Get Connected to ConnectED

connectED.mcgraw-hill.com

Your online portal to everything you need!

For Students

Leave your books at school. Now you can go online and interact with your eStudentEdition from any place, any time!

For Teachers

ConnectED is your one-stop online center for everything you need to teach, including: digital eTeacherEdition, lesson planning and scheduling tools, pacing, and assessment.

For Parents

Get homework help, help your student prepare for testing, and review math topics.

(t)Richard Hutchings, (c)STOCK4B-RF/Getty Images, (b)Jupiterimages/Thinkstock/Alamy

One Program, All Learners

Glencoe

GEOMETRY

...igned to the COMMON CORE STATE STANDARDS

McGraw Hill Education

Bothell, WA • Chicago, IL • Columbus, OH • New York, NY

connectED.mcgraw-hill.com Your Digital Math Portal

Animation 

Vocabulary 

eGlossary 

Personal Tutor  

Virtual Manipulatives 

Graphing Calculator 

Audio 

Foldables 

Self-Check Practice 

Worksheets 

In this Common Core State Standards edition of *Glencoe Geometry,* students are challenged to develop 21st century skills such as critical thinking and creative problem solving while engaging with exciting careers within Science, Technology, Engineering, and Mathematics (STEM) related fields.

Photo Credit:
Cover Hyperbolic Dodecahedron. By Paul Nylander (http://bugman123.com)

The ***McGraw-Hill*** *Companies*

connectED.mcgraw-hill.com

Send all inquiries to:
McGraw-Hill Education
STEM Learning Solutions Center
8787 Orion Place
Columbus, OH 43240

ISBN: 978-0-07-895272-2 *(Teacher Edition)*
MHID: 0-07-895272-7 *(Teacher Edition)*
ISBN: 978-0-07-895271-5 *(Student Edition)*
MHID: 0-07-895271-9 *(Student Edition)*

Printed in the United States of America.

5 6 7 8 9 QVR 16 15 14 13 12

McGraw-Hill is committed to providing instructional materials in Science, Technology, Engineering, and Mathematics (STEM) that give students a solid foundation, one that prepares them for college and careers in the 21st Century.

Contents in Brief

The correlation of the Common Core State Standards, Traditional Geometry Pathway to *Glencoe Geometry* begins on page T30.

Suggested Pacing Guide

Each chapter includes multiple days for review and assessment.

Chapter	Days
Chapter 0	Optional
Chapter 1	12 days
Chapter 2	15 days
Chapter 3	10 days
Chapter 4	12 days
Chapter 5	13 days
Chapter 6	10 days
Chapter 7	12 days
Chapter 8	14 days
Chapter 9	14 days
Chapter 10	12 days
Chapter 11	13 days
Chapter 12	13 days
Chapter 13	10 days
Total	**160 days**

Authors

Our lead authors ensure that the Macmillan/McGraw-Hill and Glencoe/McGraw-Hill mathematics programs are truly vertically aligned by beginning with the end in mind–success in Algebra 1 and beyond. By "backmapping" the content from the high school programs, all of our mathematics programs are well articulated in their scope and sequence.

Lead Authors

John A. Carter, Ph.D.

Principal
Adlai E. Stevenson High School
Lincolnshire, Illinois

Areas of Expertise: Using technology and manipulatives to visualize concepts; mathematics achievement of English-language learners

Gilbert J. Cuevas, Ph.D.

Professor of Mathematics Education
Texas State University—San Marcos
San Marcos, Texas

Areas of Expertise: Applying concepts and skills in mathematically rich contexts; mathematical representations; use of technology in the development of geometric thinking

Roger Day, Ph.D., NBCT

Mathematics Department Chairperson
Pontiac Township High School
Pontiac, Illinois

Areas of Expertise: Understanding and applying probability and statistics; mathematics teacher education

Carol Malloy, Ph.D.

Associate Professor Emerita
University of North Carolina at Chapel Hill
Chapel Hill, North Carolina

Areas of Expertise: Representations and critical thinking; student success in Algebra 1

Program Author

Jerry Cummins
Mathematics Consultant
Former President, National Council of Supervisors of Mathematics
Hinsdale, Illinois

Areas of Expertise: Graphing Technology and Mathematics

Contributing Authors

Dinah Zike FOLDABLES
Educational Consultant
Dinah-Might Activities, Inc.
San Antonio, Texas

Jay McTighe
Educational Author and Consultant
Columbia, MD

Consultants and Reviewers

These professionals were instrumental in providing valuable input and suggestions for improving the effectiveness of the mathematics instruction.

Lead Consultant

Viken Hovsepian
Professor of Mathematics
Rio Hondo College
Whittier, California

Consultants

Mathematical Content

Lead Consultant
Viken Hovsepian
Professor of Mathematics
Rio Hondo College
Whittier, California

Grant A. Fraser, Ph.D.
Professor of Mathematics
California State University, Los Angeles
Los Angeles, California

Arthur K. Wayman, Ph.D.
Professor of Mathematics Emeritus
California State University, Long Beach
Long Beach, California

Gifted and Talented

Shelbi K. Cole
Research Assistant
University of Connecticut
Storrs, Connecticut

College Readiness

Robert Lee Kimball, Jr.
Department Head, Math and Physics
Wake Technical Community College
Raleigh, North Carolina

Differentiation for English-Language Learners

Susana Davidenko
State University of New York
Cortland, New York

Alfredo Gómez
Mathematics/ESL Teacher
George W. Fowler High School
Syracuse, New York

Graphing Calculator

Ruth M. Casey
T^3 National Instructor
Frankfort, Kentucky

Mathematical Fluency

Robert M. Capraro
Associate Professor
Texas A&M University
College Station, Texas

Pre-AP

Dixie Ross
Lead Teacher for Advanced Placement Mathematics
Pflugerville High School
Pflugerville, Texas

Reading and Writing

ReLeah Cossett Lent
Author and Educational Consultant
Morganton, Georgia

Lynn T. Havens
Director of Project CRISS
Kalispell, Montana

Reviewers

Corey Andreasen
Mathematics Teacher
North High School
Sheboygan, Michigan

Mark B. Baetz
Mathematics Coordinating Teacher
Salem City Schools
Salem, Virginia

Kathryn Ballin
Mathematics Supervisor
Newark Public Schools
Newark, New Jersey

Kevin C. Barhorst
Mathematics Department Chair
Independence High School
Columbus, Ohio

Brenda S. Berg
Mathematics Teacher
Carbondale Community High School
Carbondale, Illinois

Sheryl Pernell Clayton
Mathematics Teacher
Hume Fogg Magnet School
Nashville, Tennessee

Bob Coleman
Mathematics Teacher
Cobb Middle School
Tallahassee, Florida

Jane E. Cotts
Mathematics Teacher
O'Fallon Township High School
O'Fallon, Illinois

Michael D. Cuddy
Mathematics Instructor
Zypherhills High School
Zypherhills, Florida

Melissa M. Dalton, NBCT
Mathematics Instructor
Rural Retreat High School
Rural Retreat, Virginia

Trina Louise Davis
Teacher
Fort Mill High School
Fort Mill, South Carolina

Tina S. Dohm
Mathematics Teacher
Naperville Central High School
Naperville, Illinois

Laurie L.E. Ferrari
Teacher
L'Anse Creuse High School—North
Macomb, Michigan

Patricia R. Frazier
Mathematics Department Chair/Instructor
Celina High School
Celina, Ohio

Steve Freshour
Mathematics Teacher
Parkersburg South High School
Parkersburg, West Virginia

Shirley D. Glover
Mathematics Teacher
TC Roberson High School
Asheville, North Carolina

Caroline W. Greenough
Mathematics Teacher
Cape Fear Academy
Wilmington, North Carolina

Michelle Hanneman
Mathematics Teacher
Moore High School
Moore, Oklahoma

Theresalynn Haynes
Mathematics Teacher
Glenbard East High School
Lombard, Illinois

Sandra Hester
Mathematics Teacher/AIG Specialist
North Henderson High School
Hendersonville, North Carolina

Jacob K. Holloway
Mathematics Teacher
Capitol Heights Junior High School
Montgomery, Alabama

Robert Hopp
Mathematics Teacher
Harrison High School
Harrison, Michigan

Eileen Howanitz
Mathematics Teacher/Department Chairperson
Valley View High School
Archbald, Pennsylvania

Charles R. Howard, NBCT
Mathematics Teacher
Tuscola High School
Waynesville, North Carolina

Sue Hvizdos
Mathematics Department Chairperson
Wheeling Park High School
Wheeling, West Virginia

Elaine Keller
Mathematics Teacher
Mathematics Curriculum Director K–12
Northwest Local Schools
Canal Fulton, Ohio

Sheila A. Kotter
Mathematics Educator
River Ridge High School
New Port Richey, Florida

Frank Lear
Mathematics Department Chair
Cleveland High School
Cleveland, Tennessee

Jennifer Lewis
Mathematics Teacher
Triad High School
Troy, Illinois

Catherine McCarthy
Mathematics Teacher
Glen Ridge High School
Glen Ridge, New Jersey

Jacqueline Palmquist
Mathematics Department Chair
Waubonsie Valley High School
Aurora, Illinois

Thom Schacher
Mathematics Teacher
Otsego High School
Otsego, Michigan

Laurie Shappee
Teacher/Mathematics Coordinator
Larson Middle School
Troy, Michigan

Jennifer J. Southers
Mathematics Teacher
Hillcrest High School
Simpsonville, South Carolina

Sue Steinbeck
Mathematics Department Chair
Parkersburg High School
Parkersburg, West Virginia

Kathleen D. Van Sise
Mathematics Teacher
Mandarin High School
Jacksonville, Florida

Karen Wiedman
Mathematics Teacher
Taylorville High School
Taylorville, Illinois

Glencoe Geometry Program Snapshot

Digital Light Source

What do teachers want in a mathematics program? *Glencoe Geometry* answers that question with a program that meets your needs.

SECTION 1 | Flexibility

- **Use ConnectED as Your Portal**
- **Multiple Paths to Learning**
- **Understanding by Design**
- **Connect with Digital Natives**

SECTION 2 | Differentiation

- **Teach from Your eTeacherEdition**
- **Assessment that Validates Learning**
- **Built-In Differentiated Instruction**

SECTION 3 | 21st Century Success

- **College and Work Readiness**
- **STEM Careers**
- **21st Century Skills**
- **Common Core State Standards**

Use ConnectED as Your Portal

connectED.mcgraw-hill.com

Nearly 84% of teachers say that they spend only about half of their time teaching, as opposed to disciplining or doing administrative work.

ConnectED is a time-saving online portal that has all of your digital program resources in one place. Through this portal, you can access the complete Student Edition and Teacher Edition, digital animations and tutors, editable worksheets, presentation tools, and assessment resources.

ConnectED allows you to:

- build lesson plans with easy-to-find print and digital resources
- search for activities to meet a variety of learning modalities
- teach with technology by providing virtual manipulatives, lesson animations, whole-class presentations, and more
- personalize instruction with print and digital resources
- provide students with anywhere, anytime access to student resources and tools, including eBooks, tutorials, animations, and the eGlossary
- access AdvanceTracker, which allows you to assign online assessments, track student progress, generate reports, and differentiate instruction

Multiple Paths to Learning

Students will engage with tasks they find interesting, challenging, and important. In the classroom, key factors are teacher-student relationships, pedagogy, and classroom climate.

Glencoe Geometry is designed to provide your students with a balanced approach to mathematics. Your students become successful through a variety of teaching modalities.

Keeping It Interesting

Students who are engaged are more likely to pay attention in class. ***Glencoe Geometry*** discusses topics that relate to today's students.

Content that Connects

Students use a Then, Now, Why instructional plan that connects what they know with what they are learning. New Vocabulary and Review Vocabulary help students learn to "talk math."

LESSON 4-2 Angles of Triangles

Then
- You classified triangles by their side or angle measures.

Now
1. Apply the Triangle Angle-Sum Theorem.
2. Apply Exterior Angle Theorem.

Why?
- Massachusetts Institute of Technology (MIT) sponsors the annual *Design 2.007* contest in which students design and build a robot.

One test of a robot's movements is to program it to move in a triangular path. The sum of the measures of the pivot angles through which the robot must turn will always be the same.

New Vocabulary
auxiliary line
exterior angle
remote interior angles
flow proof
corollary

1 Triangle Angle-Sum Theorem The Triangle Angle-Sum Theorem gives the relationship among the interior angle measures of any triangle.

Theorem 4.1 Triangle Angle-Sum Theorem

Words The sum of the measures of the angles of a triangle is 180.

Example $m\angle A + m\angle B + m\angle C = 180$

The proof of the Triangle Angle-Sum Theorem requires the use of an auxiliary line. An **auxiliary line** is an extra line or segment drawn in a figure to help analyze geometric relationships. As with any statement in a proof, you must justify any properties of an auxiliary line that you have drawn.

Proof Triangle Angle-Sum Theoem

Given: $\triangle ABC$

Prove: $m\angle 1 + m\angle 2 + m\angle 3 = 180$

Proof:

Statements	Reasons
1. $\triangle ABC$	1. Given
2. Draw $\overleftrightarrow{AD}$ through A parallel to $\overline{BC}$.	2. Parallel Postulate
3. $\angle 4$ and $\angle BAD$ form a linear pair.	3. Def. of a linear pair
4. $\angle 4$ and $\angle BAD$ are supplementary.	4. If 2 ∡ form a linear pair, they are supplementary.
5. $m\angle 4 + m\angle BAD = 180$	5. Def. of suppl. ∡
6. $m\angle BAD = m\angle 2 + m\angle 5$	6. Angle Addition Postulate
7. $m\angle 4 + m\angle 2 + m\angle 5 = 180$	7. Substitution
8. $\angle 4 \cong \angle 1, \angle 5 \cong \angle 3$	8. Alt. Int. ∡ Theorem
$m\angle 4 = m\angle 1, m\angle 5 = m\angle 3$	9. Def. of ≅ ∡
$\angle 1 + m\angle 2 + m\angle 3 = 180$	10. Substitution

SE Lesson Opener, p. 246

Problem-Based Learning

A wealth of problem-solving opportunities include:

- **Multiple Representations** in every chapter
- **H**igher **O**rder **T**hinking **problems** in every lesson
- Worked-out **Examples** that follow a four-step plan
- **Problem-Solving Strategy Tips** throughout
- **Test-Taking Strategies** in every chapter
- **Word-Problem Practice** masters for every lesson

54. STOCKS Technical analysts use charts to identify patterns that can suggest future activity in stock prices. Triangle charts are most useful when the fluctuation in the price of a stock is decreasing over time.

a. Classify by its sides and angles the triangle formed if a vertical line is drawn at any point on the graph.

b. How would the price have to fluctuate in order for the data to form an obtuse triangle? Draw an example to support your reasoning.

Price

Time

55. MULTIPLE REPRESENTATIONS In the diagram, the vertex *opposite* side $\overline{BC}$ is $\angle A$.

B A C

a. **Geometric** Draw four isosceles triangles, including one acute, one right, and one obtuse isosceles triangle. Label the vertices opposite the congruent sides as *A* and *C*. Label the remaining vertex *B*. Then measure the angles of each triangle and label each angle with its measure.

b. **Tabular** Measure all the angles of each triangle. Organize the measures for each triangle into a table. Include a column in your table to record the sum of these measures.

c. **Verbal** Make a conjecture about the measures of the angles that are opposite the congruent sides of an isosceles triangle. Then make a conjecture about the sum of the measures of the angles of an isosceles triangle.

d. **Algebraic** If x is the measure of one of the angles opposite one of the congruent sides in an isosceles triangle, write expressions for the measures of each of the other two angles in the triangle. Explain.

H.O.T. Problems Use Higher-Order Thinking Skills

56. ERROR ANALYSIS Elaina says that $\triangle DFG$ is obtuse. Ines disagrees, explaining that the triangle has more acute angles than obtuse angles so it must be acute. Is either of them correct? Explain your reasoning.

D 120° 38° F 22° G

REASONING Determine whether the statements below are *sometimes*, *always*, or *never* true. Explain your reasoning.

57. Equiangular triangles are also right triangles.

58. Equilateral triangles are isosceles.

59. Right triangles are equilateral.

60. CHALLENGE An equilateral triangle has sides that measure $5x + 3$ units and $7x - 5$ units. What is the perimeter of the triangle? Explain.

OPEN ENDED Draw an example of each type of triangle below using a protractor and a ruler. Label the sides and angles of each triangle with their measures. If not possible, explain why not.

61. scalene right

62. isosceles obtuse

63. equilateral obtuse

64. WRITING IN MATH Explain why classifying an equiangular triangle as an *acute* equiangular triangle is unnecessary.

connectED.mcgraw-hill.com 243

SE Multiple Representations, p. 243

Learning by Doing

Labs help to maintain learner motivation. Algebra Labs introduce and reinforce concepts using manipulatives like algebra tiles. Graphing Technology Labs allow students to explore concepts using graphing calculators, including the TI-Nspire Technology™.

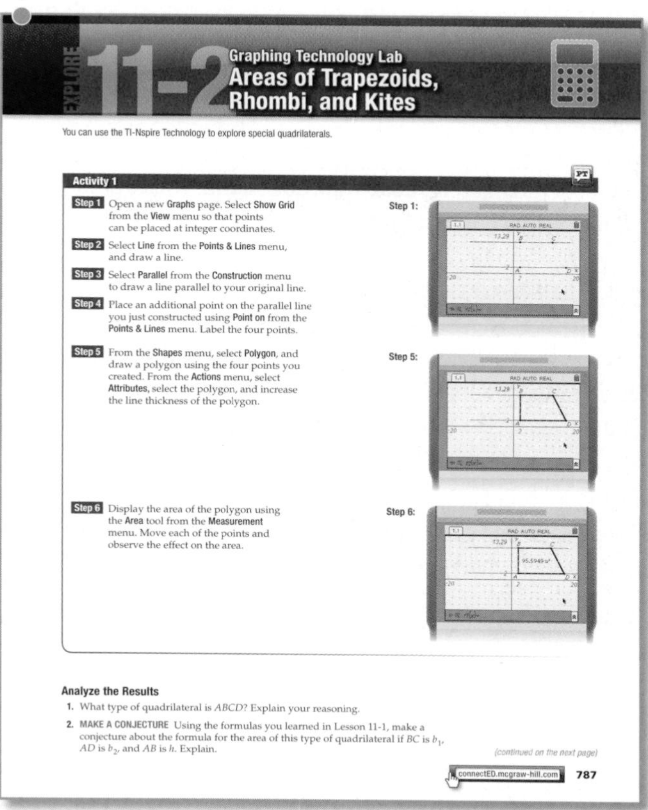

EXPLORE 11-2 Graphing Technology Lab

Areas of Trapezoids, Rhombi, and Kites

You can use the TI-Nspire Technology to explore special quadrilaterals.

Activity 1

Step 1 Open a new **Graphs** page. Select **Show Grid** from the **View** menu so that points can be placed at integer coordinates.

Step 2 Select **Line** from the **Points & Lines** menu, and draw a line.

Step 3 Select **Parallel** from the **Construction** menu to draw a line parallel to your original line.

Step 4 Place an additional point on the parallel line you just constructed using **Point on** from the **Points & Lines** menu. Label the four points.

Step 5 From the **Shapes** menu, select **Polygon**, and draw a polygon using the four points you created. From the **Actions** menu, select **Attributes**, select the polygon, and increase the line thickness of the polygon.

Step 6 Display the area of the polygon using the **Area** tool from the **Measurement** menu. Move each of the points and observe the effect on the area.

Step 1:

Step 5:

Step 6:

Analyze the Results

1. What type of quadrilateral is *ABCD*? Explain your reasoning.

2. **MAKE A CONJECTURE** Using the formulas you learned in Lesson 11-1, make a conjecture about the formula for the area of this type of quadrilateral if *BC* is b_1, *AD* is b_2, and *AB* is *h*. Explain.

(continued on the next page)

connectED.mcgraw-hill.com 787

SE Graphing Technology Lab, p. 787

Understanding by Design

What should students know and be able to do? Understanding by Design can be used to help teachers identify learning goals, develop revealing assessments of student understanding, and plan effective and engaging learning activities.

Backward Design

Understanding by Design (UbD) is a framework that uses backward design to create a coherent curriculum by considering the desired results first and then planning instruction.

The backward design process guided the development of ***Glencoe Algebra 1***, ***Glencoe Geometry***, and ***Glencoe Algebra 2***.

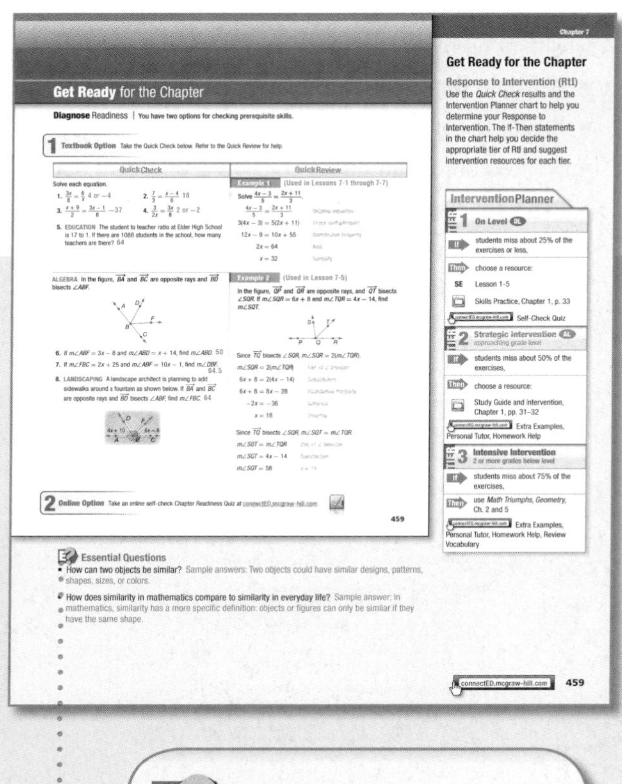

Chapter 7

Get Ready for the Chapter

Diagnose Readiness | You have two options for checking prerequisite skills.

1 Textbook Option Take the Quick Check below. Refer to the Quick Review for help.

QuickCheck

Solve each equation.

1. $\frac{3x}{8} = \frac{6}{x}$ 4 or −4
2. $\frac{7}{3} = \frac{x-4}{6}$ 18
3. $\frac{x+9}{2} = \frac{3x-1}{8}$ −37
4. $\frac{3}{2x} = \frac{3x}{8}$ 2 or −2
5. EDUCATION The student to teacher ratio at Elder High School is 17 to 1. If there are 1088 students in the school, how many teachers are there? 64

ALGEBRA In the figure, $\overrightarrow{BA}$ and $\overrightarrow{BC}$ are opposite rays and $\overrightarrow{BD}$ bisects $\angle ABF$.

6. If $m\angle ABF = 3x - 8$ and $m\angle ABD = x + 14$, find $m\angle ABD$. 50
7. If $m\angle FBC = 2x + 25$ and $m\angle ABF = 10x - 1$, find $m\angle DBF$. 64.5
8. LANDSCAPING A landscape architect is planning to add sidewalks around a fountain as shown below. If $\overrightarrow{BA}$ and $\overrightarrow{BC}$ are opposite rays and $\overrightarrow{BD}$ bisects $\angle ABF$, find $m\angle FBC$. 64

QuickReview

Example 1 (Used in Lessons 7-1 through 7-7)

Solve $\frac{4x-3}{5} = \frac{2x+11}{3}$.

$\frac{4x-3}{5} = \frac{2x+11}{3}$

$3(4x-3) = 5(2x+11)$

$12x - 9 = 10x + 55$

$2x = 64$

$x = 32$

Example 2 (Used in Lesson 7-5)

In the figure, $\overrightarrow{QP}$ and $\overrightarrow{QR}$ are opposite rays, and $\overrightarrow{QT}$ bisects $\angle SQR$. If $m\angle SQR = 6x + 8$ and $m\angle TQR = 4x - 14$, find $m\angle SQT$.

Since $\overrightarrow{TQ}$ bisects $\angle SQR$, $m\angle SQR = 2(m\angle TQR)$.

$m\angle SQR = 2(m\angle TQR)$

$6x + 8 = 2(4x - 14)$

$6x + 8 = 8x - 28$

$-2x = -36$

$x = 18$

Since $\overrightarrow{TQ}$ bisects $\angle SQR$, $m\angle SQT = m\angle TQR$

$m\angle SQT = m\angle TQR$

$m\angle SQT = 4x - 14$

$m\angle SQT = 58$

2 Online Option Take an online self-check Chapter Readiness Quiz at connectED.mcgraw-hill.com.

459

Get Ready for the Chapter

Response to Intervention (RtI) Use the *Quick Check* results and the Intervention Planner chart to help you determine your Response to Intervention. The If-Then statements in the chart help you decide the appropriate tier of RtI and suggest intervention resources for each tier.

InterventionPlanner

Tier 1 On Level OL
- If students miss about 25% of the exercises or less,
- Then choose a resource:
  - SE Lesson 1-5
  - Skills Practice, Chapter 1, p. 33
  - connectED.mcgraw-hill.com Self-Check Quiz

Tier 2 Strategic Intervention AL approaching grade level
- If students miss about 50% of the exercises,
- Then choose a resource:
  - Study Guide and Intervention, Chapter 1, pp. 31–32
  - connectED.mcgraw-hill.com Extra Examples, Personal Tutor, Homework Help

Tier 3 Intensive Intervention 2 or more grades below level
- If students miss about 75% of the exercises,
- Then use *Math Triumphs, Geometry*, Ch. 2 and 5
  - connectED.mcgraw-hill.com Extra Examples, Personal Tutor, Homework Help, Review Vocabulary

Essential Questions
- How can two objects be similar? Sample answers: Two objects could have similar designs, patterns, shapes, sizes, or colors.
- How does similarity in mathematics compare to similarity in everyday life? Sample answer: In mathematics, similarity has a more specific definition: objects or figures can only be similar if they have the same shape.

connectED.mcgraw-hill.com 459

Identifying Desired Results

The first step in developing an effective curriculum using the UbD framework is to consider the goals. What should students know and be able to do?

Glencoe Geometry addresses the big ideas of algebra and focuses student attention on **Essential Questions**, which are located within each chapter of the Student and Teacher Editions.

An Essential Question is provided at the beginning of each chapter. These thought provoking questions can be used as:

- a discussion starter for your class; throughout the discussion identify what the students already know and what they would like to know about the topic. Revisit these notes throughout the chapter.
- a benchmark of understanding; post these questions in a prominent place and have students expand upon their initial response as their understanding of the subject material grows.

Essential Questions
- How can two objects be simi
shapes, sizes, or colors.

> In mathematics, essential questions are used to develop students' understanding of key concepts as well as core processes.
>
> — Jay McTighe, co-author of Understanding by Design

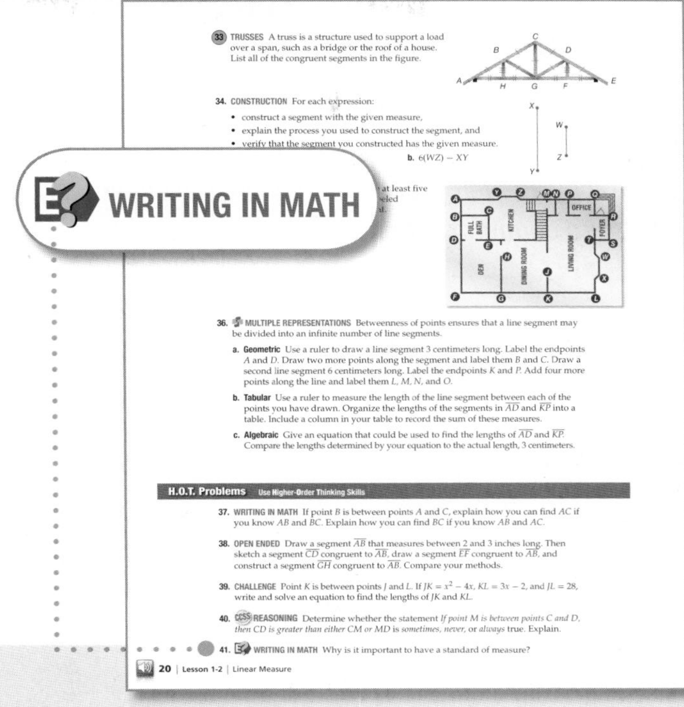

Follow-up Essential Questions can be found throughout each chapter. These questions challenge students to apply specific knowledge to a broader context, thus deepening their understanding.

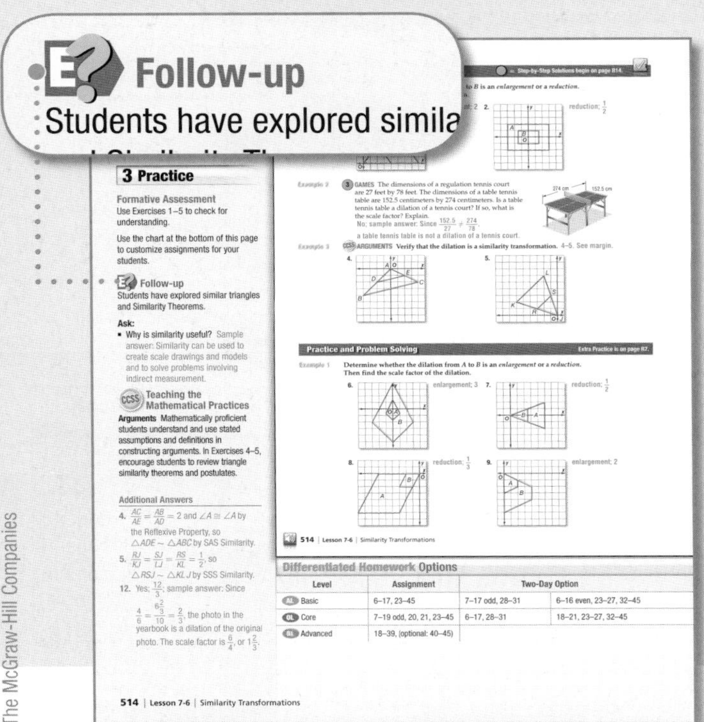

Determine Acceptable Evidence

A variety of assessment opportunities are available that enable students to show evidence of their understanding.

- **Practice and Problem Solving** and **H.O.T. Problems** allow students to explain, interpret, and apply mathematical concepts.
- **Mid-Chapter Quizzes** and **Chapter Tests** offer more traditional methods of assessment.
- **eAssessment** can also be used to customize and create assessments.

Plan Learning Experiences and Instruction

There are numerous performance activities available throughout the program, including:

- **Geometry Labs** that offer students hands-on learning experiences, and
- **Graphing Technology Labs** that use graphing calculators to aid student understanding.

You can also visit connectED.mcgraw-hill.com to choose from an extensive collection of resources to use when planning instruction, such as presentation tools, chapter projects, editable worksheets, digital animations, and eTools.

Connect with Digital Natives

connectED.mcgraw-hill.com

Today's students have an unprecedented access to and appetite for technology and new media. They perceive technology as their friend and rely on it to study, work, play, relax, and communicate.

Your students are accustomed to the role that computers play in today's world. They may well be the first generation whose primary educational tool is a computer or a cell phone. The eStudentEdition allows your students to access their math curriculum anytime, anywhere. Along with your student edition, ***Glencoe Geometry*** provides a blended instructional solution for your next-generation students.

Investigate

Animations illustrate math concepts through movement and audio.

Vocabulary tools include fun Vocabulary Review Games.

Multilingual eGlossary presents key vocabulary in 13 languages.

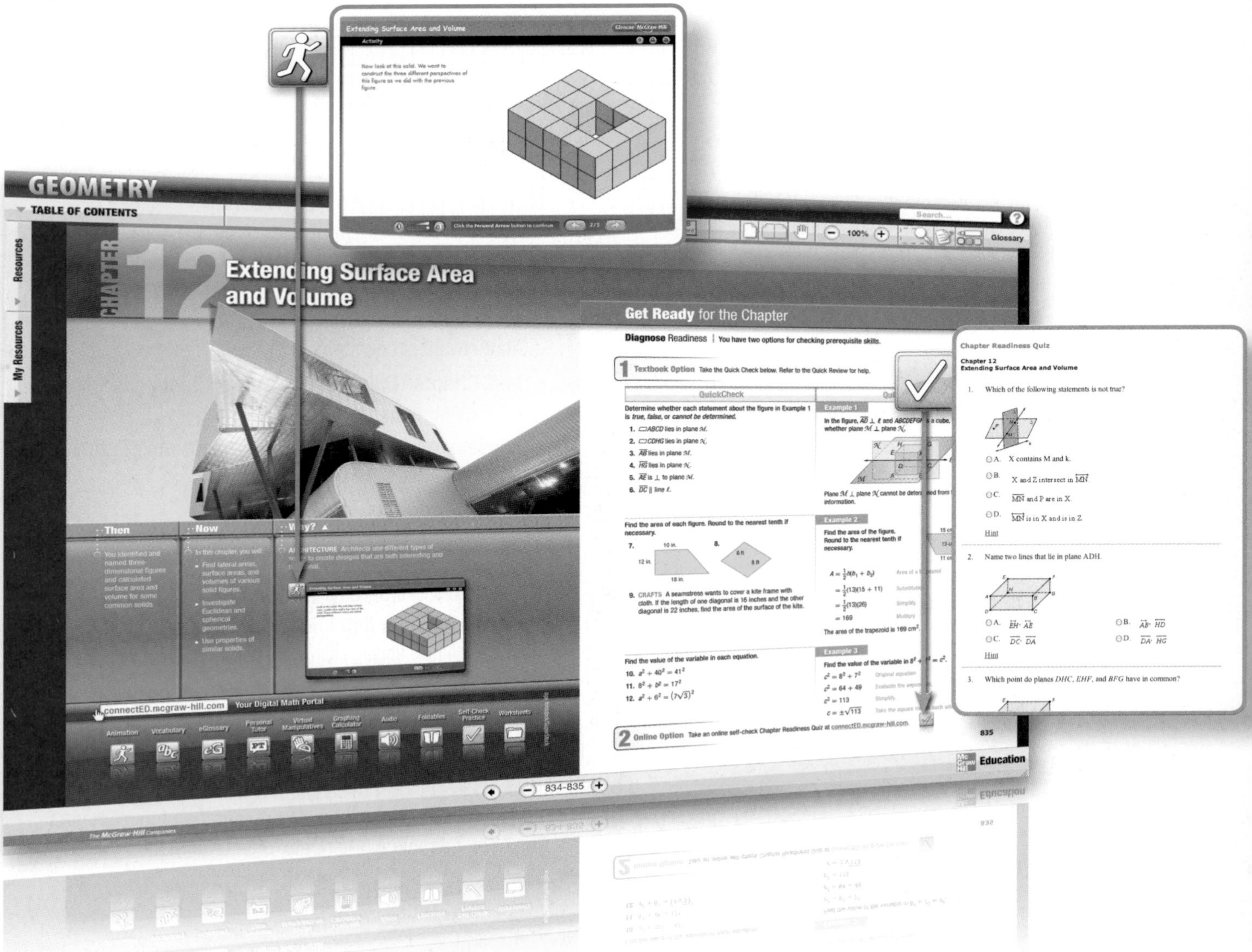

Learn

Personal Tutor presents an experienced educator explaining step-by-step solutions to problems.

Virtual Manipulatives are outstanding tools for enhancing understanding.

Graphing Calculator provides other calculator keystrokes for each Graphing Technology Lab.

Audio is provided to enhance accessibility for all students.

Foldables provide a unique way to enhance student study skills.

Practice

Self-Check Practice allows students to check their understanding and send results to their teacher.

Worksheets provide additional practice and reteaching opportunities.

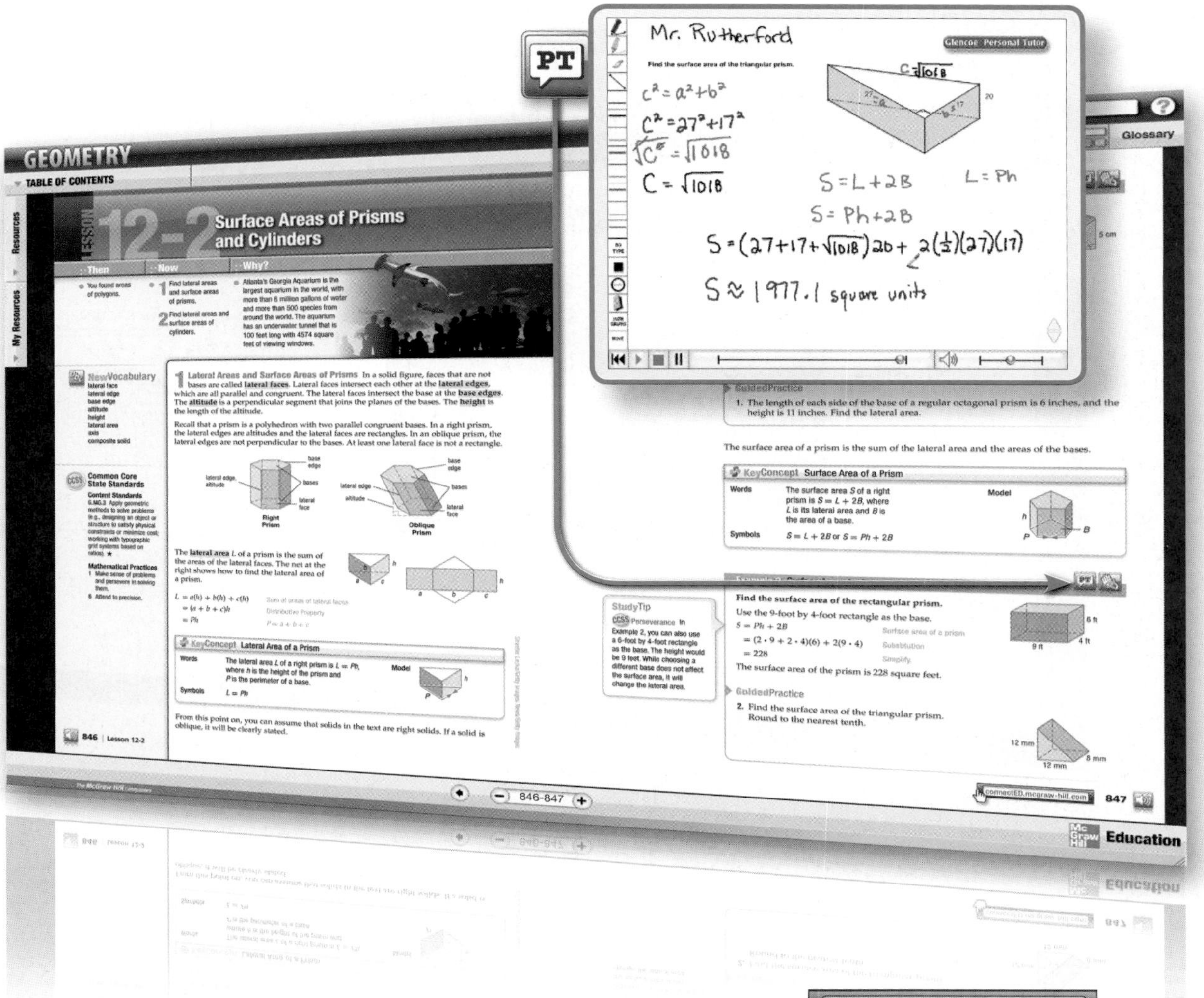

Teach from Your eTeacherEdition

connectED.mcgraw-hill.com

Nearly 90% of teachers agree that technology enhances their ability to teach.

Imagine being able to prepare and plan your instruction without having to carry your Teacher Edition home each night. Your eTeacherEdition has all of the content of your Teacher Edition, plus links to thousands of assets right at point of use.

Resources

Resources

Resources allow you to view the ancillary material for each chapter and lesson including animations, worksheets, and assessments.

My Resources

The My Resources tab allows the user to create and save their own list of resources.

Presentation Tools

Student Edition

This version of the student text is complete with links to student worksheets, Personal Tutors, and online study tools for use on your interactive whiteboard.

Interactive Classroom

These presentations provide fully worked-out, step-by-step examples and follow-up Your Turn Problems as well as direct links to animations for use on your classroom whiteboard.

Virtual Manipulatives

These tools provide your students with a digital way to explore concepts and you with a way to create problem-based learning opportunities.

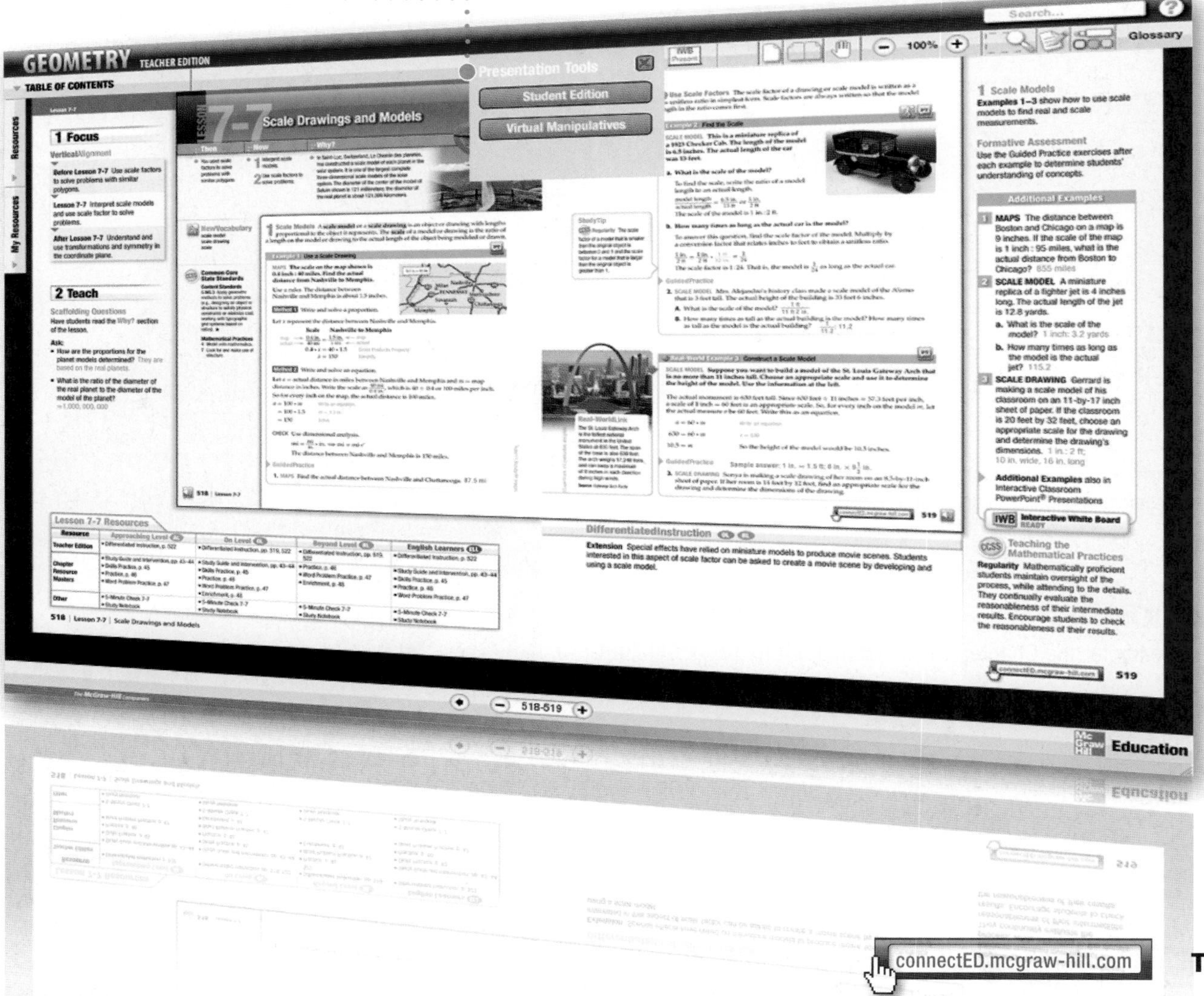

Assessment that Validates Learning

Only 48% of teachers feel that standardized tests are effective in helping them track student performance.

Glencoe Geometry offers a variety of frequent and meaningful assessments built right into the curriculum structure and teacher support materials. The program includes both traditional and nontraditional methods of assessment, including quizzes and tests, performance tasks, and open-ended assessments.

Digital assessment solutions offer additional options for creating, customizing, administering, and instantly grading assessments.

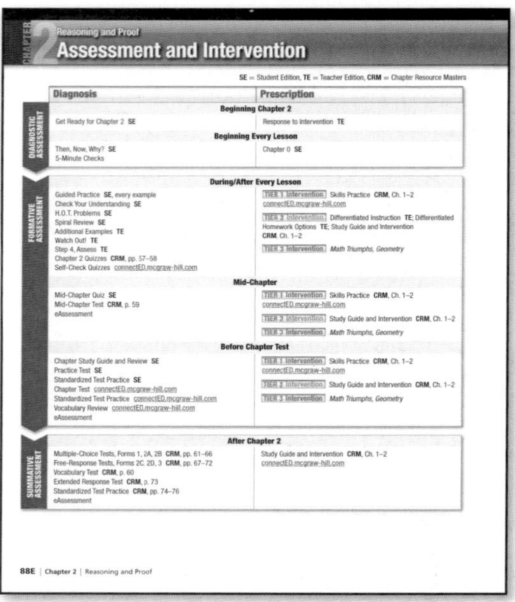

CHAPTER 2 Reasoning and Proof

Assessment and Intervention

SE = Student Edition, **TE** = Teacher Edition, **CRM** = Chapter Resource Masters

	Diagnosis	Prescription
DIAGNOSTIC ASSESSMENT	**Beginning Chapter 2**	
	Get Ready for Chapter 2 **SE**	Response to Intervention **TE**
	Beginning Every Lesson	
	Then, Now, Why? **SE** 5-Minute Checks	Chapter 0 **SE**
FORMATIVE ASSESSMENT	**During/After Every Lesson**	
	Guided Practice **SE**, every example Check Your Understanding **SE** H.O.T. Problems **SE** Spiral Review **SE** Additional Examples **TE** Watch Out! **TE** Step 4, Assess **TE** Chapter 2 Quizzes **CRM**, pp. 57–58 Self-Check Quizzes connectED.mcgraw-hill.com	TIER 1 Intervention Skills Practice **CRM**, Ch. 1–2 connectED.mcgraw-hill.com TIER 2 Intervention Differentiated Instruction **TE**; Differentiated Homework Options **TE**; Study Guide and Intervention **CRM**, Ch. 1–2 TIER 3 Intervention *Math Triumphs, Geometry*
	Mid-Chapter	
	Mid-Chapter Quiz **SE** Mid-Chapter Test **CRM**, p. 59 eAssessment	TIER 1 Intervention Skills Practice **CRM**, Ch. 1–2 connectED.mcgraw-hill.com TIER 2 Intervention Study Guide and Intervention **CRM**, Ch. 1–2 TIER 3 Intervention *Math Triumphs, Geometry*
	Before Chapter Test	
	Chapter Study Guide and Review **SE** Practice Test **SE** Standardized Test Practice **SE** Chapter Test connectED.mcgraw-hill.com Standardized Test Practice connectED.mcgraw-hill.com Vocabulary Review connectED.mcgraw-hill.com eAssessment	TIER 1 Intervention Skills Practice **CRM**, Ch. 1–2 connectED.mcgraw-hill.com TIER 2 Intervention Study Guide and Intervention **CRM**, Ch. 1–2 TIER 3 Intervention *Math Triumphs, Geometry*
SUMMATIVE ASSESSMENT	**After Chapter 2**	
	Multiple-Choice Tests, Forms 1, 2A, 2B **CRM**, pp. 61–66 Free-Response Tests, Forms 2C, 2D, 3 **CRM**, pp. 67–72 Vocabulary Test **CRM**, p. 60 Extended Response Test **CRM**, p. 73 Standardized Test Practice **CRM**, pp. 74–76 eAssessment	Study Guide and Intervention **CRM**, Ch. 1–2 connectED.mcgraw-hill.com

88E | Chapter 2 | Reasoning and Proof

TE Assessment and Intervention, p. 88E

1 Diagnostic

Initial Assessment

Assess students' knowledge at the beginning of the year with *Diagnostic and Placement Tests.* The results and scoring guides identify students who may need additional resources to meet grade-level standards.

Entry-Level Assessment

Assess students' prior knowledge at the beginning of a chapter or lesson.

Student Edition

- Get Ready for the Chapter

Teacher Edition

- Intervention Planner

Online Resources

connectED.mcgraw-hill.com

- Chapter Readiness Quiz

2 Formative

Progress Monitoring

Determine if students are progressing adequately as you teach each lesson. Use the assessments to differentiate lesson instruction and practice.

Student Edition
- Guided Practice
- Check Your Understanding
- H.O.T. Problems
- Mid-Chapter Quiz
- Study Guide and Review

Additional Resources
Chapter Resource Masters
- Mid-Chapter Test
- 4 Quizzes
- Standardized Test Practice

Digital Resources
- eAssessment

Online Resources
connectED.mcgraw-hill.com
- Self-Check Quizzes
- Mid-Chapter Test
- Study Guide and Review

3 Summative

Summative Assessment

Assess student success in learning the concepts in each chapter. Use remediation suggestions to address problem areas.

Student Edition
- Practice Test
- Standardized Test Practice

Additional Resources
Chapter Resource Masters
- Vocabulary Test
- 6 Leveled Chapter Tests
- Extended-Response Test

Digital Resources
- eAssessment
- Chapter Tests
- Cumulative Standardized Test Practice

Online Resources
connectED.mcgraw-hill.com
- Chapter Tests
- Cumulative Standardized Test Practice

Built-In Differentiated Instruction

Approximately 43% of teachers feel their classes are so mixed in terms of students' learning abilities that they can't teach them effectively.

- AL Approaching Grade Level
- OL On Grade Level
- BL Beyond Grade Level
- ELL English Language Learners

Glencoe Geometry fully supports the 3-tier RtI model with print and digital resources to diagnose students, identify areas of need, and conduct short, frequent assessments for accurate data-driven decision making. Every lesson provides easy-to-use resources that consider the needs of all students.

RtI: Response to Intervention

TIER 1 Daily Intervention

OL On grade level

Core instruction targets on-level students. Comprehensive instructional materials help you personalize instruction for every student.

- Diagnostic Teaching
- Options for Differentiated Instruction
- Leveled Exercise Sets, Resources, and Technology
- Data-Driven Decision Making

BL Beyond grade level

At every step, resources and assignments are available for advanced learners.

- Higher-Order Thinking Questions
- Differentiated Homework Options
- Enrichment Masters
- Differentiated Instruction: Extension

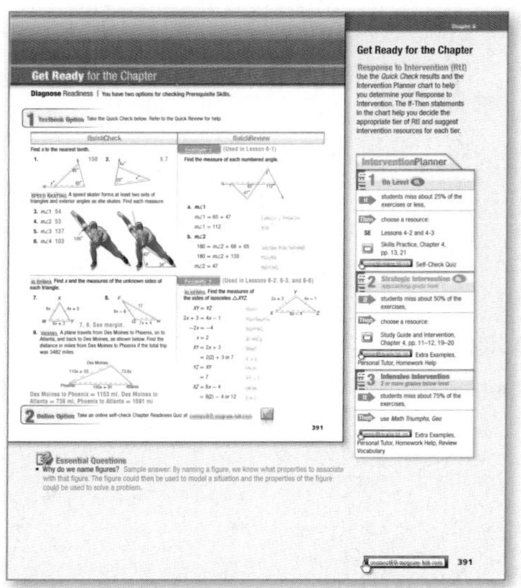

Get Ready for the Chapter

Diagnose Readiness | You have two options for checking Prerequisite Skills.

Get Ready for the Chapter

Response to Intervention (RtI) Use the Quick Check results and the Intervention Planner chart to help you determine your Response to Intervention. The If-Then statements in the chart help you decide the appropriate tier of RtI and suggest intervention resources for each tier.

Intervention Planner

Essential Questions

391

TE Get Ready for the Chapter, p. 391

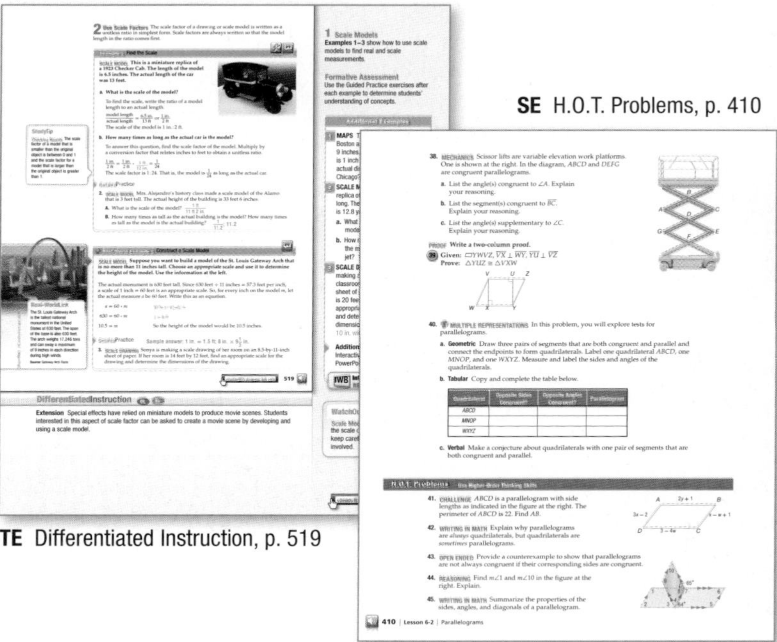

Differentiated Instruction

Extension Special effects have relied on miniature models to produce movie scenes. Students interested in this aspect of scale factor can be asked to create a movie scene by developing and using a scale model.

H.O.T. Problems Use Higher-Order Thinking Skills

410 | Lesson 6-2 | Parallelograms

TE Differentiated Instruction, p. 519

SE H.O.T. Problems, p. 410

ELL English Language Learners

Comprehensive resources are found throughout the program.

- Teacher Edition with strategies to modify activities and lesson content
- Multilingual eGlossary with definitions for each vocabulary word in 13 languages

TIER 2 StrategicIntervention

AL Approaching grade level

You can choose from a myriad of intervention tips and ancillary materials to support struggling learners.

- Using Manipulatives
- Alternate Teaching Strategies
- Online resources, including animations, examples, and Personal Tutors

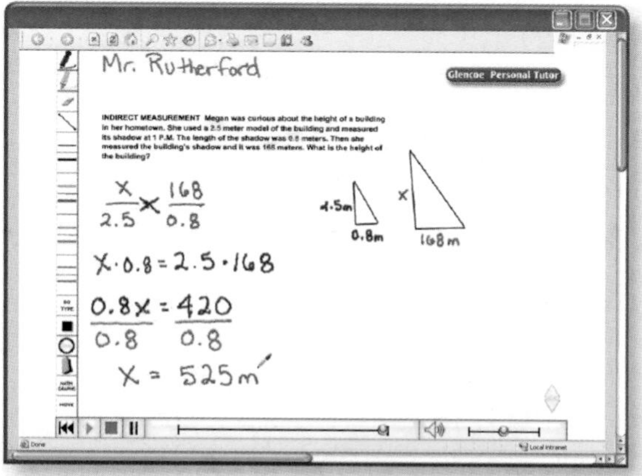

TIER 3 IntensiveIntervention

AL Significantly below grade level

For students who are far below grade level, ***Math Triumphs*** provides step-by-step instruction, vocabulary support, and meaningful practice.

Mike Kemp/Getty Images

College and Work Readiness

The U.S. Department of Labor estimates that 90% of 21st-century skilled workforce jobs will require post-secondary education. To be competitive in tomorrow's global workforce, American students must be prepared to succeed in college.

A strong high school curriculum is a good predictor of college readiness (Adelman, 2006). Students who take at least three years of college-preparatory mathematics using programs like ***Glencoe Algebra 1***, ***Glencoe Geometry***, and ***Glencoe Algebra 2*** are less likely to need remedial courses in college than students who do not (Abraham & Creech, 2002).

College Readiness

David Conley at the University of Oregon developed the following criteria for college readiness.

Key Content Knowledge

Glencoe Algebra 1, ***Glencoe Geometry***, and ***Glencoe Algebra 2*** have been aligned to rigorous state and national standards, including the *NCTM Principles & Standards for School Mathematics*, the College Board Standards for College Success, and the American Diploma Project's Benchmarks. Correlations to these standards can be found at connectED.mcgraw-hill.com.

Habits of Mind

These include critical thinking skills such as analysis, interpretation, problem solving, and reasoning. Students can hone critical higher-order thinking skills through the use of **H.O.T. (Higher Order Thinking) Problems.**

Contextual Skills

These are practical skills like understanding the admissions process and financial aid, placement testing, and communicating with professors. Throughout each Glencoe mathematics program, students are required to write, explain, justify, prove, and analyze.

Academic Behaviors

These include general skills such as reading comprehension, time management, note-taking, and metacognition. Reading Math tips and Vocabulary Links help students with reading comprehension. Study Notebooks and Anticipation Guides help students build note-taking skills and aid with metacognition.

Ariel Skelley/Photographer's Choice/Getty Images

Sources:

Abraham, A. & Creech, J. (2002). *Reducing Remedial Education.* Atlanta, GA: Southern Regional Education Board.

ACT, Inc. (2006). *Readiness for College and Readiness for Work: Same or Different?* Iowa City, IA

The Conference Board, Corporate Voices for Working Families, the Partnership for 21st Century Skills, and the Society for Human Resource Management (2006). *Are They Really Ready to Work?*

Conley, D. (2007). *Toward a More Comprehensive Conception of College Readiness.* Eugene, OR: Educational Policy Improvement Center.

Work Readiness

Work Readiness is the ability of entry-level employees to add value in front-line jobs.

Does College Readiness Lead to Success in the Workplace?

The U.S. Chamber of Commerce has created a National Work Readiness Credential that involves nine sub-skills, one of which is using math to solve problems. In a recent study, 53.5% of employers who responded reported that high school graduate entrants into the workforce are "deficient" in mathematics, while 30.4% felt that knowledge of mathematics is "very important." (Are They Really Ready to Work?, 2006)

What About Students Who Don't Plan to Go to College?

In today's technological world, math is no longer just for students who go to college. ACT compared the skills needed to succeed as a freshman in college and those needed for job-training programs. They found that students need to be educated to a comparable level in algebra, geometry, data analysis, and statistics for success in either situation (ACT, 2006).

http://ccr.mcgraw-hill.com

McGraw-Hill is committed to helping educators ensure that all students graduate from high school equipped to succeed in college or in their chosen careers. McGraw-Hill programs bridge the gap between secondary and postsecondary curricula by including pre-college content as well as the study skills and transitional life skills that are necessary for both secondary and college academic success.

Getty Images

STEM Careers

Student intentions to go to college have increased over the past 20 years. In 1988, 80% said they were likely to go to college, compared to 90% today.

Developing STEM Careers

With ***Glencoe Geometry***, you can unleash your students' curiosity about the world around them and prepare them for exciting STEM (**S**cience, **T**echnology, **E**ngineering, and **M**ath) careers.

Real-World Careers

Real-World Careers are engaging, providing information on exciting careers.

Examples

Examples are relevant, connecting in-class experiences to the world beyond the classroom.

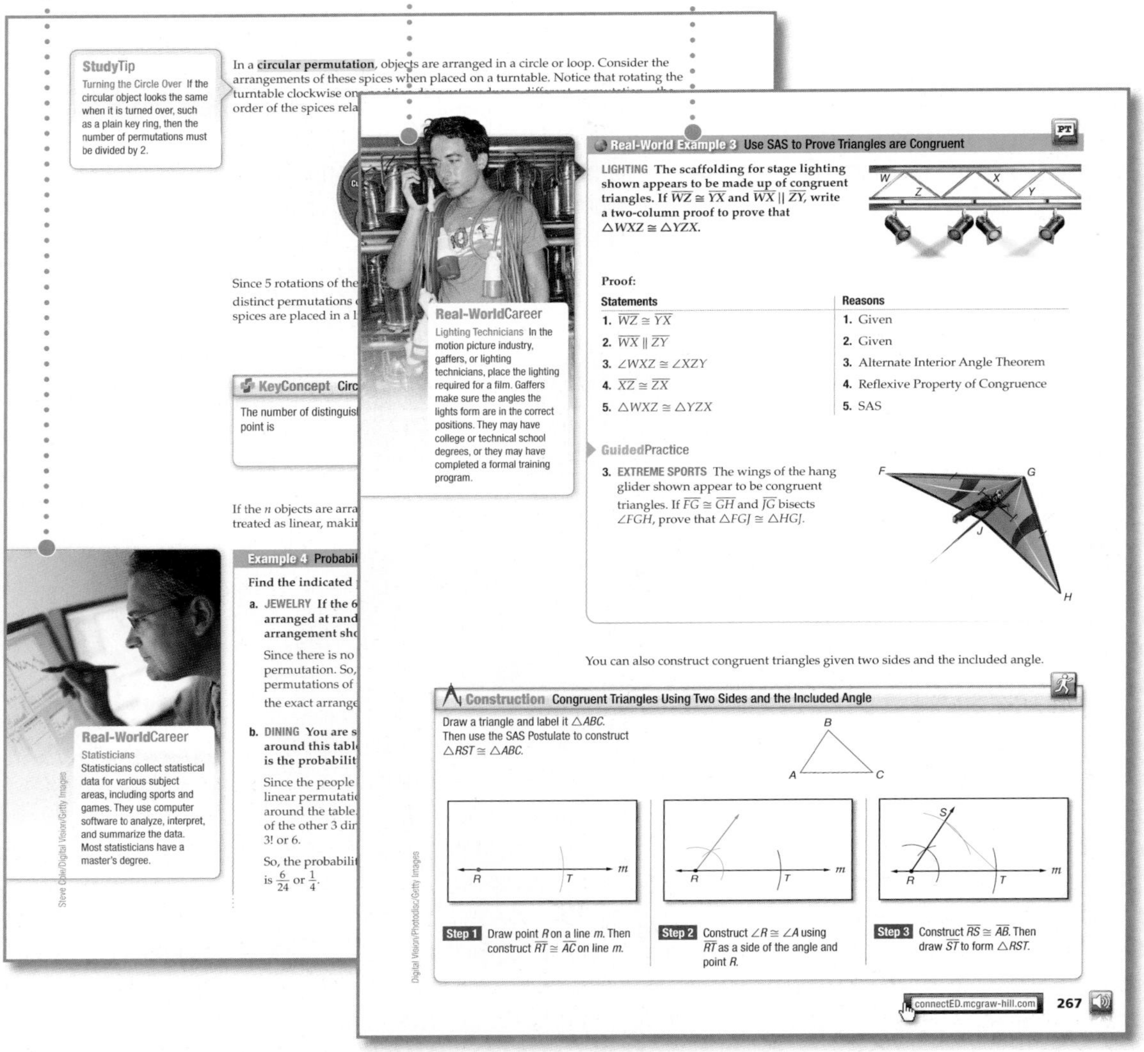

StudyTip

Turning the Circle Over If the circular object looks the same when it is turned over, such as a plain key ring, then the number of permutations must be divided by 2.

In a **circular permutation**, objects are arranged in a circle or loop. Consider the arrangements of these spices when placed on a turntable. Notice that rotating the turntable clockwise on... order of the spices rela...

Since 5 rotations of the... distinct permutations... spices are placed in a l...

KeyConcept Circ...

The number of distinguis... point is

If the *n* objects are arra... treated as linear, makin...

Real-WorldCareer

Statisticians
Statisticians collect statistical data for various subject areas, including sports and games. They use computer software to analyze, interpret, and summarize the data. Most statisticians have a master's degree.

Steve Cole/Digital Vision/Getty Images

Example 4 Probabil...

Find the indicated ...

a. JEWELRY If the 6... arranged at rand... arrangement sh...

Since there is no ... permutation. So, ... permutations of ... the exact arrange...

b. DINING You are s... around this tabl... is the probabilit...

Since the people ... linear permutati... around the table. ... of the other 3 dir... 3! or 6.

So, the probabilit... is $\frac{6}{24}$ or $\frac{1}{4}$.

Real-WorldCareer

Lighting Technicians In the motion picture industry, gaffers, or lighting technicians, place the lighting required for a film. Gaffers make sure the angles the lights form are in the correct positions. They may have college or technical school degrees, or they may have completed a formal training program.

Real-World Example 3 Use SAS to Prove Triangles are Congruent

LIGHTING The scaffolding for stage lighting shown appears to be made up of congruent triangles. If $\overline{WZ} \cong \overline{YX}$ and $\overline{WX} \parallel \overline{ZY}$, write a two-column proof to prove that $\triangle WXZ \cong \triangle YZX$.

Proof:

Statements	Reasons
1. $\overline{WZ} \cong \overline{YX}$	1. Given
2. $\overline{WX} \parallel \overline{ZY}$	2. Given
3. $\angle WXZ \cong \angle XZY$	3. Alternate Interior Angle Theorem
4. $\overline{XZ} \cong \overline{ZX}$	4. Reflexive Property of Congruence
5. $\triangle WXZ \cong \triangle YZX$	5. SAS

GuidedPractice

3. EXTREME SPORTS The wings of the hang glider shown appear to be congruent triangles. If $\overline{FG} \cong \overline{GH}$ and $\overline{JG}$ bisects $\angle FGH$, prove that $\triangle FGJ \cong \triangle HGJ$.

You can also construct congruent triangles given two sides and the included angle.

Construction Congruent Triangles Using Two Sides and the Included Angle

Draw a triangle and label it $\triangle ABC$. Then use the SAS Postulate to construct $\triangle RST \cong \triangle ABC$.

Step 1 Draw point *R* on a line *m*. Then construct $\overline{RT} \cong \overline{AC}$ on line *m*.

Step 2 Construct $\angle R \cong \angle A$ using $\overline{RT}$ as a side of the angle and point *R*.

Step 3 Construct $\overline{RS} \cong \overline{AB}$. Then draw $\overline{ST}$ to form $\triangle RST$.

Digital Vision/Photodisc/Getty Images

connectED.mcgraw-hill.com 267

21st Century Skills

The current and future health of America's 21st Century Economy depends directly on how broadly and deeply Americans reach a new level of literacy—'21st Century Literacy'—that includes strong academic skills, thinking, reasoning, teamwork skills, and proficiency in using technology.

— 21st Century Workforce Commission National Alliance of Business

Developing 21st Century Skills

The Partnership for 21st Century Skills identifies the following key student elements of a 21st century education.

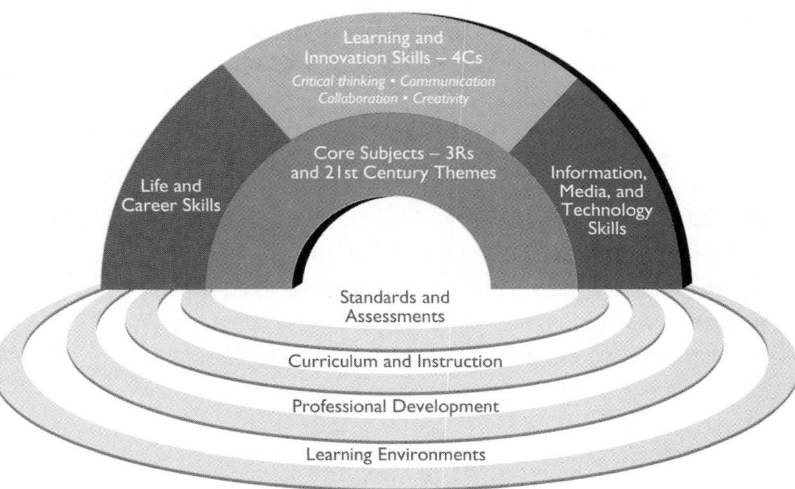

Core Subjects and 21st Century Themes

Glencoe Algebra 1, ***Glencoe Geometry***, and ***Glencoe Algebra 2*** have been aligned to rigorous state and national standards, including the Common Core State Standards, NCTM Principles & Standards for School Mathematics, and the American Diploma Project's Benchmarks. Correlations to these standards can be found at connectED.mcgraw-hill.com.

Throughout each Glencoe mathematics program, students solve problems that incorporate 21st century themes, such as financial literacy. In addition, there is also a project within each chapter that incorporates 21st Century Skills.

Learning and Innovation Skills

Students who are prepared for increasingly complex life and work environments are creative and innovative critical thinkers, problem solvers, effective communicators, and know how to work collaboratively. Throughout each Glencoe mathematics program, students are required to write, explain, justify, prove, and analyze. Students can hone critical thinking skills through the use of **H.O.T. (Higher Order Thinking) Problems** and are encouraged to work collaboratively in labs.

Life and Career Skills

McGraw-Hill is committed to helping educators ensure that all students graduate from high school equipped to succeed in college or in their chosen careers. McGraw-Hill programs bridge the gap between secondary and postsecondary curricula by including pre-college content as well as the study skills and transitional life skills that are necessary for both secondary and college academic success.

Information, Media, and Technology Skills

Throughout each Glencoe mathematics program, students use technology, including graphing calculators and the Internet, to develop 21st century mathematics knowledge and skills.

21st Century Assessments

Glencoe Algebra 1, Glencoe Geometry, and ***Glencoe Algebra 2*** offer a variety of frequent and meaningful assessments built right into the curriculum structure and teacher support materials. These programs include both traditional and nontraditional methods of assessment, including quizzes and tests, performance tasks, and open-ended assessments. Digital assessment solutions offer additional options for creating, customizing, administering, and instantly grading assessments.

Common Core State Standards

With American students fully prepared for the future, our communities will be best positioned to compete successfully in the global economy. — *Common Core State Standards Initiative*

What is the goal of the Common Core State Standards?

The mission of the *Common Core State Standards* is to provide a consistent, clear understanding of what students are expected to learn, so teachers and parents know what they need to do to help them. The standards are designed to be robust and relevant to the real world, reflecting the knowledge and skills that students need for success in college and careers.

Who wrote the standards?

The National Governors Association Center for Best Practices and the Council of Chief State School Officers worked with representatives from participating states, a wide range of educators, content experts, researchers, national organizations, and community groups.

What are the major points of the standards?

The standards seek to develop both students' mathematical understanding and their procedural skill. The *Standards for Mathematical Practice* describe varieties of expertise that mathematics teachers at all levels should seek to develop in their students. The *Standards for Mathematical Content* define what students should understand and be able to do at each level in their study of mathematics.

How do I implement the standards?

The *Common Core State Standards* are shared goals and expectations for what knowledge and skills your students need to succeed. You as a teacher, in partnership with your colleagues, principals, superintendents, decide how the standards are to be met. ***Glencoe Geometry*** is designed to help you devise lesson plans and tailor instruction to the individual needs of the students in your classroom as you meet the *Common Core State Standards.*

At the high school level the *Common Core State Standards* are organized by conceptual category. To ease implementation four model course pathways were created: traditional, integrated, accelerated traditional and accelerated integrated. ***Glencoe Algebra 1, Glencoe Geometry,*** and ***Glencoe Algebra 2*** follow the traditional pathway.

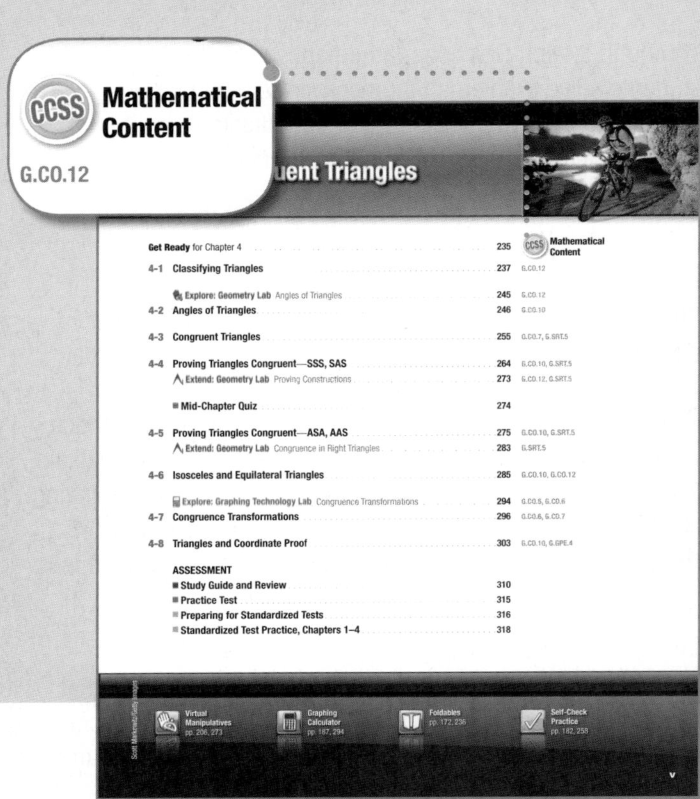

CCSS Mathematical Content

G.CO.12

...uent Triangles

How do I decode the standards?

This diagram provides clarity for decoding the standard identifiers.

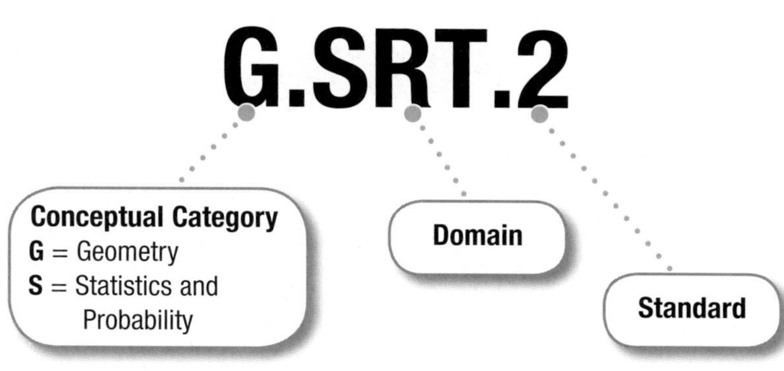

Domain Names	Abbreviations
Congruence	CO
Similarity, **R**ight Triangles, and **T**rigonometry	SRT
Circles	C
Expressing **G**eometric **P**roperties with **E**quations	GPE
Geometric **M**easurement and **D**imension	GMD
Modeling with **G**eometry	MG
Conditional **P**robability and the Rules of Probability	CP
Using Probability to **M**ake **D**ecisions	MD

There are numerous tools for implementing the Common Core State Standards available throughout the program, including:

- **Standards at point-of-use** in the Chapter Planner and in each lesson of the Teacher Edition,
- **Complete standards coverage** in ***Glencoe Geometry*** ensures that you have all the content you need to teach the standards,
- **Correlations** that show at a glance where each standard is addressed in ***Glencoe Geometry***.

You can also visit connectED.mcgraw-hill.com to learn more about the Common Core State Standards. There you can choose from an extensive collection of resources to use when planning instruction.

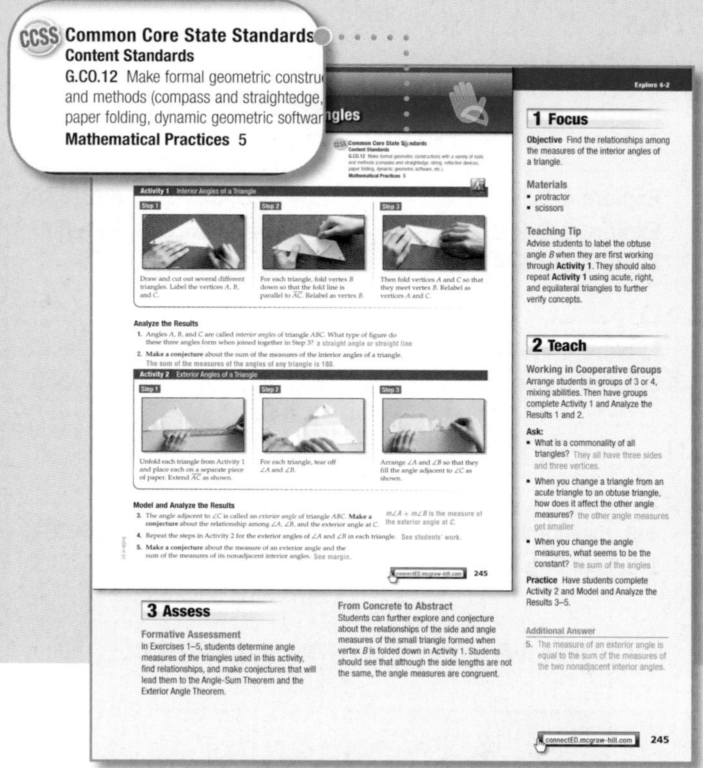

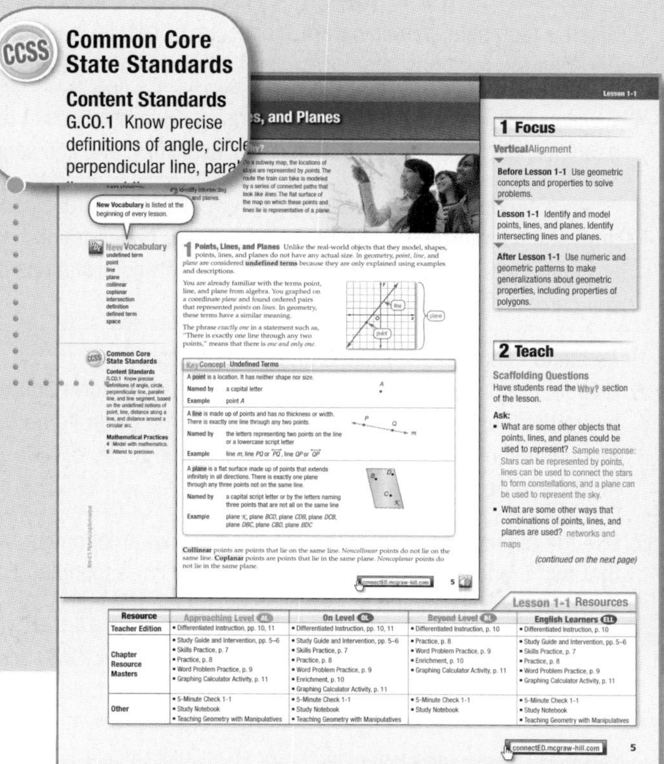

Common Core State Standards, Traditional Geometry Pathway, Correlated to *Glencoe Geometry*, Common Core Edition

Lessons in which the standard is the primary focus are indicated in **bold**.

Standards	Student Edition Lesson(s)	Student Edition Page(s)
Geometry		
Congruence G-CO		
Experiment with transformations in the plane. 1. Know precise definitions of angle, circle, perpendicular line, parallel line, and line segment, based on the undefined notions of point, line, distance along a line, and distance around a circular arc.	**1-1, 1-2, 1-3, 1-4, 3-1, 3-2, 10-1**	**5–12, 14–21, 25–35, 36–44, 173–178, 180–186, 697–705**
2. Represent transformations in the plane using, e.g., transparencies and geometry software; describe transformations as functions that take points in the plane as inputs and give other points as outputs. Compare transformations that preserve distance and angle to those that do not (e.g., translation versus horizontal stretch).	4-7, 7-6, 9-1, 9-2, **Explore 9-3,** 9-3, **Explore 9-4, 9-4, 9-6**	296–302, 511–517, 623–631, 632–638, **639,** 640–646, **650, 651–659, 674–681**
3. Given a rectangle, parallelogram, trapezoid, or regular polygon, describe the rotations and reflections that carry it onto itself.	**9-5**	**663–669**
4. Develop definitions of rotations, reflections, and translations in terms of angles, circles, perpendicular lines, parallel lines, and line segments.	**9-1, 9-2, 9-3,** Explore 9-4, 9-4	**623–631, 632–638, 640–646,** 650, 651–659
5. Given a geometric figure and a rotation, reflection, or translation, draw the transformed figure using, e.g., graph paper, tracing paper, or geometry software. Specify a sequence of transformations that will carry a given figure onto another.	**Explore 4-7, 9-1, 9-2, Explore 9-3, 9-3, Explore 9-4, 9-4**	**294–295, 623–631, 632–638, 639, 640–646, 650, 651–659**
Understand congruence in terms of rigid motions. 6. Use geometric descriptions of rigid motions to transform figures and to predict the effect of a given rigid motion on a given figure; given two figures, use the definition of congruence in terms of rigid motions to decide if they are congruent.	**Explore 4-7, 4-7,** 9-1, 9-2, 9-3, 9-4, Extend 9-6	**294–295, 296–302,** 623–631, 632–638, 640–646, 651–659, 682–683
7. Use the definition of congruence in terms of rigid motions to show that two triangles are congruent if and only if corresponding pairs of sides and corresponding pairs of angles are congruent.	**4-3,** Explore 4-7, **4-7,** 9-1, 9-2, 9-3, 9-4, Extend 9-6	**255–263,** 294–295, **296–302,** 623–631, 632–638, 640–646, 651–659, 682–683
8. Explain how the criteria for triangle congruence (ASA, SAS, and SSS) follow from the definition of congruence in terms of rigid motions.	4-7, **Extend 9-6**	296–302, **682–683**

(+) Advanced Mathematics Standards ★ Mathematical Modeling Standards

Standards	Student Edition Lesson(s)	Student Edition Page(s)
Prove geometric theorems. 9. Prove theorems about lines and angles.	**2-7, 2-8, 3-2, 3-5, 5-1**	**144–150, 151–159, 180–186, 207–214, 324–333**
10. Prove theorems about triangles.	**4-2, 4-3, 4-4, 4-5, 4-6, 4-8, 5-1, 5-2, 5-3, 5-4, 5-5, 5-6, 7-4, Explore 8-2**	**246–254, 255–263, 264–272, 275–282, 285–293, 303–309, 324–333, 335–343, 344–351, 355–362, 371–380, 490–499, 546**
11. Prove theorems about parallelograms.	**6-2, 6-3, 6-4, 6-5**	**403–411, 413–421, 423–429, 431–438**
Make geometric constructions. 12. Make formal geometric constructions with a variety of tools and methods (compass and straightedge, string, reflective devices, paper folding, dynamic geometric software, etc.).	**1-2, 1-3, 1-4, Extend 1-5, Extend 1-6, 2-7, Explore 3-2, 3-5, 3-6, 4-1, Explore 4-2, 4-4, Extend 4-4, 4-5, 4-6, Explore 5-1, Explore 5-2, Explore 5-5, Explore 6-3, 6-3, 6-4, 6-5, 7-4, 9-1, Explore 9-3, Extend 9-5, 10-3, 10-5, Extend 10-5**	**14–21, 25–35, 36–44, 55, 65–66, 144–150, 179, 207–214, 215–224, 237–244, 245, 264–272, 273, 275–282, 285–293, 323, 334, 363, 412, 413–421, 423–429, 430–438, 490–499, 623–631, 639, 670–671, 715–722, 732–739, 740**
13. Construct an equilateral triangle, a square, and a regular hexagon inscribed in a circle.	**Extend 10-5**	**740**
Similarity, Right Triangles, and Trigonometry G-SRT		
Understand similarity in terms of similarity transformations. 1. Verify experimentally the properties of dilations given by a center and a scale factor: a. A dilation takes a line not passing through the center of the dilation to a parallel line, and leaves a line passing through the center unchanged.	**Explore 9-6,** 9-6	**672–673,** 674–681
b. The dilation of a line segment is longer or shorter in the ratio given by the scale factor.	**Explore 9-6, 9-6**	**672–673, 674–681**
2. Given two figures, use the definition of similarity in terms of similarity transformations to decide if they are similar; explain using similarity transformations the meaning of similarity for triangles as the equality of all corresponding pairs of angles and the proportionality of all corresponding pairs of sides.	**7-2,** 7-3, **7-6, Extend 9-6**	**469–477,** 478–487, **511–517, 682–683**
3. Use the properties of similarity transformations to establish the AA criterion for two triangles to be similar.	7-3, 7-6, **Extend 9-6**	478–487, 511–517, **682–683**
Prove theorems involving similarity. 4. Prove theorems about triangles.	**7-3, 7-4, 7-5, 8-1**	**478–487, 490–499, 501–508, 537–545**

Standards	Student Edition Lesson(s)	Student Edition Page(s)
5. Use congruence and similarity criteria for triangles to solve problems and to prove relationships in geometric figures.	**4-3, 4-4, Extend 4-4, 4-5, Extend 4-5, 7-3, 7-4, 7-5, 7-6, 8-1**	**255–263, 264–272, 273, 275–282, 283–284, 478–487, 490–499, 501–508, 511–517, 537–545**
Define trigonometric ratios and solve problems involving right triangles. 6. Understand that by similarity, side ratios in right triangles are properties of the angles in the triangle, leading to definitions of trigonometric ratios for acute angles.	**8-3, Explore 8-4, 8-4, Extend 8-4**	**558–566, 567, 568–577, 578**
7. Explain and use the relationship between the sine and cosine of complementary angles.	**8-4**	**568–577**
8. Use trigonometric ratios and the Pythagorean Theorem to solve right triangles in applied problems.★	**8-2,** 8-4, **8-5,** 8-6	**547–555,** 568–577, **580–587,** 588–597
Apply trigonometry to general triangles. 9. (+) Derive the formula $A = \frac{1}{2}ab \sin(C)$ for the area of a triangle by drawing an auxiliary line from a vertex perpendicular to the opposite side.	**8-6**	**588–597**
10. (+) Prove the Laws of Sines and Cosines and use them to solve problems.	**8-6**	**588–597**
11. (+) Understand and apply the Law of Sines and the Law of Cosines to find unknown measurements in right and non-right triangles (e.g., surveying problems, resultant forces).	8-6, **Extend 8-6**	588–597, **598**
Circles G-C		
Understand and apply theorems about circles. 1. Prove that all circles are similar.	**10-1**	**697–705**
2. Identify and describe relationships among inscribed angles, radii, and chords.	**10-1, 10-2, 10-3, 10-4,** 10-5	**697–705, 706–714, 715–722, 723–730,** 732–739
3. Construct the inscribed and circumscribed circles of a triangle, and prove properties of angles for a quadrilateral inscribed in a circle.	**10-4, Extend 10-5**	**723–730, 740**
4. (+) Construct a tangent line from a point outside a given circle to the circle.	**10-5**	**732–739**
Find arc lengths and areas of sectors of circles. 5. Derive using similarity the fact that the length of the arc intercepted by an angle is proportional to the radius, and define the radian measure of the angle as the constant of proportionality; derive the formula for the area of a sector.	**10-2, 11-3**	**706–714, 798–804**

(+) Advanced Mathematics Standards ★ Mathematical Modeling Standards

Standards	Student Edition Lesson(s)	Student Edition Page(s)
Expressing Geometric Properties with Equations G-GPE		
Translate between the geometric description and the equation for a conic section. 1. Derive the equation of a circle of given center and radius using the Pythagorean Theorem; complete the square to find the center and radius of a circle given by an equation.	**10-8**	**757–763**
2. Derive the equation of a parabola given a focus and directrix.	**Extend 10-8**	**764–765**
Use coordinates to prove simple geometric theorems algebraically. 4. Use coordinates to prove simple geometric theorems algebraically.	**4-8, 6-2, 6-3, 6-4, 6-5, 6-6, 10-8**	**303–309, 403–411, 413–421, 423–429, 430–438, 439–448, 757–763**
5. Prove the slope criteria for parallel and perpendicular lines and use them to solve geometric problems (e.g., find the equation of a line parallel or perpendicular to a given line that passes through a given point).	**Explore 3-3, 3-3, 3-4, Extend 3-4, Extend 7-3**	**187, 188–196, 198–205, 206, 488–489**
6. Find the point on a directed line segment between two given points that partitions the segment in a given ratio.	1-3, 7-4, **8-7,** 9-6, **10-8**	25–35, 490–499, **600–608,** 674–681, **757–763**
7. Use coordinates to compute perimeters of polygons and areas of triangles and rectangles, e.g., using the distance formula.★	**1-6, 11-1**	**56–64, 779–786**
Geometric Measurement and Dimension G-GMD		
Explain volume formulas and use them to solve problems. 1. Give an informal argument for the formulas for the circumference of a circle, area of a circle, volume of a cylinder, pyramid, and cone.	**10-1, 11-3, 12-4, 12-5, 12-6**	**697–705, 798–804, 863–870, 873–879, 880–887**
3. Use volume formulas for cylinders, pyramids, cones, and spheres to solve problems.★	**1-7, 12-4, 12-5, 12-6**	**67–74, 863–870, 873–879, 880–887**
Visualize relationships between two-dimensional and three-dimensional objects. 4. Identify the shapes of two-dimensional cross-sections of three-dimensional objects, and identify three-dimensional objects generated by rotations of two-dimensional objects.	**Extend 9-3, 12-1**	**647–648, 839–844**
Modeling with Geometry G-MG		
Apply geometric concepts in modeling situations. 1. Use geometric shapes, their measures, and their properties to describe objects (e.g., modeling a tree trunk or a human torso as a cylinder).★	Throughout the text; for example, Extend 1-1, Extend 1-7, 6-1, 11-5, 12-3	Throughout the text; for example, 13, 75–77, 393–401, 818–824, 854–862
2. Apply concepts of density based on area and volume in modeling situations (e.g., persons per square mile, BTUs per cubic foot).★	**Extend 11-2,** 12-4, 12-5	**797,** 863–870, 873–879

Standards	Student Edition Lesson(s)	Student Edition Page(s)
3. Apply geometric methods to solve problems (e.g., designing an object or structure to satisfy physical constraints or minimize cost; working with typographic grid systems based on ratios).★	2-5, 3-6, 5-1, 5-2, 5-5, 6-6, 7-1, 7-7, 8-2, 10-3, 11-2, 11-4, 12-2, 12-4, 12-6, 13-4	127–134, 215–224, 324–333, 335–343, 364–370, 439–448, 461–467, 518–523, 547–555, 715–722, 789–796, 807–815, 846–853, 863–870, 880–887, 939–946
Statistics and Probability		
Conditional Probability and the Rules of Probability S-CP		
Understand independence and conditional probability and use them to interpret data. 1. Describe events as subsets of a sample space (the set of outcomes) using characteristics (or categories) of the outcomes, or as unions, intersections, or complements of other events ("or," "and," "not").	**13-5, 13-6**	**947–953, 956–963**
2. Understand that two events *A* and *B* are independent if the probability of *A* and *B* occurring together is the product of their probabilities, and use this characterization to determine if they are independent.	**13-5**	**947–953**
3. Understand the conditional probability of *A* given *B* as $\frac{P(A \text{ and } B)}{P(B)}$, and interpret independence of *A* and *B* as saying that the conditional probability of *A* given *B* is the same as the probability of *A*, and the conditional probability of *B* given *A* is the same as the probability of *B*.	**13-5**	**947–953**
4. Construct and interpret two-way frequency tables of data when two categories are associated with each object being classified. Use the two-way table as a sample space to decide if events are independent and to approximate conditional probabilities.	**Extend 13-5**	**954–955**
5. Recognize and explain the concepts of conditional probability and independence in everyday language and everyday situations.	13-5	947–953
Use the rules of probability to compute probabilities of compound events in a uniform probability model. 6. Find the conditional probability of *A* given *B* as the fraction of *B*'s outcomes that also belong to *A*, and interpret the answer in terms of the model.	13-5, Extend 13-5	947–953, 954–955
7. Apply the Addition Rule, $P(A \text{ or } B) = P(A) + P(B) - P(A \text{ and } B)$, and interpret the answer in terms of the model.	**13-6**	**956–963**
8. (+) Apply the general Multiplication Rule in a uniform probability model, $P(A \text{ and } B) = P(A)P(B\|A) = P(B)P(A\|B)$, and interpret the answer in terms of the model.	**13-5**	**947–953**

(+) Advanced Mathematics Standards ★ Mathematical Modeling Standards

Standards	Student Edition Lesson(s)	Student Edition Page(s)
9. (+) Use permutations and combinations to compute probabilities of compound events and solve problems.	**13-2**	**922–930**
Using Probability to Make Decisions S-MD		
Use probability to evaluate outcomes of decisions. 6. (+) Use probabilities to make fair decisions (e.g., drawing by lots, using a random number generator).	0-3, 13-4	P8–P9, 939–946
7. (+) Analyze decisions and strategies using probability concepts (e.g., product testing, medical testing, pulling a hockey goalie at the end of a game).	0-3, 13-3, 13-5	P8–P9, 931–937, 947–953

Common Core State Standards for Mathematical Practice, Correlated to *Glencoe Geometry*, Common Core Edition

1. **Make sense of problems and persevere in solving them.**
   Glencoe Geometry exhibits these practices throughout the entire program. Some specific lessons for review are: Lessons 1-5, 2-1, 3-5, 4-5, 5-4, 6-1, 7-5, 8-2, 9-5, 10-2, 11-2, 12-6, and 13-5.

2. **Reason abstractly and quantitatively.**
   Glencoe Geometry exhibits these practices throughout the entire program. Some specific lessons for review are: 1-3, 2-7, 3-6, 4-2, 5-3, 6-4, 7-7, 8-4, 9-6, 10-6, 11-4, Extend 12-4, and 13-2.

3. **Construct viable arguments and critique the reasoning of others.**
   Glencoe Geometry exhibits these practices throughout the entire program. Some specific lessons for review are: Lessons 1-7, 2-5, 3-5, 4-4, 5-4, 6-6, 7-4, 8-3, 9-1, 10-1, 11-5, 12-4, and 13-3.

4. **Model with mathematics.**
   Glencoe Geometry exhibits these practices throughout the entire program. Some specific lessons for review are: Lessons 1-1, 2-3, 3-1, 4-7, 5-6, 6-5, 7-7, 8-7, 9-3, 10-1, 11-4, 12-3, and 13-3.

5. **Use appropriate tools strategically.**
   Glencoe Geometry exhibits these practices throughout the entire program. Some specific lessons for review are: Extend 1-6, 2-7, Explore 3-3, Explore 4-7, Explore 5-5, Extend 6-1, 7-4, Explore 8-4, Explore 9-4, Extend 10-5, Explore 11-2, and Extend 12-4.

6. **Attend to precision.**
   Glencoe Geometry exhibits these practices throughout the entire program. Some specific lessons for review are: Extend 1-2, Lessons 2-7, 3-3, 4-4, 5-1, 6-2, 7-3, 8-1, 9-2, 10-3, 11-3, 12-5, and 13-2.

7. **Look for and make use of structure.**
   Glencoe Geometry exhibits these practices throughout the entire program. Some specific lessons for review are: Lessons 1-3, 2-1, 3-6, 4-1, Explore 5-5, 6-1, Extend 7-1, Explore 8-4, 9-5, 10-6, 11-4, 12-2, and 13-1.

8. **Look for and express regularity in repeated reasoning.**
   Glencoe Geometry exhibits these practices throughout the entire program. Some specific lessons for review are: Lessons 1-3, 2-1, Explore 3-3, 4-6, 5-3, 6-1, 7-1, 8-4, Explore 9-3, Extend 10-8, Extend 11-2, Explore 12-1, and 13-1.

Notes

Notes

Notes

Notes

CHAPTER 0 Preparing for Geometry

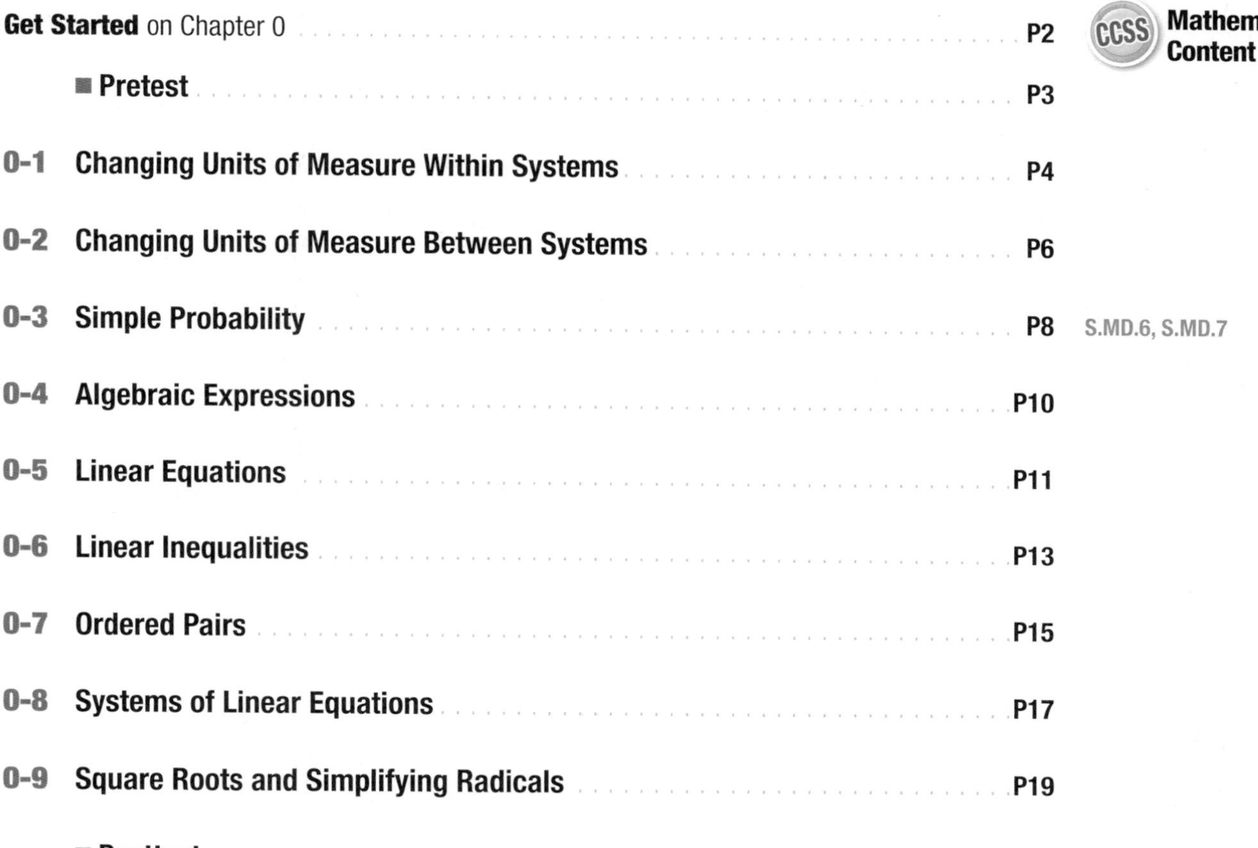

CCSS Mathematical Content

connectED.mcgraw-hill.com Your Digital Math Portal

Vocabulary p. P8

Multilingual eGlossary p. P2

Personal Tutor p. P4

Foldables p. P2

CHAPTER 1 Tools of Geometry

connectED.mcgraw-hill.com **Your Digital Math Portal**

Animation pp. 13, 120

Vocabulary pp. 78, 127

Multilingual eGlossary pp. 4, 90

Personal Tutor pp. 37, 116

CHAPTER 2 Reasoning and Proof

CCSS Mathematical Content

Virtual Manipulatives pp. 27, 102

Graphing Calculator p. 65

Foldables pp. 4, 90

Self-Check Practice pp. 8, 89

CHAPTER 3 Parallel and Perpendicular Lines

connectED.mcgraw-hill.com **Your Digital Math Portal**

Animation pp. 215, 234

Vocabulary pp. 198, 237

Multilingual eGlossary pp. 172, 236

Personal Tutor pp. 201, 297

Jeremy Woodhouse/Masterfile

CHAPTER 4 Congruent Triangles

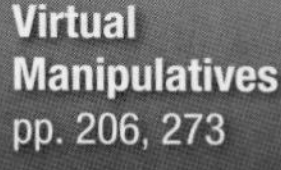

Virtual Manipulatives pp. 206, 273

Graphing Calculator pp. 187, 294

Foldables pp. 172, 236

Self-Check Practice pp. 182, 258

Scott Markewitz/Getty Images

CHAPTER 5 Relationships in Triangles

connectED.mcgraw-hill.com **Your Digital Math Portal**

Animation pp. 334, 423

Vocabulary pp. 322, 439

Multilingual eGlossary pp. 322, 392

Personal Tutor pp. 347, 402

Cusp/SuperStock

CHAPTER 6 Quadrilaterals

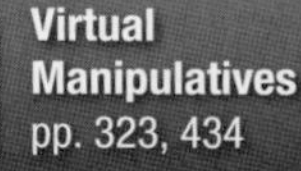

Virtual Manipulatives pp. 323, 434

Graphing Calculator pp. 363, 412

Foldables pp. 322, 392

Self-Check Practice pp. 375, 444

CHAPTER 7 Proportions and Similarity

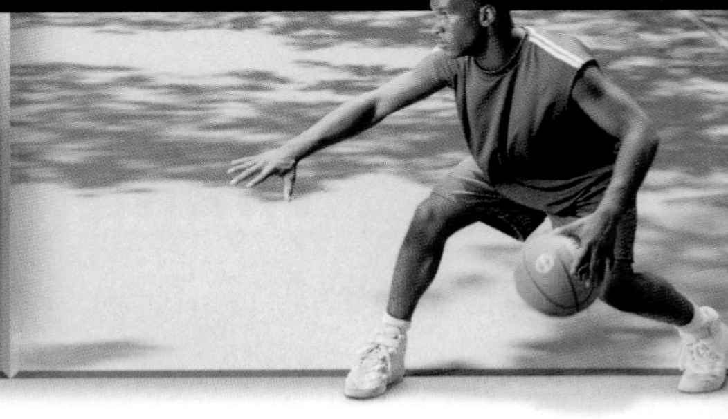

connectED.mcgraw-hill.com Your Digital Math Portal

Animation pp. 494, 534

Vocabulary pp. 524, 600

Multilingual eGlossary pp. 460, 536

Personal Tutor pp. 470, 459

CHAPTER 8
Right Triangles and Trigonometry

Virtual Manipulatives pp. 509, 569

Graphing Calculator pp. 570, 567

Foldables pp. 460, 536

Self-Check Practice pp. 483, 562

CHAPTER 9

Transformations and Symmetry

connectED.mcgraw-hill.com **Your Digital Math Portal**

Animation pp. 660, 707

Vocabulary pp. 663, 766

Multilingual eGlossary pp. 622, 696

Personal Tutor pp. 650, 758

CHAPTER 10

Circles

Mathematical Content

James Randklev/Photographer's Choice RF/Getty Images

Virtual Manipulatives
pp. 642, 740

Foldables
pp. 622, 696

Self-Check Practice
pp. 621, 745

CHAPTER 11 Areas of Polygons and Circles

connectED.mcgraw-hill.com Your Digital Math Portal

Animation pp. 806, 875

Vocabulary pp. 778, 854

Multilingual eGlossary pp. 778, 836

Personal Tutor pp. 797, 840

CHAPTER 12 Extending Surface Area and Volume

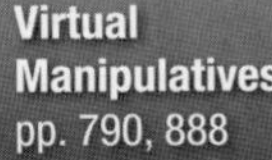
Virtual Manipulatives pp. 790, 888

Graphing Calculator pp. 787, 871

Foldables pp. 778, 836

Self-Check Practice pp. 800, 849

CHAPTER 13 Probability and Measurement

CCSS Mathematical Content

connectED.mcgraw-hill.com **Your Digital Math Portal**

Animation p. 964

Vocabulary p. 915

Multilingual eGlossary p. 914

Personal Tutor p. 956

Virtual Manipulatives p. 939

Foldables p. 914

Self-Check Practice p. 918

Image Source/SuperStock

Student Handbook

Contents

How to Use the Student Handbook

Rubberball/Getty Images

CHAPTER 0 Preparing for Geometry

Using Chapter 0

The concepts presented in Chapter 0 are review from previous courses. You may wish to use all or some of the chapter at the beginning of the school year to refresh students' skills. Or you may wish to begin with Chapter 1 and use the Chapter 0 lessons as needed to reinforce prerequisite skills as you progress through the program.

Now

Chapter 0 contains lessons on topics from previous courses. You can use this chapter in various ways.

- Begin the school year by taking the Pretest. If you need additional review, complete the lessons in this chapter. To verify that you have successfully reviewed the topics, take the Posttest.
- As you work through the text, you may find that there are topics you need to review. When this happens, complete the individual lessons that you need.
- Use this chapter for reference. When you have questions about any of these topics, flip back to this chapter to review definitions or key concepts.

Judith Worley/Painet Inc

FOLDABLES StudyOrganizer

Dinah Zike's Foldables®

Each chapter of *Glencoe Geometry* features a Foldables Study Organizer students can make to organize their notes. Encourage students to use these tools to make their study time more productive.

Get Started on the Chapter

You will review several concepts, skills, and vocabulary terms as you study Chapter 0. To get ready, identify important terms and organize your resources.

FOLDABLES StudyOrganizer

Throughout this text, you will be invited to use Foldables to organize your notes.

Why should you use them?

- They help you organize, display, and arrange information.
- They make great study guides, specifically designed for you.
- You can use them as your math journal for recording main ideas, problem-solving strategies, examples, or questions you may have.
- They give you a chance to improve your math vocabulary.

How should you use them?

- Write general information — titles, vocabulary terms, concepts, questions, and main ideas — on the front tabs of your Foldable.
- Write specific information — ideas, your thoughts, answers to questions, steps, notes, and definitions — under the tabs.
- Use the tabs for:
  - math concepts in parts, like types of triangles,
  - steps to follow, or
  - parts of a problem, like *compare* and *contrast* (2 parts) or *what*, *where*, *when*, *why*, and *how* (5 parts).
- You may want to store your Foldables in a plastic zipper bag that you have three-hole punched to fit in your notebook.

When should you use them?

- Set up your Foldable as you begin a chapter, or when you start learning a new concept.
- Write in your Foldable every day.
- Use your Foldable to review for homework, quizzes, and tests.

ReviewVocabulary

English		Español
experiment	p. P8	experimento
trial	p. P8	prueba
outcome	p. P8	resultado
event	p. P8	evento
probability	p. P8	probabilidad
theoretical probability	p. P9	probabilidad teórica
experimental probability	p. P9	probabilidad experimental
ordered pair	p. P15	par ordenado
x-coordinate	p. P15	coordenada *x*
y-coordinate	p. P15	coordenada *y*
quadrant	p. P15	cuadrante
origin	p. P15	origen
system of equations	p. P17	sistema de ecuaciones
substitution	p. P17	sustitución
elimination	p. P18	eliminación
Product Property	p. P19	Propriedad de Producto
Quotient Property	p. P19	Propriedad de Cociente

Pretest

State which metric unit you would probably use to measure each item.

1. length of a computer keyboard cm
2. mass of a large dog kg

Complete each sentence.

3. 4 ft = _?_ in. 48
4. 21 ft = _?_ yd 7
5. 180 g = _?_ kg 0.18
6. 3 T = _?_ lb 6000
7. 32 g ≈ _?_ oz 1.13
8. 3 mi ≈ _?_ km 4.8
9. 35 yd ≈ _?_ m 32
10. 5.1 L ≈ _?_ qt 5.4

11. **TUNA** A can of tuna is 6 ounces. About how many grams is it? 170

12. **CRACKERS** A box of crackers is 453 grams. About how many pounds is it? Round to the nearest pound. 1

13. **DISTANCE** A road sign in Canada gives the distance to Toronto as 140 kilometers. What is this distance to the nearest mile? 87

PROBABILITY A bag contains 3 blue chips, 7 red chips, 4 yellow chips, and 5 green chips. A chip is randomly drawn from the bag. Find each probability. 14–17. See margin.

14. P(yellow)
15. P(green)
16. P(red or blue)
17. P(not red)

Evaluate each expression if $r = 3$, $q = 1$, and $w = -2$.

18. $4r + q$ 13
19. $rw - 6$ −12
20. $\frac{r + 3q}{4r}$ $\frac{1}{2}$
21. $\frac{5w}{3r + q}$ −1
22. $|2 - r| + 17$ 18
23. $8 + |q - 5|$ 12

Solve each equation.

24. $k + 3 = 14$ 11
25. $a - 7 = 9$ 16
26. $5c = 20$ 4
27. $n + 2 = -11$ −13
28. $6t - 18 = 30$ 8
29. $4x + 7 = -1$ −2
30. $\frac{r}{4} = -8$ −32
31. $\frac{3}{5}b = -2$ $-\frac{10}{3}$
32. $-\frac{w}{2} = -9$ 18
33. $3y - 15 = y + 1$ 8
34. $27 - 6d = 7 + 4d$ 2
35. $2(m - 16) = 44$ 38

Solve each inequality.

36. $y - 13 < 2$ $\{y \mid y < 15\}$
37. $t + 8 \geq 19$ $\{t \mid t \geq 11\}$
38. $\frac{n}{4} > -6$ $\{n \mid n > -24\}$
39. $9a \leq 45$ $\{a \mid a \leq 5\}$
40. $x + 12 > -14$
41. $-2w < 24$
42. $-\frac{n}{7} \geq 3$ $\{n \mid n \leq -21\}$
43. $-\frac{b}{5} \leq -6$ $\{b \mid b \geq 30\}$

40. $\{x \mid x > -26\}$ 41. $\{w \mid w > -12\}$

Write the ordered pair for each point shown.

44. F (5, 2)
45. H (4, −2)
46. A (1, 0)
47. D (−3, 5)

Graph and label each point on the coordinate plane above.

48. $B(4, 1)$
49. $G(0, -3)$
50. $R(-2, -4)$
51. $P(-3, 3)$

52. Graph the triangle with vertices $J(1, -4)$, $K(2, 3)$, and $L(-1, 2)$. See margin.

53. Graph four points that satisfy the equation $y = 2x - 1$. See margin.

Solve each system of equations.

54. $y = 2x$, $y = -x + 6$ (2, 4)
55. $-3x - y = 4$, $4x + 2y = -8$ (0, −4)
56. $y = 2x + 1$, $y = 3x$ (1, 3)
57. $\frac{1}{2}x - y = -1$, $x - 2y = 5$ no solution
58. $x + y = -6$, $2x - y = 3$ (−1, −5)
59. $\frac{1}{3}x - 3y = -4$, $x - 9y = -12$ infinitely many solutions

Simplify.

60. $\sqrt{18}$ $3\sqrt{2}$
61. $\sqrt{\frac{25}{49}}$ $\frac{5}{7}$
62. $\sqrt{24x^2y^3}$ $2|x|y\sqrt{6y}$
63. $\frac{3}{4 - \sqrt{5}}$ $\frac{12 + 3\sqrt{5}}{11}$

Using the Pretest

The Chapter 0 Pretest assesses students' understanding of the concepts presented in Chapter 0. You may use the pretest to determine whether students need to complete each lesson in Chapter 0 before beginning the content in Chapter 1.

Additional Answers

14. $\frac{4}{19}$ or about 21%

15. $\frac{5}{19}$ or about 26%

16. $\frac{10}{19}$ or about 53%

17. $\frac{12}{19}$ or about 63%

52.

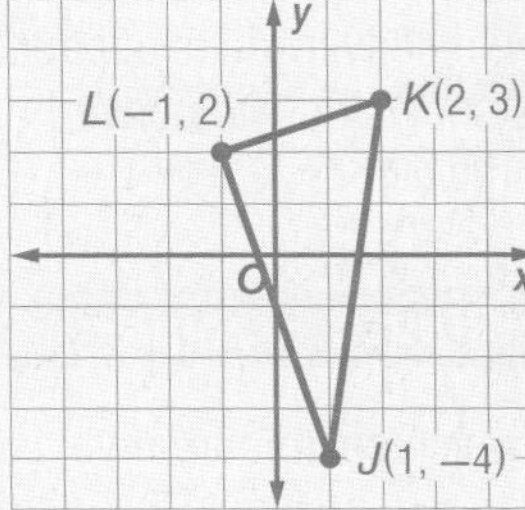

53. Sample answer:

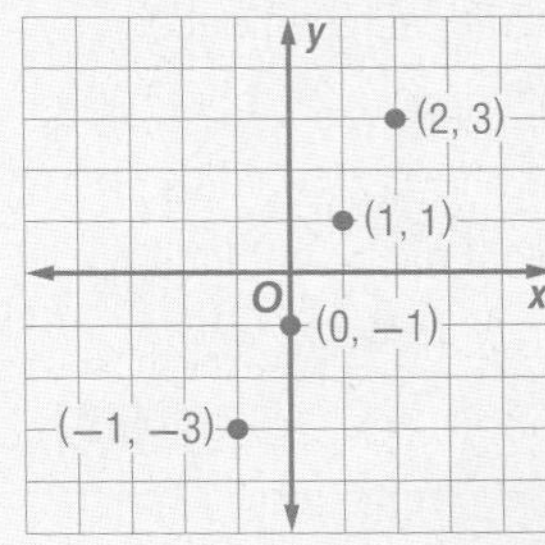

connectED.mcgraw-hill.com P3

1 Focus

VerticalAlignment

Lesson 0-1 Convert units of measure in the same system.

After Lesson 0-1 Convert units of measure between the customary and metric systems.

2 Teach

Example 1 shows how to choose the most appropriate measurement. **Examples 2 and 3** show how to convert units of length. **Example 4** shows how to convert units of capacity. **Example 5** shows how to convert units of mass and weight.

Additional Examples

1 State which customary unit you would use to measure the length of the classroom. feet

2 Complete each sentence.

a. 8.7 km = __?__ m 8700

b. 18.3 ft = __?__ yd 6.1

3 Complete each sentence.

a. 220 mm = __?__ m 0.22

b. 9,680 yd = __?__ mi 5.5

LESSON 0-1 Changing Units of Measure Within Systems

Objective

- Convert units of measure within the customary and metric systems.

Example 1 Choose Best Unit of Measure

State which metric unit you would use to measure the length of your pen.

A pen has a small length, but not very small. The *centimeter* is the appropriate unit of measure.

Metric Units of Length
1 kilometer (km) = 1000 meters (m)
1 m = 100 centimeters (cm)
1 cm = 10 millimeters (mm)

Customary Units of Length
1 foot (ft) = 12 inches (in.)
1 yard (yd) = 3 ft
1 mile (mi) = 5280 ft

- To convert from larger units to smaller units, multiply.
- To convert from smaller units to larger units, divide.
- To use dimensional analysis, multiply by the ratio of the units.

Example 2 Convert from Larger Units to Smaller Units of Length

Complete each sentence.

a. 4.2 km = __?__ m

There are 1000 meters in a kilometer.
4.2 km × 1000 = 4200 m

b. 13 yd = __?__ ft

There are 3 feet in a yard.
13 yd × 3 = 39 ft

Example 3 Convert from Smaller Units to Larger Units of Length

Complete each sentence.

a. 17 mm = __?__ m

There are 100 centimeters in a meter. First change *millimeters* to *centimeters*.

17 mm = __?__ cm — smaller unit → larger unit

17 mm ÷ 10 = 1.7 cm — Since 10 mm = 1 cm, divide by 10.

Then change *centimeters* to *meters*.

1.7 cm = __?__ m — smaller unit → larger unit

1.7 cm ÷ 100 = 0.017 m — Since 100 cm = 1 m, divide by 100.

b. 6600 yd = __?__ mi

Use dimensional analysis.

$$6600\ \text{yd} \times \frac{3\ \text{ft}}{1\ \text{yd}} \times \frac{1\ \text{mi}}{5280\ \text{ft}} = 3.75\ \text{mi}$$

Metric Units of Capacity
1 liter (L) = 1000 milliliters (mL)

Customary Units of Capacity	
1 cup (c) = 8 fluid ounces (fl oz)	1 quart (qt) = 2 pt
1 pint (pt) = 2 c	1 gallon (gal) = 4 qt

Teach with Tech

Student Response System Create 6–10 slides using two metric units of length. Ask students whether they should multiply or divide by a power of 10 to change from the first unit of measurement to the second. Have students respond with A for multiply and B for divide. Then, for each example, ask students which power of 10 should be used.

StudyTip

Dimensional Analysis You can use dimensional analysis for any conversion in this lesson.

Example 4 Convert Units of Capacity

Complete each sentence.

a. 3.7 L = __?__ mL

There are 1000 milliliters in a liter.
3.7 L × 1000 = 3700 mL

b. 16 qt = __?__ gal

There are 4 quarts in a gallon.
16 qt ÷ 4 = 4 gal

c. 7 pt = __?__ fl oz

There are 8 fluid ounces in a cup.
First change *pints* to *cups*.
7 pt = __?__ c
7 pt × 2 = 14 c
Then change *cups* to *fluid ounces*.
14 c = __?__ fl oz
14 c × 8 = 112 fl oz

d. 4 gal = __?__ pt

There are 4 quarts in a gallon.
First change *gallons* to *quarts*.
4 gal = __?__ qt
4 gal × 4 = 16 qt
Then change *quarts* to *pints*.
16 qt = __?__ pt
16 qt × 2 = 32 pt

The mass of an object is the amount of matter that it contains.

Metric Units of Mass
1 kilogram (kg) = 1000 grams (g)
1 g = 1000 milligrams (mg)

Customary Units of Weight
1 pound (lb) = 16 ounces (oz)
1 ton (T) = 2000 lb

Example 5 Convert Units of Mass

Complete each sentence.

a. 5.47 kg = __?__ mg

There are 1000 milligrams in a gram.
Change *kilograms* to *grams*.
5.47 kg = __?__ g
5.47 kg × 1000 = 5470 g
Then change *grams* to *milligrams*.
5470 g = __?__ mg
5470 g × 1000 = 5,470,000 mg

b. 5 T = __?__ oz

There are 16 ounces in a pound.
Change *tons* to *pounds*.
5 T = __?__ lb
5 T × 2000 = 10,000 lb
Then change *pounds* to *ounces*.
10,000 lb = __?__ oz
10,000 lb × 16 = 160,000 oz

Exercises

State which metric unit you would probably use to measure each item.

1. radius of a tennis ball cm
2. length of a notebook cm
3. mass of a textbook kg
4. mass of a beach ball g
5. liquid in a cup mL
6. water in a bathtub L

Complete each sentence.

7. 120 in. = __?__ ft 10
8. 18 ft = __?__ yd 6
9. 10 km = __?__ m 10,000
10. 210 mm = __?__ cm 21
11. 180 mm = __?__ m 0.18
12. 3100 m = __?__ km 3.1
13. 90 in. = __?__ yd 2.5
14. 5280 yd = __?__ mi 3
15. 8 yd = __?__ ft 24
16. 0.62 km = __?__ m 620
17. 370 mL = __?__ L 0.370
18. 12 L = __?__ mL 12,000
19. 32 fl oz = __?__ c 4
20. 5 qt = __?__ c 20
21. 10 pt = __?__ qt 5
22. 48 c = __?__ gal 3
23. 4 gal = __?__ qt 16
24. 36 mg = __?__ g 0.036
25. 13 lb = __?__ oz 208
26. 130 g = __?__ kg 0.130
27. 9.05 kg = __?__ g 9050

Additional Examples

4 Complete each sentence.

a. 12.5 L = __?__ mL 12,500
b. 24.8 qt = __?__ gal 6.2
c. 12 pt = __?__ fl oz 192
d. 7 gal = __?__ pt 56

5 Complete each sentence.

a. 7.89 kg = __?__ mg 7,890,000
b. 7 T = __?__ oz 224,000

WatchOut!

Ounces Point out to students that the number of fluid ounces in a cup is not the same as the number of ounces in a pound.

3 Assess

Formative Assessment

Use Exercises 1–27 to assess whether students understand how to convert units of measure in customary and metric units.

Ticket Out the Door Ask students to name different customary and metric units of length.

1 Focus

VerticalAlignment

Lesson 0-2 Convert units of measure between the customary and metric systems.

After Lesson 0-2 Find the probability of simple events.

2 Teach

Examples 1 and 2 show how to convert units of length. **Examples 3 and 4** show how to convert units of capacity. **Example 5** shows how to convert units of mass and weight.

Additional Examples

1 Complete each sentence.

a. 35 cm = __?__ in. 14

b. 8 mi = __?__ km 12.8

2 Complete: 1500 yd = __?__ km 1.35

3 Complete each sentence.

a. 8 L = __?__ qt 8.8

b. 3 pt = __?__ L 1.45

LESSON 0-2 Changing Units of Measure Between Systems

Objective

- Convert units of measure between the customary and metric systems.

The table below shows approximate equivalents between customary units of length and metric units of length.

Units of Length	
Customary → Metric	**Metric → Customary**
1 in. ≈ 2.5 cm	1 cm ≈ 0.4 in.
1 yd ≈ 0.9 m	1 m ≈ 1.1 yd
1 mi ≈ 1.6 km	1 km ≈ 0.6 mi

PT

Example 1 Convert Units of Length Between Systems

Complete each sentence.

a. 30 in. ≈ __?__ cm

There are approximately 2.5 centimeters in an inch.

30 in. × 2.5 = 75 cm

b. 5 km ≈ __?__ mi

There is approximately 0.6 mile in a kilometer.

5 km × 0.6 = 3 mi

PT

Example 2 Convert Units of Length Between Systems

Complete: 2000 yd ≈ __?__ km.

There is approximately 0.9 meter in a yard. First find the number of meters in 2000 yards.

2000 yd × 0.9 = 1800 m

Then change *meters* to *kilometers*. There are 1000 meters in a kilometer.

1800 m ÷ 1000 = 1.8 km

The table below shows approximate equivalents between customary units of capacity and metric units of capacity.

Units of Capacity	
Customary → Metric	**Metric → Customary**
1 qt ≈ 0.9 L	1 L ≈ 1.1 qt
1 pt ≈ 0.5 L	1 L ≈ 2.1 pt

PT

Example 3 Convert Units of Capacity Between Systems

Complete each sentence.

a. 7 qt ≈ __?__ L

There is approximately 0.9 liter in a quart.

7 qt × 0.9 = 6.3 L

b. 2 L ≈ __?__ pt

There are approximately 2.1 pints in a liter.

2 L × 2.1 = 4.2 pt

Teach with Tech

Web Search Show your students that a search engine can be used to check their answers for simple unit conversions. Demonstrate this to students by searching for a phrase such as “8 liters to gallons.”

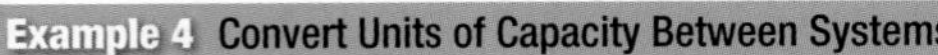
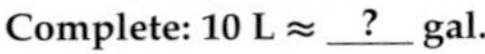

PT

Example 4 Convert Units of Capacity Between Systems

Complete: 10 L ≈ __?__ gal.

There are approximately 1.1 quarts in a liter. First find the number of quarts in 10 liters.

$10 \text{ L} \times 1.1 = 11 \text{ qt}$

Then change *quarts* to *gallons*. There are 4 quarts in a gallon.

$11 \text{ qt} \div 4 = 2.75 \text{ gal}$

You can also use dimensional analysis.

$$10 \cancel{\text{L}} \times \frac{1.1 \cancel{\text{qt}}}{1 \cancel{\text{L}}} \times \frac{1 \text{ gal}}{4 \cancel{\text{qt}}} = 2.75 \text{ gal}$$

StudyTip

Dimensional Analysis If the unit that you want to eliminate is in the numerator, make sure it is in the denominator of the ratio when you multiply. If it is in the denominator, make sure that it is in the numerator of the ratio.

The table below shows approximate equivalents between customary units of weight and metric units of mass.

Units of Weight/Mass	
Customary → Metric	**Metric → Customary**
1 oz ≈ 28.3 g	1 g ≈ 0.04 oz
1 lb ≈ 0.5 kg	1 kg ≈ 2.2 lb

PT

Example 5 Convert Units of Mass Between Systems

Complete each sentence.

a. 58.5 kg ≈ __?__ lb

There are approximately 2.2 pounds in a kilogram.

$58.5 \text{ kg} \times 2.2 = 128.7 \text{ lb}$

b. 14 oz ≈ __?__ g

There are approximately 28.3 grams in an ounce.

$14 \text{ oz} \times 28.3 = 396.2 \text{ g}$

Exercises

Complete each sentence.

1. 8 in. ≈ __?__ cm 20
2. 15 m ≈ __?__ yd 16.5
3. 11 qt ≈ __?__ L 12.1
4. 25 oz ≈ __?__ g 707.5
5. 10 mi ≈ __?__ km 16
6. 32 cm ≈ __?__ in. 12.8
7. 20 km ≈ __?__ mi 12
8. 9.5 L ≈ __?__ qt 10.45
9. 6 yd ≈ __?__ m 5.4
10. 4.3 kg ≈ __?__ lb 9.46
11. 10.7 L ≈ __?__ pt 22.47
12. 82.5 g ≈ __?__ oz 3.3
13. $2\frac{1}{4}$ lb ≈ __?__ kg 1.125
14. 10 ft ≈ __?__ m 3
15. $1\frac{1}{2}$ gal ≈ __?__ L 5.4
16. 350 g ≈ __?__ lb 0.77
17. 600 in. ≈ __?__ m 15
18. 2.1 km ≈ __?__ yd 2310
19. **CEREAL** A box of cereal is 13 ounces. About how many grams is it? 367.9 g
20. **FLOUR** A bag of flour is 2.26 kilograms. How much does it weigh? Round to the nearest pound. 5 lb
21. **SAUCE** A jar of tomato sauce is 1 pound 10 ounces. About how many grams is it? 735.8 g

Additional Examples

4 Complete: 24 L = __?__ gal 6.6

5 Complete each sentence.

a. 37.5 lb = __?__ kg 18.75

b. 90 g = __?__ oz 3.6

Tips for New Teachers

Reasoning Remind students to check the reasonableness of their answers when converting customary and metric measures. For example, ounces should always be smaller than grams and kilograms should always be smaller than pounds.

WatchOut!

Conversions Point out to students that tables provide only approximations for conversion between customary and metric measures. More precise approximations will give different answers.

3 Assess

Formative Assessment

Use Exercises 1–21 to assess whether students understand how to convert units of measure between customary and metric units.

Name the Math Have students describe the process of dimensional analysis.

1 Focus

VerticalAlignment

Lesson 0-3 Find the probability of simple events.

After Lesson 0-3 Use the order of operations to evaluate algebraic expressions.

2 Teach

Examples 1 and 2 show how to find simple probabilities by counting. **Example 3** shows how to find an experimental probability.

Additional Examples

1 Suppose that a die is rolled. What is the probability of rolling a 5? $\frac{1}{6}$

2 Suppose that a bag contains 5 white, 3 red, and 4 black marbles. What is the probability that a randomly chosen marble will not be white? $\frac{7}{12}$

LESSON 0-3 Simple Probability

Objective

- Find the probability of simple events.

NewVocabulary
experiment
trial
outcome
event
probability
theoretical probability
experimental probability

Common Core State Standards

Content Standards
S.MD.6 (+) Use probabilities to make fair decisions (e.g., drawing by lots, using a random number generator).
S.MD.7 (+) Analyze decisions and strategies using probability concepts (e.g., product testing, medical testing, pulling a hockey goalie at the end of a game).

Mathematical Practices
4 Model with mathematics.

A situation involving chance such as flipping a coin or rolling a die is an **experiment**. A single performance of an experiment such as rolling a die one time is a **trial**. The result of a trial is called an **outcome**. An **event** is one or more outcomes of an experiment.

When each outcome is equally likely to happen, the **probability** of an event is the ratio of the number of favorable outcomes to the number of possible outcomes. The probability of an event is always between 0 and 1, inclusive.

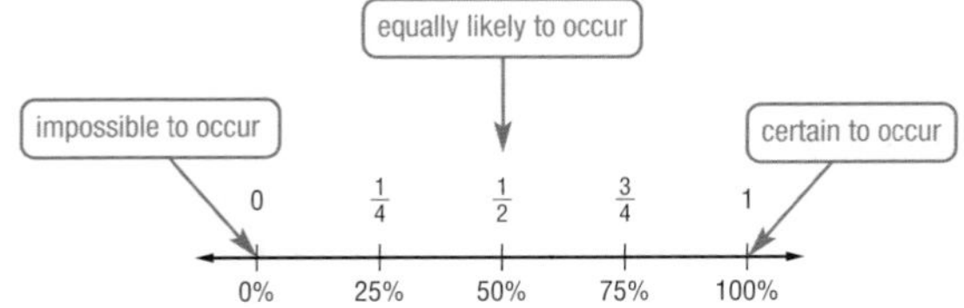

Example 1 Find Probability

Suppose a die is rolled. What is the probability of rolling an odd number?

There are 3 odd numbers on a die: 1, 3, and 5.

There are 6 possible outcomes: 1, 2, 3, 4, 5, and 6.

$$P(\text{odd}) = \frac{\text{number of favorable outcomes}}{\text{number of possible outcomes}}$$

$$= \frac{3}{6} \text{ or } \frac{1}{2}$$

The probability of rolling an odd number is $\frac{1}{2}$ or 50%.

For a given experiment, the sum of the probabilities of all possible outcomes must sum to 1.

Example 2 Find Probability

Suppose a bag contains 4 red, 3 green, 6 blue, and 2 yellow marbles. What is the probability a randomly chosen marble will not be yellow?

Since the sum of the probabilities of all of the colors must sum to 1, subtract the probability that the marble will be yellow from 1.

The probability that the marble will be yellow is $\frac{2}{15}$ because there are 2 yellow marbles and 15 total marbles.

$$P(\text{not yellow}) = 1 - P(\text{yellow})$$

$$= 1 - \frac{2}{15}$$

$$= \frac{13}{15}$$

The probability that the marble will not be yellow is $\frac{13}{15}$ or about 87%.

Teach with Tech

Portable Media Player Have students find the total number of songs on their portable media player and the number of songs for each genre of music. Ask students to find the probability that a randomly chosen song will be from that genre.

The probabilities in Examples 1 and 2 are called theoretical probabilities. The **theoretical probability** is what *should* occur. The **experimental probability** is what *actually* occurs when a probability experiment is repeated many times.

StudyTip

Experimental Probability The experimental probability of an experiment is not necessarily the same as the theoretical probability, but when an experiment is repeated many times, the experimental probability should be close to the theoretical probability.

Example 3 Find Experimental Probability

The table shows the results of an experiment in which a number cube was rolled. Find the experimental probability of rolling a 3.

Outcome	Tally	Frequency
1	𝍸 |	6
2	||||	4
3	𝍸 ||	7
4	|||	3
5	||||	4
6	|	1

$P(3) = \frac{\text{number of times 3 occurs}}{\text{total number of outcomes}}$ or $\frac{7}{25}$

The experimental probability for getting a 3 in this case is $\frac{7}{25}$ or 28%.

Exercises

A die is rolled. Find the probability of each outcome.

1. P(less than 3) $\frac{1}{3}$ or 33%
2. P(even) $\frac{1}{2}$ or 50%
3. P(greater than 2) $\frac{2}{3}$ or 67%
4. P(prime) $\frac{2}{3}$ or 67%
5. P(4 or 2) $\frac{1}{3}$ or 33%
6. P(integer) 1 or 100%

A jar contains 65 pennies, 27 nickels, 30 dimes, and 18 quarters. A coin is randomly selected from the jar. Find each probability.

11. $\frac{9}{70}$ or about 13%

7. P(penny) $\frac{13}{28}$ or about 46%
8. P(quarter) $\frac{9}{70}$ or about 13%
9. P(not dime) $\frac{11}{14}$ or about 79%
10. P(penny or dime) $\frac{19}{28}$ or about 68%
11. P(value greater than \$0.15)
12. P(not nickel) $\frac{113}{140}$ or about 81%
13. P(nickel or quarter) $\frac{9}{28}$ or about 32%
14. P(value less than \$0.20) $\frac{61}{70}$ or about 87%

PRESENTATIONS **The students in a class are randomly drawing cards numbered 1 through 28 from a hat to determine the order in which they will give their presentations. Find each probability.**

15. P(13) $\frac{1}{28}$ or about 3.6%
16. P(1 or 28) $\frac{1}{14}$ or about 7%
17. P(less than 14) $\frac{13}{28}$ or about 46%
18. P(not 1) $\frac{27}{28}$ or about 96%
19. P(not 2 or 17) $\frac{13}{14}$ or about 93%
20. P(greater than 16) $\frac{3}{7}$ or about 43%

The table shows the results of an experiment in which three coins were tossed.

Outcome	HHH	HHT	HTH	THH	TTH	THT	HTT	TTT
Tally	𝍸	𝍸	𝍸 |	𝍸 |	𝍸 ||	𝍸	𝍸 |||	𝍸 |||
Frequency	5	5	6	6	7	5	8	8

21. What is the experimental probability that all three of the coins will be heads? The theoretical probability? $\frac{1}{10}$ or 10%; $\frac{1}{8}$ or 12.5%
22. What is the experimental probability that at least two of the coins will be heads? The theoretical probability? $\frac{11}{25}$ or 44%; $\frac{1}{2}$ or 50%
23. **DECISION MAKING** You and two of your friends have pooled your money to buy a new video game. Describe a method that could be used to make a fair decision as to who gets to play the game first. See margin.
24. **DECISION MAKING** A new study finds that the incidence of heart attack while taking a certain diabetes drug is less than 5%. Should a person with diabetes take this drug? Should they take the drug if the risk is less than 1%? Explain your reasoning. See margin.

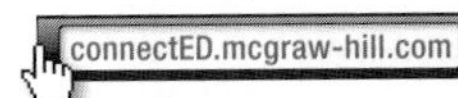

Additional Example

3 The table shows the results of an experiment in which a number cube was rolled. Find the experimental probability of rolling a 4.

Outcome	Tally	Frequency
1	||||	4
2	𝍸 |	6
3	𝍸	5
4	𝍸 ||	7
5	|||	3
6	𝍸	5

$\frac{7}{30}$

WatchOut!

Outcomes Remind students to determine the total number of possible outcomes. For example, in a bag containing different colored marbles, they will have to count the total number of marbles to determine the probability of choosing a marble of a particular color.

3 Assess

Formative Assessment

Use Exercises 1–24 to assess whether students understand how to compute simple probabilities.

Ticket Out the Door Ask students to describe the difference between theoretical and experimental probability.

Additional Answers

23. Sample answer: Assign each friend a different colored marble: red, blue, or green. Place all the marbles in a bag and without looking, select a marble from the bag. Whoever's marble is chosen gets to go first.
24. Sample answer: With either a less than 5% or 1% chance of having a heart attack, a person would still need to weigh the benefits of the drug versus the small chance of having a heart attack. A chance of less than 1% versus a chance of less than 5% should make a person who is considering taking the drug more likely to risk taking the drug to control their diabetes.

1 Focus

VerticalAlignment

Lesson 0-4 Use the order of operations to evaluate algebraic expressions.

After Lesson 0-4 Use algebra to solve linear equations.

2 Teach

Examples 1–3 show how to evaluate algebraic expressions by substitution, and using the order of operations.

Additional Examples

1 Evaluate each expression.

a. $2x + 10 - y$ if $x = -4$ and $y = 6$ -4

b. $5a^2b$ if $a = 2$ and $b = 6$ 120

2 Evaluate if $a = -3$, $b = -5$ and $c = 7$.

a. $\frac{ab - 3}{c - 1}$ 2

b. $-b(a^2 - 3c)$ -60

3 Evaluate $4|k + n| + 3|6 - p|$ if $k = -3$, $n = -5$, and $p = 4$. 38

3 Assess

Formative Assessment

Use Exercises 1–12 to assess whether students understand how to evaluate algebraic expressions.

Crystal Ball Ask students how evaluating algebraic expressions will help them solve linear equations.

LESSON 0-4 Algebraic Expressions

Objective

- Use the order of operations to evaluate algebraic expressions.

An expression is an algebraic expression if it contains sums and/or products of variables and numbers. To evaluate an algebraic expression, replace the variable or variables with known values, and then use the order of operations.

Order of Operations
Step 1 Evaluate expressions inside grouping symbols.
Step 2 Evaluate all powers.
Step 3 Do all multiplications and/or divisions from left to right.
Step 4 Do all additions and/or subtractions from left to right.

PT

Example 1 Addition/Subtraction Algebraic Expressions

Evaluate $x - 5 + y$ if $x = 15$ and $y = -7$.

$x - 5 + y = 15 - 5 + (-7)$ Substitute.

$= 10 + (-7)$ or 3 Subtract.

PT

Example 2 Multiplication/Division Algebraic Expressions

Evaluate each expression if $k = -2$, $n = -4$, and $p = 5$.

a. $\frac{2k + n}{p - 3}$

$\frac{2k + n}{p - 3} = \frac{2(-2) + (-4)}{5 - 3}$ Substitute.

$= \frac{-4 - 4}{5 - 3}$ Multiply.

$= \frac{-8}{2}$ or -4 Subtract.

b. $-3(k^2 + 2n)$

$-3(k^2 + 2n) = -3[(-2)^2 + 2(-4)]$

$= -3[4 + (-8)]$

$= -3(-4)$ or 12

PT

Example 3 Absolute Value Algebraic Expressions

Evaluate $3|a - b| + 2|c - 5|$ if $a = -2$, $b = -4$, and $c = 3$.

$3|a - b| + 2|c - 5| = 3|-2 - (-4)| + 2|3 - 5|$ Substitute for *a*, *b*, and *c*.

$= 3|2| + 2|-2|$ Simplify.

$= 3(2) + 2(2)$ or 10 Find absolute values.

Exercises

Evaluate each expression if $a = 2$, $b = -3$, $c = -1$, and $d = 4$.

1. $2a + c$ 3
2. $\frac{bd}{2c}$ 6
3. $\frac{2d - a}{b}$ -2
4. $3d - c$ 13
5. $\frac{3b}{5a + c}$ -1
6. $5bc$ 15
7. $2cd + 3ab$ -26
8. $\frac{c - 2d}{a}$ $-\frac{9}{2}$

Evaluate each expression if $x = 2$, $y = -3$, and $z = 1$.

9. $24 + |x - 4|$ 26
10. $13 + |8 + y|$ 18
11. $|5 - z| + 11$ 15
12. $|2y - 15| + 7$ 28

Teach with Tech

Interactive Whiteboard Write an algebraic expression on the board. Have students come to the board and use the highlighter tool to identify the variable. Copy the expression and have students replace the highlight with the value.

LESSON 0-5 Linear Equations

Objective

- Use algebra to solve linear equations.

If the same number is added to or subtracted from each side of an equation, the resulting equation is true.

Example 1 Addition/Subtraction Linear Equations

Solve each equation.

a. $x - 7 = 16$

$x - 7 = 16$	Original equation
$x - 7 + 7 = 16 + 7$	Add 7 to each side.
$x = 23$	Simplify.

b. $m + 12 = -5$

$m + 12 = -5$	Original equation
$m + 12 + (-12) = -5 + (-12)$	Add −12 to each side.
$m = -17$	Simplify.

c. $k + 31 = 10$

$k + 31 = 10$	Original equation
$k + 31 - 31 = 10 - 31$	Subtract 31 from each side.
$k = -21$	Simplify.

If each side of an equation is multiplied or divided by the same number, the resulting equation is true.

Example 2 Multiplication/Division Linear Equations

Solve each equation.

a. $4d = 36$

$4d = 36$	Original equation
$\frac{4d}{4} = \frac{36}{4}$	Divide each side by 4.
$x = 9$	Simplify.

b. $-\frac{t}{8} = -7$

$-\frac{t}{8} = -7$	Original equation
$-8\left(-\frac{t}{8}\right) = -8(-7)$	Multiply each side by −8.
$t = 56$	Simplify.

c. $\frac{3}{5}x = -8$

$\frac{3}{5}x = -8$	Original equation
$\frac{5}{3}\left(\frac{3}{5}\right)x = \frac{5}{3}(-8)$	Multiply each side by $\frac{5}{3}$.
$x = -\frac{40}{3}$	Simplify.

To solve equations with more than one operation, often called *multi-step equations*, undo operations by working backward.

1 Focus

VerticalAlignment

Lesson 0-5 Use algebra to solve linear equations.

After Lesson 0-5 Use algebra to solve linear inequalities.

2 Teach

Examples 1 and 2 show how to solve one-step linear equations. **Examples 3 and 4** show how to solve multi-step linear equations.

Additional Examples

1 Solve each equation.

a. $x + 8 = -5$ -13

b. $n - 15 = 3$ 18

c. $p + 27 = 12$ -15

2 Solve each equation.

a. $5g = 35$ 7

b. $-\frac{c}{6} = 8$ -48

c. $\frac{4x}{7} = -3$ $-\frac{21}{4}$

WatchOut!

Check Your Work Remind students that they can check their work by substituting the solution into the original equation.

Additional Examples

3 Solve each equation.

a. $9p + 8 = 35$ 3

b. $8x + 2 = 14x - 7$ $\frac{3}{2}$

4 Solve $4(x - 7) = 8x + 6$. $-\frac{17}{2}$

Teach with Tech

Interactive Whiteboard On the board, work through several examples solving linear equations. Save your work to a file and send it to your students so they can use it as an additional reference.

3 Assess

Formative Assessment

Use Exercises 1–36 to assess whether students understand how to solve linear equations.

Name the Math Ask students how the order of operations is used to solve linear equations.

Example 3 Multi-step Linear Equations

Solve each equation.

a. $8q - 15 = 49$

$8q - 15 = 49$	Original equation
$8q = 64$	Add 15 to each side.
$q = 8$	Divide each side by 8.

b. $12y + 8 = 6y - 5$

$12y + 8 = 6y - 5$	Original equation
$12y = 6y - 13$	Subtract 8 from each side.
$6y = -13$	Subtract $6y$ from each side.
$y = -\frac{13}{6}$	Divide each side by 6.

WatchOut!
Order of Operations
Remember that the order of operations applies when you are solving linear equations.

When solving equations that contain grouping symbols, first use the Distributive Property to remove the grouping symbols.

Example 4 Multi-step Linear Equations

Solve $3(x - 5) = 13$.

$3(x - 5) = 13$	Original equation
$3x - 15 = 13$	Distributive Property
$3x = 28$	Add 15 to each side.
$x = \frac{28}{3}$	Divide each side by 3.

Exercises

Solve each equation.

1. $r + 11 = 3$ -8
2. $n + 7 = 13$ 6
3. $d - 7 = 8$ 15
4. $\frac{8}{5}a = -6$ $-\frac{15}{4}$
5. $-\frac{p}{12} = 6$ -72
6. $\frac{x}{4} = 8$ 32
7. $\frac{12}{5}f = -18$ $-\frac{15}{2}$
8. $\frac{y}{7} = -11$ -77
9. $\frac{6}{7}y = 3$ $\frac{7}{2}$
10. $c - 14 = -11$ 3
11. $t - 14 = -29$ -15
12. $p - 21 = 52$ 73
13. $b + 2 = -5$ -7
14. $q + 10 = 22$ 12
15. $-12q = 84$ -7
16. $5t = 30$ 6
17. $5c - 7 = 8c - 4$ -1
18. $2\ell + 6 = 6\ell - 10$ 4
19. $\frac{m}{10} + 15 = 21$ 60
20. $-\frac{m}{8} + 7 = 5$ 16
21. $8t + 1 = 3t - 19$ -4
22. $9n + 4 = 5n + 18$ $\frac{7}{2}$
23. $5c - 24 = -4$ 4
24. $3n + 7 = 28$ 7
25. $-2y + 17 = -13$ 15
26. $-\frac{t}{13} - 2 = 3$ -65
27. $\frac{2}{9}x - 4 = \frac{2}{3}$ 21
28. $9 - 4g = -15$ 6
29. $-4 - p = -2$ -2
30. $21 - b = 11$ 10
31. $-2(n + 7) = 15$ $-\frac{29}{2}$
32. $5(m - 1) = -25$ -4
33. $-8a - 11 = 37$ -6
34. $\frac{7}{4}q - 2 = -5$ $-\frac{12}{7}$
35. $2(5 - n) = 8$ 1
36. $-3(d - 7) = 6$ 5

LESSON 0-6 Linear Inequalities

Objective

- Use algebra to solve linear inequalities.

Statements with greater than (>), less than (<), greater than or equal to (≥), or less than or equal to (≤) are inequalities. If any number is added or subtracted to each side of an inequality, the resulting inequality is true.

Example 1 Addition/Subtraction Linear Inequalities

Solve each inequality.

a. $x - 17 > 12$

$x - 17 > 12$	Original inequality
$x - 17 + 17 > 12 + 17$	Add 17 to each side.
$x > 29$	Simplify.

The solution set is $\{x \mid x > 29\}$.

b. $y + 11 \leq 5$

$y + 11 \leq 5$	Original inequality
$y + 11 - 11 \leq 5 - 11$	Subtract 11 from each side.
$y \leq -6$	Simplify.

The solution set is $\{y \mid y \leq -6\}$.

If each side of an inequality is multiplied or divided by a positive number, the resulting inequality is true.

Example 2 Multiplication/Division Linear Inequalities

Solve each inequality.

a. $\frac{t}{6} \geq 11$

$\frac{t}{6} \geq 11$	Original inequality
$(6)\frac{t}{6} \geq (6)11$	Multiply each side by 6.
$t \geq 66$	Simplify.

The solution set is $\{t \mid t \geq 66\}$.

b. $8p < 72$

$8p < 72$	Original inequality
$\frac{8p}{8} < \frac{72}{8}$	Divide each side by 8.
$p < 9$	Simplify.

The solution set is $\{p \mid p < 9\}$.

If each side of an inequality is multiplied or divided by the same negative number, the direction of the inequality symbol must be *reversed* so that the resulting inequality is true.

Example 3 Multiplication/Division Linear Inequalities

Solve each inequality.

a. $-5c > 30$

$-5c > 30$	Original inequality
$\frac{-5c}{-5} < \frac{30}{-5}$	Divide each side by −5. Change > to <.
$c < -6$	Simplify.

The solution set is $\{c \mid c < -6\}$.

(continued on the next page)

1 Focus

VerticalAlignment

Lesson 0-6 Use algebra to solve linear inequalities.

After Lesson 0-6 Name and graph points in the coordinate plane.

2 Teach

Examples 1–3 show how to solve one-step linear inequalities. **Example 4** shows how to solve multi-step linear inequalities.

Additional Examples

1 Solve each inequality.

a. $x - 15 < 13$ $\{x \mid x < 28\}$

b. $y + 17 \geq 9$ $\{y \mid y \geq -8\}$

2 Solve each inequality.

a. $\frac{m}{5} \leq 12$ $\{m \mid m \leq 60\}$

b. $7n > 42$ $\{n \mid n > 6\}$

3 Solve each inequality.

a. $-4d < 28$ $\{d \mid d > -7\}$

b. $-\frac{b}{11} \geq 5$ $\{b \mid b \leq -55\}$

Tips for New Teachers

Sense-Making To help students understand why they need to reverse an inequality symbol when multiplying or dividing, demonstrate by writing an inequality such as $-2 < 8$. Show that when you divide each side by −1, the inequality becomes $2 < -8$, which is incorrect. However, when you reverse the sign, the inequality becomes $2 > -8$, which is correct.

Additional Example

4 Solve each inequality.

a. $5c - 6 > 15$ $\left\{c \mid c > \frac{21}{5}\right\}$

b. $6y - 8 \leq 9y + 2$ $\left\{y \mid y \geq -\frac{10}{3}\right\}$

WatchOut!

Inequality Symbol Remind students that the direction of the inequality symbol does not change when a negative number is added or subtracted to each side of the inequality.

Teach with Tech

Portable Media Player Create a video showing your students how to graph inequalities in two variables. Place the video on your class Web page for use as an additional reference outside of class.

3 Assess

Formative Assessment

Use Exercises 1–24 to assess whether students understand how to solve linear inequalities in one variable.

Yesterday's News Ask students how solving linear equations helps them solve inequalities in one variable.

b. $-\frac{d}{13} \leq -4$

$-\frac{d}{13} \leq -4$	Original inequality
$(-13)\left(\frac{-d}{13}\right) \geq (-13)(-4)$	Multiply each side by −13. Change ≤ to ≥.
$d \geq 52$	Simplify.

The solution set is $\{d \mid d \geq 52\}$.

Inequalities involving more than one operation can be solved by undoing the operations in the same way you would solve an equation with more than one operation.

Example 4 Multi-Step Linear Inequalities

PT

Solve each inequality.

a. $-6a + 13 < -7$

$-6a + 13 < -7$	Original inequality
$-6a + 13 - 13 < -7 - 13$	Subtract 13 from each side.
$-6a < -20$	Simplify.
$\frac{-6a}{-6} > \frac{-20}{-6}$	Divide each side by −6. Change < to >.
$a > \frac{10}{3}$	Simplify.

The solution set is $\left\{a \mid a > \frac{10}{3}\right\}$.

WatchOut!

Dividing by a Negative Remember that any time you divide an inequality by a negative number you reverse the direction of the sign.

b. $4z + 7 \geq 8z - 1$

$4z + 7 \geq 8z - 1$	Original inequality
$4z + 7 - 7 \geq 8z - 1 - 7$	Subtract 7 from each side.
$4z \geq 8z - 8$	Simplify.
$4z - 8z \geq 8z - 8 - 8z$	Subtract 8z from each side.
$-4z \geq -8$	Simplify.
$\frac{-4z}{-4} \leq \frac{-8}{-4}$	Divide each side by −4. Change ≥ to ≤.
$z \leq 2$	Simplify.

The solution set is $\{z \mid z \leq 2\}$.

Exercises

1. $x - 7 < 6$ $\{x \mid x < 13\}$
2. $a + 7 \geq -5$ $\{a \mid a \geq -12\}$
3. $4y < 20$ $\{y \mid y < 5\}$
4. $-\frac{a}{8} < 5$ $\{a \mid a > -40\}$
5. $\frac{t}{6} > -7$ $\{t \mid t > -42\}$
6. $\frac{a}{11} \leq 8$ $\{a \mid a \leq 88\}$
7. $d + 8 \leq 12$ $\{d \mid d \leq 4\}$
8. $m + 14 > 10$ $\{m \mid m > -4\}$
9. $12k \geq -36$ $\{k \mid k \geq -3\}$
10. $6t - 10 \geq 4t$ $\{t \mid t \geq 5\}$
11. $3z + 8 < 2$ $\{z \mid z < -2\}$
12. $4c + 23 \leq -13$ $\{c \mid c \leq -9\}$
13. $m - 21 < 8$ $\{m \mid m < 29\}$
14. $x - 6 \geq 3$ $\{x \mid x \geq 9\}$
15. $-3b \leq 48$ $\{b \mid b \geq -16\}$
16. $-\frac{p}{5} \geq 14$ $\{p \mid p \leq -70\}$
17. $2z - 9 < 7z + 1$ $\{z \mid z > -2\}$
18. $-4h > 36$ $\{h \mid h < -9\}$
19. $\frac{2}{5}b - 6 \leq -2$ $\{b \mid b \leq 10\}$
20. $\frac{8}{3}t + 1 > -5$ $\left\{t \mid t > -\frac{9}{4}\right\}$
21. $7q + 3 \geq -4q + 25$ $\{q \mid q \geq 2\}$
22. $-3n - 8 > 2n + 7$ $\{n \mid n < -3\}$
23. $-3w + 1 \leq 8$ $\left\{w \mid w \geq -\frac{7}{3}\right\}$
24. $-\frac{4}{5}k - 17 > 11$ $\{k \mid k < -35\}$

P14 | Lesson 0-6 | Linear Inequalities

LESSON 0-7 Ordered Pairs

Objective

- Name and graph points in the coordinate plane.

NewVocabulary
ordered pair
x-coordinate
y-coordinate
quadrant
origin

Points in the coordinate plane are named by **ordered pairs** of the form (x, y). The first number, or ***x*-coordinate**, corresponds to a number on the x-axis. The second number, or ***y*-coordinate**, corresponds to a number on the y-axis.

Example 1 Writing Ordered Pairs

Write the ordered pair for each point.

a. *A*

The x-coordinate is 4.

The y-coordinate is -1.

The ordered pair is $(4, -1)$.

b. *B*

The x-coordinate is -2.

The point lies on the x-axis, so its y-coordinate is 0.

The ordered pair is $(-2, 0)$.

The x-axis and y-axis separate the coordinate plane into four regions, called **quadrants**. The point at which the axes intersect is called the **origin**. The axes and points on the axes are not located in any of the quadrants.

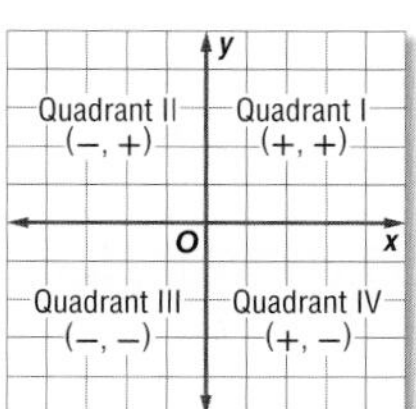

Example 2 Graphing Ordered Pairs

Graph and label each point on a coordinate plane. Name the quadrant in which each point is located.

a. $G(2, 1)$

Start at the origin. Move 2 units right, since the x-coordinate is 2. Then move 1 unit up, since the y-coordinate is 1. Draw a dot, and label it G. Point $G(2, 1)$ is in Quadrant I.

b. $H(-4, 3)$

Start at the origin. Move 4 units left, since the x-coordinate is -4. Then move 3 units up, since the y-coordinate is 3. Draw a dot, and label it H. Point $H(-4, 3)$ is in Quadrant II.

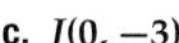

c. $J(0, -3)$

Start at the origin. Since the x-coordinate is 0, the point lies on the y-axis. Move 3 units down, since the y-coordinate is -3. Draw a dot, and label it J. Because it is on one of the axes, point $J(0, -3)$ is not in any quadrant.

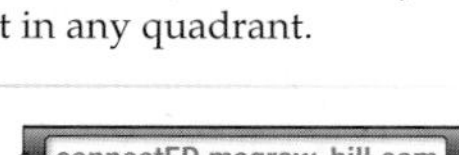

1 Focus

VerticalAlignment

Lesson 0-7 Name and graph points in the coordinate plane.

After Lesson 0-7 Solve systems of linear equations graphically.

2 Teach

Example 1 shows how to name ordered pairs, given a graph of points. **Examples 2 and 3** show how to graph ordered pairs. **Example 4** shows how to graph points that satisfy a linear equation.

Additional Example

1 Write the ordered pair for each point.

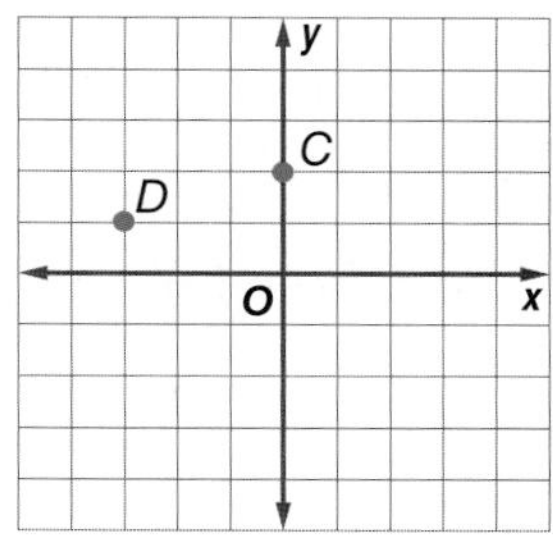

a. *C* (0, 2)

b. *D* (−3, 1)

Teach with Tech

Interactive Whiteboard Display a coordinate plane on the whiteboard. Plot several points on the plane and ask students to give the coordinates of the points. Then drag the points to other locations and repeat.

Additional Examples

2 Graph and label each point on a coordinate plane. Name the quadrant in which each point is located.

a. $P(4, 2)$ Quadrant I

b. $M(-2, 4)$ Quadrant II

c. $N(-1, 0)$ lies on the x-axis, not in a quadrant

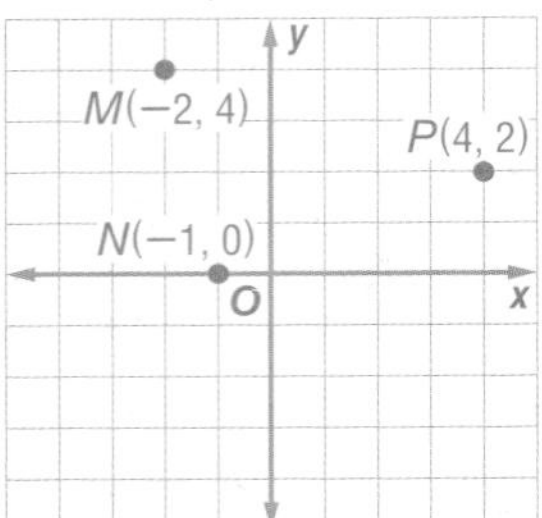

3 Graph a polygon with vertices $P(-1, 1)$, $Q(3, 1)$, $R(1, 4)$, and $S(-3, 4)$.

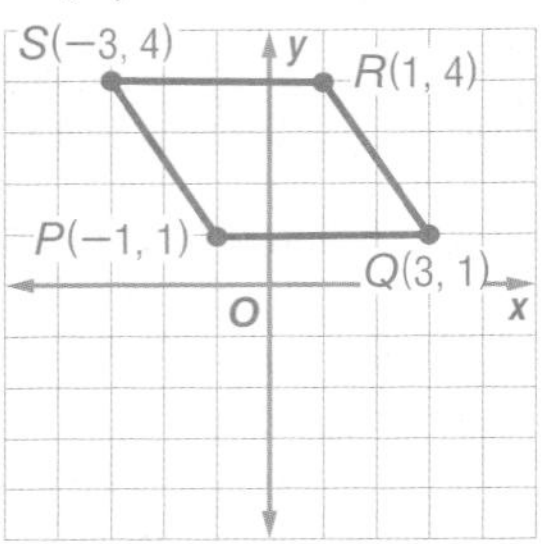

4 Graph four points that satisfy the equation $y = -x - 2$.

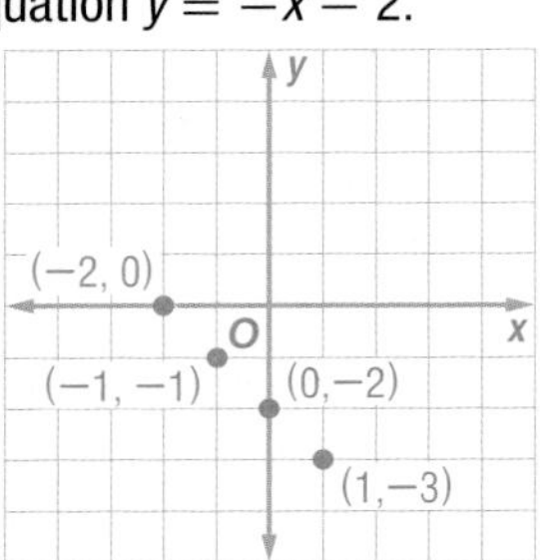

Example 3 Graphing Multiple Ordered Pairs

Graph a polygon with vertices $A(-3, 3)$, $B(1, 3)$, $C(0, 1)$, and $D(-4, 1)$.

Graph the ordered pairs on a coordinate plane. Connect each pair of consecutive points. The polygon is a parallelogram.

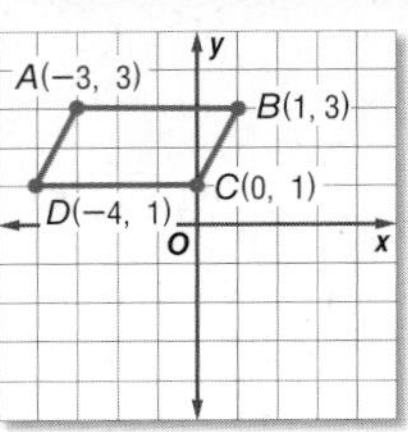

StudyTip

Lines There are infinitely many points on a line, so when you are asked to find points on a line, there are many answers.

Example 4 Graphing and Solving for Ordered Pairs

Graph four points that satisfy the equation $y = 4 - x$.

Make a table.

Choose four values for x.

Evaluate each value of x for $4 - x$.

x	$4 - x$	y	(x, y)
0	4 − 0	4	(0, 4)
1	4 − 1	3	(1, 3)
2	4 − 2	2	(2, 2)
3	4 − 3	1	(3, 1)

Plot the points.

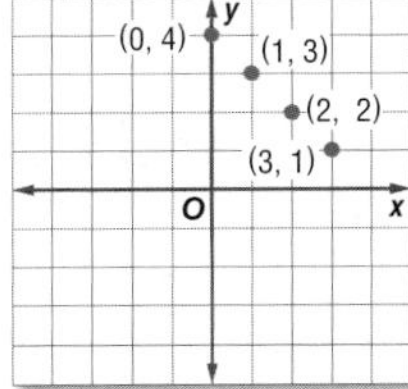

Exercises

Write the ordered pair for each point shown at the right.

1. B (−2, 3)
2. C (1, −1)
3. D (2, 2)
4. E (−3, −3)
5. F (−3, 1)
6. G (0, −3)
7. H (4, 1)
8. I (3, −2)
9. J (−1, −1)
10. K (1, 4)
11. W (3, 0)
12. M (−2, −4)
13. N (2, −4)
14. P (3, 3)
15. Q (−4, 2)

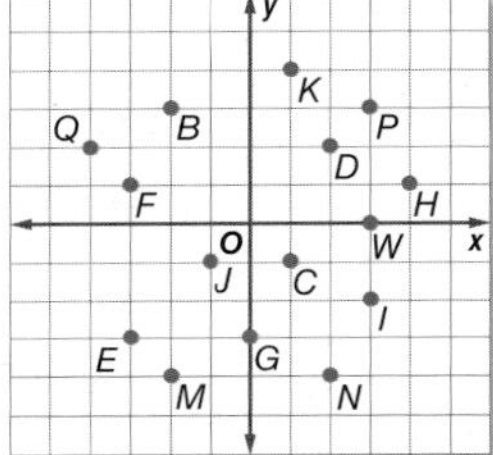

Graph and label each point on a coordinate plane. Name the quadrant in which each point is located. 16–23. See Ch. 0 Answer Appendix for graph.

16. $M(-1, 3)$ II
17. $S(2, 0)$ none
18. $R(-3, -2)$ III
19. $P(1, -4)$ IV
20. $B(5, -1)$ IV
21. $D(3, 4)$ I
22. $T(2, 5)$ I
23. $L(-4, -3)$ III

Graph the following geometric figures. 24–26. See Ch. 0 Answer Appendix.

24. a square with vertices $W(-3, 3)$, $X(-3, -1)$, $Z(1, 3)$, and $Y(1, -1)$
25. a polygon with vertices $J(4, 2)$, $K(1, -1)$, $L(-2, 2)$, and $M(1, 5)$
26. a triangle with vertices $F(2, 4)$, $G(-3, 2)$, and $H(-1, -3)$

Graph four points that satisfy each equation. 27–30. See Ch. 0 Answer Appendix.

27. $y = 2x$
28. $y = 1 + x$
29. $y = 3x - 1$
30. $y = 2 - x$

3 Assess

Formative Assessment

Use Exercises 1–30 to assess whether students understand how to name and graph points in a coordinate plane.

Name the Math Ask students to describe how to graph a point in a coordinate plane.

LESSON 0-8 Systems of Linear Equations

Objective

- Use graphing, substitution, and elimination to solve systems of linear equations.

NewVocabulary
system of equations
substitution
elimination

Two or more equations that have common variables are called a **system of equations**. The solution of a system of equations in two variables is an ordered pair of numbers that satisfies both equations. A system of two linear equations can have zero, one, or an infinite number of solutions. There are three methods by which systems of equations can be solved: graphing, elimination, and substitution.

Example 1 Graphing Linear Equations

Solve each system of equations by graphing. Then determine whether each system has *no* solution, *one* solution, or *infinitely many* solutions.

a. $y = -x + 3$
$y = 2x - 3$

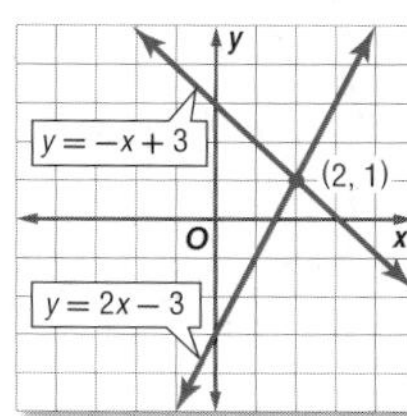

The graphs appear to intersect at (2, 1). Check this estimate by replacing x with 2 and y with 1 in each equation.

CHECK $y = -x + 3$ $\qquad$ $y = 2x - 3$

$1 \stackrel{?}{=} -2 + 3$ $\qquad$ $1 \stackrel{?}{=} 2(2) - 3$

$1 = 1$ ✓ $\qquad$ $1 = 1$ ✓

The system has one solution at (2, 1).

b. $y - 2x = 6$
$3y - 6x = 9$

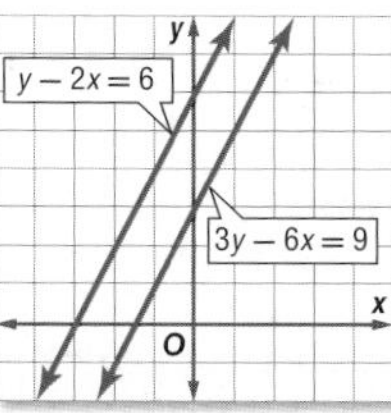

The graphs of the equations are parallel lines. Since they do not intersect, there are no solutions of this system of equations. Notice that the lines have the same slope but different y-intercepts. Equations with the same slope *and* the same y-intercepts have an infinite number of solutions.

It is difficult to determine the solution of a system when the two graphs intersect at noninteger values. There are algebraic methods by which an exact solution can be found. One such method is **substitution**.

Example 2 Substitution

Use substitution to solve the system of equations.

$y = -4x$
$2y + 3x = 8$

Since $y = -4x$, substitute $-4x$ for y in the second equation.

$2y + 3x = 8$	Second equation
$2(-4x) + 3x = 3$	$y = -4x$
$-8x + 3x = 8$	Simplify.
$-5x = 8$	Combine like terms.
$\frac{-5x}{-5} = \frac{8}{-5}$	Divide each side by −5.
$x = -\frac{8}{5}$	Simplify.

Use $y = -4x$ to find the value of y.

$y = -4x$	First equation
$= -4\left(-\frac{8}{5}\right)$	$x = -\frac{8}{5}$
$= \frac{32}{5}$	Simplify.

The solution is $\left(-\frac{8}{5}, \frac{32}{5}\right)$.

1 Focus

VerticalAlignment

Lesson 0-8 Use graphing, substitution, and elimination to solve systems of linear equations.

After Lesson 0-8 Evaluate square roots and simplify radical expressions.

2 Teach

Example 1 shows how to solve a system of linear equations graphically. **Example 2** shows how to solve a system of linear equations by using substitution. **Example 3** shows how to solve a system of linear equations by elimination.

Additional Example

1 Solve each system of equations by graphing. Then determine whether each system has *no* solution, *one* solution, or *infinitely many* solutions.

a. $y = -3x + 1$
$y = x - 3$
one solution at (1, −2)

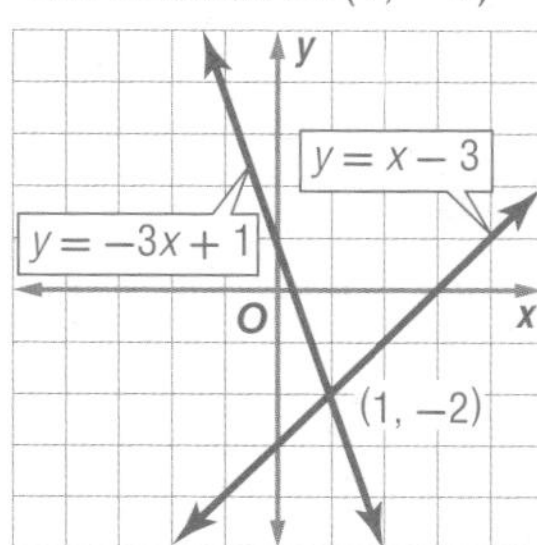

(continued on the next page)

Teach with Tech

Blog On your secure class blog, have students write a blog entry explaining how they decide when to use each of the different methods for solving a system of equations.

Additional Examples

1 **b.** $y = 2x + 3$

$-4x + 2y = 6$

infinitely many solutions

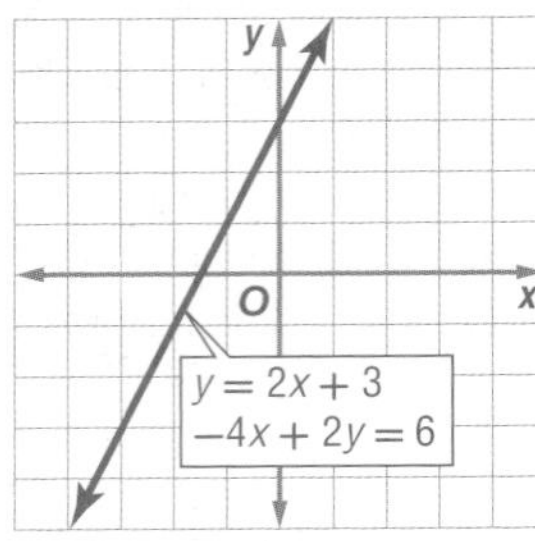

2 Use substitution to solve the system of equations.

$y = 3x$

$-2y + 9x = 5$ $\left(\frac{5}{3}, 5\right)$

3 Use elimination to solve the system of equations.

$3x + 7y = 15$

$5x + 2y = -4$

$(-2, 3)$

WatchOut!

Balanced Equations When using the elimination method, be sure to multiply both sides of the equation by the constant.

3 Assess

Formative Assessment

Use Exercises 1–15 to assess whether students understand how to solve a system of linear equations.

Ticket Out the Door Have students describe the three different methods of solving a system of linear equations.

Sometimes adding or subtracting two equations together will eliminate one variable. Using this step to solve a system of equations is called **elimination**.

PT

Example 3 Elimination

Use elimination to solve the system of equations.

$3x + 5y = 7$

$4x + 2y = 0$

Either x or y can be eliminated. In this example, we will eliminate x.

$3x + 5y = 7$ → Multiply by 4. → $12x + 20y = 28$

$4x + 2y = 0$ → Multiply by −3. → $+ (-12x) - 6y = 0$

$14y = 28$ Add the equations.

$\frac{14y}{14} = \frac{28}{14}$ Divide each side by 14.

$y = 2$ Simplify.

Now substitute 2 for y in either equation to find the value of x.

$4x + 2y = 0$ Second equation

$4x + 2(2) = 0$ $y = 2$

$4x + 4 = 0$ Simplify.

$4x + 4 - 4 = 0 - 4$ Subtract 4 from each side.

$4x = -4$ Simplify.

$\frac{4x}{4} = \frac{-4}{4}$ Divide each side by 4.

$x = -1$ Simplify.

The solution is $(-1, 2)$.

StudyTip

Checking Solutions You can confirm that your solutions are correct by substituting the values into both of the original equations.

Exercises

Solve by graphing.

1. $y = -x + 2$; $y = -\frac{1}{2}x + 1$ **(2, 0)**
2. $y = 3x - 3$; $y = x + 1$ **(2, 3)**
3. $y - 2x = 1$; $2y - 4x = 1$ **no solution**

Solve by substitution.

4. $-5x + 3y = 12$; $x + 2y = 8$ **(0, 4)**
5. $x - 4y = 22$; $2x + 5y = -21$ **(2, −5)**
6. $y + 5x = -3$; $3y - 2x = 8$ **(−1, 2)**

Solve by elimination.

7. $-3x + y = 7$; $3x + 2y = 2$ $\left(-\frac{4}{3}, 3\right)$
8. $3x + 4y = -1$; $-9x - 4y = 13$ $\left(-2, \frac{5}{4}\right)$
9. $-4x + 5y = -11$; $2x + 3y = 11$ **(4, 1)**

Name an appropriate method to solve each system of equations. Then solve the system. **10–15. See margin.**

10. $4x - y = 11$; $2x - 3y = 3$
11. $4x + 6y = 3$; $-10x - 15y = -4$
12. $3x - 2y = 6$; $5x - 5y = 5$
13. $3y + x = 3$; $-2y + 5x = 15$
14. $4x - 7y = 8$; $-2x + 5y = -1$
15. $x + 3y = 6$; $4x - 2y = -32$

Additional Answers

10. elimination or substitution, (3, 1)

11. elimination, no solution

12. graphing, (4, 3)

13. elimination or substitution, (3, 0)

14. elimination, $\left(\frac{11}{2}, 2\right)$

15. elimination or substitution, (–6, 4)

LESSON 0-9 Square Roots and Simplifying Radicals

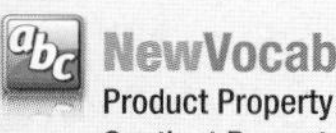

Objective

- Evaluate square roots and simplify radical expressions.

NewVocabulary
Product Property
Quotient Property

A radical expression is an expression that contains a square root. The expression is in simplest form when the following three conditions have been met.

- No radicands have perfect square factors other than 1.
- No radicands contain fractions.
- No radicals appear in the denominator of a fraction.

The **Product Property** states that for two numbers a and $b \geq 0$, $\sqrt{ab} = \sqrt{a} \cdot \sqrt{b}$.

Example 1 Product Property

Simplify.

a. $\sqrt{45}$

$\sqrt{45} = \sqrt{3 \cdot 3 \cdot 5}$ Prime factorization of 45

$= \sqrt{3^2} \cdot \sqrt{5}$ Product Property of Square Roots

$= 3\sqrt{5}$ Simplify.

b. $\sqrt{6} \cdot \sqrt{15}$

$\sqrt{6} \cdot \sqrt{15} = \sqrt{6 \cdot 15}$ Product Property

$= \sqrt{3 \cdot 2 \cdot 3 \cdot 5}$ Prime factorization

$= \sqrt{3^2} \cdot \sqrt{10}$ Product Property

$= 3\sqrt{10}$ Simplify.

For radical expressions in which the exponent of the variable inside the radical is *even* and the resulting simplified exponent is *odd*, you must use absolute value to ensure nonnegative results.

Example 2 Product Property

Simplify $\sqrt{20x^3y^5z^6}$.

$\sqrt{20x^3y^5z^6} = \sqrt{2^2 \cdot 5 \cdot x^3 \cdot y^5 \cdot z^6}$ Prime factorization

$= \sqrt{2^2} \cdot \sqrt{5} \cdot \sqrt{x^3} \cdot \sqrt{y^5} \cdot \sqrt{z^6}$ Product Property

$= 2 \cdot \sqrt{5} \cdot x \cdot \sqrt{x} \cdot y^2 \cdot \sqrt{y} \cdot |z^3|$ Simplify.

$= 2xy^2|z^3|\sqrt{5xy}$ Simplify.

The **Quotient Property** states that for any numbers a and b, where $a \geq 0$ and $b \geq 0$, $\sqrt{\frac{a}{b}} = \frac{\sqrt{a}}{\sqrt{b}}$.

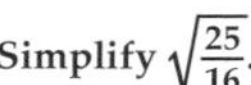

Example 3 Quotient Property

Simplify $\sqrt{\frac{25}{16}}$.

$\sqrt{\frac{25}{16}} = \frac{\sqrt{25}}{\sqrt{16}}$ Quotient Property

$= \frac{5}{4}$ Simplify.

1 Focus

VerticalAlignment

Lesson 0-9 Evaluate square roots and simplify radical expressions.

After Lesson 0-9 Use the Pythagorean Theorem and the Converse of the Pythagorean Theorem.

2 Teach

Examples 1–5 show how to simplify radical expressions.

Additional Examples

1 Simplify.
a. $\sqrt{50}$ $5\sqrt{2}$
b. $\sqrt{8} \cdot 2\sqrt{4}$ $8\sqrt{2}$

2 Simplify $\sqrt{18a^5b^4c^7}$. $3a^2b^2c^3\sqrt{2ac}$

3 Simplify $\sqrt{\frac{49}{36}}$. $\frac{7}{6}$

Teach with Tech

Interactive Whiteboard On the board, work through several examples simplifying radicals. Save your work to a file and send it to your students so they can use it as an additional reference.

Additional Examples

4 Simplify.

a. $\frac{3}{\sqrt{5}}$ $\frac{3\sqrt{5}}{5}$

b. $\frac{\sqrt{17x}}{\sqrt{20}}$ $\frac{\sqrt{85x}}{10}$

5 Simplify $\frac{8}{6-\sqrt{3}}$. $\frac{48+8\sqrt{3}}{33}$

WatchOut!

Conjugates Remind students that the operations of conjugates are opposite.

3 Assess

Formative Assessment

Use Exercises 1–20 to assess whether students understand how to simplify radical expressions.

Name the Math Ask students how to simplify a fraction that contains a radical in its denominator.

Rationalizing the denominator of a radical expression is a method used to eliminate radicals from the denominator of a fraction. To rationalize the denominator, multiply the expression by a fraction equivalent to 1 such that the resulting denominator is a perfect square.

WatchOut!

Rationalizing the Denominator Don't forget to multiply both the numerator and denominator by the radical when you rationalize the denominator.

PT

Example 4 Rationalize the Denominator

Simplify.

a. $\frac{2}{\sqrt{3}}$

$\frac{2}{\sqrt{3}} = \frac{2}{\sqrt{3}} \cdot \frac{\sqrt{3}}{\sqrt{3}}$ Multiply by $\frac{\sqrt{3}}{\sqrt{3}}$.

$= \frac{2\sqrt{3}}{3}$ Simplify.

b. $\frac{\sqrt{13y}}{\sqrt{18}}$

$\frac{\sqrt{13y}}{\sqrt{18}} = \frac{\sqrt{13y}}{\sqrt{2 \cdot 3 \cdot 3}}$ Prime factorization

$= \frac{\sqrt{13y}}{3\sqrt{2}}$ Product Property

$= \frac{\sqrt{13y}}{3\sqrt{2}} \cdot \frac{\sqrt{2}}{\sqrt{2}}$ Multiply by $\frac{\sqrt{2}}{\sqrt{2}}$.

$= \frac{\sqrt{26y}}{6}$ Product Property

Sometimes, conjugates are used to simplify radical expressions. Conjugates are binomials of the form $p\sqrt{q} + r\sqrt{t}$ and $p\sqrt{q} - r\sqrt{t}$.

PT

Example 5 Conjugates

Simplify $\frac{3}{5-\sqrt{2}}$.

$\frac{3}{5-\sqrt{2}} = \frac{3}{5-\sqrt{2}} \cdot \frac{5+\sqrt{2}}{5+\sqrt{2}}$ $\frac{5+\sqrt{2}}{5+\sqrt{2}} = 1$

$= \frac{3(5+\sqrt{2})}{5^2 - (\sqrt{2})^2}$ $(a-b)(a+b) = a^2 - b^2$

$= \frac{15+3\sqrt{2}}{25-2}$ Multiply. $(\sqrt{2})^2 = 2$

$= \frac{15+3\sqrt{2}}{23}$ Simplify.

Exercises

Simplify.

1. $\sqrt{32}$ $4\sqrt{2}$

2. $\sqrt{75}$ $5\sqrt{3}$

3. $\sqrt{50} \cdot \sqrt{10}$ $10\sqrt{5}$

4. $\sqrt{12} \cdot \sqrt{20}$ $4\sqrt{15}$

5. $\sqrt{6} \cdot \sqrt{6}$ 6

6. $\sqrt{16} \cdot \sqrt{25}$ 20

7. $\sqrt{98x^3y^6}$ $7x|y^3|\sqrt{2x}$

8. $\sqrt{56a^2b^4c^5}$ $2|a|b^2c^2\sqrt{14c}$

9. $\sqrt{\frac{81}{49}}$ $\frac{9}{7}$

10. $\sqrt{\frac{121}{16}}$ $\frac{11}{4}$

11. $\sqrt{\frac{63}{8}}$ $\frac{3\sqrt{14}}{4}$

12. $\sqrt{\frac{288}{147}}$ $\frac{4\sqrt{6}}{7}$

13. $\frac{\sqrt{10p^3}}{\sqrt{27}}$ $\frac{p\sqrt{30p}}{9}$

14. $\frac{\sqrt{108}}{\sqrt{2q^6}}$ $\frac{3\sqrt{6}}{|q^3|}$

15. $\frac{4}{5-2\sqrt{3}}$ $\frac{20+8\sqrt{3}}{13}$

16. $\frac{7\sqrt{3}}{5-2\sqrt{6}}$ $35\sqrt{3}+42\sqrt{2}$

17. $\frac{3}{\sqrt{48}}$ $\frac{\sqrt{3}}{4}$

18. $\frac{\sqrt{24}}{\sqrt{125}}$ $\frac{2\sqrt{30}}{25}$

19. $\frac{3\sqrt{5}}{2-\sqrt{2}}$ $\frac{6\sqrt{5}+3\sqrt{10}}{2}$

20. $\frac{3}{-2+\sqrt{13}}$ $\frac{2+\sqrt{13}}{3}$

Posttest

State which metric unit you would probably use to measure each item.

1. mass of a book **g**
2. length of a highway **km**

Complete each sentence.

3. 8 in. = _?_ ft $\frac{2}{3}$ **or 0.67**
4. 6 yd = _?_ ft **18**
5. 24 fl oz = _?_ pt **1.5**
6. 3.7 kg = _?_ lb **8.1**
7. 4.2 km = _?_ m **4200**
8. 285 g = _?_ kg **0.29**
9. 0.75 kg = _?_ mg **750,000**
10. 1.9 L = _?_ qt **2.1**

11. **PROBABILITY** The table shows the results of an experiment in which a number cube was rolled. Find the experimental probability of rolling a 4. $\frac{3}{25}$ **or 12%**

Outcome	Tally	Frequency
1	||||	4
2	~~||||~~ |	6
3	~~||||~~	5
4	|||	3
5	~~||||~~ ||	7

CANDY **A bag of candy contains 3 lollipops, 8 peanut butter cups, and 4 chocolate bars. A piece of candy is randomly drawn from the bag. Find each probability.**

12. P(peanut butter cup) $\frac{8}{15}$ **or about 53%**
13. P(lollipop or peanut butter cup) $\frac{11}{15}$ **or about 73%**
14. P(not chocolate bar) $\frac{11}{15}$ **or about 73%**
15. P(chocolate bar or lollipop) $\frac{7}{15}$ **or about 47%**

Evaluate each expression if $x = 2$, $y = -3$, and $z = 4$.

16. $6x - z$ **8**
17. $6y + xz$ **−10**
18. $3yz$ **−36**
19. $\frac{6z}{xy}$ **−4**
20. $\frac{y + 2x}{10z}$ $\frac{1}{40}$
21. $7 + |y - 11|$ **21**

Solve each equation.

22. $9 + s = 21$ **12**
23. $h - 8 = 12$ **20**
24. $\frac{4m}{14} = 18$ **63**
25. $\frac{2}{9}d = 10$ **45**
26. $3(20 - b) = 36$ **8**
27. $37 + w = 5w - 27$ **16**
28. $\frac{x}{6} = 7$ **42**
29. $\frac{1}{4}(n + 5) = 16$ **59**

Solve each inequality.

30. $4y - 9 > 1$ $\left\{y \mid y > \frac{5}{2}\right\}$
31. $-2z + 15 \geq 4$ $\left\{z \mid z \leq \frac{11}{2}\right\}$
32. $3r + 7 < r - 8$
33. $-\frac{2}{5}k - 20 \leq 10$ $\{k \mid k \geq -75\}$
34. $-3(b - 4) > 33$ $\{b \mid b < -7\}$
35. $2 - m \leq 6m - 12$ $\{m \mid m \geq 2\}$
36. $8 \leq r - 14$ $\{r \mid r \geq 22\}$
37. $\frac{2}{3}n < \frac{3}{9}n - 5$ $\{n \mid n < -15\}$

32. $\left\{r \mid r < -\frac{15}{2}\right\}$

Write the ordered pair for each point shown.

38. M **(0, 3)**
39. N **(−2, −5)**
40. P **(−3, 2)**
41. Q **(4, −1)**

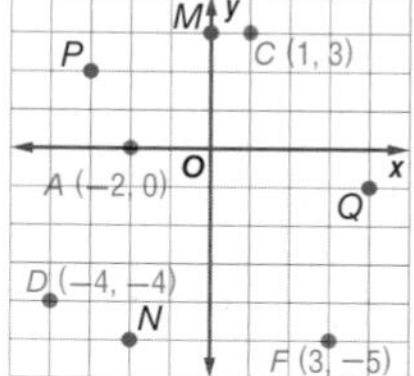

Graph and label each point on the coordinate plane above.

42. $A(-2, 0)$
43. $C(1, 3)$
44. $D(-4, -4)$
45. $F(3, -5)$

46. Graph the quadrilateral with vertices $R(2, 0)$, $S(4, -2)$, $T(4, 3)$, and $W(2, 5)$. **See margin.**

47. Graph three points that satisfy the equation $y = \frac{1}{2}x - 5$. **See margin.**

Solve each system of equations.

48. $2r + m = 11$, $6r - 2m = -2$ **(2, 7)**
49. $2x + 4y = 6$, $7x = 4 + 3y$ **(1, 1)**
50. $2c + 6d = 14$, $-\frac{7}{3} + \frac{1}{3}c = -d$ **See margin.**
51. $5a - b = 17$, $3a + 2b = 5$ **(3, −2)**
52. $6d + 3f = 12$, $2d = 8 - f$ **no solution**
53. $4x - 5y = 17$, $3x + 4y = 5$ **(3, −1)**

Simplify.

54. $\sqrt{80}$ $4\sqrt{5}$
55. $\sqrt{\frac{128}{5}}$ $\frac{8\sqrt{10}}{5}$
56. $\sqrt{36} \cdot \sqrt{81}$ **54**
57. $\sqrt{\frac{7x^3}{3}}$ $\frac{x\sqrt{21x}}{3}$
58. $\sqrt{\frac{5}{81}}$ $\frac{\sqrt{5}}{9}$
59. $\sqrt{12x^5y^2}$ $2x^2y\sqrt{3x}$

Using the Posttest

Use the Chapter 0 Posttest to assess students' understanding of the concepts after you have presented the lessons in Chapter 0. If students are still having difficulty with one or more concepts, refer to *Math Triumphs: Foundations for Geometry,* for strategies for reteaching.

Additional Answers

46.

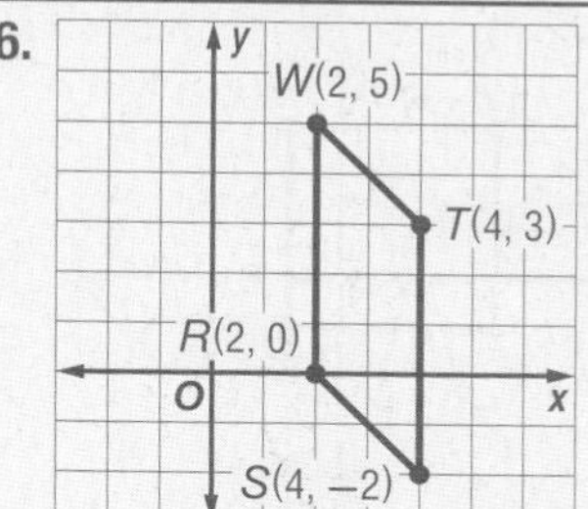

47. Sample answer:

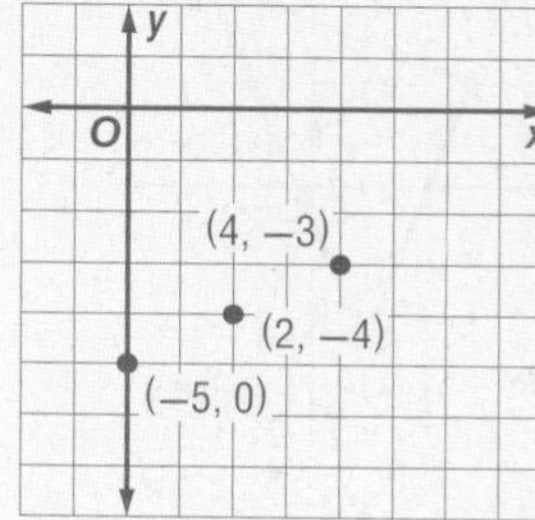

50. infinitely many solutions

Lesson 0-7

16–23.

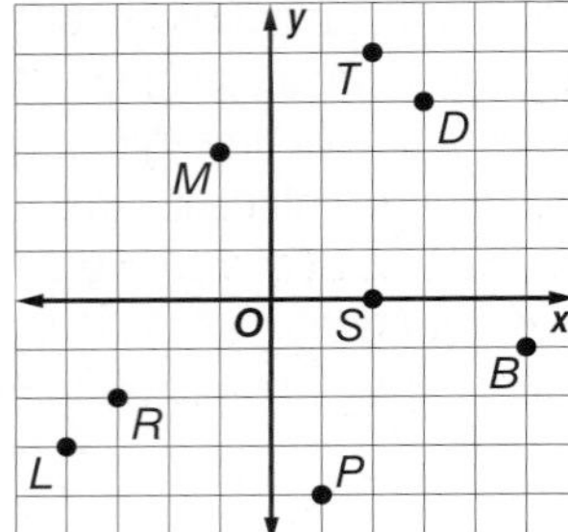

24.

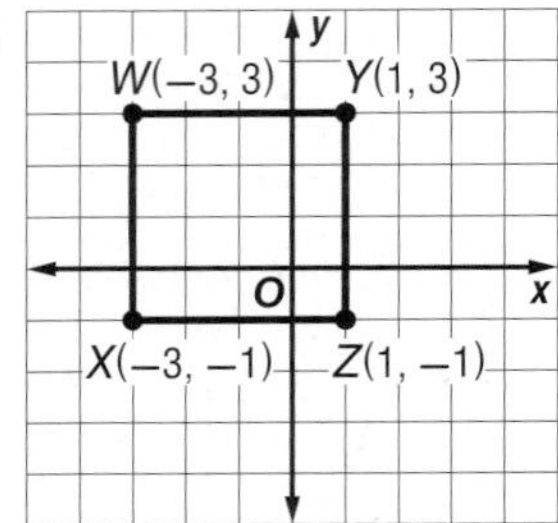

25.

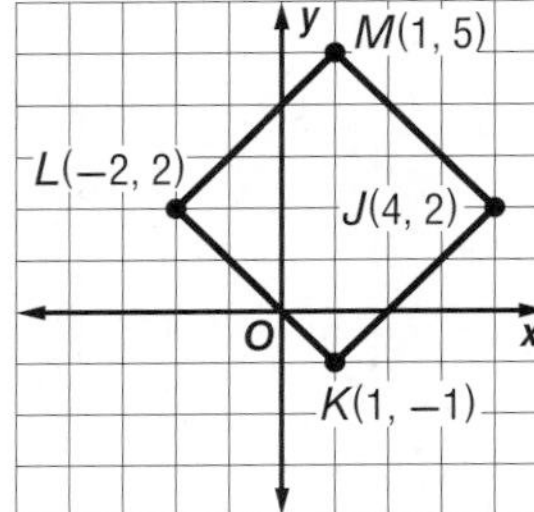

26.

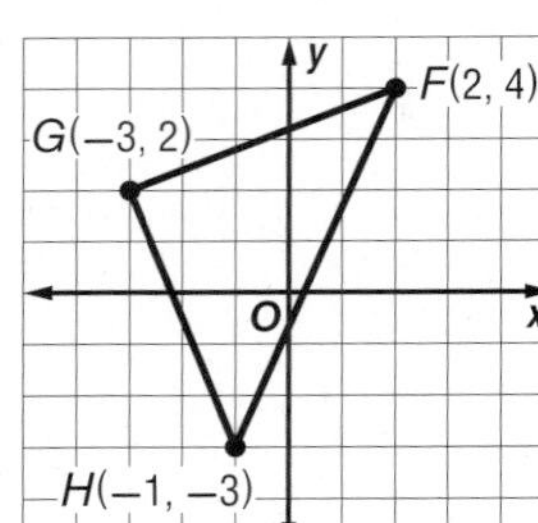

27.

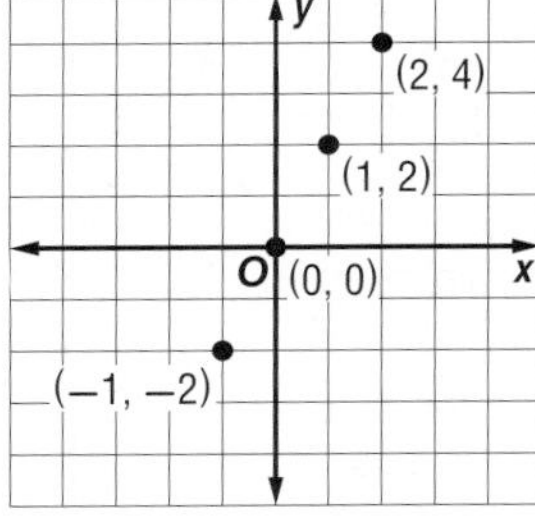

28.

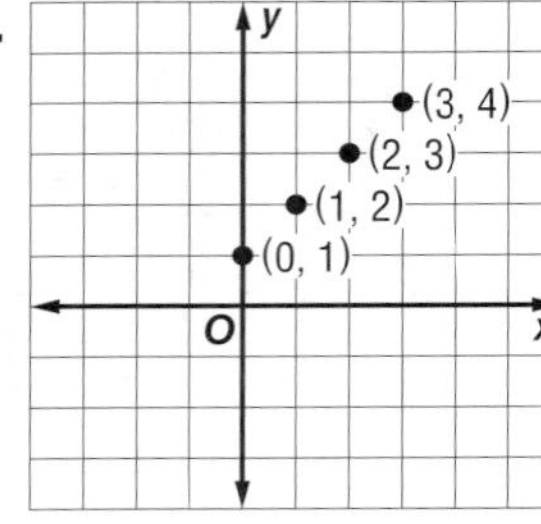

29.

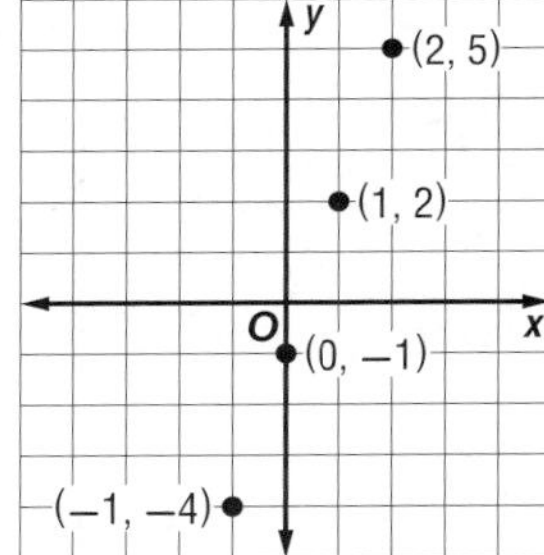

30.

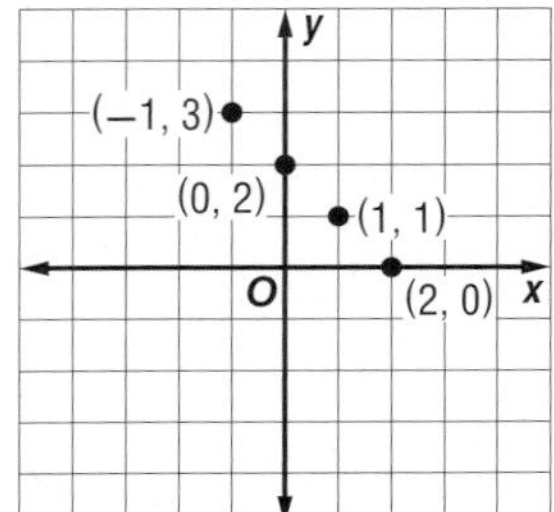

NOTES

Chapter Planner

Diagnostic Assessment
Quick Check

	LESSON 1-1 (45 min: 1.5 days; 90 min: 0.75 day)	EXTEND 1-1 (45 min: 0.5 day; 90 min: 0.25 day)	LESSON 1-2 (45 min: 1.5 days; 90 min: 0.75 day)	EXTEND 1-2 (45 min: 0.5 day; 90 min: 0.25 day)
Title	**Points, Lines, and Planes**	**Geometry Lab: Describing What You See**	**Linear Measure**	**Extension Lesson: Precision and Accuracy**
Objectives	▪ Identify and model points, lines, and planes. ▪ Identify intersecting lines and planes.	▪ Use correct mathematical terminology to describe geometric figures.	▪ Measure segments. ▪ Calculate with measures.	▪ Determine precision of measurements. ▪ Determine accuracy of measurements
Key Vocabulary	undefined term point line plane collinear coplanar space		line segment betweenness of points between congruent segments construction	precision absolute error significant digits accuracy
CCSS	G.CO.1	G.MG.1	G.CO.1, G.CO.12	
Multiple Representations	✓		✓	
Lesson Resources	connectED.mcgraw-hill.com Leveled Worksheets Vocabulary Personal Tutor Virtual Manipulatives Self-Check Quiz ▪ *5-Minute Check* ▪ *Study Notebook* ▪ *Teaching Geometry with Manipulatives*	connectED.mcgraw-hill.com Animations ▪ *Teaching Geometry with Manipulatives* **Materials:** ▪ straightedge	connectED.mcgraw-hill.com Leveled Worksheets Quiz 1 Vocabulary Personal Tutor Virtual Manipulatives Self-Check Quiz ▪ *5-Minute Check* ▪ *Study Notebook*	connectED.mcgraw-hill.com Vocabulary Personal Tutor Virtual Manipulatives **Materials:** ▪ ruler
Resources for Every Lesson	IWB eStudent Edition IWB Interactive Classroom	▪ eTeacher Edition ▪ eSolutions Manual ▪ eAssessment		
Differentiated Instruction	pp. 10, 11		pp. 15, 16, 17	

IWB All digital assets are Interactive Whiteboard ready.

Suggested Pacing			
Time Periods	Instruction	Review & Assess	Total
45-minute	12 days	2 days	14 days
90-minute	6 days	1 day	7 days

LESSON 1-3 (45 min: 1 day; 90 min: 0.5 day)	LESSON 1-4 (45 min: 1 day; 90 min: 0.5 day)	LESSON 1-5 (45 min: 1.5 days; 90 min: 0.75 day)	EXTEND 1-5 (45 min: 0.5 day; 90 min: 0.25 day)	LESSON 1-6 (45 min: 1 day; 90 min: 0.5 day)
Distance and Midpoints	**Angle Measure**	**Angle Relationships**	**Geometry Lab: Constructing Perpendiculars**	**Two-Dimensional Figures**
▪ Find the distance between two points. ▪ Find the midpoint of a segment.	▪ Measure and classify angles. ▪ Identify and use congruent angles and the bisector of an angle.	▪ Identify and use special pairs of angles. ▪ Identify perpendicular lines.	▪ Construct perpendiculars.	▪ Identify and name polygons. ▪ Find perimeter, circumference, and area of two-dimensional figures.
distance irrational number midpoint segment bisector	ray angle vertex degree right angle acute angle obtuse angle	adjacent angles linear pair vertical angles complementary angles supplementary angles perpendicular		polygon vertex of a polygon equilateral polygon regular polygon perimeter circumference area
G.CO.1, G.CO.12	G.CO.1, G.CO.12		G.CO.12	G.GPE.7
connectED.mcgraw-hill.com Leveled Worksheets Vocabulary Animations Personal Tutor Virtual Manipulatives Self-Check Quiz ▪ *5-Minute Check* ▪ *Study Notebook* ▪ *Teaching Geometry with Manipulatives*	connectED.mcgraw-hill.com Leveled Worksheets Quiz 2 Vocabulary Animations Personal Tutor Virtual Manipulatives Self-Check Quiz ▪ *5-Minute Check* ▪ *Study Notebook* ▪ *Teaching Geometry with Manipulatives*	connectED.mcgraw-hill.com Leveled Worksheets Vocabulary Personal Tutor Self-Check Quiz ▪ *5-Minute Check* ▪ *Study Notebook*	connectED.mcgraw-hill.com Animations Virtual Manipulatives ▪ *Teaching Geometry with Manipulatives* **Materials:** ▪ compass ▪ straightedge	connectED.mcgraw-hill.com Leveled Worksheets Quiz 3 Vocabulary Personal Tutor Virtual Manipulatives Self-Check Quiz ▪ *5-Minute Check* ▪ *Study Notebook*
IWB eStudent Edition IWB Interactive Classroom	▪ eTeacher Edition ▪ eSolutions Manual ▪ eAssessment			
pp. 27, 28, 32	pp. 37, 39, 40	pp. 48, 49		pp. 58, 64
	Formative Assessment Mid-Chapter Quiz			

Chapter Planner

	EXTEND 1-6 (45 min: 1 day; 90 min: 0.5 day)	LESSON 1-7 (45 min: 1 day; 90 min: 0.5 day)	EXTEND 1-7 (45 min: 1 day; 90 min: 0.5 day)
Title	**Geometry Software Lab: Two-Dimensional Figures**	**Three-Dimensional Figures**	**Geometry Lab: Two-Dimensional Representations of Three-Dimensional Objects**
Objectives	▪ Use The Geometer's Sketchpad® to draw polygons and find side lengths, angle measures, and perimeter.	▪ Identify and name three-dimensional figures. ▪ Find surface area and volume.	▪ Use orthographic views and nets to represent and construct three-dimensional figures.
Key Vocabulary		polyhedron face edge vertex prism base pyramid cylinder cone sphere regular polyhedron Platonic solid surface area volume	orthographic drawing net
CCSS	G.CO.12	G.GMD.3	G.MG.1
Multiple Representations			
Lesson Resources	connectED.mcgraw-hill.com Personal Tutor **Materials:** ▪ Geometer's Sketchpad® software	connectED.mcgraw-hill.com Leveled Worksheets Quiz 4 Vocabulary Personal Tutor Virtual Manipulatives Self-Check Quiz ▪ *5-Minute Check* ▪ *Study Notebook*	connectED.mcgraw-hill.com Vocabulary Animations Virtual Manipulatives ▪ *Teaching Geometry with Manipulatives* **Materials:** ▪ ruler ▪ scissors ▪ tape ▪ a large sheet of paper
Resources for Every Lesson	IWB eStudent Edition IWB Interactive Classroom	▪ eTeacher Edition ▪ eSolutions Manual ▪ eAssessment	
Differentiated Instruction		pp. 69, 74	

Summative Assessment
Study Guide and Review
Practice Test

IWB All digital assets are Interactive Whiteboard ready.

What the Research Says...

Students retain what they learn from their own efforts to address challenging problems that arise from situations that resonate with their own interests (Steen and Forman, 1995).

- Use the chapter project on page 2 of the Teacher Edition, as well as the other chapter projects, and allow students to pick subjects of their own choosing, based on their own interests.
- When introducing new concepts, relate them to previous learning. Ask students what they remember about the topic from the past, what they liked, or what they did not understand.

Teacher to Teacher

Nancy Trent
Teacher
The Woodlands High School
Willis, Texas

Use With Lesson 1-7

"I introduce solids by having the students construct a "Birthday Prism" from centimeter graph paper. This prism is made by using the month of their birth as the measurement for the sides of the square base and the day of the month as the measurement for the height. For example, if your birthday falls on September 30, the square bases are 9-by-9 centimeters and the height is 30 centimeters. Then the students construct a net for their prisms and determine the surface area and volume. I have also extended this activity to a "Birthday Cylinder.""

Teacher to Teacher features contain teaching suggestions from teachers who are creatively teaching Geometry in their classrooms.

Reading and Writing in Mathematics

Project CRISS

STUDY SKILL

The content frame can be used to help students compare and contrast information. The information at the right is from Lesson 1-1. Have students continue the frame for additional terms and geometric figures defined and used in this chapter.

Geometric Figure or Term	Definition	Dimension	Picture	Name	Special Features
point	Undefined; Description: a figure with no size or shape	0	A •	*A*	
line	Undefined Description: a set points	1	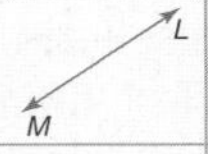	$\overleftrightarrow{LM}$	
plane	Undefined. Description: a set of points that create a flat surface	2	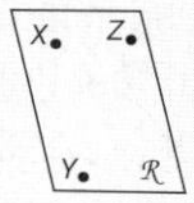	plane *R* plane *XYZ*	

Creating Independence through Student-owned Strategies

Assessment and Intervention

SE = Student Edition, **TE** = Teacher Edition, **CRM** = Chapter Resource Masters

	Diagnosis	Prescription
DIAGNOSTIC ASSESSMENT	**Beginning Chapter 1**	
	Get Ready for Chapter 1 **SE**	Response to Intervention **TE**
	Beginning Every Lesson	
	Then, Now, Why? **SE** 5-Minute Checks	Chapter 0 **SE** *Quick Review Math Handbook*
FORMATIVE ASSESSMENT	**During/After Every Lesson**	
	Guided Practice **SE**, every example Check Your Understanding **SE** H.O.T. Problems **SE** Spiral Review **SE** Additional Examples **TE** Watch Out! **TE** Step 4, Assess **TE** Chapter 1 Quizzes **CRM**, pp. 51–52 Self-Check Quizzes connectED.mcgraw-hill.com	TIER 1 Intervention Skills Practice **CRM**, Ch. 1 connectED.mcgraw-hill.com TIER 2 Intervention Differentiated Instruction **TE** Differentiated Homework Options **TE** Study Guide and Intervention **CRM**, Ch. 1 *Quick Review Math Handbook* TIER 3 Intervention *Math Triumphs, Geometry,* Ch. 1–5
	Mid-Chapter	
	Mid-Chapter Quiz **SE** Mid-Chapter Test **CRM**, p. 53 eAssessment	TIER 1 Intervention Skills Practice **CRM**, Ch. 1 connectED.mcgraw-hill.com TIER 2 Intervention Study Guide and Intervention **CRM**, Ch. 1; *Quick Review Math Handbook* TIER 3 Intervention *Math Triumphs, Geometry,* Ch. 1–5
	Before Chapter Test	
	Chapter Study Guide and Review **SE** Practice Test **SE** Standardized Test Practice **SE** Chapter Test connectED.mcgraw-hill.com Standardized Test Practice connectED.mcgraw-hill.com Vocabulary Review connectED.mcgraw-hill.com eAssessment	TIER 1 Intervention Skills Practice **CRM**, Ch. 1 connectED.mcgraw-hill.com TIER 2 Intervention Study Guide and Intervention **CRM**, Ch. 1; *Quick Review Math Handbook* TIER 3 Intervention *Math Triumphs, Geometry,* Ch. 1–5
SUMMATIVE ASSESSMENT	**After Chapter 1**	
	Multiple-Choice Tests, Forms 1, 2A, 2B **CRM**, pp. 55–60 Free-Response Tests, Forms 2C, 2D, 3 **CRM**, pp. 61–66 Vocabulary Test **CRM**, p. 54 Extended Response Test **CRM**, p. 67 Standardized Test Practice **CRM**, pp. 68–70 eAssessment	Study Guide and Intervention **CRM**, Ch. 1 *Quick Review Math Handbook* connectED.mcgraw-hill.com

Differentiated Instruction

Option 1 Reaching All Learners

Logical *Give students the following problem, explaining that they can use any means they need to solve it. (i.e. drawing a diagram, trial and error, using manipulatives, or any other problem solving strategy they choose.)*

Your classroom will receive 20 new desks. Each desk is 24 inches wide, 33 inches deep, and 30 inches high. They will be placed in four rows, spaced one foot apart, and 6 inches from the desk in front of them. How much surface area will the new desks need?

Naturalist Have students use disposable or digital cameras to take at least 12 pictures of various angles found on school grounds. Print or develop the pictures and have students measure and classify the angles in their photographs. You can have students share their most interesting photos with the class.

Option 2 Approaching Level AL

Use poster board or chart paper to draw several angles of different measures. Label each point on your drawing and display these angles in the front of the classroom. Separate students into two teams, and have them form two single file lines facing the angle drawings. Explain that each team will take turns sending a member to the front of the room. Tell them that they will classify and measure the angle you call out. Call out an angle and have the player measure and classify the angle. If either the classification or the measurement is incorrect, the other team can "steal it." The team that answers correctly earns a point. Play for as long as desired.

Option 3 English Learners ELL

Separate students into groups of three. Allow each group to choose a familiar traffic sign and create a model of it using poster board. Have them classify the shape, its angles, and calculate its perimeter and area.

Option 4 Beyond Level BL

Have students work in small groups to create a scale map of their school. They should plot important points and label them (i.e., bathrooms, specific classrooms, office, cafeteria, and so on) using coordinates. Tell students to provide a map scale so that it is possible to calculate distances from point to point.

Focus on Mathematical Content

Vertical Alignment

Before Chapter 1

Related Topics before Algebra 1

- Use the Pythagorean Theorem to find side lengths of right triangles.

Related Topics from Algebra 1

- Interpret situations in terms of given graphs or create situations that fit given graphs.
- Use symbols to represent unknowns and variables.

Chapter 1

Topics from Geometry

- Develop an awareness of the structure of a mathematical system, connecting definitions, postulates, logical reasoning, and theorems.
- Use construction to explore attributes of geometric figures and to make conjectures about geometric relationships.
- Use one- and two-dimensional coordinate systems to represent points, lines, rays, line segments, and figures.
- Find areas of regular polygons, circles, and composite figures.

After Chapter 1

Preparation for Algebra 2

- Analyze situations modeled by square root functions, formulate equations and inequalities, select a method, and solve problems.

Lesson-by-Lesson Preview

1-1 Points, Lines, and Planes

In geometry, a *point* is a location without shape or size. A *line* contains points and has no thickness or width. Points on the same line are collinear, and there is exactly one line through any two points. The intersection of two lines is a point.

A *plane* is a flat surface made of points. A plane has no depth and extends infinitely in all directions. Points on the same plane are coplanar, and the intersection of two planes is a line.

1-2 Linear Measure

A line cannot be measured because it extends infinitely in each direction. A line segment, however, has two endpoints and can be measured. Two segments with the same measure are said to be congruent. The symbol for congruence is $\cong$. An equal number of tic marks also indicates that segments are congruent.

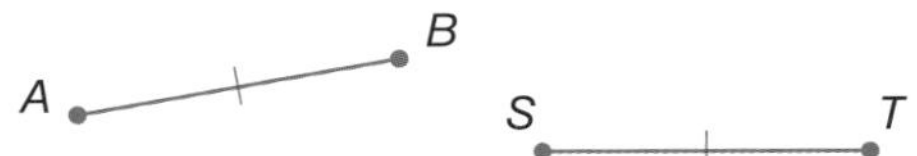

1-3 Distance and Midpoints

The coordinates of the endpoints of a segment can be used to find the length of the segment. On a number line, the distance between the endpoints is the absolute value of their difference. On a coordinate plane, you can use the Distance Formula or the Pythagorean Theorem to calculate the distance between two points.

The *midpoint* of a segment is the point halfway between its endpoints. On a number line, the coordinate of the midpoint of a segment with endpoints a and b is the sum of a and b divided by 2. To find the midpoint of a segment on the coordinate plane, use the Midpoint Formula.

1-4 Angle Measure

An *angle* is the intersection of two non-collinear rays at a common endpoint. The common endpoint is called the *vertex*, and the rays are the sides of the angle.

An angle is measured in degrees. An angle measuring exactly 90° is a right angle. Angles with measures less than 90° are acute angles, and those measuring greater than 90° are obtuse angles. Angles that have the same measure are congruent. The degree measure of an angle is represented by *m*, so to represent $\angle A$ that measures 75°, write $m\angle A = 75$.

A ray that divides an angle into two congruent angles is called an *angle* bisector.

1-5 Angle Relationships

Certain pairs of angles have special relationships. Adjacent angles are two angles that lie in the same plane, have a common vertex and a common side, but have no common interior points. Vertical angles are two non-adjacent angles formed by two intersecting lines. All vertical angles are congruent. A linear pair is a pair of adjacent angles whose non-common sides are opposite rays.

Complementary angles are a pair of angles whose angle measures have a sum of 90. Supplementary angles are two angles whose measures have a sum of 180.

If two lines intersect to form four right angles, the lines are perpendicular. Segments and rays can be perpendicular to lines or to other segments and rays. The symbol for perpendicular is $\perp$, so if line a is perpendicular to line b, write $a \perp b$.

1-6 Two-Dimensional Figures

In geometry, a *polygon* is defined as a closed figure formed by a finite number of coplanar segments. Polygons can be concave or convex. If no points of the lines are in the interior of the figure, it is convex. A convex polygon in which all sides and angles are congruent is called a *regular polygon*.

The perimeter of a polygon is the sum of the lengths of its sides. The circumference of a circle is the distance around the circle. The area is the number of square units required to cover a surface.

1-7 Three-Dimensional Figures

An orthographic drawing shows the top, left, front, and right side of an object views. An orthographic drawing can be used to render an isometric view or corner view.

A solid with all flat surfaces that encloses a single region of space is called a *polyhedron*. Each flat surface, or face, is a polygon. A regular polyhedron has all congruent edges and all of its faces are congruent regular polygons. Two common types of polyhedra are prisms and pyramids. A prism has two parallel congruent faces called *bases*. The other faces are parallelograms. A regular prism has bases that are regular polygons. A pyramid is another type of polyhedron. All the faces of a pyramid (except for the base) intersect at one vertex.

Not all solids are polyhedra. For example, a cylinder and a cone are not polyhedra because they have circular bases. A sphere, the set of points in space that are a given distance from a given point, is not a polyhedron.

Professional Development

Targeted professional development has been articulated throughout Geometry. More quality, customized professional development is available from McGraw-Hill Professional Development. Visit connectED.mcgraw-hill.com for details on each product.

- Online Lessons emphasize the strategies and techniques used to teach Geometry. Includes streaming video, interactive pages, and online tools.
- Video Workshops allow mentors, coaches, or leadership personnel to facilitate on-site workshops on educational strategies in mathematics and mathematical concepts.
- MHPD Online (www.mhpdonline.com) offers online professional development with video clips of instructional strategies, links, student activities, and news and issues in education.
- Teaching Today (teachingtoday.glencoe.com) gives secondary teachers practical strategies and materials that inspire excellence and innovation in teaching.

connectED.mcgraw-hill.com

Chapter Project

Urban Planning

Students use what they have learned about angles and polygons to complete a project.

This chapter project addresses civic literacy, as well as several specific skills identified as being essential to student success by the Framework for 21st Century Learning.

Visit connectED.mcgraw-hill.com for student and teacher handouts.

KeyVocabulary Introd uce the key vocabulary in the chapter using the method below.

Define: Adjacent angles are angles that lie in the same plane and have a common vertex and a common side, but no common interior points.

Example:

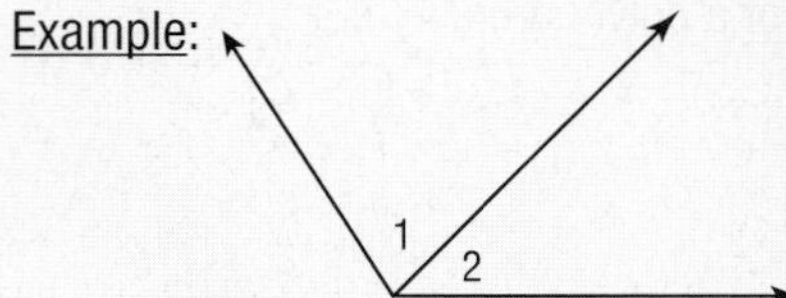

Ask: How do the angles relate to one another? What is their sum? Angles 1 and 2 are adjacent angles. The sum of their measures is about 120.

CHAPTER 1 Tools of Geometry

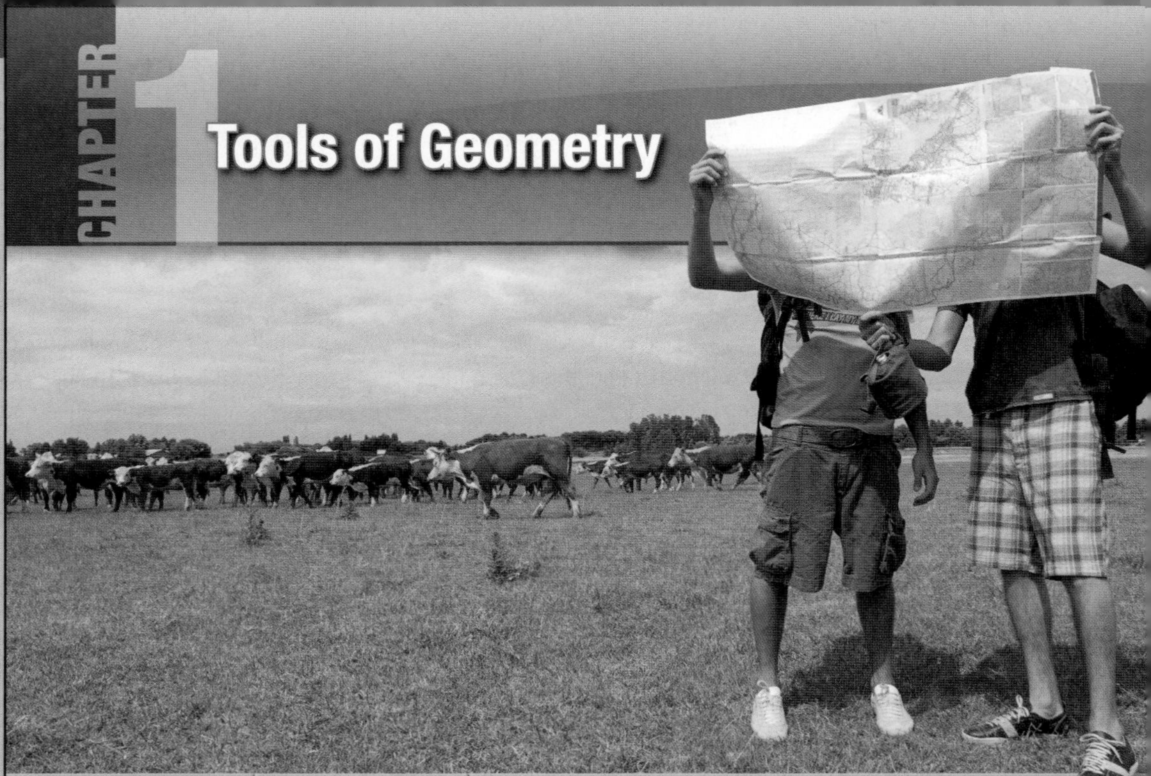

Then

- You graphed points on the coordinate plane and evaluated mathematical expressions.

Now

In this chapter, you will:

- Find distances between points and midpoints of line segments.
- Identify angle relationships.
- Find perimeters, areas, surface areas, and volumes.

Why?

- **MAPS** Geometric figures and terms can be used to represent and describe real-world situations. On a map, locations of cities can be represented by points, highways or streets by lines, and national parks by polygons that have both perimeter and area. The map itself is representative of a plane.

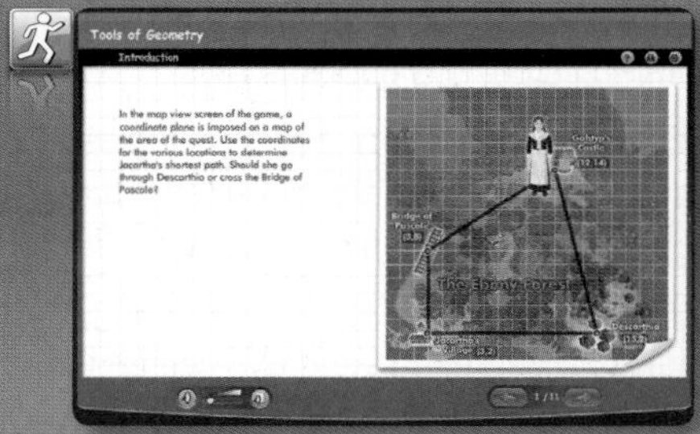

connectED.mcgraw-hill.com **Your Digital Math Portal**

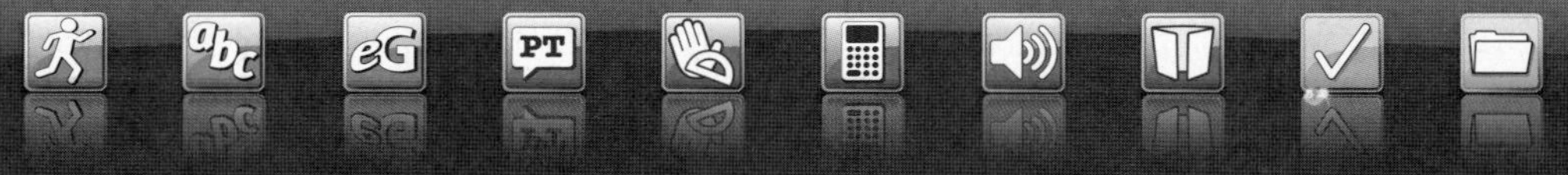

Animation | Vocabulary | eGlossary | Personal Tutor | Virtual Manipulatives | Graphing Calculator | Audio | Foldables | Self-Check Practice | Worksheets

Additional Answers (p. 3)

1.

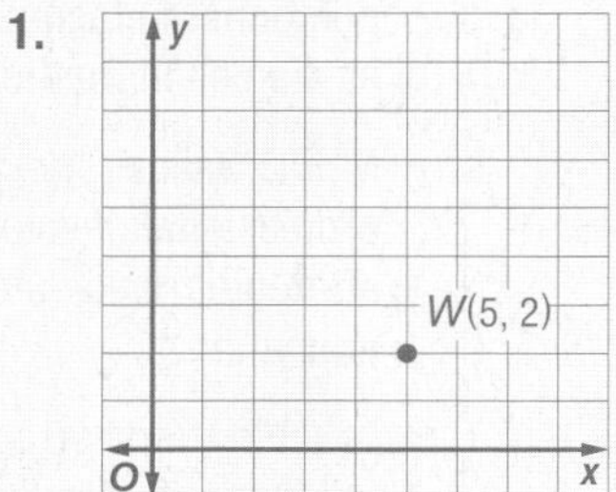

2.

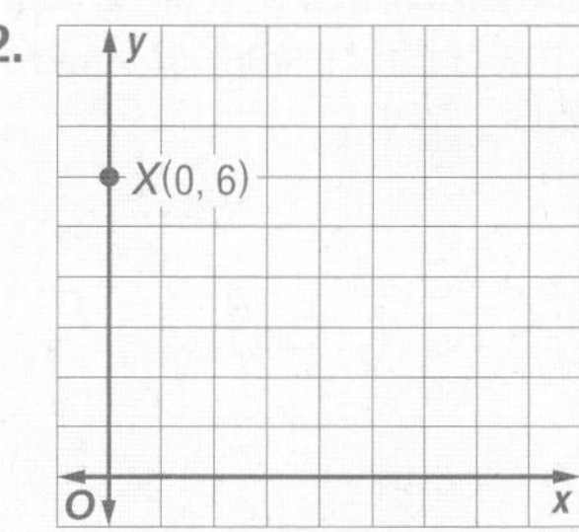

3–4. See p. 4.

Get Ready for the Chapter

Diagnose Readiness | You have two options for checking Prerequisite Skills.

1 Textbook Option Take the Quick Check below. Refer to the Quick Review for help.

QuickCheck

Graph and label each point in the coordinate plane.

1. $W(5, 2)$
2. $X(0, 6)$
3. $Y(-3, -1)$
4. $Z(4, -2)$ **1–4. See margin.**

5. **GAMES** Carolina is using the diagram to record her chess moves. She moves her knight 2 spaces up and 1 space to the left from f3. What is the location of the knight after Carolina completes her turn? **e5**

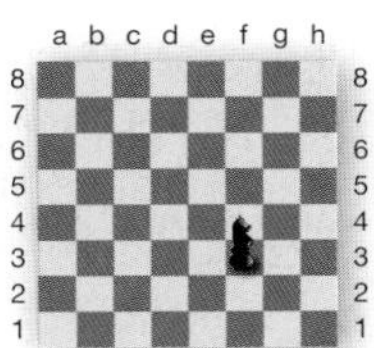

Find each sum or difference.

6. $\frac{2}{3} + \frac{5}{6}$ $1\frac{1}{2}$
7. $2\frac{1}{18} + 4\frac{3}{4}$ $6\frac{29}{36}$
8. $\frac{13}{18} - \frac{5}{9}$ $\frac{1}{6}$
9. $14\frac{3}{5} - 9\frac{7}{15}$ $5\frac{2}{15}$
10. **FOOD** Alvin ate $\frac{1}{3}$ of a pizza for dinner and took $\frac{1}{6}$ of it for lunch the next day. How much of the pizza does he have left? $\frac{1}{2}$

Evaluate each expression.

11. $(-4 - 5)^2$ **81**
12. $(6 - 10)^2$ **16**
13. $(8 - 5)^2 + [9 - (-3)]^2$ **153**

Solve each equation.

14. $6x + 5 + 2x - 11 = 90$ **12**
15. $8x - 7 = 53 - 2x$ **6**

QuickReview

Example 1 (Used in Lesson 1-1)

Graph and label the point $Q(-3, 4)$ in the coordinate plane.

Start at the origin. Since the x-coordinate is negative, move 3 units to the left. Then move 4 units up since the y-coordinate is positive. Draw a dot and label it Q.

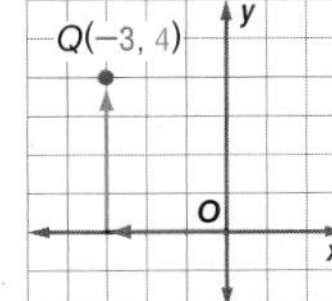

Example 2 (Used in Lesson 1-2)

Find $3\frac{1}{6} + 2\frac{3}{4}$.

$3\frac{1}{6} + 2\frac{3}{4} = \frac{19}{6} + \frac{11}{4}$ Write as improper fractions.

$= \frac{19}{6}\left(\frac{2}{2}\right) + \frac{11}{4}\left(\frac{3}{3}\right)$ The LCD is 12.

$= \frac{38}{12} + \frac{33}{12}$ Multiply.

$= \frac{71}{12}$ or $5\frac{11}{12}$ Simplify.

Example 3 (Used in Lessons 1-3 through 1-5)

Evaluate the expression $[-2 - (-7)]^2 + (1 - 8)^2$.

Follow the order of operations.

$[-2 - (-7)]^2 + (1 - 8)^2$

$= 5^2 + (-7)^2$ Subtract.

$= 25 + 49$ $5^2 = 25, (-7)^2 = 49$

$= 74$ Add.

2 Online Option Take an online self-check Chapter Readiness Quiz at connectED.mcgraw-hill.com.

Essential Question

- Why do we measure? Sample answer: Measurements provide a quantifiable way to describe real-world quantities.

Essential Questions frame each chapter. These open-ended questions guide student inquiry into the "big ideas" central to each chapter. Throughout the Student Edition, Exercises that refer to the chapter or follow up Essential Questions are indicated by the icon.

Get Ready for the Chapter

Response to Intervention (RtI)

Use the *Quick Check* results and the Intervention Planner chart to help you determine your Response to Intervention. The If-Then statements in the chart help you decide the appropriate tier of RtI and suggest intervention resources for each tier.

InterventionPlanner

Tier 1 On Level OL

If students miss about 25% of the exercises or less,

Then choose a resource:

SE Lessons 1-1, 1-2, and 1-3 through 1-5

Skills Practice, Chapter 1, pp. 7, 14, 20, 27

connectED.mcgraw-hill.com Self-Check Quiz

Tier 2 Strategic Intervention AL approaching grade level

If students miss about 50% of the exercises

Then choose a resource:

Study Guide and Intervention, Chapter 1, pp. 5–6, 12–13, 18–19, 31–32

connectED.mcgraw-hill.com Extra Examples, Personal Tutor, Homework Help

Tier 3 Intensive Intervention 2 or more grades below level

If students miss about 75% of the exercises,

Then use *Math Triumphs, Geometry*, Ch 1–5

connectED.mcgraw-hill.com Extra Examples, Personal Tutor, Homework Help, Review Vocabulary

Diagnose students' readiness for each chapter by using either the in-text **Quick Check** or the online **Chapter Readiness Quiz**. Then use the **Intervention Planner** to choose the correct program resource to reinforce each students' prerequisite skills.

connectED.mcgraw-hill.com

FOLDABLES StudyOrganizer

Dinah Zike's Foldables®

Focus Note-taking is a skill that is based upon listening or reading for main ideas and then recording those ideas for future reference.

Teach Under the tabs of their Foldable, have students take notes about points, lines, and planes; angles and angle relationships; and formulas and notes for distance, midpoint, perimeter, area, and volume. Encourage students to apply these concepts by drawing and measuring angles and line segments, and writing about the process.

When to Use It

Foldable Tabs	Lessons
Points, Lines, Planes	1-1
Distance and Midpoint	1-2 and 1-3
Angles	1-4 to 1-6
Area	1-6
Perimeter	1-6
Volume	1-7

Differentiated Instruction

Student-Built Glossary, p. 1

Students should complete the chart by providing the definition of each term and an example as they progress through Chapter 1.

This study tool can also be used to review for the chapter test.

Get Started on the Chapter

You will learn several new concepts, skills, and vocabulary terms as you study Chapter 1. To get ready, identify important terms and organize your resources. You may refer to Chapter 0 to review prerequisite skills.

FOLDABLES StudyOrganizer

Tools of Geometry Make this Foldable to help you organize your Chapter 1 notes about points, lines, and planes; angles and angle relationships; and formulas and notes for distance, midpoint, perimeter, area, and volume. Begin with a sheet of 11″ × 17″ paper.

1 **Fold** the short sides to meet in the middle.

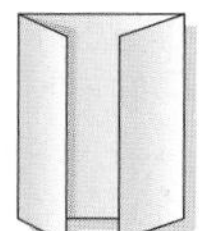

2 **Fold** the booklet in thirds lengthwise.

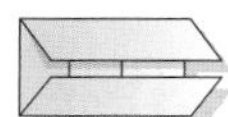

3 **Open and cut** the booklet in thirds lengthwise.

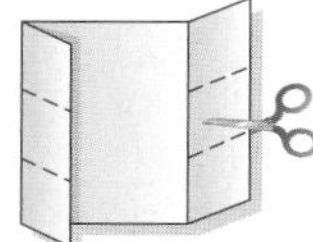

4 **Label** the tabs as shown.

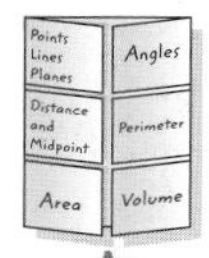

Foldables® are a unique way to enhance students' study skills. Encourage students to add to their Foldable as they work through the chapter and to use it for review for the chapter test.

NewVocabulary

English		Español
collinear	p. 5	colineal
coplanar	p. 5	coplanar
congruent	p. 16	congruente
midpoint	p. 27	punto medio
segment bisector	p. 29	bisectriz de segmento
angle	p. 36	angulo
vertex	p. 36	vertice
angle bisector	p. 39	bisectriz de un angulo
perpendicular	p. 48	perpendicular
polygon	p. 56	poligono
perimeter	p. 58	perimetro
volume	p. 69	volumen

ReviewVocabulary

ordered pair par ordenado a set of numbers or coordinates used to locate any point on a coordinate plane, written in the form (x, y)

origin origen the point where the two axes intersect at their zero points

quadrants cuadrantes the four regions into which the x-axis and y-axis separate the coordinate plane

x-coordinate coordenada x the first number in an ordered pair

y-coordinate coordenada y the second number in an ordered pair

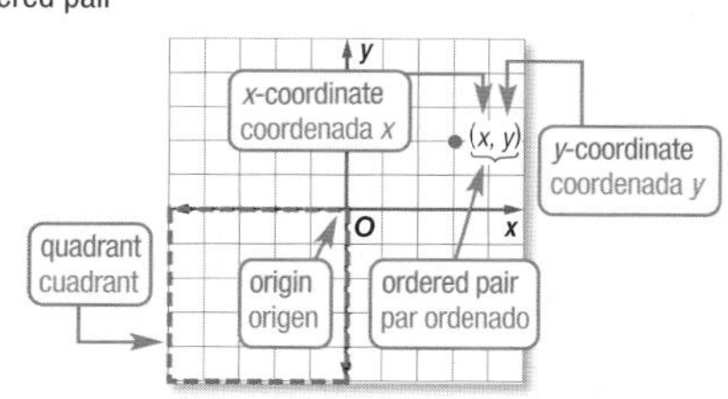

Additional Answers (Get Ready p. 3)

3.

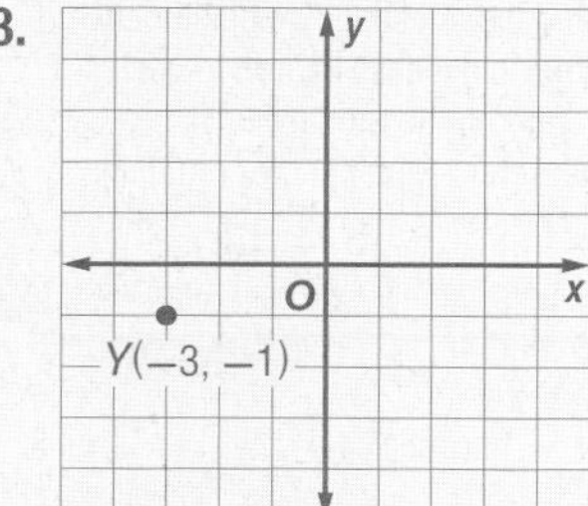

4.

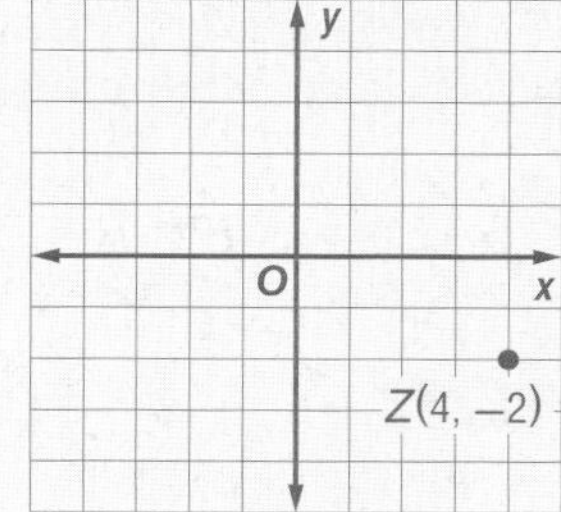

LESSON 1-1 Points, Lines, and Planes

Then	Now	Why?
● You used basic geometric concepts and properties to solve problems.	**1** Identify and model points, lines, and planes. **2** Identify intersecting lines and planes.	● On a subway map, the locations of stops are represented by *points*. The route the train can take is modeled by a series of connected paths that look like *lines*. The flat surface of the map on which these points and lines lie is representative of a *plane*.

New Vocabulary is listed at the beginning of every lesson.

NewVocabulary

undefined term
point
line
plane
collinear
coplanar
intersection
definition
defined term
space

Common Core State Standards

Content Standards
G.CO.1 Know precise definitions of angle, circle, perpendicular line, parallel line, and line segment, based on the undefined notions of point, line, distance along a line, and distance around a circular arc.

Mathematical Practices
4 Model with mathematics.
6 Attend to precision.

Brand X Pictures/Jupiterimages

1 Points, Lines, and Planes Unlike the real-world objects that they model, shapes, points, lines, and planes do not have any actual size. In geometry, *point*, *line*, and *plane* are considered **undefined terms** because they are only explained using examples and descriptions.

You are already familiar with the terms point, line, and plane from algebra. You graphed on a coordinate *plane* and found ordered pairs that represented *points* on *lines*. In geometry, these terms have a similar meaning.

The phrase *exactly one* in a statement such as, "There is exactly one line through any two points," means that there is *one and only one*.

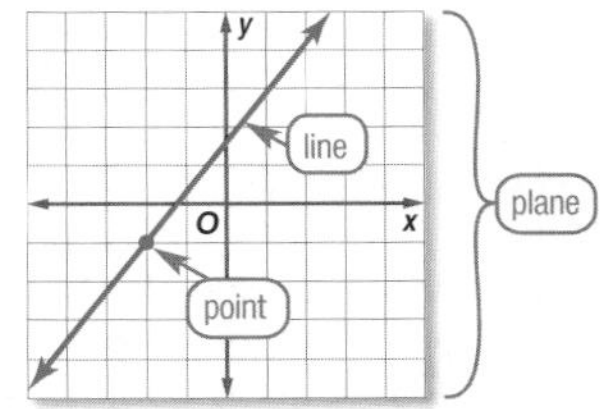

KeyConcept Undefined Terms

A **point** is a location. It has neither shape nor size.

Named by a capital letter

Example point A

A **line** is made up of points and has no thickness or width. There is exactly one line through any two points.

Named by the letters representing two points on the line or a lowercase script letter

Example line m, line PQ or $\overleftrightarrow{PQ}$, line QP or $\overleftrightarrow{QP}$

A **plane** is a flat surface made up of points that extends infinitely in all directions. There is exactly one plane through any three points not on the same line.

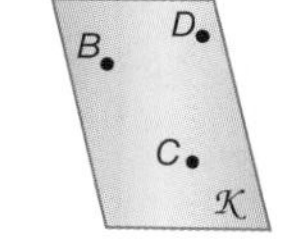

Named by a capital script letter or by the letters naming three points that are not all on the same line

Example plane $\mathcal{K}$, plane BCD, plane CDB, plane DCB, plane DBC, plane CBD, plane BDC

Collinear points are points that lie on the same line. *Noncollinear* points do not lie on the same line. **Coplanar** points are points that lie in the same plane. *Noncoplanar* points do not lie in the same plane.

1 Focus

VerticalAlignment

Before Lesson 1-1 Use geometric concepts and properties to solve problems.

Lesson 1-1 Identify and model points, lines, and planes. Identify intersecting lines and planes.

After Lesson 1-1 Use numeric and geometric patterns to make generalizations about geometric properties, including properties of polygons.

2 Teach

Scaffolding Questions

Have students read the **Why?** section of the lesson.

Ask:

- What are some other objects that points, lines, and planes could be used to represent? Sample response: Stars can be represented by points, lines can be used to connect the stars to form constellations, and a plane can be used to represent the sky.
- What are some other ways that combinations of points, lines, and planes are used? networks and maps

(continued on the next page)

Lesson 1-1 Resources

Resource	Approaching Level AL	On Level OL	Beyond Level BL	English Learners ELL
Teacher Edition	▪ Differentiated Instruction, pp. 10, 11	▪ Differentiated Instruction, pp. 10, 11	▪ Differentiated Instruction, p. 10	▪ Differentiated Instruction, p. 10
Chapter Resource Masters	▪ Study Guide and Intervention, pp. 5–6 ▪ Skills Practice, p. 7 ▪ Practice, p. 8 ▪ Word Problem Practice, p. 9 ▪ Graphing Calculator Activity, p. 11	▪ Study Guide and Intervention, pp. 5–6 ▪ Skills Practice, p. 7 ▪ Practice, p. 8 ▪ Word Problem Practice, p. 9 ▪ Enrichment, p. 10 ▪ Graphing Calculator Activity, p. 11	▪ Practice, p. 8 ▪ Word Problem Practice, p. 9 ▪ Enrichment, p. 10 ▪ Graphing Calculator Activity, p. 11	▪ Study Guide and Intervention, pp. 5–6 ▪ Skills Practice, p. 7 ▪ Practice, p. 8 ▪ Word Problem Practice, p. 9 ▪ Graphing Calculator Activity, p. 11
Other	▪ 5-Minute Check 1-1 ▪ Study Notebook ▪ Teaching Geometry with Manipulatives	▪ 5-Minute Check 1-1 ▪ Study Notebook ▪ Teaching Geometry with Manipulatives	▪ 5-Minute Check 1-1 ▪ Study Notebook	▪ 5-Minute Check 1-1 ▪ Study Notebook ▪ Teaching Geometry with Manipulatives

- Describe a point, a line, and a plane. Can you clearly define these geometric terms? What is the difference between a description and a definition? A point is like a dot, a line is like a long, straight road, and a plane is like a desktop. There are no clear definitions of these terms; a description simply describes, whereas a definition is a detail of specific criteria required for a figure.

1 Points, Lines, and Planes

Examples 1 and 2 show how to name and model points, lines, and planes by using the key concepts provided in this lesson.

Formative Assessment

Use the Guided Practice exercises after each example to determine students' understanding of concepts.

Additional Examples

1 Use the figure to name each of the following.

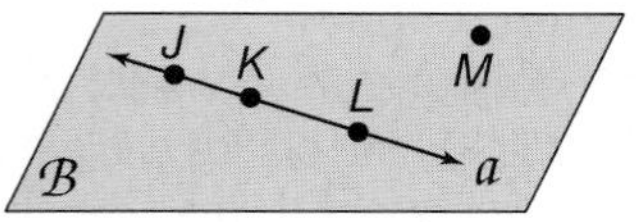

a. a line containing point K
line a, $\overleftrightarrow{JK}$, $\overleftrightarrow{JL}$, $\overleftrightarrow{KJ}$, $\overleftrightarrow{KL}$, $\overleftrightarrow{LJ}$, or $\overleftrightarrow{LK}$

b. a plane containing point L
plane B, plane JKM, plane KLM, plane JLM. Reorder the letters in these names to create 15 other acceptable names.

2 Name the geometric shape modeled by each object.

a. a 10×12 patio plane

b. a button on a table point

Additional Examples also in Interactive Classroom PowerPoint® Presentations

Example 1 Name Lines and Planes

Use the figure to name each of the following.

a. a line containing point W

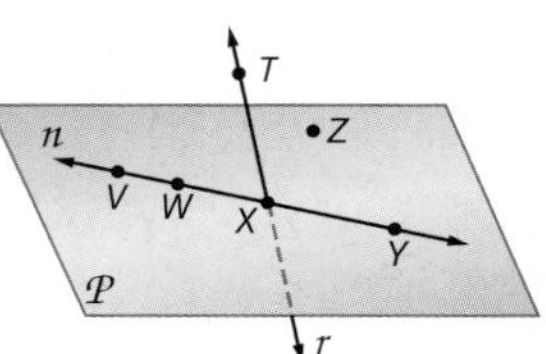

The line can be named as line n, or any two of the four points on the line can be used to name the line.

$\overleftrightarrow{VW}$ $\overleftrightarrow{WV}$ $\overleftrightarrow{VX}$ $\overleftrightarrow{XV}$ $\overleftrightarrow{VY}$ $\overleftrightarrow{YV}$
$\overleftrightarrow{WX}$ $\overleftrightarrow{XW}$ $\overleftrightarrow{WY}$ $\overleftrightarrow{YW}$ $\overleftrightarrow{XY}$ $\overleftrightarrow{YX}$

b. a plane containing point X

One plane that can be named is plane $\mathcal{P}$. You can also use the letters of any three *noncollinear* points to name this plane.

plane XZY	plane VZW	plane VZX
plane VZY	plane WZX	plane WZY

The letters of each of these names can be reordered to create other acceptable names for this plane. For example, XZY can also be written as XYZ, ZXY, ZYX, YXZ, and YZX. In all, there are 36 different three-letter names for this plane.

StudyTip
Additional Planes Although not drawn in Example 1b, there is another plane that contains point X. Since points W, T, and X are noncollinear, point X is also in plane WTX.

GuidedPractice

1A. a plane containing points T and Z TZX **1B.** a line containing point T r

Real-World Example 2 Model Points, Lines, and Planes

MESSAGE BOARD Name the geometric terms modeled by the objects in the picture.

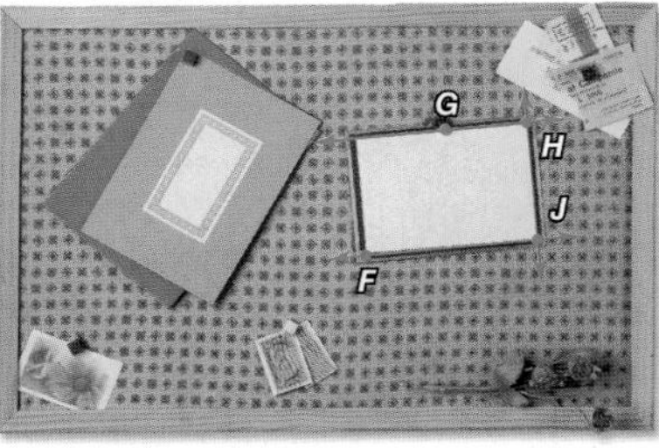

The push pin models point G.

The maroon border on the card models line GH.

The edge of the card models line HJ.

The card itself models plane FGJ.

GuidedPractice

Name the geometric term modeled by each object.

2A. stripes on a sweater lines **2B.** the corner of a box point

Real-WorldCareer
Drafter Drafters use perspective to create drawings to build everything from toys to school buildings. Drafters need skills in math and computers. They get their education at trade schools, community colleges, and some 4-year colleges. Refer to Exercises 50 and 51.

2 Intersections of Lines and Planes

The **intersection** of two or more geometric figures is the set of points they have in common. Two lines intersect in a point. Lines can intersect planes, and planes can intersect each other.

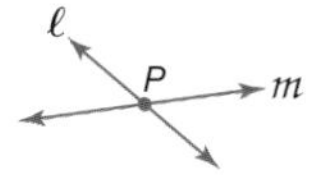

P represents the intersection of lines ℓ and m.

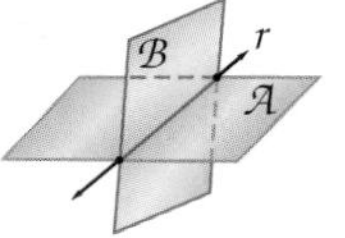

Line r represents the intersection of planes $\mathcal{A}$ and $\mathcal{B}$.

Digital Vision/Getty Images

Additional Answers (Guided Practice)

3A. Sample answer:

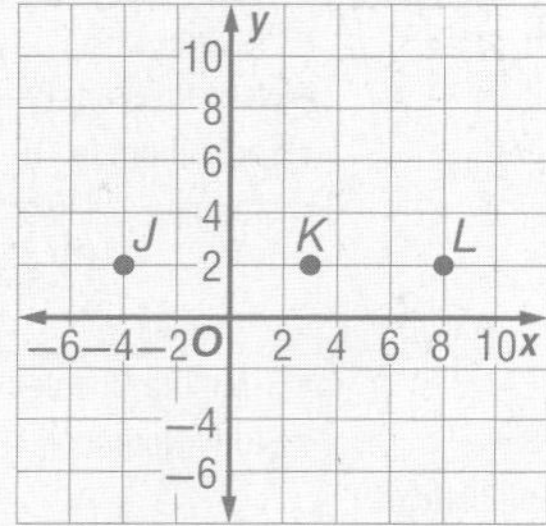

3B. Sample answer:

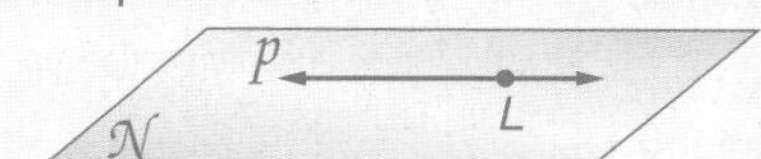

Example 3 Draw Geometric Figures

Draw and label a figure for each relationship.

a. ALGEBRA Lines AB and CD intersect at E for $A(-2, 4)$, $B(0, -2)$, $C(-3, 0)$, and $D(3, 3)$ on a coordinate plane. Point F is coplanar with these points, but not collinear with $\overleftrightarrow{AB}$ or $\overleftrightarrow{CD}$.

Graph each point and draw $\overleftrightarrow{AB}$ and $\overleftrightarrow{CD}$.

Label the intersection point as E.

An infinite number of points are coplanar with A, B, C, D and E but not collinear with $\overleftrightarrow{AB}$ and $\overleftrightarrow{CD}$. In the graph, one such point is $F(2, -3)$.

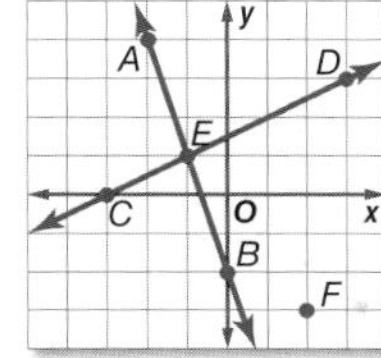

b. QR intersects plane $\mathcal{T}$ at point S.

Draw a surface to represent plane $\mathcal{T}$ and label it.

Draw a dot for point S anywhere on the plane and a dot that is not on plane $\mathcal{T}$ for point Q.

Draw a line through points Q and S. Dash the line to indicate the portion hidden by the plane. Then draw another dot on the line and label it R.

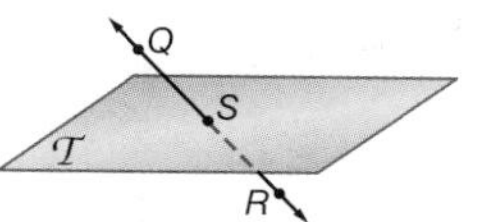

StudyTip

Three-Dimensional Drawings Because it is impossible to show an entire plane in a figure, edged shapes with different shades of color are used to represent planes.

GuidedPractice **3A–3B. See margin.**

3A. Points $J(-4, 2)$, $K(3, 2)$, and L are collinear.

3B. Line p lies in plane $\mathcal{N}$ and contains point L.

Definitions or **defined terms** are explained using undefined terms and/or other defined terms. **Space** is defined as a boundless, three-dimensional set of all points. Space can contain lines and planes.

Example 4 Interpret Drawings

a. How many planes appear in this figure?

Six: plane X, plane JDH, plane JDE, plane EDF, plane FDG, and plane HDG.

b. Name three points that are collinear.

Points J, K, and D are collinear.

c. Name the intersection of plane HDG with plane X.

Plane HDG intersects plane X in $\overleftrightarrow{HG}$.

d. At what point do $\overleftrightarrow{LM}$ and $\overleftrightarrow{EF}$ intersect? Explain.

It does not appear that these lines intersect. $\overleftrightarrow{EF}$ lies in plane X, but only point L of $\overleftrightarrow{LM}$ lies in X.

StudyTip

CCSS Precision A point has no dimension. A line exists in one dimension. However, a circle is two-dimensional, and a pyramid is three-dimensional.

GuidedPractice **4A. Points E, F, and G lie in plane X, but point D does not lie in plane X. Thus, they are not coplanar.** **4B. Point D is the only point the planes have in common.**

Explain your reasoning.

4A. Are points E, D, F, and G coplanar?

4B. At what point or in what line do planes JDH, JDE, and EDF intersect?

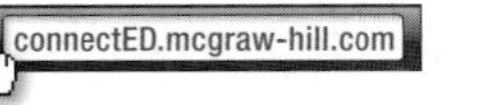

CCSS Teaching the Mathematical Practices

Precision Mathematically proficient students communicate precisely to others. Encourage students to learn and use clear definitions for the mathematical terms used throughout the program.

Teach with Tech

Interactive Whiteboard Draw a plane on the board. Select students and give them specific points and lines to draw that are either in the plane or not in the plane.

Teach with Tech features throughout the Teacher Edition offer tips on using various types of technology such as interactive whiteboards, document cameras, blogs, and more, to enhance your teaching

2 Intersection of Lines and Planes

Examples 3 and 4 show how to draw, label, and identify points, lines, and planes in space.

Additional Examples

3 Draw and label a figure for each relationship.

a. ALGEBRA Plane R contains lines $\overleftrightarrow{AB}$ and $\overleftrightarrow{DE}$, which intersect at point P. Add point C on plane R so that it is not collinear with $\overleftrightarrow{AB}$ or $\overleftrightarrow{DE}$. Sample answer:

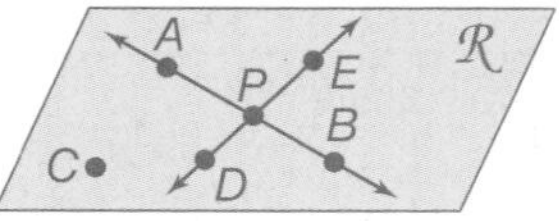

b. $\overleftrightarrow{QR}$ on a coordinate plane contains $Q(-2, 4)$ and $R(4, -4)$. Add point T so that T is collinear with these points. Sample answer:

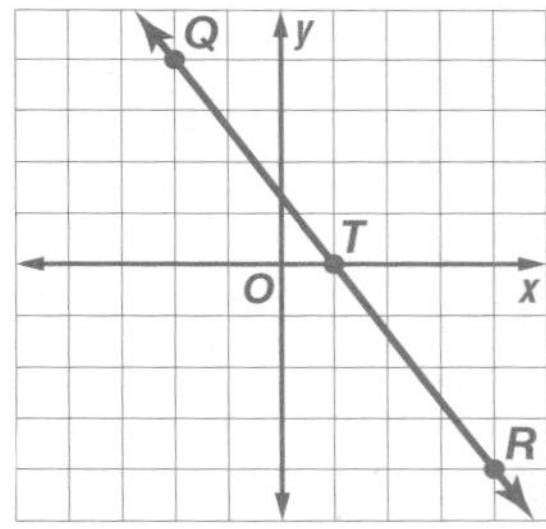

4 Use the figure for parts a–d.

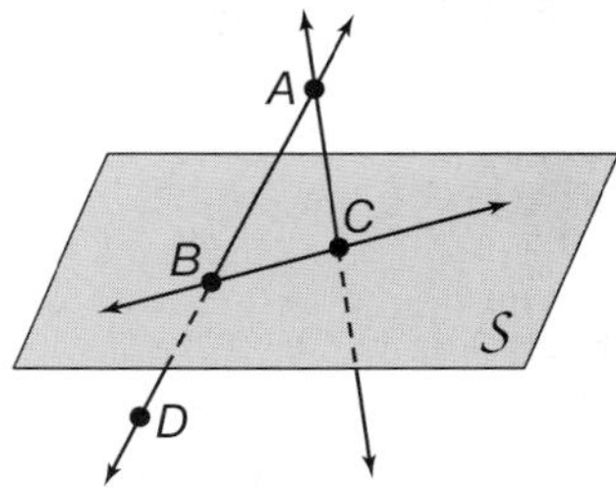

a. How many planes appear in this figure? two

b. Name three points that are collinear. A, B, and D

c. Are points A, B, C, and D coplanar? Explain. Points A, B, C, and D all lie in plane ABC, so they are coplanar.

d. At what point do $\overleftrightarrow{DB}$ and $\overleftrightarrow{CA}$ intersect? A

Check Your Understanding exercises are intended to be completed in class. **Example references** show students where to look back for review.

3 Practice

Formative Assessment

Use Exercises 1–12 to check for understanding.

Then use the chart at the bottom of this page to customize assignments for your students.

Additional Answers

6. Sample answer:

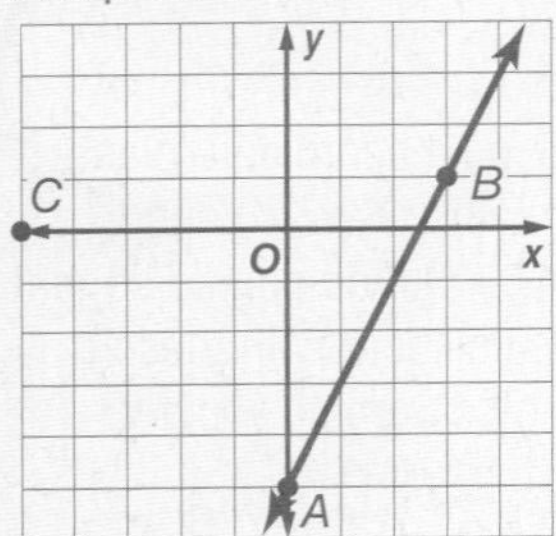

7. Sample answer:

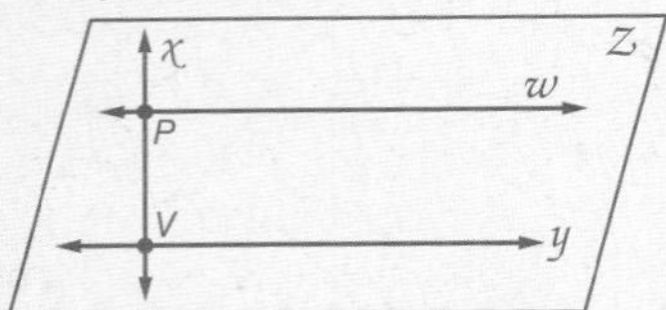

11. Yes; points *B*, *D*, and *F* lie in plane *BDF*.

Check Your Understanding

 = Step-by-Step Solutions begin on page R14. 

Example 1 **Use the figure to name each of the following.**

1. a line containing point *X* **Sample answer: *m***
2. a line containing point *Z* **Sample answer: ℓ**
3. a plane containing points *W* and *R* **𝓑**

Example 2 **Name the geometric term modeled by each object.**

4. a beam from a laser **line**
5. a floor **plane**

Example 3 **Draw and label a figure for each relationship.**

6. A line in a coordinate plane contains $A(0, -5)$ and $B(3, 1)$ and a point *C* that is not collinear with $\overleftrightarrow{AB}$. **See margin.**
7. Plane *Z* contains lines *x*, *y*, and *w*. Lines *x* and *y* intersect at point *V* and lines *x* and *w* intersect at point *P*. **See margin.**

Example 4 **Refer to the figure.**

8. How many planes are shown in the figure? **5**
9. Name three points that are collinear. **Sample answer: *A*, *H*, and *B***
10. Are points *A*, *H*, *J*, and *D* coplanar? Explain.
11. Are points *B*, *D*, and *F* coplanar? Explain. **See margin.**

10. No; points *A*, *H*, and *J* lie in plane *ABF*, but point *D* does not lie in plane *ABF*.

12. **ASTRONOMY** Ursa Minor, or the Little Dipper, is a constellation made up of seven stars in the northern sky including the star Polaris.
   a. What geometric figures are modeled by the stars? **points**
   b. Are Star 1, Star 2, and Star 3 collinear on the constellation map? Explain.
   c. Are Polaris, Star 2, and Star 6 coplanar on the map? **Yes; it appears that all three points lie in the same plane. However they are probably not coplanar in reality.**

12b. No; there is not a straight line through all three points. So the points are not collinear.

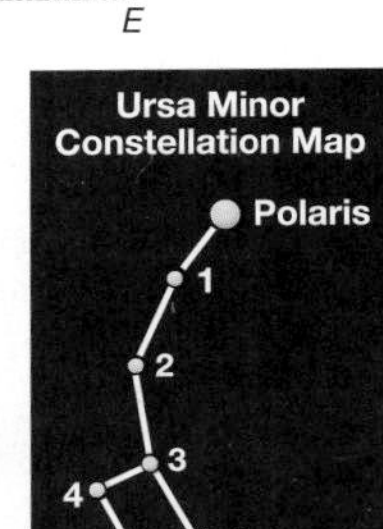

Practice and Problem Solving

Extra Practice is on page R1.

Example 1 **Refer to the figure.**

13. Name the lines that are only in plane *Q*. **Sample answer: *n* and *q***
14. How many planes are labeled in the figure? **2**
15. Name the plane containing the lines *m* and *t*. **𝓡**
16. Name the intersection of lines *m* and *t*. **C**
17. Name a point that is not coplanar with points *A*, *B*, and *C*. **Sample answer: point *P***
18. Are points *F*, *M*, *G*, and *P* coplanar? Explain.
19. Name the points not contained in a line shown. **points *A* and *P***
20. What is another name for line *t*? $\overleftrightarrow{CE}$
21. Does line *n* intersect line *q*? Explain. **Yes; line *n* intersects line *q* when the lines are extended.**

18. No; point *F* lies in plane *R*, while points *G* and *P* lie in plane *Q* and *M* lies between planes *R* and *Q*.

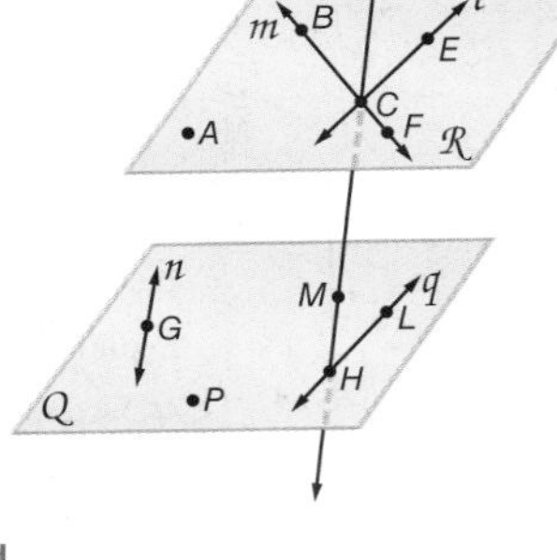

The **Differentiated Homework Options** provide leveled assignments. Many of the homework exercises are paired, so that the students could do the odds one day and the evens the next day.

Differentiated Homework Options

Level	Assignment	Two-Day Option	
AL Basic	13–48, 57, 58, 60–85	13–47 odd, 62–65	14–48 even, 57, 58, 60, 61, 66–85
OL Core	13–47 odd, 49–58, 60–85	13–48, 62–65	49–58, 60, 61, 66–79
BL Advanced	49–79, (optional: 80–85)		

Example 2 **Name the geometric term(s) modeled by each object.**

22. 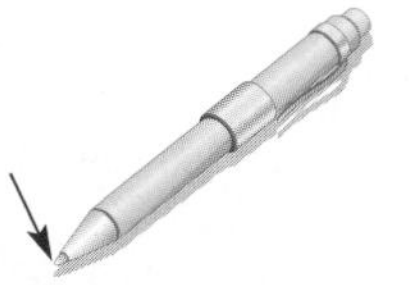 point

23. intersecting lines

24. plane; intersecting lines

25. two planes intersecting in a line

26. a blanket plane

27. a knot in a rope point

28. a telephone pole line

29. the edge of a desk line

30. two connected walls intersecting planes

31. a partially opened folder intersecting planes

Example 3 **Draw and label a figure for each relationship.** **32–39. See Ch. 1 Answer Appendix.**

32. Line m intersects plane $\mathcal{R}$ at a single point.

33. Two planes do not intersect.

34. Points X and Y lie on $\overleftrightarrow{CD}$.

35. Three lines intersect at point J but do not all lie in the same plane.

36. Points $A(2, 3)$, $B(2, -3)$, C and D are collinear, but A, B, C, D, and F are not.

37. Lines $\overleftrightarrow{LM}$ and $\overleftrightarrow{NP}$ are coplanar but do not intersect.

38. $\overleftrightarrow{FG}$ and $\overleftrightarrow{JK}$ intersect at $P(4, 3)$, where point F is at $(-2, 5)$ and point J is at $(7, 9)$.

39. Lines s and t intersect, and line v does not intersect either one.

Example 4 **CCSS MODELING** **When packing breakable objects such as glasses, movers frequently use boxes with inserted dividers like the one shown.**

40. How many planes are modeled in the picture? 15

41. What parts of the box model lines? edges

42. What parts of the box model points? vertices

Refer to the figure at the right.

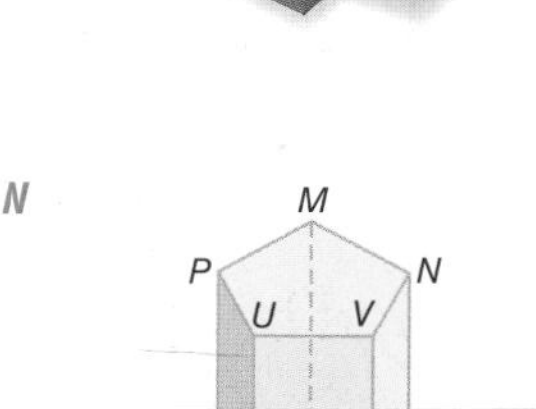

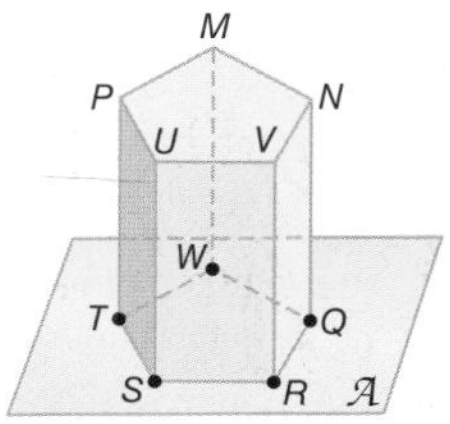

43. Name two collinear points. Sample answer: M and N

44. How many planes appear in the figure? 7

45. Do plane $\mathcal{A}$ and plane MNP intersect? Explain. No; they do not have any lines in common.

46. In what line do planes $\mathcal{A}$ and QRV intersect? $\overleftrightarrow{QR}$

47. Are points T, S, R, Q, and V coplanar? Explain. No; V does not lie in the same plane.

48. Are points T, S, R, Q, and W coplanar? Explain. Yes; all of the points lie in plane TSR.

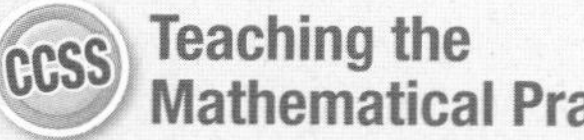

Teaching the Mathematical Practices

Modeling Mathematically proficient students can apply mathematics to solve problems arising in real life. For Exercises 40–42, encourage students to use a cardboard box to model the figure shown.

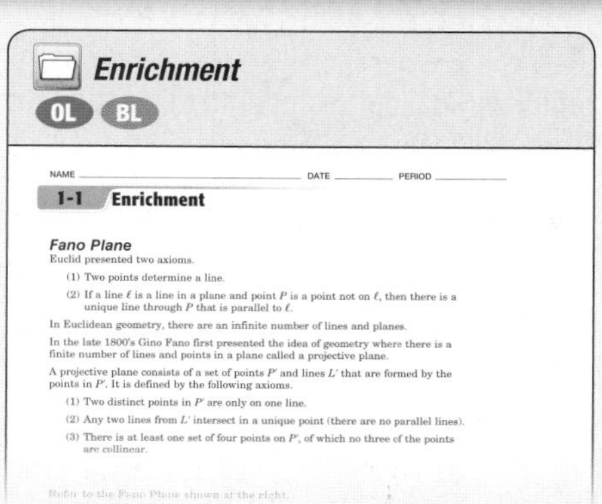

Enrichment
OL BL

NAME ______ DATE ______ PERIOD ______

1-1 Enrichment

Fano Plane

Euclid presented two axioms.

(1) Two points determine a line.

(2) If a line ℓ is a line in a plane and point P is a point not on ℓ, then there is a unique line through P that is parallel to ℓ.

In Euclidean geometry, there are an infinite number of lines and planes.

In the late 1800's Gino Fano first presented the idea of geometry where there is a finite number of lines and points in a plane called a projective plane.

A projective plane consists of a set of points P' and lines L' that are formed by the points in P'. It is defined by the following axioms.

(1) Two distinct points in P' are only on one line.

(2) Any two lines from L' intersect in a unique point (there are no parallel lines).

(3) There is at least one set of four points on P', of which no three of the points are collinear.

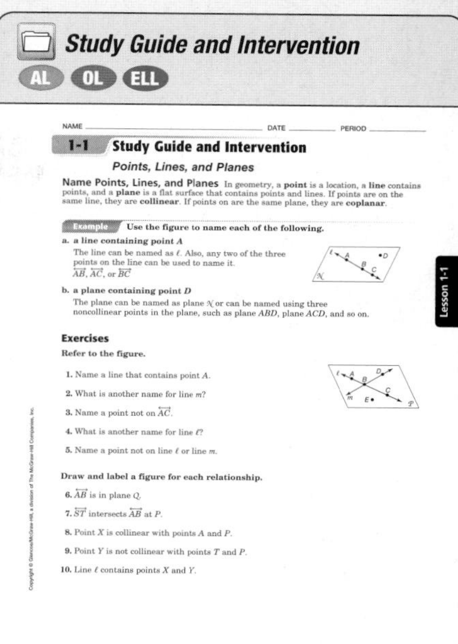

Study Guide and Intervention
AL OL ELL

NAME ______ DATE ______ PERIOD ______

1-1 Study Guide and Intervention

Points, Lines, and Planes

Name Points, Lines, and Planes In geometry, a **point** is a location, a **line** contains points, and a **plane** is a flat surface that contains points and lines. If points are on the same line, they are **collinear**. If points on are the same plane, they are **coplanar**.

Example **Use the figure to name each of the following.**

a. a line containing point A

The line can be named as ℓ. Also, any two of the three points on the line can be used to name it. $\overleftrightarrow{AB}$, $\overleftrightarrow{AC}$, or $\overleftrightarrow{BC}$

b. a plane containing point D

The plane can be named as plane $\mathcal{N}$ or can be named using three noncollinear points in the plane, such as plane ABD, plane ACD, and so on.

Exercises

Refer to the figure.

1. Name a line that contains point A.
2. What is another name for line m?
3. Name a point not on $\overleftrightarrow{AC}$.
4. What is another name for line ℓ?
5. Name a point not on line ℓ or line m.

Draw and label a figure for each relationship.

6. $\overleftrightarrow{AB}$ is in plane Q.
7. $\overleftrightarrow{ST}$ intersects $\overleftrightarrow{AB}$ at P.
8. Point X is collinear with points A and P.
9. Point Y is not collinear with points T and P.
10. Line ℓ contains points X and Y.

Lesson 1-1

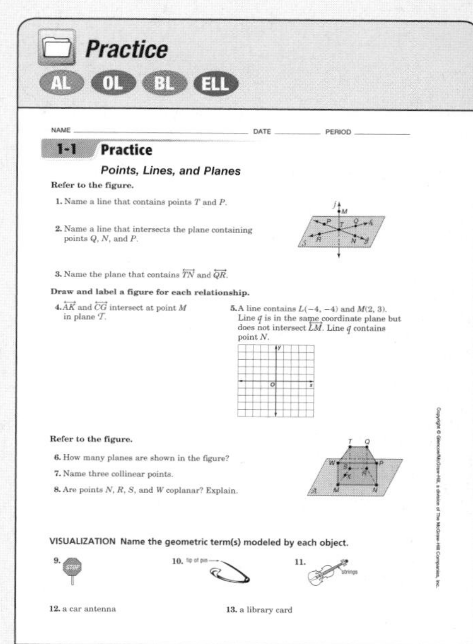

Practice
AL OL BL ELL

NAME ______ DATE ______ PERIOD ______

1-1 Practice

Points, Lines, and Planes

Refer to the figure.

1. Name a line that contains points T and P.
2. Name a line that intersects the plane containing points Q, N, and P.
3. Name the plane that contains $\overleftrightarrow{TN}$ and $\overleftrightarrow{QR}$.

Draw and label a figure for each relationship.

4. $\overleftrightarrow{AK}$ and $\overleftrightarrow{CG}$ intersect at point M in plane $\mathcal{T}$.
5. A line contains $L(-4, -4)$ and $M(2, 3)$. Line q is in the same coordinate plane but does not intersect $\overleftrightarrow{LM}$. Line q contains point N.

Refer to the figure.

6. How many planes are shown in the figure?
7. Name three collinear points.
8. Are points N, R, S, and W coplanar? Explain.

VISUALIZATION **Name the geometric term(s) modeled by each object.**

9. STOP
10. tip of pin
11. strings
12. a car antenna
13. a library card

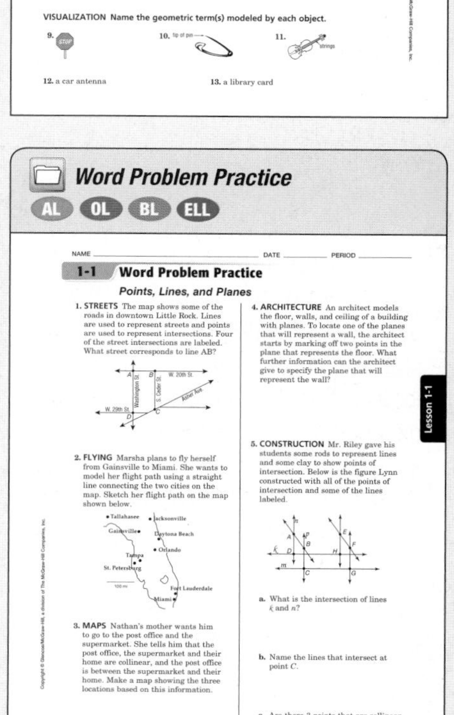

Word Problem Practice
AL OL BL ELL

NAME ______ DATE ______ PERIOD ______

1-1 Word Problem Practice

Points, Lines, and Planes

1. **STREETS** The map shows some of the roads in downtown Little Rock. Lines are used to represent streets and points are used to represent intersections. Four of the street intersections are labeled. What street corresponds to line AB?

2. **FLYING** Marsha plans to fly herself from Gainsville to Miami. She wants to model her flight path using a straight line connecting the two cities on the map. Sketch her flight path on the map shown below.

3. **MAPS** Nathan's mother wants him to go to the post office and the supermarket. She tells him that the post office, the supermarket and their home are collinear, and the post office is between the supermarket and their home. Make a map showing the three locations based on this information.

4. **ARCHITECTURE** An architect models the floor, walls, and ceiling of a building with planes. To locate one of the planes that will represent a wall, the architect starts by marking off two points in the plane that represents the floor. What further information can the architect give to specify the plane that will represent the wall?

5. **CONSTRUCTION** Mr. Riley gave his students some rods to represent lines and some clay to show points of intersection. Below is the figure Lynn constructed with all of the points of intersection and some of the lines labeled.

a. What is the intersection of lines k and n?

b. Name the lines that intersect at point C.

c. Are there 3 points that are collinear and coplanar? If so, name them.

Lesson 1-1

Additional Answers

50b.

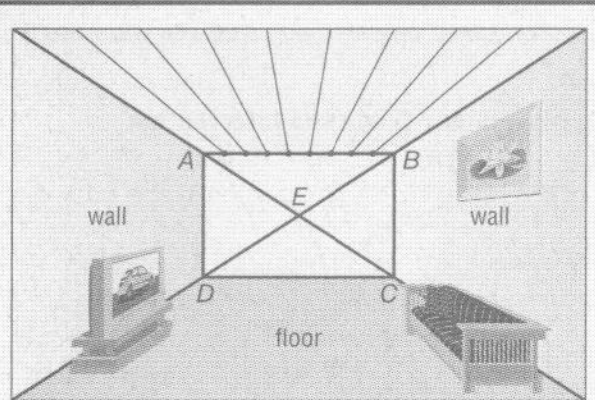

51a. Sample answer:

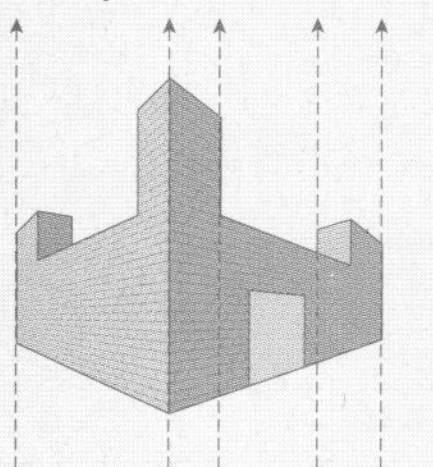

51b.

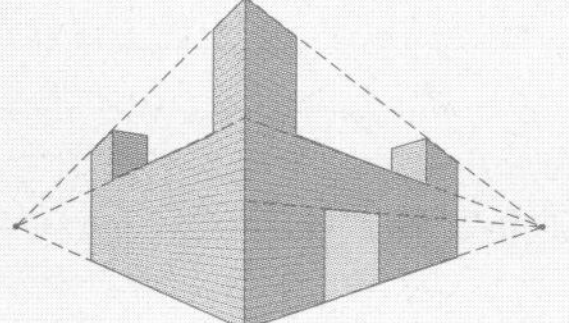

54a. Sample answer:

x	y
0	2
1	3
2	4
3	5
4	6

54b.

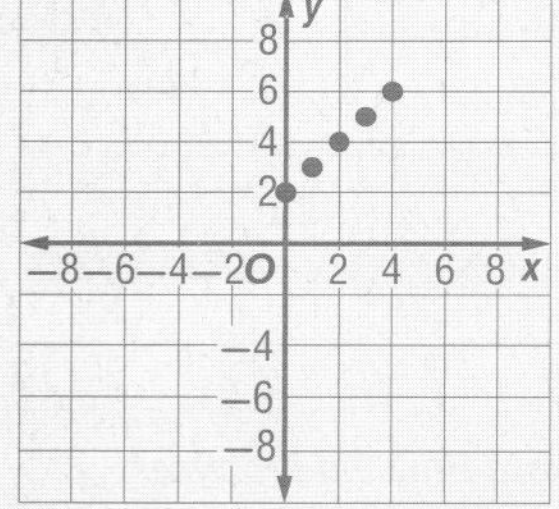

Teaching the Mathematical Practices

Arguments Mathematically proficient students make conjectures and build a logical progression of statements to explore the truth of their conjectures. In Exercise 52, point out to students that these skills in writing arguments will be useful later in this course.

Differentiated Instruction Extension activities help you cultivate skills that students will need to have success in higher mathematics.

49. **FINITE PLANES** A *finite plane* is a plane that has boundaries, or does not extend indefinitely. The street signs shown are finite planes.

a. If the pole models a line, name the geometric term that describes the intersection between the signs and the pole. **point**

b. What geometric term(s) describes the intersection between the two finite planes? Explain your answer with a diagram if necessary. **line**

50. **ONE-POINT PERSPECTIVE** One-point perspective drawings use lines to convey depth. Lines representing horizontal lines in the real object can be extended to meet at a single point called the *vanishing point*. Suppose you want to draw a tiled ceiling in the room below with nine tiles across.

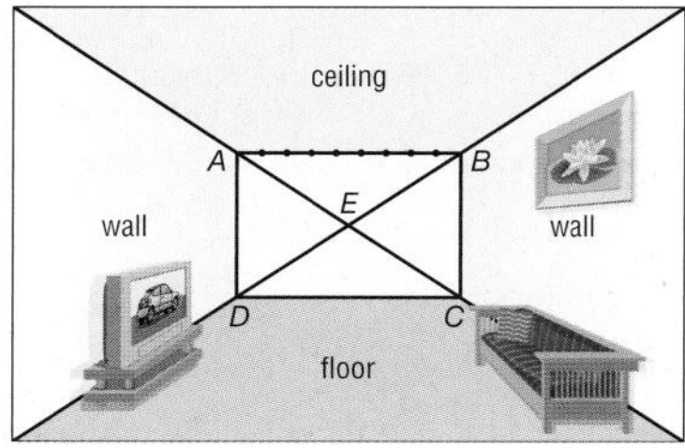

a. What point represents the vanishing point in the drawing? **Point *E***

b. Trace the figure. Then draw lines from the vanishing point through each of the eight points between *A* and *B*. Extend these lines to the top edge of the drawing. **See margin.**

c. How could you change the drawing to make the back wall of the room appear farther away? **Sample answer: Draw points *A*, *B*, *C*, and *D* closer to the vanishing point.**

51. **TWO-POINT PERSPECTIVE** Two-point perspective drawings use two vanishing points to convey depth.

a. Trace the drawing of the castle shown. Draw five of the vertical lines used to create the drawing. **a–b. See margin.**

b. Draw and extend the horizontal lines to locate the vanishing points and label them.

c. What do you notice about the vertical lines as they get closer to the vanishing point? **Sample answer: They get closer together.**

d. Draw a two-point perspective of a home or a room in a home. **See students' work.**

52. **CCSS ARGUMENTS** Name two points on the same line in the figure. How can you support your assertion? **Sample answer: *A* and *C*; use a ruler to figure out which point would be the end of the line if it continued.**

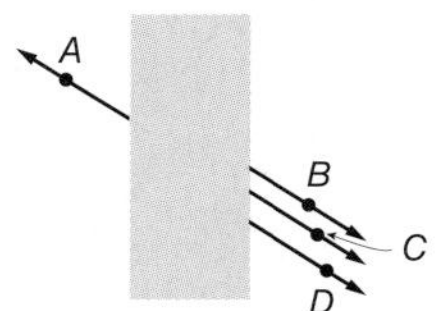

ThinkStock/Jupiterimages

Differentiated Instruction AL OL BL ELL

Extension Challenge students to develop three-dimensional models to demonstrate difficult geometric concepts related to points, lines, and planes. Some examples include:

- Develop a model to show that three points can be noncollinear.
- Develop a demonstration to show that three points are coplanar, but four points can be noncoplanar.
- Develop a three-dimensional model of lines that are not parallel and do not intersect.

53. Sample answer: The airplanes are in different horizontal planes.

53. TRANSPORTATION When two cars enter an intersection at the same time on opposing paths, one of the cars must adjust its speed or direction to avoid a collision. Two airplanes, however, can cross paths while traveling in different directions without colliding. Explain how this is possible.

54. MULTIPLE REPRESENTATIONS Another way to describe a group of points is called a locus. A **locus** is a set of points that satisfy a particular condition. In this problem, you will explore the locus of points that satisfy an equation.

a. Tabular Represent the locus of points satisfying the equation $2 + x = y$ using a table of at least five values. See margin.

b. Graphical Represent this same locus of points using a graph. See margin.

c. Verbal Describe the geometric figure that the points suggest. a line

55. PROBABILITY Three of the labeled points are chosen at random.

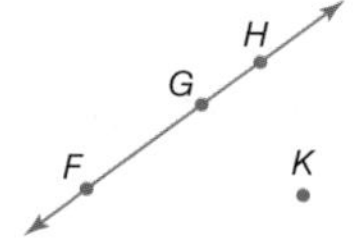

a. What is the probability that the points chosen are collinear? $\frac{1}{4}$

b. What is the probability that the points chosen are coplanar? 1

56. MULTIPLE REPRESENTATIONS In this problem, you will explore the locus of points that satisfy an inequality.

a. Tabular Represent the locus of points satisfying the inequality $y < -3x - 1$ using a table of at least ten values. See margin.

b. Graphical Represent this same locus of points using a graph. See margin.

c. Verbal Describe the geometric figure that the points suggest. the part of the coordinate plane below the line $y = -3x - 1$

Error Analysis exercises help students identify and address common errors before they occur. Prompts in the margins of the Teacher Edition help you guide students toward understanding.

H.O.T. Problems Use Higher-Order Thinking Skills

57. OPEN ENDED Sketch three planes that intersect in a line. See margin.

58. ERROR ANALYSIS Camille and Hiroshi are trying to determine the most number of lines that can be drawn using any two of four random points. Is either correct? Explain.

58. Sample answer: Hiroshi is correct; after you draw the line from the first point to the other three, one of the lines from the second point is already drawn.

Camille	Hiroshi
Since there are four points, 4 · 3 or 12 lines can be drawn between the points.	You can draw 3 · 2 · 1 or 6 lines between the points.

59. ARGUMENTS What is the greatest number of planes determined using any three of the points A, B, C, and D if no three points are collinear? 4

60. REASONING Is it possible for two points on the surface of a prism to be neither collinear nor coplanar? Justify your answer.

60. No. Sample answer: There is exactly one line through any two points and exactly one plane through any three points not on the same line. Therefore, any two points on the prism must be collinear and coplanar.

61. WRITING IN MATH Refer to Exercise 49. Give a real-life example of a finite plane. Is it possible to have a real-life object that is an infinite plane? Explain your reasoning.
Sample answer: A table is a finite plane. It is not possible to have a real-life object that is an infinite plane because all real-life objects have boundaries.

Differentiated Instruction AL OL

Naturalist Learners Explain how points, lines, and planes exist in nature. For example, planes can model leaves, lily pads, and the surface of a pond; lines can model spider webs, sunbeams, tree trunks, the edge of a riverbed, and the veins of a leaf.

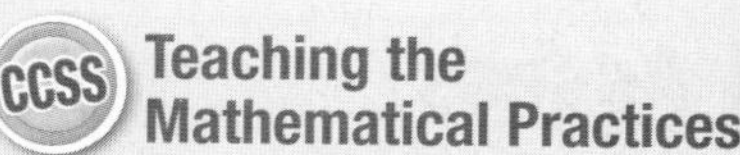

Teaching the Mathematical Practices

Arguments Mathematically proficient students can analyze situations by breaking them into cases. In Exercise 59, encourage students to visualize the situation described in the problem.

Multiple Representations

In Exercises 54 and 56, students use a table and a graph to investigate a locus of points.

WatchOut!

Error Analysis In Exercise 58, students should see that a line drawn between two points counts only one time. Camille counted each line twice, once from each point.

Additional Answers

56a. Sample answer:

x	y
−1	−4
−2	−3
−2	2
−3	−2
−3	−7
−4	−2
−4	−7
−5	−8
−5	9
−7	0

56b.

57. Sample answer:

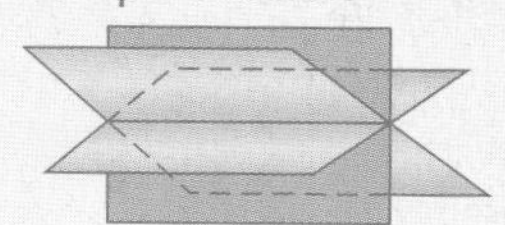

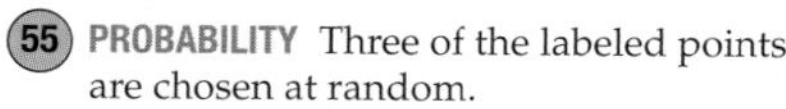

4 Assess

Name the Math Discuss how points, lines, and planes are modeled by the objects students see and use every day.

The **Four-Step Teaching Plan** shows you how to **Focus, Teach, Practice/Apply,** and **Assess** each lesson. Each lesson ends with a creative strategy for closing the lesson.

Additional Answers

75.

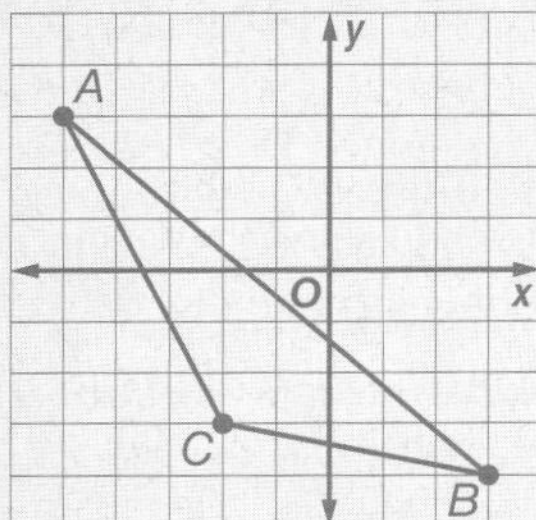

76.

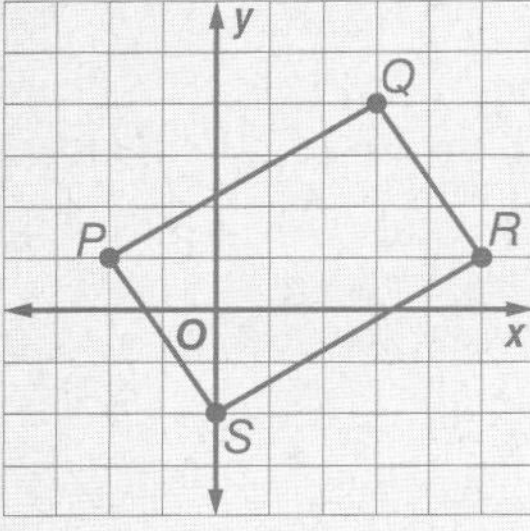

Standardized Test Practice

62. Which statement about the figure below is *not* true? **D**

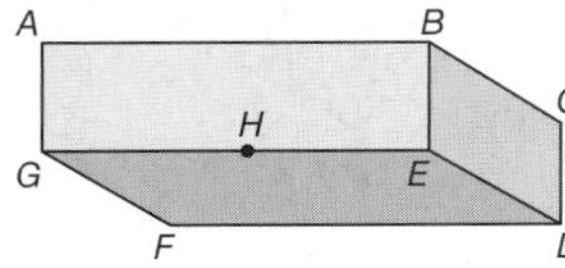

A Point H lies in planes AGE and GED.

B Planes GAB, GFD and BED intersect at point E.

C Points F, E, and B are coplanar.

D Points A, H, and D are collinear.

63. ALGEBRA What is the value of x if $3x + 2 = 8$? **H**

F -2 G 0 H 2 J 6

64. GRIDDED RESPONSE An ice chest contains 3 types of drinks: 10 apple juices, 15 grape juices, and 15 bottles of water. What is the probability that a drink selected randomly from the ice chest does *not* contain fruit juice? **3/8 or 0.375**

65. SAT/ACT A certain school's enrollment increased 6% this year over last year's enrollment. If the school now has 1378 students enrolled, how many students were enrolled last year? **B**

A 1295 C 1350 E 1500

B 1300 D 1460

Spiral Review

Simplify. (Lesson 0-9)

66. $\sqrt{72}$ **$6\sqrt{2}$**

67. $\sqrt{18} \cdot \sqrt{14}$ **$6\sqrt{7}$**

68. $\sqrt{44x^4y^3}$ **$2x^2y\sqrt{11y}$**

69. $\frac{3}{\sqrt{18}}$ **$\frac{\sqrt{2}}{2}$**

70. $\sqrt{\frac{28}{75}}$ **$\frac{2\sqrt{21}}{15}$**

71. $\frac{\sqrt{8a^6}}{\sqrt{108}}$ **$\frac{|a^3|\sqrt{6}}{9}$**

72. $\frac{5}{4 - \sqrt{2}}$ **$\frac{20 + 5\sqrt{2}}{14}$**

73. $\frac{4\sqrt{3}}{2 + \sqrt{5}}$ **$4\sqrt{15} - 8\sqrt{3}$**

74. FINANCIAL LITERACY Suppose you buy 3 shirts and 2 pairs of slacks on sale at a clothing store for $72. The next day, a friend buys 2 shirts and 4 pairs of slacks for $96. If the shirts you each bought were all the same price and the slacks were also all the same price, then what was the cost of each shirt and each pair of slacks? (Lesson 0-8) **shirt: $12; slacks: $18**

Graph the following points, and connect them in order to form a figure. (Lesson 0-7) **75–76. See margin.**

75. $A(-5, 3)$, $B(3, -4)$, and $C(-2, -3)$

76. $P(-2, 1)$, $Q(3, 4)$, $R(5, 1)$, and $S(0, -2)$

GROCERIES **Find an approximate metric weight for each item.** (Lesson 0-2)

77.

Net Wt: 15 oz

Sample answer: 424.5 g

78. FRESH SMILE Toothpaste

Net Wt: 8.2 oz

Sample answer: 232.5 g

79. TASTY TOAST MARGARINE

Net Wt: 2.5 lb

Sample answer: 1.25 kg

Skills Review

Replace each ● with >, <, or = to make a true statement.

80. $\frac{1}{4}$ in. ● $\frac{1}{2}$ in. **<**

81. $\frac{3}{4}$ in. ● $\frac{5}{8}$ in. **>**

82. $\frac{3}{8}$ in. ● $\frac{6}{16}$ in. **=**

83. 18 mm ● 2 cm **<**

84. 32 mm ● 3.2 cm **=**

85. 0.8 m ● 8 cm **>**

EXTEND 1-1 Geometry Lab: Describing What You See

When you are learning geometric concepts, it is critical to have accurate drawings to represent the information. It is helpful to know what words and phrases can be used to describe figures. Likewise, it is important to know how to read a geometric description and be able to draw the figure it describes.

Common Core State Standards
Content Standards
G.MG.1 Use geometric shapes, their measures, and their properties to describe objects (e.g., modeling a tree trunk or a human torso as a cylinder). ★
Mathematical Practices 6

The figures and descriptions below help you visualize and write about points, lines, and planes.

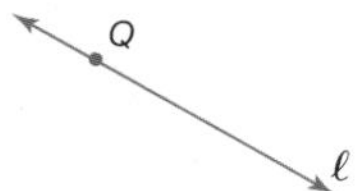

Point Q is on ℓ.
Line ℓ contains Q.
Line ℓ passes through Q.

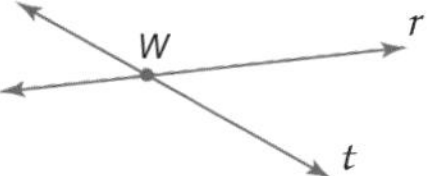

Lines r and t intersect at W.
Point W is the intersection of r and t.
Point W is on r. Point W is on t.

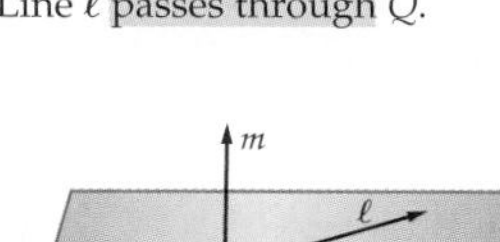

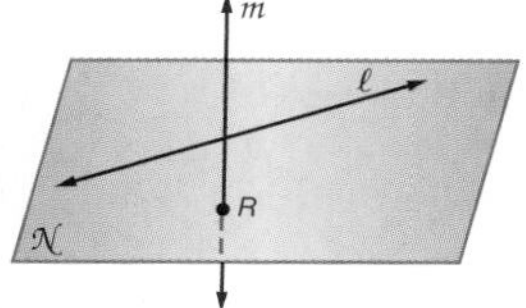

Line ℓ and point R are in $\mathcal{N}$.
Point R lies in $\mathcal{N}$.
Plane $\mathcal{N}$ contains R and ℓ.
Line m intersects $\mathcal{N}$ at R.
Point R is the intersection of m with $\mathcal{N}$.
Lines ℓ and m do not intersect.

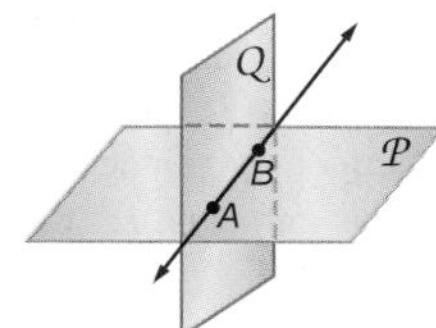

$\overleftrightarrow{AB}$ is in $\mathcal{P}$ and $\mathcal{Q}$.
Points A and B lie in both $\mathcal{P}$ and $\mathcal{Q}$.
Planes $\mathcal{P}$ and $\mathcal{Q}$ both contain $\overleftrightarrow{AB}$.
Planes $\mathcal{P}$ and $\mathcal{Q}$ intersect in $\overleftrightarrow{AB}$.
$\overleftrightarrow{AB}$ is the intersection of $\mathcal{P}$ and $\mathcal{Q}$.

Exercises

Write a description for each figure. **1–4. See margin.**

1.
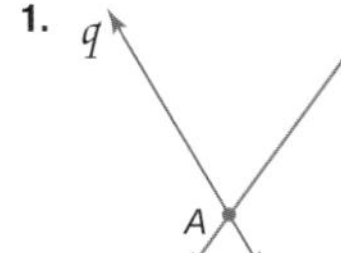

2.
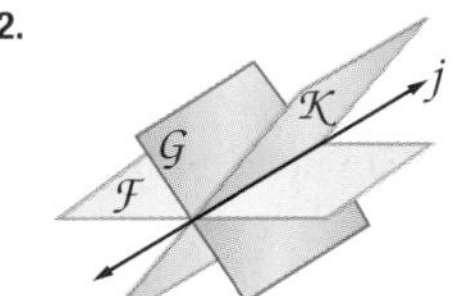

3.
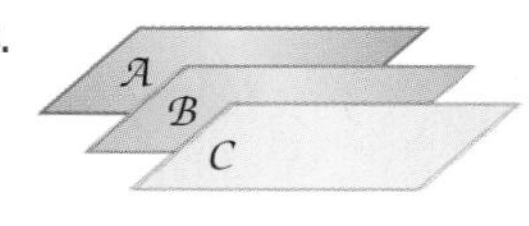

4. Draw and label a figure for the statement Planes $\mathcal{N}$ and $\mathcal{P}$ contain line a.

Additional Answers

1. Lines q and m intersect at A. Point A is the intersection of m and q. Point A is on m.
2. Line j lies in planes $\mathcal{F}$, $\mathcal{G}$, and $\mathcal{K}$.
3. Planes $\mathcal{A}$, $\mathcal{B}$, and $\mathcal{C}$ do not intersect.
4.

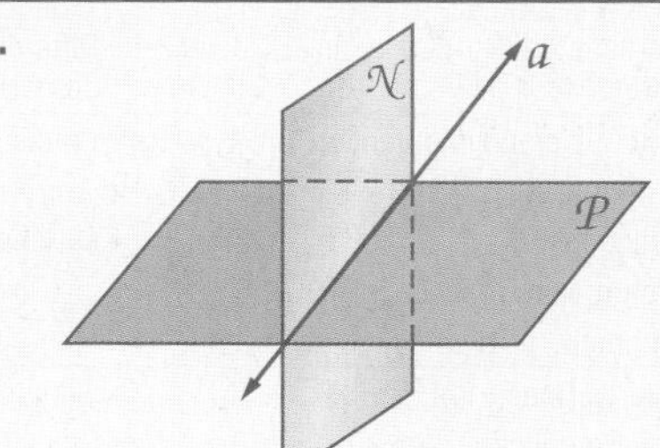

1 Focus

Objective Use correct mathematical terminology to describe geometric figures.

Materials for Each Group

- straightedge

Tips for New Teachers

Stress the importance of learning definitions and using the proper notation. A clear understanding of terms and the correct use of standard geometric notation is necessary for a strong start in geometry.

2 Teach

Working in Cooperative Groups

Organize students in groups of 2, mixing abilities. Then have students read and verify each of the descriptions. Next, have students draw and label a geometric figure that includes points, lines, and planes. Next, have students exchange figures and write descriptions, using proper terminology and notation.

Practice Have students complete Exercises 1–4.

3 Assess

Formative Assessment

Use Exercises 1–3 to assess whether students correctly use definitions and proper notations to describe geometric figures containing points, lines, and planes.

From Concrete to Abstract

Have students draw a figure that is described by the following statement.

Line p intersects line m and plane $\mathcal{R}$ at point U.

Next, compare the drawings and discuss whether different drawings accurately depict the same description.

1 Focus

VerticalAlignment

Before Lesson 1-2 Identify and model points, lines, and planes.

Lesson 1-2 Measure segments. Calculate with measures.

After Lesson 1-2 Develop an awareness of the structure of a mathematical system, connecting definitions, postulates, logical reasoning, and theorems.

2 Teach

Scaffolding Questions

Have students read the **Why?** section of the lesson.

Ask:

- What is another part of the human body that is used as a unit of measure? foot
- Is a foot a customary unit or metric unit? customary unit
- Which system of measure uses fractions and whole numbers? customary
- Which system of measure uses decimals? metric

Scaffolding Questions give direction and momentum to the lesson, clarify its purpose, and keep students on task.

LESSON 1-2 Linear Measure

Then

- You identified and modeled points, lines, and planes.

Now

1. Measure segments.
2. Calculate with measures.

Why?

- When the ancient Egyptians found a need for a measurement system, they used the human body as a guide. The cubit was the length of an arm from the elbow to the fingertips. Eventually the Egyptians standardized the length of a cubit, with ten *royal cubits* equivalent to one *rod*.

NewVocabulary
line segment
betweenness of points
between
congruent segments
construction

Common Core State Standards

Content Standards
G.CO.1 Know precise definitions of angle, circle, perpendicular line, parallel line, and line segment, based on the undefined notions of point, line, distance along a line, and distance around a circular arc.
G.CO.12 Make formal geometric constructions with a variety of tools and methods (compass and straightedge, string, reflective devices, paper folding, dynamic geometric software, etc.).

Mathematical Practices
6 Attend to precision.

1 Measure Line Segments Unlike a line, a **line segment**, or *segment*, can be measured because it has two endpoints. A segment with endpoints A and B can be named as $\overline{AB}$ or $\overline{BA}$. The *measure* of $\overline{AB}$ is written as AB. The length or measure of a segment always includes a unit of measure, such as meter or inch.

All measurements are approximations dependent upon the smallest unit of measure available on the measuring instrument.

Example 1 Length in Metric Units

Find the length of $\overline{AB}$ using each ruler.

a.

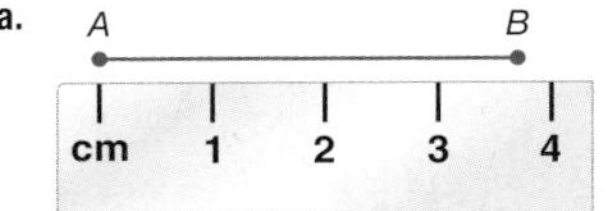

The ruler is marked in centimeters. Point B is closer to the 4-centimeter mark than to 3 centimeters.

Thus, $\overline{AB}$ is about 4 centimeters long.

b.

A B
cm 1 2 3 4

The long marks are centimeters, and the shorter marks are millimeters. There are 10 millimeters for each centimeter.

Thus, $\overline{AB}$ is about 3.7 centimeters long.

1B. Sample answer: 170 mm

GuidedPractice

1A. Measure the length of a dollar bill in centimeters. **15.6 cm**

1B. Measure the length of a pencil in millimeters.

1C. Find the length of $\overline{CD}$. **2 cm or 20 mm**

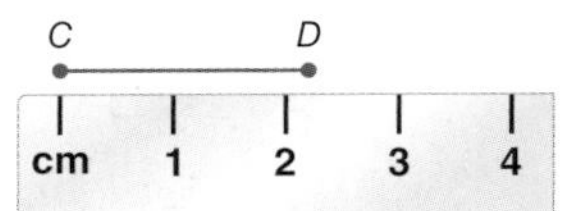

Lesson 1-2 Resources

Resource	Approaching Level AL	On Level OL	Beyond Level BL	English Learners ELL
Teacher Edition	▪ Differentiated Instruction, pp. 15, 16, 17	▪ Differentiated Instruction, pp. 15, 16, 17	▪ Differentiated Instruction, pp. 15, 16, 17	▪ Differentiated Instruction, pp. 16, 17
Chapter Resource Masters	▪ Study Guide and Intervention, pp. 12–13 ▪ Skills Practice, p. 14 ▪ Practice, p. 15 ▪ Word Problem Practice, p. 16	▪ Study Guide and Intervention, pp. 12–13 ▪ Skills Practice, p. 14 ▪ Practice, p. 15 ▪ Word Problem Practice, p. 16 ▪ Enrichment, p. 17	▪ Practice, p. 15 ▪ Word Problem Practice, p. 16 ▪ Enrichment, p. 17	▪ Study Guide and Intervention, pp. 12–13 ▪ Skills Practice, p. 14 ▪ Practice, p. 15 ▪ Word Problem Practice, p. 16
Other	▪ 5-Minute Check 1-2 ▪ Study Notebook	▪ 5-Minute Check 1-2 ▪ Study Notebook	▪ 5-Minute Check 1-2 ▪ Study Notebook	▪ 5-Minute Check 1-2 ▪ Study Notebook

StudyTip

Using a Ruler The zero point on a ruler may not be clearly marked. For some rulers, zero is the left edge of the ruler. On others, it may be a fine line farther in on the scale. If it is not clear where the zero is, align one endpoint on 1 and subtract 1 from the measurement at the other endpoint.

Example 2 Length in Standard Units

Find the length of $\overline{CD}$ using each ruler.

a.

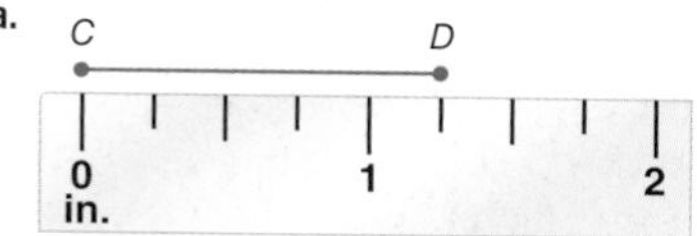

Each inch is divided into fourths.

Point D is closer to the $1\frac{1}{4}$-inch mark.

$\overline{CD}$ is about $1\frac{1}{4}$ inches long.

b.

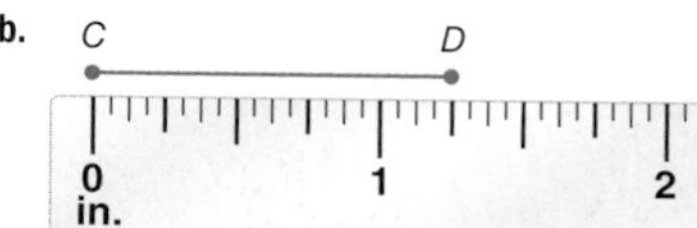

Each inch is divided into sixteenths.

Point D is closer to the $1\frac{4}{16}$-inch mark.

$\overline{CD}$ is about $1\frac{4}{16}$ or $1\frac{1}{4}$ inches long.

Guided Practice

2A. Measure the length of a dollar bill in inches. $6\frac{3}{16}$ in.

2B. Measure the length of a pencil in inches. Sample answer: $6\frac{3}{4}$ in.

2 Calculate Measures

Recall that for any two real numbers a and b, there is a real number n that is *between* a and b such that $a < n < b$. This relationship also applies to points on a line and is called **betweenness of points**. In the figure, point N is between points A and B, but points R and P are not.

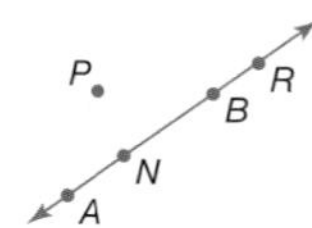

Measures are real numbers, so all arithmetic operations can be used with them. You know that the whole usually equals the sum of its parts. That is also true of line segments in geometry.

KeyConcept Betweenness of Points

Words	Model
Point M is **between** points P and Q if and only if P, Q, and M are collinear and $PM + MQ = PQ$.	PQ; P, M, Q; PM, MQ

StudyTip

Comparing Measures Because measures are real numbers, you can compare them. If points X, Y, and Z are collinear in that order, then one of these statements is true: $XY = YZ$, $XY > YZ$, or $XY < YZ$.

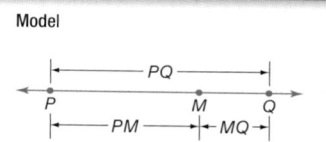

Example 3 Find Measurements by Adding

Find EG. Assume that the figure is not drawn to scale.

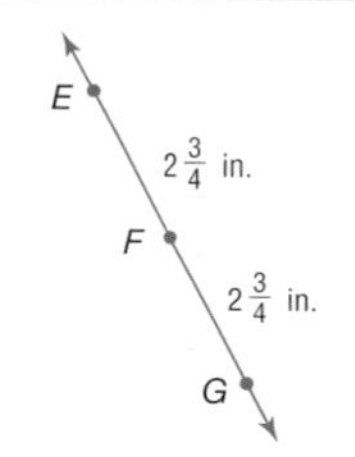

EG is the measure of $\overline{EG}$. Point F is between E and G. Find EG by adding EF and FG.

$EF + FG = EG$	Betweenness of points
$2\frac{3}{4} + 2\frac{3}{4} = EG$	Substitution
$5\frac{1}{2}$ in. $= EG$	Add.

Guided Practice

3. Find JL. Assume that the figure is not drawn to scale. 12.3 cm

Differentiated Instruction AL OL BL

Extension What do you think would happen if the divisions on a ruler were not evenly spaced? Could you be sure that measures are congruent? Explain. Sample answer: The measured length of a segment would be different, depending on which part of the ruler is used.

1 Measure Line Segments

Examples 1 and 2 show how to use a ruler to measure a line segment.

Examples illustrate all of the concepts taught in the lesson and closely mirror the questions in the exercise sets. **Guided Practice** exercises give students an opportunity to try a similar problem on their own.

Formative Assessment

Use the Guided Practice exercises after each example to determine students' understanding of concepts.

Additional Examples

1 Find the length of $\overline{AB}$ using each ruler.

a.

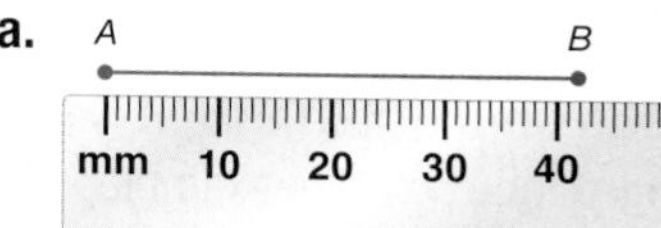

42 mm

b.

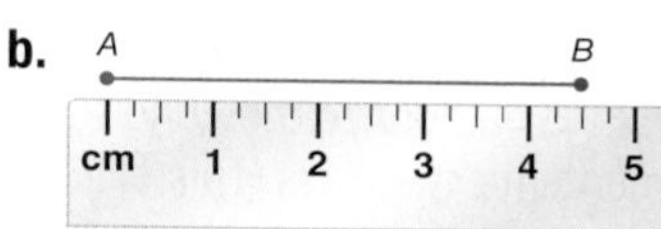

4.5 cm

2 Use a customary ruler to draw each segment.

a. $\overline{DE}$, 3 inches long
See students' work.

b. $\overline{FG}$, $2\frac{3}{4}$ inches long
See students' work.

3 Find XZ. Assume that the figure is not drawn to scale. $7\frac{1}{8}$ in.

Additional Examples also in Interactive Classroom PowerPoint® Presentations

IWB Interactive White Board READY

Additional Examples exactly parallel the examples in the text. Step-by-step solutions for these examples are included in **Interactive Classroom.**

2 Calculate Measures

Examples 3–6 show how to calculate measures by using arithmetic and algebraic operations

Additional Examples

4 Find LM. Assume that the figure is not drawn to scale. 1.4 cm

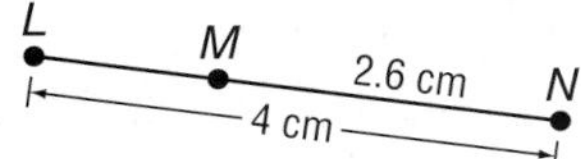

5 **ALGEBRA** Find the value of x and ST if T is between S and U, $ST = 7x$, $SU = 45$, and $TU = 5x - 3$. $x = 4$, $ST = 28$

U 5x – 3 T 7x S

Focus on Mathematical Content

Congruence Provide examples of segments with one, two, or three tick marks indicating congruence. Involve students by having them use the ≅ symbol to categorize the congruent segments for the class. This exercise reviews writing correct names and symbols.

Teach with Tech

Interactive Whiteboard Give students several exercises where the measurements of sections of segments are given in terms of a variable. Choose several students to explain to the class how they found the value of the variable and each of the measurements.

PT

Example 4 Find Measurements by Subtracting

Find AB. Assume that the figure is not drawn to scale.

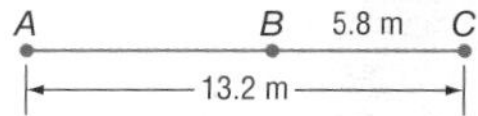

Point B is between A and C.

$AB + BC = AC$	Betweenness of points
$AB + 5.8 = 13.2$	Substitution
$AB + 5.8 - 5.8 = 13.2 - 5.8$	Subtract 5.8 from each side.
$AB = 7.4$ m	Simplify.

Guided Practice

4. Find QR. Assume that the figure is not drawn to scale. $7\frac{1}{8}$ ft

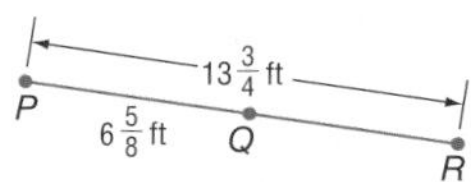

PT

Example 5 Write and Solve Equations to Find Measurements

ALGEBRA Find the value of a and XY if Y is between X and Z, $XY = 3a$, $XZ = 5a - 4$, and $YZ = 14$.

Draw a figure to represent this information.

5a – 4
3a 14
X Y Z

$XZ = XY + YZ$	Betweenness of points
$5a - 4 = 3a + 14$	Substitution
$5a - 4 - 3a = 3a + 14 - 3a$	Subtract 3a from each side.
$2a - 4 = 14$	Simplify.
$2a - 4 + 4 = 14 + 4$	Add 4 to each side.
$2a = 18$	Simplify.
$\frac{2a}{2} = \frac{18}{2}$	Divide each side by 2.
$a = 9$	Simplify.

Now find XY.

$XY = 3a$	Given
$= 3(9)$ or 27	$a = 9$

Guided Practice

5. Find x and BC if B is between A and C, $AC = 4x - 12$, $AB = x$, and $BC = 2x + 3$. $x = 15$, $BC = 33$

Segments that have the same measure are called **congruent segments**.

WatchOut!

Equal vs. Congruent Lengths are equal and segments are congruent. It is correct to say that $AB = CD$ and $\overline{AB} \cong \overline{CD}$. However, it is *not* correct to say that $\overline{AB} = \overline{CD}$ or that $AB \cong CD$.

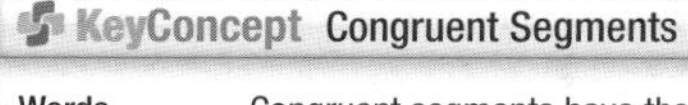

KeyConcept Congruent Segments

Words	Congruent segments have the same measure.
Symbols	≅ is read *is congruent to*. Red slashes on the figure also indicate congruence.
Example	$\overline{AB} \cong \overline{CD}$

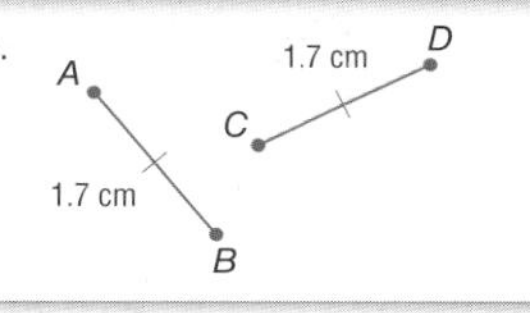

Differentiated Instruction AL OL BL ELL

Kinesthetic Learners Students can physically participate in techniques of measuring, accuracy, and the betweenness of points by grouping in threes, standing in designated spots, and using a yardstick or meterstick to measure distances between them, add distances together, and find unknown distances. They can model examples in the book or create new scenarios. If the floors or walls are tiled, they can also measure distances with one tile representing one unit increment.

Real-WorldLink

The first commercial skateboard was introduced in 1959. Now there are more than 500 skate parks in the United States.

Source: *Encyclopaedia Britannica*

Real-World Example 6 Congruent Segments

SKATE PARKS **In the graph, suppose a segment was drawn along the top of each bar. Which states would have segments that are congruent? Explain.**

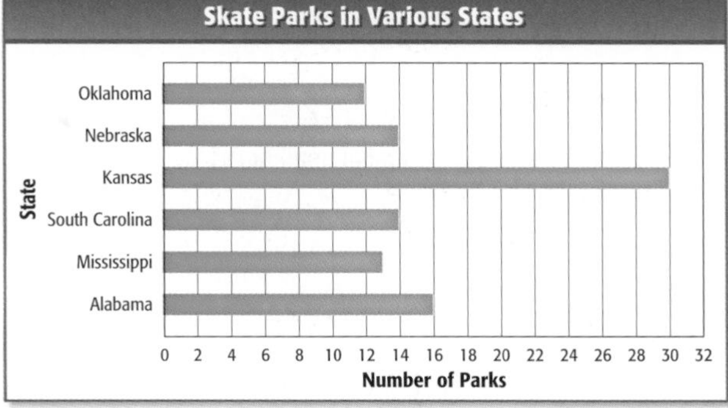

Source: SITE Design Group, Inc.

The segments on the bars for Nebraska and South Carolina would be congruent because they both represent the same number of skate parks.

GuidedPractice

6A. Suppose Oklahoma added another skate park. The segment drawn along the bar representing Oklahoma would be congruent to which other segment? **Mississippi**

6B. Name the congruent segments in the sign shown.
$\overline{AB} \cong \overline{AG}$, $\overline{BC} \cong \overline{GF}$, $\overline{CD} \cong \overline{FE}$

Drawings of geometric figures are created using measuring tools such as a ruler and protractor. **Constructions** are methods of creating these figures without the benefit of measuring tools. Generally, only a pencil, straightedge, and compass are used in constructions. *Sketches* are created without the use of any of these tools.

You can construct a segment that is congruent to a given segment.

Construction Copy a Segment

Step 1 Draw a segment $\overline{JK}$. Elsewhere on your paper, draw a line and a point on the line. Label the point Q.

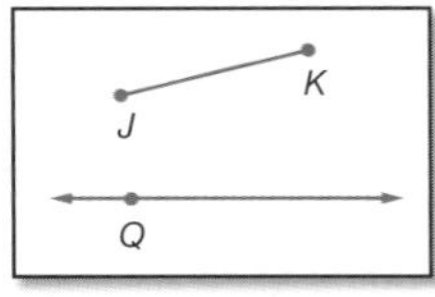

Step 2 Place the compass at point J and adjust the compass setting so that the pencil is at point K.

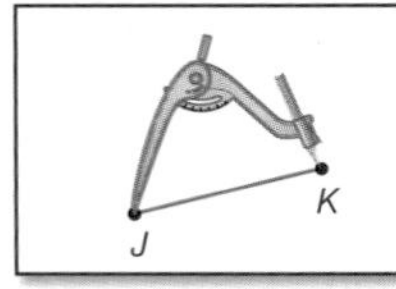

Step 3 Using that setting, place the compass point at Q and draw an arc that intersects the line. Label the point of intersection R. $\overline{JK} \cong \overline{QR}$

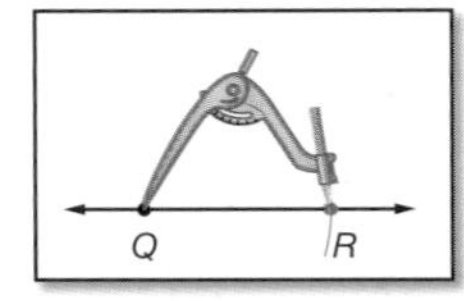

Additional Example

6 FONTS The Arial font is often used because it is easy to read. Study the word *time* shown in Arial type. Each letter can be broken into individual segments. The letter T has two segments, a short horizontal segment, and a longer vertical segment. Assume that all segments overlap where they meet. Which segments are congruent?

TIME

The five vertical segments in the letters *T*, *I*, *M*, and *E* are congruent. The four horizontal segments in *T* and *E* are congruent. The two diagonal segments in the letter *M* are congruent.

DifferentiatedInstruction AL OL BL ELL

Extension Tap into students' creativity by having them create a game that requires measurement to determine a winner. Many real-life games and sports are decided by measurement. Examples include bocce ball and javelin throw.

3 Practice

Formative Assessment

Use Exercises 1–9 to check for understanding.

Then use the chart at the bottom of this page to customize assignments for your students.

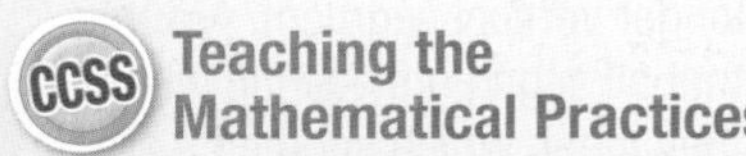

Teaching the Mathematical Practices

Structure Mathematically proficient students look closely to discern a pattern or structure. In Exercise 9, point out to students that the left side of the figure is a mirror image of the right side.

Check Your Understanding

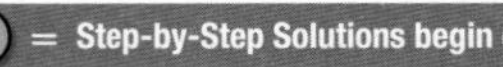
= Step-by-Step Solutions begin on page R14.

Example 1 **Find the length of each line segment or object.** 1. 5.7 cm or 57 mm

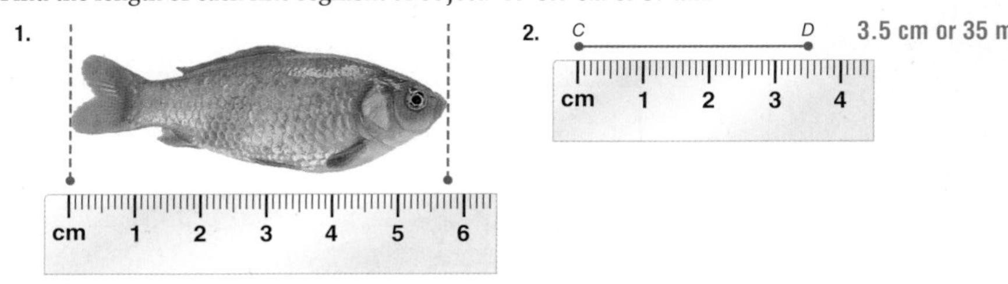

2. 3.5 cm or 35 mm

Example 2

3. 

$1\frac{7}{8}$ in.

4. 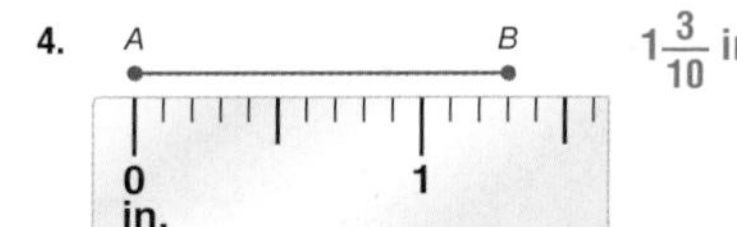

$1\frac{3}{10}$ in.

Examples 3–4 **Find the measurement of each segment. Assume that each figure is not drawn to scale.**

5. $\overline{CD}$ 3.8 in.

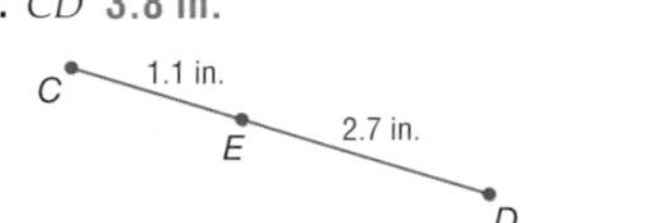

6. $\overline{RS}$ 2.4 cm

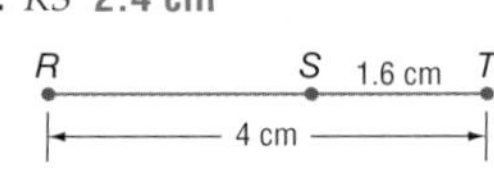

Example 5 **ALGEBRA Find the value of x and BC if B is between C and D.**

7. $CB = 2x$, $BD = 4x$, and $BD = 12$ $x = 3$; $BC = 6$

8. $CB = 4x - 9$, $BD = 3x + 5$, and $CD = 17$ $x = 3$; $BC = 3$

Example 6

9. CCSS **STRUCTURE** The Indiana State Flag was adopted in 1917. The measures of the segments between the stars and the flame are shown on the diagram in inches. List all of the congruent segments in the figure.
$\overline{AG} \cong \overline{FG}$, $\overline{BG} \cong \overline{EG}$, $\overline{CG} \cong \overline{DG}$

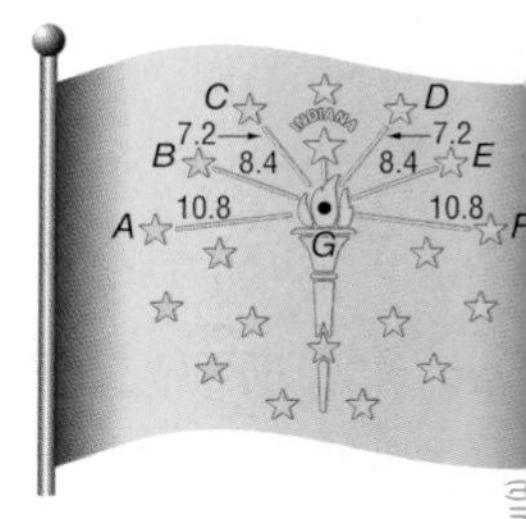

Practice and Problem Solving

Extra Practice is on page R1.

Examples 1–2 **Find the length of each line segment.**

10. 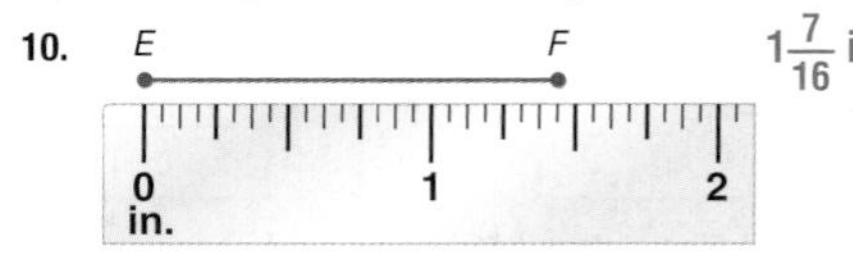

$1\frac{7}{16}$ in.

11. 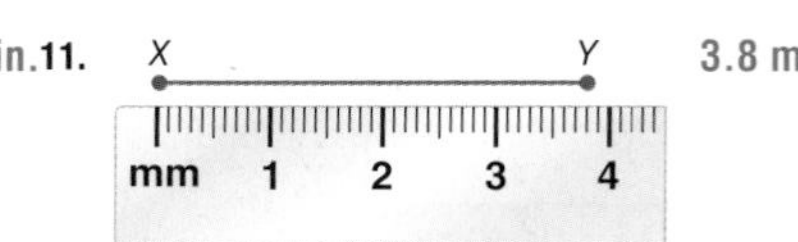

3.8 mm

Differentiated Homework Options

Level	Assignment	Two-Day Option	
AL Basic	10–32, 37, 38, 40–61	11–31 odd, 42–45	10–32 even, 37, 38, 40, 41, 46–61
OL Core	11–19 odd, 20, 21–33 odd, 34–38, 40–61	10–32, 42–45	33–38, 40, 41, 46–61
BL Advanced	34–55, (optional: 56–61)		

12. 2.4 cm or 24 mm

13.  $\frac{15}{16}$ in.

Examples 3–4 Find the measurement of each segment. Assume that each figure is not drawn to scale.

14. $\overline{EF}$ 5.3 in.

2.8 in., 2.5 in.

15. $\overline{JL}$ 1.1 cm

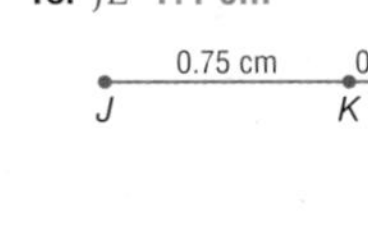

16. $\overline{PR}$ 2.1 mm

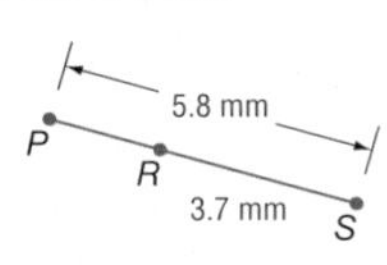

17. $\overline{SV}$ 1.5 in.

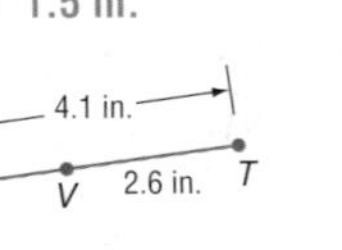

18. $\overline{WY}$ 4.4 mm

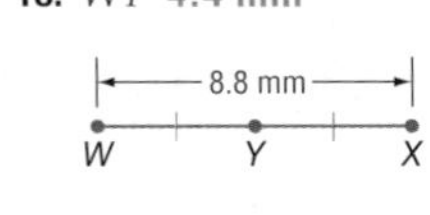

19. $\overline{FG}$ 4.2 cm

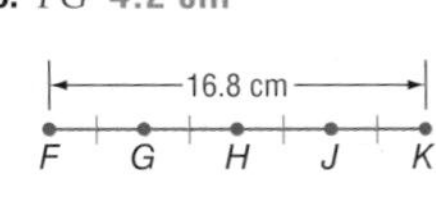

20. 2008: 20 cans, 2009: 35 cans, 2010: 30 cans; Subtract the number of cans the girls brought in from the total number of cans brought in by the girls and the boys.

20. **CCSS SENSE-MAKING** The stacked bar graph shows the number of canned food items donated by the girls and the boys in a homeroom class over three years. Use the concept of betweenness of points to find the number of cans donated by the boys for each year. Explain your method.

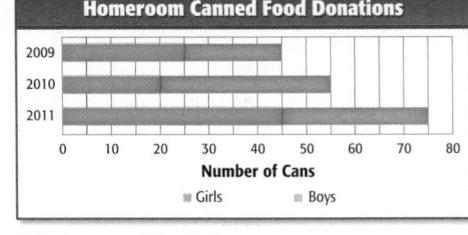

Homeroom Canned Food Donations

2009, 2010, 2011

0, 10, 20, 30, 40, 50, 60, 70, 80

Number of Cans

Girls, Boys

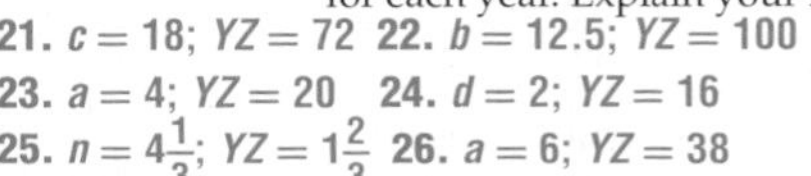

21. $c = 18$; $YZ = 72$ 22. $b = 12.5$; $YZ = 100$
23. $a = 4$; $YZ = 20$ 24. $d = 2$; $YZ = 16$
25. $n = 4\frac{1}{3}$; $YZ = 1\frac{2}{3}$ 26. $a = 6$; $YZ = 38$

Example 5 ALGEBRA Find the value of the variable and YZ if Y is between X and Z.

21. $XY = 11$, $YZ = 4c$, $XZ = 83$
22. $XY = 6b$, $YZ = 8b$, $XZ = 175$
23. $XY = 7a$, $YZ = 5a$, $XZ = 6a + 24$
24. $XY = 11d$, $YZ = 9d - 2$, $XZ = 5d + 28$
25. $XY = 4n + 3$, $YZ = 2n - 7$, $XZ = 22$
26. $XY = 3a - 4$, $YZ = 6a + 2$, $XZ = 5a + 22$

Example 6 Determine whether each pair of segments is congruent.

27. $\overline{KJ}, \overline{HL}$ yes

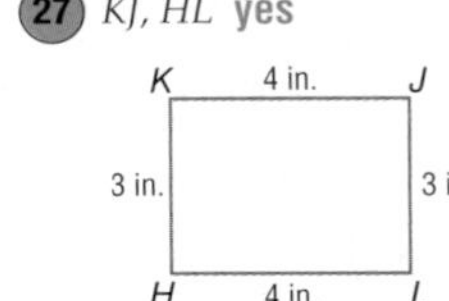

28. $\overline{AC}, \overline{BD}$ yes

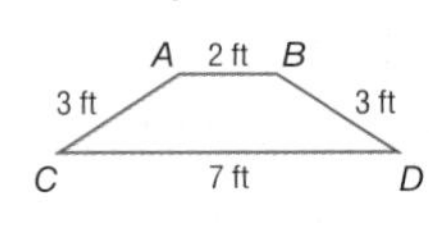

29. $\overline{EH}, \overline{FG}$ no

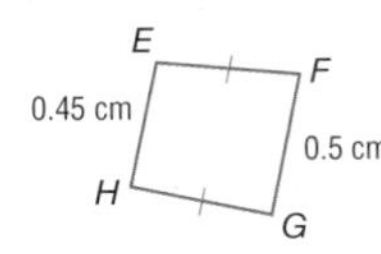

30. $\overline{VW}, \overline{UZ}$

30. cannot be determined from the information given

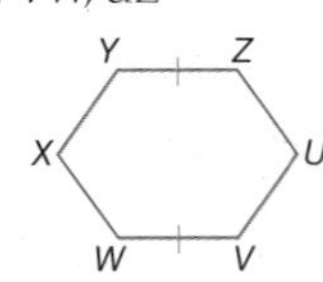

31. $\overline{MN}, \overline{RQ}$ yes

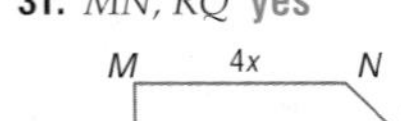

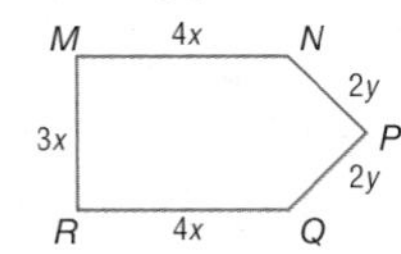

32. $\overline{SU}, \overline{VT}$ yes

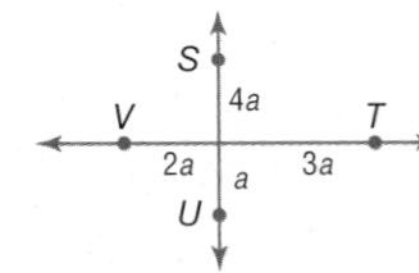

CCSS Teaching the Mathematical Practices

Sense-Making Mathematically proficient students plan a solution pathway. In Exercise 20, encourage students to form a strategy to approach the problem.

Enrichment

OL BL

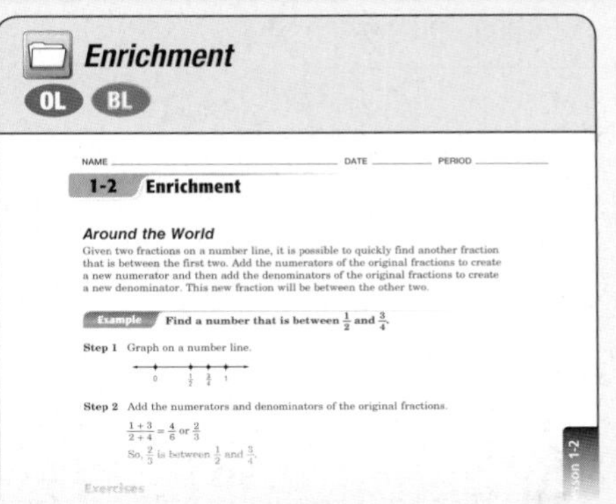

NAME ______ DATE ______ PERIOD ______

1-2 Enrichment

Around the World

Given two fractions on a number line, it is possible to quickly find another fraction that is between the first two. Add the numerators of the original fractions to create a new numerator and then add the denominators of the original fractions to create a new denominator. This new fraction will be between the other two.

Example Find a number that is between $\frac{1}{2}$ and $\frac{3}{4}$.

Step 1 Graph on a number line.

Step 2 Add the numerators and denominators of the original fractions.

$\frac{1+3}{2+4} = \frac{4}{6}$ or $\frac{2}{3}$

So, $\frac{2}{3}$ is between $\frac{1}{2}$ and $\frac{3}{4}$.

Exercises

Study Guide and Intervention

AL OL ELL

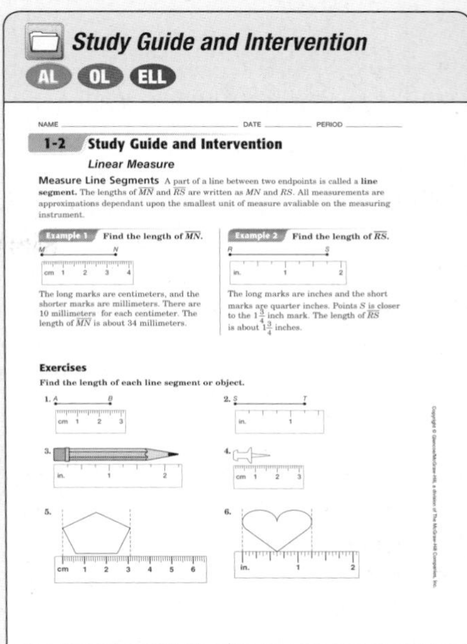

NAME ______ DATE ______ PERIOD ______

1-2 Study Guide and Intervention

Linear Measure

Measure Line Segments A part of a line between two endpoints is called a **line segment.** The lengths of $\overline{MN}$ and $\overline{RS}$ are written as MN and RS. All measurements are approximations dependant upon the smallest unit of measure avaliable on the measuring instrument.

Example 1 Find the length of $\overline{MN}$.

The long marks are centimeters, and the shorter marks are millimeters. There are 10 millimeters for each centimeter. The length of $\overline{MN}$ is about 34 millimeters.

Example 2 Find the length of $\overline{RS}$.

The long marks are inches and the short marks are quarter inches. Points S is closer to the $1\frac{3}{4}$ inch mark. The length of $\overline{RS}$ is about $1\frac{3}{4}$ inches.

Exercises

Find the length of each line segment or object.

Practice

AL OL BL ELL

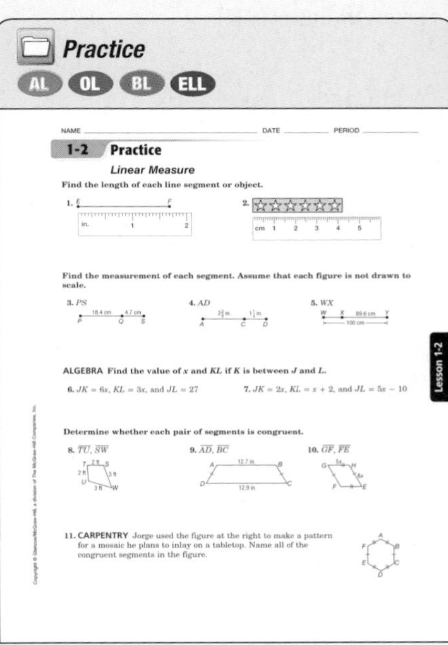

NAME ______ DATE ______ PERIOD ______

1-2 Practice

Linear Measure

Find the length of each line segment or object.

Find the measurement of each segment. Assume that each figure is not drawn to scale.

3. PS 4. AD 5. WX

ALGEBRA Find the value of x and KL if K is between J and L.

6. $JK = 6x$, $KL = 3x$, and $JL = 27$ 7. $JK = 2x$, $KL = x + 2$, and $JL = 5x - 10$

Determine whether each pair of segments is congruent.

8. $\overline{TU}, \overline{SW}$ 9. $\overline{AD}, \overline{BC}$ 10. $\overline{GF}, \overline{FE}$

11. CARPENTRY Jorge used the figure at the right to make a pattern for a mosaic he plans to inlay on a tabletop. Name all of the congruent segments in the figure.

Word Problem Practice

AL OL BL ELL

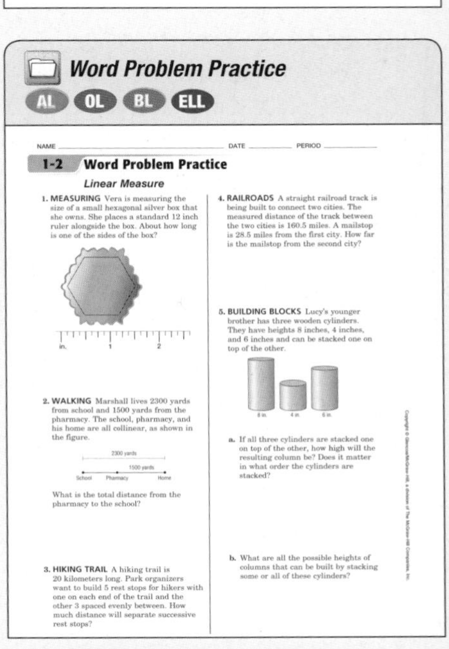

NAME ______ DATE ______ PERIOD ______

1-2 Word Problem Practice

Linear Measure

1. MEASURING Vera is measuring the size of a small hexagonal silver box that she owns. She places a standard 12 inch ruler alongside the box. About how long is one of the sides of the box?

2. WALKING Marshall lives 2300 yards from school and 1500 yards from the pharmacy. The school, pharmacy, and his home are all collinear, as shown in the figure.

What is the total distance from the pharmacy to the school?

3. HIKING TRAIL A hiking trail is 20 kilometers long. Park organizers want to build 5 rest stops for hikers with one on each end of the trail and the other 3 spaced evenly between. How much distance will separate successive rest stops?

4. RAILROADS A straight railroad track is being built to connect two cities. The measured distance of the track between the two cities is 160.5 miles. A mailstop is 28.5 miles from the first city. How far is the mailstop from the second city?

5. BUILDING BLOCKS Lucy's younger brother has three wooden cylinders. They have heights 8 inches, 4 inches, and 6 inches and can be stacked one on top of the other.

a. If all three cylinders are stacked one on top of the other, how high will the resulting column be? Does it matter in what order the cylinders are stacked?

b. What are all the possible heights of columns that can be built by stacking some or all of these cylinders?

Exercise Alert

Ruler Exercises 34 and 35 require the use of a ruler.

Multiple Representations

In Exercise 36 students investigate the concept of betweenness. They should see that between any two points on a line another point exists.

CCSS Teaching the Mathematical Practices

Reasoning Mathematically proficient students decontextualize information, represent it symbolically, and then contextualize to interpret the solution. In Exercise 40, direct students to draw a diagram to represent the information given in the problem.

Additional Answers

34a.

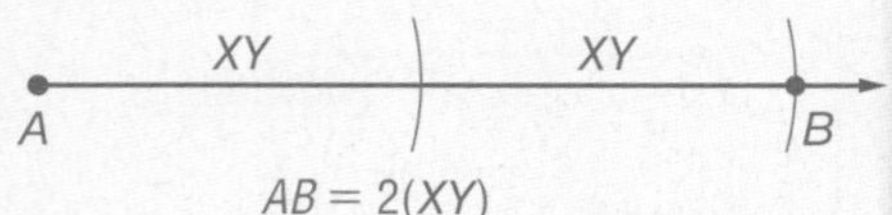

$AB = 2(XY)$

Sample answer: I measured $\overline{XY}$ with my compass and used this measurement to construct $\overline{XY}$ two times. Since I used the same arc measure to construct $\overline{XY}$ two times, the segment is $2(XY)$.

34b.

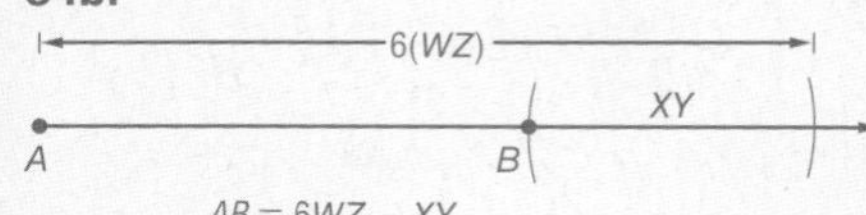

$AB = 6WZ - XY$

Sample answer: I measured $\overline{WZ}$ with my compass and constructed 6 segments equal to WZ. I measured $\overline{XY}$ and subtracted this measurement from the segment just constructed. Since I used the same arc measure to construct six WZ segments, the segment is $6(WZ)$. I then used the arc measure of XY to subtract from my previous segment. So, the resulting segment is $6(WZ) - XY$.

33. TRUSSES A truss is a structure used to support a load over a span, such as a bridge or the roof of a house. List all of the congruent segments in the figure. $\overline{AB} \cong \overline{BC} \cong \overline{CD} \cong \overline{DE} \cong \overline{DG} \cong \overline{BG} \cong \overline{CG}$, $\overline{AH} \cong \overline{HG} \cong \overline{GF} \cong \overline{FE}$, $\overline{BH} \cong \overline{DF}$, $\overline{AC} \cong \overline{EC}$, $\overline{AG} \cong \overline{HF} \cong \overline{GE}$

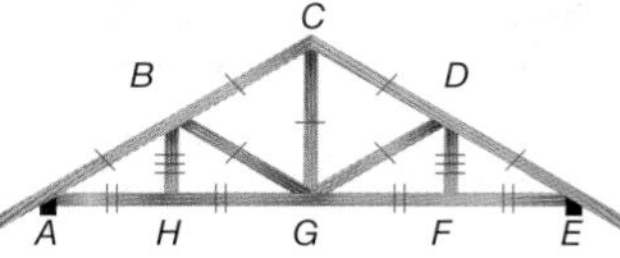

34. CONSTRUCTION For each expression:

- construct a segment with the given measure,
- explain the process you used to construct the segment, and
- verify that the segment you constructed has the given measure.

a. $2(XY)$ **See margin.** **b.** $6(WZ) - XY$ **See margin.**

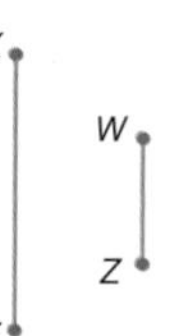

35. BLUEPRINTS Use a ruler to determine at least five pairs of congruent segments with labeled endpoints in the blueprint at the right.

Sample answer: $\overline{BD} \cong \overline{CE}$; $\overline{BD} \cong \overline{PQ}$; $\overline{YZ} \cong \overline{JK}$; $\overline{PQ} \cong \overline{RS}$; $\overline{GK} \cong \overline{KL}$

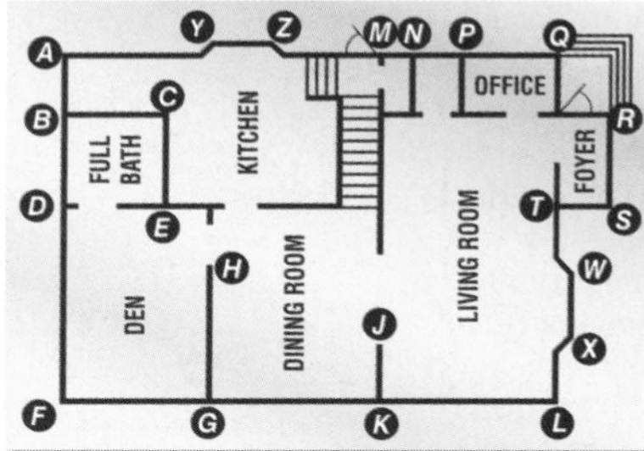

36. MULTIPLE REPRESENTATIONS Betweenness of points ensures that a line segment may be divided into an infinite number of line segments. **a–b. See margin.**

a. Geometric Use a ruler to draw a line segment 3 centimeters long. Label the endpoints A and D. Draw two more points along the segment and label them B and C. Draw a second line segment 6 centimeters long. Label the endpoints K and P. Add four more points along the line and label them L, M, N, and O.

b. Tabular Use a ruler to measure the length of the line segment between each of the points you have drawn. Organize the lengths of the segments in $\overline{AD}$ and $\overline{KP}$ into a table. Include a column in your table to record the sum of these measures.

c. Algebraic Give an equation that could be used to find the lengths of $\overline{AD}$ and $\overline{KP}$. Compare the lengths determined by your equation to the actual lengths. **$AD = AB + BC + CD$; $KP = KL + LM + MN + NO + OP$; the lengths of each segment add up to the length of the whole segment.**

H.O.T. Problems Use Higher-Order Thinking Skills

37. WRITING IN MATH If point B is between points A and C, explain how you can find AC if you know AB and BC. Explain how you can find BC if you know AB and AC.

37. If point B is between points A and C, and you know AB and BC, add AB and BC to find AC. If you know AB and AC, subtract AB from AC to find BC.

38. OPEN ENDED Draw a segment $\overline{AB}$ that measures between 2 and 3 inches long. Then sketch a segment $\overline{CD}$ congruent to $\overline{AB}$, draw a segment $\overline{EF}$ congruent to $\overline{AB}$, and construct a segment $\overline{GH}$ congruent to $\overline{AB}$. Compare your methods. **See margin.**

39. CHALLENGE Point K is between points J and L. If $JK = x^2 - 4x$, $KL = 3x - 2$, and $JL = 28$, write and solve an equation to find the lengths of JK and KL. **$JK = 12$, $KL = 16$**

40. CCSS REASONING Determine whether the statement *If point M is between points C and D, then CD is greater than either CM or MD* is *sometimes*, *never*, or *always* true. Explain. **See margin.**

41. WRITING IN MATH Why is it important to have a standard of measure? **See margin.**

H.O.T. Problems require students to use **H**igher **O**rder **T**hinking skills to solve problems.

36a. Sample answer:

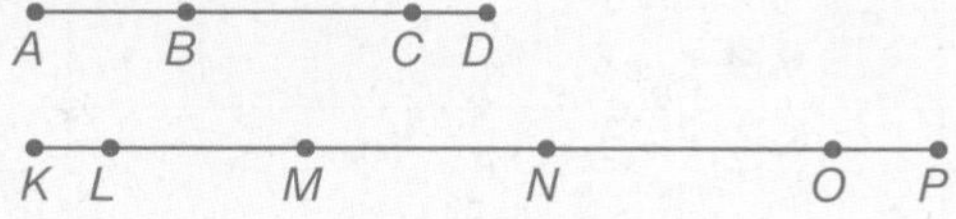

Standardized Test Practice

42. SHORT RESPONSE A 36-foot-long ribbon is cut into three pieces. The first piece of ribbon is half as long as the second piece of ribbon. The third piece is 1 foot longer than twice the length of the second piece of ribbon. How long is the longest piece of ribbon? **21 ft**

43. In the figure, points *A*, *B*, *C*, *D*, and *E* are collinear. If $AE = 38$, $BD = 15$, and $\overline{BC} \cong \overline{CD} \cong \overline{DE}$, what is the length of $\overline{AD}$? **D**

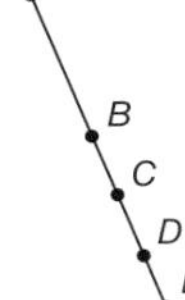

A 7.5 C 22.5
B 15 D 30.5

44. SAT/ACT If $f(x) = 7x^2 - 4x$, what is the value of $f(2)$? **K**

F −8 J 17
G 2 K 20
H 6

45. ALGEBRA
Simplify $(3x^2 - 2)(2x + 4) - 2x^2 + 6x + 7$. **D**

A $4x^2 + 14x - 1$
B $4x^2 - 14x + 15$
C $6x^3 + 12x^2 + 2x - 1$
D $6x^3 + 10x^2 + 2x - 1$

Spiral Review

Refer to the figure. (Lesson 1-1)

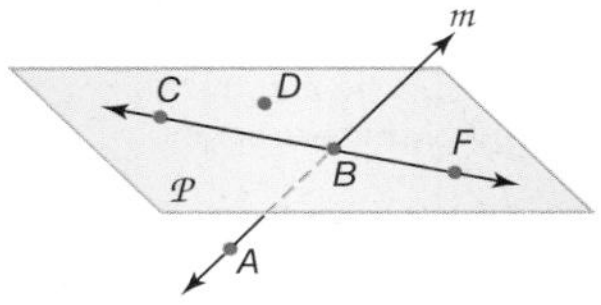

46. What are two other names for $\overleftrightarrow{AB}$? **$\overleftrightarrow{BA}$ or line *m***

47. Give another name for plane $\mathcal{P}$. **Sample answer: plane *CDF***

48. Name the intersection of plane $\mathcal{P}$ and $\overleftrightarrow{AB}$. **point *B***

49. Name three collinear points. **points *C*, *B*, and *F***

50. Name two points that are not coplanar. **Sample answer: points *A* and *D***

51. CLOCKS The period of a pendulum is the time required for it to make one complete swing back and forth. The formula of the period *P* in seconds of a pendulum is $P = 2\pi\sqrt{\frac{\ell}{32}}$, where ℓ is the length of the pendulum in feet. (Lesson 0-9)

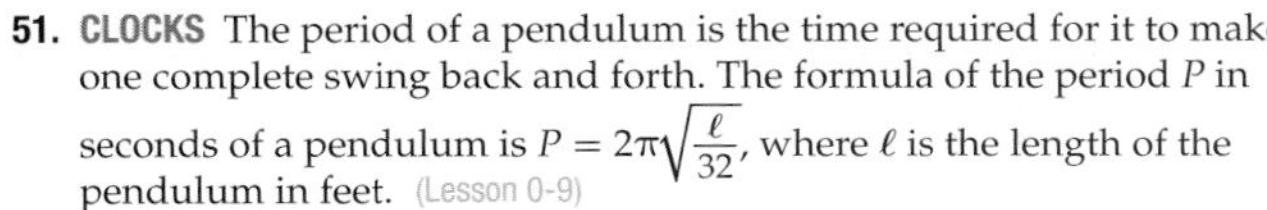

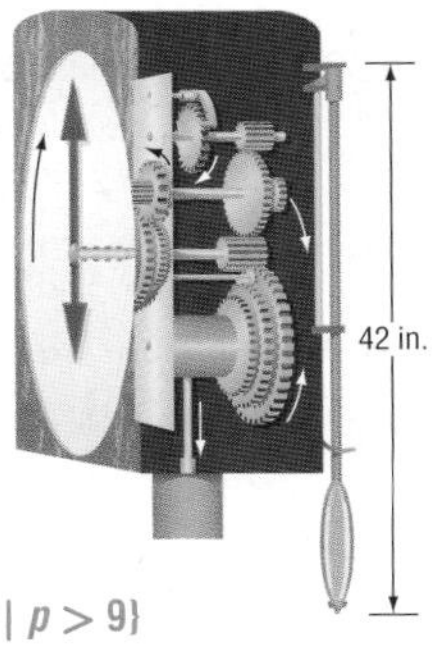

a. What is the period of the pendulum in the clock shown to the nearest tenth of a second? **about 2.1 seconds**

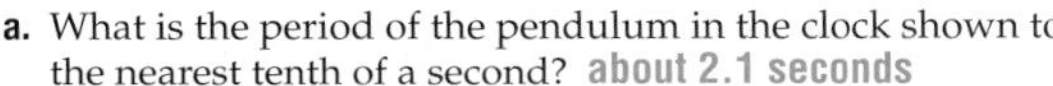

b. About how many inches long should the pendulum be in order for it to have a period of 1 second? **about 9.7 in.**

42 in.

Solve each inequality. (Lesson 0-6)

52. $-14n \geq 42$ **$\{n \mid n \leq -3\}$**

53. $p + 6 > 15$ **$\{p \mid p > 9\}$**

54. $-2a - 5 < 20$ **$\{a \mid a > -12.5\}$**

55. $5x \leq 3x - 26$ **$\{x \mid x \leq -13\}$**

Skills Review

Evaluate each expression if $a = -7$, $b = 4$, $c = -3$, and $d = 5$.

56. $b - c$ **7**

57. $|a - d|$ **12**

58. $|d - c|$ **8**

59. $\frac{b - a}{2}$ **5.5**

60. $(a - c)^2$ **16**

61. $\sqrt{(a - b)^2 + (c - d)^2}$ **$\sqrt{185}$**

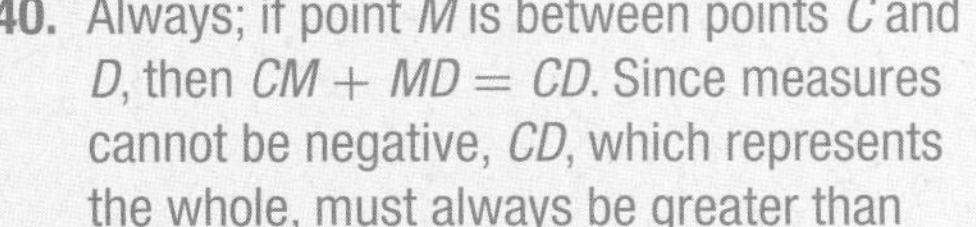

40. Always; if point *M* is between points *C* and *D*, then $CM + MD = CD$. Since measures cannot be negative, *CD*, which represents the whole, must always be greater than either of the lengths of its parts, *CM* or *MD*.

41. Sample answer: Having a standard of measure is important so that there is a reference point against which other measures can be compared and evaluated.

4 Assess

Ticket Out the Door Have students draw and label lines, planes, and simple geometric shapes. Have them turn in their drawings before they leave the classroom.

Formative Assessment

Check for student understanding of concepts in Lessons 1-1 and 1-2.

 Quiz 1, p. 51

Additional Answers

36b. Sample answer:

$\overline{AD}$	
Segment	**Length (cm)**
$\overline{AB}$	1.0
$\overline{BC}$	1.5
$\overline{CD}$	0.5
Total	3.0

$\overline{KP}$	
Segment	**Length (cm)**
$\overline{KL}$	0.5
$\overline{LM}$	1.3
$\overline{MN}$	1.6
$\overline{NO}$	1.9
$\overline{OP}$	0.7
Total	6.0

38.

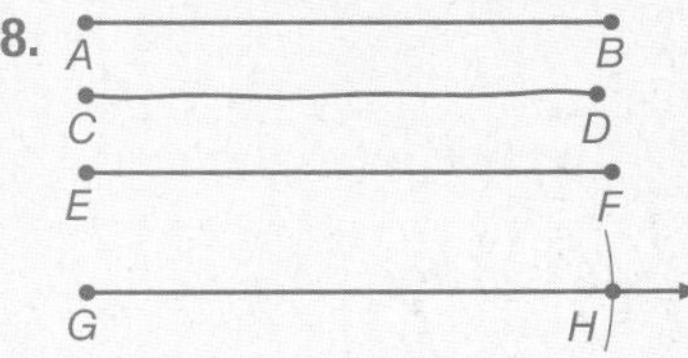

Both $\overline{AB}$ and $\overline{EF}$ were created using a ruler, while $\overline{GH}$ was created using a straightedge and compass and $\overline{CD}$ was created without any of these tools. $\overline{AB}$, $\overline{EF}$, and $\overline{GH}$ have the same measure, but $\overline{CD}$ not only does not have the same length, it isn't even a straight line.

1 Focus

Materials for Each Group
- rulers

Teaching Tip
This lesson includes topics that most students find confusing. Be diligent when discussing the definitions of absolute and relative error. Also, tell students that these concepts as well as significant digits are heavily used in science courses.

2 Teach

Working in Cooperative Groups
Allow students to work individually as the lesson content and examples are discussed. Organize students in groups of 3, mixing abilities, and have them complete the Guided Practice Examples provided in the lesson. Facilitate the group work as you monitor students' progress and understanding.

Practice Have students complete Exercises 1–23.

EXTEND 1-2 Extension Lesson Precision and Accuracy

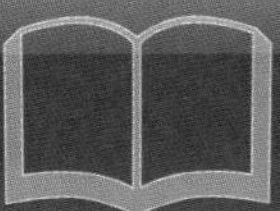

Objective

1. Determine precision of measurements.
2. Determine accuracy of measurements.

As stated in Lesson 1-2, all measurements are approximations. Two main factors are considered when determining the quality of such an approximation.

- How *precise* is the measure?
- How *accurate* is the measure?

1 Precision

Precision refers to the clustering of a group of measurements. It depends only on the smallest unit of measure available on a measuring tool. Suppose you are told that a segment measures 8 centimeters. The length, to the nearest centimeter, of each segment shown below is 8 centimeters.

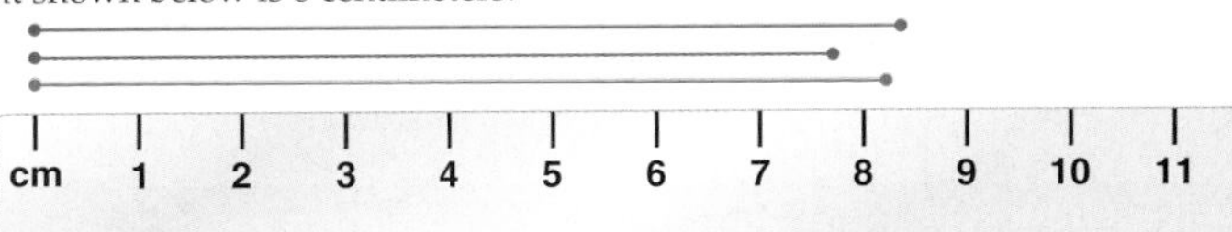

Notice that the exact length of each segment above is between 7.5 and 8.5 centimeters, or within 0.5 centimeter of 8 centimeters. The **absolute error** of a measurement is equal to one half the unit of measure. The smaller the unit of measure, the more precise the measurement.

StudyTip

Precision The absolute error of a measurement in customary units is determined before reducing the fraction. For example, if you measure the length of an object to be $1\frac{4}{16}$ inches, then the absolute error measurement is precise to within $\frac{1}{32}$ inch.

Example 1 Find Absolute Error

Find the absolute error of each measurement. Then explain its meaning.

a. 6.4 centimeters

The measure is given to the nearest 0.1 centimeter, so the absolute error of this measurement is $\frac{1}{2}(0.1)$ or 0.05 centimeter. Therefore, the exact measurement could be between 6.35 and 6.45 centimeters. The two segments below measure 6.4 ± 0.05 centimeters.

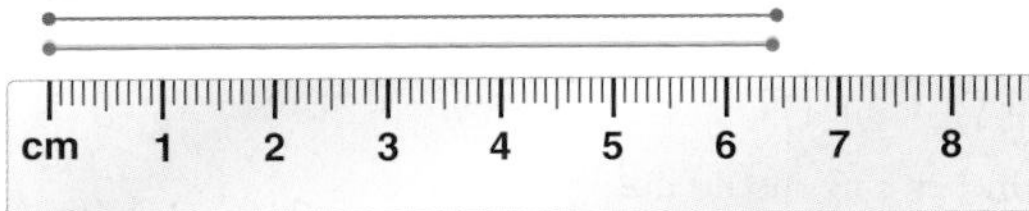

b. $2\frac{1}{4}$ inches

The measure is given to the nearest $\frac{1}{4}$ inch, so the absolute error of this measurement is $\frac{1}{2}\left(\frac{1}{4}\right)$ or $\frac{1}{8}$ inch. Therefore, the exact measurement could be between $2\frac{1}{8}$ and $2\frac{3}{8}$ inches. The two segments below measure $2\frac{1}{4} \pm \frac{1}{8}$ inches.

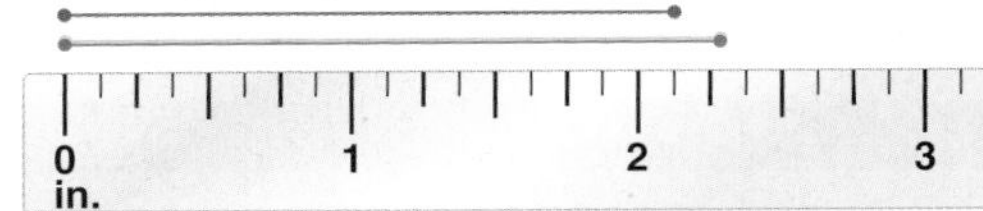

GuidedPractice

1A. $1\frac{1}{2}$ inches

1B. 4 centimeters

1A. $\frac{1}{4}$ in.; between $1\frac{1}{4}$ in. and $1\frac{3}{4}$ in.

1B. 0.5 cm; between 3.5 and 4.5 cm

Precision in a measurement is usually expressed by the number of **significant digits** reported. Reporting that the measure of $\overline{AB}$ is 4 centimeters is *less precise* than reporting that the measure of $\overline{AB}$ is 4.1 centimeters.

To determine whether digits are considered significant, use the following rules.

- Nonzero digits are always significant.
- In whole numbers, zeros are significant if they fall between nonzero digits.
- In decimal numbers greater than or equal to 1, every digit is significant.
- In decimal numbers less than 1, the first nonzero digit and every digit to the right are significant.

Real-WorldLink

Precision in measurement in the real world usually comes at a price.

- Precision in a process to 3 significant digits, commercial quality, can cost $100.
- Precision in a process to 4 significant digits, industrial quality, can cost $500.
- Precision in a process to 5 significant digits, scientific quality, can cost $2500.

Source: Southwest Texas Junior College

Example 2 Significant Digits

Determine the number of significant digits in each measurement.

a. 430.008 meters

Since this is a decimal number greater than 1, every digit is significant. So, this measurement has 6 significant digits.

b. 0.00750 centimeter

This is a decimal number less than 1. The first nonzero digit is 7, and there are two digits to the right of 7, 5 and 0. So, this measurement has 3 significant digits.

GuidedPractice

2A. 779,000 mi 3 **2B.** 50,008 ft 5 **2C.** 230.004500 m 9

2 Accuracy

Accuracy refers to how close a measured value comes to the actual or desired value. Consider the target practice results shown below.

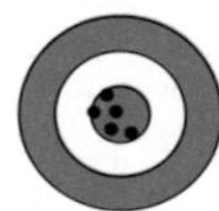
accurate and precise

accurate but not precise

precise but not accurate

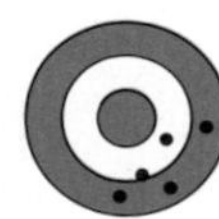
not accurate and not precise

The relative error of a measure is the ratio of the absolute error to the expected measure. A measurement with a smaller relative error is said to be more accurate.

StudyTip

Accuracy The accuracy or relative error of a measurement depends on both the absolute error and the size of the object being measured.

Example 3 Find Relative Error

MANUFACTURING A manufacturer measures each part for a piece of equipment to be 23 centimeters in length. Find the relative error of this measurement.

$$\text{relative error} = \frac{\text{absolute error}}{\text{expected measure}} = \frac{0.5\text{ cm}}{23\text{ cm}} \approx 0.022 \text{ or } 2.2\%$$

GuidedPractice

Find the relative error of each measurement.

3A. 3.2 mi about 1.6% **3B.** 1 ft 50% **3C.** 26 ft about 1.9%

WatchOut!

Accuracy vs. Precision Students have trouble determining the difference between the accuracy and the precision of a measurement. Be sure to stress the definitions of these terms as well as the differences between the terms.

3 Assess

Formative Assessment

Use Exercises 1–21 to assess whether students understand the concepts of absolute error, relative error, precision, and the proper use of significant digits.

From Concrete to Abstract

It is important that students understand that a solution to a problem or a measurement cannot be more accurate than the level of accuracy of the given values, measurements, or the measurement tools used. Ask students how this applies to reporting the solution of a basic algebraic equation like:

$$4.2x = 36.$$

The highest number of significant digits given in the problem is 2; therefore, the value of x reported should not have more than 2 significant digits.

Additional Answers

1. 0.5 yd; The exact measurement could be between 11.5 and 12.5 yd.
2. $\frac{1}{32}$ in.; The exact measurement could be between $50\frac{7}{32}$ and $50\frac{9}{32}$.
3. 0.005 ft; The exact measurement could be between 3.275 and 3.285 ft.
4. 0.0005 cm; The exact measurement could be between 2.7585 and 2.7595 cm.
5. Neither is correct; sample answer: Since the ruler is marked in $\frac{1}{16}$-inch increments, the measurement can only be precise to $\frac{1}{32}$ of an inch.

23. Sample answer: The precision of the measurement depends on the situation. For example, precision to within 0.5 mile when measuring the driving distance from one city to another is probably precise enough. However, precision to within 0.5 mile when measuring the length of a bridge or overpass would likely cause a problem, and thus, would not be precise enough.

Extension Lesson
Precision and Accuracy *Continued*

Practice and Problem Solving

Find the absolute error of each measurement. Then explain its meaning. **1–5. See margin.**

1. 12 yd
2. $50\frac{4}{16}$ in.
3. 3.28 ft
4. 2.759 cm

5. **ERROR ANALYSIS** In biology class, Manuel and Jocelyn measure a beetle as shown. Manuel says that the beetle measures between $1\frac{5}{8}$ and $1\frac{3}{4}$ inches. Jocelyn says that it measures between $1\frac{9}{16}$ and $1\frac{5}{8}$ inches. Is either of their statements about the beetle's measure correct? Explain your reasoning.

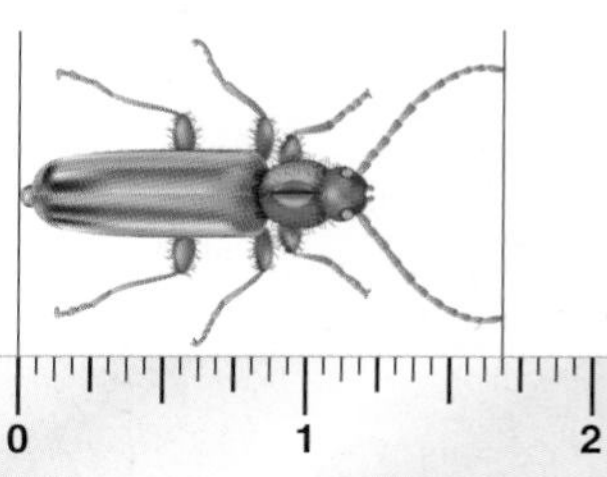

6. **PYRAMIDS** Research suggests that the design dimensions of the Great Pyramid of Giza in Egypt were 440 by 440 royal cubits. The sides of the pyramid are precise within 0.05%. What are the greatest and least possible lengths of the sides? **439.78 cubits and 440.22 cubits**

Determine the number of significant digits in each measurement.

7. 4.05 in. **3**
8. 53,000 mi **2**
9. 0.0005 mm **1**
10. 750,001 ft **6**

11. **VOLUME** When multiplying or dividing measures, the product or quotient should have only as many significant digits as the multiplied or divided measurement showing the least number of significant digits. To how many significant digits should the volume of the rectangle prism shown be reported? Report the volume to this number of significant digits.

22.37 cm
9.10 cm
85.75 cm

11. 9.10 shows the least number of significant digits—three. The product is 17,455.87025. It shows 10 significant digits, so we must round to the hundreds place in order to show only three significant digits. The final answer is 17,500 cm^3.

Find the relative error of each measurement.

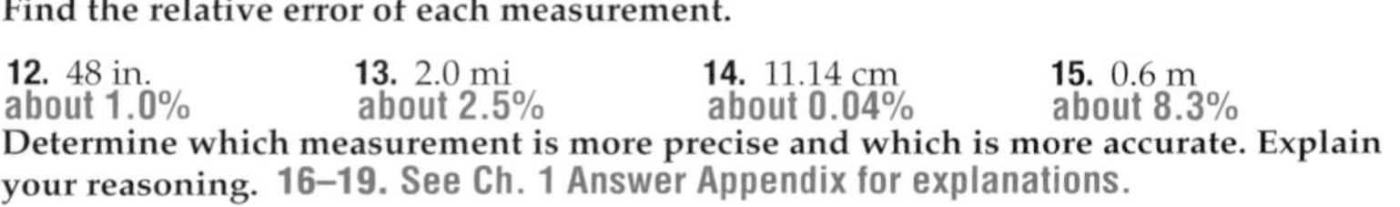

12. 48 in. **about 1.0%**
13. 2.0 mi **about 2.5%**
14. 11.14 cm **about 0.04%**
15. 0.6 m **about 8.3%**

Determine which measurement is more precise and which is more accurate. Explain your reasoning. **16–19. See Ch. 1 Answer Appendix for explanations.**

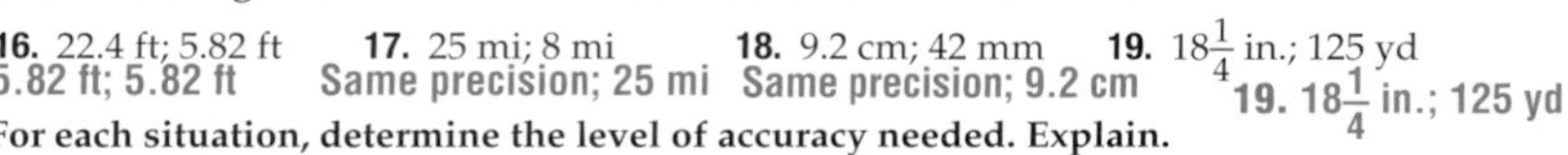

16. 22.4 ft; 5.82 ft **5.82 ft; 5.82 ft**
17. 25 mi; 8 mi **Same precision; 25 mi**
18. 9.2 cm; 42 mm **Same precision; 9.2 cm**
19. $18\frac{1}{4}$ in.; 125 yd **19. $18\frac{1}{4}$ in.; 125 yd**

For each situation, determine the level of accuracy needed. Explain.

20. You are estimating the height of a person. Which unit of measure should you use: 1 foot, 1 inch, or $\frac{1}{16}$ inch? **1 in.; See Ch.1 Answer Appendix for explanation.**
21. You are estimating the height of a mountain. Which unit of measure should you use: 1 foot, 1 inch, or $\frac{1}{16}$ inch? **1 ft; See Ch.1 Answer Appendix for explanation.**
22. **PERIMETER** The *perimeter* of a geometric figure is the sum of the lengths of its sides. Jermaine uses a ruler divided into inches and measures the sides of a rectangle to be $2\frac{1}{4}$ inches and $4\frac{3}{4}$ inches. What are the least and greatest possible perimeters of the rectangle? Explain. **13.5 in.; 14.5 in; See Ch. 1 Answer Appendix for explanation.**
23. **WRITING IN MATH** How precise is precise enough? **See margin.**

WatchOut!

Error Analysis In Exercise 5, students should look at the increments on the ruler carefully. The ruler is marked in $\frac{1}{16}$-inch increments, so the absolute error is $\frac{1}{32}$.

The beetle's measure is between $1\frac{21}{32}$ and $1\frac{23}{32}$, so neither is correct.

LESSON 1-3 Distance and Midpoints

Then

- You graphed points on the coordinate plane.

Now

1. Find the distance between two points.
2. Find the midpoint of a segment.

Why?

- The location of a city on a map is given in degrees of latitude and longitude. For short distances, the Pythagorean Theorem can be used to approximate the distance between two locations.

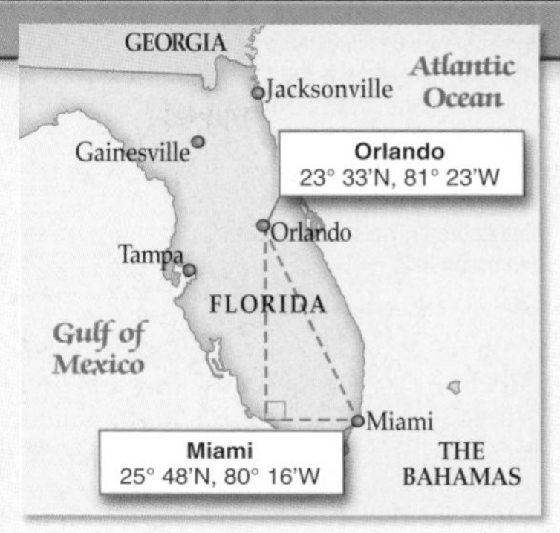

NewVocabulary
distance
irrational number
midpoint
segment bisector

Common Core State Standards

Content Standards

G.CO.1 Know precise definitions of angle, circle, perpendicular line, parallel line, and line segment, based on the undefined notions of point, line, distance along a line, and distance around a circular arc.

G.CO.12 Make formal geometric constructions with a variety of tools and methods (compass and straightedge, string, reflective devices, paper folding, dynamic geometric software, etc.).

Mathematical Practices

2 Reason abstractly and quantitatively.
7 Look for and make use of structure.

1 Distance Between Two Points

The **distance** between two points is the length of the segment with those points as its endpoints. The coordinates of the points can be used to find this length. Because $\overline{PQ}$ is the same as $\overline{QP}$, the order in which you name the endpoints is not important when calculating distance.

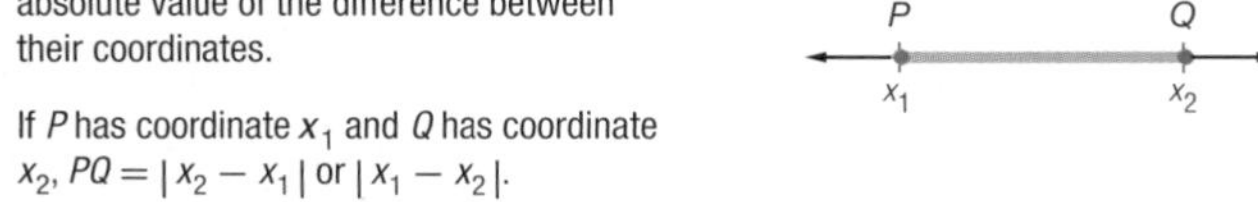

KeyConcept Distance Formula (on Number Line)

Words The distance between two points is the absolute value of the difference between their coordinates.

Symbols If P has coordinate x_1 and Q has coordinate x_2, $PQ = |x_2 - x_1|$ or $|x_1 - x_2|$.

Example 1 Find Distance on a Number Line

Use the number line to find BE.

The coordinates of B and E are −6 and 2.

$BE = |x_2 - x_1|$ Distance Formula

$= |2 - (-6)|$ $x_1 = -6$ and $x_2 = 2$

$= 8$ Simplify.

GuidedPractice

Use the number line above to find each measure.

1A. AC 3 **1B.** CF 9 **1C.** FB 11

connectED.mcgraw-hill.com 25

1 Focus

VerticalAlignment

Before Lesson 1-3 Use graphed points on the coordinate plane.

Lesson 1-3 Find the distance between two points. Find the midpoint of a segment.

After Lesson 1-3 Use distances and midpoints to solve problems and write geometric proofs.

2 Teach

Scaffolding Questions

Have students read the **Why?** section of the lesson.

Ask:

- There are 60′ in 1° longitude and 60′ in 1° latitude. What are the coordinates, in degrees, for Orlando? Miami? Orlando: 23.55°N, 81.38°W; Miami: 25.8°N, 80.27°W
- What is the length, in degrees, of each leg of the right triangle shown on the map? long leg: 2.25°; short leg: 1.11°
- Use the Pythagorean Theorem to find the distance, in degrees, between Orlando and Miami. ≈2.51°

(continued on the next page)

Lesson 1-3 Resources

Resource	Approaching Level AL	On Level OL	Beyond Level BL	English Learners ELL
Teacher Edition	▪ Differentiated Instruction, p. 28	▪ Differentiated Instruction, pp. 27, 28, 32	▪ Differentiated Instruction, pp. 27, 32	▪ Differentiated Instruction, p. 28
Chapter Resource Masters	▪ Study Guide and Intervention, pp. 18–19 ▪ Skills Practice, p. 20 ▪ Practice, p. 21 ▪ Word Problem Practice, p. 22 ▪ Spreadsheet Activity, p. 24	▪ Study Guide and Intervention, pp. 18–19 ▪ Skills Practice, p. 20 ▪ Practice, p. 21 ▪ Word Problem Practice, p. 22 ▪ Enrichment, p. 23 ▪ Spreadsheet Activity, p. 24	▪ Practice, p. 21 ▪ Word Problem Practice, p. 22 ▪ Enrichment, p. 23 ▪ Spreadsheet Activity, p. 24	▪ Study Guide and Intervention, pp. 18–19 ▪ Skills Practice, p. 20 ▪ Practice, p. 21 ▪ Word Problem Practice, p. 22 ▪ Spreadsheet Activity, p. 24
Other	▪ 5-Minute Check 1-3 ▪ Study Notebook ▪ Teaching Geometry with Manipulatives	▪ 5-Minute Check 1-3 ▪ Study Notebook ▪ Teaching Geometry with Manipulatives	▪ 5-Minute Check 1-3 ▪ Study Notebook	▪ 5-Minute Check 1-3 ▪ Study Notebook ▪ Teaching Geometry with Manipulatives

- Why must it be specified that the triangle side lengths and the distance between Orlando and Miami are measured in degrees? It must be specified that the lengths and distance are measured in degrees because the coordinates used to find the lengths are given in degrees. It is necessary to indicate that the small area of the map of Florida is transposed onto a coordinate plane so that 2-dimensional, plane figure calculations using the Pythagorean Theorem can be applied to locations (indicated by degrees latitude and longitude) that actually lie on a sphere (the Earth).

1 Distance Between Two Points

Example 1 shows how to find the distance between two points on a number line. **Example 2** shows how to use the Pythagorean Theorem or the Distance Formula to find the distance between two points on a coordinate plane.

Formative Assessment

Use the Guided Practice exercises after each example to determine students' understanding of concepts.

Additional Examples

1 Use the number line to find QR. 3

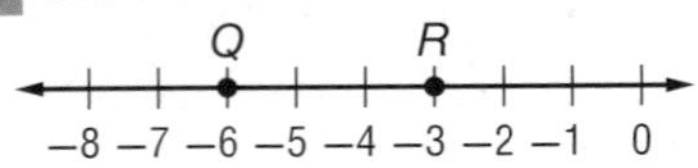

2 Find the distance between $E(-4, 1)$ and $F(3, -1)$.

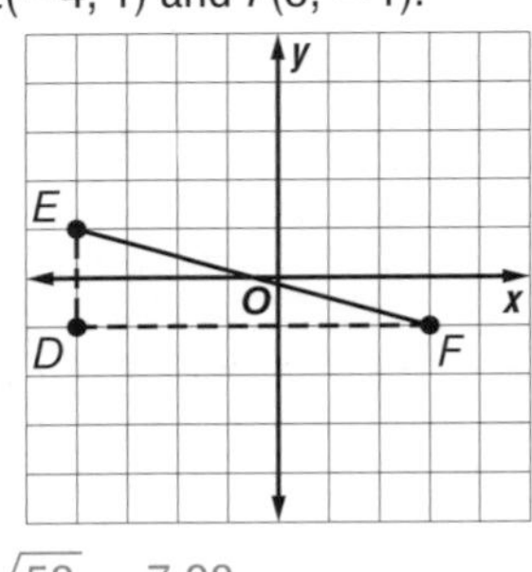

$\sqrt{53} \approx 7.28$

Additional Examples also in Interactive Classroom PowerPoint® Presentations

StudyTip

Pythagorean Theorem Recall that the Pythagorean Theorem is often expressed as $a^2 + b^2 = c^2$, where a and b are the measures of the shorter sides (legs) of a right triangle, and c is the measure of the longest side (hypotenuse). You will prove and learn about other applications of the Pythagorean Theorem in Lesson 8-2.

To find the distance between two points A and B in the coordinate plane, you can form a right triangle with $\overline{AB}$ as its hypotenuse and point C as its vertex as shown. Then use the Pythagorean Theorem to find AB.

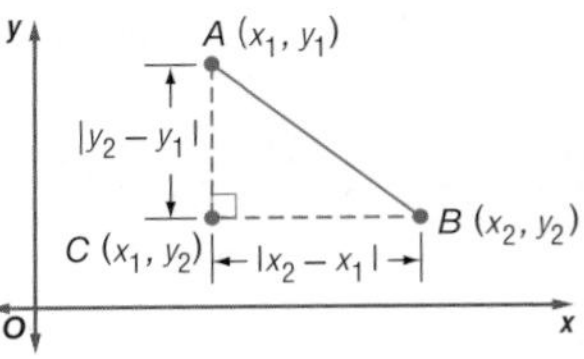

$(CB)^2 + (AC)^2 = (AB)^2$	Pythagorean Theorem
$(\lvert x_2 - x_1\rvert)^2 + (\lvert y_2 - y_1\rvert)^2 = (AB)^2$	$CB = \lvert x_2 - x_1\rvert, AC = \lvert y_2 - y_1\rvert$
$(x_2 - x_1)^2 + (y_2 - y_1)^2 = (AB)^2$	The square of a number is always positive.
$\sqrt{(x_2 - x_1)^2 + (y_2 - y_1)^2} = AB$	Take the positive square root of each side.

This gives us a Distance Formula for points in the coordinate plane. Because this formula involves taking the square root of a real number, distances can be irrational. Recall that an **irrational number** is a number that cannot be expressed as a terminating or repeating decimal.

KeyConcept Distance Formula (in Coordinate Plane)

If P has coordinates (x_1, y_1) and Q has coordinates (x_2, y_2), then

$$PQ = \sqrt{(x_2 - x_1)^2 + (y_2 - y_1)^2}.$$

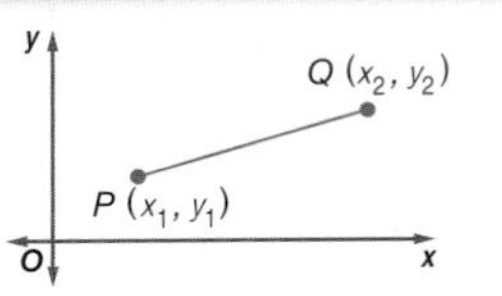

The order of the x- and y-coordinates in each set of parentheses is not important.

Example 2 Find Distance on a Coordinate Plane

Find the distance between $C(-4, -6)$ and $D(5, -1)$.

$CD = \sqrt{(x_2 - x_1)^2 + (y_2 - y_1)^2}$	Distance Formula
$= \sqrt{[5 - (-4)]^2 + [-1 - (-6)]^2}$	$(x_1, y_1) = (-4, -6)$ and $(x_2, y_2) = (5, -1)$
$= \sqrt{9^2 + 5^2}$ or $\sqrt{106}$	Subtract.

The distance between C and D is $\sqrt{106}$ units. Use a calculator to find that $\sqrt{106}$ units is approximately 10.3 units.

CHECK Graph the ordered pairs and check by using the Pythagorean Theorem.

$(CD)^2 \stackrel{?}{=} (EC)^2 + (ED)^2$

$(CD)^2 \stackrel{?}{=} 5^2 + 9^2$

$(CD)^2 \stackrel{?}{=} 106$

$CD = \sqrt{106}$ ✓

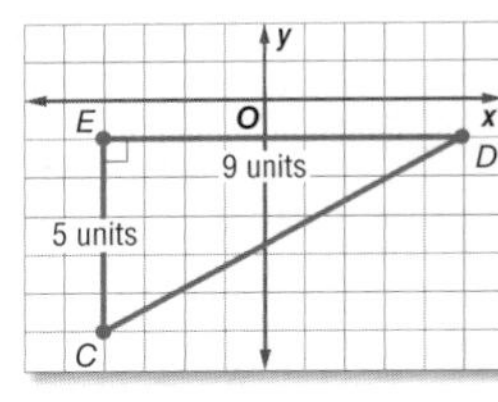

Guided Practice

Find the distance between each pair of points.

2A. $E(-5, 6)$ and $F(8, -4)$ $\sqrt{269}$ or about 16.4 units

2B. $J(4, 3)$ and $K(-3, -7)$ $\sqrt{149}$ or about 12.2 units

26 | Lesson 1-3 | Distance and Midpoints

Tips for New Teachers

Finding Distance Encourage students to use the Pythagorean Theorem to find the distance between two points several times before introducing the Distance Formula. Students tend to have difficulty remembering the Distance Formula, and this affords them an alternative to find the distance between two points.

Teach with Tech

Blog On your secure class blog, have students write a blog entry explaining how the distance formula and Pythagorean Theorem are similar to each other.

2 Midpoint of a Segment

The **midpoint** of a segment is the point halfway between the endpoints of the segment. If X is the midpoint of $\overline{AB}$, then $AX = XB$ and $\overline{AX} \cong \overline{XB}$. You can find the midpoint of a segment on a number line by finding the *mean*, or the average, of the coordinates of its endpoints.

KeyConcept Midpoint Formula (on Number Line)

If $\overline{AB}$ has endpoints at x_1 and x_2 on a number line, then the midpoint M of $\overline{AB}$ has coordinate

$$\frac{x_1 + x_2}{2}.$$

A M B
x_1 $\frac{x_1 + x_2}{2}$ x_2

> **StudyTip**
> **Alternative Method** In Example 3, the coordinate of the midpoint could also have been located by first finding the length of AB, which is $37.5 - 15$ or 22.5 inches. Half of this measure is the distance from one endpoint to the point midway between A and B, $\frac{22.5}{2}$ or 11.25. Add this distance to point A's distance from the left wall. So the midpoint between A and B is $15 + 11.25$ or 26.25 inches from the left wall.

Real-World Example 3 Find Midpoint on a Number Line

PT

DECORATING Jacinta hangs a picture 15 inches from the left side of a wall. How far from the edge of the wall should she mark the location for the nail the picture will hang on if the right edge is 37.5 inches from the wall's left side?

A B

The coordinates of the endpoints of the top of the picture frame are 15 inches and 37.5 inches. Let M be the midpoint of $\overline{AB}$.

$M = \frac{x_1 + x_2}{2}$	Midpoint Formula
$= \frac{15 + 37.5}{2}$	$x_1 = 15, x_2 = 37.5$
$= \frac{52.5}{2}$ or 26.25	Simplify.

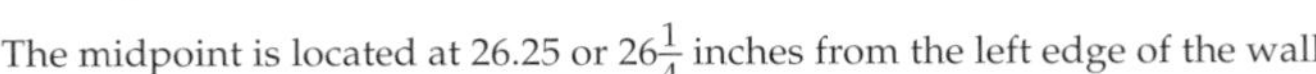

The midpoint is located at 26.25 or $26\frac{1}{4}$ inches from the left edge of the wall.

GuidedPractice

3. **TEMPERATURE** The temperature on a thermometer dropped from a reading of 25° to −8°. Find the midpoint of these temperatures. **8.5°**

You can find the midpoint of a segment on the coordinate plane by finding the average of the x-coordinates and of the y-coordinates of the endpoints.

KeyConcept Midpoint Formula (in Coordinate Plane)

If $\overline{PQ}$ has endpoints at $P(x_1, y_1)$ and $Q(x_2, y_2)$ in the coordinate plane, then the midpoint M of $\overline{PQ}$ has coordinates

$$M\left(\frac{x_1 + x_2}{2}, \frac{y_1 + y_2}{2}\right).$$

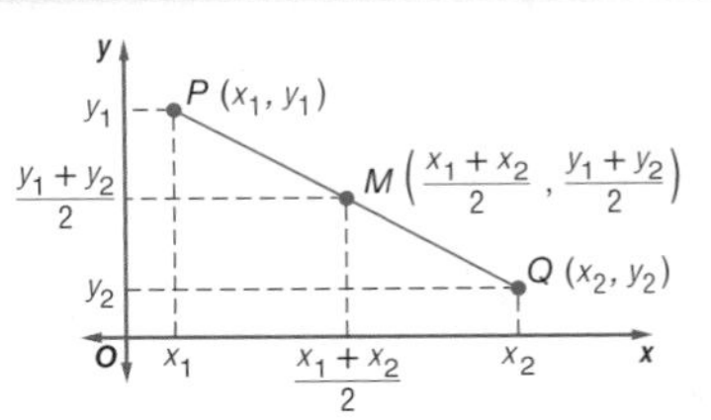

When finding the midpoint of a segment, the order of the coordinates of the endpoints is not important.

2 Midpoint of a Segment

The midpoint of a segment is the point halfway between the endpoints of the segment. **Examples 3–6** show how to find the midpoint of a segment arithmetically and algebraically on a number line and on a coordinate plane.

Additional Example

3 **DECORATING** Marco places a couch so that its end is perpendicular and 2.5 feet away from the wall. The couch is 90″ wide. How far is the midpoint of the couch back from the wall in feet? 6.25 ft

Tips for New Teachers

Midpoint Formula You may want students to develop their own midpoint formulas by testing several examples.

WatchOut!

Unlocking Misconceptions A common mistake is that students subtract the coordinates in the Midpoint Formula because subtraction is used in the distance and the slope formulas. Remind students that the midpoint is the *mean* of each coordinate and to find the mean or average, the sum is divided by the number of terms.

DifferentiatedInstruction

Extension Have students sketch three different segments that each have (0, 0) as a midpoint. Write the coordinates of the endpoints of each segment. What do you notice about the coordinates? Sample answers: In each pair, the x-coordinates and the y-coordinates are opposites.

Tips for New Teachers

Using Symbols Explain and demonstrate that a segment with points, *A*, *B*, and *C*, and tick marks on *AB* and *BC* indicates that *B* is the *midpoint* and *bisector* of $\overline{AC}$.

Additional Examples

4 Find the coordinates of *M*, the midpoint of *GH*, for *G*(8, −6) and *H*(−14, 12). (−3, 3)

5 Find the coordinates of *D* if *E*(−6, 4) is the midpoint of $\overline{DF}$ and *F* has coordinates (−5, −3). (−7, 11)

Focus on Mathematical Content

Segment Addition Traditionally, segment addition is shown in order of the points, as in $AB + BC = AC$. However, because addition is commutative, $BC + AB = AC$ is also correct.

Study Tips offer students helpful information about the topics they are studying.

Example 4 Find Midpoint in Coordinate Plane

Find the coordinates of *M*, the midpoint of $\overline{ST}$, for *S*(−6, 3) and *T*(1, 0).

$$M = \left(\frac{x_1 + x_2}{2}, \frac{y_1 + y_2}{2}\right) \quad \text{Midpoint Formula}$$

$$= \left(\frac{-6 + 1}{2}, \frac{3 + 0}{2}\right) \quad (x_1, y_1) = S(-6, 3), (x_2, y_2) = T(1, 0)$$

$$= \left(\frac{-5}{2}, \frac{3}{2}\right) \text{ or } M\left(-2\frac{1}{2}, 1\frac{1}{2}\right) \quad \text{Simplify.}$$

CHECK Graph *S*, *T*, and *M*. The distance from *S* to *M* does appear to be the same as the distance from *M* to *T*, so our answer is reasonable.

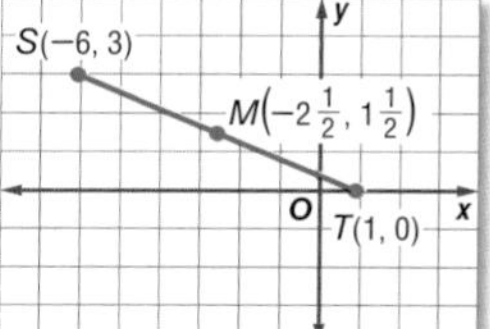

Guided Practice

Find the coordinates of the midpoint of a segment with the given coordinates.

4A. *A*(5, 12), *B*(−4, 8) $\left(\frac{1}{2}, 10\right)$

4B. *C*(−8, −2), *D*(5, 1) $\left(-1\frac{1}{2}, -\frac{1}{2}\right)$

You can also find the coordinates of the endpoint of a segment if you know the coordinates of its other endpoint and its midpoint.

Example 5 Find the Coordinates of an Endpoint

Find the coordinates of *J* if *K*(−1, 2) is the midpoint of $\overline{JL}$ and *L* has coordinates (3, −5).

Step 1 Let *J* be (x_1, y_1) and *L* be (x_2, y_2) in the Midpoint Formula.

$$K\left(\frac{x_1 + 3}{2}, \frac{y_1 + (-5)}{2}\right) = K(-1, 2) \quad (x_2, y_2) = (3, -5)$$

Step 2 Write two equations to find the coordinates of *J*.

$\frac{x_1 + 3}{2} = -1$	Midpoint Formula	$\frac{y_1 + (-5)}{2} = 2$	Midpoint Formula
$x_1 + 3 = -2$	Multiply each side by 2.	$y_1 - 5 = 4$	Multiply each side by 2.
$x_1 = -5$	Subtract 3 from each side.	$y_1 = 9$	Add 5 to each side.

The coordinates of *J* are (−5, 9).

CHECK Graph *J*, *K*, and *L*. The distance from *J* to *K* does appear to be the same as the distance from *K* to *L*, so our answer is reasonable.

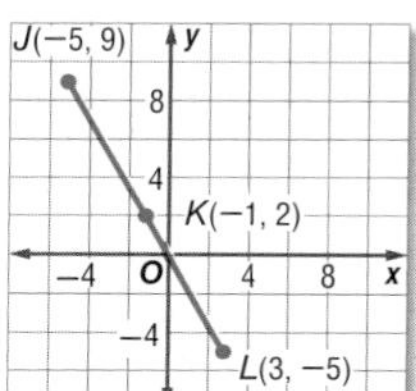

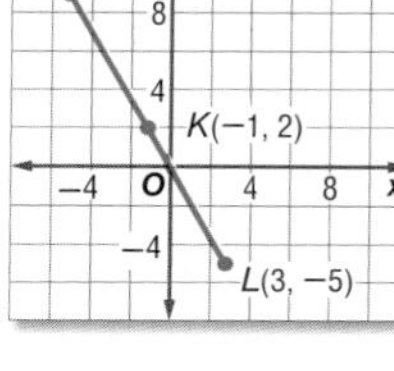

StudyTip
Check for Reasonableness Always graph the given information and the calculated coordinates of the third point to check the reasonableness of your answer.

Guided Practice

Find the coordinates of the missing endpoint if *P* is the midpoint of $\overline{EG}$.

5A. *E*(−8, 6), *P*(−5, 10) *G*(−2, 14)

5B. *P*(−1, 3), *G*(5, 6) *E*(−7, 0)

Differentiated Instruction AL OL ELL

Visual/Spatial Learners Hold a meterstick up for students to see so that the marked side is facing away from them. Ask a volunteer to mark on the back of the stick about where they visualize the middle of the meterstick to be. Have a second volunteer verify the first student's mark or add another mark. Place a pen upright on the 50-cm mark so that it shows exactly where the midpoint of the meterstick is and compare to the students' marks. Explain how people can use spatial skills to very closely identify the exact middle of many objects.

You can use algebra to find a missing measure or value in a figure that involves the midpoint of a segment.

> **StudyTip**
> **CCSS Sense-Making and Perseverance** The four-step problem solving plan is a tool for making sense of any problem. When making and executing your plan, continually ask yourself, "Does this make sense?" Monitor and evaluate your progress and change course if necessary.

Example 6 Use Algebra to Find Measures

ALGEBRA Find the measure of $\overline{PQ}$ if Q is the midpoint of $\overline{PR}$.

Understand You know that Q is the midpoint of $\overline{PR}$.
You are asked to find the measure of $\overline{PQ}$.

Plan Because Q is the midpoint, you know that $PQ = QR$. Use this equation to find a value for y.

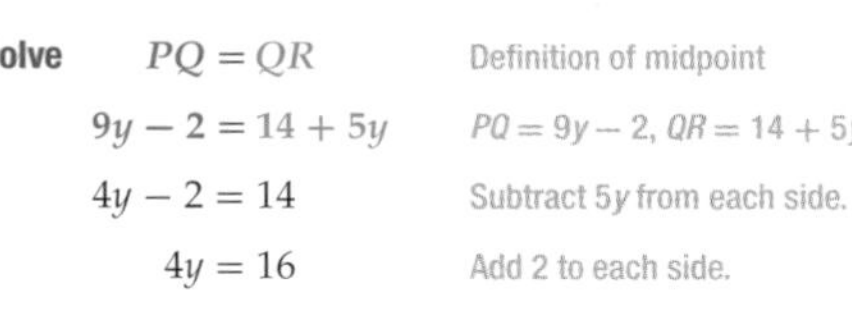

Solve

$PQ = QR$	Definition of midpoint
$9y - 2 = 14 + 5y$	$PQ = 9y - 2$, $QR = 14 + 5y$
$4y - 2 = 14$	Subtract $5y$ from each side.
$4y = 16$	Add 2 to each side.
$y = 4$	Divide each side by 4.

Now substitute 4 for y in the expression for PQ.

$PQ = 9y - 2$	Original measure
$= 9(4) - 2$	$y = 4$
$= 36 - 2$ or 34	Simplify.

The measure of $\overline{PQ}$ is 34.

Check Since $PQ = QR$, when the expression for QR is evaluated for 4, it should also be 34.

$QR = 14 + 5y$	Original measure
$\stackrel{?}{=} 14 + 5(4)$	$y = 4$
$= 34$ ✓	Simplify.

Guided Practice

6A. Find the measure of $\overline{YZ}$ if Y is the midpoint of $\overline{XZ}$ and $XY = 2x - 3$ and $YZ = 27 - 4x$. **7**

6B. Find the value of x if C is the midpoint of $\overline{AB}$, $AC = 4x + 5$, and $AB = 78$. **8.5**

> **StudyTip**
> **Segment Bisectors** There can be an infinite number of bisectors and each must contain the midpoint of the segment.

Any segment, line, or plane that intersects a segment at its midpoint is called a **segment bisector**. In the figure at the right, M is the midpoint of $\overline{PQ}$. Plane $\mathcal{A}$, $\overline{MJ}$, $\overleftrightarrow{KM}$, and point M are all bisectors of $\overline{PQ}$. We say that they *bisect* $\overline{PQ}$.

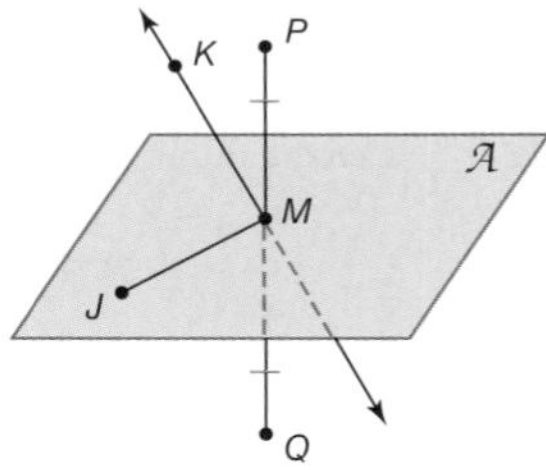

The construction on the following page shows how to construct a line that bisects a segment to find the midpoint of a given segment.

Additional Example

6 **ALGEBRA** Find the measure of $\overline{PR}$ if Q is the midpoint of $\overline{PR}$. 9

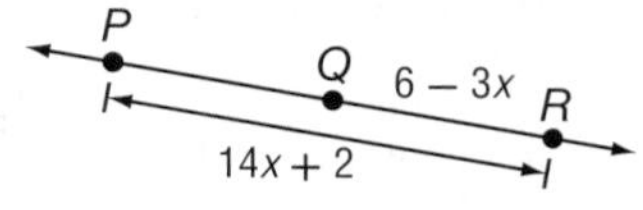

CCSS Teaching the Mathematical Practices

Sense-Making and Perseverance Mathematically proficient students start by explaining the meaning of a problem to themselves and looking for entry points. Encourage students to discuss problems with peers as they grow and apply their skills.

3 Practice

Formative Assessment

Use Exercises 1–12 to check for understanding.

Then use the chart at the bottom of this page to customize assignments for your students.

Teaching the Mathematical Practices

Reasoning Mathematically proficient students make sense of the relationship of quantities in problem situations. In Exercise 6, encourage students to contextualize their responses for Exercises 3-5 as part of their solution plan.

Additional Answers

22. 5 units
23. $\sqrt{208}$ or about 14.4 units
24. $\sqrt{200}$ or about 14.1 units
25. $\sqrt{65}$ or about 8.1 units
26. $\sqrt{20}$ or about 4.5 units
27. $\sqrt{53}$ or about 7.3 units
28. $\sqrt{37}$ or about 6.1 units
29. $\sqrt{18}$ or about 4.2 units
30. $\sqrt{29}$ or about 5.4 units

Every effort is made to show **answers** on the reduced Student Edition page, or in the margin of the Teacher Edition.

Construction Bisect a Segment

Step 1 Draw a segment and name it $\overline{AB}$. Place the compass at point A. Adjust the compass so that its width is greater than $\frac{1}{2}AB$. Draw arcs above and below $\overline{AB}$.

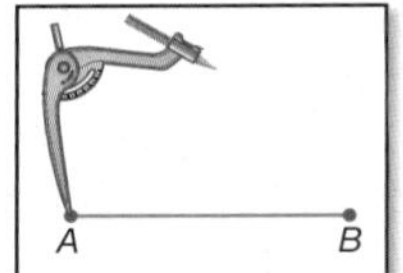

Step 2 Using the same compass setting, place the compass at point B and draw arcs above and below $\overline{AB}$ so that they intersect the two arcs previously drawn. Label the points of the intersection of the arcs as C and D.

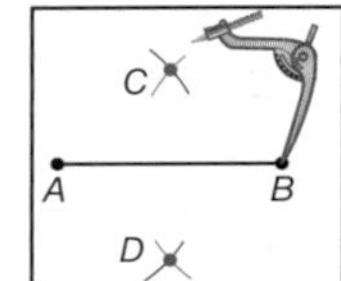

Step 3 Use a straightedge to draw $\overline{CD}$. Label the point where it intersects $\overline{AB}$ as M. Point M is the midpoint of $\overline{AB}$, and $\overline{CD}$ is a bisector of $\overline{AB}$.

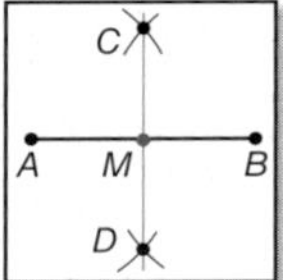

Check Your Understanding

○ = Step-by-Step Solutions begin on page R14.

Example 1 Use the number line to find each measure.

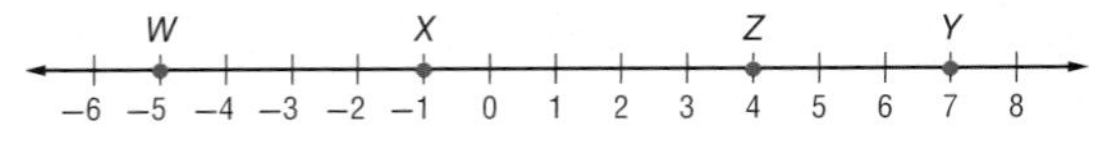

1. XY 8
2. WZ 9

Example 2 **TIME CAPSULE** Graduating classes have buried time capsules on the campus of East Side High School for over twenty years. The points on the diagram show the position of three time capsules. Find the distance between each pair of time capsules.

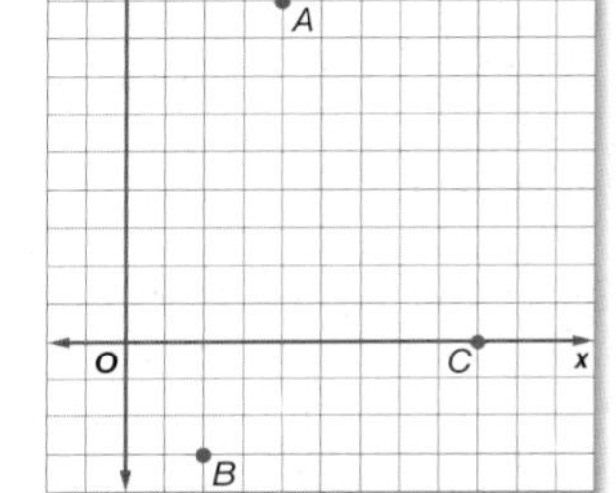

3. $A(4, 9)$, $B(2, -3)$ $\sqrt{148}$ or about 12.2 units

4. $A(4, 9)$, $C(9, 0)$ $\sqrt{106}$ or about 10.3 units

5. $B(2, -3)$, $C(9, 0)$ $\sqrt{58}$ or about 7.6 units

6. **REASONING** Which two time capsules are the closest to each other? Which are farthest apart? closest: B and C; farthest: A and B

Example 3 Use the number line to find the coordinate of the midpoint of each segment.

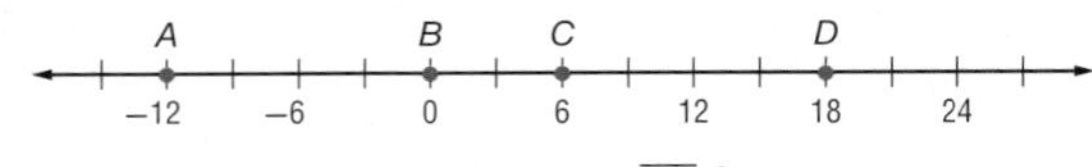

7. $\overline{AC}$ −3
8. $\overline{BD}$ 9

Example 4 Find the coordinates of the midpoint of a segment with the given endpoints.

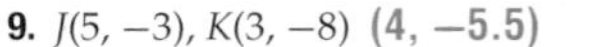

9. $J(5, -3)$, $K(3, -8)$ (4, −5.5)

10. $M(7, 1)$, $N(4, -1)$ (5.5, 0)

30 | Lesson 1-3 | Distance and Midpoints

Differentiated Homework Options

Level	Assignment	Two-Day Option	
AL Basic	13–56, 68, 69, 71–87	13–55 odd, 73–76	14–56 even, 64–69, 71, 72, 77–87
OL Core	13–55 odd, 57–60, 61–65 odd, 66–69, 71–87	13–56, 73–76	57–69, 71, 72, 77–87
BL Advanced	57–81, (optional: 82–87)		

Example 5 **11.** Find the coordinates of G if $F(1, 3.5)$ is the midpoint of $\overline{GJ}$ and J has coordinates $(6, -2)$. **(−4, 9)**

Example 6 **12.** **ALGEBRA** Point M is the midpoint of $\overline{CD}$. What is the value of a in the figure? **3**

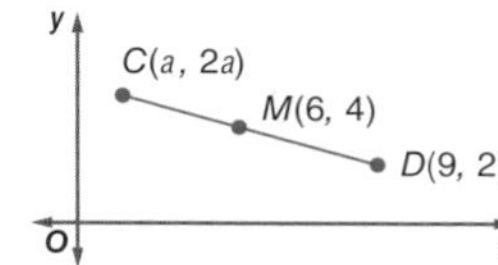

Practice and Problem Solving

Extra Practice is on page R1.

Example 1 Use the number line to find each measure.

13. JL **5** **14.** JK **3** **15.** KP **9**

16. NP **2** **17.** JP **12** **18.** LN **5**

Example 2 Find the distance between each pair of points. **22–30. See margin.**

19. $\sqrt{89}$ or about 9.4 units
20. $\sqrt{45}$ or about 6.7 units
21. $\sqrt{58}$ or about 7.6 units

19.

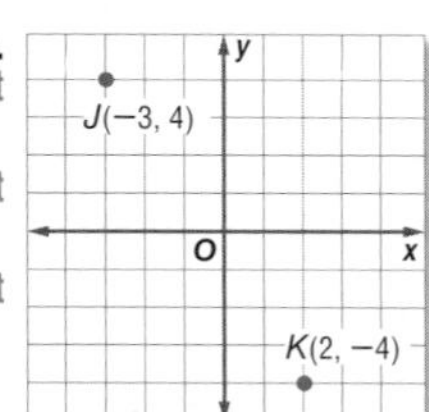

20.

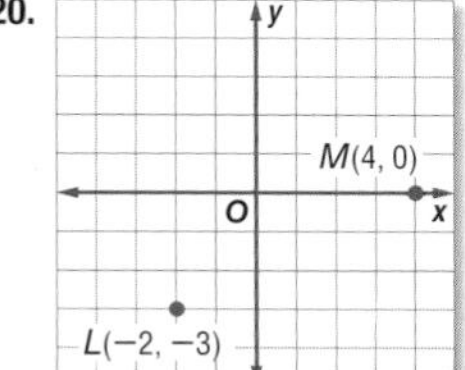

21.

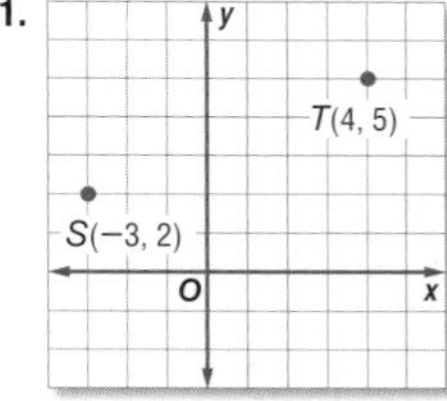

22.

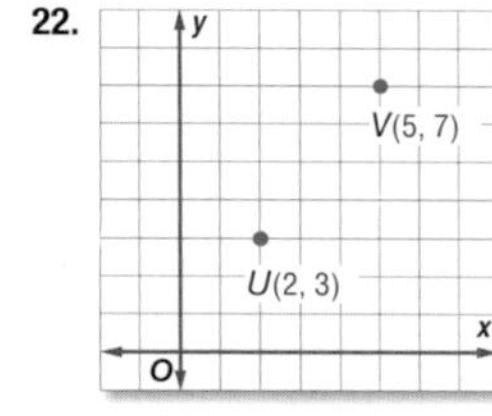

23.

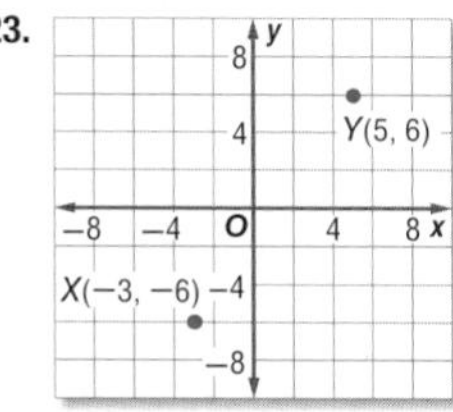

24.

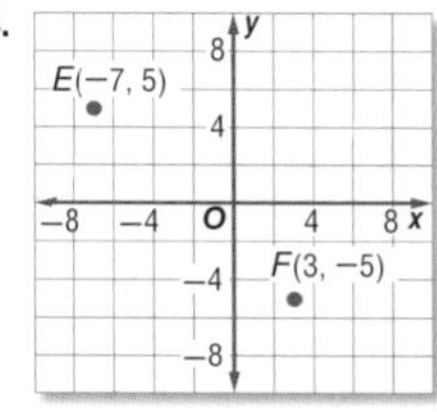

25. $X(1, 2), Y(5, 9)$ **26.** $P(3, 4), Q(7, 2)$ **27.** $M(-3, 8), N(-5, 1)$

28. $Y(-4, 9), Z(-5, 3)$ **29.** $A(2, 4), B(5, 7)$ **30.** $C(5, 1), D(3, 6)$

31. **CCSS REASONING** Vivian is planning to hike to the top of Humphreys Peak on her family vacation. The coordinates of the peak of the mountain and of the base of the trail are shown. If the trail can be approximated by a straight line, estimate the length of the trail. (*Hint:* 1 mi = 5280 ft) **4.5 mi**

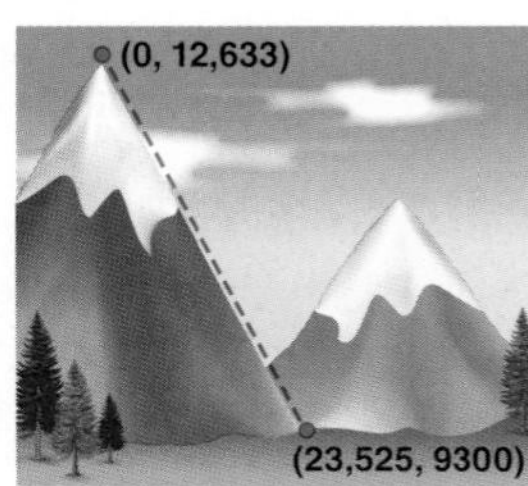

CCSS Teaching the Mathematical Practices

Reasoning Mathematically proficient students decontextualize information, represent it symbolically, and then contextualize to interpret the solution. In Exercise 31, point out to students that they are applying the Distance Formula in a real-world situation.

Enrichment

OL BL

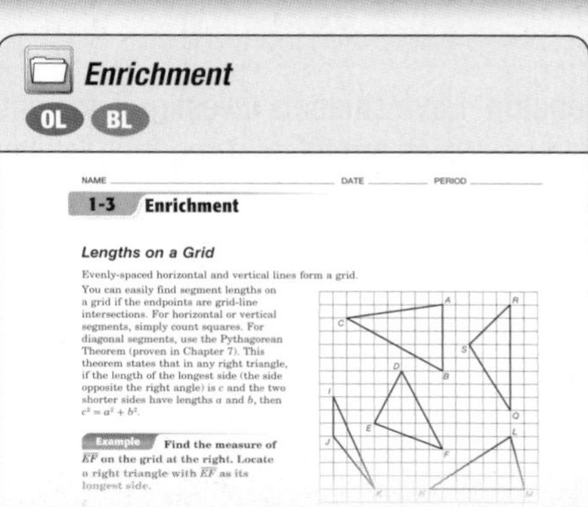

NAME ______ DATE ______ PERIOD ______

1-3 Enrichment

Lengths on a Grid

Evenly-spaced horizontal and vertical lines form a grid. You can easily find segment lengths on a grid if the endpoints are grid-line intersections. For horizontal or vertical segments, simply count squares. For diagonal segments, use the Pythagorean Theorem (proven in Chapter 7). This theorem states that in any right triangle, if the length of the longest side (the side opposite the right angle) is c and the two shorter sides have lengths a and b, then $c^2 = a^2 + b^2$.

Example Find the measure of $\overline{EF}$ on the grid at the right. Locate a right triangle with $\overline{EF}$ as its longest side.

Study Guide and Intervention

AL OL ELL

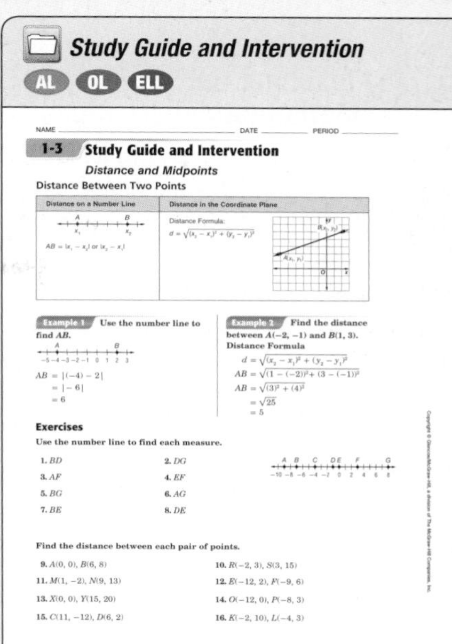

NAME ______ DATE ______ PERIOD ______

1-3 Study Guide and Intervention

Distance and Midpoints

Distance Between Two Points

Distance on a Number Line	Distance in the Coordinate Plane
$AB = \|x_1 - x_2\|$ or $\|x_2 - x_1\|$	Distance Formula: $d = \sqrt{(x_2 - x_1)^2 + (y_2 - y_1)^2}$

Example 1 Use the number line to find AB.

$AB = \|(-4) - 2\|$
$= \|-6\|$
$= 6$

Example 2 Find the distance between $A(-2, -1)$ and $B(1, 3)$.

Distance Formula

$d = \sqrt{(x_2 - x_1)^2 + (y_2 - y_1)^2}$
$AB = \sqrt{(1 - (-2))^2 + (3 - (-1))^2}$
$AB = \sqrt{(3)^2 + (4)^2}$
$= \sqrt{25}$
$= 5$

Exercises

Use the number line to find each measure.

1. BD 2. DG
3. AF 4. EF
5. BG 6. AG
7. BE 8. DE

Find the distance between each pair of points.

9. $A(0, 0), B(6, 8)$ 10. $R(-2, 3), S(3, 15)$
11. $M(1, -2), N(9, 13)$ 12. $E(-12, 2), F(-9, 6)$
13. $X(0, 0), Y(15, 20)$ 14. $O(-12, 0), P(-8, 3)$
15. $C(11, -12), D(6, 2)$ 16. $K(-2, 10), L(-4, 3)$

Practice

AL OL BL ELL

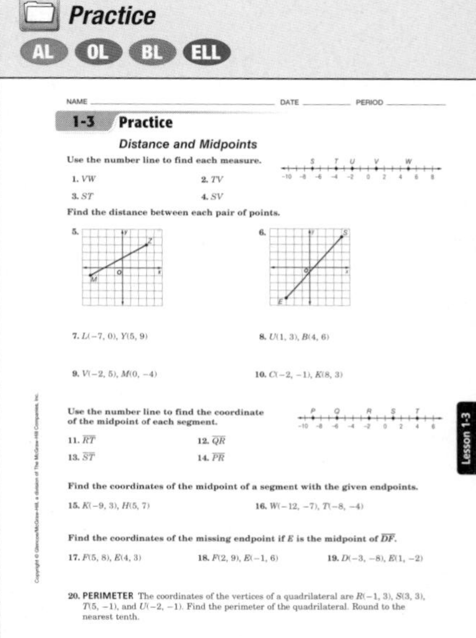

NAME ______ DATE ______ PERIOD ______

1-3 Practice

Distance and Midpoints

Use the number line to find each measure.

1. VW 2. TV
3. ST 4. SV

Find the distance between each pair of points.

5. 6.

7. $L(-7, 0), Y(5, 9)$ 8. $U(1, 3), B(4, 6)$

9. $V(-2, 5), M(0, -4)$ 10. $C(-2, -1), K(8, 3)$

Use the number line to find the coordinate of the midpoint of each segment.

11. $\overline{RT}$ 12. $\overline{QR}$
13. $\overline{ST}$ 14. $\overline{PR}$

Find the coordinates of the midpoint of a segment with the given endpoints.

15. $K(-9, 3), H(5, 7)$ 16. $W(-12, -7), T(-8, -4)$

Find the coordinates of the missing endpoint if E is the midpoint of $\overline{DF}$.

17. $F(5, 8), E(4, 3)$ 18. $F(2, 9), E(-1, 6)$ 19. $D(-3, -8), E(1, -2)$

20. **PERIMETER** The coordinates of the vertices of a quadrilateral are $R(-1, 3)$, $S(3, 3)$, $T(5, -1)$, and $U(-2, -1)$. Find the perimeter of the quadrilateral. Round to the nearest tenth.

Word Problem Practice

AL OL BL ELL

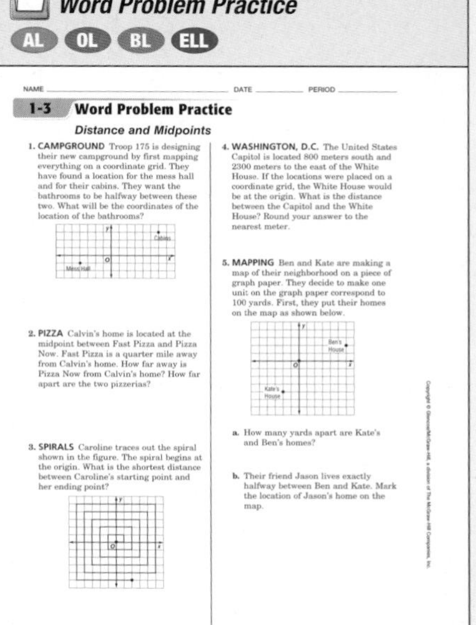

NAME ______ DATE ______ PERIOD ______

1-3 Word Problem Practice

Distance and Midpoints

1. **CAMPGROUND** Troop 175 is designing their new campground by first mapping everything on a coordinate grid. They have found a location for the mess hall and for their cabins. They want the bathrooms to be halfway between these two. What will be the coordinates of the location of the bathrooms?

2. **PIZZA** Calvin's home is located at the midpoint between Fast Pizza and Pizza Now. Fast Pizza is a quarter mile away from Calvin's home. How far away is Pizza Now from Calvin's home? How far apart are the two pizzerias?

3. **SPIRALS** Caroline traces out the spiral shown in the figure. The spiral begins at the origin. What is the shortest distance between Caroline's starting point and her ending point?

4. **WASHINGTON, D.C.** The United States Capitol is located 800 meters south and 2300 meters to the east of the White House. If the locations were placed on a coordinate grid, the White House would be at the origin. What is the distance between the Capitol and the White House? Round your answer to the nearest meter.

5. **MAPPING** Ben and Kate are making a map of their neighborhood on a piece of graph paper. They decide to make one unit on the graph paper correspond to 100 yards. First, they put their homes on the map as shown below.

a. How many yards apart are Kate's and Ben's homes?

b. Their friend Jason lives exactly halfway between Ben and Kate. Mark the location of Jason's home on the map.

Lesson 1-3

Teaching the Mathematical Practices

Modeling Mathematically proficient students can apply the mathematics they know to solve problems arising in the real world. In Exercise 32, encourage students to draw a copy of the map so they can keep track of the given information.

32. **MODELING** Penny and Akiko live in the locations shown on the map below.

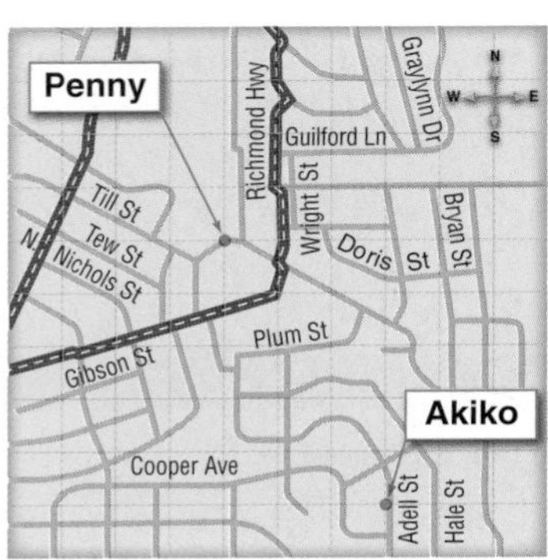

a. If each square on the grid represents one block and the bottom left corner of the grid is the location of the origin, what is the straight-line distance from Penny's house to Akiko's? **5.8 blocks**

b. If Penny moves three blocks to the north and Akiko moves 5 blocks to the west, how far apart will they be? **8.2 blocks**

Example 3 **Use the number line to find the coordinate of the midpoint of each segment.**

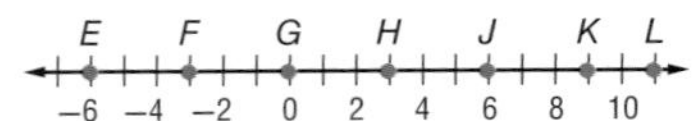

33. $\overline{HK}$ **6**　**34.** $\overline{JL}$ **8.5**　**35.** $\overline{EF}$ **−4.5**

36. $\overline{FG}$ **−1.5**　**37.** $\overline{FK}$ **3**　**38.** $\overline{EL}$ **2.5**

Example 4 **Find the coordinates of the midpoint of a segment with the given endpoints.**

39. $C(22, 4)$, $B(15, 7)$ **(18.5, 5.5)**

40. $W(12, 2)$, $X(7, 9)$ **(9.5, 5.5)**

41. $D(-15, 4)$, $E(2, -10)$ **(−6.5, −3)**

42. $V(-2, 5)$, $Z(3, -17)$ **(0.5, −6)**

43. $X(-2.4, -14)$, $Y(-6, -6.8)$ **(−4.2, −10.4)**

44. $J(-11.2, -3.4)$, $K(-5.6, -7.8)$ **(−8.4, −5.6)**

45. $R(-4, 2)$, $S(3, -1)$ **$\left(-\frac{1}{2}, \frac{1}{2}\right)$**

46. **$\left(-1, -\frac{1}{2}\right)$**

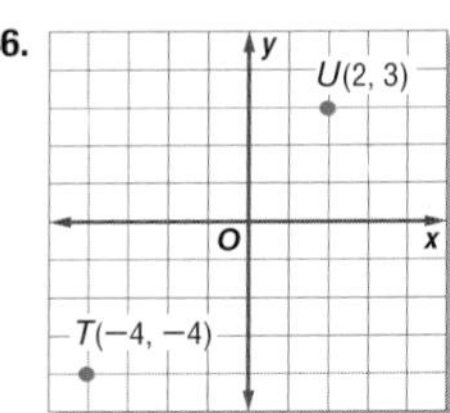

Example 5 **Find the coordinates of the missing endpoint if B is the midpoint of $\overline{AC}$.**

47. $C(-5, 4)$, $B(-2, 5)$ **A(1, 6)**

48. $A(1, 7)$, $B(-3, 1)$ **C(−7, −5)**

49. $A(-4, 2)$, $B(6, -1)$ **C(16, −4)**

50. $C(-6, -2)$, $B(-3, -5)$ **A(0, −8)**

51. $A(4, -0.25)$, $B(-4, 6.5)$ **C(−12, 13.25)**

52. $C\left(\frac{5}{3}, -6\right)$, $B\left(\frac{8}{3}, 4\right)$ **$A\left(\frac{11}{3}, 14\right)$**

Example 6 **ALGEBRA** **Suppose M is the midpoint of $\overline{FG}$. Use the given information to find the missing measure or value.**

53. $FM = 3x - 4$, $MG = 5x - 26$, $FG = ?$ **58**

54. $FM = 5y + 13$, $MG = 5 - 3y$, $FG = ?$ **16**

55. $MG = 7x - 15$, $FG = 33$, $x = ?$ **4.5**

56. $FM = 8a + 1$, $FG = 42$, $a = ?$ **2.5**

Differentiated Instruction OL BL

Extension Have students investigate the difference between driving distances and "as the crow flies" distances. Which are found using the Distance Formula? Which are found by technologies such as mapping programs?

 57 **BASKETBALL** The dimensions of a basketball court are shown below. Suppose a player throws the ball from a corner to a teammate standing at the center of the court.

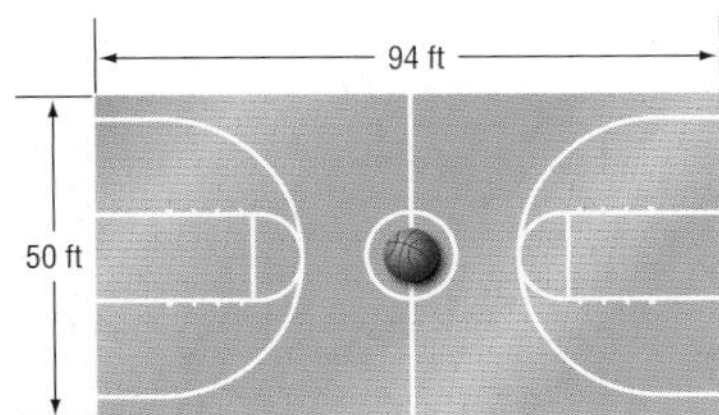

a. If center court is located at the origin, find the ordered pair that represents the location of the player in the bottom right corner. **(47, −25)**

b. Find the distance that the ball travels. **≈53.2 ft**

CCSS TOOLS **Spreadsheets can be used to perform calculations quickly. The spreadsheet below can be used to calculate the distance between two points. Values are used in formulas by using a specific cell name. The value of x_1 is used in a formula using its cell name, A2.**

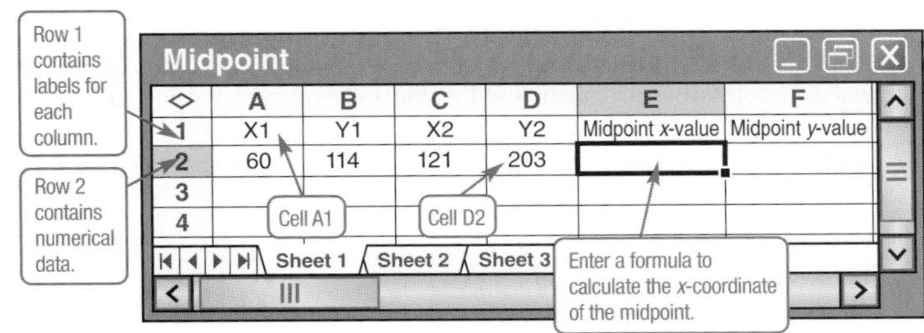

Write a formula for the indicated cell that could be used to calculate the indicated value using the coordinates (x_1, y_1) and (x_2, y_2) as the endpoint of a segment.

58. E2; the x-value of the midpoint of the segment **=AVERAGE(A2,C2)**

59. F2; the y-value of the midpoint of the segment **=AVERAGE(B2,D2)**

60. G2; the length of the segment **=SQRT((C2–A2)^2+(D2–B2)^2)**

Name the point(s) that satisfy the given condition.

61. two points on the x-axis that are 10 units from (1, 8) **(−5, 0), (7, 0)**

62. two points on the y-axis that are 25 units from (−24, 3) **(0, −4), (0, 10)**

 **63. COORDINATE GEOMETRY** Find the coordinates of B if B is the midpoint of $\overline{AC}$ and C is the midpoint of $\overline{AD}$. $\left(-1\frac{1}{2}, -1\right)$

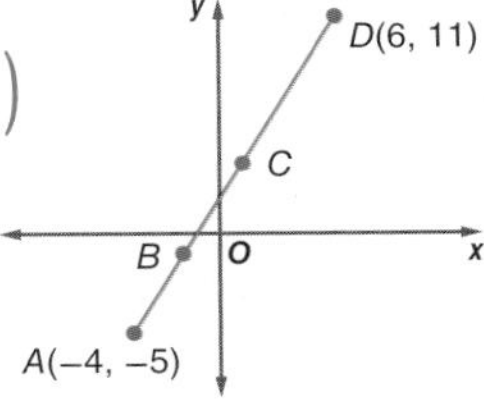

ALGEBRA **Determine the value(s) of n.**

64. $J(n, n + 2)$, $K(3n, n - 1)$, $JK = 5$ **±2**

65. $P(3n, n - 7)$, $Q(4n, n + 5)$, $PQ = 13$ **±5**

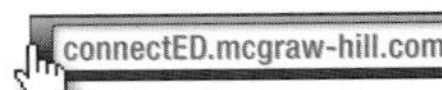

Teach with Tech

Spreadsheets Tell students that spreadsheets often use special commands to perform operations. For example, $\sqrt{x_2 - x_1}$ would be written as SQRT(A2,C2). To find the average of the numbers in a range of cells, use AVERAGE(range of cells). Use the symbol ^ to raise a number to a power.

CCSS Teaching the Mathematical Practices

Tools Mathematically proficient students consider available tools such as pencil and paper or technology to solve a problem. Point out to students that if a computer is not available, they can use the spreadsheet function on a graphing calculator.

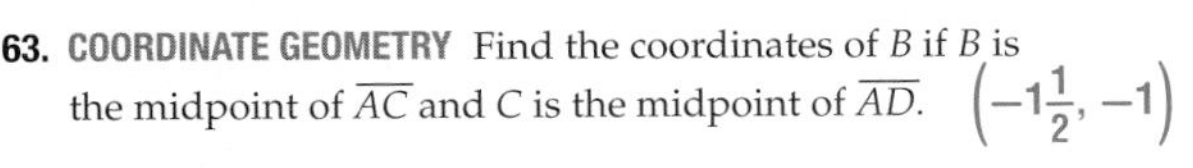

CCSS Teaching the Mathematical Practices

Perseverance Mathematically proficient students continually ask themselves, "does this make sense?" Point out to students that the latitude and longitude coordinates are analogous to the *x* and *y*-coordinates.

Multiple Representations

In Exercise 67, students use geometric figures, a table, and algebraic expressions, to investigate and conjecture about the relationship of the midpoint of the segment and the midpoint of the segment between the endpoint and the midpoint.

Tips for New Teachers

Challenge You may want to use a CHALLENGE problem, like Exercise 70, as a beginning-of-class exercise the day after the lesson is taught. This allows for an opener to homework discussion or a transition into the next lesson, and keeps students on task while daily "classroom maintenance" is performed.

Additional Answers

67a. Sample answer:

67b. Sample answer:

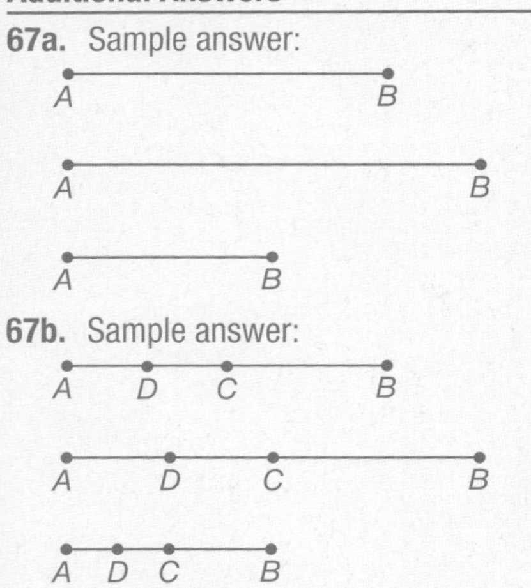

67c. Sample answer:

line	*AB* (cm)	*AC* (cm)	*AD* (cm)
1	4	2	1
2	6	3	1.5
3	3	1.5	0.75

66. CCSS **PERSEVERANCE** Wilmington, North Carolina, is located at (34.3°, 77.9°), which represents north latitude and west longitude. Winston-Salem is in the northern part of the state at (36.1°, 80.2°).

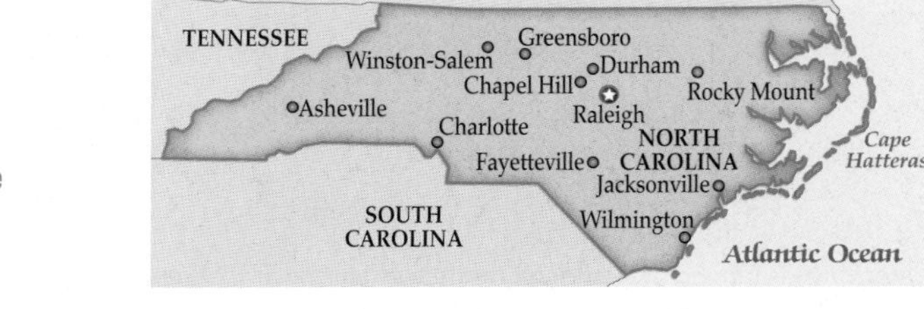

a. Find the latitude and longitude of the midpoint of the segment between Wilmington and Winston-Salem. **(35.2°, 79.1°)**

b. Use an atlas or the Internet to find a city near the location of the midpoint. **Sample answer: Fayetteville**

c. If Winston-Salem is the midpoint of the segment with one endpoint at Wilmington, find the latitude and longitude of the other endpoint. **(37.9°, 82.5°)**

d. Use an atlas or the Internet to find a city near the location of the other endpoint. **Sample answer: Prestonburg, Kentucky**

67. **MULTIPLE REPRESENTATIONS** In this problem, you will explore the relationship between a midpoint of a segment and the midpoint between the endpoint and the midpoint. **a–c. See margin.**

a. Geometric Use a straightedge to draw three different line segments. Label the endpoints *A* and *B*.

b. Geometric On each line segment, find the midpoint of $\overline{AB}$ and label it *C*. Then find the midpoint of $\overline{AC}$ and label it *D*.

c. Tabular Measure and record *AB*, *AC*, and *AD* for each line segment. Organize your results into a table.

d. Algebraic If $AB = x$, write an expression for the measures *AC* and *AD*. $AC = \frac{1}{2}x$, $AD = \frac{1}{4}x$

e. Verbal Make a conjecture about the relationship between *AB* and each segment if you were to continue to find the midpoints of a segment and a midpoint you previously found. **Sample answer: If *n* midpoints are found, then the smallest segment will have a measure of $\frac{1}{2^n}x$.**

72. Sample answer: Divide each coordinate of the endpoint that is not located at the origin by 2. For example, if the segment has coordinates (0, 0) and (−10, 6), the midpoint is located at $\left(\frac{-10}{2}, \frac{6}{2}\right)$ or (−5, 3). Using the midpoint formula, if the endpoints of the segment are (0, 0) and (*a*, *b*), the midpoint is $\left(\frac{a-0}{2}, \frac{b-0}{2}\right)$ or $\left(\frac{a}{2}, \frac{b}{2}\right)$.

H.O.T. Problems Use Higher-Order Thinking Skills

68. WRITING IN MATH Explain how the Pythagorean Theorem and the Distance Formula are related. **See margin.**

69. REASONING Is the point one third of the way from (x_1, y_1) to (x_2, y_2) *sometimes*, *always*, or *never* the point $\left(\frac{x_1 + x_2}{3}, \frac{y_1 + y_2}{3}\right)$? Explain. **Sample answer: Sometimes; when the point (x_1, y_1) has coordinates (0, 0).**

70. CHALLENGE Point *P* is located on the segment between point *A*(1, 4) and point *D*(7, 13). The distance from *A* to *P* is twice the distance from *P* to *D*. What are the coordinates of point *P*? **(5, 10)**

71. OPEN ENDED Draw a segment and name it $\overline{AB}$. Using only a compass and a straightedge, construct a segment $\overline{CD}$ such that $CD = 5\frac{1}{4}AB$. Explain and then justify your construction. **See margin.**

72. WRITING IN MATH Describe a method of finding the midpoint of a segment that has one endpoint at (0, 0). Give an example using your method, and explain why your method works.

68. Sample answer: The Pythagorean Theorem relates the lengths of the legs of a right triangle to the length of the hypotenuse using the formula $c^2 = a^2 + b^2$. If you take the square root of the formula, you get $c = \sqrt{a^2 + b^2}$. Think of the hypotenuse of the triangle as the distance between the two points, the *a* value as the horizontal distance $x_2 - x_1$, and the *b* value as the vertical distance $y_2 - y_1$. If you substitute, the Pythagorean Theorem becomes the Distance Formula, $c = \sqrt{(x_2 - x_1)^2 + (y_2 - y_1)^2}$.

Standardized Test Practice

73. Which of the following best describes the first step in bisecting $\overline{AB}$? **C**

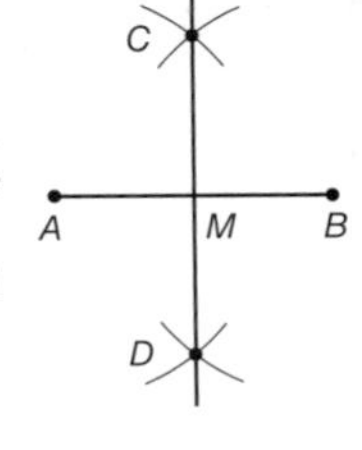

A From point A, draw equal arcs on $\overline{CD}$ using the same compass width.

B From point A, draw equal arcs above and below $\overline{AB}$ using a compass width of $\frac{1}{3}\overline{AB}$.

C From point A, draw equal arcs above and below $\overline{AB}$ using a compass width greater than $\frac{1}{2}\overline{AB}$.

D From point A, draw equal arcs above and below $\overline{AB}$ using a compass width less than $\frac{1}{2}\overline{AB}$.

74. ALGEBRA Beth paid \$74.88 for 3 pairs of jeans. All 3 pairs of jeans were the same price. How much did each pair of jeans cost? **F**

F \$24.96 **H** \$74.88
G \$37.44 **J** \$224.64

75. SAT/ACT If $5^{2x-3} = 1$, then $x =$ **C**

A 0.4 **D** 1.6
B 0.6 **E** 2
C 1.5

76. GRIDDED RESPONSE One endpoint of $\overline{AB}$ has coordinates $(-3, 5)$. If the coordinates of the midpoint of $\overline{AB}$ are $(2, -6)$, what is the approximate length of $\overline{AB}$? **24.2**

Spiral Review

Find the length of each object. (Lesson 1-2)

77. $2\frac{1}{8}$ **in.**

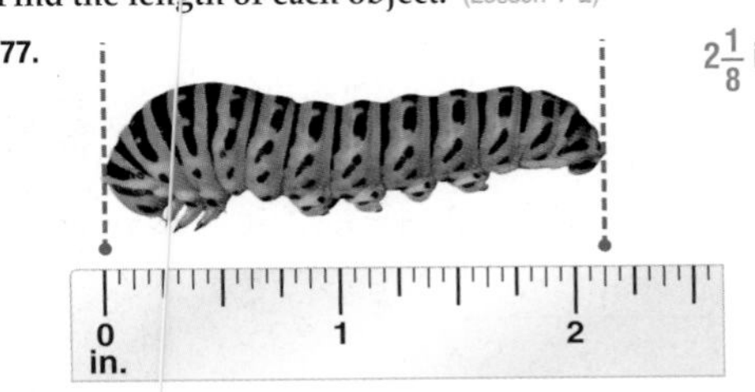

78. **38 mm or 3.8 cm**

Draw and label a figure for each relationship. (Lesson 1-1) **79–80. See margin.**

79. $\overleftrightarrow{FG}$ lies in plane M and contains point H.

80. Lines r and s intersect at point W.

81. TRUCKS A sport-utility vehicle has a maximum load limit of 75 pounds for its roof. You want to place a 38-pound cargo carrier and 4 pieces of luggage on top of the roof. Write and solve an inequality to find the average allowable weight for each piece of luggage. (Lesson 0-6) **$4x + 38 \leq 75$; 9.25 lb or less**

Skills Review

Solve each equation.

82. $8x - 15 = 5x$ **5**
83. $5y - 3 + y = 90$ **15.5**
84. $16a + 21 = 20a - 9$ **7.5**
85. $9k - 7 = 21 - 3k$ **$2\frac{1}{3}$**
86. $11z - 13 = 3z + 17$ **$3\frac{3}{4}$**
87. $15 + 6n = 4n + 23$ **4**

4 Assess

Yesterday's News Have students write a paragraph that explains how the lesson about linear measures helped them in the lesson about the Distance Formula, the Pythagorean Theorem, and the Midpoint Formula.

Additional Answers

79.

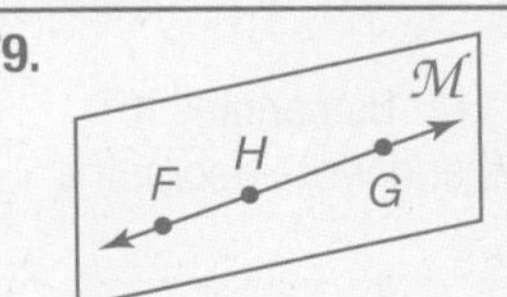

80.

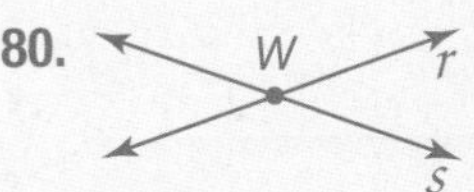

71. Sample answer:

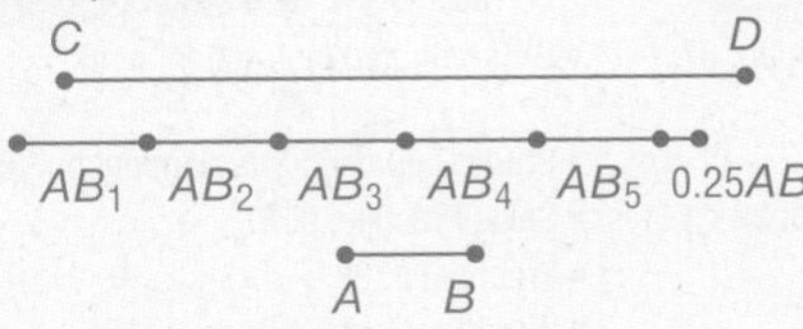

Draw $\overline{AB}$. Next, draw a construction line and place point C on it. From C, strike 6 arcs in succession of length AB. On the sixth $\overline{AB}$ length, perform a segment bisector two times to create a $\frac{1}{4}AB$ length. Label the endpoint D.

1 Focus

VerticalAlignment

Before Lesson 1-4 Measure line segments.

Lesson 1-4 Measure and classify angles. Identify and use congruent angles and the bisector of an angle.

After Lesson 1-4 Use angles to solve problems and write geometric proofs.

2 Teach

Scaffolding Questions

Have students read the **Why?** section of the lesson.

Ask:

- When is a miter joint typically used? A miter joint is typically used when a corner is built or when trim is applied to a corner.
- If the corner created by the two angles is perfect, what are the angles of the miter cuts? Each angle is 45°, creating a "perfect" right angle.
- Do the angles of the miter cuts always measure 45°? Explain. No. It is actually very uncommon for a corner to form a perfect right angle; therefore, miter cuts typically have angle measures other than 45°.

LESSON 1-4 Angle Measure

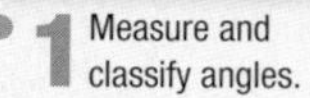

Then

- You measured line segments.

Now

1. Measure and classify angles.
2. Identify and use congruent angles and the bisector of an angle.

Why?

- One of the skills Dale must learn in carpentry class is how to cut a *miter* joint. This joint is created when two boards are cut at an angle to each other. He has learned that one miscalculation in angle measure can result in mitered edges that do not fit together.

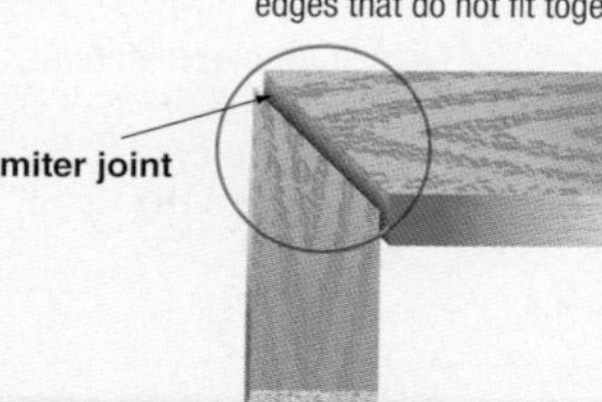

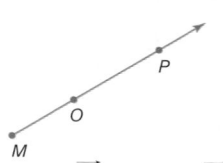

NewVocabulary

ray
opposite rays
angle
side
vertex
interior
exterior
degree
right angle
acute angle
obtuse angle
angle bisector

Common Core State Standards

Content Standards

G.CO.1 Know precise definitions of angle, circle, perpendicular line, parallel line, and line segment, based on the undefined notions of point, line, distance along a line, and distance around a circular arc.

G.CO.12 Make formal geometric constructions with a variety of tools and methods (compass and straightedge, string, reflective devices, paper folding, dynamic geometric software, etc.).

Mathematical Practices

5 Use appropriate tools strategically.

6 Attend to precision.

1 Measure and Classify Angles

A **ray** is a part of a line. It has one endpoint and extends indefinitely in one direction. Rays are named by stating the endpoint first and then any other point on the ray. The ray shown cannot be named as $\overrightarrow{OM}$ because O is not the endpoint of the ray.

M, O, P

ray MP, $\overrightarrow{MP}$, ray MO, or $\overrightarrow{MO}$

If you choose a point on a line, that point determines exactly two rays called **opposite rays**. Since both rays share a common endpoint, opposite rays are collinear

$\overrightarrow{JH}$ and $\overrightarrow{JK}$ are opposite rays.

An **angle** is formed by two *noncollinear* rays that have a common endpoint. The rays are called **sides** of the angle. The common endpoint is the **vertex**.

When naming angles using three letters, the vertex must be the second of the three letters. You can name an angle using a single letter only when there is exactly one angle located at that vertex. The angle shown can be named as $\angle X$, $\angle YXZ$, $\angle ZXY$, or $\angle 3$.

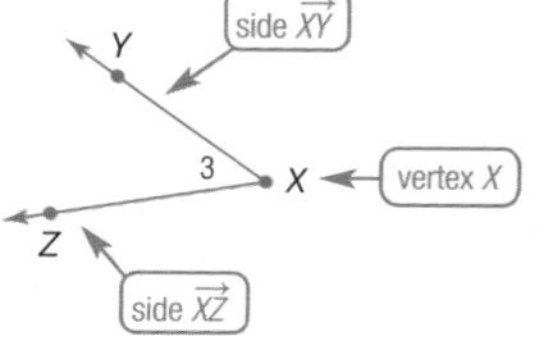

An angle divides a plane into three distinct parts.

- Points Q, M, and N lie on the angle.
- Points S and R lie in the **interior** of the angle.
- Points P and O lie in the **exterior** of the angle.

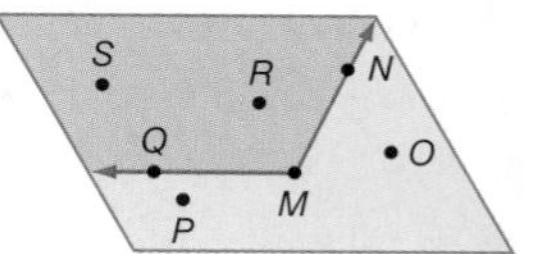

Lesson 1-4 Resources

Resource	Approaching Level AL	On Level OL	Beyond Level BL	English Learners ELL
Teacher Edition	▪ Differentiated Instruction, p. 37	▪ Differentiated Instruction, pp. 37, 39	▪ Differentiated Instruction, pp. 37, 39, 40	▪ Differentiated Instruction, p. 37
Chapter Resource Masters	▪ Study Guide and Intervention, pp. 25–26 ▪ Skills Practice, p. 27 ▪ Practice, p. 28 ▪ Word Problem Practice, p. 29	▪ Study Guide and Intervention, pp. 25–26 ▪ Skills Practice, p. 27 ▪ Practice, p. 28 ▪ Word Problem Practice, p. 29 ▪ Enrichment, p. 30	▪ Practice, p. 28 ▪ Word Problem Practice, p. 29 ▪ Enrichment, p. 30	▪ Study Guide and Intervention, pp. 25–26 ▪ Skills Practice, p. 27 ▪ Practice, p. 28 ▪ Word Problem Practice, p. 29
Other	▪ 5-Minute Check 1-4 ▪ Study Notebook ▪ Teaching Geometry with Manipulatives	▪ 5-Minute Check 1-4 ▪ Study Notebook ▪ Teaching Geometry with Manipulatives	▪ 5-Minute Check 1-4 ▪ Study Notebook	▪ 5-Minute Check 1-4 ▪ Study Notebook ▪ Teaching Geometry with Manipulatives

Real-World Example 1 Angles and Their Parts

MAPS **Use the map of a high school shown.**

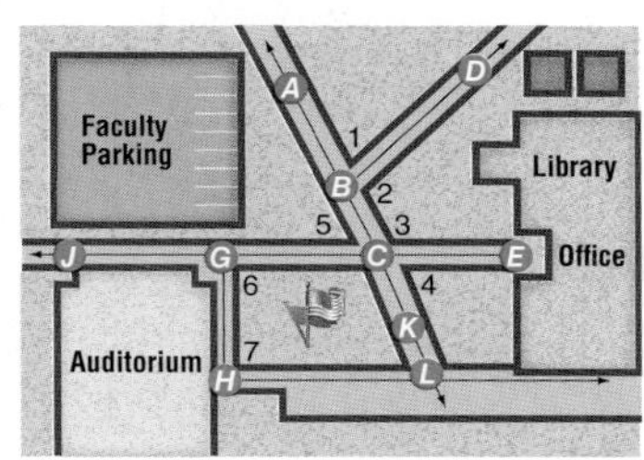

Faculty Parking
Library
Office
Auditorium

a. Name all angles that have *B* as a vertex.
∠1 or ∠*ABD*, and ∠2 or ∠*DBC*

b. Name the sides of ∠3.
$\overrightarrow{CA}$ and $\overline{CE}$ or $\overrightarrow{CB}$ and $\overline{CE}$

c. What is another name for ∠*GHL*?
∠7, ∠*H*, or ∠*LHG*

d. Name a point in the interior of ∠*DBK*.
Point *E*

StudyTip

Segments as Sides Because a ray can contain a line segment, the side of an angle can be a segment.

GuidedPractice

1A. What is the vertex of ∠5? **C**

1B. Name the sides of ∠5. **Sample answer: $\overrightarrow{CA}$ and $\overrightarrow{CJ}$**

1C. Write another name for ∠*ECL*. **∠LCE, ∠4, ∠ECK, or ∠KCE**

1D. Name a point in the exterior of ∠*CLH*. **Point D or E**

Angles are measured in units called degrees. The **degree** results from dividing the distance around a circle into 360 parts.

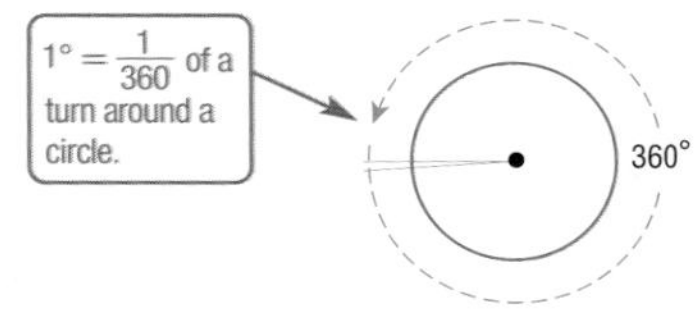

$1° = \frac{1}{360}$ of a turn around a circle.
360°

To measure an angle, you can use a *protractor*. Angle *DEF* below is a 50 degree (50°) angle. We say that the *degree measure* of ∠*DEF* is 50, or *m*∠*DEF* = 50.

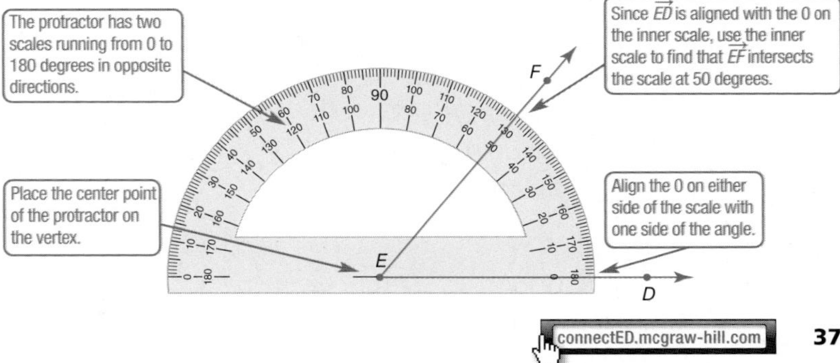

The protractor has two scales running from 0 to 180 degrees in opposite directions.
Since $\overrightarrow{ED}$ is aligned with the 0 on the inner scale, use the inner scale to find that $\overrightarrow{EF}$ intersects the scale at 50 degrees.
Place the center point of the protractor on the vertex.
Align the 0 on either side of the scale with one side of the angle.
F
E
D

1 Measure and Classify Angles

Example 1 shows how to name an angle and its parts. **Example 2** shows how to find the measures of angles and classify angles.

Formative Assessment

Use the Guided Practice exercises after each example to determine students' understanding of concepts.

Additional Example

1

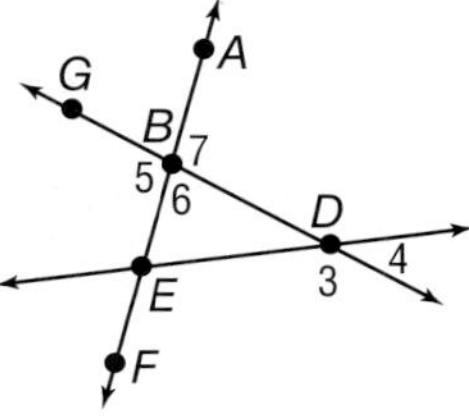

G
A
B
7
5
6
D
4
3
E
F

a. Name all angles that have *B* as a vertex. ∠5, ∠6, ∠7, ∠*ABG*

b. Name the sides of ∠5. $\overrightarrow{BG}$ and $\overrightarrow{BE}$ or $\overrightarrow{BF}$

c. Write another name for ∠6. ∠*EBD*, ∠*FBD*, ∠*DBF*, or ∠*DBE*

Additional Examples also in Interactive Classroom PowerPoint® Presentations

IWB Interactive White Board READY

Tips for New Teachers

Estimation Encourage students to estimate angle measures before measuring with a protractor. This will help them choose the correct scale on the protractor.

DifferentiatedInstruction AL OL BL ELL

Auditory/Musical Learners A metronome is a tool used to keep a constant tempo in music. It is composed of a pendulum that swings back and forth at varying speeds. The fulcrum of the pendulum acts as a vertex of the angle through which the pendulum swings. Demonstrate this by holding two pens at an angle in one hand and tapping another pen between the first two, creating a series of "ticks."

Key Concept boxes highlight definitions, formulas, and other important ideas. Multiple representations—words, symbols, examples, models—aid students' understanding.

Additional Example

2 Copy the diagram below, and extend each ray. Classify each angle as *right*, *acute*, or *obtuse*. Then use a protractor to measure the angle to the nearest degree.

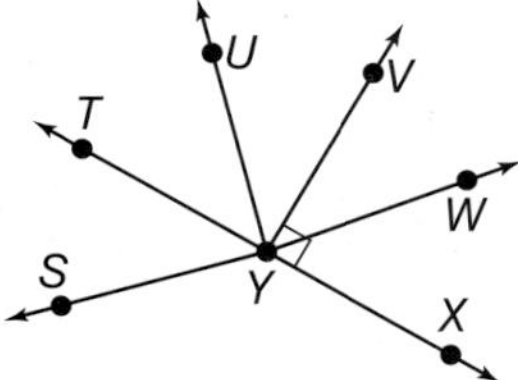

a. $\angle TYV$ 90, right

b. $\angle WYT$ 130, obtuse

c. $\angle TYU$ 45, acute

Tips for New Teachers

Patty Paper Students can use patty paper to copy diagrams that they need to measure. Patty papers are the squares of paper used to separate hamburger patties. You can also use waxed paper or tracing paper.

WatchOut!

Protractor It is common for students to misread a protractor because the rays of the angle are misaligned. Be sure to stress to students that to read the angle measure directly from the protractor, one ray must be exactly aligned with the 0 line, not the bottom of the protractor.

ReadingMath

Straight Angle Opposite rays with the same vertex form a *straight angle*. Its measure is 180. Unless otherwise specified in this book, however, the term *angle* means a nonstraight angle.

Angles can be classified by their measures as shown below.

KeyConcept Classify Angles

right angle	acute angle	obtuse angle
A (This symbol means a 90° angle.)	B	C
$m\angle A = 90$	$m\angle B < 90$	$180 > m\angle C > 90$

Example 2 Measure and Classify Angles

Copy the diagram below, and extend each ray. Classify each angle as *right*, *acute*, or *obtuse*. Then use a protractor to measure the angle to the nearest degree.

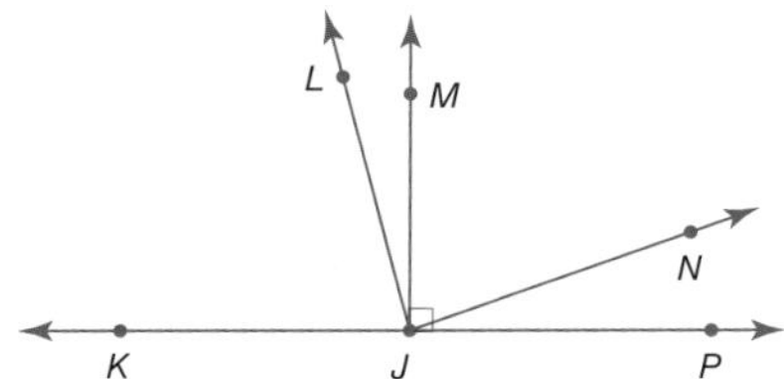

a. $\angle MJP$

$\angle MJP$ is marked as a right angle, so $m\angle MJP = 90$.

b. $\angle LJP$

Point L on angle $\angle LJP$ lies on the exterior of right angle $\angle MJP$, so $\angle LJP$ is an obtuse angle. Use a protractor to find that $m\angle LJP = 105$

CHECK Since $105 > 90$, $\angle LJP$ is an obtuse angle. ✓

c. $\angle NJP$

Point N on angle $\angle NJP$ lies on the interior of right angle $\angle MJP$, so $\angle NJP$ is an acute angle. Use a protractor to find that $m\angle NJP = 20$.

CHECK Since $20 < 90$, $\angle NJP$ is an acute angle. ✓

WatchOut!

Classify Before Measuring Classifying an angle before measuring it can prevent you from choosing the wrong scale on your protractor. In Example 2b, you must decide whether $\angle LJP$ measures 75 or 105. Since $\angle LJP$ is an obtuse angle, you can reason that the correct measure must be 105.

GuidedPractice

2A. $\angle AFB$ **acute; 20**

2B. $\angle CFA$ **right; 90**

2C. $\angle AFD$ **obtuse; 115**

2D. $\angle CFD$ **acute; 25**

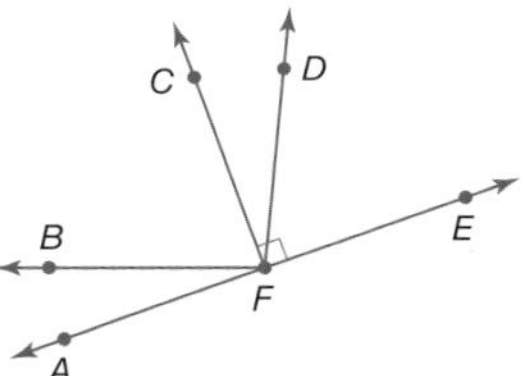

Focus on Mathematical Content

Measuring Angles Encourage students to extend the rays of angles beyond the protractor's edge when measuring. This will eliminate guesswork and ensure accurate angle measures.

Teach with Tech

Document Camera Choose a student to work through an example showing how to use a protractor to measure an angle. Be sure the student explains how he or she decided whether to read the inside or outside scale of the protractor.

2 Congruent Angles

Just as segments that have the same measure are congruent segments, angles that have the same measure are *congruent angles*.

In the figure, since $m\angle ABC = m\angle FED$, then $\angle ABC \cong \angle FED$. Matching numbers of arcs on a figure also indicate congruent angles, so $\angle CBE \cong \angle DEB$.

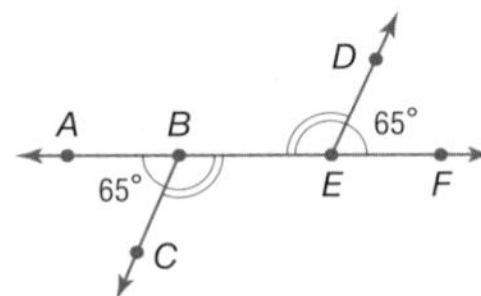

You can produce an angle congruent to a given angle using a construction.

Construction Copy an Angle

Step 1 Draw an angle like $\angle B$ on your paper. Use a straightedge to draw a ray on your paper. Label its endpoint G.

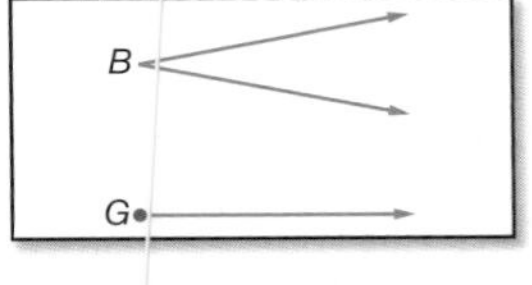

Step 2 Place the tip of the compass at point B and draw a large arc that intersects both sides of $\angle B$. Label the points of intersection A and C.

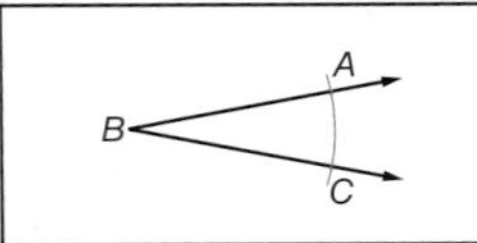

Step 3 Using the same compass setting, put the compass at point G and draw a large arc that starts above the ray and intersects the ray. Label the point of intersection H.

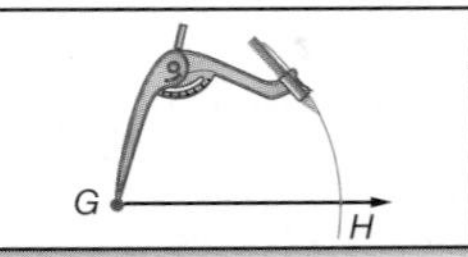

Step 4 Place the point of your compass on C and adjust so that the pencil tip is on A.

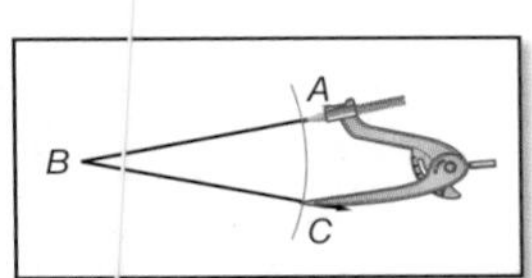

Step 5 Without changing the setting, place the compass at point H and draw an arc to intersect the larger arc you drew in Step 4. Label the point of intersection F.

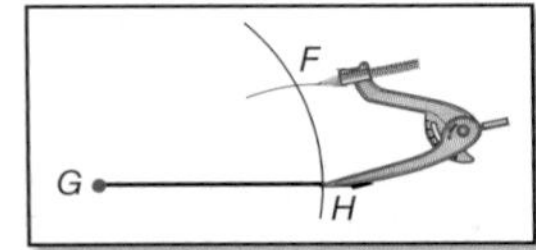

Step 6 Use a straightedge to draw $\overrightarrow{GF}$. $\angle ABC \cong \angle FGH$

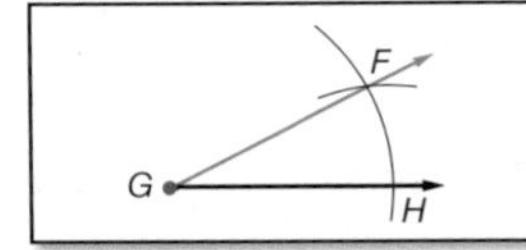

StudyTip
Segments A line segment can also bisect an angle.

A ray that divides an angle into two congruent angles is called an **angle bisector**. If $\overrightarrow{YW}$ is the angle bisector of $\angle XYZ$, then point W lies in the interior of $\angle XYZ$ and $\angle XYW \cong \angle WYZ$.

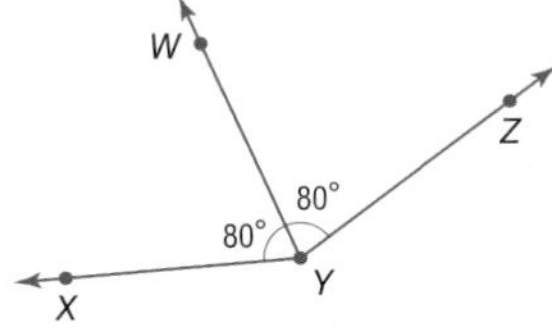

Just as with segments, when a line, segment, or ray divides an angle into smaller angles, the sum of the measures of the smaller angles equals the measure of the largest angle. So in the figure, $m\angle XYW + m\angle WYZ = m\angle XYZ$.

2 Congruent Angles

Angles that have the same measure are congruent. **Example 3** shows how to find congruent angles.

Get Animated activities are online illustrations of key concepts through animations, Interactive Labs, and BrainPOPs®.

Tips for New Teachers

Enlarge Figures Some students may feel they need to draw figures as small as they see them printed in the book. Encourage students to use a whole piece of paper for the construction. Draw the angle so that it takes up much of the top half of the paper. Then they can construct the copy on the bottom half. Working with larger figures also makes working with a compass easier.

Focus on Mathematical Content

Connections Relate new content to what students have previously learned. For example, relate angle vocabulary to that used with segments. Just as line segments with equal lengths are congruent, angles with equal measures are congruent, and the symbol used to denote this relationship for both segments and angles is ≅. Likewise, as the bisector divides a line segment into two equal segments; the angle bisector divides an angle into two equal angles.

Differentiated Instruction OL BL

Extension Tell students that $\angle RPQ$ and $\angle QPS$ are adjacent angles.

Ask:

- What three things must be true of adjacent angles? Adjacent angles must share a vertex and a side. Also, adjacent angles must not share any interior points.

Additional Example

3 INTERIOR DESIGN Wall stickers of standard shapes are often used to provide a stimulating environment for a young child's room. A five-pointed star sticker is shown with vertices labeled. Find $m\angle GBH$ and $m\angle HCI$ if $\angle GBH \cong \angle HCI$, $m\angle GBH = 2x + 5$, and $m\angle HCI = 3x - 10$.

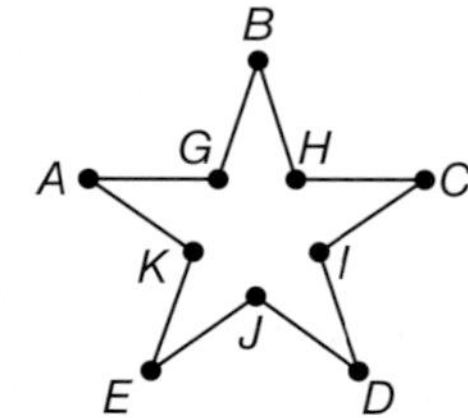

$m\angle GBH = 35$, $m\angle HCI = 35$

Example 3 Measure and Classify Angles

PT

ALGEBRA In the figure, $\overrightarrow{KJ}$ and $\overrightarrow{KM}$ are opposite rays, and $\overrightarrow{KN}$ bisects $\angle JKL$. If $m\angle JKN = 8x - 13$ and $m\angle NKL = 6x + 11$, find $m\angle JKN$.

Step 1 Solve for x.

Since $\overrightarrow{KN}$ bisects $\angle JKL$, $\angle JKN \cong \angle NKL$.

$m\angle JKN = m\angle NKL$	Definition of congruent angles
$8x - 13 = 6x + 11$	Substitution
$8x = 6x + 24$	Add 13 to each side.
$2x = 24$	Subtract $6x$ from each side.
$x = 12$	Divide each side by 2.

Step 2 Use the value of x to find $m\angle JKN$.

$m\angle JKN = 8x - 13$	Given
$= 8(12) - 13$	$x = 12$
$= 96 - 13$ or 83	Simplify.

StudyTip

Checking Solutions Check that you have computed the value of x correctly by substituting the value into the expression for $\angle NKL$. If you don't get the same measure as $\angle JKN$, you have made an error.

GuidedPractice

3. Suppose $m\angle JKL = 9y + 15$ and $m\angle JKN = 5y + 2$. Find $m\angle JKL$. **114**

You can produce the angle bisector of any angle without knowing the measure of the angle.

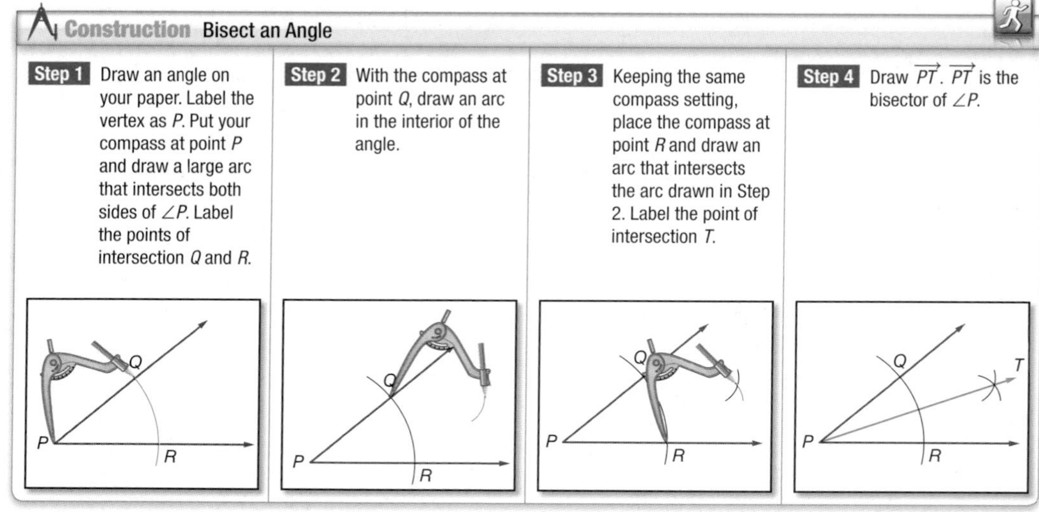

Construction Bisect an Angle

Step 1 Draw an angle on your paper. Label the vertex as P. Put your compass at point P and draw a large arc that intersects both sides of $\angle P$. Label the points of intersection Q and R.

Step 2 With the compass at point Q, draw an arc in the interior of the angle.

Step 3 Keeping the same compass setting, place the compass at point R and draw an arc that intersects the arc drawn in Step 2. Label the point of intersection T.

Step 4 Draw $\overrightarrow{PT}$. $\overrightarrow{PT}$ is the bisector of $\angle P$.

Differentiated Instruction BL

Extension Challenge students to draw a connection between angle measure and slope. Have them investigate the angles formed between lines through the origin and the x-axis using a variety of slopes.

Check Your Understanding

 = Step-by-Step Solutions begin on page R14. 

Example 1 **Use the figure at the right.**

1. Name the vertex of ∠4. U
2. Name the sides of ∠3. $\overrightarrow{XW}$, $\overrightarrow{XU}$
3. What is another name for ∠2? ∠XYU, ∠UYX
4. What is another name for ∠UXY? ∠1, ∠YXU

Example 2 **Copy the diagram shown, and extend each ray. Classify each angle as *right*, *acute*, or *obtuse*. Then use a protractor to measure the angle to the nearest degree.**

5. ∠CFD acute; 40
6. ∠AFD obtuse; 150
7. ∠BFC right; 90
8. ∠AFB acute; 25

Example 3 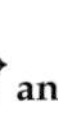 **ALGEBRA** **In the figure, $\overrightarrow{KJ}$ and $\overrightarrow{KL}$ are opposite rays. $\overrightarrow{KN}$ bisects ∠LKM.**

9. If $m\angle LKM = 7x - 5$ and $m\angle NKM = 3x + 9$, find $m\angle LKM$. 156
10. If $m\angle NKL = 7x - 9$ and $m\angle JKM = x + 3$, find $m\angle JKN$. 98

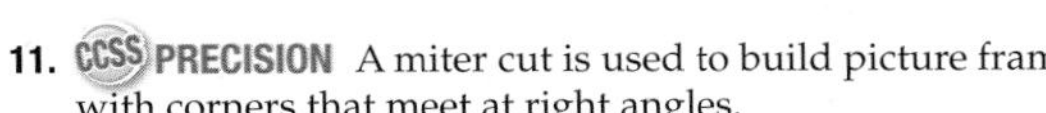

11. **CCSS PRECISION** A miter cut is used to build picture frames with corners that meet at right angles.
    a. José miters the ends of some wood for a picture frame at congruent angles. What is the degree measure of his cut? Explain and classify the angle.
    b. What does the joint represent in relation to the angle formed by the two pieces? The joint is the angle bisector of the frame angle.

11a. 45; When joined together, the angles form a right angle, which measures 90. If the two angles that form this right angle are congruent, then the measure of each angle is 90 ÷ 2 or 45. The angle of the cut is an acute angle.

Practice and Problem Solving

Extra Practice is on page R1.

Example 1 **For Exercises 12–29, use the figure at the right.**

Name the vertex of each angle.

12. ∠4 Q
13. ∠7 P
14. ∠2 R
15. ∠1 M

Name the sides of each angle.

16. ∠TPQ $\overrightarrow{PT}$, $\overrightarrow{PQ}$
17. ∠VNM $\overrightarrow{NV}$, $\overrightarrow{NM}$
18. ∠6 $\overrightarrow{NM}$, $\overrightarrow{NR}$
19. ∠3 $\overrightarrow{RP}$, $\overrightarrow{RQ}$

Write another name for each angle.

20. ∠9 ∠MRS, ∠SRM
21. ∠QPT ∠TPQ
22. ∠MQS
23. ∠5

23. ∠TPN, ∠NPT, ∠TPM, ∠MPT

22. ∠4, ∠SQM, ∠MQR, ∠RQM, ∠NQS, ∠SQN, ∠NQR, ∠RQN, ∠PQR, ∠RQP, ∠PQS, ∠SQP

24. Name an angle with vertex N that appears obtuse. Sample answer: ∠VNQ
25. Name an angle with vertex Q that appears acute. ∠4
26. Name a point in the interior of ∠VRQ. P, T
27. Name a point in the exterior of ∠MRT. S, Q
28. Name a pair of angles that share exactly one point. Sample answer: ∠6, ∠8
29. Name a pair of angles that share more than one point. Sample answer: ∠MPR, ∠PRQ

3 Practice

Formative Assessment

Use Exercises 1–11 to check for understanding.

Then use the chart at the bottom of the page to customize assignments for your students.

Teaching the Mathematical Practices

Precision Mathematically proficient students communicate precisely to others. In Exercise 11, encourage students to use clear definitions for the mathematical terms used.

Differentiated Homework Options

Level	Assignment	Two-Day Option	
AL Basic	12–42, 49, 51–75	13–41 odd, 54–57	12–42 even, 49, 51, 53, 58–75
OL Core	13–41 odd, 43–49, 51, 53–75	12–42, 54–57	43–49, 51, 53, 58–75
BL Advanced	43–69, (optional: 70–75)		

Example 2 Copy the diagram shown, and extend each ray. Classify each angle as *right, acute,* or *obtuse.* Then use a protractor to measure the angle to the nearest degree.

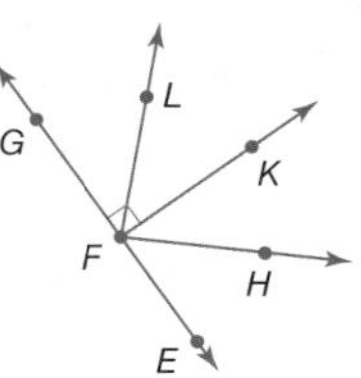

30. $\angle GFK$ **90, right**
31. $\angle EFK$ **90, right**
32. $\angle LFK$ **45, acute**
33. $\angle EFH$ **45, acute**
34. $\angle GFH$ **135, obtuse**
35. $\angle EFL$ **135, obtuse**

36. **CLOCKS** Determine at least three different times during the day when the hands on a clock form each of the following angles. Explain. **See margin.**
 a. right angle
 b. obtuse angle
 c. congruent acute angles

Example 3 **ALGEBRA** In the figure, $\overrightarrow{BA}$ and $\overrightarrow{BC}$ are opposite rays. $\overrightarrow{BH}$ bisects $\angle EBC$.

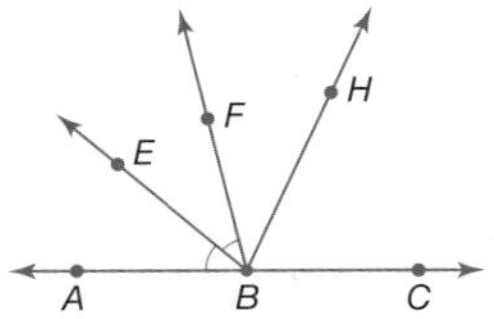

37. If $m\angle ABE = 2n + 7$ and $m\angle EBF = 4n - 13$, find $m\angle ABE$. **27**
38. If $m\angle EBH = 6x + 12$ and $m\angle HBC = 8x - 10$, find $m\angle EBH$. **78**
39. If $m\angle ABF = 7b - 24$ and $m\angle ABE = 2b$, find $m\angle EBF$. **16**
40. If $m\angle EBC = 31a - 2$ and $m\angle EBH = 4a + 45$, find $m\angle HBC$. **61**
41. If $m\angle ABF = 8s - 6$ and $m\angle ABE = 2(s + 11)$, find $m\angle EBF$. **47**
42. If $m\angle EBC = 3r + 10$ and $m\angle ABE = 2r - 20$, find $m\angle EBF$. **56**

B 43. **MAPS** Estimate the measure of the angle formed by each city or location listed, the North Pole, and the Prime Meridian.
 a. Nuuk, Greenland **about 50**
 b. Fairbanks, Alaska **about 140**
 c. Reykjavik, Iceland **about 20**
 d. Prime Meridian **0**

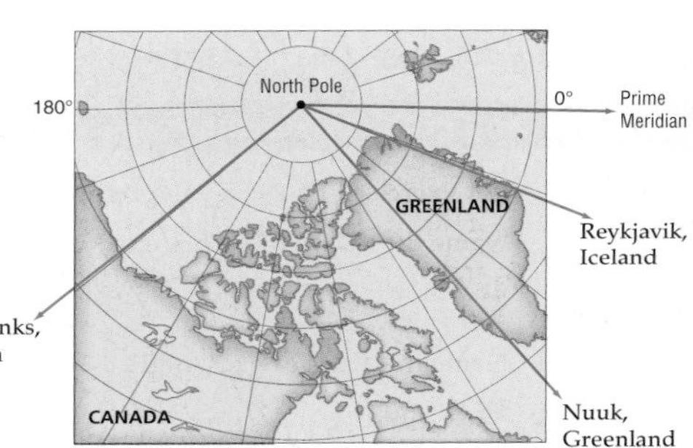

44. **CCSS TOOLS** A compass rose is a design on a map that shows directions. In addition to the directions of north, south, east, and west, a compass rose can have as many as 32 markings.
 a. With the center of the compass as its vertex, what is the measure of the angle between due west and due north? **90**
 b. What is the measure of the angle between due north and north-west? **45**
 c. How does the north-west ray relate to the angle in part **a**? **It is the angle bisector.**

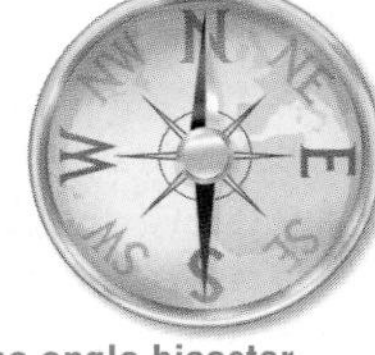

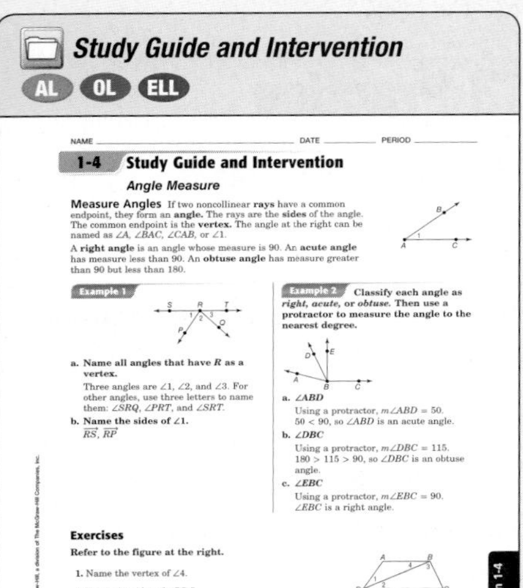

Study Guide and Intervention
AL OL ELL

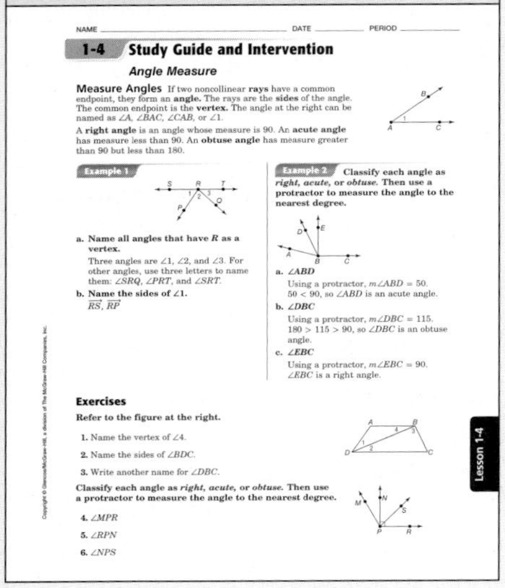

NAME ______ DATE ______ PERIOD ______

1-4 Study Guide and Intervention
Angle Measure

Measure Angles If two noncollinear **rays** have a common endpoint, they form an **angle.** The rays are the **sides** of the angle. The common endpoint is the **vertex.** The angle at the right can be named as $\angle A$, $\angle BAC$, $\angle CAB$, or $\angle 1$.

A **right angle** is an angle whose measure is 90. An **acute angle** has measure less than 90. An **obtuse angle** has measure greater than 90 but less than 180.

Example 1

a. **Name all angles that have *R* as a vertex.**
 Three angles are $\angle 1$, $\angle 2$, and $\angle 3$. For other angles, use three letters to name them: $\angle SRQ$, $\angle PRT$, and $\angle SRT$.

b. **Name the sides of $\angle 1$.**
 $\overrightarrow{RS}$, $\overrightarrow{RP}$

Example 2 **Classify each angle as *right, acute,* or *obtuse.* Then use a protractor to measure the angle to the nearest degree.**

a. $\angle ABD$
 Using a protractor, $m\angle ABD = 50$. $50 < 90$, so $\angle ABD$ is an acute angle.
b. $\angle DBC$
 Using a protractor, $m\angle DBC = 115$. $180 > 115 > 90$, so $\angle DBC$ is an obtuse angle.
c. $\angle EBC$
 Using a protractor, $m\angle EBC = 90$. $\angle EBC$ is a right angle.

Exercises

Refer to the figure at the right.

1. Name the vertex of $\angle 4$.
2. Name the sides of $\angle BDC$.
3. Write another name for $\angle DBC$.

Classify each angle as *right, acute,* or *obtuse.* Then use a protractor to measure the angle to the nearest degree.

4. $\angle MPR$
5. $\angle RPN$
6. $\angle NPS$

Lesson 1-4

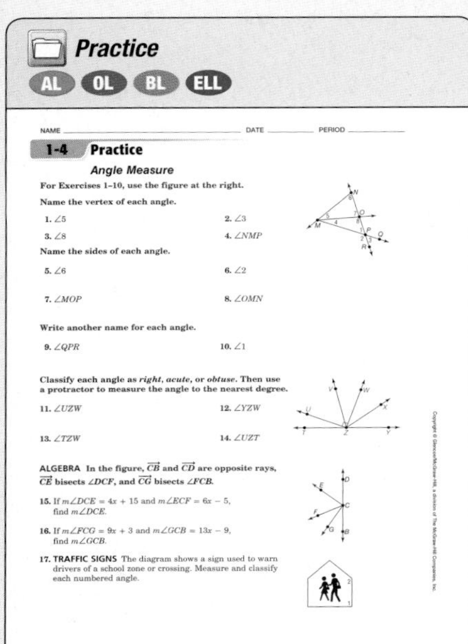

Practice
AL OL BL ELL

NAME ______ DATE ______ PERIOD ______

1-4 Practice
Angle Measure

For Exercises 1–10, use the figure at the right.

Name the vertex of each angle.

1. $\angle 5$
2. $\angle 3$
3. $\angle 8$
4. $\angle NMP$

Name the sides of each angle.

5. $\angle 6$
6. $\angle 2$
7. $\angle MOP$
8. $\angle OMN$

Write another name for each angle.

9. $\angle QPR$
10. $\angle 1$

Classify each angle as *right, acute,* or *obtuse.* Then use a protractor to measure the angle to the nearest degree.

11. $\angle UZW$
12. $\angle YZW$
13. $\angle TZW$
14. $\angle UZT$

ALGEBRA In the figure, $\overrightarrow{CB}$ and $\overrightarrow{CD}$ are opposite rays, $\overrightarrow{CE}$ bisects $\angle DCF$, and $\overrightarrow{CG}$ bisects $\angle FCB$.

15. If $m\angle DCE = 4x + 15$ and $m\angle ECF = 6x - 5$, find $m\angle DCE$.
16. If $m\angle FCG = 9x + 3$ and $m\angle GCB = 13x - 9$, find $m\angle GCB$.
17. **TRAFFIC SIGNS** The diagram shows a sign used to warn drivers of a school zone or crossing. Measure and classify each numbered angle.

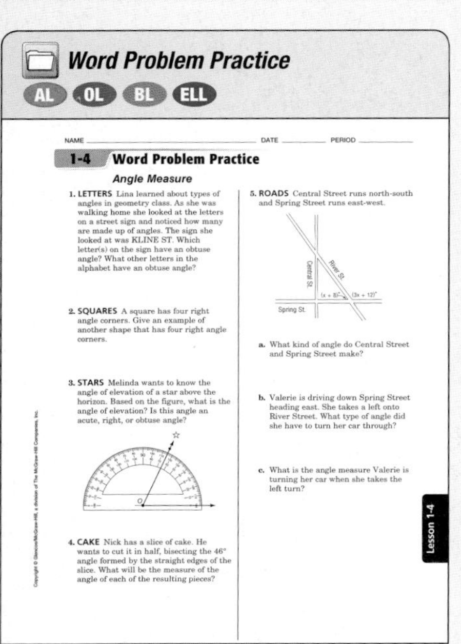

Word Problem Practice
AL OL BL ELL

NAME ______ DATE ______ PERIOD ______

1-4 Word Problem Practice
Angle Measure

1. **LETTERS** Lina learned about types of angles in geometry class. As she was walking home she looked at the letters on a street sign and noticed how many are made up of angles. The sign she looked at was KLINE ST. Which letter(s) on the sign have an obtuse angle? What other letters in the alphabet have an obtuse angle?

2. **SQUARES** A square has four right angle corners. Give an example of another shape that has four right angle corners.

3. **STARS** Melinda wants to know the angle of elevation of a star above the horizon. Based on the figure, what is the angle of elevation? Is this angle an acute, right, or obtuse angle?

4. **CAKE** Nick has a slice of cake. He wants to cut it in half, bisecting the 46° angle formed by the straight edges of the slice. What will be the measure of the angle of each of the resulting pieces?

5. **ROADS** Central Street runs north-south and Spring Street runs east-west.
 Central St.
 River St.
 Spring St.
 $(x + 8)°$
 $(3x + 12)°$
 a. What kind of angle do Central Street and Spring Street make?
 b. Valerie is driving down Spring Street heading east. She takes a left onto River Street. What type of angle did she have to turn her car through?
 c. What is the angle measure Valerie is turning her car when she takes the left turn?

Lesson 1-4

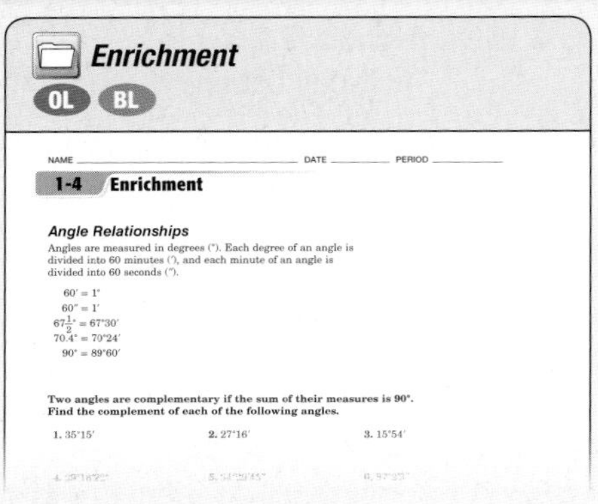

Enrichment
OL BL

NAME ______ DATE ______ PERIOD ______

1-4 Enrichment

Angle Relationships

Angles are measured in degrees (°). Each degree of an angle is divided into 60 minutes (′), and each minute of an angle is divided into 60 seconds (″).

$60' = 1°$
$60'' = 1'$
$67\frac{1}{2}° = 67°30'$
$70.4° = 70°24'$
$90° = 89°60'$

Two angles are complementary if the sum of their measures is 90°. Find the complement of each of the following angles.

1. 35°15′
2. 27°16′
3. 15°54′

Additional Answers

36a. Sample answer: 3:00, 6:16, 9:00; The angle measures at these times are 90°, which is the measure of a right angle.

36b. Sample answer: 4:00, 5:00, 7:00, 8:00; The angle measures at these times are greater than 90, or obtuse angles.

36c. Sample answer: 1:00, 2:06, 11:00; The angle measures at these times are all equal to each other or congruent and less than 90, or acute angles.

47c. about 15; If the original path of the light is extended, the measure of the angle the original path makes with the refracted path represents the number of degrees the path of the light changed. The sum of the measure of this angle and the $m\angle 3$ is 180. The measure of $\angle 3$ is $360 - (110 + 85)$ or 165, so the measure of the angle the original path makes with the refracted path is $180 - 165$ or 15.

Plot the points in a coordinate plane and sketch $\angle XYZ$. Then classify it as *right*, *acute*, or *obtuse*. **45–46. See margin.**

45. $X(5, -3)$, $Y(4, -1)$, $Z(6, -2)$

46. $X(6, 7)$, $Y(2, 3)$, $Z(4, 1)$

47 **PHYSICS** When you look at a pencil in water, it looks bent. This illusion is due to *refraction*, or the bending of light when it moves from one substance to the next.

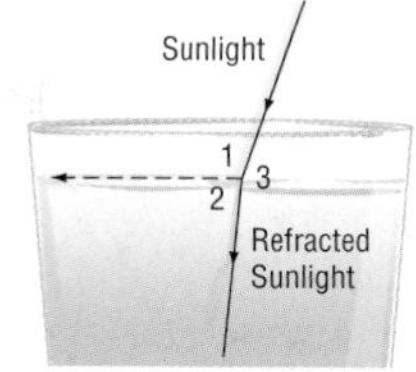

a. What is $m\angle 1$? Classify this angle as *acute*, *right*, or *obtuse*. **about 110; obtuse**

b. What is $m\angle 2$? Classify this angle as *acute*, *right*, or *obtuse*. **about 85; acute**

c. Without measuring, determine how many degrees the path of the light changes after it enters the water. Explain your reasoning.

48. **MULTIPLE REPRESENTATIONS** In this problem, you will explore the relationship of angles that compose opposite rays. **a–c. See margin.**

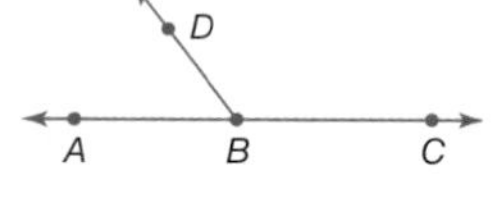

a. **Geometric** Draw four lines, each with points A, B, and C. Draw $\overrightarrow{BD}$ for each line, varying the placement of point D. Use a protractor to measure $\angle ABD$ and $\angle DBC$ for each figure.

b. **Tabular** Organize the measures for each figure into a table. Include a row in your table to record the sum of these measures.

c. **Verbal** Make a conjecture about the sum of the measures of the two angles. Explain your reasoning.

d. **Algebraic** If x is the measure of $\angle ABD$ and y is the measure of $\angle DBC$, write an equation that relates the two angle measures. $x + y = 180$

H.O.T. Problems Use Higher-Order Thinking Skills

49. OPEN ENDED Draw an obtuse angle named ABC. Measure $\angle ABC$. Construct an angle bisector $\overrightarrow{BD}$ of $\angle ABC$. Explain the steps in your construction and justify each step. Classify the two angles formed by the angle bisector. **See margin.**

50. CHALLENGE Describe how you would use a protractor to measure the angle shown. **Sample answer: Measure the acute angle and subtract this measure from 360, a full circle.**

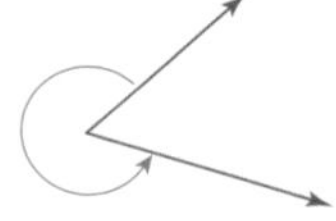

51. **CCSS ARGUMENTS** The sum of two acute angles is *sometimes*, *always*, or *never* an obtuse angle. Explain. **See margin.**

52. CHALLENGE $\overrightarrow{MP}$ bisects $\angle LMN$, $\overrightarrow{MQ}$ bisects $\angle LMP$, and $\overrightarrow{MR}$ bisects $\angle QMP$. If $m\angle RMP = 21$, find $m\angle LMN$. Explain your reasoning. **See margin.**

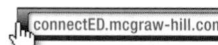

53. WRITING IN MATH Rashid says that he can estimate the measure of an acute angle using a piece of paper to within six degrees of accuracy. Explain how this would be possible. Then use this method to estimate the measure of the angle shown. **See Ch. 1 Answer Appendix.**

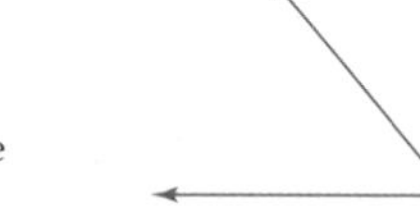

Multiple Representations

In Exercise 48, students will explore angles that compose opposite rays and determine that the angles are supplementary.

Teaching the Mathematical Practices

Arguments Mathematically proficient students are able to recognize and use counterexamples. In Exercise 51, encourage students to draw diagrams to represent the different cases.

Additional Answers

45. acute

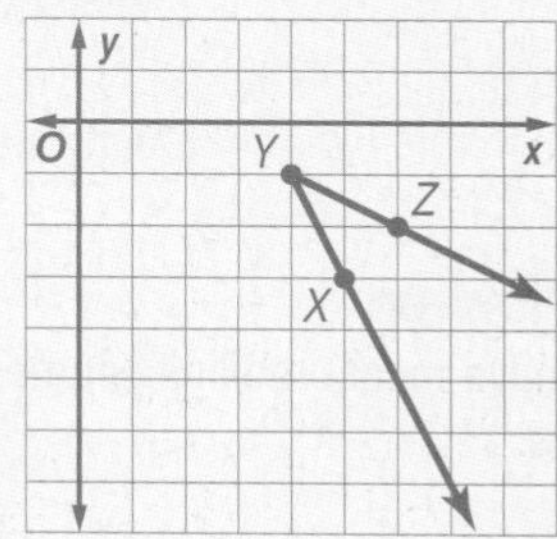

46. right

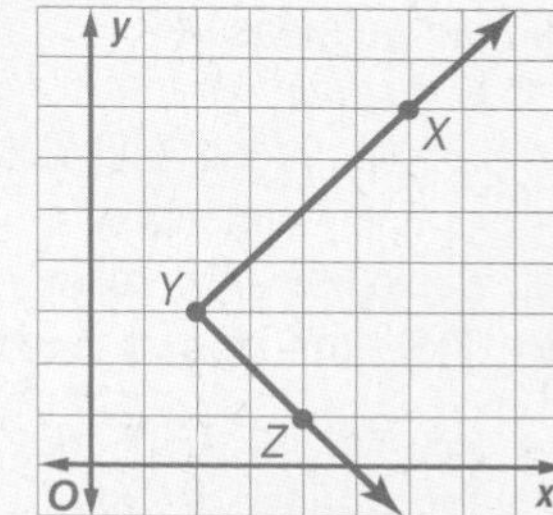

48a. Sample answer:

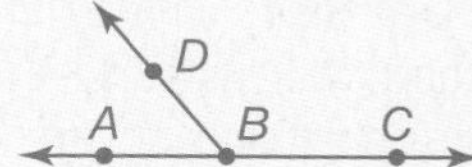

48b. Sample answer:

Angle	Measure
$\angle ABD$	50
$\angle DBC$	130
Sum	180

48c. Sample answer: The sum of the measures of the two angles will always be 180. Point B determines opposite rays $\overrightarrow{AB}$ and $\overrightarrow{BC}$, which form a line. Angles that form a straight line measure 180.

49. The two angles formed are acute angles. Sample answer: With my compass at point A, I drew an arc in the interior of the angle. With the same compass setting, I drew an arc from point C that intersected the arc from point A. From the vertex, I drew $\overrightarrow{BD}$. I used the same compass setting to draw the intersecting arcs, so $\overrightarrow{BD}$ divides $\angle ABC$ so that the measurement of $\angle ABD$ and $\angle DBC$ are equal. Therefore, $\overrightarrow{BD}$ bisects $\angle ABC$.

51. Sometimes; sample answer: For example, if you add an angle measure of 4 and an angle measure of 6, you will have an angle measure of 10, which is still acute. But if you add angles with measure of 50 and 60, you will have an obtuse angle with a measure of 110.

52. 168; If $m\angle RMP = 21$ and $\overrightarrow{MR}$ bisects $\angle QMP$, then $m\angle QMP = 2(21)$ or 42. If $m\angle QMP = 42$ and $\overrightarrow{MQ}$ bisects $\angle LMP$, then $m\angle LMP = 2(42)$ or 84. If $m\angle LMP = 84$ and $\overrightarrow{MP}$ bisects $\angle LMN$, then $m\angle LMN = 2(84)$ or 168.

4 Assess

Crystal Ball Have students write how Lesson 1-4 on angle measures will help them predict angle relationships.

Formative Assessment

Check for student understanding of concepts in Lessons 1-3 and 1-4.

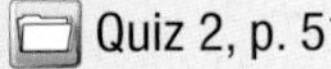 Quiz 2, p. 51

Additional Answer

55. Sample answer: Leticia's survey does not represent the entire student body because she did not take a random sample; she only took a sample of students from one major.

Follow-up

Students have measured line segments and angles.

Ask:

- How does *what* we measure influence *how* we measure? Sample answer: What we measure influences the type of tool that is used. For example, to measure an angle, you would use a protractor. To measure a line segment, you could use a ruler.

  Another factor to consider is the size of the object being measured. For example, to measure something very small or short, you could use a ruler. To measure something large or long, you could use a tape measure.

Standardized Test Practice

54. Which of the following angles measures closest to 60°? B

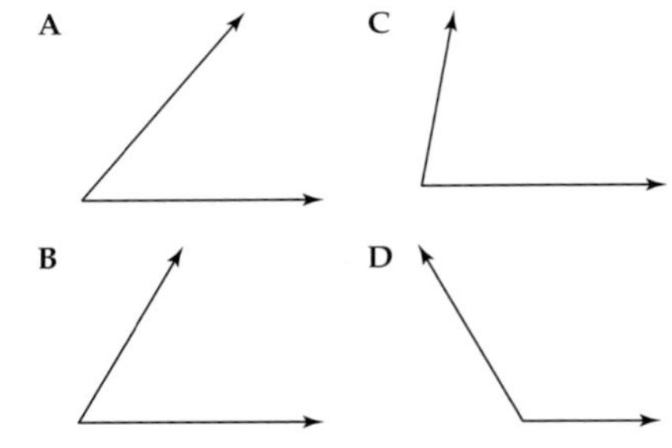

55. SHORT RESPONSE Leticia surveyed 50 English majors at a university to see if the school should play jazz music in the cafeteria during lunch. The school has 75 different majors and a total of 2000 students. Explain why the results of Leticia's survey are or are not representative of the entire student body. See margin.

56. In the figure below, if $m\angle BAC = 38$, what must be the measure of $\angle BAD$ in order for $\overrightarrow{AC}$ to be an angle bisector? G

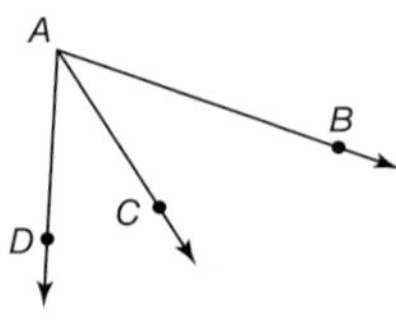

F 142 **H** 52
G 76 **J** 38

57. SAT/ACT If n is divisible by 2, 5, and 14, which of the following is also divisible by these numbers? E

A $n + 7$ **D** $n + 20$
B $n + 10$ **E** $n + 70$
C $n + 14$

Spiral Review

Find the distance between each pair of points. Round to the nearest hundredth. (Lesson 1-3)

58. $A(-1, -8), B(3, 4)$ 12.65 **59.** $C(0, 1), D(-2, 9)$ 8.25 **60.** $E(-3, -12), F(5, 4)$ 17.89

61. $G(4, -10), H(9, -25)$ 15.81 **62.** $J\left(1, \frac{1}{4}\right), K\left(-3, \frac{7}{4}\right)$ 4.27 **63.** $L\left(-5, \frac{8}{5}\right), M\left(5, \frac{2}{5}\right)$ 10.07

Find the value of the variable and ST if S is between R and T. (Lesson 1-2)

64. $RS = 7a, ST = 12a, RT = 76$ $a = 4$; $ST = 48$ **65.** $RS = 12, ST = 2x, RT = 34$ $x = 11$; $ST = 22$

66. PHOTOGRAPHY Photographers often place their cameras on tripods. In the diagram, the tripod is placed on an inclined surface, and the length of each leg is adjusted so that the camera remains level with the horizon. Are the feet of the tripod coplanar? Explain your reasoning. (Lesson 1-1) Yes; the feet of the tripod model three points that are noncollinear. Because three noncollinear points are used to name exactly one plane, the feet of the tripod are coplanar.

Complete each sentence. (Lesson 0-1)

67. 54 in. = __?__ ft 4.5 **68.** 275 mm = __?__ m 0.275 **69.** 7 gal = __?__ pt 56

Skills Review

Solve each equation.

70. $(90 - x) - x = 18$ 36 **71.** $(5x + 3) + 7x = 180$ 14.75 **72.** $(13x + 10) + 2x = 90$ $5\frac{1}{3}$

73. $(180 - x) - 4x = 56$ 24.8 **74.** $(4n + 17) + (n - 2) = 180$ 33 **75.** $(8a - 23) + (9 - 2a) = 90$ $17\frac{1}{3}$

CHAPTER 1

Mid-Chapter Quiz

Lessons 1-1 through 1-4

Use the figure to complete each of the following. (Lesson 1-1)

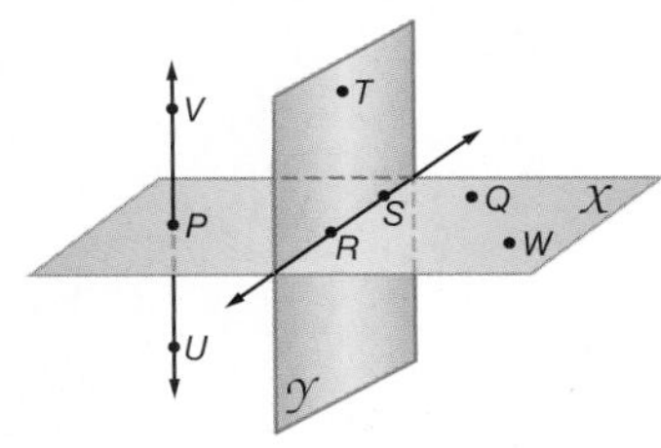

1. Name another point that is collinear with points U and V. **P**
2. What is another name for plane $\mathcal{Y}$? **plane RST**
3. Name a line that is coplanar with points P, Q, and W. **$\overleftrightarrow{RS}$**

Find the value of x and AC if B is between points A and C. (Lesson 1-2)

4. $AB = 12$, $BC = 8x - 2$, $AC = 10x$ **$x = 5$; $AC = 50$**
5. $AB = 5x$, $BC = 9x - 2$, $AC = 11x + 7.6$ **$x = 3.2$; $AC = 42.8$**
6. Find CD and the coordinate of the midpoint of $\overline{CD}$. **14; −2**

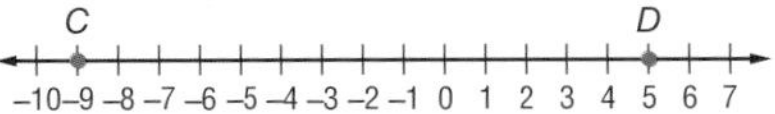

Find the coordinates of the midpoint of each segment. Then find the length of each segment. (Lesson 1-3)

7. 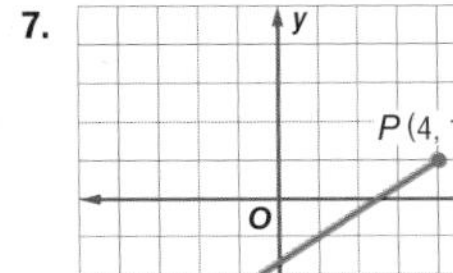 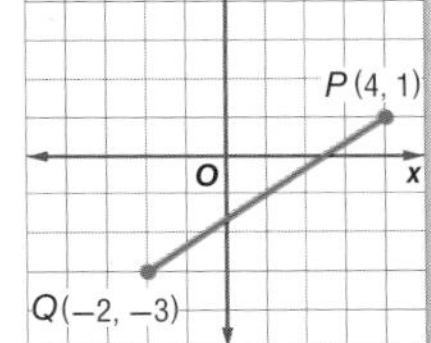

$(1, -1)$; $2\sqrt{13} \approx 7.2$

8. 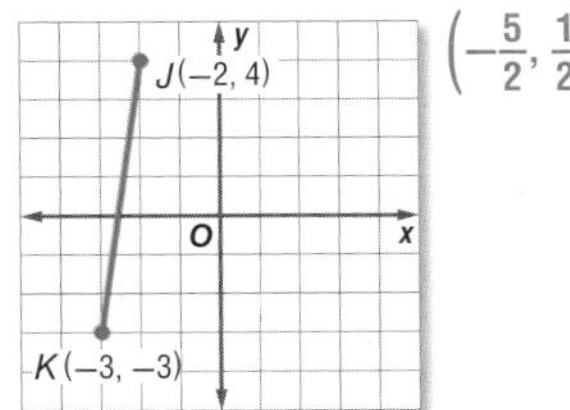

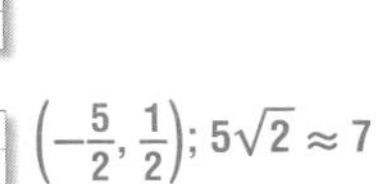
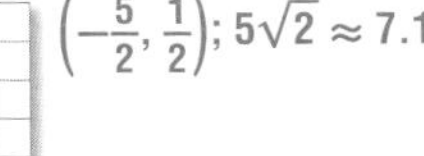
$\left(-\frac{5}{2}, \frac{1}{2}\right)$; $5\sqrt{2} \approx 7.1$

Find the coordinates of the midpoint of a segment with the given endpoints. Then find the distance between each pair of points. (Lesson 1-3)

9. $P(26, 12)$ and $Q(8, 42)$ **$(17, 27)$; $\sqrt{1224}$ or 35.0**
10. $M(6, -41)$ and $N(-18, -27)$ **$(-6, -34)$; $\sqrt{772}$ or 27.8**
11. **MAPS** A map of a town is drawn on a coordinate grid. The high school is found at point (3, 1) and town hall is found at (−5, 7). (Lesson 1-3)
    a. If the high school is at the midpoint between the town hall and the town library, at which ordered pair should you find the library? **(11, −5)**
    b. If one unit on the grid is equivalent to 50 meters, how far is the high school from town hall? **500 m**
12. **MULTIPLE CHOICE** The vertex of $\angle ABC$ is located at the origin. Point A is located at (5, 0) and Point C is located at (0, 2). How can $\angle ABC$ be classified? **C**

    A acute **C** right
    B obtuse **D** scalene

In the figure, $\overrightarrow{XA}$ and $\overrightarrow{XE}$ are opposite rays, and $\angle AXC$ is bisected by $\overrightarrow{XB}$. (Lesson 1-4)

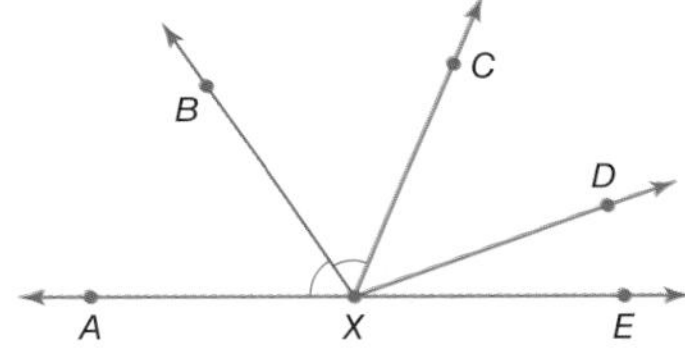

13. If $m\angle AXC = 8x - 7$ and $m\angle AXB = 3x + 10$, find $m\angle AXC$. **101**
14. If $m\angle CXD = 4x + 6$, $m\angle DXE = 3x + 1$, and $m\angle CXE = 8x - 2$, find $m\angle DXE$. **28**

Classify each angle as *acute*, *right*, or *obtuse*. (Lesson 1-4)

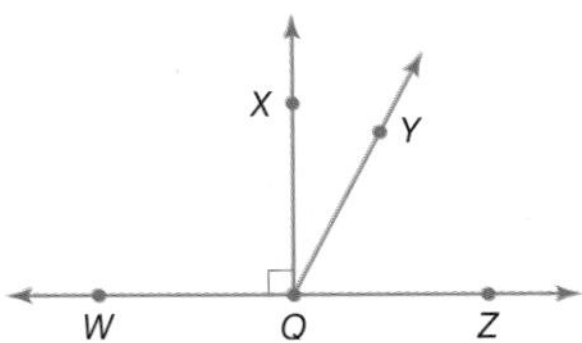
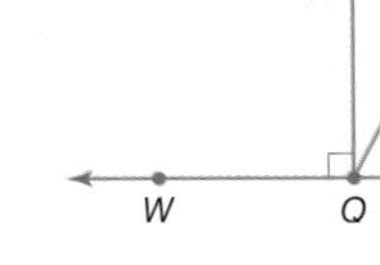

15. $\angle WQY$ **obtuse**
16. $\angle YQZ$ **acute**

Formative Assessment

Use the Mid-Chapter Quiz to assess students' progress in the first half of the chapter.

Have students review the lesson indicated for the problems that they answered incorrectly.

Summative Assessment

Mid-Chapter Test, p. 53

eAssessment Customize and create multiple versions of your Mid-Chapter Test and their answer keys.

FOLDABLES® StudyOrganizer

Dinah Zike's Foldables®

Before students complete the Mid-Chapter Quiz, encourage them to review the information from Lessons 1-1 through 1-4 in their Foldables.

The **Mid-Chapter Quiz** reviews skills and concepts presented in previous lessons.

InterventionPlanner

TIER 1 On Level OL

If students miss about 25% of the exercises or less,

Then choose a resource:

SE Lessons 1-1 through 1-4

Skills Practice, pp. 7, 14, 20 and 27

connectED.mcgraw-hill.com Self-Check Quiz

TIER 2 Strategic Intervention AL approaching grade level

If students miss about 50% of the exercises,

Then choose a resource:

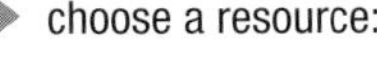
Study Guide and Intervention, pp. 5, 12, 18 and 25

Extra Examples, Personal Tutor

TIER 3 Intensive Intervention 2 or more grades below level

If students miss about 75% of the exercises,

Then use *Math Triumphs, Geometry,* Ch. 1–5

Extra Examples, Personal Tutor, Homework Help, Review Vocabulary

1 Focus

VerticalAlignment

Before Lesson 1-5 Measure and classify angles.

Lesson 1-5 Identify and use special pairs of angles. Identify perpendicular lines.

After Lesson 1-5 Identify and name polygons. Find perimeter and area of figures.

2 Teach

Scaffolding Questions

Have students read the **Why?** section of the lesson.

Ask:

- What type of triangle is modeled by the legs of the kneeling cheerleaders? What is true of all of these angles? A right angle; all are congruent.

(continued on the next page)

All of the **Lesson Resources** are leveled for students who are **approaching grade level, on grade level,** and **beyond grade level,** and for students who are **English language learners.**

LESSON 1-5 Angle Relationships

Then

- You measured and classified angles.

Now

1. Identify and use special pairs of angles.
2. Identify perpendicular lines.

Why?

- Cheerleaders position their arms and legs at specific angles to create various formations when performing at games and at competitions. Certain pairs of angles have special names and share specific relationships.

NewVocabulary

adjacent angles
linear pair
vertical angles
complementary angles
supplementary angles
perpendicular

Common Core State Standards

Content Standards

Preparation for G.SRT.7 Explain and use the relationship between the sine and cosine of complementary angles.

Mathematical Practices

2 Reason abstractly and quantitatively.

3 Construct viable arguments and critique the reasoning of others.

1 Pairs of Angles

Some pairs of angles are special because of how they are positioned in relationship to each other. Three of these angle pairs are described below.

KeyConcept Special Angle Pairs

Adjacent angles are two angles that lie in the same plane and have a common vertex and a common side, but no common interior points.

Examples $\angle 1$ and $\angle 2$ are adjacent angles.

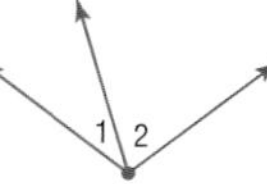

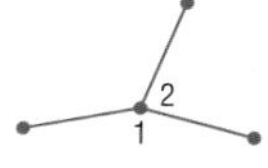

Nonexamples $\angle 3$ and $\angle ABC$ are nonadjacent angles

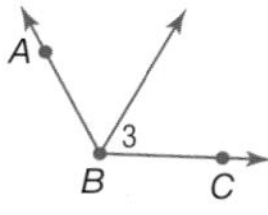

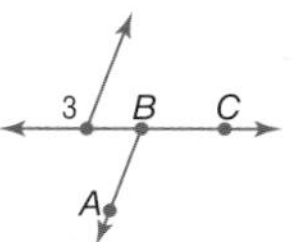

A **linear pair** is a pair of adjacent angles with noncommon sides that are opposite rays.

Example $\angle 1$ and $\angle 2$

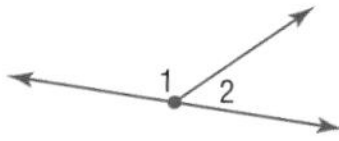

Nonexample $\angle ADB$ and $\angle ADC$

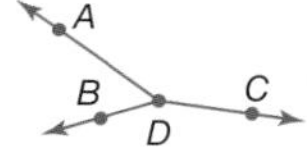

Vertical angles are two nonadjacent angles formed by two intersecting lines.

Examples $\angle 1$ and $\angle 2$; $\angle 3$ and $\angle 4$

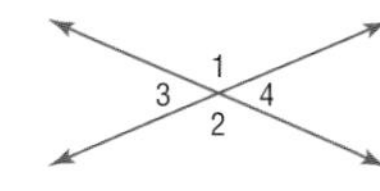

Nonexample $\angle AEB$ and $\angle DEC$

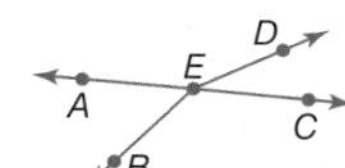

Lesson 1-5 Resources

Resource	Approaching Level AL	On Level OL	Beyond Level BL	English Learners ELL
Teacher Edition		▪ Differentiated Instruction, pp. 48, 49	▪ Differentiated Instruction, pp. 48, 49	▪ Differentiated Instruction, p. 49
Chapter Resource Masters	▪ Study Guide and Intervention, pp. 31–32 ▪ Skills Practice, p. 33 ▪ Practice, p. 34 ▪ Word Problem Practice, p. 35	▪ Study Guide and Intervention, pp. 31–32 ▪ Skills Practice, p. 33 ▪ Practice, p. 34 ▪ Word Problem Practice, p. 35 ▪ Enrichment, p. 36	▪ Practice, p. 34 ▪ Word Problem Practice, p. 35 ▪ Enrichment, p. 36	▪ Study Guide and Intervention, pp. 31–32 ▪ Skills Practice, p. 33 ▪ Practice, p. 34 ▪ Word Problem Practice, p. 35
Other	▪ 5-Minute Check 1-5 ▪ Study Notebook	▪ 5-Minute Check 1-5 ▪ Study Notebook	▪ 5-Minute Check 1-5 ▪ Study Notebook	▪ 5-Minute Check 1-5 ▪ Study Notebook

Real-World Example 1 Identify Angle Pairs

CHEERLEADING **Name an angle pair that satisfies each condition.**

a. two acute adjacent angles

$\angle HJK$, $\angle LJM$, $\angle MJN$, and $\angle NJO$ are acute angles.

$\angle LJM$ and $\angle MJN$ are acute adjacent angles, and $\angle MJN$ and $\angle NJO$ are acute adjacent angles.

b. two obtuse vertical angles

$\angle HJN$ and $\angle KJM$ are obtuse vertical angles.

Guided Practice

1A. a linear pair

1B. two acute vertical angles **$\angle HJK$ and $\angle MJN$**

1A. $\angle HJK$ and $\angle KJM$, $\angle HJL$ and $\angle LJM$, $\angle KJL$ and $\angle LJN$, $\angle KJM$ and $\angle MJN$, $\angle MJN$ and $\angle NJH$, or $\angle MJO$ and $\angle OJH$

Some pairs of angles are special because of the relationship between their angle measures.

KeyConcept Angle Pair Relationships

Vertical angles are congruent.

Examples $\angle ABC \cong \angle DBE$ and $\angle ABD \cong \angle CBE$

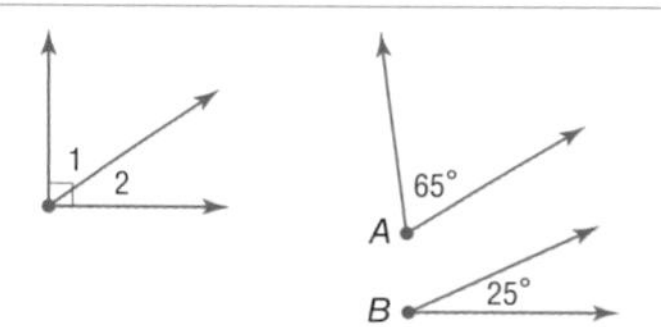

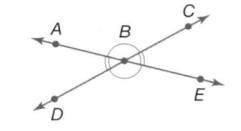

Complementary angles are two angles with measures that have a sum of 90.

Examples $\angle 1$ and $\angle 2$ are complementary.
$\angle A$ is complementary to $\angle B$.

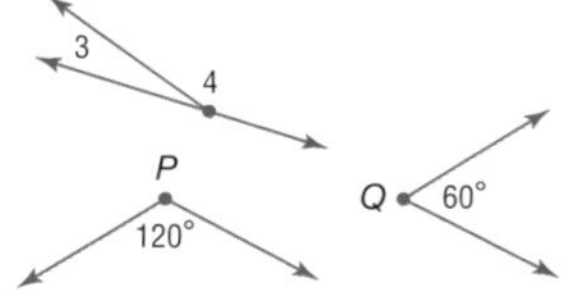

Supplementary angles are two angles with measures that have a sum of 180.

Examples $\angle 3$ and $\angle 4$ are supplementary.
$\angle P$ and $\angle Q$ are supplementary.

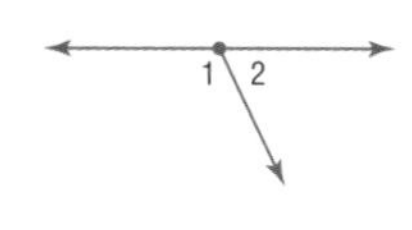

The angles in a linear pair are supplementary.

Example $m\angle 1 + m\angle 2 = 180$

StudyTip

Linear Pair vs. Supplementary Angles While the angles in a linear pair are always supplementary, some supplementary angles do not form a linear pair.

Remember that angle measures are real numbers. So the operations for real numbers and algebra can be used with angle measures.

- How can the rays of the angles formed by the arms of the center cheerleader in the back row be described? Classify the angle described. The rays of an acute angle are formed by her arms. The rays of an obtuse angle are formed by an arm and the side of her body.
- If a cheerleader holds both arms straight out, directly from the side of her body, what types of angles are formed? What are the angle measures? Her arms form a straight line, which is a 180° angle. Each arm and the corresponding side of her body form a 90° angle.

1 Pairs of Angles

Examples 1 and 2 show how to identify and find the measures of angles by using the rules of angle pairs.

Formative Assessment

Use the Guided Practice exercises after each example to determine students' understanding of concepts.

Additional Example

1 **ROADWAYS** Name an angle pair that satisfies each condition.

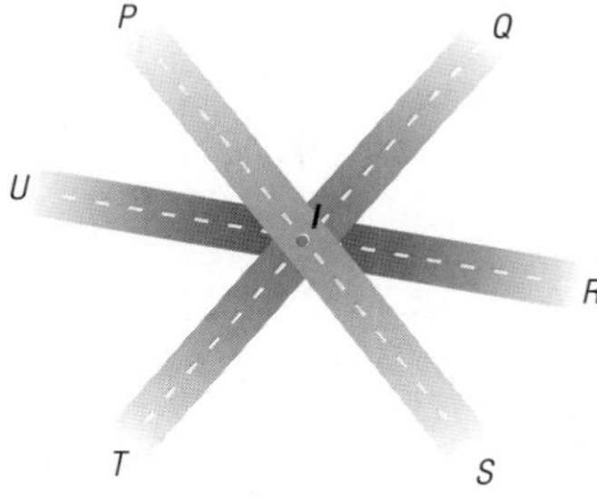

a. two angles that form a linear pair Sample answers: $\angle PIQ$ and $\angle QIS$, $\angle PIT$ and $\angle TIS$, $\angle QIU$ and $\angle UIT$

b. two acute vertical angles Sample answers: $\angle PIU$ and $\angle RIS$; $\angle PIQ$ and $\angle TIS$; $\angle RIS$ and $\angle PIU$

Additional Examples also in Interactive Classroom PowerPoint® Presentations

Tips for New Teachers

Geometry Software Have students use Geometer's Sketchpad® Software to create angles that have all of the relationships discussed in this lesson. This will help prepare them for future use of this software as well as allow for further exploration and development of understanding of these angle relationships.

Additional Example

2 ALGEBRA Find the measures of two supplementary angles if the measure of one angle is 6 less than five times the measure of the other angle. 31, 149

Focus on Mathematical Content

Stress that students should systematically write down all of the information they know about each problem and logically use each given fact to progress toward the solution. Caution students that some information they need to solve a problem may be contained in the figure and not described in the problem statement.

Teach with Tech

Student Response System Using your student response system software, develop several questions asking students to classify angle relationships.

Example 2 Angle Measure

ALGEBRA Find the measures of two supplementary angles if the difference in the measures of the two angles is 18.

Understand The problem relates the measures of two supplementary angles. You know that the sum of the measures of supplementary angles is 180. You need to find the measure of each angle.

Plan Draw two figures to represent the angles. Let the measure of one angle be x. If $m\angle A = x$, then because $\angle A$ and $\angle B$ are supplementary, $m\angle B + x = 180$ or $m\angle B = 180 - x$.

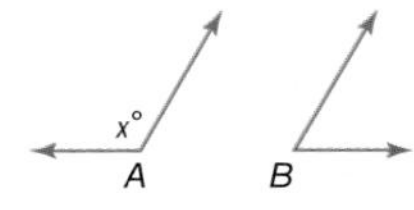

The problem states that the difference of the two angle measures is 18, or $m\angle B - m\angle A = 18$.

Problem-Solving Tip
Write an Equation While you could use the guess-and-check strategy to find two measures with a sum of 180 and a difference of 18, writing an equation is a more efficient approach to this problem.

Solve

$m\angle B - m\angle A = 18$	Given
$(180 - x) - x = 18$	$m\angle A = x$, $m\angle B = 180 - x$
$180 - 2x = 18$	Simplify.
$-2x = -162$	Subtract 180 from each side.
$x = 81$	Divide each side by −2.

Use the value of x to find each angle measure.

$m\angle A = x$ $\quad$ $m\angle B = 180 - x$

$= 81$ $\quad$ $= 180 - 81$ or 99

Check Add the angle measures to verify that the angles are supplementary.

$m\angle A + m\angle B \stackrel{?}{=} 180$

$81 + 99 = 180$ ✓

Guided Practice

2. Find the measures of two complementary angles if the measure of the larger angle is 12 more than twice the measure of the smaller angle. 26, 64

2 Perpendicular Lines

Lines, segments, or rays that form right angles are **perpendicular.**

Key Concept Perpendicular Lines

- Perpendicular lines intersect to form four right angles.
- Perpendicular lines intersect to form congruent adjacent angles.
- Segments and rays can be perpendicular to lines or other line segments and rays.
- The right angle symbol in the figure indicates that the lines are perpendicular.

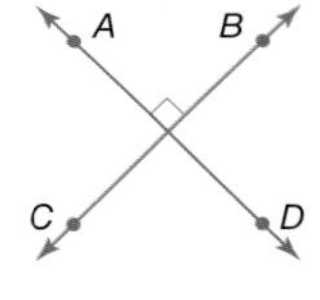

Symbol $\perp$ is read *is perpendicular to.* **Example** $\overleftrightarrow{AD} \perp \overleftrightarrow{CB}$

Differentiated Instruction OL BL

Extension Are vertical angles ever complementary or supplementary?
Yes. Vertical angles are complementary when they each measure 45. They are supplementary when they each measure 90.

Example 3 Perpendicular Lines

ALGEBRA Find x and y so that $\overleftrightarrow{PR}$ and $\overleftrightarrow{SQ}$ are perpendicular.

If $\overleftrightarrow{PR} \perp \overleftrightarrow{SQ}$, then $m\angle STR = 90$ and $m\angle PTQ = 90$.

To find x, use $\angle STW$ and $\angle WTR$.

$m\angle STR = m\angle STW + m\angle WTR$	Sum of parts = whole
$90 = 2x + (5x + 6)$	Substitution
$90 = 7x + 6$	Combine like terms.
$84 = 7x$	Subtract 6 from each side.
$12 = x$	Divide each side by 7.

To find y, use $m\angle PTQ$.

$m\angle PTQ = 4y - 2$	Given
$90 = 4y - 2$	Substitution
$92 = 4y$	Add 2 to each side.
$23 = y$	Divide each side by 4.

GuidedPractice

3. Suppose $m\angle D = 3x - 12$. Find x so that $\angle D$ is a right angle. **34**

In the figure at the right, it *appears* that $\overleftrightarrow{FG} \perp \overleftrightarrow{JK}$. However, you cannot assume this is true unless other information, such as $m\angle FHJ = 90$, is given.

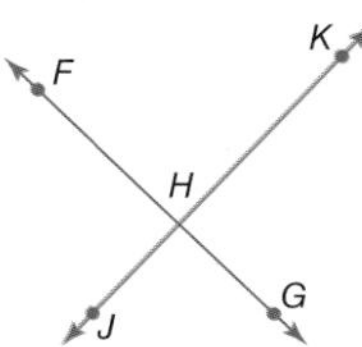

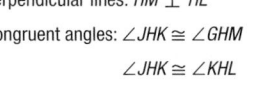

In geometry, figures are sketches used to depict a situation. They are not drawn to reflect total accuracy. There are certain relationships that you can assume to be true, but others you cannot. Study the figure and the lists below.

KeyConcept Interpreting Diagrams

CAN be Assumed	CANNOT be Assumed
All points shown are coplanar.	Perpendicular lines: $\overrightarrow{HM} \perp \overrightarrow{HL}$
G, H, and J are collinear.	Congruent angles: $\angle JHK \cong \angle GHM$
$\overrightarrow{HM}$, $\overrightarrow{HL}$, $\overrightarrow{HK}$, and $\overleftrightarrow{GJ}$ intersect at H.	$\angle JHK \cong \angle KHL$
H is between G and J.	$\angle KHL \cong \angle LHM$
L is in the interior of $\angle MHK$.	Congruent segments: $\overline{GH} \cong \overline{HJ}$
$\angle GHM$ and $\angle MHL$ are adjacent angles.	$\overline{HJ} \cong \overline{HK}$
$\angle GHL$ and $\angle LHJ$ are a linear pair.	$\overline{HK} \cong \overline{HL}$
$\angle JHK$ and $\angle KHG$ are supplementary.	$\overline{HL} \cong \overline{HG}$

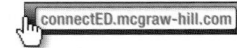

The list of statements that can be assumed is not a complete list. There are more special pairs of angles than those listed.

DifferentiatedInstruction OL BL ELL

Logical/Mathematical Learners Have students list each angle relationship presented in the Key Concept boxes of this lesson on pages 46–49. Then, have students write one or two sentences to describe each relationship and provide an example. For extra practice, have students analyze the figures found throughout the lesson and determine which angle relationships are or are not present in them.

2 Perpendicular Lines

Lines that form right angles are perpendicular. **Examples 3 and 4** show how to find the measures of angles by using the rules of perpendicular lines.

Additional Example

3 ALGEBRA Find x and y so that $\overleftrightarrow{KO}$ and $\overleftrightarrow{HM}$ are perpendicular. $x = 7$ and $y = 28$

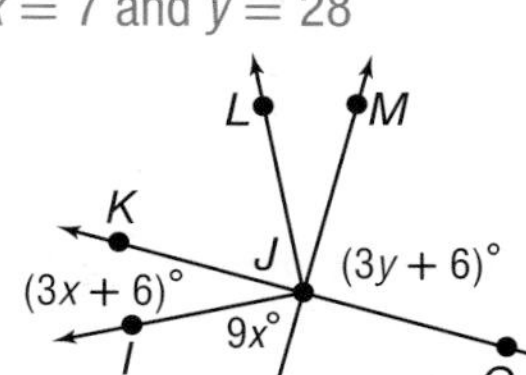

WatchOut!

Common Misconceptions Remind students that they cannot make certain assumptions about the geometric relationships of figures in a diagram. For example, just because two angles *look* like they are congruent does not necessarily mean that they are congruent.

Tips for New Teachers

Reasoning Have pairs of students sketch simple figures demonstrating angle relationships from the lesson. For example, a student can suggest that a partner draw and label a simple figure with $\angle LMP$ adjacent to $\angle PMQ$. Then have the students interpret the diagrams, discussing what can and cannot be assumed from the figures.

Additional Example

4 Determine whether each statement can be assumed from the figure below. Explain.

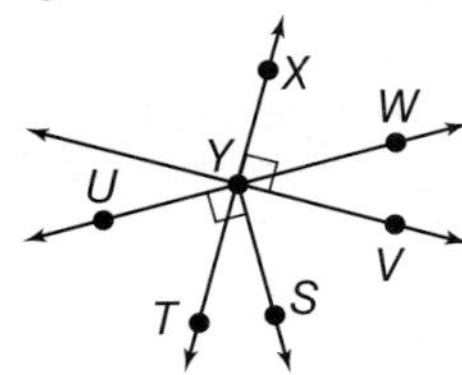

a. $m\angle VYT = 90$ Yes; $\overleftrightarrow{VY}$ and $\overleftrightarrow{TX}$ are perpendicular.

b. $\angle TYW$ and $\angle TYU$ are supplementary. Yes; they form a linear pair of angles.

c. $\angle VYW$ and $\angle TYS$ are adjacent angles. No; they do not share a common side.

3 Practice

Formative Assessment

Use Exercises 1–7 to check for understanding.

Then use the chart at the bottom of the next page to customize assignments for your students.

StudyTip

Additional Information Additional information for a figure may be given using congruent angle markings, congruent segment markings, or right angle symbols.

Example 4 Interpret Figures

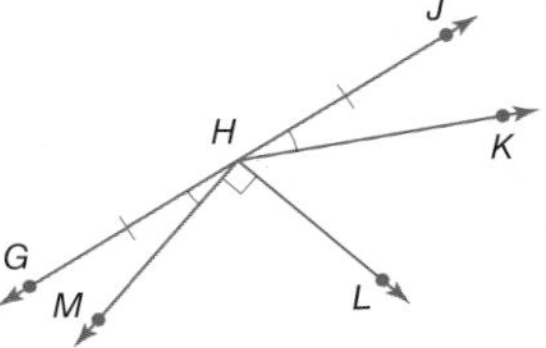

Determine whether each statement can be assumed from the figure. Explain.

a. $\angle KHJ$ and $\angle GHM$ are complementary.

No; they are congruent, but we do not know anything about their exact measures.

b. $\angle GHK$ and $\angle JHK$ are a linear pair.

Yes; they are adjacent angles whose noncommon sides are opposite rays.

c. $\overrightarrow{HL}$ is perpendicular to $\overrightarrow{HM}$.

Yes; the right angle symbol in the figure indicates that $\overrightarrow{HL} \perp \overrightarrow{HM}$.

GuidedPractice

4A. $\angle GHL$ and $\angle LHJ$ are supplementary. **4A. Yes; they form a linear pair, and angles that form a linear pair are supplementary.**

4B. $\angle GHM$ and $\angle MHK$ are adjacent angles. **4B. Yes; they share a common side and vertex and have no interior points in common.**

Check Your Understanding

○ = Step-by-Step Solutions begin on page R14.

Example 1 **Name an angle pair that satisfies each condition.**

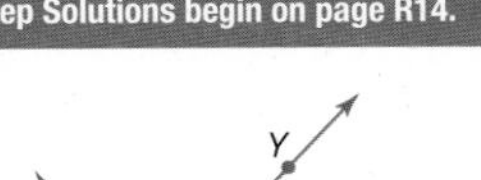
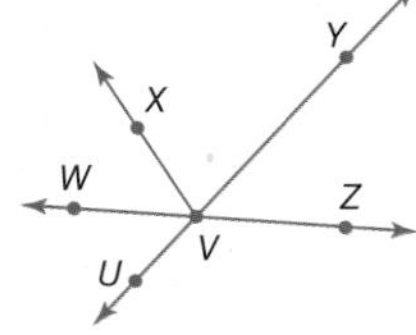

1. two acute vertical angles $\angle ZVY$, $\angle WVU$
2. two obtuse adjacent angles $\angle UVZ$, $\angle XVZ$

Examples 1–2 **3. CAMERAS** Cameras use lenses and light to capture images.

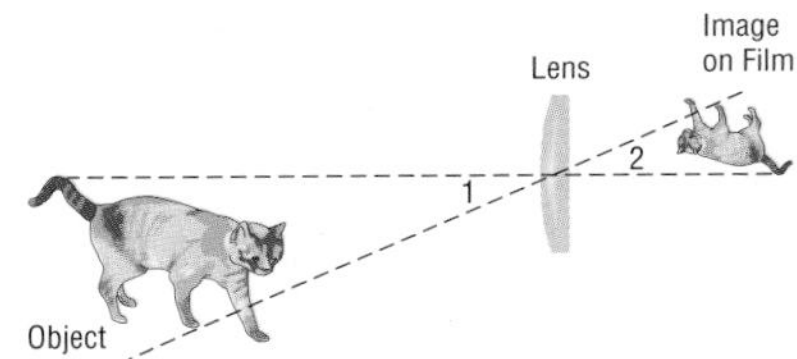

a. What type of angles are formed by the object and its image? **vertical**

b. If the measure of $\angle 2$ is 15, what is the measure of $\angle 1$? **15**

Examples 2–3 **4. ALGEBRA** The measures of two complementary angles are $7x + 17$ and $3x - 20$. Find the measures of the angles. **82.1, 7.9**

5. ALGEBRA Lines x and y intersect to form adjacent angles 2 and 3. If $m\angle 2 = 3a - 27$ and $m\angle 3 = 2b + 14$, find the values of a and b so that x is perpendicular to y. **$a = 39$; $b = 38$**

Example 4 **Determine whether each statement can be assumed from the figure. Explain.**

6. $\angle CAD$ and $\angle DAB$ are complementary. **See margin.**
7. $\angle EDB$ and $\angle BDA$ are adjacent, but they are neither complementary nor supplementary. **See margin.**

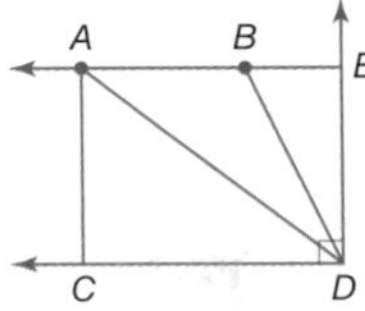

Practice and Problem Solving

Extra Practice is on page R1.

Examples 1–2 **Name an angle or angle pair that satisfies each condition.**

8. two adjacent angles **Sample answer: $\angle HGE$, $\angle DGE$**
9. two acute vertical angles **Sample answer: $\angle BFC$, $\angle DFE$**
10. two obtuse vertical angles **Sample answer: $\angle HGE$, $\angle FGD$**
11. two complementary adjacent angles **$\angle FDG$, $\angle GDE$**
12. two complementary nonadjacent angles **$\angle BCF$, $\angle BAD$**
13. two supplementary adjacent angles **Sample answer: $\angle CBF$, $\angle ABF$**
14. a linear pair whose vertex is F **Sample answer: $\angle BFC$, $\angle BFD$**
15. an angle complementary to $\angle FDG$ **$\angle GDE$**
16. an angle supplementary to $\angle CBF$ **Sample answer: $\angle JBF$**
17. an angle supplementary to $\angle JAE$ **$\angle CAE$**

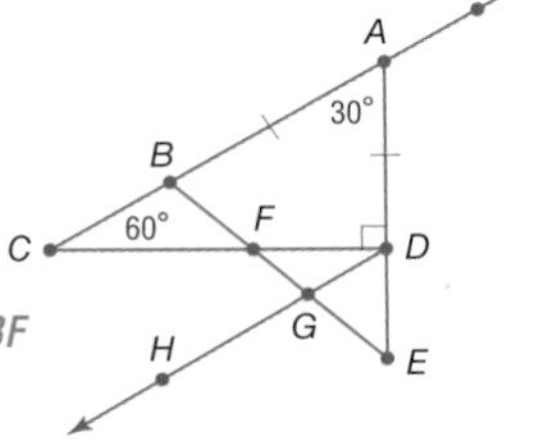

18. **CCSS REASONING** You are using a compass to drive 23° east of north. Express your direction in another way using an acute angle and two of the four directions: north, south, east, and west. Explain your reasoning. **See margin.**

Example 2 **Find the value of each variable.**

19. 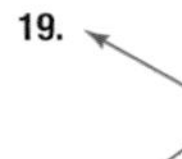 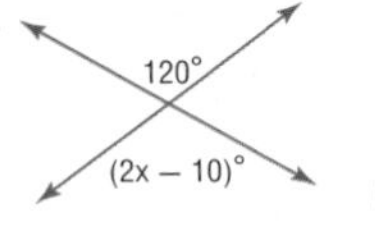 **65**

20. 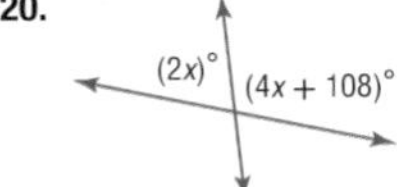 **12**

21. 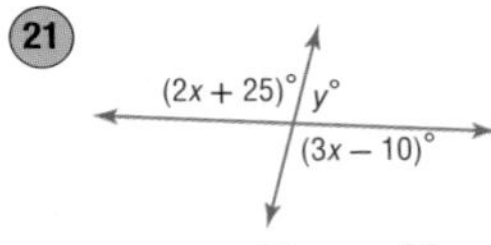 **$x = 35$; $y = 85$**

22. 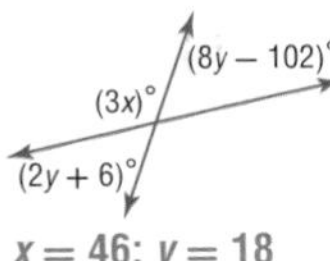 **$x = 46$; $y = 18$**

23. **$x = 48$; $y = 21$**

24. 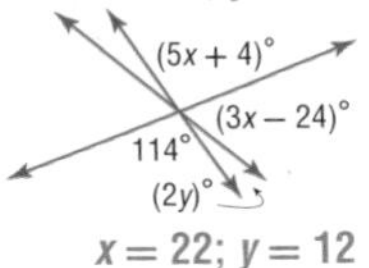 **$x = 22$; $y = 12$**

25. **ALGEBRA** $\angle E$ and $\angle F$ are supplementary. The measure of $\angle E$ is 54 more than the measure of $\angle F$. Find the measures of each angle. **$m\angle F = 63$; $m\angle E = 117$**

26. **ALGEBRA** The measure of an angle's supplement is 76 less than the measure of the angle. Find the measure of the angle and its supplement. **128; 52**

Differentiated Homework Options

Level	Assignment	Two-Day Option	
AL Basic	8–41, 49, 50, 52–67	9–41 odd, 53–56	8–40 even, 49, 50, 52, 57–67
OL Core	9–41 odd, 42–50, 52–67	8–41, 53–56	42–50, 52, 57–67
BL Advanced	42–63, (optional: 64–67)		

CCSS Teaching the Mathematical Practices

Reasoning Mathematically proficient students are able to make sense of quantities and their relationships in problem situations. In Exercise 18, encourage students to phrase the question in a different way.

Additional Answers

6. No; while $\angle CAB$ appears to be a right angle, no information verifies this.
7. Yes: they share a common side and vertex, so they are adjacent. Since $m\angle EDB + m\angle BDA + m\angle ADC = 90$, $\angle EDB$ and $\angle BDA$ cannot be complementary or supplementary.
18. Sample answer: 67° north of east; since the measure of the angle between north and east is 90, you can use the complement of the original angle and describe the direction as north of east instead of east of north.

Study Guide and Intervention

AL OL ELL

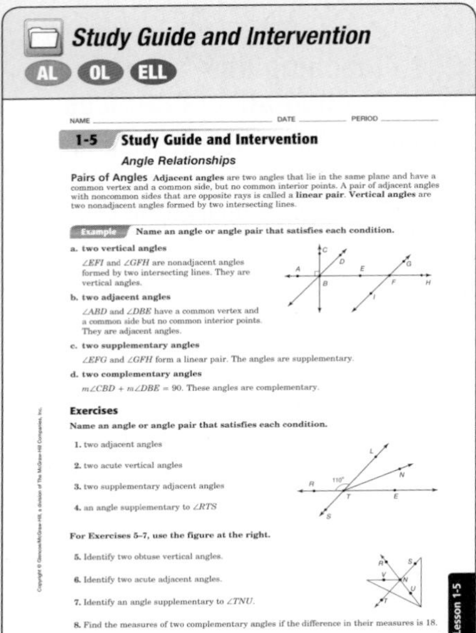
NAME ______ DATE ______ PERIOD ______

1-5 Study Guide and Intervention

Angle Relationships

Pairs of Angles Adjacent angles are two angles that lie in the same plane and have a common vertex and a common side, but no common interior points. A pair of adjacent angles with noncommon sides that are opposite rays is called a **linear pair**. **Vertical angles** are two nonadjacent angles formed by two intersecting lines.

Example Name an angle or angle pair that satisfies each condition.

a. two vertical angles
∠EFI and ∠GFH are nonadjacent angles formed by two intersecting lines. They are vertical angles.

b. two adjacent angles
∠ABD and ∠DBE have a common vertex and a common side but no common interior points. They are adjacent angles.

c. two supplementary angles
∠EFG and ∠GFH form a linear pair. The angles are supplementary.

d. two complementary angles
m∠CBD + m∠DBE = 90. These angles are complementary.

Exercises

Name an angle or angle pair that satisfies each condition.

1. two adjacent angles
2. two acute vertical angles
3. two supplementary adjacent angles
4. an angle supplementary to ∠RTS

For Exercises 5–7, use the figure at the right.

5. Identify two obtuse vertical angles.
6. Identify two acute adjacent angles.
7. Identify an angle supplementary to ∠TNU.
8. Find the measures of two complementary angles if the difference in their measures is 18.

Lesson 1-5

Practice

AL OL BL ELL

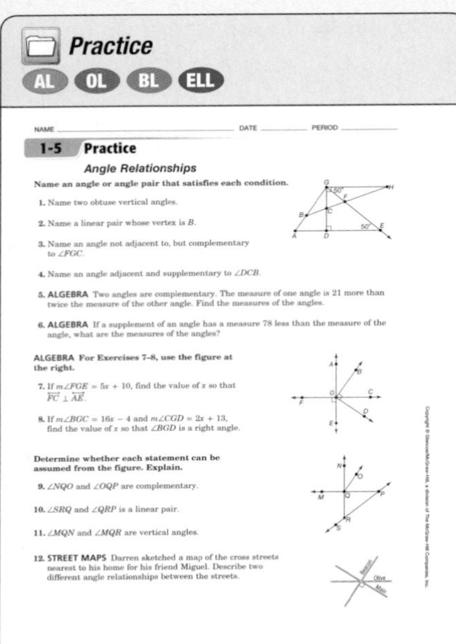
NAME ______ DATE ______ PERIOD ______

1-5 Practice

Angle Relationships

Name an angle or angle pair that satisfies each condition.

1. Name two obtuse vertical angles.
2. Name a linear pair whose vertex is B.
3. Name an angle not adjacent to, but complementary to ∠FGC.
4. Name an angle adjacent and supplementary to ∠DCB.
5. ALGEBRA Two angles are complementary. The measure of one angle is 21 more than twice the measure of the other angle. Find the measures of the angles.
6. ALGEBRA If a supplement of an angle has a measure 78 less than the measure of the angle, what are the measures of the angles?

ALGEBRA For Exercises 7–8, use the figure at the right.

7. If m∠FGE = 5x + 10, find the value of x so that $\overline{FC} \perp \overline{AE}$.
8. If m∠BGC = 16x − 4 and m∠CGD = 2x + 13, find the value of x so that ∠BGD is a right angle.

Determine whether each statement can be assumed from the figure. Explain.

9. ∠NQO and ∠OQP are complementary.
10. ∠SRQ and ∠QRP is a linear pair.
11. ∠MQN and ∠MQR are vertical angles.
12. STREET MAPS Darren sketched a map of the cross streets nearest to his home for his friend Miguel. Describe two different angle relationships between the streets.

Word Problem Practice

AL OL BL ELL

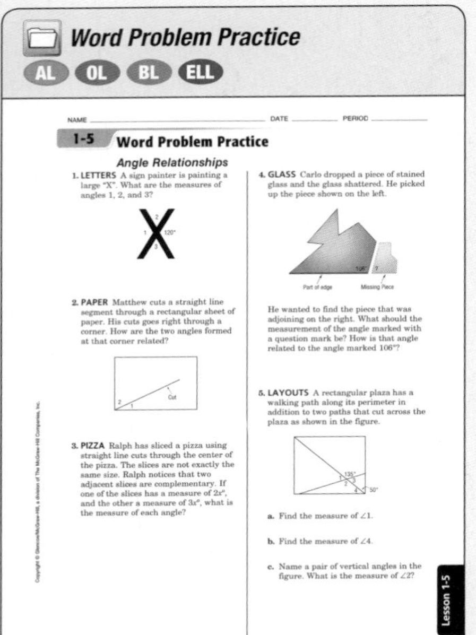
NAME ______ DATE ______ PERIOD ______

1-5 Word Problem Practice

Angle Relationships

1. LETTERS A sign painter is painting a large "X". What are the measures of angles 1, 2, and 3?
2. PAPER Matthew cuts a straight line segment through a rectangular sheet of paper. His cuts goes right through a corner. How are the two angles formed at that corner related?
3. PIZZA Ralph has sliced a pizza using straight line cuts through the center of the pizza. The slices are not exactly the same size. Ralph notices that two adjacent slices are complementary. If one of the slices has a measure of 2x°, and the other a measure of 3x°, what is the measure of each angle?
4. GLASS Carlo dropped a piece of stained glass and the glass shattered. He picked up the piece shown on the left.
He wanted to find the piece that was adjoining on the right. What should the measurement of the angle marked with a question mark be? How is that angle related to the angle marked 106°?
5. LAYOUTS A rectangular plaza has a walking path along its perimeter in addition to two paths that cut across the plaza as shown in the figure.
a. Find the measure of ∠1.
b. Find the measure of ∠4.
c. Name a pair of vertical angles in the figure. What is the measure of ∠2?

Lesson 1-5

27. ALGEBRA The measure of the supplement of an angle is 40 more than two times the measure of the complement of the angle. Find the measure of the angle. **40**

28. ALGEBRA ∠3 and ∠4 form a linear pair. The measure of ∠3 is four more than three times the measure of ∠4. Find the measure of each angle. **m∠3 = 136; m∠4 = 44**

Example 3

ALGEBRA Use the figure at the right.

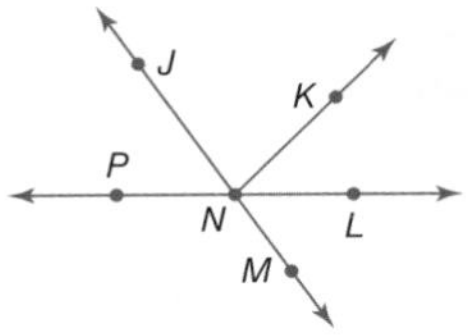

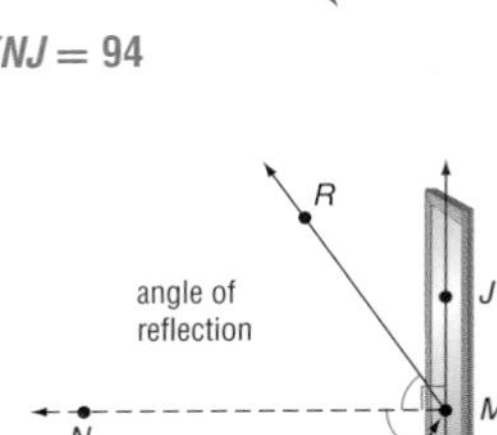

29. If m∠KNL = 6x − 4 and m∠LNM = 4x + 24, find the value of x so that ∠KNM is a right angle. **7**

30. If m∠JNP = 3x − 15 and m∠JNL = 5x + 59, find the value of x so that ∠JNP and ∠JNL are supplements of each other. **17**

31. If m∠LNM = 8x + 12 and m∠JNL = 12x − 32, find m∠JNP. **92**

32. If m∠JNP = 2x + 3, m∠KNL = 3x − 17, and m∠KNJ = 3x + 34, find the measure of each angle. **m∠JNP = 43; m∠KNL = 43; m∠KNJ = 94**

33. PHYSICS As a ray of light meets a mirror, the light is reflected. The angle at which the light strikes the mirror is the *angle of incidence*. The angle at which the light is reflected is the *angle of reflection*. The angle of incidence and the angle of reflection are congruent. In the diagram at the right, if m∠RMI = 106, find the angle of reflection and m∠RMJ. **53; 37**

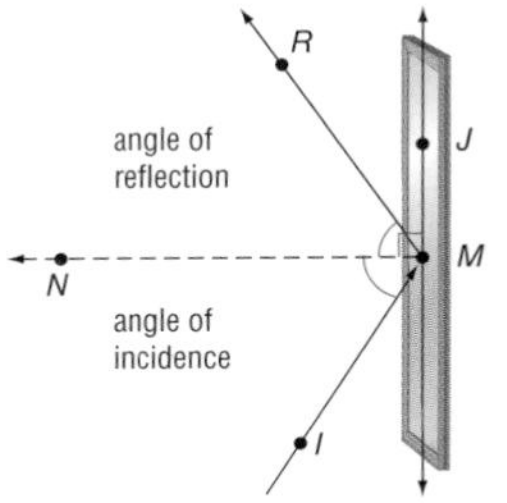

angle of reflection
angle of incidence

34. ALGEBRA Rays *AB* and *BC* are perpendicular. Point *D* lies in the interior of ∠ABC. If m∠ABD = 3r + 5 and m∠DBC = 5r − 27, find m∠ABD and m∠DBC. **m∠ABD = 47; m∠DBC = 43**

35. ALGEBRA $\overleftrightarrow{WX}$ and $\overleftrightarrow{YZ}$ intersect at point V. If m∠WVY = 4a + 58 and m∠XVY = 2b − 18, find the values of a and b so that $\overleftrightarrow{WX}$ is perpendicular to $\overleftrightarrow{YZ}$. **a = 8; b = 54**

Example 4

Determine whether each statement can be assumed from the figure. Explain.

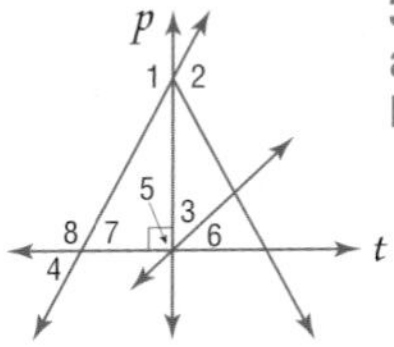

36. ∠4 and ∠7 are vertical angles. **36. Yes; the angles are nonadjacent and are formed by two lines.**

37. ∠4 and ∠8 are supplementary. **37. Yes; the angles form a linear pair.**

38. p ⊥ t **Yes; the intersection of the two lines is a right angle.**

39. ∠3 ≅ ∠6 **No; the measures of each angle are unknown.**

40. ∠5 ≅ ∠3 + ∠6

41. ∠5 and ∠7 form a linear pair. **See margin.**

40. Yes; m∠5 = 90 since it is a right angle, and m∠3 + m∠6 = 90 since it is a right angle.

42. CCSS ARGUMENTS In the diagram of the pruning shears shown, m∠1 = m∠3. What conclusion can you reach about the relationship between ∠4 and ∠2? Explain. **See margin.**

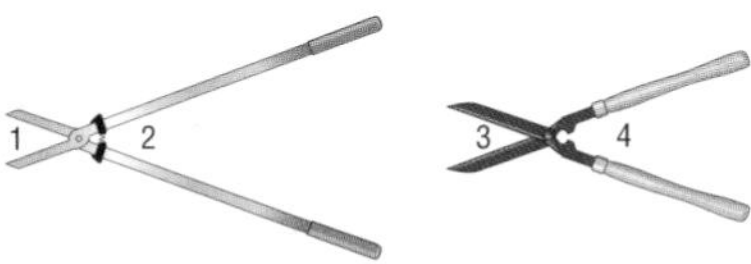

Enrichment

OL BL

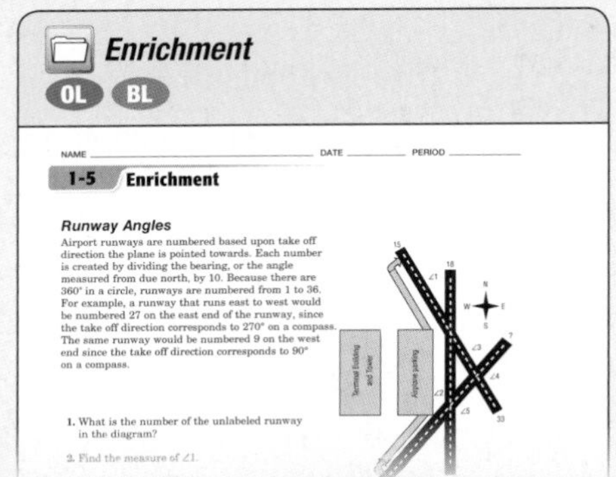
NAME ______ DATE ______ PERIOD ______

1-5 Enrichment

Runway Angles

Airport runways are numbered based upon take off direction the plane is pointed towards. Each number is created by dividing the bearing, or the angle measured from due north, by 10. Because there are 360° in a circle, runways are numbered from 1 to 36. For example, a runway that runs east to west would be numbered 27 on the east end of the runway, since the take off direction corresponds to 270° on a compass. The same runway would be numbered 9 on the west end since the take off direction corresponds to 90° on a compass.

1. What is the number of the unlabeled runway in the diagram?
2. Find the measure of ∠1.

Additional Answers

41. No; the angles are not adjacent.

42. m∠2 = m∠4; We are given that m∠1 = m∠3. Since ∠1 and ∠2 are vertical angles, ∠1 ≅ ∠2. So m∠1 = m∠2. Since ∠3 and ∠4 are vertical angles, ∠3 ≅ ∠4. So m∠3 = m∠4. Since m∠1 = m∠2 and m∠1 = m∠3, we can say that m∠2 = m∠3. Since m∠3 = m∠4 and m∠2 = m∠3, we can say that m∠2 = m∠4.

FLIGHT **The wing of the aircraft shown can pivot up to 60° in either direction from the perpendicular position.**

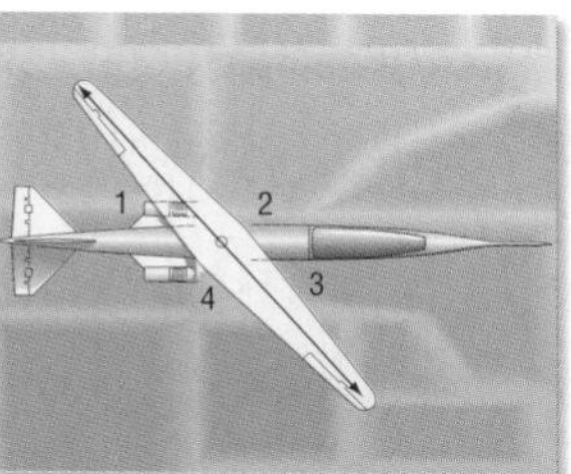

43. Identify a pair of vertical angles. **43–44. See margin.**

44. Identify two pairs of supplementary angles.

45. If $m\angle 1 = 110$, what is $m\angle 3$? $m\angle 4$? **110; 70**

46. What is the minimum possible value for $m\angle 2$? the maximum? **30; 150**

47. Is there a wing position in which none of the angles are obtuse? Explain. **See margin.**

48. **MULTIPLE REPRESENTATIONS** In this problem, you will explore the relationship between the sum of the interior angles of a triangle and the angles vertical to them.

   a. **Geometric** Draw three sets of three intersecting lines and label each as shown.

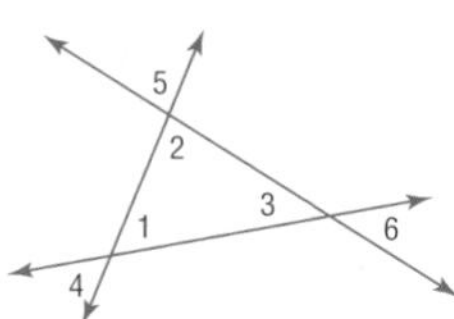

   b. **Tabular** For each set of lines, measure and record $m\angle 1$, $m\angle 2$, and $m\angle 3$ in a table. Record $m\angle 1 + m\angle 2 + m\angle 3$ in a separate column.

   c. **Verbal** Explain how you can find $m\angle 4$, $m\angle 5$, and $m\angle 6$ when you know $m\angle 1$, $m\angle 2$, and $m\angle 3$.

   d. **Algebraic** Write an equation that relates $m\angle 1 + m\angle 2 + m\angle 3$ to $m\angle 4 + m\angle 5 + m\angle 6$. Then use substitution to write an equation that relates $m\angle 4 + m\angle 5 + m\angle 6$ to an integer. **48a–d. See margin.**

H.O.T. Problems Use Higher-Order Thinking Skills

49. **CCSS REASONING** Are there angles that do not have a complement? Explain. **See margin.**

50. **OPEN ENDED** Draw a pair of intersecting lines that forms a pair of complementary angles. Explain your reasoning. **See margin.**

51. **CHALLENGE** If a line, line segment, or ray is perpendicular to a plane, it is perpendicular to every line, line segment, or ray in the plane that intersects it.

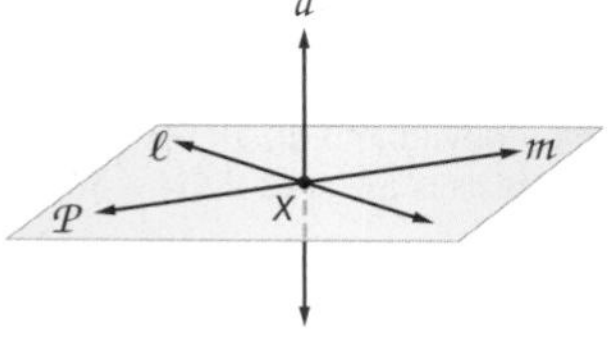

   a. If a line is perpendicular to each of two intersecting lines at their point of intersection, then the line is perpendicular to the plane determined by them. If line a is perpendicular to line ℓ and line m at point X, what must also be true? **Line a is perpendicular to plane P.**

   b. If a line is perpendicular to a plane, then any line perpendicular to the given line at the point of intersection with the given plane is in the given plane. If line a is perpendicular to plane $\mathcal{P}$ and line m at point X, what must also be true? **Line m is in plane P.**

   c. If a line is perpendicular to a plane, then every plane containing the line is perpendicular to the given plane. If line a is perpendicular to plane $\mathcal{P}$, what must also be true? **Any plane containing line a is perpendicular to plane P.**

52. **WRITING IN MATH** Describe three different ways you can determine that an angle is a right angle.

52. Sample answer: You can determine if an angle is right if it is marked with a right angle symbol, if the angle is a vertical pair with a right angle, or if the angle forms a linear pair with a right angle.

Teaching the Mathematical Practices

Arguments Mathematically proficient students understand and use stated assumptions. In Exercise 42, encourage students to look at the relationship between ∠1 and ∠2.

Exercise Alert

In Exercises 43-47, students may need clarification of the airplane construction. The wing can be positioned perpendicular to the body of the plane, or rotated to create the most efficient flight. Explain how the rotation will affect the measures of angles 1-4.

50.

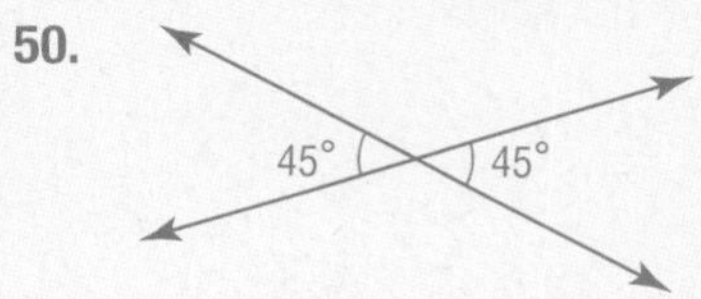

Two 45° angles are complementary.

Multiple Representations

In Exercise 48, students explore the relationship between the interior angle sum of a triangle and the measures of the angles vertical to each interior angle.

Teaching the Mathematical Practices

Reasoning Mathematically proficient students are able to contextualize abstract situations. In Exercise 49, encourage students who are struggling with this question to review the definition of *complement* first.

Additional Answers

43. Sample answer: ∠1 and ∠3

44. Sample answer: ∠1 and ∠2; ∠3 and ∠4

47. Sample answer: Yes; if the wing is not rotated at all, then all of the angles are right angles, which are neither acute nor obtuse.

48a. Sample answer:

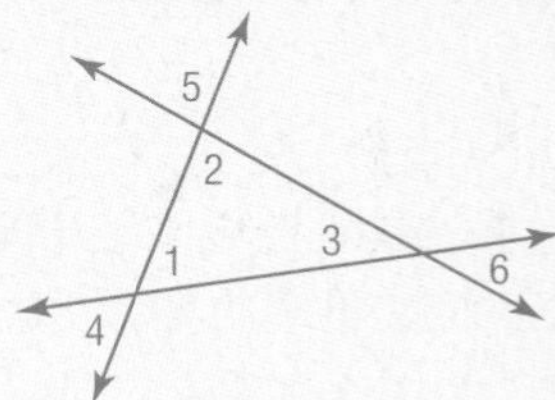

48b. Sample answer:

Set	$m\angle 1$	$m\angle 2$	$m\angle 3$	$m\angle 1 + m\angle 2 + m\angle 3$
1	30	60	90	180
2	45	55	80	180
3	20	60	100	180

48c. Sample answer: Explain how you can find $m\angle 4 = m\angle 1$, $m\angle 5 = m\angle 2$, and $m\angle 6 = m\angle 3$ because they are pairs of vertical angles.

48d. Sample answer; $m\angle 1 + m\angle 2 + m\angle 3 = m\angle 4 + m\angle 5 + m\angle 6$; $m\angle 4 + m\angle 5 + m\angle 6 = 180$.

49. Yes; angles that are right or obtuse do not have complements because their measures are greater than or equal to 90.

4 Assess

Name the Math Describing angle relationships in figures provides an opportunity for students to practice making correct assumptions and properly assessing the information given in the figures. Ask students to describe some of the figures presented in problems and examples in this lesson.

Exercise Alert

Protractor Exercises 57–59 require the use of a protractor.

Additional Answers

54. 240 chocolate chip; 120 peanut butter; 40 oatmeal raisin; Sample answer: Let $x =$ the number of oatmeal raisin cookies. The number of peanut butter cookies equals $3x$. The number of chocolate chip cookies equals $2(3x) = 6x$. The total number of cookies is $x + 3x + 6x = 400$. Solving for x, you get $x = 40$. So they need 40 oatmeal raisin, 3(40) or 120 peanut butter and 6(40) or 240 chocolate chip cookies.

60. $\left(6, -\frac{1}{2}\right)$

61. $\left(-3\frac{1}{2}, 1\right)$

62. $\left(-2, 2\frac{1}{2}\right)$

64. $\overline{AB} \cong \overline{AC}$; $\angle B \cong \angle C$

65. $\overline{FG} \cong \overline{HJ} \cong \overline{JK} \cong \overline{FL}$, $\overline{GH} \cong \overline{LK}$; $\angle F \cong \angle J$, $\angle G \cong \angle H \cong \angle K \cong \angle L$

66. $\overline{NP} \cong \overline{PQ} \cong \overline{QR} \cong \overline{RS} \cong \overline{SN}$; $\angle N \cong \angle P \cong \angle Q \cong \angle R \cong \angle S$

67. $\overline{WX} \cong \overline{XY} \cong \overline{YZ} \cong \overline{ZW}$; $\angle W \cong \angle Y$, $\angle X \cong \angle Z$

Standardized Test Practice

53. What is $m\angle RMS$ in the figure below? **B**

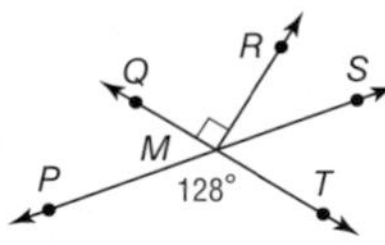

A 26

B 38

C 52

D 128

54. EXTENDED RESPONSE For a fundraiser, a theater club is making 400 cookies. They want to make twice as many chocolate chip as peanut butter cookies and three times as many peanut butter as oatmeal raisin cookies. Determine how many of each type of cookie the theater club will make. Show your work. **See margin.**

55. ALGEBRA Which inequality is graphed below? **J**

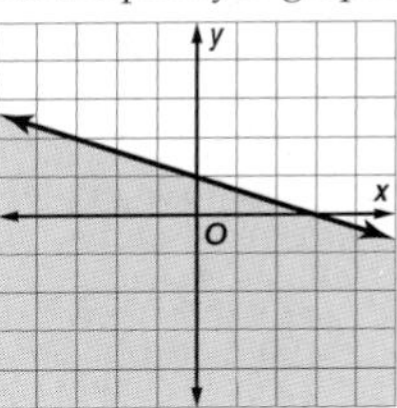

F $y > -\frac{1}{3}x + 1$ H $y \geq -\frac{1}{3}x + 1$

G $y < -\frac{1}{3}x + 1$ J $y \leq -\frac{1}{3}x + 1$

56. SAT/ACT One third of a number is three more than one fourth the same number. What is the number? **C**

A 3

B 12

C 36

D 42

E 48

Spiral Review

Copy the diagram shown and extend each ray. Classify each angle as *right, acute,* or *obtuse.* Then use a protractor to measure the angle to the nearest degree. (Lesson 1-4)

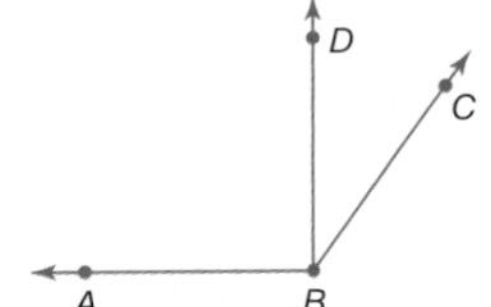

57. $\angle ABC$ **125, obtuse**

58. $\angle DBC$ **35, acute**

59. $\angle ABD$ **90, right**

Find the coordinates of the midpoint of a segment with the given endpoints. (Lesson 1-3) **60–62. See margin.**

60. $P(3, -7)$, $Q(9, 6)$ **61.** $A(-8, -5)$, $B(1, 7)$ **62.** $J(-7, 4)$, $K(3, 1)$

63. SNOWBOARDING In the design on the snowboard shown, $\overline{BD}$ bisects $\overline{SN}$ at R. If $SN = 163$ centimeters, find RN. (Lesson 1-2) **81.5 cm**

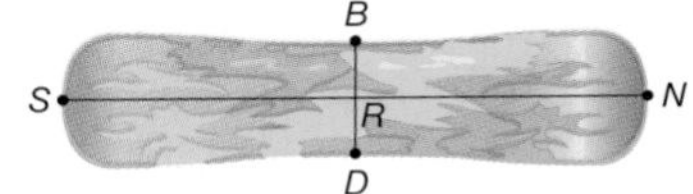

Skills Review

Name the congruent sides and angles in each figure. **64–67. See margin.**

64.

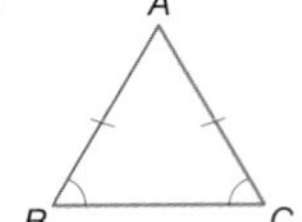

65.

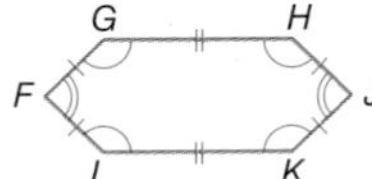

66.

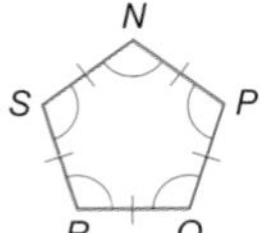

67.

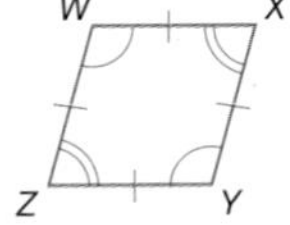

EXTEND 1-5 Geometry Lab
Constructing Perpendiculars

You can use a compass and a straightedge to construct a line perpendicular to a given line through a point on the line, or through a point *not* on the line.

CCSS Common Core State Standards
Content Standards
G.CO.12 Make formal geometric constructions with a variety of tools and methods (compass and straightedge, string, reflective devices, paper folding, dynamic geometric software, etc.).
Mathematical Practices 5

Activity Construct a Perpendicular

a. **Construct a line perpendicular to line ℓ and passing through point P on ℓ.**

Step 1

Place the compass at P. Draw arcs to the right and left of P that intersect line ℓ using the same compass setting. Label the points of intersection A and B.

Step 2

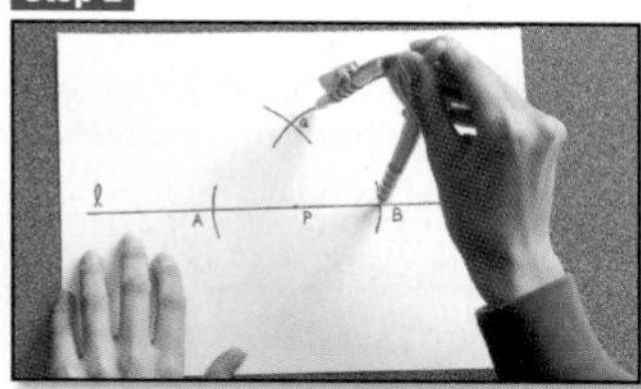

With the compass at A, draw an arc above line ℓ using a setting greater than AP. Using the same compass setting, draw an arc from B that intersects the previous arc. Label the intersection Q.

Step 3

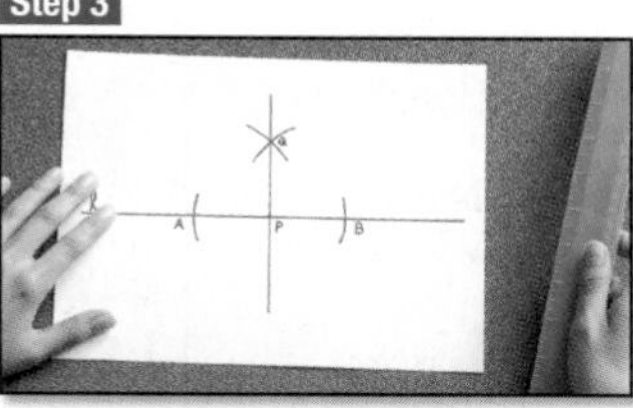

Use a straightedge to draw $\overleftrightarrow{QP}$.

b. **Construct a line perpendicular to line k and passing through point P *not* on k.**

Step 1

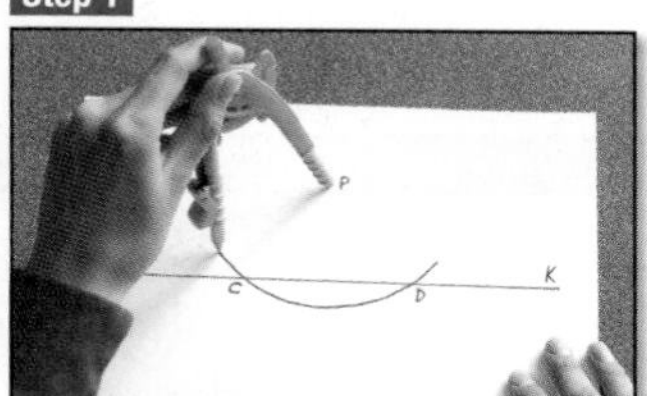

Place the compass at P. Draw an arc that intersects line k in two different places. Label the points of intersection C and D.

Step 2

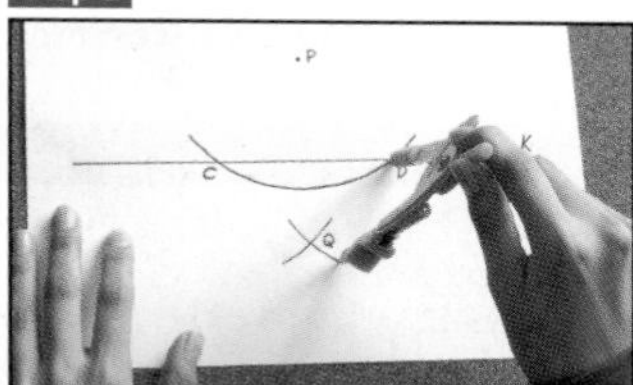

With the compass at C, draw an arc below line k using a setting greater than $\frac{1}{2}CD$. Using the same compass setting, draw an arc from D that intersects the previous arc. Label the intersection Q.

Step 3

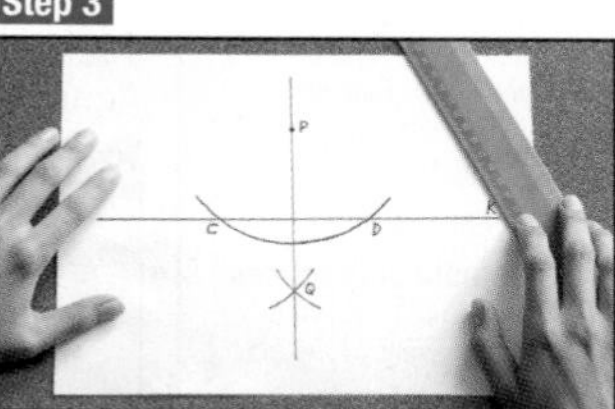

Use a straightedge to draw $\overleftrightarrow{PQ}$.

Model and Analyze the Results

1. Draw a line and construct a line perpendicular to it through a point on the line. **See students' work.**
2. Draw a line and construct a line perpendicular to it through a point not on the line. **See students' work.**
3. How is the second construction similar to the first one? **See margin.**

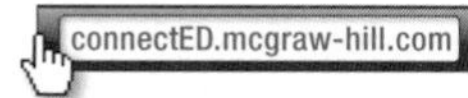

Additional Answer

3. The first step of the construction locates two points on the line. Then the process is very similar to the construction through a point on a line.

1 Focus

Objective Construct perpendiculars.

Materials

- compass
- straightedge

Teaching Tip

Stress the importance of keeping the compass setting stable when performing the construction, or the result may not be correct.

2 Teach

Working in Cooperative Groups

Arrange students in groups of 2, mixing abilities. Then have groups complete Activity **a**.

Ask:

- What is required for lines to be perpendicular? The angles formed must measure 90.
- What type of angle relationship is the result of the activity? The result forms supplementary angles.
- What is required to be able to make a line segment? two endpoints

Practice Have students complete Activity **b**.

3 Assess

Formative Assessment

Use Exercises 1 and 2 to assess whether students comprehend how to construct perpendicular lines.

From Concrete to Abstract Using the result from Activity a, have students use the arc intersections with the line as points. Next, have them connect the arc points with the perpendicular point. Have them make a conjecture about the triangle that is formed.

1 Focus

VerticalAlignment

Before Lesson 1-6 Measure figures such as line segments and angles.

Lesson 1-6 Identify and name polygons. Find perimeter or circumference and area of two-dimensional figures.

After Lesson 1-6 Formulate and test conjectures about the properties and attributes of polygons.

2 Teach

Scaffolding Questions

Have students read the **Why?** section of the lesson.

Ask:

- What are some of the geometric figures shown in the mosaic? triangles; quadrilaterals, including parallelograms and squares
- What geometric figure shown is not a polygon? circle
- What makes the circle different from the polygons used in the mosaic? The circle does not have sides or angles.

LESSON 1-6 Two-Dimensional Figures

Then

- You measured one-dimensional figures.

Now

1. Identify and name polygons.
2. Find perimeter, circumference, and area of two-dimensional figures.

Why?

- Mosaics are patterns or pictures created using small bits of colored glass or stone. They are usually set into a wall or floor and often make use of polygons.

NewVocabulary
polygon
vertex of a polygon
concave
convex
n-gon
equilateral polygon
equiangular polygon
regular polygon
perimeter
circumference
area

Common Core State Standards

Content Standards
G.GPE.7 Use coordinates to compute perimeters of polygons and areas of triangles and rectangles, e.g., using the distance formula.

Mathematical Practices
2 Reason abstractly and quantitatively.
6 Attend to precision.

1 Identify Polygons

Most of the closed figures shown in the mosaic are polygons. The term *polygon* is derived from a Greek word meaning *many angles.*

KeyConcept Polygons

A **polygon** is a closed figure formed by a finite number of coplanar segments called *sides* such that

- the sides that have a common endpoint are noncollinear, and
- each side intersects exactly two other sides, but only at their endpoints.

The vertex of each angle is a **vertex of the polygon**. A polygon is named by the letters of its vertices, written in order of consecutive vertices.

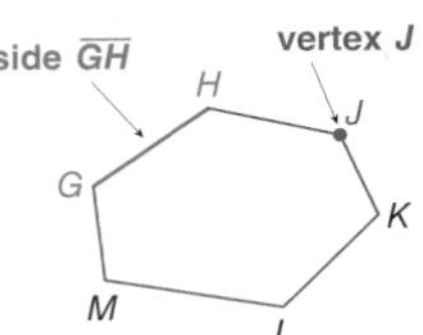

polygon *GHJKLM*

The table below shows some additional examples of polygons and some examples of figures that are not polygons.

Polygons	Not Polygons

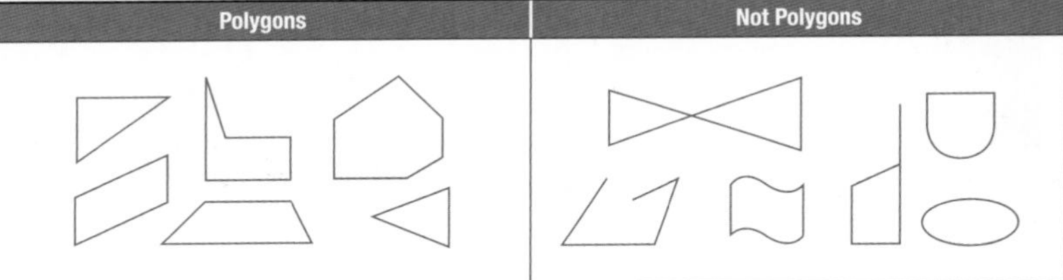

Polygons can be **concave** or **convex**. Suppose the line containing each side is drawn. If any of the lines contain any point in the interior of the polygon, then it is concave. Otherwise it is convex.

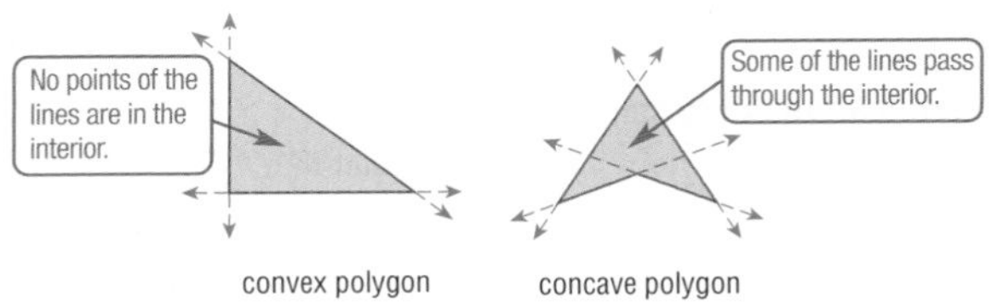

convex polygon   concave polygon

Pixoi Ltd/Alamy

56 | Lesson 1-6

Lesson 1-6 Resources

Resource	Approaching Level AL	On Level OL	Beyond Level BL	English Learners ELL
Teacher Edition	▪ Differentiated Instruction, p. 58	▪ Differentiated Instruction, pp. 58, 64	▪ Differentiated Instruction, p. 64	▪ Differentiated Instruction, p. 58
Chapter Resource Masters	▪ Study Guide and Intervention, pp. 37–38 ▪ Skills Practice, p. 39 ▪ Practice, p. 40 ▪ Word Problem Practice, p. 41	▪ Study Guide and Intervention, pp. 37–38 ▪ Skills Practice, p. 39 ▪ Practice, p. 40 ▪ Word Problem Practice, p. 41 ▪ Enrichment, p. 42	▪ Practice, p. 40 ▪ Word Problem Practice, p. 41 ▪ Enrichment, p. 42	▪ Study Guide and Intervention, pp. 37–38 ▪ Skills Practice, p. 39 ▪ Practice, p. 40 ▪ Word Problem Practice, p. 41
Other	▪ 5-Minute Check 1-6 ▪ Study Notebook	▪ 5-Minute Check 1-6 ▪ Study Notebook	▪ 5-Minute Check 1-6 ▪ Study Notebook	▪ 5-Minute Check 1-6 ▪ Study Notebook

StudyTip

Naming Polygons The Greek prefixes used to name polygons are also used to denote number. For example a *bi*cycle has two wheels, and a *tri*pod has three legs.

In general, a polygon is classified by its number of sides. The table lists some common names for various categories of polygon. A polygon with n sides is an **n-gon**. For example, a polygon with 15 sides is a 15-gon.

Number of Sides	Polygon
3	triangle
4	quadrilateral
5	pentagon
6	hexagon
7	heptagon
8	octagon
9	nonagon
10	decagon
11	hendecagon
12	dodecagon
n	n-gon

An **equilateral polygon** is a polygon in which all sides are congruent. An **equiangular polygon** is a polygon in which all angles are congruent.

A convex polygon that is both equilateral and equiangular is called a **regular polygon**. An *irregular polygon* is a polygon that is *not* regular.

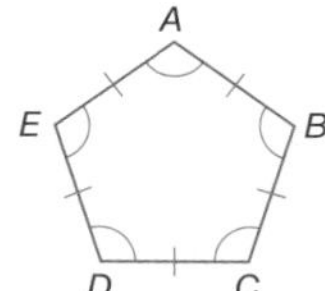

regular pentagon *ABCDE*

ReadingMath

Simple Closed Curves Polygons and circles are examples of *simple closed curves*. Such a curve begins and ends at the same point without crossing itself. The figures below are *not* simple closed curves.

Example 1 Name and Classify Polygons

Name each polygon by its number of sides. Then classify it as *convex* or *concave* and *regular* or *irregular*.

a.

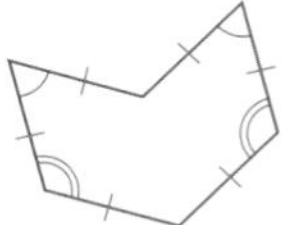

The polygon has 6 sides, so it is a hexagon.

Two of the lines containing the sides of the polygon will pass through the interior of the hexagon, so it is concave.

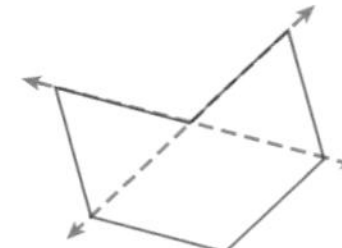

Only convex polygons can be regular, so this is an irregular hexagon.

b.

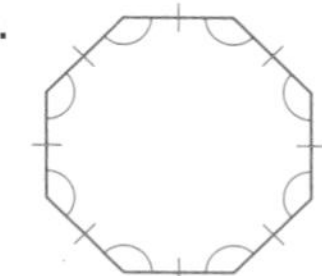

There are 8 sides, so this is an octagon.

No line containing any of the sides will pass through the interior of the octagon, so it is convex.

All of the sides are congruent, so it is equilateral. All of the angles are congruent, so it is equiangular.

Since the polygon is convex, equilateral, and equiangular, it is regular. So this is a regular octagon.

GuidedPractice

1A.

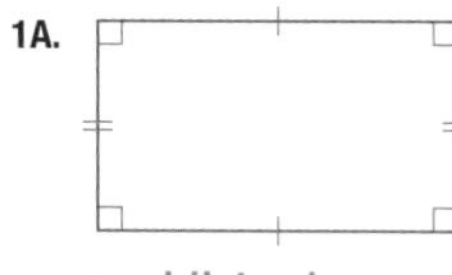

quadrilateral; convex; irregular

1B.

decagon; concave; irregular

1C.

hexagon; convex; regular

1 Identify Polygons

Example 1 shows how to use the properties of polygons to classify each polygon.

Teach with Tech

Student Response System Using your student response system software, develop several questions asking students to classify objects as convex or concave.

Formative Assessment

Use the Guided Practice exercises after each example to determine students' understanding of concepts.

Additional Example

1 Name each polygon by its number of sides. Then classify it as *convex* or *concave* and *regular* or *irregular.*

a.

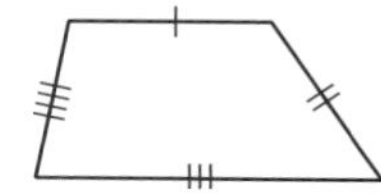

quadrilateral, convex, irregular

b.

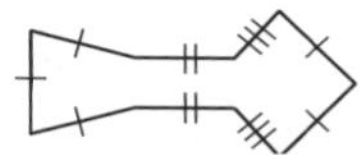

nonagon, concave, irregular

Additional Examples also in Interactive Classroom PowerPoint® Presentations

Tips for New Teachers

Classifying Polygons Stress to students that when they are asked to classify a 4-sided polygon by its number of sides, it is always classified as a quadrilateral. Some students will classify as a rectangle, square, rhombus, and so on. Point out that these classifications require that additional properties be true.

2 Perimeter, Circumference, and Area

Examples 2–4 show how to find the measures of perimeter, circumference, and area of a polygon.

Additional Example

2 Find the perimeter or circumference and area of each figure.

a. 4.6 cm; 2.3 cm

The perimeter is 13.8 cm. The area is about 10.6 cm^2.

b.

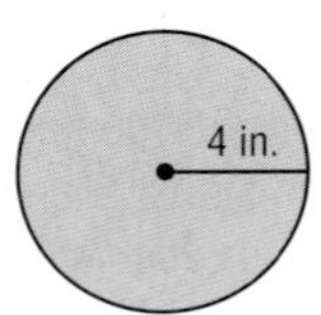

The circumference is about 25.1 inches. The area is about 50.2 square inches.

WatchOut!

Pi Approximations Alert students that approximating the circumference and area of a circle by using $\pi = 3.14$ may result in a significantly different product than when the stored value of π, [π], in a calculator is used.

Focus on Mathematical Content

Perimeter While there are formulas for the perimeters of a few special shapes, stress that the perimeter can always be found by adding the measures of all of the sides.

2 Perimeter, Circumference, and Area The **perimeter** of a polygon is the sum of the lengths of the sides of the polygon. Some shapes have special formulas for perimeter, but all are derived from the basic definition of perimeter. You will derive these formulas in Chapter 11. The **circumference** of a circle is the distance around the circle.

The **area** of a figure is the number of square units needed to cover a surface. Review the formulas for the perimeter and area of three common polygons and circle given below.

ReadingMath

Pi The symbol π is read *pi*. This is not a variable but an irrational number. The most accurate way to perform a calculation with π is to use a calculator. If no calculator is available, 3.14 is a good estimate for π.

KeyConcept Perimeter, Circumference, and Area

Triangle	Square	Rectangle	Circle
c, h, d, b	s, s, s, s	w, ℓ	r, d
$P = b + c + d$	$P = s + s + s + s$ $= 4s$	$P = \ell + w + \ell + w$ $= 2\ell + 2w$	$C = 2\pi r$ or $C = \pi d$
$A = \frac{1}{2}bh$	$A = s^2$	$A = \ell w$	$A = \pi r^2$

P = perimeter of polygon; A = area of figure; C = circumference
b = base, h = height; ℓ = length, w = width; r = radius, d = diameter

PT

Example 2 Find Perimeter and Area

Find the perimeter or circumference and area of each figure.

a.

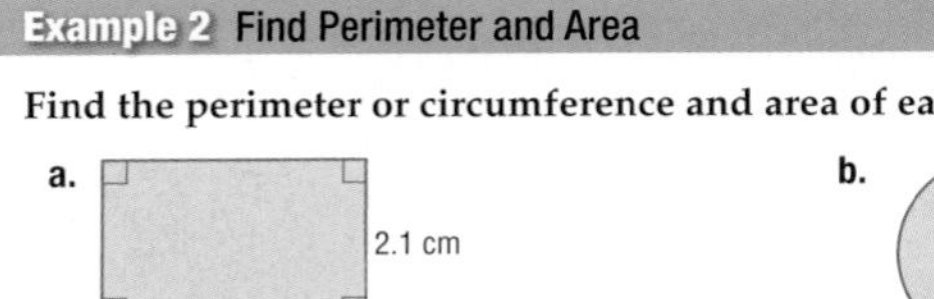

$P = 2\ell + 2w$ — Perimeter of rectangle
$= 2(3.2) + 2(2.1)$ — $\ell = 3.2$, $w = 2.1$
$= 10.6$ — Simplify.

The perimeter is 10.6 centimeters.

$A = \ell w$ — Area of rectangle
$= (3.2)(2.1)$ — $\ell = 3.2$, $w = 2.1$
$= 6.72$ — Simplify.

The area is about 6.7 square centimeters.

b.

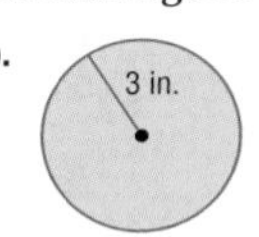

$C = 2\pi r$ — Circumference
$= 2\pi(3)$ — $r = 3$
≈ 18.85 — Use a calculator.

The circumference is about 18.9 inches.

$A = \pi r^2$ — Area of circle
$= \pi(3)^2$ — $r = 3$
≈ 28.3 — Use a calculator.

The area is about 28.3 square inches.

StudyTip

Perimeter vs. Area Since calculating the area of a figure involves multiplying two dimensions (unit × unit), *square units* are used. There is only one dimension used when finding the perimeter (the distance around), thus, it is given simply in *units*.

GuidedPractice

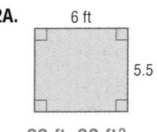

2A. 6 ft; 5.5 ft

23 ft; 33 ft^2

2B.

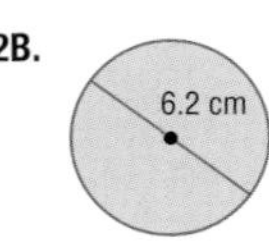

≈19.5 cm; ≈30.2 cm^2

2C.

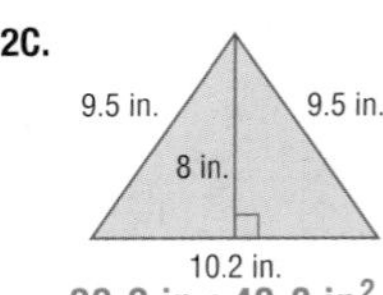

29.2 in.; 40.8 in^2

DifferentiatedInstruction AL OL ELL

If students have difficulty using or remembering the formulas for perimeter;

Then have them build their intuition by measuring cut outs of triangles, squares, and rectangles. To measure the circumference of a circle, have students use a piece of string that they can measure.

Standardized Test Example 3 Largest Area

Yolanda has 26 centimeters of cording to frame a photograph in her scrapbook. Which of these shapes would use *most* or all of the cording and enclose the *largest* area?

A right triangle with each leg about 7 centimeters long

B circle with a radius of about 4 centimeters

C rectangle with a length of 8 centimeters and a width of 4.5 centimeters

D square with a side length of 6 centimeters

Test-Taking Tip

Mental Math When you are asked to compare measures for varying figures, it can be helpful to use mental math. Estimate the perimeter or area of each figure, and then check your calculations.

Read the Test Item

You are asked to compare the area and perimeter of four different shapes.

Solve the Test Item

Find the perimeter and area of each shape.

Right Triangle

Use the Pythagorean Theorem to find the length of the hypotenuse.

$c^2 = a^2 + b^2$ Pythagorean Theorem

$c^2 = 7^2 + 7^2$ or 98 $a = 7, b = 7$

$c = \sqrt{98}$ or about 9.9 Simplify.

7 cm, 7 cm, c

Study Tip

Irrational Measures Notice that the triangle perimeter given in Example 3 is only an approximation. Because the length of the hypotenuse is an irrational number, the actual perimeter of the triangle is the irrational measure $(14 + \sqrt{98})$ centimeters.

$P = a + b + c$ Perimeter of a triangle

$\approx 7 + 7 + 9.9$ or about 23.9 cm Substitution

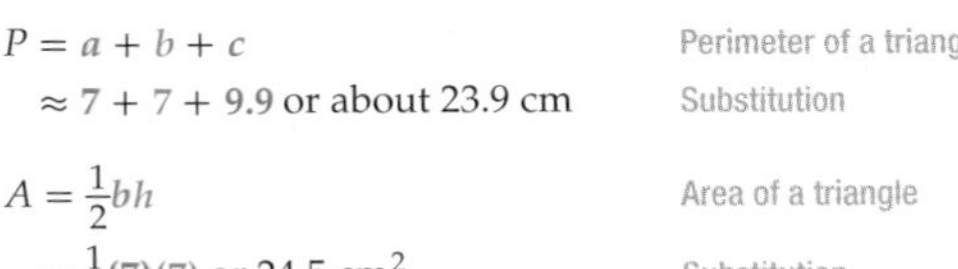

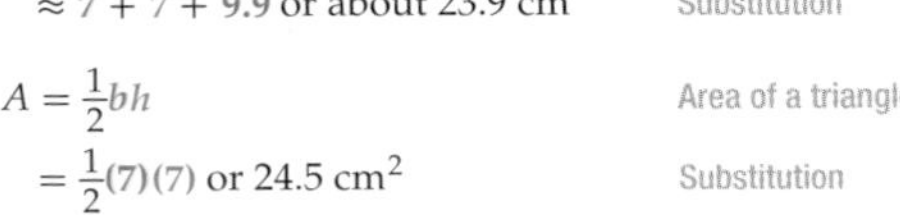

$A = \frac{1}{2}bh$ Area of a triangle

$= \frac{1}{2}(7)(7)$ or 24.5 cm^2 Substitution

Circle	Rectangle	Square
$C = 2\pi r$	$P = 2\ell + 2w$	$P = 4s$
$= 2\pi(4)$	$= 2(8) + 2(4.5)$	$= 4(6)$
≈ 25.1 cm	$= 25$ cm	$= 24$ cm
$A = \pi r^2$	$A = \ell w$	$A = s^2$
$= \pi(4)^2$	$= (8)(4.5)$	$= 6^2$
$\approx 50.3\ \text{cm}^2$	$= 36\ \text{cm}^2$	$= 36\ \text{cm}^2$

The shape that uses the most cording and encloses the largest area is the circle. The answer is B.

Guided Practice

3. Dasan has 32 feet of fencing to fence in a play area for his dog. Which shape of play area uses *most* or all of the fencing and encloses the *largest* area? F

F circle with radius of about 5 feet

G rectangle with length 5 feet and width 10 feet

H right triangle with legs of length 10 feet each

J square with side length 8 feet

Every chapter includes a worked-out **Standardized Test Example** that is similar to problems found on state assessments.

Additional Example

3 STANDARDIZED TEST EXAMPLE Terri has 19 feet of tape to mark an area in the classroom where the students may read. Which of these shapes has a perimeter or circumference that would use *most* or all of the tape? B

A square with side length of 5 feet

B circle with the radius of 3 feet

C right triangle with each leg length of 6 feet

D rectangle with a length of 8 feet and a width of 3 feet

Additional Example

4 COORDINATE GEOMETRY Find the perimeter and area of pentagon $ABCDE$ with $A(0, 4)$, $B(4, 0)$, $C(3, -4)$, $D(-3, -4)$, and $E(-3, 1)$.

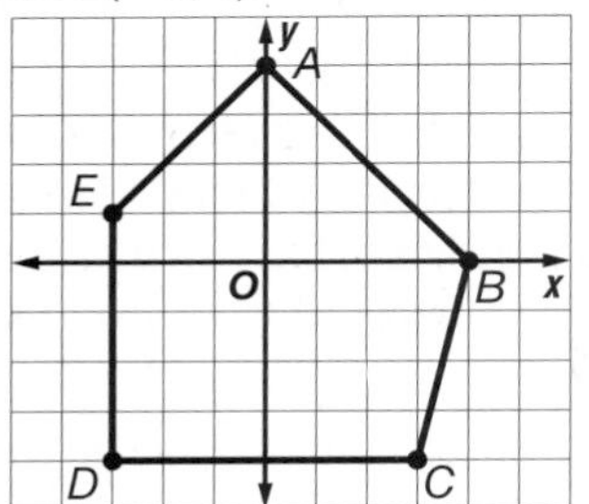

The perimeter is about 25 units and the area is 41.5 square units.

You can use the Distance Formula to find the perimeter of a polygon graphed on a coordinate plane.

Example 4 Perimeter and Area on the Coordinate Plane

COORDINATE GEOMETRY Find the perimeter and area of $\triangle PQR$ with vertices $P(-1, 3)$, $Q(-3, -1)$, and $R(4, -1)$.

Step 1 Find the perimeter of $\triangle PQR$.

Graph $\triangle PQR$.

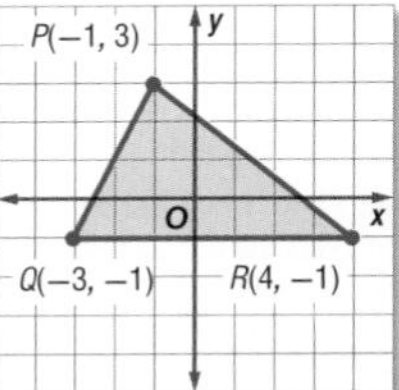

To find the perimeter of $\triangle PQR$, first find the lengths of each side. Counting the squares on the grid, we find that $QR = 7$ units. Use the Distance Formula to find the lengths of $\overline{PQ}$ and $\overline{PR}$.

$\overline{PQ}$ has endpoints at $P(-1, 3)$ and $Q(-3, -1)$.

$PQ = \sqrt{(x_2 - x_1)^2 + (y_2 - y_1)^2}$ — Distance Formula

$= \sqrt{[-1 - (-3)]^2 + [3 - (-1)]^2}$ — Substitute.

$= \sqrt{2^2 + 4^2}$ — Subtract.

$= \sqrt{20}$ or about 4.5 — Simplify.

$\overline{PR}$ has endpoints at $P(-1, 3)$ and $R(4, -1)$.

$PR = \sqrt{(x_2 - x_1)^2 + (y_2 - y_1)^2}$ — Distance Formula

$= \sqrt{(-1 - 4)^2 + [3 - (-1)]^2}$ — Substitute.

$= \sqrt{(-5)^2 + 4^2}$ — Subtract.

$= \sqrt{41}$ or about 6.4 — Simplify.

The perimeter of $\triangle PQR$ is $7 + \sqrt{20} + \sqrt{41}$ or about 17.9 units.

StudyTip

Linear and Square Units Remember to use linear units with perimeter and square units with area.

Step 2 Find the area of $\triangle PQR$.

To find the area of the triangle, find the lengths of the height and base. The height is the perpendicular distance from P to $\overline{QR}$. Counting squares on the graph, the height is 4 units. The length of $\overline{QR}$ is 7 units.

$A = \frac{1}{2}bh$ — Area of a triangle

$= \frac{1}{2}(7)(4)$ or 14 — Substitute and simplify.

The area of $\triangle PQR$ is 14 square units.

Guided Practice

4. Find the perimeter and area of $\triangle ABC$ with vertices $A(-1, 4)$, $B(-1, -1)$, and $C(6, -1)$. **$P = 12 + \sqrt{74}$ or about 20.6 units; $A = 17.5$ units^2**

60 | Lesson 1-6 | Two-Dimensional Figures

Check Your Understanding

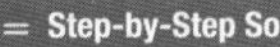 = Step-by-Step Solutions begin on page R14. 

Example 1 Name each polygon by its number of sides. Then classify it as *convex* or *concave* and *regular* or *irregular*.

1. 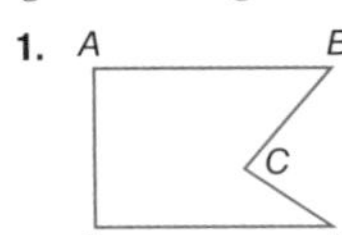

pentagon; concave; irregular

2. 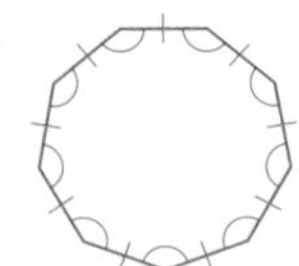 nonagon; convex; regular

SIGNS Identify the shape of each traffic sign and classify it as *regular* or *irregular*.

3. stop 

octagon; regular

4. caution or warning 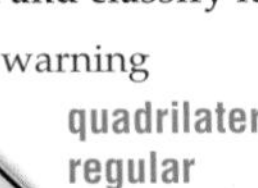 quadrilateral; regular

5. slow moving vehicle  hexagon; irregular

Example 2 Find the perimeter or circumference and area of each figure. Round to the nearest tenth.

6. 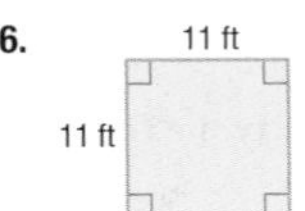

44 ft; 121 ft^2

7. 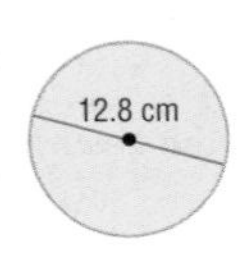

≈40.2 cm; ≈128.7 cm^2

8. 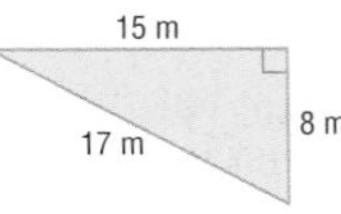

40 m; 60 m^2

Example 3

9. **MULTIPLE CHOICE** Vanesa is making a banner for the game. She has 20 square feet of fabric. What shape will use *most* or all of the fabric? **C**

A a square with a side length of 4 feet

B a rectangle with a length of 4 feet and a width of 3.5 feet

C a circle with a radius of about 2.5 feet

D a right triangle with legs of about 5 feet each

Example 4

10. CCSS **REASONING** Find the perimeter and area of $\triangle ABC$ with vertices $A(-1, 2)$, $B(3, 6)$, and $C(3, -2)$. $P = 8 + 2\sqrt{32}$ or about 19.3 units; $A = 16$ units^2

Practice and Problem Solving

Extra Practice is on page R1.

Example 1 Name each polygon by its number of sides. Then classify it as *convex* or *concave* and *regular* or *irregular*.

11. 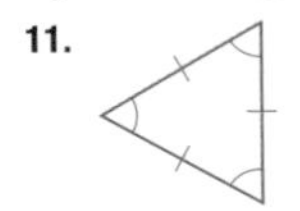 triangle; convex; regular

12. 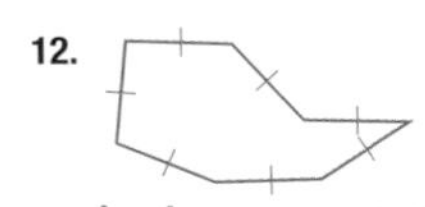 heptagon; concave; irregular

13.  octagon; concave; irregular

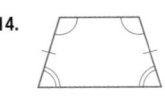

14.  quadrilateral; convex; irregular

15.  hendecagon; concave; irregular

16.  pentagon; convex; regular

Differentiated Homework Options

Level	Assignment	Two-Day Option	
AL Basic	11–28, 44, 46, 47, 49–65	11–27 odd, 50–53	12–28 even, 44, 46, 47, 49, 54–65
OL Core	11–27 odd, 29–44, 46, 47, 49–65	11–28, 50–53	29–44, 46, 47, 49, 54–65
BL Advanced	29–61, (optional: 62–65)		

3 Practice

Formative Assessment

Use Exercises 1–10 to check for understanding.

Then use the chart at the bottom of this page to customize assignments for your students.

Teaching the Mathematical Practices

Reasoning Mathematically proficient students make sense of the relationship of quantities in problem situations. In Exercise 10, encourage students to plan a solution pathway before beginning.

Examples 2–3 **Find the perimeter or circumference and area of each figure. Round to the nearest tenth.**

17.

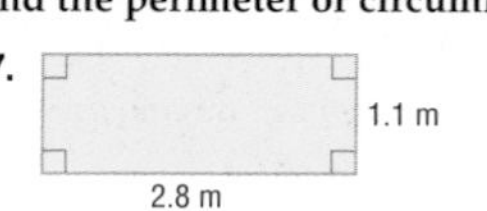

7.8 m; ≈3.1 m²

18.

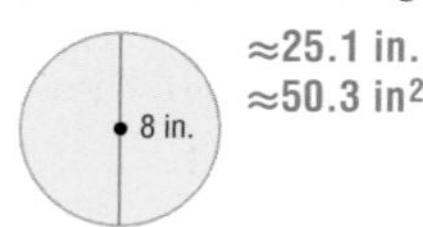

≈25.1 in.; ≈50.3 in²

19.

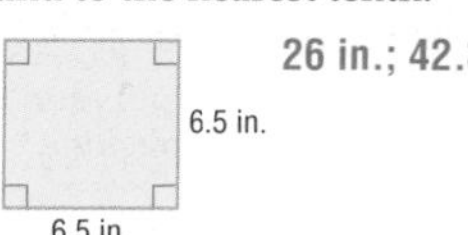

26 in.; 42.3 in²

20.

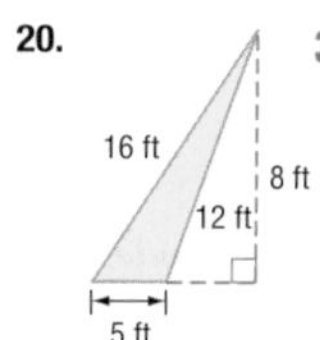

33 ft; 20 ft²

21.

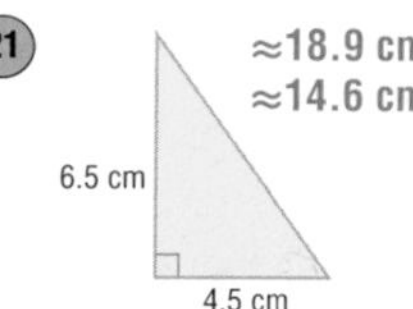

≈18.9 cm; ≈14.6 cm²

22.

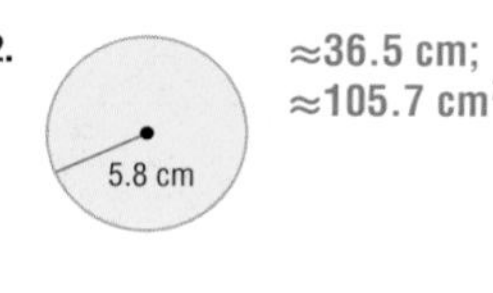

≈36.5 cm; ≈105.7 cm²

23. CRAFTS Joy has a square picture that is 4 inches on each side. The picture is framed with a length of ribbon. She wants to use the same piece of ribbon to frame a circular picture. What is the maximum radius of the circular frame? **≈2.55 in.**

24. LANDSCAPING Mr. Jackson has a circular garden with a diameter of 10 feet surrounded by edging. Using the same length of edging, he is going to create a square garden. What is the maximum side length of the square? **≈7.85 ft**

Example 4 CCSS **REASONING** **Graph each figure with the given vertices and identify the figure. Then find the perimeter and area of the figure.** **25–28. See margin.**

25. $D(-2, -2)$, $E(-2, 3)$, $F(2, -1)$

26. $J(-3, -3)$, $K(3, 2)$, $L(3, -3)$

27. $P(-1, 1)$, $Q(3, 4)$, $R(6, 0)$, $S(2, -3)$

28. $T(-2, 3)$, $U(1, 6)$, $V(5, 2)$, $W(2, -1)$

29. CHANGING DIMENSIONS Use the rectangle at the right.

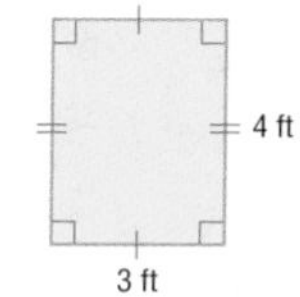

a. Find the perimeter of the rectangle. **14 ft**

b. Find the area of the rectangle. **12 ft²**

c. Suppose the length and width of the rectangle are doubled. What effect would this have on the perimeter? the area? Justify your answer. **See margin.**

d. Suppose the length and width of the rectangle are halved. What effect does this have on the perimeter? the area? Justify your answer. **See margin.**

30. CHANGING DIMENSIONS Use the triangle at the right.

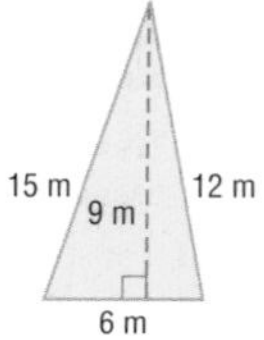

a. Find the perimeter of the triangle. **33 m**

b. Find the area of the triangle. **27 m²**

c. Suppose the side lengths and height of the triangle were doubled. What effect would this have on the perimeter? the area? Justify your answer. **See margin.**

d. Suppose the side lengths and height of the triangle were divided by three. What effect would this have on the perimeter? the area? Justify your answer. **See margin.**

31. ALGEBRA A rectangle of area 360 square yards is 10 times as long as it is wide. Find its length and width. **60 yd, 6 yd**

32. ALGEBRA A rectangle of area 350 square feet is 14 times as wide as it is long. Find its length and width. **5 ft, 70 ft**

Additional Answers

25. triangle; $P = 5 + \sqrt{32} + \sqrt{17}$ or about 14.78 units; $A = 10$ units²

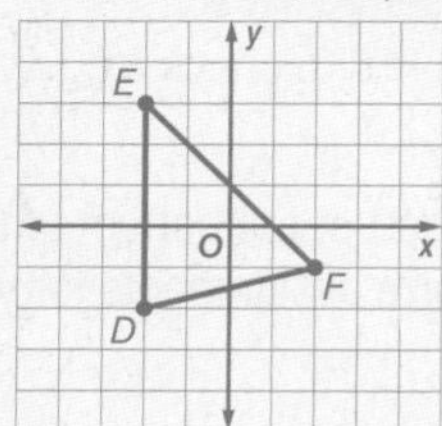

26. triangle; $P = 11 + \sqrt{61}$ or about 18.8 units; $A = 15$ units²

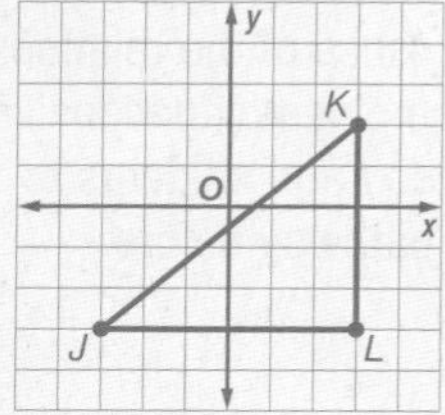

27. quadrilateral or square; $P =$ 20 units; $A = 25$ units²

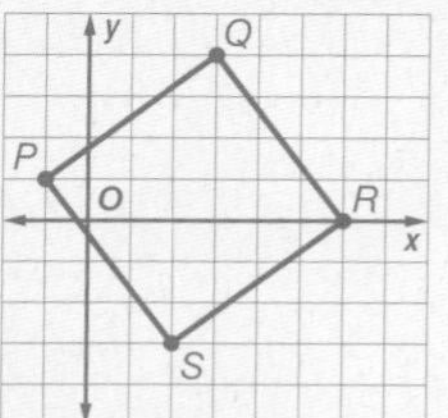

28. quadrilateral or rectangle; $P = 2\sqrt{32} + 2\sqrt{18}$ or about 19.8 units; $A = 24$ units²

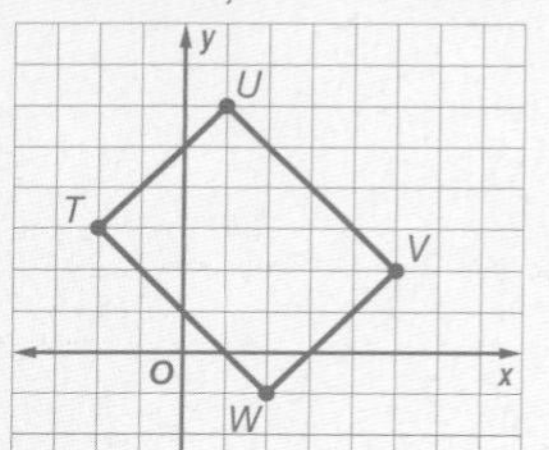

29c. The perimeter doubles; the area quadruples. The perimeter of a rectangle with dimensions 6 ft and 8 ft is 28 ft, which is twice the perimeter of the original figure since 2 • 14 ft = 28 ft. The area of a rectangle with dimensions 6 ft and 8 ft is 48 ft², which is four times the area of the original figure since 4 • 12 ft² = 48 ft².

29d. The perimeter is halved; the area is divided by 4. The perimeter of a rectangle with dimensions 1.5 ft and 2 ft is 7 ft, which is half the perimeter of the original figure since $\frac{1}{2}$ • 14 ft = 7 ft. The area of a rectangle with dimensions 1.5 ft and 2 ft is 3 ft², which is $\frac{1}{4}$ the area of the original figure since $\frac{1}{4}$ • 12 ft² = 3 ft².

30c. The perimeter doubles; the area quadruples. The perimeter of a triangle with side lengths 30 m, 24 m, and 12 m is 66 m, which is twice the perimeter of the original figure since 2 • 33 m = 66 m. The area of a triangle with base 12 m and height 18 m is 108 m², which is four times the area of the original figure since 4 • 27 m² = 108 m².

30d. The perimeter is divided by 3; the area is divided by 9. The perimeter of a triangle with side lengths 5 m, 4 m, and 2 m is 11 m, which is $\frac{1}{3}$ the perimeter of the original figure since $\frac{1}{3}$ • 33 m = 11 m. The area of a triangle with base 2 m and height 3 m is 3 m², which is $\frac{1}{9}$ the area of the original figure since $\frac{1}{9}$ • 27 m² = 3 m².

33 **DISC GOLF** The diameter of the most popular brand of flying disc used in disc golf measures between 8 and 10 inches. Find the range of possible circumferences and areas for these flying discs to the nearest tenth. **25.1 in. to 31.4 in.; 50.3 in^2 to 78.5 in^2**

ALGEBRA **Find the perimeter or circumference for each figure described.**

34. The area of a square is 36 square units. **24 units**

35. The length of a rectangle is half the width. The area is 25 square meters. **21.2 m**

36. The area of a circle is 25π square units. **10π or about 31.4 units**

37. The area of a circle is 32π square units. **$2\pi\sqrt{32}$ or about 35.5 units**

38. A rectangle's length is 3 times its width. The area is 27 square inches. **24 in.**

39. A rectangle's length is twice its width. The area is 48 square inches. **$12\sqrt{6}$ or about 29.4 in.**

CCSS PRECISION **Find the perimeter and area of each figure in inches. Round to the nearest hundredth, if necessary.**

40.

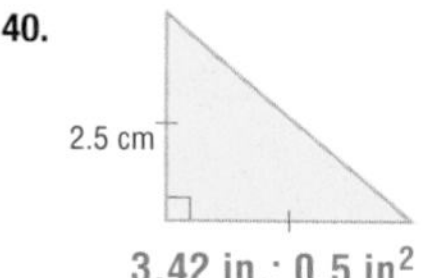

3.42 in.; 0.5 in^2

41.

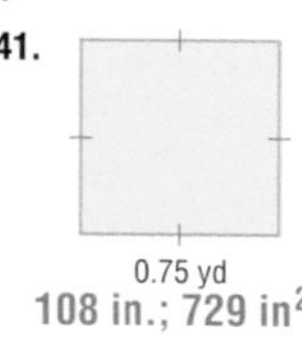

108 in.; 729 in^2

42.

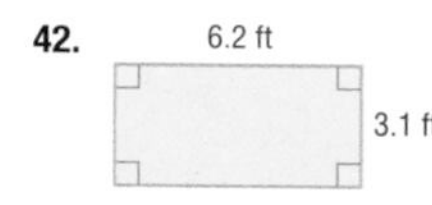

223.2 in.; 2767.68 in^2

43. 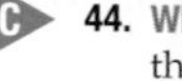 **MULTIPLE REPRESENTATIONS** Collect and measure the diameter and circumference of ten round objects using a millimeter measuring tape. **43a–d. See Ch. 1 Answer Appendix.**

Object	d	C	$\frac{C}{d}$
1			
2			
3			
⋮			
10			

a. Tabular Record the measures in a table as shown.

b. Algebraic Compute the value of $\frac{C}{d}$ to the nearest hundredth for each object and record the result.

c. Graphical Make a scatter plot of the data with d-values on the horizontal axis and C-values on the vertical axis.

d. Verbal Find an equation for a line of best fit for the data. What does this equation represent? What does the slope of the line represent?

H.O.T. Problems Use Higher-Order Thinking Skills

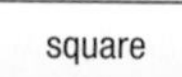

44. WHICH ONE DOESN'T BELONG? Identify the term that does not belong with the other three. Explain your reasoning. **Circle; the other shapes are polygons.**

square	circle	triangle	pentagon

45. CHALLENGE The vertices of a rectangle with side lengths of 10 and 24 units are on a circle of radius 13 units. Find the area between the figures. **290.93 units^2**

46. REASONING Name a polygon that is always regular and a polygon that is sometimes regular. Explain your reasoning. **See margin.**

47. OPEN ENDED Draw a pentagon. Is your pentagon *convex* or *concave*? Is your pentagon *regular* or *irregular*? Justify your answers. **See Ch. 1 Answer Appendix.**

48. CHALLENGE A rectangular room measures 20 feet by 12.5 feet. How many 5-inch square tiles will it take to cover the floor of this room? Explain. **See Ch. 1 Answer Appendix.**

49. WRITING IN MATH Describe two possible ways that a polygon can be equiangular but not a regular polygon. **See Ch. 1 Answer Appendix.**

Additional Answer

46. Square; by definition, all sides of a square are congruent and all angles measure 90, so therefore are congruent. Triangle; triangles can have all sides and angles congruent, just two sides and angle pairs congruent, or no sides or angles congruent.

Enrichment
OL BL

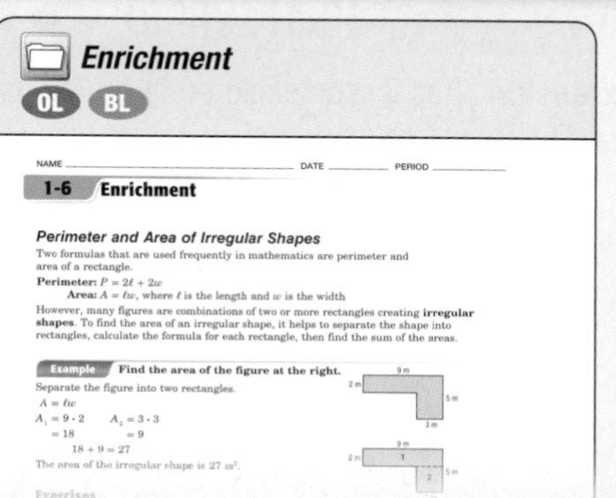

1-6 Enrichment

Perimeter and Area of Irregular Shapes

Study Guide and Intervention
AL OL ELL

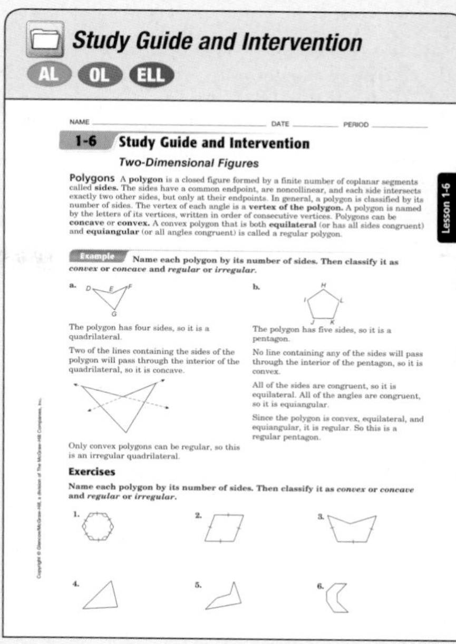

1-6 Study Guide and Intervention

Two-Dimensional Figures

Practice
AL OL BL ELL

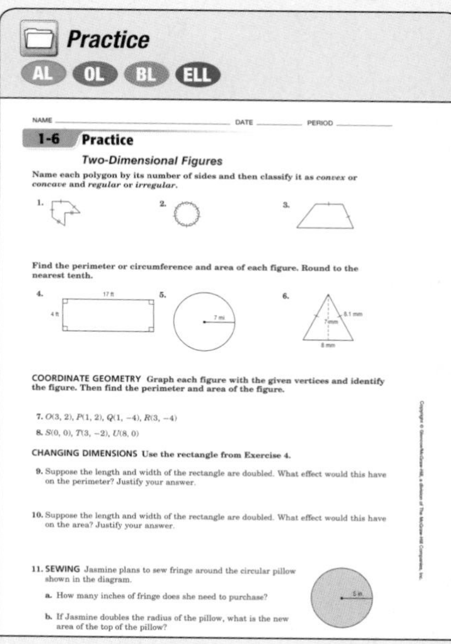

1-6 Practice

Two-Dimensional Figures

Word Problem Practice
AL OL BL ELL

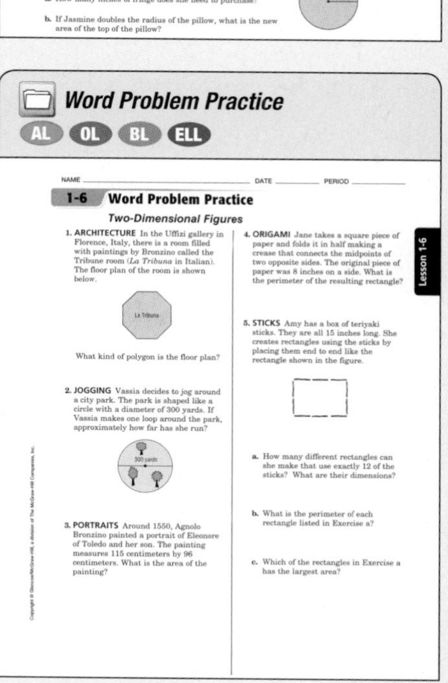

1-6 Word Problem Practice

Two-Dimensional Figures

4 Assess

Ticket out the Door Distribute a sheet of paper with several polygons on it. Have the students label each figure, classify it, use a ruler to measure the lengths of the sides, and calculate the perimeter. Have students turn in their results before they leave the classroom.

Formative Assessment

Check for student understanding of concepts in Lessons 1-5 and 1-6.

Quiz 3, p. 52

Standardized Test Practice

50. Find the perimeter of the figure. C

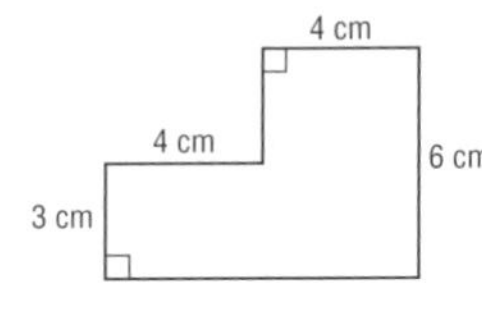

A 17 cm
B 25 cm
C 28 cm
D 31 cm

51. PROBABILITY In three successive rolls of a fair number cube, Matt rolls a 6. What is the probability of Matt rolling a 6 if the number cube is rolled a fourth time? F

F $\frac{1}{6}$
G $\frac{1}{4}$
H $\frac{1}{3}$
J 1

52. SHORT RESPONSE Miguel is planning a party for 80 guests. According to the pattern in the table, how many gallons of ice cream should Miguel buy? 20 gal

Number of Guests	Gallons of Ice Cream
8	2
16	4
24	6
32	8

53. SAT/ACT A frame 2 inches wide surrounds a painting that is 18 inches wide and 14 inches tall. What is the area of the frame? C

A 68 in^2
B 84 in^2
C 144 in^2
D 252 in^2
E 396 in^2

Spiral Review

Determine whether each statement can be assumed from the figure. Explain. (Lesson 1-5) 56. No; we do not know whether $\angle MNP$ is a right angle.

54. $\angle KJN$ is a right angle. Yes; the symbol denotes that $\angle KJN$ is a right angle.

55. $\angle PLN \cong \angle NLM$ No; we do not know anything about these measures.

56. $\angle PNL$ and $\angle MNL$ are complementary.

57. $\angle KLN$ and $\angle MLN$ are supplementary. Yes; they form a linear pair.

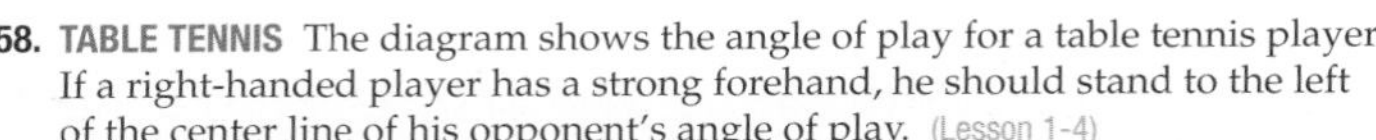

58. TABLE TENNIS The diagram shows the angle of play for a table tennis player. If a right-handed player has a strong forehand, he should stand to the left of the center line of his opponent's angle of play. (Lesson 1-4)

a. What geometric term describes the center line? angle bisector

b. If the angle of play shown in the diagram measures 43°, what is $m\angle BAD$? 21.5

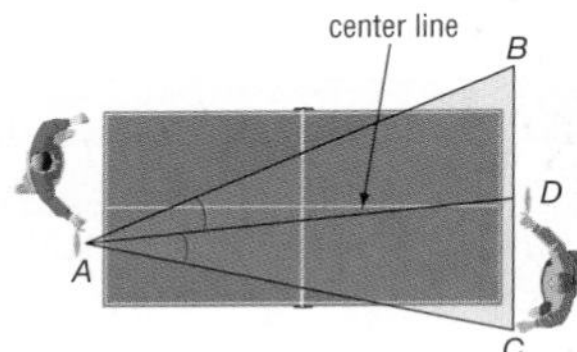

Name an appropriate method to solve each system of equations. Then solve the system. (Lesson 0-8)

59. $-5x + 2y = 13$
$2x + 3y = -9$
elimination; $x = -3$, $y = -1$

60. $y = -5x + 7$
$y = 3x - 17$
graphing; $x = 3$, $y = -8$

61. $x - 8y = 16$
$7x - 4y = -18$
substitution; $x = -4$, $y = -2.5$

Skills Review

Evaluate each expression if $P = 10$, $B = 12$, $h = 6$, $r = 3$, and $\ell = 5$. Round to the nearest tenth, if necessary.

62. $\frac{1}{2}P\ell + B$ 37

63. $\frac{1}{3}Bh$ 24

64. $\frac{1}{3}\pi r^2 h$ 56.5

65. $2\pi rh + 2\pi r^2$ 169.6

Differentiated Instruction OL BL

Extension This lesson explored two-dimensional figures. What kind of figures are three-dimensional? Solid figures such as prisms, pyramids, and spheres

EXTEND 1-6

Geometry Software Lab
Two-Dimensional Figures

You can use The Geometer's Sketchpad® to draw and investigate polygons.

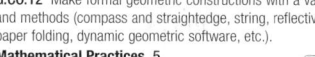

CCSS **Common Core State Standards**
Content Standards
G.CO.12 Make formal geometric constructions with a variety of tools and methods (compass and straightedge, string, reflective devices, paper folding, dynamic geometric software, etc.).
Mathematical Practices 5

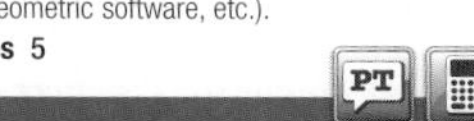

Activity 1 Draw a Polygon

Draw $\triangle XYZ$.

Step 1 Select the segment tool from the toolbar, and click to set the first endpoint X of side $\overline{XY}$. Then drag the cursor, and click again to set the other endpoint Y.

Step 2 Click on point Y to set the endpoint of $\overline{YZ}$. Drag the cursor and click to set point Z.

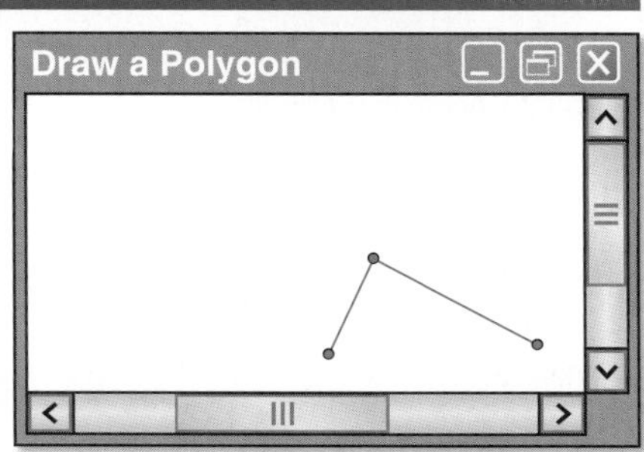

Step 3 Click on point Z to set the endpoint of $\overline{ZX}$. Then move the cursor to highlight point X. Click on X to draw $\overline{ZX}$.

Step 4 Use the pointer tool to click on points X, Y, and Z. Under the **Display** menu, select **Show Labels** to label the vertices of your triangle.

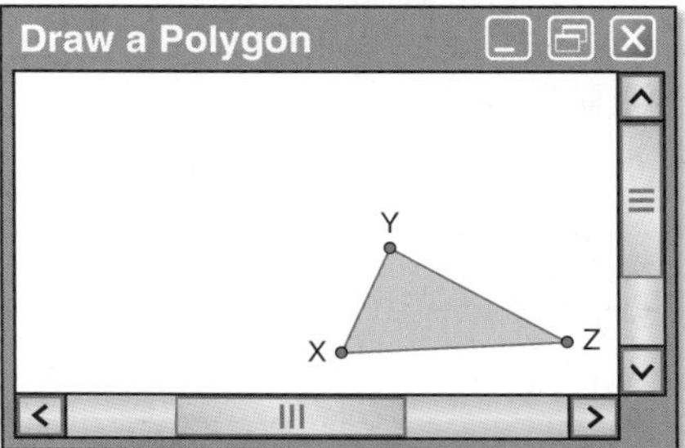

Activity 2 Measure Sides

Find XY, YZ, and ZX.

Step 1 Use the pointer tool to select $\overline{XY}$, $\overline{YZ}$, and $\overline{ZX}$.

Step 2 Select the **Length** command under the **Measure** menu to display the lengths of $\overline{XY}$, $\overline{YZ}$, and $\overline{ZX}$.

$XY = 1.79$ cm

$YZ = 3.11$ cm

$ZX = 3.48$ cm

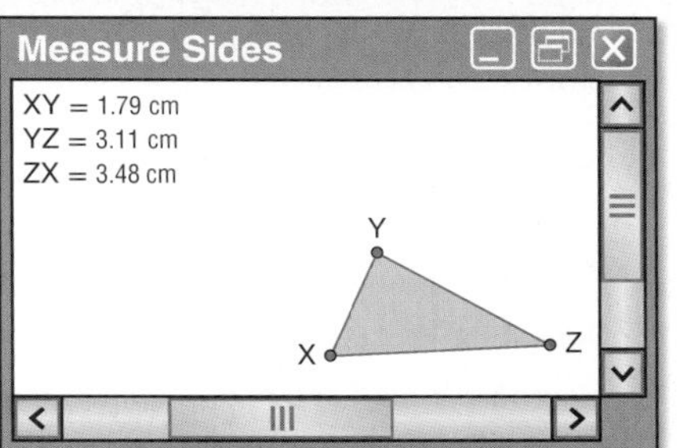

(continued on the next page)

1 Focus

Objective Use The Geometer's Sketchpad to draw polygons and find side lengths, angle measures, and perimeter.

Materials

- Geometer's Sketchpad software

Teaching Tip

Explain to students that their measurements will not be the same as the screen shown in the activity. Also, remind students to examine the measures provided by the software. An unreasonable measurement may mean the student has not selected the item correctly.

2 Teach

Working in Cooperative Groups

Arrange students in groups of 2, mixing abilities. Then have groups complete Activities 1–4. Monitor students as they work to help them avoid common mistakes when using the software.

Ask:

- Must the endpoints of a line segment be selected in a specific order to find its length? Explain. No; $XY = YX$, and so on.
- If an endpoint is selected and moved, what happens to the segment length? The Geometer's Sketchpad software automatically updates the length as it changes.
- In Activity 3, will all triangles have the same perimeter? Explain. No, the side lengths determine the perimeter, and the side lengths were drawn by the individual sketcher.
- In Activity 4, when measuring the angles, the order in which the vertices are selected is crucial. Explain why. Just as the vertex of the angle must be written between the points on the rays of the angle, the vertex of the angle must be selected second when collecting the points of the angle. For example, $\angle JHK$ is the angle with vertex at point H and rays with points J and K.

Practice Have students complete Exercises 1–5.

3 Assess

Formative Assessment

In Exercises 6–10, students derive the formula that calculates the sum of the interior angles of a polygon with *n* sides. They also recognize that changing the sides of a polygon by a common factor causes the perimeter to be changed by the same factor.

From Concrete to Abstract

Before students complete Question 4, ask them to predict what will happen to the perimeter of the quadrilateral based on what they have gathered from similar examples they have seen thus far in Lesson 1-6.

Additional Answers

4. Sample answer: When the lengths of the sides are doubled, the perimeter is doubled.
6. Sample answer: The sum of the measures of the angles of a triangle is 180°.
7. Sample answer: The sum of the measures of the angles of a quadrilateral is 360°; pentagon = 540°; hexagon = 720°.
8. Sample answer: The sum of the angles of polygons increases by 180° for each additional side.
9. Yes; sample answer: triangle: 3 sides, angle sum: 180; quadrilateral: 4 sides, angle sum: 180 + 180 = 360; pentagon: 5 sides, angle sum: 360 + 180 = 540; hexagon: 6 sides, angle sum: 540 + 180 = 720.
10. Yes; sample answer: If the sides of a polygon are *a*, *b*, *c*, and *d*, then its perimeter is $a + b + c + d$. If each of the sides are increased by a factor of *n* then the sides measure *na*, *nb*, *nc*, and *nd*, and the perimeter is $na + nb + nc + nd$. By factoring, the peimeter is $n(a + b + c + d)$, which is the original perimeter increased by the same factor as the sides.

Geometry Software Lab
Two-Dimensional Figures *Continued*

Activity 3 Find Perimeter

Find the perimeter of $\triangle XYZ$.

Step 1 Use the pointer tool to select points *X*, *Y*, and *Z*.

Step 2 Under the **Construct** menu, select **Triangle Interior**. The triangle will now be shaded.

Step 3 Select the triangle interior using the pointer.

Step 4 Choose the **Perimeter** command under the **Measure** menu to find the perimeter of $\triangle XYZ$.

The perimeter of $\triangle XYZ$ is 8.38 centimeters.

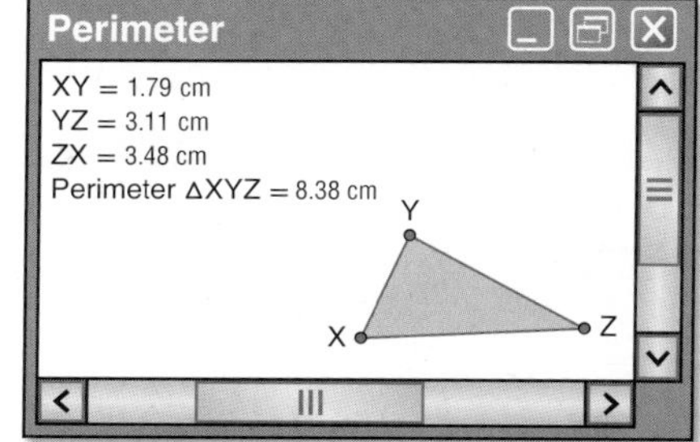

Activity 4 Measure Angles

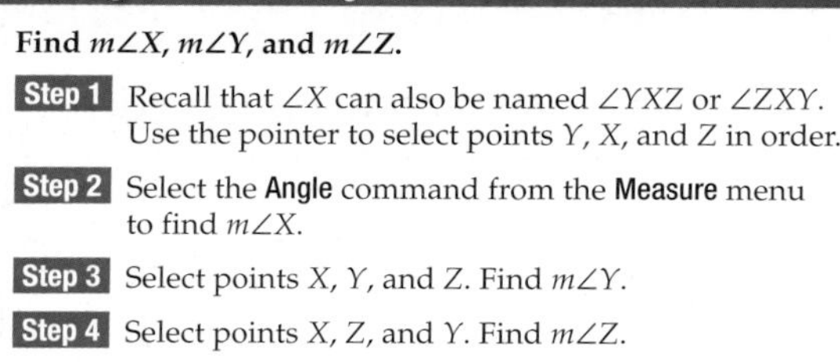

Find $m\angle X$, $m\angle Y$, and $m\angle Z$.

Step 1 Recall that $\angle X$ can also be named $\angle YXZ$ or $\angle ZXY$. Use the pointer to select points *Y*, *X*, and *Z* in order.

Step 2 Select the **Angle** command from the **Measure** menu to find $m\angle X$.

Step 3 Select points *X*, *Y*, and *Z*. Find $m\angle Y$.

Step 4 Select points *X*, *Z*, and *Y*. Find $m\angle Z$.

$m\angle X = 63.16$, $m\angle Y = 86.05$, and $m\angle Z = 30.8$.

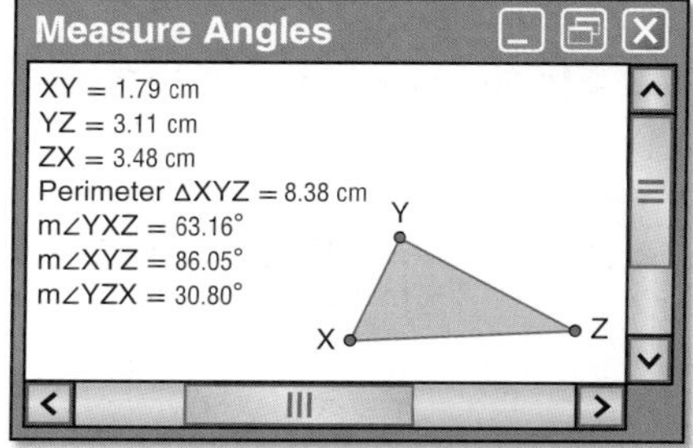

Analyze the Results **1. The sum of the side measures equals the perimeter.**

1. Add the side measures from Activity 2. How does this compare to the result in Activity 3?
2. What is the sum of the angle measures of $\triangle XYZ$? **180°**
3. Repeat the activities for each figure. **See students' work.**
   a. irregular quadrilateral **b.** square **c.** pentagon **d.** hexagon
4. Draw another quadrilateral and find its perimeter. Then enlarge your figure using the **Dilate** command. How does changing the sides affect the perimeter? **See margin.**
5. Compare your results with those of your classmates. **See students' work.**
6. Make a conjecture about the sum of the measures of the angles in any triangle. **See margin.**
7. What is the sum of the measures of the angles of a quadrilateral? pentagon? hexagon? **See margin.**
8. How are the sums of the angles of polygons related to the number of sides? **See margin.**
9. Test your conjecture on other polygons. Does your conjecture hold? Explain. **See margin.**
10. When the sides of a polygon are changed by a common factor, does the perimeter of the polygon change by the same factor as the sides? Explain. **See margin.**

LESSON 1-7 Three-Dimensional Figures

Then

- You identified and named two-dimensional figures.

Now

1. Identify and name three-dimensional figures.
2. Find surface area and volume.

Why?

- Architects often provide three-dimensional models of their ideas to clients. These models give their clients a better idea of what the completed structure will look like than a two-dimensional drawing. Three-dimensional figures, or *solids*, are made up of flat or curved surfaces.

NewVocabulary

polyhedron
face
edge
vertex
prism
base
pyramid
cylinder
cone
sphere
regular polyhedron
Platonic solid
surface area
volume

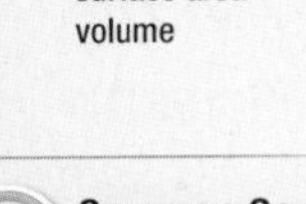

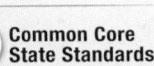

Common Core State Standards

Content Standards

G.GMD.3 Use volume formulas for cylinders, pyramids, cones, and spheres to solve problems. ★

Mathematical Practices

2 Reason abstractly and quantitatively.
6 Attend to precision.

1 Identify Three-Dimensional Figures

A solid with all flat surfaces that enclose a single region of space is called a **polyhedron**. Each flat surface or **face** is a polygon. The line segments where the faces intersect are called **edges**. The point where three or more edges intersect is called a **vertex**. Below are examples and definitions of polyhedrons and other types of solids.

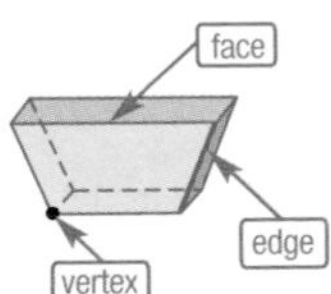

KeyConcept Types of Solids

Polyhedrons

A **prism** is a polyhedron with two parallel congruent faces called **bases** connected by parallelogram faces.

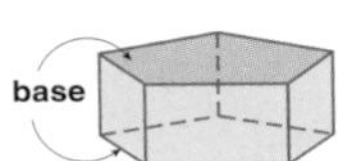

A **pyramid** is a polyhedron that has a polygonal base and three or more triangular faces that meet at a common vertex.

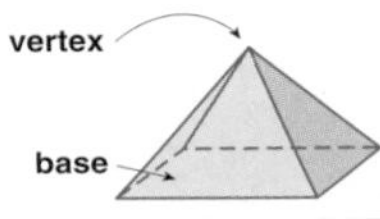

Not Polyhedrons

A **cylinder** is a solid with congruent parallel circular bases connected by a curved surface.

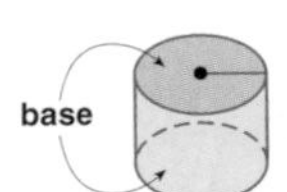

A **cone** is a solid with a circular base connected by a curved surface to a single vertex.

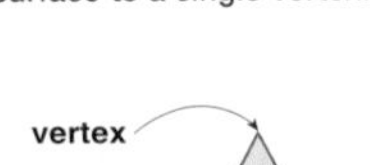
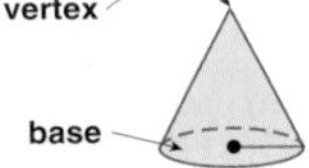

A **sphere** is a set of points in space that are the same distance from a given point. A sphere has no faces, edges, or vertices.

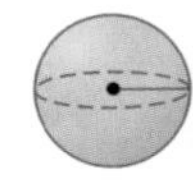

Polyhedrons or *polyhedra* are named by the shape of their bases.

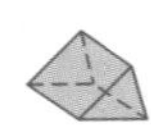

triangular prism

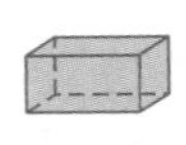
rectangular prism

pentagonal prism

triangular pyramid

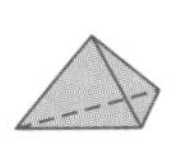
rectangular pyramid

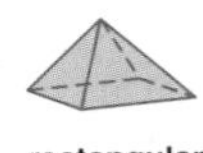

pentagonal pyramid

1 Focus

VerticalAlignment

Before Lesson 1-7 Identify and name two-dimensional figures.

Lesson 1-7 Identify and name three-dimensional figures. Find surface area and volume.

After Lesson 1-7 Use orthographic views of three-dimensional geometric figures.

2 Teach

Scaffolding Questions

Have students read the **Why?** section of the lesson.

Ask:

- What does the three-dimensional model in the picture appear to represent? Sample answer: an office building or multi-family housing units
- What geometric figures make up the sides of the model? rectangles and triangles
- What geometric figures could make up the top of a model? Explain. The top of the model could be a pyramid if the top of the building is a standard pitched roof. The top of the model could also be a simple rectangle if the building is to have a flat roof.

Lesson 1-7 Resources

Resource	Approaching Level AL	On Level OL	Beyond Level BL	English Learners ELL
Teacher Edition	▪ Differentiated Instruction, p. 69	▪ Differentiated Instruction, pp. 69, 74	▪ Differentiated Instruction, pp. 69, 74	▪ Differentiated Instruction, p. 69
Chapter Resource Masters	▪ Study Guide and Intervention, pp. 43–44 ▪ Skills Practice, p. 45 ▪ Practice, p. 46 ▪ Word Problem Practice, p. 47	▪ Study Guide and Intervention, pp. 43–44 ▪ Skills Practice, p. 45 ▪ Practice, p. 46 ▪ Word Problem Practice, p. 47 ▪ Enrichment, p. 48	▪ Practice, p. 46 ▪ Word Problem Practice, p. 47 ▪ Enrichment, p. 48	▪ Study Guide and Intervention, pp. 43–44 ▪ Skills Practice, p. 45 ▪ Practice, p. 46 ▪ Word Problem Practice, p. 47
Other	▪ 5-Minute Check 1-7 ▪ Study Notebook	▪ 5-Minute Check 1-7 ▪ Study Notebook	▪ 5-Minute Check 1-7 ▪ Study Notebook	▪ 5-Minute Check 1-7 ▪ Study Notebook

1 Identify Three-Dimensional Figures

Example 1 shows how to use the properties of three-dimensional figures to classify each object.

Formative Assessment

Use the Guided Practice exercises after each example to determine students' understanding of concepts.

Tips for New Teachers

Right Solids In this lesson, all solids are right solids. These will be defined in Lesson 12-1.

Additional Example

1 Determine whether each solid is a polyhedron. Then identify the solid. If it is a polyhedron, name the bases, faces, edges, and vertices.

a.

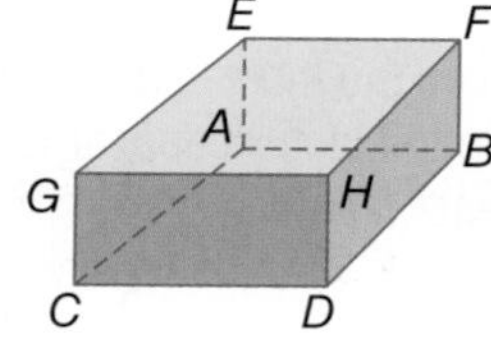

Rectangular prism;
Bases: rectangles *EFHG*, *ABDC*
Faces: rectangles *FBDH*, *EACG*, *GCDH*, *EFBA*
Edges: $\overline{EF}$, $\overline{FH}$, $\overline{HG}$, $\overline{GE}$, $\overline{EA}$, $\overline{AC}$, $\overline{CG}$, $\overline{FB}$, $\overline{BD}$, $\overline{DH}$, $\overline{AB}$, $\overline{CD}$
Vertices: *A*, *B*, *C*, *D*, *E*, *F*, *G*, *H*

b.

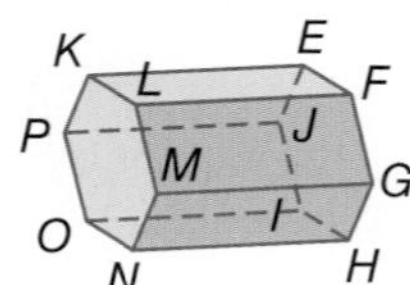

Hexagonal prism;
Bases: hexagon *EFGHIJ* and hexagon *KLMNOP*
Faces: rectangles *EFLK*, *FGML*, *GHNM*, *HNOI*, *IOPJ*, *JPKE*
Edges: $\overline{FL}$, $\overline{GM}$, $\overline{HN}$, $\overline{IO}$, $\overline{JP}$, $\overline{EK}$, $\overline{EF}$, $\overline{FG}$, $\overline{GH}$, $\overline{HI}$, $\overline{IJ}$, $\overline{JE}$, $\overline{KL}$, $\overline{LM}$, $\overline{MN}$, $\overline{NO}$, $\overline{OP}$, $\overline{PK}$
Vertices: *E*, *F*, *G*, *H*, *I*, *J*, *K*, *L*, *M*, *N*, *O*, *P*

(continued on the next page)

Example 1 Identify Solids

Determine whether each solid is a polyhedron. Then identify the solid. If it is a polyhedron, name the bases, faces, edges, and vertices.

a.

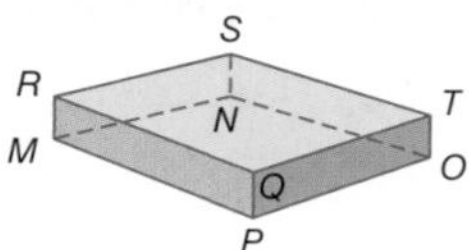

The solid is formed by polygonal faces, so it is a polyhedron. There are two parallel congruent rectangular bases, so it is a rectangular prism.

Bases: ▭*MNOP*, ▭*RSTQ*

Faces: ▭*RQPM*, ▭*RSNM*, ▭*STON*, ▭*QTOP*, ▭*RSTQ*, ▭*MNOP*

Edges: $\overline{MN}$, $\overline{NO}$, $\overline{OP}$, $\overline{PM}$, $\overline{RS}$, $\overline{ST}$, $\overline{TQ}$, $\overline{QR}$, $\overline{RM}$, $\overline{SN}$, $\overline{TO}$, $\overline{QP}$

Vertices: *M*, *N*, *O*, *P*, *Q*, *R*, *S*, *T*

b.

The solid has a curved surface, so it is not a polyhedron. It has two congruent circular bases, so it is a cylinder.

c.

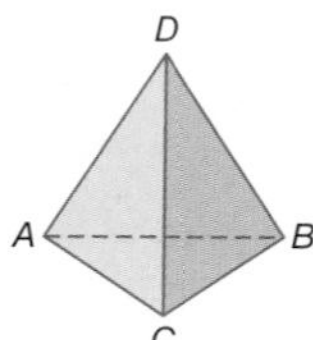

The solid is formed by polygonal faces, so it is a polyhedron. The base is a triangle, and the three faces meet in a vertex, so it is a triangular pyramid.

Bases: △*ABC*

Faces: △*ABC*, △*ADC*, △*CDB*, △*BDA*

Edges: $\overline{AB}$, $\overline{BC}$, $\overline{CA}$, $\overline{DA}$, $\overline{DB}$, $\overline{DC}$

Vertices: *A*, *B*, *C*, *D*

ReadingMath

Symbols Symbols can be used in naming the focus of polyhedra. The symbol ▭ means rectangle. The symbol △ means triangle. The symbol ⊙ means circle.

GuidedPractice

1A.

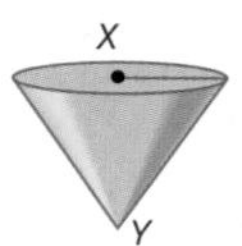

not a polyhedron; cone

1B.

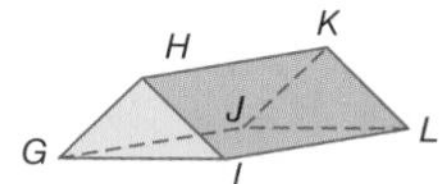

See margin.

A polyhedron is a **regular polyhedron** if all of its faces are regular congruent polygons and all of the edges are congruent. There are exactly five types of regular polyhedrons, called **Platonic Solids** because Plato used them extensively.

Math HistoryLink

Plato (427–347 B.C.) Plato, a philosopher, mathematician, and scientist, lived in Athens, Greece. He is best known for founding a school known as "The Academy." In mathematics, he was concerned with the idea of proofs, and he insisted that definitions must be accurate and hypotheses must be clear.

KeyConcept Platonic Solids

Tetrahedron	Hexahedron or Cube	Octahedron	Dodecahedron	Icosahedron
4 equilateral triangle faces	6 square faces	8 equilateral triangular faces	12 regular pentagonal faces	20 equilateral triangular faces

RICHARD NOWITZ/National Geographic Image Collection

Additional Answer (Guided Practice)

1B. a polyhedron; triangular prism; bases: △*GHI*, △*JKL*; faces: △*GHI*, △*JKL*, ▭*GHKJ*, ▭*IHKL*, ▭*GJLI*; edges: $\overline{GH}$, $\overline{HI}$, $\overline{GI}$, $\overline{GJ}$, $\overline{HK}$, $\overline{IL}$, $\overline{JK}$, $\overline{KL}$, $\overline{JL}$; vertices: *G*, *H*, *I*, *J*, *K*, *L*

Teach with Tech

Interactive Whiteboard Search the gallery of figures with your interactive whiteboard software to find precise and moveable graphics of three-dimensional figures. Display them on the board and use them as you show how to count the numbers of faces, edges, and vertices of the figures.

2 Surface Area and Volume

Surface area is a two-dimensional measurement of the surface of a solid figure. The surface area of a polyhedron is the sum of the areas of each face. **Volume** is the measure of the amount of space enclosed by a solid figure.

Review the formulas for the surface area and volume of five common solids given below. You will derive these formulas in Chapter 12.

StudyTip

Euclidean Solids The *Euclidean solids* include the cube, the pyramid, the cylinder, the cone, and the sphere.

KeyConcept Surface Area and Volume

Prism	Regular Pyramid	Cylinder	Cone	Sphere
$T = Ph + 2B$	$T = \frac{1}{2}P\ell + B$	$T = 2\pi rh + 2\pi r^2$	$T = \pi r\ell + \pi r^2$	$T = 4\pi r^2$
$V = Bh$	$V = \frac{1}{3}Bh$	$V = \pi r^2 h$	$V = \frac{1}{3}\pi r^2 h$	$V = \frac{4}{3}\pi r^3$

T = total surface area; V = volume; h = height of a solid

P = perimeter of the base; B = area of base; ℓ = slant height, r = radius

WatchOut!

Height vs. Slant Height The *height* of a pyramid or cone is not the same as its *slant height*.

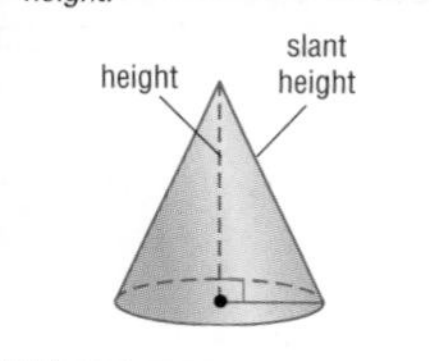

Example 2 Find Surface Area and Volume

Find the surface area and volume of the square pyramid.

5 cm; 4 cm; 6 cm

Surface Area

Since the base of the pyramid is a square, the perimeter P of the base is $4 \cdot 6$ or 24 centimeters. The area of the base B is $6 \cdot 6$ or 36 square centimeters. The slant height is 5 centimeters.

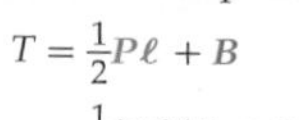

$T = \frac{1}{2}P\ell + B$ — Surface area of pyramid

$= \frac{1}{2}(24)(5) + 36$ or 96 — $P = 24$ cm, $\ell = 5$ cm, $B = 36$ cm^2

The surface area of the square pyramid is 96 square centimeters.

Volume

The height of the pyramid is 4 centimeters.

$V = \frac{1}{3}Bh$ — Volume of pyramid

$= \frac{1}{3}(36)(4)$ or 48 — $B = 36$ cm^2, $h = 4$ cm

The volume is 48 cubic centimeters.

GuidedPractice

Find the surface area and volume of each solid to the nearest tenth.

2A.

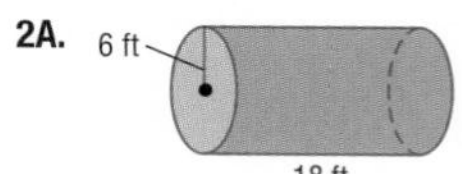

2B. 6 cm; 5.2 cm; 10 cm

2C.

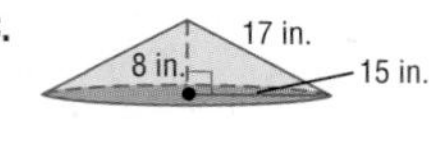

2A. 288π or about 904.8 ft^2; 648π or about 2035.8 ft^3

2B. 286.4 cm^2; 312 cm^3

2C. 480π or about 1508.0 in^2; 600π or about 1885.0 in^3

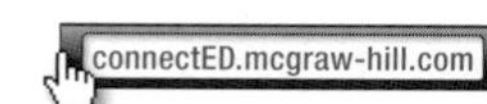

Additional Example

1 c.

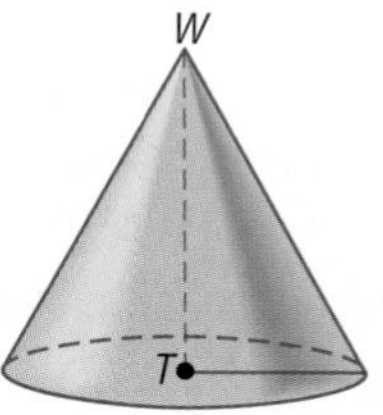

base: circle T
vertex: W
not a polyhedron

Additional Examples also in Interactive Classroom PowerPoint® Presentations

Interactive White Board READY

Focus on Mathematical Content

Cylinder Volume Point out that the formula for the volume of a cylinder is a special case of the formula for the volume of a prism. The base of a cylinder is a circle with area πr^2.

2 Surface Area and Volume

Examples 2 and 3 show how to find the surface area and volume of a three-dimensional figure.

Additional Example

2 Find the surface area and volume of the cone.

$r = 3$ cm
$h = 4$ cm
$\ell = 5$ cm

$T \approx 75.4$ cm^2; $V \approx 37.7$ cm^3

DifferentiatedInstruction AL OL BL ELL

Kinesthetic Learners When discussing surface area, provide students with the opportunity to make nets, cut them out, and then put them together to make a solid. This should help them better understand surface area.

Additional Example

3 CONTAINERS Mike is creating a mailing tube which can be used to mail posters and architectural plans. The diameter of the base is $3\frac{3}{4}$ inches, and the height is $2\frac{2}{3}$ feet. Find each measure to the nearest tenth.

a. the amount of cardboard Mike needs to make the tube ≈ 398.9 in^2

b. the volume of the tube 353.3 in^3

WatchOut!

Surface Areas Some students will find the surface area of the pool in Example 3 as if it is a standard cylinder. Point out that the solution only accounts for 1 base, the bottom of the pool, because there is no top material surface. Stress that students need to be careful of this when finding surface areas of composite figures as well.

Teaching the Mathematical Practices

Precision Mathematically proficient students are careful about specifying units of measure. Encourage students to be consistent with the units of measure.

Teaching the Mathematical Practices

Structure Mathematically proficient students look closely to discern a pattern. In Exercises 12–17, encourage students to look for a pattern.

Additional Answer

2. a polyhedron; rectangular pyramid; base: ▭$KLMN$; faces ▭$KLMN$, $\triangle JNK$, $\triangle JNM$, $\triangle JML$, $\triangle JLK$; edges: $\overline{KN}$, $\overline{NM}$, $\overline{ML}$, $\overline{LK}$, $\overline{JK}$, $\overline{JN}$, $\overline{JM}$, $\overline{JL}$; vertices: K, L, M, N, J

StudyTip

CCSS Precision Be sure that you have converted all units of measure to be consistent before you begin volume or surface area calculations.

Real-World Example 3 Surface Area and Volume

POOLS The diameter of the pool Mr. Sato purchased is 8 feet. The height of the pool is 20 inches. Find each measure to the nearest tenth.

20 in.
8 ft

a. surface area of the pool

The pool is a cylinder.

$A = 2\pi rh + \pi r^2$ — Surface area of cylinder with one base

$= 2\pi(4)\left(1\frac{2}{3}\right) + \pi(4)^2$ — $r = 4$ ft, $h = 20$ in. or $1\frac{2}{3}$ ft

≈ 92.2 — Use a calculator.

The surface area of the pool is about 92.2 square feet.

b. the volume of water needed to fill the pool to a depth of 16 inches

$V = \pi r^2 h$ — Volume of cylinder

$= \pi(4)^2\left(1\frac{1}{3}\right)$ — $r = 4$ ft, $h = 16$ in. or $1\frac{1}{3}$ ft

≈ 67.0 — Use a calculator.

The volume of water needed is approximately 67.0 cubic feet.

GuidedPractice

3. CRAFTS Jessica is making spherical candles using a mold that is 10 centimeters in diameter. Find each measure to the nearest tenth.

A. the volume of wax needed to fill the mold

B. the surface area of the finished candle

3A. 166.7π or about 523.6 cm^3

3B. 100π or about 314.2 cm^2

Check Your Understanding

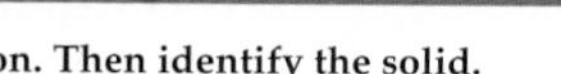

◯ = Step-by-Step Solutions begin on page R14.

Example 1 Determine whether the solid is a polyhedron. Then identify the solid. If it is a polyhedron, name the bases, faces, edges, and vertices.

1. 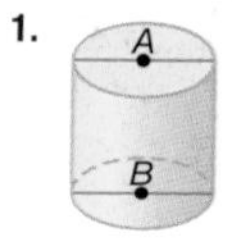

not a polyhedron; cylinder

2. 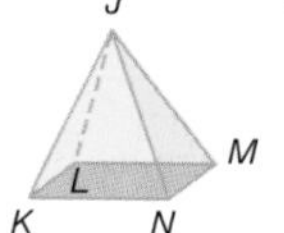

See margin.

Example 2 Find the surface area and volume of each solid to the nearest tenth.

3. 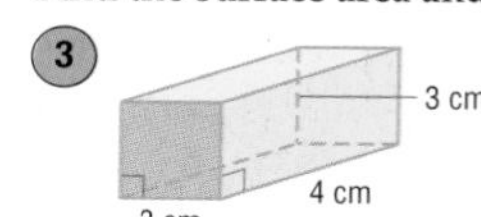

66 cm^2; 36 cm^3

4. 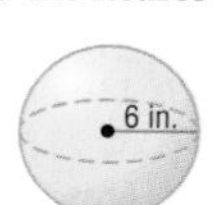

144π or about 452.4 in^2; 288π or about 904.8 in^3

Example 3 **5. PARTY FAVORS** Lawana is making cone-shaped hats 4 inches in diameter, 6.5 inches tall, with a slant height of 6.8 inches for party favors. Find each measure to the nearest tenth.

a. the volume of candy that will fill each cone ≈ 27.2 in^3

b. the area of material needed to make each hat assuming there is no overlap of material 13.6π or about 42.7 in^2

Nichola Evans/Iconica/Getty Images

Practice and Problem Solving

Extra Practice is on page R1.

Example 1 Identify the solid modeled by each object. State whether the solid modeled is a polyhedron.

6. 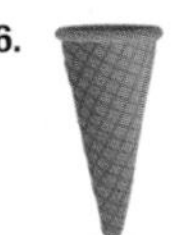

7. 

8. 

6. cone; not a polyhedron
7. pyramid; a polyhedron
8. triangular prism; a polyhedron

9.

10. 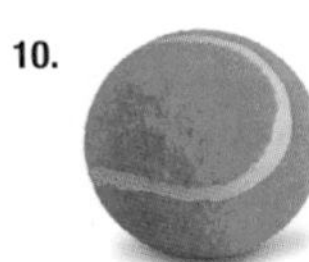

11. 

9. rectangular prism; a polyhedron
10. sphere; not a polyhedron
11. cylinder; not a polyhedron

CCSS STRUCTURE Determine whether the solid is a polyhedron. Then identify the solid. If it is a polyhedron, name the bases, faces, edges, and vertices.

12. 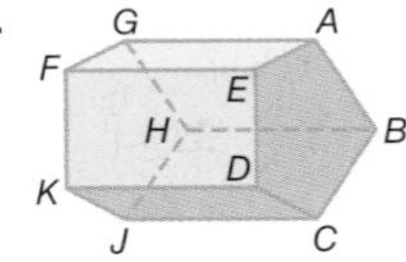

13. 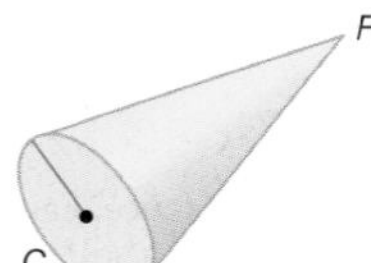

14. 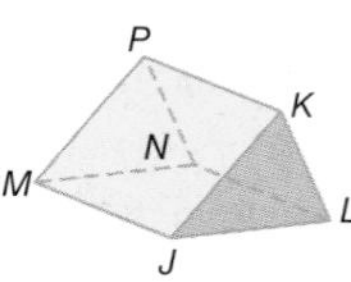

15. 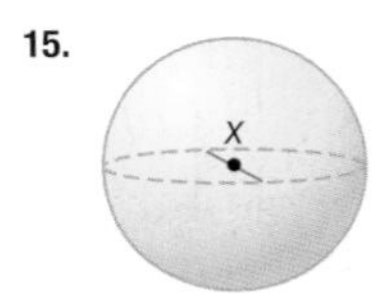

16.  

17. 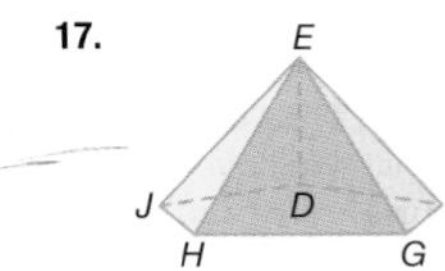

12. See margin.
13. not a polyhedron; cone
14. See margin.
15. not a polyhedron; sphere
16. not a polyhedron; cylinder
17. See margin.

Example 2 Find the surface area and volume of each solid to the nearest tenth.

18. 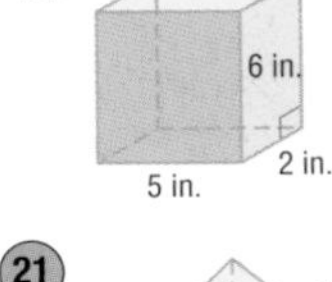

19. 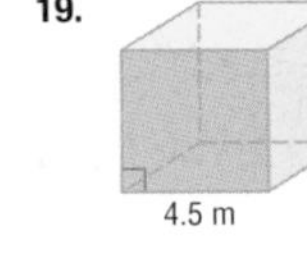

20. 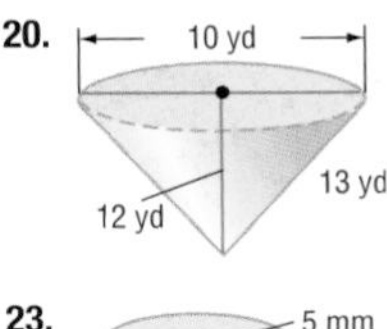

21.
10 cm
6 cm
5 cm
8 cm

22. 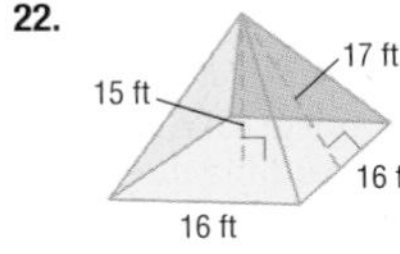

23. 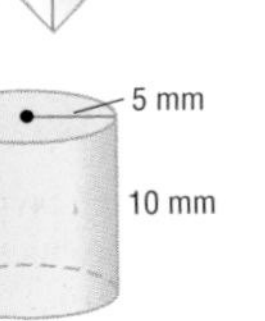

18. 104 in^2; 60 in^3
19. 121.5 m^2; 91.1 m^3
20. 90π or about 282.7 yd^2; 100π or about 314.2 yd^3
21. 168 cm^2; 120 cm^3
22. 800 ft^2; 1280 ft^3
23. 150π or about 471.2 mm^2; 250π or about 785.4 mm^3

Example 3

24. **SANDBOX** A rectangular sandbox is 3 feet by 4 feet. The depth of the box is 8 inches, but the depth of the sand is $\frac{3}{4}$ of the depth of the box. Find each measure to the nearest tenth.

a. the surface area of the sandbox assuming there is no lid 21.3 ft^2

b. the volume of sand in the sandbox 6 ft^3

Differentiated Homework Options

Level	Assignment	Two-Day Option	
AL Basic	6–26, 37, 38, 40, 42–59	6–25 odd, 43–46	6–26 even, 37, 38, 40, 42, 47–59
OL Core	7–27 odd, 28–38, 40, 42–59	6–26, 43–46	27–38, 40, 42, 47–59
BL Advanced	27–55, (optional: 56–59)		

3 Practice

Formative Assessment

Use Exercises 1–5 to check for understanding.

Then use the chart at the bottom of this page to customize assignments for your students.

Tips for New Teachers

Sense-Making Have students draw a net of a prism, pyramid, and/or cylinder and find the total area by summing the areas of the faces. Then have students find the surface area of the solid by using the surface area formula, and compare the two areas found. Note how both methods result in the same answer and are both measured in square units.

Follow-up

Students have explored area and volume.

Ask:

- How do you know what units to use when measuring? Sample answer: When dealing with length, you are only dealing with one dimension, so you could use units such as feet or meters. When dealing with area, you are dealing with two dimensions, so you could use square units such as square feet or square meters. When dealing with volume, you are dealing with three dimensions, so you could use cubic units such as cubic feet or cubic meters.

Additional Answers

12. a polyhedron; pentagonal prism; bases: *ABCDE*, *FGHJK*; faces: ▱*ABHG*, ▱*BCJH*, ▱*DCJK*, ▱*EDKF*, ▱*AEFG*; edges: $\overline{AB}$, $\overline{BC}$, $\overline{CD}$, $\overline{DE}$, $\overline{EA}$, $\overline{AG}$, $\overline{BH}$, $\overline{CJ}$, $\overline{DK}$, $\overline{EF}$, $\overline{GH}$, $\overline{HJ}$, $\overline{JK}$, $\overline{KF}$, $\overline{FG}$; vertices: *A*, *B*, *C*, *D*, *E*, *F*, *G*, *H*, *J*, *K*

14. a polyhedron; triangular prism; bases: $\triangle JLK$, $\triangle MNP$; faces: $\triangle JKL$, $\triangle MNP$, ▱*MPKJ*, ▱*PKLN*, ▱*MNLJ*; edges: $\overline{MP}$, $\overline{PK}$, $\overline{KJ}$, $\overline{JM}$, $\overline{JL}$, $\overline{KL}$, $\overline{LN}$, $\overline{MN}$, $\overline{PN}$; vertices: *M*, *P*, *L*, *J*, *N*, *K*

17. a polyhedron; pentagonal pyramid; base: *JHGFD*; faces: *JHGFD*, $\triangle JEH$, $\triangle HEG$, $\triangle GEF$, $\triangle FED$, $\triangle EDJ$; edges: $\overline{HG}$, $\overline{GF}$, $\overline{FD}$, $\overline{DJ}$, $\overline{JH}$, $\overline{EJ}$, $\overline{EH}$, $\overline{EG}$, $\overline{EF}$, $\overline{ED}$; vertices: *J*, *H*, *G*, *F*, *D*, *E*

Exercise Alert

Ruler Exercise 30 requires the use of a ruler or a tape measure.

Multiple Representations

In Exercise 36, students will explore how the change in the radius of a cone affects the cone's volume.

CCSS Teaching the Mathematical Practices

CRITIQUE Mathematically proficient students can distinguish correct logic or reasoning from that which is flawed. In Exercise 37, Emily is correct. Alex has found the area of one face and multiplied by 6, as though all of the faces were congruent. This method yields the correct surface area of a cube, not the rectangular prism shown.

25 **ART** Fernando and Humberto Campana designed the Inflating Table shown. The diameter of the table is $15\frac{1}{2}$ inches. Suppose the height of the cylinder is $11\frac{3}{4}$ inches. Find each measure to the nearest tenth. Assume that the sides of the table are perpendicular to the bases of the table.

$15\frac{1}{2}$ in.

$11\frac{3}{4}$ in.

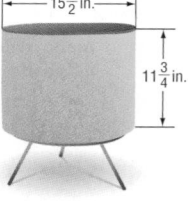

a. the volume of air that will fully inflate the table **2217.1 in^3**

b. the surface area of the table when fully inflated **949.5 in^2**

26. **CCSS SENSE-MAKING** In 1999, Marks & Spencer, a British department store, created the biggest sandwich ever made. The tuna and cucumber sandwich was in the form of a triangular prism. Suppose each slice of bread was 8 inches thick. Find each measure to the nearest tenth.

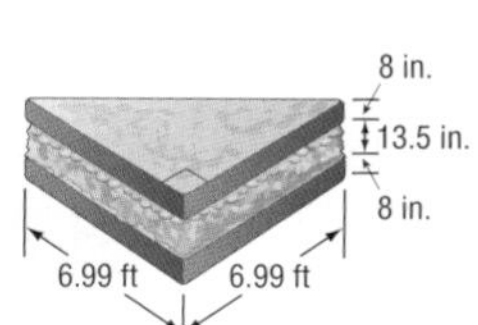

a. the surface area in square feet of the sandwich when filled **107.5 ft^2**

b. the volume of filling in cubic feet to the nearest tenth **27.5 ft^3**

27. **ALGEBRA** The surface area of a cube is 54 square inches. Find the length of each edge. **3 in.**

28. **ALGEBRA** The volume of a cube is 729 cubic centimeters. Find the length of each edge. **9 cm**

29. **PAINTING** Tara is painting her family's fence. Each post is composed of a square prism and a square pyramid. The height of the pyramid is 4 inches. Determine the surface area and volume of each post. **1212 in^2; 1776 in^3**

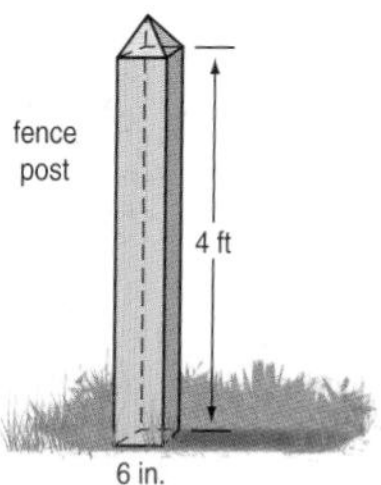

30. **COLLECT DATA** Use a ruler or tape measure and what you have learned in this lesson to find the surface area and volume of a soup can. **See students' work.**

31. **CAKES** Cakes come in many shapes and sizes. Often they are stacked in two or more layers, like those in the diagrams shown below.

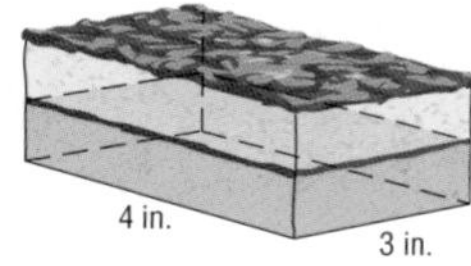

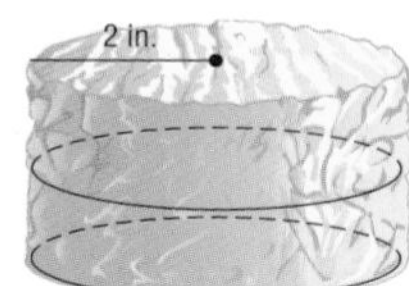

a. If each layer of the rectangular prism cake is 3 inches high, calculate the area of the cake that will be frosted assuming there is no frosting between layers. **96 in^2**

b. Calculate the area of the cylindrical cake that will be frosted, if each layer is 4 inches in height. **113.1 in^2**

c. If one can of frosting will cover 50 square inches of cake, how many cans of frosting will be needed for each cake? **prism: 2 cans; cylinder: 3 cans**

d. If the height of each layer of cake is 5 inches, what does the radius of the cylindrical cake need to be, so the same amount of frosting is used for both cakes? Explain your reasoning.

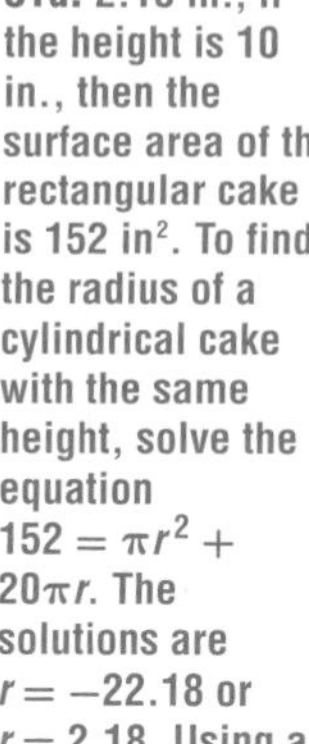

31d. **2.18 in.; if the height is 10 in., then the surface area of the rectangular cake is 152 in^2. To find the radius of a cylindrical cake with the same height, solve the equation $152 = \pi r^2 + 20\pi r$. The solutions are $r = -22.18$ or $r = 2.18$. Using a radius of 2.18 in. gives surface area of about 152 in^2.**

Additional Answers

34. Exercise 18: yes, $6 + 8 = 12 + 2$; Exercise 19: yes, $6 + 8 = 12 + 2$; Exercise 20: no, this figure is not a polyhedron, so Euler's Formula does not apply; Exercise 21: yes, $5 + 6 = 9 + 2$; Exercise 22: yes, $5 + 5 = 8 + 2$; Exercise 23: no, this figure is not a polyhedron, so Euler's Formula does not apply.

35. The volume of the original prism is 4752 cm^3. The volume of the new prism is 38,016 cm^3. The volume increased by a factor of 8 when each dimension was doubled.

36a.

Radius	Volume
1	π
2	4π
4	16π
8	64π

36b.

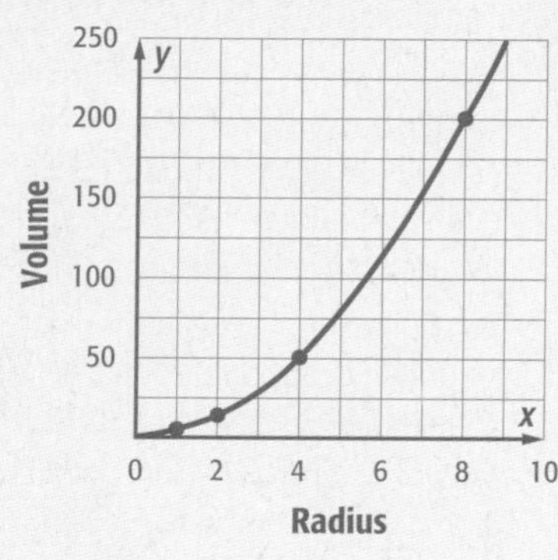

36c.

Double Radius	Volume
2	4π
4	16π
8	64π
16	256π

Doubling the radius results in an increase in the volume by a factor of 4.

36d. $V = \frac{1}{3}\pi(2r)^2h = \frac{4}{3}\pi r^2 h$

37. Neither; sample answer: the surface area is twice the sum of the areas of the top, front, and left side of the prism or $2(5 \cdot 3 + 5 \cdot 4 + 3 \cdot 4)$, which is 94 in^2.

40. Sample answer:

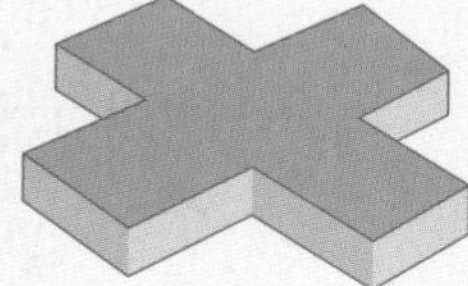

32. **CHANGING UNITS** A gift box has a surface area of 6.25 square feet. What is the surface area of the box in square inches? 900 in^2

33. **CHANGING UNITS** A square pyramid has a volume of 4320 cubic inches. What is the volume of this pyramid in cubic feet? 2.5 ft^3

34. **EULER'S FORMULA** The number of faces F, vertices V, and edges E of a polyhedron are related by Euler's (OY luhrz) Formula: $F + V = E + 2$. Determine whether Euler's Formula is true for each of the figures in Exercises 18–23. See margin.

35. **CHANGING DIMENSIONS** A rectangular prism has a length of 12 centimeters, width of 18 centimeters, and height of 22 centimeters. Describe the effect on the volume of a rectangular prism when each dimension is doubled. See margin.

36. **MULTIPLE REPRESENTATIONS** In this problem, you will investigate how changing the length of the radius of a cone affects the cone's volume. a–d. See margin.

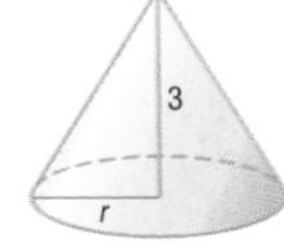

a. **Tabular** Create a table showing the volume of a cone when doubling the radius. Use radius values between 1 and 8.

b. **Graphical** Use the values from your table to create a graph of radius versus volume.

c. **Verbal** Make a conjecture about the effect of doubling the radius of a cone on the volume. Explain your reasoning.

d. **Algebraic** If r is the radius of a cone, write an expression showing the effect doubling the radius has on the cone's volume.

H.O.T. Problems Use Higher-Order Thinking Skills

37. **CCSS CRITIQUE** Alex and Emily are calculating the surface area of the rectangular prism shown. Is either of them correct? Explain your reasoning. See margin.

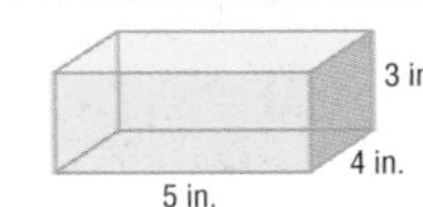

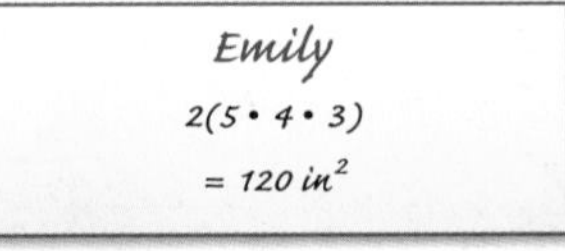

Alex
(5 • 3) • 6 faces
= 90 in²
Emily
2(5 • 4 • 3)
= 120 in²

38. Yes; all of the faces are regular congruent squares and all of the edges are congruent.

38. **REASONING** Is a cube a regular polyhedron? Explain.

39. **CHALLENGE** Describe the solid that results if the number of sides of each base increases infinitely. The bases of each solid are regular polygons inscribed in a circle.

a. pyramid cone

b. prism cylinder

40. **OPEN ENDED** Draw an irregular 14-sided polyhedron which has two congruent bases. See margin.

41. **CHALLENGE** Find the volume of a cube that has a total surface area of 54 square millimeters. 27 mm^3

42. **WRITING IN MATH** A reference sheet listed the formula for the surface area of a prism as $SA = Bh + 2B$. Use units of measure to explain why there must be a typographical error in this formula. See margin.

Additional Answer

42. Sample answer: The expression Bh is measured in cubic units and the expression $2B$ is measured in square units. Different units cannot be added, and surface area is measured in square units.

Study Guide and Intervention
AL OL ELL

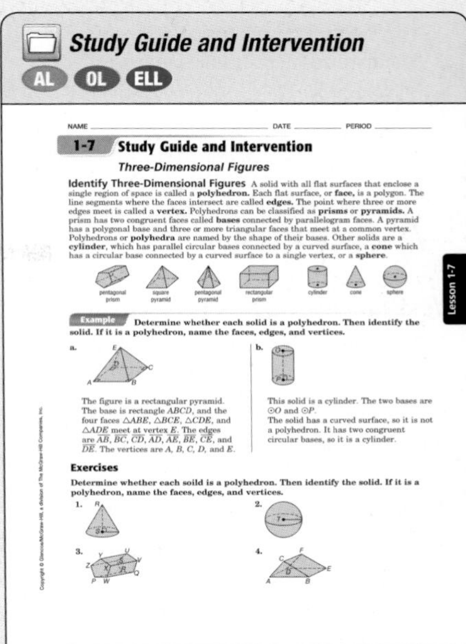

Practice
AL OL BL ELL

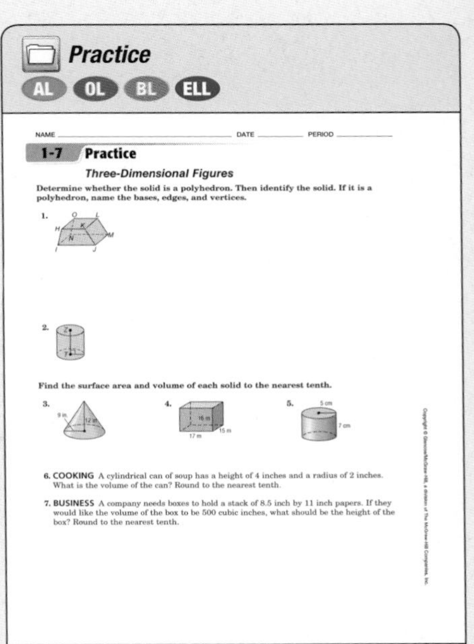

Word Problem Practice
AL OL BL ELL

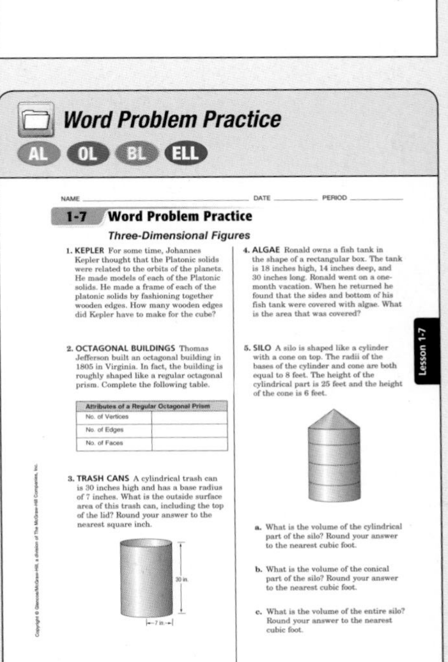

Enrichment
OL BL

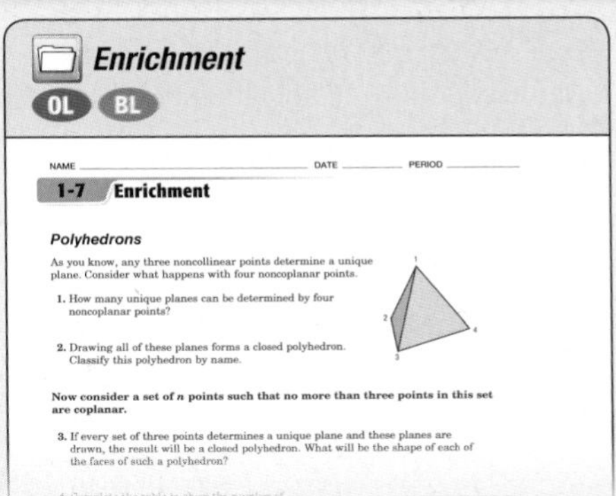

Standardized Test Practice exercises help students solidify their knowledge using exercises in a testing format.

4 Assess

Yesterday's News Have students write a paragraph that explains how the lesson about two-dimensional figures helped them in this lesson about three-dimensional figures.

Formative Assessment

Check for student understanding of concepts in Lesson 1-7.

 Quiz 4, p. 52

Additional Answers

53. The intersection of a plane and a line not in the plane is a point.

54. Two planes can intersect in a line.

55. Two lines intersect in one point.

Standardized Test Practice

43. GRIDDED RESPONSE What is the surface area of the triangular prism in square centimeters? 55.2

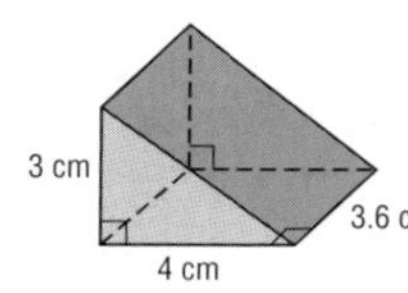

44. ALGEBRA What is the value of $(-0.8)^2 + (-0.3)^3$? B

A 0.627   C 0.370
B 0.613   D 0.327

45. The length of each side of a cube is multiplied by 5. What is the change in the volume of the cube? F

F The volume is 125 times the original volume.
G The volume is 25 times the original volume.
H The volume is 10 times the original volume.
J The volume is 5 times the original volume.

46. SAT/ACT What is the difference in surface area between a cube with an edge length of 7 inches and a cube with edge length of 4 inches? E

A 18 in^2 D 99 in^2
B 33 in^2 E 198 in^2
C 66 in^2

Spiral Review

Name each polygon by its number of sides. Then classify it as *convex* or *concave* and *regular* or *irregular*. (Lesson 1-6)

47.  quadrilateral; convex; regular

48. 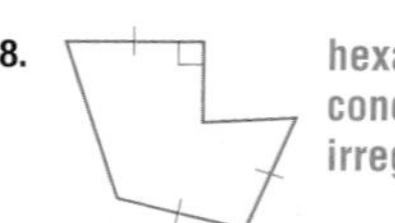 hexagon; concave; irregular

49. 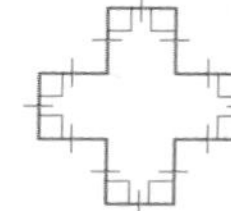 dodecagon; concave; irregular

Find the value of each variable. (Lesson 1-5)

50. 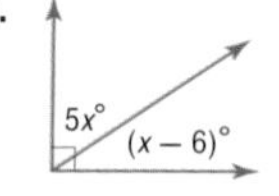

16

51. 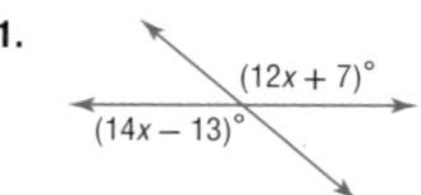

10

52. 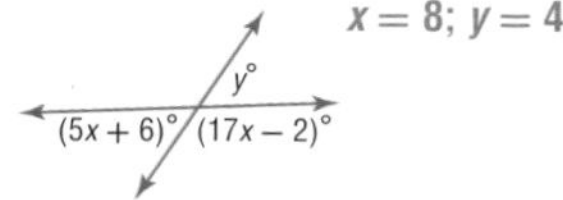

$x = 8$; $y = 46$

GAMES What type of geometric intersection is modeled in each photograph? (Lesson 1-1) 53–55. See margin.

53. 

54. 

55. 

(t)Photodisc/Getty Images, (c)Mark Ransom Photography, (r)Oxana Zubov/age fotostock

Skills Review

Sketch the next two figures in each pattern. 56–59. See Ch. 1 Answer Appendix.

56. 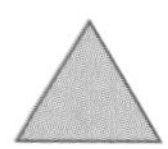   

57. 

58.  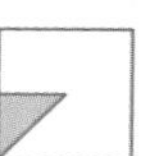 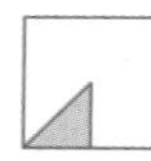 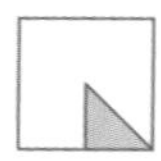

59. 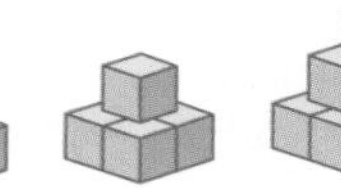

 74 | Lesson 1-7 | Three-Dimensional Figures

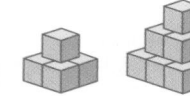

Differentiated Instruction OL BL

Extension The formula for the surface area of a sphere is $S = 4\pi r^2$.

The formula for the volume of a sphere is $V = \frac{4}{3}\pi r^3$.

A sphere of what radius has the same surface area as volume? (with different units, of course) A sphere with radius 3 has a surface area of 36π square units, and a volume of 36π cubic units.

EXTEND 1-7

Geometry Lab: Two-Dimensional Representations of Three-Dimensional Objects

If you see a three-dimensional object from only one viewpoint, you may not know its true shape. Here are four views of a square pyramid.

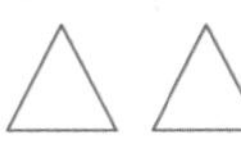

top view, left view, front view, right view

The two-dimensional views of the top, left, front, and right sides of an object are called an **orthographic drawing**.

CCSS Common Core State Standards
Content Standards
G.MG.1 Use geometric shapes, their measures, and their properties to describe objects (e.g., modeling a tree trunk or a human torso as a cylinder). ★
Mathematical Practices 5

Activity 1

Make a model of a figure for the orthographic drawing shown.

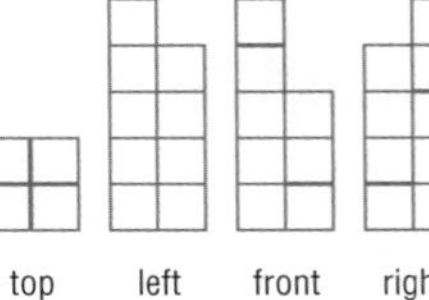

Step 1 Start with a base that matches the top view.

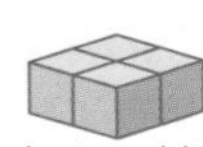

Step 2 The front view indicates that the front left side is 5 blocks high and that the right side is 3 blocks high. However, the dark segments indicate breaks in the surface.

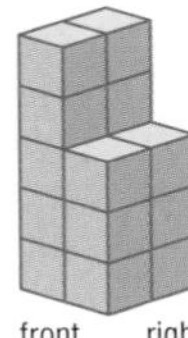

Step 3 The break on the left side of the front view indicates that the back left column is 5 blocks high, but that the front left column is only 4 blocks high, so remove 1 block from the front left column.

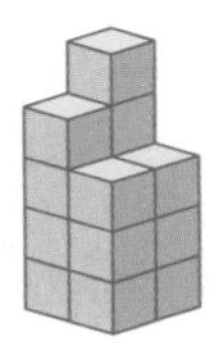

Step 4 The break on the right side of the front view indicates that the back right column is 3 blocks high, but that the front right column is only 1 block high, so remove 2 blocks from the front right column.

Step 5 Use the left and right views and the breaks in those views to confirm that you have made the correct figure.

Model and Analyze 1–2. See margin for drawings.

1. Make a model of a figure for the orthographic drawing shown.

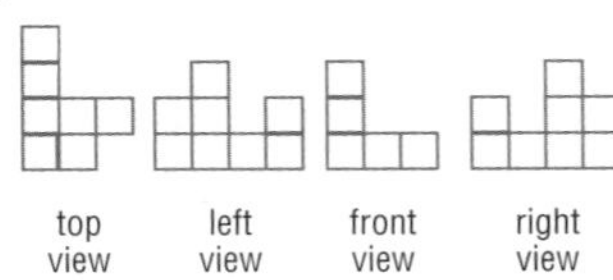

2. Make an orthographic drawing of the figure shown.

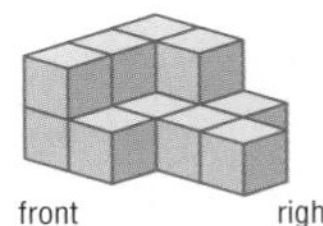

1 Focus

Objective Use orthographic views and nets to represent and construct three-dimensional figures.

Materials

- ruler, scissors, tape
- a large sheet of paper

2 Teach

Working in Cooperative Groups

Arrange students in groups of 3 or 4, mixing abilities. Then have groups complete Activities 1–3.

Ask:

- In your own words, what does the prefix *ortho* mean? Sample answer: precise
- What two shapes make up a triangular prism? triangle and rectangle
- What three-dimensional figure has the same orthographic drawing? Sample answers: sphere; cube

Practice Have students complete Exercises 1–2.

Additional Answers

1.

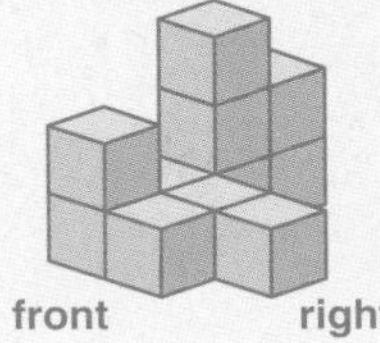

2.

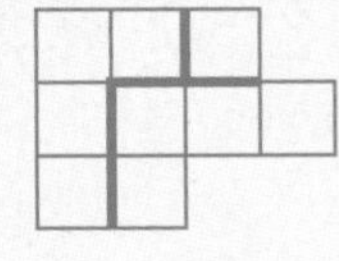
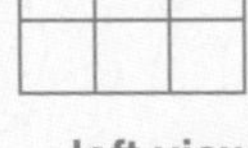
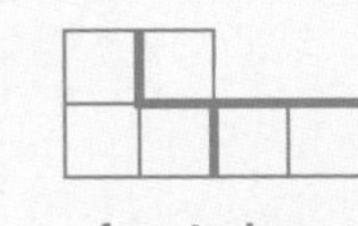
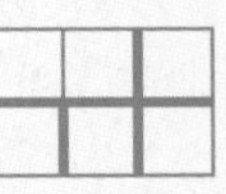

top view, left view, front view, right view

Focus on Mathematical Content

A net for a sphere can be created using several adjoining pointed ellipses or by creating a polyhedron with a large number of sides. However, since paper can only curve in one direction, it is impossible to make a perfect sphere. Thus, the spheres made from nets will be approximations.

Additional Answers

3.

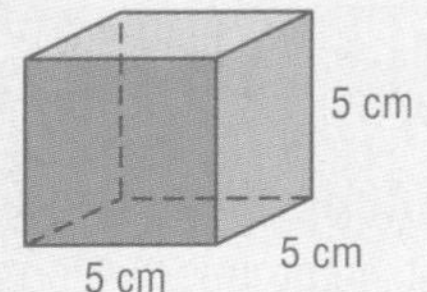

4.

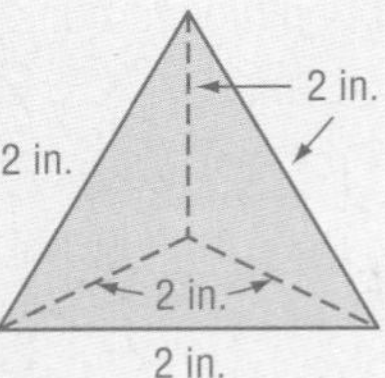

5.

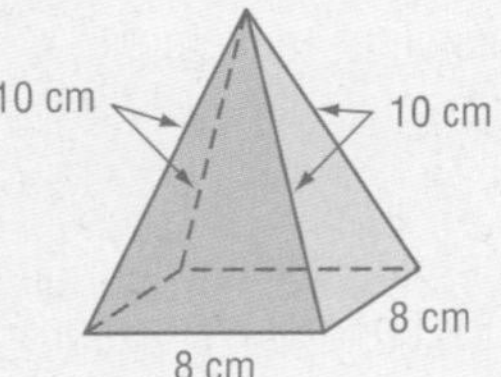

Geometry Lab

Two-Dimensional Representations of Three-Dimensional Objects *Continued*

If you cut a cardboard box at the edges and lay it flat, you will have a two-dimensional diagram called a **net** that you can fold to form a three-dimensional solid.

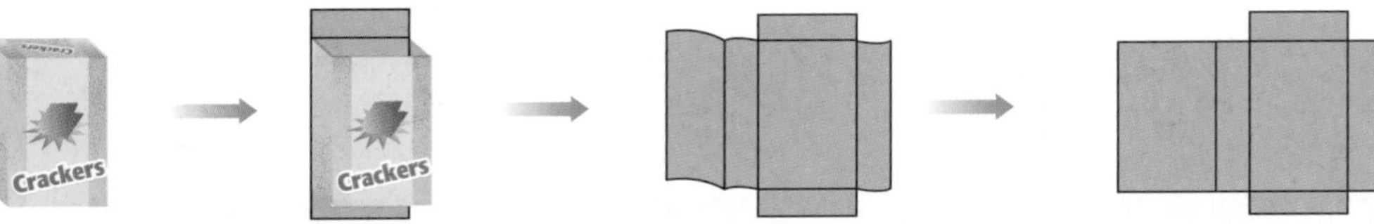

Activity 2

Make a model of a figure for the given net. Then identify the solid formed, and find its surface area.

Use a large sheet of paper, a ruler, scissors, and tape. Draw the net on the paper. Cut along the solid lines. Fold the pattern on the dashed lines and secure the edges with tape. This is the net of a triangular prism.

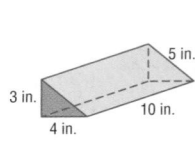

Use the net to find the surface area T.

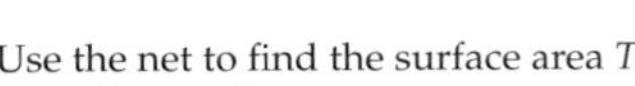

$T = 2\left[\frac{1}{2}(4)(3)\right] + 4(10) + 3(10) + 5(10)$ Area of two congruent triangles plus area of three rectangles

$= 12 + 40 + 30 + 50$ or 132 in^2 Simplify.

Model and Analyze 3–5. See margin for drawings.

Make a model of a figure for each net. Then identify the solid formed and find its surface area. If the solid has more than one name, list both. 5. square pyramid; $(64 + 32\sqrt{21})$ cm^2

3.

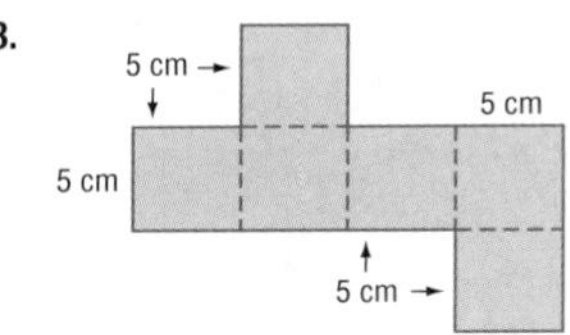

cube or hexahedron; 150 cm^2

4.

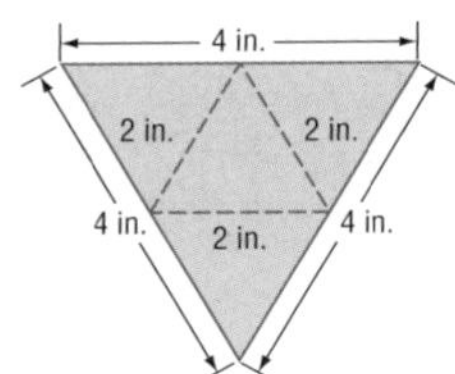

triangular pyramid or tetrahedron; $4\sqrt{3}$ in^2

5.

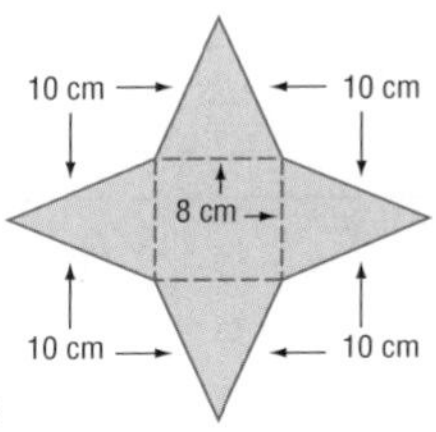

Identify the Platonic Solid that can be formed by the given net.

6.

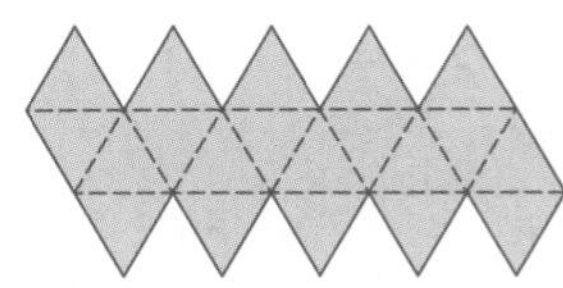

icosahedron

7.

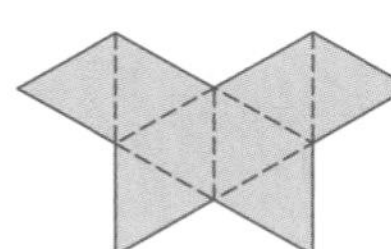

octahedron

8.

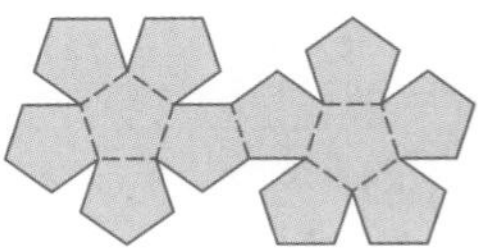

dodecahedron

To draw the net of a three-dimensional solid, visualize cutting the solid along one or more of its edges, opening up the solid, and flattening it completely.

Activity 3

Draw a net for the solid shown. Then label its dimensions.

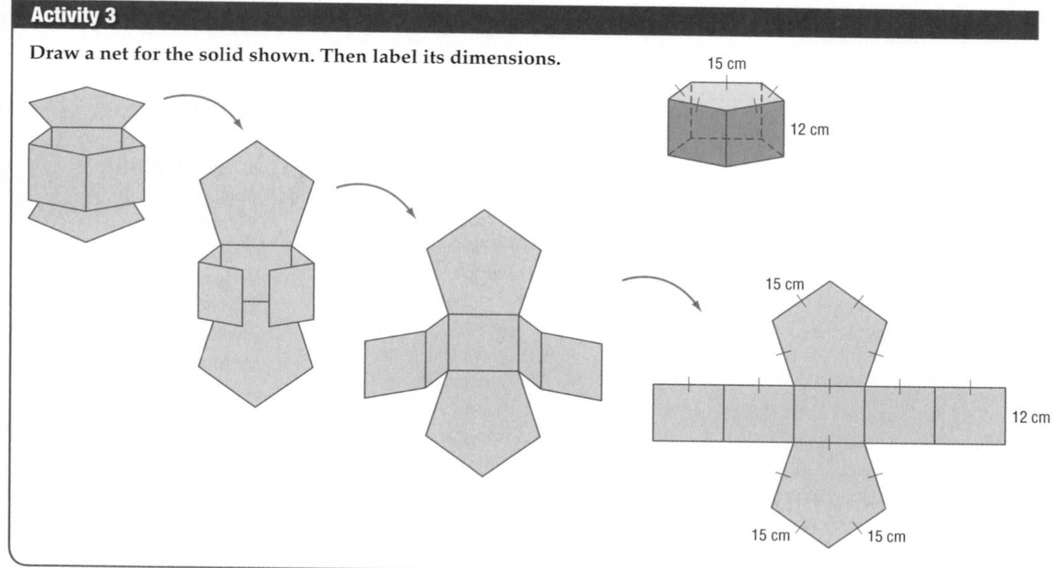

Model and Analyze 9–11. **See margin for drawings.**

Draw a net for each solid. Then label its dimensions.

9.

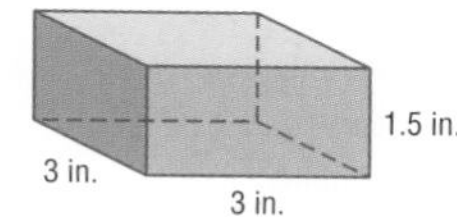

10.

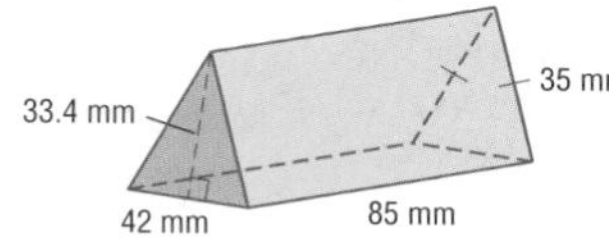

11.

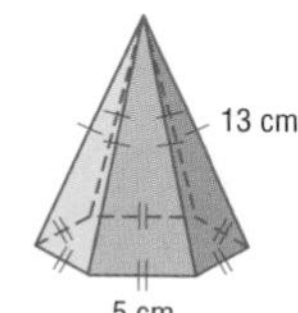

12. PACKAGING A can of pineapple is shown.

a. What shape are the top and bottom of the can? **circle**

b. If you remove the top and bottom and then make a vertical cut down the side of the can, what shape will you get when you uncurl the remaining body of the can and flatten it? **rectangle**

c. If the diameter of the can is 3 inches and its height is 2 inches, draw a net of the can and label its dimensions. Explain your reasoning. **See margin.**

12c. The diameter of the circles are the diameter of the can. The length of the rectangle is the distance around the can, or the circumference of each circle. The width of the rectangle is the height of the can.

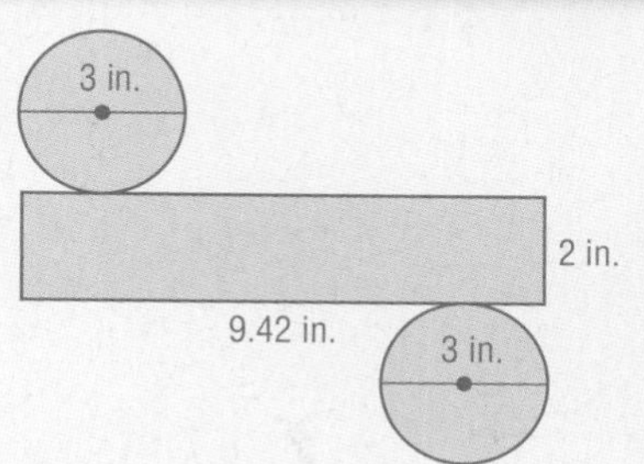

3 Assess

Formative Assessment

Use Exercises 1 and 2 to assess whether students comprehend how to make a net for a three-dimensional figure.

From Concrete to Abstract

Have students pick three objects in the classroom, and then make an orthographic drawing and a net for each object. Then have each student present their drawing, and let the class guess the object.

Additional Answers

9.

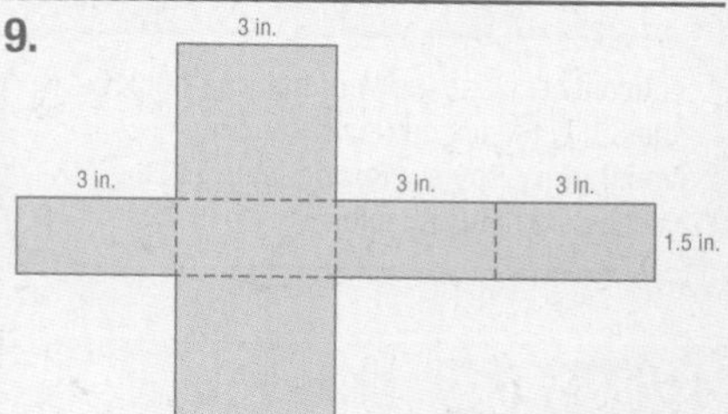

10.

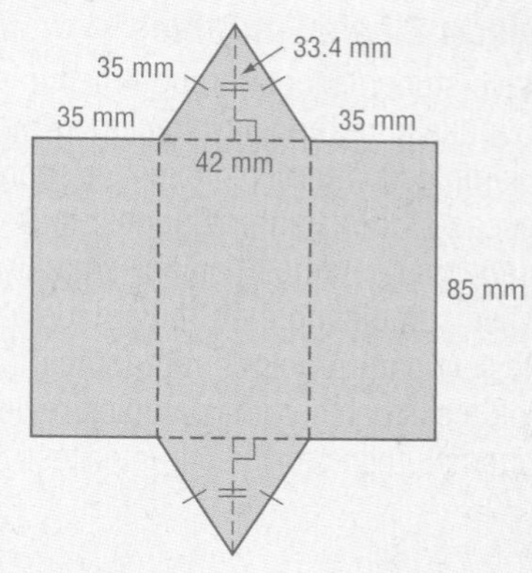

11.

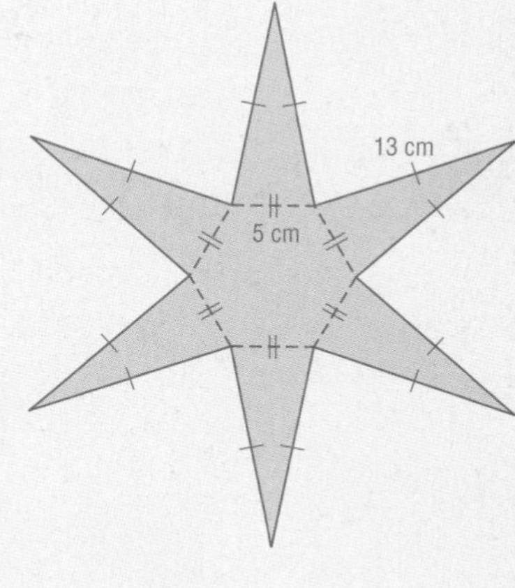

Formative Assessment

KeyVocabulary The page references after each word denote where that term was first introduced. If students have difficulty completing Exercises 1–4, remind them that they can use these page references to refresh their memories about the vocabulary terms.

Summative Assessment

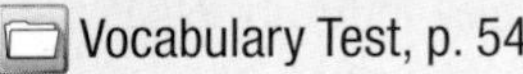
Vocabulary Test, p. 54

Vocabulary Review provides students the opportunity to check their understanding of important concepts and terminology in an online game format.

Students can use the **Vocabulary Check** in the Study Guide and Review and the **Vocabulary Review Puzzle** to review the vocabulary of the chapter.

FOLDABLES® StudyOrganizer

Dinah Zike's Foldables®

Have students look through the chapter to make sure they have included examples in their Foldables for each lesson of the chapter. Suggest that students keep their Foldables handy while completing the Study Guide and Review pages. Point out that their Foldables can serve as a quick review when studying for the chapter test.

CHAPTER 1 Study Guide and Review

Study Guide

KeyConcepts

Points, Lines, and Planes (Lesson 1-1)

- There is exactly one line through any two points.
- There is exactly one plane through any three noncollinear points.

Distance and Midpoints (Lesson 1-3)

- On a number line, the measure of a segment with endpoint coordinates a and b is $|a - b|$.
- In the coordinate plane, the distance between two points (x_1, y_1) and (x_2, y_2) is given by $d = \sqrt{(x_2 - x_1)^2 + (y_2 - y_1)^2}$.
- On a number line, the coordinate of the midpoint of a segment with endpoints a and b is $\frac{a + b}{2}$.
- In the coordinate plane, the coordinates of the midpoint of a segment with endpoints that are (x_1, y_1) and (x_2, y_2) are $\left(\frac{x_1 + x_2}{2}, \frac{y_1 + y_2}{2}\right)$.

Angles (Lessons 1-4 and 1-5)

- An angle is formed by two noncollinear rays that have a common endpoint, called its vertex. Angles can be classified by their measures.
- Adjacent angles are two coplanar angles that lie in the same plane and have a common vertex and a common side but no common interior points.
- Vertical angles are two nonadjacent angles formed by two intersecting lines.
- A linear pair is a pair of adjacent angles with noncommon sides that are opposite rays.
- Complementary angles are two angles with measures that have a sum of 90.
- Supplementary angles are two angles with measures that have a sum of 180.

FOLDABLES StudyOrganizer

Be sure the Key Concepts are noted in your Foldable.

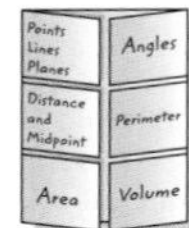

KeyVocabulary

acute angle (p. 38)
adjacent angles (p. 46)
angle (p. 36)
angle bisector (p. 39)
area (p. 58)
base (p. 67)
between (p. 15)
circumference (p. 58)
collinear (p. 5)
complementary angles (p. 47)
concave (p. 56)
cone (p. 67)
congruent (p. 16)
construction (p. 17)
convex (p. 56)
coplanar (p. 5)
cylinder (p. 67)
degree (p. 37)
distance (p. 25)
edge (p. 67)
equiangular polygon (p. 57)
equilateral polygon (p. 57)
exterior (p. 36)
face (p. 67)
interior (p. 36)
intersection (p. 6)
line (p. 5)
line segment (p. 14)
linear pair (p. 46)
midpoint (p. 27)
n-gon (p. 57)
obtuse angle (p. 38)
opposite rays (p. 36)
perimeter (p. 58)
perpendicular (p. 48)
plane (p. 5)
Platonic solid (p. 68)
point (p. 5)
polygon (p. 56)
polyhedron (p. 67)
prism (p. 67)
pyramid (p. 67)
ray (p. 36)
regular polygon (p. 57)
regular polyhedron (p. 68)
right angle (p. 38)
segment bisector (p. 29)
side (p. 36)
space (p. 7)
sphere (p. 67)
supplementary angles (p. 47)
surface area (p. 69)
undefined term (p. 5)
vertex (pp. 36, 67)
vertex of a polygon (p. 56)
vertical angles (p. 46)
volume (p. 69)

VocabularyCheck

Fill in the blank in each sentence with the vocabulary term that best completes the sentence.

1. A _____ is a flat surface made up of points that extends infinitely in all directions. **plane**
2. A set of points that all lie on the same line are said to be _____. **collinear**
3. If two lines intersect to form four right angles, the lines are _____. **perpendicular**
4. If the sum of the measures of two angles is 180, then the angles are called _____ angles. **supplementary**

Lesson-by-Lesson Review

1-1 Points, Lines, and Planes

Use the figure to complete each of the following.

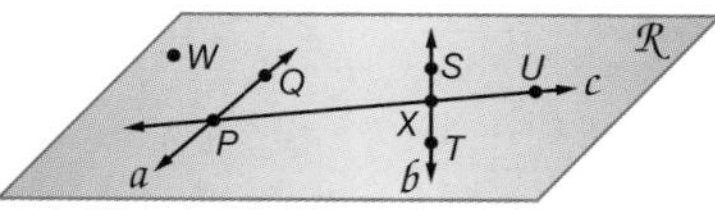

5. Name the intersection of lines a and c. point P
6. Give another name for line b. $\overleftrightarrow{ST}$
7. Name a point that is not contained in any of the three lines a, b, or c. point W
8. Give another name for plane WPX. plane $\mathcal{R}$

Name the geometric term that is best modeled by each item.

9.  line
10. 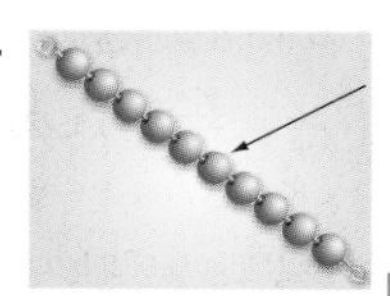 point

Example 1

Draw and label a figure for the relationship below.

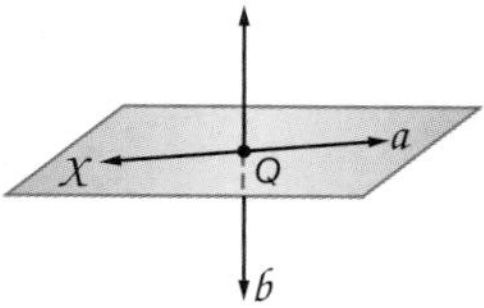

Plane $\mathcal{X}$ contains line a, line b intersects line a at point Q, but line b is not in plane $\mathcal{X}$.

Draw a surface to represent plane $\mathcal{X}$ and label it.

Draw a line in plane $\mathcal{X}$ and label it line a.

Draw a line b intersecting both the plane and line a and label the point of intersection Q.

1-2 Linear Measure

Find the value of the variable and XP, if X is between P and Q.

11. $XQ = 13$, $XP = 5x - 3$, $PQ = 40$ $x = 6$, $XP = 27$
12. $XQ = 3k$, $XP = 7k - 2$, $PQ = 6k + 16$ $k = 4.5$, $XP = 29.5$

Determine whether each pair of segments is congruent.

13. $\overline{AB}$, $\overline{CD}$ yes
14. $\overline{XY}$, $\overline{YZ}$ no

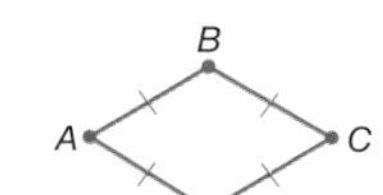

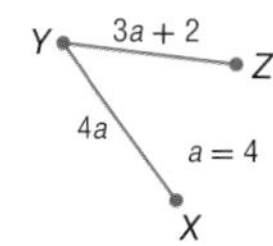

15. **DISTANCE** The distance from Salvador's job to his house is 3 times greater than the distance from his house to school. If his house is between his job and school and the distance from his job to school is 6 miles, how far is it from Salvador's house to school? 1.5 mi

Example 2

Use the figure to find the value of the variable and the length of $\overline{YZ}$.

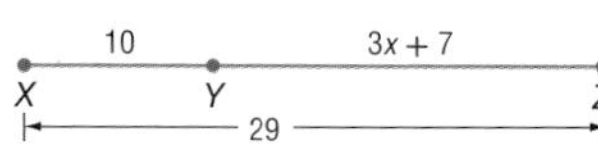

$XZ = XY + YZ$	Betweenness of points
$29 = 10 + 3x + 7$	Substitution
$29 = 3x + 17$	Simplify.
$12 = 3x$	Subtract 17 from each side.
$4 = x$	Divide each side by 3.
$YZ = 3x + 7$	Given
$= 3(4) + 7$ or 19	Substitution

So, $x = 4$ and $YZ = 19$.

Students can complete the exercises in the **Lesson-by-Lesson Review** as they prepare for the chapter test. If they need extra help, examples are provided.

Lesson-by-Lesson Review

Intervention If the given examples are not sufficient to review the topics covered by the questions, remind students that the lesson references tell them where to review that topic in their textbooks.

Two-Day Option Have students complete the Lesson-by-Lesson Review. Then you can use eAssessment to customize another review worksheet that practices all the objectives of this chapter or only the objectives on which your students need more help.

Additional Answers

26. Sample answer: $\overrightarrow{CA}$ and $\overrightarrow{CD}$
27. Sample answer: ∠A and ∠B are right, ∠E and ∠C are obtuse, and ∠D is acute.

1-3 Distance and Midpoints

Find the distance between each pair of points.

16. A(−3, 1), B(7, 13) $\sqrt{244} \approx 15.6$
17. P(2, −1), Q(10, −7) 10

Find the coordinates of the midpoint of a segment with the given endpoints.

18. L(−3, 16), M(17, 4) (7, 10)
19. C(32, −1), D(0, −12) (16, −6.5)

Find the coordinates of the missing endpoint if M is the midpoint of $\overline{XY}$.

20. X(−11, −6), M(15, 4) (41, 14)
21. M(−4, 8), Y(19, 0) (−27, 16)
22. **HIKING** Carol and Marita are hiking in a state park and decide to take separate trails. The map of the park is set up on a coordinate grid. Carol's location is at the point (7, 13) and Marita is at (3, 5).
    a. Find the distance between them. ≈8.9 units
    b. Find the coordinates of the point midway between their locations. (5, 9)

Example 3

Find the distance between X(5, 7) and Y(−7, 2).

Let $(x_1, y_1) = (5, 7)$ and $(x_2, y_2) = (-7, 2)$.

$$d = \sqrt{(x_2 - x_1)^2 + (y_2 - y_1)^2}$$
$$= \sqrt{(-7 - 5)^2 + (2 - 7)^2}$$
$$= \sqrt{(-12)^2 + (-5)^2}$$
$$= \sqrt{169} \text{ or } 13$$

The distance from X to Y is 13 units.

Example 4

Find the coordinates of the midpoint between P(−4, 13) and Q(6, 5).

Let $(x_1, y_1) = (-4, 13)$ and $(x_2, y_2) = (6, 5)$.

$$M\left(\frac{x_1 + x_2}{2}, \frac{y_1 + y_2}{2}\right) = M\left(\frac{-4 + 6}{2}, \frac{13 + 5}{2}\right)$$
$$= M(1, 9)$$

The coordinates of the midpoint are (1, 9).

1-4 Angle Measure

For Exercises 23–26, refer to the figure below.

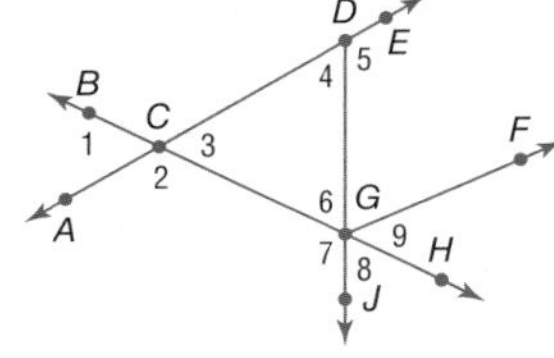

23. Name the vertex of ∠7. G
24. Write another name for ∠4. Sample answer: ∠CDG
25. Name the sides of ∠2. $\overrightarrow{CA}$ and $\overrightarrow{CH}$
26. Name a pair of opposite rays. See margin.
27. **SIGNS** A sign at West High School has the shape shown. Measure each of the angles and classify them as *right*, *acute*, or *obtuse*. See margin.

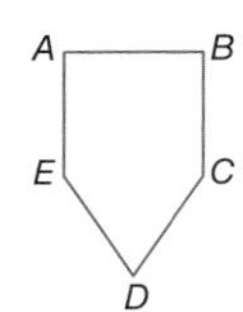

Example 5

Refer to the figure below. Name all angles that have Q as a vertex.

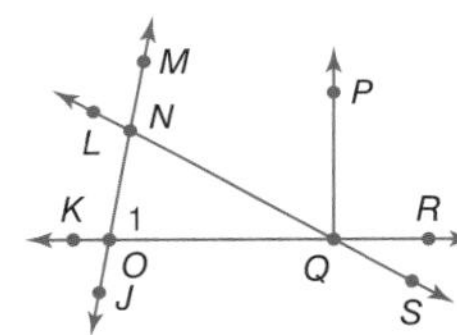

∠OQN, ∠NQP, ∠PQR, ∠RQS, ∠SQO, ∠OQP, ∠NQR, ∠PQS, ∠OQR

Example 6

In the figure above, list all other names for ∠1.

∠NOQ, ∠QON, ∠MOQ, ∠QOM, ∠MOR, ∠ROM, ∠NOR, ∠RON

80 | Chapter 1 | Study Guide and Review

1-5 Angle Relationships

For Exercises 28–30, refer to the figure below.

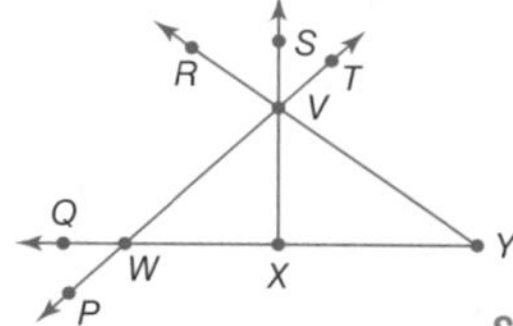

28. Name an angle supplementary to $\angle TVY$. **Sample answer: $\angle TVR$**

29. Name a pair of vertical angles with vertex W.

30. If $m\angle SXW = 5x - 16$, find the value of x so that $\overline{SX} \perp \overline{WY}$. **21.2**

31. **PARKING** The parking arm shown below rests in a horizontal position and opens to a vertical position. After the arm has moved 24°, how many more degrees does it have to move so that it is vertical? **66**

Example 7

Name a pair of supplementary angles and a pair of complementary angles in the figure below.

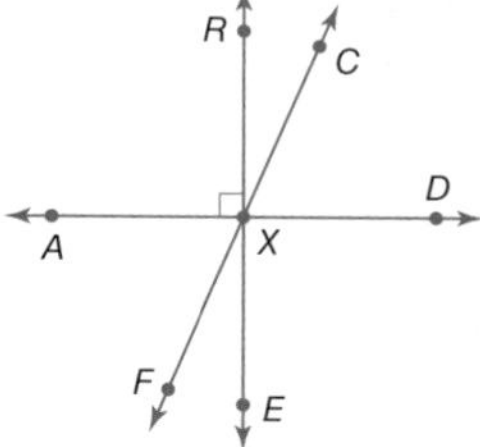

Sample answers:

Supplementary angles: $\angle RXA$ and $\angle RXD$

Complementary angles: $\angle RXC$ and $\angle CXD$

29. Sample answer: $\angle QWP$ and $\angle XWV$

1-6 Two-Dimensional Figures

Name each polygon by its number of sides. Then classify it as *convex* or *concave* and *regular* or *irregular*.

32.

triangle, convex, regular

33.

dodecahedron; concave; irregular

34. Find the perimeter of quadrilateral $ABCD$ with vertices $A(-3, 5)$, $B(0, 5)$, $C(2, 0)$, and $D(-5, 0)$.

35. **PARKS** Westside Park received 440 feet of chain-link fencing as a donation to build an enclosed play area for dogs. The park administrators need to decide what shape the area should have. They have three options: (1) a rectangle with length of 100 feet and width of 120 feet, (2) a square with sides of length 110 feet, or (3) a circle with radius of approximately 70 feet. Find the areas of all three enclosures and determine which would provide the largest area for the dogs. **See margin.**

34. $2\sqrt{29} + 10 \approx 20.8$ units

Example 8

Name the polygon by its number of sides. Then classify it as *convex* or *concave* and *regular* or *irregular*.

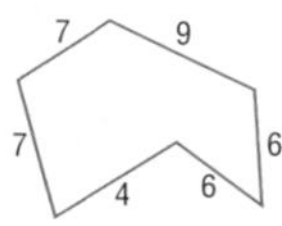

There are 6 sides, so this is a hexagon. If two of the sides are extended to make lines, they will pass through the interior of the hexagon, so it is concave. Since it is concave, it cannot be regular.

Example 9

Find the perimeter of the polygon in the figure above.

$P = s_1 + s_2 + s_3 + s_4 + s_5 + s_6$ Definition of perimeter

$= 7 + 7 + 9 + 6 + 6 + 4$ Substitution

$= 39$ Simplify.

The perimeter of the polygon is 39 units.

Additional Answer

35. Option 1 $= 12{,}000$ ft^2;
Option 2 $= 12{,}100$ ft^2;
Option 3 $\approx 15, 393.8$ ft^2;
Option 3 provides the greatest area.

connectED.mcgraw-hill.com 81

Anticipation Guide

Have students complete the Chapter 1 Anticipation Guide, and discuss how their responses have changed now that they have completed Chapter 1.

Additional Answers

36. square pyramid; base: □*ABCD*; faces: □*ABCD*, △*XAB*, △*XBC*, △*XCD*, △*XDA*; edges, $\overline{AB}$, $\overline{BC}$, $\overline{CD}$, $\overline{DA}$, $\overline{XA}$, $\overline{XB}$, $\overline{XC}$, $\overline{XD}$; vertices: *A*, *B*, *C*, *D*, *X*

37. hexagonal prism; bases: *ABCDEF* and *GHJKLM*; faces: □*ABHG*, □*BCJH*, □*CDKJ*, □*DELK*, □*EFML*, □*FAGM*; edges: $\overline{AB}$, $\overline{BC}$, $\overline{CD}$, $\overline{DE}$, $\overline{EF}$, $\overline{FA}$, $\overline{GH}$, $\overline{HJ}$, $\overline{JK}$, $\overline{KL}$, $\overline{LM}$, $\overline{MG}$, $\overline{AG}$, $\overline{BH}$, $\overline{CJ}$, $\overline{DK}$, $\overline{EL}$, $\overline{FM}$; vertices: *A*, *B*, *C*, *D*, *E*, *F*, *G*, *H*, *J*, *K*, *L*, *M*

CHAPTER 1 Study Guide and Review *Continued*

1-7 Three-Dimensional Figures

Identify each solid. Name the bases, faces, edges, and vertices. **36–37. See margin.**

36.

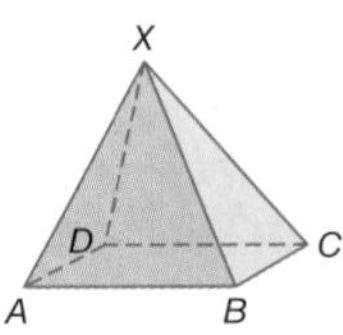

37.

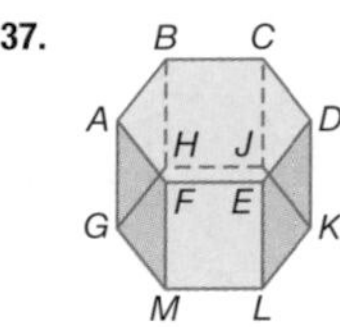

Find the surface area and volume of each solid.

38. **603.2 cm², 1131.0 cm³**

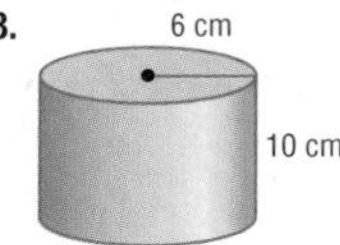

39. **384 in²; 384 in³**

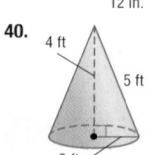

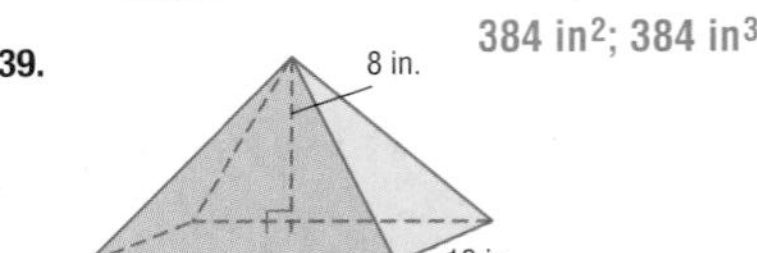

40. **75.4 ft²; 37.7 ft³**

4 ft

5 ft

3 ft

41. **72 m²; 36 m³**

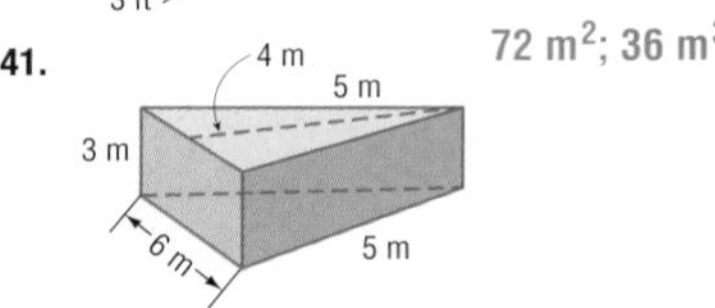

42. **BUILDING** Chris is building a trunk like the one shown below. His design is a square prism. What is the volume of the trunk? **18 ft³**

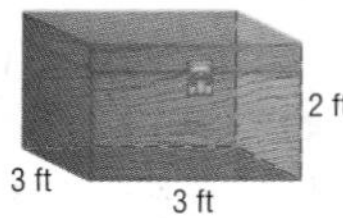

43. **HOCKEY** A regulation hockey puck is a cylinder made of vulcanized rubber 1 inch thick and 3 inches in diameter. Find the surface area and volume of a hockey puck. **≈23.6 in²; ≈7.1 in³**

Example 10

Identify the solid below. Name the bases, faces, edges, and vertices.

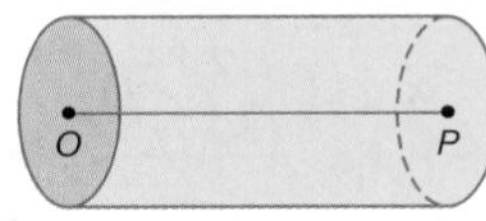

This solid has congruent circular bases in a pair of parallel planes. So, it is a cylinder.

Bases: circle *O* and circle *P*

A cylinder has no faces, edges, or vertices.

Example 11

Find the surface area and volume of the rectangular prism below.

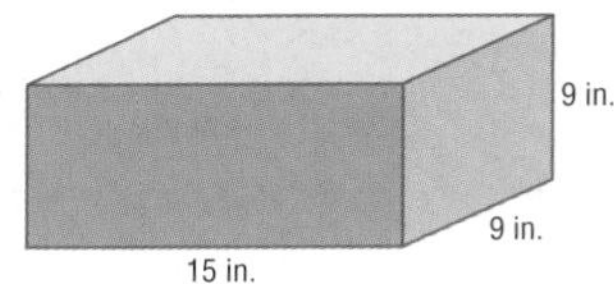

$T = Ph + 2B$	Surface area of a prism
$= (48)(9) + 2(135)$	Substitution
$= 702$	Simplify.

The surface area is 702 square inches.

$V = Bh$	Volume of a prism
$= (135)(9)$	Substitution
$= 1215$	Simplify.

The volume is 1215 cubic inches.

82 | Chapter 1 | Study Guide and Review

CHAPTER 1 Practice Test

Use the figure to name each of the following.

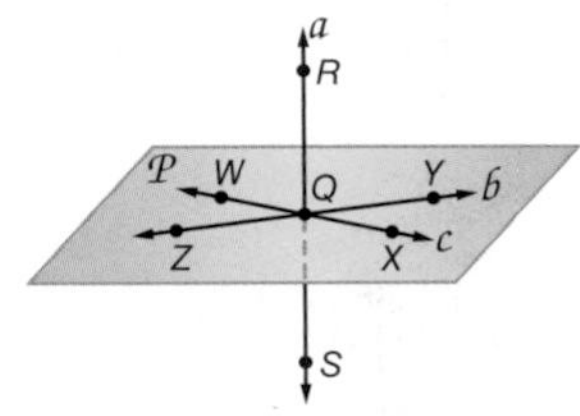

1. the line that contains points Q and Z **line b**
2. two points that are coplanar with points W, X, and Y **points Q and Z**
3. the intersection of lines a and b **point Q**

Find the value of the variable if P is between J and K.

4. $JP = 2x$, $PK = 7x$, $JK = 27$ **3**
5. $JP = 3y + 1$, $PK = 12y - 4$, $JK = 75$ **5.2**
6. $JP = 8z - 17$, $PK = 5z + 37$, $JK = 17z - 4$ **6**

Find the coordinates of the midpoint of a segment with the given endpoints.

7. (16, 5) and (28, −13) **(22, −4)**
8. (−11, 34) and (47, 0) **(18, 17)**
9. (−4, −14) and (−22, 9) **(−13, −2.5)**

Find the distance between each pair of points.

10. (43, −15) and (29, −3) **$\sqrt{340}$ or 18.4 units**
11. (21, 5) and (28, −1) **$\sqrt{85}$ or 9.2 units**
12. (0, −5) and (18, −10) **$\sqrt{349}$ or 18.7 units**
13. **ALGEBRA** The measure of $\angle X$ is 18 more than three times the measure of its complement. Find the measure of $\angle X$. **72**
14. Find the value of x that will make lines a and b perpendicular in the figure below. **12**

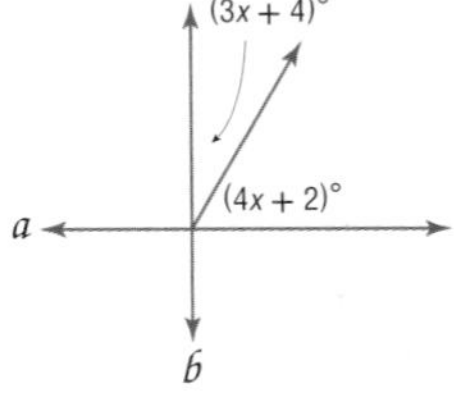

For Exercises 15–18, use the figure below.

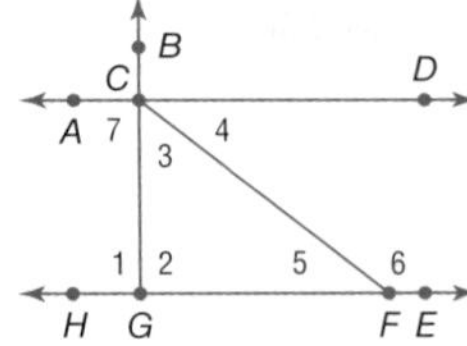

15. Name the vertex of $\angle 3$. **point C**
16. Name the sides of $\angle 1$. **$\overrightarrow{GH}$ and $\overrightarrow{GB}$**
17. Write another name for $\angle 6$. **$\angle EFC$ or $\angle CFE$**
18. Name a pair of angles that share exactly one point. **$\angle 7$ and $\angle 4$**
19. **MULTIPLE CHOICE** If $m\angle 1 = m\angle 2$, which of the following statements is true? **D**

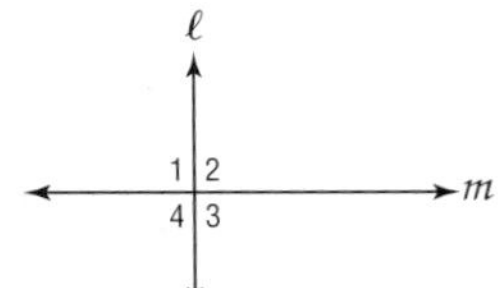

A $\angle 2 \cong \angle 4$

B $\angle 2$ is a right angle.

C $\ell \perp m$

D All of the above

Find the perimeter of each polygon.

20. triangle XYZ with vertices $X(3, 7)$, $Y(-1, -5)$, and $Z(6, -4)$ **31.1 units**
21. rectangle $PQRS$ with vertices $P(0, 0)$, $Q(0, 7)$, $R(12, 7)$, and $S(12, 0)$ **38 units**
22. **SAFETY** A severe weather siren in a local city can be heard within a radius of 1.3 miles. If the mayor of the city wants a new siren that will cover double the area of the old siren, what should the radius of the coverage area of the new siren be? Round to the nearest tenth of a mile. **1.8 mi**

Refer to the figure at the right.

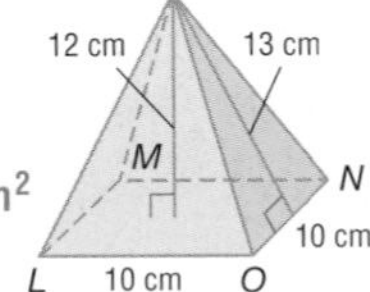

23. Name the base. **▱LMNO**
24. Find the surface area. **360 cm^2**
25. Find the volume. **400 cm^3**

Summative Assessment

Use these alternate leveled chapter tests to differentiate assessment for your students.

Leveled Chapter 1 Tests

Form	Type	Level	Page(s)
1	MC	AL	55–56
2A	MC	OL	57–58
2B	MC	OL	59–60
2C	FR	OL	61–62
2D	FR	OL	63–64
3	FR	BL	65–66
Vocabulary Test			54
Extended-Response Test			67

MC = multiple-choice questions
FR = free-response questions

Six forms of **chapter tests**, a **Vocabulary Test**, and an **Extended-Response Test** are provided for each chapter. These are available in the Chapter Resource Masters.

eAssessment Customize and create multiple versions of your Chapter test and their answer keys. All of the questions from the leveled chapter tests in the *Chapter 1 Resource Masters* are also available on eAssessment.

Intervention Planner

TIER 1 On Level OL	TIER 2 Strategic Intervention AL approaching grade level	TIER 3 Intensive Intervention 2 or more grades below level
If students miss about 25% of the exercises or less,	**If** students miss about 50% of the exercises,	**If** students miss about 75% of the exercises,
Then choose a resource:	**Then** choose a resource:	**Then** use *Math Triumphs, Geo.*, Ch. 1–5
SE Lessons 1-5, 1-6, and 1-7 Skills Practice, pp. 33, 39, and 45 connectED.mcgraw-hill.com Self-Check Quiz	Study Guide and Intervention, pp. 5, 12, 18, 25, 31, 37, 43 connectED.mcgraw-hill.com Extra Examples, Personal Tutor, Homework Help	connectED.mcgraw-hill.com Extra Examples, Personal Tutor, Homework Help, Review Vocabulary

1 Focus

Objective Understand and use key strategies to solve problems.

2 Teach

Scaffolding Questions

Ask:

- How can you organize the information given in a problem? You can underline the important given information, cross out any extraneous information, or even make a table or chart.
- What are some different ways that information can be given in a problem? Information can be given directly in the problem, in a chart or graph, or in a diagram.
- What are some key words to look for to determine what a question is asking? Look for any arithmetic terms like sum, difference, product, or quotient, and for words like least, greatest, all, or none. Be sure to answer the question that is being asked as many problems require more than one step and the solutions to those intermediate steps are frequently answer choices.
- Why is it important to check your answer? It is important that your answer makes sense and is reasonable; very minor arithmetic errors can result in solutions that are completely unreasonable.

CHAPTER 1

Preparing for Standardized Tests

Solving Math Problems

Strategies for Solving Math Problems

The first step to solving any math problem is to read the problem. When reading a math problem to get the information you need to solve, it is helpful to use special reading strategies.

Step 1

Read the problem to determine what information is given.

- **Analyze:** Determine what exactly the problem is asking you to solve.
- **Underline:** If you are able to write in your test book, underline any important information.

Step 2

Reread the problem to determine what information is needed to solve the problem.

- **Think:** How does the information fit together?
- **Key Words:** Are there any key words, variables or mathematical terms in the problem?
- **Diagrams:** Do you need to use a diagram, list or table?
- **Formulas:** Do you need a formula or an equation to solve the problem?

Step 3

Devise a plan and solve the problem. Use the information you found in Steps 1 and 2.

- **Question:** What problem are you solving?
- **Estimate:** Estimate an answer.
- **Eliminate:** Eliminate all answers that do not make sense and/or vary greatly from your estimate.

Step 4

Check your answer.

- **Reread:** Quickly reread the problem to make sure you solved the whole problem.
- **Reasonableness:** Is your answer reasonable?
- **Units:** Make sure your answer has the correct units of measurement.

Standardized Test Example

Read the problem. Identify what you need to know. Then use the information in the problem to solve.

Carmen is using a coordinate grid to make a map of her backyard. She plots the swing set at point $S(2, 5)$ and the big oak tree at point $O(-3, -6)$. If each unit on the grid represents 5 feet, what is the distance between the swing set and the oak tree? Round your answer to the nearest whole foot.

A 12 ft **B** 25 ft **C** 60 ft **D** 74 ft

Determine what exactly the problem is asking you to solve. Underline any important information.

Carmen is using a coordinate grid to make a map of her backyard. She plots the swing set at point $S(2, 5)$ and the big oak tree at point $O(-3, -6)$. If each unit on the grid represents 5 feet, what is the distance between the swing set and the oak tree? Round your answer to the nearest whole foot.

The problem is asking for the distance between the swing set and the oak tree. The key word is distance, so you know you will need to use the Distance Formula.

$d = \sqrt{(x_2 - x_1)^2 + (y_2 - y_1)^2}$ Distance Formula

$= \sqrt{(-3 - 2)^2 + (-6 - 5)^2}$ $(x_1, y_1) = (2, 5)$ and $(x_2, y_2) = (-3, -6)$

$= \sqrt{(-5)^2 + (-11)^2}$ Subtract.

$= \sqrt{25 + 121}$ or $\sqrt{146}$ Simplify.

The distance between swing set and the oak tree is $\sqrt{146}$ units. Use a calculator to find that $\sqrt{146}$ units is approximately 12.08 units.

Since each unit on the grid represents 5 feet, the distance is $(12.08) \cdot (5)$ or 60.4 ft. Therefore, the correct answer is C.

Check your answer to make sure it is reasonable, and that you have used the correct units.

Exercises

Read each question. Then fill in the correct answer on the answer document provided by your teacher or on a sheet of paper.

1. A regular pentagon has a perimeter of 24 inches. What is the measure of each side? D

   A 3 inches **C** 4 inches
   B 3.8 inches **D** 4.8 inches

2. What is the value of x in the figure at the right? G

   F 10
   G 12
   H 14
   J 15

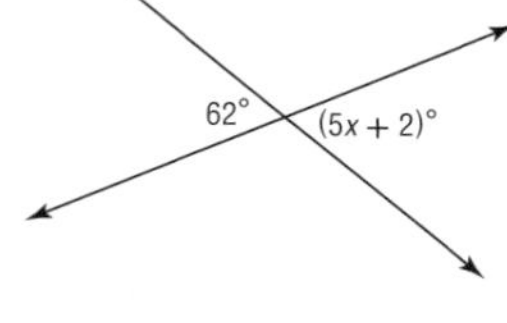

Additional Example

Manuel uses a coordinate grid to make a map of his classroom. He plots the teacher's desk at point $A(1, 4)$ and the globe at point $B(-2, -3)$. If each unit of the grid represents 3 feet, what is the distance between the desk and the globe? Round your answer to the nearest whole foot. D

A 8
B 12
C 21
D 23

3 Assess

Use Exercises 1 and 2 to assess students' understanding.

Diagnose Student Errors

Survey student responses for each item. Class trends may indicate common errors and misconceptions.

1. A only doubled one dimension
B only doubled two dimensions
C correct
D raised 2 to the fourth power, added a dimension

2. F error in calculation
G miscalculated $(-1)^2$ as -1.
H subtracted corresponding *x*- and *y*-coordinates from one point rather than the *x*- and *y*-coordinates from each of the points.
J correct

3. A describes only two points rather than all 3
B misunderstanding that points have no size and so cannot be congruent
C correct
D although $\overleftrightarrow{GH}$ and $\overleftrightarrow{FG}$ are skew lines, individual points cannot be described as skew.

4. F error in calculation
G error in calculation
H correct
J error in calculation

5. A flaw in logic
B correct
C incorrect assumption that $\triangle CDN$ is isosceles
D misuse of visual cues

6. F only adds two sides
G adds two legs and interior height
H correct
J includes interior height length in calculation

7. A correct
B misunderstanding of definition
C misunderstanding of definition
D misunderstanding of definition

CHAPTER 1 Standardized Test Practice

Cumulative, Chapter 1

Multiple Choice

Read each question. Then fill in the correct answer on the answer document provided by your teacher or on a sheet of paper.

1. If the dimensions of the prism below were doubled, by what factor would the volume of the prism increase? **C**

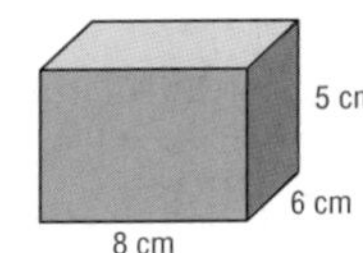

A 2   C 8
B 4   D 16

2. Find the distance between $M(-3, 1)$ and $N(2, 8)$ on a coordinate plane. **J**

F 6.1 units
G 6.9 units
H 7.3 units
J 8.6 units

3. Which of the following terms best describes points *F*, *G*, and *H*? **C**

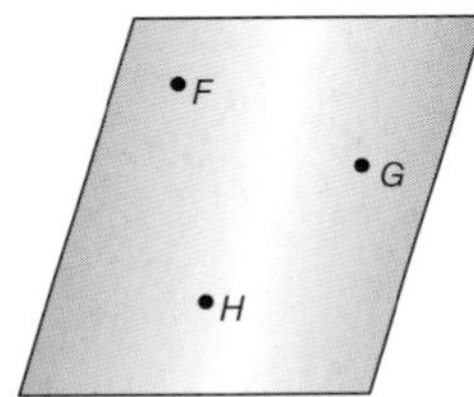

A collinear   C coplanar
B congruent   D skew

Test-Taking Tip

Question 3 Understanding the terms of geometry can help you solve problems. The term *congruent* refers to geometric figures, and *skew* refers to lines, therefore both answers can be eliminated.

4. What is the length of segment *BD*? **H**

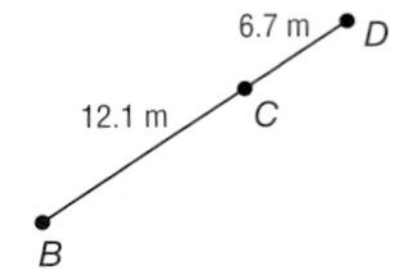

F 17.4 m   H 18.8 m
G 18.3 m   J 19.1 m

5. In the figure below, what is the measure of angle *CDN*? **B**

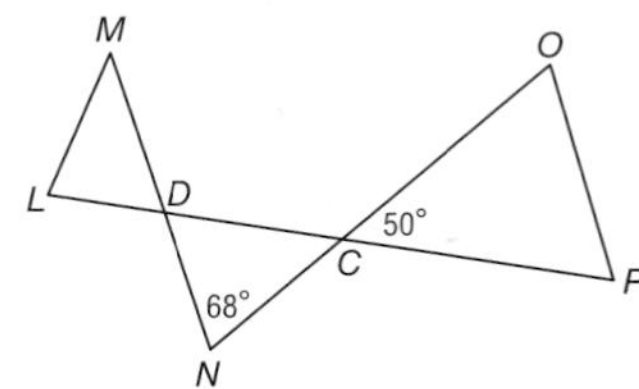

A 58°   C 68°
B 62°   D 70°

6. Find the perimeter of the figure below. **H**

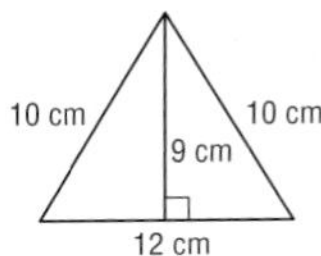

F 20 cm   H 32 cm
G 29 cm   J 41 cm

7. What is the relationship of $\angle 1$ and $\angle 2$? **A**

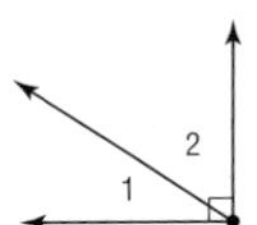

A complementary angles
B linear pair
C supplementary angles
D vertical angles

Short Response/Gridded Response

Record your answers on the answer sheet provided by your teacher or on a sheet of paper.

8. Find the distance between points R and S on the coordinate grid below. Round to the nearest tenth. **9.9 units**

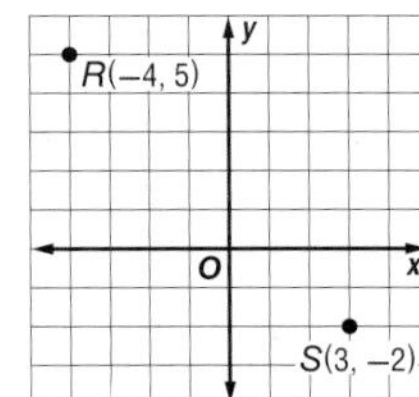

9. SHORT RESPONSE Find the value of x and AB if B is between A and C, $AB = 2x$, $AC = 6x - 5$, and $BC = 7$. **$x = 3$; $AB = 6$**

10. Suppose two lines intersect in a plane.

a. What do you know about the two pairs of vertical angles formed?

b. What do you know about the pairs of adjacent angles formed? **They are supplementary.**

10a. They have the same measure.

11. GRIDDED RESPONSE How many planes are shown in the figure below? **6**

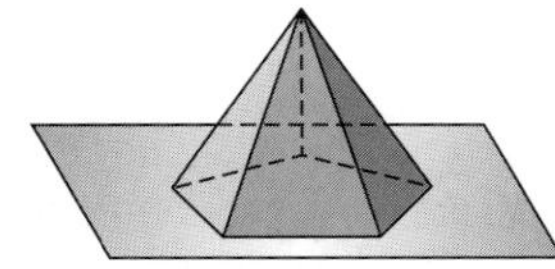

12. GRIDDED RESPONSE What is the total surface area of the cone? Round your answer to the nearest square centimeter. **314**

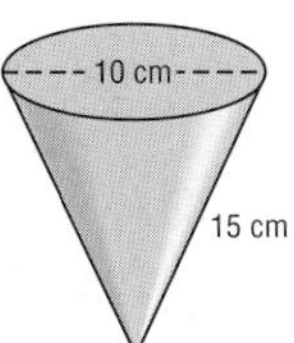

13. GRIDDED RESPONSE What is the value of x in the figure? **41**

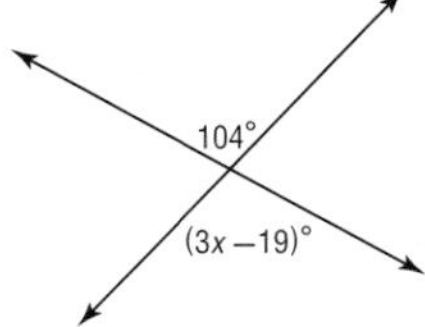

Extended Response

Record your answers on a sheet of paper. Show your work.

14. Julie's room has the dimensions shown in the figure.

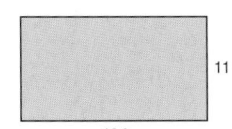

a. Find the perimeter of her room. **58 ft**

b. Find the area of her room. **198 ft^2**

c. If the length and width doubled, what effect would it have on the perimeter? **The perimeter would double.**

d. What effect would it have on the area? **The area would increase by a factor of 4.**

Need ExtraHelp?

If you missed Question...	1	2	3	4	5	6	7	8	9	10	11	12	13	14
Go to Lesson...	1-7	1-3	1-1	1-2	1-4	1-6	1-5	1-3	1-2	1-5	1-1	1-7	1-4	1-6

The items in the **Standardized Test Practice** help students practice the kinds of questions found on state assessments. The **Need Extra Help?** box allows students to diagnose and address weaknesses.

Formative Assessment

You can use these pages to benchmark student progress.

Standardized Test Practice, pp. 68–70

eAssessment Create practice tests that align to your state standards, the Common Core State Standards, and other national standards such as TIMSS and NAEP.

Answer Sheet Practice

Have students simulate taking a standardized test by recording their answers on a practice recording sheet.

Student Recording Sheet

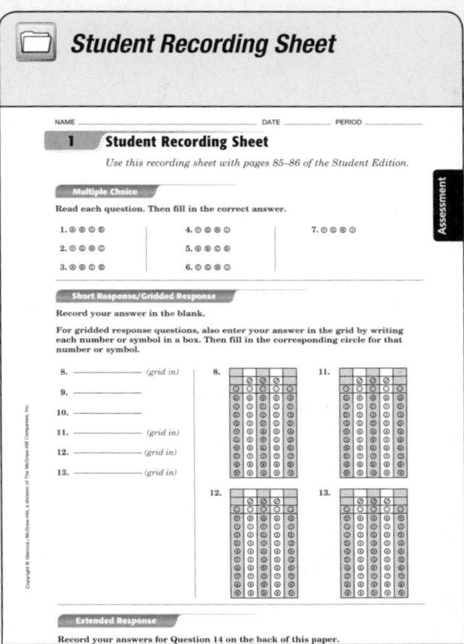

Homework Option

Get Ready for Chapter 2 Assign students the exercises on p. 89 as homework to assess whether they possess the prerequisite skills needed for the next chapter.

Lesson 1-1

32. Sample answer:

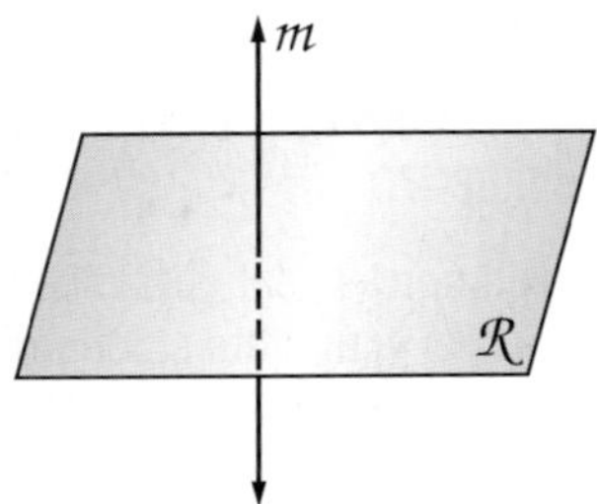

33. Sample answer:

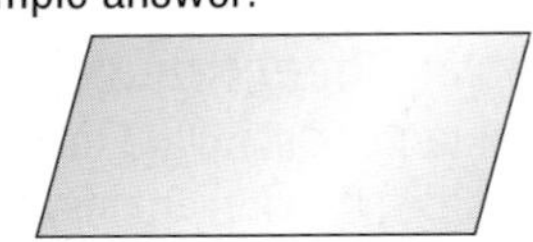

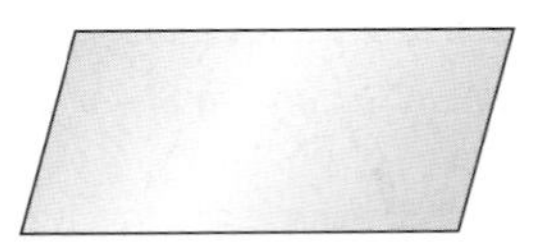

34. Sample answer:

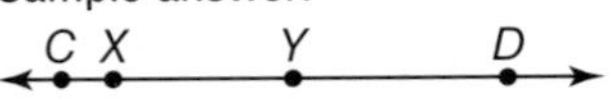

35. Sample answer:

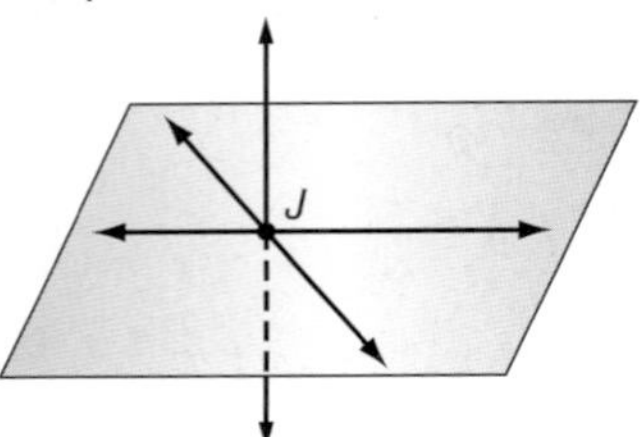

36. Sample answer:

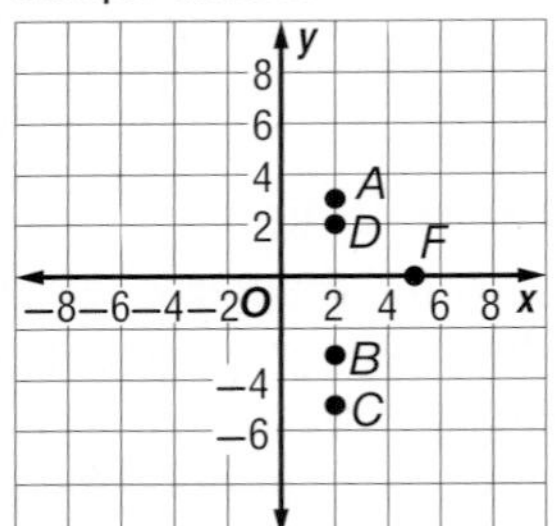

37. Sample answer:

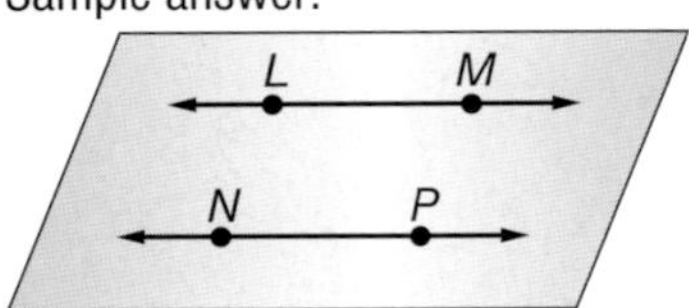

38.

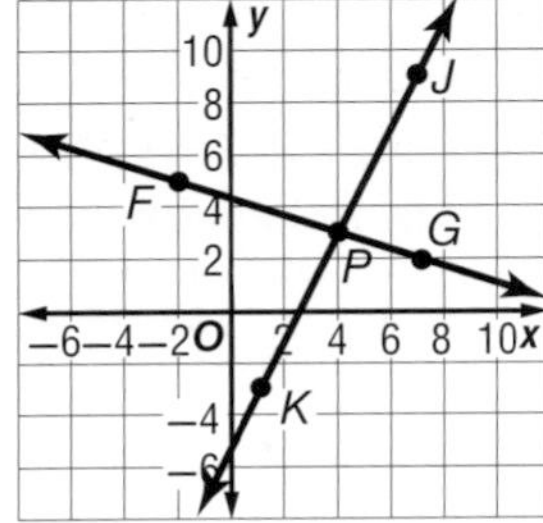

39. Sample answer:

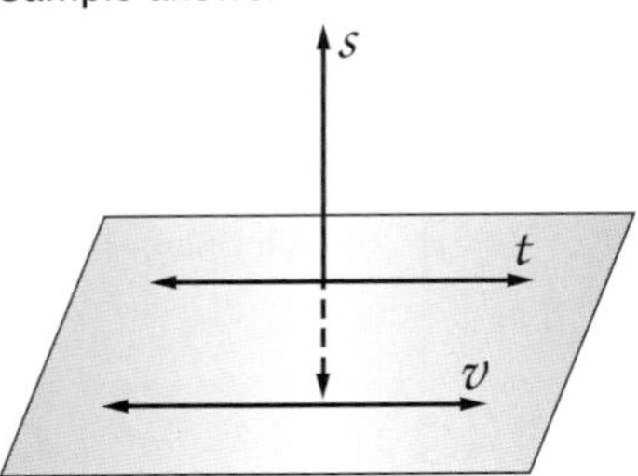

Extend Lesson 1-2

16. 22.4 ft is precise to within nearest 0.05 ft and 5.82 ft is precise to within 0.005 ft, so 5.82 ft is the more precise measurement. The relative error of 22.4 ft is $\frac{0.05 \text{ ft}}{22.4}$ or about 0.2%, while the relative error of 5.82 ft is $\frac{0.005}{5.82}$ or about 0.09%, so 5.82 ft is also more accurate.

17. Each measure is precise to within 0.5 mi, so one measure is not more precise than the other. The relative error of 13 mi is $\frac{0.5 \text{ mi}}{25 \text{ mi}}$ or 2%, while the relative error of 83 mi is $\frac{0.5 \text{ mi}}{8 \text{ mi}}$ or about 6.3%, so 8 mi is more accurate.

18. 9.2 cm is precise to within 0.05 cm or 0.5 mm and 42 mm is precise to within 0.5 mm, so one measure is not more precise than the other. The relative error of 9.2 cm ft is $\frac{0.05 \text{ cm}}{9.2 \text{ cm}}$ or about 0.5%, while the relative error of 42 mm is $\frac{0.5 \text{ mm}}{42 \text{ mm}}$ or about 1.2%, so 9.2 cm is more accurate.

19. $18\frac{1}{4}$ in. is precise to within $\frac{1}{8}$ in. and 125 yd is precise to within 0.5 yd, so $18\frac{1}{4}$ in. is the more precise measurement. The relative error of $18\frac{1}{4}$ in. is $\frac{0.125 \text{ in.}}{18.25 \text{ in.}}$ or about 0.7%, while the relative error of 125 yd is $\frac{0.5 \text{ yd}}{125 \text{ yd}}$ or 0.4%, so 125 yd is more accurate.

20. Suppose a person is 5.5 ft tall. If this height is measured to the nearest foot, the relative error would be $\frac{0.5 \text{ ft}}{5.5 \text{ ft}}$ or about 9%. If measured to the nearest inch, the relative error would be $\frac{0.5 \text{ in}}{5.5 \text{ ft}} = \frac{0.5 \text{ in.}}{65 \text{ in.}}$ or about 0.8%. If measured to the nearest $\frac{1}{16}$ in., the relative error would be $\frac{0.03125 \text{ in.}}{65 \text{ in.}}$ or about 0.05%. While measuring to the nearest $\frac{1}{16}$ in. is a more accurate measure, this level of accuracy is not necessary, about a 1% level of accuracy is sufficient, so measuring to the nearest inch is sufficient.

21. 1 ft; Suppose a mountain is 4000 ft tall. If this height is measured to the nearest foot, the relative error would be $\frac{0.5\text{ ft}}{4000\text{ ft}}$ or about 0.01%. If measured to the nearest inch, the relative error would be $\frac{0.5\text{ in}}{4000\text{ ft}} = \frac{0.5\text{ in.}}{48{,}000\text{ in.}}$ or about 0.001%. If measured to the nearest $\frac{1}{16}$ in., the relative error would be $\frac{0.03125\text{ in.}}{48{,}000\text{ in.}}$ or about 0.0007%. While measuring to the nearest $\frac{1}{16}$ in. is a more accurate measure, this level of accuracy is not necessary; about a 1% level of accuracy is sufficient, so measuring to the nearest foot is sufficient.

22. 13.5 in.; each measurement is accurate within $\frac{1}{8}$ of an inch, so the least perimeter is $2\left(2\frac{1}{8}\right)$ in. + $2\left(4\frac{5}{8}\right)$ in.; 14.5 in.; Each measurement is accurate within $\frac{1}{8}$ of an inch, so the greatest perimeter is $2\left(2\frac{3}{8}\right)$ in. + $2\left(4\frac{7}{8}\right)$ in.

Lesson 1-4

53. Sample answer: To measure an acute angle, you can fold the corner of the paper so that the edges meet. This would bisect the angle, allowing you to determine whether the angle was between 0° and 45° or between 45° and 90°. If the paper is folded two more times in the same manner and cut off this corner of the paper, the fold lines would form the increments of a homemade protractor that start at 0° on one side and progress in 90 ÷ 8 or 11.25° increments, ending at the adjacent side, which would indicate 90°. You can estimate halfway between each fold line, which would give you an accuracy of 11.25° ÷ 2 or about 6°. The actual measure of the angle shown is 52°. An estimate between 46° and 58° would be acceptable.

Lesson 1-6

43a–b. Sample answer:

Object	d (cm)	C (cm)	$\frac{C}{d}$
1	3	9.4	3.13
2	9	28.3	3.14
3	4.2	13.2	3.14
4	12	37.7	3.14
5	4.5	14.1	3.13
6	2	6.3	3.15
7	8	25.1	3.14
8	0.7	2.2	3.14
9	1.5	4.7	3.13
10	2.8	8.8	3.14

43c. Sample answer:

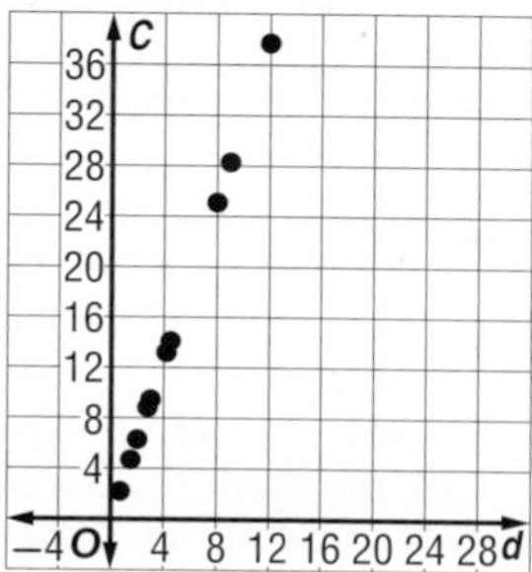

43d. Sample answer: $C = 3.14d$; the equation represents a formula for approximating the circumference of a circle. The slope represents an approximation for pi.

47. Sample answer: The pentagon is convex, since no points of the lines drawn on the edges are in the interior. The pentagon is regular since all of the angles and sides were constructed with the same measurement, making them congruent to each other.

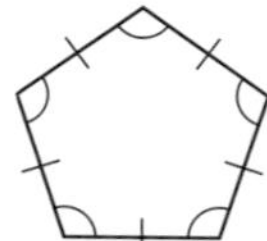

48. 1440 square tiles; Sample answer: the space is 20 × 12 or 240 inches wide and 12.5 × 12 or 150 inches wide. It will take exactly 240 in. ÷ 5 in./tile or 48 columns of tiles and 150 in. ÷ 5 in./tile or 30 rows or tiles to cover this space. So the number of tiles needed is 48 × 30 or 1440 tiles.

49. Sample answer: If a convex polygon is equiangular but not also equilateral, then it is not a regular polygon. Likewise, if a polygon is equiangular and equilateral, but not convex, then it is not a regular polygon.

Lesson 1-7

56. 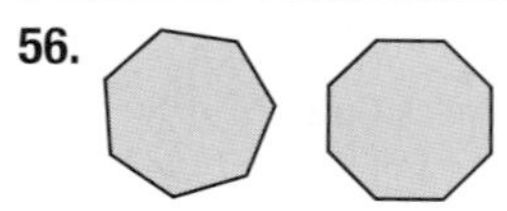

57. 

58.

59. 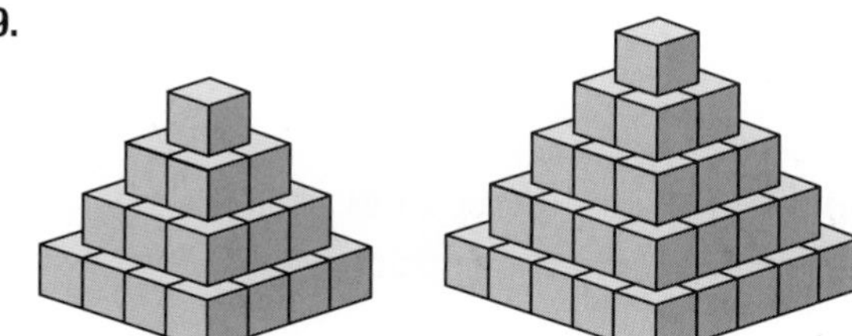

Chapter Planner

Diagnostic Assessment
Quick Check

	LESSON 2-1 (45 min: 1 day; 90 min: 0.5 day)	LESSON 2-2 (45 min: 1 day; 90 min: 0.5 day)	LESSON 2-3 (45 min: 1.5 days; 90 min: 0.5 day)
Title	**Inductive Reasoning and Conjecture**	**Logic**	**Conditional Statements**
Objectives	▪ Make conjectures based on inductive reasoning. ▪ Find counterexamples.	▪ Determine truth values of negations, conjunctions, and disjunctions and represent them using Venn diagrams. ▪ Find counterexamples.	▪ Analyze statements in if-then form. ▪ Write converses, inverses, and contrapositives.
Key Vocabulary	inductive reasoning conjecture counterexample	statement truth value negation compound statement conjunction disjunction truth table	conditional statement if-then statement conclusion related concepts converse inverse contrapositive logically equivalent
CCSS			
Multiple Representations			
Lesson Resources	connectED.mcgraw-hill.com Leveled Worksheets Vocabulary Personal Tutor Self-Check Quiz ▪ *5-Minute Check* ▪ *Study Notebook*	connectED.mcgraw-hill.com Leveled Worksheets Quiz 1 Vocabulary Personal Tutor Self-Check Quiz ▪ *5-Minute Check* ▪ *Study Notebook*	connectED.mcgraw-hill.com Leveled Worksheets Vocabulary Personal Tutor Self-Check Quiz ▪ *5-Minute Check* ▪ *Study Notebook* ▪ *Teaching Geometry with Manipulatives*
Resources for Every Lesson	IWB eStudent Edition IWB Interactive Classroom	▪ eTeacher Edition ▪ eSolutions Manual ▪ eAssessment	
Differentiated Instruction	pp. 93, 94, 98	pp. 103, 106	pp. 113, 114

IWB All digital assets are Interactive Whiteboard ready.

Suggested Pacing			
Time Periods	Instruction	Review & Assess	Total
45-minute	13 days	2 days	15 days
90-minute	5 days	1 day	6 days

EXTEND 2-3 (45 min: 0.5 day; 90 min: 0.25 day)	LESSON 2-4 (45 min: 1.5 days; 90 min: 0.5 day)	EXPLORE 2-5 (45 min: 0.5 day; 90 min: 0.25 day)	LESSON 2-5 (45 min: 2 days; 90 min: 0.5 day)
Geometry Lab: Biconditional Statements	**Deductive Reasoning**	**Geometry Lab: Necessary and Sufficient Conditions**	**Postulates and Paragraph Proofs**
▪ Identify, use, and judge the validity of biconditional statements.	▪ Use the Law of Detachment. ▪ Use the Law of Syllogism.	▪ Determine necessary and sufficient conditions for a statement to be true.	▪ Identify and use basic postulates about points, lines, and planes. ▪ Write paragraph proofs.
biconditional statements	deductive reasoning valid Law of Detachment Law of Syllogism	necessary conditions sufficient conditions	postulate axiom proof theorem deductive argument paragraph proof informal proof
			G.MG.3
connectED.mcgraw-hill.com Vocabulary Personal Tutor ▪ *Teaching Geometry with Manipulatives*	connectED.mcgraw-hill.com Leveled Worksheets Quiz 2 Vocabulary Animations Personal Tutor Self-Check Quiz ▪ *5-Minute Check* ▪ *Study Notebook* ▪ *Teaching Geometry with Manipulatives*	connectED.mcgraw-hill.com Vocabulary ▪ *Teaching Geometry with Manipulatives*	connectED.mcgraw-hill.com Leveled Worksheets Vocabulary Personal Tutor Self-Check Quiz ▪ *5-Minute Check* ▪ *Study Notebook*
IWB eStudent Edition IWB Interactive Classroom	▪ eTeacher Edition ▪ eSolutions Manual ▪ eAssessment		
	pp. 119, 124		pp. 131, 133

Formative Assessment
Mid-Chapter Quiz

Chapter Planner

	LESSON 2-6 (45 min: 1 day; 90 min: 0.5 day)	LESSON 2-7 (45 min: 2 days; 90 min: 0.75 day)	LESSON 2-8 (45 min: 2 days; 90 min: 0.75 day)
Title	**Algebraic Proof**	**Proving Segment Relationships**	**Proving Angle Relationships**
Objectives	▪ Use algebra to write two-column proofs. ▪ Use properties of equality to write geometric proofs.	▪ Write proofs involving segment addition. ▪ Write proofs involving congruence.	▪ Write proofs involving supplementary and complementary angles. ▪ Write proofs involving congruent and right angles.
Key Vocabulary	algebraic proof two-column proof formal proof		
CCSS		G.CO.9, G.CO.12	G.CO.9
Multiple Representations			
Lesson Resources	connectED.mcgraw-hill.com Leveled Worksheets Quiz 3 Vocabulary Personal Tutor Self-Check Quiz ▪ *5-Minute Check* ▪ *Study Notebook*	connectED.mcgraw-hill.com Leveled Worksheets Personal Tutor Self-Check Quiz ▪ *5-Minute Check* ▪ *Study Notebook*	connectED.mcgraw-hill.com Leveled Worksheets Quiz 4 Personal Tutor Self-Check Quiz ▪ *5-Minute Check* ▪ *Study Notebook*
Resources for Every Lesson	IWB eStudent Edition IWB Interactive Classroom	▪ eTeacher Edition ▪ eSolutions Manual ▪ eAssessment	
Differentiated Instruction	pp. 141, 142	pp. 145, 149	pp. 155, 158

Summative Assessment
Study Guide and Review
Practice Test

IWB All digital assets are Interactive Whiteboard ready.

What the Research Says...

Use a brainstorming activity to activate and build background knowledge prior to beginning a unit of study. It can also provide an assessment of what students know about the concept and indicate areas where instruction would be most needed (Taba, 1967).

- There are many vocabulary words, such as negation and disjunction, that students may be familiar with. Ask them to brainstorm and predict their definitions before giving them the actual definitions.
- The concept of two-column proofs is introduced in Lesson 2-6. Arrange students in small groups and have them create a geometric proof before introducing them to geometric proofs in the book. Have them justify their proofs.

Teacher to Teacher

Nancy Lee Keen, Teacher
Martinsville High School
Martinsville, IN

Use With Lesson 2-3

To develop the concept of conditional statements, I made posters of each of the four related conditionals. I wrote the hypotheses on yellow poster board, the conclusions on blue poster board, and NOT on red poster board. As we introduced each type of conditional, we placed the posters in the correct order.

Reading and Writing in Mathematics

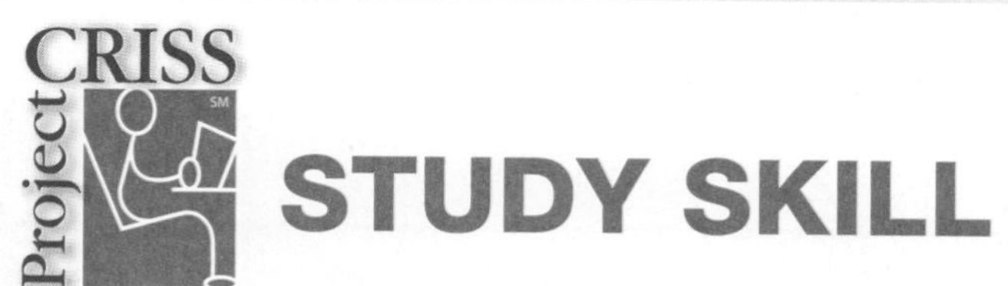

Many of the vocabulary terms introduced in Chapter 2 can be represented by symbols. Four-column notes can be a helpful way for students to organize new vocabulary terms. To reinforce understanding, students can write an explanation of each term in their own words and provide the appropriate symbol. The table below shows notes for Lesson 2-2. Students can add on to this sample with other terms from Chapter 2.

Term	Explanation	Symbol	Examples
negation	the opposite of the given statement	$\sim$	there is no school today
conjunction	a compound statement formed with the word "and"	$p \wedge q$	it is Monday and there is no school today
disjunction	a compound statement formed with the word "or"	$p \vee q$	it is Monday or there is no school today

Creating Independence through Student-owned Strategies

Reasoning and Proof

Assessment and Intervention

SE = Student Edition, **TE** = Teacher Edition, **CRM** = Chapter Resource Masters

	Diagnosis	Prescription
DIAGNOSTIC ASSESSMENT	**Beginning Chapter 2**	
	Get Ready for Chapter 2 **SE**	Response to Intervention **TE**
	Beginning Every Lesson	
	Then, Now, Why? **SE** 5-Minute Checks	Chapter 0 **SE**
FORMATIVE ASSESSMENT	**During/After Every Lesson**	
	Guided Practice **SE**, every example Check Your Understanding **SE** H.O.T. Problems **SE** Spiral Review **SE** Additional Examples **TE** Watch Out! **TE** Step 4, Assess **TE** Chapter 2 Quizzes **CRM**, pp. 57–58 Self-Check Quizzes connectED.mcgraw-hill.com	TIER 1 Intervention Skills Practice **CRM**, Ch. 1–2 connectED.mcgraw-hill.com TIER 2 Intervention Differentiated Instruction **TE**; Differentiated Homework Options **TE**; Study Guide and Intervention **CRM**, Ch. 1–2 TIER 3 Intervention *Math Triumphs, Geometry*
	Mid-Chapter	
	Mid-Chapter Quiz **SE** Mid-Chapter Test **CRM**, p. 59 eAssessment	TIER 1 Intervention Skills Practice **CRM**, Ch. 1–2 connectED.mcgraw-hill.com TIER 2 Intervention Study Guide and Intervention **CRM**, Ch. 1–2 TIER 3 Intervention *Math Triumphs, Geometry*
	Before Chapter Test	
	Chapter Study Guide and Review **SE** Practice Test **SE** Standardized Test Practice **SE** Chapter Test connectED.mcgraw-hill.com Standardized Test Practice connectED.mcgraw-hill.com Vocabulary Review connectED.mcgraw-hill.com eAssessment	TIER 1 Intervention Skills Practice **CRM**, Ch. 1–2 connectED.mcgraw-hill.com TIER 2 Intervention Study Guide and Intervention **CRM**, Ch. 1–2 TIER 3 Intervention *Math Triumphs, Geometry*
SUMMATIVE ASSESSMENT	**After Chapter 2**	
	Multiple-Choice Tests, Forms 1, 2A, 2B **CRM**, pp. 61–66 Free-Response Tests, Forms 2C, 2D, 3 **CRM**, pp. 67–72 Vocabulary Test **CRM**, p. 60 Extended Response Test **CRM**, p. 73 Standardized Test Practice **CRM**, pp. 74–76 eAssessment	Study Guide and Intervention **CRM**, Ch. 1–2 connectED.mcgraw-hill.com

Differentiated Instruction

Option 1 Reaching All Learners 

Visual Have students explore segment and angle addition by measuring objects in the classroom. Use a yardstick to find the midpoint of the classroom and a protractor to show that two right angles form a straight line.

Kinesthetic Write several if-then statements on sheets of paper cut into different figures. Write sufficient conditions for each if-then statement on paper cut into figures that are congruent to each respective if-then statement. Similarly, write necessary conditions on paper cut into similar figures that are larger than the original figures. Have students arrange the figures to demonstrate which are necessary and sufficient conditions for the if-then statements.

Option 2 Approaching Level AL

Show students how proofs proceed from assumptions to conclusions using a flow chart. The given conditions lead to the statements of the proof with each step by a justification, with the conclusion being the final statement of the proof.

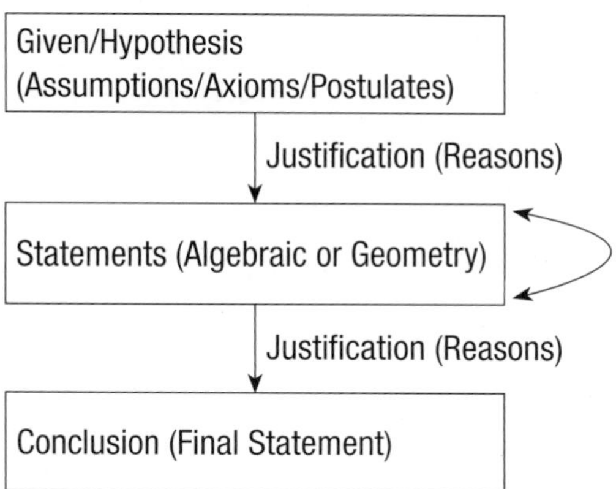

Option 3 English Learners ELL

As students learn about different forms of proofs, also describe the meanings of the following terms. Have students write the definitions in their notes.

negation: the opposite of a statement

conjunction: two statements joined together by *and*

disjunction: two statements joined together by *or*

Option 4 Beyond Level BL

Give students the following problem:

Three noncollinear points lie in a single plane. How many planes are defined by 4 noncollinear points? By 5 noncollinear points? Is there a unique answer? There are at least 1 and at most 4 planes for 4 noncollinear points. There are at least 1 and at most 10 planes for 5 noncollinear points.

Focus on Mathematical Content

Vertical Alignment

Before Chapter 2

Related Topics from Grade 8

- Communicate mathematical ideas using language, efficient tools, appropriate units, and graphical, numerical, physical, or algebraic mathematical models.
- Validate conclusions using mathematical properties and relationships.

Chapter 2

Related Topics from Geometry

- Use inductive reasoning to formulate a conjecture.
- Use logical reasoning to prove statements are true and find counterexamples to disprove statements that are false.
- Determine the validity of a conditional statement, its converse, inverse, and contrapostive.
- Use deductive reasoning to prove a statement.

After Chapter 2

Preparation for Algebra 2

- Compare and translate algebraic and graphical solutions of quadratic equations.
- Analyze situations modeled by square root functions, formulate equations or inequalities, select a method, and solve problems.

Lesson-by-Lesson Preview

2-1 Inductive Reasoning and Conjecture

A *conjecture* is an educated guess based on known information. Examining several specific situations to arrive at a conjecture is called *inductive reasoning.* If just one example contradicts the conjecture, the conjecture is not true. The false example is called a *counterexample.*

2-2 Logic

A *statement* is any sentence that is either true or false, but not both. The truth or falsity of a statement is called its *truth value.* The negation of a statement has the opposite meaning as well as an opposite truth value. This means that if a statement is represented by p, then *not* p is the negation of the statement. You can also write *not* p as $\sim p$.

Two or more statements can be joined to form a compound statement. A conjunction is a compound statement formed by joining two or more statements with the word *and* or the symbol $\wedge$. Two or more statements can also be joined to form a disjunction. A disjunction is a compound statement formed by joining two or more statements with the word *or*. The symbol $\vee$ is used in place of *or*. Conjunctions and disjunctions can be illustrated with Venn diagrams.

- **Venn Diagram**

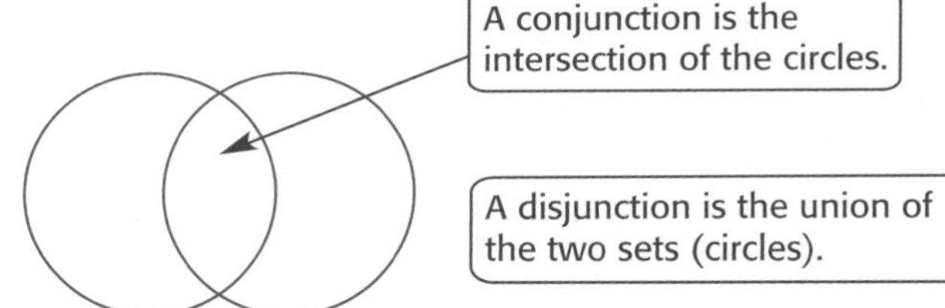

Truth tables can also be helpful in evaluating the truth values of statements.

- **Truth Tables**

p	q	$p \wedge q$
T	T	T
F	T	F
F	F	F
T	F	F

A conjunction is true only when p and q are true.

p	q	$p \vee q$
T	T	T
F	T	T
F	F	F
T	F	T

A disjunction is false only when both p and q are false.

p	$\sim p$
T	F
F	T

In a negation, if p is true, then $\sim p$ is false. If p is false, then $\sim p$ is true.

A truth table will show that a conjunction is true only when both statements are true. A disjunction, on the other hand, is true unless both statements are false.

2-3 Conditional Statements

A conditional statement is a statement that can be written in if-then form: *if p, then q*. The phrase immediately following the word *if* is called the *hypothesis*. The phrase immediately following the word *then* is called the *conclusion*. A conditional statement is true in all cases except where the hypothesis is true and the conclusion is false. Related conditionals are statements constructed from an if-then statement. A converse statement is formed by exchanging the hypothesis and the conclusion: *if q, then p*. An inverse statement is formed by negating both the hypothesis and the conclusion of the original statement: *if* $\sim p$, *then* $\sim q$. A contrapositive is formed by negating both the hypothesis and the conclusion of the converse statement: *if* $\sim q$, *then* $\sim p$.

2-4 Deductive Reasoning

Deductive reasoning uses facts, rules, definitions, or properties to reach logical conclusions. A form of deductive reasoning that is used to draw conclusions from true conditional statements is called the Law of Detachment. This law states that if $p \longrightarrow q$ is true and p is true, then q is also true. The Law of Syllogism is another law of logic. It states that if $p \longrightarrow q$ and $q \longrightarrow r$ are true, then $p \longrightarrow r$ is also true.

2-5 Postulates and Paragraph Proofs

In geometry, a *postulate* is a statement that describes a fundamental relationship between the basic terms of geometry. Postulates are accepted as true without proof.

Once a statement or conjecture has been proven to be true, it is called a *theorem*. A theorem can be used like a definition or postulate to justify that other statements are true.

A *proof* is a logical argument in which each statement you make is supported by a statement that is accepted as true. A proof states what is to be proved and develops a system of deductive reasoning.

2-6 Algebraic Proof

In algebra, properties of equality are used to solve algebraic equations and to verify relationships. A group of algebraic steps used to solve problems form a deductive argument. In geometry, a similar format is used to prove conjectures and theorems. A two-column, or formal, proof contains statements and reasons organized in two columns. Each step is called a *statement*, and the properties that justify each step are called *reasons*.

2-7 Proving Segment Relationships

As you learned in Chapter 1, a segment can be measured, and measures can be used in calculations because they are real numbers. The Ruler Postulate states that the points on any line or line segment can be paired with real numbers so that, given any two points A and B on a line, A corresponds to 0, and B corresponds to a positive real number. That number is the length of the segment. Another postulate states that if point B lies between points A and C on the same line, $AB + BC = AC$. The converse statement holds true as well.

A B C

$AB + BC = AC$

The Reflexive, Symmetric, and Transitive Properties of Equality can be used to write proofs about segment congruence. The theorem resulting from the proofs states that congruence of segments is reflexive, symmetric, and transitive.

2-8 Proving Angle Relationships

This lesson introduces postulates and theorems about angle relationships. The Protractor Postulate states, "Given $\overrightarrow{AB}$ and a number r between 0 and 180, there is exactly one ray with end-point A, extending on either side of $\overrightarrow{AB}$ such that the measure of the angle formed is r." The Angle Addition Postulate states that if R is in the interior of $\angle PQS$, then $m\angle PQR + m\angle RQS = m\angle PQS$. The converse is also true.

Mc Graw Hill Professional Development

Targeted professional development has been articulated throughout Geometry. More quality, customized professional development is available from McGraw-Hill Professional Development. Visit connectED.mcgraw-hill.com for details on each product.

- Online Lessons emphasize the strategies and techniques used to teach Geometry. Includes streaming video, interactive pages, and online tools.
- Video Workshops allow mentors, coaches, or leadership personnel to facilitate on-site workshops on educational strategies in mathematics and mathematical concepts.
- MHPD Online (www.mhpdonline.com) offers online professional development with video clips of instructional strategies, links, student activities, and news and issues in education.
- Teaching Today (teachingtoday.glencoe.com) gives secondary teachers practical strategies and materials that inspire excellence and innovation in teaching.

Chapter Project

Truth in Advertising

Students use what they have learned about conditional statements to complete a project.

This chapter project addresses business literacy, as well as several specific skills identified as being essential to student success by the Framework for 21st Century Learning.

Visit connectED.mcgraw-hill.com for student and teacher handouts.

KeyVocabulary Introduce the key vocabulary in the chapter using the routine below.

Define: A conditional statement is a statement that can be written in *if-then form*. The hypothesis is the phrase that immediately follows the word *if*. The conclusion is the phrase that immediately follows the word *then*.

Example: If you finish your homework, then you will go to the movies.

Ask: Is this statement in *if-then form*? Yes. What is the hypothesis? You finish your homework. What is the conclusion? You will go to the movies.

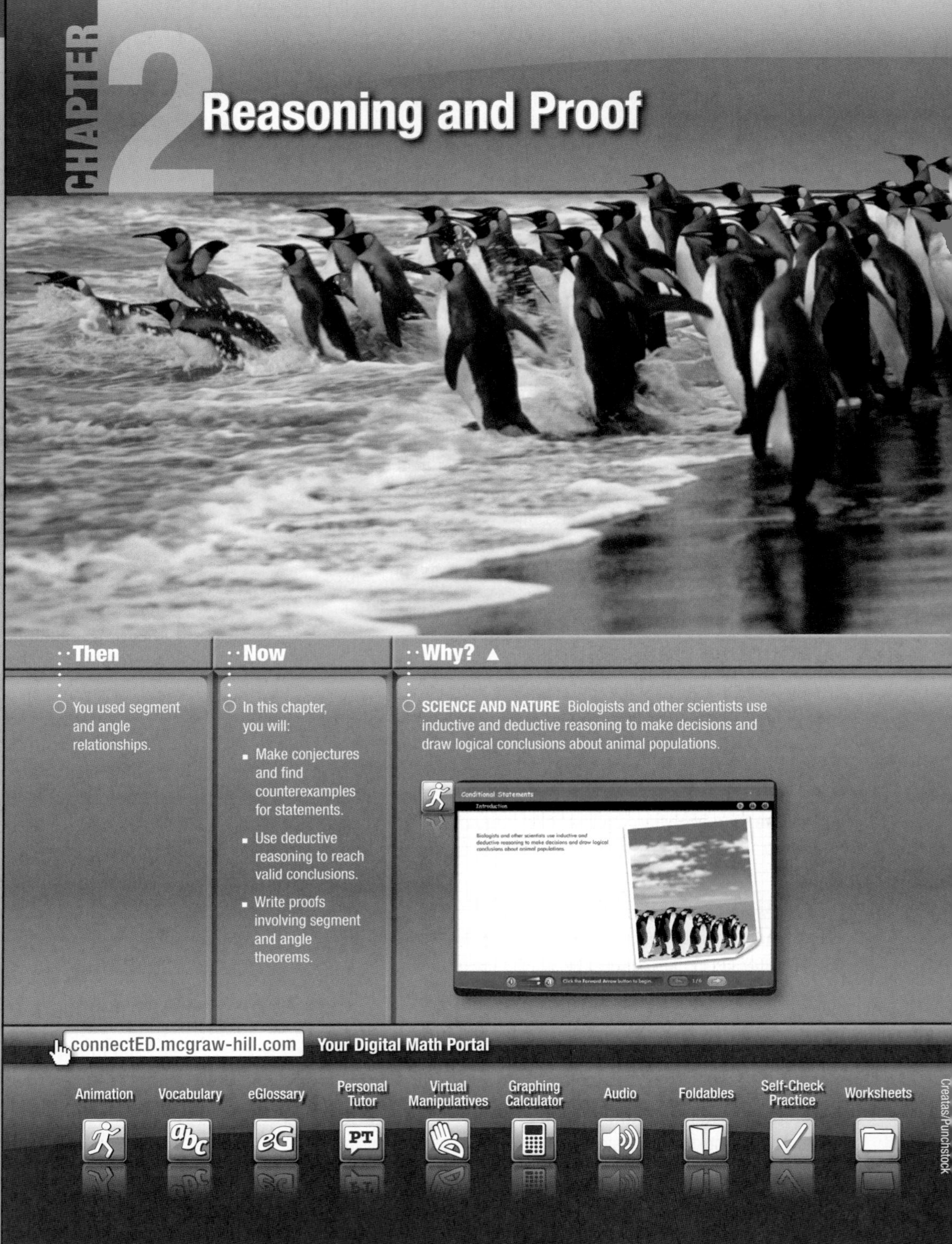

CHAPTER 2
Reasoning and Proof
Then
You used segment and angle relationships.
Now
In this chapter, you will:
Make conjectures and find counterexamples for statements.
Use deductive reasoning to reach valid conclusions.
Write proofs involving segment and angle theorems.
Why?
SCIENCE AND NATURE Biologists and other scientists use inductive and deductive reasoning to make decisions and draw logical conclusions about animal populations.
connectED.mcgraw-hill.com
Your Digital Math Portal
Animation
Vocabulary
eGlossary
Personal Tutor
Virtual Manipulatives
Graphing Calculator
Audio
Foldables
Self-Check Practice
Worksheets
Creatas/Punchstock

Get Ready for the Chapter

Diagnose Readiness | You have two options for checking prerequisite skills.

1 Textbook Option Take the Quick Check below. Refer to the Quick Review for help.

QuickCheck

Evaluate each expression for the given value of x.

1. $4x + 7; x = 6$ 31
2. $(x - 2)180; x = 8$ 1080
3. $5x^2 - 3x; x = 2$ 14
4. $\frac{x(x-3)}{2}; x = 5$ 5
5. $x + (x + 1) + (x + 2); x = 3$ 12

Write each verbal expression as an algebraic expression.

6. eight less than five times a number $5x - 8$
7. three more than the square of a number $x^2 + 3$

Solve each equation.

8. $8x - 10 = 6x$ 5
9. $18 + 7x = 10x + 39$ −7
10. $3(11x - 7) = 13x + 25$ 2.3
11. $3x + 8 = \frac{1}{2}x + 35$ 10.8
12. $\frac{2}{3}x + 1 = 5 - 2x$ 1.5
13. **CLOTHING** Nancy bought 4 shirts at the mall for $52. Write and solve an equation to find the average cost of one shirt. $4x = 52$; $13

Refer to the figure in Example 3.

14. Identify a pair of vertical angles that appear to be obtuse. $\angle BXD$, $\angle AXE$
15. Identify a pair of adjacent angles that appear to be complementary. $\angle CXD$, $\angle DXE$
16. Identify a linear pair. Sample answer: $\angle DXB$ and $\angle DXE$
17. If $m\angle DXB = 116$ and $m\angle EXA = 3x + 2$, find x. 38
18. If $m\angle BXC = 90$, $m\angle CXD = 6x - 13$, and $m\angle DXE = 10x + 7$, find x. 6

QuickReview

Example 1 (Used in Lesson 2-1)

Evaluate $x^2 - 2x + 11$ for $x = 6$.

$x^2 - 2x + 11$	Original expression
$= (6)^2 - 2(6) + 11$	Substitute 6 for x.
$= 36 - 2(6) + 11$	Evaluate the exponent.
$= 36 - 12 + 11$	Multiply.
$= 35$	Simplify.

Example 2 (Used in Lessons 2-6 through 2-8)

Solve $36x - 14 = 16x + 58$.

$36x - 14 = 16x + 58$	Original equation
$36x - 14 - 16x = 16x + 58 - 16x$	Subtract $16x$ from each side.
$20x - 14 = 58$	Simplify.
$20x - 14 + 14 = 58 + 14$	Add 14 to each side.
$20x = 72$	Simplify.
$\frac{20x}{20} = \frac{72}{20}$	Divide each side by 20.
$x = 3.6$	Simplify.

Example 3 (Used in Lesson 2-8)

If $m\angle BXA = 3x + 5$ and $m\angle DXE = 56$, find x.

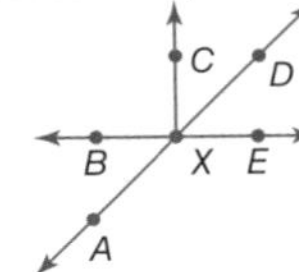

$m\angle BXA = m\angle DXE$	Vertical ∡ are ≅.
$3x + 5 = 56$	Substitution
$3x = 51$	Subtract 5 from each side.
$x = 17$	Divide each side by 3.

2 Online Option Take an online self-check Chapter Readiness Quiz at connectED.mcgraw-hill.com.

89

Get Ready for the Chapter

Response to Intervention (RtI)

Use the *Quick Check* results and the Intervention Planner chart to help you determine your Response to Intervention. The If-Then statements in the chart help you decide the appropriate tier of RtI and suggest intervention resources for each tier.

InterventionPlanner

TIER 1 On Level OL

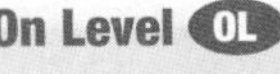

If students miss about 25% of the exercises or less,

Then choose a resource:

SE Lessons 2-1 through 2-8

Skills Practice, Chapter 2

connectED.mcgraw-hill.com Self-Check Quiz

TIER 2 Strategic Intervention AL approaching grade level

If students miss about 50% of the exercises,

Then choose a resource:

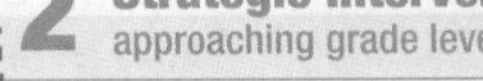
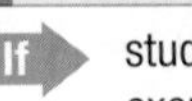
Study Guide and Intervention, Chapter 2

connectED.mcgraw-hill.com Extra Examples, Personal Tutor, Homework Help

TIER 3 Intensive Intervention 2 or more grades below level

If students miss about 75% of the exercises,

Then use *Math Triumphs, Geometry*

connectED.mcgraw-hill.com Extra Examples, Personal Tutor, Homework Help, Review Vocabulary

Essential Questions

- Why is important to be able to think logically? Sample answer: On a daily basis, we are presented with information and arguments from various sources such as television commercials and politicians. Many of these arguments are not valid. To analyze these arguments or to present valid arguments, we must be able to think logically and form valid conclusions.

FOLDABLES StudyOrganizer

Dinah Zike's Foldables®

Focus Students write about reasoning and proofs.

Teach Throughout the chapter, have students take notes under the tabs of their Foldables. Instruct students to take notes while reading each lesson and listening to instruction. They should include definitions of terms and key concepts. Encourage students to record examples of each type of logical reasoning from a lesson on the back of the Foldable.

When to use it Use the appropriate tabs as students cover each lesson in this chapter. Students should add to the vocabulary tab during each lesson.

Differentiated Instruction

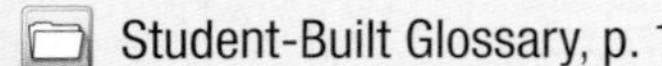 Student-Built Glossary, p. 1

Students should complete the chart by providing the definition for each term and an example as they progress through Chapter 2. This study tool can also be used to review for the chapter test.

Get Started on the Chapter

You will learn several new concepts, skills, and vocabulary terms as you study Chapter 2. To get ready, identify important terms and organize your resources. You may refer to Chapter 0 to review prerequisite skills.

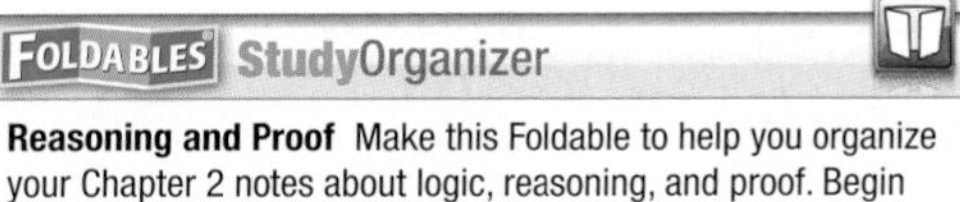

FOLDABLES StudyOrganizer

Reasoning and Proof Make this Foldable to help you organize your Chapter 2 notes about logic, reasoning, and proof. Begin with one sheet of notebook paper.

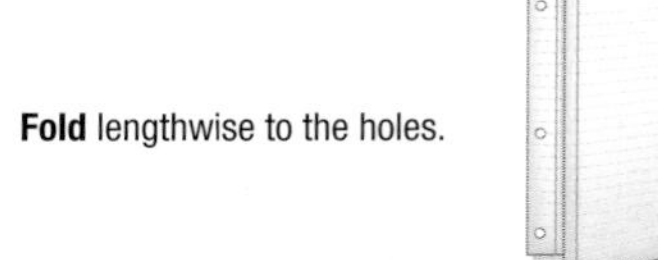

1 **Fold** lengthwise to the holes.

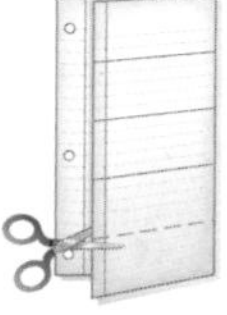

2 **Cut** five tabs in the top sheet.

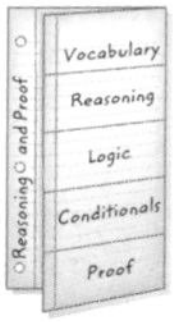

3 **Label** the tabs as shown.

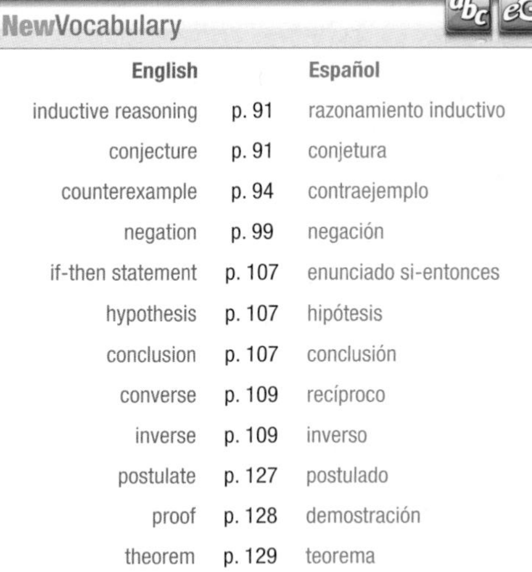

NewVocabulary

English		Español
inductive reasoning	p. 91	razonamiento inductivo
conjecture	p. 91	conjetura
counterexample	p. 94	contraejemplo
negation	p. 99	negación
if-then statement	p. 107	enunciado si-entonces
hypothesis	p. 107	hipótesis
conclusion	p. 107	conclusión
converse	p. 109	recíproco
inverse	p. 109	inverso
postulate	p. 127	postulado
proof	p. 128	demostración
theorem	p. 129	teorema

ReviewVocabulary

complementary angles ángulos complementarios two angles with measures that have a sum of 90

supplementary angles ángulos suplementarios two angles with measures that have a sum of 180

vertical angles ángulos opuestos por el vértice two nonadjacent angles formed by intersecting lines

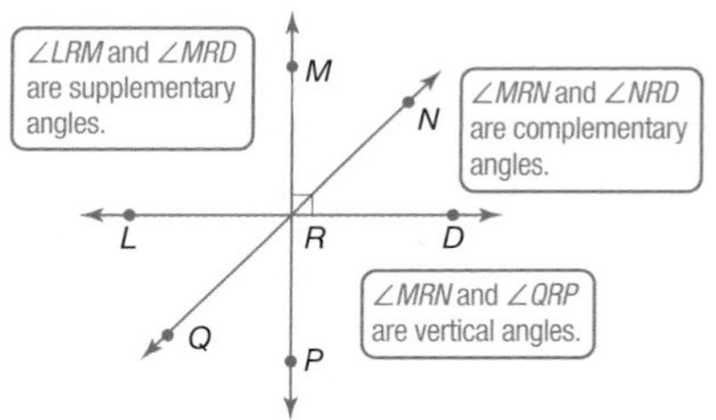

LESSON 2-1 Inductive Reasoning and Conjecture

Then

- You used data to find patterns and make predictions.

Now

1. Make conjectures based on inductive reasoning.
2. Find counterexamples.

Why?

- Market research is conducted by an analyst to answer specific questions about products. For example, a company that creates video games might hire focus group testers to play an unreleased video game. The process of using patterns to analyze the effectiveness of a product involves inductive reasoning.

NewVocabulary
inductive reasoning
conjecture
counterexample

1 Make Conjectures

Inductive reasoning is reasoning that uses a number of specific examples to arrive at a conclusion. When you assume that an observed pattern will continue, you are applying inductive reasoning. A concluding statement reached using inductive reasoning is called a **conjecture**.

Example 1 Patterns and Conjecture

Write a conjecture that describes the pattern in each sequence. Then use your conjecture to find the next item in the sequence.

a. Movie show times: 8:30 A.M., 9:45 A.M., 11:00 A.M., 12:15 P.M., . . .

Step 1 Look for a pattern.

8:30 A.M., 9:45 A.M., 11:00 A.M., 12:15 P.M., . . .

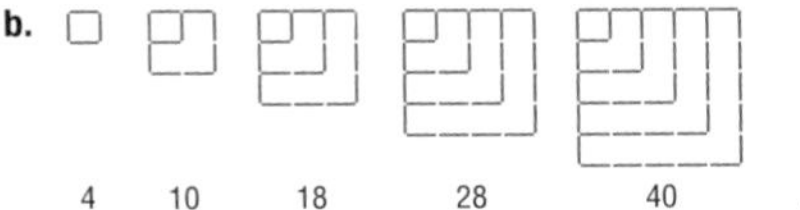

Step 2 Make a conjecture.

The show time is 1 hour and fifteen minutes greater than the previous show time. The next show time will be 12:15 P.M. + 1:15 or 1:30 P.M.

b.

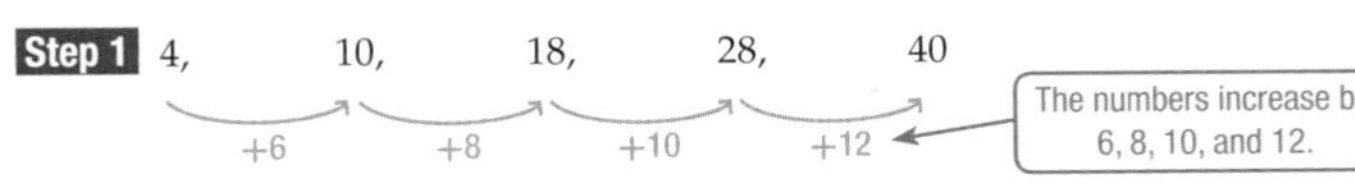

Step 1 4, 10, 18, 28, 40

+6 +8 +10 +12

The numbers increase by 6, 8, 10, and 12.

Step 2 The next figure will increase by 12 + 2 or 14 segments. So, the next figure will have 40 + 14 or 54 segments.

CHECK Draw the next figure to check your conjecture ✓

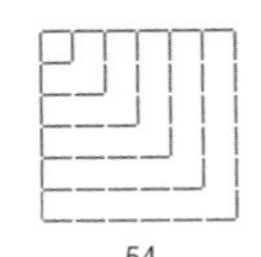

1 Focus

VerticalAlignment

Before Lesson 2-1 Represent relationships among quantities using concrete models, tables, graphs, diagrams, verbal descriptions, and equations.

Lesson 2-1 Find counterexamples. Use inductive reasoning to formulate a conjecture.

After Lesson 2-1 Use logical reasoning to prove statements are true and find counterexamples.

2 Teach

Scaffolding Questions

Have students read the **Why?** section of the lesson.

Ask:

- What other data might be of interest to a market researcher? Sample statement: Sales of the product and the products of its competitors might be of interest.
- Why would a research analyst ask questions of focus groups? Sample statement: Their opinions represent the opinions of the general public.

Lesson 2-1 Resources

Resource	Approaching Level AL	On Level OL	Beyond Level BL	English Learners ELL
Teacher Edition	▪ Differentiated Instruction, pp. 93, 94	▪ Differentiated Instruction, pp. 93, 94, 98	▪ Differentiated Instruction, pp. 94, 98	
Chapter Resource Masters	▪ Study Guide and Intervention, pp. 5–6 ▪ Skills Practice, p. 7 ▪ Practice, p. 8 ▪ Word Problem Practice, p. 9 ▪ Graphing Calculator Activity, p. 11	▪ Study Guide and Intervention, pp. 5–6 ▪ Skills Practice, p. 7 ▪ Practice, p. 8 ▪ Word Problem Practice, p. 9 ▪ Enrichment, p. 10 ▪ Graphing Calculator Activity, p. 11	▪ Practice, p. 8 ▪ Word Problem Practice, p. 9 ▪ Enrichment, p. 10 ▪ Graphing Calculator Activity, p. 11	▪ Study Guide and Intervention, pp. 5–6 ▪ Skills Practice, p. 7 ▪ Practice, p. 8 ▪ Word Problem Practice, p. 9 ▪ Graphing Calculator Activity, p. 11
Other	▪ 5-Minute Check 2-1 ▪ Study Notebook	▪ 5-Minute Check 2-1 ▪ Study Notebook	▪ 5-Minute Check 2-1 ▪ Study Notebook	▪ 5-Minute Check 2-1 ▪ Study Notebook

1 Make Conjectures

Examples 1 and 3 show how to make conjectures from patterns. **Example 2** shows how to make a conjecture about a single figure.

Additional Examples

1 Write a conjecture that describes the pattern in each sequence. Then use your conjecture to find the next item in the sequence.

a. 2, 4, 12, 48, 240

The nth term is multiplied by the number $n + 1$; 1440.

b.

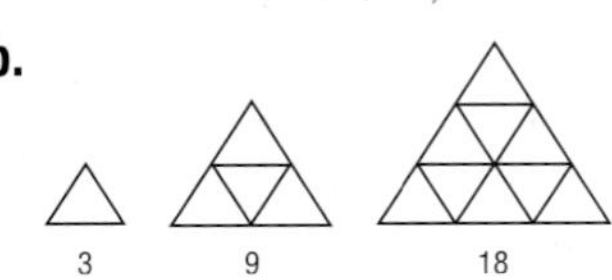

The number of segments in the nth figure increases by $3n + 3$; 30.

2 Make a conjecture about each value or geometric relationship. List or draw some examples that support your conjecture.

a. the sum of an odd number and an even number

The sum of an odd number and an even number is odd; $3 + 4 = 7, 5 + 10 = 15$.

b. For points L, M, and N, $LM = 20$, $MN = 6$, and $LN = 14$. Make a conjecture and draw a figure to illustrate your conjecture.

L, M, and N are collinear.

Teaching the Mathematical Practices

Arguments Mathematically proficient students understand and use stated assumptions, definitions, and previously established results in constructing arguments. Encouraging them to think of each problem solution as a logical progression of statements establishes good habits for this course and advanced courses.

StudyTip

Figural Patterns Patterns that involve a sequence of figures, like those in Example 1b and in Guided Practice 1C, are called *figural patterns.*

GuidedPractice

Write a conjecture that describes the pattern in each sequence. Then use your conjecture to find the next item in the sequence.

1A. Follow-up visits: Dec., May, Oct., Mar., . . .

1B. 10, 4, −2, −8, . . .

1C.

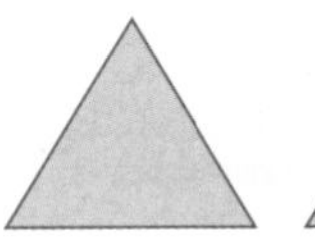
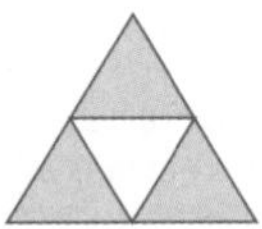
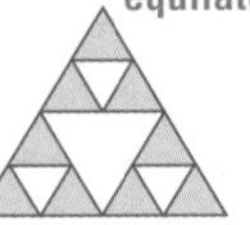

1A. The next month in the sequence is the fifth month after the preceding month; Aug.

1B. The next number in the sequence is 6 less than the preceding number; −14.

1C. Each shaded triangle in the previous figure is divided into four other equilateral triangles with a white equilateral triangle in the middle.

To make some algebraic and geometric conjectures, you will need to provide examples.

Example 2 Algebraic and Geometric Conjectures

Make a conjecture about each value or geometric relationship. List or draw some examples that support your conjecture.

a. the sum of two odd numbers

Step 1 List examples.

$1 + 3 = 4 \quad 1 + 5 = 6 \quad 3 + 5 = 8 \quad 7 + 9 = 16$

Step 2 Look for a pattern.

Notice that the sums 4, 6, 8, and 16 are all even numbers.

Step 3 Make a conjecture.

The sum of two odd numbers is an even number.

b. segments joining opposite vertices of a rectangle

Step 1

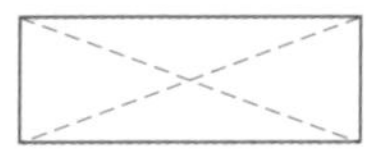
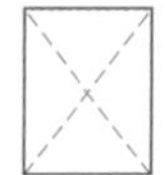

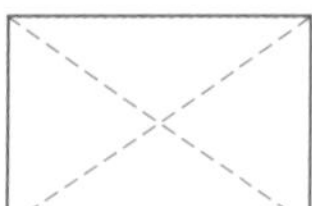

Step 2 Notice that the segments joining opposite vertices of each rectangle appear to have the same measure. Use a ruler or compass to confirm this.

Step 3 Conjecture: the segments joining opposite vertices of a rectangle are congruent.

StudyTip

Arguments Examples that support a conjecture are not enough to show that a conjecture is true. To show that an algebraic or geometric conjecture is true, you must offer a logical argument called a proof. You will learn more about proofs in Lesson 2-5.

GuidedPractice

2A. the sum of two even numbers

2B. the relationship between AB and EF, if $AB = CD$ and $CD = EF$ **See margin.**

2C. the sum of the squares of two consecutive natural numbers

2A. The sum of two even numbers is an even number; examples: $2 + 4 = 6$, $8 + 10 = 18$, $20 + 16 = 36$.

2C. The sum of the squares of two consecutive natural numbers is an odd number; examples: $1^2 + 2^2 = 5$, $2^2 + 3^2 = 13$, $5^2 + 6^2 = 61$.

Teach with Tech

Interactive Whiteboard Give students several patterns and have them make a conjecture about the next term in the pattern. Choose several students and have them share their answers and explain their reasoning.

Additional Answer (Guided Practice)

2B. $AB = EF$; examples:

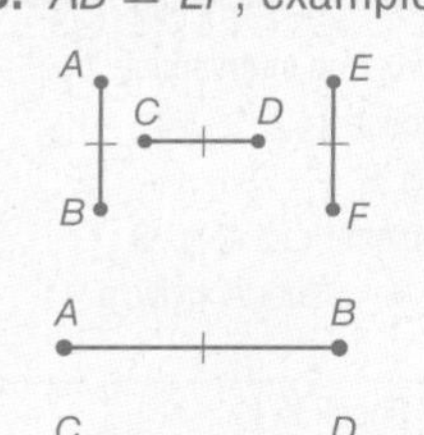

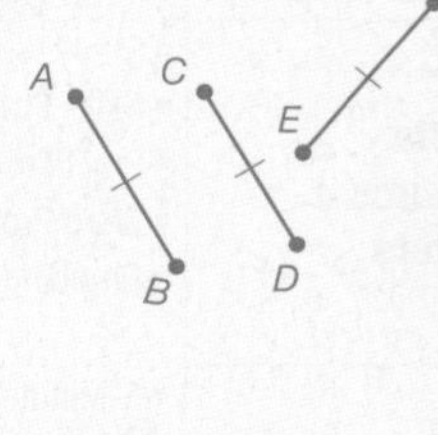

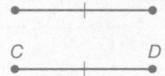

Real-world conjectures are often made based on data gathered about a specific topic of interest.

PT

Real-World Example 3 Make Conjectures from Data

BUSINESS The owner of a hair salon collected data on the number of customers her salon had each Friday, Saturday, and Sunday for 6 months to decide whether she should increase the number of stylists working each weekend. The data she collected are shown below.

Number of Customers on the Weekend

Day	Month 1	Month 2	Month 3	Month 4	Month 5	Month 6
Friday	225	255	321	406	540	450
Saturday	603	658	652	712	746	832
Sunday	552	635	642	692	685	705
Total	1380	1548	1615	1810	1971	1987

a. Make a statistical graph that best displays the data.

Since you want to look for a pattern over time, use a scatter plot to display the data. Label the horizontal axis with the months and the vertical axis with the number of customers. Plot each set of data using a different color, and include a legend.

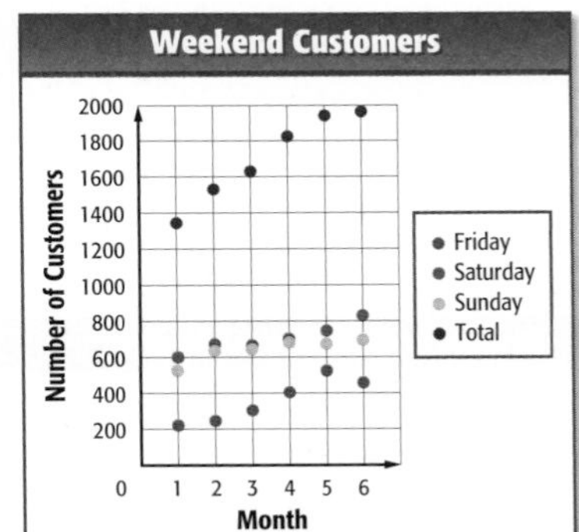

b. Make a conjecture based on the data, and explain how this conjecture is supported by your graph.

Look for patterns in the data. The number of customers on each day usually increases each month, and the total number of customers increases every single month.

Survey data supports a conjecture that the amount of business on the weekends has increased, so the owner should schedule more stylists to work on those days.

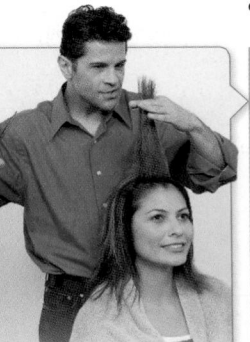

Real-WorldCareer

Hair Stylist Hair stylists work in salons where various services, including skin and nail treatments, may be provided in addition to hair care. About 48% of hair stylists are self-employed and own their own businesses. Hair stylists must attend cosmetology school and obtain a license.

GuidedPractice

3. **POSTAGE** The table at the right shows the price of postage for the years 1982 through 2009.

Year	Rate (cents)
1982	20
1987	22
1992	29
1997	32
2002	37
2007	41
2009	44

A. Make a statistical graph that best displays the data. **See margin.**

B. Predict the postage rate in 2015 based on the graph. **49 cents**

C. Does it make sense that the pattern of the data will continue over time? If not, how will it change? Explain your reasoning.

3C. Sample answer: Yes; the trend is reasonable because the price of postage will probably continue to increase over time.

Additional Example

3 SALES The table shows the total sales for the first three months a store is open. The owner wants to predict the sales for the fourth month.

Month	Sales
1	$500
2	$1500
3	$4500

a. Make a statistical graph that best displays the data.

b. Make a conjecture about the sales in the fourth month and justify your claim or prediction.

The sales triple each month, so in the fourth month there will be $13,500 in sales.

Additional Examples also in Interactive Classroom PowerPoint® Presentations

Additional Answer (Guided Practice)

3A.

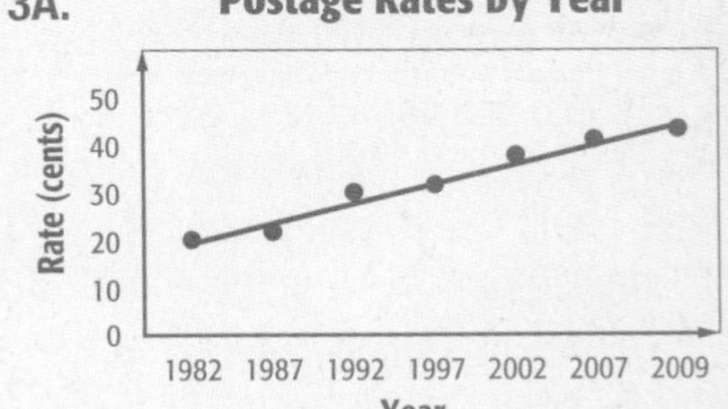

DifferentiatedInstruction AL OL

If students have trouble recognizing geometric patterns,

Then have them write down the sequence of numbers that may be contained in the pattern.

Tips for New Teachers

Reasoning Tell students to test all fundamental operations, including powers and roots, when they are looking for patterns in a series of numbers. Advise students that sometimes two operations can be used.

2 Find Counterexamples

Example 4 shows how to find a counterexample based on given information.

Additional Example

4 UNEMPLOYMENT Based on the table showing unemployment rates for various counties in Texas, find a counterexample for the following statement.

The unemployment rate is highest in the cities with the most people.

County	Population	Rate
Armstrong	2,163	3.7%
Cameron	371,825	7.2%
El Paso	713,126	7.0%
Hopkins	33,201	4.3%
Maverick	50,436	11.3%
Mitchell	9,402	6.1%

Maverick has only 50,436 people in its population, and it has a higher rate of unemployment than El Paso, which has 713,126 people in its population.

Additional Answer (Guided Practice)

4B. Sample answer: When points A, B, and D are noncollinear and points E, B and C are noncollinear, the conjecture is false. In the figure, $\angle ABC \cong \angle DBE$, but $\angle ABC$ and $\angle DBE$ are not vertical angles.

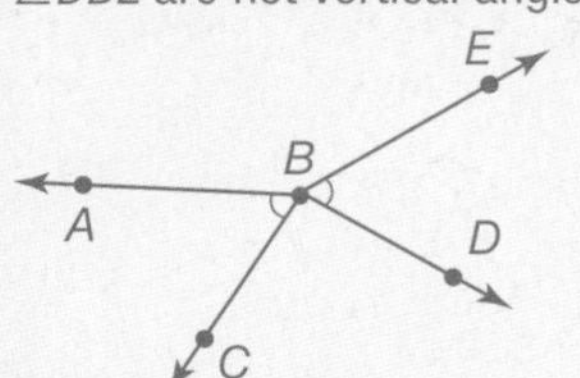

2 Find Counterexamples

To show that a conjecture is true for all cases, you must prove it. It takes only one false example, however, to show that a conjecture is not true. This false example is called a **counterexample**, and it can be a number, a drawing, or a statement.

VocabularyLink
Counterexample
Everyday Use The prefix *counter-* means *the opposite of.*
Math Use A counterexample is the opposite of an example.

Example 4 Find Counterexamples

Find a counterexample to show that each conjecture is false.

a. If n is a real number, then $n^2 > n$.

When n is 1, the conjecture is false, since $1^2 \ngtr 1$.

b. If $JK = KL$, then K is the midpoint of $\overline{JL}$.

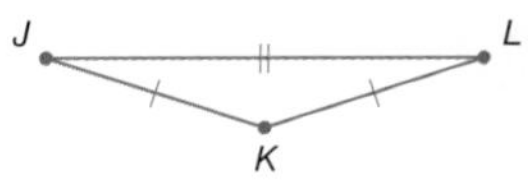

When J, K, and L are noncollinear, the conjecture is false. In the figure, $JK = KL$, but K is not the midpoint of $\overline{JL}$.

GuidedPractice

4A. If n is a real number, then $-n$ is a negative number. **4A. Sample answer: When n is -4, $-n$ is $-(-4)$ or 4, which is a positive number.**

4B. If $\angle ABC \cong \angle DBE$, then $\angle ABC$ and $\angle DBE$ are vertical angles. **See margin.**

Check Your Understanding

= Step-by-Step Solutions begin on page R14.

Example 1 **Write a conjecture that describes the pattern in each sequence. Then use your conjecture to find the next item in the sequence.**

1. Costs: \$4.50, \$6.75, \$9.00, . . . **Each cost is \$2.25 more than the previous cost; \$11.25.**

2. Appointment times: 10:15 A.M., 11:00 A.M., 11:45 A.M., . . . **Each time is 45 minutes later than the previous time; 12:30 P.M.**

3. **In each figure, the shading moves to the next point clockwise.**

4. **Each figure in the pattern has an additional circle around the outside.**

5. 3, 3, 6, 9, 15, . . . **5. Each element in the pattern is the sum of the previous two elements; 24.**

6. 2, 6, 14, 30, 62, . . . **Each element is two more than two times the previous element; 126.**

Example 2 **Make a conjecture about each value or geometric relationship.**

7. the product of two even numbers **The product of two even numbers is an even number.**

8. the relationship between a and b if $a + b = 0$ **a and b are additive inverses.**

9. the relationship between the set of points in a plane equidistant from point A **9. The set of points in a plane equidistant from point A is a circle.**

10. the relationship between $\overline{AP}$ and $\overline{PB}$ if M is the midpoint of $\overline{AB}$ and P is the midpoint of $\overline{AM}$ **$\overline{PB}$ is three times as long as $\overline{AP}$.**

DifferentiatedInstruction AL OL BL

Interpersonal Organize students into small groups. Each student should come up with at least two statements that are not always true and the other students in the group should find the counterexamples.

Example 3

11. **CELL PHONES** Refer to the table of the number of wireless subscriptions in the United States by year.

 a. Make a graph that shows U.S. wireless use from 2002 to 2007. **See margin.**

 b. Make a conjecture about U.S. wireless use in 2012.

U.S. Wireless Subscribership	
Year	Subscribers (Millions)
2002	140.8
2003	158.7
2004	182.1
2005	207.9
2006	233.0
2007	255.4

Source: Cellular Telecommunications and Internet Association

Example 4

11b. Sample answer: About 370,000,000 Americans will have wireless subscriptions in 2012.

CCSS **CRITIQUE** **Find a counterexample to show that each conjecture is false.**

12. If $\angle A$ and $\angle B$ are complementary angles, then they share a common side.

13. If a ray intersects a segment at its midpoint, then the ray is perpendicular to the segment.

Sample answer:

12. Sample answer:

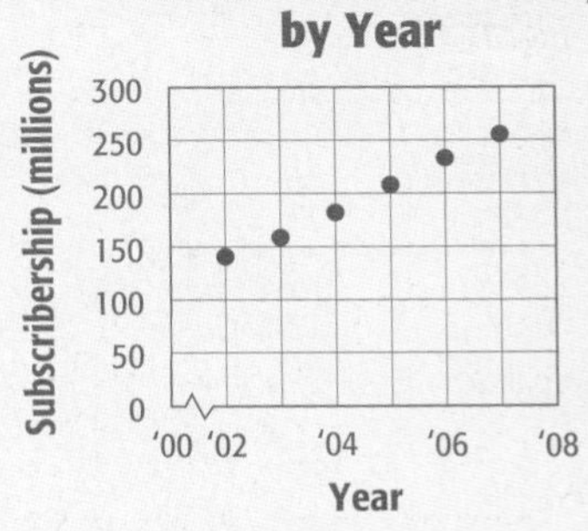

Practice and Problem Solving

Extra Practice is on page R2.

Example 1

Write a conjecture that describes the pattern in each sequence. Then use your conjecture to find the next item in the sequence. **14–19. See margin.**

14. 0, 2, 4, 6, 8
15. 3, 6, 9, 12, 15
16. 4, 8, 12, 16, 20
17. 2, 22, 222, 2222
18. 1, 4, 9, 16
19. $1, \frac{1}{2}, \frac{1}{4}, \frac{1}{8}$
20. Arrival times: 3:00 P.M., 12:30 P.M., 10:00 A.M., . . . **Each arrival time is 2 hours and 30 minutes prior to the previous arrival time; 7:30 A.M.**
21. Percent humidity: 100%, 93%, 86%, . . .
22. Work-out days: Sunday, Tuesday, Thursday, . . .
23. Club meetings: January, March, May, . . . **24–27. See Ch. 2 Answer Appendix.**

21. Each percentage is 7% less than the previous percentage; 79%.

22. Sample answer: Each work-out day is two days after the previous day; Saturday.

23. Each meeting is two months after the previous meeting; July.

24.

25.

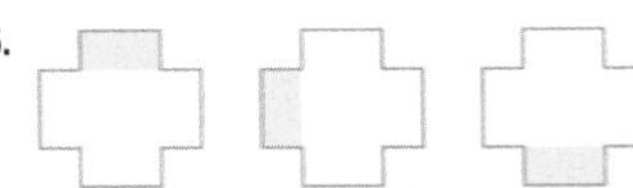

26.

27.

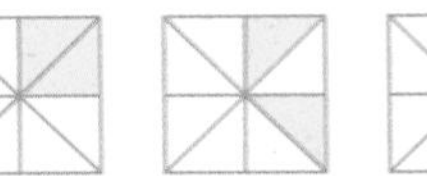

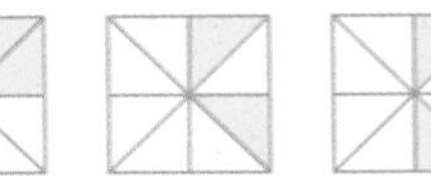

28. **FITNESS** Gabriel started training with the track team five weeks ago. During the first week, he ran 0.5 mile at each practice. The next three weeks he ran 0.75 mile, 1 mile, and 1.25 miles at each practice. If he continues this pattern, how many miles will he be running at each practice during the 7th week? **2 mi**

29. **CONSERVATION** When there is a shortage of water, some municipalities limit the amount of water each household is allowed to consume. Most cities that experience water restrictions are in the western and southern parts of the United States. Make a conjecture about why water restrictions occur in these areas. **See margin.**

30. **VOLUNTEERING** Carrie collected canned food for a homeless shelter in her area each day for one week. On day one, she collected 7 cans of food. On day two, she collected 8 cans. On day three, she collected 10 cans. On day four, she collected 13 cans. If Carrie wanted to give at least 100 cans of food to the shelter and this pattern of can collecting continued, did she meet her goal? **Yes; she collected 105 cans.**

3 Practice

Formative Assessment

Use Exercises 1–13 to check for understanding.

Use the chart at the bottom of this page to customize assignments for your students.

CCSS Teaching the Mathematical Practices

CRITIQUE Mathematically proficient students can distinguish correct logic or reasoning from that which is flawed. In Exercises 12–13, students only need to find one counterexample to show that the conjecture is false.

Additional Answers

11a.

14. Each element in the pattern is two more than the previous element; 10.
15. Each element in the pattern is three more than the previous element; 18.
16. Each element in the pattern is four more than the previous element; 24.
17. Each element has an additional two as part of the number; 22222.
18. Each element is the square of increasing natural numbers; 25.
19. Each element is one half the previous element; $\frac{1}{16}$.
29. Sample answer: It is drier in the west and hotter in the south than other parts of the country, so less water would be readily available.

Differentiated Homework Options

Level	Assignment	Two-Day Option	
AL Basic	14–45, 51–69	15–45 odd, 55–58	14–44 even, 51–54, 59–69
OL Core	14–45 odd, 46–49, 51–69	14–45, 55–58	46–49, 51–54, 59–69
BL Advanced	46–66, (optional: 67–69)		

Study Guide and Intervention

AL OL ELL

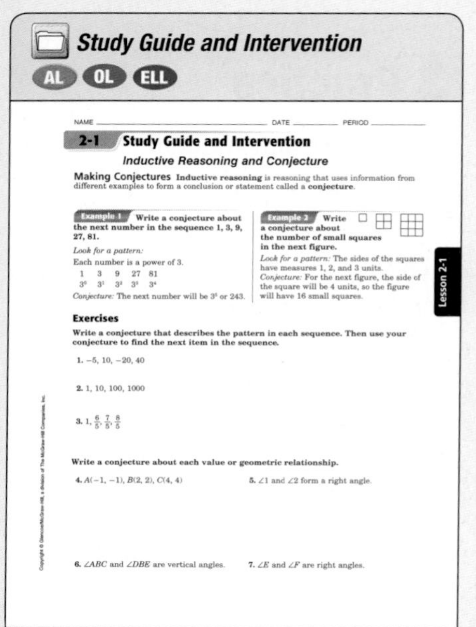
NAME ______ DATE ______ PERIOD ______

2-1 Study Guide and Intervention

Inductive Reasoning and Conjecture

Making Conjectures **Inductive reasoning** is reasoning that uses information from different examples to form a conclusion or statement called a **conjecture**.

Example 1 Write a conjecture about the next number in the sequence 1, 3, 9, 27, 81.

Look for a pattern: Each number is a power of 3.

1 3 9 27 81

3^0 3^1 3^2 3^3 3^4

Conjecture: The next number will be 3^5 or 243.

Example 2 Write a conjecture about the number of small squares in the next figure.

Look for a pattern: The sides of the squares have measures 1, 2, and 3 units.

Conjecture: For the next figure, the side of the square will be 4 units, so the figure will have 16 small squares.

Exercises

Write a conjecture that describes the pattern in each sequence. Then use your conjecture to find the next item in the sequence.

1. −5, 10, −20, 40

2. 1, 10, 100, 1000

3. $1, \frac{6}{5}, \frac{7}{5}, \frac{8}{5}$

Write a conjecture about each value or geometric relationship.

4. $A(-1, -1), B(2, 2), C(4, 4)$

5. ∠1 and ∠2 form a right angle.

6. ∠ABC and ∠DBE are vertical angles.

7. ∠E and ∠F are right angles.

Practice

AL OL BL ELL

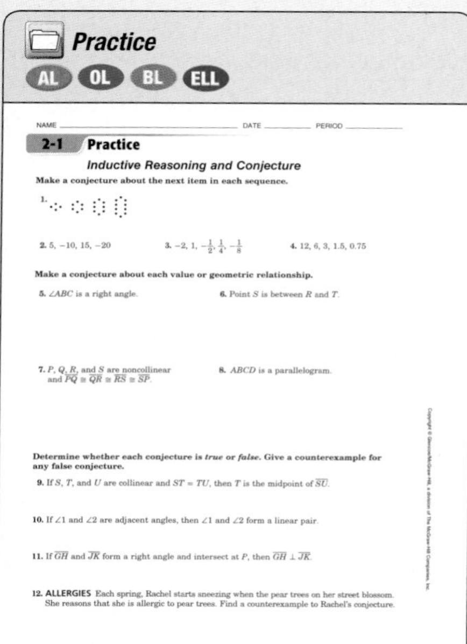
NAME ______ DATE ______ PERIOD ______

2-1 Practice

Inductive Reasoning and Conjecture

Make a conjecture about the next item in each sequence.

1.

2. 5, −10, 15, −20

3. $-2, 1, -\frac{1}{2}, \frac{1}{4}, -\frac{1}{8}$

4. 12, 6, 3, 1.5, 0.75

Make a conjecture about each value or geometric relationship.

5. ∠ABC is a right angle.

6. Point S is between R and T.

7. P, Q, R, and S are noncollinear and $\overline{PQ} \cong \overline{QR} \cong \overline{RS} \cong \overline{SP}$.

8. ABCD is a parallelogram.

Determine whether each conjecture is *true* or *false*. Give a counterexample for any false conjecture.

9. If S, T, and U are collinear and ST = TU, then T is the midpoint of $\overline{SU}$.

10. If ∠1 and ∠2 are adjacent angles, then ∠1 and ∠2 form a linear pair.

11. If $\overline{GH}$ and $\overline{JK}$ form a right angle and intersect at P, then $\overline{GH} \perp \overline{JK}$.

12. ALLERGIES Each spring, Rachel starts sneezing when the pear trees on her street blossom. She reasons that she is allergic to pear trees. Find a counterexample to Rachel's conjecture.

Word Problem Practice

AL OL BL ELL

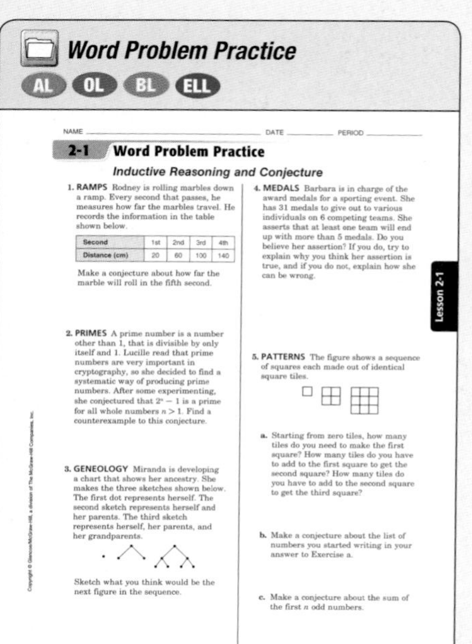
NAME ______ DATE ______ PERIOD ______

2-1 Word Problem Practice

Inductive Reasoning and Conjecture

1. RAMPS Rodney is rolling marbles down a ramp. Every second that passes, he measures how far the marbles travel. He records the information in the table shown below.

Second	1st	2nd	3rd	4th
Distance (cm)	20	60	100	140

Make a conjecture about how far the marble will roll in the fifth second.

2. PRIMES A prime number is a number other than 1, that is divisible by only itself and 1. Lucille read that prime numbers are very important in cryptography, so she decided to find a systematic way of producing prime numbers. After some experimenting, she conjectured that $2^n - 1$ is a prime for all whole numbers $n > 1$. Find a counterexample to this conjecture.

3. GENEOLOGY Miranda is developing a chart that shows her ancestry. She makes the three sketches shown below. The first dot represents herself. The second sketch represents herself and her parents. The third sketch represents herself, her parents, and her grandparents.

Sketch what you think would be the next figure in the sequence.

4. MEDALS Barbara is in charge of the award medals for a sporting event. She has 31 medals to give out to various individuals on 6 competing teams. She asserts that at least one team will end up with more than 5 medals. Do you believe her assertion? If you do, try to explain why you think her assertion is true, and if you do not, explain how she can be wrong.

5. PATTERNS The figure shows a sequence of squares each made out of identical square tiles.

a. Starting from zero tiles, how many tiles do you need to make the first square? How many tiles do you have to add to the first square to get the second square? How many tiles do you have to add to the second square to get the third square?

b. Make a conjecture about the list of numbers you started writing in your answer to Exercise a.

c. Make a conjecture about the sum of the first n odd numbers.

Example 2 **Make a conjecture about each value or geometric relationship.**

31. the product of two odd numbers **The product is an odd number.**

32. the product of two and a number, plus one **The result is odd.**

33. the relationship between a and c if $ab = bc$, $b \neq 0$ **They are equal.**

34. the relationship between a and b if $ab = 1$ **They are reciprocals.**

35. the relationship between $\overline{AB}$ and the set of points equidistant from A and B

36. the relationship between the angles of a triangle with all sides congruent

37. the relationship between the areas of a square with side x and a rectangle with sides x and $2x$ **The area of the rectangle is two times the area of the square.**

38. the relationship between the volume of a prism and a pyramid with the same base

35. The points equidistant from A and B form the perpendicular bisector of $\overline{AB}$.

36. The angles are all congruent.

38. The volume of the prism is three times the volume of the pyramid.

Example 3 39. **SPORTS** Refer to the table of Americans over the age of 7 that played hockey.

a. Make a statistical graph that best displays the data. **a–b. See margin.**

b. Make a conjecture based on the data, and explain how this conjecture is supported by your graph.

Year	Number of Participants (millions)
2000	1.9
2002	2.1
2004	2.4
2006	2.6

Example 4 **CCSS CRITIQUE** **Determine whether each conjecture is *true* or *false*. Give a counterexample for any false conjecture.** **40. False; sample answer: If $n = 2$, then $n + 1 = 3$, a prime number.**

40. If n is a prime number, then $n + 1$ is not prime.

41. If x is an integer, then $-x$ is positive. **False; sample answer: Suppose $x = 2$, then $-x = -2$.**

42. If ∠2 and ∠3 are supplementary angles, then ∠2 and ∠3 form a linear pair. **42, 43. See margin.**

43. If you have three points A, B, and C, then A, B, C are noncollinear.

44. If in $\triangle ABC$, $(AB)^2 + (BC)^2 = (AC)^2$, then $\triangle ABC$ is a right triangle. **true**

45. If the area of a rectangle is 20 square meters, then the length is 10 meters and the width is 2 meters. **False; sample answer: The length could be 4 m and the width could be 5 m.**

B **FIGURAL NUMBERS** **Numbers that can be represented by evenly spaced points arranged to form a geometric shape are called figural numbers. For each figural pattern below,**

a. write the first four numbers that are represented,

b. write a conjecture that describes the pattern in the sequence,

c. explain how this numerical pattern is shown in the sequence of figures,

d. find the next two numbers, and draw the next two figures. **46–49. See Ch. 2 Answer Appendix.**

46.

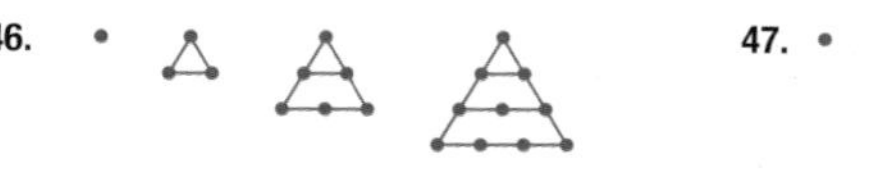

47.

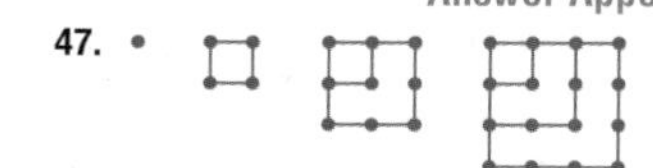

48.

49.

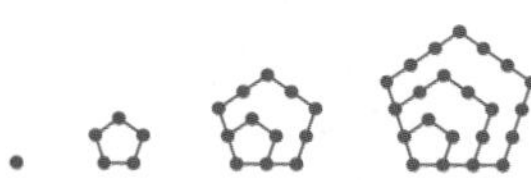

50. The sequence of odd numbers, 1, 3, 5, 7, . . . can also be a sequence of figural numbers. Use a figural pattern to represent this sequence. **See Ch. 2 Answer Appendix.**

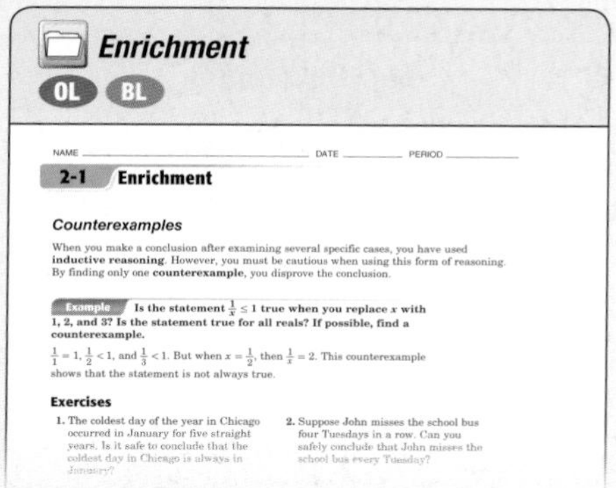

Enrichment

OL BL

NAME ______ DATE ______ PERIOD ______

2-1 Enrichment

Counterexamples

When you make a conclusion after examining several specific cases, you have used **inductive reasoning**. However, you must be cautious when using this form of reasoning. By finding only one **counterexample**, you disprove the conclusion.

Example Is the statement $\frac{1}{x} \leq 1$ true when you replace x with 1, 2, and 3? Is the statement true for all reals? If possible, find a counterexample.

$\frac{1}{1} = 1$, $\frac{1}{2} < 1$, and $\frac{1}{3} < 1$. But when $x = \frac{1}{2}$, then $\frac{1}{x} = 2$. This counterexample shows that the statement is not always true.

Exercises

1. The coldest day of the year in Chicago occurred in January for five straight years. Is it safe to conclude that the coldest day in Chicago is always in January?

2. Suppose John misses the school bus four Tuesdays in a row. Can you safely conclude that John misses the school bus every Tuesday?

Additional Answer

39a.

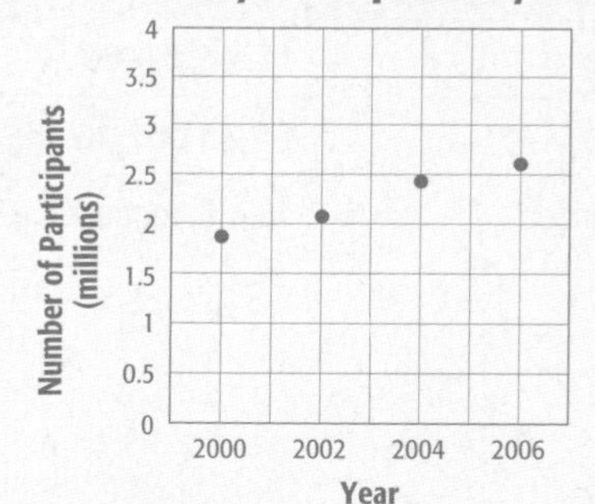

51 **GOLDBACH'S CONJECTURE** Goldbach's conjecture states that every even number greater than 2 can be written as the sum of two primes. For example, $4 = 2 + 2$, $6 = 3 + 3$, and $8 = 3 + 5$. **a. $10 = 5 + 5$, $12 = 5 + 7$, $14 = 7 + 7$, $16 = 5 + 11$, $18 = 7 + 11$, $20 = 7 + 13$**

a. Show that the conjecture is true for the even numbers from 10 to 20.

b. Given the conjecture *All odd numbers greater than 2 can be written as the sum of two primes*, is the conjecture *true* or *false*? Give a counterexample if the conjecture is false. **False; 3 cannot be written as the sum of two primes.**

52. SEGMENTS Two collinear points form one segment, as shown for $\overline{AB}$. If a collinear point is added to $\overline{AB}$, the three collinear points form three segments.

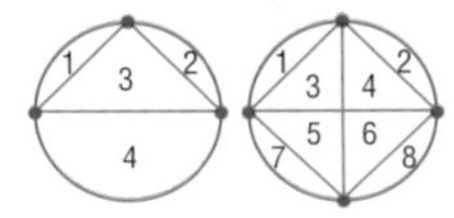

a. How many distinct segments are formed by four collinear points? by five collinear points? **6; 10**

b. Make a conjecture about the number of distinct segments formed by n collinear points. **The number of segments formed is the sum of the whole numbers less than n.**

c. Test your conjecture by finding the number of distinct segments formed by six points. **Fifteen segments are formed with six points. The conjecture is correct.**

C **53.** CCSS **TOOLS** Using dynamic geometry software, Nora calculates the perimeter P and area A of a regular hexagon with a side length of 2 units. The change to the perimeter and area after three doublings of this side length are listed in the table. Analyze the patterns in the table. Then make a conjecture as to the effects on the perimeter and area of a regular hexagon when the side length is doubled. Explain. **See Ch. 2 Answer Appendix.**

Side (units)	P (units)	A (units^2)
2	12	$6\sqrt{3}$
4	24	$24\sqrt{3}$
8	48	$96\sqrt{3}$
16	96	$384\sqrt{3}$

H.O.T. Problems Use Higher-Order Thinking Skills

54. CHALLENGE If you draw points on a circle and connect every pair of points, the circle is divided into regions. For example, two points form two regions, three points form four regions, and four points form eight regions. **a–b. See margin.**

a. Make a conjecture about the relationship between the number of points on a circle and the number of regions formed in the circle.

b. Does your conjecture hold true when there are six points? Support your answer with a diagram.

55. ERROR ANALYSIS Juan and Jack are discussing prime numbers. Juan states a conjecture that all prime numbers are odd. Jack disagrees with the conjecture and states that not all prime numbers are odd. Is either of them correct? Explain. **Jack; 2 is an even prime number.**

56. OPEN ENDED Write a number sequence that can be generated by two different patterns. Explain your patterns. **See margin.**

57. REASONING Consider the conjecture *If two points are equidistant from a third point, then the three points are collinear*. Is the conjecture *true* or *false*? If false, give a counterexample.

58. WRITING IN MATH Suppose you are conducting a survey. Choose a topic and write three questions you would include in your survey. How would you use inductive reasoning with your responses? **See margin.**

57. False; sample answer: If the two points create a straight angle that includes the third point, then the conjecture is true. If the two points do not create a straight angle with the third point, then the conjecture is false.

39b. Sample answer: More people over the age of 7 will play hockey in the future. The number of people playing hockey increases each year, so the graph suggests that even more people will play hockey in subsequent years.

42. False; sample answer:

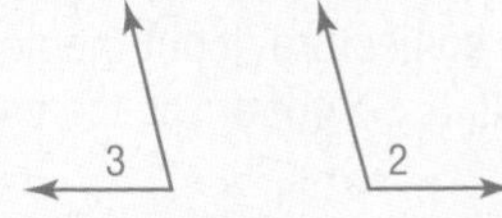

43. False; sample answer:

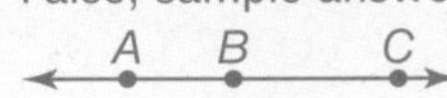

CCSS Teaching the Mathematical Practices

Tools Mathematically proficient students consider available tools such as pencil and paper or technology to solve a problem. In Exercise 53, students are to use dynamic geometry software. Encourage students to think critically about their use of the software in solving this problem as opposed to using a compass and straightedge.

Additional Answers

54a. Sample answer: The number of regions doubles when you add a point on the circle.

54b. For six points, there should be 32 regions; however only 31 regions are formed. The conjecture is false.

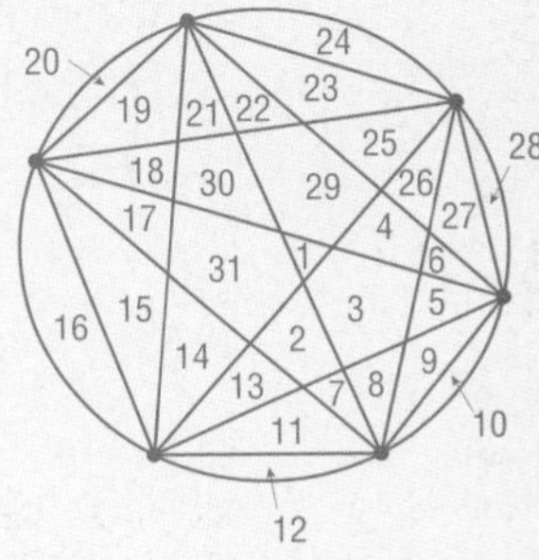

56. Sample answer: 2, 4, 8, 16, 32, ... Each number in the sequence can be generated by adding each number to itself to form the next number. Each number in the sequence is 2^n, where $n \geq 1$.

58. Sample answer: I would conduct a survey to find out the types of activities that people participate in on the weekends. I would ask the following questions: What is your age? What is your favorite weekend activity? How often do you participate in the activity? I would then use inductive reasoning to find patterns in the responses to determine if people who are the same age like to participate in the same types of activities.

4 Assess

Ticket Out the Door Ask students to write five conjectures about school rules and activities. Then have students trade papers with a partner and try to write a counterexample for each conjecture. A sample statement is: *Students must attend school Monday through Friday.*

A counterexample for this would be that Labor Day is on a Monday, but the school is closed.

Collect students' counterexamples as they exit the classroom.

Standardized Test Practice

59. Look at the pattern below.

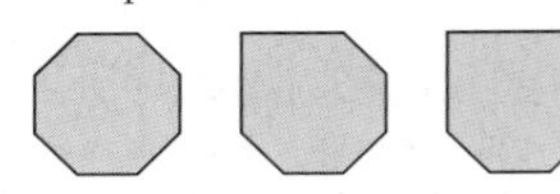

If the pattern continues, what will be the next shape? **B**

A
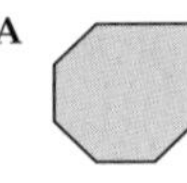

C
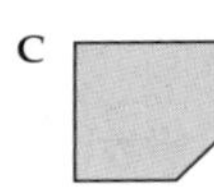

B
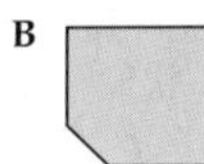

D
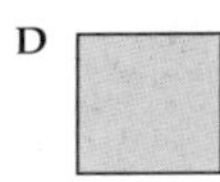

60. GRIDDED RESPONSE What is the value of the expression below if $a = 10$ and $b = 1$? **32/11**

$$2b + ab \div (a + b)$$

61. ALGEBRA A chemistry student mixed a 30% copper sulfate solution with a 40% copper sulfate solution to obtain 100 mL of a 32% copper sulfate solution. How much of the 30% copper sulfate solution did the student use in the mixture? **G**

F 90 mL

G 80 mL

H 60 mL

J 20 mL

62. SAT/ACT Which of the following is equal to $2x$? **D**

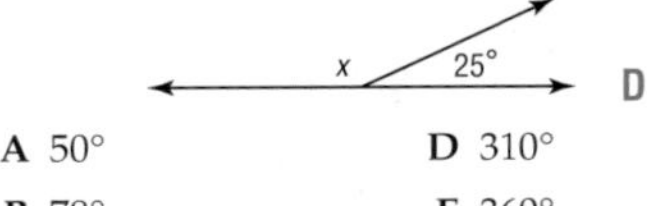

A 50°

B 78°

C 155°

D 310°

E 360°

Spiral Review

Find the surface area and volume of each solid. (Lesson 1-7)

63.
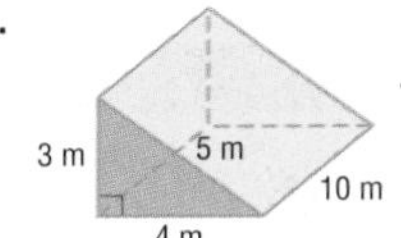

132 m²; 60 m³

64.
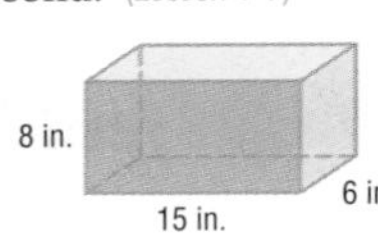

516 in²; 720 in³

65.
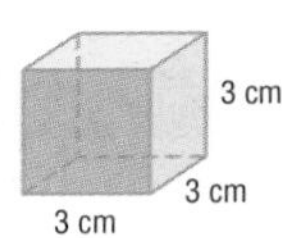

54 cm²; 27 cm³

Find the perimeter of $\triangle ABC$ to the nearest hundredth, given the coordinates of its vertices. (Lesson 1-6)

66. $A(1, 6)$, $B(1, 2)$, $C(3, 2)$ **10.47**

67. $A(-3, 2)$, $B(2, -9)$, $C(0, -10)$ **26.69**

68. ALGEBRA The measures of two complementary angles are $16z - 9$ and $4z + 3$. Find the measures of the angles. (Lesson 1-5) **67.8; 22.2**

69. FLAGS The Wyoming state flag is shown at the right. Name the geometric term modeled by this flag: point, line, or plane. (Lesson 1-1) **plane**

70. ALGEBRA Evaluate $5|x + y| - 3|2 - z|$ if $x = 3$, $y = -4$, and $z = -5$. (Lesson 0-4) **−16**

Skills Review

ALGEBRA Determine which values in the replacement set make each inequality true.

71. $x - 3 > 12$ **18**
{6, 10, 14, 18}

72. $6 + x > 9$ **8, 6, 4**
{8, 6, 4, 2}

73. $2x - 4 > 10$ **8**
{5, 6, 7, 8}

Differentiated Instruction OL BL

Extension Make a conjecture about the next two numbers in the sequence. Name the two numbers. 9, 7, 10, 8, 11, 9, 12, . . . Subtract 2, then add 3; 10, 13.

LESSON 2-2 Logic

Then	Now	Why?
You found counterexamples for false conjectures.	1 Determine truth values of negations, conjunctions, and disjunctions, and represent them using Venn diagrams. 2 Find counterexamples.	Many electrical circuits operate by evaluating a series of tests that are either true or false. For example, a single light can be controlled by two different switches connected on a circuit. The positions of both switches, either up or down, determine whether the light is on or off.

NewVocabulary
statement
truth value
negation
compound statement
conjunction
disjunction
truth table

1 Determine Truth Values

A **statement** is a sentence that is either true or false. The **truth value** of a statement is either true (T) or false (F). Statements are often represented using a letter such as p or q.

p: A rectangle is a quadrilateral. Truth value: T

The **negation** of a statement has the opposite meaning, as well as an opposite truth value. For example, the negation of the statement above is *not* p or $\sim p$.

$\sim p$: A rectangle is not a quadrilateral. Truth value: F

Two or more statements joined by the word *and* or *or* form a **compound statement**. A compound statement using the word *and* is called a **conjunction**. A conjunction is true only when both statements that form it are true.

p: A rectangle is a quadrilateral. Truth value: T
q: A rectangle is convex. Truth value: T
p and q: A rectangle is a quadrilateral, and a rectangle is convex.

Since both p and q are true, the conjunction p and q, also written $p \wedge q$, is true.

Example 1 Truth Values of Conjunctions

Use the following statements to write a compound statement for each conjunction. Then find its truth value. Explain your reasoning.

p: The figure is a triangle.
q: The figure has two congruent sides.
r: The figure has three acute angles.

a. p and r

p and r: The figure is a triangle, and the figure has three acute angles. Although p is true, r is false. So, p and r is false.

b. $q \wedge \sim r$

$q \wedge \sim r$: The figure has two congruent sides, and the figure does not have three acute angles.

Both q and $\sim r$ are true, so $q \wedge \sim r$ is true.

GuidedPractice 1A, 1B. See Ch. 2 Answer Appendix.

1A. $p \wedge q$ **1B.** not p and not r

1 Focus

VerticalAlignment

Before Lesson 2-2 Find counterexamples to false conjectures.

Lesson 2-2 Develop an awareness of the structure of a mathematical system, connecting definitions, postulates, and logical reasoning. Use logical reasoning to prove statements are true.

After Lesson 2-2 Use deductive reasoning to prove a statement.

2 Teach

Scaffolding Questions

Have students read the **Why?** section of the lesson.

Ask:

- How many combinations of on and off are there for the two light switches? 4 combinations
- How many ways can the light be turned on if both switches must be in the on position? one
- How many ways can the light be turned on if at least one switch must be in the on position? 3 ways

(continued on the next page)

Lesson 2-2 Resources

Resource	Approaching Level AL	On Level OL	Beyond Level BL	English Learners ELL
Teacher Edition	▪ Differentiated Instruction, p. 103	▪ Differentiated Instruction, pp. 103, 106	▪ Differentiated Instruction, p. 106	
Chapter Resource Masters	▪ Study Guide and Intervention, pp. 12–13 ▪ Skills Practice, p. 14 ▪ Practice, p. 15 ▪ Word Problem Practice, p. 16 ▪ Spreadsheet Activity, p. 18	▪ Study Guide and Intervention, pp. 12–13 ▪ Skills Practice, p. 14 ▪ Practice, p. 15 ▪ Word Problem Practice, p. 16 ▪ Enrichment, p. 17 ▪ Spreadsheet Activity, p. 18	▪ Practice, p. 15 ▪ Word Problem Practice, p. 16 ▪ Enrichment, p. 17 ▪ Spreadsheet Activity, p. 18	▪ Study Guide and Intervention, pp. 12–13 ▪ Skills Practice, p. 14 ▪ Practice, p. 15 ▪ Word Problem Practice, p. 16 ▪ Spreadsheet Activity, p. 18
Other	▪ 5-Minute Check 2-2 ▪ Study Notebook	▪ 5-Minute Check 2-2 ▪ Study Notebook	▪ 5-Minute Check 2-2 ▪ Study Notebook	▪ 5-Minute Check 2-2 ▪ Study Notebook

- How could the circuit work if the light was controlled by 3 different switches? Sample statement: There would be 6 combinations of off and on, and only one would have to be in the on position.

1 Determine Truth Values

Examples 1–3 show how to find the truth value of conjunctions and disjunctions of sentences.

Formative Assessment

Use the Guided Practice exercises after each example to determine students' understanding of concepts.

Additional Example

1 Use the following statements to write a compound statement for each conjunction. Then find its truth value. Explain your reasoning.

p: One foot is 14 inches.

q: September has 30 days.

r: A plane is defined by three noncollinear points.

a. *p* and *q*
One foot is 14 inches, and September has 30 days; Although *q* is true, *p* is false. So *p* and *q* is false.

b. $\sim p \wedge r$
A foot is not 14 inches, and a plane is defined by three noncollinear points; Both $\sim p$ and *r* are true, so $\sim p \wedge r$ is true.

Additional Examples also in Interactive Classroom PowerPoint® Presentations

IWB Interactive White Board READY

A compound statement that uses the word *or* is called a **disjunction**.

p: Malik studies geometry

q: Malik studies chemistry.

p or *q*: Malik studies geometry, or Malik studies chemistry.

A disjunction is true if at least one of the statements is true. If Malik studies either geometry or chemistry or both subjects, the disjunction *p* or *q*, also written as $p \vee q$, is true. If Malik studies neither geometry nor chemistry, *p* or *q* is false.

PT

Example 2 Truth Values of Disjunctions

Use the following statements to write a compound statement for each disconjunction. Then find its truth value. Explain your reasoning.

***p*: January is a fall month.**

***q*: January has only 30 days.**

***r*: January 1 is the first day of a new year.**

a. *p* or *r*

q or *r*: January has only 30 days, or January 1 is the first day of a new year.

q or *r* is true because *r* is true. It does not matter that *q* is false.

b. $p \vee q$

$p \vee q$: January is a fall month, or January has only 30 days.

Since both *p* and *q* are false, $p \vee q$ is false.

c. $\sim p \vee r$

$\sim p \vee r$: January is *not* a fall month, or January 1 is the first day of a new year.

Not *p* or *r* is true, because not *p* is true and *r* is true.

Guided Practice

2A. *r* or *p* **2B.** $q \vee \sim r$ **2C.** $p \vee \sim q$

2A. January 1 is the first day of a new year, or January is a fall month. Since *r* is true, *r* or *p* is true.
2B. January has only 30 days or January 1st is not the first day of a new year. Since both *q* and $\sim r$ are false, $q \vee \sim r$ is false.
2C. January is a fall month, or January does not have only 30 days. Since $\sim q$ is true, $p \vee \sim q$ is true.

WatchOut!
Negation Just as the opposite of an integer is not always negative, the negation of a statement is not always false. The negation of a statement has the opposite truth value of the original statement.

Concept Summary Negation, Conjunction, Disconjunction

Statement	Words	Symbols
negation	a statement that has the opposite meaning and truth value of an original statement	$\sim p$, read not *p*
conjunction	a compound statement formed by joining two or more statements using the word *and*	$p \wedge q$, read *p* and *q*
disconjunction	a compound statement formed by joining two or more statements using the word *or*	$p \vee q$, read *p* or *q*

Teach with Tech

Interactive Whiteboard On the board, write two logical statements *p* and *q*, and the symbols $\sim$, $\wedge$, and $\vee$. Drag and rearrange the symbols to form a logical statement, and show students how to create a truth table for that statement. Then rearrange the symbols to form another logical statement and create its truth table.

A convenient method for organizing the truth values of statements is to use a **truth table**. Truth tables can be used to determine truth values of negations and compound statements.

Negation

p	$\sim p$
T	F
F	T

Conjunction

p	q	$p \wedge q$
T	T	T
T	F	F
F	T	F
F	F	F

Disjunction

p	q	$p \vee q$
T	T	T
T	F	T
F	T	T
F	F	F

StudyTip

Truth Tables The truth tables for a conjunction and a disjunction are easier to recall if you remember the following.

- A conjunction is true only when both statements are true.
- A disjunction is false only when both statements are false.

You can use the truth values for negation, conjunction, and disjunction to construct truth tables for more complex compound statements.

PT

Example 3 Construct Truth Tables

Construct a truth table for $\sim p \vee q$.

① Make columns with headings that include each original statement, any negations of these statements, and the compound statement itself.

p	q	$\sim p$	$\sim p \vee q$
T	T	F	T
T	F	F	F
F	T	T	T
F	F	T	T

② List the possible combinations of truth values.

③ Use the truth values of p to determine the truth values of its negation.

④ Use the truth values for each part of the compound statement to determine the truth value of the statement.

Guided Practice

3. Construct a truth table for $\sim p \wedge \sim q$. **See Ch. 2 Answer Appendix.**

2 Venn Diagrams

Conjunctions can be illustrated with Venn diagrams. Consider the conjunction given at the beginning of the lesson.

p and q: **A rectangle is a quadrilateral,** and **a rectangle is convex.**

All Polygons

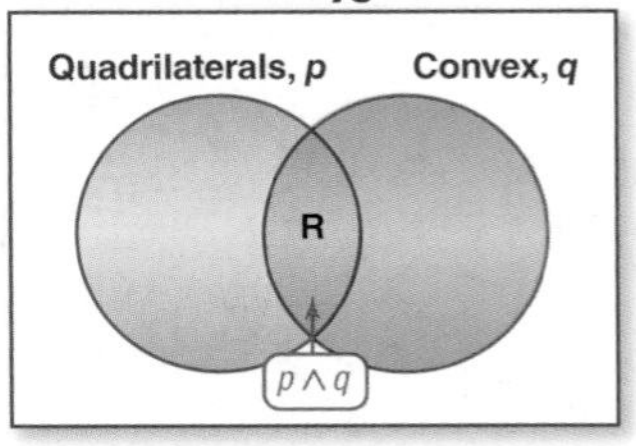

The Venn diagram shows that a rectangle (R) is located in the *intersection* of the set of quadrilaterals and the set of convex polygons. In other words, rectangles must be in the set containing quadrilaterals *and* in the set of convex polygons.

VocabularyLink

Intersection

Everyday Use the point at which two or more objects overlap

Math Use The intersection of two sets is the set of elements that are common to both.

Additional Examples

2 Use the following statements to write a compound statement for each disjunction. Then find its truth value. Explain your reasoning.

p: $\overline{AB}$ is proper notation for "segment AB."

q: Centimeters are metric units.

r: 9 is a prime number.

a. p or q
$\overline{AB}$ is proper notation for "segment AB," or centimeters are metric units; Both p and q are true, so p or q is true.

b. $q \vee r$
Centimeters are metric units, or 9 is a prime number; Since q is true, $q \vee r$ is true.

c. $\sim p \vee r$
Since both $\sim p$ and r are false, $\sim p \vee r$ is false.

3 Construct a truth table for each compound statement.

a. $\sim p \vee q$

p	q	$\sim p$	$\sim p \vee q$
T	T	F	T
T	F	F	F
F	T	T	T
F	F	T	T

b. $p \vee (\sim q \wedge r)$

p	q	r	$\sim q$	$\sim q \vee r$	$p \vee (\sim q \wedge r)$
T	T	T	F	F	T
T	F	T	T	T	T
T	T	F	F	F	T
T	F	F	T	F	T
F	T	T	F	F	F
F	F	T	T	T	T
F	T	F	F	F	F
F	F	F	T	F	F

Tips for New Teachers

Flexibility Tell students that they could potentially interchange the columns for p, q, and r in Example 3 part b, and as long as they correctly fill in the columns for $p \wedge q$ and $(p \wedge q) \vee r$, the overall outcome is the same. The result is 5 Ts and 3 Fs, but the Ts and Fs are in a different order.

WatchOut!

Conjunctions and Disjunctions Remind students that the order of statements is not important in conjunctions and disjunctions.

2 Venn Diagrams

Example 4 shows how to use a Venn diagram to make conjectures. Students should be able to make a conjecture, write a compound statement, and find its truth value.

Additional Example

4 DANCING The Venn diagram shows the number of students enrolled in Monique's Dance School for tap, jazz, and ballet classes.

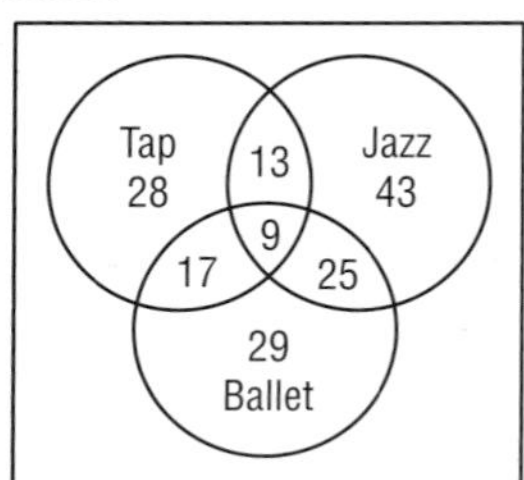

a. How many students are enrolled in all three classes? 9

b. How many students are enrolled in tap or ballet? 121

c. How many students are enrolled in jazz and ballet, but not tap? 25

Focus on Mathematical Content

Truth Tables Tell students that truth tables must display all combinations of Ts and Fs to exhaust all possible outcomes. For each statement, p, q, and r, they will need to mix the occurrences of true and false. First, they should determine the number of rows needed. Then fill the top half of the p column with the Ts and the other half with the Fs. For the q column, they can alternate T and F. If they need an r column, they can alternate sets of 2 Ts and 2 Fs all the way down, and so on. Assure students that as long as they set up the basic structure correctly, they should be able to produce the rest of the table.

A disjunction can also be illustrated with a Venn diagram. Consider the following statements.

p: A figure is a quadrilateral.

q: A figure is convex.

p or q: A figure is a quadrilateral or convex.

VocabularyLink
Union
Everyday Use the joining of two or more objects
Math Use The union of two sets is the set of elements that appear in either of the two sets.

In the Venn diagram, the disjunction is represented by the *union* of the two sets. The union includes all polygons that are quadrilaterals, convex, *or* both.

All Polygons

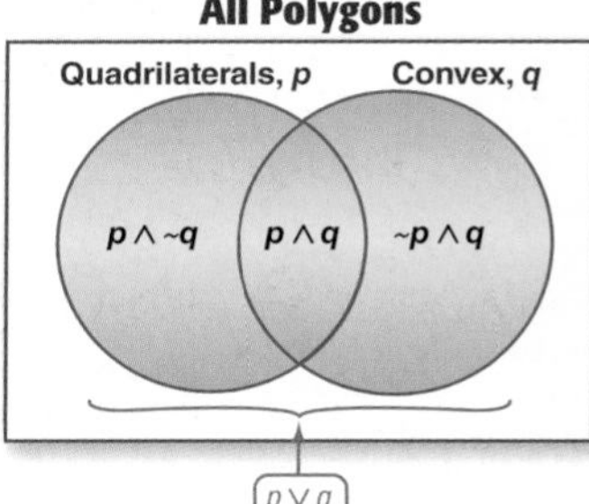

The disjunction includes these three regions:

$p \wedge {\sim}q$ quadrilaterals that are *not* convex

${\sim}p \wedge q$ convex polygons that are *not* quadrilaterals

$p \wedge q$ polygons that are both quadrilaterals and convex

Math HistoryLink
Sophie Germain
(1776–1831) Sophie Germain was born in Paris, France. Like Goldbach, she studied relationships involving prime numbers. In order to pursue her passion for mathematics, she assumed a man's identity.

Real-World Example 4 Use Venn Diagrams

SCHEDULING The Venn diagram shows the number of people who can or cannot attend the May or the June Spanish Club meetings.

Spanish Club Meeting

a. How many people can attend the May or the June meeting?

The people who can attend either the May meeting or the June meeting are represented by the union of the sets. There are $5 + 6 + 14$ or 25 people who can attend either night.

b. How many people can attend both the May and the June meetings?

The people who can attend both the May and the June meetings are represented by the intersection of the two sets. There are 6 people who can attend both meetings.

c. Describe the meetings that the 14 people located in the nonintersecting portion of the June region can attend.

These 14 people can attend the June meeting but not the May meeting.

GuidedPractice

4. PROM The Venn diagram shows the number of graduates last year who did or did not attend their junior or senior prom.

Prom Attendance

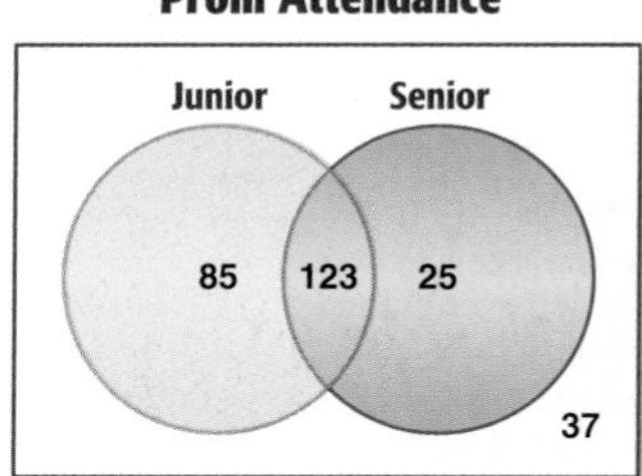

A. How many graduates attended their senior but not their junior prom? 25

B. How many graduates attended their junior and senior proms? 123

C. How many graduates did not attend either of their proms? 37

D. How many students graduated last year? Explain your reasoning.

4D. 270; The total number of students who graduated is the sum of all the elements in the entire diagram: 85 + 123 + 25 + 37 or 270.

Check Your Understanding

 = Step-by-Step Solutions begin on page R14.

Examples 1–2 **Use the following statements to write a compound statement for each conjunction or disjunction. Then find its truth value. Explain your reasoning.** 1–6. See margin.

p: A week has seven days.

q: There are 20 hours in a day.

r: There are 60 minutes in an hour.

1. p and r
2. $p \wedge q$
3. $q \vee r$
4. $\sim p$ or q
5. $p \vee r$
6. $\sim p \wedge \sim r$

Example 3

7. Copy and complete the truth table at the right.

p	q	$\sim q$	$p \vee \sim q$
T	T	F	T
T	F	T	T
F	T	F	F
F	F	T	T

Construct a truth table for each compound statement. 8, 9. See margin.

8. $p \wedge q$
9. $\sim p \vee \sim q$

Example 4

10. **CLASSES** Refer to the Venn diagram that represents the foreign language classes students selected in high school.
   a. How many students chose only Spanish? 89
   b. How many students chose Spanish and French? 15
   c. Describe the class(es) the three people in the nonintersecting portion of the French region chose. The three students chose to take only French classes.

Foreign Language Classes Selected

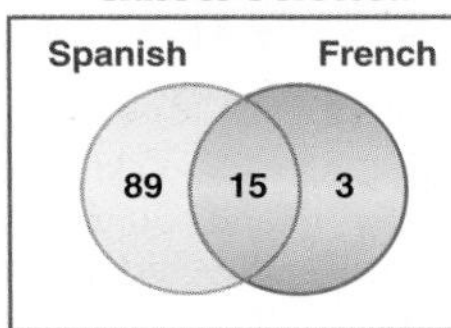

Practice and Problem Solving

Extra Practice is on page R2.

Examples 1–2 **Use the following statements and figure to write a compound statement for each conjunction or disjunction. Then find its truth value. Explain your reasoning.**

p: $\overrightarrow{DB}$ is the angle bisector of $\angle ADC$.

q: Points *C*, *D*, and *B* are collinear.

r: $\overline{AD} \cong \overline{DC}$ 11–16. See Ch. 2 Answer Appendix.

11. p and r
12. q or p
13. r or $\sim p$
14. r and q
15. $\sim p$ or $\sim r$
16. $\sim p$ and $\sim r$

CCSS REASONING Use the following statements to write a compound statement for each conjunction or disjunction. Then find its truth value. Explain your reasoning. 17–22. See Ch. 2 Answer Appendix.

p: Springfield is the capital of Illinois.

q: Illinois borders the Atlantic Ocean.

r: Illinois shares a border with Kentucky.

s: Illinois is to the west of Missouri.

17. $p \wedge r$
18. $p \wedge q$
19. $\sim r \vee s$
20. $r \vee q$
21. $\sim p \wedge \sim r$
22. $\sim s \vee \sim p$

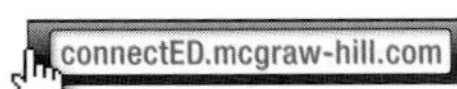

Differentiated Instruction AL OL

 students have trouble understanding how truth tables represent different statements,

 have them create truth tables that represent different statements but have the same truth entries. They should see, for example, that switching all occurrences of p and q will result in the same table.

CCSS Teaching the Mathematical Practices

Reasoning Mathematically proficient students make sense of quantities and their relationships. In Exercises 17–22, students will use contextualization skills in working with the symbolic notation of each statement.

Additional Answers

1. A week has seven days, and there are 60 minutes in an hour. p and r is true, because p is true and r is true.
2. A week has seven days, and there are 20 hours in a day. $p \wedge q$ is false, because p is true and q is false.
3. There are 20 hours in a day, or there are 60 minutes in an hour. $q \vee r$ is true, because q is false and r is true.
4. A week does not have seven days, or there are 20 hours in a day. $\sim p$ or q is false, because $\sim p$ is false and q is false.
5. A week has seven days, or there are 60 minutes in an hour. $p \vee r$ is true, because p is true and r is true.
6. A week does not have seven days, and there are not 60 minutes in an hour. $\sim p \wedge \sim r$ is false, because $\sim p$ is false and $\sim r$ is false.

8.

p	q	$p \wedge q$
T	T	T
T	F	F
F	T	F
F	F	F

9.

p	q	$\sim p$	$\sim q$	$\sim p \vee \sim q$
T	T	F	F	F
T	F	F	T	T
F	T	T	F	T
F	F	T	T	T

3 Practice

Formative Assessment

Use Exercises 1–10 to check for understanding.

Use the chart at the bottom of this page to customize assignments for your students.

Teaching the Mathematical Practices

Reasoning Mathematically proficient students decontextualize a situation. In Exercises 32 and 40, students will abstract the given situation and represent it symbolically.

Additional Answers

28.

q	r	$q \vee r$
T	T	T
T	F	T
F	T	T
F	F	F

29.

p	r	$\sim p$	$\sim p \wedge r$
T	T	F	F
T	F	F	F
F	T	T	T
F	F	T	F

30.

q	r	$\sim q$	$\sim r$	$\sim q \wedge \sim r$
T	T	F	F	F
T	F	F	T	F
F	T	T	F	F
F	F	T	T	T

32c. Yes; when the upstairs switch is down and the downstairs switch is up, the value is true in the light on column.

Example 3 Copy and complete each truth table.

23.

p	q	$\sim p$	$\sim p \wedge q$
T	T	F	F
T	F	F	F
F	T	T	T
F	F	T	F

24.

p	q	$\sim p$	$\sim q$	$\sim p \vee q$
T	T	F	F	F
T	F	F	T	T
F	T	T	F	T
F	F	T	T	T

25.

p	r	$p \wedge r$
T	T	T
T	F	F
F	T	F
F	F	F

Construct a truth table for each compound statement. 28–30. See margin.

25. $p \wedge r$
26. $r \wedge q$
27. $p \vee r$
28. $q \vee r$
29. $\sim p \wedge r$
30. $\sim q \vee \sim r$

27.

p	r	$p \vee r$
T	T	T
T	F	T
F	T	T
F	F	F

Example 4

26.

r	q	$r \wedge q$
T	T	T
T	F	F
F	T	F
F	F	F

31. **WATER SPORTS** Refer to the Venn diagram that represents the number of students who swim and dive at a high school.

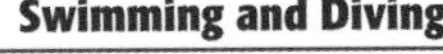

Swimming and Diving

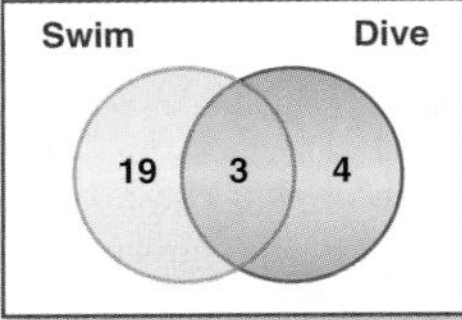

a. How many students dive? 7

b. How many students participate in swimming or diving or both? 26

c. How many students swim and dive? 3

32. **REASONING** Venus has switches at the top and bottom of her stairs to control the light for the stairwell. She notices that when the upstairs switch is up and the downstairs switch is down, the light is turned on.

Position of Switch		Light On
Upstairs	Downstairs	
up	up	F
up	down	T
down	up	T
down	down	F

a. Copy and complete the truth table.

b. If both the upstairs and downstairs switches are in the up position, will the light be on? Explain your reasoning.

32b. No; when both switches are up, the value is false in the light on column.

c. If the upstairs switch is in the down position and the downstairs switch is in the up position, will the light be on? See margin.

d. In general, how should the two switches be positioned so that the light is on? The light is on when the switches are in opposite positions.

33. **ELECTRONICS** A group of 330 teens were surveyed about what type of electronics they used. They chose from a cell phone, a portable media player, and a DVR. The results are shown in the Venn diagram.

Type of Electronics Used

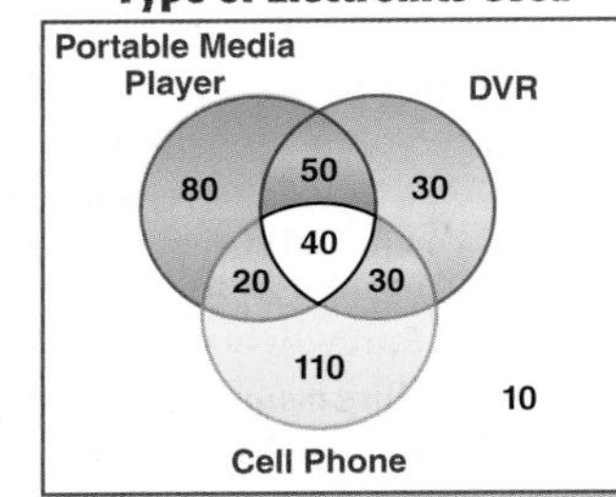

a. How many teens used only a portable media player and DVR? 50

b. How many said they used all three types of electronics? 40

c. How many said they used only a cell phone? 110

d. How many teens said they used only a portable media player and a cell phone? 20

e. Describe the electronics that the 10 teens outside of the regions use.

33e. These teens do not use any of the listed electronics.

Differentiated Homework Options

Level	Assignment	Two-Day Option	
AL Basic	11–31, 41, 48–67	11–31 odd, 50–53	12–30 even, 41, 48, 49, 54–67
OL Core	11–29 odd, 31–33, 35–39 odd, 40, 41, 48–67	11–31, 50–53	32–41, 48–49, 54–67
BL Advanced	31–63, (optional: 64–67)		

Construct a truth table for each compound statement. Determine the truth value of each compound statement if the given statements are true. 34–39. See Ch. 2 Answer Appendix.

34. $p \wedge (q \wedge r)$; p, q

35. $p \wedge (\sim q \vee r)$; p, r

36. $(\sim p \vee q) \wedge r$; q, r

37. $p \wedge (\sim q \wedge \sim r)$; p, q, r

38. $\sim p \wedge (\sim q \wedge \sim r)$; p, q, r

39. $(\sim p \vee q) \vee \sim r$; p, q

40. **CCSS REASONING** A travel agency surveyed 70 of their clients who had visited Europe about international travel. Of the 70 clients who had visited Europe, 60 had traveled to England, France, or both. Of those 60 clients, 45 had visited England, and 50 had visited France. **a–c. See Ch. 2 Answer Appendix.**
   a. Make a Venn diagram to show the results of the survey.
   b. If p represents a client who has visited England and q represents a client who has visited France, write a compound statement to represent each area of the Venn diagram. Include the compound statements on your Venn diagram.
   c. What is the probability that a randomly chosen participant in the survey will have visited both England and France? Explain your reasoning.

H.O.T. Problems Use Higher-Order Thinking Skills

41. **REASONING** Irrational numbers and integers both belong to the set of real numbers (R). Based upon the Venn diagram, is it *sometimes*, *always*, or *never* true that integers (Z) are irrational numbers (I)? Explain your reasoning.
Never; integers are rational numbers, not irrational.

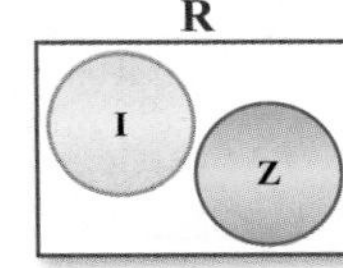

CHALLENGE To negate a statement containing the words *all* or *for every*, you can use the phrase *at least one* or *there exists*. To negate a statement containing the phrase *there exists*, use the phrase *for all* or *for every*.

p: All polygons are convex. $\sim p$: *At least one* polygon is *not* convex.

q: *There exists* a problem that has no solution. $\sim q$: *For every* problem, there is a solution.

Sometimes these phrases may be implied. For example, *The square of a real number is nonnegative* implies the following conditional and its negation.

p: *For every* real number x, $x^2 \geq 0$.

$\sim p$: *There exists* a real number x such that $x^2 < 0$.

Use the information above to write the negation of each statement.

42. Every student at Hammond High School has a locker. **There exists at least one student at Hammond High School that does not have a locker.**

43. All squares are rectangles. **There exists at least one square that is not a rectangle.**

44. There exists a real number x such that $x^2 = x$. **For every real number x, $x^2 \neq x$.**

45. There exists a student who has at least one class in C-Wing. **No students have classes in C-Wing.**

46. Every real number has a real square root. **46. There exists a real number that does not have a real square root.**

47. There exists a segment that has no midpoint. **Every segment has a midpoint.**

48. **WRITING IN MATH** Describe a situation that might be depicted using the Venn diagram shown. **See margin.**

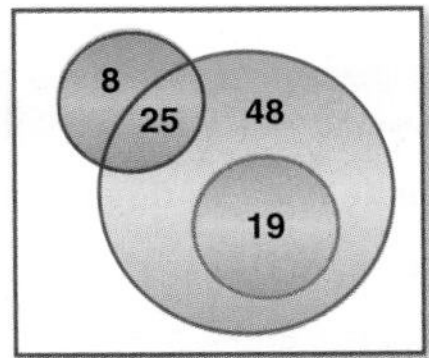

49. **OPEN ENDED** Write a compound statement that results in a true conjunction.
Sample Answer: A triangle has three sides, and a square has four sides. Both are true, so the compound statement is true.

Additional Answer

48. Sample answer: 100 people were surveyed to see if they liked vanilla, strawberry, or chocolate ice cream. There were 8 people who only liked strawberry. There were 25 people who liked both strawberry and vanilla. There were 48 people who only liked vanilla, and there were 19 people who liked both chocolate and vanilla.

Study Guide and Intervention
AL OL ELL

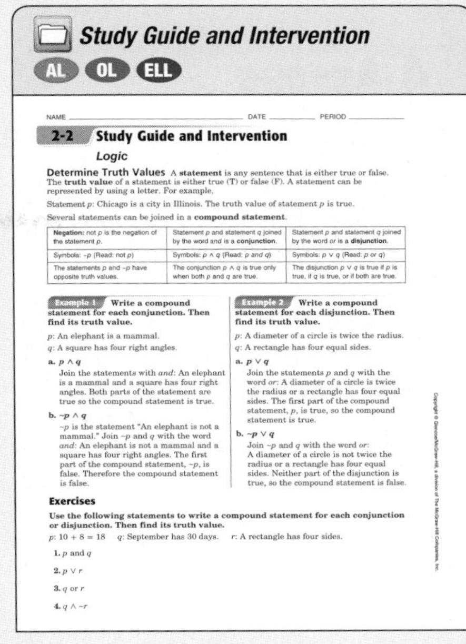

NAME DATE PERIOD

2-2 Study Guide and Intervention

Logic

Determine Truth Values A **statement** is any sentence that is either true or false. The **truth value** of a statement is either true (T) or false (F). A statement can be represented by using a letter. For example,

Statement p: Chicago is a city in Illinois. The truth value of statement p is true.

Several statements can be joined in a **compound statement**.

Negation: not p is the negation of the statement p.	Statement p and statement q joined by the word and is a conjunction.	Statement p and statement q joined by the word or is a disjunction.
Symbols: $\sim p$ (Read: not p)	Symbols: $p \wedge q$ (Read: p and q)	Symbols: $p \vee q$ (Read: p or q)
The statements p and $\sim p$ have opposite truth values.	The conjunction $p \wedge q$ is true only when both p and q are true.	The disjunction $p \vee q$ is true if p is true, if q is true, or if both are true.

Example 1 Write a compound statement for each conjunction. Then find its truth value.
p: An elephant is a mammal.
q: A square has four right angles.
a. $p \wedge q$
Join the statements with *and*: An elephant is a mammal and a square has four right angles. Both parts of the statement are true so the compound statement is true.
b. $\sim p \wedge q$
$\sim p$ is the statement "An elephant is not a mammal." Join $\sim p$ and q with the word *and*: An elephant is not a mammal and a square has four right angles. The first part of the compound statement, $\sim p$, is false. Therefore the compound statement is false.

Example 2 Write a compound statement for each disjunction. Then find its truth value.
p: A diameter of a circle is twice the radius.
q: A rectangle has four equal sides.
a. $p \vee q$
Join the statements p and q with the word *or*: A diameter of a circle is twice the radius or a rectangle has four equal sides. The first part of the compound statement, p, is true, so the compound statement is true.
b. $\sim p \vee q$
Join $\sim p$ and q with the word *or*: A diameter of a circle is not twice the radius or a rectangle has four equal sides. Neither part of the disjunction is true, so the compound statement is false.

Exercises

Use the following statements to write a compound statement for each conjunction or disjunction. Then find its truth value.
p: $10 + 8 = 18$ q: September has 30 days. r: A rectangle has four sides.

1. p and q
2. $p \vee r$
3. q or r
4. $q \wedge \sim r$

Practice
AL OL BL ELL

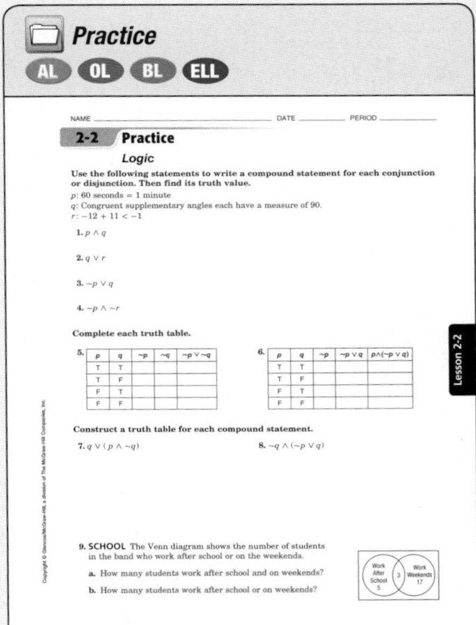

NAME DATE PERIOD

2-2 Practice

Logic

Use the following statements to write a compound statement for each conjunction or disjunction. Then find its truth value.
p: 60 seconds = 1 minute
q: Congruent supplementary angles each have a measure of 90.
r: $-12 + 11 < -1$

1. $p \wedge q$
2. $q \vee r$
3. $\sim p \vee q$
4. $\sim p \wedge \sim r$

Complete each truth table.

5.

p	q	$\sim p$	$\sim q$	$\sim p \vee \sim q$
T	T			
T	F			
F	T			
F	F			

6.

p	q	$\sim p$	$\sim p \vee q$	$p \wedge (\sim p \vee q)$
T	T			
T	F			
F	T			
F	F			

Construct a truth table for each compound statement.

7. $q \vee (p \wedge \sim q)$

8. $\sim q \wedge (\sim p \vee q)$

9. **SCHOOL** The Venn diagram shows the number of students in the band who work after school or on the weekends.
a. How many students work after school and on weekends?
b. How many students work after school or on weekends?

Work After School 5, 3, Work Weekends 17

Lesson 2-2

Word Problem Practice
AL OL BL ELL

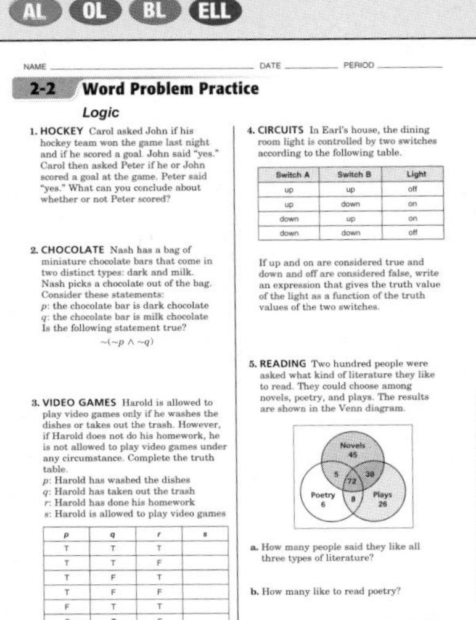

NAME DATE PERIOD

2-2 Word Problem Practice

Logic

1. **HOCKEY** Carol asked John if his hockey team won the game last night and if he scored a goal. John said "yes." Carol then asked Peter if he or John scored a goal at the game. Peter said "yes." What can you conclude about whether or not Peter scored?

2. **CHOCOLATE** Nash has a bag of miniature chocolate bars that come in two distinct types: dark and milk. Nash picks a chocolate out of the bag. Consider these statements:
p: the chocolate bar is dark chocolate
q: the chocolate bar is milk chocolate
Is the following statement true?
$\sim(\sim p \wedge \sim q)$

3. **VIDEO GAMES** Harold is allowed to play video games only if he washes the dishes or takes out the trash. However, if Harold does not do his homework, he is not allowed to play video games under any circumstance. Complete the truth table.
p: Harold has washed the dishes
q: Harold has taken out the trash
r: Harold has done his homework
s: Harold is allowed to play video games

p	q	r	s
T	T	T	
T	T	F	
T	F	T	
T	F	F	
F	T	T	
F	T	F	
F	F	T	
F	F	F	

4. **CIRCUITS** In Earl's house, the dining room light is controlled by two switches according to the following table.

Switch A	Switch B	Light
up	up	off
up	down	on
down	up	on
down	down	off

If up and on are considered true and down and off are considered false, write an expression that gives the truth value of the light as a function of the truth values of the two switches.

5. **READING** Two hundred people were asked what kind of literature they like to read. They could choose among novels, poetry, and plays. The results are shown in the Venn diagram.

Novels 45, Poetry 6, Plays 26, 5, 72, 28, 8

a. How many people said they like all three types of literature?
b. How many like to read poetry?
c. What percentage of the people who like plays also like novels and poetry?

Enrichment
OL BL

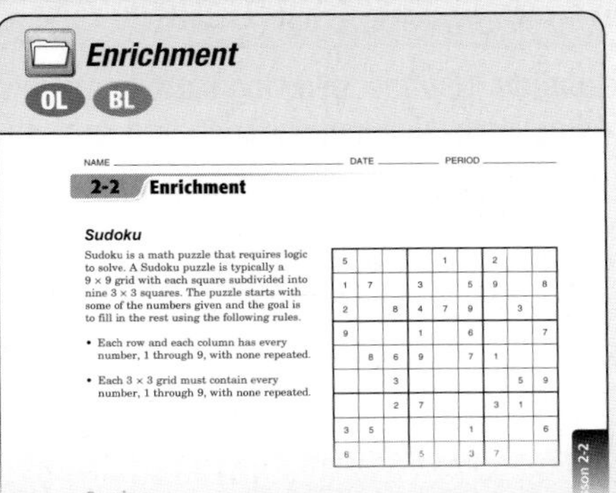

NAME DATE PERIOD

2-2 Enrichment

Sudoku

Sudoku is a math puzzle that requires logic to solve. A Sudoku puzzle is typically a 9 × 9 grid with each square subdivided into nine 3 × 3 squares. The puzzle starts with some of the numbers given and the goal is to fill in the rest using the following rules.

- Each row and each column has every number, 1 through 9, with none repeated.
- Each 3 × 3 grid must contain every number, 1 through 9, with none repeated.

connectED.mcgraw-hill.com

4 Assess

Yesterday's News Have students relate how yesterday's topic of inductive reasoning helped them with today's lesson on logic and truth tables.

Formative Assessment

Check for student understanding of Lessons 2-1 and 2-2.

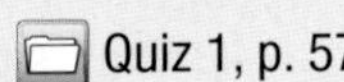 Quiz 1, p. 57

Additional Answers

51. 22 in^2; The area of a triangle is $\frac{1}{2}bh$. The base of the triangle is 11 inches and the height is 4 inches, so the area is $\frac{1}{2}(11)(4)$ or 22 in^2.

54. Inductive; sample answer: Jason noticed that chicken sandwiches were served for lunch on Tuesday and assumed that the pattern would continue, therefore he used inductive reasoning.

55. triangular prism; bases: $\triangle MNO$, $\triangle PQR$; faces: $\triangle MNO$, $\triangle PQR$, $OMPR$, $ONQR$, $PQNM$; edges: $\overline{MN}$, $\overline{NO}$, $\overline{OM}$, $\overline{PQ}$, $\overline{QR}$, $\overline{PR}$, $\overline{NQ}$, $\overline{MP}$, $\overline{OR}$; vertices: M, N, O, P, Q, and R

56. rectangular pyramid; base: $\square DEFG$; faces: $\square DEFG$, $\triangle DHG$, $\triangle GHF$, $\triangle FHE$, $\triangle DHE$; edges: $\overline{DG}$, $\overline{GF}$, $\overline{FE}$, $\overline{ED}$, $\overline{DH}$, $\overline{EH}$, $\overline{FH}$, $\overline{GH}$; vertices: D, E, F, G, and H

57. triangular pyramid; base: $\triangle HJK$; faces: $\triangle HJK$, $\triangle HLK$, $\triangle KLJ$, $\triangle HLJ$; edges: $\overline{HK}$, $\overline{KJ}$, $\overline{HJ}$, $\overline{HL}$, $\overline{KL}$, $\overline{JL}$; vertices: H, K, J, and L

Standardized Test Practice

50. Which statement about $\triangle ABC$ has the same truth value as $AB = BC$? **A**

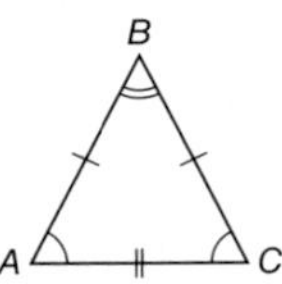

A $m\angle A = m\angle C$
B $m\angle A = m\angle B$
C $AC = BC$
D $AB = AC$

51. EXTENDED RESPONSE What is the area of the triangle shown below? Explain how you found your answer. **See margin.**

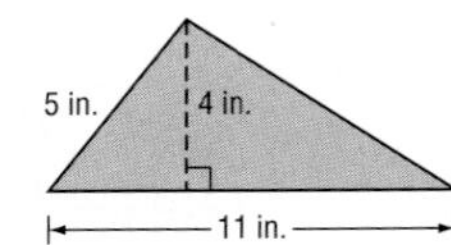

52. STATISTICS The box-and-whisker plot below represents the heights of 9th graders at a certain high school. How much greater was the median height of the boys than the median height of the girls? **F**

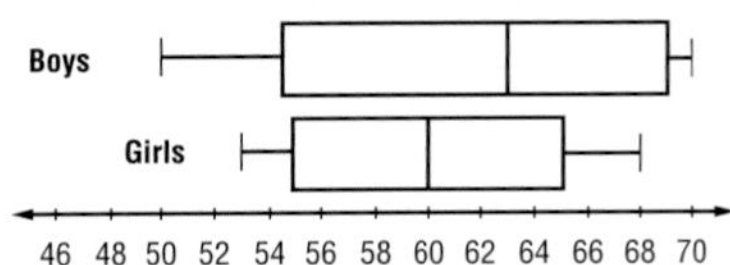

F 3 inches
G 4 inches
H 5 inches
J 6 inches

53. SAT/ACT Heather, Teresa, and Nina went shopping for new clothes. Heather spent twice as much as Teresa, and Nina spent three times what Heather spent. If they spent a total of \$300, how much did Teresa spend? **A**

A \$33.33
B \$50.00
C \$66.33
D \$100.00
E \$104.33

Spiral Review

54. LUNCH For the past four Tuesdays, Jason's school has served chicken sandwiches for lunch. Jason assumes that chicken sandwiches will be served for lunch on the next Tuesday. What type of reasoning did he use? Explain. (Lesson 2-1) **See margin.**

Identify each solid. Name the bases, faces, edges, and vertices. (Lesson 1-7) **55–57. See margin.**

55.
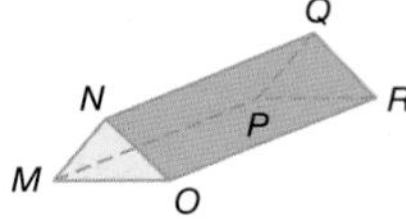

56.
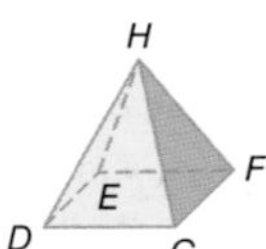

57.
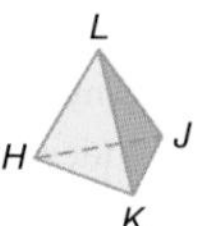

ALGEBRA **Solve each equation.** (Lesson 0-5)

58. $\frac{y}{2} - 7 = 5$ **24**
59. $3x + 9 = 6$ **−1**
60. $4(m - 5) = 12$ **8**
61. $6(w + 7) = 0$ **−7**
62. $2x - 7 = 11$ **9**
63. $\frac{y}{5} + 4 = 9$ **25**

Skills Review

ALGEBRA **Evaluate each expression for the given values.**

64. $2y + 3x$ if $y = 3$ and $x = -1$ **3**
65. $4d - c$ if $d = 4$ and $c = 2$ **14**
66. $m^2 + 7n$ if $m = 4$ and $n = -2$ **2**
67. $ab - 2a$ if $a = -2$ and $b = -3$ **10**

Differentiated Instruction OL BL

Extension Use the following statements to write a compound statement. Show whether it is a conjunction or disjunction. Then find its truth value.

p: $\triangle ABC$ is an equilateral triangle.

q: $\triangle ABC$ is a right triangle.

p or *q*; $\triangle ABC$ is an equilateral triangle, or $\triangle ABC$ is a right triangle.
Disjunction; since no image of $\triangle ABC$ is given, no truth value can be determined.

LESSON 2-3 Conditional Statements

Then
- You used logic and Venn diagrams to determine truth values of negations, conjunctions, and disjunctions.

Now
- 1 Analyze statements in if-then form.
- 2 Write the converse, inverse, and contrapositive of if-then statements.

Why?
- Call centers route calls to the appropriate departments using menus that allow callers to choose from a number of options. The recorded directions are frequently in the form of conditional statements.

NewVocabulary
conditional statement
if-then statement
hypothesis
conclusion
related conditionals
converse
inverse
contrapositive
logically equivalent

1 If-Then Statements

A **conditional statement** is a statement that can be written in *if-then form*. The direction given below is an example of a conditional statement.

If you would like to speak to a representative, **then** you will press 0 now.

KeyConcept Conditional Statement

Words	Symbols	Model
An **if-then statement** is of the form *if p, then q.*	$p \rightarrow q$ read *if p then q,* or *p implies q*	Venn diagram: circle p inside circle q; $p \rightarrow q$
The **hypothesis** of a conditional statement is the phrase immediately following the word *if.*	p	
The **conclusion** of a conditional statement is the phrase immediately following the word *then.*	q	

When a conditional statement is written as an if-then statement, you can quickly identify its hypothesis and conclusion.

Example 1 Identify the Hypothesis and Conclusion

Identify the hypothesis and conclusion of each conditional statement.

a. If the forecast is rain, then I will take an umbrella.
Hypothesis: The forecast is rain.
Conclusion: I will take an umbrella.

b. A number is divisible by 10 if its last digit is a 0.
Hypothesis: The last digit of a number is zero.
Conclusion: The number is divisible by 10.

GuidedPractice 1A, 1B. See Ch. 2 Answer Appendix.

1A. If a polygon has six sides, then it is a hexagon.
1B. Another performance will be scheduled if the first one is sold out.

1 Focus

VerticalAlignment

Before Lesson 2-3 Use logic and Venn diagrams to determine truth values of negations, conjunctions, and disjunctions. Provide counterexamples to disprove statements that are false.

Lesson 2-3 Analyze statements in if-then form. Write the converse, inverse, and contrapositive of if-then statements.

After Lesson 2-3 Use deductive reasoning to prove a statement.

2 Teach

Scaffolding Questions

Have students read the **Why?** section of the lesson.

Ask:
- What is the benefit of using menus in a call system? Sample answer: It allows customers to speak to the correct person quickly and efficiently.
- Suppose the recorded directions say, "If you would like to speak to a representative, press zero now." What are the two parts of this sentence? if you would like to speak to a representative, and press 0 now

(continued on the next page)

Lesson 2-3 Resources

Resource	Approaching Level AL	On Level OL	Beyond Level BL	English Learners ELL
Teacher Edition	▪ Differentiated Instruction, p. 114	▪ Differentiated Instruction, pp. 113, 114	▪ Differentiated Instruction, pp. 113, 114	
Chapter Resource Masters	▪ Study Guide and Intervention, pp. 19–20 ▪ Skills Practice, p. 21 ▪ Practice, p. 22 ▪ Word Problem Practice, p. 23	▪ Study Guide and Intervention, pp. 19–20 ▪ Skills Practice, p. 21 ▪ Practice, p. 22 ▪ Word Problem Practice, p. 23 ▪ Enrichment, p. 24	▪ Practice, p. 22 ▪ Word Problem Practice, p. 23 ▪ Enrichment, p. 24	▪ Study Guide and Intervention, pp. 19–20 ▪ Skills Practice, p. 21 ▪ Practice, p. 22 ▪ Word Problem Practice, p. 23
Other	▪ 5-Minute Check 2-3 ▪ Study Notebook ▪ Teaching Geometry with Manipulatives	▪ 5-Minute Check 2-3 ▪ Study Notebook ▪ Teaching Geometry with Manipulatives	▪ 5-Minute Check 2-3 ▪ Study Notebook	▪ 5-Minute Check 2-3 ▪ Study Notebook ▪ Teaching Geometry with Manipulatives

- What are possible limitations of using a menu in a call system? Sample answer: It may not be possible to list every reason a person might call.

1 If-Then Statements

Examples 1 and 2 show how to identify the hypothesis and conclusion and write them in if-then form. **Example 3** shows how to determine the truth value of a statement.

Formative Assessment

Use the Guided Practice exercises after each example to determine students' understanding of concepts.

Additional Examples

1 Identify the hypothesis and conclusion of each statement.

a. If a polygon has 6 sides, then it is a hexagon. Hypothesis: a polygon has 6 sides; Conclusion: it is a hexagon

b. Tamika will advance to the next level of play if she completes the maze in her computer game. Hypothesis: Tamika completes the maze in her computer game; Conclusion: she will advance to the next level of play

2 Identify the hypothesis and conclusion of each conditional statement. Then write each statement in if-then form.

a. Measured distance is positive. Hypothesis: a distance is measured; Conclusion: it is positive; If a distance is measured, then it is positive.

b. A five-sided polygon is a pentagon. Hypothesis: a polygon has five sides; Conclusion: it is a pentagon; If a polygon has five sides, then it is a pentagon.

ReadingMath

If and Then The word *if* is not part of the hypothesis. The word *then* is not part of the conclusion.

Many conditional statements are written without using the words *if* and *then*. To write these statements in if-then form, identify the hypothesis and conclusion.

Points will be deducted (Conclusion) from any **paper turned in after Wednesday's deadline.** (Hypothesis)

If **a paper is turned in after Wednesday's deadline**, then **points will be deducted.**

Remember, the conclusion depends upon the hypothesis.

Example 2 Write a Conditional in If-Then Form

Identify the hypothesis and conclusion for each conditional statement. Then write the statement in if-then form.

a. A mammal is a warm-blooded animal.

Hypothesis: An animal is a mammal.

Conclusion: It is warm-blooded.

If an animal is a mammal, then it is warm-blooded.

b. A prism with bases that are regular polygons is a regular prism.

Hypothesis: A prism has bases that are regular polygons.

Conclusion: It is a regular prism.

If a prism has bases that are regular polygons, then it is a regular prism.

GuidedPractice

2A. Four quarters can be exchanged for a $1 bill.

2B. The sum of the measures of two supplementary angles is 180.

2A. H: you have four quarters; C: you can exchange them for a $1 bill; If you have four quarters, then you can exchange them for a $1 bill.

2B. H: two angles are supplementary; C: the sum of the measures is 180; If two angles are supplementary, then the sum of their measures is 180.

The hypothesis and the conclusion of a conditional statement can have a truth value of true or false, as can the conditional statement itself. Consider the following conditional.

If **Tom finishes his homework**, then **he will clean his room.**

Hypothesis	Conclusion	Conditional	
Tom finishes his homework.	Tom cleans his room.	If Tom finishes his homework, then he will clean his room.	
T	T	T	If Tom *does* finish his homework and he *does* clean his room, then the conditional is true.
T	F	F	If Tom does *not* clean his room after he *does* finish his homework, then he has not fulfilled his promise and the conditional is false.
F	T	?	The conditional only indicates what will happen if Tom *does* finish his homework. He could clean his room or not clean his room if he does *not* finish his homework.
F	F	?	

ReadingMath

Not False If a statement is *not false*, logic dictates that it must be *true*.

When the hypothesis of a conditional is not met, the truth of a conditional cannot be determined. When the truth of a conditional statement cannot be determined, it is considered true by default.

Tips for New Teachers

Identifying Parts of a Conditional When determining truth values of conditional statements, tell students to use parentheses to identify the hypothesis and conclusion in each situation. Explain that if the hypothesis in the situation matches the hypothesis in the original statement, students can mark a T over the parentheses; if not, they can mark an F. They can do the same for the conclusions.

The results from the previous page can be used to create a truth table for conditional statements.

Conditional Statements

p	q	$p \to q$
T	T	T
T	F	F
F	T	T
F	F	T

Notice that a conditional is false *only* when its hypothesis is true and its conclusion is false.

Notice too that when a hypothesis is false, the conditional will *always* be considered true, regardless of whether the conclusion is true or false.

WatchOut!

Analyzing Conditionals When analyzing a conditional, do not try to determine whether the argument makes sense. Instead, analyze the form of the argument to determine whether the conclusion follows logically from the hypothesis.

To show that a conditional is true, you must show that for each case when the hypothesis is true, the conclusion is also true. To show that a conditional is false, you only need to find one counterexample.

Example 3 Truth Values of Conditionals

Determine the truth value of each conditional statement. If *true*, explain your reasoning. If *false*, give a counterexample.

a. If you divide an integer by another integer, the result is also an integer.

Counterexample: When you divide 1 by 2, the result is 0.5.
Since 0.5 is not an integer, the conclusion is false.
Since you can find a counterexample, the conditional statement is false.

b. If next month is August, then this month is July.

When the hypothesis is true, the conclusion is also true, since August is the month that follows July. So, the conditional statement is true.

c. If a triangle has four sides, then it is concave.

The hypothesis is false, since a triangle can never have four sides. A conditional with a false hypothesis is always true.

GuidedPractice

3A. If $\angle A$ is an acute angle, then $m\angle A$ is 35.   **3B.** If $\sqrt{x} = -1$, then $(-1)^2 = -1$.

3A. False; if $m\angle A = 55$, then $\angle A$ is an acute angle, but it does not measure 35.

3B. True; the hypothesis $\sqrt{x} = -1$ is false, since the square root of a number cannot be negative. Therefore, the conditional statement is true.

2 Related Conditionals

There are other statements that are based on a given conditional statement. These are known as **related conditionals**.

KeyConcept Related Conditionals

Words	Symbols	Examples
A conditional statement is a statement that can be written in the form *if p, then q.*	$p \to q$	If $m\angle A$ is 35, then $\angle A$ is an acute angle.
The **converse** is formed by exchanging the hypothesis and conclusion of the conditional.	$q \to p$	If $\angle A$ is an acute angle, then $m\angle A$ is 35.
The **inverse** is formed by negating both the hypothesis and conclusion of the conditional.	$\sim p \to \sim q$	If $m\angle A$ is *not* 35, then $\angle A$ is *not* an acute angle.
The **contrapositive** is formed by negating both the hypothesis and the conclusion of the converse of the conditional.	$\sim q \to \sim p$	If $\angle A$ is *not* an acute angle, then $m\angle A$ is *not* 35.

Additional Example

3 Determine the truth value of each conditional statement. If *true*, explain your reasoning. If *false*, give a counterexample.

a. If you subtract a whole number from another whole number, the result is also a whole number.
False; $2 - 7 = -5$.

b. If last month was February, then this month is March.
True; the hypothesis is true, and the conclusion is also true, since March is the month that follows February.

c. When a rectangle has an obtuse angle, it is a parallelogram. False; the hypothesis is false, since a rectangle can never have an obtuse angle. A conditional statement with a false hypothesis is always false.

Additional Examples also in Interactive Classroom PowerPoint® Presentations

Teach with Tech

Interactive Whiteboard Write a conditional statement on the board. Drag the hypothesis and conclusion to help write the converse, inverse, and contrapositive of the original statement.

Tips for New Teachers

Sense-Making Provide index cards for each student labeled "Hypothesis," "Conclusion," and "Implies" (or an arrow pointing to the right). Give each student two cards labeled "Not" in red ink. Ask students to use the cards to form conditional, converse, inverse, and contrapositive statements. Students should respond by placing the cards in the correct position and order to reflect the requests.

2 Related Conditionals

Example 4 shows how to write the converse, inverse, and contrapositive of a statement.

Additional Example

4 **NATURE** Write the converse, inverse, and contrapositive of the following true statement. Determine the truth value of each statement. If a statement is false, give a counterexample.

Bats are mammals that can fly.

Conditional: If an animal is a bat, then it can fly. Converse: If the animal is a mammal that can fly, then it is a bat. False; Most birds can fly and they are mammals. Inverse; If the animal is not a bat, then it is not a mammal that can fly. False; Most birds can fly and they are mammals that can fly. Contrapositive: If the animal is not a mammal that can fly, then it is not a bat. True: Since the given conditional is true, the animal cannot be a bat.

Additional Answers (Guided Practice)

4A. Converse: If two angles are congruent, then they have the same measure. True. Inverse: If two angles do not have the same measure, then they are not congruent. True. Contrapositive: If two angles are not congruent, then they do not have the same measure. True.

4B. Converse: If an animal is a rodent, then it is a hamster. False; a mouse is a rodent, but it is not a hamster. Inverse: If an animal is a not a hamster, then it is not a rodent. False; a mouse is not a hamster, but it is a rodent. Contrapositive: If an animal is not a rodent, then it is not a hamster. True.

A conditional and its contrapositive are either both true or both false. Similarly, the converse and inverse of a conditional are either both true or both false. Statements with the same truth values are said to be **logically equivalent**.

KeyConcept Logically Equivalent Statements

- A conditional and its contrapositve are logically equivalent.
- The converse and inverse of a conditional are logically equivalent.

If a conditional is true, the converse may or may not be true.

You can use logical equivalence to check the true value of statements. Notice that in Example 4, both the conditional and contrapositive are true. Also, both the converse and inverse are false.

Real-WorldLink

Cats in the genus *Panthera* include the leopard, jaguar, lion, and tiger. These are the only cats that can roar. They cannot, however, purr.

Source: *Encyclopaedia Britannica*

Real-World Example 4 Related Conditionals

NATURE Write the converse, inverse, and contrapositive of the following true statement. Then use the information at the left to determine whether each related conditional is *true* or *false*. If a statement is false, find a counterexample.

Lions are cats that can roar.

Conditional: First, rewrite the conditional in if-then form.

If an animal is a lion, then it is a cat that can roar.

Based on the information at the left, this statement is true.

Converse: If an animal is a cat that can roar, then it is a lion.

Counterexample: A tiger is a cat that can roar, but it is not a lion.

Therefore, the converse is false.

Inverse: If an animal is not a lion, then it is not a cat that can roar.

Counterexample: A tiger is not a lion, but it is a cat that can roar.

Therefore, the inverse is false.

Contrapositive: If an animal is not a cat that can roar, then it is not a lion.

Based on the information at the left, this statement is true.

CHECK Check to see that logically equivalent statements have the same truth value.

Both the conditional and contrapositive are true. ✓

Both the converse and inverse are false. ✓

GuidedPractice

Write the converse, inverse, and contrapositive of each true conditional statement. Determine whether each related conditional is *true* or *false*. If a statement is false, find a counterexample.

4A. Two angles that have the same measure are congruent. **4A, 4B. See margin.**

4B. A hamster is a rodent.

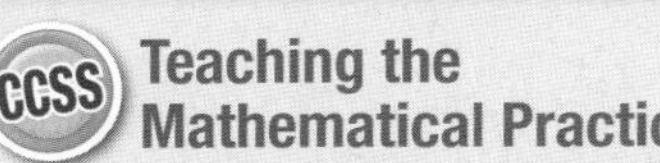

Teaching the Mathematical Practices

Arguments Mathematically proficient students analyze situations and use counterexamples. In Exercises 16–17, encourage students to check the truth of each statement.

Check Your Understanding

 = Step-by-Step Solutions begin on page R14. 

Example 1 **Identify the hypothesis and conclusion of each conditional statement.**

1. If today is Friday, then tomorrow is Saturday. H: today is Friday; C: tomorrow is Saturday
2. If $2x + 5 > 7$, then $x > 1$. H: $2x + 5 > 7$; C: $x > 1$
3. If two angles are supplementary, then the sum of the measures of the angles is 180. **3.** H: two angles are supplementary; C: the sum of the measures of the angles is 180
4. If two lines form right angles, then the lines are perpendicular. H: two lines form right angles; C: the lines are perpendicular

Example 2 **Write each statement in if-then form.**

5. Sixteen-year-olds are eligible to drive. If you are sixteen years old, then you are eligible to drive.
6. Cheese contains calcium. If it is cheese, then it contains calcium.
7. The measure of an acute angle is between 0 and 90. If the angle is acute, then its measure is between 0 and 90.
8. Equilateral triangles are equiangular. If a triangle is equilateral, then it is equiangular.

9. **WEATHER** Various kinds of precipitation form under different conditions. Write the three conditionals below in if-then form.
   a. Moisture in the air condenses and falls to form rain. If moisture in the air condenses and falls, then it rains.
   b. Supercooled moisture in cumulonimbus clouds forms hail.
   c. When the temperature is freezing in all or most of the atmosphere, precipitation falls as snow. If the temperature is freezing in all or most of the atmosphere, then precipitation falls as snow.

9b. If a cumulonimbus cloud has supercooled moisture, then hail forms.

Example 3 **Determine the truth value of each conditional statement. If *true*, explain your reasoning. If *false*, give a counterexample.** 10–15. See margin.

10. If $x^2 = 16$, then $x = 4$.
11. If you live in Charlotte, then you live in North Carolina.
12. If tomorrow is Friday, then today is Thursday.
13. If an animal is spotted, then it is a Dalmatian.
14. If the measure of a right angle is 95, then bees are lizards.
15. If pigs can fly, then $2 + 5 = 7$.

Example 4 **CCSS ARGUMENTS** **Write the converse, inverse, and contrapositive of each true conditional statement. Determine whether each related conditional is *true* or *false*. If a statement is false, find a counterexample.** 16–17. See margin.

16. If a number is divisible by 2, then it is divisible by 4.
17. All whole numbers are integers

Practice and Problem Solving

Extra Practice is on page R2.

Example 1 **Identify the hypothesis and conclusion of each conditional statement.**

18. If two angles are adjacent, then they have a common side. H: two angles are adjacent; C: they have a common side
19. If you lead, then I will follow. H: you lead; C: I will follow
20. If $3x - 4 = 11$, then $x = 5$. H: $3x - 4 = 11$; C: $x = 5$
21. If two angles are vertical, then they are congruent. H: two angles are vertical; C: they are congruent

Differentiated Homework Options

Level	Assignment	Two-Day Option	
AL Basic	18–52, 63, 65–87	19–51 odd, 69–72	18–52 even, 63, 65–68, 73–87
OL Core	19–55 odd, 57–63, 65–87	18–56, 69–72	57–63, 65, 66, 68, 73–87
BL Advanced	53–84, (optional: 85–87)		

3 Practice

Formative Assessment

Use Exercises 1–17 to check for understanding.

Use the chart at the bottom of this page to customize assignments.

Additional Answers

10. False; if $x = -4$, $(-4)^2 = 16$. The hypothesis of the conditional is true, but the conclusion is false. This counterexample shows that the conditional statement is false.
11. False; Charlotte, Michigan; The hypothesis of the conditional is true, but the conclusion is false. This counterexample shows that the conditional statement is false.
12. True; when this hypothesis is true, the conclusion is also true, since Friday is the day that follows Thursday. So, the conditional statement is true.
13. False; the animal could be a leopard. The hypothesis of the conditional is true, but the conclusion is false. This counterexample shows that the conditional statement is false.
14. True; the hypothesis is false, since the measure of a right angle is 90. A conditional with a false hypothesis is always true, so this conditional statement is true.
15. True; the hypothesis is false, since pigs cannot fly. A conditional with a false hypothesis is always true, so this conditional statement is true.
16. Converse: if a number is divisible by 4, then it is divisible by 2; true. Inverse: If a number is not divisible by 2, then it is not divisible by 4; true. Contrapositive: If a number is not divisible by 4, then it is not divisible by 2; false: Sample answer: 6 is divisible by 2 but is not divisible by 4.
17. See p. 112.

Study Guide and Intervention

AL OL ELL

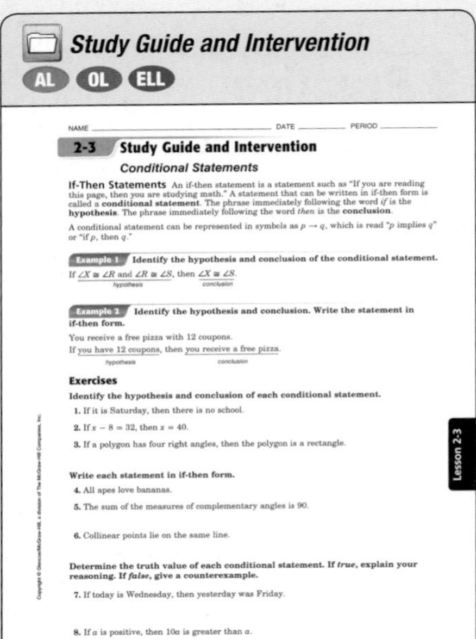

NAME ______ DATE ______ PERIOD ______

2-3 Study Guide and Intervention

Conditional Statements

If-Then Statements An if-then statement is a statement such as "If you are reading this page, then you are studying math." A statement that can be written in if-then form is called a **conditional statement**. The phrase immediately following the word *if* is the **hypothesis**. The phrase immediately following the word *then* is the **conclusion**.

A conditional statement can be represented in symbols as $p \rightarrow q$, which is read "p implies q" or "if p, then q."

Example 1 Identify the hypothesis and conclusion of the conditional statement.

If $\angle X \cong \angle R$ and $\angle R \cong \angle S$, then $\angle X \cong \angle S$.
hypothesis / conclusion

Example 2 Identify the hypothesis and conclusion. Write the statement in if-then form.

You receive a free pizza with 12 coupons.
If you have 12 coupons, then you receive a free pizza.
hypothesis / conclusion

Exercises

Identify the hypothesis and conclusion of each conditional statement.

1. If it is Saturday, then there is no school.
2. If $x - 8 = 32$, then $x = 40$.
3. If a polygon has four right angles, then the polygon is a rectangle.

Write each statement in if-then form.

4. All apes love bananas.
5. The sum of the measures of complementary angles is 90.
6. Collinear points lie on the same line.

Determine the truth value of each conditional statement. If *true*, explain your reasoning. If *false*, give a counterexample.

7. If today is Wednesday, then yesterday was Friday.
8. If a is positive, then $10a$ is greater than a.

Lesson 2-3

Practice

AL OL BL ELL

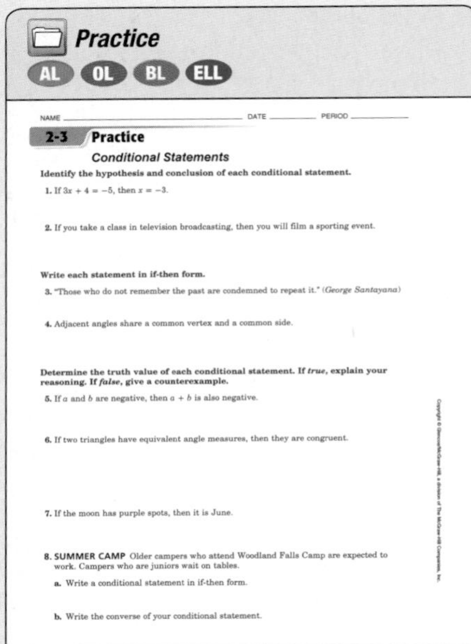

NAME ______ DATE ______ PERIOD ______

2-3 Practice

Conditional Statements

Identify the hypothesis and conclusion of each conditional statement.

1. If $3x + 4 = -5$, then $x = -3$.
2. If you take a class in television broadcasting, then you will film a sporting event.

Write each statement in if-then form.

3. "Those who do not remember the past are condemned to repeat it." (*George Santayana*)
4. Adjacent angles share a common vertex and a common side.

Determine the truth value of each conditional statement. If *true*, explain your reasoning. If *false*, give a counterexample.

5. If a and b are negative, then $a + b$ is also negative.
6. If two triangles have equivalent angle measures, then they are congruent.
7. If the moon has purple spots, then it is June.
8. **SUMMER CAMP** Older campers who attend Woodland Falls Camp are expected to work. Campers who are juniors wait on tables.
   a. Write a conditional statement in if-then form.
   b. Write the converse of your conditional statement.

Word Problem Practice

AL OL BL ELL

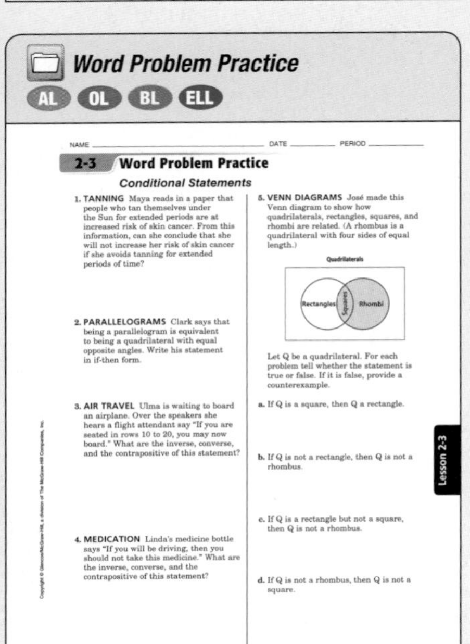

NAME ______ DATE ______ PERIOD ______

2-3 Word Problem Practice

Conditional Statements

1. **TANNING** Maya reads in a paper that people who tan themselves under the Sun for extended periods are at increased risk of skin cancer. From this information, can she conclude that she will not increase her risk of skin cancer if she avoids tanning for extended periods of time?

2. **PARALLELOGRAMS** Clark says that being a parallelogram is equivalent to being a quadrilateral with equal opposite angles. Write his statement in if-then form.

3. **AIR TRAVEL** Ulma is waiting to board an airplane. Over the speakers she hears a flight attendant say "If you are seated in rows 10 to 20, you may now board." What are the inverse, converse, and the contrapositive of this statement?

4. **MEDICATION** Linda's medicine bottle says "If you will be driving, then you should not take this medicine." What are the inverse, converse, and the contrapositive of this statement?

5. **VENN DIAGRAMS** José made this Venn diagram to show how quadrilaterals, rectangles, squares, and rhombi are related. (A rhombus is a quadrilateral with four sides of equal length.)

Let Q be a quadrilateral. For each problem tell whether the statement is true or false. If it is false, provide a counterexample.

a. If Q is a square, then Q a rectangle.
b. If Q is not a rectangle, then Q is not a rhombus.
c. If Q is a rectangle but not a square, then Q is not a rhombus.
d. If Q is not a rhombus, then Q is not a square.

Lesson 2-3

Identify the hypothesis and conclusion of each conditional statement.

22. If the degree measure of an angle is between 90 and 180, then the angle is obtuse.
23. "If there is no struggle, there is no progress." (Frederick Douglass) **H: there is no struggle; C: there is no progress**
24. If a quadrilateral has four congruent sides, then it is a square. **See margin.**
25. If a convex polygon has five sides, then it is a pentagon. **See margin.**

22. H: the degree measure of an angle is between 90 and 180; C: the angle is obtuse

Example 2 **Write each statement in if-then form.**

26. Get a free water bottle with a one-year membership. **If you buy a 1-year membership, then you get a free water bottle.**
27. Everybody at the party received a gift. **If you were at the party, then you received a gift.**
28. The intersection of two planes is a line. **If two planes intersect, then it is a line.**
29. The area of a circle is πr^2. **If a figure is a circle, then the area is πr^2.**
30. Collinear points lie on the same line. **If points are collinear, then they lie on the same line.**
31. A right angle measures 90 degrees. **If an angle is right, then the angle measures 90 degrees.**

32. **MUSIC** Different instruments are emphasized in different types of music. Write each statement in if-then form. **32–33. See Ch. 2 Answer Appendix.**
    - Jazz music often incorporates trumpet or saxophone.
    - Rock music emphasizes guitar and drums.
    - In hip-hop music, the bass is featured.

33. **ART** Write the following statement in if-then form: At the Andy Warhol Museum in Pittsburgh, Pennsylvania, most of the collection is Andy Warhol's artwork.

34. **SCIENCE** The water on Earth is constantly changing through a process called the *water cycle*. Write the three conditionals below in if-then form.

The Water Cycle

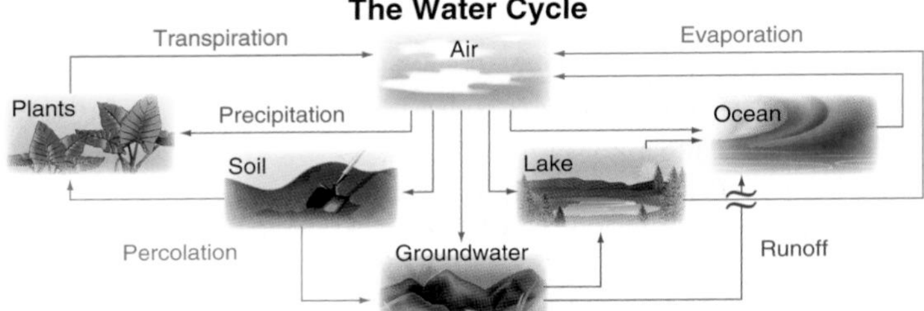

a. As runoff, water flows into bodies of water. **If water runs off, then it flows into bodies of water.**
b. Plants return water to the air through transpiration. **If plants return water to the air, then they transpire.**
c. Water bodies return water to the air through evaporation. **If water bodies return water to the air, then it is through evaporation.**

Example 3 **CCSS ARGUMENTS Determine the truth value of each conditional statement. If *true*, explain your reasoning. If *false*, give a counterexample.** **35–38. See Ch. 2 Answer Appendix.**

35. If a number is odd, then it is divisible by 5.
36. If a dog is an amphibian, then the season is summer.
37. If an angle is acute, then it has a measure of 45.
38. If a polygon has six sides, then it is a regular polygon.

Enrichment

OL BL

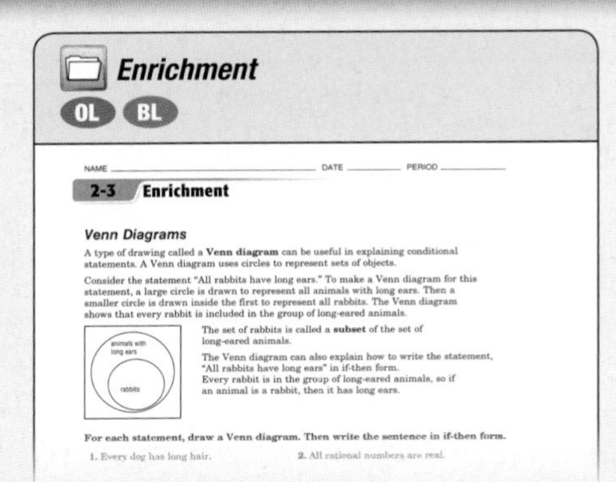

NAME ______ DATE ______ PERIOD ______

2-3 Enrichment

Venn Diagrams

A type of drawing called a **Venn diagram** can be useful in explaining conditional statements. A Venn diagram uses circles to represent sets of objects.

Consider the statement "All rabbits have long ears." To make a Venn diagram for this statement, a large circle is drawn to represent all animals with long ears. Then a smaller circle is drawn inside the first to represent all rabbits. The Venn diagram shows that every rabbit is included in the group of long-eared animals.

The set of rabbits is called a **subset** of the set of long-eared animals.

The Venn diagram can also explain how to write the statement, "All rabbits have long ears" in if-then form. Every rabbit is in the group of long-eared animals, so if an animal is a rabbit, then it has long ears.

For each statement, draw a Venn diagram. Then write the sentence in if-then form.

1. Every dog has long hair.
2. All rational numbers are real.

Additional Answers

17. If a number is a whole number, then it is an integer. Converse: If a number is an integer, then it is a whole number. False; sample answer: −3. Inverse: If a number is not a whole number, then it is not an integer. False: sample answer: −3. Contrapositive: If a number is not an integer, then it is not a whole number; true.
24. H: a quadrilateral has four congruent sides; C: it is a square.
25. H: a convex polygon has five sides; C: it is a pentagon.

Determine the truth value of each conditional statement. If *true*, explain your reasoning. If *false*, give a counterexample. 39–46. See margin.

39. If an angle's measure is 25, then the measure of the angle's complement is 65.
40. If North Carolina is south of Florida, then the capital of Ohio is Columbus.
41. If red paint and blue paint mixed together make white paint, then $3 - 2 = 0$.
42. If two angles are congruent, then they are vertical angles.
43. If an animal is a bird, then it is an eagle.
44. If two angles are acute, then they are supplementary.
45. If two lines intersect, then they form right angles.
46. If a banana is blue, then an apple is a vegetable.

Example 4 **Write the converse, inverse, and contrapositive of each true conditional statement. Determine whether each related conditional is *true* or *false*. If a statement is false, find a counterexample.** 47–52. See Ch. 2 Answer Appendix.

47. If you live in Chicago, you live in Illinois.
48. If a bird is an ostrich, then it cannot fly.
49. If two angles have the same measure, then the angles are congruent.
50. All squares are rectangles.
51. All congruent segments have the same length.
52. A right triangle has an angle measure of 90.

CCSS **ARGUMENTS** Write the statement indicated, and determine the truth value of each statement. If a statement is false, give a counterexample.

Animals with stripes are zebras. 53–56. See Ch. 2 Answer Appendix.

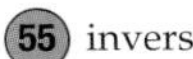

53. conditional 54. converse 55. inverse 56. contrapositive

57. **SCIENCE** Chemical compounds are grouped and described by the elements that they contain. Acids contain hydrogen (H). Bases contain hydroxide (OH). Hydrocarbons contain only hydrogen (H) and carbon (C).

Compound	Example	Chemical Formula
Acid	Hydrochloric Acid	HCl
Base	Sodium Hydroxide	NaOH
Hydrocarbon	Methane	CH_4

a. Write three conditional statements in if-then form for classifying chemical compounds. a, b. See Ch. 2 Answer Appendix.

b. Write the converse of the three true conditional statements. State whether each is *true* or *false*. If a statement is false, find a counterexample.

58. **SPORTS** In football, touchdowns are worth 6 points, extra point conversions are worth 2 points, and safeties are worth 2 points. a, b. See Ch. 2 Answer Appendix.

a. Write three conditional statements in if-then form for scoring in football.

b. Write the converse of the three true conditional statements. State whether each is *true* or *false*. If a statement is false, find a counterexample.

Additional Answers

39. True; when this hypothesis is true, the conclusion is also true, since an angle and its complement's sum is 90. So, the conditional statement is true.
40. True; the hypothesis is false, since North Carolina is not south of Florida. A conditional with a false hypothesis is always true, so this conditional statement is true.
41. True; the hypothesis is false, since red and blue paint make purple paint. A conditional with a false hypothesis is always true, so this conditional statement is true.
42. False; [two right angles in different positions]; the angles are congruent, but they are not vertical angles. The hypothesis of the conditional is true, but the conclusion is false. This counterexample shows that the conditional statement is false.
43. False; the animal could be a falcon. The hypothesis of the conditional is true, but the conclusion is false. This counterexample shows that the conditional statement is false.
44. False; [angles 1 and 2 forming a right angle]; $\angle 1$ and $\angle 2$ are acute, but the sum is 90°. The hypothesis of the conditional is true, but the conclusion is false. This counterexample shows that the conditional statement is false.
45. False; [two intersecting lines]; these lines intersect, but do not form right angles. The hypothesis of the conditional is true, but the conclusion is false. This counterexample shows that the conditional statement is false.
46. True; the hypothesis is false, since a banana is never blue. A conditional with a false hypothesis is always true, so this conditional statement is true.

Differentiated Instruction OL BL

Extension Discuss the meaning of *quadrilateral* and *rhombus* with students. Then have students write the converse of the statement *All quadrilaterals are rhombi.* Determine whether each statement is *true* or *false*.
Conditional: If a shape is a quadrilateral, then it is a rhombus; false. Converse: If a shape is a rhombus, then it is a quadrilateral; true.

Teaching the Mathematical Practices

Arguments Mathematically proficient students analyze situations and can recognize and use counterexamples. They can justify their conclusions and communicate them to others. In Exercises 53–56, point out to students that only one counterexample is needed to show that a statement is false.

 **Multiple Representations**

In Exercise 62, students use logical and verbal statements, and a Venn diagram to investigate the transitive relationship of conditional statements.

Teaching the Mathematical Practices

Critique Mathematically proficient students can distinguish correct logic from flawed reasoning. In Exercise 63, students should remember that a conditional is true except in the case where the hypothesis is true and the conclusion is false. Nicole does not identify that the hypothesis is false.

Additional Answers

62a. Sample answer: If you live in New York City, then you live in New York State; If you live in New York State, then you live in the United States; If you live in the United States, then you live in North America.

62b.

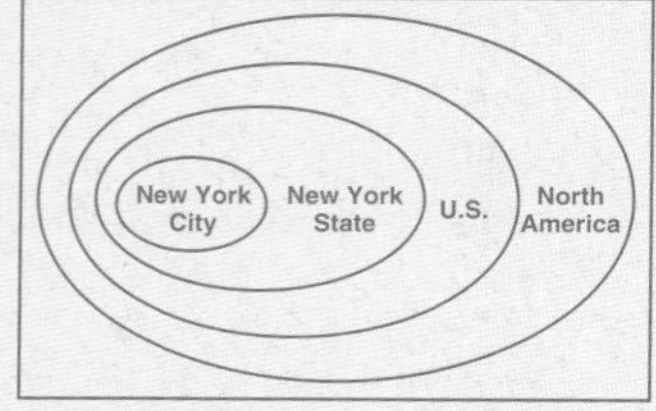

62c. If you live in New York City, then you live in North America; yes.

62d. Sample answer: If a is true, then c is true. If we know that a is true, then we know that b is true, and if we know that b is true, then we know that c is true. Therefore, when a is true, c is true.

63. Sample answer: Kiri; when the hypothesis of a conditional is false, the conditional is always true.

Use the Venn diagrams below to determine the truth value of each conditional. Explain your reasoning.

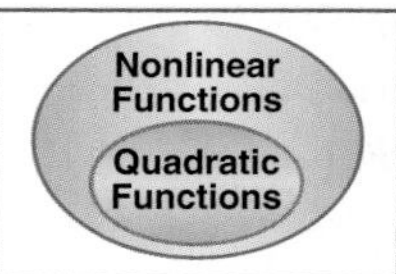

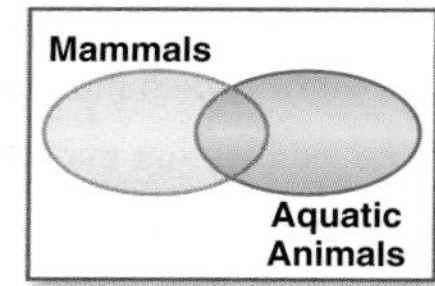

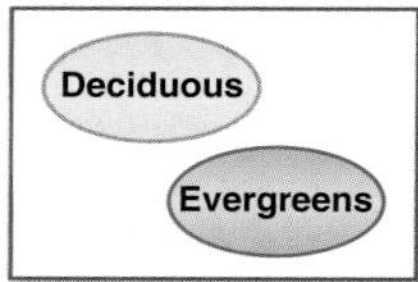

59. If a function is nonlinear, then it is quadratic. **59. False; the blue area of the Venn diagram includes nonlinear functions but not quadratic functions.**

60. If an animal is a mammal, then it cannot be aquatic. **60. False; the green area of the Venn diagram includes both mammals and aquatic animals.**

61. If a tree is deciduous, then it is not an evergreen. **61. True; the deciduous area and the evergreen area have no common areas, so a deciduous tree cannot be evergreen.**

62. **MULTIPLE REPRESENTATIONS** In this problem, you will investigate a law of logic by using conditionals. **a–d. See margin.**

a. Logical Write three true conditional statements, using each consecutive conclusion as the hypothesis for the next statement.

b. Graphical Create a Venn diagram to model your series of statements.

c. Logical Write a conditional using the hypothesis of your first conditional and the conclusion of your third conditional. Is the conditional true if the hypothesis is true?

d. Verbal Given two conditionals *If a, then b* and *If b, then c*, make a conjecture about the truth value of *c* when *a* is true. Explain your reasoning.

H.O.T. Problems Use Higher-Order Thinking Skills

63. **CCSS CRITIQUE** Nicole and Kiri are evaluating the conditional *If 15 is a prime number, then 20 is divisible by 4.* Both think that the conditional is true, but their reasoning differs. Is either of them correct? Explain. **See margin.**

Nicole	Kiri
The conclusion is true, because 20 is divisible by 4, so the conditional is true.	The hypothesis is false, because 15 is not a prime number, so the conditional is true.

64. **CHALLENGE** You have learned that statements with the same truth value are logically equivalent. Use logical equivalence to create a truth table that summarizes the conditional, converse, inverse, and contrapositive for the statements p and q. **See Ch. 2 Answer Appendix.**

65. **REASONING** You are evaluating a conditional statement in which the hypothesis is true, but the conclusion is false. Is the inverse of the statement true or false? Explain your reasoning. **True; since the conclusion is false, the converse of the statement must be true. The converse and inverse are logically equivalent, so the inverse is also true.**

66. **OPEN ENDED** Write a conditional statement in which the converse, inverse, and contrapositive are all true. Explain your reasoning. **66. Sample answer: If four is divisible by two, then birds have feathers. In order for the converse, inverse, and contrapositive to be true, the hypothesis and the conclusion must both be either true or false.**

67. **CHALLENGE** The inverse of conditional A is given below. Write conditional A, its converse, and its contrapositive. Explain your reasoning. **See margin.**

If I received a detention, then I did not arrive at school on time.

68. **WRITING IN MATH** Describe the relationship between a conditional, its converse, its inverse, and its contrapositive. **See margin.**

Differentiated Instruction AL OL BL

If students have difficulty understanding the truth value of conditional statements,

Then have students determine what type of conditional statements are never true. Have them analyze truth tables for conditional statements and find concrete examples where the hypothesis is always true and the conclusion is always false.

Standardized Test Practice

69. *If the sum of the measures of two angles is 90, then the angles are complementary angles.*

Which of the following is the converse of the conditional above? **A**

A If the angles are complementary angles, then the sum of the measures of two angles is 90.

B If the angles are not complementary angles, then the sum of the measures of the angles is 90.

C If the angles are complementary angles, then the sum of the measures of the angles is not 90.

D If the angles are not complementary angles, then the sum of the measures of two angles is not 90.

70. ALGEBRA What is $\frac{10a^2 - 15ab}{4a^2 - 9b^2}$ reduced to lowest terms? **G**

F $\frac{5a}{2a - 2b}$ H $\frac{a}{2a + 3b}$

G $\frac{5a}{2a + 3b}$ J $\frac{a}{2a - 3b}$

71. SHORT RESPONSE What is the standard notation for the following expression? **0.00462**

$$4.62 \times 10^{-3}$$

72. SAT/ACT What is the greatest common prime factor of 18 and 33? **C**

A 1 D 5

B 2 E 11

C 3

Spiral Review

Construct a truth table for each compound statement. (Lesson 2-2) **73–76. See margin.**

73. p and q **74.** p or $\sim q$ **75.** $\sim p \wedge q$ **76.** $\sim p \wedge \sim q$

Make a conjecture based on the given information. Draw a figure to illustrate your conjecture. (Lesson 2-1) **77–80. See Ch. 2 Answer Appendix for drawings.**

77. Points H, J, and K are each located on different sides of a triangle. ***H, J,* and *K* are noncollinear.**

78. Collinear points X, Y, and Z; Z is between X and Y. $XZ + ZY = XY$

79. $R(3, -4)$, $S(-2, -4)$, and $T(0, -4)$ ***R, S,* and *T* are collinear.**

80. $A(-1, -7)$, $B(4, -7)$, $C(4, -3)$, and $D(-1, -3)$ ***ABCD* is a rectangle.**

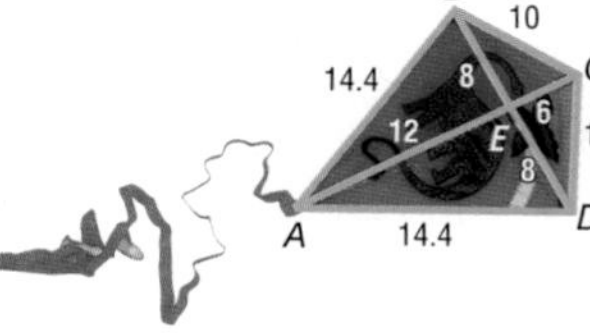

81. KITES Kite making has become an art form. The kite shown is known as a diamond kite. The measures are in inches. Name all of the congruent segments in the figure. (Lesson 1-2) $\overline{BC} \cong \overline{CD}$, $\overline{BE} \cong \overline{ED}$, $\overline{BA} \cong \overline{DA}$

Refer to the conversion charts inside the back cover of your textbook and in Lesson 0-2. (Lesson 0-2)

82. RUNNING Ling is participating in a 5-kilometer charity run next weekend. About how many miles is the race? **about 3 mi**

83. NATURE An African elephant weighs about 9 tons. About how many kilograms is this? **about 9000 kg**

84. SPORTS A football field is 120 yards long from one end zone to the other. How many feet long is a football field? **360 ft**

Skills Review

ALGEBRA Identify the operation used to change Equation (1) to Equation (2).

85. (1) $8(y - 11) = 32$ (2) $y - 11 = 4$ **Divide each side by 8.**

86. (1) $x + 9 = 4 - 3x$ (2) $4x + 9 = 4$ **Add 3x to each side.**

87. (1) $\frac{1}{3}m = 2$ (2) $m = 6$ **Multiply each side by 3.**

67. The hypothesis q of the inverse statement is *I received a detention.* The conclusion p of the inverse statement is *I did not arrive at school on time.* So the conditional A is $p \rightarrow q$: If I did not arrive at school on time, then I received a detention. So the converse of statement A is $\sim p \rightarrow \sim q$: If I arrived at school on time, then I did not receive a detention. The contrapositve of Statement A is $\sim q \rightarrow \sim p$: If I did not receive a detention, then I arrived at school on time.

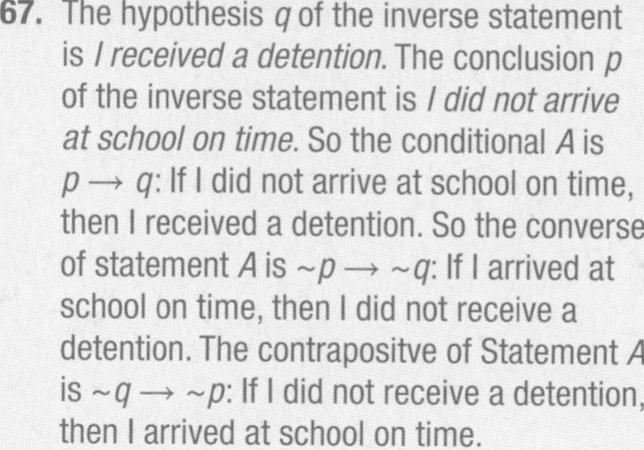

4 Assess

Crystal Ball Ask students to write how they think conditional statements will connect with tomorrow's lesson about deductive reasoning.

Additional Answers

68. Sample answer: Since they are logically equivalent, a conditional and its contrapositive always have the same truth value. The inverse and converse of a conditional are also logically equivalent and have the same truth value. The conditional and its contrapositive can have the same truth value as its inverse and converse, or it can have the opposite truth value of its inverse and converse.

73.

p	q	$p \wedge q$
T	T	T
T	F	F
F	T	F
F	F	F

74.

p	q	$\sim q$	$p \vee \sim q$
T	T	F	T
T	F	T	T
F	T	F	F
F	F	T	T

75.

p	q	$\sim p$	$p \wedge q$
T	T	F	F
T	F	F	F
F	T	T	T
F	F	T	F

76.

p	q	$\sim p$	$\sim q$	$\sim p \wedge \sim q$
T	T	F	F	F
T	F	F	T	F
F	T	T	F	F
F	F	T	T	T

1 Focus

Objective Learn to identify, use, and judge the validity of biconditional statements.

Teaching Tip

Warm students up by having them give examples of conditional statements and the converse of each statement. Have them think about the meaning of each statement, and provide examples that show that the truth of a conditional is not dependent on the truth of its converse. Ask them what the prefix "bi" means.

2 Teach

Working in Cooperative Groups

Organize students in groups of 2, mixing abilities. Then have them read and verify the examples.

Have students create a truth table that includes the conditionals and the biconditionals. Students can then match each example statement with truth values from the table.

Practice Have students complete Exercises 1–5.

3 Assess

Formative Assessment

Use Exercises 1–5 to assess whether students understand the components of a biconditional and how to determine its truth value.

From Concrete to Abstract

Use Exercise 4 to determine whether students can use biconditionals in an algebraic context.

EXTEND 2-3 Geometry Lab
Biconditional Statements

Amy is the starting pitcher for her high school softball team. If she is elected by the district coaches, she will make the All-Star Team. If she makes the All-Star Team, she has been elected by the district coaches.

p: Amy is elected by the district coaches
q: Amy makes the All-Star Team

$p \rightarrow q$: If Amy is elected by the district coaches, then she makes the All-Star Team.

$q \rightarrow p$: If Amy made the All-Star Team, then she was elected by the district coaches.

In this case, both the conditional and its converse are true. The conjunction of the two statements is called a **biconditional**.

KeyConcept Biconditional Statement

Words	A biconditional statement is the conjunction of a conditional and its converse.
Symbols	$(p \rightarrow q) \wedge (q \rightarrow p) \rightarrow (p \leftrightarrow q)$, read *p if and only if q*

If and only if can be abbreviated *iff.*

So, the biconditional statement is as follows.

$p \leftrightarrow q$: Amy makes the All-Star Team if and only if she is elected by the district coaches.

PT

Examples

Write each biconditional as a conditional and its converse. Then determine whether the biconditional is *true* or *false*. If false, give a counterexample.

a. An angle is a right angle if and only if its measure is 90.
Conditional: If an angle measures 90, then the angle is right.
Converse: If an angle is right, then the angle measures 90.
Both the conditional and the converse are true, so the biconditional is true.

b. $x > -2$ iff x is positive.
Conditional: If x is positive, then $x > -2$.
Converse: If $x > -2$, then x is positive.
Let $x = -1$. Then $-1 > -2$, but -1 is not positive. So, the biconditional is false.

Exercises

Write each biconditional as a conditional and its converse. Then determine whether the biconditional is *true* or *false*. If false, give a counterexample. 1–4. See margin.

1. Two angles are complements if and only if their measures have a sum of 90.
2. There is no school if and only if it is Saturday.
3. Two lines intersect if and only if they are not horizontal.
4. $|2x| = 4$ iff $x = 2$.
5. Use logical equivalence to create a truth table that summarizes the conditional, converse, and biconditional for statements p and q. See Ch. 2 Answer Appendix.

Additional Answers

1. Conditional: If two angles are complements, then their measures have a sum of 90.
Converse: If the measures of two angles have a sum of 90, then the angles are complements.
2. Conditional: If it is Saturday, then there is no school.
Converse: If there is no school, then it is Saturday.
False; there is no school on Sundays and holidays.
3. Conditional: If two lines intersect, then they are not horizontal.
Converse: If two lines are not horizontal, then they intersect.
False; two parallel vertical lines will not intersect.
4. Conditional: If $x = 2$, then $|2x| = 4$.
Converse: If $|2x| = 4$, then $x = 2$.
False; If $x = -2$, then $|2x| = 4$.

LESSON 2-4 Deductive Reasoning

Then

- You used inductive reasoning to analyze patterns and make conjectures.

Now

- 1 Use the Law of Detachment.
- 2 Use the Law of Syllogism.

Why?

- When detectives are trying to solve a case, they use techniques like fingerprinting to analyze evidence. Then they use this evidence to eliminate suspects and eventually identify the person responsible for the crime.

NewVocabulary

deductive reasoning
valid
Law of Detachment
Law of Syllogism

1 Law of Detachment

The process that detectives use to identify who is most likely responsible for a crime is called deductive reasoning. Unlike inductive reasoning, which uses a pattern of examples or observations to make a conjecture, **deductive reasoning** uses facts, rules, definitions, or properties to reach logical conclusions from given statements.

Real-World Example 1 Inductive and Deductive Reasoning

Determine whether each conclusion is based on *inductive* or *deductive* reasoning.

a. Every time Katie has worn her favorite socks to a softball game, she has gotten at least one hit. Katie is wearing her favorite socks to a game tonight, so she concludes that she will get at least one hit.

Katie is basing her conclusion on a pattern of observations, so she is using inductive reasoning.

b. If John is late making his car insurance payment, he will be assessed a late fee of $50. John's payment is late this month, so he concludes that he will be assessed a late fee of $50.

John is basing his conclusion on facts provided to him by his insurance company, so he is using deductive reasoning.

GuidedPractice 1A. inductive reasoning

1A. All of the signature items on the restaurant's menu shown are noted with a special symbol. Kevin orders a menu item that has this symbol next to it, so he concludes that the menu item that he has ordered is a signature item.

1B. None of the students who ride Raul's bus own a car. Ebony rides a bus to school, so Raul concludes that Ebony does not own a car.
deductive reasoning

While one counterexample is enough to disprove a conjecture reached using inductive reasoning, it is not a logically correct, or **valid**, method of proving a conjecture. To prove a conjecture requires deductive reasoning. One valid form of deductive reasoning is the **Law of Detachment**.

1 Focus

VerticalAlignment

Before Lesson 2-4 Determine the validity of a conditional statement, its converse, inverse, and contrapositive.

Lesson 2-4 Learn to use the Law of Detachment and the Law of Syllogism. Use deductive reasoning to prove a statement.

After Lesson 2-4 Use logical reasoning to prove statements are true and find counterexamples to prove statements are false.

2 Teach

Scaffolding Questions

Have students read the **Why?** section of the lesson.

Ask:

- What other evidence might a detective collect? Sample answer: descriptions from eyewitnesses and hair samples
- Why is eliminating suspects useful for detectives? Sample answer: They can focus on gathering more evidence related to a smaller number of people.

(continued on the next page)

Lesson 2-4 Resources

Resource	Approaching Level AL	On Level OL	Beyond Level BL	English Learners ELL
Teacher Edition	▪ Differentiated Instruction, p. 124	▪ Differentiated Instruction, pp. 119, 124	▪ Differentiated Instruction, p. 119	▪ Differentiated Instruction, p. 119
Chapter Resource Masters	▪ Study Guide and Intervention, pp. 25–26 ▪ Skills Practice, p. 27 ▪ Practice, p. 28 ▪ Word Problem Practice, p. 29	▪ Study Guide and Intervention, pp. 25–26 ▪ Skills Practice, p. 27 ▪ Practice, p. 28 ▪ Word Problem Practice, p. 29 ▪ Enrichment, p. 30	▪ Practice, p. 28 ▪ Word Problem Practice, p. 29 ▪ Enrichment, p. 30	▪ Study Guide and Intervention, pp. 25–26 ▪ Skills Practice, p. 27 ▪ Practice, p. 28 ▪ Word Problem Practice, p. 29
Other	▪ 5-Minute Check 2-4 ▪ Study Notebook ▪ Teaching Geometry with Manipulatives	▪ 5-Minute Check 2-4 ▪ Study Notebook ▪ Teaching Geometry with Manipulatives	▪ 5-Minute Check 2-4 ▪ Study Notebook	▪ 5-Minute Check 2-4 ▪ Study Notebook ▪ Teaching Geometry with Manipulatives

- What could be some limitations to using fingerprints as evidence? Sample answer: The person who committed the crime may not have left fingerprints.

1 Law of Detachment

Example 1 shows how to differentiate between inductive and deductive reasoning. **Example 2** shows how to use the Law of Detachment. **Example 3** shows how to use Venn diagrams to test the validity of conclusions.

Formative Assessment

Use the Guided Practice exercises after each example to determine students' understanding of concepts.

Additional Example

1 WEATHER Determine whether each conclusion is based on *inductive* or *deductive* reasoning.

a. In Miguel's town, the month of April has had the most rain for the past 5 years. He thinks that April will have the most rain this year. inductive; Miguel's conclusion is based on a pattern of observation.

b. Sandra learned that if it is cloudy at night it will not be as cold in the morning as it would be if there are no clouds at night. Sandra knows it will be cloudy tonight, so she believes it will not be cold tomorrow morning. deductive; Sandra is using facts that she has learned about clouds and temperature.

Additional Examples also in Interactive Classroom PowerPoint® Presentations

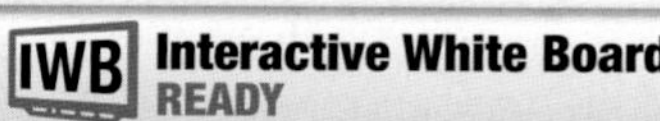
Interactive White Board READY

KeyConcept Law of Detachment

Words	If $p \rightarrow q$ is a true statement and p is true, then q is true.
Example	*Given:* If a car is out of gas, then it will not start. Sarah's car is out of gas. *Valid Conclusion:* Sarah's car will not start.

As long as the facts given are true, the conclusion reached using deductive reasoning will also be true.

StudyTip

Given Information From this point forward in this text, all given information can be assumed true.

Example 2 Law of Detachment

Determine whether each conclusion is valid based on the given information. If not, write *invalid*. Explain your reasoning.

a. Given: If two angles form a linear pair, then their noncommon sides are opposite rays.
$\angle AED$ and $\angle AEB$ form a linear pair.

Conclusion: $\overrightarrow{ED}$ and $\overrightarrow{EB}$ are opposite rays.

Step 1 Identify the hypothesis p and the conclusion q of the true conditional.

p: Two angles form a linear pair.

q: Their noncommon sides are opposite rays.

Step 2 Analyze the conclusion.

The given statement *$\angle AED$ and $\angle AEB$ form a linear pair* satisfies the hypothesis, so p is true. By the Law of Detachment, $\overrightarrow{ED}$ and $\overrightarrow{EB}$ *are opposite rays*, which matches q, is a true or valid conclusion.

b. Given: If Mika goes to the beach, she will wear sunscreen.
Mika is wearing sunscreen.

Conclusion: Mika is at the beach.

Step 1 p: Mika goes to the beach.

q: Mika wears sunscreen.

Step 2 The given statement *Mika is wearing sunscreen* satisfies the conclusion q of the true conditional. However, knowing that a conditional statement and its conclusion are true does not make the hypothesis true. Mika could be wearing sunscreen because she is at the pool. The conclusion is invalid.

GuidedPractice

2A. Given: If three points are noncollinear, they determine a plane.
Points A, B, and C lie in plane G.

Conclusion: Points A, B, and C are noncollinear. **Invalid; points A, B, and C could be collinear and form a line.**

2B. Given: If a student turns in a permission slip, then the student can go on the field trip.
Felipe turned in his permission slip.

Conclusion: Felipe can go on the field trip. **valid; Law of Detachment**

Tips for New Teachers

Law of Detachment Tell students that the Law of Detachment follows directly from what they have already learned about conditional statements and their truth tables.

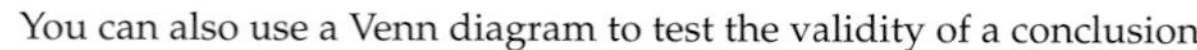

You can also use a Venn diagram to test the validity of a conclusion.

Real-WorldLink

The easiest way to distinguish monkeys from other primates is to look for a tail. Most monkey species have tails, but apes do not.

Source: *Encyclopaedia Britannica*

Example 3 Judge Conclusions Using Venn Diagrams

NATURE **Determine whether each conclusion is valid based on the given information. If not, write *invalid*. Explain your reasoning using a Venn diagram.**

Given: **If a primate is an ape, then it does not have a tail.**

Koko is a primate who does not have a tail.

Conclusion: **Koko is an ape.**

Understand Draw a Venn diagram. According to the conditional, an ape does not have a tail, so draw a circle for apes that does not intersect the circle for primates with tails.

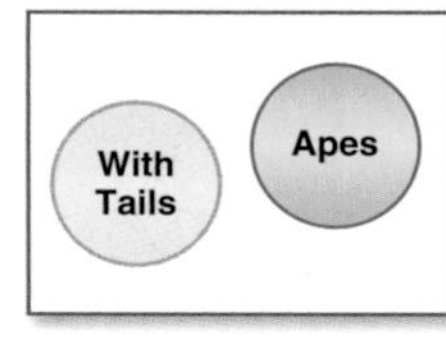

Plan Since we are only given that Koko does not have a tail, we can only conclude that Koko belongs outside the circle for primates with tails.

Solve This could put her in the area inside or outside of the Apes circle, so the conclusion is invalid.

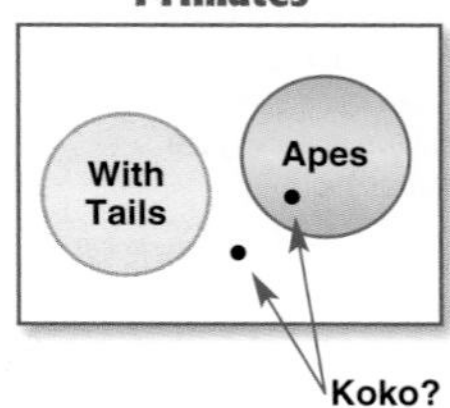

Check From the given information, we know that apes are primates that do not have tails. We also know that Koko is a primate that does not have a tail. It is possible for Koko to be a primate without a tail and still not be an ape. Therefore, the conclusion *is* invalid. ✓

StudyTip

CCSS Arguments An *argument* consists of reasons, proof, or evidence to support a position. A *logical argument* such as the one shown is supported by the rules of logic. This is different from a *statistical argument*, which is supported by examples or data.

GuidedPractice

3. **Given:** If a figure is a square, then it is a polygon. Figure A is a square.

Conclusion: Figure A is a polygon.

3. Valid; the figure is inside the square circle, which is inside the polygon circle, so the conclusion is valid.

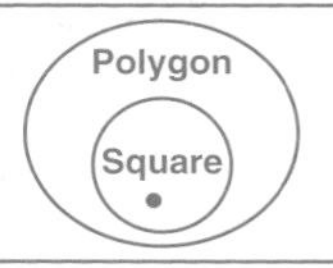

2 Law of Syllogism

The **Law of Syllogism** is another valid form of deductive reasoning. This law allows you to draw conclusions from two true conditional statements when the conclusion of one statement is the hypothesis of the other.

KeyConcept Law of Syllogism

Words	If $p \rightarrow q$ and $q \rightarrow r$ are true statements, then $p \rightarrow r$ is a true statement.
Example	*Given:* If you get a job, then you will earn money. If you earn money, then you will buy a car. *Valid Conclusion:* If you get a job, then you will buy a car.

It is important to remember that if the conclusion of the first statement is *not* the hypothesis of the second statement, no valid conclusion can be drawn.

Additional Examples

2 Determine whether the conclusion is valid based on the given information. If not, write *invalid.* Explain your reasoning.

Given: If a figure is a square, then it is a parallelogram. The figure is a parallelogram.

Conclusion: The figure is a square. Invalid conclusion; the figure could be a rectangle.

3 Determine whether the conclusion is valid based on the given information. If not, write *invalid.* Explain your reasoning using a Venn diagram.

Given: If a triangle is equilateral, then it is an acute triangle. The triangle is equilateral.

Conclusion: The triangle is acute.

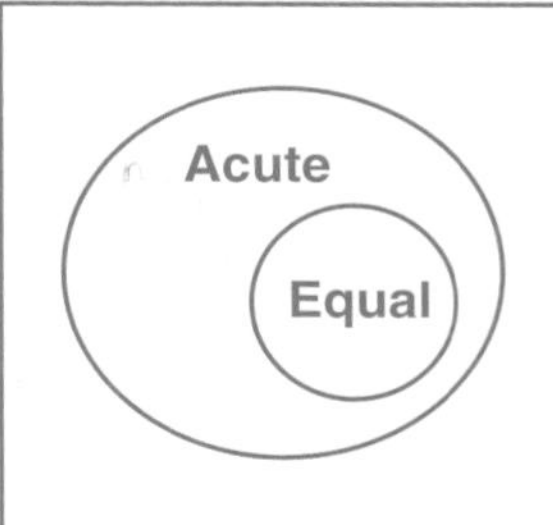

From the given information, all equilateral triangles are acute, so the conclusion is valid.

CCSS Teaching the Mathematical Practices

Arguments Mathematically proficient students justify their conclusions and communicate them to others. Encourage students to use logic or data to support their arguments.

DifferentiatedInstruction OL BL ELL

Extension Write an example to illustrate the correct use of the Law of Syllogism. Sample answer:
1) Students need to be organized.
2) If you are organized, then you have good study habits.
3) If you have good study habits, then you get good grades.
4) Students that are organized get good grades.

2 Law of Syllogism

Examples 4 and 5 show how to use the Law of Syllogism.

Additional Examples

4 STANDARDIZED TEST EXAMPLE Determine which statement follows logically from the given statements.

(1) If Jamal finishes his homework, he will go out with his friends.

(2) If Jamal goes out with his friends, he will go to the movies. B

A If Jamal goes out with his friends, then he finishes his homework.

B If Jamal finishes his homework, he will go to the movies.

C If Jamal does not go to the movies, he does not go out with his friends.

D There is no valid conclusion.

5 Draw a valid conclusion from the given statements, if possible. Then state whether your conclusion was drawn using the Law of Detachment or the Law of Syllogism. If no valid conclusion can be drawn, write *no conclusion* and explain your reasoning.

Given: If it snows more than 5 inches, school will be closed. It snows 7 inches.

p: It snows more than 5 inches. *q:* School will be closed. Since *It snows 7 inches* satisfies the hypothesis, *p* is true. By the Law of Detachment, a valid conclusion is *School is closed.*

PT

Standardized Test Example 4 Law of Syllogism

Determine which statement follows logically from the given statements.

(1) If you like musicals, then you enjoy theater productions.

(2) If you are an actor, then you enjoy theater productions.

A If you are an actor, then you like musicals.

B If you like musicals, then you are an actor.

C If you do not enjoy musicals, then you are not an actor.

D There is no valid conclusion.

Read the Test Item

Let p, q, and r represent the parts of the given conditional statements.

p: **You like musicals.**
q: **You enjoy theater productions.**
r: **You are an actor.**

Solve the Test Item

Analyze the logic of the given conditional statement using symbols.

Statement (1): $p \rightarrow q$ Statement (2): $r \rightarrow q$

Both statements are considered true. However, the Law of Syllogism does not apply since q, the conclusion of the Statement (1), is not the hypothesis of the second statement. While choices A, B, and C may be true, the logic used to draw these conclusions is not valid. Therefore, choice D is correct.

Test-Taking Tip

True vs. Valid Conclusions A true conclusion is not the same as a valid conclusion. True conclusions that are reached using invalid deductive reasoning are still invalid.

Guided Practice

4. Determine which statement follows logically from the given statements. G

(1) If you do not get enough sleep, then you will be tired.

(2) If you are tired, then you will not do well on the test.

F If you are tired, then you will not get enough sleep.

G If you do not get enough sleep, then you will not do well on the test.

H If you do not do well on the test, then you did not get enough sleep.

J There is no valid conclusion.

Example 5 Apply Laws of Deductive Reasoning

Draw a valid conclusion from the given statements, if possible. Then state whether your conclusion was drawn using the Law of Detachment or the Law of Syllogism. If no valid conclusion can be drawn, write *no valid conclusion* and explain your reasoning.

Given: If you are 16 years old, then you can apply for a driver's license. Nate is 16 years old.

p: **You are 16 years old.**

q: You can apply for a driver's license.

Since *Nate is 16 years old* satisfies the hypothesis p is true. By the Law of Detachment, a valid conclusion is *Nate can apply for a driver's license.*

Guided Practice 5. $AM = MB$; Law of Syllogism

5. Given: The midpoint divides a segment into two congruent segments. If two segments are congruent, then their measures are equal. M is the midpoint of $\overline{AB}$.

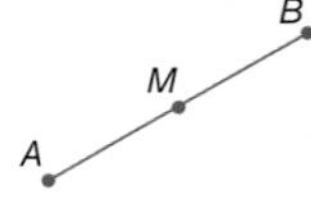

Watch Out!

Out of Order Remind students that to use the Law of Syllogism the statements must appear in the correct order; the conclusion of the first conditional must be the hypothesis of the second conditional.

Teach with Tech

Audio Recording Have students create audio recordings explaining the Law of Syllogism and the Law of Detachment in their own words. Have them provide an example for each law.

Check Your Understanding

= Step-by-Step Solutions begin on page R14.

Example 1 **Determine whether each conclusion is based on *inductive* or *deductive* reasoning.**

1. Students at Olivia's high school must have a B average in order to participate in sports. Olivia has a B average, so she concludes that she can participate in sports at school. deductive reasoning
2. Holly notices that every Saturday, her neighbor mows his lawn. Today is Saturday. Holly concludes her neighbor will mow his lawn. inductive reasoning

Example 2 **Determine whether the stated conclusion is valid based on the given information. If not, write *invalid*. Explain your reasoning.**

3. **Given:** If a number is divisible by 4, then the number is divisible by 2. 12 is divisible by 4. valid; Law of Detachment

   Conclusion: 12 is divisible by 2.

4. **Given:** If Elan stays up late, he will be tired the next day. Elan is tired.

   Conclusion: Elan stayed up late. Invalid; Elan could be tired because he worked out.

Example 3 **Determine whether the stated conclusion is valid based on the given information. If not, write *invalid*. Explain your reasoning using a Venn diagram.** 5, 6. See margin.

5. **Given:** If a beach is public, then it does not have a lifeguard. Bayview does not have a lifeguard.

   Conclusion: Bayview is a public beach.

6. **Given:** If students pass an entrance exam, they will be accepted into college. Latisha passed the entrance exam.

   Conclusion: Latisha will be accepted into college.

Example 4

7. **MULTIPLE CHOICE** Determine which statement follows logically from the given statements. C

   (1) If a triangle is a right triangle, then it has an angle that measures 90.

   (2) If a triangle has an angle that measures 90, then its acute angles are complementary.

   A If a triangle is not a right triangle, then it has an angle that measures 90.

   B If an angle of a triangle measures 90, then its acute angles are not complementary.

   C If a triangle is a right triangle, then its acute angles are complementary.

   D If a triangle has an angle that measures 90, then it is not a right triangle.

Example 5 CCSS **ARGUMENTS** **Draw a valid conclusion from the given statements, if possible. Then state whether your conclusion was drawn using the Law of Detachment or the Law of Syllogism. If no valid conclusion can be drawn, write *no valid conclusion* and explain your reasoning.**

8. **Given:** If Dalila finishes her chores, she will receive her allowance.

   If Dalila receives her allowance, she will buy a CD.

   8. If Dalila finishes her chores, she will buy a CD; Law of Syllogism.

9. **Given:** Vertical angles are congruent.

   $\angle 1 \cong \angle 2$ No valid conclusion; $\angle 1$ and $\angle 2$ do not have to be vertical in order to be congruent.

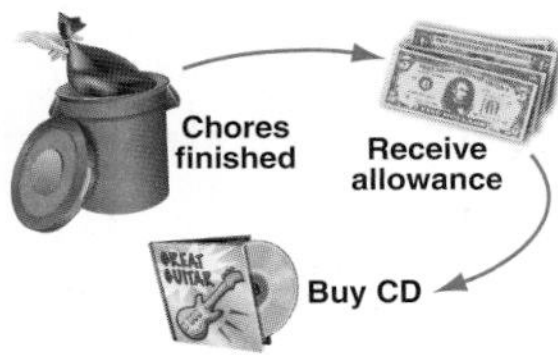

Differentiated Homework Options

Level	Assignment	Two-Day Option	
AL Basic	10–34, 42, 44–64	11–33 odd, 47–50	10–34 even, 42, 44–46, 51–64
OL Core	11–33 odd, 35–42, 44–64	10–34, 47–50	35–42, 44–46, 51–64
BL Advanced	35–58, (optional: 59–64)		

3 Practice

Formative Assessment

Use Exercises 1–9 to check for understanding.

Use the chart at the bottom of this page to customize assignments for your students.

Follow-up

Students have explored inductive reasoning, logic, and deductive reasoning.

Ask:

- What makes a logical argument? Sample answer: a series of true statements that are given in order to reach a valid conclusion

Teaching the Mathematical Practices

Arguments Mathematically proficient students understand and use stated assumptions in constructing arguments. In Exercises 8–9, encourage students to represent the statements symbolically using letters such as p, q, or r.

Additional Answers

5. Invalid: Bayview could be inside or outside the public beach's circle.

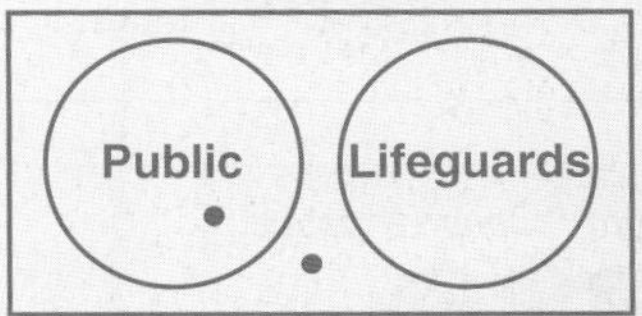

6. Valid; Latisha is inside the students who pass the entrance exam circle which puts her inside the students who are accepted into college circle, so Latisha will be accepted into college.

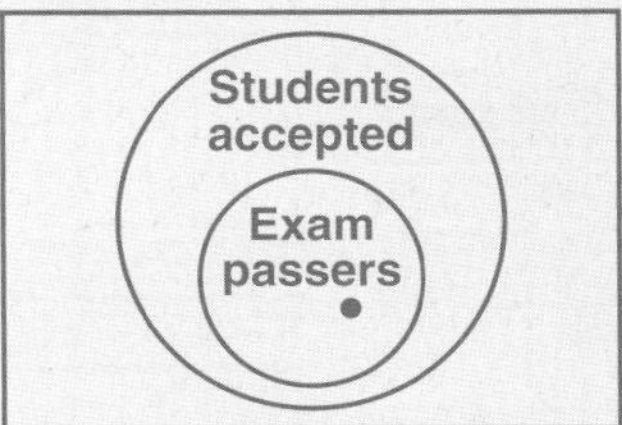

Practice and Problem Solving

Extra Practice is on page R2.

Example 1 **Determine whether each conclusion is based on *inductive* or *deductive* reasoning.**

10. At Fumio's school if you are late five times, you will receive a detention. Fumio has been late to school five times; therefore he will receive a detention. **deductive reasoning**
11. A dental assistant notices a patient has never been on time for an appointment. She concludes the patient will be late for her next appointment. **inductive reasoning**
12. A person must have a membership to work out at a gym. Jesse is working out at a gym. Jesse has a membership to the gym. **deductive reasoning**
13. If Eduardo decides to go to a concert tonight, he will miss football practice. Tonight, Eduardo went to a concert. Eduardo missed football practice. **deductive reasoning**
14. Every Wednesday Lucy's mother calls. Today is Wednesday, so Lucy concludes her mother will call. **inductive reasoning**
15. Whenever Juanita has attended a tutoring session she notices that her grades have improved. Juanita attends a tutoring session and she concludes her grades will improve. **inductive reasoning**

Example 2 CCSS **CRITIQUE** **Determine whether the stated conclusion is valid based on the given information. If not, write *invalid*. Explain your reasoning.**

16. **Given:** Right angles are congruent. $\angle 1$ and $\angle 2$ are right angles.
    Conclusion: $\angle 1 \cong \angle 2$ **valid; Law of Detachment**
17. **Given:** If a figure is a square, it has four right angles. Figure *ABCD* has four right angles.
    Conclusion: Figure *ABCD* is a square. **Invalid; the figure could be a rectangle.**
18. **Given:** An angle bisector divides an angle into two congruent angles. $\overrightarrow{KM}$ is an angle bisector of $\angle JKL$.
    Conclusion: $\angle JKM \cong \angle MKL$ **valid; Law of Detachment**

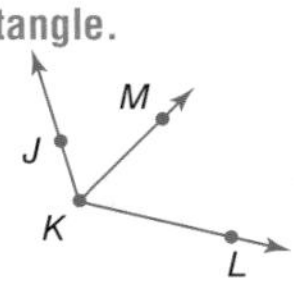

    (Figure: rays from K through J, M, and L.)
19. **Given:** If you leave your lights on while your car is off, your battery will die. Your battery is dead. **Invalid; your battery could be dead because it was old.**
    Conclusion: You left your lights on while the car was off.
20. **Given:** If Dante obtains a part-time job, he can afford a car payment. Dante can afford a car payment.
    Conclusion: Dante obtained a part-time job. **Invalid; Dante could afford a car payment because he paid off his other bills.**
21. **Given:** If 75% of the prom tickets are sold, the prom will be held at the country club. 75% of the prom tickets were sold. **valid; Law of Detachment**
    Conclusion: The prom will be held at the country club.
22. **COMPUTER GAMES** Refer to the game ratings at the right. Determine whether the stated conclusion is valid based on the given information. If not, write *invalid*. Explain your reasoning. **See margin.**
    Given: If a title is rated E, then it has content that may be suitable for ages 6 and older. Cesar buys a computer game that he believes is suitable for his little sister, who is 7.
    Conclusion: The game Cesar purchased has a rating of E.

Game Ratings

Rating	Age
EC	3 and older
E	6 and older
E10+	10 and older
T	13 and older
M	17 and older

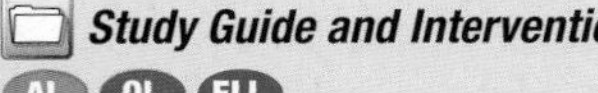

NAME ______ DATE ______ PERIOD ______

2-4 Study Guide and Intervention

Deductive Reasoning

Law of Detachment **Deductive reasoning** is the process of using facts, rules, definitions, or properties to reach conclusions. One form of deductive reasoning that draws conclusions from a true conditional $p \to q$ and a true statement p is called the **Law of Detachment**.

Law of Detachment	If $p \to q$ is true and p is true, then q is true.

Example **Determine whether each conclusion is valid based on the given information. If not, write *invalid*. Explain your reasoning.**

a. **Given: Two angles supplementary to the same angle are congruent. $\angle A$ and $\angle C$ are supplementary to $\angle B$.**
Conclusion: $\angle A$ is congruent to $\angle C$.
The statement $\angle A$ and $\angle C$ are *supplementary* to $\angle B$ is the hypothesis of the conditional. Therefore, by the Law of Detachment, the conclusion is true.

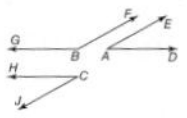

b. **Given: If Helen is going to work, then she is wearing pearls. Helen is wearing pearls.**
Conclusion: Helen is going to work.
The given statement *Helen is going to work* satisfies the conclusion of the true conditional. However, knowing that a conditional statement and its conclusion are true does not make the hypothesis true. Helen could be wearing pearls on a date. The conclusion is invalid.

Exercises

Determine whether the stated conclusion is valid based on the given information. If not, write *invalid*. Explain your reasoning.

1. **Given:** If a number is divisible by 6, then the number is divisible by 3. 18 is divisible by 6.
   Conclusion: 18 is divisible by 3.
2. **Given:** If a pet is a rabbit, then it eats carrots. Jennie's pet eats carrots.
   Conclusion: Jennie's pet is a rabbit.
3. **Given:** If a hen is a Plymouth Rock, then her eggs are brown. Berta is a Plymouth Rock hen.
   Conclusion: Berta's eggs are brown.

Lesson 2-4

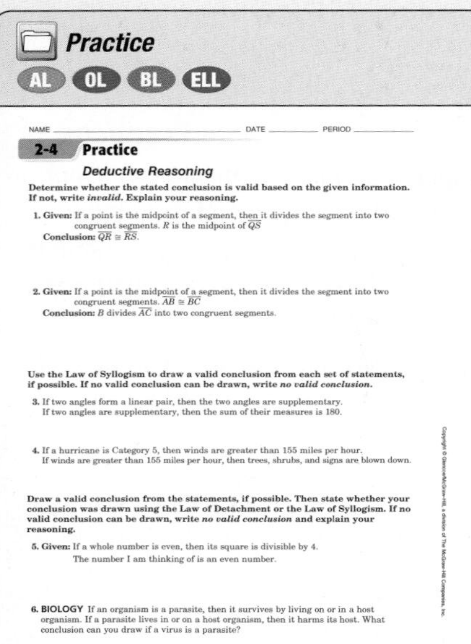

Practice AL OL BL ELL

NAME ______ DATE ______ PERIOD ______

2-4 Practice

Deductive Reasoning

Determine whether the stated conclusion is valid based on the given information. If not, write *invalid*. Explain your reasoning.

1. **Given:** If a point is the midpoint of a segment, then it divides the segment into two congruent segments. R is the midpoint of $\overline{QS}$
   Conclusion: $\overline{QR} \cong \overline{RS}$.
2. **Given:** If a point is the midpoint of a segment, then it divides the segment into two congruent segments. $\overline{AB} \cong \overline{BC}$
   Conclusion: B divides $\overline{AC}$ into two congruent segments.

Use the Law of Syllogism to draw a valid conclusion from each set of statements, if possible. If no valid conclusion can be drawn, write *no valid conclusion*.

3. If two angles form a linear pair, then the two angles are supplementary.
   If two angles are supplementary, then the sum of their measures is 180.
4. If a hurricane is Category 5, then winds are greater than 155 miles per hour.
   If winds are greater than 155 miles per hour, then trees, shrubs, and signs are blown down.

Draw a valid conclusion from the statements, if possible. Then state whether your conclusion was drawn using the Law of Detachment or the Law of Syllogism. If no valid conclusion can be drawn, write *no valid conclusion* and explain your reasoning.

5. **Given:** If a whole number is even, then its square is divisible by 4.
   The number I am thinking of is an even number.
6. **BIOLOGY** If an organism is a parasite, then it survives by living on or in a host organism. If a parasite lives in or on a host organism, then it harms its host. What conclusion can you draw if a virus is a parasite?

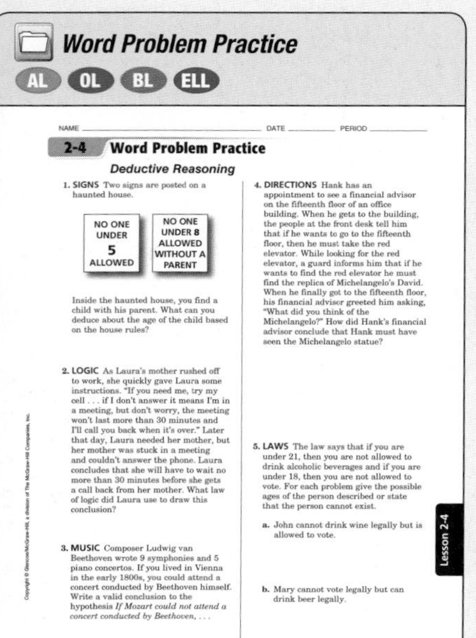

Word Problem Practice AL OL BL ELL

NAME ______ DATE ______ PERIOD ______

2-4 Word Problem Practice

Deductive Reasoning

1. **SIGNS** Two signs are posted on a haunted house.

   NO ONE UNDER 5 ALLOWED

   NO ONE UNDER 8 ALLOWED WITHOUT A PARENT

   Inside the haunted house, you find a child with his parent. What can you deduce about the age of the child based on the house rules?
2. **LOGIC** As Laura's mother rushed off to work, she quickly gave Laura some instructions. "If you need me, try my cell . . . if I don't answer it means I'm in a meeting, but don't worry, the meeting won't last more than 30 minutes and I'll call you back when it's over." Later that day, Laura needed her mother, but her mother was stuck in a meeting and couldn't answer the phone. Laura concludes that she will have to wait no more than 30 minutes before she gets a call back from her mother. What law of logic did Laura use to draw this conclusion?
3. **MUSIC** Composer Ludwig van Beethoven wrote 9 symphonies and 5 piano concertos. If you lived in Vienna in the early 1800s, you could attend a concert conducted by Beethoven himself. Write a valid conclusion to the hypothesis *If Mozart could not attend a concert conducted by Beethoven, . . .*
4. **DIRECTIONS** Hank has an appointment to see a financial advisor on the fifteenth floor of an office building. When he gets to the building, the people at the front desk tell him that if he wants to go to the fifteenth floor, then he must take the red elevator. While looking for the red elevator, a guard informs him that if he wants to find the red elevator he must find the replica of Michelangelo's David. When he finally got to the fifteenth floor, his financial advisor greeted him asking, "What did you think of the Michelangelo?" How did Hank's financial advisor conclude that Hank must have seen the Michelangelo statue?
5. **LAWS** The law says that if you are under 21, then you are not allowed to drink alcoholic beverages and if you are under 18, then you are not allowed to vote. For each problem give the possible ages of the person described or state that the person cannot exist.
   a. John cannot drink wine legally but is allowed to vote.
   b. Mary cannot vote legally but can drink beer legally.

Lesson 2-4

122 | Lesson 2-4 | Deductive Reasoning

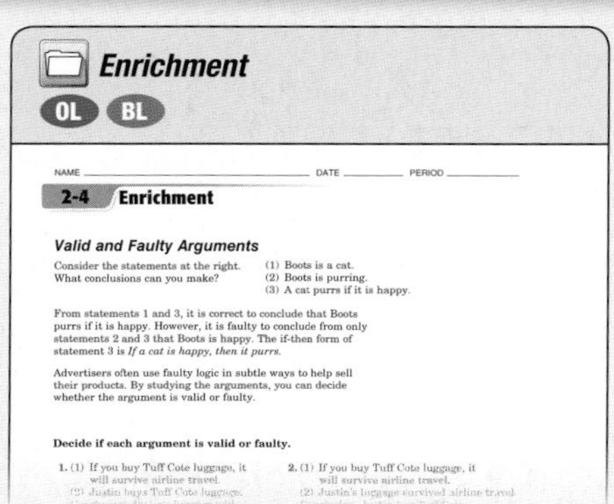

Enrichment OL BL

NAME ______ DATE ______ PERIOD ______

2-4 Enrichment

Valid and Faulty Arguments

Consider the statements at the right. What conclusions can you make?

(1) Boots is a cat.
(2) Boots is purring.
(3) A cat purrs if it is happy.

From statements 1 and 3, it is correct to conclude that Boots purrs if it is happy. However, it is faulty to conclude from only statements 2 and 3 that Boots is happy. The if-then form of statement 3 is *If a cat is happy, then it purrs.*

Advertisers often use faulty logic in subtle ways to help sell their products. By studying the arguments, you can decide whether the argument is valid or faulty.

Decide if each argument is valid or faulty.

1. (1) If you buy Tuff Cote luggage, it will survive airline travel.
   (2) Justin buys Tuff Cote luggage.
2. (1) If you buy Tuff Cote luggage, it will survive airline travel.
   (2) Justin's luggage survived airline travel.

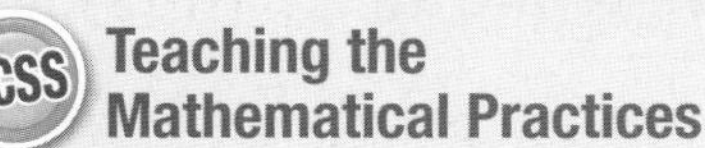

Teaching the Mathematical Practices

Critique Mathematically proficient students can distinguish correct logic from flawed reasoning. In Exercises 16–21, encourage students to identify the hypothesis and conclusion of the true conditional before analyzing the conclusion.

Example 3 **Determine whether the stated conclusion is valid based on the given information. If not, write *invalid*. Explain your reasoning using a Venn diagram.** 23–26. See margin.

23. Given: If the temperature drops below 32°F, it may snow. The temperature did not drop below 32°F on Monday.

Conclusion: It did not snow on Monday.

24. Given: If a person is a Missouri resident, he or she does not live by a beach. Michelle does not live by the beach.

Conclusion: Michelle is a Missouri resident.

25. Given: Some nurses wear blue uniforms. Sabrina is a nurse.

Conclusion: Sabrina wears a blue uniform.

26. Given: All vegetarians do not eat meat. Theo is a vegetarian.

Conclusion: Theo does not eat meat.

27 **TRANSPORTATION** There are many types of vehicles and they are classified using different sets of criteria. Determine whether the stated conclusion is valid based on the given information. If not, write *invalid*. Explain your reasoning using a Venn diagram. See Ch. 2 Answer Appendix.

Given: If a vehicle is a sport-utility vehicle, then it is a four-wheel-drive car built on a truck chassis. Ms. Rodriguez has just purchased a vehicle that has four-wheel drive.

Conclusion: Ms. Rodriguez has just purchased a sport-utility vehicle.

Examples 4–5 **28. GOLF** Zach Johnson won the Masters Tournament in 2007. Use the Law of Syllogism to draw a valid conclusion from each set of statements, if possible. If no valid conclusion can be drawn, write *no valid conclusion* and explain your reasoning.

(1) If Zach Johnson's score is lower than the other golfers at the end of the tournament, then he wins the tournament.

(2) If a golfer wins the Masters Tournament, then he gets a green jacket.

If Zach Johnson's score is lower than the other golfers at the end of the tournament, then he gets a green jacket.

CCSS ARGUMENTS **Use the Law of Syllogism to draw a valid conclusion from each set of statements, if possible. If no valid conclusion can be drawn, write *no valid conclusion* and explain your reasoning.**

29. If you interview for a job, then you wear a suit. no valid conclusion

If you interview for a job, then you will update your resume.

30. If Tina has a grade point average of 3.0 or greater, she will be on the honor roll.

If Tina is on the honor roll, then she will have her name in the school paper.

30. If Tina has a grade point average of 3.0 or greater, then she will have her name in the school paper.

31. If two lines are perpendicular, then they intersect to form right angles.

Lines r and s form right angles. no valid conclusion

32. If the measure of an angle is between 90 and 180, then it is obtuse.

If an angle is obtuse, then it is not acute. If the measure of an angle is between 90 and 180, then it is not acute.

33. If two lines in a plane are not parallel, then they intersect.

If two lines intersect, then they intersect in a point. If two lines in a plane are not parallel, then they intersect in a point.

34. If a number ends in 0, then it is divisible by 2.

If a number ends in 4, then it is divisible by 2. no valid conclusion

Focus on Mathematical Content

Formalizing Proofs Stress to students that the rules of reasoning are meant to formalize the way they intuitively draw conclusions every day. One purpose of formalizing arguments is to help you write proofs when you may not have an intuition about a question or problem.

Teaching the Mathematical Practices

Arguments Mathematically proficient students understand and use stated assumptions in constructing arguments. In Exercises 29–34, encourage students to represent the statements symbolically using letters such as p, q, or r.

Additional Answers

22. Invalid; the game could be rated EC, which is suitable for ages 3 and up.

23. Valid; Monday is outside of the days when the temperature drops below 32°F, so it cannot be inside the days when it snows circle either, so the conclusion is valid.

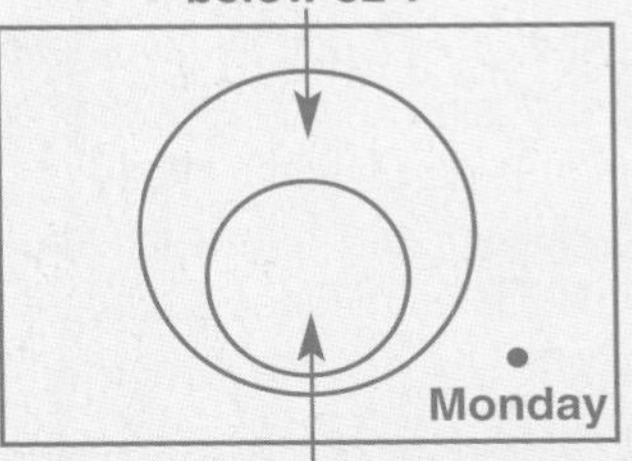

24. Invalid; Michelle could be inside the Missouri circle or inside the People who do not live by the beach circle and outside the Missouri Circle.

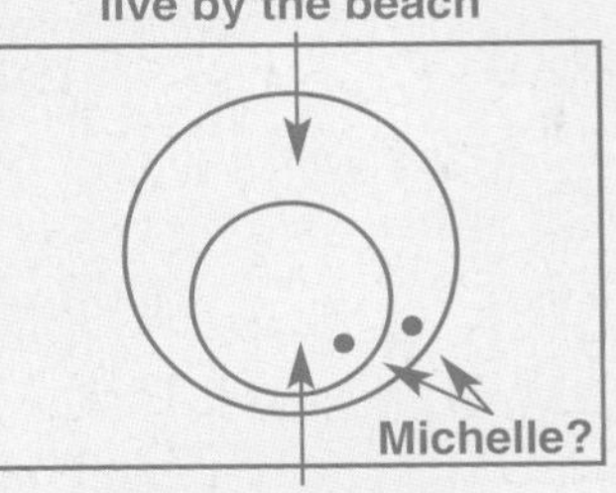

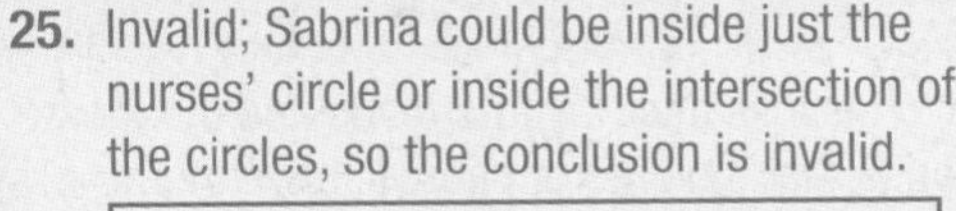

25. Invalid; Sabrina could be inside just the nurses' circle or inside the intersection of the circles, so the conclusion is invalid.

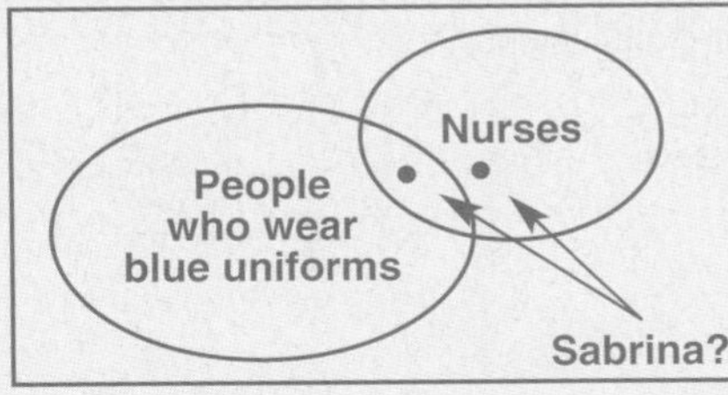

26. Valid; Theo is inside the small and large circle, so the conclusion is valid.

People who don't eat meat

Vegetarians

Theo

CCSS Teaching the Mathematical Practices

Reasoning Mathematically proficient students make sense of quantities and their relationships. In Exercise 45, point out to students that Jonah's statement can be phrased as a compound sentence. Then the compound sentence can be analyzed.

Additional Answers

41a. Florida Marlins Hits vs. At Bats

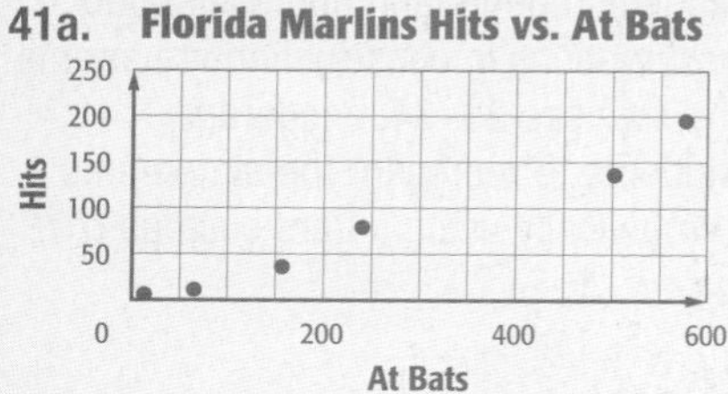

41b. Sample answer: About 91; inductive; a pattern was used to reach the conclusion.

41c. Sample answer: The player with 240 at bats got more hits; deductive; the facts provided in the table were used to reach the conclusion.

42. Sample answer: The Law of Syllogism cannot be used, because the hypothesis of the second conditional is the negation of the conclusion of the first conditional. In order to use the Law of Syllogism, the conclusion of one conditional must be the hypothesis of the second conditional.

43. Law of Detachment: $[(p \rightarrow q) \wedge p] \rightarrow q$; Law of Syllogism: $[(p \rightarrow q) \wedge (q \rightarrow r)] \rightarrow (p \rightarrow r)$

44. Sample answer: (1) If a student earns 40 credits, then he/she will graduate from high school. (2) If a student graduates from high school, then he or she will receive a diploma. Conclusion: If a student earns 40 credits, he or she will receive a diploma.

Draw a valid conclusion from the given statements, if possible. Then state whether your conclusion was drawn using the Law of Detachment or the Law of Syllogism. If no valid conclusion can be drawn, write *no valid conclusion* and explain your reasoning.

35. Given: If a figure is a square, then all the sides are congruent.
Figure *ABCD* is a square. **Figure *ABCD* has all sides congruent; Law of Detachment.**

36. Given: If two angles are complementary, the sum of the measures of the angles is 90.
$\angle 1$ and $\angle 2$ are complements of each other.

37. Given: Ballet dancers like classical music.
If you like classical music, then you enjoy the opera.

38. Given: If you are athletic, then you enjoy sports.
If you are competitive, then you enjoy sports.

39. Given: If a polygon is regular, then all of its sides are congruent.
All sides of polygon *WXYZ* are congruent.

40. Given: If Bob completes a course with a grade of C, then he will not receive credit.
If Bob does not receive credit, he will have to take the course again.

36. The sum of the measures of $\angle 1$ and $\angle 2$ is 90; Law of Detachment.
37. If you are a ballet dancer, then you enjoy the opera; Law of Syllogism.
38. No valid conclusion; the conclusion of statement (1) is not the hypothesis of statement (2).
39. No valid conclusion; knowing a conclusion is true does not imply the hypothesis will be true.
40. If Bob completes a course with a grade of C, then he will have to take the course again; Law of Syllogism.

41. DATA ANALYSIS The table shows the number of at bats and hits for some of the members of the Florida Marlins in a recent season. **a–c. See margin.**

a. Construct a scatter plot to represent the data.

b. Predict the number of hits a player with 300 at bats would get. Identify and explain your reasoning.

c. Did the player with 157 at bats or the player with 240 at bats get more hits? What type of reasoning did you use? Explain.

At Bats	Hits
13	6
576	195
240	79
502	139
157	36
64	11

Source: ESPN

H.O.T. Problems Use Higher-Order Thinking Skills

42. WRITING IN MATH Explain why the Law of Syllogism cannot be used to draw a conclusion from these conditionals. **See margin.**

If you wear winter gloves, then you will have warm hands.

If you do not have warm hands, then your gloves are too thin.

43. CHALLENGE Use the symbols from Lesson 2-2 for *conjunction* and *disjunction*, and the symbol for implies from Lesson 2-3 to represent the Law of Detachment and the Law of Syllogism symbolically. Let *p* represent the hypothesis, and let *q* represent the conclusion. **See margin.**

44. OPEN ENDED Write a pair of statements in which the Law of Syllogism can be used to reach a valid conclusion. Specify the conclusion that can be reached. **See margin.**

45. CCSS REASONING Students in Mr. Kendrick's class are divided into two groups for an activity. Students in group A must always tell the truth. Students in group B must always lie. Jonah and Janeka are in Mr. Kendrick's class. When asked if he and Janeka are in group A or B, Jonah says, "We are both in Group B." To which group does each student belong? Explain your reasoning. **See Ch. 2 Answer Appendix.**

46. WRITING IN MATH Compare and contrast inductive and deductive reasoning when making conclusions and proving conjectures. **See Ch. 2 Answer Appendix.**

Differentiated Instruction AL OL

Interpersonal Have students organize into small groups to discuss their favorite foods and the most popular foods. While they discuss why they think each food is their favorite or popular, have them describe the types of reasoning they are using to draw their conclusions.

Standardized Test Practice

47. Determine which statement follows logically from the given statements. **D**

If you order two burritos, then you also get nachos.
Michael ordered two burritos.

A Michael ordered one burrito.
B Michael will order two burritos.
C Michael ordered nachos.
D Michael got nachos.

48. ALGEBRA Solve for x: **F**

$$4(x + 2) = x - 1$$

F -3
G -5
H -6
J -8

49. SHORT RESPONSE If the perimeter of the figure shown is 52 units, what is the value of x? $\frac{26}{11}$

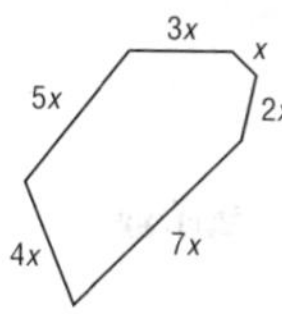

50. SAT/ACT If 30% of x is 50, then 60% of x is **E**

A 300
B 250
C 175
D 150
E 100

Spiral Review

51. TIME All states in the United States observe daylight savings time except for Arizona and Hawaii. (Lesson 2-3) **a, b. See margin.**

a. Write a true conditional statement in if-then form for daylight savings time.

b. Write the converse of the true conditional statement. State whether the statement is *true* or *false*. If false, find a counterexample.

Construct a truth table for each compound statement. (Lesson 2-2) **52–55. See margin.**

52. a and b **53.** $\sim p$ or $\sim q$ **54.** k and $\sim m$ **55.** $\sim y$ or z

ALGEBRA Find x. (Lesson 1-5)

56.

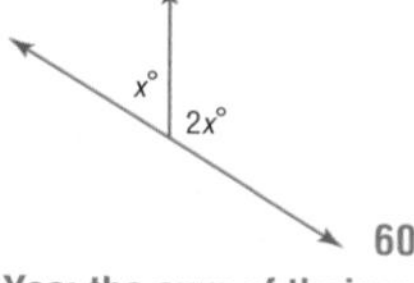

60

57.

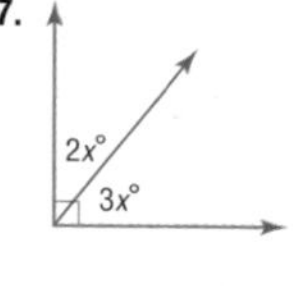

18

58.

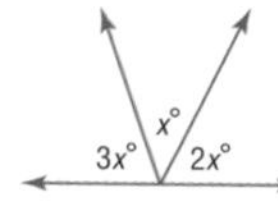

30

61. Yes; the sum of their measures is $m\angle ADC$, which is 90.

Skills Review

Determine whether each statement can be assumed from the figure. Explain.

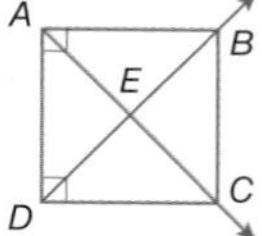

59. $\angle DAB$ is a right angle. **Yes; the symbol denotes that $\angle DAB$ is a right angle.**

60. $\angle AEB \cong \angle DEC$ **Yes; they are vertical angles.**

61. $\angle ADB$ and $\angle BDC$ are complementary.

62. $\angle DAE \cong \angle ADE$ **No; there is no indication of the measures of these angles.**

63. $\overline{AB} \perp \overline{BC}$ **No; we do not know $m\angle ABC$.**

64. $\angle AEB$ and $\angle BEC$ are supplementary. **Yes; they are a linear pair, so they are supplementary.**

4 Assess

Name the Math Students can use shapes to model the Law of Detachment and the Law of Syllogism. Provide students with two yellow squares of laminated construction paper marked with p, two blue triangles marked with q, and two red circles marked with r. Students should write a method showing how to arrange the shapes to represent the symolic relationships of the two laws.

Formative Assessment

Check for student understanding of Lessons 2-3 and 2-4.

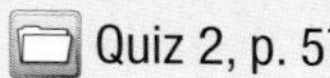
Quiz 2, p. 57

Additional Answers

51a. If you live in Hawaii or Arizona then you do not observe Daylight Savings Time.

51b. If you do not observe Daylight Savings Time, then you live in Hawaii or Arizona; true.

52.

a	b	a and b
T	T	T
T	F	F
F	T	F
F	F	F

53.

p	$\sim p$	q	$\sim q$	$\sim p$ or $\sim q$
T	F	T	F	F
T	F	F	T	T
F	T	T	F	T
F	T	F	T	T

54.

k	m	$\sim m$	k and $\sim m$
T	T	F	F
T	F	T	T
F	T	F	F
F	F	T	F

55.

y	$\sim y$	z	$\sim y$ or z
T	F	T	T
T	F	F	F
F	T	T	T
F	T	F	T

1 Focus

Objective Determine necessary and sufficient conditions for a statement to be true.

Teaching Tip

Engage students by having them give examples of statements that are always true and statements that are sometimes true. Explain that necessary and sufficient conditions are special kinds of statements that describe whether something is always true or sometimes true.

2 Teach

Working in Cooperative Groups

Arrange students in pairs, mixing abilities. Then have them read and verify the examples.

Have students think of additional examples that involve necessary and sufficient conditions.

Practice Have students complete Exercises 1–7.

3 Assess

Formative Assessment

Use Exercises 1–7 to assess whether students understand the meanings of necessary and sufficient conditions and are able to determine their truth values.

From Concrete to Abstract

Use Exercises 8–10 to determine whether students identify necessary and sufficient conditions in an algebraic context.

EXPLORE 2-5 Geometry Lab: Necessary and Sufficient Conditions

We all know that water is a *necessary* condition for plants to survive. However, it is not a *sufficient* condition. For example, plants also need sunlight to survive.

Necessary and sufficient conditions are important in mathematics. Consider the property of having four sides. While *having four sides* is a necessary condition for something being a square, that single condition is not, by itself, a sufficient condition to guarantee that it is a square. Trapezoids are four-sided figures that are not squares.

Condition	Definition	Examples
necessary	A condition *A* is said to be *necessary* for a condition *B*, if and only if the falsity or nonexistence of *A* guarantees the falsity or nonexistence of *B*.	Having opposite sides parallel is a necessary condition for something being a square.
sufficient	A condition *A* is said to be *sufficient* for a condition *B*, if and only if the truth or existence of *A* guarantees the truth or existence of *B*.	Being a square is a sufficient condition for something being a rectangle.

1. False; a rectangle does not have to have all sides equal.
3. False; a number could be less than 5 and be less than 10.
5. False; cats can also walk on 4 legs.

Exercises

Determine whether each statement is *true* or *false*. If false, give a counterexample.

1. Being a square is a necessary condition for being a rectangle.
2. Being a rectangle is a necessary condition for being a square. **true**
3. Being greater than 5 is a necessary condition for being less than 10.
4. Being less than 18 is a sufficient condition for being less than 25. **true**
5. Walking on four legs is a sufficient condition for being a dog.
6. Breathing air is a necessary condition for being a human being. **true**
7. Being an equilateral rectangle is both a necessary and sufficient condition for being a square. **true**

Determine whether I is a *necessary* condition for II, a *sufficient* condition for II, or *both*. Explain.

8. I. Two points are given. **8–10. See margin.**
   II. An equation of a line can be written.
9. I. Two planes are parallel.
   II. Two planes do not intersect.
10. I. Two angles are acute.
    II. Two angles are complementary.

Marc Romanelli/Photodisc/Getty Images

Additional Answers

8. Sufficient; an equation of a line can be written using two points. However, it is not necessary to use two points because the equation of a line can also be written using one point and the slope.
9. Both; in order to have two planes that do not intersect, it is necessary that the two planes be parallel. Also, having two planes parallel is sufficient to determine that the planes do not intersect.
10. Necessary; for two angles to be complementary, it is necessary that they be acute. It is not sufficient, however, because two 60° angles, for example, are acute but are not complementary.

LESSON 2-5 Postulates and Paragraph Proofs

Then

- You used deductive reasoning by applying the Law of Detachment and the Law of Syllogism.

Now

1. Identify and use basic postulates about points, lines, and planes.
2. Write paragraph proofs.

Why?

- If a feather and an apple are dropped from the same height in a vacuum chamber, the two objects will fall at the same rate. This demonstrates one of Sir Isaac Newton's laws of gravity and inertia. These laws are accepted as fundamental truths of physics. Some laws in geometry also must be assumed or accepted as true.

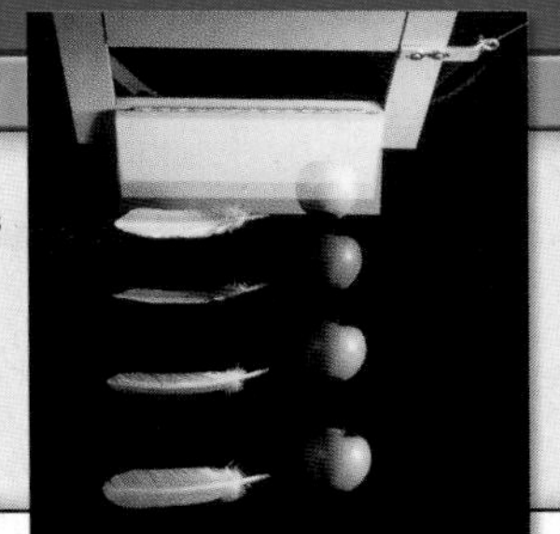

NewVocabulary
postulate
axiom
proof
theorem
deductive argument
paragraph proof
informal proof

Common Core State Standards

Content Standards
G.MG.3 Apply geometric methods to solve problems (e.g., designing an object or structure to satisfy physical constraints or minimize cost; working with typographic grid systems based on ratios). ★

Mathematical Practices
2 Reason abstractly and quantitatively.
3 Construct viable arguments and critique the reasoning of others.

1 Points, Lines, and Planes

A **postulate** or **axiom** is a statement that is accepted as true without proof. Basic ideas about points, lines, and planes can be stated as postulates.

Postulates Points, Lines, and Planes

Words	Example
2.1 Through any two points, there is exactly one line.	Line n is the only line through points P and R.
2.2 Through any three noncollinear points, there is exactly one plane.	Plane $\mathcal{K}$ is the only plane through noncollinear points A, B, and C.
2.3 A line contains at least two points.	Line n contains points P, Q, and R.
2.4 A plane contains at least three noncollinear points.	Plane $\mathcal{K}$ contains noncollinear points L, B, C, and E.
2.5 If two points lie in a plane, then the entire line containing those points lies in that plane.	Points A and B lie in plane $\mathcal{K}$, and line m contains points A and B, so line m is in plane $\mathcal{K}$.

KeyConcept Intersections of Lines and Planes

Words	Example
2.6 If two lines intersect, then their intersection is exactly one point.	Lines s and t intersect at point P.
2.7 If two planes intersect, then their intersection is a line.	Planes $\mathcal{F}$ and $\mathcal{G}$ intersect in line w.

1 Focus

VerticalAlignment

Before Lesson 2-5 Use logical reasoning to prove statements are true and find counterexamples to disprove statements are false.

Lesson 2-5 Construct and justify statements about geometric figures, using basic postulates and paragraph proofs.

After Lesson 2-5 Use deductive reasoning to prove a statement. Write two-column proofs.

2 Teach

Scaffolding Questions

Have students read the **Why?** section of the lesson.

Ask:

- Why do an apple and a feather not fall at the same rate normally? Air resistance causes the feather to fall more slowly.
- What do you think the difference is between a law and a theorem? Sample answer: Laws are accepted as truth, and theorems are proven.

Lesson 2-5 Resources

Resource	Approaching Level AL	On Level OL	Beyond Level BL	English Learners ELL
Teacher Edition	▪ Differentiated Instruction, p. 133	▪ Differentiated Instruction, pp. 131, 133	▪ Differentiated Instruction, p. 131	
Chapter Resource Masters	▪ Study Guide and Intervention, pp. 31–32 ▪ Skills Practice, p. 33 ▪ Practice, p. 34 ▪ Word Problem Practice, p. 35	▪ Study Guide and Intervention, pp. 31–32 ▪ Skills Practice, p. 33 ▪ Practice, p. 34 ▪ Word Problem Practice, p. 35 ▪ Enrichment, p. 36	▪ Practice, p. 34 ▪ Word Problem Practice, p. 35 ▪ Enrichment, p. 36	▪ Study Guide and Intervention, pp. 31–32 ▪ Skills Practice, p. 33 ▪ Practice, p. 34 ▪ Word Problem Practice, p. 35
Other	▪ 5-Minute Check 2-5 ▪ Study Notebook	▪ 5-Minute Check 2-5 ▪ Study Notebook	▪ 5-Minute Check 2-5 ▪ Study Notebook	▪ 5-Minute Check 2-5 ▪ Study Notebook

1 Points, Lines, and Planes

Examples 1 and 2 show how to identify and compare postulates. Students should be able to prove conjectures by using postulates and theorems.

Formative Assessment

Use the Guided Practice exercises after each example to determine students' understanding of concepts.

Additional Example

1 ARCHITECTURE Explain how the picture in Example 1 illustrates that each statement is true. Then state the postulate that can be used to show each statement is true.

a. Points F and G lie in plane $\mathcal{Q}$ and on line m. Line m lies entirely in plane $\mathcal{Q}$. Points F and G lie on line m, and the line lies in plane $\mathcal{Q}$. Postulate 2.5, which states that if two points lie in a plane, the entire line containing the points lies in that plane, shows that this is true.

b. Points A and C determine a line. Points A and C lie along an edge, the line that they determine. Postulate 2.1, which says through any two points there is exactly one line, shows that this is true.

Additional Examples also in Interactive Classroom PowerPoint® Presentations

IWB Interactive White Board READY

StudyTip

Undefined Terms Recall from Lesson 1-1 that points, lines, and planes are *undefined terms*. The postulates that you have learned in this lesson describe special relationships between them.

These additional postulates form a foundation for proofs and reasoning about points, lines, and planes.

Real-World Example 1 Identifying Postulates

ARCHITECTURE Explain how the picture illustrates that each statement is true. Then state the postulate that can be used to show each statement is true.

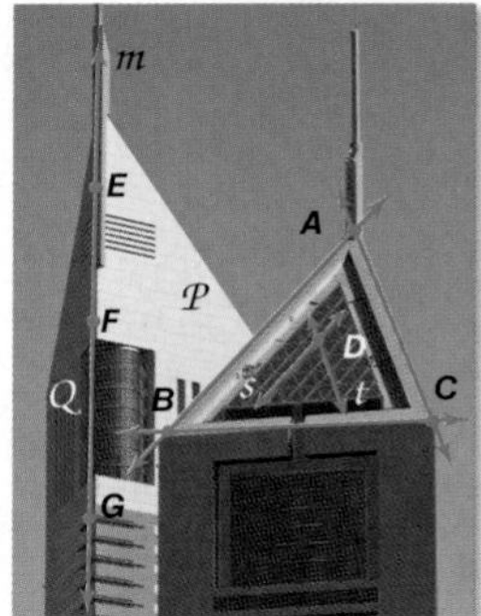

a. Line m contains points F and G. Point E can also be on line m.

The edge of the building is a straight line m. Points E, F, and G lie along this edge, so they lie along a line m. Postulate 2.3, which states that a line contains at least two points, shows that this is true.

b. Lines s and t intersect at point D.

The lattice on the window of the building forms intersecting lines. Lines s and t of this lattice intersect at only one location, point D. Postulate 2.6, which states that if two lines intersect, then their intersection is exactly one point, shows that this is true.

GuidedPractice

1A. Points A, B, and C determine a plane. **1B.** Planes $\mathcal{P}$ and $\mathcal{Q}$ intersect in line m.

1A. Points A, B, and C form the three vertices of the roof. Postulate 2.2 states that through any three noncollinear points there is exactly one plane.
1B. The edges of the sides of the roof intersect. Planes P and Q of this roof intersect only once in line m. Postulate 2.7: if two planes intersect, then their intersection is a line.

You can use postulates to explain your reasoning when analyzing statements.

Example 2 Analyze Statements Using Postulates

Determine whether each statement is *always*, *sometimes*, or *never* true. Explain your reasoning.

a. If two coplanar lines intersect, then the point of intersection lies in the same plane as the two lines.

Always; Postulate 2.5 states that if two points lie in a plane, then the entire line containing those points lies in that plane. So, since both points lie in the plane, any point on those lines, including their point of intersection, also lies in the plane.

b. Four points are noncollinear.

Sometimes; Postulate 2.3 states that a line contains at least two points. This means that a line can contain two *or more* points. So four points can be noncollinear, like A, E, C, and D, or collinear, like points A, B, C, and D.

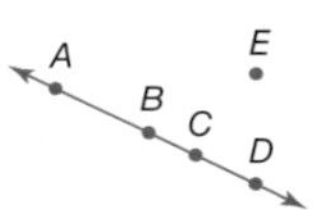

GuidedPractice

2A. Two intersecting lines determine a plane. **2B.** Three lines intersect in two points.

2A. Always; between any two intersecting lines there are always at least three noncollinear points, and Postulate 2.2 states that through any three noncollinear points there is exactly one plane.
2B. Never; in order for three lines to intersect in two points, two of the lines would have to be the same.

StudyTip

Axiomatic System An axiomatic system is a set of axioms, from which some or all axioms can be used to logically derive theorems.

2 Paragraph Proofs

To prove a conjecture, you use deductive reasoning to move from a hypothesis to the conclusion of the conjecture you are trying to prove. This is done by writing a **proof**, which is a logical argument in which each statement you make is supported by a statement that is accepted as true.

Tips for New Teachers

Formal Proofs Remind students that although postulates are not formally proven, they are accepted as true and used to prove other statements and theorems.

Teach with Tech

Wiki On your secure class wiki, have students work together to create a wiki page with several paragraph proofs. Have students work together and edit and revise each other's writing to make sure it is correct and clear.

Once a statement or conjecture has been proven, it is called a **theorem**, and it can be used as a reason to justify statements in other proofs.

KeyConcept The Proof Process

Step 1 List the given information and, if possible, draw a diagram to illustrate this information.

Step 2 State the theorem or conjecture to be proven.

Step 3 Create a **deductive argument** by forming a logical chain of statements linking the given to what you are trying to prove.

Step 4 Justify each statement with a reason. Reasons include definitions, algebraic properties, postulates, and theorems.

Step 5 State what it is that you have proven.

Given (Hypothesis) → Statements and Reasons → Prove (Conclusion)

StudyTip

Proposition A *proposition* is a statement that makes an assertion that is either false or true. In mathematics, a proposition is usually used to mean a true assertion and can be synonymous with theorem.

One method of proving statements and conjectures, a **paragraph proof**, involves writing a paragraph to explain why a conjecture for a given situation is true. Paragraph proofs are also called **informal proofs**, although the term *informal* is not meant to imply that this form of proof is any less valid than any other type of proof.

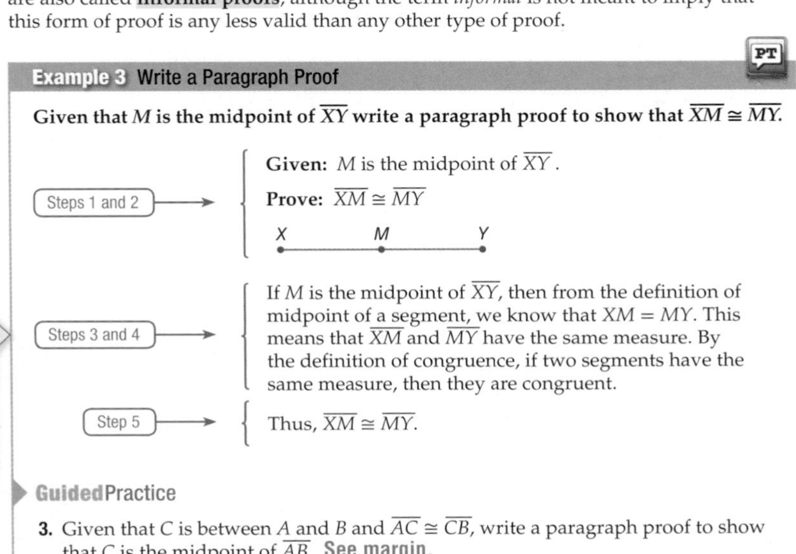

Example 3 Write a Paragraph Proof

Given that M is the midpoint of $\overline{XY}$ write a paragraph proof to show that $\overline{XM} \cong \overline{MY}$.

Steps 1 and 2 → **Given:** M is the midpoint of $\overline{XY}$.
Prove: $\overline{XM} \cong \overline{MY}$

X M Y

Steps 3 and 4 → If M is the midpoint of $\overline{XY}$, then from the definition of midpoint of a segment, we know that $XM = MY$. This means that $\overline{XM}$ and $\overline{MY}$ have the same measure. By the definition of congruence, if two segments have the same measure, then they are congruent.

Step 5 → Thus, $\overline{XM} \cong \overline{MY}$.

Problem-SolvingTip

Work Backward One strategy for writing a proof is to *work backward*. Start with what you are trying to prove, and work backward step by step until you reach the given information.

GuidedPractice

3. Given that C is between A and B and $\overline{AC} \cong \overline{CB}$, write a paragraph proof to show that C is the midpoint of $\overline{AB}$. **See margin.**

Once a conjecture has been proven true, it can be stated as a theorem and used in other proofs. The conjecture in Example 3 is known as the Midpoint Theorem.

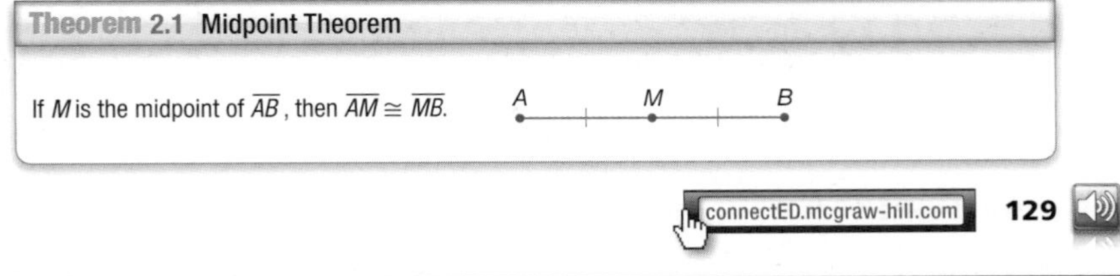

Theorem 2.1 Midpoint Theorem

If M is the midpoint of $\overline{AB}$, then $\overline{AM} \cong \overline{MB}$.

A M B

Additional Example

2 Determine whether each statement is *always, sometimes*, or *never* true. Explain.

a. If plane T contains $\overleftrightarrow{EF}$ and $\overleftrightarrow{EF}$ contains point G, then plane T contains point G. Always; Postulate 2.5 states that if two points lie in a plane, then the entire line containing those points lies in the plane.

b. $\overleftrightarrow{GH}$ contains three noncollinear points. Never; noncollinear points do not lie on the same line by definition.

2 Paragraph Proofs

Example 3 shows how to write a paragraph proof when given a statement that is accepted as true.

Additional Example

3 Given $\overleftrightarrow{AC}$ intersects $\overleftrightarrow{CD}$, write a paragraph proof to show that A, C, and D determine a plane. $\overleftrightarrow{AC}$ and $\overleftrightarrow{CD}$ must intersect at C because if two lines intersect, then their intersection is exactly one point. Point A is on $\overleftrightarrow{AC}$ and point D is on $\overleftrightarrow{CD}$. Points A, C and D are not collinear. Therefore, ACD is a plane as it contains three points not on the same line.

Focus on Mathematical Content

Postulates and Proofs Highlight the difference between postulates and proofs. Postulates are statements that are accepted as true without proof while proofs are logical arguments that are supported by postulates and theorems.

Additional Answer (Guided Practice)

3. **Given:** C is between A and B and $\overline{AC} \cong \overline{CB}$.
Prove: C is the midpoint of $\overline{AB}$.

A C B

Proof: If C is between points A and B, then by the definition of between, A, B, and C are collinear and $AC + CB = AB$. If $\overline{AC} \cong \overline{CB}$, then by the definition of congruence, they have the same measure. This means that $AC = CB$. From the definition of midpoint of a segment, if C is between points A and B, and $AC = CB$, then C is the midpoint of $\overline{AB}$.

3 Practice

Formative Assessment

Use the exercises 1–15 to check for understanding.

Use the chart at the bottom of this page to customize assignments for your students.

Additional Answers

2. The edges of the figure form intersecting lines. Lines r and n intersect at only one place, point D. Postulate 2.6, which states if two lines intersect, their intersection is exactly one point.
3. The front bottom edge of the figure is line n which contains points D, C, and E. Postulate 2.3, which states a line contains at least two points.
4. The left side of the figure or plane P contains points A, F, and D. Postulate 2.4, which states a plane contains at least three noncollinear points.
5. Points D and E, which are on line n, lie in plane Q. Postulate 2.5, which states that if two points lie in a plane, then the entire line containing those points lies in that plane.
6. Line r contains points A and D. Postulate 2.1, which states there is exactly one line through two points.

14a. 28 games

14b.

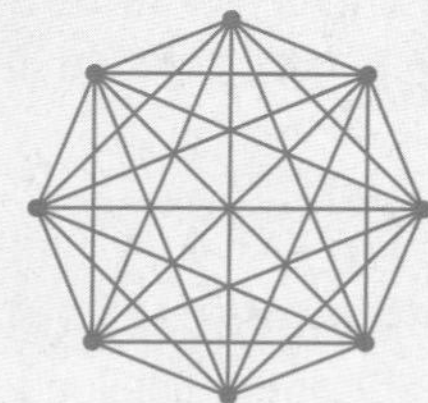

Postulate 2.1

14c. Sample answer: If there are n teams in the tournament, the number of games in the first round is $(n-1)+(n-2)+\ldots+1$.

Check Your Understanding

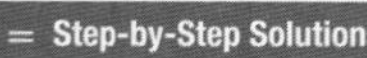

= Step-by-Step Solutions begin on page R14.

Example 1 **Explain how the figure illustrates that each statement is true. Then state the postulate that can be used to show each statement is true.** 2–6. See margin.

1. Planes $\mathcal{P}$ and Q intersect in line r.
2. Lines r and n intersect at point D.
3. Line n contains points C, D, and E.
4. Plane $\mathcal{P}$ contains the points A, F, and D.
5. Line n lies in plane Q.
6. Line r is the only line through points A and D.

1. The left side and front side have a common edge line r. Planes P and Q only intersect along line r. Postulate 2.7, which states that if two planes intersect, then their intersection is a line.

Example 2 **Determine whether each statement is *always*, *sometimes*, or *never* true. Explain your reasoning.**

7. The intersection of three planes is a line. Sometimes; if three planes intersect, then their intersection may be a line or a point.
8. Line r contains only point $\mathcal{P}$. Never; Postulate 2.3 states that a line contains at least two points.
9. Through two points, there is exactly one line. Always; Postulate 2.1 states that through any two points, there is exactly one line.

In the figure, $\overleftrightarrow{AK}$ is in plane $\mathcal{P}$ and M is on $\overleftrightarrow{NE}$. State the postulate that can be used to show each statement is true.

10. M, K, and N are coplanar. Postulate 2.2; through any three noncollinear points, there is exactly one plane.
11. $\overleftrightarrow{NE}$ contains points N and M. Postulate 2.3; a line contains at least two points.
12. N and K are collinear. Postulate 2.1; through any two points, there is exactly one line.
13. Points N, K, and A are coplanar. Postulate 2.4; a plane contains at least three noncollinear points.

14. **SPORTS** Each year, Jennifer's school hosts a student vs. teacher basketball tournament to raise money for charity. This year, there are eight teams participating in the tournament. During the first round, each team plays all of the other teams. a–c. See margin.
    a. How many games will be played in the first round?
    b. Draw a diagram to model the number of first round games. Which postulate can be used to justify your diagram?
    c. Find a numerical method that you could use regardless of the number of the teams in the tournament to calculate the number of games in the first round.

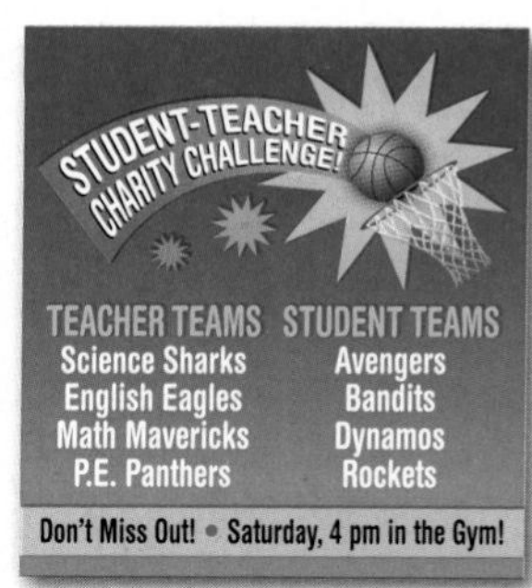

Example 3 15. CCSS **ARGUMENTS** In the figure at the right, $\overline{AE} \cong \overline{DB}$ and C is the midpoint of $\overline{AE}$ and $\overline{DB}$. Write a paragraph proof to show that $AC = CB$. See Ch. 2 Answer Appendix.

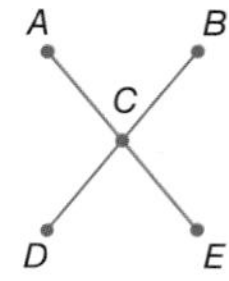

Differentiated Homework Options

Level	Assignment	Two-Day Option	
AL Basic	16–31, 45, 46, 48–65	17–31 odd, 51–54	16–30 even, 45, 46, 48–50, 55–65
OL Core	17–31 odd, 32–46, 48–65	16–32, 51–54	33–46, 48–50, 55–65
BL Advanced	33–62, (optional: 63–65)		

Practice and Problem Solving

Extra Practice is on page R2.

Example 1 **CAKES** **Explain how the picture illustrates that each statement is true. Then state the postulate that can be used to show each statement is true.** 16–23. See margin.

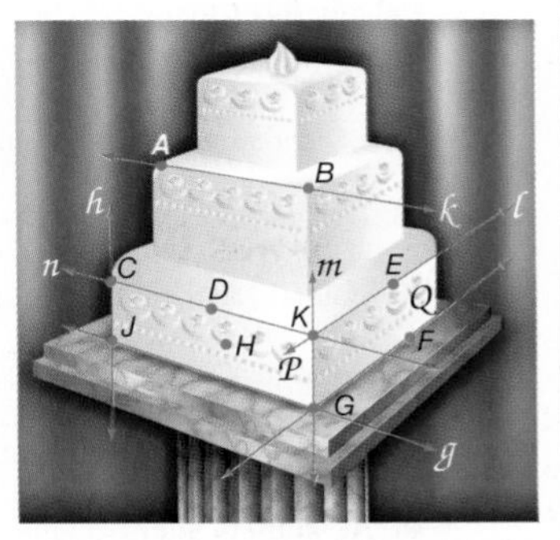

16. Lines n and ℓ intersect at point K.
17. Planes $\mathcal{P}$ and $\mathcal{Q}$ intersect in line m.
18. Points D, K, and H determine a plane.
19. Point D is also on the line n through points C and K.
20. Points D and H are collinear.
21. Points E, F, and G are coplanar.
22. $\overleftrightarrow{EF}$ lies in plane $\mathcal{Q}$.
23. Lines h and g intersect at point J.

Example 2 **Determine whether each statement is *always*, *sometimes*, or *never* true. Explain.**

24. There is exactly one plane that contains noncollinear points A, B, and C.
25. There are at least three lines through points J and K. 24–29. See Ch. 2 Answer Appendix.
26. If points M, N, and P lie in plane X, then they are collinear.
27. Points X and Y are in plane Z. Any point collinear with X and Y is in plane Z.
28. The intersection of two planes can be a point.
29. Points A, B, and C determine a plane.

Example 3

30. **PROOF** Point Y is the midpoint of $\overline{XZ}$. Z is the midpoint of $\overline{YW}$. Prove that $\overline{XY} \cong \overline{ZW}$.

31. **PROOF** Point L is the midpoint of $\overline{JK}$. $\overline{JK}$ intersects $\overline{MK}$ at K. If $\overline{MK} \cong \overline{JL}$, prove that $\overline{LK} \cong \overline{MK}$. 30–31. See Ch. 2 Answer Appendix.

32. **CCSS ARGUMENTS** Last weekend, Emilio and his friends spent Saturday afternoon at the park. There were several people there with bikes and skateboards. There were a total of 11 bikes and skateboards that had a total of 36 wheels. Use a paragraph proof to show how many bikes and how many skateboards there were. See Ch. 2 Answer Appendix.

33. **DRIVING** Keisha is traveling from point A to point B. Two possible routes are shown on the map. Assume that the speed limit on Southside Boulevard is 55 miles per hour and the speed limit on I–295 is 70 miles per hour.
    a. Which of the two routes covers the shortest distance? Explain your reasoning.
    b. If the distance from point A to point B along Southside Boulevard is 10.5 miles and the distance along I-295 is 11.6 miles, which route is faster, assuming that Keisha drives the speed limit? I-295

33a. Southside Blvd.; sample answer: Since there is a line between any two points, and Southside Blvd. is the line between point *A* and point *B*, it is the shortest route between the two.

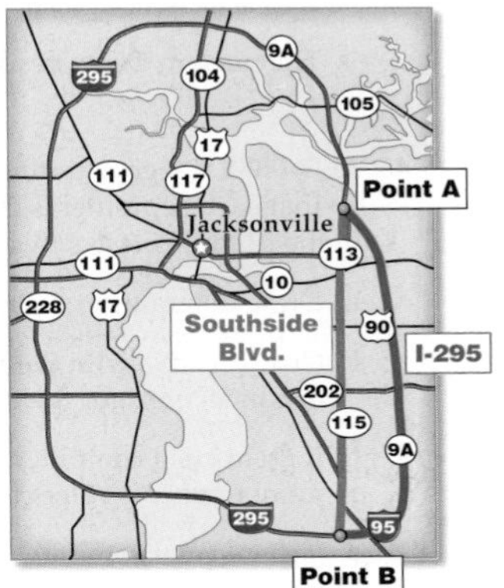

Differentiated Instruction OL BL

Extension Find the slope of each line.

Slope of s: $m = \frac{4-(-2)}{3-(-3)}$ or 1   Slope of t: $m = \frac{2-(-4)}{4-(-2)}$ or 1

Make a conjecture about slope and the appearance of these lines.
Parallel lines have the same slope.

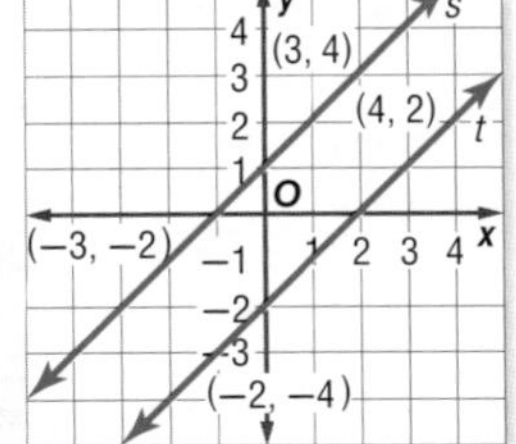

CCSS Teaching the Mathematical Practices

Arguments Mathematically proficient students understand and use stated assumptions in constructing arguments. In Exercise 32, encourage students to write down the information given in the exercise before starting on the proof.

Additional Answers

16. The top edges of the bottom layer form intersecting lines. Lines n and ℓ of this cake intersect only once at point K. Postulate 2.6; if two lines intersect, then their intersection is exactly one point.
17. The edges of the sides of the bottom layer of the cake intersect. Plane P and Q of this cake intersect only once in line m. Postulate 2.7; if two planes intersect, then their intersection is a line.
18. The bottom left part of the cake is a side. This side contains the points D, K, and H and forms a plane. Postulate 2.2; through any three noncollinear points, there is exactly one plane.
19. The top edge of the bottom layer of the cake is a straight line n. Points C, D, and K lie along this edge, so they lie along line n. Postulate 2.3; a line contains at least two points.
20. Only one line can be drawn between the points D and H. Postulate 2.1; through any two points, there is exactly one line.
21. The bottom right part of the cake is a side. The side contains points K, E, F, and G and forms a plane. Postulate 2.2; through any three noncollinear points, there is exactly one plane.
22. The bottom part of the cake is a side. Connecting the points E and F forms a line, which is contained on this side. Postulate 2.5; if two points lie in a plane, then the entire line containing those points lies in that plane.
23. The top edges of the bottom layer form intersecting lines. Lines h and g of this cake intersect only once at point J. Postulate 2.6; if two lines intersect, then their intersection is exactly one point.

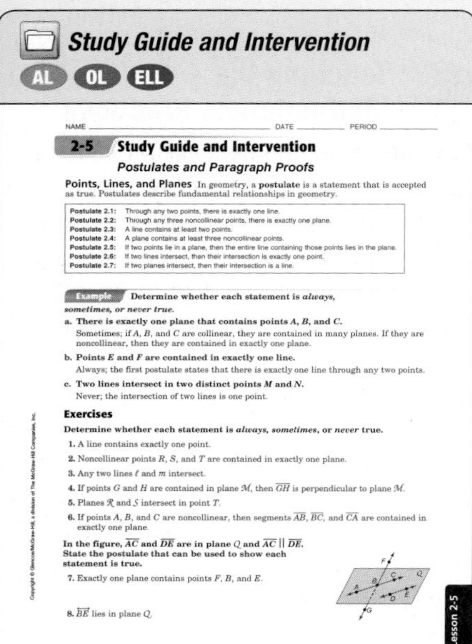

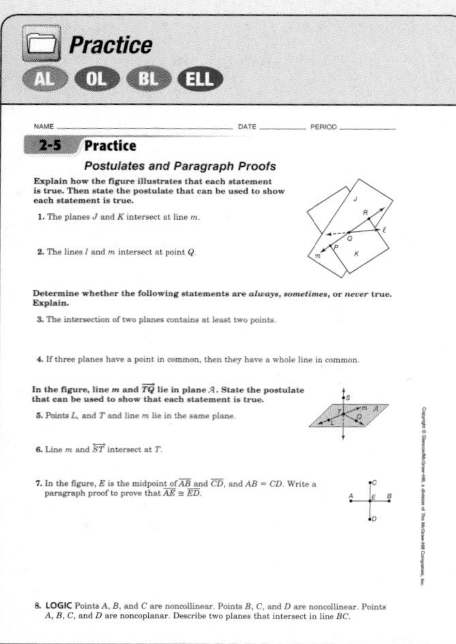

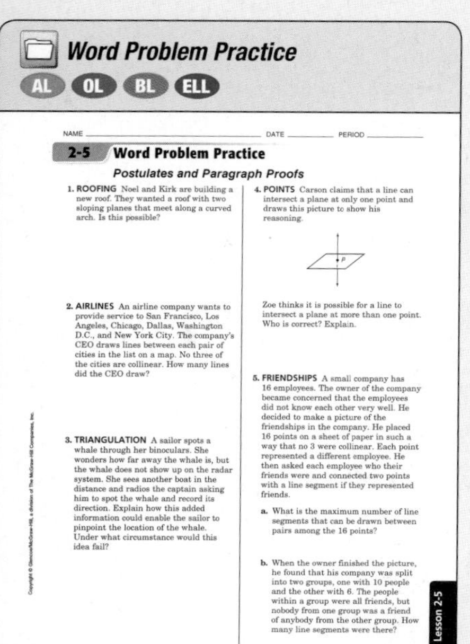

In the figure at the right, $\overleftrightarrow{CD}$ and $\overleftrightarrow{CE}$ lie in plane $\mathcal{P}$ and $\overleftrightarrow{DH}$ and $\overleftrightarrow{DJ}$ lie in plane Q. State the postulate that can be used to show each statement is true.

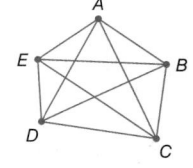

34. Points C and B are collinear. **Postulate 2.1; through any two points, there is exactly one line.**

35. $\overleftrightarrow{EG}$ contains points E, F, and G. **Postulate 2.3; a line contains at least two points.**

36. $\overleftrightarrow{DA}$ lies in plane $\mathcal{P}$. **Postulate 2.5; if two points lie in a plane, then the entire line containing those points lies in that plane.**

37. Points D and F are collinear. **Postulate 2.1; through any two points, there is exactly one line.**

38. Points C, D, and B are coplanar. **Postulate 2.2; through any three noncollinear points, there is exactly one plane.**

39. Plane Q contains the points C, H, D, and J. **39–41. See margin.**

40. $\overleftrightarrow{AC}$ and $\overleftrightarrow{FG}$ intersect at point E.

41. Plane $\mathcal{P}$ and plane Q intersect at $\overleftrightarrow{CD}$.

42. **CCSS ARGUMENTS** Roofs are designed based on the materials used to ensure that water does not leak into the buildings they cover. Some roofs are constructed from waterproof material, and others are constructed for watershed, or gravity removal of water. The pitch of a roof is the rise over the run, which is generally measured in rise per foot of run. Use the statements below to write a paragraph proof justifying the following statement: The pitch of the roof in Den's design is not steep enough. **See margin.**

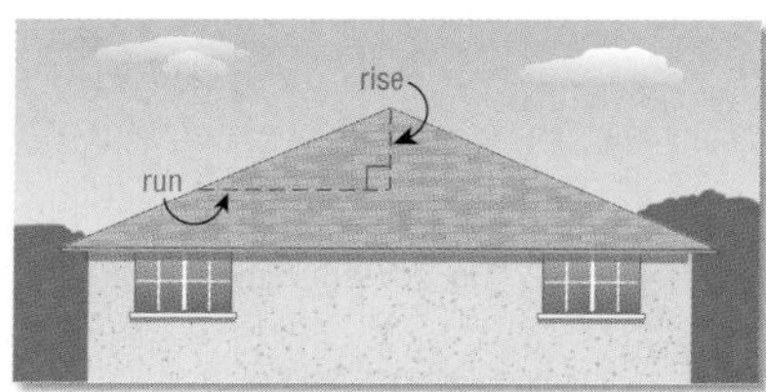

- Waterproof roofs should have a minimum slope of $\frac{1}{4}$ inch per foot.
- Watershed roofs should have a minimum slope of 4 inches per foot.
- Den is designing a house with a watershed roof.
- The pitch in Den's design is 2 inches per foot.

43. **NETWORKS** Diego is setting up a network of multiple computers so that each computer is connected to every other. The diagram at the right illustrates this network if Diego has 5 computers.

a. Draw diagrams of the networks if Diego has 2, 3, 4, or 6 computers. **a, b. See Ch. 2 Answer Appendix.**

b. Create a table with the number of computers and the number of connections for the diagrams you drew.

c. If there are n computers in the network, write an expression for the number of computers to which each of the computers is connected. $n - 1$

d. If there are n computers in the network, write an expression for the number of connections there are. $\frac{n(n-1)}{2}$

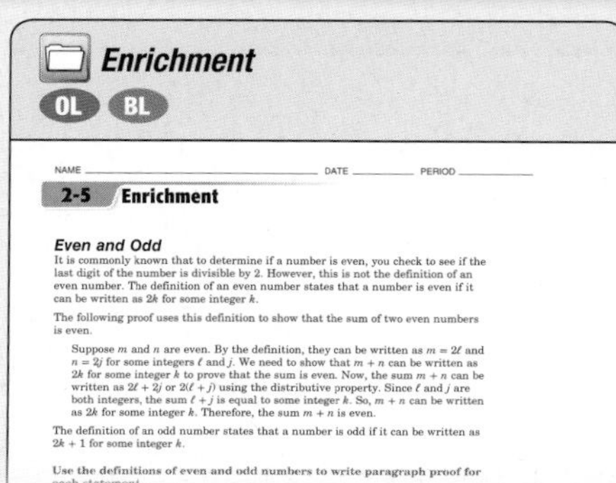

Teaching the Mathematical Practices

Arguments Mathematically proficient students understand and use stated assumptions in constructing arguments. In Exercise 42, remind students that logical progression is important in writing proofs.

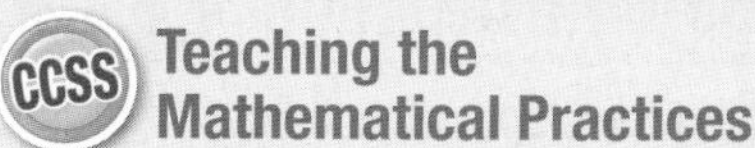

44b. Sample answer: The distance from the center of a circle to any point on the circle is equal, and through any two points, there is exactly one line. That means that there is a line between the center and each of the exits, and they are all the same length.

44. CCSS **SENSE-MAKING** The photo is of the rotunda in the capitol building in St. Paul, Minnesota. A rotunda is a round building, usually covered by a dome. Use Postulate 2.1 to help you answer parts **a–c.**

a. If you were standing in the middle of the rotunda, which arched exit is the closest to you? **All of the exits are the same distance from the center.**

b. What information did you use to formulate your answer?

c. What term describes the shortest distance from the center of a circle to a point on the circle? **radius**

H.O.T. Problems Use Higher-Order Thinking Skills

45. Lisa is correct. Sample answer: The proof should begin with the given, which is that $\overline{AB}$ is congruent to $\overline{BD}$ and A, B, and D are collinear. Therefore, Lisa began the proof correctly.

45. ERROR ANALYSIS Omari and Lisa were working on a paragraph proof to prove that if $\overline{AB}$ is congruent to $\overline{BD}$ and A, B, and D are collinear, then B is the midpoint of $\overline{AD}$. Each student started his or her proof in a different way. Is either of them correct? Explain your reasoning.

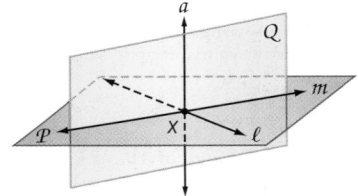

Omari	Lisa
If B is the midpoint of $\overline{AB}$, then B divides $\overline{AD}$ into two congruent segments.	$\overline{AB}$ is congruent to $\overline{BD}$ and A, B, and D are collinear.

46. OPEN ENDED Draw a figure that satisfies five of the seven postulates you have learned. Explain which postulates you chose and how your figure satisfies each postulate. **See margin.**

47. CHALLENGE Use the following true statement and the definitions and postulates you have learned to answer each question.

Two planes are perpendicular if and only if one plane contains a line perpendicular to the second plane.

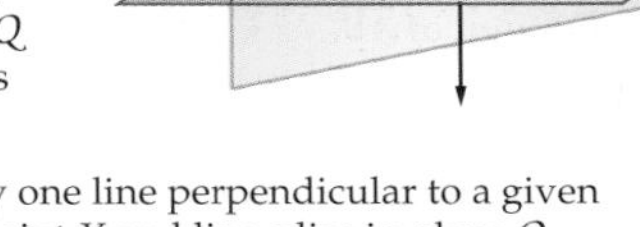

a. Through a given point, there passes one and only one plane perpendicular to a given line. If plane Q is perpendicular to line ℓ at point X and line ℓ lies in plane $\mathcal{P}$, what must also be true?

b. Through a given point, there passes one and only one line perpendicular to a given plane. If plane Q is perpendicular to plane $\mathcal{P}$ at point X and line a lies in plane Q, what must also be true?

a. Plane Q is perpendicular to plane P.
b. Line a is perpendicular to plane P.

REASONING Determine if each statement is *sometimes*, *always*, or *never* true. Explain your reasoning or provide a counterexample. **48, 49. See Ch. 2 Answer Appendix.**

48. Through any three points, there is exactly one plane.

49. Three coplanar lines have two points of intersection.

50. **WRITING IN MATH** How does writing a proof require logical thinking? **See margin.**

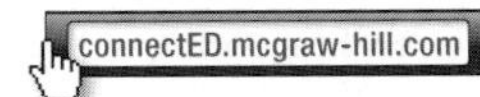

Differentiated Instruction AL OL

 students have trouble recalling the new postulates they have learned,

 have them sketch multiple examples representing each postulate from this lesson.

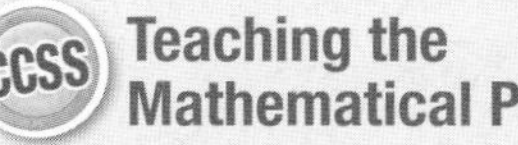

Teaching the Mathematical Practices

Sense-Making Mathematically proficient students start by explaining to themselves the meaning of a problem and looking for entry points to its solution. In Exercise 44, encourage students to imagine they are standing in the center of the rotunda as they work out the solution.

Additional Answers

39. Postulate 2.4; a plane contains at least three noncollinear points.

40. Postulate 2.6; if two lines intersect, then their intersection is exactly one point.

41. Postulate 2.7; if two planes intersect, then their intersection is a line.

42. Sample answer: Since Den is designing a watershed roof, the pitch of the roof should be a minimum of 4 inches per foot. The pitch of the roof in Den's design is 2 inches per foot, which is less than 4 inches per foot. Therefore, the pitch of the roof in Den's design is not steep enough.

46.

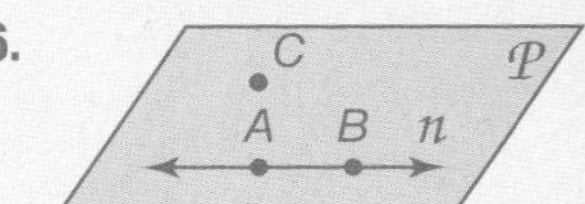

Sample answer: It satisfies Postulates 2.1 and 2.3 because points A and B are on line n. It satisfies 2.2 and 2.4 because 3 points lie in the plane. It satisfies Postulate 2.5 because points A and B lie in plane P, so line n also lies in plane P.

50. Sample answer: When writing a proof, you start with something that you know is true (the given), and then use logic to come up with a series of steps that connect the given information to what you are trying to prove.

4 Assess

Crystal Ball Have students state how writing a paragraph proof will help them as they begin to learn about algebraic proof and two-column proof.

Additional Answers

57. If people are happy, then they rarely correct their faults.
58. If a person is a champion, then that person is afraid of losing.
59. True; M is on $\overline{AB}$ and $AM + MB = AB$, so $p \wedge q$ is true.
60. True; M is on $\overline{AB}$, so $\sim p$ is false, but M is not the midpoint of $\overline{AB}$, so $\sim r$ is true. Therefore, $\sim p \vee \sim r$ is true.
61. 19 m; 20 m of edging
62. 68 in.

Standardized Test Practice

51. ALGEBRA Which is one of the solutions of the equation $3x^2 - 5x + 1 = 0$? **A**

A $\frac{5 + \sqrt{13}}{6}$ C $\frac{5}{6} - \sqrt{13}$

B $\frac{-5 - \sqrt{13}}{6}$ D $-\frac{5}{6} + \sqrt{13}$

52. GRIDDED RESPONSE Steve has 20 marbles in a bag, all the same size and shape. There are 8 red, 2 blue, and 10 yellow marbles in the bag. He will select a marble from the bag at random. What is the probability that the marble Steve selects will be yellow? **1/2 or 0.5**

53. Which statement *cannot* be true? **H**

F Three noncollinear points determine a plane.
G Two lines intersect in exactly one point.
H At least two lines can contain the same two points.
J A midpoint divides a segment into two congruent segments.

54. SAT/ACT What is the greatest number of regions that can be formed if 3 distinct lines intersect a circle? **E**

A 3   D 6
B 4   E 7
C 5

Spiral Review

Determine whether a valid conclusion can be reached from the two true statements using the Law of Detachment or the Law of Syllogism. If a valid conclusion is possible, state it and the law that is used. If a valid conclusion does not follow, write *no conclusion*. (Lesson 2-4)

55. (1) If two angles are vertical, then they do not form a linear pair. **no conclusion**
(2) If two angles form a linear pair, then they are not congruent.

56. (1) If an angle is acute, then its measure is less than 90. **$m\angle EFG$ is less than 90; detachment.**
(2) $\angle EFG$ is acute.

Write each statement in if-then form. (Lesson 2-3) **57, 58. See margin.**

57. Happy people rarely correct their faults.

58. A champion is afraid of losing.

Use the following statements to write a compound statement for each conjunction. Then find its truth value. Explain your reasoning. (Lesson 2-2) **59–62. See margin.**

p: M is on $\overline{AB}$.

q: $AM + MB = AB$

r: M is the midpoint of $\overline{AB}$.

A M B

59. $p \wedge q$

60. $\sim p \vee \sim r$

61. GARDENING A landscape designer is putting black plastic edging around a rectangular flower garden that has length 5.7 meters and width 3.8 meters. The edging is sold in 5-meter lengths. Find the perimeter of the garden and determine how much edging the designer should buy. (Lesson 1-6)

5.7 m
3.8 m 3.8 m
5.7 m

62. HEIGHT Taylor is 5 feet 8 inches tall. How many inches tall is Taylor? (Lesson 0-1)

Skills Review

ALGEBRA Solve each equation.

63. $4x - 3 = 19$ **5.5**

64. $\frac{1}{3}x + 6 = 14$ **24**

65. $5(x^2 + 2) = 30$ **2, −2**

Follow-up

Students have explored inductive and deductive reasoning.

Ask:

- How do you know when to use inductive or deductive reasoning? Sample answer: Inductive reasoning is used when making a conjecture based on observed patterns. To reach a logical conclusion, deductive reasoning should be used because it involves using known facts, rules, definitions, postulates, and theorems.

CHAPTER 2 Mid-Chapter Quiz
Lessons 2-1 through 2-5

Write a conjecture that describes the pattern in each sequence. Then use your conjecture to find the next item in the sequence. (Lesson 2-1) **1, 2. See margin.**

1. 5, 5, 10, 15, 25, . . .
2. 

Find a counterexample to show that each conjecture is false. (Lesson 2-1) **3, 4. See Ch. 2 Answer Appendix.**

3. If $AB = BC$, then B is the midpoint of $\overline{AC}$.
4. If n is a real number, then $n^3 > n$.

Use the following statements to write a compound statement for each conjunction or disjunction. Then find its truth value. Explain your reasoning. (Lesson 2-2)

p: A dollar is equal to 100 cents.
q: There are 4 quarters in a dollar.
r: February is the month before January.

5. $p \wedge r$ **5–7. See Ch. 2 Answer Appendix.**
6. p and q
7. $p \wedge \sim r$
8. Copy and complete the truth table. (Lesson 2-2)

p	q	$\sim q$	$p \vee \sim q$
T	F	T	T
F	T	F	F
F	F	T	T
T	T	F	T

Identify the hypothesis and conclusion of each conditional statement. (Lesson 2-3) **9–11. See Ch. 2 Answer Appendix.**

9. If a polygon has five sides, then it is a pentagon.
10. If $4x - 6 = 10$, then $x = 4$.
11. An angle with a measure less than 90 is an acute angle.

Determine the truth value of each conditional statement. If *true*, explain your reasoning. If *false*, give a counterexample. (Lesson 2-3)

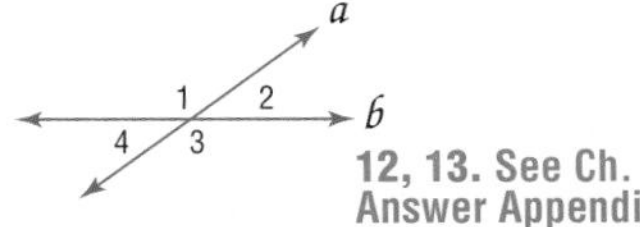

12, 13. See Ch. 2 Answer Appendix.

12. If ∠1 and ∠2 form a linear pair, they are supplementary angles.
13. If ∠1 and ∠4 form a linear pair, they are congruent angles.

Use the Venn diagrams below to determine the truth value of each conditional. Explain your reasoning. (Lesson 2-3)

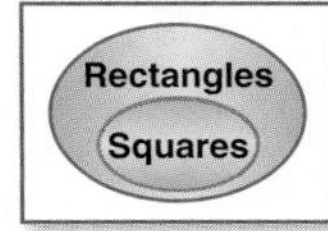

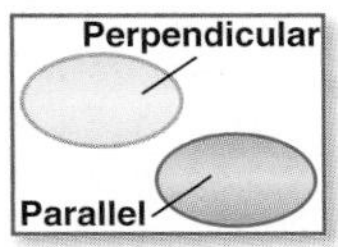

14, 15. See Ch. 2 Answer Appendix for explanations.

14. If a polygon is a square, then it is a rectangle. **true**
15. If two lines are perpendicular, then they cannot be parallel. **true**

16. **FOOTBALL** The Indianapolis Colts played the Chicago Bears in the 2007 Super Bowl. Determine whether the stated conclusion is valid based on the given information. If not, write *invalid*. Explain your reasoning. (Lesson 2-4)

    Given: The Super Bowl winner has the highest score at the end of the game. The Colts had a score of 29 and the Bears had a score of 17.
    Conclusion: The Colts won the Super Bowl.
    See Ch. 2 Answer Appendix.

17. **MULTIPLE CHOICE** Determine which statement follows logically from the given statements. (Lesson 2-4) **C**

    (1) If you are a junior in high school, then you are at least 16 years old.
    (2) If you are at least 16 years old, then you are old enough to drive.

    A If you are old enough to drive, then you are a junior in high school.
    B If you are not old enough to drive, then you are a sophomore in high school.
    C If you are a junior in high school, then you are old enough to drive.
    D No valid conclusion possible.

18–20. See Ch. 2 Answer Appendix.

Determine whether each statement is *always*, *sometimes*, or *never* true. Explain your reasoning. (Lesson 2-5)

18. Points J, K, L, and N are noncollinear and lie in the same plane M.
19. There is exactly one line through points R and S.
20. Line a contains only point Q.

Formative Assessment

Use the Mid-Chapter Quiz to assess students' progress in the first half of the chapter.

Have students review the lesson indicated for the problems they answered incorrectly.

Summative Assessment

Mid-Chapter Test, p. 59

eAssessment Customize and create multiple versions of your Mid-Chapter Test and their answer keys.

FOLDABLES StudyOrganizer

Dinah Zike's Foldables®

Before students complete the Mid-Chapter Quiz, encourage them to review the information for Lessons 2-1 through 2-5 in their Foldables.

Additional Answers

1. Each element in the pattern is the sum of the previous two elements; 40.
2. Each succeeding figure is contained inside another square.

InterventionPlanner

TIER 1 On Level OL	TIER 2 Strategic Intervention AL approaching grade level	TIER 3 Intensive Intervention 2 or more grades below level
If students miss about 25% of the exercises or less,	**If** students miss about 50% of the exercises,	**If** students miss about 75% of the exercises,
Then choose a resource: **SE** Lessons 2-1 through 2-5 Skills Practice, pp. 7, 14, 21, 27, and 33 connectED.mcgraw-hill.com Self-Check Quiz	**Then** choose a resource: Study Guide and Intervention, pp. 5, 12, 19, 25, and 31 connectED.mcgraw-hill.com Extra Examples, Personal Tutor	**Then** use *Math Triumphs, Geometry* connectED.mcgraw-hill.com Extra Examples, Personal Tutor, Homework Help, Review Vocabulary

1 Focus

VerticalAlignment

Before Lesson 2-6 Use postulates about points, lines, and planes to write paragraph proofs.

Lesson 2-6 Use algebra to write two-column proofs and use the properties of equality to write geometric proofs.

After Lesson 2-6 Construct and justify statements about geometric figures and their properties.

2 Teach

Scaffolding Questions

Have students read the **Why?** section of the lesson.

Ask:

- Does the Fahrenheit or the Celsius system have larger units for degrees? Celsius
- How can two different equations represent the same relationship? Sample answer: They can be rewritten by moving terms in the equation.

LESSON 2-6 Algebraic Proof

Then

- You used postulates about points, lines, and planes to write paragraph proofs.

Now

1. Use algebra to write two-column proofs.
2. Use properties of equality to write geometric proofs.

Why?

- The Fahrenheit scale sets the freezing and boiling points of water at 32° and 212°, respectively, while the Celsius scale sets them at 0° and 100°. You can use an algebraic proof to show that if these scales are related by the formula $C = \frac{5}{9}(F - 32)$, then they are also related by the formula $F = \frac{9}{5}C + 32$.

NewVocabulary
algebraic proof
two-column proof
formal proof

Common Core State Standards

Content Standards
Preparation for G.CO.9 Prove theorems about lines and angles.

Mathematical Practices
3 Construct viable arguments and critique the reasoning of others.

1 Algebraic Proof

Algebra is a system with sets of numbers, operations, and properties that allow you to perform algebraic operations. The following table summarizes several properties of real numbers that you studied in algebra.

KeyConcept Properties of Real Numbers

The following properties are true for any real numbers a, b, and c.

Property	Statement
Addition Property of Equality	If $a = b$, then $a + c = b + c$.
Subtraction Property of Equality	If $a = b$, then $a - c = b - c$.
Multiplication Property of Equality	If $a = b$, then $a \cdot c = b \cdot c$.
Division Property of Equality	If $a = b$ and $c \neq 0$, then, $\frac{a}{c} = \frac{b}{c}$.
Reflexive Property of Equality	$a = a$
Symmetric Property of Equality	If $a = b$, then $b = a$.
Transitive Property of Equality	If $a = b$ and $b = c$, then $a = c$.
Substitution Property of Equality	If $a = b$, then a may be replaced by b in any equation or expression.
Distributive Property	$a(b + c) = ab + ac$

An **algebraic proof** is a proof that is made up of a series of algebraic statements. The properties of equality provide justification for many statements in algebraic proofs.

Example 1 Justify Each Step When Solving an Equation

Prove that if $-5(x + 4) = 70$, then $x = -18$. Write a justification for each step.

$-5(x + 4) = 70$	Original equation or Given
$-5x + (-5)4 = 70$	Distributive Property
$-5x - 20 = 70$	Substitution Property of Equality
$-5x - 20 + 20 = 70 + 20$	Addition Property of Equality
$-5x = 90$	Substitution Property of Equality
$\frac{-5x}{-5} = \frac{90}{-5}$	Division Property of Equality
$x = -18$	Substitution Property of Equality

Lesson 2-6 Resources

Resource	Approaching Level AL	On Level OL	Beyond Level BL	English Learners ELL
Teacher Edition	▪ Differentiated Instruction, p. 141	▪ Differentiated Instruction, pp. 141, 142	▪ Differentiated Instruction, p. 142	▪ Differentiated Instruction, p. 142
Chapter Resource Masters	▪ Study Guide and Intervention, pp. 37–38 ▪ Skills Practice, p. 39 ▪ Practice, p. 40 ▪ Word Problem Practice, p. 41	▪ Study Guide and Intervention, pp. 37–38 ▪ Skills Practice, p. 39 ▪ Practice, p. 40 ▪ Word Problem Practice, p. 41 ▪ Enrichment, p. 42	▪ Practice, p. 40 ▪ Word Problem Practice, p. 41 ▪ Enrichment, p. 42	▪ Study Guide and Intervention, pp. 37–38 ▪ Skills Practice, p. 39 ▪ Practice, p. 40 ▪ Word Problem Practice, p. 41
Other	▪ 5-Minute Check 2-6 ▪ Study Notebook	▪ 5-Minute Check 2-6 ▪ Study Notebook	▪ 5-Minute Check 2-6 ▪ Study Notebook	▪ 5-Minute Check 2-6 ▪ Study Notebook

1C. $2x - 13 = -5$ (Given)
$2x - 13 + 13 = -5 + 13$ (Add. Prop)
$2x = 8$ (Subs.)
$x = 4$ (Div. Prop)

Guided Practice

State the property that justifies each statement.

1A. If $4 + (-5) = -1$, then $x + 4 + (-5) = x - 1$. **Add. Prop.**

1B. If $5 = y$, then $y = 5$. **Symm. Prop.**

1C. Prove that if $2x - 13 = -5$, then $x = 4$. Write a justification for each step.

Example 1 is a proof of the conditional statement *If* $-5(x + 4) = 70$, *then* $x = -18$. Notice that the column on the left is a step-by-step process that leads to a solution. The column on the right contains the reason for each statement.

In geometry, a similar format is used to prove conjectures and theorems. A **two-column proof** or **formal proof** contains *statements* and *reasons* organized in two columns.

Study Tip

CCSS Arguments An *algorithm* is a series of steps for carrying out a procedure or solving a problem. Proofs can be considered a type of algorithm because they go step by step.

PT

Real-World Example 2 Write an Algebraic Proof

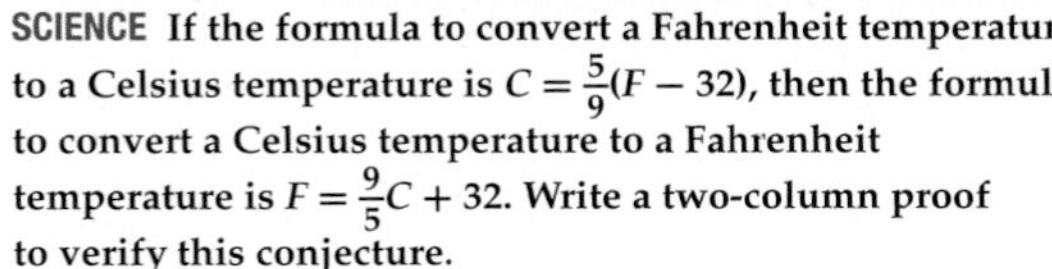

SCIENCE If the formula to convert a Fahrenheit temperature to a Celsius temperature is $C = \frac{5}{9}(F - 32)$, then the formula to convert a Celsius temperature to a Fahrenheit temperature is $F = \frac{9}{5}C + 32$. Write a two-column proof to verify this conjecture.

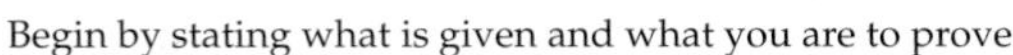

Begin by stating what is given and what you are to prove.

Given: $C = \frac{5}{9}(F - 32)$

Prove: $F = \frac{9}{5}C + 32$

Proof:

Statements	Reasons
1. $C = \frac{5}{9}(F - 32)$	1. Given
2. $\frac{9}{5}C = \frac{9}{5} \cdot \frac{5}{9}(F - 32)$	2. Multiplication Property of Equality
3. $\frac{9}{5}C = F - 32$	3. Substitution Property of Equality
4. $\frac{9}{5}C + 32 = F - 32 + 32$	4. Addition Property of Equality
5. $\frac{9}{5}C + 32 = F$	5. Substitution Property of Equality
6. $F = \frac{9}{5}C + 32$	6. Symmetric Property of Equality

Study Tip

Mental Math If your teacher permits you to do so, some steps may be eliminated by performing mental calculations. For example, steps 2 and 4 in Example 2 could be omitted. Then the reason for statement 3 would be Multiplication Property of Equality and the reason for statement 5 would be Addition Property of Equality.

Guided Practice

Write a two-column proof to verify that each conjecture is true.

2A. If $\frac{5x + 1}{2} - 8 = 0$, then $x = 3$. **See margin.**

2B. PHYSICS If the distance d moved by an object with initial velocity u and final velocity v in time t is given by $d = t \cdot \frac{u + v}{2}$, then $u = \frac{2d}{t} - v$. **See Ch. 2 Answer Appendix.**

1 Algebraic Proof

Example 1 shows how to solve an algebraic equation using the properties of equality. **Example 2** shows how to verify the equivalence of two equations by justifying each step with an algebraic property.

Additional Examples

1 Solve $2(5 - 3a) - 4(a + 7) = 92$. Write a justification for each step.

$2(5 - 3a) - 4(a + 7) = 92$ (Original Equation)
$10 - 6a - 4a - 28 = 92$ (Distr. Prop.)
$-18 - 10a = 92$ (Subst. Prop.)
$-18 - 10a + 18 = 92 + 18$ (Add. Prop.)
$-10a = 110$ (Subst. Prop.)
$\frac{-10a}{-10} = \frac{110}{-10}$ (Div. Prop.)
$a = -11$ (Subst. Prop.)

2 SCIENCE If the distance d an object travels is given by $d = 20t + 5$, the time t that the object travels is given by $t = \frac{d - 5}{20}$. Write a two-column proof to verify this conjecture.

Statements (Reasons)
1. $d = 20t + 5$ (Given)
2. $d - 5 = 20t$ (Add. Prop.)
3. $t = \frac{d - 5}{20}$ (Div. Prop.)

Additional Examples also in Interactive Classroom PowerPoint® Presentations

IWB Interactive White Board READY

CCSS Teaching the Mathematical Practices

Arguments Mathematically proficient students make conjectures and build a logical progression of statements to explore the truth of their conjectures. One way to teach logical progression is to write each statement/reason on a separate index card. Have the class organize the cards in logical progression.

Additional Answer (Guided Practice)

2A. Given: $\frac{5x + 1}{2} - 8 = 0$
Prove: $x = 3$
Proof:
Statements (Reasons)
1. $\frac{5x + 1}{2} - 8 = 0$ (Given)
2. $\frac{5x + 1}{2} = 8$ (Add. Prop.)
3. $2\left(\frac{5x + 1}{2}\right) = 2(8)$ (Mult. Prop.)
4. $5x + 1 = 16$ (Subs.)
5. $5x = 15$ (Subt. Prop.)
6. $x = 3$ (Div. Prop.)

2 Geometric Proof

Example 3 shows how to use properties to write geometric proofs.

Additional Example

3 If $\angle A \cong \angle B$, $m\angle B = 2m\angle C$, and $m\angle C = 45$, then $m\angle A = 90$. Write a two-column proof to verify this conjecture.

Statements (Reasons)

1. $\angle A \cong \angle B$; $m\angle B = 2m\angle C$; $m\angle C = 45$ (Given)
2. $m\angle A = m\angle B$ (Def. of $\cong$ angles)
3. $m\angle A = 2m\angle C$ (Tran. Prop. of =)
4. $m\angle A = 2(45)$ (Substitution)
5. $m\angle A = 90$ (Substitution)

WatchOut!

The Final Word Remind students to check that the final line of their proof matches what was asked in the question. For example, a proof may involve solving for a variable, but the question requires solving an algebraic expression with the variable.

Tips for New Teachers

Algebraic Proof In a two-column proof, each statement does not need to follow directly from the previous one, but should follow from statements above it.

Teach with Tech

Video Recording Have students work in groups to create a video showing how to write a two-column algebraic proof. Be sure they provide reasons to justify each step. Share each group's video with the class.

---

2 Geometric Proof Since geometry also uses variables, numbers, and operations, many of the properties of equality used in algebra are also true in geometry. For example, segment measures and angle measures are real numbers, so properties from algebra can be used to discuss their relationships as shown in the table below.

Property	Segments	Angles
Reflexive	$AB = AB$	$m\angle 1 = m\angle 1$
Symmetric	If $AB = CD$, then $CD = AB$.	If $m\angle 1 = m\angle 2$, then $m\angle 2 = m\angle 1$.
Transitive	If $AB = CD$ and $CD = EF$, then $AB = EF$.	If $m\angle 1 = m\angle 2$ and $m\angle 2 = m\angle 3$, then $m\angle 1 = m\angle 3$.

StudyTip

Commutative and Associative Properties Throughout this text we shall assume that if *a*, *b*, and *c* are real numbers, then the following properties are true.

Commutative Property of Addition
$a + b = b + a$

Commutative Property of Multiplication
$a \cdot b = b \cdot a$

Associative Property of Addition
$(a + b) + c = a + (b + c)$

Associative Property of Multiplication
$(a \cdot b) \cdot c = a \cdot (b \cdot c)$

These properties can be used to write geometric proofs.

Example 3 Write a Geometric Proof

If $\angle FGJ \cong \angle JGK$ and $\angle JGK \cong \angle KGH$, then $x = 6$. Write a two-column proof to verify this conjecture.

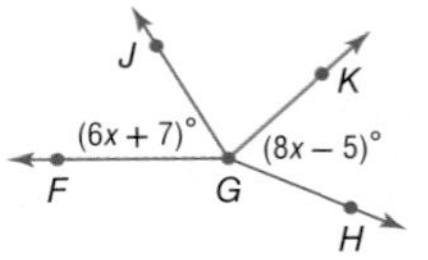

Given: $\angle FGJ \cong \angle JGK$, $\angle JGK \cong \angle KGH$, $m\angle FGJ = 6x + 7$, $m\angle KGH = 8x - 5$

Prove: $x = 6$

Proof:

Statements	Reasons
1. $m\angle FGH = 6x + 7$, $m\angle KGH = 8x - 5$; $\angle FGJ \cong \angle JGK$; $\angle JGK \cong \angle KGH$	1. Given
2. $m\angle FGJ = m\angle JGK$; $m\angle JGK = m\angle KGH$	2. Definition of congruent angles
3. $m\angle FGJ = m\angle KGH$	3. Transitive Property of Equality
4. $6x + 7 = 8x - 5$	4. Substitution Property of Equality
5. $6x + 7 + 5 = 8x - 5 + 5$	5. Addition Property of Equality
6. $6x + 12 = 8x$	6. Substitution Property of Equality
7. $6x + 12 - 6x = 8x - 6x$	7. Subtraction Property of Equality
8. $12 = 2x$	8. Substitution Property of Equality
9. $\frac{12}{2} = \frac{2x}{2}$	9. Division Property of Equality
10. $6 = x$	10. Substitution Property of Equality
11. $x = 6$	11. Symmetric Property of Equality

GuidedPractice

Write a two-column proof to verify each conjecture.

3A. If $\angle A \cong \angle B$ and $m\angle A = 37$, then $m\angle B = 37$.

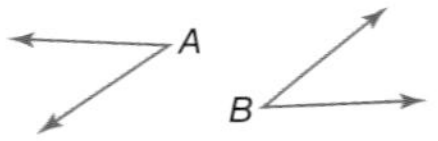

3B. If $\overline{CD} \cong \overline{EF}$, then $y = 8$.

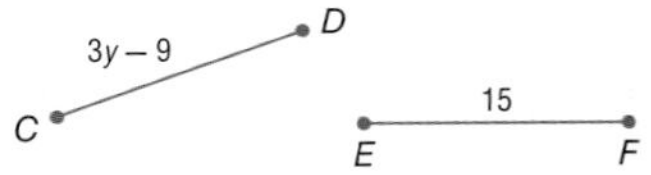

3A. Given: $\angle A \cong \angle B$ and $m\angle A = 37$
Prove: $m\angle B = 37$
Proof:
Statements (Reasons)
1. $\angle A \cong \angle B$ and $m\angle A = 37$ (Given)
2. $m\angle A = m\angle B$ (Def. of $\cong$ angles)
3. $37 = m\angle B$ (Subs.)
4. $m\angle B = 37$ (Symm. Prop.)

3B. Given: $\overline{CD} \cong \overline{EF}$, $CD = 3y - 9$, $EF = 15$
Prove: $y = 8$
Proof:
Statements (Reasons)
1. $\overline{CD} \cong \overline{EF}$ (Given)
2. $CD = EF$ (Def. of $\cong$ segs.)
3. $3y - 9 = 15$ (Subs.)
4. $3y = 24$ (Add. Prop.)
5. $y = 8$ (Div. Prop.)

Focus on Mathematical Content

Proof Writing Remind students that the reasons are given with the steps of a proof to make it rigorous and to add clarity for the reader. If students are having trouble writing a formal proof, they can write out the steps they believe lead to the solution, and then go back and add the justifications for each step. This method will help them see if they have skipped steps and help them understand how they arrived at their solution.

138 | Lesson 2-6 | Algebraic Proof

Check Your Understanding

= Step-by-Step Solutions begin on page R14.

Example 1 **State the property that justifies each statement.**

1. If $m\angle 1 = m\angle 2$ and $m\angle 2 = m\angle 3$, then $m\angle 1 = m\angle 3$. **Trans. Prop.**
2. $XY = XY$ **Refl. Prop.**
3. If $5 = x$, then $x = 5$. **Sym. Prop.**
4. If $2x + 5 = 11$, then $2x = 6$. **Subt. Prop.**

Example 2

5. Complete the following proof.

Given: $\frac{y+2}{3} = 3$

Prove: $y = 7$

Proof:

Statements	Reasons
a. ___?___ $\frac{y+2}{3} = 3$	a. Given
b. $3\left(\frac{y+2}{3}\right) = 3(3)$	b. ___?___ **Mult. Prop.**
c. ___?___ $y + 2 = 9$	c. ___?___ **Subs.**
d. $y = 7$	d. Subtraction Property

Examples 2–3 **PROOF** **Write a two-column proof to verify each conjecture.**

6. If $-4(x - 3) + 5x = 24$, then $x = 12$.
7. If $\overline{AB} \cong \overline{CD}$, then $x = 7$.

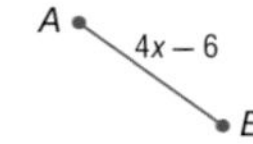

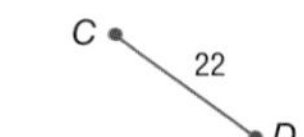

6. Given: $-4(x - 3) + 5x = 24$
Prove: $x = 12$
Proof:
Statements (Reasons)
1. $-4(x - 3) + 5x = 24$ (Given)
2. $-4x + 12 + 5x = 24$ (Dist. Prop.)
3. $x + 12 = 24$ (Subs.)
4. $x = 12$ (Subt. Prop.)

7. Given: $\overline{AB} \cong \overline{CD}$
Prove: $x = 7$
Proof:
Statements (Reasons)
1. $\overline{AB} \cong \overline{CD}$ (Given)
2. $AB = CD$ (Def. of congruent segments)
3. $4x - 6 = 22$ (Subs. Prop.)
4. $4x = 28$ (Add. Prop.)
5. $x = 7$ (Div. Prop.)

8. **CCSS ARGUMENTS** Mai-Lin measures her heart rate whenever she exercises and tries to make sure that she is staying in her target heart rate zone. The American Heart Association suggests a target heart rate of $T = 0.75(220 - a)$, where T is a person's target heart rate and a is his or her age.
   a. Prove that given a person's target heart rate, you can calculate his or her age using the formula $a = 220 - \frac{T}{0.75}$. **See Ch. 2 Answer Appendix.**
   b. If Mai-Lin's target heart rate is 153, then how old is she? What property justifies your calculation? **See Ch. 2 Answer Appendix.**

Practice and Problem Solving

Extra Practice is on page R2.

Example 1 **State the property that justifies each statement.**

9. If $a + 10 = 20$, then $a = 10$. **Subt. Prop.**
10. If $\frac{x}{3} = -15$, then $x = -45$. **Mult. Prop.**
11. If $4x - 5 = x + 12$, then $4x = x + 17$. **Add. Prop.**
12. If $\frac{1}{5}BC = \frac{1}{5}DE$, then $BC = DE$. **Mult. or Div. Prop.**

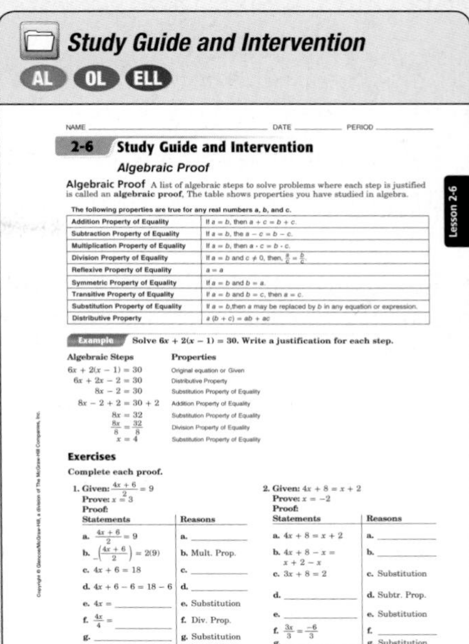

Study Guide and Intervention

AL OL ELL

NAME ______ DATE ______ PERIOD ______

2-6 Study Guide and Intervention

Algebraic Proof

Algebraic Proof A list of algebraic steps to solve problems where each step is justified is called an **algebraic proof.** The table shows properties you have studied in algebra.

The following properties are true for any real numbers *a*, *b*, and *c*.

Addition Property of Equality	If $a = b$, then $a + c = b + c$.
Subtraction Property of Equality	If $a = b$, the $a - c = b - c$.
Multiplication Property of Equality	If $a = b$, then $a \cdot c = b \cdot c$.
Division Property of Equality	If $a = b$ and $c \neq 0$, then, $\frac{a}{c} = \frac{b}{c}$.
Reflexive Property of Equality	$a = a$
Symmetric Property of Equality	If $a = b$ and $b = a$.
Transitive Property of Equality	If $a = b$ and $b = c$, then $a = c$.
Substitution Property of Equality	If $a = b$, then a may be replaced by b in any equation or expression.
Distributive Property	$a(b + c) = ab + ac$

Example Solve $6x + 2(x - 1) = 30$. Write a justification for each step.

Algebraic Steps	Properties
$6x + 2(x - 1) = 30$	Original equation or Given
$6x + 2x - 2 = 30$	Distributive Property
$8x - 2 = 30$	Substitution Property of Equality
$8x - 2 + 2 = 30 + 2$	Addition Property of Equality
$8x = 32$	Substitution Property of Equality
$\frac{8x}{8} = \frac{32}{8}$	Division Property of Equality
$x = 4$	Substitution Property of Equality

Exercises

Complete each proof.

1. Given: $\frac{4x + 6}{2} = 9$
Prove: $x = 3$
Proof:

Statements	Reasons
a. $\frac{4x + 6}{2} = 9$	a. ______
b. $\_\left(\frac{4x + 6}{2}\right) = 2(9)$	b. Mult. Prop.
c. $4x + 6 = 18$	c. ______
d. $4x + 6 - 6 = 18 - 6$	d. ______
e. $4x =$ ______	e. Substitution
f. $\frac{4x}{4} =$ ______	f. Div. Prop.
g. ______	g. Substitution

2. Given: $4x + 8 = x + 2$
Prove: $x = -2$
Proof:

Statements	Reasons
a. $4x + 8 = x + 2$	a. ______
b. $4x + 8 - x = x + 2 - x$	b. ______
c. $3x + 8 = 2$	c. Substitution
d. ______	d. Subtr. Prop.
e. ______	e. Substitution
f. $\frac{3x}{3} = \frac{-6}{3}$	f. ______
g. ______	g. Substitution

Lesson 2-6

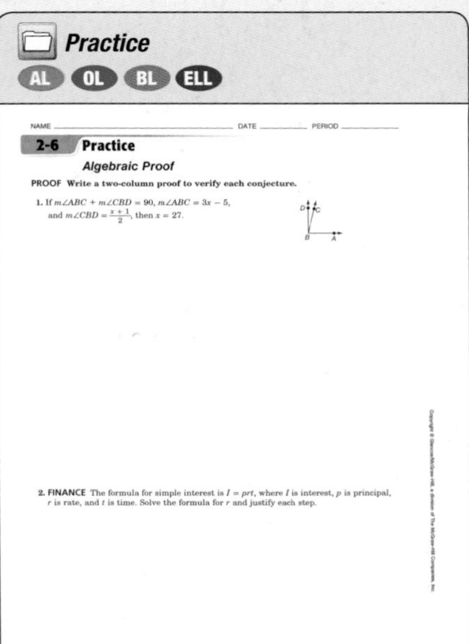

Practice

AL OL BL ELL

NAME ______ DATE ______ PERIOD ______

2-6 Practice

Algebraic Proof

PROOF **Write a two-column proof to verify each conjecture.**

1. If $m\angle ABC + m\angle CBD = 90$, $m\angle ABC = 3x - 5$, and $m\angle CBD = \frac{x + 1}{2}$, then $x = 27$.

2. **FINANCE** The formula for simple interest is $I = prt$, where I is interest, p is principal, r is rate, and t is time. Solve the formula for r and justify each step.

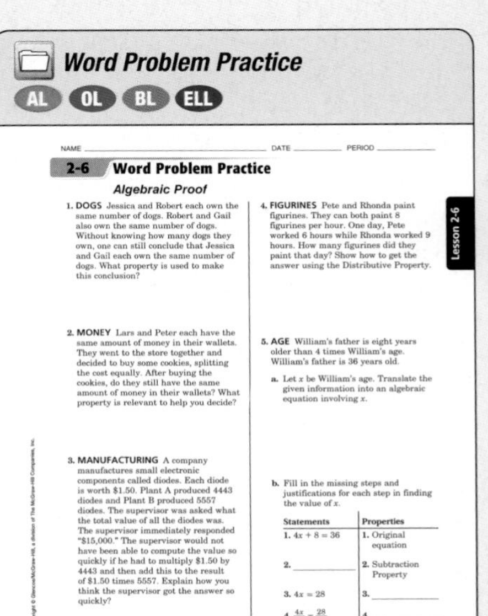

Word Problem Practice

AL OL BL ELL

NAME ______ DATE ______ PERIOD ______

2-6 Word Problem Practice

Algebraic Proof

1. **DOGS** Jessica and Robert each own the same number of dogs. Robert and Gail also own the same number of dogs. Without knowing how many dogs they own, one can still conclude that Jessica and Gail each own the same number of dogs. What property is used to make this conclusion?

2. **MONEY** Lars and Peter each have the same amount of money in their wallets. They went to the store together and decided to buy some cookies, splitting the cost equally. After buying the cookies, do they still have the same amount of money in their wallets? What property is relevant to help you decide?

3. **MANUFACTURING** A company manufactures small electronic components called diodes. Each diode is worth \$1.50. Plant A produced 4443 diodes and Plant B produced 5557 diodes. The supervisor was asked what the total value of all the diodes was. The supervisor immediately responded "\$15,000." The supervisor would not have been able to compute the value so quickly if he had to multiply \$1.50 by 4443 and then add this to the result of \$1.50 times 5557. Explain how you think the supervisor got the answer so quickly?

4. **FIGURINES** Pete and Rhonda paint figurines. They can both paint 8 figurines per hour. One day, Pete worked 6 hours while Rhonda worked 9 hours. How many figurines did they paint that day? Show how to get the answer using the Distributive Property.

5. **AGE** William's father is eight years older than 4 times William's age. William's father is 36 years old.
   a. Let x be William's age. Translate the given information into an algebraic equation involving x.
   b. Fill in the missing steps and justifications for each step in finding the value of x.

Statements	Properties
1. $4x + 8 = 36$	1. Original equation
2. ______	2. Subtraction Property
3. $4x = 28$	3. ______
4. $\frac{4x}{4} = \frac{28}{4}$	4. ______
5. ______	5. Substitution Property

Lesson 2-6

CCSS Teaching the Mathematical Practices

Arguments Mathematically proficient students build a logical progression of statements to explore the truth of their conjectures. In Exercise 8, remind students to begin by stating what they are given and what they are to prove.

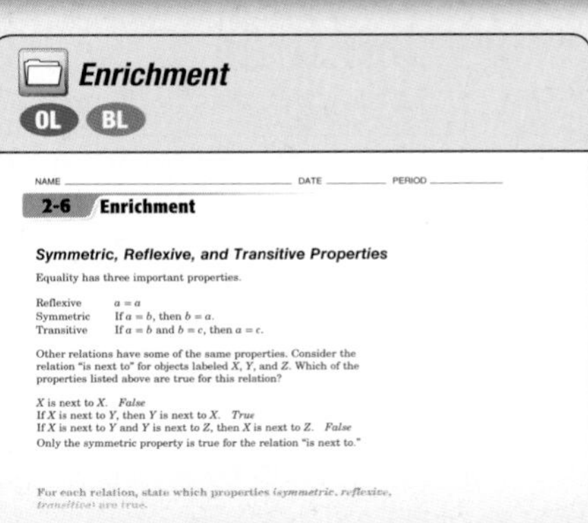

Enrichment

OL BL

NAME ______ DATE ______ PERIOD ______

2-6 Enrichment

Symmetric, Reflexive, and Transitive Properties

Equality has three important properties.

Reflexive $a = a$
Symmetric If $a = b$, then $b = a$.
Transitive If $a = b$ and $b = c$, then $a = c$.

Other relations have some of the same properties. Consider the relation "is next to" for objects labeled X, Y, and Z. Which of the properties listed above are true for this relation?

X is next to X. *False*
If X is next to Y, then Y is next to X. *True*
If X is next to Y and Y is next to Z, then X is next to Z. *False*
Only the symmetric property is true for the relation "is next to."

For each relation, state which properties (*symmetric, reflexive, transitive*) are true.

3 Practice

Formative Assessment

Use Exercises 1–8 to check for understanding.

Then use the chart at the bottom of this page to customize assignments for your students.

Additional Answers

19. Given: $-\frac{1}{3}n = 12$

Prove: $n = -36$

Proof:

Statements (Reasons)

1. $-\frac{1}{3}n = 12$ (Given)
2. $-3\left(-\frac{1}{3}n\right) = -3(12)$ (Mult. Prop.)
3. $n = -36$ (Subs.)

20. Given: $-3r + \frac{1}{2} = 4$

Prove: $r = -\frac{7}{6}$

Proof:

Statements (Reasons)

1. $-3r + \frac{1}{2} = 4$ (Given)
2. $2\left(-3r + \frac{1}{2}\right) = 2(4)$ (Mult. Prop.)
3. $-6r + 1 = 8$ (Subs.)
4. $-6r = 7$ (Subt. Prop.)
5. $r = -\frac{7}{6}$ (Div. Prop.)

21a. Given: $d = vt + \frac{1}{2}at^2$

Prove: $a = \frac{2d - 2vt}{t^2}$

Proof:

Statements (Reasons)

1. $d = vt + \frac{1}{2}at^2$ (Given)
2. $d - vt = vt - vt + \frac{1}{2}at^2$ (Subt. Prop.)
3. $d - vt = \frac{1}{2}at^2$ (Subs.)
4. $2(d - vt) = 2\left(\frac{1}{2}at^2\right)$ (Mult. Prop.)
5. $2(d - vt) = at^2$ (Subs.)
6. $2d - 2vt = at^2$ (Dist. Prop.)
7. $\frac{2d - 2vt}{t^2} = \frac{at^2}{t^2}$ (Div. Prop.)
8. $\frac{2d - 2vt}{t^2} = a$
9. $a = \frac{2d - 2vt}{t^2}$ (Sym. Prop.)

State the property that justifies each statement.

13. If $5(x + 7) = -3$, then $5x + 35 = -3$. **Dist. Prop.**

14. If $m\angle 1 = 25$ and $m\angle 2 = 25$, then $m\angle 1 = m\angle 2$. **Subs.**

15. If $AB = BC$ and $BC = CD$, then $AB = CD$. **Trans. Prop.**

16. If $3\left(x - \frac{2}{3}\right) = 4$, then $3x - 2 = 4$. **Dist. Prop.**

Example 2

CCSS ARGUMENTS Complete each proof.

17. Given: $\frac{8 - 3x}{4} = 32$

Prove: $x = -40$

Proof:

Statements	Reasons
a. $\frac{8 - 3x}{4} = 32$	a. Given
b. $4\left(\frac{8 - 3x}{4}\right) = 4(32)$	b. ___?___ **Mult. Prop.**
c. $8 - 3x = 128$	c. ___?___ **Subs.**
d. ___?___ $-3x = 120$	d. Subtraction Property
e. $x = -40$	e. ___?___ **Div. Prop.**

18. Given: $\frac{1}{5}x + 3 = 2x - 24$

Prove: $x = 15$

Proof:

Statements	Reasons
a. ___?___ $\frac{1}{5}x + 3 = 2x - 24$	a. Given
b. ___?___ $5\left(\frac{1}{5}x + 3\right) = 5(2x - 24)$	b. Multiplication Property
c. $x + 15 = 10x - 120$	c. ___?___ **Subs.**
d. ___?___ $15 = 9x - 120$	d. Subtraction Property
e. $135 = 9x$	e. ___?___ **Add. Prop.**
f. ___?___ $15 = x$	f. Division Property
g. ___?___ $x = 15$	g. Symmetric Property

Example 3

PROOF Write a two-column proof to verify each conjecture. **19, 20. See margin.**

19. If $-\frac{1}{3}n = 12$, then $n = -36$.

20. If $-3r + \frac{1}{2} = 4$, then $r = -\frac{7}{6}$.

21 **SCIENCE** Acceleration a in feet per second squared, distance traveled d in feet, velocity v in feet per second, and time t in seconds are related in the formula $d = vt + \frac{1}{2}at^2$.

a. Prove that if the values for distance, velocity, and time are known, then the acceleration of an object can be calculated using the formula $a = \frac{2d - 2vt}{t^2}$. **See margin.**

b. If an object travels 2850 feet in 30 seconds with an initial velocity of 50 feet per second, what is the acceleration of the object? What property justifies your calculation? **3 ft/s^2; Subs.**

Differentiated Homework Options

Level	Assignment	Two-Day Option	
AL Basic	9–26, 36, 38, 39, 41–58	9–25 odd, 42–45	10–26 even, 36, 38, 39, 41, 46–58
OL Core	9–25 odd, 26–36, 38, 39, 41–58	9–27, 42–45	28–36, 38, 39, 41, 46–58
BL Advanced	28–55, (optional: 56–58)		

22a. Proof:
Statements (Reasons)
1. $PV = nRT$ (Given)
2. $\frac{PV}{nR} = \frac{nRT}{nR}$ (Div. Prop.)
3. $\frac{PV}{nR} = T$ (Div. Prop.)

22. CCSS **ARGUMENTS** The Ideal Gas Law is given by the formula $PV = nRT$, where P = pressure in atmospheres, V = volume in liters, n = the amount of gas in moles, R is a constant value, and T = temperature in degrees Kelvin.

a. Prove that if the pressure, volume, and amount of the gas are known, then the formula $T = \frac{PV}{nR}$ gives the temperature of the gas.

b. If you have 1 mole of oxygen with a volume of 25 liters at a pressure of 1 atmosphere, what is the temperature of the gas? The value of R is 0.0821. What property justifies your calculation? **305 Kelvin; subs.**

PROOF **Write a two-column proof.** **23–25. See margin.**

23. If $\overline{DF} \cong \overline{EG}$, then $x = 10$.

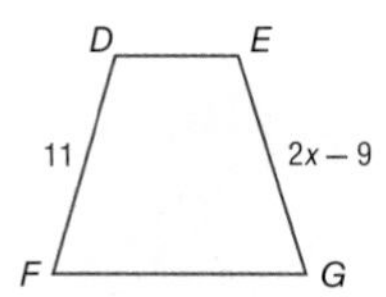

24. If $\overline{AB} \cong \overline{AC}$, then $x = 4$.

A
3x + 15
5x + 7
B
C

25. If $\angle Y \cong \angle Z$, then $x = 100$.

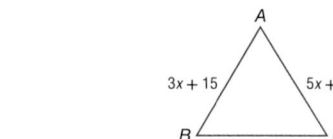

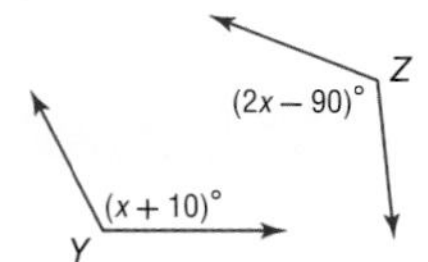

26. If $\angle MPN \cong \angle QPN$, then $x = 16$. **See Ch. 2 Answer Appendix.**

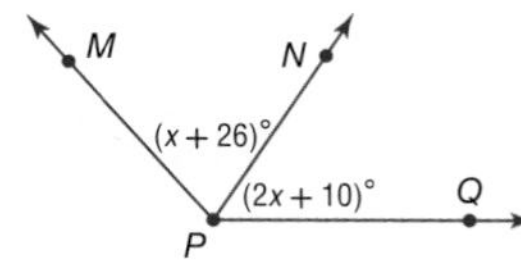

27. ELECTRICITY The voltage V of a circuit can be calculated using the formula $V = \frac{P}{I}$, where P is the power and I is the current of the circuit.

a. Write a proof to show that when the power is constant, the voltage is halved when the current is doubled. **a, b. See Ch. 2 Answer Appendix.**

b. Write a proof to show that when the current is constant, the voltage is doubled when the power is doubled.

28. MULTIPLE REPRESENTATIONS Consider a cube with a side length of s. **a, c, e. See Ch. 2 Answer Appendix.**

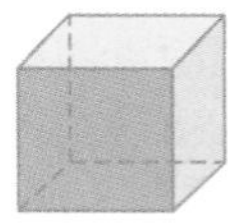
s units

a. Concrete Sketch or build a model of cubes with side lengths of 2, 4, 8, and 16 units.

b. Tabular Find the volume of each cube. Organize your results into a table like the one shown.

Side Lenth (s)	Volume (V)
2	8
4	64
8	512
16	4096

c. Verbal Use your table to make a conjecture about the change in volume when the side length of a cube is doubled. Express your conjecture in words.

d. Analytical Write your conjecture as an algebraic equation. $8V = (2s)^3$

e. Logical Write a proof of your conjecture. Be sure to write the *Given* and *Prove* statements at the beginning of your proof.

Differentiated Instruction  

Intrapersonal Provide students with algebraic and geometric proofs that are missing the justifications for each step. At least one proof should contain errors. Have students fill in the justifications and explain the errors.

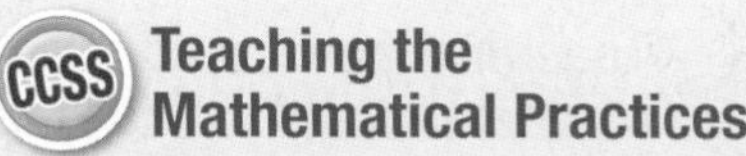

Teaching the Mathematical Practices

Arguments Mathematically proficient students build a logical progression of statements to explore the truth of their conjectures. In Exercise 22, encourage students to transform the given equation a step at a time before determining the reason for each step.

Multiple Representations

In Exercise 28, students use models, a table, verbal descriptions, and algebraic equations to investigate the volume of a cube.

Additional Answers

23. Given: $\overline{DF} \cong \overline{EG}$
Prove: $x = 10$
Proof:
Statements (Reasons)
1. $\overline{DF} \cong \overline{EG}$ (Given)
2. $DF = EG$ (Def. of $\cong$ segs)
3. $11 = 2x - 9$ (Subs.)
4. $20 = 2x$ (Add. Prop.)
5. $10 = x$ (Div. Prop.)
6. $x = 10$ (Symm. Prop.)

24. Given: $\overline{AB} \cong \overline{AC}$
Prove: $x = 4$
Proof:
Statements (Reasons)
1. $\overline{AB} \cong \overline{AC}$ (Given)
2. $AB = AC$ (Def. of $\cong$ segs)
3. $3x + 15 = 5x + 7$ (Subs.)
4. $8 = 2x$ (Subt.)
5. $4 = x$ (Div. Prop.)
6. $x = 4$ (Symm. Prop.)

25. Given: $\angle Y \cong \angle Z$
Prove: $x = 100$
Proof:
Statements (Reasons)
1. $\angle Y \cong \angle Z$ (Given)
2. $m\angle Y = m\angle Z$ (Def. of $\cong$ $\angle$s)
3. $x + 10 = 2x - 90$ (Subs.)
4. $10 = x - 90$ (Subt. Prop.)
5. $100 = x$ (Add. Prop.)
6. $x = 100$ (Sym. Prop.)

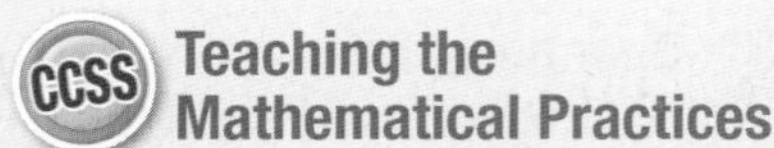

Teaching the Mathematical Practices

Sense-Making Mathematically proficient students analyze givens, constraints, relationships, and goals. In Exercise 37, encourage students to draw a diagram and label it with the information given.

Additional Answers

29. Given: $c^2 = a^2 + b^2$

Prove: $a = \sqrt{c^2 - b^2}$

Proof:

Statements (Reasons)

1. $a^2 + b^2 = c^2$ (Given)
2. $a^2 + b^2 - b^2 = c^2 - b^2$ (Subt. Prop.)
3. $a^2 = c^2 - b^2$ (Subs.)
4. $a = \pm\sqrt{c^2 - b^2}$ (Sq. Root Prop.)
5. $a = \sqrt{c^2 - b^2}$ (Length cannot be negative.)

30. The relation "has the same birthday as" is an equivalence relation because it satisfies all three properties. Sample answer: You can have the same birthday as yourself (reflexive); if you have the same birthday as your friend, then your friend has the same birthday as you (symmetric); if you have the same birthday as Bob and Bob has the same birthday as Bill, then you have the same birthday as Bill (transitive).

31. The relation "is taller than" is not an equivalence relation because it fails the Reflexive and Symmetric properties. You cannot be taller than yourself (reflexive); if you are taller than your friend, then it does not imply that your friend is taller than you (symmetric).

32. The relation "is bluer than" is not an equivalence relation because it fails the Reflexive property. A color cannot be bluer than itself.

33. The relation "$\neq$" is not an equivalence relation because it fails the Reflexive Property, since $a \neq a$ is not true.

29. PYTHAGOREAN THEOREM The Pythagorean Theorem states that in a right triangle *ABC*, the sum of the squares of the measures of the lengths of the legs, *a* and *b*, equals the square of the measure of the hypotenuse *c*, or $a^2 + b^2 = c^2$. Write a two-column proof to verify that $a = \sqrt{c^2 - b^2}$. Use the Square Root Property of Equality, which states that if $a^2 = b^2$, then $a = \pm\sqrt{b^2}$. **See margin.**

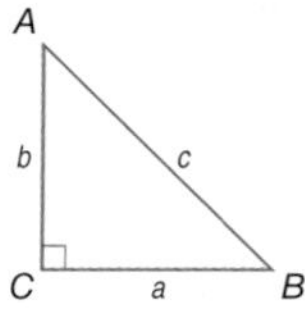

An *equivalence relation* is any relationship that satisfies the Reflexive, Symmetric, and Transitive Properties. For real numbers, equality is one type of equivalence relation. Determine whether each relation is an equivalence relation. Explain your reasoning.

30. "has the same birthday as," for the set of all human beings **30–35. See margin.**
31. "is taller than," for the set of all human beings
32. "is bluer than" for all the paint colors with blue in them
33. $\neq$, for the set of real numbers
34. $\geq$, for the set of real numbers
35. $\approx$, for the set of real numbers

H.O.T. Problems Use Higher-Order Thinking Skills

36. OPEN ENDED Give one real-world *example* and one real-world *non-example* of the Symmetric, Transitive, and Substitution properties. **See margin.**

37. SENSE-MAKING Point *P* is located on $\overline{AB}$. The length of $\overline{AP}$ is $2x + 3$, and the length of $\overline{PB}$ is $\frac{3x + 1}{2}$. Segment *AB* is 10.5 units long. Draw a diagram of this situation, and prove that point *P* is located two thirds of the way between point *A* and point *B*. **See Ch. 2 Answer Appendix.**

REASONING Classify each statement below as *sometimes*, *always*, or *never* true. Explain your reasoning.

38. If *a* and *b* are real numbers and $a + b = 0$, then $a = -b$.

39. If *a* and *b* are real numbers and $a^2 = b$, then $a = \sqrt{b}$.

38. Always; sample answer: If $a + b = 0$, then $a + b - b = 0 - b$ (Subt. Prop.) and $a = -b$ (Subs.). Therefore, the statement is always true.

39. Sometimes; sample answer: If $a^2 = 1$ and $a = 1$, then $b = \sqrt{1}$ or 1. The statement is also true if $a = -1$ and $b = 1$. If $b = 1$, then $\sqrt{b} = 1$ since the square root of a number is nonnegative. Therefore, the statement is sometimes true.

40. CHALLENGE Ayana makes a conjecture that the sum of two odd integers is an even integer. **a–d. See margin.**

a. List information that supports this conjecture. Then explain why the information you listed does not prove that this conjecture is true.

b. Two odd integers can be represented by the expressions $2n - 1$ and $2m - 1$, where *n* and *m* are both integers. Give information that supports this statement.

c. If a number is even, then it is a multiple of what number? Explain in words how you could use the expressions in part **a** and your answer to part **b** to prove Ayana's conjecture.

d. Write an algebraic proof that the sum of two odd integers is an even integer.

41. WRITING IN MATH Why is it useful to have different formats that can be used when writing a proof? **See Ch. 2 Answer Appendix**

Differentiated Instruction OL BL ELL

Extension What relationships in the triangle tree have reflexive, transitive, or symmetric relationships?

Sample answer: Acute has a transitive relationship with angles and triangles.

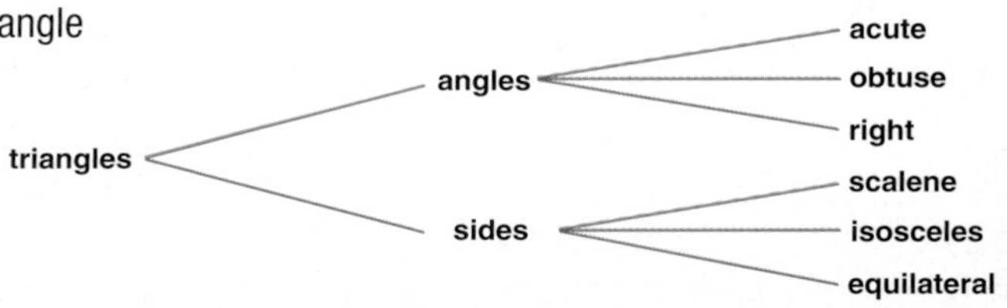

Standardized Test Practice

42. In the diagram, $m\angle CFE = 90$ and $\angle AFB \cong \angle CFD$. Which of the following conclusions does not have to be true? **B**

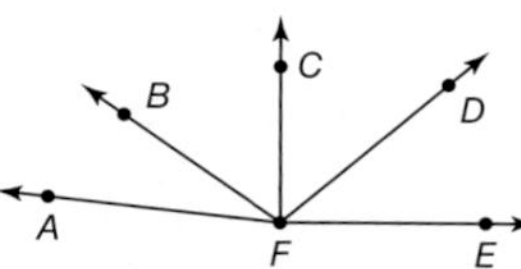

A $m\angle BFD = m\angle BFD$

B $\overline{BF}$ bisects $\angle AFD$.

C $m\angle CFD = m\angle AFB$

D $\angle CFE$ is a right angle.

43. SHORT RESPONSE Find the measure of $\angle B$ when $m\angle A = 55$ and $m\angle C = 42$. **83**

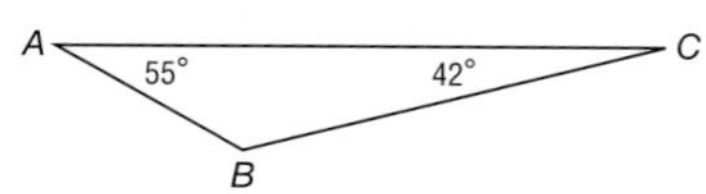

44. ALGEBRA Kendra's walk-a-thon supporters have pledged \$30 plus \$7.50 for each mile she walks. Rebecca's supporters have pledged \$45 plus \$3.75 for each mile she walks. After how many miles will Kendra and Rebecca have raised the same amount of money? **J**

F 10

G 8

H 5

J 4

45. SAT/ACT When 17 is added to $4m$, the result is $15z$. Which of the following equations represents the statement above? **E**

A $17 + 15z = 4m$

B $(4m)(15z) = 17$

C $4m - 15z = 17$

D $17(4m) = 15z$

E $4m + 17 = 15z$

Spiral Review

Determine whether the following statements are *always*, *sometimes*, or *never* true. Explain. (Lesson 2-5) **46–48. See margin.**

46. Four points will lie in one plane.

47. Two obtuse angles will be supplementary.

48. Planes $\mathcal{P}$ and Q intersect in line m. Line m lies in both plane $\mathcal{P}$ and plane Q.

49. ADVERTISING An ad for Speedy Delivery Service says *When it has to be there fast, it has to be Speedy.* Catalina needs to send a package fast. Does it follow that she should use Speedy? Explain. (Lesson 2-4) **yes; by the Law of Detachment**

Write the ordered pair for each point shown. (Lesson 0-7)

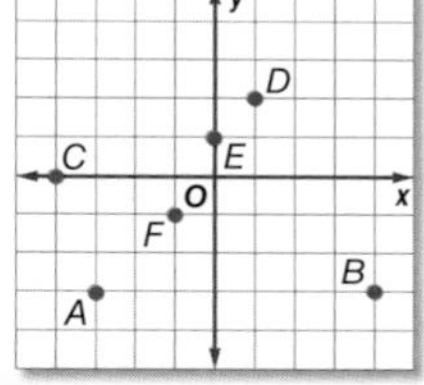

50. A **(−3, −3)**

51. B **(4, −3)**

52. C **(−4, 0)**

53. D **(1, 2)**

54. E **(0, 1)**

55. F **(−1, −1)**

Skills Review

Find the measurement of each segment. Assume that each figure is not drawn to scale.

56. $\overline{ST}$ **2.8 cm**

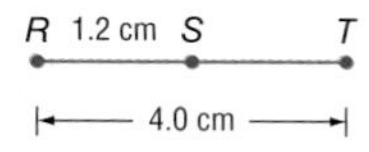

57. $\overline{WX}$ **2.4 cm**

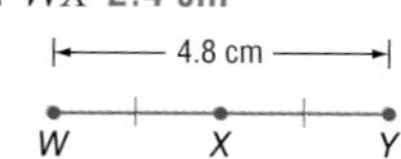
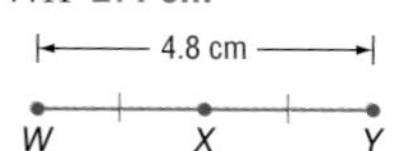

58. $\overline{BC}$ $1\frac{1}{4}$ **in.**

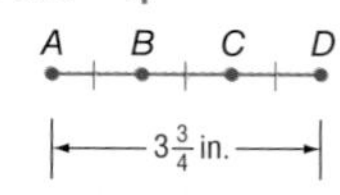

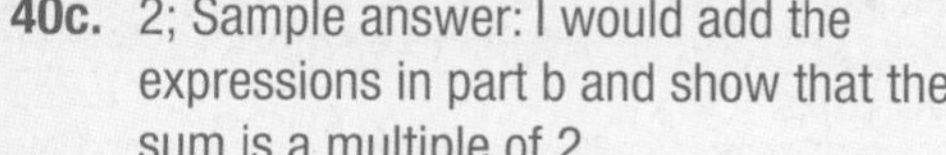

40c. 2; Sample answer: I would add the expressions in part b and show that the sum is a multiple of 2.

40d. Let two odd integers be represented by $2n - 1$ and $2m - 1$. The sum $(2n - 1) + (2m - 1)$ is equal to $2n + 2m - 2$. Each term has a two as a factor so by factoring out a 2 we get $2(n + m - 1)$. Since this expression is a multiple of 2 it is an even number. Hence, the sum of two odd integers is an even integer.

46. Sometimes; since a plane must consist of at least 3 points, the fourth point could lie in the same plane or a different one.

47. Never; the sum of the measures of two supplementary angles is 180, so two obtuse angles can never be supplementary.

48. Always; since the line is the intersection of two planes, the line lies in both of the planes.

4 Assess

Yesterday's News Have students write each proof from the examples as paragraph proofs. Have them explain how writing a paragraph proof helps organize a formal proof.

Formative Assessment

Check for student understanding of Lessons 2-5 and 2-6.

Quiz 3, p. 58

Additional Answers

34. The relation "$\geq$" is not an equivalence relation because it fails the Symmetric Property, since $2 \geq 3$ does not imply $3 \geq 2$.

35. The relation "$\approx$" is not an equivalence relation because it fails the Reflexive Property, since $a \approx a$ is not true.

36. Sample answer: Symmetric example: Sarah is Stacy's sister, and Stacy is Sarah's sister. Symmetric Non-example: If Miko is shorter than Sebastian, then Sebastian is shorter than Miko. Substitution example: When a player leaves the court in a basketball game to rest, the coach substitutes another player. Substitution Non-example: A person with a blood type of O negative can give blood to someone of any blood type, but can only receive blood type O negative. Transitive example: If Jorge is younger than Tomas and Tomas is younger than Gabby, than Jorge is younger than Gabby. Transitive Non-example: School A defeated school B, and school B defeated school C, then school A will defeat school C.

40a. Sample answer: $3 + 3 = 6$, $5 + 7 = 12$, $7 + 9 = 16$. The information listed does not represent every odd integer but only a sample of odd numbers. The sample does not show the conjecture is true for every odd number.

40b. Sample answer: $3 = 2(2) - 1$, $5 = 2(3) - 1$, $7 = 2(4) - 1$

1 Focus

VerticalAlignment

Before Lesson 2-7 Write algebraic and geometric proofs in paragraph and two-column format.

Lesson 2-7 Write proofs involving segment addition and segment congruence.

After Lesson 2-7 Use deductive reasoning to prove a statement.

2 Teach

Scaffolding Questions

Have students read the **Why?** section of the lesson.

Ask:

- Why did Emma need to measure the fabric in this way? Sample: The fabric was longer than the yardstick.
- Describe how measuring 36 and then 3 inches gives a length of 39 inches. The two lengths added together give the total length.
- How many times would Emma mark the fabric if she wanted to measure 120 inches? 3

LESSON 2-7 Proving Segment Relationships

Then

- You wrote algebraic and two-column proofs.

Now

- 1 Write proofs involving segment addition.
- 2 Write proofs involving segment congruence.

Why?

- Emma works at a fabric store after school. She measures a length of fabric by holding the straight edge of the fabric against a yardstick. To measure lengths such as 39 inches, which is longer than the yardstick, she marks a length of 36 inches. From the end of that mark, she measures an additional length of 3 inches. This ensures that the total length of fabric is 36 + 3 inches or 39 inches.

CCSS Common Core State Standards

Content Standards

G.CO.9 Prove theorems about lines and angles.

G.CO.12 Make formal geometric constructions with a variety of tools and methods (compass and straightedge, string, reflective devices, paper folding, dynamic geometric software, etc.).

Mathematical Practices

2 Reasoning abstractly and quantitatively.

3 Construct viable arguments and critique the reasoning of others.

1 Ruler Postulate In Lesson 1-2, you measured segments with a ruler by matching the mark for zero with one endpoint and then finding the number on the ruler that corresponded to the other endpoint. This illustrates the Ruler Postulate.

Postulate 2.8 Ruler Postulate

Words The points on any line or line segment can be put into one-to-one correspondence with real numbers.

Symbols Given any two points A and B on a line, if A corresponds to zero, then B corresponds to a positive real number.

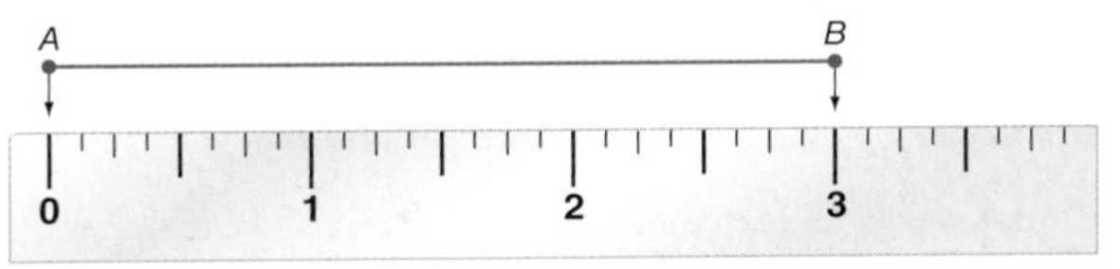

In Lesson 1-2, you also learned about what it means for a point to be *between* two other points. This relationship can be expressed as the Segment Addition Postulate.

Postulate 2.9 Segment Addition Postulate

Words If A, B, and C are collinear, then point B is between A and C if and only if $AB + BC = AC$.

Symbols

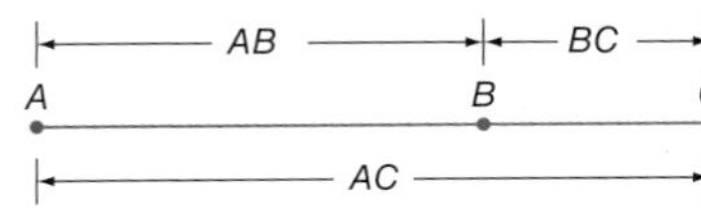

The Segment Addition Postulate is used as a justification in many geometric proofs.

 144 | Lesson 2-7

Lesson 2-7 Resources

Resource	Approaching Level AL	On Level OL	Beyond Level BL	English Learners ELL
Teacher Edition	▪ Differentiated Instruction, p. 145	▪ Differentiated Instruction, pp. 145, 149	▪ Differentiated Instruction, p. 149	
Chapter Resource Masters	▪ Study Guide and Intervention, pp. 43–44 ▪ Skills Practice, p. 45 ▪ Practice, p. 46 ▪ Word Problem Practice, p. 47	▪ Study Guide and Intervention, pp. 43–44 ▪ Skills Practice, p. 45 ▪ Practice, p. 46 ▪ Word Problem Practice, p. 47 ▪ Enrichment, p. 48	▪ Practice, p. 46 ▪ Word Problem Practice, p. 47 ▪ Enrichment, p. 48	▪ Study Guide and Intervention, pp. 43–44 ▪ Skills Practice, p. 45 ▪ Practice, p. 46 ▪ Word Problem Practice, p. 47
Other	▪ 5-Minute Check 2-7 ▪ Study Notebook	▪ 5-Minute Check 2-7 ▪ Study Notebook	▪ 5-Minute Check 2-7 ▪ Study Notebook	▪ 5-Minute Check 2-7 ▪ Study Notebook

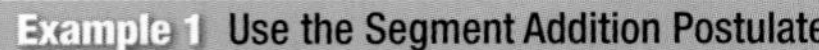

Example 1 Use the Segment Addition Postulate

Prove that if $\overline{CE} \cong \overline{FE}$ and $\overline{ED} \cong \overline{EG}$ then $\overline{CD} \cong \overline{FG}$.

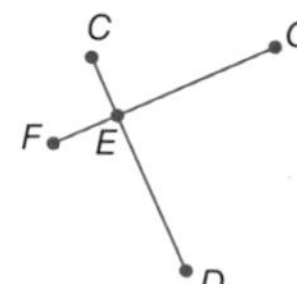

Given: $\overline{CE} \cong \overline{FE}$; $\overline{ED} \cong \overline{EG}$

Prove: $\overline{CD} \cong \overline{FG}$

Proof:

Statements	Reasons
1. $\overline{CE} \cong \overline{FE}$; $\overline{ED} \cong \overline{EG}$	1. Given
2. $CE = FE$; $ED = EG$	2. Definition of congruence
3. $CE + ED = CD$	3. Segment Addition Postulate
4. $FE + EG = CD$	4. Substitution (Steps 2 & 3)
5. $FE + EG = FG$	5. Segment Addition Postulate
6. $CD = FG$	6. Substitution (Steps 4 & 5)
7. $\overline{CD} \cong \overline{FG}$	7. Definition of congruence

ReadingMath

Substitution Property The Substitution Property of Equality is often just written as *Substitution.*

GuidedPractice

Copy and complete the proof.

1. **Given:** $\overline{JL} \cong \overline{KM}$

Prove: $\overline{JK} \cong \overline{LM}$

Proof:

Statements	Reasons
a. $\overline{JL} \cong \overline{KM}$	**a.** Given
b. $JL = KM$	**b.** ___?___ Def. of ≅
c. $JK + KL =$ ___?___ (JL); $KL + LM =$ ___?___ (KM)	**c.** Segment Addition Postulate
d. $JK + KL = KL + LM$	**d.** ___?___ Subs.
e. $JK + KL - KL = KL + LM - KL$	**e.** Subtraction Property of Equality
f. ___?___ $JK = LM$	**f.** Substitution
g. $\overline{JK} \cong \overline{LM}$	**g.** Definition of congruence

2 Segment Congruence

In Lesson 2-6, you saw that segment measures are reflexive, symmetric, and transitive. Since segments with the same measure are congruent, congruence of segments is also reflexive, symmetric, and transitive.

VocabularyLink

Symmetric

Everyday Use balanced or proportional

Math Use If $a = b$, then $b = a$.

Theorem 2.2 Properties of Segment Congruence

Reflexive Property of Congruence	$\overline{AB} \cong \overline{AB}$
Symmetric Property of Congruence	If $\overline{AB} \cong \overline{CD}$, then $\overline{CD} \cong \overline{AB}$.
Transitive Property of Congruence	If $\overline{AB} \cong \overline{CD}$ and $\overline{CD} \cong \overline{EF}$, then $\overline{AB} \cong \overline{EF}$.

You will prove the Symmetric and Reflexive Properties in Exercises 6 and 7, respectively.

1 Segment Addition

Example 1 shows how to use properties and postulates to prove segment addition.

Formative Assessment

Use the Guided Practice exercises after each example to determine students' understanding of concepts.

Additional Example

1 Prove that if $\overline{AB} \cong \overline{CD}$, then $\overline{AC} \cong \overline{BD}$.

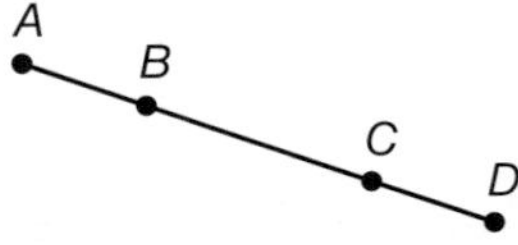

Proof:

Statements (Reasons)

1. $\overline{AB} \cong \overline{CD}$ (Given)
2. $AB = CD$ (Def. of ≅ segs.)
3. $BC = BC$ (Refl. Prop. of =)
4. $AB + BC = AC$ (Seg. Add. Post.)
5. $CD + BC = AC$ (Substi. Prop. of =)
6. $CD + BC = BD$ (Seg. Add. Post.)
7. $AC = BD$ (Trans. Prop. of =)
8. $\overline{AC} \cong \overline{BD}$ (Def. of ≅ segs.)

Additional Examples also in Interactive Classroom PowerPoint® Presentations

Interactive White Board READY

WatchOut!

End it Right In Example 1, the question asks to prove that two segments are congruent. Explain to students that the last line of the proof is needed to accurately describe the relationship of the segments as the question asks.

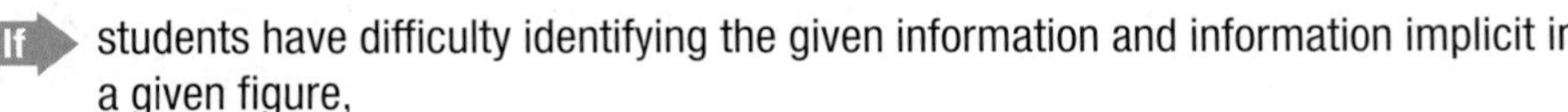

DifferentiatedInstruction AL OL

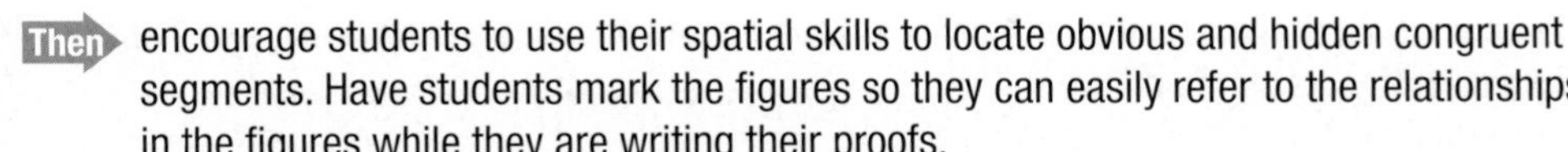

If students have difficulty identifying the given information and information implicit in a given figure,

Then encourage students to use their spatial skills to locate obvious and hidden congruent segments. Have students mark the figures so they can easily refer to the relationships in the figures while they are writing their proofs.

Tips for New Teachers

Knowledge Building Point out that with each new lesson, students are accumulating knowledge of more postulates and theorems that they can use for writing proofs. Encourage students to practice using these concepts as much as possible before moving on to the next lesson to strengthen their ability to recall important facts for proof-writing.

2 Segment Congruence

Example 2 shows how to use properties and postulates to prove segment congruence.

Additional Example

2 **BADGE** Jamie is designing a badge for her club. The length of the top edge of the badge is equal to the length of the left edge of the badge. The top edge of the badge is congruent to the right edge of the badge, and the right edge of the badge is congruent to the bottom edge of the badge. Prove that the bottom edge of the badge is congruent to the left edge of the badge.

Given: $WY = YZ$
$\overline{YZ} \cong \overline{XZ}$
$\overline{XZ} \cong \overline{WX}$

Prove: $\overline{WX} \cong \overline{WY}$

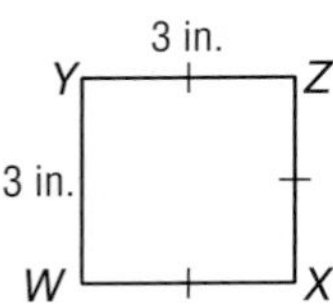

Proof:

Statements (Reasons)

1. $WY = YZ$ (Given)
2. $\overline{WY} \cong \overline{YZ}$ (Def. of $\cong$ segs.)
3. $\overline{YZ} \cong \overline{XZ}$, $\overline{XZ} \cong \overline{WX}$ (Given)
4. $\overline{YZ} \cong \overline{WX}$ (Trans. Prop.)
5. $\overline{WX} \cong \overline{WY}$ (Substitution)

Proof Transitive Property of Congruence

Given: $\overline{AB} \cong \overline{CD}$, $\overline{CD} \cong \overline{EF}$

Prove: $\overline{AB} \cong \overline{EF}$

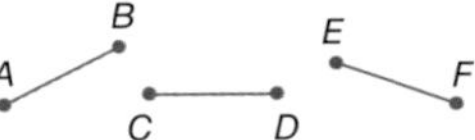

Paragraph Proof:

Since $\overline{AB} \cong \overline{CD}$ and $\overline{CD} \cong \overline{EF}$, $AB = CD$ and $CD = EF$ by the definition of congruent segments. By the Transitive Property of Equality, $AB = EF$. Thus, $\overline{AB} \cong \overline{EF}$ by the definition of congruence.

Real-World Example 2 Proof Using Segment Congruence

PT

VOLUNTEERING The route for a charity fitness run is shown. Checkpoints X and Z are the midpoints between the starting line and Checkpoint Y and Checkpoint Y and the finish line F, respectively. If Checkpoint Y is the same distance from Checkpoints X and Z, prove that the route from Checkpoint Z to the finish line is congruent to the route from the starting line to Checkpoint X.

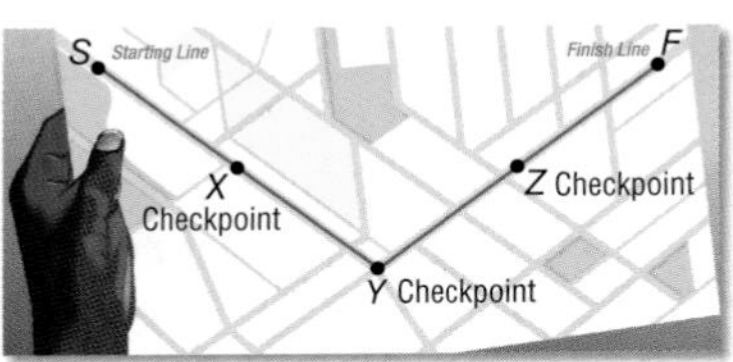

Real-WorldLink

According to a recent poll, 70% of teens who volunteer began doing so before age 12. Others said they would volunteer if given more opportunities to do so.

Source: Youth Service America

Given: X is the midpoint of $\overline{SY}$. Z is the midpoint of $\overline{YF}$. $XY = YZ$

Prove: $\overline{ZF} \cong \overline{SX}$

Two-Column Proof:

Statements	Reasons
1. X is the midpoint of $\overline{SY}$. Z is the midpoint of $\overline{YF}$. $XY = YZ$	1. Given
2. $\overline{SX} \cong \overline{XY}$; $\overline{YZ} \cong \overline{ZF}$	2. Definition of midpoint
3. $\overline{XY} \cong \overline{YZ}$	3. Definition of congruence
4. $\overline{SX} \cong \overline{YZ}$	4. Transitive Property of Congruence
5. $\overline{SX} \cong \overline{ZF}$	5. Transitive Property of Congruence
6. $\overline{ZF} \cong \overline{SX}$	6. Symmetric Property of Congruence

GuidedPractice

2. CARPENTRY A carpenter cuts a 2″ × 4″ board to a desired length. He then uses this board as a pattern to cut a second board congruent to the first. Similarly, he uses the second board to cut a third board and the third board to cut a fourth board. Prove that the last board cut has the same measure as the first.

2. Given: $\overline{KL} \cong \overline{MN}$, $\overline{MN} \cong \overline{PQ}$, $\overline{PQ} \cong \overline{RS}$
Prove: $RS = KL$
Proof: If $\overline{KL} \cong \overline{MN}$ and $\overline{MN} \cong \overline{PQ}$, then by the Transitive Property of Congruence, $\overline{KL} \cong \overline{PQ}$. If $\overline{PQ} \cong \overline{RS}$, then $\overline{KL} \cong \overline{RS}$ by the Transitive Property of Congruence. $\overline{RS} \cong \overline{KL}$ by the Symmetric Property of Congruence and $RS = KL$ by the definition of congruence. So, the first board cut has the same measure as the last board cut.

Focus on Mathematical Content

Line Segments It is important to know that the art and diagrams that go along with problems may not always be to scale. Two segments may be assumed to be congruent in a question, but if measured with a ruler they could be different. On the other hand, certain combinations of lines can create an optical illusion and lines that are the same length may not appear so.

Teach with Tech

Interactive Whiteboard Work through several proofs on the board and save your work. Post your notes on a class Web page so students will have an additional reference outside of class.

Check Your Understanding

 = Step-by-Step Solutions begin on page R14.  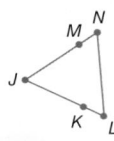

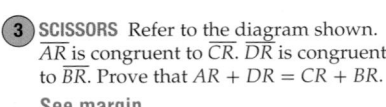

Example 1

1. CCSS **ARGUMENTS** Copy and complete the proof.

Given: $\overline{LK} \cong \overline{NM}$, $\overline{KJ} \cong \overline{MJ}$

Prove: $\overline{LJ} \cong \overline{NJ}$

Proof:

Statements	Reasons
a. $\overline{LK} \cong \overline{NM}$, $\overline{KJ} \cong \overline{MJ}$	a. ? **Given**
b. ? **$LK = NM$, $KJ = MJ$**	b. Def. of congruent segments
c. $LK + KJ = NM + MJ$	c. ? **Add. Prop.**
d. ? **$LJ = LK + KJ$; $NJ = NM + MJ$**	d. Segment Addition Postulate
e. $LJ = NJ$	e. ? **Subs.**
f. $\overline{LJ} \cong \overline{NJ}$	f. ? **Def. ≅ segs.**

Example 2

2. **PROOF** Prove the following. **See margin.**

Given: $\overline{WX} \cong \overline{YZ}$

Prove: $\overline{WY} \cong \overline{XZ}$

3. **SCISSORS** Refer to the diagram shown. $\overline{AR}$ is congruent to $\overline{CR}$. $\overline{DR}$ is congruent to $\overline{BR}$. Prove that $AR + DR = CR + BR$. **See margin.**

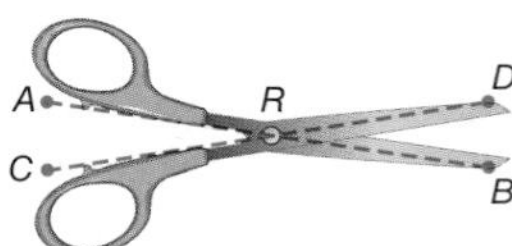

Practice and Problem Solving

Extra Practice is on page R2.

Example 1

4. CCSS **ARGUMENTS** Copy and complete the proof.

Given: C is the midpoint of $\overline{AE}$.
C is the midpoint of $\overline{BD}$.
$\overline{AE} \cong \overline{BD}$

Prove: $\overline{AC} \cong \overline{CD}$

Proof:

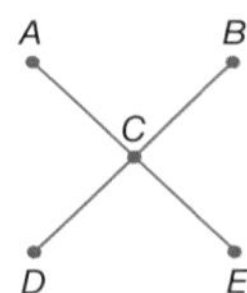

Statements	Reasons
a. ?	a. Given
b. $AC = CE$, $BC = CD$	b. ? **Def of midpoint**
c. $AE = BD$	c. ? **Def ≅ segs.**
d. ? **$AE = AC + CE$, $BD = BC + CD$**	d. Segment Addition Postulate
e. $AC + CE = BC + CD$	e. ? **Subs.**
f. $AC + AC = CD + CD$	f. ? **Subs.**
g. ? **$2AC = 2CD$**	g. Simplify.
h. ? **$AC = CD$**	h. Division Property
i. $\overline{AC} \cong \overline{CD}$	i. ? **Def ≅ segs.**

4a. C **is the midpoint of** $\overline{AE}$. C **is the midpoint of** $\overline{BD}$. $\overline{AE} \cong \overline{BD}$

Differentiated Homework Options

Level	Assignment	Two-Day Option	
AL Basic	4–13, 17, 19–36	5–13 odd, 23–26	4–12 even, 17, 19–22, 27–36
OL Core	5–13 odd, 15–17, 19–36	4–13, 23–26	14–17, 19–22, 27–36
BL Advanced	14–33, (optional: 34–36)		

3 Practice

Formative Assessment

Use Exercises 1–3 to check for understanding.

Use the chart at the bottom of this page to customize assignments for your students.

CCSS Teaching the Mathematical Practices

Arguments Mathematically proficient students understand and use stated assumptions, definitions, and previously established results in constructing arguments. In Exercises 1 and 4, encourage students to copy the figures onto their paper and label each with the given information.

Additional Answers

2. Given: $\overline{WX} \cong \overline{YZ}$

Prove: $\overline{WY} \cong \overline{XZ}$

Proof:

Statements (Reasons)

1. $\overline{WX} \cong \overline{YZ}$ (Given)
2. $WX = YZ$ (Def. ≅ segs.)
3. $XY = XY$ (Refl. Prop.)
4. $WX + XY = XY + YZ$ (Add. Property)
5. $WY = WX + XY$; $XZ = XY + YZ$ (Seg. Add. Post.)
6. $WY = XZ$ (Subs.)
7. $\overline{WY} \cong \overline{XZ}$ (Def. ≅ segs.)

3. Given: $\overline{AR} \cong \overline{CR}$; $\overline{DR} \cong \overline{BR}$

Prove: $AR + DR = CR + BR$

Proof:

Statements (Reasons)

1. $\overline{AR} \cong \overline{CR}$; $\overline{DR} \cong \overline{BR}$ (Given)
2. $AR = CR$, $DR = BR$ (Def. of ≅ segs.)
3. $AR + DR = CR + DR$ (Add. Prop.)
4. $AR + DR = CR + BR$ (Subs.)

Study Guide and Intervention

AL OL ELL

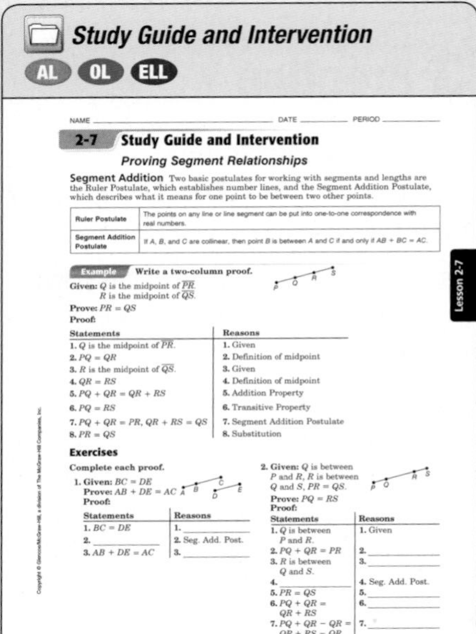
NAME ______ DATE ______ PERIOD ______

2-7 Study Guide and Intervention

Proving Segment Relationships

Segment Addition Two basic postulates for working with segments and lengths are the Ruler Postulate, which establishes number lines, and the Segment Addition Postulate, which describes what it means for one point to be between two other points.

Ruler Postulate	The points on any line or line segment can be put into one-to-one correspondence with real numbers.
Segment Addition Postulate	If A, B, and C are collinear, then point B is between A and C if and only if AB + BC = AC.

Example Write a two-column proof.

Given: Q is the midpoint of $\overline{PR}$. R is the midpoint of $\overline{QS}$.

Prove: PR = QS

Proof:

Statements	Reasons
1. Q is the midpoint of $\overline{PR}$.	1. Given
2. PQ = QR	2. Definition of midpoint
3. R is the midpoint of $\overline{QS}$.	3. Given
4. QR = RS	4. Definition of midpoint
5. PQ + QR = QR + RS	5. Addition Property
6. PQ = RS	6. Transitive Property
7. PQ + QR = PR, QR + RS = QS	7. Segment Addition Postulate
8. PR = QS	8. Substitution

Exercises

Complete each proof.

1. Given: BC = DE
Prove: AB + DE = AC
Proof:

Statements	Reasons
1. BC = DE	1. ______
2. ______	2. Seg. Add. Post.
3. AB + DE = AC	3. ______

2. Given: Q is between P and R, R is between Q and S, PR = QS.
Prove: PQ = RS
Proof:

Statements	Reasons
1. Q is between P and R.	1. Given
2. PQ + QR = PR	2. ______
3. R is between Q and S.	3. ______
4. ______	4. Seg. Add. Post.
5. PR = QS	5. ______
6. PQ + QR = QR + RS	6. ______
7. PQ + QR − QR = QR + RS − QR	7. ______
8. ______	8. Substitution

Lesson 2-7

Practice

AL OL BL ELL

NAME ______ DATE ______ PERIOD ______

2-7 Practice

Proving Segment Relationships

Complete the following proof.

1. Given: $\overline{AB} \cong \overline{DE}$
B is the midpoint of $\overline{AC}$.
E is the midpoint of $\overline{DF}$.
Prove: $\overline{BC} \cong \overline{EF}$
Proof:

Statements	Reasons
a. ______	a. Given
b. AB = DE	b. ______
c. ______	c. Definition of Midpoint
d. BC = DE	d. ______
e. BC = EF	e. ______
f. ______	f. ______

2. TRAVEL Refer to the figure. DeAnne knows that the distance from Grayson to Apex is the same as the distance from Redding to Pine Bluff. Prove that the distance from Grayson to Redding is equal to the distance from Apex to Pine Bluff.

Word Problem Practice

AL OL BL ELL

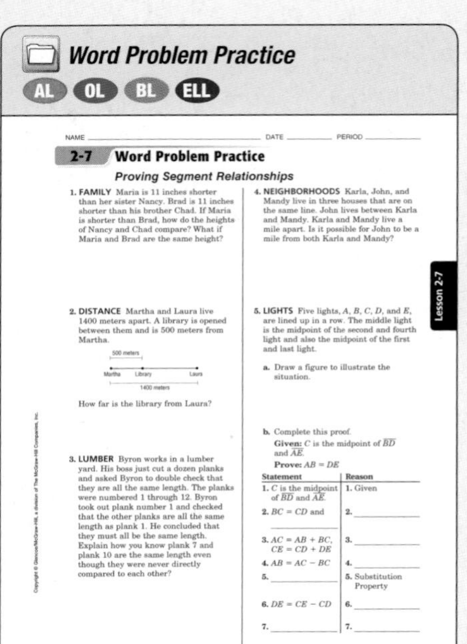
NAME ______ DATE ______ PERIOD ______

2-7 Word Problem Practice

Proving Segment Relationships

1. FAMILY Maria is 11 inches shorter than her sister Nancy. Brad is 11 inches shorter than his brother Chad. If Maria is shorter than Brad, how do the heights of Nancy and Chad compare? What if Maria and Brad are the same height?

2. DISTANCE Martha and Laura live 1400 meters apart. A library is opened between them and is 500 meters from Martha.

How far is the library from Laura?

3. LUMBER Byron works in a lumber yard. His boss just cut a dozen planks and asked Byron to double check that they are all the same length. The planks were numbered 1 through 12. Byron took out plank number 1 and checked that the other planks are all the same length as plank 1. He concluded that they must all be the same length. Explain how you know plank 7 and plank 10 are the same length even though they were never directly compared to each other?

4. NEIGHBORHOODS Karla, John, and Mandy live in three houses that are on the same line. John lives between Karla and Mandy. Karla and Mandy live a mile apart. Is it possible for John to be a mile from both Karla and Mandy?

5. LIGHTS Five lights, A, B, C, D, and E, are lined up in a row. The middle light is the midpoint of the second and fourth light and also the midpoint of the first and last light.

a. Draw a figure to illustrate the situation.

b. Complete this proof.
Given: C is the midpoint of $\overline{BD}$ and $\overline{AE}$.
Prove: AB = DE

Statement	Reason
1. C is the midpoint of $\overline{BD}$ and $\overline{AE}$.	1. Given
2. BC = CD and ______	2. ______
3. AC = AB + BC, CE = CD + DE	3. ______
4. AB = AC − BC	4. ______
5. ______	5. Substitution Property
6. DE = CE − CD	6. ______
7. ______	7. ______

Lesson 2-7

Example 2 5. **TILING** A tile setter cuts a piece of tile to a desired length. He then uses this tile as a pattern to cut a second tile congruent to the first. He uses the first two tiles to cut a third tile whose length is the sum of the measures of the first two tiles. Prove that the measure of the third tile is twice the measure of the first tile. **See Ch. 2 Answer Appendix.**

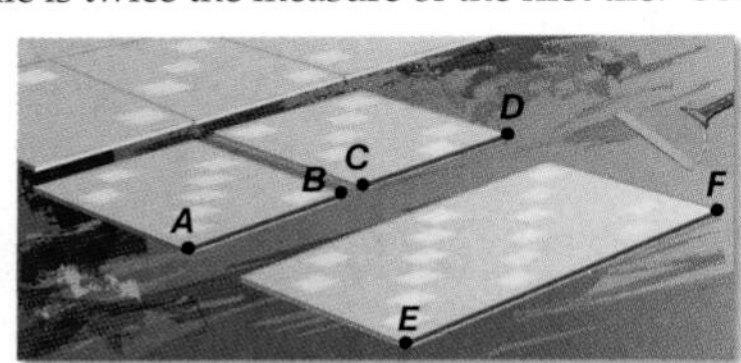

CCSS ARGUMENTS **Prove each theorem.** **6, 7. See Ch. 2 Answer Appendix.**

6. Symmetric Property of Congruence (Theorem 2.2)

7. Reflexive Property of Congruence (Theorem 2.2)

8. **TRAVEL** Four cities in New York are connected by Interstate 90: Buffalo, Utica, Albany, and Syracuse. Buffalo is the farthest west. **a, b. See Ch. 2 Answer Appendix.**

- Albany is 126 miles from Syracuse and 263 miles from Buffalo.
- Buffalo is 137 miles from Syracuse and 184 miles from Utica.

a. Draw a diagram to represent the locations of the cities in relation to each other and the distances between each city. Assume that Interstate 90 is straight.

b. Write a paragraph proof to support your conclusion.

PROOF **Prove the following.** **9–12. See Ch. 2 Answer Appendix.**

9. If $\overline{SC} \cong \overline{HR}$ and $\overline{HR} \cong \overline{AB}$, then $\overline{SC} \cong \overline{AB}$.

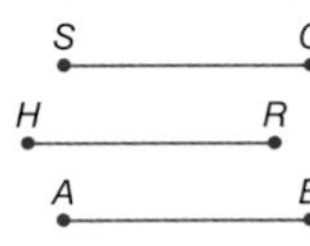

10. If $\overline{VZ} \cong \overline{VY}$ and $\overline{WY} \cong \overline{XZ}$, then $\overline{VW} \cong \overline{VX}$.

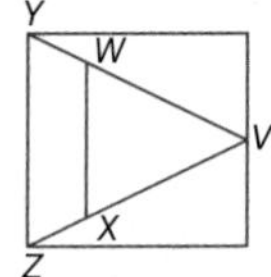

11. If E is the midpoint of $\overline{DF}$ and $\overline{CD} \cong \overline{FG}$, then $\overline{CE} \cong \overline{EG}$.

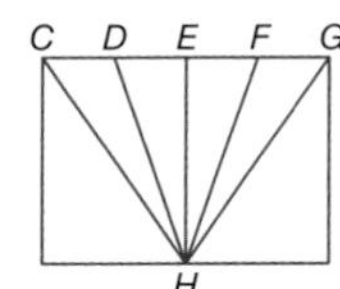

12. If B is the midpoint of $\overline{AC}$, D is the midpoint of $\overline{CE}$, and $\overline{AB} \cong \overline{DE}$, then $AE = 4AB$.

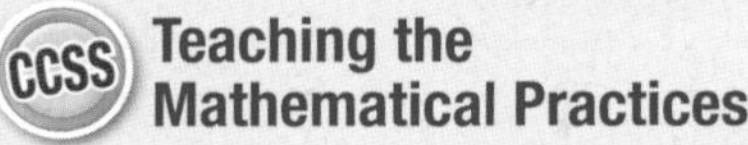

13. **OPTICAL ILLUSION** $\overline{AC} \cong \overline{GI}$, $\overline{FE} \cong \overline{LK}$, and $AC + CF + FE = GI + IL + LK$. **a, b. See Ch. 2 Answer Appendix.**

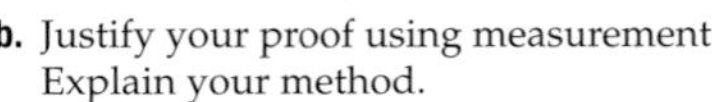

a. Prove that $\overline{CF} \cong \overline{IL}$.

b. Justify your proof using measurement. Explain your method.

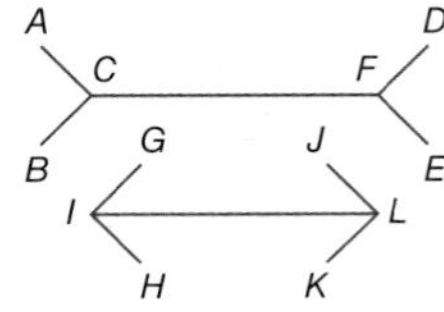

Enrichment

OL BL

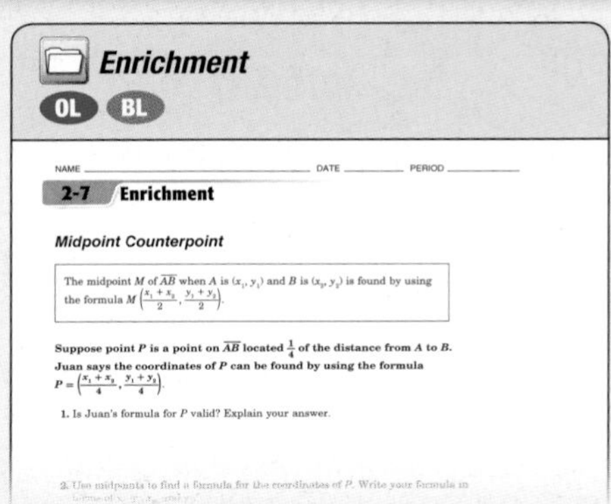
NAME ______ DATE ______ PERIOD ______

2-7 Enrichment

Midpoint Counterpoint

The midpoint M of $\overline{AB}$ when A is (x_1, y_1) and B is (x_2, y_2) is found by using the formula $M\left(\frac{x_1 + x_2}{2}, \frac{y_1 + y_2}{2}\right)$.

Suppose point P is a point on $\overline{AB}$ located $\frac{1}{4}$ of the distance from A to B. Juan says the coordinates of P can be found by using the formula $P = \left(\frac{x_1 + x_2}{4}, \frac{y_1 + y_2}{4}\right)$.

1. Is Juan's formula for P valid? Explain your answer.

CCSS Teaching the Mathematical Practices

Arguments Mathematically proficient students understand and use stated assumptions, definitions, and previously established results in constructing arguments. In Exercises 6–7, students should draw diagrams for each proof and identify the given statements as well as the statement to prove in order to prove the properties.

14. **CONSTRUCTION** Construct a segment that is twice as long as $\overline{PQ}$. Explain how the Segment Addition Postulate can be used to justify your construction. **See Ch. 2 Answer Appendix.**

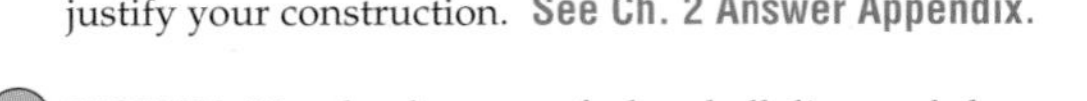

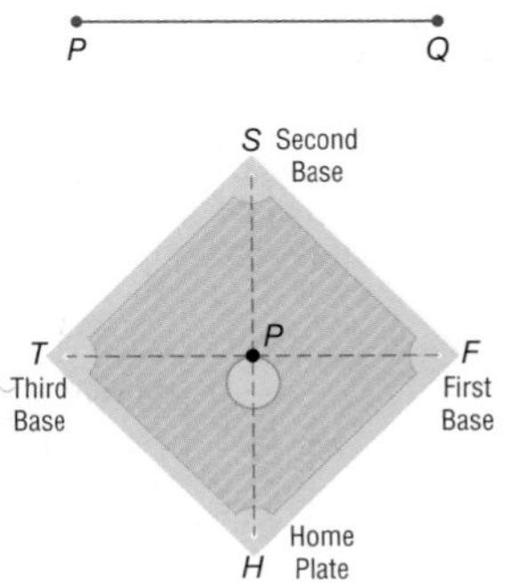

15. **BASEBALL** Use the diagram of a baseball diamond shown.
    a. On the diagram, $\overline{SH} \cong \overline{TF}$. P is the midpoint of $\overline{SH}$ and $\overline{TF}$. Using a two-column proof, prove that $\overline{SP} \cong \overline{TP}$. **See margin.**
    b. The distance from home plate to second base is 127.3 feet. What is the distance from first base to second base? **90 ft**

16. **MULTIPLE REPRESENTATIONS** A is the midpoint of $\overline{PQ}$, B is the midpoint of $\overline{PA}$, and C is the midpoint of $\overline{PB}$. **a–e. See Ch. 2 Answer Appendix.**
    a. **Geometric** Make a sketch to represent this situation.
    b. **Algebraic** Make a conjecture as to the algebraic relationship between PC and PQ.
    c. **Geometric** Copy segment $\overline{PQ}$ from your sketch. Then construct points B and C on $\overline{PQ}$. Explain how you can use your construction to support your conjecture.
    d. **Concrete** Use a ruler to draw a segment congruent to $\overline{PQ}$ from your sketch and to draw points B and C on $\overline{PQ}$. Use your drawing to support your conjecture.
    e. **Logical** Prove your conjecture.

H.O.T. Problems Use Higher-Order Thinking Skills

17. **CCSS CRITIQUE** In the diagram, $\overline{AB} \cong \overline{CD}$ and $\overline{CD} \cong \overline{BF}$. Examine the conclusions made by Leslie and Shantice. Is either of them correct? **See margin.**

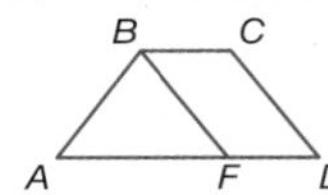

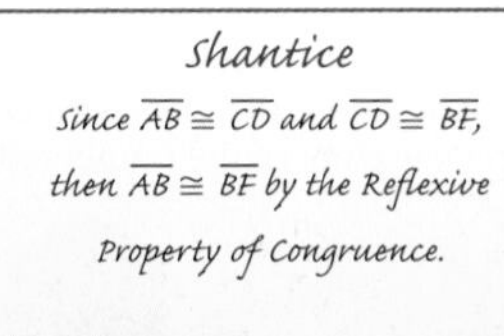

Leslie
Since $\overline{AB} \cong \overline{CD}$ and $\overline{CD} \cong \overline{BF}$, then $\overline{AB} \cong \overline{AF}$ by the Transitive Property of Congruence

Shantice
Since $\overline{AB} \cong \overline{CD}$ and $\overline{CD} \cong \overline{BF}$, then $\overline{AB} \cong \overline{BF}$ by the Reflexive Property of Congruence.

18. **CHALLENGE** $ABCD$ is a square. Prove that $\overline{AC} \cong \overline{BD}$. **See Ch. 2 Answer Appendix.**

19. **WRITING IN MATH** Does there exist an Addition Property of Congruence? Explain. **See margin.**

20. **REASONING** Classify the following statement as *true* or *false*. If false, provide a counterexample. **See Ch. 2 Answer Appendix.**

    If A, B, C, D, and E are collinear with B between A and C, C between B and D, and D between C and E, and AC = BD = CE, then AB = BC = DE.

21. **OPEN ENDED** Draw a representation of the Segment Addition Postulate in which the segment is two inches long, contains four collinear points, and contains no congruent segments. **See Ch. 2 Answer Appendix.**

22. **WRITING IN MATH** Compare and contrast paragraph proofs and two-column proofs. **See Ch. 2 Answer Appendix.**

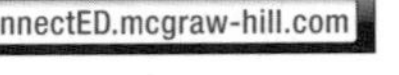

Differentiated Instruction OL BL

Extension

Given: $BD = EC$
$DA = AE$

Prove: $BA = AC$

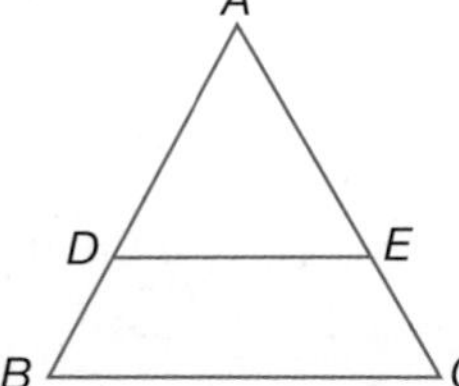

Proof:

Statement (reason)

1. $BD = EC$; $DA = AE$ (Given)
2. $BD + DA = EC + AE$ (Add. Prop. of =)
3. $BD + DA = BA$; $EC + AE = AC$ (Seg. Add. Post.)
4. $BA = AC$ (Substitution)

Exercise Alert

Compass and Straightedge Exercise 14 requires students to use a compass and straightedge.

Compass and Ruler Exercise 16 requires students to use a compass and a ruler.

Multiple Representations

In Exercise 16, students use geometric sketches, algebraic conjecture, and direct measurement to investigate midpoints of a line.

CCSS Teaching the Mathematical Practices

Critique Mathematically proficient students can distinguish correct logic from flawed reasoning. In Exercise 17, Leslie applied the property correctly but incorrectly stated that $\overline{AB} \cong \overline{AF}$. Shantice also applied the property correctly but mistakenly cited the Reflexive Property.

Additional Answers

15a. Given: $\overline{SH} \cong \overline{TF}$; P is the midpoint of $\overline{SH}$ and $\overline{TF}$.

Prove: $\overline{SP} \cong \overline{TP}$

Proof:

Statements (Reasons)

1. $\overline{SH} \cong \overline{TF}$; P is the midpoint of $\overline{SH}$, P is the midpoint of $\overline{TF}$. (Given)
2. $SH = TF$ (Def. of $\cong$ Segs.)
3. $SP = PH$, $TP = PF$ (Def. of Midpoint)
4. $SH = SP + PH$, $TF = TP + PF$ (Seg. Add. Post.)
5. $SP + PH = TP + PF$ (Subs.)
6. $SP + SP = TP + TP$ (Subs.)
7. $2SP = 2TP$ (Subs.)
8. $SP = TP$ (Div. Prop.)
9. $\overline{SP} \cong \overline{TP}$ (Def. of $\cong$ segs.)

17. Neither; since $\overline{AB} \cong \overline{CD}$ and $\overline{CD} \cong \overline{BF}$, then $\overline{AB} \cong \overline{BF}$ by the Transitive Property of Congruence.

19. No; congruence refers to segments. Segments cannot be added, only the measures of segments.

4 Assess

Name the Math Give each student a ruler to measure a finger from the tip to the first knuckle. Next, have each student measure from the first knuckle to the second knuckle. Have students find the length from the tip of the finger to second knuckle and determine whether the measurements taken on the corresponding finger of the other hand are congruent. Have them write the postulates or theorems that they used.

Additional Answer

27. Given: $AC = DF$, $AB = DE$

Prove: $BC = EF$

Proof:

Statements (Reasons)

1. $AC = DF$, $AB = DE$ (Given)
2. $AC = AB + BC$; $DF = DE + EF$ (Seg. Add. Post.)
3. $AB + BC = DE + EF$ (Subs.)
4. $BC = EF$ (Subt. Prop.)

Standardized Test Practice

23. ALGEBRA The chart below shows annual recycling by material in the United States. About how many pounds of aluminum are recycled each year? **D**

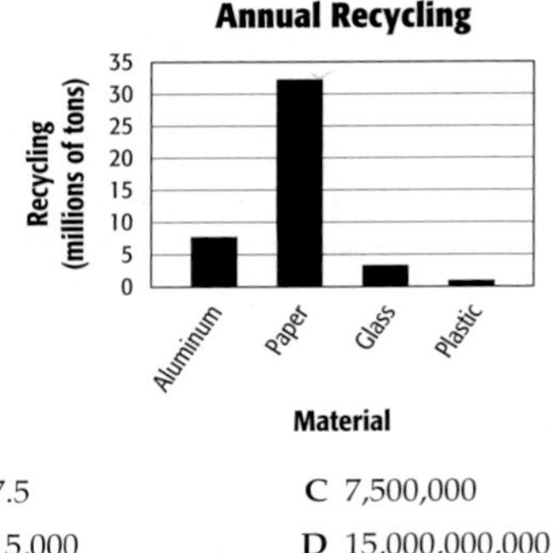

A 7.5
B 15,000
C 7,500,000
D 15,000,000,000

24. ALGEBRA Which expression is equivalent to $\frac{12x^{-4}}{4x^{-8}}$? **G**

F $\frac{1}{3x^4}$
G $3x^4$
H $8x^2$
J $\frac{x^4}{3}$

25. SHORT RESPONSE The measures of two complementary angles are in the ratio 4 : 1. What is the measure of the smaller angle? **18**

26. SAT/ACT Julie can word process 40 words per minute. How many minutes will it take Julie to word process 200 words? **C**

A 0.5
B 2
C 5
D 10
E 12

Spiral Review

27. PROOF **Write a two-column proof.** (Lesson 2-6)
Given: $AC = DF$
$AB = DE$
Prove: $BC = EF$ **See margin.**

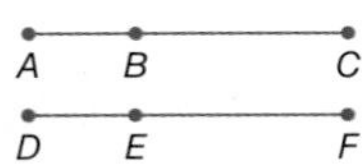

28. MODELS Brian is using six squares of cardboard to form a rectangular prism. What geometric figure do the pieces of cardboard represent, and how many lines will be formed by their intersections? (Lesson 2-5) **planes; 12**

29. PATTERN BLOCKS Pattern blocks can be arranged to fit in a circular pattern without leaving spaces. Remember that the measurement around a full circle is 360°. Determine the degree measure of the numbered angles shown below. (Lesson 1-4) **60, 30, 90, 60, 120, 60**

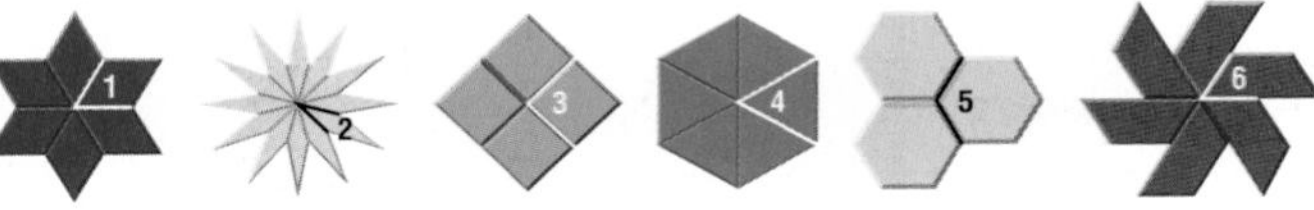

Simplify. (Lesson 0-9)

30. $\sqrt{48}$ **$4\sqrt{3}$**
31. $\sqrt{162}$ **$9\sqrt{2}$**
32. $\sqrt{25a^6b^4}$ **$5|a^3|b^2$**
33. $\sqrt{45xy^8}$ **$3y^4\sqrt{5x}$**

Skills Review

ALGEBRA **Find x.**

34. $(5x - 2)°$, $(8x + 1)°$ **7**

35. $14x°$, $(8x + 4)°$ **8**

36. $2x°$, $4x°$ **15**

Additional Answer (Lesson 2-8, Guided Practice)

1. $m\angle 1 + m\angle 2 + m\angle 3 = m\angle ABC$ (Ang. Add. Pos.)
$23 + 90 + m\angle 3 = 131$ ($m\angle 2 = 90$)
$113 + m\angle 3 = 131$ (Subs.)
$113 + m\angle 3 - 113 = 131 - 113$ (Subt. Prop.)
$m\angle 3 = 18$ (Subs.)

LESSON 2-8 Proving Angle Relationships

Then

- You identified and used special pairs of angles.

Now

1. Write proofs involving supplementary and complementary angles.
2. Write proofs involving congruent and right angles.

Why?

- Jamal's school is building a walkway that will include bricks with the names of graduates from each class. All of the bricks are rectangular, so when the bricks are laid, all of the angles form linear pairs.

Common Core State Standards

Content Standards
G.CO.9 Prove theorems about lines and angles.

Mathematical Practices
3 Construct viable arguments and critique the reasoning of others.
6 Attend to precision.

1 Supplementary and Complementary Angles

The Protractor Postulate illustrates the relationship between angle measures and real numbers.

Postulate 2.10 Protractor Postulate

Words Given any angle, the measure can be put into one-to-one correspondence with real numbers between 0 and 180.

Example If $\overrightarrow{BA}$ is placed along the protractor at 0°, then the measure of $\angle ABC$ corresponds to a positive real number.

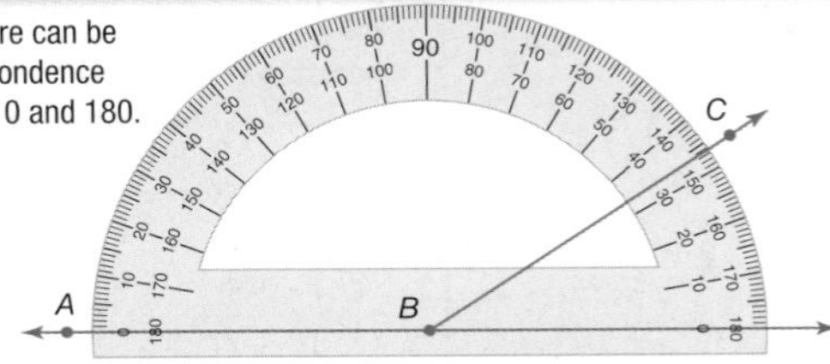

In Lesson 2-7, you learned about the Segment Addition Postulate. A similar relationship exists between the measures of angles.

Postulate 2.11 Angle Addition Postulate

D is in the interior of $\angle ABC$ if and only if $m\angle ABD + m\angle DBC = m\angle ABC$.

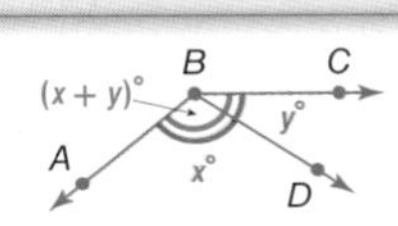

Example 1 Use the Angle Addition Postulate

Find $m\angle 1$ if $m\angle 2 = 56$ and $m\angle JKL = 145$.

$m\angle 1 + m\angle 2 = m\angle JKL$	Angle Addition Postulate
$m\angle 1 + 56 = 145$	$m\angle 2 = 56$ $m\angle JKL = 145$
$m\angle 1 + 56 - 56 = 145 - 56$	Subtraction Property of Equality
$m\angle 1 = 89$	Substitution

J K L 2 1

GuidedPractice

1. If $m\angle 1 = 23$ and $m\angle ABC = 131$, find the measure of $\angle 3$. Justify each step. **See margin.**

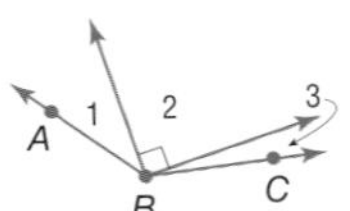

1 Focus

VerticalAlignment

Before Lesson 2-8 Use logical reasoning to prove statements are true. Identify and use special pairs of angles.

Lesson 2-8 Write proofs involving supplementary and complementary angles. Write proofs involving congruent and right angles. Use deductive reasoning to prove a statement.

After Lesson 2-8 Use deductive reasoning to prove a statement.

2 Teach

Scaffolding Questions

Have students read the **Why?** section of the lesson.

Ask:

- What do the angles of rectangles and squares have in common? They all measure 90.
- If a square and a rectangle are adjacent, what is the sum of the measure of any two adjacent angles? 180
- If 5 squares and 5 rectangles are all put in a row, how many linear pairs are formed? 8

Lesson 2-8 Resources

Resource	Approaching Level AL	On Level OL	Beyond Level BL	English Learners ELL
Teacher Edition	▪ Differentiated Instruction, p. 155	▪ Differentiated Instruction, p. 155	▪ Differentiated Instruction, p. 158	▪ Differentiated Instruction, p. 155
Chapter Resource Masters	▪ Study Guide and Intervention, pp. 49–50 ▪ Skills Practice, p. 51 ▪ Practice, p. 52 ▪ Word Problem Practice, p. 53	▪ Study Guide and Intervention, pp. 49–50 ▪ Skills Practice, p. 51 ▪ Practice, p. 52 ▪ Word Problem Practice, p. 53 ▪ Enrichment, p. 54	▪ Practice, p. 52 ▪ Word Problem Practice, p. 53 ▪ Enrichment, p. 54	▪ Study Guide and Intervention, pp. 49–50 ▪ Skills Practice, p. 51 ▪ Practice, p. 52 ▪ Word Problem Practice, p. 53
Other	▪ 5-Minute Check 2-8 ▪ Study Notebook	▪ 5-Minute Check 2-8 ▪ Study Notebook	▪ 5-Minute Check 2-8 ▪ Study Notebook	▪ 5-Minute Check 2-8 ▪ Study Notebook

1 Supplementary and Complementary Angles

Examples 1 and 2 show how to use the supplementary and complementary theorems to find the measures of unknown angles.

Formative Assessment

Use the Guided Practice exercises after each example to determine students' understanding of concepts.

Additional Examples

1 **CONSTRUCTION** Using a protractor, a construction worker measures that the angle a beam makes with ceiling is 42°. What is the measure of the angle the beam makes with the wall? 48

2 **TIME** At 4 o'clock, the angle between the hour and minute hands of a clock is 120°. When the second hand bisects the angle between the hour and minute hands, what are the measures of the angles between the minute and second hands and between the second and hour hands? They are both 60 by the definition of angle bisector and the Angle Addition Postulate.

Additional Examples also in Interactive Classroom PowerPoint® Presentations

Tips for New Teachers

Congruent Angles Remind students that angles can be congruent and that the measure of angles can be equal. To say that two angles are equal would mean that they are the same object in a figure.

The Angle Addition Postulate can be used with other angle relationships to provide additional theorems relating to angles.

StudyTip

Linear Pair Theorem The Supplement Theorem may also be known as the *Linear Pair Theorem.*

Theorems

2.3 Supplement Theorem If two angles form a linear pair, then they are supplementary angles.

Example $m\angle 1 + m\angle 2 = 180$

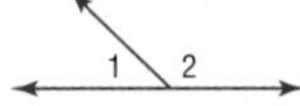

2.4 Complement Theorem If the noncommon sides of two adjacent angles form a right angle, then the angles are complementary angles.

Example $m\angle 1 + m\angle 2 = 90$

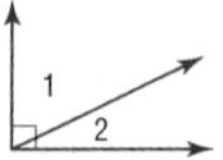

You will prove Theorems 2.3 and 2.4 in Exercises 16 and 17, respectively.

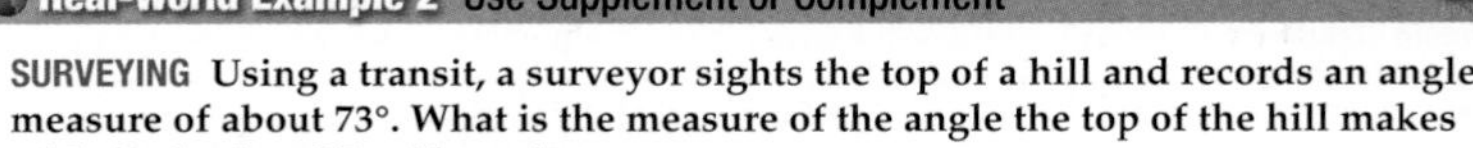

Real-World Example 2 Use Supplement or Complement

SURVEYING Using a transit, a surveyor sights the top of a hill and records an angle measure of about 73°. What is the measure of the angle the top of the hill makes with the horizon? Justify each step.

Understand Make a sketch of the situation. The surveyor is measuring the angle of his line of sight below the vertical. Draw a vertical ray and a horizontal ray from the point where the surveyor is sighting the hill, and label the angles formed. We know that the vertical and horizontal rays form a right angle.

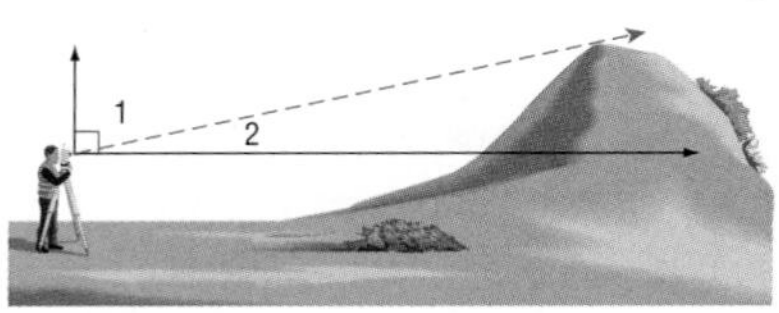

Plan Since ∠1, and ∠2 form a right angle, you can use the Complement Theorem.

Solve

$m\angle 1 + m\angle 2 = 90$	Complement Theorem
$73 + m\angle 2 = 90$	$m\angle 1 = 73$
$73 + m\angle 2 - 73 = 90 - 73$	Subtraction Property of Equality
$m\angle 2 = 17$	Substitution

The top of the hill makes a 17° angle with the horizon.

Check Since we know that the sum of the angles should be 90, check your math. The sum of 17 and 73 is 90. ✓

ReviewVocabulary

supplementary angles two angles with measures that add to 180

complementary angles two angles with measures that add to 90

linear pair a pair of adjacent angles with noncommon sides that are opposite rays

GuidedPractice

2. ∠6 and ∠7 form linear pair. If $m\angle 6 = 3x + 32$ and $m\angle 7 = 5x + 12$, find x, $m\angle 6$, and $m\angle 7$. Justify each step. **See margin.**

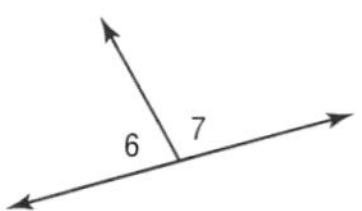

Additional Answer (Guided Practice)

2.
$m\angle 6 + m\angle 7 = 180$ (≅ Suppl. Thm.)
$3x + 32 + 5x + 12 = 180$ (Subs.)
$8x + 44 = 180$ (Subs.)
$8x + 44 - 44 = 180 - 44$ (Subt. Prop.)
$8x = 136$ (Subs.)
$\frac{8x}{8} = \frac{136}{8}$ (Div. Prop.)
$x = 17$ (Subs.)

$m\angle 6 = 3x + 32$ (Given)
$= 3(17) + 32$ or 83 (Subs.)
$m\angle 7 = 5x + 12$ (Given)
$= 5(17) + 12$ or 97 (Subs.)

2 Congruent Angles

Congruent Angles The properties of algebra that applied to the congruence of segments and the equality of their measures also hold true for the congruence of angles and the equality of their measures.

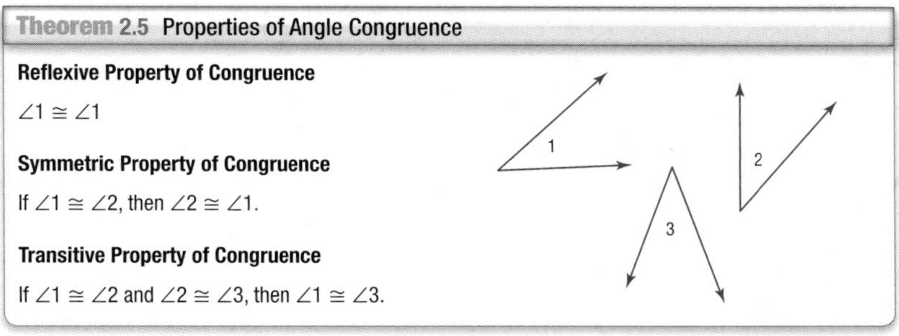

Theorem 2.5 Properties of Angle Congruence

Reflexive Property of Congruence

$\angle 1 \cong \angle 1$

Symmetric Property of Congruence

If $\angle 1 \cong \angle 2$, then $\angle 2 \cong \angle 1$.

Transitive Property of Congruence

If $\angle 1 \cong \angle 2$ and $\angle 2 \cong \angle 3$, then $\angle 1 \cong \angle 3$.

You will prove the Reflexive and Transitive Properties of Congruence in Exercises 18 and 19, respectively.

Proof Symmetric Property of Congruence

Given: $\angle A \cong \angle B$

Prove: $\angle B \cong \angle A$

Paragraph Proof:

We are given $\angle A \cong \angle B$. By the definition of congruent angles, $m\angle A = m\angle B$. Using the Symmetric Property of Equality, $m\angle B = m\angle A$. Thus, $\angle B \cong \angle A$ by the definition of congruent angles.

Algebraic properties can be applied to prove theorems for congruence relationships involving supplementary and complementary angles.

ReadingMath

Abbreviations and Symbols
The notation $\measuredangle$ means *angles.*

Theorems

2.6 Congruent Supplements Theorem
Angles supplementary to the same angle or to congruent angles are congruent.

Abbreviation *$\measuredangle$ suppl. to same $\angle$ or $\cong$ $\measuredangle$ are $\cong$.*

Example If $m\angle 1 + m\angle 2 = 180$ and $m\angle 2 + m\angle 3 = 180$, then $\angle 1 \cong \angle 3$.

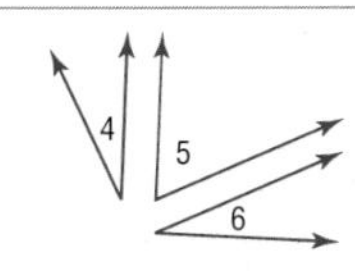

2.7 Congruent Complements Theorem
Angles complementary to the same angle or to congruent angles are congruent.

Abbreviation *$\measuredangle$ compl. to same $\angle$ or $\cong$ $\measuredangle$ are $\cong$.*

Example If $m\angle 4 + m\angle 5 = 90$ and $m\angle 5 + m\angle 6 = 90$, then $\angle 4 \cong \angle 6$.

You will prove one case of Theorem 2.6 in Exercise 6.

Teach with Tech

Video Recording Create a video of the examples you show in class. Post the recording to a video sharing Web site for students to view outside of class.

Focus on Mathematical Content

Writing Proofs The Symmetric Property is often assumed in proofs to reduce the number of steps in a proof. The rigor of proof is left up to the teacher, but this text will assume Symmetric Property statements in future chapters.

2 Congruent and Right Angles

Examples 3 and 4 show students how to prove congruency and find measurements of unknown angles.

WatchOut!

Answer the Question Instruct students to read problems carefully so they can be sure to provide the information requested. In the Guided Practice questions for Examples 2 and 4, point out that students are to find angle measures, not just the value of the variable. However, they have to use the value of the variable to find the correct answer.

Additional Example

3 In the figure, ∠1 and ∠4 form a linear pair, and $m\angle 3 + m\angle 1 = 180$. Prove that ∠3 and ∠4 are congruent.

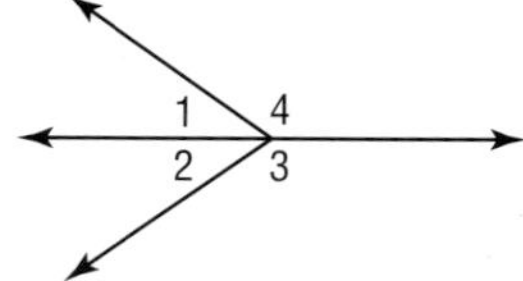

Statements (Reasons)

1. $m\angle 3 + m\angle 1 = 180$; ∠1 and ∠4 form a linear pair. (Given)
2. ∠1 and ∠4 are supplementary. (Linear pairs are supplementary.)
3. ∠3 and ∠1 are supplementary. (Def. of suppl. ∠s)
4. ∠3 ≅ ∠4 (Angles supplementary to same ∠ are ≅.)

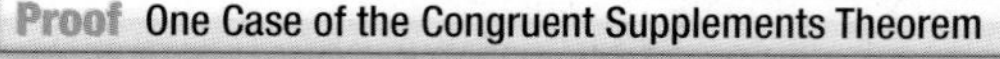

Proof One Case of the Congruent Supplements Theorem

Given: ∠1 and ∠2 are supplementary.
∠2 and ∠3 are supplementary.

Prove: ∠1 ≅ ∠3

Proof:

Statements	Reasons
1. ∠1 and ∠2 are supplementary. ∠2 and ∠3 are supplementary.	1. Given
2. $m\angle 1 + m\angle 2 = 180$; $m\angle 2 + m\angle 3 = 180$	2. Definition of supplementary angles
3. $m\angle 1 + m\angle 2 = m\angle 2 + m\angle 3$	3. Substitution
4. $m\angle 2 = m\angle 2$	4. Reflexive Property
5. $m\angle 1 = m\angle 3$	5. Subtraction Property
6. ∠1 ≅ ∠3	6. Definition of congruent angles

Example 3 Proofs Using Congruent Comp. or Suppl. Theorems

PT

Prove that vertical angles 2 and 4 in the photo at the left are congruent.

Given: ∠2 and ∠4 are vertical angles.

Prove: ∠2 ≅ ∠4

Proof:

Statements	Reasons
1. ∠2 and ∠4 are vertical angles.	1. Given
2. ∠2 and ∠4 are nonadjacent angles formed by intersecting lines.	2. Definition of vertical angles
3. ∠2 and ∠3 from a linear pair. ∠3 and ∠4 form a linear pair.	3. Definition of a linear pair
4. ∠2 and ∠3 are supplementary. ∠3 and ∠4 are supplementary.	4. Supplement Theorem
5. ∠2 ≅ ∠4	5. ∠s suppl. to same ∠ or ≅ ∠s are ≅.

Real-WorldLink

The 100-story John Hancock Building uses huge X-braces in its design. These diagonals are connected to the exterior columns, making it possible for strong wind forces to be carried from the braces to the exterior columns and back.

Source: PBS

GuidedPractice

3. In the figure, ∠ABE and ∠DBC are right angles. Prove that ∠ABD ≅ ∠EBC. **See margin.**

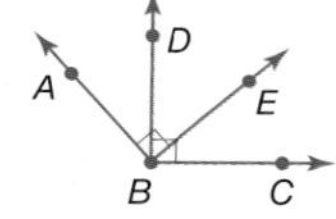

ReviewVocabulary

Vertical Angles two nonadjacent angles formed by intersecting lines

Note that in Example 3, ∠1 and ∠3 are vertical angles. The conclusion in the example supports the following Vertical Angles Theorem.

Theorem 2.8 Vertical Angles Theorem

If two angles are vertical angles, then they are congruent.

Abbreviation *Vert. ∠s are ≅.*

Example ∠1 ≅ ∠3 and ∠2 ≅ ∠4

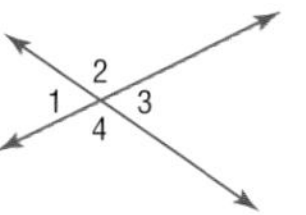

You will prove Theorem 2.8 in Exercise 28.

Tips for New Teachers

Examples Before explaining the formal proof, have students think of possible angle measures that could be used to support the Congruent Supplement Theorem.

Additional Answer (Guided Practice)

3. **Given:** ∠ABE and ∠DBC are right angles.

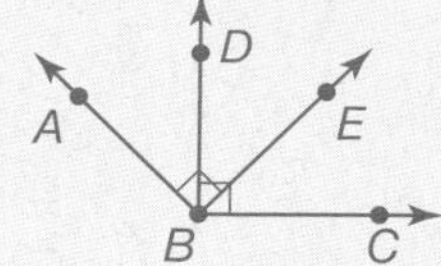

Prove: ∠ABD ≅ ∠EBC

Proof:

Statements (Reasons)

1. ∠ABE and ∠DBC are right angles. (Given)
2. $m\angle ABE = 90$; $m\angle DBC = 90$ (Def. of rt. ∠)
3. ∠ABD and ∠DBE are complementary; ∠DBE and ∠EBC are complementary. (≅ Comp. Thm.)
4. ∠ABD ≅ ∠EBC (∠s comp. to same ∠ or ≅ ∠s are ≅.)

4. $m\angle 3 = m\angle 4$ (Vert. ∠s Thm.)
$6x + 2 = 8x - 14$ (Subs.)
$6x + 2 + 14 = 8x - 14 + 14$ (Add. Prop.)
$6x + 16 = 8x$ (Subs.)
$6x + 16 - 6x = 8x - 6x$ (Subt. Prop.)
$16 = 2x$ (Subs.)
$\frac{16}{2} = \frac{2x}{2}$ (Div. Prop.)
$8 = x$ (Subs.)
$m\angle 3 = 6x + 2$ (Given)
$m\angle 3 = 6(8) + 2$ or 50 (Subs.)
$m\angle 4 = m\angle 3$ (Vert. ∠s Thm.)
$m\angle 4 = 50$ (Subs.)

Example 4 Use Vertical Angles

Prove that if $\overrightarrow{DB}$ bisects $\angle ADC$, then $\angle 2 \cong \angle 3$.

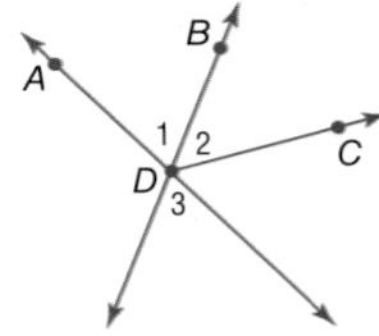

Given: $\overrightarrow{DB}$ bisects $\angle ADC$.

Prove: $\angle 2 \cong \angle 3$

Proof:

Statements	Reasons
1. $\overrightarrow{DB}$ bisects $\angle ADC$.	1. Given
2. $\angle 1 \cong \angle 2$	2. Definition of angle bisector
3. $\angle 1$ and $\angle 3$ are vertical angles.	3. Definition of vertical angles
4. $\angle 3 \cong \angle 1$	4. Vert. ∠s are ≅.
5. $\angle 3 \cong \angle 2$	5. Transitive Property of Congruence
6. $\angle 2 \cong \angle 3$	6. Symmetric Property of Congruence

GuidedPractice

4. If $\angle 3$ and $\angle 4$ are vertical angles, $m\angle 3 = 6x + 2$, and $m\angle 4 = 8x - 14$, find $m\angle 3$ and $m\angle 4$. Justify each step.

Additional Example

4 If $\angle 1$ and $\angle 2$ are vertical angles and $m\angle 1 = d - 32$ and $m\angle 2 = 175 - 2d$, find $m\angle 1$ and $m\angle 2$. Justify each step. 37; 37

Statements (Reasons)

1. $\angle 1$ and $\angle 2$ are vertical angles. (Given)
2. $\angle 1 \cong \angle 2$ (Vert. ∠s are congruent.)
3. $m\angle 1 = m\angle 2$ (Definition of congruence)
4. $d - 32 = 175 - 2d$ (Substitution Property of Equality)
5. $3d = 207$ (Additive Property of Equality)
6. $d = 69$ (Division Property of Equality)
7. $m\angle 1 = 37$ (Substitution Property of Equality)
8. $m\angle 2 = 37$ (Substitution Property of Equality)

The theorems in this lesson can be used to prove the following right angle theorems.

ReadingMath

Perpendicular Recall from Lesson 1-5 that the symbol ⊥ means *is perpendicular to*.

Theorems Right Angle Theorems

Theorem	Example
2.9 Perpendicular lines intersect to form four right angles. **Example** If $\overleftrightarrow{AC} \perp \overleftrightarrow{DB}$, then $\angle 1$, $\angle 2$, $\angle 3$, and $\angle 4$ are rt. ∠s.	(figure: A, B, C, D, 1, 2, 3, 4)
2.10 All right angles are congruent. **Example** If $\angle 1$, $\angle 2$, $\angle 3$, and $\angle 4$ are rt. ∠s, then $\angle 1 \cong \angle 2 \cong \angle 3 \cong \angle 4$.	
2.11 Perpendicular lines form congruent adjacent angles. **Example** If $\overleftrightarrow{AC} \perp \overleftrightarrow{DB}$, then $\angle 1 \cong \angle 2$, $\angle 2 \cong \angle 4$, $\angle 3 \cong \angle 4$, and $\angle 1 \cong \angle 3$.	
2.12 If two angles are congruent and supplementary, then each angle is a right angle. **Example** If $\angle 5 \cong \angle 6$ and $\angle 5$ is suppl. to $\angle 6$, then $\angle 5$ and $\angle 6$ are rt. ∠s.	(figure: 5, 6)
2.13 If two congruent angles form a linear pair, then they are right angles. **Example** If $\angle 7$ and $\angle 8$ form a linear pair, then $\angle 7$ and $\angle 8$ are rt. ∠s.	(figure: 7, 8)

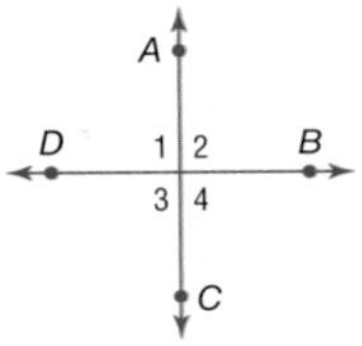

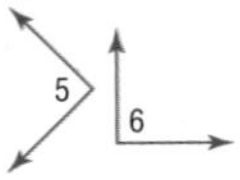

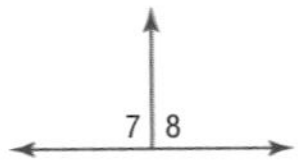

You will prove Theorems 2.9–2.13 in Exercises 22–26.

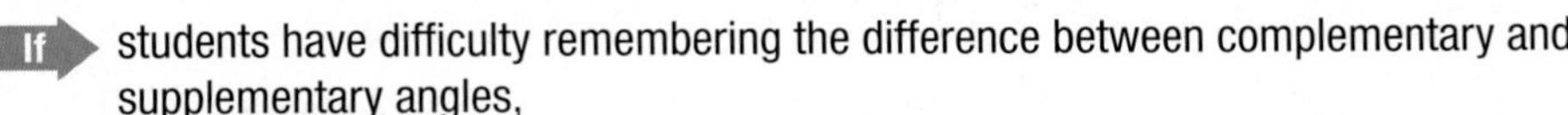

If students have difficulty remembering the difference between complementary and supplementary angles,

Then have them write a short poem or rhyme to help them remember the definitions.

3 Practice

Formative Assessment

Use Exercises 1–7 to check for understanding.

Use the chart at the bottom of this page to customize assignments for your students.

Additional Answers

1. $m\angle 1 = 90$, $m\angle 3 = 64$; Comp. Thm.
2. $m\angle 2 = 53$, $m\angle 3 = 37$; Comp. Thm.
3. $m\angle 4 = 114$, $m\angle 5 = 66$; Suppl. Thm.
4. $m\angle 4 = 129$, $m\angle 5 = 51$; Suppl. Thm.
5. **Given:** $\angle 2 \cong \angle 6$

   Prove: $\angle 4 \cong \angle 8$

   Proof:

   Statements (Reasons)

   1. $\angle 2 \cong \angle 6$ (Given)
   2. $m\angle 2 + m\angle 4 = 180$, $m\angle 6 + m\angle 8 = 180$ (Suppl. Thm.)
   3. $m\angle 2 + m\angle 8 = 180$ (Subs.)
   4. $m\angle 2 - m\angle 2 + m\angle 4 = 180 - m\angle 2$, $m\angle 2 - m\angle 2 + m\angle 8 = 180 - m\angle 2$ (Subt. Prop.)
   5. $m\angle 4 = 180 - m\angle 2$, $m\angle 8 = 180 - m\angle 2$ (Subt. Prop.)
   6. $m\angle 4 = m\angle 8$ (Subs.)
   7. $\angle 4 \cong \angle 8$ (Def. ≅ ∠s)
7. **Given:** $\angle 4 \cong \angle 7$

   Prove: $\angle 5 \cong \angle 6$

   Proof:

   Statements (Reasons)

   1. $\angle 4 \cong \angle 7$ (Given)
   2. $\angle 4 \cong \angle 5$ and $\angle 6 \cong \angle 7$ (Vert. ∠s Thm.)
   3. $\angle 7 \cong \angle 5$ (Subs.)
   4. $\angle 5 \cong \angle 6$ (Subs.)

Check Your Understanding

 = Step-by-Step Solutions begin on page R14.

Example 1 **Find the measure of each numbered angle, and name the theorems that justify your work.** 1–4. See margin.

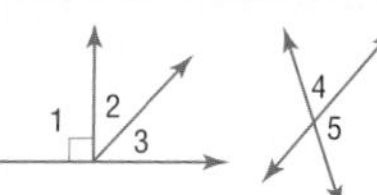

1. $m\angle 2 = 26$
2. $m\angle 2 = x$, $m\angle 3 = x - 16$
3. $m\angle 4 = 2x$, $m\angle 5 = x + 9$
4. $m\angle 4 = 3(x - 1)$, $m\angle 5 = x + 7$

Example 2

5. **PARKING** Refer to the diagram of the parking lot at the right. Given that $\angle 2 \cong \angle 6$, prove that $\angle 4 \cong \angle 8$. See margin.

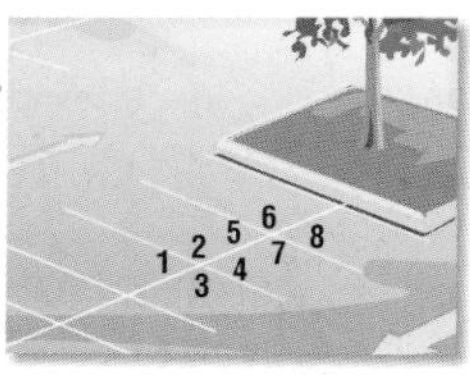

Example 3

6. **PROOF** Copy and complete the proof of one case of Theorem 2.6.

   Given: $\angle 1$ and $\angle 3$ are complementary. $\angle 2$ and $\angle 3$ are complementary.

   Prove: $\angle 1 \cong \angle 2$

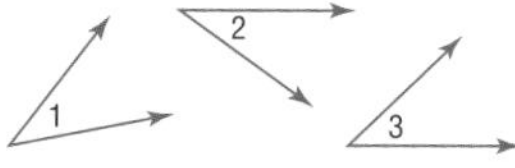

Proof:

Statements	Reasons
a. $\angle 1$ and $\angle 3$ are complementary. $\angle 2$ and $\angle 3$ are complementary.	a. ___?___ Given
b. $m\angle 1 + m\angle 3 = 90$; $m\angle 2 + m\angle 3 = 90$	b. ___?___ Def. of comp. ∠s
c. $m\angle 1 + m\angle 3 = m\angle 2 + m\angle 3$	c. ___?___ Subs.
d. ___?___ $m\angle 3 = m\angle 3$	d. Reflexive Property
e. $m\angle 1 = m\angle 2$	e. ___?___ Subt. Prop.
f. $\angle 1 \cong \angle 2$	f. ___?___ Def ≅ ∠s

Example 4

7. **PROOF** Write a two-column proof.

   Given: $\angle 4 \cong \angle 7$

   Prove: $\angle 5 \cong \angle 6$ See margin.

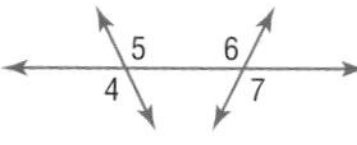

Practice and Problem Solving

Extra Practice is on page R2.

Examples 1–3 **Find the measure of each numbered angle, and name the theorems used that justify your work.**

8. $m\angle 5 = m\angle 6$

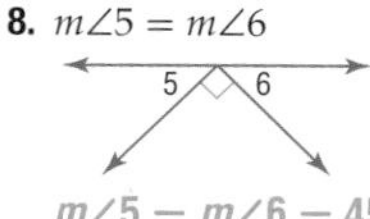

$m\angle 5 = m\angle 6 = 45$ (≅ Supp. Thm.)

9. $\angle 2$ and $\angle 3$ are complementary. $\angle 1 \cong \angle 4$ and $m\angle 2 = 28$

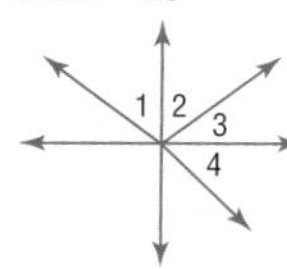

$m\angle 3 = 62$, $m\angle 1 = m\angle 4 = 45$ (≅ Comp. and Supp. Thm.)

10. $\angle 2$ and $\angle 4$ and $\angle 4$ and $\angle 5$ are supplementary. $m\angle 4 = 105$

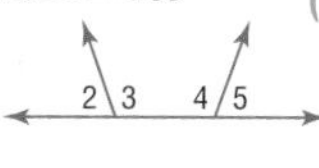

$m\angle 2 = 75$, $m\angle 3 = 105$, $m\angle 5 = 75$ (≅ Supp. Thm.)

Differentiated Homework Options

Level	Assignment	Two-Day Option	
AL Basic	8–15, 31, 32, 34–53	9–15 odd, 36–39	8–14 even, 31, 32, 34, 35, 40–53
OL Core	9–15 odd, 16–32, 34–53	8–15, 36–39	16–32, 34, 35, 40–53
BL Advanced	16–48, (optional: 49–53)		

Find the measure of each numbered angle and name the theorems used that justify your work.

11. $m\angle 9 = 3x + 12$
$m\angle 10 = x - 24$

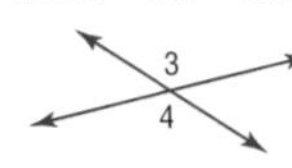

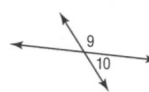

12. $m\angle 3 = 2x + 23$
$m\angle 4 = 5x - 112$

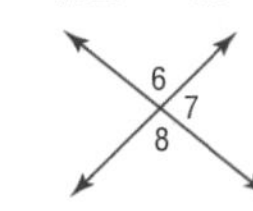

13. $m\angle 6 = 2x - 21$
$m\angle 7 = 3x - 34$

11. $m\angle 9 = 156$, $m\angle 10 = 24$ (≅ Supp. Thm.)
12. $m\angle 3 = 113$, $m\angle 4 = 113$ (Vert. ⦞ Thm.)
13. $m\angle 6 = 73$, $m\angle 7 = 107$, $m\angle 8 = 73$ (≅ Supp. Thm. and Vert. ⦞ Thm.)

Example 4 **PROOF** Write a two-column proof. **14, 15. See Ch. 2 Answer Appendix.**

14. **Given:** $\angle ABC$ is a right angle.
Prove: $\angle ABD$ and $\angle CBD$ are complementary.

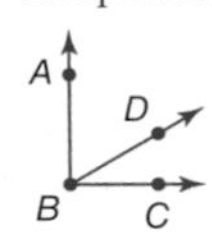

15. **Given:** $\angle 5 \cong \angle 6$
Prove: $\angle 4$ and $\angle 6$ are supplementary.

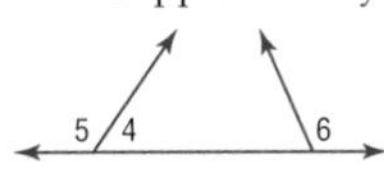

B Write a proof for each theorem. **16–19. See Ch. 2 Answer Appendix.**

16. Supplement Theorem
17. Complement Theorem
18. Reflexive Property of Angle Congruence
19. Transitive Property of Angle Congruence

20. **FLAGS** Refer to the Florida state flag at the right. Prove that the sum of the four angle measures is 360. **See Ch. 2 Answer Appendix.**

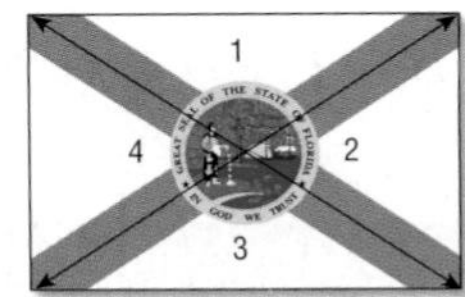

21. **CCSS ARGUMENTS** The diamondback rattlesnake is a pit viper with a diamond pattern on its back. An enlargement of a skin is shown below. If $\angle 1 \cong \angle 4$, prove that $\angle 2 \cong \angle 3$. **See Ch. 2 Answer Appendix.**

PROOF Use the figure to write a proof of each theorem. **22–26. See Ch. 2 Answer Appendix.**

22. Theorem 2.9
23. Theorem 2.10
24. Theorem 2.11
25. Theorem 2.12
26. Theorem 2.13

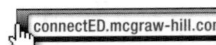

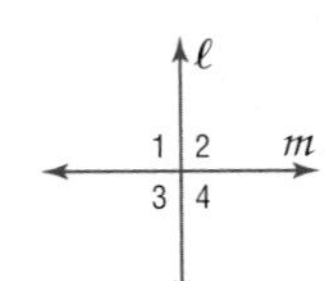

Teaching the Mathematical Practices

Arguments Mathematically proficient students understand and use stated assumptions, definitions, and previously established results in constructing arguments. In Exercise 21, encourage students to determine the relationship between $\angle 1$ and $\angle 2$ and $\angle 3$ and $\angle 4$ first.

Enrichment
OL BL

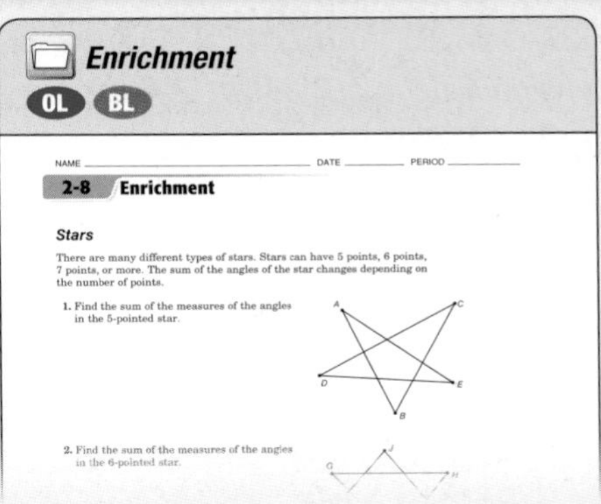

2-8 Enrichment

Stars

There are many different types of stars. Stars can have 5 points, 6 points, 7 points, or more. The sum of the angles of the star changes depending on the number of points.

1. Find the sum of the measures of the angles in the 5-pointed star.

2. Find the sum of the measures of the angles in the 6-pointed star.

Study Guide and Intervention
AL OL ELL

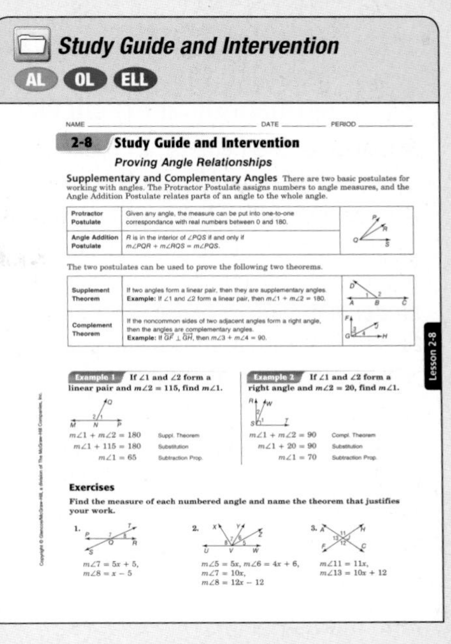

2-8 Study Guide and Intervention

Proving Angle Relationships

Supplementary and Complementary Angles There are two basic postulates for working with angles. The Protractor Postulate assigns numbers to angle measures, and the Angle Addition Postulate relates parts of an angle to the whole angle.

The two postulates can be used to prove the following two theorems.

Exercises

Find the measure of each numbered angle and name the theorem that justifies your work.

Practice
AL OL BL ELL

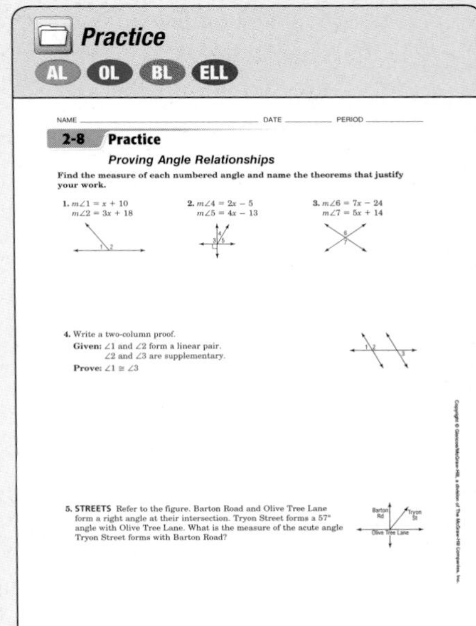

2-8 Practice

Proving Angle Relationships

Find the measure of each numbered angle and name the theorems that justify your work.

4. Write a two-column proof.

5. STREETS Refer to the figure. Barton Road and Olive Tree Lane form a right angle at their intersection. Tryon Street forms a 57° angle with Olive Tree Lane. What is the measure of the acute angle Tryon Street forms with Barton Road?

Word Problem Practice
AL OL BL ELL

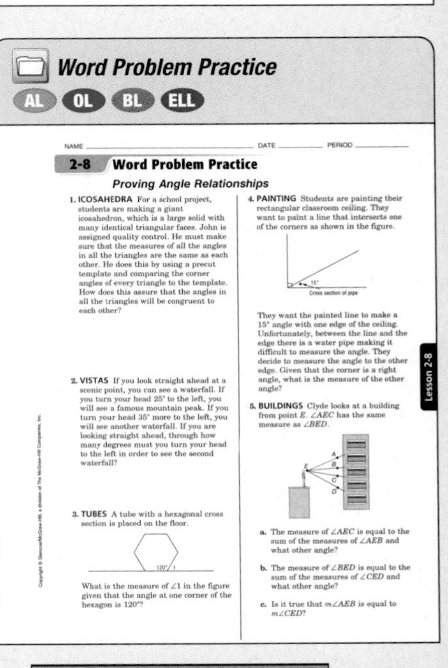

2-8 Word Problem Practice

Proving Angle Relationships

1. ICOSAHEDRA

2. VISTAS

3. TUBES

4. PAINTING

5. BUILDINGS

Teaching the Mathematical Practices

Arguments Mathematically proficient students understand and use stated assumptions, definitions, and previously established results in constructing arguments. In Exercise 27, encourage students to write a two-column proof first to ensure that they have a valid reason for each statement.

Multiple Representations

In Exercise 30, students use geometric sketches, verbal description, and proof to investigate angles in a triangle.

Additional Answers

27. Since the path of the pendulum forms a right angle, $\angle ABC$ is a right angle, or measures 90. $\overrightarrow{BR}$ divides $\angle ABC$ into $\angle ABR$ and $\angle CBR$. By the Angle Addition Postulate, $m\angle ABR + m\angle CBR = m\angle ABC$, and, using substitution, $m\angle ABR + m\angle CBR = 90$. Substituting again, $m\angle 1 + m\angle 2 = 90$. We are given that $m\angle 1$ is 45, so, substituting, $45 + m\angle 2 = 90$. Using the Subtraction Property, $45 - 45 + m\angle 2 = 90 - 45$, or $m\angle 2 = 45$. Since $m\angle 1$ and $m\angle 2$ are equal, $\overrightarrow{BR}$ is the bisector of $\angle ABC$ by the definition of angle bisector.

28. Given: $\angle 1$ and $\angle 3$ are vertical angles.

Prove: $\angle 1 \cong \angle 3$

Proof: Since $\angle 1$ and $\angle 3$ are vertical angles, they are formed by intersecting lines. Then we know that $\angle 1$ and $\angle 2$ are a linear pair and $\angle 2$ and $\angle 3$ are also a linear pair. By Theorem 2.3, $\angle 1$ and $\angle 2$ are supplementary angles and $\angle 2$ and $\angle 3$ are supplementary angles. Then by the Transitive Property of Congruence, $\angle 1 \cong \angle 3$.

35. Sample answer: Since protractors have the scale for both acute and obtuse angles along the top, the supplement is the measure of the given angle on the other scale.

27. ARGUMENTS To mark a specific tempo, the weight on the pendulum of a metronome is adjusted so that it swings at a specific rate. Suppose $\angle ABC$ in the photo is a right angle. If $m\angle 1 = 45$, write a paragraph proof to show that $\overrightarrow{BR}$ bisects $\angle ABC$. **See margin.**

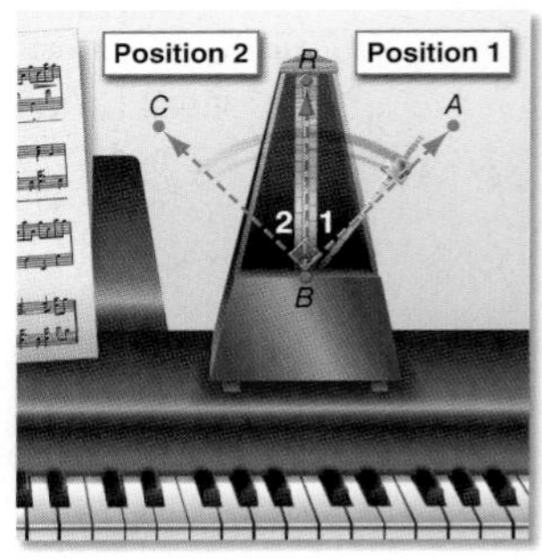

28. PROOF Write a proof of Theorem 2.8. **See margin.**

29. GEOGRAPHY Utah, Colorado, Arizona, and New Mexico all share a common point on their borders called Four Corners. This is the only place where four states meet in a single point. If $\angle 2$ is a right angle, prove that lines ℓ and m are perpendicular. **See Ch. 2 Answer Appendix.**

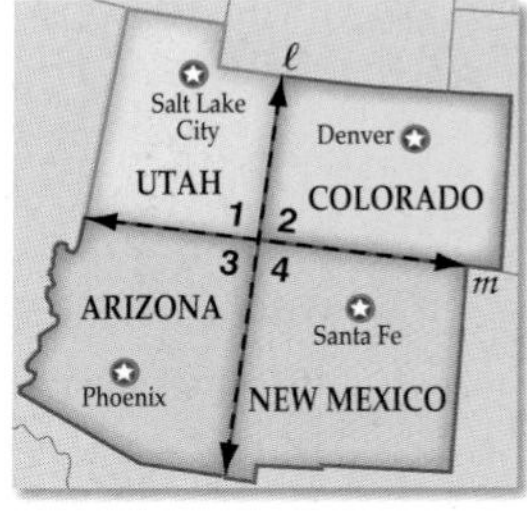

30. MULTIPLE REPRESENTATIONS In this problem, you will explore angle relationships.

a. Geometric Draw a right angle ABC. Place point D in the interior of this angle and draw $\overrightarrow{BD}$. Draw $\overrightarrow{KL}$ and construct $\angle JKL$ congruent to $\angle ABD$.

b. Verbal Make a conjecture as to the relationship between $\angle JKL$ and $\angle DBC$.

c. Logical Prove your conjecture. **a–c. See Ch. 2 Answer Appendix.**

H.O.T. Problems Use Higher-Order Thinking Skills

31. OPEN ENDED Draw an angle WXZ such that $m\angle WXZ = 45$. Construct $\angle YXZ$ congruent to $\angle WXZ$. Make a conjecture as to the measure of $\angle WXY$, and then prove your conjecture. **See Ch. 2 Answer Appendix.**

32. WRITING IN MATH Write the steps that you would use to complete the proof below.

Given: $\overline{BC} \cong \overline{CD}$, $AB = \frac{1}{2}BD$

Prove: $\overline{AB} \cong \overline{CD}$

A B C D

Sample answer: First, show that $BC = CD$ and $BC + CD = BD$. Then use substitution to show that $CD + CD = BD$ and $2CD = BD$. Divide to show that $CD = \frac{1}{2}BD$, so $AB = CD$. That means that $\overline{AB} \cong \overline{CD}$.

33. CHALLENGE In this lesson, one case of the Congruent Supplements Theorem was proven. In Exercise 6, you proved the same case for the Congruent Complements Theorem. Explain why there is another case for each of these theorems. Then write a proof of this second case for each theorem. **See Ch. 2 Answer Appendix.**

34. REASONING Determine whether the following statement is *sometimes*, *always*, or *never* true. Explain your reasoning.

If one of the angles formed by two intersecting lines is acute, then the other three angles formed are also acute. **See Ch. 2 Answer Appendix.**

35. WRITING IN MATH Explain how you can use your protractor to quickly find the measure of the supplement of an angle. **See margin.**

Differentiated Instruction BL

Extension Find $m\angle C$ if $\angle C \cong \angle A$, $m\angle A = 3x$, $m\angle B = x + 20$, and $\angle A$ and $\angle B$ are supplementary. Verify your answer.

1. $m\angle A + m\angle B = 180$ (Def. of Supp. ∠s)
2. $3x + x + 20 = 180$ (Substitution)
3. $x = 40$ (Substitution)
4. $m\angle A = m\angle C$ (Def. of ≅ ∠s)
5. $m\angle C = 3x$ (Substitution)
6. $m\angle C = 3(40)$ (Substitution)
7. $m\angle C = 120$ (Substitution)

Standardized Test Practice

36. GRIDDED RESPONSE What is the mode of this set of data? **4**

4, 3, −2, 1 , 4, 0, 1, 4

37. Find the measure of $\angle CFD$. **A**

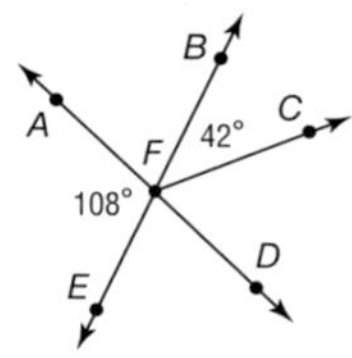

A 66° C 108°

B 72° D 138°

38. ALGEBRA Simplify. **H**

$$4(3x - 2)(2x + 4) + 3x^2 + 5x - 6$$

F $9x^2 + 3x - 14$

G $9x^2 + 13x - 14$

H $27x^2 + 37x - 38$

J $27x^2 + 27x - 26$

39. SAT/ACT On a coordinate grid where each unit represents 1 mile, Isabel's house is located at (3, 0) and a mall is located at (0, 4). What is the distance between Isabel's house and the mall? **B**

A 3 miles D 13 miles

B 5 miles E 25 miles

C 12 miles

Spiral Review

40. MAPS On a U.S. map, there is a scale that lists kilometers on the top and miles on the bottom.

0 km	20	40	50	60	80	100
0 mi			31			62

Suppose $\overline{AB}$ and $\overline{CD}$ are segments on this map. If $AB = 100$ kilometers and $CD = 62$ miles, is $\overline{AB} \cong \overline{CD}$? Explain. (Lesson 2-7) **See margin.**

State the property that justifies each statement. (Lesson 2-6)

41. If $y + 7 = 5$, then $y = -2$. **Subt. Prop.**

42. If $MN = PQ$, then $PQ = MN$. **Symm. Prop.**

43. If $a - b = x$ and $b = 3$, then $a - 3 = x$. **Subs.**

44. If $x(y + z) = 4$, then $xy + xz = 4$. **Dist. Prop.**

Determine the truth value of the following statement for each set of conditions.
If you have a fever, then you are sick. (Lesson 2-3)

45. You do not have a fever, and you are sick. **true**

46. You have a fever, and you are not sick. **false**

47. You do not have a fever, and you are not sick. **true**

48. You have a fever, and you are sick. **true**

Skills Review

Refer to the figure.

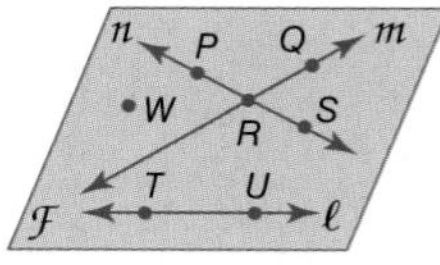

49. Name a line that contains point P. **line n**

50. Name the intersection of lines n and m. **point R**

51. Name a point not contained in lines ℓ, m, or n. **point W**

52. What is another name for line n? **Sample answer: $\overleftrightarrow{PR}$**

53. Does line ℓ intersect line m or line n? Explain. **See margin.**

4 Assess

Ticket Out the Door Give students a list of theorems from this chapter. Have each choose a theorem and write a summary of it without using their books. Have students turn in the summaries as they leave the classroom.

Formative Assessment

Check for student understanding of Lessons 2-7 and 2-8.

Quiz 4, p. 58

Additional Answers

40. Yes; according to the scale, 100 km and 62 mi are the same length. So, $AB = CD$. By the definition of the congruence, $\overline{AB} \cong \overline{CD}$.

53. Yes; it intersects both m and n when all three lines are extended.

Formative Assessment

KeyVocabulary The page references after each word denote where that term was first introduced. If students have difficulty answering questions 1–10, remind them that they can use these page references to refresh their memories about the vocabulary terms.

Summative Assessment

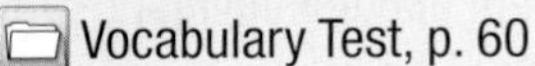

Vocabulary Test, p. 60

Vocabulary Review

Vocabulary Review provides students the opportunity to check their understanding of important concepts and terminology in an online game format.

FOLDABLES® StudyOrganizer

Dinah Zike's Foldables®

Have students look through the chapter to make sure they have included examples in their Foldables for each tab. Suggest that students keep their Foldables handy while completing the Study Guide and Review pages. Point out that their Foldables can serve as a quick review tool for studying for the chapter test.

Additional Answers

1. false; theorem
3. true
4. false; inverse
7. true

CHAPTER 2 Study Guide and Review

Study Guide

KeyConcepts

Inductive Reasoning and Logic (Lessons 2-1 and 2-2)

- Inductive reasoning: a conjecture is reached based on observations of a previous pattern
- Counterexample: an example that proves a conjecture is false
- Negation of statement p: *not* p
- Conjunction: a compound statement formed with the word *and*
- Disjunction: a compound statement formed with the word *or*

Conditional Statements (Lesson 2-3)

- An if-then statement is written in the form if p, then q in which p is the hypothesis and q is the conclusion.

statement	$p \rightarrow q$
converse	$q \rightarrow p$
inverse	not $p \rightarrow$ not q
contrapositive	not $q \rightarrow$ not p

Deductive Reasoning (Lesson 2-4)

- Law of Detachment: If $p \rightarrow q$ is true and p is true, then q is also true.
- Law of Syllogism: If $p \rightarrow q$ and $q \rightarrow r$ are true, then $p \rightarrow r$ is also true.

Proof (Lessons 2-5 through 2-8)

Step 1 List the given information and draw a diagram, if possible.

Step 2 State what is to be proved.

Step 3 Create a deductive argument.

Step 4 Justify each statement with a reason.

Step 5 State what you have proved.

FOLDABLES StudyOrganizer

Be sure the Key Concepts are noted in your Foldable.

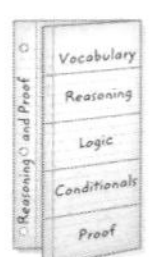

KeyVocabulary

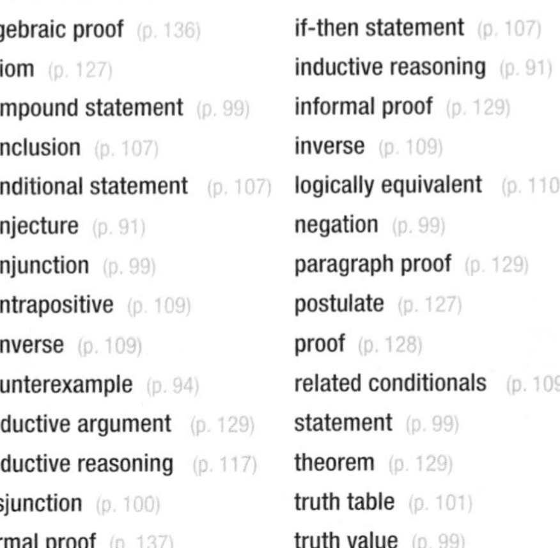

algebraic proof (p. 136)	if-then statement (p. 107)
axiom (p. 127)	inductive reasoning (p. 91)
compound statement (p. 99)	informal proof (p. 129)
conclusion (p. 107)	inverse (p. 109)
conditional statement (p. 107)	logically equivalent (p. 110)
conjecture (p. 91)	negation (p. 99)
conjunction (p. 99)	paragraph proof (p. 129)
contrapositive (p. 109)	postulate (p. 127)
converse (p. 109)	proof (p. 128)
counterexample (p. 94)	related conditionals (p. 109)
deductive argument (p. 129)	statement (p. 99)
deductive reasoning (p. 117)	theorem (p. 129)
disjunction (p. 100)	truth table (p. 101)
formal proof (p. 137)	truth value (p. 99)
hypothesis (p. 107)	two-column proof (p. 137)

VocabularyCheck

State whether each sentence is *true* or *false*. If *false*, replace the underlined term to make a true sentence. 1, 3, 4, 7. See margin

1. A postulate is a statement that requires proof.
2. The first part of an if-then statement is the conjecture. false; hypothesis
3. Deductive reasoning uses the laws of mathematics to reach logical conclusions from given statements.
4. The contrapositive is formed by negating the hypothesis and conclusion of a conditional.
5. A conjunction is formed by joining two or more statements with the word *and*. true
6. A theorem is a statement that is accepted as true without proof. false; postulate
7. The converse is formed by exchanging the hypothesis and conclusion of a conditional.
8. To show that a conjecture is false, you would provide a disjunction. false; counterexample
9. The inverse of a statement p would be written in the form *not p*. false; negation
10. In a two-column proof, the properties that justify each step are called reasons. true

Lesson-by-Lesson Review

2-1 Inductive Reasoning and Conjecture

Determine whether each conjecture is *true* or *false*. If false, give a counterexample.

11. If ∠1 and ∠2 are supplementary angles, then ∠1 and ∠2 form a linear pair.

12. If $W(-3, 2)$, $X(-3, 7)$, $Y(6, 7)$, $Z(6, 2)$, then quadrilateral *WXYZ* is a rectangle. true

13. **PARKS** Jacinto enjoys hiking with his dog in the forest at his local park. While on vacation in Smoky Mountain National Park in Tennessee, he was disappointed that dogs were not allowed on most hiking trails. Make a conjecture about why his local park and the national park have differing rules with regard to pets. See margin.

11. False; two nonadjacent supplementary angles

Example 1

Determine whether each conjecture is *true* or *false*. If false, give a counterexample.

a. $c = d$, $d = c$ is an example of a property of real numbers.

$c = d$, $d = c$ is an example of the Symmetric Property of real numbers, so the conjecture is true.

b. If $AB + CD = AD$, then *B* and *C* are between *A* and *D*.

This conjecture is false. In the figure below, $AB + CD = AD$, but *B* and *C* are not between *A* and *D*.

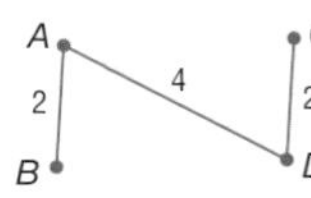

2-2 Logic

Use the following statements to write a compound statement for each conjunction or disjunction. Then find its truth value. Explain.

p: A plane contains at least three noncollinear points.

q: A square yard is equivalent to three square feet.

r: The sum of the measures of two complementary angles is 180. 14–16. See margin.

14. $\sim q \vee r$ **15.** $p \wedge \sim r$ **16.** $\sim p \vee q$

17. **PETS** The Venn diagram shows the results of a pet store survey to determine the pets customers owned.

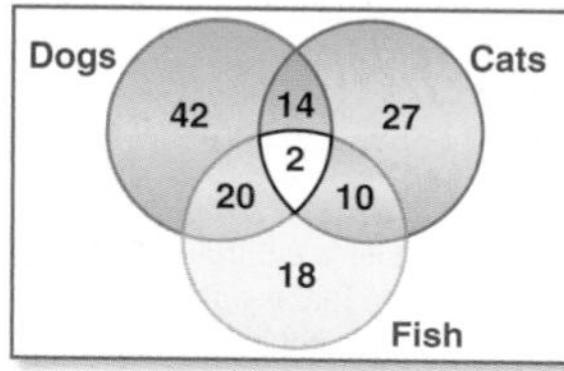

a. How many customers had only fish? 18

b. How many had only cats and dogs? 14

c. How many had dogs as well as fish? 22

Example 2

Use the following statements to write a compound statement for each conjunction or disjunction. Then find its truth value. Explain.

p: x^2 is a nonnegative number.

q: Adjacent angles lie in the same plane.

r: A negative number is not a real number.

a. $\sim q \wedge r$

$\sim q \wedge r$: Adjacent angles do not lie in the same plane, and a negative number is not a real number.

Since both $\sim q$ and *r* are false, $\sim q \wedge r$ is false.

b. *p* or *r*

p or *r*: x^2 is a nonnegative number, or a negative number is not a real number.

p or *r* is true because *p* is true. It does not matter that *r* is false.

Lesson-by-Lesson Review

Daily Intervention If the given examples are not sufficient to review the topics covered by the questions, remind students that the lesson references tell them where to review that topic in their textbooks.

Two-Day Option Have students complete the Lesson-by-Lesson Review. Then you can use eAssessment to customize another review worksheet that practices all the objectives of this chapter or only the objectives on which your students need more help.

Additional Answers

13. Sample answer: Dogs or other pets may threaten or chase wildlife that might not be present in his local park.

14. A square yard is not equivalent to three square feet or the sum of the measures of two complementary angles is 180; true.

15. A plane contains at least three noncollinear points and the sum of the measures of two complementary angles is not 180; true.

16. A plane does not contain at least three noncollinear points or a square yard is equivalent to three square feet; false.

Additional Answers

20. Converse: If two angles have the same degree measure, then they are congruent. True.

    Inverse: If two angles are not congruent, then they do not have the same degree measure. True.

    Contrapositive: If two angles do not have the same degree measure, then they are not congruent. True.

21. *PQRS* is a parallelogram; Law of Detachment.
22. Invalid; the Law of Syllogism does not apply since the conclusion of the first statement is not the hypothesis of the second statement.
23. Valid; Law of Detachment

CHAPTER 2 Study Guide and Review *Continued*

2-3 Conditional Statements

Determine the truth value of each conditional statement. If *true*, explain your reasoning. If *false*, give a counterexample.

18. If you square an integer, then the result is a positive integer. **true**
19. If a hexagon has eight sides, then all of its angles will be obtuse. **true**
20. Write the converse, inverse, and contrapositive of the following true conditional. Then, determine whether each related conditional is *true* or *false*. If a statement is false, find a counterexample. **See margin.**

    If two angles are congruent, then they have the same degree measure.

Example 3

Write the *converse*, *inverse*, and *contrapositive* of the following true conditional.

If a figure is a square, then it is a parallelogram.

Converse:	If a figure is a parallelogram, then it is a square.
Inverse:	If a figure is not a square, then it is not a parallelogram.
Contrapositive:	If a figure is not a parallelogram, then it is not a square.

2-4 Deductive Reasoning

Draw a valid conclusion from the given statements, if possible. Then state whether your conclusion was drawn using the Law of Detachment or the Law of Syllogism. If no valid conclusion can be drawn, write *no valid conclusion* and explain your reasoning. **21–23. See margin.**

21. **Given:** If a quadrilateral has diagonals that bisect each other, then it is a parallelogram.

    The diagonals of quadrilateral *PQRS* bisect each other.
22. **Given:** If Liana struggles in science class, then she will receive tutoring.

    If Liana stays after school on Thursday, then she will receive tutoring.
23. **EARTHQUAKES** Determine whether the stated conclusion is valid based on the given information. If not, write *invalid*. Explain.

    Given: If an earthquake measures a 7.0 or higher on the Richter scale, then it is considered a major earthquake that could cause serious damage. The 1906 San Francisco earthquake measured 8.0 on the Richter scale.

    Conclusion: The 1906 San Francisco earthquake was a major earthquake that caused serious damage.

Example 4

Use the Law of Syllogism to determine whether a valid conclusion can be reached from the following statements.

(1) If the measure of an angle is greater than 90, then it is an obtuse angle.

(2) If an angle is an obtuse angle, then it is not a right angle.

p: the measure of an angle is greater than 90

q: the angle is an obtuse angle

r: the angle is not a right angle

Statement (1): $p \rightarrow q$

Statement (2): $q \rightarrow r$

Since the given statements are true, use the Law of Syllogism to conclude that $p \rightarrow r$. That is, *If the measure of an angle is greater than 90, then it is not a right angle.*

2-5 Postulates and Paragraph Proofs

Determine whether each statement is *always, sometimes,* or *never* true. Explain. **24–27. See margin.**

24. Two planes intersect at a point.

25. Three points are contained in more than one plane.

26. If line m lies in plane $\mathcal{X}$ and line m contains a point Q, then point Q lies in plane $\mathcal{X}$.

27. If two angles are complementary, then they form a right angle.

28. **NETWORKING** Six people are introduced at a business convention. If each person shakes hands with each of the others, how many handshakes will be exchanged? Include a model to support your reasoning. **See margin.**

Example 5

Determine whether each statement is *always, sometimes,* or *never* true. Explain.

a. ***If points X, Y, and Z lie in plane $\mathcal{R}$, then they are not collinear.***

Sometimes; the fact that X, Y, and Z are contained in plane $\mathcal{R}$ has no bearing on whether those points are collinear or not.

b. **For any two points A and B, there is exactly one line that contains them.**

Always; according to Postulate 2-1, there is exactly one line through any two points.

2-6 Algebraic Proof

State the property that justifies each statement.

29. If $7(x-3)=35$, then $35=7(x-3)$. **Symm. Prop.**

30. If $2x+19=27$, then $2x=8$. **Subt. Prop.**

31. $5(3x+1)=15x+5$ **Distr. Prop.**

32. $7x-2=7x-2$ **Reflex. Prop.**

33. If $12=2x+8$ and $2x+8=3y$, then $12=3y$. **Trans. Prop.**

34. Copy and complete the following proof.

Given: $6(x-4)=42$

Prove: $x=11$

Statements	Reasons
a. $6(x-4)=42$	**a.** ? **Given**
b. $6x-24=42$	**b.** ? **Dist. Prop.**
c. $6x=66$	**c.** ? **Add. Prop.**
d. $x=11$	**d.** ? **Div. Prop.**

35. Write a two-column proof to show that if $PQ=RS$, $PQ=5x+9$, and $RS=x-31$, then $x=-10$. **See margin.**

36. **GRADES** Jerome received the same quarter grade as Paula. Paula received the same quarter grade as Heath. Which property would show that Jerome and Heath received the same grade? **Trans. Prop.**

Example 6

Write a two-column proof.

Given: $\frac{5x-3}{6}=2x+1$

Prove: $x=-\frac{9}{7}$

Proof:

Statements	Reasons
1. $\frac{5x-3}{6}=2x+1$	**1.** Given
2. $5x-3=6(2x+1)$	**2.** Multiplication Property of Equality
3. $5x-3=12x+6$	**3.** Distributive Property of Equality
4. $-3=7x+6$	**4.** Subtraction Property of Equality
5. $-9=7x$	**5.** Subtraction Property of Equality
6. $-\frac{9}{7}=x$	**6.** Division Property of Equality
7. $x=-\frac{9}{7}$	**7.** Symmetric Property of Equality

163

Additional Answers

24. Never; if two planes intersect, they form a line.

25. Sometimes; if the three points are collinear, they will be contained in multiple planes, but if they are noncollinear, they will be contained in only one plane.

26. Always; if a plane contains a line, then every point of that line lies in the plane.

27. Sometimes; if the angles are adjacent, they will form a right angle, but if they are not adjacent, they will not.

28. 15 handshakes;

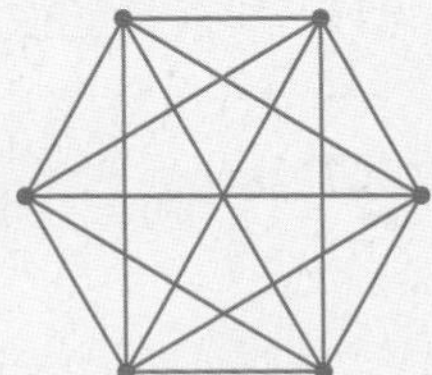

35. **Statements (Reasons)**

1. $PQ=RS$, $PQ=5x+9$, $RS=x-31$ (Given)
2. $5x+9=x-31$ (Subs. Prop.)
3. $4x+9=-31$ (Subt. Prop.)
4. $4x=-40$ (Subt. Prop.)
5. $x=-10$ (Div. Prop.)

Anticipation Guide

Have students complete the Chapter 2 Anticipation Guide, and discuss how their responses have changed now that they have completed Chapter 2.

Additional Answers

37. Statements (Reasons)

1. X is the midpoint of $\overline{WY}$ and $\overline{VZ}$. (Given)
2. $\overline{WX} \cong \overline{YX}$, $\overline{VX} \cong \overline{ZX}$ (Def. of midpoint)
3. $WX = YX$, $VX = ZX$ (Def. of $\cong$)
4. $VX = VW + WX$, $ZX = ZY + YX$ (Seg. Add. Post.)
5. $VW + WX = ZY + YX$ (Subs.)
6. $VW = ZY$ (Subt. Prop.)

38. Statements (Reasons)

1. $AB = DC$ (Given)
2. $BC = BC$ (Refl. Prop.)
3. $AB + BC = DC + BC$ (Add. Prop.)
4. $AB + BC = AC$, $DC + BC = DB$ (Seg. Add. Post.)
5. $AC = DB$ (Subs.)

43. Statements (Reasons)

1. $\angle 1 \cong \angle 4$, $\angle 2 \cong \angle 3$ (Given)
2. $m\angle 1 = m\angle 4$, $m\angle 2 = m\angle 3$ (Def. of $\cong$)
3. $m\angle 1 + m\angle 2 = m\angle 3 + m\angle 4$ (Add. Prop.)
4. $m\angle 1 + m\angle 2 = m\angle AFC$, $m\angle 3 + m\angle 4 = m\angle EFC$ ($\angle$ Add. Post.)
5. $m\angle AFC = m\angle EFC$ (Subs.)
6. $\angle AFC \cong \angle EFC$ (Def. of $\cong$)

CHAPTER 2 Study Guide and Review *Continued*

2-7 Proving Segment Relationships

Write a two-column proof. **37, 38. See margin.**

37. Given: X is the midpoint of $\overline{WY}$ and $\overline{VZ}$.
Prove: $VW = ZY$

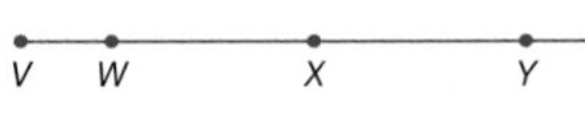

38. Given: $AB = DC$
Prove: $AC = DB$

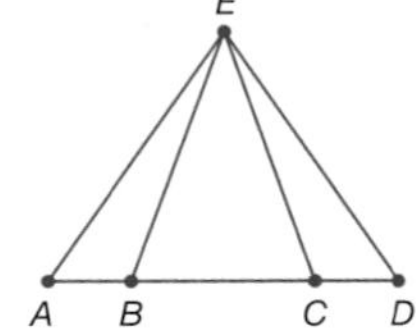

39. GEOGRAPHY Leandro is planning to drive from Kansas City to Minneapolis along Interstate 35. The map he is using gives the distance from Kansas City to Des Moines as 194 miles and from Des Moines to Minneapolis as 243 miles. What allows him to conclude that the distance he will be driving is 437 miles from Kansas City to Minneapolis? Assume that Interstate 35 forms a straight line. **Seg. Add. Post.**

Example 7

Write a two-column proof.

Given: B is the midpoint of $\overline{AC}$.
C is the midpoint of $\overline{BD}$.
Prove: $\overline{AB} \cong \overline{CD}$

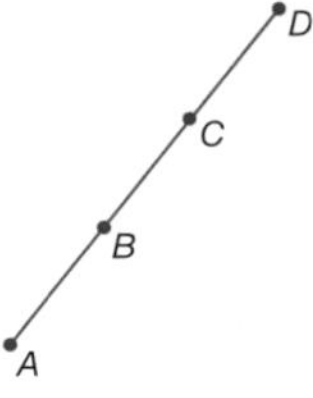

Proof:

Statements	Reasons
1. B is the midpoint of $\overline{AC}$.	1. Given
2. $\overline{AB} \cong \overline{BC}$	2. Definition of midpoint
3. C is the midpoint of $\overline{BD}$.	3. Given
4. $\overline{BC} \cong \overline{CD}$	4. Definition of midpoint
5. $\overline{AB} \cong \overline{CD}$	5. Transitive Property of Equality

2-8 Proving Angle Relationships

Find the measure of each angle.

40. $\angle 5$ **90**

41. $\angle 6$ **127**

42. $\angle 7$ **53**

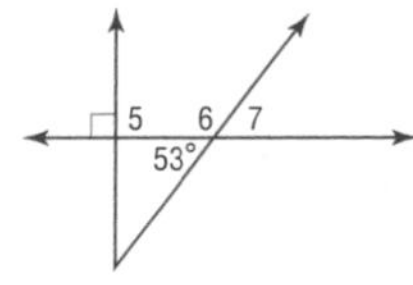

43. PROOF Write a two-column proof.
Given: $\angle 1 \cong \angle 4$, $\angle 2 \cong \angle 3$ **See margin.**
Prove: $\angle AFC \cong \angle EFC$

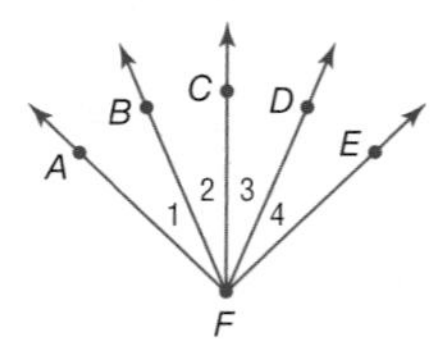

Example 8

Find the measure of each numbered angle if $m\angle 1 = 72$ and $m\angle 3 = 26$.

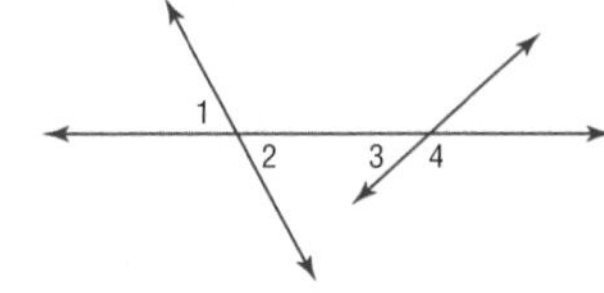

$m\angle 2 = 72$, since $\angle 1$ and $\angle 2$ are vertical angles.

$\angle 3$ and $\angle 4$ form a linear pair and must be supplementary angles.

$26 + m\angle 4 = 180$ Definition of supplementary angles

$m\angle 4 = 154$ Subtract 26 from each side.

Additional Answers (Practice Test)

1. Each consecutive term is the next multiple of 15; 75.
2. The triangle rotates to the right 90° and the shading moves from left to top to right;

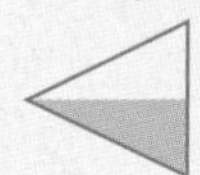

3. $5 < -3$ and all vertical angles are congruent; false.
4. $5 < -3$ or all vertical angles are congruent, and if $4x = 36$, then $x = 9$; true.
5. **Proof:** Since $\overline{JK} \cong \overline{CB}$ and $\overline{KL} \cong \overline{AB}$, $JK = BC$ and $KL = AB$ by the definition of congruent segments. By the Addition Property, $JK + KL = CB + AB$. Using the Segment Addition Postulate, $JL = JK + KL$ and $AC = AB + BC$. By substitution, $JL = AC$. Because the measures are equal, $\overline{JL} \cong \overline{AC}$ by the definition of congruent segments.

CHAPTER 2 Practice Test

Write a conjecture that describes the pattern in each sequence. Then use your conjecture to find the next item in the sequence. **1, 2. See margin.**

1. 15, 30, 45, 60
2. 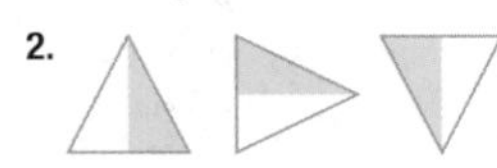

Use the following statements to write a compound statement for each conjunction or disjunction. Then find its truth value.

p: $5 < -3$

q: All vertical angles are congruent.

r: If $4x = 36$, then $x = 9$.

3. p and q **3, 4. See margin.**
4. $(p \vee q) \wedge r$

5. **PROOF** Write a paragraph proof. **See margin.**

   Given: $\overline{JK} \cong \overline{CB}$, $\overline{KL} \cong \overline{AB}$

   Prove: $\overline{JL} \cong \overline{AC}$

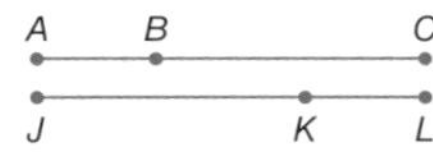

6. **SPORTS** Refer to the Venn diagram that represents the sports students chose to play at South High School last year.

Sports

Soccer: 76 | Both: 23 | Tennis: 62

   a. Describe the sports that the students in the nonintersecting portion of the tennis region chose. **These students only played tennis.**

   b. How many students played soccer and tennis? **23**

7. Determine whether the stated conclusion is valid based on the given information. If not, write *invalid*. Explain your reasoning.

   Given: If a lawyer passes the bar exam, then he or she can practice law. Candice passed the bar exam.

   Conclusion: Candice can practice law. **valid; Law of Detachment**

8. **PROOF** Copy and complete the following proof.

   Given: $3(x - 4) = 2x + 7$

   Prove: $x = 19$

   Proof:

Statements	Reasons
a. $3(x - 4) = 2x + 7$	a. Given
b. $3x - 12 = 2x + 7$	b. __?__ **Dist. Prop.**
c. __?__ **$x - 12 = 7$**	c. Subtraction Property
d. $x = 19$	d. __?__ **Add. Prop.**

Determine whether each statement is *always*, *sometimes*, or *never* true.

9. Two angles that are supplementary form a linear pair. **sometimes**
10. If B is between A and C, then $AC + AB = BC$. **never**
11. If two lines intersect to form congruent adjacent angles, then the lines are perpendicular. **always**

Find the measure of each numbered angle, and name the theorems that justify your work. **12, 13. See margin.**

12. $m\angle 1 = x$, $m\angle 2 = x - 6$

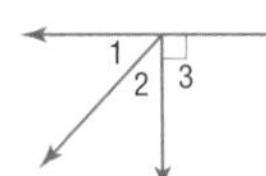

13. $m\angle 7 = 2x + 15$, $m\angle 8 = 3x$

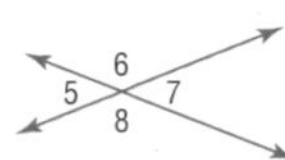

Write each statement in if-then form. **14, 15. See margin.**

14. An acute angle measures less than 90.
15. Two perpendicular lines intersect to form right angles.

16. **MULTIPLE CHOICE** If a triangle has one obtuse angle, then it is an obtuse triangle.

    Which of the following statements is the contrapositive of the conditional above? **C**

    A If a triangle is not obtuse, then it has one obtuse angle.

    B If a triangle does not have one obtuse angle, then it is not an obtuse triangle.

    C If a triangle is not obtuse, then it does not have one obtuse angle.

    D If a triangle is obtuse, then it has one obtuse angle.

Summative Assessment

Use these alternate leveled chapter tests to differentiate assessment for your students.

Leveled Chapter 2 Tests

Form	Type	Level	Page(s)
1	MC	AL	61–62
2A	MC	OL	63–64
2B	MC	OL	65–66
2C	FR	OL	67–68
2D	FR	OL	69–70
3	FR	BL	71–72
Vocabulary Test			60
Extended-Response Test			73

MC = multiple-choice questions

FR = free-response questions

eAssessment Customize and create multiple versions of your chapter test and their answer keys. All of the questions from the leveled chapter tests in the *Chapter 2 Resource Masters* are also available on eAssessment.

Additional Answers

12. $m\angle 1 = 48$, $m\angle 2 = 42$, Comp. Thm.; $m\angle 3 = 90$, Given.
13. $m\angle 7 = 81$, $m\angle 8 = 99$, Supp. Thm.; $m\angle 5 = 81$, $m\angle 6 = 99$, Vert. Angles Thm.
14. If an angle is acute, then it measures less than 90.
15. If two lines are perpendicular, then they form right angles.

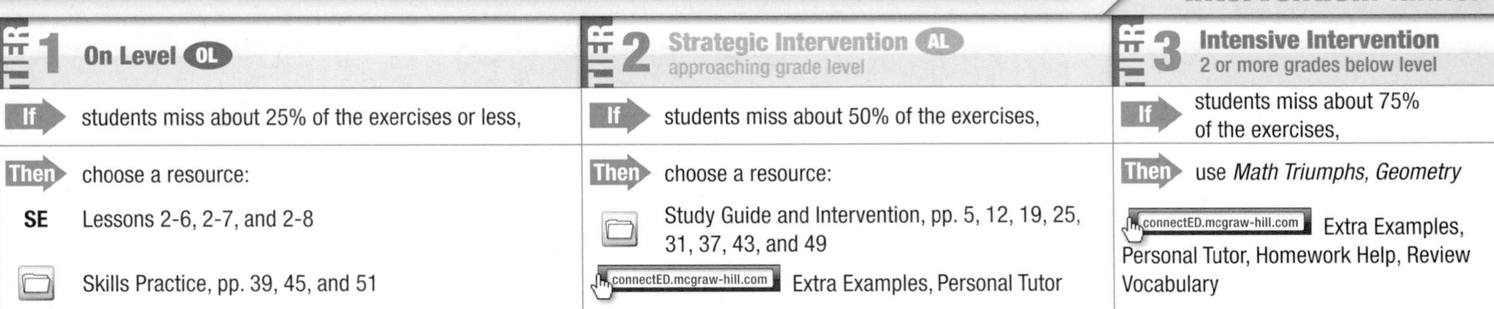

InterventionPlanner

Tier 1 On Level OL	Tier 2 Strategic Intervention AL approaching grade level	Tier 3 Intensive Intervention 2 or more grades below level
If students miss about 25% of the exercises or less,	**If** students miss about 50% of the exercises,	**If** students miss about 75% of the exercises,
Then choose a resource:	**Then** choose a resource:	**Then** use *Math Triumphs, Geometry*
SE Lessons 2-6, 2-7, and 2-8 Skills Practice, pp. 39, 45, and 51 connectED.mcgraw-hill.com Self-Check Quiz	Study Guide and Intervention, pp. 5, 12, 19, 25, 31, 37, 43, and 49 connectED.mcgraw-hill.com Extra Examples, Personal Tutor	connectED.mcgraw-hill.com Extra Examples, Personal Tutor, Homework Help, Review Vocabulary

1 Focus

Objective Understand and use the fundamental tools of logical reasoning to solve problems.

2 Teach

Scaffolding Questions

Ask:

- How can counterexamples be used to solve a problem? Sample answer: Counterexamples can be used to eliminate answer choices that contradict the question that is being asked.
- What are some different ways you can visually represent information given in a problem? Sample answer: You can use a diagram, chart, or table to visually represent the information given in a problem.
- What two types of reasoning are used when writing proofs? Inductive and deductive reasoning can be used to write proofs.

CHAPTER 2

Preparing for Standardized Tests

Logical Reasoning

Solving geometry problems frequently requires the use of logical reasoning. You can use the fundamentals of logical reasoning to help you solve problems on standardized tests.

Strategies for Using Logical Reasoning

Step 1

Read the problem to determine what information you are given and what you need to find out in order to answer the question.

Step 2

Determine if you can apply one of the principles of logical reasoning to the problem.

- **Counterexample**: A counterexample contradicts a statement that is known to be true.

  Identify any answer choices that contradict the problem statement and eliminate them.

- **Postulates:** A postulate is a statement that describes a fundamental relationship in geometry.

  Determine if you can apply a postulate to draw a logical conclusion.

Step 3

If you cannot reach a conclusion using only the principles in Step 2, determine if one of the tools below would be helpful.

- **Patterns:** Look for a pattern to make a conjecture.
- **Truth Tables:** Use a truth table to organize the truth values of the statement provided in the problem.
- **Venn Diagrams:** Use a Venn Diagram to clearly represent the relationships between members of groups.
- **Proofs:** Use deductive and inductive reasoning to reach a conclusion in the form of a proof.

Step 4

If you still cannot reach a conclusion using the tools in Step 3, make a **conjecture**, or educated guess, about which answer choice is most reasonable. Then mark the problem so that you can return to it if you have extra time at the end of the exam.

166 | Chapter 2 | Preparing for Standardized Tests

Standardized Test Example

Read the problem. Identify what you need to know. Then use the information in the problem to solve.

In a school of 292 students, 94 participate in sports, 122 participate in academic clubs, and 31 participate in both. How many students at the school do not participate in sports or academic clubs?

A 95
B 107
C 122
D 138

Read the problem carefully. There are no clear counterexamples, and a postulate cannot be used to draw a logical conclusion. Therefore, consider the tools that you can use to organize the information.

A Venn diagram can be used to show the intersection of two sets. Make a Venn diagram with the information provided in the problem statement.

Determine how many students participate in only sports or academic clubs.

Only sports: $94 - 31 = 63$

Only academic clubs: $122 - 31 = 91$

School Participation

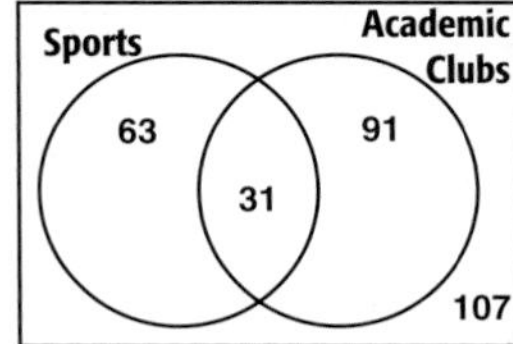

Use the information to calculate the number of students who do not participate in either sports or academic clubs.

$292 - 63 - 91 - 31 = 107$

There are 107 students who do not participate in either sports or academic clubs. The correct answer is B.

Additional Example

In a school of 367 students, 185 have a dog as a pet, 163 have a cat as a pet, and 97 have both a cat and a dog. How many students in the school do not have a dog or a cat? B

A 8
B 116
C 270
D 348

3 Assess

Use Exercises 1 and 2 to assess students' understanding.

Exercises

Read each question. Then fill in the correct answer on the answer document provided by your teacher or on a sheet of paper.

1. Determine the truth of the following statement. If the statement is false, give a counterexample. D

   The product of two even numbers is even.

   A false; $8 \times 4 = 32$
   B false; $7 \times 6 = 42$
   C false; $3 \times 10 = 30$
   D true

2. Find the next item in the pattern. H

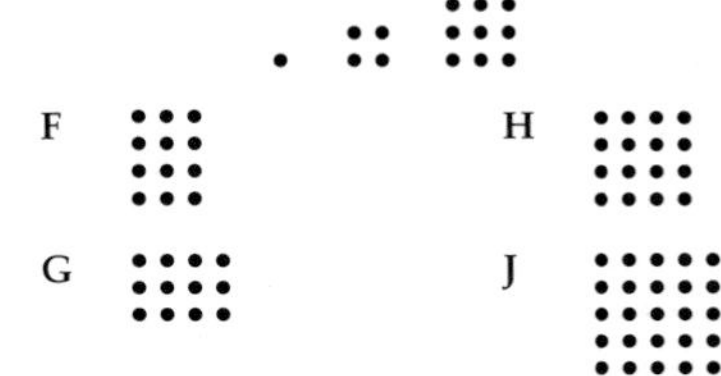

connectED.mcgraw-hill.com 167

Diagnose Student Errors

Survey student responses for each item. Class trends may indicate common errors and misconceptions.

1. A $\sim p$ is false
B q is false
C correct
D $\sim p$ is false

2. F correct
G the sum is 180
H this is Substitution Property
J this is Substitution Property

3. A two acute angles can not be supplementary
B correct
C two obtuse angles can not be supplementary
D two right angles are supplementary and may form a linear pair

4. F there could be other reasons the game is cancelled
G correct
H contradicts second statement
J there could be other reasons the game is cancelled

5. A definition of vertical angles
B definition of linear pair
C definition of vertical angles
D correct

6. F contains shortest length, but not minimum area
G not the minimum area
H not the minimum area
J correct

CHAPTER 2

Standardized Test Practice

Cumulative, Chapters 1 through 2

Multiple Choice

Read each question. Then fill in the correct answer on the answer document provided by your teacher or on a sheet of paper.

1. Which conjunction is true for statements p and q below? C

p: There are four letters in MATH.

q: There are two vowels in MATH.

A $\sim p \wedge \sim q$

B $p \wedge q$

C $p \wedge \sim q$

D $\sim p \wedge q$

2. In the diagram below, $\angle 1 \cong \angle 3$. F

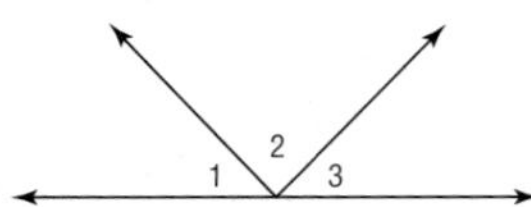

Which of the following conclusions does not have to be true?

F $m\angle 1 - m\angle 2 + m\angle 3 = 90$

G $m\angle 1 + m\angle 2 + m\angle 3 = 180$

H $m\angle 1 + m\angle 2 = m\angle 2 + m\angle 3$

J $m\angle 2 - m\angle 1 = m\angle 2 - m\angle 3$

3. *Two supplementary angles always form a linear pair.* B

Which of the following best describes a *counterexample* to the assertion above?

A two acute angles

B two nonadjacent angles

C two obtuse angles

D two right angles

> **Test-Taking Tip**
>
> Question 3 A *counterexample* is an example used to show that a given statement is not always true.

4. Determine which statement follows logically from the given statements. G

If it rains today, the game will be cancelled.

Cancelled games are made up on Saturdays.

F If a game is cancelled, it was because of rain.

G If it rains today, the game will be made up on Saturday.

H Some cancelled games are not made up on Saturdays.

J If it does not rain today, the game will not be made up on Saturday.

5. In the diagram, $\overline{BD}$ intersects $\overline{AE}$ at C. Which of the following conclusions does *not* have to be true? D

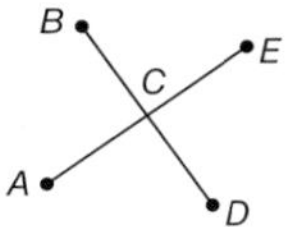

A $\angle ACB \cong \angle ECD$

B $\angle ACB$ and $\angle ACD$ form a linear pair.

C $\angle BCE$ and $\angle ACD$ are vertical angles.

D $\angle BCE$ and $\angle ECD$ are complementary angles.

6. A farmer needs to make a 1000-square-foot rectangular enclosure for her cows. She wants to save money by purchasing the least amount of fencing possible to enclose the area. What whole-number dimensions will require the least amount of fencing? J

F 8 ft by 125 ft

G 10 ft by 100 ft

H 20 ft by 50 ft

J 25 ft by 40 ft

Short Response/Gridded Response

Record your answers on the answer sheet provided by your teacher or on a sheet of paper.

7. Points A, B, C, and D are collinear, with point B between points A and C and point C between points B and D. Complete the statement.

   $AB + \underline{\ ?\ } = AD$ **BD**

8. **GRIDDED RESPONSE** Suppose line m contains points D, E, and F. If $DE = 12$ millimeters, $EF = 15$ millimeters, and point D is between points E and F, what is the length of $\overline{DF}$? Express your answer in millimeters. **3**

9. Use the proof to answer the question.

   Given: $\angle A$ is the complement of $\angle B$. $m\angle B = 46$

   Prove: $m\angle A = 44$

   Proof:

Statements	Reasons
1. A is the complement of $\angle B$; $m\angle B = 46$.	1. Given
2. $m\angle A + m\angle B = 90$	2. Def. of comp. angles
3. $m\angle A + 46 = 90$	3. Substitution Prop.
4. $m\angle A + 46 - 46 = 90 - 46$	4. ___?___
5. $m\angle A = 44$	5. Substitution Prop.

   What reason can be given to justify Statement 4? **Subt. Prop.**

10. Write the contrapositive of the statement.

    If an angle measures greater than 90°, then it is obtuse.

    10. If an angle is not obtuse, then it does not measure greater than 90°.

11. **GRIDDED RESPONSE** Point E is the midpoint of $\overline{DF}$. If $DE = 8x - 3$ and $EF = 3x + 7$, what is x? **2**

Extended Response

Record your answers on a sheet of paper. Show your work.

12. Consider the pattern.

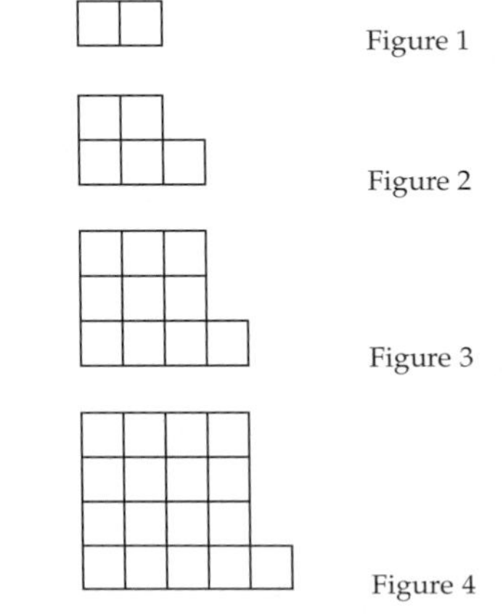

   a. Make a conjecture about the number of squares in each figure.

   b. Write an algebraic expression that can be used to find the number of squares in the nth figure in the pattern. $n^2 + 1$

   c. How many squares will be needed to make the 6th figure of the pattern? **37**

   a. Sample answer: The number of squares is the figure number squared, plus 1.

Need ExtraHelp?

If you missed Question...	1	2	3	4	5	6	7	8	9	10	11	12
Go to Lesson...	2-2	2-8	2-1	2-4	2-7	1-6	1-2	1-2	2-8	2-3	1-3	2-1

Formative Assessment

You can use these pages to benchmark student progress.

Standardized Test Practice, pp. 74–76

Answer Sheet Practice

Have students simulate taking a standardized test by recording their answers on a practice recording sheet.

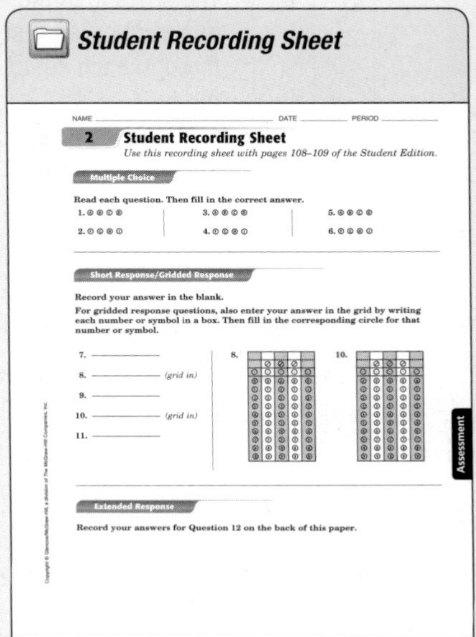

eAssessment Create practice tests that align to your state standards, the Common Core State Standards, and other national standards such as TIMSS and NAEP.

Homework Option

Get Ready for Chapter 3 Assign students the exercises on p. 171 as homework to assess whether they possess the prerequisite skills needed for the next chapter.

Lesson 2-1

24.  The direction of the arrow in the pattern rotates clockwise from one figure to the next.

25. 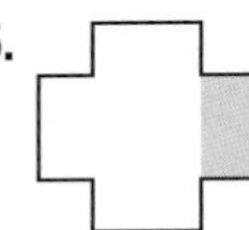 In each figure, the shading moves to the next area of the figure counter clockwise.

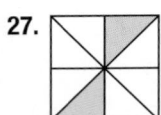

26. Each figure in the pattern is the next largest regular polygon.

27. The shading of the lower triangle in the upper right quadrant of the first figure moves clockwise through each set of triangles from one figure to the next.

46a. 1, 3, 6, 10

46b. Sample answer: Add the position number to the previous number to get the next number in the sequence.

46c. Sample answer: Each figure is the previous figure with an additional row added that has one more point in it than in the last row.

46d. 15, 21

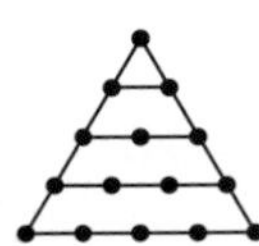 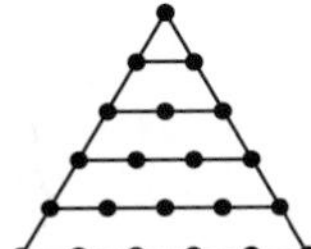

47a. 1, 4, 9, 16

47b. Sample answer: Start by adding 3 to 1 to get the second number, 4. Continue adding the next odd number to the previous number to get the next number in the sequence.

47c. Sample answer: Each figure is the previous figure with an additional row and column of points added, which is 2(position number) – 1. One is subtracted since 2(position number) counts the corner point twice. 2(position number) – 1 is always an odd number.

47d. 25, 36

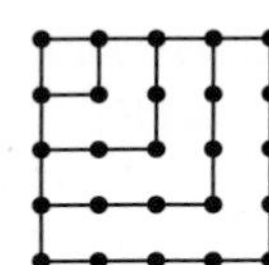 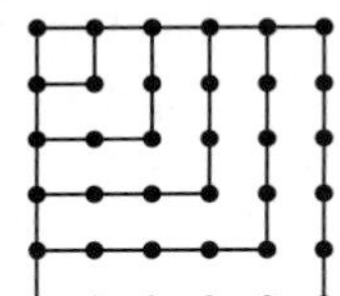

48a. 2, 6, 12, 20

48b. Sample answer: Start by adding the even number 4 to the first number to get the second number, 6. To get each of the next numbers, add the next even number to the previous number in the sequence.

48c. Sample answer: The second figure is the previous figure with 4 points added to make a rectangle. The third figure is the previous figure with 6 points added, which is 2 more than the last number of points added. The fourth figure is the previous figure with 8 points added, which is 2 more than the last number of points added.

48d. 30, 42

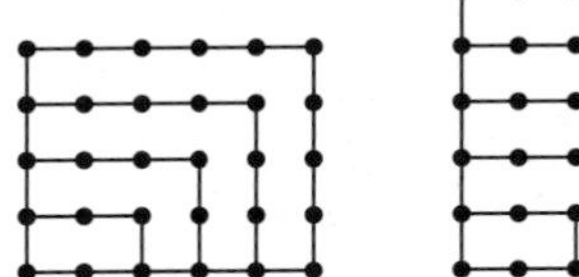

49a. 1, 5, 12, 22

49b. Sample answer: Start by adding 4 to 1 to get the second number, 5. Increase the amount added to the previous number by 3 each time to get the next number in sequence. So, add $4 + 3$ or 7 to 5 to get 12, and add $4 + 3 + 3$ or 10 to 12 to get 22.

49c. Sample answer: The second figure is the previous figure with 4 points added to make a pentagon. The third figure is the previous figure with 7 more points added, which is 3 more than the last number of points added. The fourth figure is the previous figure with 10 points added, which is 3 more than the last number of points added.

49d. 35, 51

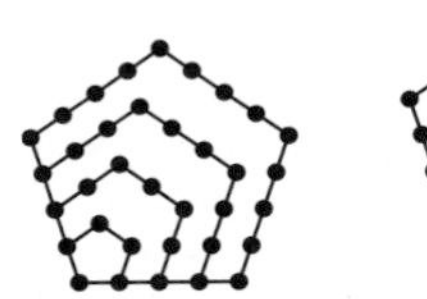 

50. Sample answer:

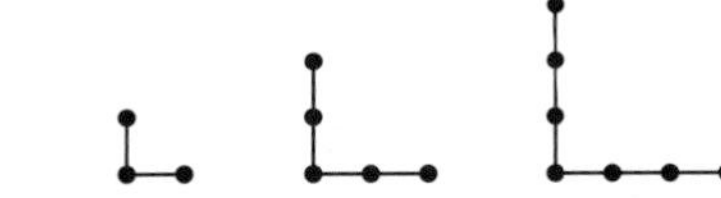

53. In the sequence of perimeters, each measure is twice the previous measure. Therefore, doubling the side length of a regular hexagon appears to also double its perimeter. In the sequence of areas, each measure is four times the previous measure. Therefore, doubling the side length of a regular hexagon appears to quadruple its area.

Lesson 2-2 (Guided Practice)

1A. The figure is a triangle, and the figure has two congruent sides. Both *p* and *q* are true, so $p \wedge q$ is true.

1B. The figure is not a triangle, and the figure does not have three acute angles. While not *r* is true, not *p* is false. So, not *p* and not *r* is false.

3.

P	q	$\sim p$	$\sim q$	$\sim p \wedge \sim q$
T	T	F	F	F
T	F	F	T	F
F	T	T	F	F
F	F	T	T	T

Lesson 2-2

11. $\overrightarrow{DB}$ is the angle bisector of $\angle ADC$, and $\overline{AD} \cong \overline{DC}$. p and r is true because p is true and r is true.

12. Points C, D, and B are collinear, or $\overrightarrow{DB}$ is the angle bisector of $\angle ADC$. q or p is true because q is false and p is true.

13. $\overline{AD} \cong \overline{DC}$ or $\overrightarrow{DB}$ is not the angle bisector of $\angle ADC$. r or $\sim p$ is true because r is true and $\sim p$ is false.

14. $\overline{AD} \cong \overline{DC}$ and Points C, D, and B are collinear. r and q is false because r is true and q is false.

15. $\overrightarrow{DB}$ is not the angle bisector of $\angle ADC$, or $\overline{AD} \not\cong \overline{DC}$. $\sim p$ or $\sim r$ is false because $\sim p$ is false and $\sim r$ is false.

16. $\overline{DB}$ is not the angle bisector of $\angle ADC$, and $\overline{AD} \neq \overline{DC}$. $\sim p$ and $\sim r$ is false because $\sim p$ is false and $\sim r$ is false.

17. Springfield is the capital of Illinois, and Illinois shares a border with Kentucky. $p \wedge r$ is true because p is true and r is true.

18. Springfield is the capital of Illinois, and Illinois borders the Atlantic Ocean. $p \wedge q$ is false because p is true and q is false.

19. Illinois does not share a border with Kentucky, or Illinois is to the west of Missouri. $\sim r \vee s$ is false because $\sim r$ is false and s is false.

20. Illinois shares a border with Kentucky, or Illinois borders the Atlantic Ocean. $r \vee q$ is true because r is true and q is false.

21. Springfield is not the capital of Illinois, and Illinois does not share a border with Kentucky. $\sim p \wedge \sim r$ is false because $\sim p$ is false and $\sim r$ is false.

22. Illinois is not to the west of Missouri, or Springfield is not the capital of Illinois. $\sim s \vee \sim p$ is true because $\sim s$ is true and $\sim p$ is false.

34. If p and q are true, then $p \wedge (q \wedge r)$ is true if r is true and false if r is false.

p	q	r	$q \wedge r$	$p \wedge (q \wedge r)$
T	T	T	T	T
T	F	T	F	F
T	T	F	F	F
T	F	F	F	F
F	T	T	T	F
F	F	T	F	F
F	T	F	F	F
F	F	F	F	F

35. If p and r are true, and q is true or false, then $p \wedge (\sim q \vee r)$ is true.

p	q	$\sim q$	r	$\sim q \vee r$	$p \wedge (\sim q \vee r)$
T	T	F	T	T	T
T	F	T	T	T	T
T	T	F	F	F	F
T	F	T	F	T	T
F	T	F	T	T	F
F	F	T	T	T	F
F	T	F	F	F	F
F	F	T	F	T	F

36. If p is true or false, then $(\sim p \vee q) \wedge r$ is true.

p	q	$\sim p$	$\sim p \vee q$	r	$(\sim p \vee q) \wedge r$
T	T	F	T	T	T
T	F	F	F	T	F
T	T	F	T	F	F
T	F	F	F	F	F
F	T	T	T	T	T
F	F	T	T	T	T
F	T	T	T	F	F
F	F	T	T	F	F

37. true

p	q	$\sim q$	r	$\sim r$	$\sim q \wedge \sim r$	$p \vee (\sim q \wedge \sim r)$
T	T	F	T	F	F	T
T	F	T	T	F	F	T
T	T	F	F	T	F	T
T	F	T	F	T	T	T
F	T	F	T	F	F	F
F	F	T	T	F	F	F
F	T	F	F	T	F	F
F	F	T	F	T	T	T

38. false

p	$\sim p$	q	$\sim q$	r	$\sim r$	$\sim q \wedge \sim r$	$p \wedge (\sim q \wedge \sim r)$
T	F	T	F	T	F	F	F
T	F	F	T	T	F	F	F
T	F	T	F	F	T	F	F
T	F	F	T	F	T	T	F
F	T	T	F	T	F	F	F
F	T	F	T	T	F	F	F
F	T	T	F	F	T	F	F
F	T	F	T	F	T	T	T

39. If r is true or false, then $(\sim p \vee q) \vee \sim r$ is true.

p	$\sim p$	q	r	$\sim r$	$(\sim p \vee q)$	$(\sim p \vee q) \vee \sim r)$
T	F	T	T	F	T	T
T	F	F	T	F	F	F
T	F	T	F	T	T	T
T	F	F	F	T	F	T
F	T	T	T	F	T	T
F	T	F	T	F	T	T
F	T	T	F	T	T	T
F	T	F	F	T	T	T

40a.

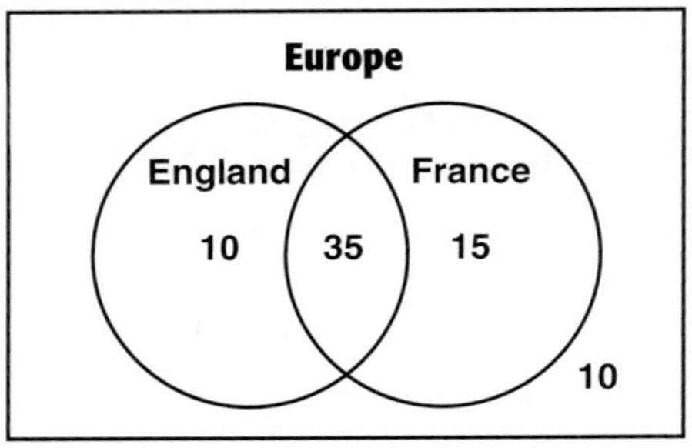

Europe

England 10 | 35 | France 15 | 10

40b.

Europe

England 10 $p \wedge \sim q$ | 35 $p \wedge q$ | France 15 $q \wedge \sim p$ | 10 $\sim p \wedge \sim q$

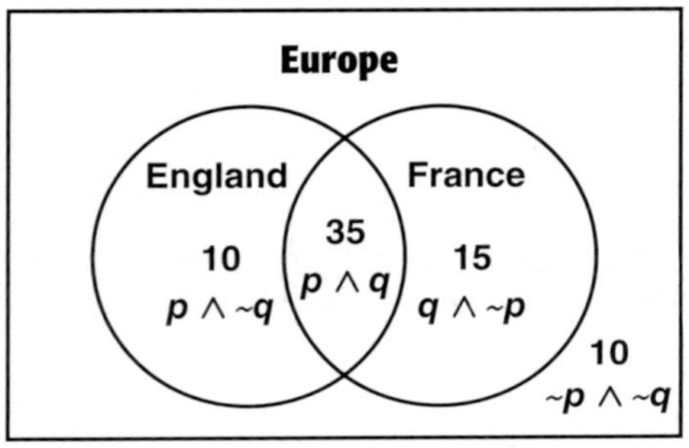

40c. $\frac{1}{2}$; Sample answer: Since 35 of those surveyed have visited both England and France and there are 70 total survey participants, the probability that a randomly chosen participant would have visited both England and France is $\frac{35}{70}$ or $\frac{1}{2}$.

Lesson 2-3 (Guided Practice)

1A. H: a polygon has six sides; C: the polygon is a hexagon.

1B. H: the first performance is sold out; C: another performance will be scheduled.

Lesson 2-3

32. If you listen to jazz music, then you will likely hear trumpet or saxophone. If you listen to rock music, then you will likely hear guitar and drums. If you listen to hip-hop music, then you will likely hear bass.

33. If the museum is the Andy Warhol Museum, then most of the collection is Andy Warhol's artwork.

35. False; 9 is an odd number, but not divisible by 5. The hypothesis of the conditional is true, but the conclusion is false. This counterexample shows that the conditional statement is false.

36. True; the hypothesis is false, since a dog is not an amphibian. A conditional with a false hypothesis is always true, so this conditional statement is true.

37. False; 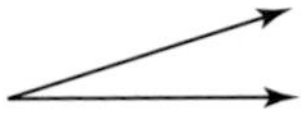 ; the angle drawn is an acute angle whose measure is not 45. The hypothesis of the conditional is true, but the conclusion is false. This counterexample shows that the conditional statement is false.

38. False; 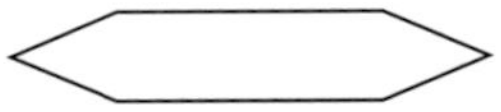 ; this polygon has six sides, but is not regular. The hypothesis of the conditional is true, but the conclusion is false. This counterexample shows that the conditional statement is false.

47. Converse: If you live in Illinois, then you live in Chicago. False: You can live in Springfield. Inverse: If you do not live in Chicago, then you do not live in Illinois. False: You can live in Springfield. Contrapositive: If you do not live in Illinois, then you do not live in Chicago; true.

48. Converse: If a bird cannot fly, then it is an ostrich. False; The bird could be a penguin. Inverse: If a bird is not an ostrich, then it can fly. False; The bird could be a penguin. Contrapositive: If a bird can fly, then the bird is not an ostrich; true.

49. Converse: If two angles are congruent, then they have the same measure; true. Inverse: If two angles do not have the same measure, then the angles are not congruent; true. Contrapositive: If two angles are not congruent, then they do not have the same measure; true.

50. If a figure is a square, then it is a rectangle. Converse: If a figure is a rectangle, then it is a square. False. A rectangle does not have to have all sides congruent. Inverse: If a figure is not a square, then it is not a rectangle. False. The figure could be a rectangle, even though it is not a square. Contrapositive: If a figure is not a rectangle, then it is not a square; true.

51. If segments are congruent, then they have the same length. Converse: If segments have the same length, then they are congruent; true. Inverse: If segments are not congruent, then they do not have the same length; true. Contrapositive: If segments do not have the same length, then they are not congruent; true.

52. If a triangle is right, then it has an angle measure of 90. Converse: If a triangle has an angle measure of 90, then it is a right triangle; true. Inverse: If a triangle is not right, then it does not have an angle measure of 90; true. Contrapositive: If a triangle does not have an angle measure of 90, then it is not a right triangle; true.

53. If an animal has stripes, then it is a zebra; false: a zebra duiker has stripes.

54. If an animal is a zebra, then it has stripes; true.

55. If an animal does not have stripes, then it is not a zebra; true.

56. If an animal is not a zebra, then it does not have stripes; false: a zebra duiker has stripes.

57a. Sample answer: If a compound is an acid, it contains hydrogen. If a compound is a base, it contains hydroxide. If a compound is a hydrocarbon, it contains only hydrogen and carbon.

57b. Sample answer: If a compound contains hydrogen, it is an acid. False; a hydrocarbon contains hydrogen. If a compound contains hydroxide, it is a base; true. If a compound contains only hydrogen and carbon, it is a hydrocarbon; true.

58a. Sample answer: If a football team makes a touchdown, they get 6 points; If a football team makes a two-point conversion, they get 2 points; If a football team makes a safety, they get 2 points.

58b. Sample answer: If a football team gets 6 points, they made a touchdown. True; If a football team gets 2 points, they made a two-point conversion. False; they could have gotten a safety; If a football team gets 2 points, they made a safety. False; they could have gotten a two-point conversion.

64.

p	q	Conditional $p \rightarrow q$	Converse $q \rightarrow p$	Inverse $\sim p \rightarrow \sim q$	Contrapositive $\sim q \rightarrow \sim p$
T	T	T	T	T	T
T	F	F	T	T	F
F	T	T	F	F	T
F	F	T	T	T	T

77.

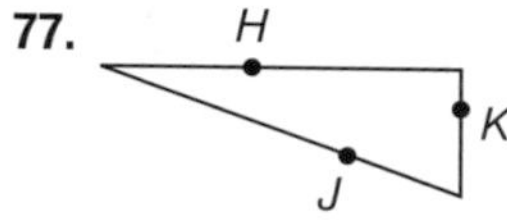

78. X Y Z

79.

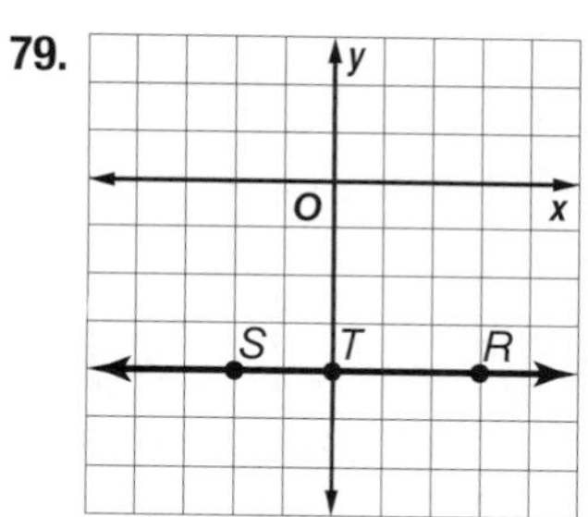

80.

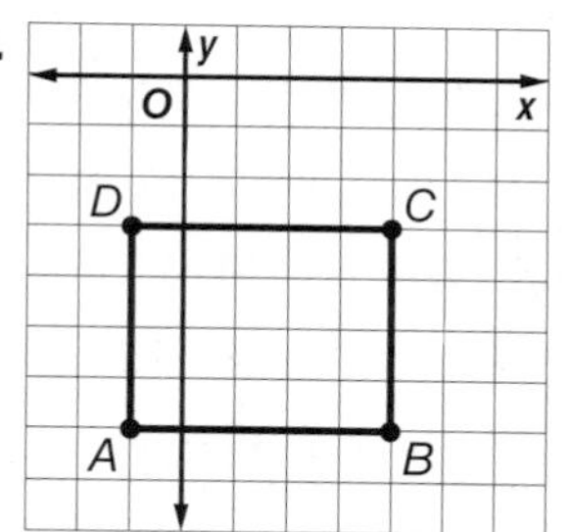

Extend 2-3

5.

p	q	$p \rightarrow q$	$q \rightarrow p$	$p \leftrightarrow q$
T	T	T	T	T
T	F	F	T	F
F	T	T	F	F
F	F	T	T	T

Lesson 2-4

27. Invalid; Ms. Rodriquez's car might be a four-wheel drive vehicle that is not a sport-utility vehicle.

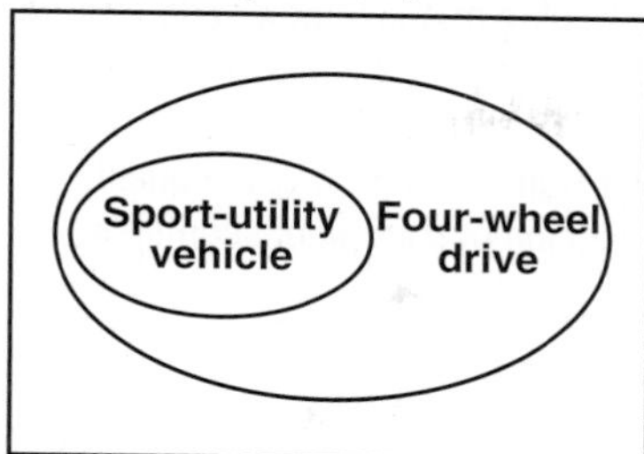

45. Jonah's statement can be restated as, "Jonah is in group B and Janeka is in group B." In order for this compound statement to be true, both parts of the statement must be true. If Jonah was in group A, he would not be able to say that he is in group B, since students in group A must always tell the truth. Therefore the statement that Jonah is in group B is true. For the compound statement to be false, the statement that Janeka is in group B must be false. Therefore, Jonah is in group B and Janeka is in group A.

46. Sample answer: Inductive reasoning uses several specific examples to reach a conclusion, while deductive reasoning relies on established facts, rules, definitions, and/or properties to reach a conclusion. One counterexample is enough to disprove a conjecture reached using inductive or deductive reasoning. Deductive reasoning, however, is the only valid method of proving a conjecture. Inductive reasoning cannot be used to prove a conjecture.

Lesson 2-5

15. Since C is the midpoint of $\overline{AE}$ and $\overline{DB}$, $CA = CE = \frac{1}{2}AE$ and $CD = CB = \frac{1}{2}DB$ by the definition of midpoint. We are given $\overline{AE} \cong \overline{DB}$, so $AE = DB$ by the definition of congruent segments. By the multiplication property, $\frac{1}{2}DB = \frac{1}{2}AE$. So, by substitution, $AC = CB$.

24. Always; Postulate 2.2 states that through any three noncollinear points, there is exactly one plane.

25. Never; Postulate 2.1 states through any two points, there is exactly one line.

26. Sometimes; the points do not have to be collinear to lie in a plane.

27. Always; Postulate 2.5 states if two points lie in a plane, then the entire line containing those points lies in that plane.

28. Never; Postulate 2.7 states if two planes intersect, then their intersection is a line.

29. Sometimes; the points must be noncollinear.

30. Given: Point Y is the midpoint of $\overline{XZ}$.
Z is the midpoint of $\overline{YW}$.

Prove: $\overline{XY} \cong \overline{ZW}$

Proof: We are given that Y is the midpoint of $\overline{XZ}$ and Z is the midpoint of $\overline{YW}$. By the definition of midpoint, $\overline{XY} \cong \overline{YZ}$ and $\overline{YZ} \cong \overline{ZW}$. Using the definition of congruent segments, $XY = YZ$ and $YZ = ZW$. $XY = ZW$ by the Transitive Property of Equality. Thus, $\overline{XY} \cong \overline{ZW}$ by the definition of congruent segments.

31. Given: L is the midpoint of $\overline{JK}$.
$\overline{JK}$ intersects $\overline{MK}$ at K. $\overline{MK} \cong \overline{JL}$

Prove: $\overline{LK} \cong \overline{MK}$

Proof: We are given that L is the midpoint of $\overline{JK}$ and $\overline{MK} \cong \overline{JL}$. By the Midpoint Theorem, $\overline{JL} \cong \overline{LK}$. By the Transitive Property of Equality, $\overline{LK} \cong \overline{MK}$.

32. Sample answer: From the given information, there are a total of 11 bikes and skateboards, so if b represents bikes and s represents skateboards, $b + s = 11$. The equation can also be written $s = 11 - b$. There are a total of 36 wheels, so $2b + 4s = 36$, since each bike has two wheels and each skateboard has four wheels. Substitute the equation $s = 11 - b$ into the equation $2b + 4s = 36$ to eliminate one variable, resulting in $2b + 4(11 - b) = 36$. Simplify the equation to $2b + 44 - 4b = 36$ and solve to get $b = 4$. If there are 4 bikes, there are $11 - 4$, or 7 skateboards. Therefore, there are 4 bikes and 7 skateboards.

43a.

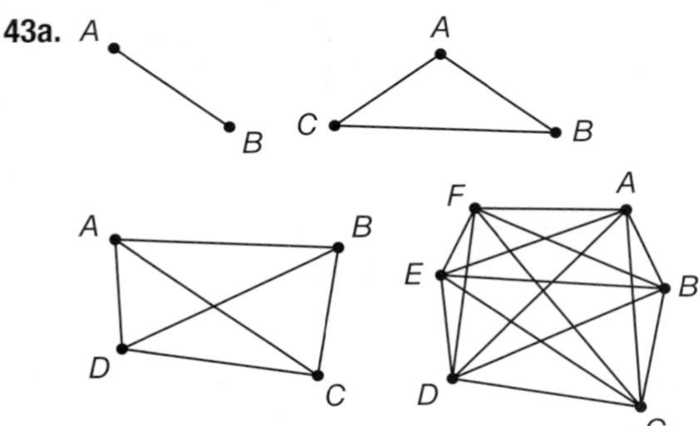

43b.

Number of Computers	Number of Connections
2	1
3	3
4	6
5	10
6	15

48. Sometimes; if the points were noncollinear, there would be exactly one plane by Postulate 2.2 shown by Figure 1. If the points were collinear, there would be infinitely many planes. Figure 2 shows what two planes through collinear points would look like. More planes would rotate around the three points.

Figure 1

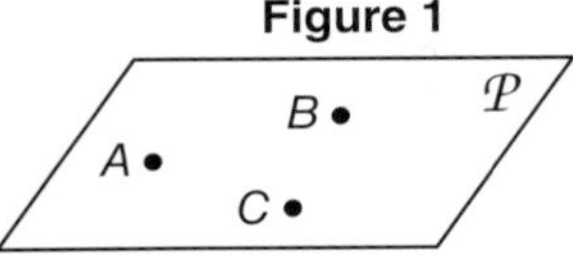

Figure 2

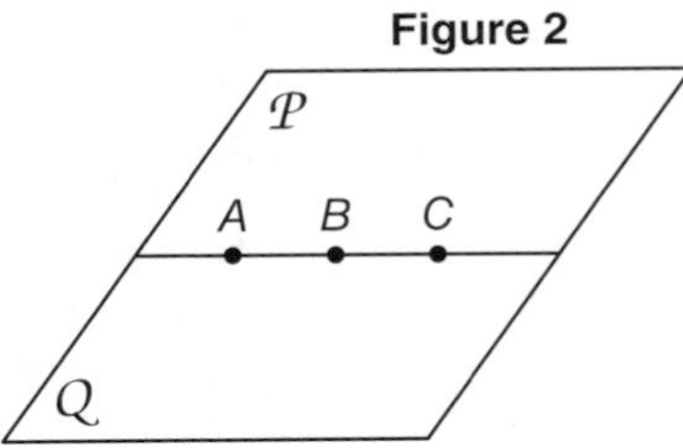

49. Sometimes; three coplanar lines may have 0, 1, 2, or 3 points of intersection, as shown in the figures below.

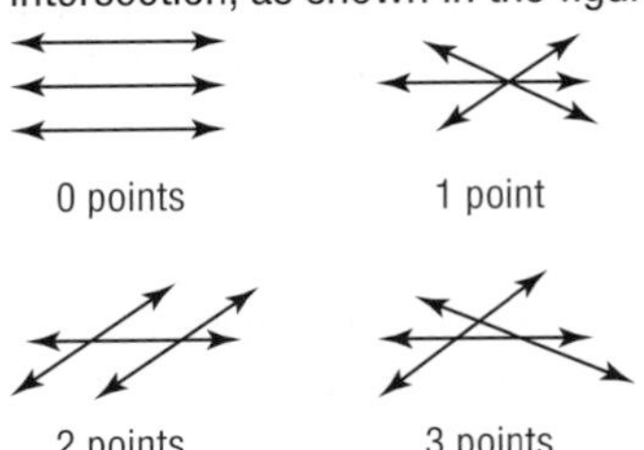

Postulates 2.1 – 2.5 were used. Through points A and B there is exactly one line, n, satisfying Postulate 2.1. For the noncollinear points A, B, and C there is exactly one plane, P, satisfying Postulate 2.2. Line n contains points A and B, satisfying Postulate 2.3. Plane P contains the noncollinear points A, B, and C, satisfying Postulate 2.4. Line n, containing points A and B, lies entirely in plane P, satisfying Postulate 2.5.

Mid-Chapter Quiz

3. False; A, B, and C do not have to be collinear.

4. When n is 1, the conjecture is false, since $1^3 > 1$.

5. False; \$1 = 100¢ and January is the month before February.

6. True; \$1 = 100¢ and 4 quarters = \$1.

7. True; \$1 = 100¢ and February is *not* the month before January.

9. H: a polygon has five sides; C: it is a pentagon

10. H: $4x - 6 = 10$; C: $x = 4$

11. H: an angle has a measure less than 90

C: it is an acute angle

12. True; $m\angle 1 + m\angle 2 = 180$.

13. False; $\angle 1$ and $\angle 3$ are congruent angles.

14. All squares are rectangles.

15. Perpendicular lines intersect and parallel lines never intersect.

16. Valid; the Colts had the highest score in the Super Bowl. The team with the highest score is the winner, therefore the Colts won the Super Bowl.

18. Sometimes; Postulate 2.4 states that a plane contains at least 3 noncollinear points.

19. Always; Postulate 2.1 states through any two points, there is exactly one line.

20. Never; Postulate 2.3 states a line contains at least two points.

Lesson 2-6 (Guided Practice)

2B. $d = t \cdot \frac{u+v}{2}$ (Given)

$\frac{d}{t} = \frac{u+v}{2}$ (Div. Prop.)

$2\left(\frac{d}{t}\right) = 2\left(\frac{u+v}{2}\right)$ (Mult. Prop.)

$\frac{2d}{t} = u + v$ (Subs.)

$\frac{2d}{t} - v = u$ (Subt. Prop.)

$u = \frac{2d}{t} - v$ (Symm. Prop.)

Lesson 2-6

8a. Proof:

Statements (Reasons)

1. $T = 0.75(220 - a)$ (Given)
2. $\frac{T}{0.75} = 220 - a$ (Div. Prop.)
3. $\frac{T}{0.75} - 220 = -a$ (Subt. Prop.)
4. $-\frac{T}{0.75} + 220 = a$ (Mult. Prop.)
5. $a = -\frac{T}{0.75} + 220$ (Symm. Prop.)
6. $a = 220 - \frac{T}{0.75}$ (Comm. Prop.)

8b. 16 years old; Sample answer: Substitution

26. Given: $\angle MPN \cong \angle QPN$

Prove: $x = 16$

Proof:

Statements (Reasons)

1. $\angle MPN \cong \angle QPN$ (Given)
2. $m\angle MPN = m\angle QPN$ (Def. of $\cong$ ∡s)
3. $x + 26 = 2x + 10$ (Subs.)
4. $16 = x$ (Subt. Prop.)
5. $x = 16$ (Symm. Prop.)

27a. Given: $V = \frac{P}{I}$

Prove: $\frac{V}{2} = \frac{P}{2I}$

Proof:

Statements (Reasons)

1. $V = \frac{P}{I}$ (Given)
2. $\frac{1}{2} \cdot V = \frac{1}{2} \cdot \frac{P}{I}$ (Mult. Prop.)
3. $\frac{V}{2} = \frac{P}{2I}$ (Mult. Prop.)

27b. Given: $V = \frac{P}{I}$

Prove: $2V = \frac{2P}{I}$

Proof:

Statements (Reasons)

1. $V = \frac{P}{I}$ (Given)
2. $2 \cdot V = 2 \cdot \frac{P}{I}$ (Mult. Prop.)
3. $2V = \frac{2P}{I}$ (Mult. Prop.)

28a.

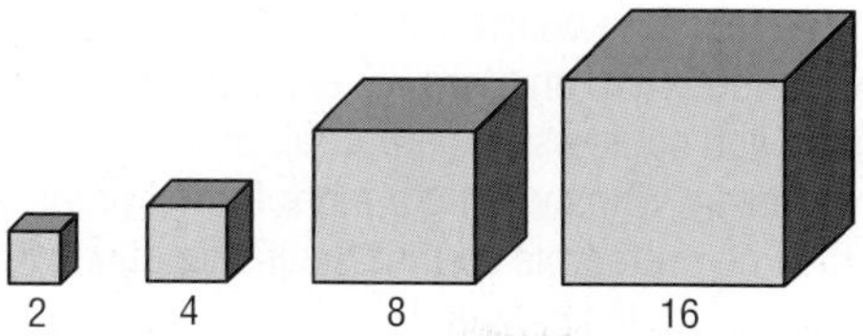

28c. Sample answer: When the side length of a cube doubles, the volume is 8 times greater.

28e. Given: a cube with side length s and volume V

Prove: $8V = (2s)^3$

Proof:

Statements (Reasons)

1. side length $= s$ (Given)
2. volume $= V$ (Given)
3. $V = s^3$ (Def. of volume of a cube)
4. $V = s \cdot s \cdot s$ (Def. of exponent)
5. $2 \cdot 2 \cdot 2 \cdot V = 2 \cdot s \cdot 2 \cdot s \cdot 2 \cdot s$ (Mult. Prop.)
6. $8V = (2s)(2s)(2s)$ (Mult. Prop.)
7. $8V = (2s)^3$ (Def. of exponent)

37. Given: $AP = 2x + 3$

$PB = \frac{3x+1}{2}$

$AB = 10.5$

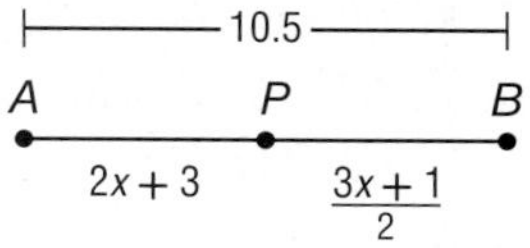

Prove: $\frac{AP}{AB} = \frac{2}{3}$

Proof:

Statements (Reasons)

1. $AP = 2x + 3$, $PB = \frac{3x+1}{2}$, $AB = 10.5$ (Given)
2. $AP + PB = AB$ (Def. of a segment)
3. $2x + 3 + \frac{3x+1}{2} = 10.5$ (Subt.)
4. $2 \cdot \left(2x + 3 + \frac{3x+1}{2}\right) = 2 \cdot 10.5$ (Mult. Prop.)
5. $2 \cdot \left(2x + 3 + \frac{3x+1}{2}\right) = 21$ (Subs. Prop.)
6. $2 \cdot 2x + 2 \cdot 3 + 2 \cdot \frac{3x+1}{2} = 21$ (Dist. Prop.)
7. $4x + 6 + 3x + 1 = 21$ (Mult. Prop.)
8. $7x + 7 = 21$ (Add. Prop.)
9. $7x + 7 - 7 = 21 - 7$ (Subt. Prop.)
10. $7x = 14$ (Subs.)
11. $x = 2$ (Div. Prop.)
12. $AP = 2(2) + 3$ (Subs.)
13. $AP = 4 + 3$ (Mult. Prop.)
14. $AP = 7$ (Add. Prop.)
15. $\frac{AP}{AB} = \frac{7}{10.5}$ (Subs.)
16. $\frac{AP}{AB} = 0.\overline{6}$ (Div. Prop.)
17. $\frac{2}{3} = 0.\overline{6}$ (Div. Prop.)
18. $\frac{AP}{AB} = \frac{2}{3}$ (Trans. Prop.)

41. Sample answer: Depending on the purpose of the proof, one format may be preferable to another. For example, when writing an informal proof, you could use a paragraph proof to quickly convey your reasoning. When writing a more formal proof, a two-column proof may be preferable so that the justifications for each step are organized and easy to follow.

Lesson 2-7

5. **Given:** $\overline{AB} \cong \overline{CD}$, $AB + CD = EF$
   Prove: $2AB = EF$
   Proof:
   Statements (Reasons)
   1. $\overline{AB} \cong \overline{CD}$, $AB + CD = EF$ (Given)
   2. $AB = CD$ (Def. of ≅ segs.)
   3. $AB + AB = EF$ (Subs.)
   4. $2AB = EF$ (Subs. Prop.)

6. **Given:** $\overline{AB} \cong \overline{CD}$
   Prove: $\overline{CD} \cong \overline{AB}$
   Proof:
   Statements (Reasons)
   1. $\overline{AB} \cong \overline{CD}$ (Given)
   2. $AB = CD$ (Def. of ≅ segs.)
   3. $CD = AB$ (Symm. Prop.)
   4. $\overline{CD} \cong \overline{AB}$ (Def. of ≅ segs.)

7. **Given:** $\overline{AB}$
   Prove: $\overline{AB} \cong \overline{AB}$
   Proof:
   Statements (Reasons)
   1. $\overline{AB}$ (Given)
   2. $AB = AB$ (Refl. Prop.)
   3. $\overline{AB} \cong \overline{AB}$ (Def. of ≅ segs.)

8a.

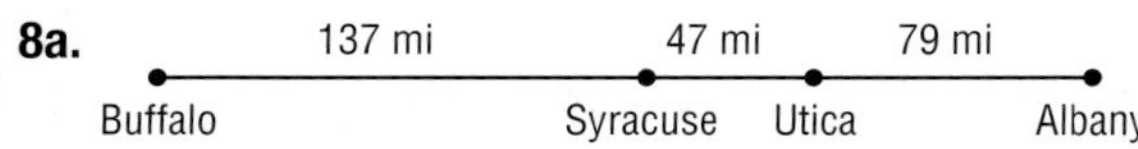

8b. Given: Buffalo, Utica, Albany, and Syracuse are collinear.
Buffalo is the farthest west.
Albany is 126 miles from Syracuse.
Albany is 263 miles from Buffalo.
Buffalo is 137 miles from Syracuse.
Buffalo is 184 miles from Utica.
Prove: The cities from west to east are Buffalo, Syracuse, Utica, and Albany.
It is 137 miles from Buffalo to Syracuse.
It is 47 miles from Syracuse to Utica.
It is 79 miles from Utica to Albany.

Proof:
We are given that all of the points are collinear. Since Syracuse is 137 miles from Buffalo and Albany is 263 miles from Buffalo, Syracuse is between Buffalo and Albany. Since Utica is 184 miles from Buffalo, and Syracuse is 137 miles from Buffalo, Syracuse is between Utica and Buffalo. Since Albany is 253 miles from Buffalo, and Utica is 184 miles from Buffalo, Utica is between Albany and Buffalo. Therefore, from east to west, the cities are Buffalo, Syracuse, Utica, and Albany.

Syracuse is 137 miles from Buffalo and Utica is 184 miles from Buffalo, so, using the Segment Addition Postulate, Syracuse is 184 − 137, or 47 miles from Utica. The distance from Buffalo to Albany is 263 miles and the distance from Buffalo to Utica is 184 miles, so, using the Segment Addition Postulate, the distance from Utica to Albany is 263 − 184, or 79 miles.

9. **Given:** $\overline{SC} \cong \overline{HR}$ and $\overline{HR} \cong \overline{AB}$
   Prove: $\overline{SC} \cong \overline{AB}$
   Proof:
   Statements (Reasons)
   1. $\overline{SC} \cong \overline{HR}$ and $\overline{HR} \cong \overline{AB}$ (Given)
   2. $SC = HR$ and $HR = AB$ (Def. of ≅ segs.)
   3. $SC = AB$ (Trans. Prop.)
   4. $\overline{SC} \cong \overline{AB}$ (Def. of ≅ segs.)

10. **Given:** $\overline{VZ} \cong \overline{VY}$ and $\overline{WY} \cong \overline{XZ}$
    Prove: $\overline{VW} \cong \overline{VX}$
    Proof:
    Statements (Reasons)
    1. $\overline{VZ} \cong \overline{VY}$ and $\overline{WY} \cong \overline{XZ}$ (Given)
    2. $VZ = VY$ and $WY = XZ$ (Def. of ≅ segs.)
    3. $VZ = VX + XZ$ and $VY = VW + WY$ (Seg. Add. Postulate)
    4. $VX + XZ = VW + WY$ (Subs.)
    5. $VX + WY = VW + WY$ (Subs.)
    6. $VX = VW$ (Subt. Prop.)
    7. $VW = VX$ (Symm. Prop.)
    8. $\overline{VW} \cong \overline{VX}$ (Def. of ≅ segs.)

11. **Given:** E is the midpoint of $\overline{DF}$ and $\overline{CD} \cong \overline{FG}$.
    Prove: $\overline{CE} \cong \overline{EG}$
    Proof:
    Statements (Reasons)
    1. E is the midpoint of $\overline{DF}$ and $\overline{CD} \cong \overline{FG}$. (Given)
    2. $DE = EF$ (Def. of midpoint)
    3. $CD = FG$ (Def. of ≅ segs.)
    4. $CD + DE = EF + FG$ (Add. Prop.)
    5. $CE = CD + DE$ and $EG = EF + FG$ (Seg. Add. Post.)
    6. $CE = EG$ (Subs.)
    7. $\overline{CE} \cong \overline{EG}$ (Def. of ≅ segs.)

12. Given: B is the midpoint of $\overline{AC}$, D is the midpoint of $\overline{CE}$, and $\overline{AB} \cong \overline{DE}$.

Prove: $AE = 4AB$

Proof:

Statements (Reasons)

1. B is the midpoint of $\overline{AC}$, D is the midpoint of $\overline{CE}$, and $\overline{AB} \cong \overline{DE}$. (Given)
2. $AB = BC$ and $CD = DE$ (Def. of midpoint)
3. $AB = DE$ (Def. of $\cong$ segs.)
4. $AC = AB + BC$ and $CE = CD + DE$ (Seg. Add. Post.)
5. $AE = AC + CE$ (Seg. Add. Post.)
6. $AE = AB + BC + CD + DE$ (Subs.)
7. $AE = AB + AB + AB + AB$ (Subs.)
8. $AE = 4AB$ (Subs.)

13a Given: $\overline{AC} \cong \overline{GI}$, $\overline{FE} \cong \overline{LK}$, $AC + CF + FE = GI + IL + LK$

Prove: $\overline{CF} \cong \overline{IL}$

Proof:

Statements (Reasons)

1. $\overline{AC} \cong \overline{GI}$, $\overline{FE} \cong \overline{LK}$, $AC + CF + FE = GI + IL + LK$ (Given)
2. $AC + CF + FE = AC + IL + LK$ (Subs.)
3. $AC - AC + CF + FE = AC - AC + IL + LK$ (Subt. Prop.)
4. $CF + FE = IL + LK$ (Subs. Prop.)
5. $CF + FE = IL + FE$ (Subs.)
6. $CF + FE - FE = IL + FE - FE$ (Subt. Prop.)
7. $CF = IL$ (Subs. Prop.)
8. $\overline{CF} \cong \overline{IL}$ (Def. of $\cong$ segs.)

13b. Sample answer: I measured $\overline{CF}$ and $\overline{IL}$, and both were 1.5 inches long, so the two segments are congruent.

14.

Sample answer: I placed an initial point A on a line ℓ and constructed a point B on the line so that AB is equal to PQ. Using point B as an initial point, I marked point C on the line so that BC is also equal to PQ. The length of the whole segment AC is $AB + BC$ according to the Additional Postulate and $AB = BC = PQ$. Using substitution $AC = PQ + PQ$, or $AC = 2PQ$, so $\overline{AC}$ is twice as long as $\overline{PQ}$.

16a.

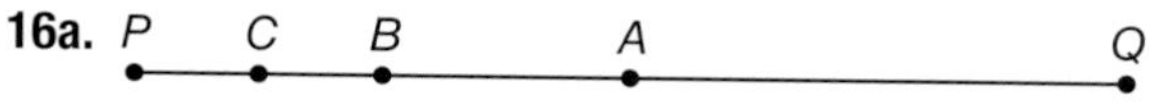

16b. $8PC = PQ$

16c. P C B Q

I can measure $\overline{PC}$ and mark off segments of that length along $\overline{PQ}$, and count how many segments were formed.

16d. P C B Q

$8PC = PQ$

16e. Given: A is the midpoint of $\overline{PQ}$, B is the midpoint of $\overline{PA}$, and C is the midpoint of $\overline{PB}$.

Prove: $8PC = PQ$

Proof:

Statements (Reasons)

1. A is the midpoint of $\overline{PQ}$, B is the midpoint of $\overline{PA}$, and C is the midpoint of $\overline{PB}$. (Given)
2. $PA = AQ$, $PB = BA$, $PC = CB$ (Def. of Midpoint)
3. $PC + CB = PB$ (Seg. Add. Post.)
4. $PC + PC = PB$ (Subs.)
5. $2PC = PB$ (Subs.)
6. $PB + BA = PA$ (Seg. Add. Post.)
7. $PB + PB = PA$ (Subs.)
8. $2PB = PA$ (Add. Prop.)
9. $2(2PC) = PA$ (Subs.)
10. $4PC = PA$ (Subs.)
11. $PA + AQ = PQ$ (Seg. Add. Post.)
12. $PA + PA = PQ$ (Subs.)
13. $2PA = PQ$ (Subs.)
14. $2(4PC) = PQ$ (Subs.)
15. $8PC = PQ$ (Subs.)

18. Given: $ABCD$ is a square.

Prove: $\overline{AC} \cong \overline{BD}$

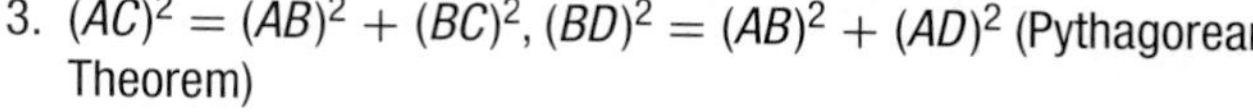

Proof:

Statements (Reasons)

1. $ABCD$ is a square. (Given)
2. $AB = BC = CD = DA$ (Def. of a square)
3. $(AC)^2 = (AB)^2 + (BC)^2$, $(BD)^2 = (AB)^2 + (AD)^2$ (Pythagorean Theorem)
4. $(BD)^2 = (AB)^2 + (BC)^2$ (Subt.)
5. $(AC)^2 = (BD)^2$ (Trans. Prop.)
6. $AC = \pm\sqrt{(BD)^2}$ (Sq. Root Prop.)
7. $AC = \sqrt{(BD)^2}$ (By definition, length must be positive.)
8. $AC = BD$ (Def. of Sq. Root)
9. $\overline{AC} \cong \overline{BD}$ (Def. of $\cong$ segs.)

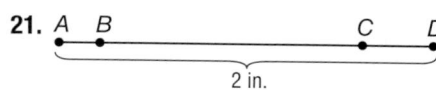

20. False; sample answer: $AB = BD = CE = 10$, but $AB = 7$, $BC = 3$, $CD = 7$ and $DE = 3$.

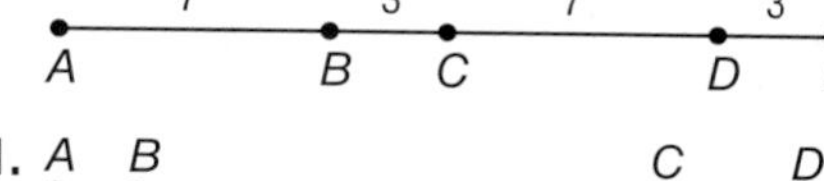

21. A B C D

2 in.

22. Paragraph proofs and two-column proofs both use deductive reasoning presented in a logical order along with the postulates, theorems, and definitions used to support the steps of the proofs. Paragraph proofs are written as a paragraph with the reasons for each step incorporated into the sentences. Two-column proofs are numbered and itemized. Each step of the proof is provided on a separate line with the support for that step in the column beside the step.

Lesson 2-8

14. Proof:

Statements (Reasons)

1. $\angle ABC$ is a right angle. (Given)
2. $m\angle ABC = 90$ (Def. of rt. angle)
3. $m\angle ABC = m\angle ABD + m\angle CBD$ ($\angle$ Add. Post.)
4. $m\angle ABD + m\angle CBD = 90$ (Subs.)
6. $\angle ABD$ and $\angle CBD$ are complementary. (Def. of compl. $\angle$s)

15. Proof:

Statements (Reasons)

1. $\angle 5 \cong \angle 6$ (Given)
2. $m\angle 5 = m\angle 6$ (Def. of $\cong$ $\angle$s)
3. $\angle 4$ and $\angle 5$ are supplementary. (Def. of linear pairs)
4. $m\angle 4 + m\angle 5 = 180$ (Def. of supp. $\angle$s)
5. $m\angle 4 + m\angle 6 = 180$ (Subs.)
6. $\angle 4$ and $\angle 6$ are supplementary. (Def. of supp. $\angle$s)

16. Given: Two $\angle$s form a linear pair.

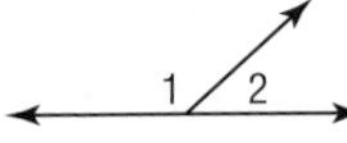

Prove: The $\angle$s are supplementary.

Paragraph Proof:

When 2 $\angle$s form a linear pair, the resulting $\angle$ is a straight $\angle$ whose measure is 180. By definition, 2 $\angle$s are supp. if the sum of their measures is 180. By the Angle Addition Post., $m\angle 1 + m\angle 2 = 180$. Thus, if 2 $\angle$s form a linear pair, then the angles are suppl.

17. Given: $\angle ABC$ is a right angle.

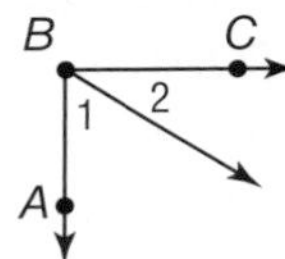

Prove: $\angle 1$ and $\angle 2$ are complementary $\angle$s.

Proof:

Statements (Reasons)

1. $\angle ABC$ is a right angle. (Given)
2. $m\angle ABC = 90$ (Def. of rt. $\angle$s)
3. $m\angle ABC = m\angle 1 + m\angle 2$ ($\angle$ Add. Post.)
4. $90 = m\angle 1 + m\angle 2$ (Subst.)
5. $\angle 1$ and $\angle 2$ are complementary angles. (Def. of comp. $\angle$s)

18. Given: $\angle A$

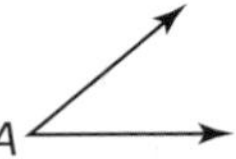

Prove: $\angle A \cong \angle A$

Proof:

Statements (Reasons)

1. $\angle A$ is an angle. (Given)
2. $m\angle A = m\angle A$ (Refl. Prop.)
3. $\angle A \cong \angle A$ (Def. of $\cong$ $\angle$s)

19. Given: $\angle 1 \cong \angle 2$, $\angle 2 \cong \angle 3$

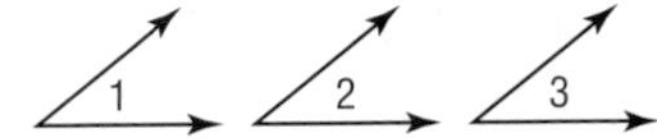

Prove: $\angle 1 \cong \angle 3$

Proof:

Statements (Reasons)

1. $\angle 1 \cong \angle 2$, $\angle 2 \cong \angle 3$ (Given)
2. $m\angle 1 = m\angle 2$, $m\angle 2 = m\angle 3$ (Def. of $\cong$ $\angle$s)
3. $m\angle 1 = m\angle 3$ (Trans. Prop.)
4. $\angle 1 \cong \angle 3$ (Def. of $\cong$ $\angle$s)

20. Given:

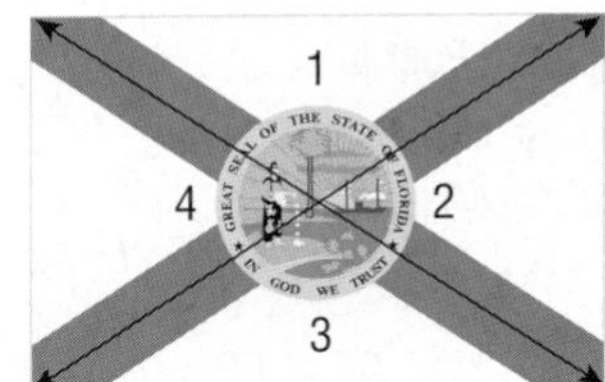

Prove: $m\angle 1 + m\angle 2 + m\angle 3 + m\angle 4 = 360$

Proof:

Statements (Reasons)

1. 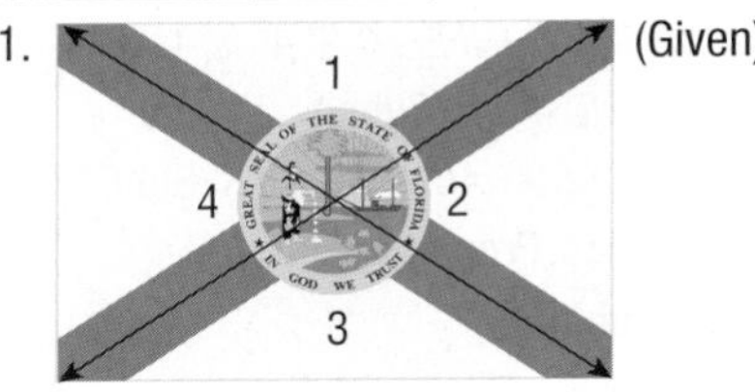

(Given)
2. $m\angle 1 + m\angle 2 = 180$, $m\angle 3 + m\angle 4 = 180$ (Suppl. Thm.)
3. $m\angle 1 + m\angle 2 + m\angle 3 = 180 + m\angle 3$ (Add. Prop.)
4. $m\angle 1 + m\angle 2 + m\angle 3 + m\angle 4 = 180 + m\angle 3 + m\angle 4$ (Add. Prop.)
5. $m\angle 1 + m\angle 2 + m\angle 3 + m\angle 4 = 180 + 180$ (Subs.)
6. $m\angle 1 + m\angle 2 + m\angle 3 + m\angle 4 = 360$ (Add. Prop.)

21. Given: $\angle 1 \cong \angle 4$

Prove: $\angle 2 \cong \angle 3$

Proof:

Statements (Reasons)

1. $\angle 1 \cong \angle 4$ (Given)
2. $\angle 1 \cong \angle 2$, $\angle 3 \cong \angle 4$ (Vert. $\angle$s are $\cong$.)
3. $\angle 1 \cong \angle 3$ (Trans. Prop.)
4. $\angle 2 \cong \angle 3$ (Subs.)

22. Given: $\ell \perp m$

Prove: $\angle 2$, $\angle 3$, $\angle 4$ are rt. $\angle$s

Proof:

Statements (Reasons)

1. $\ell \perp m$ (Given)
2. $\angle 1$ is a right angle. (Def. of $\perp$)
3. $m\angle 1 = 90$ (Def. of rt. $\angle$s)
4. $\angle 1 \cong \angle 4$ (Vert. $\angle$s $\cong$)
5. $m\angle 1 = m\angle 4$ (Def. of vertical $\angle$s)
6. $m\angle 4 = 90$ (Subs.)
7. $\angle 1$ and $\angle 2$ form a linear pair. $\angle 3$ and $\angle 4$ form a linear pair. (Def. of linear pairs)
8. $m\angle 1 + m\angle 2 = 180$, $m\angle 4 + m\angle 3 = 180$ (Linear pairs are supplementary.)
9. $90 + m\angle 2 = 180$, $90 + m\angle 3 = 180$ (Subs.)
10. $m\angle 2 = 90$, $m\angle 3 = 90$ (Subt. Prop.)
11. $\angle 2$, $\angle 3$, $\angle 4$ are rt. $\angle$s. (Def. of rt. $\angle$s (Steps 6, 10))

23. Given: $\angle 1$ and $\angle 2$ are rt. $\angle$s.

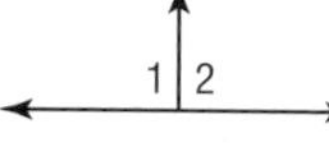

Prove: $\angle 1 \cong \angle 2$

Proof:

Statements (Reasons)

1. $\angle 1$ and $\angle 2$ are rt. $\angle$s. (Given)
2. $m\angle 1 = 90$, $m\angle 2 = 90$ (Def. of rt. $\angle$s)
3. $m\angle 1 = m\angle 2$ (Subs.)
4. $\angle 1 \cong \angle 2$ (Def. of $\cong$ $\angle$s)

24. Given: $\ell \perp m$

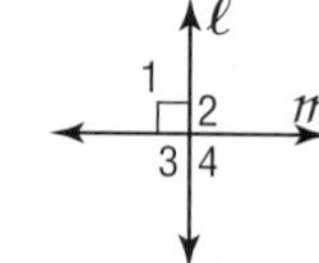

Prove: $\angle 1 \cong \angle 2$

Proof:

Statements (Reasons)

1. $\ell \perp m$ (Given)
2. $\angle 1$ and $\angle 2$ rt. $\angle$s ($\perp$ lines intersect to form 4 rt. $\angle$s.)
3. $\angle 1 \cong \angle 2$ (All rt. $\angle$s $\cong$.)

25. Given: $\angle 1 \cong \angle 2$, $\angle 1$ and $\angle 2$ are supplementary.

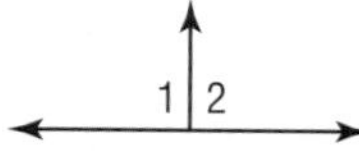

Prove: $\angle 1$ and $\angle 2$ are rt. $\angle$s.

Proof:

Statements (Reasons)

1. $\angle 1 \cong \angle 2$, $\angle 1$ and $\angle 2$ are supplementary. (Given)
2. $m\angle 1 + m\angle 2 = 180$ (Def. of $\angle$s)
3. $m\angle 1 = m\angle 2$ (Def. of $\cong$ $\angle$s)
4. $m\angle 1 + m\angle 1 = 180$ (Subs.)
5. $2(m\angle 1) = 180$ (Subs.)
6. $m\angle 1 = 90$ (Div. Prop.)
7. $m\angle 2 = 90$ (Subs. (steps 3, 6))
8. $\angle 1$ and $\angle 2$ are rt. $\angle$s. (Def. of rt. $\angle$s)

26. Given: $\angle 1 \cong \angle 2$

Prove: $\angle 1$ and $\angle 2$ are rt. $\angle$s.

Proof:

Statements (Reasons)

1. $\angle 1 \cong \angle 2$ (Given)
2. $\angle 1$ and $\angle 2$ form a linear pair. (Def. of linear pair)
3. $\angle 1$ and $\angle 2$ are supplementary. (Linear pairs are supplementary.)
4. $\angle 1$ and $\angle 2$ are rt. $\angle$s. (If $\angle$s $\cong$ and suppl., they are rt. $\angle$s.)

29. Given: $\angle 2$ is a right angle.

Prove: $\ell \perp m$

Proof:

Statements (Reasons)

1. $\angle 2$ is a right angle. (Given)
2. $m\angle 2 = 90$ (Def. of a rt. $\angle$)
3. $\angle 2 \cong \angle 3$ (Vert. $\angle$s are $\cong$.)
4. $m\angle 3 = 90$ (Subs.)
5. $m\angle 1 + m\angle 2 = 180$ (Supp. Th.)
6. $m\angle 1 + 90 = 180$ (Subs.)
7. $m\angle 1 + 90 - 90 = 180 - 90$ (Subt. Prop.)
8. $m\angle 1 = 90$ (Subs.)
9. $\angle 1 \cong \angle 4$ (Vert. $\angle$s are $\cong$.)
10. $\angle 4 \cong \angle 1$ (Symm. Prop.)
11. $m\angle 4 = m\angle 1$ (Def. of $\cong$ $\angle$s)
12. $m\angle 4 = 90$ (Subs.)
13. $\ell \perp m$ (Perpendicular lines intersect to form four right angles.)

30a.

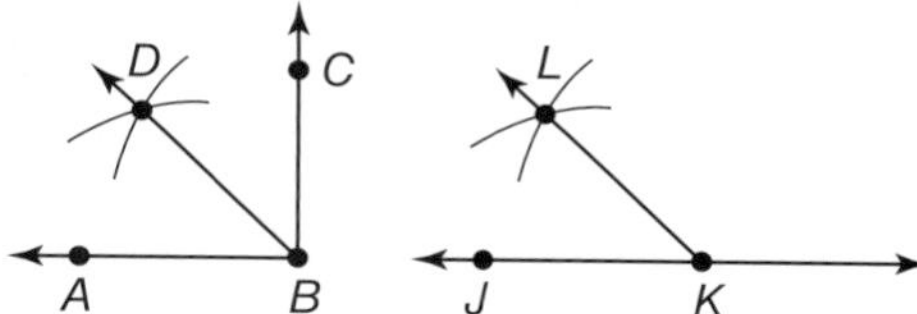

30b. Sample answer: $\angle DBC$ and $\angle JKL$ are complementary.

30c. Given: $\angle ABD$ and $\angle DBC$ are complementary. $\angle ABD \cong \angle JKL$

Prove: $\angle DBC$ and $\angle JKL$ are complementary.

Proof:

Statements (Reasons)

1. $\angle ABD$ and $\angle DBC$ are complementary $\angle ABD \cong \angle JKL$. (Given)
2. $m\angle DBC + m\angle ABD = 90$ (Def. of comp. $\angle$s)
3. $m\angle ABD = m\angle JKL$ (Def. of $\cong$ $\angle$s)
4. $m\angle DBC + m\angle JKL = 90$ (Subs.)
5. $\angle DBC$ and $\angle JKL$ are complementary. (Def. of comp. $\angle$s)

31. Given: $\overline{XZ}$ bisects $\angle WXY$, and $m\angle WXZ = 45$.

Prove: $\angle WXY$ is a right angle.

Proof:

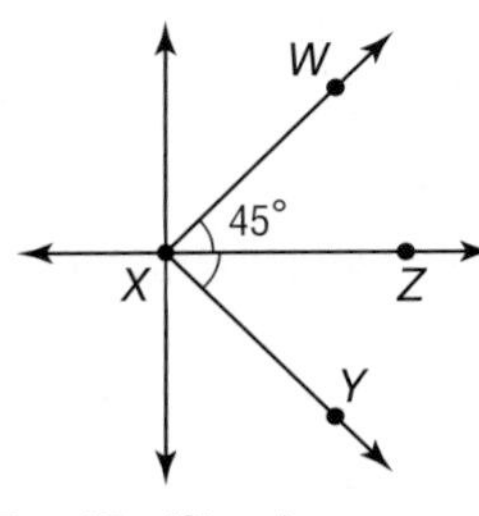

Statements (Reasons)

1. $\overline{XZ}$ bisects $\angle WXY$, and $m\angle WXZ = 45$. (Given)
2. $\angle WXZ \cong \angle ZXY$ (Def. of $\angle$ bisector)
3. $m\angle WXZ = m\angle ZXY$ (Def. of $\cong$ ⦣s)
4. $m\angle ZXY = 45$ (Subs.)
5. $m\angle WXY = m\angle WXZ + m\angle ZXY$ ($\angle$ Add. Post.)
6. $m\angle WXY = 45 + 45$ (Subs.)
7. $m\angle WXY = 90$ (Subs.)
8. $\angle WXY$ is a right angle. (Def. of rt. $\angle$)

33. Each of these theorems uses the words "or to congruent angles" indicating that this case of the theorem must also be proven true. The other proofs only addressed the "to the same angle" case of the theorem.

Given: $\angle ABC \cong \angle DEF$, $\angle GHI$ is complementary to $\angle ABC$, $\angle JKL$ is complementary to $\angle DEF$.

Prove: $\angle GHI \cong \angle JKL$

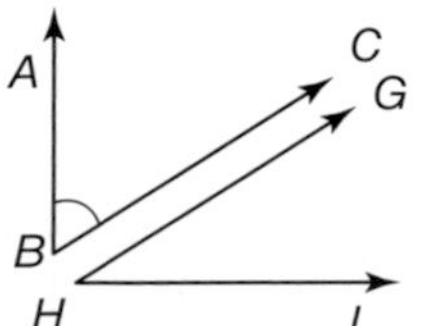

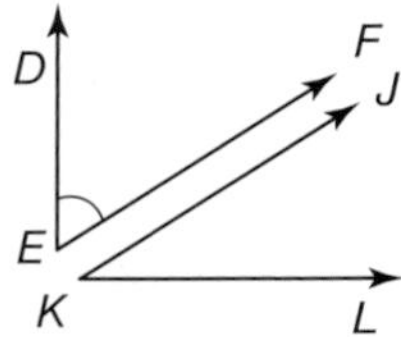

Proof:

Statements (Reasons)

1. $\angle ABC \cong \angle DEF$, $\angle GHI$ is complementary to $\angle ABC$, $\angle JKL$ is complementary to $\angle DEF$. (Given)
2. $m\angle ABC + m\angle GHI = 90$, $\angle DEF + \angle JKL = 90$ (Def. of compl. ⦣s)
3. $m\angle ABC + m\angle JKL = 90$ (Subs.)
4. $90 = m\angle ABC + m\angle JKL$ (Symm. Prop.)
5. $m\angle ABC + m\angle GHI = m\angle ABC + m\angle JKL$ (Trans. Prop.)
6. $m\angle ABC - m\angle ABC + m\angle GHI = m\angle ABC - m\angle ABC + m\angle JKL$ (Subt. Prop.)
7. $m\angle GHI = m\angle JKL$ (Subs. Prop.)
8. $\angle GHI \cong \angle JKL$ (Def. of $\cong$ ⦣s)

Given: $\angle ABC \cong \angle DEF$, $\angle GHI$ is supplementary to $\angle ABC$, $\angle JKL$ is supplementary to $\angle DEF$.

Prove: $\angle GHI \cong \angle JKL$

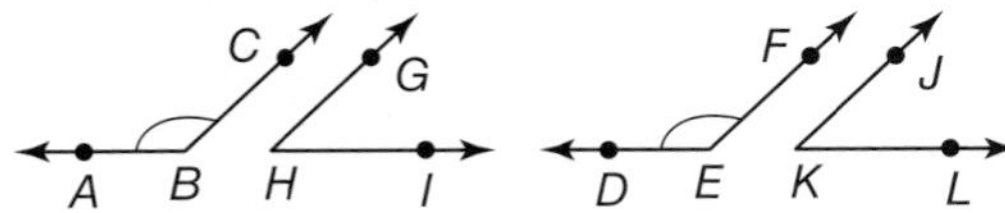

Proof:

Statements (Reasons)

1. $\angle ABC \cong \angle DEF$, $\angle GHI$ is supplementary to $\angle ABC$, $\angle JKL$ is supplementary to $\angle DEF$. (Given)
2. $m\angle ABC + m\angle GHI = 180$, $m\angle DEF + m\angle JKL = 180$ (Def. of suppl. ⦣s)
3. $m\angle ABC + m\angle JKL = 180$ (Subs.)
4. $180 = m\angle ABC + m\angle JKL$ (Symm. Property)
5. $m\angle ABC + m\angle GHI = m\angle ABC + m\angle JKL$ (Trans. Prop.)
6. $m\angle ABC - m\angle ABC + m\angle GHI = m\angle ABC - m\angle ABC + m\angle JKL$ (Subt. Prop.)
7. $m\angle GHI = m\angle JKL$ (Subs. Prop.)
8. $\angle GHI \cong \angle JKL$ (Def. of $\cong$ ⦣s)

34. Never; adjacent angles formed by two intersecting lines form a linear pair. If one angle in this linear pair is acute, then its measure is less than 90. The supplement of any angle will be greater than 90 because subtracting a number less than 90 from 180 must always result in a measure greater than 90.

Chapter Planner

	Diagnostic Assessment Quick Check LESSON 3-1 45 min: 1 day 90 min: 0.75 day	EXPLORE 3-2 45 min: 1 day 90 min: 0.5 day	LESSON 3-2 45 min: 1 day 90 min: 0.75 day
Title	**Parallel Lines and Transversals**	**Geometry Software Lab: Angles and Parallel Lines**	**Angles and Parallel Lines**
Objectives	▪ Identify the relationship between two lines or two planes. ▪ Name angle pairs formed by parallel lines and transversals.	▪ Use Geometer's Sketchpad to investigate angles formed by two parallel lines and a transversal.	▪ Use theorems to determine the relationships between specific pairs of angles. ▪ Use algebra to find angle measurements.
Key Vocabulary	parallel lines, parallel planes skew lines transversal interior angles, exterior angles consecutive interior angles alternate interior/exterior angles corresponding angles		
CCSS	G.CO.1	G.CO.12	G.CO.1, G.CO.9
Multiple Representations			
Lesson Resources	connectED.mcgraw-hill.com Leveled Worksheets Vocabulary Personal Tutor Self-Check Quiz ▪ *5-Minute Check* ▪ *Study Notebook* ▪ *Teaching Geometry with Manipulatives*	connectED.mcgraw-hill.com Personal Tutor **Materials:** ▪ computers with Geometer's Sketchpad software	connectED.mcgraw-hill.com Leveled Worksheets Quiz 1 Personal Tutor Self-Check Quiz ▪ *5-Minute Check* ▪ *Study Notebook*
Resources for Every Lesson	IWB eStudent Edition IWB Interactive Classroom	▪ eTeacher Edition ▪ eSolutions Manual ▪ eAssessment	
Differentiated Instruction	pp. 175, 178		pp. 181, 185

IWB All digital assets are Interactive Whiteboard ready.

Suggested Pacing			
Time Periods	Instruction	Review & Assess	Total
45-minute	8 days	2 days	10 days
90-minute	6 days	1 day	7 days

EXPLORE 3-3 (45 min: 0.5 day; 90 min: 0.5 day)	LESSON 3-3 (45 min: 1 day; 90 min: 0.75 day)	LESSON 3-4 (45 min: 1 day; 90 min: 0.75 day)	EXTEND 3-4 (45 min: 0.5 day; 90 min: 0.5 day)
Graphing Technology Lab: Investigating Slope	**Slopes of Lines**	**Equations of Lines**	**Geometry Lab: Equations of Perpendicular Bisectors**
▪ Use a graphing calculator to investigate slope.	▪ Find slopes of lines. ▪ Use slope to identify parallel and perpendicular lines.	▪ Write an equation of a line given information about the graph. ▪ Solve problems by writing equations.	▪ Explore figures on a coordinate plane.
	slope rate of change	slope-intercept form point-slope form	
G.GPE.5	G.GPE.5	G.GPE.5	G.GPE.5
connectED.mcgraw-hill.com **Materials:** ▪ graphing calculators with data collection devices	connectED.mcgraw-hill.com Leveled Worksheets Quiz 2 Vocabulary Animations Personal Tutor Virtual Manipulatives Self-Check Quiz ▪ *5-Minute Check* ▪ *Study Notebook*	connectED.mcgraw-hill.com Leveled Worksheets Vocabulary Personal Tutor Virtual Manipulatives Self-Check Quiz ▪ *5-Minute Check* ▪ *Study Notebook* ▪ *Teaching Geometry with Manipulatives*	connectED.mcgraw-hill.com Virtual Manipulatives ▪ *Teaching Geometry with Manipulatives* **Materials:** ▪ grid paper
IWB eStudent Edition IWB Interactive Classroom	▪ eTeacher Edition ▪ eSolutions Manual ▪ eAssessment		
	pp. 192, 195	pp. 200, 205	

Formative Assessment
Mid-Chapter Quiz

Chapter Planner

	LESSON 3-5 (45 min: 1 day; 90 min: 0.75 day)	LESSON 3-6 (45 min: 1 day; 90 min: 0.75 day)
Title	**Proving Lines Parallel**	**Perpendiculars and Distance**
Objectives	▪ Recognize angle pairs that occur with parallel lines. ▪ Prove that two lines are parallel.	▪ Find the distance between a point and a line. ▪ Find the distance between two parallel lines.
Key Vocabulary		equidistant
CCSS	G.CO.9, G.CO.12	G.CO.12, G.MG.3
Multiple Representations		
Lesson Resources	connectED.mcgraw-hill.com Leveled Worksheets Quiz 3 Animations Personal Tutor Self-Check Quiz ▪ *5-Minute Check* ▪ *Study Notebook* ▪ *Teaching Geometry with Manipulatives*	connectED.mcgraw-hill.com Leveled Worksheets Quiz 4 Vocabulary Animations Personal Tutor Virtual Manipulatives Self-Check Quiz ▪ *5-Minute Check* ▪ *Study Notebook* ▪ *Teaching Geometry with Manipulatives*
Resources for Every Lesson	IWB eStudent Edition IWB Interactive Classroom	▪ eTeacher Edition ▪ eSolutions Manual ▪ eAssessment
Differentiated Instruction	pp. 209, 210	pp. 216, 223

Summative Assessment
Study Guide and Review
Practice Test

IWB All digital assets are Interactive Whiteboard ready.

What the Research Says...

Gagne and Driscoll (1988) state that the learning of a skill typically requires the explicit prior development of simpler component skills.

- Stress that the concept of parallel lines taught throughout Chapter 3 is a concept that is further developed through the course.
- The relationship between angles, transversals, slope, and parallel lines is relied upon to write proofs.

Teacher to Teacher

Cynthia W. Poche, Teacher
Salmen High School
Slidell, LA

Use With Lesson 3-5

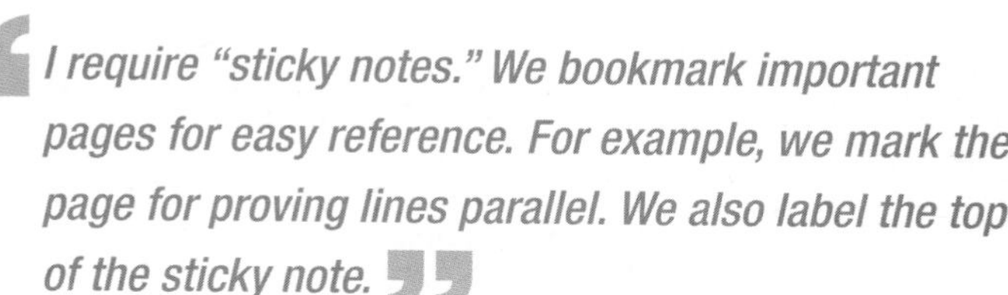

"I require "sticky notes." We bookmark important pages for easy reference. For example, we mark the page for proving lines parallel. We also label the top of the sticky note."

Reading and Writing in Mathematics

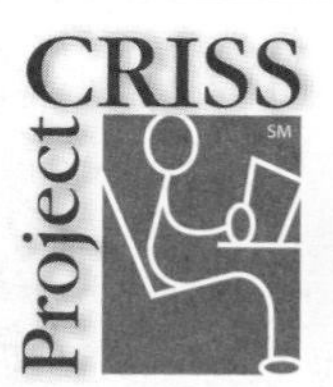

STUDY SKILL

Concept maps can be developed as part of a class discussion to help students understand mathematical relationships. After students have read Lesson 3-2, write "Angles Formed by Parallel Lines and a Transversal" on the board. Allow students to complete the concept map. Encourage them to make drawings to accompany their descriptions. Students can develop similar concept maps as part of class discussions on Slopes of Lines (Lesson 3-3), Equations of Lines (Lesson 3-4), and other topics in Chapter 3.

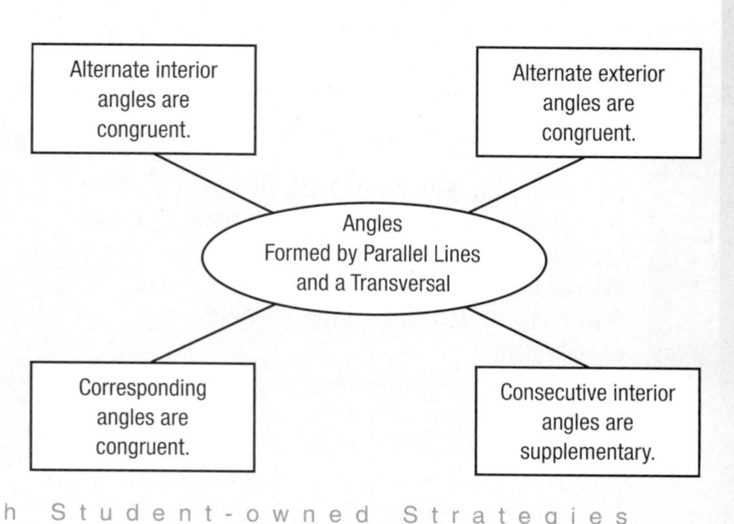

Creating Independence through Student-owned Strategies

CHAPTER 3 Parallel and Perpendicular Lines

Assessment and Intervention

SE = Student Edition, **TE** = Teacher Edition, **CRM** = Chapter Resource Masters

	Diagnosis	Prescription
DIAGNOSTIC ASSESSMENT	**Beginning Chapter 3**	
	Get Ready for Chapter 3 **SE**	Response to Intervention **TE**
	Beginning Every Lesson	
	Then, Now, Why? **SE** 5-Minute Checks	Chapter 0 **SE**
FORMATIVE ASSESSMENT	**During/After Every Lesson**	
	Guided Practice **SE**, every example Check Your Understanding **SE** H.O.T. Problems **SE** Spiral Review **SE** Additional Examples **TE** Watch Out! **TE** Step 4, Assess **TE** Chapter 3 Quizzes **CRM**, pp. 45–46 Self-Check Quizzes connectED.mcgraw-hill.com	TIER 1 Intervention Skills Practice **CRM**, Ch. 1–3 connectED.mcgraw-hill.com TIER 2 Intervention Differentiated Instruction **TE** Differentiated Homework Options **TE** Study Guide and Intervention **CRM**, Ch. 1–3 TIER 3 Intervention *Math Triumphs, Geometry,* Ch. 4
	Mid-Chapter	
	Mid-Chapter Quiz **SE** Mid-Chapter Test **CRM**, p. 47 eAssessment	TIER 1 Intervention Skills Practice **CRM**, Ch. 1–3 connectED.mcgraw-hill.com TIER 2 Intervention Study Guide and Intervention **CRM**, Ch. 1–3 TIER 3 Intervention *Math Triumphs, Geometry,* Ch. 4
	Before Chapter Test	
	Chapter Study Guide and Review **SE** Practice Test **SE** Standardized Test Practice **SE** Chapter Test connectED.mcgraw-hill.com Standardized Test Practice connectED.mcgraw-hill.com Vocabulary Review connectED.mcgraw-hill.com eAssessment	TIER 1 Intervention Skills Practice **CRM**, Ch. 1–3 connectED.mcgraw-hill.com TIER 2 Intervention Study Guide and Intervention **CRM**, Ch. 1–3 TIER 3 Intervention *Math Triumphs, Geometry,* Ch. 4
SUMMATIVE ASSESSMENT	**After Chapter 3**	
	Multiple-Choice Tests, Forms 1, 2A, 2B **CRM**, pp. 49–54 Free-Response Tests, Forms 2C, 2D, 3 **CRM**, pp. 55–60 Vocabulary Test **CRM**, p. 48 Extended Response Test **CRM**, p. 61 Standardized Test Practice **CRM**, pp. 62–64 eAssessment	Study Guide and Intervention **CRM**, Ch. 1–3 connectED.mcgraw-hill.com

CHAPTER 3 Parallel and Perpendicular Lines

Differentiated Instruction

Option 1 Reaching All Learners

Interpersonal Have each student write a fraction on an index card to represent the slope of a line. Then have each student trade cards with another student. Each student should write the slope of a line that is either parallel to or perpendicular to the slope of the first line on the other student's card. Have students return the card to the original owner, who will then label the relationship of the lines as either parallel or perpendicular and construct an accurate drawing of the two lines.

Intrapersonal Have students construct a drawing of two or three parallel lines cut by a transversal and number each angle. Then have them classify the relationship between each pair of angles as alternate interior, alternate exterior, corresponding, or consecutive interior and complementary or supplementary.

Option 2 Approaching Level AL

Mark two parallel lines and a transversal on the floor. Have pairs of students stand in the angles that are congruent or supplementary and explain whether the angles are alternate interior, alternate exterior, and so on.

Option 3 English Learners ELL

Have students identify parallel and perpendicular lines drawn on paper. Have students look around the room for real-life examples and brainstorm real-life examples from outside the classroom. Encourage students to bring examples of figures that have parallel and perpendicular edges from home.

Option 4 Beyond Level BL

In this chapter, students look at several real-world examples of slopes, angles, transversals, and parallel lines (the Sears Tower, electrical wires, and so on.). Have students choose a well-known architectural structure to research. The research should include the location as well as the date and purpose of the construction. Students will use the information to create a poster to present to the class. The poster should include the research paper, a picture of the structure, and a sketch of the structure with labels for the various line relationships (parallel, perpendicular, transversal, and skew), the measure of the slopes of lines, and angle relationships (alternate interior, alternate exterior, corresponding, and consecutive interior).

Focus on Mathematical Content

Vertical Alignment

Before Chapter 3

Related Topics before Grade 8

- Compare and contrast proportional and nonproportional linear relationships.
- Identify and apply mathematics to everyday experience, to activities in and outside of school, with other disciplines, and with other mathematical topics.

Related Topics from Algebra 1

- Graph and write equations of lines.

Chapter 3

Related Topics from Geometry

- Make conjectures about lines and determine the validity of the conjectures.
- Make conjectures about angles and determine the validity of the conjectures.
- Use slopes of equations of lines to investigate geometric relationships, including parallel lines and perpendicular lines.
- Use one- and two-dimensional coordinate systems to represent lines.

After Chapter 3

Continuing Geometry

- Formulate and test conjectures.

Preparation for Algebra 2

- Identify and sketch graphs of parent functions, including linear.

Lesson-by-Lesson Preview

3-1 Parallel Lines and Transversals

Coplanar lines that do not intersect are called *parallel lines*. Planes that do not intersect are called *parallel planes*. The notation || is used to show parallelism. Noncoplanar lines are called *skew lines*.

A line that intersects two or more lines in a plane at different points is called a *transversal*. The intersection of these lines creates a variety of angle relationships. Each intersection creates four angles. Each angle has a corresponding angle at the other intersection.

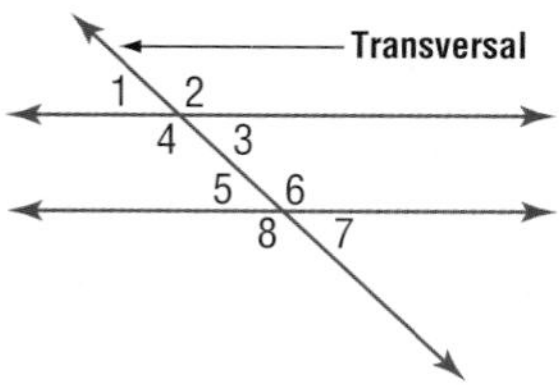

- Interior angles lie inside the parallel lines.
  $\angle 3$, $\angle 4$, $\angle 5$, $\angle 6$
- Exterior angles lie outside the parallel lines.
  $\angle 1$, $\angle 2$, $\angle 7$, $\angle 8$
- Alternate interior angles are on opposite sides of the transversal and inside the parallel lines.
  $\angle 3$ and $\angle 5$, $\angle 4$ and $\angle 6$
- Alternate exterior angles are on opposite sides of the transversal and outside the parallel lines.
  $\angle 1$ and $\angle 7$, $\angle 2$ and $\angle 8$
- Corresponding angles are in the same position on the parallel lines in relation to the transversal.
  $\angle 1$ and $\angle 5$, $\angle 2$ and $\angle 6$, $\angle 3$ and $\angle 7$, $\angle 4$ and $\angle 8$

3-2 Angles and Parallel Lines

When a transversal intersects a pair of parallel lines, the corresponding angles are congruent. This postulate is called the Corresponding Angles Postulate. In this same situation, alternate interior angles and alternate exterior angles are also congruent. Furthermore, each pair of consecutive interior angles is supplementary.

The Perpendicular Transversal Theorem states that, in a plane, if a transversal is perpendicular to one of two parallel lines, it is also perpendicular to the other. Students use their knowledge of how transversals create congruent and supplementary angles to calculate angle measures.

3-3 Slope of Lines

The slope of a line is the ratio of its vertical rise to its horizontal run.

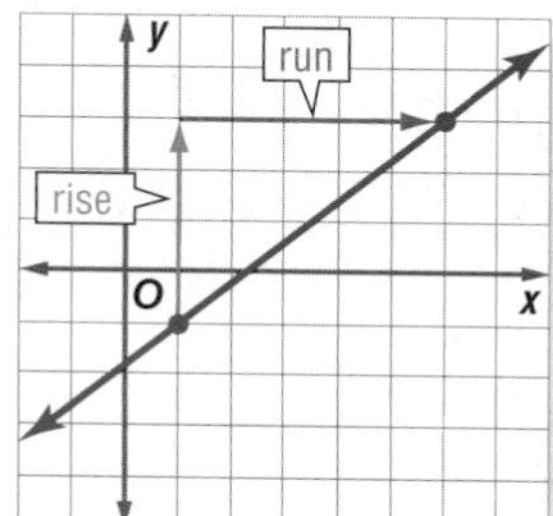

$\frac{\text{rise}}{\text{run}} = \frac{4}{5} = \text{slope}$

The slope of a vertical line is undefined, and the slope of a horizontal line is zero. Two nonvertical lines have the same slope if and only if they are parallel. Two nonvertical lines are perpendicular if and only if the product of their slopes is -1. This means that you can use slope to identify parallel and perpendicular lines. You can also use slope to graph parallel and perpendicular lines. In the example above, a perpendicular line would have a slope of $-\frac{5}{4}$ because $\frac{4}{5}\left(-\frac{5}{4}\right) = -1$.

3-4 Equations of Lines

This lesson presents two basic forms for the equations of lines. One is called the slope-intercept form. It is written as $y = mx + b$, where m is the slope and b is the y-intercept. The point-slope form is the second form. It is written as $y - y_1 = m(x - x_1)$ where (x_1, y_1) are the coordinates of any point contained in the line.

You can write linear equations to solve real-world problems. Slope often represents a rate of change. This rate can be used to determine cost or other information.

3-5 Proving Lines Parallel

Lines can be proved parallel if certain angle conditions are met. If two lines in a plane are cut by a transversal so that corresponding angles are congruent, then the lines are parallel. This postulate justifies the construction of parallel lines. A transversal is drawn through a given point to intersect a given line. The given point becomes the vertex for constructing an angle congruent to the one formed by the line and the transversal. Using a compass and straightedge, copy the given angle. The result is a pair of parallel lines cut by a transversal. This construction leads to the Parallel Postulate: If given a line and a point not on the line, then there exists exactly one line through the point that is parallel to the given line.

Because parallel lines create pairs of angles with special relationships, those pairs of angles can be used to prove that lines are parallel. Some of the conditions that verify parallel lines are:

- congruent corresponding angles,
- congruent alternate exterior angles,
- congruent alternate interior angles,
- consecutive interior angles that are supplementary, and
- lines that are perpendicular to the same line.

3-6 Perpendiculars and Distance

The distance from a line to a point not on the line is the length of the segment perpendicular to the line from the point. This is the shortest distance from the point to the line. You can construct a perpendicular segment by using a compass and straightedge. Distance can be used to determine parallel lines. Two lines in a plane are parallel if they are equidistant everywhere. Equidistant means that the distance between two lines is always the same.

To find the distance between two parallel lines, measure the length of a perpendicular segment whose endpoints lie on each of the two lines. You need to measure in only one place because the distance remains consistent. This also means that if two lines are equidistant from a third line, then the two lines are parallel to each other.

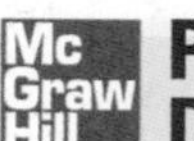

Professional Development

Targeted professional development has been articulated throughout Geometry. More quality, customized professional development is available from McGraw-Hill Professional Development. Visit connectED.mcgraw-hill.com for details on each product.

- Online Lessons emphasize the strategies and techniques used to teach Geometry. Includes streaming video, interactive pages, and online tools.
- Video Workshops allow mentors, coaches, or leadership personnel to facilitate on-site workshops on educational strategies in mathematics and mathematical concepts.
- MHPD Online (www.mhpdonline.com) offers online professional development with video clips of instructional strategies, links, student activities, and news and issues in education.
- Teaching Today (teachingtoday.glencoe.com) gives secondary teachers practical strategies and materials that inspire excellence and innovation in teaching.

Chapter Project

For the Birds

Students use what they have learned about parallel and perpendicular lines to complete a project.

This chapter project addresses environmental literacy, as well as several specific skills identified as being essential to student success by the Framework for 21st Century Learning.

Visit connectED.mcgraw-hill.com for student and teacher handouts.

KeyVocabulary Introduce the Key Vocabulary in the chapter by using the routine below.

Define: Parallel lines are coplanar lines that never intersect.

Example: The lines on a sheet of notebook paper are parallel.

Ask: True or False? If the lines on the notebook paper are parallel, then they must be coplanar. True True or False? If the lines on the notebook paper are coplanar, then they must be parallel. False What would be an example of coplanar lines that are not parallel?

Sample answer: intersecting lines drawn on notebook paper

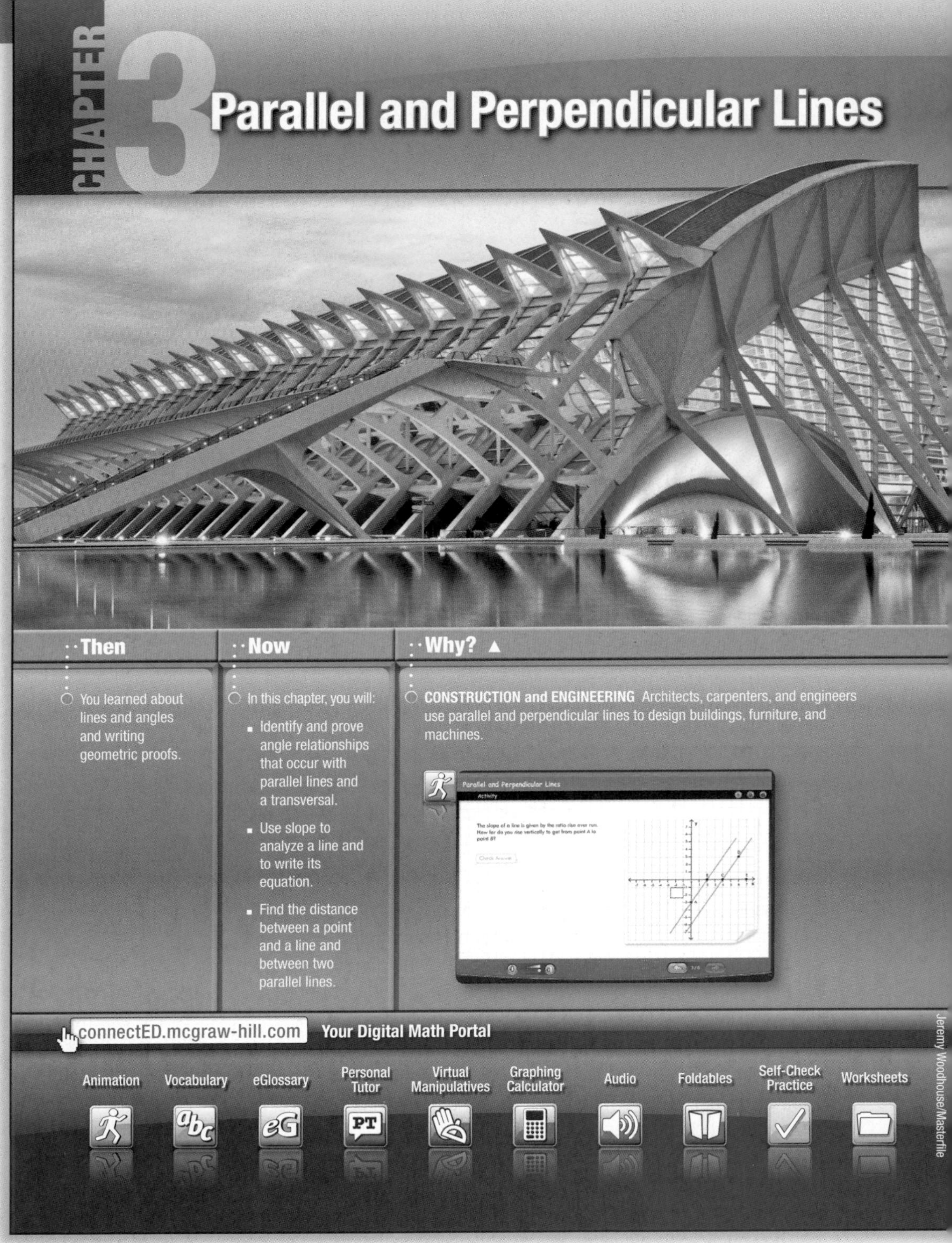

CHAPTER 3
Parallel and Perpendicular Lines
Then
You learned about lines and angles and writing geometric proofs.
Now
In this chapter, you will:
Identify and prove angle relationships that occur with parallel lines and a transversal.
Use slope to analyze a line and to write its equation.
Find the distance between a point and a line and between two parallel lines.
Why?
CONSTRUCTION and ENGINEERING Architects, carpenters, and engineers use parallel and perpendicular lines to design buildings, furniture, and machines.
Parallel and Perpendicular Lines
Activity
connectED.mcgraw-hill.com
Your Digital Math Portal
Animation
Vocabulary
eGlossary
Personal Tutor
Virtual Manipulatives
Graphing Calculator
Audio
Foldables
Self-Check Practice
Worksheets
Jeremy Woodhouse/Masterfile

Get Ready for the Chapter

Diagnose Readiness | You have two options for checking prerequisite skills.

1 Textbook Option Take the Quick Check below. Refer to the Quick Review for help.

QuickCheck

Refer to the figure to identify each of the following.

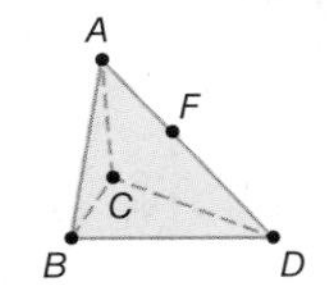

1. How many planes are shown in this figure? **4**
2. Name three points that are collinear. ***A*, *F*, and *D***
3. Are points *C* and *D* coplanar? Explain. **See margin.**
4. **PHOTOGRAPHY** Tina is taking a picture of her friends. If she sets a tripod level on the ground, will the bottom of each of the three legs of the tripod be coplanar? **yes**

QuickReview

Example 1 (Used in Lesson 3-1)

Refer to the figure.

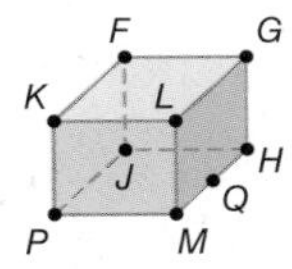

a. How many planes are shown in this figure?
Six: plane *FGLK*, plane *JHMP*, plane *FKPJ*, plane *GLMH*, plane *FGHJ*, and plane *KLMP*

b. Name three points that are collinear.
Points *M*, *Q*, and *H* are collinear.

c. Are points *F*, *K*, and *J* coplanar? Explain.
Yes. Points *F*, *K*, and *J* all lie in plane *FKPJ*.

Find each angle measure.

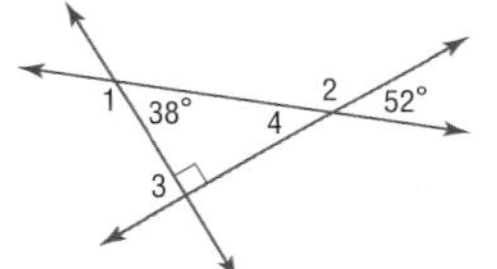

5. $\angle 1$ **142**
6. $\angle 2$ **128**
7. $\angle 3$ **90**
8. $\angle 4$ **52**

Example 2 (Used in Lessons 3-2 and 3-5)

Find $m\angle 1$.

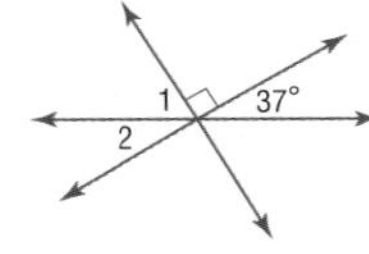

$m\angle 1 + 37 + 90 = 180$ Add.
$m\angle 1 = 53$ Simplify.

Find the value of *x* for the given values of *a* and *b*.

9. $a + 8 = -4(x - b)$, for $a = 8$ and $b = 3$ **−1**
10. $b = 3x + 4a$, for $a = -9$ and $b = 12$ **16**
11. $\frac{a+2}{b+13} = 5x$, for $a = 18$ and $b = -1$ $\frac{1}{3}$
12. **MINIATURE GOLF** A miniature golf course offers a $1 ice cream cone with each round of golf purchased. If five friends each had a cone after golfing and spend a total of $30, how much does one round of golf cost? **$5**

Example 3 (Used in Lessons 3-3 through 3-6)

Find *x* in $a + 8 = b(x - 7)$ if $a = 12$ and $b = 10$.

$a + 8 = b(x - 7)$	Write the equation.
$12 + 8 = 10(x - 7)$	$a = 12$ and $b = 10$
$20 = 10x - 70$	Simplify.
$90 = 10x$	Add.
$x = 9$	Divide.

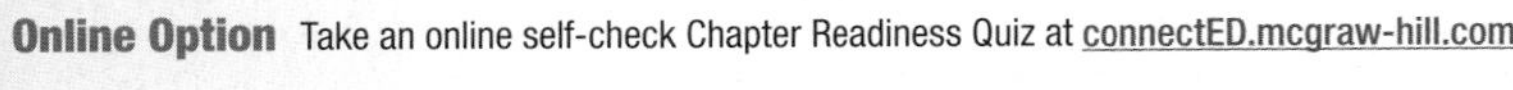

2 Online Option Take an online self-check Chapter Readiness Quiz at connectED.mcgraw-hill.com.

171

Essential Questions

- Why do we have undefined terms such as *point* and *line*? Sample answer: We have to start somewhere, so we start with a set of terms with meanings that are accepted as true.
- How can we use undefined terms? Sample answer: We can use them to define more terms. Then, we can use these definitions to write postulates and theorems and to develop properties.

Get Ready for the Chapter

Response to Intervention (RtI)

Use the *Quick Check* results and the Intervention Planner chart to help you determine your Response to Intervention. The If-Then statements in the chart help you decide the appropriate tier of RtI and suggest intervention resources for each tier.

InterventionPlanner

TIER 1 On Level OL

 students miss about 25% of the exercises or less,

 choose a resource:

SE Lessons 0-4, 1-1, and 1-5

 Skills Practice, Chapter 1, pp. 7, 33

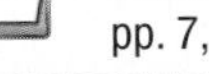 Self-Check Quiz

TIER 2 Strategic Intervention AL approaching grade level

 students miss about 50% of the exercises,

 choose a resource:

 Study Guide and Intervention, Chapter 1, pp. 5–6, 31–32

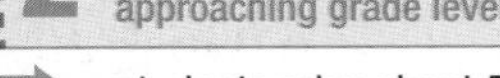 Extra Examples, Personal Tutor, Homework Help

TIER 3 Intensive Intervention 2 or more grades below level

 students miss about 75% of the exercises,

Then use *Math Triumphs, Geo.*, Ch. 4

 Extra Examples, Personal Tutor, Homework Help, Review Vocabulary

Additional Answer

3. Yes, points *C* and *D* lie in plane *CBD*.

FOLDABLES StudyOrganizer

Dinah Zike's Foldables®

Focus Students write about parallel and perpendicular lines.

Teach Students need study cards, either 3″ × 5″ index cards, or sheets of notebook paper cut into quarter sections. As students learn about parallel lines and transversals, have them draw a diagram on one side of the card and describe in writing what they have drawn on the other side. Store parallel line cards in the appropriate pocket of the foldable. Continue through the chapter also making cards for perpendicular lines.

When to use it Use the appropriate tabs as students cover each lesson in this chapter. Students can add to the vocabulary tab during each lesson.

For a more durable Foldable, have students add a folded sheet of construction paper as a cover before stapling and cutting the 11 × 17 paper.

Differentiated Instruction

Student-Built Glossary, pp. 1–2

Students complete the chart by providing the definition of each term and an example as they progress through Chapter 3.

This study tool can also be used to review for the chapter test.

Get Started on the Chapter

You will learn several new concepts, skills, and vocabulary terms as you study Chapter 3. To get ready, identify important terms and organize your resources. You may wish to refer to Chapter 0 to review prerequisite skills.

FOLDABLES StudyOrganizer

Parallel and Perpendicular Lines Make this Foldable to help you organize your Chapter 3 notes about relationships between lines. Begin with a sheet of 11″ × 17″ paper and six index cards.

1 **Fold** lengthwise about 3″ from the bottom.

2 **Fold** the paper in thirds.

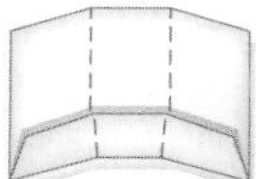

3 **Open** and staple the edges on either side to form three pockets.

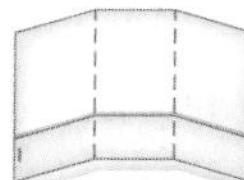

4 **Label** the pockets as shown. Place two index cards in each pocket.

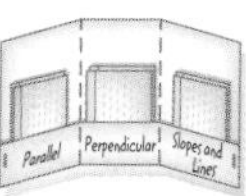

NewVocabulary

English		Español
parallel lines	p. 173	rectas paralelas
skew lines	p. 173	rectas alabeadas
parallel planes	p. 173	planos paralelos
transversal	p. 174	transversal
interior angles	p. 174	ángulos interiores
exterior angles	p. 174	ángulos externos
corresponding angles	p. 174	ángulos correspondientes
slope	p. 188	pendiente
rate of change	p. 189	tasa de cambio
slope-intercept form	p. 198	forma pendiente-intersección
point-slope form	p. 198	forma punto-pendiente
equidistant	p. 218	equidistante

ReviewVocabulary

congruent angles ángulos congruentes two angles that have the same degree measure

perpendicular perpendicular two lines, segments, or rays that intersect to form right angles

vertical angles ángulos opusetos por el vértice two nonadjacent angles formed by intersecting lines

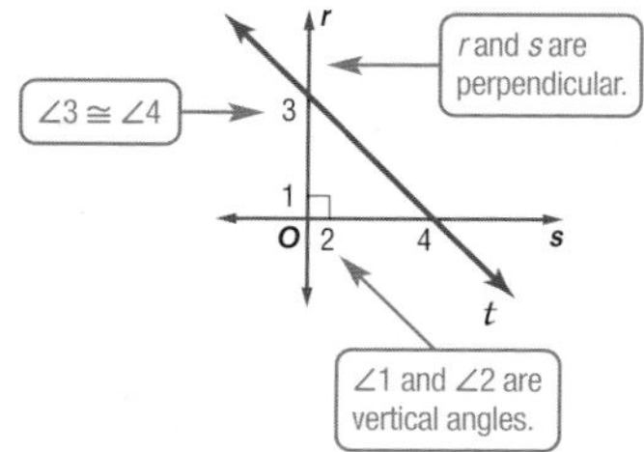

LESSON 3-1 Parallel Lines and Transversals

Then

- You used angle and line segment relationships to prove theorems.

Now

1. Identify the relationships between two lines or two planes.
2. Name angle pairs formed by parallel lines and transversals.

Why?

- An Ames room creates the illusion that a person standing in the right corner is much larger than a person standing in the left corner.

From a front viewing hole the front and back walls appear parallel, when in fact they are slanted. The ceiling and floor appear horizontal, but are actually tilted.

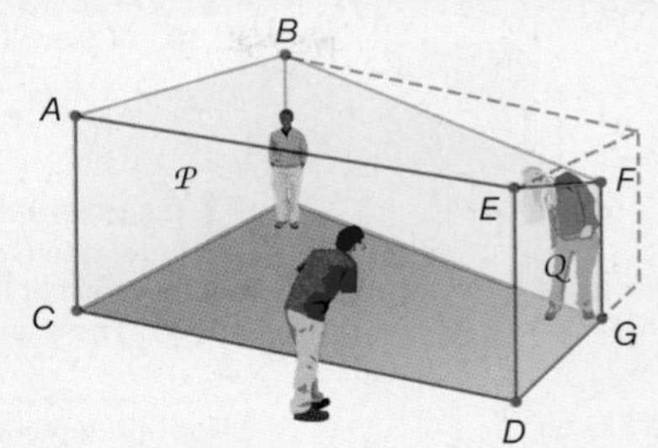

New Vocabulary
parallel lines
skew lines
parallel planes
transversal
interior angles
exterior angles
consecutive interior angles
alternate interior angles
alternate exterior angles
corresponding angles

Common Core State Standards

Content Standards
G.CO.1 Know precise definitions of angle, circle, perpendicular line, parallel line, and line segment, based on the undefined notions of point, line, distance along a line, and distance around a circular arc.

Mathematical Practices
1 Make sense of problems and persevere in solving them.
3 Construct viable arguments and critique the reasoning of others.

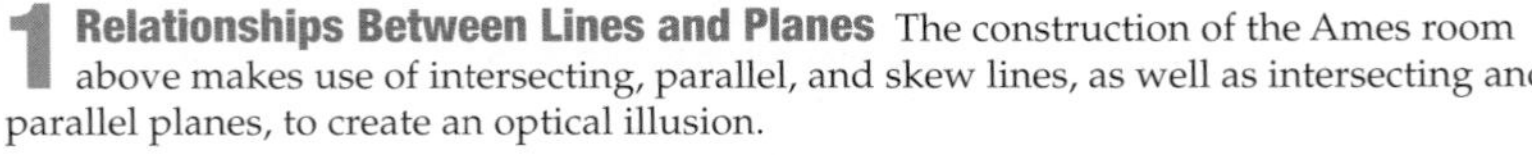

1 Relationships Between Lines and Planes

The construction of the Ames room above makes use of intersecting, parallel, and skew lines, as well as intersecting and parallel planes, to create an optical illusion.

KeyConcepts Parallel and Skew

Parallel lines are coplanar lines that do not intersect.
Example $\overleftrightarrow{JK} \parallel \overleftrightarrow{LM}$

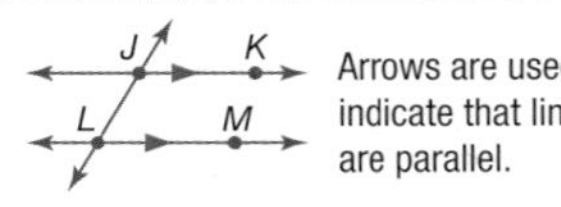

Arrows are used to indicate that lines are parallel.

Skew lines are lines that do not intersect and are not coplanar.
Example Lines ℓ and m are skew.

Parallel planes are planes that do not intersect.
Example Planes $\mathcal{A}$ and $\mathcal{B}$ are parallel.

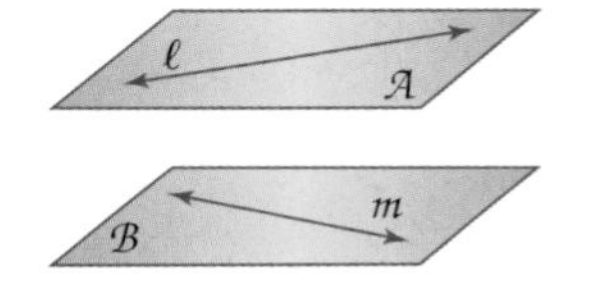

$\overleftrightarrow{JK} \parallel \overleftrightarrow{LM}$ is read as *line JK is parallel to line LM*.

If segments or rays are contained within lines that are parallel or skew, then the segments or rays are parallel or skew.

PT

Real-World Example 1 Identify Parallel and Skew Relationships

Identify each of the following using the wedge of cheese below.

a. **all segments parallel to $\overline{JP}$**

$\overline{KQ}$ and $\overline{LR}$

b. **a segment skew to $\overline{KL}$**

$\overline{JP}$, $\overline{PQ}$, or $\overline{PR}$

c. **a plane parallel to plane PQR**

Plane JKL is the only plane parallel to plane PQR.

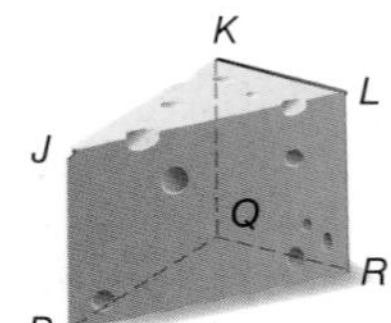
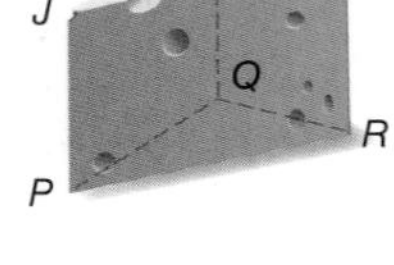

1 Focus

Vertical Alignment

Before Lesson 3-1 Use angle and line segment relationships to prove theorems.

Lesson 3-1 Identify relationships between two lines or two planes. Name angle pairs formed by parallel lines and transversals.

After Lesson 3-1 Use slopes of equations of lines to investigate geometric relationships, including parallel lines and perpendicular lines.

2 Teach

Scaffolding Questions

Have students read the **Why?** section of the lesson.

Ask:

- Does an object appear larger than it really is in the front of an Ames room or in the back? front
- How could the use of slanted lines make objects appear larger or smaller than they really are? Sample answer: The distance between the lines changes. When the lines are closer together, an object between them appears larger. When the lines are farther apart, the object appears smaller.

Lesson 3-1 Resources

Resource	Approaching Level AL	On Level OL	Beyond Level BL	English Learners ELL
Teacher Edition	▪ Differentiated Instruction, p. 175	▪ Differentiated Instruction, pp. 175, 178	▪ Differentiated Instruction, pp. 175, 178	▪ Differentiated Instruction, p. 175
Chapter Resource Masters	▪ Study Guide and Intervention, pp. 5–6 ▪ Skills Practice, p. 7 ▪ Practice, p. 8 ▪ Word Problem Practice, p. 9	▪ Study Guide and Intervention, pp. 5–6 ▪ Skills Practice, p. 7 ▪ Practice, p. 8 ▪ Word Problem Practice, p. 9 ▪ Enrichment, p. 10	▪ Practice, p. 8 ▪ Word Problem Practice, p. 9 ▪ Enrichment, p. 10	▪ Study Guide and Intervention, pp. 5–6 ▪ Skills Practice, p. 7 ▪ Practice, p. 8 ▪ Word Problem Practice, p. 9
Other	▪ 5-Minute Check 3-1 ▪ Study Notebook ▪ Teaching Geometry with Manipulatives	▪ 5-Minute Check 3-1 ▪ Study Notebook ▪ Teaching Geometry with Manipulatives	▪ 5-Minute Check 3-1 ▪ Study Notebook	▪ 5-Minute Check 3-1 ▪ Study Notebook ▪ Teaching Geometry with Manipulatives

1 Relationships Between Lines and Planes

Example 1 shows how to identify relationships between parallel planes. Students should be able to identify a plane in a drawing and all planes that are parallel to it.

Formative Assessment

Use the Guided Practice exercises after each example to determine students' understanding of concepts.

Additional Example

1 Identify each of the following using the box below.

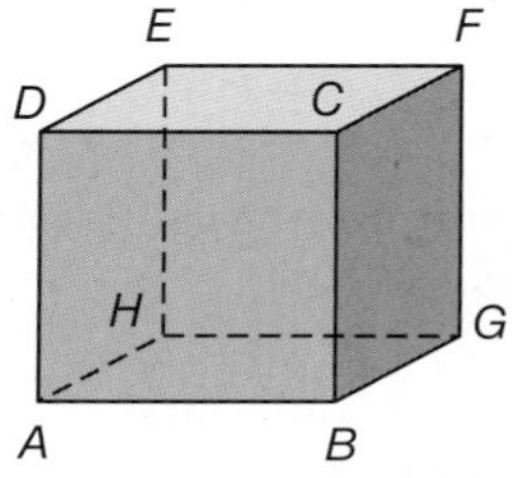

a. all segments parallel to $\overline{BC}$ $\overline{AD}$, $\overline{EH}$, $\overline{FG}$

b. a segment skew to EH $\overline{AB}$, $\overline{CD}$, $\overline{BG}$, or $\overline{CF}$

c. a plane parallel to plane *ABG* plane *CDE*

Additional Examples also in Interactive Classroom PowerPoint® Presentations

2 Transversal Angle Pair Relationships

Example 2 shows how to identify angle relationships from a set of parallel lines cut by a transversal. **Example 3** shows how to identify sets of lines to which each given line is a transversal.

WatchOut!

Parallel vs. Skew
In Check Your Progress 1A, $\overleftrightarrow{FE}$ is *not* skew to $\overleftrightarrow{BC}$. Instead, these lines are parallel in plane *BCF*.

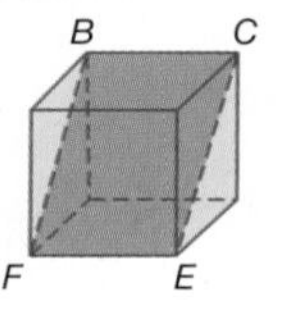

GuidedPractice

Identify each of the following using the cube shown.

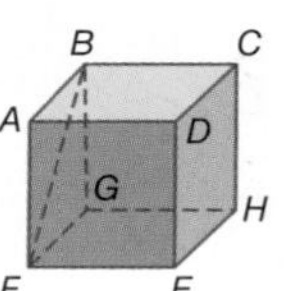

1A. all segments skew to $\overleftrightarrow{BC}$ $\overleftrightarrow{AF}$, $\overleftrightarrow{DE}$, $\overleftrightarrow{FG}$, $\overleftrightarrow{HE}$

1B. a segment parallel to $\overleftrightarrow{EH}$ $\overleftrightarrow{AB}$, $\overleftrightarrow{CD}$, or $\overleftrightarrow{FG}$

1C. all planes parallel to plane *DCH* plane *ABG*

2 Transversal Angle Pair Relationships A line that intersects two or more coplanar lines at two different points is called a **transversal**. In the diagram below, line *t* is a transversal of lines *q* and *r*. Notice that line *t* forms a total of eight angles with lines *q* and *r*. These angles, and specific pairings of these angles, are given special names.

ReadingMath

Same-Side Interior Angles
Consecutive interior angles are also called *same-side interior angles.*

KeyConcept Transversal Angle Pair Relationships

Four **interior angles** lie in the region between lines *q* and *r*.	∠3, ∠4, ∠5, ∠6	
Four **exterior angles** lie in the two regions that are not between lines *q* and *r*.	∠1, ∠2, ∠7, ∠8	
Consecutive interior angles are interior angles that lie on the same side of transversal *t*.	∠4 and ∠5, ∠3 and ∠6	
Alternate interior angles are nonadjacent interior angles that lie on opposite sides of transversal *t*.	∠3 and ∠5, ∠4 and ∠6	
Alternate exterior angles are nonadjacent exterior angles that lie on opposite sides of transversal *t*.	∠1 and ∠7, ∠2 and ∠8	
Corresponding angles lie on the same side of transversal *t* and on the same side of lines *q* and *r*.	∠1 and ∠5, ∠2 and ∠6 ∠3 and ∠7, ∠4 and ∠8	

exterior t 1 2 4 3 q interior 6 r 5 7 8 exterior

Example 2 Classify Angle Pair Relationships

Refer to the figure below. Classify the relationship between each pair of angles as ***alternate interior, alternate exterior, corresponding,*** **or** ***consecutive interior*** **angles.**

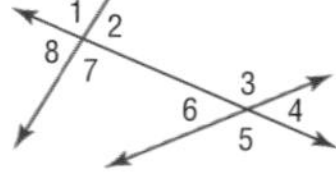

a. ∠1 and ∠5
alternate exterior

b. ∠6 and ∠7
consecutive interior

c. ∠2 and ∠4
corresponding

d. ∠2 and ∠6
alternate interior

GuidedPractice

2A. ∠3 and ∠7 **2B.** ∠5 and ∠7 **2C.** ∠4 and ∠8 **2D.** ∠2 and ∠3

2A. alternate interior
2B. corresponding
2C. alternate exterior
2D. consecutive interior

WatchOut!

Line Segments When deciding if line segments intersect, do not extend the lines to decide if they would intersect if they continued further. Line segments have a fixed length.

Teach with Tech

Interactive Whiteboard Draw a three-dimensional figure on the board (such as a rectangular prism or square pyramid). Choose students to come to the board and highlight the edges that are parallel to each other.

When more than one line can be considered a transversal, first identify the transversal for a given angle pair by locating the line that connects the vertices of the angles.

StudyTip

Nonexample In the figure below, line c is *not* a transversal of lines a and b, since line c intersects lines a and b in only one point.

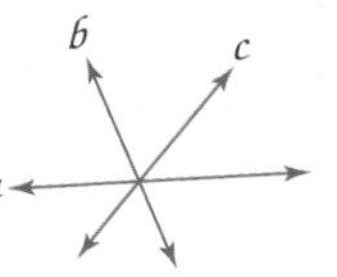

Example 3 Identify Transversals and Classify Angle Pairs

Identify the transversal connecting each pair of angles in the photo. Then classify the relationship between each pair of angles.

a. $\angle 1$ **and** $\angle 3$

The transversal connecting $\angle 1$ and $\angle 3$ is line h. These are alternate exterior angles.

b. $\angle 5$ **and** $\angle 6$

The transversal connecting $\angle 5$ and $\angle 6$ is line k. These are consecutive interior angles.

c. $\angle 2$ **and** $\angle 6$

The transversal connecting $\angle 2$ and $\angle 6$ is line ℓ. These are corresponding angles.

GuidedPractice

3A. $\angle 3$ and $\angle 5$ **3B.** $\angle 2$ and $\angle 8$

3C. $\angle 5$ and $\angle 7$ **3D.** $\angle 2$ and $\angle 9$

3A. line j; alternate exterior
3B. line ℓ; alternate interior
3C. line k; corresponding
3D. line ℓ; consecutive interior

Check Your Understanding

= Step-by-Step Solutions begin on page R14.

Example 1 **Refer to the figure at the right to identify each of the following.**

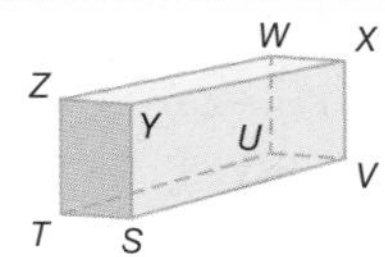

1. a plane parallel to plane ZWX **TUV**
2. a segment skew to $\overline{TS}$ that contains point W **$\overline{WZ}$, $\overline{WU}$**
3. all segments parallel to $\overline{SV}$ **$\overline{YX}$, $\overline{TU}$, $\overline{ZW}$**
4. **CONSTRUCTION** Use the diagram of the partially framed storage shed shown to identify each of the following.

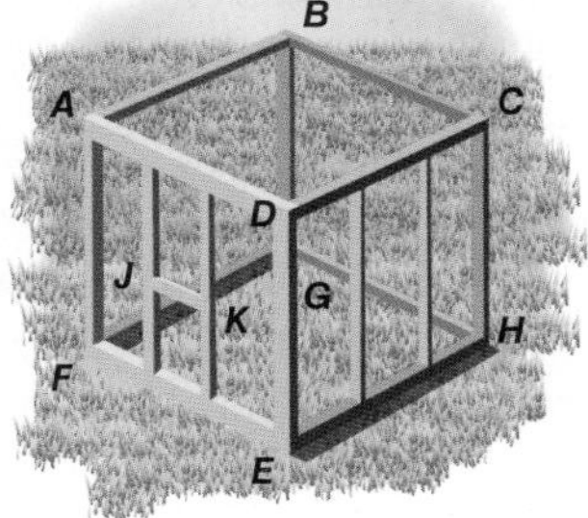

   a. Name three pairs of parallel planes.
   b. Name three segments parallel to $\overline{DE}$.
   c. Name two segments parallel to $\overline{FE}$.
   d. Name two pairs of skew segments.

4a. plane $ABCD \parallel$ plane $FGHE$; plane $ADEF \parallel$ plane $BCHG$; plane $DCHE \parallel$ plane $ABGF$
4b. $\overline{CH}$, $\overline{BG}$, $\overline{AF}$
4c. Sample answer: $\overline{AD}$ and $\overline{BC}$
4d. Sample answer: $\overline{JK}$ and $\overline{BG}$; $\overline{JK}$ and $\overline{CH}$

Example 2 **Classify the relationship between each pair of angles as *alternate interior, alternate exterior, corresponding,* or *consecutive interior* angles.**

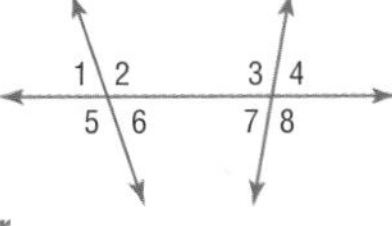

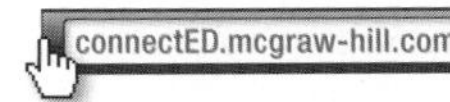

5. $\angle 1$ and $\angle 8$ **alternate exterior**
6. $\angle 2$ and $\angle 4$ **corresponding**
7. $\angle 3$ and $\angle 6$ **alternate interior**
8. $\angle 6$ and $\angle 7$ **consecutive interior**

Additional Examples

2 Refer to the figure below. Classify the relationship between each pair of angles as *alternate interior, alternate exterior, corresponding,* or *consecutive interior* angles.

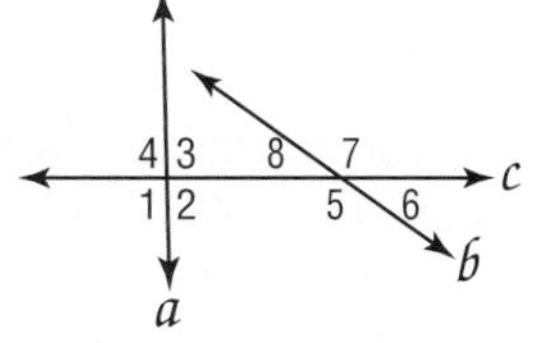

a. $\angle 2$ and $\angle 6$ corresponding
b. $\angle 1$ and $\angle 7$ alternate exterior
c. $\angle 3$ and $\angle 8$ consecutive interior
d. $\angle 3$ and $\angle 5$ alternate interior

3 **BUS STATION** The driveways at a bus station are shown. Identify the transversal connecting each pair of angles in the figure. Then classify the relationship between each pair of angles.

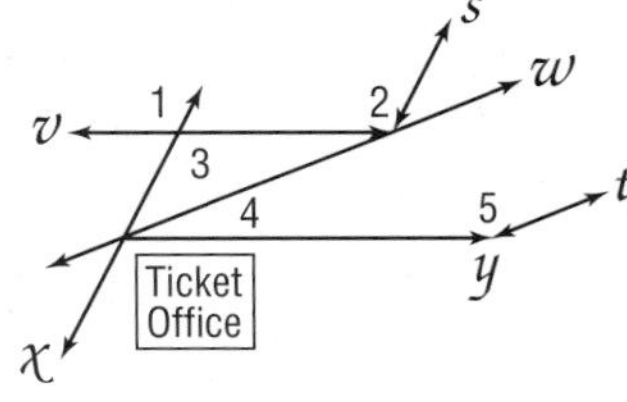

a. $\angle 1$ and $\angle 2$ v; corresponding
b. $\angle 2$ and $\angle 3$ v; alternate interior
c. $\angle 4$ and $\angle 5$ y; consecutive interior

DifferentiatedInstruction AL OL BL ELL

Interpersonal Have students organize into small groups. Provide them with figures of lines and transversals and have them play a guessing game. One student will think of an angle and provide clues about the angle's relationship to the other angles with the vocabulary from the lesson. The other students will use the clues to guess the angle.

Tips for New Teachers

Transversals To help students identify transversals, draw the figure shown below. Remind students that any one of the three lines could be considered the transversal because each intersects the other two lines. Demonstrate the concept by identifying various angle relationships.

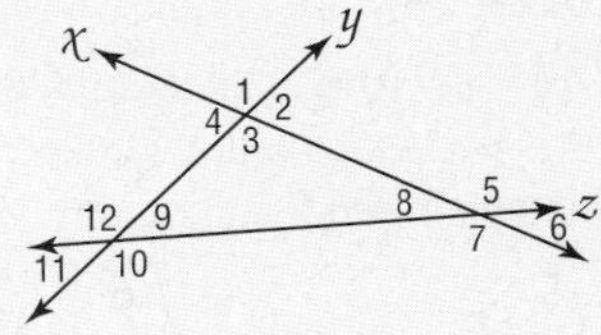

3 Practice

Formative Assessment

Use Exercises 1–12 to check for understanding.

Then use the chart at the bottom of this page to customize assignments for your students.

Focus on Mathematical Content

Transversals When classifying angles, it is important to determine which line is considered the transversal. The relationship of one angle to another is dependent on the transversal.

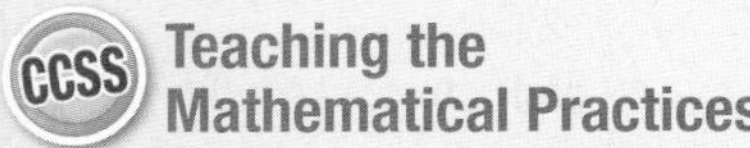

Precision Mathematically proficient students use clear definitions in discussion with others and in their own reasoning. For Exercises 21–30, encourage students to learn the similarities and differences amongst the pairs of angles.

Additional Answers

21. line *s*; corresponding
22. line *r*; consecutive interior
23. line *t*; alternate interior
24. line *v*; corresponding
25. line *t*; alternate exterior
26. line *s*; alternate interior
27. line *t*; consecutive interior
28. line *v*; alternate exterior
29. line *s*; alternate exterior
30. line *v*; alternate interior
31. line *a*; vertical
32. line *a*; consecutive interior
33. line *c*; alternate interior
34. line *d* or line *f*; linear pair
35. line *f*; corresponding
36. line *a*; alternate interior

37a. Sample answer: Since the lines are coplanar and they cannot touch, they are parallel.

44a. $\overline{AB} \parallel \overline{CD}$; The distance between the segments is the same anywhere on the segment.

Example 3 **Identify the transversal connecting each pair of angles. Then classify the relationship between each pair of angles.**

9. $\angle 2$ and $\angle 4$ **line *n*; corresponding**
10. $\angle 5$ and $\angle 6$ **line *p*; alternate exterior**
11. $\angle 4$ and $\angle 7$ **line *m*; consecutive interior**
12. $\angle 2$ and $\angle 7$ **line *p*; alternate interior**

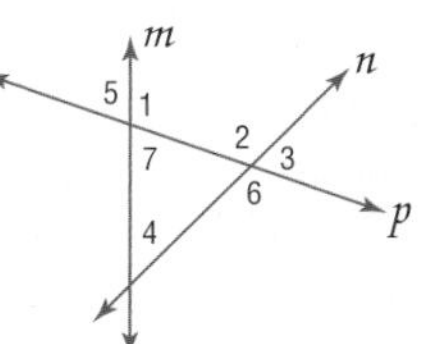

Practice and Problem Solving

Extra Practice is on page R3.

Example 1 **Refer to the figure to identify each of the following.**

13. all segments parallel to $\overline{DM}$ **$\overline{CL}$, $\overline{EN}$, $\overline{BK}$, $\overline{AJ}$**
14. a plane parallel to plane *ACD* **JLM**
15. a segment skew to $\overline{BC}$ **$\overline{EN}$, $\overline{AJ}$, $\overline{DM}$, $\overline{NM}$, $\overline{NJ}$, $\overline{JK}$ or $\overline{ML}$**
16. all planes intersecting plane *EDM* **DCL, NML, AED, AEN**
17. all segments skew to $\overline{AE}$ **$\overline{KL}$, $\overline{CL}$, $\overline{BK}$, $\overline{ML}$, $\overline{DM}$, $\overline{NM}$, $\overline{KJ}$**
18. a segment parallel to $\overline{EN}$ **$\overline{AJ}$, $\overline{BK}$, $\overline{CL}$, or $\overline{DM}$**
19. a segment parallel to $\overline{AB}$ through point *J* **$\overline{JK}$**
20. a segment skew to $\overline{CL}$ through point *E* **$\overline{AE}$, $\overline{ED}$**

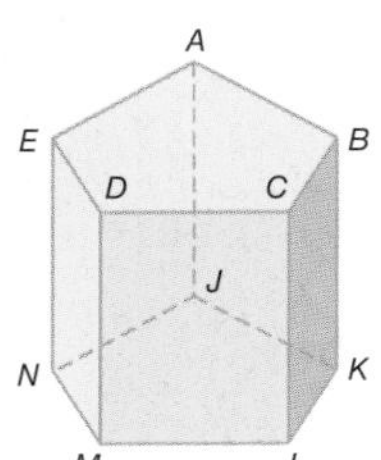

Examples 2–3 **CCSS PRECISION** **Identify the transversal connecting each pair of angles. Then classify the relationship between each pair of angles as *alternate interior, alternate exterior, corresponding,* or *consecutive interior* angles.** **21–30. See margin.**

21. $\angle 4$ and $\angle 9$
22. $\angle 5$ and $\angle 7$
23. $\angle 3$ and $\angle 5$
24. $\angle 10$ and $\angle 11$
25. $\angle 1$ and $\angle 6$
26. $\angle 6$ and $\angle 8$
27. $\angle 2$ and $\angle 3$
28. $\angle 9$ and $\angle 10$
29. $\angle 4$ and $\angle 11$
30. $\angle 7$ and $\angle 11$

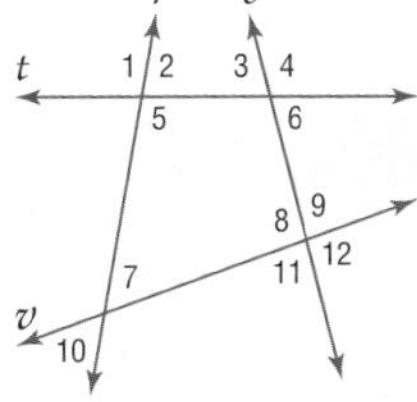

Example 3 **SAFETY** **Identify the transversal connecting each pair of angles in the photo of a fire escape shown. Then classify the relationship between each pair of angles.** **31–36. See margin.**

31. $\angle 1$ and $\angle 2$
32. $\angle 2$ and $\angle 4$
33. $\angle 4$ and $\angle 5$
34. $\angle 6$ and $\angle 7$
35. $\angle 7$ and $\angle 8$
36. $\angle 2$ and $\angle 3$

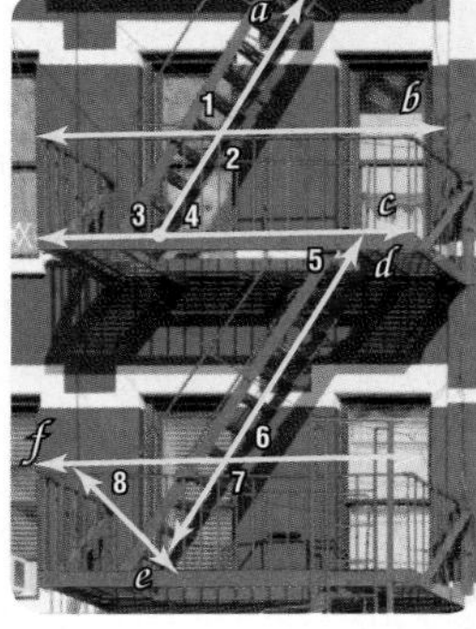

37. **POWER** Power lines are not allowed to intersect.
    a. What must be the relationship between power lines *p* and *m*? Explain your reasoning. **See margin.**
    b. What is the relationship between line *q* and lines *p* and *m*? **Line *q* is a transversal of lines *p* and *m*.**

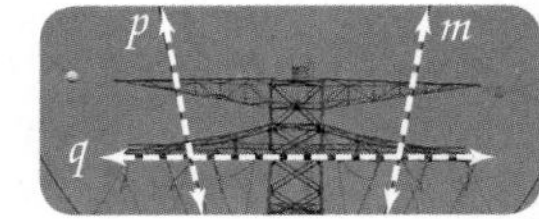

Differentiated Homework Options

Level	Assignment	Two-Day Option	
AL Basic	13–37, 46, 48–63	13–37 odd, 51–54	14–36 even, 46, 48–50, 55–63
OL Core	13–45 odd, 46, 48–63	13–37, 51–54	38–46, 48–50, 55–63
BL Advanced	38–60, (optional: 61–63)		

B Describe the relationship between each pair of segments as *parallel*, *skew*, or *intersecting*.

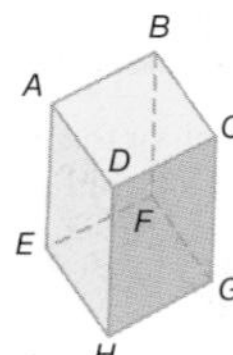

38. $\overline{FG}$ and $\overline{BC}$ **parallel**

39. $\overline{AB}$ and $\overline{CG}$ **skew**

40. $\overline{DH}$ and $\overline{HG}$ **intersecting**

41. $\overline{DH}$ and $\overline{BF}$ **parallel**

42. $\overline{EF}$ and $\overline{BC}$ **skew**

43. $\overline{CD}$ and $\overline{AD}$ **intersecting**

44. **CCSS SENSE-MAKING** The illusion at the right is created using squares and straight lines.

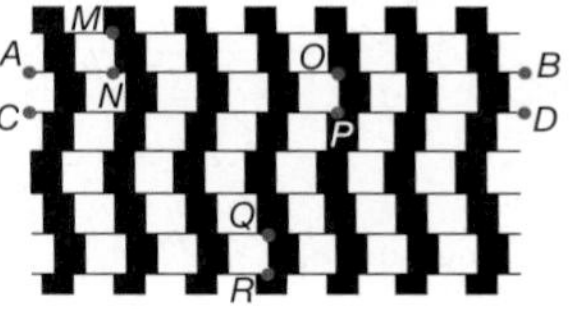

a. How are $\overline{AB}$ and $\overline{CD}$ related? Justify your reasoning. **See margin.**

b. How are $\overline{MN}$ and $\overline{QR}$ related? $\overline{AB}$, $\overline{CD}$, and $\overline{OP}$? **$\overline{MN} \parallel \overline{QR}$; $\overline{OP}$ is a transversal between $\overline{AB}$ and $\overline{CD}$.**

C 45. **ESCALATORS** Escalators consist of steps on a continuous loop that is driven by a motor. At the top and bottom of the platform, the steps collapse to provide a level surface for entrance and exit.

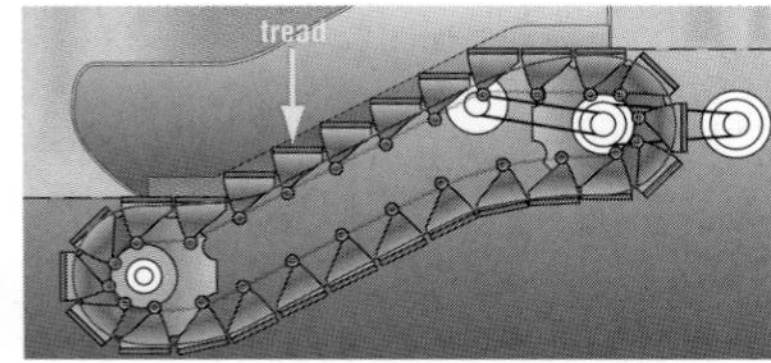

a. What is the relationship between the treads of the ascending stairs? **parallel**

b. What is the relationship between the treads of the two steps at the top of the incline? **coplanar**

c. How do the treads of the steps on the incline of the escalator relate to the treads of the steps on the bottom of the escalator? **skew**

H.O.T. Problems Use Higher-Order Thinking Skills

46. **OPEN ENDED** Plane $\mathcal{P}$ contains lines a and b. Line c intersects plane $\mathcal{P}$ at point J. Lines a and b are parallel, lines a and c are skew, and lines b and c are not skew. Draw a figure based upon this description. **See Ch. 3 Answer Appendix.**

47. **CHALLENGE** Suppose points A, B, and C lie in plane $\mathcal{P}$, and points D, E, and F lie in plane $\mathcal{Q}$. Line m contains points D and F and does not intersect plane $\mathcal{P}$. Line n contains points A and E. **a. See Ch. 3 Answer Appendix.**

a. Draw a diagram to represent the situation.

b. What is the relationship between planes $\mathcal{P}$ and $\mathcal{Q}$? **parallel**

c. What is the relationship between lines m and n? **skew**

48. Sometimes; $\overleftrightarrow{AB}$ is either skew or parallel to $\overleftrightarrow{CD}$ because the lines will never intersect and are not coplanar.

REASONING **Plane $\mathcal{X}$ and plane $\mathcal{Y}$ are parallel and plane $\mathcal{Z}$ intersects plane $\mathcal{X}$. Line $\overleftrightarrow{AB}$ is in plane $\mathcal{X}$, line $\overleftrightarrow{CD}$ is in plane $\mathcal{Y}$, and line $\overleftrightarrow{EF}$ is in plane $\mathcal{Z}$. Determine whether each statement is *always*, *sometimes*, or *never* true. Explain.**

48. $\overleftrightarrow{AB}$ is skew to $\overleftrightarrow{CD}$.

49. $\overleftrightarrow{AB}$ intersects $\overleftrightarrow{EF}$.

49. Sometimes; $\overleftrightarrow{AB}$ intersects $\overleftrightarrow{EF}$ depending on where the planes intersect.

50. **WRITING IN MATH** Can a pair of planes be described as skew? Explain. **See Ch. 3 Answer Appendix.**

CCSS Teaching the Mathematical Practices

Sense-Making Mathematically proficient students look for entry points to the solution of a problem. In exercise 44, the optical illusion makes it difficult to see how the points are related. Students can use a straightedge to help identify the segments.

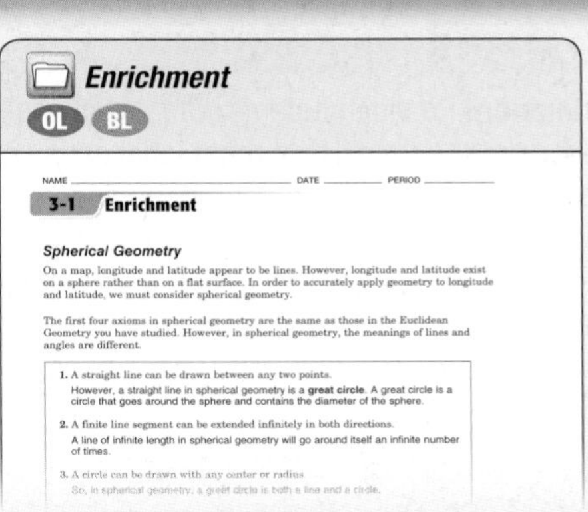

Enrichment

OL BL

NAME ______ DATE ______ PERIOD ______

3-1 Enrichment

Spherical Geometry

On a map, longitude and latitude appear to be lines. However, longitude and latitude exist on a sphere rather than on a flat surface. In order to accurately apply geometry to longitude and latitude, we must consider spherical geometry.

The first four axioms in spherical geometry are the same as those in the Euclidean Geometry you have studied. However, in spherical geometry, the meanings of lines and angles are different.

1. A straight line can be drawn between any two points.
   However, a straight line in spherical geometry is a **great circle**. A great circle is a circle that goes around the sphere and contains the diameter of the sphere.
2. A finite line segment can be extended infinitely in both directions.
   A line of infinite length in spherical geometry will go around itself an infinite number of times.
3. A circle can be drawn with any center or radius.
   So, in spherical geometry, a great circle is both a line and a circle.

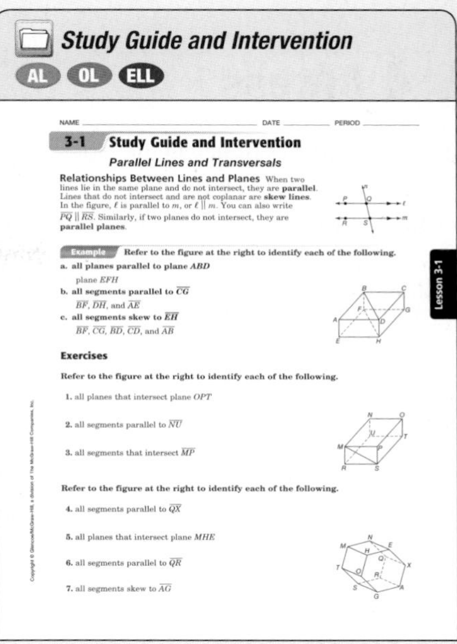

Study Guide and Intervention

AL OL ELL

NAME ______ DATE ______ PERIOD ______

3-1 Study Guide and Intervention

Parallel Lines and Transversals

Relationships Between Lines and Planes When two lines lie in the same plane and do not intersect, they are **parallel**. Lines that do not intersect and are not coplanar are **skew lines**. In the figure, ℓ is parallel to m, or $\ell \parallel m$. You can also write $\overline{PQ} \parallel \overline{RS}$. Similarly, if two planes do not intersect, they are **parallel planes**.

Example Refer to the figure at the right to identify each of the following.

a. all planes parallel to plane ABD
   plane EFH

b. all segments parallel to $\overline{CG}$
   $\overline{BF}$, $\overline{DH}$, and $\overline{AE}$

c. all segments skew to $\overline{EH}$
   $\overline{BF}$, $\overline{CG}$, $\overline{BD}$, $\overline{CD}$, and $\overline{AB}$

Exercises

Refer to the figure at the right to identify each of the following.

1. all planes that intersect plane OPT
2. all segments parallel to $\overline{NU}$
3. all segments that intersect $\overline{MP}$

Refer to the figure at the right to identify each of the following.

4. all segments parallel to $\overline{QX}$
5. all planes that intersect plane MHE
6. all segments parallel to $\overline{QR}$
7. all segments skew to $\overline{AG}$

Lesson 3-1

Copyright © Glencoe/McGraw-Hill, a division of The McGraw-Hill Companies, Inc.

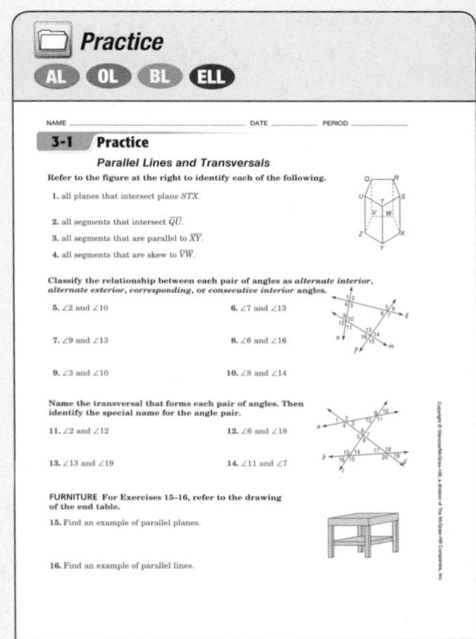

Practice

AL OL BL ELL

NAME ______ DATE ______ PERIOD ______

3-1 Practice

Parallel Lines and Transversals

Refer to the figure at the right to identify each of the following.

1. all planes that intersect plane STX.
2. all segments that intersect $\overline{QU}$.
3. all segments that are parallel to $\overline{XY}$.
4. all segments that are skew to $\overline{VW}$.

Classify the relationship between each pair of angles as *alternate interior*, *alternate exterior*, *corresponding*, or *consecutive interior* angles.

5. $\angle 2$ and $\angle 10$
6. $\angle 7$ and $\angle 13$
7. $\angle 9$ and $\angle 13$
8. $\angle 6$ and $\angle 16$
9. $\angle 3$ and $\angle 10$
10. $\angle 8$ and $\angle 14$

Name the transversal that forms each pair of angles. Then identify the special name for the angle pair.

11. $\angle 2$ and $\angle 12$
12. $\angle 6$ and $\angle 18$
13. $\angle 13$ and $\angle 19$
14. $\angle 11$ and $\angle 7$

FURNITURE For Exercises 15–16, refer to the drawing of the end table.

15. Find an example of parallel planes.
16. Find an example of parallel lines.

Copyright © Glencoe/McGraw-Hill, a division of The McGraw-Hill Companies, Inc.

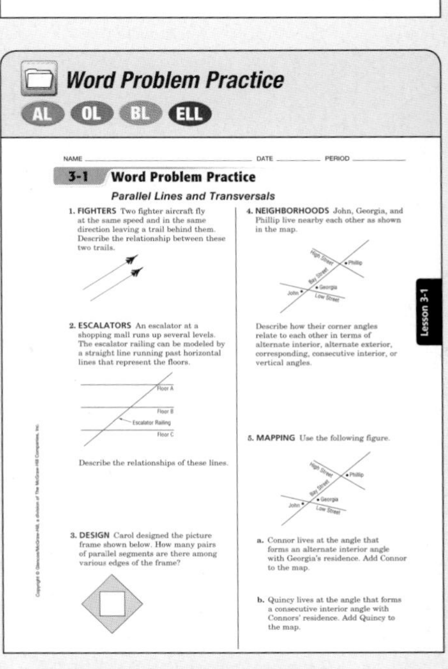

Word Problem Practice

AL OL BL ELL

NAME ______ DATE ______ PERIOD ______

3-1 Word Problem Practice

Parallel Lines and Transversals

1. **FIGHTERS** Two fighter aircraft fly at the same speed and in the same direction leaving a trail behind them. Describe the relationship between these two trails.

2. **ESCALATORS** An escalator at a shopping mall runs up several levels. The escalator railing can be modeled by a straight line running past horizontal lines that represent the floors.

   Describe the relationships of these lines.

3. **DESIGN** Carol designed the picture frame shown below. How many pairs of parallel segments are there among various edges of the frame?

4. **NEIGHBORHOODS** John, Georgia, and Phillip live nearby each other as shown in the map.

   Describe how their corner angles relate to each other in terms of alternate interior, alternate exterior, corresponding, consecutive interior, or vertical angles.

5. **MAPPING** Use the following figure.

   a. Connor lives at the angle that forms an alternate interior angle with Georgia's residence. Add Connor to the map.

   b. Quincy lives at the angle that forms a consecutive interior angle with Connors' residence. Add Quincy to the map.

Lesson 3-1

Copyright © Glencoe/McGraw-Hill, a division of The McGraw-Hill Companies, Inc.

4 Assess

Ticket Out the Door As the students leave the room, ask them to identify intersecting lines in the classroom, and classify pairs of angles formed when a transversal intersects two other lines.

Additional Answer

58. Given: $\overline{WY} \cong \overline{ZX}$
A is the midpoint of $\overline{WY}$.
A is the midpoint of $\overline{ZX}$.

Prove: $\overline{WA} \cong \overline{ZA}$

Proof:

Statements (Reasons)

1. $\overline{WY} \cong \overline{ZX}$
   A is the midpoint of $\overline{WY}$.
   A is the midpoint of $\overline{ZX}$. (Given)
2. $WY = ZX$ (Def. of $\cong$ segments)
3. $WA = AY$, $ZA = AX$ (Def. of midpoint)
4. $WY = WA + AY$, $ZX = ZA + AX$ (Seg. Add. Post.)
5. $WA + AY = ZA + AX$ (Substitution)
6. $WA + WA = ZA + ZA$ (Substitution)
7. $2WA = 2ZA$ (Substitution)
8. $WA = ZA$ (Division Property)
9. $\overline{WA} \cong \overline{ZA}$ (Def. of $\cong$ segments)

Standardized Test Practice

51. Which of the following angle pairs are alternate exterior angles? **B**

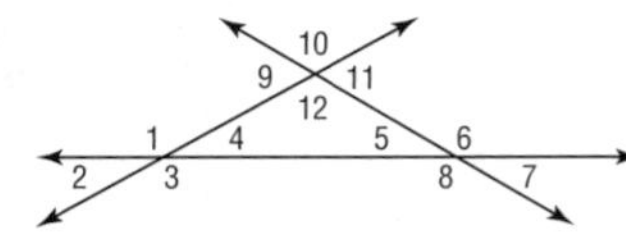

A $\angle 1$ and $\angle 5$
C $\angle 2$ and $\angle 10$
B $\angle 2$ and $\angle 6$
D $\angle 5$ and $\angle 9$

52. What is the measure of $\angle XYZ$? **H**

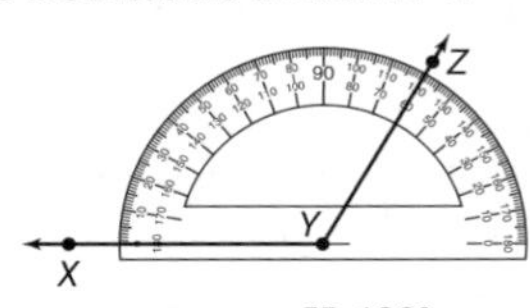

F $30°$
H $120°$
G $60°$
J $150°$

53. SHORT RESPONSE Name the coordinates of the points representing the x- and y-intercepts of the graph shown below. **(0, 4), (−6, 0)**

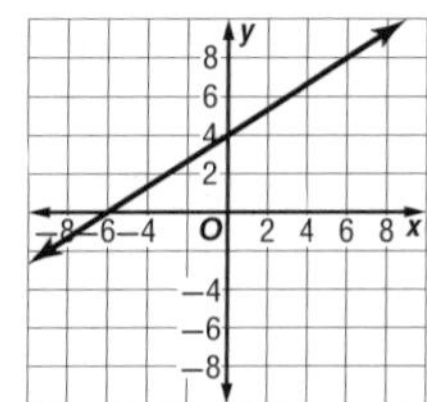

54. SAT/ACT Of the following, the one that is *not* equivalent to 485 is: **C**

A $(3 \times 100) + (4 \times 10) + 145$
B $(3 \times 100) + (18 \times 10) + 5$
C $(4 \times 100) + (8 \times 10) + 15$
D $(4 \times 100) + (6 \times 10) + 25$
E $(4 \times 100) + (5 \times 10) + 35$

Spiral Review

Find the measure of each numbered angle. (Lesson 2-8)

55. $m\angle 9 = 2x - 4$, $m\angle 10 = 2x + 4$ **$m\angle 9 = 86$, $m\angle 10 = 94$**

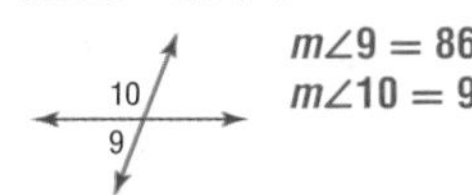

56. $m\angle 11 = 4x$, $m\angle 12 = 2x - 6$ **$m\angle 11 = 124$, $m\angle 12 = 56$**

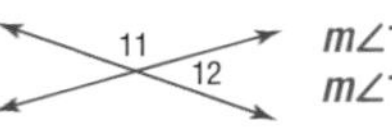

57. $m\angle 19 = 100 + 20x$, $m\angle 20 = 20x$ **$m\angle 19 = 140$, $m\angle 20 = 40$**

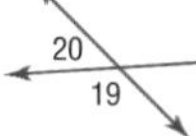

58. PROOF Prove the following. (Lesson 2-7) **See margin.**

Given: $\overline{WY} \cong \overline{ZX}$
A is the midpoint of $\overline{WY}$.
A is the midpoint of $\overline{ZX}$.

Prove: $\overline{WA} \cong \overline{ZA}$

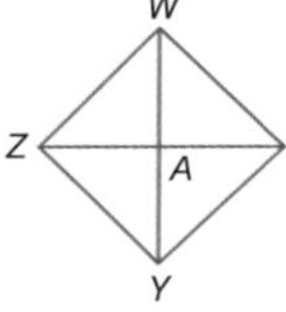

ALGEBRA **Use the figure at the right.** (Lesson 1-5)

59. If $m\angle CFD = 12a + 45$, find a so that $\overrightarrow{FC} \perp \overrightarrow{FD}$. **3.75**

60. If $m\angle AFB = 8x - 6$ and $m\angle BFC = 14x + 8$, find the value of x so that $\angle AFC$ is a right angle. **4**

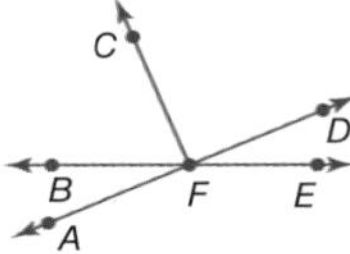

Skills Review

Find x.

61. **90**

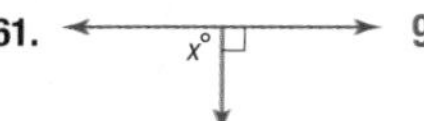

62. **102**

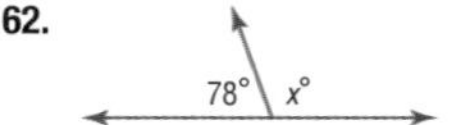

63. **45**

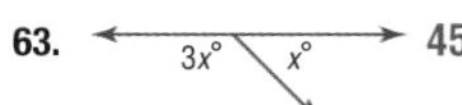

Differentiated Instruction OL BL

Extension Provide students with a drawing such as the one at the right. Have them label each angle and identify pairs of alternate interior angles, corresponding angles, and so on. Tell students that as they prepare to begin a study in proof, it is important to completely understand the initial concepts presented in this lesson.

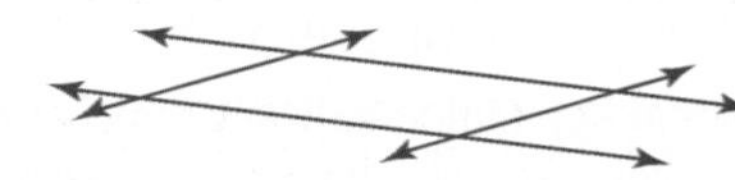

EXPLORE 3-2 Geometry Software Lab
Angles and Parallel Lines

You can use The Geometer's Sketchpad® to explore the angles formed by two parallel lines and a transversal.

CCSS Common Core State Standards
Content Standards
G.CO.12 Make formal geometric constructions with a variety of tools and methods (compass and straightedge, string, reflective devices, paper folding, dynamic geometric software, etc.).
Mathematical Practices 5

Activity Parallel Lines and a Transversal

Step 1 **Draw a line.**

Draw and label points F and G. Then use the line tool to draw $\overleftrightarrow{FG}$.

Step 2 **Draw a parallel line.**

Draw a point that is not on $\overleftrightarrow{FG}$ and label it J. Select $\overleftrightarrow{FG}$ and point J, and then choose **Parallel Line** from the **Construct** menu. Draw and label a point K on this parallel line.

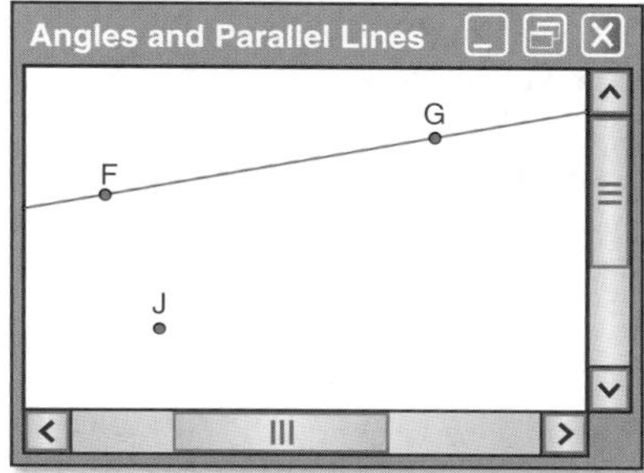

Step 3 **Draw a transversal.**

Draw and label point A on $\overleftrightarrow{FG}$ and point B on $\overleftrightarrow{JK}$. Select A and B and then choose **Line** from the **Construct** menu to draw transversal $\overleftrightarrow{AB}$. Then draw and label points C and D on $\overleftrightarrow{AB}$ as shown.

Step 4 **Measure each angle.**

Measure all eight angles formed by these lines. For example, select points F, A, then C, and choose **Angle** from the **Measure** menu to find $m\angle FAC$.

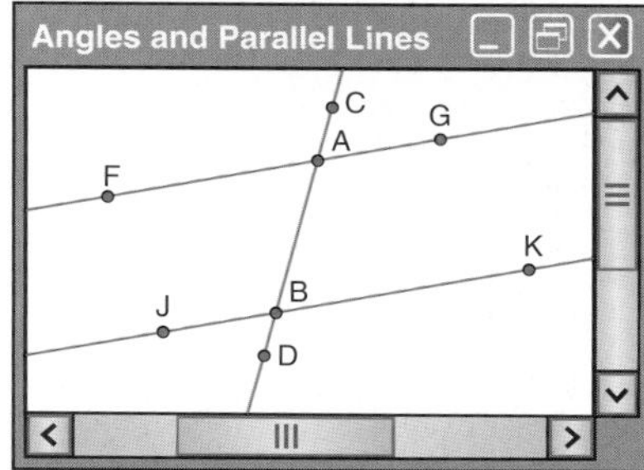

Analyze the Results 1–2. See Ch. 3 Answer Appendix.

1. Record the measures from Step 4 in a table like this one. Which angles have the same measure?

Angle	∠FAC	∠CAG	∠GAB	∠FAB	∠JBA	∠ABK	∠KBD	∠JBD
1st Measure	114	66	114	66	114	66	114	66

2. Drag point C or D to move transversal $\overleftrightarrow{AB}$ so that it intersects the two parallel lines at a different angle. Add a row **2nd Measure** to your table and record the new measures. Repeat these steps until your table has 3rd, 4th, and 5th Measure rows of data.

3. Using the angles listed in the table, identify and describe the relationship between all angle pairs that have the following special names. Then write a conjecture in if-then form about each angle pair when formed by any two parallel lines cut by a transversal. **a–d. See Ch. 3 Answer Appendix.**

   a. corresponding
   b. alternate interior
   c. alternate exterior
   d. consecutive interior

4. Drag point C or D so that the measure of any of the angles is 90. **a–b. See Ch. 3 Answer Appendix.**

   a. What do you notice about the measures of the other angles?
   b. Make a conjecture about a transversal that is perpendicular to one of two parallel lines.

From Concrete to Abstract

Give students a model with two lines cut by a transversal with the angle measures provided. Tell students to show whether the lines are parallel.

1 Focus

Objective Use Geometer's Sketchpad to investigate angles formed by two parallel lines and a transversal.

Materials

- computers with Geometer's Sketchpad software

Teaching Tip

Show students how to drag and move lines so the transversal intersects the parallel lines.

2 Teach

Working Independently or in Pairs

Have students work alone or in pairs of mixed abilities. Then have students complete the Activity and Exercises 1–2.

Discuss with the class how they think the relationship between the angles will change when the transversal is rotated. Also discuss what the relationship may be between the angles formed by a transversal that is perpendicular to one of the lines. Then have them complete the exercises to test their conjectures.

Practice Have students complete Exercises 3 and 4.

3 Assess

Formative Assessment

Use Exercises 1–4 to assess whether students comprehend the relationships between angles formed by two parallel lines cut by a transversal.

1 Focus

VerticalAlignment

Before Lesson 3-2 Identify the relationships between two lines or planes. Name angle pairs formed by parallel lines and transversals.

Lesson 3-2 Use theorems to determine the relationships between specific pairs of angles. Use algebra to find angle measurements.

After Lesson 3-2 Use slopes of equations of lines to investigative geometric relationships, incuding parallel lines and perpendicular lines.

2 Teach

Scaffolding Questions

Have students read the **Why?** section of the lesson.

Ask:

- What shapes are formed by the scaffolding? triangles and rectangles
- Are the platforms parallel or perpendicular to one another? parallel
- How many traversals are there on one level of the scaffolding? 6

LESSON 3-2 Angles and Parallel Lines

Then	Now	Why?
● You named angle pairs formed by parallel lines and transversals.	● 1 Use theorems to determine the relationships between specific pairs of angles. 2 Use algebra to find angle measurements.	● Construction and maintenance workers often use an access scaffold. This structure provides support and access to elevated areas. The transversal *t* shown provides structural support to the two parallel working areas.

CCSS Common Core State Standards

Content Standards

G.CO.1 Know precise definitions of angle, circle, perpendicular line, parallel line, and line segment, based on the undefined notions of point, line, distance along a line, and distance around a circular arc.

G.CO.9 Prove theorems about lines and angles.

Mathematical Practices

1 Make sense of problems and persevere in solving them.

3 Construct viable arguments and critique the reasoning of others.

1 Parallel Lines and Angle Pairs

In the photo, line t is a transversal of lines a and b, and $\angle 1$ and $\angle 2$ are corresponding angles. Since lines a and b are parallel, there is a special relationship between corresponding angle pairs.

Postulate 3.1 Corresponding Angles Postulate

If two parallel lines are cut by a transversal, then each pair of corresponding angles is congruent.

Examples $\angle 1 \cong \angle 3$, $\angle 2 \cong \angle 4$, $\angle 5 \cong \angle 7$, $\angle 6 \cong \angle 8$

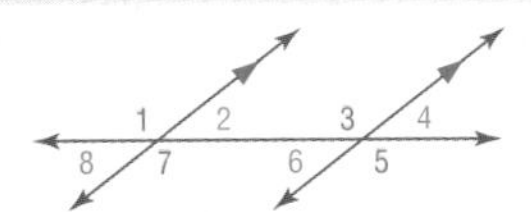

PT

Example 1 Use Corresponding Angles Postulate

In the figure, $m\angle 5 = 72$. Find the measure of each angle. Tell which postulate(s) or theorem(s) you used.

a. $\angle 4$

$\angle 4 \cong \angle 5$	Corresponding Angles Postulate
$m\angle 4 = m\angle 5$	Definition of congruent angles
$m\angle 4 = 72$	Substitution

b. $\angle 2$

$\angle 2 \cong \angle 4$	Vertical Angles Theorem
$\angle 4 \cong \angle 5$	Corresponding Angles Postulate
$\angle 2 \cong \angle 5$	Transitive Property of Congruence
$m\angle 2 = m\angle 5$	Definition of congruent angles
$m\angle 2 = 72$	Substitution

GuidedPractice **1A–1C. See Ch. 3 Answer Appendix.**

In the figure, suppose that $m\angle 8 = 105$. Find the measure of each angle. Tell which postulate(s) or theorem(s) you used.

1A. $\angle 1$ **1B.** $\angle 2$ **1C.** $\angle 3$

In Example 1, $\angle 2$ and $\angle 5$ are congruent alternate exterior angles. This and other examples suggest the following theorems about the other angle pairs formed by two parallel lines cut by a transversal.

180 | Lesson 3-2

Lesson 3-2 Resources

Resource	Approaching Level AL	On Level OL	Beyond Level BL	English Learners ELL
Teacher Edition	▪ Differentiated Instruction, p. 181	▪ Differentiated Instruction, pp. 181, 185	▪ Differentiated Instruction, pp. 181, 185	▪ Differentiated Instruction, p. 181
Chapter Resource Masters	▪ Study Guide and Intervention, pp. 11–12 ▪ Skills Practice, p. 13 ▪ Practice, p. 14 ▪ Word Problem Practice, p. 15	▪ Study Guide and Intervention, pp. 11–12 ▪ Skills Practice, p. 13 ▪ Practice, p. 14 ▪ Word Problem Practice, p. 15 ▪ Enrichment, p. 16	▪ Practice, p. 14 ▪ Word Problem Practice, p. 15 ▪ Enrichment, p. 16	▪ Study Guide and Intervention, pp. 11–12 ▪ Skills Practice, p. 13 ▪ Practice, p. 14 ▪ Word Problem Practice, p. 15
Other	▪ 5-Minute Check 3-2 ▪ Study Notebook	▪ 5-Minute Check 3-2 ▪ Study Notebook	▪ 5-Minute Check 3-2 ▪ Study Notebook	▪ 5-Minute Check 3-2 ▪ Study Notebook

StudyTip

Angle Relationships These theorems generalize the relationships between specific pairs of angles. If you get confused about the relationships, you can verify them with the methods you used in Example 1, using only corresponding, vertical, and supplementary angles.

Theorems Parallel Lines and Angle Pairs

3.1 Alternate Interior Angles Theorem If two parallel lines are cut by a transversal, then each pair of alternate interior angles is congruent.

Examples $\angle 1 \cong \angle 3$ and $\angle 2 \cong \angle 4$

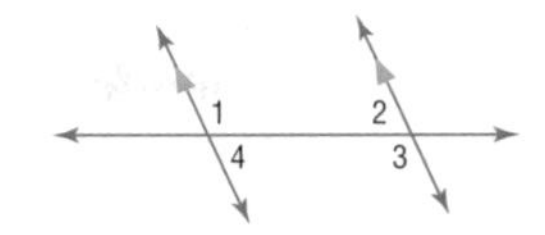

3.2 Consecutive Interior Angles Theorem If two parallel lines are cut by a transversal, then each pair of consecutive interior angles is supplementary.

Examples $\angle 1$ and $\angle 2$ are supplementary. $\angle 3$ and $\angle 4$ are supplementary.

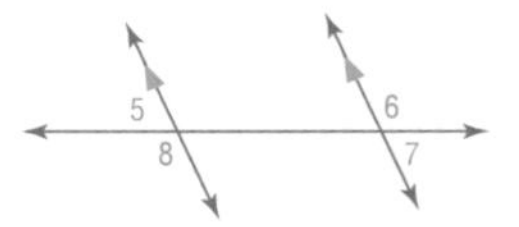

3.3 Alternate Exterior Angles Theorem If two parallel lines are cut by a transversal, then each pair of alternate exterior angles is congruent.

Examples $\angle 5 \cong \angle 7$ and $\angle 6 \cong \angle 8$

You will prove Theorems 3.2 and 3.3 in Exercises 30 and 35, respectively.

Since postulates are accepted without proof, you can use the Corresponding Angles Postulate to prove each of the theorems above.

Proof Alternate Interior Angles Theorem

Given: $a \parallel b$

t is a transversal of a and b.

Prove: $\angle 4 \cong \angle 5$, $\angle 3 \cong \angle 6$

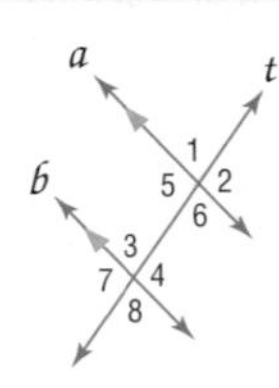

Paragraph Proof: We are given that $a \parallel b$ with a transversal t. By the Corresponding Angles Postulate, corresponding angles are congruent. So, $\angle 2 \cong \angle 4$ and $\angle 6 \cong \angle 8$. Also, $\angle 5 \cong \angle 2$ and $\angle 8 \cong \angle 3$ because vertical angles are congruent. Therefore, $\angle 5 \cong \angle 4$ and $\angle 3 \cong \angle 6$ since congruence of angles is transitive.

Real-World Example 2 Use Theorems about Parallel Lines

COMMUNITY PLANNING **Redding Lane and Creek Road are parallel streets that intersect Park Road along the west side of Wendell Park. If $m\angle 1 = 118$, find $m\angle 2$.**

Creek Road
Park Road
Wendell Park
Redding Lane

$\angle 2 \cong \angle 1$ Alternate Interior Angles Postulate

$m\angle 2 = m\angle 1$ Definition of congruent angles

$m\angle 2 = 118$ Substitution

Real-WorldLink

Some cities require that streets in newly planned subdivisions intersect at no less than a 60° angle.

GuidedPractice 2A. 80°; Supplement Theorem, Alternate Exterior Angles 2B. 70°; Alternate Exterior Angles

COMMUNITY PLANNING **Refer to the diagram above to find each angle measure. Tell which postulate(s) or theorem(s) you used.**

2A. If $m\angle 1 = 100$, find $m\angle 4$.

2B. If $m\angle 3 = 70$, find $m\angle 4$.

1 Parallel Lines and Angle Pairs

Examples 1 and 2 show how to determine an angle measurement when given two parallel lines cut by a transversal and one angle's measure.

Formative Assessment

Use the Guided Practice exercises after each example to determine students' understanding of concepts.

Additional Example

1 In the figure, $m\angle 11 = 51$. Find the measure of each angle. Tell which postulates (or theorems) you used.

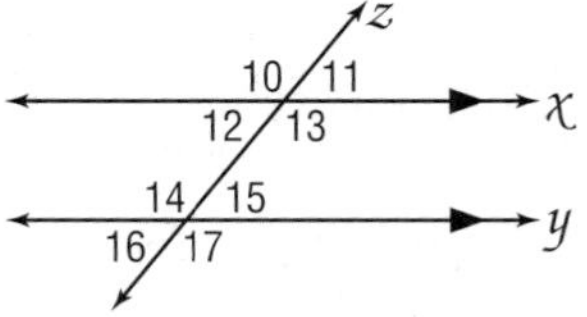

a. $m\angle 15$ 51; Corresponding Angles Postulate

b. $m\angle 16$ 51; Vertical Angles Theorem, Corresponding Angles Postulate

Additional Examples also in Interactive Classroom PowerPoint® Presentations

Teach with Tech

Student Response System Show students a diagram of two parallel lines with a transversal. Number the angles 1 through 8. Choose an angle and have students respond with the number of an alternate interior angle. Repeat this activity and have students identify alternate exterior angles, vertical angles, and supplementary angles.

DifferentiatedInstruction AL OL BL ELL

Kinesthetic Learners Use masking tape to mark two parallel lines and a transversal on the floor. Have pairs of students stand in angles that are congruent or supplementary, and have them explain whether their angles are alternate interior, alternate exterior, corresponding, or consecutive interior angles.

Additional Example

2 FLOOR TILES The following diagram represents floor tiles in Michelle's house. If $m\angle 2 = 125$, find $m\angle 3$.

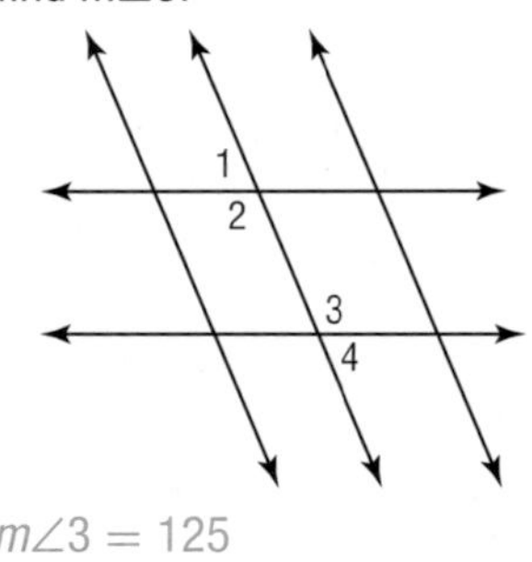

$m\angle 3 = 125$

2 Algebra and Angle Measures

Example 3 uses an algebraic expression to represent an angle measurement. Students should be able to solve for the variable algebraically, then substitute the solution for the variable in the expression to then find the angle's measure.

Additional Example

3 ALGEBRA Use the figure below to find the indicated variable. Explain your reasoning.

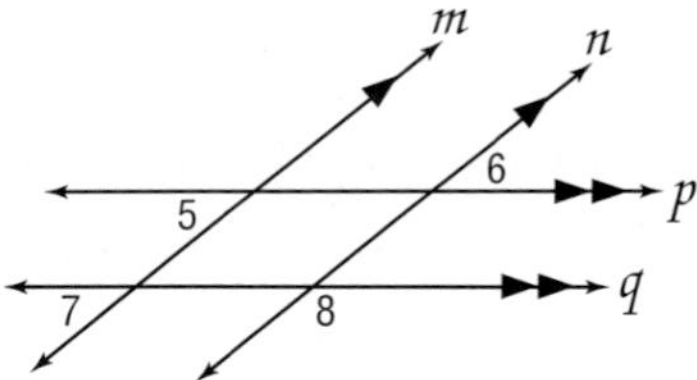

a. If $m\angle 5 = 2x - 10$, and $m\angle 7 = x + 15$, find x. 25; Corresponding Angles Postulate

b. Find y, if $m\angle 6 = 4(y - 25)$ and $m\angle 8 = 4y$. 35; Alt. Ext. Angles Thm., Supplement Thm.

Teaching the Mathematical Practices

Precision Mathematically proficient students use clear definitions in discussion with others and in their own reasoning. Remind students to be mindful that their assumptions are valid.

2 Algebra and Angle Measures

The special relationships between the angles formed by two parallel lines and a transversal can be used to find unknown values.

Example 3 Find Values of Variables

ALGEBRA Use the figure at the right to find the indicated variable. Explain your reasoning.

a. If $m\angle 4 = 2x - 17$ and $m\angle 1 = 85$, find x.

$\angle 3 \cong \angle 1$	Vertical Angles Theorem
$m\angle 3 = m\angle 1$	Definition of congruent angles
$m\angle 3 = 85$	Substitution

Since lines r and s are parallel, $\angle 4$ and $\angle 3$ are supplementary by the Consecutive Interior Angles Theorem.

$m\angle 3 + m\angle 4 = 180$	Definition of supplementary angles
$85 + 2x - 17 = 180$	Substitution
$2x + 68 = 180$	Simplify.
$2x = 112$	Subtract 68 from each side.
$x = 56$	Divide each side by 2.

b. Find y if $m\angle 3 = 4y + 30$ and $m\angle 7 = 7y + 6$.

$\angle 3 \cong \angle 7$	Alternate Interior Angles Theorem
$m\angle 3 = m\angle 7$	Definition of congruent angles
$4y + 30 = 7y + 6$	Substitution
$30 = 3y + 6$	Subtract 4y from each side.
$24 = 3y$	Subtract 6 from each side.
$8 = y$	Divide each side by 3.

StudyTip

Precision The postulates and theorems you will be studying in this lesson only apply to *parallel* lines cut by a transversal. You should assume that lines are parallel only if the information is given or the lines are marked with parallel arrows.

GuidedPractice 3A–3B. See margin.

3A. If $m\angle 2 = 4x + 7$ and $m\angle 7 = 5x - 13$, find x.

3B. Find y if $m\angle 5 = 68$ and $m\angle 3 = 3y - 2$.

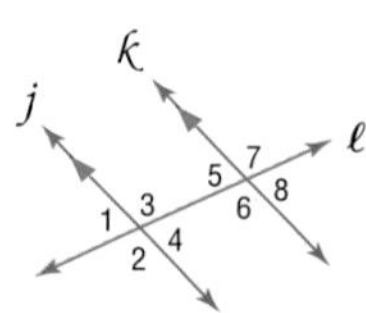

A special relationship exists when the transversal of two parallel lines is a perpendicular line.

Theorem 3.4 Perpendicular Transversal Theorem

In a plane, if a line is perpendicular to one of two parallel lines, then it is perpendicular to the other.

Examples If line $a \parallel$ line b and line $a \perp$ line t, then line $b \perp$ line t.

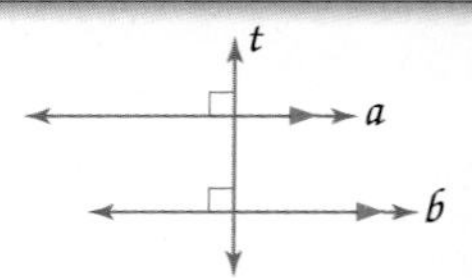

You will prove Theorem 3.4 in Exercise 37.

ReadingMath

perpendicular Recall from Lesson 1-5 that line $b \perp$ line t is read as *Line b is perpendicular to line t.*

Additional Answers (Guided Practice)

3A. Since lines j and k are parallel, $\angle 2$ and $\angle 7$ are congruent by the Alternate Exterior Angles Theorem.

$m\angle 2 = m\angle 7$	Definition of congruent
$4x + 7 = 5x - 13$	Substitution
$4x + 20 = 5x$	Add 13 to each side.
$20 = x$	Subtract $4x$ from each side.

3B. Since lines j and k are parallel, $\angle 3$ and $\angle 5$ are supplementary by the Consecutive Interior Angles Theorem.

$m\angle 5 + m\angle 3 = 180$	Definition of supplementary
$68 + 3y - 2 = 180$	Substitution
$3y + 66 = 180$	Simplify.
$3y = 114$	Subtract 64 from each side.
$x = 38$	Divide each side by 3.

Check Your Understanding

 = Step-by-Step Solutions begin on page R14. 

Example 1 **In the figure, $m\angle 1 = 94$. Find the measure of each angle. Tell which postulate(s) or theorem(s) you used.** 1–3. See margin.

1. $\angle 3$
2. $\angle 5$
3. $\angle 4$

Example 2 **In the figure, $m\angle 4 = 101$. Find the measure of each angle. Tell which postulate(s) or theorem(s) you used.** 4–6. See margin.

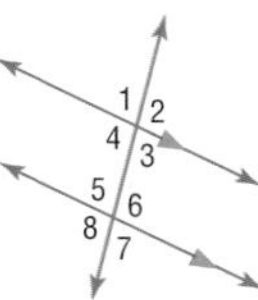

4. $\angle 6$
5. $\angle 7$
6. $\angle 5$

7. **ROADS** In the diagram, the guard rail is parallel to the surface of the roadway and the vertical supports are parallel to each other. Find the measures of angles 2, 3, and 4. $m\angle 2 = 93$, $m\angle 3 = 87$, $m\angle 4 = 87$

Example 3 **Find the value of the variable(s) in each figure. Explain your reasoning.** 8–10. See margin.

8.
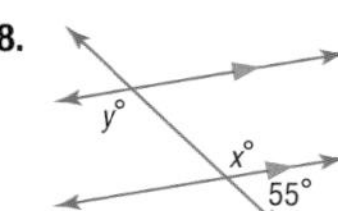

9.
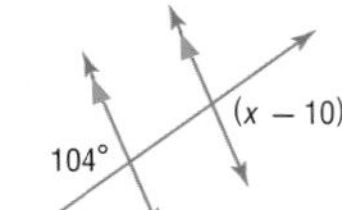

10.
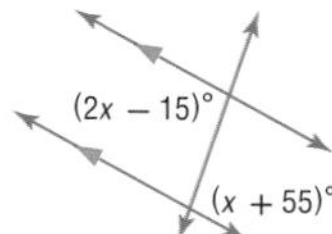

Practice and Problem Solving

Extra Practice is on page R3.

Examples 1–2 **In the figure, $m\angle 11 = 62$ and $m\angle 14 = 38$. Find the measure of each angle. Tell which postulate(s) or theorem(s) you used.** 11–19. See margin.

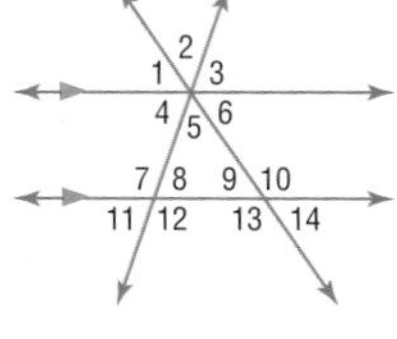

11. $\angle 4$
12. $\angle 3$
13. $\angle 12$
14. $\angle 8$
15. $\angle 6$
16. $\angle 2$
17. $\angle 10$
18. $\angle 5$
19. $\angle 1$

Example 3 20. supplementary; Consecutive Interior Angles

CCSS **MODELING** A solar dish collects energy by directing radiation from the Sun to a receiver located at the focal point of the dish. Assume that the radiation rays are parallel. Determine the relationship between each pair of angles, and explain your reasoning.

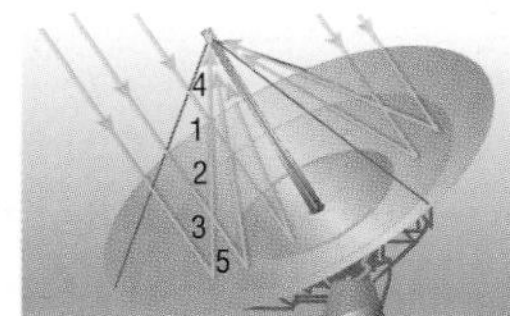

21. congruent; Corresponding Angles
22. congruent; Alternate Exterior Angles
23. See margin.

20. $\angle 1$ and $\angle 2$

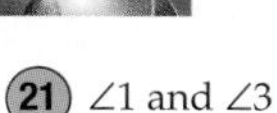 21. $\angle 1$ and $\angle 3$

22. $\angle 4$ and $\angle 5$

23. $\angle 3$ and $\angle 4$

Differentiated Homework Options

Level	Assignment	Two-Day Option	
AL Basic	11–26, 42–44, 46–61	11–25 odd, 47–50	12–26 even, 42–44, 46, 51–61
OL Core	11–29 odd, 30–44, 46–61	11–26, 47–50	27–44, 46, 51–61
BL Advanced	27–55, (optional 56–61)		

3 Practice

Formative Assessment

Use Exercises 1–10 to check for understanding.

Use the chart at the bottom of this page to customize assignments for your students.

Teaching the Mathematical Practices

Modeling Mathematically proficient students can apply the mathematics they know to solve problems arising in the real world. In Exercises 20–23, encourage students to copy the diagram onto their papers. Using a different color for the transversal may help students see the relationships between the angles marked.

Additional Answers

1. 94; Corresponding Angle Postulate
2. 94; Alt. Ext. ∠s Thm.
3. 86; Corresponding Angle Postulate and Supplement Angle Thm.
4. 101; Alt. Int. ∠s Thm.
5. 79; Vertical Angle Thm. and Cons. Int. ∠s Thm.
6. 79; Cons. Int. ∠s Thm.
8. $x = 125$ by the Supplement Thm.; $y = 125$ by the Alt. Int. ∠s Thm.
9. $x = 114$ by the Alt. Ext. ∠s Thm.
10. $x = 70$ by the Alt. Int. ∠s Thm.
11. 62; Corr. ∠s Post.
12. 62; Corresponding ∠s Post. and Vertical ∠s Thm. or Alt. Ext. ∠s Thm.
13. 118; Def. Supp. ∠s
14. 62; Vertical Angle Thm.
15. 38; Corr. ∠s Post.
16. 80; Alt. Ext. ∠s Post. and Supp. ∠ Thm.
17. 142; Supplement Angles Thm.
18. 80; Vertical Angles Thm.
19. 38; Alt. Ext. ∠s Thm.
23. supplementary; since $\angle 3$ and $\angle 5$ are a linear pair, they are supplementary. $\angle 4$ and $\angle 5$ are congruent because they are alternate exterior angles, so $\angle 3$ is supplementary to $\angle 4$.

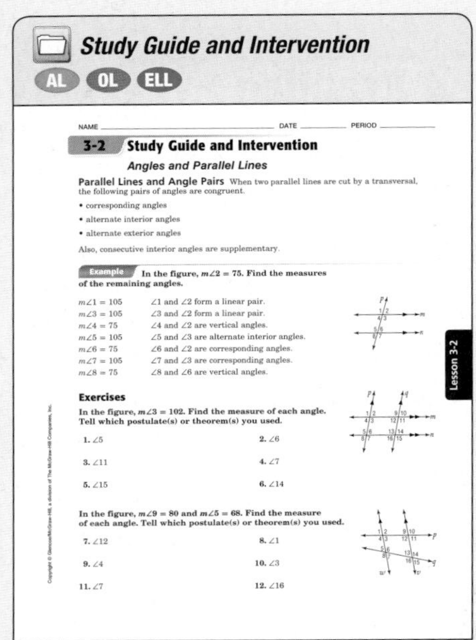

Study Guide and Intervention

AL OL ELL

NAME ________________ DATE ________ PERIOD ________

3-2 Study Guide and Intervention

Angles and Parallel Lines

Parallel Lines and Angle Pairs When two parallel lines are cut by a transversal, the following pairs of angles are congruent.

- corresponding angles
- alternate interior angles
- alternate exterior angles

Also, consecutive interior angles are supplementary.

Example In the figure, $m\angle 2 = 75$. Find the measures of the remaining angles.

$m\angle 1 = 105$ — $\angle 1$ and $\angle 2$ form a linear pair.
$m\angle 3 = 105$ — $\angle 3$ and $\angle 2$ form a linear pair.
$m\angle 4 = 75$ — $\angle 4$ and $\angle 2$ are vertical angles.
$m\angle 5 = 105$ — $\angle 5$ and $\angle 3$ are alternate interior angles.
$m\angle 6 = 75$ — $\angle 6$ and $\angle 2$ are corresponding angles.
$m\angle 7 = 105$ — $\angle 7$ and $\angle 3$ are corresponding angles.
$m\angle 8 = 75$ — $\angle 8$ and $\angle 6$ are vertical angles.

Exercises

In the figure, $m\angle 3 = 102$. Find the measure of each angle. Tell which postulate(s) or theorem(s) you used.

1. $\angle 5$ 2. $\angle 6$
3. $\angle 11$ 4. $\angle 7$
5. $\angle 15$ 6. $\angle 14$

In the figure, $m\angle 9 = 80$ and $m\angle 5 = 68$. Find the measure of each angle. Tell which postulate(s) or theorem(s) you used.

7. $\angle 12$ 8. $\angle 1$
9. $\angle 4$ 10. $\angle 3$
11. $\angle 7$ 12. $\angle 16$

Lesson 3-2

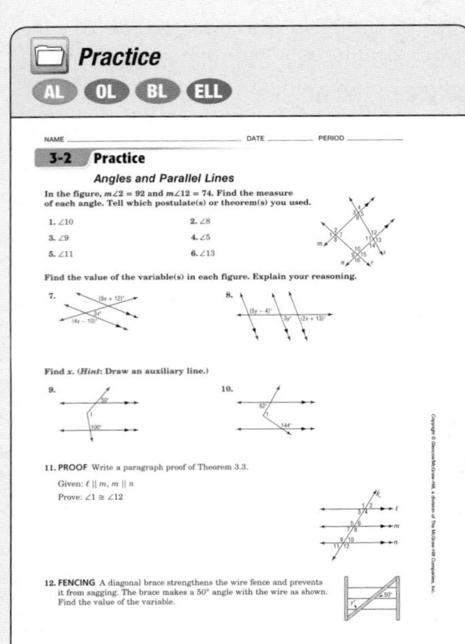

Practice

AL OL BL ELL

NAME ________________ DATE ________ PERIOD ________

3-2 Practice

Angles and Parallel Lines

In the figure, $m\angle 2 = 92$ and $m\angle 12 = 74$. Find the measure of each angle. Tell which postulate(s) or theorem(s) you used.

1. $\angle 10$ 2. $\angle 8$
3. $\angle 9$ 4. $\angle 5$
5. $\angle 11$ 6. $\angle 13$

Find the value of the variable(s) in each figure. Explain your reasoning.

7. 8.

Find x. (*Hint*: Draw an auxiliary line.)

9. 10.

11. **PROOF** Write a paragraph proof of Theorem 3.3.
Given: $\ell \parallel m$, $m \parallel n$
Prove: $\angle 1 \cong \angle 12$

12. **FENCING** A diagonal brace strengthens the wire fence and prevents it from sagging. The brace makes a 50° angle with the wire as shown. Find the value of the variable.

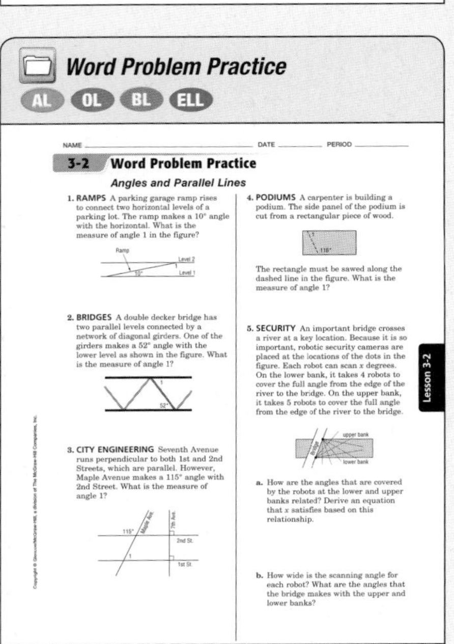

Word Problem Practice

AL OL BL ELL

NAME ________________ DATE ________ PERIOD ________

3-2 Word Problem Practice

Angles and Parallel Lines

1. **RAMPS** A parking garage ramp rises to connect two horizontal levels of a parking lot. The ramp makes a 10° angle with the horizontal. What is the measure of angle 1 in the figure?

2. **BRIDGES** A double decker bridge has two parallel levels connected by a network of diagonal girders. One of the girders makes a 52° angle with the lower level as shown in the figure. What is the measure of angle 1?

3. **CITY ENGINEERING** Seventh Avenue runs perpendicular to both 1st and 2nd Streets, which are parallel. However, Maple Avenue makes a 115° angle with 2nd Street. What is the measure of angle 1?

4. **PODIUMS** A carpenter is building a podium. The side panel of the podium is cut from a rectangular piece of wood.

The rectangle must be sawed along the dashed line in the figure. What is the measure of angle 1?

5. **SECURITY** An important bridge crosses a river at a key location. Because it is so important, robotic security cameras are placed at the locations of the dots in the figure. Each robot can scan x degrees. On the lower bank, it takes 4 robots to cover the full angle from the edge of the river to the bridge. On the upper bank, it takes 5 robots to cover the full angle from the edge of the river to the bridge.

a. How are the angles that are covered by the robots at the lower and upper banks related? Derive an equation that x satisfies based on this relationship.

b. How wide is the scanning angle for each robot? What are the angles that the bridge makes with the upper and lower banks?

Lesson 3-2

Find the value of the variable(s) in each figure. Explain your reasoning.

24–29. See margin.

24.

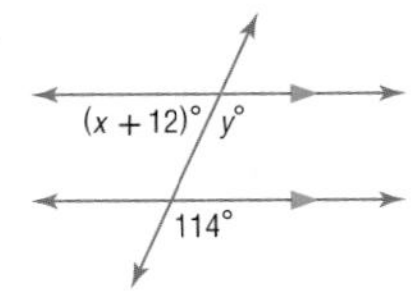

25.

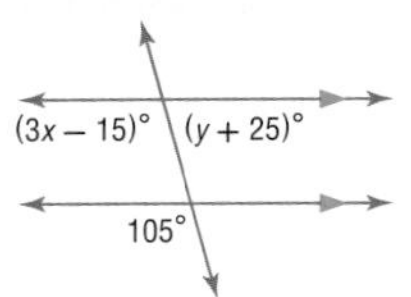

26.

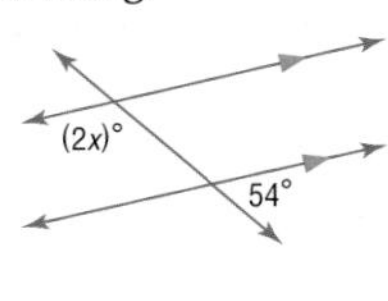

B **27.**

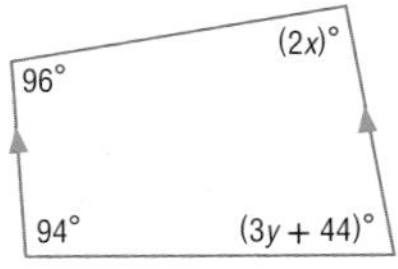

28.

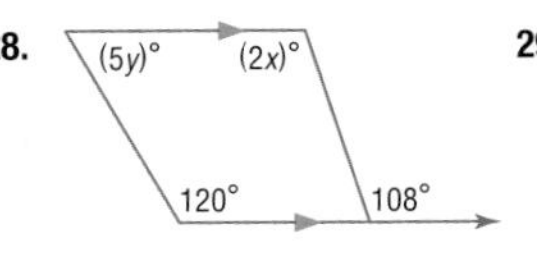

29.

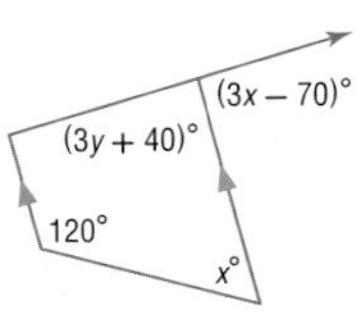

30. PROOF Copy and complete the proof of Theorem 3.2.

Given: $m \parallel n$; ℓ is a transversal.

Prove: $\angle 1$ and $\angle 2$ are supplementary; $\angle 3$ and $\angle 4$ are supplementary.

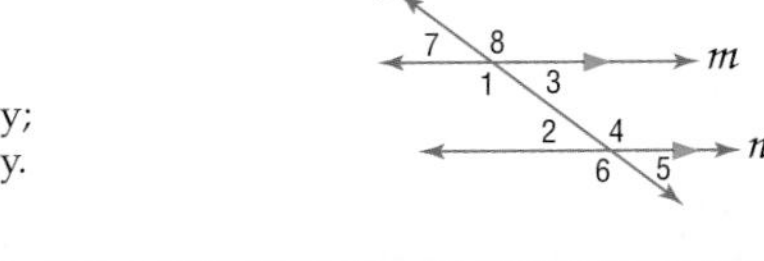

Proof: a. $m \parallel n$; ℓ is a transversal.

Statements	Reasons
a. ?	a. Given
b. $\angle 1$ and $\angle 3$ form a linear pair; $\angle 2$ and $\angle 4$ form a linear pair.	b. ? Def. of linear pair
c. ?	c. If two angles form a linear pair, then they are supplementary.
d. $\angle 1 \cong \angle 4$, $\angle 2 \cong \angle 3$	d. ? Alt. Int. ∠s Theorem
e. $m\angle 1 = m\angle 4$, $m\angle 2 = m\angle 3$	e. Definition of Congruence
f. ?	f. ? Substitution

f. $\angle 1$ and $\angle 2$ are supp. $\angle 3$ and $\angle 4$ are supp.

30c. $\angle 1$ and $\angle 3$ are supplementary. $\angle 2$ and $\angle 4$ are supplementary.

31. Congruent; Alternate Interior Angles
32. Congruent; Corresponding Angles
33. Congruent; vertical angles are congruent
34. Complementary; because the vertical and horizontal lines are perpendicular, they form right angles.

STORAGE When industrial shelving needs to be accessible from either side, additional support is provided on the side by transverse members. Determine the relationship between each pair of angles and explain your reasoning.

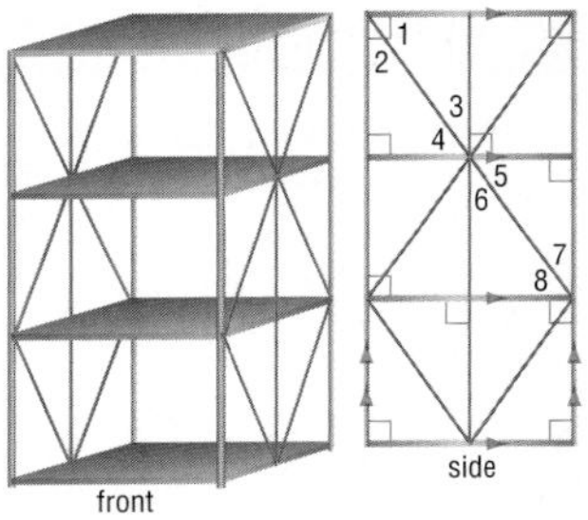

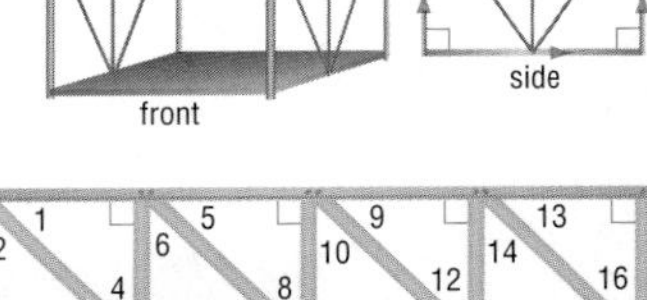

31. $\angle 1$ and $\angle 8$ **32.** $\angle 1$ and $\angle 5$

33. $\angle 3$ and $\angle 6$ **34.** $\angle 1$ and $\angle 2$

35. CCSS **ARGUMENTS** Write a two-column proof of the Alternate Exterior Angles Theorem. (Theorem 3.3) See Ch. 3 Answer Appendix.

36. BRIDGES Refer to the diagram of the double decker Michigan Avenue Bridge in Chicago, Illinois, at the right. The two levels of the bridge, and its diagonal braces, are parallel. a–c. See Ch. 3 Answer Appendix.

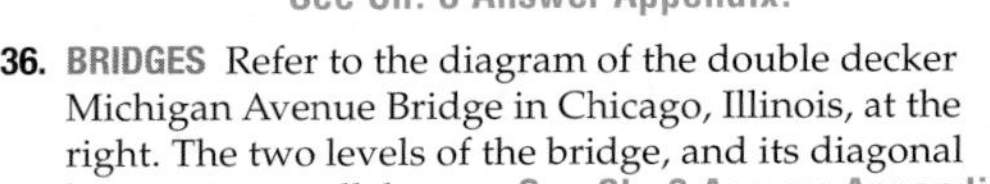

a. How are the measures of the odd-numbered angles related? Explain.

b. How are the measures of the even-numbered angles related? Explain.

c. How are any pair of angles in which one is odd and the other is even related?

d. What geometric term(s) can be used to relate the two roadways contained by the bridge? parallel planes

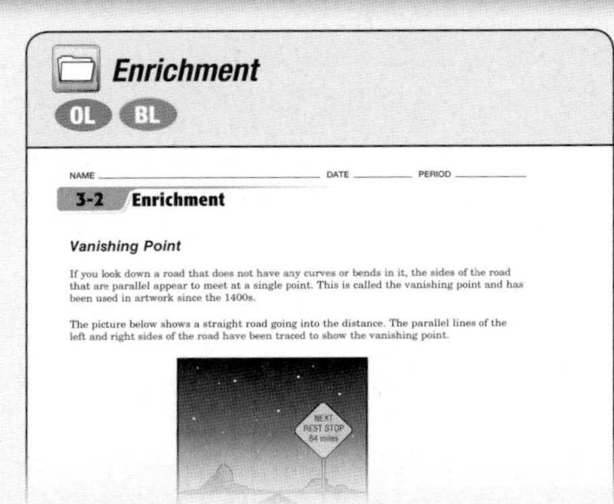

Enrichment

OL BL

NAME ________________ DATE ________ PERIOD ________

3-2 Enrichment

Vanishing Point

If you look down a road that does not have any curves or bends in it, the sides of the road that are parallel appear to meet at a single point. This is called the vanishing point and has been used in artwork since the 1400s.

The picture below shows a straight road going into the distance. The parallel lines of the left and right sides of the road have been traced to show the vanishing point.

Additional Answers

24–29. See Ch. 3 Answer Appendix for explanations.

24. $x = 54$, $y = 114$

25. $x = 40$, $y = 50$

26. $x = 63$

27. $x = 42$, $y = 14$

28. $x = 54$, $y = 12$

29. $x = 60$, $y = 10$

37. PROOF In a plane, prove that if a line is perpendicular to one of two parallel lines, then it is perpendicular to the other. (Theorem 3.4) See margin.

CCSS TOOLS **Find x. (*Hint:* Draw an auxiliary line.)**

38. 22 **39** 130

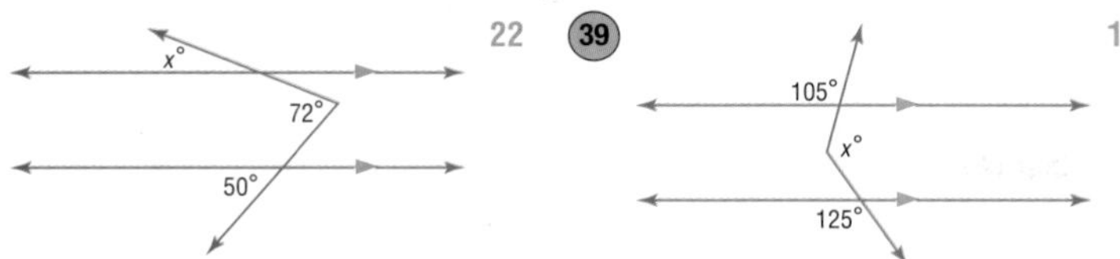

40. PROBABILITY Suppose you were to pick any two angles in the figure below.

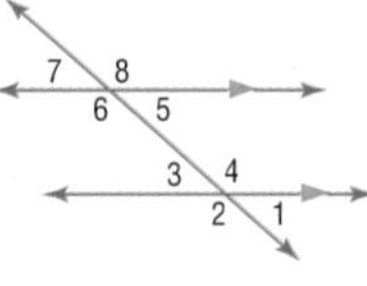

a. How many possible angle pairings are there? Explain. **a–c.** See margin.

b. Describe the possible relationships between the measures of the angles in each pair. Explain.

c. Describe the likelihood of randomly selecting a pair of congruent angles. Explain your reasoning.

41c. Sample answer: Angles on the exterior of a pair of parallel lines located on the same side of the transversal are supplementary.

41. MULTIPLE REPRESENTATIONS In this problem, you will investigate the relationship between same-side exterior angles. **a, b, e.** See Ch. 3 Answer Appendix.

a. **Geometry** Draw five pairs of parallel lines, m and n, a and b, r and s, j and k, and x and y, cut by a transversal t, and measure the four angles on one side of t.

b. **Tabular** Record your data in a table.

c. **Verbal** Make a conjecture about the relationship between the pair of angles formed on the exterior of parallel lines and on the same side of the transversal.

d. **Logical** What type of reasoning did you use to form your conjecture? Explain. Inductive; a pattern was used to make a conjecture.

e. **Proof** Write a proof of your conjecture.

42–44. See Ch. 3 Answer Appendix.

H.O.T. Problems Use Higher-Order Thinking Skills

42. WRITING IN MATH If line a is parallel to line b and $\angle 1 \cong \angle 2$, describe the relationship between lines b and c. Explain your reasoning.

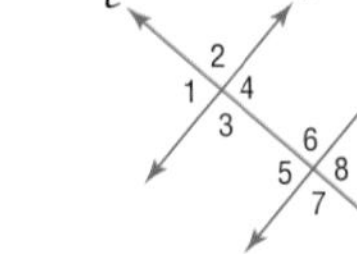

43. WRITING IN MATH Compare and contrast the Alternate Interior Angles Theorem and the Consecutive Interior Angles Theorem.

46. One; sample answer: Once the measure of one angle is known, the rest of the angles are either congruent or supplementary to the given angle.

44. OPEN ENDED Draw a pair of parallel lines cut by a transversal and measure the two exterior angles on the same side of the transversal. Include the measures on your drawing. Based on the pattern you have seen for naming other pairs of angles, what do you think the name of the pair you measured would be?

45. CHALLENGE Find x and y.

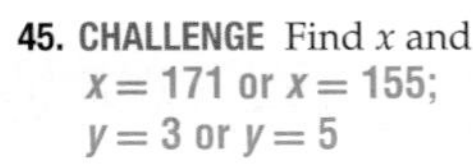

$x = 171$ or $x = 155$; $y = 3$ or $y = 5$

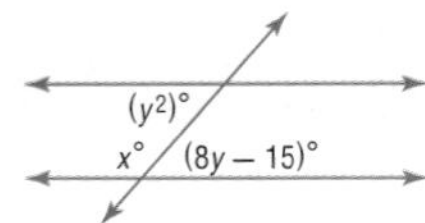

46. REASONING Determine the minimum number of angle measures you would have to know to find the measures of all the angles formed by two parallel lines cut by a transversal. Explain.

Differentiated Instruction OL BL

Extension Remember from algebra that the slope of a line is defined as the rise over the run, or $\frac{\text{rise}}{\text{run}}$. On a coordinate plane, draw two parallel lines at $y = 6$ and $y = 1$. Now draw a transversal at some angle across those two lines. Find the slope of the transverse line. Answers will vary. What are the slopes of the parallel lines? zero

Teaching the Mathematical Practices

Tools Mathematically proficient students consider the available tools when solving a problem. Encourage students to copy the diagrams onto their papers and to add auxiliary parallel lines.

Additional Answers

37. Given: $m \parallel n$, $t \perp m$

Prove: $t \perp n$

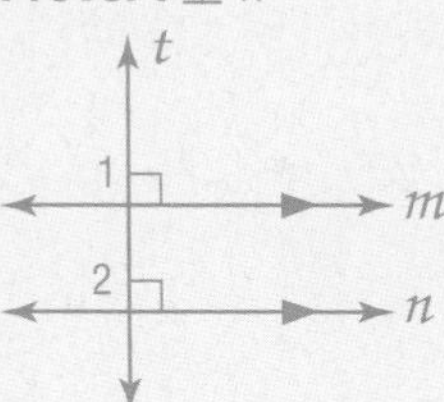

Proof:

Statements (Reasons)

1. $m \parallel n$, $t \perp m$ (Given)
2. $\angle 1$ is a right angle. (Def. of $\perp$)
3. $m\angle 1 = 90$ (Def. of rt. ∠s)
4. $\angle 1 \cong \angle 2$ (Corr. ∠s Post.)
5. $m\angle 1 = m\angle 2$ (Def. of ≅ ∠s)
6. $m\angle 2 = 90$ (Subs.)
7. $\angle 2$ is a right angle. (Def. of rt. ∠s)
8. $t \perp n$ (Def. of $\perp$ lines)

40a. Sample answer: There are 28 possible angle pairings. The first angle can be paired with seven others, then the second angle can be paired with six others since it has already been paired with the first angle. The number of pairings is the sum of the number of angles each subsequent angle can be paired with, $7 + 6 + 5 + 4 + 3 + 2 + 1$ or 28 pairings.

40b. Sample answer: There are two possible relationships between the pairs of angles. Two angles chosen will be either congruent or supplementary.

40c. Sample answer: Twelve of the 28 angle pairs are congruent. So the likelihood of selecting a pair of congruent angles is $\frac{12}{28}$ or $\frac{3}{7}$.

4 Assess

Yesterday's News Working in small groups, have students take turns describing to their group how the lesson on parallel lines and transversals helped them learn about angle relationships.

Formative Assessment

Check for student understanding of Lessons 3-1 and 3-2.

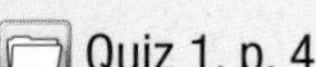 Quiz 1, p. 45

Standardized Test Practice

47. Suppose $\angle 4$ and $\angle 5$ form a linear pair. If $m\angle 1 = 2x$, $m\angle 2 = 3x - 20$, and $m\angle 3 = x - 4$, what is $m\angle 3$? **C**

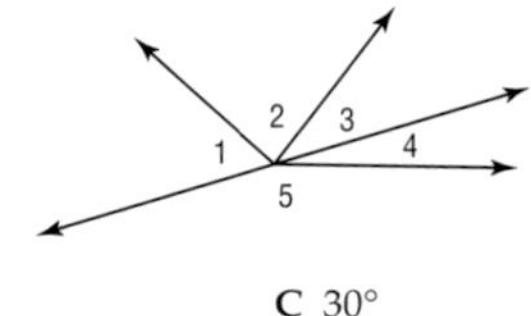

A 26° C 30°
B 28° D 32°

48. SAT/ACT A farmer raises chickens and pigs. If his animals have a total of 120 heads and a total of 300 feet, how many chickens does the farmer have? **J**

F 60 H 80
G 70 J 90

49. SHORT RESPONSE If $m \parallel n$, then which of the following statements must be true? **I and II**

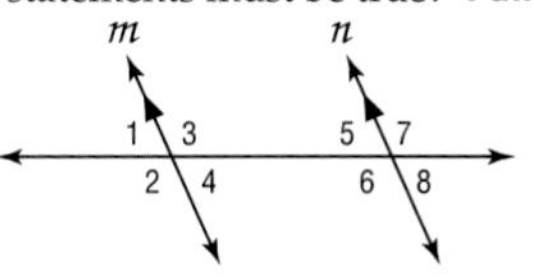

I. $\angle 3$ and $\angle 6$ are Alternate Interior Angles.
II. $\angle 4$ and $\angle 6$ are Consecutive Interior Angles.
III. $\angle 1$ and $\angle 7$ are Alternate Exterior Angles.

50. ALGEBRA If $-2 + x = -6$, then $-17 - x = ?$ **A**

A -13 D 13
B -4 E 21
C 9

Spiral Review

51. AVIATION Airplanes are assigned an altitude level based on the direction they are flying. If one airplane is flying northwest at 34,000 feet and another airplane is flying east at 25,000 feet, describe the type of lines formed by the paths of the airplanes. Explain your reasoning. (Lesson 3-1)
Skew lines; the planes are flying in different directions and at different altitudes.

Use the given statement to find the measure of each numbered angle. (Lesson 2-8)

52. $\angle 1$ and $\angle 2$ form a linear pair and $m\angle 2 = 67$.

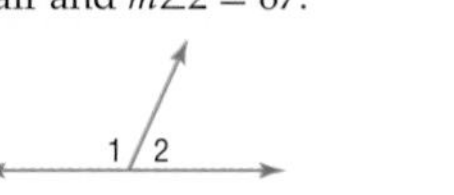

$m\angle 1 = 113$

53. $\angle 6$ and $\angle 8$ are; complementary $m\angle 8 = 47$.

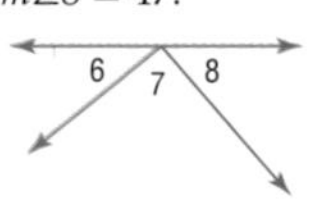

$m\angle 6 = 43$, $m\angle 7 = 90$

54. $m\angle 4 = 32$
$m\angle 3 = 90$, $m\angle 5 = 58$

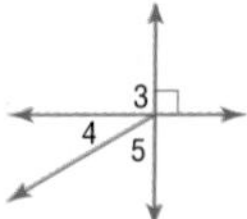

55. TRAINS A train company wants to provide routes to New York City, Dallas, Chicago, Los Angeles, San Francisco, and Washington, D.C. An engineer draws lines between each pair of cities on a map. No three of the cities are collinear. How many lines did the engineer draw? (Lesson 2-5) **15**

Skills Review

Simplify each expression.

56. $\frac{6-5}{4-2}$ $\frac{1}{2}$

57. $\frac{-5-2}{4-7}$ $\frac{7}{3}$

58. $\frac{-11-4}{12-(-9)}$ $-\frac{5}{7}$

59. $\frac{16-12}{15-11}$ 1

60. $\frac{10-22}{8-17}$ $\frac{4}{3}$

61. $\frac{8-17}{12-(-3)}$ $-\frac{3}{5}$

Follow-up

Students have explored angle relationships formed by parallel lines cut by a transversal.

Ask:

- How are lines used to define angle pairs? Sample answer: The intersections of different types and numbers of lines are used to define certain angle pairs. For example, the intersection of two lines defines linear, supplementary, complementary, and vertical angles. The intersections of two or more coplanar lines define interior, exterior, and corresponding angles.
- Why do we name angle pairs? Sample answer: Once angle pairs are named, they can be used to write postulates, prove theorems, and solve problems.

EXPLORE 3-3 Graphing Technology Lab: Investigating Slope

The rate of change of the steepness of a line is called the *slope*. Slope can be used to investigate the relationship between real-world quantities.

CCSS Common Core State Standards
Content Standards
G.GPE.5 Prove the slope criteria for parallel and perpendicular lines and use them to solve geometric problems (e.g., find the equation of a line parallel or perpendicular to a given line that passes through a given point).
Mathematical Practices 5

Set Up the Lab

- Connect a data collection device to a graphing calculator. Place the device on a desk or table so that it can read the motion of a walker.
- Mark the floor at distances of 1 meter and 6 meters from the device.

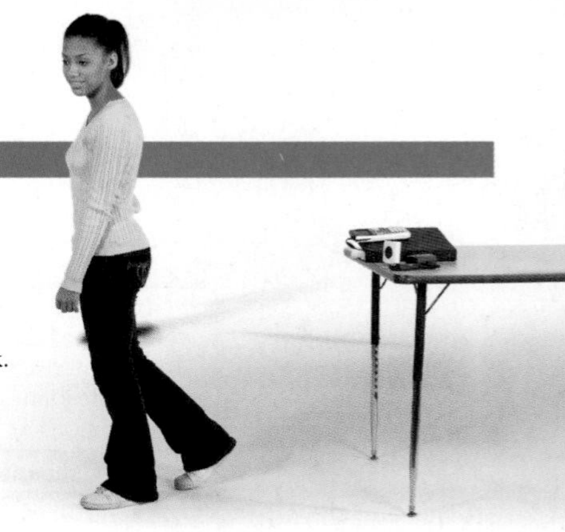

Activity

Step 1 Have one group member stand at the 1-meter mark. When another group member presses the button to begin collecting data, the walker should walk away from the device at a slow, steady pace.

Step 2 Stop collecting data when the walker passes the 6-meter mark. Save the data as Trial 1.

Step 3 Repeat the experiment, walking more quickly. Save the data as Trial 2.

Step 4 For Trial 3, repeat the experiment by slowly walking toward the data collection device.

Step 5 Repeat the experiment, walking quickly toward the device. Save the data as Trial 4.

Analyze the Results 1–5. See margin.

1. Compare and contrast the graphs for Trials 1 and 2. How do the graphs for Trials 1 and 3 compare?

2. Use the **TRACE** feature of the calculator to find the coordinates of two points on each graph. Record the coordinates in a table like the one shown. Then use the points to find the slope of the line.

Trial	Point A (x_1, y_1)	Point B (x_2, y_2)	Slope $= \frac{y_2 - y_1}{x_2 - x_1}$
1			
2			
3			
4			

3. Compare and contrast the slopes for Trials 1 and 2. How do the slopes for Trials 1 and 2 compare to the slopes for Trials 3 and 4?

4. The slope of a line describes the rate of change of the quantities represented by the x- and y-values. What is represented by the rate of change in this experiment?

5. **MAKE A CONJECTURE** What would the graph look like if you were to collect data while the walker was standing still? Use the data collection device to test your conjecture.

1 Focus

Objective Use a graphing calculator to investigate slope.

Materials

- graphing calculators with data collection device

2 Teach

Working in Cooperative Groups

Arrange students in groups of mixed abilities. Have students complete the activity.

After the students have completed the activity, discuss which trial had the steeper slope and the possible reasons for this. Ask how differences in the rate of change relate to changes in the slopes. Explain that calculus is based on the study of changes in the rate of change.

Practice Have students complete Exercises 1–5.

3 Assess

Formative Assessment

Use Exercises 1–5 to assess whether students comprehend the relationships between the slope and the rate of change.

From Concrete to Abstract

Give students coordinate graph paper to draw two lines, one with a negative slope and one with a positive slope. Tell students to trade with a partner and find the slope and equation of the lines.

Additional Answers

1. Sample answer: The graph of Trial 1 is not as steep as the graph of Trial 2 and the graph of Trial 3 is not as steep as the graph of Trial 4. But the graph of Trial 1 slopes up from left to right and the graph of Trial 3 slopes down from left to right.
2. See students' work.
3. Sample answer: The slope for Trial 2 is greater than the slope for Trial 1. The slopes of Trial 1 and 2 are positive and the slopes for Trial 3 and 4 are negative.
4. The slope represents the rate of change of the walker's position in relation to the data collection device, that is, the walker's speed.
5. The slope of the graph would be 0, so the graph would be a horizontal line.

1 Focus

VerticalAlignment

Before Lesson 3-3 Use properties of parallel lines to determine congruent angles.

Lesson 3-3 Find slopes of lines. Use slope to identify parallel and perpendicular lines.

After Lesson 3-3 Formulate and test conjectures about the properties and attributes of polygons and their component parts.

2 Teach

Scaffolding Questions

Have students read the **Why?** section of the lesson.

Ask:

- What difficulty level is a slope with a 13% gradient? the easiest
- If a trail has a 20% gradient, how many feet does it fall for every 100 feet traveled? 20 feet
- Could a ski slope have a 90% gradient? Sample: No, this would be too steep.

1 Slope of a Line

Example 1 shows how to use the ratio of vertical rise to horizontal run to find the slope of a line. Parts **c** and **d** address lines that have a slope of zero and lines that have undefined slope.

LESSON 3-3 Slopes of Lines

Then

- You used the properties of parallel lines to determine congruent angles.

Now

1. Find slopes of lines.
2. Use slope to identify parallel and perpendicular lines.

Why?

- Ski resorts assign ratings to their ski trails according to their difficulty. A primary factor in determining this rating is a trail's steepness or *slope gradient.* A trail with a 6% or $\frac{6}{100}$ grade falls 6 feet vertically for every 100 feet traveled horizontally.

The easiest trails, labeled ●, have slopes ranging from 6% to 25%, while more difficult trails, labeled ♦ or ♦♦, have slopes of 40% or greater.

NewVocabulary
slope
rate of change

Common Core State Standards

Content Standards
G.GPE.5 Prove the slope criteria for parallel and perpendicular lines and use them to solve geometric problems (e.g., find the equation of a line parallel or perpendicular to a given line that passes through a given point).

Mathematical Practices
4 Model with mathematics.
7 Look for and make use of structure.
8 Look for and express regularity in repeated reasoning.

1 Slope of a Line The steepness or slope of a hill is described by the ratio of the hill's vertical rise to its horizontal run. In algebra, you learned that the slope of a line in the coordinate plane can be calculated using any two points on the line.

KeyConcept Slope of a Line

In a coordinate plane, the **slope** of a line is the ratio of the change along the *y*-axis to the change along the *x*-axis between any two points on the line.

The slope m of a line containing two points with coordinates (x_1, y_1) and (x_2, y_2) is given by the formula

$$m = \frac{y_2 - y_1}{x_2 - x_1}, \text{ where } x_1 \neq x_2.$$

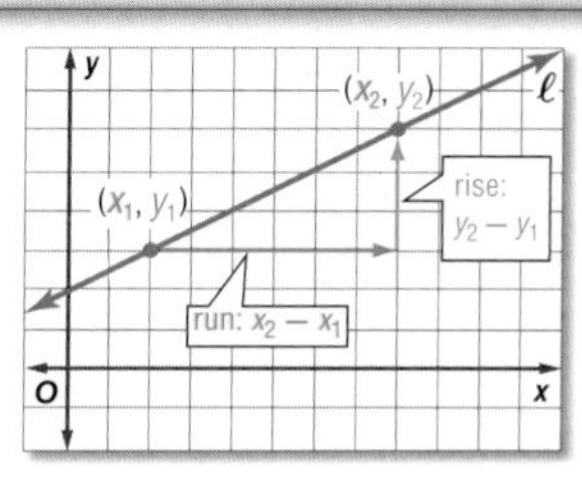

$$m = \frac{\text{rise}}{\text{run}} = \frac{y_2 - y_1}{x_2 - x_1}$$

Example 1 Find the Slope of a Line

Find the slope of each line.

a.

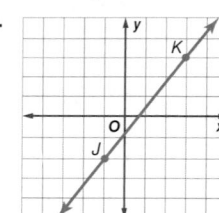

Substitute $(-1, -2)$ for (x_1, y_1) and $(3, 3)$ for (x_2, y_2).

$m = \frac{y_2 - y_1}{x_2 - x_1}$ Slope Formula

$= \frac{3 - (-2)}{3 - (-1)}$ Substitution

$= \frac{5}{4}$ Simplify.

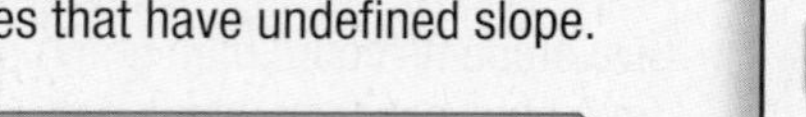

Lesson 3-3 Resources

Resource	Approaching Level AL	On Level OL	Beyond Level BL	English Learners ELL
Teacher Edition	▪ Differentiated Instruction, pp. 192, 195	▪ Differentiated Instruction, pp. 192, 195	▪ Differentiated Instruction, p. 195	▪ Differentiated Instruction, p. 195
Chapter Resource Masters	▪ Study Guide and Intervention, pp. 17–18 ▪ Skills Practice, pp. 19 ▪ Practice, p. 20 ▪ Word Problem Practice, p. 21 ▪ Spreadsheet Activity, p. 23	▪ Study Guide and Intervention, pp. 17–18 ▪ Skills Practice, p. 19 ▪ Practice, p. 20 ▪ Word Problem Practice, p. 21 ▪ Enrichment, p. 22 ▪ Spreadsheet Activity, p. 23	▪ Practice, p. 20 ▪ Word Problem Practice, p. 21 ▪ Enrichment, p. 22 ▪ Spreadsheet Activity, p. 23	▪ Study Guide and Intervention, pp. 17–18 ▪ Skills Practice, p. 19 ▪ Practice, p. 20 ▪ Word Problem Practice, p. 21 ▪ Spreadsheet Activity, p. 23
Other	▪ 5-Minute Check 3-3 ▪ Study Notebook	▪ 5-Minute Check 3-3 ▪ Study Notebook	▪ 5-Minute Check 3-3 ▪ Study Notebook	▪ 5-Minute Check 3-3 ▪ Study Notebook

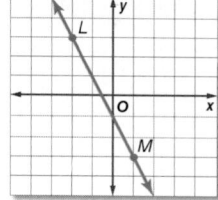

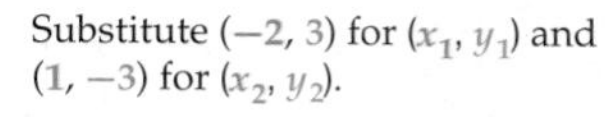

b. Substitute $(-2, 3)$ for (x_1, y_1) and $(1, -3)$ for (x_2, y_2).

$m = \frac{y_2 - y_1}{x_2 - x_1}$ Slope Formula

$= \frac{-3 - 3}{1 - (-2)}$ Substitution

$= -2$ Simplify.

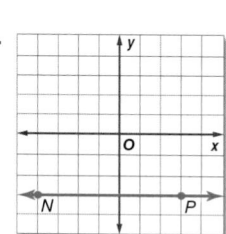

c. Substitute $(-4, -3)$ for (x_1, y_1) and $(3, -3)$ for (x_2, y_2).

$m = \frac{y_2 - y_1}{x_2 - x_1}$ Slope Formula

$= \frac{-3 - (-3)}{3 - (-4)}$ Substitution

$= \frac{0}{7}$ or 0 Simplify.

d.

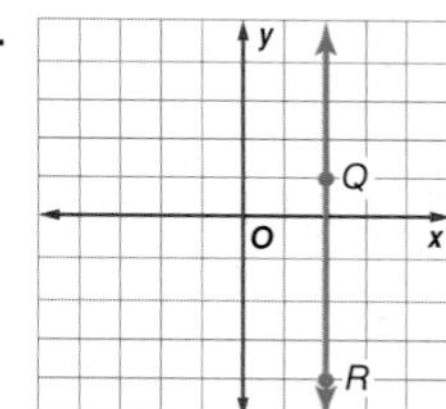

Substitute $(2, 1)$ for (x_1, y_1) and $(2, -4)$ for (x_2, y_2).

$m = \frac{y_2 - y_1}{x_2 - x_1}$ Slope Formula

$= \frac{-4 - 1}{2 - 2}$ Substitution

$= \frac{-5}{0}$ Simplify.

This slope is **undefined**.

StudyTip

Dividing by 0 The slope $\frac{-5}{0}$ is undefined because there is no number that you can multiply by 0 and get -5. Since this is true for any number, all numbers divided by 0 will have an undefined slope. All vertical lines have undefined slopes.

GuidedPractice 1A. $\frac{1}{3}$ 1B. $-\frac{1}{14}$

1A. the line containing $(6, -2)$ and $(-3, -5)$

1B. the line containing $(8, -3)$ and $(-6, -2)$

1C. the line containing $(4, 2)$ and $(4, -3)$ undefined

1D. the line containing $(-3, 3)$ and $(4, 3)$ 0

Example 1 illustrates the four different types of slopes.

ConceptSummary Classifying Slopes

Positive Slope	Negative Slope	Zero Slope	Undefined Slope
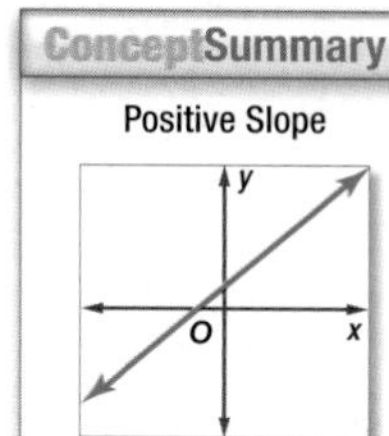	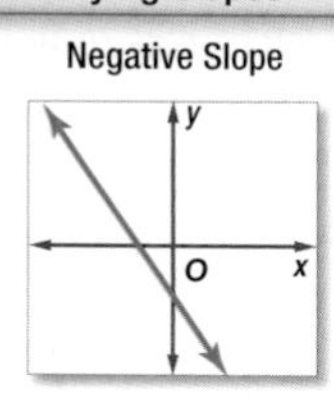	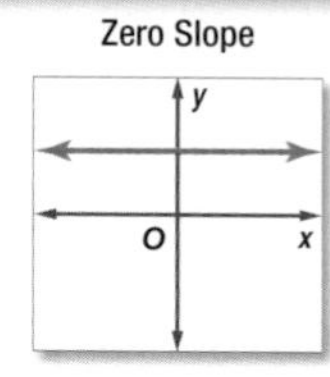	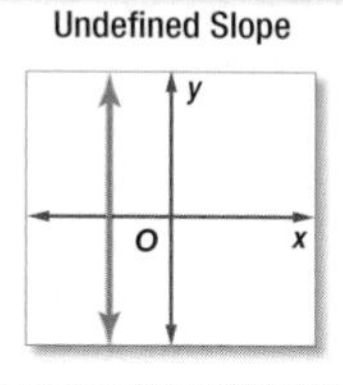

Slope can be interpreted as a **rate of change**, describing how a quantity y changes in relation to quantity x. The slope of a line can also be used to identify the coordinates of any point on the line.

Formative Assessment

Use the Guided Practice exercises after each example to determine students' understanding of concepts.

Additional Example

1 Find the slope of each line.

a.

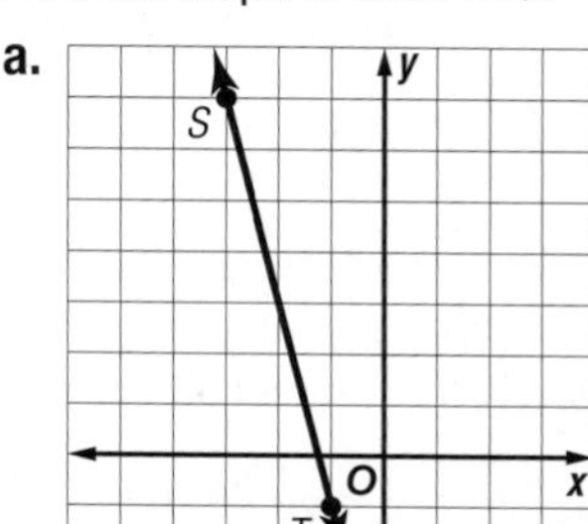

$-\frac{8}{2}$ or -4

b.

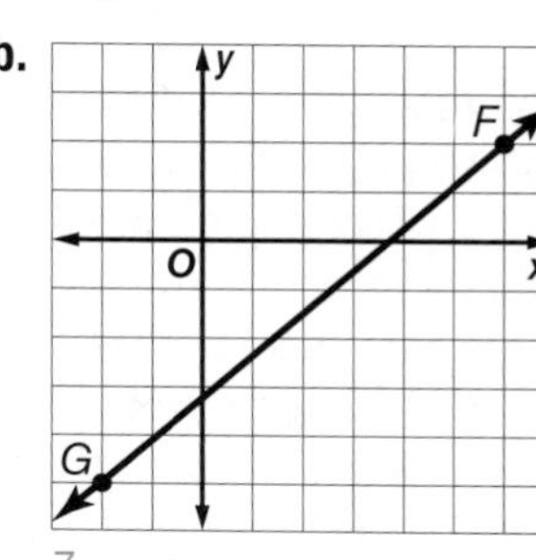

$\frac{7}{8}$

c.

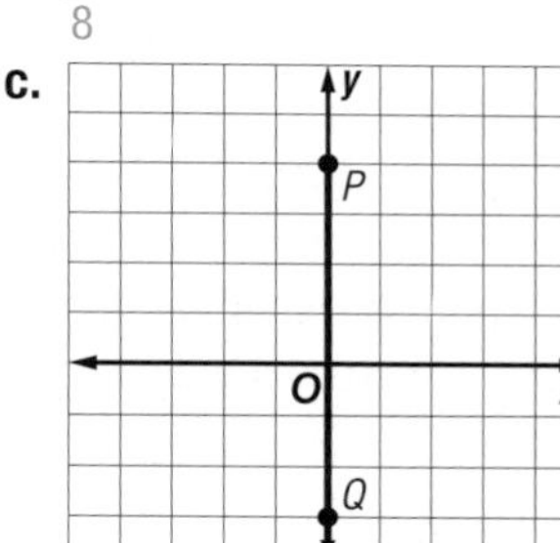

$-\frac{7}{0}$ or undefined

d.

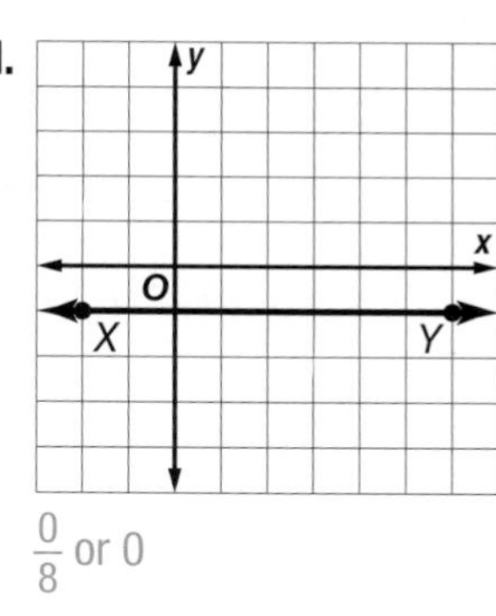

$\frac{0}{8}$ or 0

Focus on Mathematical Content

Slope Formula As long as coordinates from a single ordered pair are placed in the slope formula in the same order, the value of the slope will not change. In Example 1b, have students confirm that the slope of $\overleftrightarrow{LM}$ does not change if they use the ordered pairs in reverse order.

Slope of $\overleftrightarrow{LM}$: $m = \frac{3 - (-3)}{-2 - 1} = -\frac{6}{3}$ or -2

Additional Example

2 **RECREATION** In 2000, the annual sales for one manufacturer of camping equipment was \$48.9 million. In 2005, the total sales were \$85.9 million. If sales increase at the same rate, what will be the total sales in 2015? about \$159.9 million

Additional Examples also in Interactive Classroom PowerPoint® Presentations

Tips for New Teachers

Sense-Making Have students draw a line on graph paper (through two points) that has a positive slope, a negative slope, a slope of zero, and an undefined slope. Next, have them find the slope of each line. Then have students explain how you can determine visually whether the slope of a line will be positive, negative, zero, or undefined.

Teach with Tech

Video On your favorite video sharing site, have students search for a rap or song to help them remember the Slope Formula. One such song can be sung to the tune of "Row, Row, Row Your Boat."

m equals *y* sub 2
Minus *y* sub 1
All over *x* sub 2
Minus *x* sub 1.

Real-WorldCareer

Flight Attendants Flight attendants check tickets, assist passengers with boarding and carry-ons, and provide an overview of emergency equipment and procedures. A high school diploma is required, but airlines increasingly favor bi- or multi-lingual candidates with college degrees.

PT

Real-World Example 2 Use Slope as Rate of Change

TRAVEL A pilot flies a plane from Columbus, Ohio, to Orlando, Florida. After 0.5 hour, the plane reaches its cruising altitude and is 620 miles from Orlando. Half an hour later, the plane is 450 miles from Orlando. How far was the plane from Orlando 1.25 hours after takeoff?

Understand Use the data given to graph the line that models the distance from Orlando y in miles as a function of time x in hours.

Assume that speed is constant. Plot the points (0.5, 620) and (1.0, 450), and draw a line through them.

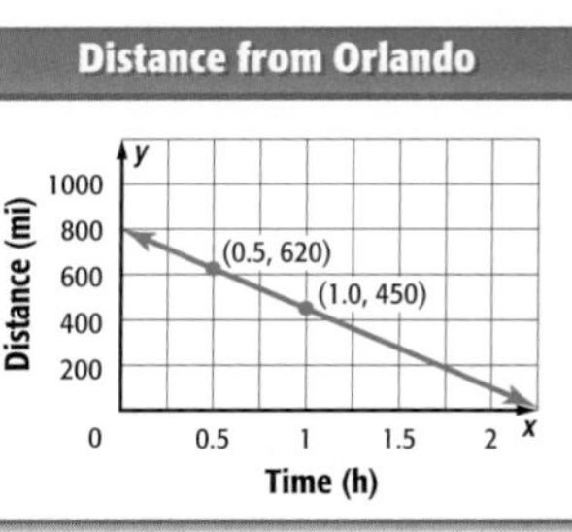

You want to find the distance from Orlando after 1.25 hours.

From the graph we can estimate that after 1.25 hours, the distance was a little less than 400 miles.

Plan Find the slope of the line graphed. Use this rate of change in the plane's distance from Orlando per hour to find the distance from Orlando after 1.25 hours.

Solve Use the Slope Formula to find the slope of the line.

$$m = \frac{y_2 - y_1}{x_2 - x_1} = \frac{(450 - 620) \text{ miles}}{(1.0 - 0.5) \text{ hours}} = \frac{-170 \text{ miles}}{0.5 \text{ hour}} \text{ or } -\frac{340 \text{ miles}}{1 \text{ hour}}$$

The plane traveled at an average speed of 340 miles per hour. The negative sign indicates a *decrease* in distance over time.

Use the slope of the line and one known point on the line to calculate the distance y when the time x is 1.25.

$m = \frac{y_2 - y_1}{x_2 - x_1}$ Slope Formula

$-340 = \frac{y_2 - 620}{1.25 - 0.5}$ $m = -340$, $x_1 = 0.5$, $y_1 = 620$, and $x_2 = 1.25$

$-340 = \frac{y_2 - 620}{0.75}$ Simplify.

$-255 = y_2 - 620$ Multiply each side by 0.75.

$365 = y_2$ Add 620 to each side.

Thus, the distance from Orlando after 1.25 hours is 365 miles.

Check Since 365 is close to the estimate, our answer is reasonable. ✓

GuidedPractice

2B. 150; The number of songs downloaded legally increased by 150 million songs per year.

2. DOWNLOADS In 2006, 500 million songs were legally downloaded from the Internet. In 2004, 200 million songs were legally downloaded.

A. Use the data given to graph the line that models the number of songs legally downloaded y as a function of time x in years. See margin.

B. Find the slope of the line, and interpret its meaning.

C. If this trend continues at the same rate, how many songs will be legally downloaded in 2020? 2.6 billion songs

WatchOut!

Negative Coordinates Tell students to be careful when calculating slope of points that contain negative coordinates. Students should write the complete formula for slope, substitute the coordinates, and then simplify.

Additional Answer (Guided Practice)

2A.

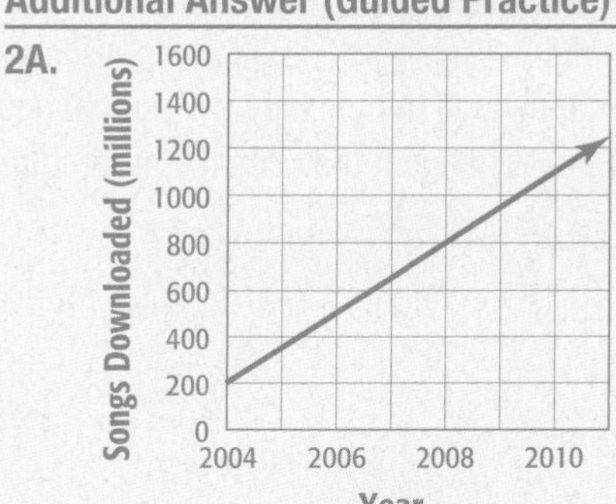

2 Parallel and Perpendicular Lines

Parallel and Perpendicular Lines You can use the slopes of two lines to determine whether the lines are parallel or perpendicular. Lines with the same slope are parallel.

Postulates Parallel and Perpendicular Lines

3.2 Slopes of Parallel Lines Two nonvertical lines have the same slope if and only if they are parallel. All vertical lines are parallel.

Example Parallel lines ℓ and m have the same slope, 4.

3.3 Slopes of Perpendicular Lines Two nonvertical lines are perpendicular if and only if the product of their slopes is -1. Vertical and horizontal lines are perpendicular.

Example line $m \perp$ line p
product of slopes $= 4 \cdot -\frac{1}{4}$ or -1

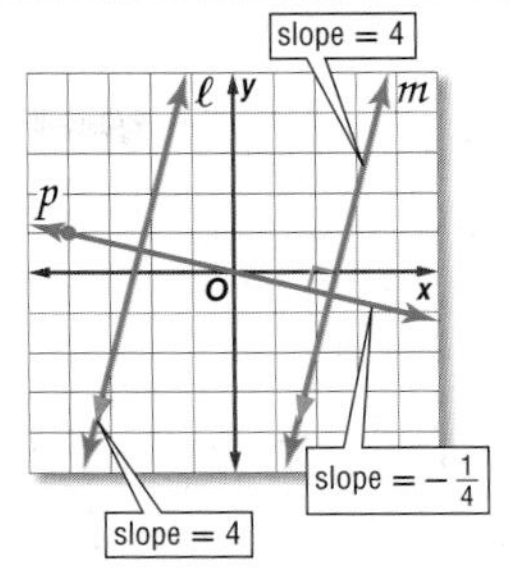

Example 3 Determine Line Relationships

Determine whether $\overleftrightarrow{AB}$ and $\overleftrightarrow{CD}$ are *parallel, perpendicular,* or *neither* for $A(1, 1)$, $B(-1, -5)$, $C(3, 2)$, and $D(6, 1)$. Graph each line to verify your answer.

Step 1 Find the slope of each line.

slope of $\overleftrightarrow{AB} = \frac{-5-1}{-1-1} = \frac{-6}{-2}$ or 3 slope of $\overleftrightarrow{CD} = \frac{1-2}{6-3}$ or $\frac{-1}{3}$

Step 2 Determine the relationship, if any, between the lines.

The two lines do not have the same slope, so they are *not* parallel. To determine if the lines are perpendicular, find the product of their slopes.

$3\left(-\frac{1}{3}\right) = -1$ Product of slopes for $\overleftrightarrow{AB}$ and $\overleftrightarrow{CD}$

Since the product of their slopes is -1, $\overleftrightarrow{AB}$ is perpendicular to $\overleftrightarrow{CD}$.

CHECK When graphed, the two lines appear to intersect and form four right angles. ✔

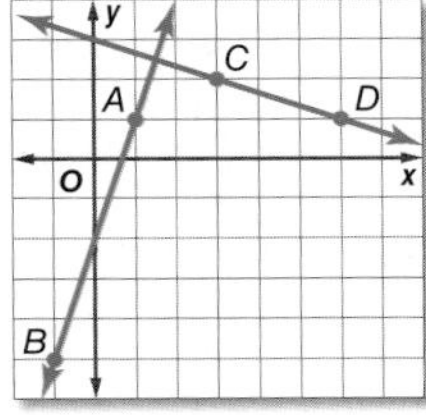

StudyTip

Slopes of Perpendiculars If a line ℓ has a slope of $\frac{a}{b}$, then the slope of a line perpendicular to line ℓ is the opposite reciprocal, $-\frac{b}{a}$, since $\frac{a}{b}\left(-\frac{b}{a}\right) = -1$.

Guided Practice

Determine whether $\overleftrightarrow{AB}$ and $\overleftrightarrow{CD}$ are *parallel, perpendicular,* or *neither.* Graph each line to verify your answer.

3A. $A(14, 13)$, $B(-11, 0)$, $C(-3, 7)$, $D(-4, -5)$ **3A–3B. See margin.**

3B. $A(3, 6)$, $B(-9, 2)$, $C(5, 4)$, $D(2, 3)$

2 Parallel and Perpendicular Lines

Example 3 shows how to determine whether lines are parallel, perpendicular, or neither. **Example 4** shows how to use slope to graph a line.

Additional Example

3 Determine whether $\overleftrightarrow{FG}$ and $\overleftrightarrow{HJ}$ are *parallel, perpendicular,* or *neither* for $F(1, -3)$, $G(-2, -1)$, $H(5, 0)$, and $J(6, 3)$. Graph each line to verify your answer.

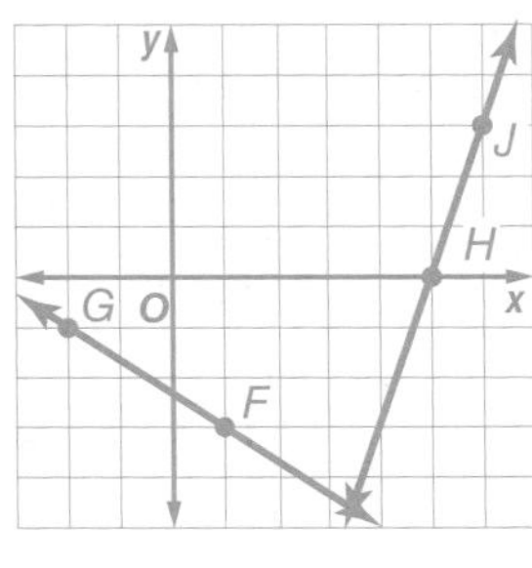

neither

Additional Answers (Guided Practice)

3A. neither

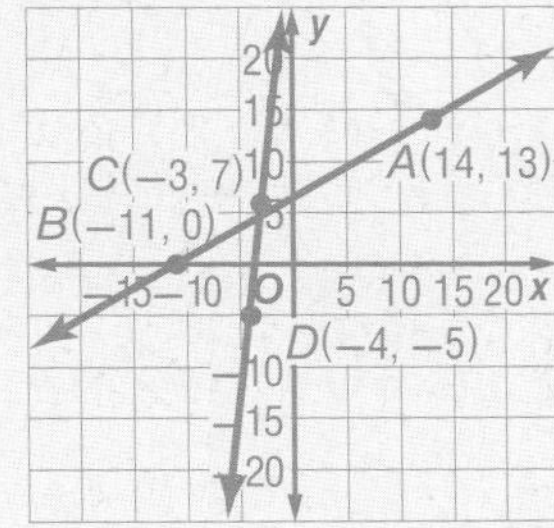

3B. parallel

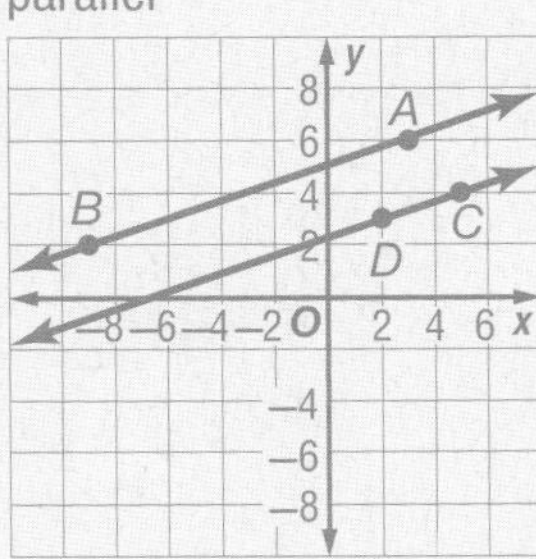

Additional Example

4 Graph the line that contains $Q(5, 1)$ and is parallel to $\overleftrightarrow{MN}$ with $M(-2, 4)$ and $N(2, 1)$.

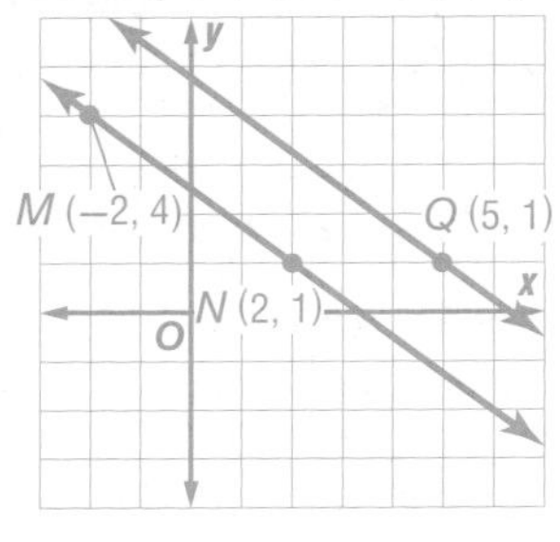

Additional Answer (Guided Practice)

4.

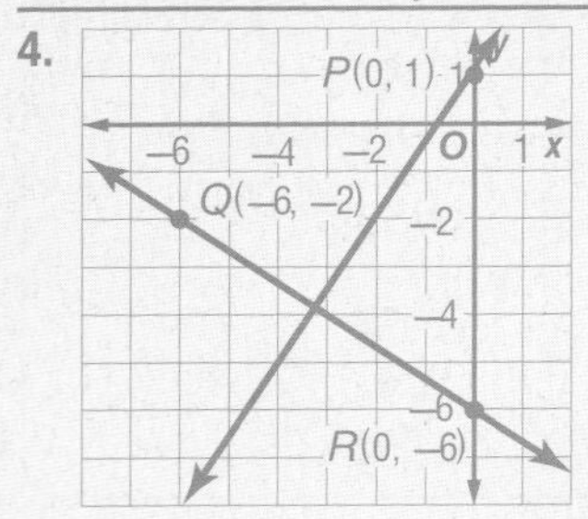

Additional Answers

4a.

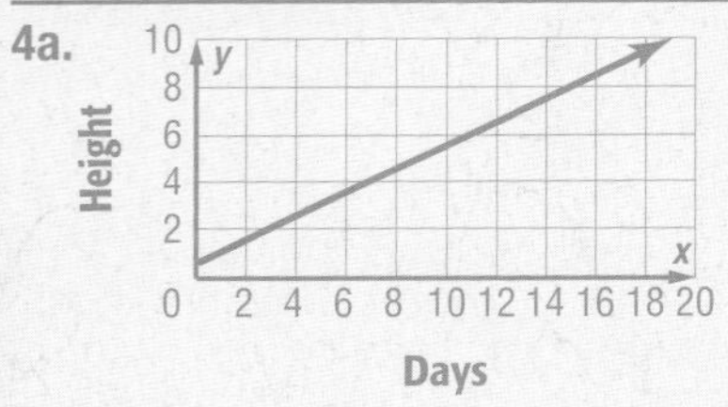

5–8. See Ch. 3 Answer Appendix for graphs.

5. perpendicular
6. neither
7. parallel
8. perpendicular

Example 4 Use Slope to Graph a Line

Graph the line that contains $A(-3, 0)$ and is perpendicular to $\overleftrightarrow{CD}$ with $C(-2, -3)$ and $D(2, 0)$.

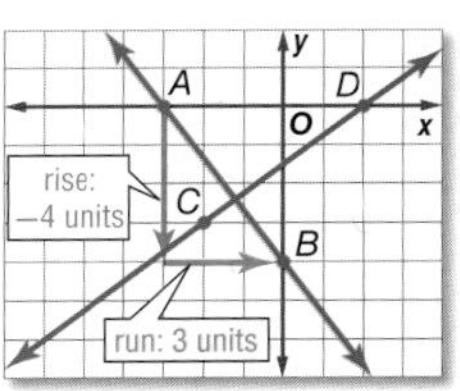

The slope of $\overleftrightarrow{CD}$ is $\frac{0-(-3)}{2-(-2)}$ or $\frac{3}{4}$.

Since $\frac{3}{4}\left(\frac{4}{-3}\right) = -1$, the slope of the line perpendicular to $\overleftrightarrow{CD}$ through A is $-\frac{4}{3}$ or $\frac{-4}{3}$.

To graph the line, start at point A. Move down 4 units and then right 3 units. Label the point B and draw $\overleftrightarrow{AB}$.

GuidedPractice

4. Graph the line that contains $P(0, 1)$ and is perpendicular to $\overleftrightarrow{QR}$ with $Q(-6, -2)$ and $R(0, -6)$. See margin.

Check Your Understanding

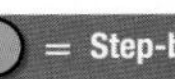 = Step-by-Step Solutions begin on page R14.

Example 1 **Find the slope of each line.**

1.

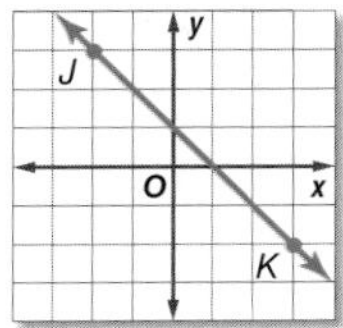

−1

2.

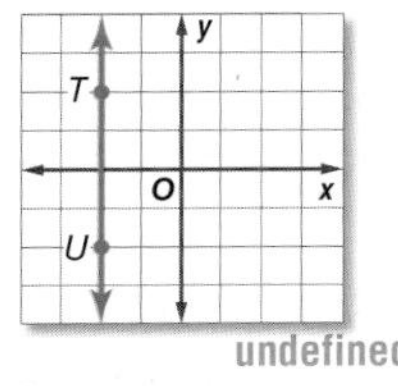

undefined

3.

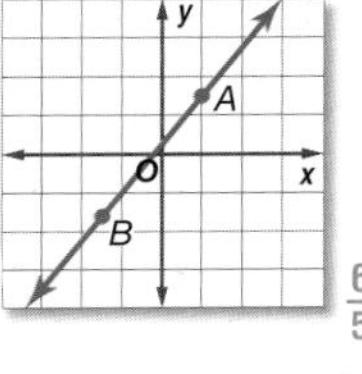

$\frac{6}{5}$

Example 2 **4. BOTANY** Kudzu is a fast-growing vine found in the southeastern United States. An initial measurement of the length of a kudzu vine was 0.5 meter. Seven days later the plant was 4 meters long.

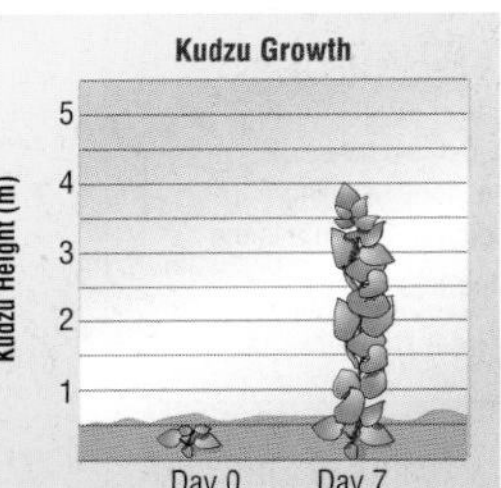

a. Graph the line that models the length of the plant over time. See margin.

b. What is the slope of your graph? What does it represent? $\frac{1}{2}$; The plant grows 0.5 m a day.

c. Assuming that the growth rate of the plant continues, how long will the plant be after 15 days? 8 m

Example 3 **Determine whether $\overleftrightarrow{WX}$ and $\overleftrightarrow{YZ}$ are *parallel*, *perpendicular*, or *neither*. Graph each line to verify your answer.** 5–8. See margin.

5. $W(2, 4)$, $X(4, 5)$, $Y(4, 1)$, $Z(8, -7)$

6. $W(1, 3)$, $X(-2, -5)$, $Y(-6, -2)$, $Z(8, 3)$

7. $W(-7, 6)$, $X(-6, 9)$, $Y(6, 3)$, $Z(3, -6)$

8. $W(1, -3)$, $X(0, 2)$, $Y(-2, 0)$, $Z(8, 2)$

Example 4 **Graph the line that satisfies each condition.** 9–11. See Ch. 3 Answer Appendix.

9. passes through $A(3, -4)$, parallel to $\overleftrightarrow{BC}$ with $B(2, 4)$ and $C(5, 6)$

10. slope = 3, passes through $A(-1, 4)$

11. passes through $P(7, 3)$, perpendicular to $\overleftrightarrow{LM}$ with $L(-2, -3)$ and $M(-1, 5)$

DifferentiatedInstruction AL OL

 students have a difficult time remembering the meanings of values of slopes,

 have students sing a simple song about the different lines that have positive, negative, zero, or an undefined slope.

Practice and Problem Solving

Extra Practice is on page R3.

Example 1 **Find the slope of each line.**

12. 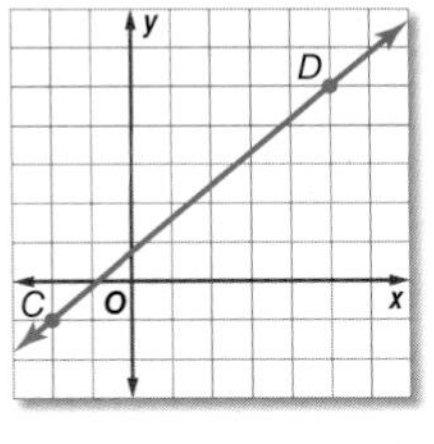 $\frac{6}{7}$

13. 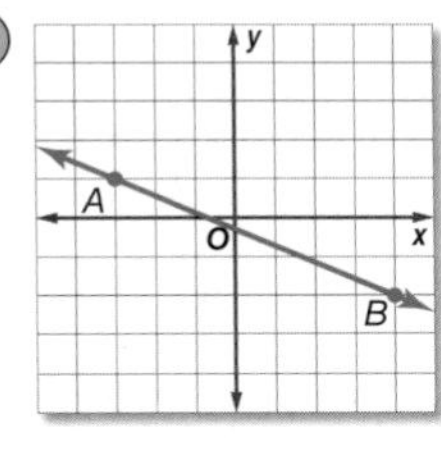 $-\frac{3}{7}$

14. 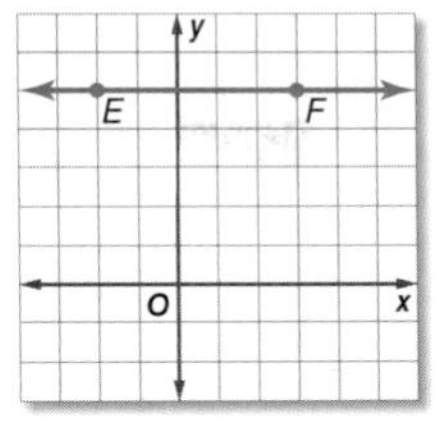 0

15. 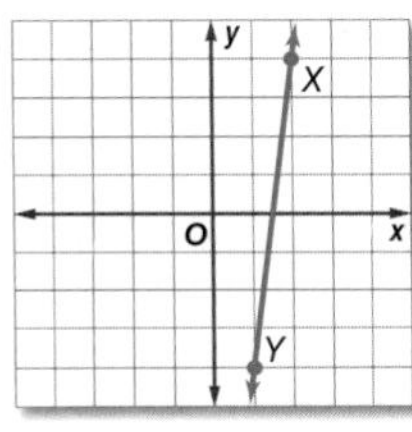 8

16. 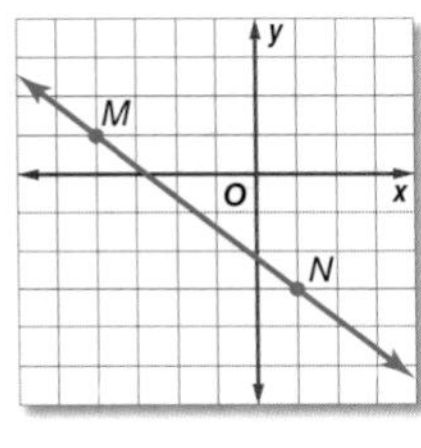 $-\frac{4}{5}$

17. 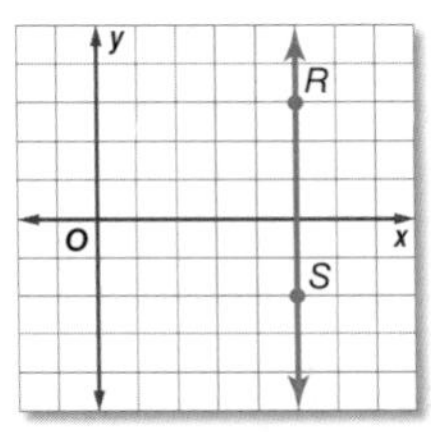 undefined

Determine the slope of the line that contains the given points.

18. $C(3, 1), D(-2, 1)$ 0

19. $E(5, -1), F(2, -4)$ 1

20. $G(-4, 3), H(-4, 7)$ undefined

21. $J(7, -3), K(-8, -3)$ 0

22. $L(8, -3), M(-4, -12)$ $\frac{3}{4}$

23. $P(-3, -5), Q(-3, -1)$ undefined

24. $R(2, -6), S(-6, 5)$ $-\frac{11}{8}$

25. $T(-6, -11), V(-12, -10)$ $-\frac{1}{6}$

Example 2 **26.** CCSS **MODELING** In 2004, 8 million Americans over the age of 7 participated in mountain biking, and in 2006, 8.5 million participated.

a. Create a graph to show the number of participants in mountain biking based on the change in participation from 2004 to 2006. See margin.

b. Based on the data, what is the growth per year of the sport? 250,000 people per year

c. If participation continues at the same rate, what will be the participation in 2013 to the nearest 10,000? 10,250,000

27. **FINANCIAL LITERACY** Suppose an MP3 player cost \$499 in 2003 and \$249.99 in 2009.

a. Graph a trend line to predict the price of the MP3 player for 2003 through 2009. See margin.

b. Based on the data, how much does the price drop per year? \$41.50

c. If the trend continues, what will be the cost of an MP3 player in 2013? \$84

Example 3 **Determine whether $\overleftrightarrow{AB}$ and $\overleftrightarrow{CD}$ are *parallel, perpendicular,* or *neither.* Graph each line to verify your answer.** 28–33. See margin.

28. $A(1, 5), B(4, 4), C(9, -10), D(-6, -5)$

29. $A(-6, -9), B(8, 19), C(0, -4), D(2, 0)$

30. $A(4, 2), B(-3, 1), C(6, 0), D(-10, 8)$

31. $A(8, -2), B(4, -1), C(3, 11), D(-2, -9)$

32. $A(8, 4), B(4, 3), C(4, -9), D(2, -1)$

33. $A(4, -2), B(-2, -8), C(4, 6), D(8, 5)$

3 Practice

Formative Assessment

Use Exercises 1–11 to check for understanding.

Use the chart at the bottom of this page to customize assignments for your students.

CCSS Teaching the Mathematical Practices

Modeling Mathematically proficient students can apply the mathematics they know to solve problems arising in the real world. They also routinely interpret their results in the context of the situation. In Exercise 26, encourage students to explain the relationship of slope to the price drop per year.

26a.

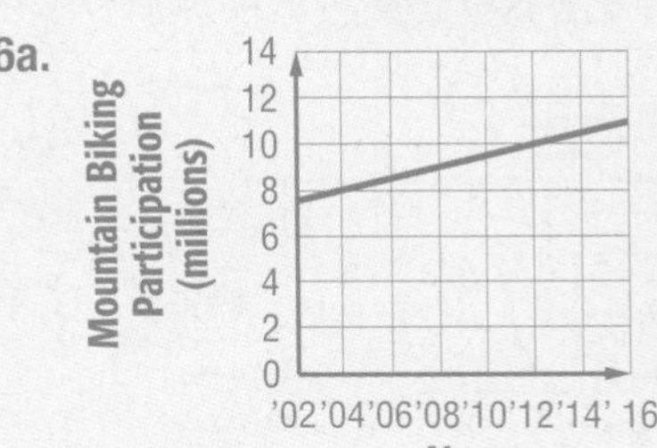

27a.

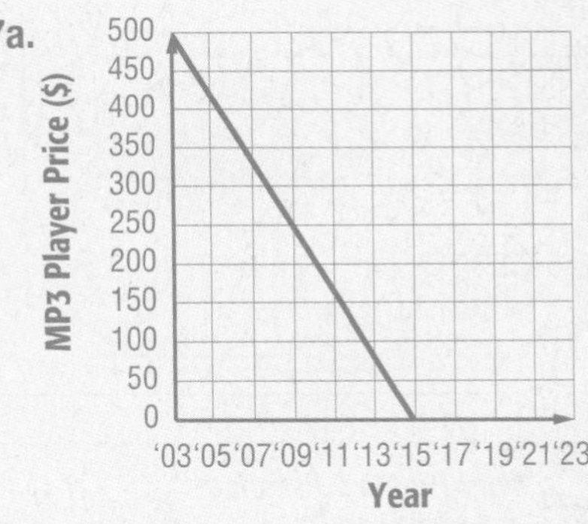

28–33. See Ch. 3 Answer Appendix for graphs.

28. parallel

29. parallel

30. neither

31. perpendicular

32. perpendicular

33. neither

Differentiated Homework Options

Level	Assignment	Two-Day Option	
AL Basic	12–39, 52–55, 57–74	13–39 odd, 58–61	12–38 even, 52–55, 57, 62–74
OL Core	13–49 odd, 50–55, 57–74	12–39, 58–61	40–55, 57, 62–74
BL Advanced	40–71, (optional: 72–74)		

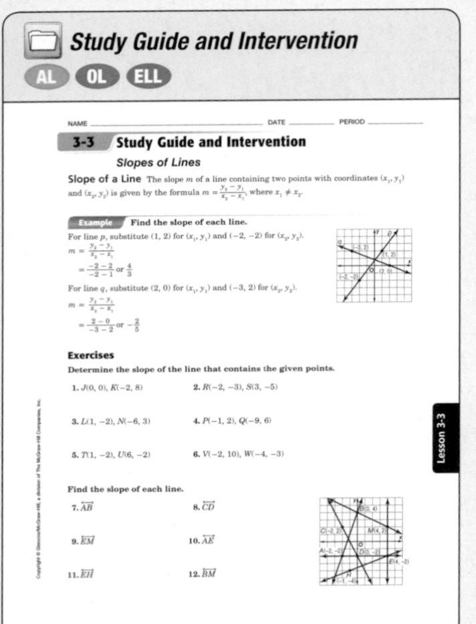

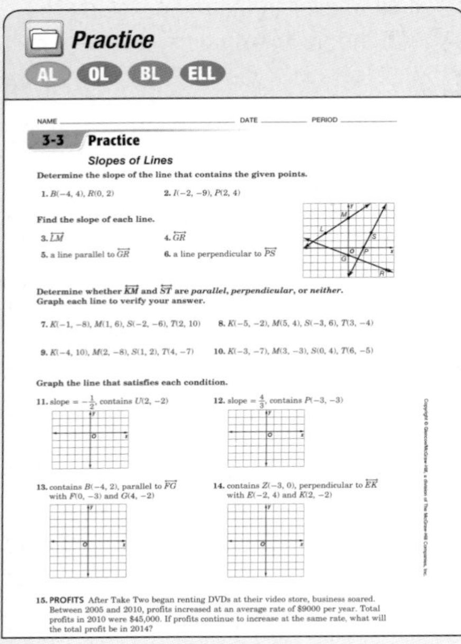

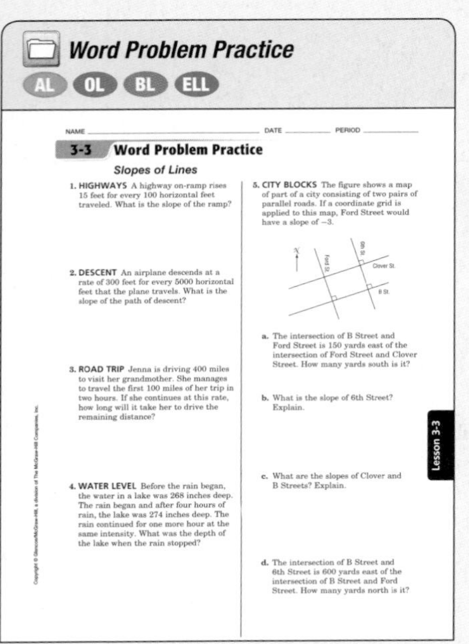

Example 4 **Graph the line that satisfies each condition.** 34–39. See Ch. 3 Answer Appendix.

34. passes through $A(2, -5)$, parallel to $\overleftrightarrow{BC}$ with $B(1, 3)$ and $C(4, 5)$

35. slope $= -2$, passes through $H(-2, -4)$

36. passes through $K(3, 7)$, perpendicular to $\overleftrightarrow{LM}$ with $L(-1, -2)$ and $M(-4, 8)$

37. passes through $X(1, -4)$, parallel to $\overleftrightarrow{YZ}$ with $Y(5, 2)$ and $Z(-3, -5)$

38. slope $= \frac{2}{3}$, passes through $J(-5, 4)$

39. passes through $D(-5, -6)$, perpendicular to $\overleftrightarrow{FG}$ with $F(-2, -9)$ and $G(1, -5)$

40. STADIUMS Before it was demolished, the RCA Dome was home to the Indianapolis Colts. The attendance in 2001 was 450,746, and the attendance in 2005 was 457,373.

B

a. What is the approximate rate of change in attendance from 2001 to 2005? 1657

b. If this rate of change continues, predict the attendance for 2012. 468,973

c. Will the attendance continue to increase indefinitely? Explain.

d. The Colts have now built a new, larger stadium. Do you think their decision was reasonable? Why or why not?

40c. No; the attendance can only continue to increase until the capacity of the stadium is reached.

40d. Sample answer: Yes; since their attendance is growing, a new stadium will allow them to accommodate more fans.

Determine which line passing through the given points has a steeper slope.

41. Line 1: (0, 5) and (6, 1) Line 2
Line 2: (−4, 10) and (8, −5)

42. Line 1: (0, −4) and (2, 2) Line 1
Line 2: (0, −4) and (4, 5)

43. Line 1: (−9, −4) and (7, 0) Line 2
Line 2: (0, 1) and (7, 4)

44. Line 1: (−6, 7) and (9, −3) Line 1
Line 2: (−9, 9) and (3, 5)

45. CCSS MODELING Michigan provides habitat for two endangered species, the bald eagle and the gray wolf. The graph shows the Michigan population of each species in 1992 and 2006.

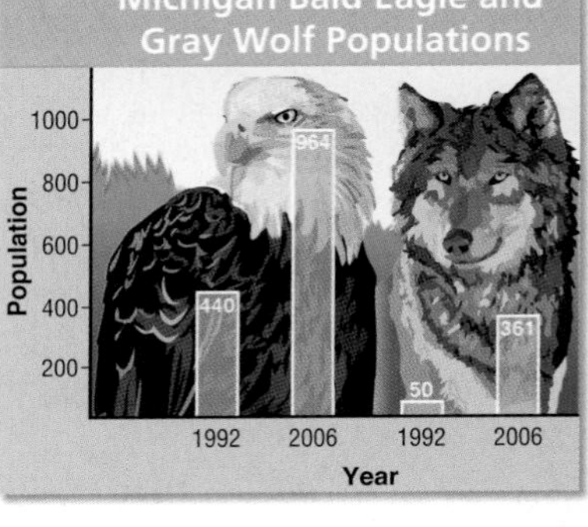

a. Which species experienced a greater rate of change in population? the bald eagle

b. Make a line graph showing the growth of both populations. See Ch. 3 Answer Appendix.

c. If both species continue to grow at their respective rates, what will the population of each species be in 2012? 1189 bald eagles; 494 gray wolves

Find the value of x or y that satisfies the given conditions. Then graph the line. 46–49. See Ch. 3 Answer Appendix.

46. The line containing $(4, -1)$ and $(x, -6)$ has a slope of $-\frac{5}{2}$.

47. The line containing $(-4, 9)$ and $(4, 3)$ is parallel to the line containing $(-8, 1)$ and $(4, y)$.

48. The line containing $(8, 7)$ and $(7, -6)$ is perpendicular to the line containing $(2, 4)$ and $(x, 3)$.

49. The line containing $(1, -3)$ and $(3, y)$ is parallel to the line containing $(5, -6)$ and $(9, y)$.

50. SCHOOLS In 2000, Jefferson High School had 1125 students. By 2006, the student body had increased to 1425 students. When Fairview High School was built in 2001, it had 1275 students. How many students did Fairview High School have in 2006 if the student body grew at the same rate as Jefferson High School? 1525 students

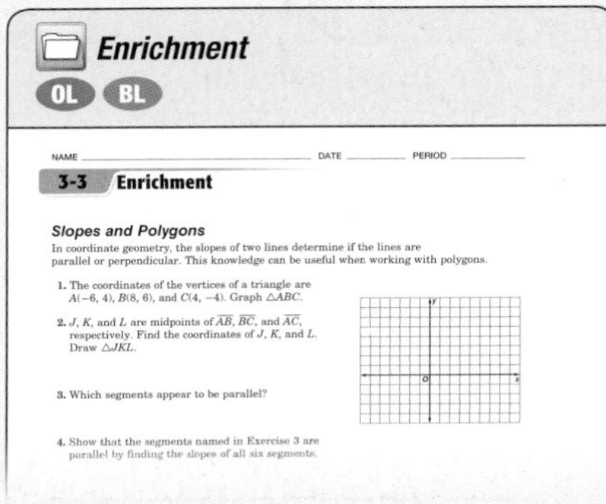

CCSS Teaching the Mathematical Practices

Modeling Mathematically proficient students can apply the mathematics they know to solve problems arising in the real world. They also routinely interpret their results in the context of the situation. In Exercise 45, encourage students to explain how the concept of slope is useful for situations in which future predictions are needed.

51 **MUSIC** Maggie and Mikayla want to go to the music store near Maggie's house after school. They can walk 3.5 miles per hour and ride their bikes 10 miles per hour. **51a–b. See margin.**

a. Create a table to show how far Maggie and Mikayla can travel walking and riding their bikes. Include distances for 0, 1, 2, 3, and 4 hours.

b. Create a graph to show how far Maggie and Mikayla can travel based on time for both walking and riding their bikes. Be sure to label the axes of your graph.

c. What does the slope represent in your graph? **their speed**

d. Maggie's mom says they can only go if they can make it to the music store and back in less than two hours. If they want to spend at least 30 minutes in the music store and it is four miles away, can they make it? Should they walk or ride their bikes? Explain your reasoning. **See margin.**

H.O.T. Problems Use Higher-Order Thinking Skills

52. WRITE A QUESTION A classmate says that all lines have positive or negative slope. Write a question that would challenge his conjecture. **Sample answer: What about vertical lines?**

53. ERROR ANALYSIS Terrell and Hale calculated the slope of the line passing through the points $Q(3, 5)$ and $R(-2, 2)$. Is either of them correct? Explain your reasoning.

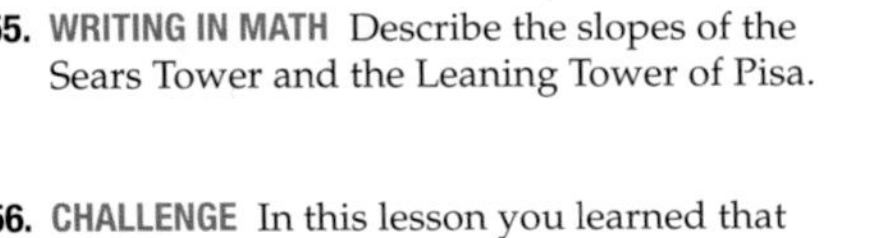

Terrell; Hale subtracted the x-coordinates in the wrong order.

54c. Sample answer: Since the slope of $\overline{AB}$ is undefined and the slope of $\overline{BC}$ is zero, the lines are perpendicular to each other. Therefore, the lines form right angles with measures of 90°. The same logic applies to all the sides.

54. CCSS REASONING Draw a square $ABCD$ with opposite vertices at $A(2, -4)$ and $C(10, 4)$.

a. Find the other two vertices of the square and label them B and D.

b. Show that $\overline{AD} \parallel \overline{BC}$ and $\overline{AB} \parallel \overline{DC}$. **a–b. See margin.**

c. Show that the measure of each angle inside the square is equal to 90.

55. The Sears Tower has a vertical or undefined slope and the Leaning Tower of Pisa has a positive slope.

55. WRITING IN MATH Describe the slopes of the Sears Tower and the Leaning Tower of Pisa.

Sears Tower

Leaning Tower of Pisa

56. CHALLENGE In this lesson you learned that $m = \frac{y_2 - y_1}{x_2 - x_1}$. Use an algebraic proof to show that the slope can also be calculated using the equation $m = \frac{y_1 - y_2}{x_1 - x_2}$.

56–57. See Ch. 3 Answer Appendix.

57. WRITING IN MATH Find two additional points that lie along the same line as $X(3, -1)$ and $Y(-1, 7)$. Generalize a method you can use to find additional points on the line from any given point.

Differentiated Instruction AL OL BL ELL

Extension Have students graph $y = x^2$ on a coordinate plane. They can use a graphing calculator to generate the graph. Explain that a tangent line intersects the graph in one place. Have them predict where the tangent line of their function will be located. Have them sketch the line and predict the slope of the line. Explain to students that they will learn more about tangent lines to functions as they begin their study of calculus.

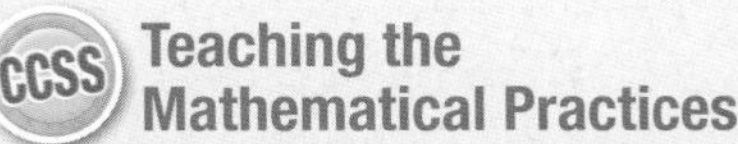

CCSS Teaching the Mathematical Practices

Reasoning Mathematically proficient students make sense of quantities and their relationships in problem situations. In Exercise 54, encourage students to use graph paper to graph the vertices given and to draw the square.

Additional Answers

51a.

Time (hours)	Distance Walking (miles)	Distance Riding Bikes (miles)
0	0	0
1	3.5	10
2	7	20
3	10.5	30
4	14	40

51b.

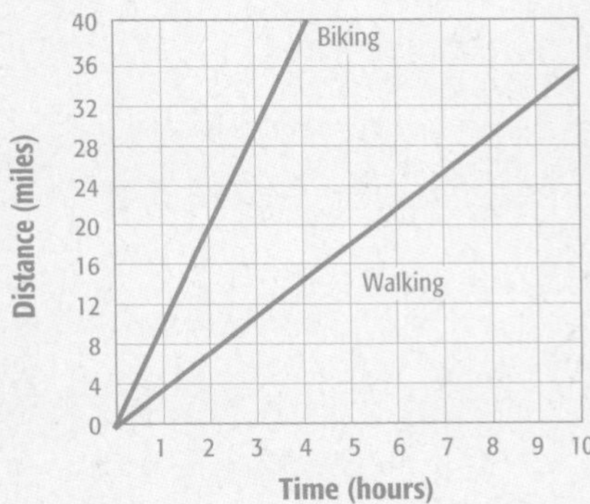

51d. Sample answer: Yes, they can make it if they ride their bikes. If they walk, it takes over two hours to go eight miles, so they wouldn't be home in time and they wouldn't get to spend any time in the store. If they ride their bikes, they can travel there in 24 minutes. If they spend 30 minutes in the store and spend 24 minutes riding home, the total amount of time they will use is 24 + 30 + 24 = 78 minutes, which is 1 hour and 18 minutes.

54a. Sample answer: $B(2, 4)$ and $D(10, -4)$

54b. Sample answer: The slopes of $\overline{AB}$ and $\overline{DC}$ are undefined, so they are parallel to each other. The slopes of $\overline{AD}$ and $\overline{BC}$ are 0, so they are parallel to each other.

4 Assess

Name the Math Have students write a paragraph explaining how to use the slopes of two lines to determine whether they are perpendicular.

Formative Assessment
Check for student understanding of Lesson 3-3.

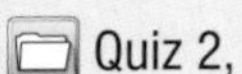 Quiz 2, p. 45

Standardized Test Practice

58. What is the slope of a line perpendicular to the line through the points $(-1, 6)$ and $(3, -4)$? D

A $m = -\frac{5}{2}$

B $m = -1$

C $m = -\frac{2}{5}$

D $m = \frac{2}{5}$

59. SHORT RESPONSE A set of 25 cards is randomly placed face down on a table. 15 cards have only the letter A written on the face, and 10 cards have only the letter B. Patrick turned over 1 card. What is the probability of this card having the letter B written on its face? 2:5

60. ALGEBRA Jamie is collecting money to buy an $81 gift for her teacher. She has already contributed $24. She will collect $3 from each contributing student. How many other students must contribute? J

F 3 students

G 9 students

H 12 students

J 19 students

61. SAT/ACT The area of a circle is 20π square centimeters. What is its circumference? C

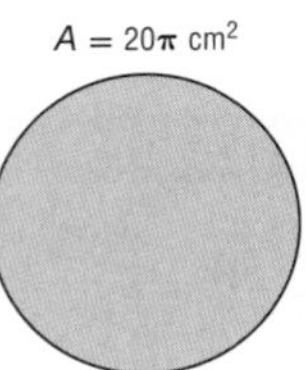

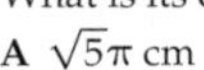

A $\sqrt{5}\pi$ cm

B $2\sqrt{5}\pi$ cm

C $4\sqrt{5}\pi$ cm

D 20π cm

E 40π cm

Spiral Review

In the figure, $a \parallel b$, $c \parallel d$, and $m\angle 4 = 57$. Find the measure of each angle. (Lesson 3-2)

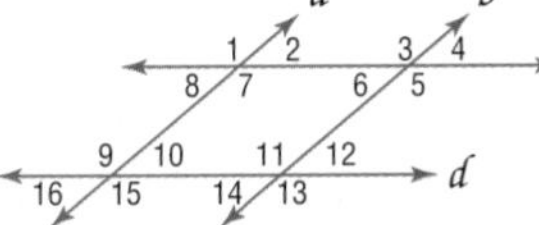

62. $\angle 5$ 123

63. $\angle 1$ 123

64. $\angle 8$ 57

65. $\angle 10$ 57

Refer to the diagram at the right. (Lesson 3-1)

66. Name all segments parallel to $\overline{TU}$. $\overline{BC}$, $\overline{EF}$, $\overline{QR}$

67. Name all planes intersecting plane BCR.

68. Name all segments skew to $\overline{DE}$. $\overline{AP}$, $\overline{BQ}$, $\overline{CR}$, $\overline{FU}$, $\overline{PU}$, $\overline{QR}$, $\overline{RS}$, $\overline{TU}$

67. *ABC, ABQ, PQR, CDS, APU, DET*

Determine whether the stated conclusion is valid based on the given information. If not, write *invalid*. Explain your reasoning. (Lesson 2-4)

69. Given: $\angle B$ and $\angle C$ are vertical angles.
Conclusion: $\angle B \cong \angle C$ valid

70. Given: $\angle W \cong \angle Y$
Conclusion: $\angle W$ and $\angle Y$ are vertical angles.
Invalid; congruent angles do not have to be vertical.

71. CONSTRUCTION There are four buildings on the Mansfield High School Campus, no three of which stand in a straight line. How many sidewalks need to be built so that each building is directly connected to every other building? (Lesson 1-1) 6

Skills Review

Solve for y.

72. $3x + y = 5$ $y = -3x + 5$

73. $4x + 2y = 6$ $y = -2x + 3$

74. $4y - 3x = 5$ $y = \frac{3}{4}x + \frac{5}{4}$

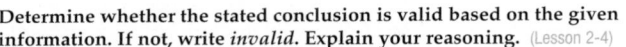

196 | Lesson 3-3 | Slopes of Lines

CHAPTER 3 Mid-Chapter Quiz
Lessons 3-1 through 3-3

Identify the transversal connecting each pair of angles. Then classify the relationship between each pair of angles as *alternate interior, alternate exterior, corresponding,* or *consecutive interior* angles. (Lesson 3-1)

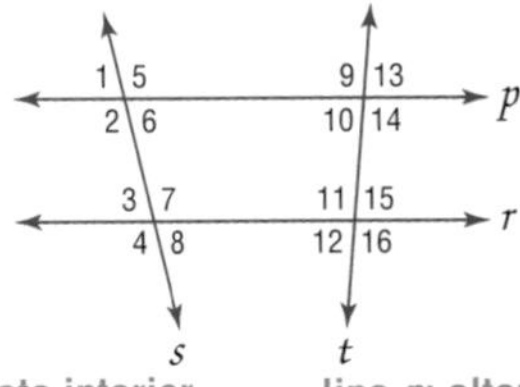

1. ∠6 and ∠3 **line *s*; alternate interior**
2. ∠1 and ∠14 **line *p*; alternate exterior**
3. ∠10 and ∠11 **line *t*; consecutive interior**
4. ∠5 and ∠7 **line *s*; corresponding**

Refer to the figure to identify each of the following. (Lesson 3-1)

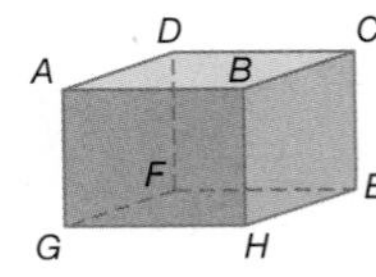

5. a plane parallel to plane *ABCD* **FGHE**
6. a segment skew to $\overline{GH}$ that contains point *D* **$\overline{AD}$, $\overline{DF}$**
7. all segments parallel to $\overline{HE}$ **$\overline{GF}$, $\overline{AD}$, $\overline{BC}$**

8. **MULTIPLE CHOICE** Which term best describes ∠4 and ∠8? (Lesson 3-1) **A**

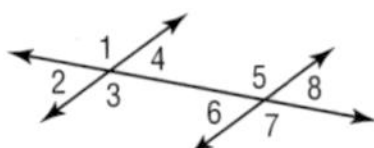

A corresponding
B alternate exterior
C alternate interior
D consecutive interior

In the figure, $m\angle 4 = 104$, $m\angle 14 = 118$. Find the measure of each angle. Tell which postulate(s) or theorem(s) you used. (Lesson 3-2) **9–12. See margin.**

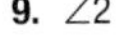

9. ∠2
10. ∠9
11. ∠10
12. ∠7

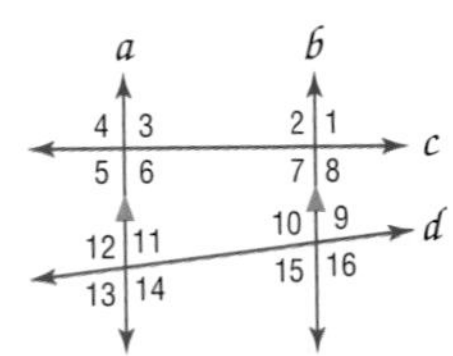

13. Find *x*. (Lesson 3-2) **48**

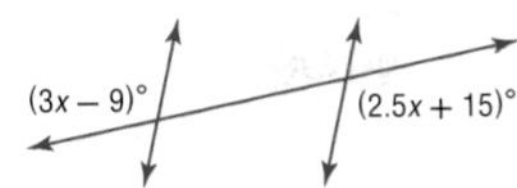

14. **MODEL TRAINS** Amy is setting up two parallel train tracks so that a third track runs diagonally across the first two. To properly place a switch, she needs the angle between the diagonal and the top right portion of the second track to be twice as large as the angle between the diagonal and bottom right portion of the first track. What is the measure of the angle between the diagonal and the top right portion of the second track? (Lesson 3-2) **120**

Determine whether $\overleftrightarrow{AB}$ and $\overleftrightarrow{XY}$ are *parallel, perpendicular,* or *neither*. Graph each line to verify your answer. (Lesson 3-3)

15. *A*(2, 0), *B*(4, −5), *X*(−3, 3), *Y*(−5, 8)
16. *A*(1, 1), *B*(6, −9), *X*(4, −10), *Y*(7, −4)

15–16. See Ch. 3 Answer Appendix.

Find the slope of each line. (Lesson 3-3)

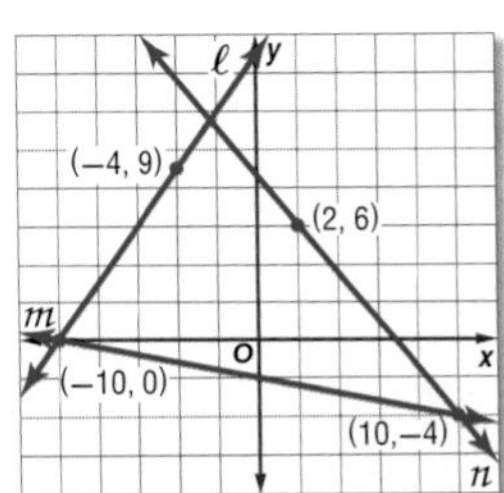

17. line ℓ **$\frac{3}{2}$**
18. a line parallel to *m* **$-\frac{1}{5}$**
19. a line perpendicular to *n* **$\frac{4}{5}$**

20. **SALES** The 2008 and 2011 sales figures for Vaughn Electronics are in the table below. (Lesson 3-3)

Year	Approximate Sales ($)
2008	240,000
2011	330,000

a. What is the rate of change in approximate sales from 2008 to 2011? **$30,000 per year**

b. If this rate of change continues, predict the approximate sales for the year 2015. **$450,000**

Formative Assessment

Use the Mid-Chapter Quiz to assess students' progress in the first half of the chapter.

Have students review the lesson indicated for the problems they answered incorrectly.

Summative Assessment

Mid-Chapter Test, p. 47

Customize and create multiple versions of your Mid-Chapter Quiz and their answer keys.

FOLDABLES® StudyOrganizer

Dinah Zike's Foldables®

Before students complete the Mid-Chapter Quiz, encourage them to review the information they have recorded in their Foldables.

Additional Answers

9. 104; ∠2 ≅ ∠4 by Corr. ∠s Thm.
10. 62; ∠14 is supplementary to ∠15 by Cons. Int ∠s Thm. and ∠15 ≅ ∠9 by Vert. ∠s Thm.
11. 118; ∠14 ≅ ∠10 by Alt. Int. ∠s Thm.
12. 76; ∠4 ≅ ∠6 by Vert. ∠s Thm. and ∠7 is supplementary to ∠6 by Cons. Int. ∠s Thm.

InterventionPlanner

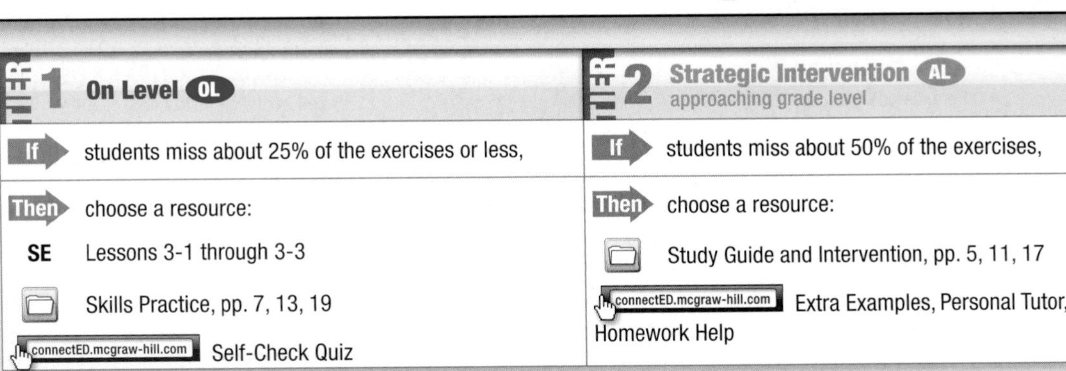

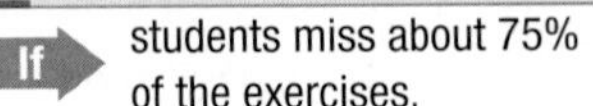

Tier 1 On Level OL	Tier 2 Strategic Intervention AL approaching grade level	Tier 3 Intensive Intervention 2 or more grades below level
If students miss about 25% of the exercises or less,	**If** students miss about 50% of the exercises,	**If** students miss about 75% of the exercises,
Then choose a resource:	**Then** choose a resource:	**Then** use *Math Triumphs, Geo.*, Ch. 4
SE Lessons 3-1 through 3-3	Study Guide and Intervention, pp. 5, 11, 17	connectED.mcgraw-hill.com Extra Examples, Personal Tutor, Homework Help, Review Vocabulary
Skills Practice, pp. 7, 13, 19	connectED.mcgraw-hill.com Extra Examples, Personal Tutor, Homework Help	
connectED.mcgraw-hill.com Self-Check Quiz		

1 Focus

VerticalAlignment

Before Lesson 3-4 Graph and write equations of lines given characteristics such as two points, a point and a slope, or a slope and *y*-intercept.

Lesson 3-4 Write an equation of a line given information about the graph. Solve problems by writing equations.

After Lesson 3-4 Identify and sketch graphs of parent functions, including linear.

2 Teach

Scaffolding Questions

Have students read the **Why?** section of the lesson.

Ask:

- How much is a ticket for traveling 80 miles per hour? \$52.50
- What are two points on the graph of the equation? Sample answer: (10, 42.5), (15, 52.5)
- What is the slope of the line? 2

LESSON 3-4 Equations of Lines

Then

- You found the slopes of lines.

Now

1. Write an equation of a line given information about the graph.
2. Solve problems by writing equations.

Why?

- On an interstate near Lauren's hometown, the minimum fine for speeding ten or fewer miles per hour over the speed limit of 65 miles per hour is \$42.50. There is an additional charge of \$2 for each mile per hour over this initial ten miles per hour. The total charge, not including court costs, can be represented by the equation $C = 42.5 + 2m$.

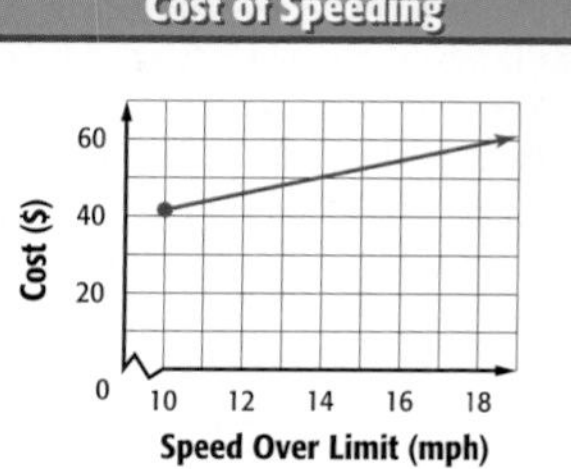

NewVocabulary
slope-intercept form
point-slope form

Common Core State Standards

Content Standards
G.GPE.5 Prove the slope criteria for parallel and perpendicular lines and use them to solve geometric problems (e.g., find the equation of a line parallel or perpendicular to a given line that passes through a given point).

Mathematical Practices
4 Model with mathematics.
8 Look for and express regularity in repeated reasoning.

1 Write Equations of Lines

You may remember from algebra that an equation of a nonvertical line can be written in different but equivalent forms.

KeyConcept Nonvertical Line Equations

The **slope-intercept form** of a linear equation is $y = mx + b$, where m is the slope of the line and b is the y-intercept.

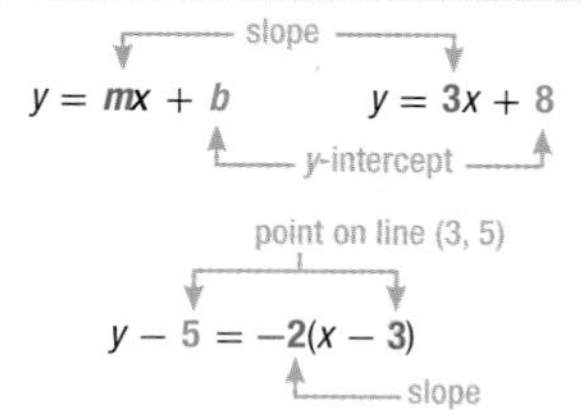

The **point-slope form** of a linear equation is $y - y_1 = m(x - x_1)$, where (x_1, y_1) is any point on the line and m is the slope of the line.

point on line (3, 5)

$y - 5 = -2(x - 3)$

slope

When given the slope and either the y-intercept or a point on a line, you can use these forms to write the equation of the line.

Example 1 Slope and y-intercept

Write an equation in slope-intercept form of the line with slope 3 and *y*-intercept of −2. Then graph the line.

$y = mx + b$	Slope-intercept form
$y = 3x + (-2)$	$m = 3, b = -2$
$y = 3x - 2$	Simplify.

Plot a point at the y-intercept, −2. Use the slope of 3 or $\frac{3}{1}$ to find another point 3 units up and 1 unit to the right of the y-intercept. Then draw the line through these two points.

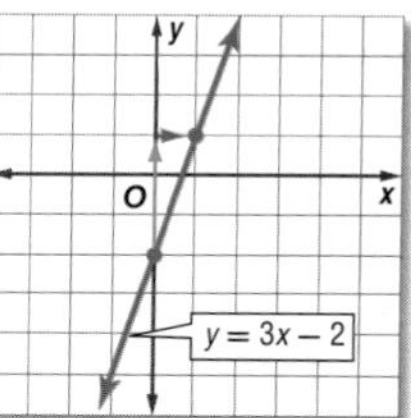

GuidedPractice

1. Write an equation in slope-intercept form of the line with slope $-\frac{1}{2}$ and y-intercept of 8. Then graph the line. See Ch. 3 Answer Appendix.

198 | Lesson 3-4

Lesson 3-4 Resources

Resource	Approaching Level AL	On Level OL	Beyond Level BL	English Learners ELL
Teacher Edition	▪ Differentiated Instruction, p. 200	▪ Differentiated Instruction, pp. 200, 205	▪ Differentiated Instruction, pp. 200, 205	▪ Differentiated Instruction, p. 200
Chapter Resource Masters	▪ Study Guide and Intervention, pp. 24–25 ▪ Skills Practice, p. 26 ▪ Practice, p. 27 ▪ Word Problem Practice, p. 28	▪ Study Guide and Intervention, pp. 24–25 ▪ Skills Practice, p. 26 ▪ Practice, p. 27 ▪ Word Problem Practice, p. 28 ▪ Enrichment, p. 29	▪ Practice, p. 27 ▪ Word Problem Practice, p. 28 ▪ Enrichment, p. 29	▪ Study Guide and Intervention, pp. 24–25 ▪ Skills Practice, p. 26 ▪ Practice, p. 27 ▪ Word Problem Practice, p. 28
Other	▪ 5-Minute Check 3-4 ▪ Study Notebook ▪ Teaching Geometry with Manipulatives	▪ 5-Minute Check 3-4 ▪ Study Notebook ▪ Teaching Geometry with Manipulatives	▪ 5-Minute Check 3-4 ▪ Study Notebook	▪ 5-Minute Check 3-4 ▪ Study Notebook ▪ Teaching Geometry with Manipulatives

Example 2 Slope and a Point on the Line

Write an equation in point-slope form of the line with slope $-\frac{3}{4}$ that contains (−2, 5). Then graph the line.

$y - y_1 = m(x - x_1)$ — Point-Slope form

$y - 5 = -\frac{3}{4}[x - (-2)]$ — $m = -\frac{3}{4}$, $(x_1, y_1) = (-2, 5)$

$y - 5 = -\frac{3}{4}(x + 2)$ — Simplify.

Graph the given point (−2, 5). Use the slope $-\frac{3}{4}$ or $\frac{-3}{4}$ to find another point 3 units down and 4 units to the right. Then draw the line through these two points.

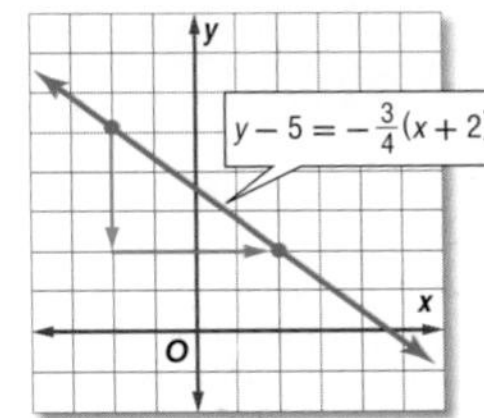

WatchOut!

Substituting Negative Coordinates When substituting negative coordinates, use parentheses to avoid making errors with the signs.

Guided Practice

2. Write an equation in point-slope form of the line with slope 4 that contains (−3, −6). Then graph the line. **See Ch. 3 Answer Appendix.**

When the slope of a line is not given, use two points on the line to calculate the slope. Then use the point-slope or slope-intercept form to write an equation of the line.

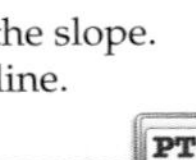

Example 3 Two Points

Write an equation of the line through each pair of points in slope-intercept form.

a. (0, 3) and (−2, −1)

Step 1 Find the slope of the line through the points.

$m = \frac{y_2 - y_1}{x_2 - x_1} = \frac{-1 - 3}{-2 - 0} = \frac{-4}{-2}$ or 2 — Use the Slope Formula.

Step 2 Write an equation of the line.

$y = mx + b$ — Slope-Intercept form

$y = 2x + 3$ — $m = 2$; (0, 3) is the y-intercept.

b. (−7, 4) and (9, −4)

Step 1 $m = \frac{y_2 - y_1}{x_2 - x_1} = \frac{-4 - 4}{9 - (-7)} = \frac{-8}{16}$ or $-\frac{1}{2}$ — Use the Slope Formula.

Step 2 $y - y_1 = m(x - x_1)$ — Point-Slope form

$y - 4 = -\frac{1}{2}[x - (-7)]$ — $m = -\frac{1}{2}$, $(x_1, y_1) = (-7, 4)$

$y - 4 = -\frac{1}{2}(x + 7)$ — Simplify.

$y - 4 = -\frac{1}{2}x - \frac{7}{2}$ — Distribute.

$y = -\frac{1}{2}x + \frac{1}{2}$ — Add 4 to each side: $\frac{7}{2} + 4 = -\frac{7}{2} + \frac{8}{2} = \frac{1}{2}$

StudyTip

CCSS Perseverance In Example 3b, you could also use the slope-intercept form and one point to find the y-intercept and write the equation.

$y = mx + b$
$4 = -\frac{1}{2}(-7) + b$
$4 = \frac{7}{2} + b$
$4 - \frac{7}{2} = b$
$b = \frac{1}{2}$

So, $y = -\frac{1}{2}x + \frac{1}{2}$.

Guided Practice

3A. (−2, 4) and (8, 10) $y = \frac{3}{5}x + \frac{26}{5}$

3B. (−1, 3) and (7, 3) $y = 3$

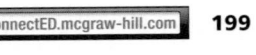

1 Write Equation of Lines

Examples 1–4 show how to write a linear equation using the slope-intercept form or point-slope form of a line. Students should be able to use given values to write a linear equation either in slope-intercept form or point-slope form. **Example 5** shows how to find a line that is perpendicular to a given line through a given point.

Formative Assessment

Use the Guided Practice exercises after each example to determine students' understanding of concepts.

Additional Examples

1 Write an equation in slope-intercept form of the line with slope of 6 and y-intercept of −3. Then graph the line. $y = 6x - 3$

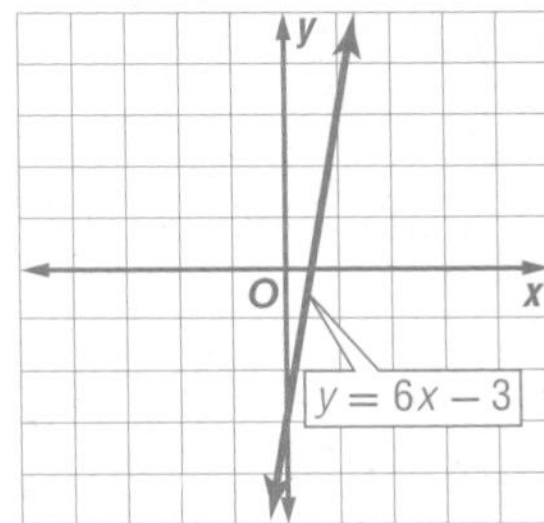

2 Write an equation in point-slope form of the line with slope $-\frac{3}{5}$ that contains (−10, 8). Then graph the line. $y - 8 = -\frac{3}{5}(x + 10)$

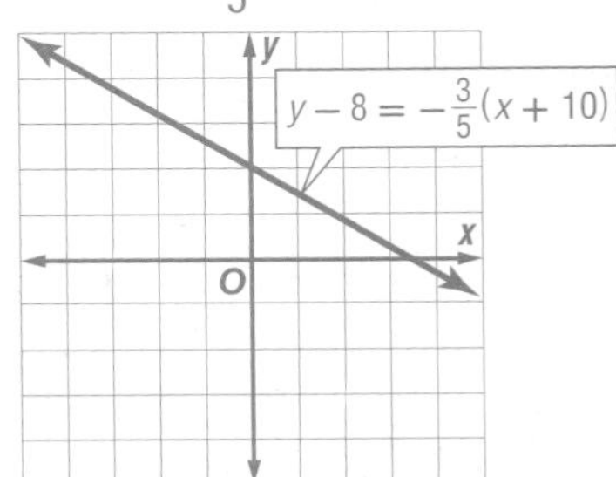

Additional Examples also in Interactive Classroom PowerPoint® Presentations

IWB Interactive White Board READY

Tips for New Teachers

Using Graphs Some students have difficulty writing a linear equation using the point-slope form from a word problem. The students should make a graph with each axis representing the variables for the given values. This method allows the students to substitute values for the slope and intercept.

CCSS Teaching the Mathematical Practices

Perseverance Mathematically proficient students check their answers to problems using a different method. They can understand the approaches of others to solving complex problems. Encourage students to look for alternate ways to solve problems.

Additional Examples

3 Write an equation of the line through each pair of points in slope-intercept form.

a. (4, 9) and (−2, 0) $y = \frac{3}{2}x + 3$

b. (−3, −7) and (−1, 3) $y = 5x + 8$

4 Write an equation of the line through (5, −2) and (0, −2) in slope-intercept form. $y = -2$

5 Write an equation in slope-intercept form for a line perpendicular to the line $y = \frac{1}{5}x + 2$ through (2, 0). $y = -5x + 10$

WatchOut!

Equations of Lines When converting the point-slope form of the equation of a line into slope-intercept form, remember to distribute across the parentheses.

Teach with Tech

Interactive Whiteboard Drag a coordinate grid on the board. Draw a line on the grid, and have students write the equation of the line in slope-intercept form. Then drag the line to another location on the board and repeat the process. Discuss how the equations are similar and different.

Math HistoryLink

Gaspard Monge (1746–1818) Monge presented the point-slope form of an equation of a line in a paper published in 1784.

Example 4 Horizontal Line

Write an equation of the line through (−2, 6) and (5, 6) in slope-intercept form.

Step 1 $m = \frac{y_2 - y_1}{x_2 - x_1} = \frac{6 - 6}{5 - (-2)} = \frac{0}{7}$ or 0 This is a horizontal line.

Step 2

$y - y_1 = m(x - x_1)$ Point-Slope form

$y - 6 = 0[x - (-2)]$ $m = -\frac{1}{2}, (x_1, y_1) = (-2, 6)$

$y - 6 = 0$ Simplify.

$y = 6$ Add 6 to each side.

GuidedPractice $y = 0$

4. Write an equation of the line through (5, 0) and (−1, 0) in slope-intercept form.

The equations of horizontal and vertical lines involve only one variable.

KeyConcepts Horizontal and Vertical Line Equations

The equation of a horizontal line is $y = b$, where b is the y-intercept of the line.

Example $y = -3$

The equation of a vertical line is $x = a$, where a is the x-intercept of the line.

Example $x = -2$

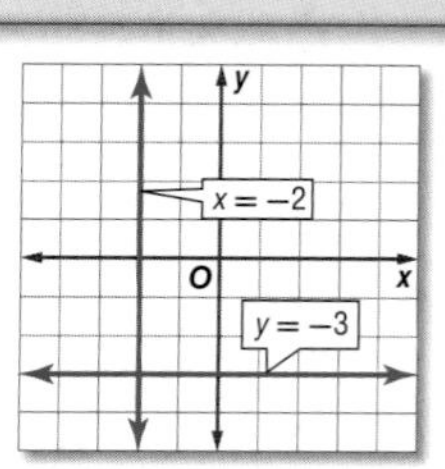

Parallel lines that are not vertical have equal slopes. Two nonvertical lines are perpendicular if the product of their slope is −1. Vertical and horizontal lines are always perpendicular to one another.

Example 5 Write Equations of Parallel or Perpendicular Lines

Write an equation in slope-intercept form for a line perpendicular to $y = -3x + 2$ containing (4, 0).

The slope of $y = -3x + 2$ is −3, so the slope of a line perpendicular to it is $\frac{1}{3}$.

$y = mx + b$ Slope-Intercept form

$0 = \frac{1}{3}(4) + b$ $m = \frac{1}{3}$ and $(x, y) = (4, 0)$

$0 = \frac{4}{3} + b$ Simplify.

$-\frac{4}{3} = b$ Subtract $\frac{4}{3}$ from each side.

So, the equation is $y = \frac{1}{3}x + \left(-\frac{4}{3}\right)$ or $y = \frac{1}{3}x - 1\frac{1}{3}$.

GuidedPractice

5. Write an equation in slope-intercept form for a line parallel to $y = -\frac{3}{4}x + 3$ containing (−3, 6). $y = -\frac{3}{4}x + \frac{15}{4}$

DifferentiatedInstruction AL OL BL ELL

Logical Explain to students that when they find the equation of a graph they should always check their work. Working independently, have students look at the examples in this lesson and substitute points on the line into the final equation. They should see that the substitution results in a true equation.

ReadingMath

Linear The word *linear* indicates a line. The graph of a linear equation is a line.

2 Write Equations to Solve Problems

Many real-world situations can be modeled using a linear equation.

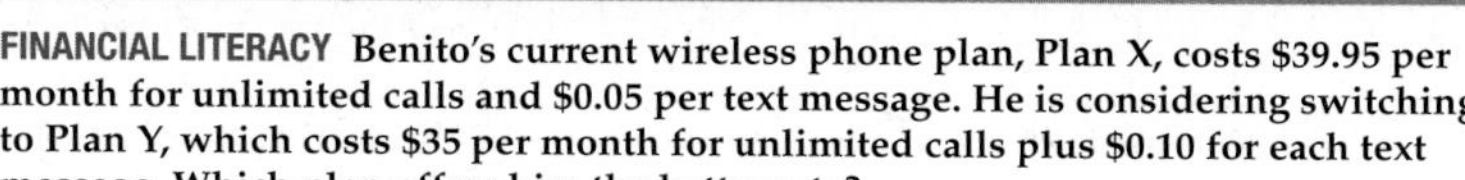

Real-World Example 6 Write Linear Equations

FINANCIAL LITERACY Benito's current wireless phone plan, Plan X, costs $39.95 per month for unlimited calls and $0.05 per text message. He is considering switching to Plan Y, which costs $35 per month for unlimited calls plus $0.10 for each text message. Which plan offers him the better rate?

Understand Plan X costs $39.95 per month plus $0.05 per text message. Plan Y costs $35 per month plus $0.10 per text message. You want to compare the two plans to determine when the cost of one plan is less than the other.

Plan Write an equation to model the total monthly cost C of each plan for t text messages sent or received. Then graph the equations in order to compare the two plans.

Solve The rates of increase, or slopes m, in the total costs are 0.05 for Plan X and 0.10 for Plan Y. When the number of text messages is 0, the total charge is just the monthly fee. So, the y-intercept b is 39.95 for Plan X and 35 for Plan Y.

Plan X		Plan Y
$C = mt + b$	Slope-intercept form	$C = mt + b$
$C = \mathbf{0.05}t + \mathbf{39.95}$	Substitute for m and b.	$C = \mathbf{0.10}t + \mathbf{35}$

Graph the two equations on the same coordinate plane.

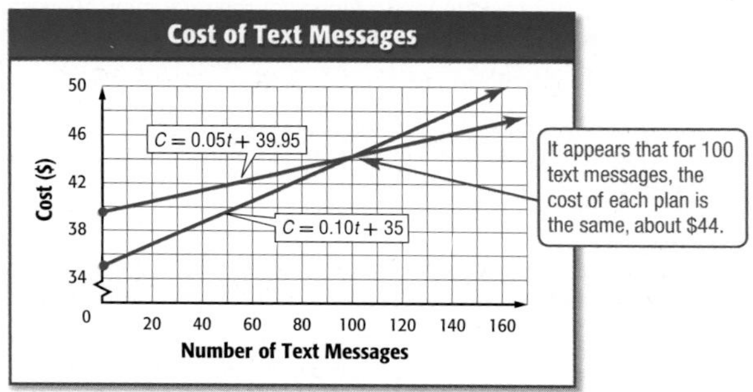

From the graph, it appears that if Benito sends or receives less than about 100 text messages, Plan Y offers the lower rate. For more than 100 messages, Plan X is lower.

Check Check your estimate. For 100 text messages, Plan X costs 0.05(100) + 39.95 or 44.95, and Plan Y costs 0.1(100) + 35 or 45. Adjusting our estimate, we find that when the number of messages is 99, both plans cost $44.90. ✓

Problem-SolvingTip

Draw a Graph In Example 6, although Plan Y has a lower monthly fee, the charge per text message is higher. This makes the plans more difficult to compare. A graph can often give you a better comparison of two linear situations.

GuidedPractice

6. Suppose the rate for Plan Y was $44 a month and $0.02 per text message. Which plan would offer Benito the better rate? Justify your answer. **See margin.**

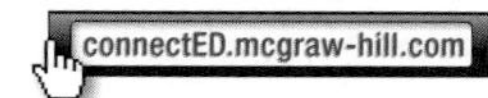

2 Write Equations to Solve Problems

Example 6 shows how to solve a real-world problem using a linear equation.

Additional Example

6 RENTAL COSTS An apartment complex charges $525 per month plus a $750 annual maintenance fee.

a. Write an equation to represent the total first year's cost A for r months of rent. $A = 525r + 750$

b. Compare this rental cost to a complex which charges a $200 annual maintenance fee but $600 per month for rent. If a person expects to stay in an apartment for one year, which complex offers the better rate? The first complex offers the better rate: the first year costs $7050 instead of $7400.

Focus on Mathematical Content

Equations of Lines The equation of a line may be written in many different ways. The point-slope form can be written with any point that the line passes through, or the slope-intercept form can be used. These equations are equivalent by using the algebraic properties of equality.

Additional Answer (Guided Practice)

6. $C = 0.05t + 39.95$, $C = 0.02t + 44$; For 135 messages, the rates are the same. For fewer than 135 messages, Brady's current plan offers the lower rate. For greater than 135 messages, the alternative plan offers the lower rate.

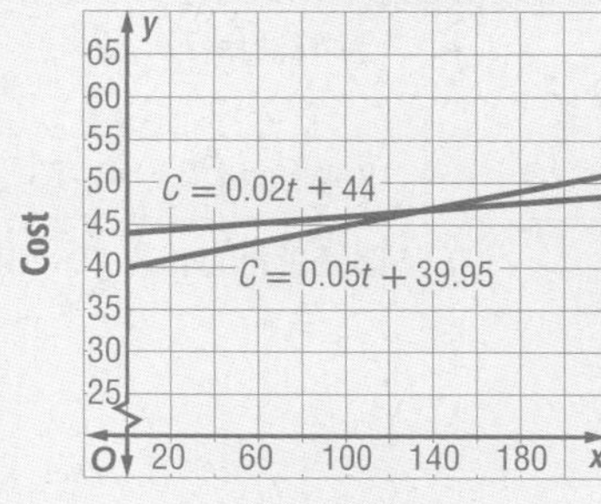

3 Practice

Formative Assessment

Use Exercises 1–12 to check for understanding.

Use the chart at the bottom of this page to customize assignments for your students.

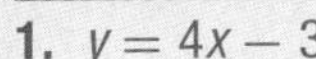

Additional Answers

1. $y = 4x - 3$

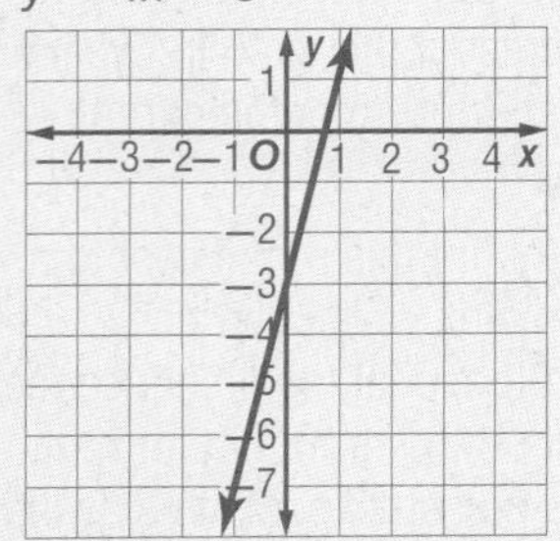

2. $y = \frac{1}{2}x - 1$

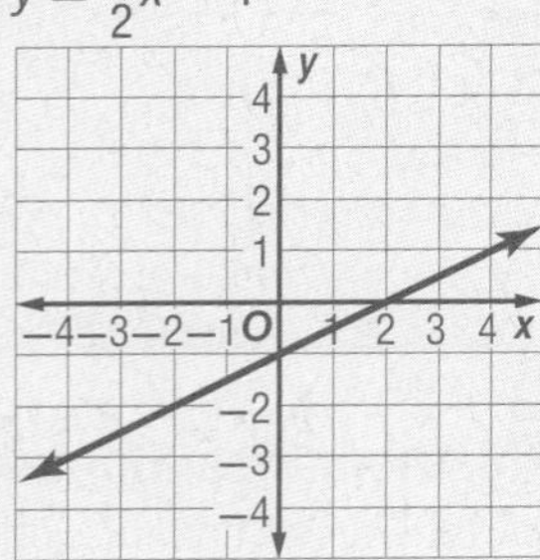

3. $y = -\frac{2}{3}x + 5$

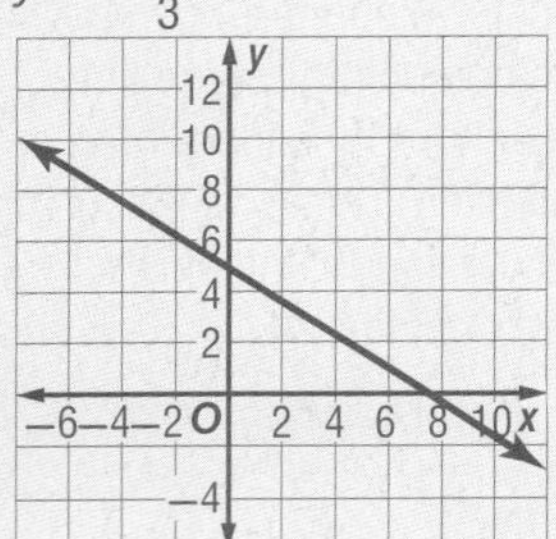

4–6. See Ch. 3 Answer Appendix for graphs.

4. $y + 2 = 5(x - 3)$
5. $y + 3 = \frac{1}{4}(x + 2)$
6. $y - 6 = -4.25(x + 4)$
7. $y = \frac{5}{4}x - 1$
8. $y = 3x - 9$
9. $y = \frac{9}{7}x - \frac{19}{7}$

Check Your Understanding

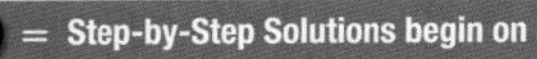

= Step-by-Step Solutions begin on page R14.

Example 1 **Write an equation in slope-intercept form of the line having the given slope and y-intercept. Then graph the line.** **1–3. See margin.**

1. m: 4, y-intercept: -3
2. m: $\frac{1}{2}$, y-intercept: -1
3. m: $-\frac{2}{3}$, y-intercept: 5

Example 2 **Write an equation in point-slope form of the line having the given slope that contains the given point. Then graph the line.** **4–6. See margin.**

4. $m = 5$, $(3, -2)$
5. $m = \frac{1}{4}$, $(-2, -3)$
6. $m = -4.25$, $(-4, 6)$

Examples 3–4 **Write an equation of the line through each pair of points in slope-intercept form.** **7–9. See margin.**

7.

x	y
0	−1
4	4

8.

x	y
4	3
1	−6

9.

x	y
6	5
−1	−4

Example 5

10. Write an equation in slope-intercept form for a line perpendicular to $y = -2x + 6$ containing (3, 2). $y = \frac{1}{2}x + \frac{1}{2}$
11. Write an equation in slope-intercept form for a line parallel to $y = 4x - 5$ containing $(-1, 5)$. $y = 4x + 9$

Example 6

12. **CCSS MODELING** Kameko currently subscribes to Ace Music, an online music service, but she is considering switching to another online service, Orange Tunes. The plan for each online music service is shown.

a. Write an equation to represent the total monthly cost for each plan. $y = 10$, $y = 0.79x + 5$
b. Graph the equations. See Ch. 3 Answer Appendix.
c. If Kameko downloads 15 songs per month, should she keep her current plan, or change to the other plan? Explain. She should switch to the other plan. She would spend $16.85 per month with her current plan and $10 per month with the other plan.

Practice and Problem Solving

Extra Practice is on page R3.

Example 1 **Write an equation in slope-intercept form of the line having the given slope and y-intercept or points. Then graph the line.** **13–18. See Ch. 3 Answer Appendix.**

13. m: -5, y-intercept: -2
14. m: -7, b: -4
15. m: 9, b: 2
16. m: 12, y-intercept: $\frac{4}{5}$
17. m: $-\frac{3}{4}$, (0, 4)
18. m: $\frac{5}{11}$, (0, −3)

Example 2 **Write an equation in point-slope form of the line having the given slope that contains the given point. Then graph the line.** **19–24. See Ch. 3 Answer Appendix.**

19. $m = 2$, (3, 11)
20. $m = 4$, $(-4, 8)$
21. $m = -7$, (1, 9)
22. $m = \frac{5}{7}$, $(-2, -5)$
23. $m = -\frac{4}{5}$, $(-3, -6)$
24. $m = -2.4$, $(14, -12)$

Examples 3–4 **Write an equation of the line through each pair of points in slope-intercept form.**

25. $(-1, -4)$ and $(3, -4)$ $y = -4$
26. $(2, -1)$ and $(2, 6)$ $x = 2$
27. $(-3, -2)$ and $(-3, 4)$ $x = -3$
28. (0, 5) and (3, 3) $y = -\frac{2}{3}x + 5$
29. $(-12, -6)$ and (8, 9) $y = \frac{3}{4}x + 3$
30. (2, 4) and $(-4, -11)$ $y = \frac{5}{2}x - 1$

Differentiated Homework Options

Level	Assignment	Two-Day Option	
AL Basic	13–42, 56–73	13–41 odd, 60–63	14–42 even, 56–59, 64–73
OL Core	13–41 odd, 53, 56–73	13–42, 60–63	43–54, 56–59, 64–73
BL Advanced	43–69, (optional: 70–73)		

Write an equation in slope-intercept form for each line shown or described.

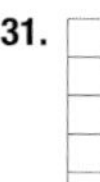

31. 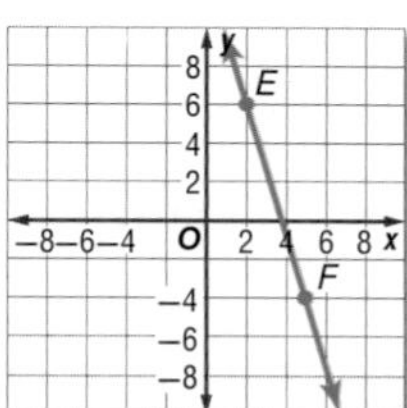

$y = -\frac{10}{3}x + \frac{38}{3}$

32. 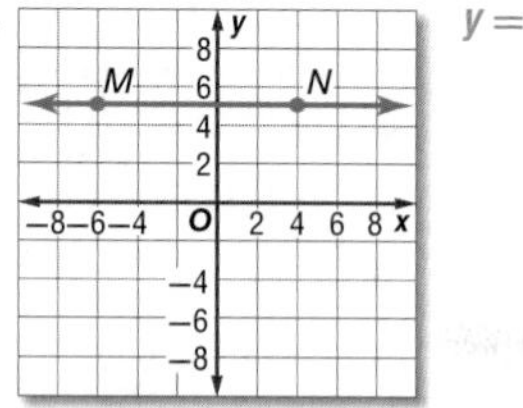

$y = 5$

33.

x	−1	3
y	−2	4

$y = \frac{3}{2}x - \frac{1}{2}$

34.

x	−4	−8
y	−5	−13

$y = 2x + 3$

35. x-intercept = 3, y-intercept = −2 35. $y = \frac{2}{3}x - 2$

36. x-intercept = $-\frac{1}{2}$, y-intercept = 4 $y = 8x + 4$

Example 5 Write an equation in slope-intercept form for each line described.

37. passes through (−7, −4), perpendicular to $y = \frac{1}{2}x + 9$ $y = -2x - 18$

38. passes through (−1, −10), parallel to $y = 7$ $y = -10$

39. passes through (6, 2), parallel to $y = -\frac{2}{3}x + 1$ $y = -\frac{2}{3}x + 6$

40. passes through (−2, 2), perpendicular to $y = -5x - 8$ $y = \frac{1}{5}x + \frac{12}{5}$

Example 6 **41** **PLANNING** Karen is planning a graduation party for the senior class. She plans to rent a meeting room at the convention center that costs \$400. There is an additional fee of \$5.50 for each person who attends the party.

a. Write an equation to represent the cost y of the party if x people attend. $y = 5.5x + 400$

b. Graph the equation. See margin.

c. There are 285 people in Karen's class. If $\frac{2}{3}$ of these people attend, how much will the party cost? \$1445

d. If the senior class has raised \$2000 for the party, how many people can attend? 290

42. **CCSS MODELING** Victor is saving his money to buy a new satellite radio for his car. He wants to save enough money for the radio and one year of satellite radio service before he makes the purchase. He started saving for the radio with \$50 that he got for his birthday. Since then, he has been adding \$15 every week after he cashes his paycheck.

a. Write an equation to represent Victor's savings y after x weeks. $y = 15x + 50$

b. Graph the equation. See Ch. 3 Answer Appendix.

c. How long will it take Victor to save \$150? 7 wk

d. A satellite radio costs \$180. Satellite radio service costs \$10 per month. If Victor started saving two weeks ago, how much longer will it take him to save enough money? Explain. See Ch. 3 Answer Appendix.

B Name the line(s) on the graph shown that match each description.

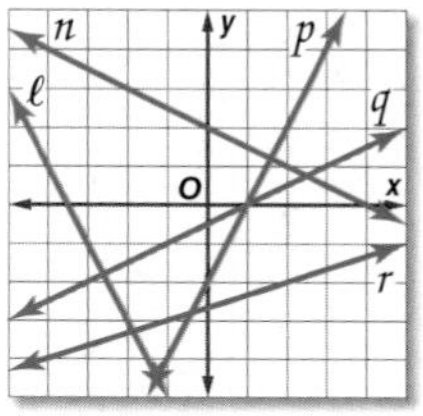

43. parallel to $y = 2x - 3$ p

44. perpendicular to $y = \frac{1}{2}x + 7$ ℓ

45. intersecting, but not perpendicular to $y = \frac{1}{2}x - 5$ n, p, or r

Determine whether the lines are *parallel*, *perpendicular*, or *neither*.

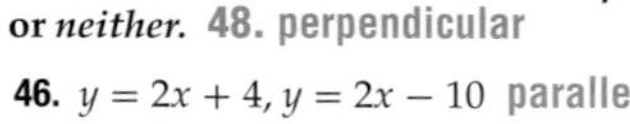

48. perpendicular

46. $y = 2x + 4$, $y = 2x - 10$ parallel

47. $y = -\frac{1}{2}x - 12$, $y = 2x + 7$ perpendicular

48. $y - 4 = 3(x + 5)$, $y + 3 = -\frac{1}{3}(x + 1)$

49. $y - 3 = 6(x + 2)$, $y + 3 = -\frac{1}{3}(x - 4)$ neither

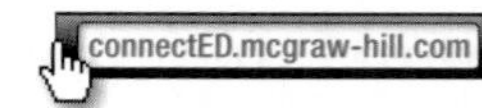

Additional Answer

41b. **Cost of Graduation Party**

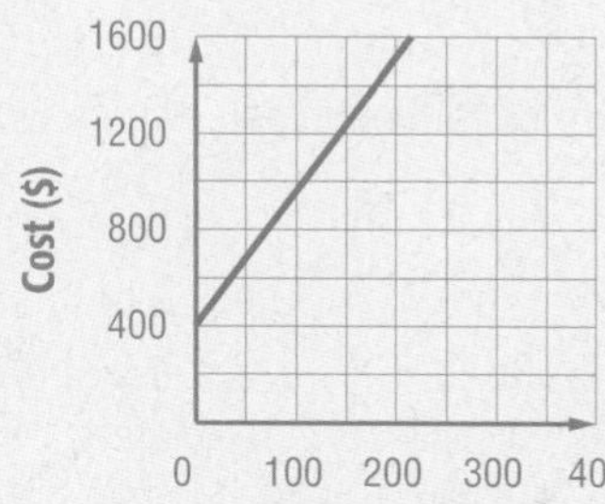

Enrichment

OL BL

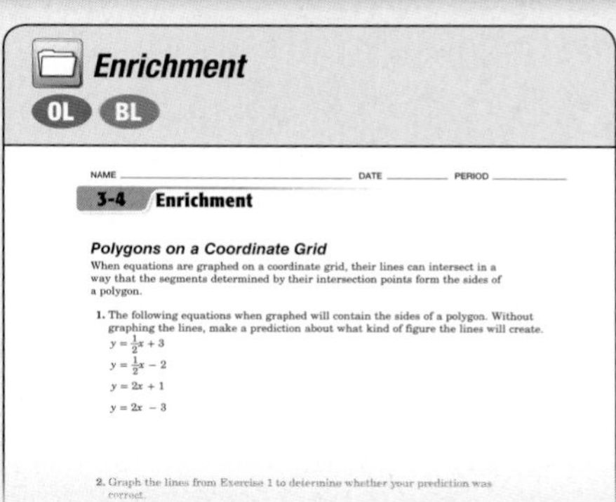

NAME ________ DATE ________ PERIOD ________

3-4 Enrichment

Polygons on a Coordinate Grid

When equations are graphed on a coordinate grid, their lines can intersect in a way that the segments determined by their intersection points form the sides of a polygon.

1. The following equations when graphed will contain the sides of a polygon. Without graphing the lines, make a prediction about what kind of figure the lines will create.

$y = \frac{1}{2}x + 3$

$y = \frac{1}{2}x - 2$

$y = 2x + 1$

$y = 2x - 3$

2. Graph the lines from Exercise 1 to determine whether your prediction was correct.

Study Guide and Intervention

AL OL ELL

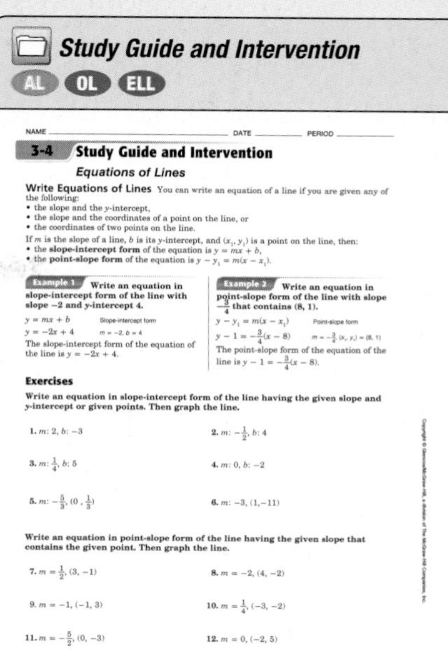

NAME ________ DATE ________ PERIOD ________

3-4 Study Guide and Intervention

Equations of Lines

Write Equations of Lines You can write an equation of a line if you are given any of the following:
- the slope and the y-intercept,
- the slope and the coordinates of a point on the line, or
- the coordinates of two points on the line.

If m is the slope of a line, b is its y-intercept, and (x_1, y_1) is a point on the line, then:
- the **slope-intercept form** of the equation is $y = mx + b$,
- the **point-slope form** of the equation is $y - y_1 = m(x - x_1)$.

Example 1 Write an equation in slope-intercept form of the line with slope −2 and y-intercept 4.

$y = mx + b$ Slope-intercept form

$y = -2x + 4$ $m = -2, b = 4$

The slope-intercept form of the equation of the line is $y = -2x + 4$.

Example 2 Write an equation in point-slope form of the line with slope $-\frac{3}{4}$ that contains (8, 1).

$y - y_1 = m(x - x_1)$ Point-slope form

$y - 1 = -\frac{3}{4}(x - 8)$ $m = -\frac{3}{4}$, $(x_1, y_1) = (8, 1)$

The point-slope form of the equation of the line is $y - 1 = -\frac{3}{4}(x - 8)$.

Exercises

Write an equation in slope-intercept form of the line having the given slope and y-intercept or given points. Then graph the line.

1. m: 2, b: −3
2. m: $-\frac{1}{2}$, b: 4
3. m: $\frac{1}{4}$, b: 5
4. m: 0, b: −2
5. m: $-\frac{5}{3}$, $(0, \frac{1}{3})$
6. m: −3, (1, −11)

Write an equation in point-slope form of the line having the given slope that contains the given point. Then graph the line.

7. $m = \frac{1}{2}$, (3, −1)
8. $m = -2$, (4, −2)
9. $m = -1$, (−1, 3)
10. $m = \frac{1}{4}$, (−3, −2)
11. $m = -\frac{5}{2}$, (0, −3)
12. $m = 0$, (−2, 5)

Practice

AL OL BL ELL

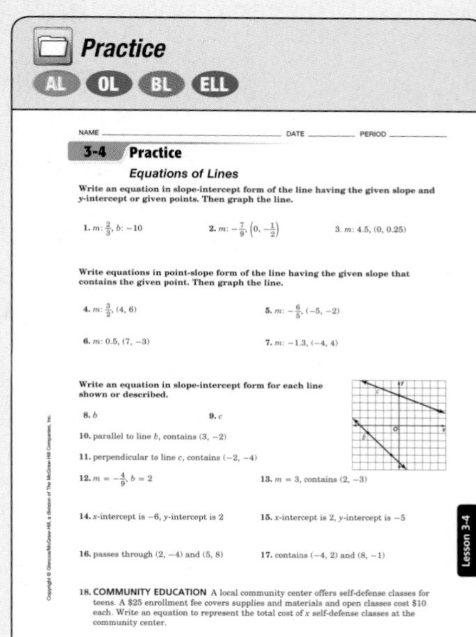

NAME ________ DATE ________ PERIOD ________

3-4 Practice

Equations of Lines

Write an equation in slope-intercept form of the line having the given slope and y-intercept or given points. Then graph the line.

1. m: $\frac{2}{3}$, b: −10
2. m: $-\frac{7}{9}$, $(0, -\frac{1}{2})$
3. m: 4.5, (0, 0.25)

Write equations in point-slope form of the line having the given slope that contains the given point. Then graph the line.

4. m: $\frac{3}{2}$, (4, 6)
5. m: $-\frac{6}{5}$, (−5, −2)
6. m: 0.5, (7, −3)
7. m: −1.3, (−4, 4)

Write an equation in slope-intercept form for each line shown or described.

8. b
9. c
10. parallel to line b, contains (3, −2)
11. perpendicular to line c, contains (−2, −4)
12. $m = -\frac{4}{9}$, $b = 2$
13. $m = 3$, contains (2, −3)
14. x-intercept is −6, y-intercept is 2
15. x-intercept is 2, y-intercept is −5
16. passes through (2, −4) and (5, 8)
17. contains (−4, 2) and (8, −1)
18. **COMMUNITY EDUCATION** A local community center offers self-defense classes for teens. A \$25 enrollment fee covers supplies and materials and open classes cost \$10 each. Write an equation to represent the total cost of x self-defense classes at the community center.

Lesson 3-4

Word Problem Practice

AL OL BL ELL

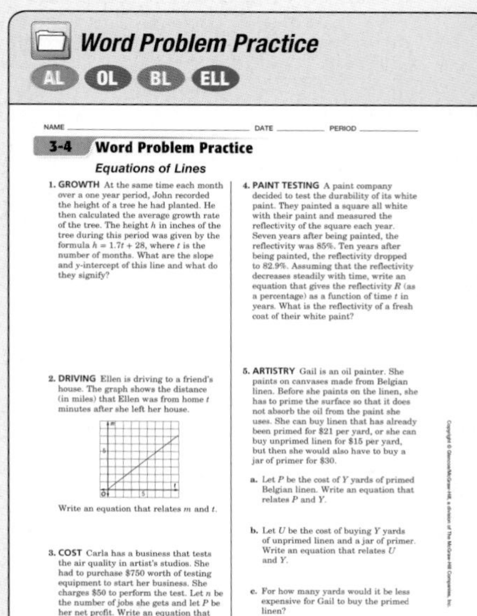

NAME ________ DATE ________ PERIOD ________

3-4 Word Problem Practice

Equations of Lines

1. **GROWTH** At the same time each month over a one year period, John recorded the height of a tree he had planted. He then calculated the average growth rate of the tree. The height h in inches of the tree during this period was given by the formula $h = 1.7t + 28$, where t is the number of months. What are the slope and y-intercept of this line and what do they signify?

2. **DRIVING** Ellen is driving to a friend's house. The graph shows the distance (in miles) that Ellen was from home t minutes after she left her house.

Write an equation that relates m and t.

3. **COST** Carla has a business that tests the air quality in artist's studios. She had to purchase \$750 worth of testing equipment to start her business. She charges \$50 to perform the test. Let n be the number of jobs she gets and let P be her net profit. Write an equation that relates P and n. How many jobs does she need to make \$750?

4. **PAINT TESTING** A paint company decided to test the durability of its white paint. They painted a square all white with their paint and measured the reflectivity of the square each year. Seven years after being painted, the reflectivity was 85%. Ten years after being painted, the reflectivity dropped to 82.9%. Assuming that the reflectivity decreases steadily with time, write an equation that gives the reflectivity R (as a percentage) as a function of time t in years. What is the reflectivity of a fresh coat of their white paint?

5. **ARTISTRY** Gail is an oil painter. She paints on canvases made from Belgian linen. Before she paints on the linen, she has to prime the surface so that it does not absorb the oil from the paint she uses. She can buy linen that has already been primed for \$21 per yard, or she can buy unprimed linen for \$15 per yard, but then she would also have to buy a jar of primer for \$30.

a. Let P be the cost of Y yards of primed Belgian linen. Write an equation that relates P and Y.

b. Let U be the cost of buying Y yards of unprimed linen and a jar of primer. Write an equation that relates U and Y.

c. For how many yards would it be less expensive for Gail to buy the primed linen?

Multiple Representations

In Exercise 52, students use a table, a verbal description, and an algebraic equation to investigate slopes of lines in a system of equations that has one solution, no solution, or infinitely many solutions.

Teaching the Mathematical Practices

Critique Mathematically proficient students can distinguish correct logic from flawed reasoning. In Exercise 58, students should recognize that if Josefina simplified her equation, it would be identical to Mark's answer. Remind students that the slope-intercept form and the point-slope form result in equivalent forms of an equation of a line.

50. Write an equation in slope-intercept form for a line containing (4, 2) that is parallel to the line $y - 2 = 3(x + 7)$. $y = 3x - 10$

51 Write an equation for a line containing (−8, 12) that is perpendicular to the line containing the points (3, 2) and (−7, 2). $x = -8$

52. Write an equation in slope-intercept form for a line containing (5, 3) that is parallel to the line $y + 11 = \frac{1}{2}(4x + 6)$. $y = 2x - 7$

53. POTTERY A community center offers pottery classes. A $40 enrollment fee covers supplies and materials, including one bag of clay. Extra bags of clay cost $15 each. Write an equation to represent the cost of the class and x bags of clay. $C = 15(x - 1) + 40$ or $C = 15x + 25$

54. MULTIPLE REPRESENTATIONS In Algebra 1, you learned that the solution of a system of two linear equations is an ordered pair that is a solution of both equations. Consider lines q, r, s, and t with the equations given. a–d. See margin.

line q: $y = 3x + 2$ line r: $y = 0.5x - 3$ line s: $2y = x - 6$ line t: $y = 3x - 3$

a. **Tabular** Make a table of values for each equation for $x = -3, -2, -1, 0, 1, 2,$ and 3. Which pairs of lines appear to represent a system of equations with one solution? no solution? infinitely many solutions? Use your tables to explain your reasoning.

b. **Graphical** Graph the equations on the same coordinate plane. Describe the geometric relationship between each pair of lines, including points of intersection.

c. **Analytical** How could you have determined your answers to part **a** using only the equations of the lines?

d. **Verbal** Explain how to determine whether a given system of two linear equations has one solution, no solution, or infinitely many solutions using a table, a graph, or the equations of the lines.

H.O.T. Problems Use Higher-Order Thinking Skills

55. CHALLENGE Find the value of n so that the line perpendicular to the line with the equation $-2y + 4 = 6x + 8$ passes through the points at $(n, -4)$ and $(2, -8)$. 14

56. REASONING Determine whether the points at (−2, 2), (2, 5), and (6, 8) are collinear. Justify your answer. See Ch. 3 Answer Appendix.

57. OPEN ENDED Write equations for two different pairs of perpendicular lines that intersect at the point at (−3, −7). Sample answer: $y = 2x - 1$, $y = -\frac{1}{2}x - \frac{17}{2}$

58. CRITIQUE Mark and Josefina wrote an equation of a line with slope −5 that passes through the point (−2, 4). Is either of them correct? Explain your reasoning.

Mark	Josefina
$y - 4 = -5(x - (-2))$	$y - 4 = -5(x - (-2))$
$y - 4 = -5(x + 2)$	$y - 4 = -5(x + 2)$
$y - 4 = -5x - 10$	
$y = -5x - 6$	

Both; Mark wrote the equation in slope-intercept form and Josefina wrote the equation in point-slope form.

59. WRITING IN MATH When is it easier to use the point-slope form to write an equation of a line and when is it easier to use the slope-intercept form?

59. Sample answer: When given the slope and y-intercept, the slope-intercept form is easier to use. When given two points, the point-slope form is easier to use. When given the slope and a point, the point-slope form is easier to use.

Additional Answers

54a.

line q $y = 3x + 2$	
x	y
−3	−7
−2	−4
−1	−1
0	2
1	5
2	8
3	11

line r $y = 0.5x - 3$	
x	y
−3	−4.5
−2	−4
−1	−3.5
0	−3
1	−2.5
2	−2
3	−1.5

line s $2y = x - 6$	
x	y
−3	−4.5
−2	−4
−1	−3.5
0	−3
1	−2.5
2	−2
3	−1.5

line t $y = 3x - 3$	
x	y
−3	−12
−2	−9
−1	−6
0	−3
1	0
2	3
3	6

Sample answer: The system of equations represented by lines q and r and by lines q and s each appear to have one solution, since each pairing of tables has the ordered pair (−2, −4) in common. The system of equations represented by lines r and t and by lines s and t each appear to have one solution, since each pairing of tables has the ordered pair (0, −3) in common. The system of equations represented by lines q and t appears to have no solution, since the y-values of the ordered pairs with the same x-values will always differ by 5. The system of equations represented by lines r and s appears to have infinitely many solutions since the pair of tables has all ordered pairs in common.

54b.

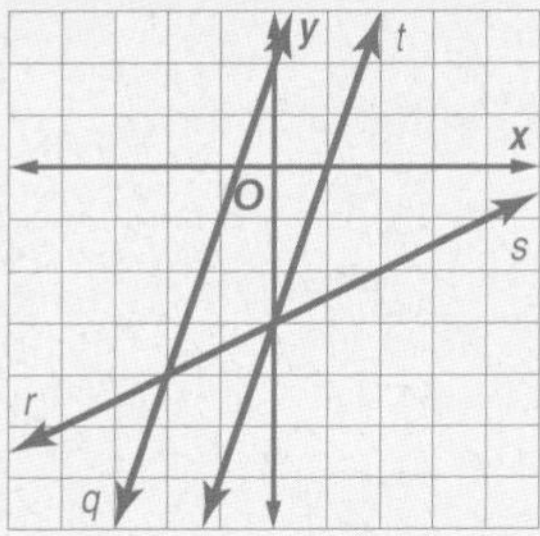

Sample answer: Lines q and t are parallel. Lines r and s coincide. Lines q and r intersect at point (−2, −4). Lines r and t intersect at point (0, −3).

Standardized Test Practice

60. Which graph best represents a line passing through the point (−2, −3)? C

A

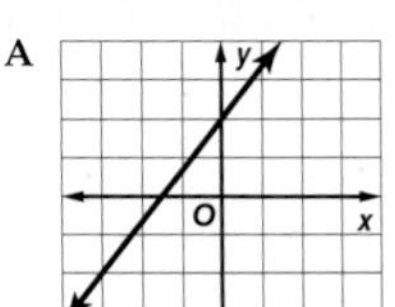

C

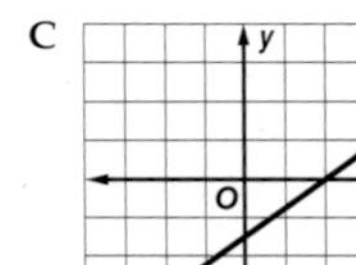

B

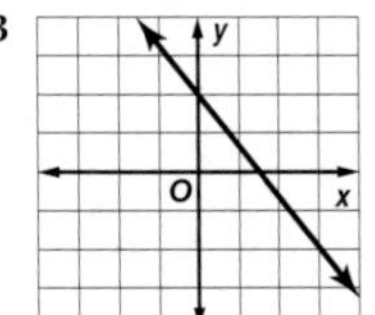

D

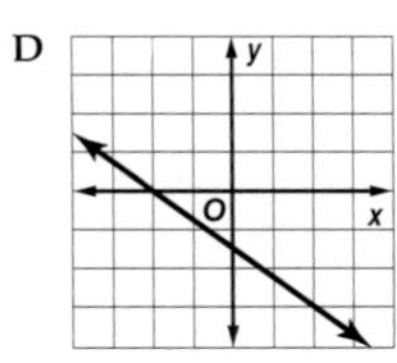

61. Which equation describes the line that passes through the point at (−2, 1) and is perpendicular to the line $y = \frac{1}{3}x + 5$? H

F $y = 3x + 7$ H $y = -3x - 5$

G $y = \frac{1}{3}x + 7$ J $y = -\frac{1}{3}x - 5$

62. GRIDDED RESPONSE At Jefferson College, 80% of students have cell phones. Of the students who have cell phones, 70% have computers. What percent of the students at Jefferson College have both a cell phone and a computer? 56

63. SAT/ACT Which expression is equivalent to $4(x - 6) - \frac{1}{2}(x^2 + 8)$? E

A $4x^2 + 4x - 28$ D $3x - 20$

B $-\frac{1}{2}x^2 + 4x - 20$ E $-\frac{1}{2}x^2 + 4x - 28$

C $-\frac{1}{2}x^2 + 6x - 24$

Spiral Review

Determine the slope of the line that contains the given points. (Lesson 3-3)

64. $J(4, 3)$, $K(5, -2)$ −5

65. $X(0, 2)$, $Y(-3, -4)$ 2

66. $A(2, 5)$, $B(5, 1)$ $-\frac{4}{3} \approx -1.3$

Find x and y in each figure. (Lesson 3-2)

67. $x = 3$, $y \approx 26.33$

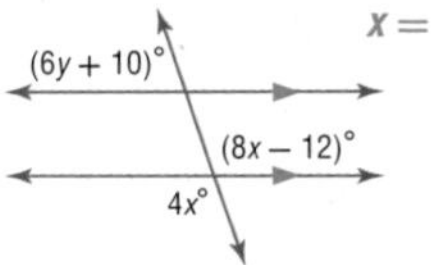

68. $x = 16$, $y = 8.7$

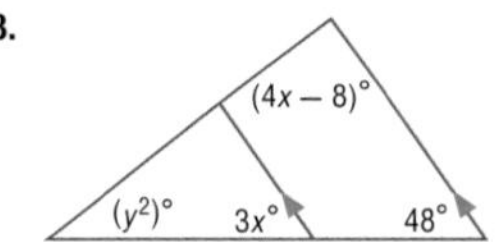

69. DRIVING Lacy's home is located at the midpoint between Newman's Gas Station and Gas-O-Rama. Newman's Gas Station is a quarter mile away from Lacy's home. How far away is Gas-O-Rama from Lacy's home? How far apart are the two gas stations? (Lesson 1-3)
Gas-O-Rama is also a quarter mile from Lacy's home; the two gas stations are half a mile apart.

Skills Review

Determine the relationship between each pair of angles.

70. ∠1 and ∠12 alternate exterior

71. ∠7 and ∠10 consecutive interior

72. ∠4 and ∠8 corresponding

73. ∠2 and ∠11 alternate exterior

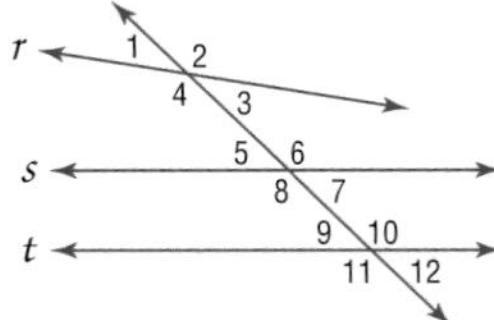

Differentiated Instruction OL BL

Extension Have students define a situation where there is a profit equation and an expense equation, and graph each equation on the same grid. The point of intersection of the two lines is called the "break-even point." For example, at Ken's lemonade stand, Ken earns $0.25 per glass of lemonade sold. His expenses are $2.50 for a pitcher and $0.05 per glass of lemonade he makes. Graph the equations $y = 0.25x$ and $y = 0.05x + 2.5$. The point of intersection (12.5, 3.125) tells Ken he must sell at least 13 glasses of lemonade per pitcher to make a profit.

4 Assess

Yesterday's News Have students write how yesterday's lesson in slopes of lines helped them in learning to write equations of lines. They should give at least two examples that support their reasoning.

Additional Answers

54c. Sample answer: Compare the slopes of the lines and their y-intercepts. Line q has slope 3 and y-intercept 2, line r has slope 0.5 and y-intercept −3, line s has slope 0.5 and y-intercept −3, and line t has slope 3 and y-intercept −3. Since lines q and r have different slopes and lines r and t have different slopes, each pair of lines intersect, and therefore each related system of equations has one solution. Since lines q and t have the same slope but different y-intercepts, the lines are parallel, and therefore the related system of equations has no solution. Since lines r and s have the same slope and the same y-intercept, the lines coincide, and therefore the related system of equations has infinitely many solutions.

54d. Sample answer: A system of equations that has one solution will have only one ordered pair that is common to each table of values, a graph of intersecting lines, and equations that have different slopes. A system of equations that has no solution will have not have any ordered pairs common to each table of values, a graph of parallel lines, and equations that have the same slope, but different y-intercepts. A system of equations that has infinitely many solutions will have identical tables of values, a graph of coinciding lines, and equations that have the same slope and the same y-intercept.

1 Focus

Objective Explore figures on a coordinate plane.

Materials for Each Group

- grid paper

Easy to Make Manipulatives

Teaching Geometry with Manipulatives templates for:

- grid paper, p. 1

2 Teach

Working Independently or in Pairs

Students can work individually on this activity or in pairs of mixed abilities. Have students read through the activity.

After they have read the activity, discuss the steps required to find the perpendicular bisector. Ask why it is necessary to find the midpoint of the given line segment and its slope. Have the students decide if the order of Steps 1 and 2 is important.

Practice Have students complete Exercises 1–7.

3 Assess

Formative Assessment

Use Exercise 1–7 to assess whether students understand how to write an equation and graph a line that is a perpendicular bisector.

From Concrete to Abstract

Tell students to write about this activity using their own words and examples. Tell them to define a perpendicular bisector and explain the steps, with diagrams, of how to write an equation and draw a graph of a perpendicular bisector.

EXTEND 3-4 Geometry Lab
Equations of Perpendicular Bisectors

You can apply what you have learned about slope and equations of lines to geometric figures on a plane.

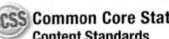

CCSS Common Core State Standards
Content Standards
G.GPE.5 Prove the slope criteria for parallel and perpendicular lines and use them to solve geometric problems (e.g., find the equation of a line parallel or perpendicular to a given line that passes through a given point).
Mathematical Practices 8

Activity

Find the equation of a line that is a perpendicular bisector of a segment AB with endpoints $A(-3, 3)$ and $B(4, 0)$.

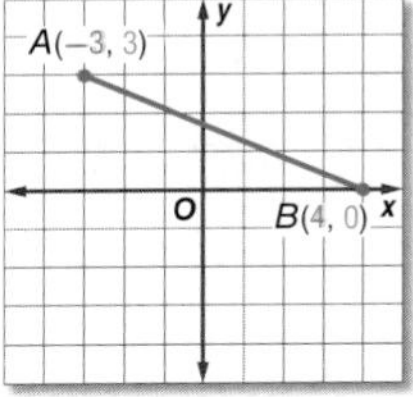

Step 1 A segment bisector contains the midpoint of the segment. Use the Midpoint Formula to find the midpoint M of $\overline{AB}$.

$$M\left(\frac{x_1 + x_2}{2}, \frac{y_1 + y_2}{2}\right) = M\left(\frac{-3 + 4}{2}, \frac{3 + 0}{2}\right)$$
$$= M\left(\frac{1}{2}, \frac{3}{2}\right)$$

Step 2 A perpendicular bisector is perpendicular to the segment through the midpoint. In order to find the slope of the bisector, first find the slope of $\overline{AB}$.

$$m = \frac{y_2 - y_1}{x_2 - x_1} \quad \text{Slope Formula}$$
$$= \frac{0 - 3}{4 - (-3)} \quad x_1 = -3,\ x_2 = 4,\ y_1 = 3,\ y_2 = 0$$
$$= -\frac{3}{7} \quad \text{Simplify.}$$

Step 3 Now use the point-slope form to write the equation of the line. The slope of the bisector is $\frac{7}{3}$ since $-\frac{3}{7}\left(\frac{7}{3}\right) = -1$

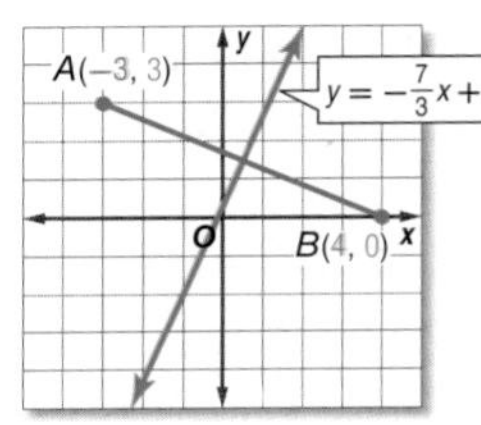

$$y - y_1 = m(x - x_1) \quad \text{Point-slope form}$$
$$y - \frac{3}{2} = \frac{7}{3}\left(x - \frac{1}{2}\right) \quad m = \frac{7}{3},\ (x_1, y_1) = \left(\frac{1}{2}, \frac{3}{2}\right)$$
$$y - \frac{3}{2} = \frac{7}{3}x - \frac{7}{6} \quad \text{Distributive Property}$$
$$y = \frac{7}{3}x + \frac{1}{3} \quad \text{Add } \frac{3}{2} \text{ to each side.}$$

Exercises

Find the equation of a line that is the perpendicular bisector $\overline{PQ}$ for the given endpoints.

1. $P(5, 2), Q(7, 4)$ $y = -x + 9$
2. $P(-3, 9), Q(-1, 5)$ $y = \frac{1}{2}x + 8$
3. $P(-6, -1), Q(8, 7)$ $y = -\frac{7}{4}x + \frac{19}{4}$
4. $P(-2, 1), Q(0, -3)$ $y = \frac{1}{2}x - \frac{1}{2}$
5. $P(0, 1.6), Q(0.5, 2.1)$ $y = -x + 2.1$
6. $P(-7, 3), Q(5, 3)$ $x = -1$
7. **CHALLENGE** Find the equations of the lines that contain the sides of $\triangle XYZ$ with vertices $X(-2, 0)$, $Y(1, 3)$, and $Z(3, -1)$. $y = x + 2$; $y = -2x + 5$; $y = -\frac{1}{5}x - \frac{2}{5}$

LESSON 3-5 Proving Lines Parallel

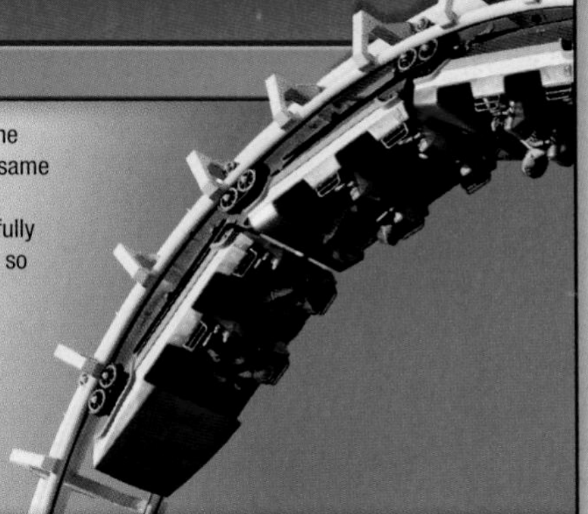

Then

- You used slopes to identify parallel and perpendicular lines.

Now

1. Recognize angle pairs that occur with parallel lines.
2. Prove that two lines are parallel.

Why?

- When you see a roller coaster track, the two sides of the track are always the same distance apart, even though the track curves and turns. The tracks are carefully constructed to be parallel at all points so that the car is secure on the track.

Common Core State Standards

Content Standards

G.CO.9 Prove theorems about lines and angles.

G.CO.12 Make formal geometric constructions with a variety of tools and methods (compass and straightedge, string, reflective devices, paper folding, dynamic geometric software, etc.).

Mathematical Practices

1. Make sense of problems and persevere in solving them.
3. Construct viable arguments and critique the reasoning of others.

1 Identify Parallel Lines

The two sides of the track of a roller coaster are parallel, and all of the supports along the track are also parallel. Each of the angles formed between the track and the supports are corresponding angles. We have learned that corresponding angles are congruent when lines are parallel. The converse of this relationship is also true.

Postulate 3.4 Converse of Corresponding Angles Postulate

If two lines are cut by a transversal so that corresponding angles are congruent, then the lines are parallel.

Examples If $\angle 1 \cong \angle 3$, $\angle 2 \cong \angle 4$, $\angle 5 \cong \angle 7$, $\angle 6 \cong \angle 8$, then $a \parallel b$.

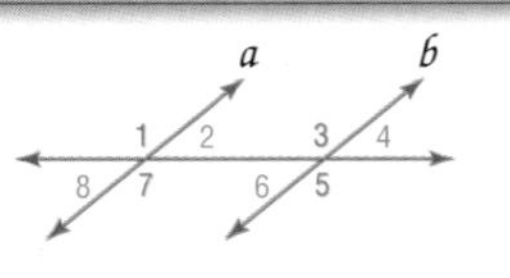

The Converse of the Corresponding Angles Postulate can be used to construct parallel lines.

Construction Parallel Line Through a Point Not on the Line

Step 1 Use a straightedge to draw $\overleftrightarrow{AB}$. Draw a point C that is not on $\overleftrightarrow{AB}$. Draw $\overleftrightarrow{CA}$.

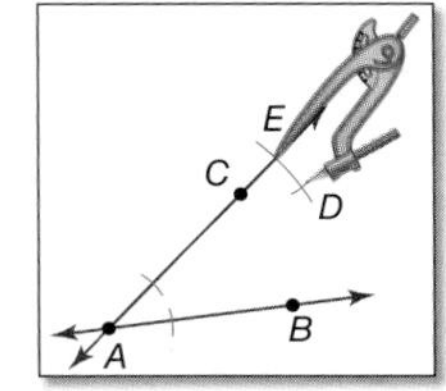

Step 2 Copy $\angle CAB$ so that C is the vertex of the new angle. Label the intersection points D and E.

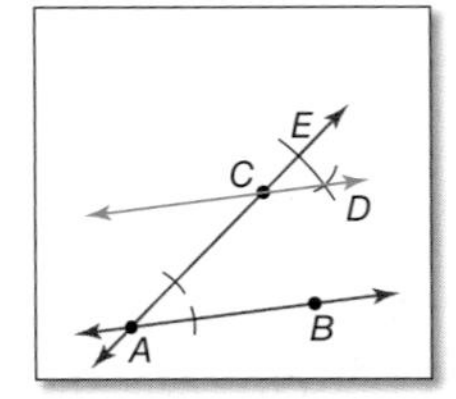

Step 3 Draw CD. Because $\angle ECD \cong \angle CAB$ by construction and they are corresponding angles, $\overleftrightarrow{AB} \parallel \overleftrightarrow{CD}$.

1 Focus

Vertical Alignment

Before Lesson 3-5 Use slopes of lines to identify parallel and perpendicular lines.

Lesson 3-5 Recognize the angle relationships that occur when parallel lines are cut by a transversal.
Use angle relationships to prove that lines are parallel.

After Lesson 3-5 Find the distance between two parallel lines and the distance between a point and a line.

2 Teach

Scaffolding Questions

Have students read the **Why?** section of the lesson.

Ask:

- Why are the two sides of the track constructed to be parallel at all points? Sample answer: The cars would not be able to move safely on the track if the two sides were not parallel.
- If one of the support bars that joins the two sides of the track is perpendicular to one side of the tracks, what is the measure of the angle created by the bar and the other side of the track? 90

Lesson 3-5 Resources

Resource	Approaching Level AL	On Level OL	Beyond Level BL	English Learners ELL
Teacher Edition	▪ Differentiated Instruction, p. 209	▪ Differentiated Instruction, pp. 209, 210	▪ Differentiated Instruction, pp. 209, 210	▪ Differentiated Instruction, p. 209
Chapter Resource Masters	▪ Study Guide and Intervention, pp. 30–31 ▪ Skills Practice, p. 32 ▪ Practice, p. 33 ▪ Word Problem Practice, p. 34	▪ Study Guide and Intervention, pp. 30–31 ▪ Skills Practice, p. 32 ▪ Practice, p. 33 ▪ Word Problem Practice, p. 34 ▪ Enrichment, p. 35	▪ Practice, p. 33 ▪ Word Problem Practice, p. 34 ▪ Enrichment, p. 35	▪ Study Guide and Intervention, pp. 30–31 ▪ Skills Practice, p. 32 ▪ Practice, p. 33 ▪ Word Problem Practice, p. 34
Other	▪ 5-Minute Check 3-5 ▪ Study Notebook ▪ Teaching Geometry with Manipulatives	▪ 5-Minute Check 3-5 ▪ Study Notebook ▪ Teaching Geometry with Manipulatives	▪ 5-Minute Check 3-5 ▪ Study Notebook	▪ 5-Minute Check 3-5 ▪ Study Notebook ▪ Teaching Geometry with Manipulatives

1 Identify Parallel Lines

Examples 1 and 2 show how to determine that lines are parallel. Students should be able to use known theorems and postulates to identify parallel lines.

Formative Assessment

Use the Guided Practice exercises after each example to determine students' understanding of concepts.

Additional Example

1 Given the following information, is it possible to prove that any of the lines shown are parallel? If so, state the postulate or theorem that justifies your answer.

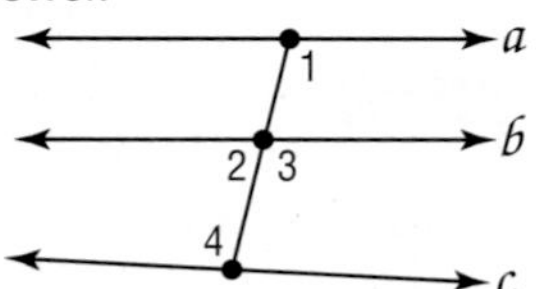

a. $\angle 1 \cong \angle 3$ $a \parallel b$ by Corresponding Angles Converse

b. $m\angle 1 = 103$ and $m\angle 4 = 100$ a is not parallel to c by the Alternate Interior Angles Converse

Additional Examples also in Interactive Classroom PowerPoint® Presentations

The construction establishes that there is *at least* one line through C that is parallel to $\overleftrightarrow{AB}$. The following postulate guarantees that this line is the *only* one.

> **StudyTip**
>
> Euclid's Postulates The father of modern geometry, Euclid (c. 300 B.C.) realized that only a few postulates were needed to prove the theorems in his day. Postulate 3.5 is one of Euclid's five original postulates. Postulate 2.1 and Theorem 2.10 also reflect two of Euclid's postulates.

Postulate 3.5 Parallel Postulate

If given a line and a point not on the line, then there exists exactly one line through the point that is parallel to the given line.

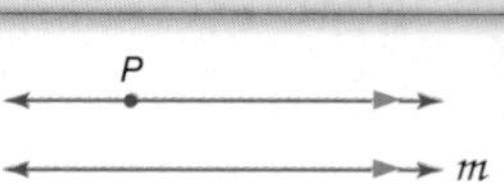

Parallel lines that are cut by a transversal create several pairs of congruent angles. These special angle pairs can also be used to prove that a pair of lines are parallel.

Theorems Proving Lines Parallel

Theorem	Example
3.5 Alternate Exterior Angles Converse If two lines in a plane are cut by a transversal so that a pair of alternate exterior angles is congruent, then the two lines are parallel.	If $\angle 1 \cong \angle 3$, then $p \parallel q$.
3.6 Consecutive Interior Angles Converse If two lines in a plane are cut by a transversal so that a pair of consecutive interior angles is supplementary, then the lines are parallel.	If $m\angle 4 + m\angle 5 = 180$, then $p \parallel q$.
3.7 Alternate Interior Angles Converse If two lines in a plane are cut by a transversal so that a pair of alternate interior angles is congruent, then the lines are parallel.	If $\angle 6 \cong \angle 8$, then $p \parallel q$.
3.8 Perpendicular Transversal Converse In a plane, if two lines are perpendicular to the same line, then they are parallel.	If $p \perp r$ and $q \perp r$, then $p \parallel q$.

You will prove Theorems 3.5, 3.6, 3.7, and 3.8 in Exercises 6, 23, 31, and 30, respectively.

Example 1 Identify Parallel Lines

Given the following information, determine which lines, if any, are parallel. State the postulate or theorem that justifies your answer.

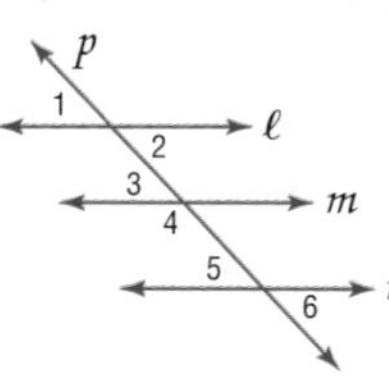

a.  $\angle 1 \cong \angle 6$

$\angle 1$ and $\angle 6$ are alternate exterior angles of lines ℓ and n.

Since $\angle 1 \cong \angle 6$, $\ell \parallel n$ by the Converse of the Alternate Exterior Angles Theorem.

b. $\angle 2 \cong \angle 3$

$\angle 2$ and $\angle 3$ are alternate interior angles of lines ℓ and m.

Since $\angle 2 \cong \angle 3$, $\ell \parallel m$ by the Converse of the Alternate Interior Angles Theorem.

Tips for New Teachers

Reasoning Encourage students to make connections with previous concepts by comparing the theorems and postulates in this lesson to those in Lesson 3-2. Ask students to explain any connections in logic that they find.

208 | Lesson 3-5 | Proving Lines Parallel

1A. $a \parallel b$; Alt. Int. ∠s Converse
1B. $\ell \parallel m$; Converse of Corr. ∠s Post.
1C. $a \parallel b$; Alt. Ext. ∠s Converse
1D. not possible
1E. $\ell \parallel m$; Consec. Int. ∠s Converse
1F. not possible

Guided Practice

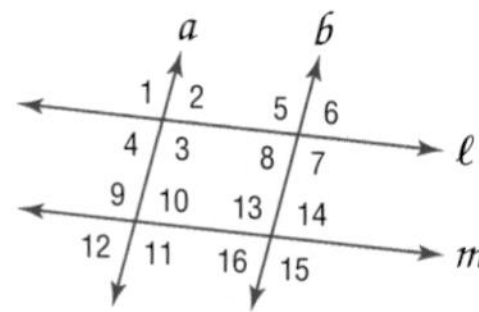

1A. $\angle 2 \cong \angle 8$ **1B.** $\angle 3 \cong \angle 11$

1C. $\angle 12 \cong \angle 14$ **1D.** $\angle 1 \cong \angle 15$

1E. $m\angle 8 + m\angle 13 = 180$ **1F.** $\angle 8 \cong \angle 6$

Angle relationships can be used to solve problems involving unknown values.

Standardized Test Example 2 Use Angle Relationships

OPEN ENDED **Find $m\angle MRQ$ so that $a \parallel b$. Show your work.**

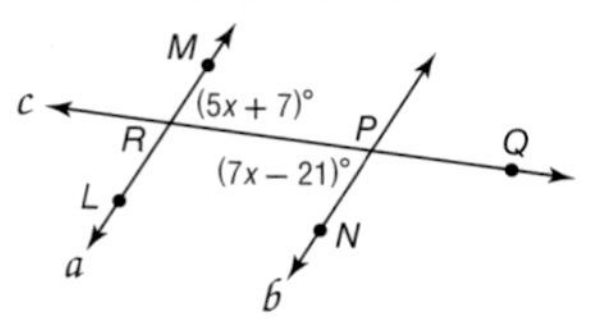

Read the Test Item

From the figure, you know that $m\angle MRQ = 5x + 7$ and $m\angle RPN = 7x - 21$. You are asked to find the measure of $\angle MRQ$.

Solve the Test Item

$\angle MRQ$ and $\angle RPN$ are alternate interior angles. For lines a and b to be parallel, alternate interior angles must be congruent, so $\angle MRQ \cong \angle RPN$. By the definition of congruence, $m\angle MRQ = m\angle RPN$. Substitute the given angle measures into this equation and solve for x.

$m\angle MRQ = m\angle RPN$	Alternate interior angles
$5x + 7 = 7x - 21$	Substitution
$7 = 2x - 21$	Subtract 5x from each side.
$28 = 2x$	Add 21 to each side.
$14 = x$	Divide each side by 2.

Now, use the value of x to find $\angle MRQ$.

$m\angle MRQ = 5x + 7$	Substitution
$= 5(14) + 7$	$x = 14$
$= 77$	Simplify.

CHECK Check your answer by using the value of x to find $m\angle RPN$.

$m\angle RP = 7x - 21$
$= 7(14) - 21$ or 77 ✓

Since $m\angle MRQ = m\angle RPN$, $\angle MRQ \cong \angle RPN$ and $a \parallel b$. ✓

StudyTip

Finding What Is Asked For Be sure to reread test questions carefully to be sure you are answering the question that was asked. In Example 2, a common error would be to stop after you have found the value of x and say that the solution of the problem is 14.

Guided Practice

2. Find y so that $e \parallel f$. Show your work.
20

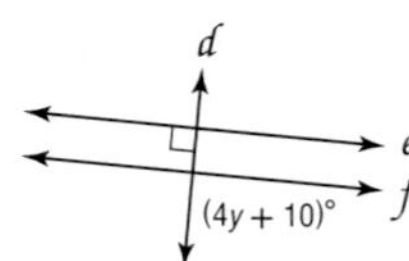

Additional Example

2 STANDARDIZED TEST PRACTICE Find $m\angle ZYN$ so that $\overleftrightarrow{PQ} \parallel \overleftrightarrow{MN}$. Show your work.

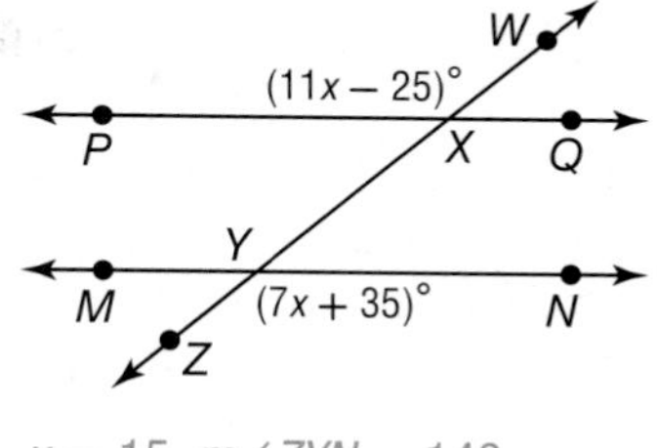

$x = 15$, $m\angle ZYN = 140$

Focus on Mathematical Content

Reasoning Many students think that the postulates and theorems in this lesson are the same as those in Lesson 3-2. Help them focus on the difference that in this lesson they are **concluding** that lines are parallel (the **then** clause), while in Lesson 3-2 they were **starting** with parallel lines (the **if** clause).

Teach with Tech

Document Camera Show a parallelogram on a coordinate plane, and orient it so that none of the sides are horizontal or vertical line segments. Tell students they need to prove that the opposite sides of the figure are parallel. Choose four students, and have each student find the slope of one side of the figure. Then choose another student to explain how these slopes prove the opposite sides are parallel.

Differentiated Instruction AL OL BL ELL

Logical Instruct students to draw two lines cut by a transversal with given specific angle measure criteria. The students may work together in small groups of 3 or 4 to discuss whether the lines must be parallel. Facilitate the discussions so that students discern that more angle measures can be found with certainty when the lines are parallel than when the lines are not parallel.

2 Prove Lines Parallel

Example 3 describes how to prove that lines are parallel by using a real-world example.

Additional Example

3 CONSTRUCTION In the window shown, the diamond grid pattern is constructed by hand. Is it possible to ensure that the wood pieces that run the same direction are parallel? If so, explain how. If not, explain why not.

Sample answer: Measure the corresponding angles formed by two consecutive grid lines and the intersecting grid line traveling in the opposite direction. If these angles are congruent, then the grid lines that run in the same direction are parallel by the Converse of the Corresponding Angles Postulate.

Additional Answer (Guided Practice)

3. Not possible; the alternate exterior angles, alternate interior angles, or corresponding angles are not congruent so the lines are not parallel. The consecutive interior angles are not supplementary so the lines are not parallel.

Additional Answers

1. $j \parallel k$; Converse of Corresponding Angles Postulate
2. $j \parallel k$; Alternate Interior Angles Converse
3. $\ell \parallel m$; Alternate Exterior Angles Converse
4. $\ell \parallel m$; Consecutive Interior Angles Converse

StudyTip

Proving Lines Parallel When two parallel lines are cut by a transversal, the angle pairs formed are either congruent or supplementary. When a pair of lines forms angles that do not meet this criterion, the lines cannot possibly be parallel.

2 Prove Lines Parallel

The angle pair relationships formed by a transversal can be used to prove that two lines are parallel.

PT

Real-World Example 3 Prove Lines Parallel

HOME FURNISHINGS In the ladder shown, each rung is perpendicular to the two rails. Is it possible to prove that the two rails are parallel and that all of the rungs are parallel? If so, explain how. If not, explain why not.

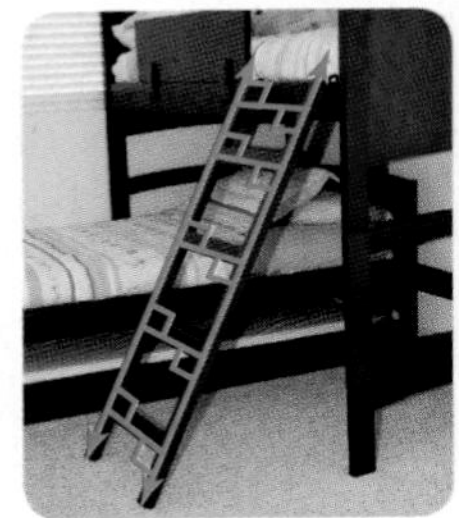

Since both rails are perpendicular to each rung, the rails are parallel by the Perpendicular Transversal Converse. Since any pair of rungs is perpendicular to the rails, they are also parallel.

GuidedPractice

3. **ROWING** In order to move in a straight line with maximum efficiency, rower's oars should be parallel. Refer to the photo at the right. Is it possible to prove that any of the oars are parallel? If so, explain how. If not, explain why not. **See margin.**

Check Your Understanding

= Step-by-Step Solutions begin on page R14.

Example 1 **Given the following information, determine which lines, if any, are parallel. State the postulate or theorem that justifies your answer.** **1–4. See margin.**

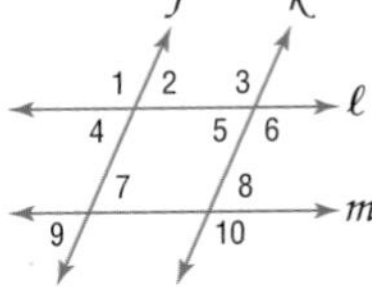

1. $\angle 1 \cong \angle 3$
2. $\angle 2 \cong \angle 5$
3. $\angle 3 \cong \angle 10$
4. $m\angle 6 + m\angle 8 = 180$

Example 2

5. **SHORT RESPONSE** Find x so that $m \parallel n$. Show your work. **20**

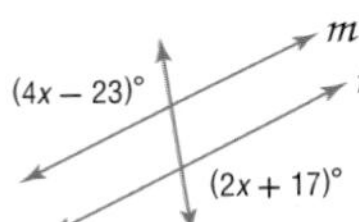

Example 3

6. **PROOF** Copy and complete the proof of Theorem 3.5.

Given: $\angle 1 \cong \angle 2$

Prove: $\ell \parallel m$

Proof:

Statements	Reasons
a. $\angle 1 \cong \angle 2$	a. Given
b. $\angle 2 \cong \angle 3$	b. ___?___ Vertical ∠s are ≅.
c. $\angle 1 \cong \angle 3$	c. Transitive Property
d. ___?___ $\ell \parallel m$	d. ___?___ If corr. ∠s are ≅, then lines are ∥.

DifferentiatedInstruction OL BL

Extension Have students re-format some of the proofs from this lesson. They can generate the proof from Example 3 as a paragraph proof or as a flow proof.

210 | Lesson 3-5 | Proving Lines Parallel

7. **RECREATION** Is it possible to prove that the backrest and footrest of the lounging beach chair are parallel? If so, explain how. If not, explain why not.

Yes; sample answer: Since the alternate exterior angles are congruent, the backrest and footrest are parallel.

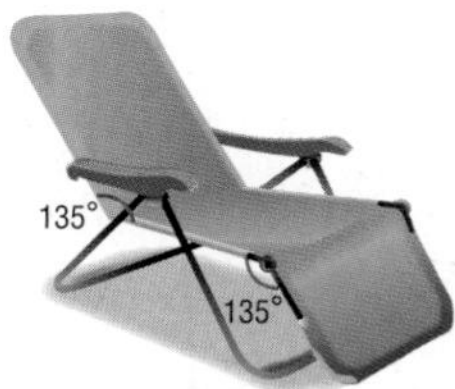

Practice and Problem Solving

Extra Practice is on page R3.

Example 1 **Given the following information, determine which lines, if any, are parallel. State the postulate or theorem that justifies your answer.** **8–15. See margin.**

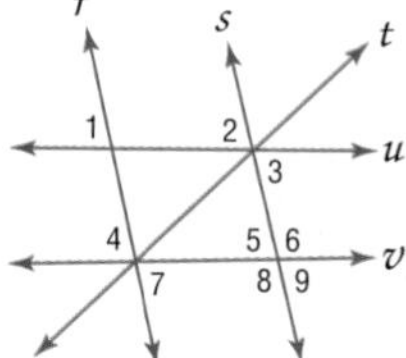

8. $\angle 1 \cong \angle 2$
9. $\angle 2 \cong \angle 9$
10. $\angle 5 \cong \angle 7$
11. $m\angle 7 + m\angle 8 = 180$
12. $m\angle 3 + m\angle 6 = 180$
13. $\angle 3 \cong \angle 5$
14. $\angle 3 \cong \angle 7$
15. $\angle 4 \cong \angle 5$

Example 2 **Find x so that $m \parallel n$. Identify the postulate or theorem you used.**

16.

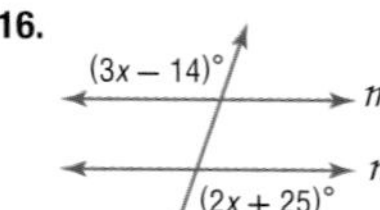

39; Alt. Ext. ∡ Conv.

17.

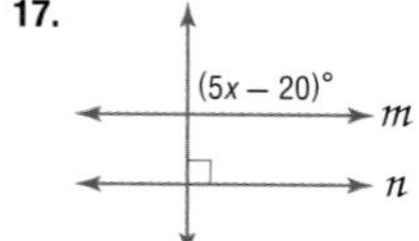

22; Conv. Corr. ∡ Post.

18.

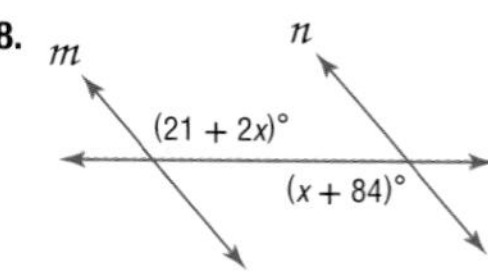

63; Alt. Int. ∡ Conv.

19.

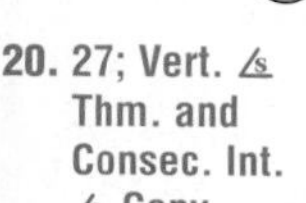

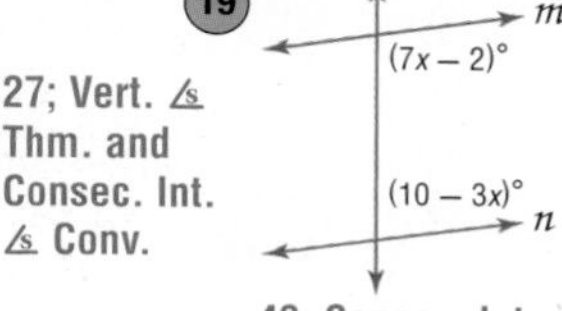

43; Consec. Int. ∡ Conv.

20.

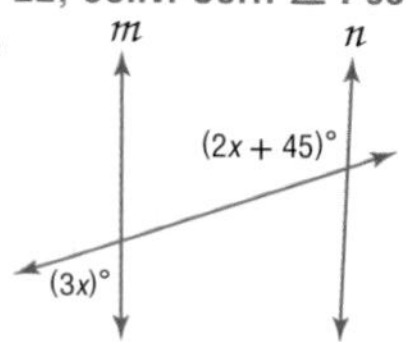

20. 27; Vert. ∡ Thm. and Consec. Int. ∡ Conv.

21.

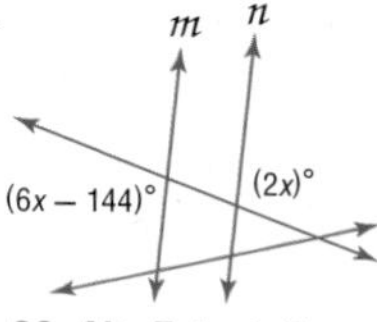

36; Alt. Ext. ∡ Conv.

22. **CCSS SENSE-MAKING** Wooden picture frames are often constructed using a miter box or miter saw. These tools allow you to cut at an angle of a given size. If each of the four pieces of framing material is cut at a 45° angle, will the sides of the frame be parallel? Explain your reasoning. **See margin.**

Example 3 23. **PROOF** Copy and complete the proof of Theorem 3.6.

Given: $\angle 1$ and $\angle 2$ are supplementary.

Prove: $\ell \parallel m$

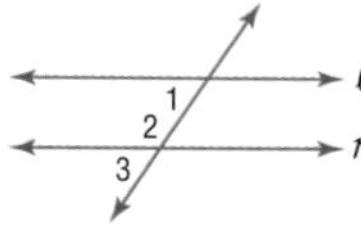

Proof:

Statements	Reasons
a. ___?___	a. Given
b. $\angle 2$ and $\angle 3$ form a linear pair.	b. ___?___ **Def. of linear pair.**
c. ___?___	c. ___?___ **Suppl. Thm.**
d. $\angle 1 \cong \angle 3$	d. ___?___ **≅ Suppl. Thm.**
e. $\ell \parallel m$	e. ___?___

23a. ∠1 and ∠2 are supplementary.
23c. ∠2 and ∠3 are supplementary.
23e. Converse of Corr. ∡ Post.

Differentiated Homework Options

Level	Assignment	Two-Day Option	
AL Basic	8–30, 37–40, 42–57	9–29 odd, 44–47	8–30 even, 37–40, 42, 43, 48–57
OL Core	9–35 odd, 36–40, 42–57	8–30, 44–47	31–40, 42, 43, 48–57
BL Advanced	31–56, (optional: 57)		

3 Practice

Formative Assessment

Use Exercises 1–7 to check for understanding.

Use the chart at the bottom of this page to customize assignments for your students.

Teaching the Mathematical Practices

Sense-making Mathematically proficient students look for entry points to a solution. They analyze givens, constraints, relationships, and goals. In Exercise 22, encourage students to draw a diagram with the parallel sides and transversals labeled.

Additional Answers

8. $r \parallel s$; Converse of Corresponding Angles Postulate
9. $u \parallel v$; Alternate Exterior Angles Converse
10. $r \parallel s$; Alternate Interior Angles Converse
11. $r \parallel s$; Consecutive Interior Angles Converse
12. $u \parallel v$; Consecutive Interior Angles Converse
13. $u \parallel v$; Alternate Interior Angles Converse
14. No lines can be proven ||.
15. $r \parallel s$; Converse of Corresponding Angles Postulate
22. Yes; when two pieces are put together, they form a 90° angle. Two lines that are perpendicular to the same line are parallel.

24. **CRAFTS** Jacqui is making a stained glass piece. She cuts the top and bottom pieces at a 30° angle. If the corners are right angles, explain how Jacqui knows that each pair of opposite sides are parallel.
Since the corners are rt. ∠s, each pr. of opp. sides is ⊥ to the same line. Therefore, each pr. of opposite sides is ∥.

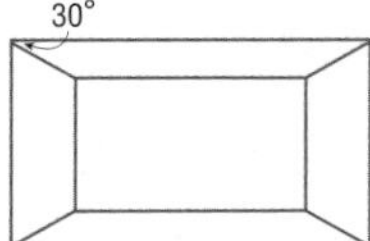

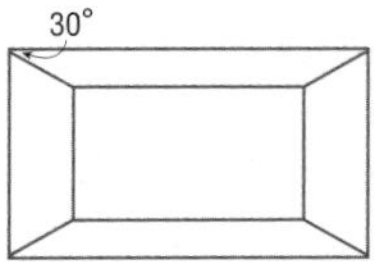

PROOF Write a two-column proof for each of the following. **25–28. See Ch. 3 Answer Appendix.**

25. **Given:** $\angle 1 \cong \angle 3$
$\overline{AC} \parallel \overline{BD}$
Prove: $\overline{AB} \parallel \overline{CD}$

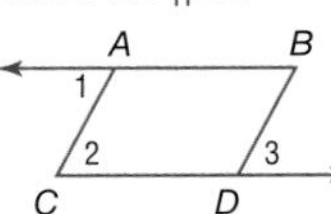

26. **Given:** $\overline{WX} \parallel \overline{YZ}$
$\angle 2 \cong \angle 3$
Prove: $\overline{WY} \parallel \overline{XZ}$

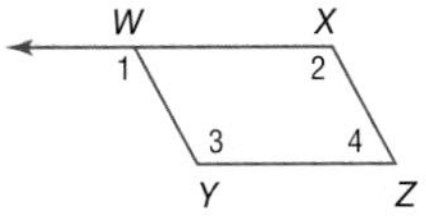

27. **Given:** $\angle ABC \cong \angle ADC$
$m\angle A + m\angle ABC = 180$
Prove: $\overline{AB} \parallel \overline{CD}$

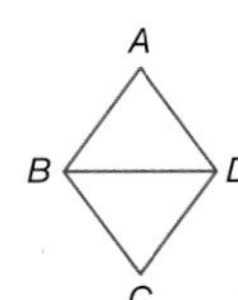

28. **Given:** $\angle 1 \cong \angle 2$
$\overline{LJ} \perp \overline{ML}$
Prove: $\overline{KM} \perp \overline{ML}$

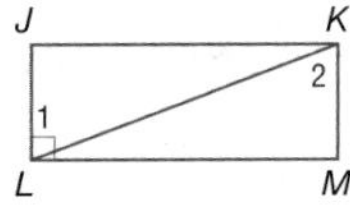

29. **MAILBOXES** Mail slots are used to make the organization and distribution of mail easier. In the mail slots shown, each slot is perpendicular to each of the sides. Explain why you can conclude that the slots are parallel.
See margin.

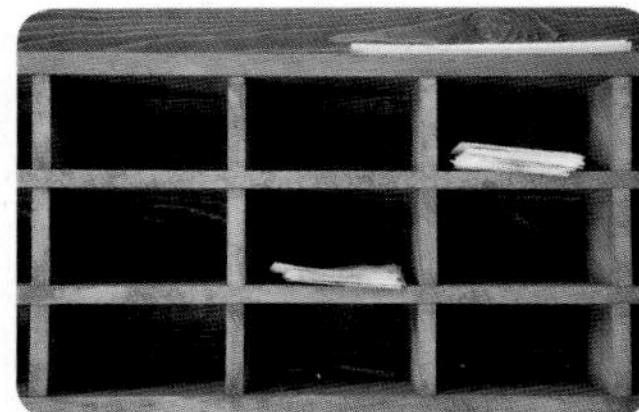

30. **PROOF** Write a paragraph proof of Theorem 3.8. **30–31. See Ch. 3 Answer Appendix.**

31. **PROOF** Write a two-column proof of Theorem 3.7.

32. **CCSS REASONING** Based upon the information given in the photo of the staircase at the right, what is the relationship between each step? Explain your answer.
Each of the steps is parallel to one other because the corresponding angles are congruent.

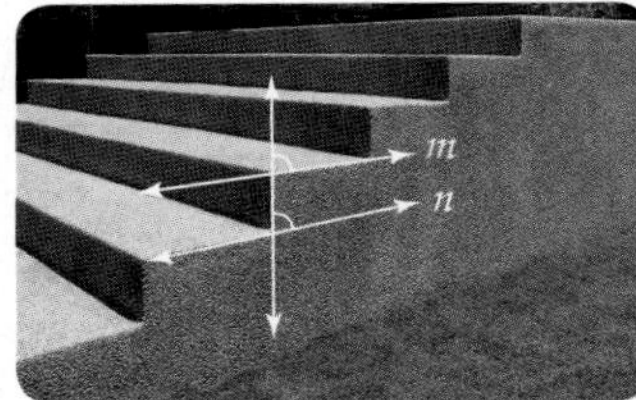

Determine whether lines r and s are parallel. Justify your answer. **33–35. See Ch. 3 Answer Appendix.**

33.

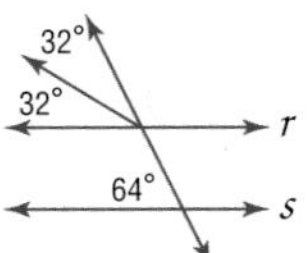

34.

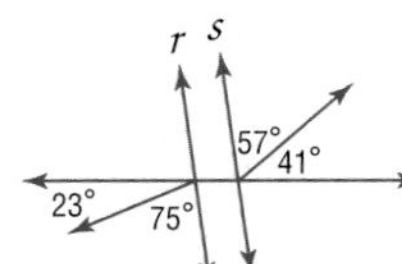

35.

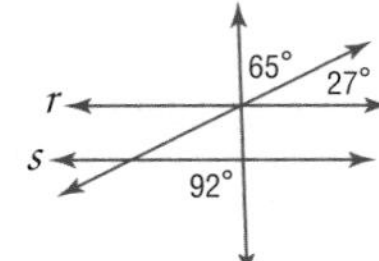

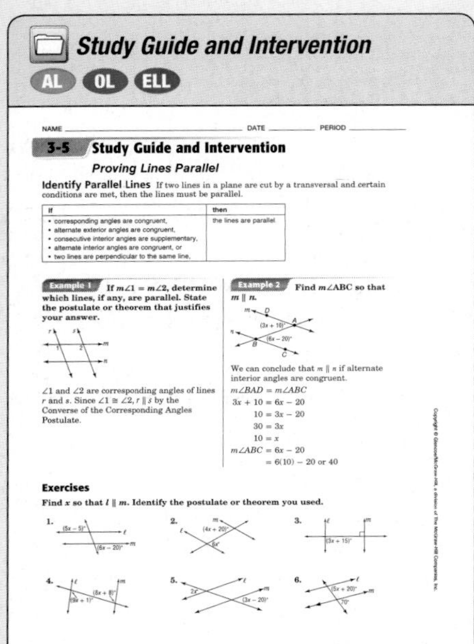

Study Guide and Intervention

AL OL ELL

NAME ______ DATE ______ PERIOD ______

3-5 Study Guide and Intervention

Proving Lines Parallel

Identify Parallel Lines If two lines in a plane are cut by a transversal and certain conditions are met, then the lines must be parallel.

If	then
• corresponding angles are congruent, • alternate exterior angles are congruent, • consecutive interior angles are supplementary, • alternate interior angles are congruent, or • two lines are perpendicular to the same line,	the lines are parallel

Example 1 If $m\angle 1 = m\angle 2$, determine which lines, if any, are parallel. State the postulate or theorem that justifies your answer.

$\angle 1$ and $\angle 2$ are corresponding angles of lines r and s. Since $\angle 1 \cong \angle 2$, $r \parallel s$ by the Converse of the Corresponding Angles Postulate.

Example 2 Find $m\angle ABC$ so that $m \parallel n$.

We can conclude that $m \parallel n$ if alternate interior angles are congruent.

$m\angle BAD = m\angle ABC$
$3x + 10 = 6x - 20$
$10 = 3x - 20$
$30 = 3x$
$10 = x$
$m\angle ABC = 6x - 20$
$= 6(10) - 20$ or 40

Exercises

Find x so that $\ell \parallel m$. Identify the postulate or theorem you used.

1. 2. 3. 4. 5. 6.

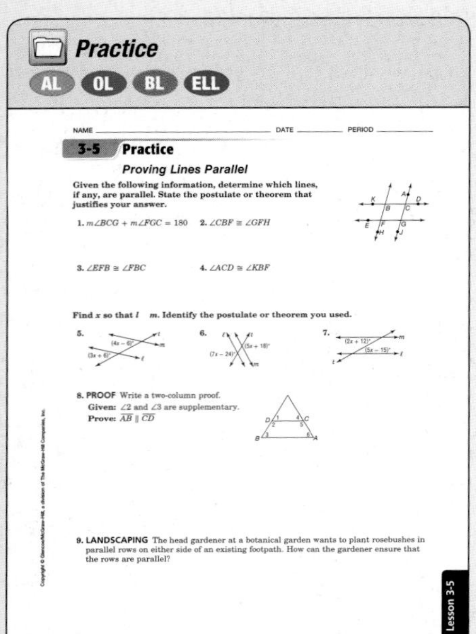

Practice

AL OL BL ELL

NAME ______ DATE ______ PERIOD ______

3-5 Practice

Proving Lines Parallel

Given the following information, determine which lines, if any, are parallel. State the postulate or theorem that justifies your answer.

1. $m\angle BCG + m\angle FGC = 180$
2. $\angle CBF \cong \angle GFH$
3. $\angle EFB \cong \angle FBC$
4. $\angle ACD \cong \angle KBF$

Find x so that l m. Identify the postulate or theorem you used.

5. 6. 7.

8. **PROOF** Write a two-column proof.
Given: $\angle 2$ and $\angle 3$ are supplementary.
Prove: $\overline{AB} \parallel \overline{CD}$

9. **LANDSCAPING** The head gardener at a botanical garden wants to plant rosebushes in parallel rows on either side of an existing footpath. How can the gardener ensure that the rows are parallel?

Lesson 3-5

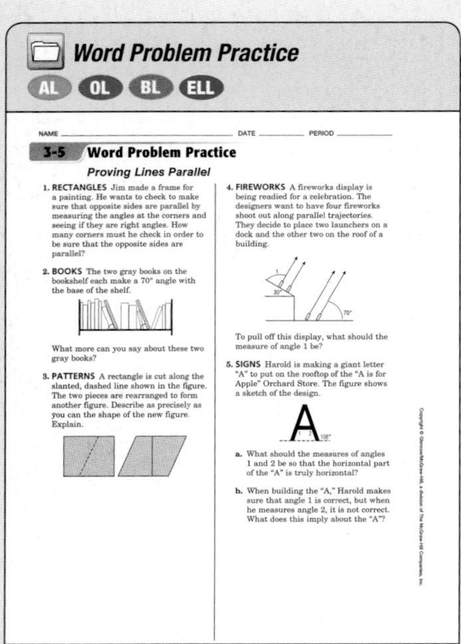

Word Problem Practice

AL OL BL ELL

NAME ______ DATE ______ PERIOD ______

3-5 Word Problem Practice

Proving Lines Parallel

1. **RECTANGLES** Jim made a frame for a painting. He wants to check to make sure that opposite sides are parallel by measuring the angles at the corners and seeing if they are right angles. How many corners must he check in order to be sure that the opposite sides are parallel?

2. **BOOKS** The two gray books on the bookshelf each make a 70° angle with the base of the shelf.
What more can you say about these two gray books?

3. **PATTERNS** A rectangle is cut along the slanted, dashed line shown in the figure. The two pieces are rearranged to form another figure. Describe as precisely as you can the shape of the new figure. Explain.

4. **FIREWORKS** A fireworks display is being readied for a celebration. The designers want to have four fireworks shoot out along parallel trajectories. They decide to place two launchers on a dock and the other two on the roof of a building.
To pull off this display, what should the measure of angle 1 be?

5. **SIGNS** Harold is making a giant letter "A" to put on the rooftop of the "A is for Apple" Orchard Store. The figure shows a sketch of the design.
a. What should the measures of angles 1 and 2 be so that the horizontal part of the "A" is truly horizontal?
b. When building the "A," Harold makes sure that angle 1 is correct, but when he measures angle 2, it is not correct. What does this imply about the "A"?

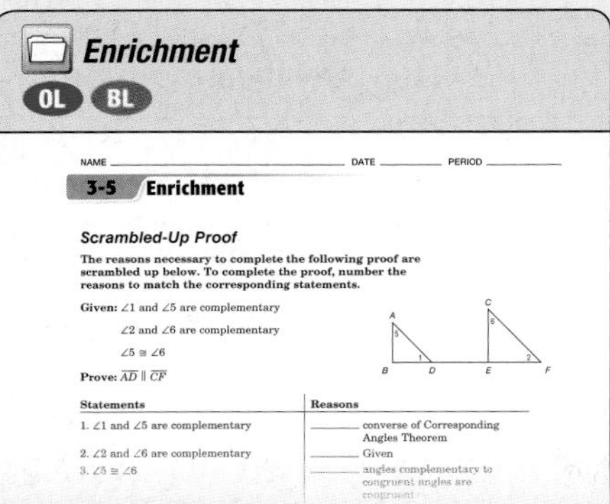

Enrichment

OL BL

NAME ______ DATE ______ PERIOD ______

3-5 Enrichment

Scrambled-Up Proof

The reasons necessary to complete the following proof are scrambled up below. To complete the proof, number the reasons to match the corresponding statements.

Given: $\angle 1$ and $\angle 5$ are complementary
$\angle 2$ and $\angle 6$ are complementary
$\angle 5 \cong \angle 6$
Prove: $\overline{AD} \parallel \overline{CF}$

Statements	Reasons
1. $\angle 1$ and $\angle 5$ are complementary	______ converse of Corresponding Angles Theorem
2. $\angle 2$ and $\angle 6$ are complementary	______ Given
3. $\angle 5 \cong \angle 6$	______ angles complementary to congruent angles are congruent

Additional Answer

29. The Converse of the Perpendicular Transversal Theorem states that two coplanar lines perpendicular to the same line are parallel. Since the slots are perpendicular to each of the sides, the slots are parallel.

36. **MULTIPLE REPRESENTATIONS** In this problem, you will explore the shortest distance between two parallel lines.

a. **Geometric** Draw three sets of parallel lines k and ℓ, s and t, and x and y. For each set, draw the shortest segment $\overline{BC}$ and label points A and D as shown below. See margin.

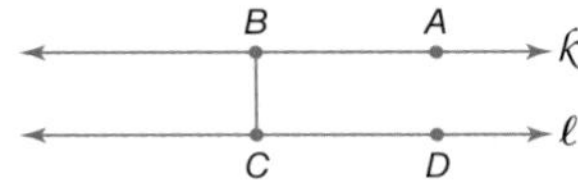

b. **Tabular** Copy the table below, measure $\angle ABC$ and $\angle BCD$, and complete the table.

Set of Parallel Lines	$m\angle ABC$	$m\angle BCD$
k and ℓ	90	90
s and t	90	90
x and y	90	90

c. **Verbal** Make a conjecture about the angle the shortest segment forms with both parallel lines. Sample answer: The angle that the segment forms with the parallel lines will always measure 90.

H.O.T. Problems Use Higher-Order Thinking Skills

37. Daniela; $\angle 1$ and $\angle 2$ are alternate interior angles for $\overline{WX}$ and $\overline{YZ}$, so if alternate interior angles are congruent, then the lines are parallel.

37. **ERROR ANALYSIS** Sumi and Daniela are determining which lines are parallel in the figure at the right. Sumi says that since $\angle 1 \cong \angle 2$, $\overline{WY} \parallel \overline{XZ}$. Daniela disagrees and says that since $\angle 1 \cong \angle 2$, $\overline{WX} \parallel \overline{YZ}$. Is either of them correct? Explain.

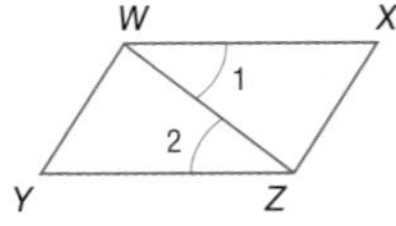

38. **CCSS REASONING** Is Theorem 3.8 still true if the two lines are not coplanar? Draw a figure to justify your answer. See margin.

39. **CHALLENGE** Use the figure at the right to prove that two lines parallel to a third line are parallel to each other. See Ch. 3 Answer Appendix.

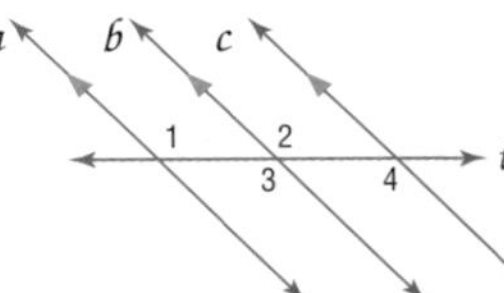

40. **OPEN ENDED** Draw a triangle ABC. See margin.

a. Construct the line parallel to $\overline{BC}$ through point A.

b. Use measurement to justify that the line you constructed is parallel to $\overline{BC}$.

c. Use mathematics to justify this construction.

41–43. See Ch. 3 Answer Appendix.

41. **CHALLENGE** Refer to the figure at the right.

a. If $m\angle 1 + m\angle 2 = 180$, prove that $a \parallel c$.

b. Given that $a \parallel c$, if $m\angle 1 + m\angle 3 = 180$, prove that $t \perp c$.

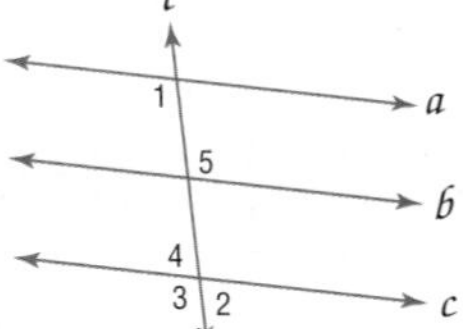

42. **WRITING IN MATH** Summarize the five methods used in this lesson to prove that two lines are parallel.

43. **WRITING IN MATH** Can a pair of angles be supplementary and congruent? Explain your reasoning.

Multiple Representations

In Exercise 36, students use geometric sketches, a table, and verbal description to investigate the shortest distance between two parallel lines.

WatchOut!

Error Analysis In Exercise 37, students should recognize that $\overline{WZ}$ can be a transversal of $\overline{WY}$ and $\overline{XZ}$ as well as $\overline{WX}$ and $\overline{YZ}$. In both cases, $\angle 1$ and $\angle 2$ are congruent alternate interior angles, so $\overline{WY} \parallel \overline{XZ}$ and $\overline{WX} \parallel \overline{YZ}$. Sumi and Daniela are both correct.

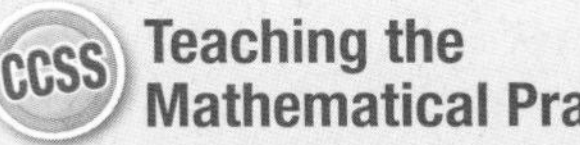

Teaching the Mathematical Practices

Reasoning Mathematically proficient students are able to decontextualize a given situation and represent it symbolically. In Exercise 38, refer students to the description of the Perpendicular Transversal Converse theorem.

Additional Answers

36a.

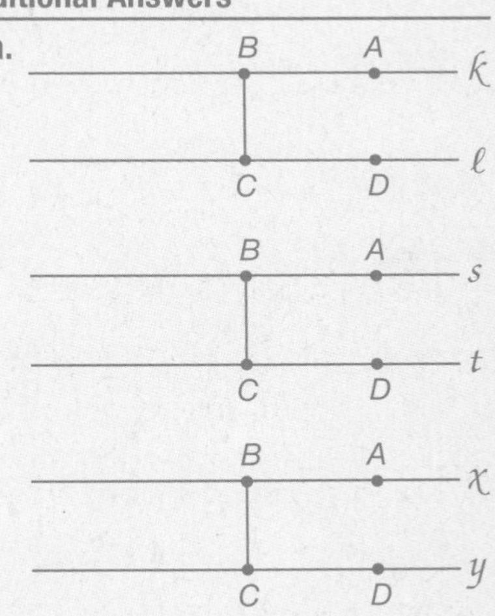

38. No; sample answer: In the figure shown, $\overline{AB} \perp \overline{BC}$ and $\overline{GC} \perp \overline{BC}$, but $\overline{AB} \not\perp \overline{GC}$.

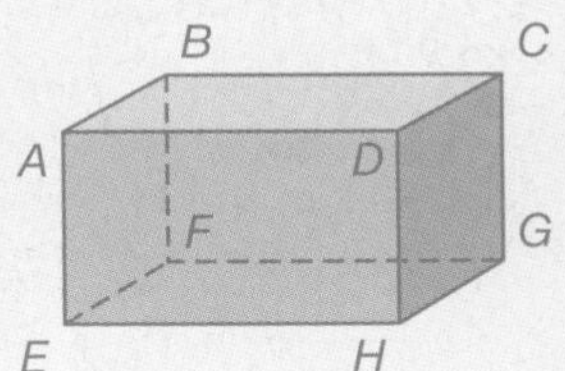

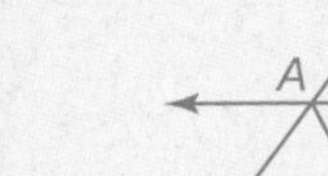

40a.

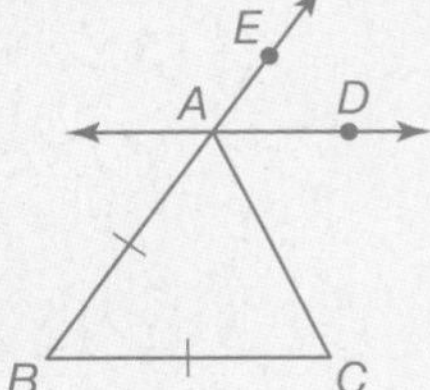

40b. Sample answer: Using a straightedge, the lines are equidistant. So they are parallel.

40c. Sample answer: $\overleftrightarrow{AB}$ is a transversal for $\overleftrightarrow{BC}$ and $\overleftrightarrow{AD}$. $\angle ABC$ was copied to construct $\angle EAD$. So, $\angle ABC \cong \angle EAD$. $\angle ABC$ and $\angle EAD$ are corresponding angles, so by the converse of corresponding angles postulate, $\overleftrightarrow{AD} \parallel \overleftrightarrow{BC}$.

4 Assess

Ticket Out the Door As students leave the classroom, have them write on a piece of paper the procedure for constructing a line parallel to a given line through a point not on the line.

Formative Assessment

Check for student understanding of Lessons 3-4 and 3-5.

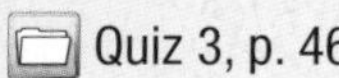

Quiz 3, p. 46

Additional Answers

52. 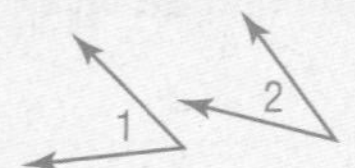

53. 

Standardized Test Practice

44. Which of the following facts would be sufficient to prove that line d is parallel to $\overline{XZ}$? **B**

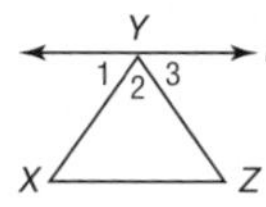

A $\angle 1 \cong \angle 3$ **C** $\angle 1 \cong \angle Z$
B $\angle 3 \cong \angle Z$ **D** $\angle 2 \cong \angle X$

45. ALGEBRA The expression $\sqrt{52} + \sqrt{117}$ is equivalent to **G**

F 13   **H** $6\sqrt{13}$
G $5\sqrt{13}$ **J** $13\sqrt{13}$

46. What is the approximate surface area of the figure? **D**

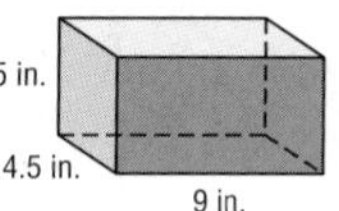

A 101.3 in^2 **C** 202.5 in^2
B 108 in^2 **D** 216 in^2

47. SAT/ACT If $x^2 = 25$ and $y^2 = 9$, what is the greatest possible value of $(x - y)^2$? **J**

F 4   **J** 64
G 16   **K** 70
H 58

Spiral Review

Write an equation in slope-intercept form of the line having the given slope and y-intercept. (Lesson 3-4)

48. m: 2.5, (0, 0.5) $y = 2.5x + 0.5$

49. m: $\frac{4}{5}$, (0, −9) $y = \frac{4}{5}x - 9$

50. m: $-\frac{7}{8}$, $\left(0, -\frac{5}{6}\right)$ $y = -\frac{7}{8}x - \frac{5}{6}$

51. ROAD TRIP Anne is driving 400 miles to visit Niagara Falls. She manages to travel the first 100 miles of her trip in two hours. If she continues at this rate, how long will it take her to drive the remaining distance? (Lesson 3-3) **6 hours**

Find a counterexample to show that each conjecture is false. (Lesson 2-1)

52. Given: $\angle 1$ and $\angle 2$ are complementary angles. **52–53. See margin.**

Conjecture: $\angle 1$ and $\angle 2$ form a right angle.

53. Given: points W, X, Y, and Z

Conjecture: W, X, Y, and Z are noncollinear.

Find the perimeter or circumference and area of each figure. Round to the nearest tenth. (Lesson 1-6)

54. 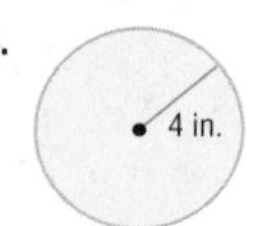

≈25.1 in.; ≈50.3 in^2

55. 3.2 m, 1.1 m

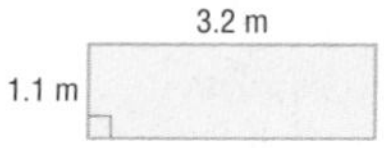

8.6 m; ≈3.5 m^2

56. 4 cm, 6 cm

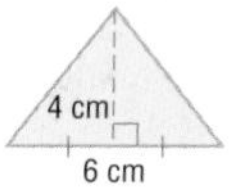

16 cm; 12 cm^2

Skills Review

57. Find x and y so that $\overline{BE}$ and $\overline{AD}$ are perpendicular. **10, 8.3**

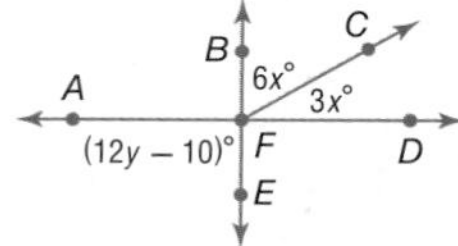

214 | Lesson 3-5 | Proving Lines Parallel

LESSON 3-6 Perpendiculars and Distance

Then

- You proved that two lines are parallel using angle relationships.

Now

1. Find the distance between a point and a line.
2. Find the distance between parallel lines.

Why?

- A *plumb bob* is made of string with a specially designed weight. When the weight is suspended and allowed to swing freely, the point of the bob is precisely below the point to which the string is fixed.

The plumb bob is useful in establishing what is the true vertical or *plumb* when constructing a wall or when hanging wallpaper.

NewVocabulary
equidistant

Common Core State Standards

Content Standards

G.CO.12 Make formal geometric constructions with a variety of tools and methods (compass and straightedge, string, reflective devices, paper folding, dynamic geometric software, etc.).

G.MG.3 Apply geometric methods to solve problems (e.g., designing an object or structure to satisfy physical constraints or minimize cost; working with typographic grid systems based on ratios). ★

Mathematical Practices

2 Reason abstractly and quantitatively.
4 Model with mathematics.

1 Distance From a Point to a Line

The plumb bob also indicates the shortest distance between the point at which it is attached on the ceiling and a level floor below. This perpendicular distance between a point and a line is the shortest in all cases.

KeyConcept Distance Between a Point and a Line

Words The distance between a line and a point not on the line is the length of the segment perpendicular to the line from the point.

Model

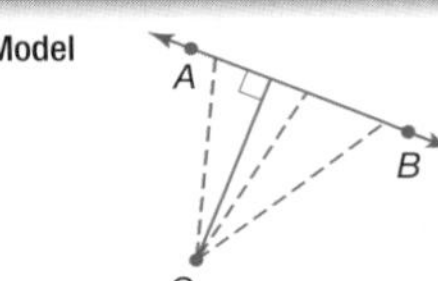

The construction of a line perpendicular to an existing line through a point not on the existing line in Extend Lesson 1-5 establishes that there is *at least one* line through a point P that is perpendicular to a line AB. The following postulate states that this line is the *only* line through P perpendicular to $\overleftrightarrow{AB}$.

Postulate 3.6 Perpendicular Postulate

Words If given a line and a point not on the line, then there exists exactly one line through the point that is perpendicular to the given line.

Model

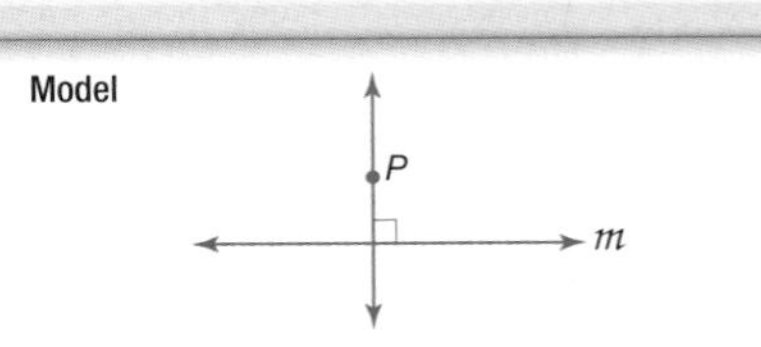

1 Focus

VerticalAlignment

Before Lesson 3-6 Use angle relationships to prove that two lines are parallel.

Lesson 3-6 Find the distance between a point and a line. Find the distance between two parallel lines.

After Lesson 3-6 Make conjectures about lines and determine the validity of the conjectures.

2 Teach

Scaffolding Questions

Have students read the **Why?** section of the lesson.

Ask:

- What are other professions that may use a plumb bob? Plumb bobs are used by carpenters and surveyors.
- Why is it important to use a tool to ensure the accuracy of the true vertical alignment of a structure? Structures are more stable and structurally sound when properly aligned both vertically and horizontally.
- What tool is equivalent to the plumb bob for ensuring horizontal alignment of a structure? a level

Lesson 3-6 Resources

Resource	Approaching Level AL	On Level OL	Beyond Level BL	English Learners ELL
Teacher Edition	▪ Differentiated Instruction, p. 216	▪ Differentiated Instruction, p. 216	▪ Differentiated Instruction, p. 223	▪ Differentiated Instruction, p. 216
Chapter Resource Masters	▪ Study Guide and Intervention, pp. 36–37 ▪ Skills Practice, p. 38 ▪ Practice, p. 39 ▪ Word Problem Practice, p. 40	▪ Study Guide and Intervention, pp. 36–37 ▪ Skills Practice, p. 38 ▪ Practice, p. 39 ▪ Word Problem Practice, p. 40 ▪ Enrichment, p. 41 ▪ Graphing Calculator Activity, p. 42	▪ Practice, p. 39 ▪ Word Problem Practice, p. 40 ▪ Enrichment, p. 41	▪ Study Guide and Intervention, pp. 36–37 ▪ Skills Practice, p. 38 ▪ Practice, p. 39 ▪ Word Problem Practice, p. 40
Other	▪ 5-Minute Check 3-6 ▪ Study Notebook ▪ Teaching Geometry with Manipulatives	▪ 5-Minute Check 3-6 ▪ Study Notebook ▪ Teaching Geometry with Manipulatives	▪ 5-Minute Check 3-6 ▪ Study Notebook	▪ 5-Minute Check 3-6 ▪ Study Notebook ▪ Teaching Geometry with Manipulatives

1 Distance From a Point to a Line

Example 1 shows how to determine the distance from a line to a point not on the line by constructing a line segment perpendicular to the original line. **Example 2** shows how to use coordinate geometry to find the distance from a line to a point not on the line.

Formative Assessment

Use the Guided Practice exercises after each example to determine students' understanding of concepts.

Additional Example

1 **CONSTRUCTION** A certain roof truss is designed so that the center post extends from the peak of the roof (point A) to the main beam. Construct and name the segment whose length represents the shortest length of wood that will be needed to connect the peak of the roof to the main beam. $\overline{AB}$

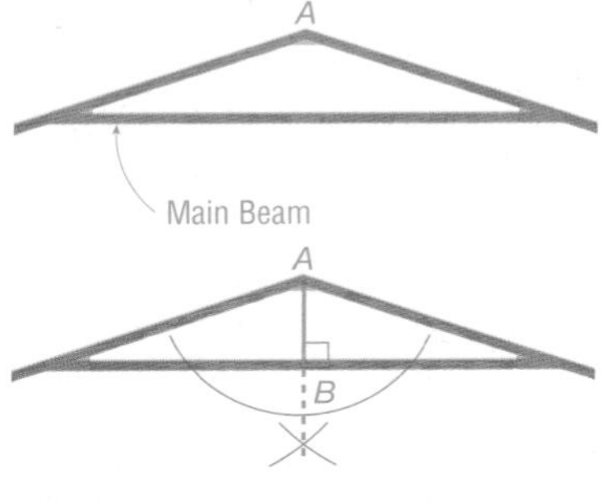

Additional Examples also in Interactive Classroom PowerPoint® Presentations

Additional Answer (Guided Practice)

1. $\overline{QT}$ represents the distance from Q to $\overleftrightarrow{PR}$.

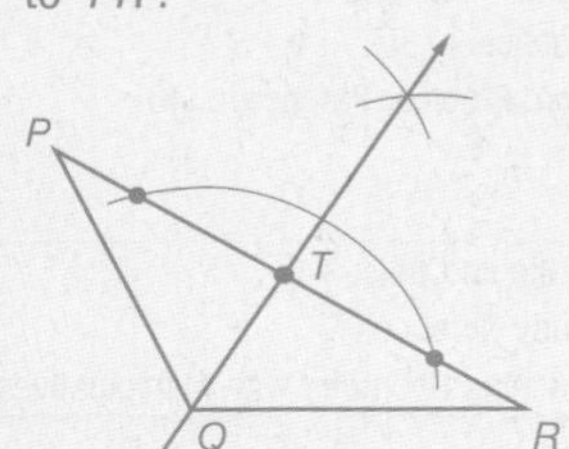

Real-World Career

Landscape Architect Landscape architects enjoy working with their hands and possess strong analytical skills. Creative vision and artistic talent are also desirable qualities. Typically, a bachelor's degree is required of landscape architects, but a master's degree may be required for specializations such as golf course design.

Real-World Example 1 Construct Distance From a Point to a Line

LANDSCAPING **A landscape architect notices that one part of a yard does not drain well. She wants to tap into an existing underground drain represented by line m. Construct and name the segment with the length that represents the shortest amount of pipe she will need to lay to connect this drain to point A.**

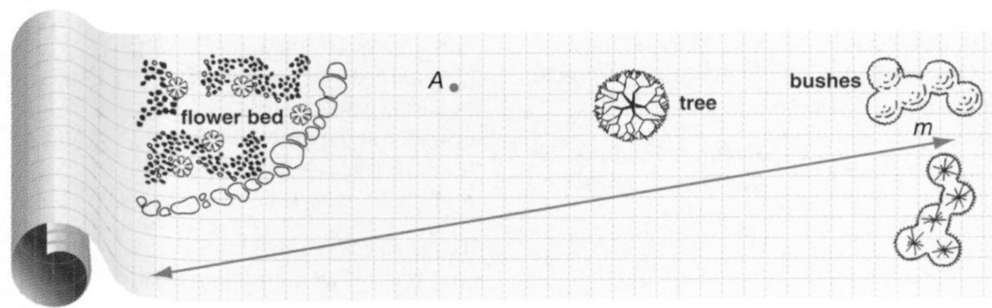

The distance from a line to a point not on the line is the length of the segment perpendicular to the line from the point. Locate points B and C on line m equidistant from point A.

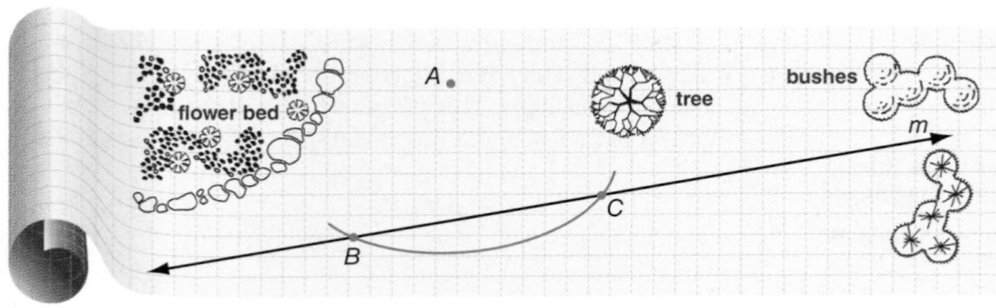

Locate a third point on line m equidistant from B and C. Label this point D. Then draw $\overleftrightarrow{AD}$ so that $\overleftrightarrow{AD} \perp \overleftrightarrow{BC}$.

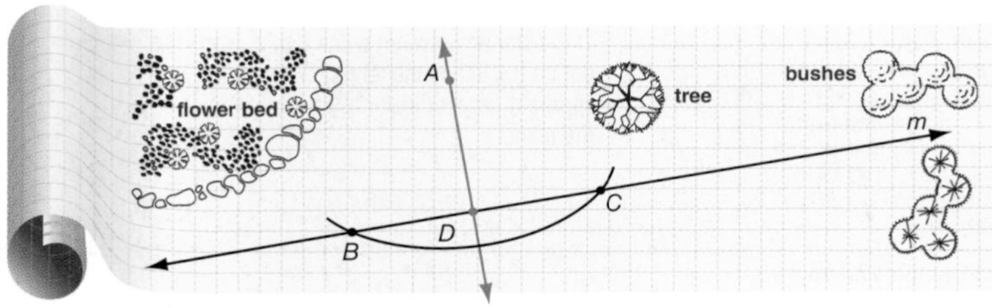

The measure of $\overline{AD}$ represents the shortest amount of pipe the architect will need to lay to connect the drain to point A.

Study Tip

Drawing the Shortest Distance You can use tools like the corner of a piece of paper to help you draw a perpendicular segment from a point to a line, but only a compass and a straightedge can be used to construct this segment.

Guided Practice

1. Copy the figure. Then construct and name the segment that represents the distance from Q to $\overleftrightarrow{PR}$. See margin.

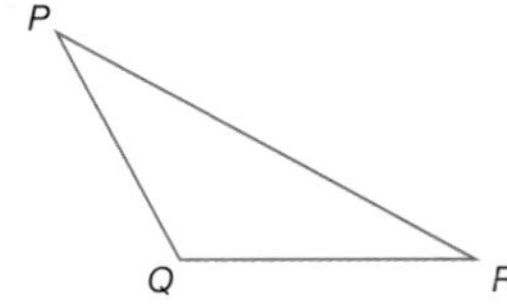

Differentiated Instruction AL OL ELL

Kinesthetic Learners Identify examples of parallel lines in the classroom, like the grout lines of the tile floor or the frame of the chalkboard. Have students work in pairs to measure the distance of various points along one line to a fixed point on another line. Have students discuss their findings. Facilitate the discussions so that students are able to see the relationships of the segments and distances between parallel lines.

StudyTip

Distance to Axes Note that the distance from a point to the x-axis can be determined by looking at the y-coordinate, and the distance from a point to the y-axis can be determined by looking at the x-coordinate.

Example 2 Distance from a Point to a Line on Coordinate Plane

COORDINATE GEOMETRY **Line ℓ contains points at $(-5, 3)$ and $(4, -6)$. Find the distance between line ℓ and point $P(2, 4)$.**

Step 1 Find the equation of the line ℓ.

Begin by finding the slope of the line through points $(-5, 3)$ and $(4, -6)$.

$$m = \frac{y_2 - y_1}{x_2 - x_1} = \frac{-6 - 3}{4 - (-5)} = \frac{-9}{9} \text{ or } -1$$

Then write the equation of this line using the point $(4, -6)$ on the line.

$y = mx + b$	Slope-intercept form
$-6 = -1(4) + b$	$m = -1, (x, y) = (4, -6)$
$-6 = -4 + b$	Simplify.
$-2 = b$	Add 4 to each side.

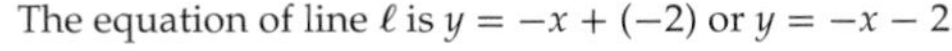

The equation of line ℓ is $y = -x + (-2)$ or $y = -x - 2$.

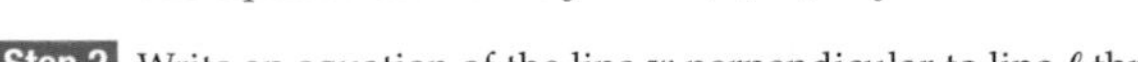

Step 2 Write an equation of the line w perpendicular to line ℓ through $P(2, 4)$.

Since the slope of line ℓ is -1, the slope of a line p is 1. Write the equation of line w through $P(2, 4)$ with slope 1.

$y = mx + b$	Slope-intercept form
$4 = 1(2) + b$	$m = -1, (x, y) = (2, 4)$
$4 = 2 + b$	Simplify.
$2 = b$	Subtract 2 from each side.

The equation of line w is $y = x + 2$.

StudyTip

Elimination Method To review **solving systems of equations** using the elimination method, see p. P18.

Step 3 Solve the system of equations to determine the point of intersection.

line ℓ: $y = -x - 2$

line w: $(+)\ y = x + 2$

$2y = 0$	Add the two equations.
$y = 0$	Divide each side by 2.

Solve for x.

$0 = x + 2$	Substitute 0 for y in the second equation.
$-2 = x$	Subtract 2 from each side.

The point of intersection is $(-2, 0)$. Let this be point Q.

Step 4 Use the Distance Formula to determine the distance between $P(2, 4)$ and $Q(-2, 0)$.

$d = \sqrt{(x_2 - x_1)^2 + (y_2 - y_1)^2}$	Distance formula
$= \sqrt{(-2 - 2)^2 + (0 - 4)^2}$	$x_2 = -2, x_1 = 2, y_2 = 0, y_1 = 4$
$= \sqrt{32}$	Simplify.

The distance between the point and the line is $\sqrt{32}$ or about 5.66 units.

Focus on Mathematical Content

Angles Formed by Perpendicular Lines By definition, perpendicular lines form right angles. Because right angles are congruent, the angles formed by perpendicular lines are congruent and adjacent. In contrast, if two lines form congruent adjacent angles, then the lines are perpendicular.

Additional Example

2 **COORDINATE GEOMETRY** Line s contains points at $(0, 0)$ and $(-5, 5)$. Find the distance between line s and point $V(1, 5)$.

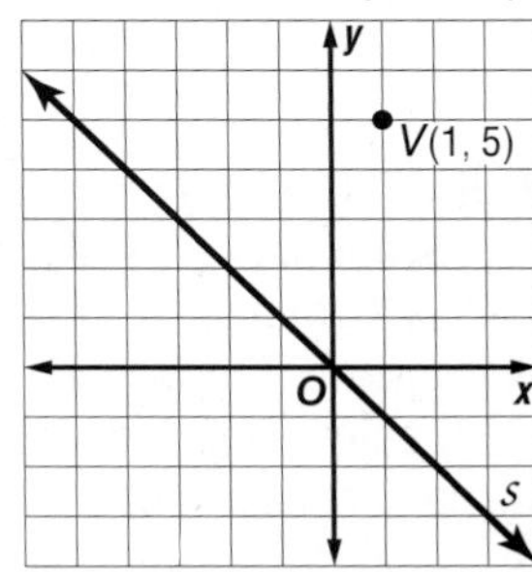

Sample answer: $d = \sqrt{18}$ or about 4.24 units

Teach with Tech

Audio Recording Have students explain in their own words why the distance from a point to a line is the length of the perpendicular segment from the point to the line. Then, post the audio files on your class Web site.

2 Distance Between Parallel Lines

Equidistant means that the distance between two lines measured along any line perpendicular to both lines is always the same. In **Example 3,** the students will find the distance between parallel lines algebraically.

Additional Example

3 Find the distance between the parallel lines a and b with equations $y = 2x + 3$ and $y = 2x - 1$, respectively. about 1.79 units

Tips for New Teachers

Real-Life Connections Ask students to identify a straight path in a park, playground, or field. They should visualize any point in the park that is not on the path, and imagine going from that point directly to the path. Then they should verify that their movement to the path was perpendicular to the path.

GuidedPractice

2. Line ℓ contains points at (1, 2) and (5, 4). Construct a line perpendicular to ℓ through $P(1, 7)$. Then find the distance from P to ℓ. $\sqrt{20} \approx 4.47$

StudyTip

Equidistant You will use this concept of *equidistant* to describe special points and lines relating to the sides and angles of triangles in Lesson 5-1.

2 Distance Between Parallel Lines By definition, parallel lines do not intersect. An alternate definition states that two lines in a plane are parallel if they are everywhere **equidistant**. Equidistant means that the distance between two lines measured along a perpendicular line to the lines is always the same.

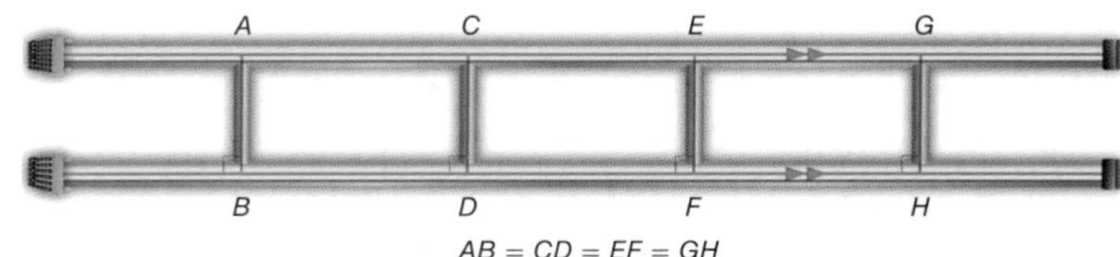

$AB = CD = EF = GH$

This leads to the definition of the distance between two parallel lines.

KeyConcept Distance Between Parallel Lines

The distance between two parallel lines is the perpendicular distance between one of the lines and any point on the other line.

StudyTip

Locus of Points Equidistant from Two Parallel Lines Conversely, the locus of points in a plane that are equidistant from two parallel lines is a third line that is parallel to and centered between the two parallel lines.

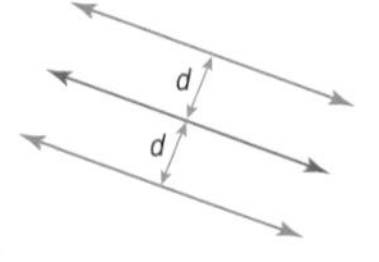

Recall from Lesson 1-1 that a *locus* is the set of all points that satisfy a given condition. Parallel lines can be described as the locus of points in a plane equidistant from a given line.

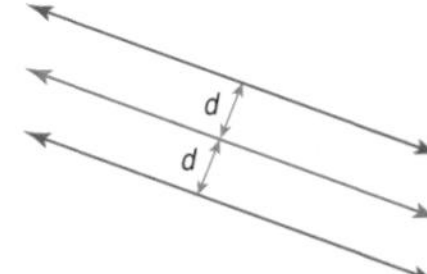

Theorem 3.9 Two Lines Equidistant from a Third

In a plane, if two lines are each equidistant from a third line, then the two lines are parallel to each other.

You will prove Theorem 3.9 in Exercise 30.

Example 3 Distance Between Parallel Lines

Find the distance between the parallel lines ℓ and m with equations $y = 2x + 1$ and $y = 2x - 3$, respectively.

You will need to solve a system of equations to find the endpoints of a segment that is perpendicular to both ℓ and m. From their equations, we know that the slope of line ℓ and line m is 2.

Sketch line p through the y-intercept of line m, (0, −3), perpendicular to lines m and ℓ.

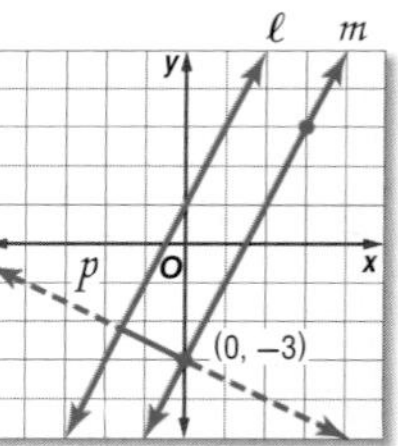

218 | Lesson 3-6 | Perpendiculars and Distance

Step 1 Write an equation of line p. The slope of p is the opposite reciprocal of 2, or $-\frac{1}{2}$. Use the y-intercept of line m, (0, −3), as one of the endpoints of the perpendicular segment.

$$(y - y_1) = m(x - x_1) \quad \text{Point-slope form}$$

$$[y - (-3)] = -\frac{1}{2}(x - 0) \quad x_1 = 0,\ y_1 = 3, \text{ and } m = -\frac{1}{2}$$

$$y + 3 = -\frac{1}{2}x \quad \text{Simplify.}$$

$$y = -\frac{1}{2}x - 3 \quad \text{Subtract 3 from each side.}$$

Step 2 Use a system of equations to determine the point of intersection of lines ℓ and p.

ℓ: $y = 2x + 1$

p: $y = -\frac{1}{2}x - 3$

$$2x + 1 = -\frac{1}{2}x - 3 \quad \text{Substitute } 2x + 1 \text{ for } y \text{ in the second equation.}$$

$$2x + \frac{1}{2}x = -3 - 1 \quad \text{Group like terms on each side.}$$

$$\frac{5}{2}x = -4 \quad \text{Simplify on each side.}$$

$$x = -\frac{8}{5} \quad \text{Multiply each side by } \frac{2}{5}.$$

$$y = -\frac{1}{2}\left(-\frac{8}{5}\right) - 3 \quad \text{Substitute } -\frac{8}{5} \text{ for } x \text{ in the equation for } p.$$

$$= -\frac{11}{5} \quad \text{Simplify.}$$

The point of intersection is $\left(-\frac{8}{5}, -\frac{11}{5}\right)$ or (−1.6, −2.2).

StudyTip

Substitution Method To review solving systems of equations using the substitution method, see p. P17.

Step 3 Use the Distance Formula to determine the distance between (0, −3) and (−1.6, −2.2).

$$d = \sqrt{(x_2 - x_1)^2 + (y_2 - y_1)^2} \quad \text{Distance Formula}$$

$$= \sqrt{(-1.6 - 0)^2 + [-2.2 - (-3)]^2} \quad x_2 = -1.6,\ x_1 = 0,\ y_2 = -2.2, \text{ and } y_1 = -3$$

$$\approx 1.8 \quad \text{Simplify using a calculator.}$$

The distance between the lines is about 1.8 units.

GuidedPractice

3A. Find the distance between the parallel lines r and s whose equations are $y = -3x - 5$ and $y = -3x + 6$, respectively. $\sqrt{12.1} \approx 3.48$

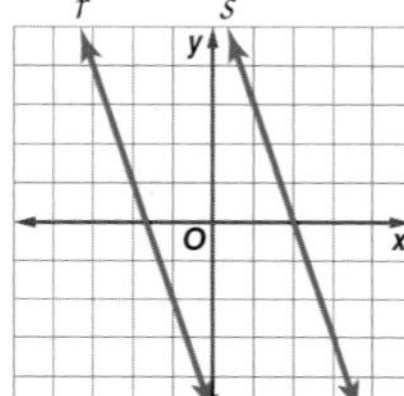

3B. Find the distance between parallel lines a and b with equations $x + 3y = 6$ and $x + 3y = -14$, respectively.

$\sqrt{40} \approx 6.32$

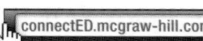

connectED.mcgraw-hill.com 219

3 Practice

Formative Assessment

Use Exercise 1-8 to check for understanding.

Use the chart at the bottom of this page to customize assignments for your students.

Teaching the Mathematical Practices

Structure Mathematically proficient students look closely to discern a pattern. In Exercise 3, students may have difficulty visualizing the pattern. Have the students act out the problem.

Additional Answers

1.

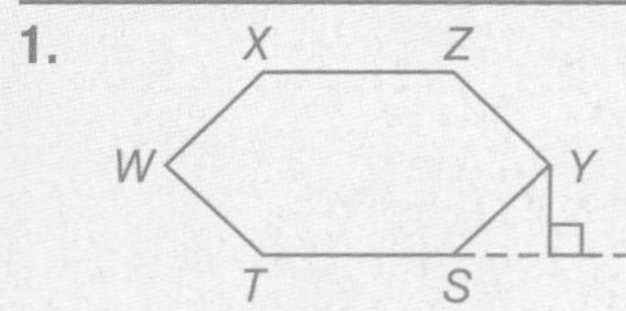

2.

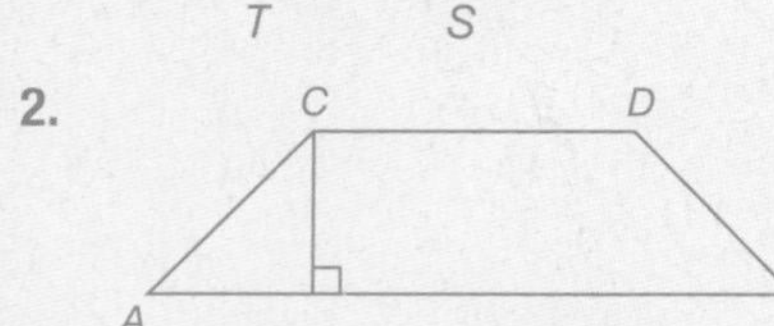

30. **Given:** ℓ is equidistant to m, and n is equidistant to m.

Prove: $\ell \parallel n$

Proof:

Statements (Reasons)

1. ℓ is equidistant to m, and n is equidistant to m. (Given)
2. $\ell \parallel m$ and $m \parallel n$ (Def. of equidistant)
3. slope of ℓ = slope of m slope of m = slope of n (Def. of $\parallel$ lines)
4. slope of ℓ = slope of n (Substitution)
5. $\ell \parallel n$ (Def. of $\parallel$ lines)

34. Alma can measure the perpendicular distance between the posters in two different places. If these distances are equal, then the posters are parallel.

Check Your Understanding

 = Step-by-Step Solutions begin on page R14.

Example 1 **Copy each figure. Construct the segment that represents the distance indicated.**

1. Y to $\overleftrightarrow{TS}$ See margin.

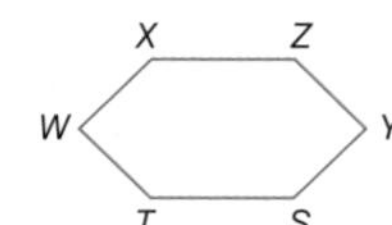

2. C to $\overleftrightarrow{AB}$ See margin.

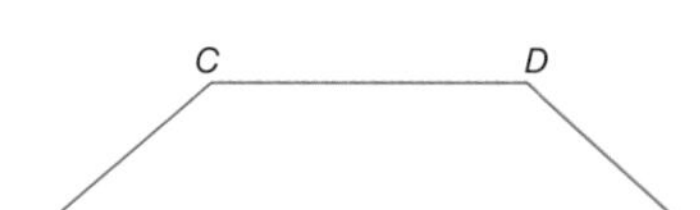

3. **CCSS STRUCTURE** After forming a line, every even member of a marching band turns to face the home team's end zone and marches 5 paces straight forward. At the same time, every odd member turns in the opposite direction and marches 5 paces straight forward. Assuming that each band member covers the same distance, what formation should result? Justify your answer.

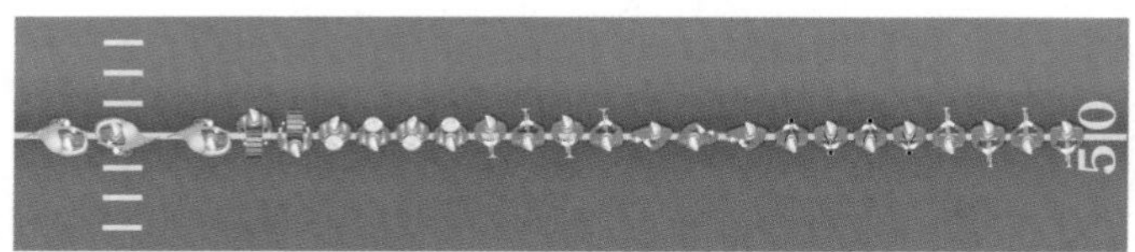

Example 2 **COORDINATE GEOMETRY Find the distance from P to ℓ.**

4. Line ℓ contains points (4, 3) and (−2, 0). Point P has coordinates (3, 10). $3\sqrt{5}$ units
5. Line ℓ contains points (−6, 1) and (9, −4). Point P has coordinates (4, 1). $\sqrt{10}$ units
6. Line ℓ contains points (4, 18) and (−2, 9). Point P has coordinates (−9, 5). $\sqrt{13}$ units

Example 3 **Find the distance between each pair of parallel lines with the given equations.**

7. $y = -2x + 4$ $2\sqrt{5}$ units
$y = -2x + 14$

8. $y = 7$ 10 units
$y = -3$

3. The formation should be that of two parallel lines that are also parallel to the 50-yard line; the band members have formed two lines that are equidistant from the 50-yard line, so by Theorem 3.9, the two lines formed are parallel.

Practice and Problem Solving

Extra Practice is on page R3.

Example 1 **Copy each figure. Construct the segment that represents the distance indicated.** 9–12. See Ch. 3 Answer Appendix.

9. Q to $\overline{RS}$

10. A to $\overline{BC}$

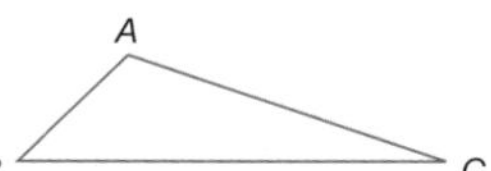

11. H to $\overline{FG}$

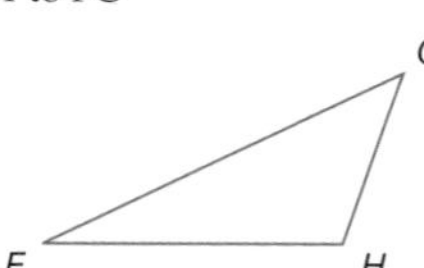

12. K to $\overline{LM}$

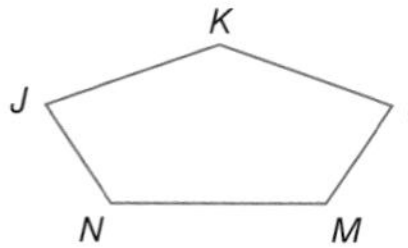

Differentiated Homework Options

Level	Assignment	Two-Day Option	
AL Basic	9–29, 41, 42, 44–65	9–29 odd, 48–51	10–28 even, 41, 42, 44–47, 52–65
OL Core	9–33 odd, 34–42, 44–65	9–29, 48–51	30–42, 44–47, 52–65
BL Advanced	30–59, (optional: 60–65)		

13. **DRIVEWAYS** In the diagram at the right, is the driveway shown the shortest possible one from the house to the road? Explain why or why not.

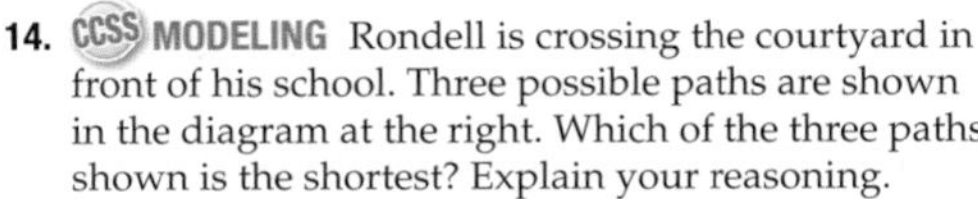

No; a driveway perpendicular to the road would be the shortest. The angle the driveway makes with the road is less than 90°, so it is not the shortest possible driveway.

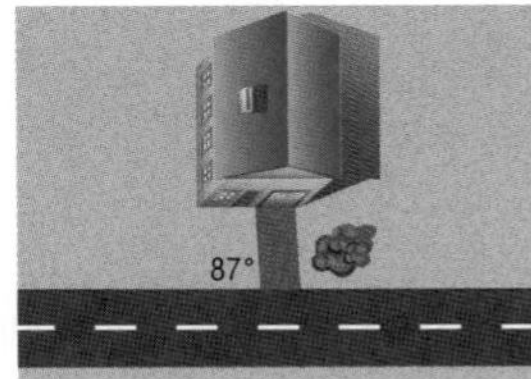

14. **CCSS MODELING** Rondell is crossing the courtyard in front of his school. Three possible paths are shown in the diagram at the right. Which of the three paths shown is the shortest? Explain your reasoning.

Path B; The shortest possible distance would be the perpendicular distance from one side of the courtyard to the other. Since Path B is the closest to 90°, it is the shortest of the three paths shown.

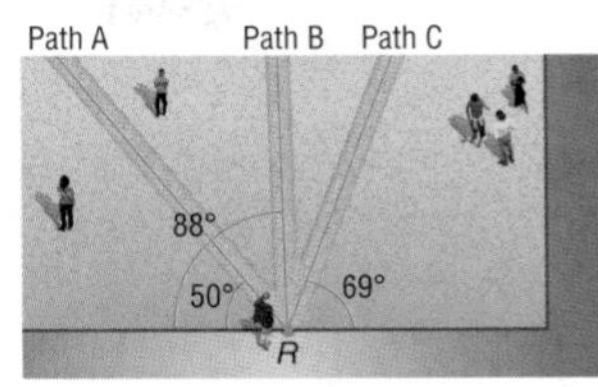

Example 2 **COORDINATE GEOMETRY** **Find the distance from P to ℓ.**

15. Line ℓ contains points $(0, -3)$ and $(7, 4)$. Point P has coordinates $(4, 3)$. $\sqrt{2}$ units

16. Line ℓ contains points $(11, -1)$ and $(-3, -11)$. Point P has coordinates $(-1, 1)$. $\sqrt{74}$ units

17. Line ℓ contains points $(-2, 1)$ and $(4, 1)$. Point P has coordinates $(5, 7)$. 6 units

18. Line ℓ contains points $(4, -1)$ and $(4, 9)$. Point P has coordinates $(1, 6)$. 3 units

19. Line ℓ contains points $(1, 5)$ and $(4, -4)$. Point P has coordinates $(-1, 1)$. $\sqrt{10}$ units

20. Line ℓ contains points $(-8, 1)$ and $(3, 1)$. Point P has coordinates $(-2, 4)$. 3 units

Example 3 **Find the distance between each pair of parallel lines with the given equations.**

21. $y = -2$, $y = 4$ 6 units

22. $x = 3$, $x = 7$ 4 units

23. $y = 5x - 22$, $y = 5x + 4$ $\sqrt{26}$ units

24. $y = \frac{1}{3}x - 3$, $y = \frac{1}{3}x + 2$ $1.5\sqrt{10}$ units

25. $x = 8.5$, $x = -12.5$ 21 units

26. $y = 15$, $y = -4$ 19 units

27. $y = \frac{1}{4}x + 2$, $4y - x = -60$ $4\sqrt{17}$ units

28. $3x + y = 3$, $y + 17 = -3x$ $2\sqrt{10}$ units

29. $y = -\frac{5}{4}x + 3.5$, $4y + 10.6 = -5x$ $\sqrt{14.76}$ units

B 30. **PROOF** Write a two-column proof of Theorem 3.9. See margin.

Find the distance from the line to the given point.

31. $y = -3, (5, 2)$ 5 units

32. $y = \frac{1}{6}x + 6, (-6, 5)$ 0 units

33. $x = 4, (-2, 5)$ 6 units

34. **POSTERS** Alma is hanging two posters on the wall in her room as shown. How can Alma use perpendicular distances to confirm that the posters are parallel? See margin.

Teaching the Mathematical Practices

Modeling Mathematically proficient students can apply the mathematics they know to solve problems arising in the real world. They also routinely interpret their results in the context of the situation. In Exercise 14, point out to students that Path B is not perpendicular to the line containing R.

Enrichment

OL BL

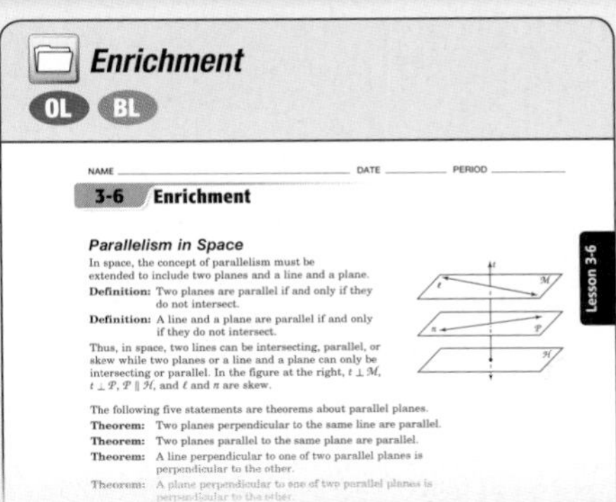

3-6 Enrichment

Parallelism in Space

Study Guide and Intervention

AL OL ELL

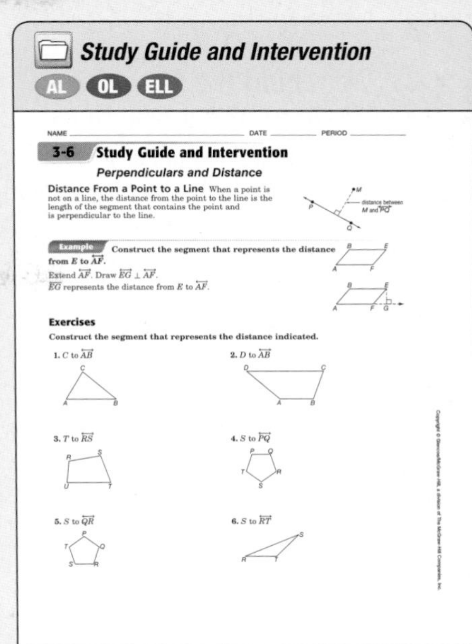

3-6 Study Guide and Intervention

Perpendiculars and Distance

Practice

AL OL BL ELL

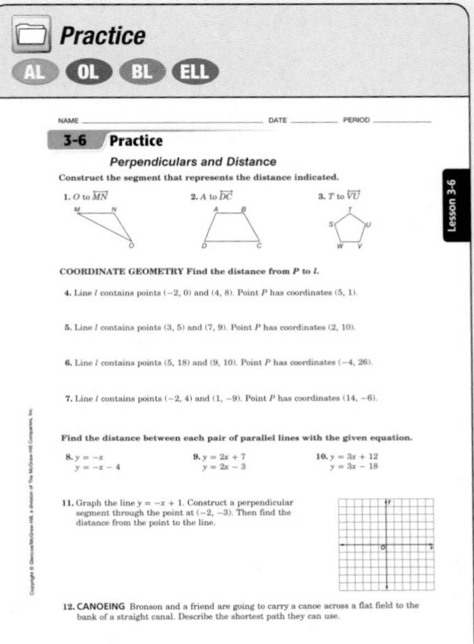

3-6 Practice

Perpendiculars and Distance

Word Problem Practice

AL OL BL ELL

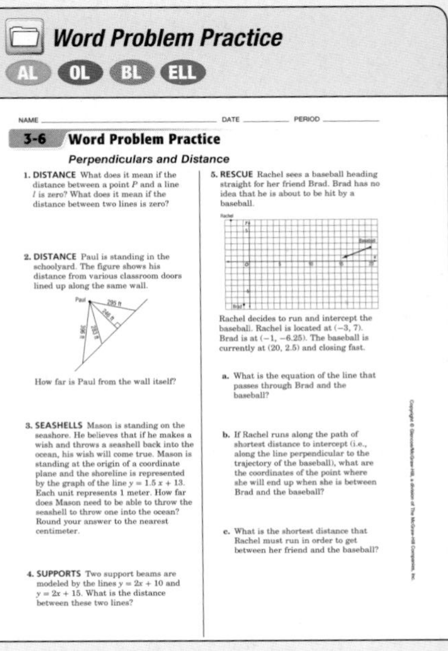

3-6 Word Problem Practice

Perpendiculars and Distance

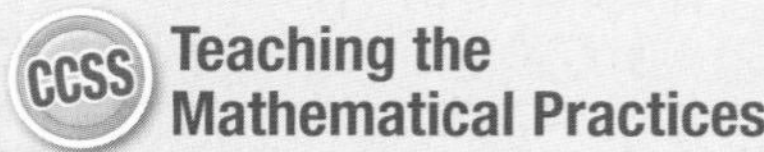

Teaching the Mathematical Practices

Sense-making Mathematically proficient students look for entry points to a solution. They analyze givens, constraints, relationships, and goals. In Exercise 22, encourage students to use their graph to find the coordinates of A and B.

Multiple Representations

In Exercise 39, students use a geometric sketch and verbal description to explore the area of triangles formed by points on parallel lines.

Additional Answers

35. He can conclude that the right and left sides of the bulletin board are not parallel, since the perpendicular distance between one line and any point on the other line must be equal be the same anywhere on the lines for the two lines to be parallel.

36. Sample answer: The lines are perpendicular; the slope of ℓ is -1 and the slope of $\overleftrightarrow{PQ}$ is 1. Since the slopes are negative reciprocals, the lines are perpendicular.

38a.

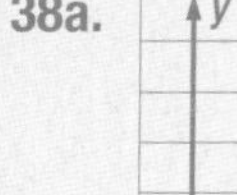

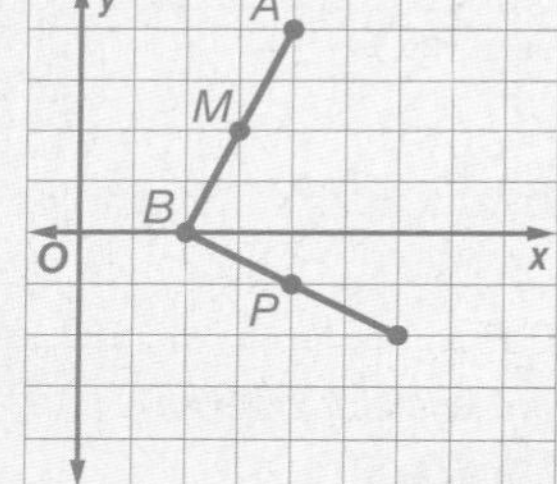

43. $a = \pm 1$; $y = \frac{1}{2}x + 6$ and $y = \frac{1}{2}x + \frac{7}{2}$ or $y = -\frac{1}{2}x + 6$ and $y = -\frac{1}{2}x + \frac{7}{2}$

45a. Sample answer:

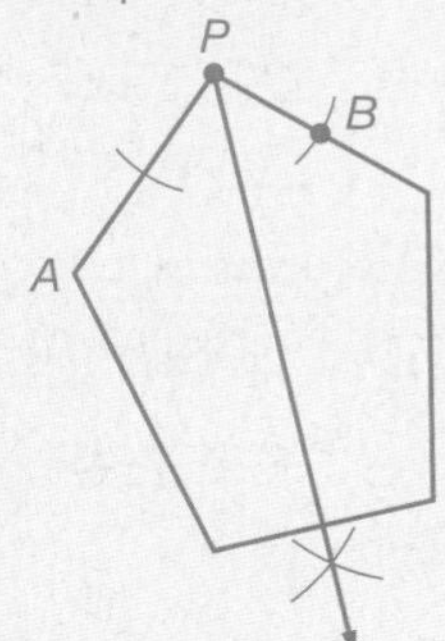

35. **SCHOOL SPIRIT** Brock is decorating a hallway bulletin board to display pictures of students demonstrating school spirit. He cuts off one length of border to match the width of the top of the board, and then uses that strip as a template to cut a second strip that is exactly the same length for the bottom.

DON'T MESS WITH THE BEST!

When stapling the bottom border in place, he notices that the strip he cut is about a quarter of an inch too short. Describe what he can conclude about the bulletin board. Explain your reasoning. **See margin.**

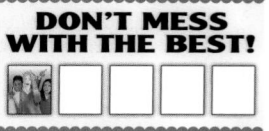

CONSTRUCTION **Line ℓ contains points at $(-4, 3)$ and $(2, -3)$. Point P at $(-2, 1)$ is on line ℓ. Complete the following construction.**

Step 1

Graph line ℓ and point P, and put the compass at point P. Using the same compass setting, draw arcs to the left and right of P. Label these points A and B.

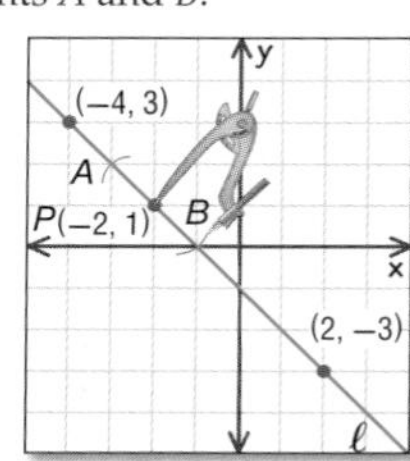

Step 2

Open the compass to a setting greater than AP. Put the compass at point A and draw an arc above line ℓ.

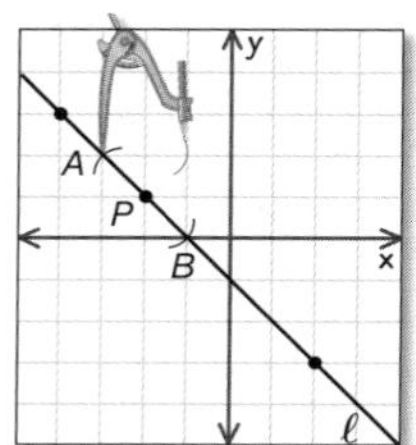

Step 3

Using the same compass setting, put the compass at point B and draw an arc above line ℓ. Label the point of intersection Q. Then draw $\overleftrightarrow{PQ}$.

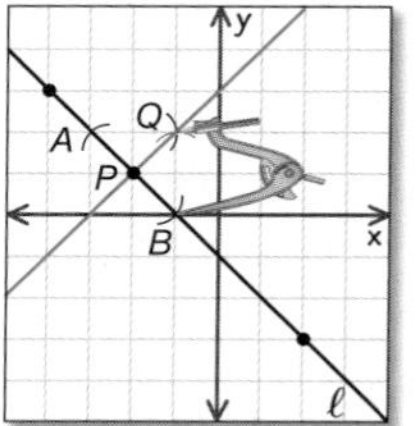

36. What is the relationship between line ℓ and $\overleftrightarrow{PQ}$? Verify your conjecture using the slopes of the two lines. **See margin.**

37. Repeat the construction above using a different line and point on that line. **See students' work.**

38.  **SENSE-MAKING** $\overline{AB}$ has a slope of 2 and midpoint $M(3, 2)$. A segment perpendicular to $\overline{AB}$ has midpoint $P(4, -1)$ and shares endpoint B with $\overline{AB}$.

a. Graph the segments. **See margin.**

b. Find the coordinates of A and B. **$A(4, 4)$, $B(2, 0)$**

39. **MULTIPLE REPRESENTATIONS** In this problem, you will explore the areas of triangles formed by points on parallel lines.

a. Geometric Draw two parallel lines and label them as shown. **See students' work.**

39b. Place point C any place on line m. The area of the triangle is $\frac{1}{2}$ the height of the triangle times the length of the base of the triangle. The numbers stay constant regardless of the location of C on line m.

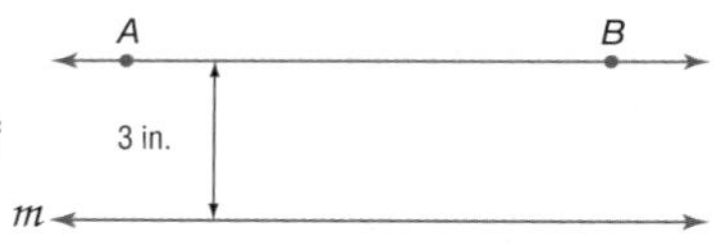

b. Verbal Where would you place point C on line m to ensure that triangle ABC would have the largest area? Explain your reasoning.

c. Analytical If $AB = 11$ inches, what is the maximum area of $\triangle ABC$? **16.5 in^2**

40. PERPENDICULARITY AND PLANES Make a copy of the diagram below to answer each question, marking the diagram with the given information.

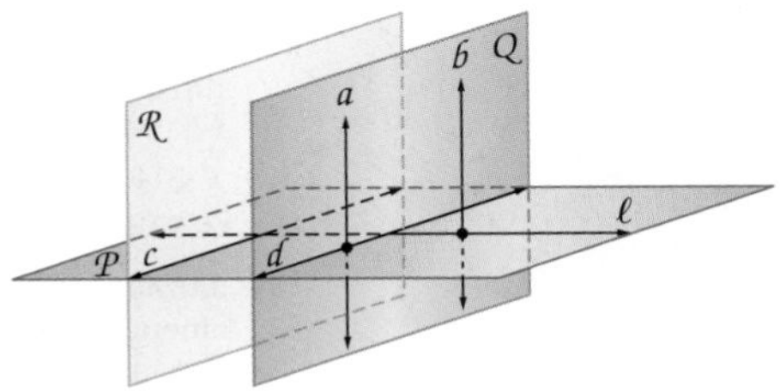

a. If two lines are perpendicular to the same plane, then they are coplanar. If both line a and line b are perpendicular to plane $\mathcal{P}$, what must also be true? **Lines a and b are coplanar.**

b. If a plane intersects two parallel planes, then the intersections form two parallel lines. If planes $\mathcal{R}$ and $\mathcal{Q}$ are parallel and they intersect plane $\mathcal{P}$, what must also be true? **$c \parallel d$**

c. If two planes are perpendicular to the same line, then they are parallel. If both plane $\mathcal{Q}$ and plane $\mathcal{R}$ are perpendicular to line ℓ, what must also be true? **$R \parallel Q$**

H.O.T. Problems Use Higher-Order Thinking Skills

41. Shenequa; the distance between points A and C is 1.2 cm. The distance between points B and D is 1.35 cm. Since the lines are not equidistant everywhere, the lines will eventually intersect when extended.

41. ERROR ANALYSIS Han draws the segments $\overline{AB}$ and $\overline{CD}$ shown below using a straightedge. He claims that these two lines, if extended, will never intersect. Shenequa claims that they will. Is either of them correct? Justify your answer.

42. CHALLENGE Describe the locus of points that are equidistant from two intersecting lines, and sketch an example. **See Ch. 3 Answer Appendix.**

43. CHALLENGE Suppose a line perpendicular to a pair of parallel lines intersects the lines at the points $(a, 4)$ and $(0, 6)$. If the distance between the parallel lines is $\sqrt{5}$, find the value of a and the equations of the parallel lines. **See margin.**

44. REASONING Determine whether the following statement is *sometimes*, *always*, or *never* true. Explain.

The distance between a line and a plane can be found. **Sometimes; the distance can only be found if the line is parallel to the plane.**

45. OPEN ENDED Draw an irregular convex pentagon using a straightedge. **a–c. See margin.**

a. Use a compass and straightedge to construct a line between one vertex and a side opposite the vertex.

b. Use measurement to justify that the line constructed is perpendicular to the side chosen.

c. Use mathematics to justify this conclusion.

46. CCSS SENSE-MAKING Rewrite Theorem 3.9 in terms of two planes that are equidistant from a third plane. Sketch an example. **See margin.**

47. WRITING IN MATH Summarize the steps necessary to find the distance between a pair of parallel lines given the equations of the two lines. **See margin.**

Differentiated Instruction BL

Logical Learners Ask students to prove that if two parallel planes are intersected by a third plane, then the lines of intersection are parallel. Refer students to the illustration for Exercise 40. Students should realize that the third plane intersects the two parallel planes at a line. Because it is given that the two planes are parallel, any pair of lines created by the intersection of a third plane will also be parallel.

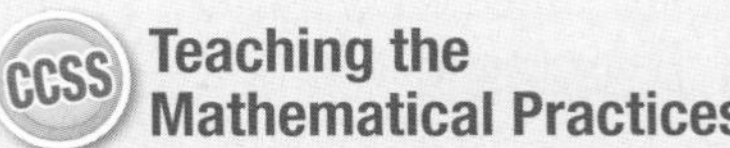

Teaching the Mathematical Practices

Sense-making Mathematically proficient students look for entry points to a solution. They analyze givens, constraints, relationships, and goals. In Exercise 46, encourage students to look at the relationship between a line and a plane.

Additional Answers

45b. Sample answer: Using a protractor, the measurement of the constructed angle is equal to 90. So, the line constructed from vertex P is perpendicular to the nonadjacent side chosen.

45c. Sample answer: The same compass setting was used to construct points A and B. Then the same compass setting was used to construct the perpendicular line to the side chosen. Since the compass setting was equidistant in both steps a perpendicular line was constructed.

46. If two planes are each equidistant form a third plane, then the two planes are parallel to each other.

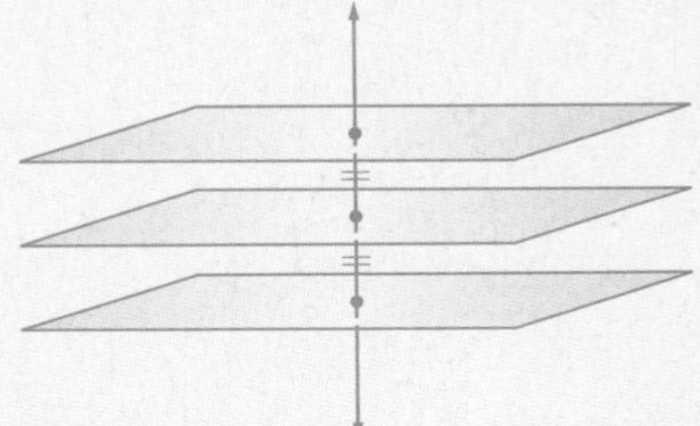

47. Sample answer: First, a point on one of the parallel lines is found. Then the line perpendicular to the pair of parallel lines is found. Then the point of intersection is found between the perpendicular line and the other line not used in the first step. Last, the Distance Formula is used to determine the distance between the pair of intersection points. This value is the distance between the pair of parallel lines.

4 Assess

Name the Math Each student should mark a point on a piece of paper and place a ruler on the same paper to represent a line. Then they should write instructions how to find the distance from the point to the line represented by the ruler. Students should measure the distance, and justify their answers.

Formative Assessment

Check for student understanding of Lesson 3-6.

 Quiz 4, p. 46

Additional Answers

48a.

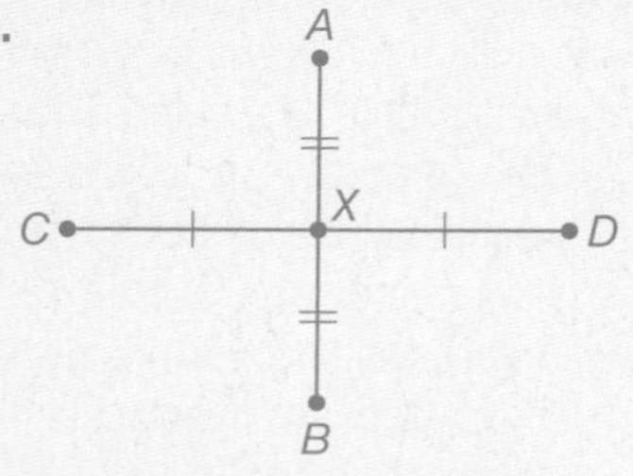

52. Slope of a: $m = \frac{(-4-2)}{(1+3)} = -\frac{3}{2}$;

Slope of b: $m = \frac{(-1-2)}{(5-3)} = -\frac{3}{2}$;

Since the slopes are equal, $a \parallel b$.

57. **Given:** $AB = BC$

Prove: $AC = 2BC$

Statements (Reasons)

1. $AB = BC$ (Given)
2. $AC = AB + BC$ (Seg. Add. Post.)
3. $AC = BC + BC$ (Substitution)
4. $AC = 2BC$ (Substitution)

58. **Given:** $\overline{JK} \cong \overline{KL}$, $\overline{HJ} \cong \overline{GH}$, $\overline{KL} \cong \overline{HJ}$

Prove: $\overline{GH} \cong \overline{JK}$

Statements (Reasons)

1. $\overline{JK} \cong \overline{KL}$, $\overline{KL} \cong \overline{HJ}$ (Given)
2. $\overline{JK} \cong \overline{HJ}$ (Transitive Property of Congruence)
3. $\overline{HJ} \cong \overline{GH}$ (Given)
4. $\overline{JK} \cong \overline{GH}$ (Transitive Property of Congruence)
5. $\overline{GH} \cong \overline{JK}$ (Symmetric Property of Congruence)

Standardized Test Practice

48. **EXTENDED RESPONSE** Segment AB is perpendicular to segment CD. Segment AB and segment CD bisect each other at point X.
    a. Draw a figure to represent the problem. **a. See margin.**
    b. Find $\overline{BD}$ if $AB = 12$ and $CD = 16$. **10**
    c. Find $\overline{BD}$ if $AB = 24$ and $CD = 18$. **15**

49. A city park is square and has an area of 81,000 square feet. Which of the following is the closest to the length of one side of the park? **C**

    A 100 ft C 300 ft
    B 200 ft D 400 ft

50. **ALGEBRA** Pablo bought a sweater on sale for 25% off the original price and another 40% off the discounted price. If the sweater originally cost \$48, what was the final price of the sweater? **G**

    F \$14.40 H \$31.20
    G \$21.60 J \$36.00

51. **SAT/ACT** After N cookies are divided equally among 8 children, 3 remain. How many would remain if $(N + 6)$ cookies were divided equally among the 8 children? **B**

    A 0 C 2 E 6
    B 1 D 4

Spiral Review

52. Refer to the figure at the right. Determine whether $a \parallel b$. Justify your answer. (Lesson 3-5) **See margin.**

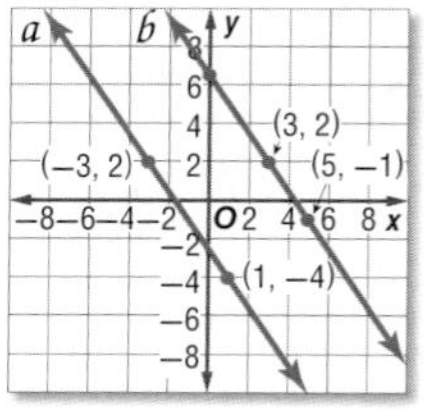

Write an equation in point-slope form of the line having the given slope that contains the given point. (Lesson 3-4)

53. $m: \frac{1}{4}, (3, -1)$ $y + 1 = \frac{1}{4}(x - 3)$
54. $m: 0, (-2, 6)$ $y - 6 = 0$
55. $m: -1, (-2, 3)$ $y - 3 = -(x + 2)$
56. $m: -2, (-6, -7)$ $y + 7 = -2(x + 6)$

Prove the following. (Lesson 2-7)

57. If $AB = BC$, then $AC = 2BC$. **See margin.**

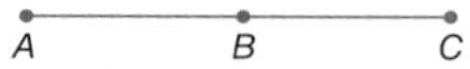

58. **Given:** $\overline{JK} \cong \overline{KL}$, $\overline{HJ} \cong \overline{GH}$, $\overline{KL} \cong \overline{HJ}$ **See margin.**

Prove: $\overline{GH} \cong \overline{JK}$

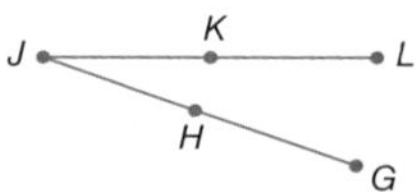

59. **MAPS** Darnell sketched a map for his friend of the cross streets nearest to his home. Describe two different angle relationships between the streets. (Lesson 1-5)

Sample answer: Robin ⊥ Cardinal; Bluebird divides two of the angles formed by Robin and Cardinal into pairs of complementary angles.

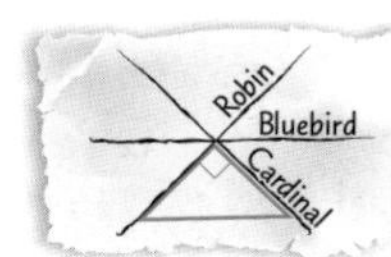

Skills Review

Use the Distance Formula to find the distance between each pair of points.

60. $A(0, 0), B(15, 20)$ **25**
61. $O(-12, 0), P(-8, 3)$ **5**
62. $C(11, -12), D(6, 2)$ $\sqrt{221} \approx 14.9$
63. $R(-2, 3), S(3, 15)$ **13**
64. $M(1, -2), N(9, 13)$ **17**
65. $Q(-12, 2), T(-9, 6)$ **5**

 **Follow-up**

Students have explored parallel, skew and perpendicular lines.

Ask:

- Why do we describe relationships between lines? Sample answer: to associate properties with the lines
- How can pairs of lines be named? Sample answers: parallel, perpendicular, skew, coplanar

224 | Lesson 3-6 | Perpendiculars and Distance

CHAPTER 3 Study Guide and Review

Study Guide

KeyConcepts

Transversals (Lessons 3-1 and 3-2)

- When a transversal intersects two lines, the following types of angles are formed: exterior, interior, consecutive interior, alternate interior, alternate exterior, and corresponding.
- If two parallel lines are cut by a transversal, then:
  - each pair of corresponding angles is congruent,
  - each pair of alternate interior angles is congruent,
  - each pair of consecutive interior angles is supplementary, and
  - each pair of alternate exterior angles is congruent.

Slope (Lessons 3-3 and 3-4)

- The slope m of a line containing two points with coordinates (x_1, y_1) and (x_2, y_2) is $m = \frac{y_2 - y_1}{x_2 - x_1}$, where $x_1 \neq x_2$.

Proving Lines Parallel (Lesson 3-5)

- If two lines in a plane are cut by a transversal so that any one of the following is true, then the two lines are parallel:
  - a pair of corresponding angles is congruent,
  - a pair of alternate exterior angles is congruent,
  - a pair of alternate interior angles is congruent, or
  - a pair of consecutive interior angles is supplementary.
- In a plane, if two lines are perpendicular to the same line, then they are parallel.

Distance (Lesson 3-6)

- The distance from a line to a point not on the line is the length of the segment perpendicular to the line from the point.
- The distance between two parallel lines is the perpendicular distance between one of the lines and any point on the other line.

FOLDABLES StudyOrganizer

Be sure the Key Concepts are noted in your Foldable.

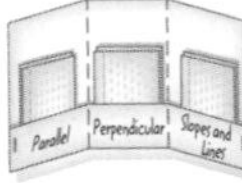

KeyVocabulary

alternate exterior angles (p. 174)
alternate interior angles (p. 174)
consecutive interior angles (p. 174)
corresponding angles (p. 174)
equidistant (p. 218)
parallel lines (p. 173)
parallel planes (p. 173)
point-slope form (p. 198)
rate of change (p. 189)
skew lines (p. 173)
slope (p. 188)
slope-intercept form (p. 198)
transversal (p. 174)

VocabularyCheck

State whether each sentence is *true* or *false*. If *false*, replace the underlined word or number to make a true sentence.

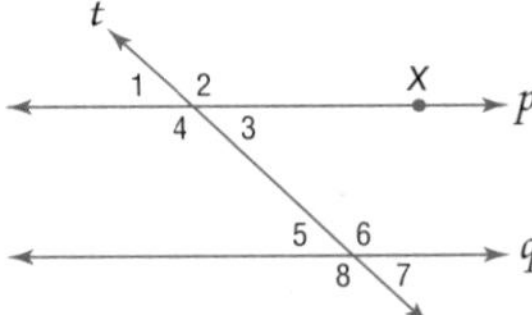

1. If $\angle 1 \cong \angle 5$, then lines p and q are <u>skew</u> lines. false; parallel
2. Angles 4 and 6 are <u>alternate</u> interior angles. true
3. Angles 1 and 7 are alternate <u>exterior</u> angles. true
4. If lines p and q are parallel, then angles 3 and 6 are <u>congruent</u>. false; supplementary
5. The distance from point X to line q is the length of the segment <u>perpendicular</u> to line q from X. true
6. Line t is called the <u>transversal</u> for lines p and q. true
7. If $p \parallel q$, then $\angle 2$ and $\angle 8$ are <u>supplementary</u>. false; congruent
8. Angles 4 and 8 are <u>corresponding</u> angles. true

Formative Assessment

KeyVocabulary The page references after each word denote where that term was first introduced. If students have difficulty answering Exercises 1–8, remind them that they can use these page references to refresh their memories about the vocabulary terms.

Summative Assessment

Vocabulary Test, p. 48

Vocabulary Review

Vocabulary Review provides students the opportunity to check their understanding of important concepts and terminology in an online game format.

FOLDABLES StudyOrganizer

Dinah Zike's Foldables®

Have students look through the chapter to make sure they have included examples in their Foldables for each tab. Suggest that students keep their Foldables handy while completing the Study Guide and Review pages. Point out that their Foldables can serve as a quick review tool for studying for the chapter test.

Lesson-by-Lesson Review

Daily Intervention If the given examples are not sufficient to review the topics covered by the questions, remind students that the lesson references tell them where to review that topic in their textbook.

Two-Day Option Have students complete the Lesson-by-Lesson Review. Then you can use eAssessment to customize another review worksheet that practices all the objectives of this chapter or only the objectives on which your students need more help.

Additional Answers

9. corresponding
10. alternate interior
11. alternate exterior
12. consecutive interior
14. 123; Alt. Ext. ∠s Thm.
15. 57; ∠5 ≅ ∠13 by Corr. ∠s Post. and ∠13 and ∠14 form a linear pair.
16. 57; ∠1 ≅ ∠9 by Corr. ∠s Post. and ∠9 and ∠16 form a linear pair.
17. 123; ∠11 ≅ ∠5 by Alt. Int. ∠s Thm. and ∠5 ≅ ∠1 by Alt. Ext. ∠s Thm.
18. 57; ∠1 ≅ ∠5 by Alt. Ext. ∠s Thm. and ∠4 and ∠5 form a linear pair.
19. 57; ∠1 ≅ ∠3 by Corr. ∠s Post. and ∠3 and ∠6 form a linear pair.

CHAPTER 3 Study Guide and Review *Continued*

Lesson-by-Lesson Review

3-1 Parallel Lines and Transversals

Classify the relationship between each pair of angles as *alternate interior, alternate exterior, corresponding,* or *consecutive interior* angles. 9–12. See margin.

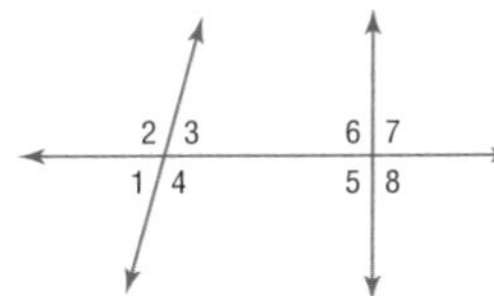

9. ∠1 and ∠5
10. ∠4 and ∠6
11. ∠2 and ∠8
12. ∠4 and ∠5
13. **BRIDGES** The Roebling Suspension Bridge extends over the Ohio River connecting Cincinnati, Ohio, to Covington, Kentucky. Describe the type of lines formed by the bridge and the river. skew lines

Example 1

Refer to the figure below. Classify the relationship between each pair of angles as *alternate interior, alternate exterior, corresponding,* or *consecutive interior* angles.

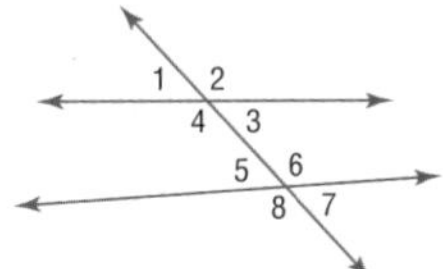

a. ∠3 and ∠6
consecutive interior

b. ∠2 and ∠6
corresponding

c. ∠1 and ∠7
alternate exterior

d. ∠3 and ∠5
alternate interior

3-2 Angles and Parallel Lines

In the figure, $m\angle 1 = 123$. Find the measure of each angle. Tell which postulate(s) or theorem(s) you used. 14–19. See margin.

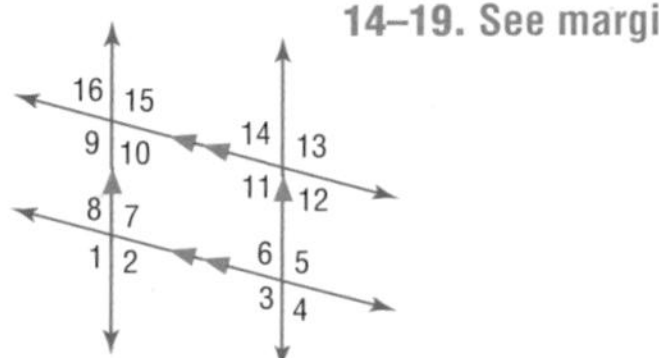

14. ∠5
15. ∠14
16. ∠16
17. ∠11
18. ∠4
19. ∠6

20. **MAPS** The diagram shows the layout of Elm, Plum, and Oak streets. Find the value of *x*. 125

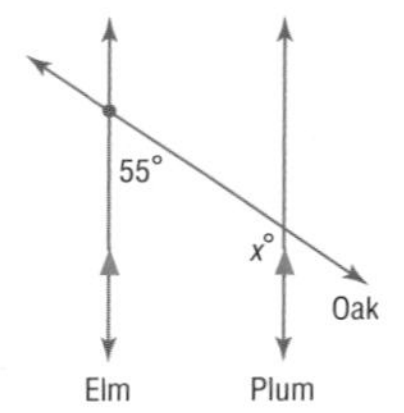

Example 2

ALGEBRA If $m\angle 5 = 7x - 5$ and $m\angle 4 = 2x + 23$, find *x*. Explain your reasoning.

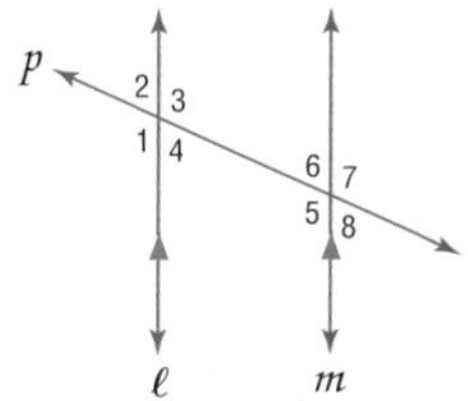

$m\angle 4 + m\angle 5 = 180$	Def. of Supp. ∠s
$(2x + 23) + (7x - 5) = 180$	Substitution
$9x + 18 = 180$	Simplify.
$9x = 162$	Subtract.
$x = 18$	Divide.

Since lines ℓ and *m* are parallel, ∠4 and ∠5 are supplementary by the Consecutive Interior Angles Theorem.

3-3 Slopes of Lines

Determine whether $\overleftrightarrow{AB}$ and $\overleftrightarrow{XY}$ are *parallel, perpendicular,* or *neither.* Graph each line to verify your answer. **21–23. See margin.**

21. $A(5, 3)$, $B(8, 0)$, $X(-7, 2)$, $Y(1, 10)$

22. $A(-3, 9)$, $B(0, 7)$, $X(4, 13)$, $Y(-5, 7)$

23. $A(8, 1)$, $B(-2, 7)$, $X(-6, 2)$, $Y(-1, -1)$

Graph the line that satisfies each condition. **24–25. See margin.**

24. contains $(-3, 4)$ and is parallel to $\overleftrightarrow{AB}$ with $A(2, 5)$ and $B(9, 2)$

25. contains $(1, 3)$ and is perpendicular to $\overleftrightarrow{PQ}$ with $P(4, -6)$ and $Q(6, -1)$

26. AIRPLANES Two Oceanic Airlines planes are flying at the same altitude. Using satellite imagery, each plane's position can be mapped onto a coordinate plane. Flight 815 was mapped at (23, 17) and (5, 11) while Flight 44 was mapped at (3, 15) and (9, 17). Determine whether their paths are *parallel, perpendicular,* or *neither.* parallel

Example 3

Graph the line that contains $C(0, -4)$ and is perpendicular to $\overleftrightarrow{AB}$ with $A(5, -4)$ and $B(0, -2)$.

The slope of $\overleftrightarrow{AB}$ is $\frac{-2-(-4)}{0-5}$ or $-\frac{2}{5}$.

Since $-\frac{2}{5}\left(\frac{5}{2}\right) = -1$, the slope of the line perpendicular to $\overleftrightarrow{AB}$ through C is $\frac{5}{2}$.

To graph the line, start at C. Move up 5 units and then right 2 units. Label the point D and draw $\overleftrightarrow{CD}$.

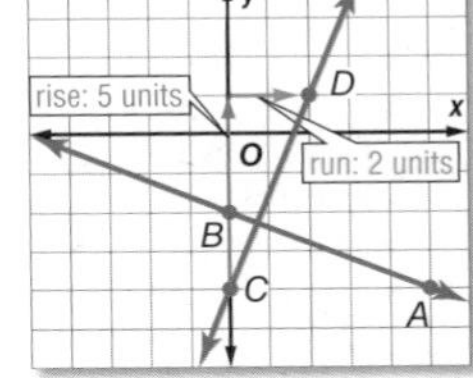

3-4 Equations of Lines

Write an equation in point-slope form of the line having the given slope that contains the given point.

27. $m = 2$, $(4, -9)$ $y + 9 = 2(x - 4)$

28. $m = -\frac{3}{4}$, $(8, -1)$ $y + 1 = -\frac{3}{4}(x - 8)$

Write an equation in slope-intercept form of the line having the given slope and y-intercept.

29. m: 5, y-intercept: -3 $y = 5x - 3$

30. m: $\frac{1}{2}$, y-intercept: 4 $y = \frac{1}{2}x + 4$

Write an equation in slope-intercept form for each line.

31. $(-3, 12)$ and $(15, 0)$ $y = -\frac{2}{3}x + 10$

32. $(-7, 2)$ and $(5, 8)$ $y = \frac{1}{2}x + \frac{11}{2}$

33. WINDOW CLEANING Ace Window Cleaning Service charges \$50 for the service call and \$20 for each hour spent on the job. Write an equation in slope-intercept form that represents the total cost C in terms of the number of hours h. $C = 20h + 50$

Example 4

Write an equation of the line through (2, 5) and (6, 3) in slope-intercept form.

Step 1 Find the slope of the line through the points.

$m = \frac{y_2 - y_1}{x_2 - x_1}$ Slope Formula

$= \frac{3-5}{6-2}$ $x_1 = 2$, $y_1 = 5$, $x_2 = 6$, and $y_2 = 3$

$= \frac{-2}{4}$ or $-\frac{1}{2}$ Simplify.

Step 2 Write an equation of the line.

$y - y_1 = m(x - x_1)$ Point-slope form

$y - 5 = -\frac{1}{2}[x - (2)]$ $m = -\frac{1}{2}$, $(x_1, y_1) = (2, 5)$

$y - 5 = -\frac{1}{2}x + 1$ Simplify.

$y = -\frac{1}{2}x + 6$ Add 5 to each side.

Additional Answers

21. perpendicular

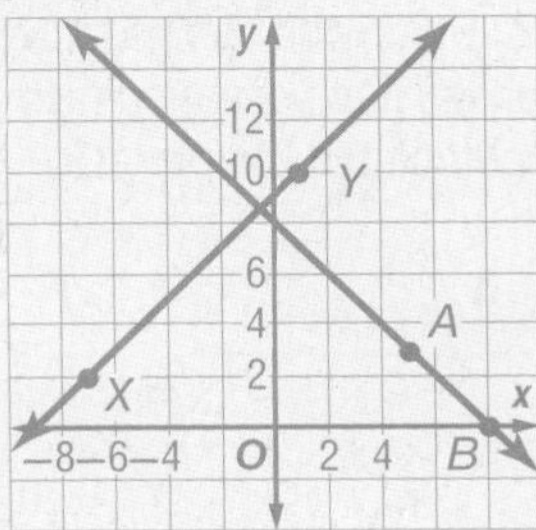

22. neither

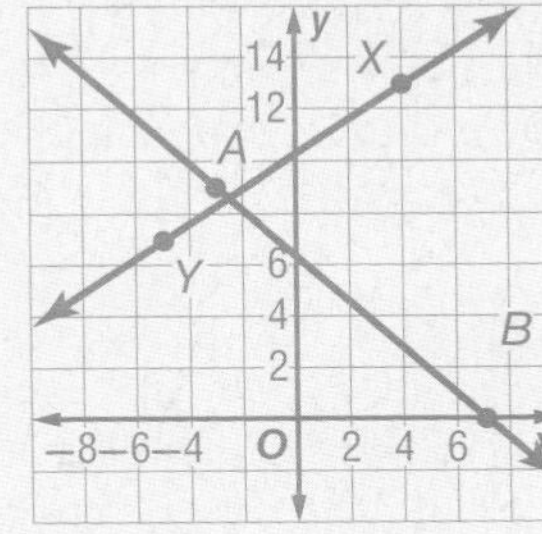

23. parallel

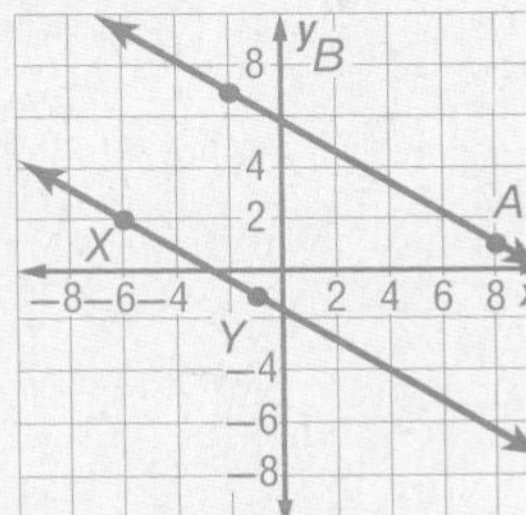

24.

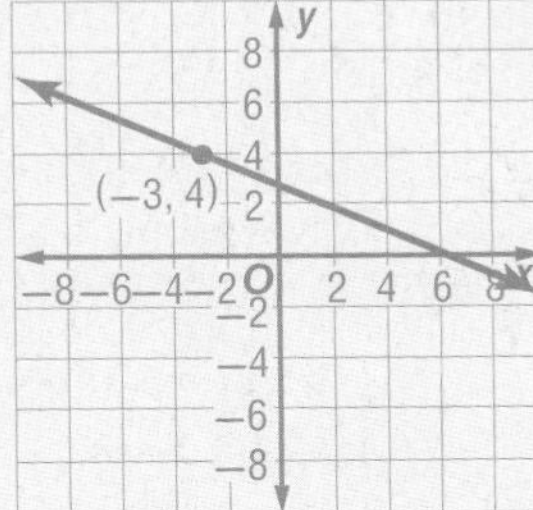

25.

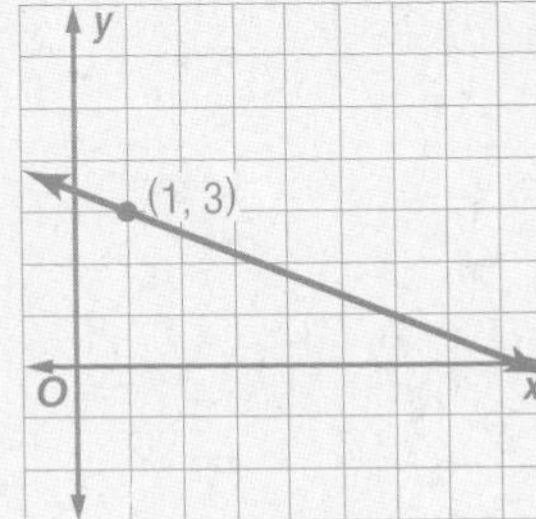

Anticipation Guide

Have students complete the Chapter 3 Anticipation Guide and discuss how their responses have changed now that they have completed Chapter 3.

Additional Answers

34. $w \parallel x$; Consecutive Interior Angles Converse Thm.

35. none

36. $w \parallel x$; Corresponding Angles Converse Postulate

37. $v \parallel z$; Alternate Exterior Angles Converse Thm.

40.

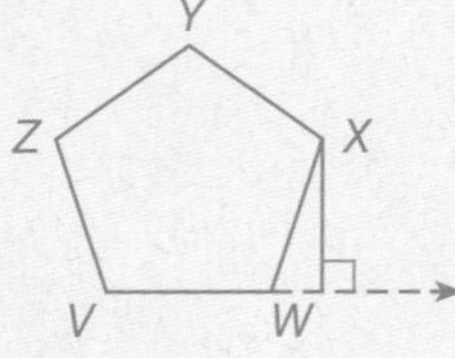

41.

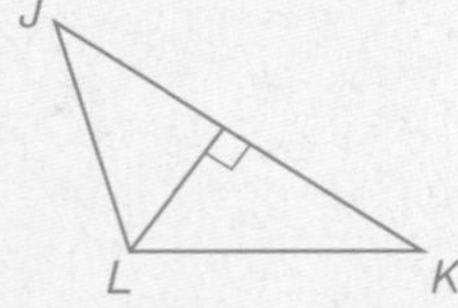

42. The second row is equidistant at all points from the first row.

Additional Answers (Practice Test)

8. 84; Cons. Int. Angles Thm.

9. 138; Supplementary Angles Thm.

10. 42; Alternate Interior Angles Thm.

12a. Fit-N-Trim: $y = 80x$,
Fit-For-Life: $y = 55x + 75$

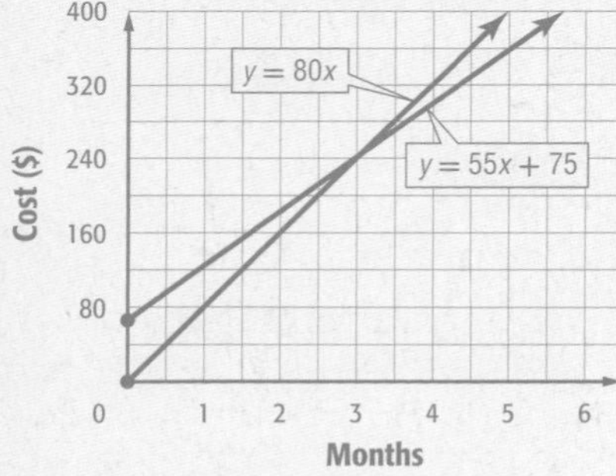

12b. No; the lines intersect because the slopes of the two lines, 80 and 55, are not equal.

12c. From the graph, it appears that if you attend the center for less than 3 month, Fit-N-Trim offers the lower rate. If you intend to attend for more than 3 months, Fit-For-Life offers the better rate.

CHAPTER 3 Study Guide and Review *Continued*

3-5 Proving Lines Parallel

Given the following information, determine which lines, if any, are parallel. State the postulate or theorem that justifies your answer. **34–37. See margin.**

34. $\angle 7 \cong \angle 10$

35. $\angle 2 \cong \angle 10$

36. $\angle 1 \cong \angle 3$

37. $\angle 3 \cong \angle 11$

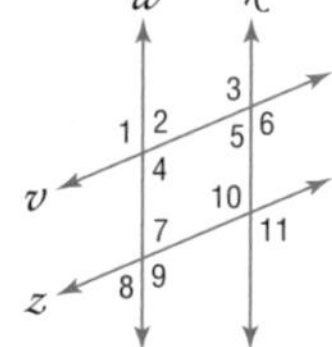

38. Find x so that $p \parallel q$. Identify the postulate or theorem you used.

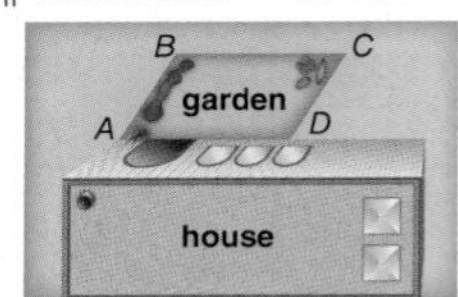

9; converse of Cons. Int. ∠s Thm.

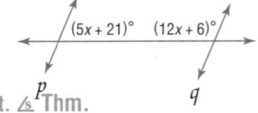

39. LANDSCAPING Find the measure needed for $m\angle ADC$ that will make $\overline{AB} \parallel \overline{CD}$ if $m\angle BAD = 45$. **135**

Example 5

Given the following information, determine which lines, if any, are parallel. State the postulate or theorem that justifies your answer.

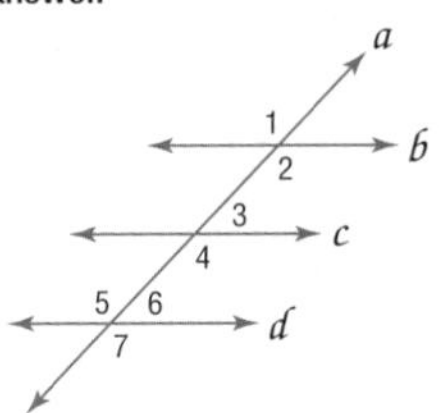

a. $\angle 1 \cong \angle 7$

$\angle 1$ and $\angle 7$ are alternate exterior angles of lines b and d.

Since $\angle 1 \cong \angle 7$, $b \parallel d$ by the Converse of the Alternate Exterior Angles Theorem.

b. $\angle 4 \cong \angle 5$

$\angle 4$ and $\angle 5$ are alternate interior angles of lines c and d.

Since $\angle 4 \cong \angle 5$, $c \parallel d$ by the Converse of the Alternate Interior Angles Theorem.

3-6 Perpendiculars and Distance

Copy each figure. Draw the segment that represents the distance indicated. **40–42. See margin.**

40. X to $\overline{VW}$

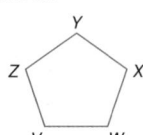

41. L to $\overline{JK}$

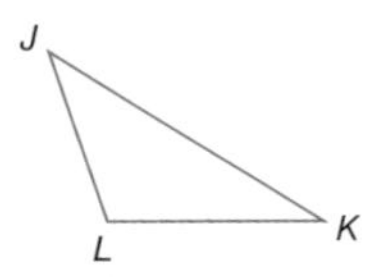

42. HOME DÉCOR Scott wants to hang two rows of framed pictures in parallel lines on his living room wall. He first spaces the nails on the wall in a line for the top row. Next, he hangs a weighted plumb line from each nail and measures an equal distance below each nail for the second row. Why does this ensure that the two rows of pictures will be parallel?

Example 6

Copy the figure. Draw the segment that represents the distance from point A to $\overline{CD}$.

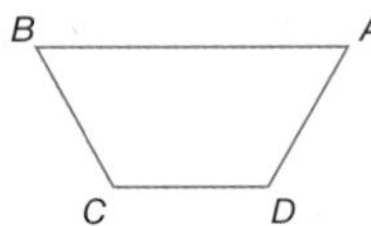

The distance from a line to a point not on the line is the length of the segment perpendicular to the line that passes through the point.

Extend $\overline{CD}$ and draw the segment perpendicular to $\overline{CD}$ from A.

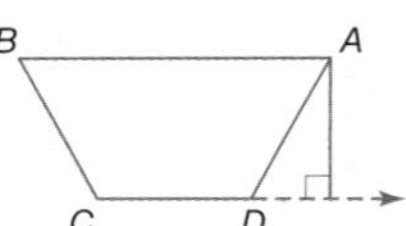

228 | Chapter 3 | Study Guide and Review

CHAPTER 3 Practice Test

Classify the relationship between each pair of angles as *alternate interior, alternate exterior, corresponding,* or *consecutive interior* angles.

1. ∠6 and ∠3 alternate exterior
2. ∠4 and ∠7
3. ∠5 and ∠4

2. consecutive interior
3. alternate interior

Determine the slope of the line that contains the given points. 4. undefined

4. $G(8, 1), H(8, -6)$
5. $A(0, 6), B(4, 0)$ $-\frac{3}{2}$
6. $E(6, 3), F(-6, 3)$ 0
7. $E(5, 4), F(8, 1)$ −1

In the figure, $m\angle 8 = 96$ and $m\angle 12 = 42$. Find the measure of each angle. Tell which postulate(s) or theorem(s) you used.

8. ∠9
9. ∠11
10. ∠6

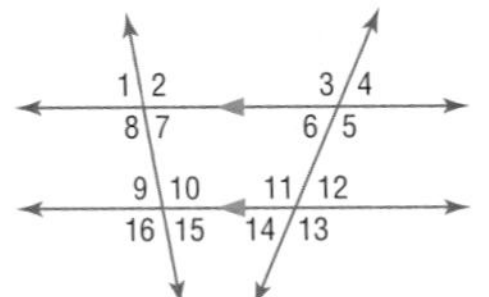

8–10. See margin.

11. Find the value of x in the figure below. 128

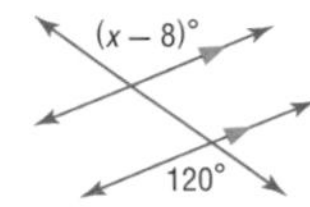

12. **FITNESS** You would like to join a fitness center. Fit-N-Trim charges $80 per month. Fit-For-Life charges a one-time membership fee of $75 and $55 per month. a–c. See margin.
   a. Write and graph two equations in slope-intercept form to represent the cost y to attend each fitness center for x months.
   b. Are the lines you graphed in part a parallel? Explain why or why not.
   c. Which fitness center offers the better rate? Explain.

Write an equation in slope-intercept form for each line described.

13. passes through $(-8, 1)$, perpendicular to $y = 2x - 17$ $y = -\frac{1}{2}x - 3$
14. passes through $(0, 7)$, parallel to $y = 4x - 19$ $y = 4x + 7$
15. passes through $(-12, 3)$, perpendicular to $y = -\frac{2}{3}x - 11$ $y = \frac{3}{2}x + 21$

Find the distance between each pair of parallel lines with the given equations.

16. $y = x - 11$, $y = x - 7$ $\sqrt{8} \approx 2.8$
17. $y = -2x + 1$, $y = -2x + 16$ $\sqrt{45} \approx 6.7$

18. **MULTIPLE CHOICE** Which segment is skew to $\overline{CD}$? D

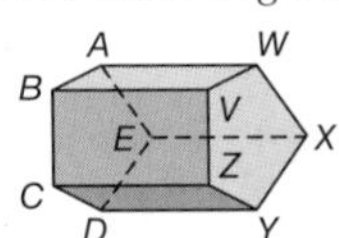

A $\overline{ZY}$ C $\overline{DE}$
B $\overline{AB}$ D $\overline{VZ}$

19. Find x so that $a \parallel b$. Identify the postulate or theorem you used. 14; converse of Cons. Int. ∠s Thm.

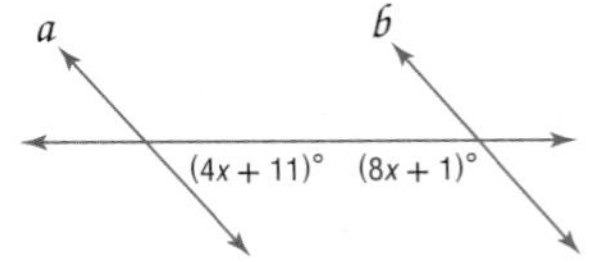

COORDINATE GEOMETRY Find the distance from P to ℓ.

20. Line ℓ contains points $(-4, 2)$ and $(3, -5)$. Point P has coordinates $(1, 2)$. $\frac{5\sqrt{2}}{2} \approx 3.5$
21. Line ℓ contains points $(6, 5)$ and $(2, 3)$. Point P has coordinates $(2, 6)$. $\frac{6\sqrt{5}}{5} \approx 2.7$

Given the following information, determine which lines, if any, are parallel. State the postulate or theorem that justifies your answer. 22–24. See margin.

22. ∠4 ≅ ∠10
23. ∠9 ≅ ∠6
24. ∠7 ≅ ∠11

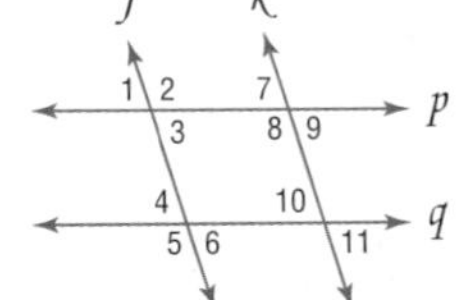

25. **JOBS** Hailey works at a gift shop. She is paid $10 per hour plus a 15% commission on merchandise she sells. Write an equation in slope-intercept form that represents her earnings in a week if she sold $550 worth of merchandise. See margin.

connectED.mcgraw-hill.com 229

Summative Assessment

Use these alternate leveled chapter tests to differentiate assessment for your students.

Leveled Chapter 3 Tests

Form	Type	Level	Page(s)
1	MC	AL	49–50
2A	MC	OL	51–52
2B	MC	OL	53–54
2C	FR	OL	55–56
2D	FR	OL	57–58
3	FR	BL	59–60
Vocabulary Test			48
Extended-Response Test			61

MC = multiple-choice questions
FR = free-response questions

eAssessment Customize and create multiple versions of your chapter tests and their answer keys. All of the questions from the leveled chapter tests in the *Chapter 3 Resource Masters* are also available on eAssessment with the standards that each item assesses.

Additional Answers

22. $j \parallel k$; Corresponding Angles Converse Post.
23. No lines can be proven ∥.
24. $p \parallel q$; Alternate Exterior Angles Converse Thm.
25. $y = 10x + 82.5$, where x = number of hours worked

InterventionPlanner

TIER 1 On Level OL

If students miss about 25% of the exercises or less,

Then choose a resource:

SE Lessons 3-1, 3-2, 3-3, 3-4, 3-5, and 3-6

Skills Practice, pp. 7, 13, 19, 26, 32, and 38

connectED.mcgraw-hill.com Self-Check Quiz

TIER 2 Strategic Intervention AL approaching grade level

If students miss about 50% of the exercises,

Then choose a resource:

Study Guide and Intervention, pp. 5, 11, 17, 24, 30, and 36

connectED.mcgraw-hill.com Extra Examples, Personal Tutor, Homework Help

TIER 3 Intensive Intervention 2 or more grades below level

If students miss about 75% of the exercises,

Then use *Math Triumphs, Geo.*, Ch. 4

connectED.mcgraw-hill.com Extra Examples, Personal Tutor, Homework Help, Review Vocabulary

1 Focus

Objective Solve gridded response standardized test problems.

2 Teach

Scaffolding Questions

Ask:

- How is solving a multiple choice question the same as or different than solving one for which you do not have answer choices? Sample answer: If you are not given answer choices, you cannot solve by eliminating possibilities.
- How can you check to see if your answer for a gridded response question is reasonable? Sample answer: If your answer cannot be entered in the grid, then it is not reasonable.

CHAPTER 3 Preparing for Standardized Tests

Gridded Response Questions

In addition to multiple-choice, short-answer, and extended-response questions, you will likely encounter gridded-response questions on standardized tests. After solving a gridded-response question, you must print your answer on an answer sheet and mark in the correct circles on the grid to match your answer. Answers to gridded-response questions may be whole numbers, decimals, or fractions.

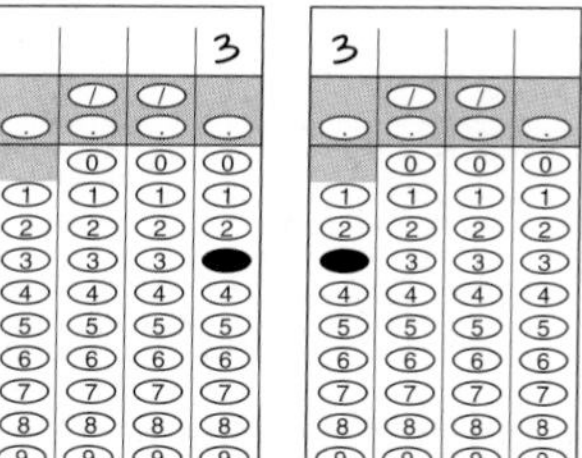

Whole Numbers

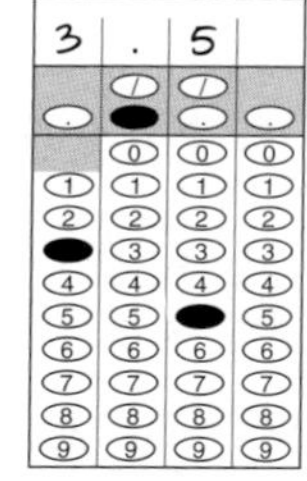

Decimals

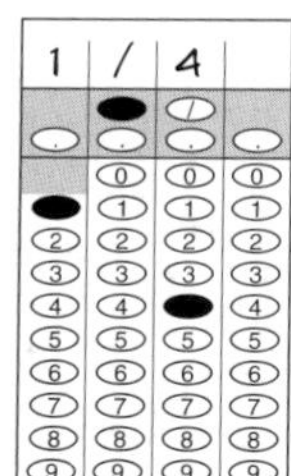

Fractions

Strategies for Solving Gridded-Response Questions

Step 1

Read the problem carefully and solve.

- Be sure your answer makes sense.
- If time permits, check your answer.

Step 2

Print your answer in the answer boxes.

- Print only one digit or symbol in each answer box.
- Do not write any digits or symbols outside the answer boxes.
- Write answer as a whole number, decimal, or fraction.

Step 3

Fill in the grid.

- Fill in only one bubble for every answer box that you have written in. Be sure not to fill in a bubble under a blank answer box.
- Fill in each bubble completely and clearly.

Standardized Test Example

Read the problem. Identify what you need to know. Then use the information in the problem to solve.

GRIDDED RESPONSE In the figure below, $\angle ABC$ is intersected by parallel lines ℓ and m. What is the measure of $\angle ABC$? Express your answer in degrees.

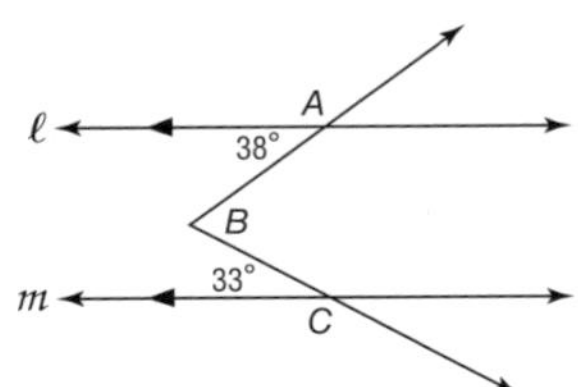

Redraw the figure and add a third line parallel to lines ℓ and m through point B. Find the angle measures using alternate interior angles.

Solve the Problem

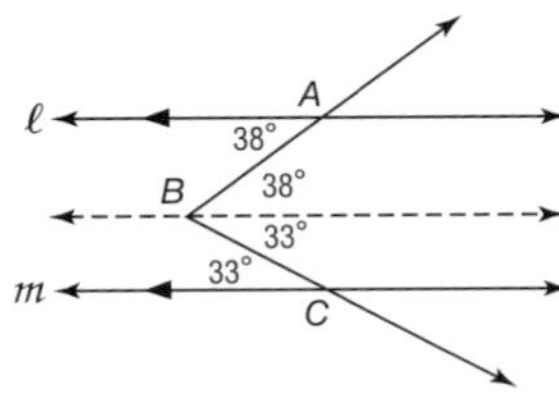

$m\angle ABC = 38 + 33 = 71$

Fill in the Grid

7 1

Print your answer in the answer box and fill in the grid.

Exercises

Read each question. Then fill in the correct answer on the answer document provided by your teacher or on a sheet of paper.

1. **GRIDDED RESPONSE** What is the slope of the line that contains the points $R(-2, 1)$ and $S(10, 6)$? Express your answer as a fraction. 5/12

2. **GRIDDED RESPONSE** Solve for x in the figure below. 31

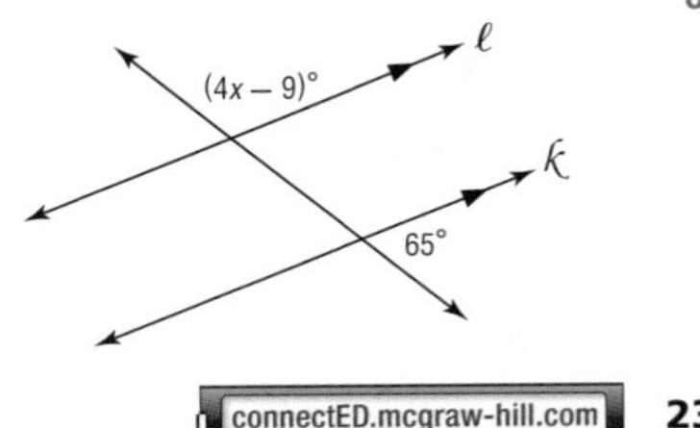

Additional Example

What is the slope of the line that contains the points represented by the table below? 4

x	y
−4	−18
−2	−10
2	6
4	14

3 Assess

Use Exercises 1 and 2 to assess students' understanding.

connectED.mcgraw-hill.com 231

Diagnose Student Errors

Survey student responses for each item. Class trends may indicate common errors and misconceptions.

1. A did not apply Vertical Angles Theorem
B did not apply Alternate Interior Angles Theorem
C did not apply Alternate Exterior Angles Theorem
D correct

2. F correct
G one addend is even
H both the addends and the sum are even
J one addend is even

3. A correct
B disregarded that the rise is slightly more than 1
C error in calculation
D error in calculation

4. F formula error
G correct
H error in calculation
J error in calculation

5. A error in calculation
B error in calculation
C correct
D error in calculation

6. F correct
G visual estimation
H error in calculation
J error in calculation

7. A error in calculation
B correct
C error in calculation
D error in calculation

CHAPTER 3

Standardized Test Practice

Cumulative, Chapters 1 through 3

Multiple Choice

Read each question. Then fill in the correct answer on the answer document provided by your teacher or on a sheet of paper.

1. If $a \parallel b$ in the diagram below, which of the following may *not* be true? **D**

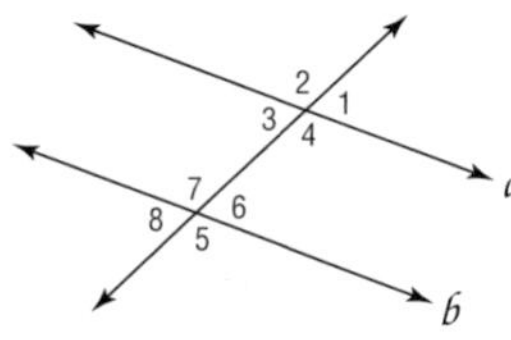

A $\angle 1 \cong \angle 3$ C $\angle 2 \cong \angle 5$
B $\angle 4 \cong \angle 7$ D $\angle 8 \cong \angle 2$

2. Which of the following best describes a *counterexample* to the assertion below? **F**

The sum of two odd numbers is odd.

F $3 + 3 = 6$ H $6 + 2 = 8$
G $5 + 4 = 9$ J $4 + 9 = 13$

3. What is the slope of the line? **A**

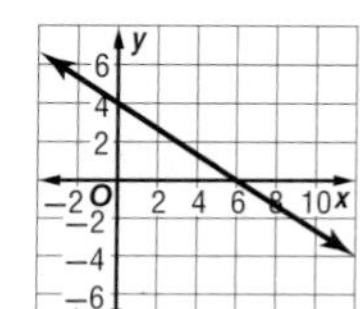

A $-\frac{2}{3}$ C $-\frac{2}{5}$
B $-\frac{1}{2}$ D $-\frac{1}{6}$

4. Line k contains points at (4, 1) and (−5, −5). Find the distance between line k and point $F(-4, 0)$. **G**

F 3.3 units H 4.0 units
G 3.6 units J 4.2 units

5. The globe has a diameter of 22 inches. What is the volume of the globe? **C**

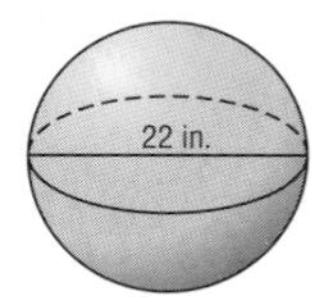

A 1520.5 in^3 C 5575.3 in^3
B 1741.4 in^3 D 6014.8 in^3

6. What is $m\angle 1$ in the figure below? **F**

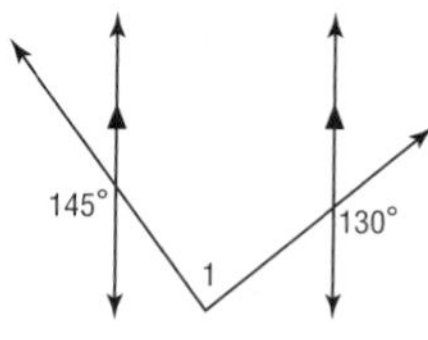

F 85 H 95
G 90 J 100

7. Jason is saving money to buy a car stereo. He has \$45 saved, and he can save \$15 per week. If the stereo that he wants is \$210, how many weeks will it take Jason to buy the stereo? **B**

A 10 C 12
B 11 D 13

> **Test-TakingTip**
>
> **Question 6** *Drawing a diagram* can help you solve problems. Draw a third parallel line through the vertex of angle 1. Then use the properties of parallel lines and transversals to solve the problem.

Short Response/Gridded Response

Record your answers on the answer sheet provided by your teacher or on a sheet of paper.

8. **GRIDDED RESPONSE** For a given line and a point not on the line, how many lines exist that pass through the point and are parallel to the given line? 1

9. **GRIDDED RESPONSE** Find the slope of the line that contains the points (4, 3) and (−2, −5). 4/3

10. Complete the proof.

    Given: $\angle 1 \cong \angle 2$

    Prove: $a \parallel b$

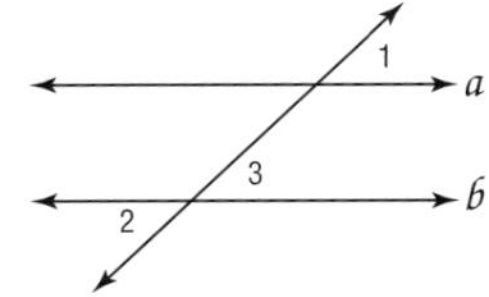

Proof: 2. Vertical angles are congruent.

Statements	Reasons
1. $\angle 1 \cong \angle 2$	1. Given
2. $\angle 2 \cong \angle 3$	2. ___?___
3. $\angle 1 \cong \angle 3$	3. Transitive Prop.
4. $a \parallel b$	4. If corresponding angles are congruent, then the lines are parallel.

11. Write the contrapositive of the statement.

    If a figure is a square, then the figure is a parallelogram.
    If a figure is not a parallelogram, then the figure is not a square.

Extended Response

Record your answers on a sheet of paper. Show your work.

12. Refer to the figure to identify each of the following.

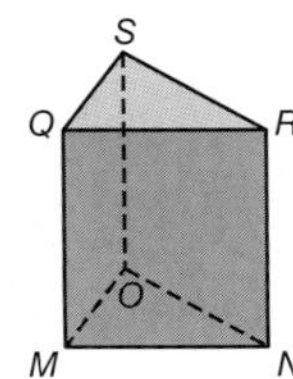

   a. all segments parallel to $\overline{MQ}$ segments NR and OS

   b. all planes intersecting plane SRN planes QMN, SOM, QRS, OMN

   c. a segment skew to $\overline{ON}$ segment MQ

13. Use this graph to answer each question.

   a. What is the equation of line m? $y = \frac{5}{6}x - 5$

   b. What is the slope of a line that is parallel to line m? $\frac{5}{6}$

   c. What is the slope of a line that is perpendicular to *line m*? $-\frac{6}{5}$

Need ExtraHelp?

If you missed Question...	1	2	3	4	5	6	7	8	9	10	11	12	13
Go to Lesson...	3-2	2-1	3-3	3-6	1-7	3-2	3-4	3-6	3-3	3-1	2-3	3-1	3-4

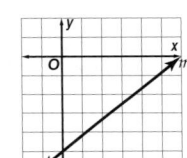

Formative Assessment

You can use these pages to benchmark student progress. The objectives are listed with each question.

Standardized Test Practice, pp. 62–64

Answer Sheet Practice

Have students simulate taking a standardized test by recording their answers on a practice recording sheet.

Student Recording Sheet

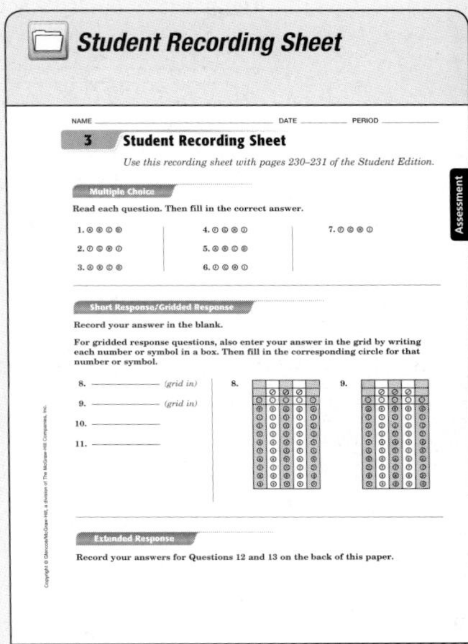

eAssessment Create practice tests that align to your state standards, the Common Core State Standards, and other national standards such as TIMSS and NAEP.

Homework Option

Get Ready for Chapter 4 Assign students the exercises on page 235 as homework to assess whether they possess the prerequisite skills for the next chapter.

Lesson 3-1

46.

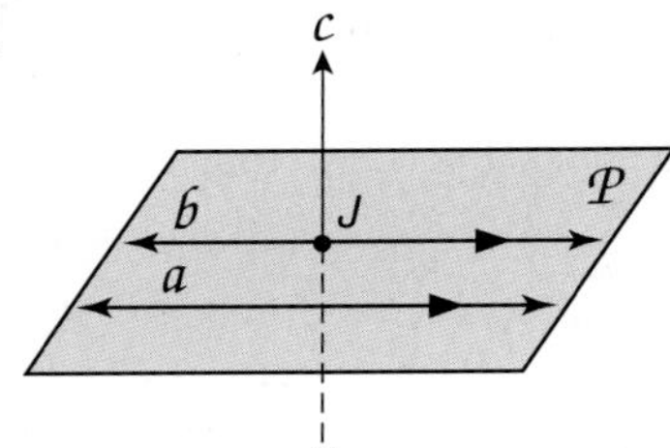

47a.

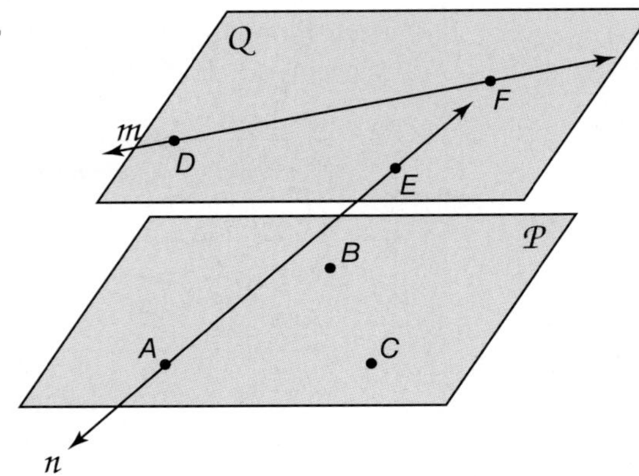

50. No; sample answer: From the definition of skew lines, the lines must not intersect and cannot be coplanar. Different planes cannot be coplanar, but they are always parallel or intersecting. Therefore, skew lines must be on planes that are parallel or intersecting.

Explore 3-2

1. $\angle FAC$, $\angle GAB$, $\angle JBA$, and $\angle KBD$ have the same measure. $\angle CAG$, $\angle FAB$, $\angle ABK$, and $\angle JBD$ have the same measure.

2. Sample answer:

Angle	$\angle FAC$	$\angle CAG$	$\angle GAB$	$\angle FAB$	$\angle JBA$	$\angle ABK$	$\angle KBD$	$\angle JBD$
1st Measure	114	66	114	66	114	66	114	66
2nd Measure	87	93	87	93	87	93	87	93
3rd Measure	45	135	45	135	45	135	45	135
4th Measure	122	58	122	58	122	58	122	58
5th Measure	150	30	150	30	150	30	150	30

3a. Corresponding: $\angle FAC$ and $\angle JBA$, $\angle CAG$ and $\angle ABK$, $\angle GAB$ and $\angle KBD$, $\angle FAB$ and $\angle JBD$; If two parallel lines are cut by a transversal, then corresponding angle pairs are congruent.

3b. Alternate exterior: $\angle FAB$ and $\angle ABK$, $\angle GAB$ and $\angle JBA$; If two parallel lines are cut by a transversal, then alternate interior angles are congruent.

3c. Alternate exterior: $\angle FAC$ and $\angle KBD$, $\angle CAG$ and $\angle JBD$; If two parallel lines are cut by a transversal, then alternate exterior angles are congruent.

3d. Consecutive interior: $\angle FAB$ and $\angle JBA$, $\angle GAB$ and $\angle ABK$; If two parallel lines are cut by a transversal, then consecutive interior angles are supplementary.

4a. Sample answer: All of the angles measure 90.

4b. Sample answer: If two parallel lines are cut by a transversal so that it is perpendicular to one of the lines, then the transversal is perpendicular to the other line.

Lesson 3-2 (Guided Practice)

1A. 105; Corresponding Angles Postulate

1B. 75°; $\angle 2$ is supplementary to $\angle 1$; Supplement Theorem

1C. 75; $\angle 3 \cong \angle 2$; Vertical Angles Theorem

Lesson 3-2

24. $y = 114$ by the Corresponding Angles Postulate; $x = 54$ by the Supplement Theorem

25. $x = 40$ by the Corresponding Angles Postulate; $y = 50$ by the Supplement Theorem

26. $x = 63$ by the Vertical Angle Theorem and the Consecutive Interior Angles Theorem

27. $x = 42$ by the Consecutive Interior Angles Theorem; $y = 14$ by the Consecutive Interior Angles Theorem

28. $x = 54$ by the Alternate Interior Angles Theorem; $y = 12$ by the Consecutive Interior Angles Theorem

29. $x = 60$ by the Consecutive Interior Angles Theorem; $y = 10$ by the Supplement Theorem

35. Given: $\ell \parallel m$

Prove: $\angle 1 \cong \angle 8$
$\angle 2 \cong \angle 7$

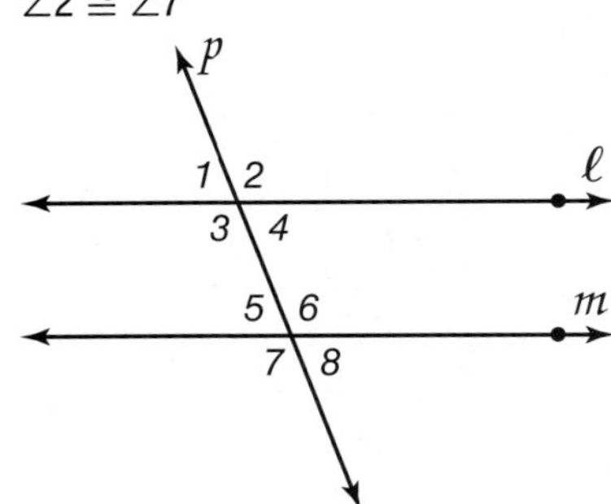

Proof:

Statements (Reasons)

1. $\ell \parallel m$ (Given)
2. $\angle 1 \cong \angle 5$, $\angle 2 \cong \angle 6$ (Corr. $\angle$s Post.)
3. $\angle 5 \cong \angle 8$, $\angle 6 \cong \angle 7$ (Vertical $\angle$s Thm.)
4. $\angle 1 \cong \angle 8$, $\angle 2 \cong \angle 7$ (Trans. Prop.)

36a. Congruent; all of the odd numbered angles are alternate interior angles related by the diagonal transversals or are complements of even numbered alternate interior angles related by the vertical transversals, so they are all congruent.

36b. Congruent; all of the even numbered angles are alternate interior angles related by either the diagonal transversals or the vertical transversals, so they are all congruent.

36c. Complementary; since the vertical supports and the horizontal supports are perpendicular, angle pairs like $\angle 1$ and $\angle 2$ must be complementary. Since all of the odd numbered angles are congruent and all of the even numbered angles are congruent, any pair of angles that has one odd and one even number will be complementary.

41a. Sample answer for m and n:

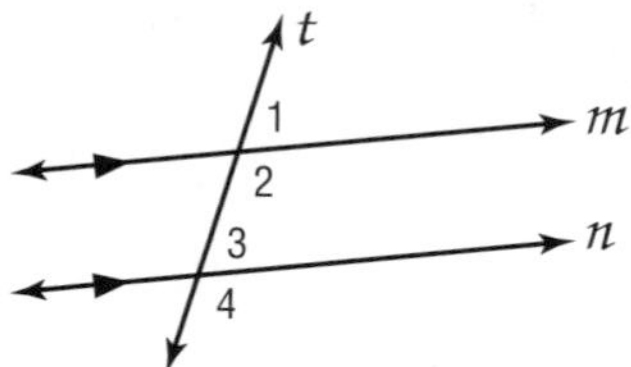

41b. Sample answer:

$m\angle 1$	$m\angle 2$	$m\angle 3$	$m\angle 4$
60	120	60	120
45	135	45	135
70	110	70	110
90	90	90	90
25	155	25	155

41e. Given: parallel lines m and n cut by transversal t
Prove: $\angle 1$ and $\angle 4$ are supplementary.

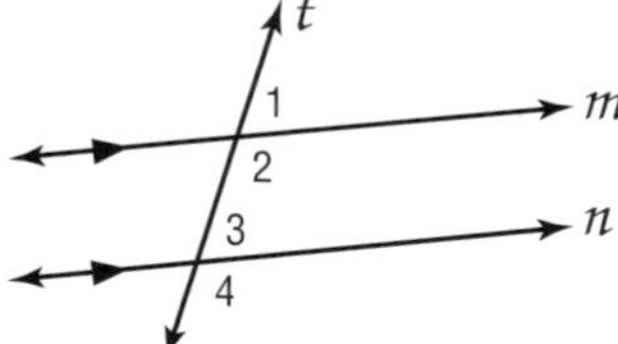

Proof:

Statements (Reasons)

1. Lines m and n are parallel and cut by transversal t. (Given)
2. $m\angle 1 + m\angle 2 = 180$ (Suppl. Thm.)
3. $\angle 2 \cong \angle 4$ (Corr. ∠s are ≅.)
4. $m\angle 2 = m\angle 4$ (Def. of congruence.)
5. $m\angle 1 + m\angle 4 = 180$ (Subs.)
6. $\angle 1$ and $\angle 4$ are supplementary. (Def. of supplementary ∠s.)

42. Lines b and c are perpendicular. Since $\angle 1$ and $\angle 2$ form a linear pair, $m\angle 1 + m\angle 2 = 180$. $\angle 1 \cong \angle 2$, so $m\angle 1 = m\angle 2$. Substituting, $m\angle 1 + m\angle 1 = 180$, so $m\angle 1 = 90$ and $m\angle 2 = 90$. So, lines a and c are perpendicular. By Theorem 3.4, since transversal c is perpendicular to line a and lines a and b are parallel, then line c is perpendicular to line b.

43. In both theorems, a pair of angles is formed when two parallel lines are cut by a transversal. However, in the Alternate Interior Angles Theorem, each pair of alternate interior angles that is formed are congruent, whereas in the Consecutive Interior Angles Theorem, each pair of angles formed is supplementary.

44.

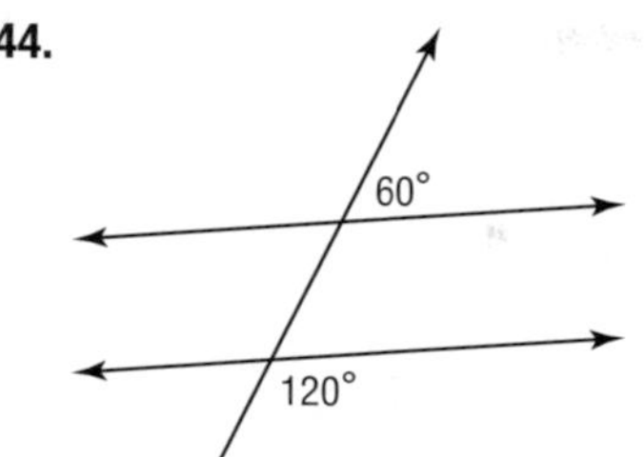

Consecutive Exterior Angles or Same-Side Exterior Angles

Lesson 3-3

5.

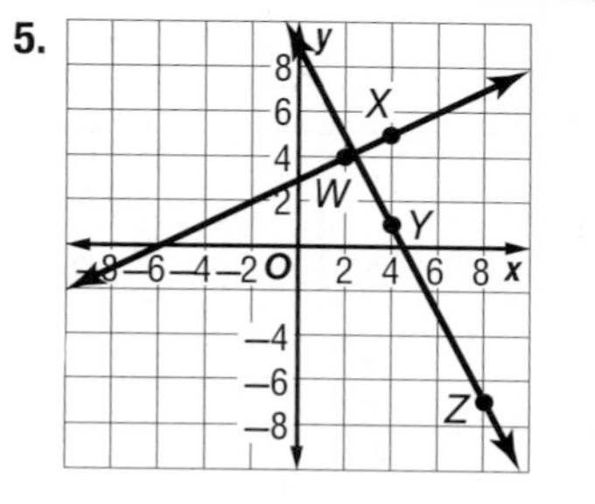

6.

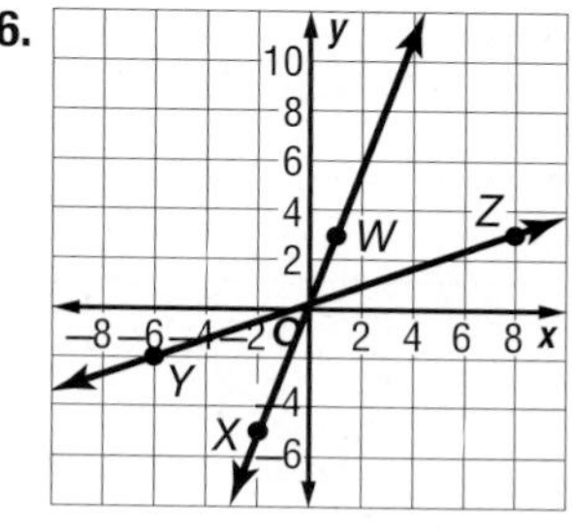

7.

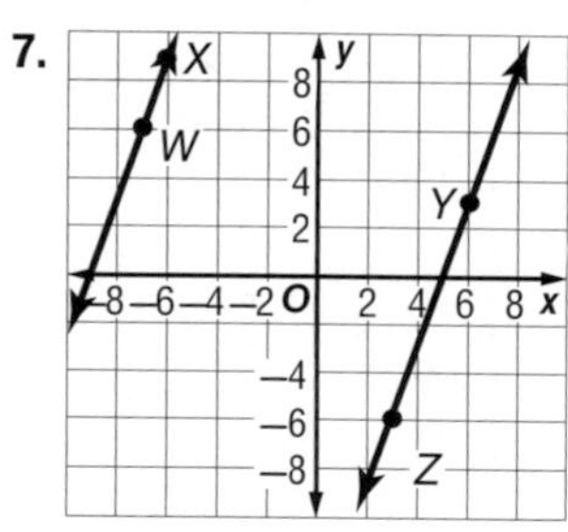

8.

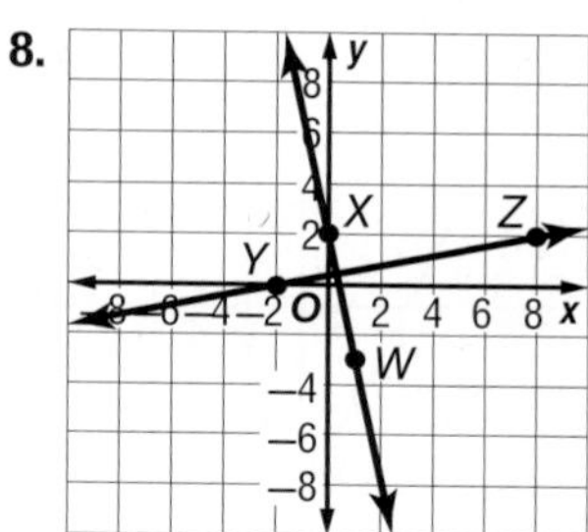

9.

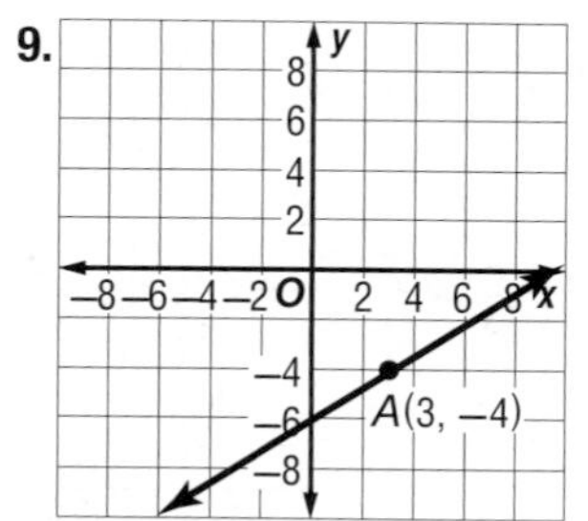

10.

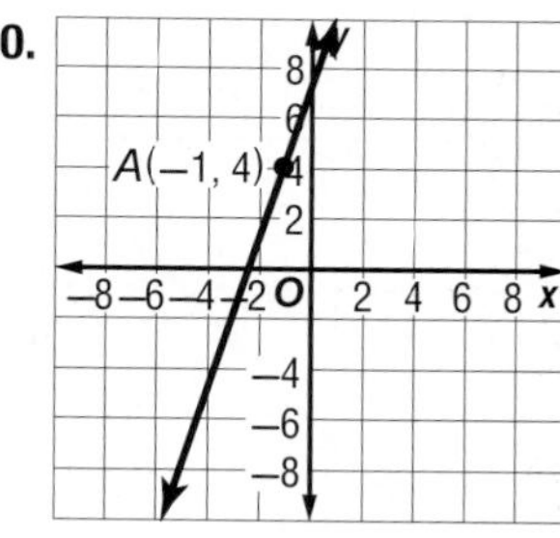

11.

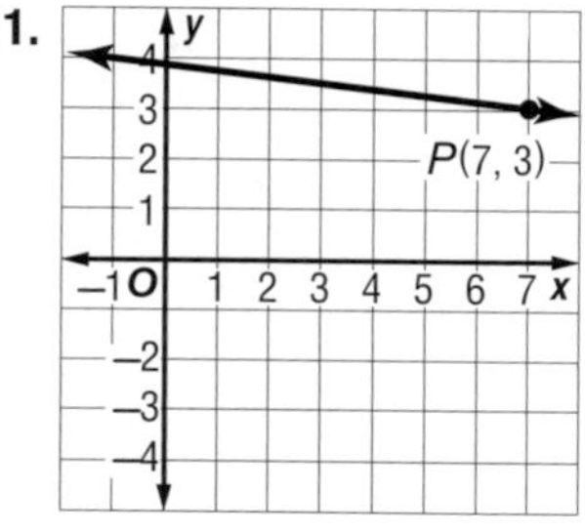

28.

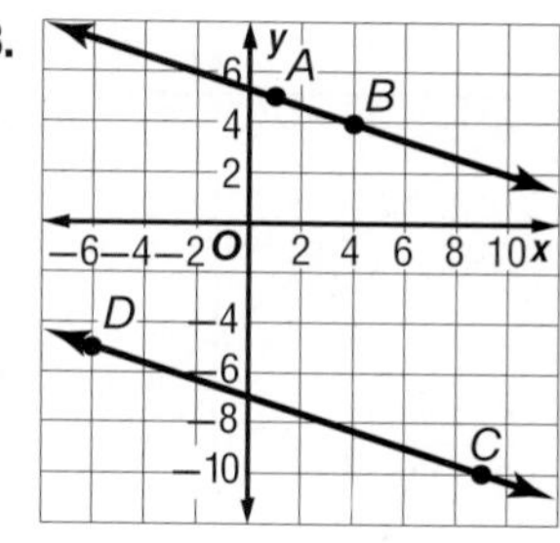

29. 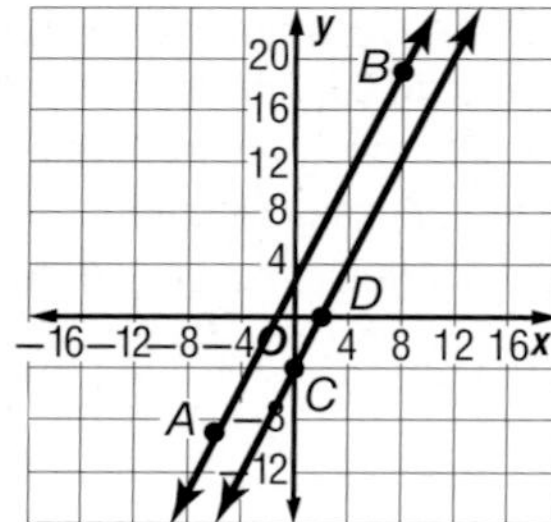

30. 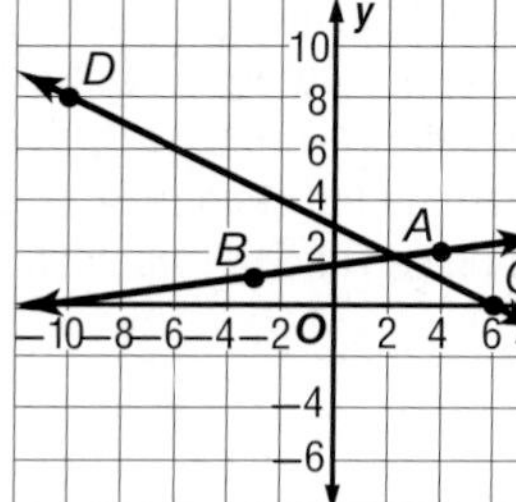

31. 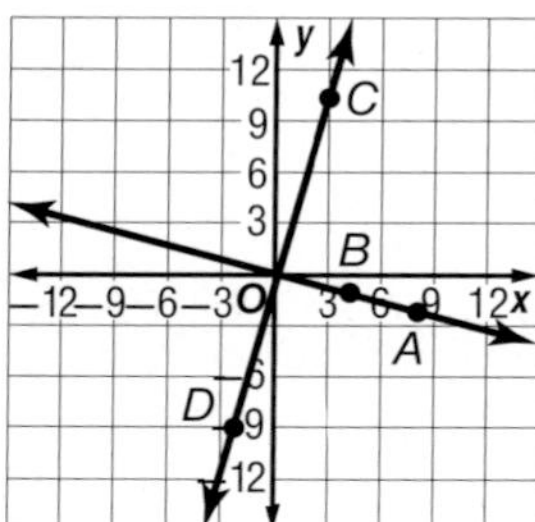

32. 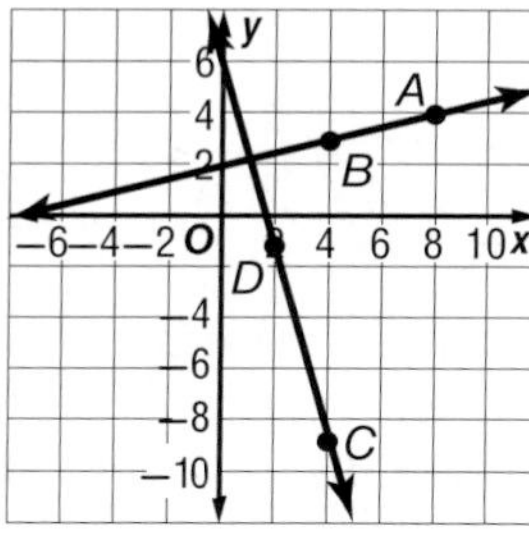

33. 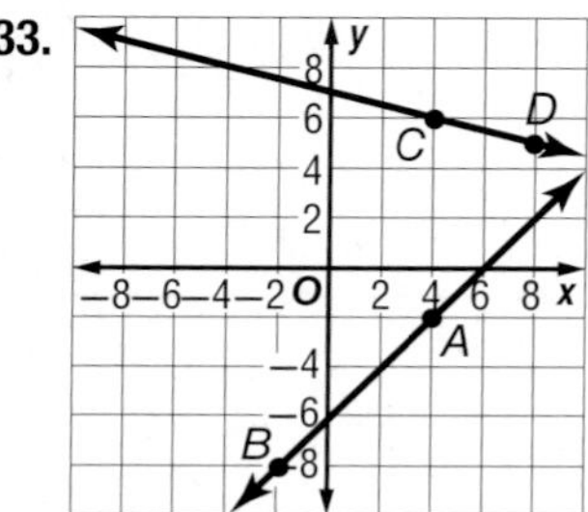

34. 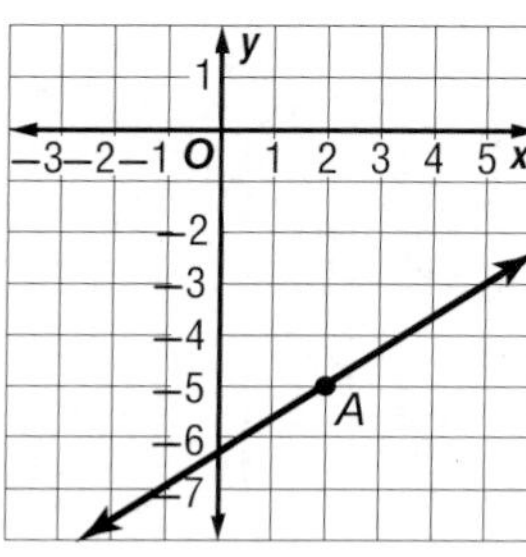

35. 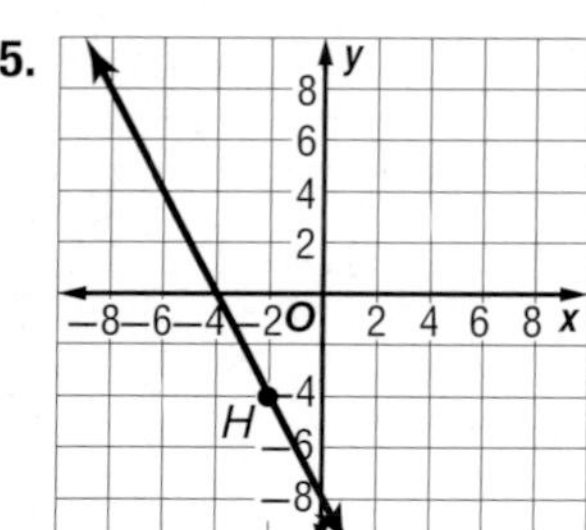

36. 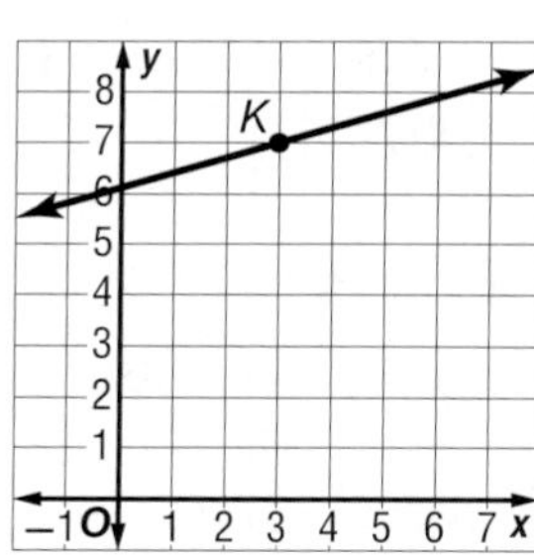

37. 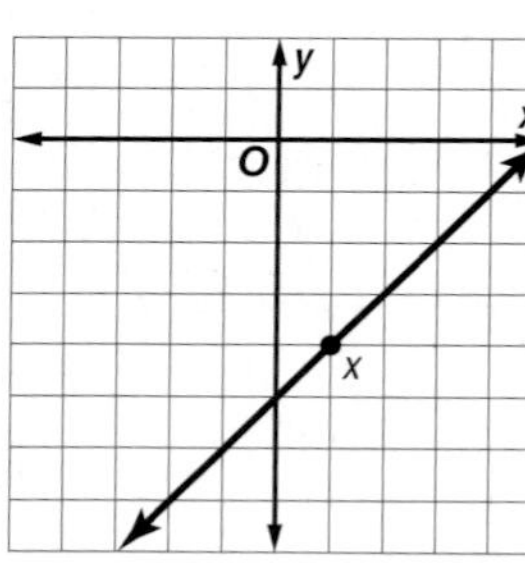

38. 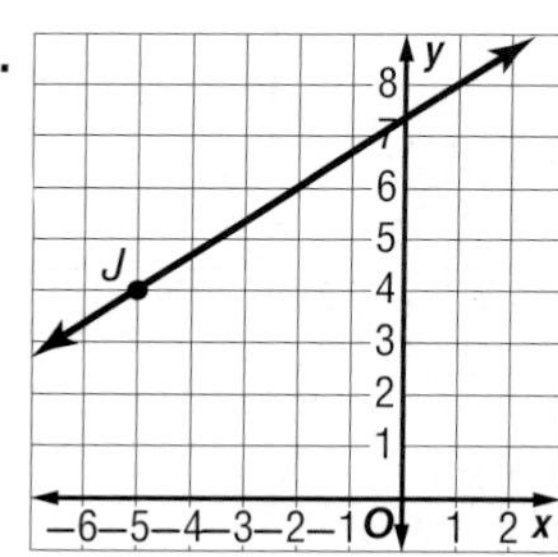

39. 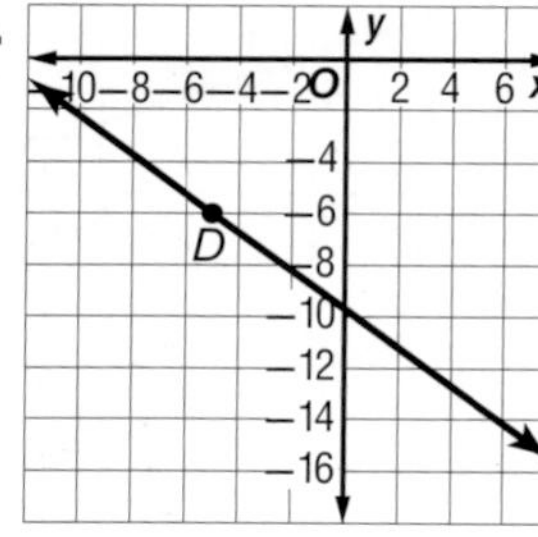

45b. 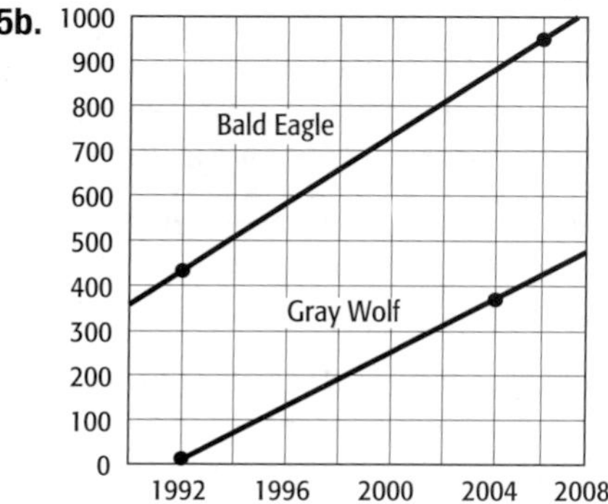

46. $x = 6$;

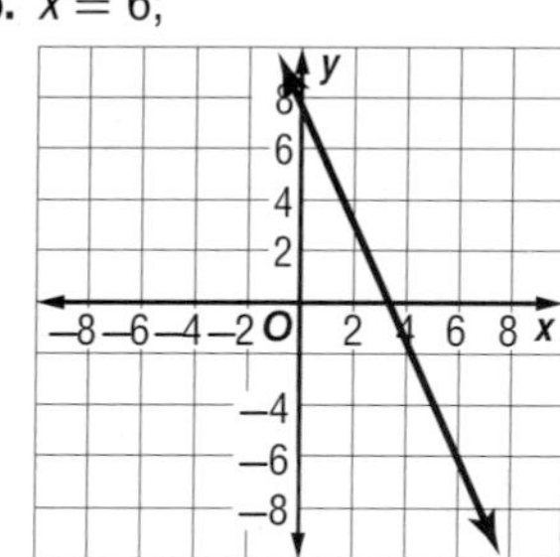

47. $y = -8$;

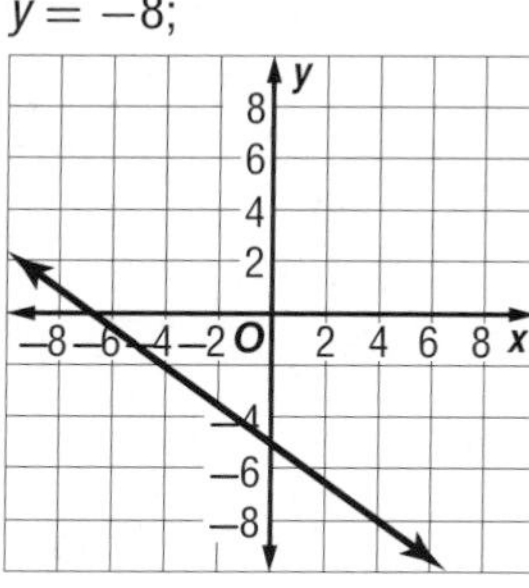

48. $x = 15$;

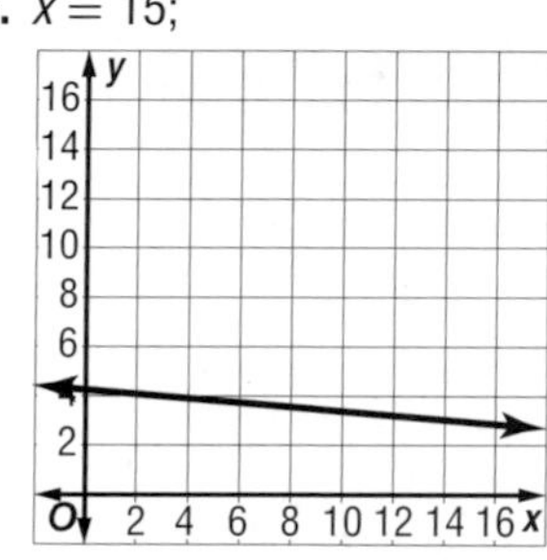

49. $y = 0$;

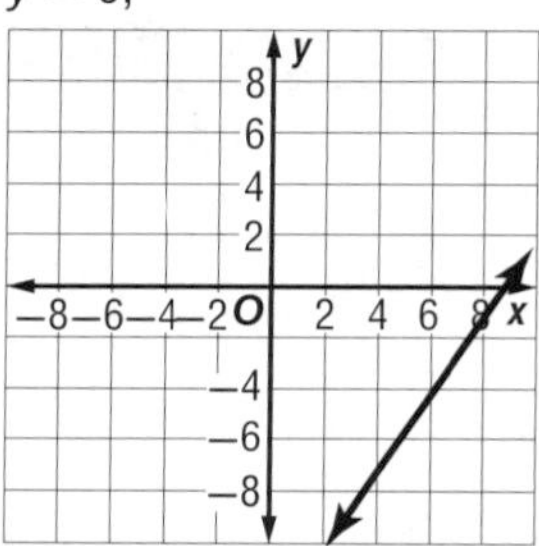

56. Sample answer:

Given: $m = \frac{y_2 - y_1}{x_2 - x_1}$

Prove: $m = \frac{y_1 - y_2}{x_1 - x_2}$

Proof:

Statements (Reasons)

1. $m = \frac{y_2 - y_1}{x_2 - x_1}$ (Given)
2. $m = \frac{-(y_2 - y_1)}{-(x_2 - x_1)}$ (Mult. Prop.)
3. $m = \frac{-y_2 + y_1}{-x_2 + x_1}$ (Dist. Prop.)
4. $m = \frac{y_1 - y_2}{x_1 - x_2}$ (Comm. Prop. of Addition)

57. Sample answer: (4, −3) and (5, −5) lie along the same line as points X and Y. The slope between all of the points is −2. To find additional points, you can take any point on the line and subtract 2 from the y-coordinate and add 1 to the x-coordinate.

Mid-Chapter Quiz

15.
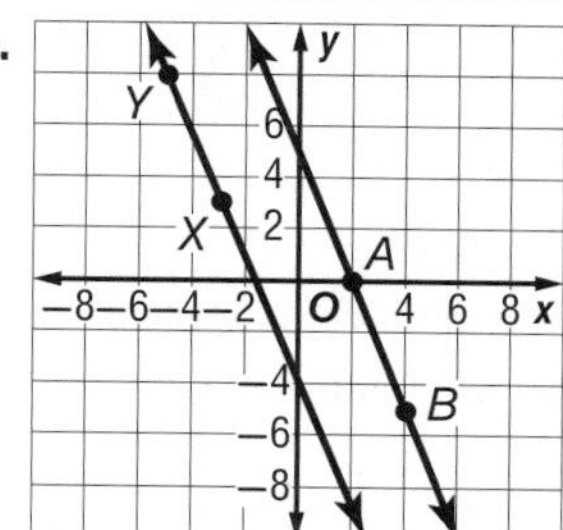

16.
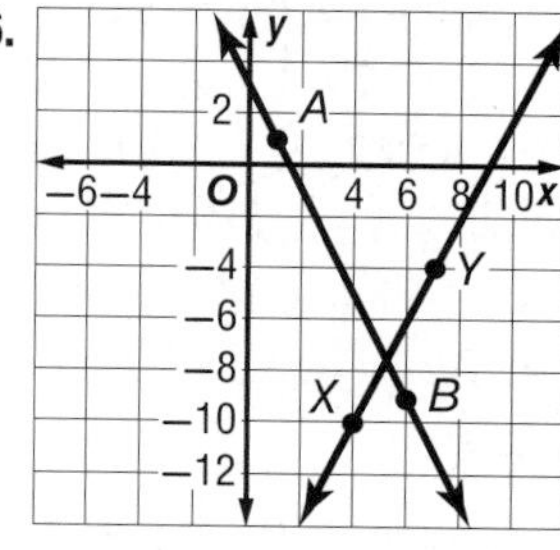

Lesson 3-4 (Guided Practice)

1. $y = -\frac{1}{2}x + 8$
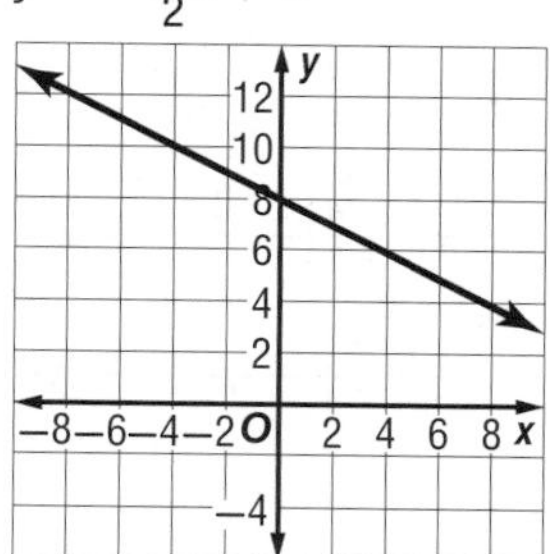

2. $y + 6 = 4(x + 3)$
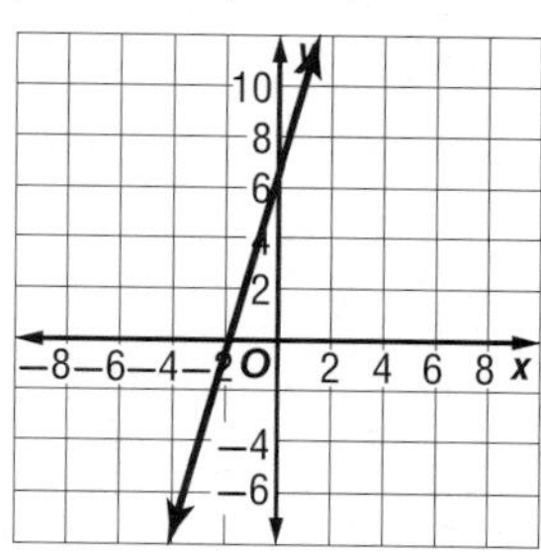

Lesson 3-4

4.
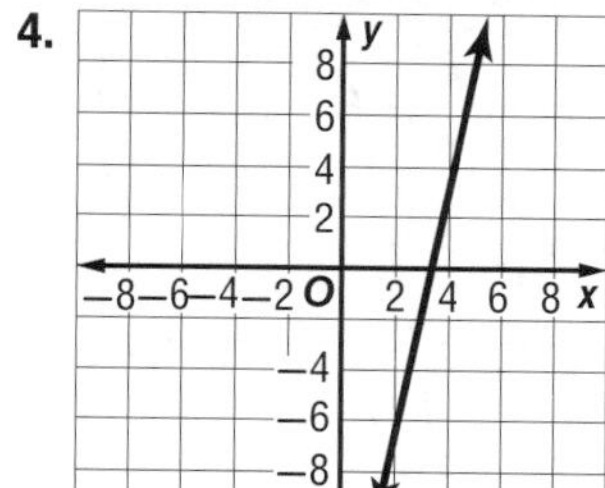

5.
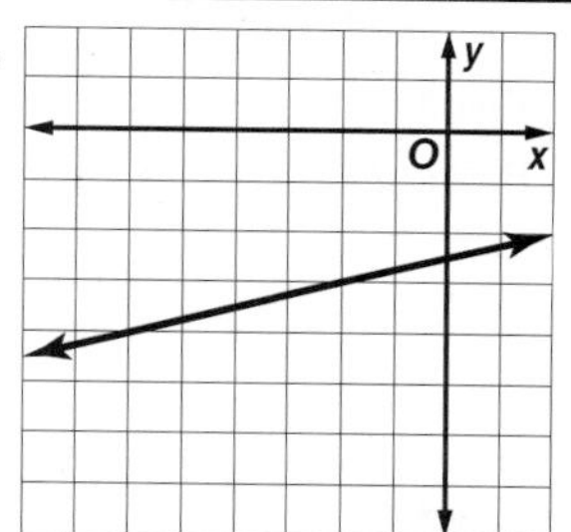

6.
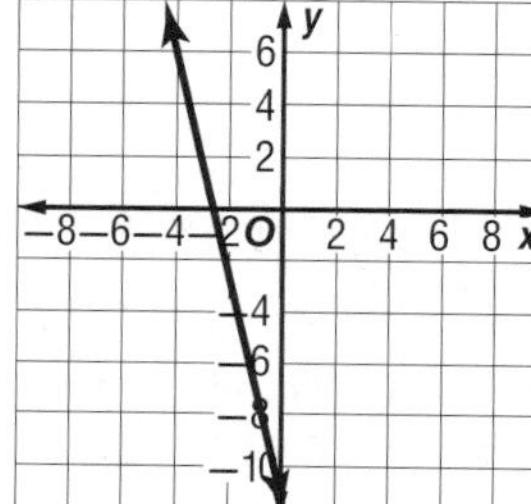

12b.
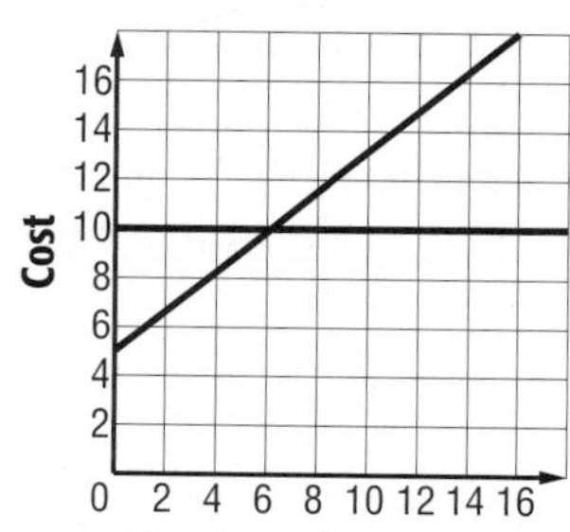

13. $y = -5x - 2$
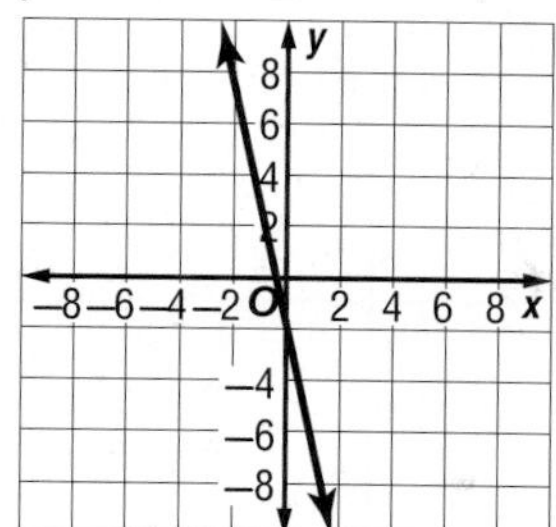

14. $y = -7x - 4$
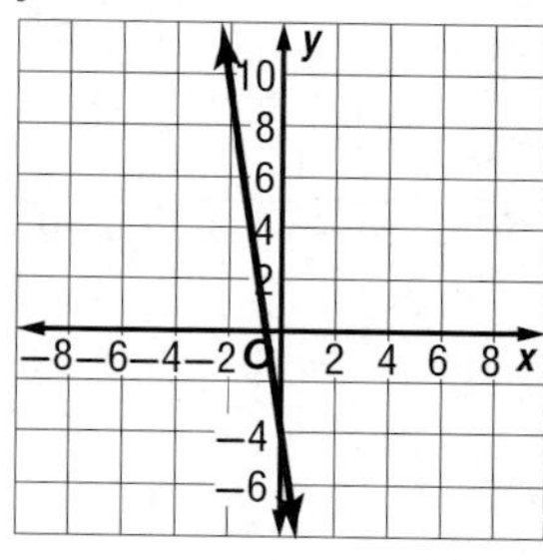

15. $y = 9x + 2$
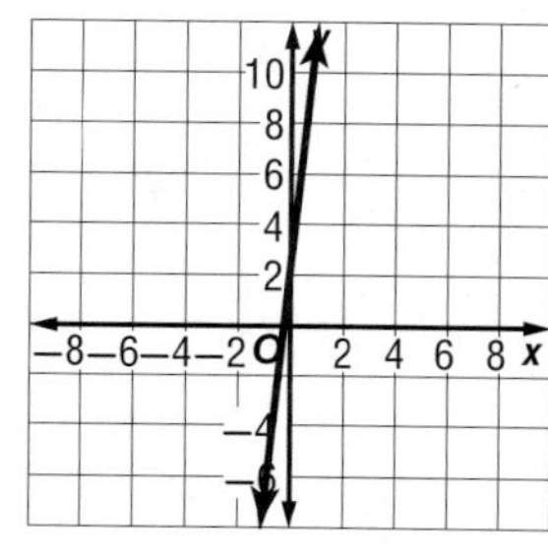

16. $y = 12x + \frac{4}{5}$
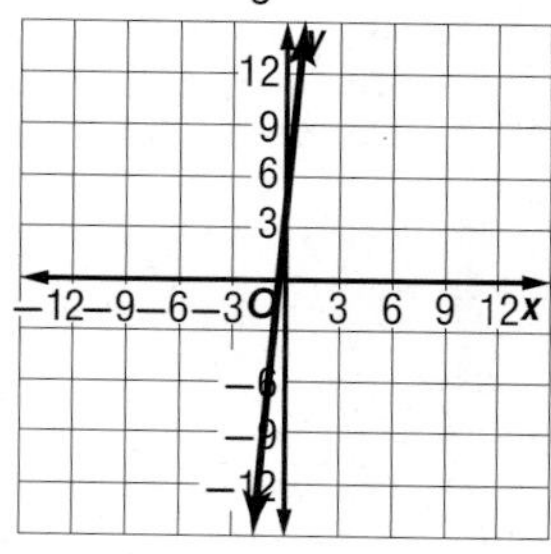

17. $y = -\frac{3}{4}x + 4$
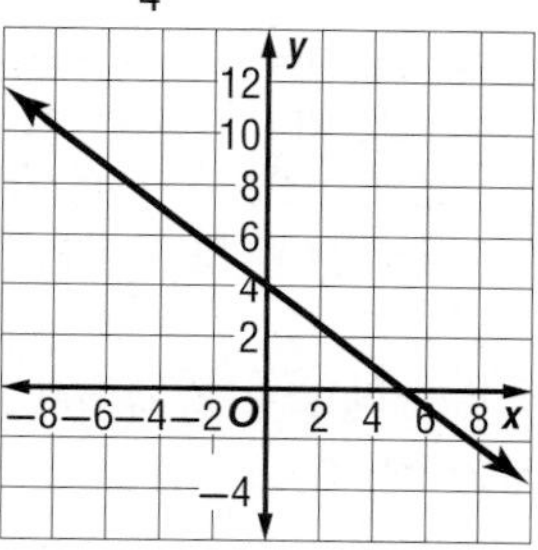

18. $y = \frac{5}{11}x - 3$
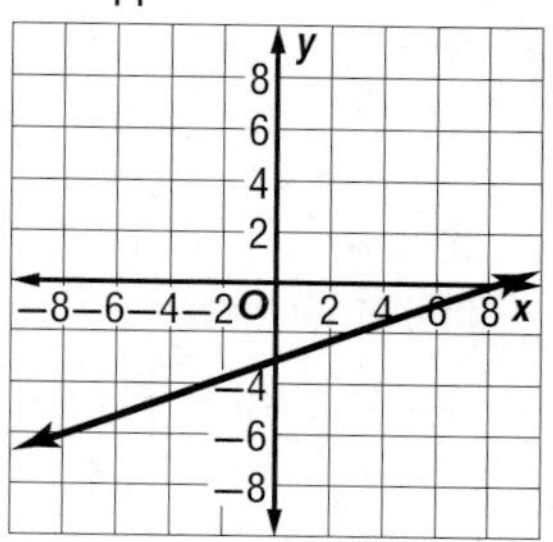

19. $y - 11 = 2(x - 3)$
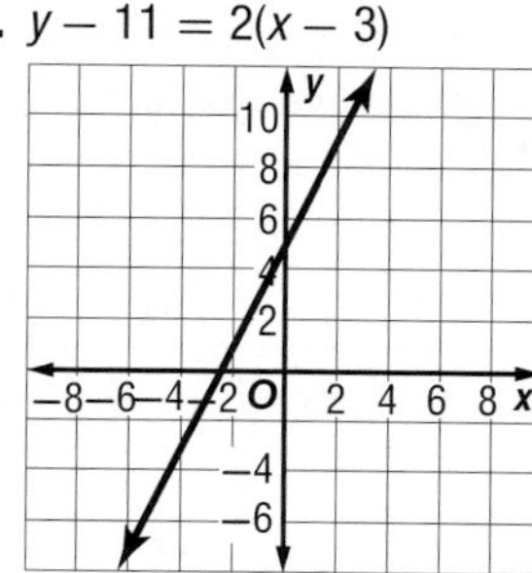

20. $y - 8 = 4(x + 4)$
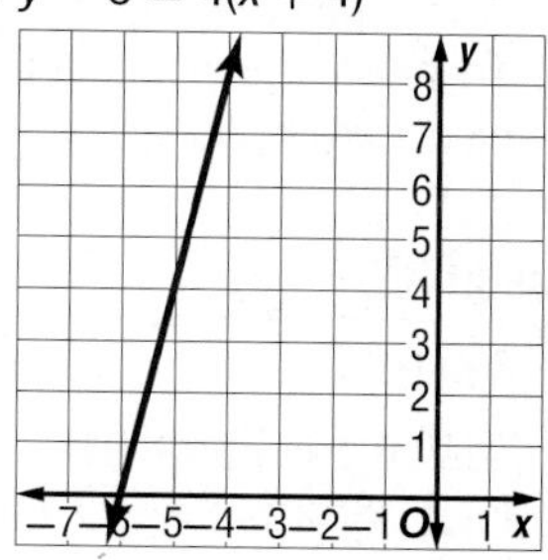

21. $y - 9 = -7(x - 1)$
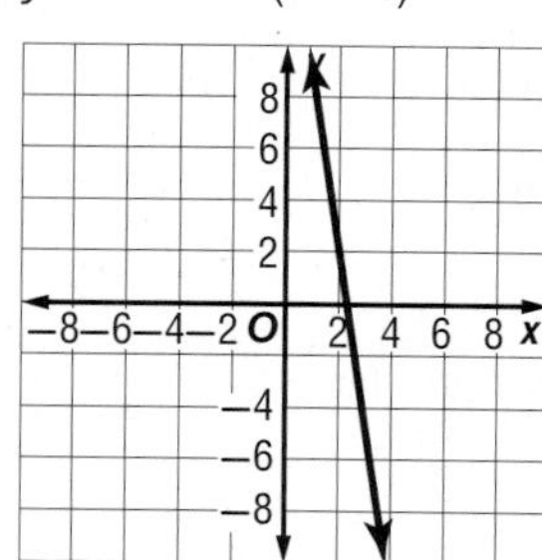

22. $y + 5 = \frac{5}{7}(x + 2)$
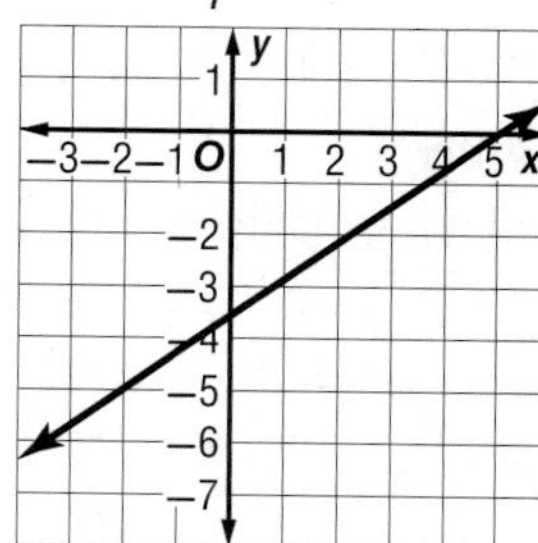

23. $y + 6 = -\frac{4}{5}(x + 3)$

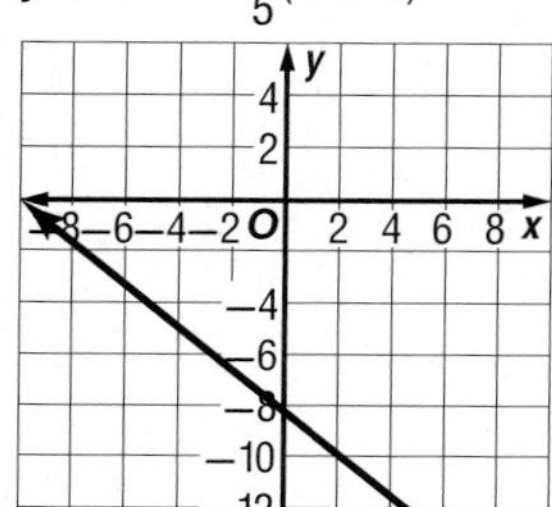

24. $y + 12 = -2.4(x - 14)$

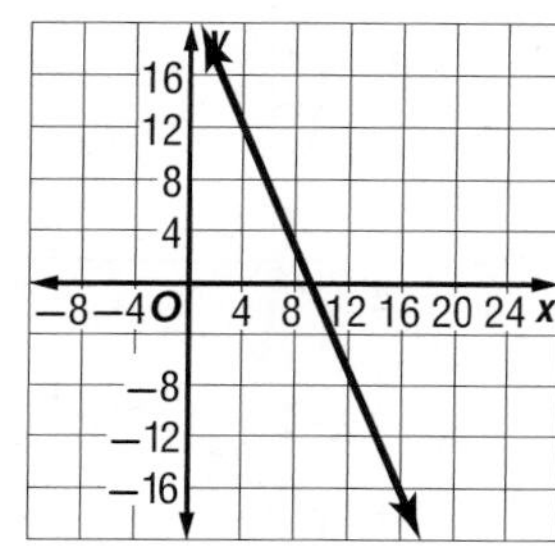

42b.

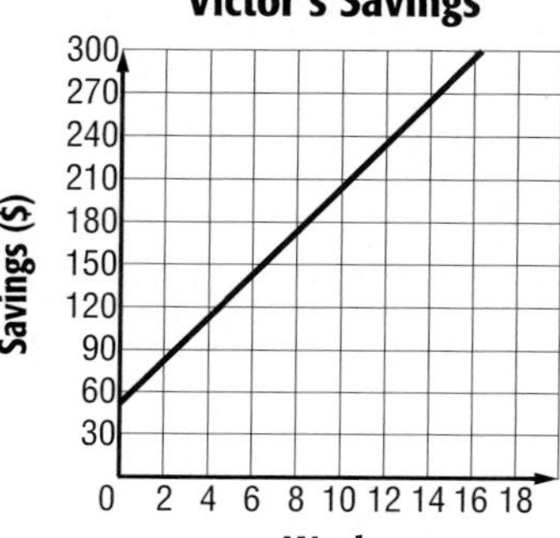

42d. 15; If Victor started saving two weeks ago, he already has $50 + $15 + $15 or $80. He needs to save $180 + 12($10) or $300. He still needs to save $300 − $80 or $220. Dividing $220 by $15, it will take 15 more weeks for Victor to save enough money.

56. Yes; the slope of the line through the points (−2, 2) and (2, 5) is $\frac{3}{4}$. The slope of the line through the points (2, 5) and (6, 8) is $\frac{3}{4}$. Since these lines have the same slope and have a point in common their equations would be the same. Therefore, the points are all on the same line and all the points are collinear.

Lesson 3-5

25. Proof:

Statements (Reasons)

1. $\angle 1 \cong \angle 3$, $\overline{AC} \parallel \overline{BD}$ (Given)
2. $\angle 2 \cong \angle 3$ (Corr. ∡ Postulate)
3. $\angle 1 \cong \angle 2$ (Trans. Prop.)
4. $\overline{AB} \parallel \overline{CD}$ (If alternate ∡ are ≅, then lines are ||.)

26. Proof:

Statements (Reasons)

1. $\overline{WX} \parallel \overline{YZ}$, $\angle 2 \cong \angle 3$ (Given)
2. $\angle 2$ and $\angle 4$ are supplementary. (Cons. Int. ∡)
3. $m\angle 2 + m\angle 4 = 180$ (Def. of suppl. ∡)
4. $m\angle 3 + m\angle 4 = 180$ (Substitution)
5. $\angle 3$ and $\angle 4$ are supplementary. (Def of suppl. ∡)
6. $\overline{WY} \parallel \overline{XZ}$ (If cons. int. ∡ are suppl., then lines are ||.)

27. Proof:

Statements (Reasons)

1. $\angle ABC \cong \angle ADC$, $m\angle A + m\angle ABC = 180$ (Given)
2. $m\angle ABC = m\angle ADC$ (Def. of ≅ ∡)
3. $m\angle A + m\angle ADC = 180$ (Substitution)
4. $\angle A$ and $\angle ADC$ are supplementary. (Def. of suppl. ∡)
5. $\overline{AB} \parallel \overline{CD}$ (If consec. int. ∡ are suppl., then lines are ||.)

28. Proof:

Statements (Reasons)

1. $\angle 1 \cong \angle 2$, $\overline{LJ} \perp \overline{ML}$ (Given)
2. $\overline{LJ} \parallel \overline{KM}$ (If alt. int. ∡ are ≅, then lines are ||.)
3. $\overline{KM} \perp \overline{ML}$ (Perpendicular Transversal Theorem)

30. Given: $\ell \perp t, m \perp t$

Prove: $\ell \parallel m$

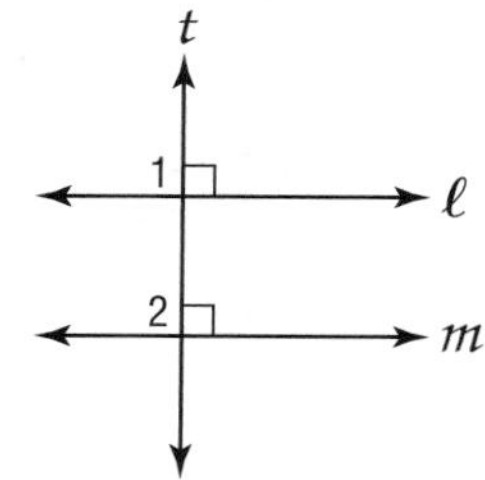

Proof:

Since $\ell \perp t$ and $m \perp t$, the measures of $\angle 1$ and $\angle 2$ are 90. Since $\angle 1$ and $\angle 2$ have the same measure, they are congruent. By the Converse of the Corresponding Angles Postulate, $\ell \parallel m$.

31. Given: $\angle 1 \cong \angle 2$

Prove: $\ell \parallel m$

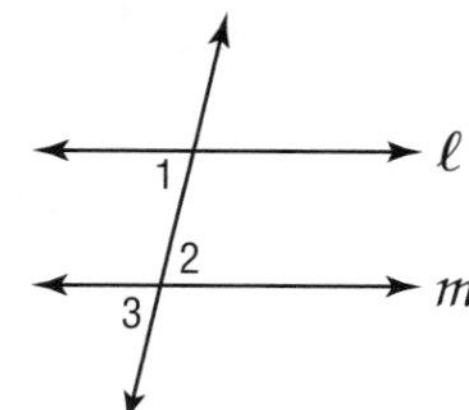

Proof:

Statements (Reasons)

1. $\angle 1 \cong \angle 2$ (Given)
2. $\angle 2 \cong \angle 3$ (Vertical ∡ are ≅)
3. $\angle 1 \cong \angle 3$ (Transitive Prop.)
4. $\ell \parallel m$ (If corr ∡ are ≅, then lines are ||.)

33. $r \parallel s$; Sample answer: The corresponding angles are congruent. Since the measures of the angles are equal, the lines are parallel.

34. $r \parallel s$; Sample answer: The alternate exterior angles are congruent. Since the measures of the angles are equal, the lines are parallel.

35. $r \parallel s$; Sample answer: The alternate exterior angles are congruent. Since the measures of the angles are equal, the lines are parallel.

39. Sample answer:

Given: $a \parallel b$ and $b \parallel c$

Prove: $a \parallel c$

Proof:

Statements (Reasons)

1. $a \parallel b$ and $b \parallel c$ (Given)
2. $\angle 1 \cong \angle 3$ (Alt. Int. $\angle$s Thm.)
3. $\angle 3 \cong \angle 2$ (Vert. $\angle$s are $\cong$)
4. $\angle 2 \cong \angle 4$ (Alt. Int. $\angle$s Thm.)
5. $\angle 1 \cong \angle 4$ (Trans. Prop.)
6. $a \parallel c$ (Alt. Int. $\angle$s Conv. Thm.)

41a. We know that $m\angle 1 + m\angle 2 = 180$. Since $\angle 2$ and $\angle 3$ are linear pairs, $m\angle 2 + m\angle 3 = 180$. By substitution, $m\angle 1 + m\angle 2 = m\angle 2 + m\angle 3$. By subtracting $m\angle 2$ from both sides we get $m\angle 1 = m\angle 3$. $\angle 1 \cong \angle 3$, by the definition of congruent angles. Therefore, $a \parallel c$ since the corresponding angles are congruent.

41b. We know that $a \parallel c$ and $m\angle 1 + m\angle 3 = 180$. Since $\angle 1$ and $\angle 3$ are corresponding angles, they are congruent and their measures are equal. By substitution, $m\angle 3 + m\angle 3 = 180$ or $2\,m\angle 3 = 180$. By dividing both sides by 2, we get $m\angle 3 = 90$. Therefore, $t \perp c$ since they form a right angle.

42. Sample answer: Use a pair of alternate exterior angles that are congruent and cut by transversal; show that a pair of consecutive interior angles are supplementary; show that alternate interior angles are congruent; show two coplanar lines are perpendicular to same line; show corresponding angles are congruent.

43. Yes; sample answer: A pair of angles can be both supplementary and congruent if the measure of both angles is 90, since the sum of the angle measures would be 180.

Lesson 3-6

9.

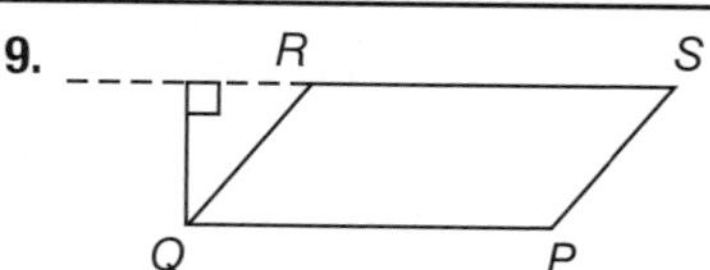

10.

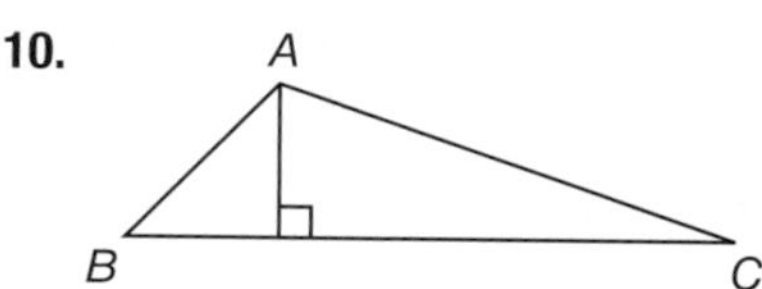

11.

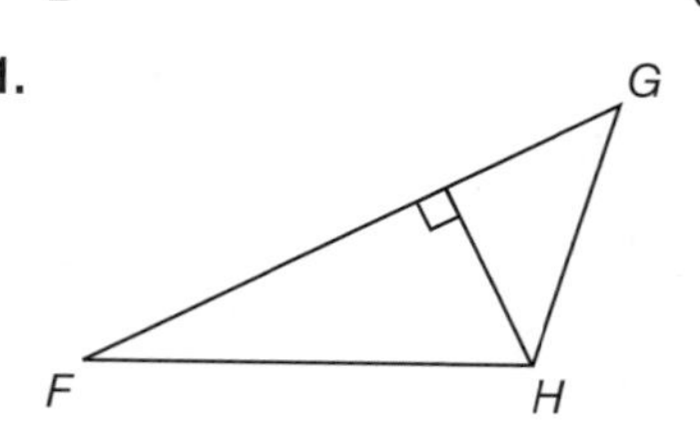

12.

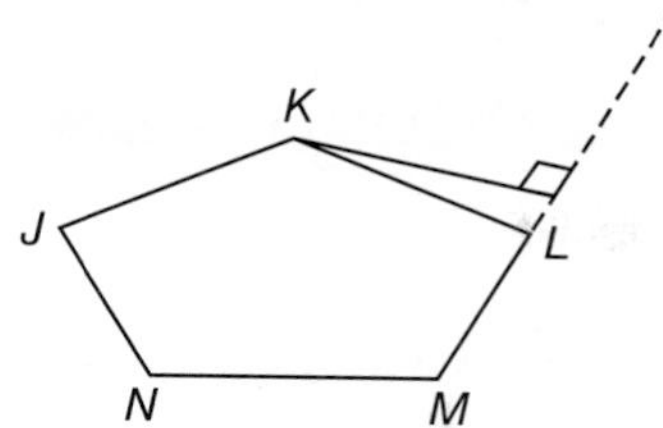

42. Sample answer: $\overleftrightarrow{AB}$ and $\overleftrightarrow{CD}$ intersect at X to form 2 pairs of vertical angles. The locus of points equidistant from lines $\overleftrightarrow{AB}$ and $\overleftrightarrow{CD}$ lie along $\overleftrightarrow{EF}$, and $\overleftrightarrow{GH}$, which bisect each pair of vertical angles. $\overleftrightarrow{EF}$ and $\overleftrightarrow{GH}$ are perpendicular.

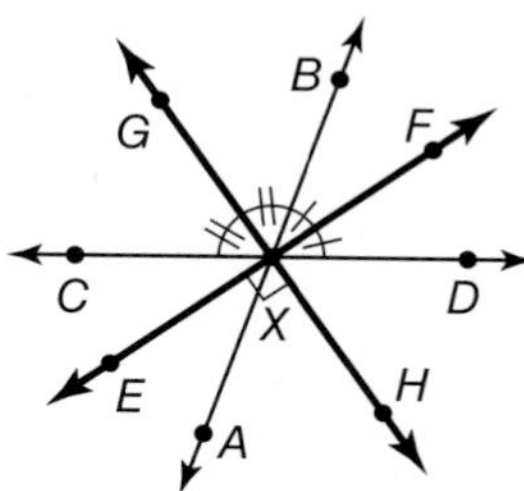

Chapter Planner

	Diagnostic Assessment Quick Check		
	LESSON 4-1 **45 min:** 1 day **90 min:** 0.5 day	**EXPLORE 4-2** **45 min:** 0.5 day **90 min:** 0.25 day	**LESSON 4-2** **45 min:** 1.5 days **90 min:** 0.75 day
Title	**Classifying Triangles**	**Geometry Lab: Angles of Triangles**	**Angles of Triangles**
Objectives	▪ Identify and classify triangles by angle measures and side measures.	▪ Find the relationships among the measures of the interior angles of a triangle.	▪ Apply the Triangle Angle-Sum Theorem. ▪ Apply the Exterior Angle Theorem.
Key Vocabulary	acute triangle equilangular triangle obtuse triangle right triangle equilateral triangle isosceles triangle scalene triangle		auxiliary line exterior angle remote interior angle flow proof corollary
CCSS	G.CO.12	G.CO.12	G.CO.10
Multiple Representations			
Lesson Resources	connectED.mcgraw-hill.com Leveled Worksheets Vocabulary Personal Tutor Self-Check Quiz ▪ *5-Minute Check* ▪ *Study Notebook*	connectED.mcgraw-hill.com Animations ▪ *Teaching Geometry with Manipulatives* **Materials:** ▪ protractor ▪ scissors	connectED.mcgraw-hill.com Leveled Worksheets Quiz 1 Vocabulary Personal Tutor Self-Check Quiz ▪ *5-Minute Check* ▪ *Study Notebook* ▪ *Teaching Geometry with Manipulatives*
Resources for Every Lesson	IWB eStudent Edition IWB Interactive Classroom	▪ eTeacher Edition ▪ eSolutions Manual ▪ eAssessment	
Differentiated Instruction	pp. 238, 239, 242		pp. 248, 252

IWB All digital assets are Interactive Whiteboard ready.

Suggested Pacing			
Time Periods	Instruction	Review & Assess	Total
45-minute	12 days	2 days	14 days
90-minute	6 days	1 day	7 days

LESSON 4-3 **45 min:** 1 day **90 min:** 0.5 day	LESSON 4-4 **45 min:** 1.5 days **90 min:** 0.75 day	EXTEND 4-4 **45 min:** 0.5 day **90 min:** 0.25 day	LESSON 4-5 **45 min:** 1.5 days **90 min:** 0.75 day
Congruent Triangles	**Proving Triangles Congruent—SSS, SAS**	**Geometry Lab: Proving Constructions**	**Proving Triangles Congruent—ASA, AAS**
▪ Name and use corresponding parts of congruent polygons. ▪ Prove triangles congruent using the definition of congruence.	▪ Use the SSS and SAS Postulates to test for triangle congruence.	▪ Prove constructions using congruent measurements.	▪ Use the ASA and AAS Postulates to test for triangle congruence.
congruent congruent polygon corresponding parts	included angle		included side
G.CO.7, G.SRT.5	G.CO.10, G.SRT.5	G.CO.12, G.SRT.5	G.CO.10, G.SRT.5
connectED.mcgraw-hill.com Leveled Worksheets Vocabulary Personal Tutor Self-Check Quiz ▪ *5-Minute Check* ▪ *Study Notebook* ▪ *Teaching Geometry with Manipulatives*	connectED.mcgraw-hill.com Leveled Worksheets Quiz 2 Vocabulary Animations Personal Tutor Self-Check Quiz ▪ *5-Minute Check* ▪ *Study Notebook* ▪ *Teaching Geometry with Manipulatives*	connectED.mcgraw-hill.com Animations Virtual Manipulatives ▪ *Teaching Geometry with Manipulatives* **Materials:** ▪ compass ▪ straightedge	connectED.mcgraw-hill.com Leveled Worksheets Vocabulary Animations Personal Tutor Self-Check Quiz ▪ *5-Minute Check* ▪ *Study Notebook*
IWB eStudent Edition IWB Interactive Classroom	▪ eTeacher Edition ▪ eSolutions Manual ▪ eAssessment		
pp. 256, 257, 261	pp. 265, 272		pp. 277, 282
		Formative Assessment Mid-Chapter Quiz	

Chapter Planner

	EXTEND 4-5 (45 min: 0.5 day; 90 min: 0.25 day)	LESSON 4-6 (45 min: 1 day; 90 min: 0.5 day)	EXPLORE 4-7 (45 min: 0.5 day; 90 min: 0.25 day)
Title	**Geometry Lab: Congruence in Right Triangles**	**Isosceles and Equilateral Triangles**	**Graphing Technology Lab: Congruence Tranformations**
Objectives	▪ Explore congruence in right triangles.	▪ Use properties of isosceles and equilateral triangles.	▪ Use a graphing calculator to perform transformations on triangles in the coordinate plane. ▪ Test congruence of transformations of triangles.
Key Vocabulary		legs of an isosceles triangle vertex angle base angles	
CCSS	G.SRT.5	G.CO.10, G.CO.12	G.CO.5, G.CO.6
Multiple Representations			
Lesson Resources	connectED.mcgraw-hill.com Animations Virtual Manipulatives ▪ *Teaching Geometry with Manipulatives* **Materials:** ▪ rulers ▪ protractors	connectED.mcgraw-hill.com Leveled Worksheets Quiz 3 Vocabulary Personal Tutor Self-Check Quiz ▪ *5-Minute Check* ▪ *Study Notebook* ▪ *Teaching Geometry with Manipulatives*	connectED.mcgraw-hill.com Personal Tutor **Materials:** ▪ TI-Nspire technology
Resources for Every Lesson	IWB eStudent Edition IWB Interactive Classroom	▪ eTeacher Edition ▪ eSolutions Manual ▪ eAssessment	
Differentiated Instruction		pp. 287, 288	

IWB All digital assets are Interactive Whiteboard ready.

Suggested Pacing			
Time Periods	Instruction	Review & Assess	Total
45-minute	12 days	2 days	14 days
90-minute	6 days	1 day	7 days

LESSON 4-7 — 45 min: 1.5 days, 90 min: 0.75 day	LESSON 4-8 — 45 min: 1 day, 90 min: 0.5 day
Congruence Transformations	**Triangles and Coordinate Proof**
▪ Identify reflections, translations, and rotations. ▪ Verify congruence after a congruence transformation.	▪ Position and label triangles for use in coordinate proofs. ▪ Write coordinate proofs.
transformation preimage image congruence transformation isometry reflection translation rotation	coordinate proof
G.CO.6, G.CO.7	G.CO.10, G.GPE.4
connectED.mcgraw-hill.com Leveled Worksheets Vocabulary Animations Virtual Manipulatives Personal Tutor Self-Check Quiz ▪ *5-Minute Check* ▪ *Study Notebook*	connectED.mcgraw-hill.com Leveled Worksheets Vocabulary Quiz 4 Animations Personal Tutor Self-Check Quiz ▪ *5-Minute Check* ▪ *Study Notebook*
IWB eStudent Edition IWB Interactive Classroom	▪ eTeacher Edition ▪ eSolutions Manual ▪ eAssessment
pp. 297, 301, 302	pp. 305, 309
	Summative Assessment Study Guide and Review Practice Test

What the Research Says...

Formative Assessment—ongoing assessments designed to make students' thinking visible to both teachers and students—are essential. They permit the teacher to grasp the students' preconceptions, understand where the students are in the 'developmental corridor' from informal to formal thinking, and design instruction accordingly (Bransford et al., 2000).

- Determine students' preconceived ideas about the concepts in the chapter by utilizing the Chapter 4 Anticipation Guide. Make certain to emphasize the areas of misconceptions that are clarified during the lesson.
- Use the Assessment Activity at the end of each lesson to assess students' understanding of the concepts of the lesson.

Teacher to Teacher

Karyn S. Cummins, Teacher
Franklin Central High School
Indianapolis, IN

Use With Lesson 4-5

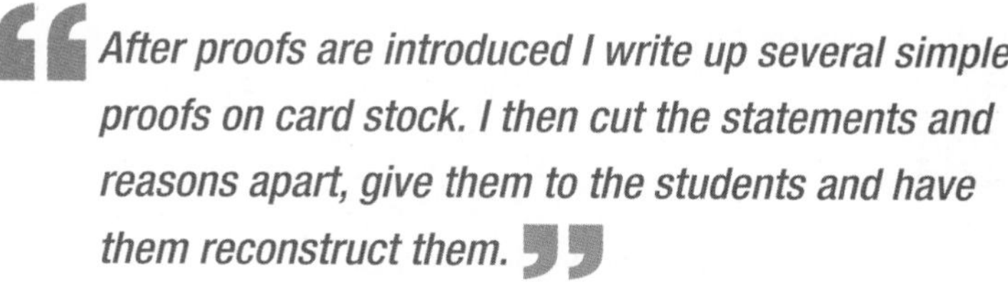

"After proofs are introduced I write up several simple proofs on card stock. I then cut the statements and reasons apart, give them to the students and have them reconstruct them."

CHAPTER 4

Congruent Triangles
Assessment and Intervention

SE = Student Edition, **TE** = Teacher Edition, **CRM** = Chapter Resource Masters

	Diagnosis	Prescription
DIAGNOSTIC ASSESSMENT	**Beginning Chapter 4**	
	Get Ready for Chapter 4 **SE**	Response to Intervention **TE**
	Beginning Every Lesson	
	Then, Now, Why? **SE** 5-Minute Checks	Chapter 0 **SE**
FORMATIVE ASSESSMENT	**During/After Every Lesson**	
	Guided Practice **SE**, every example Check Your Understanding **SE** H.O.T. Problems **SE** Spiral Review **SE** Additional Examples **TE** Watch Out! **TE** Step 4, Assess **TE** Chapter 4 Quizzes **CRM**, pp. 57–58 Self-Check Quizzes connectED.mcgraw-hill.com	TIER 1 Intervention Skills Practice **CRM**, Ch. 1–4 connectED.mcgraw-hill.com TIER 2 Intervention Differentiated Instruction **TE**; Differentiated Homework Options **TE**; Study Guide and Intervention **CRM**, Ch. 1–4 TIER 3 Intervention *Math Triumphs, Geometry,* Ch. 5
	Mid-Chapter	
	Mid-Chapter Quiz **SE** Mid-Chapter Test **CRM**, p. 59 eAssessment	TIER 1 Intervention Skills Practice **CRM**, Ch. 1–4 connectED.mcgraw-hill.com TIER 2 Intervention Study Guide and Intervention **CRM**, Ch. 1–4 TIER 3 Intervention *Math Triumphs, Geometry,* Ch. 5
	Before Chapter Test	
	Chapter Study Guide and Review **SE** Practice Test **SE** Standardized Test Practice **SE** Chapter Test connectED.mcgraw-hill.com Standardized Test Practice connectED.mcgraw-hill.com Vocabulary Review connectED.mcgraw-hill.com eAssessment	TIER 1 Intervention Skills Practice **CRM**, Ch. 1–4 connectED.mcgraw-hill.com TIER 2 Intervention Study Guide and Intervention **CRM**, Ch. 1–4 TIER 3 Intervention *Math Triumphs, Geometry,* Ch. 5
SUMMATIVE ASSESSMENT	**After Chapter 4**	
	Multiple-Choice Tests, Forms 1, 2A, 2B **CRM**, pp. 61–66 Free-Response Tests, Forms 2C, 2D, 3 **CRM**, pp. 67–72 Vocabulary Test **CRM**, p. 60 Extended Response Test **CRM**, p. 73 Standardized Test Practice **CRM**, pp. 74–77 eAssessment	Study Guide and Intervention **CRM**, Ch. 1–4 connectED.mcgraw-hill.com

Differentiated Instruction

Option 1 Reaching All Learners

Kinesthetic Mark a coordinate plane on the floor with tape. Have students form vertices of figures, holding yarn or string between them to form sides. Have them make each of the triangles they have studied in this chapter. Ask them to compare and contrast the triangles.

Naturalist Have students use examples from the chapter and their own observations to classify triangles found in nature. For example, some leaves and trees grow in a triangular shape. Cats have triangular ears. Some algae are triangular in structure.

Visual Rotations, reflections, and translations can be used to create tremendous works of art. Have students begin with a single figure in the coordinate plane and use various transformations to create a work of art. Students should record each transformation they used to create their design.

Option 2 Approaching Level AL

Have small groups of students work together and use a coordinate plane marked on a corkboard to make the triangles that have been studied in this chapter. Have students use pushpins for vertices and string for sides. Have them explain the characteristics of each triangle and classify them.

Option 3 English Learners ELL

Write several proofs on note cards. Cut the statements and the reasons apart. Distribute them to students with the reasons in one shuffled stack and the statements in another. Have students match the statements with the reasons.

Option 4 Beyond Level BL

Have students create an example bank for their classmates. Have them create examples of triangle congruency. They should write SSS, SAS, ASA, or AAS on one side of a card or poster along with the definitions of each. On the other side, they should illustrate an example.

Challenge students to create all the types of triangles possible. Have students organize their attempts in a table like the one below. Students should draw an example of each type of triangle, or write an explanation of why it is not possible.

	acute	right	obtuse	equiangular
scalene				
isosceles				
equilateral				

Focus on Mathematical Content

VerticalAlignment

Before Chapter 4

Related Topics from Grade 8

- Use geometric concepts and properties to solve problems.
- Graph on a coordinate plane.

Chapter 4

Related Topics from Geometry

- Make conjectures about polygons.
- Use numeric and geometric patterns to make generalizations about geometric properties.
- Use logical reasoning to prove statements are true.

After Chapter 4

Preparation for Precalculus

- Solve problems from physical situations using trigonometry, including the use of Law of Sines, Law of Cosines, and area formulas.

Lesson-by-Lesson Preview

4-1 Classifying Triangles

Triangles can be classified based on their angle measures. In an acute triangle, all of the angles are acute. In an obtuse triangle, one of the angles is obtuse. In a right triangle, one angle measures 90. When all of the angles of a triangle are congruent, it is called an equiangular triangle.

Triangles can also be classified according to their number of congruent sides. No two sides of a scalene triangle are congruent. At least two sides of an isosceles triangle are congruent. All of the sides of an equilateral triangle are congruent. Equilateral triangles are a special kind of isosceles triangle.

4-2 Angles of Triangles

The Angle Sum Theorem states that the sum of the measures of the interior angles of a triangle is always 180. This theorem can be applied to any triangle. It also leads to the Third Angle Theorem: If two angles of one triangle are congruent to two angles of a second triangle, then the third angles of the triangles are congruent. Each angle of a triangle has an exterior angle, which is formed by one side of the triangle and the extension of another side. The interior angles of the triangle not adjacent to a given exterior angle are called remote interior angles. The measure of an exterior angle of a triangle is equal to the sum of the measures of the two remote interior angles. This is the Exterior Angle Theorem.

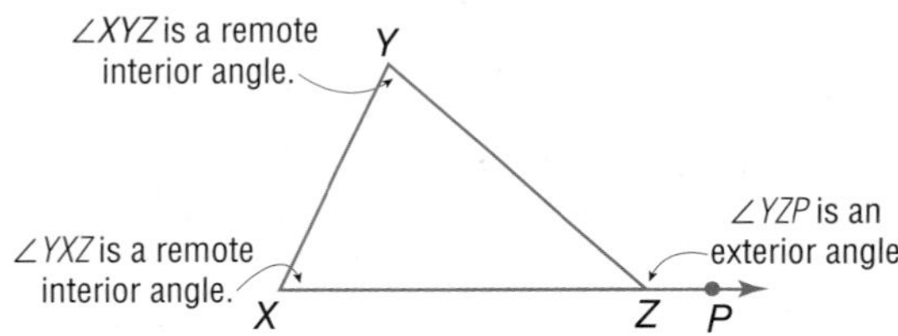

$m\angle XYZ + m\angle YXZ = m\angle YZP$

4-3 Congruent Triangles

Two triangles are congruent *if and only if* their corresponding parts are congruent. Certain transformations, including a slide, flip, and turn, do not affect congruence. These transformations are called *congruence transformations*.

Congruence of triangles, like that of angles and segments, is reflexive, symmetric, and transitive.

4-4 Proving Triangles Congruent—SSS, SAS

In this lesson you will construct a triangle in which three sides are congruent to the three sides of a given triangle. This activity demonstrates the Side-Side-Side Postulate, also written SSS. You will also construct a triangle in which two sides and the included angle are congruent to two sides and the included angle of a given triangle. This activity demonstrates the Side-Angle-Side Postulate, also written SAS.

4-5 Proving Triangles Congruent—ASA, AAS

The Angle-Side-Angle Postulate, written as ASA, works because the measures of two angles of a triangle and the side between them form a unique triangle. The postulate states that if two angles and the included side of one triangle are congruent to the corresponding two angles and included side of another triangle, then the triangles are congruent.

The Angle-Angle-Side, or AAS, Theorem follows from the ASA Postulate: If two angles and a nonincluded side of one triangle are congruent to the corresponding two angles and side of a second triangle, then the two triangles are congruent.

Right triangles have their own theorems to prove congruence. One of those is the LL Congruence Theorem, which is the SAS Postulate applied to right triangles. It states that if the legs of one right triangle are congruent to the corresponding legs of another right triangle, then the triangles are congruent. The HL Postulate is based on SSA, a test that works only for right triangles. It states that if the hypotenuse and leg of one right triangle are congruent to the hypotenuse and corresponding leg of another right triangle, then the triangles are congruent.

4-6 Isosceles and Equilateral Triangles

Isosceles triangles have special terminology for their parts. The angle formed by the congruent sides is called the *vertex angle*. The two angles formed by the base and one of the congruent sides are called *base angles*. The congruent sides are called *legs*. Isosceles triangles also have special properties recognized in the Isosceles Triangle Theorem and its converse: If two sides of a triangle are congruent, then the angles opposite those sides are congruent.

This theorem leads to corollaries about the angles of an equilateral triangle. The first states that a triangle is equilateral if and only if it is equiangular. The second states that each angle of an equilateral triangle measures 60°.

4-7 Congruence Transformations

A transformation is an operation that maps one geometric figure, the preimage, onto another geometric figure, the image. A congruence transformation is one in which the position of the image may differ from the preimage, but the two figures are congruent. Reflections, translations, and rotations are three types of congruence transformations. Congruence transformations are also verified by using properties of congruent triangles.

4-8 Triangles and Coordinate Proof

The coordinate plane can be used in combination with algebra in a coordinate proof. Before beginning a coordinate proof, you will need to place the figure in the coordinate plane. It is important that you use coordinates that make computation as simple as possible. Using the origin as a vertex or center will help, and you should place at least one side of a polygon on an axis. If possible, keep the figure within the first quadrant.

Once the triangle is placed, you can proceed with the proof. The Distance Formula, Slope Formula, and Midpoint Formula are often used in coordinate proofs.

Mc Graw Hill Professional Development

Targeted professional development has been articulated throughout Geometry. More quality, customized professional development is available from McGraw-Hill Professional Development. Visit connectED.mcgraw-hill.com for details on each product.

- Online Lessons emphasize the strategies and techniques used to teach Geometry. Includes streaming video, interactive pages, and online tools.
- Video Workshops allow mentors, coaches, or leadership personnel to facilitate on-site workshops on educational strategies in mathematics and mathematical concepts.
- MHPD Online (www.mhpdonline.com) offers online professional development with video clips of instructional strategies, links, student activities, and news and issues in education.
- Teaching Today (teachingtoday.glencoe.com) gives secondary teachers practical strategies and materials that inspire excellence and innovation in teaching.

Chapter Project

Make Your Mark

Students use what they have learned about triangles and congruence transformations to complete a project.

This chapter project addresses global awareness, as well as several specific skills identified as being essential to student success by the Framework for 21st Century Learning.

Visit connectED.mcgraw-hill.com for student and teacher handouts.

KeyVocabulary Introduce the key vocabulary in the chapter using the method below.

Define: An isosceles triangle is a triangle that has at least two congruent sides.

Example:

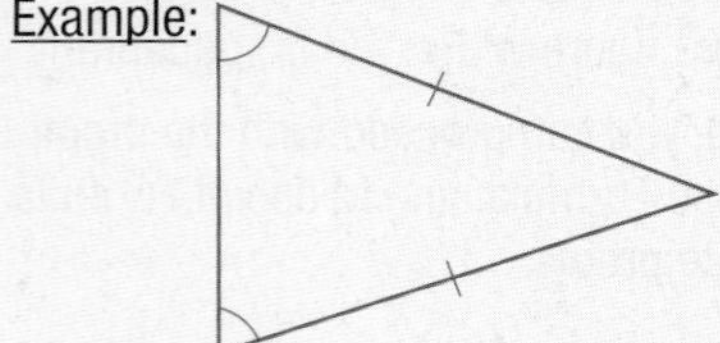

Ask: Do you think the third angle is always the smallest? Sample answer: No; the sum of the measures of the angles opposite the congruent sides could be less than 90, making the measure of the third angle obtuse and therefore the largest angle in the triangle.

CHAPTER 4 Congruent Triangles

Then

You learned about segments, angles, and discovered relationships between their measures.

Now

In this chapter, you will:

- Apply special relationships about the interior and exterior angles of triangles.
- Identify corresponding parts of congruent triangles and prove triangles congruent.
- Learn about the special properties of isosceles and equilateral triangles

Why?

FITNESS Triangles are used to add strength to many structures, including fitness equipment such as bike frames.

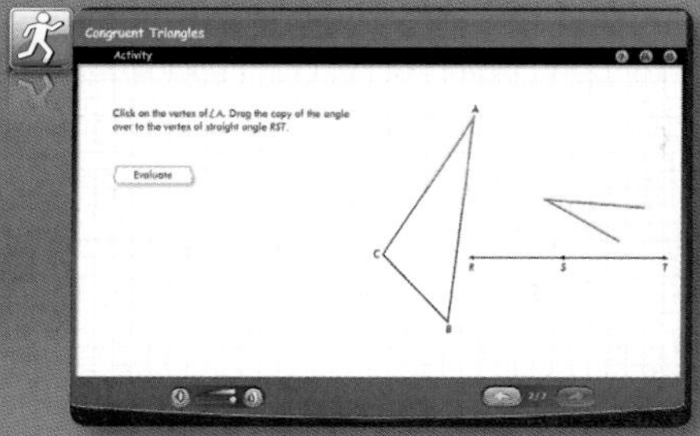

connectED.mcgraw-hill.com Your Digital Math Portal

Animation | Vocabulary | eGlossary | Personal Tutor | Virtual Manipulatives | Graphing Calculator | Audio | Foldables | Self-Check Practice | Worksheets

Get Ready for the Chapter

Diagnose Readiness | You have two options for checking prerequisite skills.

1 Textbook Option Take the Quick Check below. Refer to the Quick Review for help.

QuickCheck

Classify each angle as *right*, *acute*, or *obtuse*.

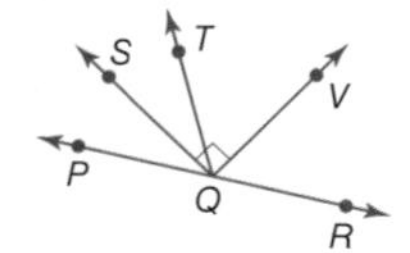

1. $m\angle VQS$ **right**
2. $m\angle TQV$ **acute**
3. $m\angle PQV$ **obtuse**

4. **ORIGAMI** The origami fold involves folding a strip of paper so that the lower edge of the strip forms a right angle with itself. Identify each angle as *right*, *acute*, or *obtuse*.
∠1, right; ∠2, acute; ∠3, obtuse

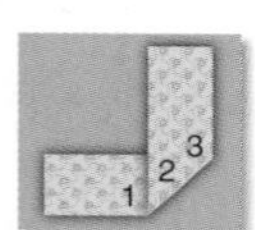

ALGEBRA Use the figure to find the indicated variable(s). Explain your reasoning.

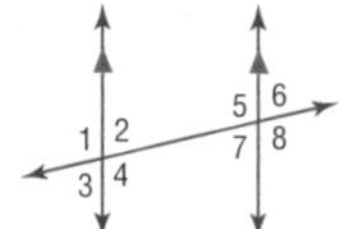

5. Find x if $m\angle 3 = x - 12$ and $m\angle 6 = 72$.
84°; alternate exterior angles
6. If $m\angle 4 = 2y + 32$ and $m\angle 5 = 3y - 3$, find y.
35°; alternate interior angles

Find the distance between each pair of points. **7–10. See margin.**

7. $F(3, 6)$, $G(7, -4)$
8. $X(-2, 5)$, $Y(1, 11)$
9. $R(8, 0)$, $S(-9, 6)$
10. $A(14, -3)$, $B(9, -9)$
11. **MAPS** Miranda laid a coordinate grid on a map of a state where each 1 unit is equal to 10 miles. If her city is located at $(-8, -12)$ and the state capital is at $(0, 0)$, find the distance from her city to the capital to the nearest tenth of a mile.
144.2 miles

QuickReview

Example 1 (Used in Lesson 4-1)

Classify each angle as *right*, *acute*, or *obtuse*.

a. $m\angle ABG$
Point G on angle $\angle ABG$ lies on the exterior of right angle $\angle ABF$, so $\angle ABG$ is an obtuse angle.

b. $m\angle DBA$
Point D on angle $\angle DBA$ lies on the interior of right angle $\angle FBA$, so $\angle DBA$ is an acute angle.

Example 2 (Used in Lessons 4-2 through 4-5)

In the figure, $m\angle 4 = 42$. Find $m\angle 7$.

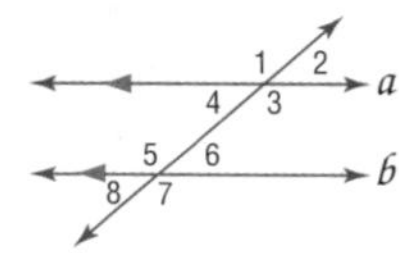

$\angle 7$ and $\angle 1$ are alternate interior angles, so they are congruent. $\angle 1$ and $\angle 4$ are a linear pair, so they are supplementary. Therefore, $\angle 7$ is supplementary to $\angle 1$. The measure of $\angle 7$ is $180 - 42$ or 138.

Example 3 (Used in Lessons 4-4, 4-7, and 4-8)

Find the distance between $J(5, 2)$ and $K(11, -7)$.

$JK = \sqrt{(x_2 - x_1)^2 + (y_2 - y_1)^2}$ Distance Formula

$= \sqrt{(11 - 5)^2 + [(-7) - 2]^2}$ Substitute.

$= \sqrt{6^2 + (-9)^2}$ Subtract.

$= \sqrt{36 + 81}$ or $\sqrt{117}$ Simplify.

2 Online Option Take an online self-check Chapter Readiness Quiz at connectED.mcgraw-hill.com.

235

Essential Questions

- How can you compare two objects? Sample answer: You can compare their characteristics, such as size, color, and shape.
- How can you tell if two objects are congruent? Sample answer: You can measure all of the parts of each of object and then compare them.
- How can you tell if two triangles are congruent? Sample answer: You can measure all of the sides and angles of each triangle, and then compare them to see if the corresponding parts are congruent.

Get Ready for the Chapter

Response to Intervention (RtI)

Use the *Quick Check* results and the Intervention Planner chart to help you determine your Response to Intervention. The If-Then statements in the chart help you decide the appropriate tier of RtI and suggest intervention resources for each tier.

InterventionPlanner

TIER 1 On Level OL

 students miss about 25% of the exercises or less,

 choose a resource:

SE Lessons 1-3, 1-4, and 3-2

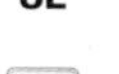 Skills Practice, Chapter 1, pp. 20, 27, Chapter 3, p. 13

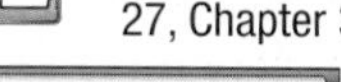 Self-Check Quiz

TIER 2 Strategic Intervention AL approaching grade level

 students miss about 50% of the exercises,

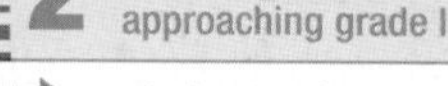

 choose a resource:

 Study Guide and Intervention, Chapter 1, pp. 18–19, 25–26, Chapter 3, pp. 11–12

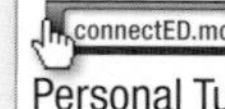 Extra Examples, Personal Tutor, Homework Help

TIER 3 Intensive Intervention 2 or more grades below level

 students miss about 75% of the exercises,

 use *Math Triumphs, Geometry*, Ch. 5

connectED.mcgraw-hill.com Extra Examples, Personal Tutor, Homework Help, Review Vocabulary

Additional Answers

7. ≈10.8
8. ≈6.7
9. ≈18.0
10. ≈7.8

FOLDABLES StudyOrganizer

Dinah Zike's Foldables®

Focus Students use their Foldable to take notes, define terms, record concepts, and write examples about triangles.

Teach After students make their Foldable journal, have them label the pages to correspond to the eight lessons in this chapter. The journal can be used to take notes, as well as to describe the progress of learning, personal associations that come to mind, and to list examples of ways their new knowledge has been used, or could be used, in their daily lives.

When to Use It Use the appropriate tabs as students cover each lesson in this chapter. Students can add to the vocabulary tab during each lesson.

Differentiated Instruction

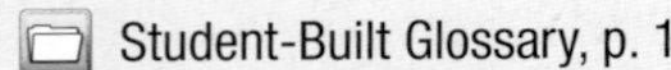

Student-Built Glossary, p. 1

Students complete the chart by providing the definition of each term and an example as they progress through Chapter 4. This study tool can also be used to review for the chapter test.

Get Started on the Chapter

You will learn several new concepts, skills, and vocabulary terms as you study Chapter 4. To get ready, identify important terms and organize your resources. You may wish to refer to Chapter 0 to review prerequisite skills.

FOLDABLES StudyOrganizer

Congruent Triangles Make this Foldable to help you organize your Chapter 4 notes about congruent triangles. Begin with a sheet of $8\frac{1}{2}$" × 11" paper.

1 **Fold** into a taco forming a square. Cut off the excess paper strip formed by the square.

2 **Open** the fold and refold it the opposite way forming another taco and an X fold pattern.

3 **Open** and fold the corners toward the center point of the X forming a small square.

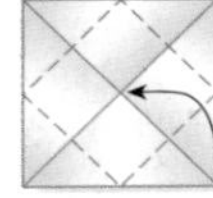

4 **Label** the flaps as shown.

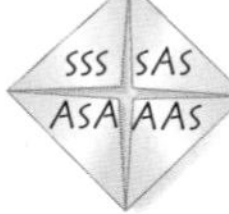

NewVocabulary

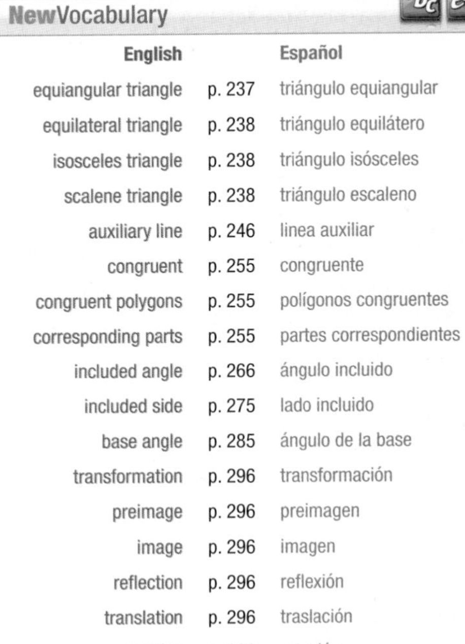

English		Español
equiangular triangle	p. 237	triángulo equiangular
equilateral triangle	p. 238	triángulo equilátero
isosceles triangle	p. 238	triángulo isósceles
scalene triangle	p. 238	triángulo escaleno
auxiliary line	p. 246	linea auxiliar
congruent	p. 255	congruente
congruent polygons	p. 255	polígonos congruentes
corresponding parts	p. 255	partes correspondientes
included angle	p. 266	ángulo incluido
included side	p. 275	lado incluido
base angle	p. 285	ángulo de la base
transformation	p. 296	transformación
preimage	p. 296	preimagen
image	p. 296	imagen
reflection	p. 296	reflexión
translation	p. 296	traslación
rotation	p. 296	rotación

ReviewVocabulary

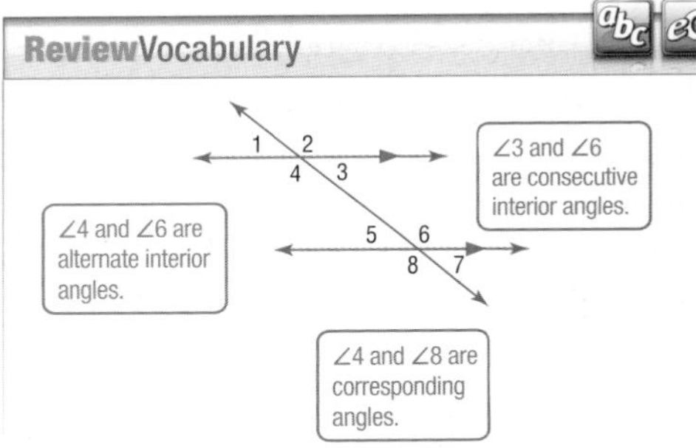

236 | Chapter 4 | Congruent Triangles

LESSON 4-1 Classifying Triangles

:: Then	:: Now	:: Why?
● You measured and classified angles.	● **1** Identify and classify triangles by angle measures. **2** Identify and classify triangles by side measures.	● Radio transmission towers are designed to support antennas for broadcasting radio or television signals. The structure of the tower shown reveals a pattern of triangular braces.

NewVocabulary
acute triangle
equiangular triangle
obtuse triangle
right triangle
equilateral triangle
isosceles triangle
scalene triangle

Common Core State Standards

Content Standards
G.CO.12 Make formal geometric constructions with a variety of tools and methods (compass and straightedge, string, reflective devices, paper folding, dynamic geometric software, etc.).

Mathematical Practices
2 Reason abstractly and quantitatively.
6 Attend to precision.

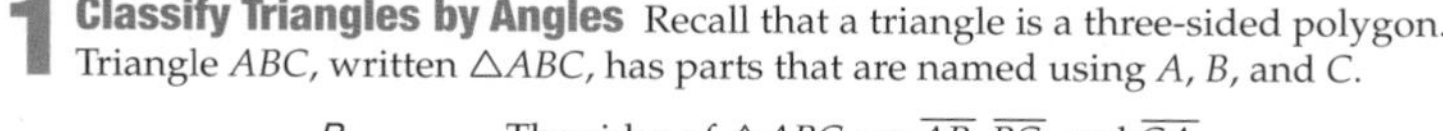

1 Classify Triangles by Angles

Recall that a triangle is a three-sided polygon. Triangle ABC, written $\triangle ABC$, has parts that are named using A, B, and C.

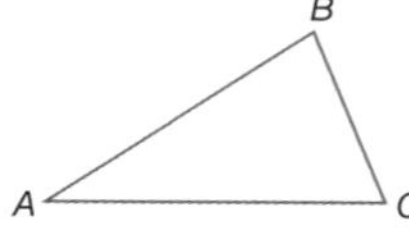

The sides of $\triangle ABC$ are $\overline{AB}$, $\overline{BC}$, and $\overline{CA}$.

The vertices are points A, B, and C.

The angles are $\angle BAC$ or $\angle A$, $\angle ABC$ or $\angle B$, and $\angle BCA$ or $\angle C$.

Triangles can be classified in two ways—by their angles or by their sides. All triangles have at least two acute angles, but the third angle is used to classify the triangle.

KeyConcept Classifications of Triangles by Angles

acute triangle	equiangular triangle	obtuse triangle	right triangle
3 acute angles	3 congruent acute angles	1 obtuse angle	1 right angle

An equiangular triangle is a special kind of acute triangle.

When classifying triangles, be as specific as possible. While a triangle with three congruent acute angles is an acute triangle, it is more specific to classify it as an equiangular triangle.

Example 1 Classify Triangles by Angles

PT

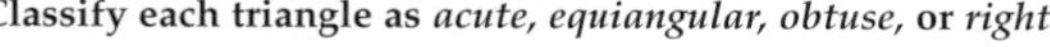

Classify each triangle as *acute*, *equiangular*, *obtuse*, or *right*.

a.

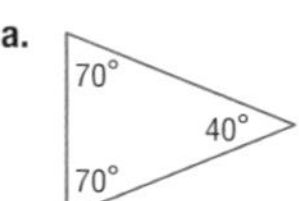

The triangle has three acute angles that are not all equal. It is an acute triangle.

b.

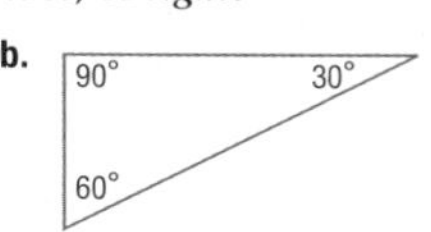

One angle of the triangle measures 90, so it is a right angle. Since the triangle has a right angle, it is a right triangle.

1 Focus

VerticalAlignment

Before Lesson 4-1 Measure and classify angles.

Lesson 4-1 Identify and classify triangles by angle measures and side measures.

After Lesson 4-1 Use congruence transformations to make conjectures and justify properties of geometric figures.

2 Teach

Scaffolding Questions

Have students read the **Why?** section of the lesson.

Ask:

- What appears to be true about the lengths of the three tower braces that form a triangle? The lengths of the braces are the same.
- It appears that the three angles of the triangles formed by the braces are congruent. If this is true, what is the measure of each of the angles? 60
- If the braces formed noncongruent angles, could the lengths of the braces still be congruent? No, a triangle with three equal sides must also have three congruent angles.

Lesson 4-1 Resources

Resource	Approaching Level AL	On Level OL	Beyond Level BL	English Learners ELL
Teacher Edition	▪ Differentiated Instruction, p. 238	▪ Differentiated Instruction, pp. 238, 239	▪ Differentiated Instruction, pp. 238, 239	▪ Differentiated Instruction, pp. 238, 239
Chapter Resource Masters	▪ Study Guide and Intervention, pp. 5–6 ▪ Skills Practice, p. 7 ▪ Practice, p. 8 ▪ Word Problem Practice, p. 9	▪ Study Guide and Intervention, pp. 5–6 ▪ Skills Practice, p. 7 ▪ Practice, p. 8 ▪ Word Problem Practice, p. 9 ▪ Enrichment, p. 10	▪ Practice, p. 8 ▪ Word Problem Practice, p. 9 ▪ Enrichment, p. 10	▪ Study Guide and Intervention, pp. 5–6 ▪ Skills Practice, p. 7 ▪ Practice, p. 8 ▪ Word Problem Practice, p. 9
Other	▪ 5-Minute Check 4-1 ▪ Study Notebook	▪ 5-Minute Check 4-1 ▪ Study Notebook	▪ 5-Minute Check 4-1 ▪ Study Notebook	▪ 5-Minute Check 4-1 ▪ Study Notebook

1 Classify Triangles by Angles

Examples 1 and 2 show how to classify triangles using the angle measurements.

Formative Assessment

Use the Guided Practice exercises after each example to determine students' understanding of concepts.

Additional Examples

1 Classify each triangle as *acute*, *equiangular*, *obtuse*, or *right*.

a.

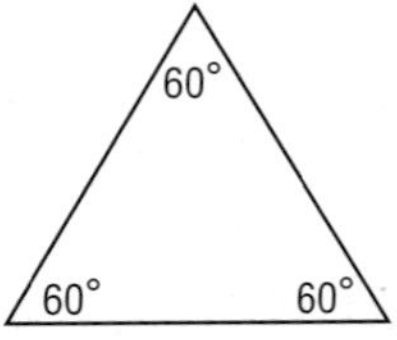

The triangle has three congruent angles. It is an equiangular triangle.

b.

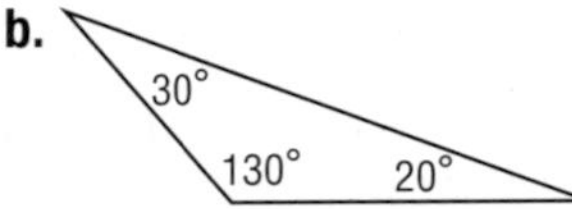

One angle of the triangle measures 130, so it is an obtuse angle. The triangle has an obtuse angle, so it is an obtuse triangle.

2 Classify $\triangle XYZ$ as *acute*, *equiangular*, *obtuse*, or *right*. Explain your reasoning.

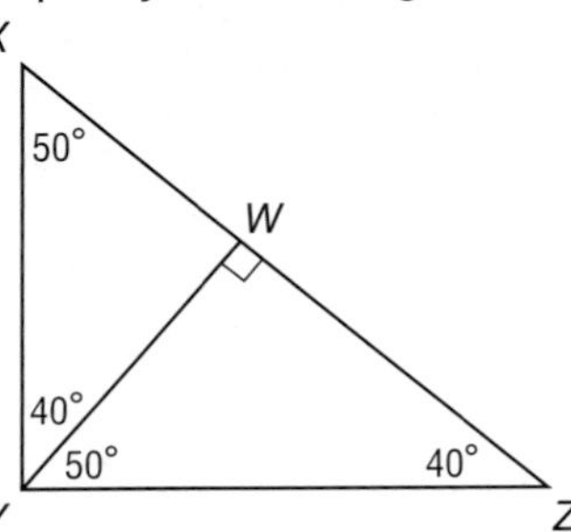

Point W is in the interior of $\angle XYZ$, so by the Angle Addition Postulate, $m\angle XYW + m\angle WYZ = m\angle XYZ$. By substitution, $m\angle XYZ = 40 + 50$ or 90. Since $\triangle XYZ$ has a right angle, it is a right triangle.

ReviewVocabulary

acute angle an angle with a degree measure less than 90

right angle an angle with a degree measure of 90

obtuse angle an angle with a degree measure greater than 90

GuidedPractice

Classify each triangle as *acute, equiangular, obtuse,* or *right*.

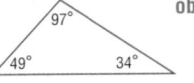

1A. 97°, 49°, 34° — obtuse

1B.

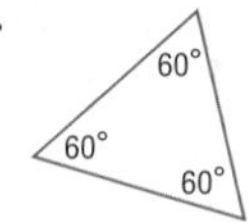

equiangular

Example 2 Classify Triangles by Angles Within Figures

Classify $\triangle PQR$ as *acute, equiangular, obtuse,* or *right*. Explain your reasoning.

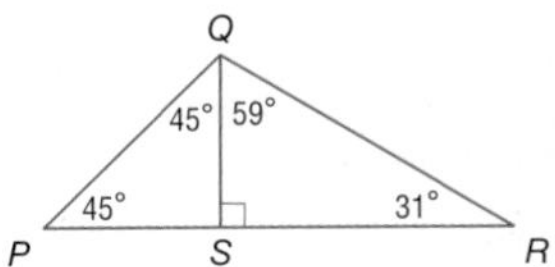

Point S is in the interior of $\angle PQR$, so by the Angle Addition Postulate, $m\angle PQR = m\angle PQS + m\angle SQR$. By substitution, $m\angle PQR = 45 + 59$ or 104.

Since $\triangle PQR$ has one obtuse angle, it is an obtuse triangle.

GuidedPractice

2. Use the diagram to classify $\triangle PQS$ as *acute, equiangular, obtuse* or *right*. Explain your reasoning. **Right; $\triangle PQS$ has one right angle.**

2 Classify Triangles by Sides

Triangles can also be classified according to the number of congruent sides they have. To indicate that sides of a triangle are congruent, an equal number of hash marks is drawn on the corresponding sides.

KeyConcept Classifications of Triangles by Sides

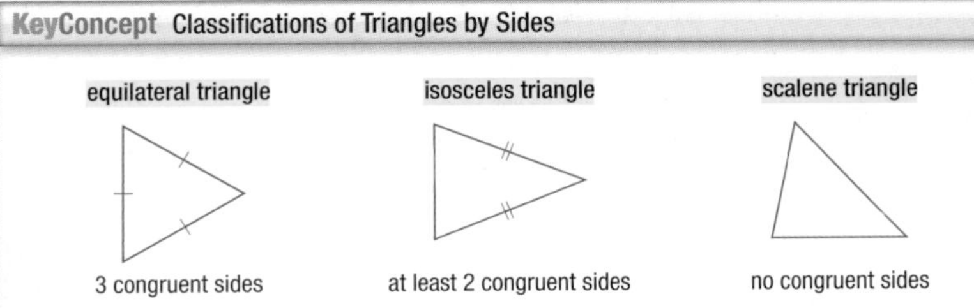

An equilateral triangle is a special kind of isosceles triangle.

Real-WorldLink

In many cars, hazard lights are activated by pushing a small button located near the steering column. The switch is usually an icon shaped like an equilateral triangle.

Source: General Motors

Real-World Example 3 Classify Triangles by Sides

MUSIC Classify the sound box of the Russian lute below as *equilateral, isosceles,* or *scalene*.

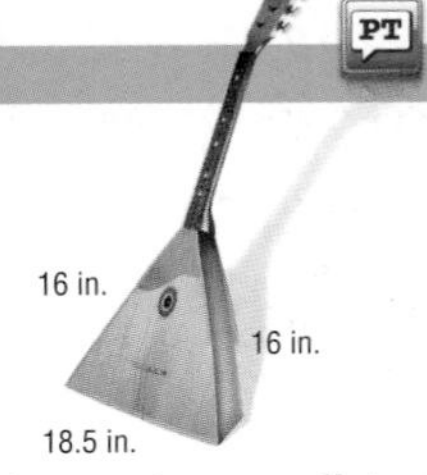

Two sides have the same measure, 16 inches, so the triangle has two congruent sides. The triangle is isosceles.

GuidedPractice

3. DRIVING SAFETY Classify the button in the picture at the left by its sides. **equilateral**

DifferentiatedInstruction AL OL BL ELL

Interpersonal Students work in groups of 2 or 3 to explore the triangle classifications. Ask students to explore and discuss questions such as these: Can you draw an equiangular triangle with a 90° angle? Can you draw a right triangle that has an obtuse angle? Facilitate the discussions so that students discover which triangle classifications are mutually exclusive and which are not.

Example 4 Classify Triangles by Sides Within Figures

If point M is the midpoint of $\overline{JL}$, classify $\triangle JKM$ as *equilateral*, *isosceles*, or *scalene*. Explain your reasoning.

By the definition of midpoint, $JM = ML$.

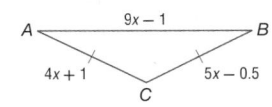

$JM + ML = JL$	Segment Addition Postulate
$ML + ML = 1.5$	Substitution
$2ML = 1.5$	Simplify.
$ML = 0.75$	Divide each side by 2.

$JM = ML$ or 0.75. Since $\overline{KM} \cong \overline{ML}$, $KM = ML$ or 0.75.

Since $KJ = JM = KM = 0.75$, the triangle has three sides with the same measure. Therefore, the triangle has three congruent sides, so it is equilateral.

GuidedPractice **4. Isosceles; two sides of the triangle are congruent.**

4. Classify $\triangle KML$ as *equilateral*, *isosceles*, or *scalene*. Explain your reasoning.

You can also use the properties of isosceles and equilateral triangles to find missing values.

Example 5 Finding Missing Values

ALGEBRA Find the measures of the sides of isosceles triangle ABC.

Step 1 Find x.

$AC = CB$	Given
$4x + 1 = 5x - 0.5$	Substitution
$1 = x - 0.5$	Subtract $4x$ from each side.
$1.5 = x$	Add 0.5 to each side.

Step 2 Substitute to find the length of each side.

$AC = 4x + 1$	Given
$= 4(1.5) + 1$ or 7	$x = 1.5$
$CB = AC$	Given
$= 7$	$AC = 7$
$AB = 9x - 1$	Given
$= 9(1.5) - 1$	$x = 1.5$
$= 12.5$	Simplify.

StudyTip

CCSS Perseverance In Example 5, to check your answer, test to see if $CB = AC$ when 1.5 is substituted for x in the expression for CB, $5x - 0.5$.

$CB = 5x - 0.5$
$= 5(1.5) - 0.5$ or 7 ✓

GuidedPractice

5. Find the measures of the sides of equilateral triangle FGH. $FG = GH = HF = 21$

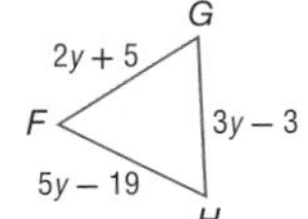

DifferentiatedInstruction   

Extension Have students refer to the picture of the triangular braces at the top of page 237 and compare the triangles formed. Are the sides congruent? Are the angles congruent? Are the triangles congruent? Have them make a conjecture about the shared angles and sides of the two triangles. The corresponding sides are congruent, and the triangles are congruent.

2 Classify Triangles by Sides

Examples 3–5 show how to classify triangles by using the number of congruent sides.

Additional Examples

3 ARCHITECTURE The triangular truss below is modeled for steel construction. Classify $\triangle JMN$, $\triangle JKO$, and $\triangle OLN$ as *acute*, *equiangular*, *obtuse*, or *right*.

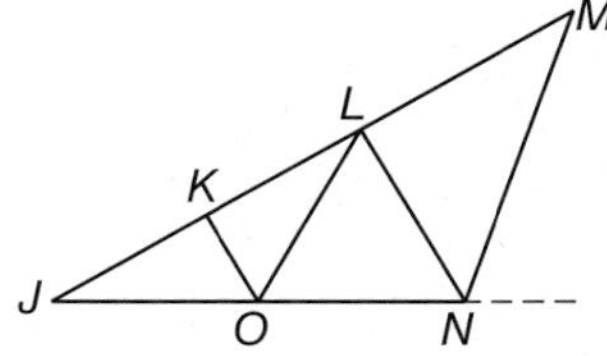

$\triangle JMN$ is obtuse. $\triangle JKO$ is right. $\triangle OLN$ is equiangular.

4 If point Y is the midpoint of $\overline{VX}$, and $WY = 3.0$ units, classify $\triangle VWY$ as *equilateral*, *isosceles*, or *scalene*. Explain your reasoning.

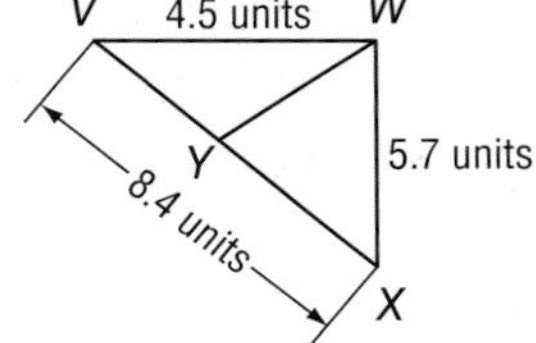

Scalene; the three sides of the triangle have different lengths.

5 ALGEBRA Find the measures of the sides of isosceles triangle KLM with base $\overline{KL}$.

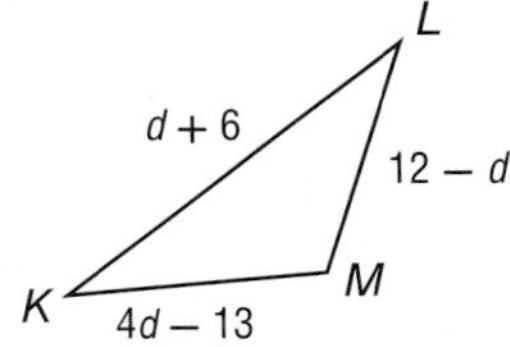

$KM = LM = 7$, $KL = 11$

Additional Examples also in Interactive Classroom PowerPoint® Presentations

Teach with Tech

Student Response System Use your student response system software to build slides that show students a series of triangles and ask them what type of triangle is shown. First, have students classify the triangles by angles. Then have them classify the triangles by sides. Provide students with a key for how to respond.

WatchOut!

Keep Going! Remind students that in Exercises 12 and 13, to answer the questions completely you need to do more than solve for *x*. Once *x* is found, it is substituted into the expressions for each side length.

Tips for New Teachers

Sense-Making Remind students that an acute triangle must have *three* acute angles. Therefore, when classifying a triangle, if the triangle has *one* angle that is not acute it must be a right or obtuse triangle.

3 Practice

Formative Assessment

Use Exercises 1–14 to check for understanding.

Use the chart at the bottom of this page to customize assignments for your students.

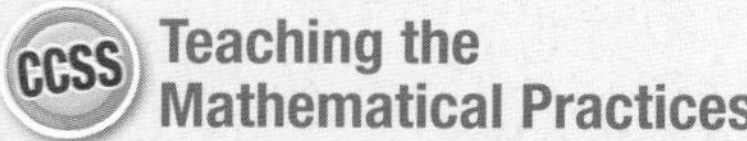

Teaching the Mathematical Practices

Precision Mathematically proficient students use clear definitions in discussion with others and in their own reasoning. In Exercises 7–8 and 21–26, encourage students to choose the most accurate term for each triangle.

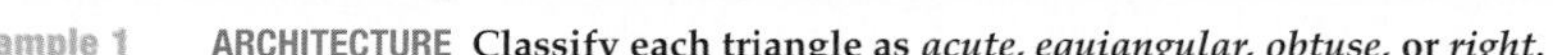

Check Your Understanding

 = Step-by-Step Solutions begin on page R14.

Example 1 **ARCHITECTURE** Classify each triangle as *acute, equiangular, obtuse,* or *right.*

1. 

right

2. 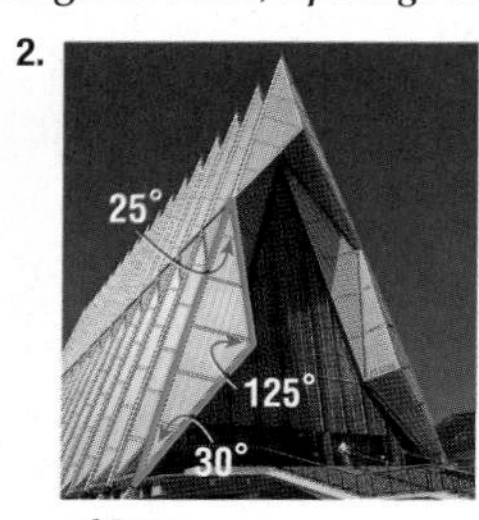

obtuse

3. 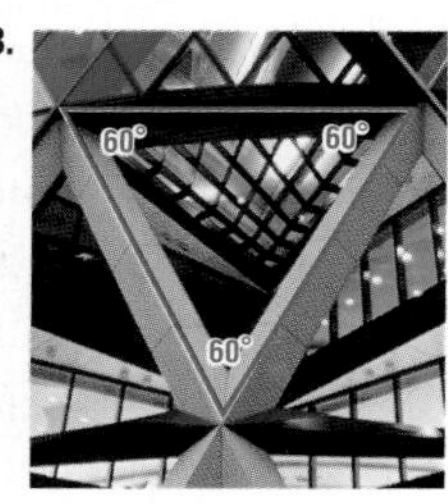

equiangular

Example 2 **Classify each triangle as *acute, equiangular, obtuse,* or *right.* Explain your reasoning.**

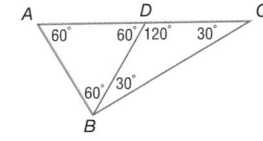

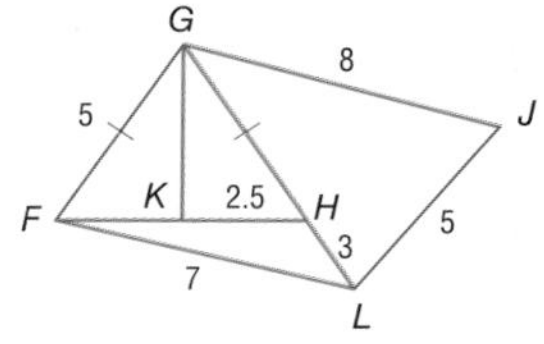

4. $\triangle ABD$ equiangular; All three angles are 60°.
5. $\triangle BDC$ obtuse; $\angle BDC > 90°$
6. $\triangle ABC$ right; $\angle ABC = 90°$

Example 3 **CCSS PRECISION** Classify each triangle as *equilateral, isosceles,* or *scalene.*

7. 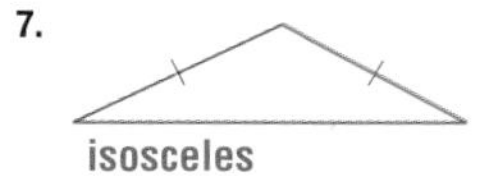
isosceles

8. 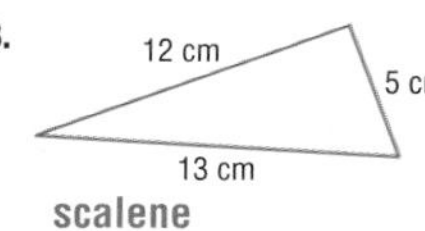

scalene

Example 4 **If point *K* is the midpoint of $\overline{FH}$, classify each triangle in the figure at the right as *equilateral, isosceles,* or *scalene.***

9. $\triangle FGH$ equilateral
10. $\triangle GJL$ isosceles
11. $\triangle FHL$ scalene

Example 5 **ALGEBRA Find *x* and the measures of the unknown sides of each triangle.**

12. 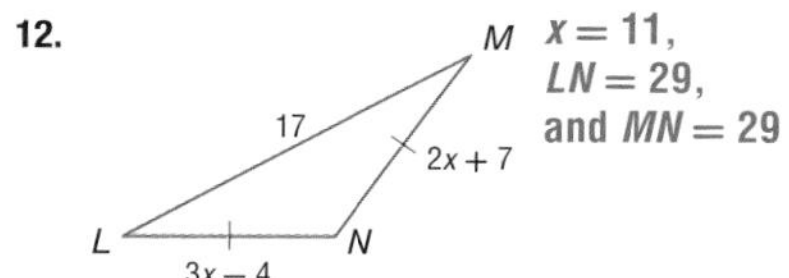

$x = 11$, $LN = 29$, and $MN = 29$

13. 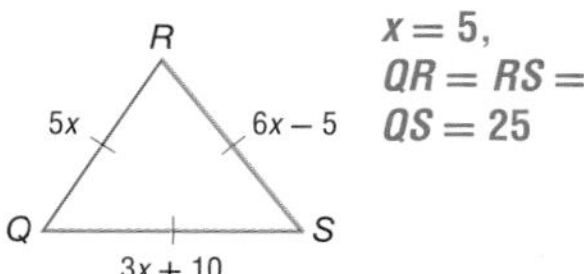

$x = 5$, $QR = RS = QS = 25$

14. **JEWELRY** Suppose you are bending stainless steel wire to make the earring shown. The triangular portion of the earring is an isosceles triangle. If 1.5 centimeters are needed to make the hook portion of the earring, how many earrings can be made from 45 centimeters of wire? Explain your reasoning.
4; The total amount of wire needed, including the hook, is 2.1 + 3.2 + 3.2 + 1.5 or 10 cm. 45 cm ÷ 10 cm/earring = 4.5 earrings. There is not enough wire to make 5 earrings, only 4 can be made from 45 cm of wire.

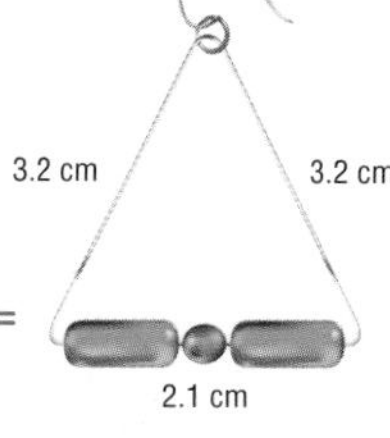

Differentiated Homework Options

Level	Assignment	Two-Day Option	
AL Basic	15–37, 56–59, 61–85	15–37 odd, 65–68	16–36 even, 56–59, 61–64, 69–85
OL Core	15–53 odd, 54–59, 61–85	15–37, 65–68	38–59, 61–64, 69–85
BL Advanced	38–81, (optional: 82–85)		

Practice and Problem Solving

Extra Practice is on page R4.

Example 1 Classify each triangle as *acute, equiangular, obtuse,* or *right.*

15. 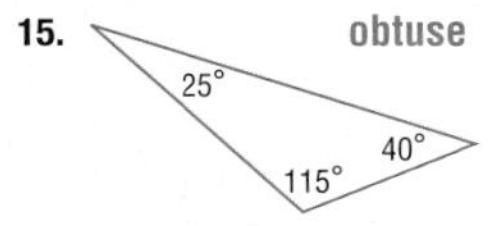

obtuse

16. 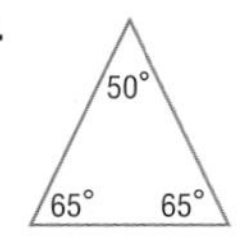

acute

17. 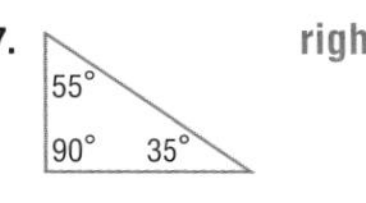

right

18. 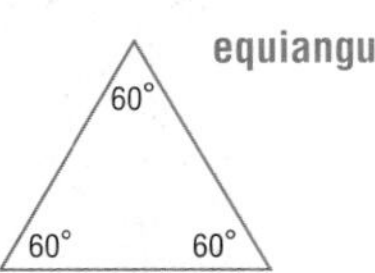

equiangular

19. 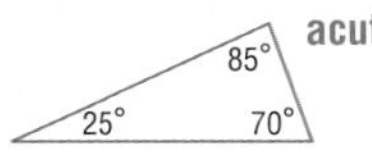

acute

20. 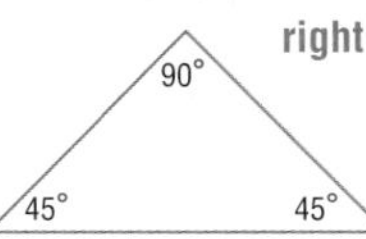

right

Example 2  **PRECISION** Classify each triangle as *acute, equiangular, obtuse,* or *right.*

21. $\triangle UYZ$ obtuse
22. $\triangle BCD$ right
23. $\triangle ADB$ acute
24. $\triangle UXZ$ acute
25. $\triangle UWZ$ right
26. $\triangle UXY$ equiangular

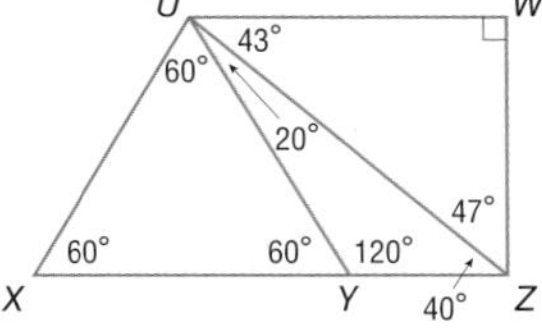

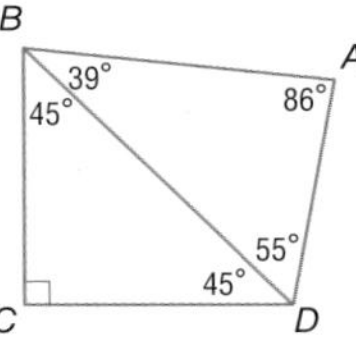

Example 3 Classify each triangle as *equilateral, isosceles,* or *scalene.*

27. 
equilateral

28. 
isosceles

29. 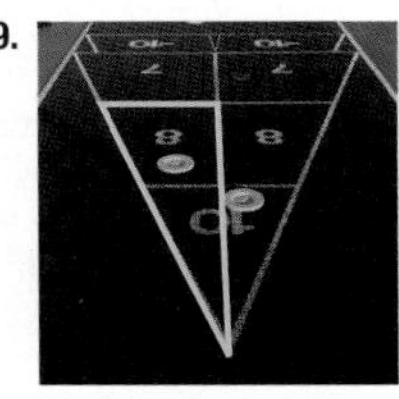
scalene

Example 4 If point C is the midpoint of $\overline{BD}$ and point E is the midpoint of $\overline{DF}$, classify each triangle as *equilateral, isosceles,* or *scalene.*

30. $\triangle ABC$ scalene
31. $\triangle AEF$ scalene
32. $\triangle ADF$ isosceles
33. $\triangle ACD$ scalene
34. $\triangle AED$ scalene
35. $\triangle ABD$ equilateral

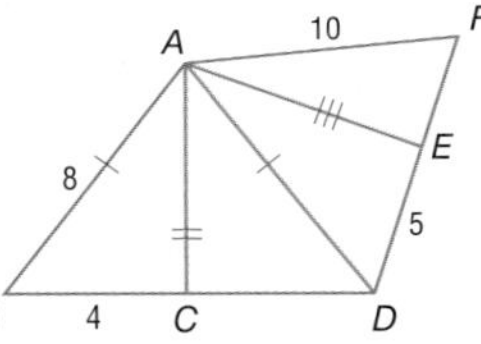

Example 5

36. **ALGEBRA** Find x and the length of each side if $\triangle ABC$ is an isosceles triangle with $\overline{AB} \cong \overline{BC}$. $x = 7$; $AB = 7$, $BC = 7$, $CA = 4$

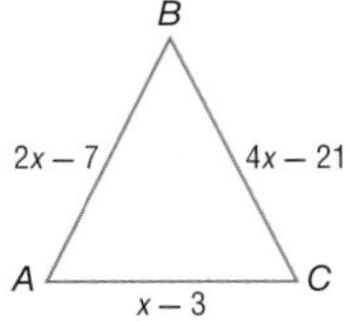

(37) **ALGEBRA** Find x and the length of each side if $\triangle FGH$ is an equilateral triangle. $x = 3$; $FG = GH = HF = 19$

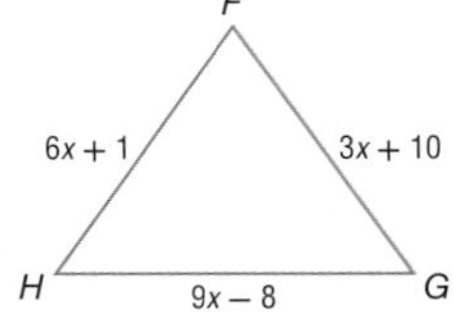

Enrichment

OL BL

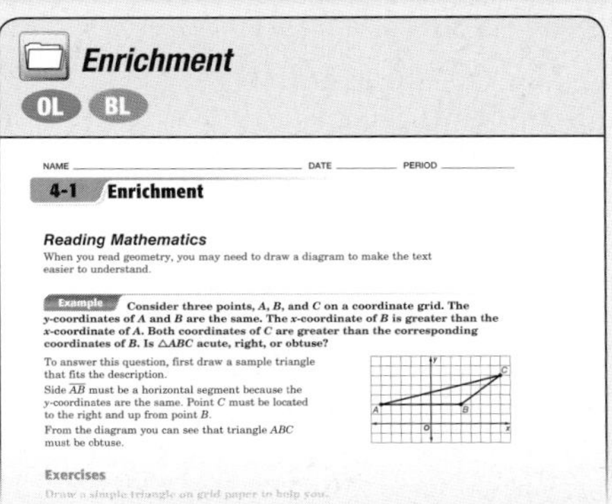
NAME _______ DATE _______ PERIOD _______

4-1 Enrichment

Reading Mathematics

When you read geometry, you may need to draw a diagram to make the text easier to understand.

Example Consider three points, A, B, and C on a coordinate grid. The y-coordinates of A and B are the same. The x-coordinate of B is greater than the x-coordinate of A. Both coordinates of C are greater than the corresponding coordinates of B. Is △ABC acute, right, or obtuse?

To answer this question, first draw a sample triangle that fits the description.
Side AB must be a horizontal segment because the y-coordinates are the same. Point C must be located to the right and up from point B.
From the diagram you can see that triangle ABC must be obtuse.

Exercises

Study Guide and Intervention

AL OL ELL

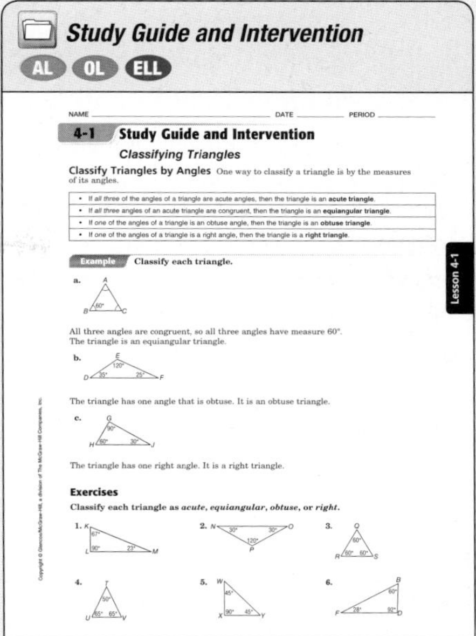
NAME _______ DATE _______ PERIOD _______

4-1 Study Guide and Intervention

Classifying Triangles

Classify Triangles by Angles One way to classify a triangle is by the measures of its angles.

- If all three of the angles of a triangle are acute angles, then the triangle is an **acute triangle**.
- If all three angles of an acute triangle are congruent, then the triangle is an **equiangular triangle**.
- If one of the angles of a triangle is an obtuse angle, then the triangle is an **obtuse triangle**.
- If one of the angles of a triangle is a right angle, then the triangle is a **right triangle**.

Example Classify each triangle.

a. All three angles are congruent, so all three angles have measure 60°. The triangle is an equiangular triangle.

b. The triangle has one angle that is obtuse. It is an obtuse triangle.

c. The triangle has one right angle. It is a right triangle.

Exercises

Classify each triangle as *acute, equiangular, obtuse,* or *right.*

1. 2. 3. 4. 5. 6.

Lesson 4-1

Practice

AL OL BL ELL

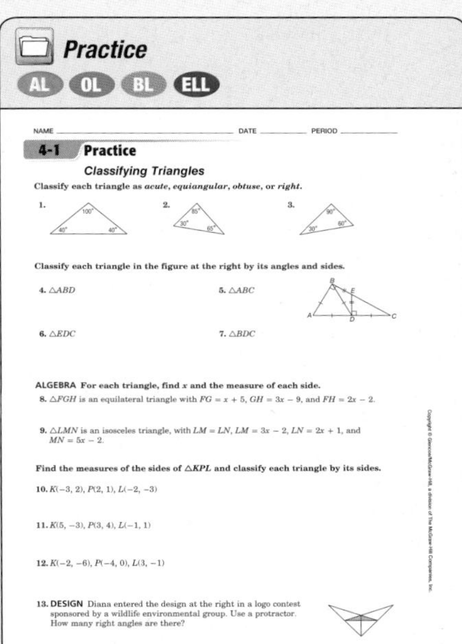
NAME _______ DATE _______ PERIOD _______

4-1 Practice

Classifying Triangles

Classify each triangle as *acute, equiangular, obtuse,* or *right.*

1. 2. 3.

Classify each triangle in the figure at the right by its angles and sides.

4. △ABD
5. △ABC
6. △EDC
7. △BDC

ALGEBRA For each triangle, find x and the measure of each side.

8. △FGH is an equilateral triangle with FG = x + 5, GH = 3x − 9, and FH = 2x − 2.

9. △LMN is an isosceles triangle, with LM = LN, LM = 3x − 2, LN = 2x + 1, and MN = 5x − 2.

Find the measures of the sides of △KPL and classify each triangle by its sides.

10. K(−3, 2), P(2, 1), L(−2, −3)

11. K(5, −3), P(3, 4), L(−1, 1)

12. K(−2, −6), P(−4, 0), L(3, −1)

13. DESIGN Diana entered the design at the right in a logo contest sponsored by a wildlife environmental group. Use a protractor. How many right angles are there?

Word Problem Practice

AL OL BL ELL

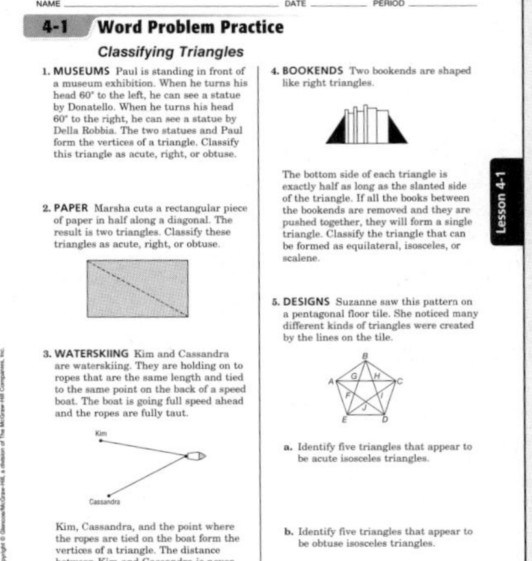
NAME _______ DATE _______ PERIOD _______

4-1 Word Problem Practice

Classifying Triangles

1. **MUSEUMS** Paul is standing in front of a museum exhibition. When he turns his head 60° to the left, he can see a statue by Donatello. When he turns his head 60° to the right, he can see a statue by Della Robbia. The two statues and Paul form the vertices of a triangle. Classify this triangle as acute, right, or obtuse.

2. **PAPER** Marsha cuts a rectangular piece of paper in half along a diagonal. The result is two triangles. Classify these triangles as acute, right, or obtuse.

3. **WATERSKIING** Kim and Cassandra are waterskiing. They are holding on to ropes that are the same length and tied to the same point on the back of a speed boat. The boat is going full speed ahead and the ropes are fully taut.

Kim, Cassandra, and the point where the ropes are tied on the boat form the vertices of a triangle. The distance between Kim and Cassandra is never equal to the length of the ropes. Classify the triangle as equilateral, isosceles, or scalene.

4. **BOOKENDS** Two bookends are shaped like right triangles.

The bottom side of each triangle is exactly half as long as the slanted side of the triangle. If all the books between the bookends are removed and they are pushed together, they will form a single triangle. Classify the triangle that can be formed as equilateral, isosceles, or scalene.

5. **DESIGNS** Suzanne saw this pattern on a pentagonal floor tile. She noticed many different kinds of triangles were created by the lines on the tile.

a. Identify five triangles that appear to be acute isosceles triangles.

b. Identify five triangles that appear to be obtuse isosceles triangles.

Lesson 4-1

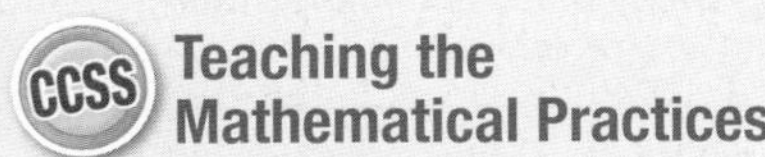

Teaching the Mathematical Practices

Precision Mathematically proficient students use clear definitions in discussion with others and in their own reasoning. In Exercises 40–42, encourage students to choose the most accurate term for each triangle.

Exercise Alert

Compass and Straightedge Exercise 53 requires the use of a compass and straightedge.

Additional Answers

38. ∠1: right scalene, ∠2: right scalene, ∠3: obtuse scalene, ∠4: acute isosceles, ∠5: right scalene, ∠6: obtuse scalene

39. Because the base of the prism formed is an equilateral triangle, the mirror tile must be cut into three strips of congruent width. Since the original tile is a 12-inch square, each strip will be 12 inches long by 12 ÷ 3 or 4 inches wide.

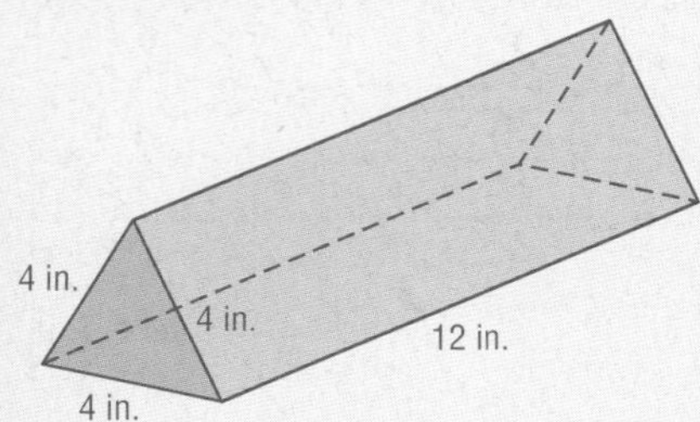

43. scalene; $XZ = 3\sqrt{5}$, $XY = \sqrt{113}$, $YZ = 2\sqrt{26}$

44. isosceles; $XZ = \sqrt{29}$, $XY = \sqrt{29}$, $YZ = 4$

45. isosceles; $XZ = 2$, $XY = 2\sqrt{2}$, $YZ = 2$

46. scalene; $XZ = 8$, $XY = \sqrt{82}$, $YZ = \sqrt{130}$

47. Given: $m\angle ADC = 120$

Prove: $\triangle DBC$ is acute.

Proof: ∠ADC and ∠BDC form a linear pair. ∠ADC and ∠BDC are supplementary because if two angles form a linear pair, then they are supplementary. So, $m\angle ADC + m\angle BDC = 180$. We know $m\angle ADC = 120$, so by substitution, $120 + m\angle BDC = 180$. Subtract to find that $m\angle BDC = 60$. We already know that ∠B is acute because △ABC is acute. ∠BCD must also be acute because ∠C is acute and $m\angle C = m\angle ACD + m\angle BCD$. △DBC is acute by definition.

38. GRAPHIC ART Refer to the illustration shown. Classify each numbered triangle in *Kat* by its angles and by its sides. Use the corner of a sheet of notebook paper to classify angle measures and a ruler to measure sides. **See margin.**

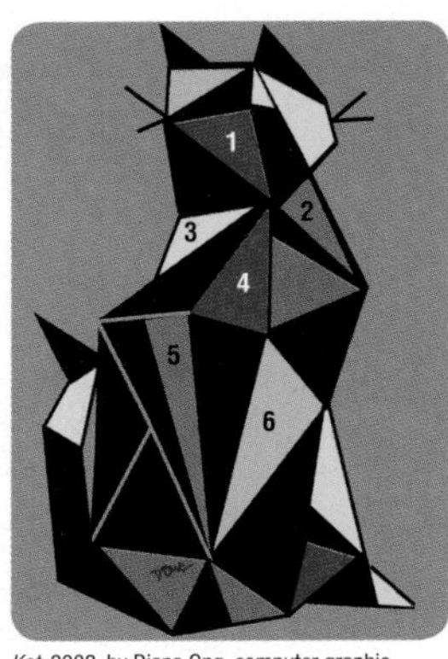

Kat, 2002, by Diana Ong, computer graphic

39. KALEIDOSCOPE Josh is building a kaleidoscope using PVC pipe, cardboard, bits of colored paper, and a 12-inch square mirror tile. The mirror tile is to be cut into strips and arranged to form an open prism with a base like that of an equilateral triangle. Make a sketch of the prism, giving its dimensions. Explain your reasoning. **See margin.**

CCSS PRECISION Classify each triangle in the figure by its angles and sides.

40. △ABE **isosceles right**

41. △EBC **isosceles obtuse**

42. △BDC **scalene right**

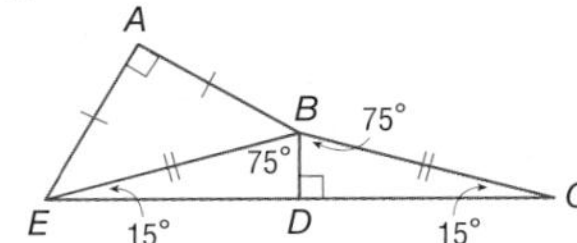

COORDINATE GEOMETRY Find the measures of the sides of △XYZ and classify each triangle by its sides. **43–46. See margin.**

43. X(−5, 9), Y(2, 1), Z(−8, 3)

44. X(7, 6), Y(5, 1), Z(9, 1)

45. X(3, −2), Y(1, −4), Z(3, −4)

46. X(−4, −2), Y(−3, 7), Z(4, −2)

47. PROOF Write a paragraph proof to prove that △DBC is an acute triangle if $m\angle ADC = 120$ and △ABC is acute. **See margin.**

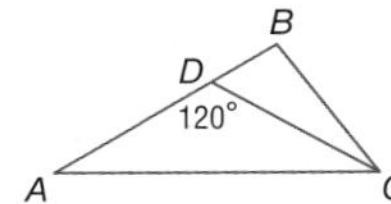

48. PROOF Write a two-column proof to prove that △BCD is equiangular if △ACE is equiangular and $\overline{BD} \parallel \overline{AE}$. **See Ch. 4 Answer Appendix.**

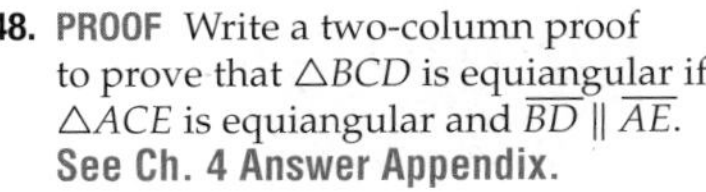

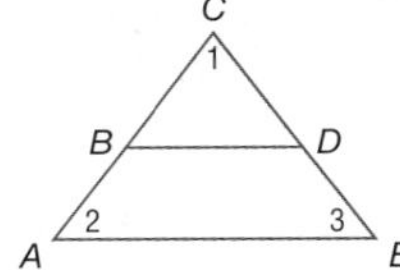

ALGEBRA For each triangle, find *x* and the measure of each side.

49. △FGH is an equilateral triangle with $FG = 3x - 10$, $GH = 2x + 5$, and $HF = x + 20$. **49.** $x = 15$; $FG = 35$, $GH = 35$, $HF = 35$

50. △JKL is isosceles with $\overline{JK} \cong \overline{KL}$, $JK = 4x - 1$, $KL = 2x + 5$, and $LJ = 2x - 1$. $x = 3$; $JK = 11$, $KL = 11$, $LJ = 5$

51. △MNP is isosceles with $\overline{MN} \cong \overline{NP}$. MN is two less than five times x, NP is seven more than two times x, and PM is two more than three times x. $x = 3$; $MN = 13$, $NP = 13$, $PM = 11$

52. △RST is equilateral. RS is three more than four times x, ST is seven more than two times x, and TR is one more than five times x. $x = 2$; $RS = ST = TR = 11$

53. CONSTRUCTION Construct an equilateral triangle. Verify your construction using measurement and justify it using mathematics. (*Hint:* Use the construction for copying a segment.) **See Ch. 4 Answer Appendix.**

54. STOCKS Technical analysts use charts to identify patterns that can suggest future activity in stock prices. Symmetrical triangle charts are most useful when the fluctuation in the price of a stock is decreasing over time.

a. Classify by its sides and angles the triangle formed if a vertical line is drawn at any point on the graph. **isosceles; acute**

b. How would the price have to fluctuate in order for the data to form an obtuse triangle? Draw an example to support your reasoning. **See Ch. 4 Answer Appendix.**

55. MULTIPLE REPRESENTATIONS In the diagram, the vertex *opposite* side $\overline{BC}$ is $\angle A$. **a–d. See margin.**

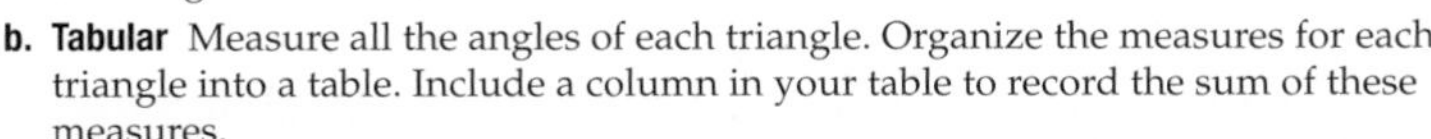

a. Geometric Draw four isosceles triangles, including one acute, one right, and one obtuse isosceles triangle. Label the vertices opposite the congruent sides as *A* and *C*. Label the remaining vertex *B*. Then measure the angles of each triangle and label each angle with its measure.

b. Tabular Measure all the angles of each triangle. Organize the measures for each triangle into a table. Include a column in your table to record the sum of these measures.

c. Verbal Make a conjecture about the measures of the angles that are opposite the congruent sides of an isosceles triangle. Then make a conjecture about the sum of the measures of the angles of an isosceles triangle.

d. Algebraic If *x* is the measure of one of the angles opposite one of the congruent sides in an isosceles triangle, write expressions for the measures of each of the other two angles in the triangle. Explain.

56. Sample answer: Elaina; all triangles have at least two acute angles, so using Ines' reasoning all triangles would be classified as acute. Instead, triangles are classified by their third angle. If the third angle is also acute, then the triangle is acute. If the third angle is obtuse, as in the triangle shown, the triangle is classified as obtuse.

H.O.T. Problems Use Higher-Order Thinking Skills

56. ERROR ANALYSIS Elaina says that $\triangle DFG$ is obtuse. Ines disagrees, explaining that the triangle has more acute angles than obtuse angles so it must be acute. Is either of them correct? Explain your reasoning.

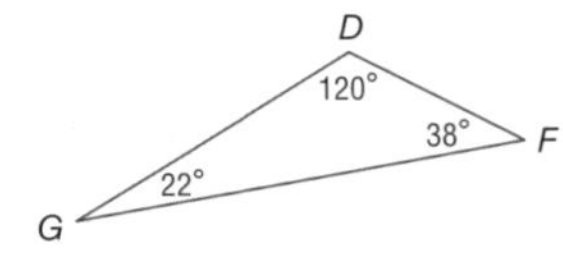

PRECISION Determine whether the statements below are *sometimes*, *always*, or *never* true. Explain your reasoning. **57–60. See Ch. 4 Answer Appendix.**

57. Equiangular triangles are also right triangles.

58. Equilateral triangles are isosceles.

59. Right triangles are equilateral.

60. CHALLENGE An equilateral triangle has sides that measure $5x + 3$ units and $7x - 5$ units. What is the perimeter of the triangle? Explain.

OPEN ENDED Draw an example of each type of triangle below using a protractor and a ruler. Label the sides and angles of each triangle with their measures. If not possible, explain why not. **61–64. See Ch. 4 Answer Appendix.**

61. scalene right **62.** isosceles obtuse **63.** equilateral obtuse

64. WRITING IN MATH Explain why classifying an equiangular triangle as an *acute* equiangular triangle is unnecessary.

Multiple Representations

In Exercise 55, students investigate the angles of an isosceles triangle using sketches, a table, a verbal description, and an algebraic description.

WatchOut!

Error Analysis For Exercise 56, students should see that Elaina is correct. Discuss that a triangle can have only one obtuse angle and so every obtuse triangle will also have two acute angles. In fact, every triangle has at least two acute angles; therefore, Ines' logic is flawed.

Exercise Alert

Protractor and Ruler Exercises 61–63 require the use of a protractor and a ruler.

Additional Answers

55a. Sample answer:

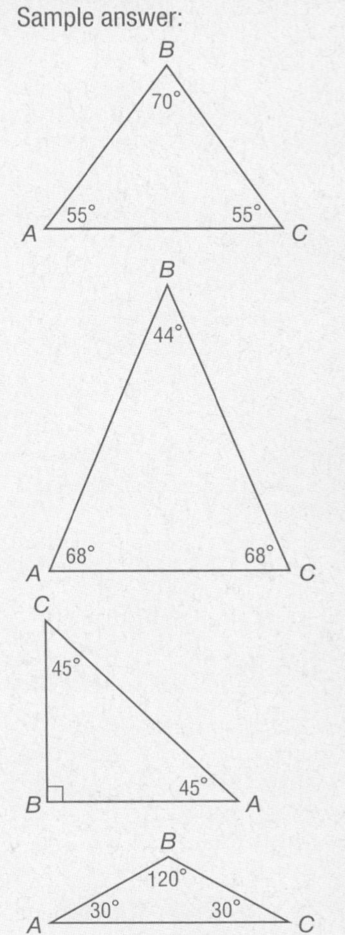

55b.

$m\angle A$	$m\angle C$	$m\angle B$	Sum of Angle Measures
55	55	70	180
68	68	44	180
45	45	90	180
30	30	120	180

55c. Sample answer: In an isosceles triangle, the angles opposite the congruent sides have the same measure. The sum of the measures of the angles of an isosceles triangle is 180.

55d. x and $180 - 2x$; If the measures of the angles opposite the congruent sides of an isosceles triangle have the same measure, then if one angle measures x, then the other angle also measures x. The sum of the measures of the angles of an isosceles triangle is 180, thus the measure of the third angle is $180 - 2x$.

4 Assess

Crystal Ball Have students write about how the information learned about classifying triangles applies to finding the measurements of angles of triangles by using the symbols $<$, $>$, or $=$. For example, an obtuse triangle has an angle greater than 90 degrees.

Additional Answers

77. H: you have a driver's license; C: you are at least 16 years old

79. Plane *AEB* intersects with plane $\mathcal{N}$ in $\overline{AB}$.

81. Points *D*, *C*, and *B* lie in plane $\mathcal{N}$, but point *E* does not lie in plane $\mathcal{N}$. Thus, they are not coplanar.

Standardized Test Practice

65. Which type of triangle can serve as a counterexample to the conjecture below? **A**

If two angles of a triangle are acute, then the measure of the third angle must be greater than or equal to 90.

A equilateral **C** right
B obtuse **D** scalene

66. ALGEBRA A baseball glove originally cost \$84.50. Kenji bought it at 40% off. How much was deducted from the original price? **H**

F \$50.70 **H** \$33.80
G \$44.50 **J** \$32.62

67. GRIDDED RESPONSE Jorge is training for a 20-mile race. Jorge runs 7 miles on Monday, Tuesday, and Friday, and 12 miles on Wednesday and Saturday. After 6 weeks of training, Jorge will have run the equivalent of how many races? **13.5**

68. SAT/ACT What is the slope of the line determined by the equation $2x + y = 5$? **B**

A $-\frac{5}{2}$ **D** 2
B -2 **E** $\frac{5}{2}$
C -1

Spiral Review

Find the distance between each pair of parallel lines with the given equations. (Lesson 3-6)

69. $x = -2$, $x = 5$ **7**

70. $y = -6$, $y = 1$ **7**

71. $y = 2x + 3$, $y = 2x - 7$ $\mathbf{2\sqrt{5}}$

72. $y = x + 2$, $y = x - 4$ $\mathbf{3\sqrt{2}}$

73. FOOTBALL When striping the practice football field, Mr. Hawkins first painted the sidelines. Next he marked off 10-yard increments on one sideline. He then constructed lines perpendicular to the sidelines at each 10-yard mark. Why does this guarantee that the 10-yard lines will be parallel? (Lesson 3-5)
Two lines in a plane that are perpendicular to the same line are parallel.

Identify the hypothesis and conclusion of each conditional statement. (Lesson 2-3)

74. If three points lie on a line, then they are collinear. **H: three points lie on a line; C: the points are collinear**

75. If you are a teenager, then you are at least 13 years old. **H: you are a teenager; C: you are at least 13 years old**

76. If $2x + 6 = 10$, then $x = 2$. **H: $2x + 6 = 10$; C: $x = 2$**

77. If you have a driver's license, then you are at least 16 years old. **See margin.**

Refer to the figure at the right. (Lesson 1-1)

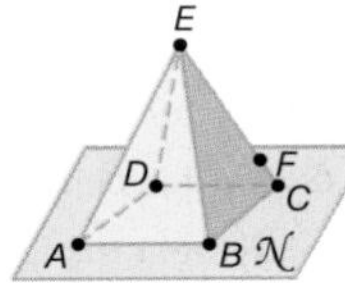

78. How many planes appear in this figure? **5**

79. Name the intersection of plane *AEB* with plane $\mathcal{N}$. **See margin.**

80. Name three points that are collinear. ***E*, *F*, *C***

81. Are points *D*, *E*, *C*, and *B* coplanar? **See margin.**

Skills Review

Identify each pair of angles as *alternate interior*, *alternate exterior*, *corresponding*, or *consecutive interior angles*.

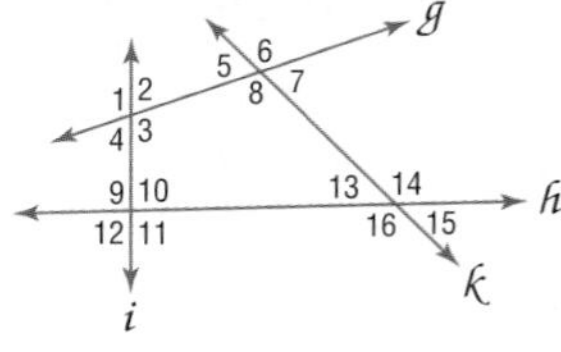

82. $\angle 5$ and $\angle 3$ **alt. int.**

83. $\angle 9$ and $\angle 4$ **cons. int.**

84. $\angle 11$ and $\angle 13$ **alt. int.**

85. $\angle 1$ and $\angle 11$ **alt. ext.**

244 | Lesson 4-1 | Classifying Triangles

EXPLORE 4-2

Geometry Lab
Angles of Triangles

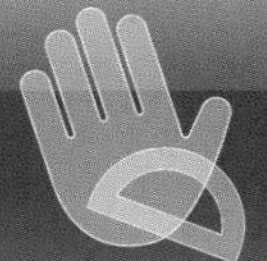

In this lab, you will find special relationships among the angles of a triangle.

CCSS Common Core State Standards
Content Standards
G.CO.12 Make formal geometric constructions with a variety of tools and methods (compass and straightedge, string, reflective devices, paper folding, dynamic geometric software, etc.).
Mathematical Practices 5

Activity 1 Interior Angles of a Triangle

Step 1

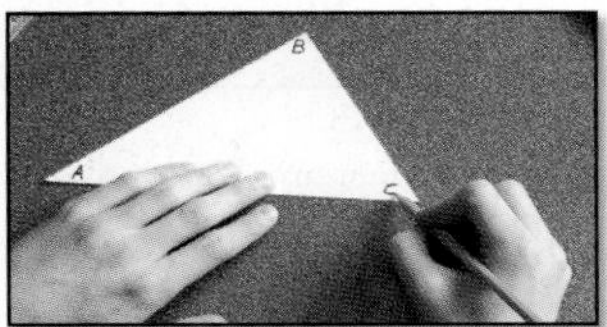

Draw and cut out several different triangles. Label the vertices *A*, *B*, and *C*.

Step 2

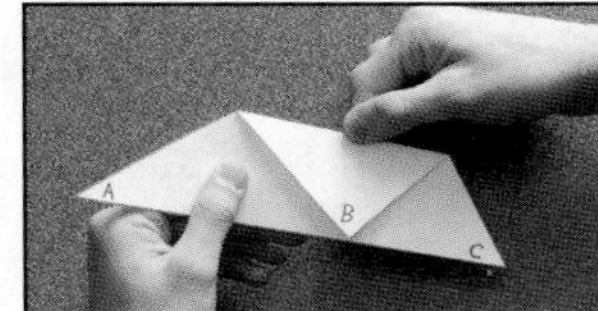

For each triangle, fold vertex *B* down so that the fold line is parallel to $\overline{AC}$. Relabel as vertex *B*.

Step 3

Then fold vertices *A* and *C* so that they meet vertex *B*. Relabel as vertices *A* and *C*.

Analyze the Results

1. Angles *A*, *B*, and *C* are called *interior angles* of triangle *ABC*. What type of figure do these three angles form when joined together in Step 3? **a straight angle or straight line**
2. **Make a conjecture** about the sum of the measures of the interior angles of a triangle. **The sum of the measures of the angles of any triangle is 180.**

Activity 2 Exterior Angles of a Triangle

Step 1

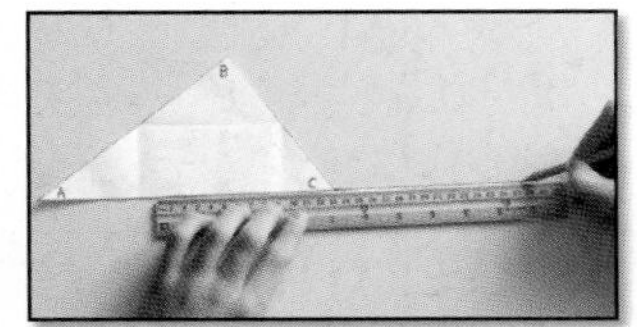

Unfold each triangle from Activity 1 and place each on a separate piece of paper. Extend $\overline{AC}$ as shown.

Step 2

For each triangle, tear off $\angle A$ and $\angle B$.

Step 3

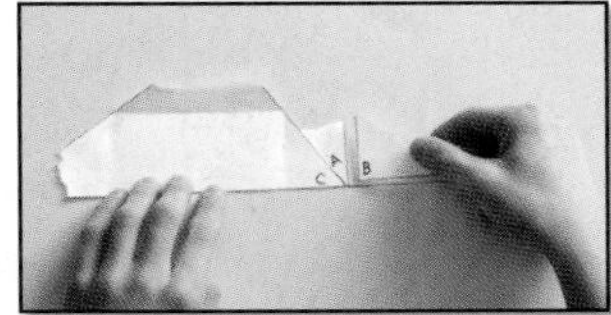

Arrange $\angle A$ and $\angle B$ so that they fill the angle adjacent to $\angle C$ as shown.

Model and Analyze the Results

3. The angle adjacent to $\angle C$ is called an *exterior angle* of triangle *ABC*. **Make a conjecture** about the relationship among $\angle A$, $\angle B$, and the exterior angle at *C*. **$m\angle A + m\angle B$ is the measure of the exterior angle at *C*.**
4. Repeat the steps in Activity 2 for the exterior angles of $\angle A$ and $\angle B$ in each triangle. **See students' work.**
5. **Make a conjecture** about the measure of an exterior angle and the sum of the measures of its nonadjacent interior angles. **See margin.**

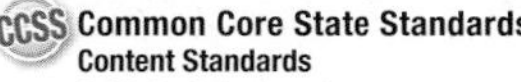

1 Focus

Objective Find the relationships among the measures of the interior angles of a triangle.

Materials

- protractor
- scissors

Teaching Tip

Advise students to label the obtuse angle *B* when they are first working through **Activity 1**. They should also repeat **Activity 1** using acute, right, and equilateral triangles to further verify concepts.

2 Teach

Working in Cooperative Groups

Arrange students in groups of 3 or 4, mixing abilities. Then have groups complete Activity 1 and Analyze the Results 1 and 2.

Ask:

- What is a commonality of all triangles? They all have three sides and three vertices.
- When you change a triangle from an acute triangle to an obtuse triangle, how does it affect the other angle measures? the other angle measures get smaller
- When you change the angle measures, what seems to be the constant? the sum of the angles

Practice Have students complete Activity 2 and Model and Analyze the Results 3–5.

Additional Answer

5. The measure of an exterior angle is equal to the sum of the measures of the two nonadjacent interior angles.

3 Assess

Formative Assessment

In Exercises 1–5, students determine angle measures of the triangles used in this activity, find relationships, and make conjectures that will lead them to the Angle-Sum Theorem and the Exterior Angle Theorem.

From Concrete to Abstract

Students can further explore and conjecture about the relationships of the side and angle measures of the small triangle formed when vertex *B* is folded down in Activity 1. Students should see that although the side lengths are not the same, the angle measures are congruent.

1 Focus

VerticalAlignment

Before Lesson 4-2 Classify triangles by side lengths and angle measures.

Lesson 4-2 Apply the Triangle Angle-Sum Theorem and the Exterior Angle Theorem.

After Lesson 4-2 Use congruence transformations to make conjectures and justify properties of geometric figures.

2 Teach

Scaffolding Questions

Have students read the **Why?** section of the lesson.

Ask:

- What measurement other than the pivot angle must be programmed so that the robot will move in a triangular path? The distance the robot will travel before pivoting.
- The pivot angles shown in the picture are all acute angles. Must each pivot angle be an acute angle? No, the pivot angle could be a right or an obtuse angle.
- The narrative states that the sum of the measures of the pivot angles must always be the same. What is that sum? 180; The sum of the measures of the interior angles of a triangle is always 180.

LESSON 4-2 Angles of Triangles

Then

- You classified triangles by their side or angle measures.

Now

1. Apply the Triangle Angle-Sum Theorem.
2. Apply Exterior Angle Theorem.

Why?

- Massachusetts Institute of Technology (MIT) sponsors the annual *Design 2.007* contest in which students design and build a robot.

One test of a robot's movements is to program it to move in a triangular path. The sum of the measures of the pivot angles through which the robot must turn will always be the same.

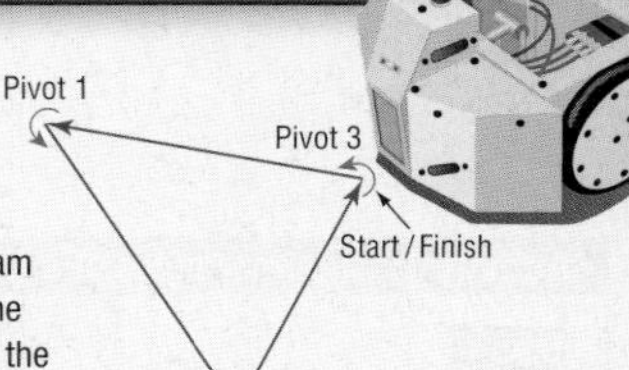

NewVocabulary
auxiliary line
exterior angle
remote interior angles
flow proof
corollary

Common Core State Standards

Content Standards
G.CO.10 Prove theorems about triangles.

Mathematical Practices
1 Make sense of problems and persevere in solving them.
3 Construct viable arguments and critique the reasoning of others.

1 Triangle Angle-Sum Theorem

The Triangle Angle-Sum Theorem gives the relationship among the interior angle measures of any triangle.

Theorem 4.1 Triangle Angle-Sum Theorem

Words The sum of the measures of the angles of a triangle is 180.

Example $m\angle A + m\angle B + m\angle C = 180$

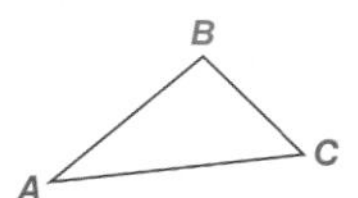

The proof of the Triangle Angle-Sum Theorem requires the use of an auxiliary line. An **auxiliary line** is an extra line or segment drawn in a figure to help analyze geometric relationships. As with any statement in a proof, you must justify any properties of an auxiliary line that you have drawn.

Proof Triangle Angle-Sum Theorem

Given: $\triangle ABC$

Prove: $m\angle 1 + m\angle 2 + m\angle 3 = 180$

Proof:

Statements	Reasons
1. $\triangle ABC$	1. Given
2. Draw $\overleftrightarrow{AD}$ through A parallel to $\overline{BC}$.	2. Parallel Postulate
3. $\angle 4$ and $\angle BAD$ form a linear pair.	3. Def. of a linear pair
4. $\angle 4$ and $\angle BAD$ are supplementary.	4. If 2 ∡ form a linear pair, they are supplementary.
5. $m\angle 4 + m\angle BAD = 180$	5. Def. of suppl. ∡
6. $m\angle BAD = m\angle 2 + m\angle 5$	6. Angle Addition Postulate
7. $m\angle 4 + m\angle 2 + m\angle 5 = 180$	7. Substitution
8. $\angle 4 \cong \angle 1, \angle 5 \cong \angle 3$	8. Alt. Int. ∡ Theorem
9. $m\angle 4 = m\angle 1, m\angle 5 = m\angle 3$	9. Def. of ≅ ∡
10. $m\angle 1 + m\angle 2 + m\angle 3 = 180$	10. Substitution

Lesson 4-2 Resources

Resource	Approaching Level AL	On Level OL	Beyond Level BL	English Learners ELL
Teacher Edition	▪ Differentiated Instruction, p. 248	▪ Differentiated Instruction, pp. 248, 252	▪ Differentiated Instruction, p. 252	▪ Differentiated Instruction, p. 252
Chapter Resource Masters	▪ Study Guide and Intervention, pp. 11–12 ▪ Skills Practice, p. 13 ▪ Practice, p. 14 ▪ Word Problem Practice, p. 15 ▪ Cabri Jr. Activity, p. 17 ▪ Geometer's Sketchpad Activity, p. 18	▪ Study Guide and Intervention, pp. 11–12 ▪ Skills Practice, p. 13 ▪ Practice, p. 14 ▪ Word Problem Practice, p. 15 ▪ Enrichment, p. 16 ▪ Technology Activities, pp. 17–18	▪ Practice, p. 14 ▪ Word Problem Practice, p. 15 ▪ Enrichment, p. 16 ▪ Cabri Jr. Activity, p. 17 ▪ Geometer's Sketchpad Activity, p. 18	▪ Study Guide and Intervention, pp. 11–12 ▪ Skills Practice, p. 13 ▪ Practice, p. 14 ▪ Word Problem Practice, p. 15 ▪ Cabri Jr. Activity, p. 17 ▪ Geometer's Sketchpad Activity, p. 18
Other	▪ 5-Minute Check 4-2 ▪ Study Notebook ▪ Teaching Geometry with Manipulatives	▪ 5-Minute Check 4-2 ▪ Study Notebook ▪ Teaching Geometry with Manipulatives	▪ 5-Minute Check 4-2 ▪ Study Notebook	▪ 5-Minute Check 4-2 ▪ Study Notebook ▪ Teaching Geometry with Manipulatives

The Triangle Angle-Sum Theorem can be used to determine the measure of the third angle of a triangle when the other two angle measures are known.

Real-WorldLink

The pass-and-move soccer drill incorporates several fundamental aspects of passing. All passes in this drill are made in a triangle, which is the basis of all ball movement. Additionally, the players are forced to move immediately after passing the ball.

Real-World Example 1 Use the Triangle Angle-Sum Theorem

PT

SOCCER The diagram shows the path of the ball in a passing drill created by four friends. Find the measure of each numbered angle.

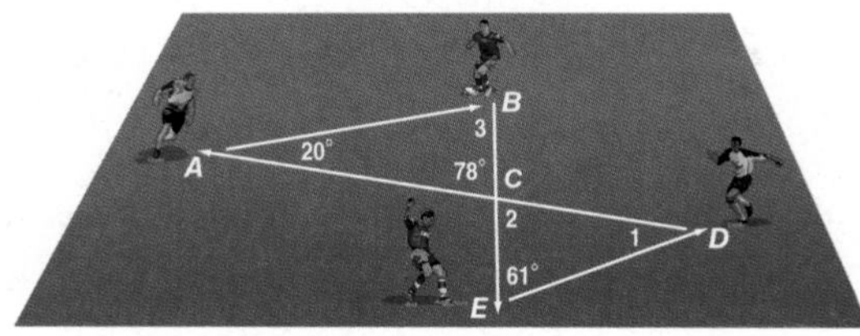

Understand Examine the information given in the diagram. You know the measures of two angles of one triangle and only one measure of another. You also know that $\angle ACB$ and $\angle 2$ are vertical angles.

Plan Find $m\angle 3$ using the Triangle Angle-Sum Theorem, because the measures of two angles of $\angle ABC$ are known. Use the Vertical Angles Theorem to find $m\angle 2$. Then you will have enough information to find the measure of $\angle 1$ in $\triangle CDE$.

Solve

$m\angle 3 + m\angle BAC + m\angle ACB = 180$ Triangle Angle-Sum Theorem

$m\angle 3 + 20 + 78 = 180$ Substitution

$m\angle 3 + 98 = 180$ Simplify.

$m\angle 3 = 82$ Subtract 98 from each side.

$\angle ACB$ and $\angle 2$ are congruent vertical angles. So, $m\angle 2 = 78$.

Use $m\angle 2$ and $\angle CED$ of $\triangle CDE$ to find $m\angle 1$.

$m\angle 1 + m\angle 2 + m\angle CED = 180$ Triangle Angle-Sum Theorem

$m\angle 1 + 78 + 61 = 180$ Substitution

$m\angle 1 + 139 = 180$ Simplify.

$m\angle 1 = 41$ Subtract 139 from each side.

Check The sums of the measures of the angles of $\triangle ABC$ and $\triangle CDE$ should be 180.

$\triangle ABC$: $m\angle 3 + m\angle BAC + m\angle ACB = 82 + 20 + 78$ or 180 ✓

$\triangle CDE$: $m\angle 1 + m\angle 2 + m\angle CED = 41 + 78 + 61$ or 180 ✓

Problem-SolvingTip

CCSS Sense-Making Often a complex problem can be more easily solved if you first break it into more manageable parts. In Example 1, before you can find $m\angle 1$, you must first find $m\angle 2$.

GuidedPractice

Find the measures of each numbered angle.

1A.

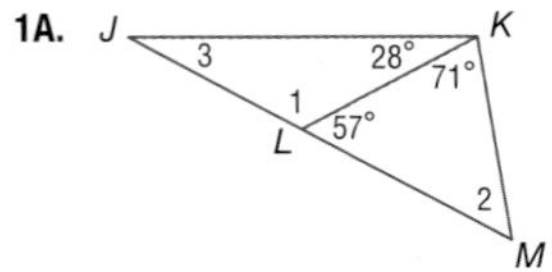

$m\angle 1 = 123$, $m\angle 2 = 52$, $m\angle 3 = 29$

1B.

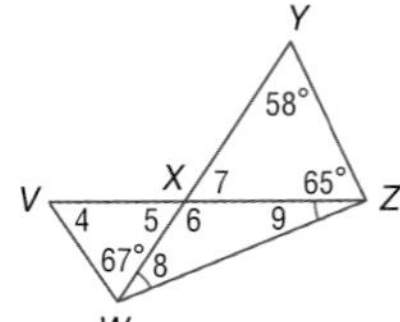

1B. $m\angle 4 = 56$, $m\angle 5 = 57$, $m\angle 6 = 123$, $m\angle 7 = 57$, $m\angle 8 = m\angle 9 = 28.5$

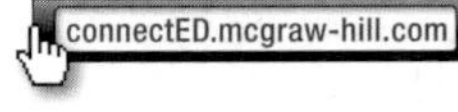

1 Triangle Angle-Sum Theorem

Example 1 shows how to find the missing angle measures by using previously learned theorems and the Triangle Angle-Sum Theorem.

Formative Assessment

Use the Guided Practice exercises after each example to determine students' understanding of concepts.

Additional Example

1 SOFTBALL The diagram shows the path of the softball in a drill developed by four players. Find the measure of each numbered angle.

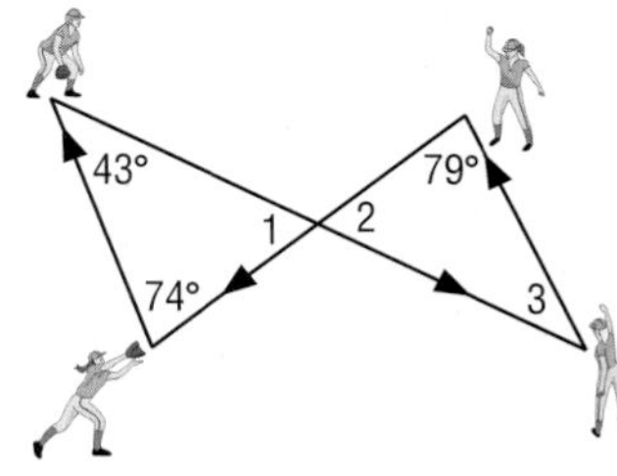

$m\angle 1 = 63$, $m\angle 2 = 63$, $m\angle 3 = 38$

Additional Examples also in Interactive Classroom PowerPoint® Presentations

Focus on Mathematical Content

Prior Knowledge In Chapter 3, students used angle relationships to find angle measures. In this lesson, students will apply their knowledge of vertical angles, supplementary angles, and complementary angles along with the Triangle Angle-Sum Theorem and the Exterior Angle Theorem to find missing angle measures.

Teach with Tech

Computer Projector Use geometry software to draw various triangles. Then construct the angles of the triangles. Arrange the angles together to illustrate their relationships.

CCSS Teaching the Mathematical Practices

Sense-Making Mathematically proficient students look for entry points into a solution. They consider simpler forms of the original problem in order to gain insight into its solution. Encourage students to break complicated solutions into manageable parts.

Tips for New Teachers

Exterior Angles Have students discover Theorem 4.2 by providing them with multiple examples where the two remote interior angles are given. Ask them to find the exterior angle.

2 Exterior Angle Theorem In addition to its three interior angles, a triangle can have **exterior angles** formed by one side of the triangle and the extension of an adjacent side. Each exterior angle of a triangle has two **remote interior angles** that are not adjacent to the exterior angle.

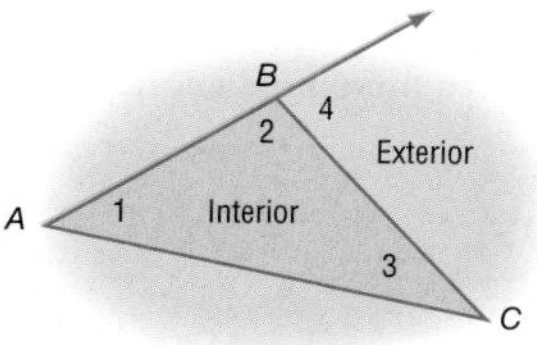

$\angle 4$ is an exterior angle of $\triangle ABC$. Its two remote interior angles are $\angle 1$ and $\angle 3$.

Theorem 4.2 Exterior Angle Theorem

The measure of an exterior angle of a triangle is equal to the sum of the measures of the two remote interior angles.

Example $m\angle A + m\angle B = m\angle 1$

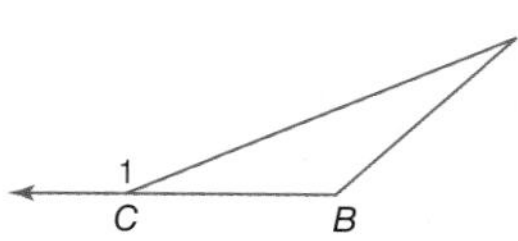

ReadingMath

Flowchart Proof A flow proof is sometimes called a *flowchart* proof.

A **flow proof** uses statements written in boxes and arrows to show the logical progression of an argument. The reason justifying each statement is written below the box. You can use a flow proof to prove the Exterior Angle Theorem.

StudyTip

Flow Proofs Flow proofs can be written vertically or horizontally.

Proof Exterior Angle Theorem

Given: $\triangle ABC$

Prove: $m\angle A + m\angle B = m\angle 1$

Flow Proof:

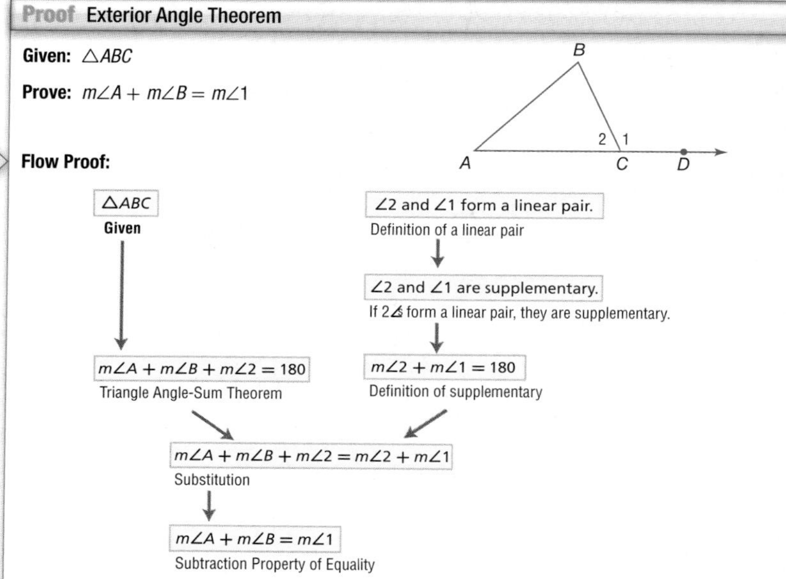

The Exterior Angle Theorem can also be used to find missing measures.

Differentiated Instruction AL OL

Visual/Spatial Learner Tell students that the Triangle Angle-Sum Theorem and Exterior Angle Theorem are both based on the idea that a straight angle measures 180°. Show that if they cut the angles of any triangle and place them adjacent to one another, they form a straight line. This visually demonstrates why the sum of the measures of the interior angles of a triangle is 180.

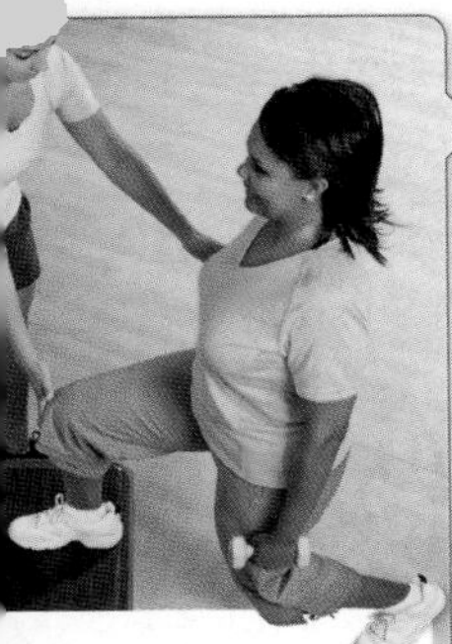

Real-World Example 2 Use the Exterior Angle Theorem

FITNESS Find the measure of $\angle JKL$ in the Triangle Pose shown.

$m\angle KLM + m\angle LMK = m\angle JKL$	Exterior Angle Theorem
$x + 50 = 2x - 15$	Substitution
$50 = x - 15$	Subtract x from each side.
$65 = x$	Add 15 to each side.

So, $m\angle JKL = 2(65) - 15$ or 115.

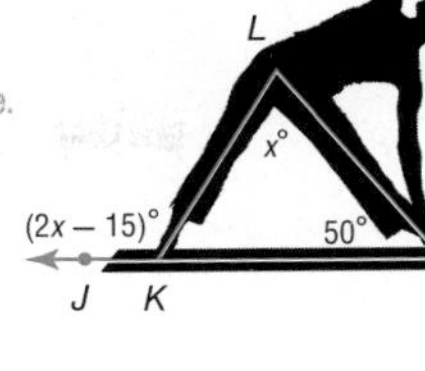

Guided Practice

2. **CLOSET ORGANIZING** Tanya mounts the shelving bracket shown to the wall of her closet. What is the measure of $\angle 1$, the angle that the bracket makes with the wall? 130

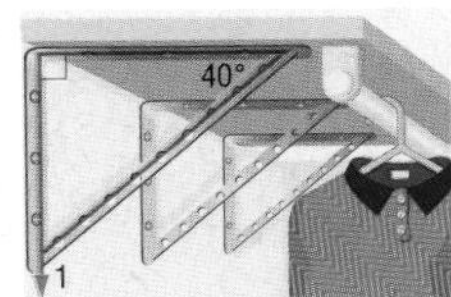

Real-World Career

Personal Trainer Personal trainers instruct and motivate individuals in exercise activities. They demonstrate various exercises and help clients improve their exercise techniques. Personal trainers must obtain certification in the fitness field.

A **corollary** is a theorem with a proof that follows as a direct result of another theorem. As with a theorem, a corollary can be used as a reason in a proof. The corollaries below follow directly from the Triangle Angle-Sum Theorem.

Corollaries Triangle Angle-Sum Corollaries

4.1 The acute angles of a right triangle are complementary.

Abbreviation: *Acute ∠s of a rt. △ are comp.*

Example: If $\angle C$ is a right angle, then $\angle A$ and $\angle B$ are complementary.

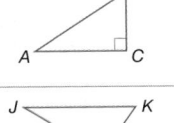

4.2 There can be at most one right or obtuse angle in a triangle.

Example: If $\angle L$ is a right or an obtuse angle, then $\angle J$ and $\angle K$ must be acute angles.

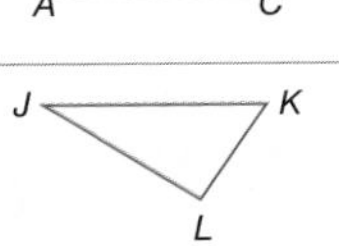

You will prove Corollaries 4.1 and 4.2 in Exercises 34 and 35.

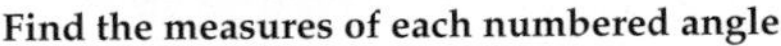

Example 3 Find Angle Measures in Right Triangles

Find the measures of each numbered angle.

$m\angle 1 + m\angle TYZ = 90$	Acute ∠s of a rt. △ are comp.
$m\angle 1 + 52 = 90$	Substitution
$m\angle 1 = 38$	Subtract 52 from each side.

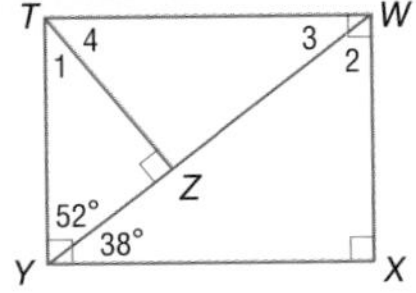

Guided Practice

3A. $\angle 2$ 52 **3B.** $\angle 3$ 38 **3C.** $\angle 4$ 52

Study Tip

Check for Reasonableness When you are solving for the measure of one or more angles of a triangle, always check to make sure that the sum of the angle measures is 180.

2 Exterior Angle Theorem

Example 2 shows how to find missing angle measures by using previously learned theorems and the Exterior Angle Theorem. **Example 3** uses a corollary to find the measure of an angle.

Additional Examples

2 **GARDENING** Find the measure of $\angle FLW$ in the fenced flower garden shown.

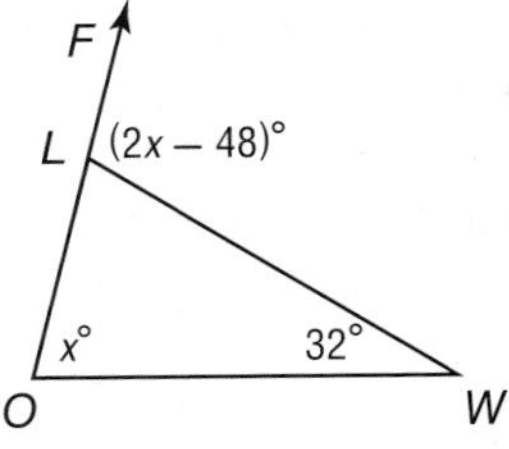

$m\angle FLW = 112$

3 Find the measure of each numbered angle.

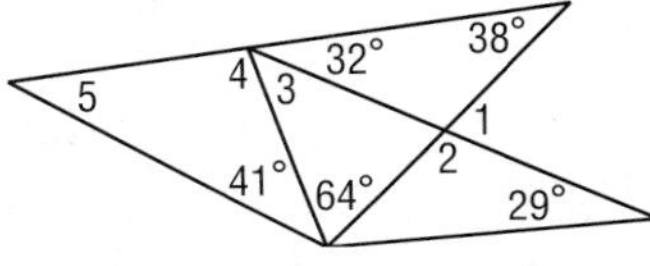

$m\angle 1 = 70$, $m\angle 2 = 110$, $m\angle 3 = 46$, $m\angle 4 = 102$, and $m\angle 5 = 37$

Tips for New Teachers

Numbered Angles It may not be possible to find the measures of numbered angles in the order in which they are numbered. Encourage students to find missing angle measures in an order that is logical and helpful for them.

Watch Out!

Triangle Angle-Sum Theorem When finding missing measures of a triangle, check the solution by seeing if the measures of the angles of the triangle sum to 180.

3 Practice

Formative Assessment

Use Exercises 1–11 to check for understanding.

Use the chart at the bottom of this page to customize assignments for your students.

Teaching the Mathematical Practices

Regularity Mathematically proficient students look for general methods while maintaining oversight of the process. In Exercises 9–11 and 24–29, encourage students to look for a triangle with two given angle measures.

Check Your Understanding

Example 1 Find the measures of each numbered angle.

1. 

58

2. 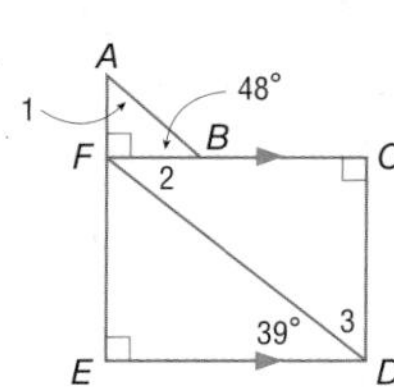

$m\angle 1 = 42$, $m\angle 2 = 39$, $m\angle 3 = 51$

Example 2 Find each measure.

3. $m\angle 2$ 80

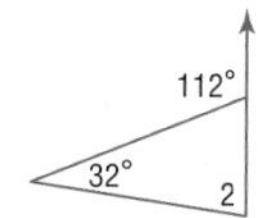

4. $m\angle MPQ$ 101

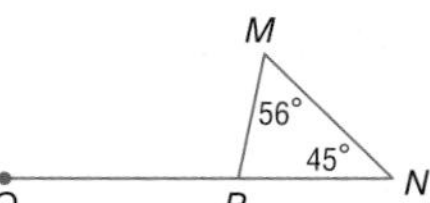

DECK CHAIRS The brace of this deck chair forms a triangle with the rest of the chair's frame as shown. If $m\angle 1 = 102$ and $m\angle 3 = 53$, find each measure.

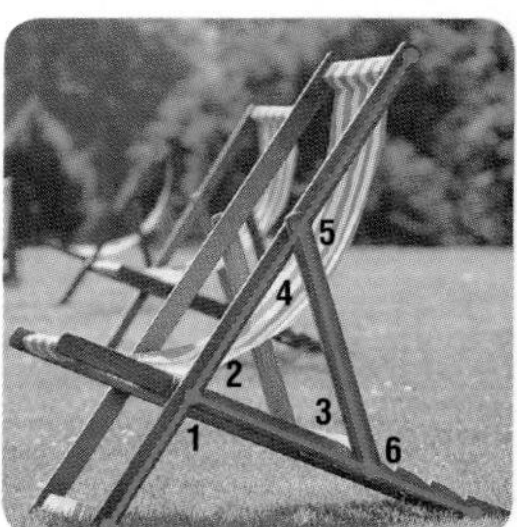

5. $m\angle 4$ 49
6. $m\angle 6$ 127
7. $m\angle 2$ 78
8. $m\angle 5$ 131

Example 3 CCSS REGULARITY Find each measure.

9. $m\angle 1$ 61
10. $m\angle 3$ 12
11. $m\angle 2$ 151

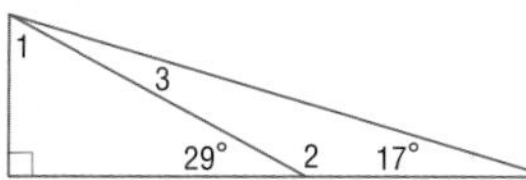

Practice and Problem Solving

Extra Practice is on page R4.

Example 1 Find the measure of each numbered angle.

12. 

60

13. 

30

14. 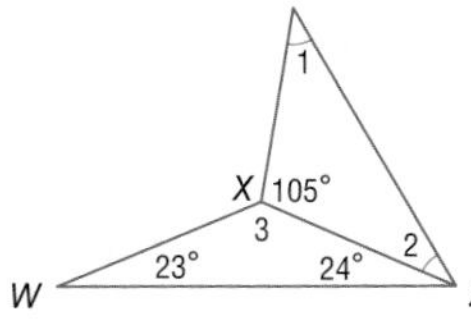

14. $m\angle 1 = 37.5$, $m\angle 2 = 37.5$, $m\angle 3 = 133$

15. L M 31° 2 N 1 Q 3 22° P

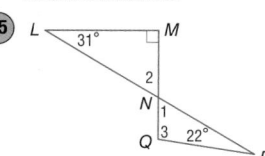

15. $m\angle 1 = 59$, $m\angle 2 = 59$, $m\angle 3 = 99$

Differentiated Homework Options

Level	Assignment	Two-Day Option	
AL Basic	12–29, 46–48, 50–67	13–29 odd, 52–55	12–28 even, 46–48, 50, 51, 56–67
OL Core	12–37 odd, 38–48, 50–67	12–29, 52–55	30–48, 50, 51, 56–67
BL Advanced	30–62, (optional: 63–67)		

16. **AIRPLANES** The path of an airplane can be modeled using two sides of a triangle as shown. The distance covered during the plane's ascent is equal to the distance covered during its descent.

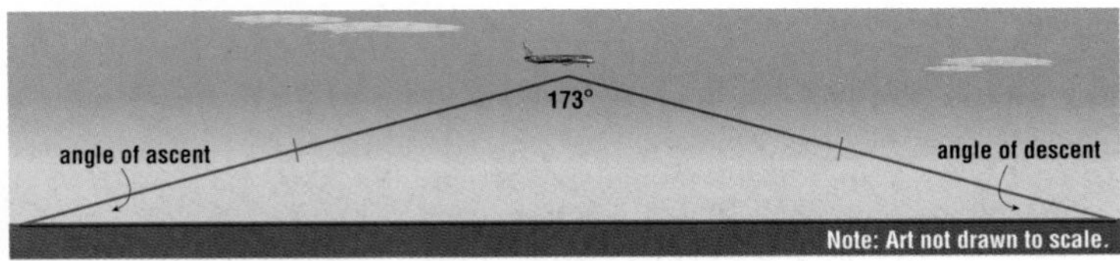

a. Classify the model using its sides and angles. **isosceles, obtuse**

b. The angles of ascent and descent are congruent. Find their measures. **3.5**

Example 2 **Find each measure.**

17. $m\angle 1$ **79**

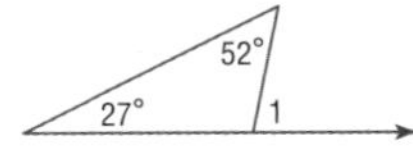

18. $m\angle 3$ **65**

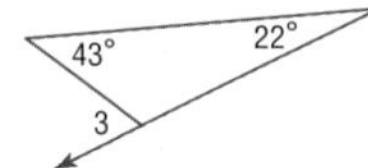

19. $m\angle 2$ **21**

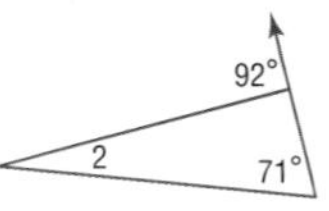

20. $m\angle 4$ **33**

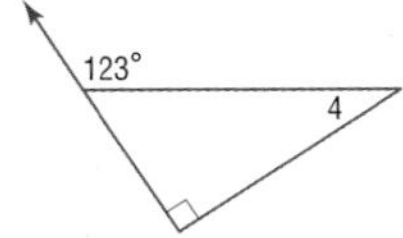

21. $m\angle ABC$ **51**

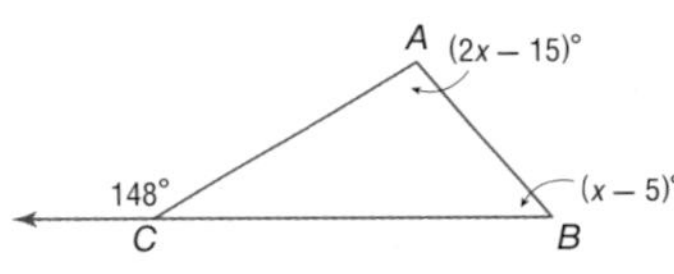

22. $m\angle JKL$ **31**

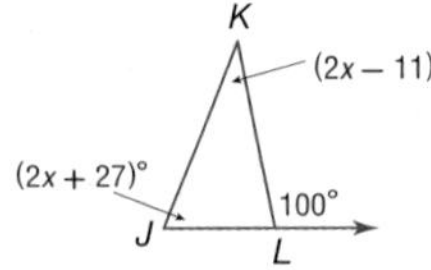

Example 3 23. **WHEELCHAIR RAMP** Suppose the wheelchair ramp shown makes a 12° angle with the ground. What is the measure of the angle the ramp makes with the van door? **78**

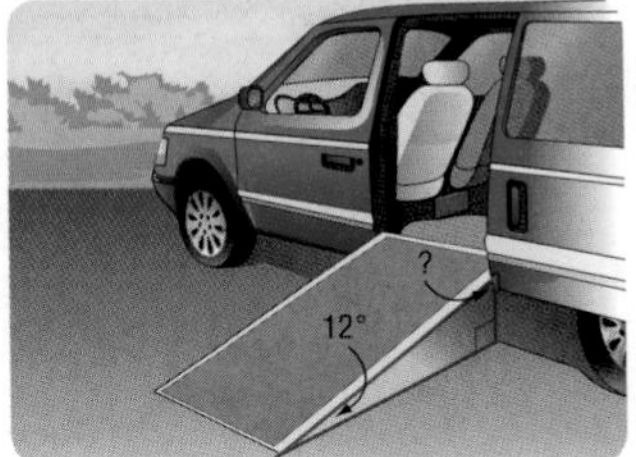

CCSS REGULARITY **Find each measure.**

24. $m\angle 1$ **62**

25. $m\angle 2$ **39**

26. $m\angle 3$ **26**

27. $m\angle 4$ **55**

28. $m\angle 5$ **55**

29. $m\angle 6$ **35**

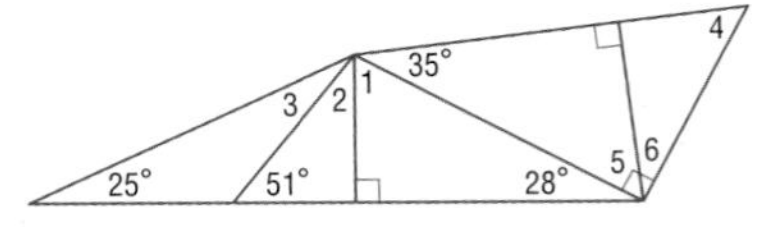

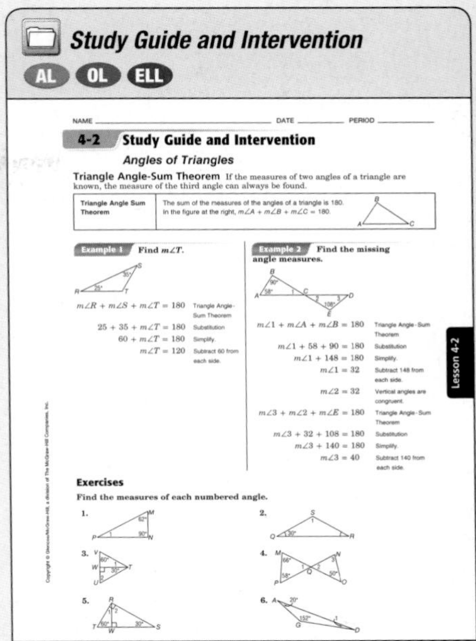

Study Guide and Intervention

AL OL ELL

4-2 Study Guide and Intervention

Angles of Triangles

Triangle Angle-Sum Theorem If the measures of two angles of a triangle are known, the measure of the third angle can always be found.

Triangle Angle Sum Theorem	The sum of the measures of the angles of a triangle is 180. In the figure at the right, $m\angle A + m\angle B + m\angle C = 180$.

Example 1 Find $m\angle T$.

$m\angle R + m\angle S + m\angle T = 180$ Triangle Angle-Sum Theorem
$25 + 35 + m\angle T = 180$ Substitution
$60 + m\angle T = 180$ Simplify.
$m\angle T = 120$ Subtract 60 from each side.

Example 2 Find the missing angle measures.

$m\angle 1 + m\angle A + m\angle B = 180$ Triangle Angle-Sum Theorem
$m\angle 1 + 58 + 90 = 180$ Substitution
$m\angle 1 + 148 = 180$ Simplify.
$m\angle 1 = 32$ Subtract 148 from each side.
$m\angle 2 = 32$ Vertical angles are congruent.
$m\angle 3 + m\angle 2 + m\angle E = 180$ Triangle Angle-Sum Theorem
$m\angle 3 + 32 + 108 = 180$ Substitution
$m\angle 3 + 140 = 180$ Simplify.
$m\angle 3 = 40$ Subtract 140 from each side.

Exercises

Find the measures of each numbered angle.

1. 2. 3. 4. 5. 6.

Lesson 4-2

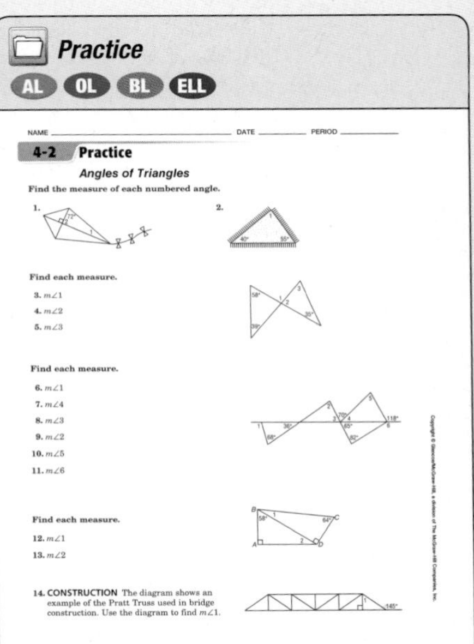

Practice

AL OL BL ELL

4-2 Practice

Angles of Triangles

Find the measure of each numbered angle.

1. 2.

Find each measure.

3. $m\angle 1$
4. $m\angle 2$
5. $m\angle 3$

Find each measure.

6. $m\angle 1$
7. $m\angle 4$
8. $m\angle 3$
9. $m\angle 2$
10. $m\angle 5$
11. $m\angle 6$

Find each measure.

12. $m\angle 1$
13. $m\angle 2$

14. CONSTRUCTION The diagram shows an example of the Pratt Truss used in bridge construction. Use the diagram to find $m\angle 1$.

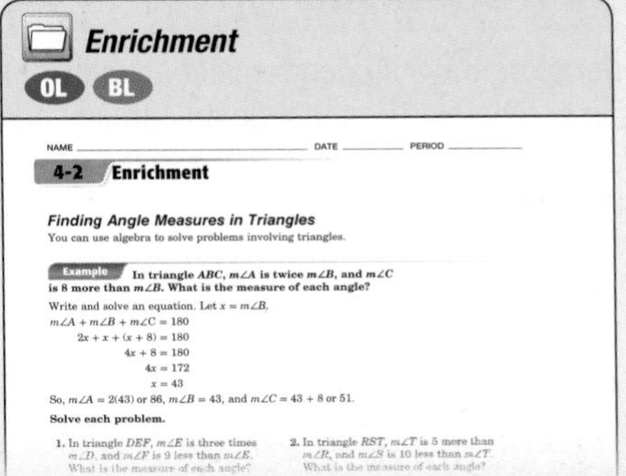

Enrichment

OL BL

4-2 Enrichment

Finding Angle Measures in Triangles

You can use algebra to solve problems involving triangles.

Example In triangle ABC, $m\angle A$ is twice $m\angle B$, and $m\angle C$ is 8 more than $m\angle B$. What is the measure of each angle?

Write and solve an equation. Let $x = m\angle B$.

$m\angle A + m\angle B + m\angle C = 180$
$2x + x + (x + 8) = 180$
$4x + 8 = 180$
$4x = 172$
$x = 43$

So, $m\angle A = 2(43)$ or 86, $m\angle B = 43$, and $m\angle C = 43 + 8$ or 51.

Solve each problem.

1. In triangle DEF, $m\angle E$ is three times $m\angle D$, and $m\angle F$ is 9 less than $m\angle E$. What is the measure of each angle?

2. In triangle RST, $m\angle T$ is 5 more than $m\angle R$, and $m\angle S$ is 10 less than $m\angle T$. What is the measure of each angle?

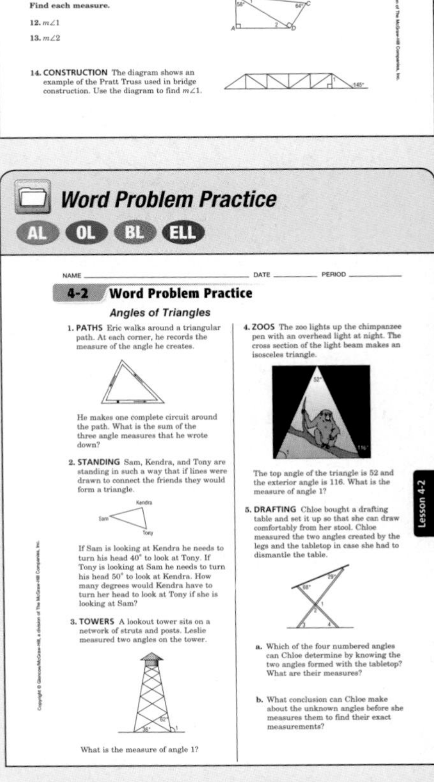

Word Problem Practice

AL OL BL ELL

4-2 Word Problem Practice

Angles of Triangles

1. PATHS Eric walks around a triangular path. At each corner, he records the measure of the angle he creates.

He makes one complete circuit around the path. What is the sum of the three angle measures that he wrote down?

2. STANDING Sam, Kendra, and Tony are standing in such a way that if lines were drawn to connect the friends they would form a triangle.

If Sam is looking at Kendra he needs to turn his head 40° to look at Tony. If Tony is looking at Sam he needs to turn his head 50° to look at Kendra. How many degrees would Kendra have to turn her head to look at Tony if she is looking at Sam?

3. TOWERS A lookout tower sits on a network of struts and posts. Leslie measured two angles on the tower.

What is the measure of angle 1?

4. ZOOS The zoo lights up the chimpanzee pen with an overhead light at night. The cross section of the light beam makes an isosceles triangle.

The top angle of the triangle is 52 and the exterior angle is 116. What is the measure of angle 1?

5. DRAFTING Chloe bought a drafting table and set it up so that she can draw comfortably from her stool. Chloe measured the two angles created by the legs and the tabletop in case she had to dismantle the table.

a. Which of the four numbered angles can Chloe determine by knowing the two angles formed with the tabletop? What are their measures?

b. What conclusion can Chloe make about the unknown angles before she measures them to find their exact measurements?

Lesson 4-2

connectED.mcgraw-hill.com

251

Additional Answers

34. Given: $\triangle RST$

$\angle R$ is a right angle.

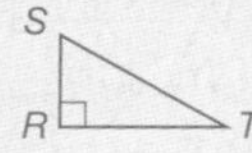

Prove: $\angle S$ and $\angle T$ are complementary.

Proof:

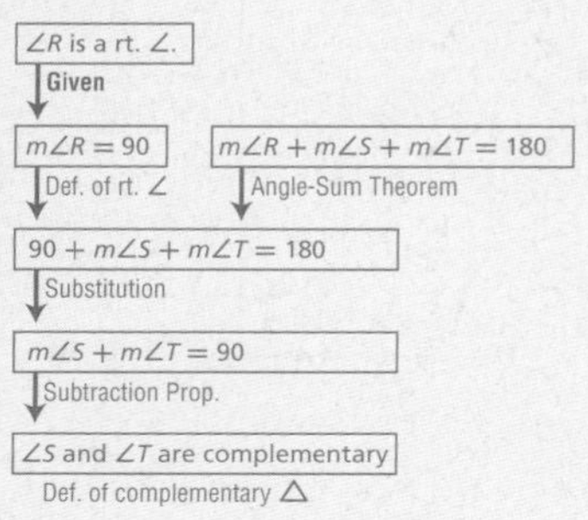

35. Given: $\triangle MNO$

$\angle M$ is a right angle.

Prove: There can be at most one right angle in a triangle.

Proof: In $\triangle MNO$, M is a right angle. $m\angle M + m\angle N + m\angle O = 180$. $m\angle M = 90$, so $m\angle N + m\angle O = 90$. If N were a right angle, then $m\angle O = 0$. But that is impossible, so there cannot be two right angles in a triangle.

Given: $\triangle PQR$

$\angle P$ is obtuse.

Prove: There can be at most one obtuse angle in a triangle.

Proof: In $\angle PQR$, $\angle P$ is obtuse. So $m\angle P > 90$. $m\angle P + m\angle Q + m\angle R = 180$. It must be that $m\angle Q + m\angle R < 90$. So, $\angle Q$ and $\angle R$ must be acute.

40. True; sample answer: Since the sum of the two acute angles is greater than 90, the measure of the third angle is a number greater than 90 subtracted from 180, which must be less than 90. Therefore, the triangle has three acute angles and is acute.

41. $z < 23$; Sample answer: Since the sum of the measures of the angles of a triangle is 180 and $m\angle X = 157$, $157 + m\angle Y + m\angle Z = 180$, so $m\angle Y + m\angle Z = 23$. If $m\angle Y$ was 0, then $m\angle Z$ would equal 23. But since an angle must have a measure greater than 0, $m\angle Z$ must be less than 23, so $z < 23$.

ALGEBRA Find the value of x. Then find the measure of each angle.

30.

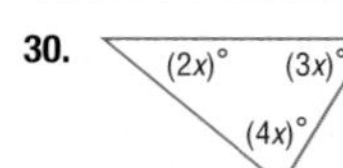

$x = 20$; 40, 60, 80

31.

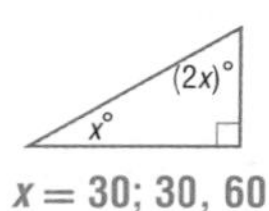

$x = 30$; 30, 60

32. (Figure: $(5x + 62)°$, $37°$, $(3x + 47)°$) $x = 11$; 80, 117

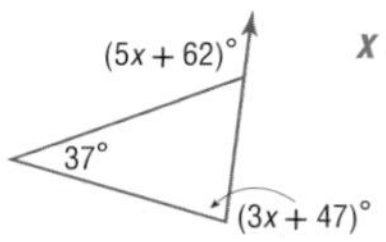

33. GARDENING A landscaper is forming an isosceles triangle in a flowerbed using chrysanthemums. She wants $m\angle A$ to be three times the measure of $\angle B$ and $\angle C$. What should the measure of each angle be? $m\angle A = 108$, $m\angle B = m\angle C = 36$

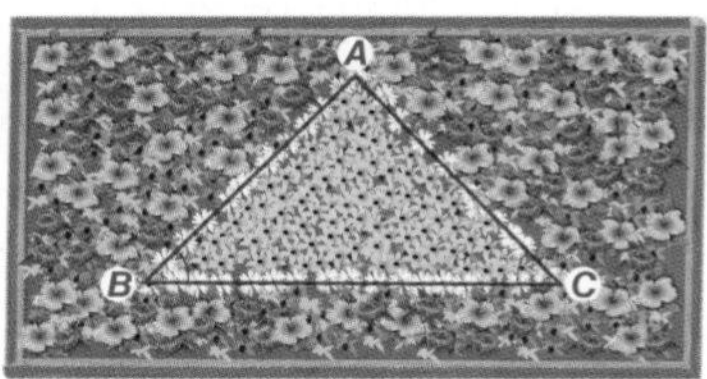

PROOF Write the specified type of proof. **34–35. See margin.**

34. flow proof of Corollary 4.1

35. paragraph proof of Corollary 4.2

CCSS REGULARITY Find the measure of each numbered angle.

36.

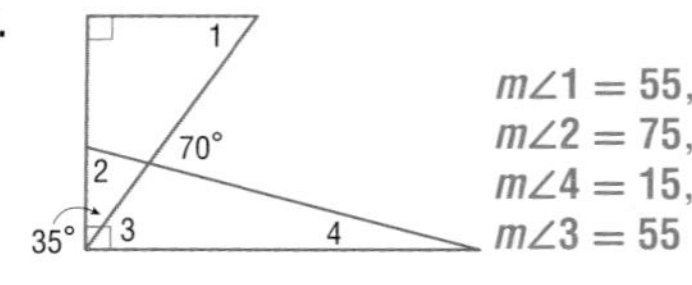

$m\angle 1 = 55$, $m\angle 2 = 75$, $m\angle 4 = 15$, $m\angle 3 = 55$

37. (Figure: angles 1–8, 110°, 30°, 130°)

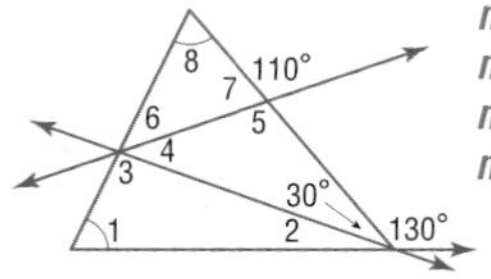

$m\angle 1 = 65$, $m\angle 2 = 20$, $m\angle 3 = 95$, $m\angle 4 = 40$, $m\angle 5 = 110$, $m\angle 6 = 45$, $m\angle 7 = 70$, $m\angle 8 = 65$

38. ALGEBRA Classify the triangle shown by its angles. Explain your reasoning.

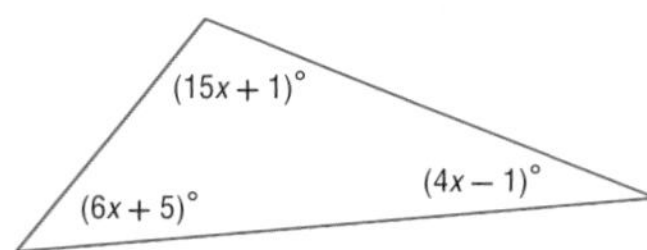

38. Obtuse; the sum of the measures of the three angles of a triangle is 180. So, $(15x + 1) + (6x + 5) + (4x - 1) = 180$ and $x = 7$. Substituting 7 into the expressions for each angle, the angle measures are 106, 47, and 27. Since the triangle has an obtuse angle, it is obtuse.

39. ALGEBRA The measure of the larger acute angle in a right triangle is two degrees less than three times the measure of the smaller acute angle. Find the measure of each angle. 67°, 23°

40. Determine whether the following statement is *true* or *false*. If false, give a counterexample. If true, give an argument to support your conclusion. **See margin.**

If the sum of two acute angles of a triangle is greater than 90, then the triangle is acute.

41. ALGEBRA In $\triangle XYZ$, $m\angle X = 157$, $m\angle Y = y$, and $m\angle Z = z$. Write an inequality to describe the possible measures of $\angle Z$. Explain your reasoning. **See margin.**

42. CARS Refer to the photo at the right.

a. Find $m\angle 1$ and $m\angle 2$. $m\angle 1 = 141$; $m\angle 2 = 39$

b. If the support for the hood were shorter than the one shown, how would $m\angle 1$ change? Explain. **See margin.**

c. If the support for the hood were shorter than the one shown, how would $m\angle 2$ change? Explain. **See margin.**

Differentiated Instruction OL BL ELL

Extension Have students select a vertex of a hexagon and draw interior straight lines to other vertices that do not already have an existing line. Ask how many triangles are formed. How many triangles are formed using a heptagon? Write an algebraic equation that works for n sides and t triangles. 4; 5; $t = n - 2$

 **PROOF** **Write the specified type of proof.**

43. two-column proof **See margin.**
Given: $RSTUV$ is a pentagon.
Prove: $m\angle S + m\angle STU + m\angle TUV + m\angle V + m\angle VRS = 540$

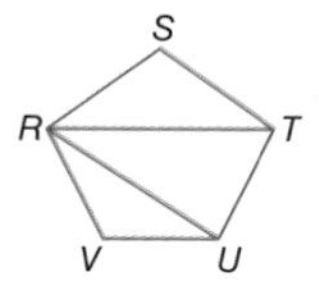

44. flow proof **See margin.**
Given: $\angle 3 \cong \angle 5$
Prove: $m\angle 1 + m\angle 2 = m\angle 6 + m\angle 7$

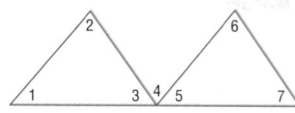

45. **MULTIPLE REPRESENTATIONS** In this problem, you will explore the sum of the measures of the exterior angles of a triangle. **a–e. See Ch. 4 Answer Appendix.**

a. **Geometric** Draw five different triangles, extending the sides and labeling the angles as shown. Be sure to include at least one obtuse, one right, and one acute triangle.

b. **Tabular** Measure the exterior angles of each triangle. Record the measures for each triangle and the sum of these measures in a table.

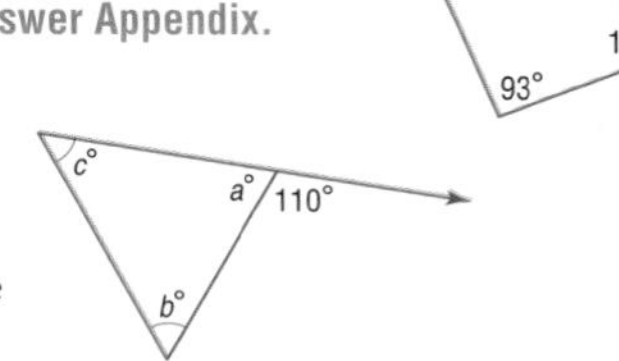

c. **Verbal** Make a conjecture about the sum of the exterior angles of a triangle. State your conjecture using words.

d. **Algebraic** State the conjecture you wrote in part **c** algebraically.

e. **Analytical** Write a paragraph proof of your conjecture.

H.O.T. Problems Use Higher-Order Thinking Skills

46. **CCSS CRITIQUE** Curtis measured and labeled the angles of the triangle as shown. Arnoldo says that at least one of his measures is incorrect. Explain in at least two different ways how Arnoldo knows that this is true. **See Ch. 4 Answer Appendix.**

47. **WRITING IN MATH** Explain how you would find the missing measures in the figure shown. **See Ch. 4 Answer Appendix.**

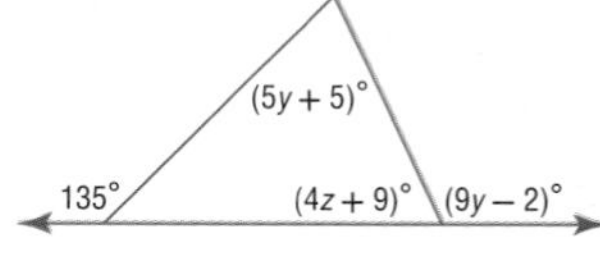

48. **OPEN ENDED** Construct a right triangle and measure one of the acute angles. Find the measure of the second acute angle using calculation and explain your method. Confirm your result using a protractor. **See Ch. 4 Answer Appendix.**

49. **CHALLENGE** Find the values of y and z in the figure at the right. **$y = 13$, $z = 14$**

50. **REASONING** If an exterior angle adjacent to $\angle A$ is acute, is $\triangle ABC$ acute, right, obtuse, or can its classification not be determined? Explain your reasoning.

50. Obtuse; since the exterior angle is acute, the sum of the remote interior angles must be acute, which means the third angle must be obtuse. Therefore, the triangle must be obtuse.

51. **WRITING IN MATH** Explain why a triangle cannot have an obtuse, acute, and a right exterior angle. **See Ch. 4 Answer Appendix.**

Multiple Representations

In Exercise 45, students investigate the sum of the measures of the exterior angles of a triangle using geometric sketches, a table, a verbal description, and a paragraph proof.

Exercise Alert

Compass, Straightedge, and Protractor Exercise 48 requires the use of a compass, a straightedge, and a protractor.

CCSS Teaching the Mathematical Practices

Critique Mathematically proficient students can distinguish correct logic from flawed reasoning. In Exercise 46, Arnoldo can justify his claim by showing that the sum of the interior angles of the triangle is 37 + 93 + 130 = 260, which cannot be correct because the sum of the interior angles of a triangle must be 180. Also a triangle can have at most one obtuse angle. Therefore, the triangle with angles that measure 93° and 103° is not possible.

Additional Answers

42b. Sample answer: The measure of $\angle 1$ would get larger if the support were shorter because the hood would be closer to the leg of the triangle that is along the fender of the car.

42c. Sample answer: The measure of $\angle 2$ would get smaller if the support were shorter because $\angle 1$ would get larger and they are a linear pair.

43. Proof: Statements (Reasons)

1. $RSTUV$ is a pentagon. (Given)
2. $m\angle S + m\angle 1 + m\angle 2 = 180$; $m\angle 3 + m\angle 4 + m\angle 7 = 180$; $m\angle 6 + m\angle V + m\angle 5 = 180$ ($\angle$ Sum Thm.)
3. $m\angle S + m\angle 1 + m\angle 2 + m\angle 3 + m\angle 4 + m\angle 7 + m\angle 6 + m\angle V + m\angle 5 = 540$ (Add. Prop.)
4. $m\angle VRS = m\angle 1 + m\angle 4 + m\angle 5$; $m\angle TUV = m\angle 7 + m\angle 6$; $m\angle STU = m\angle 2 + m\angle 3$ ($\angle$ Addition)
5. $m\angle S + m\angle STU + m\angle TUV + m\angle V + m\angle VRS = 540$ (Subst.)

CCSS Teaching the Mathematical Practices

Regularity Mathematically proficient students look for general methods while maintaining oversight of the process. In Exercises 36–37, encourage students to look for a triangle with two given angle measures first and then solve each missing angle measure one at time.

44. Proof:

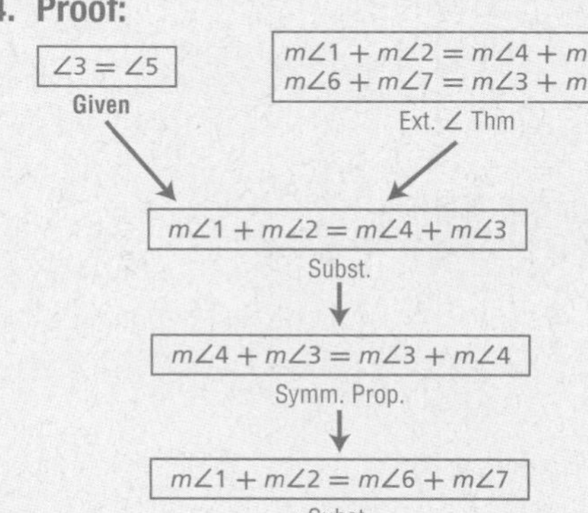

∠3 = ∠5
Given
m∠1 + m∠2 = m∠4 + m∠5; m∠6 + m∠7 = m∠3 + m∠4
Ext. ∠ Thm
m∠1 + m∠2 = m∠4 + m∠3
Subst.
m∠4 + m∠3 = m∠3 + m∠4
Symm. Prop.
m∠1 + m∠2 = m∠6 + m∠7
Subst.

4 Assess

Name the Math Draw an acute triangle with angles that measure 44 and 56. Draw an obtuse triangle with angles that measure 110 and 40. Draw an isosceles triangle with two angles measuring 75. Students should use the theorems in this lesson to find the missing angle measures in each triangle and then write their response.

Formative Assessment

Check for student understanding of concepts in Lessons 4-1 and 4-2.

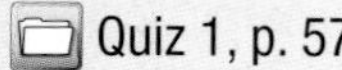
Quiz 1, p. 57

Additional Answers

61. Each set of figures has one more triangle than the previous set and the direction of the triangles alternate between pointing up and pointing to the right;

62. Each figure has a row of blocks added to the base of the previous figure. The row of blocks added contains one more block than the number of blocks in the last row of the previous figure;

Standardized Test Practice

52. **PROBABILITY** Mr. Glover owns a video store and wants to survey his customers to find what type of movies he should buy. Which of the following options would be the best way for Mr. Glover to get accurate survey results? **D**
   - **A** surveying customers who come in from 9 P.M. until 10 P.M.
   - **B** surveying customers who come in on the weekend
   - **C** surveying the male customers
   - **D** surveying at different times of the week and day

53. **SHORT RESPONSE** Two angles of a triangle have measures of 35° and 80°. Find the values of the exterior angle measures of the triangle. **100°, 115°, 145°**

54. **ALGEBRA** Which equation is equivalent to $7x - 3(2 - 5x) = 8x$? **G**
   - **F** $2x - 6 = 8$
   - **G** $22x - 6 = 8x$
   - **H** $-8x - 6 = 8x$
   - **J** $22x + 6 = 8x$

55. **SAT/ACT** Joey has 4 more video games than Solana and half as many as Melissa. If together they have 24 video games, how many does Melissa have? **E**
   - **A** 7
   - **B** 9
   - **C** 12
   - **D** 13
   - **E** 14

Spiral Review

Classify each triangle as *acute, equiangular, obtuse,* or *right.* (Lesson 4-1)

56. 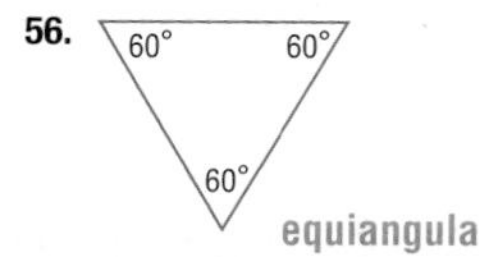

equiangular

57. 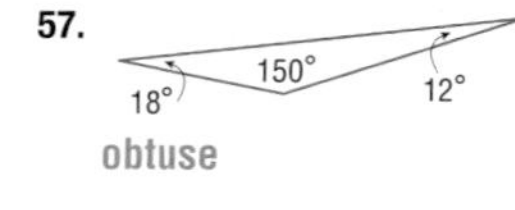

obtuse

58. 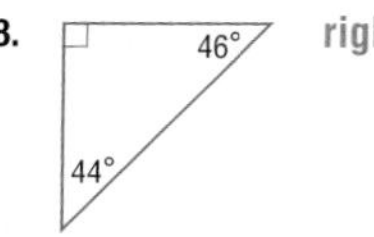

right

COORDINATE GEOMETRY Find the distance from *P* to *ℓ*. (Lesson 3-6)

59. Line ℓ contains points (0, −2) and (1, 3). Point *P* has coordinates (−4, 4). $\sqrt{26}$ **units**

60. Line ℓ contains points (−3, 0) and (3, 0). Point *P* has coordinates (4, 3). **3 units**

Write a conjecture that describes the pattern in each sequence. Then use your conjecture to find the next item in the sequence. (Lesson 2-1)

61. 
See margin.

62.  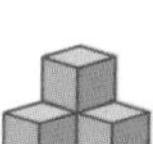 
See margin.

Skills Review

State the property that justifies each statement.

63. If $\frac{x}{2} = 7$, then $x = 14$. **Multiplication Property**

64. If $x = 5$ and $b = 5$, then $x = b$. **Substitution Property**

65. If $XY - AB = WZ - AB$, then $XY = WZ$. **Addition Property**

66. If $m\angle A = m\angle B$ and $m\angle B = m\angle C$, $m\angle A = m\angle C$. **Transitive Property**

67. If $m\angle 1 + m\angle 2 = 90$ and $m\angle 2 = m\angle 3$, then $m\angle 1 + m\angle 3 = 90$. **Substitution Property**

254 | Lesson 4-2 | Angles of Triangles

LESSON 4-3 Congruent Triangles

Then
- You identified and used congruent angles.

Now
1. Name and use corresponding parts of congruent polygons.
2. Prove triangles congruent using the definition of congruence.

Why?
- As an antitheft device, many manufacturers make car stereos with removable faceplates. The shape and size of the faceplate and of the space where it fits must be exactly the same for the faceplate to properly attach to the car's dashboard.

NewVocabulary
congruent
congruent polygons
corresponding parts

Common Core State Standards

Content Standards
G.CO.7 Use the definition of congruence in terms of rigid motions to show that two triangles are congruent if and only if corresponding pairs of sides and corresponding pairs of angles are congruent.
G.SRT.5 Use congruence and similarity criteria for triangles to solve problems and to prove relationships in geometric figures.

Mathematical Practices
6 Attend to precision.
3 Construct viable arguments and critique the reasoning of others.

1 Congruence and Corresponding Parts

If two geometric figures have exactly the same shape and size, they are **congruent**.

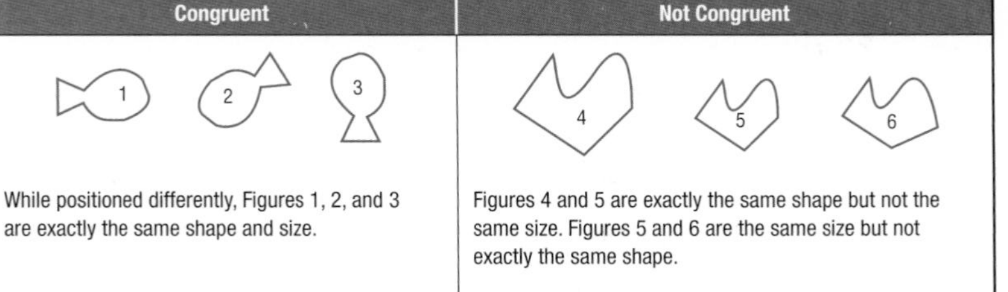

Congruent	Not Congruent
While positioned differently, Figures 1, 2, and 3 are exactly the same shape and size.	Figures 4 and 5 are exactly the same shape but not the same size. Figures 5 and 6 are the same size but not exactly the same shape.

In two **congruent polygons**, all of the parts of one polygon are congruent to the **corresponding parts** or matching parts of the other polygon. These corresponding parts include *corresponding angles* and *corresponding sides.*

KeyConcept Definition of Congruent Polygons

Words Two polygons are congruent if and only if their corresponding parts are congruent.

Example

Corresponding Angles
$\angle A \cong \angle H$ $\quad \angle B \cong \angle J$ $\quad \angle C \cong \angle K$

Corresponding Sides
$\overline{AB} \cong \overline{HJ}$ $\quad \overline{BC} \cong \overline{JK}$ $\quad \overline{AC} \cong \overline{HK}$

Congruence Statement
$\triangle ABC \cong \triangle HJK$

Model

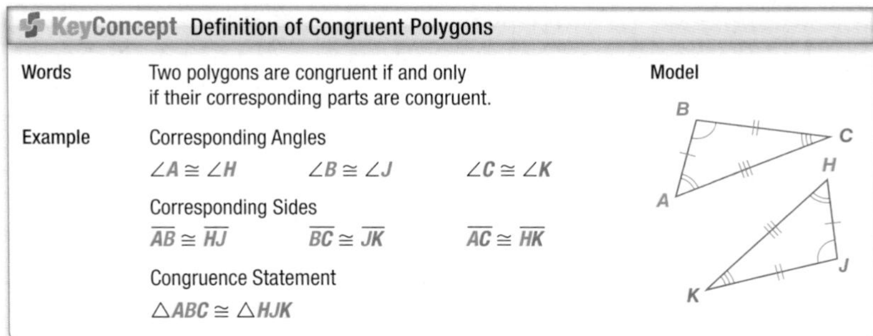

Other congruence statements for the triangles above exist. Valid congruence statements for congruent polygons list corresponding vertices in the same order.

Valid Statement	Not a Valid Statement
$\triangle BCA \cong \triangle JKH$	$\triangle ABC \cong \triangle HKJ$

1 Focus

VerticalAlignment

Before Lesson 4-3 Identify and use congruent angles.

Lesson 4-3 Name and use corresponding parts of congruent triangles. Prove triangles congruent using the definition of congruence.

After Lesson 4-3 Use congruence transformations to make conjectures and justify properties of geometric figures.

2 Teach

Scaffolding Questions

Have students read the **Why?** section of the lesson.

Ask:
- Why must the shape and size of the faceplate exactly match the space where it fits? If they do not match, the faceplate might not attach correctly, or might not attach at all.
- What other parts of the faceplate must match the space exactly? The slots for the knobs and buttons must be exactly the same size and shape as the actual knobs and buttons.
- What is a consequence of the faceplate not attaching properly? It will not be an effective antitheft device.

Lesson 4-3 Resources

Resource	Approaching Level AL	On Level OL	Beyond Level BL	English Learners ELL
Teacher Edition	▪ Differentiated Instruction, pp. 256, 261	▪ Differentiated Instruction, pp. 256, 257, 261	▪ Differentiated Instruction, pp. 257, 261	▪ Differentiated Instruction, p. 256
Chapter Resource Masters	▪ Study Guide and Intervention, pp. 19–20 ▪ Skills Practice, p. 21 ▪ Practice, p. 22 ▪ Word Problem Practice, p. 23	▪ Study Guide and Intervention, pp. 19–20 ▪ Skills Practice, p. 21 ▪ Practice, p. 22 ▪ Word Problem Practice, p. 23 ▪ Enrichment, p. 24	▪ Practice, p. 22 ▪ Word Problem Practice, p. 23 ▪ Enrichment, p. 24	▪ Study Guide and Intervention, pp. 19–20 ▪ Skills Practice, p. 21 ▪ Practice, p. 22 ▪ Word Problem Practice, p. 23
Other	▪ 5-Minute Check 4-3 ▪ Study Notebook ▪ Teaching Geometry with Manipulatives	▪ 5-Minute Check 4-3 ▪ Study Notebook ▪ Teaching Geometry with Manipulatives	▪ 5-Minute Check 4-3 ▪ Study Notebook	▪ 5-Minute Check 4-3 ▪ Study Notebook ▪ Teaching Geometry with Manipulatives

1 Congruence and Corresponding Parts

Example 1 shows that if the corresponding parts of two triangles are congruent, then the triangles are congruent. **Example 2** uses congruence to find missing values.

Formative Assessment

Use the Guided Practice exercises after each example to determine students' understanding of concepts.

Additional Examples

1 Show that the polygons are congruent by identifying all of the congruent corresponding parts. Then write a congruence statement.

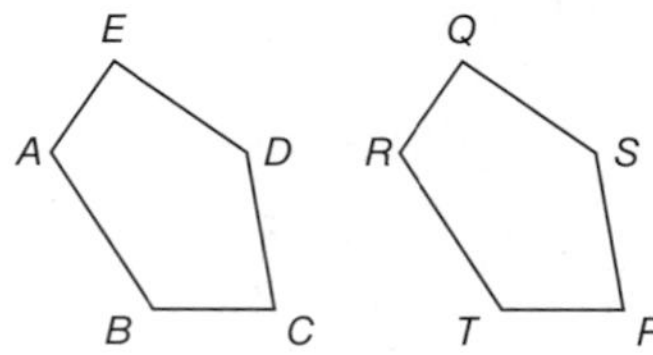

$\angle A \cong \angle R$, $\angle B \cong \angle T$, $\angle C \cong \angle P$, $\angle D \cong \angle S$, $\angle E \cong \angle Q$
$\overline{AB} \cong \overline{RT}$, $\overline{BC} \cong \overline{TP}$, $\overline{CD} \cong \overline{PS}$, $\overline{DE} \cong \overline{SQ}$, $\overline{EA} \cong \overline{QR}$

All corresponding parts of the two polygons are congruent. Therefore, $ABCDE \cong RTPSQ$.

2 In the diagram, $\triangle ITP \cong \triangle NGO$. Find the values of x and y.

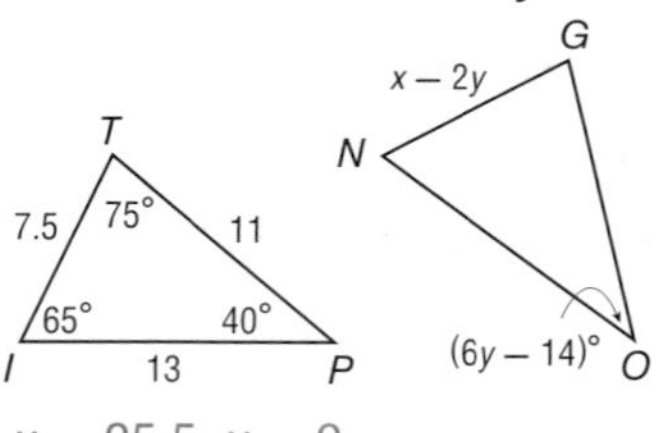

$x = 25.5$, $y = 9$

Additional Examples also in Interactive Classroom PowerPoint® Presentations

IWB Interactive White Board READY

Math HistoryLink

Johann Carl Friedrich Gauss (1777–1855) Gauss developed the congruence symbol to show that two sides of an equation were the same even if they weren't equal. He made many advances in math and physics, including a proof of the fundamental theorem of algebra.

Source: The Granger Collection, New York

PT

Example 1 Identify Corresponding Congruent Parts

Show that the polygons are congruent by identifying all the congruent corresponding parts. Then write a congruence statement.

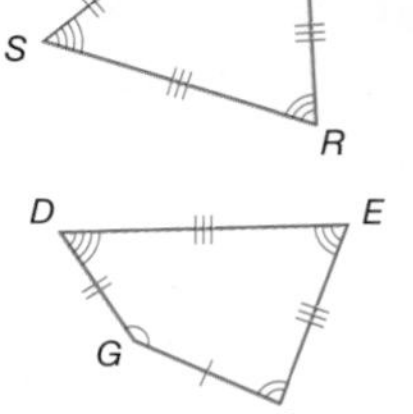

Angles: $\angle P \cong \angle G$, $\angle Q \cong \angle F$, $\angle R \cong \angle E$, $\angle S \cong \angle D$

Sides: $\overline{PQ} \cong \overline{GF}$, $\overline{QR} \cong \overline{FE}$, $\overline{RS} \cong \overline{ED}$, $\overline{SP} \cong \overline{DG}$

All corresponding parts of the two polygons are congruent. Therefore, polygon $PQRS \cong$ polygon $GFED$.

GuidedPractice **1A–1B. See margin.**

1A.

1B.

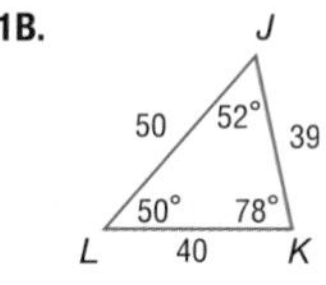

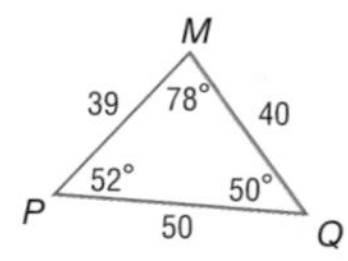

The phrase "if and only if" in the congruent polygon definition means that both the conditional and its converse are true. So, if two polygons are congruent, then their corresponding parts are congruent. For triangles, we say *Corresponding parts of congruent triangles are congruent*, or CPCTC.

PT

Example 2 Use Corresponding Parts of Congruent Triangles

In the diagram, $\triangle ABC \cong \triangle DFE$. Find the values of x and y.

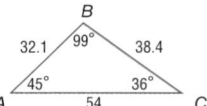

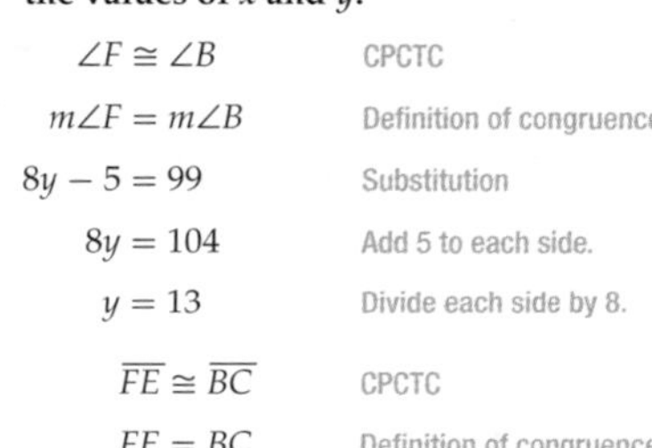

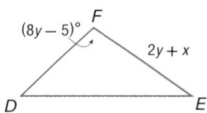

$\angle F \cong \angle B$	CPCTC
$m\angle F = m\angle B$	Definition of congruence
$8y - 5 = 99$	Substitution
$8y = 104$	Add 5 to each side.
$y = 13$	Divide each side by 8.
$\overline{FE} \cong \overline{BC}$	CPCTC
$FE = BC$	Definition of congruence
$2y + x = 38.4$	Substitution
$2(13) + x = 38.4$	Substitution
$26 + x = 38.4$	Simplify.
$x = 12.4$	Subtract 26 from each side.

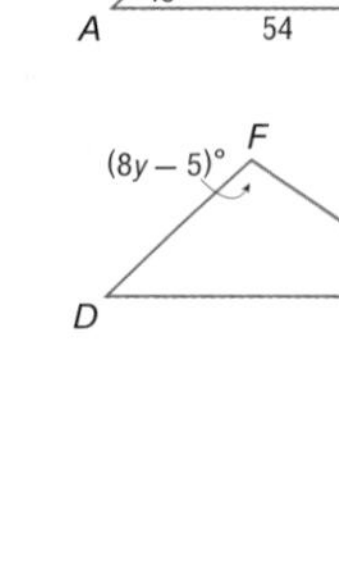

StudyTip

Using a Congruence Statement You can use a congruence statement to help you correctly identify corresponding sides.

$\triangle ABC \cong \triangle DFE$
$\overline{BC} \cong \overline{FE}$

GuidedPractice

2. In the diagram, $\triangle RSV \cong \triangle TVS$. Find the values of x and y.
$x = 12$; $y = 12.5$

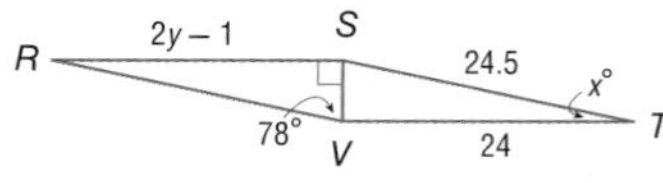

DifferentiatedInstruction AL OL ELL

Auditory/Musical Learners Explain to students that congruency can be appealing to both the eyes and the ears. Point out that if students use beats to model two congruent equilateral triangles, they could use three equally-spaced drum beats for the first and then repeat the exact same rhythm for the second. An isosceles beat could consist of two quick beats and one slow beat or vice versa. Tell students that often in music, a "congruent" rhythm is used throughout a song. A popular example is the song, "Louie, Louie."

2 Prove Triangles Congruent

The Triangle Angle-Sum Theorem you learned in Lesson 4-2 leads to another theorem about the angles in two triangles.

Theorem 4.3 Third Angles Theorem

Words: If two angles of one triangle are congruent to two angles of a second triangle, then the third angles of the triangles are congruent.

Example: If $\angle C \cong \angle K$ and $\angle B \cong \angle J$, then $\angle A \cong \angle L$.

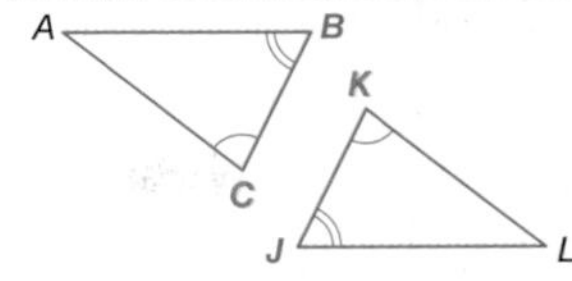
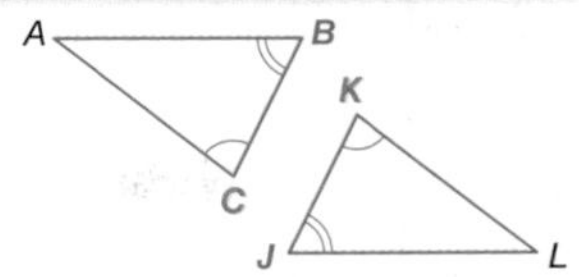

You will prove this theorem in Exercise 21.

Real-World Example 3 Use the Third Angles Theorem

PARTY PLANNING The planners of the Senior Banquet decide to fold the dinner napkins using the Triangle Pocket Fold so that they can place a small gift in the pocket. If $\angle NPQ \cong \angle RST$, and $m\angle NPQ = 40$, find $m\angle SRT$.

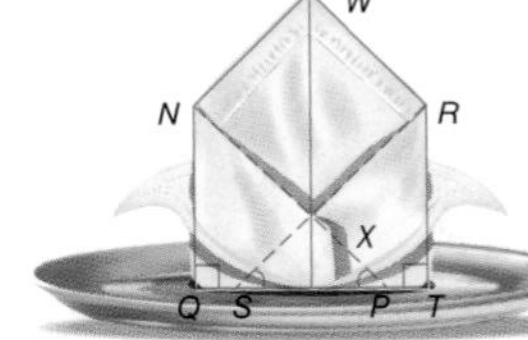

$\angle NPQ \cong \angle RST$, and since all right angles are congruent, $\angle NQP \cong \angle RTS$. So by the Third Angles Theorem, $\angle QNP \cong \angle SRT$. By the definition of congruence, $m\angle QNP = m\angle TRS$.

$m\angle QNP + m\angle NPQ = 90$	The acute angles of a right triangle are complementary.
$m\angle QNP + 40 = 90$	Substitution
$m\angle QNP = 50$	Subtract 40 from each side.

By substitution, $m\angle SRT = m\angle QNP$ or 50.

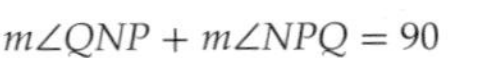

Real-WorldLink

Using some basic skills with napkin folding can add an elegant touch to any party. Many of the folds use triangles.

GuidedPractice

3. In the diagram above, if $\angle WNX \cong \angle WRX$, $\overline{WX}$ bisects $\angle NXR$, $m\angle WNX = 88$, and $m\angle NXW = 49$, find $m\angle NWR$. Explain your reasoning.

3. 86; since $\angle WNX \cong \angle WRX$ and $\angle NXW \cong \angle RWX$, $\angle NWX \cong \angle RWX$. $\angle NWX = 180 - 88 - 49$ or $43°$, so $\angle NWR$ is $2 \times 43°$ or 86.

Example 4 Prove That Two Triangles are Congruent

Write a two-column proof.

Given: $\overline{DE} \cong \overline{GE}$, $\overline{DF} \cong \overline{GF}$, $\angle D \cong \angle G$, $\angle DFE \cong \angle GFE$

Prove: $\triangle DEF \cong \triangle GEF$

Proof:

Statements	Reasons
1. $\overline{DE} \cong \overline{GE}$, $\overline{DF} \cong \overline{GF}$	1. Given
2. $\overline{EF} \cong \overline{EF}$	2. Reflexive Property of Congruence
3. $\angle D \cong \angle G$, $\angle DFE \cong \angle GFE$	3. Given
4. $\angle DEF \cong \angle GEF$	4. Third Angles Theorem
5. $\triangle DEF \cong \triangle GEF$	5. Definition of Congruent Polygons

StudyTip

Reflexive Property
When two triangles share a common side, use the Reflexive Property of Congruence to establish that the common side is congruent to itself.

2 Prove Triangles Congruent

Example 3 uses triangle congruence to solve a real-world example. **Example 4** shows how to write a proof for triangle congruence.

Additional Examples

3 ARCHITECTURE A drawing of a tower's roof is composed of congruent triangles all converging at a point at the top. If $\angle J \cong \angle K$ and $m\angle J = 72$, find $m\angle JIH$.

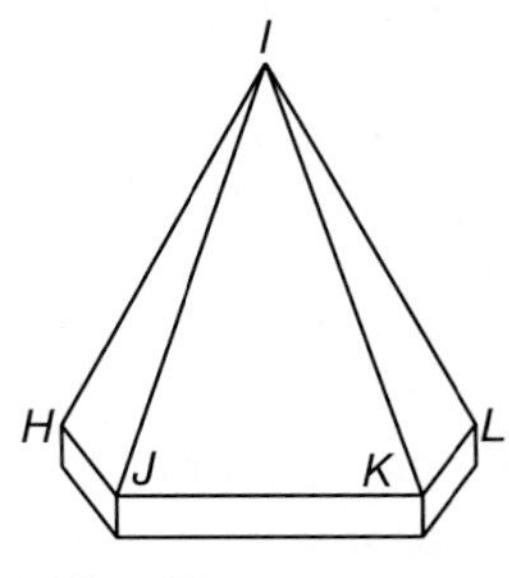

$m\angle JIH = 36$

4 Write a two-column proof.

Given: $\angle L \cong \angle P$, $\overline{LM} \cong \overline{PO}$, $\overline{LN} \cong \overline{PN}$, $\overline{MN} \cong \overline{OP}$

Prove: $\triangle LMN \cong \triangle PON$

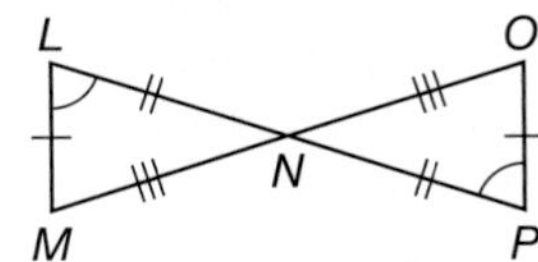

Proof:

Statements (Reasons)

1. $\angle L \cong \angle P$, $\overline{LM} \cong \overline{PO}$, $\overline{LN} \cong \overline{PN}$, $\overline{MN} \cong \overline{OP}$ (Given)
2. $\angle LNM \cong \angle PNO$ (Vertical ∠s Thm)
3. $\angle M \cong \angle O$ (Third ∠s Thm)
4. $\triangle LMN \cong \triangle PON$ (CPCTC)

DifferentiatedInstruction OL BL

Extension Have students draw $\triangle ABC$ with vertices $A(-8, 8)$, $B(-2, 5)$, and $C(-8, 2)$. Next, have students draw $\triangle PTS$ with vertices $P(8, 8)$, $T(2, 5)$, and $S(8, 2)$. Ask students how they can verify that the corresponding sides of the triangles are congruent. Further, facilitate discussion about whether the corresponding angles of $\triangle ABC$ and $\triangle PTS$ are congruent. Students can use the distance formula to prove that corresponding sides are congruent. Further discussion about the angles may include suggestions that the triangles are exactly the same because one is a reflection of the other, or that the equal side lengths require equal angles.

Additional Answers (Guided Practice)

1A. $\angle A \cong \angle W$, $\angle B \cong \angle X$, $\angle C \cong \angle Y$, $\angle D \cong \angle Z$; $\overline{AB} \cong \overline{WX}$, $\overline{BC} \cong \overline{XY}$, $\overline{CD} \cong \overline{YZ}$, $\overline{DA} \cong \overline{ZW}$; polygon $ABCD \cong$ polygon $WXYZ$

1B. $\angle J \cong \angle P$, $\angle K \cong \angle M$, $\angle L \cong \angle Q$; $\overline{JK} \cong \overline{PM}$, $\overline{KL} \cong \overline{MQ}$, $\overline{LJ} \cong \overline{QP}$; $\triangle JKL \cong \triangle PMQ$

Teach with Tech

Interactive Whiteboard Display two congruent triangles on the board. Drag one of the triangles to show your students that it fits exactly on top of the other triangle. Use this visual to show which parts of the triangles correspond to each other.

WatchOut!

Congruent vs. Similar To prove that a polygon is congruent, it is necessary to show that all of the sides and angles have the same measures. If only the angles are shown to be congruent, this only proves that the polygons are similar.

Tips for New Teachers

Visualize Congruency Students can use tick marks on sides and angles to help visually organize the corresponding parts of congruent triangles.

Focus on Mathematical Content

Common Misconceptions Point out that figures will not always be marked and that it is up to students to use their knowledge of geometric concepts to prove congruence. Stress the importance of using only information that is given and not forming any assumptions about two figures based only on appearance.

3 Practice

Formative Assessment

Use Exercises 1–8 to check for understanding.

Use the chart at the bottom of the next page to customize assignments for your students.

4.
Proof:
Statements (Reasons)
1. $\angle J \cong \angle P$, $\overline{JK} \cong \overline{PM}$, $\overline{JL} \cong \overline{PL}$, and L bisects $\overline{KM}$. (Given)
2. $\angle JLK \cong \angle PLM$ (Vert. ∠s are ≅.)
3. $\overline{LK} \cong \overline{LM}$ (Def. of segment bisector)
4. $\angle K \cong \angle M$ (Third ∠ Thm.)
5. $\triangle JLK \cong \triangle PLM$ (CPCTC)

GuidedPractice

4. Write a two column proof.

Given: $\angle J \cong \angle P$, $\overline{JK} \cong \overline{PM}$, $\overline{JL} \cong \overline{PL}$, and L bisects $\overline{KM}$.

Prove: $\triangle JLK \cong \triangle PLM$

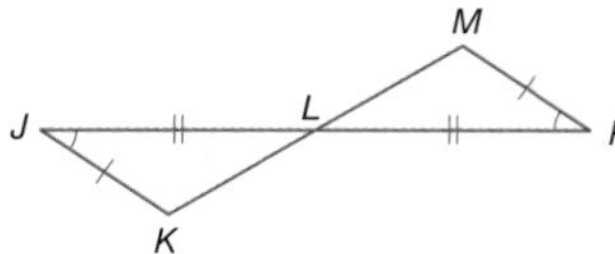

Like congruence of segments and angles, congruence of triangles is reflexive, symmetric, and transitive.

Theorem 4.4 Properties of Triangle Conguruence

Reflexive Property of Triangle Congruence

$\triangle ABC \cong \triangle ABC$

Symmetric Property of Triangle Congruence

If $\triangle ABC \cong \triangle EFG$, then $\triangle EFG \cong \triangle ABC$.

Transitive Property of Triangle Congruence

If $\triangle ABC \cong \triangle EFG$ and $\triangle EFG \cong \triangle JKL$, then $\triangle ABC \cong \triangle JKL$.

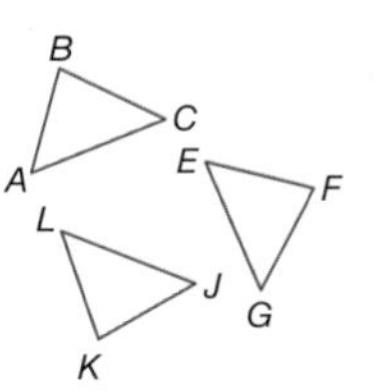

You will prove the reflexive, symmetric, and transitive parts of Theorem 4.4 in Exercises 27, 22, and 26, respectively.

1. $\angle Y \cong \angle S$, $\angle X \cong \angle R$, $\angle XZY \cong \angle RZS$, $\overline{YX} \cong \overline{SR}$, $\overline{YZ} \cong \overline{SZ}$, $\overline{XZ} \cong \overline{RZ}$; $\triangle YXZ \cong \triangle SRZ$
2. $\angle A \cong \angle E$, $\angle B \cong \angle F$, $\angle C \cong \angle G$, $\angle D \cong \angle H$, $\overline{AB} \cong \overline{EF}$, $\overline{CD} \cong \overline{GH}$, $\overline{AD} \cong \overline{EH}$; $\overline{BC} \cong \overline{FG}$; polygon $ABCD \cong$ polygon $EFGH$

Check Your Understanding

= Step-by-Step Solutions begin on page R14.

Example 1 **Show that polygons are congruent by identifying all congruent corresponding parts. Then write a congruence statement.**

1.

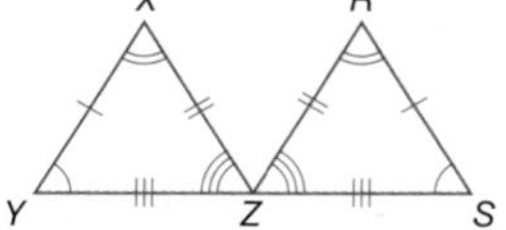

2.

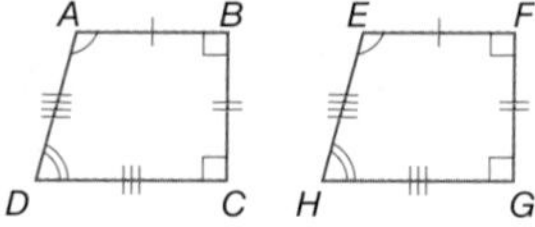

3. $\frac{1}{2}$ in.; Sample answer: The nut is congruent to the opening for the $\frac{1}{2}$ in. socket.

3. TOOLS Sareeta is changing the tire on her bike and the nut securing the tire looks like the one shown. Which of the sockets below should she use with her wrench to remove the tire? Explain your reasoning.

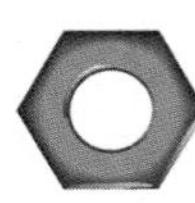

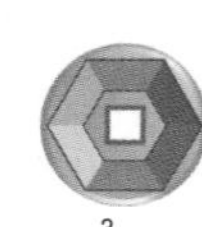

$\frac{3}{8}$ in.

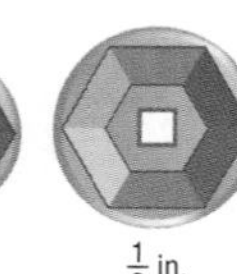

$\frac{1}{2}$ in.

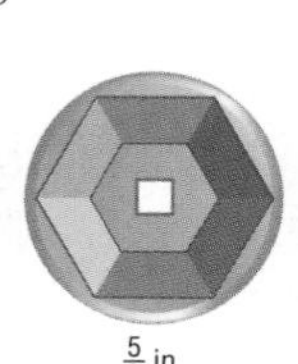

$\frac{5}{8}$ in.

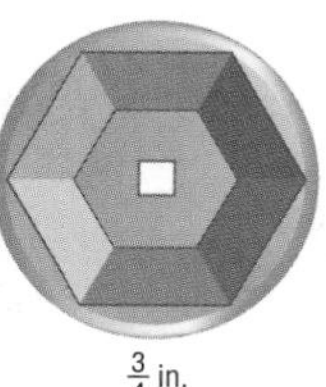

$\frac{3}{4}$ in.

258 | Lesson 4-3 | Congruent Triangles

Example 2 In the figure, $\triangle LMN \cong \triangle QRS$.

4. Find x. 20

5. Find y. 50

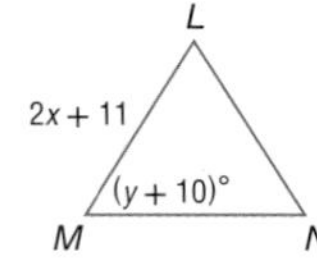

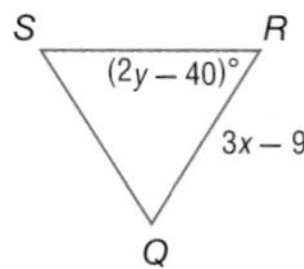

Example 3 CCSS **REGULARITY** Find x. Explain your reasoning. 6–7. See margin.

6. B G F (2x)° 80° A C H

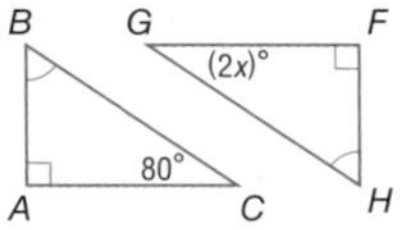

7.

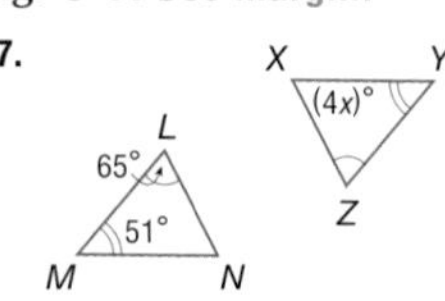

Example 4 8. **PROOF** Write a paragraph proof.

Given: $\angle WXZ \cong \angle YXZ$, $\angle XZW \cong \angle XZY$, $\overline{WX} \cong \overline{YX}$, $\overline{WZ} \cong \overline{YZ}$

Prove: $\triangle WXZ \cong \triangle YXZ$ See margin.

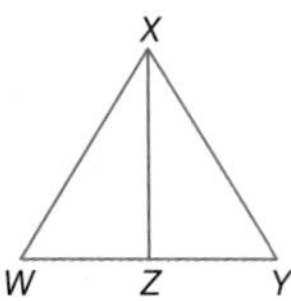

Practice and Problem Solving

Extra Practice is on page R4.

Example 1 Show that polygons are congruent by identifying all congruent corresponding parts. Then write a congruence statement.

9. $\angle X \cong \angle A$, $\angle Y \cong \angle B$, $\angle Z \cong \angle C$, $\overline{XY} \cong \overline{AB}$, $\overline{XZ} \cong \overline{AC}$, $\overline{YZ} \cong \overline{BC}$; $\triangle XYZ \cong \triangle ABC$

9.

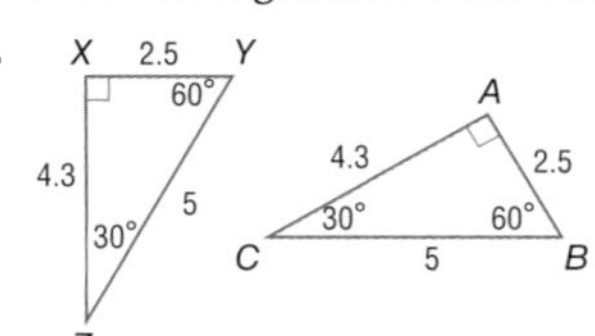

10.

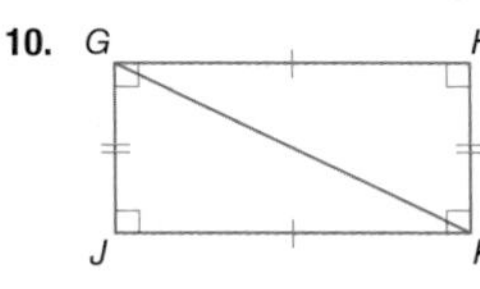

$\angle J \cong \angle H$, $\angle JGK \cong \angle HKG$, $\angle KGH \cong \angle GKJ$, $\overline{GJ} \cong \overline{KH}$, $\overline{JK} \cong \overline{HG}$, $\overline{GK} \cong \overline{GK}$; $\triangle GJK \cong \triangle KHG$

11. $\angle R \cong \angle J$, $\angle T \cong \angle K$, $\angle S \cong \angle L$, $\overline{RT} \cong \overline{JK}$, $\overline{TS} \cong \overline{KL}$, $\overline{RS} \cong \overline{JL}$; $\triangle RTS \cong \triangle JKL$

11.

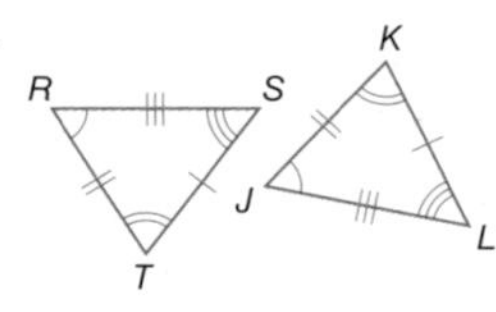

12.

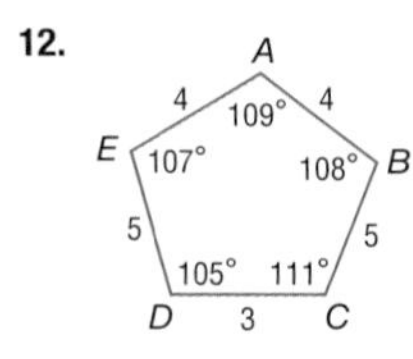

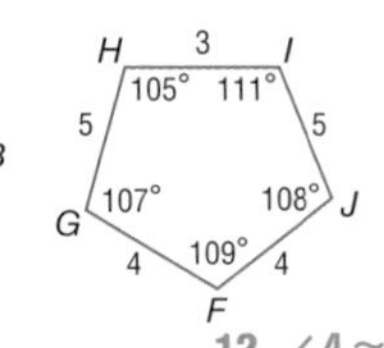

12. $\angle A \cong \angle F$, $\angle B \cong \angle J$, $\angle C \cong \angle I$, $\angle D \cong \angle H$, $\angle E \cong \angle G$, $\overline{AB} \cong \overline{FJ}$, $\overline{BC} \cong \overline{JI}$, $\overline{CD} \cong \overline{IH}$, $\overline{DE} \cong \overline{HG}$, $\overline{AE} \cong \overline{FG}$; polygon $ABCDE \cong$ polygon $FJIHG$

Example 2 Polygon $BCDE \cong$ polygon $RSTU$. Find each value.

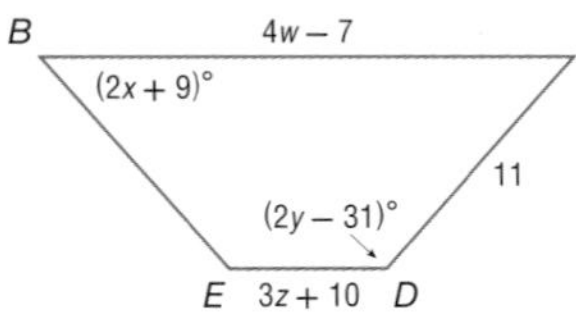

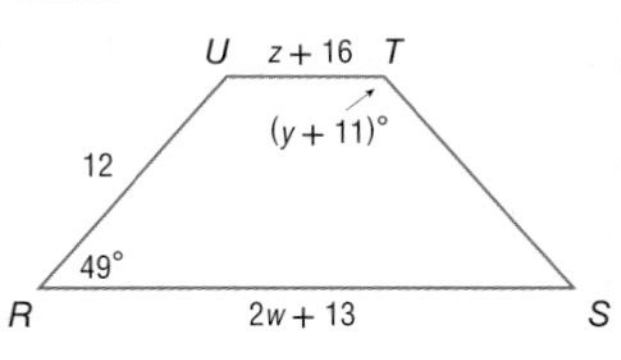

13. x 20

14. y 42

15. z 3

16. w 10

CCSS Teaching the Mathematical Practices

Regularity Mathematically proficient students look for general methods while maintaining oversight of the process, while attending to the details. In Exercises 6–7, encourage students to list the information given in each figure.

Additional Answers

6. 40; $\angle G$ corresponds to $\angle C$, so $2x = 80$.

7. 16; $\angle N$ corresponds to $\angle X$. By the Third Angles Theorem, $m\angle N = 64$, so $4x = 64$.

8. We know that $\overline{WX} \cong \overline{YX}$, $\overline{WZ} \cong \overline{YZ}$, $\overline{XZ} \cong \overline{XZ}$ by the Reflexive Property. We also know $\angle WXZ \cong \angle YXZ$, $\angle XZW \cong \angle XZY$ and by the Third Angles Theorem, $\angle W \cong \angle Y$. So, $\triangle WXZ \cong \triangle YXZ$, by the definition of congruent polygons.

Differentiated Homework Options

Level	Assignment	Two-Day Option	
AL Basic	9–27, 36–38, 40–58	9–27 odd, 43–47	10–26 even, 36–38, 40–42, 48–58
OL Core	9–31 odd, 32–38, 40, 41, 43–58	9–27, 44–47	28–38, 40–43, 48–58
BL Advanced	28–57, (optional: 58)		

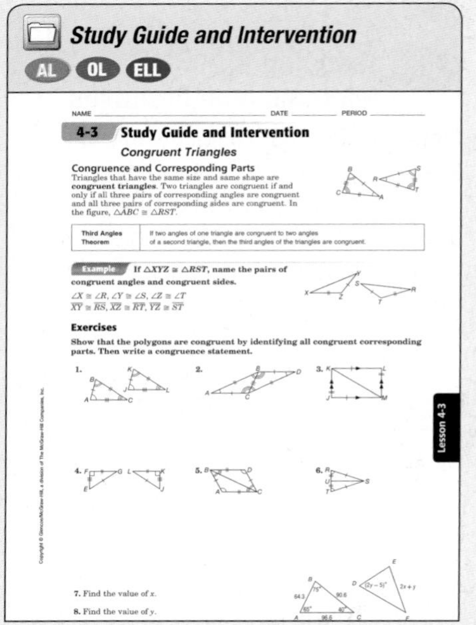

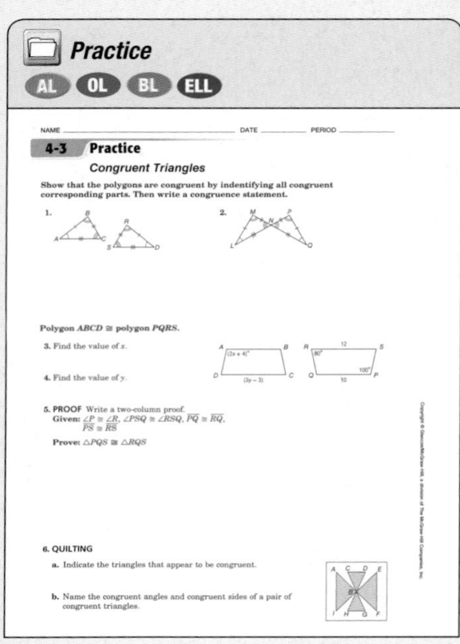

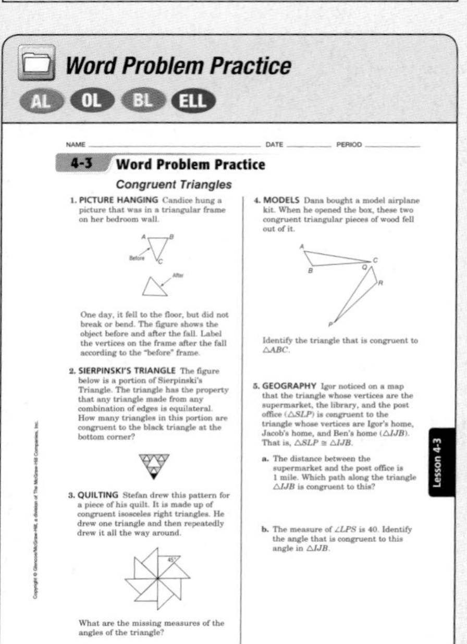

17. **SAILING** To ensure that sailboat races are fair, the boats and their sails are required to be the same size and shape. **17a–c. See Ch. 4 Answer Appendix.**
    a. Write a congruence statement relating the triangles in the photo.
    b. Name six pairs of congruent segments.
    c. Name six pairs of congruent angles.

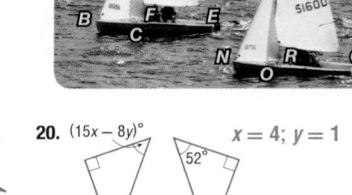

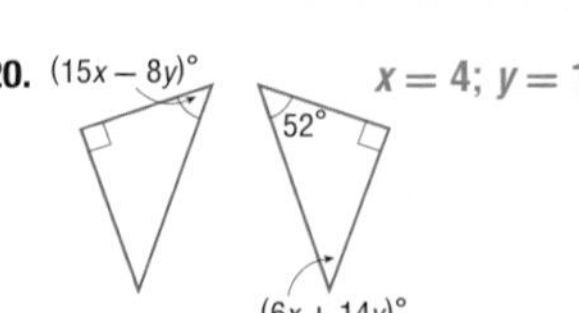

Example 3 Find x and y.

18. 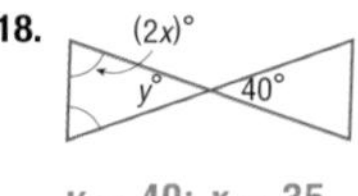

$y = 40$; $x = 35$

19. 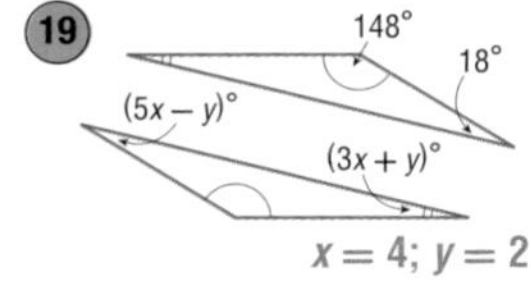

$x = 4$; $y = 2$

20. $x = 4$; $y = 1$

Example 4

21. **PROOF** Write a two-column proof of Theorem 4.3. **See Ch. 4 Answer Appendix.**

22. **PROOF** Put the statements used to prove the statement below in the correct order. Provide the reasons for each statement. **See Ch. 4 Answer Appendix.**

Congruence of triangles is symmetric. (Theorem 4.4)

Given: $\triangle RST \cong \triangle XYZ$

Prove: $\triangle XYZ \cong \triangle RST$

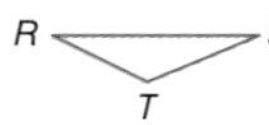 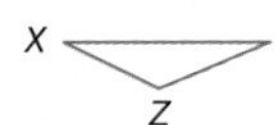

Proof:

$\angle X \cong \angle R$, $\angle Y \cong \angle S$, $\angle Z \cong \angle T$, $\overline{XY} \cong \overline{RS}$, $\overline{YZ} \cong \overline{ST}$, $\overline{XZ} \cong \overline{RT}$	$\angle R \cong \angle X$, $\angle S \cong \angle Y$, $\angle T \cong \angle Z$, $\overline{RS} \cong \overline{XY}$, $\overline{ST} \cong \overline{YZ}$, $\overline{RT} \cong \overline{XZ}$	$\triangle RST \cong \triangle XYZ$	$\triangle XYZ \cong \triangle RST$
?	?	?	?

CCSS ARGUMENTS Write a two-column proof.

23. **Given:** $\overline{BD}$ bisects $\angle B$. $\overline{BD} \perp \overline{AC}$
Prove: $\angle A \cong \angle C$
See Ch. 4 Answer Appendix.

24. **Given:** $\angle P \cong \angle T$, $\angle S \cong \angle Q$, $\overline{TR} \cong \overline{PR}$, $\overline{RP} \cong \overline{RQ}$, $\overline{RT} \cong \overline{RS}$, $\overline{PQ} \cong \overline{TS}$
Prove: $\triangle PRQ \cong \triangle TRS$
See Ch. 4 Answer Appendix.

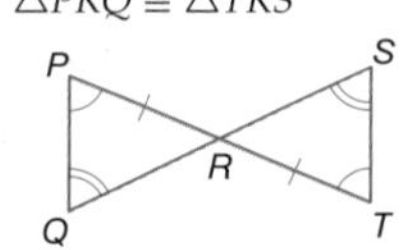

25. **SCRAPBOOKING** Lanie is using a flower-shaped corner decoration punch for a scrapbook she is working on. If she punches the corners of two pages as shown, what property guarantees that the punched designs are congruent? Explain.

25. Sample answer: Both of the punched flowers are congruent to the flower on the stamp, because it was used to create the images. According to the Transitive Property of Polygon Congruence, the two stamped images are congruent to each other because they are both congruent to the flowers on the punch.

PROOF Write the specified type of proof of the indicated part of Theorem 4.4.

26. Congruence of triangles is transitive. (paragraph proof) **See Ch. 4 Answer Appendix.**

27. Congruence of triangles is reflexive. (flow proof) **See Ch. 4 Answer Appendix.**

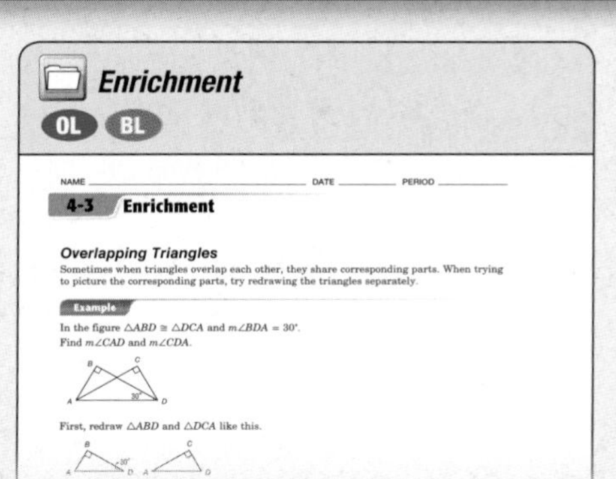

CCSS Teaching the Mathematical Practices

Arguments Mathematically proficient students make conjectures and build a logical progression of statements to explore the truth of their conjectures. In Exercises 23–24, encourage students to copy the figures onto their papers and add to it as they write the proof.

 **ALGEBRA** Draw and label a figure to represent the congruent triangles. Then find x and y. **28–30. See margin.**

28. $\triangle ABC \cong \triangle DEF$, $AB = 7$, $BC = 9$, $AC = 11 + x$, $DF = 3x - 13$, and $DE = 2y - 5$

29. $\triangle LMN \cong \triangle RST$, $m\angle L = 49$, $m\angle M = 10y$, $m\angle S = 70$, and $m\angle T = 4x + 9$

30. $\triangle JKL \cong \triangle MNP$, $JK = 12$, $LJ = 5$, $PM = 2x - 3$, $m\angle L = 67$, $m\angle K = y + 4$ and $m\angle N = 2y - 15$

31a. $\overline{AB} \cong \overline{CB}$, $\overline{AB} \cong \overline{DE}$, $\overline{AB} \cong \overline{FE}$, $\overline{CB} \cong \overline{DE}$, $\overline{CB} \cong \overline{FE}$, $\overline{DE} \cong \overline{FE}$, $\overline{AC} \cong \overline{DF}$

31 **PENNANTS** Scott is in charge of roping off an area of 100 square feet for the band to use during a pep rally. He is using a string of pennants that are congruent isosceles triangles.

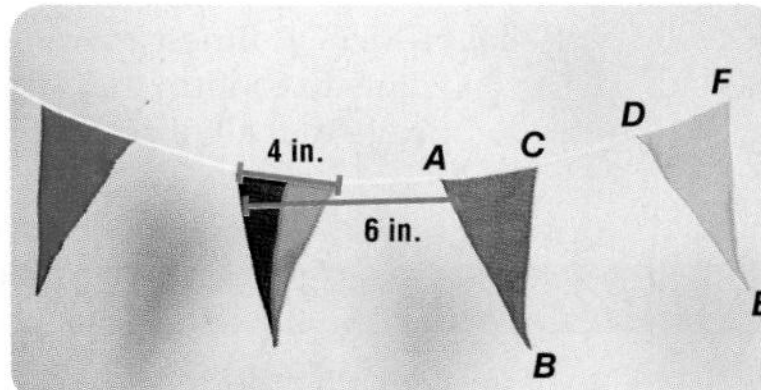

a. List seven pairs of congruent segments in the photo.

b. If the area he ropes off is a square, how long will the pennant string need to be? **40 ft**

c. How many pennants will be on the string? **80**

32. CCSS **SENSE-MAKING** In the photo of New York City's Chrysler Building at the right, $\overline{TS} \cong \overline{ZY}$, $\overline{XY} \cong \overline{RS}$, $\overline{TR} \cong \overline{ZX}$, $\angle X \cong \angle R$, $\angle T \cong \angle Z$, $\angle Y \cong \angle S$, and $\triangle HGF \cong \triangle LKJ$. **a–c. See margin.**

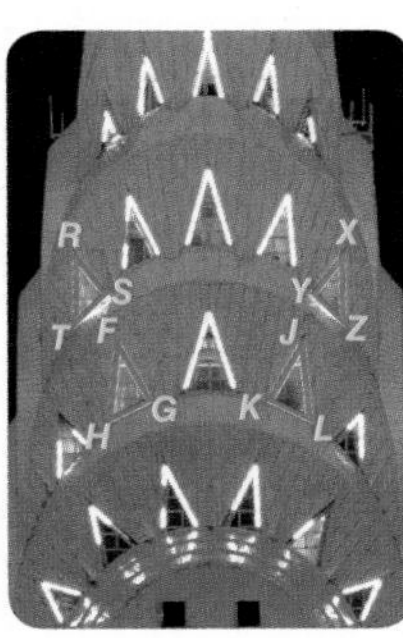

a. Which triangle, if any, is congruent to $\triangle YXZ$? Explain your reasoning.

b. Which side(s) are congruent to $\overline{JL}$? Explain your reasoning.

c. Which angle(s) are congruent to $\angle G$? Explain your reasoning.

33. **MULTIPLE REPRESENTATIONS** In this problem, you will explore the statement *The areas of congruent triangles are equal.* **a–f. See Ch. 4 Answer Appendix.**

a. Verbal Write a conditional statement to represent the relationship between the areas of a pair of congruent triangles.

b. Verbal Write the converse of your conditional statement. Is the converse *true* or *false*? Explain your reasoning.

c. Geometric If possible, draw two equilateral triangles that have the same area but are not congruent. If not possible, explain why not.

d. Geometric If possible, draw two rectangles that have the same area but are not congruent. If not possible, explain why not.

e. Geometric If possible, draw two squares that have the same area but are not congruent. If not possible, explain why not.

f. Verbal For which polygons will the following conditional and its converse both be true? Explain your reasoning.

If a pair of __________ are congruent, then they have the same area.

Differentiated Instruction OL BL

Extension Graph paper makes creating different types of congruent triangles much easier. Ask students to create a design that includes at least 10 different pairs of congruent triangles. Challenge students to explain how they know that each pair of triangles is congruent and to compare the creation of congruent triangles on graph paper to finding the slope of a line.

CCSS Teaching the Mathematical Practices

Sense-Making Mathematically proficient students look for entry points into a solution. They consider simpler forms of the original problem in order to gain insight into its solution. In Exercise 32, encourage students to draw a larger version of the triangles on their paper. Then label the figure with each of the given statements.

Multiple Representations

In Exercise 33, students use verbal descriptions and geometric sketches to investigate the areas of congruent triangles.

Additional Answers

28.

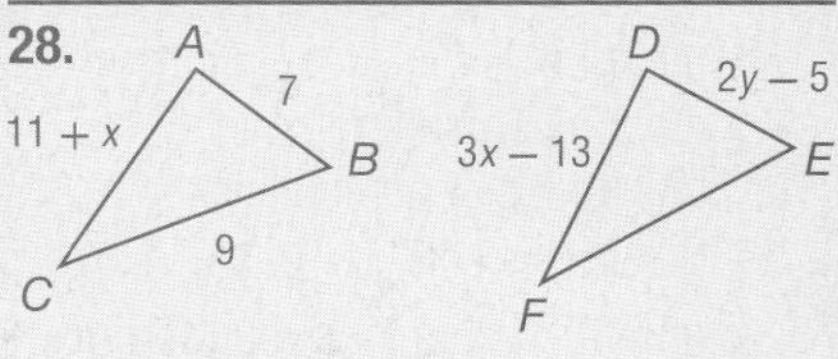

$x = 12$; $y = 6$

29.

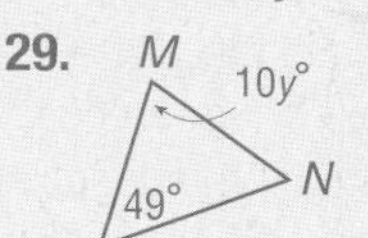

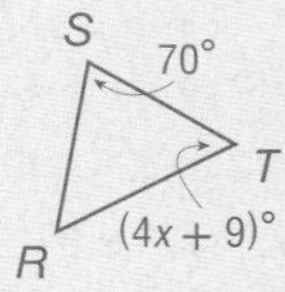

$x = 13$; $y = 7$

30.

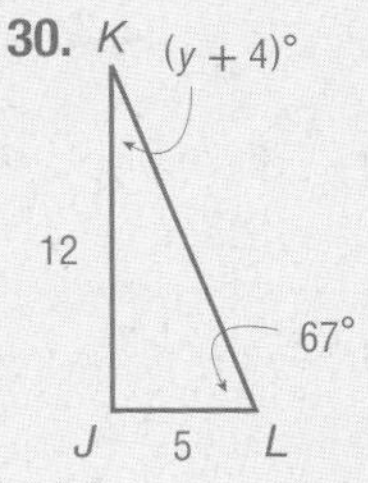

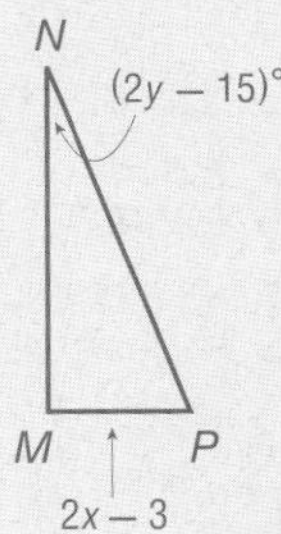

$x = 4$; $y = 19$

32a. $\triangle SRT$; The corresponding parts of the triangles are congruent, therefore the triangles are congruent.

32b. $\overline{FH}$; We are given that $\triangle HGF \cong \triangle LKJ$, and $\overline{JL}$ corresponds with $\overline{FH}$. Since corresponding parts of congruent triangles are congruent, $\overline{JL} \cong \overline{FH}$.

32c. $\angle K$; we are given that $\triangle HGF \cong \triangle LKJ$, and $\angle G$ corresponds with $\angle K$. Since corresponding parts of congruent triangles are congruent, $\angle G \cong \angle K$.

WatchOut!

Error Analysis In Exercise 37, both are correct! Both congruence statements list all corresponding parts of the two triangles in the correct order.

Additional Answers

34d. 4 in.; Sample answer: Because the polygons that make the pattern are regular, all of the sides of the triangles must be equal, so the triangles are equilateral. That means that CB is equal to AC and CE, so AE is $2(CB)$, or 4 inches.

34e. 60°; Sample answer: Because the triangles are regular, they must be equilateral, and all of the angles of an equilateral triangle are 60°.

35. diameter, radius, or circumference; Sample answer: Two circles are the same size if they have the same diameter, radius, or circumference, so she can determine if the hoops are congruent if she measures any of them.

36. Sample answer: When naming congruent triangles, it is important that the corresponding vertices be in the same location for both triangles because the location indicates congruence. For example if $\triangle ABC$ is congruent to $\triangle DEF$, then $\angle A \cong \angle D$, $\angle B \cong \angle E$, and $\angle C \cong \angle F$.

37. Both; Sample answer: $\angle A$ corresponds with $\angle Y$, $\angle B$ corresponds with $\angle X$, and $\angle C$ corresponds with $\angle Z$. $\triangle CAB$ is the same triangle as $\triangle ABC$ and $\triangle ZXY$ is the same triangle as $\triangle XYZ$.

38. Sample answer: Do you think that the sum of the angles of a quadrilateral is constant? If so, do you think that the final pair of corresponding angles will be congruent if three other pairs of corresponding angles are congruent for a pair of quadrilaterals?

34. PATTERNS The pattern shown is created using regular polygons. **d, e. See margin.**

a. What two polygons are used to create the pattern? **hexagons and triangles**

b. Name a pair of congruent triangles. **Sample answer: $\triangle ABC \cong \triangle DEC$**

c. Name a pair of corresponding angles. **Sample answer: $\angle B$ and $\angle E$**

d. If $CB = 2$ inches, what is AE? Explain.

e. What is the measure of $\angle D$? Explain.

35. FITNESS A fitness instructor is starting a new aerobics class using fitness hoops. She wants to confirm that all of the hoops are the same size. What measure(s) can she use to prove that all of the hoops are congruent? Explain your reasoning. **See margin.**

H.O.T. Problems Use Higher-Order Thinking Skills

36. WRITING IN MATH Explain why the order of the vertices is important when naming congruent triangles. Give an example to support your answer. **See margin.**

37. ERROR ANALYSIS Jasmine and Will are evaluating the congruent figures below. Jasmine says that $\triangle CAB \cong \triangle ZYX$ and Will says that $\triangle ABC \cong \triangle YXZ$. Is either of them correct? Explain. **See margin.**

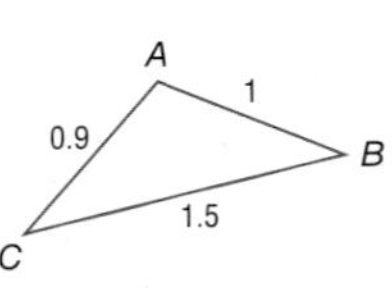

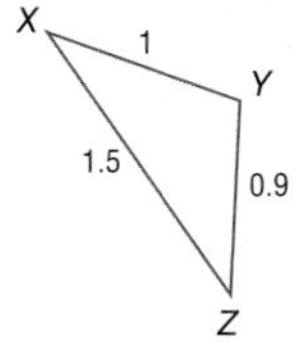

38. WRITE A QUESTION A classmate is using the Third Angles Theorem to show that if 2 corresponding pairs of the angles of two triangles are congruent, then the third pair is also congruent. Write a question to help him decide if he can use the same strategy for quadrilaterals. **See margin.**

39. CHALLENGE Find x and y if $\triangle PQS \cong \triangle RQS$. **$x = 16$, $y = 8$**

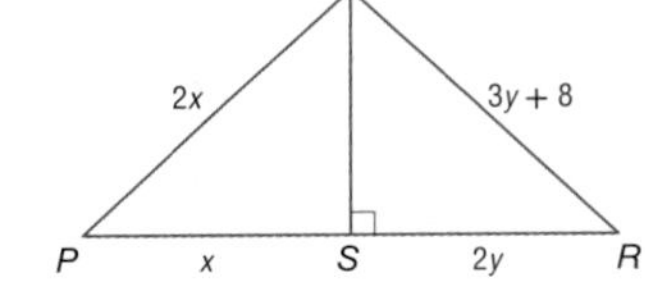

CCSS ARGUMENTS Determine whether each statement is *true* or *false*. If false, give a counterexample. If true, explain your reasoning. 40–42. See margin.

40. Two triangles with two pairs of congruent corresponding angles and three pairs of congruent corresponding sides are congruent.

41. Two triangles with three pairs of corresponding congruent angles are congruent.

42. CHALLENGE Write a paragraph proof to prove polygon $ABED \cong$ polygon $FEBC$.

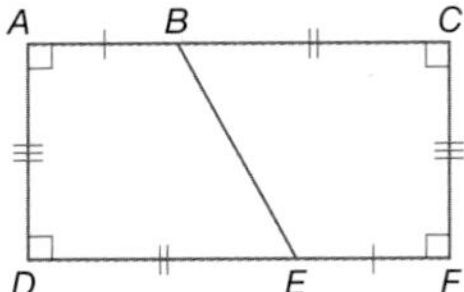

43. WRITING IN MATH Determine whether the following statement is *always, sometimes,* or *never* true. Explain your reasoning. **See margin.**

Equilateral triangles are congruent.

40. True; Sample answer: Using the Third Angles Theorem, the third pair of angles is also congruent and all corresponding sides are congruent, so since CPCTC, the triangles are congruent.

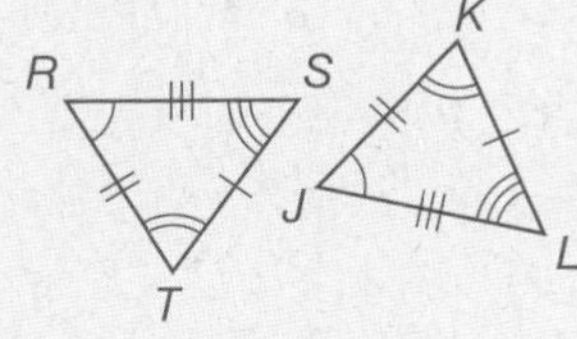

41. False; $\angle A \cong \angle X$, $\angle B \cong \angle Y$, $\angle C \cong \angle Z$, but corresponding sides are not congruent.

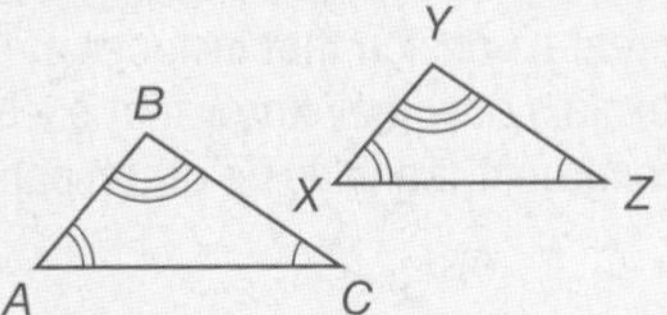

262 | Lesson 4-3 | Congruent Triangles

Standardized Test Practice

44. Barrington cut four congruent triangles off the corners of a rectangle to make an octagon as shown below. What is the area of the octagon? B

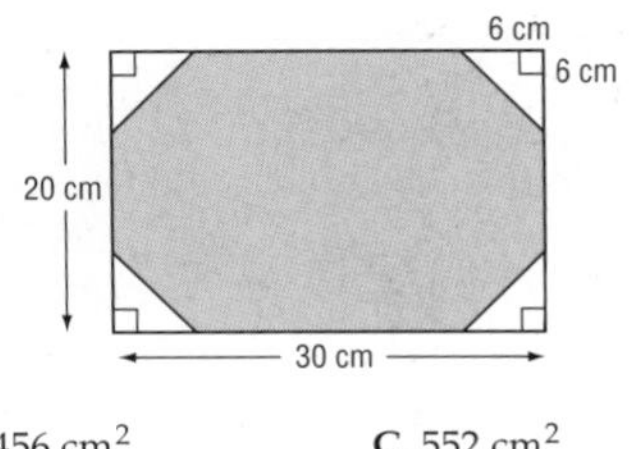

A 456 cm^2 C 552 cm^2
B 528 cm^2 D 564 cm^2

45. GRIDDED RESPONSE Triangle ABC is congruent to $\triangle HIJ$. The vertices of $\triangle ABC$ are $A(-1, 2)$, $B(0, 3)$ and $C(2, -2)$. What is the measure of side $\overline{HJ}$? 5

46. ALGEBRA Which is a factor of $x^2 + 19x - 42$? H

F $x + 14$ H $x - 2$
G $x + 2$ J $x - 14$

47. SAT/ACT Mitsu travels a certain distance at 30 miles per hour and returns the same route at 65 miles per hour. What is his average speed in miles per hour for the round trip? C

A 32.5 D 47.5
B 35.0 E 55.3
C 41.0

Spiral Review

Find each measure in the triangle at the right. (Lesson 4-2)

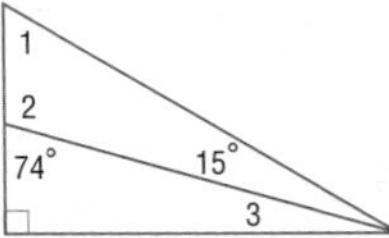

48. $m\angle 2$ 106 **49.** $m\angle 1$ 59 **50.** $m\angle 3$ 16

COORDINATE GEOMETRY Find the measures of the sides of $\triangle JKL$ and classify each triangle by the measures of its sides. (Lesson 4-1) **51–54. See margin.**

51. $J(-7, 10)$, $K(15, 0)$, $L(-2, -1)$ **52.** $J(9, 9)$, $K(12, 14)$, $L(14, 6)$

53. $J(4, 6)$, $K(4, 11)$, $L(9, 6)$ **54.** $J(16, 14)$, $K(7, 6)$, $L(-5, -14)$

Determine whether each statement is *always, sometimes,* or *never* true. (Lesson 1-5)

55. Two angles that form a linear pair are supplementary. always

56. If two angles are supplementary, then one of the angles is obtuse. sometimes

57. CARPENTRY A carpenter must cut two pieces of wood at angles so that they fit together to form the corner of a picture frame. What type of angles must he use to make sure that a 90° corner results? (Lesson 1-5) complementary angles

Skills Review

58. Copy and complete the proof.

Given: $\overline{MN} \cong \overline{PQ}$, $\overline{PQ} \cong \overline{RS}$
Prove: $\overline{MN} \cong \overline{RS}$
Proof:

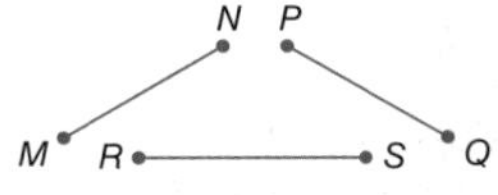

Statements	Reasons
a. ___?___ $\overline{MN} \cong \overline{PQ}$, $\overline{PQ} \cong \overline{RS}$	a. Given
b. $MN = PQ$, $PQ = RS$	b. ___?___ Def. $\cong$ segments
c. ___?___ $MN = RS$	c. ___?___ Transitive Prop. (=)
d. $\overline{MN} \cong \overline{RS}$	d. Definition of congruent segments

CCSS Teaching the Mathematical Practices

Arguments Mathematically proficient students can recognize and use counterexamples. In Exercises 40–41, encourage students to draw a figure that matches the description in each exercise.

4 Assess

Crystal Ball Have students predict how identifying corresponding congruent parts of a triangle will help them prove that the triangles are congruent. As the students leave the room, have them turn in their responses.

Additional Answers

42.

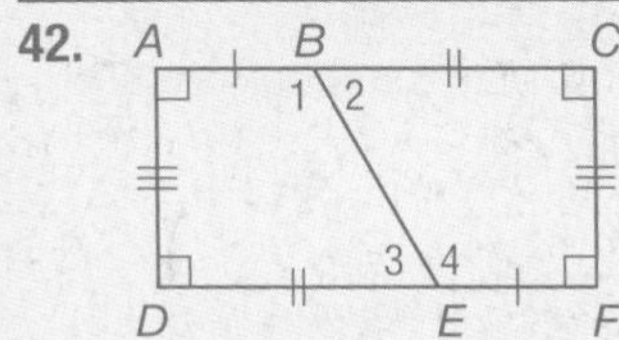

We know that $\overline{AB} \cong \overline{FE}$, $\overline{ED} \cong \overline{BC}$, and $\overline{AD} \cong \overline{FC}$. By the reflexive property, $\overline{BE} \cong \overline{EB}$. $\angle A \cong F$ and $\angle D \cong \angle C$ since all right angles are congruent. Since $\overline{AC}$ and $\overline{DF}$ are both perpendicular to $\overline{CF}$, $\overline{AC} \parallel \overline{DF}$ (Theorem 3.8). $\angle 1 \cong \angle 4$ and $\angle 2 \cong \angle 3$ because alternate interior angles are congruent to each other. Since all corresponding parts are congruent, polygon $ABED \cong$ polygon $FEBC$.

43. Sometimes; Equilateral triangles will be congruent if one pair of corresponding sides are congruent.

51. $JK = 2\sqrt{146}$, $KL = \sqrt{290}$, $JL = \sqrt{146}$; scalene

52. $JK = \sqrt{34}$, $KL = 2\sqrt{17}$, $JL = \sqrt{34}$; isosceles

53. $JK = 5$, $KL = 5\sqrt{2}$, $JL = 5$; isosceles

54. $JK = \sqrt{145}$, $KL = 4\sqrt{34}$, $JL = 35$; scalene

1 Focus

Vertical Alignment

Before Lesson 4-4 Prove triangles congruent using the definition of congruence.

Lesson 4-4 Use the SSS and SAS Postulates to test for triangle congruence.

After Lesson 4-4 Formulate and test conjectures about the properties and attributes of polygons.

2 Teach

Scaffolding Questions

Have students read the **Why?** section of the lesson.

Ask:

- How might the board be affected if the side arms are not the same distance from the top of the board? The board might wobble.
- What must be true if $\triangle ABC \cong \triangle XYZ$? All three corresponding sides and angles must be congruent.
- How is the congruence of the triangles discussed affected if the side arms are not positioned the same distance from the top of the board? The triangles formed will not be congruent.

LESSON 4-4 Proving Triangles Congruent–SSS, SAS

Then

- You proved triangles congruent using the definition of congruence.

Now

1. Use the SSS Postulate to test for triangle congruence.
2. Use the SAS Postulate to test for triangle congruence.

Why?

- An A-frame sandwich board is a convenient way to display information. Not only does it fold flat for easy storage, but with each sidearm locked into place, the frame is extremely sturdy. With the sidearms the same length and positioned the same distance from the top on either side, the open frame forms two congruent triangles.

New Vocabulary
included angle

Common Core State Standards

Content Standards
G.CO.10 Prove theorems about triangles.
G.SRT.5 Use congruence and similarity criteria for triangles to solve problems and to prove relationships in geometric figures.

Mathematical Practices
3 Construct viable arguments and critique the reasoning of others.
1 Make sense of problems and persevere in solving them.

1 SSS Postulate In Lesson 4-3, you proved that two triangles were congruent by showing that all six pairs of corresponding parts were congruent. It is possible to prove two triangles congruent using fewer pairs.

The sandwich board demonstrates that if two triangles have the same three side lengths, then they are congruent. This is expressed in the postulate below.

Postulate 4.1 Side-Side-Side (SSS) Congruence

If three sides of one triangle are congruent to three sides of a second triangle, then the triangles are congruent.

Example If Side $\overline{AB} \cong \overline{DE}$,
Side $\overline{BC} \cong \overline{EF}$, and
Side $\overline{AC} \cong \overline{DF}$,
then $\triangle ABC \cong \triangle DEF$.

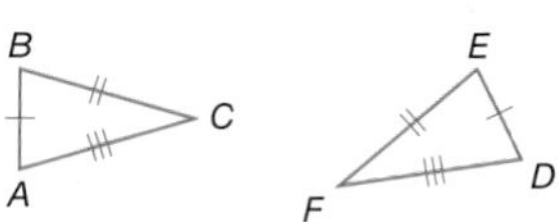

Example 1 Use SSS to Prove Triangles Congruent

Write a flow proof.

Given: $\overline{GH} \cong \overline{KJ}$, $\overline{HL} \cong \overline{JL}$, and L is the midpoint of $\overline{GK}$.

Prove: $\triangle GHL \cong \triangle KJL$

H J G L K

Flow Proof:

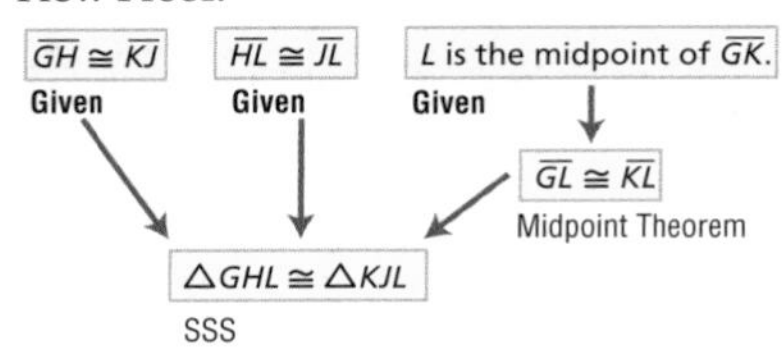

Guided Practice

1. Write a flow proof. See Ch. 4 Answer Appendix.

Given: $\triangle QRS$ is isosceles with $\overline{QR} \cong \overline{SR}$. $\overline{RT}$ bisects $\overline{QS}$ at point T.

Prove: $\triangle QRT \cong \triangle SRT$

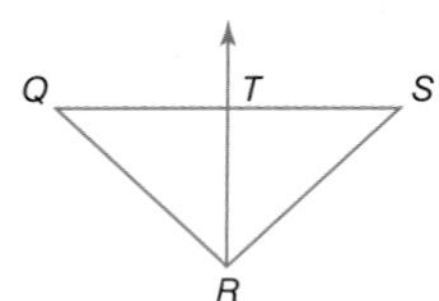

264 | Lesson 4-4

Lesson 4-4 Resources

Resource	Approaching Level AL	On Level OL	Beyond Level BL	English Learners ELL
Teacher Edition		▪ Differentiated Instruction, pp. 265, 272	▪ Differentiated Instruction, pp. 265, 272	
Chapter Resource Masters	▪ Study Guide and Intervention, pp. 25–26 ▪ Skills Practice, p. 27 ▪ Practice, p. 28 ▪ Word Problem Practice, p. 29	▪ Study Guide and Intervention, pp. 25–26 ▪ Skills Practice, p. 27 ▪ Practice, p. 28 ▪ Word Problem Practice, p. 29 ▪ Enrichment, p. 30	▪ Practice, p. 28 ▪ Word Problem Practice, p. 29 ▪ Enrichment, p. 30	▪ Study Guide and Intervention, pp. 25–26 ▪ Skills Practice, p. 27 ▪ Practice, p. 28 ▪ Word Problem Practice, p. 29
Other	▪ 5-Minute Check 4-4 ▪ Study Notebook ▪ Teaching Geometry with Manipulatives	▪ 5-Minute Check 4-4 ▪ Study Notebook ▪ Teaching Geometry with Manipulatives	▪ 5-Minute Check 4-4 ▪ Study Notebook	▪ 5-Minute Check 4-4 ▪ Study Notebook ▪ Teaching Geometry with Manipulatives

Standardized Test Example 2 SSS on the Coordinate Plane

EXTENDED RESPONSE **Triangle *ABC* has vertices *A*(1, 1), *B*(0, 3), and *C*(2, 5). Triangle *EFG* has vertices *E*(1, −1), *F*(2, −5), and *G*(4, −4).**

a. **Graph both triangles on the same coordinate plane.**

b. **Use your graph to make a conjecture as to whether the triangles are congruent. Explain your reasoning.**

c. **Write a logical argument using coordinate geometry to support the conjecture you made in part b.**

Read the Test Item

You are asked to do three things in this problem. In part **a**, you are to graph $\triangle ABC$ and $\triangle EFG$ on the same coordinate plane. In part **b**, you should make a conjecture that $\triangle ABC \cong \triangle EFG$ or $\triangle ABC \ncong \triangle EFG$ based on your graph. Finally, in part **c**, you are asked to prove your conjecture.

Test-TakingTip

CSS Tools When you are solving problems using the coordinate plane, remember to use tools like the Distance, Midpoint, and Slope Formulas to solve problems and to check your solutions.

Solve the Test Item

a. y, C, B, A, O, E, x, G, F

b. From the graph, it appears that the triangles do not have the same shape, so we can conjecture that they are not congruent.

c. Use the Distance Formula to show that not all corresponding sides have the same measure.

$AB = \sqrt{(0-1)^2 + (3-1)^2} = \sqrt{1+4}$ or $\sqrt{5}$

$EF = \sqrt{(2-1)^2 + [-5-(-1)]^2} = \sqrt{1+16}$ or $\sqrt{17}$

$BC = \sqrt{(2-0)^2 + (5-3)^2} = \sqrt{4+4}$ or $\sqrt{8}$

$FG = \sqrt{(4-2)^2 + [-4-(-5)]^2} = \sqrt{4+1}$ or $\sqrt{5}$

$AC = \sqrt{(2-1)^2 + (5-1)^2} = \sqrt{1+16}$ or $\sqrt{17}$

$EG = \sqrt{(4-1)^2 + [-4-(-1)]^2} = \sqrt{9+9}$ or $\sqrt{18}$

While $AB = FG$ and $AC = EF$, $BC \neq EG$. Since SSS congruence is not met, $\triangle ABC \ncong \triangle EFG$.

ReadingMath

Symbols $\triangle ABC \ncong \triangle EFG$ is read as *triangle ABC is not congruent to triangle EFG.*

GuidedPractice

2. Triangle *JKL* has vertices *J*(2, 5), *K*(1, 1), and *L*(5, 2). Triangle *NPQ* has vertices *N*(−3, 0), *P*(−7, 1), and *Q*(−4, 4). **2a–c. See Ch. 4 Answer Appendix.**

a. Graph both triangles on the same coordinate plane.

b. Use your graph to make a conjecture as to whether the triangles are congruent. Explain your reasoning.

c. Write a logical argument using coordinate geometry to support the conjecture you made in part **b**.

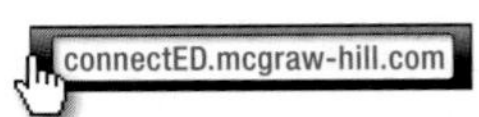

1 SSS Postulate

Examples 1 and 2 show how to prove two triangles are congruent by using Postulate 4.1.

Formative Assessment

Use the Guided Practice exercises after each example to determine students' understanding of concepts.

Additional Example

1 Write a flow proof.

Given: $\overline{QU} \cong \overline{AD}$, $\overline{QD} \cong \overline{AU}$

Prove: $\triangle QUD \cong \triangle ADU$

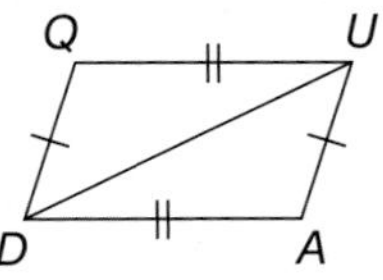

Flow Proof:

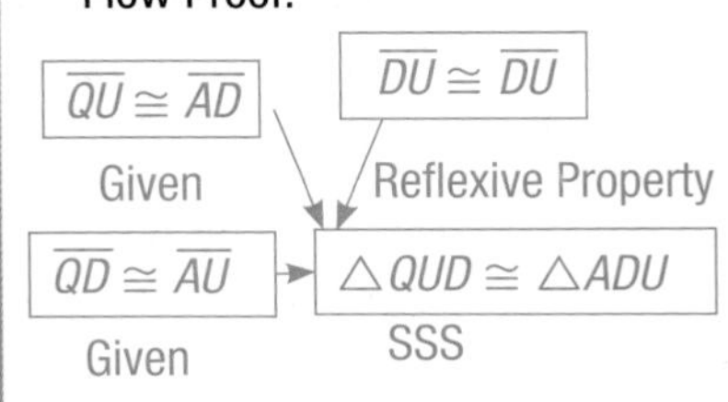

Additional Examples also in Interactive Classroom PowerPoint® Presentations

IWB Interactive White Board READY

CCSS Teaching the Mathematical Practices

Tools Mathematically proficient students consider available tools when solving a problem. Encourage students to continually review their notes to keep definitions, theorems, and postulates in the forefront of their minds.

DifferentiatedInstruction OL BL

Logical/Mathematical Learners Students can use a systematic approach to write the proofs for problems and examples in this lesson. Have students start by looking for possible methods of proof using SSS or SAS. They should examine the problem to determine how much necessary information is given and how they can find any other information that they need for the proof. Finally, they can draw on prior knowledge of midpoints, distances, angle relationships, and so on, to extract any other necessary information and compile the facts for the final proof.

Additional Example

2 EXTENDED RESPONSE Triangle *DVW* has vertices $D(-5, -1)$, $V(-1, -2)$, and $W(-7, -4)$. Triangle *LPM* has vertices $L(1, -5)$, $P(2, -1)$, and $M(4, -7)$.

a. Graph both triangles on the same coordinate plane.

b. Use your graph to make a conjecture as to whether the triangles are congruent. Explain your reasoning.

c. Write a logical argument that uses coordinate geometry to support the conjecture you made in part **b**.

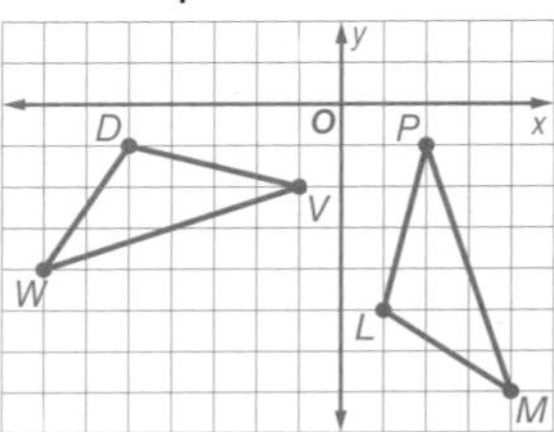

$WD = ML$, $DV = LP$, and $VW = PM$. By definition of congruent segments, all corresponding segments are congruent. Therefore, $\triangle WDV \cong \triangle MLP$ by SSS.

Focus on Mathematical Content

Naming Triangles Explain to students that when listing congruent triangles, it is important to list triangle congruence in the same order as their corresponding congruent parts. If $\triangle PKR \cong \triangle JKL$ uses appropriate order to indicate the corresponding sides and angles that are congruent in the two triangles, it would be incorrect to write $\triangle PRK \cong \triangle JKL$.

WatchOut!

Include the Angle The SAS Postulate can only be used when the angle is between two adjacent sides.

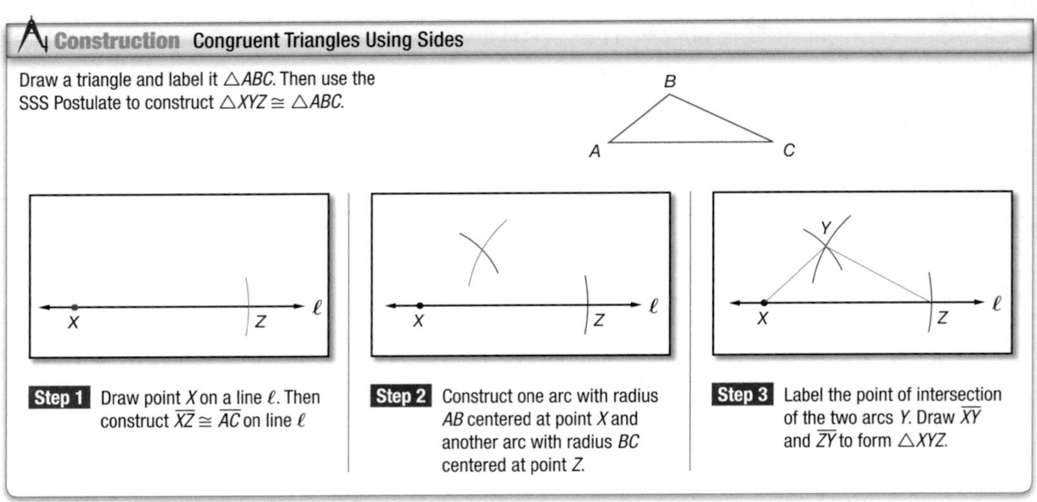

Construction Congruent Triangles Using Sides

Draw a triangle and label it $\triangle ABC$. Then use the SSS Postulate to construct $\triangle XYZ \cong \triangle ABC$.

Step 1 Draw point *X* on a line ℓ. Then construct $\overline{XZ} \cong \overline{AC}$ on line ℓ.

Step 2 Construct one arc with radius *AB* centered at point *X* and another arc with radius *BC* centered at point *Z*.

Step 3 Label the point of intersection of the two arcs *Y*. Draw $\overline{XY}$ and $\overline{ZY}$ to form $\triangle XYZ$.

2 SAS Postulate The angle formed by two adjacent sides of a polygon is called an **included angle**. Consider included angle *JKL* formed by the hands on the first clock shown below. Any time the hands form an angle with the same measure, the distance between the ends of the hands $\overline{JL}$ and $\overline{PR}$ will be the same.

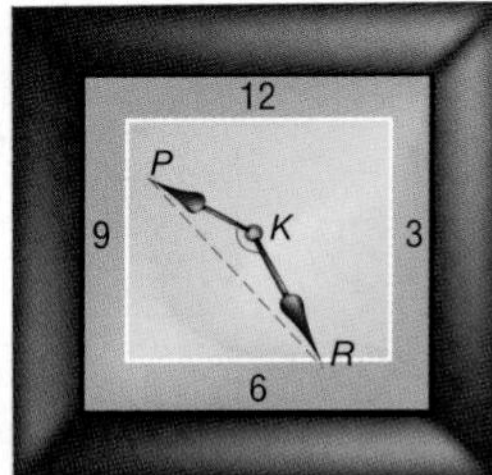

$\triangle PKR \cong \triangle JKL$

Any two triangles formed using the same side lengths and included angle measure will be congruent. This illustrates the following postulate.

StudyTip

Side-Side-Angle The measures of two sides and a nonincluded angle are not sufficient to prove two triangles congruent.

Postulate 4.2 Side-Angle-Side (SAS) Congruence

Words If two sides and the included angle of one triangle are congruent to two sides and the included angle of a second triangle, then the triangles are congruent.

Example If Side $\overline{AB} \cong \overline{DE}$,
Angle $\angle B \cong \angle E$, and
Side $\overline{BC} \cong \overline{EF}$,
then $\triangle ABC \cong \triangle DEF$.

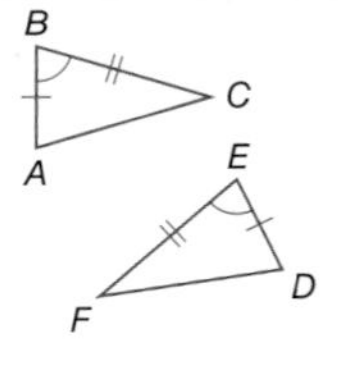

Real-WorldCareer

Lighting Technicians In the motion picture industry, gaffers, or lighting technicians, place the lighting required for a film. Gaffers make sure the angles the lights form are in the correct positions. They may have college or technical school degrees, or they may have completed a formal training program.

Real-World Example 3 Use SAS to Prove Triangles are Congruent

LIGHTING The scaffolding for stage lighting shown appears to be made up of congruent triangles. If $\overline{WX} \cong \overline{YZ}$ and $\overline{WX} \parallel \overline{ZY}$, write a two-column proof to prove that $\triangle WXZ \cong \triangle YZX$.

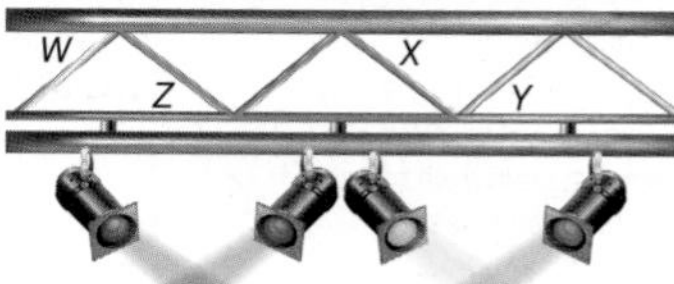

Proof:

Statements	Reasons
1. $\overline{WX} \cong \overline{YZ}$	1. Given
2. $\overline{WX} \parallel \overline{ZY}$	2. Given
3. $\angle WXZ \cong \angle XZY$	3. Alternate Interior Angle Theorem
4. $\overline{XZ} \cong \overline{ZX}$	4. Reflexive Property of Congruence
5. $\triangle WXZ \cong \triangle YZX$	5. SAS

GuidedPractice

3. **EXTREME SPORTS** The wings of the hang glider shown appear to be congruent triangles. If $\overline{FG} \cong \overline{GH}$ and $\overline{JG}$ bisects $\angle FGH$, prove that $\triangle FGJ \cong \triangle HGJ$. **See margin.**

You can also construct congruent triangles given two sides and the included angle.

Construction Congruent Triangles Using Two Sides and the Included Angle

Draw a triangle and label it $\triangle ABC$. Then use the SAS Postulate to construct $\triangle RST \cong \triangle ABC$.

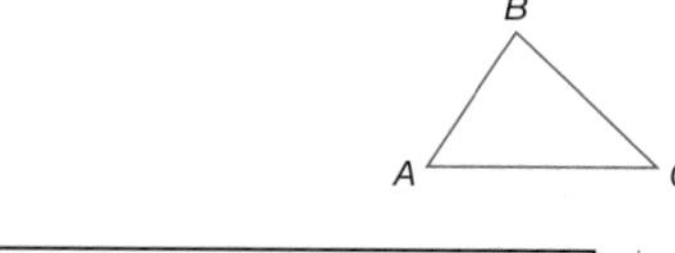

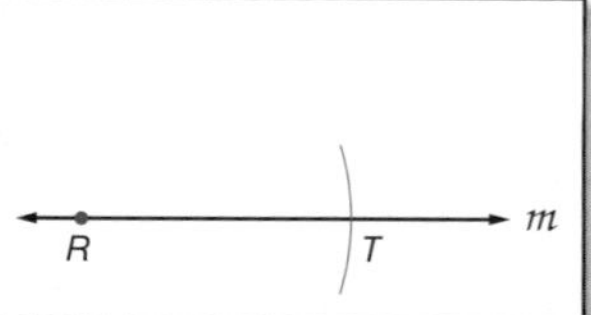

Step 1 Draw point R on a line m. Then construct $\overline{RT} \cong \overline{AC}$ on line m.

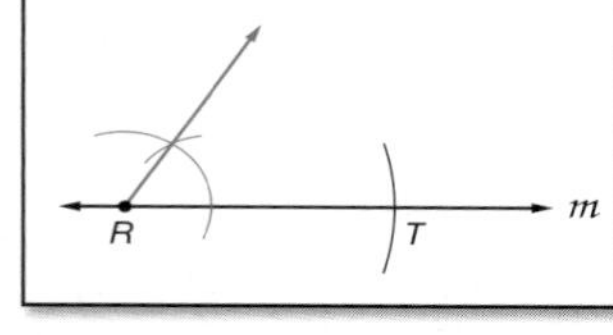

Step 2 Construct $\angle R \cong \angle A$ using $\overline{RT}$ as a side of the angle and point R.

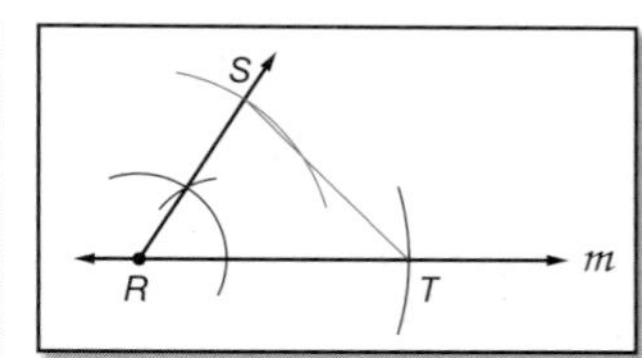

Step 3 Construct $\overline{RS} \cong \overline{AB}$. Then draw $\overline{ST}$ to form $\triangle RST$.

2 SAS Postulate

Examples 3 and 4 show how to prove that triangles are congruent when two sides and the included angle of one triangle are congruent to two sides and the included angle of another triangle.

Additional Example

3 **ENTOMOLOGY** The wings of one type of moth form two triangles. Write a two-column proof to prove that $\triangle FEG \cong \triangle HIG$ if $\overline{EI} \cong \overline{FH}$, and G is the midpoint of both $\overline{EI}$ and $\overline{FH}$.

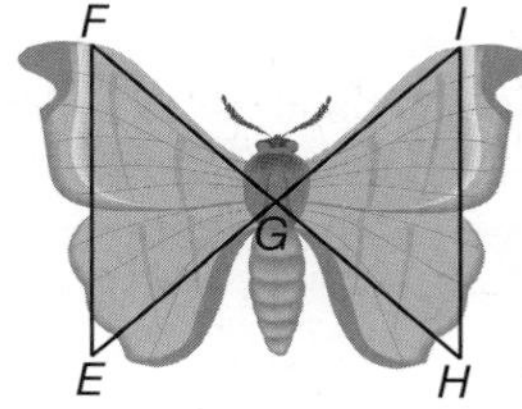

Statements (Reasons)

1. $\overline{EI} \cong \overline{FH}$; G is the midpoint of $\overline{EI}$; G is the midpoint of $\overline{FH}$. (Given)
2. $\overline{FG} \cong \overline{HG}$; $\overline{EG} \cong \overline{IG}$ (Midpoint Theorem)
3. $\angle FGE \cong \angle HGI$ (Vertical Angles Theorem)
4. $\triangle FEG \cong \triangle HIG$ (SAS)

Additional Answer (Guided Practice)

3. **Given:** $\overline{FG} \cong \overline{GH}$; $\overline{JG}$ bisects $\angle FGH$.
Prove: $\triangle FGJ \cong \triangle HGJ$

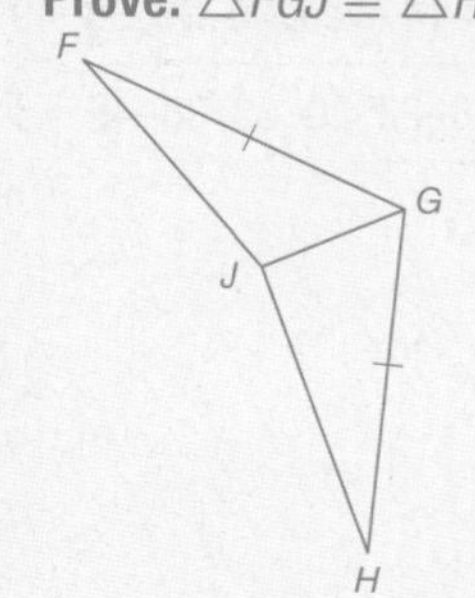

Proof:

Statements (Reasons)

1. $\overline{FG} \cong \overline{GH}$, $\overline{JG}$ bisects $\angle FGH$. (Given)
2. $\angle FGJ \cong \angle HGJ$ (Def. of $\angle$ bisector)
3. $\overline{GJ} \cong \overline{GJ}$ (Reflex. Prop. $\cong$)
4. $\triangle FGJ \cong \triangle HGJ$ (SAS)

Additional Example

4 Write a paragraph proof.

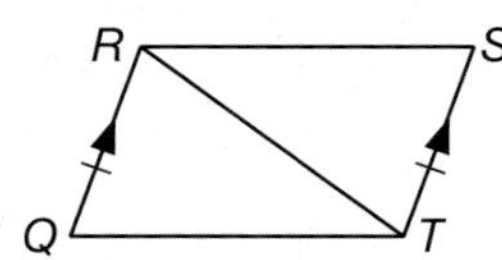

Given: $\overline{RQ} \parallel \overline{TS}$

$\overline{RQ} \cong \overline{TS}$

Prove: $\angle Q \cong \angle S$

Because $\overline{RQ} \parallel \overline{TS}$, alternate interior angles $\angle QRT$ and $\angle STR$, are congruent. That is, $\angle QRT \cong \angle STR$. $\overline{RQ} \cong \overline{TS}$ and $\overline{RT} \cong \overline{RT}$ by the Reflexive Property. Therefore, $\triangle QRT \cong \triangle STR$ by SAS. By CPCTC, $\angle Q \cong \angle S$.

3 Practice

Formative Assessment

Use Exercises 1–4 to check for understanding.

Use the chart at the bottom of this page to customize assignments for your students.

Additional Answer (Guided Practice)

4. Write a two-column proof.

Given: $\overline{MN} \cong \overline{PN}$, $\overline{LM} \cong \overline{LP}$

Prove: $\angle LNM \cong \angle LNP$

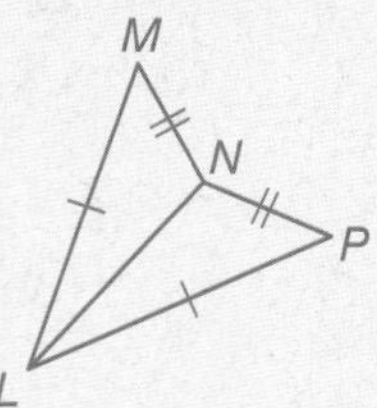

Statements (Reasons)

1. $\overline{MN} \cong \overline{PN}$, $\overline{LM} \cong \overline{LP}$ (Given)
2. $\overline{LN} \cong \overline{LN}$ (Refl. Prop. of Congruence)
3. $\triangle LNM \cong \triangle LNP$ (SSS)
4. $\angle LNM \cong \angle LNP$ (CPCTC)

StudyTip

Overlapping Figures When triangles overlap, it can be helpful to draw each triangle separately and label the congruent parts. In Example 4, the figure could have been separated as shown.

Example 4 Use SAS or SSS in Proofs

Write a paragraph proof.

Given: $\overline{BC} \cong \overline{DC}$, $\angle BCF \cong \angle DCE$, $\overline{FC} \cong \overline{EC}$

Prove: $\angle CFD \cong \angle CEB$

Proof:

Since $\overline{BC} \cong \overline{DC}$, $\angle BCF \cong \angle DCE$, and $\overline{FC} \cong \overline{EC}$, then $\triangle BCF \cong \triangle DCE$ by SAS. By CPCTC, $\angle CFB \cong \angle CED$. $\angle CFD$ forms a linear pair with $\angle CFB$, and $\angle CEB$ forms a linear pair with $\angle CED$. By the Congruent Supplements Theorem, $\angle CFD$ is supplementary to $\angle CFB$ and $\angle CEB$ is supplementary to $\angle CED$. Since angles supplementary to the same angle or congruent angles are congruent, $\angle CFD \cong \angle CEB$.

GuidedPractice

4. Write a two-column proof. See margin.

Given: $\overline{MN} \cong \overline{PN}$, $\overline{LM} \cong \overline{LP}$

Prove: $\angle LNM \cong \angle LNP$

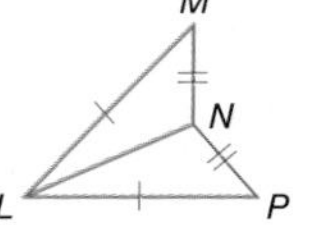

Check Your Understanding

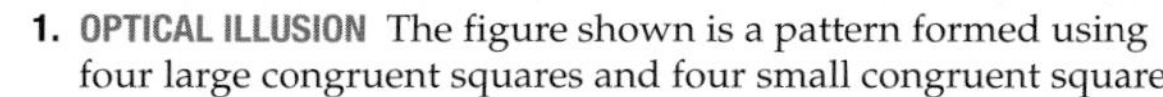

= Step-by-Step Solutions begin on page R14.

Example 1

1. **OPTICAL ILLUSION** The figure shown is a pattern formed using four large congruent squares and four small congruent squares.
   a. How many different-sized triangles are used to create the illusion? two
   b. Use the Side-Side-Side Congruence Postulate to prove that $\triangle ABC \cong \triangle CDA$. See Ch. 4 Answer Appendix.
   c. What is the relationship between $\overleftrightarrow{AB}$ and $\overleftrightarrow{CD}$? Explain your reasoning. See Ch. 4 Answer Appendix.

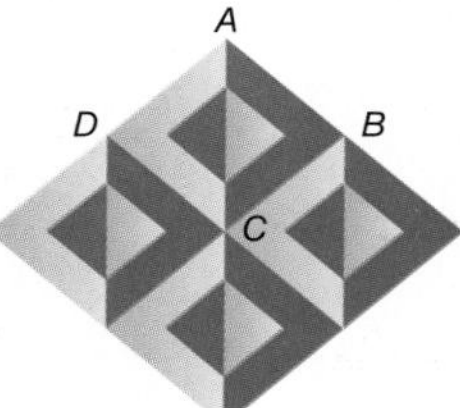

Example 2

2. **EXTENDED RESPONSE** Triangle ABC has vertices $A(-3, -5)$, $B(-1, -1)$, and $C(-1, -5)$. Triangle XYZ has vertices $X(5, -5)$, $Y(3, -1)$, and $Z(3, -5)$. **a–c.** See Ch. 4 Answer Appendix.
   a. Graph both triangles on the same coordinate plane.
   b. Use your graph to make a conjecture as to whether the triangles are congruent. Explain your reasoning.
   c. Write a logical argument using coordinate geometry to support your conjecture.

Example 3

3. **EXERCISE** In the exercise diagram, if $\overline{LP} \cong \overline{NO}$, $\angle LPM \cong \angle NOM$, and $\triangle MOP$ is equilateral, write a paragraph proof to show that $\triangle LMP \cong \triangle NMO$. See Ch. 4 Answer Appendix.

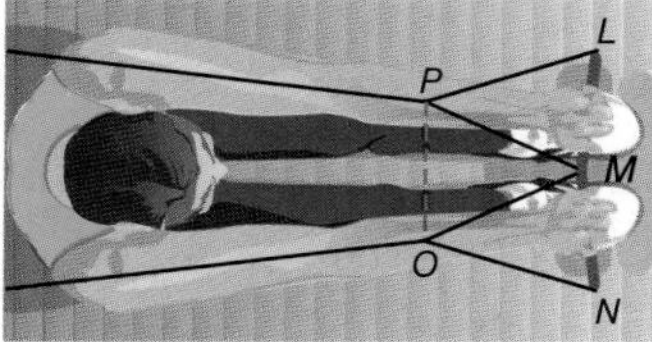

Differentiated Homework Options

Level	Assignment	Two-Day Option	
AL Basic	5–15, 30–49	5–15 odd, 34–37	6–14 even, 30–33, 38–49
OL Core	5–27 odd, 30–49	5–15, 34–37	16–28, 30–33, 38–49
BL Advanced	16–45, (optional: 46–49)		

Example 4 **4. Write a two-column proof.** See margin.

Given: $\overline{BA} \cong \overline{DC}$, $\angle BAC \cong \angle DCA$
Prove: $\overline{BC} \cong \overline{DA}$

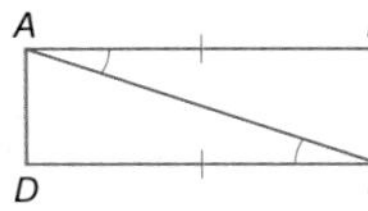

Practice and Problem Solving

Extra Practice is on page R4.

Example 1 **PROOF Write the specified type of proof.** 5–6. See margin.

5. paragraph proof

Given: $\overline{QR} \cong \overline{SR}$, $\overline{ST} \cong \overline{QT}$
Prove: $\triangle QRT \cong \triangle SRT$

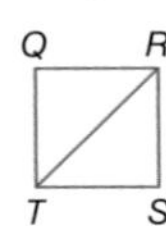

6. two-column proof

Given: $\overline{AB} \cong \overline{ED}$, $\overline{CA} \cong \overline{CE}$; $\overline{AC}$ bisects $\overline{BD}$.
Prove: $\triangle ABC \cong \triangle EDC$

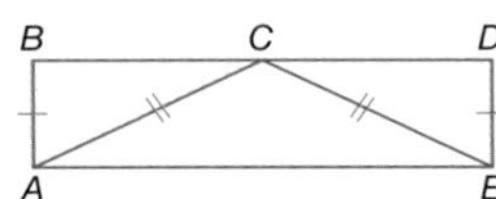

7. BRIDGES The Sunshine Skyway Bridge in Florida is the world's longest cable-stayed bridge, spanning 4.1 miles of Tampa Bay. It is supported using steel cables suspended from two concrete supports. If the supports are the same height above the roadway and perpendicular to the roadway, and the topmost cables meet at a point midway between the supports, prove that the two triangles shown in the photo are congruent. See margin.

Example 2 **CCSS SENSE-MAKING Determine whether $\triangle MNO \cong \triangle QRS$. Explain.** 8–11. See margin.

8. $M(2, 5)$, $N(5, 2)$, $O(1, 1)$, $Q(-4, 4)$, $R(-7, 1)$, $S(-3, 0)$

9. $M(0, -1)$, $N(-1, -4)$, $O(-4, -3)$, $Q(3, -3)$, $R(4, -4)$, $S(3, 3)$

10. $M(0, -3)$, $N(1, 4)$, $O(3, 1)$, $Q(4, -1)$, $R(6, 1)$, $S(9, -1)$

11. $M(4, 7)$, $N(5, 4)$, $O(2, 3)$, $Q(2, 5)$, $R(3, 2)$, $S(0, 1)$

Example 3 **PROOF Write the specified type of proof.** 12–13. See Ch. 4 Answer Appendix.

12. two-column proof

Given: $\overline{BD} \perp \overline{AC}$, $\overline{BD}$ bisects $\overline{AC}$.
Prove: $\triangle ABD \cong \triangle CBD$

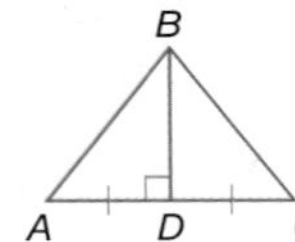

13. paragraph proof

Given: R is the midpoint of $\overline{QS}$ and $\overline{PT}$.
Prove: $\triangle PRQ \cong \triangle TRS$

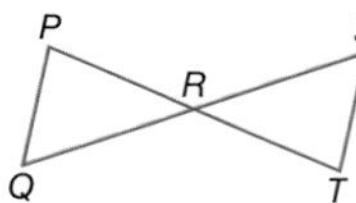

Additional Answers

4. Proof:

Statements (Reasons)

1. $\overline{BA} \cong \overline{DC}$, $\angle BAC \cong \angle DCA$ (Given)
2. $\overline{AC} \cong \overline{CA}$ (Reflex. Prop. $\cong$)
3. $\triangle BCA \cong \triangle DAC$ (SAS)
4. $\overline{BC} \cong \overline{DA}$ (CPCTC)

5. Proof: We know that $\overline{QR} \cong \overline{SR}$ and $\overline{ST} \cong \overline{QT}$. $\overline{RT} \cong \overline{RT}$ by the Reflexive Property. Since $\overline{QR} \cong \overline{SR}$, $\overline{ST} \cong \overline{QT}$, and $\overline{RT} \cong \overline{RT}$, $\triangle QRT \cong \triangle SRT$ by SSS.

6. Proof:

Statements (Reasons)

1. $\overline{AB} \cong \overline{ED}$, $\overline{CA} \cong \overline{CE}$, and $\overline{AC}$ bisects $\overline{BD}$ (Given)
2. C is the midpoint of $\overline{BD}$ (Def. of Segment Bisectors)
3. $\overline{BC} \cong \overline{CD}$ (Midpoint Thm.)
4. $\triangle ABC \cong \triangle EDC$ (SSS)

7. Given: $\overline{AB} \cong \overline{ED}$, $\angle ABC$ and $\angle EDC$ are right angles, and C is the midpoint of $\overline{BD}$.

Prove: $\triangle ABC \cong \triangle EDC$

Proof:

Statements (Reasons)

1. $\overline{AB} \cong \overline{ED}$, $\angle ABC$ and $\angle EDC$ are right angles, and C is the midpoint of $\overline{BD}$. (Given)
2. $\angle ABC \cong \angle EDC$ (All rt. $\angle$s $\cong$)
3. $\overline{BC} \cong \overline{DC}$ (Midpoint Thm.)
4. $\triangle ABC \cong \triangle EDC$ (SAS)

8. $MN = \sqrt{18}$, $NO = \sqrt{17}$, $MO = \sqrt{17}$, $QR = \sqrt{18}$, $RS = \sqrt{17}$, and $QS = \sqrt{17}$. Each pair of corresponding sides has the same measure so they are congruent. $\triangle MNO \cong \triangle QRS$ by SSS.

9. $MN = \sqrt{10}$, $NO = \sqrt{10}$, $MO = \sqrt{20}$, $QR = \sqrt{2}$, $RS = \sqrt{50}$, and $QS = 6$. The corresponding sides are not congruent, so the triangles are not congruent.

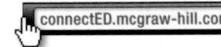

CCSS Teaching the Mathematical Practices

Sense-Making Mathematically proficient students look for entry points into a solution. They plan a solution pathway rather than simply jumping into a solution attempt. In Exercises 8–11, encourage students to make a plan to solve each problem first.

10. $MN = \sqrt{50}$, $NO = \sqrt{13}$, $MO = 5$, $QR = \sqrt{8}$, $RS = \sqrt{13}$, and $QS = 5$. The corresponding sides are not congruent, so the triangles are not congruent.

11. $MN = \sqrt{10}$, $NO = \sqrt{10}$, $MO = \sqrt{20}$, $QR = \sqrt{10}$, $RS = \sqrt{10}$, and $QS = \sqrt{20}$. Each pair of corresponding sides has the same measure, so they are congruent. $\triangle MNO \cong \triangle QRS$ by SSS.

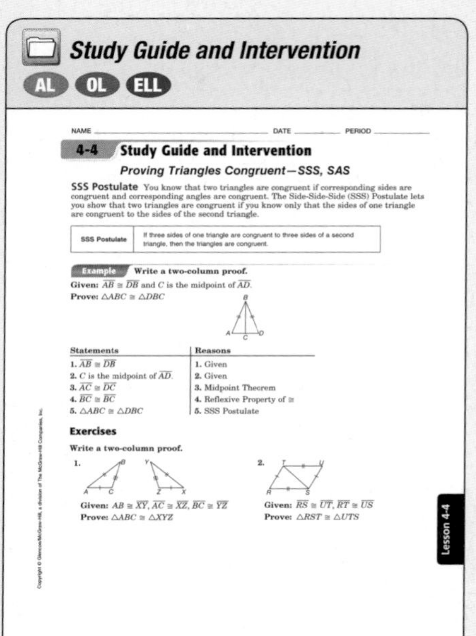

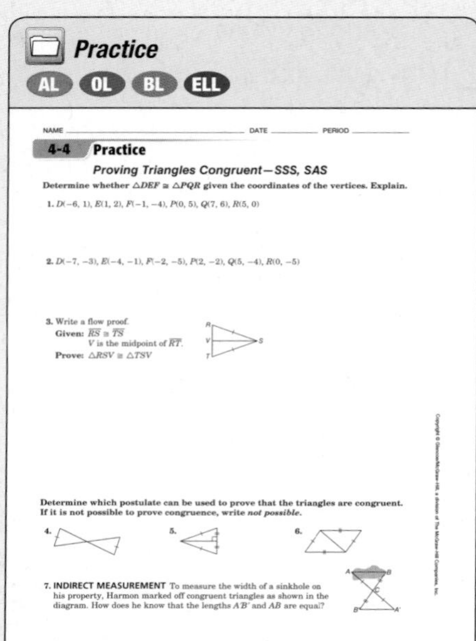

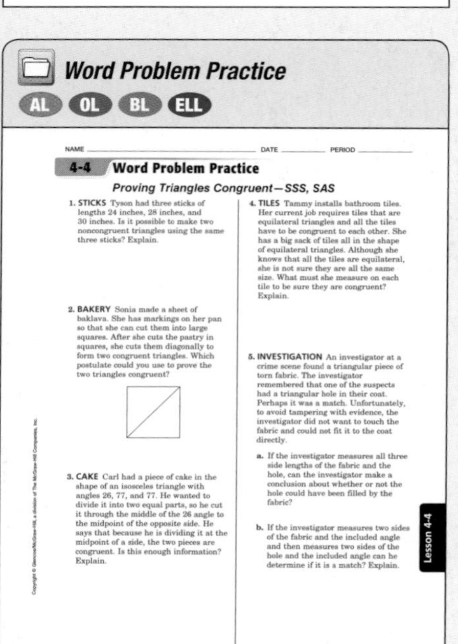

Example 4 **PROOF** **Write the specified type of proof.** **14–15. See Ch. 4 Answer Appendix.**

14. flow proof

Given: $\overline{JM} \cong \overline{NK}$; L is the midpoint of $\overline{JN}$ and $\overline{KM}$.

Prove: $\angle MJL \cong \angle KNL$

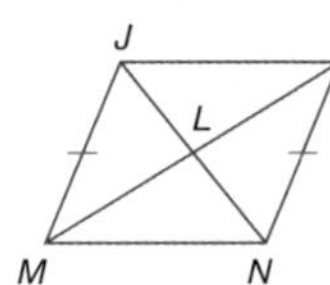

15. paragraph proof

Given: $\triangle XYZ$ is equilateral. $\overline{WY}$ bisects $\angle XYZ$.

Prove: $\overline{XW} \cong \overline{ZW}$

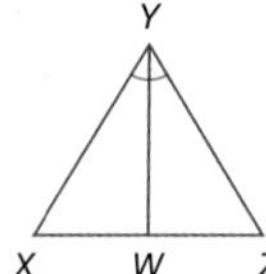

B **CCSS ARGUMENTS** **Determine which postulate can be used to prove that the triangles are congruent. If it is not possible to prove congruence, write *not possible*.**

16. 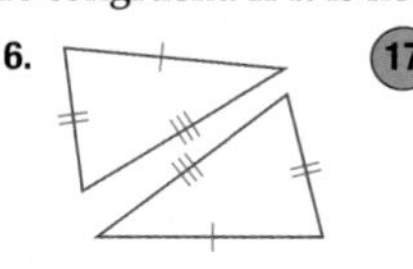 **SSS**

17. 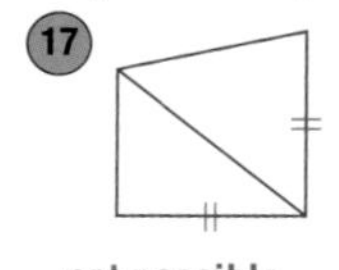 **not possible**

18. 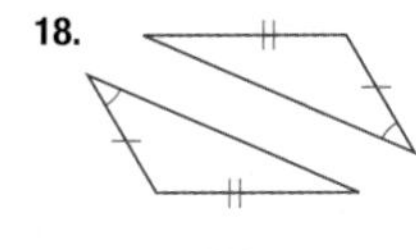 **not possible**

19. 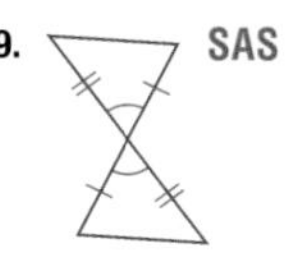 **SAS**

20. SIGNS Refer to the diagram at the right.

a. Identify the three-dimensional figure represented by the wet floor sign. **triangular pyramid**

b. If $\overline{AB} \cong \overline{AD}$ and $\overline{CB} \cong \overline{DC}$, prove that $\triangle ACB \cong \triangle ACD$.

c. Why do the triangles not look congruent in the diagram?

b, c. See Ch. 4 Answer Appendix.

PROOF **Write a flow proof.** **21–22. See Ch. 4 Answer Appendix.**

21. Given: $\overline{MJ} \cong \overline{ML}$; K is the midpoint of $\overline{JL}$.

Prove: $\triangle MJK \cong \triangle MLK$

22. Given: $\triangle TPQ \cong \triangle SPR$; $\angle TQR \cong \angle SRQ$

Prove: $\triangle TQR \cong \triangle SRQ$

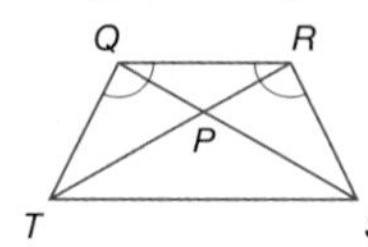

23. SOFTBALL Use the diagram of a fast-pitch softball diamond shown. Let F = first base, S = second base, T = third base, P = pitching point, and R = home plate. **See Ch. 4 Answer Appendix.**

a. Write a two-column proof to prove that the distance from first base to third base is the same as the distance from home plate to second base.

b. Write a two-column proof to prove that the angle formed between second base, home plate, and third base is the same as the angle formed between second base, home plate, and first base.

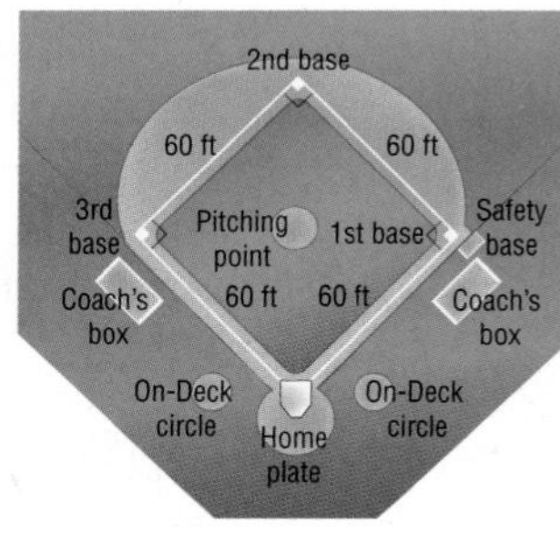

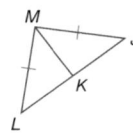

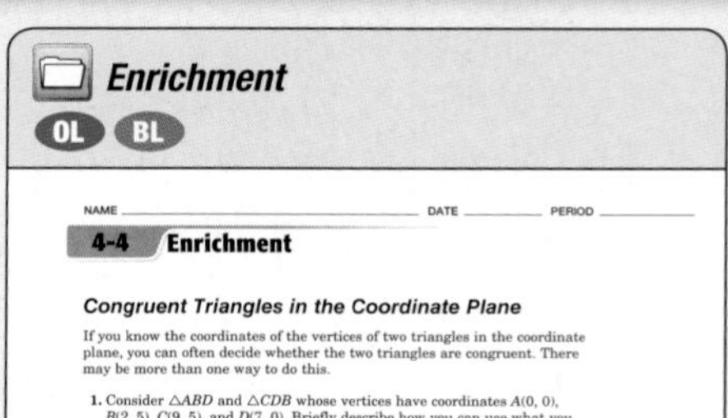

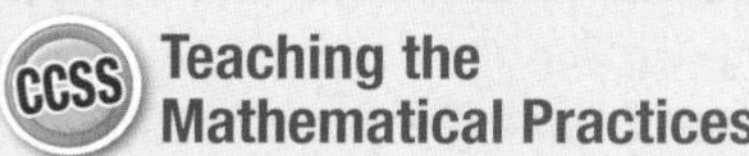

Teaching the Mathematical Practices

Arguments Mathematically proficient students make conjectures and build a logical progression of statements to explore the truth of their conjectures. In Exercises 16–19, encourage students to review the postulates before beginning the exercises.

PROOF Write a two-column proof. **24–25. See margin.**

24. Given: $\overline{YX} \cong \overline{WZ}$, $\overline{YX} \parallel \overline{ZW}$
Prove: $\triangle YXZ \cong \triangle WZX$

25. Given: $\triangle EAB \cong \triangle DCB$
Prove: $\triangle EAD \cong \triangle DCE$

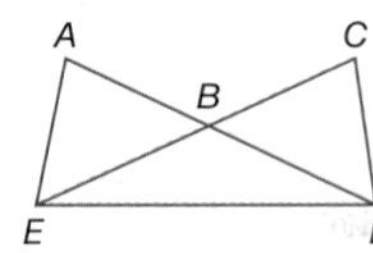

26. **CCSS ARGUMENTS** Write a paragraph proof.
Given: $\overline{HL} \cong \overline{HM}$, $\overline{PM} \cong \overline{KL}$, $\overline{PG} \cong \overline{KJ}$, $\overline{GH} \cong \overline{JH}$
Prove: $\angle G \cong \angle J$ **See Ch. 4 Answer Appendix.**

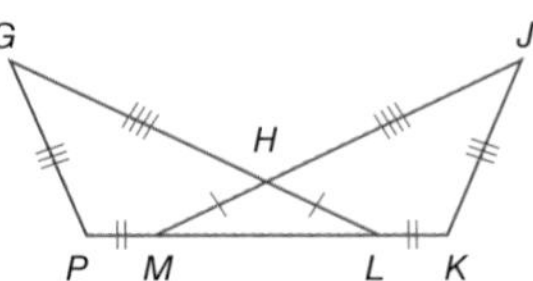

ALGEBRA Find the value of the variable that yields congruent triangles. Explain.

27. $\triangle WXY \cong \triangle WXZ$ **$y = 4$; By CPCTC, $\angle WXZ \cong \angle WXY$, and $\overline{YX} \cong \overline{ZX}$.**

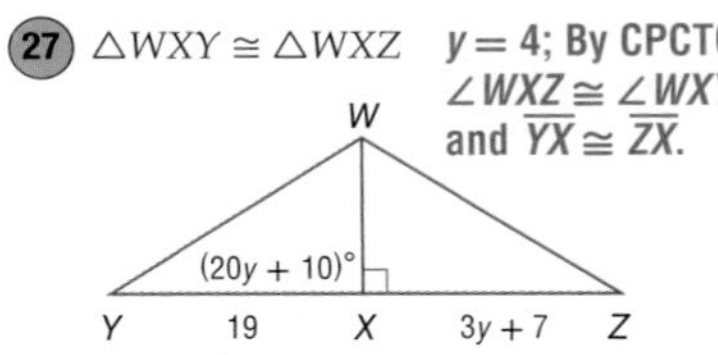

28. $\triangle ABC \cong \triangle FGH$ **$x = 3$; By CPCTC, $\overline{AC} \cong \overline{FH}$, and $\overline{BC} \cong \overline{GH}$.**

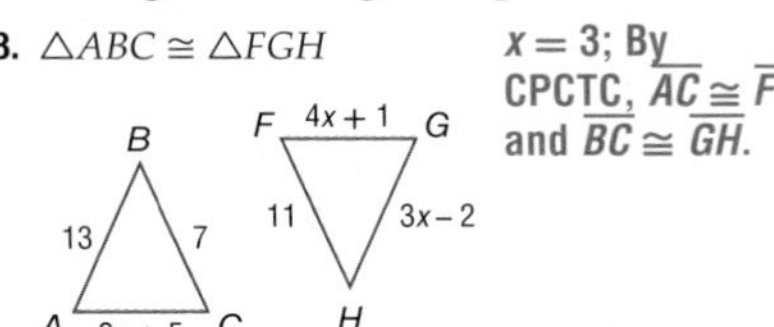

H.O.T. Problems Use Higher-Order Thinking Skills

29. CHALLENGE Refer to the graph shown. **See Ch. 4 Answer Appendix.**

a. Describe two methods you could use to prove that $\triangle WYZ$ is congruent to $\triangle WYX$. You may not use a ruler or a protractor. Which method do you think is more efficient? Explain.

b. Are $\triangle WYZ$ and $\triangle WYX$ congruent? Explain your reasoning.

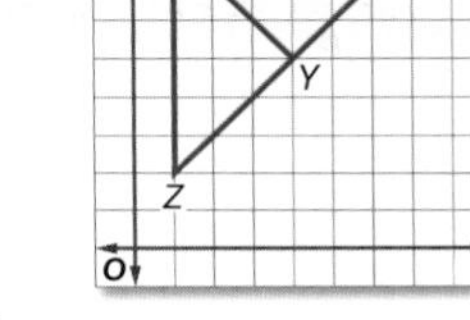

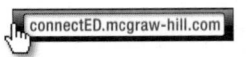

30. REASONING Determine whether the following statement is *true* or *false*. If true, explain your reasoning. If *false*, provide a counterexample.

If the congruent sides in one isosceles triangle have the same measure as the congruent sides in another isosceles triangle, then the triangles are congruent. **See margin.**

31. ERROR ANALYSIS Bonnie says that $\triangle PQR \cong \triangle XYZ$ by SAS. Shada disagrees. She says that there is not enough information to prove that the two triangles are congruent. Is either of them correct? Explain.

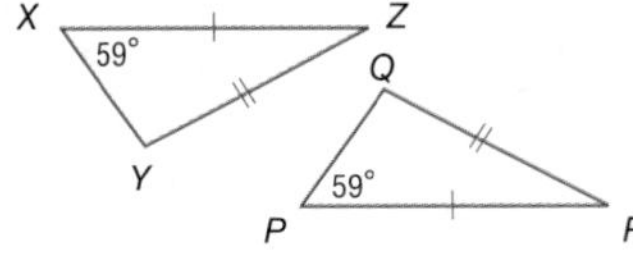

31. Shada; for SAS the angle must be the included angle and here it is not included.

32. OPEN ENDED Use a straightedge to draw obtuse triangle *ABC*. Then construct $\triangle XYZ$ so that it is congruent to $\triangle ABC$ using either SSS or SAS. Justify your construction mathematically and verify it using measurement.

32. Sample answer: Using a ruler I measured all of the sides and they are congruent so the triangles are congruent by SSS.

33. WRITING IN MATH Two pairs of corresponding sides of two right triangles are congruent. Are the triangles congruent? Explain your reasoning. **See Ch. 4 Answer Appendix.**

WatchOut!

Error Analysis In Exercise 31, Shada is correct. Although there are two congruent corresponding sides and one congruent corresponding angle in the triangles shown, the angle marked is not formed by the congruent sides; and therefore, is not the included angle. To apply the SAS Postulate, the angle must be the included angle. There is no additional information given or that can be deduced from the figure, so there is not enough information to determine whether the triangles are congruent.

Exercise Alert

Compass and Straightedge Exercise 32 requires the use of a compass and a straightedge.

Additional Answers

24. Proof:

Statements (Reasons)

1. $\overline{YX} \cong \overline{WZ}$, $\overline{YX} \parallel \overline{ZW}$ (Given)
2. $\angle YXZ \cong \angle WZX$ (Alt. Int. ⦞)
3. $\overline{XZ} \cong \overline{ZX}$ (Reflex. Prop.)
4. $\triangle YXZ \cong \triangle WZX$ (SAS)

25. Proof:

Statements (Reasons)

1. $\triangle EAB \cong \triangle DCB$ (Given)
2. $\overline{EA} \cong \overline{DC}$ (CPCTC)
3. $\overline{ED} \cong \overline{DE}$ (Reflex. Prop.)
4. $\overline{AB} \cong \overline{CB}$ (CPCTC)
5. $\overline{DB} \cong \overline{EB}$ (CPCTC)
6. $AB = CB$, $DB = EB$ (Def. ≅ segments)
7. $AB + DB = CB + EB$ (Add. Prop. =)
8. $AD = AB + DB$, $CE = CB + EB$ (Segment addition)
9. $AD = CE$ (Subst. Prop. =)
10. $\overline{AD} \cong \overline{CE}$ (Def. ≅ segments)
11. $\triangle EAD \cong \triangle DCE$ (SSS)

CCSS Teaching the Mathematical Practices

Arguments Mathematically proficient students understand and use stated assumptions, definitions, and previously established results in constructing arguments. In Exercise 26, encourage students to determine whether SSS or SAS could be used in the proof.

30. false; sample answer:

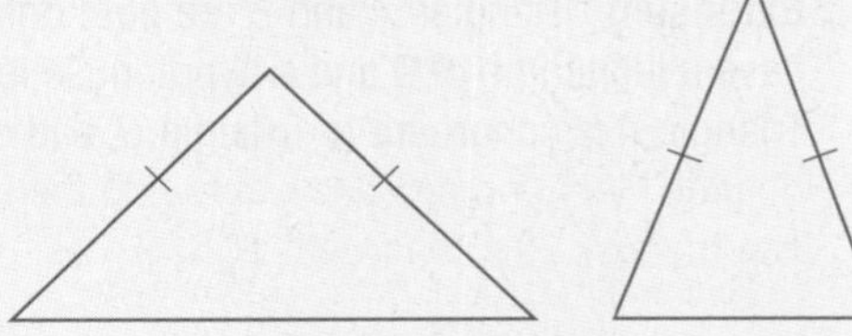

4 Assess

Name The Math Ask students to write in their own words how they can use SSS and SAS to prove triangle congruence.

Formative Assessment

Check for student understanding of concepts in Lessons 4-3 and 4-4.

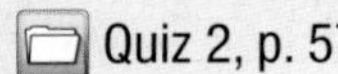 Quiz 2, p. 57

Additional Answers

36. $\frac{3}{20}$; First you have to find how many students there are in the class. There are $1 + 2 + 3 + 14$ or 20. Then the probability of randomly choosing a student with blue eyes is the number of students with blue eyes divided by 20. Since there are 3 students with blue eyes, the probability is $\frac{3}{20}$.

44. False; if $x = -5$, $(-5)^2 = 25$. The hypothesis of the conditional is true, but the conclusion is false. This counterexample shows that the conditional statement is false.

45. False; a 16-year-old could be a freshman, sophomore, junior, or senior. The hypothesis of the conditional is true, but the conclusion is false. This counterexample shows that the conditional statement is false.

Standardized Test Practice

34. ALGEBRA The Ross Family drove 300 miles to visit their grandparents. Mrs. Ross drove 70 miles per hour for 65% of the trip and 35 miles per hour or less for 20% of the trip that was left. Assuming that Mrs. Ross never went over 70 miles per hour, how many miles did she travel at a speed between 35 and 70 miles per hour? **B**

A 195 C 21

B 84 D 18

35. In the figure, $\angle C \cong \angle Z$ and $\overline{AC} \cong \overline{XZ}$.

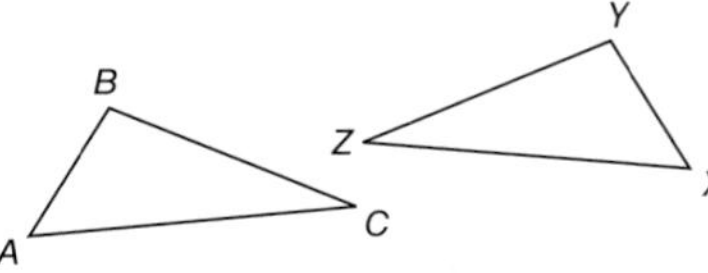

What additional information could be used to prove that $\triangle ABC \cong \triangle XYZ$? **F**

F $\overline{BC} \cong \overline{YZ}$

G $\overline{AB} \cong \overline{XY}$

H $\overline{BC} \cong \overline{XZ}$

J $\overline{XZ} \cong \overline{XY}$

36. EXTENDED RESPONSE The graph below shows the eye colors of all of the students in a class. What is the probability that a student chosen at random from this class will have blue eyes? Explain your reasoning. **See margin.**

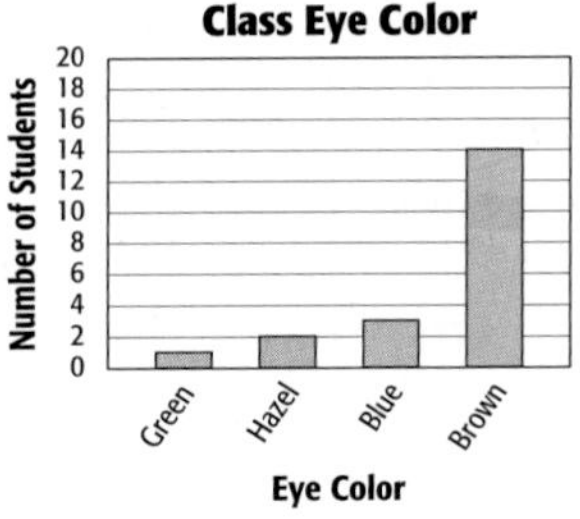

37. SAT/ACT If $4a + 6b = 6$ and $-2a + b = -7$, what is the value of a? **D**

A −2

B −1

C 2

D 3

E 4

Spiral Review

In the diagram, $\triangle LMN \cong \triangle QRS$. (Lesson 4-3)

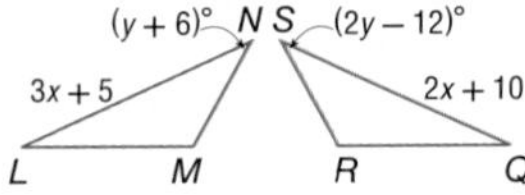

38. Find x. **5**

39. Find y. **18**

40. ASTRONOMY The Big Dipper is a part of the larger constellation Ursa Major. Three of the brighter stars in the constellation form $\triangle RSA$. If $m\angle R = 41$ and $m\angle S = 109$, find $m\angle A$. (Lesson 4-2) **30**

Write an equation in slope-intercept form for each line. (Lesson 3-4)

41. $(-5, -3)$ and $(10, -6)$ $y = -\frac{1}{5}x - 4$

42. $(4, -1)$ and $(-2, -1)$ $y = -1$

43. $(-4, -1)$ and $(-8, -5)$ $y = x + 3$

Determine the truth value of each conditional statement. If *true*, explain your reasoning. If *false*, give a counterexample. (Lesson 2-3) **44–45. See margin.**

44. If $x^2 = 25$, then $x = 5$.

45. If you are 16, you are a junior in high school.

Skills Review

State the property that justifies each statement.

46. $AB = AB$ **Reflexive Prop.**

47. If $EF = GH$ and $GH = JK$, then $EF = JK$. **Transitive Prop.**

48. If $a^2 = b^2 - c^2$, then $b^2 - c^2 = a^2$. **Symmetric Prop.**

49. If $XY + 20 = YW$ and $XY + 20 = DT$, then $YW = DT$. **Substitution Prop.**

Differentiated Instruction OL BL

Extension Triangles *A* and *B* are both right triangles and each have a leg length of 9 and a hypotenuse length of 15. Prove that Triangle *A* is congruent to Triangle *B*, and explain your reasoning. Use the Pythagorean Theorem to find the unknown leg length, 12. The triangles are congruent by SSS.

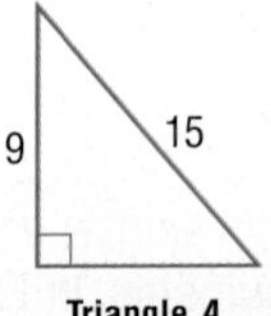

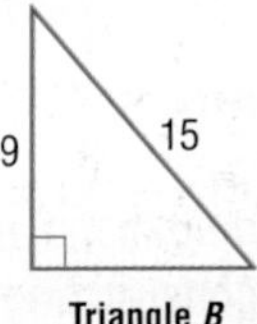

EXTEND 4-4 Geometry Lab: Proving Constructions

When you perform a construction using a straightedge and compass, you assume that segments constructed using the same compass setting are congruent. You can use this information, along with definitions, postulates, and theorems to prove constructions.

Common Core State Standards
Content Standards
G.CO.12 Make formal geometric constructions with a variety of tools and methods (compass and straightedge, string, reflective devices, paper folding, dynamic geometric software, etc.).
G.SRT.5 Use congruence and similarity criteria for triangles to solve problems and to prove relationships in geometric figures.
Mathematical Practices 3, 5

Activity

Follow the steps below to bisect an angle. Then prove the construction.

Step 1

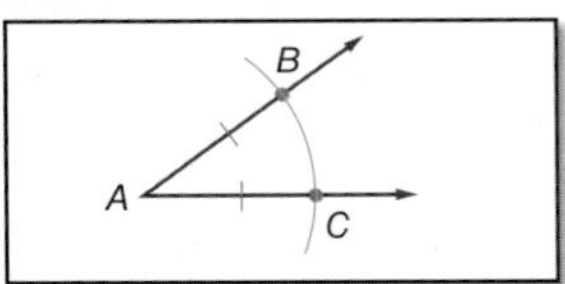

Draw any angle with vertex A. Place the compass point at A and draw an arc that intersects both sides of $\angle A$. Label the points B and C. Mark the congruent segments.

Step 2

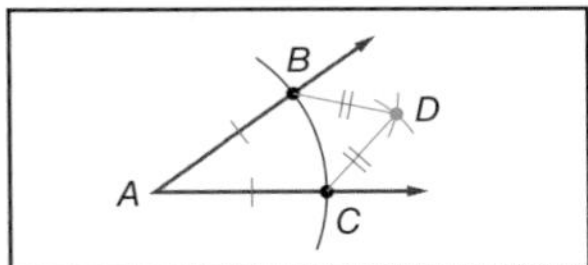

With the compass point at B, draw an arc in the interior of $\angle A$. With the same radius, draw an arc from C intersecting the first arc at D. Draw the segments $\overline{BD}$ and $\overline{CD}$. Mark the congruent segments.

Step 3

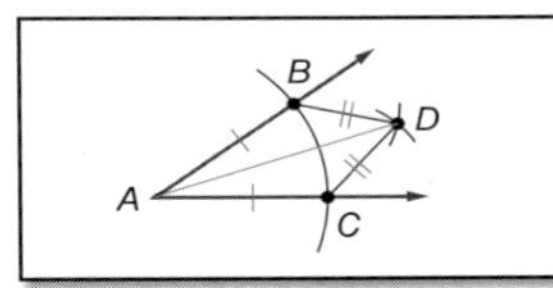

Draw $\overline{AD}$.

Given: Description of steps and diagram of construction

Prove: $\overline{AD}$ bisects $\angle BAC$.

Proof:

Statements	Reasons
1. $\overline{AB} \cong \overline{AC}$	1. The same compass setting was used from point A to construct points B and C.
2. $\overline{BD} \cong \overline{CD}$	2. The same compass setting was used from points B and C to construct point D.
3. $\overline{AD} \cong \overline{AD}$	3. Reflexive Property
4. $\triangle ABD \cong \triangle ACD$	4. SSS Postulate
5. $\angle BAD \cong \angle CAD$	5. CPCTC
6. $\overline{AD}$ bisects $\angle BAC$.	6. Definition of angle bisector

Exercises

1. Construct a line parallel to a given line through a given point. Write a two-column proof of your construction.
2. Construct an equilateral triangle. Write a paragraph proof of your construction.
3. **CHALLENGE** Construct the bisector of a segment that is also perpendicular to the segment and write a two-column proof of your construction. (*Hint:* You will need to use more than one pair of congruent triangles.).

1–3. See Ch. 4 Answer Appendix.

1 Focus

Objective Prove constructions using congruent measurements.

Materials for Each Group

- compass
- straightedge

2 Teach

Working in Cooperative Groups

Arrange students in groups of 2, mixing abilities. Then have students complete the activity.

Ask:

- How do you know which segments are congruent in Step 1? $\overline{AB} \cong \overline{AC}$ because the segments were created using the same compass setting. This ensures that the segments are the same length.
- How do you make sure that $\overline{BD}$ and $\overline{CD}$ are congruent? Care must be taken to maintain the same compass setting to guarantee equal measures from one segment to another.
- Are $\overline{AB}$, $\overline{AC}$, $\overline{BD}$, and $\overline{CD}$ congruent segments? What must happen in order for all of these segments to be congruent to each other? Not necessarily; All four of these lengths are the same only if the same compass setting is maintained for all four measurements.
- A common error in the proof is to state that $\triangle ABC \cong \triangle DBC$. What is the error? The error is in stating that the congruent parts are in each of the individual triangles rather than in corresponding parts of two different triangles.

Practice Have students complete Exercises 1–3.

3 Assess

Formative Assessment

Use Exercises 1–2 to assess whether students comprehend how to prove a construction.

From Concrete to Abstract

Use what you know about the angles discussed in the lab to show that $\overline{AD}$ bisects $\angle BAC$ algebraically. Because $\angle BAD \cong \angle CAD$, $m\angle BAD = m\angle CAD$. Also, $m\angle BAD + m\angle CAD = m\angle BAC$. Using substitution,

$$m\angle BAD + m\angle BAD = m\angle BAC$$
$$2m\angle BAD = m\angle BAC$$
$$m\angle BAD = \frac{m\angle BAC}{2}$$
$$m\angle CAD = \frac{m\angle BAC}{2}$$

Therefore, $\overline{AD}$ bisects $\angle BAC$.

Formative Assessment

Use the Mid-Chapter Quiz to assess students' progress in the first half of the chapter.

For problems answered incorrectly, have students review the lessons indicated in parentheses.

Summative Assessment

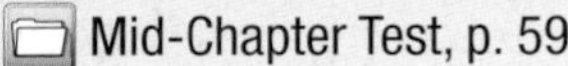

Mid-Chapter Test, p. 59

eAssessment Customize and create multiple versions of your Mid-Chapter Test and their answer keys.

FOLDABLES StudyOrganizer

Dinah Zike's Foldables®

Before students complete the Mid-Chapter Quiz, encourage them to review the information for Lessons 4-1 through 4-4 in their Foldables.

Additional Answers

20. Statements (Reasons)
    1. $\triangle LMN$ is isos. with $\overline{LM} \cong \overline{NM}$. (Given)
    2. $\overline{MO}$ bisects $\angle LMN$. (Given)
    3. $\angle 1 \cong \angle 2$ (Def. of $\angle$ bisector)
    4. $\overline{MO} \cong \overline{MO}$ (Refl. Prop.)
    5. $\triangle MLO \cong \triangle MNO$ (SAS)

CHAPTER 4 Mid-Chapter Quiz

Lessons 4-1 through 4-4

1. **COORDINATE GEOMETRY** Classify $\triangle ABC$ with vertices $A(-2, -1)$, $B(-1, 3)$, and $C(2, 0)$ as *scalene, equilateral,* or *isosceles.* (Lesson 4-1) **isosceles**

2. **MULTIPLE CHOICE** Which of the following are the measures of the sides of isosceles triangle QRS? (Lesson 4-1) **A**

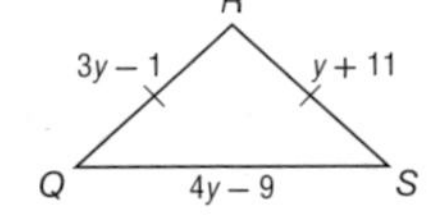

A	17, 17, 15	**C**	14, 15, 14
B	15, 15, 16	**D**	14, 14, 16

3. **ALGEBRA** Find x and the length of each side if $\triangle WXY$ is an equilateral triangle with sides $\overline{WX} = 6x - 12$, $\overline{XY} = 2x + 10$, and $\overline{WY} = 4x - 1$. (Lesson 4-1) $x = 5.5$; $WX = XY = WY = 21$

Find the measure of each angle indicated. (Lesson 4-2)

4. $m\angle 1$ **108**
5. $m\angle 2$ **34**
6. $m\angle 3$ **66**

7. **ASTRONOMY** Leo is a constellation that represents a lion. Three of the brighter stars in the constellation form $\triangle LEO$. If the angles have measures as shown in the figure, find $m\angle OLE$. (Lesson 4-2) **66**

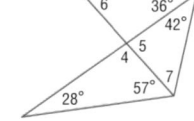

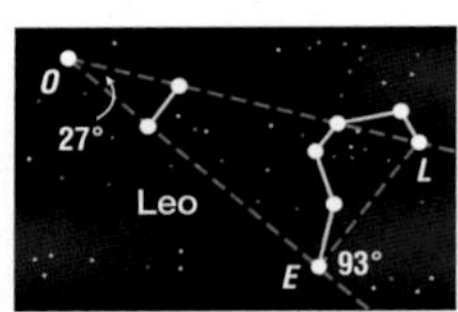

Find the measure of each numbered angle. (Lesson 4-2)

8. $m\angle 4$ **95**
9. $m\angle 5$ **85**
10. $m\angle 6$ **49**
11. $m\angle 7$ **53**

In the diagram, $\triangle RST \cong \triangle ABC$. (Lesson 4-3)

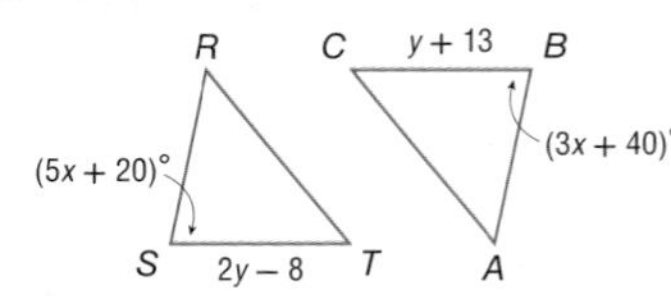

12. Find x. **10**
13. Find y. **21**

14. **ARCHITECTURE** The diagram shows an A-frame house with various points labeled. Assume that segments and angles that appear to be congruent in the diagram are congruent. Indicate which triangles are congruent. (Lesson 4-3) **See Ch. 4 Answer Appendix.**

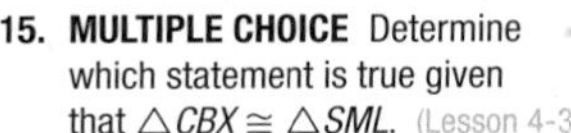

15. **MULTIPLE CHOICE** Determine which statement is true given that $\triangle CBX \cong \triangle SML$. (Lesson 4-3) **J**

F	$\overline{MO} \cong \overline{SL}$	**H**	$\angle X \cong \angle S$
G	$\overline{XC} \cong \overline{ML}$	**J**	$\angle XCB \cong \angle LSM$

16. **BRIDGES** A bridge truss is shown in the diagram below, where $\overline{AC} \perp \overline{BD}$ and B is the midpoint of $\overline{AC}$. What method can be used to prove that $\triangle ABD \cong \triangle CBD$? (Lesson 4-4) **SAS**

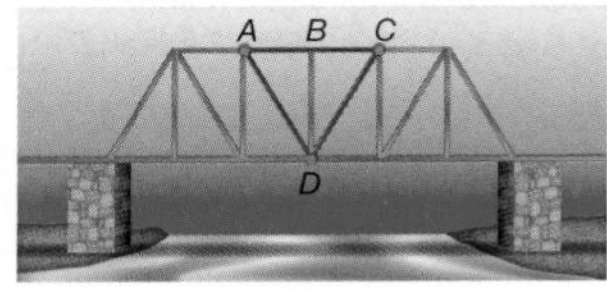

Determine whether $\triangle PQR \cong \triangle XYZ$. (Lesson 4-4)

17. $P(3, -5)$, $Q(11, 0)$, $R(1, 6)$, $X(5, 1)$, $Y(13, 6)$, $Z(3, 12)$ **yes**
18. $P(-3, -3)$, $Q(-5, 1)$, $R(-2, 6)$, $X(2, -6)$, $Y(3, 3)$, $Z(5, -1)$ **no**
19. $P(8, 1)$, $Q(-7, -15)$, $R(9, -6)$, $X(5, 11)$, $Y(-10, -5)$, $Z(6, 4)$ **yes**

20. **Write a two-column proof.** (Lesson 4-4) **See margin.**

Given: $\triangle LMN$ is isos. with $\overline{LM} \cong \overline{NM}$, and $\overline{MO}$ bisects $\angle LMN$.

Prove: $\triangle MLO \cong \triangle MNO$

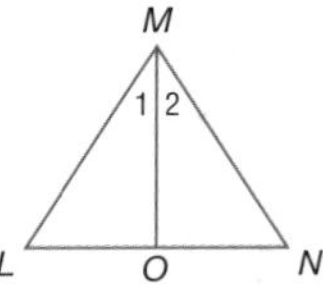

InterventionPlanner

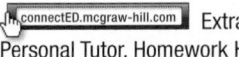

TIER 1 On Level OL	TIER 2 Strategic Intervention AL approaching grade level	TIER 3 Intensive Intervention 2 or more grades below level
If students miss about 25% of the exercises or less,	**If** students miss about 50% of the exercises,	**If** students miss about 75% of the exercises,
Then choose a resource:	**Then** choose a resource:	**Then** use *Math Triumphs, Geometry,* Ch. 5
SE Lessons 4-1 through 4-4	Study Guide and Intervention, pp. 5, 11, 19, and 25	connectED.mcgraw-hill.com Extra Examples, Personal Tutor, Homework Help, Review Vocabulary
Skills Practice, pp. 7, 13, 21, and 27	connectED.mcgraw-hill.com Extra Examples, Personal Tutor, Homework Help	
connectED.mcgraw-hill.com Self-Check Quiz		

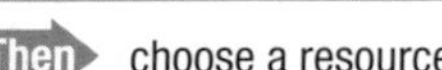
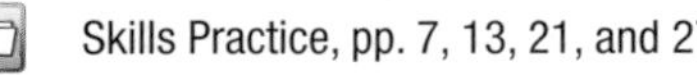

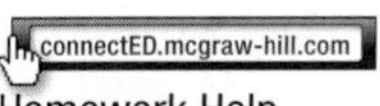

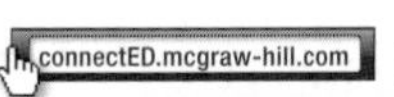

4-5 Proving Triangles Congruent—ASA, AAS

Then

- You proved triangles congruent using SSS and SAS.

Now

1. Use the ASA Postulate to test for congruence.
2. Use the AAS Theorem to test for congruence.

Why?

- Competitive sweep rowing, also called *crew*, involves two or more people who sit facing the stern of the boat, with each rower pulling one oar. In high school competitions, a race, called a *regatta*, usually requires a body of water that is more than 1500 meters long. Congruent triangles can be used to measure distances that are not easily measured directly, like the length of a regatta course.

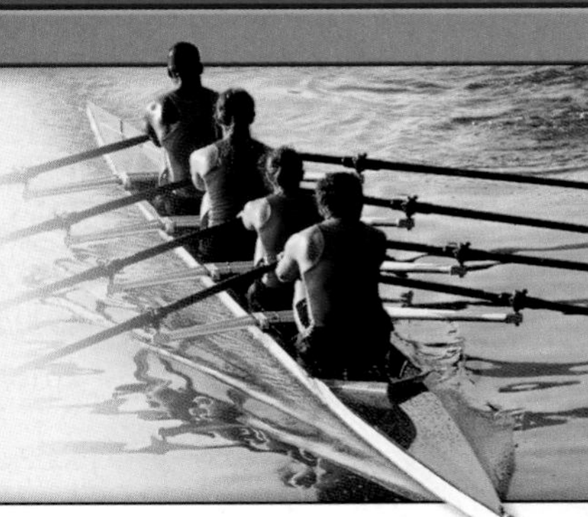

NewVocabulary
included side

Common Core State Standards

Content Standards
G.CO.10 Prove theorems about triangles.
G.SRT.5 Use congruence and similarity criteria for triangles to solve problems and to prove relationships in geometric figures.

Mathematical Practices
3 Construct viable arguments and critique the reasoning of others.
5 Use appropriate tools strategically.

1 ASA Postulate

An **included side** is the side located between two consecutive angles of a polygon. In $\triangle ABC$ at the right, $\overline{AC}$ is the included side between $\angle A$ and $\angle C$.

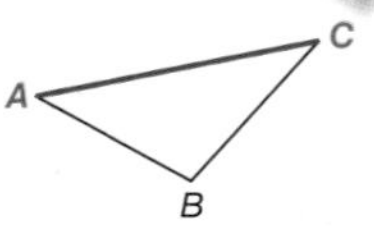

Postulate 4.3 Angle-Side-Angle (ASA) Congruence

If two angles and the included side of one triangle are congruent to two angles and the included side of another triangle, then the triangles are congruent.

Example If Angle $\angle A \cong \angle D$,
Side $\overline{AB} \cong \overline{DE}$, and
Angle $\angle B \cong \angle E$,
then $\triangle ABC \cong \triangle DEF$.

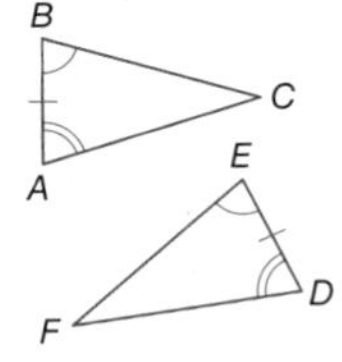

Construction Congruent Triangles Using Two Angles and Included Side

Draw a triangle and label it $\triangle ABC$. Then use the ASA Postulate to construct $\triangle XYZ \cong \triangle ABC$.

Step 1

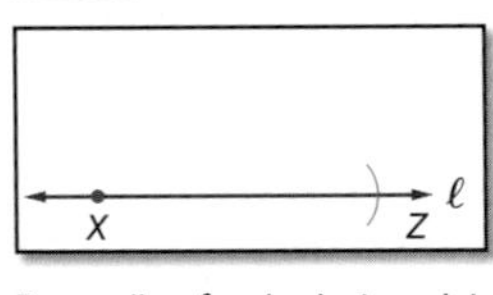

Draw a line ℓ and select a point X. Construct $\overline{XZ}$ such that $\overline{XZ} \cong \overline{AC}$.

Step 2

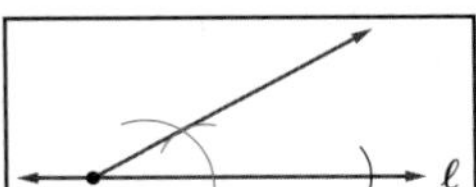

Construct an angle congruent to $\angle A$ at X using $\overleftrightarrow{XZ}$ as a side of the angle.

Step 3

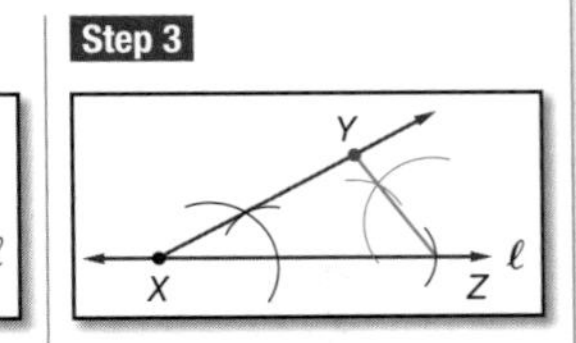

Construct an angle congruent to $\angle C$ at Z using $\overleftrightarrow{XZ}$ as a side of the angle. Label the point where the new sides of the angles meet as Y.

1 Focus

VerticalAlignment

Before Lesson 4-5 Prove triangles are congruent using the SSS and SAS Postulates.

Lesson 4-5 Use the ASA and AAS Postulates to test for triangle congruence.

After Lesson 4-5 Use triangle congruence postulates to make conjectures and justify properties of geometric figures.

2 Teach

Scaffolding Questions

Have students read the **Why?** section of the lesson.

Ask:

- In the passage, there is a claim that the length of a regatta course can be measured indirectly. To what surface would you transfer the length of the course? the ground or the shore
- To estimate the distance from the shore to the starting point of the race course, stand at a point perpendicular to the starting line of the race and look directly at the starting point of the race. Keeping your eyes locked in place and your neck stiff, turn your body to establish the same line of sight to a point along the ground.

(continued on the next page)

Lesson 4-5 Resources

Resource	Approaching Level AL	On Level OL	Beyond Level BL	English Learners ELL
Teacher Edition		▪ Differentiated Instruction, pp. 277, 282	▪ Differentiated Instruction, pp. 277, 282	▪ Differentiated Instruction, p. 277
Chapter Resource Masters	▪ Study Guide and Intervention, pp. 31–32 ▪ Skills Practice, p. 33 ▪ Practice, p. 34 ▪ Word Problem Practice, p. 35	▪ Study Guide and Intervention, pp. 31–32 ▪ Skills Practice, p. 33 ▪ Practice, p. 34 ▪ Word Problem Practice, p. 35 ▪ Enrichment, p. 36	▪ Practice, p. 34 ▪ Word Problem Practice, p. 35 ▪ Enrichment, p. 36	▪ Study Guide and Intervention, pp. 31–32 ▪ Skills Practice, p. 33 ▪ Practice, p. 34 ▪ Word Problem Practice, p. 35
Other	▪ 5-Minute Check 4-5 ▪ Study Notebook	▪ 5-Minute Check 4-5 ▪ Study Notebook	▪ 5-Minute Check 4-5 ▪ Study Notebook	▪ 5-Minute Check 4-5 ▪ Study Notebook

Then measure the distance from where you are standing to the point on the ground. You have just created two congruent triangles; how can you prove it? Because you are perpendicular to the ground, two congruent, right angles are formed. The angles formed by your line of sight are the same and your height is also the same in both triangles. Therefore, the two triangles formed are congruent by ASA, and so by CPCTC, the distances are the same.

1 ASA Postulate

Example 1 shows how to use the ASA Postulate in a proof.

Formative Assessment

Use the Guided Practice exercises after each Example to determine students' understanding of concepts.

Additional Example

1 Write a two-column proof.

Given: L is the midpoint of $\overline{WE}$. $\overline{WR} \parallel \overline{ED}$

Prove: $\triangle WRL \cong \triangle EDL$

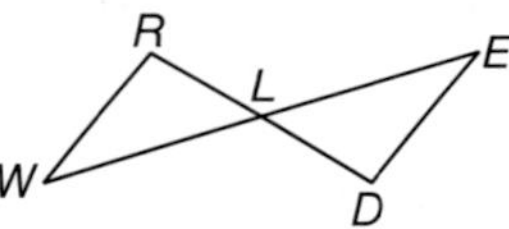

Proof:

Statements (Reasons)

1. L is the midpoint of $\overline{WE}$ (Given)
2. $\overline{WL} \cong \overline{LE}$ (Midpoint Theorem)
3. $\overline{WR} \parallel \overline{ED}$ (Given)
4. $\angle W \cong \angle E$ (Alternate Interior Angles Theorem)
5. $\angle WLR \cong \angle ELD$ (Vertical Angles Theorem)
6. $\triangle WRL \cong \triangle EDL$ (ASA)

Additional Examples also in Interactive Classroom PowerPoint® Presentations

IWB Interactive White Board READY

PT

Example 1 Use ASA to Prove Triangles Congruent

Write a two-column proof.

Given: $\overline{QS}$ bisects $\angle PQR$; $\angle PSQ \cong \angle RSQ$.

Prove: $\triangle PQS \cong \triangle RQS$

Proof:

Statements	Reasons
1. $\overline{QS}$ bisects $\angle PQR$; $\angle PSQ \cong \angle RSQ$.	**1.** Given
2. $\angle PQS \cong \angle RQS$	**2.** Definition of Angle Bisector
3. $\overline{QS} \cong \overline{QS}$	**3.** Reflexive Property of Congruence
4. $\triangle PQS \cong \triangle RQS$	**4.** ASA

Guided Practice

1. Write a flow proof. See margin.
Given: $\overline{ZX}$ bisects $\angle WZY$; $\overline{XZ}$ bisects $\angle YXW$.
Prove: $\triangle WXZ \cong \triangle XZY$

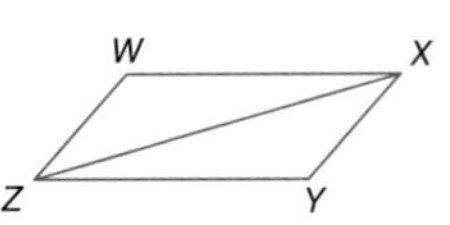

2 AAS Theorem

The congruence of two angles and a nonincluded side are also sufficient to prove two triangles congruent. This congruence relationship is a theorem because it can be proved using the Third Angles Theorem.

Theorem 4.5 Angle-Angle-Side (AAS) Congruence

If two angles and the nonincluded side of one triangle are congruent to the corresponding two angles and side of a second triangle, then the two triangles are congruent.

Example If Angle $\angle A \cong \angle D$,
Angle $\angle B \cong \angle E$, and
Side $\overline{BC} \cong \overline{EF}$,
then $\triangle ABC \cong \triangle DEF$.

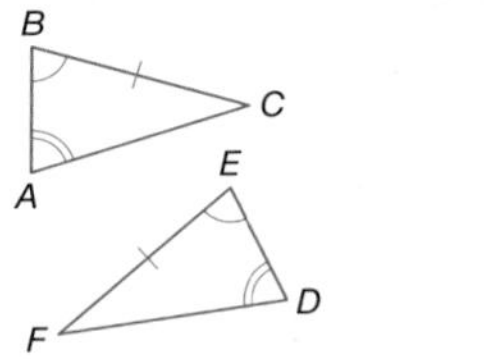

Proof Angle-Angle-Side Theorem

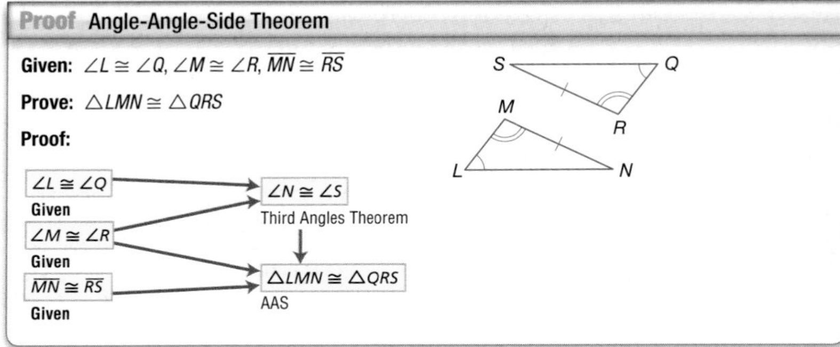

Given: $\angle L \cong \angle Q$, $\angle M \cong \angle R$, $\overline{MN} \cong \overline{RS}$

Prove: $\triangle LMN \cong \triangle QRS$

Proof:

Additional Answer (Guided Practice)

1.

Statement	Reason
$\overline{ZX}$ bisects $\angle WZY$	Given
$\angle WZX \cong \angle YZX$	Def. of bisects
$\overline{ZX}$ bisects $\angle YXW$	Given
$\angle WXZ \cong \angle YXZ$	Def. of bisects
$\overline{ZX} \cong \overline{ZX}$	Refl. Prop.
$\triangle WXZ \cong \triangle XZY$	ASA

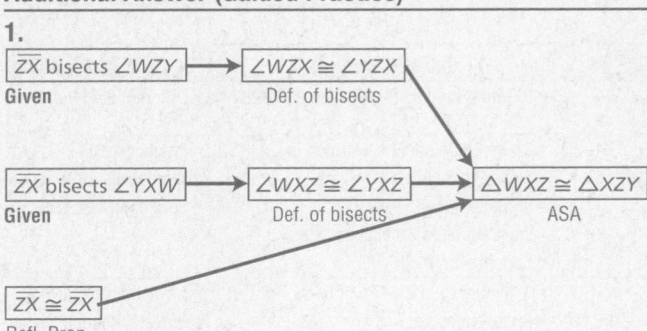

Focus on Mathematical Content

Intervention A student may ask about proving congruence with SSA. Point out that two triangles with two pairs of sides and the non-included angles congruent are not necessarily congruent. The locations of the angles with respect to the sides of a triangle are crucial for proving congruency.

Example 2 Use AAS to Prove Triangles Congruent

Write a two-column proof.

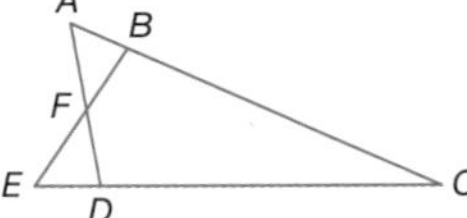

Given: $\angle DAC \cong \angle BEC$
$\overline{DC} \cong \overline{BC}$

Prove: $\triangle ACD \cong \triangle ECB$

Proof: We are given that $\angle DAC \cong \angle BEC$ and $\overline{DC} \cong \overline{BC}$. $\angle C \cong \angle C$ by the Reflexive Property. By AAS, $\triangle ACD \cong \triangle ECB$.

Guided Practice

See Ch. 4 Answer Appendix.

2. Write a flow proof.
Given: $\overline{RQ} \cong \overline{ST}$ and $\overline{RQ} \parallel \overline{ST}$
Prove: $\triangle RUQ \cong \triangle TUS$

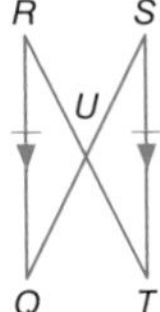

You can use congruent triangles to measure distances that are difficult to measure directly.

Real-World Example 3 Apply Triangle Congruence

COMMUNITY SERVICE Jeremias is working with a community service group to build a bridge across a creek at a local park. The bridge will span the creek between points *C* and *B*. Jeremias located a fixed point *D* to use as a reference point so that the segments have the relationships shown. *A* is the midpoint of $\overline{CD}$ and *DE* is 15 feet. How long does the bridge need to be?

In order to determine the length of $\overline{CB}$, we must first prove that the two triangles Jeremias has created are congruent.

- Since $\overline{CD}$ is perpendicular to both $\overline{CB}$ and $\overline{DE}$, the segments form right angles as shown on the diagram.
- All right angles are congruent, so $\angle BCA \cong \angle EDA$.
- Point *A* is the midpoint of $\overline{CD}$, so $\overline{CA} \cong \overline{AD}$.
- $\angle BAC$ and $\angle EAD$ are vertical angles, so they are congruent.

Therefore, by ASA, $\triangle BAC \cong \triangle EAD$.

Since $\triangle BAC \cong \triangle EAD$, $\overline{DE} \cong \overline{CB}$ by CPCTC. Since the measure of $\overline{DE}$ is 15 feet, the measure of $\overline{CB}$ is also 15 feet. Therefore, the bridge needs to be 15 feet long.

Study Tip

Angle-Angle-Angle In Example 3, $\angle B$ and $\angle E$ are congruent by the Third Angles Theorem. Congruence of all three corresponding angles is not sufficient, however, to prove two triangles congruent.

Differentiated Instruction OL BL ELL

Intrapersonal Ask students to study the proofs for the examples in this lesson and note the properties that recur, such as the reflexive properties of angles, segments, bisectors, midpoints, and so on. Students can start a list of things to watch for when they are working on proofs and include recurring properties, theorems, formulas and methods that they can refer to in later lessons. They can also look at the order of the steps in paragraph proofs, flow proofs, and two-column proofs for similarities and differences.

2 AAS Theorem

Example 2 shows how to prove two triangles are congruent by using Theorem 4.5. **Example 3** shows how to use congruent triangles to indirectly measure distances.

Additional Examples

2 Write a paragraph proof.

Given: $\angle NKL \cong \angle NJM$
$\overline{KL} \cong \overline{JM}$

Prove: $\overline{LN} \cong \overline{MN}$

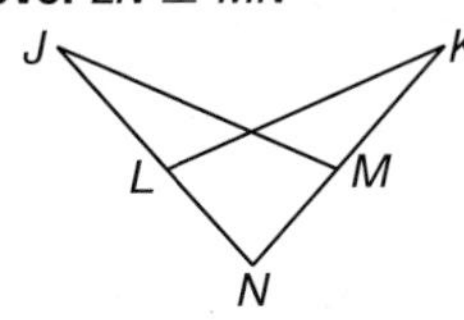

Proof: $\angle NKL \cong \angle NJM$, $\overline{KL} \cong \overline{MN}$, and $\angle N \cong \angle N$ by the Reflexive Property. Therefore, $\triangle JNM \cong \triangle KNL$ by AAS. By CPCTC, $\overline{LN} \cong \overline{MN}$.

3 **MANUFACTURING** Barbara designs a paper template for a certain envelope. She designs the top and bottom flaps to be isosceles triangles that have congruent bases and base angles. If $EV = 8$ cm and the height of the isosceles triangle is 3 cm, find *PO*.

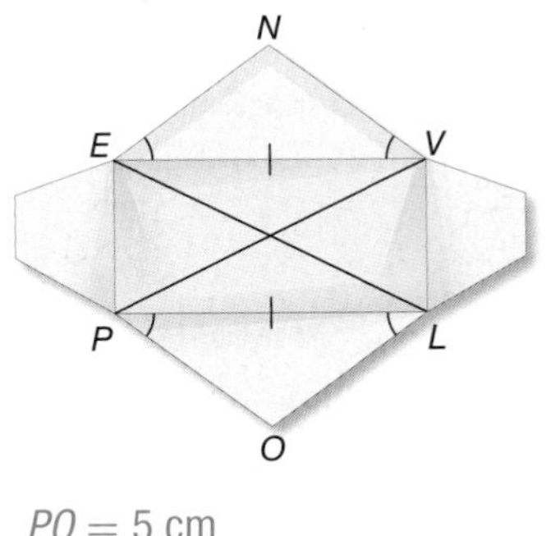

$PO = 5$ cm

Watch Out!

Where's the side? The AAS Postulate can only be used when the side is *not* between the two angles.

Teach with Tech

Video Recording Have students work in groups to create videos explaining how to prove that two triangles are congruent using ASA and/or AAS. Post the videos to a video sharing Web site and have each group watch the other groups' videos.

3 Practice

Formative Assessment

Use Exercises 1–5 to check for understanding.

Use the chart at the bottom of the next page to customize assignments for your students.

Additional Answer (Guided Practice)

3. We are given that $\overline{BC} \perp \overline{AC}$, $\overline{DE} \perp \overline{CE}$, $\angle BAC \cong \angle DCE$, and $\overline{AB} \cong \overline{CD}$. Since $\overline{BC} \perp \overline{AC}$ and $\overline{DE} \perp \overline{CE}$, $\angle BCA$ and $\angle DEC$ are right angles. $\angle BCA \cong \angle DEC$ because all right angles are congruent to each other. Then by the Angle-Angle-Side Postulate, $\triangle BAC \cong \triangle DCE$. So, $\overline{BC} \cong \overline{DE}$ by CPCTC.

Additional Answers

1. **Proof:**

Statements (Reasons)

1. $\overline{CB}$ bisects $\angle ABD$ and $\angle ACD$. (Given)
2. $\angle ABC \cong \angle DBC$ (Def. of $\angle$ bisector)
3. $\overline{BC} \cong \overline{BC}$ (Refl. Prop.)
4. $\angle ACB \cong \angle DCB$ (Def. of $\angle$ bisector)
5. $\triangle ABC \cong \triangle DBC$ (ASA)

GuidedPractice

3. In the sign scaffold shown at the right, $\overline{BC} \perp \overline{AC}$ and $\overline{DE} \perp \overline{CE}$. $\angle BAC \cong \angle DCE$, and $\overline{AB} \cong \overline{CD}$. Write a paragraph proof to show that $\overline{BC} \cong \overline{DE}$. **See margin.**

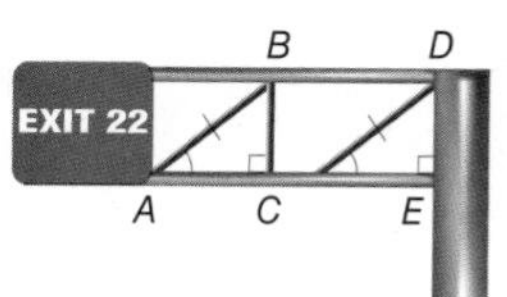

You have learned several methods for proving triangle congruence.

ConceptSummary Proving Triangles Congruent

SSS	SAS	ASA	AAS
Three pairs of corresponding sides are congruent.	Two pairs of corresponding sides and their included angles are congruent.	Two pairs of corresponding angles and their included sides are congruent.	Two pairs of corresponding angles and the corresponding nonincluded sides are congruent.

Check Your Understanding = Step-by-Step Solutions begin on page R14.

Example 1 **PROOF** Write the specified type of proof. **1–4. See margin.**

1. two-column proof

Given: $\overline{CB}$ bisects $\angle ABD$ and $\angle ACD$.

Prove: $\triangle ABC \cong \triangle DBC$

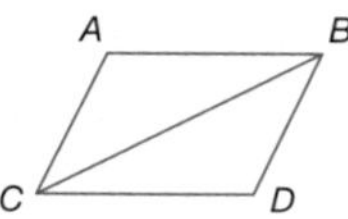

2. flow proof

Given: $\overline{JK} \parallel \overline{LM}$, $\overline{JL} \parallel \overline{KM}$

Prove: $\triangle JML \cong \triangle MJK$

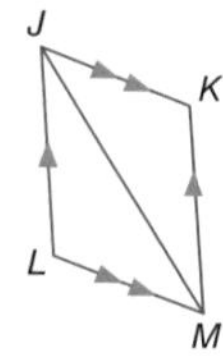

Example 2

3. paragraph proof

Given: $\angle K \cong \angle M$, $\overline{JK} \cong \overline{JM}$, $\overline{JL}$ bisects $\angle KLM$.

Prove: $\triangle JKL \cong \triangle JML$

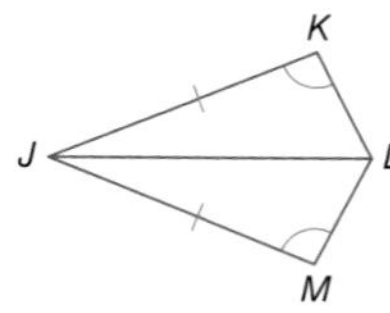

4. two-column proof

Given: $\overline{GH} \parallel \overline{FJ}$, $m\angle G = m\angle J = 90$

Prove: $\triangle HJF \cong \triangle FGH$

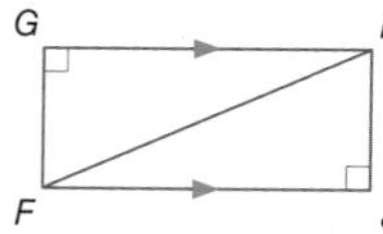

2.

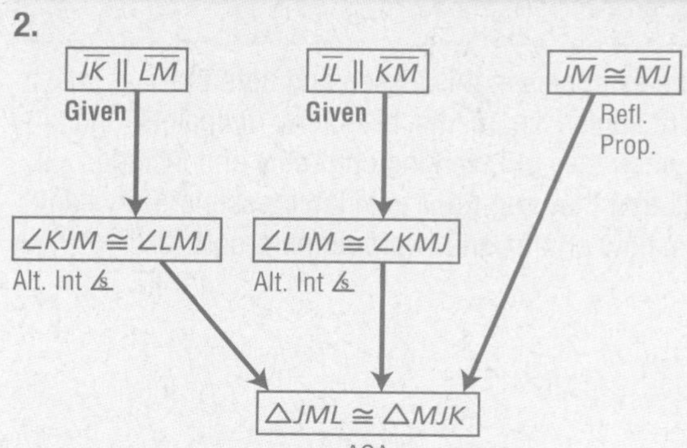

3. **Proof:** We are given $\angle K \cong \angle M$, $\overline{JK} \cong \overline{JM}$, and $\overline{JL}$ bisects $\angle KLM$. Since $\overline{JL}$ bisects $\angle KLM$, we know $\angle KLJ \cong \angle MLJ$. So, $\triangle JKL \cong \triangle JML$ is congruent by the Angle-Angle-Side Congruence Theorem.

Example 3 **5** **BRIDGE BUILDING** A surveyor needs to find the distance from point A to point B across a canyon. She places a stake at A, and a coworker places a stake at B on the other side of the canyon. The surveyor then locates C on the same side of the canyon as A such that $\overline{CA} \perp \overline{AB}$. A fourth stake is placed at E, the midpoint of $\overline{CA}$. Finally, a stake is placed at D such that $\overline{CD} \perp \overline{CA}$ and D, E, and B are sited as lying along the same line.

a. Explain how the surveyor can use the triangles formed to find AB. See margin.

b. If $AC = 1300$ meters, $DC = 550$ meters, and $DE = 851.5$ meters, what is AB? Explain your reasoning.
550 m; Since $DC = 550$ m and $\overline{DC} \cong \overline{AB}$, then by the definition of congruence, $AB = 550$ m.

Practice and Problem Solving

Extra Practice is on page R4.

Example 1 **PROOF** Write a paragraph proof. 6–7. See margin.

6. Given: $\overline{CE}$ bisects $\angle BED$; $\angle BCE$ and $\angle ECD$ are right angles.
Prove: $\triangle ECB \cong \triangle ECD$

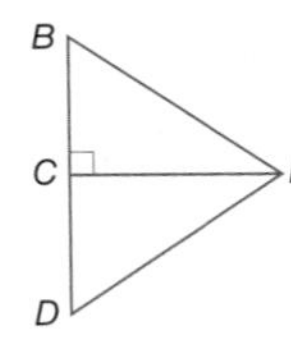

7. Given: $\angle W \cong \angle Y$, $\overline{WZ} \cong \overline{YZ}$, $\overline{XZ}$ bisects $\angle WZY$.
Prove: $\triangle XWZ \cong \triangle XYZ$

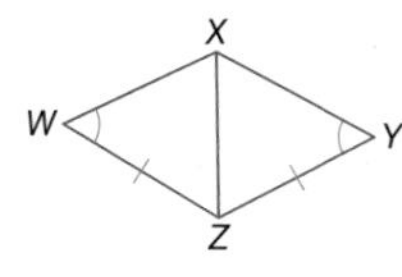

8. TOYS The object of the toy shown is to make the two spheres meet and strike each other repeatedly on one side of the wand and then again on the other side. If $\angle JKL \cong \angle MLK$ and $\angle JLK \cong \angle MKL$, prove that $\overline{JK} \cong \overline{ML}$. See margin.

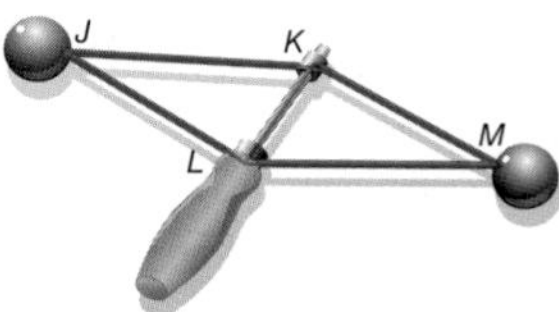

Example 2 **PROOF** Write a two-column proof. 9–10. See Ch. 4 Answer Appendix.

9 **Given:** V is the midpoint of $\overline{YW}$; $\overline{UY} \parallel \overline{XW}$.
Prove: $\triangle UVY \cong \triangle XVW$

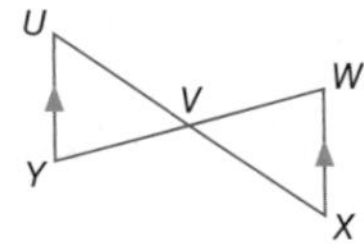

10. Given: $\overline{MS} \cong \overline{RQ}$, $\overline{MS} \parallel \overline{RQ}$
Prove: $\triangle MSP \cong \triangle RQP$

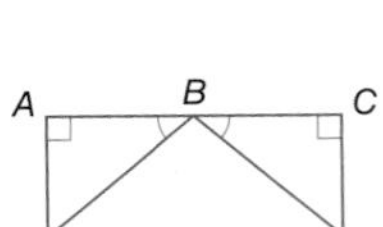

11. CCSS **ARGUMENTS** Write a flow proof.
Given: $\angle A$ and $\angle C$ are right angles. $\angle ABE \cong \angle CBD$, $\overline{AE} \cong \overline{CD}$
Prove: $\overline{BE} \cong \overline{BD}$ See Ch. 4 Answer Appendix.

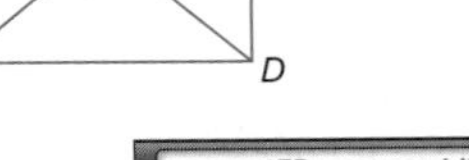

Differentiated Homework Options

Level	Assignment	Two-Day Option	
AL Basic	6–13, 22–24, 26–38	7–13 odd, 27–30	6–12 even, 22–24, 26, 31–38
OL Core	7–15 odd, 16, 17–21 odd, 22–24, 26–38	6–13, 27–30	14–24, 26, 31–38
BL Advanced	14–36, (optional: 37, 38)		

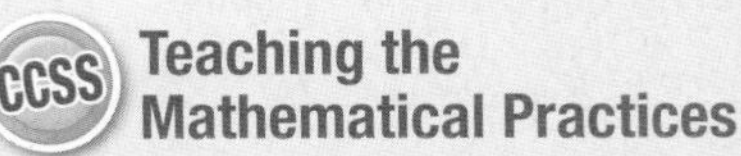

Teaching the Mathematical Practices

Arguments Mathematically proficient students understand and use stated assumptions, definitions, and previously established results in constructing arguments. In Exercise 11, encourage students to determine whether SSS, SAS, or ASA could be used in the proof.

Additional Answers

4. Proof:

Statements (Reasons)

1. $\overline{GH} \parallel \overline{FJ}$, $m\angle G = m\angle J = 90$ (Given)
2. $m\angle G \cong m\angle J$ (Def. of $\cong$ ∠s.)
3. $\angle GHF \cong \angle JFH$ (Alt. Int. ∠s are $\cong$.)
4. $\overline{HF} \cong \overline{FH}$ (Ref. Prop.)
5. $\triangle HJF \cong \triangle FGH$ (AAS)

5a. We know $\angle BAE$ and $\angle DCE$ are congruent because they are both right angles. $\overline{AE}$ is congruent to $\overline{EC}$ by the Midpoint Theorem. From the Vertical Angles Theorem, $\angle DEC \cong \angle BEA$. By ASA, the surveyor knows that $\triangle DCE \cong \triangle BAE$. By CPCTC, $\overline{DC} \cong \overline{AB}$, so the surveyor can measure $\overline{DC}$ and know the distance between A and B.

6. Proof: We are given that $\overline{CE}$ bisects $\angle BED$ and $\angle BCE$ and $\angle ECD$ are right angles. Since all right angles are congruent, $\angle BCE \cong \angle ECD$. By the definition of angle bisector, $\angle BEC \cong \angle DEC$. The Reflexive Property tells us that $\overline{EC} \cong \overline{EC}$. By Angle-Side-Angle Congruence Postulate, $\triangle ECB \cong \triangle ECD$.

7. Proof: It is given that $\angle W \cong \angle Y$, $\overline{WZ} \cong \overline{YZ}$, and $\overline{XZ}$ bisects $\angle WZY$. By the definition of angle bisector, $\angle WZX \cong \angle YZX$. The Angle-Side-Angle Congruence Postulate tells us that $\triangle XWZ \cong \triangle XYZ$.

8. Proof:

Statements (Reasons)

1. $\angle JKL \cong \angle MLK$, $\angle JLK \cong \angle MKL$ (Given)
2. $\overline{KL} \cong \overline{KL}$ (Refl. Prop.)
3. $\triangle KLM \cong \triangle LKJ$ (ASA)
4. $\overline{JK} \cong \overline{ML}$ (CPCTC)

Study Guide and Intervention

AL OL ELL

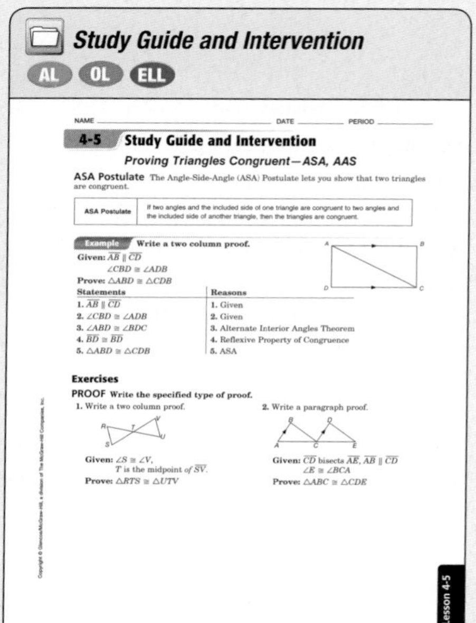
NAME ______ DATE ______ PERIOD ______

4-5 Study Guide and Intervention

Proving Triangles Congruent—ASA, AAS

ASA Postulate The Angle-Side-Angle (ASA) Postulate lets you show that two triangles are congruent.

ASA Postulate	If two angles and the included side of one triangle are congruent to two angles and the included side of another triangle, then the triangles are congruent.

Example Write a two column proof.

Given: $\overline{AB} \parallel \overline{CD}$, $\angle CBD \cong \angle ADB$

Prove: $\triangle ABD \cong \triangle CDB$

Statements	Reasons
1. $\overline{AB} \parallel \overline{CD}$	1. Given
2. $\angle CBD \cong \angle ADB$	2. Given
3. $\angle ABD \cong \angle BDC$	3. Alternate Interior Angles Theorem
4. $\overline{BD} \cong \overline{BD}$	4. Reflexive Property of Congruence
5. $\triangle ABD \cong \triangle CDB$	5. ASA

Exercises

PROOF Write the specified type of proof.

1. Write a two column proof.
Given: $\angle S \cong \angle V$, T is the midpoint of $\overline{SV}$.
Prove: $\triangle RTS \cong \triangle UTV$

2. Write a paragraph proof.
Given: $\overline{CD}$ bisects $\overline{AE}$, $\overline{AB} \parallel \overline{CD}$, $\angle E \cong \angle BCA$
Prove: $\triangle ABC \cong \triangle CDE$

Lesson 4-5

Practice

AL OL BL ELL

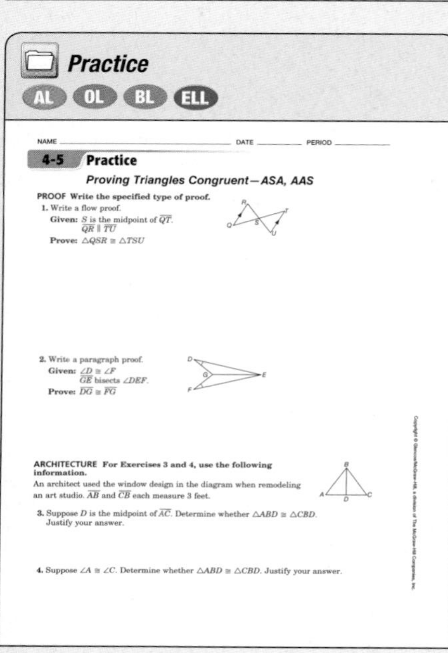
NAME ______ DATE ______ PERIOD ______

4-5 Practice

Proving Triangles Congruent—ASA, AAS

PROOF Write the specified type of proof.

1. Write a flow proof.
Given: S is the midpoint of $\overline{QT}$. $\overline{QR} \parallel \overline{TU}$
Prove: $\triangle QSR \cong \triangle TSU$

2. Write a paragraph proof.
Given: $\angle D \cong \angle F$, $\overline{GE}$ bisects $\angle DEF$.
Prove: $\overline{DG} \cong \overline{FG}$

ARCHITECTURE For Exercises 3 and 4, use the following information.
An architect used the window design in the diagram when remodeling an art studio. $\overline{AB}$ and $\overline{CB}$ each measure 3 feet.

3. Suppose D is the midpoint of $\overline{AC}$. Determine whether $\triangle ABD \cong \triangle CBD$. Justify your answer.

4. Suppose $\angle A \cong \angle C$. Determine whether $\triangle ABD \cong \triangle CBD$. Justify your answer.

Word Problem Practice

AL OL BL ELL

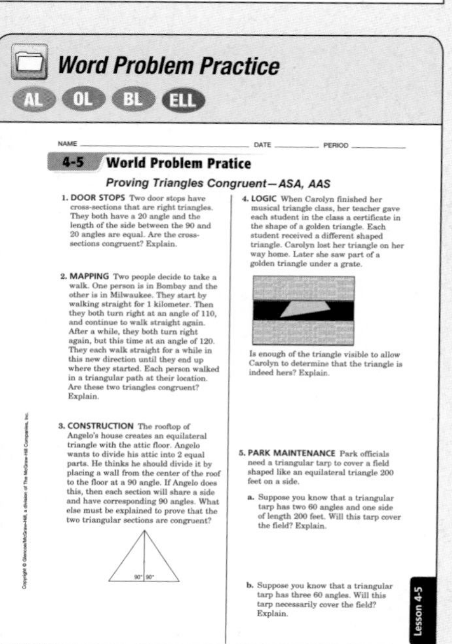
NAME ______ DATE ______ PERIOD ______

4-5 World Problem Pratice

Proving Triangles Congruent—ASA, AAS

1. DOOR STOPS Two door stops have cross-sections that are right triangles. They both have a 20 angle and the length of the side between the 90 and 20 angles are equal. Are the cross-sections congruent? Explain.

2. MAPPING Two people decide to take a walk. One person is in Bombay and the other is in Milwaukee. They start by walking straight for 1 kilometer. Then they both turn right at an angle of 110, and continue to walk straight again. After a while, they both turn right again, but this time at an angle of 120. They each walk straight for a while in this new direction until they end up where they started. Each person walked in a triangular path at their location. Are these two triangles congruent? Explain.

3. CONSTRUCTION The rooftop of Angelo's house creates an equilateral triangle with the attic floor. Angelo wants to divide his attic into 2 equal parts. He thinks he should divide it by placing a wall from the center of the roof to the floor at a 90 angle. If Angelo does this, then each section will share a side and have corresponding 90 angles. What else must be explained to prove that the two triangular sections are congruent?

4. LOGIC When Carolyn finished her musical triangle class, her teacher gave each student in the class a certificate in the shape of a golden triangle. Each student received a different shaped triangle. Carolyn lost her triangle on her way home. Later she saw part of a golden triangle under a grate.

Is enough of the triangle visible to allow Carolyn to determine that the triangle is indeed hers? Explain.

5. PARK MAINTENANCE Park officials need a triangular tarp to cover a field shaped like an equilateral triangle 200 feet on a side.

a. Suppose you know that a triangular tarp has two 60 angles and one side of length 200 feet. Will this tarp cover the field? Explain.

b. Suppose you know that a triangular tarp has three 60 angles. Will this tarp necessarily cover the field? Explain.

Lesson 4-5

12. **PROOF** Write a flow proof.

Given: $\overline{KM}$ bisects $\angle JML$; $\angle J \cong \angle L$.

Prove: $\overline{JM} \cong \overline{LM}$ **See Ch. 4 Answer Appendix.**

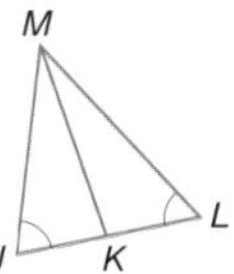

Example 3

13. **CCSS MODELING** A high school wants to hold a 1500-meter regatta on Lake Powell but is unsure if the lake is long enough. To measure the distance across the lake, the crew members locate the vertices of the triangles below and find the measures of the lengths of $\triangle HJK$ as shown below.

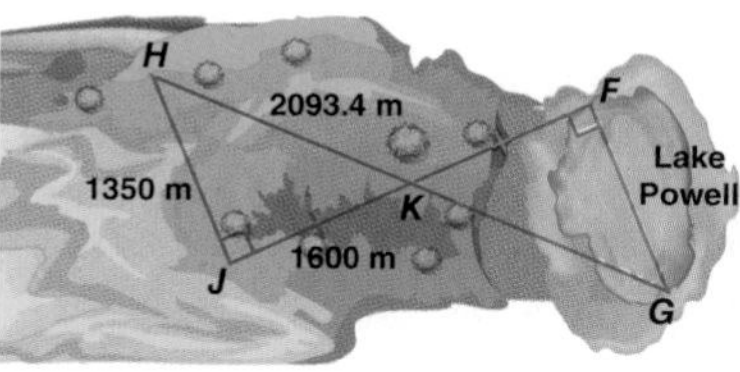

a. Explain how the crew team can use the triangles formed to estimate the distance FG across the lake. **See Ch. 4 Answer Appendix.**

b. Using the measures given, is the lake long enough for the team to use as the location for their regatta? Explain your reasoning. **No; $HJ = 1350$ m, so $FG = 1350$ m. If the regatta is to be 1500 m, the lake is not long enough, since $1350 < 1500$.**

B **ALGEBRA** Find the value of the variable that yields congruent triangles.

14. $\triangle BCD \cong \triangle WXY$ **$x = 3$**

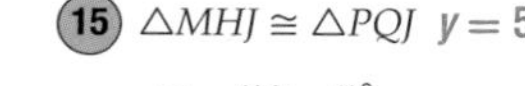

15. $\triangle MHJ \cong \triangle PQJ$ **$y = 5$**

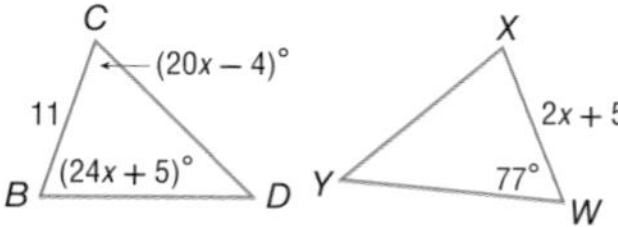

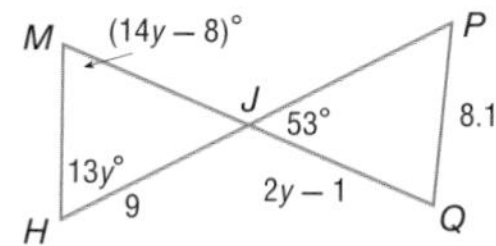

16. **THEATER DESIGN** The trusses of the roof of the outdoor theater shown below appear to be several different pairs of congruent triangles. Assume that trusses that appear to lie on the same line actually lie on the same line. **16a–c. See Ch. 4 Answer Appendix.**

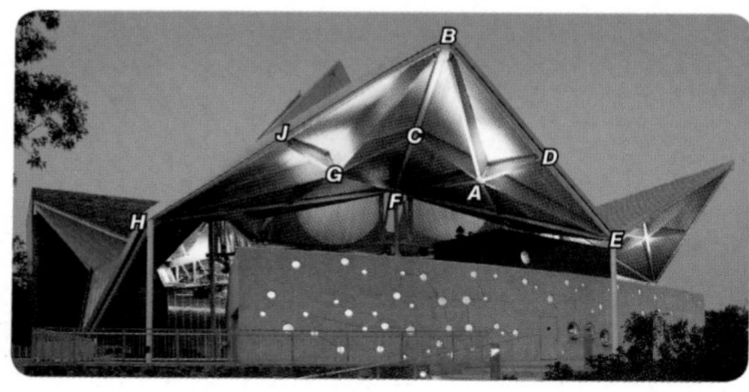

a. If $\overline{AB}$ bisects $\angle CBD$ and $\angle CAD$, prove that $\triangle ABC \cong \triangle ABD$.

b. If $\triangle ABC \cong \triangle ABD$ and $\angle FCA \cong \angle EDA$, prove that $\triangle CAF \cong \triangle DAE$.

c. If $\overline{HB} \cong \overline{EB}$, $\angle BHG \cong \angle BEA$, $\angle HGJ \cong \angle EAD$, and $\angle JGB \cong \angle DAB$, prove that $\triangle BHG \cong \triangle BEA$.

Enrichment

OL BL

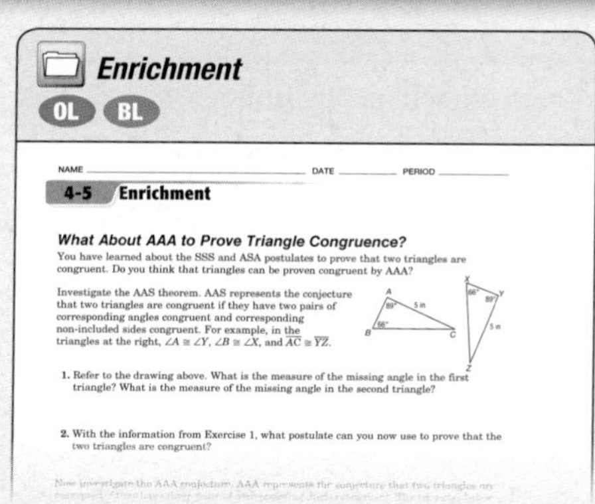
NAME ______ DATE ______ PERIOD ______

4-5 Enrichment

What About AAA to Prove Triangle Congruence?

You have learned about the SSS and ASA postulates to prove that two triangles are congruent. Do you think that triangles can be proven congruent by AAA?

Investigate the AAS theorem. AAS represents the conjecture that two triangles are congruent if they have two pairs of corresponding angles congruent and corresponding non-included sides congruent. For example, in the triangles at the right, $\angle A \cong \angle Y$, $\angle B \cong \angle X$, and $\overline{AC} \cong \overline{YZ}$.

1. Refer to the drawing above. What is the measure of the missing angle in the first triangle? What is the measure of the missing angle in the second triangle?

2. With the information from Exercise 1, what postulate can you now use to prove that the two triangles are congruent?

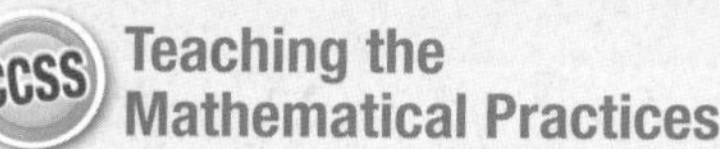

Teaching the Mathematical Practices

Modeling Mathematically proficient students can apply mathematics to solve problems arising in real life. For Exercise 13, encourage students to work together to plan a solution pathway.

280 | Lesson 4-5 | Proving Triangles Congruent—ASA, AAS

PROOF **Write a paragraph proof.** 17–18. See margin.

17. **Given:** $\overline{AE} \perp \overline{DE}$, $\overline{EA} \perp \overline{AB}$, C is the midpoint of $\overline{AE}$.
Prove: $\overline{CD} \cong \overline{CB}$

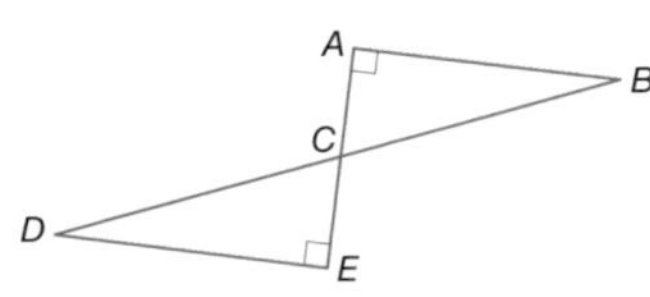

18. **Given:** $\angle F \cong \angle J$, $\overline{FH} \parallel \overline{GJ}$
Prove: $\overline{FH} \cong \overline{JG}$

PROOF **Write a two-column proof.** 19–20. See margin.

19. **Given:** $\angle K \cong \angle M$, $\overline{KP} \perp \overline{PR}$, $\overline{MR} \perp \overline{PR}$
Prove: $\angle KPL \cong \angle MRL$

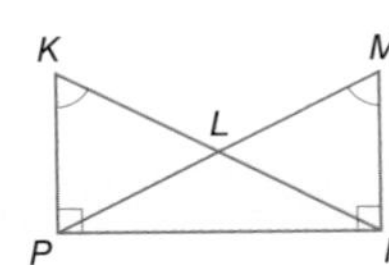

20. **Given:** $\overline{QR} \cong \overline{SR} \cong \overline{WR} \cong \overline{VR}$
Prove: $\overline{QT} \cong \overline{WU}$

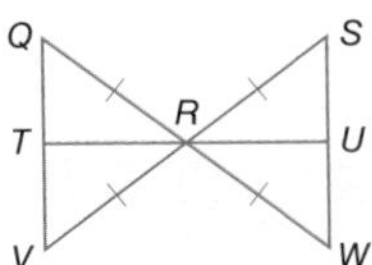

21 **FITNESS** The seat tube of a bicycle forms a triangle with each seat and chain stay as shown. If each seat stay makes a 44° angle with its corresponding chain stay and each chain stay makes a 68° angle with the seat tube, show that the two seat stays are the same length. See Ch. 4 Answer Appendix.

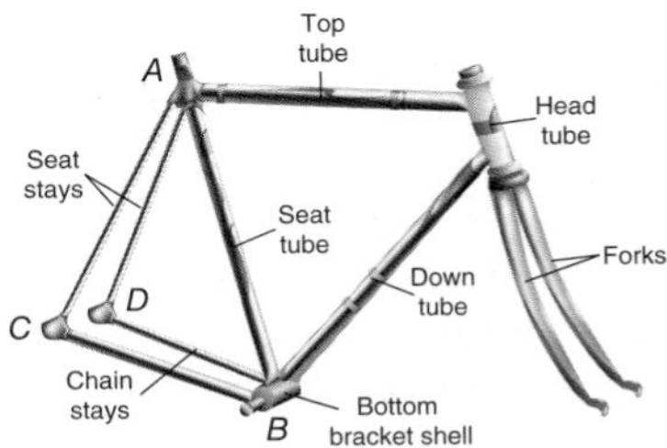

23. Tyrone; Lorenzo showed that all three corresponding angles were congruent, but AAA is not a proof of triangle congruence.

H.O.T. Problems Use Higher-Order Thinking Skills

22. **OPEN ENDED** Draw and label two triangles that could be proved congruent by ASA. See margin.

23. CCSS **CRITIQUE** Tyrone says it is not possible to show that $\triangle ADE \cong \triangle ACB$. Lorenzo disagrees, explaining that since $\angle ADE \cong \angle ACB$, and $\angle A \cong \angle A$ by the Reflexive Property, $\triangle ADE \cong \triangle ACB$. Is either of them correct? Explain.

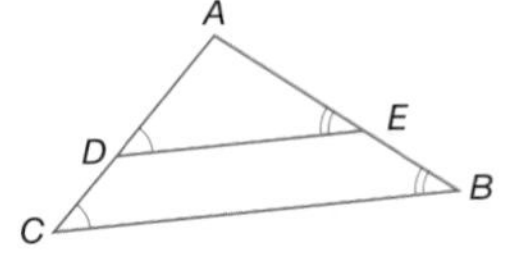

24. **REASONING** Find a counterexample to show why SSA (Side-Side-Angle) cannot be used to prove the congruence of two triangles. See Ch. 4 Answer Appendix.

25. **CHALLENGE** Using the information given in the diagram, write a flow proof to show that $\triangle PVQ \cong \triangle SVT$. See Ch. 4 Answer Appendix.

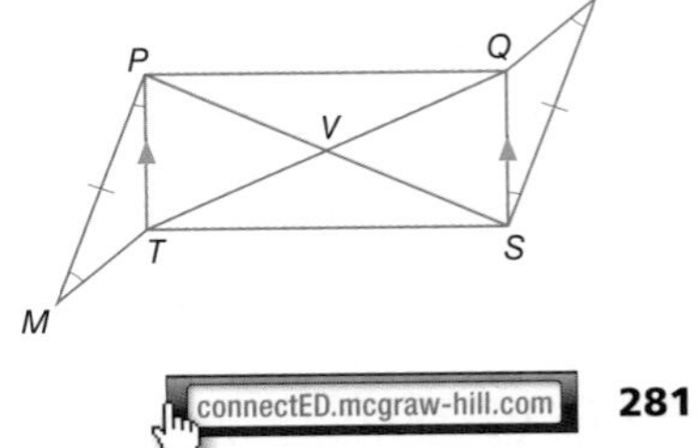

26. **WRITING IN MATH** How do you know what method (SSS, SAS, etc.) to use when proving triangle congruence? Use a chart to explain your reasoning. See Ch. 4 Answer Appendix.

CCSS Teaching the Mathematical Practices

Critique Mathematically proficient students can distinguish correct logic from flawed reasoning. In Exercise 23, Tyrone is correct. Lorenzo has shown that all three pairs of corresponding angles of the congruent triangles are congruent, but this does not prove that $\triangle ADE \cong \triangle ACB$. In fact, triangles that have corresponding congruent angles can have different side lengths.

Additional Answers

17. **Proof:** We are given that $\overline{AE}$ is perpendicular to $\overline{DE}$, $\overline{EA}$ is perpendicular to $\overline{AB}$, and C is the midpoint of $\overline{AE}$. Since $\overline{AE}$ is perpendicular to $\overline{DE}$, $m\angle CED = 90$. Since $\overline{EA}$ is perpendicular to $\overline{AB}$, $m\angle BAC = 90$. $\angle CED \cong \angle BAC$ because all right angles are congruent. $\overline{AC} \cong \overline{CE}$ from the Midpt. Thm. $\angle ECD \cong \angle ACB$ because they are vertical angles. Angle-Side-Angle gives us that $\triangle CED \cong \triangle CAB$. $\overline{CD} \cong \overline{CB}$ because corresponding parts of congruent triangles are congruent.

18. **Proof:** $\angle F \cong \angle J$ and $\overline{FH} \parallel \overline{GJ}$ because it is given. $\angle FHG \cong \angle JGH$ because they are alternate interior angles. By the Reflexive Property, $\overline{GH} \cong \overline{GH}$. So $\triangle GHJ \cong \triangle HGF$ by the Angle-Angle-Side postulate. Then $\overline{FH} \cong \overline{JG}$ since corresponding parts of congruent triangles are congruent.

19. **Proof:**

Statements (Reasons)

1. $\angle K \cong \angle M$, $\overline{KP} \perp \overline{PR}$, $\overline{MR} \perp \overline{PR}$ (Given)
2. $\angle KPR$ and $\angle MRP$ are both right angles. (Def. of $\perp$)
3. $\angle KPR \cong \angle MRP$ (All rt. ∠s are congruent.)
4. $\overline{PR} \cong \overline{PR}$ (Refl. Prop.)
5. $\triangle KPR \cong \triangle MRP$ (AAS)
6. $\overline{KP} \cong \overline{MR}$ (CPCTC)
7. $\angle KLP \cong \angle MLR$ (Vertical angles are $\cong$.)
8. $\triangle KLP \cong \triangle MLR$ (AAS)
9. $\angle KPL \cong \angle MRL$ (CPCTC)

20. **Proof:**

Statements (Reasons)

1. $\overline{QR} \cong \overline{SR} \cong \overline{WR} \cong \overline{VR}$ (Given)
2. $\angle QRV \cong \angle SRW$ (Vert. ∠s are $\cong$.)
3. $\triangle VRQ \cong \triangle SRW$ (SAS)
4. $\angle VQR \cong \angle SWR$ (CPCTC)
5. $\angle QRT \cong \angle URW$ (Vert. ∠s are $\cong$.)
6. $\triangle URW \cong \triangle TRQ$ (ASA)
7. $\overline{QT} \cong \overline{WU}$ (CPCTC)

22. Sample answer: $\triangle ABC \cong \triangle DEF$

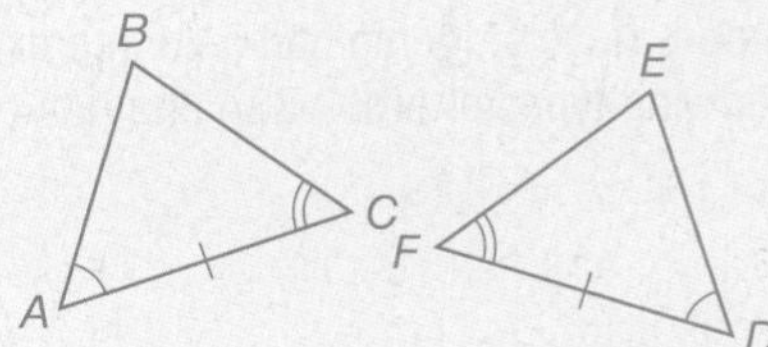

4 Assess

Yesterday's News Have students observe and study the Key Concepts on pp. 264, 266, 275, and 276. Have them write a conclusion about any similarities and differences between yesterday's concepts of SSS and SAS and today's concepts of ASA and AAS.

Additional Answers

31. $AB = \sqrt{125}$, $BC = \sqrt{221}$, $AC = \sqrt{226}$, $XY = \sqrt{125}$, $YZ = \sqrt{221}$, $XZ = \sqrt{226}$. The corresponding sides have the same measure and are congruent. $\triangle ABC \cong \triangle XYZ$ by SSS.

32. $AB = 5$, $BC = 2$, $AC = \sqrt{29}$, $XY = 5$, $YZ = 2$, $XZ = \sqrt{29}$; the corresponding sides have the same measure and are congruent. $\triangle ABC \cong \triangle XYZ$ by SSS.

33. $x = 19$; $y = 3$

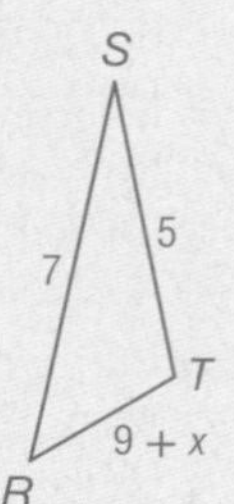

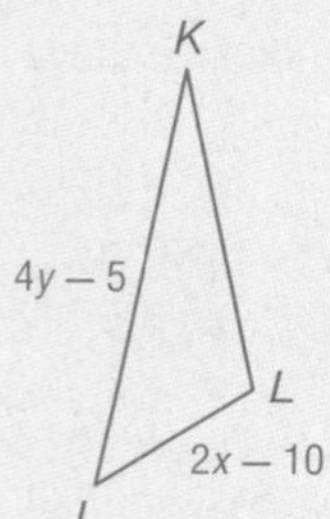

37. Proof:

Statements (Reasons)

1. $\angle 2 \cong \angle 1$, $\angle 1 \cong \angle 3$ (Given)
2. $\angle 2 \cong \angle 3$ (Trans. Prop.)
3. $AB \parallel DE$ (If alt. int. ∠s are ≅, lines are ∥.)

38. Proof:

Statements (Reasons)

1. $\angle MJK \cong \angle KLM$, $\angle LMJ$ and $\angle KLM$ are suppl. (Given)
2. $m\angle MJK = m\angle KLM$ (Def. of ≅ ∠s)
3. $m\angle LMJ + m\angle KLM = 180$ (Def. of ≅ suppl. ∠s)
4. $m\angle LMJ + m\angle MJK = 180$ (Subst.)
5. $\angle LMJ$ and $\angle MJK$ are suppl. (Def. of suppl. ∠s)
6. $\overline{KJ} \parallel \overline{LM}$ (If cons. int. ∠s are suppl., lines are ∥.)

Standardized Test Practice

27. Given: $\overline{BC}$ is perpendicular to $\overline{AD}$; $\angle 1 \cong \angle 2$.

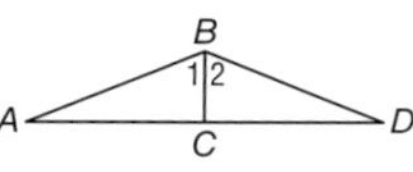

Which theorem or postulate could be used to prove $\triangle ABC \cong \triangle DBC$? **B**

A AAS
B ASA
C SAS
D SSS

28. SHORT RESPONSE Write an expression that can be used to find the values of $s(n)$ in the table. $\frac{1}{4}n + 3$

n	−8	−4	−1	0	1
$s(n)$	1.00	2.00	2.75	3.00	3.25

29. ALGEBRA If −7 is multiplied by a number greater than 1, which of the following describes the result? **J**

F a number greater than 7
G a number between −7 and 7
H a number greater than −7
J a number less than −7

30. SAT/ACT $\sqrt{121 + 104} = ?$ **A**

A 15
B 21
C 25
D 125
E 225

Spiral Review

Determine whether $\triangle ABC \cong \triangle XYZ$. Explain. (Lesson 4-4) **31–32. See margin.**

31. $A(6, 4)$, $B(1, -6)$, $C(-9, 5)$, $X(0, 7)$, $Y(5, -3)$, $Z(15, 8)$

32. $A(0, 5)$, $B(0, 0)$, $C(-2, 0)$, $X(4, 8)$, $Y(4, 3)$, $Z(6, 3)$

33. ALGEBRA If $\triangle RST \cong \triangle JKL$, $RS = 7$, $ST = 5$, $RT = 9 + x$, $JL = 2x - 10$, and $JK = 4y - 5$, draw and label a figure to represent the congruent triangles. Then find x and y. (Lesson 4-3) **See margin.**

34. FINANCIAL LITERACY Maxine charges $5 to paint a mailbox and $4 per hour to mow a lawn. Write an equation to represent the amount of money Maxine can earn from a homeowner who has his or her mailbox painted and lawn mowed. (Lesson 3-4) $y = 4x + 5$

Copy and complete each truth table. (Lesson 2-2)

35.

p	q	$\sim p$	$\sim p \vee q$
F	T	T	T
T	T	F	T
F	F	T	T
T	F	F	F

36.

p	q	$\sim q$	$\sim q \wedge p$
F	T	F	F
T	F	T	T
T	T	F	F
F	F	T	T

Skills Review

PROOF **Write a two-column proof for each of the following.** **37–38. See margin.**

37. **Given:** $\angle 2 \cong \angle 1$
$\angle 1 \cong \angle 3$

Prove: $\overline{AB} \parallel \overline{DE}$

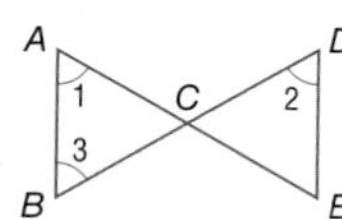

38. **Given:** $\angle MJK \cong \angle KLM$
$\angle LMJ$ and $\angle KLM$ are supplementary.

Prove: $\overline{KJ} \parallel \overline{LM}$

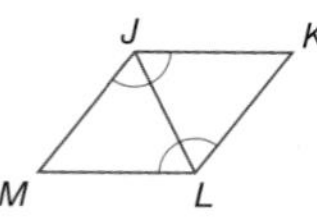

Differentiated Instruction OL BL

Extension Have students find a counterexample for the following types of proof: SSA and AAA.

Sample answer for AAA: $\angle A \cong \angle D$; $\angle B \cong \angle E$, and $\angle C \cong \angle F$. Since $AC = 6$ and $DF = 12$, $\overline{AC} \not\cong \overline{DF}$; therefore $\triangle ABC \not\cong \triangle DEF$.

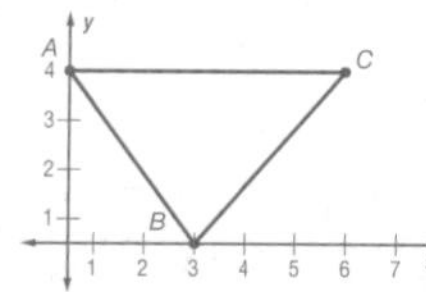

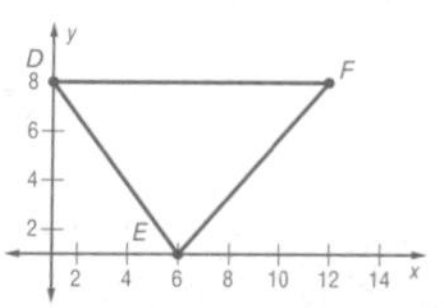

EXTEND 4-5 Geometry Lab: Congruence in Right Triangles

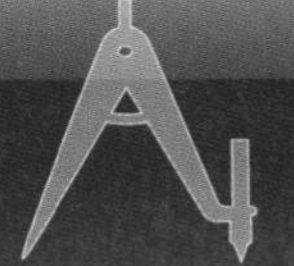

In Lessons 4-4 and 4-5, you learned theorems and postulates to prove triangles congruent. How do these theorems and postulates apply to right triangles?

Common Core State Standards
Content Standards
G.SRT.5 Use congruence and similarity criteria for triangles to solve problems and to prove relationships in geometric figures.
Mathematical Practices 5

Study each pair of right triangles.

a.
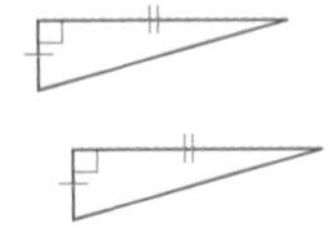

b.

c.
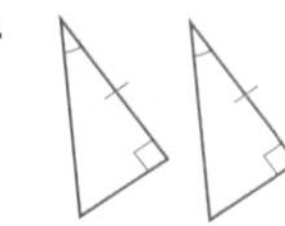

Analyze

1. Is each pair of triangles congruent? If so, which congruence theorem or postulate applies? Yes, a. SAS, b. AAS, c. ASA
2. Rewrite the congruence rules from Exercise 1 using *leg*, (L), or *hypotenuse*, (H), to replace *side*. Omit the *A* for any right angle since we know that all right triangles contain a right angle and all right angles are congruent. a. LL, b. HA, c. LA
3. **MAKE A CONJECTURE** If you know that the corresponding legs of two right triangles are congruent, what other information do you need to declare the triangles congruent? Explain. None; two pairs of legs congruent is sufficient for proving right triangles congruent.

In Lesson 4-5, you learned that SSA is not a valid test for determining triangle congruence. Can SSA be used to prove right triangles congruent?

Activity SSA and Right Triangles

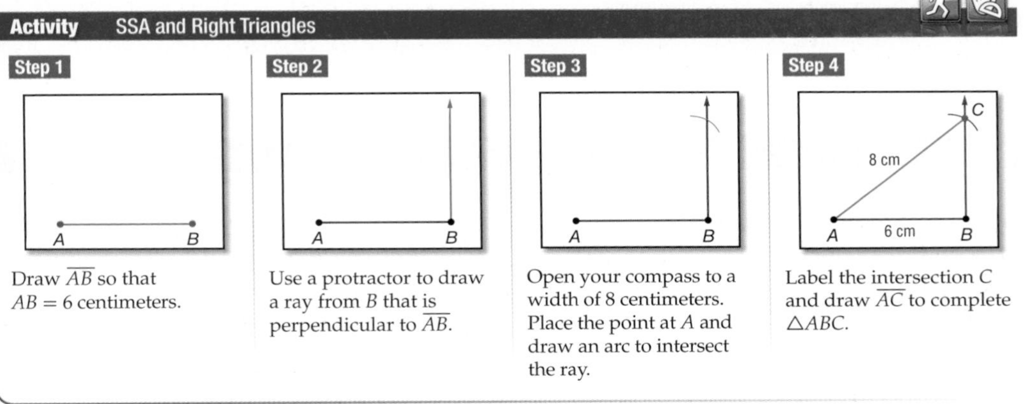

Step 1 Draw $\overline{AB}$ so that $AB = 6$ centimeters.

Step 2 Use a protractor to draw a ray from B that is perpendicular to $\overline{AB}$.

Step 3 Open your compass to a width of 8 centimeters. Place the point at A and draw an arc to intersect the ray.

Step 4 Label the intersection C and draw $\overline{AC}$ to complete $\triangle ABC$.

Analyze

4. Does the model yield a unique triangle? yes
5. Can you use the lengths of the hypotenuse and a leg to show right triangles are congruent? yes
6. **Make a conjecture** about the case of SSA that exists for right triangles. SSA is a valid test of congruence for right triangles.

(continued on the next page)

1 Focus

Objective Explore congruence in right triangles.

Materials

- rulers
- protractors

2 Teach

Working in Cooperative Groups

Arrange students in groups of 3 or 4, mixing abilities. Then have groups complete Exercises 1–3, the activity, and Exercises 4–6.

Ask:

- How are right triangles labeled differently than other triangles? They have a right triangle symbol.
- What other unique features do right triangles have? The sides adjacent to the right angle are called legs, and the side opposite the right angle is called the hypotenuse.
- Is there another type of triangle that has special names for its parts? isosceles

Practice Have students complete Exercises 7–15.

Follow-up

Students have explored triangle congruence postulates and theorems.

Ask:

- Why are rules about triangle congruence useful? Sample answer: Rules such as postulates and theorems about triangles congruence allow you to prove that two triangles are congruent using only three corresponding congruent triangle parts. So, by using these rules, you don't have to test all of the sides and angles of the triangles to prove that they are congruent.

3 Assess

Formative Assessment

Use Exercises 10–13 to assess whether students comprehend how to write a paragraph proof. Use Exercises 14–15 to assess whether students understand when to apply Right Triangle Congruence Theorems in proofs.

From Concrete to Abstract

Have students write an algebraic equation for a right triangle that will prove that the sum of the remaining angles is 90. If $m\angle C = 90$ and $m\angle A + m\angle B + m\angle C = 180$ by the Angle Sum Theorem, then $m\angle A + m\angle B = 90$.

Additional Answers

12. Case 1:

Given: $\triangle ABC$ and $\triangle DEF$ are right triangles. $\overline{AC} \cong \overline{DF}$, $\angle C \cong \angle F$

Prove: $\triangle ABC \cong \triangle DEF$

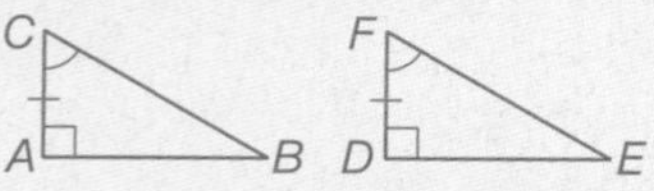

Proof: It is given that $\triangle ABC$ and $\triangle DEF$ are right traingles, $\overline{AC} \cong \overline{DF}$, $\angle C \cong \angle F$. By the definition of right triangles, $\angle A$ and $\angle D$ are right angles. Thus, $\angle A \cong \angle D$ since all right angles are congruent. $\triangle ABC \cong \triangle DEF$ by ASA.

Case 2:

Given: $\triangle ABC$ and $\triangle EFD$ are right triangles. $\overline{CB} \cong \overline{DF}$, $\angle B \cong \angle F$

Prove: $\triangle ABC \cong \triangle EFD$

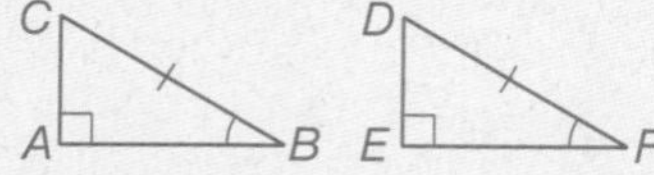

Proof: It is given that $\triangle ABC$ and $\triangle EFD$ are right triangles, $\overline{CB} \cong \overline{DF}$, $\angle B \cong \angle F$. By the definition of right triangle, $\angle A$ and $\angle E$ are right angles. Thus, $\angle A \cong \angle E$ since all right angles are congruent. $\triangle ABC \cong \triangle EFD$ by AAS.

13. Given: $\triangle ABC$ and $\triangle DEF$ are right triangles.

$\overline{BC} \cong \overline{EF}$

$\overline{AB} \cong \overline{DE}$

Prove: $\triangle ABC \cong \triangle DEF$

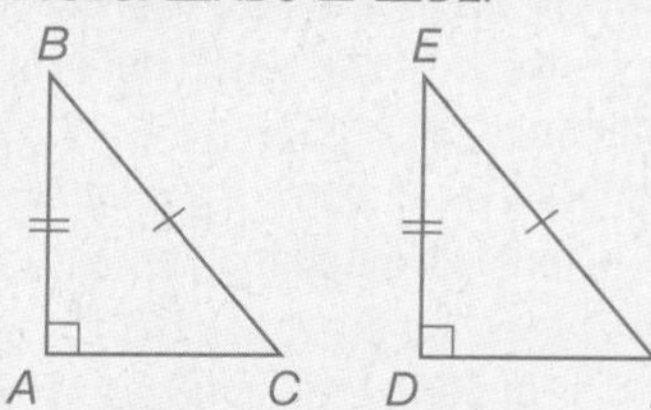

Proof: Statements (Reasons)

1. $\triangle ABC$ and $\triangle DEF$ are right triangles, $\overline{BC} \cong \overline{EF}$, $\overline{AB} \cong \overline{DE}$ (Given)
2. $AB = DE$, $BC = EF$ (Def. of $\cong$)
3. $(AB)^2 + (CA)^2 = (BC)^2$, $(DE)^2 + (FD)^2 = (EF)^2$ (Pythagorean Thm.)
4. $(AB)^2 + (CA)^2 = (DE)^2 + (FD)^2$ (Subs. Prop.)
5. $(AB)^2 + (CA)^2 = (AB)^2 + (FD)^2$ (Subs. Prop.)
6. $(CA)^2 = (FD)^2$ (Subt. Prop.)
7. $CA = FD$ (A property of square roots)
8. $\overline{CA} \cong \overline{FD}$ (Def. of $\cong$ segments)
9. $\triangle ABC \cong \triangle DEF$ (SSS)

Geometry Lab
Congruence in Right Triangles *Continued*

Your work on the previous page provides evidence for four ways to prove right triangles congruent.

Theorem Right Triangle Congruence

Theorem 4.6 Leg-Leg Congruence
If the legs of one right triangle are congruent to the corresponding legs of another right triangle, then the triangles are congruent.

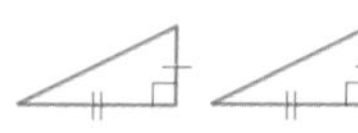

Abbreviation *LL*

Theorem 4.7 Hypotenuse-Angle Congruence
If the hypotenuse and acute angle of one right triangle are congruent to the hypotenuse and corresponding acute angle of another right triangle, then the two triangles are congruent.

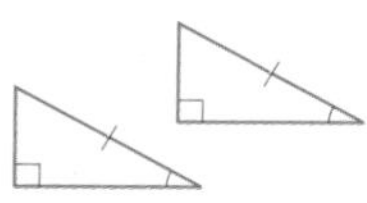

Abbreviation *HA*

Theorem 4.8 Leg-Angle Congruence
If one leg and an acute angle of one right triangle are congruent to the corresponding leg and acute angle of another right triangle, then the triangles are congruent.

Abbreviation *LA*

Theorem 4.9 Hypotenuse-Leg Congruence
If the hypotenuse and a leg of one right triangle are congruent to the hypotenuse and corresponding leg of another right triangle, then the triangles are congruent.

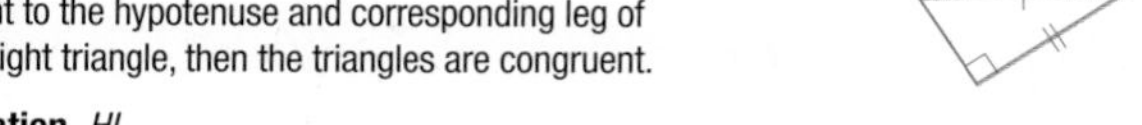

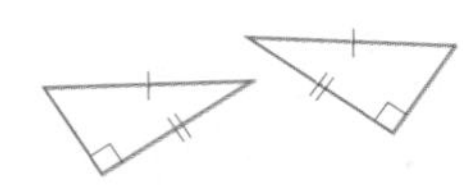

Abbreviation *HL*

Exercises

Determine whether each pair of triangles is congruent. If yes, tell which postulate or theorem applies.

7. 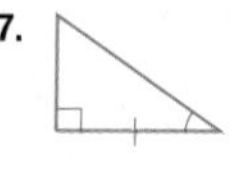 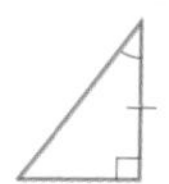 yes, LA

8.   no

9. 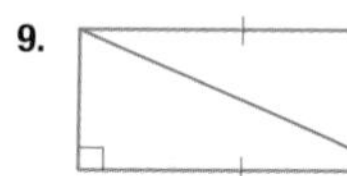 yes, HL

PROOF **Write a proof for each of the following.** **10–11. See Ch. 4 Answer Appendix. 12–13. See margin.**

10. Theorem 4.6
11. Theorem 4.7
12. Theorem 4.8 (*Hint*: There are two possible cases.)
13. Theorem 4.9 (*Hint*: Use the Pythagorean Theorem.)

Use the figure at the right. **14–15. See Ch. 4 Answer Appendix.**

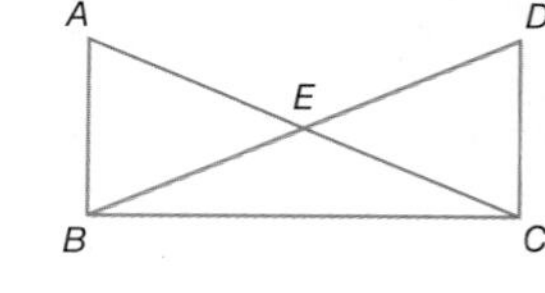

14. **Given:** $\overline{AB} \perp \overline{BC}$, $\overline{DC} \perp \overline{BC}$, $\overline{AC} \cong \overline{BD}$
Prove: $\overline{AB} \cong \overline{DC}$

15. **Given:** $\overline{AB} \parallel \overline{DC}$, $\overline{AB} \perp \overline{BC}$, E is the midpoint of $\overline{AC}$ and $\overline{BD}$.
Prove: $\overline{AC} \cong \overline{DB}$

LESSON 4-6 Isosceles and Equilateral Triangles

Then
- You identified isosceles and equilateral triangles.

Now
1. Use properties of isosceles triangles.
2. Use properties of equilateral triangles.

Why?
- The tracks on the roller coaster have triangular reinforcements between the tracks for support and stability. The triangle supports in the photo are isosceles triangles.

NewVocabulary
legs of an isosceles triangle
vertex angle
base angles

Common Core State Standards

Content Standards
G.CO.10 Prove theorems about triangles.
G.CO.12 Make formal geometric constructions with a variety of tools and methods (compass and straightedge, string, reflective devices, paper folding, dynamic geometric software, etc.).

Mathematical Practices
2 Reason abstractly and quantitatively.
3 Construct viable arguments and critique the reasoning of others.

1 Properties of Isosceles Triangles

Recall that isosceles triangles have at least two congruent sides. The parts of an isosceles triangle have special names.

The two congruent sides are called the **legs of an isosceles triangle**, and the angle with sides that are the legs is called the **vertex angle**. The side of the triangle opposite the vertex angle is called the *base*. The two angles formed by the base and the congruent sides are called the **base angles**.

$\angle 1$ is the vertex angle.

$\angle 2$ and $\angle 3$ are the base angles.

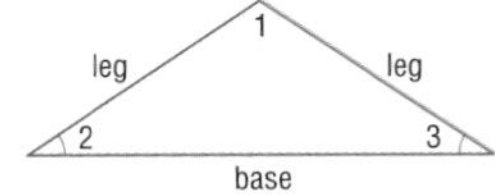

Theorems Isosceles Triangle

4.10 Isosceles Triangle Theorem
If two sides of a triangle are congruent, then the angles opposite those sides are congruent.

Example If $\overline{AC} \cong \overline{BC}$, then $\angle 2 \cong \angle 1$.

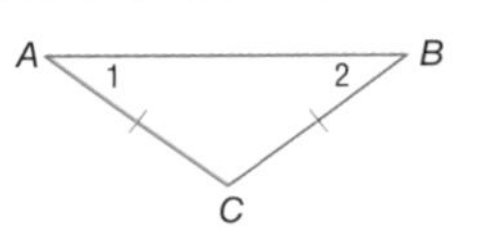

4.11 Converse of Isosceles Triangle Theorem
If two angles of a triangle are congruent, then the sides opposite those angles are congruent.

Example If $\angle 1 \cong \angle 2$, then $\overline{FE} \cong \overline{DE}$.

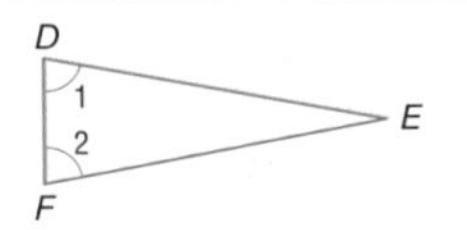

You will prove Theorem 4.11 in Exercise 37.

Example 1 Congruent Segments and Angles

a. Name two unmarked congruent angles.

$\angle ACB$ is opposite $\overline{AB}$ and $\angle B$ is opposite $\overline{AC}$, so $\angle ACB \cong \angle B$.

b. Name two unmarked congruent segments.

$\overline{AD}$ is opposite $\angle ACD$ and $\overline{AC}$ is opposite $\angle D$, so $\overline{AD} \cong \overline{AC}$.

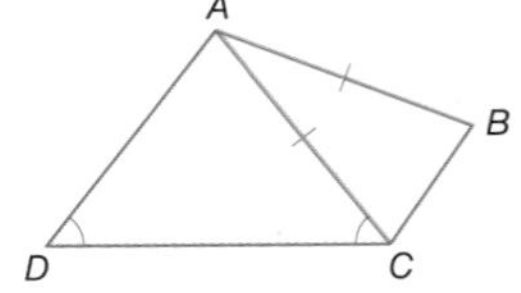

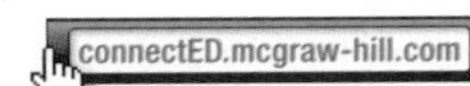

1 Focus

VerticalAlignment

Before Lesson 4-6 Identify isosceles and equilateral triangles.

Lesson 4-6 Use properties of isosceles and equilateral triangles.

After Lesson 4-6 Use congruence transformations to make conjectures and justify properties of geometric figures.

2 Teach

Scaffolding Questions

Have students read the **Why?** section of the lesson.

Ask:
- Why are the triangles isosceles? Because each triangle has two congruent sides.
- What appears to be true about the angles opposite the equal sides? The angles appear to be congruent.
- What type of triangle results if the third side of the triangle is congruent to the other 2 sides? an equilateral triangle
- What do you think is true of the three angles if the three sides are congruent? The angles are also congruent, and each measures 60.

Lesson 4-6 Resources

Resource	Approaching Level AL	On Level OL	Beyond Level BL	English Learners ELL
Teacher Edition	▪ Differentiated Instruction, p. 287	▪ Differentiated Instruction, pp. 287, 288	▪ Differentiated Instruction, p. 288	▪ Differentiated Instruction, p. 287
Chapter Resource Masters	▪ Study Guide and Intervention, pp. 37–38 ▪ Skills Practice, p. 39 ▪ Practice, p. 40 ▪ Word Problem Practice, p. 41	▪ Study Guide and Intervention, pp. 37–38 ▪ Skills Practice, p. 39 ▪ Practice, p. 40 ▪ Word Problem Practice, p. 41 ▪ Enrichment, p. 42	▪ Practice, p. 40 ▪ Word Problem Practice, p. 41 ▪ Enrichment, p. 42	▪ Study Guide and Intervention, pp. 37–38 ▪ Skills Practice, p. 39 ▪ Practice, p. 40 ▪ Word Problem Practice, p. 41
Other	▪ 5-Minute Check 4-6 ▪ Study Notebook ▪ Teaching Geometry with Manipulatives	▪ 5-Minute Check 4-6 ▪ Study Notebook ▪ Teaching Geometry with Manipulatives	▪ 5-Minute Check 4-6 ▪ Study Notebook	▪ 5-Minute Chec 4-6 ▪ Study Notebook ▪ Teaching Geometry with Manipulatives

1 Properties of Isosceles Triangles

Example 1 shows how to use the Isosceles Triangle Theorem to name congruent sides and angles.

Formative Assessment

Use the Guided Practice exercises after each example to determine students' understanding of concepts.

Additional Example

1

a. Name two unmarked congruent angles. $\angle A$ and $\angle BCA$

b. Name two unmarked congruent segments. $\overline{BD} \cong \overline{BC}$

Additional Examples also in Interactive Classroom PowerPoint® Presentations

IWB Interactive White Board READY

Teach with Tech

Video Recording Have students work in groups to create videos showing how to prove that triangles are either isosceles or equilateral. Share each group's video with the class.

GuidedPractice

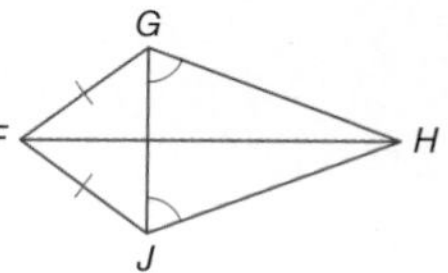

1A. Name two unmarked congruent angles.

1B. Name two unmarked congruent segments.

1A. $\angle FGJ$ and $\angle FJG$
1B. $\overline{GH}$ and $\overline{JH}$

To prove the Isosceles Triangle Theorem, draw an auxiliary line and use the two triangles formed.

Proof Isosceles Triangle Theorem

Given: $\triangle LMP$; $\overline{LM} \cong \overline{LP}$

Prove: $\angle M \cong \angle P$

Proof:

Statements	Reasons
1. Let N be the midpoint of $\overline{MP}$.	1. Every segment has exactly one midpoint.
2. Draw an auxiliary segment $\overline{LN}$.	2. Two points determine a line.
3. $\overline{MN} \cong \overline{PN}$	3. Midpoint Theorem
4. $\overline{LN} \cong \overline{LN}$	4. Reflexive Property of Congruence
5. $\overline{LM} \cong \overline{LP}$	5. Given
6. $\triangle LMN \cong \triangle LPN$	6. SSS
7. $\angle M \cong \angle P$	7. CPCTC

2 Properties of Equilateral Triangles

The Isosceles Triangle Theorem leads to two corollaries about the angles of an equilateral triangle.

ReviewVocabulary
equilateral triangle a triangle with three congruent sides

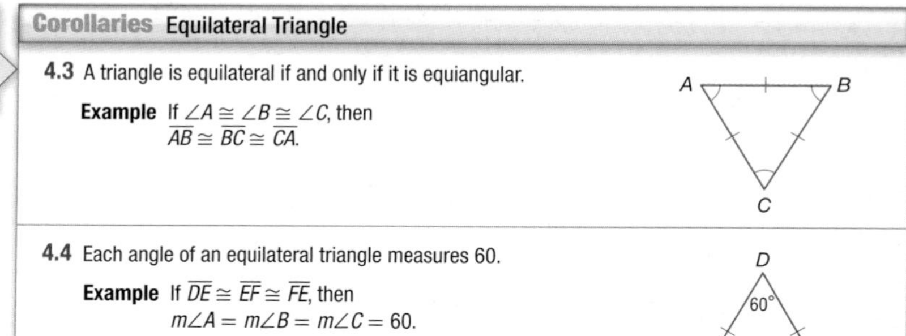

Corollaries Equilateral Triangle

4.3 A triangle is equilateral if and only if it is equiangular.

Example If $\angle A \cong \angle B \cong \angle C$, then $\overline{AB} \cong \overline{BC} \cong \overline{CA}$.

4.4 Each angle of an equilateral triangle measures 60.

Example If $\overline{DE} \cong \overline{EF} \cong \overline{FE}$, then $m\angle A = m\angle B = m\angle C = 60$.

You will prove Corollaries 4.3 and 4.4 in Exercises 35 and 36.

Tips for New Teachers

Vary Orientation Because parts of isosceles triangles have special names, students frequently make mistakes when classifying isosceles triangles. Make sure that you present isosceles triangles in different orientations so that students can identify the congruent sides and base angles.

Tips for New Teachers

Angle Congruence Use patty paper to demonstrate the relationship between the base angles of an isosceles triangle. Draw the figure and fold the paper in half.

Example 2 Find Missing Measures

Find each measure.

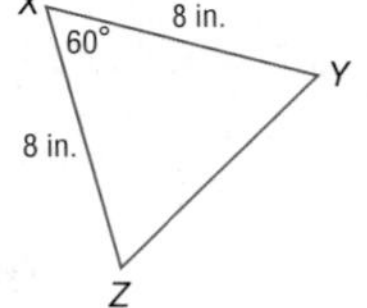

a. $m\angle Y$

Since $XY = XZ$, $\overline{XY} \cong \overline{XZ}$. By the Isosceles Triangle Theorem, base angles Z and Y are congruent, so $m\angle Z = m\angle Y$. Use the Triangle Sum Theorem to write and solve an equation to find $m\angle Y$.

$m\angle X + m\angle Y + m\angle Z = 180$	Triangle Sum Theorem
$60 + m\angle Y + m\angle Y = 180$	$m\angle X = 60$, $m\angle Z = m\angle Y$
$60 + 2(m\angle Y) = 180$	Simplify.
$2(m\angle Y) = 120$	Subtract 60 from each side.
$m\angle Y = 60$	Divide each side by 2.

StudyTip

Isosceles Triangles As you discovered in Example 2, any isosceles triangle that has one 60° angle must be an equilateral triangle.

b. YZ

$m\angle Z = m\angle Y$, so $m\angle Z = 60$ by substitution. Since $m\angle X = 60$, all three angles measure 60, so the triangle is equiangular. Because an equiangular triangle is also equilateral, $XY = XZ = ZY$. Since $XY = 8$ inches, $YZ = 8$ inches by substitution.

GuidedPractice

2A. $m\angle M$ **30**

2B. PN **11 cm**

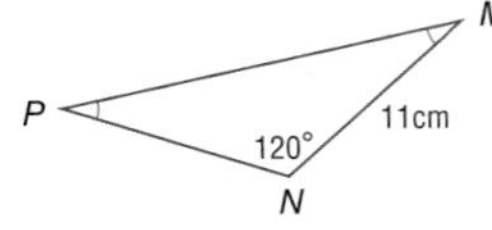

You can use the properties of equilateral triangles and algebra to find missing values.

Example 3 Find Missing Values

ALGEBRA Find the value of each variable.

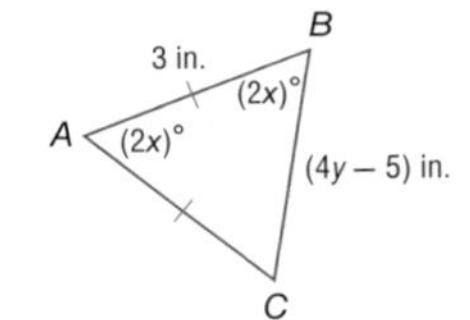

Since $\angle B = \angle A$, $\overline{AC} \cong \overline{BC}$ by the Converse of the Isosceles Triangle Theorem. All of the sides of the triangle are congruent, so the triangle is equilateral. Each angle of an equilateral triangle measures 60°, so $2x = 60$ and $x = 30$.

The triangle is equilateral, so all of the sides are congruent, and the lengths of all of the sides are equal.

$AB = BC$	Definition of equilateral triangle
$3 = 4y - 5$	Substitution
$8 = 4y$	Add 5 to each side.
$2 = y$	Divide each side by 4.

GuidedPractice

3. Find the value of each variable.
$x = 7$, $y = 2$

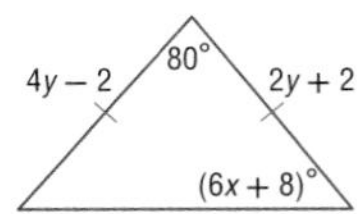
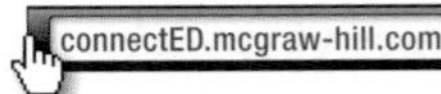

2 Properties of Equilateral Triangles

Examples 2 and 3 show how to use the properties of equilateral triangles to find missing measures and values. **Example 4** shows how to apply the triangle congruence properties to prove that a triangle is equilateral.

Additional Examples

2 Find each measure.

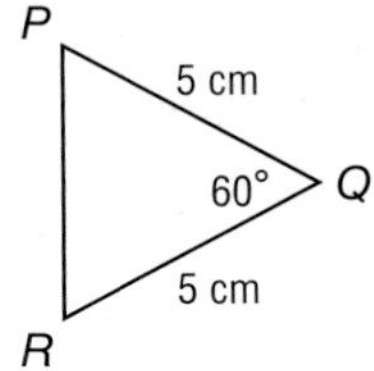

a. $m\angle R$ 60

b. PR 5 cm

3 **ALGEBRA** Find the value of each variable.

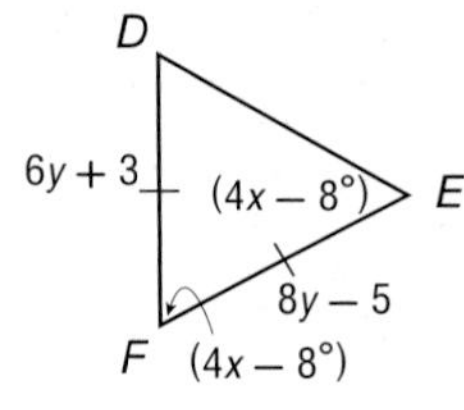

$x = 17$, $y = 4$

DifferentiatedInstruction AL OL ELL

Interpersonal Have groups of students work on Exercises 1–3 in Guided Practice. Encourage groups to discuss the properties of isosceles and equilateral triangles while they are figuring out the proofs.

Additional Example

4

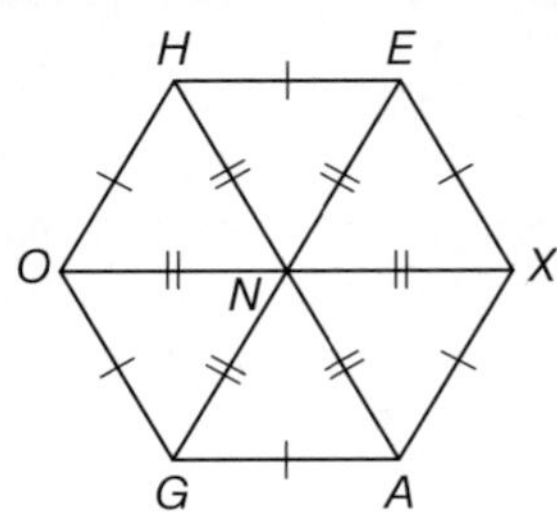

Given: *HEXAGO* is a regular polygon. $\triangle ONG$ is equilateral, *N* is the midpoint of $\overline{GE}$, and $\overline{EX} \parallel \overline{OG}$.

Prove: $\triangle ENX$ is equilateral.

Proof:

Statements (Reasons)

1. *HEXAGO* is a regular polygon. (Given)
2. $\triangle ONG$ is equilateral. (Given)
3. $\overline{EX} \cong \overline{XA} \cong \overline{AG} \cong \overline{GO} \cong \overline{OH} \cong \overline{HE}$ (Definition of a regular hexagon)
4. *N* is the midpoint of $\overline{GE}$. (Given)
5. $\overline{NG} \cong \overline{NE}$ (Midpoint Theorem)
6. $\overline{EX} \parallel \overline{OG}$ (Given)
7. $\angle NEX \cong \angle NGO$ (Alternate Exterior Angles Theorem)
8. $\triangle ONG \cong \triangle ENX$ (SAS)
9. $\overline{OG} \cong \overline{NO} \cong \overline{GN}$ (Definition of Equilateral Triangle)
10. $\overline{NO} \cong \overline{NX}$, $\overline{GN} \cong \overline{EN}$ (CPCTC)
11. $\overline{XE} \cong \overline{NX} \cong \overline{EN}$ (Substitution)
12. $\triangle ENX$ is equilateral. (Definition of Equilateral Triangle)

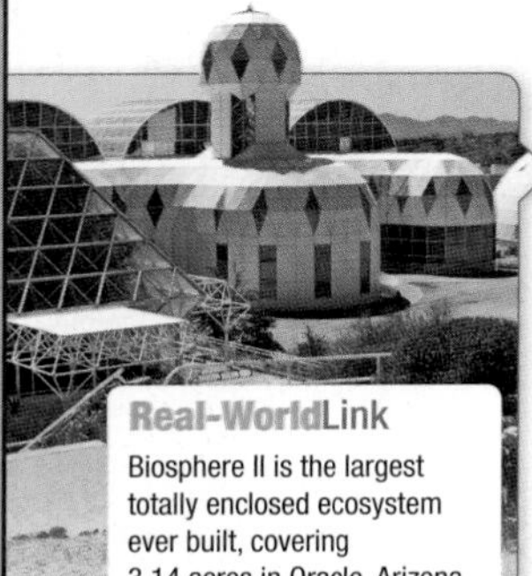

Real-WorldLink

Biosphere II is the largest totally enclosed ecosystem ever built, covering 3.14 acres in Oracle, Arizona. The controlled-environment facility is 91 feet at its highest point, and it has 6500 windows that enclose a volume of 7.2 million cubic feet.

Source: University of Arizona

PT

Real-World Example 4 Apply Triangle Congruence

ENVIRONMENT Refer to the photo of Biosphere II at the right. $\triangle ACE$ is an equilateral triangle. *F* is the midpoint of $\overline{AE}$, *D* is the midpoint of $\overline{EC}$, and *B* is the midpoint of $\overline{CA}$. Prove that $\triangle FBD$ is also equilateral.

A F B E D C

Given: $\triangle ACE$ is equilateral. *F* is the midpoint of $\overline{AE}$, *D* is the midpoint of $\overline{EC}$, and *B* is the midpoint of $\overline{CA}$.

Prove: $\triangle FBD$ is equilateral.

Proof:

Statements	Reasons
1. $\triangle ACE$ is equilateral.	1. Given
2. *F* is the midpoint of *AE*, *D* is the midpoint of *EC*, and *B* is the midpoint of *CA*.	2. Given
3. $m\angle A = 60$, $m\angle C = 60$, $m\angle E = 60$	3. Each angle of an equilateral triangle measures 60.
4. $\angle A \cong \angle C \cong \angle E$	4. Definition of congruence and substitution
5. $\overline{AE} \cong \overline{EC} \cong \overline{CA}$	5. Definition of equilateral triangle
6. $AE = EC = CA$	6. Definition of congruence
7. $\overline{AF} \cong \overline{FE}$, $\overline{ED} \cong \overline{DC}$, $\overline{CB} \cong \overline{BA}$	7. Midpoint Theorem
8. $AF = FE$, $ED = DC$, $CB = BA$	8. Definition of congruence
9. $AF + FE = AE$, $ED + DC = EC$, $CB + BA = CA$	9. Segment Addition Postulate
10. $AF + AF = AE$, $FE + FE = AE$, $ED + ED = EC$, $DC + DC = EC$, $CB + CB = CA$, $BA + BA = CA$	10. Substitution
11. $2AF = AE$, $2FE = AE$, $2ED = EC$, $2DC = EC$, $2CB = CA$, $2BA = CA$	11. Addition Property
12. $2AF = AE$, $2FE = AE$, $2ED = AE$, $2DC = AE$, $2CB = AE$, $2BA = AE$	12. Substitution Property
13. $2AF = 2ED = 2CB$, $2FE = 2DC = 2BA$	13. Transitive Property
14. $AF = ED = CB$, $FE = DC = BA$	14. Division Property
15. $\overline{AF} \cong \overline{ED} \cong \overline{CB}$, $\overline{FE} \cong \overline{DC} \cong \overline{BA}$	15. Definition of congruence
16. $\triangle AFB \cong \triangle EDF \cong \triangle CBD$	16. SAS
17. $\overline{DF} \cong \overline{FB} \cong \overline{BD}$	17. CPCTC
18. $\triangle FBD$ is equilateral.	18. Definition of equilateral triangle

GuidedPractice

4. Given that $\triangle ACE$ is equilateral, $\overline{FB} \parallel \overline{EC}$, $\overline{FD} \parallel \overline{BC}$, $\overline{BD} \parallel \overline{EF}$, and *D* is the midpoint of $\overline{EC}$, prove that $\triangle FED \cong \triangle BDC$. **See Ch. 4 Answer Appendix.**

DifferentiatedInstruction OL BL

Extension Find the measure of vertex angle *A*. Explain.

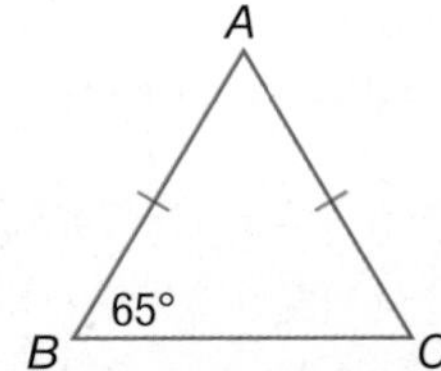

Since $\overline{AB} \cong \overline{AC}$, $\triangle ABC$ is isosceles. The Isosceles Angle Theorem states that if two sides of a triangle are congruent, then the angles opposite those sides are congruent. So, $m\angle C = 65$. The Angle-Sum Theorem states that the sum of the measures of the angles of a triangle is 180. So, $m\angle A = 180 - 65 - 65 = 50$.

288 | Lesson 4-6 | Isosceles and Equilateral Triangles

Check Your Understanding

 = Step-by-Step Solutions begin on page R14.

Example 1 **Refer to the figure at the right.**

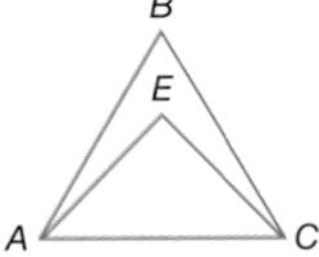

1. If $\overline{AB} \cong \overline{CB}$, name two congruent angles. $\angle BAC$ and $\angle BCA$

2. If $\angle EAC \cong \angle ECA$, name two congruent segments. $\overline{EA}$ and $\overline{EC}$

Example 2 **Find each measure.**

3. FH 12

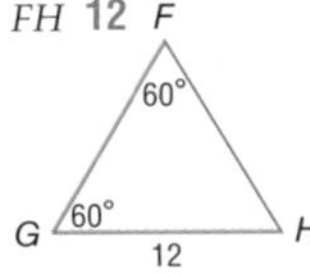

4. $m\angle MRP$ 60

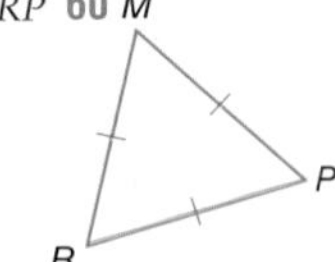

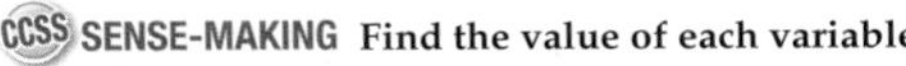

Example 3 CCSS **SENSE-MAKING** **Find the value of each variable.**

5. 12

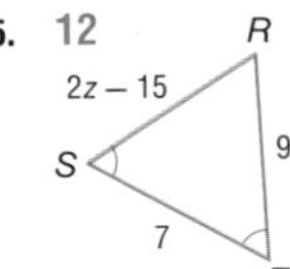

6. 16

W
8
X
62°
8
(4x – 2)°
Y

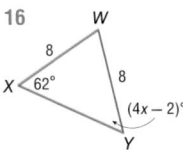

Example 4 **7. PROOF** **Write a two-column proof.**

Given: $\triangle ABC$ is isosceles; $\overline{EB}$ bisects $\angle ABC$.

Prove: $\triangle ABE \cong \triangle CBE$ See margin.

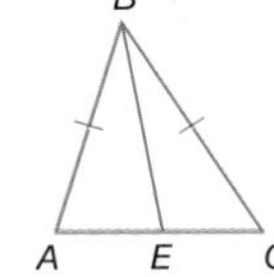

8. ROLLER COASTERS The roller coaster track shown in the photo on page 285 appears to be composed of congruent triangles. A portion of the track is shown.

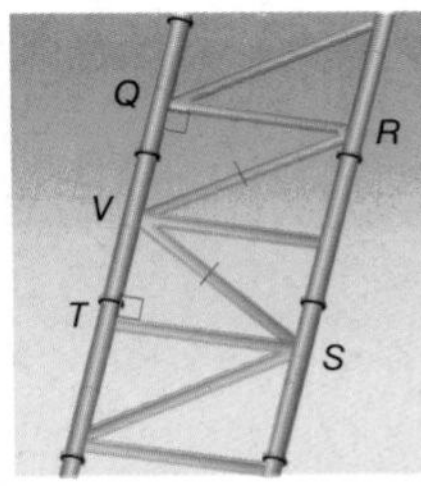

a. If $\overline{QR}$ and $\overline{ST}$ are perpendicular to $\overline{QT}$, $\triangle VSR$ is isosceles with base $\overline{SR}$, and $\overline{QT} \parallel \overline{SR}$, prove that $\triangle RQV \cong \triangle STV$. See margin.

b. If $VR = 2.5$ meters and $QR = 2$ meters, find the distance between $\overline{QR}$ and $\overline{ST}$. Explain your reasoning.

The Pythagorean Theorem tells us that $QV = \sqrt{2.5^2 - 2^2}$ or 1.5 m. By CPCTC we know that $VT = 1.5$ m. The Seg. Add. Post. says $QV + VT = QT$. By substitution, we have $1.5 + 1.5 = QT$. So $QT = 3$ m.

Practice and Problem Solving

Extra Practice is on page R4.

Example 1 **Refer to the figure at the right.**

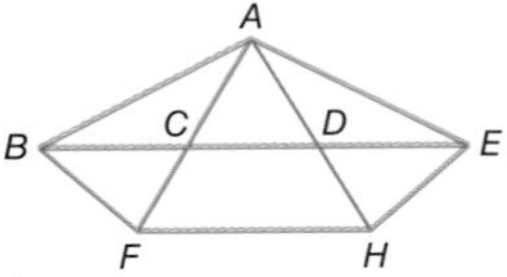

9. If $\overline{AB} \cong \overline{AE}$, name two congruent angles. $\angle ABE$ and $\angle AEB$

10. If $\angle ABF \cong \angle AFB$, name two congruent segments. $\overline{AB}$ and $\overline{AF}$

11. If $\overline{CA} \cong \overline{DA}$, name two congruent angles. $\angle ACD$ and $\angle ADC$

12. If $\angle DAE \cong \angle DEA$, name two congruent segments. $\overline{AD}$ and $\overline{DE}$

13. If $\angle BCF \cong \angle BFC$, name two congruent segments. $\overline{BF}$ and $\overline{BC}$

14. If $\overline{FA} \cong \overline{AH}$, name two congruent angles. $\angle AFH$ and $\angle AHF$

Differentiated Homework Options

Level	Assignment	Two-Day Option	
AL Basic	9–24, 46–67	9–23 odd, 52–55	10–24 even, 46–51, 56–67
OL Core	9–23 odd, 25–29, 31–43 odd, 44, 46–67	9–24, 52–55	25–29, 31–43, 46–51, 56–67
BL Advanced	25–66, (optional: 67)		

3 Practice

Formative Assessment

Use Exercises 1–8 to check for understanding.

Then use the chart at the bottom of this page to customize assignments for your students.

CCSS Teaching the Mathematical Practices

Sense-Making Mathematically proficient students look for entry points into a solution. They plan a solution pathway rather than simply jumping into a solution attempt. In Exercises 5–6, encourage students to refer to the Isosceles Triangle Theorem.

Additional Answers

7. Proof:

Statements (Reasons)

1. $\triangle ABC$ is isosceles; $\overline{EB}$ bisects $\angle ABC$. (Given)
2. $\overline{AB} \cong \overline{BC}$ (Def. of isosceles)
3. $\angle ABE \cong \angle CBE$ (Def. of $\angle$ bisector)
4. $\overline{BE} \cong \overline{BE}$ (Refl. Prop.)
5. $\triangle ABE \cong \triangle CBE$ (SAS)

8a. Given: $\overline{QR}$ and $\overline{ST}$ are perpendicular to $\overline{QT}$, $\triangle VSR$ is isosceles with base $\overline{SR}$, and $\overline{QT} \parallel \overline{SR}$.

Prove: $\triangle RQV \cong \triangle STV$

Proof:

Statements (Reasons)

1. $\overline{QR}$ and $\overline{ST}$ are perpendicular to $\overline{QT}$, $\triangle VSR$ is isosceles with base $\overline{SR}$, and $\overline{QT} \parallel \overline{SR}$. (Given)
2. $\angle RQV$ and $\angle STV$ are right angles. (Def. of $\perp$)
3. $\angle RQV \cong \angle STV$ (All rt. ∠s are ≅.)
4. $\overline{VR} \cong \overline{VS}$ (Def. of isosceles)
5. $\angle VSR \cong \angle VRS$ (Isos. △ Thm.)
6. $\angle QVR \cong \angle VRS$, $\angle TVS \cong \angle VSR$ (Alt. Int. ∠s Thm.)
7. $\angle TVS \cong \angle QVR$ (Trans. Property)
8. $\triangle RQV \cong \triangle STV$ (AAS)

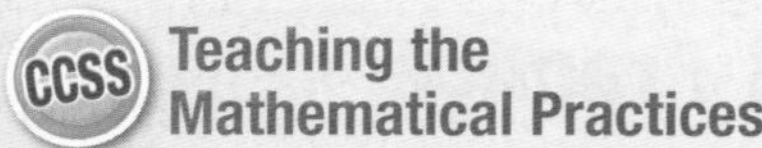

Teaching the Mathematical Practices

Regularity Mathematically proficient students look for general methods while maintaining oversight of the process. In Exercises 19–22, encourage students to analyze each figure to determine which theorems apply.

Additional Answers

25a. 65°; Since $\triangle ABC$ is isosceles, $\angle ABC \cong \angle ACB$, so $180 - 50 = 130$ and $130 \div 2 = 65$.

25b. Proof: Statements (Reasons)

1. $\overline{AB} \cong \overline{AC}$, $\overline{BE} \cong \overline{CD}$ (Given)
2. $AB = AC$, $BE = CD$ (Def. of $\cong$)
3. $AB + BE = AE$, $AC + CD = AD$ (Seg. Add. Post.)
4. $AB + BE = AC + CD$ (Add. Prop. =)
5. $AE = AD$ (Subst.)
6. $\overline{AE} \cong \overline{AD}$ (Def. of $\cong$)
7. $\triangle AED$ is isosceles. (Def. of isosceles)

25c. Proof: Statements (Reasons)

1. $\overline{AB} \cong \overline{AC}$, $\overline{BC} \parallel \overline{ED}$, and $\overline{ED} \cong \overline{AD}$ (Given)
2. $\angle ABC \cong \angle ACB$ (Isos. $\triangle$ Thm.)
3. $m\angle ABC = m\angle ACB$ (Def. of $\cong$ ∡)
4. $\angle ABC \cong \angle AED$, $\angle ACB \cong \angle ADE$ (Corr. ∡)
5. $m\angle ABC = m\angle AED$, $m\angle ACB = m\angle ADE$ (Def. of $\cong$ ∡)
6. $m\angle AED = m\angle ACB$ (Subst.)
7. $m\angle AED = m\angle ADE$ (Subst.)
8. $\angle AED \cong \angle ADE$ (Def. of $\cong$ ∡)
9. $\overline{AD} \cong \overline{AE}$ (Conv. of Isos. $\triangle$ Thm.)
10. $\triangle ADE$ is equilateral. (Def. of equilateral $\triangle$)

Example 2 Find each measure.

15. $m\angle BAC$ **60**

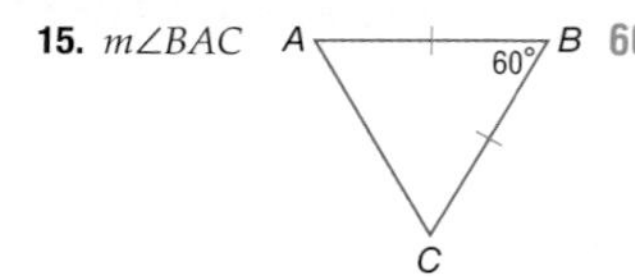

16. $m\angle SRT$ **65**

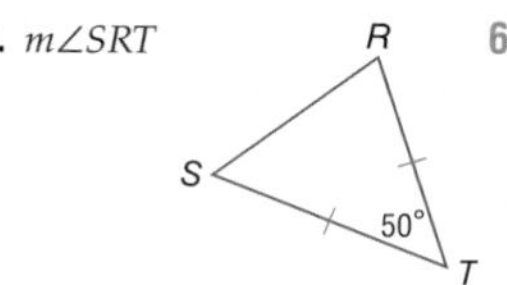

17. TR **4**

18. CB **3**

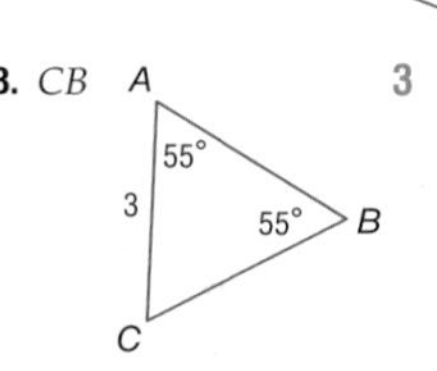

Example 3 CCSS **REGULARITY** Find the value of each variable.

19. $x = 5$

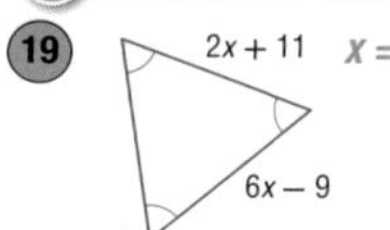

20. $x = 13$

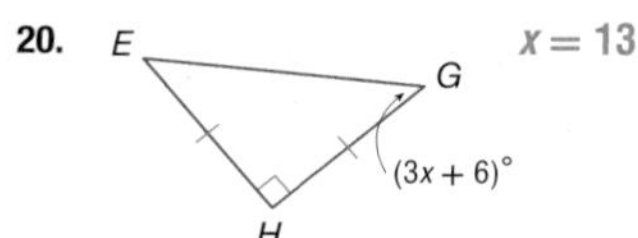

21. $x = 11$, $y = 11$

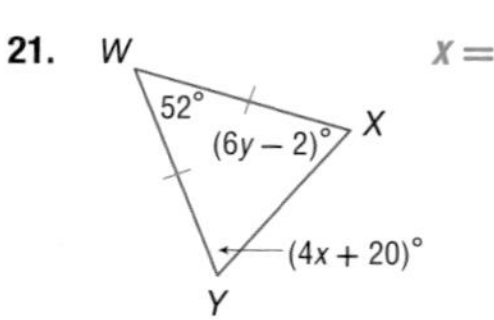

22. $x = 1.4$, $y = -1$

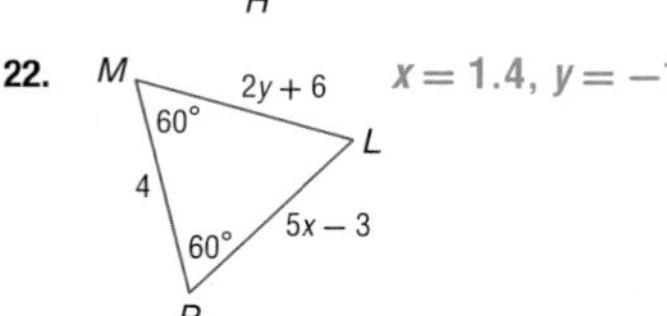

Example 4 **PROOF** Write a paragraph proof. **23–24. See Ch. 4 Answer Appendix.**

23. **Given:** $\triangle HJM$ is isosceles, and $\triangle HKL$ is equilateral. $\angle JKH$ and $\angle HKL$ are supplementary and $\angle HLK$ and $\angle MLH$ are supplementary.
Prove: $\angle JHK \cong \angle MHL$

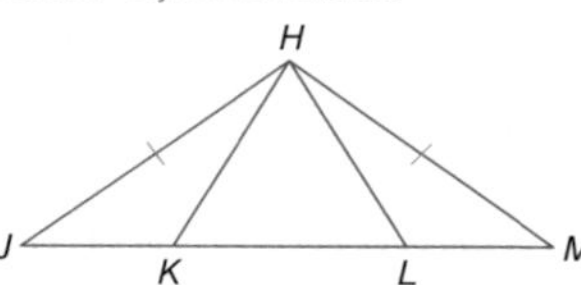

24. **Given:** $\overline{XY} \cong \overline{XZ}$
W is the midpoint of $\overline{XY}$.
Q is the midpoint of $\overline{XZ}$.
Prove: $\overline{WZ} \cong \overline{QY}$

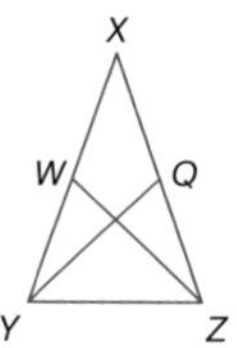

25. **BABYSITTING** While babysitting her neighbor's children, Elisa observes that the supports on either side of a park swing set form two sets of triangles. Using a jump rope to measure, Elisa is able to determine that $\overline{AB} \cong \overline{AC}$, but $\overline{BC} \not\cong \overline{AB}$. **a–d. See margin.**

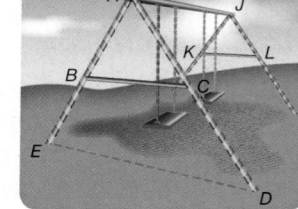

a. Elisa estimates $m\angle BAC$ to be 50. Based on this estimate, what is $m\angle ABC$? Explain.

b. If $\overline{BE} \cong \overline{CD}$, show that $\triangle AED$ is isosceles.

c. If $\overline{BC} \parallel \overline{ED}$ and $\overline{ED} \cong \overline{AD}$, show that $\triangle AED$ is equilateral.

d. If $\triangle JKL$ is isosceles, what is the minimum information needed to prove that $\triangle ABC \cong \triangle JLK$? Explain your reasoning.

25d. One pair of congruent corresponding sides and one pair of congruent corresponding angles; since you know that the triangle is isosceles, if one leg is congruent to a leg of $\triangle ABC$, then you know that both pairs of legs are congruent. Because the base angles of an isosceles triangle are congruent, if you know that $\angle K \cong \angle B$, you know that $\angle K \cong \angle L$, $\angle B \cong \angle C$, and $\angle C \cong \angle L$. Therefore, with one pair of congruent corresponding sides and one pair of congruent corresponding angles, the triangles can be proved congruent using either ASA or SAS.

26. CHIMNEYS In the picture, $\overline{BD} \perp \overline{AC}$ and $\triangle ABC$ is an isosceles triangle with base $\overline{AC}$. Show that the chimney of the house, represented by $\overline{BD}$, bisects the angle formed by the sloped sides of the roof, $\angle ABC$. **See Ch. 4 Answer Appendix.**

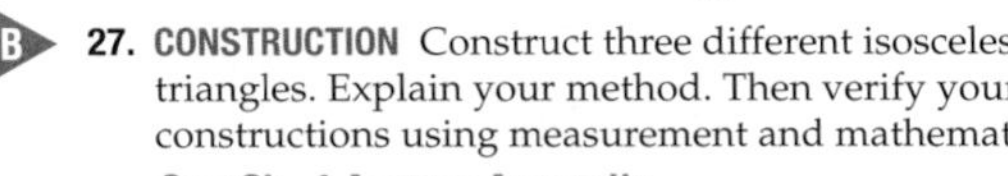

B **27. CONSTRUCTION** Construct three different isosceles right triangles. Explain your method. Then verify your constructions using measurement and mathematics. **See Ch. 4 Answer Appendix.**

28. PROOF Based on your construction in Exercise 27, make and prove a conjecture about the relationship between the base angles of an isosceles right triangle. **See margin.**

CCSS REGULARITY **Find each measure.**

29 $m\angle CAD$ **44**

30. $m\angle ACD$ **44**

31. $m\angle ACB$ **136**

32. $m\angle ABC$ **22**

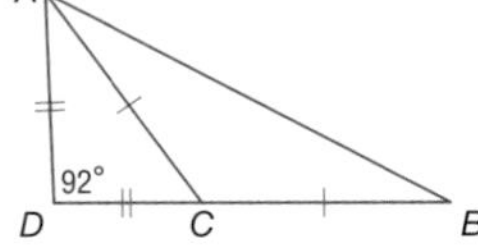

33. FITNESS In the diagram, the rider will use his bike to hop across the tops of each of the concrete solids shown. If each triangle is isosceles with vertex angles G, H, and J, and $\overline{BG} \cong \overline{HC}$, $\overline{HD} \cong \overline{JF}$, $\angle G \cong \angle H$, and $\angle H \cong \angle J$, show that the distance from B to F is three times the distance from D to F. **See Ch. 4 Answer Appendix.**

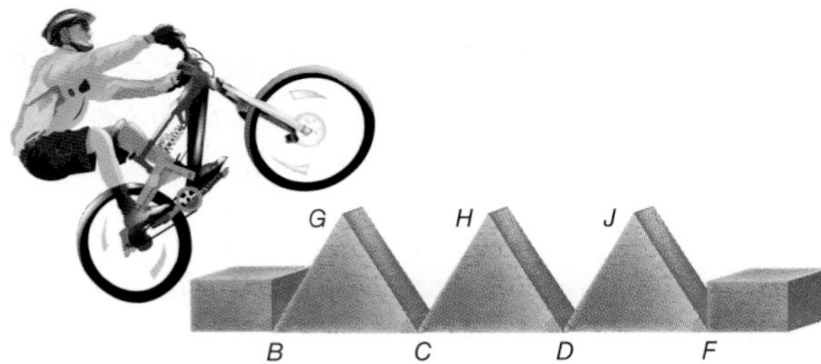

34. Given: $\triangle XWV$ is isosceles; $\overline{ZY} \perp \overline{YV}$.

Prove: $\angle X$ and $\angle YZV$ are complementary. **See Ch. 4 Answer Appendix.**

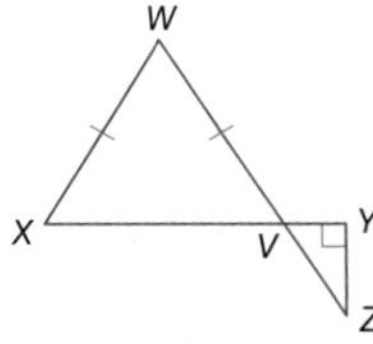

PROOF **Write a two-column proof of each corollary or theorem.** **35–37. See Ch. 4 Answer Appendix.**

35. Corollary 4.3 **36.** Corollary 4.4 **37.** Theorem 4.11

Find the value of each variable.

38. **3**

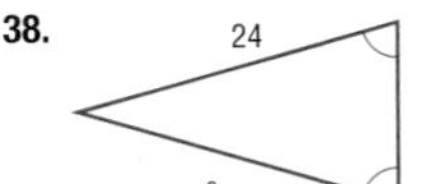

39. **14**

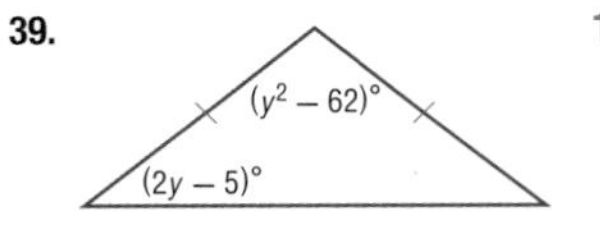

Additional Answer

28. Conjecture: The measures of the base angles of an isosceles right triangle are 45. **Proof:** The base angles are congruent because it is an isosceles triangle. Let the measure of each acute angle be x. The acute angles of a right triangle are complementary, so $x + x = 90$ and $x = 45$.

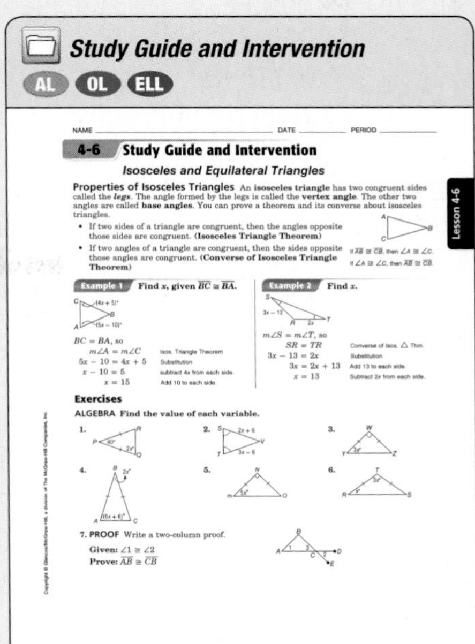

Study Guide and Intervention

AL OL ELL

NAME ____ DATE ____ PERIOD ____

4-6 Study Guide and Intervention

Isosceles and Equilateral Triangles

Properties of Isosceles Triangles An **isosceles triangle** has two congruent sides called the **legs**. The angle formed by the legs is called the **vertex angle**. The other two angles are called **base angles**. You can prove a theorem and its converse about isosceles triangles.

- If two sides of a triangle are congruent, then the angles opposite those sides are congruent. (**Isosceles Triangle Theorem**)
- If two angles of a triangle are congruent, then the sides opposite those angles are congruent. (**Converse of Isosceles Triangle Theorem**)

Example 1 Find x, given $\overline{BC} \cong \overline{BA}$.

$BC = BA$, so
$m\angle A = m\angle C$ Isos. Triangle Theorem
$5x - 10 = 4x + 5$ Substitution
$x - 10 = 5$ Subtract 4x from each side.
$x = 15$ Add 10 to each side.

Example 2 Find x.

$m\angle S = m\angle T$, so
$SR = TR$ Converse of Isos. △ Thm.
$3x - 13 = 2x$ Substitution
$3x = 2x + 13$ Add 13 to each side.
$x = 13$ Subtract 2x from each side.

Exercises

ALGEBRA Find the value of each variable.

1. 2. 3. 4. 5. 6.

7. **PROOF** Write a two-column proof.
Given: $\angle 1 \cong \angle 2$
Prove: $\overline{AB} \cong \overline{CB}$

Lesson 4-6

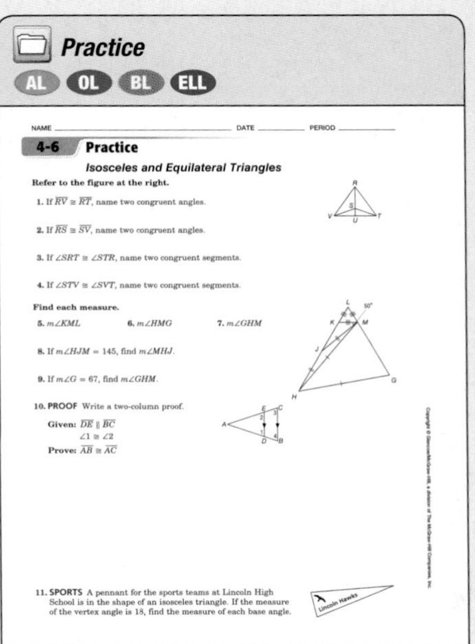

Practice

AL OL BL ELL

NAME ____ DATE ____ PERIOD ____

4-6 Practice

Isosceles and Equilateral Triangles

Refer to the figure at the right.

1. If $\overline{RV} \cong \overline{RT}$, name two congruent angles.
2. If $\overline{RS} \cong \overline{SV}$, name two congruent angles.
3. If $\angle SRT \cong \angle STR$, name two congruent segments.
4. If $\angle STV \cong \angle SVT$, name two congruent segments.

Find each measure.

5. $m\angle KML$ 6. $m\angle HMG$ 7. $m\angle GHM$
8. If $m\angle HJM = 145$, find $m\angle MHJ$.
9. If $m\angle G = 67$, find $m\angle GHM$.

10. **PROOF** Write a two-column proof.
Given: $\overline{DE} \parallel \overline{BC}$, $\angle 1 \cong \angle 2$
Prove: $\overline{AB} \cong \overline{AC}$

11. **SPORTS** A pennant for the sports teams at Lincoln High School is in the shape of an isosceles triangle. If the measure of the vertex angle is 18, find the measure of each base angle.

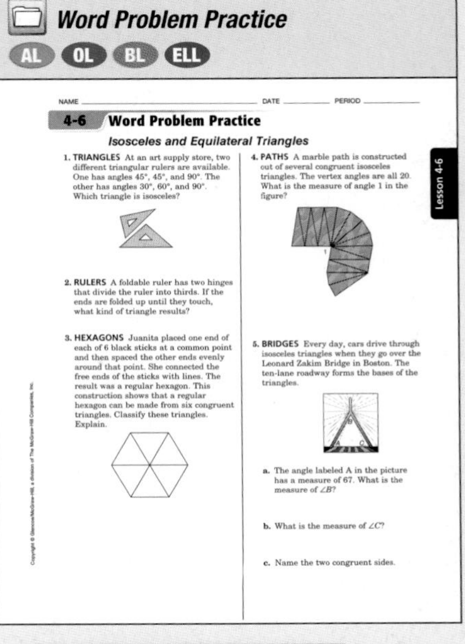

Word Problem Practice

AL OL BL ELL

NAME ____ DATE ____ PERIOD ____

4-6 Word Problem Practice

Isosceles and Equilateral Triangles

1. **TRIANGLES** At an art supply store, two different triangular rulers are available. One has angles 45°, 45°, and 90°. The other has angles 30°, 60°, and 90°. Which triangle is isosceles?

2. **RULERS** A foldable ruler has two hinges that divide the ruler into thirds. If the ends are folded up until they touch, what kind of triangle results?

3. **HEXAGONS** Juanita placed one end of each of 6 black sticks at a common point and then spaced the other ends evenly around that point. She connected the free ends of the sticks with lines. The result was a regular hexagon. This construction shows that a regular hexagon can be made from six congruent triangles. Classify these triangles. Explain.

4. **PATHS** A marble path is constructed out of several congruent isosceles triangles. The vertex angles are all 20. What is the measure of angle 1 in the figure?

5. **BRIDGES** Every day, cars drive through isosceles triangles when they go over the Leonard Zakim Bridge in Boston. The ten-lane roadway forms the bases of the triangles.

a. The angle labeled A in the picture has a measure of 67. What is the measure of $\angle B$?

b. What is the measure of $\angle C$?

c. Name the two congruent sides.

Lesson 4-6

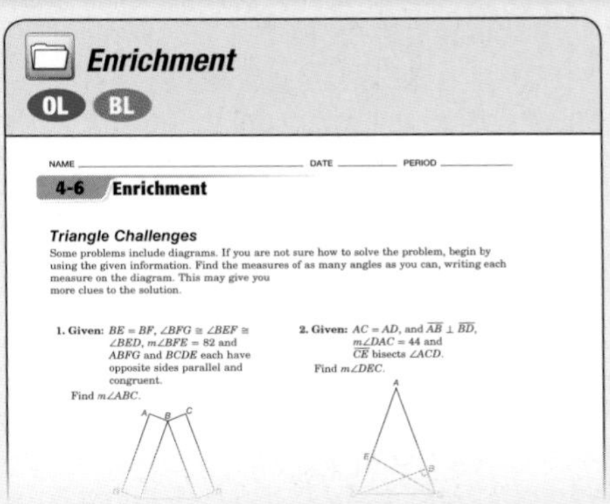

Enrichment

OL BL

NAME ____ DATE ____ PERIOD ____

4-6 Enrichment

Triangle Challenges

Some problems include diagrams. If you are not sure how to solve the problem, begin by using the given information. Find the measures of as many angles as you can, writing each measure on the diagram. This may give you more clues to the solution.

1. Given: $BE = BF$, $\angle BFG \cong \angle BEF \cong \angle BED$, $m\angle BFE = 82$ and $ABFG$ and $BCDE$ each have opposite sides parallel and congruent.
Find $m\angle ABC$.

2. Given: $AC = AD$, and $\overline{AB} \perp \overline{BD}$, $m\angle DAC = 44$ and $\overline{CE}$ bisects $\angle ACD$.
Find $m\angle DEC$.

connectED.mcgraw-hill.com

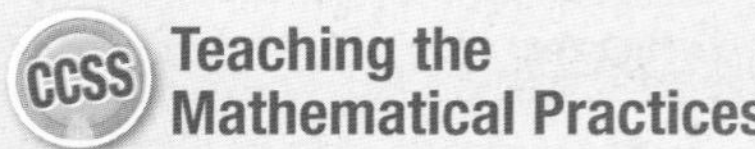

Teaching the Mathematical Practices

Precision Mathematically proficient students use clear definitions in discussion with others and in their own reasoning. In Exercises 46–47, point out to students that it may be easier to think of examples first and then counterexamples.

WatchOut!

Error Analysis In Exercise 48, neither is correct. $\overline{GF} \cong \overline{HF}$ and $m\angle G = m\angle H$ by the Isosceles Triangle Theorem. If $m\angle G = m\angle H = x$, $2x + 70 = 180$, $2x = 110$, and $x = 55$. So, $m\angle G = x = 55$.

GAMES Use the diagram of a game timer shown to find each measure.

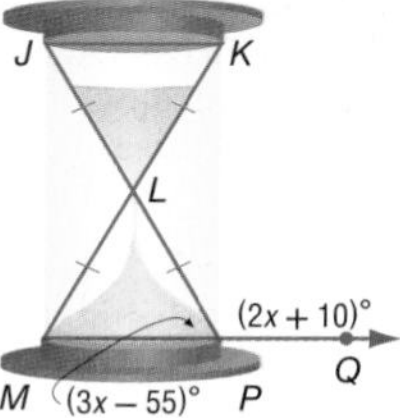

40. $m\angle LPM$ 80
41. $m\angle LMP$ 80
42. $m\angle JLK$ 20
43. $m\angle JKL$ 80

44. **MULTIPLE REPRESENTATIONS** In this problem, you will explore possible measures of the interior angles of an isosceles triangle given the measure of one exterior angle.

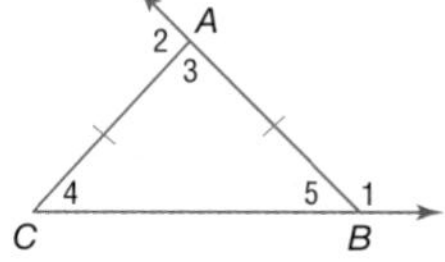

a. **Geometric** Use a ruler and a protractor to draw three different isosceles triangles, extending one of the sides adjacent to the vertex angle and to one of the base angles, and labeling as shown. See margin.

b. **Tabular** Use a protractor to measure and record $m\angle 1$ for each triangle. Use $m\angle 1$ to calculate the measures of $\angle 3$, $\angle 4$, and $\angle 5$. Then find and record $m\angle 2$ and use it to calculate these same measures. Organize your results in two tables. See margin.

c. **Verbal** Explain how you used $m\angle 1$ to find the measures of $\angle 3$, $\angle 4$, and $\angle 5$. Then explain how you used $m\angle 2$ to find these same measures. See margin.

d. **Algebraic** If $m\angle 1 = x$, write an expression for the measures of $\angle 3$, $\angle 4$, and $\angle 5$. Likewise, if $m\angle 2 = x$, write an expression for these same angle measures. $m\angle 5 = 180 - x$, $m\angle 4 = 180 - x$, $m\angle 3 = 2x - 180$; $m\angle 3 = 180 - x$, $m\angle 4 = \frac{x}{2}$, $m\angle 5 = \frac{x}{2}$

H.O.T. Problems Use Higher-Order Thinking Skills

45. **CHALLENGE** In the figure at the right, if $\triangle WJZ$ is equilateral and $\angle ZWP \cong \angle WJM \cong \angle JZL$, prove that $\overline{WP} \cong \overline{ZL} \cong \overline{JM}$. See Ch. 4 Answer Appendix.

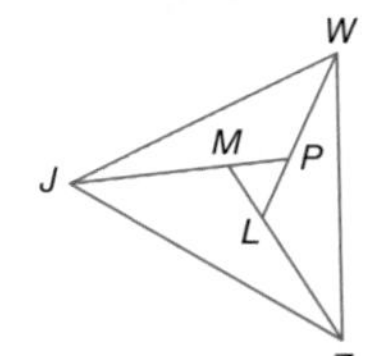

PRECISION Determine whether the following statements are *sometimes*, *always*, or *never* true. Explain.

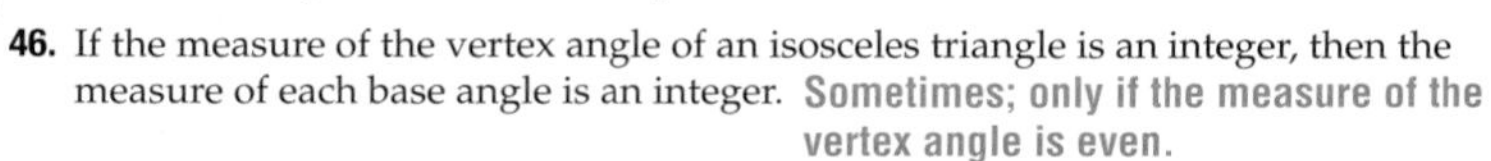

46. If the measure of the vertex angle of an isosceles triangle is an integer, then the measure of each base angle is an integer. Sometimes; only if the measure of the vertex angle is even.

47. If the measures of the base angles of an isosceles triangle are integers, then the measure of its vertex angle is odd.

47. Never; the measure of the vertex angle will be 180 − 2 (measure of the base angle) so if the base angles are integers, then 2(measure of the base angle) will be even and 180 − 2(measure of the base angle) will be even.

48. **ERROR ANALYSIS** Alexis and Miguela are finding $m\angle G$ in the figure shown. Alexis says that $m\angle G = 35$, while Miguela says that $m\angle G = 60$. Is either of them correct? Explain your reasoning. Neither; $m\angle G = \frac{180 - 70}{2}$ or 55.

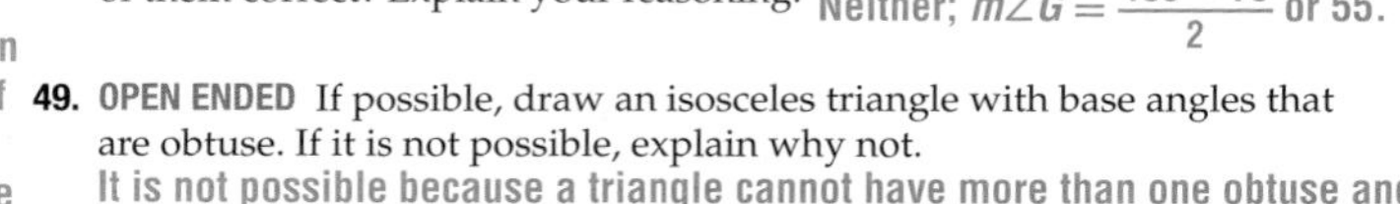

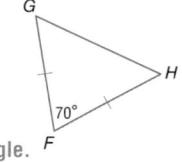

49. **OPEN ENDED** If possible, draw an isosceles triangle with base angles that are obtuse. If it is not possible, explain why not. It is not possible because a triangle cannot have more than one obtuse angle.

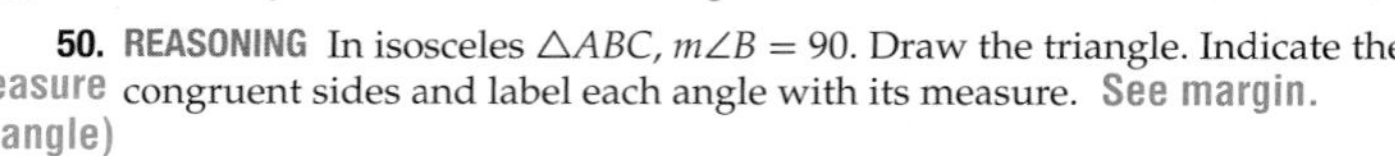

50. **REASONING** In isosceles $\triangle ABC$, $m\angle B = 90$. Draw the triangle. Indicate the congruent sides and label each angle with its measure. See margin.

51. **WRITING IN MATH** How can triangle classifications help you prove triangle congruence? See margin.

Additional Answers

44a.

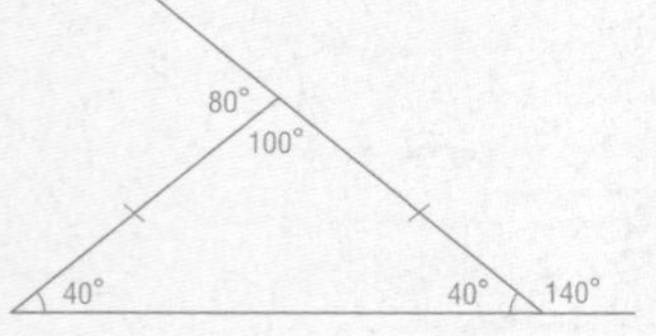

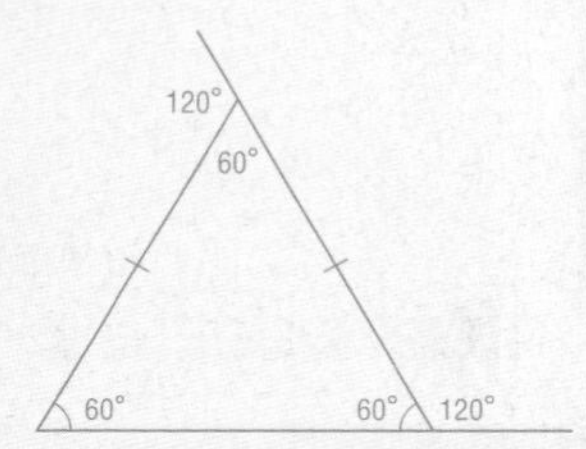

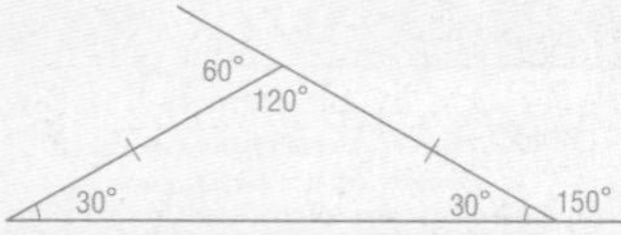

44b.

$m\angle 1$	$m\angle 3$	$m\angle 4$	$m\angle 5$
140	100	40	40
120	60	60	60
150	120	30	30

$m\angle 2$	$m\angle 3$	$m\angle 4$	$m\angle 5$
80	100	40	40
120	60	60	60
60	120	30	30

44c. $\angle 5$ is supplementary to $\angle 1$, so $m\angle 5 = 180 - m\angle 1$. $\angle 4 \cong \angle 5$, so $m\angle 4 = m\angle 5$. The sum of the angle measures in a triangle must be 180, so $m\angle 3 = 180 - m\angle 4 - m\angle 5$. $\angle 2$ is supplementary to $\angle 3$, so $m\angle 3 = 180 - m\angle 2$. $m\angle 2$ is twice as much as $m\angle 4$ and $m\angle 5$, so $m\angle 4 = m\angle 5 = \frac{m\angle 2}{2}$.

50.

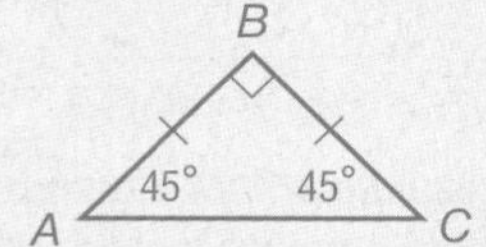

51. Sample answer: If a triangle is already classified, you can use the previously proven properties of that type of triangle in the proof. Doing this can save you steps when writing the proof.

Standardized Test Practice

52. ALGEBRA What quantity should be added to both sides of this equation to complete the square? **D**

$$x^2 - 10x = 3$$

A -25 **C** 5
B -5 **D** 25

53. SHORT RESPONSE In a school of 375 students, 150 students play sports and 70 students are involved in the community service club. 30 students play sports and are involved in the community service club. How many students are *not* involved in either sports or the community service club? **185**

54. In the figure $\overline{AE}$ and $\overline{BD}$ bisect each other at point C.

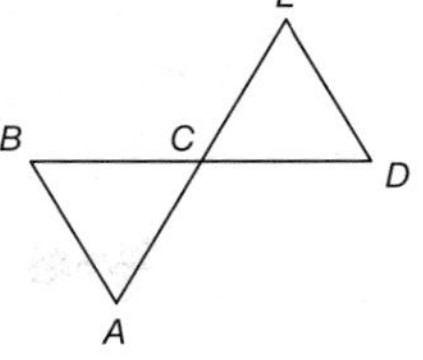

Which additional piece of information would be enough to prove that $\overline{DE} \cong \overline{DC}$? **F**

F $\angle A \cong \angle BCA$ **H** $\angle ACB \cong \angle EDC$
G $\angle B \cong \angle D$ **J** $\angle A \cong \angle B$

55. SAT/ACT If $x = -3$, then $4x^2 - 7x + 5 =$ **E**

A 2 **C** 20 **E** 62
B 14 **D** 42

56. $\triangle ADC \cong \triangle ABC$; since $\overline{AC} \cong \overline{AC}$, the two triangles are congruent by AAS.

Spiral Review

56. If $m\angle ADC = 35$, $m\angle ABC = 35$, $m\angle DAC = 26$, and $m\angle BAC = 26$, determine whether $\triangle ADC \cong \triangle ABC$. (Lesson 4-5)

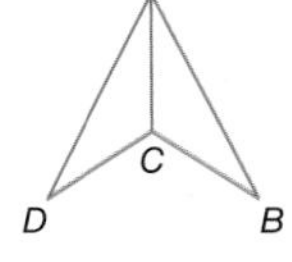

Determine whether $\triangle STU \cong \triangle XYZ$. Explain. (Lesson 4-4) **57–58. See margin.**

57. $S(0, 5)$, $T(0, 0)$, $U(1, 1)$, $X(4, 8)$, $Y(4, 3)$, $Z(6, 3)$

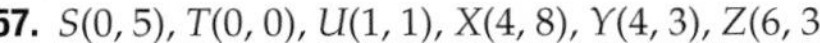

58. $S(2, 2)$, $T(4, 6)$, $U(3, 1)$, $X(-2, -2)$, $Y(-4, 6)$, $Z(-3, 1)$

59. PHOTOGRAPHY Film is fed through a traditional camera by gears that catch the perforation in the film. The distance from A to C is the same as the distance from B to D. Show that the two perforated strips are the same width. (Lesson 2-7) **See margin.**

State the property that justifies each statement. (Lesson 2-6)

60. If $x(y + z) = a$, then $xy + xz = a$. **Dist. Prop.**

61. If $n - 17 = 39$, then $n = 56$. **Add. Prop.**

62. If $m\angle P + m\angle Q = 110$ and $m\angle R = 110$, then $m\angle P + m\angle Q = m\angle R$. **Substitution**

63. If $cv = md$ and $md = 15$, then $cv = 15$. **Trans. Prop.**

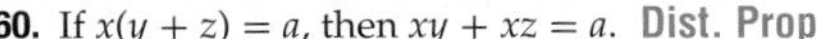

Refer to the figure at the right. (Lesson 1-1)

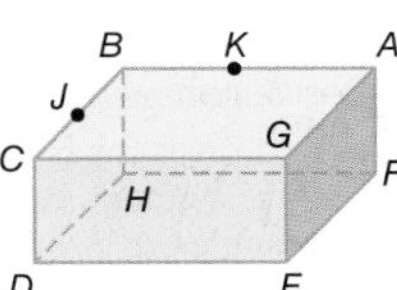

64. How many planes appear in this figure? **6**

65. Name three points that are collinear. ***A*, *K*, *B* or *B*, *J*, *C***

66. Are points A, C, D, and J coplanar?
No; *A*, *C*, and *J* lie in plane *ABC*, but *D* does not.

Skills Review

67. PROOF If $\angle ACB \cong \angle ABC$, then $\angle XCA \cong \angle YBA$. **See margin.**

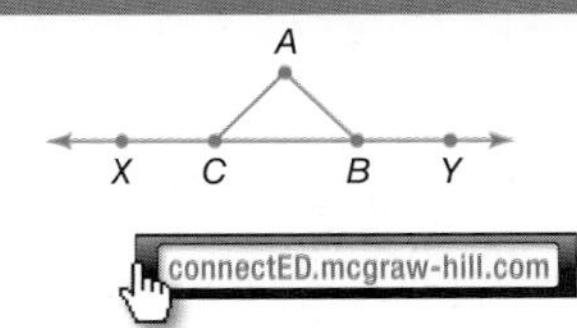

4 Assess

Crystal Ball Have students predict how the methods of proof they have learned so far in this chapter will help them in the next lesson.

Formative Assessment

Check for student understanding of Lessons 4-5 and 4-6.

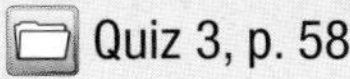 Quiz 3, p. 58

Additional Answers

57. $SU = \sqrt{17}$, $TU = \sqrt{2}$, $ST = 5$, $XZ = \sqrt{29}$, $YZ = 2$, $XY = 5$; the corresponding sides are not congruent; the triangles are not congruent.

58. $SU = \sqrt{2}$, $TU = \sqrt{26}$, $ST = \sqrt{20}$, $XZ = \sqrt{10}$, $YZ = \sqrt{26}$, $XY = \sqrt{68}$; the corresponding sides are not congruent; the triangles are not congruent.

59. Given: $AC = BD$
Prove: $AB = CD$

A B C D

Proof:

Statement (Reasons)

1. $AC = BD$ (Given)
2. $AC = AB + BC$
   $BD = BC + CD$ (Seg. Add. Post.)
3. $AB + BC = BC + CD$ (Subst.)
4. $\overline{BC} \cong \overline{BC}$ (Reflexive)
5. $BC = BC$ (Def. of $\cong$ Segs.)
6. $AB = CD$ (Subt. Prop.)

67. Proof:

Statement (Reasons)

1. $\angle ACB \cong \angle ABC$ (Given)
2. $\angle XCA$ and $\angle ACB$ are a linear pair. $\angle ABC$ and $\angle ABY$ are a linear pair. (Def. of Linear Pair)
3. $\angle XCA$, $\angle ACB$ and $\angle ABC$, $\angle ABY$ are suppl. (Suppl. Thm.)
4. $\angle XCA \cong \angle YBA$ ($\angle$s suppl. to $\cong$ $\angle$s are $\cong$.)

1 Focus

Objective

- Use a graphing calculator to perform transformations on triangles in the coordinate plane.
- Test congruence of transformations of triangles.

Materials for Each Group

- TI-Nspire technology

Teaching Tip

- Allow students to experiment and explore the TI-Nspire technology **Graphs** feature before beginning the lab. If the TI-Nspire technology is a new technology for most students, prepare a more structured introduction to the **Graphs** page.
- To change the viewing window, select **Windows Settings** from the **Window/ Zoom** menu. Adjust the **XMin, Xmax, Ymin** and **YMax** to match the screen shot.

2 Teach

Working in Cooperative Groups

Organize students in groups of 2, mixing abilities. If possible, each student should complete the lab on a TI-Nspire technology, but students should work together to troubleshoot any technology problems and to discuss Exercises 1–5.

Have students complete Activities 1–3 along with Exercises 1–3, respectively. Facilitate the use of the technology so that the objective of the lab is not lost by simply trying to construct the geometric figures.

Practice Have students complete Exercises 1–4.

EXPLORE 4-7 Graphing Technology Lab
Congruence Transformations

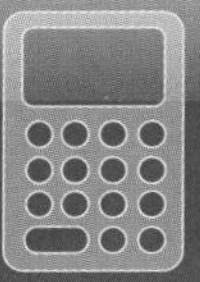

You can use TI-Nspire technology to perform *transformations* on triangles in the coordinate plane and test for congruence.

CCSS Common Core State Standards
Content Standards
G.CO.5 Given a geometric figure and a rotation, reflection, or translation, draw the transformed figure using, e.g., graph paper, tracing paper, or geometry software. Specify a sequence of transformations that will carry a given figure onto another.
G.CO.6 Use geometric descriptions of rigid motions to transform figures and to predict the effect of a given rigid motion on a given figure; given two figures, use the definition of congruence in terms of rigid motions to decide if they are congruent.
Mathematical Practices 5

PT

Activity 1 Translate a Triangle and Test for Congruence

Step 1 Open a new **Graphs** page. Select **Show Grid** from the **View** menu. Use the **Window/Zoom** menu to adjust the window size.

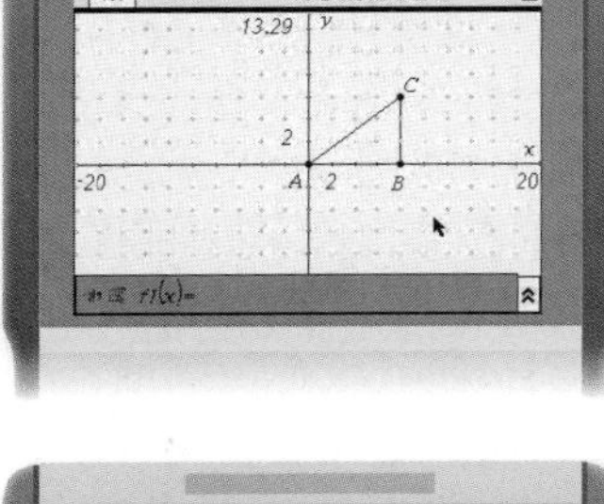

Step 2 Select **Triangle** from the **Shapes** menu and draw a right triangle with legs measuring 6 units and 8 units as shown by placing the first point at (0, 0), the second point at (8, 0), and the third point at (8, 6). Use the **Text** tool under the **Actions** menu to label the vertices of the triangle as *A*, *B*, and *C*.

Step 3 Select **Translation** from the **Transformation** menu. Then select $\triangle ABC$ and point *A*. Translate or *slide* the right triangle 8 units down and 14 units left. Label the corresponding vertices of the image as A', B', and C'.

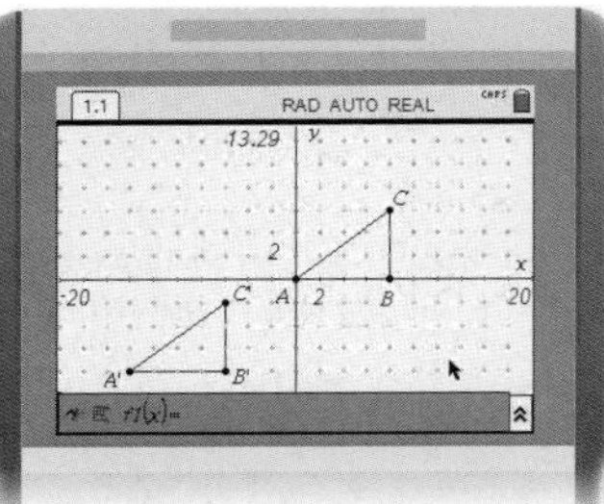

Step 4 To verify that $\triangle A'B'C'$ is congruent to $\triangle ABC$, select **Length** from the **Measurement** menu. Then select any two endpoints and press the **ENTER** key to determine the length of the segment. Repeat this for each segment of each triangle.

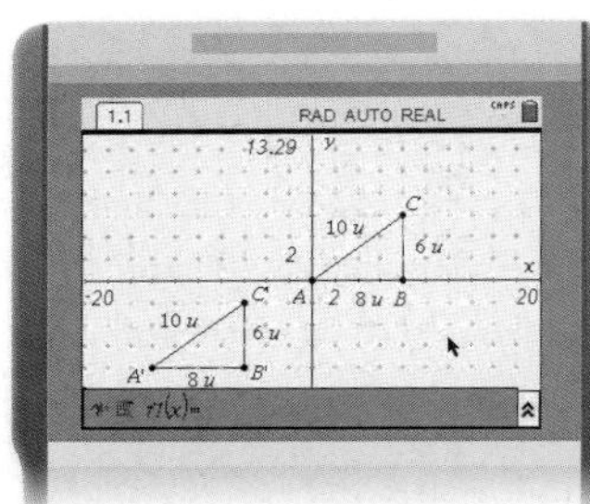

In addition to measuring lengths, the TI-Nspire can also be used to measure angles. This will allow you to use other tests for triangle congruence that involve angle measure.

Activity 2 Reflect a Triangle and Test for Congruence

Step 1 Open a new **Graphs** page, show the grid, and redraw $\triangle ABC$ from Activity 1.

Step 2 Select **Reflection** from the **Transformation** menu. Then select $\triangle ABC$ and then the y-axis to reflect or *flip* $\triangle ABC$ in the y-axis. Label the corresponding vertices of the image as A', B', and C'.

Step 3 Use the **Angle** tool from the **Measurement** menu to find $m\angle A$ and $m\angle A'$. Use the **Length** tool from the **Measurement** menu to find AB, $A'B'$, AC, and $A'C'$.

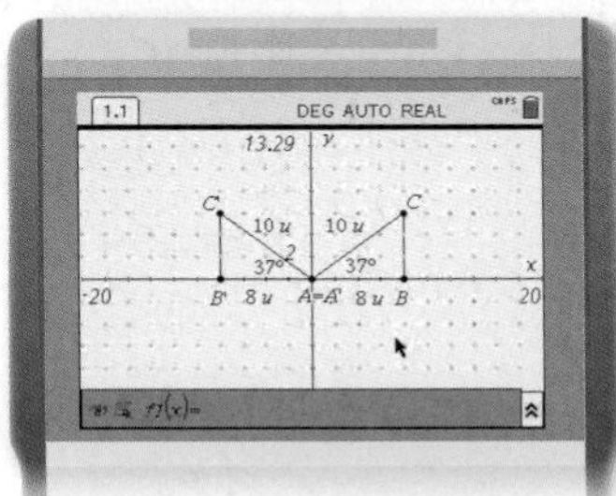

To rotate a figure about the origin using TI-Nspire technology, use the Rotation tool to select the figure, then the point (0, 0), then draw an angle of rotation.

Activity 3 Rotate a Triangle and Test for Congruence

Step 1 Open a new **Graphs** page, show the grid, and redraw $\triangle ABC$ from Activity 1.

Step 2 Select **Rotation** from the **Transformation** menu. Then select $\triangle ABC$, select the origin, and type in a number for the angle of rotation.

Step 3 Use the **Angle** tool from the **Measurement** menu to find $m\angle A$, $m\angle A'$, $m\angle C$, and $m\angle C'$. Use the **Length** tool from the **Measurement** menu to find AC and $A'C'$.

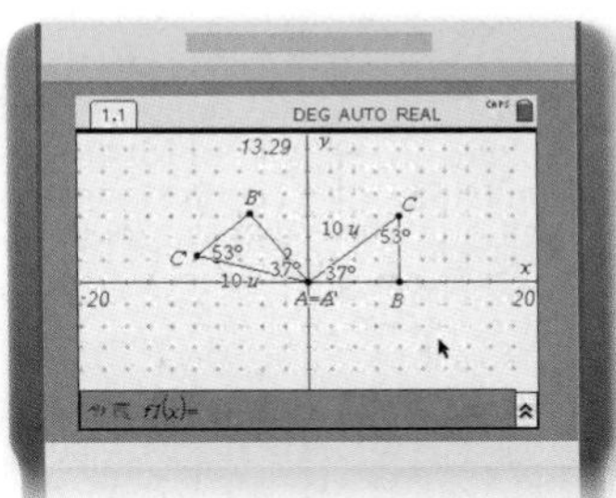

Analyze the Results

Determine whether $\triangle ABC$ and $\triangle A'B'C'$ are congruent. Explain your reasoning. 1–4. See margin.

1. Activity 1
2. Activity 2
3. Activity 3
4. Explain why $\triangle A'B'C'$ in Activity 3 does not appear to be congruent to $\triangle ABC$.
5. **MAKE A CONJECTURE** Repeat Activities 1–3 using a different triangle XYZ. Analyze your results and compare them to those found in Exercises 1–3. Make a conjecture as to the relationship between a triangle and its transformed image under a translation, reflection, or a rotation. See margin.
6. Do the measurements and observations you made in Activities 1–3 constitute a proof of the conjecture you made in Exercise 5? Explain. See margin.

3 Assess

Formative Assessment

Use Exercise 5 to assess whether students understand how to perform and analyze congruence transformations on the TI-Nspire technology.

From Concrete to Abstract

Have students identify the coordinates of $\triangle XYZ$ and $\triangle X'Y'Z'$. Next, students should use the Distance Formula to verify triangle congruence algebraically.

Additional Answers

1. Yes; since $AB = A'B'$, $CB = C'B'$, and $AC = A'C'$, $\overline{AB} \cong \overline{A'B'}$, $\overline{BC} \cong \overline{B'C'}$, and $\overline{AC} \cong \overline{A'C'}$, by the definition of congruence. So by SSS, $\triangle ABC \cong \triangle A'B'C'$.
2. Yes; since $m\angle A = m\angle A'$, $\angle A \cong \angle A'$. Likewise, since $AC = A'C'$ and $AB = A'B'$, $\overline{AB} \cong \overline{A'B'}$ and $\overline{AC} \cong \overline{A'C'}$. Therefore by SAS, $\triangle ABC \cong \triangle A'B'C'$.
3. Yes; since $m\angle A = m\angle A'$ and $m\angle C$ and $m\angle C'$, $\angle A \cong \angle A'$ and $\angle C = \angle C'$. Likewise, since and $AC = A'C'$, $\overline{AC} \cong \overline{A'C'}$. Therefore by ASA, $\triangle ABC \cong \triangle A'B'C'$.
4. The viewing window is rectangular and not square. The x-axis is labeled in increments of 1, while the y-axis is labeled in increments of 2. This distorts the actual shape of $\triangle ABC$ and $\triangle A'B'C$.
5. See students' work. Conjecture: A triangle and its transformed image under a translation, reflection, or a rotation are congruent.
6. No; the conjecture made in Exercise 5 was reached using inductive reasoning, which is not a valid way to prove a conjecture.

1 Focus

Standards Alignment

Before Lesson 4-7 Prove triangles congruent.

Lesson 4-7 Identify reflections, translations, and rotations. Verify congruence after a congruence transformation.

After Lesson 4-7 Use coordinate geometry to prove and verify congruence algebraically.

2 Teach

Scaffolding Questions

Have students read the **Why?** section of the lesson.

Ask:

- What is the repeating figure used on the fabric in the photo? a fish
- How is the figure repeated in the pattern? The figure is repeated by sliding the fish to another location on the fabric.
- How do you know that the adjacent fish are not reflections of each other? The reflected fish would either face each other or face in opposite directions.

LESSON 4-7 Congruence Transformations

Then	Now	Why?
You proved whether two triangles were congruent.	1 Identify reflections, translations, and rotations. 2 Verify congruence after a congruence transformation.	The fashion industry often uses prints that display patterns. Many of these patterns are created by taking one figure and sliding it to create another figure in a different location, flipping the figure to create a mirror image of the original, or turning the original figure to create a new one.

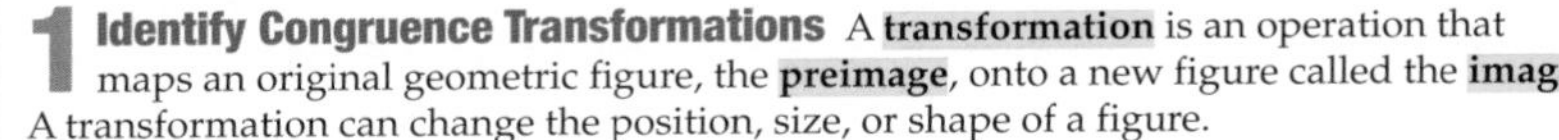

New Vocabulary

transformation
preimage
image
congruence transformation
isometry
reflection
translation
rotation

Common Core State Standards

Content Standards

G.CO.6 Use geometric descriptions of rigid motions to transform figures and to predict the effect of a given rigid motion on a given figure; given two figures, use the definition of congruence in terms of rigid motions to decide if they are congruent.

G.CO.7 Use the definition of congruence in terms of rigid motions to show that two triangles are congruent if and only if corresponding pairs of sides and corresponding pairs of angles are congruent.

Mathematical Practices

1 Make sense of problems and persevere in solving them.

7 Look for and make use of structure.

1 Identify Congruence Transformations

A **transformation** is an operation that maps an original geometric figure, the **preimage**, onto a new figure called the **image**. A transformation can change the position, size, or shape of a figure.

A transformation can be noted using an arrow. The transformation statement $\triangle ABC \rightarrow \triangle XYZ$ tells you that A is mapped to X, B is mapped to Y, and C is mapped to Z.

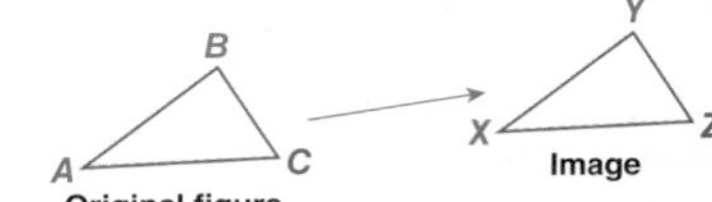

A **congruence transformation**, also called a *rigid transformation* or an **isometry**, is one in which the position of the image may differ from that of the preimage, but the two figures remain congruent. The three main types of congruence transformations are shown below.

Key Concept Reflections, Translations, and Rotations

A **reflection** or *flip* is a transformation over a line called the *line of reflection*. Each point of the preimage and its image are the same distance from the line of reflection.

Example

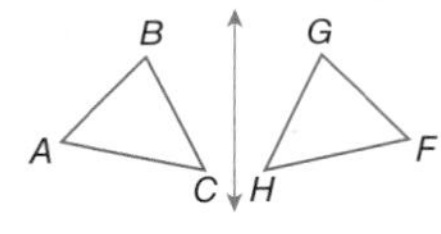

$\triangle ABC \longrightarrow \triangle FGH$

A **translation** or *slide* is a transformation that moves all points of the original figure the same distance in the same direction.

Example

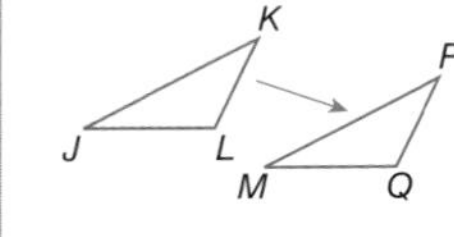

$\triangle JKL \longrightarrow \triangle MPQ$

A **rotation** or *turn* is a transformation around a fixed point called the *center of rotation*, through a specific angle, and in a specific direction. Each point of the original figure and its image are the same distance from the center.

Example

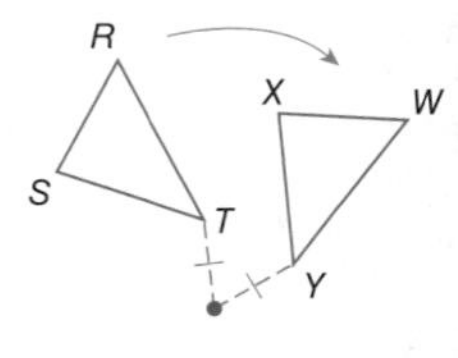

$\triangle RST \longrightarrow \triangle WXY$

Lesson 4-7 Resources

Resource	Approaching Level AL	On Level OL	Beyond Level BL	English Learners ELL
Teacher Edition	▪ Differentiated Instruction, p. 297	▪ Differentiated Instruction, pp. 297, 301, 302	▪ Differentiated Instruction, pp. 297, 301, 302	▪ Differentiated Instruction, p. 297
Chapter Resource Masters	▪ Study Guide and Intervention, pp. 43–44 ▪ Skills Practice, p. 45 ▪ Practice, p. 46 ▪ Word Problem Practice, p. 47	▪ Study Guide and Intervention, pp. 43–44 ▪ Skills Practice, p. 45 ▪ Practice, p. 46 ▪ Word Problem Practice, p. 47 ▪ Enrichment, p. 48	▪ Practice, p. 46 ▪ Word Problem Practice, p. 47 ▪ Enrichment, p. 48	▪ Study Guide and Intervention, pp. 43–44 ▪ Skills Practice, p. 45 ▪ Practice, p. 46 ▪ Word Problem Practice, p. 47
Other	▪ 5-Minute Check 4-7 ▪ Study Notebook	▪ 5-Minute Check 4-7 ▪ Study Notebook	▪ 5-Minute Check 4-7 ▪ Study Notebook	▪ 5-Minute Check 4-7 ▪ Study Notebook

StudyTip

Transformations Not all transformations preserve congruence. Only transformations that do not change the size or shape of the figure are congruence transformations. You will learn more about transformations in Chapter 9.

Example 1 Identify Congruence Transformations

Identify the type of congruence transformation shown as a *reflection, translation,* or *rotation.*

a.

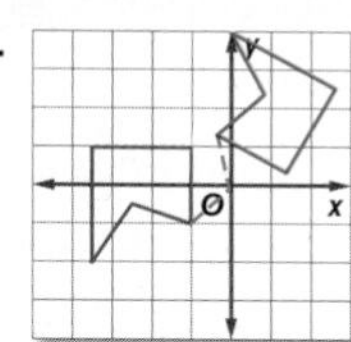

Each vertex and its image are the same distance from the origin. The angles formed by each pair of corresponding points and the origin are congruent. This is a rotation.

b.

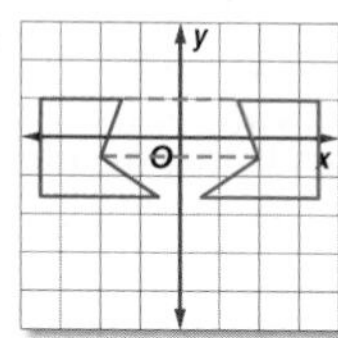

Each vertex and its image are the same distance from the *y*-axis. This is a reflection.

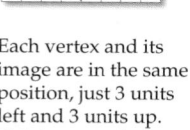

c.

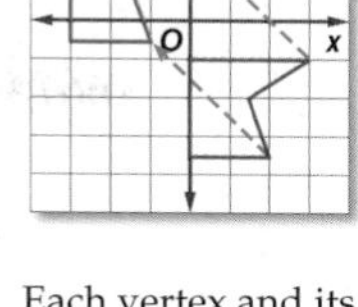

Each vertex and its image are in the same position, just 3 units left and 3 units up. This is a translation.

GuidedPractice **1A.** reflection **1B.** rotation **1C.** translation

1A.

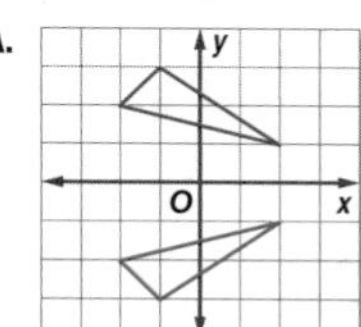

1B.

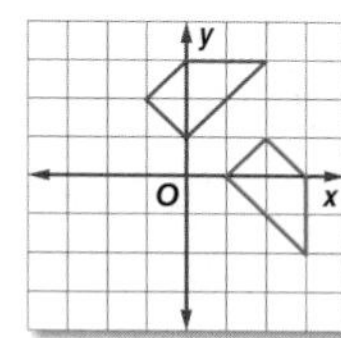

1C.

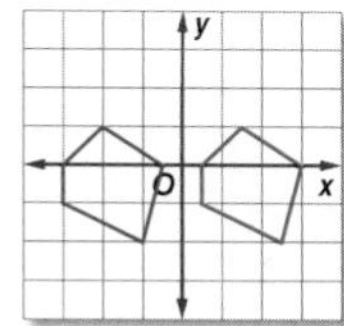

Some real-world motions or objects can be represented by transformations.

Real-World Example 2 Identify a Real-World Transformation

GAMES Refer to the information at the left. Identify the type of congruence transformation shown in the diagram as a *reflection, translation,* or *rotation.*

The position of the weight at different times is an example of a rotation. The center of rotation is the person's ankle.

Real-WorldLink

The game shown above involves a weight attached to a ring that you can place around your ankle. As the rope passes in front of your other foot, you skip over it.

GuidedPractice **2A.** translation **2B.** reflection

Identify the type of congruence transformation shown as a *reflection, translation,* or *rotation.*

2A.

2B.

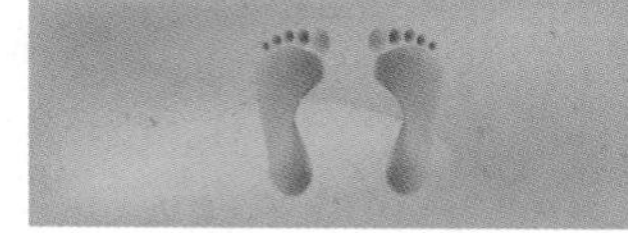

DifferentiatedInstruction AL OL BL ELL

Naturalist Have students photograph or draw representations of the congruence transformations found in nature. Each photo or drawing should include a description of the transformation shown.

1 Identify Congruence Transformations

Examples 1 and 2 show how to identify which type of congruence transformation is shown.

Formative Assessment

Use the Guided Practice exercises after each Example to determine students' understanding of concepts.

Additional Example

1 Identify the type of congruence transformation shown as a *reflection*, *translation*, or *rotation*.

a.

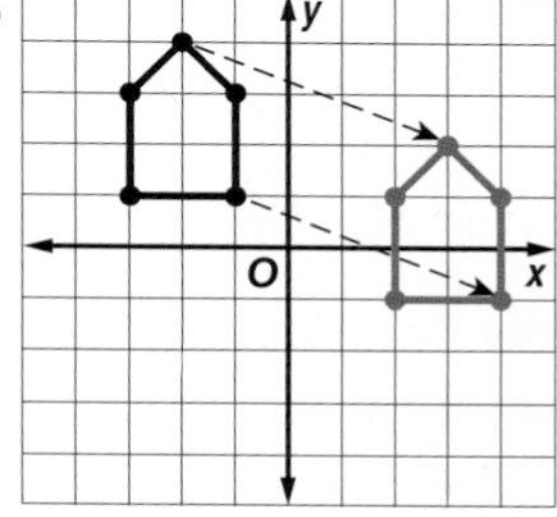

This is a translation.

b.

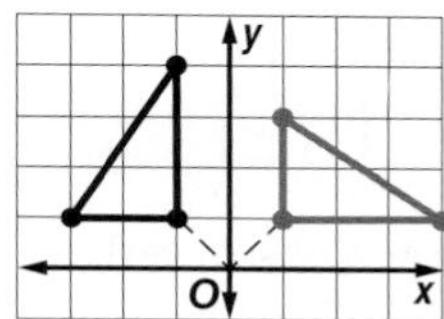

This is a rotation.

c.

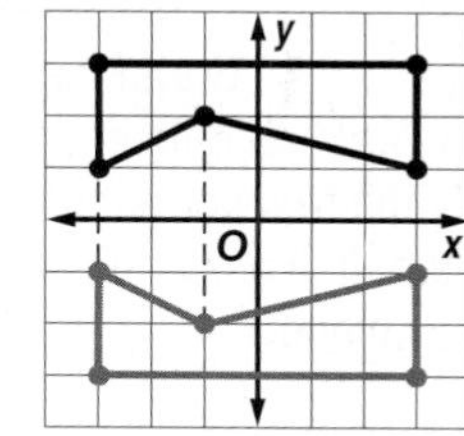

This is a reflection over the *x*-axis.

Additional Examples also in Interactive Classroom PowerPoint® Presentations

Interactive White Board READY

Additional Example

2 BRIDGES Refer to the picture below. Identify the type of congruence transformation shown by the image of the bridge in the river as a *reflection*, *translation*, or *rotation*.

The image is a reflection; the line at which the bridge meets the water is the line of reflection.

2 Verify Congruence

Example 3 shows how to use coordinate geometry to verify triangle congruence after a congruence transformation.

Additional Example

3 Triangle PQR with vertices $P(4, 2)$, $Q(3, -3)$, and $R(5, -2)$ is a transformation of $\triangle JKL$ with vertices $J(-2, 0)$, $K(-3, -5)$, and $L(-1, -4)$. Graph the original figure and its image. Identify the transformation and verify that it is a congruence transformation.

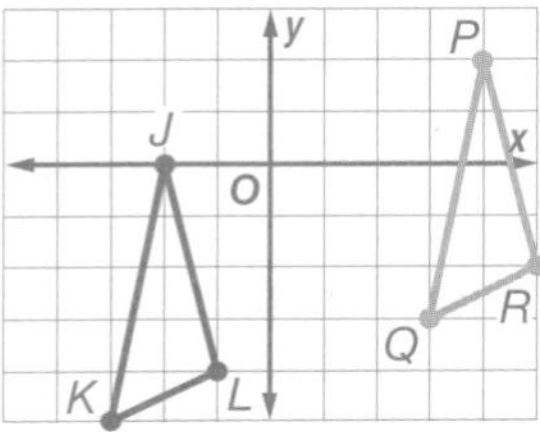

$\triangle PQR$ is a translation of $\triangle JKL$. Because $PQ = JK = \sqrt{26}$, $QR = KL = \sqrt{5}$, and $PR = JL = \sqrt{17}$, $\overline{PQ} \cong \overline{JK}$, $\overline{QR} \cong \overline{KL}$, and $\overline{PR} \cong \overline{JL}$. $\triangle JKL \cong \triangle PQR$ by SSS.

2 Verify Congruence

You can verify that reflections, translations, and rotations of triangles produce congruent triangles using SSS.

Example 3 Verify Congruence after a Transformation

Triangle XZY with vertices $X(2, -8)$, $Z(6, -7)$, and $Y(4, -2)$ is a transformation of $\triangle ABC$ with vertices $A(2, 8)$, $B(6, 7)$, and $C(4, 2)$. Graph the original figure and its image. Identify the transformation and verify that it is a congruence transformation.

Understand You are asked to identify the type of transformation—reflection, translation, or rotation. Then, you need to show that the two figures are congruent.

Plan Use the Distance Formula to find the measure of each side. Then show that the two triangles are congruent by SSS.

Solve Graph each figure. The transformation appears to be a reflection over the x-axis. Find the measures of the sides of each triangle.

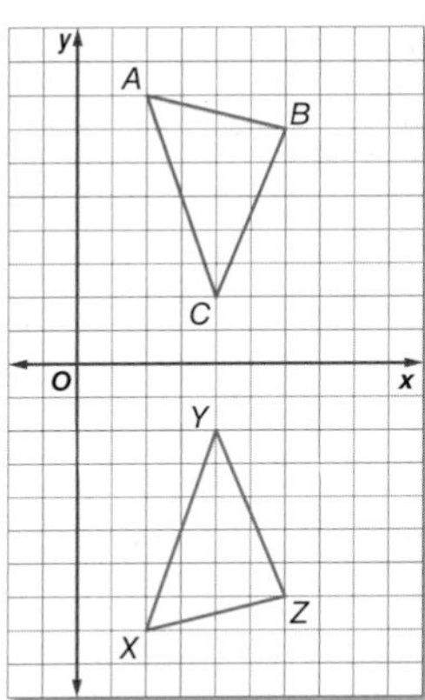

$AB = \sqrt{(6-2)^2 + (7-8)^2}$ or $\sqrt{17}$

$BC = \sqrt{(6-4)^2 + (7-2)^2}$ or $\sqrt{29}$

$AC = \sqrt{(4-2)^2 + (2-8)^2}$ or $\sqrt{40}$

$XZ = \sqrt{(6-2)^2 + [-7-(-8)]^2}$ or $\sqrt{17}$

$ZY = \sqrt{(6-4)^2 + [-7-(-2)]^2}$ or $\sqrt{29}$

$XY = \sqrt{(2-4)^2 + [-8-(-2)]^2}$ or $\sqrt{40}$

Since $AB = XZ$, $BC = ZY$, and $AC = XY$, $\overline{AB} \cong \overline{XZ}$, $\overline{BC} \cong \overline{ZY}$, and $\overline{AC} \cong \overline{XY}$. By SSS, $\triangle ABC \cong \triangle XZY$.

Check Use the definition of a reflection. Use a ruler to measure and compare the segments connecting each vertex and its image to the line of symmetry. These segments are congruent, so the triangles are congruent. ✓

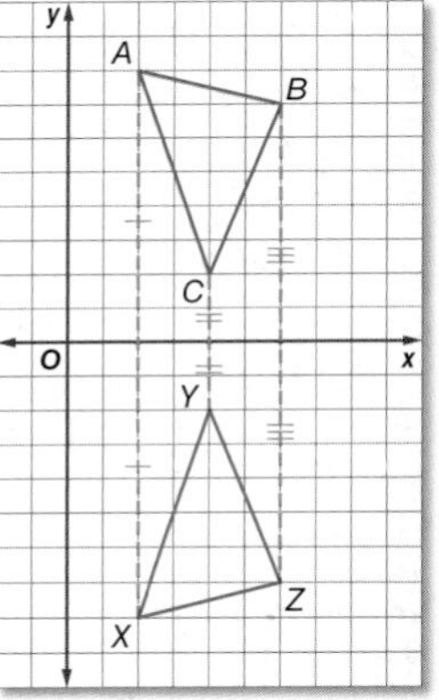

StudyTip

Isometry While an isometry preserves congruence, a *direct isometry* also preserves orientation or order of lettering. An *indirect* or *opposite isometry* changes this order, such as from clockwise to counterclockwise. The reflection shown in Example 3 is an example of an indirect isometry.

GuidedPractice

3. Triangle JKL with vertices $J(-2, 2)$, $K(-8, 5)$, and $L(-4, 6)$ is a transformation of $\triangle PQR$ with vertices $P(2, -2)$, $Q(8, -5)$, and $R(4, -6)$. Graph the original figure and its image. Identify the transformation and verify that it is a congruence transformation. **See margin.**

Focus on Mathematical Content

Algebra Point out the connection between algebra and geometry in Example 3. Algebra is used to verify that a geometric congruence transformation results in congruent figures.

Teach with Tech

Photo Editing Software Give students several digital pictures of triangles. Have them use a photo editing program to rotate, flip, and reposition the pictures on the screen. Show students that these transformations do not affect the size or shape of the triangle.

Check Your Understanding

 = Step-by-Step Solutions begin on page R14.

Example 1 Identify the type of congruence transformation shown as a *reflection, translation,* or *rotation.*

1. 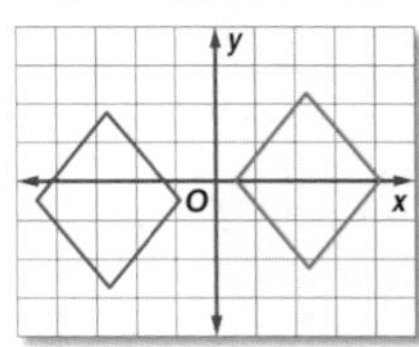 translation

2. 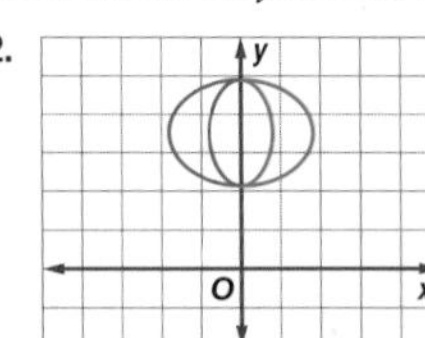 reflection

Example 2

3. 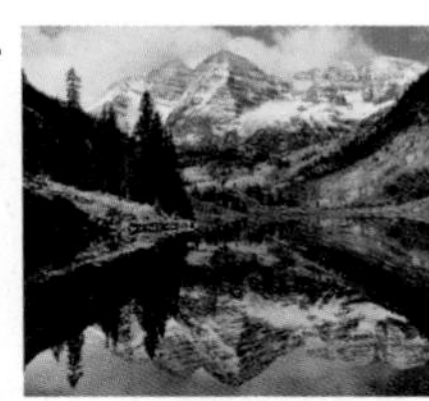 reflection

4.  rotation

Example 3 COORDINATE GEOMETRY Identify each transformation and verify that it is a congruence transformation.

5. 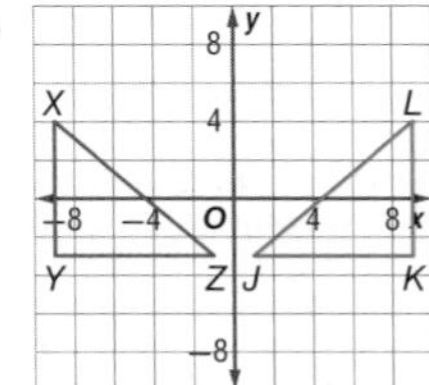 See margin

6. 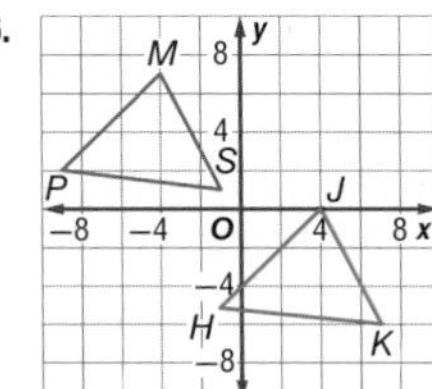 See margin.

Practice and Problem Solving

Extra Practice is on page R4.

Example 1 CCSS STRUCTURE Identify the type of congruence transformation shown as a *reflection, translation,* or *rotation.*

7. reflection
8. translation or reflection

7. 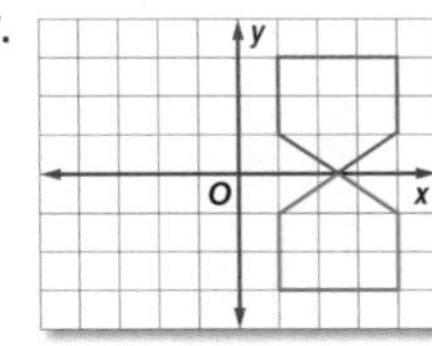

8. 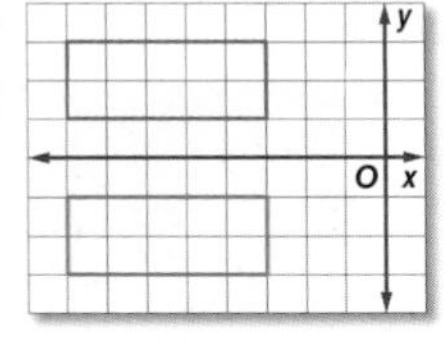

9. 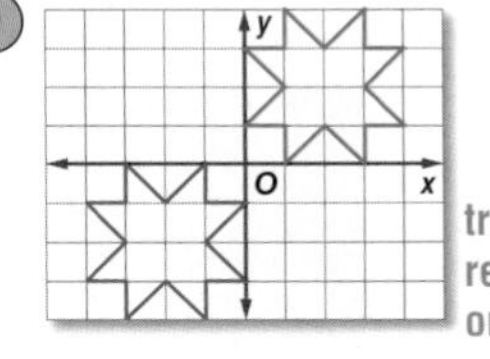 translation, reflection, or rotation

10. rotation
11. rotation

10. 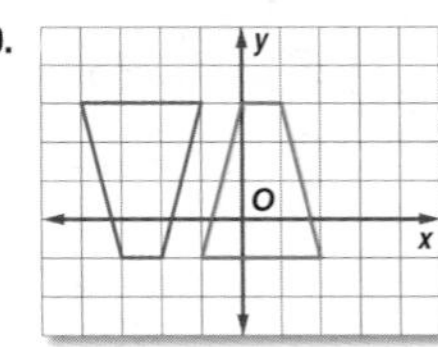

11. 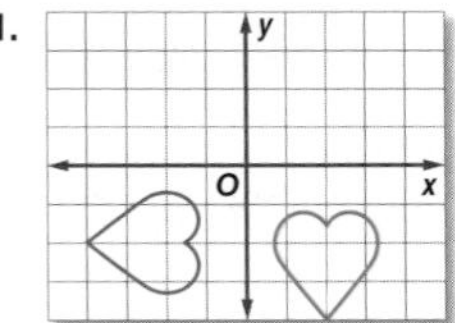

12. 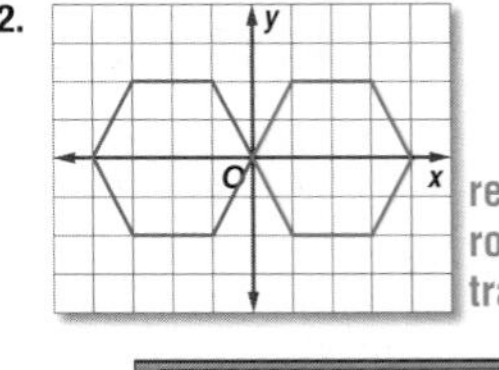 reflection, rotation, or translation

Differentiated Homework Options

Level	Assignment	Two-Day Option	
AL Basic	7–20, 32–51	7–19 odd, 37–40	8–20 even, 32–36, 41–51
OL Core	7–27 odd, 28–30, 32–51	7–20, 37–40	21–30, 32–36, 41–51
BL Advanced	21–45, (optional: 46–51)		

3 Practice

Formative Assessment

Use Exercises 1–6 to check for understanding.

Use the chart at the bottom of this page to customize assignments for your students.

Teaching the Mathematical Practices

Structure Mathematically proficient students look closely to discern a pattern or structure. In Exercises 7–12, point out to students that the original figure is in blue and the image is green.

Additional Answer (Guided Practice)

3. 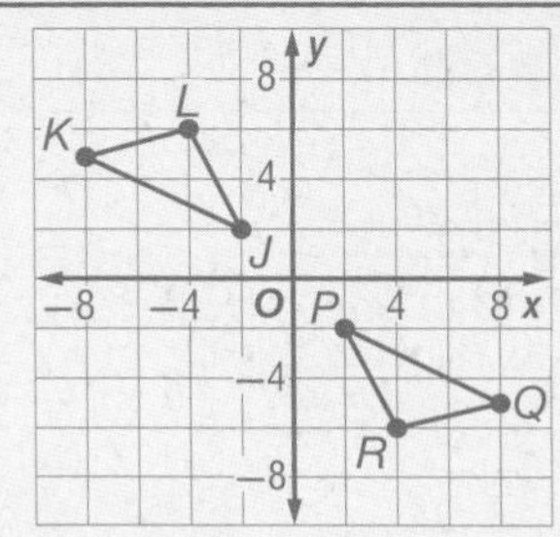

$\triangle JKL$ is a rotation of $\triangle PQR$. $PQ = \sqrt{45}$, $QR = \sqrt{17}$, $PR = \sqrt{20}$, $JK = \sqrt{45}$, $KL = \sqrt{17}$, and $JL = \sqrt{20}$. Since $PQ = JL$, $QR = KL$, and $PR = JK$, $\overline{PQ} \cong \overline{JL}$, $\overline{QR} \cong \overline{KL}$, and $\overline{PR} \cong \overline{JK}$. $\triangle PQR \cong \triangle JKL$.

Additional Answers

5. $\triangle LKJ$ is a reflection of $\triangle XYZ$. $XY = 7$, $YZ = 8$, $XZ = \sqrt{113}$, $KJ = 8$, $LJ = \sqrt{113}$, and $LK = 7$. $\triangle XYZ \cong \triangle LKJ$ by SSS.

6. $\triangle JHK$ is a translation of $\triangle MPS$. $MP = \sqrt{50}$, $PS = \sqrt{65}$, $SM = \sqrt{45}$, $JH = \sqrt{50}$, $JK = \sqrt{45}$, and $HK = \sqrt{65}$. $\triangle JHK \cong \triangle MPS$ by SSS.

Study Guide and Intervention

AL OL ELL

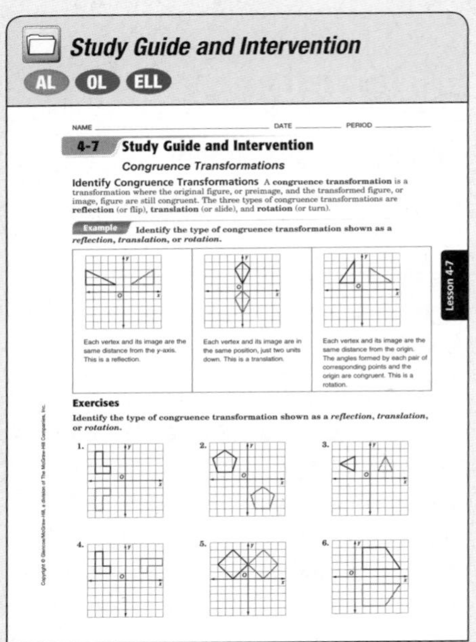

NAME ______ DATE ______ PERIOD ______

4-7 Study Guide and Intervention

Congruence Transformations

Identify Congruence Transformations A **congruence transformation** is a transformation where the original figure, or preimage, and the transformed figure, or image, figure are still congruent. The three types of congruence transformations are **reflection** (or flip), **translation** (or slide), and **rotation** (or turn).

Example Identify the type of congruence transformation shown as a *reflection, translation,* or *rotation.*

Each vertex and its image are the same distance from the y-axis. This is a reflection.	Each vertex and its image are in the same position, just two units down. This is a translation.	Each vertex and its image are the same distance from the origin. The angles formed by each pair of corresponding points and the origin are congruent. This is a rotation.

Exercises

Identify the type of congruence transformation shown as a *reflection, translation,* or *rotation.*

1. 2. 3. 4. 5. 6.

Practice

AL OL BL ELL

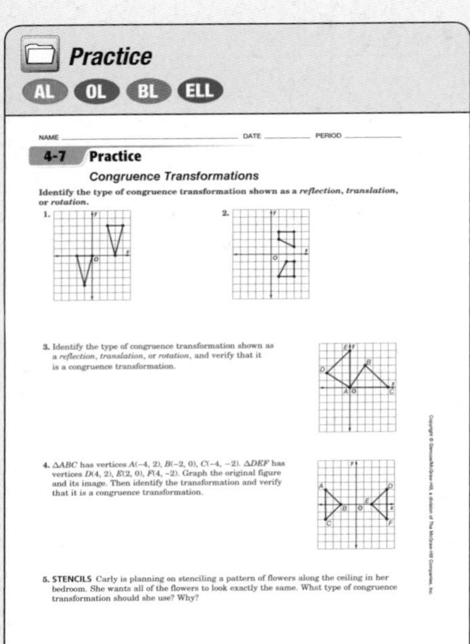

NAME ______ DATE ______ PERIOD ______

4-7 Practice

Congruence Transformations

Identify the type of congruence transformation shown as a *reflection, translation,* or *rotation.*

1. 2.

3. Identify the type of congruence transformation shown as a *reflection, translation,* or *rotation,* and verify that it is a congruence transformation.

4. △ABC has vertices A(−4, 2), B(−2, 0), C(−4, −2). △DEF has vertices D(4, 2), E(2, 0), F(4, −2). Graph the original figure and its image. Then identify the transformation and verify that it is a congruence transformation.

5. STENCILS Carly is planning on stenciling a pattern of flowers along the ceiling in her bedroom. She wants all of the flowers to look exactly the same. What type of congruence transformation should she use? Why?

Word Problem Practice

AL OL BL ELL

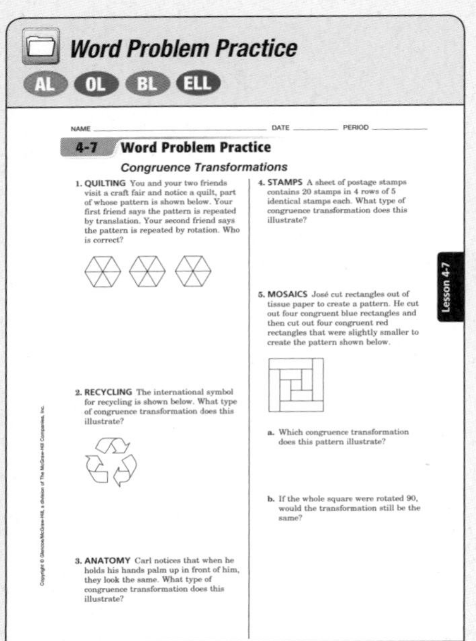

NAME ______ DATE ______ PERIOD ______

4-7 Word Problem Practice

Congruence Transformations

1. QUILTING You and your two friends visit a craft fair and notice a quilt, part of whose pattern is shown below. Your first friend says the pattern is repeated by translation. Your second friend says the pattern is repeated by rotation. Who is correct?

2. RECYCLING The international symbol for recycling is shown below. What type of congruence transformation does this illustrate?

3. ANATOMY Carl notices that when he holds his hands palm up in front of him, they look the same. What type of congruence transformation does this illustrate?

4. STAMPS A sheet of postage stamps contains 20 stamps in 4 rows of 5 identical stamps each. What type of congruence transformation does this illustrate?

5. MOSAICS José cut rectangles out of tissue paper to create a pattern. He cut out four congruent blue rectangles and then cut out four congruent red rectangles that were slightly smaller to create the pattern shown below.

a. Which congruence transformation does this pattern illustrate?

b. If the whole square were rotated 90, would the transformation still be the same?

Example 2 Identify the type of congruence transformation shown in each picture as a *reflection, translation,* or *rotation.*

13.  translation

14.  reflection

15.  rotation

16.  translation

Example 3 **COORDINATE GEOMETRY** Graph each pair of triangles with the given vertices. Then, identify the transformation, and verify that it is a congruence transformation. **17–20. See Ch. 4 Answer Appendix.**

17. $M(-7, -1), P(-7, -7), R(-1, -4)$; $T(7, -1), V(7, -7), S(1, -4)$

18. $A(3, 9), B(3, 7), C(7, 7)$; $S(3, 5), T(3, 3), R(7, 3)$

19. $A(-4, 5), B(0, 2), C(-4, 2)$; $X(-5, -4), Y(-2, 0), Z(-2, -4)$

20. $A(2, 2), B(4, 7), C(6, 2)$; $D(2, -2), F(4, -7), G(6, -2)$

B **CONSTRUCTION** Identify the type of congruence transformation performed on each given triangle to generate the other triangle in the truss with matching left and right sides shown below.

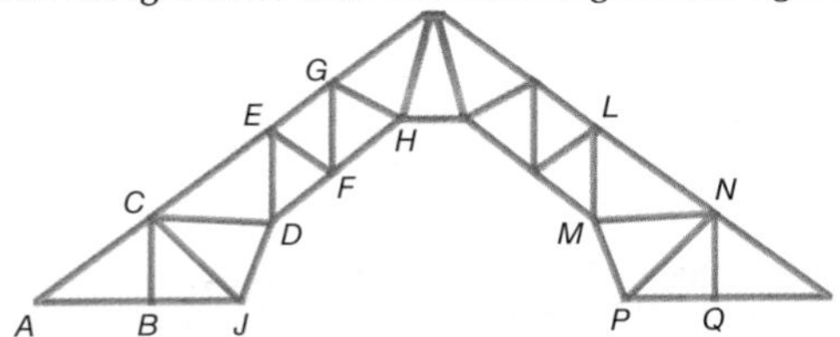

21. $\triangle NMP$ to $\triangle CJD$ **rrotation**

22. $\triangle EFD$ to $\triangle GHF$ **translation**

23. $\triangle CBJ$ to $\triangle NQP$ **reflection**

AMUSEMENT RIDES Identify the type of congruence transformation shown in each picture as a *reflection, translation,* or *rotation.*

24. rotation
25. rotation
26. translation

24.  25.  26.

28. vertical: A, H, I, M, O, T, U, V, W, X, and Y; horizontal: B, C, D, E, H, I, K, O, and X

27. Rotation; the knob is the center of rotation.

27. **SCHOOL** Identify the transformations that are used to open a combination lock on a locker. If appropriate, identify the line of symmetry or center of rotation.

C 28. **CCSS STRUCTURE** Determine which capital letters of the alphabet have vertical and/or horizontal lines of reflection.

Enrichment

OL BL

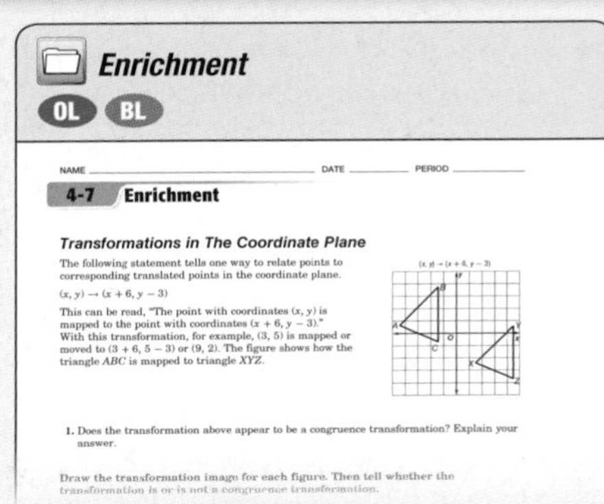

NAME ______ DATE ______ PERIOD ______

4-7 Enrichment

Transformations in The Coordinate Plane

The following statement tells one way to relate points to corresponding translated points in the coordinate plane.

(x, y) → (x + 6, y − 3)

This can be read, "The point with coordinates (x, y) is mapped to the point with coordinates (x + 6, y − 3)." With this transformation, for example, (3, 5) is mapped or moved to (3 + 6, 5 − 3) or (9, 2). The figure shows how the triangle ABC is mapped to triangle XYZ.

1. Does the transformation above appear to be a congruence transformation? Explain your answer.

Draw the transformation image for each figure. Then tell whether the transformation is or is not a congruence transformation.

CCSS Teaching the Mathematical Practices

Structure Mathematically proficient students look closely to discern a pattern or structure. In Exercise 28, encourage students to write each letter of the alphabet to see which have lines of reflection.

29. **DECORATING** Tionne is redecorating her bedroom. She can use stencils or a stamp to create the design shown.

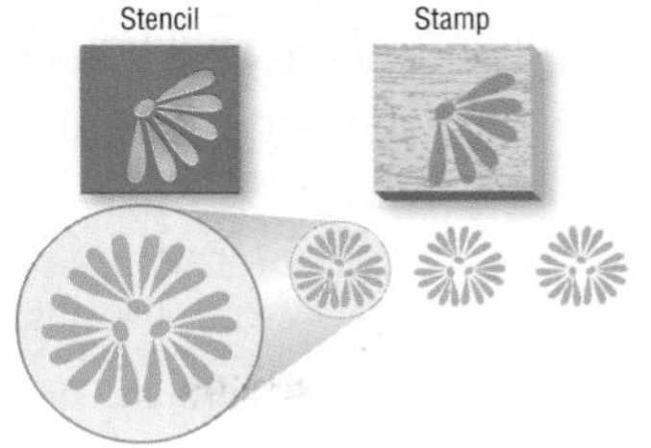

a. If Tionne used the stencil, what type of transformation was used to produce each flower in the design? reflection or rotation

b. What type of transformation was used if she used the stamp to produce each flower in the design? rotation

30. **MULTIPLE REPRESENTATIONS** In this problem, you will investigate the relationship between the ordered pairs of a figure and its translated image.

a. **Geometric** Draw congruent rectangles *ABCD* and *WXYZ* on a coordinate plane. See margin.

b. **Verbal** How do you get from a vertex on *ABCD* to the corresponding vertex on *WXYZ* using only horizontal and vertical movement?

c. **Tabular** Copy the table shown. Use your rectangles to fill in the *x*-coordinates, the *y*-coordinates, and the unknown value in the transformation column. See margin.

Rectangle *ABCD*	Transformation	Rectangle *WXYZ*
A(?, ?)	$(x_1 + ?, y_1 + ?)$	*W*(?, ?)
B(?, ?)	$(x_1 + ?, y_1 + ?)$	*X*(?, ?)
C(?, ?)	$(x_1 + ?, y_1 + ?)$	*Y*(?, ?)
D(?, ?)	$(x_1 + ?, y_1 + ?)$	*Z*(?, ?)

d. **Algebraic** Function notation $(x, y) \rightarrow (x + a, y + b)$, where a and b are real numbers, represents a mapping from one set of coordinates onto another. Complete the following notation that represents the rule for the translation $ABCD \rightarrow WXYZ$: $(x, y) \rightarrow (x + a, y + b)$. Sample answer: $(x, y) \rightarrow (x + 5, y + 3)$

30b. Sample answer: You get from a vertex on *ABCD* to the corresponding vertex on *WXYZ* by moving 5 units to the right and 3 units up.

H.O.T. Problems Use Higher-Order Thinking Skills

31. **CHALLENGE** Use the diagram at the right.

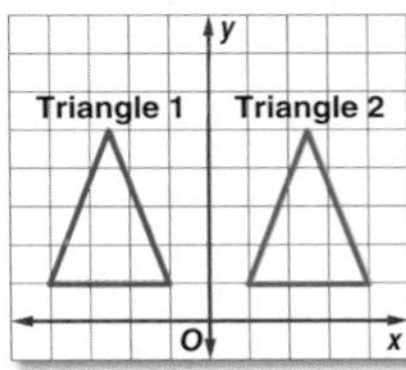

a. Identify two transformations of Triangle 1 that can result in Triangle 2. translation, reflection

b. What must be true of the triangles in order for more than one transformation on a preimage to result in the same image? Explain your reasoning.

31b. Sample answer: The triangles must be either isosceles or equilateral. When triangles are isosceles or equilateral, they have a line of symmetry, so reflections result in the same figure.

32. **CCSS REASONING** A *dilation* is another type of transformation. In the diagram, a small paper clip has been dilated to produce a larger paper clip. Explain why dilations are not a congruence transformation. The images produced are not congruent to the original image.

OPEN ENDED **Describe a real-world example of each of the following, other than those given in this lesson.**

33. reflection **34.** translation **35.** rotation

33. Sample answer: A person looking in a mirror sees a reflection of himself or herself.

36. **WRITING IN MATH** In the diagram at the right $\triangle DEF$ is called a *glide reflection* of $\triangle ABC$. Based on the diagram, define a glide reflection. Is a glide reflection a congruence transformation? Include a definition of congruence transformation in your response. Explain your reasoning. See margin.

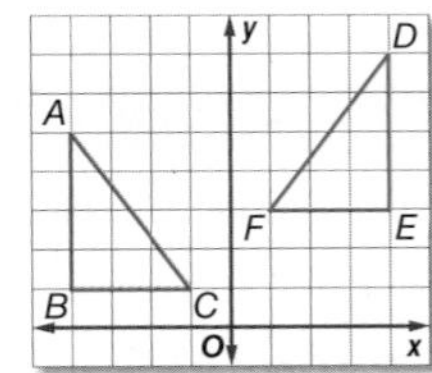

34. Sample answer: A marching band moves across the field in a formation.
35. Sample answer: A faucet handle rotates when you turn the water on.

Differentiated Instruction  

Extension Rotations, reflections, and translations are used to create many works of art. Have students explore using these transformations to create patterns. Students should begin with a single figure in the coordinate plane and use various transformations to turn their figure into an artful pattern. Students should record each pattern used so that the design can be repeated.

Multiple Representations

In Exercise 30, students use geometric sketches, a verbal description, a table, and algebraic expressions to investigate the relationship between ordered pairs of a figure and its translated image.

Teaching the Mathematical Practices

Reasoning Mathematically proficient students make sense of quantities and their relationships in problem situations. In Exercise 32, encourage students to compare the dilation to the translation, reflection, and rotation.

Additional Answers

30a. Sample answer:

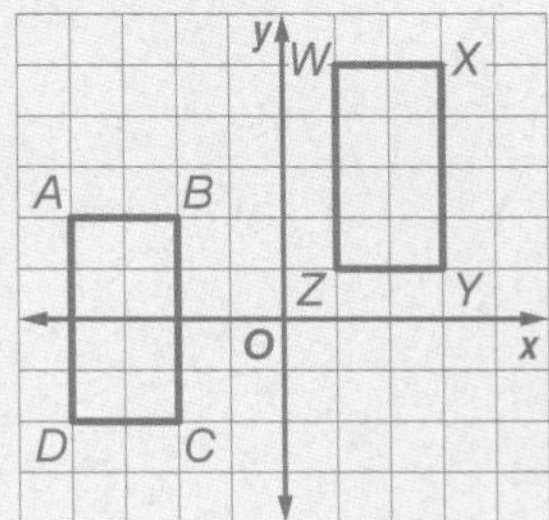

30c. Sample answer:

Rectangle *ABCD*	Transformation	Rectangle *WXYZ*
A(−4, 2)	(−4 + 5, 2 + 3)	*W*(1, 5)
B(−2, 2)	(−2 + 5, 2 + 3)	*X*(3, 5)
C(−2, −2)	(−2 + 5, −2 + 3)	*Y*(3, 1)
D(−4, −2)	(−4 + 5, −2 + 3)	*Z*(1, 1)

36. Sample answer: A glide reflection is a reflection over a line and then a translation in a direction that is parallel to the line of reflection. In a congruence transformation, the preimage and image are congruent. Yes; a glide reflection is a congruence transformation. In the diagram, $AB = DE$, $BC = EF$, and $AC = DF$, so $\overline{AB} \cong \overline{DE}$, $\overline{BC} \cong \overline{EF}$, and $\overline{AC} \cong \overline{DF}$, so $\triangle ABC \cong \triangle DEF$.

4 Assess

Yesterday's News Have students write how what they learned in the previous Chapter 4 lessons has helped them with the concepts in Lesson 4-7.

Follow-up

Students have explored congruence transformations.

Ask:

- Where can congruence transformations be found in everyday life? Sample answer: Video games often use translations and rotations; the image of a person in a mirror is a reflection; the movement of turning a puzzle piece around is a rotation.

Standardized Test Practice

37. SHORT RESPONSE Cindy is shopping for a new desk chair at a store where the desk chairs are 50% off. She also has a coupon for 50% off any one item. Cindy thinks that she can now get the desk chair for free. Is this true? If not, what will be the percent off she will receive with both the sale and the coupon? **no; 75%**

38. Identify the congruence transformation shown. **C**

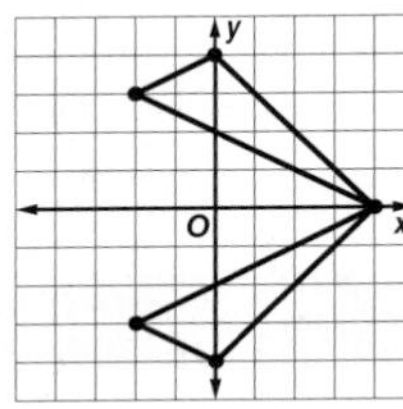

A dilation
B reflection
C rotation
D translation

39. Look at the graph below. What is the slope of the line shown? **J**

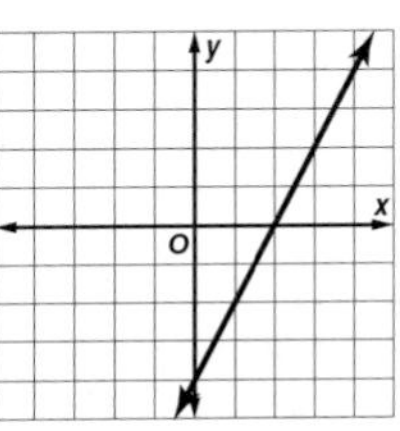

F −2
G −1
H 1
J 2

40. SAT/ACT What is the y-intercept of the line determined by the equation $3x - 4 = 12y - 3$? **B**

A −12
B $-\frac{1}{12}$
C $\frac{1}{12}$
D $\frac{1}{4}$
E 12

Spiral Review

Find each measure. (Lesson 4-6)

41. YZ **4**

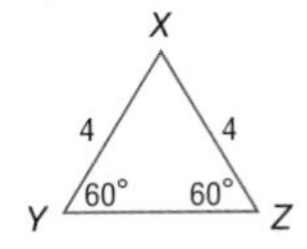

42. $m\angle JLK$ **40**

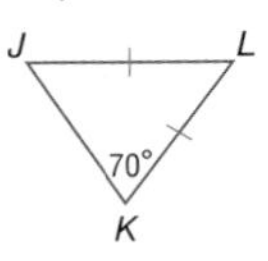

43. AB **10**

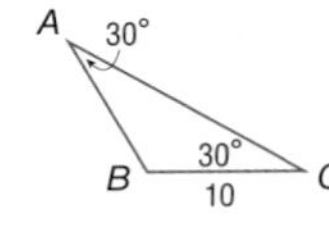

44. PROOF Write a paragraph proof. (Lesson 4-5)

Given: $\angle YWZ \cong \angle XZW$ and $\angle YZW \cong \angle XWZ$

Prove: $\triangle WXZ \cong \triangle ZYW$

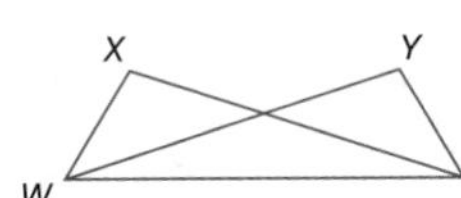

It is given that $\angle YWZ \cong \angle XZW$ and $\angle YZW \cong \angle XWZ$. By the Reflexive Property, $\overline{WZ} \cong \overline{WZ}$. Then $\triangle WXZ \cong \triangle ZYW$ by ASA.

45. ROLLER COASTERS The sign in front of the Electric Storm roller coaster states that all riders must be at least 54 inches tall to ride. If Andy is 5 feet 8 inches tall, can he ride the Electric Storm? Which law of logic leads you to this conclusion? (Lesson 2-4) **yes; Law of Detachment**

Skills Review

Find the coordinates of the midpoint of a segment with the given endpoints.

46. $A(10, -12), C(5, -6)$ **(7.5, −9)**

47. $A(13, 14), C(3, 5)$ **(8, 9.5)**

48. $A(-28, 8), C(-10, 2)$ **(−19, 5)**

49. $A(-12, 2), C(-3, 5)$ **(−7.5, 3.5)**

50. $A(0, 0), C(3, -4)$ **(1.5, −2)**

51. $A(2, 14), C(0, 5)$ **(1, 9.5)**

Differentiated Instruction OL BL

Extension Have students draw a triangle in Quadrant I. Then have students apply each of the three congruence transformations so that Quadrant II, Quadrant III, and Quadrant IV each contain a triangle congruent to the original triangle.

302 | Lesson 4-7 | Congruence Transformations

LESSON 4-8 Triangles and Coordinate Proof

Then

You used coordinate geometry to prove triangle congruence.

Now

1 Position and label triangles for use in coordinate proofs.

2 Write coordinate proofs.

Why?

A global positioning system (GPS) receives transmissions from satellites that allow the exact location of a car to be determined. The information can be used with navigation software to provide driving directions.

NewVocabulary
coordinate proof

Common Core State Standards

Content Standards
G.CO.10 Prove theorems about triangles.
G.GPE.4 Use coordinates to prove simple geometric theorems algebraically.

Mathematical Practices
3 Construct viable arguments and critique the reasoning of others.
2 Reason abstractly and quantitatively.

1 Position and Label Triangles

As with global positioning systems, knowing the coordinates of a figure in a coordinate plane allows you to explore its properties and draw conclusions about it. **Coordinate proofs** use figures in the coordinate plane and algebra to prove geometric concepts. The first step in a coordinate proof is placing the figure on the coordinate plane.

Example 1 Position and Label a Triangle

Position and label right triangle MNP on the coordinate plane so that leg $\overline{MN}$ is a units long and leg $\overline{NP}$ is b units long.

- The length(s) of the side(s) that are along the axes will be easier to determine than the length(s) of side(s) that are not along an axis. Since this is a right triangle, two sides can be located on an axis.
- Placing the right angle of the triangle, $\angle N$, at the origin will allow the two legs to be along the x- and y-axes.
- Position the triangle in the first quadrant.
- Since M is on the y-axis, its x-coordinate is 0. Its y-coordinate is a because the leg is a units long.
- Since P is on the x-axis, its y-coordinate is 0. Its x-coordinate is b because the leg is b units long.

y
M (0, a)
P (b, 0)
O N (0, 0) x

GuidedPractice See Ch. 4 Answer Appendix.

1. Position and label isosceles triangle JKL on the coordinate plane so that its base $\overline{JL}$ is a units long, vertex K is on the y-axis, and the height of the triangle is b units.

KeyConcept Placing Triangles on Coordinate Plane

Step 1 Use the origin as a vertex or center of the triangle.

Step 2 Place at least one side of a triangle on an axis.

Step 3 Keep the triangle within the first quadrant if possible.

Step 4 Use coordinates that make computations as simple as possible.

1 Focus

VerticalAlignment

Before Lesson 4-8 Use coordinate geometry to prove triangle congruence.

Lesson 4-8 Position and label triangles for use in coordinate proofs. Write coordinate proofs.

After Lesson 4-8 Use congruence transformations to make conjectures and justify properties of geometric figures including figures on a coordinate plane.

2 Teach

Scaffolding Questions

Have students read the **Why?** section of the lesson.

Ask:

- How is the coordinate system used by a GPS similar to the geometric coordinate system? The x-axis is the equator and the y-axis is the prime meridian.
- How do you suspect that the satellite determines where you are located on Earth? Accept all reasonable responses.
- What do you need to know to find the distance between two points on a coordinate plane? You need to know the coordinates of each point.

Lesson 4-8 Resources

Resource	Approaching Level AL	On Level OL	Beyond Level BL	English Learners ELL
Teacher Edition	▪ Differentiated Instruction, p. 305	▪ Differentiated Instruction, pp. 305, 309	▪ Differentiated Instruction, pp. 305, 309	
Chapter Resource Masters	▪ Study Guide and Intervention, pp. 49–50 ▪ Skills Practice, p. 51 ▪ Practice, p. 52 ▪ Word Problem Practice, p. 53	▪ Study Guide and Intervention, pp. 49–50 ▪ Skills Practice, p. 51 ▪ Practice, p. 52 ▪ Word Problem Practice, p. 53 ▪ Enrichment, p. 54	▪ Practice, p. 52 ▪ Word Problem Practice, p. 53 ▪ Enrichment, p. 54	▪ Study Guide and Intervention, pp. 49–50 ▪ Skills Practice, p. 51 ▪ Practice, p. 52 ▪ Word Problem Practice, p. 53
Other	▪ 5-Minute Check 4-8 ▪ Study Notebook	▪ 5-Minute Check 4-8 ▪ Study Notebook	▪ 5-Minute Check 4-8 ▪ Study Notebook	▪ 5-Minute Check 4-8 ▪ Study Notebook

Example 2 Identify Missing Coordinates

Name the missing coordinates of isosceles triangle *XYZ*.

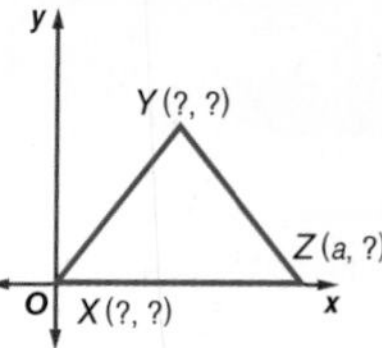

Vertex X is positioned at the origin; its coordinates are (0, 0).

Vertex Z is on the x-axis, so its y-coordinate is 0. The coordinates of vertex Z are $(a, 0)$.

$\triangle XYZ$ is isosceles, so using a vertical segment from Y to to the x-axis and the Hypotenuse-Leg Theorem shows that the x-coordinate of Y is halfway between 0 and a or $\frac{a}{2}$. We cannot write the y-coordinate in terms of a, so call it b. The coordinates of point Y are $\left(\frac{a}{2}, b\right)$.

StudyTip

Right Angle The intersection of the x- and y-axis forms a right angle, so it is a convenient place to locate the right angle of a figure such as a right triangle.

GuidedPractice

2. Name the missing coordinates of isosceles right triangle ABC. **$A(0, a)$, $B(0, 0)$, $C(a, 0)$**

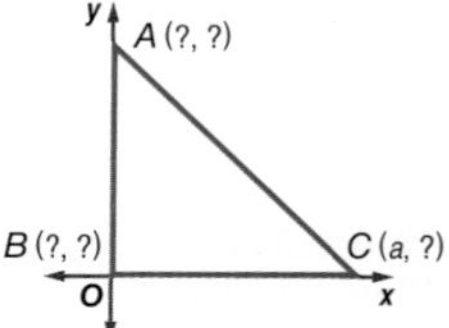

2 Write Coordinate Proofs

After a triangle is placed on the coordinate plane and labeled, we can use coordinate proofs to verify properties and to prove theorems.

StudyTip

Coordinate Proof The guidelines and methods used in this lesson apply to all polygons, not just triangles.

Example 3 Write a Coordinate Proof

Write a coordinate proof to show that a line segment joining the midpoints of two sides of a triangle is parallel to the third side.

Place a vertex at the origin and label it A. Use coordinates that are multiples of 2 because the Midpoint Formula involves dividing the sum of the coordinates by 2.

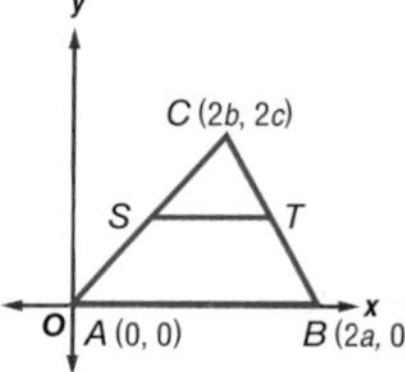

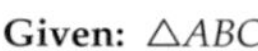

Given: $\triangle ABC$
S is the midpoint of $\overline{AC}$.
T is the midpoint of $\overline{BC}$.

Prove: $\overline{ST} \parallel \overline{AB}$

Proof:

By the Midpoint Formula, the coordinates of S are $\left(\frac{2b+0}{2}, \frac{2c+0}{2}\right)$ or (b, c) and the coordinates of T are $\left(\frac{2a+2b}{2}, \frac{0+2c}{2}\right)$ or $(a + b, c)$.

By the Slope Formula, the slope of $\overline{ST}$ is $\frac{c-c}{a+b-b}$ or 0 and the slope of $\overline{AB}$ is $\frac{0-0}{2a-0}$ or 0.

Since $\overline{ST}$ and $\overline{AB}$ have the same slope, $\overline{ST} \parallel \overline{AB}$.

Additional Answer (Guided Practice)

4. Let O represent Odessa, A represent Albany, and S represent San Angleo.
$\overline{OA} = \sqrt{(31.9 - 32.7)^2 + (102.3 - 99.3)^2} \approx 3.10$;
$\overline{AS} = \sqrt{(32.7 - 31.4)^2 + (99.3 - 100.5)^2} \approx 1.77$;
$\overline{OS} = \sqrt{(31.9 - 31.4)^2 + (102.3 - 100.5)^2} \approx 1.87$; $AS \approx OS$, $\triangle OAS$ is approximately isosceles. Therefore, the West Texas Triangle is approximately isosceles.

1 Position and Label Triangles

Examples 1 and 2 show how to use coordinate proofs to prove geometric concepts.

Formative Assessment

Use the Guided Practice exercises after each example to determine students' understanding of concepts.

Additional Examples

1 Position and label right triangle XYZ with leg $\overline{XZ}$ d units long on the coordinate plane.

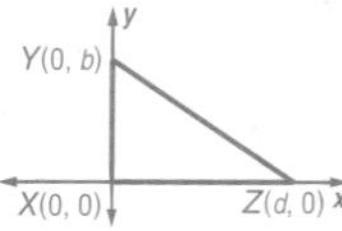

2 Name the missing coordinates of isosceles right triangle QRS. $Q(0, 0)$, $S(c, c)$

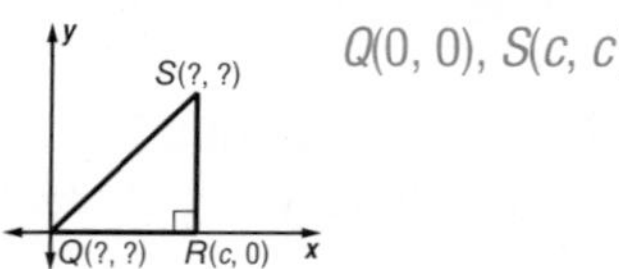

Additional Examples also in Interactive Classroom PowerPoint® Presentations

2 Write Coordinate Proofs

Examples 3 and 4 shows students how to use properties and theorems to write coordinate proofs.

Additional Example

3 Write a coordinate proof to prove that the segment that joins the vertex angle of an isosceles triangle to the midpoint of its base is perpendicular to the base.

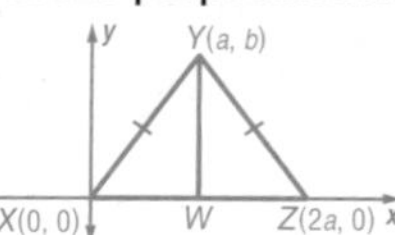

The midpoint of $\overline{XZ}$ is $(a, 0)$. The slope of $\overline{YW}$ is undefined, and the slope of $\overline{XZ}$ is 0. So, $\overline{YW} \perp \overline{XZ}$.

GuidedPractice

3. Write a coordinate proof to show that $\triangle ABX \cong \triangle CDX$. **See Ch. 4 Answer Appendix.**

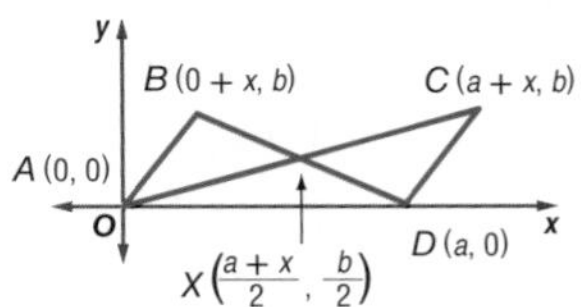

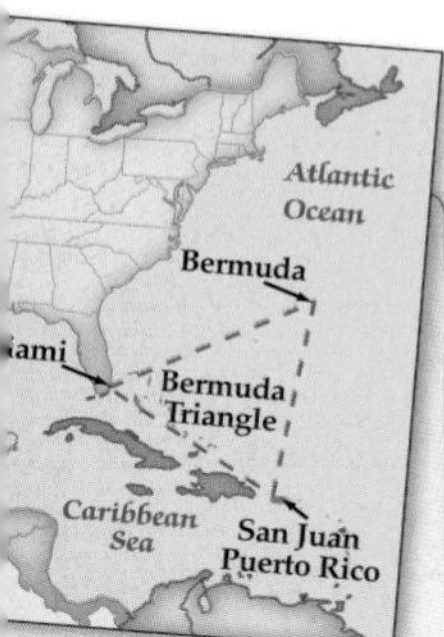

Real-WorldLink

More than 50 ships and 20 airplanes have mysteriously disappeared from a section of the North Atlantic Ocean off of North America commonly referred to as the Bermuda Triangle.

Source: *Encyclopaedia Britannica*

The techniques used for coordinate proofs can be used to solve real-world problems.

PT

Real-World Example 4 Classify Triangles

GEOGRAPHY The Bermuda Triangle is a region formed by Miami, Florida, San Jose, Puerto Rico, and Bermuda. The approximate coordinates of each location, respectively, are 25.8°N 80.27°W, 18.48°N 66.12°W, and 33.37°N 64.68°W. Write a coordinate proof to prove that the Bermuda Triangle is scalene.

The first step is to label the coordinates of each location. Let M represent Miami, B represent Bermuda, and P represent Puerto Rico.

$B(33.37, 64.68)$

$M(25.8, 80.27)$

$P(18.48, 66.12)$

If no two sides of $\triangle MPB$ are congruent, then the Bermuda Triangle is scalene. Use the Distance Formula and a calculator to find the distance between each location.

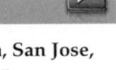

$$MB = \sqrt{(33.37 - 25.8)^2 + (64.68 - 80.27)^2}$$

$$\approx 17.33$$

$$MP = \sqrt{(25.8 - 18.48)^2 + (80.27 - 66.12)^2}$$

$$\approx 15.93$$

$$PB = \sqrt{(33.37 - 18.48)^2 + (64.68 - 66.12)^2}$$

$$\approx 14.96$$

Since each side is a different length, $\triangle MPB$ is scalene. Therefore, the Bermuda Triangle is scalene.

GuidedPractice

4. **GEOGRAPHY** In 2006, a group of art museums collaborated to form the West Texas Triangle to promote their collections. This region is formed by the cities of Odessa, Albany, and San Angelo. The approximate coordinates of each location, respectively, are 31.9°N 102.3°W, 32.7°N 99.3°W, and 31.4°N 100.5°W. Write a coordinate proof to prove that the West Texas Triangle is approximately isosceles. **See margin.**

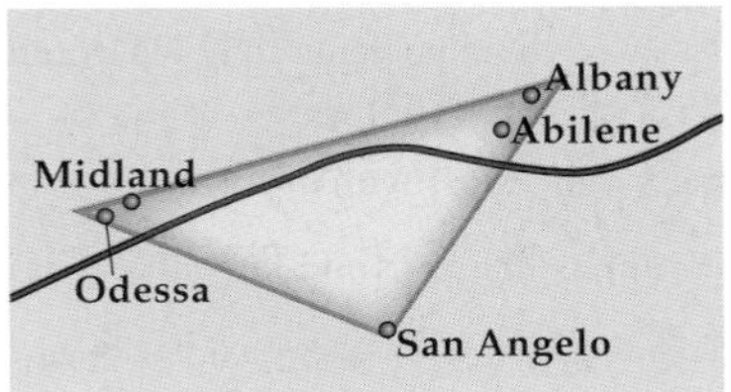

DifferentiatedInstruction   

Visual/Spatial Supply students with an overhead or see-through copy of a map. Have students choose three destinations and use these vertices to draw a triangle. Next, students place the see-through map on a coordinate plane. Encourage students to experiment with this placement. Finally, have students use coordinate proof to classify the triangle.

Teach with Tech

Interactive Whiteboard Project a triangle onto the board and draw a coordinate plane so that one of the vertices is located at a point (a, b) in the first quadrant. Then redraw the coordinate plane so that vertex is now located at (0, 0). Show your students that this typically helps to simplify the computations.

Tips for New Teachers

Reasoning Since coordinate proofs use a combination of geometry and algebra, remind students that they will need to use the distance, slope, and midpoint formulas, as well as postulates and theorems. Advise students to look for key words such as "length" or "parallel" in word problems, which may imply that a particular formula can be used to solve the problem.

Additional Example

4 **DRAFTING** Write a coordinate proof to prove that this drafter's tool is shaped like a right triangle. The length of one side is 10 inches and the length of another side is 5.75 inches.

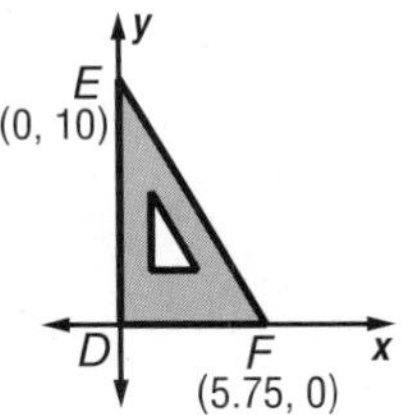

Slope of $\overline{ED}$ is undefined. Slope of $\overline{DF}$ is 0. $\overline{ED} \perp \overline{DF}$, so $\triangle DEF$ is a right triangle. The drafter's tool is shaped like a right triangle.

Focus on Mathematical Content

Numeric First Advise students that they may want to place a figure using numeric coordinates first and then translate to variable coordinates to write their proofs.

3 Practice

Formative Assessment

Use Exercises 1–6 to check for understanding.

Use the chart at the bottom of this page to customize assignments for your students.

Teaching the Mathematical Practices

Arguments Mathematically proficient students understand and use stated assumptions, definitions, and previously established results in constructing arguments. In Exercise 5, encourage students to make a plan for their proof before starting.

Additional Answer

5. $DC = \sqrt{(-a-(-a))^2 + (b-0)^2}$ or b

$GH = \sqrt{(a-a)^2 + (b-0)^2}$ or b

Since $DC = GH$, $\overline{DC} \cong \overline{GH}$.

$DF = \sqrt{(0+a)^2 + \left(\frac{b}{2}-b\right)^2}$ or $\sqrt{a^2 + \frac{b^2}{4}}$

$GF = \sqrt{(a-0)^2 + \left(b-\frac{b}{2}\right)^2}$ or $\sqrt{a^2 + \frac{b^2}{4}}$

$CF = \sqrt{(0+a)^2 + \left(\frac{b}{2}-0\right)^2}$ or $\sqrt{a^2 + \frac{b^2}{4}}$

$HF = \sqrt{(a-0)^2 + \left(0-\frac{b}{2}\right)^2}$ or $\sqrt{a^2 + \frac{b^2}{4}}$

Since $DF = GF = CF = HF$, $\overline{DF} \cong \overline{GF} \cong \overline{CF} \cong \overline{HF}$.

$\triangle FGH \cong \triangle FDC$ by SSS.

Check Your Understanding

= Step-by-Step Solutions begin on page R14.

Example 1 **Position and label each triangle on the coordinate plane.** **1–2. See Ch. 4 Answer Appendix.**

1. right $\triangle ABC$ with legs $\overline{AC}$ and $\overline{AB}$ so that $\overline{AC}$ is $2a$ units long and leg $\overline{AB}$ is $2b$ units long
2. isosceles $\triangle FGH$ with base $\overline{FG}$ that is $2a$ units long

Example 2 **Name the missing coordinate(s) of each triangle.**

3. **$T(2a, 0)$**

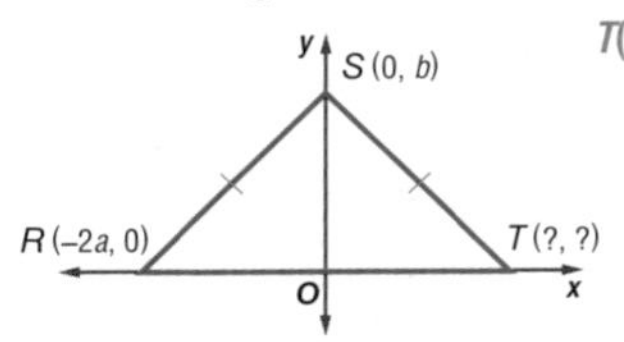

4. **$W(0, 0)$, $Z(a, \sqrt{3}a)$**

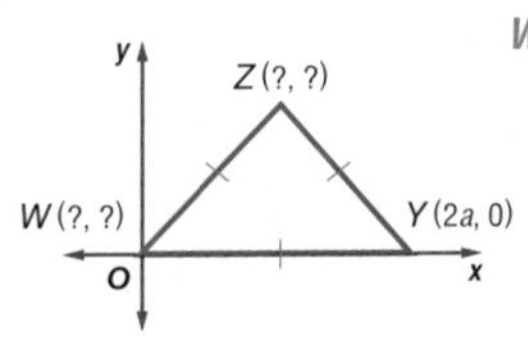

Example 3

5. **CCSS ARGUMENTS** Write a coordinate proof to show that $\triangle FGH \cong \triangle FDC$. **See margin.**

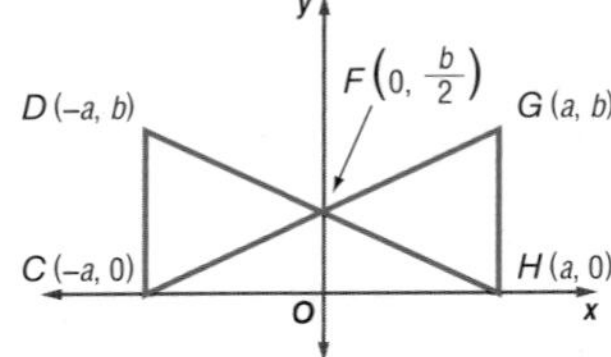

Example 4

6. **FLAGS** Write a coordinate proof to prove that the large triangle in the center of the flag is isosceles. The dimensions of the flag are 4 feet by 6 feet and point B of the triangle bisects the bottom of the flag. **See Ch. 4 Answer Appendix.**

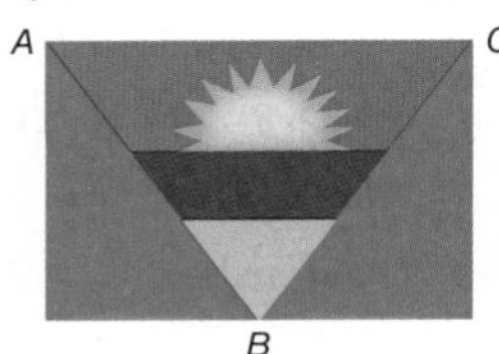

Practice and Problem Solving

Extra Practice is on page R4.

Example 1 **Position and label each triangle on the coordinate plane.** **7–12. See Ch. 4 Answer Appendix.**

7. isosceles $\triangle ABC$ with base $\overline{AB}$ that is a units long
8. right $\triangle XYZ$ with hypotenuse $\overline{YZ}$, the length of $\overline{XY}$ is b units long, and the length of $\overline{XZ}$ is three times the length of $\overline{XY}$
9. isosceles right $\triangle RST$ with hypotenuse $\overline{RS}$ and legs $3a$ units long
10. right $\triangle JKL$ with legs $\overline{JK}$ and $\overline{KL}$ so that $\overline{JK}$ is a units long and leg $\overline{KL}$ is $4b$ units long
11. equilateral $\triangle GHJ$ with sides $\frac{1}{2}a$ units long
12. equilateral $\triangle DEF$ with sides $4b$ units long

Differentiated Homework Options

Level	Assignment	Two-Day Option	
AL Basic	7–24, 30, 34, 36–51	7–21 odd, 38–41	8–24 even, 30, 34, 36, 37, 42–51
OL Core	7–23 odd, 25–30, 34, 36–51	7–24, 38–41	25–30, 34, 36, 37, 42–51
BL Advanced	25–48, (optional: 49–51)		

Example 2 Name the missing coordinate(s) of each triangle.

13.

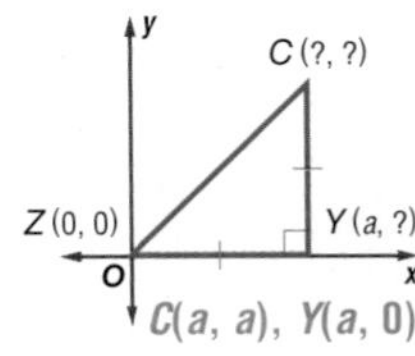

$C(a, a)$, $Y(a, 0)$

14.

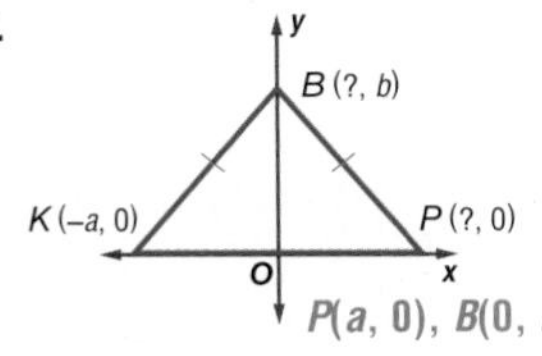

$P(a, 0)$, $B(0, b)$

15. $J(?, b)$, $N(?, 0)$, $L(3a, ?)$

$N(0, 0)$, $J(1.5a, b)$, $L(3a, 0)$

16.

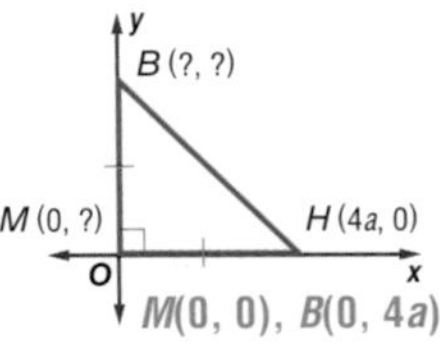

$M(0, 0)$, $B(0, 4a)$

17.

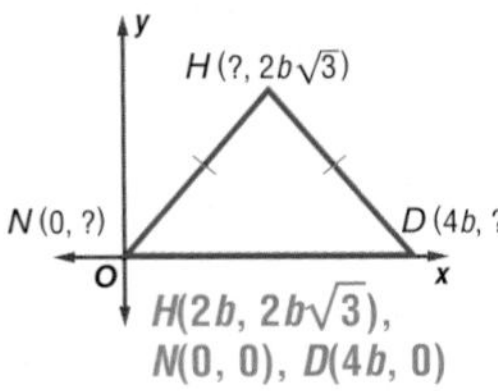

$H(2b, 2b\sqrt{3})$, $N(0, 0)$, $D(4b, 0)$

18.

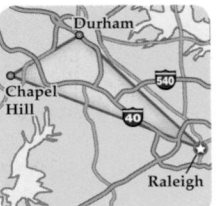

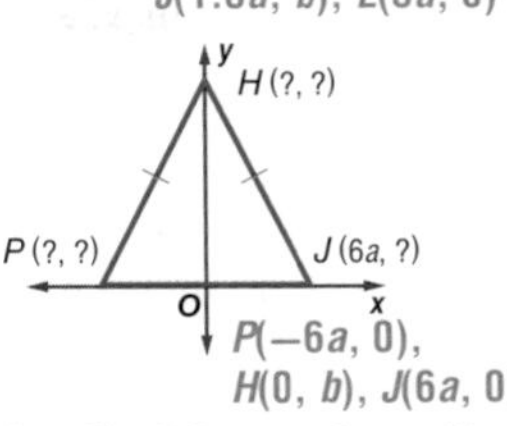

$P(-6a, 0)$, $H(0, b)$, $J(6a, 0)$

Example 3  **ARGUMENTS** **Write a coordinate proof for each statement.** 19–20. See Ch. 4 Answer Appendix.

19. The segments joining the base vertices to the midpoints of the legs of an isosceles triangle are congruent.

20. The three segments joining the midpoints of the sides of an isosceles triangle form another isosceles triangle.

Example 4 **PROOF** **Write a coordinate proof for each statement.** 21–22. See Ch. 4 Answer Appendix.

21. The measure of the segment that joins the vertex of the right angle in a right triangle to the midpoint of the hypotenuse is one-half the measure of the hypotenuse.

22. If a line segment joins the midpoints of two sides of a triangle, then its length is equal to one half the length of the third side.

23. RESEARCH TRIANGLE The cities of Raleigh, Durham, and Chapel Hill, North Carolina, form what is known as the Research Triangle. The approximate latitude and longitude of Raleigh are 35.82°N 78.64°W, of Durham are 35.99°N 78.91°W, and of Chapel Hill are 35.92°N 79.04°W. Show that the triangle formed by these three cities is scalene. See Ch. 4 Answer Appendix.

24. PARTY PLANNING Three friends live in houses with backyards adjacent to a neighborhood bike path. They decide to have a round-robin party using their three homes, inviting their friends to start at one house and then move to each of the other two. If one friend's house is centered at the origin, then the location of the other homes are (5, 12) and (13, 0). Write a coordinate proof to prove that the triangle formed by these three homes is isosceles. See Ch. 4 Answer Appendix.

B **Draw $\triangle XYZ$ and find the slope of each side of the triangle. Determine whether the triangle is a right triangle. Explain.** 25–26. See margin.

25. $X(0, 0)$, $Y(2h, 2h)$, $Z(4h, 0)$

26. $X(0, 0)$, $Y(1, h)$, $Z(2h, 0)$

27. CAMPING Two families set up tents at a state park. If the ranger's station is located at (0, 0), and the locations of the tents are (0, 25) and (12, 9), write a coordinate proof to prove that the figure formed by the locations of the ranger's station and the two tents is a right triangle. See Ch. 4 Answer Appendix.

C **28. PROOF** Write a coordinate proof to prove that $\triangle ABC$ is an isosceles triangle if the vertices are $A(0, 0)$, $B(a, b)$, and $C(2a, 0)$. See Ch. 4 Answer Appendix.

Additional Answers

25. slope of $\overline{XY} = 1$, slope of $\overline{YZ} = -1$, slope of $\overline{ZX} = 0$; since $1(-1) = -1$, $\overline{XY} \perp \overline{YZ}$. Therefore $\triangle XYZ$ is a right triangle.

26. slope of $\overline{XY} = h$, slope of $\overline{YZ} = \frac{h}{1 - 2h}$, slope of $\overline{ZX} = 0$; no two slopes have a product of -1, so $\triangle XYZ$ is not a right triangle.

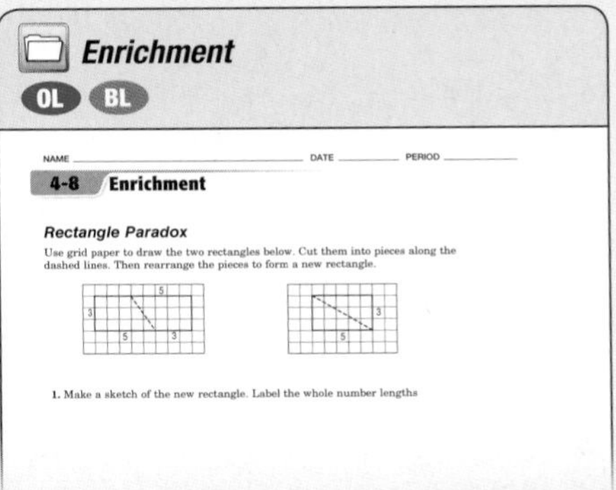

Enrichment OL BL

NAME DATE PERIOD

4-8 Enrichment

Rectangle Paradox

Use grid paper to draw the two rectangles below. Cut them into pieces along the dashed lines. Then rearrange the pieces to form a new rectangle.

1. Make a sketch of the new rectangle. Label the whole number lengths

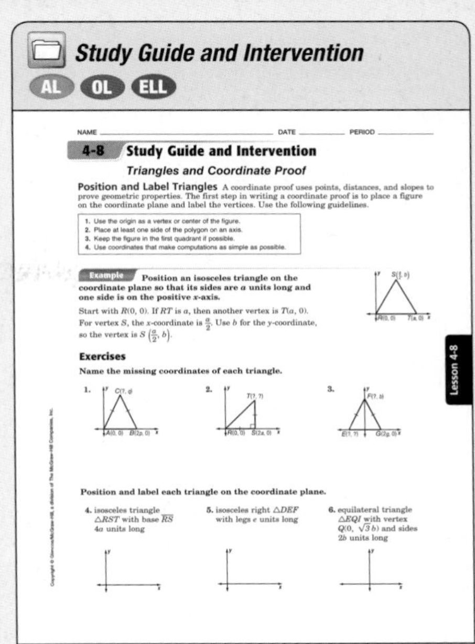

Study Guide and Intervention AL OL ELL

NAME DATE PERIOD

4-8 Study Guide and Intervention

Triangles and Coordinate Proof

Position and Label Triangles A coordinate proof uses points, distances, and slopes to prove geometric properties. The first step in writing a coordinate proof is to place a figure on the coordinate plane and label the vertices. Use the following guidelines.

1. Use the origin as a vertex or center of the figure.
2. Place at least one side of the polygon on an axis.
3. Keep the figure in the first quadrant if possible.
4. Use coordinates that make computations as simple as possible.

Example Position an isosceles triangle on the coordinate plane so that its sides are *a* units long and one side is on the positive *x*-axis.

Start with *R*(0, 0). If $\overline{RT}$ is *a*, then another vertex is *T*(*a*, 0). For vertex *S*, the *x*-coordinate is $\frac{a}{2}$. Use *b* for the *y*-coordinate, so the vertex is $S\left(\frac{a}{2}, b\right)$.

Exercises

Name the missing coordinates of each triangle.

Position and label each triangle on the coordinate plane.

4. isosceles triangle $\triangle RST$ with base $\overline{RS}$ 4*a* units long
5. isosceles right $\triangle DEF$ with legs *e* units long
6. equilateral triangle $\triangle EQI$ with vertex $Q(0, \sqrt{3}b)$ and sides 2*b* units long

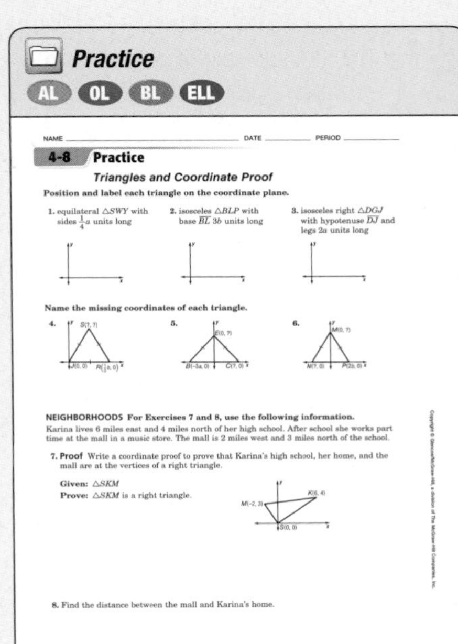

Practice AL OL BL ELL

NAME DATE PERIOD

4-8 Practice

Triangles and Coordinate Proof

Position and label each triangle on the coordinate plane.

1. equilateral $\triangle SWY$ with sides $\frac{1}{4}a$ units long
2. isosceles $\triangle BLP$ with base $\overline{BL}$ 3*b* units long
3. isosceles right $\triangle DGJ$ with hypotenuse $\overline{DJ}$ and legs 2*a* units long

Name the missing coordinates of each triangle.

NEIGHBORHOODS For Exercises 7 and 8, use the following information.
Karina lives 6 miles east and 4 miles north of her high school. After school she works part time at the mall in a music store. The mall is 2 miles west and 3 miles north of the school.

7. **Proof** Write a coordinate proof to prove that Karina's high school, her home, and the mall are at the vertices of a right triangle.
Given: $\triangle SKM$
Prove: $\triangle SKM$ is a right triangle.

8. Find the distance between the mall and Karina's home.

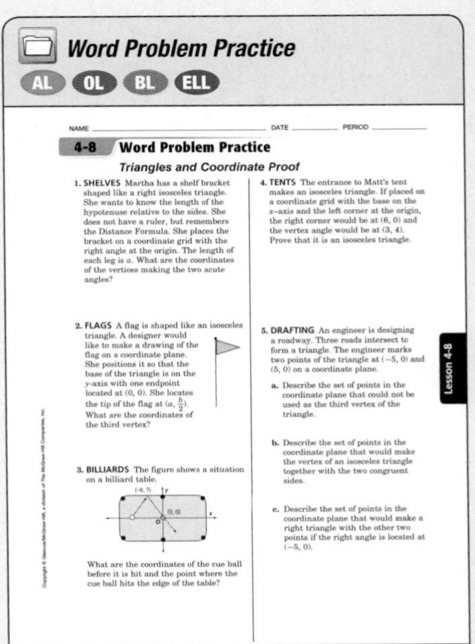

Word Problem Practice AL OL BL ELL

NAME DATE PERIOD

4-8 Word Problem Practice

Triangles and Coordinate Proof

1. **SHELVES** Martha has a shelf bracket shaped like a right isosceles triangle. She wants to know the length of the hypotenuse relative to the sides. She does not have a ruler, but remembers the Distance Formula. She places the bracket on a coordinate grid with the right angle at the origin. The length of each leg is *a*. What are the coordinates of the vertices making the two acute angles?

2. **FLAGS** A flag is shaped like an isosceles triangle. A designer would like to make a drawing of the flag on a coordinate plane. She positions it so that the base of the triangle is on the *y*-axis with one endpoint located at (0, 0). She locates the tip of the flag at $\left(a, \frac{b}{2}\right)$. What are the coordinates of the third vertex?

3. **BILLIARDS** The figure shows a situation on a billiard table.

What are the coordinates of the cue ball before it is hit and the point where the cue ball hits the edge of the table?

4. **TENTS** The entrance to Matt's tent makes an isosceles triangle. If placed on a coordinate grid with the base on the *x*-axis and the left corner at the origin, the right corner would be at (6, 0) and the vertex angle would be at (3, 4). Prove that it is an isosceles triangle.

5. **DRAFTING** An engineer is designing a roadway. Three roads intersect to form a triangle. The engineer marks two points of the triangle at (−5, 0) and (5, 0) on a coordinate plane.

a. Describe the set of points in the coordinate plane that could not be used as the third vertex of the triangle.

b. Describe the set of points in the coordinate plane that would make the vertex of an isosceles triangle together with the other two congruent sides.

c. Describe the set of points in the coordinate plane that would make a right triangle with the other two points if the right angle is located at (−5, 0).

Additional Answers

29a.

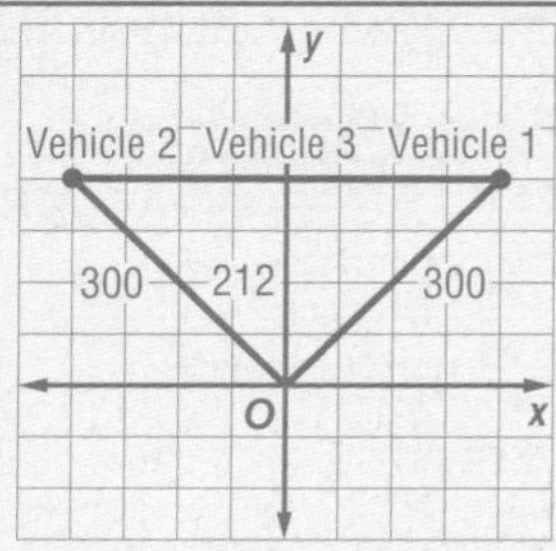

The equation of the line along which the first vehicle lies is $y = x$. The slope is 1 because the vehicle travels the same number of units north as it does east of the origin and the y-intercept is 0. The equation of the line along which the second vehicle lies is $y = -x$. The slope is -1 because the vehicle travels the same number of units north as it does west of the origin and the y-intercept is 0.

29c. First vehicle, $(150\sqrt{2}, 150\sqrt{2})$; second vehicle, $(-150\sqrt{2}, 150\sqrt{2})$; third vehicle, (0, 212); the paths taken by the first two vehicles form the hypotenuse of a right triangle. Using the Pythagorean Theorem, the distance between the third vehicle and the first and second vehicle can be calculated. The third vehicle travels due north and therefore, remains on the y-axis.

29d. The y-coordinates of the first two vehicles are $150\sqrt{2} \approx 212.13$, while the y-coordinate of the third vehicle is 212. Since all three vehicles have approximately the same y-coordinate, they are approximately collinear. The midpoint of the first and second vehicle is $\left(\frac{150\sqrt{2} - 150\sqrt{2}}{2}, \frac{212 + 212}{2}\right)$ or (0, 212), the location of the third vehicle.

29 **WATER SPORTS** Three personal watercraft vehicles launch from the same dock. The first vehicle leaves the dock traveling due northeast, while the second vehicle travels due northwest. Meanwhile, the third vehicle leaves the dock traveling due north.

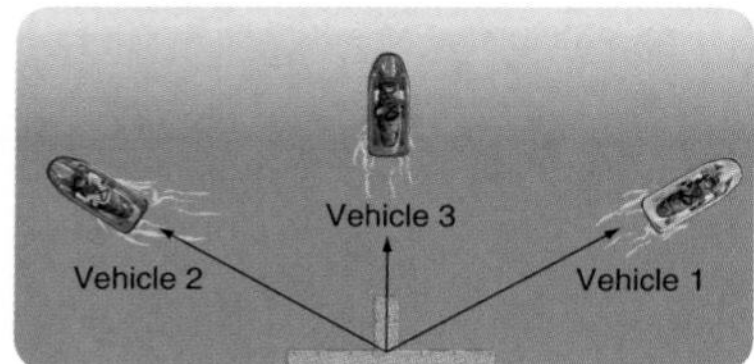

The first and second vehicles stop about 300 yards from the dock, while the third stops about 212 yards from the dock.

a. If the dock is located at (0, 0), sketch a graph to represent this situation. What is the equation of the line along which the first vehicle lies? What is the equation of the line along which the second vehicle lies? Explain your reasoning. **See margin.**

b. Write a coordinate proof to prove that the dock, the first vehicle, and the second vehicle form an isosceles right triangle.

c. Find the coordinates of the locations of all three watercrafts. Explain your reasoning. **See margin.**

d. Write a coordinate proof to prove that the positions of all three watercrafts are approximately collinear and that the third watercraft is at the midpoint between the other two. **See margin.**

29b. The paths taken by both the first and second vehicles are 300 yards long. Therefore the paths are congruent. If two sides of a triangle are congruent, then the triangle is isosceles.

H.O.T. Problems Use Higher-Order Thinking Skills

30. **REASONING** The midpoints of the sides of a triangle are located at $(a, 0)$, $(2a, b)$ and (a, b). If one vertex is located at the origin, what are the coordinates of the other vertices? Explain your reasoning. **See margin.**

CHALLENGE **Find the coordinates of point L so $\triangle JKL$ is the indicated type of triangle. Point J has coordinates (0, 0) and point K has coordinates $(2a, 2b)$.**

31–33. Sample answers given.

31. scalene triangle $(a, 0)$

32. right triangle $(2a, 0)$ or $(0, 2b)$

33. isosceles triangle $(4a, 0)$

34. **OPEN ENDED** Draw an isosceles right triangle on the coordinate plane so that the midpoint of its hypotenuse is the origin. Label the coordinates of each vertex. **See Ch. 4 Answer Appendix.**

35. **CHALLENGE** Use a coordinate proof to show that if you add n units to each x-coordinate of the vertices of a triangle and m to each y-coordinate, the resulting figure is congruent to the original triangle. **See Ch. 4 Answer Appendix.**

36.  **REASONING** A triangle has vertex coordinates (0, 0) and $(a, 0)$. If the coordinates of the third vertex are in terms of a, and the triangle is isosceles, identify the coordinates and position the triangle on the coordinate plane. **See margin.**

37. **WRITING IN MATH** Explain why following each guideline below for placing a triangle on the coordinate plane is helpful in proving coordinate proofs.

a. Use the origin as a vertex of the triangle. **a–c. See margin.**

b. Place at least one side of the triangle on the x- or y-axis.

c. Keep the triangle within the first quadrant if possible.

30. $(2a, 0)$, $(2a, 2b)$; Using the midpoint formula,

$(a, 0) = \left(0 + \frac{x_2}{2}, 0 + \frac{y_2}{2}\right)$,

so $x_2 = 2a$ and $y_2 = 0$

$(a, b) = \left(0 + \frac{x_2}{2}, 0 + \frac{y_2}{2}\right)$,

so $x_2 = 2a$ and $y_2 = 2b$

CCSS Teaching the Mathematical Practices

Reasoning Mathematically proficient students have the ability to decontextualize a situation and to contextualize abstract information. In Exercise 36, encourage students to contextualize the information given by drawing a figure that meets the criteria.

Standardized Test Practice

38. GRIDDED RESPONSE In the figure below, $m\angle B = 76$. The measure of $\angle A$ is half the measure of $\angle B$. What is $m\angle C$? **66**

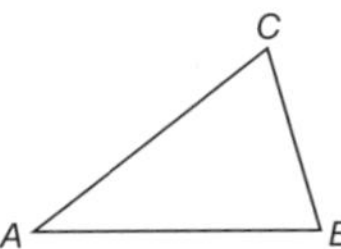

39. ALGEBRA What is the x-coordinate of the solution to the system of equations shown below? **D**

$$\begin{cases} 2x - 3y = 3 \\ -4x + 2y = -18 \end{cases}$$

A −6 C 3
B −3 D 6

40. What are the coordinates of point R in the triangle? **G**

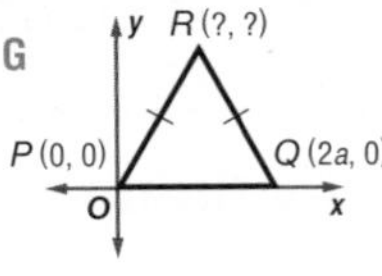

F $\left(\frac{a}{2}, a\right)$ H $\left(\frac{b}{2}, a\right)$

G (a, b) J $\left(\frac{b}{2}, \frac{a}{2}\right)$

41. SAT/ACT For all x,
$17x^5 + 3x^2 + 2 - (-4x^5 + 3x^3 - 2) =$ **C**

A $13x^5 + 3x^3 + 3x^2$
B $13x^5 + 6x^2 + 4$
C $21x^5 - 3x^3 + 3x^2 + 4$
D $21x^5 + 3x^2 + 3x^3$
E $21x^5 + 3x^3 + 3x^2 + 4$

Spiral Review

Identify the type of congruence transformation shown as a *reflection, translation,* or *rotation*. (Lesson 4-7)

42.

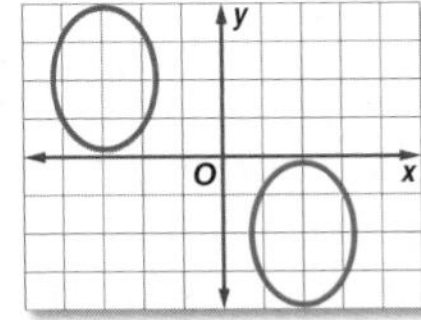

translation or rotation

43.

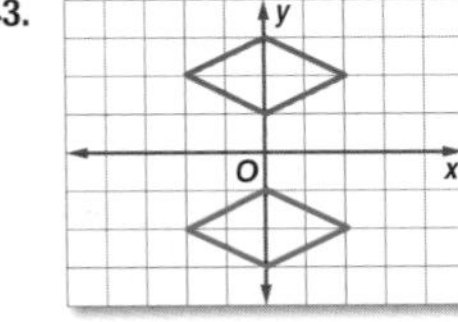

reflection, translation, or rotation

44.

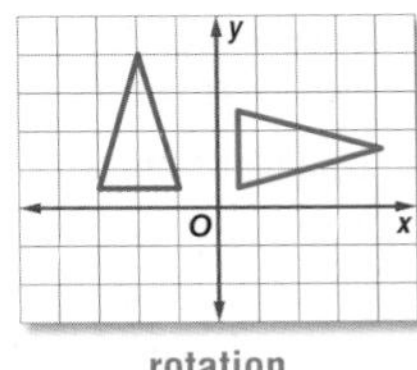

rotation

Refer to the figure at the right. (Lesson 4-6)

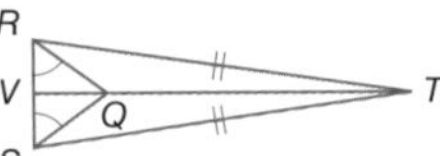

45. Name two congruent angles. $\angle TSR \cong \angle TRS$

46. Name two congruent segments. $\overline{RQ} \cong \overline{QS}$

47. Name a pair of congruent triangles. $\triangle RQV \cong \triangle SQV$

45–47. Sample answer given.

48. RAMPS The Americans with Disabilities Act requires that wheelchair ramps have at least a 12-inch run for each rise of 1 inch. (Lesson 3-3)

a. Determine the slope represented by this requirement. $\frac{1}{12}$

b. The maximum length that the law allows for a ramp is 30 feet. How many inches tall is the highest point of this ramp? **30 in.**

Skills Review

Find the distance between each pair of points. Round to the nearest tenth.

49. $X(5, 4)$ and $Y(2, 1)$ **4.2**

50. $A(1, 5)$ and $B(-2, -3)$ **8.5**

51. $J(-2, 6)$ and $K(1, 4)$ **3.6**

Differentiated Instruction OL BL

Extension Use coordinate geometry to prove the Midpoint Formula.

Given: A has coordinates $A(x_1, y_1)$ and B has coordinates $B(x_2, y_2)$

Prove: $M\left(\frac{x_1 + x_2}{2}, \frac{y_1 + y_2}{2}\right)$ is the midpoint of $\overline{AB}$.

Hint: Let $x_2 = x_1 + 2t$ and $y_2 = y_1 + 2u$ for some real numbers t and u. See Ch. 4 Answer Appendix.

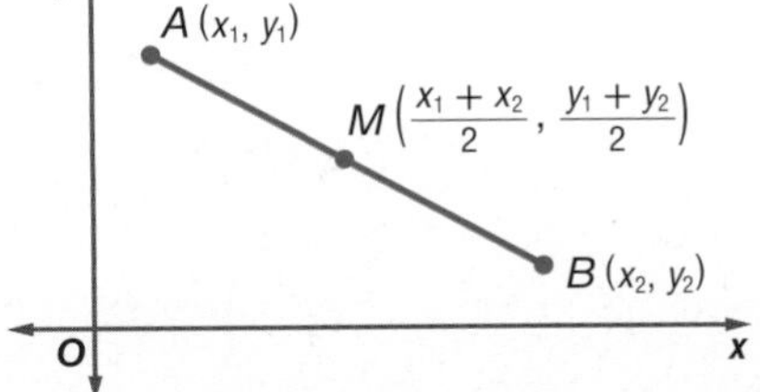

4 Assess

Name The Math Have students verbalize how they would place certain figures in a coordinate plane and how they would label the vertices. Students can discuss different ideas about placement and how they can simplify coordinate proofs by using the origin and simple labeling techniques.

Formative Assessment

Check for student understanding of concepts in Lesson 4-8.

 Quiz 4, p. 58

Additional Answers

36. Sample answer: (0, *a*);

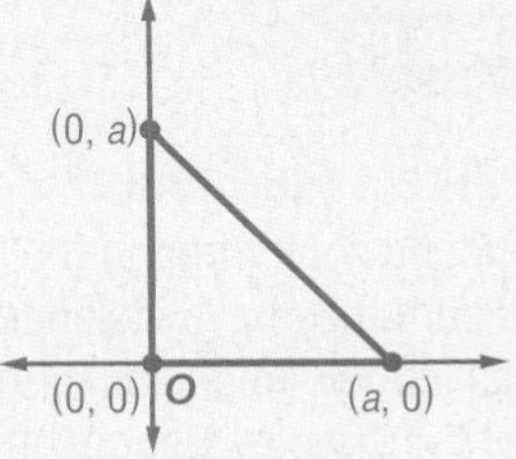

37a. Using the origin as a vertex of the triangle makes calculations easier because the coordinates are (0, 0).

37b. Placing at least one side of the triangle on the *x*- or *y*-axis makes it easier to calculate the length of the side since one of the coordinates will be 0.

37c. Keeping a triangle within the first quadrant makes all of the coordinates positive, and makes the calculations easier.

Formative Assessment

KeyVocabulary The page references after each word denote where that term was first introduced. If students have difficulty completing Exercises 1–10, remind them that they can use these page references to refresh their memories about the vocabulary terms.

Summative Assessment

Vocabulary Test, p. 60

Vocabulary Review

Vocabulary Review provides students the opportunity to check their understanding of important concepts and terminology in an online game format.

FOLDABLES StudyOrganizer

Dinah Zike's Foldables®

Have students look through the chapter to make sure they have included examples in their Foldables for each lesson of the chapter. Suggest that students keep their Foldables handy while completing the Study Guide and Review pages. Point out that their Foldables can serve as a quick review tool for studying for the chapter test.

CHAPTER 4 Study Guide and Review

Study Guide

KeyConcepts

Classifying Triangles (Lesson 4-1)

- Triangles can be classified by their angles as acute, obtuse, or right, and by their sides as scalene, isosceles, or equilateral.

Angles of Triangles (Lesson 4-2)

- The measure of an exterior angle is equal to the sum of its two remote interior angles.

Congruent Triangles (Lesson 4-3 through 4-5)

- SSS: If all of the corresponding sides of two triangles are congruent, then the triangles are congruent.
- SAS: If two pairs of corresponding sides of two triangles and the included angles are congruent, then the triangles are congruent.
- ASA: If two pairs of corresponding angles of two triangles and the included sides are congruent, then the triangles are congruent.
- AAS: If two pairs of corresponding angles of two triangles are congruent, and a corresponding pair of nonincluded sides is congruent, then the triangles are congruent.

Isosceles and Equilateral Triangles (Lesson 4-6)

- The base angles of an isosceles triangle are congruent and a triangle is equilateral if it is equiangular.

Transformations and Coordinate Proofs (Lessons 4-7 and 4-8)

- In a congruence transformation, the position of the image may differ from the preimage, but the two figures remain congruent.
- Coordinate proofs use algebra to prove geometric concepts.

FOLDABLES StudyOrganizer

Be sure the Key Concepts are noted in your Foldable.

KeyVocabulary

acute triangle (p. 237)
auxiliary line (p. 246)
base angles (p. 285)
congruence transformation (p. 296)
congruent polygons (p. 255)
coordinate proof (p. 303)
corollary (p. 249)
corresponding parts (p. 255)
equiangular triangle (p. 237)
equilateral triangle (p. 238)
exterior angle (p. 248)
flow proof (p. 248)
included angle (p. 266)
included side (p. 275)
isosceles triangle (p. 238)
obtuse triangle (p. 237)
reflection (p. 296)
remote interior angles (p. 248)
right triangle (p. 237)
rotation (p. 296)
scalene triangle (p. 238)
translation (p. 296)
vertex angle (p. 285)

VocabularyCheck

State whether each sentence is *true* or *false*. If *false*, replace the underlined word or phrase to make a true sentence.

1. An equiangular triangle is also an example of an <u>acute</u> triangle. **true**
2. A triangle with an angle that measures greater than 90° is a <u>right</u> triangle. **false; obtuse**
3. An <u>equilateral</u> triangle is always equiangular. **true**
4. A <u>scalene</u> triangle has at least two congruent sides. **false; isosceles**
5. The <u>vertex</u> angles of an isosceles triangle are congruent. **false; base**
6. An <u>included</u> side is the side located between two consecutive angles of a polygon. **true**
7. The three types of <u>congruence transformations</u> are rotation, reflection, and translation. **true**
8. A <u>rotation</u> moves all points of a figure the same distance and in the same direction. **false; translation**
9. A <u>flow proof</u> uses figures in the coordinate plane and algebra to prove geometric concepts. **false; coordinate proof**
10. The measure of an <u>exterior angle</u> of a triangle is equal to the sum of the measures of its two remote interior angles. **true**

Lesson-by-Lesson Review

4-1 Classifying Triangles

Classify each triangle as *acute*, *equiangular*, *obtuse*, or *right*.

11. $\triangle ADB$ obtuse
12. $\triangle BCD$ right
13. $\triangle ABC$ right

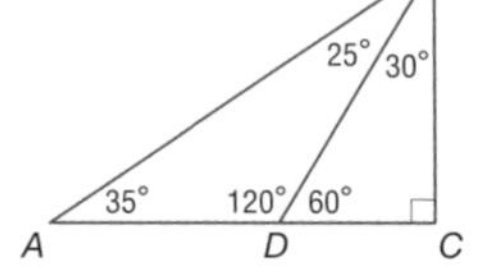

ALGEBRA Find x and the measures of the unknown sides of each triangle.

14.

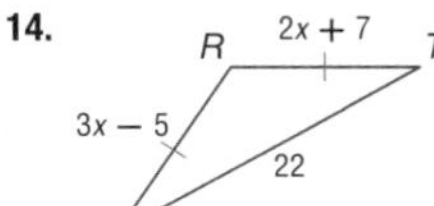
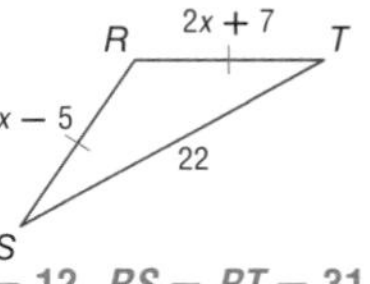

15.

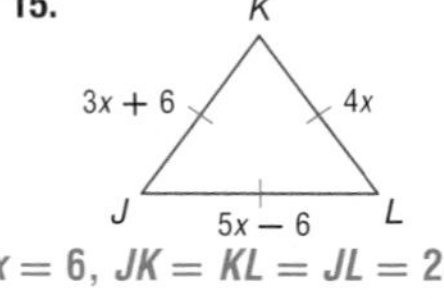

$x = 12$, $RS = RT = 31$ $x = 6$, $JK = KL = JL = 24$

16. **MAPS** The distance from Chicago to Cleveland to Cincinnati and back to Chicago is 900 miles. The distance from Chicago to Cleveland is 50 miles more than the distance from Cincinnati to Chicago, and the distance from Cleveland to Cincinnati is 50 miles less than the distance from Cincinnati to Chicago. Find each distance and classify the triangle formed by the three cities. Cin. to Chi. = 300 miles, Cin. to Clev. = 250, Chi. to Clev. = 350; scalene

Example 1

Classify each triangle as *acute*, *equiangular*, *obtuse*, or *right*.

a.

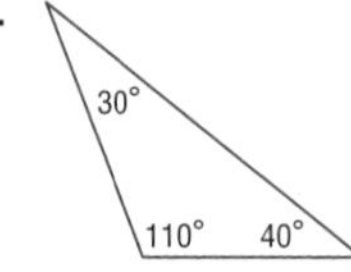

Since the triangle has one obtuse angle, it is an obtuse triangle.

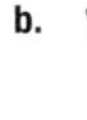
b.

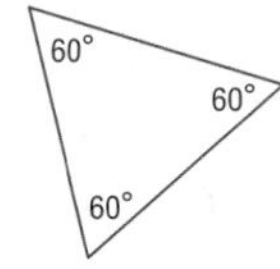

The triangle has three acute angles that are all equal. It is an equiangular triangle.

4-2 Angles of Triangles

Find the measure of each numbered angle.

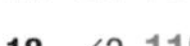

17. $\angle 1$ 70
18. $\angle 2$ 110
19. $\angle 3$ 82

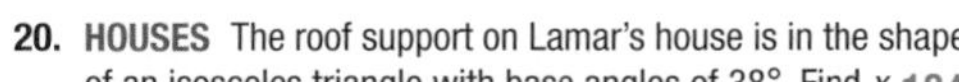

20. **HOUSES** The roof support on Lamar's house is in the shape of an isosceles triangle with base angles of 38°. Find x. 104

Example 2

Find the measure of each numbered angle.

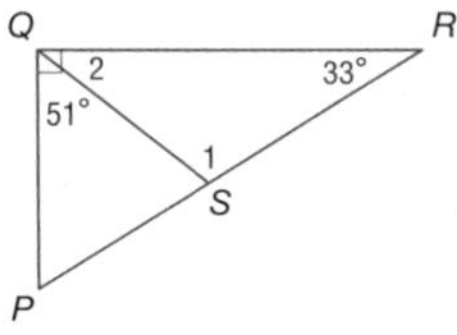

$m\angle 2 + m\angle PQS = 90$	
$m\angle 2 + 51 = 90$	Substitution
$m\angle 2 = 39$	Subtract 51 from each side.
$m\angle 1 + m\angle 2 + 33 = 180$	Triangle Sum Theorem
$m\angle 1 + 39 + 33 = 180$	Substitution
$m\angle 1 + 72 = 180$	Simplify.
$m\angle 1 = 108$	Subtract.

Lesson-by-Lesson Review

Intervention If the given examples are not sufficient to review the topics covered by the questions, remind students that the lesson references tell them where to review that topic in their textbook.

Two-Day Option Have students complete the Lesson-by-Lesson Review. Then you can use eAssessment to customize another review worksheet that practices all the objectives of this chapter or only the objectives on which your students need more help.

connectED.mcgraw-hill.com 311

Additional Answers

21. $\angle D \cong \angle J$, $\angle A \cong \angle F$, $\angle C \cong \angle H$, $\angle B \cong \angle G$, $\overline{AB} \cong \overline{FG}$, $\overline{BC} \cong \overline{HG}$, $\overline{DC} \cong \overline{JH}$, $\overline{DA} \cong \overline{JF}$; polygon $ABCD \cong$ polygon $FGHJ$
22. $\angle X \cong \angle J$, $\angle Y \cong \angle K$, $\angle Z \cong \angle L$, $\overline{XY} \cong \overline{JK}$, $\overline{YZ} \cong \overline{KL}$, $\overline{XZ} \cong \overline{JL}$; $\triangle XYZ \cong \triangle JKL$
23. $\triangle BFG \cong \triangle CGH \cong \triangle DHE \cong \triangle AEF$, $\triangle EFG \cong \triangle FGH \cong \triangle GHE \cong \triangle HEF$
24. Yes, by SSS. $AB = XY = 5$, $BC = YZ = \sqrt{26}$, $ZX = CA = \sqrt{29}$
25. No, the corresponding sides of the two triangles are not congruent.

CHAPTER 4 Study Guide and Review *Continued*

4-3 Congruent Triangles

Show that the polygons are congruent by identifying all congruent corresponding parts. Then write a congruence statement. 21–23. See margin.

21.

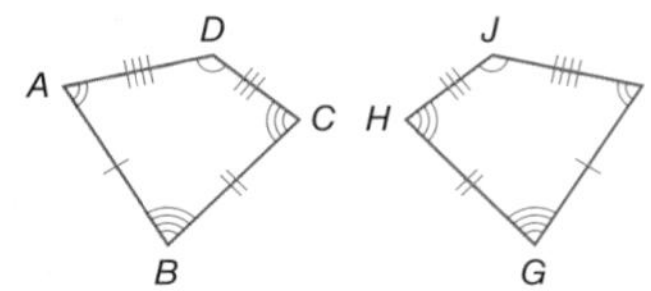

22.

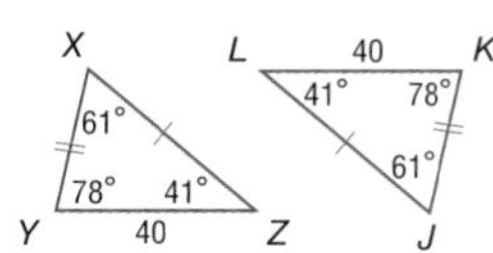

23. MOSAIC TILING A section of a mosaic tiling is shown. Name the triangles that appear to be congruent.

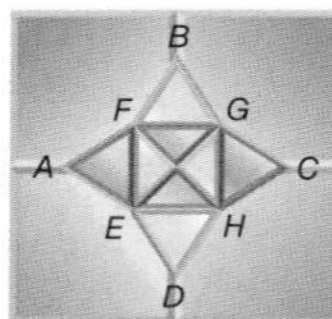

Example 3

Show that the polygons are congruent by identifying all the congruent corresponding parts. Then write a congruence statement.

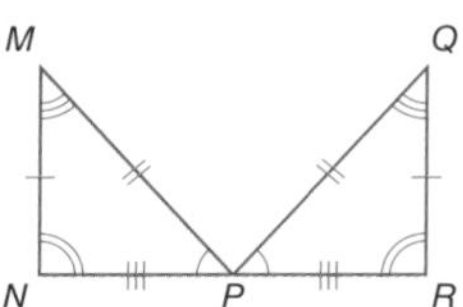

Angles: $\angle N \cong \angle R$, $\angle M \cong \angle Q$, $\angle MPN \cong \angle QPR$

Sides: $\overline{MN} \cong \overline{QR}$, $\overline{MP} \cong \overline{QP}$, $\overline{NP} \cong \overline{RP}$

All corresponding parts of the two triangles are congruent. Therefore, $\triangle MNP \cong \triangle QRP$.

4-4 Proving Triangles Congruent—SSS, SAS

Determine whether $\triangle ABC \cong \triangle XYZ$. Explain. 24–25. See margin.

24. $A(5, 2)$, $B(1, 5)$, $C(0, 0)$, $X(-3, 3)$, $Y(-7, 6)$, $Z(-8, 1)$

25. $A(3, -1)$, $B(3, 7)$, $C(7, 7)$, $X(-7, 0)$, $Y(-7, 4)$, $Z(1, 4)$

Determine which postulate can be used to prove that the triangles are congruent. If it is not possible to prove that they are congruent, write *not possible*.

26. SAS

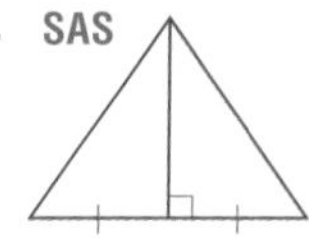

27. not possible

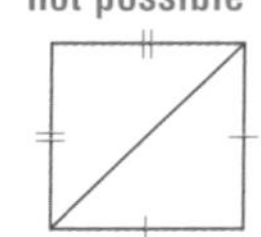

28. PARKS The diagram shows a park in the shape of a pentagon with five sidewalks of equal length leading to a central point. If all the angles at the central point have the same measure, how could you prove that $\triangle ABX \cong \triangle DCX$? The triangles are congruent by SAS.

B, A, C, X, E, D

Example 4

Write a two-column proof.

Given: $\triangle KPL$ is equilateral.
$\overline{JP} \cong \overline{MP}$,
$\angle JPK \cong \angle MPL$

Prove: $\triangle JPK \cong \triangle MPL$

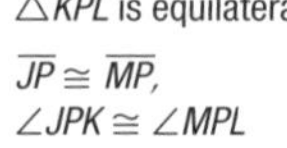

Statements	Reasons
1. $\triangle KPL$ is equilateral.	1. Given
2. $\overline{PK} \cong \overline{PL}$	2. Def. of Equilateral $\triangle$
3. $\overline{JP} \cong \overline{MP}$	3. Given
4. $\angle JPK \cong \angle MPL$	4. Given
5. $\triangle JPK \cong \triangle MPL$	5. SAS

4-5 Proving Triangles Congruent—ASA, AAS

Write a two-column proof. 29–30. See margin.

29. Given: $\overline{AB} \parallel \overline{DC}$, $\overline{AB} \cong \overline{DC}$

Prove: $\triangle ABE \cong \triangle CDE$

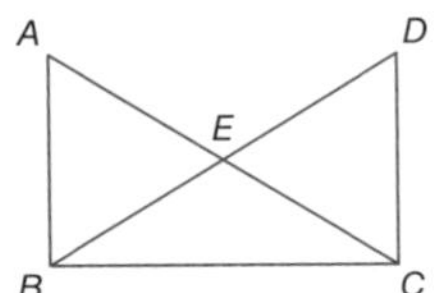

30. KITES Denise's kite is shown in the figure at the right. Given that $\overline{WY}$ bisects both $\angle XWZ$ and $\angle XYZ$, prove that $\triangle WXY \cong \triangle WZY$.

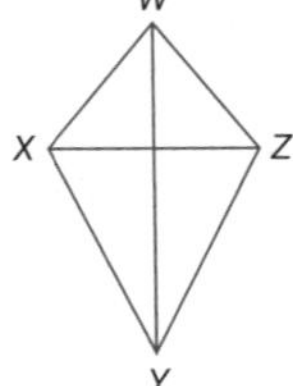

Example 5

Write a flow proof.

Given: $\overline{PQ}$ bisects $\angle RPS$.
$\angle R \cong \angle S$

Prove: $\triangle RPQ \cong \triangle SPQ$

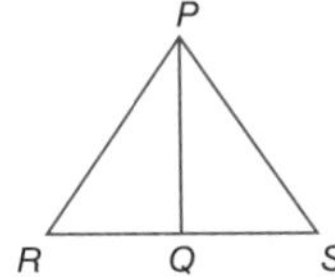

Flow Proof:

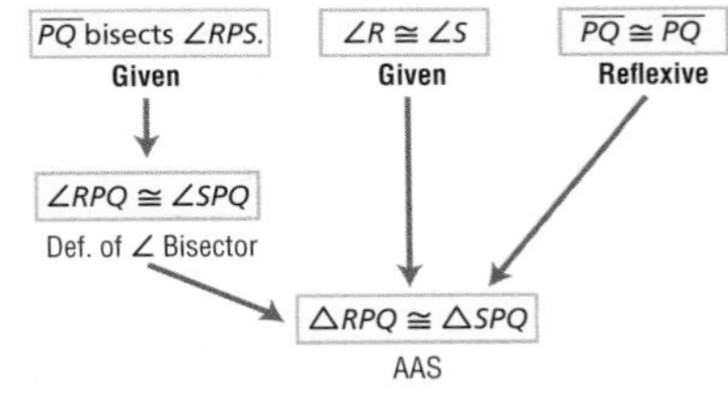

4-6 Isosceles and Equilateral Triangles

Find the value of each variable.

31. 3

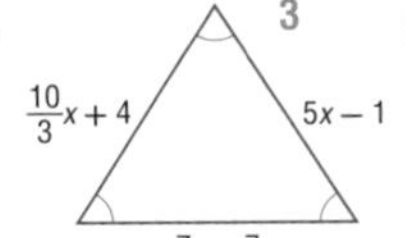

32. 76

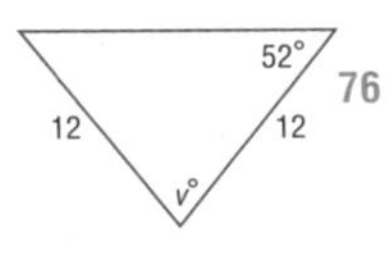

33. PAINTING Pam is painting using a wooden easel. The support bar on the easel forms an isosceles triangle with the two front supports. According to the figure below, what are the measures of the base angles of the triangle? 77.5

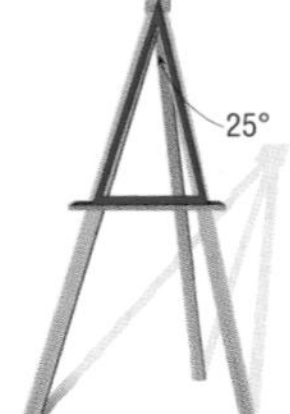

Example 6

Find each measure.

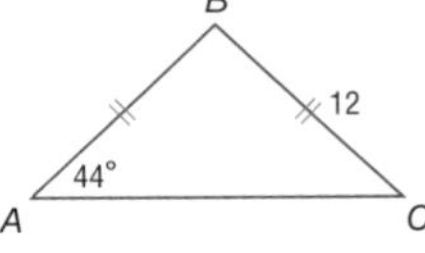

a. $m\angle B$

Since $AB = BC$, $\overline{AB} \cong \overline{BC}$. By the Isosceles Triangle Theorem, base angles A and C are congruent, so $m\angle A = m\angle C$. Use the Triangle Sum Theorem to write and solve an equation to find $m\angle B$.

$m\angle A + m\angle B + m\angle C = 180$	△ Sum Theorem
$44 + m\angle B + 44 = 180$	$m\angle A = m\angle C = 44$
$88 + m\angle B = 180$	Simplify.
$m\angle B = 92$	Subtract.

b. AB

$AB = BC$, so $\triangle ABC$ is isosceles. Since $BC = 12$, $AB = 12$ by substitution.

Additional Answers

29. Statements (Reasons)

1. $\overline{AB} \parallel \overline{DC}$ (Given)
2. $\angle A \cong \angle DCE$ (Alternate Interior ∠s Thm.)
3. $\overline{AB} \cong \overline{DC}$ (Given)
4. $\angle ABE \cong \angle D$ (Alternate Interior ∠s Thm.)
5. $\triangle ABE \cong \triangle CDE$ (ASA)

30. Statements (Reasons)

1. $\overline{WY}$ bisects both $\angle XWZ$ and $\angle XYZ$. (Given)
2. $\angle XWY \cong \angle ZWY$ (Def. of ∠ Bisector)
3. $\overline{WY} \cong \overline{WY}$ (Reflexive Property)
4. $\angle XYW \cong \angle ZYW$ (Def. of ∠ Bisector)
5. $\angle WXY \cong \angle WZY$ (ASA)

Anticipation Guide

Have students complete the Chapter 4 Anticipation Guide and discuss how their responses have changed now that they have completed Chapter 4.

Additional Answers

38. 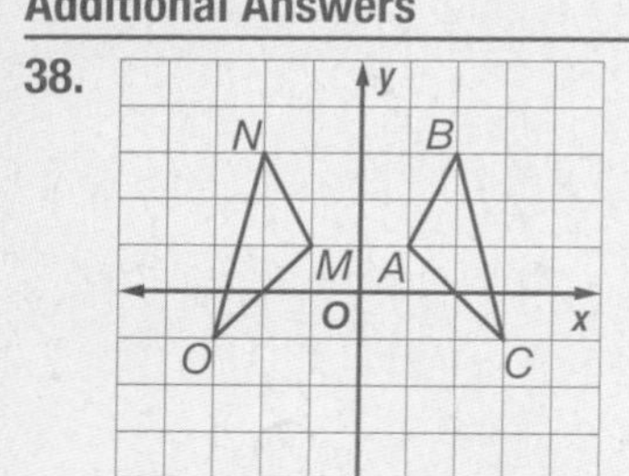

39. 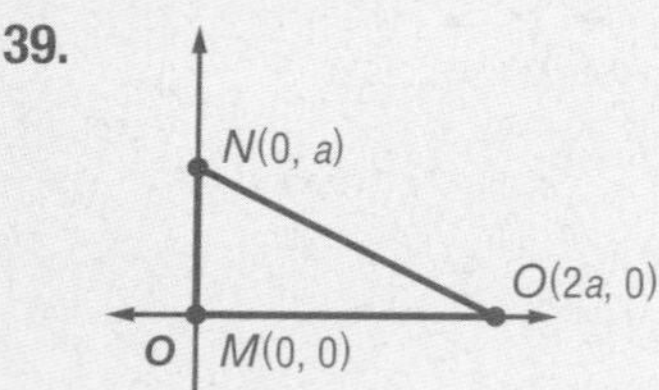

40. 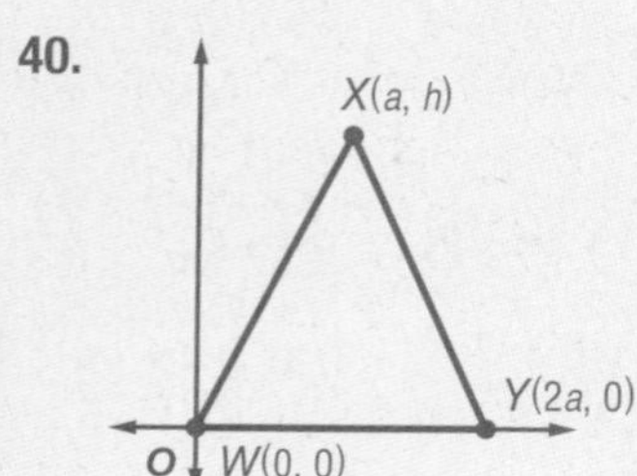

CHAPTER 4 Study Guide and Review *Continued*

4-7 Congruence Transformations

Identify the type of congruence transformation shown as a *reflection, translation,* or *rotation.*

34. translation

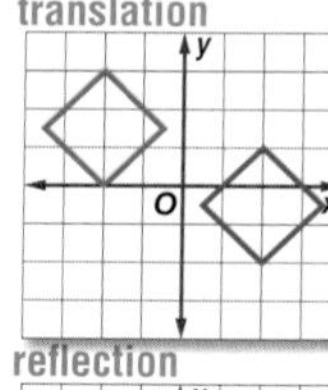

35. reflection

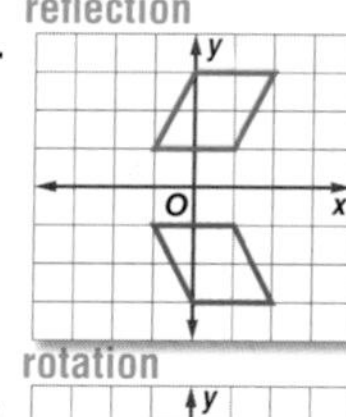

36. reflection

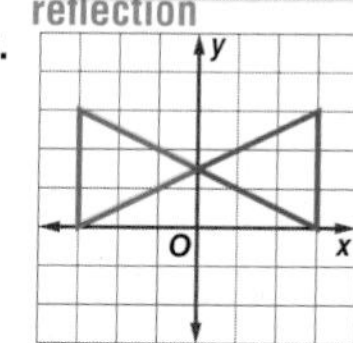

37. rotation

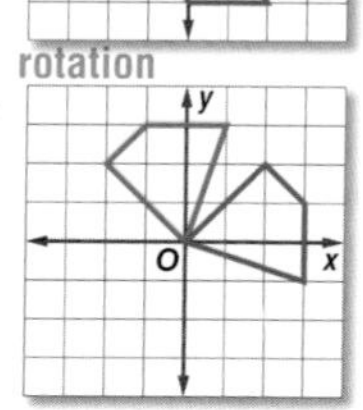

38. Triangle ABC with vertices $A(1, 1)$, $B(2, 3)$, and $C(3, -1)$ is a transformation of $\triangle MNO$ with vertices $M(-1, 1)$, $N(-2, 3)$, and $O(-3, -1)$. Graph the original figure and its image. Identify the transformation and verify that it is a congruence transformation. **Reflection; see margin for graph.**

Example 7

Triangle RST with vertices $R(4, 1)$, $S(2, 5)$, and $T(-1, 0)$ is a transformation of $\triangle CDF$ with vertices $C(1, -3)$, $D(-1, 1)$, and $F(-4, -4)$. Identify the transformation and verify that it is a congruence transformation.

Graph each figure. The transformation appears to be a translation. Find the lengths of the sides of each triangle.

$RS = \sqrt{(4-2)^2 + (1-5)^2}$ or $\sqrt{20}$

$TS = \sqrt{(-1-2)^2 + (0-5)^2}$ or $\sqrt{34}$

$RT = \sqrt{(-1-4)^2 + (0-1)^2}$ or $\sqrt{26}$

$CD = \sqrt{(-1-1)^2 + [1-(-3)]^2}$ or $\sqrt{20}$

$DF = \sqrt{[-4-(-1)]^2 + (-4-1)^2}$ or $\sqrt{34}$

$CF = \sqrt{(-4-1)^2 + [-4-(-3)]^2}$ or $\sqrt{26}$

Since each vertex of $\triangle CDF$ has undergone a transformation 3 units to the right and 4 units up, this is a translation.

Since $RS = CD$, $TS = DF$, and $RT = CF$, $\overline{RS} \cong \overline{CD}$, $\overline{TS} \cong \overline{DF}$, and $\overline{RT} \cong \overline{CF}$. By SSS, $\triangle RST \cong \triangle CDF$.

4-8 Triangles and Coordinate Proof

Position and label each triangle on the coordinate plane.

39. right $\triangle MNO$ with right angle at point M and legs of lengths a and $2a$. **See margin.**

40. isosceles $\triangle WXY$ with height h and base $\overline{WY}$ with length $2a$. **See margin.**

41. GEOGRAPHY Jorge plotted the cities of Dallas, San Antonio, and Houston as shown. Write a coordinate proof to show that the triangle formed by these cities is scalene. **See margin.**

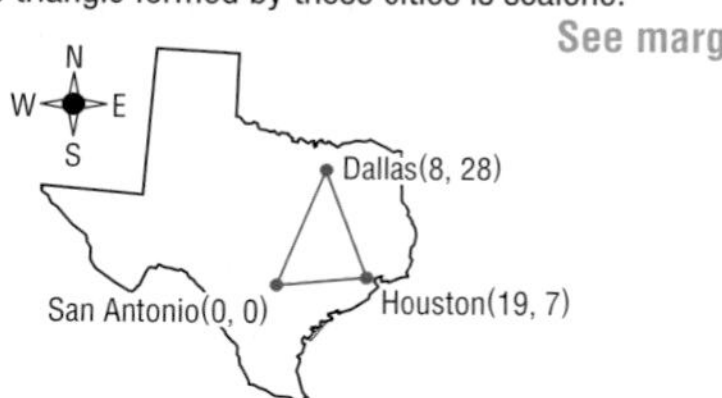

Example 8

Position and label an equilateral triangle $\triangle XYZ$ with side lengths of $2a$.

- Use the origin for one of the three vertices of the triangle.
- Place one side of the triangle along the positive side of the x-axis.
- The third point should be located above the midpoint of the base of the triangle.

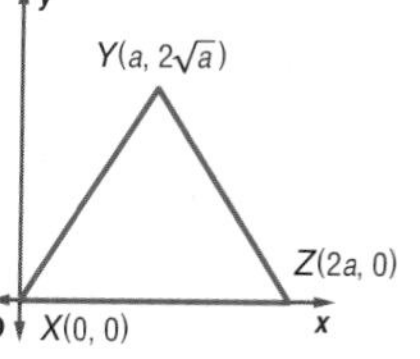

41. Proof:

Statements (Reasons)

1. $D(8, 28)$, $S(0, 0)$, and $H(19, 7)$ (Given)
2. $\overline{DS} = \sqrt{(8-0)^2 + (28-0)^2}$ or $\sqrt{848}$ (Distance Formula)
3. $\overline{SH} = \sqrt{(19-0)^2 + (7-0)^2}$ or $\sqrt{410}$ (Distance Formula)
4. $\overline{DH} = \sqrt{(8-19)^2 + (28-7)^2}$ or $\sqrt{562}$ (Distance Formula)
5. $\overline{DS} \ncong \overline{SH} \ncong \overline{DH}$
6. $\triangle DSH$ is a scalene triangle. (Definition of scalene)

CHAPTER 4 Practice Test

Classify each triangle as *acute, equiangular, obtuse,* or *right.*

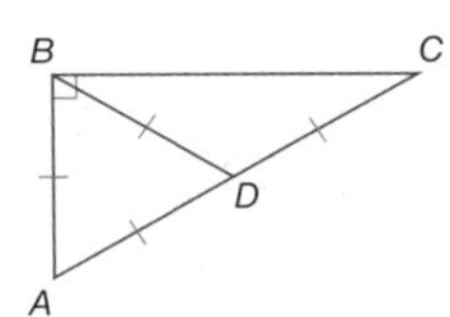

1. $\triangle ABD$ **equiangular**
2. $\triangle ABC$ **right**
3. $\triangle BDC$ **obtuse**

Find the measure of each numbered angle.

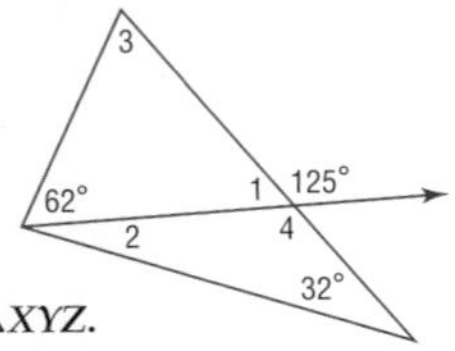

4. $\angle 1$ **55**
5. $\angle 2$ **23**
6. $\angle 3$ **63**
7. $\angle 4$ **125**

In the diagram, $\triangle RST \cong \triangle XYZ$.

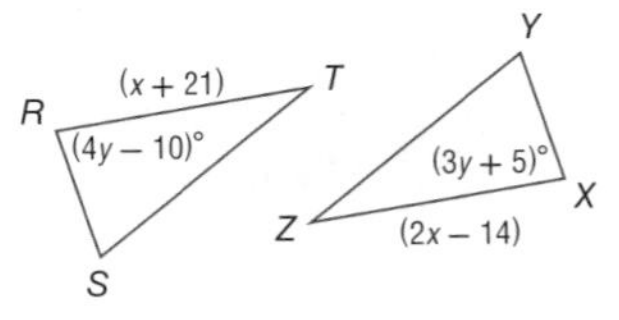

8. Find x. **35**
9. Find y. **15**
10. **PROOF** Write a flow proof.
    Given: $\overline{XY} \parallel \overline{WZ}$ and $\overline{XW} \parallel \overline{YZ}$
    Prove: $\triangle XWZ \cong \triangle ZYX$
    See Ch. 4 Answer Appendix.

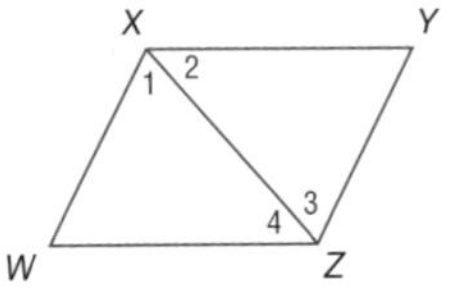

11. **MULTIPLE CHOICE** Find x. **C**

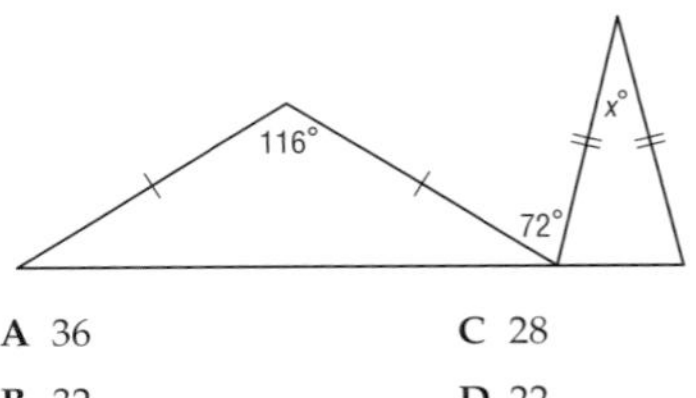

A 36 C 28
B 32 D 22

12. Determine whether $\triangle TJD \cong \triangle SEK$ given $T(-4, -2)$, $J(0, 5)$, $D(1, -1)$, $S(-1, 3)$, $E(3, 10)$, and $K(4, 4)$. Explain. **Yes, by SSS.**

Determine which postulate or theorem can be used to prove each pair of triangles congruent. If it is not possible to prove them congruent, write *not possible.*

13. **AAS**

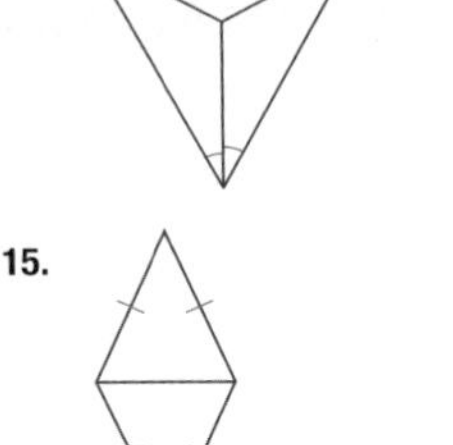

14. **SSS**

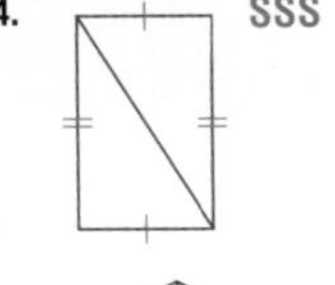

15. **not possible**

16. **SAS**

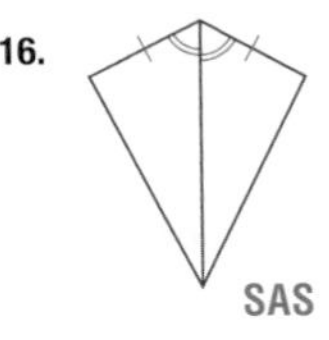

17. **LANDSCAPING** Angie has laid out a design for a garden consisting of two triangular areas as shown below. The points are $A(0, 0)$, $B(0, 5)$, $C(3, 5)$, $D(6, 5)$, and $E(6, 0)$. Name the type of congruence transformation for the preimage $\triangle ABC$ to $\triangle EDC$. **reflection**

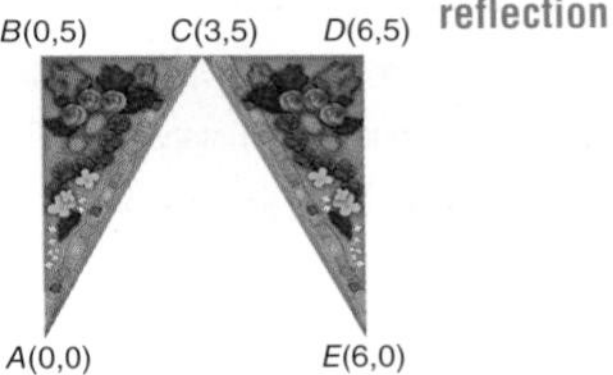

Find the measure of each numbered angle.

18. $\angle 1$ **66**
19. $\angle 2$ **24**

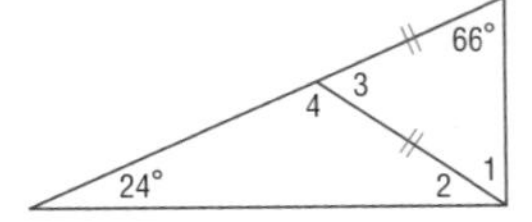

20. **PROOF** $\triangle ABC$ is a right isosceles triangle with hypotenuse $\overline{AB}$. M is the midpoint of $\overline{AB}$. Write a coordinate proof to show that $\overline{CM}$ is perpendicular to $\overline{AB}$. **See Chapter 4 Answer Appendix.**

Summative Assessment

Use these alternate leveled chapter tests to differentiate assessment for your students.

Leveled Chapter 4 Tests

Form	Type	Level	Page(s)
1	MC	AL	61–62
2A	MC	OL	63–64
2B	MC	OL	65–66
2C	FR	OL	67–68
2D	FR	OL	69–70
3	FR	BL	71–72
Vocabulary Test			60
Extended-Response Test			73

MC = multiple-choice questions
FR = free-response questions

eAssessment Customize and create multiple versions of your chapter test and their answer keys. All of the questions from the leveled chapter tests in the Chapter 4 *Resource Masters* are also available on eAssessment.

InterventionPlanner

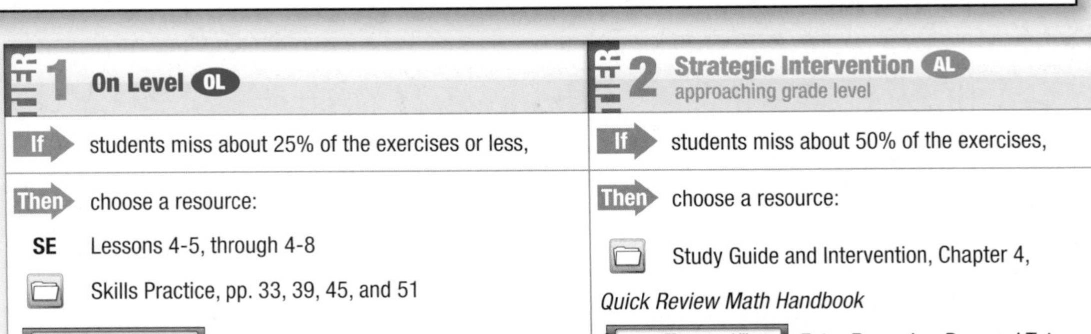

TIER 1 On Level OL

If students miss about 25% of the exercises or less,

Then choose a resource:

SE Lessons 4-5, through 4-8

Skills Practice, pp. 33, 39, 45, and 51

connectED.mcgraw-hill.com Self-Check Quiz

TIER 2 Strategic Intervention AL approaching grade level

If students miss about 50% of the exercises,

Then choose a resource:

Study Guide and Intervention, Chapter 4,

Quick Review Math Handbook

connectED.mcgraw-hill.com Extra Examples, Personal Tutor, Homework Help

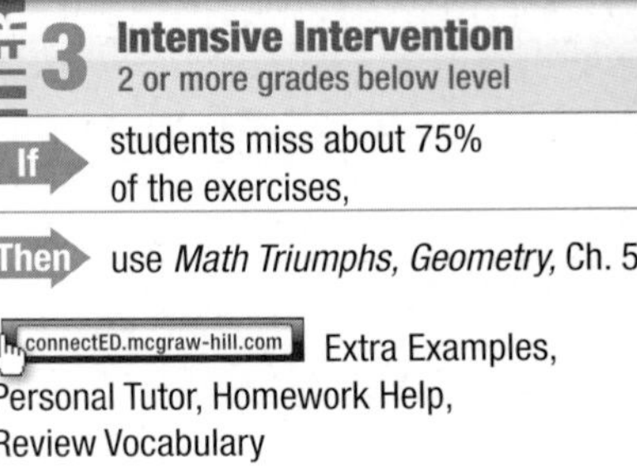

TIER 3 Intensive Intervention 2 or more grades below level

If students miss about 75% of the exercises,

Then use *Math Triumphs, Geometry,* Ch. 5

connectED.mcgraw-hill.com Extra Examples, Personal Tutor, Homework Help, Review Vocabulary

CHAPTER 4 Preparing for Standardized Tests

Short-Answer Questions

Short-answer questions require you to provide a solution to the problem, along with a method, explanation, and/or justification used to arrive at the solution.

Short-answer questions are typically graded using a **rubric**, or a scoring guide.

The following is an example of a short-answer question scoring rubric.

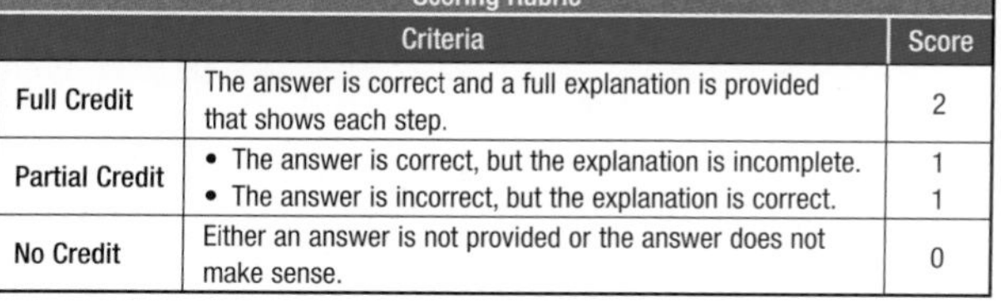

Scoring Rubric		
	Criteria	Score
Full Credit	The answer is correct and a full explanation is provided that shows each step.	2
Partial Credit	• The answer is correct, but the explanation is incomplete. • The answer is incorrect, but the explanation is correct.	1 1
No Credit	Either an answer is not provided or the answer does not make sense.	0

Strategies for Solving Short-Answer Questions

Step 1

Read the problem to gain an understanding of what you are trying to solve.

- Identify relevant facts.
- Look for key words and mathematical terms.

Step 2

Make a plan and solve the problem.

- Explain your reasoning or state your approach to solving the problem.
- Show all of your work or steps.
- Check your answer if time permits.

Standardized Test Example

Read the problem. Identify what you need to know. Then use the information in the problem to solve. Show your work.

Triangle ABC is an isosceles triangle with base $\overline{BC}$. What is the perimeter of the triangle?

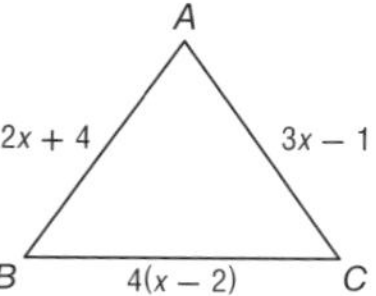

1 Focus

Objective Understand the components of short answer questions and develop methods to solve them.

2 Teach

Scaffolding Questions

Ask:

- What are some ways in which solving a short answer question is different than solving a multiple choice question? How are they similar? Sample answer: You must show your work for short answer questions. This is not necessary for multiple choice questions. Short answer questions are graded using a rubric, so partial credit is possible. With multiple choice questions, the answer is either right or wrong. Both types of questions require careful reading.
- Why is it important to explain your reasoning when you answer a short answer question? Sample answer: Only correct answers accompanied by complete correct explanations receive full credit.
- Why is it important to check your answer? Sample answer: Careless errors will result in only partial or no credit.

Read the problem carefully. You are told that $\triangle ABC$ is isosceles with base $\overline{BC}$. You are asked to find the perimeter of the triangle.

Make a plan and solve the problem.

The legs of an isosceles triangle are congruent. So, $\overline{AB} \cong \overline{AC}$ or $AB = AC$. Solve for x.

$$AB = AC$$
$$2x + 4 = 3x - 1$$
$$2x - 3x = -1 - 4$$
$$-x = -5$$
$$x = 5$$

Next, find the length of each side.

$AB = 2(5) + 4 = 14$ units

$AC = 3(5) - 1 = 14$ units

$BC = 4(5 - 2) = 12$ units

The perimeter of $\triangle ABC$ is $14 + 14 + 12 = 40$ units.

The steps, calculations, and reasoning are clearly stated. The student also arrives at the correct answer. So, this response is worth the full 2 points.

Exercises

Read each problem. Identify what you need to know. Then use the information in the problem to solve. Show your work.

1. Classify $\triangle DEF$ according to its angle measures. **obtuse**

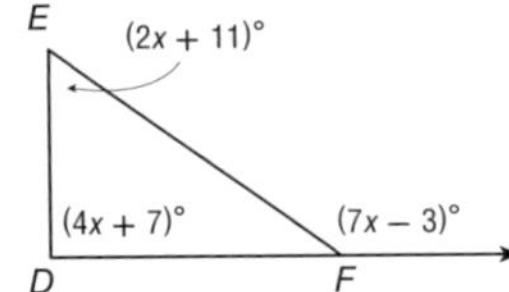

2. In the figure below, $\triangle RST \cong \triangle VUT$. What is the area of $\triangle RST$? **300 square units**

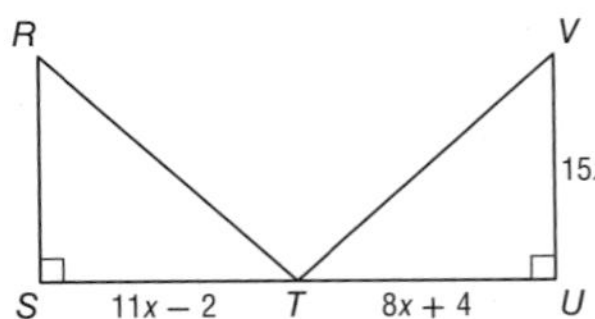

3. A farmer needs to make a 48-square-foot rectangular enclosure for chickens. He wants to save money by purchasing the least amount of fencing possible to enclose the area. What whole-number dimensions will require the least amount of fencing? **8 ft × 6 ft**

4. What is $m\angle 1$ in degrees? **85°**

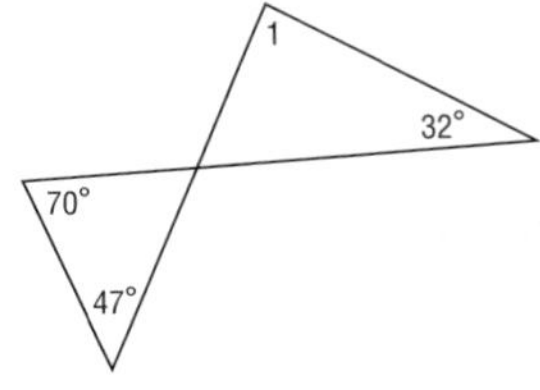

5. Write an equation of the line containing the points (2, 4) and (0, –2). **$y = 3x - 2$**

Additional Example

Triangle DEF is an isosceles triangle with base $\overline{DE}$. What is the perimeter of the triangle?

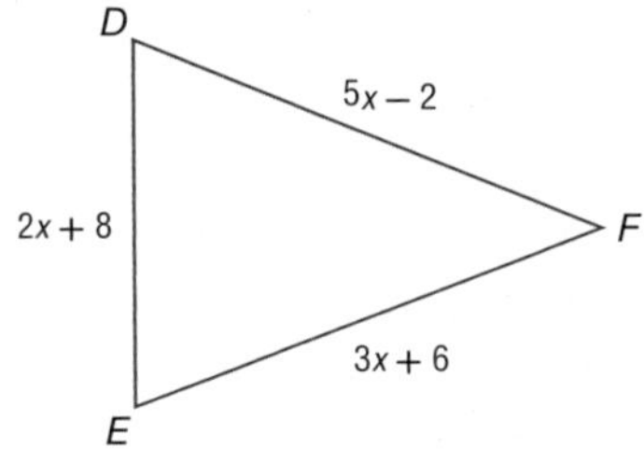

The legs of an isosceles triangle are congruent. Therefore $\overline{DF} \cong \overline{EF}$, or $DF = EF$.

Solving for x,

$$5x - 2 = 3x + 6$$
$$2x = 8$$
$$x = 4$$

Therefore, the side lengths are $DF = 18$, $EF = 18$, and $DE = 16$.

The perimeter of $\triangle DEF$ is $18 + 18 + 16 = 52$ units.

3 Assess

Use Exercises 1–5 to assess students' understanding.

Diagnose Student Errors

Survey student responses for each item. Class trends may indicate common errors and misconceptions.

1. A guess
B miscalculation
C found supplemental angle
D correct

2. F use of incorrect vocabulary
G use of incorrect vocabulary
H correct
J use of incorrect vocabulary

3. A guess
B guess
C does not classify by side lengths
D correct

4. F first segment incorrect
G first segment incorrect
H correct
J first segment incorrect

5. A did not cube factor
B squared factor
C correct
D raised factor to fourth power

6. F correct
G arithmetic error
H arithmetic error
J incorrectly used fact about isosceles triangle

7. A arithmetic error
B correct
C found complement of given angle
D this is the other base angle

CHAPTER 4

Standardized Test Practice

Cumulative, Chapters 1 through 4

Multiple Choice

Read each question. Then fill in the correct answer on the answer document provided by your teacher or on a sheet of paper.

1. If $m\angle 1 = 110°$, what must $m\angle 2$ equal for lines x and z to be parallel? D

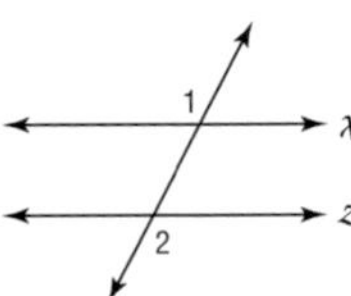

A 30° B 60° C 70° D 110°

2. Which of the following terms best describes the transformation below? G

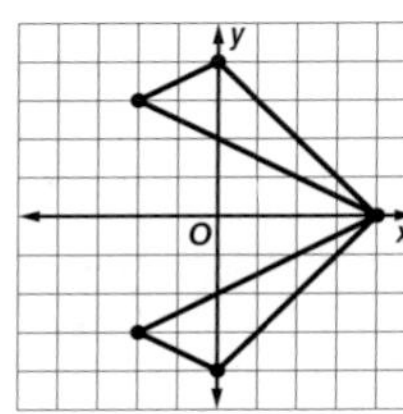

F dilation
G reflection
H rotation
J translation

3. Classify the triangle below according to its side lengths. D

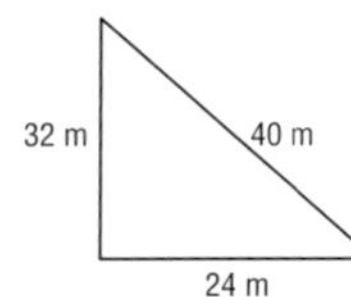

A equilateral
B isosceles
C right
D scalene

Test-Taking Tip

Question 3 Read the problem statement carefully to make sure you select the correct answer.

4. Given: $\overline{WX} \cong \overline{JK}$, $\overline{YX} \cong \overline{IK}$, $\angle X \cong \angle K$ H

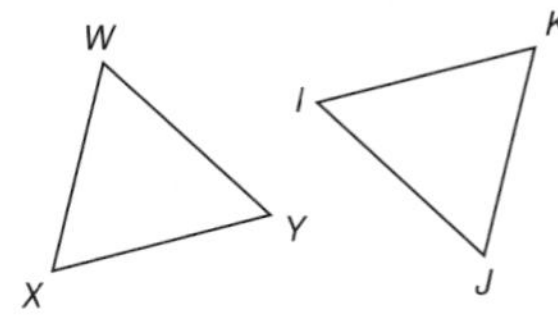

Which of the following lists the correct triangle congruence?

F $\triangle WXY \cong \triangle KIJ$
G $\triangle WXY \cong \triangle IKJ$
H $\triangle WXY \cong \triangle JKI$
J $\triangle WXY \cong \triangle IJK$

5. Suppose the dimensions of the prism below are tripled. By what factor will the volume of the prism increase? C

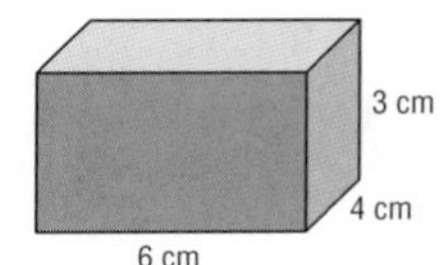

A 3 B 9 C 27 D 81

6. What is the measure of angle R below? F

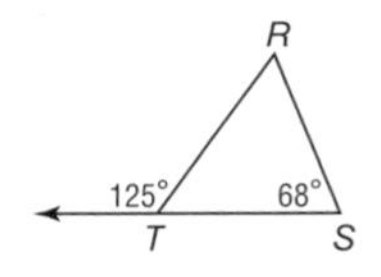

F 57° G 59° H 65° J 68°

7. Suppose one base angle of an isosceles triangle has a measure of 44°. What is the measure of the vertex angle? B

A 108°
B 92°
C 56°
D 44°

Short Response/Gridded Response

Record your answers on the answer sheet provided by your teacher or on a sheet of paper.

8. **GRIDDED RESPONSE** In the figure below, $\triangle NDG \cong \triangle LGD$. What is the value of x? 54

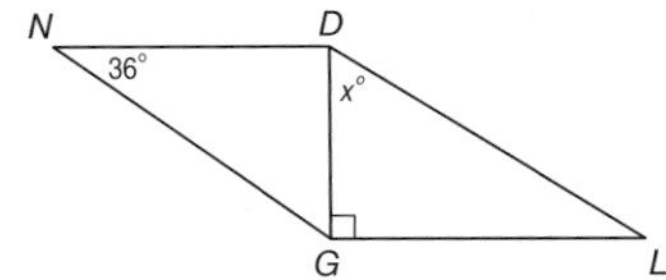

9. **GRIDDED RESPONSE** Suppose line ℓ contains points A, B, and C. If $AB = 7$ inches, $AC = 32$ inches, and point B is between points A and C, what is the length of $\overline{BC}$? Express your answer in inches. 25

10. Write the converse of the statement.

If you are the winner, then I am the loser.

If I am the loser, then you are the winner.

11. Use the figure and the given information below.

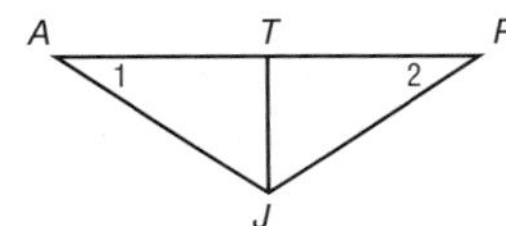

Given: $\overline{JT} \perp \overline{AP}$
$\angle 1 \cong \angle 2$

Since $JT \perp AP$, $\angle JTA \cong \angle JTP$. $\angle 1 \cong \angle 2$ and $\overline{JT} \cong \overline{JT}$. So, $\triangle PTJ \cong \triangle ATJ$ by AAS.

Which congruence theorem could you use to prove $\triangle PTJ \cong \triangle ATJ$ with only the information given? Explain.

12. Write an equation in slope intercept form for the line which goes through the points (0, 3) and (4, −5). $y = -2x + 3$

13. **GRIDDED RESPONSE** Find $m\angle TUV$ in the figure. 53

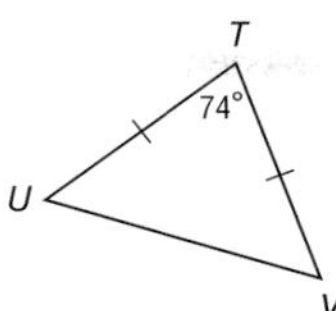

14. Suppose two sides of triangle ABC are congruent to two sides of triangle MNO. Also, suppose one of the nonincluded angles of $\triangle ABC$ is congruent to one of the nonincluded angles of $\triangle MNO$. Are the triangles congruent? If so, write a paragraph proof showing the congruence. If not, sketch a counterexample. See margin.

Extended Response

Record your answers on a sheet of paper. Show your work.

15. Use a coordinate grid to write a coordinate proof of the following statement.

If the vertices of a triangle are $A(0, 0)$, $B(2a, b)$, and $C(4a, 0)$, then the triangle is isosceles.

a. Plot the vertices on a coordinate grid to model the problem. See margin.

b. Use the Distance Formula to write an expression for AB. $AB = \sqrt{4a^2 + b^2}$

c. Use the Distance Formula to write an expression for BC. $BC = \sqrt{4a^2 + b^2}$

d. Use your results from parts **b** and **c** to draw a conclusion about $\triangle ABC$. Since $AB = BC$, $\overline{AB} \cong \overline{BC}$. So, $\triangle ABC$ is isosceles.

Need ExtraHelp?

If you missed Question...	1	2	3	4	5	6	7	8	9	10	11	12	13	14	15
Go to Lesson...	3-2	4-7	4-1	4-3	1-7	4-2	4-6	4-3	1-2	2-3	4-5	3-4	4-6	4-4	4-8

Formative Assessment

You can use these pages to benchmark student progress.

Standardized Test Practice, pp. 74–77

eAssessment Create practice tests that align to your state standards, the Common Core State Standards, and other national standards such as TIMSS and NAEP.

Answer Sheet Practice

Have students simulate taking a standardized test by recording their answers on a practice recording sheet.

Student Recording Sheet

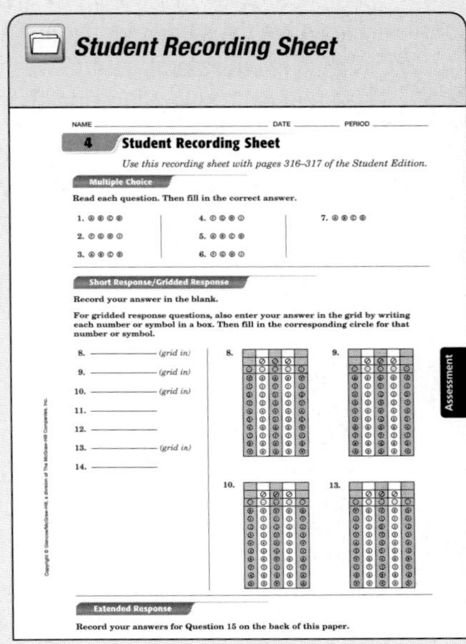
NAME ____ DATE ____ PERIOD ____

4 **Student Recording Sheet**

Use this recording sheet with pages 316–317 of the Student Edition.

Multiple Choice

Read each question. Then fill in the correct answer.

Short Response/Gridded Response

Record your answer in the blank.

For gridded response questions, also enter your answer in the grid by writing each number or symbol in a box. Then fill in the corresponding circle for that number or symbol.

Extended Response

Record your answers for Question 15 on the back of this paper.

Homework Option

Get Ready for Chapter 5 Assign students the exercises on page 321 as homework to assess whether they possess the prerequisite skills for the next chapter.

Additional Answers

14. No; sample counterexample:

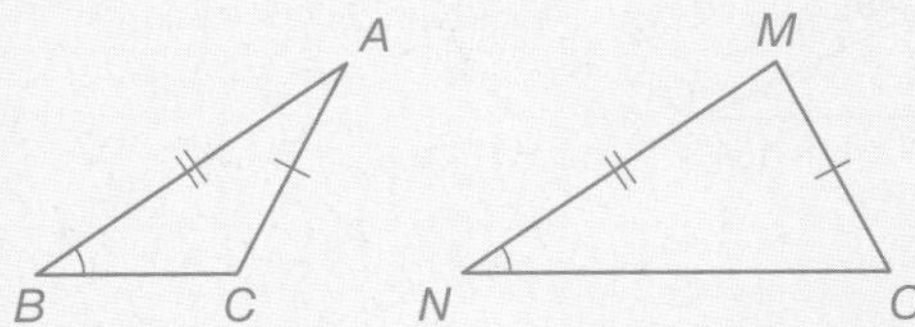

15a.

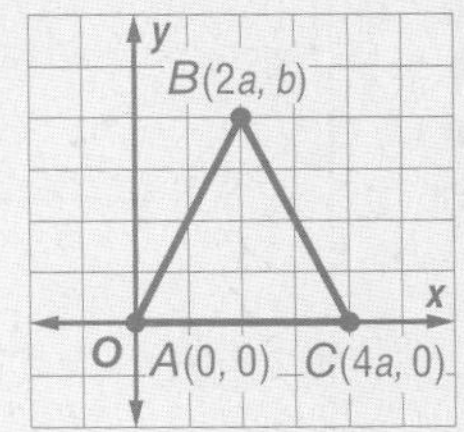

Lesson 4-1

48. Given: $\triangle ACE$ is equiangular and $\overline{BD} \parallel \overline{AE}$.

Prove: $\triangle BCD$ is equiangular.

Proof:

Statements (Reasons)

1. $\triangle ACE$ is equiangular and $\overline{BD} \parallel \overline{AE}$. (Given)
2. $\angle 1 \cong \angle 2 \cong \angle 3$ (Def. of equiangular $\triangle$)
3. $\angle 2 \cong \angle CBD$ and $\angle 3 \cong CDB$ (Corr. ∠s Post.)
4. $\angle 1 \cong \angle CBD \cong \angle CDB$ (Substitution)
5. $\triangle BCD$ is equiangular. (Def. of equiangular $\triangle$)

53.

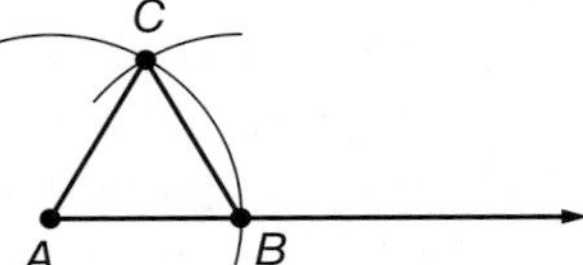

Sample answer: In $\triangle ABC$, $AB = BC = AC = 1.3$ cm. Since all sides have the same length, they are all congruent. Therefore the triangle is equilateral. $\triangle ABC$ was constructed using AB as the length of each side. Since the arc for each segment is the same, the triangle is equilateral.

54b. Sample answer: The fluctuation would have to be high and decrease quickly in order to form an obtuse triangle.

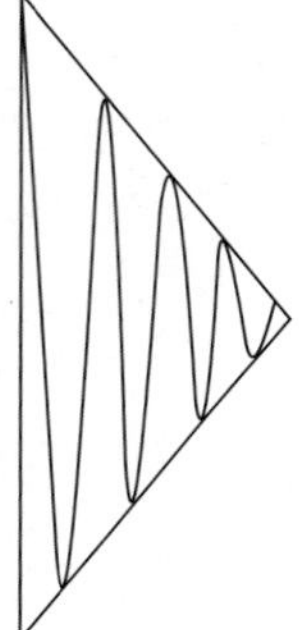

57. Never; all equiangular triangles have three 60° angles, so they do not have a 90° angle. Therefore they cannot be right triangles.

58. Always; all equilateral triangles have three equal sides and isosceles triangles have at least two equal sides, so all triangles with three equal sides are isosceles.

59. Never; all equilateral triangles are also equiangular, which means all of the angles are 60°. A right triangle has one 90° angle.

60. Sample answer: Since the triangle is equilateral, the sides are equal. Setting $5x + 3$ equal to $7x - 5$ and solving, x is 4. The length of one side is $5(4) + 3$ or 23 units. The perimeter of an equilateral triangle is the sum of the three sides or three times one side. The perimeter is 3(23) or 69 units.

61. Sample answer:

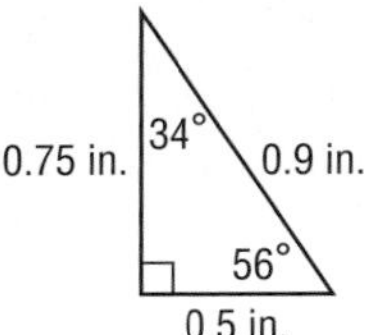

62. Sample answer:

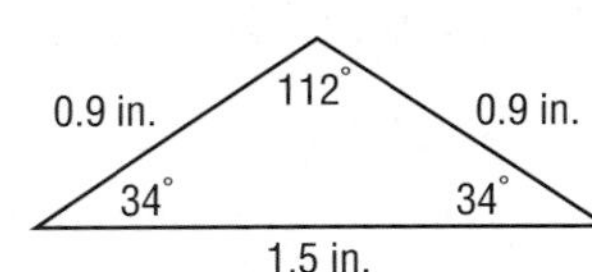

63. Not possible; all equilateral triangles have three acute angles.

64. Sample answer: An acute triangle has three acute angles and an equiangular triangle has three angles that measure 60°. Since an angle that measures 60° is an acute angle, all equiangular triangles are acute. Therefore, acute equiangular is redundant.

Lesson 4-2

45a. Sample answer:

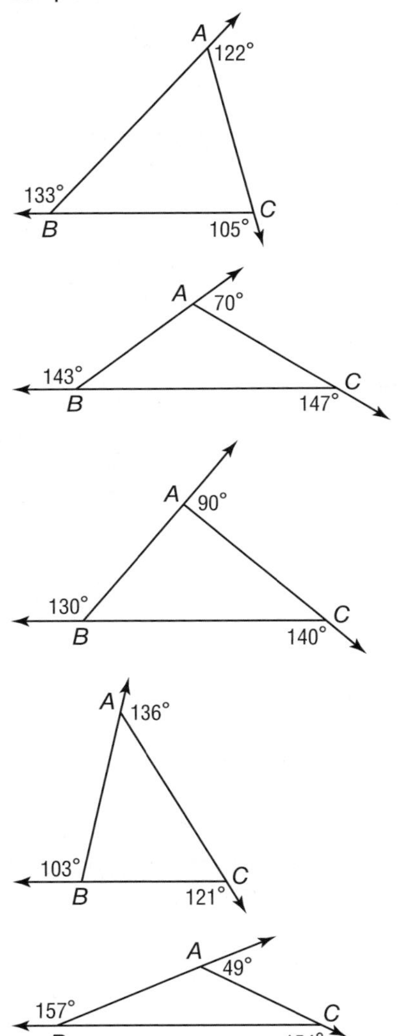

45b. Sample answer:

$m\angle 1$	$m\angle 2$	$m\angle 3$	Sum of Angle Measures
122	105	133	360
70	147	143	360
90	140	130	360
136	121	103	360
49	154	157	360

45c. Sample answer: The sum of the measures of the exterior angles of a triangle is 360.

45d.

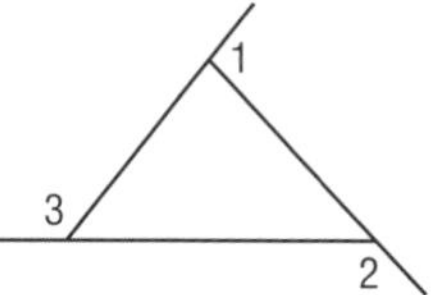

$m\angle 1 + m\angle 2 + m\angle 3 = 360$

45e. The Exterior Angle Theorem tells us that $m\angle 3 = m\angle BAC + m\angle BCA$, $m\angle 2 = m\angle BAC + m\angle CBA$, $m\angle 1 = m\angle CBA + m\angle BCA$. Through substitution, $m\angle 1 + m\angle 2 + m\angle 3 = m\angle CBA + m\angle BCA + m\angle BAC + m\angle CBA + m\angle BAC + m\angle BCA$. Which can be simplified to $m\angle 1 + m\angle 2 + m\angle 3 = 2m\angle CBA + 2m\angle BCA + 2m\angle BAC$. The Distributive Property can be applied and gives $m\angle 1 + m\angle 2 + m\angle 3 = 2(m\angle CBA + m\angle BCA + m\angle BAC)$. The Triangle Angle-Sum Theorem tells us that $m\angle CBA + m\angle BCA + m\angle BAC = 180$. Through substitution we have $m\angle 1 + m\angle 2 + m\angle 3 = 2(180) = 360$.

46. Sample answer: Corollary 4.2 states that there can be at most one right or obtuse angle in a triangle. Since this triangle is labeled with two obtuse angle measures, 93 and 130, at least one of these measures must be incorrect. Since by the Triangle Angle Sum Theorem the sum of the interior angles of the triangle must be 180 and $37 + 93 + 130 \neq 180$, at least one of these measures must be incorrect.

47. The measure of $\angle a$ is the supplement of the exterior angle with measure 110, so $\angle a = 180 - 110$ or 70. Because the angles with measures b and c are congruent, $b = c$. Using the Exterior Angle Theorem, $b + c = 110$. By substitution, $b + b = 110$, so $2b = 110$ and $b = 55$. Because $b = c$, $c = 55$.

48. Sample answer:

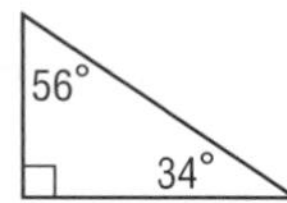

I found the measure of the second angle by subtracting the first angle from 90° since the acute angles of a right triangle are complementary.

51. Sample answer: Since an exterior angle is acute, the adjacent angle must be obtuse. Since another exterior angle is right, the adjacent angle must be right. A triangle cannot contain both a right and an obtuse angle because it would be more than 180 degrees. Therefore, a triangle cannot have an obtuse, acute, and a right exterior angle.

Lesson 4-3

17a. $\triangle ABC \cong \triangle MNO$; $\triangle DEF \cong \triangle PQR$

17b. $\overline{AB} \cong \overline{MN}$, $\overline{BC} \cong \overline{NO}$, $\overline{AC} \cong \overline{MO}$, $\overline{DE} \cong \overline{PQ}$, $\overline{EF} \cong \overline{QR}$, $\overline{DF} \cong \overline{PR}$

17c. $\angle A \cong \angle M$, $\angle B \cong \angle N$, $\angle C \cong \angle O$, $\angle D \cong \angle P$, $\angle E \cong \angle Q$, $\angle F \cong \angle R$

21. Given: $\angle A \cong \angle D$
$\angle B \cong \angle E$

Prove: $\angle C \cong \angle F$

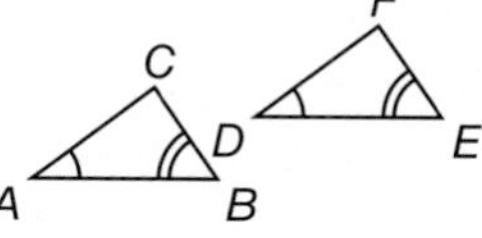

Proof:

Statements (Reasons)

1. $\angle A \cong \angle D$, $\angle B \cong \angle E$ (Given)
2. $m\angle A = m\angle D$, $m\angle B = m\angle E$ (Def. of $\cong$ ⦞)
3. $m\angle A + m\angle B + m\angle C = 180$, $m\angle D + m\angle E + m\angle F = 180$ ($\angle$ Sum Theorem)
4. $m\angle A + m\angle B + m\angle C = m\angle D + m\angle E + m\angle F$ (Trans. Prop.)
5. $m\angle D + m\angle E + m\angle C = m\angle D + m\angle E + m\angle F$ (Subst.)
6. $m\angle C = m\angle F$ (Subt. Prop.)
7. $\angle C \cong \angle F$ (Def. of $\cong$ ⦞)

22. Proof:

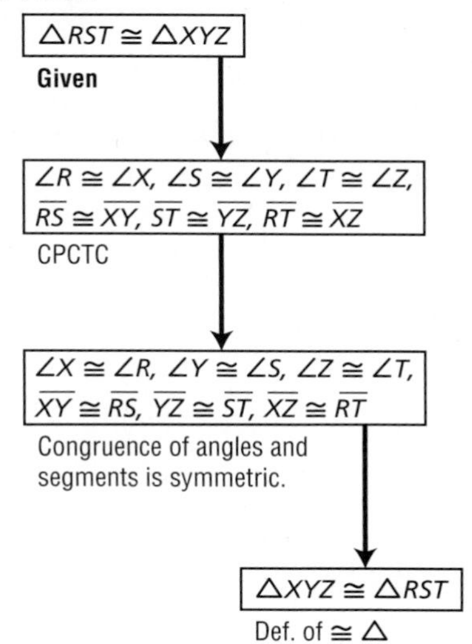

$\triangle RST \cong \triangle XYZ$
Given
$\angle R \cong \angle X$, $\angle S \cong \angle Y$, $\angle T \cong \angle Z$, $\overline{RS} \cong \overline{XY}$, $\overline{ST} \cong \overline{YZ}$, $\overline{RT} \cong \overline{XZ}$
CPCTC
$\angle X \cong \angle R$, $\angle Y \cong \angle S$, $\angle Z \cong \angle T$, $\overline{XY} \cong \overline{RS}$, $\overline{YZ} \cong \overline{ST}$, $\overline{XZ} \cong \overline{RT}$
Congruence of angles and segments is symmetric.
$\triangle XYZ \cong \triangle RST$
Def. of $\cong$ $\triangle$

23. Proof:

Statements (Reasons)

1. $\overline{BD}$ bisects $\angle B$, $\overline{BD} \perp \overline{AC}$. (Given)
2. $\angle ABD \cong \angle DBC$ (Def. of angle bisector)
3. $\angle ADB$ and $\angle BDC$ are right angles. ($\perp$ lines form rt. ⦞.)
4. $\angle ADB \cong \angle BDC$ (All rt. ⦞ are $\cong$.)
5. $\angle A \cong \angle C$ (Third ⦞ Thm.)

24. Proof:

Statements (Reasons)

1. $\angle P \cong \angle T$, $\angle S \cong \angle Q$, $\overline{TR} \cong \overline{PR}$, $\overline{RP} \cong \overline{RQ}$, $\overline{RT} \cong \overline{RS}$, $\overline{PQ} \cong \overline{TS}$ (Given)
2. $\overline{PR} \cong \overline{QR}$, $\overline{TR} \cong \overline{SR}$ (Symm. Prop.)
3. $\overline{TR} \cong \overline{QR}$ (Trans. Prop)
4. $\overline{QR} \cong \overline{TR}$ (Symm. Prop.)
5. $\overline{QR} \cong \overline{SR}$ (Trans. Prop.)
6. $\angle PRQ \cong \angle TRS$ (Vert. ∠s are ≅.)
7. $\triangle PRQ \cong \triangle TRS$ (Def. of ≅ △s)

26. Given: $\triangle ABC \cong \triangle DEF$, $\triangle DEF \cong \triangle GHI$

Prove: $\triangle ABC \cong \triangle GHI$

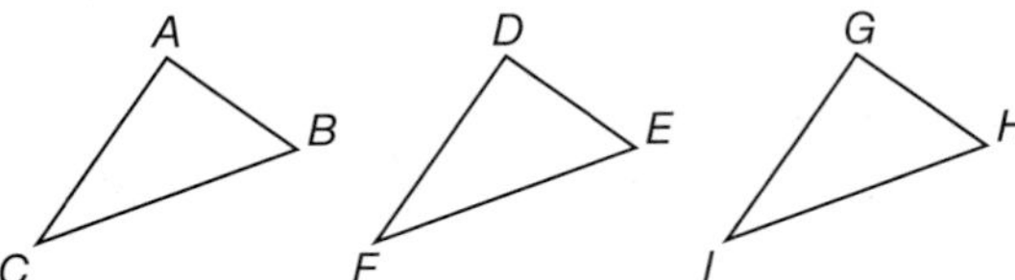

Proof:

We know that $\triangle ABC \cong \triangle DEF$. Because corresponding parts of congruent triangles are congruent, $\angle A \cong \angle D$, $\angle B \cong \angle E$, $\angle C \cong \angle F$, $\overline{AB} \cong \overline{DE}$, $\overline{BC} \cong \overline{EF}$, $\overline{AC} \cong \overline{DF}$. We also know that $\triangle DEF \cong \triangle GHI$. So $\angle D \cong \angle G$, $\angle E \cong \angle H$, $\angle F \cong \angle I$, $\overline{DE} \cong \overline{GH}$, $\overline{EF} \cong \overline{HI}$, $\overline{DF} \cong \overline{GI}$, by CPCTC. Therefore, $\angle A \cong \angle G$, $\angle B \cong \angle H$, $\angle C \cong \angle I$, $\overline{AB} \cong \overline{GH}$, $\overline{BC} \cong \overline{HI}$, $\overline{AC} \cong \overline{GI}$ because congruence of angles and segments is transitive. Thus, $\triangle ABC \cong \triangle GHI$ by the definition of congruent triangles.

27. Given: $\triangle DEF$

Prove: $\triangle DEF \cong \triangle DEF$

Proof:

E
D F

$\triangle DEF$
Given

$\overline{DE} \cong \overline{DE}$, $\overline{EF} \cong \overline{EF}$, $\overline{DF} \cong \overline{DF}$
Congruence of segments is reflexive.

$\angle D \cong \angle D$, $\angle E \cong \angle E$, $\angle F \cong \angle F$
Congruence of △ is reflexive.

$\triangle DEF \cong \triangle DEF$
Def. of ≅ △

33a. If two triangles are congruent, then their areas are equal.

33b. If the areas of a pair of triangles are equal, then the triangles are congruent; false; If one triangle has a base of 2 and a height of 6 and a second triangle has a base of 3 and a height of 4, then their areas are equal, but they are not congruent.

33c. No; sample answer: Any pair of equilateral triangles that have the same base also have the same height, so it is not possible to draw a pair of equilateral triangles with the same area that are not congruent.

33d. yes; sample answer:

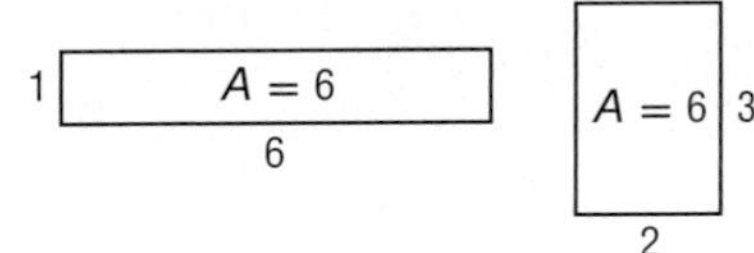

33e. No; any pair of squares that have the same area have the same side length, which is the square root of the area. If their areas are equal, they are congruent.

33f. Regular *n*-gons; If two regular *n*-gons are congruent, then they have the same area. All regular *n*-gons have the same shape, but may have different sizes. If two regular *n*-gons have the same area, then they not only have the same shape but also the same size. Therefore, they are congruent.

Lesson 4-4 (Guided Practice)

1. Proof:

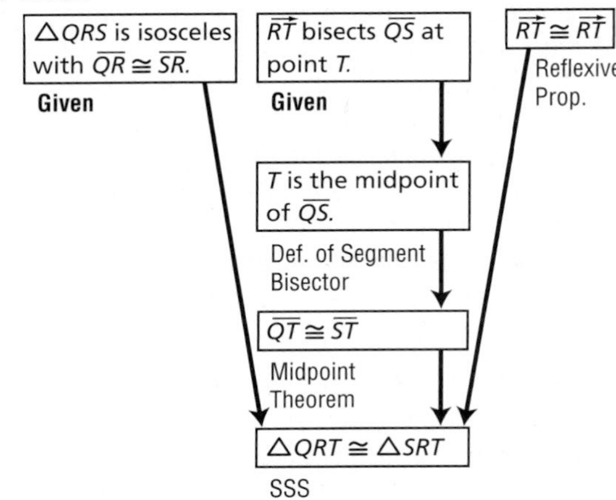

2a.

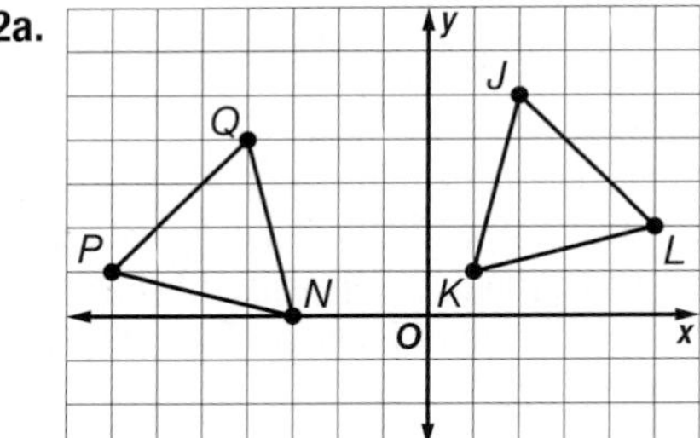

2b. From the graphs, it appears that the triangles have the same shape and size, so we can conjecture that the two triangles are congruent.

2c.

$JL = \sqrt{(2-5)^2 + (5-2)^2}$
$= \sqrt{9+9}$ or $\sqrt{18}$

$QP = \sqrt{[-4-(-7)]^2 + (4-1)^2}$
$= \sqrt{9+9}$ or $\sqrt{18}$

$LK = \sqrt{(5-1)^2 + (2-1)^2}$
$= \sqrt{16+1}$ or $\sqrt{17}$

$PN = \sqrt{[-7-(-3)]^2 + (1-0)^2}$
$= \sqrt{16+1}$ or $\sqrt{17}$

$KJ = \sqrt{(2-1)^2 + (5-1)^2}$
$= \sqrt{1+16}$ or $\sqrt{17}$

$NQ = \sqrt{[-4-(-3)]^2 + (4-0)^2}$
$= \sqrt{1+16}$ or $\sqrt{17}$

$JL = QP$, $LK = PN$, and $KJ = NQ$. By definition of congruent segments, all corresponding segments are congruent. Therefore $\triangle JKL \cong \triangle QNP$ by SSS.

Lesson 4-4

1b. Given: *ABCD* is a square

Prove: $\triangle ABC \cong \triangle CDA$

Proof:

Statements (Reasons)

1. *ABCD* is a square (Given)
2. $\overline{AB} \cong \overline{CD}$, $\overline{BC} \cong \overline{DA}$ (Def. of a square)
3. $\overline{AC} \cong \overline{CA}$ (Reflex. Prop. $\cong$)
4. $\triangle ABC \cong \triangle CDA$ (SSS)

1c. Sample answer: $\overleftrightarrow{AB} \parallel \overleftrightarrow{CD}$; $\overleftrightarrow{AC}$ is a transversal to $\overleftrightarrow{AB}$ and $\overleftrightarrow{CD}$, so $\angle CAB$ and $\angle ACD$ are alternate interior angles. Since $\triangle ABC \cong \triangle CDA$, $\angle CAB$ and $\angle ACD$ are congruent corresponding angles. Therefore, the lines are parallel.

2a.

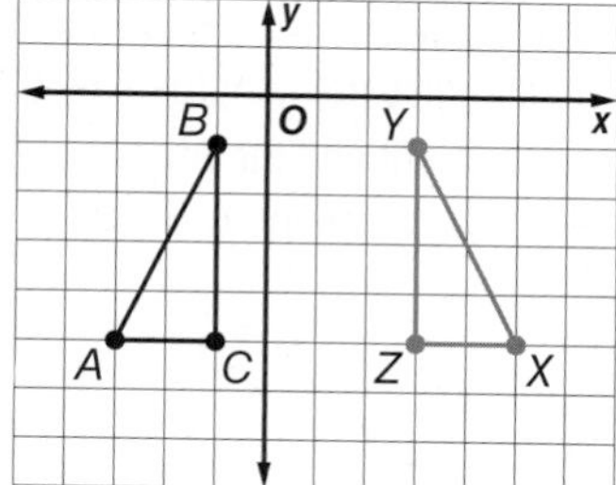

2b. The triangles look the same size and shape so we can conjecture that they are congruent.

2c. $AB = \sqrt{20}$, $XY = \sqrt{20}$, $BC = 4$, $YZ = 4$, $AC = 2$, and $XZ = 2$. The corresponding sides have the same measure and are congruent. So, $\triangle ABC \cong \triangle XYZ$ by SSS.

3. Sample answer: We are given that $\overline{LP} \cong \overline{NO}$ and $\angle LPM \cong \angle NOM$. Since $\triangle MOP$ is equilateral, $\overline{MO} \cong \overline{MP}$ by the definition of an equilateral triangle. Therefore, $\triangle LMP$ is congruent to $\triangle NMO$ by the Side-Angle-Side Congruence Postulate.

12. Proof:

Statements (Reasons)

1. $\overline{BD} \perp \overline{AC}$; $\overline{BD}$ bisects $\overline{AC}$. (Given)
2. $\angle BDA$ and $\angle BDC$ are right angles. (Def. of $\perp$)
3. $\angle BDA \cong \angle BDC$ (all right angles are $\cong$)
4. $\overline{AD} \cong \overline{DC}$ (Def. of bisects)
5. $\overline{BD} \cong \overline{BD}$ (Ref. Prop.)
6. $\triangle ABD \cong \triangle CBD$ (SAS)

13. Since *R* is the midpoint of $\overline{QS}$ and $\overline{PT}$, $\overline{PR} \cong \overline{RT}$ and $\overline{RQ} \cong \overline{RS}$ by definition of a midpoint. $\angle PRQ \cong \angle TRS$ by the Vertical Angles Theorem.

So, $\triangle PRQ \cong \triangle TRS$ by SAS.

14. Proof:

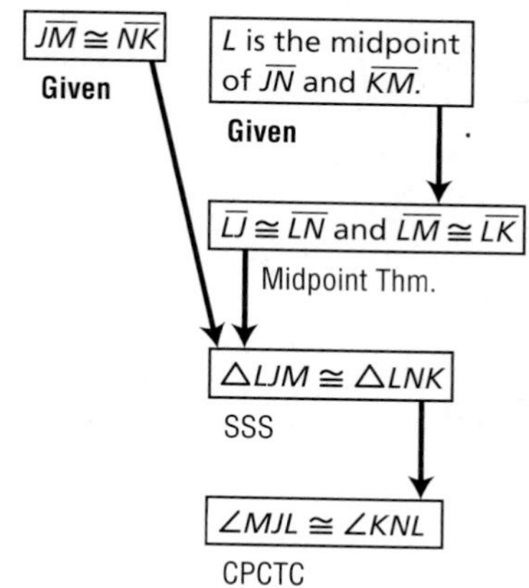

15. Proof: We know that $\overline{WY}$ bisects $\angle Y$, so $\angle XYW \cong \angle ZYW$. Also, $\overline{YW} \cong \overline{YW}$ by the Reflexive Property. Since $\triangle XYZ$ is equilateral it is a special type of isosceles triangle, so $\overline{XY} \cong \overline{ZY}$. By the Side-Angle-Side Congruence Postulate, $\triangle XYW \cong \triangle ZYW$. By CPCTC, $\overline{XW} \cong \overline{ZW}$.

20b. Given: $\overline{AB} \cong \overline{AD}$ and $\overline{CB} \cong \overline{DC}$

Prove: $\triangle ACB \cong \triangle ACD$

Proof:

Statements (Reasons)

1. $\overline{AB} \cong \overline{AD}$ and $\overline{CB} \cong \overline{DC}$ (Given)
2. $\overline{AC} \cong \overline{AC}$ (Refl. Prop.)
3. $\triangle ACB \cong \triangle ACD$ (SSS)

20c. Sample answer: The object is three-dimensional, so when it is viewed in two dimensions, the perspective makes it look like the triangles are differently shaped.

21. Proof:

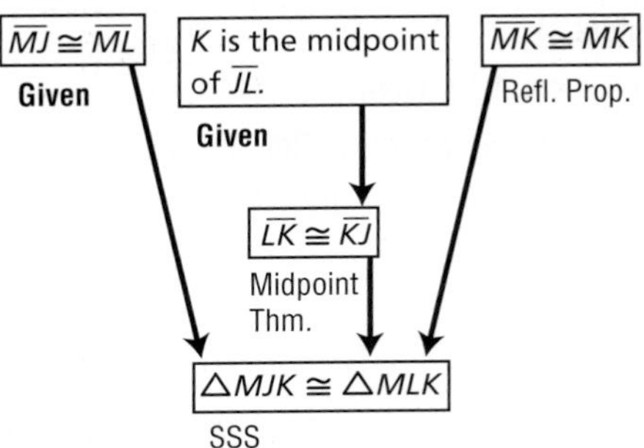

22. Proof:

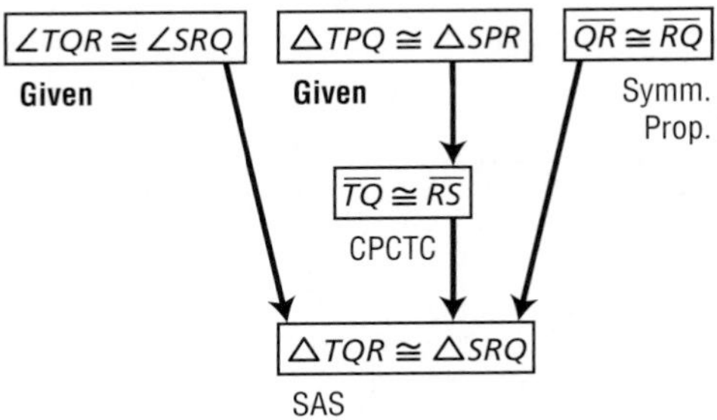

23a. Given: $\overline{TS} \cong \overline{SF} \cong \overline{FR} \cong \overline{RT}$ $\angle TSF$, $\angle SFR$, $\angle FRT$, and $\angle RTS$ are right angles.

Prove: $\overline{RS} \cong \overline{TF}$

Proof:

<u>**Statements (Reasons)**</u>

1. $\overline{TS} \cong \overline{SF} \cong \overline{FR} \cong \overline{RT}$ (Given)
2. $\angle TSF$, $\angle SFR$, $\angle FRT$, and $\angle RTS$ are right angles. (Given)
3. $\angle STR \cong \angle TRF$ (All rt $\angle$s are $\cong$.)
4. $\triangle STR \cong \triangle TRF$ (SAS)
5. $\overline{RS} \cong \overline{TF}$ (CPCTC)

23b. Given: $\overline{TS} \cong \overline{SF} \cong \overline{FH} \cong \overline{HT}$; $\angle TSF$, $\angle SFH$, $\angle FHT$, and $\angle HTS$ are right $\angle$s.

Prove: $\angle SRT \cong \angle SRF$

Proof:

<u>**Statements (Reasons)**</u>

1. $\overline{TS} \cong \overline{SF} \cong \overline{FR} \cong \overline{RT}$ (Given)
2. $\angle TSF$, $\angle SFR$, $\angle FRT$, and $\angle RTS$ are right angles. (Given)
3. $\angle STR \cong \angle SFR$ (All rt $\angle$s are $\cong$.)
4. $\triangle STR \cong \triangle SFR$ (SAS)
5. $\angle SRT \cong \angle SRF$ (CPCTC)\

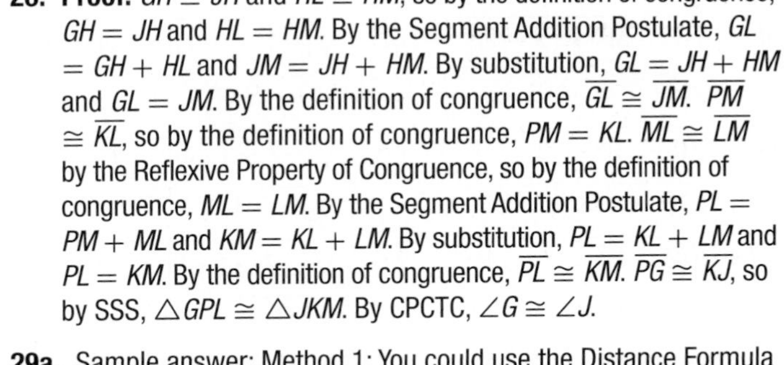

26. Proof: $\overline{GH} \cong \overline{JH}$ and $\overline{HL} \cong \overline{HM}$, so by the definition of congruence, $GH = JH$ and $HL = HM$. By the Segment Addition Postulate, $GL = GH + HL$ and $JM = JH + HM$. By substitution, $GL = JH + HM$ and $GL = JM$. By the definition of congruence, $\overline{GL} \cong \overline{JM}$. $\overline{PM} \cong \overline{KL}$, so by the definition of congruence, $PM = KL$. $\overline{ML} \cong \overline{LM}$ by the Reflexive Property of Congruence, so by the definition of congruence, $ML = LM$. By the Segment Addition Postulate, $PL = PM + ML$ and $KM = KL + LM$. By substitution, $PL = KL + LM$ and $PL = KM$. By the definition of congruence, $\overline{PL} \cong \overline{KM}$. $\overline{PG} \cong \overline{KJ}$, so by SSS, $\triangle GPL \cong \triangle JKM$. By CPCTC, $\angle G \cong \angle J$.

29a. Sample answer: Method 1: You could use the Distance Formula to find the length of each of the sides, and then use the Side-Side-Side Congruence Postulate to prove the triangles congruent. Method 2: You could find the slopes of $\overline{ZX}$ and $\overline{WY}$ to prove that they are perpendicular and that $\angle WYZ$ and $\angle WYX$ are both right angles. You can use the Distance Formula to prove that $\overline{XY}$ is congruent to $\overline{ZY}$. Since the triangles share the leg $\overline{WY}$, you can use the Side-Angle-Side Congruence Postulate; Sample answer: I think that method 2 is more efficient, because you only have two steps instead of three.

29b. Sample answer: Yes; the slope of $\overline{WY}$ is –1 and the slope of $\overline{ZX}$ is 1, and –1 and 1 are opposite reciprocals, so $\overline{WY}$ is perpendicular to $\overline{ZX}$. Since they are perpendicular, $\angle WYZ$ and $\angle WYX$ are both 90°. Using the Distance Formula, the length of $\overline{ZY}$ is $\sqrt{(4-1)^2 + (5-2)^2}$ or $3\sqrt{2}$, and the length of $\overline{XY}$ is $\sqrt{(7-4)^2 + (8-5)^2}$ or $3\sqrt{2}$. Since $\overline{WY}$ is congruent to $\overline{WY}$, $\triangle WYZ$ is congruent to $\triangle WYX$ by the Side-Angle-Side Congruence Postulate.

33. Case 1: You know the hypotenuses are congruent and one of the legs are congruent. Then the Pythagorean Theorem says that the other legs are congruent so the triangles are congruent by SSS. Case 2: You know the legs are congruent and the right angles are congruent, then the triangles are congruent by SAS.

Extend 4-4

1. Given: Diagram of Construction

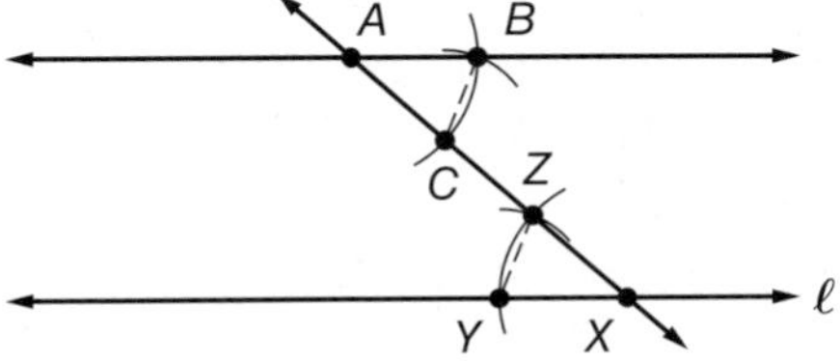

Prove: $\overline{AB} \parallel \overline{YX}$

Proof:

Statements (Reasons)

1. $\overline{AB} \cong \overline{AC} \cong \overline{XY} \cong \overline{XZ}$ (The same compass setting was used from point *A* to construct points *B* and *C* and from point *X* to construct points *Y* and *Z*.)
2. $\overline{BC} \cong \overline{YZ}$ (The same compass setting was used from point *C* to construct point *B* and from point *Y* to construct point *Z*.
3. $\triangle ABC \cong \triangle XYZ$ (SSS)
4. $\angle BAC \cong \angle YXZ$ (CPCTC)
5. $\overline{AB} \parallel \overline{YX}$ (Alt. Int. ∠s Conv.)

2. Given: Diagram of Construction

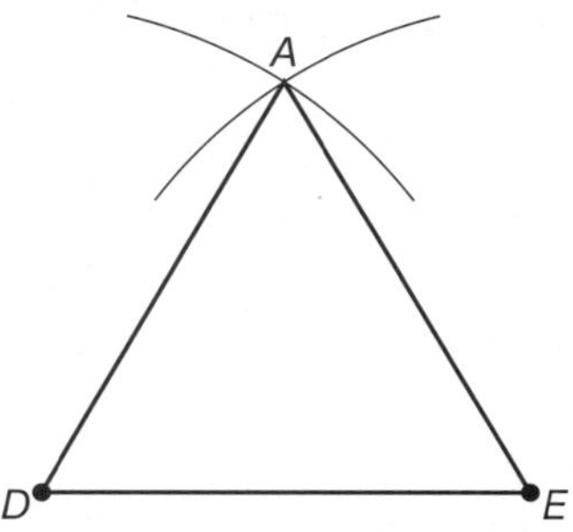

Prove: $\triangle DAE$ is equilateral.

Proof: $\overline{DE} \cong \overline{DA} \cong \overline{AE}$ since the compass was set to the length of $\overline{DE}$ and used to construct point *A* from points *D* and *E*. Therefore, by the definition of an equilateral triangle, $\triangle DAE$ is equilateral.

3. Given: Diagram of Construction

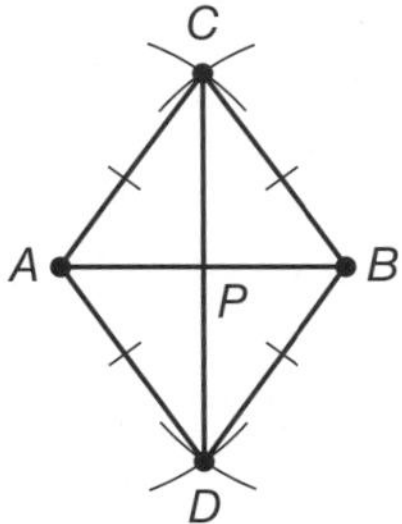

Prove: $\overline{CD} \perp \overline{AB}$ and $\overline{AP} \cong \overline{BP}$

Proof:

Statements (Reasons)

1. $\overline{AD} \cong \overline{AC} \cong \overline{BD}$ (The same compass setting was used from points *A* and *B* to construct points *C* and *D*.)
2. $\overline{CD} \cong \overline{CD}$ (Refl. Prop.)
3. $\triangle ACD \cong \triangle BCD$ (SSS)
4. $\angle ACP \cong \angle BCP$ (CPCTC)
5. $\overline{CP} \cong \overline{CP}$ (Refl. Prop.)
6. $\triangle ACP \cong \triangle BCP$ (SSS)
7. $\overline{AP} \cong \overline{BP}$ (CPCTC)
8. $\angle CPA \cong \angle CPB$ (CPCTC)
9. $m\angle CPA = m\angle CPB$ (Def. of $\cong$)
10. $\angle CPA$ is adjacent to $\angle CPB$. (Def. of adjacent ∠s)
11. $\overline{CD} \perp \overline{AB}$ (By definition, perpendicular lines intersect to form congruent adjacent angles.)

Mid-Chapter Quiz

14. $\triangle BED \cong \triangle CFG$; $\triangle BJH \cong \triangle CKM$; $\triangle BPN \cong \triangle CQS$; $\triangle DIH \cong \triangle GLM$; $\triangle DON \cong \triangle GRS$

Lesson 4-5 (Guided Practice)

2. Proof:

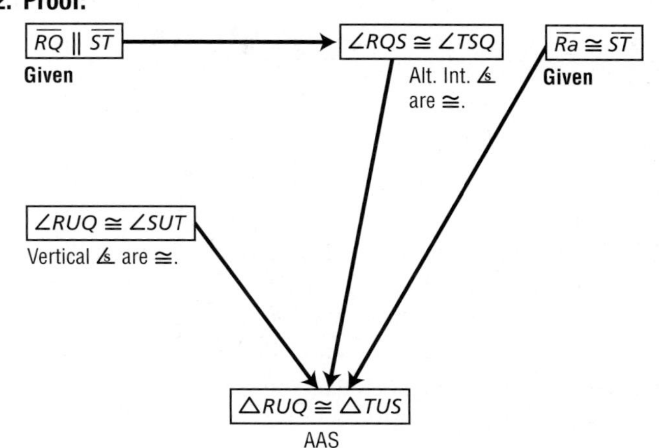

Lesson 4-5

9. Proof:

Statements (Reasons)

1. *V* is the midpoint of $\overline{YW}$; $\overline{UY} \parallel \overline{XW}$. (Given)
2. $\overline{YV} \cong \overline{VW}$ (Midpoint Theorem)
3. $\angle VWX \cong \angle VYU$ (Alt. Int. ∠ Thm.)
4. $\angle VUY \cong \angle VXW$ (Alt. Int. ∠ Thm.)
5. $\triangle UVY \cong \triangle XVW$ (AAS)

10. Proof:

Statements (Reasons)

1. $\overline{MS} \cong \overline{RQ}$, $\overline{MS} \parallel \overline{RQ}$ (Given)
2. $\angle SPM \cong \angle QPR$ (Vert. ∠s are $\cong$.)
3. $\angle SMP \cong \angle QRP$ (Alt. Int. ∠ Thm.)
4. $\triangle MSP \cong \triangle RQP$ (AAS)

11. Proof:

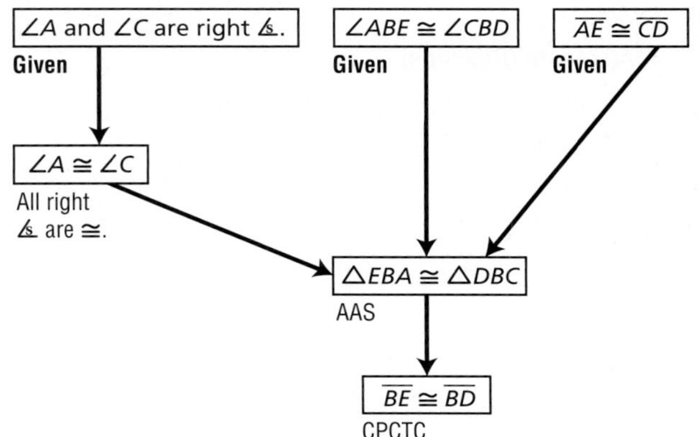

12. Proof:

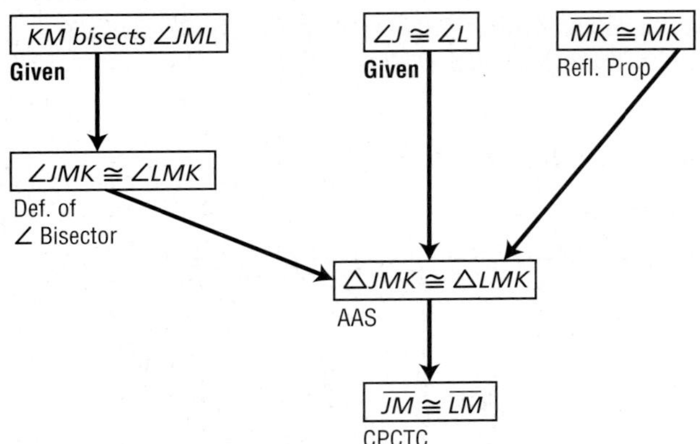

13a. $\angle HJK \cong \angle GFK$ since all right angles are congruent. We are given that $\overline{JK} \cong \overline{KF}$. $\angle HKJ$ and $\angle FKG$ are vertical angles, so $\angle HKJ \cong \angle FKG$ by the Vertical Angles Theorem. By ASA, $\triangle HJK \cong \triangle GFK$, so $\overline{FG} \cong \overline{HJ}$ by CPCTC.

16a. Given: $\overline{AB}$ bisects $\angle CBD$ and $\angle CAD$.

Prove: $\triangle ABC \cong \triangle ABD$.

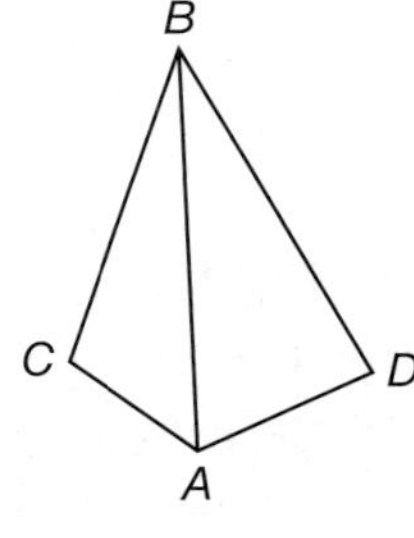

Proof:

Statements (Reasons)

1. $\overline{AB}$ bisects $\angle CBD$ and $\angle CAD$. (Given)
2. $\angle ABC \cong \angle ABD$, $\angle CAB \cong \angle DAB$ (Def. of bisect)
3. $\overline{AB} \cong \overline{AB}$ (Refl. Prop.)
4. $\triangle ABC \cong \triangle ABD$ (ASA)

16b. Given: $\triangle ABC \cong \triangle ABD$, $\angle FCA \cong \angle EDA$

Prove: $\triangle CAF \cong \triangle DAE$

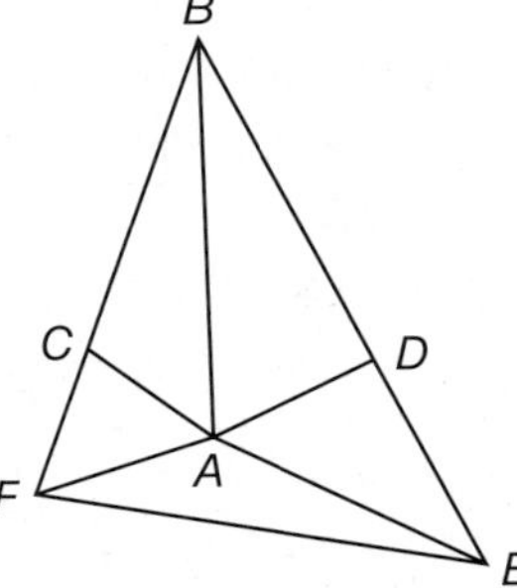

Proof:

Statements (Reasons)

1. $\triangle ABC \cong \triangle ABD$, $\angle FCA \cong \angle EDA$ (Given)
2. $\overline{CA} \cong \overline{DA}$ (CPCTC)
3. $\angle CAF \cong \angle DAE$ (Vert. $\angle$s are $\cong$.)
4. $\triangle CAF \cong \triangle DAE$ (ASA)

16c. Given: $\overline{HB} \cong \overline{EB}$, $\angle BHG \cong \angle BEA$, $\angle HGJ \cong \angle EAD$, $\angle JGB \cong \angle DAB$

Prove: $\triangle BHG \cong \triangle BEA$

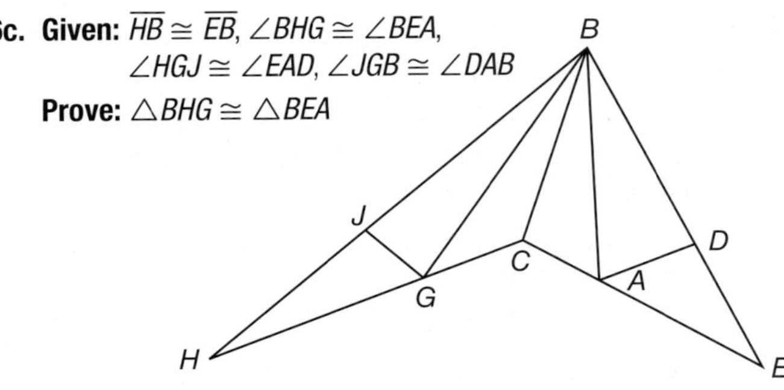

Proof:

Statements (Reasons)

1. $\overline{HB} \cong \overline{EB}$, $\angle BHG \cong \angle BEA$, $\angle HGJ \cong \angle EAD$, $\angle JGB \cong \angle DAB$ (Given)
2. $m\angle HGJ = m\angle EAD$, $m\angle JGB = m\angle DAB$ (Def. of $\cong$)
3. $m\angle HGJ + m\angle JGB = m\angle HGB$, $m\angle EAD + m\angle DAB = m\angle EAB$ (Add Prop of $=$)
4. $m\angle EAD + m\angle DAB = m\angle HGB$, $m\angle EAD + m\angle DAB = m\angle EAB$ (Angle Add. Post.)
5. $m\angle HGB = m\angle EAB$ (Subst.)
6. $\angle HGB \cong \angle EAB$ (Def. of congruence)
7. $\triangle BHG \cong \triangle BEA$ (AAS)

21. Proof:

Statements (Reasons)

1. $m\angle ACB = 44$, $m\angle ADB = 44$, $m\angle CBA = 68$, $m\angle DBA = 68$ (Given)
2. $m\angle ACB = m\angle ADB$, $m\angle CBA = m\angle DBA$ (Subst.)
3. $\angle ACB \cong \angle ADB$, $\angle CBA \cong \angle DBA$ (Def. of $\cong$)
4. $\overline{AB} \cong \overline{AB}$ (Refl. Prop.)
5. $\triangle ADB \cong \triangle ACB$ (AAS)
6. $\overline{AC} \cong \overline{AD}$ (CPCTC)

24. Sample answer: $\overline{AB} \cong \overline{XY}$, $\overline{BC} \cong \overline{YZ}$, and $\angle C \cong \angle Z$. $\triangle ABC \not\cong \triangle XYZ$.

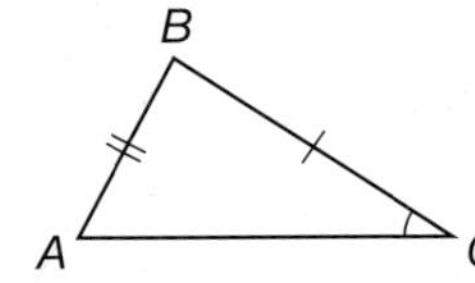

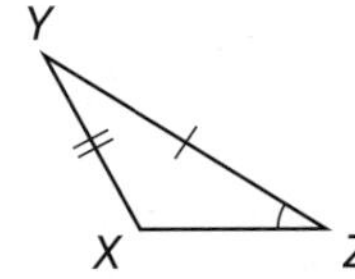

Chapter 4 Answer Appendix

25. Proof:

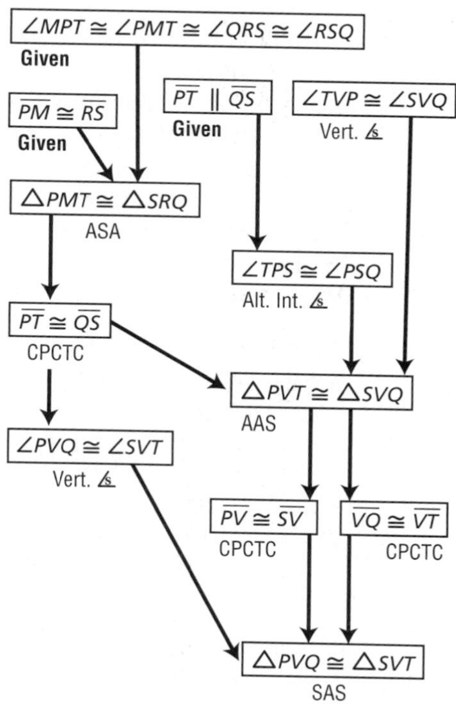

26. Sample answer:

Method	Use when...
Definition of Congruent Triangles	All corresponding parts of one triangle are congruent to the corresponding parts of the other triangle.
SSS	The three sides of one triangle must be congruent to the three sides of the other triangle.
SAS	Two sides and the included angle of one triangle must be congruent to two sides and the included angle of the other triangle.
ASA	Two angles and the included side of one triangle must be congruent to two angles and the included side of the other triangle.
AAS	Two angles and a nonincluded side of one triangle must be congruent to two angles and the corresponding nonincluded side of the other triangle.

Extend 4-5

10. Given: $\triangle DEF$ and $\triangle RST$ are right triangles. $\angle E$ and $\angle S$ are right angles. $\overline{EF} \cong \overline{ST}$, $\overline{ED} \cong \overline{SR}$

Prove: $\triangle DEF \cong \triangle RST$

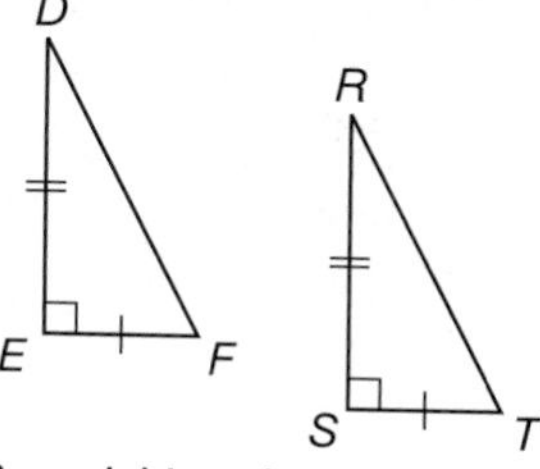

Proof: We are given that $\overline{EF} \cong \overline{ST}$, $\overline{ED} \cong \overline{SR}$, and $\angle E$ and $\angle S$ are right angles. Since all right angles are congruent, $\angle E \cong \angle S$. Therefore, by SAS, $\triangle DEF \cong \triangle RST$.

11. Given: $\triangle ABC$ and $\triangle XYZ$ are right triangles. $\angle A$ and $\angle X$ are right angles. $\overline{BC} \cong \overline{YZ}$ $\angle B \cong \angle Y$

Prove: $\triangle ABC \cong \triangle XYZ$

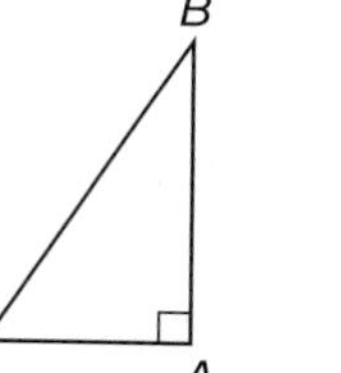

Proof: We are given that $\triangle ABC$ and $\triangle XYZ$ are right triangles with right angles $\angle A$ and $\angle X$, $\overline{BC} \cong \overline{YZ}$, and $\angle B \cong \angle Y$. Since all right angles are congruent, $\angle A \cong \angle X$. Therefore, $\triangle ABC \cong \triangle XYZ$ by AAS.

14. Proof:

Statements (Reasons)

1. $\overline{AB} \perp \overline{BC}$, $\overline{DC} \perp \overline{BC}$ (Given)
2. $\angle ABC$ is a right angle, $\angle DCB$ is a right angle. ($\perp$ lines form rt. ∠s)
3. $\triangle ABC$ is a right triangle, $\triangle DCB$ is a right triangle. (Def. of rt. △)
4. $\overline{AC} \cong \overline{BD}$ (Given)
5. $\overline{BC} \cong \overline{BC}$ (Refl. Prop. of Congruence)
6. $\triangle ABC \cong \triangle DCB$ (HL)
7. $\overline{AB} \cong \overline{DC}$ (CPCTC)

15. Proof:

Statements (Reasons)

1. $\overline{AB} \parallel \overline{DC}$, $\overline{AB} \parallel \overline{BC}$ (Given)
2. $\overline{DC} \perp \overline{BC}$ (In a plane, if a line is perpendicualr to one of two parallel lines, then it is perpendicular to the other.)
3. $\angle ABC$ is a right angle, $\angle DCB$ is a right angle. ($\perp$ lines form rt. $\angle$s)
4. $\triangle ABC$ is a right triangle, $\triangle DCB$ is a right triangle. (Def. of rt. $\triangle$)
5. E is the midpoint of $\overline{AC}$ and $\overline{BD}$. (Given)
6. $\overline{AE} \cong \overline{EC}$, $\overline{BE} \cong \overline{ED}$ (Midpt. Thm.)
7. $\angle AEB \cong \angle CED$ (Vertical $\angle$s are $\cong$)
8. $\triangle AEB \cong \triangle CED$ (SAS)
9. $\overline{AB} \cong \overline{CD}$ (CPCTC)
10. $\overline{BC} \cong \overline{BC}$ (Refl. Prop. of Congruence)
11. $\triangle ABC \cong \triangle DCB$ (LL)
12. $\overline{AC} \cong \overline{DB}$ (CPCTC)

Lesson 4-6 (Guided Practice)

4. Given: $\triangle ACE$ is equilateral, $\overline{FB} \parallel \overline{EC}$, $\overline{FD} \parallel \overline{BC}$, $\overline{BD} \parallel \overline{EF}$ and D is the midpoint of $\overline{EC}$.

Prove: $\triangle FED \cong \triangle BDC$

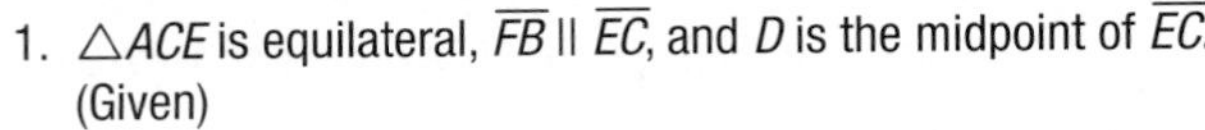

Proof:

Statements (Reasons)

1. $\triangle ACE$ is equilateral, $\overline{FB} \parallel \overline{EC}$, and D is the midpoint of $\overline{EC}$. (Given)
2. $m\angle E = 60$, $m\angle C = 60$ (Each $\angle$ of an equilateral $\triangle$ measures 60.)
3. $m\angle E = m\angle C$ (Trans. Prop.)
4. $\angle E \cong \angle C$ (Def. of congruence)
5. $\overline{ED} \cong \overline{DC}$ (Midpt. Thm.)
6. $\angle CBD \cong \angle BDF$, $\angle EFD \cong \angle BDF$ (Alt. Int. $\angle$s Thm.)
7. $\angle CBD \cong \angle EFD$ (Trans. Prop.)
8. $\triangle FED \cong \triangle BDC$ (AAS)

Lesson 4-6

23. Proof: We are given that $\triangle HJM$ is an isosceles triangle and $\triangle HKL$ is an equilateral triangle, $\angle JKH$ and $\angle HKL$ are supplementary and $\angle HLK$ and $\angle MLH$ are supplementary. From the Isosceles Triangle Theorem, we know that $\angle HJK \cong \angle HML$. Since $\triangle HKL$ is an equilateral triangle, we know $\angle HLK \cong \angle LKH \cong \angle KHL$ and $\overline{HL} \cong \overline{KL} \cong \overline{HK}$. $\angle JKH$, $\angle HKL$ and $\angle HLK$, $\angle MLH$ are supplementary, and $\angle HKL \cong \angle HLK$, we know $\angle JKH \cong \angle MLH$ by the Congruent Supplements Theorem. By AAS, $\triangle JHK \cong \triangle MLH$. By CPCTC, $\angle JHK \cong \angle MHL$.

24. Proof: We are given $\overline{XY} \cong \overline{XZ}$, W is the midpoint of $\overline{XY}$, and Q is the midpoint of $\overline{XZ}$. Since W is the midpoint of $\overline{XY}$, we know that $\overline{XW} \cong \overline{WY}$. Similarly, since Q is the midpoint of $\overline{XZ}$, $\overline{XQ} \cong \overline{QZ}$. The Segment Addition Postulate gives us $XW + WY = XY$ and $XQ + QZ = XZ$. Substitution gives $XW + WY = XQ + QZ$ and $WY + WY = QZ + QZ$. So, $2WY = 2QZ$. If we divide each side by 2, we have $WY = QZ$. The Isosceles Triangle Theorem says $\angle XYZ \cong \angle XZY$. $\overline{YZ} \cong \overline{ZY}$ by the Reflexive Property. By SAS, $\triangle WYZ \cong \triangle QZY$. So, $\overline{WZ} \cong \overline{QY}$ by CPCTC.

26. Given: $\overline{BD} \perp \overline{AC}$ and $\triangle ABC$ is an isosceles with base $\overline{AC}$.

Prove: $\overline{BD}$ bisects the angle formed by the sloped sides of the roof, $\angle ABC$.

Proof:

Statements (Reasons)

1. $\overline{BD} \perp \overline{AC}$, and $\triangle ABC$ is an isosceles with base $\overline{AC}$. (Given)
2. $\angle BDA$ and $\angle BDC$ are rt. $\angle$s. (Def. of $\perp$)
3. $\angle BDA \cong \angle BDC$ (All rt. $\angle$s are $\cong$.)
4. $\overline{AB} \cong \overline{BC}$ (Def. of Isos.)
5. $\angle BAD \cong \angle BCD$ (Isos. $\triangle$ Thm.)
6. $\triangle BAD \cong \triangle BCD$ (AAS)
7. $\angle ABD \cong \angle CBD$ (CPCTC)
8. $\overline{BD}$ bisects the angle formed by the sloped sides of the roof, $\angle ABC$. (Def. of $\angle$ bisector)

27.

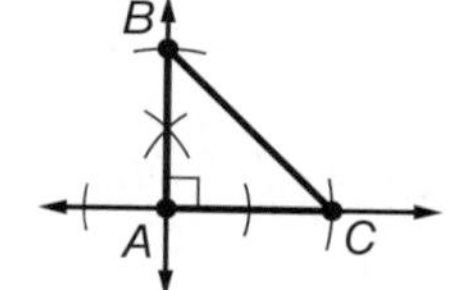

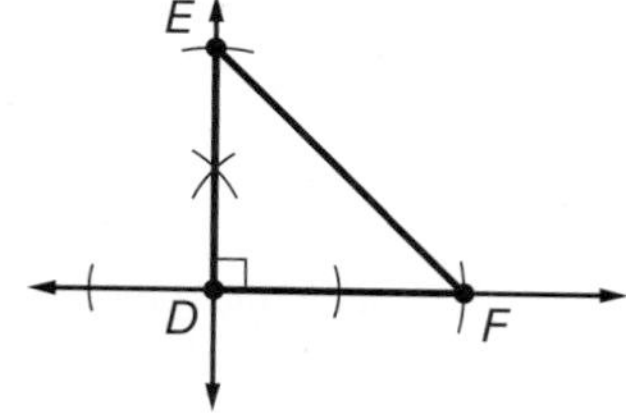

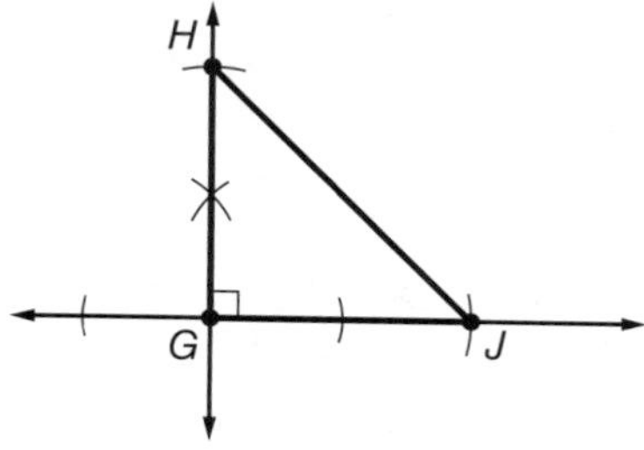

Sample answer: I constructed a pair of perpendicular segments and then used the same compass setting to mark points equidistant from their intersection. I measured both legs for each triangle. Since $AB = AC = 1.3$ cm, $DE = DF = 1.9$ cm, and $GH = GJ = 2.3$ cm, the triangles are isosceles. I used a protractor to confirm that $\angle A$, $\angle D$, and $\angle G$ are all right angles.

33. Given: Each triangle is isosceles, $\overline{BG} \cong \overline{HC}$, $\overline{HD} \cong \overline{JF}$, $\angle G \cong \angle H$, and $\angle H \cong \angle J$.

Prove: The distance from B to F is three times the distance from D to F.

Proof:

Statements (Reasons)

1. Each triangle is isosceles, $\overline{BG} \cong \overline{HC}$, $\overline{HD} \cong \overline{JF}$, $\angle G \cong \angle H$, and $\angle H \cong \angle J$. (Given)
2. $\angle G \cong \angle J$ (Trans. Prop.)
3. $\overline{BG} \cong \overline{CG}$, $\overline{HC} \cong \overline{HD}$, $\overline{JD} \cong \overline{JF}$ (Def. of Isosceles)
4. $\overline{BG} \cong \overline{JD}$ (Trans. Prop.)
5. $\overline{HC} \cong \overline{JD}$ (Trans. Prop.)
6. $\overline{CG} \cong \overline{JF}$ (Trans. Prop.)
7. $\triangle BCG \cong \triangle CDH \cong \triangle DFJ$ (SAS)
8. $\overline{BC} \cong \overline{CD} \cong \overline{DF}$ (CPCTC)
9. $BC = CD = DF$ (Def. of congruence)
10. $BC + CD + DF = BF$ (Seg. Add. Post.)
11. $DF + DF + DF = BF$ (Subst.)
12. $3DF = BF$ (Addition)

34. Proof:

Statements (Reasons)

1. $\triangle XWV$ is isosceles; $\overline{ZY} \perp \overline{YV}$. (Given)
2. $\angle X \cong \angle WVX$ (Isos. $\triangle$ Thm.)
3. $\angle WVX \cong \angle YVZ$ (Vert $\angle$s are $\cong$.)
4. $\angle X \cong \angle YVZ$ (Trans. Prop.)
5. $m\angle X = m\angle YVZ$ (Def. of $\cong$ $\angle$s)
6. $m\angle VYZ = 90$ ($\perp$ lines form rt $\angle$s.)
7. $\triangle ZVY$ is a right triangle. (Def of rt. $\triangle$)
8. $\angle YZV$ and $\angle YVZ$ are complementary. (The acute $\angle$s of a rt. $\triangle$ are comp.)
9. $m\angle YZV + m\angle YVZ = 90$ (Def. Of Compl. $\angle$s)
10. $m\angle YZV + m\angle X = 90$ (Subst.)
11. $\angle X$ and $\angle YZV$ are complementary (Def. of Compl. $\angle$s)

35. Case I

B
A C

Given: $\triangle ABC$ is an equilateral triangle.

Prove: $\triangle ABC$ is an equiangular triangle.

Proof:

Statements (Reasons)

1. $\triangle ABC$ is an equilateral triangle. (Given)
2. $\overline{AB} \cong \overline{AC} \cong \overline{BC}$ (Def. of equilateral $\triangle$)
3. $\angle A \cong \angle B \cong \angle C$ (Isosceles $\triangle$ Th.)
4. $\triangle ABC$ is an equiangular triangle. (Def. of equiangular)

Case II

B
A C

Given: $\triangle ABC$ is an equiangular triangle.

Prove: $\triangle ABC$ is an equilateral triangle.

Proof:

Statements (Reasons)

1. $\triangle ABC$ is an equiangular triangle. (Given)
2. $\angle A \cong \angle B \cong \angle C$ (Def. of equiangular $\triangle$)
3. $\overline{AB} \cong \overline{AC} \cong \overline{BC}$ (If 2 $\angle$s of a $\triangle$ are $\cong$ then the sides opp. those $\angle$s are $\cong$.)
4. $\triangle ABC$ is an equilateral triangle. (Def. of equilateral)

36. Given: $\triangle ABC$ is an equilateral triangle.

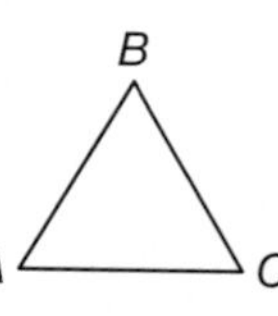

Prove: $m\angle A = m\angle B = m\angle C = 60$

Proof:

Statements (Reasons)

1. $\triangle ABC$ is an equilateral triangle. (Given)
2. $\overline{AB} \cong \overline{AC} \cong \overline{BC}$ (Def. of equilateral $\triangle$)
3. $\angle A \cong \angle B \cong \angle C$ (Isosceles $\triangle$ Thm.)
4. $m\angle A = m\angle B = m\angle C$ (Def. of $\cong$ $\angle$s)
5. $m\angle A + m\angle B + m\angle C = 180$ (Triangle Angle-Sum Thm.)
6. $3m\angle A = 180$ (Subst.)
7. $m\angle A = 60$ (Div. Prop.)
8. $m\angle A = m\angle B = m\angle C = 60$ (Subst.)

37. Given: $\triangle ABC$; $\angle A \cong \angle C$
Prove: $\overline{AB} \cong \overline{CB}$

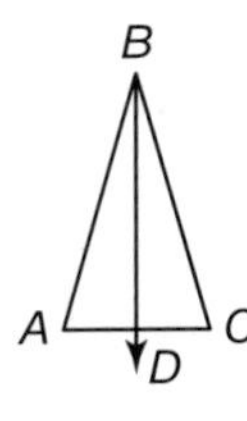

Proof:

Statements (Reasons)

1. Let $\overrightarrow{BD}$ bisect $\angle ABC$. (Protractor Post.)
2. $\angle ABD \cong \angle CBD$ (Def. of $\angle$ bisector)
3. $\angle A \cong \angle C$ (Given)
4. $\overline{BD} \cong \overline{BD}$ (Refl. Prop.)
5. $\triangle ABD \cong \triangle CBD$ (AAS)
6. $\overline{AB} \cong \overline{CB}$ (CPCTC)

45. Given: $\triangle WJZ$ is equilateral, and $\angle ZWP \cong \angle WJM \cong \angle JZL$.
Prove: $\overline{WP} \cong \overline{ZL} \cong \overline{JM}$

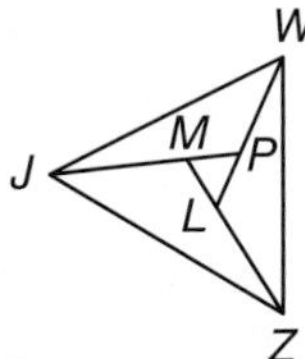

Proof:

We know that $\triangle WJZ$ is equilateral, since an equilateral $\triangle$ is equiangular, $\angle ZWJ \cong \angle WJZ \cong \angle JZW$. So, $m\angle ZWJ = m\angle WJZ = m\angle JZW$, by the definition of congruence. Since $\angle ZWP \cong \angle WJM \cong \angle JZL$, $m\angle ZWP = m\angle WJM = m\angle JZL$, by the definition of congruence. By the Angle Addition Postulate, $m\angle ZWJ = m\angle ZWP + m\angle PWJ$, $m\angle WJZ = m\angle WJM + m\angle MJZ$, $m\angle JZW = m\angle JZL + m\angle LZW$. By substitution, $m\angle ZWP + m\angle PWJ = m\angle WJM + m\angle MJZ = m\angle JZL + m\angle LZW$.

Again by substitution, $m\angle ZWP + m\angle PWJ = m\angle ZWP + m\angle PJZ = m\angle ZWP + m\angle LZW$. By the Subtraction Property, $m\angle PWJ = m\angle PJZ = m\angle LZW$. By the definition of congruence, $\angle PWJ \cong \angle PJZ \cong \angle LZW$. So, by ASA, $\triangle WZL \cong \triangle ZJM \cong \triangle JWP$. By CPCTC, $\overline{WP} \cong \overline{ZL} \cong \overline{JM}$.

Lesson 4-7

17.

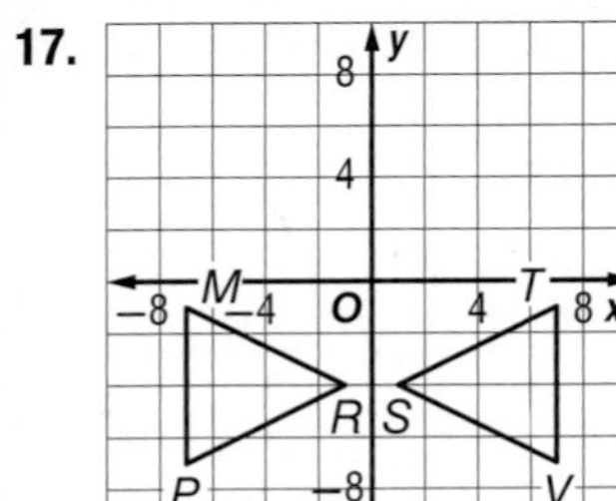

$\triangle TVS$ is a reflection of $\triangle MPR$. $MP = 6$, $PR = \sqrt{45}$, $MR = \sqrt{45}$, $ST = \sqrt{45}$, $TV = 6$, $SV = \sqrt{45}$. $\triangle MPR \cong \triangle TVS$ by SSS.

18.

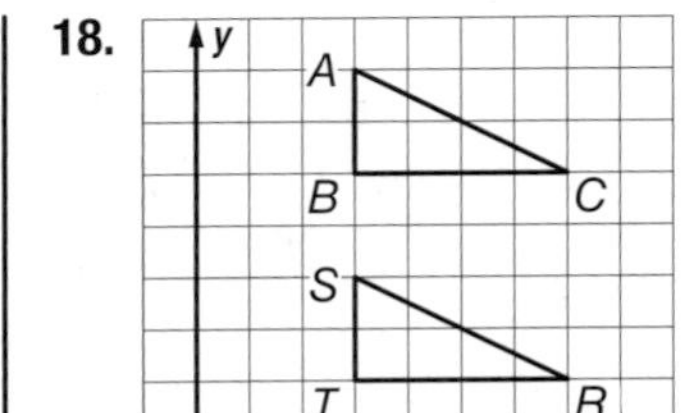

$\triangle ABC$ is a translation of $\triangle STR$. $AB = 2$, $BC = 4$, $AC = \sqrt{20}$, $ST = 2$, $TR = 4$, $SR = \sqrt{20}$. $\triangle ABC \cong \triangle STR$ by SSS.

19.

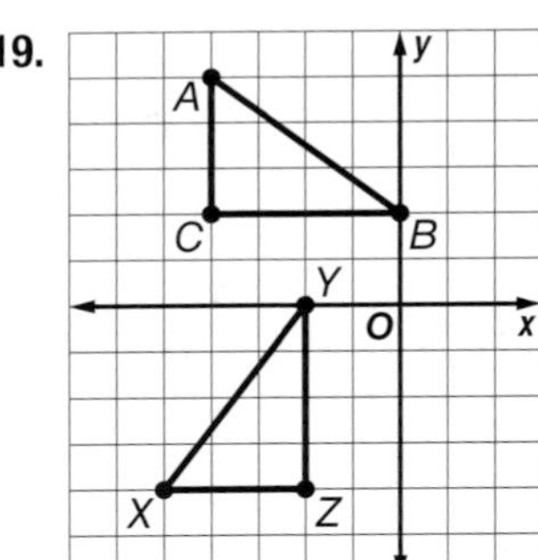

$\triangle XYZ$ is a rotation of $\triangle ABC$. $AB = 5$, $BC = 4$, $AC = 3$, $XY = 5$, $YZ = 4$, $XZ = 3$. Since $AB = XY$, $BC = YZ$, and $AC = XZ$, $\overline{AB} \cong \overline{XY}$, $\overline{BC} \cong \overline{YZ}$, and $\overline{AC} \cong \overline{XZ}$, $\triangle ABC \cong \triangle XYZ$ by SSS.

20.

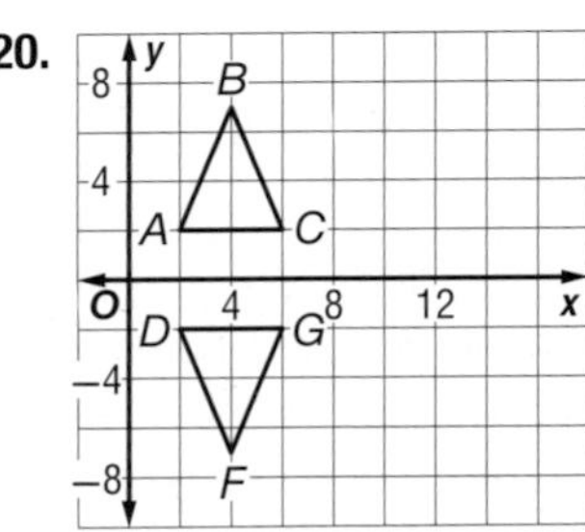

$\triangle ABC$ is a reflection of $\triangle DFG$. $AB = \sqrt{29}$, $AC = 4$, $BC = \sqrt{29}$, $DG = 4$, $FG = \sqrt{29}$, $DF = \sqrt{29}$. $\triangle ABC \cong \triangle DFG$ by SSS.

Lesson 4-8 (Guided Practice)

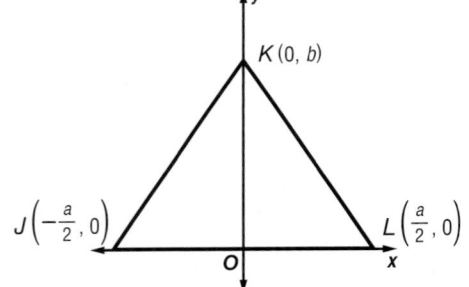

1.

y

$K(0, b)$

$J\left(-\frac{a}{2}, 0\right)$ $L\left(\frac{a}{2}, 0\right)$

O x

3. Given: $\triangle ABX$ and $\triangle CDX$

Prove: $\triangle ABX \cong \triangle CDX$

Proof:

The midpoint of $\overline{AC}$ is $\left(\frac{0+a+x}{2}, \frac{0+b}{2}\right)$ or $\left(\frac{a+x}{2}, \frac{b}{2}\right)$, and the midpoint of $\overline{BD}$ is $\left(\frac{0+x+a}{2}, \frac{b+0}{2}\right)$ or $\left(\frac{a+x}{2}, \frac{b}{2}\right)$.

Because X is located at $\left(\frac{a+x}{2}, \frac{b}{2}\right)$, it is the midpoint of $\overline{AC}$ and $\overline{BD}$. By the definition of a segment bisector, $\overline{AC}$ bisects $\overline{BD}$ and $\overline{BD}$ bisects $\overline{AC}$. Therefore, $\overline{BX} \cong \overline{XD}$ and $\overline{AX} \cong \overline{XC}$.

From the Midpoint Formula,

$CD = \sqrt{[(a+x)-a]^2 + (b-0)^2}$ or $\sqrt{x^2+b^2}$, and

$AB = \sqrt{[(0+x)-0]^2 + (b-0)^2}$ or $\sqrt{x^2+b^2}$.

Therefore, $\overline{CD} \cong \overline{AB}$ by the def. of $\cong$, and $\triangle ABX \cong \triangle CDX$ by SSS.

Lesson 4-8 (Differentiated Instruction)

Proof: Let $x_2 = x_1 + 2t$ and $y_2 = y_1 + 2u$ for some real numbers t and u. Then $B(x_2, y_2) = B(x_1 + 2t, y_1 + 2u)$ and

$M\left(\frac{x_1+x_2}{2}, \frac{y_1+y_2}{2}\right) = M\left(\frac{x_1+(x_1+2t)}{2}, \frac{y_1+(y_1+2u)}{2}\right)$ or

$M(x_1 + t, y_1 + u)$. The slope of $\overline{AB}$ is $\frac{y_1-(y_1+2u)}{x_1-(x_1+2t)}$ or $\frac{u}{t}$ and slope of $\overline{AM}$ is $\frac{y_1-(y_1+u)}{x_1-(x_1+t)}$ or $\frac{u}{t}$. Since these slopes are equal, point M lies on $\overline{AB}$. Using the Distance Formula,

$AM = \sqrt{(x_1-(x_1+t))^2 + (y_1-(y_1+u))^2}$ or $\sqrt{t^2+u^2}$ and

$MB = \sqrt{((x_1+t)-(x_1+2t))^2 + ((y_1+u)-(y_1+2u))^2}$ or

$\sqrt{t^2+u^2}$. Since $AM = MB$, $M\left(\frac{x_1+x_2}{2}, \frac{y_1+y_2}{2}\right)$ is the midpoint of $\overline{AB}$.

Lesson 4-8

1\.

y
C (0, 2a)
B (2b, 0)
O A (0, 0)
x

2\.

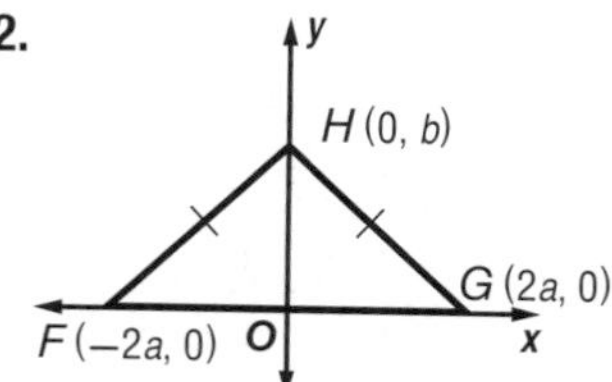

6. Given: $\triangle ABC$

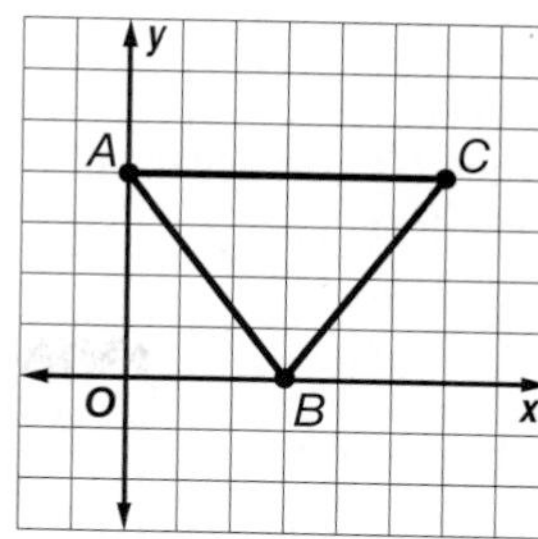

Prove: $\triangle ABC$ is isosceles.

Proof: Use the Distance Formula to find AB and BC.

$AB = \sqrt{(4-0)^2 + (0-3)^2}$ or $\sqrt{25}$ or 5

$BC = \sqrt{(4-0)^2 + (6-3)^2}$ or $\sqrt{25}$ or 5

Since $AB = BC$, $\overline{AB} \cong \overline{BC}$. Since the legs are congruent, $\triangle ABC$ is isosceles.

7\.

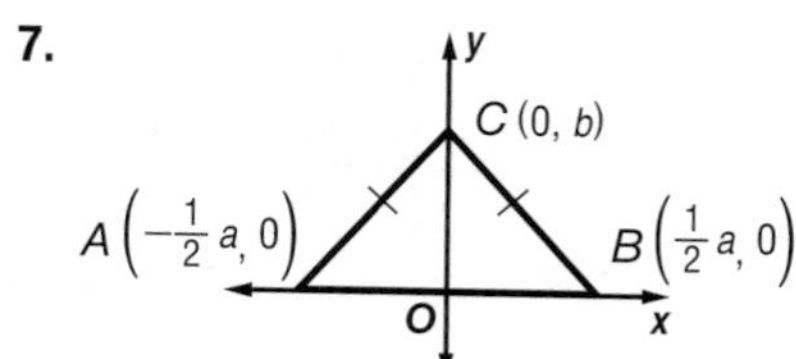

8\.

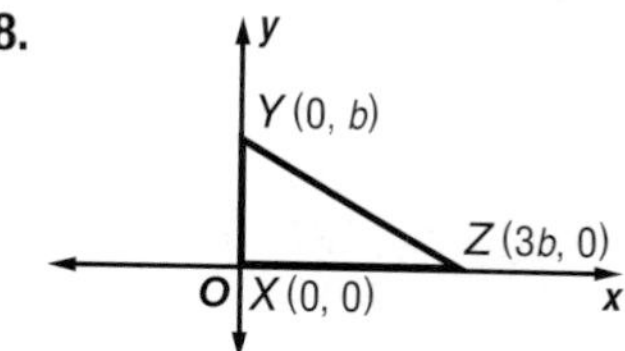

9\.

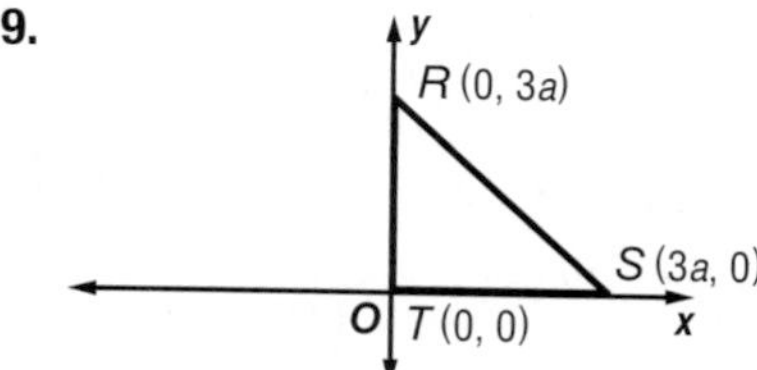

10\.

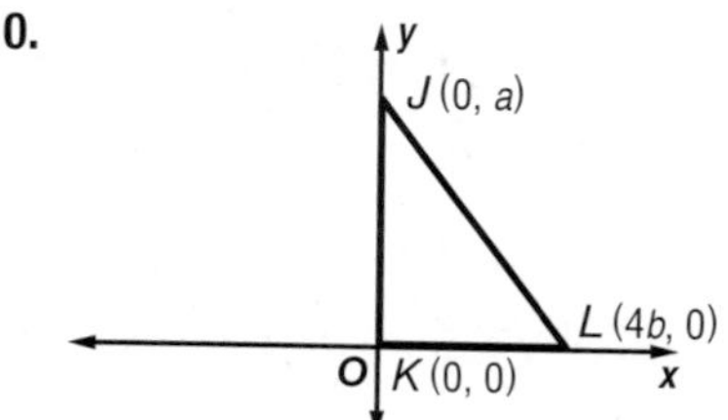

11\.

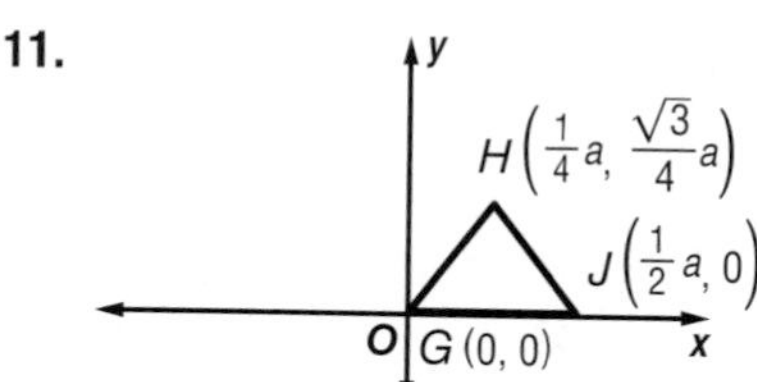

12\.

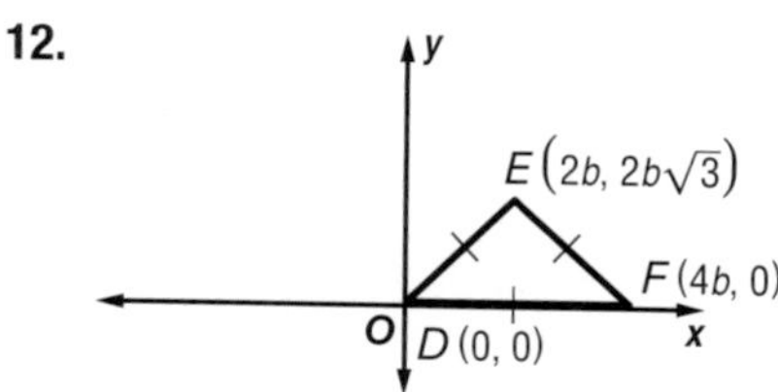

Chapter 4 Answer Appendix

19. Given: Isosceles $\triangle ABC$ with $\overline{AC} \cong \overline{BC}$; R and S are midpoints of legs $\overline{AC}$ and $\overline{BC}$.

Prove: $\overline{AS} \cong \overline{BR}$

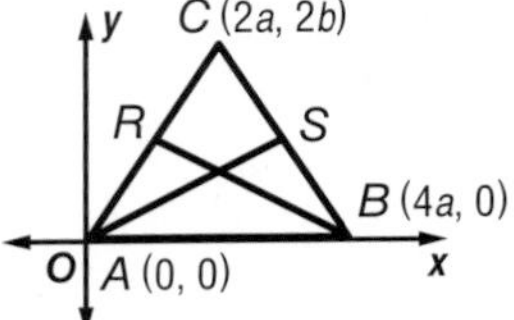

Proof:

The coordinates of S are $\left(\frac{2a+4a}{2}, \frac{2b+0}{2}\right)$ or $(3a, b)$.

The coordinates of R are $\left(\frac{2a+0}{2}, \frac{2b+0}{2}\right)$ or (a, b).

$AS = \sqrt{(3a-0)^2 + (b-0)^2}$ or $\sqrt{9a^2 + b^2}$

$BR = \sqrt{(4a-a)^2 + (0-b)^2}$ or $\sqrt{9a^2 + b^2}$

Since $AS = BR$, $\overline{AS} \cong \overline{BR}$.

20. Given: Isosceles triangle ABC; $\overline{BC} \cong \overline{AC}$; R, S, and T are midpoints of their respective sides.

Prove: $\triangle RST$ is isosceles.

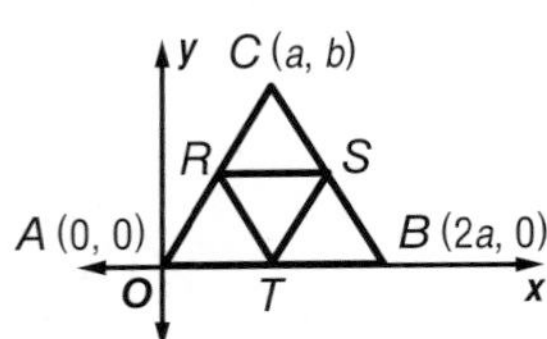

Proof:

Midpoint R is $\left(\frac{a+0}{2}, \frac{b+0}{2}\right)$ or $\left(\frac{a}{2}, \frac{b}{2}\right)$.

Midpoint S is $\left(\frac{a+2a}{2}, \frac{b+0}{2}\right)$ or $\left(\frac{3a}{2}, \frac{b}{2}\right)$.

Midpoint T is $\left(\frac{2a+0}{2}, \frac{0+0}{2}\right)$ or $(a, 0)$.

$RT = \sqrt{\left(\frac{a}{2} - a\right)^2 + \left(\frac{b}{2} - 0\right)^2}$ or $\sqrt{\left(\frac{a}{2}\right)^2 + \left(\frac{b}{2}\right)^2}$

$ST = \sqrt{\left(\frac{3a}{2} - a\right)^2 + \left(\frac{b}{2} - 0\right)^2}$ or $\sqrt{\left(\frac{a}{2}\right)^2 + \left(\frac{b}{2}\right)^2}$

$RT = ST$ and $\overline{RT} \cong \overline{ST}$ and $\triangle RST$ is isosceles.

21. Given: Right $\triangle ABC$ with right $\angle BAC$; P is the midpoint of $\overline{BC}$.

Prove: $AP = \frac{1}{2}BC$

Proof:

Midpoint P is $\left(\frac{0+2c}{2}, \frac{2b+0}{2}\right)$ or (c, b).

$AP = \sqrt{(c-0)^2 + (b-0)^2}$ or $\sqrt{c^2 + b^2}$

$BC = \sqrt{(2c-0)^2 + (0-2b)^2} = \sqrt{4c^2 + 4b^2}$ or $2\sqrt{c^2 + b^2}$

$\frac{1}{2}BC = \sqrt{c^2 + b^2}$

So, $AP = \frac{1}{2}BC$.

22. Given: $\triangle ABC$

S is the midpoint of $\overline{AC}$.

T is the midpoint of $\overline{BC}$.

Prove: $ST = \frac{1}{2}AB$

Proof:

The coordinates of S are $\left(\frac{b}{2}, \frac{c}{2}\right)$ and the coordinates of T are $\left(\frac{a+b}{2}, \frac{c}{2}\right)$

$ST = \sqrt{\left(\frac{a+b}{2} - \frac{b}{2}\right)^2 + \left(\frac{c}{2} - \frac{c}{2}\right)^2}$ or $\frac{a}{2}$

$AB = \sqrt{(a-0)^2 + (0-0)^2}$ or a

$ST = \frac{1}{2}AB$

23. The distance between Raleigh and Durham is about 0.32 units, between Raleigh and Chapel Hill is about 0.41 units, and between Durham and Chapel Hill is about 0.15 units. Since none of these distances are the same, the Research Triangle is scalene.

24. $FS = \sqrt{(5-0)^2 + (12-0)^2}$ or 13

$FT = \sqrt{(13-0)^2 + (0-0)^2}$ or 13

Since the distance between the first house at (0, 0) and the third house at (13, 0) is the same as the distance between the first house at (0, 0) and the second house at (5, 12), the triangle formed by the three homes is isosceles.

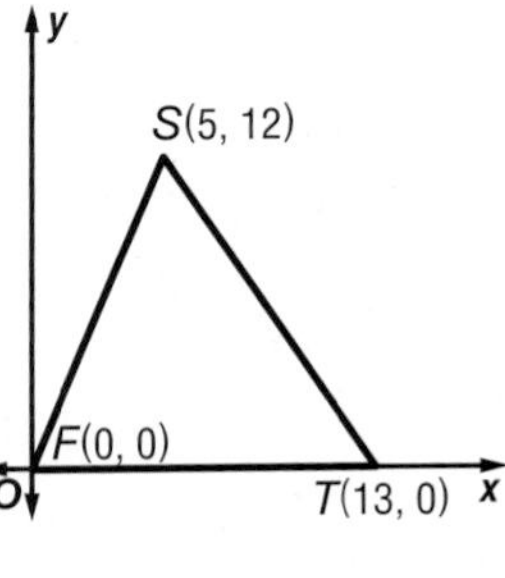

27. The slope between the tents is $-\frac{4}{3}$. The slope between the ranger's station and the tent located at (12, 9) is $\frac{3}{4}$. Since $-\frac{4}{3} \cdot \frac{3}{4} = -1$, the triangle formed by the tents and ranger's station is a right triangle.

28. Given: vertices $A(0, 0)$, $B(a, b)$, and $C(2a, 0)$

Prove: $\triangle ABC$ is isosceles.

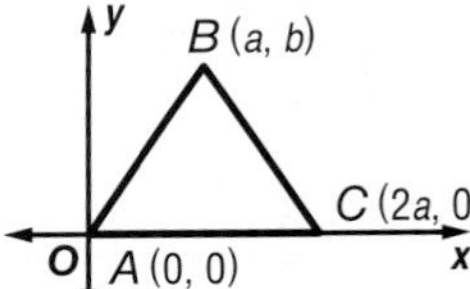

Proof:

$AB = \sqrt{(a-0)^2 + (b-0)^2}$ or $\sqrt{a^2 + b^2}$

$BC = \sqrt{(2a-a)^2 + (0-b)^2}$ or $\sqrt{a^2 + b^2}$

Since, $AB = BC$, $\overline{AB} \cong \overline{BC}$. So, $\triangle ABC$ is isosceles.

34. Sample answer:

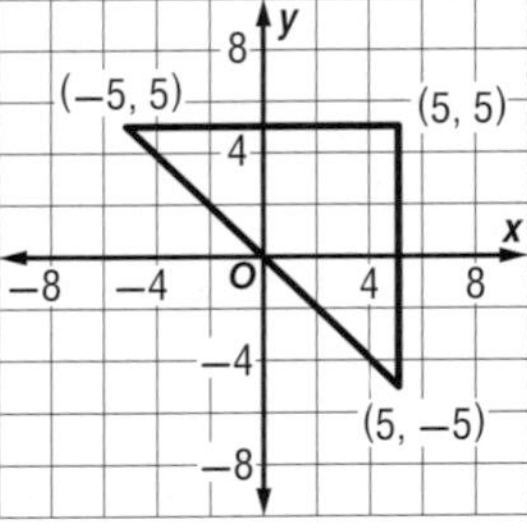

35. Given: $\triangle ABC$ with coordinates $A(0, 0)$, $B(a, b)$, and $C(c, d)$ and $\triangle DEF$ with coordinates $D(0 + n, 0 + m)$, $E(a + n, b + m)$, and $F(c + n, d + m)$

Prove: $\triangle DEF \cong \triangle ABC$

Proof:

$AB = \sqrt{(a - 0)^2 + (b - 0)^2}$ or $\sqrt{a^2 + b^2}$

$DE = \sqrt{[a + n - (0 + n)]^2 + [b + m - (0 + m)]^2}$ or $\sqrt{a^2 + b^2}$

Since $AB = DE$, $\overline{AB} \cong \overline{DE}$.

$BC = \sqrt{(c - a)^2 + (d - b)^2}$ or $\sqrt{c^2 - 2ac + a^2 + d^2 - 2bd + b^2}$

$EF = \sqrt{[c + n - (a + n)]^2 + [d + m - (b + m)]^2}$ or $\sqrt{c^2 - 2ac + a^2 + d^2 - 2bd + b^2}$

Since $BC = EF$, $\overline{BC} \cong \overline{EF}$.

$CA = \sqrt{(c - 0)^2 + (d - 0)^2}$ or $\sqrt{c^2 + d^2}$

$FD = \sqrt{[0 + n - (c + n)]^2 + [0 + m - (d + m)]^2}$ or $\sqrt{c^2 + d^2}$

Since $CA = FD$, $\overline{CA} \cong \overline{FD}$.

Therefore, $\triangle DEF \cong \triangle ABC$ by the SSS Postulate.

Practice Test

10. Proof:

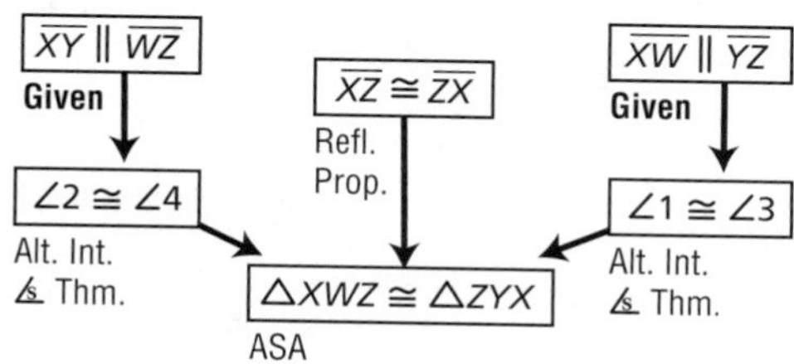

20. Sample Answer:

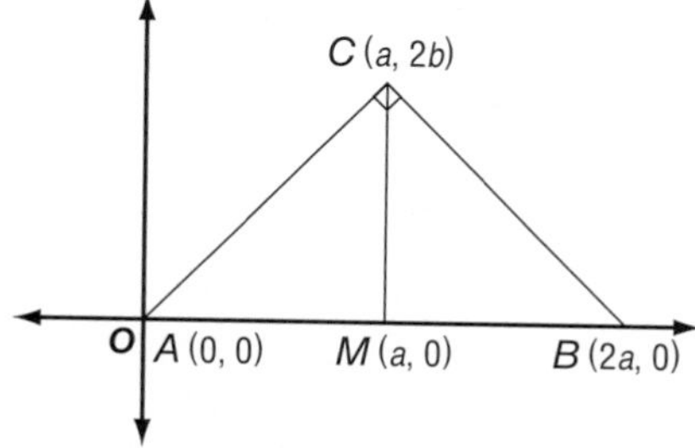

The midpoint of $\overline{AB}$ is $(a, 0)$. The slope of $\overline{CM}$ is undefined, so $\overline{CM}$ is a vertical line. The slope of $\overline{AB}$ is 0, so it is horizontal. Therefore, $\overline{AB} \perp \overline{CM}$.

Chapter Planner

Diagnostic Assessment
Quick Check

	EXPLORE 5-1 (45 min: 0.5 day; 90 min: 0.25 day)	LESSON 5-1 (45 min: 1 day; 90 min: 0.5 day)	EXPLORE 5-2 (45 min: 0.5 day; 90 min: 0.25 day)
Title	**Geometry Lab: Constructing Bisectors**	**Bisectors of Triangles**	**Geometry Lab: Constructing Medians and Altitudes**
Objectives	■ Construct perpendicular bisectors and angle bisectors of triangles.	■ Identify and use perpendicular bisectors in triangles. ■ Identify and use angle bisectors in triangles.	■ Construct medians and altitudes of triangles.
Key Vocabulary		perpendicular bisector point of concurrency circumcenter, incenter	
CCSS	G.CO.12	G.CO.10, G.MG.3	G.CO.12
Multiple Representations			
Lesson Resources	connectED.mcgraw-hill.com Animations Virtual Manipulatives ■ *Teaching Geometry with Manipulatives*	connectED.mcgraw-hill.com Leveled Worksheets Vocabulary Personal Tutor Self-Check Quiz ■ *5-Minute Check* ■ *Study Notebook* ■ *Teaching Geometry with Manipulatives*	connectED.mcgraw-hill.com Animations Virtual Manipulatives ■ *Teaching Geometry with Manipulatives* **Materials:** ■ straightedge ■ string ■ thumbtack
Resources for Every Lesson	IWB eStudent Edition IWB Interactive Classroom	■ eTeacher Edition ■ eSolutions Manual ■ eAssessment	
Differentiated Instruction		pp. 325, 333	

IWB All digital assets are Interactive Whiteboard ready.

Suggested Pacing			
Time Periods	Instruction	Review & Assess	Total
45-minute	10 days	2 days	12 days
90-minute	5 days	1 day	6 days

LESSON 5-2 (45 min: 1.5 days; 90 min: 0.75 day)	LESSON 5-3 (45 min: 1 day; 90 min: 0.5 day)	EXPLORE 5-4 (45 min: 0.5 day; 90 min: 0.25 day)	LESSON 5-4 (45 min: 1 day; 90 min: 0.5 day)
Medians and Altitudes of Triangles	**Inequalities in One Triangle**	**Geometry Lab: Matrix Logic**	**Indirect Proof**
▪ Identify and use medians in triangles. ▪ Identify and use altitudes in triangles.	▪ Recognize and apply properties of inequalities to the measures of the angles of a triangle. ▪ Recognize and apply properties of inequalities to the relationships between the angles and the sides of a triangle.	▪ Use matrix logic.	▪ Write indirect algebraic proofs. ▪ Write indirect geometric proofs.
median, centroid altitude, orthocenter		matrix logic	indirect reasoning indirect proof proof by contradiction
G.CO.10, G.MG.3	G.CO.10		G.CO.10
connectED.mcgraw-hill.com Leveled Worksheets Quiz 1 Vocabulary Personal Tutor Virtual Manipulatives Self-Check Quiz ▪ *5-Minute Check* ▪ *Study Notebook* ▪ *Teaching Geometry with Manipulatives*	connectED.mcgraw-hill.com Leveled Worksheets Quiz 2 Personal Tutor Self-Check Quiz ▪ *5-Minute Check* ▪ *Study Notebook*	connectED.mcgraw-hill.com Vocabulary Animations **Materials:** ▪ grid paper	connectED.mcgraw-hill.com Leveled Worksheets Vocabulary Animations Personal Tutor Self-Check Quiz ▪ *5-Minute Check* ▪ *Study Notebook*
IWB eStudent Edition IWB Interactive Classroom	▪ eTeacher Edition ▪ eSolutions Manual ▪ eAssessment		
p. 338	pp. 346, 347		pp. 357, 361

Formative Assessment
Mid-Chapter Quiz

Chapter Planner

	EXPLORE 5-5 (45 min: 0.5 day; 90 min: 0.25 day)	LESSON 5-5 (45 min: 1.5 days; 90 min: 0.75 day)	LESSON 5-6 (45 min: 2 days; 90 min: 1 day)
Title	**Graphing Technology Lab: The Triangle Inequality**	**The Triangle Inequality**	**Inequalities in Two Triangles**
Objectives	■ Use technology to investigate triangle inequalities.	■ Use the Triangle Inequality Theorem to identify possible triangles. ■ Prove triangle relationships using the Triangle Inequality Theorem.	■ Apply the Hinge Theorem or its converse to make comparisons in two triangles. ■ Prove triangle relationships using the Hinge Theorem or its converse.
Key Vocabulary			
CCSS	G.CO.12	G.CO.10, G.MG.3	G.CO.10
Multiple Representations			
Lesson Resources	connectED.mcgraw-hill.com Personal Tutor **Materials:** ■ TI-83/84 Plus or other graphing calculator	connectED.mcgraw-hill.com Leveled Worksheets Quiz 3 Personal Tutor Self-Check Quiz ■ *5-Minute Check* ■ *Study Notebook* ■ *Teaching Geometry with Manipulatives*	connectED.mcgraw-hill.com Leveled Worksheets Quiz 4 Personal Tutor Self-Check Quiz ■ *5-Minute Check* ■ *Study Notebook*
Resources for Every Lesson	IWB eStudent Edition IWB Interactive Classroom	■ eTeacher Edition ■ eSolutions Manual ■ eAssessment	
Differentiated Instruction		pp. 365, 366	pp. 372, 378

Summative Assessment
Study Guide and Review
Practice Test

What the Research Says...

Lampert and Cobb (2003) found evidence that talking about mathematics can give rise to opportunities for students to learn by reflecting on and objectifying prior activity.

- Have students work cooperatively when completing Explore Lessons 5-1, and 5-4 and the Geometry Labs within the lessons. This leads to discussions, debate, and shared ideas about the concepts being taught.
- Arrange students in small groups of mixed abilities to complete the included differentiated instructional activities for Chapter 5. Have students confer when analyzing the results and completing the activities. Allow them an opportunity to reflect and summarize at the end of the activity.

Teacher to Teacher

Douglas E. Hall
Chaparral High School
Las Vegas, NV

Use With All Lessons

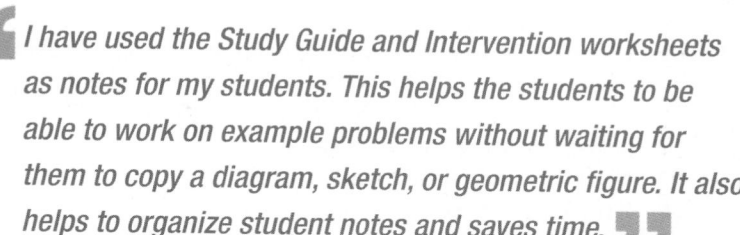

"I have used the Study Guide and Intervention worksheets as notes for my students. This helps the students to be able to work on example problems without waiting for them to copy a diagram, sketch, or geometric figure. It also helps to organize student notes and saves time."

STUDY SKILL

A vocabulary map can help students understand the meaning of a newly introduced term. The sample vocabulary map at the right describes point concurrency. Let students work in cooperative groups or pairs to develop maps for other terms and concepts.

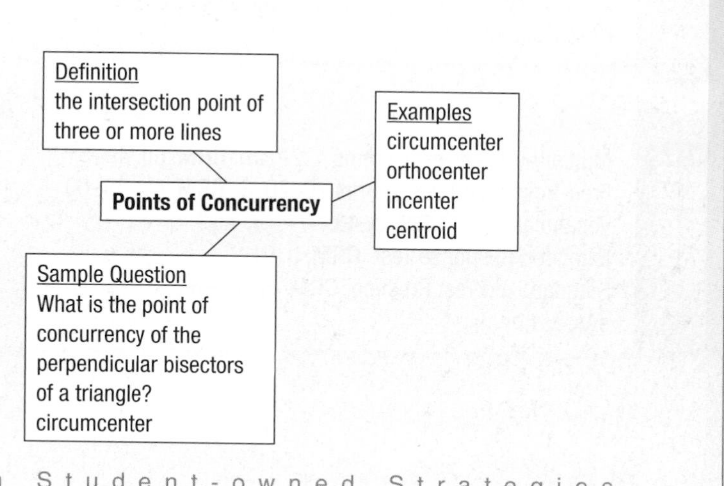

Definition
the intersection point of three or more lines
Points of Concurrency
Examples
circumcenter
orthocenter
incenter
centroid
Sample Question
What is the point of concurrency of the perpendicular bisectors of a triangle?
circumcenter

Creating Independence through Student-owned Strategies

CHAPTER 5

Relationships in Triangles

Assessment and Intervention

SE = Student Edition, TE = Teacher Edition, CRM = Chapter Resource Masters

	Diagnosis	Prescription
DIAGNOSTIC ASSESSMENT	**Beginning Chapter 5**	
	Get Ready for Chapter 5 **SE**	Response to Intervention **TE**
	Beginning Every Lesson	
	Then, Now, Why? **SE** 5-Minute Checks	Chapter 0 **SE**
FORMATIVE ASSESSMENT	**During/After Every Lesson**	
	Guided Practice **SE**, every example Check Your Understanding **SE** H.O.T. Problems **SE** Spiral Review **SE** Additional Examples **TE** Watch Out! **TE** Step 4, Assess **TE** Chapter 5 Quizzes **CRM**, pp. 45–46 Self-Check Quizzes connectED.mcgraw-hill.com	TIER 1 Intervention Skills Practice **CRM**, Ch. 1–5 connectED.mcgraw-hill.com TIER 2 Intervention Differentiated Instruction **TE**; Differentiated Homework Options **TE**; Study Guide and Intervention **CRM**, Ch. 1–5 TIER 3 Intervention *Math Triumphs, Geo.,* Ch. 3 and 4
	Mid-Chapter	
	Mid-Chapter Quiz **SE** Mid-Chapter Test **CRM**, p. 47 eAssessment	TIER 1 Intervention Skills Practice **CRM**, Ch. 1–5 connectED.mcgraw-hill.com TIER 2 Intervention Study Guide and Intervention **CRM**, Ch. 1–5 TIER 3 Intervention *Math Triumphs, Geo.,* Ch. 3 and 4
	Before Chapter Test	
	Chapter Study Guide and Review **SE** Practice Test **SE** Standardized Test Practice **SE** Chapter Test connectED.mcgraw-hill.com Standardized Test Practice connectED.mcgraw-hill.com Vocabulary Review connectED.mcgraw-hill.com eAssessment	TIER 1 Intervention Skills Practice **CRM**, Ch. 1–5 connectED.mcgraw-hill.com TIER 2 Intervention Study Guide and Intervention **CRM**, Ch. 1–5 TIER 3 Intervention *Math Triumphs, Geo.,* Ch. 3 and 4
SUMMATIVE ASSESSMENT	**After Chapter 5**	
	Multiple-Choice Tests, Forms 1, 2A, 2B **CRM**, pp. 49–54 Free-Response Tests, Forms 2C, 2D, 3 **CRM**, pp. 55–60 Vocabulary Test **CRM**, p. 48 Extended Response Test **CRM**, p. 61 Standardized Test Practice **CRM**, pp. 62–64 eAssessment	Study Guide and Intervention **CRM**, Ch. 1–5 connectED.mcgraw-hill.com

Differentiated Instruction

Option 1 Reaching All Learners

Visual Set up a cork board in front of the class with pushpins to use as vertices of triangles and varied lengths of colored yarn to use as the sides, bisectors, medians, and altitudes of triangles. Students can take turns using the pushpins and yarn to model different types of triangles and to place angle bisectors, segment bisectors, medians, and altitudes of triangles.

Interpersonal Have students work in small groups to research the origins of geometry, including the work of Euclid. Have them investigate the way constructions in triangles were first developed. For example, ancient Greeks could not compute midpoint because their number system did not have integers or rational numbers. It was made up of only whole numbers. Therefore, the Greeks could not measure an arbitrary line and divide it by 2 to find the midpoint. This problem led to the use of a compass and a straight edge. Have students work together to create a visual display of their learning to share with other groups.

Kinesthetic Many students enter geometry under the assumption that any three sides can be put together to make a triangle and the idea of the Triangle Inequality Theorem contradicts this assumption. Students can use different length segments (cut in various lengths using straws, for example) and experiment to find out which lengths can be used to make triangles and which cannot. See if students can develop a "rule" to determine whether or not three side lengths can be used to make a triangle prior to introducing the Triangle Inequality.

Option 2 Approaching Level AL

Have students work in small mixed-ability groups to prove triangle relationships with inequalities. Draw several sets of triangles on the board along with possible relationships between angles and sides of the triangles. Have students decide whether the inequality statements are true, and have them write out an explanation of their reasoning.

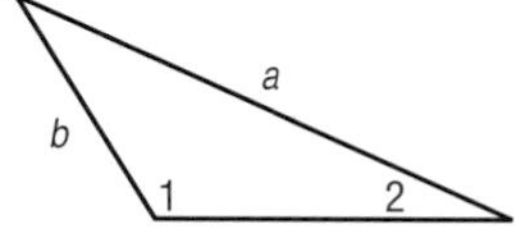

Option 3 English Learners ELL

Organize students in groups. Have group members search through the chapter and create a dictionary of prefixes to help them as they proceed through the geometry lessons. For example, the prefix *circum* means *about* or *around*. The word *circumcenter* refers to the center of a circle around a triangle that contains the vertices of the triangle.

Option 4 Beyond Level BL

Have students investigate careers in which a strong background in geometry is necessary. Architects need to be able to evaluate layouts and see them spatially, using geometric formulas to ensure that structures are sound and visually pleasing. Interior designers use triangulation to place artwork and other accessories in a room, making the ordinary beautiful. Students can choose to interview someone in their chosen field, read about the job, or survey examples of the work of someone currently in the field. They should present what they have learned as a poster or in a report and share it with the class, demonstrating a real-life application of triangle relationships and other geometric concepts.

Focus on Mathematical Content

VerticalAlignment

Before Chapter 5

Related Topics from Grade 8

- Determine linear relationships.
- Graph on a coordinate plane.

Previous Topics from Algebra 1

- Represent relationships using tables and graphs.
- Solve linear equations.

Chapter 5

Related Topics from Geometry

- Use slope and equations of lines to investigate geometric relationships, including special segments of triangles.
- Recognize and know historical development of geometric systems and know that mathematics was developed for a variety of purposes.
- Analyze geometric relationships in order to verify conjectures.

After Chapter 5

Preparation for Precalculus

- Solve problems from physical situations using trigonometry, including the use of Law of Sines, Law of Cosines, and area formulas.

Lesson-by-Lesson Preview

5-1 Bisectors of Triangles

A *perpendicular bisector* of a side of a triangle is a line, a segment, or a ray that passes through the midpoint of the side and is perpendicular to the side. Perpendicular bisectors have special properties. Any point on the perpendicular bisector of a segment is equidistant from the endpoints of the segment. The converse of this statement is also true. The point of concurrency of the perpendicular bisectors of a triangle is called the circumcenter. The *circumcenter* of a triangle is equidistant from the vertices of the triangle.

Angle bisectors also have special properties. Any point on the angle bisector is equidistant from the sides of the angle, and any point in the interior of an angle that is equidistant from the sides of the angle lies on the angle bisector. The intersection of the angle bisectors of a triangle is called the *incenter*. The incenter of a triangle is equidistant from the sides of the triangle.

5-2 Medians and Altitudes of Triangles

A *median* is a line segment with endpoints that are a vertex of a triangle and the midpoint of the side opposite the vertex. The point of concurrency for the medians of a triangle is called a *centroid*. The centroid of a triangle is located on a median at a point two-thirds of the distance from a vertex to the midpoint of the side opposite the vertex.

An *altitude* of a triangle is a segment perpendicular to a side of the triangle that has a vertex as one endpoint and a point on the line containing the side opposite the vertex as the other endpoint. The intersection of the altitudes of a triangle is called the *orthocenter*.

Name	Type	Point of Concurrency
perpendicular bisector	line, segment, or ray	circumcenter
angle bisector	line, segment, or ray	incenter
median	segment	centroid
altitude	segment	orthocenter

5-3 Inequalities in One Triangle

In algebra, students learned the concept of inequality: For any real numbers a and b, $a > b$ if and only if there is a positive number c such that $a = b + c$. Students also studied several properties of inequalities for real numbers. In this lesson students apply these concepts to angles.

The Exterior Angle Inequality Theorem states that if an angle is an exterior angle of a triangle, then its measure is greater than the measure of either of its corresponding remote interior angles. Another inequality theorem in geometry is based on the relationship between a side and the vertex opposite that side. If one side of a triangle is longer than another side, then the angle opposite the longer side has a greater measure than the angle opposite the shorter side. The converse is also true: if one angle of a triangle has a greater measure than another angle, then the side opposite the greater angle is longer than the side opposite the lesser angle.

5-4 Indirect Proof

Indirect proof, or *proof by contradiction*, is a method of proving that a statement is true by first assuming that it is false. The next steps of the indirect proof show that this assumption leads to a contradiction of the hypothesis or some other established fact, such as a definition, postulate, theorem, or corollary. Finally, the assumption is rejected because it leads to a contradiction, therefore, the original statement is accepted as true. Indirect proof can be used in both algebra and geometry.

5-5 The Triangle Inequality

The Triangle Inequality Theorem states that the sum of the lengths of any two sides of a triangle is greater than the length of the third side. This theorem can be used to determine whether three segments with given lengths form a triangle.

The perpendicular segment from a point to a line is the shortest segment from that point to the line. This theorem can be proved using the Exterior Angle Inequality Theorem and leads to a corollary that the perpendicular segment from a point to a plane is the shortest segment from the point to the plane.

5-6 Inequalities in Two Triangles

This lesson extends Theorem 5.11 to two triangles. That theorem states that if two sides of a triangle are congruent to two sides of another triangle and the included angle in one triangle has a greater measure than the included angle in the other triangle, then the third side of the first triangle is longer than the third side of the second triangle. This is called the Hinge Theorem. The converse of the Hinge Theorem is also true. If two sides of a triangle are congruent to two sides of another triangle and the third side in one triangle is longer than the third side in the other, then the angle between the pair of congruent sides in the first triangle is greater than the corresponding angle in the second triangle.

Mc Graw Hill Professional Development

Targeted professional development has been articulated throughout Geometry. More quality, customized professional development is available from McGraw-Hill Professional Development. Visit connectED.mcgraw-hill.com for details on each product.

- Online Lessons emphasize the strategies and techniques used to teach Geometry. Includes streaming video, interactive pages, and online tools.
- Video Workshops allow mentors, coaches, or leadership personnel to facilitate on-site workshops on educational strategies in mathematics and mathematical concepts.
- MHPD Online (www.mhpdonline.com) offers online professional development with video clips of instructional strategies, links, student activities, and news and issues in education.
- Teaching Today (teachingtoday.glencoe.com) gives secondary teachers practical strategies and materials that inspire excellence and innovation in teaching.

Chapter Project

Architecture: Triangular Design

Students use what they have learned about special segments of triangles to complete a project.

This chapter project addresses global awareness, as well as several specific skills identified as being essential to student success by the Framework for 21st Century Learning.

Visit connectED.mcgraw-hill.com for student and teacher handouts.

KeyVocabulary Introduce the key vocabulary in the chapter using the method below.

Define: The circumcenter of a triangle is the point of concurrency of the perpendicular bisectors.

Example:

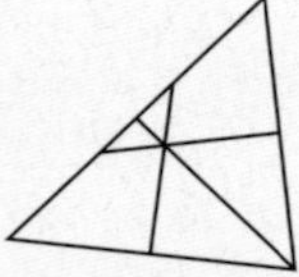

Ask: Will the circumcenter always lie in the interior of a triangle? No. If the triangle is obtuse, the circumcenter will lie outside the triangle. If the triangle is right, the circumcenter will lie on a side of the triangle.

CHAPTER 5 Relationships in Triangles

Then

You learned how to classify triangles.

Now

In this chapter, you will:

- Learn about special segments and points related to triangles.
- Learn about relationships between the sides and angles of triangles.
- Learn to write indirect proofs.

Why?

INTERIOR DESIGN Triangle relationships are used to find and compare angle measures and distances. Interior designers use the relationships in triangles to maximize efficiency and create balance in their designs.

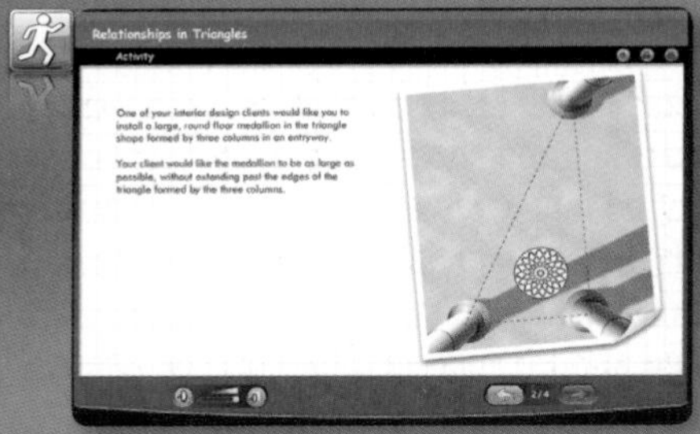

connectED.mcgraw-hill.com **Your Digital Math Portal**

Animation | Vocabulary | eGlossary | Personal Tutor | Virtual Manipulatives | Graphing Calculator | Audio | Foldables | Self-Check Practice | Worksheets

Additional Answers (Get Ready p. 321)

4. $\angle 3$ and $\angle 4$ are supplementary.

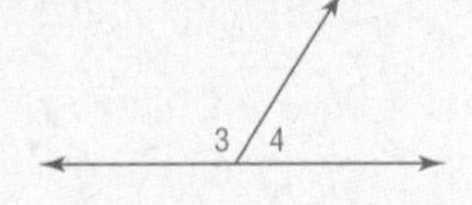

5. $JK = KL = LM = MJ$

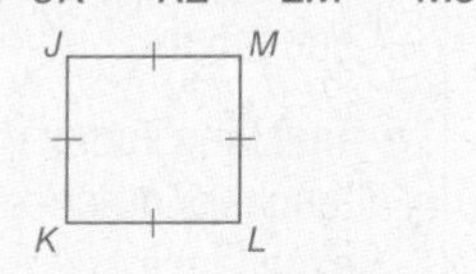

6. $\angle ABD \cong \angle DBC$

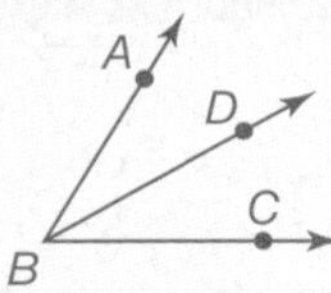

7. Sometimes; the conjecture is true when E is between D and F, otherwise it is false.

Get Ready for the Chapter

Diagnose Readiness | You have two options for checking prerequisite skills.

1 Textbook Option Take the Quick Check below. Refer to the Quick Review for help.

QuickCheck

Find each measure.

1. BC 9

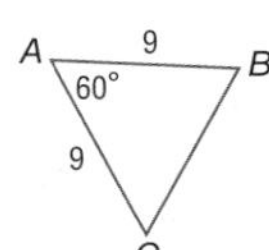

2. $m\angle RST$ 55

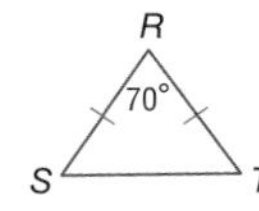

3. **GARDENS** Bronson is creating a right triangular flower bed. If two of the sides of the flower bed are 7 feet long each, what is the length of the third side to the nearest foot? **10 ft**

Make a conjecture based on the given information.

4. $\angle 3$ and $\angle 4$ are a linear pair. **4–7. See margin.**
5. $JKLM$ is a square.
6. $\overrightarrow{BD}$ is an angle bisector of $\angle ABC$.
7. **REASONING** Determine whether the following conjecture is *always*, *sometimes*, or *never* true based on the given information. Justify your reasoning.
   Given: collinear points D, E, and F
   Conjecture: $DE + EF = DF$

Solve each inequality.

8. $x + 13 < 41$ $x < 28$
9. $x - 6 > 2x$ $-6 > x$
10. $6x + 9 < 7x$ $x > 9$
11. $8x + 15 > 9x - 26$ $x < 41$
12. **MUSIC** Nina added 15 more songs to her MP3 player, resulting in a total of more than 120 songs. How many songs were originally on the player? **Sample answer: $x > 105$**

QuickReview

Example 1 (Used in Lessons 5-1 through 5-3)

Find each measure.

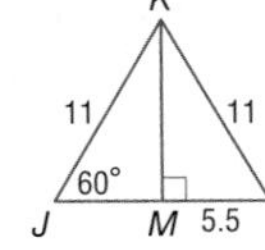

a. JM

$m\angle J = m\angle L$, so $m\angle L = 60$ and $\overline{JM} \cong \overline{LM}$ by the Converse of the Isosceles Triangle Theorem. Since $LM = 5.5$, $JM = 5.5$ by substitution.

b. $m\angle JKL$

$m\angle J + m\angle JKL + m\angle L = 180$	△ Sum Theorem
$60 + m\angle JKL + 60 = 180$	$m\angle J = m\angle L = 60$
$120 + m\angle JKL = 180$	Simplify.
$m\angle JKL = 60$	Subtract.

Example 2 (Used in Lesson 5-4)

K is the midpoint of $\overline{JL}$. Make a conjecture based on the given information and draw a figure to illustrate your conjecture.

Given: K is the midpoint of $\overline{JL}$. J, K, and L are collinear points, and K lies an equal distance between J and L.

Conjecture: $\overline{JK} \cong \overline{KL}$

Check: Draw $\overline{JL}$. This illustrates the conjecture.

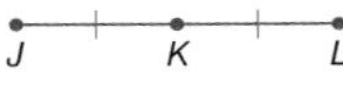

Example 3 (Used in Lessons 5-5 and 5-6)

Solve $3x + 5 > 2x$.

$3x + 5 > 2x$	Given
$3x - 3x + 5 > 2x - 3x$	Subtract.
$5 > -x$	Simplify.
$-5 < x$	Divide.

2 Online Option Take an online self-check Chapter Readiness Quiz at connectED.mcgraw-hill.com.

321

Essential Questions

- What makes a triangle a triangle? Sample answer: three sides, three angles, angle measures that sum to 180
- How are the sides and angles of a triangle related? Sample answers: The longest side is opposite the greatest angle and the smallest side is opposite the smallest angle.

Get Ready for the Chapter

Response to Intervention (RtI)

Use the *Quick Check* results and the Intervention Planner chart to help you determine your Response to Intervention. The If-Then statements in the chart help you decide the appropriate tier of RtI and suggest intervention resources for each tier.

InterventionPlanner

TIER 1 On Level OL

If students miss about 25% of the exercises or less,

Then choose a resource:

SE Lessons 0-6, 2-1, and 4-2

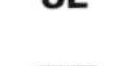

Skills Practice, Chapter 2, p. 7, Chapter 4, p. 13

connectED.mcgraw-hill.com Self-Check Quiz

TIER 2 Strategic Intervention AL approaching grade level

If students miss about 50% of the exercises,

Then choose a resource:

Study Guide and Intervention, Chapter 2, pp. 5–6, Chapter 4, pp. 11–12

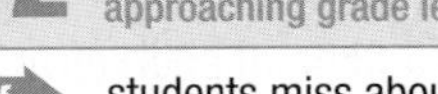

connectED.mcgraw-hill.com Extra Examples, Personal Tutor, Homework Help

TIER 3 Intensive Intervention 2 or more grades below level

If students miss about 75% of the exercises,

Then use *Math Triumphs, Geometry,* Chs. 3 and 4

connectED.mcgraw-hill.com Extra Examples, Personal Tutor, Homework Help, Review Vocabulary

FOLDABLES® StudyOrganizer

Dinah Zike's Foldables®

Focus Students take notes, define terms, record concepts, and write proofs about the relationships in triangles.

Teach After students make their Foldable, have them label the tabs to correspond to the six lessons in this chapter. Students should write a descriptive paragraph about the concepts, vocabulary, and theorems of each lesson, and make special note of any graphics that can enhance this description.

When to Use It Use the appropriate tabs as students cover each lesson in this chapter. The vocabulary tab can be added to each lesson.

Differentiated Instruction

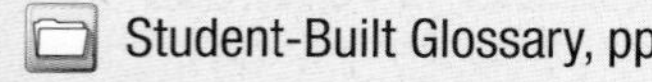

Student-Built Glossary, pp. 1–2

Students complete the chart by providing the definition of each term and an example as they progress through Chapter 5. This study tool can also be used to review for the chapter test.

Get Started on the Chapter

You will learn several new concepts, skills, and vocabulary terms as you study Chapter 5. To get ready, identify important terms and organize your resources. You may wish to refer to Chapter 0 to review prerequisite skills.

FOLDABLES StudyOrganizer

Relationships in Triangles Make this Foldable to help you organize your Chapter 5 notes about relationships in triangles. Begin with seven sheets of grid paper.

1. **Stack** the sheets. Fold the top right corner to the bottom edge to form an isosceles right triangle.

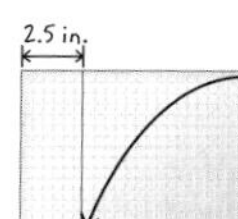

2. **Fold** the rectangular part in half.

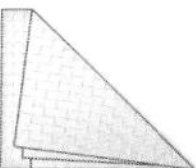

3. **Staple** the sheets along the rectangular fold in four places.

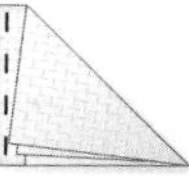

4. **Label** each sheet with a lesson number and the rectangular tab with the chapter title.

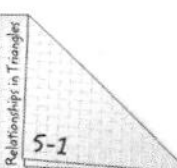

NewVocabulary

English		Español
perpendicular bisector	p. 324	mediatriz
concurrent lines	p. 325	rectas concurrentes
point of concurrency	p. 325	punto de concurrencia
circumcenter	p. 325	circuncentro
incenter	p. 328	incentro
median	p. 335	mediana
centroid	p. 335	baricentro
altitude	p. 337	altura
orthocenter	p. 337	ortocentro
indirect reasoning	p. 355	razonamiento indirecto
indirect proof	p. 355	demostración indirecta
proof by contradiction	p. 355	demostración por contradicción

ReviewVocabulary

angle bisector bisectriz de un ángulo a ray that divides an angle into two congruent angles (Lesson 1-4)

midpoint punto medio the point on a segment exactly halfway between the endpoints of the segment (Lesson 1-3)

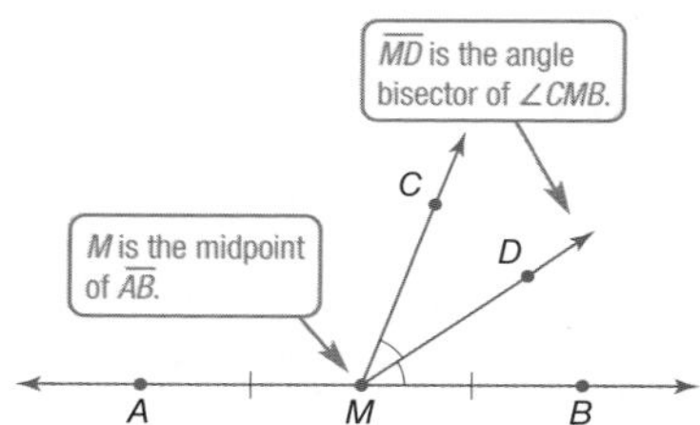

EXPLORE 5-1 Geometry Lab: Constructing Bisectors

Paper folding can be used to construct special segments in triangles.

CCSS Common Core State Standards
Content Standards
G.CO.12 Make formal geometric constructions with a variety of tools and methods (compass and straightedge, string, reflective devices, paper folding, dynamic geometric software, etc.).
Mathematical Practices 5

Construction: Perpendicular Bisector

Construct a perpendicular bisector of the side of a triangle.

Step 1

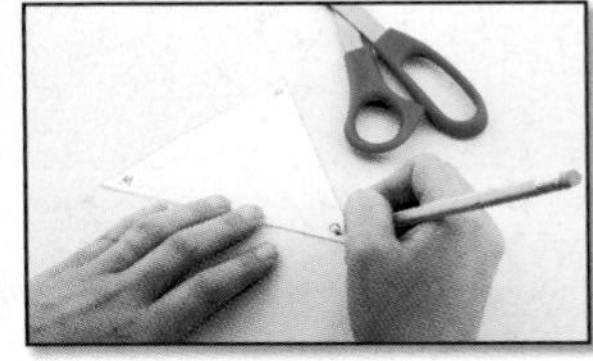

Draw, label, and cut out $\triangle MPQ$.

Step 2

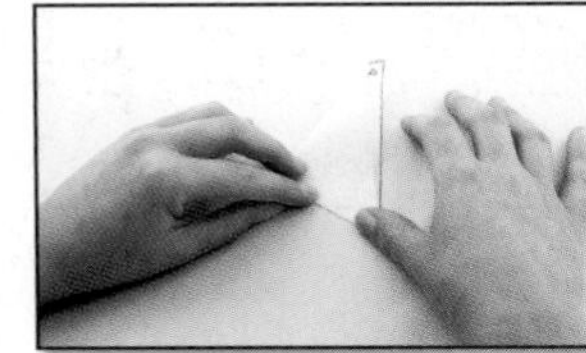

Fold the triangle in half along $\overline{MQ}$ so that vertex M touches vertex Q.

Step 3

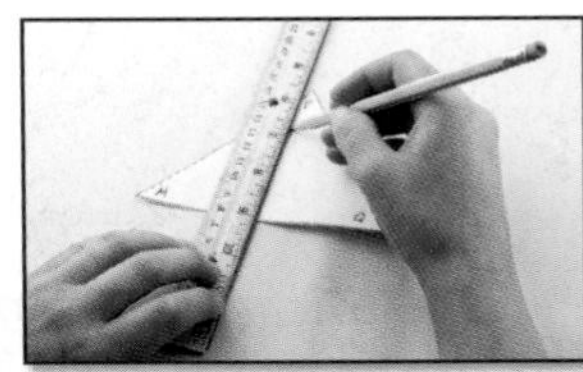

Use a straightedge to draw $\overline{AB}$ along the fold. $\overline{AB}$ is the perpendicular bisector of $\overline{MQ}$.

An angle bisector in a triangle is a line containing a vertex of the triangle and bisecting that angle.

Construction: Angle Bisector

Construct an angle bisector of a triangle.

Step 1

Draw, label, and cut out $\triangle ABC$.

Step 2

Fold the triangle in half through vertex A, such that sides $\overline{AC}$ and $\overline{AB}$ are aligned.

Step 3

Label point L at the crease along edge $\overline{BC}$. Use a straightedge to draw $\overline{AL}$ along the fold. $\overline{AL}$ is an angle bisector of $\triangle ABC$.

Model and Analyze

1. Construct the perpendicular bisectors of the other two sides of $\triangle MPQ$. Construct the angle bisectors of the other two angles of $\triangle ABC$. What do you notice about their intersections? **See students' work. They intersect at the same point.**

Repeat the two constructions for each type of triangle. **2–4. See students' work.**

2. acute
3. obtuse
4. right

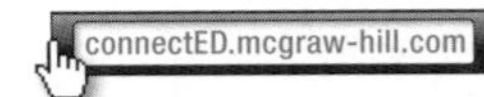

1 Focus

Objective Construct perpendicular bisectors and angle bisectors of triangles.

Teaching Tip

The activity demonstrates two different constructions on an acute scalene triangle. Students could use patty paper to draw and trace two acute scalene triangles with the same side lengths, angle measures, and orientation in three different places on one sheet of paper. When students are finished with the constructions, they can see the differences between the perpendicular and angle bisectors for the same triangle.

Alternative Method

The constructions presented in this lesson can also be completed using classic ruler and compass methods.

2 Teach

Working in Cooperative Groups

Arrange students in groups of 3 with mixed abilities. Each student completes one of the three steps in the construction activities. Rotate the steps for Constructions 1 and 2.

Practice Have the students complete Exercise 1 while performing the activities.

3 Assess

Formative Assessment

Use Exercises 2–4 to assess whether students understand the concept and construction of perpendicular and angle bisectors.

From Concrete to Abstract

Give students the three types of triangles mentioned in Exercises 2–4. Tell them that you want to have each triangle balance on a pencil. Have them pick a construction method and explain.

1 Focus

Vertical Alignment

Before Lesson 5-1 Use segment and angle bisectors.

Lesson 5-1 Identify and use perpendicular bisectors and angle bisectors in triangles.

After Lesson 5-1 Connect algebraic and geometric representation of functions.

2 Teach

Scaffolding Questions

Have students read the **Why?** section of the lesson.

Ask:

- Why could a work triangle be useful in designing a kitchen? It reduces the number of steps taken.
- Where could an island be placed in this triangle? A point equidistant from the refrigerator, stove, and sink.
- Is this point always at the midpoint of each side of the triangle? Why? Sample answer: No, in the picture it is not at the midpoint of the side connecting the stove and sink.

LESSON 5-1 Bisectors of Triangles

Then

- You used segment and angle bisectors.

Now

1. Identify and use perpendicular bisectors in triangles.
2. Identify and use angle bisectors in triangles.

Why?

- Creating a work triangle in a kitchen can make food preparation more efficient by cutting down on the number of steps you have to take. To locate the point that is equidistant from the sink, stove, and refrigerator, you can use the perpendicular bisectors of the triangle.

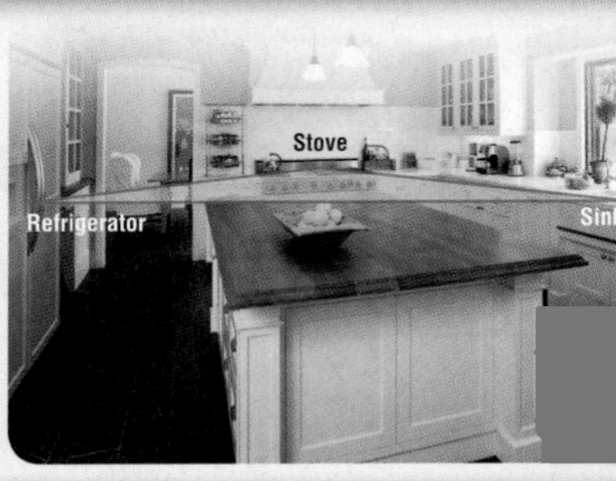

New Vocabulary

perpendicular bisector
concurrent lines
point of concurrency
circumcenter
incenter

Common Core State Standards

Content Standards

G.CO.10 Prove theorems about triangles.

G.MG.3 Apply geometric methods to solve problems (e.g., designing an object or structure to satisfy physical constraints or minimize cost; working with typographic grid systems based on ratios). ★

Mathematical Practices

1. Make sense of problems and persevere in solving them.
3. Construct viable arguments and critique the reasoning of others.

1 Perpendicular Bisectors

In Lesson 1-3, you learned that a segment bisector is any segment, line, or plane that intersects a segment at its midpoint. If a bisector is also perpendicular to the segment, it is called a **perpendicular bisector**.

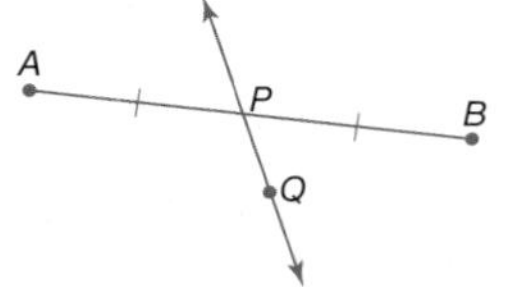

$\overleftrightarrow{PQ}$ is a bisector of $\overline{AB}$.

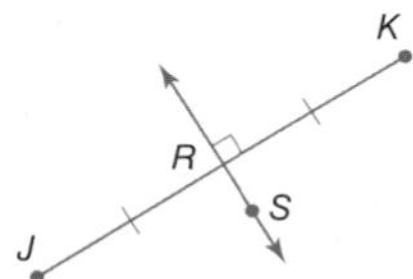

$\overleftrightarrow{RS}$ is a perpendicular bisector of $\overline{JK}$.

Recall that a *locus* is a set of points that satisfies a particular condition. The perpendicular bisector of a segment is the locus of points in a plane equidistant from the endpoints of the segment. This leads to the following theorems.

Theorems Perpendicular Bisectors

5.1 Perpendicular Bisector Theorem

If a point is on the perpendicular bisector of a segment, then it is equidistant from the endpoints of the segment.

Example: If $\overline{CD}$ is a $\perp$ bisector of $\overline{AB}$, then $AC = BC$.

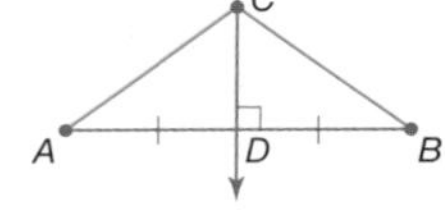

5.2 Converse of the Perpendicular Bisector Theorem

If a point is equidistant from the endpoints of a segment, then it is on the perpendicular bisector of the segment.

Example: If $AE = BE$, then E lies on $\overline{CD}$, the $\perp$ bisector of $\overline{AB}$.

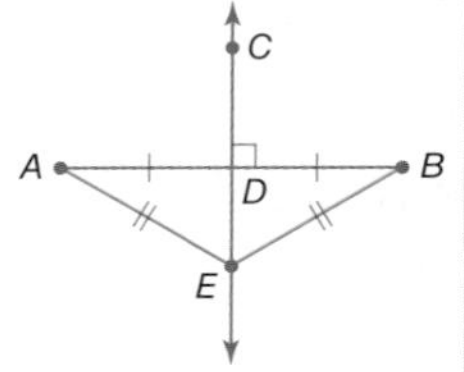

You will prove Theorems 5.1 and 5.2 in Exercises 39 and 37, respectively.

Lesson 5-1 Resources

Resource	Approaching Level AL	On Level OL	Beyond Level BL	English Learners ELL
Teacher Edition	▪ Differentiated Instruction, p. 325	▪ Differentiated Instruction, pp. 325, 333	▪ Differentiated Instruction, p. 333	▪ Differentiated Instruction, p. 325
Chapter Resource Masters	▪ Study Guide and Intervention, pp. 5–6 ▪ Skills Practice, p. 7 ▪ Practice, p. 8 ▪ Word Problem Practice, p. 9	▪ Study Guide and Intervention, pp. 5–6 ▪ Skills Practice, p. 7 ▪ Practice, p. 8 ▪ Word Problem Practice, p. 9 ▪ Enrichment, p. 10	▪ Practice, p. 8 ▪ Word Problem Practice, p. 9 ▪ Enrichment, p. 10	▪ Study Guide and Intervention, pp. 5–6 ▪ Skills Practice, p. 7 ▪ Practice, p. 8 ▪ Word Problem Practice, p. 9
Other	▪ 5-Minute Check 5-1 ▪ Study Notebook ▪ Teaching Geometry with Manipulatives	▪ 5-Minute Check 5-1 ▪ Study Notebook ▪ Teaching Geometry with Manipulatives	▪ 5-Minute Check 5-1 ▪ Study Notebook	▪ 5-Minute Check 5-1 ▪ Study Notebook ▪ Teaching Geometry with Manipulatives

StudyTip

Perpendicular Bisectors The perpendicular bisector of a side of a triangle does not necessarily pass through a vertex of the triangle. For example, in $\triangle XYZ$ below, the perpendicular bisector of $\overline{XY}$ does not pass through point Z.

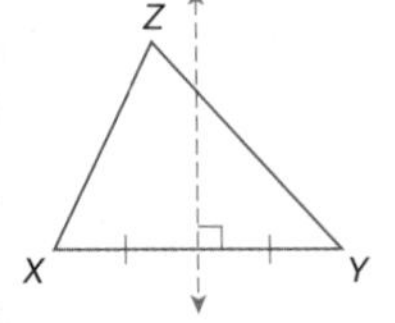

Example 1 Use the Perpendicular Bisector Theorems

Find each measure.

a. AB

From the information in the diagram, we know that $\overleftrightarrow{CA}$ is the perpendicular bisector of $\overline{BD}$.

$AB = AD$	Perpendicular Bisector Theorem
$AB = 4.1$	Substitution

b. WY

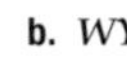

Since $WX = ZX$ and $\overleftrightarrow{XY} \perp \overline{WZ}$, $\overleftrightarrow{XY}$ is the perpendicular bisector of $\overline{WZ}$ by the Converse of the Perpendicular Bisector Theorem. By the definition of segment bisector, $WY = YZ$. Since $YZ = 3$, $WY = 3$.

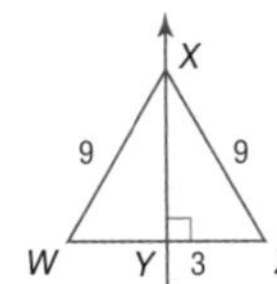

c. RT

$\overleftrightarrow{SR}$ is the perpendicular bisector of $\overline{QT}$.

$RT = RQ$	Perpendicular Bisector Theorem
$4x - 7 = 2x + 3$	Substitution
$2x - 7 = 3$	Subtract $2x$ from each side.
$2x = 10$	Add 7 to each side.
$x = 5$	Divide each side by 2.

So $RT = 4(5) - 7$ or 13.

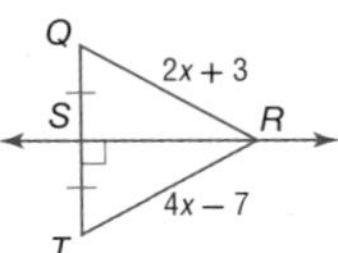

GuidedPractice

1A. If $WX = 25.3$, $YZ = 22.4$, and $WZ = 25.3$, find XY. **22.4**

1B. If m is the perpendicular bisector of XZ and $WZ = 14.9$, find WX. **14.9**

1C. If m is the perpendicular bisector of XZ, $WX = 4a - 15$, and $WZ = a + 12$, find WX. **21**

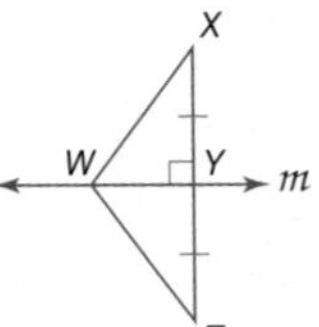

When three or more lines intersect at a common point, the lines are called **concurrent lines**. The point where concurrent lines intersect is called the **point of concurrency**.

A triangle has three sides, so it also has three perpendicular bisectors. These bisectors are concurrent lines. The point of concurrency of the perpendicular bisectors is called the **circumcenter** of the triangle.

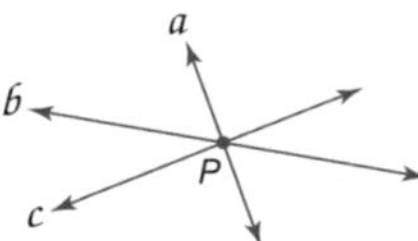

Lines a, b, and c are concurrent at P.

Theorem 5.3 Circumcenter Theorem

Words The perpendicular bisectors of a triangle intersect at a point called the *circumcenter* that is equidistant from the vertices of the triangle.

Example If P is the circumcenter of $\triangle ABC$, then $PB = PA = PC$.

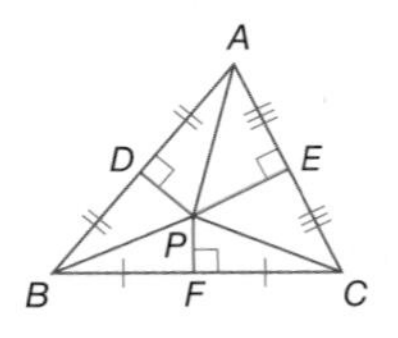

1 Perpendicular Bisectors

Example 1 shows how to use angle bisectors to find measures in a figure. **Example 2** shows how to use the circumcenter to locate a point in a figure.

Formative Assessment

Use the Guided Practice exercises after each example to determine students' understanding of concepts.

Additional Example

1 Find each measure.

a. BC

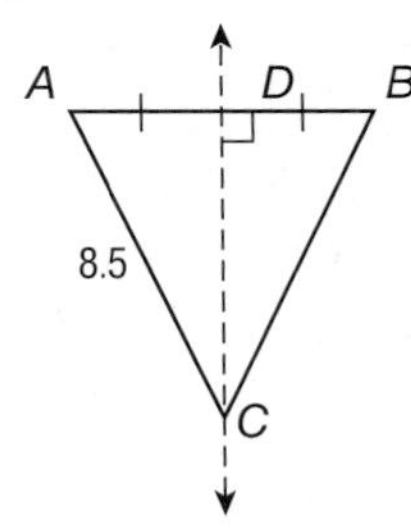

8.5

b. XY

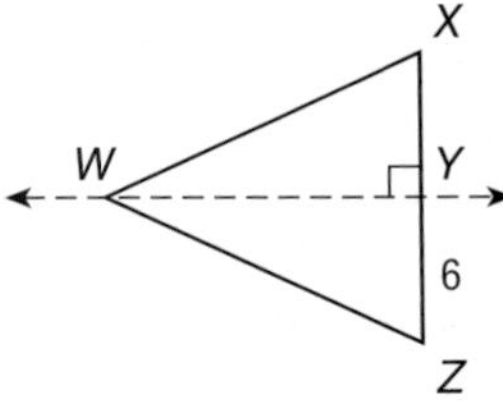

6

c. PQ

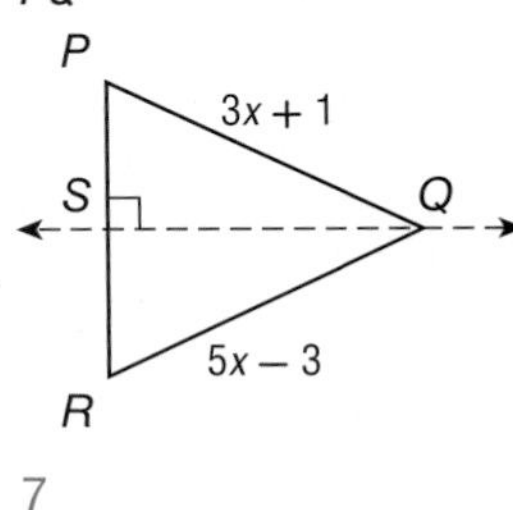

7

Additional Examples also in Interactive Classroom PowerPoint® Presentations

Interactive White Board READY

DifferentiatedInstruction AL OL ELL

Visual Learners Expect some students to find the concepts and vocabulary in this lesson confusing. Allow extra time for all the concepts in this lesson. After each concept, suggest that students add to a class poster that illustrates the different concepts and facts about them. Also review concepts as you complete them, discussing their similarities and differences.

Additional Example

2 GARDEN A triangular-shaped garden is shown. Can a fountain be placed at the circumcenter and still be inside the garden?

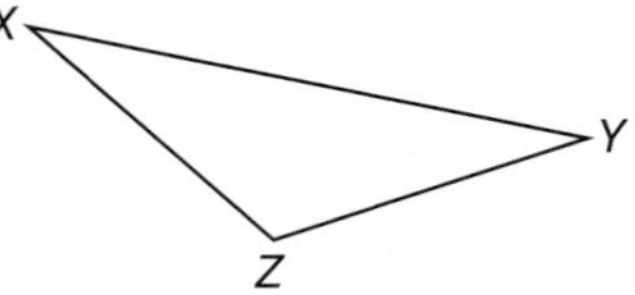

No, the circumcenter of an obtuse triangle is in the exterior of the triangle.

Tips for New Teachers

Clarify Vocabulary Explain that a circumcenter does not necessarily have to lie in the interior of a triangle. Draw an obtuse isosceles triangle with angles 10°, 10°, and 160° to demonstrate a circumcenter outside of a triangle.

Focus on Mathematical Content

Word Understanding This lesson has many terms that have a prefix or suffix attached to the root word center. Emphasize to students that each prefix or suffix will help them understand. For example, **circum** means around or encircling. The circumcenter of a triangle is the center of a circle circumscribed about the triangle.

ReadingMath

Circum– The prefix *circum–* means *about* or *around.* The circumcenter is the center of a circle around a triangle that contains the vertices of the triangle.

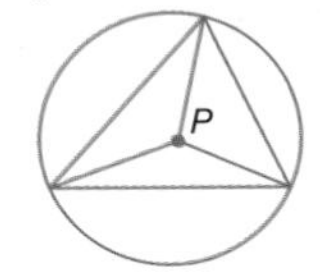

The circumcenter can be on the interior, exterior, or side of a triangle.

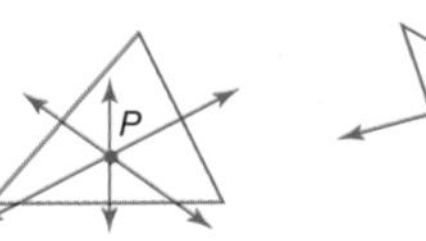

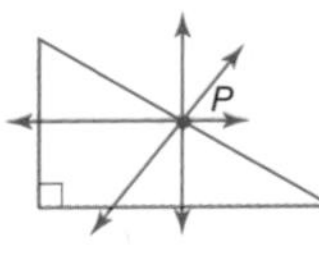

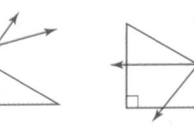

acute triangle obtuse triangle right triangle

Proof Circumcenter Theorem

Given: $\overline{PD}$, $\overline{PF}$, and $\overline{PE}$ are perpendicular bisectors of $\overline{AB}$, $\overline{AC}$, and $\overline{BC}$, respectively.

Prove: $AP = CP = BP$

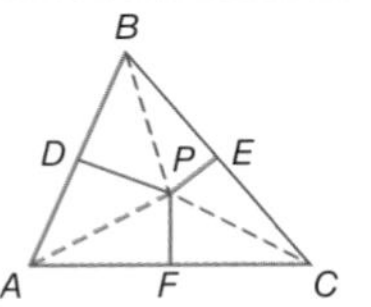

Paragraph Proof:

Since P lies on the perpendicular bisector of $\overline{AC}$, it is equidistant from A and C. By the definition of equidistant, $AP = CP$. The perpendicular bisector of $\overline{BC}$ also contains P. Thus, $CP = BP$. By the Transitive Property of Equality, $AP = BP$. Thus, $AP = CP = BP$.

Real-WorldLink

Some basic rules of thumb for a kitchen work triangle are that the sides of the triangle should be no greater than 9 feet and no less than 4 feet. Also, the perimeter of the triangle should be no more than 26 feet and no less than 12 feet.

Source: Merillat

PT

Real-World Example 2 Use the Circumcenter Theorem

INTERIOR DESIGN A stove S, sink K, and refrigerator R are positioned in a kitchen as shown. Find the location for the center of an island work station so that it is the same distance from these three points.

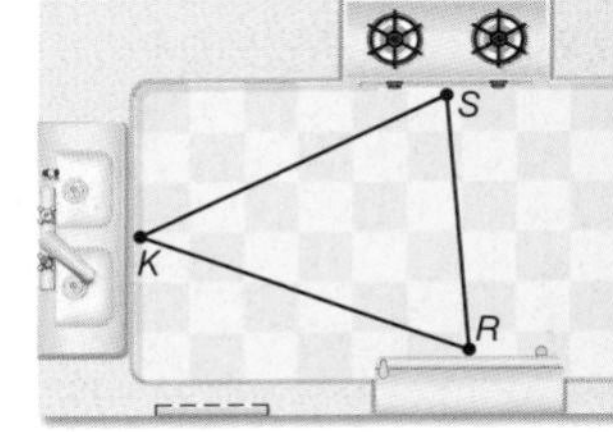

By the Circumcenter Theorem, a point equidistant from three points is found by using the perpendicular bisectors of the triangle formed by those points.

Copy $\triangle SKR$, and use a ruler and protractor to draw the perpendicular bisectors. The location for the center of the island is C, the circumcenter of $\triangle SKR$.

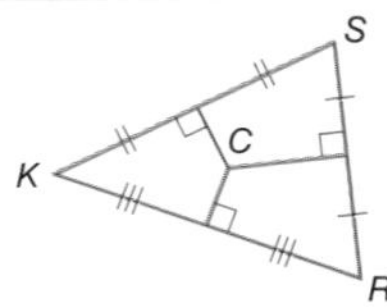

GuidedPractice

2. To water his triangular garden, Alex needs to place a sprinkler equidistant from each vertex. Where should Alex place the sprinkler? **See margin.**

2 Angle Bisectors Recall from Lesson 1-4 that an angle bisector divides an angle into two congruent angles. The angle bisector can be a line, segment, or ray.

The bisector of an angle can be described as the locus of points in the interior of the angle equidistant from the sides of the angle. This description leads to the following theorems.

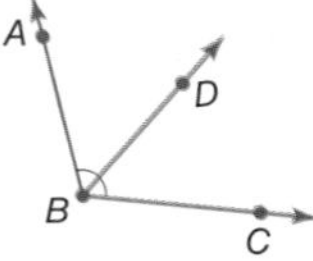

$\overrightarrow{BD}$ is the angle bisector of $\angle ABC$.

Additional Answer (Guided Practice)

2.

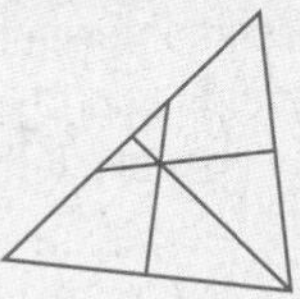

Theorems Angle Bisectors

5.4 Angle Bisector Theorem

If a point is on the bisector of an angle, then it is equidistant from the sides of the angle.

Example: If $\overrightarrow{BF}$ bisects $\angle DBE$, $\overline{FD} \perp \overrightarrow{BD}$, and $\overline{FE} \perp \overrightarrow{BE}$, then $DF = FE$.

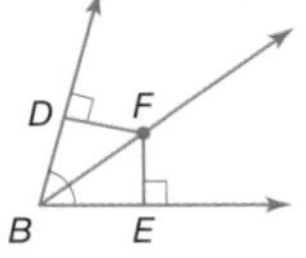

5.5 Converse of the Angle Bisector Theorem

If a point in the interior of an angle is equidistant from the sides of the angle, then it is on the bisector of the angle.

Example: If $\overline{FD} \perp \overrightarrow{BD}$, $\overline{FE} \perp \overrightarrow{BE}$, and $DF = FE$, then $\overrightarrow{BF}$ bisects $\angle DBE$.

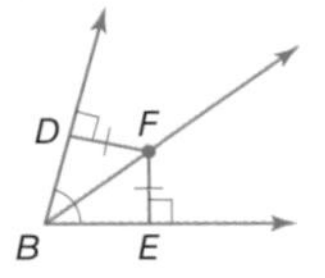

You will prove Theorems 5.4 and 5.5 in Exercises 43 and 40.

Example 3 Use the Angle Bisector Theorems

Find each measure.

a. XY

$XY = XW$ Angle Bisector Theorem

$XY = 7$ Substitution

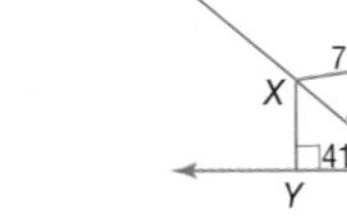

b. $m\angle JKL$

Since $\overline{LJ} \perp \overrightarrow{KJ}$, $\overline{LM} \perp \overrightarrow{KM}$, $\overline{LJ} \cong \overline{LM}$, L is equidistant from the sides of $\angle JKM$. By the Converse of the Angle Bisector Theorem, $\overrightarrow{KL}$ bisects $\angle JKM$.

$\angle JKL \cong \angle LKM$ Definition of angle bisector

$m\angle JKL = m\angle LKM$ Definition of congruent angles

$m\angle JKL = 37$ Substitution

c. SP

$SP = SM$ Angle Bisector Theorem

$6x - 7 = 3x + 5$ Substitution

$3x - 7 = 5$ Subtract $3x$ from each side.

$3x = 12$ Add 7 to each side.

$x = 4$ Divide each side by 3.

So, $SP = 6(4) - 7$ or 17

> **StudyTip**
> **Angle Bisector** For part **b**, only that $JL = LM$ would not be enough information to conclude that $\overrightarrow{KL}$ bisects $\angle JKM$.

GuidedPractice

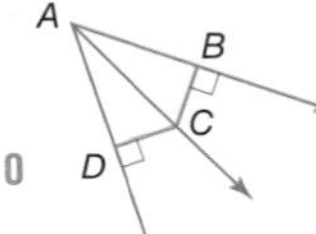

3A. If $m\angle BAC = 38$, $BC = 5$, and $DC = 5$, find $m\angle DAC$. 38

3B. If $m\angle BAC = 40$, $m\angle DAC = 40$, and $DC = 10$, find BC. 10

3C. If $\overrightarrow{AC}$ bisects $\angle DAB$, $BC = 4x + 8$, and $DC = 9x - 7$, find BC. 20

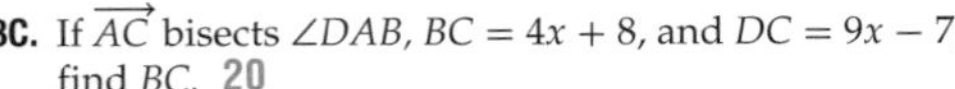

2 Angle Bisectors

Example 3 shows how to use the Angle Bisector Theorem. **Example 4** shows how to use the Incenter Theorem.

Additional Example

3 Find each measure.

a. DB

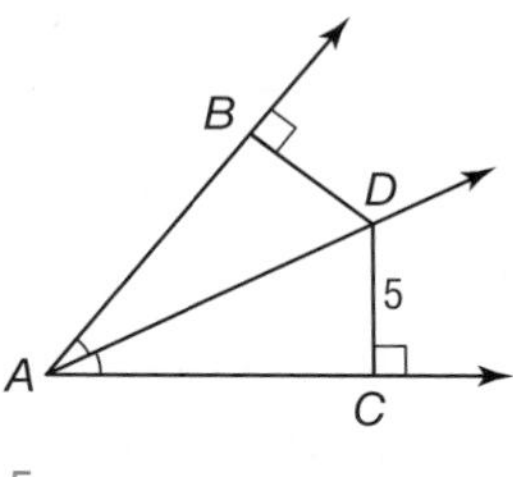

5

b. $m\angle WYZ$

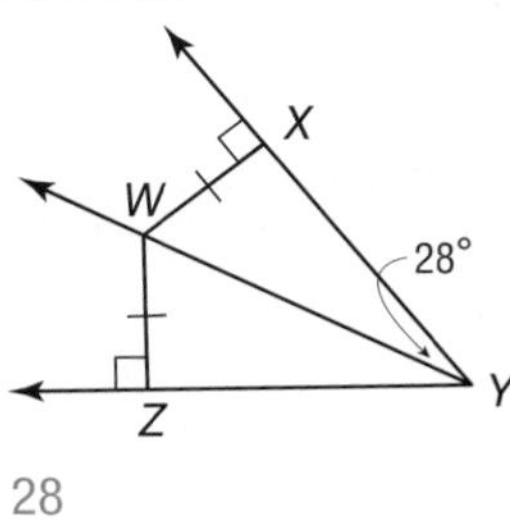

28

c. QS

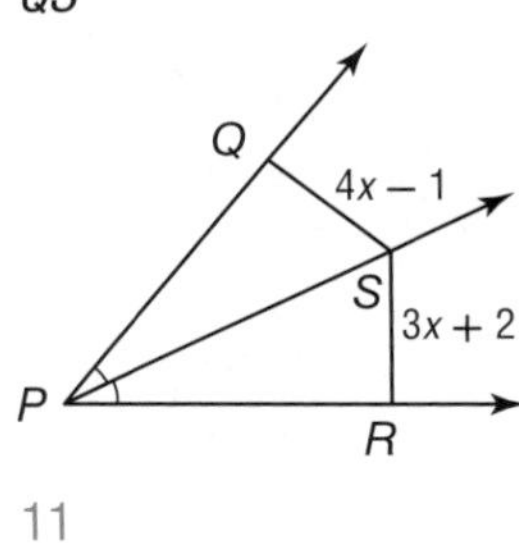

11

> **WatchOut!**
> **Substitution** In part **c** of Example 3, it is not enough to solve for the variable x. To find the length of $\overline{SP}$, you need to evaluate $6x - 7$.

Teach with Tech

Interactive Whiteboard Assign several exercises to the class that give the measures of each half of a bisected angle as an algebraic expression. Choose several students to work through the exercises in front of the class, showing how to find both the value of the variable and the measure of the angle.

Tips for New Teachers

Definitions Have students look up the definitions of bisectors, medians, and altitudes. They should compare the mathematical definitions to the real-world definitions to get a holistic understanding of the meanings.

Additional Example

4 Find each measure if S is the incenter of $\triangle MNP$.

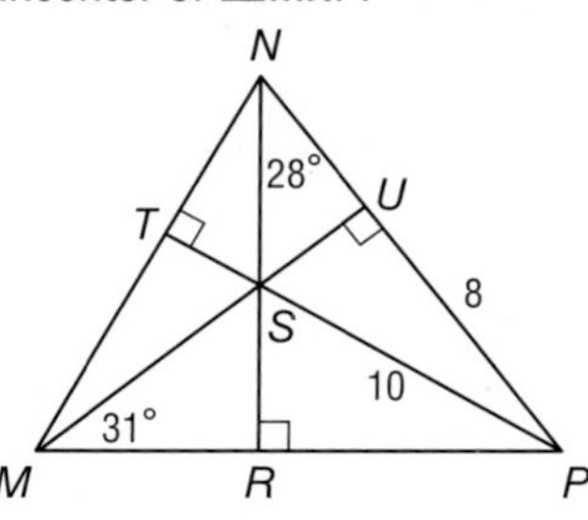

a. SU 6

b. $m\angle SPU$ 31

ReadingMath

Incenter The incenter is the center of a circle that intersects each side of the triangle at one point. For this reason, the incenter always lies in the interior of a triangle.

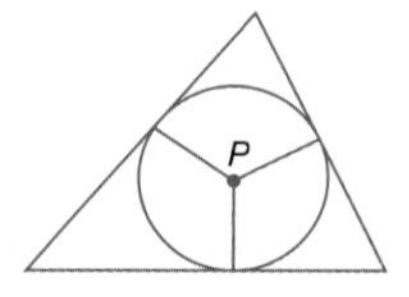

Similar to perpendicular bisectors, since a triangle has three angles, it also has three angle bisectors. The angle bisectors of a triangle are concurrent, and their point of concurrency is called the **incenter** of a triangle.

Theorem 5.6 Incenter Theorem

Words The angle bisectors of a triangle intersect at a point called the *incenter* that is equidistant from the sides of the triangle.

Example If P is the incenter of $\triangle ABC$, then $PD = PE = PF$.

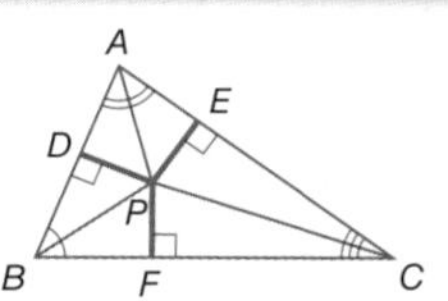

You will prove Theorem 5.6 in Exercise 38.

Example 4 Use the Incenter Theorem

Find each measure if J is the incenter of $\triangle ABC$.

a. JF

By the Incenter Theorem, since J is equidistant from the sides of $\triangle ABC$, $JF = JE$. Find JF by using the Pythagorean Theorem.

$a^2 + b^2 = c^2$	Pythagorean Theorem
$JE^2 + 12^2 = 15^2$	Substitution
$JE^2 + 144 = 225$	$12^2 = 144$ and $15^2 = 225$.
$JE^2 = 81$	Subtract 144 from each side.
$JE = \pm 9$	Take the square root of each side.

Since length cannot be negative, use only the positive square root, 9. Since $JE = JF$, $JF = 9$.

b. $m\angle JAC$

Since $\overrightarrow{BJ}$ bisects $\angle CBE$, $m\angle CBE = 2m\angle JBE$. So $m\angle CBE = 2(34)$ or 68. Likewise, $m\angle DCF = 2m\angle DCJ$, so $m\angle DCF = 2(32)$ or 64.

$m\angle CBE + m\angle DCF + m\angle FAE = 180$	Triangle Angle Sum Theorem
$68 + 64 + m\angle FAE = 180$	$m\angle CBE = 68$, $m\angle DCF = 64$
$132 + m\angle FAE = 180$	Simplify.
$m\angle FAE = 48$	Subtract 132 from each side.

Since $\overrightarrow{AJ}$ bisects $\angle FAE$, $2m\angle JAC = m\angle FAE$. This means that $m\angle JAC = \frac{1}{2}m\angle FAE$, so $m\angle JAC = \frac{1}{2}(48)$ or 24.

GuidedPractice

If P is the incenter of $\triangle XYZ$, find each measure.

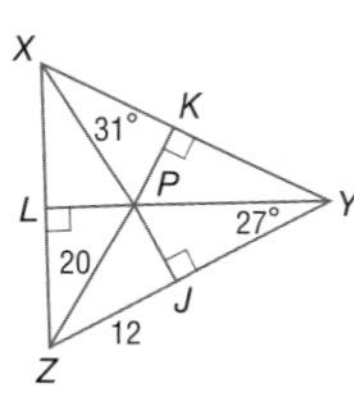

4A. PK **16**

4B. $m\angle LZP$ **32**

328 | Lesson 5-1 | Bisectors of Triangles

Check Your Understanding

 = Step-by-Step Solutions begin on page R14. 

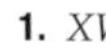

Example 1 Find each measure.

1. XW **12**

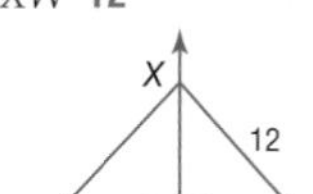

2. AC **14**

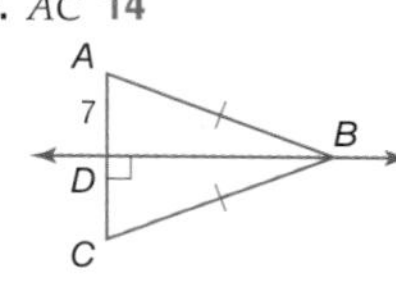

3. LP **15**

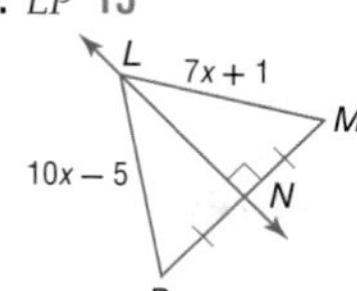

Example 2 **4. ADVERTISING** Four friends are passing out flyers at a mall food court. Three of them take as many flyers as they can and position themselves as shown. The fourth one keeps the supply of additional flyers. Copy the positions of points A, B, and C. Then position the fourth friend at D so that she is the same distance from each of the other three friends. **See margin.**

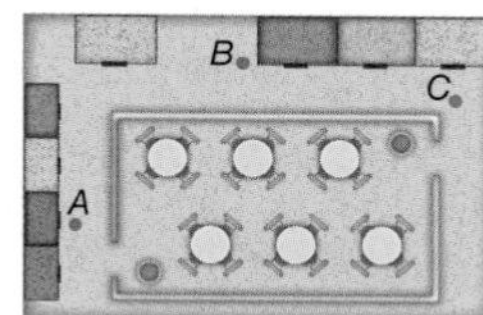

Example 3 Find each measure.

5. CP **8**

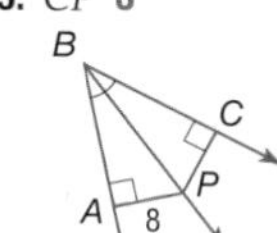

6. $m\angle WYZ$ **23**

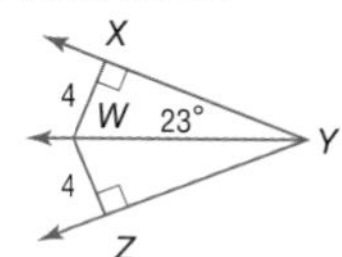

7. QM **12**

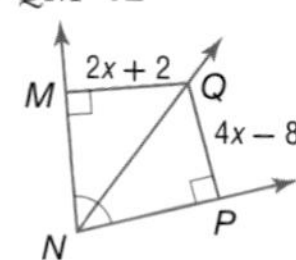

Example 4 **8.** CCSS **SENSE-MAKING** Find JQ if Q is the incenter of $\triangle JLN$. **18.8**

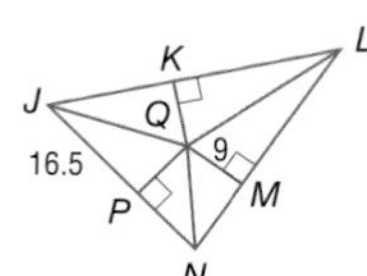

Practice and Problem Solving

Extra Practice is on page R5.

Example 1 Find each measure.

9. NP **14**

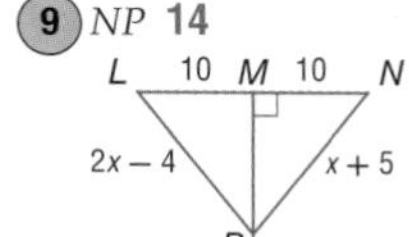

10. PS **9**

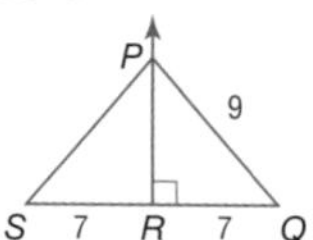

11. KL **6**

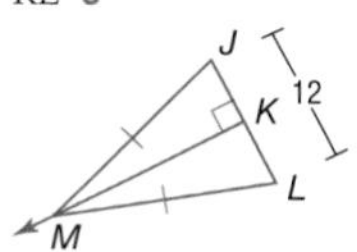

12. EG **10**

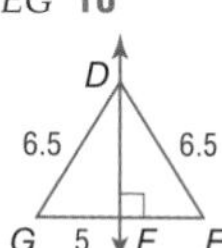

13. CD **4**

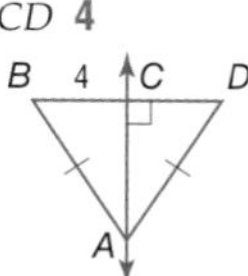

14. SW **16**

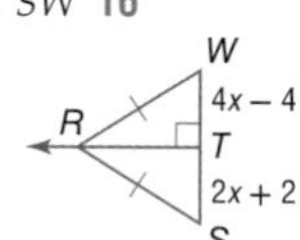

Differentiated Homework Options

Level	Assignment	Two-Day Option	
AL Basic	9–30, 48–51, 54–69	9–29 odd, 55–58	10–30 even, 48–51, 54, 59–69
OL Core	9–35 odd, 36, 37–43 odd, 44, 45, 47, 48–51, 54–69	9–30, 55–58	31–51, 54, 59–69
BL Advanced	32–67, (optional: 68, 69)		

3 Practice

Formative Assessment

Use Exercises 1–8 to check for understanding.

Use the chart at the bottom of this page to customize assignments for your students.

Teaching the Mathematical Practices

Sense-Making Mathematically proficient students look for entry points into a solution. They plan a solution pathway rather than simply jumping into a solution attempt. In Exercise 8, encourage students to make a plan to solve the problem first.

Additional Answer

4.

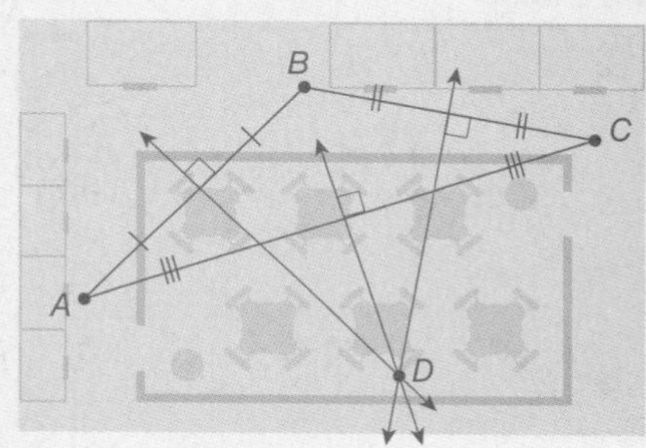

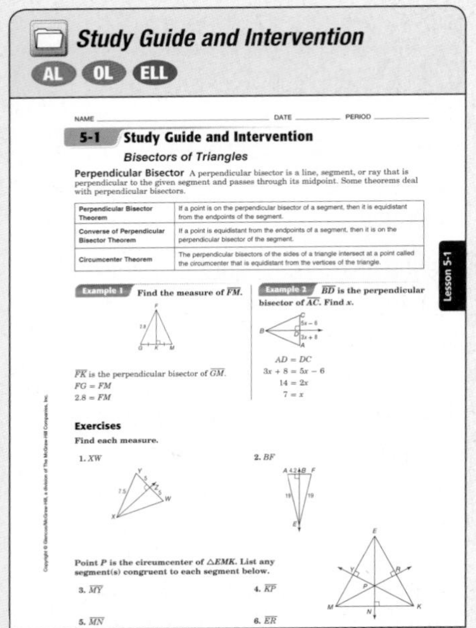

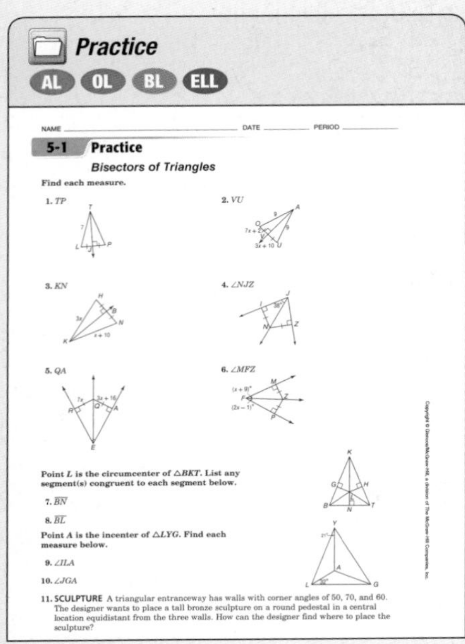

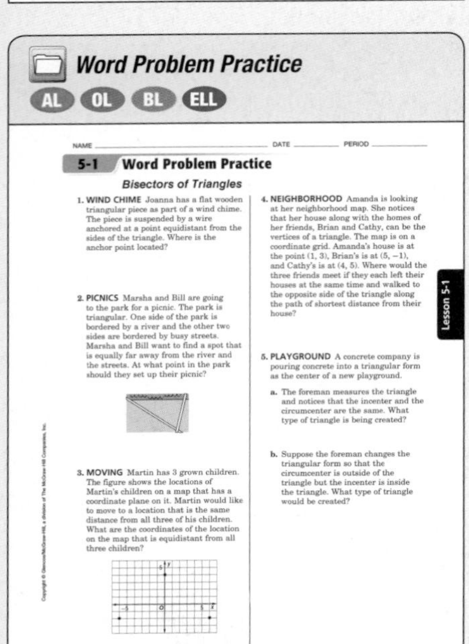

Example 2

15. **STATE FAIR** The state fair has set up the location of the midway, livestock competition, and food vendors. The fair planners decide that they want to locate the portable restrooms the same distance from each location. Copy the positions of points M, L, and F. Then find the location for the restrooms and label it R. **See Ch. 5 Answer Appendix.**

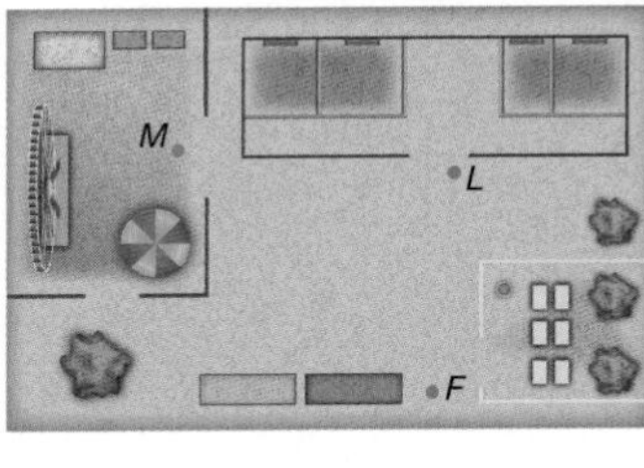

16. **SCHOOL** A school system has built an elementary, middle, and high school at the locations shown in the diagram. Copy the positions of points E, M, and H. Then find the location for the bus yard B that will service these schools so that it is the same distance from each school. **See margin.**

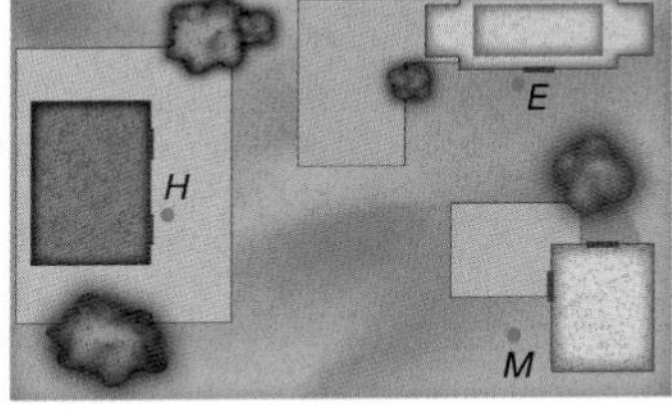

Point D is the circumcenter of $\triangle ABC$. List any segment(s) congruent to each segment.

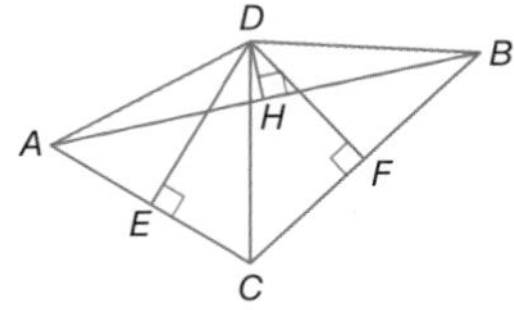

17. $\overline{AD}$ **$\overline{CD}$, $\overline{BD}$**
18. $\overline{BF}$ **$\overline{CF}$**
19. $\overline{AH}$ **$\overline{BH}$**
20. $\overline{DC}$ **$\overline{DA}$, $\overline{DB}$**

Example 3

Find each measure.

21. AF **11**

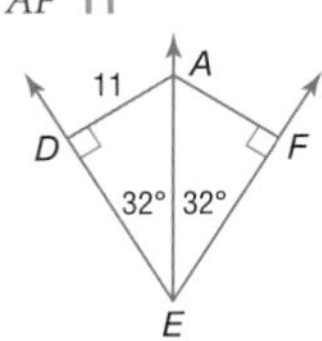

22. $m\angle DBA$ **17**

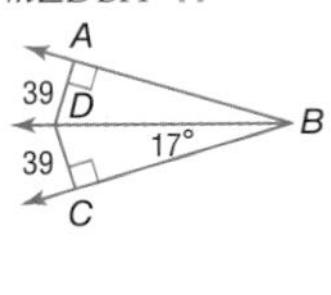

23. $m\angle PNM$ **88**

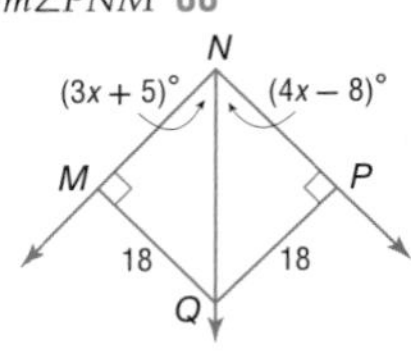

24. XA **4**

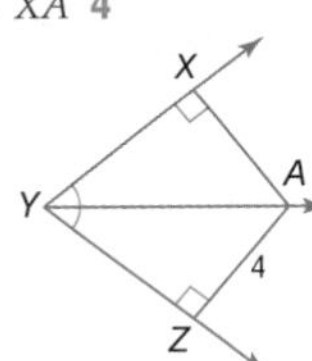

25. $m\angle PQS$ **42**

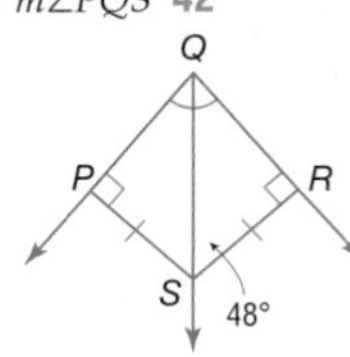

26. PN **30**

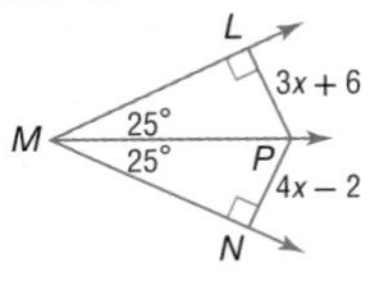

Example 4

CCSS SENSE-MAKING **Point P is the incenter of $\triangle AEC$. Find each measure below.**

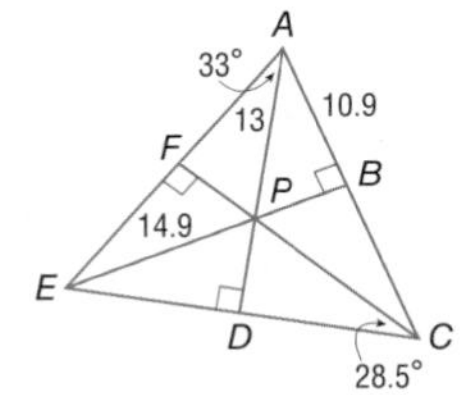

27. PB **7.1**
28. DE **13.1**
29. $m\angle DAC$ **33**
30. $m\angle DEP$ **28.5**

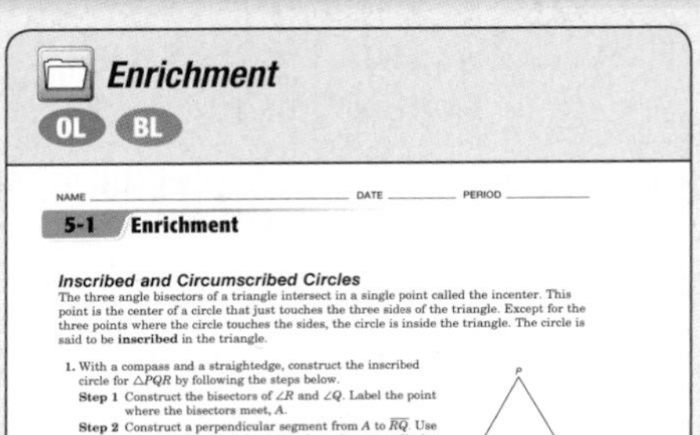

CCSS Teaching the Mathematical Practices

Sense-Making Mathematically proficient students look for entry points into a solution. They plan a solution pathway rather than simply jumping into a solution attempt. In Exercises 27–30, encourage students to make a plan to solve the problem first.

31 **INTERIOR DESIGN** You want to place a centerpiece on a corner table so that it is located the same distance from each edge of the table. Make a sketch to show where you should place the centerpiece. Explain your reasoning. **See margin.**

Determine whether there is enough information given in each diagram to find the value of x. Explain your reasoning. **32. No; we need to know if the segments are perpendicular to the rays.**

B **32.**

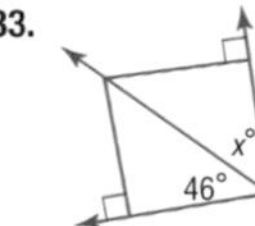

33.

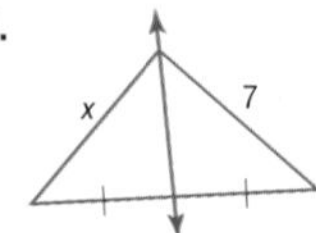

34.

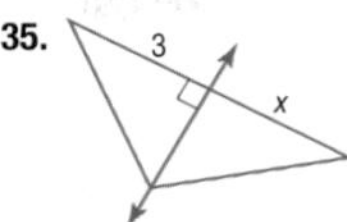

35.

33. No; we need to know if the perpendicular segments are equal to each other.
34. No; we need to know if the segment bisector is a perpendicular bisector.
35. No; we need to know whether the hypotenuse of the triangles are congruent.

36. SOCCER A soccer player P is approaching the opposing team's goal as shown in the diagram. To make the goal, the player must kick the ball between the goal posts at L and R. The goalkeeper faces the kicker. He then tries to stand so that if he needs to dive to stop a shot, he is as far from the left-hand side of the shot angle as the right-hand side. **a–c. See margin.**

a. Describe where the goalkeeper should stand. Explain your reasoning.
b. Copy $\triangle PRL$. Use a compass and a straightedge to locate a point G where the goalkeeper should stand.
c. If the ball is kicked so it follows the path from P to R, construct the shortest path the goalkeeper should take to block the shot. Explain your reasoning.

PROOF **Write a two-column proof.** **37–38. See Ch. 5 Answer Appendix.**

37. Theorem 5.2
Given: $\overline{CA} \cong \overline{CB}$, $\overline{AD} \cong \overline{BD}$
Prove: C and D are on the perpendicular bisector of $\overline{AB}$.

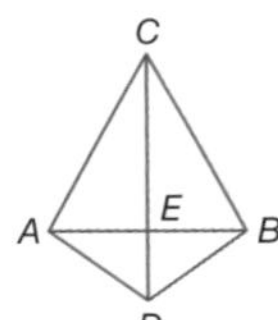

38. Theorem 5.6
Given: $\triangle ABC$, angle bisectors $\overline{AD}$, $\overline{BE}$, and $\overline{CF}$, $\overline{KP} \perp \overline{AB}$, $\overline{KQ} \perp \overline{BC}$, $\overline{KR} \perp \overline{AC}$
Prove: $KP = KQ = KR$

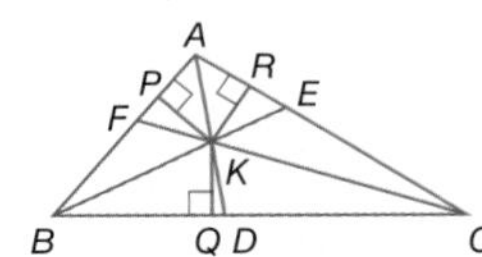

CCSS ARGUMENTS **Write a paragraph proof of each theorem.**

39. Theorem 5.1 **See Ch. 5 Answer Appendix.**

40. Theorem 5.5 **See Ch. 5 Answer Appendix.**

COORDINATE GEOMETRY **Write an equation in slope-intercept form for the perpendicular bisector of the segment with the given endpoints. Justify your answer.**

41. $A(-3, 1)$ and $B(4, 3)$ **See margin.**

42. $C(-4, 5)$ and $D(2, -2)$ **See margin.**

41. $y = -\frac{7}{2}x + \frac{15}{4}$; The perpendicular bisector bisects the segment at the midpoint of the segment. The midpoint is $\left(\frac{1}{2}, 2\right)$. The slope of the given segment is $\frac{2}{7}$, so the slope of the perpendicular bisector is $-\frac{7}{2}$.

42. $y = \frac{6}{7}x + \frac{33}{14}$; The perpendicular bisector bisects the segment at the midpoint of the segment. The midpoint is $\left(-1, \frac{3}{2}\right)$. The slope of the given segment is $-\frac{7}{6}$, so the slope of the perpendicular bisector is $\frac{6}{7}$.

Exercise Alert

Compass and Straightedge
Exercises 4, 15, 16, 36, 44, and 49 require the use of a compass and a straightedge.

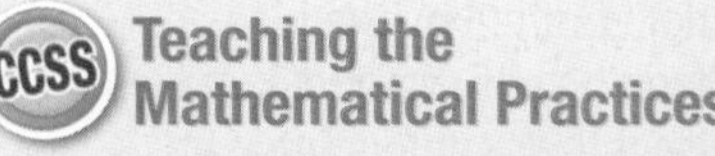

CCSS Teaching the Mathematical Practices

Arguments Mathematically proficient students understand and use stated assumptions, definitions, and previously established results in constructing arguments. In Exercises 39–40, encourage students to draw each figure before starting the proof.

Additional Answers

16.

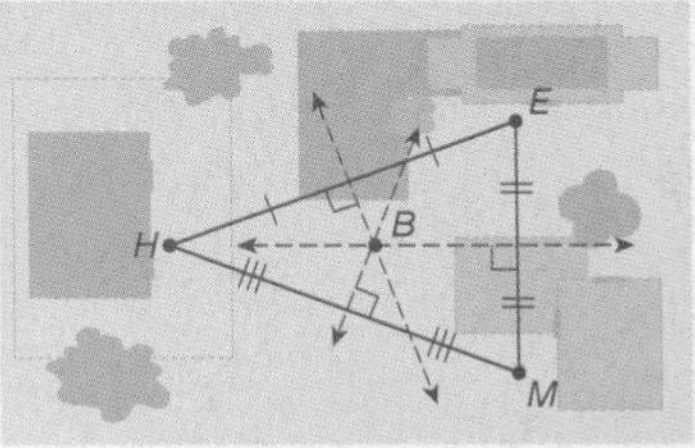

31.

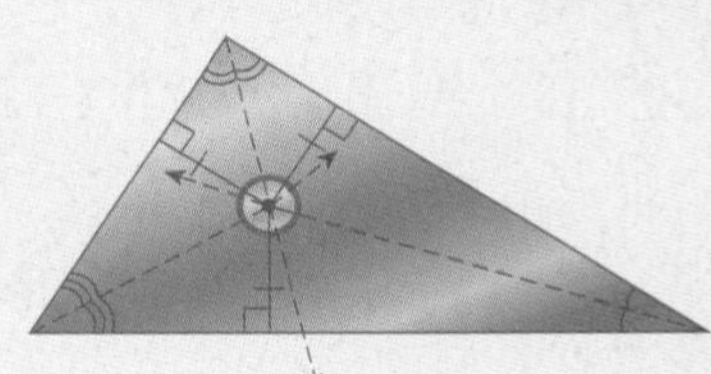

Find the point of concurrency of the angle bisectors of the triangle, the incenter. This point is equidistant from each side of the triangle.

36a. The goalkeeper should stand along the angle bisector of the opponent's shot angle, since the distance to either side of the angle is the same along this line.

36b.

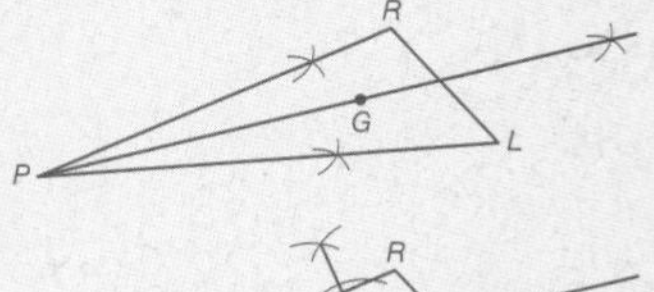

36c.

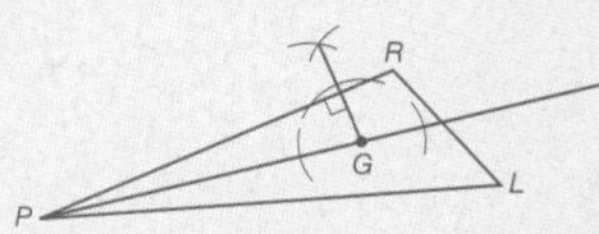

The shortest distance to a line from a point not on the line is the length of the segment perpendicular to the line from the point.

WatchOut!

Error Analysis In Exercise 48, students should see that there is no information given about the angle formed by the bisector. Claudio sees that the line does bisect the segment into two equal lengths, but thinks it is perpendicular only because it appears that way.

Additional Answers

43. Given: $\overline{PX}$ bisects $\angle QPR$. $\overline{XY} \perp \overline{PQ}$ and $\overline{XZ} \perp \overline{PR}$

Prove: $\overline{XY} \cong \overline{XZ}$

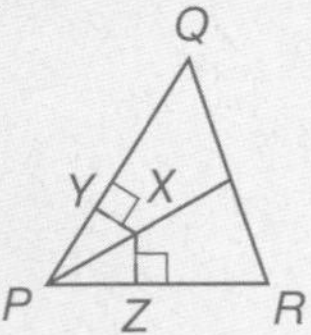

Proof:

Statements (Reasons)

1. $\overline{PX}$ bisects $\angle QPR$, $\overline{XY} \perp \overline{PQ}$ and $\overline{XZ} \perp \overline{PR}$. (Given)
2. $\angle YPX \cong \angle ZPX$ (Definition of angle bisector)
3. $\angle PYX$ and $\angle PZX$ are right angles. (Definition of perpendicular)
4. $\angle PYX \cong \angle PZX$ (Right angles are congruent.)
5. $\overline{PX} \cong \overline{PX}$ (Reflexive Property)
6. $\triangle PYX \cong \triangle PZX$ (AAS)
7. $\overline{XY} \cong \overline{XZ}$ (CPCTC)

44.

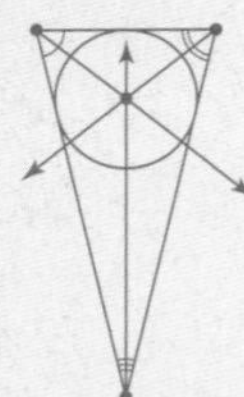

When the circle is as large as possible, it will touch all three sides of the pennant. We need to find the incenter of the triangle by finding the intersection point of the angle bisectors.

43. **PROOF** Write a two-column proof of Theorem 5.4. **See margin.**

44. **GRAPHIC DESIGN** Mykia is designing a pennant for her school. She wants to put a picture of the school mascot inside a circle on the pennant. Copy the outline of the pennant and locate the point where the center of the circle should be to create the largest circle possible. Justify your drawing. **See margin.**

COORDINATE GEOMETRY **Find the coordinates of the circumcenter of the triangle with the given vertices. Explain.**

45. $A(0, 0)$, $B(0, 6)$, $C(10, 0)$ **See margin.**

46. $J(5, 0)$, $K(5, -8)$, $L(0, 0)$ **See margin.**

47. **LOCUS** Consider $\overline{CD}$. Describe the set of all points in space that are equidistant from C and D.
a plane perpendicular to the plane in which $\overline{CD}$ lies and bisecting $\overline{CD}$

48. Caitlyn; K is only on the perpendicular bisector of $\overline{LM}$ if $\overline{LK} \cong \overline{MK}$, but we are not given this information in the diagram.

H.O.T. Problems Use Higher-Order Thinking Skills

48. **ERROR ANALYSIS** Claudio says that from the information supplied in the diagram, he can conclude that K is on the perpendicular bisector of $\overline{LM}$. Caitlyn disagrees. Is either of them correct? Explain your reasoning.

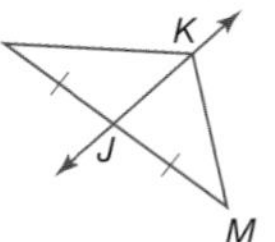

49. **OPEN ENDED** Draw a triangle with an incenter located inside the triangle but a circumcenter located outside. Justify your drawing by using a straightedge and a compass to find both points of concurrency. **See margin.**

CCSS ARGUMENTS **Determine whether each statement is *sometimes, always,* or *never* true. Justify your reasoning using a counterexample or proof.**

50. The angle bisectors of a triangle intersect at a point that is equidistant from the vertices of the triangle. **See Ch. 5 Answer Appendix.**

51. In an isosceles triangle, the perpendicular bisector of the base is also the angle bisector of the opposite vertex. **See Ch. 5 Answer Appendix.**

CHALLENGE **Write a two-column proof for each of the following.**

52. **Given:** Plane $\mathcal{Y}$ is a perpendicular bisector of $\overline{DC}$. **See Ch. 5 Answer Appendix.**
Prove: $\angle ADB \cong \angle ACB$

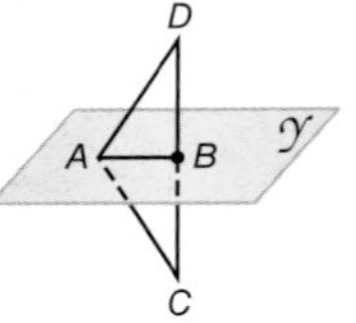

53. **Given:** Plane $\mathcal{Z}$ is an angle bisector of $\angle KJH$, $\overline{KJ} \cong \overline{HJ}$ **See Ch. 5 Answer Appendix.**
Prove: $\overline{MH} \cong \overline{MK}$

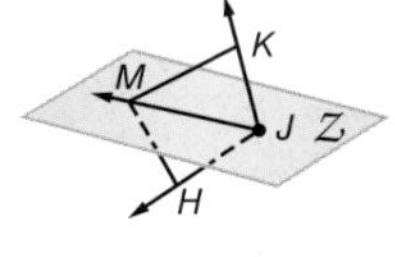

54. **WRITING IN MATH** Compare and contrast the perpendicular bisectors and angle bisectors of a triangle. How are they alike? How are they different? Be sure to compare their points of concurrency. **See margin.**

45. The equation of a line of one of the perpendicular bisectors is $y = 3$. The equation of a line of another perpendicular bisector is $x = 5$. These lines intersect at $(5, 3)$. The circumcenter is located at $(5, 3)$.

46. The equation of a line of one perpendicular bisector is $y = -4$. The equation of a line of another perpendicular bisector is $x = 2.5$. These lines intersect at $(2.5, -4)$. The circumcenter is located at $(2.5, -4)$.

49. Sample answer:

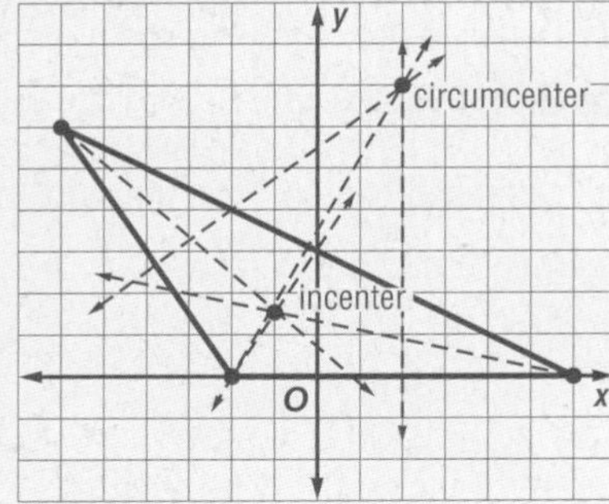

Standardized Test Practice

55. ALGEBRA An object is projected straight upward with initial velocity v meters per second from an initial height of s meters. The height h in meters of the object after t seconds is given by $h = -10t^2 + vt + s$. Sherise is standing at the edge of a balcony 54 meters above the ground and throws a ball straight up with an initial velocity of 12 meters per second. After how many seconds will it hit the ground? **A**

A 3 seconds
B 4 seconds
C 6 seconds
D 9 seconds

56. SAT/ACT For $x \neq -3$, $\frac{3x+9}{x+3} =$ **K**

F $x + 12$
G $x + 9$
H $x + 3$
J x
K 3

57. A line drawn through which of the following points would be a perpendicular bisector of $\triangle JKL$? **D**

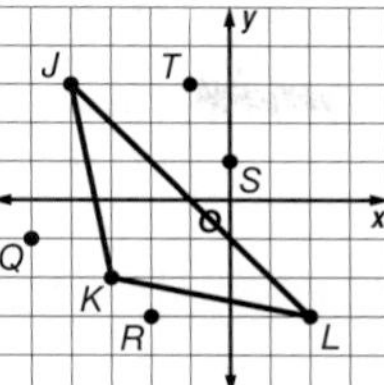

A T and K
B L and Q
C J and R
D S and K

58. SHORT RESPONSE Write an equation in slope-intercept form that describes the line containing the points (−1, 0) and (2, 4). $y = \frac{4}{3}x + \frac{4}{3}$

Spiral Review

Name the missing coordinate(s) of each triangle. (Lesson 4-8)

59.

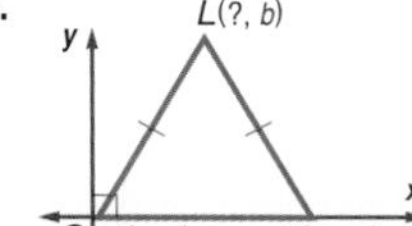

$L(a, b)$

60.

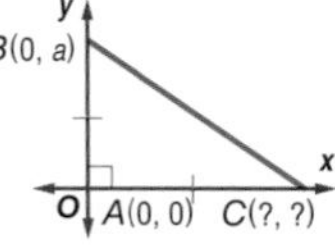

$C(a, 0)$

61.

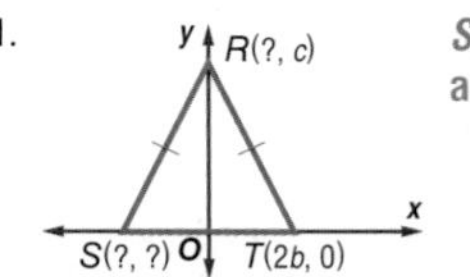

$S(-2b, 0)$ and $R(0, c)$

COORDINATE GEOMETRY Graph each pair of triangles with the given vertices. Then identify the transformation and verify that it is a congruence transformation. (Lesson 4-7) **62–63. See margin.**

62. $A(-2, 4)$, $B(-2, -2)$, $C(4, 1)$;
$R(12, 4)$, $S(12, -2)$, $T(6, 1)$

63. $J(-3, 3)$, $K(-3, 1)$, $L(1, 1)$;
$X(-3, -1)$, $Y(-3, -3)$, $Z(1, -3)$

Find the distance from the line to the given point. (Lesson 3-6)

64. $y = 5$, $(-2, 4)$ **1**

65. $y = 2x + 2$, $(-1, -5)$ $\sqrt{5}$

66. $2x - 3y = -9$, $(2, 0)$ $\sqrt{13}$

67. AUDIO ENGINEERING A studio engineer charges a flat fee of $450 for equipment rental and $42 an hour for recording and mixing time. Write the equation that shows the cost to hire the studio engineer as a function of time. How much would it cost to hire the studio engineer for 17 hours? (Lesson 3-4) $m = 42t + 450$; **$1164**

Skills Review

PROOF Write a two-column proof for each of the following. **68–69. See Ch. 5 Answer Appendix.**

68. Given: $\triangle XKF$ is equilateral.
$\overline{XJ}$ bisects $\angle X$.
Prove: J is the midpoint of $\overline{KF}$.

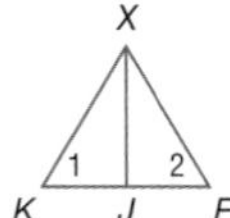

69. Given: $\triangle MLP$ is isosceles.
N is the midpoint of $\overline{MP}$.
Prove: $\overline{LN} \perp \overline{MP}$

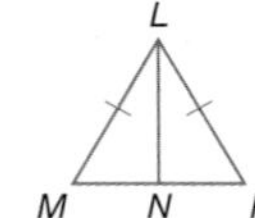

Differentiated Instruction OL BL

Extension In groups have the students discuss what geometric term represents the center of a star and explain.

Sample answer: Circumenter; the circumcenter of a figure is equidistant from the vertices of the figure.

CCSS Teaching the Mathematical Practices

Arguments Mathematically proficient students are able to analyze situations by breaking them into cases and can recognize and use counterexamples. In Exercises 50–51, encourage students to draw each figure first.

4 Assess

Name the Math Have students sketch an irregular figure with five sides. Have them describe a way to find its center of gravity.

Additional Answers

54. The bisectors each bisect something, but the perpendicular bisectors bisect segments while angle bisectors bisect angles. They each will intersect at a point of concurrency. The point of concurrency for perpendicular bisectors is the circumcenter. The point of concurrency for angle bisectors is the incenter. The incenter always lies in the triangle, while the circumcenter can be inside, outside, or on the triangle.

62.

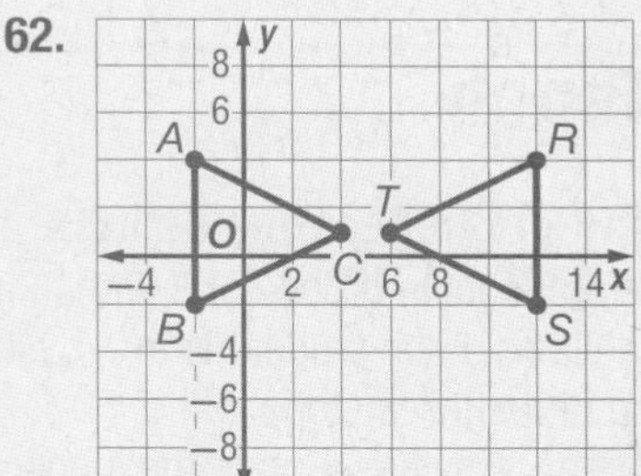

$\triangle RST$ is a reflection of $\triangle ABC$; $AB = 6$, $BC = \sqrt{45}$, $AC = \sqrt{45}$, $TR = \sqrt{45}$, $RS = 6$, $TS = \sqrt{45}$. $\triangle ABC \cong \triangle RST$ by SSS.

63.

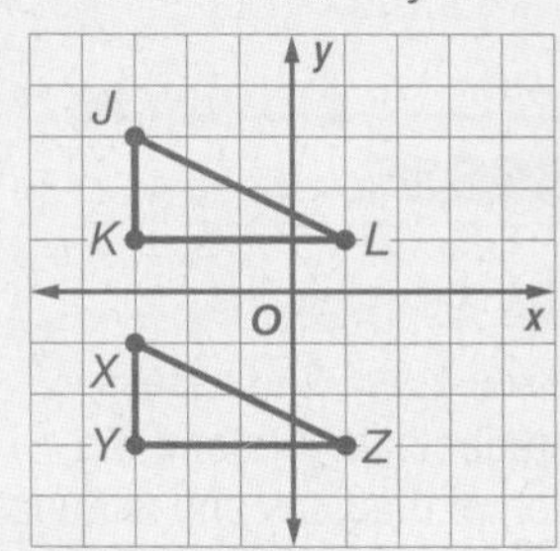

$\triangle JKL$ is a translation of $\triangle XYZ$; $JK = 2$, $KL = 4$, $JL = \sqrt{20}$; $XY = 2$, $YZ = 4$, $XZ = \sqrt{20}$. $\triangle JKL \cong \triangle XYZ$ by SSS.

1 Focus

Objective Construct medians and altitudes of triangles.

Materials for Each Group

- straightedge
- string
- thumbtack

Teaching Tip

The activity demonstrates two different constructions on an acute scalene triangle. Students could use patty paper to draw and trace two acute scalene triangles with the same side lengths, angle measures, and orientation in three different places on one sheet of paper. When students are finished with the constructions, they can see the differences between the medians and altitudes for the same triangle.

Alternative Method

The constructions presented in this lesson can also be completed using classic ruler and compass methods.

2 Teach

Working in Cooperative Groups

Arrange students in groups of 3 with mixed abilities. Each student is to pick one of the three steps in the construction activities. Rotate the steps for Constructions 1 and 2.

Practice Have students complete Exercises 1 and 2.

EXPLORE 5-2 Geometry Lab: Constructing Medians and Altitudes

A *median* of a triangle is a segment with endpoints that are a vertex and the midpoint of the side opposite that vertex. You can use the construction for the midpoint of a segment to construct a median.

Wrap the end of string around a pencil. Use a thumbtack to fix the string to a vertex.

CCSS Common Core State Standards
Content Standards
G.CO.12 Make formal geometric constructions with a variety of tools and methods (compass and straightedge, string, reflective devices, paper folding, dynamic geometric software, etc.).
Mathematical Practices 5

Construction 1 Median of a Triangle

Step 1

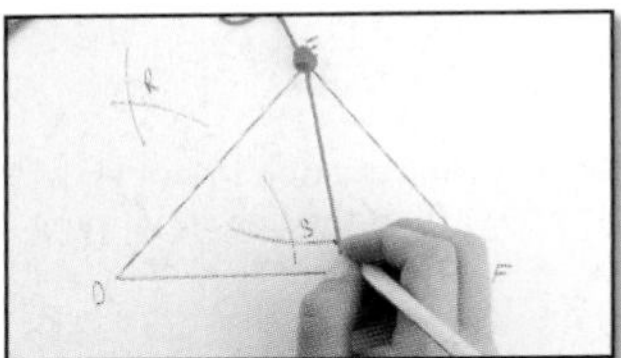

Place the thumbtack on vertex D and then on vertex E to draw intersecting arcs above and below $\overline{DE}$. Label the points of intersection R and S.

Step 2

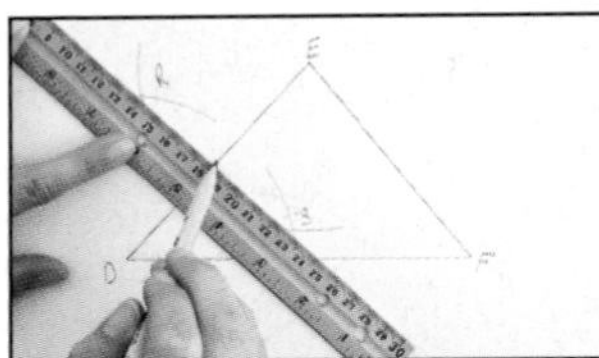

Use a straightedge to find the point where $\overline{RS}$ intersects $\overline{DE}$. Label the point M. This is the midpoint of $\overline{DE}$.

Step 3

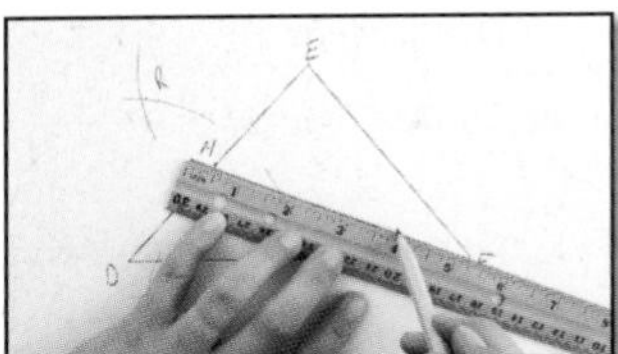

Draw a line through F and M. $\overline{FM}$ is a median of $\triangle DEF$.

An *altitude* of a triangle is a segment from a vertex of the triangle to the opposite side and is perpendicular to the opposite side.

Construction 2 Altitude of a Triangle

Step 1

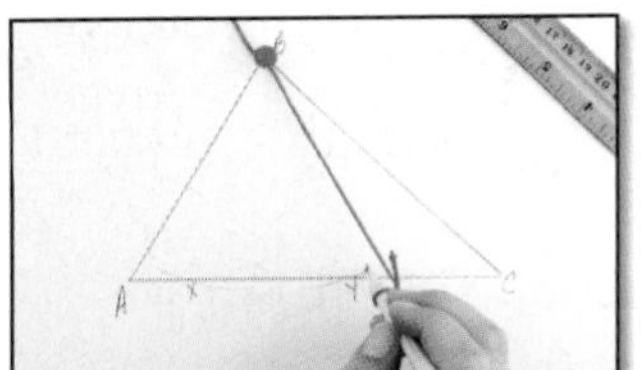

Place the thumbtack on vertex B and draw two arcs intersecting $\overline{AC}$. Label the points where the arcs intersect the sides as X and Y.

Step 2

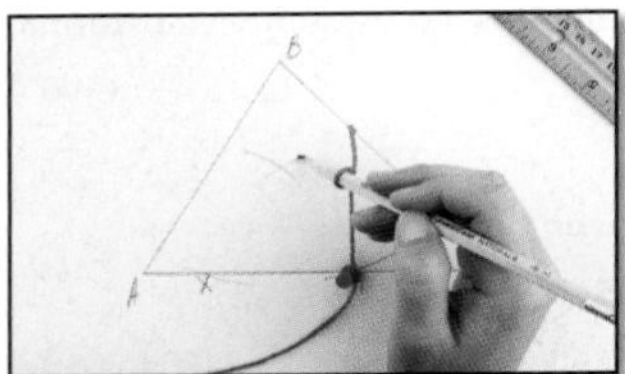

Adjust the length of the string so that it is greater than $\frac{1}{2}XY$. Place the tack on X and draw an arc above $\overline{AC}$. Use the same length of string to draw an arc from Y. Label the points of intersection of the arcs H.

Step 3

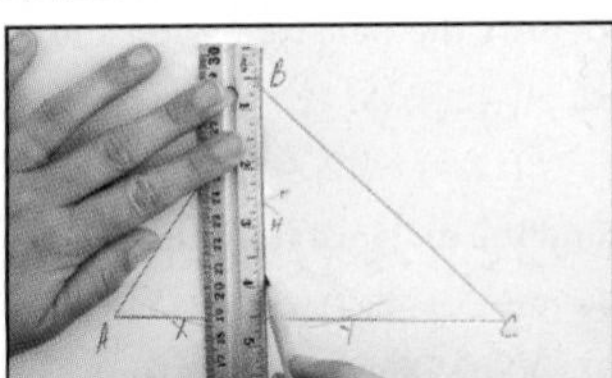

Use a straightedge to draw $\overleftrightarrow{BH}$. Label the point where $\overleftrightarrow{BH}$ intersects $\overline{AC}$ as D. $\overline{BD}$ is an altitude of $\triangle ABC$ and is perpendicular to $\overline{AC}$.

Model and Analyze 1–2. See margin.

1. Construct the medians of the other two sides of $\triangle DEF$. What do you notice about the medians of a triangle?
2. Construct the altitudes to the other two sides of $\triangle ABC$. What do you observe?

3 Assess

Formative Assessment

Use Exercises 1 and 2 to assess whether students understand the construction of medians and altitudes.

From Concrete to Abstract

Have students compare the intersections of the medians and altitudes they constructed with the incenter and circumcenter of the triangle.

Additional Answers

1. They intersect at the same point.
2. They intersect at the same point.

334 | Explore 5-2 | Geometry Lab: Constructing Medians and Altitudes

LESSON 5-2 Medians and Altitudes of Triangles

Then

- You identified and used perpendicular and angle bisectors in triangles.

Now

1. Identify and use medians in triangles.
2. Identify and use altitudes in triangles.

Why?

- A mobile is a *kinetic* or moving sculpture that uses the principles of balance and equilibrium. Simple mobiles consist of several rods attached by strings from which objects of varying weights hang. The hanging objects balance each other and can rotate freely. To ensure that a triangle in a mobile hangs parallel to the ground, artists have to find the triangle's balancing point.

NewVocabulary
median
centroid
altitude
orthocenter

Common Core State Standards

Content Standards
G.CO.10 Prove theorems about triangles.
G.MG.3 Apply geometric methods to solve problems (e.g., designing an object or structure to satisfy physical constraints or minimize cost; working with typographic grid systems based on ratios). ★

Mathematical Practices
6 Attend to precision.
3 Construct viable arguments and critique the reasoning of others.

1 Medians

A **median** of a triangle is a segment with endpoints being a vertex of a triangle and the midpoint of the opposite side.

Every triangle has three medians that are concurrent. The point of concurrency of the medians of a triangle is called the **centroid** and is always inside the triangle.

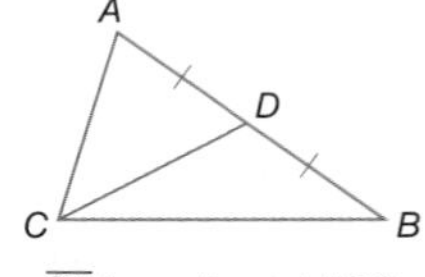

$\overline{CD}$ is a median of $\triangle ABC$.

Theorem 5.7 Centroid Theorem

The medians of a triangle intersect at a point called the centroid that is two thirds of the distance from each vertex to the midpoint of the opposite side.

Example If P is the centroid of $\triangle ABC$, then $AP = \frac{2}{3}AK$, $BP = \frac{2}{3}BL$, and $CP = \frac{2}{3}CJ$.

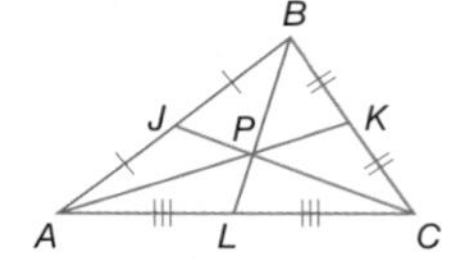

You will prove Theorem 5.7 in Exercise 36.

Example 1 Use the Centroid Theorem

In $\triangle ABC$, Q is the centroid and $BE = 9$. Find BQ and QE.

$BQ = \frac{2}{3}BE$ — Centroid Theorem

$= \frac{2}{3}(9)$ or 6 — $BE = 9$

$BQ + QE = 9$ — Segment Addition

$6 + QE = 9$ — $BQ = 6$

$QE = 3$ — Subtract 6 from each side.

GuidedPractice In $\triangle ABC$ above, $FC = 15$. Find each length.

1A. FQ 5

1B. QC 10

1 Focus

VerticalAlignment

Before Lesson 5-2 Identify and use perpendicular and angle bisectors in triangles.

Lesson 5-2 Identify and use medians and altitudes in triangles.

After Lesson 5-2 Recognize and apply properties of inequalities to the angles and sides of a triangle.

2 Teach

Scaffolding Questions

Have students read the **Why?** section of the lesson.

Ask:

- What does *kinetic* mean? moving
- At what point should a mobile be hung to be parallel to the ground? the balancing point
- Is the balancing point of a mobile always at its center? Why? Sample answer: No, in the picture it is not, and this is due to the difference in the weights of the objects.

Lesson 5-2 Resources

Resource	Approaching Level AL	On Level OL	Beyond Level BL	English Learners ELL
Teacher Edition	▪ Differentiated Instruction, p. 338	▪ Differentiated Instruction, p. 338	▪ Differentiated Instruction, p. 338	▪ Differentiated Instruction, p. 338
Chapter Resource Masters	▪ Study Guide and Intervention, pp. 11–12 ▪ Skills Practice, p. 13 ▪ Practice, p. 14 ▪ Word Problem Practice, p. 15	▪ Study Guide and Intervention, pp. 11–12 ▪ Skills Practice, p. 13 ▪ Practice, p. 14 ▪ Word Problem Practice, p. 15 ▪ Enrichment, p. 16	▪ Practice, p. 14 ▪ Word Problem Practice, p. 15 ▪ Enrichment, p. 16	▪ Study Guide and Intervention, pp. 11–12 ▪ Skills Practice, p. 13 ▪ Practice, p. 14 ▪ Word Problem Practice, p. 15
Other	▪ 5-Minute Check 5-2 ▪ Study Notebook ▪ Teaching Geometry with Manipulatives	▪ 5-Minute Check 5-2 ▪ Study Notebook ▪ Teaching Geometry with Manipulatives	▪ 5-Minute Check 5-2 ▪ Study Notebook	▪ 5-Minute Check 5-2 ▪ Study Notebook ▪ Teaching Geometry with Manipulatives

1 Medians

Examples 1 and 2 show how to use the Centroid Theorem to find segment lengths. **Example 3** shows how to find the centroid by using the coordinate plane.

Formative Assessment

Use the Guided Practice exercises after each example to determine students' understanding of the concepts.

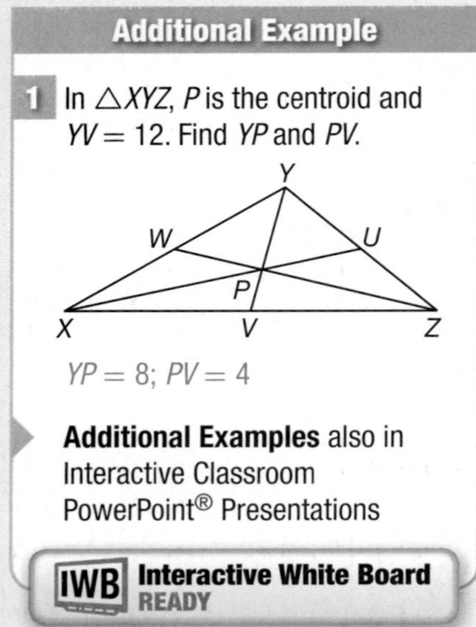

Additional Example

1 In $\triangle XYZ$, P is the centroid and $YV = 12$. Find YP and PV.

$YP = 8$; $PV = 4$

Additional Examples also in Interactive Classroom PowerPoint® Presentations

IWB Interactive White Board READY

Teach with Tech

Interactive Whiteboard Work through an example on the board and save your work. Post your notes on a class Web page so students will have an additional reference outside of class.

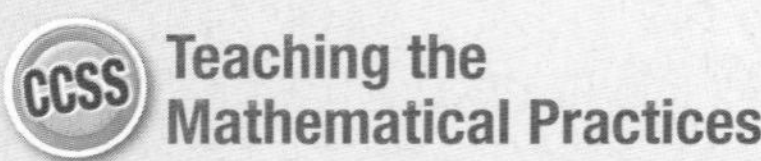

Teaching the Mathematical Practices

Reasoning Mathematically proficient students make sense of quantities and their relationships in problem situations. Encourage students to contextualize the abstract in a problem.

StudyTip

CCSS Reasoning In Example 2, you can also use number sense to find KP. Since $KP = \frac{2}{3}KT$, $PT = \frac{1}{3}KT$ and $KP = 2PT$. Therefore, if $PT = 2$, then $KP = 2(2)$ or 4.

Example 2 Use the Centroid Theorem

In $\triangle JKL$, $PT = 2$. Find KP.

Since $\overline{JR} \cong \overline{RK}$, R is the midpoint of $\overline{JK}$ and $\overline{LR}$ is a median of $\triangle JKL$. Likewise, S and T are the midpoints of $\overline{KL}$ and $\overline{LJ}$ respectively, so $\overline{JS}$ and $\overline{KT}$ are also medians of $\triangle JKL$. Therefore, point P is the centroid of $\triangle JKL$.

$KP = \frac{2}{3}KT$	Centroid Theorem
$KP = \frac{2}{3}(KP + PT)$	Segment Addition and Substitution
$KP = \frac{2}{3}(KP + 2)$	$PT = 2$
$KP = \frac{2}{3}KP + \frac{4}{3}$	Distributive Property
$\frac{1}{3}KP = \frac{4}{3}$	Subtract $\frac{2}{3}KP$ from each side.
$KP = 4$	Multiply each side by 3.

GuidedPractice

In $\triangle JKL$ above, $RP = 3.5$ and $JP = 9$. Find each measure.

2A. PL 7 **2B.** PS 4.5

All polygons have a balance point or centroid. The centroid is also the balancing point or *center of gravity* for a triangular region. The center of gravity is the point at which the region is stable under the influence of gravity.

Real-World Example 3 Find the Centroid on Coordinate Plane

PERFORMANCE ART A performance artist plans to balance triangular pieces of metal during her next act. When one such triangle is placed on the coordinate plane, its vertices are located at (1, 10), (5, 0), and (9, 5). What are the coordinates of the point where the artist should support the triangle so that it will balance?

Understand You need to find the centroid of the triangle with the given coordinates. This is the point at which the triangle will balance.

Plan Graph and label the triangle with vertices $A(1, 10)$, $B(5, 0)$, and $C(9, 5)$. Since the centroid is the point of concurrency of the medians of a triangle, use the Midpoint Theorem to find the midpoint of one of the sides of the triangle. The centroid is two-thirds the distance from the opposite vertex to that midpoint.

Math HistoryLink

Pierre de Fermat (1601–1665) Another triangle center is the Fermat point, which minimizes the sum of the distances from the three vertices. Fermat is one of the best-known mathematicians for writing proofs.

Solve Graph $\triangle ABC$.

Find the midpoint D of side $\overline{AB}$ with endpoints $A(1, 10)$ and $B(5, 0)$.

$D\left(\frac{1+5}{2}, \frac{10+0}{2}\right) = D(3, 5)$

Graph point D. Notice that $\overline{DC}$ is a horizontal line. The distance from $D(3, 5)$ to $C(9, 5)$ is $9 - 3$ or 6 units.

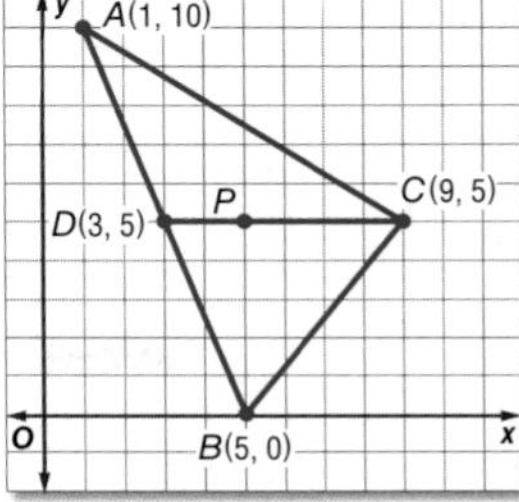

If P is the centroid of $\triangle ABC$, then $PC = \frac{2}{3}DC$. So the centroid is $\frac{2}{3}(6)$ or 4 units to the left of C. The coordinates of P are $(9 - 4, 5)$ or $(5, 5)$.

The performer should balance the triangle at the point (5, 5).

Check Use a different median to check your answer. The midpoint F of side $\overline{AC}$ is $F\left(\frac{1+9}{2}, \frac{10+5}{2}\right)$ or $F(5, 7.5)$. $\overline{BF}$ is a vertical line, so the distance from B to F is $7.5 - 0$ or 7.5. $\overline{PB} = \frac{2}{3}(7.5)$ or 5, so P is 5 units up from B. The coordinates of P are $(5, 0 + 5)$ or $(5, 5)$. ✓

GuidedPractice

3. A second triangle has vertices at (0, 4), (6, 11.5), and (12, 1). What are the coordinates of the point where the artist should support the triangle so that it will balance? Explain your reasoning. **See margin.**

2 Altitudes

An **altitude** of a triangle is a segment from a vertex to the line containing the opposite side and perpendicular to the line containing that side. An altitude can lie in the interior, exterior, or on the side of a triangle.

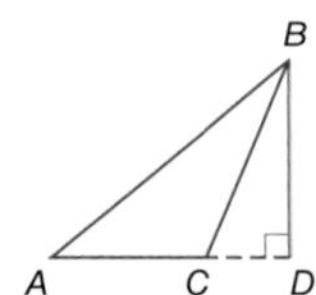

$\overline{BD}$ is an altitude from B to $\overline{AC}$.

ReadingMath

Height of a Triangle The length of an altitude is known as the *height* of the triangle. The height of a triangle is used to calculate the triangle's area.

Every triangle has three altitudes. If extended, the altitudes of a triangle intersect in a common point.

KeyConcept Orthocenter

The lines containing the altitudes of a triangle are concurrent, intersecting at a point called the **orthocenter**.

Example The lines containing altitudes $\overline{AF}$, $\overline{CD}$, and $\overline{BG}$ intersect at P, the orthocenter of $\triangle ABC$.

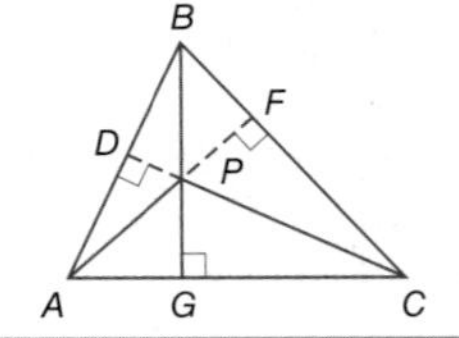

Additional Examples

2 In $\triangle ABC$, $CG = 4$. Find GE.

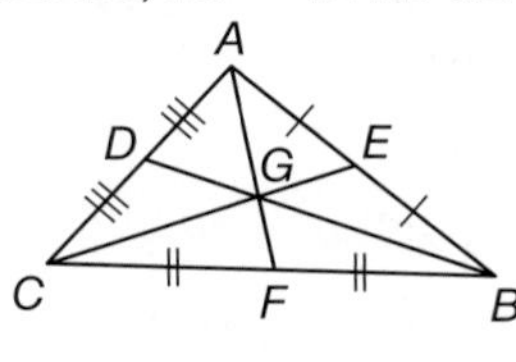

2

3 **SCULPTURE** An artist is designing a sculpture that balances a triangle on top of a pole. In the artist's design on the coordinate plane, the vertices are located at (1, 4), (3, 0), and (3, 8). What are the coordinates of the point where the artist should place the pole under the triangle so that it will balance? $\left(\frac{7}{3}, 4\right)$

WatchOut!

Orthocenter The orthocenter may not lie in the interior of the triangle.

Additional Answer (Guided Practice)

3. (6, 5.5)

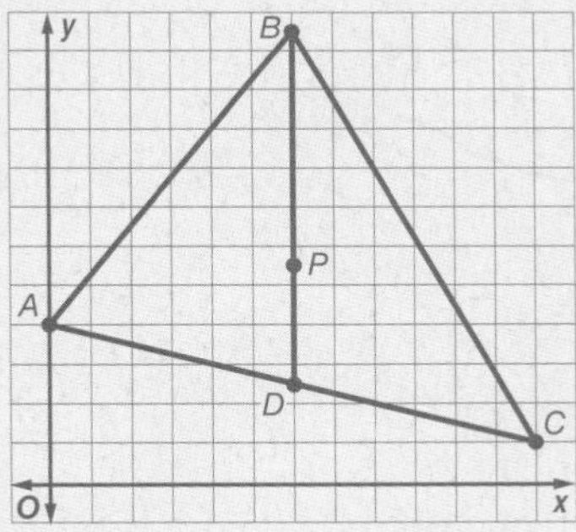

The midpoint of side $\overline{AC}$ is $D\left(\frac{0+12}{2}, \frac{4+1}{2}\right)$ or $D(6, 2.5)$. $\overline{BD}$ is a vertical line, so the distance from B to D is $11.5 - 2.5$ or 9. $PB = \frac{2}{3}(9)$ or 6, so P is 6 units down from B. The coordinates of P are $(6, 11.5 - 6)$ or $(6, 5.5)$.

2 Altitudes

Example 4 shows how to find the orthocenter of a triangle on the coordinate plane.

Additional Example

4 **COORDINATE GEOMETRY** The vertices of $\triangle HIJ$ are $H(1, 2)$, $I(-3, -3)$, and $J(-5, 1)$. Find the coordinates of the orthocenter of $\triangle HIJ$.

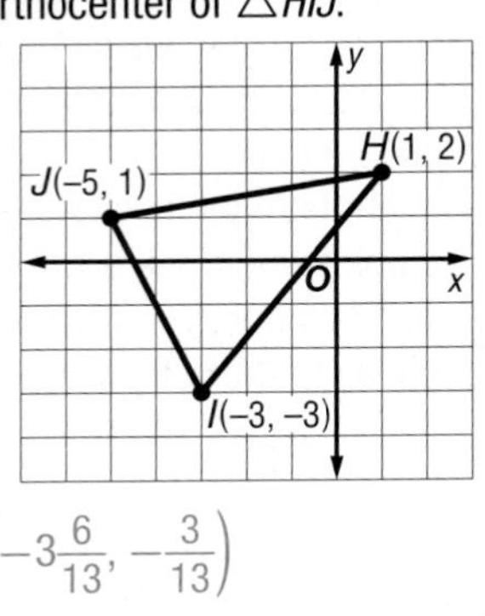

$\left(-3\frac{6}{13}, -\frac{3}{13}\right)$

Focus on Mathematical Content

Centroid and Orthocenter In an acute triangle, the centroid and orthocenter may appear to be the same point. This only occurs when each median of the triangle is the same as each perpendicular bisector.

Example 4 Find the Orthocenter on a Coordinate Plane

COORDINATE GEOMETRY The vertices of $\triangle FGH$ are $F(-2, 4)$, $G(4, 4)$, and $H(1, -2)$. Find the coordinates of the orthocenter of $\triangle FGH$.

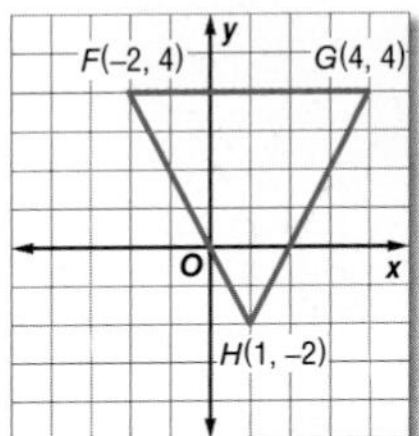

Step 1 Graph $\triangle FGH$. To find the orthocenter, find the point where two of the three altitudes intersect.

Step 2 Find an equation of the altitude from F to $\overline{GH}$. The slope of $\overline{GH}$ is $\frac{4-(-2)}{4-1}$ or 2, so the slope of the altitude, which is perpendicular to $\overline{GH}$, is $-\frac{1}{2}$.

$y - y_1 = m(x - x_1)$ Point-slope form

$y - 4 = -\frac{1}{2}[x - (-2)]$ $m = -\frac{1}{2}$ and $(x_1, y_1) = F(-2, 4)$.

$y - 4 = -\frac{1}{2}(x + 2)$ Simplify.

$y - 4 = -\frac{1}{2}x - 1$ Distributive Property

$y = -\frac{1}{2}x + 3$ Add 4 to each side.

Find an equation of the altitude from G to $\overline{FH}$. The slope of $\overline{FH}$ is $\frac{-2-4}{1-(-2)}$ or -2, so the slope of the altitude is $\frac{1}{2}$.

$y - y_1 = m(x - x_1)$ Point-slope form

$y - 4 = \frac{1}{2}(x - 4)$ $m = \frac{1}{2}$ and $(x_1, y_1) = G(4, 4)$

$y - 4 = \frac{1}{2}x - 2$ Distributive Property

$y = \frac{1}{2}x + 2$ Add 4 to each side.

Step 3 Solve the resulting system of equations $\begin{cases} y = -\frac{1}{2}x + 3 \\ y = \frac{1}{2}x + 2 \end{cases}$ to find the point of intersection of the altitudes.

Adding the two equations to eliminate x results in $2y = 5$ or $y = \frac{5}{2}$.

$y = \frac{1}{2}x + 2$ Equation of altitude from G

$\frac{5}{2} = \frac{1}{2}x + 2$ $y = \frac{5}{2}$

$\frac{1}{2} = \frac{1}{2}x$ Subtract $\frac{4}{2}$ or 2 from each side.

$1 = x$ Multiply each side by 2.

The coordinates of the orthocenter of $\triangle JKL$ are $\left(1, \frac{5}{2}\right)$ or $\left(1, 2\frac{1}{2}\right)$.

StudyTip

Check for Reasonableness Use the corner of a sheet of paper to draw the altitudes of each side of the triangle.

The intersection is located at approximately $\left(1, 2\frac{1}{2}\right)$, so the answer is reasonable.

Guided Practice

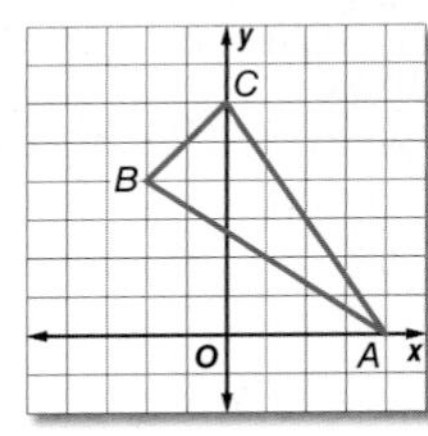

4. Find the coordinates of the orthocenter of $\triangle ABC$ graphed at the right. $\left(-\frac{4}{5}, 4\frac{4}{5}\right)$

Differentiated Instruction AL OL BL ELL

Visual/Spatial Learners Tell students to fold a sheet of paper in four sections labeled Circumcenter, Incenter, Centroid, and Orthocenter. Have students draw a copy of the same triangle in each section of the paper and use their spatial skills to determine the approximate position of the circumcenter, incenter, centroid, and orthocenter of the triangle. Then students can use metric rulers, compasses, and protractors to see how close their approximations are.

ConceptSummary Special Segments and Points in Triangles

Name	Example	Point of Concurrency	Special Property	Example
perpendicular bisector		circumcenter	The circumcenter *P* of $\triangle ABC$ is equidistant from each vertex.	
angle bisector		incenter	The incenter *Q* of $\triangle ABC$ is equidistant from each side of the triangle.	
median		centroid	The centroid *R* of $\triangle ABC$ is two thirds of the distance from each vertex to the midpoint of the opposite side.	
altitude		orthocenter	The lines containing the altitudes of $\triangle ABC$ are concurrent at the orthocenter *S*.	

Check Your Understanding

= Step-by-Step Solutions begin on page R14.

Examples 1–2 **In $\triangle ACE$, *P* is the centroid, $PF = 6$, and $AD = 15$. Find each measure.**

1. PC 12
2. AP 10

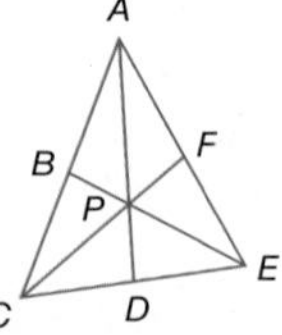

Example 3

3. **INTERIOR DESIGN** An interior designer is creating a custom coffee table for a client. The top of the table is a glass triangle that needs to balance on a single support. If the coordinates of the vertices of the triangle are at (3, 6), (5, 2), and (7, 10), at what point should the support be placed? (5, 6)

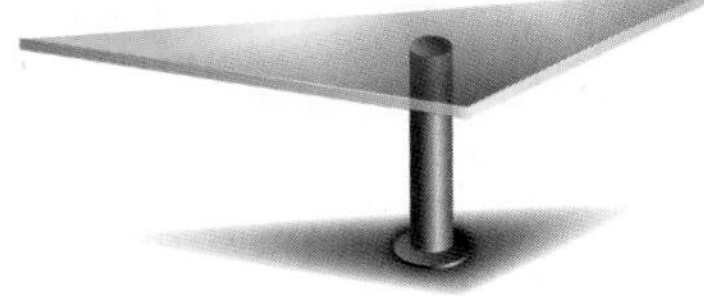

Example 4

4. **COORDINATE GEOMETRY** Find the coordinates of the orthocenter of $\triangle ABC$ with vertices $A(-3, 3)$, $B(-1, 7)$, and $C(3, 3)$. $(-1, 5)$

3 Practice

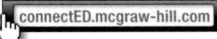

Formative Assessment

Use Exercises 1–4 to check for understanding.

Then use the chart at the bottom of the next page to customize assignments for your students.

Tips for New Teachers

Sense-Making It may be hard for students to differentiate between the four points of concurrency of a triangle. Have students draw a diagram using a protractor and ruler for each of the points. Encourage students to make a connection between the segments they are drawing and the corresponding point of concurrency.

CCSS Teaching the Mathematical Practices

Sense-making Mathematically proficient students look for entry points to a solution. They analyze givens, constraints, relationships, and goals. They plan a solution pathway. In Exercise 20, encourage students to make a plan to solve the problem first.

Additional Answers

31. **Given:** $\triangle XYZ$ is isosceles. $\overline{WY}$ bisects $\angle Y$.

Prove: $\overline{WY}$ is a median.

Proof: Since $\triangle XYZ$ is isosceles, $\overline{XY} \cong \overline{YZ}$. By the definition of angle bisector, $\angle XYW \cong \angle ZYW$. $\overline{YW} \cong \overline{YW}$ by the Reflexive Property. So, by SAS, $\triangle XYW \cong \triangle ZYW$. By CPCTC, $\overline{XW} \cong \overline{ZW}$. By the definition of a midpoint, W is the midpoint of $\overline{XZ}$. By the definition of a median, $\overline{WY}$ is a median.

32. **Given:** $\triangle XYZ$ with medians $\overline{XR}$, $\overline{YS}$, and $\overline{ZQ}$.

Prove: $\frac{XP}{PR} = 2$

Proof:

Statements (Reasons)

1. $\triangle XYZ$ with medians $\overline{XR}$, $\overline{YS}$, and $\overline{ZQ}$. (Given)
2. $XP = \frac{2}{3}XR$ (Centroid Thm.)
3. $XR = XP + PR$ (Seg. Add. Post.)
4. $XP = \frac{2}{3}(XP + PR)$ (Subst.)
5. $XP = \frac{2}{3}XP + \frac{2}{3}PR$ (Dist. Prop.)
6. $\frac{1}{3}XP = \frac{2}{3}PR$ (Subt. Prop.)
7. $XP = 2PR$ (Mult. Prop.)
8. $\frac{XP}{PR} = 2$ (Div. Prop.)

Practice and Problem Solving

Extra Practice is on page R5.

Examples 1–2 In $\triangle SZU$, $UJ = 9$, $VJ = 3$, and $ZT = 18$. Find each length.

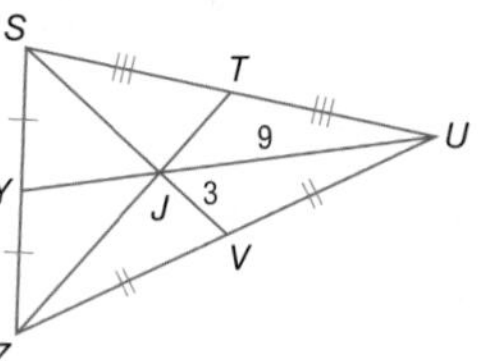

5. YJ 4.5
6. SJ 6
7. YU 13.5
8. SV 9
9. JT 6
10. ZJ 12

Example 3 **COORDINATE GEOMETRY** Find the coordinates of the centroid of each triangle with the given vertices.

11. $A(-1, 11)$, $B(3, 1)$, $C(7, 6)$ (3, 6)
12. $X(5, 7)$, $Y(9, -3)$, $Z(13, 2)$ (9, 2)

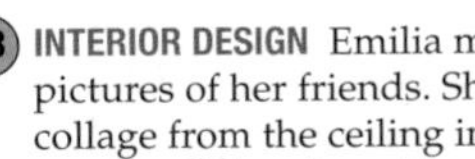

13. **INTERIOR DESIGN** Emilia made a collage with pictures of her friends. She wants to hang the collage from the ceiling in her room so that it is parallel to the ceiling. A diagram of the collage is shown in the graph at the right. At what point should she place the string? (3, 4)

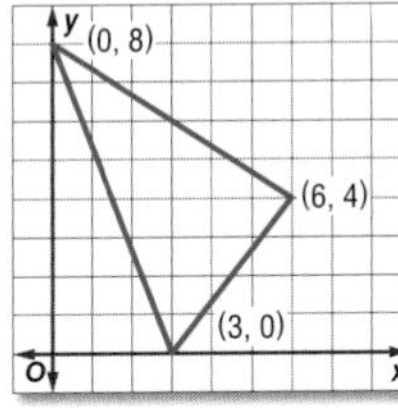

Example 4 **COORDINATE GEOMETRY** Find the coordinates of the orthocenter of each triangle with the given vertices.

14. $J(3, -2)$, $K(5, 6)$, $L(9, -2)$ (5, −1)
15. $R(-4, 8)$, $S(-1, 5)$, $T(5, 5)$ (−4, −4)

Identify each segment $\overline{BD}$ as a(n) altitude, median, or perpendicular bisector.

16. altitude

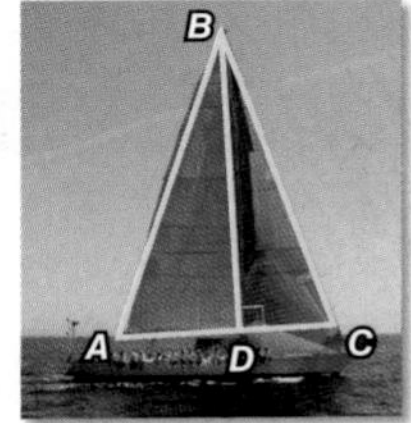

17. median

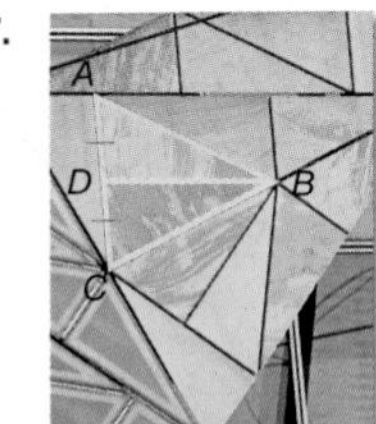

18. perpendicular bisector, altitude, median

19. median

20. **CCSS SENSE-MAKING** In the figure at the right, if J, P, and L are the midpoints of $\overline{KH}$, $\overline{HM}$, and $\overline{MK}$, respectively, find x, y, and z.
$x = 4.75$, $y = 6$, $z = 1$

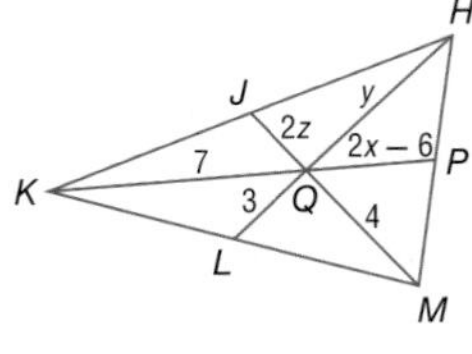

Differentiated Homework Options

Level	Assignment	Two-Day Option	
AL Basic	5–15, 37, 38, 40, 42–56	5–19 odd, 44–47	6–18 even, 37, 38, 40, 42, 43, 48–56
OL Core	5–25 odd, 26, 27–37 odd, 38, 40, 42–56	5–19, 44–47	20–38, 40, 42, 43, 48–56
BL Advanced	20–55, (optional: 56)		

26. Circumcenter, incenter, centroid, orthocenter; sample answer: The angle bisector of each angle also bisects the opposite side and is perpendicular to the opposite side of the triangle, so it also represents the perpendicular bisector, the median, and the altitude. That means that the blue peg represents all of the centers, including the circumcenter, incenter, centroid, and orthocenter.

Copy and complete each statement for $\triangle RST$ for medians $\overline{RM}$, $\overline{SL}$ and $\overline{TK}$, and centroid J.

21. $SL = x(JL)$ 3

22. $JT = x(TK)$ $\frac{2}{3}$

23. $JM = x(RJ)$ $\frac{1}{2}$

ALGEBRA Use the figure at the right.

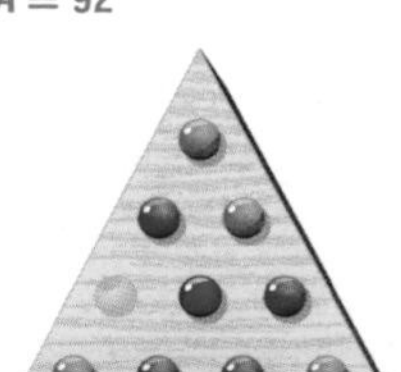

24. If $\overline{EC}$ is an altitude of $\triangle AED$, $m\angle 1 = 2x + 7$, and $m\angle 2 = 3x + 13$, find $m\angle 1$ and $m\angle 2$. $m\angle 1 = 35$, $m\angle 2 = 55$

25. Find the value of x if $AC = 4x - 3$, $DC = 2x + 9$, $m\angle ECA = 15x + 2$, and $\overline{EC}$ is a median of $\triangle AED$. Is $\overline{EC}$ also an altitude of $\triangle AED$? Explain. 6; no; because $m\angle ECA = 92$

26. **GAMES** The game board shown is shaped like an equilateral triangle and has indentations for game pieces. The game's objective is to remove pegs by jumping over them until there is only one peg left. Copy the game board's outline and determine which of the points of concurrency the blue peg represents: *circumcenter, incenter, centroid,* or *orthocenter*. Explain your reasoning.

CCSS ARGUMENTS Use the given information to determine whether $\overline{LM}$ is a *perpendicular bisector, median,* and/or an *altitude* of $\triangle JKL$.

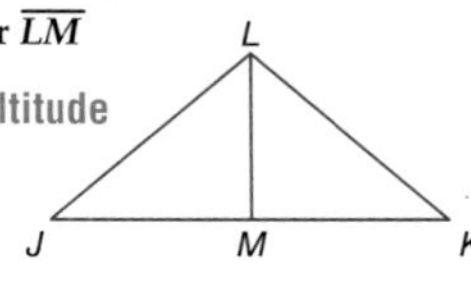

27. $\overline{LM} \perp \overline{JK}$ altitude

28. $\triangle JLM \cong \triangle KLM$ perpendicular bisector, median, altitude

29. $\overline{JM} \cong \overline{KM}$ median

30. $\overline{LM} \perp \overline{JK}$ and $\overline{JL} \cong \overline{KL}$ perpendicular bisector, median, altitude

31. **PROOF** Write a paragraph proof.

Given: $\triangle XYZ$ is isosceles. $\overline{WY}$ bisects $\angle Y$.

Prove: $\overline{WY}$ is a median. See margin.

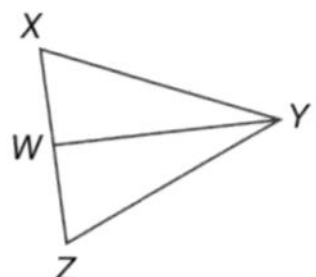

32. **PROOF** Write an algebraic proof.

Given: $\triangle XYZ$ with medians $\overline{XR}$, $\overline{YS}$, $\overline{ZQ}$

Prove: $\frac{XP}{PR} = 2$ See margin.

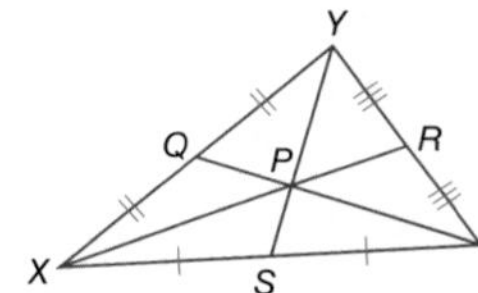

33. **MULTIPLE REPRESENTATIONS** In this problem, you will investigate the location of the points of concurrency for any equilateral triangle. a–c. See Ch. 5 Answer Appendix.

a. **Concrete** Construct three different equilateral triangles on tracing paper and cut them out. Fold each triangle to locate the circumcenter, incenter, centroid, and orthocenter.

b. **Verbal** Make a conjecture about the relationships among the four points of concurrency of any equilateral triangle.

c. **Graphical** Position an equilateral triangle and its circumcenter, incenter, centroid, and orthocenter on the coordinate plane using variable coordinates. Determine the coordinates of each point of concurrency.

ALGEBRA In $\triangle JLP$, $m\angle JMP = 3x - 6$, $JK = 3y - 2$, and $LK = 5y - 8$.

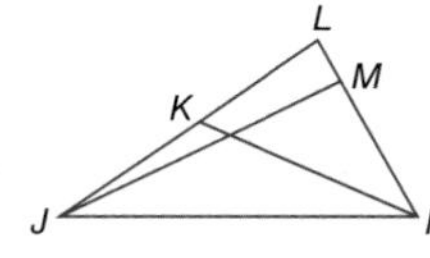

34. If $\overline{JM}$ is an altitude of $\triangle JLP$, find x. 32

35. Find LK if $\overline{PK}$ is a median. 7

CCSS Teaching the Mathematical Practices

Arguments Mathematically proficient students understand and use stated assumptions, definitions, and previously established results in constructing arguments. In Exercises 27–30, encourage students to draw a figure for each exercise with the given information labeled.

Enrichment
OL BL

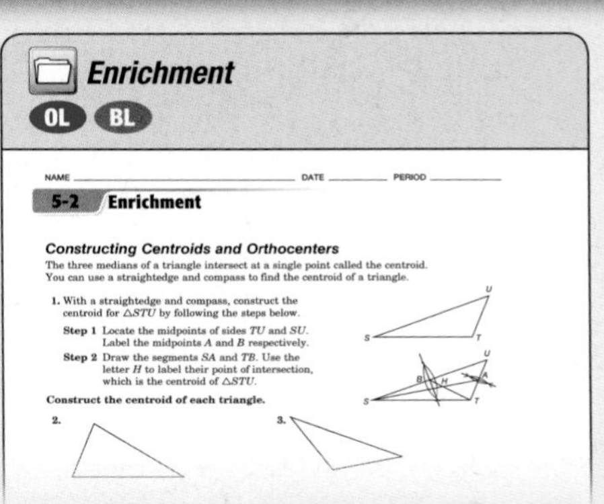

Study Guide and Intervention
AL OL ELL

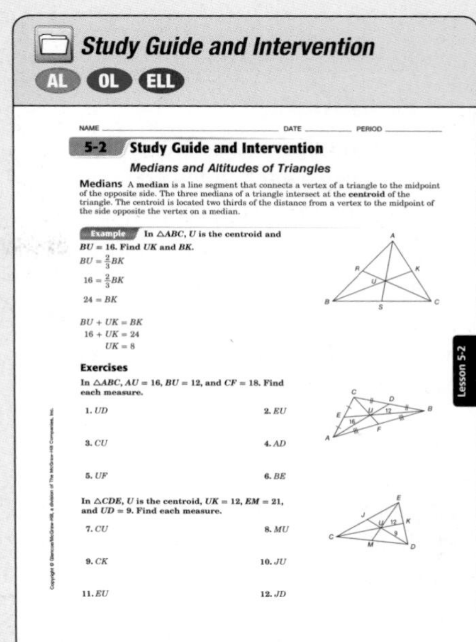

Practice
AL OL BL ELL

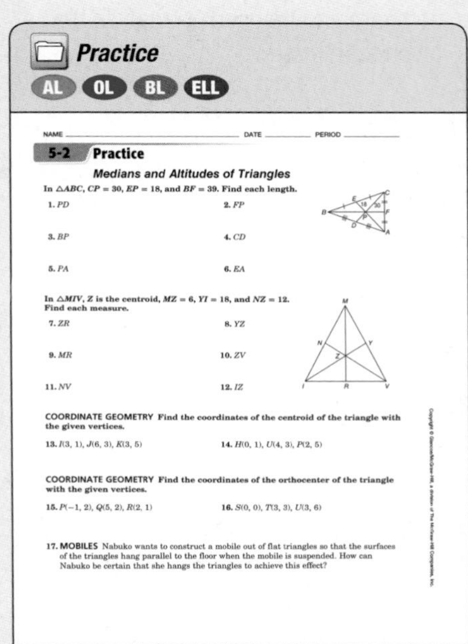

Word Problem Practice
AL OL BL ELL

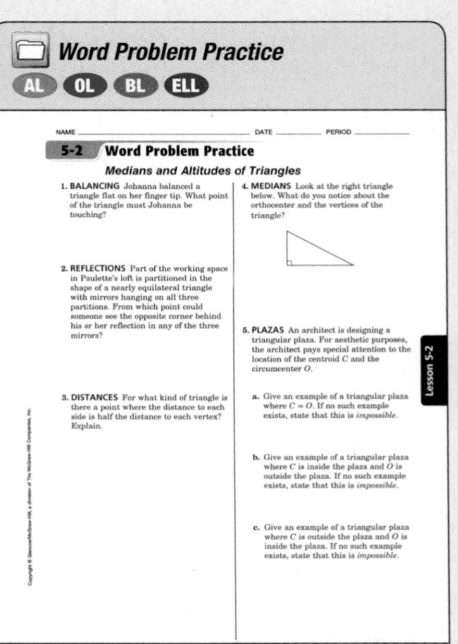

WatchOut!

Error Analysis In Exercise 37, Luke has switched the segments from the Centroid Theorem. Remind students that in questions with geometric figures, they should use the figure to check the reasonableness of their answer.

CCSS Teaching the Mathematical Practices

Arguments Mathematically proficient students are able to analyze situations by breaking them into cases and can recognize and use counterexamples. In Exercise 38, dynamic geometry software can be used to analyze the given statement.

Additional Answers

37. Sample answer: Kareem is correct. According to the Centroid Theorem, $AP = \frac{2}{3}AD$. The segment lengths are transposed.

38. True; sample answer: In a right triangle, the altitudes from the two nonright vertices will always be the legs of the triangle, which intersect at the vertex that contains the right angle. The altitude to the hypotenuse of the triangle originates at the vertex, so the three altitudes intersect there. Therefore, the vertex of a right triangle will always be the orthocenter.

39. $\left(1, \frac{5}{3}\right)$; Sample answer: I found the midpoint of $\overline{AC}$ and used it to find the equation for the line that contains point B and the midpoint of $\overline{AC}$, $y = \frac{10}{3}x - \frac{5}{3}$. I also found the midpoint of $\overline{BC}$ and the equation for the line between point A and the midpoint of $\overline{BC}$, $y = -\frac{1}{3}x + 2$. I solved the system of two equations for x and y to get the coordinates of the centroid, $\left(1, \frac{5}{3}\right)$.

36. PROOF **Write a coordinate proof to prove the Centroid Theorem.**

Given: $\triangle ABC$, medians $\overline{AR}$, $\overline{BS}$, and $\overline{CQ}$

Prove: The medians intersect at point P and P is two thirds of the distance from each vertex to the midpoint of the opposite side.

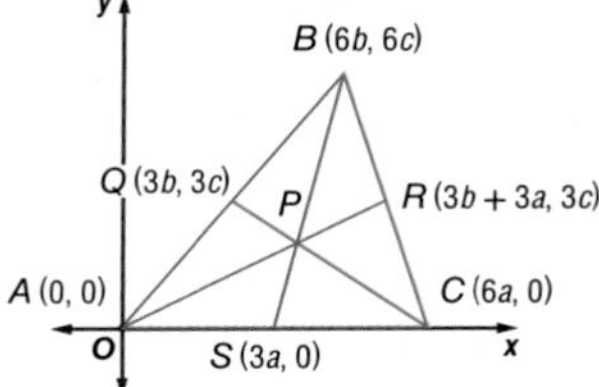

(*Hint*: First, find the equations of the lines containing the medians. Then find the coordinates of point P and show that all three medians intersect at point P. Next, use the Distance Formula and multiplication to show $AP = \frac{2}{3}AR$, $BP = \frac{2}{3}BS$, and $CP = \frac{2}{3}CQ$.) **See Ch. 5 Answer Appendix.**

H.O.T. Problems Use Higher-Order Thinking Skills

37. ERROR ANALYSIS Based on the figure at the right, Luke says that $\frac{2}{3}AP = AD$. Kareem disagrees. Is either of them correct? Explain your reasoning. **See margin.**

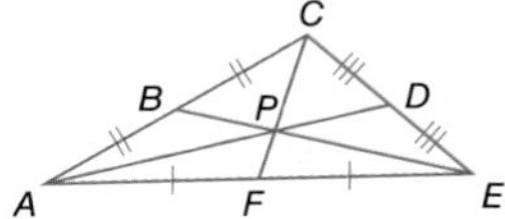

38. CCSS ARGUMENTS Determine whether the following statement is *true* or *false*. If true, explain your reasoning. If false, provide a counterexample. **See margin.**

The orthocenter of a right triangle is always located at the vertex of the right angle.

39. CHALLENGE $\triangle ABC$ has vertices $A(-3, 3)$, $B(2, 5)$, and $C(4, -3)$. What are the coordinates of the centroid of $\triangle ABC$? Explain the process you used to reach your conclusion. **See margin.**

40. WRITING IN MATH Compare and contrast the perpendicular bisectors, medians, and altitudes of a triangle. **See Ch. 5 Answer Appendix.**

41. CHALLENGE In the figure at the right, segments $\overline{AD}$ and $\overline{CE}$ are medians of $\triangle ACB$, $\overline{AD} \perp \overline{CE}$, $AB = 10$, and $CE = 9$. Find CA. $2\sqrt{13}$

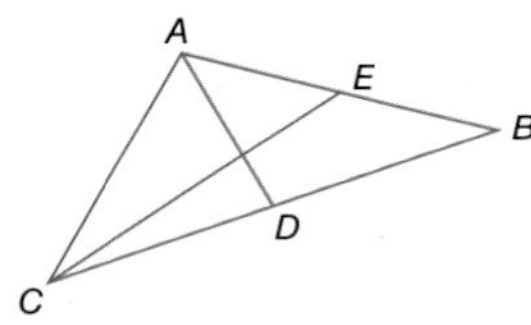

42. OPEN ENDED In this problem, you will investigate the relationships among three points of concurrency in a triangle. **a–d. See margin.**

a. Draw an acute triangle and find the circumcenter, centroid, and orthocenter.

b. Draw an obtuse triangle and find the circumcenter, centroid, and orthocenter.

c. Draw a right triangle and find the circumcenter, centroid, and orthocenter.

d. Make a conjecture about the relationships among the circumcenter, centroid, and orthocenter.

43. WRITING IN MATH Use area to explain why the centroid of a triangle is its center of gravity. Then use this explanation to describe the location for the balancing point for a rectangle. **See margin.**

42a.

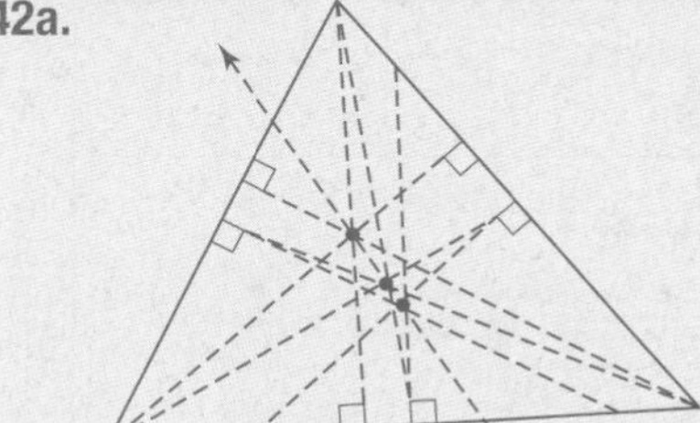

42b.

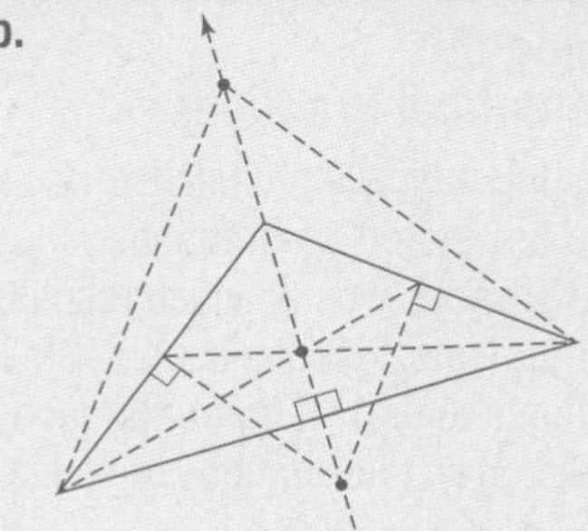

Standardized Test Practice

44. In the figure below, $\overline{GJ} \cong \overline{HJ}$. Which must be true? **C**

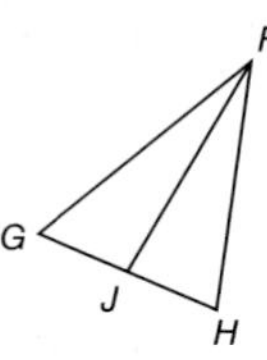

A $\overline{FJ}$ is an altitude of $\triangle FGH$.

B $\overline{FJ}$ is an angle bisector of $\triangle FGH$.

C $\overline{FJ}$ is a median of $\triangle FGH$.

D $\overline{FJ}$ is a perpendicular bisector of $\triangle FGH$.

45. GRIDDED RESPONSE What is the x-intercept of the graph of $4x - 6y = 12$? **3**

46. ALGEBRA Four students have volunteered to fold pamphlets for a local community action group. Which student is the fastest? **H**

Student	Folding Speed
Neiva	1 page every 3 seconds
Sarah	2 pages every 10 seconds
Quinn	30 pages per minute
Deron	45 pages in 2 minutes

F Deron

G Neiva

H Quinn

J Sarah

47. SAT/ACT 80 percent of 42 is what percent of 16? **B**

A 240

B 210

C 150

D 50

E 30

Spiral Review

Find each measure. (Lesson 5-1)

48. LM **12**

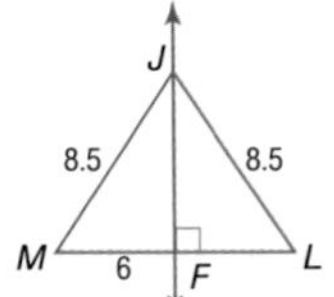

49. DF **5**

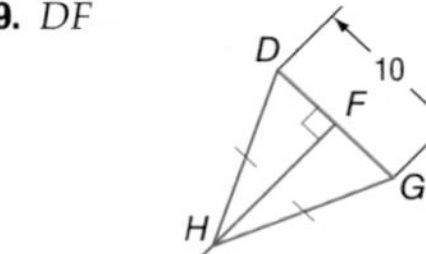

50. TQ **12**

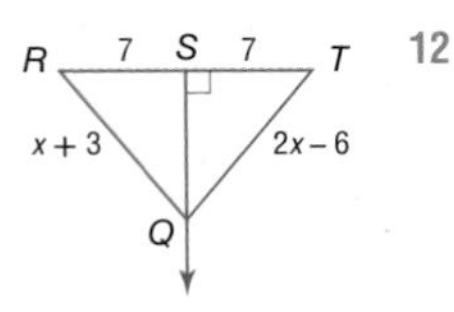

Position and label each triangle on the coordinate plane. (Lesson 4-8) **51–52. See margin.**

51. right $\triangle XYZ$ with hypotenuse $\overline{XZ}$, ZY is twice XY, and $\overline{XY}$ is b units long

52. isosceles $\triangle QRT$ with base $\overline{QR}$ that is b units long

Determine whether $\overleftrightarrow{RS}$ and $\overleftrightarrow{JK}$ are *parallel*, *perpendicular*, or *neither*. Graph each line to verify your answer. (Lesson 3-3) **53–54. See margin.**

53. $R(5, -4)$, $S(10, 0)$, $J(9, -8)$, $K(5, -13)$

54. $R(1, 1)$, $S(9, 8)$, $J(-6, 1)$, $K(2, 8)$

55. HIGHWAYS Near the city of Hopewell, Virginia, Route 10 runs perpendicular to Interstate 95 and Interstate 295. Show that the angles at the intersections of Route 10 with Interstate 95 and Interstate 295 are congruent. (Lesson 2-8) **Because the lines are perpendicular, the angles formed are right angles. All right angles are congruent. Therefore, $\angle 1$ is congruent to $\angle 2$.**

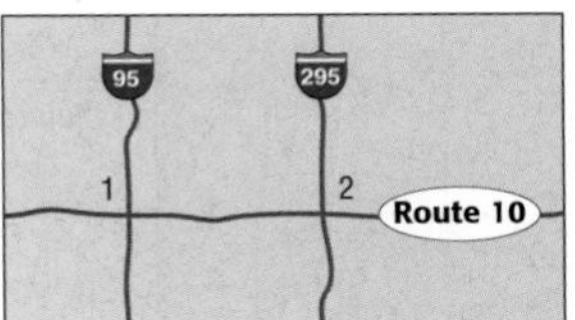

Skills Review

PROOF Write a flow proof of the Exterior Angle Theorem.

56. Given: $\triangle XYZ$

Prove: $m\angle X + m\angle Z = m\angle 1$ **See Ch. 5 Answer Appendix.**

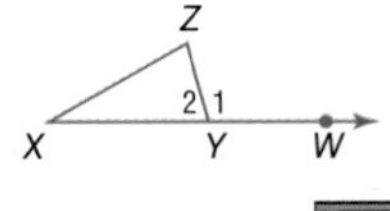

53. neither

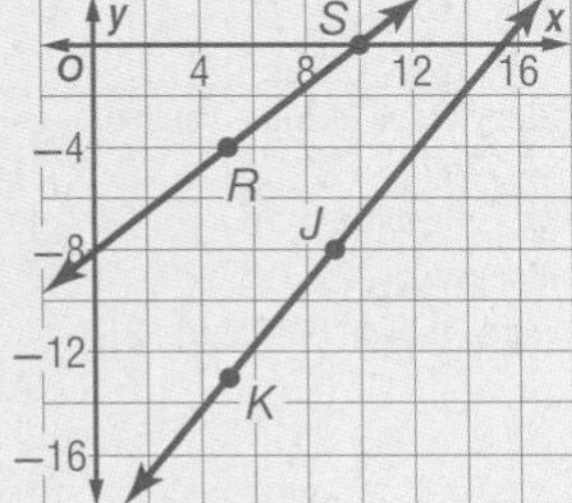

54. parallel

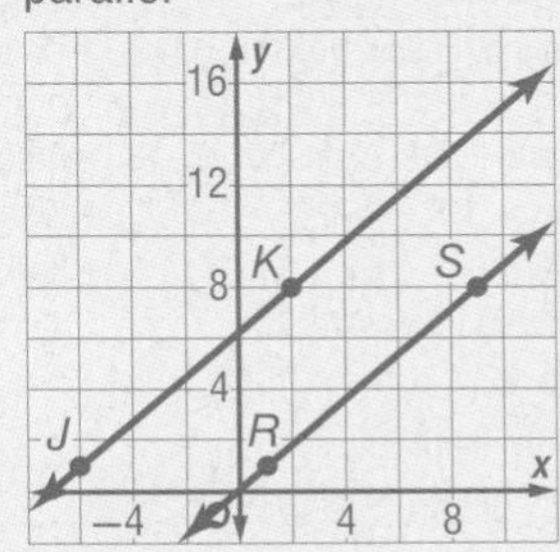

4 Assess

Ticket out the Door Have students write a short description that explains the differences between the median and altitude, and the centroid and orthocenter of a triangle.

Formative Assessment

Check for student understanding of Lessons 5-1 and 5-2.

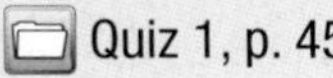

Additional Answers

42c.

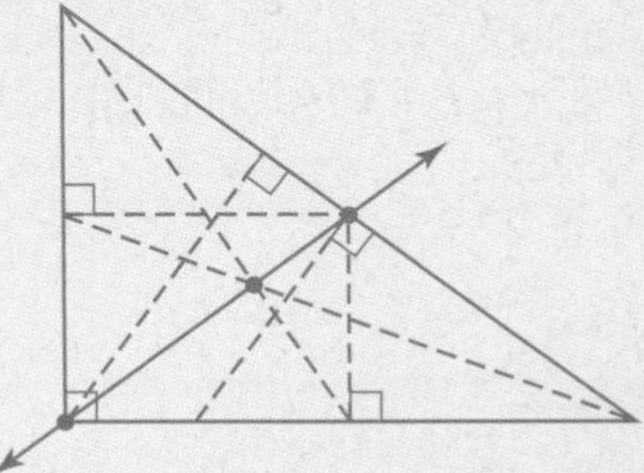

42d. Sample answer: The circumcenter, centroid, and orthocenter are all collinear.

43. Sample answer: Each median divides the triangle into two smaller triangles of equal area, so the triangle can be balanced along any one of those lines. To balance the triangle on one point, you need to find the point where these three balance lines intersect. The balancing point for a rectangle is the intersection of the segments connecting the midpoints of the opposite sides, since each segment connecting these midpoints of a pair of opposite sides divides the rectangle into two parts with equal area.

51.

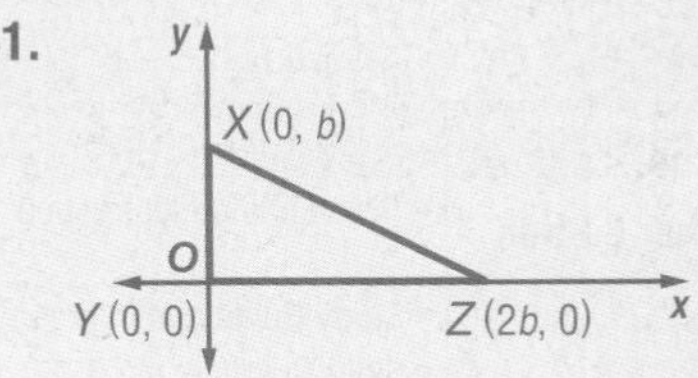

52.

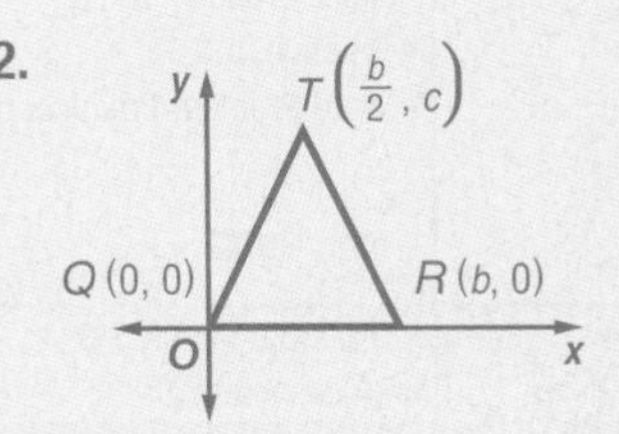

1 Focus

VerticalAlignment

Before Lesson 5-3 Find the relationship between the angle measures of a triangle.

Lesson 5-3 Recognize and apply properties of inequalities to the measures of the angles of triangles and between the angles and sides of a triangle.

After Lesson 5-3 Use and extend similarity properties to explore and justify conjectures about geometric figures.

2 Teach

Scaffolding Questions

Have students read the **Why?** section of the lesson.

Ask:

- Which is the largest angle of the triangle in the picture? the angle at the top
- Which is the longest side of the triangle? the bottom side
- What is the relationship between the largest angle and the longest side? Sample answer: The longest side is opposite the largest angle.

LESSON 5-3 Inequalities in One Triangle

Then

- You found the relationship between the angle measures of a triangle.

Now

1. Recognize and apply properties of inequalities to the measures of the angles of a triangle.
2. Recognize and apply properties of inequalities to the relationships between the angles and sides of a triangle.

Why?

- To create the appearance of depth in a room, interior designers use a technique called *triangulation.* A basic example of this technique is the placement of an end table on each side of a sofa with a painting over the sofa.

The measures of the base angles of the triangle should be less than the measure of the other angle.

CCSS Common Core State Standards

Content Standards
G.CO.10 Prove theorems about triangles.

Mathematical Practices
1 Make sense of problems and persevere in solving them.
3 Construct viable arguments and critique the reasoning of others.

1 Angle Inequalities

In algebra, you learned about the inequality relationship between two real numbers. This relationship is often used in proofs.

KeyConcept Definition of Inequality

Words	For any real numbers a and b, $a > b$ if and only if there is a positive number c such that $a = b + c$.
Example	If $5 = 2 + 3$, then $5 > 2$ and $5 > 3$.

The table below lists some of the properties of inequalities you studied in algebra.

KeyConcept Properties of Inequality for Real Numbers

The following properties are true for any real numbers a, b, and c.

Property	
Comparison Property of Inequality	$a < b$, $a = b$, or $a > b$
Transitive Property of Inequality	**1.** If $a < b$ and $b < c$, then $a < c$. **2.** If $a > b$ and $b > c$, then $a > c$.
Addition Property of Inequality	**1.** If $a > b$, then $a + c > b + c$. **2.** If $a < b$, then $a + c < b + c$.
Subtraction Property of Inequality	**1.** If $a > b$, then $a - c > b - c$. **2.** If $a < b$, then $a - c < b - c$.

The definition of inequality and the properties of inequalities can be applied to the measures of angles and segments, since these are real numbers. Consider $\angle 1$, $\angle 2$, and $\angle 3$ in the figure shown.

By the Exterior Angle Theorem, you know that $m\angle 1 = m\angle 2 + m\angle 3$.

Since the angle measures are positive numbers, we can also say that

$$m\angle 1 > m\angle 2 \quad \text{and} \quad m\angle 1 > m\angle 3$$

by the definition of inequality. This result suggests the following theorem.

Lesson 5-3 Resources

Resource	Approaching Level AL	On Level OL	Beyond Level BL	English Learners ELL
Teacher Edition	▪ Differentiated Instruction, p. 346	▪ Differentiated Instruction, pp. 346, 347	▪ Differentiated Instruction, pp. 346, 347	
Chapter Resource Masters	▪ Study Guide and Intervention, pp. 17–18 ▪ Skills Practice, p. 19 ▪ Practice, p. 20 ▪ Word Problem Practice, p. 21	▪ Study Guide and Intervention, pp. 17–18 ▪ Skills Practice, p. 19 ▪ Practice, p. 20 ▪ Word Problem Practice, p. 21 ▪ Enrichment, p. 22 ▪ Cabri Jr. Activity, p. 23 ▪ Geometer's Sketchpad Activity, p. 24	▪ Practice, p. 20 ▪ Word Problem Practice, p. 21 ▪ Enrichment, p. 22	▪ Study Guide and Intervention, pp. 17–18 ▪ Skills Practice, p. 19 ▪ Practice, p. 20 ▪ Word Problem Practice, p. 21
Other	▪ 5-Minute Check 5-3 ▪ Study Notebook	▪ 5-Minute Check 5-3 ▪ Study Notebook	▪ 5-Minute Check 5-3 ▪ Study Notebook	▪ 5-Minute Check 5-3 ▪ Study Notebook

ReviewVocabulary

Remote Interior Angle Each exterior angle of a triangle has two *remote interior angles* that are not adjacent to the exterior angle.

Theorem 5.8 Exterior Angle Inequality

The measure of an exterior angle of a triangle is greater than the measure of either of its corresponding remote interior angles.

Example: $m\angle 1 > m\angle A$
$m\angle 1 > m\angle B$

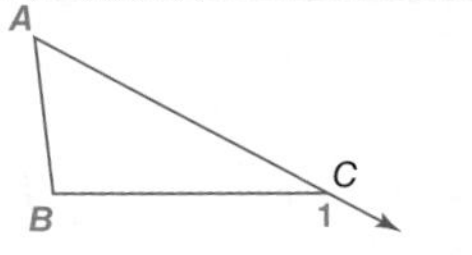

The proof of Theorem 5.8 is in Lesson 5-4.

Example 1 Use the Exterior Angle Inequality Theorem

Use the Exterior Angle Inequality Theorem to list all of the angles that satisfy the stated condition.

a. measures less than $m\angle 7$

$\angle 7$ is an exterior angle to $\triangle KML$, with $\angle 4$ and $\angle 5$ as corresponding remote interior angles. By the Exterior Angle Inequality Theorem, $m\angle 7 > m\angle 4$ and $m\angle 7 > m\angle 5$.

$\angle 7$ is also an exterior angle to $\triangle JKL$, with $\angle 1$ and $\angle JKL$ as corresponding remote interior angles. So, $m\angle 7 > m\angle 1$ and $m\angle 7 > m\angle JKL$. Since $m\angle JKL = m\angle 2 + m\angle 4$, by substitution $m\angle 7 > m\angle 2 + m\angle 4$. Therefore, $m\angle 7 > m\angle 2$.

So, the angles with measures less than $m\angle 7$ are $\angle 1$, $\angle 2$, $\angle 4$, $\angle 5$.

b. measures greater than $m\angle 6$

$\angle 3$ is an exterior angle to $\triangle KLM$. So by the Exterior Angle Inequality Theorem, $m\angle 3 > m\angle 6$. Because $\angle 8$ is an exterior angle to $\triangle JKL$, $m\angle 8 > m\angle 6$. Thus, the measures of $\angle 3$ and $\angle 8$ are greater than $m\angle 6$.

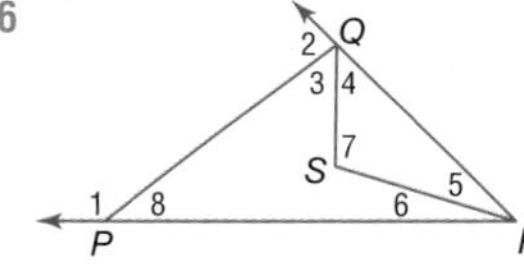

GuidedPractice

1A. measures less than $m\angle 1$ $\angle 3$, $\angle 4$, $\angle 5$, $\angle 6$

1B. measures greater than $m\angle 8$ $\angle 2$

Q
P
R
S
1 2 3 4 5 6 7 8

WatchOut!

Identifying Side Opposite Be careful to correctly identify the side opposite an angle. The sides that form the angle cannot be the sides opposite the angle.

2 Angle-Side Inequalities

In Lesson 4-6, you learned that if two sides of a triangle are congruent, or the triangle is isosceles, then the angles opposite those sides are congruent. What relationship exists if the sides are not congruent? Examine the longest and shortest sides and smallest and largest angles of a scalene obtuse triangle.

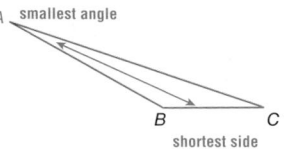

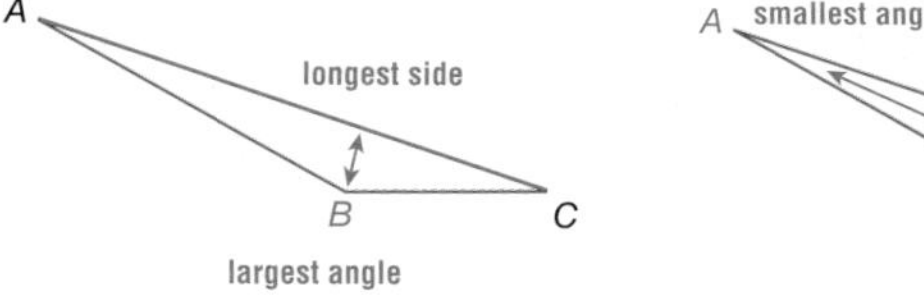

Notice that the longest side and largest angle of $\triangle ABC$ are opposite each other. Likewise, the shortest side and smallest angle are opposite each other.

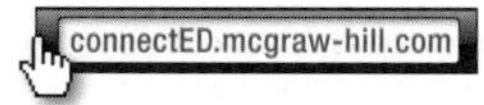

1 Angle Inequalities

Example 1 shows how to use the Exterior Angle Inequality Theorem.

Formative Assessment

Use the Guided Practice exercises after each example to determine students' understanding of concepts.

Additional Example

1 Use the Exterior Angle Inequality to list all of the angles that satisfy the stated condition.

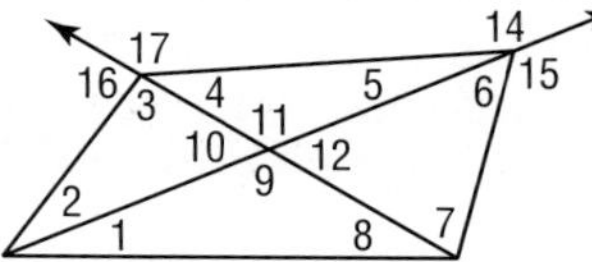

a. measures less than $m\angle 14$ $\angle 4$, $\angle 11$, $\angle 9$, $\angle 3$, $\angle 2$, $\angle 6$, $\angle 7$

b. measures greater than $m\angle 5$ $\angle 10$, $\angle 16$, $\angle 12$, $\angle 15$, $\angle 17$

Additional Examples also in Interactive Classroom PowerPoint® Presentations

IWB Interactive White Board READY

Tips for New Teachers

Exterior Angles Theorem 5.8 is true because $\angle 1$ is supplementary to the interior adjacent angle and the sum of the measures of the interior angles is 180.

Focus on Mathematical Content

Comparing Theorems You can summarize Theorems 5.9 and 5.10 by saying that the shorter segment is opposite the smaller angle, and the longer segment is opposite the larger angle.

2 Angle-Side Inequalities

Examples 2–4 show how to determine the relationship between the measures of given angles and sides of a triangle. Students should be able to use Theorems 5.9 and 5.10 to determine the angle-side relationship.

Additional Example

2 List the angles of $\triangle ABC$ in order from smallest to largest.

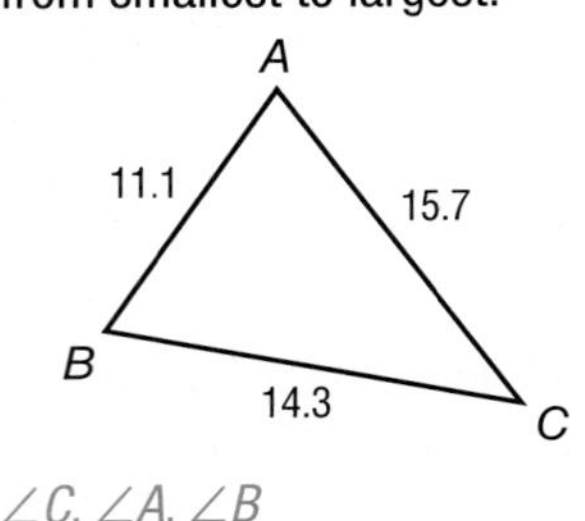

$\angle C$, $\angle A$, $\angle B$

WatchOut!

Symbols for Angles and Inequalities The symbol for angle ($\angle$) looks similar to the symbol for less than (<), especially when handwritten. Be careful to write the symbols correctly in situations where both are used.

The side-angle relationships in an obtuse scalene triangle are true for all triangles, and are stated using inequalities in the theorems below.

Theorems Angle-Side Relationships in Triangles

5.9 If one side of a triangle is longer than another side, then the angle opposite the longer side has a greater measure than the angle opposite the shorter side.

Example: $XY > YZ$, so $m\angle Z > m\angle X$.

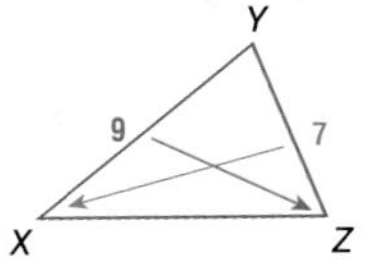

5.10 If one angle of a triangle has a greater measure than another angle, then the side opposite the greater angle is longer than the side opposite the lesser angle.

Example: $m\angle J > m\angle K$, so $KL > JL$.

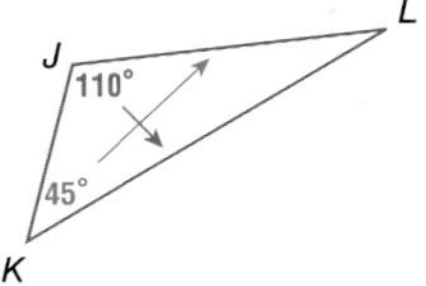

Proof Theorem 5.9

Given: $\triangle ABC$, $AB > BC$

Prove: $m\angle BCA > m\angle A$

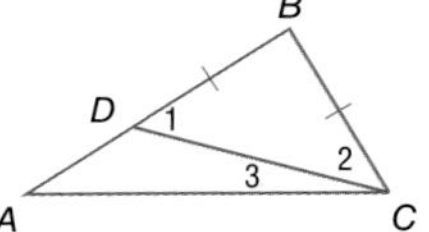

Proof:

Since $AB > BC$ in the given $\triangle ABC$, there exists a point D on $\overline{AB}$ such that $BD = BC$. Draw $\overline{CD}$ to form isosceles $\triangle BCD$. By the Isosceles Triangle Theorem, $\angle 1 \cong \angle 2$, so $m\angle 1 = m\angle 2$ by the definition of congruent angles.

By the Angle Addition Postulate, $m\angle BCA = m\angle 2 + m\angle 3$, so $m\angle BCA > m\angle 2$ by the definition of inequality. By substitution, $m\angle BCA > m\angle 1$.

By the Exterior Angle Inequality Theorem, $m\angle 1 > m\angle A$. Therefore, because $m\angle BCA > m\angle 1$ and $m\angle 1 > m\angle A$, by the Transitive Property of Inequality, $m\angle BCA > m\angle A$.

You will prove Theorem 5.10 in Lesson 5-4, Exercise 31.

Example 2 Order Triangle Angle Measures

List the angles of $\triangle PQR$ in order from smallest to largest.

The sides from shortest to longest are $\overline{PR}$, $\overline{PQ}$, $\overline{QR}$. The angles opposite these sides are $\angle Q$, $\angle R$, and $\angle P$, respectively. So the angles from smallest to largest are $\angle Q$, $\angle R$, and $\angle P$.

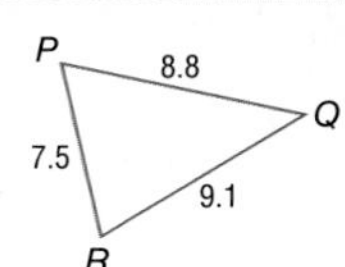

GuidedPractice

2. List the angles and sides of $\triangle ABC$ in order from smallest to largest. $\overline{AC}$, $\overline{AB}$, $\overline{CB}$; $\angle B$, $\angle C$, $\angle A$

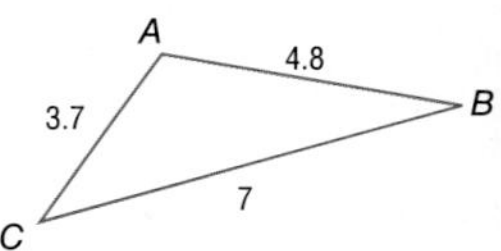

DifferentiatedInstruction AL OL BL

Logical Learners Ask students to summarize, in paragraph form, the proof of Theorem 5.9 using their own words. Tell them they do not have to use the exact order of the formal proof, but they should have a logical flow from the beginning to the end of the paragraph. Instead of using formal reasons, students could explain the concepts of the properties, definitions, postulates, and theorems used in the proof.

Example 3 Order Triangle Side Lengths

List the sides of $\triangle FGH$ in order from shortest to longest.

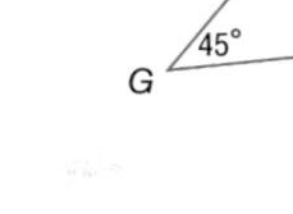

First find the missing angle measure using the Triangle Angle Sum Theorem.

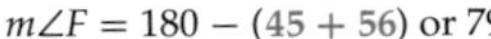

$m\angle F = 180 - (45 + 56)$ or 79

So, the angles from smallest to largest are $\angle G$, $\angle H$, and $\angle F$. The sides opposite these angles are $\overline{FH}$, $\overline{FG}$, and $\overline{GH}$, respectively. So, the sides from shortest to longest are $\overline{FH}$, $\overline{FG}$, $\overline{GH}$.

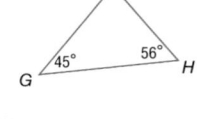

GuidedPractice

3. List the angles and sides of $\triangle WXY$ in order from smallest to largest. $\overline{WY}$, $\overline{YX}$, $\overline{WX}$; $\angle X$, $\angle W$, $\angle Y$

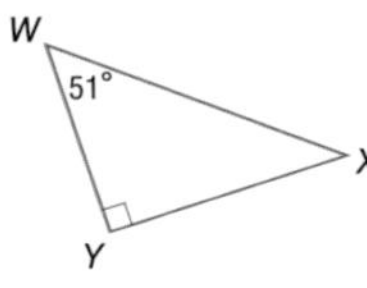

You can use angle-side relationships in triangles to solve real-world problems.

Real-World Example 4 Angle-Side Relationships

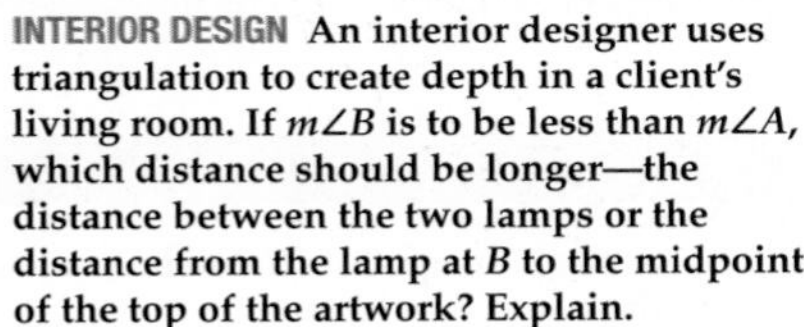

INTERIOR DESIGN An interior designer uses triangulation to create depth in a client's living room. If $m\angle B$ is to be less than $m\angle A$, which distance should be longer—the distance between the two lamps or the distance from the lamp at B to the midpoint of the top of the artwork? Explain.

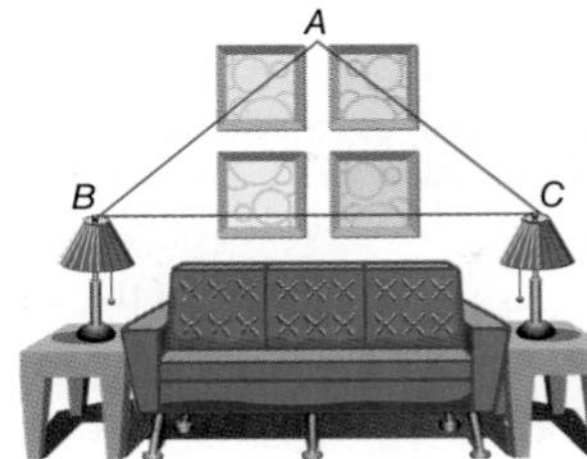

According to Theorem 5.10, in order for $m\angle B < m\angle A$, the length of the side opposite $\angle B$ must be less than the length of the side opposite $\angle A$. Since $\overline{AC}$ is opposite $\angle B$, and $\overline{BC}$ is opposite $\angle A$, then $AC < BC$ and $BC > AC$. So BC, the distance between the lamps, must be greater than the distance from the lamp at B to the midpoint of the top of the artwork.

GuidedPractice

4. **LIFEGUARDING** During lifeguard training, an instructor simulates a person in distress so that trainees can practice their rescue skills. If the instructor, Trainee 1, and Trainee 2 are located in the positions shown on the diagram, which of the two trainees is closest to the instructor? Trainee 1

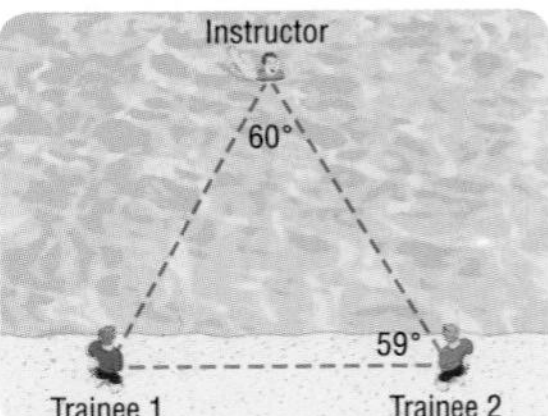

Real-WorldCareer

Interior Designer An interior designer decorates a space so that it is visually pleasing and comfortable for people to live or work in. Designers must know color and paint theory, lighting design, and space planning. A bachelor's degree is recommended for entry-level positions. Graduates usually enter a 1- to 3-year apprenticeship before taking a licensing exam.

DifferentiatedInstruction

Extension You are given the angle measures of a triangle. How will you know how to order the sides from shortest to longest? Using Theorems 5.9 and 5.10, the side opposite the smallest angle is the shortest side and the side opposite the largest angle is the longest side.

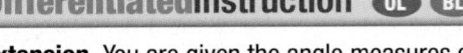

Additional Examples

3 List the sides of $\triangle ABC$ in order from shortest to longest.

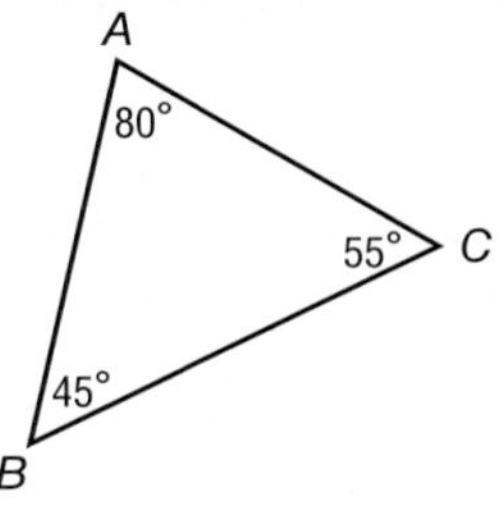

$\overline{AC}$, $\overline{AB}$, $\overline{BC}$

4 **HAIR ACCESSORIES** Ebony is following directions for folding a handkerchief to make a bandana for her hair. After she folds the handkerchief in half, the directions tell her to tie the two smaller angles of the triangle under her hair. If she folds the handkerchief with the dimensions shown, which two ends should she tie?

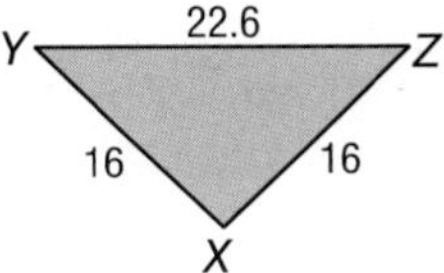

the ends marked Y and Z

Teach with Tech

Blog On your secure class blog, have students write a blog entry summarizing the relationship between angle measures and side lengths in a triangle. Allow students to be informal and check for their general understanding of the concept.

3 Practice

Formative Assessment

Use Exercises 1–7 to check for understanding.

Use the chart at the bottom of this page to customize assignments for your students.

Follow-up

Students have explored inequalities in one triangle.

Ask:

- How are inequalities related to sides and angles of triangles? Sample answers: The angle opposite a longer side of a triangle has a greater measure than the angle opposite a shorter side; the sum of the lengths of any two sides of a triangle must be greater than the length of the third side.

Additional Answers

20. Ben; sample answer: Using the Triangle Sum Theorem, the measure of the angle across from the segment between Hannah and Gilberto is 70. Since $48 < 70$, the pass from Hannah to Ben would be shorter.

21. If $m\angle X = 90$, then $m\angle Y + m\angle Z = 90$, so $m\angle Y < 90$ by the definition of inequality. So $m\angle X > m\angle Y$. According to Theorem 5.9, if $m\angle X > m\angle Y$, then the length of the side opposite $\angle X$ must be greater than the length of the side opposite $\angle Y$. Since $\overline{YZ}$ is opposite $\angle X$, and $\overline{XZ}$ is opposite $\angle Y$, then $YZ > XZ$. So YZ, the length of the top surface of the ramp, must be greater than the length of the ramp.

Check Your Understanding

 = Step-by-Step Solutions begin on page R14.

Example 1 Use the Exterior Angle Inequality Theorem to list all of the angles that satisfy the stated condition.

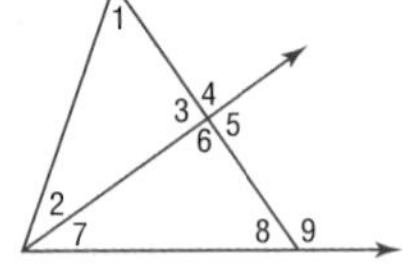

1. measures less than $m\angle 4$ $\angle 1$, $\angle 2$
2. measures greater than $m\angle 7$ $\angle 5$, $\angle 9$
3. measures greater than $m\angle 2$ $\angle 4$
4. measures less than $m\angle 9$ $\angle 6$, $\angle 7$

Examples 2–3 List the angles and sides of each triangle in order from smallest to largest.

5. 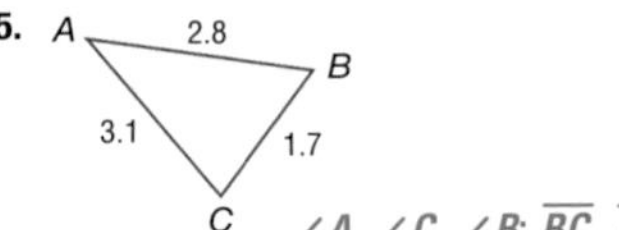

$\angle A$, $\angle C$, $\angle B$; $\overline{BC}$, $\overline{AB}$, $\overline{AC}$

6. 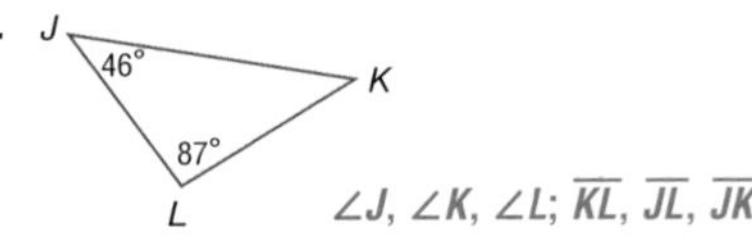

$\angle J$, $\angle K$, $\angle L$; $\overline{KL}$, $\overline{JL}$, $\overline{JK}$

Example 4

7. **HANG GLIDING** The supports on a hang glider form triangles like the one shown. Which is longer—the support represented by $\overline{AC}$ or the support represented by $\overline{BC}$? Explain your reasoning. $\overline{BC}$; Sample answer: Since the angle across from segment $\overline{BC}$ is larger than the angle across from $\overline{AC}$, $\overline{BC}$ is longer.

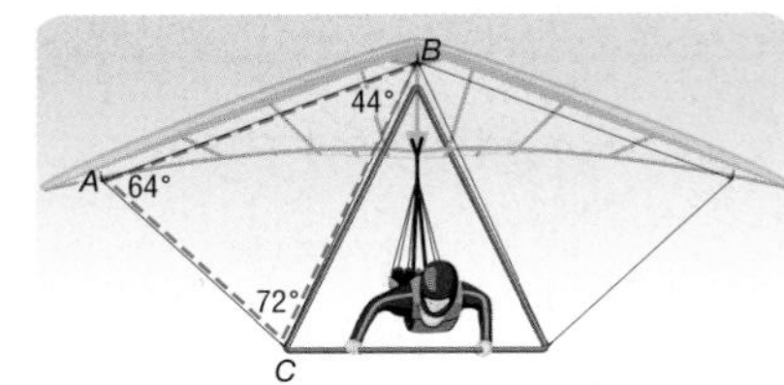

Practice and Problem Solving

Extra Practice is on page R5.

Example 1  **SENSE-MAKING** Use the Exterior Angle Inequality Theorem to list all of the angles that satisfy the stated condition.

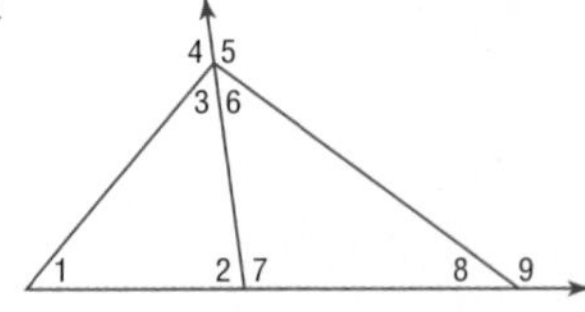

8. measures greater than $m\angle 2$ $\angle 4$
9. measures less than $m\angle 4$ $\angle 1$, $\angle 2$
10. measures less than $m\angle 5$ $\angle 7$, $\angle 8$
11. measures less than $m\angle 9$ $\angle 1$, $\angle 3$, $\angle 6$, $\angle 7$
12. measures greater than $m\angle 8$ $\angle 2$, $\angle 5$
13. measures greater than $m\angle 7$ $\angle 5$, $\angle 9$

Examples 2–3 List the angles and sides of each triangle in order from smallest to largest.

14. $\angle W$, $\angle Y$, $\angle Z$; $\overline{YZ}$, $\overline{WZ}$, $\overline{WY}$

17. $\angle L$, $\angle P$, $\angle M$; $\overline{PM}$, $\overline{ML}$, $\overline{PL}$

18. $\angle A$, $\angle B$, $\angle C$; $\overline{BC}$, $\overline{AC}$, $\overline{AB}$

14. 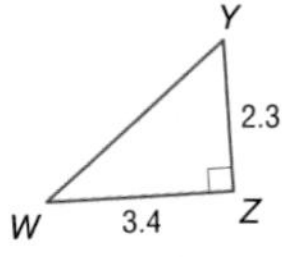

15. 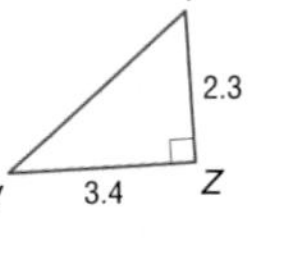
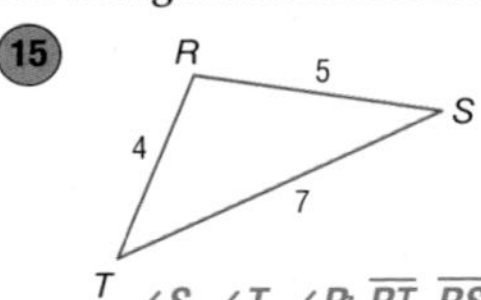

$\angle S$, $\angle T$, $\angle R$; $\overline{RT}$, $\overline{RS}$, $\overline{ST}$

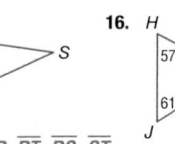

16. H $\angle H$, $\angle J$, $\angle K$; $\overline{JK}$, $\overline{HK}$, $\overline{HJ}$

17. 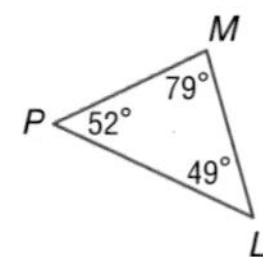

18. 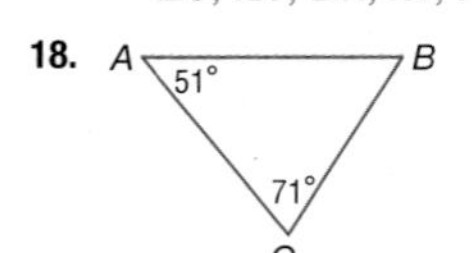

19. 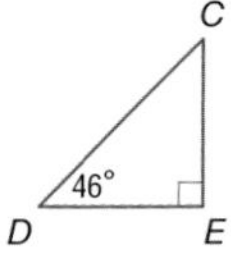

$\angle C$, $\angle D$, $\angle E$; $\overline{DE}$, $\overline{CE}$, $\overline{CD}$

Differentiated Homework Options

Level	Assignment	Two-Day Option	
AL Basic	8–21, 43, 45, 46, 48–61	9–21 odd, 49–52	8–20 even, 43, 45, 46, 48, 53–61
OL Core	9–21 odd, 22–43, 45, 46, 48–61	9–21, 49–52	22–43, 45, 46, 48, 53–61
BL Advanced	22–58, (optional: 59–61)		

Example 4

20. **SPORTS** Ben, Gilberto, and Hannah are playing Ultimate. Hannah is trying to decide if she should pass to Ben or Gilberto. Which player should she choose in order to have the shorter passing distance? Explain your reasoning. **See margin.**

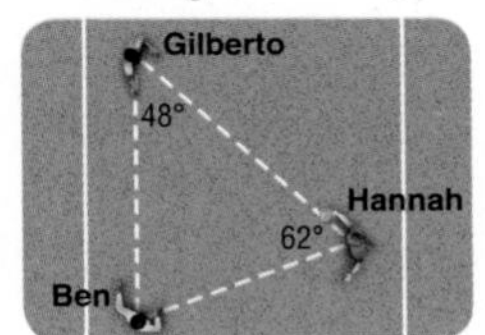

21. **RAMPS** The wedge below represents a bike ramp. Which is longer, the length of the ramp $\overline{XZ}$ or the length of the top surface of the ramp $\overline{YZ}$? Explain your reasoning using Theorem 5.9. **See margin.**

List the angles and sides of each triangle in order from smallest to largest.

22.

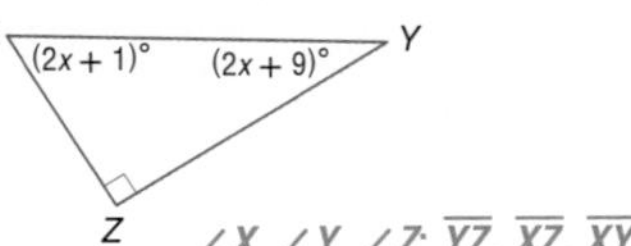

$\angle X, \angle Y, \angle Z; \overline{YZ}, \overline{XZ}, \overline{XY}$

23.

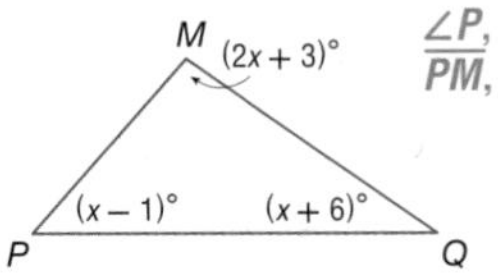

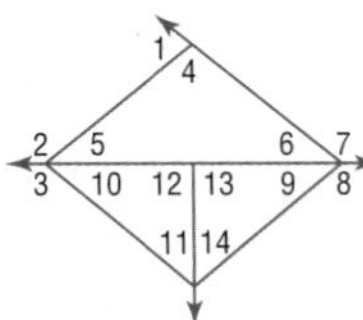

$\angle P, \angle Q, \angle M; \overline{MQ}, \overline{PM}, \overline{PQ}$

Use the figure at the right to determine which angle has the greatest measure.

24. $\angle 1, \angle 5, \angle 6$ $\angle 1$

25. $\angle 2, \angle 4, \angle 6$ $\angle 2$

26. $\angle 7, \angle 4, \angle 5$ $\angle 7$

27. $\angle 3, \angle 11, \angle 12$ $\angle 3$

28. $\angle 3, \angle 9, \angle 14$ $\angle 3$

29. $\angle 8, \angle 10, \angle 11$ $\angle 8$

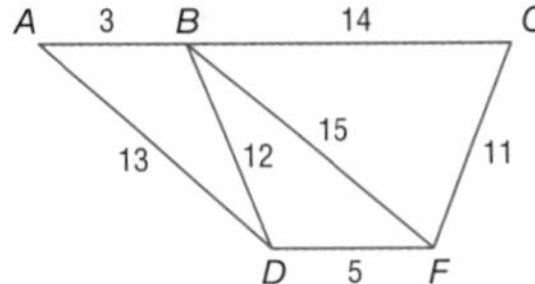

CCSS SENSE-MAKING **Use the figure at the right to determine the relationship between the measures of the given angles.**

30. $\angle ABD, \angle BDA$ $m\angle ABD > m\angle BDA$

31. $\angle BCF, \angle CFB$ $m\angle BCF > m\angle CFB$

32. $\angle BFD, \angle BDF$ $m\angle BFD < m\angle BDF$

33. $\angle DBF, \angle BFD$ $m\angle DBF < m\angle BFD$

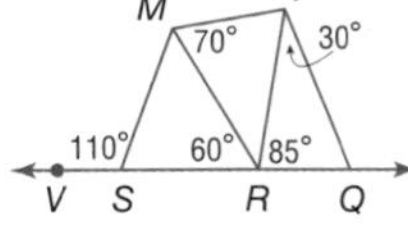

Use the figure at the right to determine the relationship between the given lengths.

34. SM, MR $SM < MR$

35. RP, MP $RP > MP$

36. RQ, PQ $RQ < PQ$

37. RM, RQ $RM > RQ$

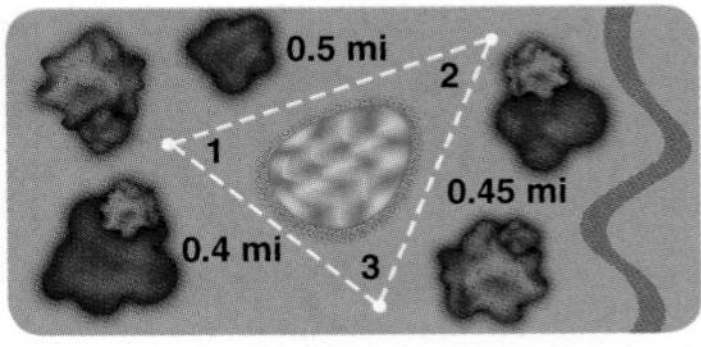

38. **HIKING** Justin and his family are hiking around a lake as shown in the diagram at the right. Order the angles of the triangle formed by their path from largest to smallest. $m\angle 3 > m\angle 1 > m\angle 2$

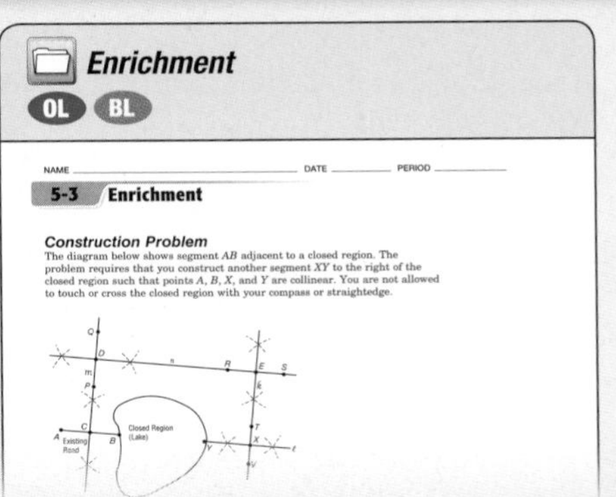

CCSS Teaching the Mathematical Practices

Sense-making Mathematically proficient students look for entry points to a solution. They analyze givens, constraints, relationships, and goals. In Exercises 30–33, analyze the angle-side relationship for each triangle.

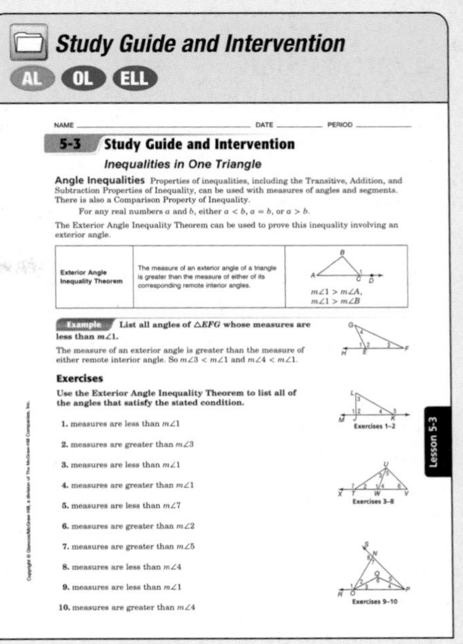

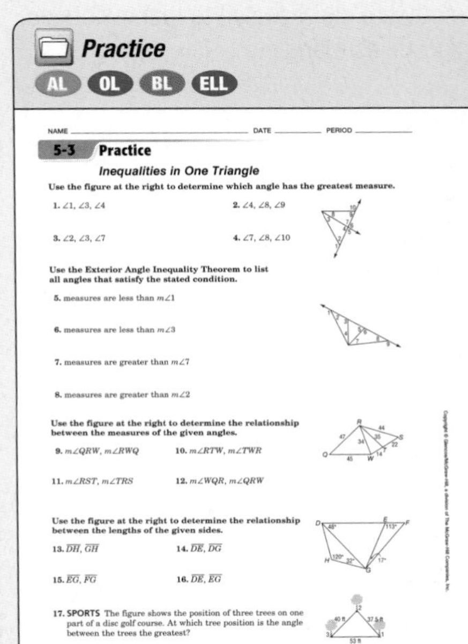

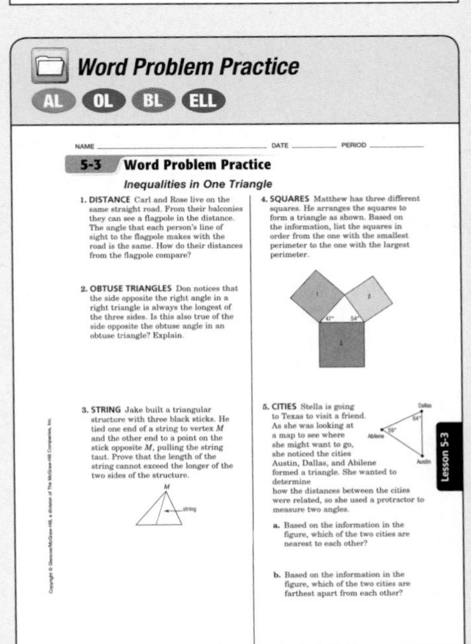

Enrichment

OL BL

5-3 Enrichment

Construction Problem

The diagram below shows segment AB adjacent to a closed region. The problem requires that you construct another segment XY to the right of the closed region such that points A, B, X, and Y are collinear. You are not allowed to touch or cross the closed region with your compass or straightedge.

Exercise Alert

Ruler Exercises 42 and 44 require the use of a ruler.

Multiple Representations

In Exercise 42, students use sketches, tables, algebraic computation, and verbal description to investigate the relationship between the sides of a triangle.

CCSS Teaching the Mathematical Practices

Arguments Mathematically proficient students are able to analyze situations by breaking them into cases and can recognize and use counterexamples. In Exercise 46, dynamic geometry software can be used to manipulate an isosceles triangle.

Additional Answers

42c. Sample answer:

Triangle	BC	CA	BC + CA	AB
Acute	2.4	3.2	5.6	2
Obtuse	3.4	5.0	8.4	2.6
Right	2.8	3.8	6.6	2.7

Triangle	AB	CA	AB + CA	BC
Acute	2	3.2	5.2	2.4
Obtuse	2.6	5.0	7.6	3.4
Right	2.7	3.8	6.5	2.8

43. Sample answer: $\angle R$ is an exterior angle to $\triangle PQR$, so by the Exterior Angle Inequality, $m\angle R$ must be greater than $m\angle Q$. The markings indicate that $\angle R \cong \angle Q$, indicating that $m\angle R = m\angle Q$. This is a contradiction of the Exterior Angle Inequality Theorem, so the markings are incorrect.

44. Sample answer: Since $\angle A$ is the largest angle, the side opposite it, $\overline{CB}$, is the longest side. Since $\angle C$ is the smallest angle, $\overline{AB}$ is the shortest side.

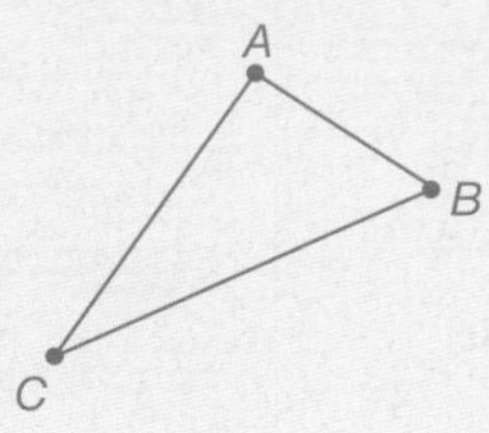

COORDINATE GEOMETRY List the angles of each triangle with the given vertices in order from smallest to largest. Justify your answer.

39. $A(-4, 6), B(-2, 1), C(5, 6)$ **39.** $\angle C$, $\angle A$, $\angle B$, because $AB = \sqrt{29} \approx 5.4$, $BC = \sqrt{74} \approx 8.6$, and $AC = 9$.

40. $X(-3, -2), Y(3, 2), Z(-3, -6)$ $\angle Y$, $\angle Z$, $\angle X$, because $XZ = 4$, $XY = \sqrt{52} \approx 7.2$, and $YZ = 10$.

41. List the side lengths of the triangles in the figure from shortest to longest. Explain your reasoning. AB, BC, AC, CD, BD; In $\triangle ABC$, $AB < BC < AC$ and in $\triangle BCD$, $BC < CD < BD$. By the figure $AC < CD$, so $BC < AC < CD$.

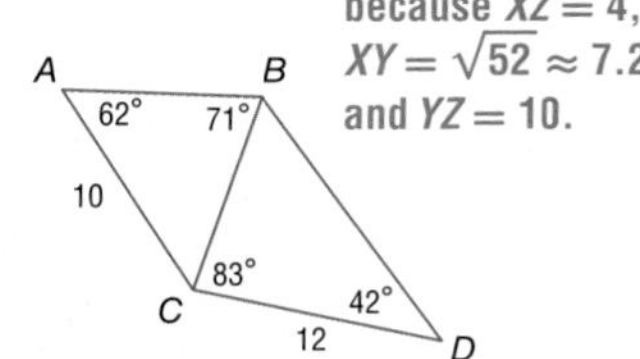

42. MULTIPLE REPRESENTATIONS In this problem, you will explore the relationship between the sides of a triangle. **a.** See Ch. 5 Answer Appendix.

a. Geometric Draw three triangles, including one acute, one obtuse, and one right angle. Label the vertices of each triangle A, B, and C.

b. Tabular Measure the length of each side of the three triangles. Then copy and complete the table. Sample answers given in table.

Triangle	AB	BC	AB + BC	CA
Acute	2	2.4	4.4	3.2
Obtuse	2.6	3.4	6.0	5.0
Right	2.7	2.8	5.5	3.8

c. Tabular Create two additional tables like the one above, finding the sum of BC and CA in one table and the sum of AB and CA in the other. See margin.

d. Algebraic Write an inequality for each of the tables you created relating the measure of the sum of two of the sides to the measure of the third side of a triangle. $AB + BC > CA$, $BC + CA > AB$, $AB + CA > BC$

e. Verbal Make a conjecture about the relationship between the measure of the sum of two sides of a triangle and the measure of the third side.

42e. Sample answer: The sum of the measures of two sides of a triangle is greater than the measure of the third side of the triangle.

H.O.T. Problems Use Higher-Order Thinking Skills

43. WRITING IN MATH Analyze the information given in the diagram and explain why the markings must be incorrect. See margin.

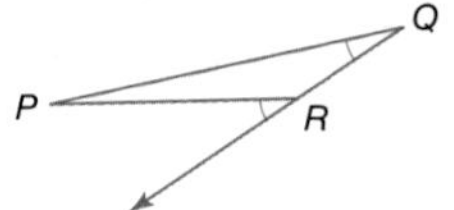

44. CHALLENGE Using only a ruler, draw $\triangle ABC$ such that $m\angle A > m\angle B > m\angle C$. Justify your drawing. See margin.

45. OPEN ENDED Give a possible measure for $\overline{AB}$ in $\triangle ABC$ shown. Explain your reasoning. See margin.

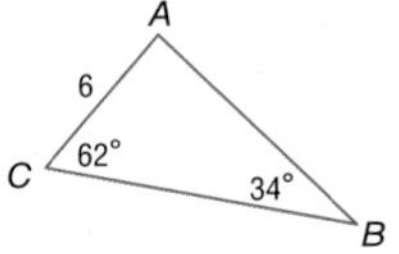

46. CCSS ARGUMENTS Is the base of an isosceles triangle *always*, *sometimes*, or *never* the longest side of the triangle? Explain. See margin.

47. CHALLENGE Use the side lengths in the figure to list the numbered angles in order from smallest to largest given that $m\angle 2 = m\angle 5$. Explain your reasoning. See margin.

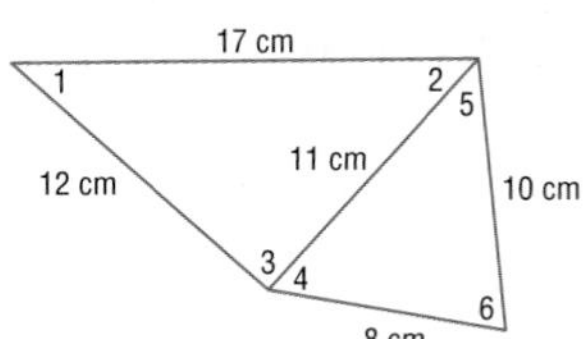

48. WRITING IN MATH Why is the hypotenuse always the longest side of a triangle? See margin.

45. Sample answer: 10; $m\angle C > m\angle B$, so if $AB > AC$, Theorem 5.10 is satisfied. Since $10 > 6$, $AB > AC$.

46. Sometimes; sample answer: If the measures of the base angles are less than 60°, then the base will be the longest leg. If the measures of the base angles are greater than 60°, then the base will be the shortest leg.

47. $m\angle 1$, $m\angle 2 = m\angle 5$, $m\angle 4$, $m\angle 6$, $m\angle 3$; Sample answer: The side opposite $\angle 5$ is the smallest side in that triangle and $m\angle 2 = m\angle 5$, so we know that $m\angle 4$ and $m\angle 6$ are both greater than $m\angle 2$ and $m\angle 5$. The side opposite $\angle 6$ is greater than the side opposite $\angle 4$. Since the side opposite $\angle 2$ is greater than the side opposite $\angle 1$, we know that $m\angle 1 < m\angle 2$ and $m\angle 5$. Since $m\angle 2 = m\angle 5$, $m\angle 1 + m\angle 3 = m\angle 4 + m\angle 6$. Since $m\angle 1 < m\angle 4$, then $m\angle 3 > m\angle 6$.

350 | Lesson 5-3 | Inequalities in One Triangle

Standardized Test Practice

49. STATISTICS The chart shows the number and types of DVDs sold at three stores. D

DVD Type	Store 1	Store 2	Store 3
Comedy	75	80	92
Action	54	37	65
Horror	30	48	62
Science Fiction	21	81	36
Total	180	246	255

According to the information in the chart, which of these statements is true?

A The mean number of DVDs sold per store was 56.

B Store 1 sold twice as many action and horror films as store 3 sold of science fiction.

C Store 2 sold fewer comedy and science fiction than store 3 sold.

D The mean number of science fiction DVDs sold per store was 46.

50. Two angles of a triangle have measures 45° and 92°. What type of triangle is it? F

F obtuse scalene H acute scalene

G obtuse isosceles J acute isosceles

51. EXTENDED RESPONSE At a five-star restaurant, a waiter earns a total of t dollars for working h hours in which he receives \$198 in tips and makes \$2.50 per hour. **a.** $t = 2.5h + 198$

a. Write an equation to represent the total amount of money the waiter earns.

b. If the waiter earned a total of \$213, how many hours did he work? 6

c. If the waiter earned \$150 in tips and worked for 12 hours, what is the total amount of money he earned? \$180

52. SAT/ACT Which expression has the *least* value? E

A $|-99|$ D $|-28|$

B $|45|$ E $|15|$

C $|-39|$

Spiral Review

In $\triangle XYZ$, P is the centroid, $KP = 3$, and $XJ = 8$. Find each length. (Lesson 5-2)

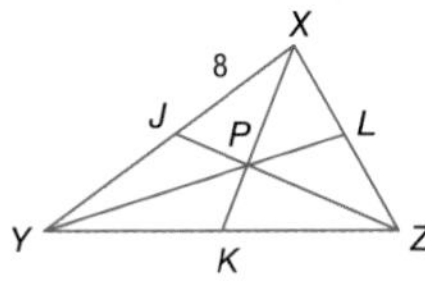

53. XK 9

54. YJ 8

COORDINATE GEOMETRY Write an equation in slope-intercept form for the perpendicular bisector of the segment with the given endpoints. Justify your answer. (Lesson 5-1) **55–57. See margin.**

55. $D(-2, 4)$ and $E(3, 5)$

56. $D(-2, -4)$ and $E(2, 1)$

57. JETS The United States Navy Flight Demonstration Squadron, the Blue Angels, flies in a formation that can be viewed as two triangles with a common side. Write a two-column proof to prove that $\triangle SRT \cong \triangle QRT$ if T is the midpoint of $\overline{SQ}$ and $\overline{SR} \cong \overline{QR}$. (Lesson 4-4)

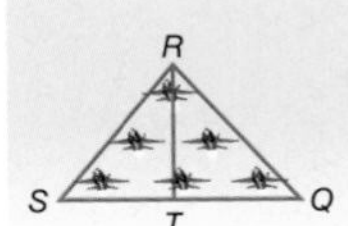

58. POOLS A rectangular pool is 20 feet by 30 feet. The depth of the pool is 60 inches, but the depth of the water is $\frac{3}{4}$ of the depth of the pool. Find each measure to the nearest tenth. (Lesson 1-7)

a. the surface area of the pool 1700 ft^2

b. the volume of water in the pool 2250 ft^3

Skills Review

Determine whether each statement is true or false if $x = 8$, $y = 2$, and $z = 3$.

59. $z(x - y) = 13$ false

60. $2x = 3yz$ false

61. $x + y > z + y$ true

4 Assess

Name The Math Select examples from the lesson or practice exercises and call on different students to discuss angle inequalities and angle-side relationships using geometric terminology. Be sure students properly name angles and sides and use terms like greater/lesser measure for angles and longer/shorter or greater/lesser measure for sides.

Formative Assessment

Check for student understanding of Lesson 5-3.

 Quiz 2, p. 45

Additional Answers

48. Sample answer: Since the hypotenuse is across from the right angle and both of the other angles in a right triangle are always acute, the hypotenuse is always the longest side and is always opposite the largest angle of the triangle.

55. $y = -5x + 7$; The perpendicular bisector bisects the segment at the midpoint of the segment. The midpoint is $\left(\frac{1}{2}, \frac{9}{2}\right)$. The slope of the given segment is $\frac{1}{5}$, so the slope of the perpendicular bisector is -5.

56. $y = -\frac{4}{5}x - \frac{3}{2}$; The perpendicular bisector bisects the segment at the midpoint of the segment. The midpoint is $\left(0, -\frac{3}{2}\right)$. The slope of the given segment is $\frac{5}{4}$, so the slope of the perpendicular bisector is $-\frac{4}{5}$.

57. Given: T is the midpoint of $\overline{SQ}$.
$\overline{SR} \cong \overline{QR}$

Prove: $\triangle SRT \cong \triangle QRT$

Proof:

Statements (Reasons)

1. T is the midpoint of $\overline{SQ}$. (Given)
2. $\overline{ST} \cong \overline{TQ}$ (Def. of midpoint)
3. $\overline{SR} \cong \overline{QR}$ (Given)
4. $\overline{RT} \cong \overline{RT}$ (Reflexive Prop.)
5. $\triangle SRT \cong \triangle QRT$ (SSS)

Formative Assessment

Use the Mid-Chapter Quiz to assess students' progress in the first half of the chapter.

Have students review the lesson indicated for the problems they answered incorrectly.

Summative Assessment

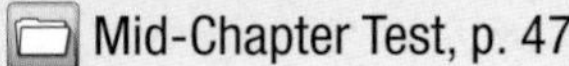
Mid-Chapter Test, p. 47

eAssessment Customize and create multiple versions of your Mid-Chapter Test and their answer keys.

FOLDABLES StudyOrganizer

Dinah Zike's Foldables®

Before students complete the Mid-Chapter Quiz, encourage them to review the information they have recorded for Lessons 5-1 through 5-3 in their Foldables.

Additional Answers

13. The three entrances to the school form a triangle. If each of the three altitudes of the triangle are extended, they will intersect at the orthocenter.
14. $\angle T, \angle S, \angle R; \overline{RS}, \overline{RT}, \overline{ST}$
15. $\angle G, \angle H, \angle F; \overline{FH}, \overline{GF}, \overline{GH}$
17. $\angle 4, \angle 3$
18. $\angle 8, \angle 9, \angle 10$
19. $\angle 6, \angle 2, \angle 4, \angle 3$

CHAPTER 5 Mid-Chapter Quiz

Lessons 5-1 through 5-3

Find each measure. (Lesson 5-1)

1. AB **29**

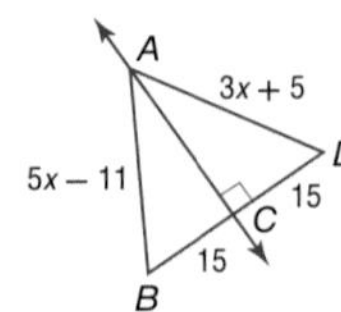

2. JL **12**

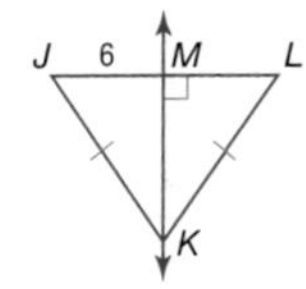

3. **CAMP** Camp Onawatchi ends with a game of capture the flag. If the starting locations of three teams are shown in the diagram below, with the flag at a point equidistant from each team's base, how far from each base is the flag in feet? (Lesson 5-1) **50**

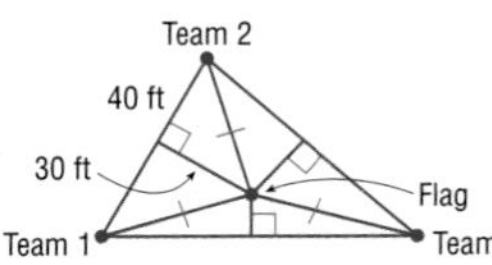

Find each measure. (Lesson 5-1)

4. $\angle MNP$ **130**

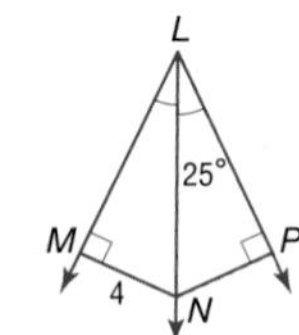

5. XY **21**

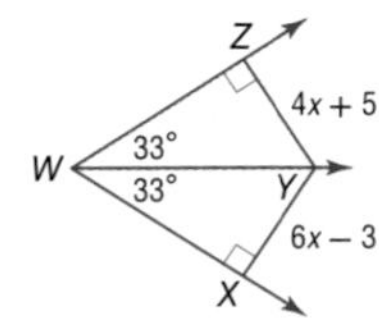

In $\triangle RST$, Z is the centroid and $RZ = 18$. Find each length. (Lesson 5-2)

6. ZV **9**
7. SZ **10**
8. SR **28**

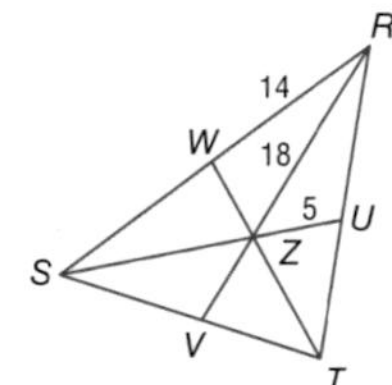

COORDINATE GEOMETRY Find the coordinates of the centroid of each triangle with the given vertices. (Lesson 5-2)

9. $A(1, 7)$, $B(4, 2)$, $C(7, 7)$ $\left(4, \frac{16}{3}\right)$
10. $X(-11, 0)$, $Y(-11, -8)$, $Z(-1, -4)$ $\left(-\frac{23}{3}, -4\right)$
11. $R(-6, 4)$, $S(-2, -2)$, $T(2, 4)$ $(-2, 2)$
12. $J(-5, 5)$, $K(-5, -1)$, $L(1, 2)$ $(-3, 2)$

13. **ARCHITECTURE** An architect is designing a high school building. Describe how to position the central office so that it is at the intersection of each hallway connected to the three entrances to the school. (Lesson 5-2) **See margin.**

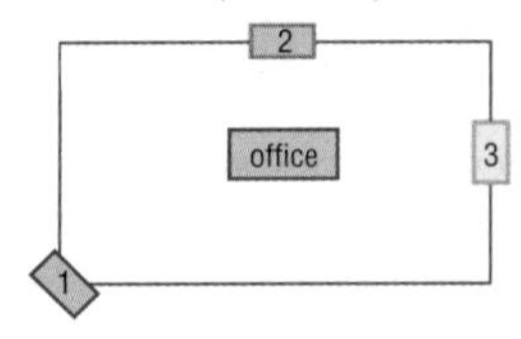

List the angles and sides of each triangle in order from smallest to largest. (Lesson 5-3) **14–15. See margin.**

14.
15.

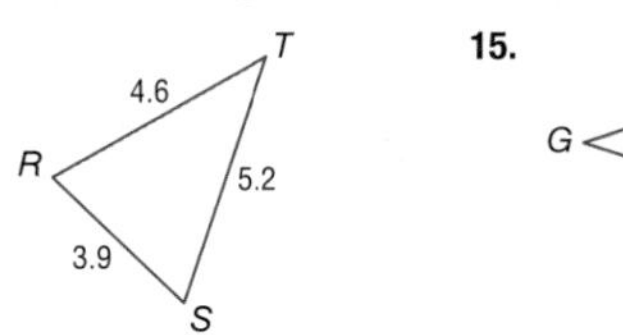

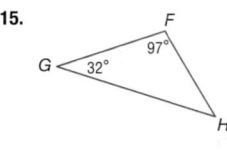

16. **VACATION** Kailey plans to fly over the route marked on the map of Hawaii below. (Lesson 5-3)

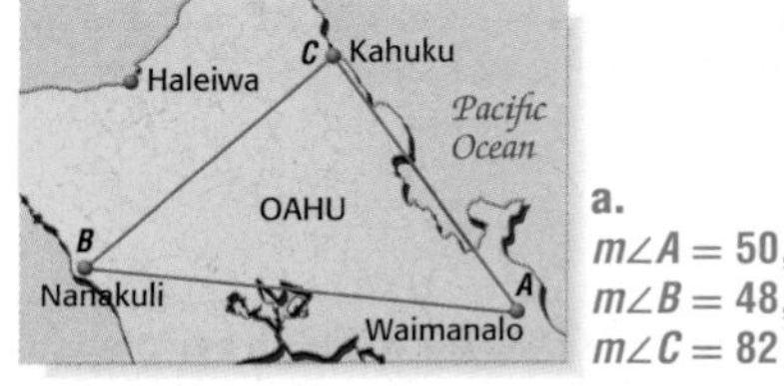

a. $m\angle A = 50$, $m\angle B = 48$, $m\angle C = 82$

a. If $m\angle A = 2 + m\angle B$ and $m\angle C = 2(m\angle B) - 14$, what are the measures of the three angles?

b. What are the lengths of Kailey's trip in order of least to greatest? ***AC, BC, BA***

c. The length of the entire trip is about 68 miles. The middle leg is 11 miles greater than one-half the length of the shortest leg. The longest leg is 12 miles greater than three-fourths of the shortest leg. What are the lengths of the legs of the trip? **20 mi, 21 mi, 27 mi**

17–19. See margin.

Use the Exterior Angle Inequality Theorem to list all of the angles that satisfy the stated condition. (Lesson 5-3)

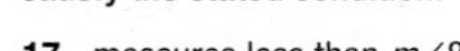

17. measures less than $m\angle 8$
18. measures greater than $m\angle 3$
19. measures less than $m\angle 10$

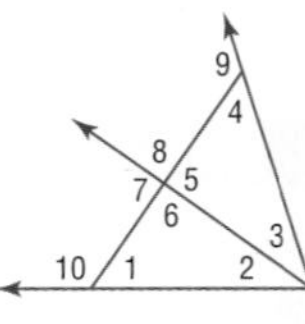

352 | Chapter 5 | Mid-Chapter Quiz

InterventionPlanner

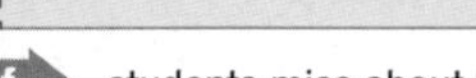

TIER 1 On Level OL	TIER 2 Strategic Intervention AL approaching grade level	TIER 3 Intensive Intervention 2 or more grades below level
If students miss about 25% of the exercises or less,	**If** students miss about 50% of the exercises,	**If** students miss about 75% of the exercises,
Then choose a resource:	**Then** choose a resource:	**Then** use *Math Triumphs, Geo.*, Chs. 3 and 4
SE Lessons 5-1, 5-2, and 5-3  Skills Practice, pp. 7, 13, and 19  Self-Check Quiz	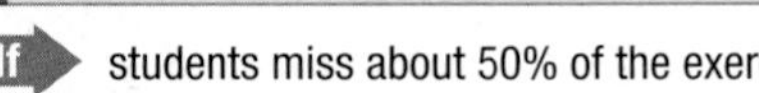  Study Guide and Intervention, pp. 5–6, 11–12, and 17–18 connectED.mcgraw-hill.com Extra Examples, Personal Tutor, Homework Help	 connectED.mcgraw-hill.com Extra Examples, Personal Tutor, Homework Help, Review Vocabulary

EXPLORE 5-4 Geometry Lab: Matrix Logic

Matrix logic uses a rectangular array in which you record what you have learned from clues in order to solve a logic or reasoning problem. Once all the rows and columns are filled, you can deduce the answer.

FOOD **Matt, Abby, Javier, Corey, and Keisha go to an Italian restaurant. Each orders their favorite dish: ravioli, pizza, lasagna, manicotti, or spaghetti. Javier loves ravioli, but Matt does not like pasta dishes. Abby does not like lasagna or manicotti. Corey's favorite dish does not end in the letter i. What does each person order?**

Step 1 Create an appropriate matrix.

Use a 5×5 matrix that includes each person's name as the header for each row and their possible favorite foods as the header for each column.

Step 2 Use each clue and logical reasoning to fill in the matrix.

- Since Javier loves ravioli, place a ✓ in Javier's row under ravioli and an × in every other cell in his row. Since only one person likes each dish, you can place an × in every other cell in the ravioli column.

Name	ravioli	pizza	lasagna	manicotti	spaghetti
Matt	×	✓	×	×	×
Abby	×	×			
Javier	✓	×	×	×	×
Corey	×	×			
Keisha	×	×			

- Since Matt does not like pasta, you know that Matt cannot like manicotti, ravioli, lasagna, or spaghetti, which are all pasta dishes. Therefore, Matt must like pizza. Place a ✓ in Matt's row under pizza. Place an × in every other cell in Matt's row and in every other cell in the pizza column.

- Since Abby does not like lasagna or manicotti, place an × in Abby's row under lasagna and manicotti. This leaves only spaghetti without an × for Abby's row. Therefore, you can conclude that Abby must like spaghetti. Place a ✓ in that cell and an × in every other cell in the spaghetti column.

Name	ravioli	pizza	lasagna	manicotti	spaghetti
Matt	×	✓	×	×	×
Abby	×	×	×	×	✓
Javier	✓	×	×	×	×
Corey	×	×			×
Keisha	×	×			×

- From the matrix, you can see that Corey's favorite dish must be either lasagna or manicotti. However, since Corey's favorite dish does not end in the letter i, you can conclude that Corey must like lasagna. In Corey's row, place a ✓ under lasagna and an × under manicotti.

- This leaves only one empty cell in Keisha's row, so you can conclude that her favorite dish is manicotti.

Name	ravioli	pizza	lasagna	manicotti	spaghetti
Matt	×	✓	×	×	×
Abby	×	×	×	×	✓
Javier	✓	×	×	×	×
Corey	×	×	✓	×	×
Keisha	×	×	×	✓	×

(Column header: Favorite Dish)

Step 3 Use your matrix to state the answer to the problem.

From the matrix you can state that Matt orders pizza, Abby orders spaghetti, Javier orders ravioli, Corey orders lasagna, and Keisha orders manicotti.

Girl Movie Restaurant

Boy

Restaurant

Movie

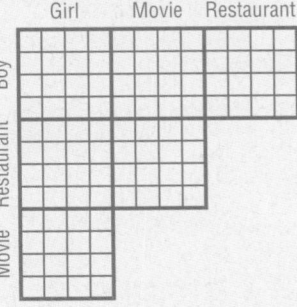

1 Focus

Objective

- Use matrix logic.

Materials for Each Group

- grid paper

Teaching Tips

- If students need extra practice, they can find many interactive matrix logic puzzles online.
- Encourage students to check their final answers against the clues given.

2 Teach

Working in Cooperative Groups

Organize students into pairs, mixing abilities. Have pairs help each other to complete the exercises.

Practice Have students complete Exercises 1–4.

3 Assess

Formative Assessment

Use Exercises 1 and 2 on the next page to assess whether students understand how to use a matrix to solve a logic problem.

From Concrete to Abstract

Ask students what the matrix would look like to solve a logic puzzle that involved four variables (girl name, boy name, restaurant name, and movie title) if each of these variables had four choices. See figure at the left. Then ask them to generalize how many $n \times n$ squares would be needed to create the matrix for a logic puzzle that involved m variables that each had n choices. $\frac{m^2 - m}{2}$ squares that are $n \times n$.

Additional Answers

1.

		Sport			
		basketball	football	track	tennis
Name	Trey	X	X	✓	X
	Nathan	X	X	X	✓
	Parker	✓	X	X	X
	Chen	X	✓	X	X

2.

		Birth Order				
		1st	2nd	3rd	4th	5th
Name	Grace	X	✓	X	X	X
	Hannah	X	X	✓	X	X
	Thomas	X	X	X	X	✓
	Sarah	✓	X	X	X	X
	Samuel	X	X	X	✓	X

3.

		Pet			Pet Name		
		dog	rabbit	cat	Sweet Pea	Zuzu	Roscoe
Name	Alejandra	X	X	✓	✓	X	X
	Tamika	✓	X	X	X	✓	X
	Emily	X	✓	X	X	X	✓
Pet Name	Sweet Pea	X	X	✓			
	Zuzu	✓	X	X			
	Roscoe	X	✓	X			

4.

		Sides			Angles		
		scalene	isosceles	equilateral	acute	right	obtuse
Name	Kasa	X	✓	X	X	X	✓
	Marcus	✓	X	X	X	✓	X
	Jason	X	X	✓	✓	X	X
Angles	acute	X	X	✓			
	right	✓	X	X			
	obtuse	X	✓	X			

Geometry Lab

Matrix Logic *Continued*

Exercises

Use a matrix to solve each problem. 1–4. See margin for matrices.

1. **SPORTS** Trey, Nathan, Parker, and Chen attend the same school. Each participates in a different school sport: basketball, football, track, or tennis. Use the following clues to determine in which sport each student participates.
   - Nathan does not like track or basketball.
   - Trey does not participate in football or tennis.
   - Parker prefers an indoor winter sport.
   - Chen scored four touchdowns in the final game of the season.

   Trey, track; Nathan, tennis; Parker, basketball; Chen, football

2. **FAMILY** The Martin family has five children. Use the following clues to determine in what order the children were born.
   - Grace is older than Hannah.
   - Thomas is younger than Sarah.
   - Hannah is older than Thomas and Samuel.
   - Samuel is older than Thomas.
   - Sarah is older than Grace.

   Sarah, then Grace, then Hannah, then Samuel, and then Thomas

3. **PETS** Alejandra, Tamika, and Emily went to a pet store. Each girl chose a different pet to adopt: a dog, a rabbit, or a cat. Each girl named her pet Sweet Pea, Zuzu, or Roscoe. Use the following clues and the matrix shown to determine the animal each girl adopted and what name she gave her pet.
   - The girl who adopted a dog did not name it Sweet Pea.
   - Tamika's pet, who she named Zuzu, is not the type of animal that hops.
   - Roscoe, who is not a cat, was adopted by Emily.
   - The rabbit was not adopted by Alejandra.

   Alejandra, cat named Sweet Pea; Tamika, dog named Zuzu; Emily, rabbit named Roscoe

		Pet			Pet Name		
		dog	rabbit	cat	Sweet Pea	Zuzu	Roscoe
Names	Alejandra						
	Tamika						
	Emily						
Pet Name	Sweet Pea						
	Zuzu						
	Roscoe						

4. **GEOMETRY** Kasa, Marcus, and Jason each drew a triangle, no two of which share the same side or angle classification. Use the following clues to determine what type of triangle each person has drawn.
   - Kasa did not draw an equilateral triangle.
   - Marcus' triangle has one angle that measures 25 and another that measures 65.
   - Jason drew a triangle with at least one pair of congruent sides.
   - The obtuse triangle has two congruent angles.

   Kasa, isosceles, obtuse; Marcus, scalene, right; Jason, equilateral, acute

LESSON 5-4 Indirect Proof

Then

- You wrote paragraph, two-column, and flow proofs.

Now

1. Write indirect algebraic proofs.
2. Write indirect geometric proofs.

Why?

Matthew: "I'm almost positive Friday is not a teacher work day, but I can't prove it."

Kim: "Let's assume that Friday *is* a teacher work day. What day is our next Geometry test?"

Ana: "Hmmm . . . according to the syllabus, it's this Friday. But we don't have tests on teacher work days—we're not in school."

Jamal: "Exactly—so that proves it! This Friday can't be a teacher work day."

NewVocabulary
indirect reasoning
indirect proof
proof by contradiction

Common Core State Standards

Content Standards
G.CO.10 Prove theorems about triangles.

Mathematical Practices
3 Construct viable arguments and critique the reasoning of others.
2 Reason abstractly and quantitatively.

1 Indirect Algebraic Proof

The proofs you have written have been *direct proofs*—you started with a true hypothesis and proved that the conclusion was true. In the example above, the students used **indirect reasoning**, by assuming that a conclusion was false and then showing that this assumption led to a contradiction.

In an **indirect proof** or **proof by contradiction**, you temporarily assume that what you are trying to prove is false. By showing this assumption to be logically impossible, you prove your assumption false and the original conclusion true. Sometimes this is called *proof by negation.*

KeyConcept How to Write an Indirect Proof

Step 1 Identify the conclusion you are asked to prove. Make the assumption that this conclusion is false by assuming that the opposite is true.

Step 2 Use logical reasoning to show that this assumption leads to a contradiction of the hypothesis, or some other fact, such as a definition, postulate, theorem, or corollary.

Step 3 Point out that since the assumption leads to a contradiction, the original conclusion, what you were asked to prove, must be true.

Example 1 State the Assumption for Starting an Indirect Proof

State the assumption necessary to start an indirect proof of each statement.

a. If 6 is a factor of n, then 2 is a factor of n.

The conclusion of the conditional statement is *2 is a factor of n*. The negation of the conclusion is *2 is not a factor of n*.

b. $\angle 3$ is an obtuse angle.

If *$\angle 3$ is an obtuse angle* is false, then *$\angle 3$ is not an obtuse angle* must be true.

GuidedPractice

1A. $x > 5$ $x \leq 5$

1B. $\triangle XYZ$ is an equilateral triangle. $\triangle XYZ$ is not an equilateral triangle.

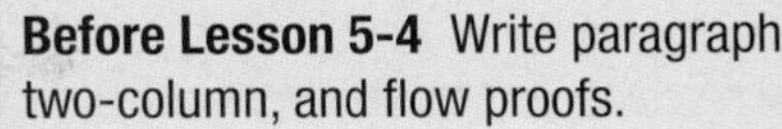

1 Focus

VerticalAlignment

Before Lesson 5-4 Write paragraph, two-column, and flow proofs.

Lesson 5-4 Write indirect algebraic and geometric proofs.

After Lesson 5-4 Make conjectures about angles, lines, polygons, circles, and three-dimensional figures and determine the validity of the conjectures.

2 Teach

Scaffolding Questions

Have students read the **Why?** Section of the lesson.

Ask:

- What question is used to prove that Friday is not a teacher work day? What day is our next geometry test?
- Who provides the reason that Friday is not a teacher work day? Ana
- What could have proved directly that Friday is a teacher work day? Sample answer: The syllabus states that Friday is a teacher work day.

Lesson 5-4 Resources

Resource	Approaching Level AL	On Level OL	Beyond Level BL	English Learners ELL
Teacher Edition		▪ Differentiated Instruction, pp. 357, 361	▪ Differentiated Instruction, pp. 357, 361	
Chapter Resource Masters	▪ Study Guide and Intervention, pp. 25–26 ▪ Skills Practice, p. 27 ▪ Practice, p. 28 ▪ Word Problem Practice, p. 29	▪ Study Guide and Intervention, pp. 25–26 ▪ Skills Practice, p. 27 ▪ Practice, p. 28 ▪ Word Problem Practice, p. 29 ▪ Enrichment, p. 30	▪ Practice, p. 28 ▪ Word Problem Practice, p. 29 ▪ Enrichment, p. 30	▪ Study Guide and Intervention, pp. 25–26 ▪ Skills Practice, p. 27 ▪ Practice, p. 28 ▪ Word Problem Practice, p. 29
Other	▪ 5-Minute Check 5-4 ▪ Study Notebook	▪ 5-Minute Check 5-4 ▪ Study Notebook	▪ 5-Minute Check 5-4 ▪ Study Notebook	▪ 5-Minute Check 5-4 ▪ Study Notebook

1 Indirect Algebraic Proof

Examples 1–4 show the steps for writing an indirect proof. Students should be able to state the assumption and use indirect proofs.

Formative Assessment

Use the Guided Practice exercises after each example to determine students' understanding of concepts.

Additional Examples

1 State the assumption necessary to start an indirect proof of each statement.

a. $\overline{EF}$ is not a perpendicular bisector. $\overline{EF}$ is a perpendicular bisector.

b. If B is the midpoint of $\overline{LH}$ and $LH = 26$, then $\overline{BH}$ is congruent to $\overline{LB}$. $\overline{BH}$ is not congruent to $\overline{LB}$.

2 Write an indirect proof to show that if $-2x + 11 < 7$, then $x > 2$.

Assume that $x < 2$ or $x = 2$. Make a table.

x	$-2x + 11$
2	7
1	9
0	11
−1	13
−2	15

In both cases, the assumption leads to a contradiction, therefore $x > 2$ must be true.

Additional Examples also in Interactive Classroom PowerPoint® Presentations

Interactive White Board READY

Indirect proofs can be used to prove algebraic concepts.

Example 2 Write an Indirect Algebraic Proof

Write an indirect proof to show that if $-3x + 4 > 16$, then $x < -4$.

Given: $-3x + 4 > 16$

Prove: $x < -4$

Step 1 **Indirect Proof:**
The negation of $x < -4$ is $x \geq -4$. So, assume that $x > -4$ or $x = -4$ is true.

Step 2 Make a table with several possibilities for x assuming $x > -4$ or $x = -4$.

x	−4	−3	−2	−1	0
$-3x + 4$	16	13	10	7	4

When $x > -4$, $-3x + 4 < 16$ and when $x = -4$, $-3x + 4 = 16$.

Step 3 In both cases, the assumption leads to the contradiction of the given information that $-3x + 4 > 16$. Therefore, the assumption that $x \geq -4$ must be false, so the original conclusion that $x < -4$ must be true.

ReadingMath

Contradiction
A contradiction is a principle of logic stating that an assumption cannot be both A and the opposite of A at the same time.

GuidedPractice

Write an indirect proof of each statement. 2A–2B. See Ch. 5 Answer Appendix.

2A. If $7x > 56$, then $x > 8$.

2B. If $-c$ is positive, then c is negative.

Indirect reasoning and proof can be used in everyday situations.

Real-World Example 3 Indirect Algebraic Proof

PROM COSTS Javier asked his friend Christopher the cost of his meal and his date's meal when he went to dinner for prom. Christopher could not remember the individual costs, but he did remember that the total bill, not including tip, was over \$60. Use indirect reasoning to show that at least one of the meals cost more than \$30.

Let the cost of one meal be x and the cost of the other meal be y.

Step 1 **Given:** $x + y > 60$

Prove: $x > 30$ or $y > 30$

Indirect Proof:
Assume that $x \leq 30$ and $y \leq 30$.

Step 2 If $x \leq 30$ and $y \leq 30$, then $x + y \leq 30 + 30$ or $x + y \leq 60$. This is a contradiction because we know that $x + y > 60$.

Step 3 Since the assumption that $x \leq 30$ and $y \leq 30$ leads to a contradiction of a known fact, the assumption must be false. Therefore, the conclusion that $x > 30$ or $y > 30$ must be true. Thus, at least one of the meals had to cost more than \$30.

Real-WorldLink

\$100–\$300 the range in price of a girl's prom dress

\$75–\$125 the range in cost for a tuxedo rental

around \$150 the cost of a fancy dinner for two

\$100–\$200 the range in cost of prom tickets per couple

Source: PromSpot

GuidedPractice

3. TRAVEL Cleavon traveled over 360 miles on his trip, making just two stops. Use indirect reasoning to prove that he traveled more than 120 miles on one leg of his trip. See Ch. 5 Answer Appendix.

WatchOut!

Contradictions A proof by contradiction can only work if there is a hypothesis that is assumed to be true.

Focus on Mathematical Content

Reading Solving word problems depends on students' understanding of the key words indicating the type of math needed. Analyze the wording to determine the actual situation in each indirect proof.

Indirect proofs are often used to prove concepts in number theory. In such proofs, it is helpful to remember that you can represent an even number with the expression $2k$ and an odd number with the expression $2k + 1$ for any integer k.

Example 4 Indirect Proofs in Number Theory

Write an indirect proof to show that if $x + 2$ is an even integer, then x is an even integer.

Step 1 **Given:** $x + 2$ is an even integer.

Prove: x is an even integer.

Indirect Proof:
Assume that x is an odd integer. This means that $x = 2k + 1$ for some integer k.

Step 2 $x + 2 = (2k + 1) + 2$ — Substitution of assumption

$= (2k + 2) + 1$ — Commutative Property

$= 2(k + 1) + 1$ — Distributive Property

Now determine whether $2(k + 1) + 1$ is an even or odd integer. Since k is an integer, $k + 1$ is also an integer. Let m represent the integer $k + 1$.

$2(k + 1) + 1 = 2m + 1$ — Substitution

So, $x + 2$ can be represented by $2m + 1$, where m is an integer. But this representation means that $x + 2$ is an odd integer, which contradicts the given statement that $x + 2$ is an even integer.

Step 3 Since the assumption that x is an odd integer leads to a contradiction of the given statement, the original conclusion that x is an even integer must be true.

WatchOut!

CCSS Arguments Proof by contradiction and using a counterexample are not the same. A counterexample helps you disprove a conjecture. It cannot be used to prove a conjecture.

GuidedPractice

4. Write an indirect proof to show that if the square of an integer is odd, then the integer is odd. **See Ch. 5 Answer Appendix.**

2 Indirect Proof with Geometry

Indirect reasoning can be used to prove statements in geometry, such as the Exterior Angle Inequality Theorem.

Example 5 Geometry Proof

If an angle is an exterior angle of a triangle, prove that its measure is greater than the measure of either of its corresponding remote interior angles.

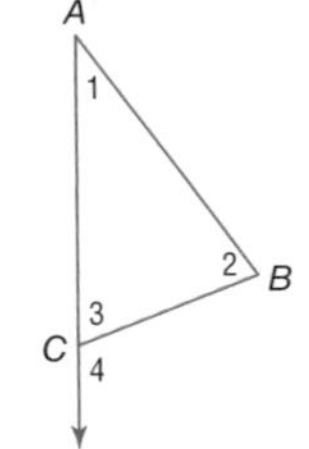

Step 1 Draw a diagram of this situation. Then identify what you are given and what you are asked to prove.

Given: $\angle 4$ is an exterior angle of $\triangle ABC$.

Prove: $m\angle 4 > m\angle 1$ and $m\angle 4 > m\angle 2$.

Indirect Proof:
Assume that $m\angle 4 \not> m\angle 1$ or $m\angle 4 \not> m\angle 2$.
In other words, $m\angle 4 \leq m\angle 1$ or $m\angle 4 \leq m\angle 2$.

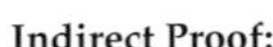

(continued on the next page)

Additional Examples

3 **EDUCATION** Marta signed up for three classes at a community college for a little under \$156. There was an administration fee of \$15, and the class costs are equal. How can you show that each class cost less than \$47?
Given: Marta spent less than \$156. Prove: At least one of the classes x cost less than \$47. That is, if $3x + 15 < 156$, then $x < 47$. Step 1: Assume $x \geq 47$. Step 2: $47 + 47 + 47 + 15 \geq 156$. Step 3: This contradicts the statement that the total cost was less than \$156, so the assumption that $x \geq 47$ must be false. Therefore, one class must cost less than 47.

4 Write an indirect proof to show that if x is a prime number not equal to 3, then $\frac{x}{3}$ is not an integer.
Step 1: Assume $\frac{x}{3}$ is an integer.
Step 2: $\frac{x}{3} = n$ (Substitution of assumption)
$x = 3n$ (Multiplication Property)
Step 3: This contradicts that x is prime, because n divides x and $n \neq 1$ since $x \neq 3$. Therefore $\frac{x}{3}$ is not an integer.

DifferentiatedInstruction OL BL

Logical Learners Point out that students are used to working forward to solve equations and inequalities, and they may be tempted to solve algebraic problems as a step in writing indirect proofs. Tell students that although this method works, it is not representative of an indirect proof, and they should avoid solving the algebraic problems in this lesson. Rather, they should use methods similar to the steps demonstrated for Example 2.

Teach with Tech

Video Recording Create a video showing how to create a proof by contradiction. Then post it to a video sharing Web site. This may be a difficult concept for some students, so it could be helpful for them to replay your exact explanation of how to write this kind of proof.

CCSS Teaching the Mathematical Practices

Arguments Mathematically proficient students can recognize and use counterexamples. Encourage students to write down the different methods of proof (proof by contradiction, two-column proof, flow proof, etc.) in their notebooks for quick reference while working on homework.

2 Indirect Proof with Geometry

Example 5 shows how to use the indirect reasoning in a geometry problem.

Additional Example

5 Given: $\triangle JKL$ with side lengths 5, 7, and 8 as shown.

Prove: $m\angle K < m\angle L$

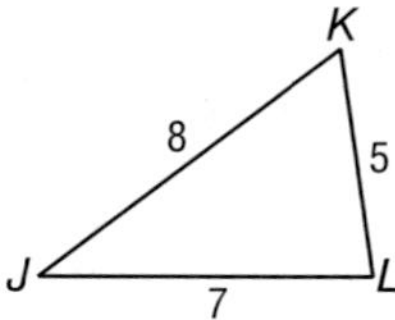

Step 1: Assume $m\angle K \geq m\angle L$.
Step 2: By angle-side relationships, $JL \geq JK$.
Step 3: This contradicts the given side lengths, so the assumption $m\angle K \geq m\angle L$ must be false. Therefore, $m\angle K < m\angle L$.

Additional Answer (Guided Practice)

5. **Given:** $\overline{MO} \cong \overline{ON}$, $\overline{MP} \ncong \overline{NP}$

Prove: $\angle MOP \ncong \angle NOP$

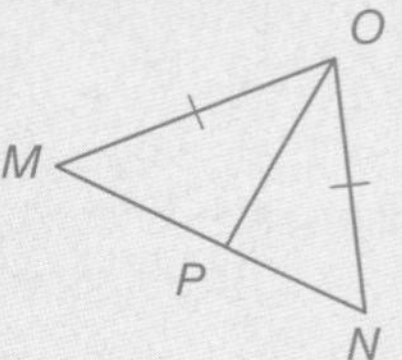

Indirect Proof:

Step 1: Assume that $\angle MOP \cong \angle NOP$.

Step 2: We know that $\overline{MO} \cong \overline{ON}$, and $\overline{OP} \cong \overline{OP}$ by the Reflexive Property. If $\angle MOP \cong \angle NOP$, then $\triangle MOP \cong \triangle NOP$ by SAS. Then, $\overline{MP} \cong \overline{NP}$ by CPCTC.

Step 3: The conclusion that $\overline{MP} \cong \overline{NP}$ contradicts the given information. Thus, the assumption is false. Therefore, $\angle MOP \ncong \angle NOP$.

Step 2 You need only show that the assumption $m\angle 4 \leq m\angle 1$ leads to a contradiction. The argument for $m\angle 4 \leq m\angle 2$ follows the same reasoning.

$m\angle 4 \leq m\angle 1$ means that either $m\angle 4 = m\angle 1$ or $m\angle 4 < m\angle 1$.

Case 1 $m\angle 4 = m\angle 1$

$m\angle 4 = m\angle 1 + m\angle 2$	Exterior Angle Theorem
$m\angle 4 = m\angle 4 + m\angle 2$	Substitution
$0 = m\angle 2$	Subtract $m\angle 4$ from each side.

This contradicts the fact that the measure of an angle is greater than 0, so $m\angle 4 \neq m\angle 1$.

Case 2 $m\angle 4 < m\angle 1$

By the Exterior Angle Theorem, $m\angle 4 = m\angle 1 + m\angle 2$. Since angle measures are positive, the definition of inequality implies that $m\angle 4 > m\angle 1$. This contradicts the assumption that $m\angle 4 < m\angle 1$.

Step 3 In both cases, the assumption leads to the contradiction of a theorem or definition. Therefore, the original conclusion that $m\angle 4 > m\angle 1$ and $m\angle 4 > m\angle 2$ must be true.

StudyTip

Recognizing Contradictions Remember that the contradiction in an indirect proof is not always of the given information or the assumption. It can be of a known fact or definition, such as in Case 1 of Example 5—the measure of an angle must be greater than 0.

GuidedPractice

5. Write an indirect proof. See margin.

Given: $\overline{MO} \cong \overline{ON}$, $\overline{MP} \ncong \overline{NP}$

Prove: $\angle MOP \ncong \angle NOP$

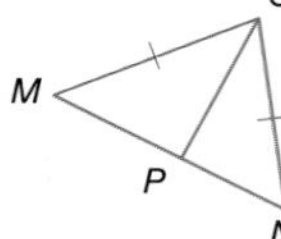

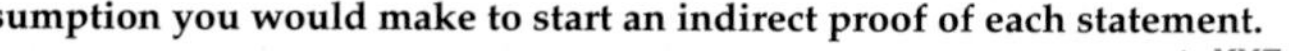
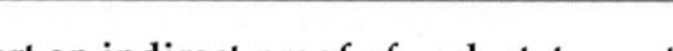

Check Your Understanding

= Step-by-Step Solutions begin on page R14.

Example 1 **State the assumption you would make to start an indirect proof of each statement.**

1. $\overline{AB} \cong \overline{CD}$ $\overline{AB} \ncong \overline{CD}$
2. $\triangle XYZ$ is a scalene triangle. $\triangle XYZ$ is an isosceles or equilateral triangle.
3. If $4x < 24$, then $x < 6$. $x \geq 6$
4. $\angle A$ is not a right angle. $\angle A$ is a right angle.

Example 2 **Write an indirect proof of each statement.** 5–6. See Ch. 5 Answer Appendix.

5. If $2x + 3 < 7$, then $x < 2$.
6. If $3x - 4 > 8$, then $x > 4$.

Example 3

7. **LACROSSE** Christina scored 13 points for her high school lacrosse team during the last six games. Prove that her average points per game was less than 3. See Ch. 5 Answer Appendix.

Example 4

8. Write an indirect proof to show that if $5x - 2$ is an odd integer, then x is an odd integer. See Ch. 5 Answer Appendix.

Example 5 **Write an indirect proof of each statement.** 9–10. See Ch. 5 Answer Appendix.

9. The hypotenuse of a right triangle is the longest side.
10. If two angles are supplementary, then they both cannot be obtuse angles.

358 | Lesson 5-4 | Indirect Proof

Practice and Problem Solving

Extra Practice is on page R5.

Example 1 **State the assumption you would make to start an indirect proof of each statement.**

11. If $2x > 16$, then $x > 8$. $x \leq 8$

12. $\angle 1$ and $\angle 2$ are not supplementary angles. $\angle 1$ and $\angle 2$ are supplementary angles.

13. If two lines have the same slope, the lines are parallel. The lines are not parallel.

14. If the consecutive interior angles formed by two lines and a transversal are supplementary, the lines are parallel. The lines are not parallel.

15. If a triangle is not equilateral, the triangle is not equiangular. The triangle is equiangular.

16. An odd number is not divisible by 2. An odd number is divisible by 2.

Example 2 **Write an indirect proof of each statement.** 17–20. See Ch. 5 Answer Appendix.

17. If $2x - 7 > -11$, then $x > -2$.

18. If $5x + 12 < -33$, then $x < -9$.

19. If $-3x + 4 < 7$, then $x > -1$.

20. If $-2x - 6 > 12$, then $x < -9$.

Example 3

21. **COMPUTER GAMES** Kwan-Yong bought two computer games for just over \$80 before tax. A few weeks later, his friend asked how much each game cost. Kwan-Yong could not remember the individual prices. Use indirect reasoning to show that at least one of the games cost more than \$40. See margin.

22. **FUNDRAISING** Jamila's school is having a Fall Carnival to raise money for a local charity. The cost of an adult ticket to the carnival is \$6 and the cost of a child's ticket is \$2.50. If 375 total tickets were sold and the profit was more than \$1460, prove that at least 150 adult tickets were sold. See margin.

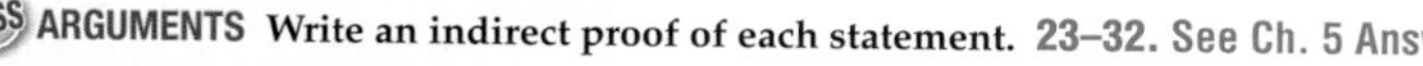

Examples 4–5 CCSS **ARGUMENTS** **Write an indirect proof of each statement.** 23–32. See Ch. 5 Answer Appendix.

23. **Given:** xy is an odd integer.
    Prove: x and y are both odd integers.

24. **Given:** n^2 is even.
    Prove: n^2 is divisible by 4.

25. **Given:** x is an odd number.
    Prove: x is not divisible by 4.

26. **Given:** xy is an even integer.
    Prove: x or y is an even integer.

27. **Given:** $XZ > YZ$
    Prove: $\angle X \not\cong \angle Y$

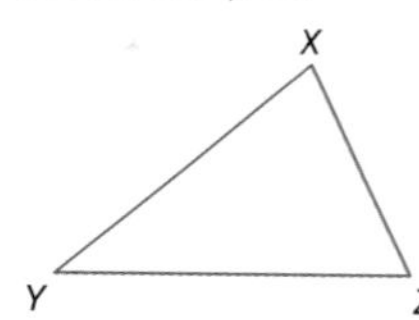

28. **Given:** $\triangle ABC$ is equilateral.
    Prove: $\triangle ABC$ is equiangular.

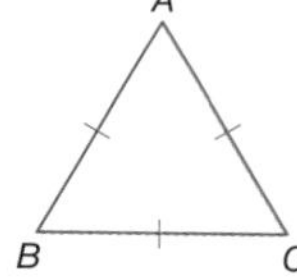

29. In an isosceles triangle neither of the base angles can be a right angle.

30. A triangle can have only one right angle.

31. Write an indirect proof for Theorem 5.10.

32. Write an indirect proof to show that if $\frac{1}{b} < 0$, then b is negative.

Differentiated Homework Options

Level	Assignment	Two-Day Option	
AL Basic	11–30, 40, 41, 43–59	11–29 odd, 45–48	12–30 even, 40, 41, 43, 49–59
OL Core	11–29 odd, 31–41, 43–59	11–30, 45–48	31–41, 43, 49–59
BL Advanced	31–56, (optional: 57–59)		

3 Practice

Formative Assessment

Use Exercises 1–10 to check for understanding.

Use the chart at the bottom of this page to customize assignments for your students.

Teaching the Mathematical Practices

Arguments Mathematically proficient students understand and use stated assumptions, definitions, and previously established results in constructing arguments. In Exercises 23–32, encourage students to plan their proofs before starting.

Additional Answers

21. Let the cost of one game be x and the other be y.

    Step 1 Given: $x + y > 80$

    Prove: $x > 40$ or $y > 40$

    Indirect Proof:

    Assume that $x \leq 40$ *and* $y \leq 40$.

    Step 2 If $x \leq 40$ and $y \leq 40$, then $x + y \leq 40 + 40$ or $x + y \leq 80$. This is a contradiction because we know that $x + y > 80$.

    Step 3 Since the assumption that $x \leq 40$ and $y \leq 40$ leads to a contradiction of a known fact, the assumption must be false. Therefore, the conclusion that $x > 40$ or $y > 40$ must be true. Thus, at least one of the games had to cost more than \$40.

22. **Step 1** Assume that fewer than 150 adult tickets were sold.

    Step 2 If 149 adult tickets were sold, 375 − 149, or 226 child tickets were sold. The total profit for 149 adult tickets and 226 child tickets is (149)(\$6) + (226)(\$2.50) or \$1459.

    Step 3 The conclusion is false, so the assumption must be false. Therefore, the number of adult tickets sold is greater than or equal to 150.

33. BASKETBALL In basketball, there are three possible ways to score three points in a single possession. A player can make a basket from behind the three-point line, a player may be fouled while scoring a two-point shot and be allowed to shoot one free throw, or a player may be fouled behind the three-point line and be allowed to shoot three free throws. When Katsu left to get in the concession line, the score was 28 home team to 26 visiting team. When she returned, the score was 28 home team to 29 visiting team. Katsu concluded that a player on the visiting team had made a three-point basket. Prove or disprove her assumption using an indirect proof. **See margin.**

34. GAMES A computer game involves a knight on a quest for treasure. At the end of the journey, the knight approaches the two doors shown below.

One of these doors leads to a ferocious dragon.

Behind this door is a treasure, and behind the other door is a ferocious dragon.

A servant tells the knight that one of the signs is true and the other is false. Use indirect reasoning to determine which door the knight should choose. Explain your reasoning. **See margin.**

35 SURVEYS Luisa's local library conducted an online poll of teens to find out what activities teens participate in to preserve the environment. The results of the poll are shown in the graph.

a. Prove: *More than half of teens polled said that they recycle to preserve the environment.*

a–b. See Ch. 5 Answer Appendix.

b. If 400 teens were polled, verify that 92 said that they participate in Earth Day.

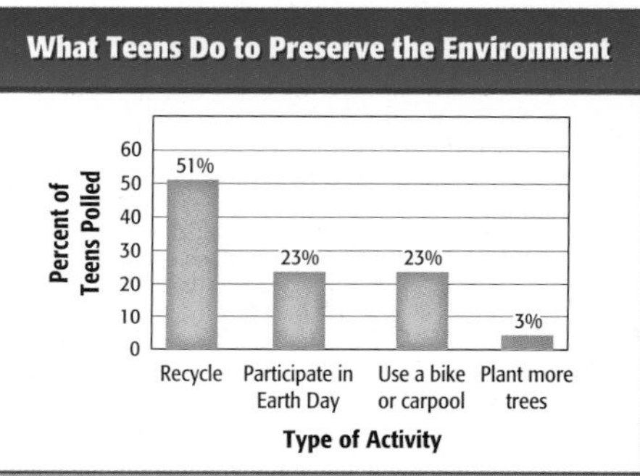

Use a bike or carpool
Plant more trees

36. CCSS REASONING James, Hector, and Mandy all have different color cars. Only one of the statements below is true. Use indirect reasoning to determine which statement is true. Explain. **Statement 2; sample answer: If you assume that statement 2 is not true, or "Hector has a red car," it contradicts statement 1 "James has a red car," so statement 2 is true. If you assume that statements 1 and 3 are not true, neither of the other remaining statements contradict the assumption.**

(1) James has a red car.

(2) Hector does not have a red car.

(3) Mandy does not have a blue car.

Study Guide and Intervention

AL OL ELL

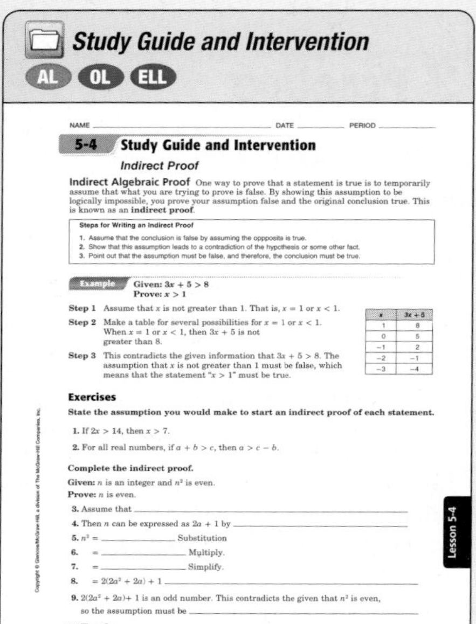

NAME ______ DATE ______ PERIOD ______

5-4 Study Guide and Intervention

Indirect Proof

Indirect Algebraic Proof One way to prove that a statement is true is to temporarily assume that what you are trying to prove is false. By showing this assumption to be logically impossible, you prove your assumption false and the original conclusion true. This is known as an **indirect proof**.

Steps for Writing an Indirect Proof
1. Assume that the conclusion is false by assuming the oppposite is true.
2. Show that this assumption leads to a contradiction of the hypothesis or some other fact.
3. Point out that the assumption must be false, and therefore, the conclusion must be true.

Example **Given:** $3x + 5 > 8$
Prove: $x > 1$

Step 1 Assume that x is not greater than 1. That is, $x = 1$ or $x < 1$.

Step 2 Make a table for several possibilities for $x = 1$ or $x < 1$. When $x = 1$ or $x < 1$, then $3x + 5$ is not greater than 8.

Step 3 This contradicts the given information that $3x + 5 > 8$. The assumption that x is not greater than 1 must be false, which means that the statement "$x > 1$" must be true.

x	$3x + 5$
1	8
0	5
−1	2
−2	−1
−3	−4

Exercises

State the assumption you would make to start an indirect proof of each statement.

1. If $2x > 14$, then $x > 7$.

2. For all real numbers, if $a + b > c$, then $a > c - b$.

Complete the indirect proof.

Given: n is an integer and n^2 is even.
Prove: n is even.

3. Assume that ______
4. Then n can be expressed as $2a + 1$ by ______
5. $n^2 =$ ______ Substitution
6. $=$ ______ Multiply.
7. $=$ ______ Simplify.
8. $= 2(2a^2 + 2a) + 1$ ______
9. $2(2a^2 + 2a) + 1$ is an odd number. This contradicts the given that n^2 is even, so the assumption must be ______
10. Therefore, ______

Lesson 5-4

Practice

AL OL BL ELL

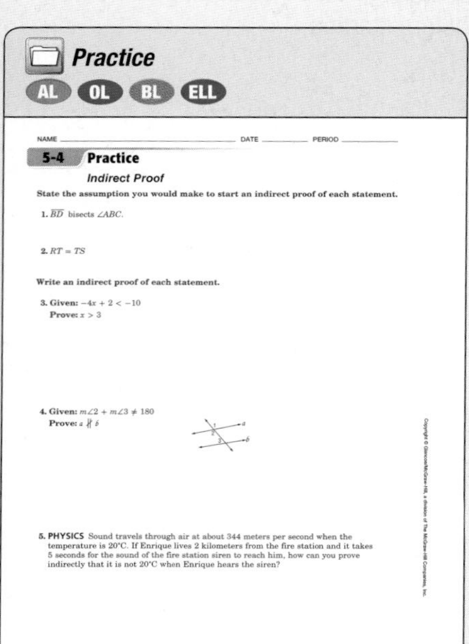

NAME ______ DATE ______ PERIOD ______

5-4 Practice

Indirect Proof

State the assumption you would make to start an indirect proof of each statement.

1. $\overline{BD}$ bisects $\angle ABC$.

2. $RT = TS$

Write an indirect proof of each statement.

3. Given: $-4x + 2 < -10$
Prove: $x > 3$

4. Given: $m\angle 2 + m\angle 3 \neq 180$
Prove: $a \nparallel b$

5. PHYSICS Sound travels through air at about 344 meters per second when the temperature is 20°C. If Enrique lives 2 kilometers from the fire station and it takes 5 seconds for the sound of the fire station siren to reach him, how can you prove indirectly that it is not 20°C when Enrique hears the siren?

Word Problem Practice

AL OL BL ELL

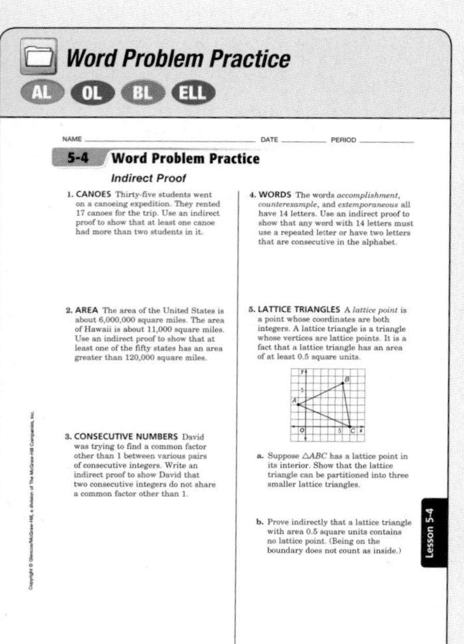

NAME ______ DATE ______ PERIOD ______

5-4 Word Problem Practice

Indirect Proof

1. CANOES Thirty-five students went on a canoeing expedition. They rented 17 canoes for the trip. Use an indirect proof to show that at least one canoe had more than two students in it.

2. AREA The area of the United States is about 6,000,000 square miles. The area of Hawaii is about 11,000 square miles. Use an indirect proof to show that at least one of the fifty states has an area greater than 120,000 square miles.

3. CONSECUTIVE NUMBERS David was trying to find a common factor other than 1 between various pairs of consecutive integers. Write an indirect proof to show David that two consecutive integers do not share a common factor other than 1.

4. WORDS The words *accomplishment*, *counterexample*, and *extemporaneous* all have 14 letters. Use an indirect proof to show that any word with 14 letters must use a repeated letter or have two letters that are consecutive in the alphabet.

5. LATTICE TRIANGLES A *lattice point* is a point whose coordinates are both integers. A lattice triangle is a triangle whose vertices are lattice points. It is a fact that a lattice triangle has an area of at least 0.5 square units.

a. Suppose $\triangle ABC$ has a lattice point in its interior. Show that the lattice triangle can be partitioned into three smaller lattice triangles.

b. Prove indirectly that a lattice triangle with area 0.5 square units contains no lattice point. (Being on the boundary does not count as inside.)

Lesson 5-4

Enrichment

OL BL

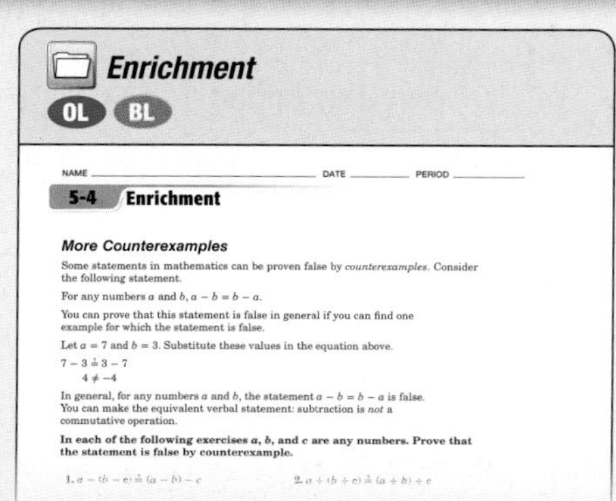

NAME ______ DATE ______ PERIOD ______

5-4 Enrichment

More Counterexamples

Some statements in mathematics can be proven false by *counterexamples*. Consider the following statement.

For any numbers a and b, $a - b = b - a$.

You can prove that this statement is false in general if you can find one example for which the statement is false.

Let $a = 7$ and $b = 3$. Substitute these values in the equation above.

$7 - 3 \stackrel{?}{=} 3 - 7$
$4 \neq -4$

In general, for any numbers a and b, the statement $a - b = b - a$ is false. You can make the equivalent verbal statement: subtraction is *not* a commutative operation.

In each of the following exercises a, b, and c are any numbers. Prove that the statement is false by counterexample.

1. $a - (b - c) \stackrel{?}{=} (a - b) - c$ **2.** $a \div (b \div c) \stackrel{?}{=} (a \div b) \div c$

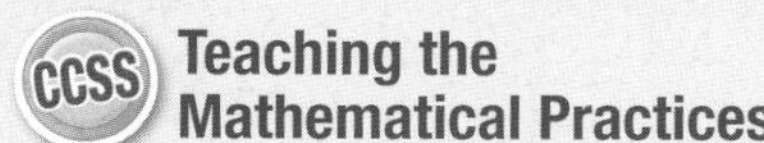

Teaching the Mathematical Practices

Reasoning Mathematically proficient students make sense of quantities and their relationships in problem situations. In Exercise 36, point out to students that in an indirect proof, they are to assume that one of the statements is not true.

Determine whether each statement about the shortest distance between a point and a line or plane can be proved using a direct or indirect proof. Then write a proof of each statement. 37–38. See Ch. 5 Answer Appendix.

37. Given: $\overline{AB} \perp$ line p

Prove: $\overline{AB}$ is the shortest segment from A to line p.

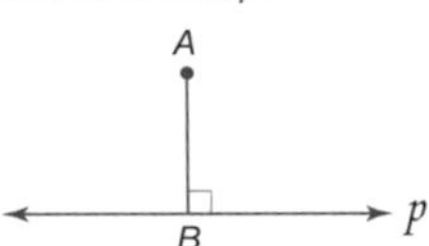

38. Given: $\overline{PQ} \perp$ plane M

Prove: $\overline{PQ}$ is the shortest segment from P to plane M.

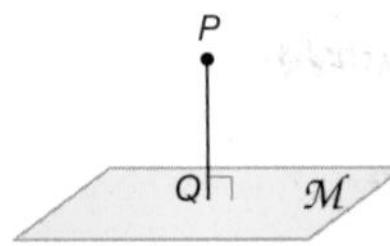

39. **NUMBER THEORY** In this problem, you will make and prove a conjecture about a number theory relationship.

a. Write an expression for *the sum of the cube of a number and three.* $n^3 + 3$

b. Create a table that includes the value of the expression for 10 different values of n. Include both odd and even values of n. See Ch. 5 Answer Appendix.

c. Write a conjecture about n when the value of the expression is even.

d. Write an indirect proof of your conjecture. See Ch. 5 Answer Appendix.

39c. Sample answer: When $n^3 + 3$ is even, n is odd.

H.O.T. Problems Use Higher-Order Thinking Skills

40. **WRITING IN MATH** Explain the procedure for writing an indirect proof. See Ch. 5 Answer Appendix.

41. **OPEN ENDED** Write a statement that can be proven using indirect proof. Include the indirect proof of your statement. See Ch. 5 Answer Appendix.

42. **CHALLENGE** If x is a rational number, then it can be represented by the quotient $\frac{a}{b}$ for some integers a and b, if $b \neq 0$. An irrational number cannot be represented by the quotient of two integers. Write an indirect proof to show that the product of a nonzero rational number and an irrational number is an irrational number. See Ch. 5 Answer Appendix.

43. CCSS **CRITIQUE** Amber and Raquel are trying to verify the following statement using indirect proof. Is either of them correct? Explain your reasoning.

If the sum of two numbers is even, then the numbers are even.

Amber	Raquel
The statement is true. If one of the numbers is even and the other number is zero, then the sum is even. Since the hypothesis is true even when the conclusion is false, the statement is true.	The statement is true. If the two numbers are odd, then the sum is even. Since the hypothesis is true when the conclusion is false, the statement is true.

Neither; sample answer: Since the hypothesis is true when the conclusion is false, the statement is false.

44. **WRITING IN MATH** Refer to Exercise 8. Write the contrapositive of the statement and write a direct proof of the contrapositive. How are the direct proof of the contrapositive of the statement and the indirect proof of the statement related? See Ch. 5 Answer Appendix.

Differentiated Instruction OL BL

Extension Write an indirect proof for the following statement.

The equation $x^2 - y^2 = 1$ has no positive integer solutions.

Step 1 Assume that there is a solution (x, y) to $x^2 - y^2 = 1$, where x and y are positive integers.

Step 2 The expression $x^2 - y^2$ factors to $(x - y)(x + y)$. If x and y are integers, then either $x - y = 1$ and $x + y = 1$ or $x - y = -1$ and $x + y = -1$. Solving the system of equations in the first case, we find that $x = 1$ and $y = 0$. Since 0 is not a positive number, this contradicts our assumption. In the second case, we find that $x = -1$ and $y = 0$, which also contradicts our assumption.

Step 3 Therefore, the original statement that $x^2 - y^2 = 1$ has no positive integer solutions must be true.

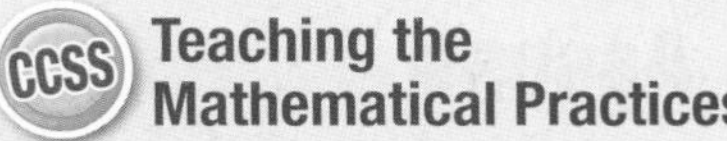

Teaching the Mathematical Practices

Critique Mathematically proficient students can distinguish correct logic from flawed reasoning. In Exercise 43, students should recognize that it is enough to disprove a statement with one counterexample, as Raquel does. Amber was incorrect to say that when the hypothesis is true and the conclusion is false that the statement is true.

Additional Answers

33. We know that the other team scored 3 points, and Katsu thinks that they made a three-point shot. We also know that a player can score 3 points by making a basket and a foul shot.

Step 1 Assume that a player for the other team made a two-point basket and a foul shot.

Step 2 The other team's score before Katsu left was 26, so their score after a two-point basket and a foul shot would be 26 + 3 or 29.

Step 3 The score is correct when we assume that the other team made a two-point basket and a foul shot, so Katsu's assumption may not be correct. The other team could have made a three-point basket or a two-point basket and a foul shot.

34. The door on the left. If the sign on the door on the right were true, then both signs would be true. But one sign is false, so the sign on the door on the right must be false.

4 Assess

Ticket out the Door On their way out the door, have students explain why the altitude to a side of a triangle cannot be longer than the other two sides of the triangle.

Additional Answer

49. Given: $\overline{RQ}$ bisects $\angle SRT$.

Prove: $m\angle SQR > m\angle SRQ$

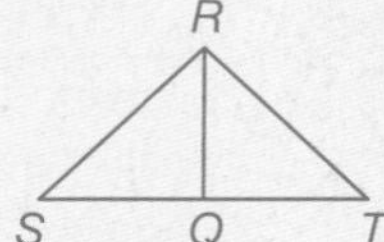

Proof:

Statements (Reasons)

1. $\overline{RQ}$ bisects $\angle SRT$. (Given)
2. $\angle SRQ \cong \angle QRT$ (Def. of angle bisector)
3. $m\angle QRS = m\angle QRT$ (Def. of $\cong$ $\triangle$s)
4. $m\angle SQR = m\angle T + m\angle QRT$ (Exterior Angle Theorem)
5. $m\angle SQR > m\angle QRT$ (Def. of Inequality)
6. $m\angle SQR > m\angle SRQ$ (Substitution)

Standardized Test Practice

45. SHORT RESPONSE Write an equation in slope-intercept form to describe the line that passes through the point (5, 3) and is parallel to the line represented by the equation $-2x + y = -4$. $y = 2x - 7$

46. Statement: If $\angle A \cong \angle B$ and $\angle A$ is supplementary to $\angle C$, then $\angle B$ is supplementary to $\angle C$.

Dia is proving the statement above by contradiction. She began by assuming that $\angle B$ is not supplementary to $\angle C$. Which of the following definitions will Dia use to reach a contradiction? D

A definition of congruence
B definition of a linear pair
C definition of a right angle
D definition of supplementary angles

47. List the angles of $\triangle MNO$ in order from smallest to largest if $MN = 9$, $NO = 7.5$, and $OM = 12$. J

F $\angle N, \angle O, \angle M$
G $\angle O, \angle M, \angle N$
H $\angle O, \angle N, \angle M$
J $\angle M, \angle O, \angle N$

48. SAT/ACT If $b > a$, which of the following must be true? A

A $-a > -b$
B $3a > b$
C $a^2 < b^2$
D $a^2 < ab$
E $-b > -a$

Spiral Review

49. PROOF Write a two-column proof. (Lesson 5-3) See margin.
Given: $\overline{RQ}$ bisects $\angle SRT$.
Prove: $m\angle SQR > m\angle SRQ$

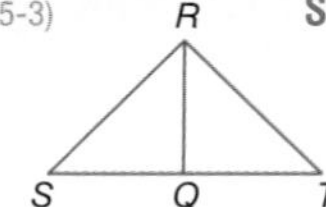

COORDINATE GEOMETRY **Find the coordinates of the circumcenter of each triangle with the given vertices.** (Lesson 5-1)

50. $D(-3, 3)$, $E(3, 2)$, $F(1, -4)$ **50.** $\left(-\frac{17}{38}, -\frac{7}{38}\right)$

51. $A(4, 0)$, $B(-2, 4)$, $C(0, 6)$ $\left(1\frac{2}{5}, 2\frac{3}{5}\right)$

Find each measure. (Lesson 4-2)

52. $m\angle 1$ 26

53. $m\angle 4$ 64

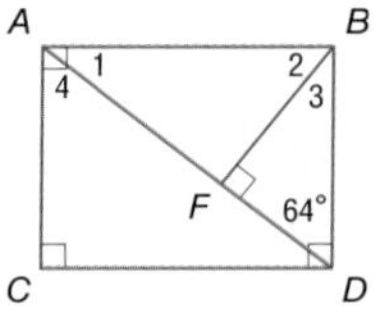

COORDINATE GEOMETRY **Find the distance between each pair of parallel lines with the given equations.** (Lesson 3-6)

54. $x + 3y = 6$
$x + 3y = -14$ $\sqrt{40} \approx 6.3$

55. $y = 2x + 2$
$y = 2x - 3$ $\sqrt{5} \approx 2.2$

56. RECYCLING Refer to the Venn diagram that represents the number of neighborhoods in a city with a curbside recycling program for paper or aluminum. (Lesson 2-2)

a. How many neighborhoods recycle aluminum? 24
b. How many neighborhoods recycle paper or aluminum or both? 36
c. How many neighborhoods recycle paper and aluminum? 4

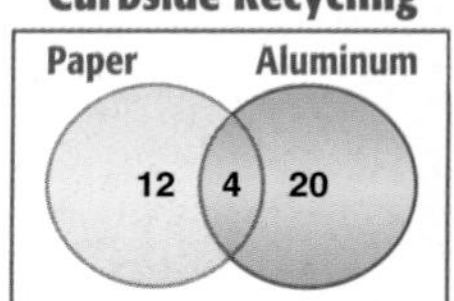

Skills Review

Determine whether each inequality is *true* or *false*.

57. $23 - 11 > 9$ true

58. $41 - 19 < 21$ false

59. $57 + 68 < 115$ false

362 | Lesson 5-4 | Indirect Proof

EXPLORE 5-5

Graphing Technology Lab
The Triangle Inequality

You can use the Cabri™ Jr. application on a TI-83/84 Plus graphing calculator to discover properties of triangles.

Common Core State Standards
Content Standards
G.CO.12 Make formal geometric constructions with a variety of tools and methods (compass and straightedge, string, reflective devices, paper folding, dynamic geometric software, etc.).
Mathematical Practices 5

Activity 1

Construct a triangle. Observe the relationship between the sum of the lengths of two sides and the length of the other side.

Step 1 Construct a triangle using the triangle tool on the **F2** menu. Then use the **Alph-Num** tool on the **F5** menu to label the vertices as *A*, *B*, and *C*.

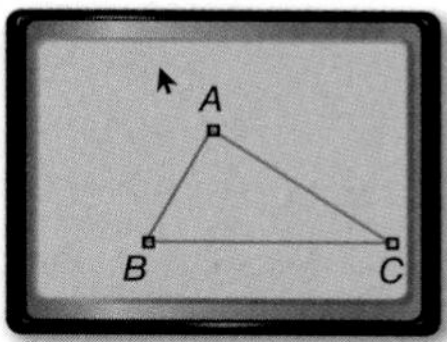

Step 1

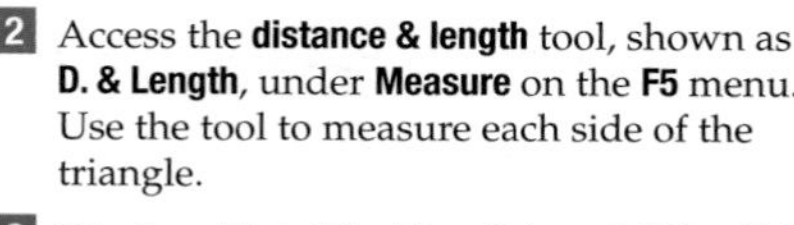

Step 2 Access the **distance & length** tool, shown as **D. & Length**, under **Measure** on the **F5** menu. Use the tool to measure each side of the triangle.

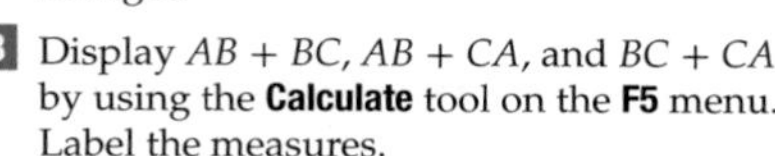

Step 3 Display $AB + BC$, $AB + CA$, and $BC + CA$ by using the **Calculate** tool on the **F5** menu. Label the measures.

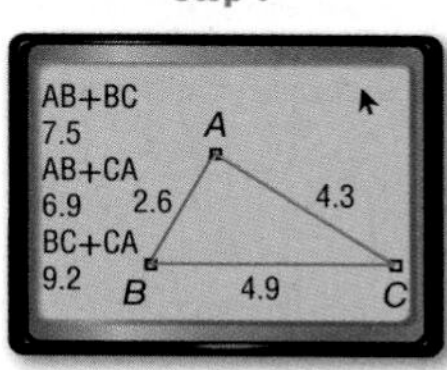

Steps 2 and 3

Step 4 Click and drag the vertices to change the shape of the triangle.

Analyze the Results

1. Replace each ● with <, >, or = to make a true statement.
$AB + BC$ ● CA $AB + BC > CA$ $AB + CA$ ● BC $AB + CA > BC$ $BC + CA$ ● AB $BC + CA > AB$
2. Click and drag the vertices to change the shape of the triangle. Then review your answers to Exercise 1. What do you observe? The inequalities are all still the same.
3. Click on point *A* and drag it to lie on line *BC*. What do you observe about *AB*, *BC*, and *CA*? Are *A*, *B*, and *C* the vertices of a triangle? Explain.
Sample answer: $AB + BC = CA$; No, the points are not the vertices of a triangle because they are collinear.
4. **Make a conjecture** about the sum of the lengths of two sides of a triangle and the length of the third side. The sum of the lengths of two sides of a triangle is greater than the length of the third side.
5. Do the measurements and observations you made in the Activity and in Exercises 1–3 constitute a proof of the conjecture you made in Exercise 4? Explain. See margin.
6. Replace each ● with <, >, or = to make a true statement.
$|AB - BC|$ ● CA $|AB - CA|$ ● BC $|BC - CA|$ ● AB
Then click and drag the vertices to change the shape of the triangle and review your answers. What do you observe? $|AB - BC| < CA$; $|AB - CA| < BC$; $|BC - CA| < AB$; The inequalities are all still the same.
7. How could you use your observations to determine the possible lengths of the third side of a triangle if you are given the lengths of the other two sides? See margin.

1 Focus

Objective Use technology to investigate triangle inequalities.

Materials

- TI-83/84 Plus graphing calculator

2 Teach

Working Independently

Students can work alone or in pairs of mixed abilities. Tell students to do the activity while answering Exercises 1–6.

Ask students how their conjecture in Exercise 4 relates to what they have observed. Have students determine how to click and drag vertex *A* so that it is the shortest distance from vertex *B*.

Practice Have students complete Exercise 7 individually.

3 Assess

Formative Assessment

Use Exercises 1–7 to assess if students comprehend the relationships between the sides lengths of triangles.

From Concrete to Abstract

Have students draw a triangle on grid paper. Tell them to exchange their triangle with a partner. Have students find the lengths of the sides and write inequalities to express the relationships between the lengths.

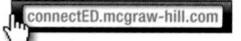

Additional Answers

5. No; the conjecture made in Exercise 4 was reached using inductive reasoning, which is not a valid way to prove a conjecture.
7. The length of the third side will be less than the sum of the lengths of the other two sides and greater than the absolute value of the difference of the lengths of the other two sides.

1 Focus

VerticalAlignment

Before Lesson 5-5 Recognize and apply properties of inequalities to the relationships between the angles and sides of triangles.

Lesson 5-5 Use the Triangle Inequality Theorem to identify possible triangles and prove triangle relationships.

After Lesson 5-5 Make conjectures about angles, lines, polygons, circles, and three-dimensional figures and determine the validity of the conjectures.

2 Teach

Scaffolding Questions

Have students read the **Why?** section of the lesson.

Ask:

- What are the lengths of the three scraps from each attempt? first: 3 in., 6 in., 8 in.; second: 3 in., 3 in., 8 in.
- What is the sum of the two shorter lengths for each attempt? first: 9 in.; second: 6 in.

(continued on the next page)

LESSON 5-5 The Triangle Inequality

Then	Now	Why?
You recognized and applied properties of inequalities to the relationships between the angles and sides of a triangle.	1 Use the Triangle Inequality Theorem to identify possible triangles. 2 Prove triangle relationships using the Triangle Inequality Theorem.	On a home improvement show, a designer wants to use scrap pieces of cording from another sewing project to decorate the triangular throw pillows that she and the homeowner have made. To minimize waste, she wants to use the scraps without cutting them. She selects three scraps at random and tries to form a triangle. Two such attempts are shown.

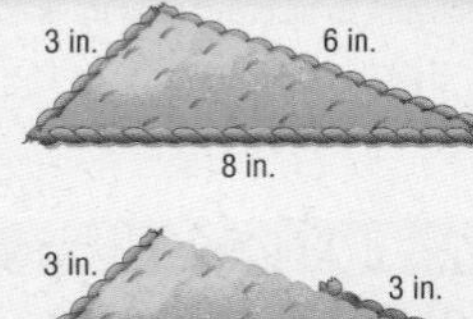

Common Core State Standards

Content Standards

G.CO.10 Prove theorems about triangles.

G.MG.3 Apply geometric methods to solve problems (e.g., designing an object or structure to satisfy physical constraints or minimize cost; working with typographic grid systems based on ratios). ★

Mathematical Practices

1 Make sense of problems and persevere in solving them.

2 Reason abstractly and quantitatively.

1 The Triangle Inequality While a triangle is formed by three segments, a special relationship must exist among the lengths of the segments in order for them to form a triangle.

Theorem 5.11 Triangle Inequality Theorem

The sum of the lengths of any two sides of a triangle must be greater than the length of the third side.

Examples $PQ + QR > PR$
$QR + PR > PQ$
$PR + PQ > QR$

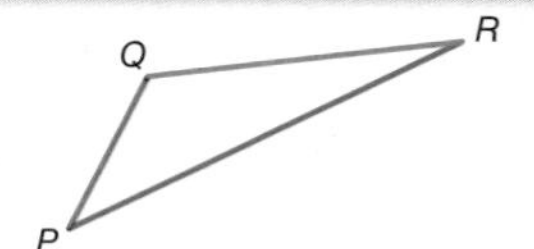

You will prove Theorem 5.11 in Exercise 23.

To show that it is not possible to form a triangle with three side lengths, you need only show that one of the three triangle inequalities is not true.

Example 1 Identify Possible Triangles Given Side Lengths

Is it possible to form a triangle with the given side lengths? If not, explain why not.

a. 8 in., 15 in., 17 in.

Check each inequality.

$8 + 15 \overset{?}{>} 17$ $\quad 23 > 17$ ✓

$8 + 17 \overset{?}{>} 15$ $\quad 25 > 15$ ✓

$15 + 17 \overset{?}{>} 8$ $\quad 32 > 8$ ✓

Since the sum of each pair of side lengths is greater than the third side length, sides with lengths 8, 15, and 17 inches will form a triangle.

b. 6 m, 8 m, 14 m

$6 + 8 \overset{?}{>} 14$

$14 \not> 14$ ✗

Since the sum of one pair of side lengths is not greater than the third side length, sides with lengths 6, 8, and 14 meters will not form a triangle.

GuidedPractice 1A. yes; $15 + 16 > 30$; $15 + 30 > 16$; $16 + 30 > 15$

1A. 15 yd, 16 yd, 30 yd

1B. 2 ft, 8 ft, 11 ft no; $2 + 8 \not> 11$

Lesson 5-5 Resources

Resource	Approaching Level AL	On Level OL	Beyond Level BL	English Learners ELL
Teacher Edition	▪ Differentiated Instruction, p. 365	▪ Differentiated Instruction, pp. 365, 366	▪ Differentiated Instruction, pp. 365, 366	
Chapter Resource Masters	▪ Study Guide and Intervention, pp. 31–32 ▪ Skills Practice, p. 33 ▪ Practice, p. 34 ▪ Word Problem Practice, p. 35	▪ Study Guide and Intervention, pp. 31–32 ▪ Skills Practice, p. 33 ▪ Practice, p. 34 ▪ Word Problem Practice, p. 35 ▪ Enrichment, p. 36	▪ Practice, p. 34 ▪ Word Problem Practice, p. 35 ▪ Enrichment, p. 36	▪ Study Guide and Intervention, pp. 31–32 ▪ Skills Practice, p. 33 ▪ Practice, p. 34 ▪ Word Problem Practice, p. 35
Other	▪ 5-Minute Check 5-5 ▪ Study Notebook ▪ Teaching Geometry with Manipulatives	▪ 5-Minute Check 5-5 ▪ Study Notebook ▪ Teaching Geometry with Manipulatives	▪ 5-Minute Check 5-5 ▪ Study Notebook	▪ 5-Minute Check 5-5 ▪ Study Notebook ▪ Teaching Geometry with Manipulatives

When the lengths of two sides of a triangle are known, the third side can be any length in a range of values. You can use the Triangle Inequality Theorem to determine the range of possible lengths for the third side.

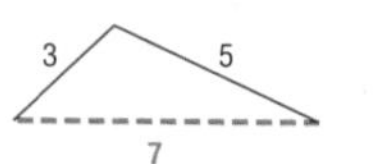

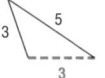

Standardized Test Example 2 Find Possible Side Lengths

If the measures of two sides of a triangle are 3 feet and 7 feet, which is the *least* possible whole number measure for the third side?

A 3 ft **B** 4 ft **C** 5 ft **D** 10 ft

Read the Test Item

You need to determine which value is the least possible measure for the third side of a triangle with sides that measure 3 feet and 7 feet.

Solve the Test Item

To determine the least possible measure from the choices given, first determine the range of possible measures for the third side.

Draw a diagram and let x represent the length of the third side.

Next, set up and solve each of the three triangle inequalities.

$3 + 7 > x$	$3 + x > 7$	$x + 7 > 3$
$10 > x$ or $x < 10$	$x > 4$	$x > -4$

Notice that $x > -4$ is always true for any whole number measure for x. Combining the two remaining inequalities, the range of values that fit both inequalities is $x > 4$ and $x < 10$, which can be written as $4 < x < 10$.

The least whole number value between 4 and 10 is 5. So the correct answer is choice C.

Guided Practice

2. Which of the following could *not* be the value of n? J

F 7 **H** 13

G 10 **J** 22

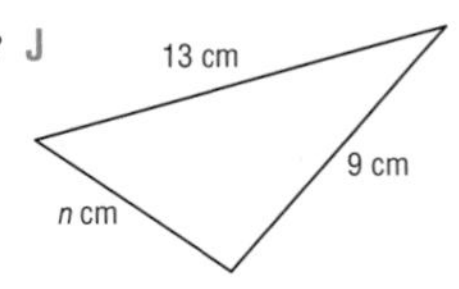

Test-Taking Tip

Testing Choices If you are short on time, you can test each choice to find the correct answer and eliminate any remaining choices.

Reading Math

Multiple Inequality Symbols The compound inequality $4 < x < 10$ is read *x is between 4 and 10.*

2 Proofs Using the Triangle Inequality Theorem

You can use the Triangle Inequality Theorem as a reason in proofs.

Differentiated Instruction

Naturalist Learners Explain that even naturally occurring triangles must follow the principles presented in this lesson. Ask students to find examples to explore and test the Triangle Inequality Theorem, such as bird beaks, leaves, star constellations, animal tracks, and so on. The stars Vega, Deneb, and Altair form a right triangle, called the "Summer Triangle." Students can research to find estimated distances between the stars and verify that even in nature, the theorem is true.

- How does the sum compare to the third scrap in each attempt? In the first attempt, the sum is greater than the third side, and in the second the sum is smaller.
- Use this information to make a conjecture about the relationships between the two shorter sides and the third side of a triangle. Sample answer: The sum of the two shorter sides must be greater than the third side.

1 The Triangle Inequality

Examples 1 and 2 show how to identify and determine side lengths of a triangle. Students will use inequalities to determine side lengths.

Formative Assessment

Use the Guided Practice exercises after each example to determine students' understanding of concepts.

Additional Examples

1 Is it possible to form a triangle with the given side lengths? If not, explain why not.

a. $6\frac{1}{2}, 6\frac{1}{2}, 14\frac{1}{2}$

no; $6\frac{1}{2} + 6\frac{1}{2} < 14\frac{1}{2}$

b. 6.8, 7.2, 5.1 yes

2 STANDARDIZED TEST EXAMPLE In $\triangle PQR$, $PQ = 7.2$ and $QR = 5.2$. Which measure cannot be PR? D

A 7 **B** 9 **C** 11 **D** 13

Teach with Tech

Interactive Whiteboard Draw three line segments on the board, so that the sum of the lengths of the two shortest segments is less than or equal to the length of the longest segment (do not display the measurements). Select students to come to the board to rotate and drag the line segments to try to form a triangle. When students find that this is not possible, have them measure the length of each segment and support their findings using triangle inequality.

2 Proofs Using the Triangle Inequality Theorem

Example 3 shows how to use the Triangle Inequality Theorem to write a proof about distances.

Additional Example

3 TRAVEL The towns of Jefferson, Kingston, and Newbury are shown in the map below. Prove that driving first from Jefferson to Kingston and then Kingston to Newbury is a greater distance than driving from Jefferson to Newbury.

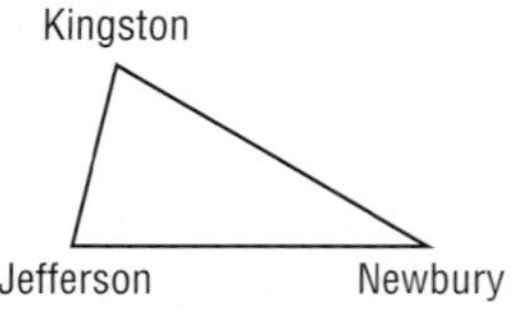

Abbreviating the vertices as J, K, and N, $JK + KN > JN$.

Additional Examples also in Interactive Classroom PowerPoint® Presentations

Tips for New Teachers

The Triangle Inequality By the Segment Addition Postulate, if the sum of any two line segments is equal to the length of a third line segment, then the three endpoints are collinear. Therefore, the three line segments can not form a triangle.

Additional Answer (Guided Practice)

3. Statements (Reasons)
   1. $GL = LK$ (Given)
   2. $JH + GH > GJ$ (Triangle Inequality Thm.)
   3. $GJ = GL + LJ$ (Seg. Add. Post.)
   4. $JH + GH > GL + LJ$ (Subst.)
   5. $JH + GH > LK + LJ$ (Subst.)
   6. $LK + LJ > JK$ ($\triangle$ Ineq. Thm.)
   7. $JH + GH > JK$ (Transitive Prop.)

Real-WorldLink

A direct flight is not the same as a nonstop flight. For a direct flight, passengers do not change planes, but the plane may make one or more stops before continuing to its final destination.

Real-World Example 3 Proof Using Triangle Inequality Theorem

TRAVEL The distance from Colorado Springs, Springs, Colorado, to Abilene, Texas, is the same as the distance from Colorado Springs to Tulsa, Oklahoma. Prove that a direct flight from Colorado Springs to Tulsa through Lincoln, Nebraska, is a greater distance than a nonstopflight from Colorado Springs to Abilene.

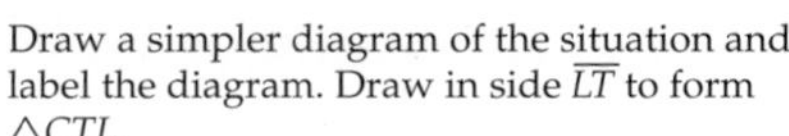

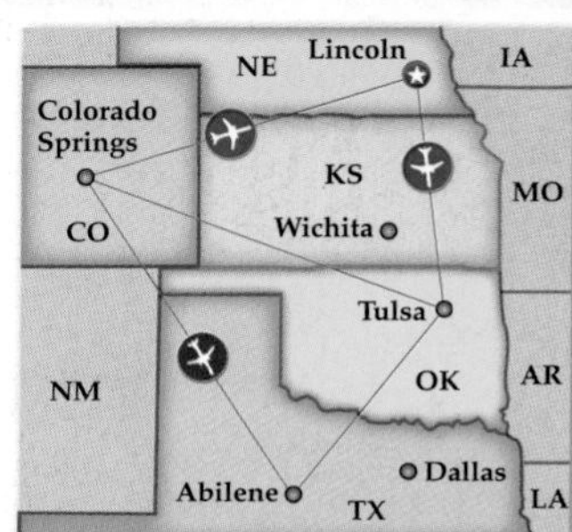

Draw a simpler diagram of the situation and label the diagram. Draw in side $\overline{LT}$ to form $\triangle CTL$.

Given: $CA = CT$

Prove: $CL + LT > CA$

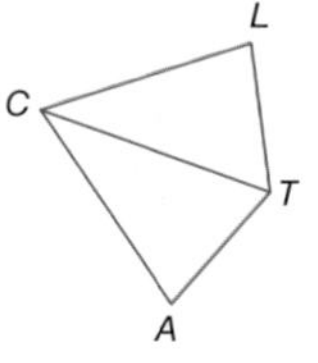

Proof:

Statements	Reasons
1. $CA = CT$	1. Given
2. $CL + LT > CT$	2. Triangle Inequality Theorem
3. $CL + LT > CA$	3. Substitution

GuidedPractice

3. Write a two-column proof.

   Given: $GL = LK$

   Prove: $JH + GH > JK$
   See margin.

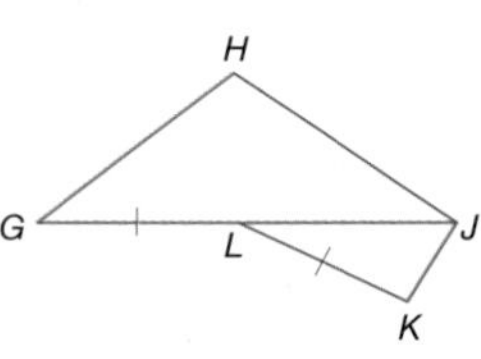

Check Your Understanding

= Step-by-Step Solutions begin on page R14.

Example 1 **Is it possible to form a triangle with the given side lengths? If not, explain why not.**

1. 5 cm, 7 cm, 10 cm
2. 3 in., 4 in., 8 in. no; $3 + 4 \not> 8$
3. 6 m, 14 m, 10 m

Example 2

4. **MULTIPLE CHOICE** If the measures of two sides of a triangle are 5 yards and 9 yards, what is the least possible measure of the third side if the measure is an integer? B

   A 4 yd **B** 5 yd **C** 6 yd **D** 14 yd

Example 3

5. **PROOF** Write a two-column proof.

   Given: $\overline{XW} \cong \overline{YW}$

   Prove: $YZ + ZW > XW$ See margin.

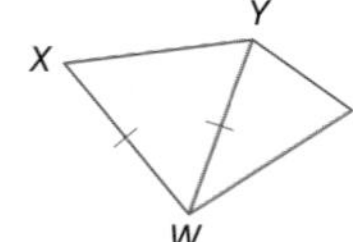

1. yes; $5 + 7 > 10$, $5 + 10 > 7$, and $7 + 10 > 5$
3. yes; $6 + 14 > 10$, $6 + 10 > 14$, and $10 + 14 > 6$

DifferentiatedInstruction OL BL

Extension A park designer is planning a new park that will be in the shape of a triangle. The designer informed the city council members that the borders of the park have measures of 180 feet, 150 feet, and 340 feet. One of the council members asked the designer to go back to the site and measure again. In detail, explain why. The Triangle Inequality Theorem states that the sum of the lengths of any two sides of a triangle is greater that the length of the third side. Since $180 + 150 = 330$, which is less than the third side, the measurements cannot make a triangle.

Practice and Problem Solving

Extra Practice is on page R5.

Example 1 **Is it possible to form a triangle with the given side lengths? If not, explain why not.**

6. 4 ft, 9 ft, 15 ft **6–11. See margin.**
7. 11 mm, 21 mm, 16 mm
8. 9.9 cm, 1.1 cm, 8.2 cm
9. 2.1 in., 4.2 in., 7.9 in.
10. $2\frac{1}{2}$ m, $1\frac{3}{4}$ m, $5\frac{1}{8}$ m
11. $1\frac{1}{5}$ km, $4\frac{1}{2}$ km, $3\frac{3}{4}$ km

Example 2 **Find the range for the measure of the third side of a triangle given the measures of two sides.**

12. 4 ft, 8 ft **$4 \text{ ft} < n < 12 \text{ ft}$**
13. 5 m, 11 m **$6 \text{ m} < n < 16 \text{ m}$**
14. 2.7 cm, 4.2 cm **$1.5 \text{ cm} < n < 6.9 \text{ cm}$**
15. 3.8 in., 9.2 in. **$5.4 \text{ in.} < n < 13 \text{ in.}$**
16. $\frac{1}{2}$ km, $3\frac{1}{4}$ km **$2\frac{3}{4} \text{ km} < n < 3\frac{3}{4} \text{ km}$**
17. $2\frac{1}{3}$ yd, $7\frac{2}{3}$ yd **$5\frac{1}{3} \text{ yd} < n < 10 \text{ yd}$**

Example 3 **PROOF Write a two-column proof.**

18. **Given:** $\angle BCD \cong \angle CDB$ **See Ch. 5 Answer Appendix.**
Prove: $AB + AD > BC$

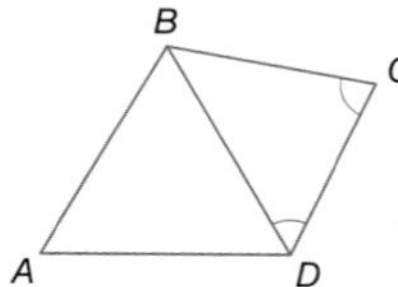

19. **Given:** $\overline{JL} \cong \overline{LM}$ **See Ch. 5 Answer Appendix.**
Prove: $KJ + KL > LM$

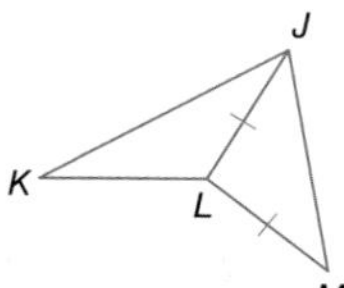

  **SENSE-MAKING Determine the possible values of *x*.**

20. **$6 < x < 17$**

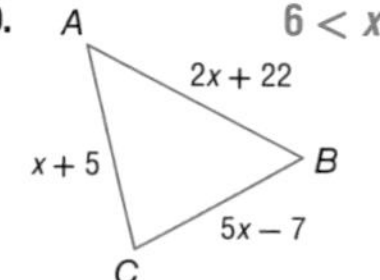

21. **$\frac{7}{5} < x < 21$**

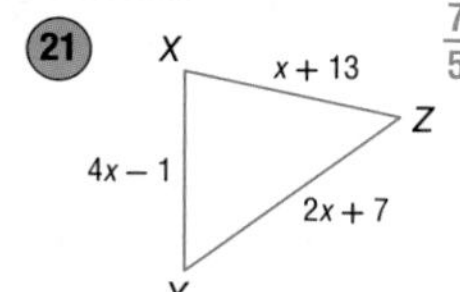

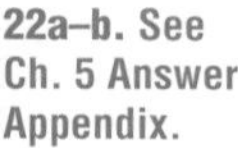

22a–b. See Ch. 5 Answer Appendix.

22. **DRIVING** Takoda wants to take the most efficient route from his house to a soccer tournament at The Sportsplex. He can take County Line Road or he can take Highway 4 and then Route 6 to the get to The Sportsplex.
   a. Which of the two possible routes is the shortest? Explain your reasoning.
   b. Suppose Takoda always drives below the speed limit. If the speed limit on County Line Road is 30 miles per hour and on both Highway 4 and Route 6 it is 55 miles per hour, which route will be faster? Explain.

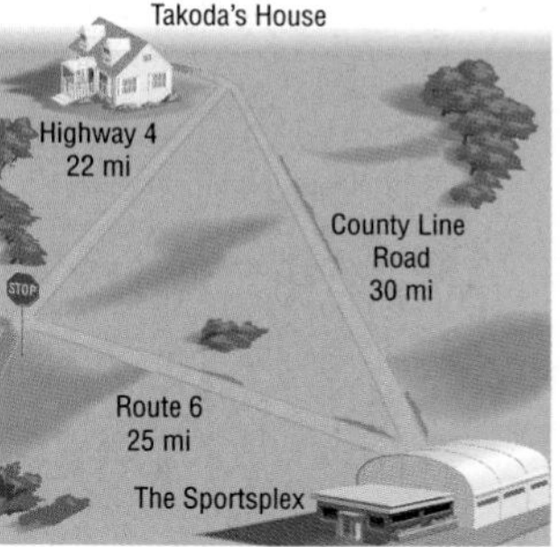

23. **PROOF Write a two-column proof.** **See Ch. 5 Answer Appendix.**
Given: $\triangle ABC$
Prove: $AC + BC > AB$ (Triangle Inequality Theorem)
(*Hint*: Draw auxiliary segment $\overline{CD}$, so that C is between B and D and $\overline{CD} \cong \overline{AC}$.)

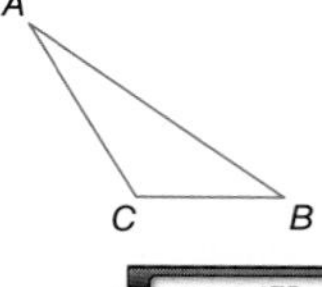

Differentiated Homework Options

Level	Assignment	Two-Day Option	
AL Basic	6–19, 44, 45, 47–64	7–19 odd, 49–52	6–18 even, 44, 45, 47, 48, 53–64
OL Core	7–19 odd, 21–42, 44, 45, 47–64	6–19, 49–52	20–42, 44, 45, 47, 48, 53–64
BL Advanced	20–60, (optional: 61–64)		

3 Practice

Formative Assessment

Use Exercises 1–5 to check for understanding.

Use the chart at the bottom of this page to customize assignments for your students.

Teaching the Mathematical Practices

Sense-Making Mathematically proficient students look for entry points into a solution. They plan a solution pathway rather than simply jumping into a solution attempt. In Exercises 20–21, point out to students that they should use the Triangle Inequality Theorem.

Additional Answers

5. **Given:** $\overline{XW} \cong \overline{YW}$
Prove: $YZ + ZW > XW$

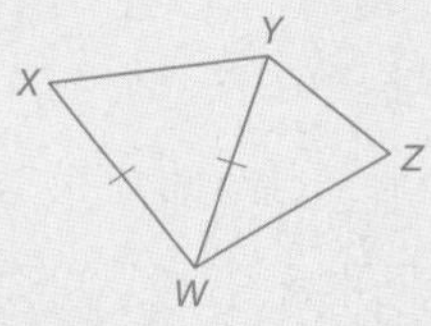

Statements (Reasons)
1. $\overline{XW} \cong \overline{YW}$ (Given)
2. $XW = YW$ (Def. of $\cong$ segments)
3. $YZ + ZW > YW$ ($\triangle$ Inequality Thm.)
4. $YZ + ZW > XW$ (Subst.)

6. no; $4 + 9 \ngtr 15$
7. yes; $11 + 21 > 16$, $11 + 16 > 21$, and $16 + 21 > 11$
8. no; $1.1 + 8.2 \ngtr 9.9$
9. no; $2.1 + 4.2 \ngtr 7.9$
10. no; $2\frac{1}{2} + 1\frac{3}{4} \ngtr 5\frac{1}{8}$
11. yes; $1\frac{1}{5} + 4\frac{1}{2} > 3\frac{3}{4}$, $1\frac{1}{5} + 3\frac{3}{4} > 4\frac{1}{2}$, $4\frac{1}{2} + 3\frac{3}{4} > 1\frac{1}{5}$

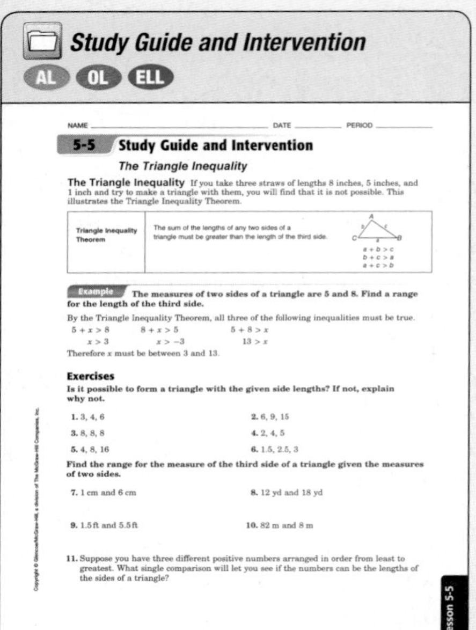

Study Guide and Intervention

AL OL ELL

NAME ______ DATE ______ PERIOD ______

5-5 Study Guide and Intervention

The Triangle Inequality

The Triangle Inequality If you take three straws of lengths 8 inches, 5 inches, and 1 inch and try to make a triangle with them, you will find that it is not possible. This illustrates the Triangle Inequality Theorem.

Triangle Inequality Theorem	The sum of the lengths of any two sides of a triangle must be greater than the length of the third side.	$a + b > c$ $b + c > a$ $a + c > b$

Example **The measures of two sides of a triangle are 5 and 8. Find a range for the length of the third side.**

By the Triangle Inequality Theorem, all three of the following inequalities must be true.

$5 + x > 8$ $\quad 8 + x > 5$ $\quad 5 + 8 > x$

$x > 3$ $\quad x > -3$ $\quad 13 > x$

Therefore x must be between 3 and 13.

Exercises

Is it possible to form a triangle with the given side lengths? If not, explain why not.

1. 3, 4, 6
2. 6, 9, 15
3. 8, 8, 8
4. 2, 4, 5
5. 4, 8, 16
6. 1.5, 2.5, 3

Find the range for the measure of the third side of a triangle given the measures of two sides.

7. 1 cm and 6 cm
8. 12 yd and 18 yd
9. 1.5 ft and 5.5 ft
10. 82 m and 8 m
11. Suppose you have three different positive numbers arranged in order from least to greatest. What single comparison will let you see if the numbers can be the lengths of the sides of a triangle?

Lesson 5-5

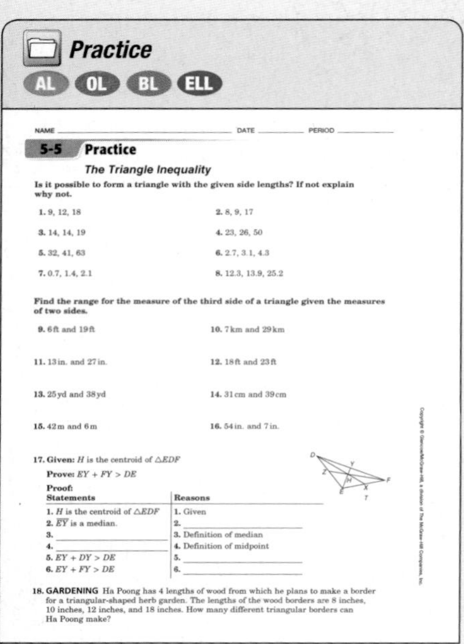

Practice

AL OL BL ELL

NAME ______ DATE ______ PERIOD ______

5-5 Practice

The Triangle Inequality

Is it possible to form a triangle with the given side lengths? If not explain why not.

1. 9, 12, 18
2. 8, 9, 17
3. 14, 14, 19
4. 23, 26, 50
5. 32, 41, 63
6. 2.7, 3.1, 4.3
7. 0.7, 1.4, 2.1
8. 12.3, 13.9, 25.2

Find the range for the measure of the third side of a triangle given the measures of two sides.

9. 6 ft and 19 ft
10. 7 km and 29 km
11. 13 in. and 27 in.
12. 18 ft and 23 ft
13. 25 yd and 38 yd
14. 31 cm and 39 cm
15. 42 m and 6 m
16. 54 in. and 7 in.

17. **Given:** H is the centroid of $\triangle EDF$

Prove: $EY + FY > DE$

Proof:

Statements	Reasons
1. H is the centroid of $\triangle EDF$	1. Given
2. $\overline{EY}$ is a median.	2. ______
3. ______	3. Definition of median
4. ______	4. Definition of midpoint
5. $EY + DY > DE$	5. ______
6. $EY + FY > DE$	6. ______

18. **GARDENING** Ha Poong has 4 lengths of wood from which he plans to make a border for a triangular-shaped herb garden. The lengths of the wood borders are 8 inches, 10 inches, 12 inches, and 18 inches. How many different triangular borders can Ha Poong make?

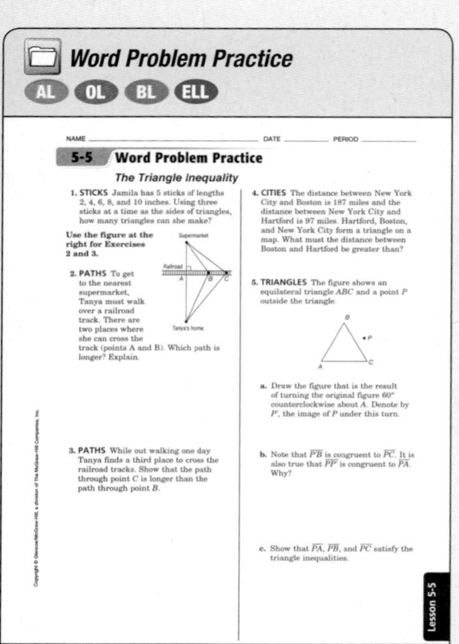

Word Problem Practice

AL OL BL ELL

NAME ______ DATE ______ PERIOD ______

5-5 Word Problem Practice

The Triangle Inequality

1. **STICKS** Jamila has 5 sticks of lengths 2, 4, 6, 8, and 10 inches. Using three sticks at a time as the sides of triangles, how many triangles can she make?

Use the figure at the right for Exercises 2 and 3.

2. **PATHS** To get to the nearest supermarket, Tanya must walk over a railroad track. There are two places where she can cross the track (points A and B). Which path is longer? Explain.

3. **PATHS** While out walking one day Tanya finds a third place to cross the railroad tracks. Show that the path through point C is longer than the path through point B.

4. **CITIES** The distance between New York City and Boston is 187 miles and the distance between New York City and Hartford is 97 miles. Hartford, Boston, and New York City form a triangle on a map. What must the distance between Boston and Hartford be greater than?

5. **TRIANGLES** The figure shows an equilateral triangle ABC and a point P outside the triangle.

a. Draw the figure that is the result of turning the original figure 60° counterclockwise about A. Denote by P', the image of P under this turn.

b. Note that $\overline{P'B}$ is congruent to $\overline{PC}$. It is also true that $\overline{PP'}$ is congruent to $\overline{PA}$. Why?

c. Show that $\overline{PA}$, $\overline{PB}$, and $\overline{PC}$ satisfy the triangle inequalities.

Lesson 5-5

24. **SCHOOL** When Toya goes from science class to math class, she usually stops at her locker. The distance from her science classroom to her locker is 90 feet, and the distance from her locker to her math classroom is 110 feet. What are the possible distances from science class to math class if she takes the hallway that goes directly between the two classrooms? **The distance is greater than 20 ft and less than 200 ft.**

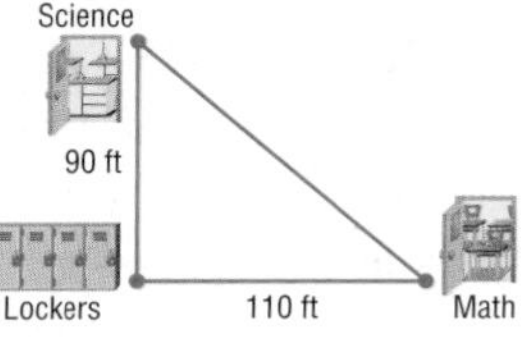

Find the range of possible measures of x if each set of expressions represents measures of the sides of a triangle.

25. $x, 4, 6$ $\quad 2 < x < 10$
26. $8, x, 12$ $\quad 4 < x < 20$
27. $x + 1, 5, 7$ $\quad 1 < x < 11$
28. $x - 2, 10, 12$ $\quad 4 < x < 24$
29. $x + 2, x + 4, x + 6$ $\quad x > 0$
30. $x, 2x + 1, x + 4$ $\quad x > \frac{3}{2}$

31. **DRAMA CLUB** Anthony and Catherine are working on a ramp up to the stage for the drama club's next production. Anthony's sketch of the ramp is shown below. Catherine is concerned about the measurements and thinks they should recheck the measures before they start cutting the wood. Is Catherine's concern valid? Explain your reasoning. See Ch. 5 Answer Appendix.

32. **CCSS SENSE-MAKING** Aisha is riding her bike to the park and can take one of two routes. The most direct route from her house is to take Main Street, but it is safer to take Route 3 and then turn right on Clay Road as shown. The additional distance she will travel if she takes Route 3 to Clay Road is between how many miles? **0 and 12**

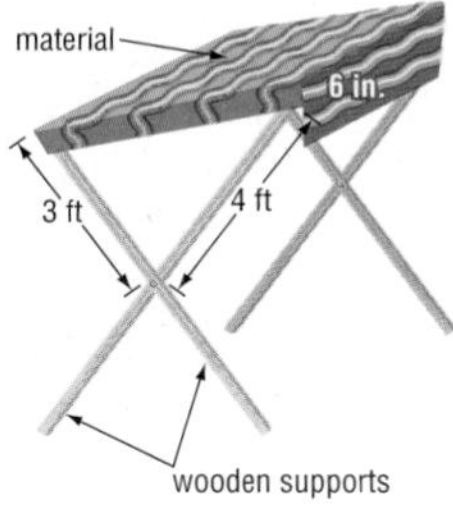

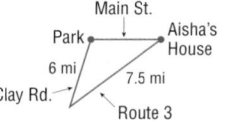

33. **DESIGN** Carlota designed an awning that she and her friends could take to the beach. Carlota decides to cover the top of the awning with material that will drape 6 inches over the front. What length of material should she buy to use with her design so that it covers the top of the awning, including the drape, when the supports are open as far as possible? Assume that the width of the material is sufficient to cover the awning. **She should buy no more than 7.5 ft.**

material
6 in.
3 ft
4 ft
wooden supports

ESTIMATION **Without using a calculator, determine if it is possible to form a triangle with the given side lengths. Explain.** 34–37. See margin.

34. $\sqrt{8}$ ft, $\sqrt{2}$ ft, $\sqrt{35}$ ft
35. $\sqrt{99}$ yd, $\sqrt{48}$ yd, $\sqrt{65}$ yd
36. $\sqrt{3}$ m, $\sqrt{15}$ m, $\sqrt{24}$ m
37. $\sqrt{122}$ in., $\sqrt{5}$ in., $\sqrt{26}$ in.

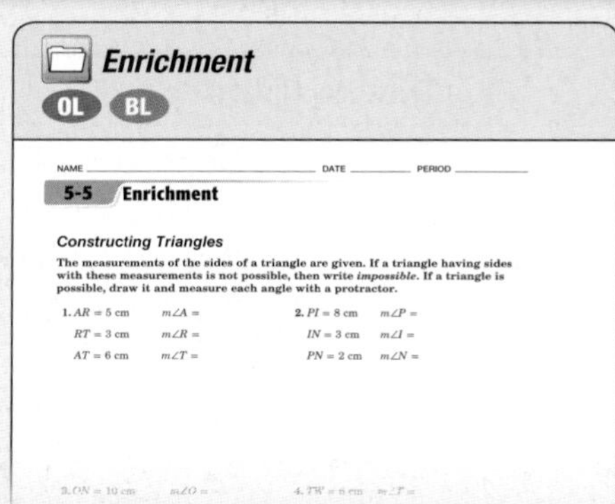

Enrichment

OL BL

NAME ______ DATE ______ PERIOD ______

5-5 Enrichment

Constructing Triangles

The measurements of the sides of a triangle are given. If a triangle having sides with these measurements is not possible, then write *impossible*. If a triangle is possible, draw it and measure each angle with a protractor.

1. $AR = 5$ cm $\quad m\angle A =$
$RT = 3$ cm $\quad m\angle R =$
$AT = 6$ cm $\quad m\angle T =$

2. $PI = 8$ cm $\quad m\angle P =$
$IN = 3$ cm $\quad m\angle I =$
$PN = 2$ cm $\quad m\angle N =$

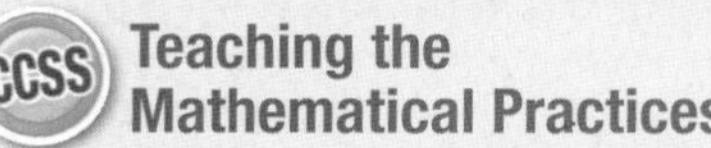

Teaching the Mathematical Practices

Sense-Making Mathematically proficient students look for entry points into a solution. They plan a solution pathway rather than simply jumping into a solution attempt. In Exercise 32, point out to students that they should use the Triangle Inequality Theorem.

CCSS REASONING **Determine whether the given coordinates are the vertices of a triangle. Explain.**

38. $X(1, -3)$, $Y(6, 1)$, $Z(2, 2)$
yes; $XY + YZ > XZ$, $XY + XZ > YZ$, and $XZ + YZ > XY$

39. $F(-4, 3)$, $G(3, -3)$, $H(4, 6)$ yes; $FG + GH > FH$, $FG + FH > GH$, and $GH + FH > FG$

40. $J(-7, -1)$, $K(9, -5)$, $L(21, -8)$
no; $JK + KL = JL$

41. $Q(2, 6)$, $R(6, 5)$, $S(1, 2)$ yes; $QR + QS > RS$, $QR + RS > QS$, and $QS + RS > QR$

42. **MULTIPLE REPRESENTATIONS** In this problem, you will use inequalities to make comparisons between the sides and angles of two triangles.

a. **Geometric** Draw three pairs of triangles that have two pairs of congruent sides and one pair of sides that is not congruent. Mark each pair of congruent sides. Label each triangle pair ABC and DEF, where $\overline{AB} \cong \overline{DE}$ and $\overline{AC} \cong \overline{DF}$. See Ch. 5 Answer Appendix.

b. **Tabular** Copy the table below. Measure and record the values of BC, $m\angle A$, EF, and $m\angle D$ for each triangle pair.

Triangle Pair	BC	$m\angle A$	EF	$m\angle D$
1	0.75	26	2	105
2	0.3	15	1	97
3	0.8	44	1.4	101

c. **Verbal** Make a conjecture about the relationship between the angles opposite the noncongruent sides of a pair of triangles that have two pairs of congruent legs.
Sample answer: The angle opposite the longer of the two noncongruent sides is greater than the angle opposite the shorter of the two noncongruent sides.

H.O.T. Problems Use Higher-Order Thinking Skills

43. **CHALLENGE** What is the range of possible perimeters for figure $ABCDE$ if $AC = 7$ and $DC = 9$? Explain your reasoning. See margin.

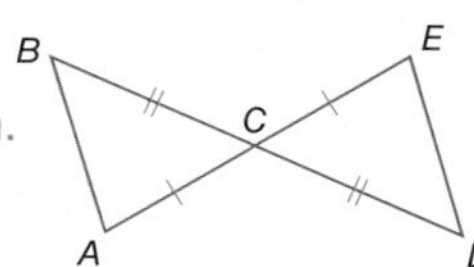

44. **REASONING** What is the range of lengths of each leg of an isosceles triangle if the measure of the base is 6 inches? Explain. See margin.

45. **WRITING IN MATH** What can you tell about a triangle when given three side lengths? Include at least two items. See margin.

46. **CHALLENGE** The sides of an isosceles triangle are whole numbers, and its perimeter is 30 units. What is the probability that the triangle is equilateral? $\frac{1}{7}$

47. **OPEN ENDED** The length of one side of a triangle is 2 inches. Draw a triangle in which the 2-inch side is the shortest side and one in which the 2-inch side is the longest side. Include side and angle measures on your drawing. See Ch. 5 Answer Appendix.

48. **WRITING IN MATH** Suppose your house is $\frac{3}{4}$ mile from a park and the park is 1.5 miles from a shopping center. a–b. See Ch. 5 Answer Appendix.

a. If your house, the park, and the shopping center are noncollinear, what do you know about the distance from your house to the shopping center? Explain your reasoning.

b. If the three locations are collinear, what do you know about the distance from your house to the shopping center? Explain your reasoning.

44. Each leg must be greater than 3 inches. Sample answer: When you use the Triangle Inequality Theorem to find the minimum leg length, the solution is greater than 3 inches. When you use it to find the maximum leg length, the inequality is $0 < 6$, which is always true. Therefore, there is no maximum length.

45. Sample answers: whether or not the side lengths actually form a triangle, what the smallest and largest angles are, whether the triangle is equilateral, isosceles, or scalene

CCSS Teaching the Mathematical Practices

Reasoning Mathematically proficient students make sense of quantities and their relationships in problem situations. In Exercises 38–41, encourage students to graph each ordered pair.

Multiple Representations

In Exercise 42, students use geometric sketches, a table, and verbal description to investigate the relationship between two sides and angles of a triangle.

Additional Answers

34. No; $\sqrt{8} \approx 2.9$ since $\sqrt{9} = 3$, $\sqrt{2} \approx 1.5$ since $\sqrt{4} = 2$ and $\sqrt{1} = 1$, and $\sqrt{35} \approx 5.9$ since $\sqrt{36} = 6$. So, $2.9 + 1.5 \not> 5.9$.

35. Yes; $\sqrt{99} \approx 9.9$ since $\sqrt{100} = 10$, $\sqrt{48} \approx 6.9$ since $\sqrt{49} = 7$, and $\sqrt{65} \approx 8.1$ since $\sqrt{64} = 8$. $6.9 + 8.1 > 9.9$ so it is possible.

36. Yes; $\sqrt{3} \approx 1.9$ since $\sqrt{4} = 2$, $\sqrt{15} \approx 3.9$ since $\sqrt{16} = 4$, and $\sqrt{24} \approx 4.9$ since $\sqrt{25} = 5$. $1.9 + 3.9 > 4.9$ so it is possible.

37. no; $\sqrt{122} \approx 11.1$ since $\sqrt{121} = 11$, $\sqrt{5} \approx 2.1$ since $\sqrt{4} = 2$, and $\sqrt{26} \approx 5.1$ since $\sqrt{25} = 5$. So, $2.1 + 5.1 \not> 11.1$.

43. The perimeter is greater than 36 and less than 64. Sample answer: From the diagram we know that $\overline{AC} \cong \overline{EC}$ and $\overline{DC} \cong \overline{BC}$, and $\angle ACB \cong \angle ECD$ because vertical angles are congruent, so $\triangle ACB \cong \triangle ECD$. Using the Triangle Inequality Theorem, the minimum value of AB and ED is 2 and the maximum value is 16. Therefore, the minimum value of the perimeter is greater than $2(2 + 7 + 9)$ or 36, and the maximum value of the perimeter is less than $2(16 + 7 + 9)$ or 64.

4 Assess

Crystal Ball To enhance understanding of the lesson concepts, tell students to rewrite the theorems and corollary from this lesson in their own words and predict how these will help in Lesson 5-6.

Formative Assessment

Check for student understanding of Lessons 5-4 and 5-5.

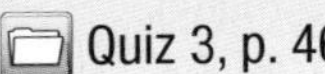
Quiz 3, p. 46

Additional Answers

61. $x = 2$; $JK = KL = JL = 14$
62. $x = 9$; $AB = BC = 23$
63. $x = 7$; $SR = RT = 24$, $ST = 19$

Standardized Test Practice

49. If $\overline{DC}$ is a median of $\triangle ABC$ and $m\angle 1 > m\angle 2$, which of the following statements is not true? B

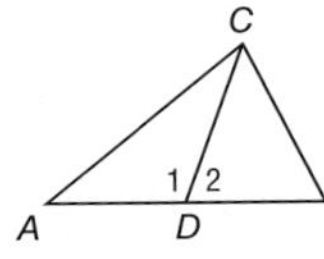

A $AD = BD$ C $AC > BC$
B $m\angle ADC = m\angle BDC$ D $m\angle 1 > m\angle B$

50. SHORT RESPONSE A high school soccer team has a goal of winning at least 75% of their 15 games this season. In the first three weeks, the team has won 5 games. How many more games must the team win to meet their goal? 7

51. Which of the following is a logical conclusion based on the statement and its converse below?

Statement: If a polygon is a rectangle, then it has four sides.

Converse: If a polygon has four sides, then it is a rectangle. H

F The statement and its converse are both true.
G The statement is false; the converse is false.
H The statement is true; the converse is false.
J The statement is false; the converse is true.

52. SAT/ACT When 7 is subtracted from $14w$, the result is z. Which of the following equations represents this statement? D

A $7 - 14w = z$ D $z = 14w - 7$
B $z = 14w + 7$ E $7 + 14w = 7z$
C $7 - z = 14w$

Spiral Review

State the assumption you would make to start an indirect proof of each statement. (Lesson 5-4)

53. If $4y + 17 = 41$, then $y = 6$. $y > 6$ or $y < 6$

54. If two lines are cut by a transversal and a pair of alternate interior angles are congruent, then the two lines are parallel. The two lines are not parallel.

55. GEOGRAPHY The distance between San Jose, California, and Las Vegas, Nevada, is about 375 miles. The distance from Las Vegas to Carlsbad, California, is about 243 miles. Use the Triangle Inequality Theorem to find the possible distance between San Jose and Carlsbad. (Lesson 5-3) $132 \text{ mi} \le d \le 618 \text{ mi}$

Find x so that $m \parallel n$. Identify the postulate or theorem you used. (Lesson 3-5)

56.

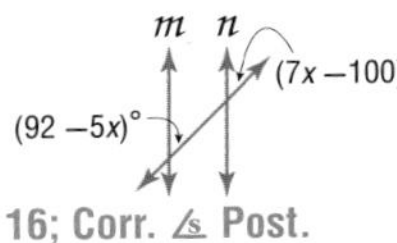

16; Corr. ∠s Post.

57.

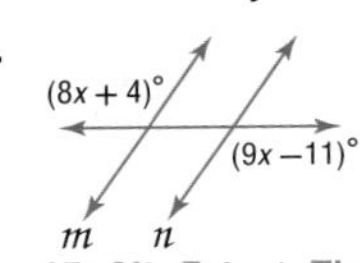

15; Alt. Ext. ∠s Thm.

58.

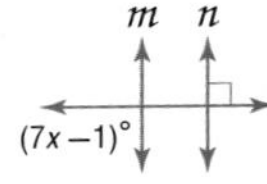

13; Alt. Ext. ∠s Thm.

ALGEBRA Find x and JK if J is between K and L. (Lesson 1-2)

59. $KJ = 3x$, $JL = 6x$, and $KL = 12$ $x = \frac{4}{3} \approx 1.3$; $JK = 4$

60. $KJ = 3x - 6$, $JL = x + 6$, and $KL = 24$ $x = 6$; $JK = 12$

Skills Review

Find x and the measures of the unknown sides of each triangle. 61–63. See margin.

61.

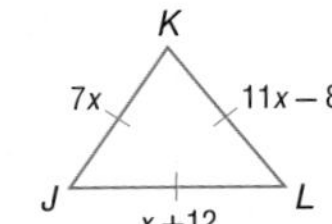

62.

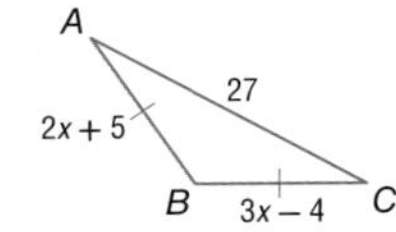

63.

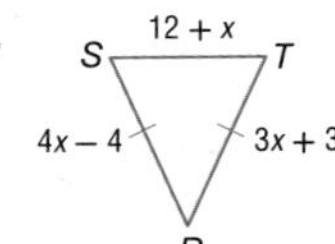

370 | Lesson 5-5 | The Triangle Inequality

LESSON 5-6 Inequalities in Two Triangles

Then

You used inequalities to make comparisons in one triangle.

Now

1 Apply the Hinge Theorem or its converse to make comparisons in two triangles.

2 Prove triangle relationships using the Hinge Theorem or its converse.

Why?

A car jack is used to lift a car. The jack shown below is one of the simplest still in use today. Notice that as the jack is lowered, the legs of isosceles $\triangle ABC$ remain congruent, but the included angle A widens and $\overline{BC}$, the side opposite $\angle A$, lengthens.

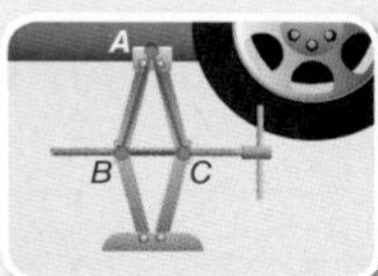

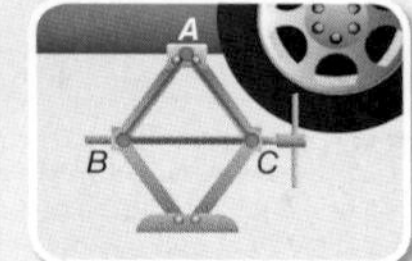

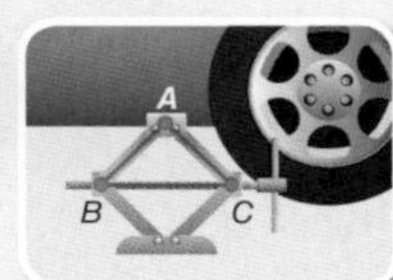

Common Core State Standards

Content Standards

G.CO.10 Prove theorems about triangles.

Mathematical Practices

3 Construct viable arguments and critique the reasoning of others.

1 Make sense of problems and persevere in solving them.

1 Hinge Theorem

The observation in the example above is true of any type of triangle and illustrates the following theorems.

Theorems Inequalities in Two Triangles

5.13 Hinge Theorem If two sides of a triangle are congruent to two sides of another triangle, and the included angle of the first is larger than the included angle of the second triangle, then the third side of the first triangle is longer than the third side of the second triangle.

Example: If $\overline{AB} \cong \overline{FG}$, $\overline{AC} \cong \overline{FH}$, and $m\angle A > m\angle F$, then $BC > GH$.

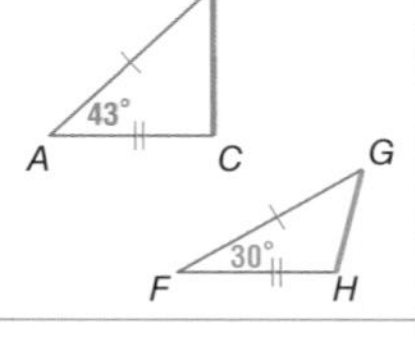

5.14 Converse of the Hinge Theorem If two sides of a triangle are congruent to two sides of another triangle, and the third side in the first is longer than the third side in the second triangle, then the included angle measure of the first triangle is greater than the included angle measure in the second triangle.

Example: If $\overline{JL} \cong \overline{PR}$, $\overline{KL} \cong \overline{QR}$, and $PQ > JK$, then $m\angle R > m\angle L$.

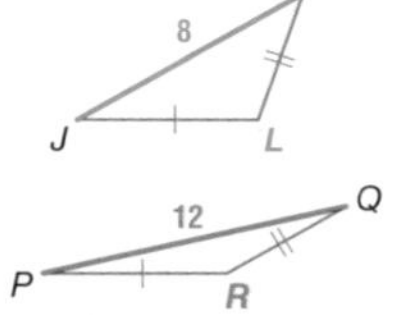

The proof of Theorem 5.13 is on p. 372. You will prove Theorem 5.14 in Exercise 28.

Example 1 Use the Hinge Theorem and its Converse

Compare the given measures.

a. WX and XY

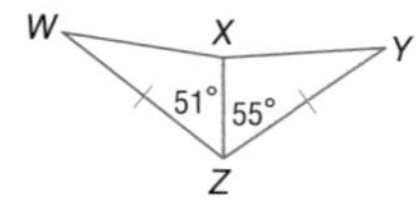

In $\triangle WXZ$ and $\triangle YXZ$, $\overline{WZ} \cong \overline{YZ}$, $\overline{XZ} \cong \overline{XZ}$, and $\angle YZX > \angle WZX$. By the Hinge Theorem, $m\angle WZX < m\angle YZX$, so $WX < XY$.

b. $m\angle FCD$ and $m\angle BFC$

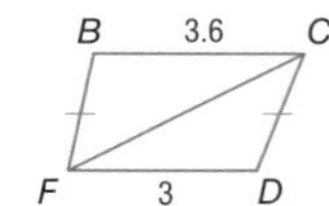

In $\triangle BCF$ and $\triangle DFC$, $\overline{BF} \cong \overline{DC}$, $\overline{FC} \cong \overline{CF}$, and $BC > FD$. By the Converse of the Hinge Theorem, $\angle BFC > \angle DCF$.

connectED.mcgraw-hill.com 371

1 Focus

VerticalAlignment

Before Lesson 5-6 Use inequalities to make comparisons in one triangle.

Lesson 5-6 Apply the Hinge Theorem or its converse to make comparisons in two triangles and prove triangle relationships.

After Lesson 5-6 Make conjectures about angles, lines, polygons, circles, and three-dimensional figures and determine the validity of the conjectures.

2 Teach

Scaffolding Questions

Have students read the **Why?** section of the lesson.

Ask:

- Is $\angle A$ larger when the car is higher or when it is lower? lower
- Is $\overline{BC}$ longer when the car is higher or when it is lower? lower
- The legs of the triangles are always congruent, but how do $m\angle ABC$ and $m\angle ACB$ change? They get smaller.

Lesson 5-6 Resources

Resource	Approaching Level AL	On Level OL	Beyond Level BL	English Learners ELL
Teacher Edition	▪ Differentiated Instruction, p. 372	▪ Differentiated Instruction, pp. 372, 378	▪ Differentiated Instruction, p. 378	
Chapter Resource Masters	▪ Study Guide and Intervention, pp. 37–38 ▪ Skills Practice, p. 39 ▪ Practice, p. 40 ▪ Word Problem Practice, p. 41	▪ Study Guide and Intervention, pp. 37–38 ▪ Skills Practice, p. 39 ▪ Practice, p. 40 ▪ Word Problem Practice, p. 41 ▪ Enrichment, p. 42	▪ Practice, p. 40 ▪ Word Problem Practice, p. 41 ▪ Enrichment, p. 42	▪ Study Guide and Intervention, pp. 37–38 ▪ Skills Practice, p. 39 ▪ Practice, p. 40 ▪ Word Problem Practice, p. 41
Other	▪ 5-Minute Check 5-6 ▪ Study Notebook	▪ 5-Minute Check 5-6 ▪ Study Notebook	▪ 5-Minute Check 5-6 ▪ Study Notebook	▪ 5-Minute Check 5-6 ▪ Study Notebook

1 Hinge Theorem

Examples 1 and 2 show how to use the Hinges Theorem to create an inequality of two triangles. **Example 3** shows how to use inequalities to prove triangle relationships.

Formative Assessment

Use the Guided Practice exercises after each example to determine students' understanding of concepts.

Additional Example

1 Compare the given measures.

a. AD and BD

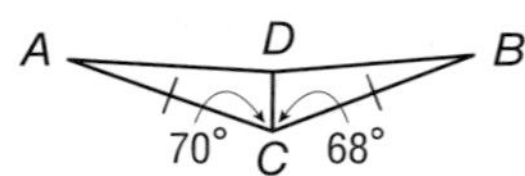

By the Hinge Theorem, $AD > BD$.

b. $m\angle ABD$ and $m\angle BDC$

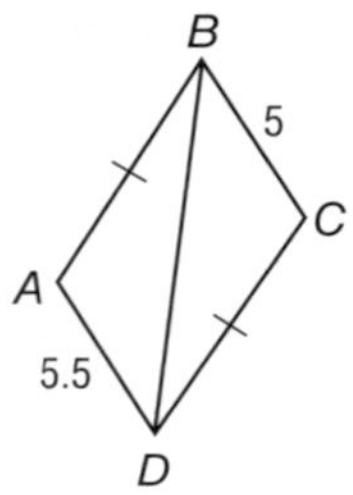

By the Converse to the Hinge Theorem, $m\angle ABD > m\angle BDC$.

Additional Examples also in Interactive Classroom PowerPoint® Presentations

GuidedPractice

Compare the given measures.

1A. JK and MQ $JK > MQ$

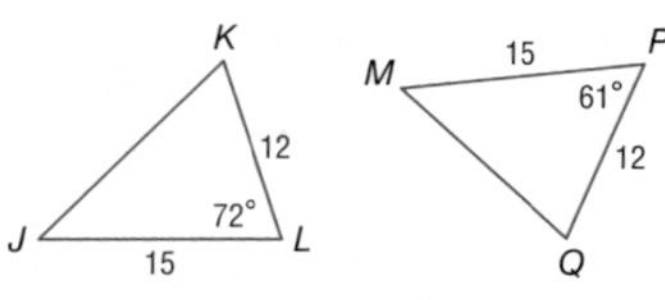

1B. $m\angle SRT$ and $m\angle VRT$ $m\angle SRT < m\angle VRT$

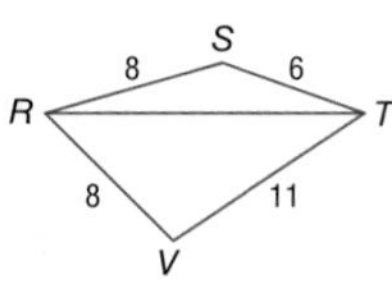

Proof Hinge Theorem

Given: $\triangle ABC$ and $\triangle DEF$, $\overline{AC} \cong \overline{DF}$, $\overline{BC} \cong \overline{EF}$, $m\angle F > m\angle C$

Prove: $DE > AB$

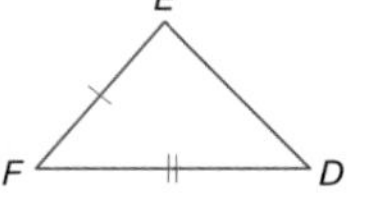

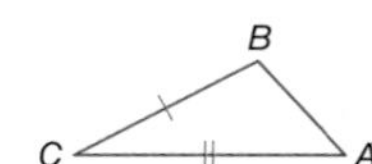

Proof:

We are given that $\overline{AC} \cong \overline{DF}$ and $\overline{BC} \cong \overline{EF}$. We also know that $m\angle F > m\angle C$.

Draw auxiliary ray FP such that $m\angle DFP = m\angle C$ and that $\overline{PF} \cong \overline{BC}$. This leads to two cases.

Case 1 P lies on $\overline{DE}$.

Then $\triangle FPD \cong \triangle CBA$ by SAS. Thus, $PD = BA$ by CPCTC and the definition of congruent segments.

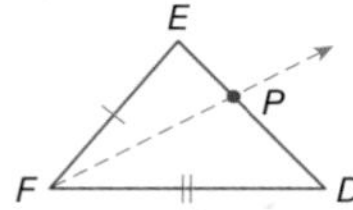

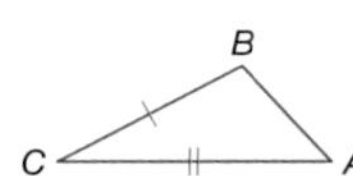

By the Segment Addition Postulate, $DE = EP + PD$. Also, $DE > PD$ by the definition of inequality. Therefore, $DE > AB$ by substitution.

Case 2 P does not lie on $\overline{DE}$.

Then let the intersection of $\overline{FP}$ and $\overline{ED}$ be point T, and draw another auxiliary segment $\overline{FQ}$ such that Q is on $\overline{DE}$ and $\angle EFQ \cong \angle QFP$. Then draw auxiliary segments $\overline{PD}$ and $\overline{PQ}$.

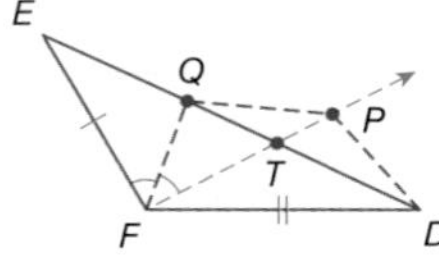

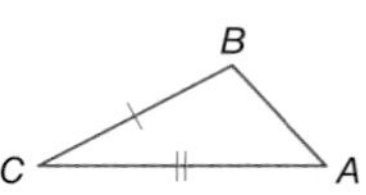

Since $\overline{FP} \cong \overline{BC}$ and $\overline{BC} \cong \overline{EF}$, we have $\overline{FP} \cong \overline{EF}$ by the Transitive Property. Also $\overline{QF}$ is congruent to itself by the Reflexive Property. Thus, $\triangle EFQ \cong \triangle PFQ$ by SAS. By CPCTC, $\overline{EQ} \cong \overline{PQ}$ or $EQ = PQ$. Also, $\triangle FPD \cong \triangle CBA$ by SAS. So, $\overline{PD} \cong \overline{BA}$ by CPCTC and $PD = BA$.

In $\triangle QPD$, $QD + PQ > PD$ by the Triangle Inequality Theorem. By substitution, $QD + EQ > PD$. Since $ED = QD + EQ$ by the Segment Addition Postulate, $ED > PD$. Using substitution, $ED > BA$ or $DE > AB$.

StudyTip

SAS and SSS Inequality Theorem The Hinge Theorem is also called the SAS Inequality Theorem. The Converse of the Hinge Theorem is also called the SSS Inequality Theorem.

DifferentiatedInstruction AL OL

Logical/Mathematical Learners Tell students that the inequality theorems in this lesson are extremely logical, so students can rely on reasoning skills to remember them. Encourage students to examine the two theorems for similarities. Explain that students can simply remember that a longer side will always be opposite a larger angle, and a shorter side will always be opposite a smaller angle. Also, both theorems involve two triangles with an angle included between two congruent sides.

Real-WorldLink

There are over 225,000 miles of groomed and marked snowmobile trails in North America.

Source: International Snowmobile Manufacturers Association

You can use the Hinge Theorem to solve real-world problems.

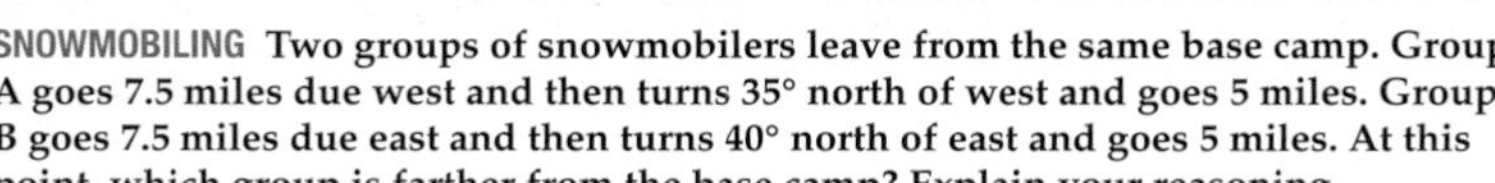

SNOWMOBILING Two groups of snowmobilers leave from the same base camp. Group A goes 7.5 miles due west and then turns 35° north of west and goes 5 miles. Group B goes 7.5 miles due east and then turns 40° north of east and goes 5 miles. At this point, which group is farther from the base camp? Explain your reasoning.

Understand Using the sets of directions given in the problem, you need to determine which snowmobile group is farther from the base camp. A turn of 35° north of west is correctly interpreted as shown.

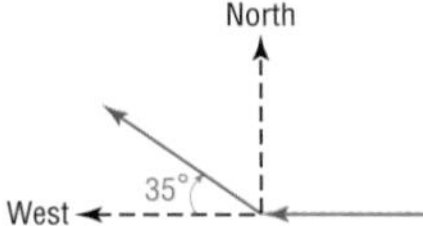

Plan Draw a diagram of the situation.

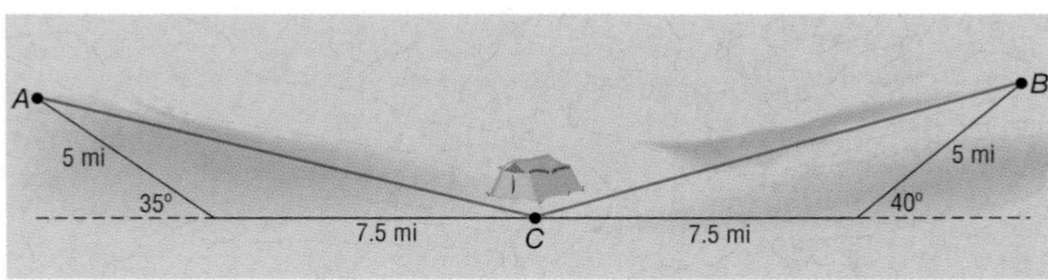

The paths taken by each group and the straight-line distance back to the camp form two triangles. Each group goes 7.5 miles and then turns and goes 5 miles.

Use linear pairs to find the measures of the included angles. Then apply the Hinge Theorem to compare the distance each group is from base camp.

Solve The included angle for the path made by Group A measures $180 - 35$ or 145. The included angle for the path made by Group B is $180 - 40$ or 140.

Since $145 > 140$, $AC > BC$ by the Hinge Theorem. So Group A is farther from the base camp.

Check Group B turned 5° more than Group A did back toward base camp, so they should be closer to base camp than Group A. Thus, Group A should be farther from the base camp. ✔

Problem-SolvingTip

Draw a Diagram Draw a diagram to help you see and correctly interpret a problem that has been described in words.

GuidedPractice

2A. SKIING Two groups of skiers leave from the same lodge. Group A goes 4 miles due east and then turns 70° north of east and goes 3 miles. Group B goes 4 miles due west and then turns 75° north of west and goes 3 miles. At this point, which group is *farther* from the lodge? Explain your reasoning. See margin.

2B. SKIING In problem 2A, suppose Group A instead went 4 miles west and then turned 45° north of west and traveled 3 miles. Which group would be *closer* to the lodge? Explain your reasoning. See margin.

When the included angle of one triangle is greater than the included angle in a second triangle, the Converse of the Hinge Theorem is used.

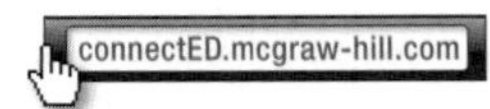

Focus on Mathematical Content

Organization Place congruence marks and other helpful notations on figures before writing a proof to help organize all given information and facilitate the proof-writing process. These planning steps also help clarify the relationships that already exist and those that are to be proved.

WatchOut!

Hinge Theorem To use the Hinge Theorem or its converse, the angle must be between the two congruent sides.

Additional Example

2 **HEALTH** Doctors use a straight-leg-raising test to determine the amount of pain felt in a person's back. The patient lies flat on the examining table, and the doctor raises each leg until the patient experiences pain in the back area. Nitan can tolerate the doctor raising his right leg 35° and his left leg 65° from the table. Which leg can Nitan raise higher above the table? his left leg

Additional Answers (Guided Practice)

2A. Group A; the included angle for the path made by Group A measures $180 - 70$ or 110. The included angle for the path made by Group B is $180 - 75$ or 105. Since $110 > 105$, by the Hinge Theorem $AC > BC$. So, Group A is farther.

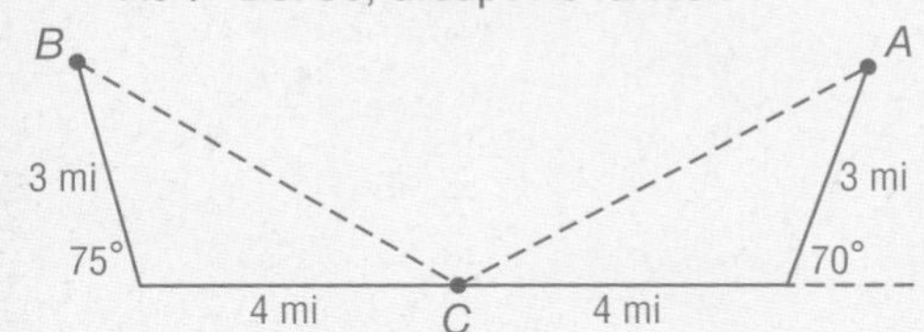

2B. Group A; the included angle for the path made by Group A measures $180 - 45$ or 135. The included angle for the path made by Group B is $180 - 75$ or 105. Since $135 > 105$, by the Hinge Theorem $AC > BC$. So, Group B is closer to the lodge.

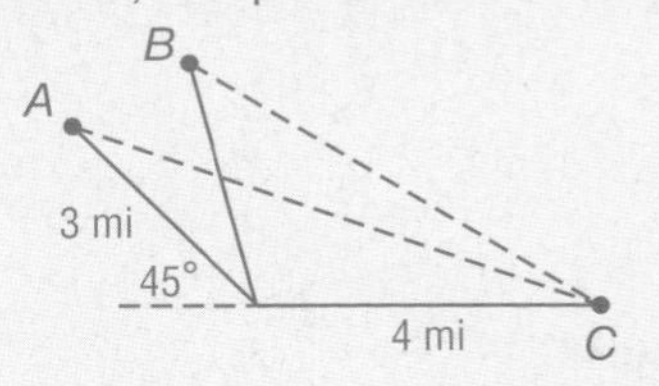

Additional Example

3 **ALGEBRA** Find the range of possible values for a.

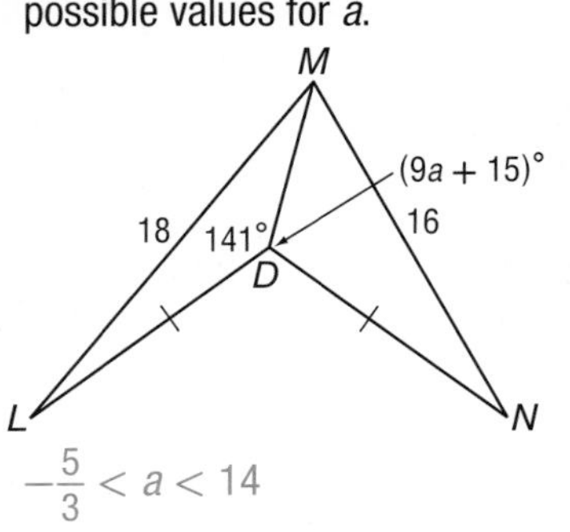

$-\frac{5}{3} < a < 14$

2 Prove Relationships in Two Triangles

Examples 4 and 5 show how to use the Hinge Theorem and its converse to prove triangle relationships.

Additional Example

4 **Given:** $JK = HL$
$m\angle JKH + m\angle HKL < m\angle JHK + m\angle KHL$

Prove: $JH < KL$

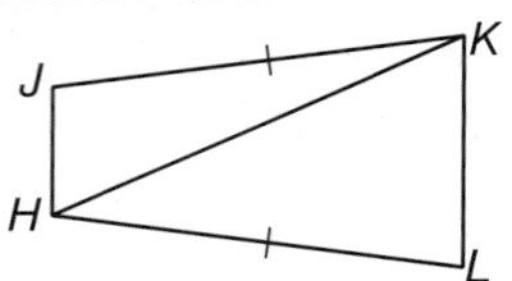

Proof:

Statements (Reasons)

1. $JK = HL$ (Given)
2. $HK = HK$ (Reflexive Prop.)
3. $m\angle JKH + m\angle HKL < m\angle JHK + m\angle KHL$ (Given)
4. $m\angle HKL = m\angle JHK$ (Alt. Int. angles are $\cong$)
5. $m\angle JKH + m\angle JHK < m\angle JHK + m\angle KHL$ (Subst.)
6. $m\angle JKH < m\angle KHL$ (Subtraction Prop. of Ineq.)
7. $JH < KL$ (Hinge Theorem)

StudyTip

Using Additional Facts When finding a range for the possible values for x, you may need to use one of the following facts.

- The measure of any angle is always greater than 0 and less than 180.
- The measure of any segment is always greater than 0.

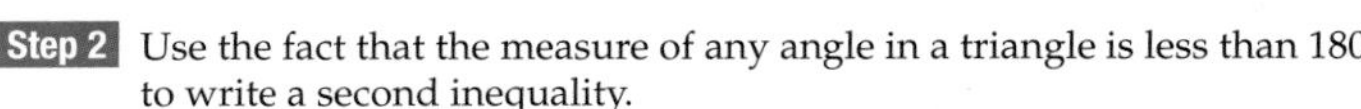

Example 3 Apply Algebra to the Relationships in Triangles

ALGEBRA Find the range of possible values for x.

Step 1 From the diagram, we know that $\overline{JH} \cong \overline{GH}$, $\overline{EH} \cong \overline{EH}$, and $JE > EG$.

$m\angle JHE > m\angle EHG$	Converse of the Hinge Theorem
$6x + 15 > 65$	Substitution
$x > 8\frac{1}{3}$	Solve for x.

Step 2 Use the fact that the measure of any angle in a triangle is less than 180 to write a second inequality.

$m\angle JHE < 180$	
$6x + 15 < 180$	Substitution
$x < 27.5$	Solve for x.

Step 3 Write $x > 8\frac{1}{3}$ and $x < 27.5$ as the compound inequality $8\frac{1}{3} < x < 27.5$.

GuidedPractice

3. Find the range of possible values for x.
$-0.4 < x < 9$

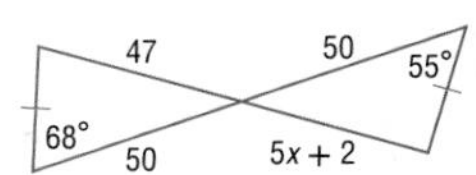

2 Prove Relationships In Two Triangles

You can use the Hinge Theorem and its converse to prove relationships in two triangles.

Example 4 Prove Triangle Relationships Using Hinge Theorem

Write a two-column proof.

Given: $\overline{AB} \cong \overline{AD}$

Prove: $EB > ED$

Proof:

Statements	Reasons
1. $\overline{AB} \cong \overline{AD}$	1. Given
2. $\overline{AE} \cong \overline{AE}$	2. Reflexive Property
3. $m\angle EAB = m\angle EAD + m\angle DAB$	3. Angle Addition Postulate
4. $m\angle EAB > m\angle EAD$	4. Definition of Inequality
5. $EB > ED$	5. Hinge Theorem

GuidedPractice

4. Write a two-column proof.
Given: $\overline{RQ} \cong \overline{ST}$
Prove: $RS > TQ$

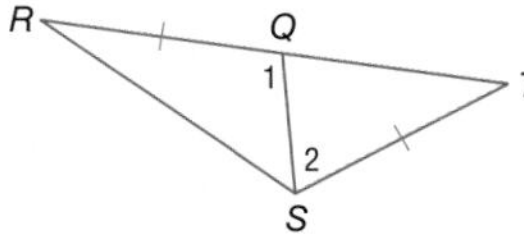

4.
Given: $\overline{RQ} \cong \overline{ST}$
Prove: $RS > TQ$
Proof:
Statements (Reasons)
1. $\overline{RQ} \cong \overline{ST}$ (Given)
2. $\overline{QS} \cong \overline{QS}$ (Reflexive Prop.)
3. $\angle 1$ is an exterior angle of $\triangle QST$. (Def. of ext. $\angle$)
4. $m\angle 1 > m\angle 2$ (If an $\angle$ is an ext. $\angle$ of a $\triangle$, then its measure is greater than the measure of either corr. remote int. $\angle$.)
5. $RS > TQ$ (SAS Inequality)

Teach with Tech

Interactive Whiteboard Show students two triangles with various angle measures, side measures, and congruence markings. Choose two sides of the triangles and ask students to name which has a greater length. Provide students with a key to use for their responses.

5.
Given: $\overline{NK}$ is a median of $\triangle JMN$.
$JN > NM$
Prove: $m\angle 1 > m\angle 2$
Proof:
Statements (Reasons)
1. $\overline{NK}$ is a median of $\triangle JMN$. (Given)
2. K is the midpoint of $\overline{JM}$. (Def. of median)
3. $\overline{JK} \cong \overline{KM}$ (Midpoint Th.)
4. $\overline{KN} \cong \overline{KN}$ (Reflexive Prop.)
5. $JN > NM$ (Given)
6. $m\angle 1 > m\angle 2$ (SSS Inequality)

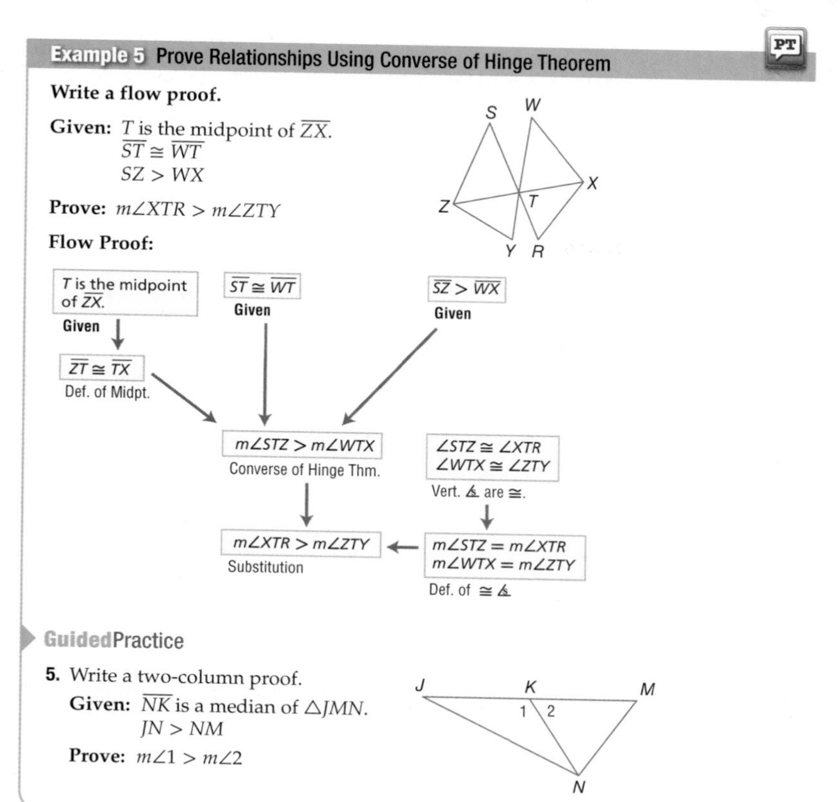

Example 5 Prove Relationships Using Converse of Hinge Theorem

Write a flow proof.

Given: T is the midpoint of $\overline{ZX}$.
$\overline{ST} \cong \overline{WT}$
$SZ > WX$

Prove: $m\angle XTR > m\angle ZTY$

Flow Proof:

T is the midpoint of $\overline{ZX}$. (Given) → $\overline{ZT} \cong \overline{TX}$ (Def. of Midpt.)

$\overline{ST} \cong \overline{WT}$ (Given)

$\overline{SZ} > \overline{WX}$ (Given)

→ $m\angle STZ > m\angle WTX$ (Converse of Hinge Thm.)

$\angle STZ \cong \angle XTR$, $\angle WTX \cong \angle ZTY$ (Vert. ∠s are ≅.) → $m\angle STZ = m\angle XTR$, $m\angle WTX = m\angle ZTY$ (Def. of ≅ ∠s)

→ $m\angle XTR > m\angle ZTY$ (Substitution)

Guided Practice

5. Write a two-column proof.
Given: $\overline{NK}$ is a median of $\triangle JMN$.
$JN > NM$
Prove: $m\angle 1 > m\angle 2$

Check Your Understanding

= Step-by-Step Solutions begin on page R14.

Example 1 **Compare the given measures.**

1. $m\angle ACB$ and $m\angle GDE$ $m\angle ACB > m\angle GDE$

2. JL and KM $JL < KM$

3. QT and ST $QT < ST$

4. $m\angle XWZ$ and $m\angle YZW$ $m\angle XWZ > m\angle YZW$

Additional Example

5 **Given:** $ST = PQ$
$SR = QR$
$SP > ST$

Prove: $m\angle SRP > m\angle PRQ$

Proof:

Statements (Reasons)
1. $SR = QR$ (Given)
2. $PR = PR$ (Reflexive)
3. $ST = PQ$ (Given)
4. $SP > ST$ (Given)
5. $SP > PQ$ (Substitution)
6. $m\angle SRP > m\angle PRQ$ (Converse of the Hinge Theorem)

Tips for New Teachers

Reasoning Show students that they can separate a figure that is made up of two or more triangles and draw a new diagram, to clarify which side and angle measures of the triangles are congruent.

3 Practice

Formative Assessment

Use Exercises 1–9 to check for understanding.

Use the chart at the bottom of the next page to customize assignments for your students.

Follow-up

Students have explored inequalities in one and two triangles.

Ask:

- How are the angles and/or sides of two triangles related? Sample answer: If two sides in one triangle are congruent to two sides in another and the included angle of the first is larger than the included angle of the second, then the third side of the first is longer than the third side of the second.

Teaching the Mathematical Practices

Arguments Mathematically proficient students understand and use stated assumptions, definitions, and previously established results in constructing arguments. In Exercises 8–9 and 23–26, encourage students to review the theorems presented in this chapter while planning their proofs.

Additional Answers

5b. $\angle D$; Sample answer: Since $EF > BC$, according to the Converse of the Hinge Theorem, $m\angle D > m\angle A$.

8. Given: $\triangle YZX$, $\overline{YZ} \cong \overline{XW}$

Prove: $ZX > YW$

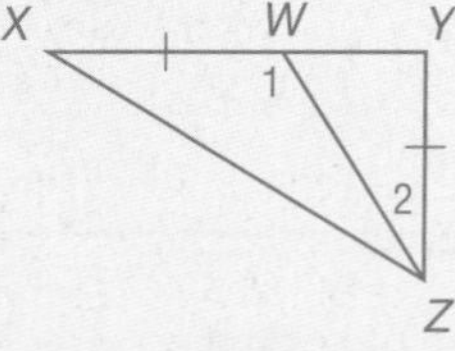

Statements (Reasons)

1. $\triangle YZX$, $\overline{YZ} \cong \overline{XW}$ (Given)
2. $\overline{ZW} \cong \overline{ZW}$ (Reflexive Property)
3. $\angle 1$ is an exterior angle of $\triangle YZW$. (Def. of ext. $\angle$)
4. $m\angle 1 > m\angle 2$ (Exterior Angle Inequality Theorem)
5. $ZX > YW$ (SAS Inequality)

9. Given: $\overline{AD} \cong \overline{CB}$, $DC < AB$

Prove: $m\angle CBD < m\angle ADB$

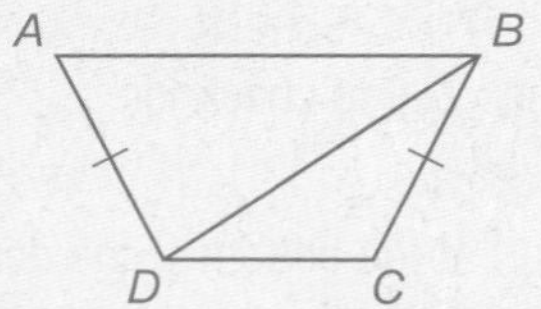

Statements (Reasons)

1. $\overline{AD} \cong \overline{CB}$ (Given)
2. $\overline{DB} \cong \overline{DB}$ (Reflexive Property)
3. $DC < AB$ (Given)
4. $m\angle CBD < m\angle ADB$ (SSS Inequality)

Example 2

5. SWINGS The position of the swing changes based on how hard the swing is pushed.

a. Which pairs of segments are congruent? **5a.** $\overline{AB} \cong \overline{DE}$, $\overline{AC} \cong \overline{DF}$

b. Is the measure of $\angle A$ or the measure of $\angle D$ greater? Explain. **See margin.**

Example 3

Find the range of possible values for x.

6. $\frac{7}{2} < x < 24$

7. $\frac{5}{3} < x < 8$

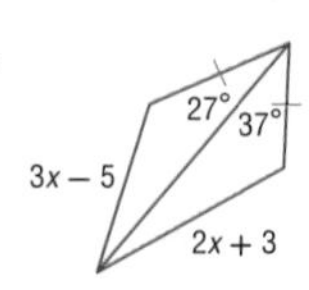

Examples 4–5 **ARGUMENTS** **Write a two-column proof.** **8–9. See margin.**

8. Given: $\triangle YZX$, $\overline{YZ} \cong \overline{XW}$

Prove: $ZX > YW$

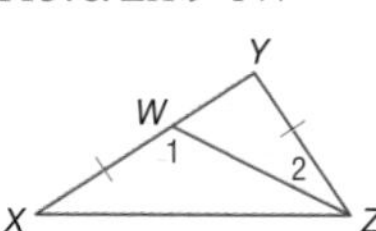

9. Given: $\overline{AD} \cong \overline{CB}$, $DC < AB$

Prove: $m\angle CBD < m\angle ADB$

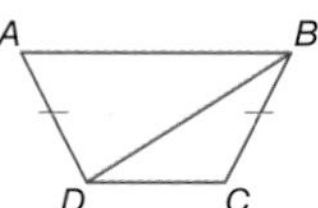

Practice and Problem Solving

Extra Practice is on page R5.

Example 1

Compare the given measures.

10. $m\angle BAC$ and $m\angle DGE$ — $m\angle BAC < m\angle DGE$

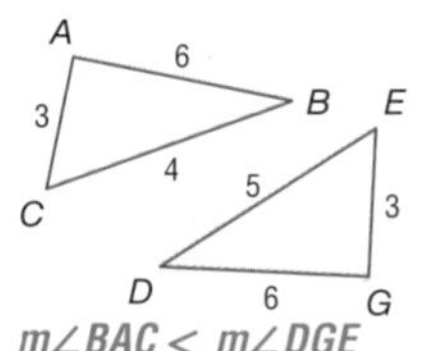

11. $m\angle MLP$ and $m\angle TSR$ — $m\angle MLP < m\angle TSR$

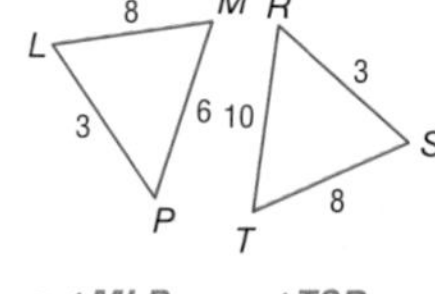

12. SR and XY — $SR > XY$

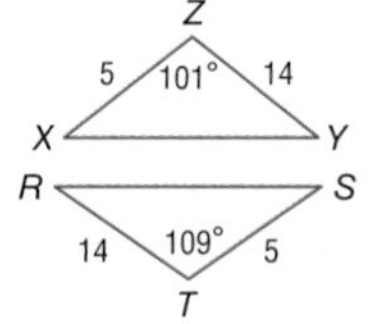

13. $m\angle TUW$ and $m\angle VUW$ — $m\angle TUW < m\angle VUW$

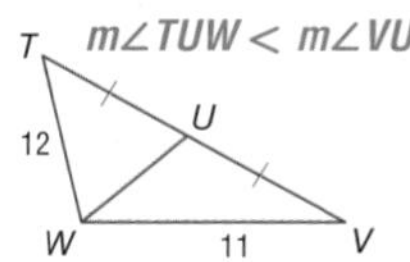

14. PS and SR — $PS < SR$

Q 10 P, 29°, 38°, 10, R, S

15. JK and HJ — $JK > HJ$

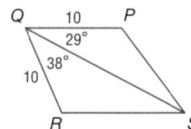

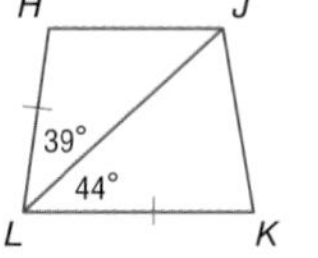

Example 2

16. CAMPING Pedro and Joel are camping in a national park. One morning, Pedro decides to hike to the waterfall. He leaves camp and goes 5 miles east then turns 15° south of east and goes 2 more miles. Joel leaves the camp and travels 5 miles west, then turns 35° north of west and goes 2 miles to the lake for a swim. **16a–b. See Ch. 5 Answer Appendix.**

a. When they reach their destinations, who is closer to the camp? Explain your reasoning. Include a diagram.

b. Suppose instead of turning 35° north of west, Joel turned 10° south of west. Who would then be farther from the camp? Explain your reasoning. Include a diagram.

Differentiated Homework Options

Level	Assignment	Two-Day Option	
AL Basic	9–26, 39, 41–58	9–25 odd, 43–46	10–26 even, 39, 41, 42, 47–58
OL Core	9–29 odd, 30, 31–39 odd, 41–58	9–26, 43–46	27–37, 41, 42, 47–58
BL Advanced	27–55, (optional: 56–58)		

Example 3 Find the range of possible values for x.

17. $2 < x < 6$

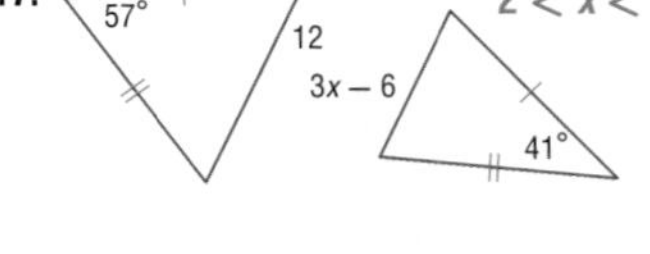

18. $-4.5 < x < 33$

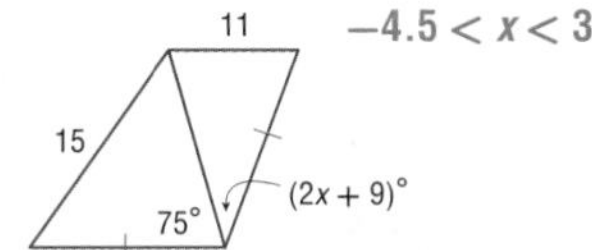

19. $-20 < x < 21$

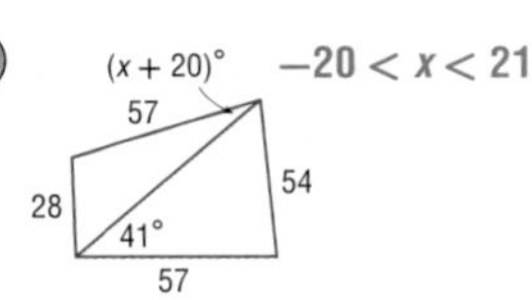

20. $x > 7$

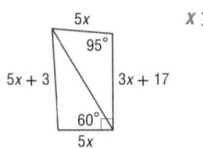

5x, 95°, 5x + 3, 3x + 17, 60°, 5x

21. CRANES In the diagram, a crane is shown lifting an object to two different heights. The length of the crane's arm is fixed, and $\overline{MP} \cong \overline{RT}$. Is $\overline{MN}$ or $\overline{RS}$ shorter? Explain your reasoning.

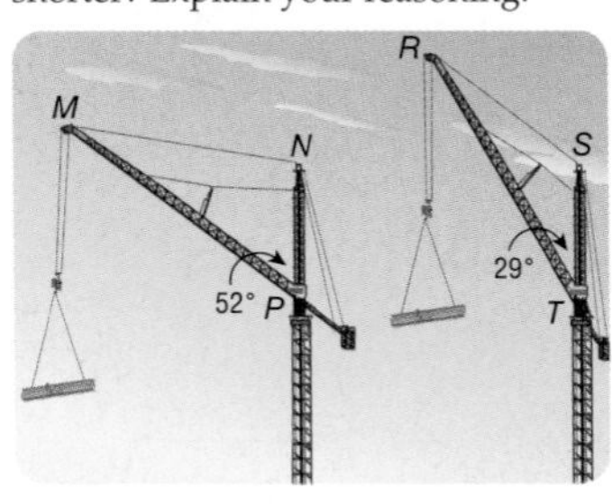

21. $\overline{RS}$; sample answer: The height of the crane is the same and the length of the crane arm is fixed, so according to the Hinge Theorem, the side opposite the smaller angle is shorter. Since $29° < 52°$, $\overline{RS} < \overline{MN}$.

22. LOCKERS Neva and Shawn both have their lockers open as shown in the diagram. Whose locker forms a larger angle? Explain your reasoning.

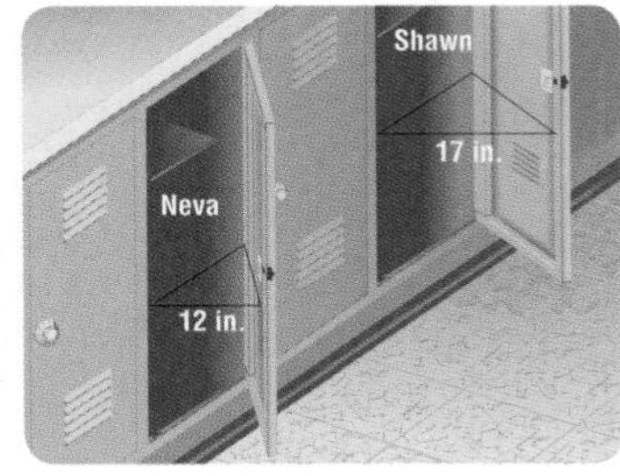

22. Shawn; sample answer: Since the lengths of the openings of the lockers and the lengths of the doors of the lockers are equal, use the Converse of the Hinge Theorem to determine that, since 17 in. > 12 in., the angle of the opening of Shawn's locker is greater than the angle of the opening of Neva's.

Examples 4–5 CCSS **ARGUMENTS** Write a two-column proof. 23–26. See Ch. 5 Answer Appendix.

23. Given: $\overline{LK} \cong \overline{JK}$, $\overline{RL} \cong \overline{RJ}$
K is the midpoint of $\overline{QS}$.
$m\angle SKL > m\angle QKJ$

Prove: $RS > QR$

Q, J, R, K, L, S

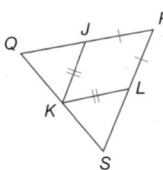

24. Given: $\overline{VR} \cong \overline{RT}$, $\overline{WV} \cong \overline{WT}$
$m\angle SRV > m\angle QRT$
R is the midpoint of $\overline{SQ}$.

Prove: $WS > WQ$

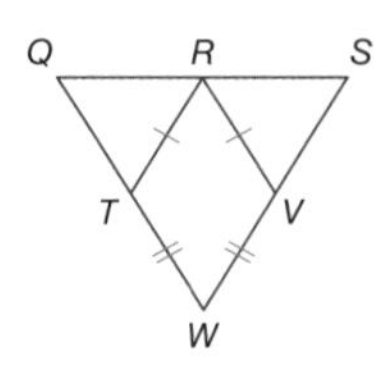

25. Given: $\overline{XU} \cong \overline{VW}$, $VW > XW$
$\overline{XU} \parallel \overline{VW}$

Prove: $m\angle XZU > m\angle UZV$

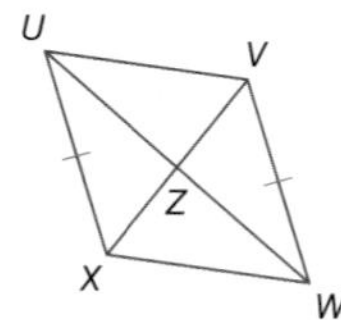

26. Given: $\overline{AF} \cong \overline{DJ}$, $\overline{FC} \cong \overline{JB}$
$AB > DC$

Prove: $m\angle AFC > m\angle DJB$

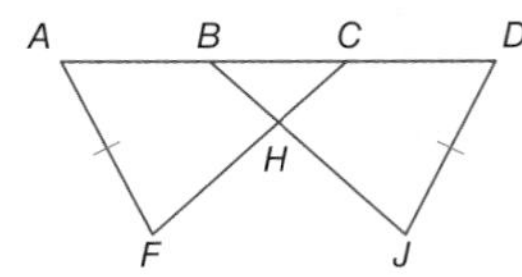

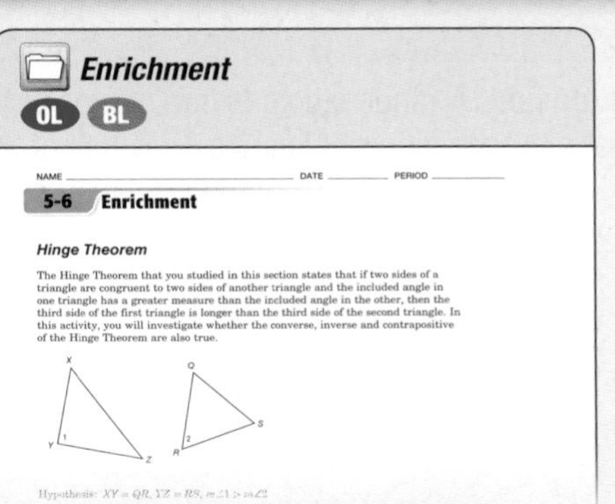
Enrichment
OL BL
5-6 Enrichment
Hinge Theorem

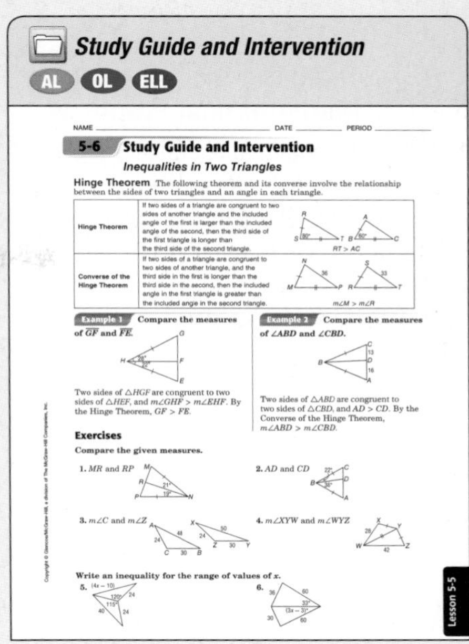
Study Guide and Intervention
AL OL ELL
5-6 Study Guide and Intervention
Inequalities in Two Triangles

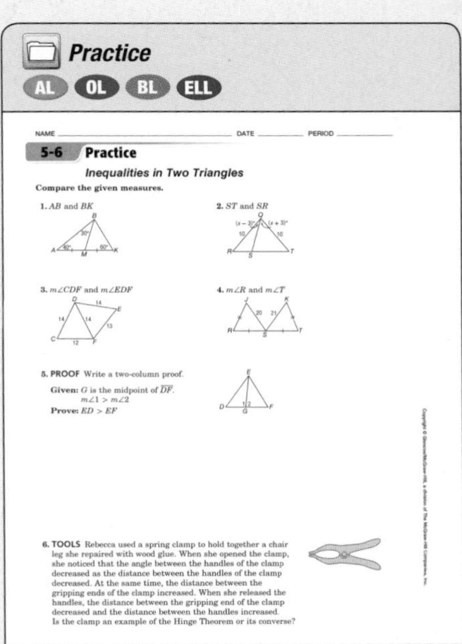
Practice
AL OL BL ELL
5-6 Practice
Inequalities in Two Triangles

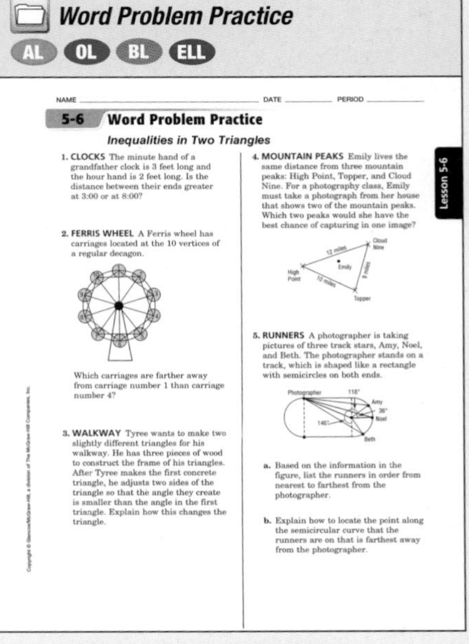
Word Problem Practice
AL OL BL ELL
5-6 Word Problem Practice
Inequalities in Two Triangles

connectED.mcgraw-hill.com 377

27 EXERCISE Anica is doing knee-supported bicep curls as part of her strength training.

a. Is the distance from Anica's fist to her shoulder greater in Position 1 or Position 2? Justify your answer using measurement. **See Ch. 5 Answer Appendix.**

b. Is the measure of the angle formed by Anica's elbow greater in Position 1 or Position 2? Explain your reasoning. **See Ch. 5 Answer Appendix.**

28. PROOF Use an indirect proof to prove the SSS Inequality Theorem (Theorem 5.14).

Given: $\overline{RS} \cong \overline{UW}$
$\overline{ST} \cong \overline{WV}$
$RT > UV$

Prove: $m\angle S > m\angle W$ **See margin.**

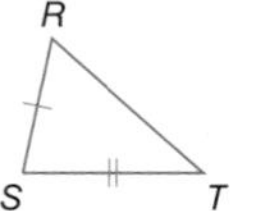

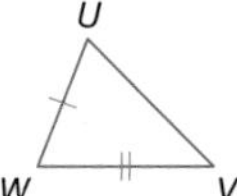

29. PROOF If $\overline{PR} \cong \overline{PQ}$ and $SQ > SR$, write a two-column proof to prove $m\angle 1 < m\angle 2$. **See margin.**

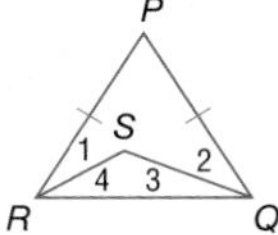

30. SCAVENGER HUNT Stephanie, Mario, Lee, and Luther are participating in a scavenger hunt as part of a geography lesson. Their map shows that the next clue is 50 feet due east and then 75 feet 35° east of north starting from the fountain in the school courtyard. When they get ready to turn and go 75 feet 35° east of north, they disagree about which way to go, so they split up and take the paths shown in the diagram below.

30a. Luther and Stephanie; sample answer: The directions from the map were 35° east of north, which makes a 125° angle with the direction due west. Since their angle is 125° with the direction due west, they chose the path 35° east of north.

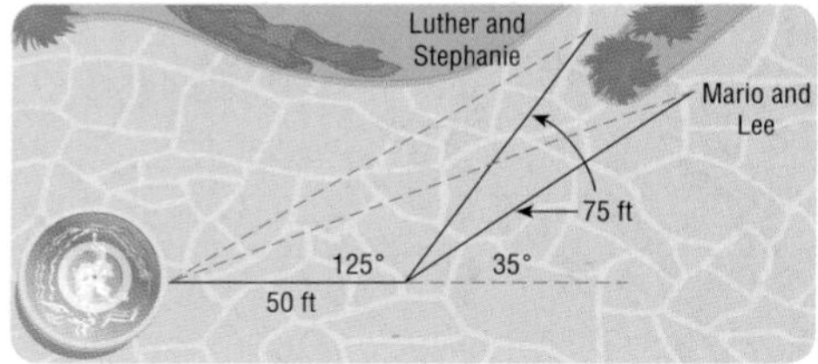

a. Which pair chose the correct path? Explain your reasoning.

b. Which pair is closest to the fountain when they stop? Explain your reasoning. **See margin.**

CCSS SENSE-MAKING Use the figure at the right to write an inequality relating the given pair of angle or segment measures.

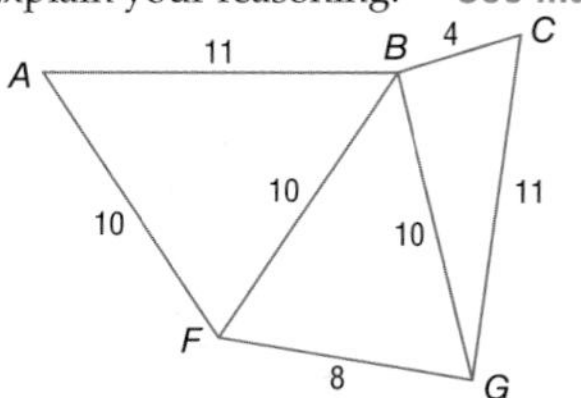

31. CB and AB **$CB < AB$**

32. $m\angle FBG$ and $m\angle BFA$ **$m\angle FBG < m\angle BFA$**

33. $m\angle BGC$ and $m\angle FBA$ **$m\angle BGC < m\angle FBA$**

CCSS Teaching the Mathematical Practices

Sense-Making Mathematically proficient students look for entry points into a solution. They plan a solution pathway rather than simply jumping into a solution attempt. In Exercises 31–33, encourage students to use side-angle relationships in analyzing the figure shown.

Additional Answers

28. Indirect Proof

Step 1: Assume that $m\angle S \leq m\angle W$.

Step 2: If $m\angle S \leq m\angle W$, then either $m\angle S < m\angle W$ or $m\angle S = m\angle W$.

Case 1: If $m\angle S < m\angle W$, then $RT < UV$ by the SAS Inequality.

Case 2: If $m\angle S = m\angle W$, then $\triangle RST \cong \triangle UVW$ by SAS, and $\overline{RT} \cong \overline{UV}$ by CPCTC. Thus $RT = UV$.

Step 3: Both cases contradict the given $RT > UV$. Therefore, the assumption must be false, and the conclusion, $m\angle S > m\angle W$, must be true.

29. Statements (Reasons)

1. $\overline{PR} \cong \overline{PQ}$ (Given)
2. $\angle PRQ \cong \angle PQR$ (Isos. △ Thm.)
3. $m\angle PRQ = m\angle 1 + m\angle 4$, $m\angle PQR = m\angle 2 + m\angle 3$ (Angle Add. Post.)
4. $m\angle PRQ = m\angle PQR$ (Def. of ≅ ∠s)
5. $m\angle 1 + m\angle 4 = m\angle 2 + m\angle 3$ (Subst.)
6. $SQ > SR$ (Given)
7. $m\angle 4 > m\angle 3$ (Angle-Side Relationship Thm.)
8. $m\angle 4 = m\angle 3 + x$ (Def. of inequality)
9. $m\angle 1 + m\angle 4 - m\angle 4 = m\angle 2 + m\angle 3 - (m\angle 3 + x)$ (Subt. Prop.)
10. $m\angle 1 = m\angle 2 - x$ (Subt.)
11. $m\angle 1 + x = m\angle 2$ (Add. Prop.)
12. $m\angle 1 < m\angle 2$ (Def. of inequality)

Differentiated Instruction OL BL

Extension Arrange students into groups of 2. Have each student design a baseball field with 4 sides that are each different lengths. Only half of the lengths and angles should be labeled. Have students exchange their designs and determine if the non-labeled lengths are greater than or less than the given lengths.

Use the figure at the right to write an inequality relating the given pair of angles or segment measures.

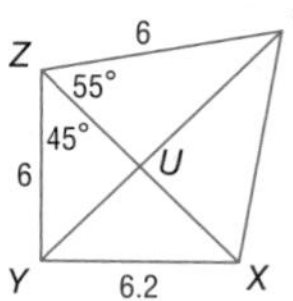

34. $m\angle ZUY$ and $m\angle ZUW$ $\angle ZUY > \angle ZUW$

35 WU and YU $WU > YU$

36. WX and XY $WX > XY$

37. **MULTIPLE REPRESENTATIONS** In this problem, you will investigate properties of polygons.

a. Geometric Draw a three-sided, a four-sided, and a five-sided polygon. Label the 3-sided polygon ABC, the four-sided polygon $FGHJ$, and the five-sided polygon $PQRST$. Use a protractor to measure and label each angle. See Ch. 5 Answer Appendix.

b. Tabular Copy and complete the table below.

Number of sides	Angle Measures				Sum of Angles
3	$m\angle A$	59	$m\angle C$	45	180
	$m\angle B$	76			
4	$m\angle F$	90	$m\angle H$	90	360
	$m\angle G$	90	$m\angle J$	90	
5	$m\angle P$	105	$m\angle S$	116	540
	$m\angle Q$	100	$m\angle T$	123	
	$m\angle R$	96			

37c. Sample answer: The sum of the angles of the polygon is equal to 180 times two less than the number of sides of the polygon.

c. Verbal Make a conjecture about the relationship between the number of sides of a polygon and the sum of the measures of the angles of the polygon.

d. Logical What type of reasoning did you use in part **c**? Explain.

e. Algebraic Write an algebraic expression for the sum of the measures of the angles for a polygon with n sides. $(n - 2)180$

37d. Inductive; sample answer: Since I used a pattern to determine the relationship, the reasoning I used was inductive.

H.O.T. Problems Use Higher-Order Thinking Skills

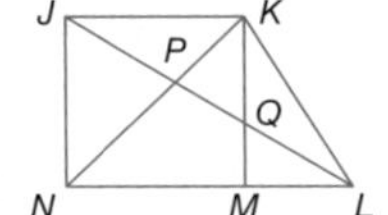

38. **CHALLENGE** If $m\angle LJN > m\angle KJL$, $KJ \cong JN$, and $JN \perp NL$, which is greater, $m\angle LKN$ or $m\angle LNK$? Explain your reasoning.

38–42. See margin.

39. **OPEN ENDED** Give a real-world example of an object that uses a hinge. Draw two sketches in which the hinge on your object is adjusted to two different positions. Use your sketches to explain why Theorem 5.13 is called the Hinge Theorem.

40. **CHALLENGE** Given $\triangle RST$ with median $\overline{RQ}$, if RT is greater than or equal to RS, what are the possible classifications of $\triangle RQT$? Explain your reasoning.

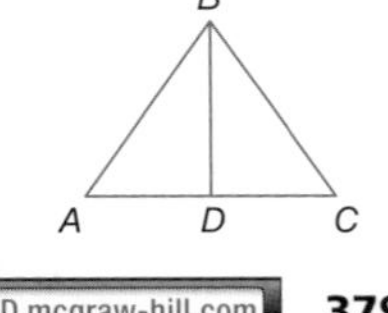

41. **CCSS PRECISION** If $\overline{BD}$ is a median and $AB < BC$, then $\angle BDC$ is *always*, *sometimes*, or *never* an acute angle. Explain.

42. **WRITING IN MATH** Compare and contrast the Hinge Theorem to the SAS Postulate for triangle congruence.

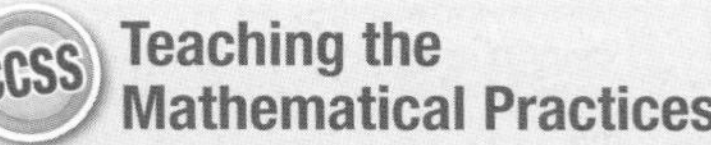

Teaching the Mathematical Practices

Precision Mathematically proficient students use clear definitions in discussion with others and in their own reasoning. In Exercise 41, encourage students to review the terms used in this exercise.

Additional Answers

30b. Luther and Stephanie; sample answer: Luther and Stephanie create a path leaving a 125° angle while Mario and Lee create an angle of 145°.

38. In $\triangle JKL$ and $\triangle JNL$, it is given that $\overline{KJ} \cong \overline{JN}$ and $m\angle LJN > m\angle KJL$, and $\overline{JL} \cong \overline{JL}$, so according to the Converse of the Hinge Theorem, $LN > LK$. In $\triangle LKN$, $LN > LK$ which means that $m\angle LKN > m\angle LNK$.

39. A door; as the door opens, the door opening increases as the angle made by the hinge increases. As the door closes, the door opening decreases as the angle made by the hinge decreases. This is similar to the side opposite the angle in a triangle, because as the side opposite an angle increases the measure of the angle also increases. As the side decrease, the angle also decreases.

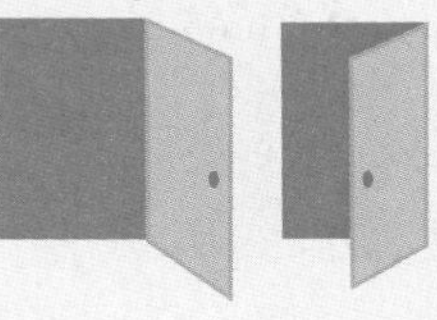

40. Right or obtuse; sample answer: If $RT = RS$, then the triangle is isosceles, and the median is also perpendicular to $\overline{TS}$. That would mean that both triangles formed by the median, $\triangle RQT$ and $\triangle RQS$, are right. If $RT > RS$, that means that $m\angle RQT > m\angle RQS$. Since they are a linear pair and the sum of the angles measures must be 180, $m\angle RQT$ must be greater than 90 and $\triangle RQT$ is obtuse.

41. Never; from the Converse of the Hinge Theorem, $\angle ADB < \angle BDC$. $\angle ADB < \angle BDC$ form a linear pair. So, $m\angle ADB + m\angle BDC = 180$. Since, $m\angle BDC > m\angle ADB$, $m\angle BDC$ must be greater than 90 and $m\angle ADB$ must be smaller than 90. So, by the definition of obtuse and acute angles, $m\angle BDC$ is always obtuse and $m\angle ADB$ is always acute.

42. Both the SAS Postulate for triangle congruence and the Hinge Theorem require that you have two pairs of corresponding side congruent and consider the included angle. Using the SAS Postulate for triangle congruence, if the corresponding included angles are congruent, then the two triangles are congruent. Using the Hinge Theorem, if the one of the included angles is greater than the corresponding angle in the other triangle, then the side opposite the greater angle is longer than the side opposite the lesser angle in the other triangle.

4 Assess

Name the Math Select or create examples of proofs using the Hinge Theorem and its converse. For each example, allow students to give statements and reasons in the order necessary to complete the proof.

Formative Assessment

Check for student understanding of Lesson 5-6.

 Quiz 4, p. 46

Additional Answers

50. Let the cost of Tavia's cruise be x and the other be y.

Step 1 Given: $x + y > 500$

Prove: $x > 250$ or $y > 250$

Indirect Proof:

Assume that $x \leq 250$ and $y \leq 250$.

Step 2 If $x \leq 250$ and $y \leq 250$, then $x + y \leq 250 + 250$ or $x + y \leq 500$. This is a contradiction because we know that $x + y > 500$.

Step 3 Since the assumption that $x \leq 250$ and $y \leq 250$ leads to a contradiction of a known fact, the assumption must be false. Therefore, the conclusion that $x > 250$ or $y > 250$ must be true. Thus, the cost of at least one cruise had to cost more than \$250.

51. $x = 8$

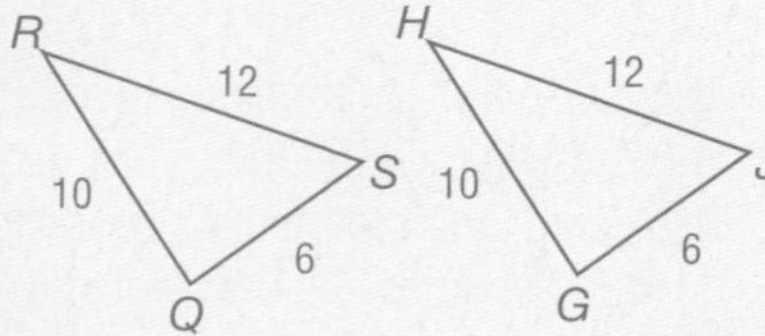

52. $x = 2$

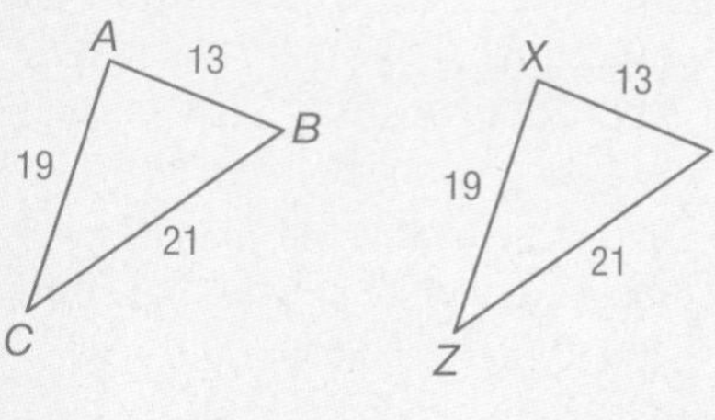

Standardized Test Practice

43. SHORT RESPONSE Write an inequality to describe the possible range of values for x. $2.8 < x < 12$

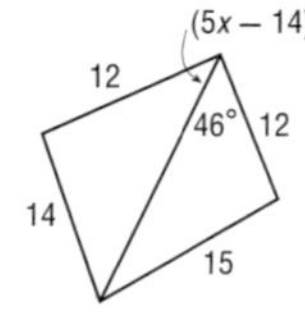

44. Which of the following is the inverse of the statement *If it is snowing, then Steve wears his snow boots?* **B**

A If Steve wears his snow boots, then it is snowing.

B If it is not snowing, then Steve does not wear his snow boots.

C If it is not snowing, then Steve wears his snow boots.

D If it never snows, then Steve does not own snow boots.

45. ALGEBRA Which linear function best describes the graph shown? **F**

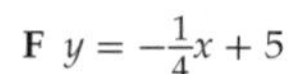

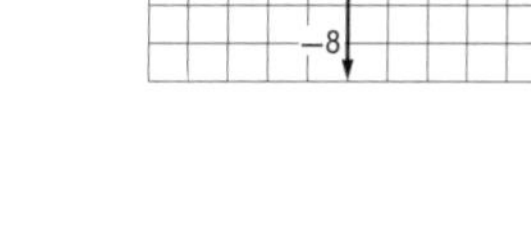

F $y = -\frac{1}{4}x + 5$

G $y = -\frac{1}{4}x - 5$

H $y = \frac{1}{4}x + 5$

J $y = \frac{1}{4}x - 5$

46. SAT/ACT If the side of a square is $x + 3$, then the diagonal of the square is **B**

A $x^2 + 1$

B $x\sqrt{2} + 3\sqrt{2}$

C $2x + 6$

D $x^2\sqrt{2} + 6$

E $x^2 + 9$

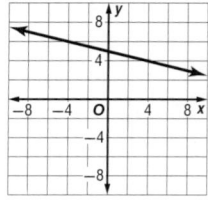

Spiral Review

Find the range for the measure of the third side of a triangle given the measures of two sides. (Lesson 5-5)

47. 3.2 cm, 4.4 cm $1.2 \text{ cm} < n < 7.6 \text{ cm}$

48. 5 ft, 10 ft $5 \text{ ft} < n < 15 \text{ ft}$

49. 3 m, 9 m $6 \text{ m} < n < 12 \text{ m}$

50. CRUISES Ally asked Tavia the cost of a cruise she and her best friend went on after graduation. Tavia could not remember how much it cost per person, but she did remember that the total cost was over \$500. Use indirect reasoning to show that the cost for one person was more than \$250. (Lesson 5-4) **See margin.**

Draw and label a figure to represent the congruent triangles. Then find x. (Lesson 4-3) **51–52. See margin.**

51. $\triangle QRS \cong \triangle GHJ$, $RS = 12$, $QR = 10$, $QS = 6$, and $HJ = 2x - 4$.

52. $\triangle ABC \cong \triangle XYZ$, $AB = 13$, $AC = 19$, $BC = 21$, and $XY = 3x + 7$.

Use the figure at the right. (Lesson 1-4)

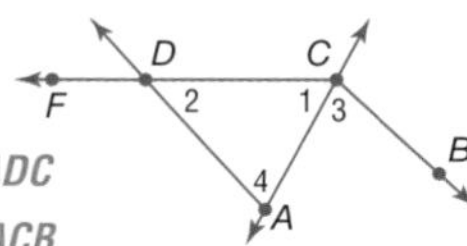

53. Name the vertex of $\angle 4$. *A*

54. What is another name for $\angle 2$? $\angle CDA$, $\angle ADC$

55. What is another name for $\angle BCA$? $\angle 3$, $\angle ACB$

Skills Review

Find the value of the variable(s) in each figure. Explain your reasoning. **56–58. See margin.**

56.

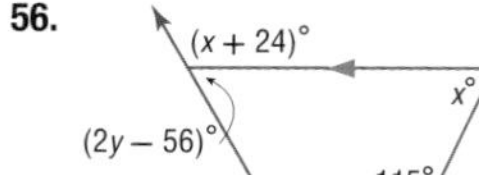

57.

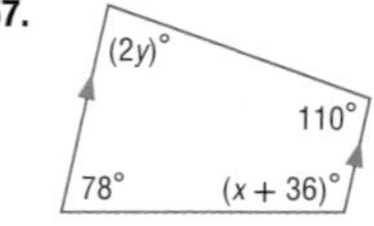

58.

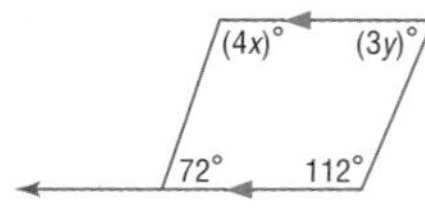

56. $x = 65$ by the Consecutive Interior Angles Theorem; $y = 73.5$ by the Supplement Theorem

57. $x = 66$ by the Consecutive Interior Angles Theorem; $y = 35$ by the Consecutive Interior Angles Theorem

58. $x = 27$ by the Consecutive Interior Angles Theorem; $y = 22\frac{2}{3}$ by the Consecutive Interior Angles Theorem

380 | Lesson 5-6 | Inequalities in Two Triangles

5 Study Guide and Review

Study Guide

KeyConcepts

Special Segments in Triangles (Lessons 5-1 and 5-2)

- The special segments of triangles are perpendicular bisectors, angle bisectors, medians, and altitudes.
- The intersection points of each of the special segments of a triangle are called the points of concurrency.
- The points of concurrency for a triangle are the circumcenter, incenter, centroid, and orthocenter.

Indirect Proof (Lesson 5-4)

- Writing an Indirect Proof:
  1. Assume that the conclusion is false.
  2. Show that this assumption leads to a contradiction.
  3. Since the false conclusion leads to an incorrect statement, the original conclusion must be true.

Triangle Inequalities (Lessons 5-3, 5-5, and 5-6)

- The largest angle in a triangle is opposite the longest side, and the smallest angle is opposite the shortest side.
- The sum of the lengths of any two sides of a triangle is greater than the length of the third side.
- **SAS Inequality** (Hinge Theorem): In two triangles, if two sides are congruent, then the measure of the included angle determines which triangle has the longer third side.
- **SSS Inequality**: In two triangles, if two corresponding sides of each triangle are congruent, then the length of the third side determines which triangle has the included angle with the greater measure.

FOLDABLES StudyOrganizer

Be sure the Key Concepts are noted in your Foldable.

KeyVocabulary

altitude (p. 337)
centroid (p. 335)
circumcenter (p. 325)
concurrent lines (p. 325)
incenter (p. 328)
indirect proof (p. 355)
indirect reasoning (p. 355)
median (p. 335)
orthocenter (p. 337)
perpendicular bisector (p. 324)
point of concurrency (p. 325)
proof by contradiction (p. 355)

VocabularyCheck

State whether each sentence is *true* or *false*. If *false*, replace the underlined term to make a true sentence.

1. The altitudes of a triangle intersect at the centroid. **false; orthocenter**
2. The point of concurrency of the medians of a triangle is called the incenter. **false; angle bisectors**
3. The point of concurrency is the point at which three or more lines intersect. **true**
4. The circumcenter of a triangle is equidistant from the vertices of the triangle. **true**
5. To find the centroid of a triangle, first construct the angle bisectors. **false; median**
6. The perpendicular bisectors of a triangle are concurrent lines. **true**
7. To start a proof by contradiction, first assume that what you are trying to prove is true. **false; false**
8. A proof by contradiction uses indirect reasoning. **true**
9. A median of a triangle connects the midpoint of one side of the triangle to the midpoint of another side of the triangle. **false; the vertex opposite that side**
10. The incenter is the point at which the angle bisectors of a triangle intersect. **true**

Formative Assessment

KeyVocabulary The page references after each word denote where that term was first introduced. If students have difficulty completing Exercises 1–10, remind them that they can use these page references to refresh their memories about the vocabulary terms.

Summative Assessment

Vocabulary Test, p. 48

Vocabulary Review

Vocabulary Review provides students the opportunity to check their understanding of important concepts and terminology in an online game format.

FOLDABLES StudyOrganizer

Dinah Zike's Foldables®

Have students look through the chapter to make sure they have included the key concepts under the proper lesson tab in their Foldables. Suggest that students keep their Foldables handy while completing the Study Guide and Review pages. Point out that their Foldables can serve as a quick review tool for studying for the chapter test.

Lesson-by-Lesson Review

Intervention If the given examples are not sufficient to review the topics covered by the questions, remind students that the lesson references tell them where to review that topic in their textbook.

Two-Day Option Have students complete the Lesson-by-Lesson Review. Then you can use eAssessment to customize another review worksheet that practices all the objectives of this chapter or only the objectives on which your students need more help.

Additional Answers

14.

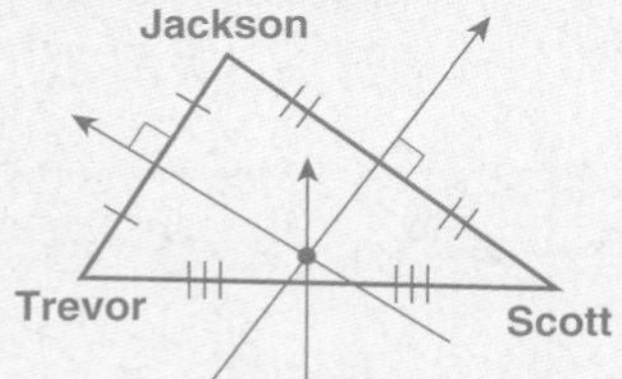

17. $\angle S, \angle R, \angle T; \overline{RT}, \overline{TS}, \overline{SR}$

18. $\angle N, \angle L, \angle M; \overline{ML}, \overline{MN}, \overline{LN}$

21. $\triangle FGH$ is not congruent to $\triangle MNO$.

22. $\triangle KLM$ is not a right triangle.

24. Let the measure of one angle be x and the measure of the other angle be y. By the definition of complementary angles, $x + y = 90$.

Step 1 Assume that the angle with the measure x is a right angle. Then $x = 90$.

Step 2 Since $x = 90$, then $x + y > 90$. This is a contradiction because we know that $x + y = 90$.

Step 3 Since the assumption that one angle is a right angle leads to a contradiction, the assumption must be false. Therefore, the conclusion that neither angle is a right angle must be true.

CHAPTER 5 Study Guide and Review *Continued*

Lesson-by-Lesson Review

5-1 Bisectors of Triangles

11. Find EG if G is the incenter of $\triangle ABC$. 5

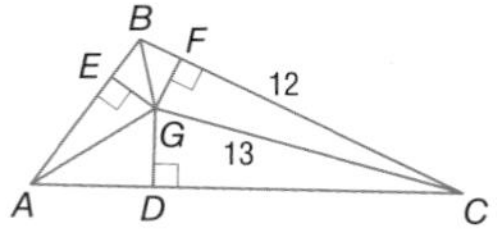

Find each measure.

12. RS 9

13. XZ 34

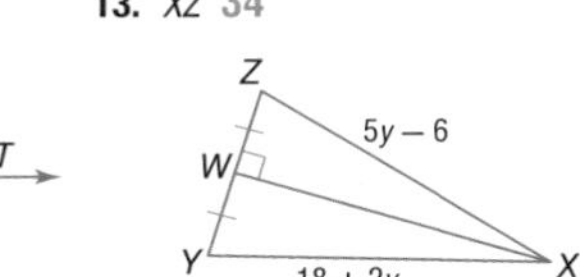

14. BASEBALL Jackson, Trevor, and Scott are warming up before a baseball game. One of their warm-up drills requires three players to form a triangle, with one player in the middle. Where should the fourth player stand so that he is the same distance from the other three players? See margin.

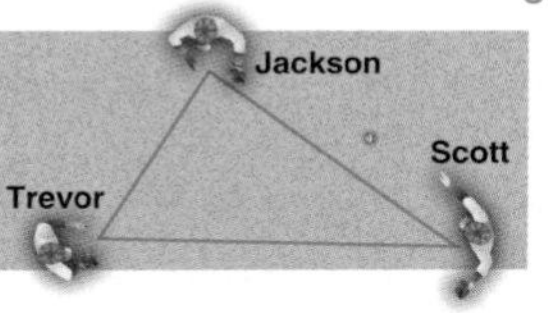

Example 1

Find each measure if Q is the incenter of $\triangle JKL$.

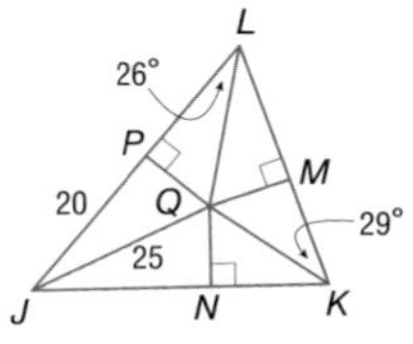

a. $\angle QJK$

$m\angle KLP + m\angle MKN + m\angle NJP = 180$	$\triangle$ Sum Theorem
$2(26) + 2(29) + m\angle NJP = 180$	Substitution
$110 + m\angle NJP = 180$	Simplify.
$m\angle NJP = 70$	Subtract.

Since $\overrightarrow{JQ}$ bisects $\angle NJP$, $2m\angle QJK = m\angle NJP$. So, $m\angle QJK = \frac{1}{2}m\angle NJP$, so $m\angle QJK = \frac{1}{2}(70)$ or 35.

b. QP

$a^2 + b^2 = c^2$	Pythagorean Theorem
$(QP)^2 + 20^2 = 25^2$	Substitution
$(QP)^2 + 400 = 625$	$20^2 = 400$ and $25^2 = 625$
$(QP)^2 = 225$	Subtract.
$QP = 15$	Simplify.

5-2 Medians and Altitudes of Triangles

15. The vertices of $\triangle DEF$ are $D(0, 0)$, $E(0, 7)$, and $F(6, 3)$. Find the coordinates of the orthocenter of $\triangle DEF$. (2, 3)

16. PROM Georgia is on the prom committee. She wants to hang a dozen congruent triangles from the ceiling so that they are parallel to the floor. She sketched out one triangle on a coordinate plane with coordinates (0, 4), (3, 8), and (6, 0). If each triangle is to be hung by one chain, what are the coordinates of the point where the chain should attach to the triangle? (3, 4)

Example 2

In $\triangle EDF$, T is the centroid and $FT = 12$. Find TQ.

$FT = \frac{2}{3}FQ$	
$FT = \frac{2}{3}(FT + TQ)$	
$12 = \frac{2}{3}(12 + TQ)$	$FT = 12$
$12 = 8 + \frac{2}{3}TQ$	Distributive Property
$4 = \frac{2}{3}TQ$	Subtract.
$6 = TQ$	Multiply.

5-3 Inequalities in One Triangle

List the angles and sides of each triangle in order from smallest to largest. **17–18. See margin.**

17.

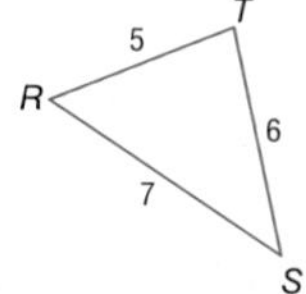

18.

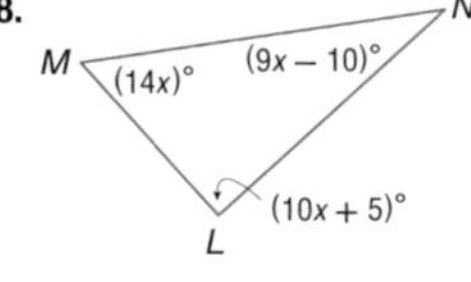

19. **NEIGHBORHOODS** Anna, Sarah, and Irene live at the intersections of the three roads that make the triangle shown. If the girls want to spend the afternoon together, is it a shorter path for Anna to stop and get Sarah and go onto Irene's house, or for Sarah to stop and get Irene and then go on to Anna's house? **The shorter path is for Sarah to get Irene and then go to Anna's house.**

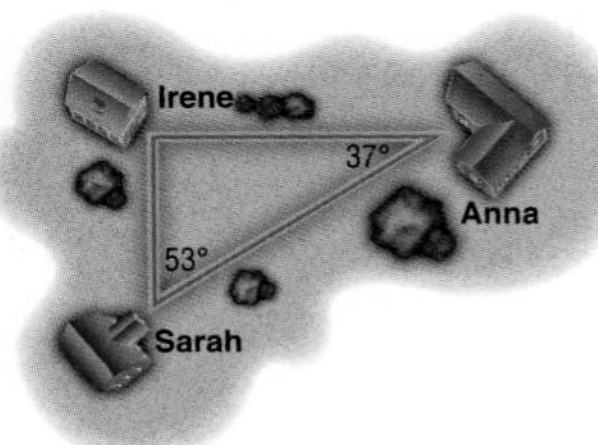

Example 3

List the angles and sides of $\triangle ABC$ in order from smallest to largest.

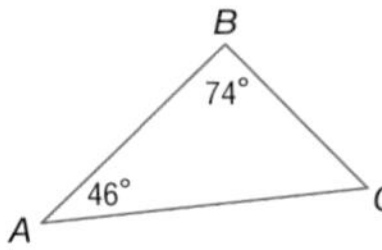

a. First, find the missing angle measure using the Triangle Sum Theorem.

$m\angle C = 180 - (46 + 74)$ or 60

So, the angles from smallest to largest are $\angle A$, $\angle C$, and $\angle B$.

b. The sides from shortest to longest are $\overline{BC}$, $\overline{AB}$, and $\overline{AC}$.

5-4 Indirect Proof

State the assumption you would make to start an indirect proof of each statement.

20. $m\angle A \geq m\angle B$ **$m\angle A < m\angle B$**

21. $\triangle FGH \cong \triangle MNO$ **See margin.**

22. $\triangle KLM$ is a right triangle. **See margin.**

23. If $3y < 12$, then $y < 4$. **$y \geq 4$**

24. Write an indirect proof to show that if two angles are complementary, neither angle is a right angle.

25. **MOVIES** Isaac bought two DVD's and spent over $50. Use indirect reasoning to show that at least one of the DVD's he purchased was over $25.

24–25. See margin.

Example 4

State the assumption necessary to start an indirect proof of each statement.

a. $\overline{XY} \not\cong \overline{JK}$

$\overline{XY} \cong \overline{JK}$

b. If $3x < 18$, then $x < 6$.

The conclusion of the conditional statement is $x < 6$. The negation of the conclusion is $x \geq 6$.

c. $\angle 2$ is an acute angle.

If $\angle 2$ *is an acute angle* is false, then $\angle 2$ *is not an acute angle* must be true. This means that $\angle 2$ *is an obtuse or right angle* must be true.

Additional Answer

25. Let the cost of one DVD be x, and the cost of the other DVD be y.

Given: $x + y > 50$

Prove: $x > 25$ or $y > 25$

Indirect proof:

Step 1 Assume that $x \leq 25$ and $y \leq 25$.

Step 2 If $x \leq 25$ and $y \leq 25$, then $x + y \leq 25 + 25$, or $x + y \leq 50$. This is a contradiction because we know that $x + y > 50$.

Step 3 Since the assumption that $x \leq 25$ and $y \leq 25$ leads to a contradiction of a known fact, the assumption must be false. Therefore, the conclusion that $x > 25$ or $y > 25$ must be true. Thus, at least one DVD had to be over $25.

connectED.mcgraw-hill.com 383

Anticipation Guide

Have students complete the Chapter 5 Anticipation Guide, and discuss how their responses have changed now that they have completed Chapter 5.

Additional Answers

28. Let x be the length of the third side. 2 ft $< x <$ 12 ft
29. Let x be the length of the third side. 6.5 cm $< x <$ 14.5 cm
30. The distance is greater than 1 mile and less than 5 miles.

Additional Answer (Practice Test)

5. **Given:** $5x + 7 \geq 52$

Prove: $x \geq 9$

Proof:

Step 1: Assume that $x < 9$.

Step 2: Make a table with several possibilities for x, assuming $x < 9$.

x	8	7	0	−2
$5x + 7$	47	42	7	−3

When $x < 9$, $5x + 7 < 52$.

Step 3: The assumption leads to the contradiction of the given information that $5x + 7 \geq 52$. Therefore the assumption that $x < 9$ must be false, so the original conclusion that $x \geq 9$ must be true.

CHAPTER 5 Study Guide and Review *Continued*

5-5 The Triangle Inequality

Is it possible to form a triangle with the given lengths? If not, explain why not.

26. 5, 6, 9 yes
27. 3, 4, 8 no; $3 + 4 < 8$

Find the range for the measure of the third side of a triangle given the measure of two sides.

28. 5 ft, 7 ft See margin.
29. 10.5 cm, 4 cm See margin.
30. **BIKES** Leonard rides his bike to visit Josh. Since High Street is closed, he has to travel 2 miles down Main Street and turn to travel 3 miles farther on 5th Street. If the three streets form a triangle with Leonard and Josh's house as two of the vertices, find the range of the possible distance between Leonard and Josh's houses when traveling straight down High Street. See margin.

Example 5

Is it possible to form a triangle with the lengths 7, 10, and 9 feet? If not, explain why not.

Check each inequality.

$7 + 10 > 9$	$7 + 9 > 10$	$10 + 9 > 7$
$17 > 9$ ✓	$16 > 10$ ✓	$19 > 7$ ✓

Since the sum of each pair of side lengths is greater than the third side length, sides with lengths 7, 10, and 9 feet will form a triangle.

5-6 Inequalities in Two Triangles

Compare the given measures.

31. $m\angle ABC$, $m\angle DEF$
32. QT and RS $QT > RS$

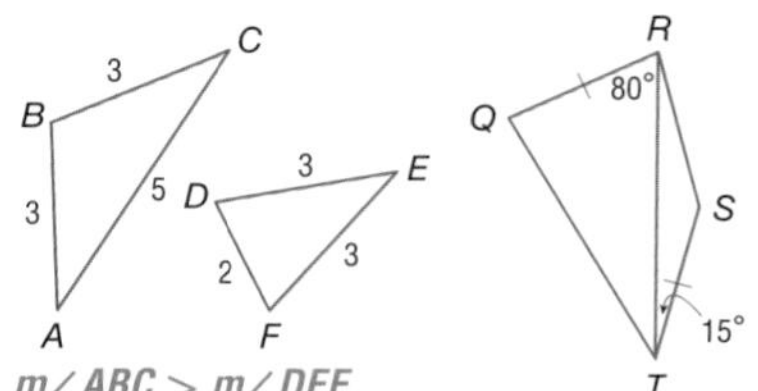

$m\angle ABC > m\angle DEF$

33. **BOATING** Rose and Connor each row across a pond heading to the same point. Neither of them has rowed a boat before, so they both go off course as shown in the diagram. After two minutes, they have each traveled 50 yards. Who is closer to their destination? Rose

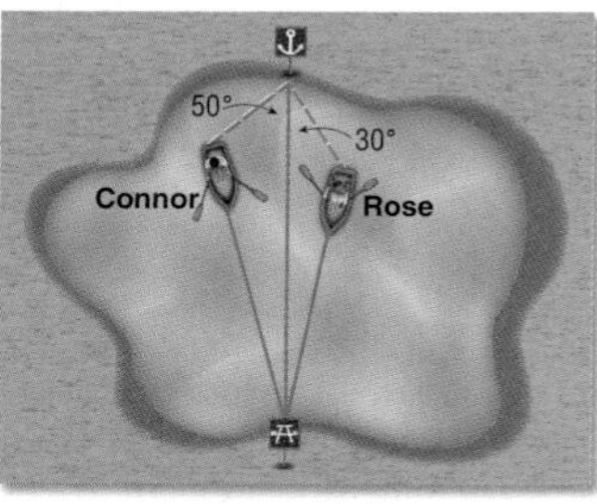

Example 6

Compare the given measures.

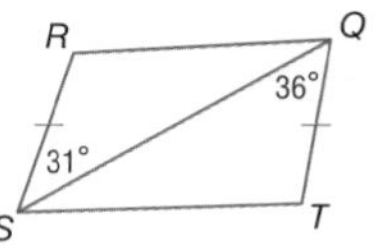

a. RQ and ST

In $\triangle QRS$ and $\triangle STQ$, $\overline{RS} \cong \overline{TQ}$, $\overline{QS} \cong \overline{QS}$, and $\angle SQT > \angle RSQ$. By the Hinge Theorem, $m\angle SQT < m\angle RSQ$, so $RQ < ST$.

b. $m\angle JKM$ and $m\angle LKM$

In $\triangle JKM$ and $\triangle LKM$, $\overline{JM} \cong \overline{LM}$, $\overline{KM} \cong \overline{KM}$, and $LK > JK$. By the Converse of the Hinge Theorem, $\angle LKM > \angle JKM$.

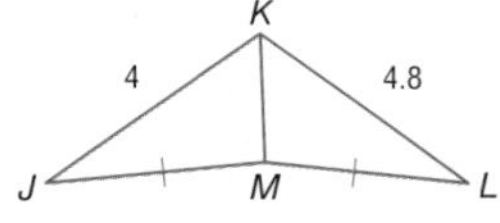

Additional Answer (Practice Test)

23. **Given:** $\overline{RQ}$ bisects $\angle SRT$.

Prove: $m\angle SQR > m\angle SRQ$

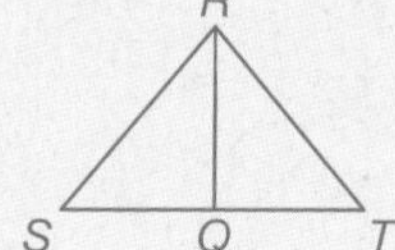

Proof:

<u>Statements (Reasons)</u>

1. $\overline{RQ}$ bisects $\angle SRT$. (Given)
2. $\angle SRQ \cong \angle QRT$ (Def. of bisector)
3. $m\angle QRS = m\angle QRT$ (Def. of $\cong$ ∠s)
4. $m\angle SQR = m\angle T + m\angle QRT$ (Exterior Angle Theorem)
5. $m\angle SQR > m\angle QRT$ (Def. of Inequality)
6. $m\angle SQR > m\angle SRQ$ (Substitution)

CHAPTER 5 Practice Test

1. **GARDENS** Maggie wants to plant a circular flower bed within a triangular area set off by three pathways. Which point of concurrency related to triangles would she use for the center of the largest circle that would fit inside the triangle? **incenter**

In $\triangle CDF$, K is the centroid and $DK = 16$. Find each length.

2. KH **8**
3. CD **18**
4. FG **18**

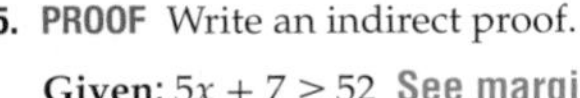

5. **PROOF** Write an indirect proof.

   Given: $5x + 7 \geq 52$ **See margin.**

   Prove: $x \geq 9$

Find each measure.

6. $m\angle TQR$ **43**
7. XZ **23**

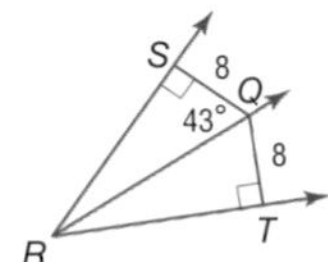

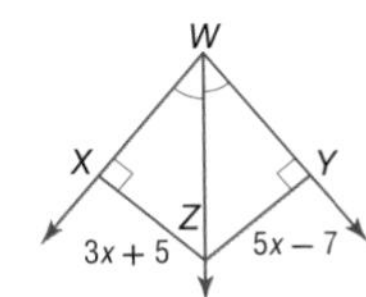

8. **GEOGRAPHY** The distance from Tonopah to Round Mountain is equal to the distance from Tonopah to Warm Springs. The distance from Tonopah to Hawthorne is the same as the distance from Tonopah to Beatty. Determine which distance is greater, Round Mountain to Hawthorne or Warm Springs to Beatty. **Warm Springs to Beatty**

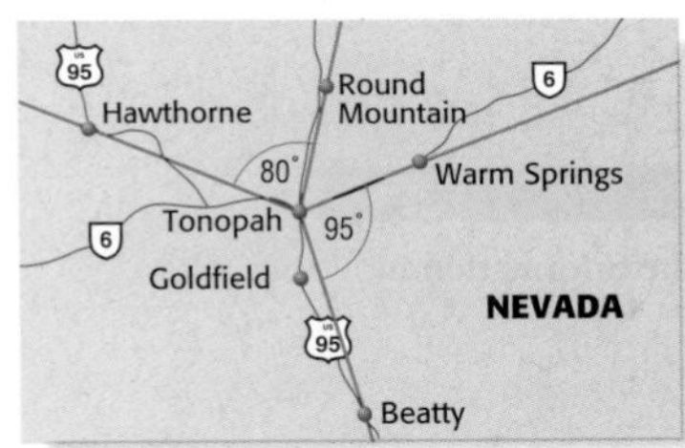

9. **MULTIPLE CHOICE** If the measures of two sides of a triangle are 3.1 feet and 4.6 feet, which is the *least* possible whole number measure for the third side? **B**

   A 1.6 feet C 7.5 feet

   B 2 feet D 8 feet

Point H is the incenter of $\triangle ABC$. Find each measure.

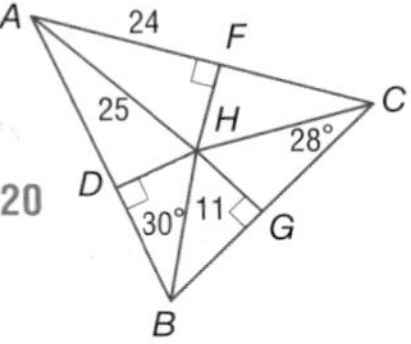

10. DH **7**
11. BD **8.5**
12. $m\angle HAC$ **32**
13. $m\angle DHG$ **120**

14. **MULTIPLE CHOICE** If the lengths of two sides of a triangle are 5 and 11, what is the range of possible lengths for the third side? **H**

    F $6 < x < 10$ H $6 < x < 16$

    G $5 < x < 11$ J $x < 5$ or $x > 11$

Compare the given measures.

15. AB and BC **$AB < BC$**
16. $\angle RST$ and $\angle JKL$ **$m\angle RST > m\angle JKL$**

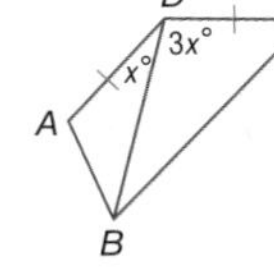

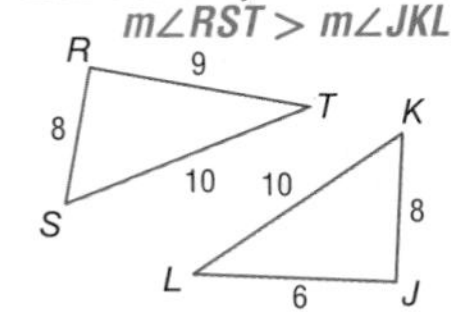

State the assumption necessary to start an indirect proof of each statement. **17. 4 is not a factor of n.**

17. If 8 is a factor of n, then 4 is a factor of n.
18. $m\angle M > m\angle N$ **$m\angle M \leq m\angle N$**
19. If $3a + 7 \leq 28$, then $a \leq 7$. **$a > 7$**

Use the figure to determine which angle has the greatest measure.

20. $\angle 1, \angle 5, \angle 6$ **$\angle 1$**
21. $\angle 9, \angle 8, \angle 3$ **$\angle 8$**
22. $\angle 4, \angle 3, \angle 2$ **$\angle 4$**

23. **PROOF** Write a two-column proof. **See margin.**

    Given: $\overline{RQ}$ bisects $\angle SRT$.

    Prove: $m\angle SQR > m\angle SRQ$

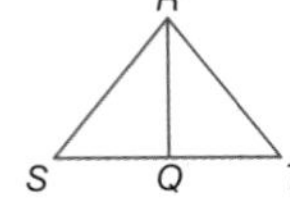

Find the range for the measure of the third side of a triangle given the measures of the two sides.

24. 10 ft, 16 ft **6 ft < x < 26 ft**
25. 23 m, 39 m **16 m < x < 62 m**

Summative Assessment

Use these alternate leveled chapter tests to differentiate assessment for your students.

Leveled Chapter 5 Tests

Form	Type	Level	Page(s)
1	MC	AL	49–50
2A	MC	OL	51–52
2B	MC	OL	53–54
2C	FR	OL	55–56
2D	FR	OL	57–58
3	FR	BL	59–60
Vocabulary Test			48
Extended-Response Test			61

MC = multiple-choice questions
FR = free-response questions

eAssessment Customize and create multiple versions of your chapter tests and their answer keys. All of the questions from the leveled chapter tests in the *Chapter 5 Resource Masters* are also available on eAssessment.

InterventionPlanner

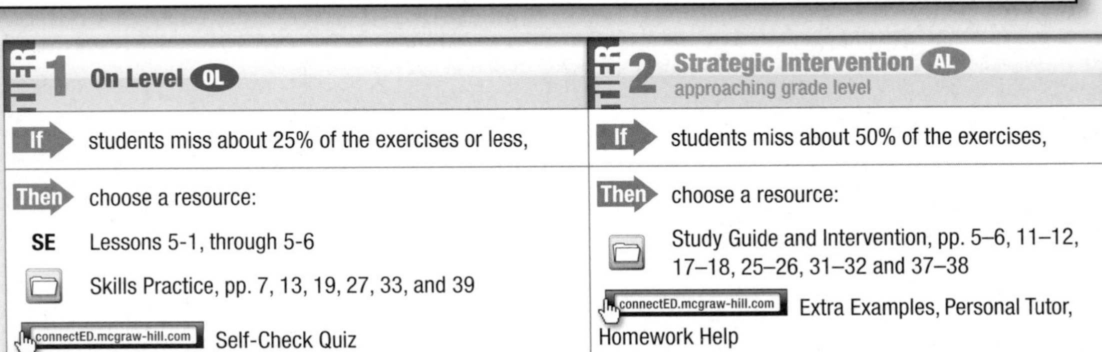

Tier 1 On Level OL

If students miss about 25% of the exercises or less,

Then choose a resource:

SE Lessons 5-1, through 5-6

Skills Practice, pp. 7, 13, 19, 27, 33, and 39

connectED.mcgraw-hill.com Self-Check Quiz

Tier 2 Strategic Intervention AL approaching grade level

If students miss about 50% of the exercises,

Then choose a resource:

Study Guide and Intervention, pp. 5–6, 11–12, 17–18, 25–26, 31–32 and 37–38

connectED.mcgraw-hill.com Extra Examples, Personal Tutor, Homework Help

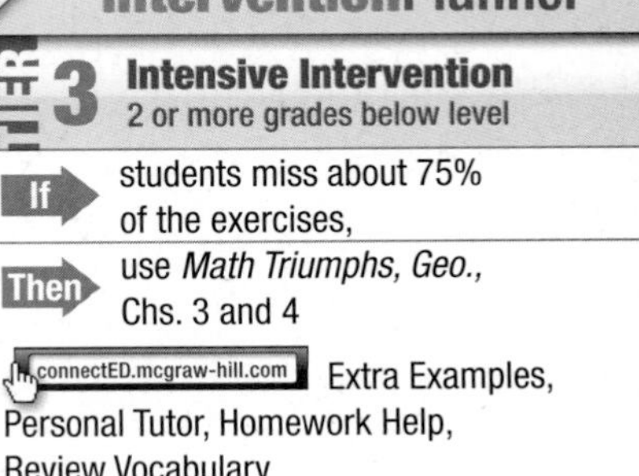

Tier 3 Intensive Intervention 2 or more grades below level

If students miss about 75% of the exercises,

Then use *Math Triumphs, Geo.*, Chs. 3 and 4

connectED.mcgraw-hill.com Extra Examples, Personal Tutor, Homework Help, Review Vocabulary

1 Focus

Objective Learn the strategy of eliminating unreasonable answers to help solve multiple choice questions.

2 Teach

Scaffolding Questions

Ask:

- Explain how eliminating unreasonable answers can help solve multiple choice questions. Sample answer: Eliminating unreasonable answers helps to narrow down the answer choices.
- What are some further questions you could ask about what information a question asks for? Sample answer: While reading the question you could determine what you are being asked to solve, whether the correct answer is a whole number, fraction, or decimal, and what units (if any) the solution should have.
- What are some examples from this chapter where you can eliminate numeric answers that are too large or small? Sample answer: When solving a problem, if the answer you find is an angle measure of a triangle that is greater than or equal to 180 or makes the sum of the angle measures of a triangle greater than 180, you should eliminate that answer choice.

CHAPTER 5 Preparing for Standardized Tests

Eliminate Unreasonable Answers

You can eliminate unreasonable answers to determine the correct answer when solving multiple choice test items.

Strategies for Eliminating Unreasonable Answers

Step 1

Read the problem statement carefully to determine exactly what you are being asked to find.

- What am I being asked to solve?
- Is the correct answer a whole number, fraction, or decimal?
- Do I need to use a graph or table?
- What units (if any) will the correct answer have?

Step 2

Carefully look over each possible answer choice and evaluate for reasonableness. Do not write any digits or symbols outside the answer boxes.

- Identify any answer choices that are clearly incorrect and eliminate them.
- Eliminate any answer choices that are not in the proper format.
- Eliminate any answer choices that do not have the correct units.

Step 3

Solve the problem and choose the correct answer from those remaining. Check your answer.

Standardized Test Example

Read the problem. Identify what you need to know. Then use the information in the problem to solve.

What is the measure of $\angle KLM$?

A 32

B 44

C 78

D 94

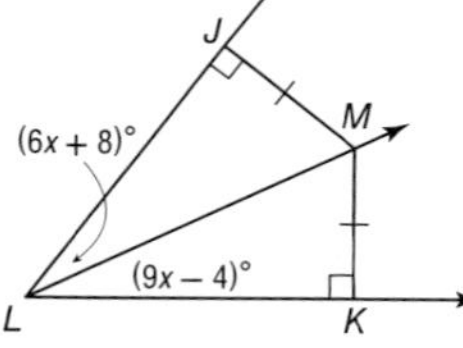

386 | Chapter 5 | Preparing for Standardized Tests

Read the problem and study the figure carefully. Triangle KLM is a right triangle. Since the sum of the interior angles of a triangle is 180°, $m\angle KLM + m\angle LMK$ must be equal to 90°. Otherwise, the sum would exceed 180°. Since answer choice D is an obtuse angle, it can be eliminated as unreasonable. The correct answer must be A, B, or C.

Solve the problem. According to the converse of the Angle Bisector Theorem, if a point in the interior of an angle is equidistant from the sides of the angle, then it is on the bisector of the angle. Point M is equidistant from rays LJ and LK, so it lies on the angle bisector of $\angle JLK$. Therefore, $\angle JLM$ must be congruent to $\angle KLM$. Set up and solve an equation for x.

$$6x + 8 = 9x - 4$$
$$-3x = -12$$
$$x = 4$$

So, the measure of $\angle KLM$ is $[9(4) - 4]°$, or 32°. The correct answer is A.

Exercises

Read each question. Then fill in the correct answer on the answer document provided by your teacher or on a sheet of paper.

1. Point P is the centroid of triangle QUS. If QP = 14 centimeters, what is the length of $\overline{QT}$? D

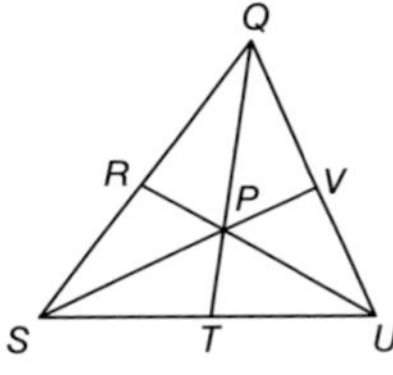

A 7 cm
B 12 cm
C 18 cm
D 21 cm

2. What is the area, in square units, of the triangle shown below? H

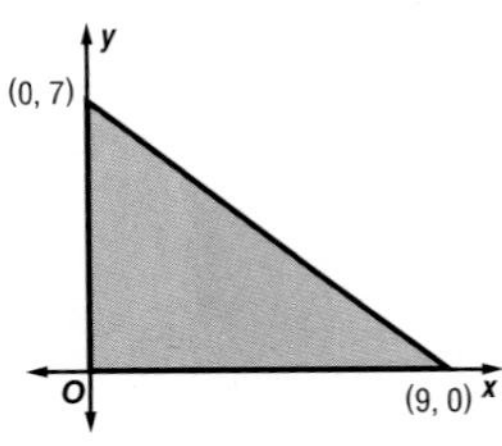

F 8
G 27.4
H 31.5
J 63

3. What are the coordinates of the orthocenter of the triangle below? C

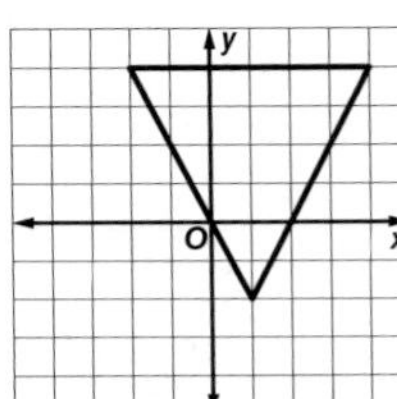

A $\left(-\frac{3}{4}, -1\right)$
B $\left(-\frac{4}{3}, 1\right)$
C $\left(1, \frac{5}{2}\right)$
D $\left(1, \frac{9}{4}\right)$

4. If $\triangle ABC$ is isosceles and $m\angle A = 94$, which of the following *must* be true? J

F $m\angle B = 94$
G $m\angle B = 47$
H $AB = BC$
J $AB = AC$

5. Which of the following could *not* be the dimensions of a triangle? B

A 1.9, 3.2, 4
B 1.6, 3, 4.6
C 3, 7.2, 7.5
D 2.6, 4.5, 6

Additional Example

What is the measure of $\overline{AD}$? D

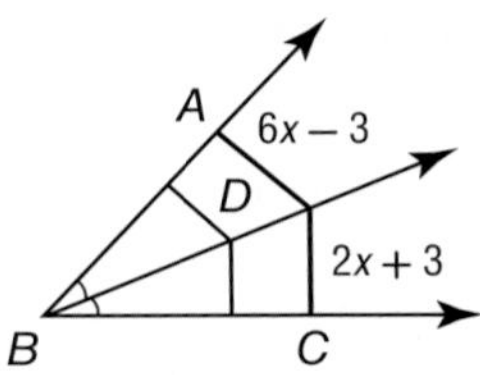

A −8
B −2
C 2
D 7

3 Assess

Use Exercises 1–5 to assess students' understanding.

Diagnose Student Errors

Survey student responses for each item. Class trends may indicate common errors and misconceptions.

1. A arithmetic error
B arithmetic error
C arithmetic error
D correct

2. F guess
G guess
H guess
J correct

3. A assumes the conclusion
B assumes the conclusion
C assumes the conclusion
D correct

4. F correct
G guess
H guess
J guess

5. A wrong formula
B correct
C wrong slope
D wrong slope

6. F correct
G guess
H guess
J order reversed

7. A forgets case of acute angle
B correct
C forgets case of right angle
D guess

8. F classified by the given angles only
G incorrect definition
H correct
J guess from appearance of figure

CHAPTER 5

Standardized Test Practice

Cumulative, Chapters 1 through 5

Multiple Choice

Read each question. Then fill in the correct answer on the answer document provided by your teacher or on a sheet of paper.

1. Solve for x. D

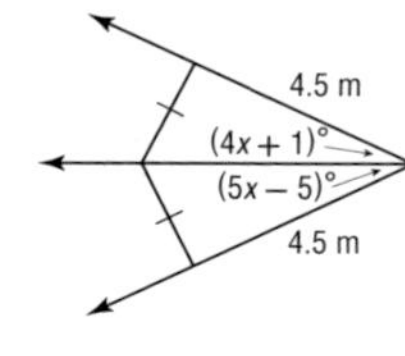

A 3
B 4
C 5
D 6

2. Which of the following could not be the value of x? J

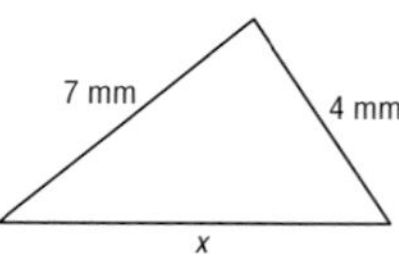

F 8 mm
G 9 mm
H 10 mm
J 11 mm

3. Jesse claims that if you live in Lexington, then you live in Kentucky. Which assumption would you need to make to form an indirect proof of this claim? D

A Suppose someone lives in Kentucky, but not in Lexington.

B Suppose someone lives in Kentucky and in Lexington.

C Suppose someone lives in Lexington and in Kentucky.

D Suppose someone lives in Lexington, but not in Kentucky.

4. Which of the following best describes the shortest distance from a vertex of a triangle to the opposite side? F

F altitude
G diameter
H median
J segment

5. Lin started mowing lawns. Let x represent the number of weeks after he began mowing lawns, and y represent the number of customers. Use the points (3, 4) and (9, 6) to find the equation of a line that can be used to predict how many customers Lin has by the end of a certain week. B

A $y = \frac{1}{3}x$
B $y = \frac{1}{3}x + 3$
C $y = \frac{2}{3}x + 2$
D $y = \frac{2}{3}x$

6. What is the correct relationship between the angle measures of $\triangle PQR$? F

F $m\angle R < m\angle Q < m\angle P$
G $m\angle R < m\angle P < m\angle Q$
H $m\angle Q < m\angle P < m\angle R$
J $m\angle P < m\angle Q < m\angle R$

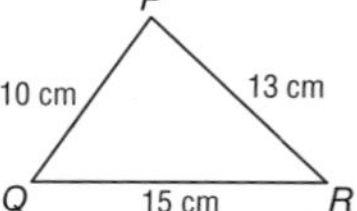

7. Which assumption would you need to make in order to start an indirect proof of the statement? B

Angle S is not an obtuse angle.

A $\angle S$ is a right angle.
B $\angle S$ is an obtuse angle.
C $\angle S$ is an acute angle.
D $\angle S$ is not an acute angle.

8. Classify the triangle below according to its angle measures. H

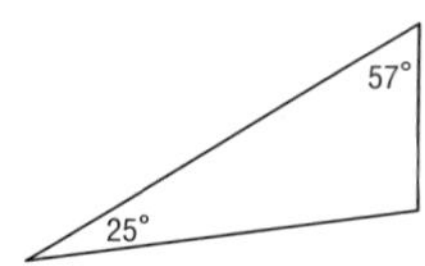

F acute
G equiangular
H obtuse
J right

Test-Taking Tip

Question 2 The sum of any two sides of a triangle must be greater than the third side.

Short Response/Gridded Response

Record your answers on the answer sheet provided by your teacher or on a sheet of paper.

9. **GRIDDED RESPONSE** If the measures of two sides of a triangle are 9 centimeters and 15 centimeters, what is the least possible measure of the third side in centimeters if the measure is an integer? 7

10. What are the coordinates of the orthocenter of the triangle below?

$\left(-\frac{2}{3}, 6\frac{2}{3}\right)$

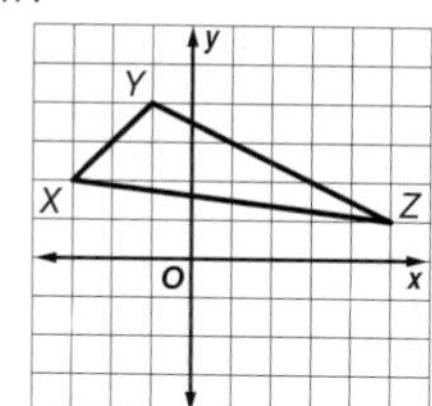

11. List the sides of the triangle below in order from shortest to longest. *RS, RT, ST*

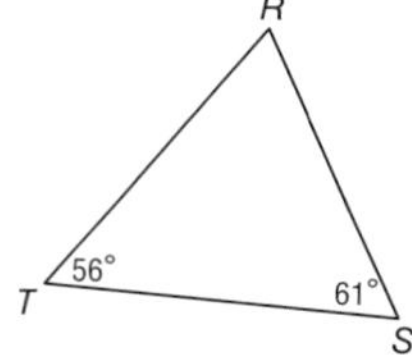

12. Suppose two lines intersect in a plane to form four angles.

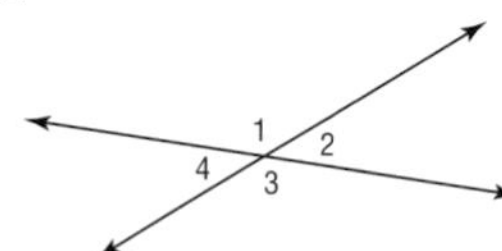

What do you know about the pairs of adjacent angles formed? Explain. They are supplementary. Each pair of adjacent angles forms a linear pair.

13. Eric and Heather are each taking a group of campers hiking in the woods. Eric's group leaves camp and goes 2 miles east, then turns 20° south of east and goes 4 more miles. Heather's group leaves camp and travels 2 miles west, then turns 30° north of west and goes 4 more miles. How many degrees south of east would Eric have needed to turn in order for his group and Heather's group to be the same distance from camp after the two legs of the hike? 30°

14. **GRIDDED RESPONSE** Solve for *x* in the triangle below. 15

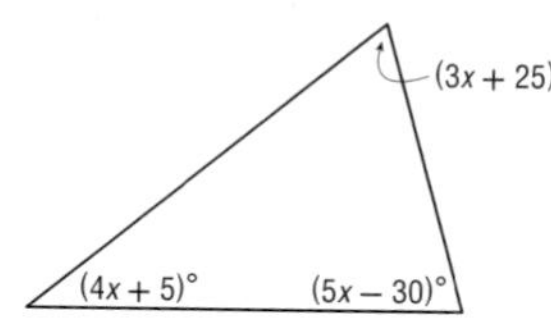

Extended Response

Record your answers on a sheet of paper. Show your work.

15. Refer to the figure to answer each question.

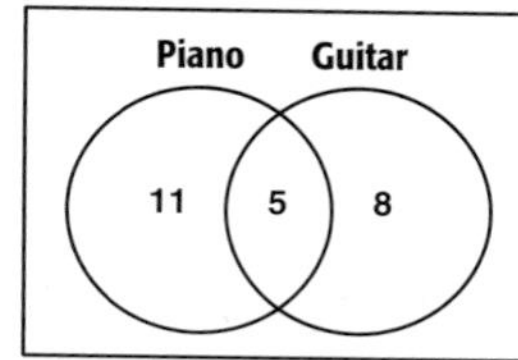

a. How many students play the guitar? 13

b. How many students play the piano? 16

c. How many students play both piano and guitar? 5

Need ExtraHelp?

If you missed Question...	1	2	3	4	5	6	7	8	9	10	11	12	13	14	15
Go to Lesson...	5-1	5-5	5-4	5-2	3-4	5-3	5-4	4-1	5-5	5-2	5-3	1-5	5-6	4-2	2-2

Formative Assessment

You can use these pages to benchmark student progress.

Chapter 5 Resource Masters

Standardized Test Practice, pp. 62–64

Answer Sheet Practice

Have students simulate taking a standardized test by recording their answers on a practice recording sheet.

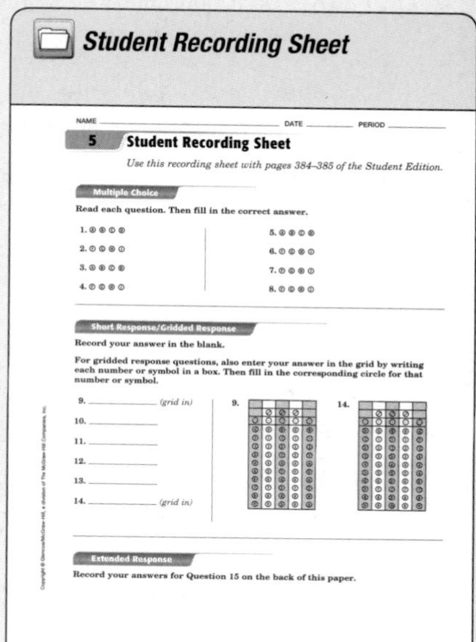

Student Recording Sheet

NAME ____ DATE ____ PERIOD ____

5 Student Recording Sheet

Use this recording sheet with pages 384–385 of the Student Edition.

Multiple Choice

Read each question. Then fill in the correct answer.

1. 2. 3. 4. 5. 6. 7. 8.

Short Response/Gridded Response

Record your answer in the blank.

For gridded response questions, also enter your answer in the grid by writing each number or symbol in a box. Then fill in the corresponding circle for that number or symbol.

9. ____ (grid in)
10. ____
11. ____
12. ____
13. ____
14. ____ (grid in)

Extended Response

Record your answers for Question 15 on the back of this paper.

eAssessment Create practice tests that align to your state standards, the Common Core State Standards, and other national standards such as TIMSS and NAEP.

Homework Option

Get Ready for Chapter 6 Assign students the exercises on page 391 as homework to assess whether they possess the prerequisite skills for the next chapter.

Lesson 5-1

15.

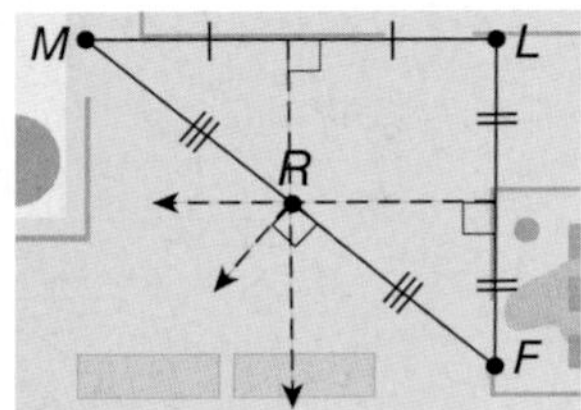

37. Proof:

Statements (Reasons)

1. $\overline{CA} \cong \overline{CB}$, $\overline{AD} \cong \overline{BD}$ (Given)
2. $\overline{CD} \cong \overline{CD}$ (Congruence of segments is reflexive.)
3. $\triangle ACD \cong \triangle BCD$ (SSS)
4. $\angle ACD \cong \angle BCD$ (CPCTC)
5. $\overline{CE} \cong \overline{CE}$ (Congruence of segments is reflexive.)
6. $\triangle CEA \cong \triangle CEB$ (SAS)
7. $\overline{AE} \cong \overline{BE}$ (CPCTC)
8. E is the midpoint of $\overline{AB}$. (Def. of midpoint)
9. $\angle CEA \cong \angle CEB$ (CPCTC)
10. $\angle CEA$ and $\angle CEB$ form a linear pair. (Def. of linear pair)
11. $\angle CEA$ and $\angle CEB$ are supplementary. (Suppl. Thm.)
12. $m\angle CEA + m\angle CEB = 180$ (Def. of supplementary)
13. $m\angle CEA + m\angle CEA = 180$ (Substitution Prop.)
14. $2m\angle CEA = 180$ (Substitution Prop.)
15. $m\angle CEA = 90$ (Division Prop.)
16. $\angle CEA$ and $\angle CEB$ are rt. $\angle$. (Def. of rt. $\angle$)
17. $\overline{CD} \perp \overline{AB}$ (Def. of $\perp$)
18. $\overline{CD}$ is the $\perp$ bisector of $\overline{AB}$. (Def. of $\perp$ bisector)
19. C and D are on the $\perp$ bisector of $\overline{AB}$. (Def. of point on a line)

38. Proof:

Statements (Reasons)

1. $\triangle ABC$, angle bisectors $\overline{AD}$, $\overline{BE}$, and $\overline{CF}$, $\overline{KP} \perp \overline{AB}$, $\overline{KQ} \perp \overline{BC}$, $\overline{KR} \perp \overline{AC}$ (Given)
2. $KP = KQ$, $KQ = KR$, $KP = KR$ (Any point on the $\angle$ bisector is equidistant from the sides of the angle.)
3. $KP = KQ = KR$ (Transitive Property)

39. Given: $\overline{CD}$ is the $\perp$ bisector of $\overline{AB}$.
E is a point on CD.

Prove: $EA = EB$

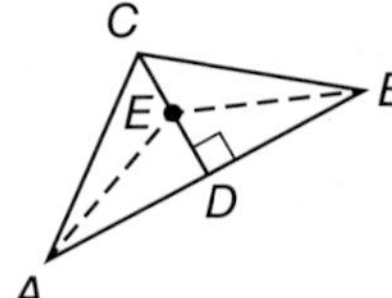

Proof: $\overline{CD}$ is the $\perp$ bisector of $\overline{AB}$. By definition of bisector, D is the midpoint of $\overline{AB}$. Thus, $\overline{AD} \cong \overline{BD}$ by the Midpoint Theorem. $\angle CDA$ and $\angle CDB$ are right angles by the definition of perpendicular. Since all right angles are congruent, $\angle CDA \cong \angle CDB$. Since E is a point on $\overline{CD}$, $\angle EDA$ and $\angle EDB$ are right angles and are congruent. By the Reflexive Property, $\overline{ED} \cong \overline{ED}$. Thus $\triangle EDA \cong \triangle EDB$ by SAS. $\overline{EA} \cong \overline{EB}$ because CPCTC, and by definition of congruence, $EA = EB$.

40. Given: $\angle BAC$
P is in the interior of $\angle BAC$;
$PD = PE$

Prove: $\overrightarrow{AP}$ is the angle bisector of $\angle BAC$.

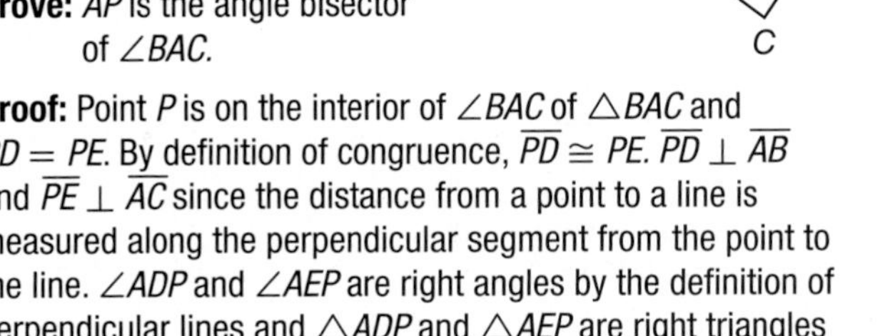

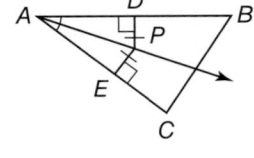

Proof: Point P is on the interior of $\angle BAC$ of $\triangle BAC$ and $PD = PE$. By definition of congruence, $\overline{PD} \cong \overline{PE}$. $\overline{PD} \perp \overline{AB}$ and $\overline{PE} \perp \overline{AC}$ since the distance from a point to a line is measured along the perpendicular segment from the point to the line. $\angle ADP$ and $\angle AEP$ are right angles by the definition of perpendicular lines and $\triangle ADP$ and $\triangle AEP$ are right triangles by the definition of right triangles. By the Reflexive Property, $\overline{AP} \cong \overline{AP}$. Thus, $\triangle ADP \cong \triangle AEP$ by HL. $\angle DAP \cong \angle EAP$ because CPCTC, and $\overrightarrow{AP}$ is the angle bisector of $\angle BAC$ by the definition of angle bisector.

50. Sometimes; if the triangle is equilateral, then this is true, but if the triangle is isosceles or scalene, the statement is false.

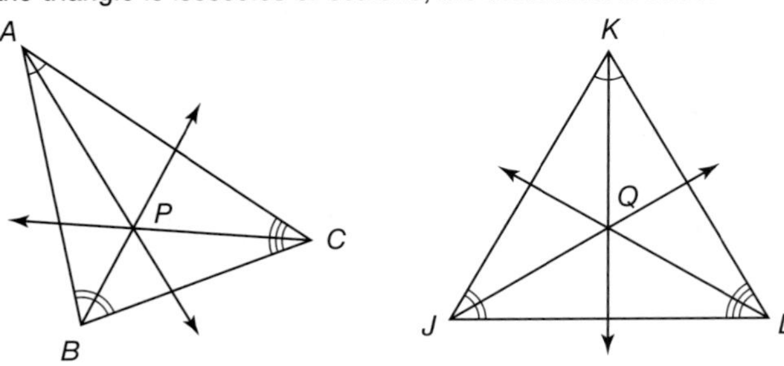

$AP \neq BP \neq CP$. $JQ = KQ = LQ$

51. always

Given: $\triangle ABC$ is isosceles with legs $\overline{AB}$ and $\overline{BC}$; $\overline{BD}$ is the $\perp$ bisector of $\overline{AC}$.

Prove: $\overline{BD}$ is the angle bisector of $\angle ABC$.

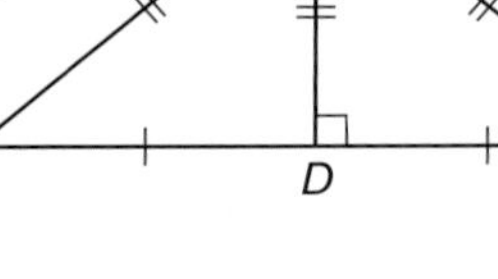

Proof:

Statements (Reasons)

1. $\triangle ABC$ is isosceles with legs $\overline{AB}$ and $\overline{BC}$. (Given)
2. $\overline{AB} \cong \overline{BC}$ (Def. of isosceles $\triangle$)
3. $\overline{BD}$ is the $\perp$ bisector of $\overline{AC}$. (Given)
4. D is the midpoint of $\overline{AC}$. (Def. of segment bisector)
5. $\overline{AD} \cong \overline{DC}$ (Def. of midpoint)
6. $\overline{BD} \cong \overline{BD}$ (Reflexive Property)
7. $\triangle ABD \cong \triangle CBD$ (SSS)
8. $\angle ABD \cong \angle CBD$ (CPCTC)
9. $\overline{BD}$ is the angle bisector of $\angle ABC$. (Def. $\angle$ bisector)

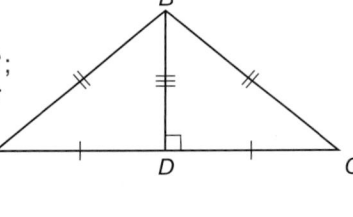

52. Proof:

Statements (Reasons)

1. Plane $\mathcal{Y}$ is a perpendicular bisector of $\overline{DC}$. (Given)
2. $\angle DBA$ and $\angle CBA$ are rt $\measuredangle$s, $\overline{DB} \cong \overline{CB}$ (Def. of $\perp$ bisector)
3. $\angle DBA \cong \angle CBA$ (Right angles are congruent.)
4. $\overline{AB} \cong \overline{AB}$ (Reflexive Property)
5. $\triangle DBA \cong \triangle CBA$ (SAS)
6. $\angle ADB \cong \angle ACB$ (CPCTC)

53. Proof:

Statements (Reasons)

1. Plane $\mathcal{Z}$ is an angle bisector of $\angle KJH$; $\overline{KJ} \cong \overline{HJ}$ (Given)
2. $\angle KJM \cong \angle HJM$ (Definition of angle bisector)
3. $\overline{JM} \cong \overline{JM}$ (Reflexive Property)
4. $\triangle KJM \cong \triangle HJM$ (SAS)
5. $\overline{MH} \cong \overline{MK}$ (CPCTC)

68. Proof:

Statements (Reasons)

1. $\triangle XKF$ is equilateral. (Given)
2. $\angle 1 \cong \angle 2$ (Equilateral $\triangle$s are equiangular.)
3. $\overline{KX} \cong \overline{FX}$ (Def. of equilateral $\triangle$)
4. $\overline{XJ}$ bisects $\angle X$. (Given)
5. $\angle KXJ \cong \angle FXJ$ (Def. of $\angle$ bisector)
6. $\triangle KXJ \cong \triangle FXJ$ (ASA)
7. $\overline{KJ} \cong \overline{FJ}$ (CPCTC)
8. J is the midpoint of $\overline{KF}$. (Def. of midpoint)

69. Proof:

Statements (Reasons)

1. $\triangle MLP$ is isosceles. (Given)
2. $\overline{ML} \cong \overline{PL}$ (Definition of isosceles $\triangle$)
3. $\angle M \cong \angle P$ (Isosceles $\triangle$ Th.)
4. N is the midpoint of $\overline{MP}$. (Given)
5. $\overline{MN} \cong \overline{PN}$ (Def. of midpoint)
6. $\triangle MNL \cong \triangle PNL$ (SAS)
7. $\angle LNM \cong \angle LNP$ (CPCTC)
8. $m\angle LNM = m\angle LNP$ (Def. of $\cong$ $\measuredangle$s)
9. $\angle LNM$ and $\angle LNP$ are a linear pair. (Def. of a linear pair)
10. $m\angle LNM + m\angle LNP = 180$ (Sum of measures of linear pair of $\measuredangle$s $= 180$)
11. $2m\angle LNM = 180$ (Substitution)
12. $m\angle LNM = 90$ (Division)
13. $\angle LNM$ is a right angle. (Def. of rt. $\angle$)
14. $\overline{LN} \perp \overline{MP}$ (Def. of $\perp$)

Lesson 5-2

33a.

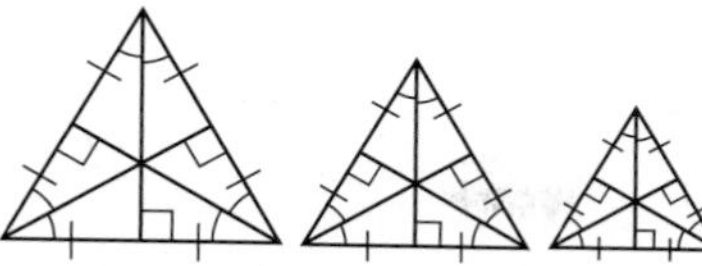

33b. Sample answer: The four points of concurrency of an equilateral triangle are all the same point.

33c.

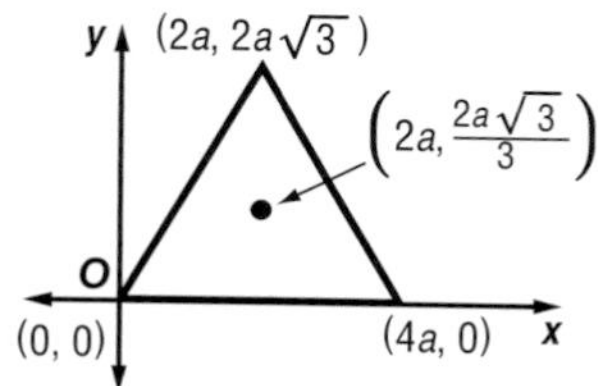

36. Proof: slope of $\overline{AR} = \dfrac{3c}{3b+3a} = \dfrac{c}{b+a}$,

slope of $\overline{BS} = \dfrac{6c}{6b-3a} = \dfrac{2c}{2b-a}$,

slope of $\overline{CQ} = \dfrac{3c}{3b-6a} = \dfrac{c}{b-2a}$

$\overline{AR}$ contained in the line $y = \left(\dfrac{c}{b+a}\right)x$,

$\overline{BS}$ contained in the line $y = \dfrac{2c}{2b+a}(x-3a)$,

$\overline{CQ}$ contained in the line $y = \dfrac{c}{b-2a}(x-6a)$

To find the coordinates of P, find the intersection point of two medians, $\overline{BS}$ and $\overline{CQ}$.

$y = \dfrac{2c}{2b-a}(x-3a)$ and $y = \dfrac{c}{b-2a}(x-6a)$

$\dfrac{2c}{2b-a}(x-3a) = \dfrac{c}{b-2a}(x-6a)$.

$2c(x-3a)(b-2a) = c(x-6a)(2b-a)$

$2c(bx-2ax-3ab+6a^2) = c(2bx-ax-12ab+6a^2)$

$2bcx-4acx-6abc+12a^2c = 2bcx-acx-12abc+6a^2c$

$-3acx = -6abc-6a^2c$

$x = 2b+2a$

Find y.

$y = \dfrac{2c}{2b-a}(x-3a) = \dfrac{2c}{2b-a}(2b+2a-3a) =$

$\dfrac{2c(2b-a)}{2b-a} = 2c$

So the coordinates of P are $(2b+2a, 2c)$. Now, show that P is on $\overline{AR}$.

$y = \left(\dfrac{c}{b+a}\right)(2b+2a) = \dfrac{2c(b+a)}{b+a} = 2c$.

Thus, the three medians intersect at the same point.

Find the lengths of $\overline{AR}$, $\overline{AP}$, $\overline{BS}$, $\overline{BP}$, $\overline{CQ}$, and $\overline{CP}$ using the Distance Formula.

$AR = \sqrt{((3b+3a)-0)^2+(3c-0)^2}$

$= \sqrt{(3(b+a))^2+(3c)^2}$

$= \sqrt{9((b+a)^2+c^2)}$

$= 3\sqrt{(b+a)^2+c^2}$

$$AP = \sqrt{((2b + 2a) - 0)^2 + (2c - 0)^2}$$
$$= \sqrt{(2(b + a))^2 + (2c)^2}$$
$$= \sqrt{4\left((b + a)^2 + c^2\right)}$$
$$= 2\sqrt{(b + a)^2 + c^2}$$
$$BS = \sqrt{(6b - 3a)^2 + (6c - 0)^2}$$
$$= \sqrt{(3(2b - a))^2 + (3(2c))^2}$$
$$= \sqrt{9(2b - a)^2 + 9(2c)^2}$$
$$= 3\sqrt{(2b - a)^2 + 4c^2}$$
$$BP = \sqrt{(6b - (2b + 2a))^2 + (6c - 2c)^2}$$
$$= \sqrt{(4b - 2a)^2 + (4c)^2}$$
$$= \sqrt{2(2b - a)^2 + 2(2c)^2}$$
$$= 2\sqrt{(2b - a)^2 + 4c^2}$$
$$CQ = \sqrt{(6a - 3b)^2 + (0 - 3c)^2}$$
$$= \sqrt{(3(2a - b))^2 + (-3c)^2}$$
$$= \sqrt{9\left((2a - b)^2 + c^2\right)}$$
$$= 3\sqrt{(2a - b)^2 + c^2}$$
$$CP = \sqrt{(6a - (2b + 2a)) + (0 - 2c)^2}$$
$$= \sqrt{(4a - 2b)^2 + (-2c)^2}$$
$$= \sqrt{(2(2a - b))^2 + 4c^2}$$
$$= \sqrt{4(2a - b)^2 + 4c^2}$$
$$= 2\sqrt{(2a - b)^2 + c^2}$$

Show that the P is two thirds of the distance from the vertices to the midpoints.

$$\frac{2}{3}AR = \frac{2}{3}\left(3\sqrt{(b + a)^2 + c^2}\right)$$
$$= 2\sqrt{(b + a)^2 + c^2} \text{ or } AP$$
$$\frac{2}{3}BS = \frac{2}{3}\left(3\sqrt{(2b - a)^2 + 4c^2}\right)$$
$$= 2\sqrt{(2b - a)^2 + 4c^2} \text{ or } BP$$
$$\frac{2}{3}CQ = \frac{2}{3}\left(3\sqrt{(2a - b)^2 + c^2}\right)$$
$$= 2\sqrt{(2a - b)^2 + c^2} \text{ or } CP$$

Thus, $AP = \frac{2}{3}AR$, $BP = \frac{2}{3}BS$, and $CP = \frac{2}{3}CQ$.

40. Sample answer: The perpendicular bisector and the median pass through a common point on the side of the triangle, but only the median always passes through the vertex opposite the side. The perpendicular bisector and the altitude are both perpendicular to the side, but do not necessarily pass through a common point on the side of the triangle. The median and the altitude both pass through the vertex, but do not necessarily pass through a common point on the side of the triangle.

56.

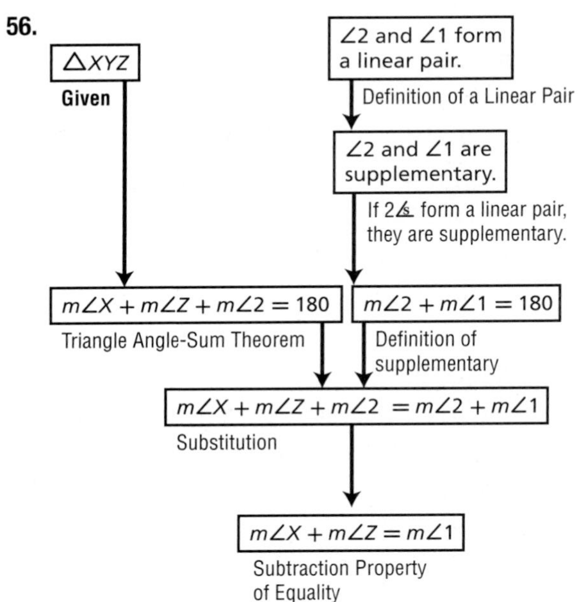

Lesson 5-3

42a.

B
A C

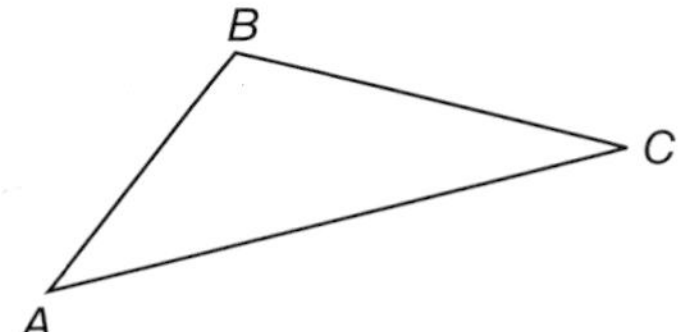

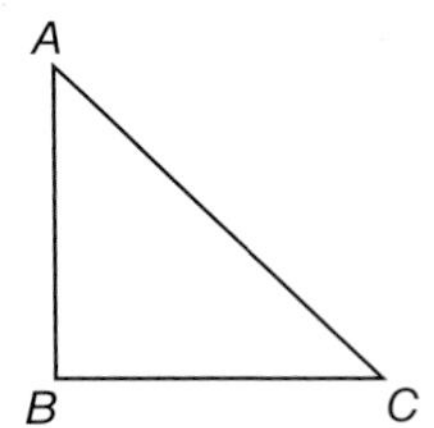

Lesson 5-4 (Guided Practice)

2A. Given: $7x > 56$

Prove: $x > 8$

Indirect Proof: Step 1 Assume that $x < 8$ or $x = 8$.

Step 2

x	4	5	6	7	8
$7x$	28	35	42	49	56

When $x < 8$, $7x < 56$ and when $x = 8$, $7x = 56$.

Step 3 In both cases, the assumption leads to the contradiction of the given information that $7x > 56$. Therefore, the assumption that $x \leq 8$ must be false and the original conclusion that $x > 8$ must be true.

2B. Given: $-c > 0$

Prove: $c < 0$

Indirect Proof: Step 1 Assume that $c > 0$ or $c = 0$.

Step 2

c	0	1	2	3	4
$-c$	0	-1	-2	-3	-4

If $c > 0$, then $-c < 0$. If $c = 0$, then $-c = 0$.

Step 3 In both cases, the assumption leads to the contradiction of the given information that $-c > 0$. Therefore, the assumption that $c > 0$ must be false and the original conclusion that $c < 0$ must be true. Since $c < 0$ is true, c must be a negative number.

3. Let x = distance traveled on the first leg of his trip, y = distance traveled on the second leg of his trip, and z = distance traveled on the third leg of his trip.

Given: $x + y + z > 360$

Prove: $x > 120$ or $y > 120$ or $z > 120$

Indirect Proof: Step 1 Assume that no leg of his trip was more than 120 miles. That is, $x \leq 120$, $y \leq 120$, and $z \leq 120$.

Step 2 If $x \leq 120$, $y \leq 120$, and $z \leq 120$, then $x + y + z \leq 120 + 120 + 120$ or $x + y + z \leq 360$.

Step 3 This is a contradiction of the given statement. Therefore, the assumption is false and $x > 120$ or $y > 120$ or $z > 120$. That is, he traveled more than 120 miles on one leg of his trip.

4. Given: x^2 is an odd integer.

Prove: x is an odd integer.

Indirect Proof: Step 1 Assume that x is an even integer. This means that $x = 2k$ for some integer k.

Step 2

$x^2 = (2k)^2$	Substitution of assumption
$= 4k^2$	Simplify.
$= (2 \cdot 2)k^2$	Multiplication Property
$= 2(2k^2)$	Associative Property of Multiplication

Since k is an integer, $2k^2$ is also an integer. Let m represent the integer $2k^2$. So x^2 can be represented by $2m$, where m is an integer. This means that x^2 is an even integer, but this contradicts the given statement that x^2 is an odd integer.

Step 3 Since the assumption that x is even leads to a contradiction of the given, the original conclusion that x is odd must be true.

Lesson 5-4

5. Given: $2x + 3 < 7$

Prove: $x < 2$

Indirect Proof: Step 1 Assume that $x > 2$ or $x = 2$ is true.

Step 2

x	2	3	4	5	6
$2x + 3$	7	9	11	13	15

When $x > 2$, $2x + 3 > 7$ and when $x = 2$, $2x + 3 = 7$.

Step 3 In both cases, the assumption leads to the contradiction of the given information that $2x + 3 < 7$. Therefore, the assumption that $x \geq 2$ must be false, so the original conclusion that $x < 2$ must be true.

6. Given: $3x - 4 > 8$

Prove: $x > 4$

Indirect Proof: Step 1 Assume that $x < 4$ or $x = 4$ is true.

Step 2

x	0	1	2	3	4
$3x - 4$	-4	-1	2	5	8

When $x < 4$, $3x - 4 < 8$ and when $x = 4$, $3x - 4 = 8$.

Step 3 In both cases, the assumption leads to the contradiction of the given information that $3x - 4 > 8$. Therefore, the assumption that $x \leq 4$ must be false, so the original conclusion that $x > 4$ must be true.

7. Use a = average or $\dfrac{\text{number of points scored}}{\text{number of games played}}$.

Indirect Proof:

Step 1 Assume that Christina's average points per game was greater than or equal to 3, $a \geq 3$.

Step 2

CASE 1	CASE 2
$a = 3$	$a > 3$
$3 \stackrel{?}{=} \frac{13}{6}$	$\frac{13}{6} \stackrel{?}{>} 3$
$3 \neq 2.2$	$2.2 \not> 3$

Step 3 The conclusions are false, so the assumption must be false. Therefore, Christina's average points per game was less than 3.

8. Given: $5x - 2$ is an odd integer.

Prove: x is an odd integer.

Indirect Proof: Step 1 Assume that x is not an odd integer. That is, assume that x is an even integer.

Step 2 Let $x = 2k$ for some integer k.

$5x - 2 = 5(2k) - 2$	Subst. of assumption
$= 10k - 2$	Mult. Prop.
$= 2(5k - 1)$	Dist. Prop.

Since k is an integer, $5k - 1$ is also an integer. Let p represent the integer $5k - 1$. So $5x - 2$ can be represented by $2p$, where p is an integer. This means that $5x - 2$ is an even integer, but this contradicts the given that $5x - 2$ is an odd integer.

Step 3 Since the assumption that x is an even integer leads to a contradiction of the given, the original conclusion that x is an odd integer must be true.

9. Given: $\triangle ABC$ is a right triangle; $\angle C$ is a right angle.

Prove: $AB > BC$ and $AB > AC$

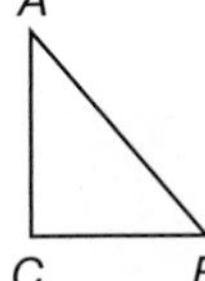

Indirect Proof: Step 1 Assume that the hypotenuse of a right triangle is not the longest side. That is, $AB < BC$ and $AB < AC$.

Step 2 If $AB < BC$, then $m\angle C < m\angle A$. Since $m\angle C = 90$, $m\angle A > 90$. So, $m\angle C + m\angle A > 180$. By the same reasoning, $m\angle C + m\angle B > 180$.

Step 3 Both relationships contradict the fact that the sum of the measures of the angles of a triangle equals 180. Therefore, the hypotenuse must be the longest side of a right triangle.

10. Given: $\angle A$ and $\angle B$ are supplementary.

Prove: $\angle A$ and $\angle B$ cannot both be obtuse angles.

Indirect Proof: Step 1 Assume that $\angle A$ and $\angle B$ are both obtuse angles.

Step 2 By the definition of obtuse angles, $m\angle A > 90$ and $m\angle B > 90$. So, $m\angle A + m\angle B > 180$.

Step 3 This contradicts the given information, $m\angle A + m\angle B = 180$. Therefore, the original conclusion that $\angle A$ and $\angle B$ cannot both be obtuse angles must be true.

17. Given: $2x - 7 > -11$

Prove: $x > -2$

Indirect Proof: Step 1 Assume that $x \leq -2$ is true.

Step 2

x	−6	−5	−4	−3	−2
$2x - 7$	−19	−17	−15	−13	−11

When $x < -2$, $2x - 7 < -11$ and when $x = -2$, $2x - 7 = -11$.

Step 3 In both cases, the assumption leads to the contradiction of the given information that $2x - 7 > -11$. Therefore, the assumption that $x \leq -2$ must be false, so the original conclusion that $x > -2$ must be true.

18. Given: $5x + 12 < -33$

Prove: $x < -9$

Indirect Proof: Step 1 Assume that $x \geq -9$ is true.

Step 2

x	−9	−8	−7	−6	−5
$5x + 12$	−33	−28	−23	−18	−13

When $x > -9$, $5x + 12 > -33$ and when $x = -9$, $5x + 12 = -33$.

Step 3 In both cases, the assumption leads to the contradiction of the given information that $5x + 12 < -33$. Therefore, the assumption that $x \geq -9$ must be false, so the original conclusion that $x < -9$ must be true.

19. Given: $-3x + 4 < 7$

Prove: $x > -1$

Indirect Proof: Step 1 Assume that $x \leq -1$ is true.

Step 2

x	−5	−4	−3	−2	−1
$-3x + 4$	19	16	13	10	7

When $x < -1$, $-3x + 4 > 7$ and when $x = -1$, $-3x + 4 = 7$.

Step 3 In both cases, the assumption leads to the contradiction of the given information that $-3x + 4 < 7$. Therefore, the assumption that $x \leq -1$ must be false, so the original conclusion that $x > -1$ must be true.

20. Given: $-2x - 6 > 12$

Prove: $x < -9$

Indirect Proof: Step 1 Assume that $x \geq -9$ is true.

Step 2

x	−9	−8	−7	−6	−5
$-2x - 6$	12	10	8	6	4

When $x > -9$, $-2x - 6 < 12$ and when $x = -9$, $-2x - 6 = 12$.

Step 3 In both cases, the assumption leads to the contradiction of the given information that $-2x - 6 > 12$. Therefore, the assumption that $x \geq -9$ must be false, so the original conclusion that $x < -9$ must be true.

23. **Given:** xy is an odd integer.

Prove: x and y are odd integers.

Indirect Proof: Step 1 Assume that x and y are not both odd integers. That is, assume that either x or y is an even integer.

Step 2 You only need to show that the assumption that x is an even integer leads to a contradiction, since the argument for y is an even integer follows the same reasoning. So, assume that x is an even integer and y is an odd integer. This means that $x = 2k$ for some integer k and $y = 2m + 1$ for some integer m.

$xy = (2k)(2m + 1)$	Subst. of assumption
$= 4km + 2k$	Dist. Prop.
$= 2(km + k)$	Dist. Prop.

Since k and m are integers, $km + k$ is also an integer. Let p represent the integer $km + k$. So xy can be represented by $2p$, where p is an integer. This means that xy is an even integer, but this contradicts the given that xy is an odd integer.

Step 3 Since the assumption that x is an even integer and y is an odd integer leads to a contradiction of the given, the original conclusion that x and y are both odd integers must be true.

24. **Given:** n^2 is even.

Prove: n^2 is divisible by 4.

Indirect Proof: Step 1 Assume n^2 is not divisible by 4. In other words, 4 is not a factor of n^2.

Step 2 If the square of a number is even, then the number is also even. So, if n^2 is even, n must be even. Let $n = 2a$.

$n = 2a$

$n^2 = (2a)^2$ or $4a^2$

4 is a factor of n^2, which contradicts the assumption.

Step 3 Since the assumption that n^2 is not divisible by 4 leads to a contradiction of the assumption, the original conclusion that n^2 is divisible by 4 must be true.

25. **Given:** x is an odd number.

Prove: x is not divisible by 4.

Indirect Proof: Step 1 Assume x is divisible by 4. In other words, 4 is a factor of x.

Step 2 Let $x = 4n$, for some integer n.

$x = 2(2n)$

So, 2 is a factor of x which means x is an even number, but this contradicts the given information.

Step 3 Since the assumption that x is divisible by 4 leads to a contradiction of the given, the original conclusion x is not divisible by 4 must be true.

26. **Given:** xy is an even integer.

Prove: x or y is an even integer.

Indirect Proof: Step 1 Assume x and y are odd integers.

Step 2 Let $x = 2n + 1$ and $y = 2k + 1$, for some integer n and k.

$xy = (2n + 1)(2k + 1)$	Subst.
$= 4nk + 2n + 2k + 1$	Dist. Prop.
$= 2(2nk + n + k) + 1$	Dist. Prop.

Since k and n are integers, $2nk + n + k$ is also an integer. Let p represent the integer $2nk + n + k$. So xy can be represented by $2p + 1$, where p is an integer. This means that xy is an odd integer, but this contradicts the given that xy is an even integer.

Step 3 Since the assumption that x and y are odd integers leads to a contradiction of the given, the original conclusion x or y is an even integer must be true.

27. **Given:** $XZ > YZ$

Prove: $\angle X \not\cong \angle Y$

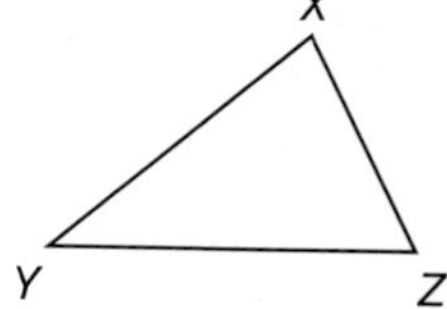

Indirect Proof: Step 1 Assume that $\angle X \cong \angle Y$.

Step 2 $\overline{XZ} \cong \overline{YZ}$ by the converse of the isosceles △ theorem.

Step 3 This contradicts the given information that $XZ > YZ$. Therefore, the assumption $\angle X \cong \angle Y$ must be false, so the original conclusion $\angle X \not\cong \angle Y$ must be true.

28. **Given:** $\triangle ABC$ is equilateral.

Prove: $\triangle ABC$ is equiangular.

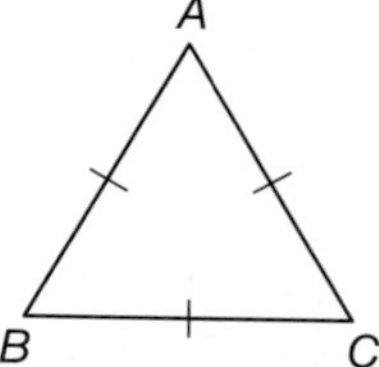

Indirect Proof: Step 1 Assume that $\triangle ABC$ is not equiangular.

Step 2 Then $m\angle B > m\angle C$. Then $AC > AB$ by Angle–Side Relationships in Triangles Theorem.

Step 3 This contradicts the given information that $\triangle ABC$ is equilateral. Therefore, the assumption that $\triangle ABC$ is not equiangular must be false, so the original conclusion $\triangle ABC$ is equiangular must be true.

29. **Given:** $\triangle ABC$ is isosceles.

Prove: Neither of the base angles is a right angle.

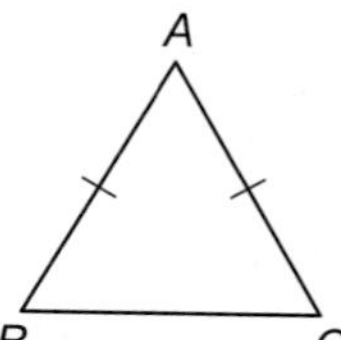

Indirect Proof: Step 1 Assume that $\angle B$ is a right angle.

Step 2 By the Isosceles △ Theorem, $\angle C$ is also a right angle.

Step 3 This contradicts the fact that a triangle can have no more than one right angle. Therefore, the assumption that $\angle B$ is a right angle must be false, so the original conclusion neither of the base angles is a right angle must be true.

30. Given: $\triangle ABC$

Prove: $\triangle ABC$ has no more than one right angle.

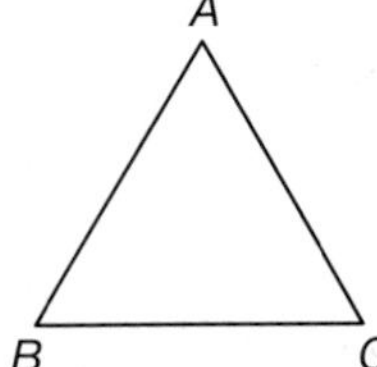

Indirect Proof: Step 1 Assume that $\triangle ABC$ has more than one right angle.

Step 2 If $\angle B$ and $\angle C$ are right angles, then $m\angle B + m\angle C =$ 180. The $m\angle A + m\angle B + m\angle C = 180$ because the angles of a triangle add to 180. By substitution, $m\angle A + 180 = 180$, so $m\angle A = 0$.

Step 3 This contradicts the given information, $\triangle ABC$. Therefore, the assumption that $\triangle ABC$ has more than one right angle must be false, so the original conclusion, $\triangle ABC$ has no more than one right angle, must be true.

31. Given: $m\angle A > m\angle ABC$

Prove: $BC > AC$

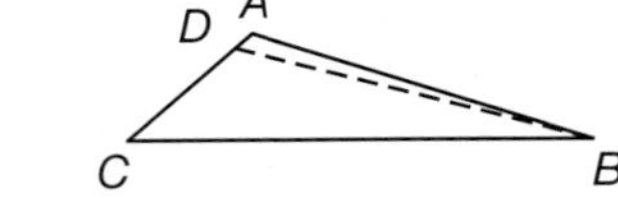

Proof:

Assume $BC \not> AC$. By the Comparison Property, $BC = AC$ or $BC < AC$.

Case 1: If $BC = AC$, then $\angle ABC \cong \angle A$ by the Isosceles Triangle Theorem. (If two sides of a triangle are congruent, then the angles opposite those sides are congruent.) But, $\angle ABC \cong \angle A$ contradicts the given statement that $m\angle A > m\angle ABC$. So, $BC \neq AC$.

Case 2: If $BC < AC$, then there must be a point D between A and C so that $\overline{DC} \cong \overline{BC}$. Draw the auxiliary segment $\overline{BD}$. Since $DC = BC$, by the Isosceles Triangle Theorem $\angle BDC \cong \angle DBC$. Now $\angle BDC$ is an exterior angle of $\triangle BAD$ and by the Exterior Angles Inequality Theorem (the measure of an exterior angle of a triangle is greater than the measure of either corresponding remote interior angle) $m\angle BDC > m\angle A$. By the Angle Addition Postulate, $m\angle ABC = m\angle ABD + m\angle DBC$. Then by the definition of inequality, $m\angle ABC > m\angle DBC$. By Substitution and the Transitive Property of Inequality, $m\angle ABC > m\angle A$. But this contradicts the given statement that $m\angle A > m\angle ABC$. In both cases, a contradiction was found, and hence our assumption must have been false. Therefore, $BC > AC$.

32. Given: $\frac{1}{b} < 0$

Prove: b is negative.

Indirect Proof: Step 1 Assume that $b > 0$. $b \neq 0$ since that would make $\frac{1}{b}$ undefined.

Step 2 $b > 0$

$\frac{1}{b} > 0$; A positive number divided by a positive number is positive.

Step 3 $\frac{1}{b} > 0$ contradicts the given, so the assumption must be false. Thus, b must be negative.

35a. Indirect Proof: Step 1 50% is half, and the statement says more than half of the teens polled said that they recycle, so assume that less than 50% recycle.

Step 2 The data shows that 51% of teens said that they recycle, and 51% > 50%, so the number of teens that recycle is not less than half.

Step 3 This contradicts the data given. Therefore, the assumption is false, and the conclusion more than half of the teens polled said they recycle must be true.

35b. $400 \cdot 23\% \stackrel{?}{=} 92$

$400 \cdot 0.23 \stackrel{?}{=} 92$

$92 = 92$

37. indirect proof

Given: $\overline{AB} \perp p$

Prove: $\overline{AB}$ is the shortest segment from A to p.

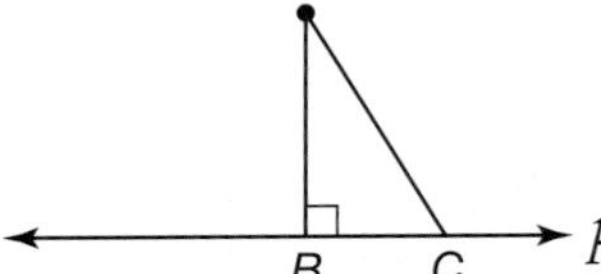

Indirect Proof: Step 1 Assume $\overline{AB}$ is not the shortest segment from A to p.

Step 2 Since $\overline{AB}$ is not the shortest segment from A to p, there is a point C such that $\overline{AC}$ is the shortest distance. $\triangle ABC$ is a right triangle with hypotenuse $\overline{AC}$, the longest side of $\triangle ABC$ since it is across from the largest angle in $\triangle ABC$ by the Angle–Side Relationships in Triangles Theorem.

Step 3 This contradicts the fact that $\overline{AC}$ is the shortest side. Therefore, the assumption is false, and the conclusion, $\overline{AB}$ is the shortest side, must be true.

38. direct proof

Given: $\overline{PQ} \perp$ plane M

Prove: $\overline{PQ}$ is the shortest segment from P to plane $\mathcal{M}$.

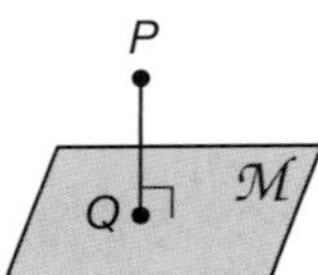

Proof:

By definition, $\overline{PQ}$ is perpendicular to plane $\mathcal{M}$ if it is perpendicular to every line in $\mathcal{M}$ that intersects it. But since the perpendicular segment from a point to a line is the shortest segment from the point to the line, that perpendicular segment is the shortest segment from the point to each of these lines. Therefore, $\overline{PQ}$ is the shortest segment from P to $\mathcal{M}$.

39b. Sample answer:

n	$n^3 + 3$
2	11
3	30
10	1003
11	1334
24	13,827
25	15,628
100	1,000,003
101	1,030,304
526	145,531,579
527	146,363,186

39d. Indirect Proof: Step 1 Assume that n is even. Let $n = 2k$, where k some integer.

Step 2

$n^3 + 3 = (2k)^3 + 3$ Substitute assumption

$= 8k^3 + 3$ Simplify.

$= (8k^3 + 2) + 1$ Replace 3 with 2 + 1 and group the first two terms.

$= 2(4k^3 + 1) + 1$ Distributive Property

Since k is an integer, $4k^3 + 1$ is also an integer. Therefore, $n^3 + 3$ is odd.

Step 3 This contradicts the given information that $n^3 + 3$ is even. Therefore, the assumption is false, so the conclusion that n is odd must be true.

40. Sample answer: First identify the statement you need to prove and assume temporarily that this statement is false by assuming that the opposite of the statement is true. Next, reason logically until you reach a contradiction. Finally, point out that the statement you wanted to prove must be true because the contradiction proves that the temporary assumption you made was false.

41. Sample answer: $\triangle ABC$ is scalene.

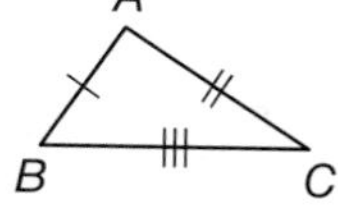

Given: $\triangle ABC$; $AB \neq BC$; $BC \neq AC$; $AB \neq AC$

Prove: $\triangle ABC$ is scalene.

Indirect Proof: Step 1 Assume that $\triangle ABC$ is not scalene.

Case 1: $\triangle ABC$ is isosceles.

Step 2 If $\triangle ABC$ is isosceles, then $AB = BC$, $BC = AC$, or $AB = AC$.

Step 3 This contradicts the given information, so $\triangle ABC$ is not isosceles.

Case 2: $\triangle ABC$ is equilateral.

In order for a triangle to be equilateral, it must also be isosceles, and Case 1 proved that $\triangle ABC$ is not isosceles. Thus, $\triangle ABC$ is not equilateral. Therefore, $\triangle ABC$ is scalene.

42. Given: x is a nonzero rational number and y is an irrational number.

Prove: xy is irrational.

Indirect Proof: Step 1 Since we are given that x is a nonzero rational, $x = \frac{a}{b}$ for some integers a and b, $b \neq 0$. Substituting, $xy = \frac{a}{b} \cdot y$ or $\frac{ay}{b}$.

Assume that xy is a rational number. Then $xy = \frac{c}{d}$ for some integers c and d, $d \neq 0$.

Step 2 $xy = \frac{ay}{b}$ x is a rational number.

$\frac{c}{d} = \frac{ay}{b}$ Substitution of assumption

$cb = ayd$ Multiply each side by db. This is possible because $b \neq 0$ and $d \neq 0$.

$\frac{cb}{ad} = y$ Solve for y by dividing each side by ad. $a \neq 0$ since $x = \frac{a}{b}$ and x is nonzero.

Since a, b, c, and d are integers and $a, d \neq 0$, $\frac{cb}{ad}$ is the quotient of two integers. Therefore, y is a rational number. This contradicts the given statement that y is an irrational number.

Step 3 Since the assumption that xy is a rational number leads to a contradiction of the given, the original conclusion that xy is irrational must be true.

44. If x is not an odd integer, then $5x - 2$ is not an odd integer. Sample answer: If x is not an odd integer, then it is an even integer. If x is an even integer, then $5x$ is also even because the product of any number and an even number is even. $5x - 2$ is also even, because two subtracted from an even number is even. Therefore, the statement *If x is not an odd integer, then $5x - 2$ is not an odd integer* is true; The direct proof of the contrapositive of the statement and the indirect proof of the statement make the same assumptions and reach the same conclusions.

Lesson 5-5

18. Proof:

Statements (Reasons)

1. $\angle BCD \cong \angle CDB$ (Given)
2. $\overline{BC} \cong \overline{BD}$ (Conv. Isos. $\triangle$ Thm.)
3. $BC = BD$ (Def. of $\cong$ segments)
4. $AB + AD > BD$ ($\triangle$ Inequal. Thm.)
5. $AB + AD > BC$ (Subst.)

19. Proof:

<u>**Statements (Reasons)**</u>

1. $\overline{JL} \cong \overline{LM}$ (Given)
2. $JL = LM$ (Def. of $\cong$ segments)
3. $KJ + KL > JL$ ($\triangle$ Inequal. Thm.)
4. $KJ + KL > LM$ (Subst.)

22a. County Line Road; sample answer: In a triangle, the sum of two of the sides is always greater than the third side, so the sum of the distance on Highway 4 and the distance on Route 6 is greater than the distance on County Line Road.

22b. Highway 4 to Route 6; sample answer: Since Takoda can drive 30 miles per hour on County Line Road and the distance is 30 miles, it will take him 1 hour. He has to drive 47 miles on Highway 4 and Route 6, and the speed limit is 55 miles per hour, so it will take him 0.85 hour or about 51 minutes. The route on Highway 4 and Route 6 will take less time than the route on County Line Road.

23. Proof:

<u>**Statements (Reasons)**</u>

1. Construct $\overline{CD}$ so that C is between B and D and $\overline{CD} \cong \overline{AC}$. (Ruler Post.)
2. $CD = AC$ (Def. of $\cong$ segments)
3. $\angle CAD \cong \angle ADC$ (Isos. $\triangle$ Thm)
4. $m\angle CAD = m\angle ADC$ (Def. of $\cong$ $\angle$s)
5. $m\angle BAC + m\angle CAD = m\angle BAD$ ($\angle$ Add. Post.)
6. $m\angle BAC + m\angle ADC = m\angle BAD$ (Subst.)
7. $m\angle ADC < m\angle BAD$ (Def. of inequality)
8. $AB < BD$ (Theorem 5.10)
9. $BD = BC + CD$ (Seg. Add. Post.)
10. $AB < BC + CD$ (Subst.)
11. $AB < BC + AC$ (Subst. (Steps 2, 10))

31. Yes; sample answer: The measurements on the drawing do not form a triangle. According to the Triangle Inequality Theorem, the sum of the lengths of any two sides of a triangle is greater than the length of the third side. The lengths in the drawing are 1 ft, $3\frac{7}{8}$ ft, and $6\frac{3}{4}$ ft. Since $1 + 3\frac{7}{8} \not> 6\frac{3}{4}$, the triangle is impossible. They should recalculate their measurements before they cut the wood.

42a.

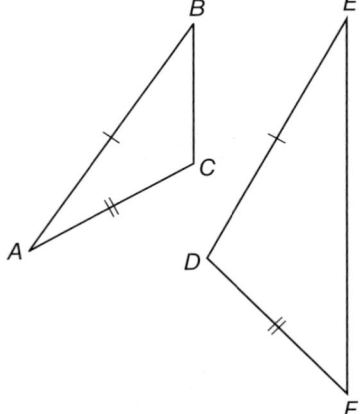

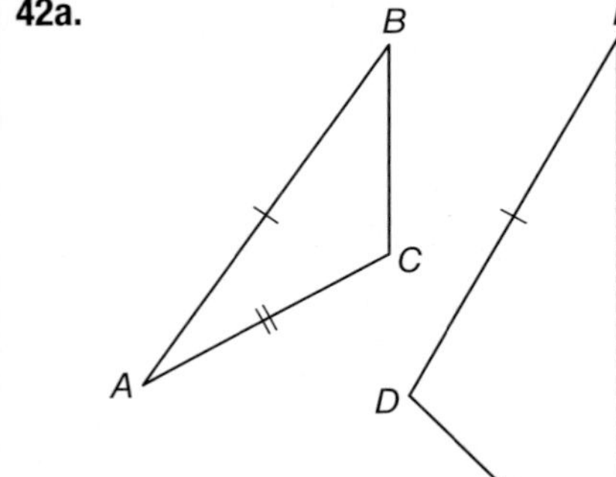

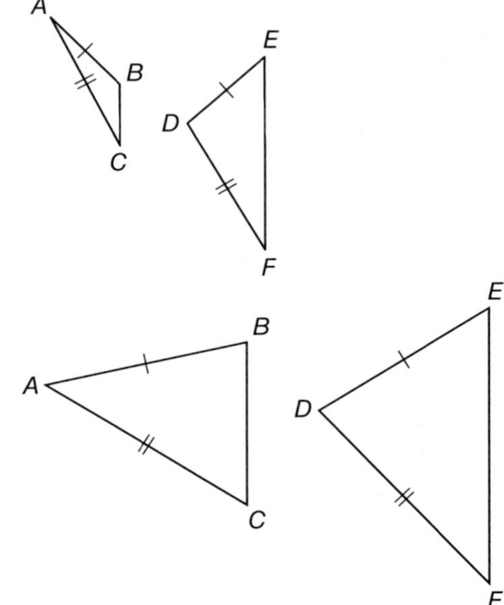

47.

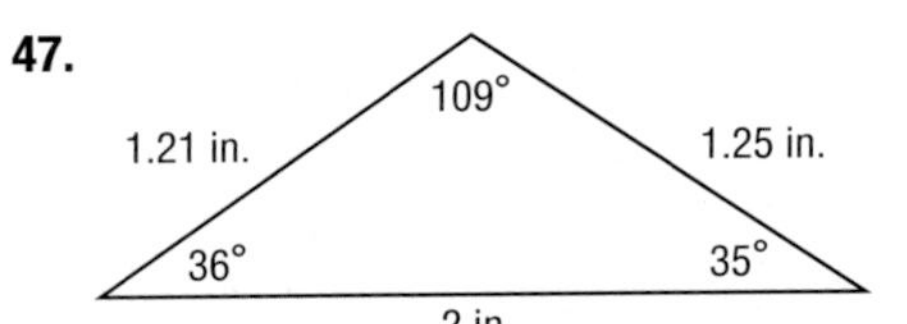

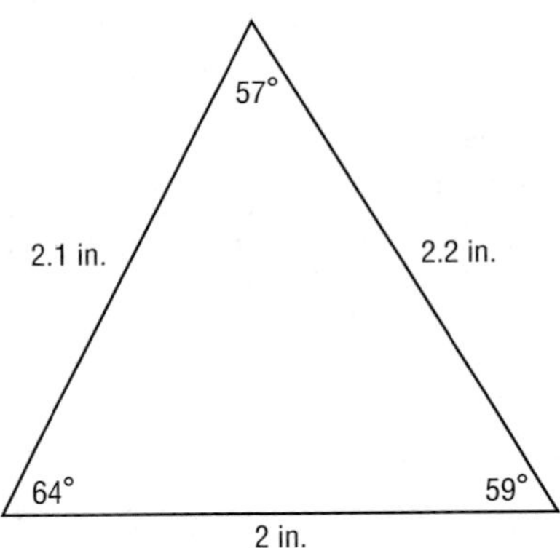

48a. Sample answer: By the Triangle Inequality Theorem, the distance from my house to the shopping center is greater than $\frac{3}{4}$ mile and less than $2\frac{1}{4}$ miles.

48b. Sample answer: The park can be between my house and the shopping center, which means that the distance from my house to the shopping center is $2\frac{1}{4}$ miles, or my house can be between the park and the shopping center, which means that the distance from my house to the shopping center is 34 mile.

Lesson 5-6

16a. Joel; sample answer: Pedro turned 15° south, so the measure of the angle across from the side of the triangle that represents his distance from the camp is 180 − 15 or 165. Joel turned 35° north, so the measure of the angle across from the side of the triangle that represents his distance from the camp is 180 − 35 or 145. By the Hinge Theorem, since 145 < 165, Joel is closer to the camp.

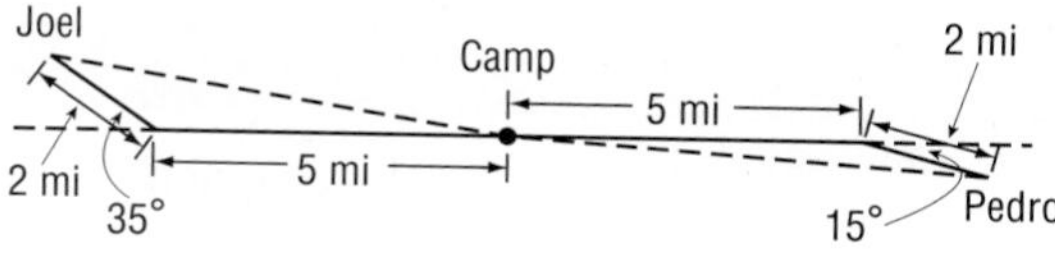

16b. Joel; sample answer: Pedro turned 15° south, so the measure of the angle across from the side of the triangle that represents his distance from the camp is 180 − 15 or 165°. Joel turned 10° south, so the measure of the angle across from the side of the triangle that represents his distance from the camp is 180 − 10 or 170. By the Hinge Theorem, since 170 > 165, Joel is farther from the camp.

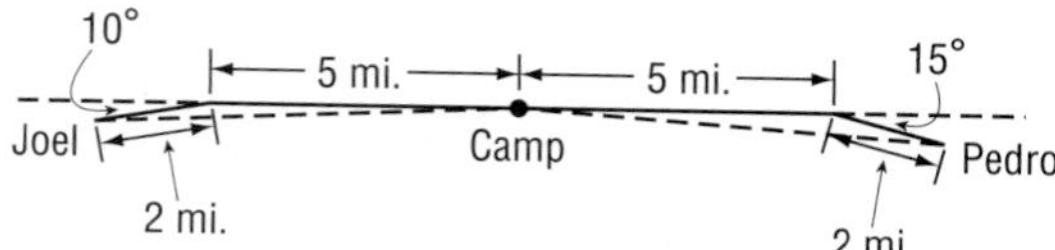

23. Proof:

Statements (Reasons)

1. $\overline{LK} \cong \overline{JK}$, $\overline{RL} \cong \overline{RJ}$, K is the midpoint of $\overline{QS}$, $m\angle SKL > m\angle QKJ$ (Given)
2. $SK = QK$ (Def. of midpoint)
3. $SL > QJ$ (Hinge Thm.)
4. $RL = RJ$ (Def. of ≅ segs.)
5. $SL + RL > RL + RJ$ (Add. Prop.)
6. $SL + RL > QJ + RJ$ (Subst.)
7. $RS = SL + RL$, $QR = QJ + RJ$ (Seg. Add. Post.)
8. $RS > QR$ (Subst.)

24. Proof:

Statements (Reasons)

1. $\overline{VR} \cong \overline{RT}$; R is the midpoint of $\overline{SQ}$. (Given)
2. $SR = QR$ (Def. of midpoint)
3. $\overline{SR} \cong \overline{QR}$ (Def. of ≅ segs)
4. $m\angle SRV > m\angle QRT$ (Given)
5. $VS > TQ$ (SAS Inequality)
6. $\overline{WV} \cong \overline{WT}$ (Given)
7. $WV = WT$ (Def. of ≅ segs)
8. $WV + VS > WV + TQ$ (Add. Prop.)
9. $WV + VS > WT + TQ$ (Subst.)
10. $WV + VS = WS$, $WT + TQ = WQ$ (Seg. Add. Post.)
11. $WS > WQ$ (Subst.)

25. Proof:

Statements (Reasons)

1. $\overline{XU} \cong \overline{VW}$, $\overline{XU} \parallel \overline{VW}$ (Given)
2. $\angle UXV \cong \angle XVW$, $\angle XUW \cong \angle UWV$ (Alt. Int. ∠s Thm.)
3. $\triangle XZU \cong \triangle VZW$ (ASA)
4. $\overline{XZ} \cong \overline{VZ}$ (CPCTC)
5. $\overline{WZ} \cong \overline{WZ}$ (Refl. Prop.)
6. $VW > XW$ (Given)
7. $m\angle VZW > m\angle XZW$ (Converse of Hinge Thm.)
8. $\angle VZW \cong \angle XZU$, $\angle XZW \cong \angle VZU$ (Vert. ∠s are ≅)
9. $m\angle VZW = m\angle XZU$, $m\angle XZW = m\angle VZU$ (Def. of ≅ ∠s)
10. $m\angle XZU > m\angle UZV$ (Subst.)

26. Proof:

Statements (Reasons)

1. $\overline{AF} \cong \overline{DJ}$, $\overline{FC} \cong \overline{JB}$, $AB > DC$ (Given)
2. $\overline{BC} \cong \overline{BC}$ (Refl. Prop.)
3. $BC = BC$ (Def. of ≅ segs.)
4. $AB + BC = AC$, $DC + CB = DB$ (Seg. Add. Post.)
5. $AB + BC > DC + CB$ (Add. Prop.)
6. $AC > DB$ (Subst.)
7. $m\angle AFC > m\angle DJB$ (Converse of Hinge Thm.)

27a. Position 2; sample answer: If you measure the distance from her shoulder to her fist for each position, it is 1.6 cm for Position 1 and 2 cm for Position 2. Therefore, the distance from her shoulder to her fist is greater in position 2.

27b. Position 2; sample answer: Using the measurements in part a and the Converse of the Hinge Theorem, you know that the measure of the angle opposite the larger side is larger, so the angle formed by Anica's elbow is greater in Position 2.

37a.

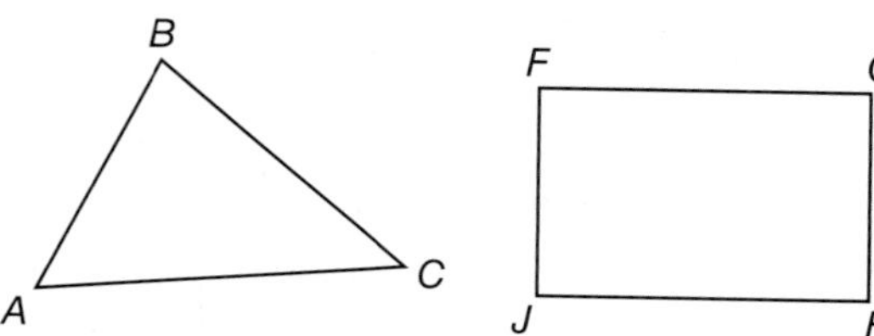

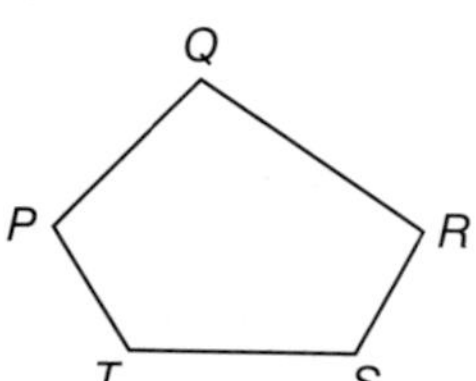

Chapter Planner

	Diagnostic Assessment Quick Check		
	LESSON 6-1 45 min: 1 day 90 min: 0.5 day	**EXTEND 6-1** 45 min: 0.5 day 90 min: 0.5 day	**LESSON 6-2** 45 min: 1 day 90 min: 0.5 day
Title	**Angles of Polygons**	**Spreadsheet Lab: Angles of Polygons**	**Parallelograms**
Objectives	■ Find and use the sum of the measures of the interior angles of a polygon. ■ Find and use the sum of the measures of the exterior angles of a polygon.	■ Explore the sum of the measures of the interior and exterior angles of a polygon using a spreadsheet.	■ Recognize and apply the properties of the sides and angles of parallelograms. ■ Recognize and apply the properties of the diagonals of parallelograms.
Key Vocabulary	diagonal		parallelogram
CCSS	G.MG.1		G.CO.11, G.GPE.4
Multiple Representations			
Lesson Resources	connectED.mcgraw-hill.com Leveled Worksheets Vocabulary Personal Tutor Virtual Manipulatives Self-Check Quiz ■ *5-Minute Check* ■ *Study Notebook* ■ *Teaching Geometry with Manipulatives*	connectED.mcgraw-hill.com Personal Tutor **Materials:** ■ computer ■ spreadsheet program	connectED.mcgraw-hill.com Leveled Worksheets Quiz 1 Vocabulary Personal Tutor Virtual Manipulatives Self-Check Quiz ■ *5-Minute Check* ■ *Study Notebook*
Resources for Every Lesson	IWB eStudent Edition IWB Interactive Classroom	■ eTeacher Edition ■ eSolutions Manual ■ eAssessment	
Differentiated Instruction	pp. 394, 396		pp. 405, 408

IWB All digital assets are Interactive Whiteboard ready.

Suggested Pacing			
Time Periods	Instruction	Review & Assess	Total
45-minute	7 days	2 days	9 days
90-minute	4 days	1 day	5 days

EXPLORE 6-3 (45 min: 0.5 day; 90 min: 0.5 day)	LESSON 6-3 (45 min: 1 day; 90 min: 0.5 day)	LESSON 6-4 (45 min: 1 day; 90 min: 0.5 day)	LESSON 6-5 (45 min: 1 day; 90 min: 0.5 day)	LESSON 6-6 (45 min: 1 day; 90 min: 0.5 day)
Graphing Technology Lab: Parallelograms	**Tests for Parallelograms**	**Rectangles**	**Rhombi and Squares**	**Trapezoids and Kites**
▪ Use the Cabri Junior application on a TI-83/84 Plus graphing calculator to discover properties of parallelograms.	▪ Recognize the conditions that ensure a quadrilateral is a parallelogram. ▪ Prove that a set of points form a parallelogram in the coordinate plane.	▪ Recognize and apply properties of rectangles ▪ Determine whether parallelograms are rectangles.	▪ Recognize and apply properties of rhombi and squares. ▪ Determine whether quadrilaterals are rectangles, rhombi, or squares.	▪ Recognize and apply the properties of trapezoids, including the medians of trapezoids. ▪ Recognize and apply the properties of kites.
		rectangle	rhombus square	trapezoid, bases, legs of a trapezoid, base angles, isosceles trapezoid, midsegment of a trapezoid, kite
G.CO.12	G.CO.11, G.GPE.4	G.CO.11, G.GPE.4	G.CO.11, G.GPE.4	G.GPE.4, G.MG.3
connectED.mcgraw-hill.com Personal Tutor **Materials:** ▪ TI-83/84 Plus or other graphing calculator	connectED.mcgraw-hill.com Leveled Worksheets Quiz 2 Vocabulary Personal Tutor Virtual Manipulatives Self-Check Quiz ▪ *5-Minute Check* ▪ *Study Notebook* ▪ *Teaching Geometry with Manipulatives*	connectED.mcgraw-hill.com Leveled Worksheets Vocabulary Animations Personal Tutor Virtual Manipulatives Self-Check Quiz ▪ *5-Minute Check* ▪ *Study Notebook* ▪ *Teaching Geometry with Manipulatives*	connectED.mcgraw-hill.com Leveled Worksheets Quiz 3 Vocabulary Animations Personal Tutor Virtual Manipulatives Self-Check Quiz ▪ *5-Minute Check* ▪ *Study Notebook* ▪ *Teaching Geometry with Manipulatives*	connectED.mcgraw-hill.com Leveled Worksheets Quiz 4 Animations Personal Tutor Virtual Manipulatives Self-Check Quiz ▪ *5-Minute Check* ▪ *Study Notebook*
IWB eStudent Edition IWB Interactive Classroom	▪ eTeacher Edition ▪ eSolutions Manual ▪ eAssessment			
	pp. 415, 420, 421	pp. 424, 429	pp. 433, 434, 437	pp. 441, 443, 446

Formative Assessment
Mid-Chapter Quiz

Summative Assessment
Study Guide and Review
Practice Test

CHAPTER 6 Quadrilaterals

Chapter Planner

What the Research Says...

Wenglinsky (2000) found that students whose teachers conduct hands-on learning activities outperform their peers by more than 70% of a grade level in math on the National Assessment of Educational Progress, a study of over 7000 students.

- Give students ample opportunity to do the Geometry Labs located in each lesson. Repeat labs at the end of the lesson if there is any confusion about the concept.
- In Lessons 6-4, 6-5, and 6-6, allow students to find these quadrilaterals in the classroom or use pattern blocks. They can trace the shapes onto paper, or use one view of the figure and mark the diagonal with tape or string.

Teacher to Teacher

Debbie Witherspoon
Mathematics Teacher
Mansfield High School
Mansfield, Texas

Use With ALL Lessons

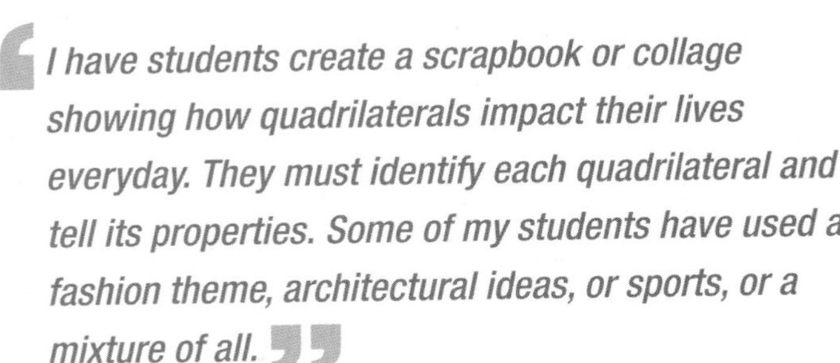

“I have students create a scrapbook or collage showing how quadrilaterals impact their lives everyday. They must identify each quadrilateral and tell its properties. Some of my students have used a fashion theme, architectural ideas, or sports, or a mixture of all.”

Reading and Writing in Mathematics

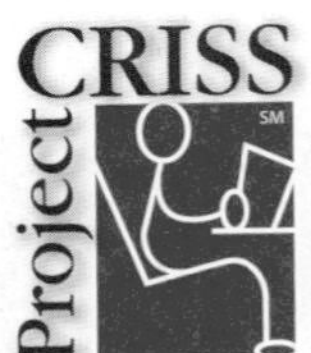
Project CRISS SM

STUDY SKILL

Creating Venn diagrams can be done as a cooperative activity after students have studied a topic. Give groups of students large sheets of paper and colored markers. Have them select similar items, such as geometric figures, to compare. The Venn diagram at the right compares the Angle Sum Theorem for interior and exterior angles of polygons (Lesson 6-1).

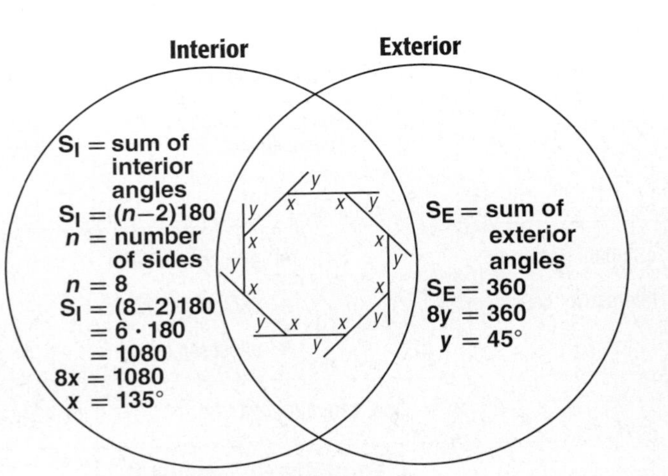
Interior
Exterior
S_I = sum of interior angles
$S_I = (n-2)180$
n = number of sides
$n = 8$
$S_I = (8-2)180$
$= 6 \cdot 180$
$= 1080$
$8x = 1080$
$x = 135°$
S_E = sum of exterior angles
$S_E = 360$
$8y = 360$
$y = 45°$
x
y

Creating Independence through Student-owned Strategies

Notes

Assessment and Intervention

SE = Student Edition, **TE** = Teacher Edition, **CRM** = Chapter Resource Masters

	Diagnosis	Prescription
DIAGNOSTIC ASSESSMENT	**Beginning Chapter 6**	
	Get Ready for Chapter 6 **SE**	Response to Intervention **TE**
	Beginning Every Lesson	
	Then, Now, Why? **SE** 5-Minute Checks	Chapter 0 **SE**
FORMATIVE ASSESSMENT	**During/After Every Lesson**	
	Guided Practice **SE**, every example Check Your Understanding **SE** H.O.T. Problems **SE** Spiral Review **SE** Additional Examples **TE** Watch Out! **TE** Step 4, Assess **TE** Chapter 6 Quizzes **CRM**, pp. 45–46 Self-Check Quizzes connectED.mcgraw-hill.com	**TIER 1 Intervention** Skills Practice **CRM**, Ch. 1–6 connectED.mcgraw-hill.com **TIER 2 Intervention** Differentiated Instruction **TE**; Differentiated Homework Options **TE**; Study Guide and Intervention **CRM**, Ch. 1–6 **TIER 3 Intervention** *Math Triumphs, Geo.*
	Mid-Chapter	
	Mid-Chapter Quiz **SE** Mid-Chapter Test **CRM**, p. 47 eAssessment	**TIER 1 Intervention** Skills Practice **CRM**, Ch. 1–6 connectED.mcgraw-hill.com **TIER 2 Intervention** Study Guide and Intervention **CRM**, Ch. 1–6 **TIER 3 Intervention** *Math Triumphs, Geo.*
	Before Chapter Test	
	Chapter Study Guide and Review **SE** Practice Test **SE** Standardized Test Practice **SE** Chapter Test connectED.mcgraw-hill.com Standardized Test Practice connectED.mcgraw-hill.com Vocabulary Review connectED.mcgraw-hill.com eAssessment	**TIER 1 Intervention** Skills Practice **CRM**, Ch. 1–6 connectED.mcgraw-hill.com **TIER 2 Intervention** Study Guide and Intervention **CRM**, Ch. 1–6 **TIER 3 Intervention** *Math Triumphs, Geo.*
SUMMATIVE ASSESSMENT	**After Chapter 6**	
	Multiple-Choice Tests, Forms 1, 2A, 2B **CRM**, pp. 49–54 Free-Response Tests, Forms 2C, 2D, 3 **CRM**, pp. 55–60 Vocabulary Test **CRM**, p. 48 Extended Response Test **CRM**, p. 61 Standardized Test Practice **CRM**, pp. 62–64 eAssessment	Study Guide and Intervention **CRM**, Ch. 1–6 connectED.mcgraw-hill.com

Differentiated Instruction

Option 1 Reaching All Learners

Visual/Spatial Display pictures of one-patch quilts. (A one-patch quilt is one that uses the same basic shape repeated throughout the quilt. It can be cut apart to form additional shapes, but all start from that same basic patch. For example, if the basic patch is a hexagon, it can be cut into isosceles trapezoids, rhombi, isosceles triangles, equilateral triangles, and kites.) Working individually, students will create and color a one-patch quilt design based on a regular hexagon. Once the designs are finished, ask students to measure the angles and test a conjecture about the sum of the measures of the interior angles of a polygon. Have them use the formula $(n - 2)180$ where n is the number of sides. Then, have the students write a short report explaining their calculations, congruency and other properties of regular polygons as well as symmetry that is present within their designs. Display the quilt designs in the classroom.

Option 2 Approaching Level AL

Give students the following problem:

In a regular octagon, what is the measure of each interior and exterior angle? Explain your thinking in words, numbers, equations or drawings.

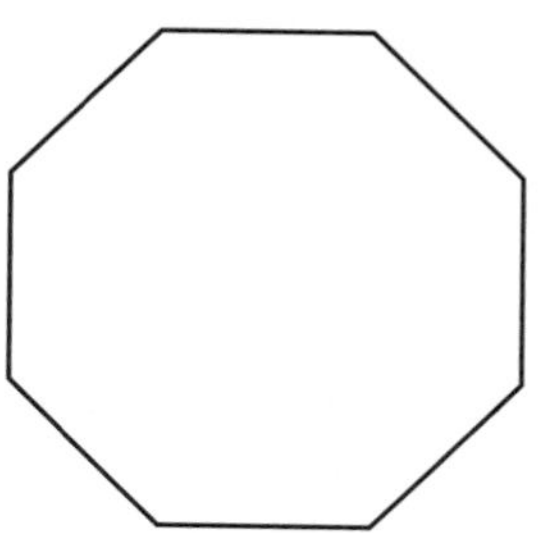

Option 3 English Learners ELL

Naming polygons can be difficult for English learners. Help them remember the different characteristics of named polygons with a card ring. Have them write the name of a polygon on one side of a card and the definition and a picture of the same polygon on the other side of the card. Then, have them use a hole-punch to make a hole in the top left corner of each card, securing the card with a book ring.

Option 4 Beyond Level BL

Using the Internet, have students search for Escher and his work. Have students read about his influences and the ways he integrates geometry, specifically angles of polygons, flips and rotations into his work. Then, ask students to pick one of his works to analyze. Students should hand in a print-out of an Escher picture with notes on why they found the picture striking. They should note the geometric characteristics of the work, including its shapes, symmetries, reflections, rotations, and perspective.

Focus on Mathematical Content

Vertical Alignment

Before Chapter 6

Related Topics from Grade 8

- Use geometric concepts and properties to solve problems in fields such as art and architecture.
- Identify and apply mathematics to everyday experience, to activities in and outside of school, with other disciplines, and with other mathematical topics.
- Communicate mathematical ideas using language, efficient tools, appropriate units, and graphical, numerical, physical, or algebraic mathematical models.

Chapter 6

Related Topics from Geometry

- Use numeric and geometric patterns to make generalizations about geometric properties, including properties of polygons.
- Formulate and test conjectures about the properties and attributes of polygons.
- Derive and use formulas involving length, slope, and midpoint.
- Formulate and test conjectures about the properties and attributes of polygons.

After Chapter 6

Preparation for Precalculus

- Use properties of conic sections to describe physical phenomena such as the reflective properties of light and sound.
- Use the concept of vectors to model situations defined by magnitude and direction.

Lesson-by-Lesson Preview

6-1 Angles of Polygons

The Interior Angle Sum Theorem states that if a convex polygon has n sides and S is the sum of the measures of its interior angles, then $S = 180(n - 2)$. This equation can also be used to find the measure of each interior angle in a regular polygon. Moreover, it can be used to find the number of sides in a polygon if the sum of the interior angle measures is known.

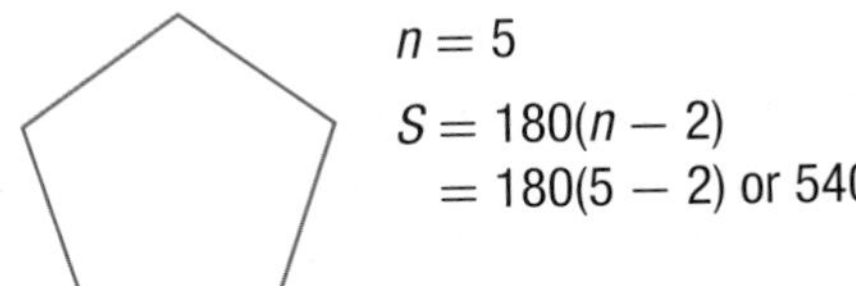

$n = 5$

$S = 180(n - 2)$
$= 180(5 - 2)$ or 540

The sum of the exterior angles of a convex polygon is always 360, no matter the number of sides. This is called the Exterior Angle Sum Theorem.

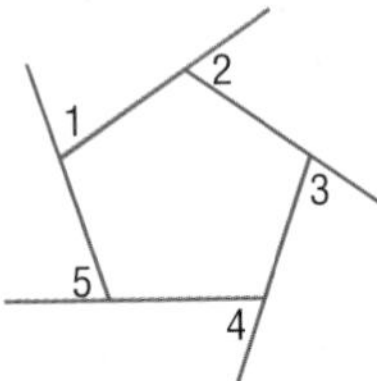

$$m\angle 1 + m\angle 2 + m\angle 3 + m\angle 4 + m\angle 5 = 360$$

6-2 Parallelograms

A *parallelogram* is a quadrilateral with both pairs of opposite sides parallel. Parallelograms have several special properties that help to define them. First, opposite sides of a parallelogram are congruent, and opposite angles of a parallelogram are congruent. Second, consecutive angles in a parallelogram are supplementary. Third, if a parallelogram has one right angle, it has four right angles. Finally, the diagonals of a parallelogram bisect each other, and each diagonal separates the parallelogram into two congruent triangles.

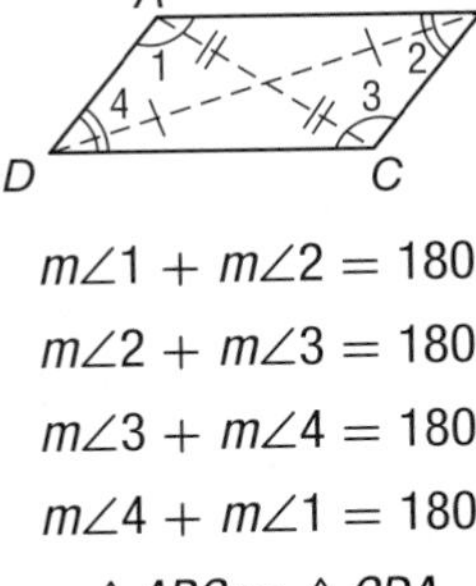

$$m\angle 1 + m\angle 2 = 180$$
$$m\angle 2 + m\angle 3 = 180$$
$$m\angle 3 + m\angle 4 = 180$$
$$m\angle 4 + m\angle 1 = 180$$
$$\triangle ABC \cong \triangle CDA$$

6-3 Tests for Parallelograms

In addition to the definition of a parallelogram as having opposite sides parallel, there are other tests to determine whether a quadrilateral is a parallelogram. For example, if both pairs of opposite sides of a quadrilateral are congruent, then the quadrilateral is a parallelogram. If both pairs of opposite angles of a quadrilateral are congruent, then it is a parallelogram. If the diagonals of a quadrilateral bisect each other, the quadrilateral is a parallelogram. If one pair of opposite sides of a quadrilateral is both parallel and congruent, then it is a parallelogram.

If a quadrilateral is graphed on the coordinate plane, you can use the Distance Formula and the Slope Formula to determine if it is a parallelogram. The Slope Formula is used to determine whether opposite sides are parallel. The Distance Formula is used to test opposite sides for congruence.

6-4 Rectangles

A *rectangle* is a quadrilateral with four right angles. Since both pairs of opposite sides are congruent, a rectangle has all the properties of a parallelogram. A rectangle has special properties of its own as well. For example, the diagonals of a rectangle are congruent. Congruent diagonals, in fact, can be used to prove that a parallelogram is a rectangle.

If a quadrilateral is graphed on a coordinate plane, the Slope Formula can be used to determine whether consecutive sides are perpendicular. If they are, then the quadrilateral is a rectangle. The Distance Formula can also be used to prove that a quadrilateral is a rectangle. You can use the Distance Formula to calculate the measures of the diagonals. If the diagonals are congruent, then the parallelogram is a rectangle.

6-5 Rhombi and Squares

A *rhombus* is a quadrilateral with all four sides congruent. Since opposite sides are congruent, the rhombus is a parallelogram. Therefore, all the properties of parallelograms can be applied to rhombi. Rhombi also have special properties of their own. The diagonals of a rhombus are perpendicular. The converse of this theorem also holds true. If the diagonals of a parallelogram are perpendicular, then the parallelogram is a rhombus.

If a quadrilateral is both a rhombus and a rectangle, then it is a square. A square is extremely specialized, having all the properties of a parallelogram, a rectangle, and a rhombus. It is important to note that while a square is a rhombus, a rhombus is not necessarily a square.

6-6 Trapezoids and Kites

A *trapezoid* is a quadrilateral with exactly one pair of parallel sides. The parallel sides are called *bases*, and the nonparallel sides are called *legs*. A base and a leg form a base angle. If the legs are congruent, then the trapezoid is an isosceles trapezoid. Both pairs of base angles of an isosceles trapezoid are congruent. The diagonals of an isosceles trapezoid are also congruent.

The segment that joins the midpoints of the legs of a trapezoid is the median. The median of a trapezoid is parallel to the bases, and its measure is one-half the sum of the measures of the bases. This is true for all trapezoids, not only isosceles trapezoids.

Mc Graw Hill Professional Development

Targeted professional development has been articulated throughout Geometry. More quality, customized professional development is available from McGraw-Hill Professional Development. Visit connectED.mcgraw-hill.com for details on each product.

- Online Lessons emphasize the strategies and techniques used to teach Geometry. Includes streaming video, interactive pages, and online tools.
- Video Workshops allow mentors, coaches, or leadership personnel to facilitate on-site workshops on educational strategies in mathematics and mathematical concepts.
- MHPD Online (www.mhpdonline.com) offers online professional development with video clips of instructional strategies, links, student activities, and news and issues in education.
- Teaching Today (teachingtoday.glencoe.com) gives secondary teachers practical strategies and materials that inspire excellence and innovation in teaching.

Chapter Project

Fashion Forward

Students use what they have learned about quadrilaterals to complete a project.

This chapter project addresses entrepreneurial literacy, as well as several specific skills identified as being essential to student success by the Framework for 21st Century Learning.

Visit connectED.mcgraw-hill.com for student and teacher handouts.

KeyVocabulary Introduce the key vocabulary in the chapter using the routine below.

Define: A parallelogram is a quadrilateral with both pairs of opposite sides parallel?

Example:

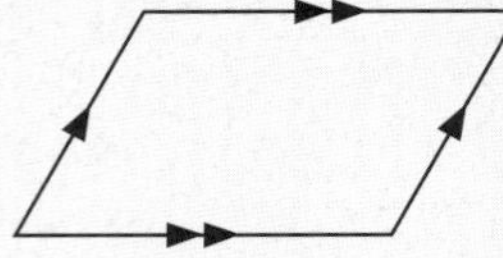

Ask: How do you think the lengths of the opposite sides are related? How do you think the measures of the opposite angles are related?

CHAPTER 6 Quadrilaterals

Then

You classified polygons. You recognized and applied properties of polygons.

Now

In this chapter, you will:

- Find and use the sum of the measures of the interior and exterior angles of a polygon.
- Recognize and apply properties of quadrilaterals.
- Compare quadrilaterals.

Why? ▲

FUN AND GAMES The properties of quadrilaterals can be used to find various angle measures and side lengths such as the measures of angles in game equipment, playing fields, and game boards.

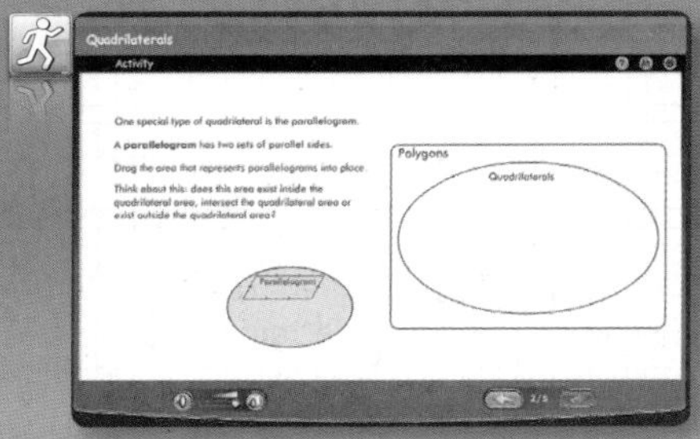

connectED.mcgraw-hill.com Your Digital Math Portal

Animation | Vocabulary | eGlossary | Personal Tutor | Virtual Manipulatives | Graphing Calculator | Audio | Foldables | Self-Check Practice | Worksheets

Additional Answers (p. 391)

7. $x = 1$, $WX = XY = YW = 9$

8. $x = 5$, $FG = GH = 39$

Get Ready for the Chapter

Diagnose Readiness | You have two options for checking Prerequisite Skills.

1 Textbook Option Take the Quick Check below. Refer to the Quick Review for help.

QuickCheck

Find x to the nearest tenth.

1. 150 **2.** 9.7

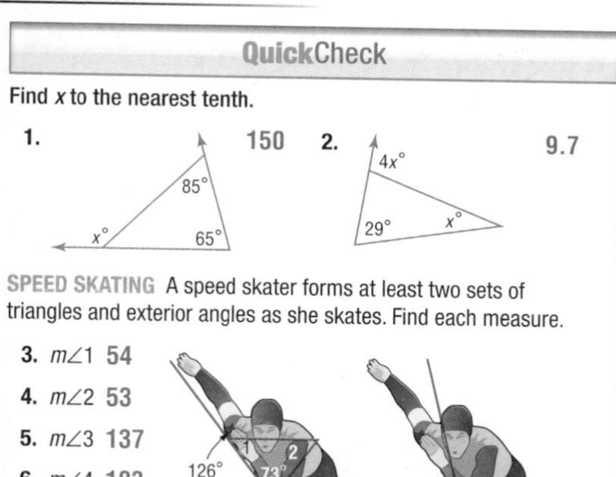

SPEED SKATING A speed skater forms at least two sets of triangles and exterior angles as she skates. Find each measure.

3. $m\angle 1$ 54

4. $m\angle 2$ 53

5. $m\angle 3$ 137

6. $m\angle 4$ 103

ALGEBRA Find x and the measures of the unknown sides of each triangle.

7.

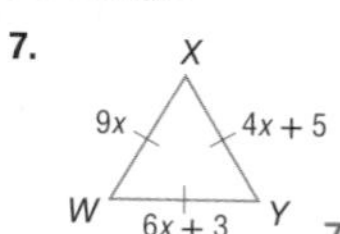

8.

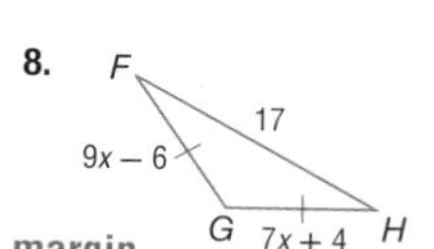

7, 8. See margin.

9. **TRAVEL** A plane travels from Des Moines to Phoenix, on to Atlanta, and back to Des Moines, as shown below. Find the distance in miles for each leg of the trip if the total trip was 3482 miles.

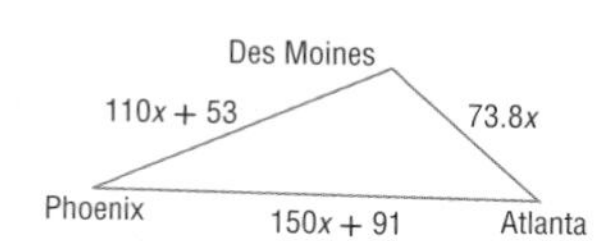

Des Moines to Phoenix = 1153 mi, Des Moines to Atlanta = 738 mi, Phoenix to Atlanta = 1591 mi

QuickReview

Example 1 (Used in Lesson 6-1)

Find the measure of each numbered angle.

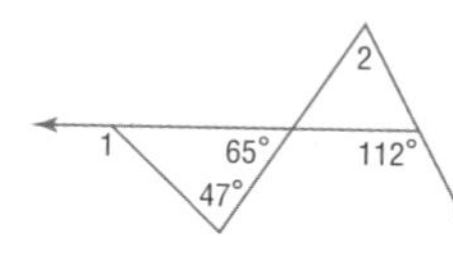

a. $m\angle 1$

$m\angle 1 = 65 + 47$ Exterior ∠ Theorem

$m\angle 1 = 112$ Add.

b. $m\angle 2$

$180 = m\angle 2 + 68 + 65$ Triangle Sum Theorem

$180 = m\angle 2 + 133$ Simplify.

$m\angle 2 = 47$ Subtract.

Example 2 (Used in Lessons 6-2, 6-3, and 6-6)

ALGEBRA Find the measures of the sides of isosceles $\triangle XYZ$.

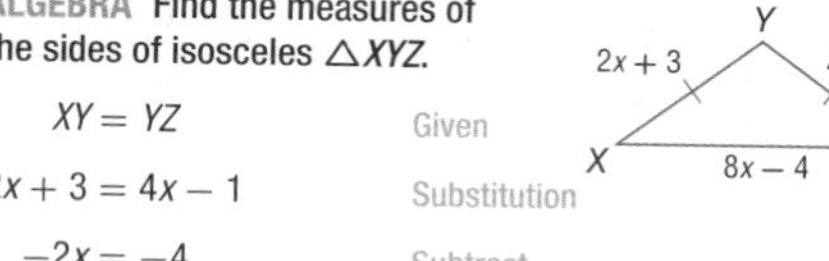

$XY = YZ$ Given

$2x + 3 = 4x - 1$ Substitution

$-2x = -4$ Subtract.

$x = 2$ Simplify.

$XY = 2x + 3$ Given

$= 2(2) + 3$ or 7 $x = 2$

$YZ = XY$ Given

$= 7$ $XY = 7$

$XZ = 8x - 4$ Given

$= 8(2) - 4$ or 12 $x = 2$

2 Online Option Take an online self-check Chapter Readiness Quiz at connectED.mcgraw-hill.com.

391

Essential Questions

- Why do we name figures? Sample answer: By naming a figure, we know what properties to associate with that figure. The figure could then be used to model a situation and the properties of the figure could be used to solve a problem.

Get Ready for the Chapter

Response to Intervention (RtI)

Use the *Quick Check* results and the Intervention Planner chart to help you determine your Response to Intervention. The If-Then statements in the chart help you decide the appropriate tier of RtI and suggest intervention resources for each tier.

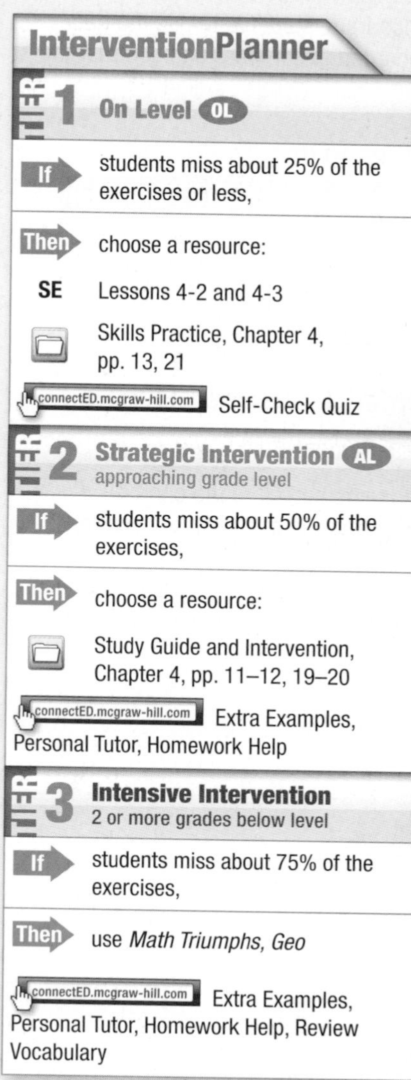

InterventionPlanner

TIER 1 On Level OL

If students miss about 25% of the exercises or less,

Then choose a resource:

SE Lessons 4-2 and 4-3

Skills Practice, Chapter 4, pp. 13, 21

connectED.mcgraw-hill.com Self-Check Quiz

TIER 2 Strategic Intervention AL approaching grade level

If students miss about 50% of the exercises,

Then choose a resource:

Study Guide and Intervention, Chapter 4, pp. 11–12, 19–20

connectED.mcgraw-hill.com Extra Examples, Personal Tutor, Homework Help

TIER 3 Intensive Intervention 2 or more grades below level

If students miss about 75% of the exercises,

Then use *Math Triumphs, Geo*

connectED.mcgraw-hill.com Extra Examples, Personal Tutor, Homework Help, Review Vocabulary

FOLDABLES StudyOrganizer

Dinah Zike's Foldables®

Focus Students write notes about each lesson in this chapter.

Teach Have students make and label the Foldable as illustrated.

Students use their Foldables to take notes, define terms, record concepts, and apply properties of quadrilaterals. Encourage students to use the data recorded to compare and contrast the five quadrilaterals studied.

When to Use It

Foldable Tabs	Lesson(s)
Parallelograms	6-2, 6-3
Rectangles	6-2, 6-4
Squares and Rhombi	6-5
Trapezoids and Kites	6-6

Differentiated Instruction

Student-Built Glossary, pp. 1–2

Students complete the chart by providing the definition of each term and an example as they progress through Chapter 6. This study tool can also be used to review for the chapter test.

Get Started on the Chapter

You will learn several new concepts, skills, and vocabulary terms as you study Chapter 6. To get ready, identify important terms and organize your resources. You may wish to refer to Chapter 0 to review prerequisite skills.

FOLDABLES StudyOrganizer

Quadrilaterals Make this Foldable to help you organize your Chapter 6 notes about quadrilaterals. Begin with one sheet of notebook paper.

1 **Fold** lengthwise to the holes.

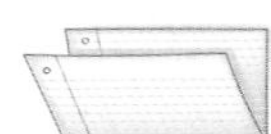

2 **Fold** along the width of the paper twice and unfold the paper.

3 **Cut** along the fold marks on the left side of the paper.

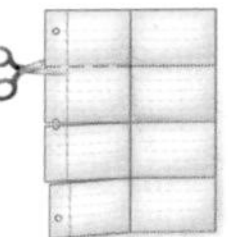

4 **Label** as shown.

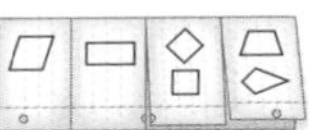

NewVocabulary

English		Español
diagonal	p. 393	diagonal
parallelogram	p. 403	paralelogramo
rectangle	p. 423	rectángulo
rhombus	p. 430	rombo
square	p. 431	cuadrado
trapezoid	p. 439	trapecio
base	p. 439	base
legs	p. 439	catetos
isosceles trapezoid	p. 439	trapecio isósceles
midsegment of a trapezoid	p. 441	segmento medio de un trapecio

ReviewVocabulary

exterior angle ángulo externo an angle formed by one side of a triangle and the extension of another side

remote interior angle ángulos internos no adyacentes the angles of a triangle that are not adjacent to a given exterior angle

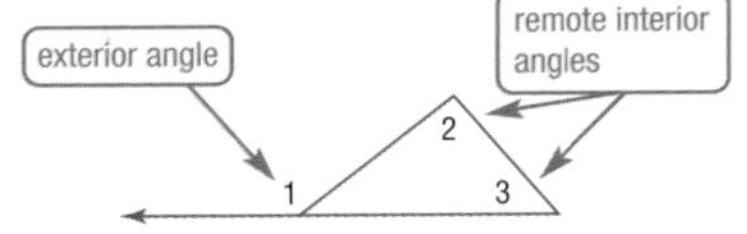

slope pendiente for a (nonvertical) line containing two points (x_1, y_1) and (x_2, y_2), the number m given by the formula $m = \frac{(y_2 - y_1)}{(x_2 - x_1)}$ where $x_2 \neq x_1$

LESSON 6-1

Angles of Polygons

:: Then	:: Now	:: Why?
You named and classified polygons.	**1** Find and use the sum of the measures of the interior angles of a polygon. **2** Find and use the sum of the measures of the exterior angles of a polygon.	To create their honeycombs, young worker honeybees excrete flecks of wax that are carefully molded by other bees to form hexagonal cells. The cells are less than 0.1 millimeter thick, but they support almost 25 times their own weight. The cell walls all stand at exactly the same angle to one another. This angle is the measure of the interior angle of a regular hexagon.

NewVocabulary
diagonal

Common Core State Standards

Content Standards
G.MG.1 Use geometric shapes, their measures, and their properties to describe objects (e.g., modeling a tree trunk or a human torso as a cylinder). ★

Mathematical Practices
4 Model with mathematics.
3 Construct viable arguments and critique the reasoning of others.

1 Polygon Interior Angles Sum

A **diagonal** of a polygon is a segment that connects any two nonconsecutive vertices.

The vertices of polygon *PQRST* that are not consecutive with vertex *P* are vertices *R* and *S*. Therefore, polygon *PQRST* has two diagonals from vertex *P*, $\overline{PR}$ and $\overline{PS}$. Notice that the diagonals from vertex *P* separate the polygon into three triangles.

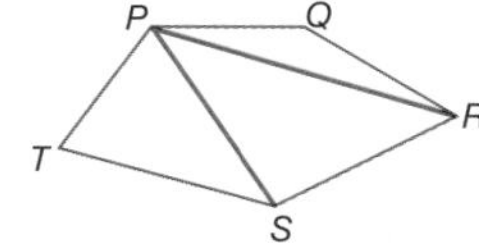

The sum of the angle measures of a polygon is the sum of the angle measures of the triangles formed by drawing all the possible diagonals from one vertex.

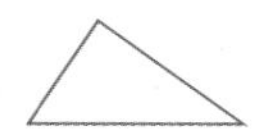
Triangle

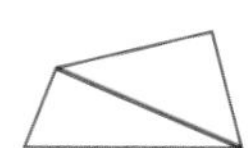
Quadrilateral

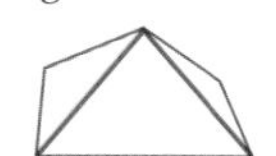
Pentagon

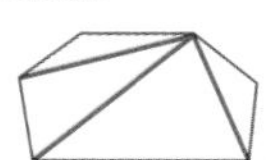
Hexagon

Since the sum of the angle measures of a triangle is 180, we can make a table and look for a pattern to find the sum of the angle measures for any convex polygon.

Polygon	Number of Sides	Number of Triangles	Sum of Interior Angle Measures
Triangle	3	1	(1)180 or 180
Quadrilateral	4	2	(2)180 or 360
Pentagon	5	3	(3)180 or 540
Hexagon	6	4	(4)180 or 720
n-gon	*n*	$n - 2$	$(n - 2)180$

This leads to the following theorem.

Theorem 6.1 Polygon Interior Angles Sum

The sum of the interior angle measures of an *n*-sided convex polygon is $(n - 2) \cdot 180$.

Example $m\angle A + m\angle B + m\angle C + m\angle D + m\angle E = (5 - 2) \cdot 180$

$= 540$

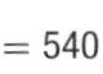

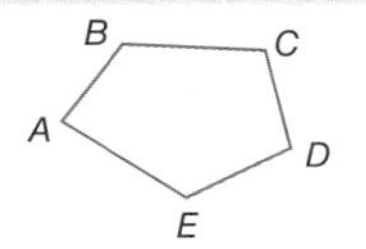

You will prove Theorem 6.1 for octagons in Exercise 42.

1 Focus

VerticalAlignment

Before Lesson 6-1 Name and classify polygons.

Lesson 6-1 Find and use the sum of the measures of the interior angles of a polygon. Find and use the sum of the measures of the exterior angles of a polygon.

After Lesson 6-1 Recognize and apply properties of the sides and angles of parallelograms.

2 Teach

Scaffolding Questions

Have students read the **Why?** section of the lesson.

Ask:

- Each cell has how many interior angles? 6
- What comparisons can you make about each of the interior angles of each cell and generally about all of the cells? Every interior angle of each cell is the same. Every cell is the same. All the interior angles of all the cells are the same.

(continued on the next page)

Lesson 6-1 Resources

Resource	Approaching Level AL	On Level OL	Beyond Level BL	English Learners ELL
Teacher Edition	▪ Differentiated Instruction, p. 394	▪ Differentiated Instruction, pp. 394, 396	▪ Differentiated Instruction, pp. 394, 396	
Chapter Resource Masters	▪ Study Guide and Intervention, pp. 5–6 ▪ Skills Practice, p. 7 ▪ Practice, p. 8 ▪ Word Problem Practice, p. 9	▪ Study Guide and Intervention, pp. 5–6 ▪ Skills Practice, p. 7 ▪ Practice, p. 8 ▪ Word Problem Practice, p. 9 ▪ Enrichment, p. 10	▪ Practice, p. 8 ▪ Word Problem Practice, p. 9 ▪ Enrichment, p. 10	▪ Study Guide and Intervention, pp. 5–6 ▪ Skills Practice, p. 7 ▪ Practice, p. 8 ▪ Word Problem Practice, p. 9
Other	▪ 5-Minute Check 6-1 ▪ Study Notebook ▪ Teaching Geometry with Manipulatives	▪ 5-Minute Check 6-1 ▪ Study Notebook ▪ Teaching Geometry with Manipulatives	▪ 5-Minute Check 6-1 ▪ Study Notebook	▪ 5-Minute Check 6-1 ▪ Study Notebook ▪ Teaching Geometry with Manipulatives

- The sum of the measures of the interior angles of a hexagon is 720. What is the measure of one interior angle of a honeycomb cell? 120
- A reflex angle is the angle on the outside of the vertex. What would be the measure of a reflex angle of a honeycomb cell? Explain your reasoning. 240; A circle measures 360°. If the interior angle of a honeycomb cell measures 120, then the difference of 360 and 120 must equal the measure of the reflex angle.

1 Polygon Interior Angles Sum

Examples 1–3 show how to find the interior angle sum of a polygon using the Interior Angles Sum Theorem.

Formative Assessment

Use the Guided Practice exercises after each example to determine students' understanding of concepts.

Additional Example

1 **a.** Find the sum of the measures of the interior angles of a convex nonagon. 1260

b. Find the measure of each interior angle of parallelogram *RSTU*.

S $(11x + 4)°$ $5x°$ T
R $5x°$ $(11x + 4)°$ U

$m\angle R = m\angle T = 55$;
$m\angle S = m\angle U = 125$

Additional Examples also in Interactive Classroom PowerPoint® Presentations

Interactive White Board READY

You can use the Polygon Interior Angles Sum Theorem to find the sum of the interior angles of a polygon and to find missing measures in polygons.

Study Tip

Naming Polygons
Remember, a polygon with *n*-sides is an *n-gon*, but several polygons have special names.

Number of Sides	Polygon
3	triangle
4	quadrilateral
5	pentagon
6	hexagon
7	heptagon
8	octagon
9	nonagon
10	decagon
11	hendecagon
12	dodecagon
n	*n*-gon

Example 1 Find the Interior Angles Sum of a Polygon

a. Find the sum of the measures of the interior angles of a convex heptagon.

A heptagon has seven sides. Use the Polygon Interior Angles Sum Theorem to find the sum of its interior angle measures.

$(n - 2) \cdot 180 = (7 - 2) \cdot 180$ $\quad n = 7$

$= 5 \cdot 180$ or 900 $\quad$ Simplify.

The sum of the measures is 900.

CHECK Draw a convex polygon with seven sides. Use a protractor to measure each angle to the nearest degree. Then find the sum of these measures.

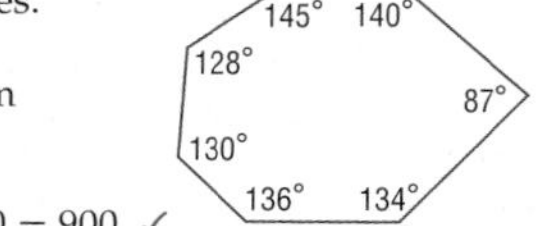

$128 + 145 + 140 + 87 + 134 + 136 + 130 = 900$ ✓

b. ALGEBRA Find the measure of each interior angle of quadrilateral *ABCD*.

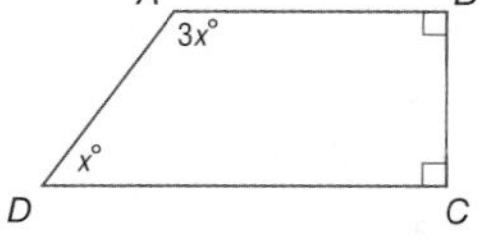

Step 1 Find *x*.

Since there are 4 angles, the sum of the interior angle measures is $(4 - 2) \cdot 180$ or 360.

$360 = m\angle A + m\angle B + m\angle C + m\angle D$	Sum of interior angle measures
$360 = 3x + 90 + 90 + x$	Substitution
$360 = 4x + 180$	Combine like terms.
$180 = 4x$	Subtract 180 from each side.
$45 = x$	Divide each side by 4.

Step 2 Use the value of *x* to find the measure of each angle.

$m\angle A = 3x$ $\quad$ $m\angle B = 90$ $\quad$ $m\angle D = x$
$= 3(45)$ or 135 $\quad$ $m\angle C = 90$ $\quad$ $= 45$

Guided Practice

1A. Find the sum of the measures of the interior angles of a convex octagon. **1080**

1B. Find the measure of each interior angle of pentagon *HJKLM* shown

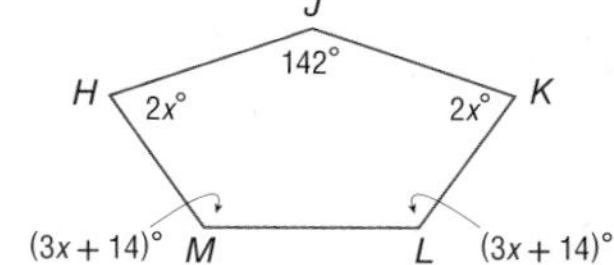

1B. $m\angle H = 74$, $m\angle J = 142$, $m\angle K = 74$, $m\angle L = 125$, $m\angle M = 125$

Recall from Lesson 1-6 that in a regular polygon, all of the interior angles are congruent. You can use this fact and the Polygon Interior Angle Sum Theorem to find the interior angle measure of any regular polygon.

Differentiated Instruction AL OL BL

Logical Have students use a straightedge to construct an irregular polygon that has five or more sides. Have students use a protractor to measure and label half of the interior angles of the figure and the exterior angles of the remaining vertices. Instruct students to trade drawings with another student and measure and label the remaining interior and exterior angles without using a protractor. Students should then return the drawing to the owner. Answers can be checked by using a protractor.

ReviewVocabulary

regular polygon
a convex polygon in which all of the sides are congruent and all of the angles are congruent

Real-World Example 2 Interior Angle Measure of Regular Polygon

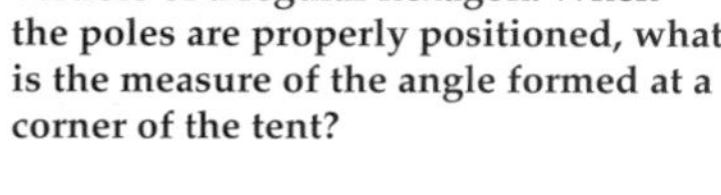

TENTS The poles for a tent form the vertices of a regular hexagon. When the poles are properly positioned, what is the measure of the angle formed at a corner of the tent?

Understand Draw a diagram of the situation.

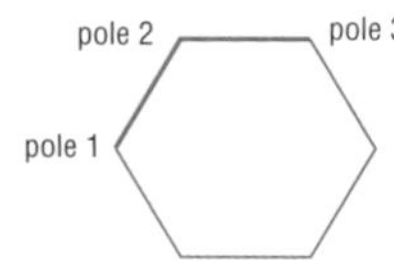

The measure of the angle formed at a corner of the tent is an interior angle of a regular hexagon.

Plan Use the Polygon Interior Angles Sum Theorem to find the sum of the measures of the angles. Since the angles of a regular polygon are congruent, divide this sum by the number of angles to find the measure of each interior angle.

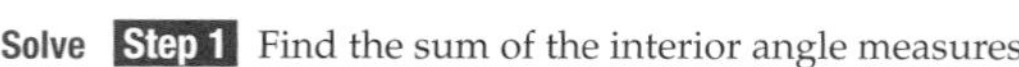

Solve **Step 1** Find the sum of the interior angle measures.

$$(n-2) \cdot 180 = (6-2) \cdot 180 \quad n = 6$$
$$= 4 \cdot 180 \text{ or } 720 \quad \text{Simplify.}$$

Step 2 Find the measure of one interior angle.

$$\frac{\text{sum of interior angle measures}}{\text{number of congruent angles}} = \frac{720}{6} \quad \text{Substitution}$$
$$= 120 \quad \text{Divide.}$$

The angle at a corner of the tent measures 120.

Check To verify that this measure is correct, use a ruler and a protractor to draw a regular hexagon using 120 as the measure of each interior angle. The last side drawn should connect with the beginning point of the first segment drawn. ✓

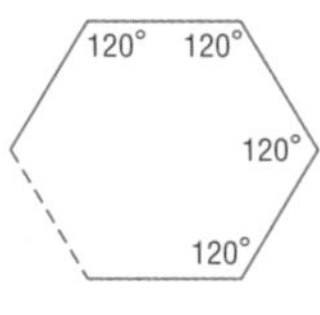

Real-WorldLink

Susan B. Anthony was a leader of the women's suffrage movement in the late 1800s, which eventually led to the Nineteenth Amendment giving women the right to vote. In 1979, the Susan B. Anthony one-dollar coin was first minted, making her the first woman to be depicted on U.S. currency.

Source: *Encyclopaedia Britannica*

GuidedPractice

2A. COINS Find the measure of each interior angle of the regular hendecagon that appears on the face of a Susan B. Anthony one-dollar coin. **$147\frac{3}{11}$**

2B. HOT TUBS A certain company makes hot tubs in a variety of different shapes. Find the measure of each interior angle of the nonagon model. **140**

Given the interior angle measure of a regular polygon, you can also use the Polygon Interior Angles Sum Theorem to find a polygon's number of sides.

Teach with Tech

Computer Projector Use geometry software to draw various polygons. Have students take turns measuring the interior angles and finding the sum of the measures of each polygon. Have students summarize their results and explain it to the class. Save their work and distribute it to the class.

Tips for New Teachers

Sense-Making Remind students that if they forget the equation for the sum of the interior angles of a polygon, they can draw all possible diagonals from one vertex and then multipying the number of triangles that are formed by 180. Show an example using a pentagon or hexagon.

Additional Example

2 **ARCHITECTURE** A mall is designed so that five walkways meet at a food court that is in the shape of a regular pentagon. Find the measure of one of the interior angles of the pentagon. 108

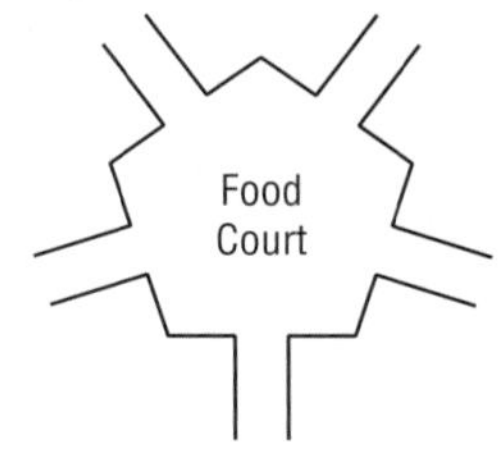

WatchOut!

Interior Angles Students should be sure to check for what information a question asks. Does the question ask for the measure of one interior angle, or the sum of the measures of the interior angles?

Additional Example

3 The measure of an interior angle of a regular polygon is 150. Find the number of sides in the polygon. 12

Focus on Mathematical Content

Exterior Angles The measure of an exterior angle of a polygon can be found by using the supplemental angles theorem. If the measure of the interior angle of a polygon is known, the measure of the exterior angle of the same vertex is equal to the difference of 180° (the measure of a straight line) and the measure of the interior angle.

Example 3 Find Number of Sides Given Interior Angle Measure

The measure of an interior angle of a regular polygon is 135. Find the number of sides in the polygon.

Let n = the number of sides in the polygon. Since all angles of a regular polygon are congruent, the sum of the interior angle measures is $135n$. By the Polygon Interior Angles Sum Theorem, the sum of the interior angle measures can also be expressed as $(n - 2) \cdot 180$.

$135n = (n - 2) \cdot 180$	Write an equation.
$135n = 180n - 360$	Distributive Property
$-45n = -360$	Subtract $180n$ from each side.
$n = 8$	Divide each side by -45.

The polygon has 8 sides.

GuidedPractice

3. The measure of an interior angle of a regular polygon is 144. Find the number of sides in the polygon. **10**

ReviewVocabulary

exterior angle an angle formed by one side of a polygon and the extension of another side

2 Polygon Exterior Angles Sum Does a relationship exist between the number of sides of a convex polygon and the sum of its exterior angle measures? Examine the polygons below in which an exterior angle has been measured at each vertex.

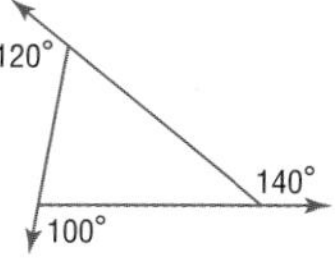

$120 + 100 + 140 = \mathbf{360}$

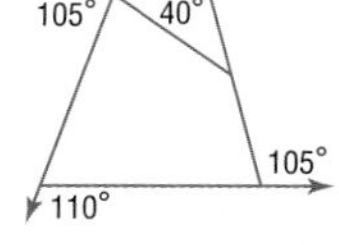

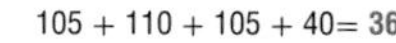
$105 + 110 + 105 + 40 = \mathbf{360}$

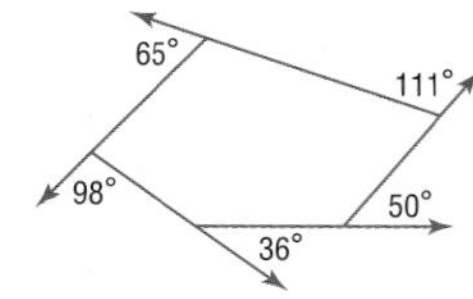

$65 + 98 + 36 + 50 + 111 = \mathbf{360}$

Notice that the sum of the exterior angle measures in each case is 360. This suggests the following theorem.

Theorem 6.2 Polygon Exterior Angles Sum

The sum of the exterior angle measures of a convex polygon, one angle at each vertex, is 360.

Example

$m\angle 1 + m\angle 2 + m\angle 3 + m\angle 4 + m\angle 5 + m\angle 6 = 360$

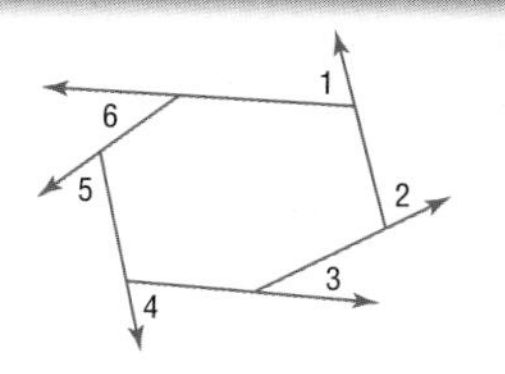

You will prove Theorem 6.2 in Exercise 43.

DifferentiatedInstruction OL BL

Extension Have students draw a concave polygon. They should measure the interior angles and the exterior angles with a protractor. Have them see if Theorem 6.1 and Theorem 6.2 hold true to their measurements. See students' work.

Example 4 Find Exterior Angle Measures of a Polygon

a. ALGEBRA Find the value of x in the diagram.

Use the Polygon Exterior Angles Sum Theorem to write an equation. Then solve for x.

$$(2x - 5) + 5x + 2x + (6x - 5) + (3x + 10) = 360$$

$$(2x + 5x + 2x + 6x + 3x) + [-5 + (-5) + 10] = 360$$

$$18x = 360$$

$$x = \frac{360}{18} \text{ or } 20$$

StudyTip

CCSS Perseverance To find the measure of each exterior angle of a regular polygon, you can find the measure of each interior angle and subtract this measure from 180, since an exterior angle and its corresponding interior angle are supplementary.

b. Find the measure of each exterior angle of a regular nonagon.

A regular nonagon has 9 congruent sides and 9 congruent interior angles. The exterior angles are also congruent, since angles supplementary to congruent angles are congruent. Let n = the measure of each exterior angle and write and solve an equation.

$9n = 360$ Polygon Exterior Angles Sum Theorem

$n = 40$ Divide each side by 9.

The measure of each exterior angle of a regular nonagon is 40.

GuidedPractice

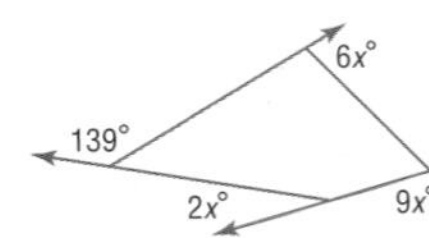

4A. Find the value of x in the diagram. **13**

4B. Find the measure of each exterior angle of a regular dodecagon. **30**

Check Your Understanding

= Step-by-Step Solutions begin on page R14.

Example 1 **Find the sum of the measures of the interior angles of each convex polygon.**

1. decagon **1440**

2. pentagon **540**

Find the measure of each interior angle.

3.

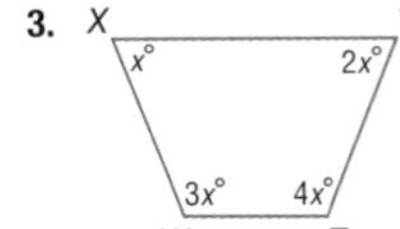

4.

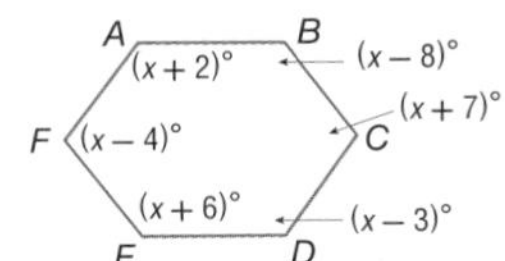

3. $m\angle X = 36$, $m\angle Y = 72$, $m\angle Z = 144$, $m\angle W = 108$

4. $m\angle A = 122$, $m\angle B = 112$, $m\angle C = 127$, $m\angle D = 117$, $m\angle E = 126$, $m\angle F = 116$

Example 2 **5** **AMUSEMENT** The Wonder Wheel at Coney Island in Brooklyn, New York, is a regular polygon with 16 sides. What is the measure of each interior angle of the polygon? **157.5**

Example 3 **The measure of an interior angle of a regular polygon is given. Find the number of sides in the polygon.**

6. 150 **12**

7. 170 **36**

2 Polygon Exterior Angles Sum

Example 4 shows how to use the Exterior Angles Sum Theorem when given a convex polygon.

Additional Example

4 a. Find the value of x in the diagram.

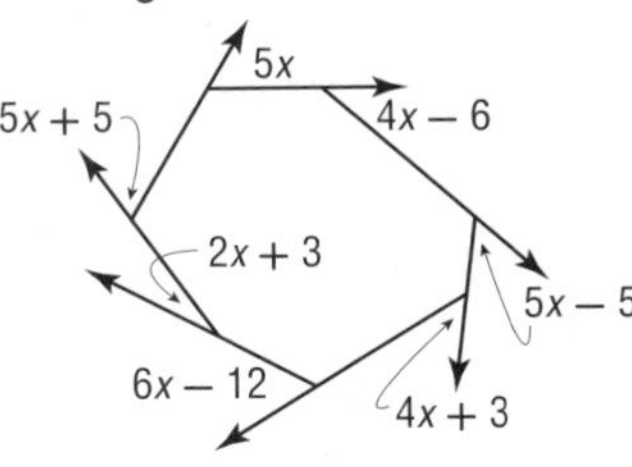

12

b. Find the measure of each exterior angle of a regular decagon. 36

CCSS Teaching the Mathematical Practices

Perseverance Mathematically proficient students check their answers to problems using a different method, and they continually ask themselves, "does this make sense?" Encourage students to use alternative methods of problem solving.

3 Practice

Formative Assessment

Use Exercises 1–11 to check for understanding.

Then use the chart at the bottom of the next page to customize assignments for your students.

Teaching the Mathematical Practices

Modeling Mathematically proficient students can apply the mathematics they know to solve problems arising in everyday life. In Exercises 25 and 44, encourage students to use the diagrams given to identify information important to solving each problem.

Additional Answers

42. Draw all of the diagonals from one vertex in an octagon.

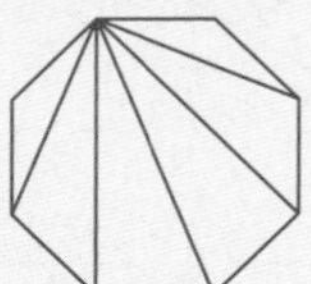

Notice that the polygon is divided up into 6 triangles. The sum of the measures of the interior angles of each triangle is 180, so the sum of the measures of the interior angles of the octagon is $6 \cdot 180 = 1080 = (8 - 2) \cdot 180$ or $(n - 2) \cdot 180$ if $n =$ the number of sides of the polygon.

43. Consider the sum of the measures of the exterior angles N for an n-gon.

$N =$ sum of measures of linear pairs − sum of measures of interior angles

$= 180n - 180(n - 2)$

$= 180n - 180n + 360$

$= 360$

So, the sum of the exterior angle measures is 360 for any convex polygon.

Example 4 **Find the value of x in each diagram.**

8. 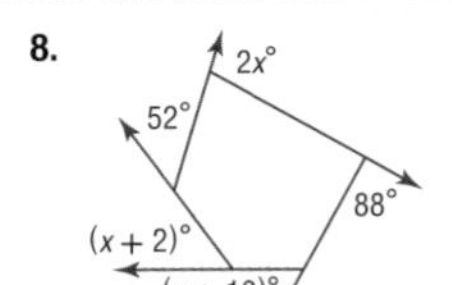

52

9. 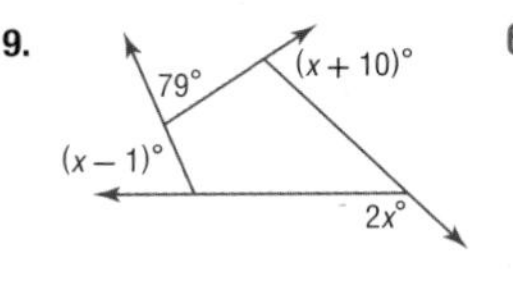

68

Find the measure of each exterior angle of each regular polygon.

10. quadrilateral **90** **11.** octagon **45**

Practice and Problem Solving

Extra Practice is on page R6.

Example 1 **Find the sum of the measures of the interior angles of each convex polygon.**

12. dodecagon **1800** **13.** 20-gon **3240** **14.** 29-gon **4860** **15.** 32-gon **5400**

Find the measure of each interior angle.

16. 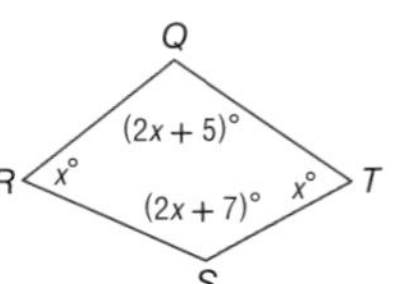

17. 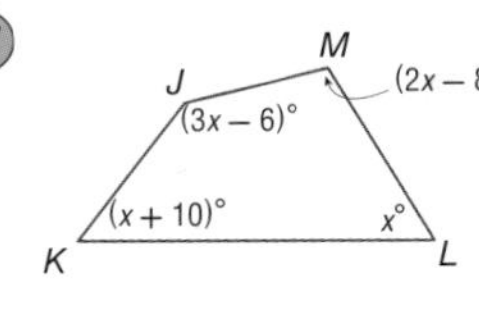

18. 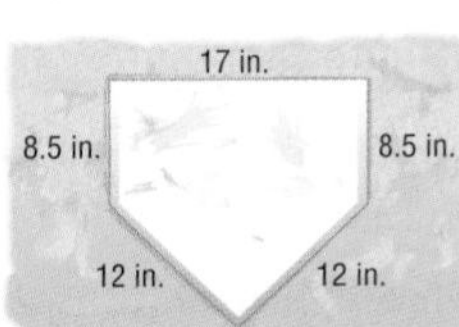

19. 

16. $m\angle Q = 121$, $m\angle R = 58$, $m\angle S = 123$, $m\angle T = 58$
17. $m\angle J = 150$, $m\angle K = 62$, $m\angle L = 52$, $m\angle M = 96$
18. $m\angle A = 90$, $m\angle B = 90$, $m\angle C = 128$, $m\angle D = 74$, $m\angle E = 158$
19. $m\angle U = 60$, $m\angle V = 193$, $m\angle W = 76$, $m\angle Y = 68$, $m\angle Z = 143$

20. **BASEBALL** In baseball, home plate is a pentagon. The dimensions of home plate are shown. What is the sum of the measures of the interior angles of home plate? **540**

17 in.
8.5 in.
8.5 in.
12 in.
12 in.

Example 2 **Find the measure of each interior angle of each regular polygon.**

21. dodecagon **150** **22.** pentagon **108** **23.** decagon **144** **24.** nonagon **140**

25.  **MODELING** Hexagonal chess is played on a regular hexagonal board comprised of 92 small hexagons in three colors. The chess pieces are arranged so that a player can move any piece at the start of a game.

a. What is the sum of the measures of the interior angles of the chess board? **720**

b. Does each interior angle have the same measure? If so, give the measure. Explain your reasoning.

25b. Yes, 120; sample answer: Since the hexagon is regular, the measures of the angles are equal. That means each angle is 720 ÷ 6 or 120.

Example 3 **The measure of an interior angle of a regular polygon is given. Find the number of sides in the polygon.**

26. 60 **3** **27.** 90 **4** **28.** 120 **6** **29.** 156 **15**

Differentiated Homework Options

Level	Assignment	Two-Day Option	
AL Basic	12–38, 49, 51–66	13–37 odd, 54–57	12–38 even, 49, 51–53, 58–66
OL Core	13–41 odd, 42–45, 47, 49, 58–66	12–38, 54–57	39, 41–45, 47, 49, 51–53, 58–66
BL Advanced	39–64, (optional: 65, 66)		

Example 4 **Find the value of x in each diagram.**

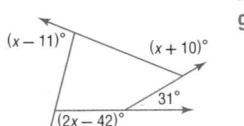

30. 93

31. 71

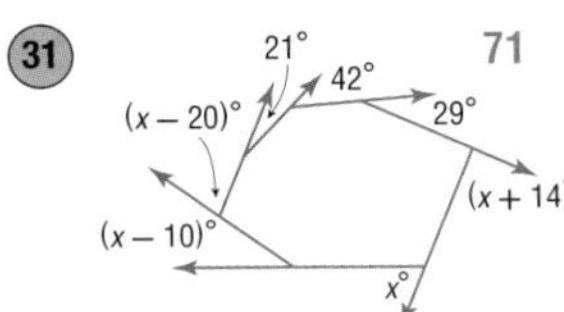

32. 44

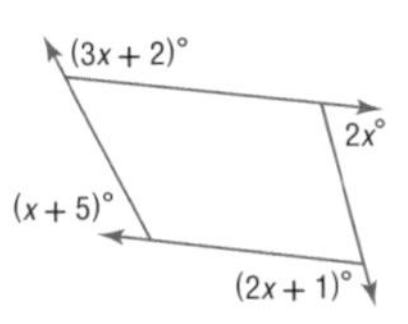

33. 37

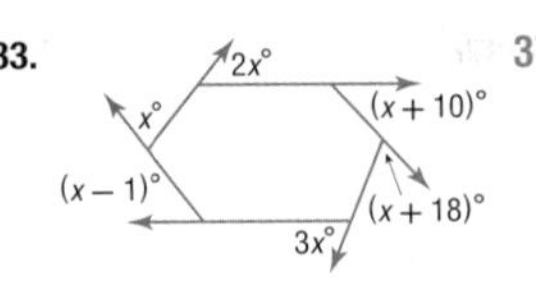

Find the measure of each exterior angle of each regular polygon.

34. decagon 36 **35.** pentagon 72 **36.** hexagon 60 **37.** 15-gon 24

38. COLOR GUARD During the halftime performance for a football game, the color guard is planning a new formation in which seven members stand around a central point and stretch their flag to the person immediately to their left as shown.

a. What is the measure of each exterior angle of the formation? about 51.4

b. If the perimeter of the formation is 38.5 feet, how long is each flag? 5.5 ft

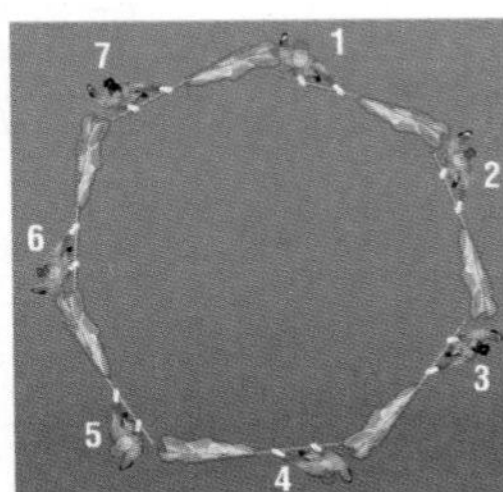

B **Find the measures of an exterior angle and an interior angle given the number of sides of each regular polygon. Round to the nearest tenth, if necessary.**

39. 7 51.4, 128.6 **40.** 13 27.7, 152.3 **41.** 14 25.7, 154.3

42. PROOF Write a paragraph proof to prove the Polygon Interior Angles Sum Theorem for octagons. See margin.

43. PROOF Use algebra to prove the Polygon Exterior Angles Sum Theorem. See margin.

44. CCSS MODELING The aperture on the camera lens shown is a regular 14-sided polygon.

a. What is the measure of each interior angle of the polygon? about 154.3

b. What is the measure of each exterior angle of the polygon? about 25.7

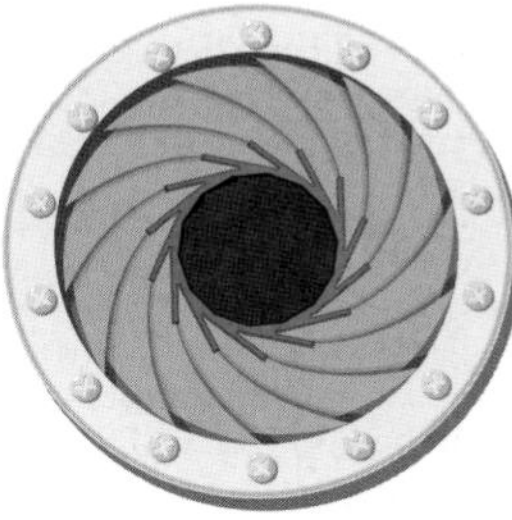

ALGEBRA **Find the measure of each interior angle.**

45. decagon, in which the measures of the interior angles are $x + 5$, $x + 10$, $x + 20$, $x + 30$, $x + 35$, $x + 40$, $x + 60$, $x + 70$, $x + 80$, and $x + 90$ 105, 110, 120, 130, 135, 140, 160, 170, 180, 190

46. polygon $ABCDE$, in which the measures of the interior angles are $6x$, $4x + 13$, $x + 9$, $2x - 8$, $4x - 1$ $m\angle A = 186$, $m\angle B = 137$, $m\angle C = 40$, $m\angle D = 54$, $m\angle E = 123$

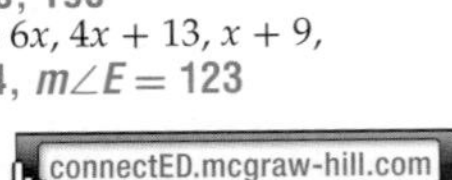

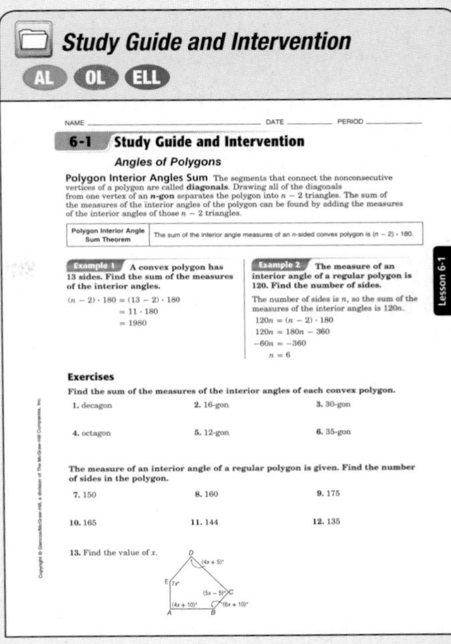

Study Guide and Intervention

AL OL ELL

NAME ______ DATE ______ PERIOD ______

6-1 Study Guide and Intervention

Angles of Polygons

Polygon Interior Angles Sum The segments that connect the nonconsecutive vertices of a polygon are called **diagonals**. Drawing all of the diagonals from one vertex of an ***n*-gon** separates the polygon into $n - 2$ triangles. The sum of the measures of the interior angles of the polygon can be found by adding the measures of the interior angles of those $n - 2$ triangles.

Polygon Interior Angle Sum Theorem	The sum of the interior angle measures of an n-sided convex polygon is $(n - 2) \cdot 180$.

Example 1 **A convex polygon has 13 sides. Find the sum of the measures of the interior angles.**

$(n - 2) \cdot 180 = (13 - 2) \cdot 180$
$= 11 \cdot 180$
$= 1980$

Example 2 **The measure of an interior angle of a regular polygon is 120. Find the number of sides.**

The number of sides is n, so the sum of the measures of the interior angles is $120n$.

$120n = (n - 2) \cdot 180$
$120n = 180n - 360$
$-60n = -360$
$n = 6$

Exercises

Find the sum of the measures of the interior angles of each convex polygon.

1. decagon 2. 16-gon 3. 30-gon

4. octagon 5. 12-gon 6. 35-gon

The measure of an interior angle of a regular polygon is given. Find the number of sides in the polygon.

7. 150 8. 160 9. 175

10. 165 11. 144 12. 135

13. Find the value of x.

Lesson 6-1

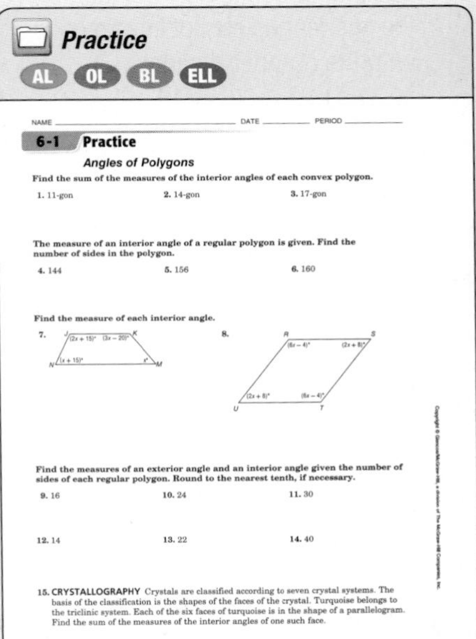

Practice

AL OL BL ELL

NAME ______ DATE ______ PERIOD ______

6-1 Practice

Angles of Polygons

Find the sum of the measures of the interior angles of each convex polygon.

1. 11-gon 2. 14-gon 3. 17-gon

The measure of an interior angle of a regular polygon is given. Find the number of sides in the polygon.

4. 144 5. 156 6. 160

Find the measure of each interior angle.

7. 8.

Find the measures of an exterior angle and an interior angle given the number of sides of each regular polygon. Round to the nearest tenth, if necessary.

9. 16 10. 24 11. 30

12. 14 13. 22 14. 40

15. **CRYSTALLOGRAPHY** Crystals are classified according to seven crystal systems. The basis of the classification is the shapes of the faces of the crystal. Turquoise belongs to the triclinic system. Each of the six faces of turquoise is in the shape of a parallelogram. Find the sum of the measures of the interior angles of one such face.

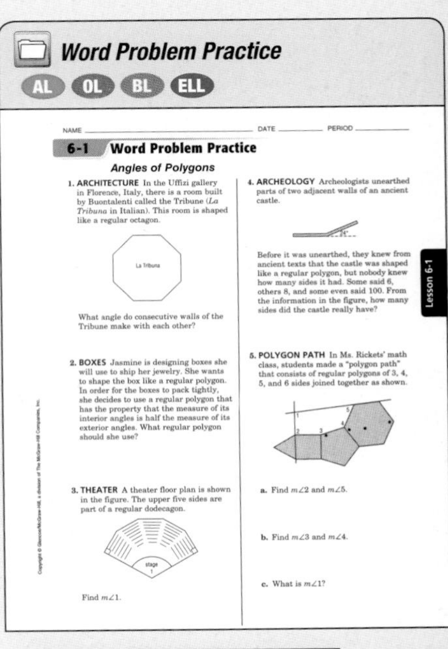

Word Problem Practice

AL OL BL ELL

NAME ______ DATE ______ PERIOD ______

6-1 Word Problem Practice

Angles of Polygons

1. **ARCHITECTURE** In the Uffizi gallery in Florence, Italy, there is a room built by Buontalenti called the Tribune (*La Tribuna* in Italian). This room is shaped like a regular octagon.

What angle do consecutive walls of the Tribune make with each other?

2. **BOXES** Jasmine is designing boxes she will use to ship her jewelry. She wants to shape the box like a regular polygon. In order for the boxes to pack tightly, she decides to use a regular polygon that has the property that the measure of its interior angles is half the measure of its exterior angles. What regular polygon should she use?

3. **THEATER** A theater floor plan is shown in the figure. The upper five sides are part of a regular dodecagon.

Find $m\angle 1$.

4. **ARCHEOLOGY** Archeologists unearthed parts of two adjacent walls of an ancient castle.

Before it was unearthed, they knew from ancient texts that the castle was shaped like a regular polygon, but nobody knew how many sides it had. Some said 6, others 8, and some even said 100. From the information in the figure, how many sides did the castle really have?

5. **POLYGON PATH** In Ms. Rickets' math class, students made a "polygon path" that consists of regular polygons of 3, 4, 5, and 6 sides joined together as shown.

a. Find $m\angle 2$ and $m\angle 5$.

b. Find $m\angle 3$ and $m\angle 4$.

c. What is $m\angle 1$?

Lesson 6-1

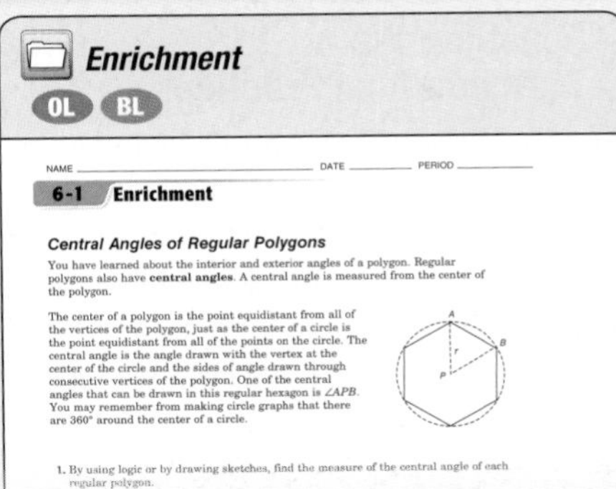

Enrichment

OL BL

NAME ______ DATE ______ PERIOD ______

6-1 Enrichment

Central Angles of Regular Polygons

You have learned about the interior and exterior angles of a polygon. Regular polygons also have **central angles**. A central angle is measured from the center of the polygon.

The center of a polygon is the point equidistant from all of the vertices of the polygon, just as the center of a circle is the point equidistant from all of the points on the circle. The central angle is the angle drawn with the vertex at the center of the circle and the sides of angle drawn through consecutive vertices of the polygon. One of the central angles that can be drawn in this regular hexagon is $\angle APB$. You may remember from making circle graphs that there are 360° around the center of a circle.

1. By using logic or by drawing sketches, find the measure of the central angle of each regular polygon.

Multiple Representations

In Exercise 48, students use geometric sketches, a table, and verbal description to investigate angle and side relationships in special quadrilaterals.

Exercise Alert

Ruler and Compass and Protractor Exercise 48 requires the use of a ruler, a compass and protractor.

WatchOut!

Error Analysis For Exercise 49, students should realize that the sum of the measures of the exterior angles of all polygons is equal to 360. It is only the sum of the interior angles that increases with the number of sides.

Additional Answers

48a. Sample answer:

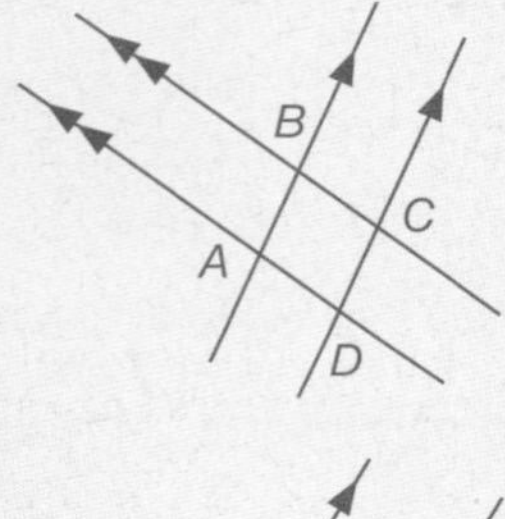

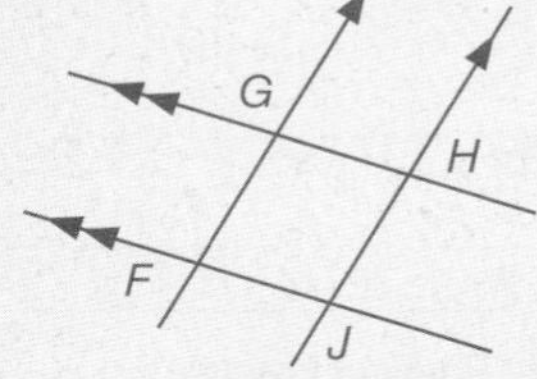

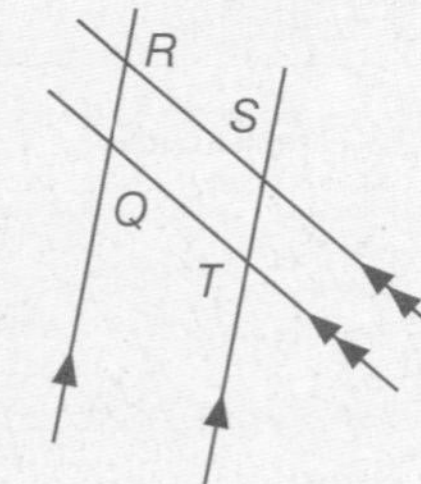

49. Liam; by the Exterior Angle Sum Theorem, the sum of the measures of any convex polygon is 360.

47. THEATER The drama club would like to build a theater in the round, so the audience can be seated on all sides of the stage, for its next production.

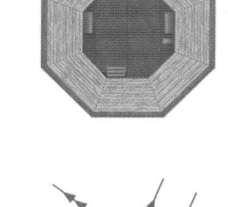

a. The stage is to be a regular octagon with a total perimeter of 60 feet. To what length should each board be cut to form the sides of the stage? 7.5 ft

b. At what angle should each board be cut so that they will fit together as shown? Explain your reasoning.

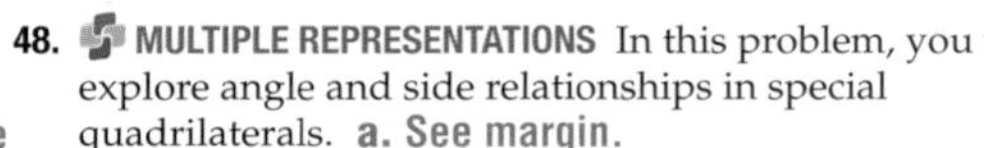

48. MULTIPLE REPRESENTATIONS In this problem, you will explore angle and side relationships in special quadrilaterals. **a. See margin.**

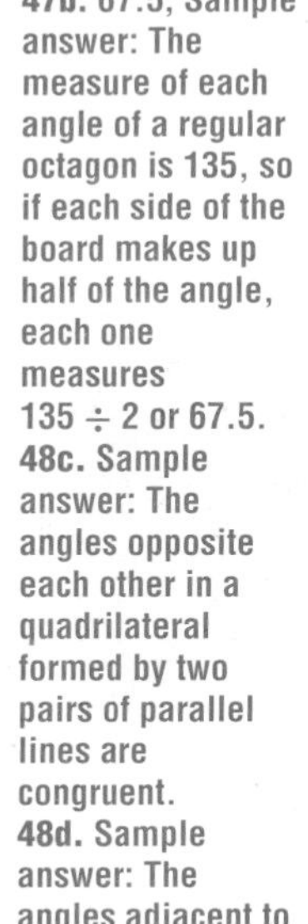

47b. 67.5; Sample answer: The measure of each angle of a regular octagon is 135, so if each side of the board makes up half of the angle, each one measures 135 ÷ 2 or 67.5.

48c. Sample answer: The angles opposite each other in a quadrilateral formed by two pairs of parallel lines are congruent.

48d. Sample answer: The angles adjacent to each other in a quadrilateral formed by two pairs of parallel lines are supplementary.

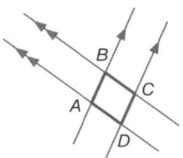

a. **Geometric** Draw two pairs of parallel lines that intersect like the ones shown. Label the quadrilateral formed by *ABCD*. Repeat these steps to form two additional quadrilaterals, *FGHJ* and *QRST*.

b. **Tabular** Copy and complete the table below.

Quadrilateral	Lengths and Measures							
ABCD	$m\angle A$	101	$m\angle B$	79	$m\angle C$	101	$m\angle D$	79
	AB	0.6 cm	*BC*	0.6 cm	*CD*	0.6 cm	*DA*	0.6 cm
FGHJ	$m\angle F$	76	$m\angle G$	104	$m\angle H$	76	$m\angle J$	104
	FG	1 cm	*GH*	0.9 cm	*HJ*	1 cm	*JF*	0.9 cm
QRST	$m\angle Q$	121	$m\angle R$	59	$m\angle S$	121	$m\angle T$	59
	QR	0.5 cm	*RS*	1.2 cm	*ST*	0.5 cm	*TQ*	1.2 cm

c. **Verbal** Make a conjecture about the relationship between the angles opposite each other in a quadrilateral formed by two pairs of parallel lines.

d. **Verbal** Make a conjecture about the relationship between two consecutive angles in a quadrilateral formed by two pairs of parallel lines.

e. **Verbal** Make a conjecture about the relationship between the sides opposite each other in a quadrilateral formed by two pairs of parallel lines. Sample answer: The sides opposite each other in a quadrilateral formed by two pairs of parallel lines are congruent.

H.O.T. Problems Use Higher-Order Thinking Skills

49. ERROR ANALYSIS Marcus says that the sum of the exterior angles of a decagon is greater than that of a heptagon because a decagon has more sides. Liam says that the sum of the exterior angles for both polygons is the same. Is either of them correct? Explain your reasoning. **See margin.**

50. CHALLENGE Find the values of *a*, *b*, and *c* if *QRSTVX* is a regular hexagon. Justify your answer. **See Ch. 6 Answer Appendix.**

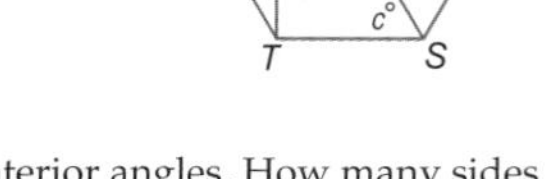

51. ARGUMENTS If two sides of a regular hexagon are extended to meet at a point in the exterior of the polygon, will the triangle formed *always*, *sometimes*, or *never* be equilateral? Justify your answer. **51–53. See margin.**

52. OPEN ENDED Sketch a polygon and find the sum of its interior angles. How many sides does a polygon with twice this interior angles sum have? Justify your answer.

53. WRITING IN MATH Explain how triangles are related to the Interior Angles Sum Theorem.

Teaching the Mathematical Practices

Arguments Mathematically proficient students understand and use stated assumptions and definitions in constructing arguments. They make conjectures and build a logical progression of statements to explore the truth of their conjectures. In Exercise 51, encourage students to draw a diagram of the situation described.

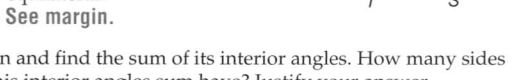

Standardized Test Practice

54. If the polygon shown is regular, what is $m\angle ABC$? **A**

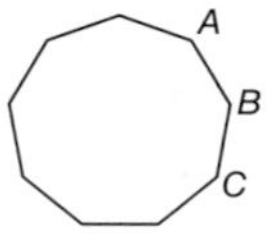

A 140

B 144

C 162

D 180

55. SHORT RESPONSE Figure *ABCDE* is a regular pentagon with line ℓ passing through side *AE*. What is $m\angle y$? **72**

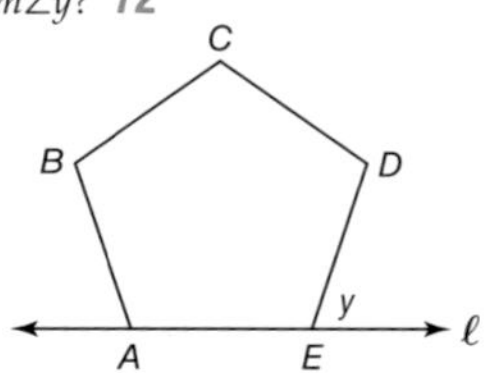

56. ALGEBRA $\frac{3^2 \cdot 4^5 \cdot 5^3}{5^3 \cdot 3^3 \cdot 4^6} =$ **G**

F $\frac{1}{60}$

G $\frac{1}{12}$

H $\frac{3}{4}$

J 12

57. SAT/ACT The sum of the measures of the interior angles of a polygon is twice the sum of the measures of its exterior angles. What type of polygon is it? **C**

A square

B pentagon

C hexagon

D octagon

E nonagon

Spiral Review

Compare the given measures. (Lesson 5-6)

58. $m\angle DCE$ and $m\angle SRT$ **$m\angle DCE > m\angle SRT$**

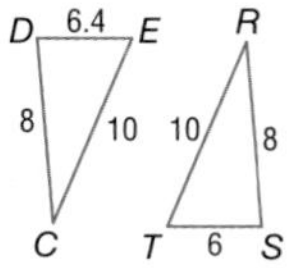

59. *JM* and *ML* **$ML < JM$**

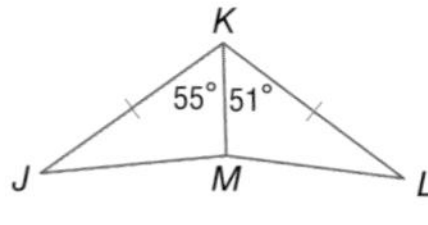

60. *WX* and *ZY* **$WX < ZY$**

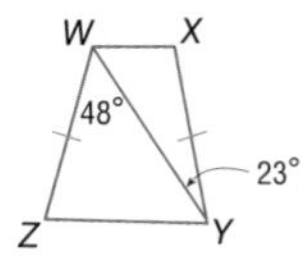

61. HISTORY The early Egyptians used to make triangles by using a rope with knots tied at equal intervals. Each vertex of the triangle had to occur at a knot. How many different triangles can be formed using the rope below? (Lesson 5-5) **3**

Show that the triangles are congruent by identifying all congruent corresponding parts. Then write a congruence statement. (Lesson 4-3) **62–64. See margin.**

62.

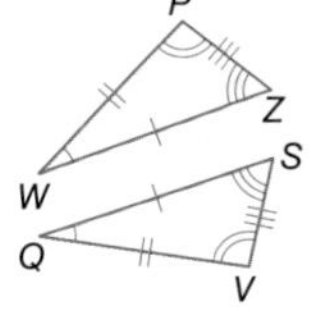

63.

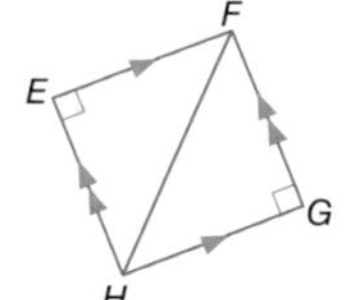

64.

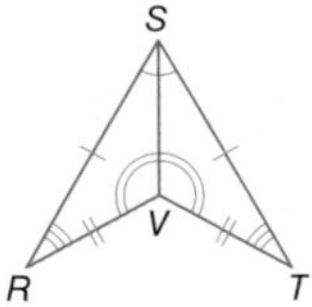

Skills Review

In the figure, $\ell \parallel m$ and $\overline{AC} \parallel \overline{BD}$. Name all pairs of angles for each type indicated. **65, 66. See margin.**

65. alternate interior angles

66. consecutive interior angles

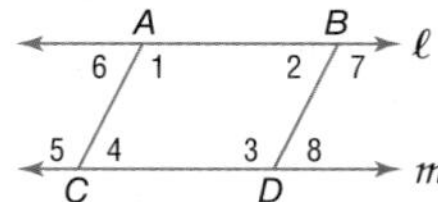

62. $\angle W \cong \angle Q$; $\angle P \cong \angle V$; $\angle Z \cong \angle S$; $\overline{WP} \cong \overline{QV}$; $\overline{PZ} \cong \overline{VS}$; $\overline{WZ} \cong \overline{QS}$; $\triangle WPZ \cong \triangle QVS$

63. $\angle E \cong \angle G$; $\angle EFH \cong \angle GHF$; $\angle EHF \cong \angle GFH$; $\overline{EF} \cong \overline{GH}$; $\overline{EH} \cong \overline{GF}$; $\overline{FH} \cong \overline{HF}$; $\triangle EFH \cong \triangle GHF$

64. $\angle R \cong \angle T$; $\angle RSV \cong \angle TSV$; $\angle RVS \cong \angle TVS$; $\overline{RS} \cong \overline{TS}$; $\overline{SV} \cong \overline{SV}$; $\overline{RV} \cong \overline{TV}$; $\triangle RSV \cong \triangle TSV$

65. $\angle 1$ and $\angle 5$, $\angle 4$ and $\angle 6$, $\angle 2$ and $\angle 8$, $\angle 3$ and $\angle 7$

66. $\angle 1$ and $\angle 4$, $\angle 2$ and $\angle 3$, $\angle 1$ and $\angle 2$, $\angle 3$ and $\angle 4$

4 Assess

Crystal Ball Have students describe how to find the sum of the measures of the interior angles of a polygon and how this process may connect to the next lesson about angles of parallelograms.

Additional Answers

51. Always; by the Exterior Angles Sum Theorem, $m\angle QPR = 60$ and $m\angle QRP = 60$. Since the sum of the interior angle measures of a triangle is 180, the measure of $\angle PQR = 180 - m\angle QPR - m\angle QRP = 180 - 60 - 60 = 60$. So, $\triangle PQR$ is an equilateral triangle.

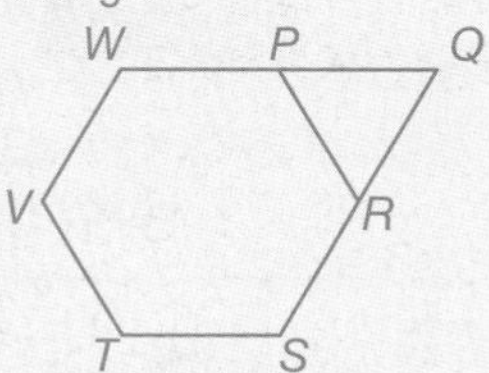

52. 8; Sample answer:

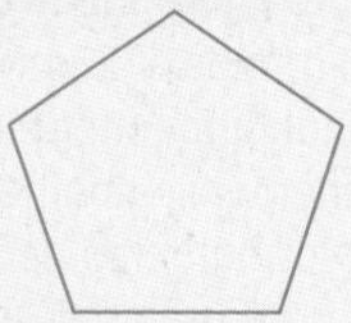

Interior angles sum $= (5 - 2) \cdot 180$ or 540. Twice this sum is 2(540) or 1080. A polygon with this interior angles sum is the solution to $(n - 2) \cdot 180 = 1080$, $n = 8$.

53. The Interior Angles Sum Theorem is derived from the pattern between the number of sides in a polygon and the number of triangles. The formula is the product of the sum of the measures of the angles in a triangle, 180, and the number of triangles in the polygon.

1 Focus

Objective Explore the sum of the measures of the interior and exterior angles of a polygon using a spreadsheet.

Materials

- computer
- spreadsheet program

Teaching Tip

Students may use the "Fill-down" feature of a spreadsheet to enter the data in columns one and two. Students should notice that they can find the sum of the interior angles for a many-sided polygon this way, including a polygon with 115 sides (Exercise 7).

2 Teach

Working in Cooperative Groups

Arrange students in groups of 2, mixing abilities. Ask one student to enter the data into the computer while another student reads the information to be entered. Then have groups complete Exercises 1–4.

Ask:

- What is the advantage of a spreadsheet? You are able to enter data once and then build upon that data.
- What is the disadvantage of using a spreadsheet? Typing mistakes can make your outcomes incorrect.

Practice Have students complete Exercises 5–8.

EXTEND 6-1

Spreadsheet Lab: Angles of Polygons

It is possible to find the interior and exterior measurements along with the sum of the interior angles of any regular polygon with *n* number of sides by using a spreadsheet.

PT

Activity

Design a spreadsheet using the following steps.

- Label the columns as shown in the spreadsheet below.
- Enter the digits 3–10 in the first column.
- The number of triangles in a polygon is 2 fewer than the number of sides. Write a formula for Cell B1 to subtract 2 from each number in Cell A1.
- Enter a formula for Cell C1 so the spreadsheet will calculate the sum of the measures of the interior angles. Remember that the formula is $S = (n - 2)180$.
- Continue to enter formulas so that the indicated computation is performed. Then, copy each formula through Row 9. The final spreadsheet will appear as below.

Polygons and Angles

	A	B	C	D	E	F
1	Number of Sides	Number of Triangles	Sum of Measures of Interior Angles	Measure of Each Interior Angle	Measure of Each Exterior Angle	Measures of Exterior Angles
2	3	1	180	60	120	360
3	4	2	360	90	90	360
4	5	3	540	108	72	360
5	6	4	720	120	60	360
6	7	5	900	128.57	51.43	360
7	8	6	1080	135	45	360
8	9	7	1260	140	40	360
9	10	8	1440	144	36	360

Sheet 1 Sheet 2 Sheet 3

Exercises

1. Write the formula to find the measure of each interior angle in the polygon. =C2/A2
2. Write the formula to find the sum of the measures of the exterior angles. =A2*E2
3. What is the measure of each interior angle if the number of sides is 1? 2? −180, 0
4. Is it possible to have values of 1 and 2 for the number of sides? Explain. No, a polygon is a closed figure formed by coplanar segments.

For Exercises 5–8, use the spreadsheet.

5. How many triangles are in a polygon with 17 sides? 15
6. Find the measure of an exterior angle of a regular polygon with 16 sides. 22.5
7. Find the measure of an interior angle of a regular polygon with 115 sides. 176.9
8. If the measure of the exterior angles is 0, find the measure of the interior angles. Is this possible? Explain. Each interior angle measures 180. This is not possible for a polygon.

3 Assess

Formative Assessment

In Exercises 5–8, check student answers to assess if students have entered their formulas correctly into the spreadsheet.

From Concrete to Abstract

Have students predict the interior and exterior angles of a regular convex polygon with 360 sides using the information from above.

LESSON 6-2 Parallelograms

Then

- You classified polygons with four sides as quadrilaterals.

Now

1. Recognize and apply properties of the sides and angles of parallelograms.
2. Recognize and apply properties of the diagonals of parallelograms.

Why?

- The arm of the basketball goal shown can be adjusted to a height of 10 feet or 5 feet. Notice that as the height is adjusted, each pair of opposite sides of the quadrilateral formed by the arms remains parallel.

NewVocabulary
parallelogram

Common Core State Standards

Content Standards
G.CO.11 Prove theorems about parallelograms.
G.GPE.4 Use coordinates to prove simple geometric theorems algebraically.

Mathematical Practices
4 Model with mathematics.
3 Construct viable arguments and critique the reasoning of others.

1 Sides and Angles of Parallelograms

A **parallelogram** is a quadrilateral with both pairs of opposite sides parallel. To name a parallelogram, use the symbol ▱. In ▱$ABCD$, $\overline{BC} \parallel \overline{AD}$ and $\overline{AB} \parallel \overline{DC}$ by definition.

Other properties of parallelograms are given in the theorems below.

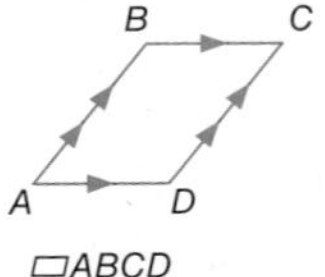

▱ABCD

Theorem Properties of Parallelograms

6.3 If a quadrilateral is a parallelogram, then its opposite sides are congruent.

Abbreviation *Opp. sides of a ▱ are ≅.*

Example If $JKLM$ is a parallelogram, then $\overline{JK} \cong \overline{ML}$ and $\overline{JM} \cong \overline{KL}$.

6.4 If a quadrilateral is a parallelogram, then its opposite angles are congruent.

Abbreviation *Opp. ∡ of a ▱ are ≅.*

Example If $JKLM$ is a parallelogram, then $\angle J \cong \angle L$ and $\angle K \cong \angle M$.

6.5 If a quadrilateral is a parallelogram, then its consecutive angles are supplementary.

Abbreviation *Cons. ∡ in a ▱ are supplementary.*

Example If $JKLM$ is a parallelogram, then $x + y = 180$.

6.6 If a parallelogram has one right angle, then it has four right angles.

Abbreviation *If a ▱ has 1 rt. ∠, it has 4 rt. ∠s.*

Example In ▱$JKLM$, if $\angle J$ is a right angle, then $\angle K$, $\angle L$, and $\angle M$ are also right angles.

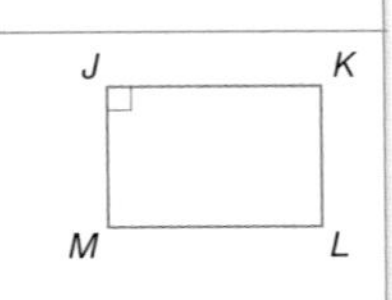

You will prove Theorems 6.3, 6.5, and 6.6 in Exercises 28, 26, and 7, respectively.

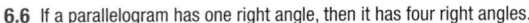

1 Focus

VerticalAlignment

Before Lesson 6-2 Classify polygons with four sides as quadrilaterals.

Lesson 6-2 Recognize and apply properties of the sides and angles of parallelograms. Recognize and apply properties of the diagonals of parallelograms.

After Lesson 6-2 Recognize the conditions that ensure that a quadrilateral is a parallelogram.

2 Teach

Scaffolding Questions

Have students read the **Why?** section of the lesson.

Ask:

- What properties make the figure formed by the arms, the post, and the goal a parallelogram? The arms are always parallel and the post and the goal are always parallel.
- What happens to the measure of the angles as the goal is lowered from 10 feet to 5 feet? The acute angles become obtuse and the obtuse angles become acute.

(continued on the next page)

Lesson 6-2 Resources

Resource	Approaching Level AL	On Level OL	Beyond Level BL	English Learners ELL
Teacher Edition	▪ Differentiated Instruction, p. 405	▪ Differentiated Instruction, pp. 405, 408	▪ Differentiated Instruction, p. 408	
Chapter Resource Masters	▪ Study Guide and Intervention, pp. 11–12 ▪ Skills Practice, p. 13 ▪ Practice, p. 14 ▪ Word Problem Practice, p. 15	▪ Study Guide and Intervention, pp. 11–12 ▪ Skills Practice, p. 13 ▪ Practice, p. 14 ▪ Word Problem Practice, p. 15 ▪ Enrichment, p. 16	▪ Practice, p. 14 ▪ Word Problem Practice, p. 15 ▪ Enrichment, p. 16	▪ Study Guide and Intervention, pp. 11–12 ▪ Skills Practice, p. 13 ▪ Practice, p. 14 ▪ Word Problem Practice, p. 15
Other	▪ 5-Minute Check 6-2 ▪ Study Notebook	▪ 5-Minute Check 6-2 ▪ Study Notebook	▪ 5-Minute Check 6-2 ▪ Study Notebook	▪ 5-Minute Check 6-2 ▪ Study Notebook

- What conjectures can you make about the relationship among and between the four angles regardless of the height of the goal? The sum of the four angle measures will always equal 360. Opposite angles will always be congruent. If one of the angle measures equals 90, then all of the angle measures will equal 90.

1 Sides and Angles of Parallelograms

Example 1 shows how to use the properties of parallelograms to find missing measures.

Formative Assessment

Use the Guided Practice exercises after each example to determine students' understanding of concepts.

Additional Example

1

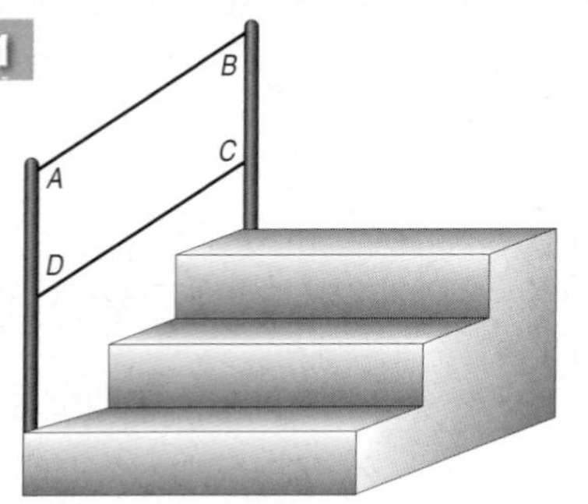

CONSTRUCTION In $\square ABCD$, suppose $m\angle B = 32$, $CD = 80$ inches, $BC = 15$ inches. Find each measure.

a. AD 15 in.

b. $m\angle C$ 148

c. $m\angle D$ 32

Additional Examples also in Interactive Classroom PowerPoint® Presentations

StudyTip

Including a Figure Theorems are presented in general terms. In a proof, you must include a drawing so that you can refer to segments and angles specifically.

Proof Theorem 6.4

Write a two-column proof of Theorem 6.4.

Given: $\square FGHJ$

Prove: $\angle F \cong \angle H$, $\angle J \cong \angle G$

Proof:

Statements	Reasons
1. $\square FGHJ$	1. Given
2. $\overline{FG} \parallel \overline{JH}$; $\overline{FJ} \parallel \overline{GH}$	2. Definition of parallelogram
3. $\angle F$ and $\angle J$ are supplementary. $\angle J$ and $\angle H$ are supplementary. $\angle H$ and $\angle G$ are supplementary.	3. If parallel lines are cut by a transversal, consecutive interior angles are supplementary.
4. $\angle F \cong \angle H$, $\angle J \cong \angle G$	4. Supplements of the same angles are congruent.

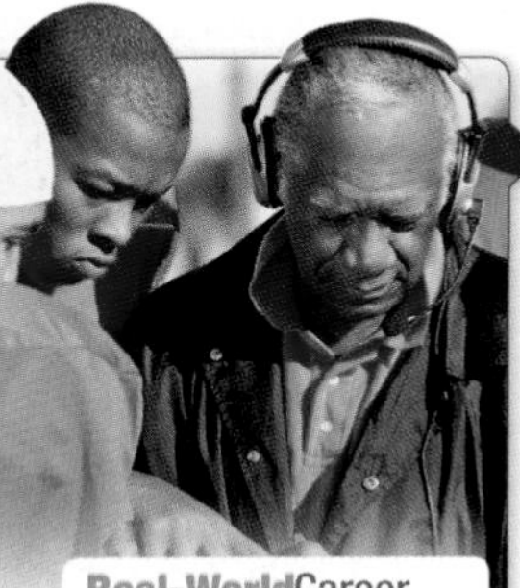

Real-WorldCareer

Coach Coaches organize amateur and professional atheletes, teaching them the fundamentals of a sport. They manage teams during both practice sessions and competitions. Additional tasks may include selecting and issuing sports equiment, materials, and supplies. Head coaches at public secondary schools usually have a bachelor's degree.

Real-World Example 1 Use Properties of Parallelograms

BASKETBALL In $\square ABCD$, suppose $m\angle A = 55$, $AB = 2.5$ feet, and $BC = 1$ foot. Find each measure.

a. DC

$DC = AB$ — Opp. sides of a $\square$ are $\cong$.

$= 2.5$ ft — Substitution

b. $m\angle B$

$m\angle B + m\angle A = 180$ — Cons. ∡ in a $\square$ are supplementary.

$m\angle B + 55 = 180$ — Substitution

$m\angle B = 125$ — Subtract 55 from each side.

c. $m\angle C$

$m\angle C = m\angle A$ — Opp. ∡ of a $\square$ are $\cong$.

$= 55$ — Substitution

GuidedPractice

1. MIRRORS The wall-mounted mirror shown uses parallelograms that change shape as the arm is extended. In $\square JKLM$, suppose $m\angle J = 47$. Find each measure.

A. $m\angle L$ 47 **B.** $m\angle M$ 133

C. Suppose the arm was extended further so that $m\angle J = 90$. What would be the measure of each of the other angles? Justify your answer.

1C. Each of the other angle measures would be 90 by Theorem 6.6.

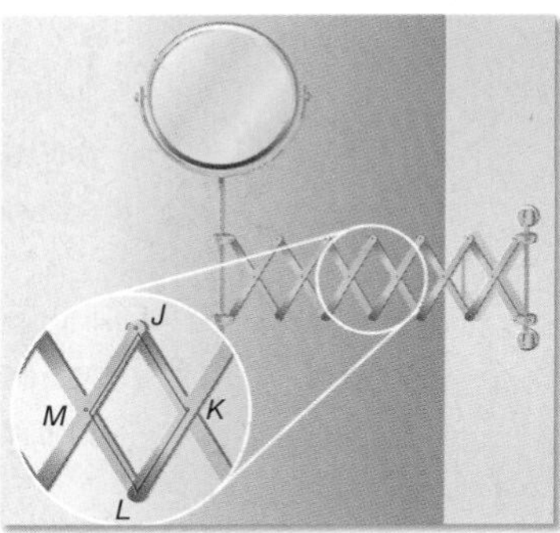

WatchOut!

Parallelograms Theorems 6.3–6.6 apply only if you already know the figure is a parallelogram. In particular, the converse of Theorem 6.6 is not true.

Tips for New Teachers

Parallelograms Before telling students Theorems 6.3-6.6, have them brainstorm what properties they think will be true for a parallelogram.

2 Diagonals of Parallelograms

The diagonals of a parallelogram have special properties as well.

Theorem Diagonals of Parallelograms

6.7 If a quadrilateral is a parallelogram, then its diagonals bisect each other.

Abbreviation *Diag. of a ▱ bisect each other.*

Example If *ABCD* is a parallelogram, then $\overline{AP} \cong \overline{PC}$ and $\overline{DP} \cong \overline{PB}$.

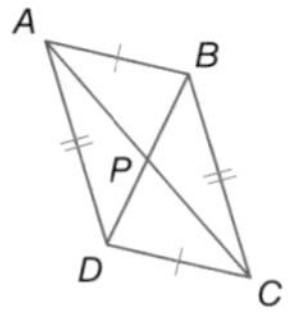

6.8 If a quadrilateral is a parallelogram, then each diagonal separates the parallelogram into two congruent triangles.

Abbreviation *Diag. separates a ▱ into 2 ≅ △s.*

Example If *ABCD* is a parallelogram, then $\triangle ABD \cong \triangle CDB$.

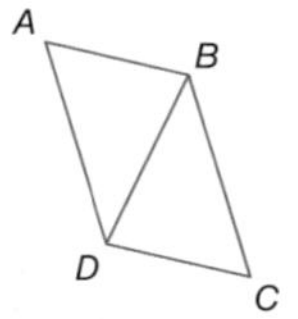

You will prove Theorems 6.7 and 6.8 in Exercises 29 and 27, respectively.

Example 2 Use Properties of Parallelograms and Algebra

ALGEBRA If *QRST* is a parallelogram, find the value of the indicated variable.

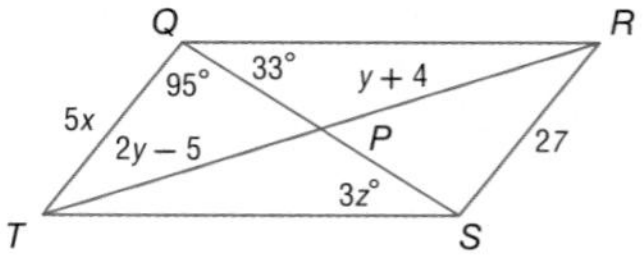

a. x

$\overline{QT} \cong \overline{RS}$	Opp. sides of a ▱ are ≅.
$QT = RS$	Definition of congruence
$5x = 27$	Substitution
$x = 5.4$	Divide each side by 5.

b. y

$\overline{TP} \cong \overline{PR}$	Diag. of a ▱ bisect each other.
$TP = PR$	Definition of congruence
$2y - 5 = y + 4$	Substitution
$y = 9$	Subtract *y* and add 5 to each side.

c. z

$\triangle TQS \cong \triangle RSQ$	Diag. separates a ▱ into 2 ≅ △s.
$\angle QST \cong \angle SQR$	CPCTC
$m\angle QST = m\angle SQR$	Definition of congruence
$3z = 33$	Substitution
$z = 11$	Divide each side by 3.

StudyTip
Congruent Triangles
A parallelogram with two diagonals divides the figure into two pairs of congruent triangles.

GuidedPractice

Find the value of each variable in the given parallelogram.

2A.

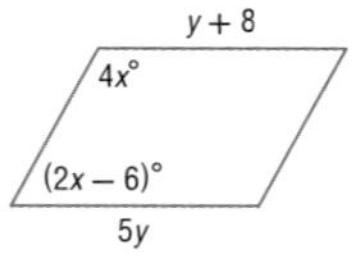

$x = 31$, $y = 2$

2B.

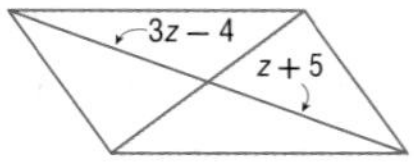

$z = 4.5$

2 Diagonals of Parallelograms

Examples 2–4 shows how to use theorems to prove that diagonals of a parallelogram bisect each other.

Additional Example

2 If *WXYZ* is a parallelogram, find the value of the indicated variable.

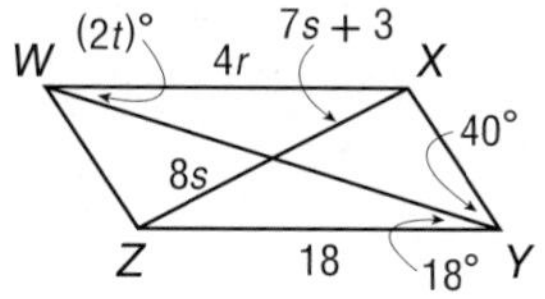

a. r 4.5

b. s 3

c. t 9

Focus on Mathematical Content

Transversals The diagonals of a parallelogram are transversals, and therefore the alternate interior angles are congruent.

Teach with Tech

Interactive Whiteboard Give students several exercises to find the lengths of the diagonals of a parallelogram. Then choose several students to show and explain their work to the class. Save their work and distribute to the class.

DifferentiatedInstruction AL OL

Visual/Spatial Learners Stress that in some parallelograms, the diagonals appear to bisect the opposite angles, but this is not a property of parallelograms. Caution students not to assume that angles are bisected. In Lesson 6-5, students will study rhombi and squares. The diagonals do bisect the opposite angles in these parallelograms.

Additional Examples

3 What are the coordinates of the intersection of the diagonals of parallelogram *MNPR*, with vertices $M(-3, 0)$, $N(-1, 3)$, $P(5, 4)$, and $R(3, 1)$? (1, 2)

4 Write a paragraph proof.

Given: ▱*ABCD*, $\overline{AC}$ and $\overline{BD}$ are diagonals, and point *P* is the intersection of $\overline{AC}$ and $\overline{BD}$.

Prove: $\overline{AC}$ and $\overline{BD}$ bisect each other.

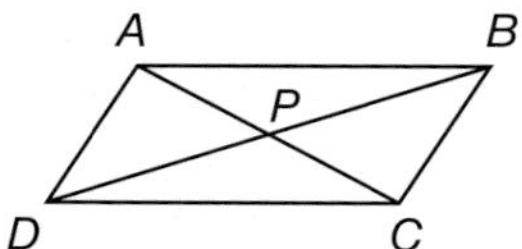

ABCD is a parallelogram and $\overline{AC}$ and $\overline{BD}$ are diagonals; therefore, $\overline{AB} \parallel \overline{DC}$, and $\overline{AC}$ is a transversal. $\angle BAC \cong \angle DCA$ and $\angle ABD \cong \angle CDB$ by the Alt. Int. ∠s Thm. $\overline{AB} \cong \overline{CD}$ since opp. sides of a ▱ are ≅. $\triangle APB \cong \triangle CPD$ by ASA. So, by the properties of congruent triangles $\overline{BP} \cong \overline{DP}$ and $\overline{AP} \cong \overline{CP}$. Therefore, $\overline{AC}$ and $\overline{BD}$ bisect each other.

CCSS Teaching the Mathematical Practices

Regularity Mathematically proficient students maintain oversight of the process, while attending to the details. They continually evaluate the reasonableness of their intermediate results. Encourage students to check the reasonableness of their results.

You can use Theorem 6.7 to determine the coordinates of the intersection of the diagonals of a parallelogram on a coordinate plane given the coordinates of the vertices.

Example 3 Parallelograms and Coordinate Geometry

COORDINATE GEOMETRY Determine the coordinates of the intersection of the diagonals of ▱*FGHJ* with vertices $F(-2, 4)$, $G(3, 5)$, $H(2, -3)$, and $J(-3, -4)$.

Since the diagonals of a parallelogram bisect each other, their intersection point is the midpoint of $\overline{FH}$ and $\overline{GJ}$. Find the midpoint of $\overline{FH}$ with endpoints $(-2, 4)$ and $(2, -3)$.

$$\left(\frac{x_1 + x_2}{2}, \frac{y_1 + y_2}{2}\right) = \left(\frac{-2 + 2}{2}, \frac{4 + (-3)}{2}\right) \quad \text{Midpoint Formula}$$

$$= (0, 0.5) \quad \text{Simplify.}$$

The coordinates of the intersection of the diagonals of ▱*FGHJ* are (0, 0.5).

CHECK Find the midpoint of $\overline{GJ}$ with endpoints (3, 5) and (−3, −4).

$$\left(\frac{3 + (-3)}{2}, \frac{5 + (-4)}{2}\right) = (0, 0.5) \checkmark$$

Study Tip

Regularity Graph the parallelogram in Example 3 and the point of intersection of the diagonals you found. Draw the diagonals. The point of intersection appears to be correct.

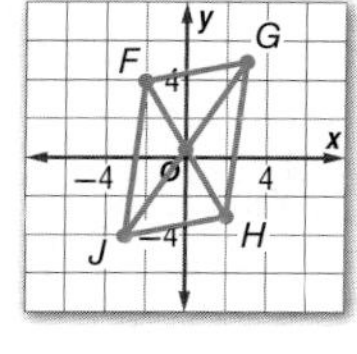

Guided Practice

3. **COORDINATE GEOMETRY** Determine the coordinates of the intersection of the diagonals of *RSTU* with vertices $R(-8, -2)$, $S(-6, 7)$, $T(6, 7)$, and $U(4, -2)$. (−1, 2.5)

You can use the properties of parallelograms and their diagonals to write proofs.

Example 4 Proofs Using the Properties of Parallelograms

Write a paragraph proof.

Given: ▱*ABDG*, $\overline{AF} \cong \overline{CF}$

Prove: $\angle BDG \cong \angle C$

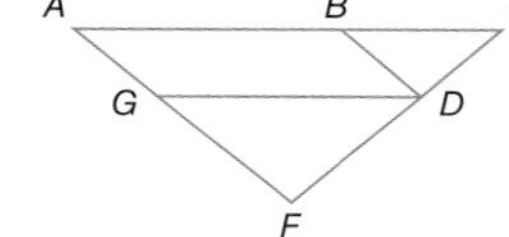

Proof:

We are given *ABDG* is a parallelogram. Since opposite angles in a parallelogram are congruent, $\angle BDG \cong \angle A$. We are also given that $\overline{AF} \cong \overline{CF}$. By the Isosceles Triangle Theorem, $\angle A \cong \angle C$. So, by the Transitive Property of Congruence, $\angle BDG \cong \angle C$.

Guided Practice

4. Write a two-column proof.

Given: ▱*HJKP* and ▱*PKLM*

Prove: $\overline{HJ} \cong \overline{ML}$

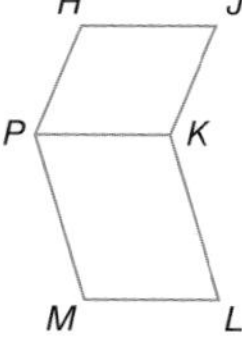

4.
Given: ▱*HJKP* and ▱*PKLM*
Prove: $\overline{HJ} \cong \overline{ML}$

Proof:
Statements (Reasons)
1. ▱ *HJKP* and ▱*PKLM* (Given)
2. $\overline{HJ} \cong \overline{PK}$, $\overline{PK} \cong \overline{ML}$ (Opp. sides of ▱ are ≅.)
3. $\overline{HJ} \cong \overline{ML}$ (Trans. Prop.)

Check Your Understanding

 = Step-by-Step Solutions begin on page R14. 

Example 1

1. **NAVIGATION** To chart a course, sailors use a *parallel ruler.* One edge of the ruler is placed along the line representing the direction of the course to be taken. Then the other ruler is moved until its edge reaches the compass rose printed on the chart. Reading the compass determines which direction to travel. The rulers and the crossbars of the tool form ▱*MNPQ*.

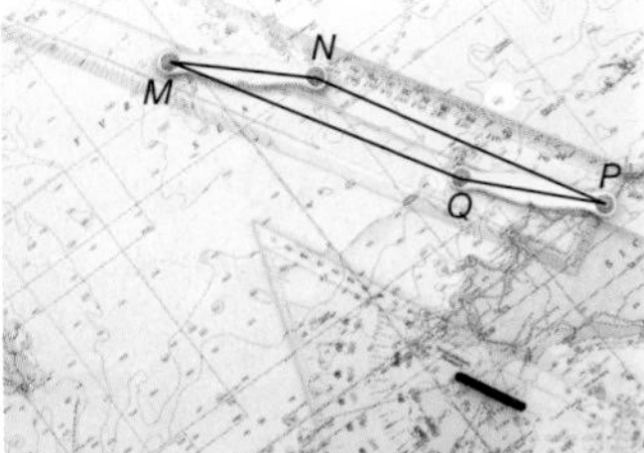

   a. If $m\angle NMQ = 32$, find $m\angle MNP$. 148
   b. If $m\angle MQP = 125$, find $m\angle MNP$. 125
   c. If $MQ = 4$, what is NP? 4

Example 2

ALGEBRA **Find the value of each variable in each parallelogram.**

2. 38

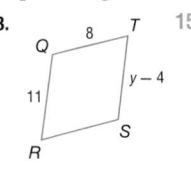

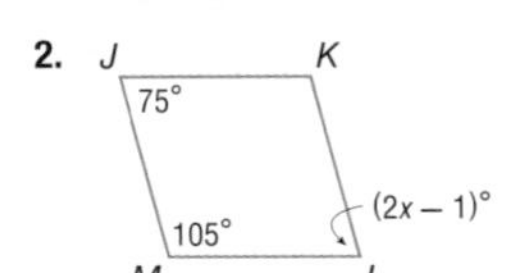

3. 15

Q 8 T
11
y – 4
R S

4. a = 9, b = 8

W X
10
2
a – 7
Y
2b – 6
Z

5. w = 5, b = 4

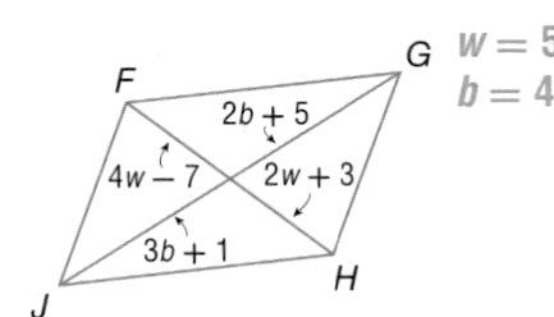

Example 3

6. **COORDINATE GEOMETRY** Determine the coordinates of the intersection of the diagonals of ▱*ABCD* with vertices $A(-4, 6)$, $B(5, 6)$, $C(4, -2)$, and $D(-5, -2)$. (0, 2)

Example 4

CCSS ARGUMENTS **Write the indicated type of proof.** 7, 8. See margin.

7. paragraph

   Given: ▱*ABCD*, ∠*A* is a right angle.
   Prove: ∠*B*, ∠*C*, and ∠*D* are right angles. (Theorem 6.6)

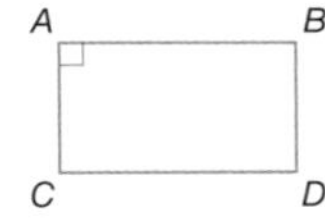

8. two-column

   Given: *ABCH* and *DCGF* are parallelograms.
   Prove: ∠*A* ≅ ∠*F*

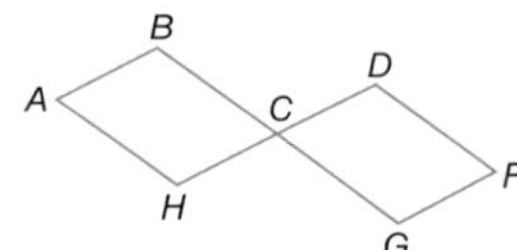

Practice and Problem Solving

Extra Practice is on page R6.

Example 1

Use ▱*PQRS* to find each measure.

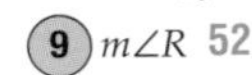

9. $m\angle R$ 52
10. QR 3
11. QP 5
12. $m\angle S$ 128

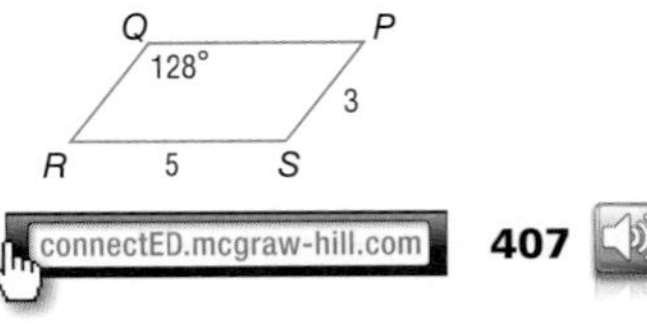

Differentiated Homework Options

Level	Assignment	Two-Day Option	
AL Basic	9–25, 42–62	9–25 odd, 46–49	10–24 even, 42–45, 50–62
OL Core	9–37 odd, 38–40, 42–62	9–25, 46–49	27–40, 42–45, 50–62
BL Advanced	26–59, (optional: 60–62)		

3 Practice

Formative Assessment

Use Exercises 1–8 to check for understanding.

Then use the chart at the bottom of this page to customize assignments for your students.

CCSS Teaching the Mathematical Practices

Arguments Mathematically proficient students understand and use stated assumptions and definitions in constructing arguments. They make conjectures and build a logical progression of statements to explore the truth of their conjectures. In Exercises 7–8, encourage students to review the properties of parallelograms before starting the proofs.

Additional Answers

7. **Given:** ▱*ABCD*, ∠*A* is a right angle.

   Prove: ∠*B*, ∠*C*, and ∠*D* are right angles. (Theorem 6.6)

   Proof: By definition of a parallelogram, $\overline{AB} \parallel \overline{CD}$. Since ∠*A* is a right angle, $\overline{AC} \perp \overline{AB}$. By the Perpendicular Transversal Theorem, $\overline{AC} \perp \overline{CD}$. ∠*C* is a right angle, because perpendicular lines form a right angle. ∠*B* ≅ ∠*C* and ∠*A* ≅ ∠*D* because opposite angles in a parallelogram are congruent. ∠*C* and ∠*D* are right angles, since all right angles are congruent.

8. **Given:** *ABCH* and *DCGF* are parallelograms.

   Prove: ∠*A* ≅ ∠*F*

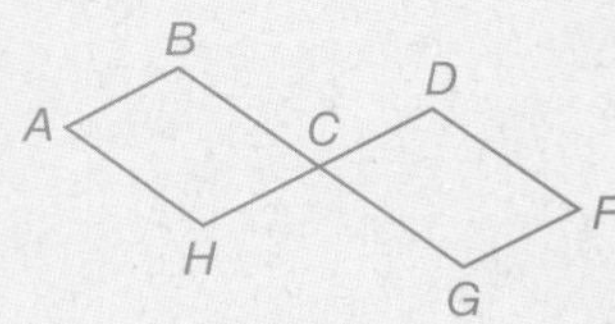

Proof:

Statements (Reasons)

1. *ABCH* and *DCGF* are parallelograms. (Given)
2. ∠*BCH* ≅ ∠*DCG* (Vert. ∠s are ≅)
3. ∠*A* ≅ ∠*BCH* and ∠*DCG* ≅ ∠*F* (Opp. ∠s of a ▱ are ≅.)
4. ∠*A* ≅ ∠*F* (Subst.)

13. HOME DECOR The slats on Venetian blinds are designed to remain parallel in order to direct the path of light coming in a window. In ▱$FGHJ$, $FJ = \frac{3}{4}$ inch, $FG = 1$ inch, and $m\angle JHG = 62$. Find each measure.

a. JH 1 in.

b. GH $\frac{3}{4}$ in.

c. $m\angle JFG$ 62

d. $m\angle FJH$ 118

14. CCSS MODELING Wesley is a member of the kennel club in his area. His club uses accordion fencing like the section shown at the right to block out areas at dog shows.

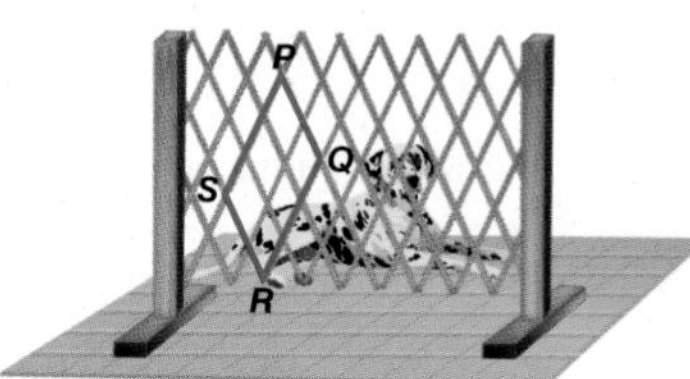

a. Identify two pairs of congruent segments. $\overline{PS} \cong \overline{QR}$, $\overline{PQ} \cong \overline{SR}$

b. Identify two pairs of supplementary angles. Sample answer: $\angle P$ and $\angle Q$, $\angle S$ and $\angle R$

Example 2 **ALGEBRA Find the value of each variable in each parallelogram.**

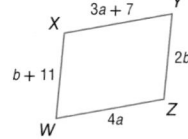

15. $a = 7$, $b = 11$
16. $x = 79$, $y = 101$
17. $x = 5$, $y = 17$
18. $a = 2$, $b = 3$
19. $x = 58$, $y = 63.5$
20. $z = 2$, $y = 5$

15.

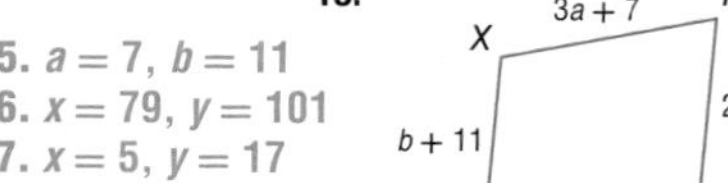

16.

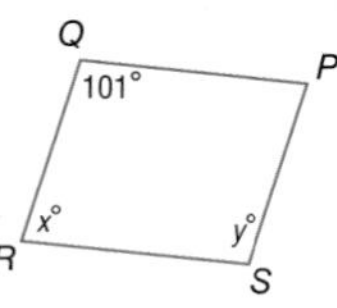

17.

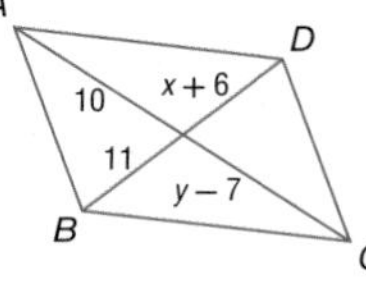

18.

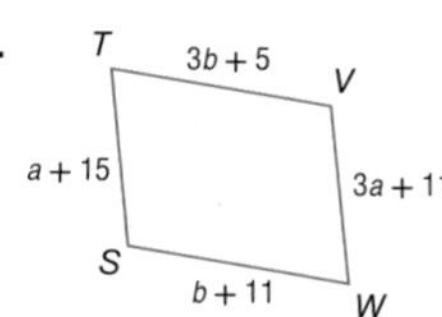

19.

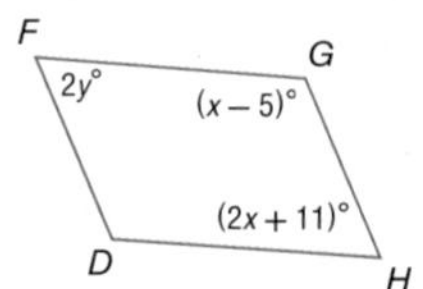

20.

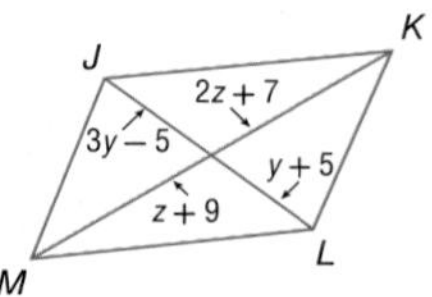

Example 3 **COORDINATE GEOMETRY Find the coordinates of the intersection of the diagonals of ▱$WXYZ$ with the given vertices.**

21. $W(-1, 7)$, $X(8, 7)$, $Y(6, -2)$, $Z(-3, -2)$ (2.5, 2.5)

22. $W(-4, 5)$, $X(5, 7)$, $Y(4, -2)$, $Z(-5, -4)$ (0, 1.5)

Example 4 **PROOF Write a two-column proof.** 23, 24. See margin.

23. Given: $WXTV$ and $ZYVT$ are parallelograms.
Prove: $\overline{WX} \cong \overline{ZY}$

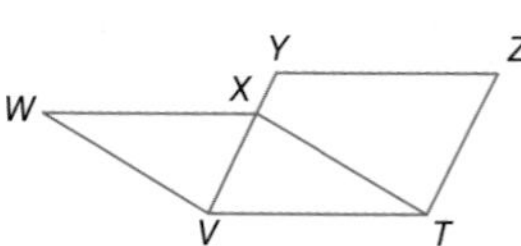

24. Given: ▱$BDHA$, $\overline{CA} \cong \overline{CG}$
Prove: $\angle BDH \cong \angle G$

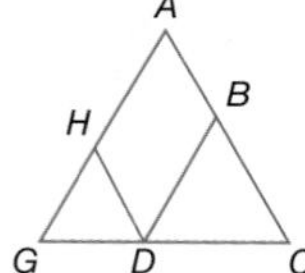

CCSS Teaching the Mathematical Practices

Modeling Mathematically proficient students can apply the mathematics they know to solve problems arising in everyday life. In Exercise 14, encourage students to copy the parallelogram onto their papers.

Additional Answers

23. Given: $WXTV$ and $ZYVT$ are parallelograms.
Prove: $\overline{WX} \cong \overline{ZY}$

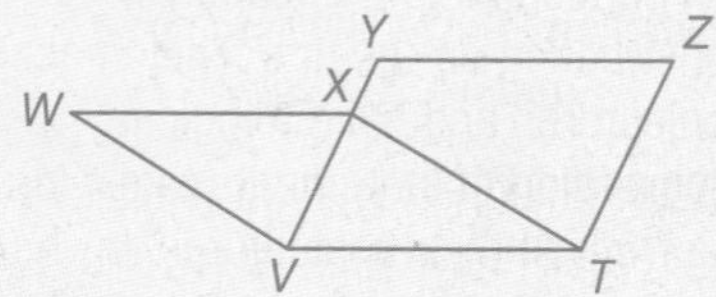

Proof:

Statements (Reasons)

1. $WXTV$ and $ZYVT$ are parallelograms. (Given)
2. $\overline{WX} \cong \overline{VT}$, $\overline{VT} \cong \overline{YZ}$ (Opp. sides of a ▱ are ≅.)
3. $\overline{WX} \cong \overline{ZY}$ (Trans. Prop.)

24. Given: ▱$BDHA$, $\overline{CA} \cong \overline{CG}$
Prove: $\angle BDH \cong \angle G$

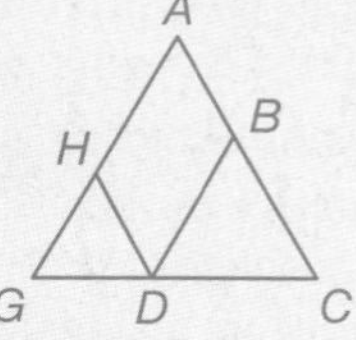

Proof:

Statements (Reasons)

1. ▱$BDHA$, $\overline{CA} \cong \overline{CG}$ (Given)
2. $\angle A \cong \angle BDH$ (Opp. ∠s of a ▱ are ≅.)
3. $\angle A \cong \angle G$ (Isos. △ Thm.)
4. $\angle BDH \cong \angle G$ (Trans. Prop.)

Differentiated Instruction OL BL

Extension Have students construct a parallelogram that lies within all four quadrants of a coordinate grid. Then have students draw the diagonals of the figure. Next, have students draw two dilations of the figure on the same coordinate grid using scale factors 0.5 and 2. Students should include the diagonals on the dilation figures also. Have students journal about the relationship between the interior angles of all three figures and the diagonals of all three figures. Performing dilations on a parallelogram does not change the measure of the interior angles of the subsequent figures. All of the corresponding diagonals are parallel.

25. FLAGS Refer to the Alabama state flag at the right. **See Ch. 6 Answer Appendix.**

Given: $\triangle ACD \cong \triangle CAB$

Prove: $\overline{DP} \cong \overline{PB}$

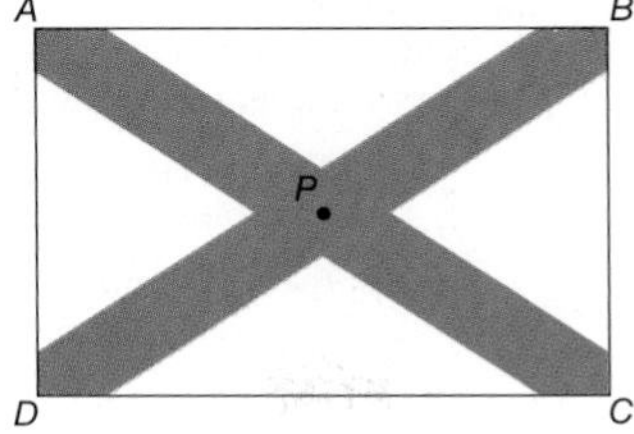

CCSS ARGUMENTS Write the indicated type of proof. 26–29. See Ch. 6 Answer Appendix.

26. two-column
Given: ▱$GKLM$
Prove: $\angle G$ and $\angle K$, $\angle K$ and $\angle L$, $\angle L$ and $\angle M$, and $\angle M$ and $\angle G$ are supplementary. (Theorem 6.5)

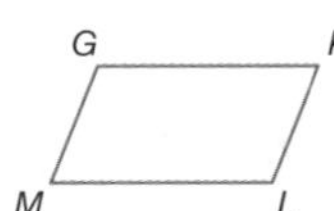

27. two-column
Given: ▱$WXYZ$
Prove: $\triangle WXZ \cong \triangle YZX$ (Theorem 6.8)

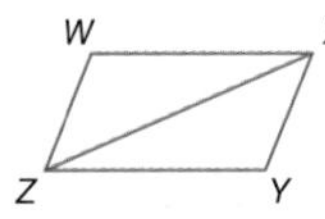

28. two-column
Given: ▱$PQRS$
Prove: $\overline{PQ} \cong \overline{RS}$, $\overline{QR} \cong \overline{SP}$ (Theorem 6.3)

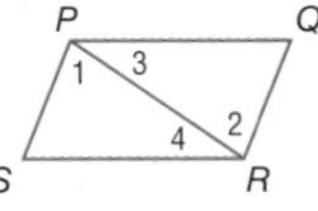

29. paragraph
Given: ▱$ACDE$ is a parallelogram.
Prove: $\overline{EC}$ bisects $\overline{AD}$. (Theorem 6.7)

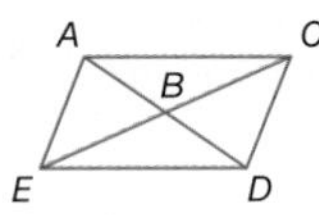

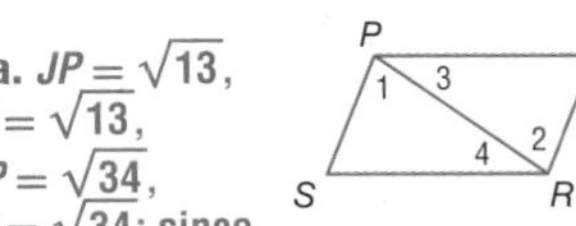

30a. $JP = \sqrt{13}$, $LP = \sqrt{13}$, $MP = \sqrt{34}$, $KP = \sqrt{34}$; since $JP = LP$ and $MP = KP$, the diagonals bisect each other.
30b. No; $JP + LP \neq MP + KP$.
30c. No; the slope of $\overline{JK} = 0$ and the slope of $\overline{JM} = 2$. The slopes are not negative reciprocals of each other.

30. COORDINATE GEOMETRY Use the graph shown.

a. Use the Distance Formula to determine if the diagonals of $JKLM$ bisect each other. Explain.

b. Determine whether the diagonals are congruent. Explain.

c. Use slopes to determine if the consecutive sides are perpendicular. Explain.

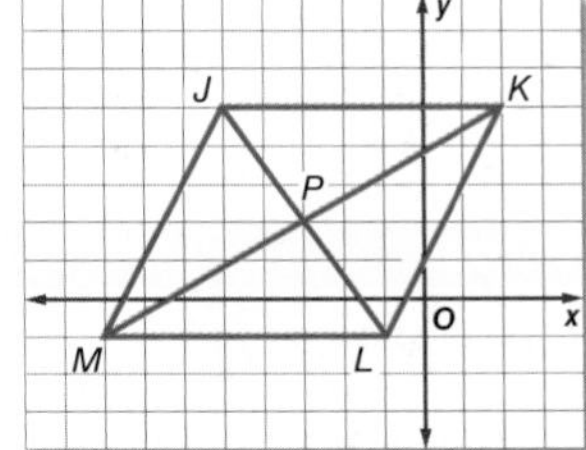

ALGEBRA Use ▱$ABCD$ to find each measure or value.

31. x **3**

32. y **6**

33. $m\angle AFB$ **131**

34. $m\angle DAC$ **72**

35. $m\angle ACD$ **29**

36. $m\angle DAB$ **101**

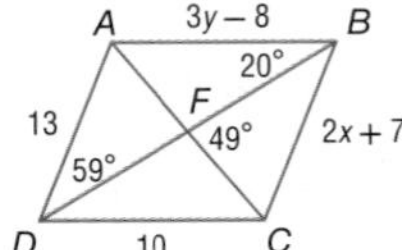

37. COORDINATE GEOMETRY ▱$ABCD$ has vertices $A(-3, 5)$, $B(1, 2)$, and $C(3, -4)$. Determine the coordinates of vertex D if it is located in Quadrant III. **(–1, –1)**

CCSS Teaching the Mathematical Practices

Arguments Mathematically proficient students understand and use stated assumptions and definitions in constructing arguments. They make conjectures and build a logical progression of statements to explore the truth of their conjectures. In Exercises 26–29, encourage students to work together to write the proofs.

Enrichment
OL BL

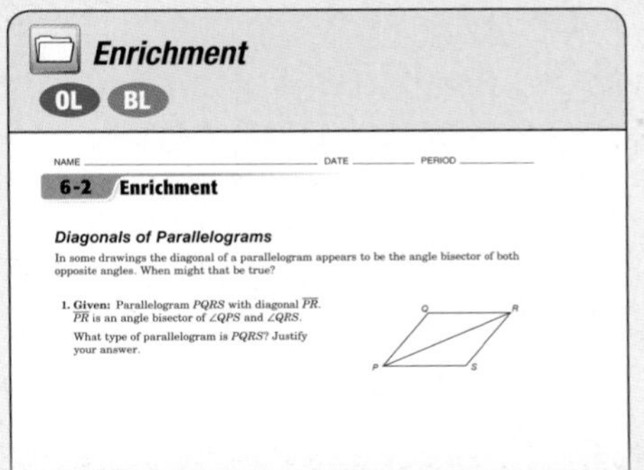

NAME ______ DATE ______ PERIOD ______

6-2 Enrichment

Diagonals of Parallelograms

In some drawings the diagonal of a parallelogram appears to be the angle bisector of both opposite angles. When might that be true?

1. Given: Parallelogram $PQRS$ with diagonal $\overline{PR}$. $\overline{PR}$ is an angle bisector of $\angle QPS$ and $\angle QRS$. What type of parallelogram is $PQRS$? Justify your answer.

Study Guide and Intervention
AL OL ELL

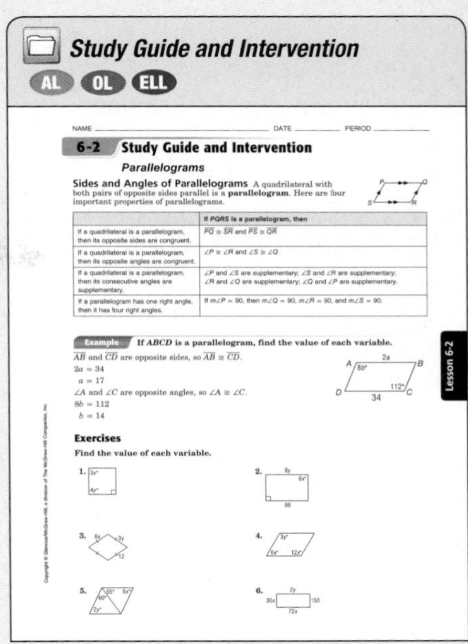

NAME ______ DATE ______ PERIOD ______

6-2 Study Guide and Intervention

Parallelograms

Sides and Angles of Parallelograms A quadrilateral with both pairs of opposite sides parallel is a **parallelogram**. Here are four important properties of parallelograms.

	If PQRS is a parallelogram, then
If a quadrilateral is a parallelogram, then its opposite sides are congruent.	$\overline{PQ} \cong \overline{SR}$ and $\overline{PS} \cong \overline{QR}$
If a quadrilateral is a parallelogram, then its opposite angles are congruent.	$\angle P \cong \angle R$ and $\angle S \cong \angle Q$
If a quadrilateral is a parallelogram, then its consecutive angles are supplementary.	$\angle P$ and $\angle S$ are supplementary; $\angle S$ and $\angle R$ are supplementary; $\angle R$ and $\angle Q$ are supplementary; $\angle Q$ and $\angle P$ are supplementary.
If a parallelogram has one right angle, then it has four right angles.	If $m\angle P = 90$, then $m\angle Q = 90$, $m\angle R = 90$, and $m\angle S = 90$.

Example If $ABCD$ is a parallelogram, find the value of each variable.

$\overline{AB}$ and $\overline{CD}$ are opposite sides, so $\overline{AB} \cong \overline{CD}$.
$2a = 34$
$a = 17$
$\angle A$ and $\angle C$ are opposite angles, so $\angle A \cong \angle C$.
$8b = 112$
$b = 14$

Exercises

Find the value of each variable.

Lesson 6-2

Practice
AL OL BL ELL

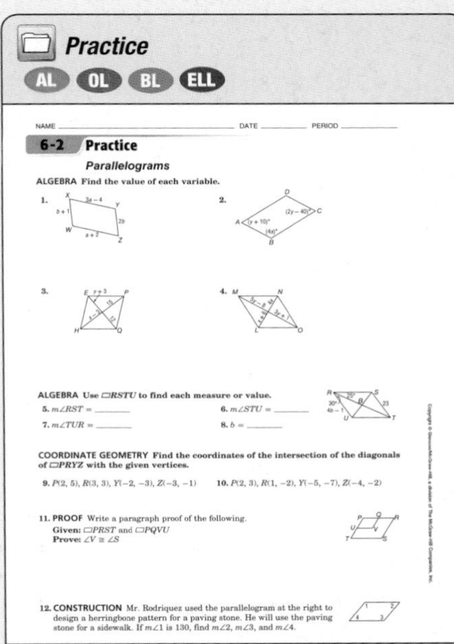

NAME ______ DATE ______ PERIOD ______

6-2 Practice

Parallelograms

ALGEBRA Find the value of each variable.

ALGEBRA Use ▱$RSTU$ to find each measure or value.

5. $m\angle RST$ = ______ 6. $m\angle STU$ = ______
7. $m\angle TUR$ = ______ 8. b = ______

COORDINATE GEOMETRY Find the coordinates of the intersection of the diagonals of ▱$PRYZ$ with the given vertices.

9. $P(2, 5)$, $R(3, 3)$, $Y(-2, -3)$, $Z(-3, -1)$ 10. $P(2, 3)$, $R(1, -2)$, $Y(-5, -7)$, $Z(-4, -2)$

11. **PROOF** Write a paragraph proof of the following.
Given: ▱$PRST$ and ▱$PQVU$
Prove: $\angle V \cong \angle S$

12. **CONSTRUCTION** Mr. Rodriques used the parallelogram at the right to design a herringbone pattern for a paving stone. He will use the paving stone for a sidewalk. If $m\angle 1$ is 130, find $m\angle 2$, $m\angle 3$, and $m\angle 4$.

Word Problem Practice
AL OL BL ELL

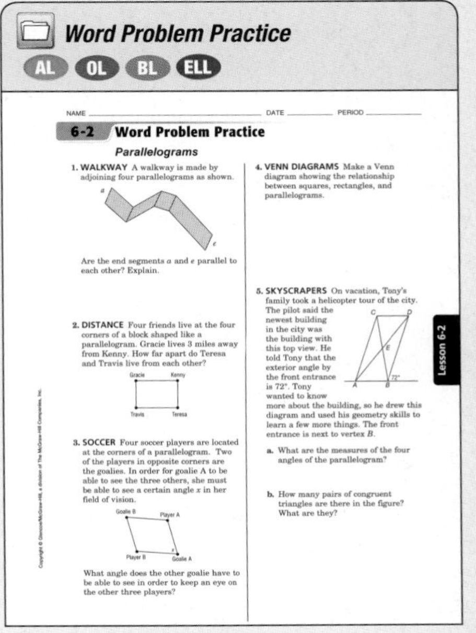

NAME ______ DATE ______ PERIOD ______

6-2 Word Problem Practice

Parallelograms

1. **WALKWAY** A walkway is made by adjoining four parallelograms as shown.

Are the end segments a and e parallel to each other? Explain.

2. **DISTANCE** Four friends live at the four corners of a block shaped like a parallelogram. Gracie lives 3 miles away from Kenny. How far apart do Teresa and Travis live from each other?

3. **SOCCER** Four soccer players are located at the corners of a parallelogram. Two of the players in opposite corners are the goalies. In order for goalie A to be able to see the three others, she must be able to see a certain angle x in her field of vision.

What angle does the other goalie have to be able to see in order to keep an eye on the other three players?

4. **VENN DIAGRAMS** Make a Venn diagram showing the relationship between squares, rectangles, and parallelograms.

5. **SKYSCRAPERS** On vacation, Tony's family took a helicopter tour of the city. The pilot said the newest building in the city was the building with this top view. He told Tony that the exterior angle by the front entrance is 72°. Tony wanted to know more about the building, so he drew this diagram and used his geometry skills to learn a few more things. The front entrance is next to vertex B.

a. What are the measures of the four angles of the parallelogram?

b. How many pairs of congruent triangles are there in the figure? What are they?

Lesson 6-2

Exercise Alert

Ruler, Protractor, and Compass Exercise 40 requires the use of a ruler, a protractor, and a compass.

Multiple Representations

In Exercise 40, students use geometric sketches, a table, and verbal description to investigate a test for when a quadrilateral is a parallelogram.

Additional Answers

38a. $\angle C$, $\angle E$, $\angle G$; sample answer: $\angle C$ is congruent to $\angle A$ because opposite angles of parallelograms are congruent. $\angle E$ is congruent to $\angle A$ because the parallelograms are congruent, and $\angle G$ is congruent to $\angle E$ because opposite angles of parallelograms are congruent and congruent to $\angle A$ by the Transitive Property.

38b. $\overline{AD}$, $\overline{DE}$, $\overline{GF}$; sample answer: $\overline{AD}$ is congruent to $\overline{BC}$ because opposite sides of parallelograms are congruent. $\overline{DE}$ is congruent to $\overline{BC}$ because the parallelograms are congruent, and $\overline{GF}$ is congruent to $\overline{DE}$ because opposite sides of parallelograms are congruent and congruent to $\overline{BC}$ by the Transitive Property.

38c. $\angle ABC$, $\angle ADC$, $\angle EDG$, $\angle EFG$; sample answer: Angles ABC and ADC are supplementary to $\angle C$ because consecutive angles of parallelograms are supplementary. $\angle EDG$ is supplementary to $\angle C$ because it is congruent to $\angle ADC$ by the Vertical angles Theorem and supplementary to $\angle C$ by substitution. $\angle EFG$ is congruent to $\angle EDG$ because opposite angles of parallelograms are congruent and it is supplementary to $\angle C$ by substitution.

39. Given: ▱$YWVZ$, $\overline{VX} \perp \overline{WY}$, $\overline{YU} \perp \overline{VZ}$

Prove: $\triangle YUZ \cong \triangle VXW$

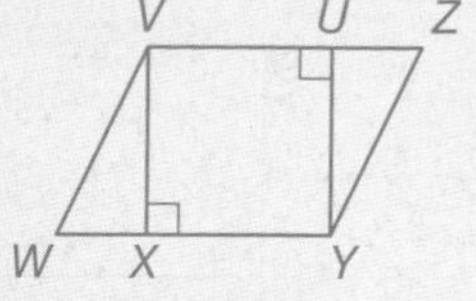

38. MECHANICS Scissor lifts are variable elevation work platforms. One is shown at the right. In the diagram, $ABCD$ and $DEFG$ are congruent parallelograms. **a–c. See margin.**

a. List the angle(s) congruent to $\angle A$. Explain your reasoning.

b. List the segment(s) congruent to $\overline{BC}$. Explain your reasoning.

c. List the angle(s) supplementary to $\angle C$. Explain your reasoning.

PROOF **Write a two-column proof.**

39. **Given:** ▱$YWVZ$, $\overline{VX} \perp \overline{WY}$, $\overline{YU} \perp \overline{VZ}$
Prove: $\triangle YUZ \cong \triangle VXW$ **See margin.**

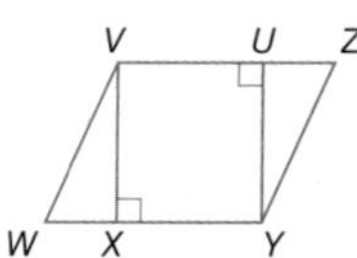

40. MULTIPLE REPRESENTATIONS In this problem, you will explore tests for parallelograms.

a. **Geometric** Draw three pairs of segments that are both congruent and parallel and connect the endpoints to form quadrilaterals. Label one quadrilateral $ABCD$, one $MNOP$, and one $WXYZ$. Measure and label the sides and angles of the quadrilaterals. **See margin.**

b. **Tabular** Copy and complete the table below.

Quadrilateral	Opposite Sides Congruent?	Opposite Angles Congruent?	Parallelogram
ABCD	yes	yes	yes
MNOP	yes	yes	yes
WXYZ	yes	yes	yes

c. **Verbal** Make a conjecture about quadrilaterals with one pair of segments that are both congruent and parallel. **Sample answer: If a quadrilateral has a pair of sides that are ≅ and ∥, then the quadrilateral is a parallelogram.**

45. Sample answer: In a parallelogram, the opp. sides and ∡ are ≅. Two consecutive ∡ in a ▱ are supplementary. If one angle of a ▱ is right, then all the angles are right. The diagonals of a parallelogram bisect each other.

H.O.T. Problems Use Higher-Order Thinking Skills

41. CHALLENGE $ABCD$ is a parallelogram with side lengths as indicated in the figure at the right. The perimeter of $ABCD$ is 22. Find AB. **7**

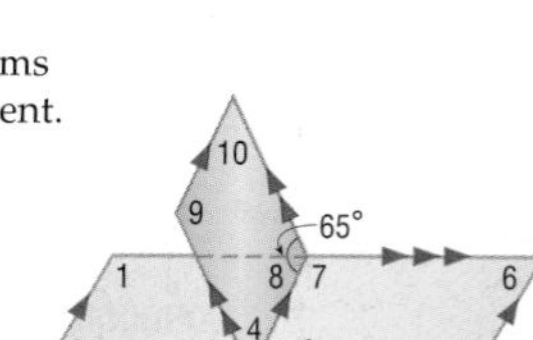

42. WRITING IN MATH Explain why parallelograms are *always* quadrilaterals, but quadrilaterals are *sometimes* parallelograms. **See margin.**

43. OPEN ENDED Provide a counterexample to show that parallelograms are not always congruent if their corresponding sides are congruent. **See margin.**

44. CCSS REASONING Find $m\angle 1$ and $m\angle 10$ in the figure at the right. Explain. **See margin.**

45. WRITING IN MATH Summarize the properties of the sides, angles, and diagonals of a parallelogram.

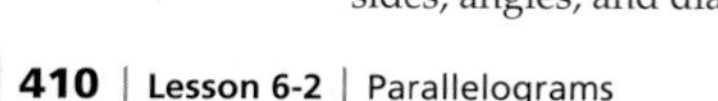

Proof:

Statements (Reasons)

1. ▱$YWVZ$, $\overline{VX} \perp \overline{WY}$, $\overline{YU} \perp \overline{VZ}$ (Given)
2. $\angle Z \cong \angle W$ (Opp. ∡ of a ▱ are ≅.)
3. $\overline{WV} \cong \overline{ZY}$ (Opp. sides of a ▱ are ≅.)
4. $\angle VXW$ and $\angle YUZ$ are rt. ∡. (⊥ lines form rt. ∡.)
5. $\triangle VXW$ and $\triangle YUZ$ are rt. ⊿. (Def. of rt. ⊿)
6. $\triangle YUZ \cong \triangle VXW$ (HA)

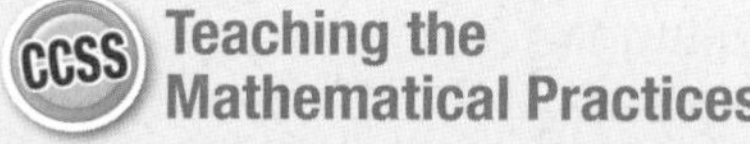

Teaching the Mathematical Practices

Reasoning Mathematically proficient students make sense of quantities and their relationships in problem situations. Encourage students to analyze the diagram to find the relationship between $\angle 1$ and $\angle 10$.

Standardized Test Practice

46. Two consecutive angles of a parallelogram measure $3x + 42$ and $9x - 18$. What are the measures of the angles? D

A 13, 167 C 39, 141
B 58.5, 31.5 D 81, 99

47. GRIDDED RESPONSE Parallelogram *MNPQ* is shown. What is the value of x? 13

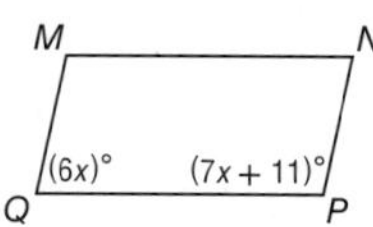

48. ALGEBRA In a history class with 32 students, the ratio of girls to boys is 5 to 3. How many more girls are there than boys? G

F 2 G 8 H 12 J 15

49. SAT/ACT The table shows the heights of the tallest buildings in Kansas City, Missouri. To the nearest tenth, what is the positive difference between the median and the mean of the data? B

Name	Height (m)
One Kansas City Place	193
Town Pavillion	180
Hyatt Regency	154
Power and Light Building	147
City Hall	135
1201 Walnut	130

A 5
B 6
C 7
D 8
E 10

Spiral Review

The measure of an interior angle of a regular polygon is given. Find the number of sides in the polygon. (Lesson 6-1)

50. 108 5 **51.** 140 9 **52.** ≈ 147.3 11 **53.** 160 18 **54.** 135 8 **55.** 176.4 100

56. LANDSCAPING When landscapers plant new trees, they usually brace the tree using a stake tied to the trunk of the tree. Use the SAS or SSS Inequality to explain why this is an effective method for keeping a newly planted tree perpendicular to the ground. Assume that the tree does not lean forward or backward. (Lesson 5-6) See margin.

Determine whether the solid is a polyhedron. Then identify the solid. If it is a polyhedron, name the bases, faces, edges, and vertices. (Lesson 1-7)

57.

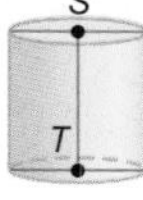

not a polyhedron; cylinder

58.

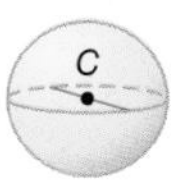

not a polyhedron; sphere

59.

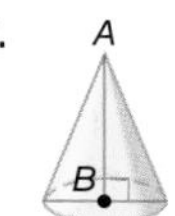

not a polyhedron; cone

Skills Review

The vertices of a quadrilateral are $W(3, -1)$, $X(4, 2)$, $Y(-2, 3)$ and $Z(-3, 0)$. Determine whether each segment is a side or diagonal of the quadrilateral, and find the slope of each segment.

60. $\overline{YZ}$ side; 3 **61.** $\overline{YW}$ diagonal; $-\frac{4}{5}$ **62.** $\overline{ZW}$ side; $-\frac{1}{6}$

40a. Sample answer:

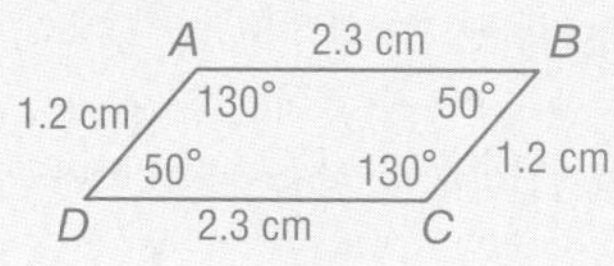

W 2.8 cm X
122° 58°
1.7 cm 1.7 cm
58° 122°
Z 2.8 cm Y

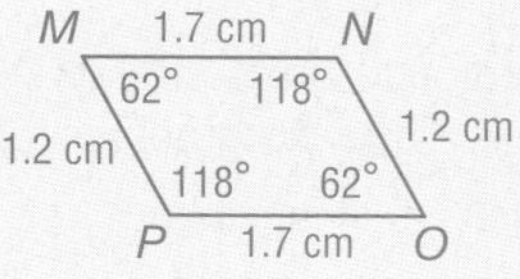

4 Assess

Ticket Out the Door Ask students to make a list of all the properties of parallelograms they have learned. Have students turn in their statements before they leave the classroom.

Formative Assessment

Check for student understanding of Lessons 6-1 and 6-2.

Quiz 1, p. 45

Additional Answers

42. A parallelogram is a polygon with four sides in which the opposite sides and angles are congruent. Quadrilaterals are defined as four-sided polygons. Since a parallelogram always has four sides, it is always a quadrilateral. A quadrilateral is only a parallelogram when the opposite sides and angles of the polygon are congruent.

43.

44. $m\angle 1 = 116$, $m\angle 10 = 115$; sample answer: $m\angle 8 = 64$ because alternate interior angles are congruent. $\angle 1$ is supplementary to $\angle 8$ because consecutive angles in a parallelogram are supplementary, so $m\angle 1$ is 116. $\angle 10$ is supplementary to the 65° angle because consecutive angles in a parallelogram are supplementary, so $m\angle 10$ is $180 - 65$ or 115.

56. By the SAS Inequality Theorem, if the tree started to lean, one of the angles of the triangle formed by the tree, the ground, and the stake would change, and the side opposite that angle would change as well. However, with the stake in the ground and fixed to the tree, no side of the triangle can change length. Thus, no angle can change. This ensures that the tree will stay perpendicular to the ground.

1 Focus

Objective Use the Cabri Junior application on a TI-83/84 Plus graphing calculator to discover properties of parallelograms.

Materials

- TI-83/84 Plus graphing calculator

2 Teach

Working Independently

Have students work alone, or in pairs, mixing abilities. Have students complete Steps 1–5.

Ask:

- What can you say about the lengths of $\overline{CA}$ and $\overline{DB}$? The lengths are congruent because $\overline{AB} \parallel \overline{CD}$.
- What is the purpose of using the slope tool in this activity? If two lines have the same slope, it means they are parallel and parallel sides indicate a parallelogram.

Practice Have students work independently to complete Exercises 1–5.

3 Assess

Formative Assessment

Use Exercises 4 and 5 to assess whether students comprehend the properties of a parallelogram.

From Concrete to Abstract

Tell students to look around the class and find examples of parallelograms. Ask students how they can tell whether the examples are quadrilaterals or quadrilaterals that are true parallelograms.

EXPLORE 6-3 Graphing Technology Lab: Parallelograms

You can use the Cabri™ Jr. application on a TI-83/84 Plus graphing calculator to discover properties of parallelograms.

CCSS Common Core State Standards
Content Standards
G.CO.12 Make formal geometric constructions with a variety of tools and methods (compass and straightedge, string, reflective devices, paper folding, dynamic geometric software, etc.).
Mathematical Practices 5

Activity

Construct a quadrilateral with one pair of sides that are both parallel and congruent.

Step 1 Construct a segment using the **Segment** tool on the **F2** menu. Label the segment $\overline{AB}$. This is one side of the quadrilateral.

Step 2 Use the **Parallel** tool on the **F3** menu to construct a line parallel to the segment. Pressing ENTER will draw the line and a point on the line. Label the point *C*.

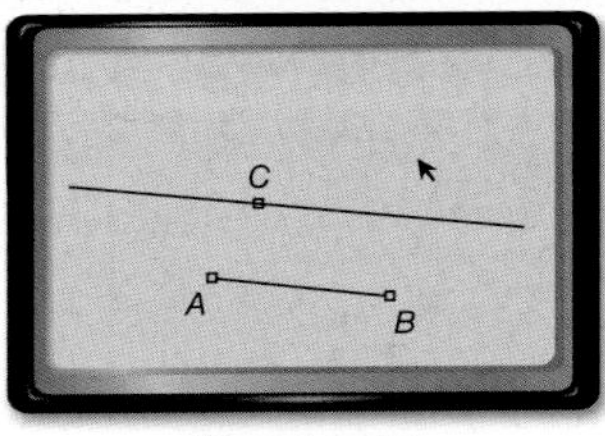

Steps 1 and 2

Step 3 Access the **Compass** tool on the **F3** menu. Set the compass to the length of $\overline{AB}$ by selecting one endpoint of the segment and then the other. Construct a circle centered at *C*.

Step 4 Use the **Point Intersection** tool on the **F2** menu to draw a point at the intersection of the line and the circle. Label the point *D*. Then use the **Segment** tool on the **F2** menu to draw $\overline{AC}$ and $\overline{BD}$.

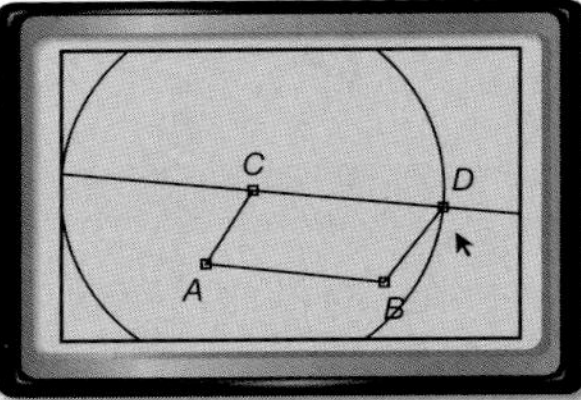

Steps 3 and 4

Step 5 Use the **Hide/Show** tool on the **F5** menu to hide the circle. Then access **Slope** tool under **Measure** on the **F5** menu. Display the slopes of $\overline{AB}$, $\overline{BD}$, $\overline{CD}$, and $\overline{AC}$.

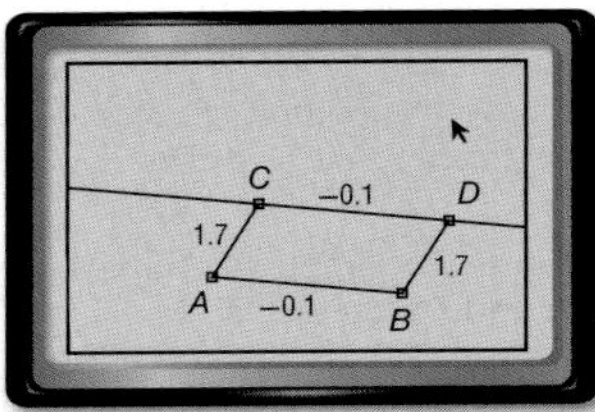

Step 5

Analyze the Results 1–5. See margin.

1. What is the relationship between sides $\overline{AB}$ and $\overline{CD}$? Explain how you know.
2. What do you observe about the slopes of opposite sides of the quadrilateral? What type of quadrilateral is *ABDC*? Explain.
3. Click on point *A* and drag it to change the shape of *ABDC*. What do you observe?
4. Make a conjecture about a quadrilateral with a pair of opposite sides that are both congruent and parallel.
5. Use a graphing calculator to construct a quadrilateral with both pairs of opposite sides congruent. Then analyze the slopes of the sides of the quadrilateral. Make a conjecture based on your observations.

Extend the Activity

Ask:

- Suppose there is a quadrilateral with one pair of sides parallel and congruent. Is this a parallelogram? Yes.

Additional Answers

1. $\overline{AB} \parallel \overline{CD}$ and $\overline{AB} \cong \overline{CD}$; the line containing $\overline{CD}$ was constructed to be parallel to $\overline{AB}$. The compass was used to ensure that $\overline{AB} \cong \overline{CD}$.
2. The slopes are equal. *ABDC* is a parallelogram because opposite sides are parallel.
3. The slopes of the opposite sides remain equal.
4. The quadrilateral is a parallelogram.
5. Sample answer: A quadrilateral with both pairs of opposite sides congruent is a parallelogram.

LESSON 6-3 Tests for Parallelograms

Then

- You recognized and applied properties of parallelograms.

Now

1. Recognize the conditions that ensure a quadrilateral is a parallelogram.
2. Prove that a set of points forms a parallelogram in the coordinate plane.

Why?

- Lexi and Rosalinda cut strips of bulletin board paper at an angle to form the hallway display shown. Their friends asked them how they cut the strips so that their sides were parallel without using a protractor.

Rosalinda explained that since the left and right sides of the paper were parallel, she only needed to make sure that the sides were cut to the same length to guarantee that a strip would form a parallelogram.

Common Core State Standards

Content Standards

G.CO.11 Prove theorems about parallelograms.

G.GPE.4 Use coordinates to prove simple geometric theorems algebraically.

Mathematical Practices

3 Construct viable arguments and critique the reasoning of others.

2 Reason abstractly and quantitatively.

1 Conditions for Parallelograms

If a quadrilateral has each pair of opposite sides parallel, it is a parallelogram by definition.

This is not the only test, however, that can be used to determine if a quadrilateral is a parallelogram.

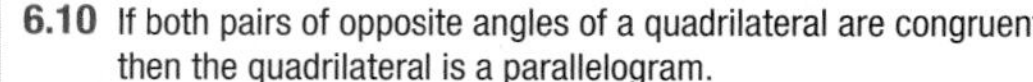

Theorems Conditions for Parallelograms

6.9 If both pairs of opposite sides of a quadrilateral are congruent, then the quadrilateral is a parallelogram.

Abbreviation *If both pairs of opp. sides are ≅, then quad. is a ▱.*

Example If $\overline{AB} \cong \overline{DC}$ and $\overline{AD} \cong \overline{BC}$, then *ABCD* is a parallelogram.

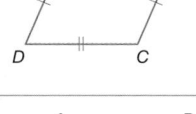

6.10 If both pairs of opposite angles of a quadrilateral are congruent, then the quadrilateral is a parallelogram.

Abbreviation *If both pairs of opp. ∠s are ≅, then quad. is a ▱.*

Example If $\angle A \cong \angle C$ and $\angle B \cong \angle D$, then *ABCD* is a parallelogram.

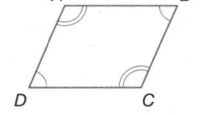

6.11 If the diagonals of a quadrilateral bisect each other, then the quadrilateral is a parallelogram.

Abbreviation *If diag. bisect each other, then quad. is a ▱.*

Example If $\overline{AC}$ and $\overline{DB}$ bisect each other, then *ABCD* is a parallelogram.

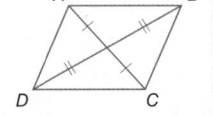

6.12 If one pair of opposite sides of a quadrilateral is both parallel and congruent, then the quadrilateral is a parallelogram.

Abbreviation *If one pair of opp. sides is ≅ and ||, then the quad. is a ▱.*

Example If $\overline{AB} \parallel \overline{DC}$ and $\overline{AB} \cong \overline{DC}$, then *ABCD* is a parallelogram.

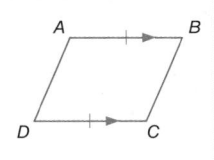

You will prove Theorems 6.10, 6.11, and 6.12 in Exercises 30, 32, and 33, respectively.

1 Focus

Vertical Alignment

Before Lesson 6-3 Recognize and apply properties of parallelograms.

Lesson 6-3 Recognize the conditions that ensure a quadrilateral is a parallelogram. Prove that a set of points forms a parallelogram in the coordinate plane.

After Lesson 6-3 Use and extend similarity properties to explore and justify conjectures about rectangles.

2 Teach

Scaffolding Questions

Have students read the **Why?** section of the lesson.

Ask:

- How did Rosalinda cut each piece of paper? Draw a diagram.

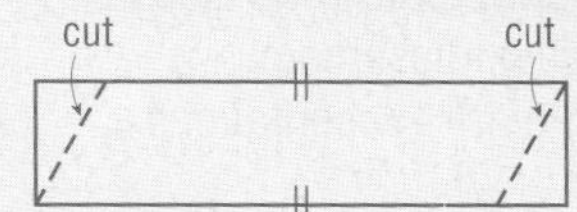

- How could Lexi verify that Rosalinda's method worked? Sample answer: She could measure each angle and verify that consecutive angles are supplementary, since if this is true, opposite sides are parallel.

Lesson 6-3 Resources

Resource	Approaching Level AL	On Level OL	Beyond Level BL	English Learners ELL
Teacher Edition	▪ Differentiated Instruction, p. 415	▪ Differentiated Instruction, pp. 415, 420	▪ Differentiated Instruction, pp. 415, 420, 421	
Chapter Resource Masters	▪ Study Guide and Intervention, pp. 17–18 ▪ Skills Practice, p. 19 ▪ Practice, p. 20 ▪ Word Problem Practice, p. 21	▪ Study Guide and Intervention, pp. 17–18 ▪ Skills Practice, p. 19 ▪ Practice, p. 20 ▪ Word Problem Practice, p. 21 ▪ Enrichment, p. 22	▪ Practice, p. 20 ▪ Word Problem Practice, p. 21 ▪ Enrichment, p. 22	▪ Study Guide and Intervention, pp. 17–18 ▪ Skills Practice, p. 19 ▪ Practice, p. 20 ▪ Word Problem Practice, p. 21
Other	▪ 5-Minute Check 6-3 ▪ Study Notebook ▪ Teaching Geometry with Manipulatives	▪ 5-Minute Check 6-3 ▪ Study Notebook ▪ Teaching Geometry with Manipulatives	▪ 5-Minute Check 6-3 ▪ Study Notebook	▪ 5-Minute Check 6-3 ▪ Study Notebook ▪ Teaching Geometry with Manipulatives

1 Conditions for Parallelograms

Examples 1–3 show how to use new theorems, which are converse of the theorems in Lesson 6-2, to prove a parallelogram.

Formative Assessment

Use the Guided Practice exercises after each example to determine students' understanding of concepts.

Additional Example

1 Determine whether the quadrilateral is a parallelogram. Justify your answer.

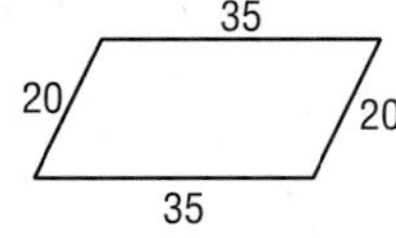

Each pair of opposite sides has the same measure. Therefore, they are congruent. If both pairs of opposite sides are congruent, the quadrilateral is a parallelogram.

Additional Examples also in Interactive Classroom PowerPoint® Presentations

Proof Theorem 6.9

Write a paragraph proof of Theorem 6.9.

Given: $\overline{WX} \cong \overline{ZY}$, $\overline{WZ} \cong \overline{XY}$

Prove: $WXYZ$ is a parallelogram.

Paragraph Proof:

Two points determine a line, so we can draw auxiliary line $\overline{ZX}$ to form $\triangle ZWX$ and $\triangle XYZ$. We are given that $\overline{WX} \cong \overline{ZY}$ and $\overline{WZ} \cong \overline{XY}$. Also, $\overline{ZX} \cong \overline{XZ}$ by the Reflexive Property of Congruence. So $\triangle ZWX \cong \triangle XYZ$ by SSS. By CPCTC, $\angle WXZ \cong \angle YZX$ and $\angle WZX \cong \angle YXZ$. This means that $\overline{WX} \parallel \overline{ZY}$ and $\overline{WZ} \parallel \overline{XY}$ by the Alternate Interior Angles Converse. Opposite sides of $WXYZ$ are parallel, so by definition $WXYZ$ is a parallelogram.

Example 1 Identify Parallelograms

Determine whether the quadrilateral is a parallelogram. Justify your answer.

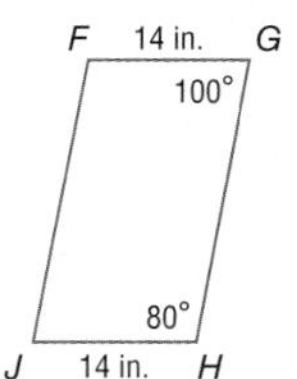

Opposite sides $\overline{FG}$ and $\overline{JH}$ are congruent because they have the same measure. Also, since $\angle FGH$ and $\angle GHJ$ are supplementary consecutive interior angles, $\overline{FG} \parallel \overline{JH}$. Therefore, by Theorem 6.12, $FGHJ$ is a parallelogram.

Guided Practice

1A.

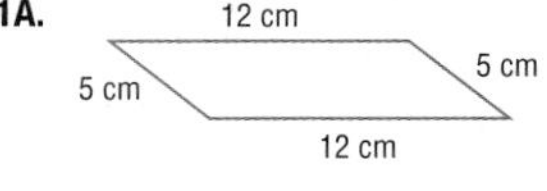

1B.

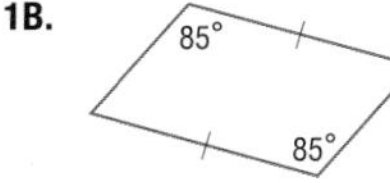

1A. Yes; both pairs of opposites sides are congruent.
1B. No; none of the tests for parallelograms are fulfilled.

You can use the conditions of parallelograms to prove relationships in real-world situations.

Real-World Example 2 Use Parallelograms to Prove Relationships

FISHING The diagram shows a side view of the tackle box at the left. In the diagram, $PQ = RS$ and $PR = QS$. Explain why the upper and middle trays remain parallel no matter to what height the trays are raised or lowered.

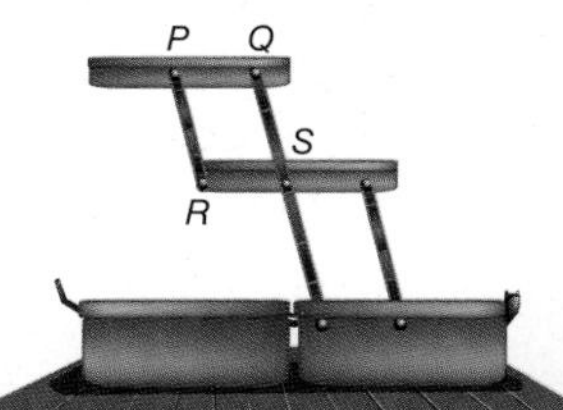

Since both pairs of opposite sides of quadrilateral $PQSR$ are congruent, $PQRS$ is a parallelogram by Theorem 6.9. By the definition of a parallelogram, opposite sides are parallel, so $\overline{PQ} \parallel \overline{RS}$. Therefore, no matter the vertical position of the trays, they will always remain parallel.

Real-WorldLink

A 2- or 3-cantilever tackle box is often used to organize lures and other fishing supplies. The trays lift up and away so that all items in the box are easily accessible.

Guided Practice

2. **BANNERS** In the example at the beginning of the lesson, explain why the cuts made by Lexi and Rosalinda are parallel. **See Ch. 6 Answer Appendix.**

WatchOut!

Parallelograms A quadrilateral needs to pass only one of the five tests to be proved a parallelogram. All of the properties of a parallelogram do not need to be proven.

You can also use the conditions of parallelograms along with algebra to find missing values that make a quadrilateral a parallelogram.

Example 3 Use Parallelograms and Algebra to Find Values

If $FK = 3x - 1$, $KG = 4y + 3$, $JK = 6y - 2$, and $KH = 2x + 3$, find x and y so that the quadrilateral is a parallelogram.

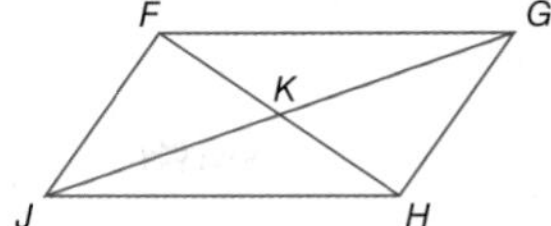

By Theorem 6.11, if the diagonals of a quadrilateral bisect each other, then it is a parallelogram. So find x such that $\overline{FK} \cong \overline{KH}$ and y such that $\overline{JK} \cong \overline{KG}$.

$FK = KH$	Definition of $\cong$
$3x - 1 = 2x + 3$	Substitution
$x - 1 = 3$	Subtract $2x$ from each side.
$x = 4$	Add 1 to each side.
$JK = KG$	Definition of $\cong$
$6y - 2 = 4y + 3$	Substitution
$2y - 2 = 3$	Subtract $4y$ from each side.
$2y = 5$	Add 2 to each side.
$y = 2.5$	Divide each side by 2.

So, when x is 4 and y is 2.5, quadrilateral $FGHJ$ is a parallelogram.

GuidedPractice

Find x and y so that each quadrilateral is a parallelogram.

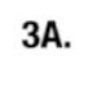
3A.
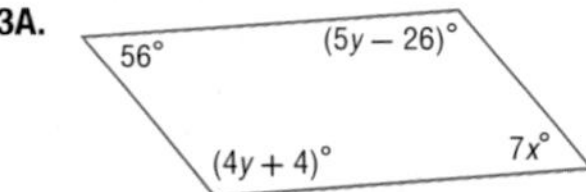

3B.
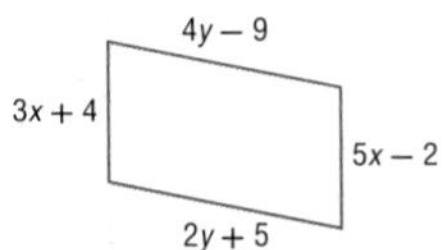

You have learned the conditions of parallelograms. The following list summarizes how to use the conditions to prove a quadrilateral is a parallelogram.

Concept Summary

Prove that a Quadrilateral Is a Parallelogram

- Show that both pairs of opposite sides are parallel. (Definition)
- Show that both pairs of opposite sides are congruent. (Theorem 6.9)
- Show that both pairs of opposite angles are congruent. (Theorem 6.10)
- Show that the diagonals bisect each other. (Theorem 6.11)
- Show that a pair of opposite sides is both parallel and congruent. (Theorem 6.12)

VatchOut!

arallelograms In Example , if x is 4, then y must be .5 in order for $FGHJ$ to be a arallelogram. In other words, x is 4 and y is 1, then $FGHJ$ s not a parallelogram.

3A. $x = 8$, $y = 30$
3B. $x = 3$, $y = 7$

Additional Example

2 MECHANICS Scissor lifts, like the platform lift shown below, are commonly applied to tools intended to lift heavy items. In the diagram, $\angle A \cong \angle C$ and $\angle B \cong \angle D$. Explain why consecutive angles will always be supplementary regardless of the height of the platform.

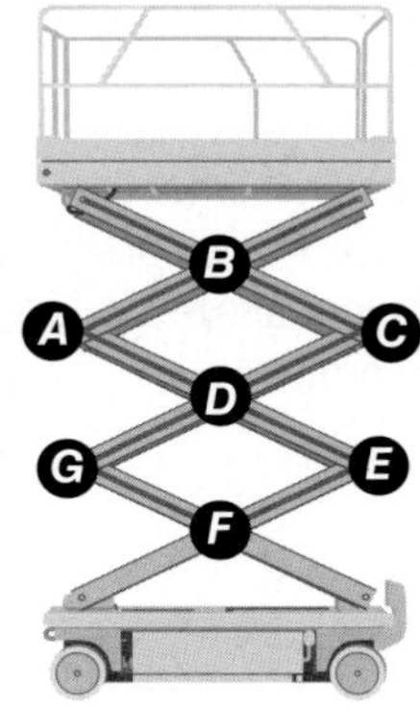

Since both pairs of opposite angles of quadrilateral $ABCD$ are congruent, $ABCD$ is a parallelogram by Theorem 6.10. Theorem 6.5 states that consecutive angles of parallelograms are supplementary. Therefore, $m\angle A + m\angle B = 180$ and $m\angle C + m\angle D = 180$. By substitution, $m\angle A + m\angle D = 180$ and $m\angle C + m\angle B = 180$.

Tips for New Teachers

Reasoning Ask students to describe an alternate method that could be used to complete a proof by discussing the five conditions of parallelograms. Remind students that there are often multiple strategies that can be used, although one may be the most efficient.

DifferentiatedInstruction AL OL BL

Intrapersonal Learners Have students choose a partner. Instruct one student to draw a parallelogram in a plane. Then ask the partner to prove that the quadrilateral is a parallelogram. Next switch roles and do the activity again.

Additional Example

3 Find x and y so that the quadrilateral is a parallelogram.

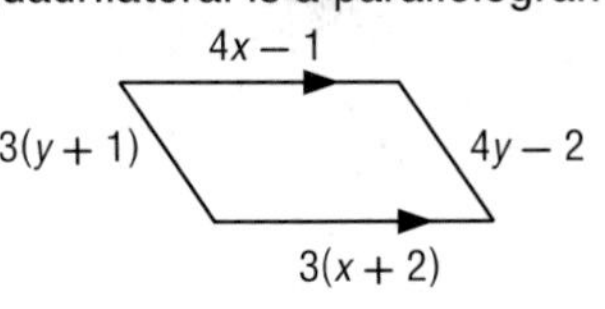

$x = 7$; $y = 5$

2 Parallelograms on the Coordinate Plane

Examples 4 and 5 show how to use coordinate plane formulas to determine whether a quadrilateral is a parallelogram.

Additional Examples

4 COORDINATE GEOMETRY Graph quadrilateral *QRST* with vertices *Q*(−1, 3), *R*(3, 1), *S*(2, −3), and *T*(−2, −1). Determine whether the quadrilateral is a parallelogram. Justify your answer by using the Slope Formula.

slope of $\overline{QR} = -\frac{1}{2}$

slope of $\overline{ST} = -\frac{1}{2}$

slope of $\overline{RS} = 4$

slope of $\overline{TQ} = 4$

QRST is a parallelogram by definition.

5 Write a coordinate proof of the following statement. If both pairs of opposite sides of a quadrilateral are congruent, the quadrilateral is a parallelogram.

Position quadrilateral *ABCD* on a coordinate plane such that $\overline{AB} \cong \overline{DC}$ and $\overline{AD} \cong \overline{BC}$. Use quadrilateral *A*(0, 0), *B*(*a*, 0), *C*(*b* + *a*, *c*), and *D*(*b*, *c*).

Given: quadrilateral *ABCD*, $\overline{AB} \cong \overline{DC}$, $\overline{AD} \cong \overline{BC}$

Prove: *ABCD* is a paralelogram.

By definition a quadrilateral is a parallelogram if opposite sides are parallel. Use the Slope Formula.

Slope of $\overline{AD} = \frac{c-0}{b-0} = \frac{c}{b}$

Slope of $\overline{BC} = \frac{c-0}{b-0} = \frac{c}{b}$

The slopes of $\overline{AB}$ and $\overline{CD}$ are 0.

Since $\overline{AB}$ and $\overline{CD}$ have the same slopes and $\overline{AD}$ and $\overline{BC}$ have the same slopes, $\overline{AB} \parallel \overline{CD}$ and $\overline{AD} \parallel \overline{BC}$. So quadrilateral *ABCD* is a parallelogram because opposite sides are parallel.

StudyTip

Midpoint Formula
To show that a quadrilateral is a parallelogram, you can also use the Midpoint Formula. If the midpoint of each diagonal is the same point, then the diagonals bisect each other.

2 Parallelograms on the Coordinate Plane We can use the Distance, Slope, and Midpoint Formulas to determine whether a quadrilateral in the coordinate plane is a parallelogram.

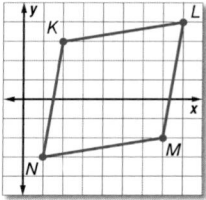

Example 4 Parallelograms and Coordinate Geometry

COORDINATE GEOMETRY Graph quadrilateral *KLMN* with vertices *K*(2, 3), *L*(8, 4), *M*(7, −2), and *N*(1, −3). Determine whether the quadrilateral is a parallelogram. Justify your answer using the Slope Formula.

If the opposite sides of a quadrilateral are parallel, then it is a parallelogram.

slope of $\overline{KL} = \frac{4-3}{8-2}$ or $\frac{1}{6}$

slope of $\overline{NM} = \frac{-2-(-3)}{7-1}$ or $\frac{1}{6}$

slope of $\overline{KN} = \frac{-3-3}{1-2} = \frac{-6}{-1}$ or 6

slope of $\overline{LM} = \frac{-2-4}{7-8} = \frac{-6}{-1}$ or 6

Since opposite sides have the same slope, $\overline{KL} \parallel \overline{NM}$ and $\overline{KN} \parallel \overline{LM}$. Therefore, *KLMN* is a parallelogram by definition.

GuidedPractice

Determine whether the quadrilateral is a parallelogram. Justify your answer using the given formula.

4A. *A*(3, 3), *B*(8, 2), *C*(6, −1), *D*(1, 0); Distance Formula **4A–B. See margin.**

4B. *F*(−2, 4), *G*(4, 2), *H*(4, −2), *J*(−2, −1); Midpoint Formula

In Chapter 4, you learned that variable coordinates can be assigned to the vertices of triangles. Then the Distance, Slope, and Midpoint Formulas were used to write coordinate proofs of theorems. The same can be done with quadrilaterals.

ReviewVocabulary

coordinate proof a proof that uses figures in the coordinate plane and algebra to prove geometric concepts

Example 5 Parallelograms and Coordinate Proofs

Write a coordinate proof for the following statement.

If one pair of opposite sides of a quadrilateral is both parallel and congruent, then the quadrilateral is a parallelogram.

Step 1 Position quadrilateral *ABCD* on the coordinate plane such that $\overline{AB} \parallel \overline{DC}$ and $\overline{AB} \cong \overline{DC}$.

- Begin by placing the vertex *A* at the origin.
- Let $\overline{AB}$ have a length of *a* units. Then *B* has coordinates (*a*, 0).
- Since horizontal segments are parallel, position the endpoints of $\overline{DC}$ so that they have the same *y*-coordinate, *c*.
- So that the distance from *D* to *C* is also *a* units, let the *x*-coordinate of *D* be *b* and of *C* be *b* + *a*.

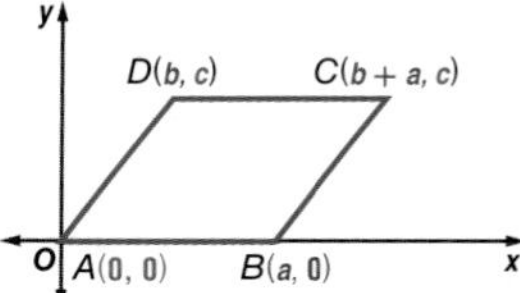

Teach with Tech

Wiki Have students work in pairs to create a wiki page listing and explaining different ways to prove a quadrilateral is a parallelogram. Students should work together to edit and revise their work to be sure it is correct and clear.

Math HistoryLink

René Descartes (1596–1650)
René Descartes was a French mathematician who was the first to use a coordinate grid. It has been said that he first thought of locating a point on a plane with a pair of numbers when he was watching a fly on the ceiling, but this is a myth.

Step 2 Use your figure to write a proof.

Given: quadrilateral $ABCD$, $\overline{AB} \parallel \overline{DC}$, $\overline{AB} \cong \overline{DC}$

Prove: $ABCD$ is a parallelogram.

Coordinate Proof:

By definition, a quadrilateral is a parallelogram if opposite sides are parallel. We are given that $\overline{AB} \parallel \overline{DC}$, so we need only show that $\overline{AD} \parallel \overline{BC}$.

Use the Slope Formula.

slope of $\overline{AD} = \frac{c-0}{b-0} = \frac{c}{b}$ slope of $\overline{BC} = \frac{c-0}{b+a-a} = \frac{c}{b}$

Since $\overline{AD}$ and $\overline{BC}$ have the same slope, $\overline{AD} \parallel \overline{BC}$. So quadrilateral $ABCD$ is a parallelogram because opposite sides are parallel.

GuidedPractice

5. Write a coordinate proof of this statement: *If a quadrilateral is a parallelogram, then opposite sides are congruent.* **See margin.**

Check Your Understanding

= Step-by-Step Solutions begin on page R14.

Example 1 **Determine whether each quadrilateral is a parallelogram. Justify your answer.**

1. 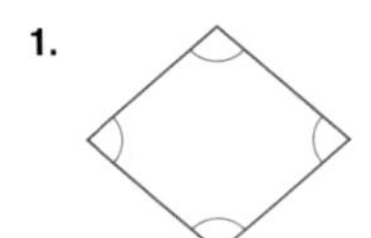 Yes; each pair of opposite angles are congruent.

2. 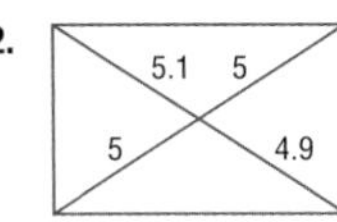

No; none of the tests for ▱ are fulfilled.

Example 2

3. **KITES** Charmaine is building the kite shown below. She wants to be sure that the string around her frame forms a parallelogram before she secures the material to it. How can she use the measures of the wooden portion of the frame to prove that the string forms a parallelogram? Explain your reasoning.

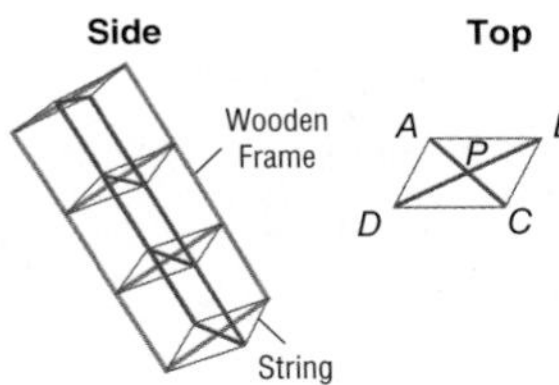

3. $AP = CP$, $BP = DP$; sample answer: If the diagonals of a quadrilateral bisect each other, then the quadrilateral is a parallelogram, so if $AP = CP$ and $BP = DP$, then the string forms a parallelogram.

Example 3 **ALGEBRA** **Find x and y so that the quadrilateral is a parallelogram.**

4. 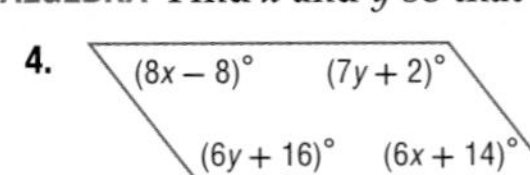

$x = 11$, $y = 14$

5. 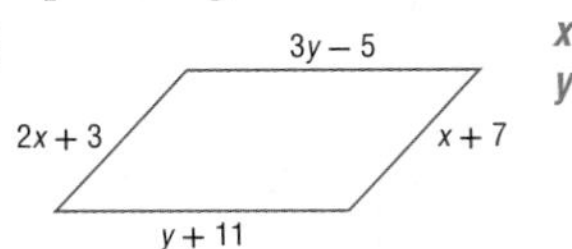

$x = 4$, $y = 8$

5. **Given:** $ABCD$ is a parallelogram.
Prove: $\overline{AB} \cong \overline{DC}$ and $\overline{AD} \cong \overline{BC}$

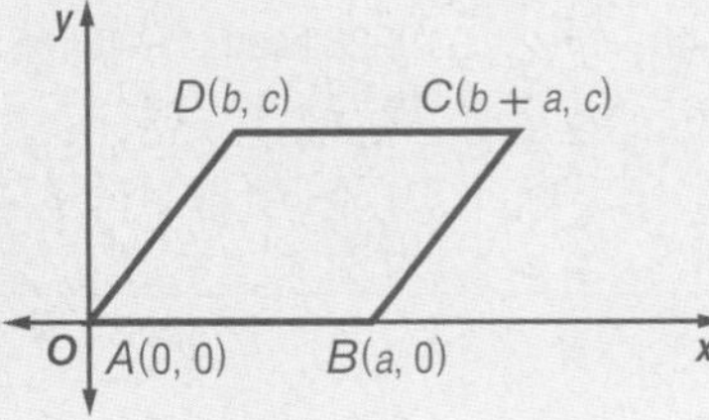

Coordinate Proof:

$AB = \sqrt{(a-0)^2 + (0-0)^2}$ or a

$DC = \sqrt{(b+a-b)^2 + (c-c)^2}$ or a

$AD = \sqrt{(c-0)^2 + (b-0)^2}$ or $\sqrt{c^2 + b^2}$

$BC = \sqrt{(a-(b+a))^2 + (c-0)^2}$

$= \sqrt{b^2 + c^2}$ or $\sqrt{c^2 + b^2}$

Since $AB = DC$ and $AD = BC$, then $\overline{AB} \cong \overline{DC}$ and $\overline{AD} \cong \overline{BC}$.

3 Practice

Formative Assessment

Use Exercises 1–8 to check for understanding.

Then use the chart at the bottom of the next page to customize assignments for your students.

Additional Answers (Guided Practice)

4A.

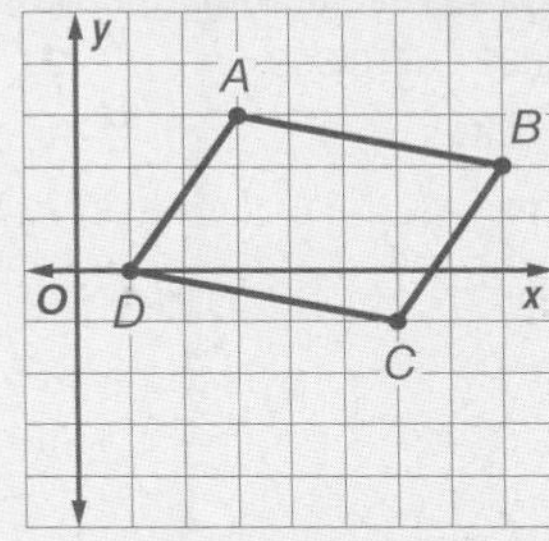

If both pairs of opposite sides of a quadrilateral are congruent, then it is a parallelogram. $AB = \sqrt{26}$; $DC = \sqrt{26}$; $AD = \sqrt{13}$; $BC = \sqrt{13}$. Since $AB = DC$ and $AD = BC$, $\overline{AB} \cong \overline{DC}$, and $\overline{AD} \cong \overline{BC}$. Therefore, $ABCD$ is a parallelogram by Theorem 6.9.

4B.

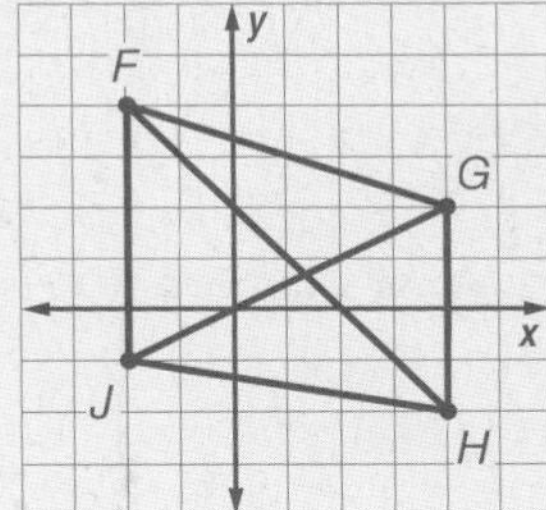

If the diagonals of a quadrilateral bisect each other, then it is a parallelogram. The diagonals of a quadrilateral bisect each other if their midpoints coincide. The midpoint of diagonal $\overline{FH} = (1, 1)$. The midpoint of diagonal $\overline{JG} = (1, 0.5)$. Since the midpoint of diagonals $\overline{FH}$ and $\overline{JG}$ do not have the same coordinates, quadrilateral $FGHJ$ is not a parallelogram.

Teaching the Mathematical Practices

Arguments Mathematically proficient students understand and use stated assumptions and definitions in constructing arguments. They make conjectures and build a logical progression of statements to explore the truth of their conjectures. They justify their conclusions. In Exercises 9–14, encourage students to review the properties of parallelograms before starting these exercises.

Additional Answers

6. No; both pairs of opposite sides must be parallel; since the slope of $\overline{BC} \neq$ slope of $\overline{AD}$, $ABCD$ is not a parallelogram.

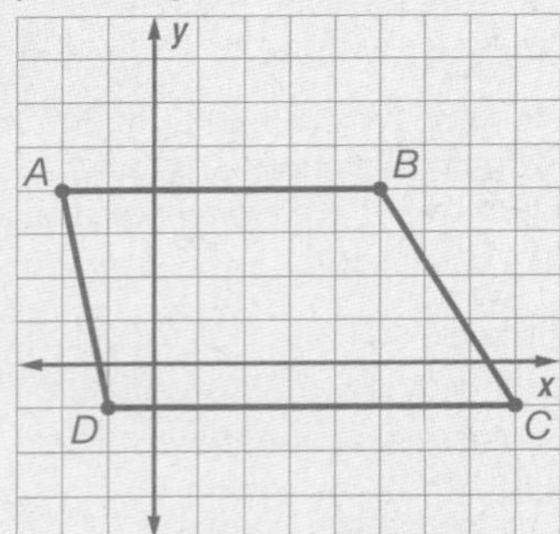

7. Yes; the midpoint of $\overline{WY}$ and $\overline{XZ}$ is $\left(-2, \frac{1}{2}\right)$. By the definition of midpoint, $\overline{WM} \cong \overline{MY}$, and $\overline{ZM} \cong \overline{MX}$. Since the diagonals bisect each other, $WXYZ$ is a parallelogram.

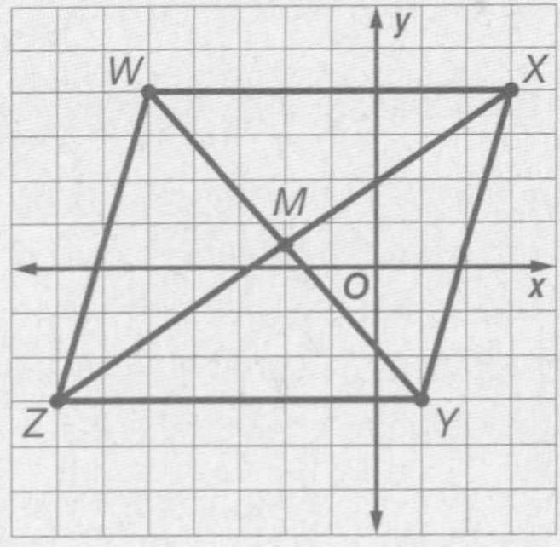

Example 4 **COORDINATE GEOMETRY** Graph each quadrilateral with the given vertices. Determine whether the figure is a parallelogram. Justify your answer with the method indicated.

6. $A(-2, 4)$, $B(5, 4)$, $C(8, -1)$, $D(-1, -1)$; Slope Formula **6, 7. See margin.**

7. $W(-5, 4)$, $X(3, 4)$, $Y(1, -3)$, $Z(-7, -3)$; Midpoint Formula

Example 5 8. Write a coordinate proof for the statement: *If a quadrilateral is a parallelogram, then its diagonals bisect each other.* **See Ch. 6 Answer Appendix.**

Practice and Problem Solving

Extra Practice is on page R6.

Example 1 **CCSS ARGUMENTS** Determine whether each quadrilateral is a parallelogram. Justify your answer.

9. 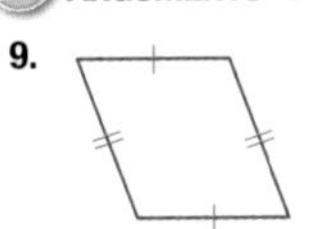

10. 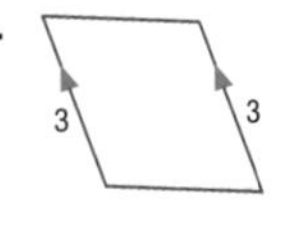

11. 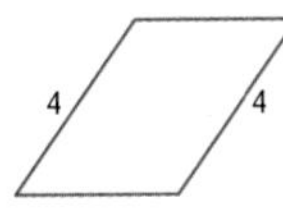

12. 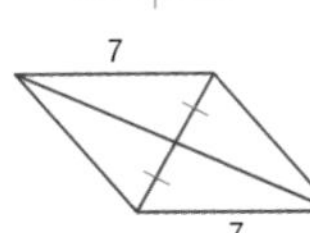

13. 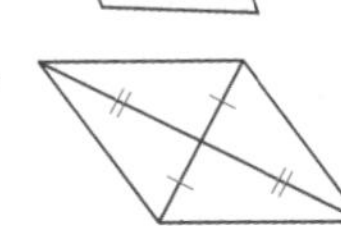

14. 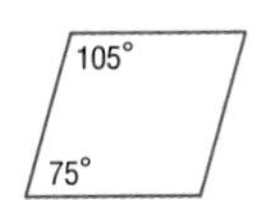

9. Yes; both pairs of opp. sides are ≅.
10. Yes; one pair of opp. sides is || and ≅.
11. No; none of the tests for ▱ are fulfilled.
12. No; none of the tests for ▱ are fulfilled.
13. Yes; the diagonals bisect each other.
14. No; none of the tests for ▱ are fulfilled.

Example 2 15. **PROOF** If $ACDH$ is a parallelogram, B is the midpoint of $\overline{AC}$, and F is the midpoint of $\overline{HD}$, write a flow proof to prove that $ABFH$ is a parallelogram.

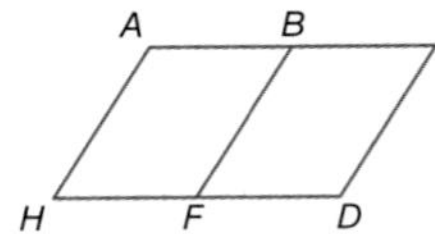

16. **PROOF** If WXYZ is a parallelogram, $\angle W \cong \angle X$, and M is the midpoint of $\overline{WX}$, write a paragraph proof to prove that ZMY is an isosceles triangle.

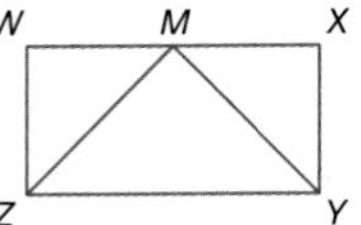

15–17. See Ch. 6 Answer Appendix.

17. **REPAIR** Parallelogram lifts are used to elevate large vehicles for maintenance. In the diagram, $ABEF$ and $BCDE$ are parallelograms. Write a two-column proof to show that $ACDF$ is also a parallelogram.

Example 3 **ALGEBRA** Find x and y so that the quadrilateral is a parallelogram.

18. 

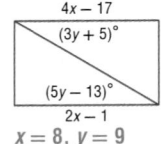

$x = 2$, $y = 29$

19.

$x = 8$, $y = 9$

20. 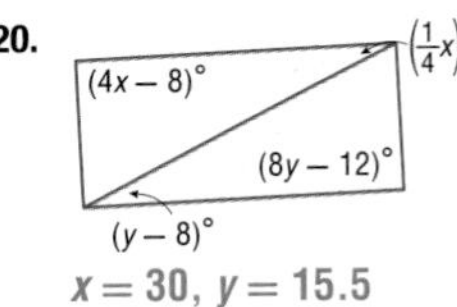

$x = 30$, $y = 15.5$

Differentiated Homework Options

Level	Assignment	Two-Day Option	
AL Basic	9–29, 41–43, 45–59	9–29 odd, 46–49	10–28 even, 41–43, 45, 50–59
OL Core	9–31 odd, 35, 37, 39, 41–43, 45–59	9–29, 46–49	31, 35–37, 39, 41–43, 45, 50–59
BL Advanced	30–57, (optional: 58, 59)		

ALGEBRA **Find x and y so that the quadrilateral is a parallelogram.**

21. 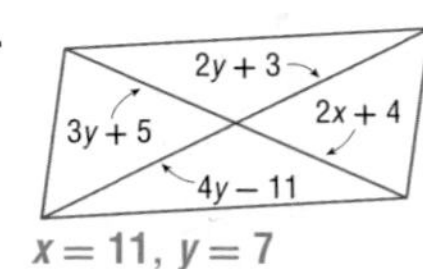

$x = 11, y = 7$

22. 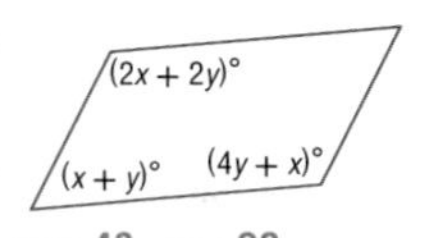

$x = 40, y = 20$

23. 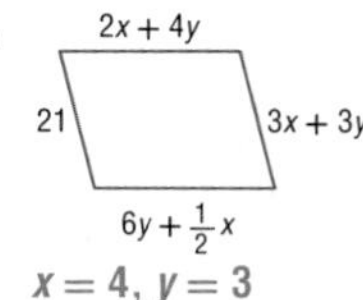

$6y + \frac{1}{2}x$

$x = 4, y = 3$

Example 4 **COORDINATE GEOMETRY** **Graph each quadrilateral with the given vertices. Determine whether the figure is a parallelogram. Justify your answer with the method indicated.** 24–27. See Ch. 6 Answer Appendix.

24. $A(-3, 4)$, $B(4, 5)$, $C(5, -1)$, $D(-2, -2)$; Slope Formula

25. $J(-4, -4)$, $K(-3, 1)$, $L(4, 3)$, $M(3, -3)$; Distance Formula

26. $V(3, 5)$, $W(1, -2)$, $X(-6, 2)$, $Y(-4, 7)$; Slope Formula

27. $Q(2, -4)$, $R(4, 3)$, $S(-3, 6)$, $T(-5, -1)$; Distance and Slope Formulas

Example 5 **28.** Write a coordinate proof for the statement: *If both pairs of opposite sides of a quadrilateral are congruent, then the quadrilateral is a parallelogram.* 28–30. See Ch. 6 Answer Appendix.

29. Write a coordinate proof for the statement: *If a parallelogram has one right angle, it has four right angles.*

B **30.** **PROOF** Write a paragraph proof of Theorem 6.10.

31 **PANTOGRAPH** A pantograph is a device that can be used to copy an object and either enlarge or reduce it based on the dimensions of the pantograph.

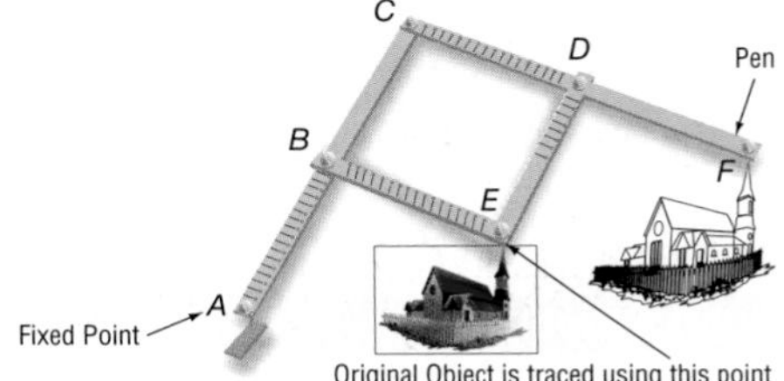

a. If $\overline{AC} \cong \overline{CF}$, $\overline{AB} \cong \overline{CD} \cong \overline{BE}$, and $\overline{DF} \cong \overline{DE}$, write a paragraph proof to show that $\overline{BE} \parallel \overline{CD}$. See Ch. 6 Answer Appendix.

b. The scale of the copied object is the ratio of CF to BE. If AB is 12 inches, DF is 8 inches, and the width of the original object is 5.5 inches, what is the width of the copy? about 9.2 in.

PROOF **Write a two-column proof.** 32–34. See Ch. 6 Answer Appendix.

32. Theorem 6.11

33. Theorem 6.12

34. **CONSTRUCTION** Explain how you can use Theorem 6.11 to construct a parallelogram. Then construct a parallelogram using your method.

C CCSS **REASONING** **Name the missing coordinates for each parallelogram.**

35 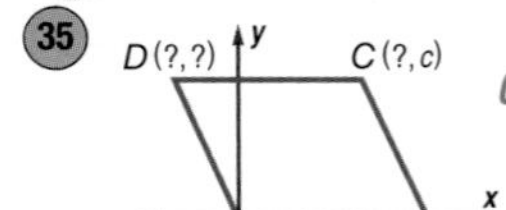

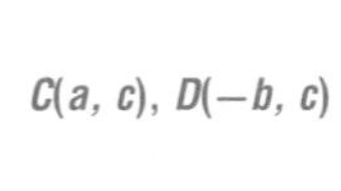
$C(a, c)$, $D(-b, c)$

36. 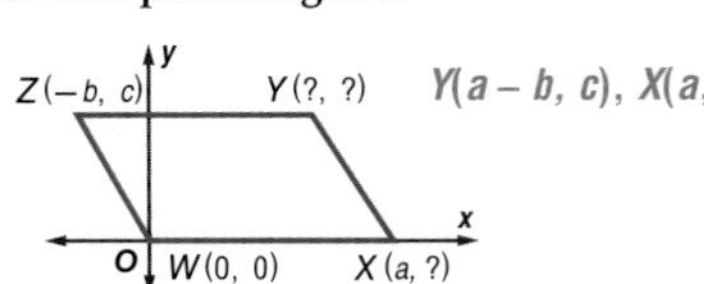

$Y(a - b, c)$, $X(a, 0)$

CCSS Teaching the Mathematical Practices

Reasoning Mathematically proficient students make sense of quantities and their relationships in problem situations. In Exercises 35–36, encourage students to use the properties of parallelograms to find the relationship between the ordered pairs of each.

Enrichment

OL BL

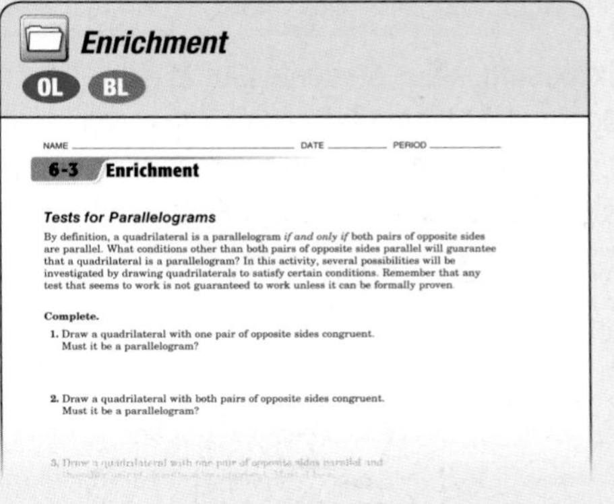

Study Guide and Intervention

AL OL ELL

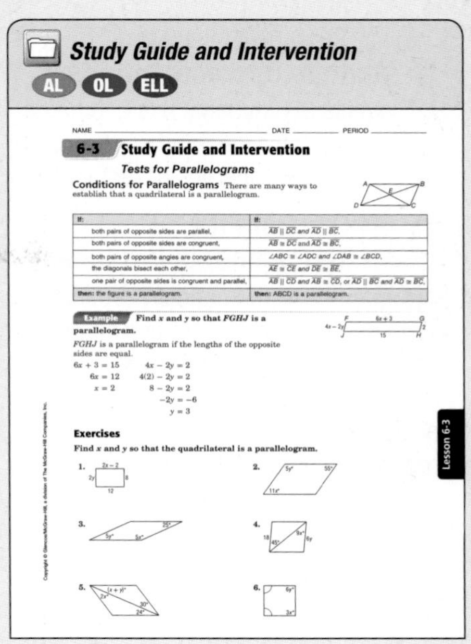

Practice

AL OL BL ELL

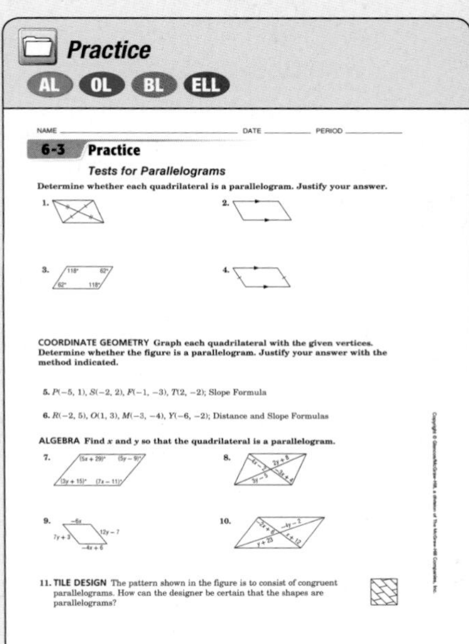

Word Problem Practice

AL OL BL ELL

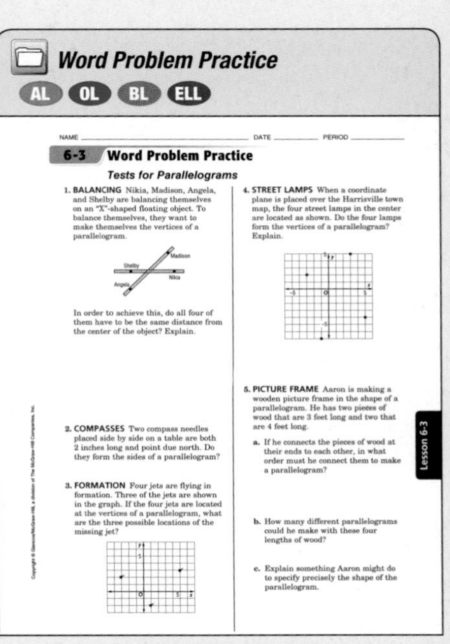

Multiple Representations

In Exercise 39, students use geometric sketches, a table, and verbal description to explore the properties of rectangles.

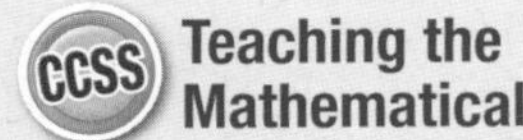

Teaching the Mathematical Practices

Arguments Mathematically proficient students understand and use stated assumptions and definitions in constructing arguments. In Exercise 42, encourage students to review the properties of parallelograms before starting these exercises.

Additional Answers

37. Sample answer: Since the two vertical rails are both perpendicular to the ground, he knows that they are parallel to each other. If he measures the distance between the two rails at the top of the steps and at the bottom of the steps, and they are equal, then one pair of sides of the quadrilateral formed by the handrails is both parallel and congruent, so the quadrilateral is a parallelogram. Since the quadrilateral is a parallelogram, the two hand rails are parallel by definition.

39a. Sample answer:

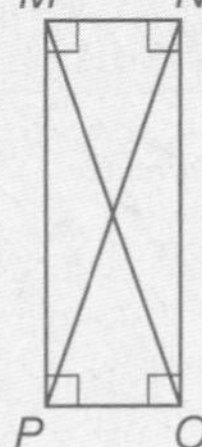

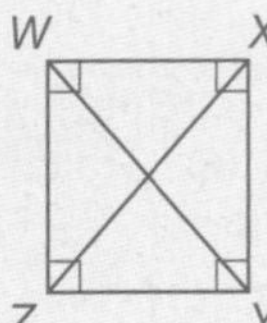

39c. Sample answer: The diagonals of a rectangle are congruent.

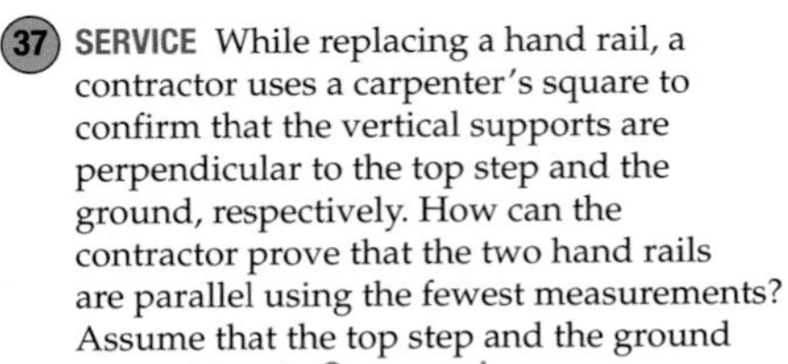

37 **SERVICE** While replacing a hand rail, a contractor uses a carpenter's square to confirm that the vertical supports are perpendicular to the top step and the ground, respectively. How can the contractor prove that the two hand rails are parallel using the fewest measurements? Assume that the top step and the ground are both level. **See margin.**

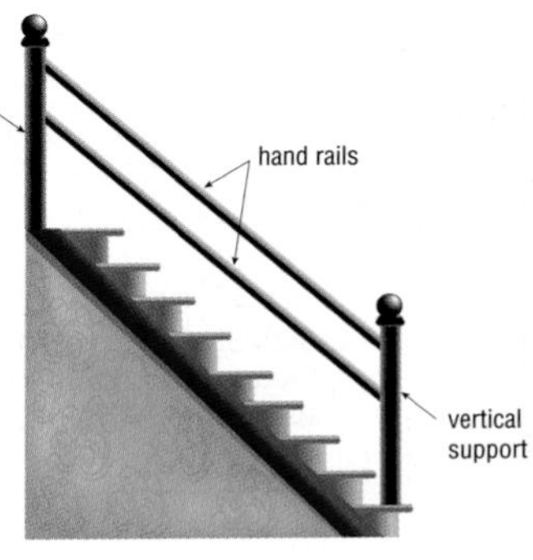

38. **PROOF** Write a coordinate proof to prove that the segments joining the midpoints of the sides of any quadrilateral form a parallelogram. **See Ch. 6 Answer Appendix.**

39. **MULTIPLE REPRESENTATIONS** In this problem, you will explore the properties of rectangles. A rectangle is a quadrilateral with four right angles.

a. **Geometric** Draw three rectangles with varying lengths and widths. Label one rectangle *ABCD*, one *MNOP*, and one *WXYZ*. Draw the two diagonals for each rectangle. **a, c. See margin.**

b. **Tabular** Measure the diagonals of each rectangle, and complete the table at the right.

c. **Verbal** Write a conjecture about the diagonals of a rectangle.

Rectangle	Side	Length
ABCD	$\overline{AC}$	3.3 cm
	$\overline{BD}$	3.3 cm
MNOP	$\overline{MO}$	2.8 cm
	$\overline{NP}$	2.8 cm
WXYZ	$\overline{WY}$	2.0 cm
	$\overline{XZ}$	2.0 cm

41. Sample answer: The theorems are converses of each other. The hypothesis of Theorem 6.3 is "a figure is a ▱", and the hypothesis of 6.9 is "both pairs of opp. sides of a quadrilateral are ≅". The conclusion of Theorem 6.3 is "opp. sides are ≅", and the conclusion of 6.9 is "the quadrilateral is a ▱".

H.O.T. Problems Use Higher-Order Thinking Skills

40. **CHALLENGE** The diagonals of a parallelogram meet at the point (0, 1). One vertex of the parallelogram is located at (2, 4), and a second vertex is located at (3, 1). Find the locations of the remaining vertices. **(−3, 1) and (−2, −2)**

41. **WRITING IN MATH** Compare and contrast Theorem 6.9 and Theorem 6.3.

42. **CCSS ARGUMENTS** If two parallelograms have four congruent corresponding angles, are the parallelograms *sometimes*, *always*, or *never* congruent? **42, 43. See margin.**

43. **OPEN ENDED** Position and label a parallelogram on the coordinate plane differently than shown in either Example 5, Exercise 35, or Exercise 36.

44. **CHALLENGE** If *ABCD* is a parallelogram and $\overline{AJ} \cong \overline{KC}$, show that quadrilateral *JBKD* is a parallelogram. **44, 45. See Ch. 6 Answer Appendix.**

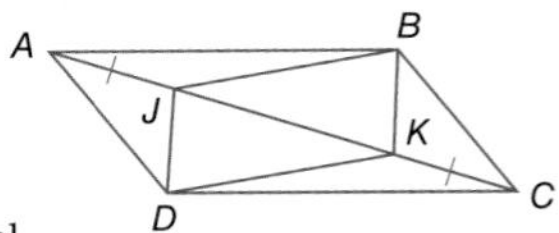

45. **WRITING IN MATH** How can you prove that a quadrilateral is a parallelogram?

Differentiated Instruction OL BL

Extension Have students plot $P(-4, -3)$, $L(-1, 2)$, and $S(5, 1)$ on a coordinate plane. Have them locate and plot a fourth point T that will create a parallelogram. They should prove that the figure is a parallelogram by using the theorems in this lesson. The coordinate for the fourth point is (2, −4). This point creates a parallelogram and is proven by either the distance formula or the slope formula. Example answer: slope of $\overline{PL} = \frac{5}{3}$, $\overline{LS} = -\frac{1}{6}$, $\overline{ST} = \frac{5}{3}$, and $\overline{TP} = -\frac{1}{6}$. Since opposite sides have same slope, $\overline{PL} \parallel \overline{ST}$ and $\overline{LS} \parallel \overline{TP}$. Therefore, *PLST* is a parallelogram by definition.

Standardized Test Practice

46. If sides $\overline{AB}$ and $\overline{DC}$ of quadrilateral $ABCD$ are parallel, which additional information would be sufficient to prove that quadrilateral $ABCD$ is a parallelogram? **B**

A $\overline{AB} \cong \overline{AC}$ **C** $\overline{AC} \cong \overline{BD}$

B $\overline{AB} \cong \overline{DC}$ **D** $\overline{AD} \cong \overline{BC}$

47. SHORT RESPONSE Quadrilateral $ABCD$ is shown. AC is 40 and BD is $\frac{3}{5}AC$. $\overline{BD}$ bisects $\overline{AC}$. For what value of x is $ABCD$ a parallelogram? **4**

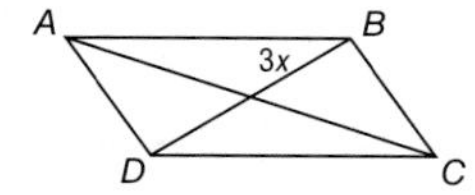

48. ALGEBRA Jarod's average driving speed for a 5-hour trip was 58 miles per hour. During the first 3 hours, he drove 50 miles per hour. What was his average speed in miles per hour for the last 2 hours of his trip? **F**

F 70 **H** 60

G 66 **J** 54

49. SAT/ACT A parallelogram has vertices at (0, 0), (3, 5), and (0, 5). What are the coordinates of the fourth vertex? **E**

A (0, 3) **D** (0, −3)

B (5, 3) **E** (3, 0)

C (5, 0)

Spiral Review

COORDINATE GEOMETRY Find the coordinates of the intersection of the diagonals of ▱$ABCD$ with the given vertices. (Lesson 6-2)

50. $A(-3, 5)$, $B(6, 5)$, $C(5, -4)$, $D(-4, -4)$ **(1, 0.5)**

51. $A(2, 5)$, $B(10, 7)$, $C(7, -2)$, $D(-1, -4)$ **(4.5, 1.5)**

Find the value of x. (Lesson 6-1)

52. **55**

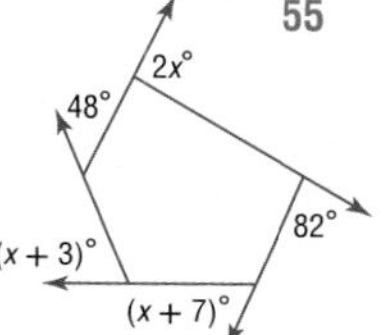

53. **35**

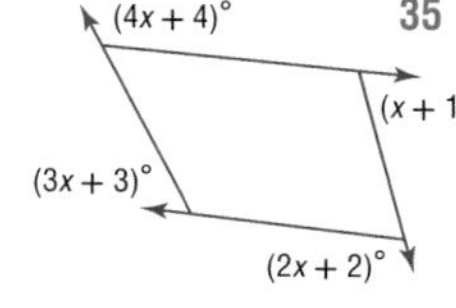

54. **58**

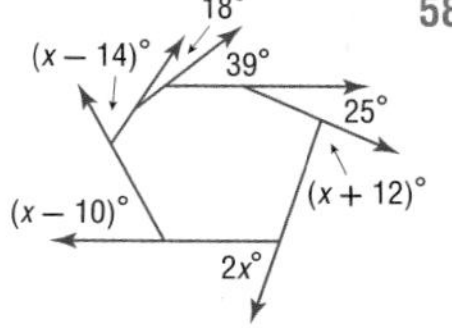

55. FITNESS Toshiro was at the gym for just over two hours. He swam laps in the pool and lifted weights. Prove that he did one of these activities for more than an hour. (Lesson 5-4) **See margin.**

PROOF Write a flow proof. (Lesson 4-5) **56, 57. See Ch. 6 Answer Appendix.**

56. Given: $\overline{EJ} \parallel \overline{FK}$, $\overline{JG} \parallel \overline{KH}$, $\overline{EF} \cong \overline{GH}$
Prove: $\triangle EJG \cong \triangle FKH$

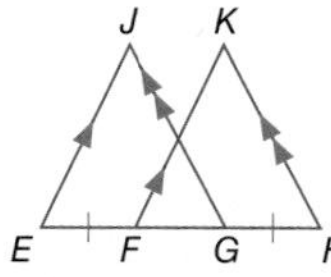

57. Given: $\overline{MN} \cong \overline{PQ}$, $\angle M \cong \angle Q$, $\angle 2 \cong \angle 3$
Prove: $\triangle MLP \cong \triangle QLN$

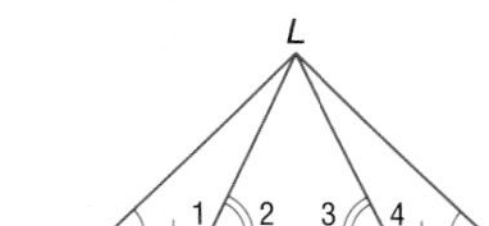

Skills Review

Use slope to determine whether XY and YZ are *perpendicular* or *not perpendicular*.

58. $X(-2, 2)$, $Y(0, 1)$, $Z(4, 1)$ **not perpendicular**

59. $X(4, 1)$, $Y(5, 3)$, $Z(6, 2)$ **not perpendicular**

DifferentiatedInstruction BL

Extension Have students draw a parallelogram on the coordinate plane with coordinates (0, 0), (2, 4), (8, 4), and (6, 0). Next, connect the points (2, 4) and (5, 0), (3, 4) and (6, 0), (0, 0) and (6, 4), and (2, 0) and (8, 4). What shape is formed by the intersections of the four line segments? parallelogram

4 Assess

Yesterday's News Have students write a paragraph that explains how the lesson about parallelograms helped them in the lesson about tests for parallelograms.

Formative Assessment

Check for student understanding of Lesson 6-3.

 Quiz 2, p. 45

Additional Answers

42. Sometimes; sample answer: The two parallelograms could be congruent, but you can also make the parallelogram bigger or smaller without changing the angle measures by changing the side lengths.

43.

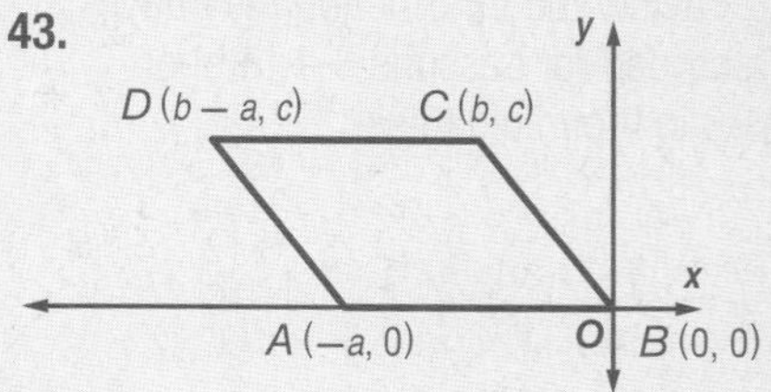

55. Given: $P + W > 2$ (P is time spent in the pool; W is time spent lifting weights.)

Prove: $P > 1$ or $W > 1$

Proof:

Step 1: Assume $P \leq 1$ and $W \leq 1$.

Step 2: $P + W \leq 2$

Step 3: This contradicts the given statement. Therefore he did at least one of these activities for more than an hour.

Formative Assessment

Use the Mid-Chapter Quiz to assess students' progress in the first half of the chapter.

Have students review the lesson indicated for the problems they answered incorrectly.

Summative Assessment

Mid-Chapter Test, p. 47

eAssessment Customize and create multiple versions of your Mid-Chapter Tests and their answer keys.

FOLDABLES StudyOrganizer

Dinah Zike's Foldables®

Before students complete the Mid-Chapter Quiz, encourage them to review the information they have recorded for Lessons 6-1 through 6-3 in their Foldables.

Additional Answers

5. $m\angle A = 158$, $m\angle B = 46$, $m\angle C = 110$, $m\angle D = 46$
6. $m\angle P = 61$, $m\angle Q = 106$, $m\angle R = 122$, $m\angle S = 71$
16. Sample answer: Make sure that opposite sides are congruent or make sure that opposite angles are congruent.

CHAPTER 6 Mid-Chapter Quiz

Lessons 6-1 through 6-3

Find the sum of the measures of the interior angles of each convex polygon. (Lesson 6-1)

1. pentagon **540**
2. heptagon **900**
3. 18-gon **2880**
4. 23-gon **3780**

Find the measure of each interior angle. (Lesson 6-1)

5. 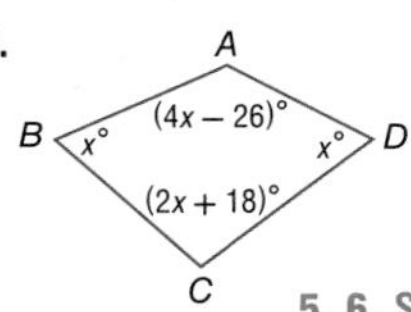

6. 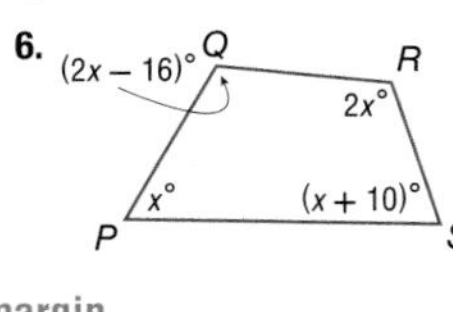

5, 6. See margin.

The sum of the measures of the interior angles of a regular polygon is given. Find the number of sides in the polygon. (Lesson 6-1)

7. 720 **6**
8. 1260 **9**
9. 1800 **12**
10. 4500 **27**

Find the value of x in each diagram. (Lesson 6-1)

11. 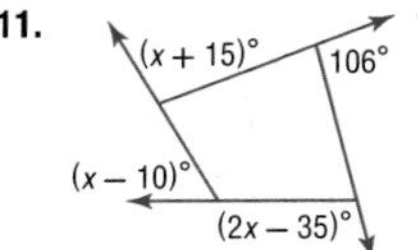

71

12. 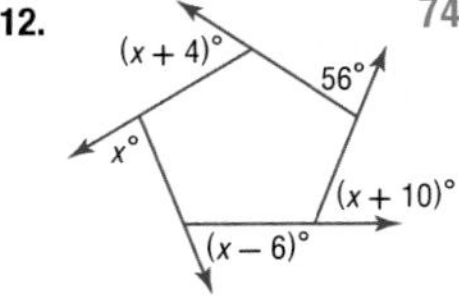

74

Use ▱WXYZ to find each measure. (Lesson 6-2)

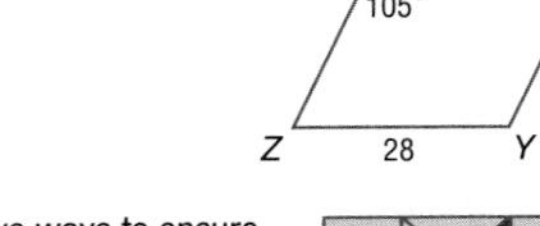

13. $m\angle WZY$ **75**
14. WZ **24**
15. $m\angle XYZ$ **105**

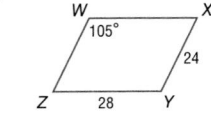

16. **DESIGN** Describe two ways to ensure that the pieces of the design at the right would fit properly together. (Lesson 6-2) **See margin.**

ALGEBRA Find the value of each variable in each parallelogram. (Lesson 6-2)

17. 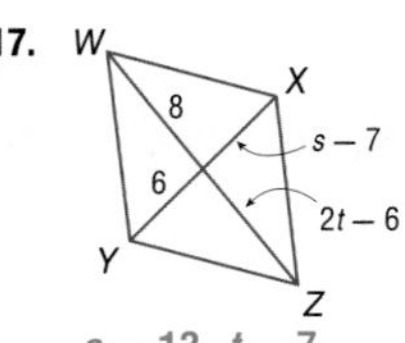

$s = 13$, $t = 7$

18. 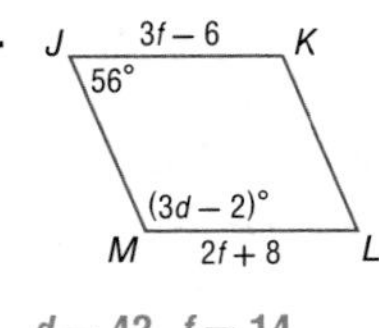

$d = 42$, $f = 14$

19. **PROOF** Write a two-column proof. (Lesson 6-2)
Given: ▱GFBA and ▱HACD
Prove: $\angle F \cong \angle D$ **See Ch. 6 Answer Appendix.**

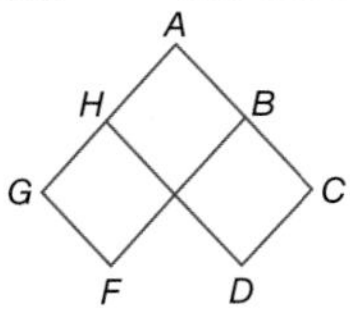

Find x and y so that each quadrilateral is a parallelogram. (Lesson 6-3)

20. 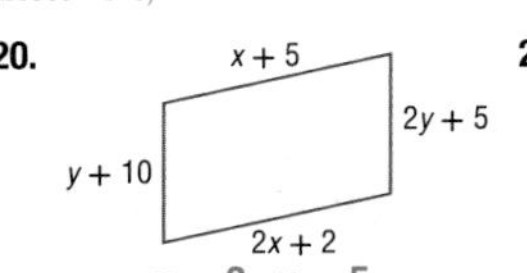

$x = 3$, $y = 5$

21. 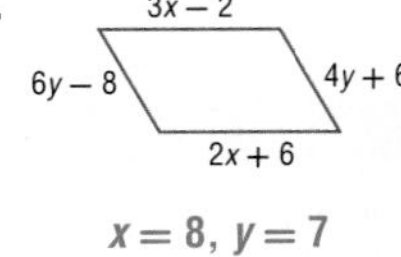

$x = 8$, $y = 7$

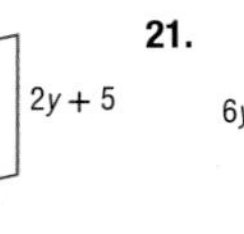

22. **MUSIC** Why will the keyboard stand with legs joined at the midpoints always remain parallel to the floor? (Lesson 6-3) **See Ch. 6 Answer Appendix.**

23. **MULTIPLE CHOICE** Which of the following quadrilaterals is not a parallelogram? (Lesson 6-3) **D**

A 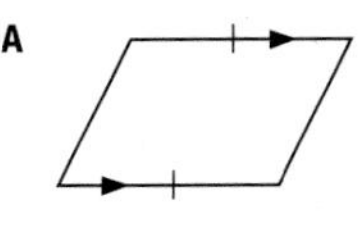

C 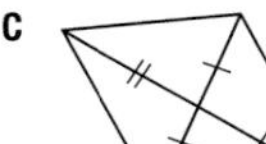

B 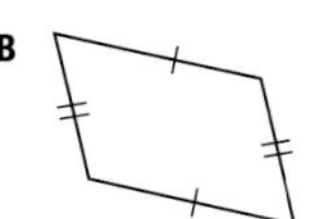

D 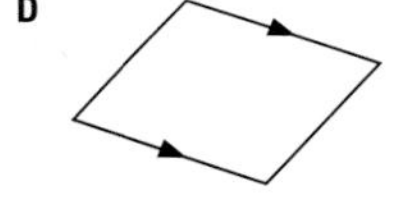

COORDINATE GEOMETRY Determine whether the figure is a parallelogram. Justify your answer with the method indicated. (Lesson 6-3) **24, 25. See Ch. 6 Answer Appendix.**

24. $A(-6, -5)$, $B(-1, -4)$, $C(0, -1)$, $D(-5, -2)$; Distance Formula
25. $Q(-5, 2)$, $R(-3, -6)$, $S(2, 2)$, $T(-1, 6)$; Slope Formula

422 | Chapter 6 | Mid-Chapter Quiz

InterventionPlanner

Tier 1 On Level OL	Tier 2 Strategic Intervention AL approaching grade level	Tier 3 Intensive Intervention 2 or more grades below level
If students miss about 25% of the exercises or less,	**If** students miss about 50% of the exercises,	**If** students miss about 75% of the exercises,
Then choose a resource: **SE** Lessons 6-1, 6-2, and 6-3  Skills Practice, pp. 7, 13 and 19  connectED.mcgraw-hill.com Self-Check Quiz	**Then** choose a resource:  Study Guide and Intervention, pp. 5, 11 and 17  connectED.mcgraw-hill.com Extra Examples, Personal Tutor, Homework Help	**Then** use *Math Triumphs, Geo.* 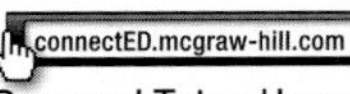 connectED.mcgraw-hill.com Extra Examples, Personal Tutor, Homework Help, Review Vocabulary

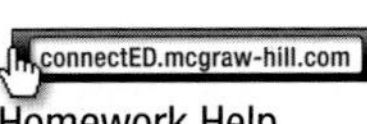

LESSON 6-4 Rectangles

:: Then	:: Now	:: Why?
You used properties of parallelograms and determined whether quadrilaterals were parallelograms.	1 Recognize and apply properties of rectangles. 2 Determine whether parallelograms are rectangles.	Leonardo is in charge of set design for a school play. He needs to use paint to create the appearance of a doorway on a lightweight solid wall. The doorway is to be a rectangle 36 inches wide and 80 inches tall. How can Leonardo be sure that he paints a rectangle?

NewVocabulary
rectangle

Common Core State Standards

Content Standards
G.CO.11 Prove theorems about parallelograms.
G.GPE.4 Use coordinates to prove simple geometric theorems algebraically.

Mathematical Practices
3 Construct viable arguments and critique the reasoning of others.
5 Use appropriate tools strategically.

1 Properties of Rectangles

A **rectangle** is a parallelogram with four right angles. By definition, a rectangle has the following properties.

- All four angles are right angles.
- Opposite sides are parallel and congruent.
- Opposite angles are congruent.
- Consecutive angles are supplementary.
- Diagonals bisect each other.

In addition, the diagonals of a rectangle are congruent.

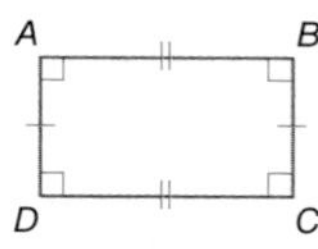

Rectangle *ABCD*

Theorem 6.13 Diagonals of a Rectangle

If a parallelogram is a rectangle, then its diagonals are congruent.

Abbreviation *If a ▱ is a rectangle, diag. are ≅.*

Example If ▱*JKLM* is a rectangle, then $\overline{JL} \cong \overline{MK}$.

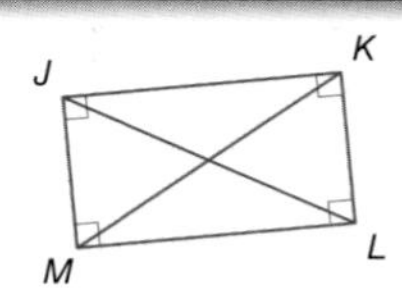

You will prove Theorem 6.13 in Exercise 33.

Real-World Example 1 Use Properties of Rectangles

EXERCISE A rectangular park has two walking paths as shown. If $PS = 180$ meters and $PR = 200$ meters, find QT.

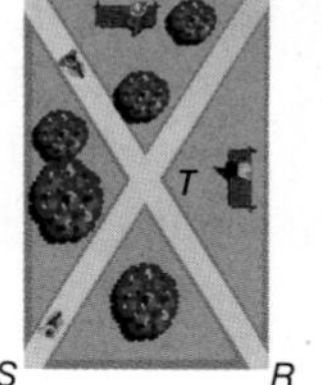

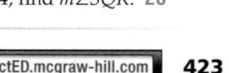

$\overline{QS} \cong \overline{PR}$	If a ▱ is a rectangle, diag. are ≅.
$QS = PR$	Definition of congruence
$QS = 200$	Substitution

Since *PQRS* is a rectangle, it is a parallelogram. The diagonals of a parallelogram bisect each other, so $QT = ST$.

$QT + ST = QS$	Segment Addition
$QT + QT = QS$	Substitution
$2QT = QS$	Simplify.
$QT = \frac{1}{2}QS$	Divide each side by 2.
$QT = \frac{1}{2}(200)$ or 100	Substitution

GuidedPractice Refer to the figure in Example 1.

1A. If $TS = 120$ meters, find PR. 240

1B. If $m\angle PRS = 64$, find $m\angle SQR$. 26

1 Focus

VerticalAlignment

Before Lesson 6-4 Use properties of parallelograms and determine whether quadrilaterals are parallelograms.

Lesson 6-4 Recognize and apply properties of rectangles. Determine whether parallelograms are rectangles.

After Lesson 6-4 Use deductive reasoning to prove a statement.

2 Teach

Scaffolding Questions

Have students read the **Why?** section of the lesson.

Ask:

- How would you approach the problem if you were Leonardo? What will Leonardo have to do to that ensure the door is a rectangle? Sample answer: Measure 80 inches up from the floor, then 36 inches across at a right angle, and then back down to the floor. Make sure that the corners of the door form right angles. Make sure that the sides of the door are the same length, and that the top of the door and the bottom of the door are the same length.

(continued on the next page)

Lesson 6-4 Resources

Resource	Approaching Level AL	On Level OL	Beyond Level BL	English Learners ELL
Teacher Edition	▪ Differentiated Instruction, p. 424	▪ Differentiated Instruction, pp. 424, 429	▪ Differentiated Instruction, pp. 424, 429	
Chapter Resource Masters	▪ Study Guide and Intervention, pp. 23–24 ▪ Skills Practice, p. 25 ▪ Practice, p. 26 ▪ Word Problem Practice, p. 27 ▪ Cabri Jr Activity, p. 29 ▪ Geometer's Sketchpad, p. 30	▪ Study Guide and Intervention, pp. 23–24 ▪ Skills Practice and Practice, pp. 25, 26 ▪ Word Problem Practice, p. 27 ▪ Enrichment, p. 28 ▪ Cabri Jr Activity, p. 29 ▪ Geometer's Sketchpad, p. 30	▪ Practice, p. 26 ▪ Word Problem Practice, p. 27 ▪ Enrichment, p. 28 ▪ Cabri Jr Activity, p. 29 ▪ Geometer's Sketchpad, p. 30	▪ Study Guide and Intervention, pp. 23–24 ▪ Skills Practice, p. 25 ▪ Practice, p. 26 ▪ Word Problem Practice, p. 27 ▪ Cabri Jr Activity, p. 29 ▪ Geometer's Sketchpad, p. 30
Other	▪ 5-Minute Check 6-4 ▪ Study Notebook ▪ Teaching Geometry with Manipulatives	▪ 5-Minute Check 6-4 ▪ Study Notebook ▪ Teaching Geometry with Manipulatives	▪ 5-Minute Check 6-4 ▪ Study Notebook	▪ 5-Minute Check 6-4 ▪ Study Notebook ▪ Teaching Geometry with Manipulatives

- Assuming that the floor is level, how could Leonardo check that the door is a rectangle without measuring the sides or angles? Measure the diagonals. If they are congruent, the figure is a rectangle.

1 Properties of Rectangles

Examples 1 and 2 show how to prove that quadrilaterals are rectangles algebraically using properties and theorems of rectangles.

Formative Assessment

Use the Guided Practice exercises after each example to determine students' understanding of concepts.

Additional Examples

1 **CONSTRUCTION** A rectangular garden gate is reinforced with diagonal braces to prevent it from sagging. If $JK = 12$ feet, and $LN = 6.5$ feet, find KM.

$KM = 13$ ft

2 Quadrilateral $RSTU$ is a rectangle. If $m\angle RTU = 8x + 4$ and $m\angle SUR = 3x - 2$, find x. 8

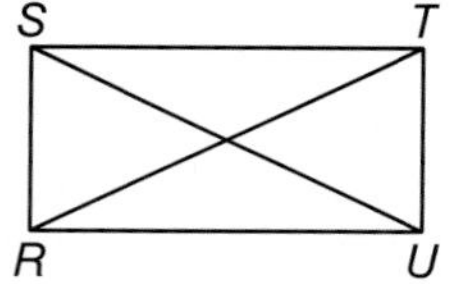

Additional Examples also in Interactive Classroom PowerPoint® Presentations

You can use the properties of rectangles along with algebra to find missing values.

StudyTip

Right Angles Recall from Theorem 6-6 that if a parallelogram has one right angle, then it has four right angles.

Example 2 Use Properties of Rectangles and Algebra

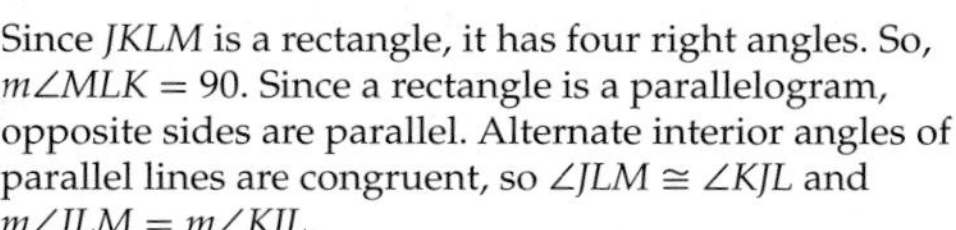

ALGEBRA Quadrilateral $JKLM$ is a rectangle. If $m\angle KJL = 2x + 4$ and $m\angle JLK = 7x + 5$, find x.

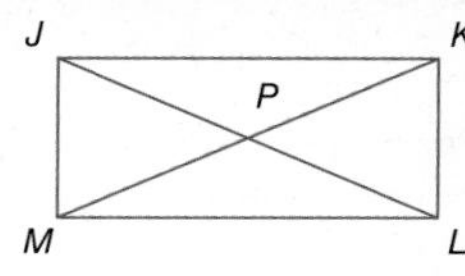

Since $JKLM$ is a rectangle, it has four right angles. So, $m\angle MLK = 90$. Since a rectangle is a parallelogram, opposite sides are parallel. Alternate interior angles of parallel lines are congruent, so $\angle JLM \cong \angle KJL$ and $m\angle JLM = m\angle KJL$.

$m\angle JLM + m\angle JLK = 90$	Angle Addition
$m\angle KJL + m\angle JLK = 90$	Substitution
$2x + 4 + 7x + 5 = 90$	Substitution
$9x + 9 = 90$	Add like terms.
$9x = 81$	Subtract 9 from each side.
$x = 9$	Divide each side by 9.

Guided Practice

2. Refer to the figure in Example 2. If $JP = 3y - 5$ and $MK = 5y + 1$, find y. 11

2 Prove that Parallelograms are Rectangles

The converse of Theorem 6.13 is also true.

Theorem 6.14 Diagonals of a Rectangle

If the diagonals of a parallelogram are congruent, then the parallelogram is a rectangle.

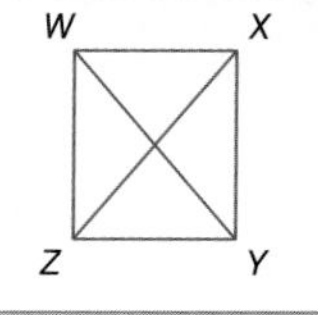

Abbreviation *If diag. of a ▱ are ≅, then ▱ is a rectangle.*

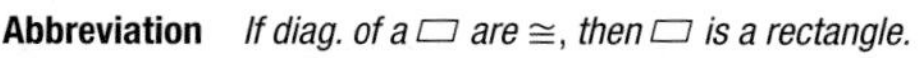

Example If $\overline{WY} \cong \overline{XZ}$ in ▱$WXYZ$, then ▱$WXYZ$ is a rectangle.

You will prove Theorem 6.14 in Exercise 34.

Real-World Link

The game of dodgeball is played on a rectangular playing field ideally 60 feet long and 30 feet wide. The field is divided into two equal sections by a center-line and attack-lines that are 3 meters (9.8 feet) from, and parallel to, the centerline.

Source: National Amateur Dodgeball Assoc.

Real-World Example 3 Providing Rectangle Relationships

DODGEBALL A community recreation center has created an outdoor dodgeball playing field. To be sure that it meets the ideal playing field requirements, they measure the sides of the field and its diagonals. If $AB = 60$ feet, $BC = 30$ feet, $CD = 60$ feet, $AD = 30$ feet, $AC = 67$ feet, and $BD = 67$ feet, explain how the recreation center can be sure that the playing field is rectangular.

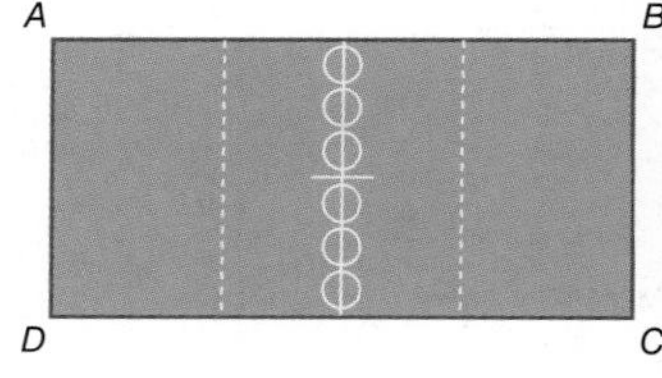

Since $AB = CD$, $BC = AD$, and $AC = BD$, $\overline{AB} \cong \overline{CD}$, $\overline{BC} \cong \overline{AD}$, and $\overline{AC} \cong \overline{BD}$. Because $\overline{AB} \cong \overline{CD}$ and $\overline{BC} \cong \overline{AD}$, $ABCD$ is a parallelogram. Since $\overline{AC}$ and $\overline{BD}$ are congruent diagonals in ▱$ABCD$, ▱$ABCD$ is a rectangle.

Differentiated Instruction AL OL BL

Kinesthetic Learners Have students use two equal-length pieces of string, masking tape, and a smooth surface to mark off quadrilaterals. Secure the two pieces of string to the surface so that they intersect. Use the masking tape to form a quadrilateral by connecting the ends of the strings. Repeat several times, having the strings intersect at different points. Students should see that the quadrilateral is a rectangle only when the strings intersect at their midpoints.

Real-WorldLink

The Mosaic Youth Theater in Detroit, Michigan, is a professional performing arts training program for young people ages 12 to 18. Students are involved in all aspects of performances, including set and lighting design, set construction, stage management, sound, and costumes.

GuidedPractice

3. SET DESIGN Refer to the beginning of the lesson. Leonardo measures the sides of his figure and confirms that they have the desired measures as shown. Using a carpenter's square, he also confirms that the measure of the bottom left corner of the figure is a right angle. Can he conclude that the figure is a rectangle? Explain. **See margin.**

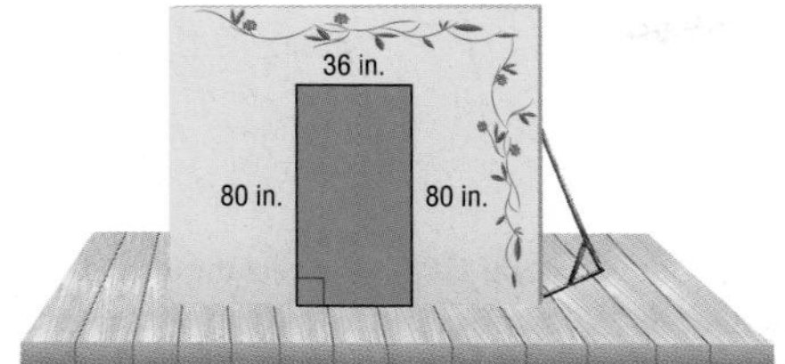

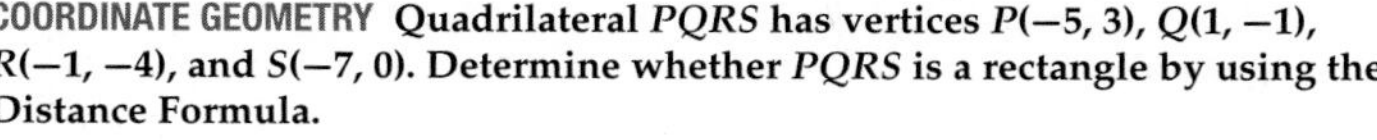

You can also use the properties of rectangles to prove that a quadrilateral positioned on a coordinate plane is a rectangle given the coordinates of the vertices.

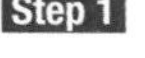

Example 4 Rectangles and Coordinate Geometry

COORDINATE GEOMETRY Quadrilateral *PQRS* has vertices *P*(−5, 3), *Q*(1, −1), *R*(−1, −4), and *S*(−7, 0). Determine whether *PQRS* is a rectangle by using the Distance Formula.

Step 1 Use the Distance Formula to determine whether *PQRS* is a parallelogram by determining if opposite sides are congruent.

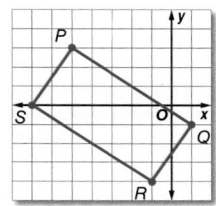

$PQ = \sqrt{(-5-1)^2 + [3-(-1)]^2}$ or $\sqrt{52}$

$RS = \sqrt{[-1-(-7)]^2 + (-4-0)^2}$ or $\sqrt{52}$

$PS = \sqrt{[-5-(-7)]^2 + (3-0)^2}$ or $\sqrt{13}$

$QR = \sqrt{[1-(-1)]^2 + [-1-(-4)]^2}$ or $\sqrt{13}$

Since opposite sides of the quadrilateral have the same measure, they are congruent. So, quadrilateral *PQRS* is a parallelogram.

Step 2 Determine whether the diagonals of ▱*PQRS* are congruent.

$PR = \sqrt{[-5-(-1)]^2 + [3-(-4)]^2}$ or $\sqrt{65}$

$QS = \sqrt{[1-(-7)]^2 + (-1-0)^2}$ or $\sqrt{65}$

Since the diagonals have the same measure, they are congruent. So, ▱*PQRS* is a rectangle.

StudyTip

Rectangles and Parallelograms A rectangle is a parallelogram, but a parallelogram is not necessarily a rectangle.

GuidedPractice

4. Quadrilateral *JKLM* has vertices *J*(−10, 2), *K*(−8, −6), *L*(5, −3), and *M*(2, 5). Determine whether *JKLM* is a rectangle using the Slope Formula. **No; $\overline{JK}$ and $\overline{ML}$ are not parallel.**

2 Prove that Parallelograms are Rectangles

Examples 3 and 4 show how to prove that parallelograms are rectangles by using Theorem 6.14.

Additional Examples

3 ART Some artists stretch their own canvas over wooden frames. This allows them to customize the size of a canvas. In order to ensure that the frame is rectangular before stretching the canvas, an artist measures the sides and the diagonals of the frame. If $AB = 12$ inches, $BC = 35$ inches, $CD = 12$ inches, $DA = 35$ inches, $BD = 37$ inches, and $AC = 37$ inches, explain how an artist can be sure that the frame is rectangular.

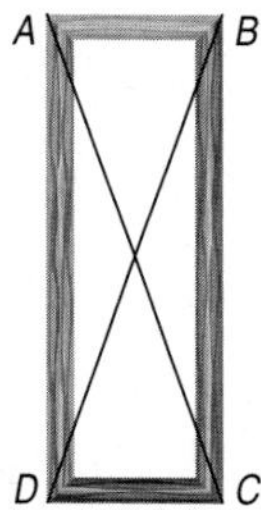

$\overline{AB} \cong \overline{DC}$ and $\overline{AD} \cong \overline{BC}$; therefore, *ABCD* is a parallelogram. $\overline{AC} \cong \overline{BD}$; therefore, ▱*ABCD* is a rectangle.

4 Quadrilateral *JKLM* has vertices *J*(−2, 3), *K*(1, 4), *L*(3, −2), and *M*(0, −3). Determine whether *JKLM* is a rectangle by using the Distance Formula.

Because $JK = ML = \sqrt{10}$ and $JM = KL = \sqrt{40}$, *JKLM* is a parallelogram.

Because $KM = JL = \sqrt{50}$, *JKLM* is a rectangle.

Teach with Tech

Blog On your secure class blog, have students write a blog entry explaining two different ways to prove that a parallelogram is a rectangle.

Additional Answer (Guided Practice)

3. Yes; since opposite sides are congruent, the doorway is a parallelogram. If one angle in a parallelogram is a right angle, then all angles are right angles. Since the bottom left angle of the doorway is a right angle, all angles of the doorway are right angles, so by definition, the doorway is rectangular.

3 Practice

Formative Assessment

Use Exercises 1–9 to check for understanding.

Then use the chart at the bottom of this page to customize assignments for your students.

Teaching the Mathematical Practices

Regularity Mathematically proficient students look both for general methods and for shortcuts. In Exercises 14–19, encourage students to use the properties of rectangles to find each of the indicated measures.

Additional Answers

7. **Given:** *ABDE* is a rectangle; $\overline{BC} \cong \overline{DC}$.

Prove: $\overline{AC} \cong \overline{EC}$

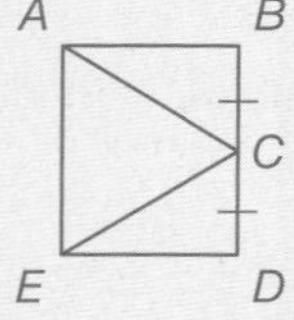

Proof:

Statements (Reasons)

1. *ABDE* is a rectangle; $\overline{BC} \cong \overline{DC}$. (Given)
2. *ABDE* is a parallelogram. (Def. of rectangle)
3. $\overline{AB} \cong \overline{DE}$ (Opp. sides of a ▱ are ≅.)
4. ∠*B* and ∠*D* are right angles. (Def. of rectangle)
5. ∠*B* ≅ ∠*D* (All rt ∠s are ≅.)
6. △*ABC* ≅ △*EDC* (SAS)
7. $\overline{AC} \cong \overline{EC}$ (CPCTC)

Check Your Understanding

= Step-by-Step Solutions begin on page R14.

Example 1 **FARMING** An X-brace on a rectangular barn door is both decorative and functional. It helps to prevent the door from warping over time. If $ST = 3\frac{13}{16}$ feet, $PS = 7$ feet, and $m\angle PTQ = 67$, find each measure.

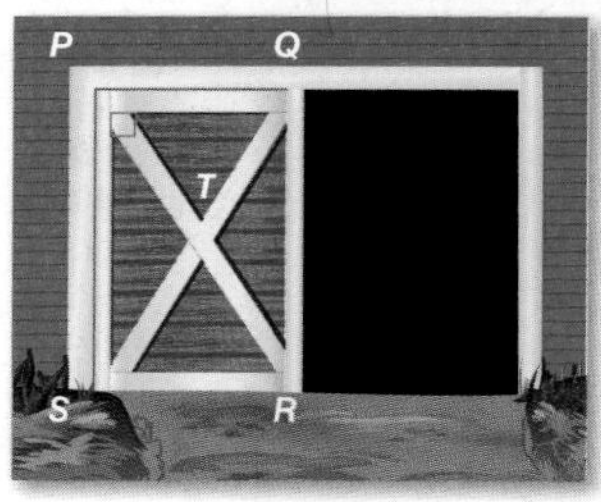

1. QR 7 ft
2. SQ $7\frac{5}{8}$ ft
3. $m\angle TQR$ 33.5
4. $m\angle TSR$ 56.5

Example 2 **ALGEBRA** Quadrilateral *DEFG* is a rectangle.

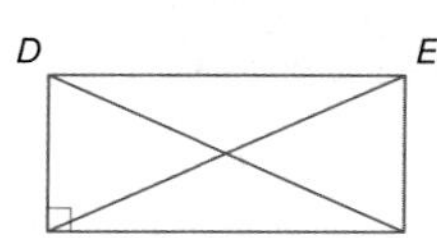

5. If $FD = 3x - 7$ and $EG = x + 5$, find EG. 11
6. If $m\angle EFD = 2x - 3$ and $m\angle DFG = x + 12$, find $m\angle EFD$. 51

Example 3

7. **PROOF** If *ABDE* is a rectangle and $\overline{BC} \cong \overline{DC}$, prove that $\overline{AC} \cong \overline{EC}$. See margin.

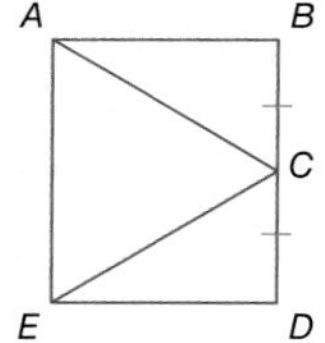

Example 4 **COORDINATE GEOMETRY** Graph each quadrilateral with the given vertices. Determine whether the figure is a rectangle. Justify your answer using the indicated formula. 8–9. See Ch. 6 Answer Appendix.

8. $W(-4, 3)$, $X(1, 5)$, $Y(3, 1)$, $Z(-2, -2)$; Slope Formula
9. $A(4, 3)$, $B(4, -2)$, $C(-4, -2)$, $D(-4, 3)$; Distance Formula

Practice and Problem Solving

Extra Practice is on page R6.

Example 1 **FENCING** X-braces are also used to provide support in rectangular fencing. If $AB = 6$ feet, $AD = 2$ feet, and $m\angle DAE = 65$, find each measure.

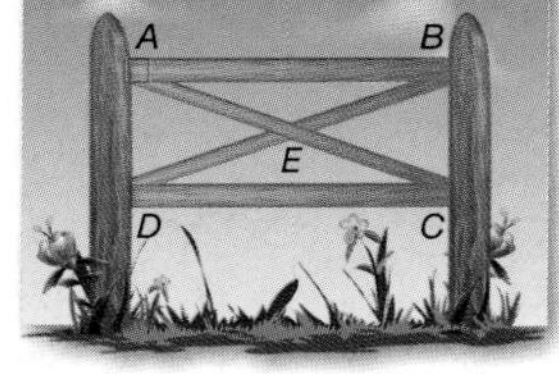

10. BC 2 ft
11. DB 6.3 ft
12. $m\angle CEB$ 50
13. $m\angle EDC$ 25

Example 2 **REGULARITY** Quadrilateral *WXYZ* is a rectangle.

14. If $ZY = 2x + 3$ and $WX = x + 4$, find WX. 5
15. If $PY = 3x - 5$ and $WP = 2x + 11$, find ZP. 43
16. If $m\angle ZYW = 2x - 7$ and $m\angle WYX = 2x + 5$, find $m\angle ZYW$. 39
17. If $ZP = 4x - 9$ and $PY = 2x + 5$, find ZX. 38
18. If $m\angle XZY = 3x + 6$ and $m\angle XZW = 5x - 12$, find $m\angle YXZ$. 48
19. If $m\angle ZXW = x - 11$ and $m\angle WZX = x - 9$, find $m\angle ZXY$. 46

Differentiated Homework Options

Level	Assignment	Two-Day Option	
AL Basic	10–25, 46–64	11–25 odd, 50–53	10–24 even, 46–49, 54–64
OL Core	11–31 odd, 32, 33–43 odd, 46–64	10–25, 50–53	26–44, 46–49, 54–64
BL Advanced	26–61, (optional: 62–64)		

Example 3 **PROOF** **Write a two-column proof.** 20–25. See Ch. 6 Answer Appendix.

20. **Given:** $ABCD$ is a rectangle.
Prove: $\triangle ADC \cong \triangle BCD$

21. **Given:** $QTVW$ is a rectangle.
$\overline{QR} \cong \overline{ST}$
Prove: $\triangle SWQ \cong \triangle RVT$

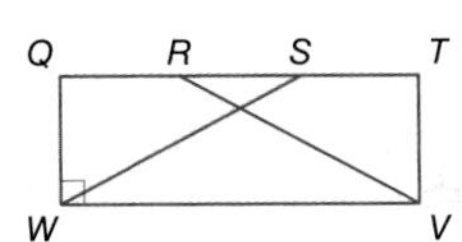

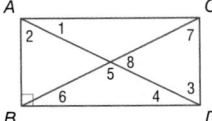

32. 3 ft 3 in.; sample answer: In order for the bookshelf to be square, the lengths of all of the metal supports should be equal. Since I knew the length of the bookshelves and the distance between them, I used the Pythagorean Theorem to find the lengths of the metal supports.

Example 4 **COORDINATE GEOMETRY** **Graph each quadrilateral with the given vertices. Determine whether the figure is a rectangle. Justify your answer using the indicated formula.**

22. $W(-2, 4), X(5, 5), Y(6, -2), Z(-1, -3)$; Slope Formula

23. $J(3, 3), K(-5, 2), L(-4, -4), M(4, -3)$; Distance Formula

24. $Q(-2, 2), R(0, -2), S(6, 1), T(4, 5)$; Distance Formula

25. $G(1, 8), H(-7, 7), J(-6, 1), K(2, 2)$; Slope Formula

B **Quadrilateral $ABCD$ is a rectangle. Find each measure if $m\angle 2 = 40$.**

26. $m\angle 1$ 50
27. $m\angle 7$ 40
28. $m\angle 3$ 40
29. $m\angle 5$ 80
30. $m\angle 6$ 50
31. $m\angle 8$ 100

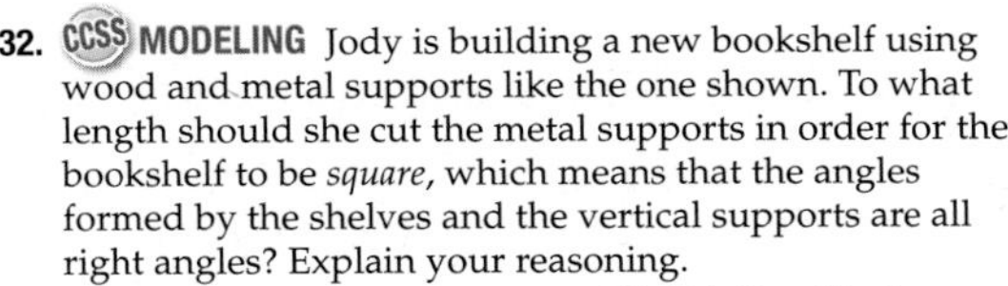

32. **CCSS MODELING** Jody is building a new bookshelf using wood and metal supports like the one shown. To what length should she cut the metal supports in order for the bookshelf to be *square*, which means that the angles formed by the shelves and the vertical supports are all right angles? Explain your reasoning.

PROOF **Write a two-column proof.** 33, 34. See Ch. 6 Answer Appendix.

33. Theorem 6.13
34. Theorem 6.14

PROOF **Write a paragraph proof of each statement.** 35, 36. See Ch. 6 Answer Appendix.

35. If a parallelogram has one right angle, then it is a rectangle.

36. If a quadrilateral has four right angles, then it is a rectangle.

37. **CONSTRUCTION** Construct a rectangle using the construction for congruent segments and the construction for a line perpendicular to another line through a point on the line. Justify each step of the construction. See Ch. 6 Answer Appendix.

38. **SPORTS** The end zone of a football field is 160 feet wide and 30 feet long. Kyle is responsible for painting the field. He has finished the end zone. Explain how Kyle can confirm that the end zone is the regulation size and be sure that it is also a rectangle using only a tape measure. See Ch. 6 Answer Appendix.

ALGEBRA **Quadrilateral $WXYZ$ is a rectangle.**

39. If $XW = 3$, $WZ = 4$, and $XZ = b$, find YW. 5

40. If $XZ = 2c$ and $ZY = 6$, and $XY = 8$, find WY. 10

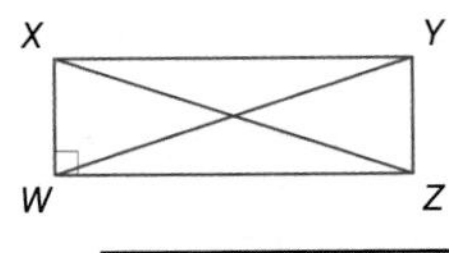

CCSS Teaching the Mathematical Practices

Modeling Mathematically proficient students can apply the mathematics they know to solve problems arising in everyday life. In Exercise 32, point out to students that the properties of parallelograms apply to rectangles.

Enrichment

OL BL

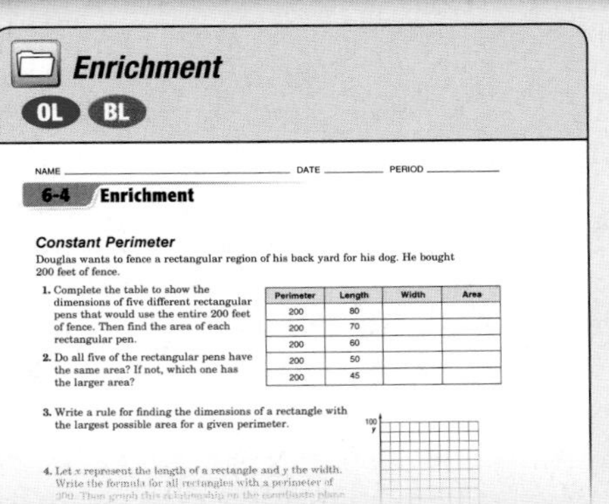

6-4 Enrichment

Constant Perimeter

Douglas wants to fence a rectangular region of his back yard for his dog. He bought 200 feet of fence.

1. Complete the table to show the dimensions of five different rectangular pens that would use the entire 200 feet of fence. Then find the area of each rectangular pen.

Perimeter	Length	Width	Area
200	80		
200	70		
200	60		
200	50		
200	45		

2. Do all five of the rectangular pens have the same area? If not, which one has the larger area?

3. Write a rule for finding the dimensions of a rectangle with the largest possible area for a given perimeter.

Study Guide and Intervention

AL OL ELL

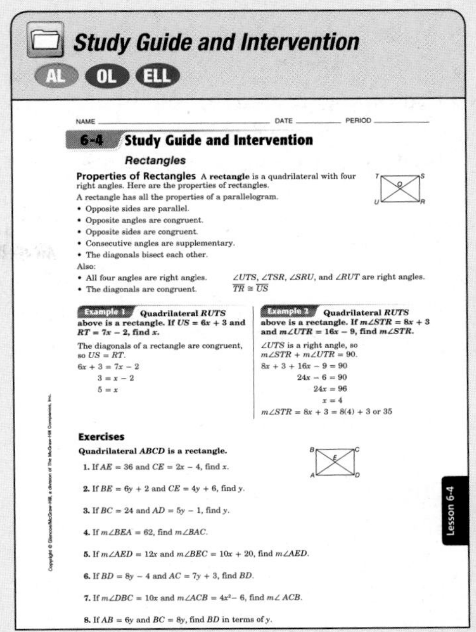

6-4 Study Guide and Intervention

Rectangles

Properties of Rectangles A rectangle is a quadrilateral with four right angles. Here are the properties of rectangles.
A rectangle has all the properties of a parallelogram.
• Opposite sides are parallel.
• Opposite angles are congruent.
• Opposite sides are congruent.
• Consecutive angles are supplementary.
• The diagonals bisect each other.
Also:
• All four angles are right angles.
• The diagonals are congruent.

Exercises

Quadrilateral ABCD is a rectangle.

Practice

AL OL BL ELL

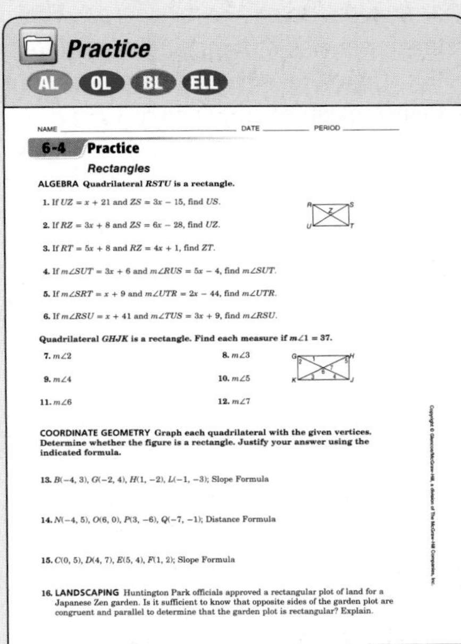

6-4 Practice

Rectangles

COORDINATE GEOMETRY Graph each quadrilateral with the given vertices. Determine whether the figure is a rectangle. Justify your answer using the indicated formula.

Word Problem Practice

AL OL BL ELL

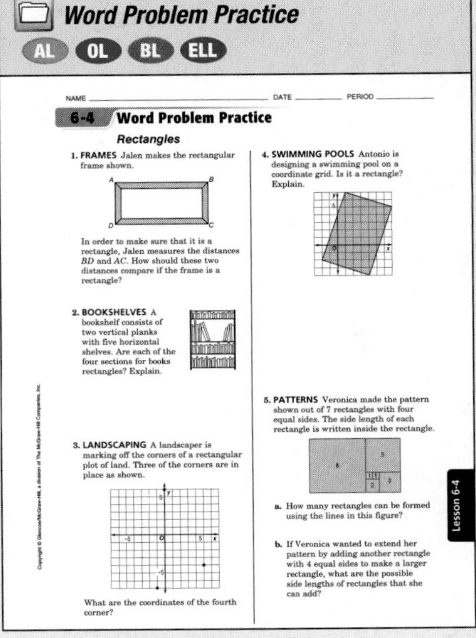

6-4 Word Problem Practice

Rectangles

Exercise Alert

Protractor, Compass, and Ruler Exercise 44 requires the use of a protractor, a compass, and a ruler.

Multiple Representations

In Exercise 44, students use geometric sketches, a table, and verbal description to investigate properties of special parallelograms.

CCSS Teaching the Mathematical Practices

Critique Mathematically proficient students can distinguish correct logic from flawed reasoning. For Exercise 46, students should realize that any two congruent acute triangles can be arranged to form a parallelogram. The interior angles of a rectangle measure 90°. Therefore, only two congruent right triangles can be arranged to form a rectangle.

Additional Answers

42. Given: *ABCD* is a rectangle.

Prove: $\overline{AC} \cong \overline{DB}$

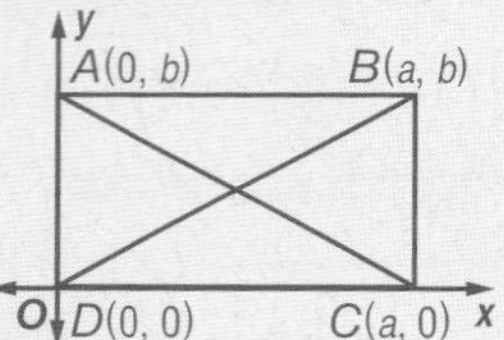

Proof:

Use the Distance Formula to find $AC = \sqrt{a^2 + b^2}$ and $BD = \sqrt{a^2 + b^2}$. *AC* and *DB* have the same length, so they are congruent.

43. Given: ▱*ABCD* and $\overline{AC} \cong \overline{BD}$

Prove: ▱*ABCD* is a rectangle.

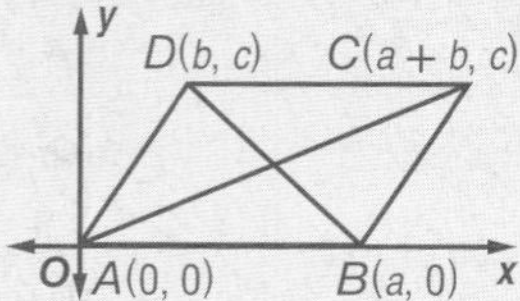

Proof:

$AC = \sqrt{(a + b - 0)^2 + (c - 0)^2}$

$BD = \sqrt{(b - a)^2 + (c - 0)^2}$

But $AC = BD$ and

$\sqrt{(a + b - 0)^2 + (c - 0)^2} = \sqrt{(b - a)^2 + (c - 0)^2}$.

$$(a + b - 0)^2 + (c - 0)^2 = (b - a)^2 + (c - 0)^2$$
$$(a + b)^2 + c^2 = (b - a)^2 + c^2$$
$$a^2 + 2ab + b^2 + c^2 = b^2 - 2ab + a^2 + c^2$$
$$2ab = -2ab$$
$$4ab = 0$$
$$a = 0 \text{ or } b = 0$$

Because *A* and *B* are different points, $a \neq 0$. Then $b = 0$. The slope of $\overline{AD}$ is undefined and the slope of $\overline{AB} = 0$. Thus, $\overline{AD} \perp \overline{AB}$. $\angle DAB$ is a right angle and *ABCD* is a rectangle.

41. SIGNS The sign below is in the foyer of Nyoko's school. Based on the dimensions given, can Nyoko be sure that the sign is a rectangle? Explain your reasoning.

No; sample answer: Both pairs of opposite sides are congruent, so the sign is a parallelogram, but no measure is given that can be used to prove that it is a rectangle.

PROOF **Write a coordinate proof of each statement.** 42, 43. See margin.

42. The diagonals of a rectangle are congruent.

43. If the diagonals of a parallelogram are congruent, then it is a rectangle.

44. **MULTIPLE REPRESENTATIONS** In the problem, you will explore properties of other special parallelograms.

a. Geometric Draw three parallelograms, each with all four sides congruent. Label one parallelogram *ABCD*, one *MNOP*, and one *WXYZ*. Draw the two diagonals of each parallelogram and label the intersections *R*. See margin.

b. Tabular Use a protractor to measure the appropriate angles and complete the table below.

Parallelogram	*ABCD*		*MNOP*		*WXYZ*	
Angle	∠*ARB*	∠*BRC*	∠*MRN*	∠*NRO*	∠*WRX*	∠*XRY*
Angle Measure	90°	90°	90°	90°	90°	90°

c. Verbal Make a conjecture about the diagonals of a parallelogram with four congruent sides.

44c. Sample answer: The diagonals of a parallelogram with four congruent sides are perpendicular.

49. Sample answer: All rectangles are parallelograms because, by definition, both pairs of opposite sides are parallel. Parallelograms with right angles are rectangles, so some parallelograms are rectangles, but others with non-right angles are not.

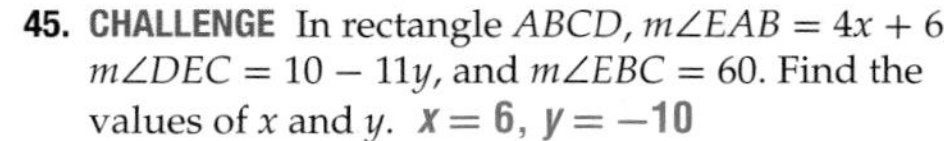

H.O.T. Problems Use Higher-Order Thinking Skills

45. CHALLENGE In rectangle *ABCD*, $m\angle EAB = 4x + 6$, $m\angle DEC = 10 - 11y$, and $m\angle EBC = 60$. Find the values of *x* and *y*. $x = 6$, $y = -10$

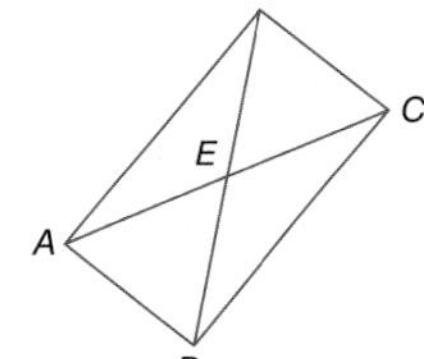

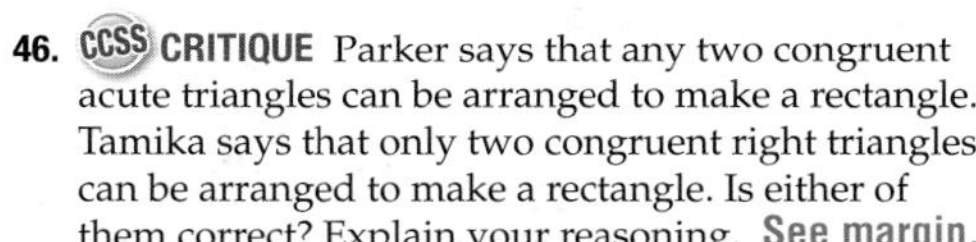

46. CCSS CRITIQUE Parker says that any two congruent acute triangles can be arranged to make a rectangle. Tamika says that only two congruent right triangles can be arranged to make a rectangle. Is either of them correct? Explain your reasoning. See margin.

47. REASONING In the diagram at the right, lines *n*, *p*, *q*, and *r* are parallel and lines *ℓ* and *m* are parallel. How many rectangles are formed by the intersecting lines? 6

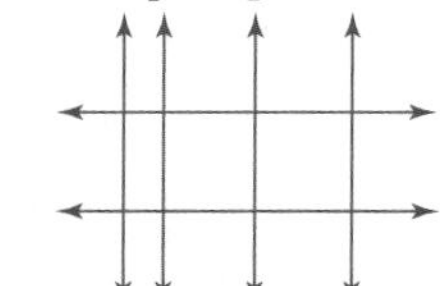

48. OPEN ENDED Write the equations of four lines having intersections that form the vertices of a rectangle. Verify your answer using coordinate geometry. See margin.

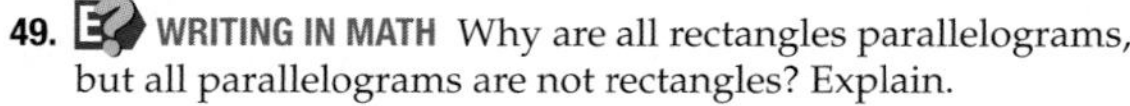

49. WRITING IN MATH Why are all rectangles parallelograms, but all parallelograms are not rectangles? Explain.

Standardized Test Practice

50. If $FJ = -3x + 5y$, $FM = 3x + y$, $GH = 11$, and $GM = 13$, what values of x and y make parallelogram $FGHJ$ a rectangle? **A**

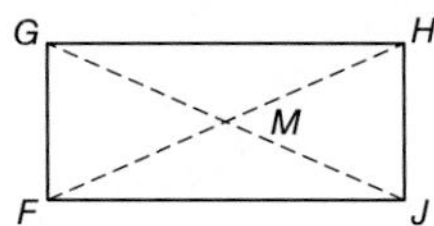

A $x = 3, y = 4$
B $x = 4, y = 3$
C $x = 7, y = 8$
D $x = 8, y = 7$

51. ALGEBRA A rectangular playground is surrounded by an 80-foot fence. One side of the playground is 10 feet longer than the other. Which of the following equations could be used to find r, the shorter side of the playground? **J**

F $10r + r = 80$
G $4r + 10 = 80$
H $r(r + 10) = 80$
J $2(r + 10) + 2r = 80$

52. SHORT RESPONSE What is the measure of $\angle APB$? **112**

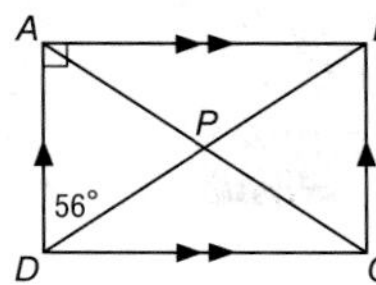

53. SAT/ACT If p is odd, which of the following must also be odd? **E**

A $2p$
B $2p + 2$
C $\frac{p}{2}$
D $2p - 2$
E $p + 2$

Spiral Review

ALGEBRA Find x and y so that the quadrilateral is a parallelogram. (Lesson 6-3)

54. 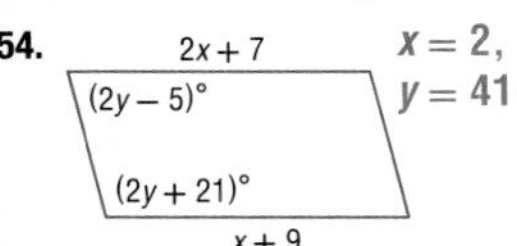

 $x = 2$, $y = 41$

55. 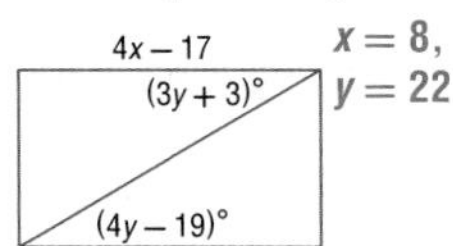

$x = 8$, $y = 22$

56. 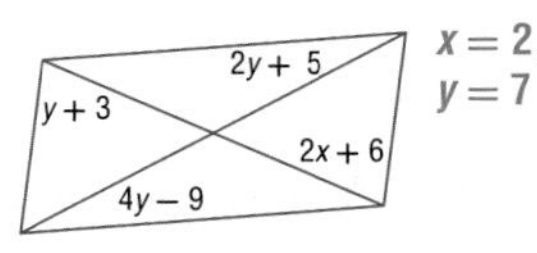

$x = 2$, $y = 7$

57. COORDINATE GEOMETRY Find the coordinates of the intersection of the diagonals of $\square ABCD$ with vertices $A(1, 3)$, $B(6, 2)$, $C(4, -2)$, and $D(-1, -1)$. (Lesson 6-2) **(2.5, 0.5)**

Refer to the figure at the right. (Lesson 4-6)

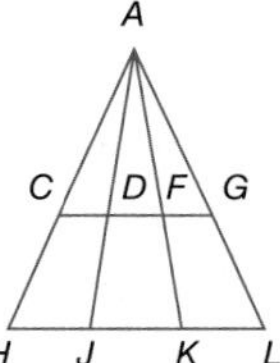

58. If $\overline{AC} \cong \overline{AF}$, name two congruent angles. $\angle ACF$ and $\angle AFC$

59. If $\angle AHJ \cong \angle AJH$, name two congruent segments. $\overline{AH}$ and $\overline{AJ}$

60. If $\angle AJL \cong \angle ALJ$, name two congruent segments. $\overline{AJ}$ and $\overline{AL}$

61. If $\overline{JA} \cong \overline{KA}$, name two congruent angles. $\angle AJK$ and $\angle AKJ$

Skills Review

Find the distance between each pair of points.

62. (4, 2), (2, −5) $\sqrt{53}$

63. (0, 6), (−1, −4) $\sqrt{101}$

64. (−4, 3), (3, −4) $7\sqrt{2}$

Differentiated Instruction OL BL

Extension Have students review Lessons 6-1 through 6-4. Have them write a conjecture about the result when diagonals are formed in a rhombus or square.
Lesson 6-4 shows that if a parallelogram is a rectangle, then the diagonals are congruent. Because Lesson 6-4 focuses on diagonal length, the next step is to focus on how the diagonals intersect. A sample conjecture is that the diagonals of a rhombus or square are perpendicular.

4 Assess

Name the Math Have students show how to write a two-column proof to show that a quadrilateral with congruent diagonals is a rectangle.

Additional Answers

44a. Sample answer:

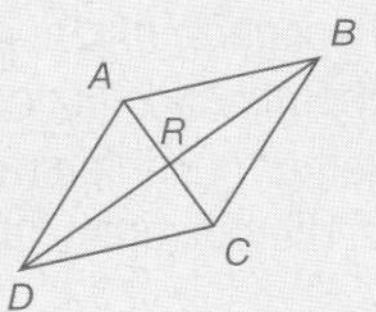

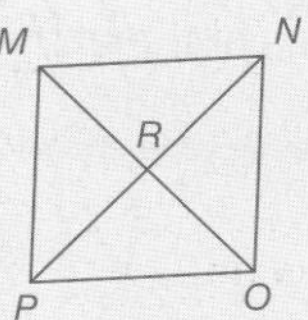

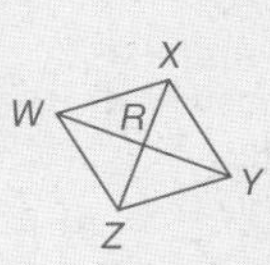

46. Tamika; Sample answer: When two congruent triangles are arranged to form a quadrilateral, two of the angles are formed by a single vertex of a triangle. In order for the quadrilateral to be a rectangle, one of the angles in the congruent triangles has to be a right angle.

48. Sample answer: $x = 0$, $x = 6$, $y = 0$, $y = 4$;

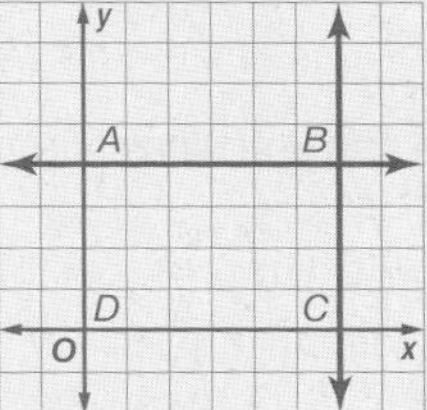

The length of $\overline{AB}$ is 6 − 0 or 6 units and the length of $\overline{CD}$ is 6 − 0 or 6 units. The slope of AB is 0 and the slope of DC is 0. Since a pair of sides of the quadrilateral is both parallel and congruent, by Theorem 6.12, the quadrilateral is a parallelogram. Since $\overline{AB}$ is horizontal and $\overline{BC}$ is vertical, the lines are perpendicular and the measure of the angle they form is 90. By Theorem 6.6, if a parallelogram has one right angle, it has four right angles. Therefore, by definition, the parallelogram is a rectangle.

1 Focus

VerticalAlignment

Before Lesson 6-5 Use properties of parallelograms and rectangles to determine whether quadrilaterals are parallelograms and/or rectangles.

Lesson 6-5 Recognize and apply the properties of rhombi and squares. Determine whether quadrilaterals are rectangles, rhombi, or squares.

After Lesson 6-5 Recognize and apply the properties of trapezoids and kites.

2 Teach

Scaffolding Questions

Have students read the **Why?** section of the lesson.

Ask:

- Why can a rhombus and a square also be classified as equilateral parallelograms? Because all four sides are the same length and because opposite sides are parallel.
- In what ways can you classify rhombi and squares? A rhombus is an equilateral parallelogram. A square is a rhombus with all angles measuring 90.

(continued on the next page)

LESSON 6-5 Rhombi and Squares

Then

- You determined whether quadrilaterals were parallelograms and/or rectangles.

Now

1. Recognize and apply the properties of rhombi and squares.
2. Determine whether quadrilaterals are rectangles, rhombi, or squares.

Why?

- Some fruits, nuts, and vegetables are packaged using bags made out of rhombus-shaped tubular netting. Similar shaped nylon netting is used for goals in such sports as soccer, hockey, and football. A rhombus and a square are both types of equilateral parallelograms.

NewVocabulary
rhombus
square

Common Core State Standards

Content Standards
G.CO.11 Prove theorems about parallelograms.
G.GPE.4 Use coordinates to prove simple geometric theorems algebraically.

Mathematical Practices
3 Construct viable arguments and critique the reasoning of others.
2 Reason abstractly and quantitatively.

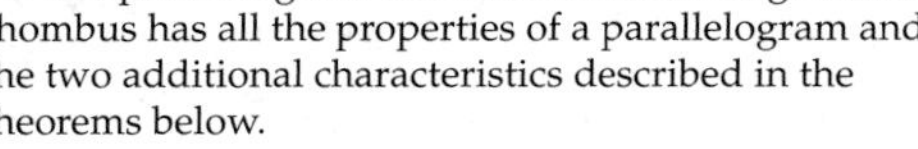

1 Properties of Rhombi and Squares

A **rhombus** is a parallelogram with all four sides congruent. A rhombus has all the properties of a parallelogram and the two additional characteristics described in the theorems below.

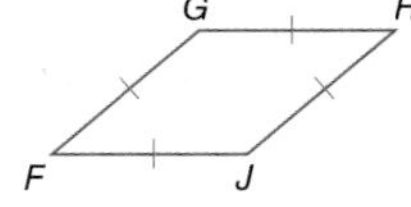

Theorems Diagonals of a Rhombus

6.15 If a parallelogram is a rhombus, then its diagonals are perpendicular.

Example If ▱$ABCD$ is a rhombus, then $\overline{AC} \perp \overline{BD}$.

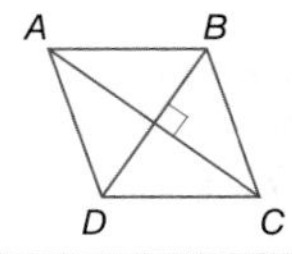

6.16 If a parallelogram is a rhombus, then each diagonal bisects a pair of opposite angles.

Example If ▱$NPQR$ is a rhombus, then $\angle 1 \cong \angle 2$, $\angle 3 \cong \angle 4$, $\angle 5 \cong \angle 6$, and $\angle 7 \cong \angle 8$.

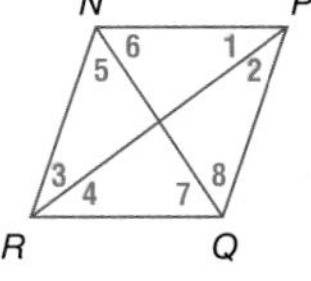

You will prove Theorem 6.16 in Exercise 34.

Proof Theorem 6.15

Given: $ABCD$ is a rhombus.

Prove: $\overline{AC} \perp \overline{BD}$

Paragraph Proof:

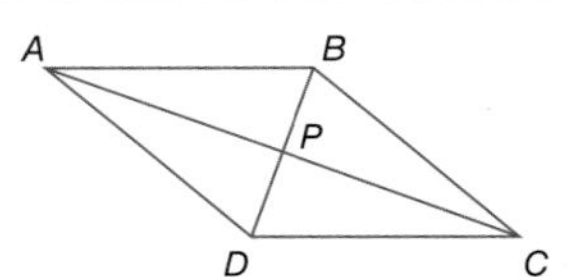

Since $ABCD$ is a rhombus, by definition $\overline{AB} \cong \overline{BC}$. A rhombus is a parallelogram and the diagonals of a parallelogram bisect each other, so $\overline{BD}$ bisects $\overline{AC}$ at P. Thus, $\overline{AP} \cong \overline{PC}$. $\overline{BP} \cong \overline{BP}$ by the Reflexive Property. So, $\triangle APB \cong \triangle CPB$ by SSS. $\angle APB \cong \angle CPB$ by CPCTC. $\angle APB$ and $\angle CPB$ also form a linear pair. Two congruent angles that form a linear pair are right angles. $\angle APB$ is a right angle, so $\overline{AC} \perp \overline{BD}$ by the definition of perpendicular lines.

Lesson 6-5 Resources

Resource	Approaching Level AL	On Level OL	Beyond Level BL	English Learners ELL
Teacher Edition	▪ Differentiated Instruction, p. 433	▪ Differentiated Instruction, pp. 433, 434, 437	▪ Differentiated Instruction, pp. 434, 437	
Chapter Resource Masters	▪ Study Guide and Intervention, pp. 31–32 ▪ Skills Practice, p. 33 ▪ Practice, p. 34 ▪ Word Problem Practice, p. 35	▪ Study Guide and Intervention, pp. 31–32 ▪ Skills Practice, p. 33 ▪ Practice, p. 34 ▪ Word Problem Practice, p. 35 ▪ Enrichment, p. 36	▪ Practice, p. 34 ▪ Word Problem Practice, p. 35 ▪ Enrichment, p. 36	▪ Study Guide and Intervention, pp. 31–32 ▪ Skills Practice, p. 33 ▪ Practice, p. 34 ▪ Word Problem Practice, p. 35
Other	▪ 5-Minute Check 6-5 ▪ Study Notebook ▪ Teaching Geometry with Manipulatives	▪ 5-Minute Check 6-5 ▪ Study Notebook ▪ Teaching Geometry with Manipulatives	▪ 5-Minute Check 6-5 ▪ Study Notebook	▪ 5-Minute Check 6-5 ▪ Study Notebook ▪ Teaching Geometry with Manipulatives

ReadingMath

Rhombi The plural form of rhombus is *rhombi*, pronounced ROM-bye.

Example 1 Use Properties of a Rhombus

The diagonals of rhombus *FGHJ* intersect at *K*. Use the given information to find each measure or value.

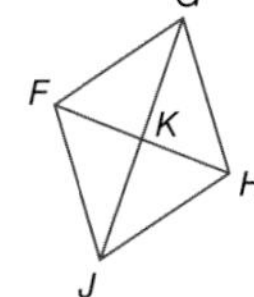

a. If $m\angle FJH = 82$, find $m\angle KHJ$.

Since *FGHJ* is a rhombus, diagonal $\overline{JG}$ bisects $\angle FJH$. Therefore, $m\angle KJH = \frac{1}{2}m\angle FJH$. So $m\angle KJH = \frac{1}{2}(82)$ or 41. Since the diagonals of a rhombus are perpendicular, $m\angle JKH = 90$ by the definition of perpendicular lines.

$m\angle KJH + m\angle JKH + m\angle KHJ = 180$	Triangle Sum Theorem
$41 + 90 + m\angle KHJ = 180$	Substitution
$131 + m\angle KHJ = 180$	Simplify.
$m\angle KHJ = 49$	Subtract 131 from each side.

b. ALGEBRA If $GH = x + 9$ and $JH = 5x - 2$, find x.

$\overline{GH} \cong \overline{JH}$	By definition, all sides of a rhombus are congruent.
$GH = JH$	Definition of congruence
$x + 9 = 5x - 2$	Substitution
$9 = 4x - 2$	Subtract *x* from each side.
$11 = 4x$	Add 2 to each side.
$2.75 = x$	Divide each side by 4.

GuidedPractice

Refer to rhombus *FGHJ* above.

1A. If $FK = 5$ and $FG = 13$, find KJ. 12

1B. ALGEBRA If $m\angle JFK = 6y + 7$ and $m\angle KFG = 9y - 5$, find y. 4

A **square** is a parallelogram with four congruent sides and four right angles. Recall that a parallelogram with four right angles is a rectangle, and a parallelogram with four congruent sides is a rhombus. Therefore, a parallelogram that is both a rectangle and a rhombus is also a square.

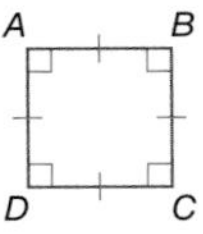

Square *ABCD*

The Venn diagram summarizes the relationships among parallelograms, rhombi, rectangles, and squares.

ConceptSummary Parallelograms

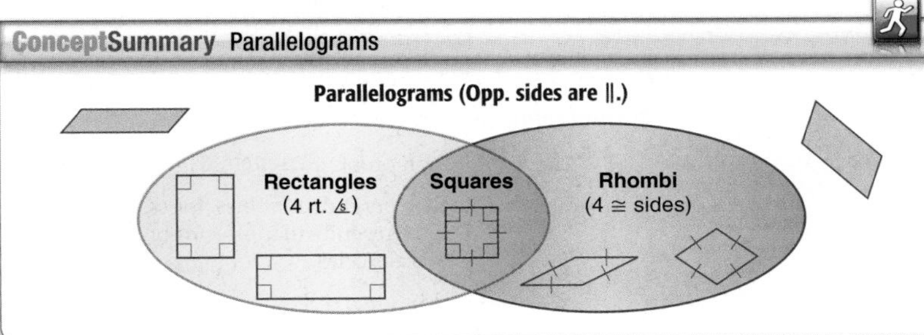

Focus on Mathematical Content

Classifying Rhombi A rhombus meets the minimum properties of a kite.

1. Two disjoint pairs of consecutive sides are congruent.
2. The diagonals are perpendicular.
3. One diagonal is the perpendicular bisector of the other.
4. One of the diagonals bisects a pair of opposite angles.
5. One pair of opposite angles are congruent.

Therefore, a rhombus can be classified as a specialized kite.

- Is it possible for a rhombus to have exactly one 90° angle? Exactly two? Explain your reasoning. A rhombus cannot have exactly one 90° angle because opposite sides are congruent, so opposite angles are congruent. A rhombus cannot have exactly two 90° angles because then it would have to have two more 90° angles. A rhombus can have four 90° angles and therefore be a square, or it can have no angles that measure 90.

1 Properties of Rhombi and Squares

Example 1 shows how to use the properties of rhombi algebraically.

Formative Assessment

Use the Guided Practice exercises after each example to determine students' understanding of concepts.

Additional Example

1 The diagonals of rhombus *WXYZ* intersect at *V*. Use the given information to find each measure or value.

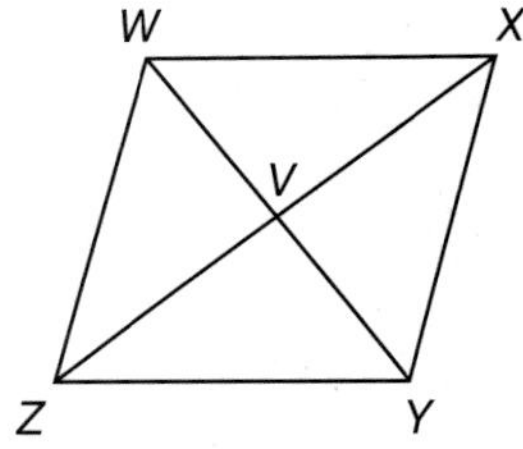

a. If $m\angle WZX = 39.5$, find $m\angle ZYX$. 101

b. ALGEBRA If $WX = 8x - 5$ and $WZ = 6x + 3$, find x. 4

Additional Examples also in Interactive Classroom PowerPoint® Presentations

Tips for New Teachers

Squares Since a square is both a parallelogram and a rhombus, all of the properties of parallelograms and rhombi will apply to squares.

2 Prove that Quadrilaterals are Rhombi or Squares

Examples 2–4 show how to use the properties of a rhombus or a square in proofs.

Additional Example

2 Write a paragraph proof.

Given: *LMNP* is a parallelogram. $\angle 1 \cong \angle 2$ and $\angle 2 \cong \angle 6$

Prove: *LMNP* is a rhombus.

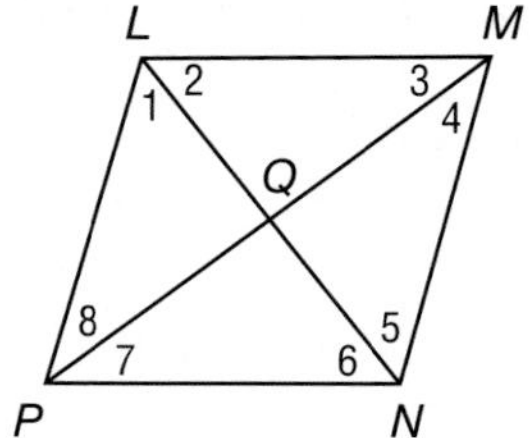

$\overline{LN}$ bisects $\angle L$ and $\angle N$; therefore, by Theorem 6.18 *LMNP* is a rhombus.

Additional Answer (Guided Practice)

2. Given: $\overline{SQ}$ is the perpendicular bisector of $\overline{PR}$. $\overline{PR}$ is the perpendicular bisector of $\overline{SQ}$.

$\triangle RMS$ is isosceles.

Prove: *PQRS* is a square.

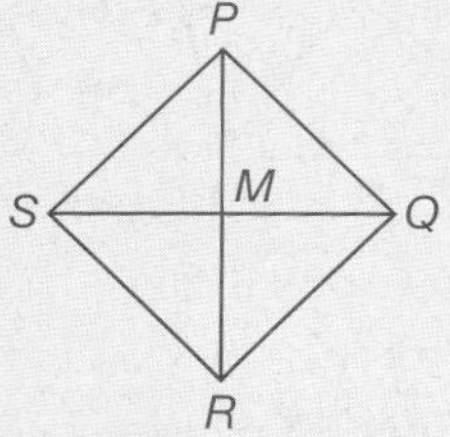

Paragraph Proof:

Since $\overline{SQ}$ is the perpendicular bisector of $\overline{PR}$, $\overline{QS} \perp \overline{PR}$ and $\overline{MP} \cong \overline{MR}$ by definition. Since $\overline{PR}$ is the perpendicular bisector of $\overline{SQ}$, $\overline{MS} \cong \overline{QM}$. Since $\triangle RMS$ is isosceles, $\overline{MS} \cong \overline{MR}$ by definition. By substitution, $\overline{MS} \cong \overline{MP}$. So by the definition of congruence and the Transitive Property, $MS = MP = QM = MR$. By Segment Addition, $MS + MQ = SQ$ and $MP + MR = PR$. By substitution, $MS + MS = SQ$ and $MS + MS = PR$ and $SQ = PR$. So by the definition of congruence, $\overline{SQ} \cong \overline{PR}$. Since the diagonals of *PQRS* bisect each other, *PQRS* is a parallelogram. Since the diagonals are congruent, ▱*PQRS* is a rectangle. Since the diagonals are perpendicular, ▱*PQRS* is a rhombus. Since ▱*PQRS* is a rectangle and a rhombus, it is a square.

All of the properties of parallelograms, rectangles, and rhombi apply to squares. For example, the diagonals of a square bisect each other (parallelogram), are congruent (rectangle), and are perpendicular (rhombus).

2 Prove that Quadrilaterals are Rhombi or Squares The theorems below provide conditions for rhombi and squares.

StudyTip
Common Misconception
Theorems 6.17, 6.18, and 6.19 apply only if you already know that a quadrilateral is a parallelogram.

Theorems Conditions for Rhombi and Squares

6.17 If the diagonals of a parallelogram are perpendicular, then the parallelogram is a rhombus. (Converse of Theorem. 6.15)

Example If $\overline{JL} \perp \overline{KM}$, then ▱*JKLM* is a rhombus.

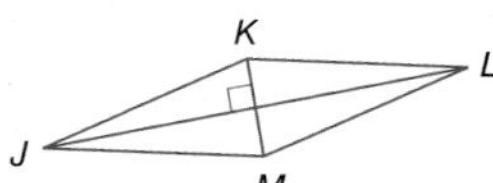

6.18 If one diagonal of a parallelogram bisects a pair of opposite angles, then the parallelogram is a rhombus. (Converse of Theorem. 6.16)

Example If $\angle 1 \cong \angle 2$ and $\angle 3 \cong \angle 4$, or $\angle 5 \cong \angle 6$ and $\angle 7 \cong \angle 8$, then ▱*WXYZ* is a rhombus.

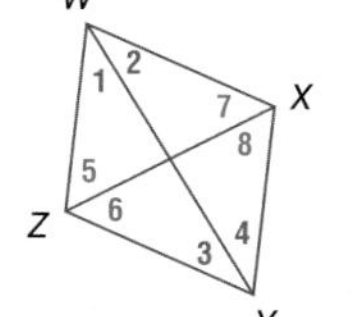

6.19 If one pair of consecutive sides of a parallelogram are congruent, the parallelogram is a rhombus.

Example If $\overline{AB} \cong \overline{BC}$, then ▱*ABCD* is a rhombus.

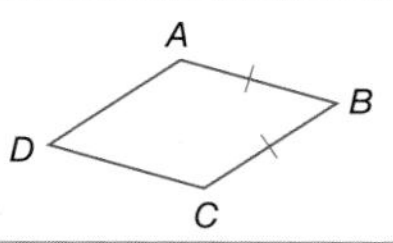

6.20 If a quadrilateral is both a rectangle and a rhombus, then it is a square.

You will prove Theorems 6.17–6.20 in Exercises 35–38, respectively.

You can use the properties of rhombi and squares to write proofs.

StudyTip
Congruent Triangles
Since a rhombus has four congruent sides, one diagonal separates the rhombus into two congruent isosceles triangles. Drawing two diagonals separates the rhombus into four congruent right triangles.

PT

Example 2 Proofs Using Properties of Rhombi and Squares

Write a paragraph proof.

Given: *JKLM* is a parallelogram.

$\triangle JKL$ is isosceles.

Prove: *JKLM* is a rhombus.

Paragraph Proof:

Since it is given that $\triangle JKL$ is isosceles, $\overline{KL} \cong \overline{JK}$ by definition. These are consecutive sides of the given parallelogram *JKLM*. So, by Theorem 6.19, *JKLM* is a rhombus.

GuidedPractice

2. Write a paragraph proof. **See margin.**

Given: $\overline{SQ}$ is the perpendicular bisector of $\overline{PR}$.
$\overline{PR}$ is the perpendicular bisector of $\overline{SQ}$.
$\triangle RMS$ is isosceles.

Prove: *PQRS* is a square.

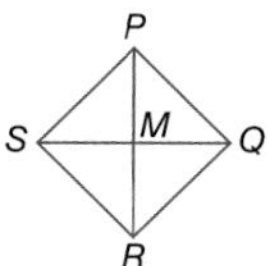

WatchOut!
Rhombi Theorems 6.17-6.19 only apply if you already know that the figure is a parallelogram.

Real-WorldLink

Archaeology is the study of artifacts that provide information about human life and activities in the past. Since humans only began writing about 5000 years ago, information from periods before that time must be gathered from the objects that archeologists locate.

Source: Encyclopeadia Britannica

Real-World Example 3 Use Conditions for Rhombi and Squares

ARCHAEOLOGY The key to the successful excavation of an archaeological site is accurate mapping. How can archaeologists be sure that the region they have marked off is a 1-meter by 1-meter square?

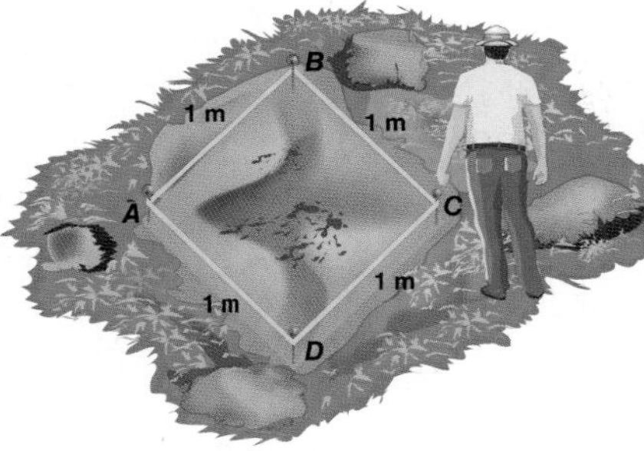

Each side of quadrilateral *ABCD* measures 1 meter. Since opposite sides are congruent, *ABCD* is a parallelogram. Since consecutive sides of ▱*ABCD* are congruent, it is a rhombus. If the archaeologists can show that ▱*ABCD* is also a rectangle, then by Theorem 6.20, ▱*ABCD* is a square.

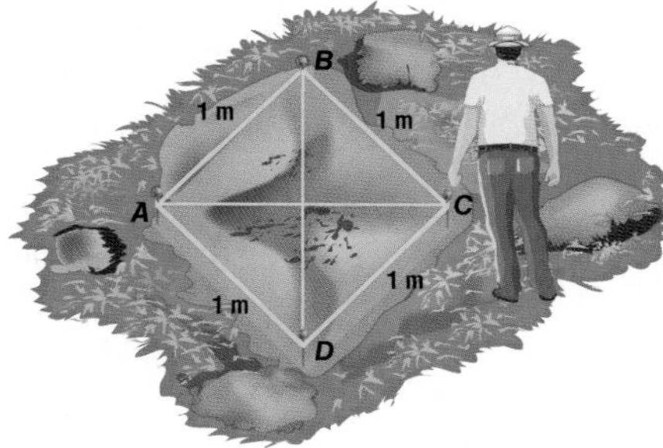

If the diagonals of a parallelogram are congruent, then the parallelogram is a rectangle. So if the archeologists measure the length of string needed to form each diagonal and find that these lengths are equal, then *ABCD* is a square.

GuidedPractice

3. **QUILTING** Kathy is designing a quilt with blocks like the one shown.

A. If she marks the diagonals of each yellow piece and determines that each pair of diagonals is perpendicular, can she conclude that each yellow piece is a rhombus? Explain.

B. If all four angles of the green piece have the same measure and the bottom and left sides have the same measure, can she conclude that the green piece is a square? Explain.

3A. No; she can only make this conclusion if she also knows that the quadrilateral is a parallelogram.
3B. Yes; if all four angles have the same measure, then the measure of each angle is $360 \div 4$ or 90. Thus, opposite angles are congruent, so the piece is a parallelogram. If the measure of each angle is 90, then the quadrilateral has four right angles, so it is also a rectangle. If consecutive sides are congruent, then it is also a square.

In Chapter 4, you used coordinate geometry to classify triangles. Coordinate geometry can also be used to classify quadrilaterals.

Additional Example

3 GARDENING Hector is measuring the boundary of a new garden. He wants the garden to be square. He has set each of the corner stakes 6 feet apart. What does Hector need to know to make sure that the garden is square?

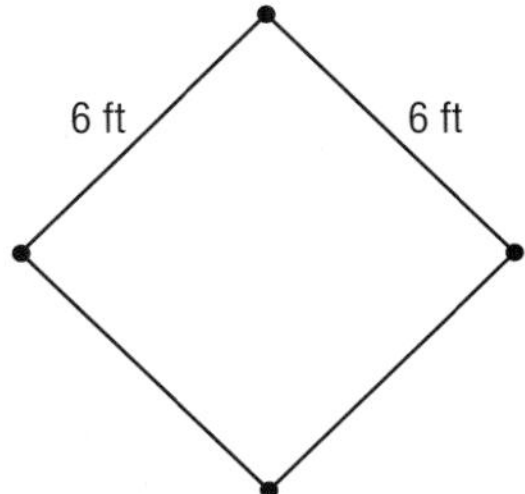

Since opposite sides are congruent, the garden is a parallelogram. Since consecutive sides are congruent, the garden is a rhombus. Hector needs to know if the diagonals of the garden are congruent. If they are, then the garden is a rectangle. By Theorem 6.20, it is a square.

Teach with Tech

Video Recording Have students work in pairs to create a video describing the properties of rhombi and squares. Be sure they name all properties of these figures, including those common to other parallelograms.

DifferentiatedInstruction AL OL

Visual/Spatial Learners Students may not believe that a rhombus has perpendicular diagonals. Ask groups of students to cut out four congruent right triangles. Make sure each group's triangles are unique to that group. Ask them to join the four triangles at the right angle vertices. The triangles should form a rhombus. Groups should share the results with the class.

Additional Example

4 Determine whether parallelogram *ABCD* is a *rhombus*, a *rectangle*, or a *square* for $A(-2, -1)$, $B(-1, 3)$, $C(3, 2)$, and $D(2, -2)$. List all that apply. Explain

$AC = \sqrt{34}$; $BD = \sqrt{34}$;

slope of $\overline{AC} = \frac{3}{5}$;

slope of $\overline{BD} = -\frac{5}{3}$.

Because the slope of $\overline{AC}$ is the negative reciprocal of the slope of $\overline{BD}$, the diagonals are perpendicular. The lengths of $\overline{AC}$ and $\overline{BD}$ are the same. *ABCD* is a rhombus, a rectangle, and a square.

Additional Answers

3. **Given:** *ABCD* is a rhombus with diagonal $\overline{DB}$.
   Prove: $AP \cong CP$
   Statements (Reasons)
   1. *ABCD* is a rhombus with diagonal $\overline{DB}$. (Given)
   2. $\angle ABP \cong \angle CBP$ (Diag. of rhombus bisects $\angle$)
   3. $\overline{PB} \cong \overline{PB}$ (Refl. Prop.)
   4. $\overline{AB} \cong \overline{CB}$ (Def. of rhombus)
   5. $\triangle APB \cong \triangle CPB$ (SAS)
   6. $\overline{AP} \cong \overline{CP}$ (CPCTC)
4. Sample answer: Since each side of the board is 8 squares in length and each of the squares is congruent, the lengths of all four sides of the board are equal. Since we know that each of the four quadrilaterals that form the corners of the board are squares, we know that the measure of the angle of each vertex of the board is 90. Therefore, the board is a square.

Problem-SolvingTip

Make a Graph When analyzing a figure using coordinate geometry, graph the figure to help formulate a conjecture and also to help check the reasonableness of the answer you obtain algebraically.

StudyTip

Square and Rhombus
A square is a rhombus, but a rhombus is not necessarily a square.

Example 4 Classify Quadrilaterals Using Coordinate Geometry

COORDINATE GEOMETRY Determine whether ▱*JKLM* with vertices $J(-7, -2)$, $K(0, 4)$, $L(9, 2)$, and $M(2, -4)$ is a *rhombus*, a *rectangle*, or a *square*. List all that apply. Explain.

Understand Plot and connect the vertices on a coordinate plane.

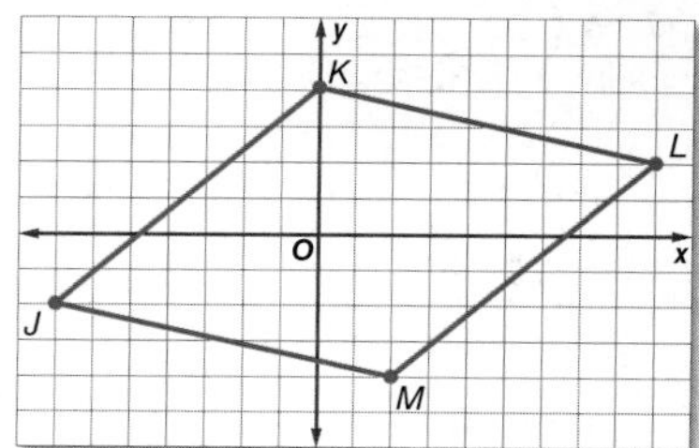

It appears from the graph that the parallelogram has four congruent sides, but no right angles. So, it appears that the figure is a rhombus, but not a square or a rectangle.

Plan If the diagonals of the parallelogram are congruent, then it is a rectangle. If they are perpendicular, then it is a rhombus. If they are both congruent and perpendicular, the parallelogram is a rectangle, a rhombus, and a square.

Solve **Step 1** Use the Distance Formula to compare the diagonal lengths.

$KM = \sqrt{(2-0)^2 + (-4-4)^2} = \sqrt{68}$ or $2\sqrt{17}$

$JL = \sqrt{[9-(-7)]^2 + [2-(-2)]^2} = \sqrt{272}$ or $4\sqrt{17}$

Since $2\sqrt{17} \neq 4\sqrt{17}$, the diagonals are not congruent. So, ▱*JKLM* is *not* a rectangle. Since the figure is not a rectangle, it also *cannot* be a square.

Step 2 Use the Slope Formula to determine whether the diagonals are perpendicular.

slope of $\overline{KM} = \frac{-4-4}{2-0} = \frac{-8}{2}$ or -4

slope of $\overline{JL} = \frac{2-(-2)}{9-(-7)} = \frac{4}{16}$ or $\frac{1}{4}$

Since the product of the slopes of the diagonals is -1, the diagonals are perpendicular, so ▱*JKLM* is a rhombus.

Check $JK = \sqrt{[4-(-2)]^2 + [0-(-7)]^2}$ or $\sqrt{85}$

$KL = \sqrt{(9-0)^2 + (2-4)^2}$ or $\sqrt{85}$

So, ▱*JKLM* is a rhombus by Theorem 6.20.

Since the slope of $\overline{JK} = \frac{4-(-2)}{0-(-7)}$ or $\frac{6}{7}$, the slope of $\overline{KL} = \frac{2-4}{9-0}$ or $-\frac{2}{9}$, and the product of these slopes is not -1, consecutive sides $\overline{JK}$ and $\overline{KL}$ are not perpendicular. Therefore, $\angle JKL$ is not a right angle. So ▱*JKLM* is not a rectangle or a square. ✓

GuidedPractice

4. Given $J(5, 0)$, $K(8, -11)$, $L(-3, -14)$, $M(-6, -3)$, determine whether parallelogram *JKLM* is a *rhombus*, a *rectangle*, or a *square*. List all that apply. Explain.

4. Square, rectangle, rhombus; all sides are congruent and perpendicular.

DifferentiatedInstruction OL BL

Extension Have students imagine that they work at a picture frame shop. A customer asks them to make a frame out of four identical pieces of wood. Write a description for future employees to test that the picture frame is square. Sample answer: Measure the diagonals of the frame. If the diagonals bisect each other, then the frame is a parallelogram. Next, measure the angles formed by the diagonal bisectors. If the diagonals are perpendicular, then the frame is square.

Check Your Understanding

 = Step-by-Step Solutions begin on page R14.

Example 1 **ALGEBRA** **Quadrilateral *ABCD* is a rhombus. Find each value or measure.**

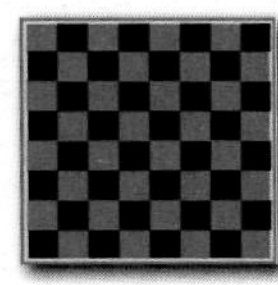

1. If $m\angle BCD = 64$, find $m\angle BAC$. **32**
2. If $AB = 2x + 3$ and $BC = x + 7$, find CD. **11**

Examples 2–3 3. **PROOF** Write a two-column proof to prove that if $ABCD$ is a rhombus with diagonal $\overline{DB}$, then $\overline{AP} \cong \overline{CP}$.

3, 4. See margin.

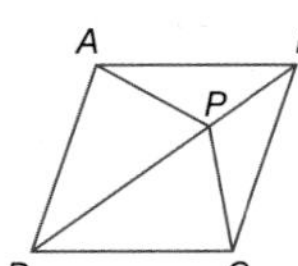

4. **GAMES** The checkerboard below is made up of 64 congruent black and red squares. Use this information to prove that the board itself is a square.

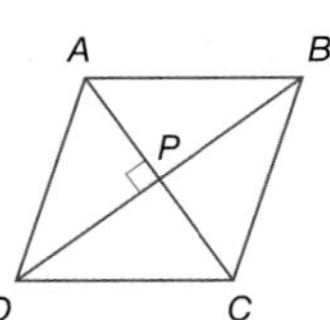

Example 4 **COORDINATE GEOMETRY** **Given each set of vertices, determine whether ▱*QRST* is a *rhombus*, a *rectangle*, or a *square*. List all that apply. Explain.**

5. $Q(1, 2), R(-2, -1), S(1, -4), T(4, -1)$
   Rectangle, rhombus, square; consecutive sides are ⊥, all sides are ≅.
6. $Q(-2, -1), R(-1, 2), S(4, 1), T(3, -2)$
   None; the diagonals are not congruent or perpendicular.

Practice and Problem Solving

Extra Practice is on page R6.

Example 1 **ALGEBRA** **Quadrilateral *ABCD* is a rhombus. Find each value or measure.**

7. If $AB = 14$, find BC. **14**
8. If $m\angle BCD = 54$, find $m\angle BAC$. **27**
9. If $AP = 3x - 1$ and $PC = x + 9$, find AC. **28**
10. If $DB = 2x - 4$ and $PB = 2x - 9$, find PD. **5**
11. If $m\angle ABC = 2x - 7$ and $m\angle BCD = 2x + 3$, find $m\angle DAB$. **95**
12. If $m\angle DPC = 3x - 15$, find x. **35**

Example 2 **CCSS ARGUMENTS** **Write a two-column proof.** **13. See margin.**

13. **Given:** $\overline{WZ} \parallel \overline{XY}$, $\overline{WX} \parallel \overline{ZY}$
    $\overline{WZ} \cong \overline{ZY}$
    Prove: $WXYZ$ is a rhombus.

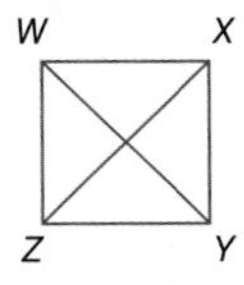

14. **Given:** $QRST$ is a parallelogram.
    $\overline{TR} \cong \overline{QS}$, $m\angle QPR = 90$
    Prove: $QRST$ is a square.

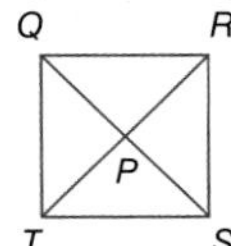

15. **Given:** $JKQP$ is a square.
    $\overline{ML}$ bisects $\overline{JP}$ and $\overline{KQ}$.
    Prove: $JKLM$ is a parallelogram.

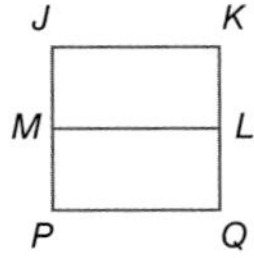

16. **Given:** $ACDH$ and $BCDF$ are parallelograms; $\overline{BF} \cong \overline{AB}$.
    Prove: $ABFH$ is a rhombus. **14–16. See Ch. 6 Answer Appendix.**

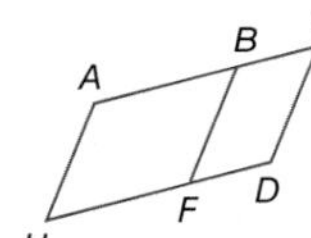

3 Practice

Formative Assessment

Use Exercises 1–6 to check for understanding.

Then use the chart at the bottom of this page to customize assignments for your students.

CCSS Teaching the Mathematical Practices

Arguments Mathematically proficient students understand and use stated assumptions and definitions in constructing arguments. They make conjectures and build a logical progression of statements to explore the truth of their conjectures. In Exercises 13–16, encourage students to review the properties of each quadrilateral studied.

Additional Answers

13. **Given:** $\overline{WZ} \parallel \overline{XY}$, $\overline{WX} \parallel \overline{ZY}$, $\overline{WZ} \cong \overline{ZY}$
    Prove: $WXYZ$ is a rhombus.

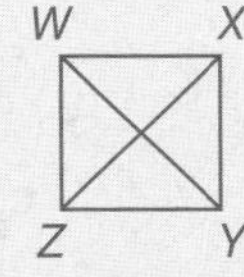

Statements (Reasons)

1. $\overline{WZ} \parallel \overline{XY}$, $\overline{WX} \parallel \overline{ZY}$, $\overline{WZ} \cong \overline{ZY}$ (Given)
2. $WXYZ$ is a ▱. (Both pairs of opp. sides are ∥.)
3. $WXYZ$ is a rhombus. (If one pair of consecutive sides of a ▱ are ≅, the ▱ is a rhombus.)

Differentiated Homework Options

Level	Assignment	Two-Day Option	
AL Basic	7–22, 46, 47, 49–65	7–21 odd, 51–54	8–22 even, 45, 47, 49, 50, 55–65
OL Core	7–41 odd, 43–47, 49–65	7–21, 51–54	22–47, 49, 50, 55–65
BL Advanced	23–62, (optional: 63–65)		

Example 3

17. ROADWAYS Main Street and High Street intersect as shown in the diagram. Each of the crosswalks is the same length. Classify the quadrilateral formed by the crosswalks. Explain your reasoning. **See margin.**

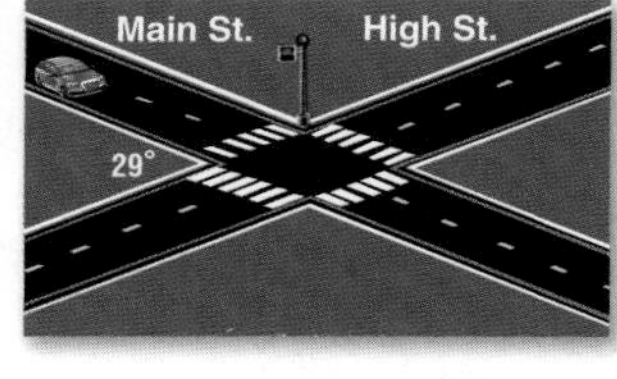

18. CCSS MODELING A landscaper has staked out the area for a square garden as shown. She has confirmed that each side of the quadrilateral formed by the stakes is congruent and that the diagonals are perpendicular. Is this information enough for the landscaper to be sure that the garden is a square? Explain your reasoning. **See margin.**

Example 4

COORDINATE GEOMETRY Given each set of vertices, determine whether $\square JKLM$ is a *rhombus*, a *rectangle*, or a *square*. List all that apply. Explain.

19. $J(-4, -1), K(1, -1), L(4, 3), M(-1, 3)$

20. $J(-3, -2), K(2, -2), L(5, 2), M(0, 2)$

21. $J(-2, -1), K(-4, 3), L(1, 5), M(3, 1)$ **None; the diagonals are not ≅ or ⊥.**

22. $J(-1, 1), K(4, 1), L(4, 6), M(-1, 6)$

19. Rhombus; the diagonals are ⊥.
20. Rhombus; the diagonals are ⊥.
22. Square, rectangle, rhombus; all sides are ≅ and ⊥.

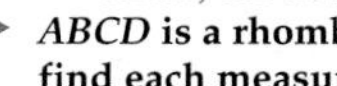

B ABCD is a rhombus. If $PB = 12$, $AB = 15$, and $m\angle ABD = 24$, find each measure.

23. AP **9**

24. CP **9**

25. $m\angle BDA$ **24**

26. $m\angle ACB$ **66**

WXYZ is a square. If $WT = 3$, find each measure.

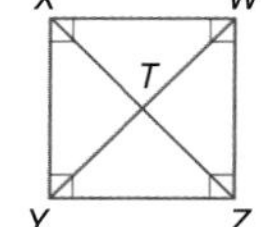

27. ZX **6**

28. XY **$3\sqrt{2}$**

29. $m\angle WTZ$ **90**

30. $m\angle WYX$ **45**

Classify each quadrilateral.

31.

square

32.

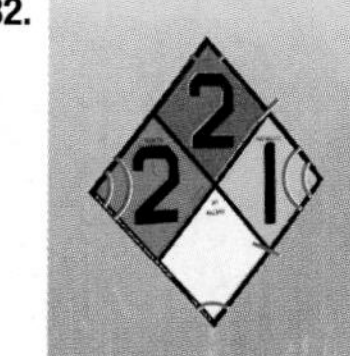

rhombus

33.

rectangle

PROOF Write a paragraph proof. **34–38. See Ch. 6 Answer Appendix.**

34. Theorem 6.16

35. Theorem 6.17

36. Theorem 6.18

37. Theorem 6.19

38. Theorem 6.20

CONSTRUCTION Use diagonals to construct each figure. Justify each construction.

39. rhombus

40. square

39, 40. See Ch. 6 Answer Appendix.

PROOF Write a coordinate proof of each statement. **41, 42. See Ch. 6 Answer Appendix.**

41. The diagonals of a square are perpendicular.

42. The segments joining the midpoints of the sides of a rectangle form a rhombus.

Study Guide and Intervention

AL OL ELL

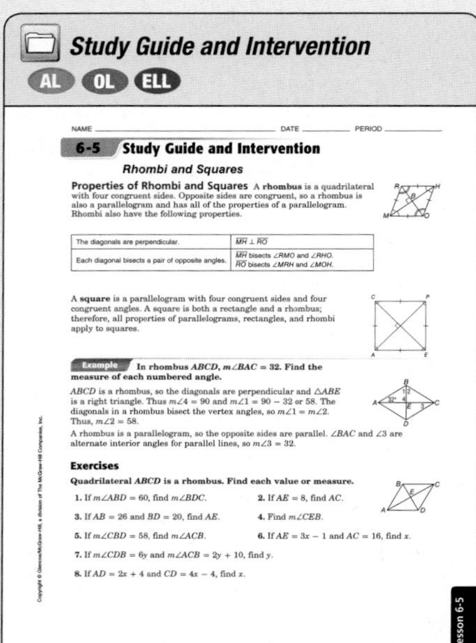

NAME ______ DATE ______ PERIOD ______

6-5 Study Guide and Intervention

Rhombi and Squares

Properties of Rhombi and Squares A **rhombus** is a quadrilateral with four congruent sides. Opposite sides are congruent, so a rhombus is also a parallelogram and has all of the properties of a parallelogram. Rhombi also have the following properties.

The diagonals are perpendicular.	$\overline{MH} \perp \overline{RO}$
Each diagonal bisects a pair of opposite angles.	$\overline{MH}$ bisects $\angle RMO$ and $\angle RHO$. $\overline{RO}$ bisects $\angle MRH$ and $\angle MOH$.

A **square** is a parallelogram with four congruent sides and four congruent angles. A square is both a rectangle and a rhombus; therefore, all properties of parallelograms, rectangles, and rhombi apply to squares.

Example In rhombus *ABCD*, $m\angle BAC = 32$. Find the measure of each numbered angle.

ABCD is a rhombus, so the diagonals are perpendicular and $\triangle ABE$ is a right triangle. Thus $m\angle 4 = 90$ and $m\angle 1 = 90 - 32$ or 58. The diagonals in a rhombus bisect the vertex angles, so $m\angle 1 = m\angle 2$. Thus, $m\angle 2 = 58$.

A rhombus is a parallelogram, so the opposite sides are parallel. $\angle BAC$ and $\angle 3$ are alternate interior angles for parallel lines, so $m\angle 3 = 32$.

Exercises

Quadrilateral *ABCD* is a rhombus. Find each value or measure.

1. If $m\angle ABD = 60$, find $m\angle BDC$.
2. If $AE = 8$, find AC.
3. If $AB = 26$ and $BD = 20$, find AE.
4. Find $m\angle CEB$.
5. If $m\angle CBD = 58$, find $m\angle ACB$.
6. If $AE = 3x - 1$ and $AC = 16$, find x.
7. If $m\angle CDB = 6y$ and $m\angle ACB = 2y + 10$, find y.
8. If $AD = 2x + 4$ and $CD = 4x - 4$, find x.

Lesson 6-5

Practice

AL OL BL ELL

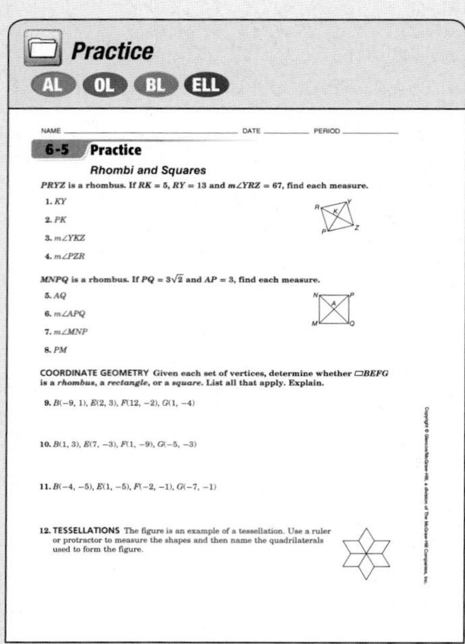

NAME ______ DATE ______ PERIOD ______

6-5 Practice

Rhombi and Squares

***PRYZ* is a rhombus. If $RK = 5$, $RY = 13$ and $m\angle YRZ = 67$, find each measure.**

1. KY
2. PK
3. $m\angle YKZ$
4. $m\angle PZR$

***MNPQ* is a rhombus. If $PQ = 3\sqrt{2}$ and $AP = 3$, find each measure.**

5. AQ
6. $m\angle APQ$
7. $m\angle MNP$
8. PM

COORDINATE GEOMETRY Given each set of vertices, determine whether $\square BEFG$ is a *rhombus*, a *rectangle*, or a *square*. List all that apply. Explain.

9. $B(-9, 1), E(2, 3), F(12, -2), G(1, -4)$
10. $B(1, 3), E(7, -3), F(1, -9), G(-5, -3)$
11. $B(-4, -5), E(1, -5), F(-2, -1), G(-7, -1)$
12. **TESSELLATIONS** The figure is an example of a tessellation. Use a ruler or protractor to measure the shapes and then name the quadrilaterals used to form the figure.

Word Problem Practice

AL OL BL ELL

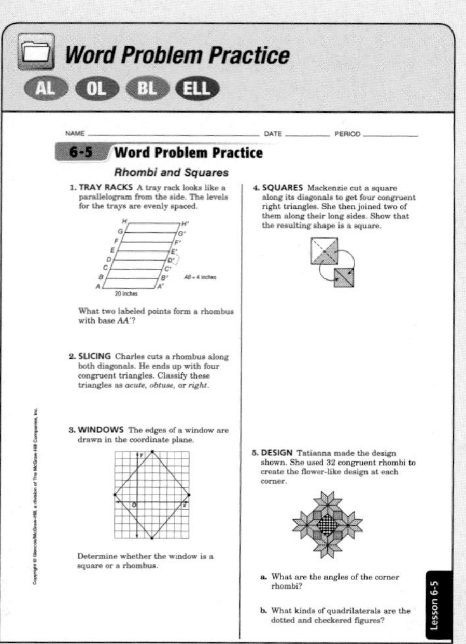

NAME ______ DATE ______ PERIOD ______

6-5 Word Problem Practice

Rhombi and Squares

1. **TRAY RACKS** A tray rack looks like a parallelogram from the side. The levels for the trays are evenly spaced.

   What two labeled points form a rhombus with base AA'?

2. **SLICING** Charles cuts a rhombus along both diagonals. He ends up with four congruent triangles. Classify these triangles as *acute*, *obtuse*, or *right*.

3. **WINDOWS** The edges of a window are drawn in the coordinate plane.

   Determine whether the window is a square or a rhombus.

4. **SQUARES** Mackenzie cut a square along its diagonals to get four congruent right triangles. She then joined two of them along their long sides. Show that the resulting shape is a square.

5. **DESIGN** Tatianna made the design shown. She used 32 congruent rhombi to create the flower-like design at each corner.

   a. What are the angles of the corner rhombi?

   b. What kinds of quadrilaterals are the dotted and checkered figures?

Lesson 6-5

Enrichment

OL BL

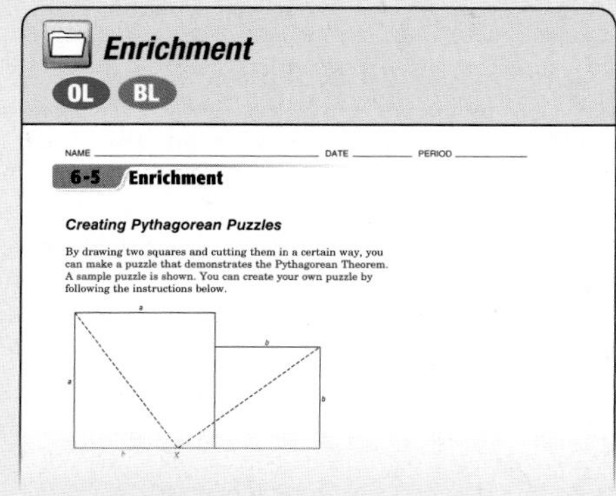

NAME ______ DATE ______ PERIOD ______

6-5 Enrichment

Creating Pythagorean Puzzles

By drawing two squares and cutting them in a certain way, you can make a puzzle that demonstrates the Pythagorean Theorem. A sample puzzle is shown. You can create your own puzzle by following the instructions below.

CCSS Teaching the Mathematical Practices

Modeling Mathematically proficient students can apply the mathematics they know to solve problems arising in everyday life. In Exercise 18, encourage students to use the theorems about squares when planning their arguments.

43. **DESIGN** The tile pattern below consists of regular octagons and quadrilaterals. Classify the quadrilaterals in the pattern and explain your reasoning.

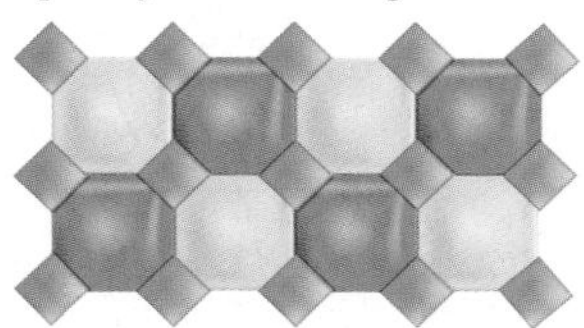

See Ch. 6 Answer Appendix.

44. **REPAIR** The window pane shown needs to be replaced. What are the dimensions of the replacement pane?

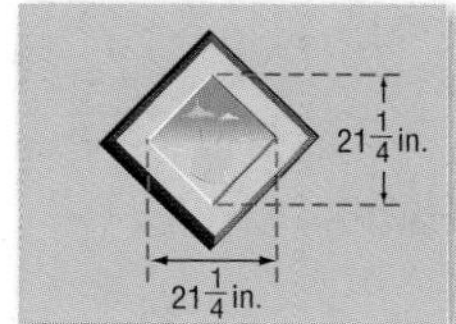

square; 15 in.

45. **MULTIPLE REPRESENTATIONS** In this problem, you will explore the properties of kites, which are quadrilaterals with exactly two distinct pairs of adjacent congruent sides.

a. **Geometric** Draw three kites with varying side lengths. Label one kite $ABCD$, one $PQRS$, and one $WXYZ$. Then draw the diagonals of each kite, labeling the point of intersection N for each kite. See Ch. 6 Answer Appendix.

b. **Tabular** Measure the distance from N to each vertex. Record your results in a table like the one shown.

Figure	Distance from N to Each Vertex Along Shorter Diagonal		Distance from N to Each Vertex Along Longer Diagonal	
$ABCD$	0.8 cm	0.8 cm	0.9 cm	1.5 cm
$PQRS$	1.2 cm	1.2 cm	0.3 cm	0.9 cm
$WXYZ$	0.2 cm	0.2 cm	1.1 cm	0.4 cm

B, A, N, C, D

Kite $ABCD$

c. **Verbal** Make a conjecture about the diagonals of a kite.
Sample answer: The shorter diagonal of a kite is bisected by the longer diagonal.

46. Neither; sample answer: Since they do not know that the sides of the parallelogram are congruent, only that the diagonals are congruent, they can only conclude that the parallelogram is a rectangle.

H.O.T. Problems Use Higher-Order Thinking Skills

46. **ERROR ANALYSIS** In parallelogram $PQRS$, $\overline{PR} \cong \overline{QS}$. Lola thinks that the parallelogram is a square, and Xavier thinks that it is a rhombus. Is either of them correct? Explain your reasoning.

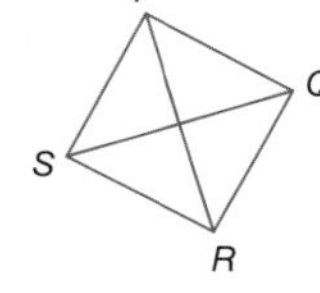

47. **CCSS ARGUMENTS** Determine whether the statement is *true* or *false*. Then write the converse, inverse, and contrapositive of the statement and determine the truth value of each. Explain your reasoning. See Ch. 6 Answer Appendix.

If a quadrilateral is a square, then it is a rectangle.

48. **CHALLENGE** The area of square $ABCD$ is 36 square units and the area of $\triangle EBF$ is 20 square units. If $\overline{EB} \perp \overline{BF}$ and $\overline{AE} = 2$, find the length of $\overline{CF}$. 2

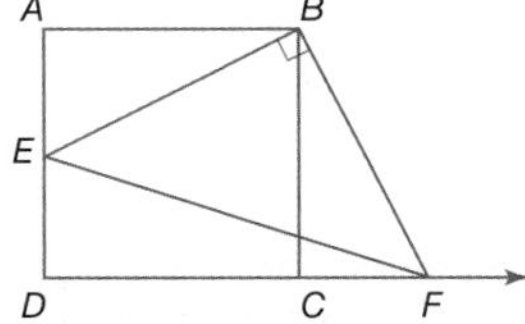

49. **OPEN ENDED** Find the vertices of a square with diagonals that are contained in the lines $y = x$ and $y = -x + 6$. Justify your reasoning.

49. Sample answer: (0, 0), (6, 0), (0, 6), (6, 6); the diagonals are perpendicular, and any four points on the lines equidistant from the intersection of the lines will be the vertices of a square.

50. **WRITING IN MATH** Compare all of the properties of the following quadrilaterals: parallelograms, rectangles, rhombi, and squares. See Ch. 6 Answer Appendix.

Multiple Representations

In Exercise 45, students use geometric sketches, a table, and verbal description to investigate the properties of kites.

WatchOut!

Error Analysis For Exercise 46, students should realize that although the diagonals of a square and a rhombus are congruent, that fact alone is not sufficient proof of either. More information about the parallelogram or its diagonals is needed. All rectangles, however, have congruent diagonals by Theorem 6.14. The parallelogram must be a rectangle, but not necessarily a square or a rhombus.

CCSS Teaching the Mathematical Practices

Arguments Mathematically proficient students understand and use stated assumptions and definitions in constructing arguments. They make conjectures and build a logical progression of statements to explore the truth of their conjectures. In Exercise 47, encourage students to make a truth table.

Additional Answers

17. Rhombus; Sample answer: The measure of angle formed between the two streets is 29, and vertical angles are congruent, so the measure of one angle of the quadrilateral is 29. Since the crosswalks are the same length, the sides of the quadrilateral are congruent. Therefore, they form a rhombus.

18. No; sample answer: Since the four sides of the quadrilateral are congruent and the diagonals are perpendicular, the figure is either a square or a rhombus. To be sure that the garden is a square, she also needs to confirm that the diagonals are congruent.

Differentiated Instruction OL BL

Extension Have students create a children's story together based on the following theme. Squares are a very elite group because the requirements for obtaining membership to the "square group" are very stringent. The squares then gradually increase membership by changing the classification of their group by decreasing the number of requirements needed to be in the group.

4 Assess

Yesterday's News Have the students observe and study the Concept Summary. Have them write a conclusion about any similarities and differences between yesterday's concept of rectangles and today's concept of rhombi and squares.

Formative Assessment

Check for student understanding of Lessons 6-4 and 6-5.

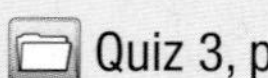 Quiz 3, p. 46

Additional Answers

58. No; none of the tests for parallelograms are fulfilled.

59. Yes; both pairs of opposite sides are congruent.

60. Yes; one pair of opposite sides is parallel and congruent.

61. No; the Triangle Inequality Theorem states that the sum of the lengths of any two sides of a triangle must be greater than the length of the third side. Since $22 + 23 = 45$, the sides of Monifa's backyard cannot be 22 ft, 23 ft and 45 ft.

62. $\triangle ABC$ is a reflection of $\triangle XYZ$. $AB = 5$, $BC = 4$, $AC = \sqrt{41}$, $XY = 5$, $YZ = 4$, $XZ = \sqrt{41}$. $\triangle ABC \cong \triangle XYZ$ by SSS.

Standardized Test Practice

51. *JKLM* is a rhombus. If $CK = 8$ and $JK = 10$, find *JC*. **B**

A 4   C 8
B 6   D 10

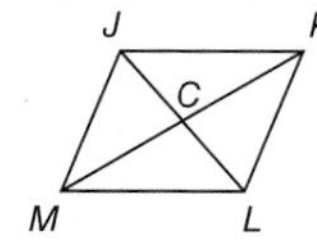

52. EXTENDED RESPONSE The sides of square *ABCD* are extended by sides of equal length to form square *WXYZ*.

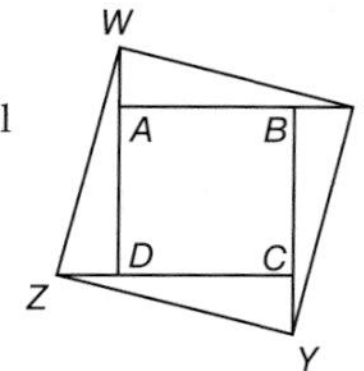

a. If $CY = 3$ cm and the area of *ABCD* is 81 cm^2, find the area of *WXYZ*. **153 cm²**

b. If the areas of *ABCD* and *WXYZ* are 49 cm^2 and 169 cm^2 respectively, find *DZ*. **5 cm**

c. If $AB = 2CY$ and the area of $ABCD = g$ square meters, find the area of *WXYZ* in square meters. **2.5g**

53. ALGEBRA What values of *x* and *y* make quadrilateral *ABCD* a parallelogram? **H**

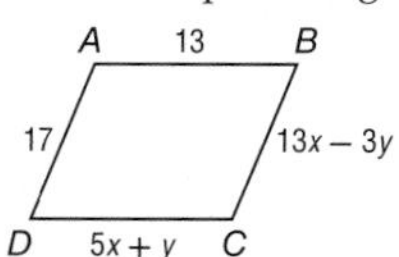

F $x = 3, y = 2$
G $x = \frac{3}{2}, y = -1$
H $x = 2, y = 3$
J $x = 3, y = -1$

54. SAT/ACT What is 6 more than the product of -3 and a certain number *x*? **D**

A $-3x - 6$ D $-3x + 6$
B $-3x$ E $6 + 3x$
C $-x$

Spiral Review

Quadrilateral *ABDC* is a rectangle. Find each measure if $m\angle 1 = 38$. (Lesson 6-4)

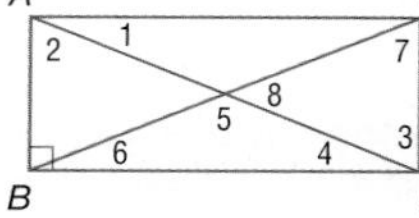

55. $m\angle 2$ **52**   **56.** $m\angle 5$ **104**   **57.** $m\angle 6$ **38**

Determine whether each quadrilateral is a parallelogram. Justify your answer. (Lesson 6-3) **58–60. See margin.**

58.

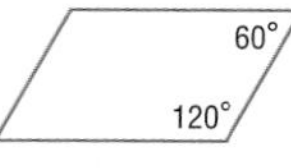

59.

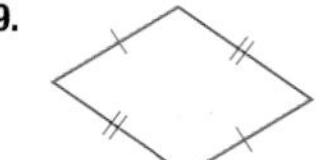

60.

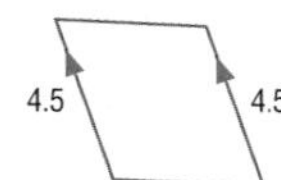

61. MEASUREMENT Monifa says that her backyard is shaped like a triangle and that the lengths of its sides are 22 feet, 23 feet, and 45 feet. Do you think these measurements are correct? Explain your reasoning. (Lesson 5-5) **See margin.**

62. COORDINATE GEOMETRY Identify the transformation and verify that it is a congruence transformation. (Lesson 4-7) **See margin.**

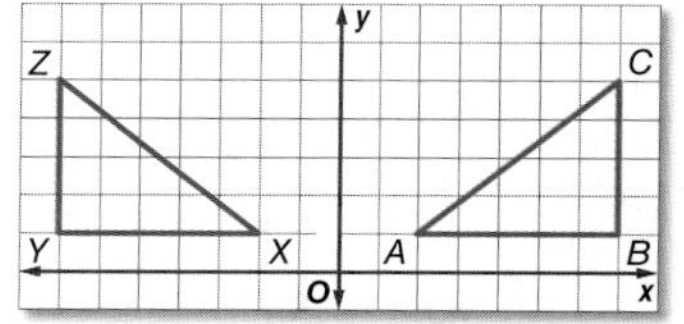

Skills Review

Solve each equation.

63. $\frac{1}{2}(5x + 7x - 1) = 11.5$ **2**   **64.** $\frac{1}{2}(10x + 6x + 2) = 7$ $\frac{3}{4}$ **65.** $\frac{1}{2}(12x + 6 - 8x + 7) = 9$ $\frac{5}{4}$

Follow-up

Students have explored the characteristics of parallelograms, rectangles, rhombi, and squares.

Ask:

- What should you consider when naming a parallelogram? Sample answer: whether diagonals are congruent, whether diagonals are perpendicular, whether diagonals bisect opposite pairs of angles, whether sides are congruent, whether all four angles are right angles

LESSON 6-6 Trapezoids and Kites

Then
- You used properties of special parallelograms.

Now
1. Apply properties of trapezoids.
2. Apply properties of kites.

Why?
- In gymnastics, vaulting boxes made out of high compression foam are used as spotting platforms, vaulting horses, and steps. The left and right side of each section is a *trapezoid*.

NewVocabulary
trapezoid
bases
legs of a trapezoid
base angles
isosceles trapezoid
midsegment of a trapezoid
kite

Common Core State Standards

Content Standards

G.GPE.4 Use coordinates to prove simple geometric theorems algebraically.

G.MG.3 Apply geometric methods to solve problems (e.g., designing an object or structure to satisfy physical constraints or minimize cost; working with typographic grid systems based on ratios). ★

Mathematical Practices
1. Make sense of problems and persevere in solving them.
2. Reason abstractly and quantitatively.

1 Properties of Trapezoids

A **trapezoid** is a quadrilateral with exactly one pair of parallel sides. The parallel sides are called **bases**. The nonparallel sides are called **legs**. The **base angles** are formed by the base and one of the legs. In trapezoid $ABCD$, $\angle A$ and $\angle B$ are one pair of base angles and $\angle C$ and $\angle D$ are the other pair. If the legs of a trapezoid are congruent, then it is an **isosceles trapezoid**.

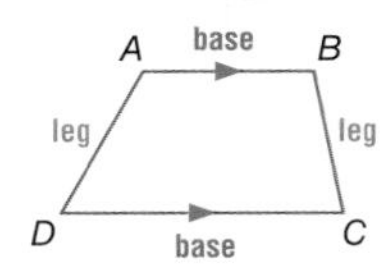

Theorems Isosceles Trapezoids

6.21 If a trapezoid is isosceles, then each pair of base angles is congruent.

Example If trapezoid $FGHJ$ is isosceles, then $\angle G \cong \angle H$ and $\angle F \cong \angle J$.

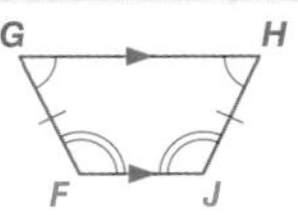

6.22 If a trapezoid has one pair of congruent base angles, then it is an isosceles trapezoid.

Example If $\angle L \cong \angle M$, then trapezoid $KLMP$ is isosceles.

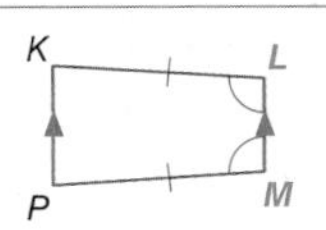

6.23 A trapezoid is isosceles if and only if its diagonals are congruent.

Example If trapezoid $QRST$ is isosceles, then $\overline{QS} \cong \overline{RT}$. Likewise, if $\overline{QS} \cong \overline{RT}$, then trapezoid $QRST$ is isosceles.

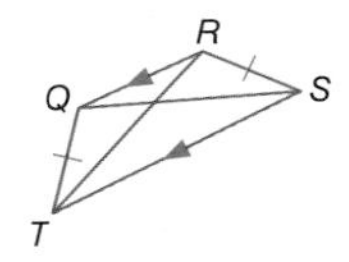

You will prove Theorem 6.21, Theorem 6.22, and the other part of Theorem 6.23 in Exercises 28, 29, and 30.

Proof Part of Theorem 6.23

Given: $ABCD$ is an isosceles trapezoid.

Prove: $\overline{AC} \cong \overline{BD}$

$ABCD$ is an isosceles trapezoid. (Given)
→ $\overline{DC} \cong \overline{CD}$ (Reflexive Property)
→ $\overline{AD} \cong \overline{BC}$ (Def. Isos. Trapezoid)
→ $\angle ADC \cong \angle BCD$ (Base ∠s of trapezoid are ≅.)
→ $\triangle ADC \cong \triangle BCD$ (SAS)
→ $\overline{AC} \cong \overline{BD}$ (CPCTC)

1 Focus

Vertical Alignment

Before Lesson 6-6 Use properties of special parallelograms.

Lesson 6-6 Recognize and apply the properties of trapezoids.
Recognize and apply the properties of kites.

After Lesson 6-6 Use deductive reasoning to prove a statement.

2 Teach

Scaffolding Questions

Have students read the **Why?** section of the lesson.

Ask:
- What characteristic differentiates a trapezoid from a parallelogram? A trapezoid has only one pair of parallel sides.
- Why would a vaulting horse shaped like a trapezoid be more stable than one that is shaped like a rectangle? One base is wider; therefore the vaulting horse is less likely to tip over than it would be if it were shaped like a rectangle of the same height and width.

(continued on the next page)

Lesson 6-6 Resources

Resource	Approaching Level AL	On Level OL	Beyond Level BL	English Learners ELL
Teacher Edition	▪ Differentiated Instruction, p. 443	▪ Differentiated Instruction, pp. 441, 443, 446	▪ Differentiated Instruction, pp. 441, 446	
Chapter Resource Masters	▪ Study Guide and Intervention, pp. 37–38 ▪ Skills Practice, p. 39 ▪ Practice, p. 40 ▪ Word Problem Practice, p. 41	▪ Study Guide and Intervention, pp. 37–38 ▪ Skills Practice, p. 39 ▪ Practice, p. 40 ▪ Word Problem Practice, p. 41 ▪ Enrichment, p. 42	▪ Practice, p. 40 ▪ Word Problem Practice, p. 41 ▪ Enrichment, p. 42	▪ Study Guide and Intervention, pp. 37–38 ▪ Skills Practice, p. 39 ▪ Practice, p. 40 ▪ Word Problem Practice, p. 41
Other	▪ 5-Minute Check 6-6 ▪ Study Notebook	▪ 5-Minute Check 6-6 ▪ Study Notebook	▪ 5-Minute Check 6-6 ▪ Study Notebook	▪ 5-Minute Check 6-6 ▪ Study Notebook

- Look at the illustration of the four staked vaulting boxes. What conjectures can you make about the angles of the trapezoids that form the end of the box? The corresponding angles of the four trapezoids must be congruent to the upper base of the figure below. Therefore, the trapezoids that form the ends of the vaulting box must be similar.

1 Properties of Trapezoids

Examples 1–3 show how to use theorems to prove or identify that a figure is a trapezoid.

Formative Assessment

Use the Guided Practice exercises after each example to determine students' understanding of concepts.

Additional Example

1 **BASKET** Each side of the basket shown is an isosceles trapezoid. If $m\angle JML = 130$, $KN = 6.7$ feet, and $MN = 3.6$ feet, find each measure.

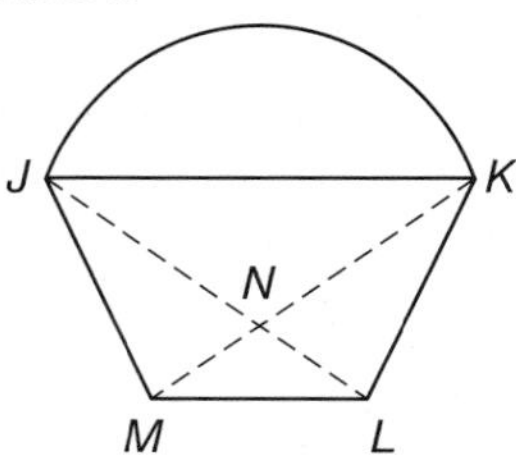

a. $m\angle MJK$ 50

b. JL 10.3

Additional Examples also in Interactive Classroom PowerPoint® Presentations

Real-WorldLink

Speakers are amplifiers that intensify sound waves so that they are audible to the unaided ear. Amplifiers exist in devices such as televisions, stereos, and computers.

Source: How Stuff Works

Real-World Example 1 Use Properties of Isosceles Trapezoids

MUSIC **The speaker shown is an isosceles trapezoid. If $m\angle FJH = 85$, $FK = 8$ inches, and $JG = 19$ inches, find each measure.**

a. $m\angle FGH$

Since $FGHJ$ is an isosceles trapezoid, $\angle FJH$ and $\angle GHJ$ are congruent base angles. So, $m\angle GHJ = m\angle FJH = 85$.

Since $FGHJ$ is a trapezoid, $\overline{FG} \parallel \overline{JH}$.

$m\angle FGH + m\angle GHJ = 180$	Consecutive Interior Angles Theorem
$m\angle FGH + 85 = 180$	Substitution
$m\angle FGH = 95$	Subtract 85 from each side.

b. KH

Since $FGHJ$ is an isosceles trapezoid, diagonals $\overline{FH}$ and $\overline{JG}$ are congruent.

$FH = JG$	Definition of congruent
$FK + KH = JG$	Segment Addition
$8 + KH = 19$	Substitution
$KH = 11$ cm	Subtract 8 from each side.

StudyTip

Isosceles Trapezoids The base angles of a trapezoid are only congruent if the trapezoid is isosceles.

GuidedPractice

1. **CAFETERIA TRAYS** To save space at a square table, cafeteria trays often incorporate trapezoids into their design. If $WXYZ$ is an isosceles trapezoid and $m\angle YZW = 45$, $WV = 15$ centimeters, and $VY = 10$ centimeters, find each measure.

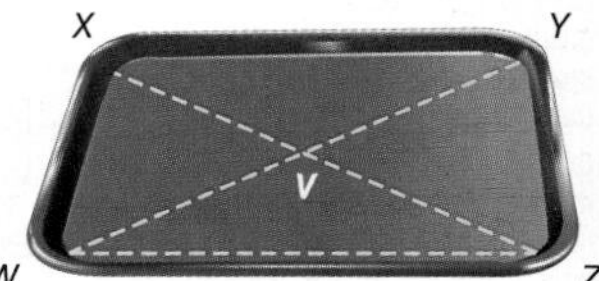

A. $m\angle XWZ$ 45 **B.** $m\angle WXY$ 135

C. XZ 25 cm **D.** XV 10 cm

You can use coordinate geometry to determine whether a trapezoid is an isosceles trapezoid.

Example 2 Isosceles Trapezoids and Coordinate Geomerty

COORDINATE GEOMETRY **Quadrilateral $ABCD$ has vertices $A(-3, 4)$, $B(2, 5)$, $C(3, 3)$, and $D(-1, 0)$. Show that $ABCD$ is a trapezoid and determine whether it is an isosceles trapezoid.**

Graph and connect the vertices of $ABCD$.

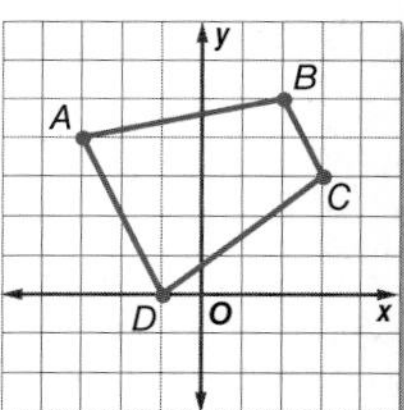

Step 1 Use the Slope Formula to compare the slopes of opposite sides $\overline{BC}$ and $\overline{AD}$ and of opposite sides $\overline{AB}$ and $\overline{DC}$. A quadrilateral is a trapezoid if exactly one pair of opposite sides are parallel.

Opposite sides $\overline{BC}$ and $\overline{AD}$:

slope of $\overline{BC} = 3 - \frac{5}{3} - 2 = -\frac{2}{1}$ or -2

slope of $\overline{AD} = \frac{0 - 4}{-1 - (-3)} = \frac{-4}{2}$ or -2

Since the slopes of $\overline{BC}$ and $\overline{AD}$ are equal, $\overline{BC} \parallel \overline{AD}$.

Opposite sides $\overline{AB}$ and $\overline{DC}$:

slope of $\overline{AB} = \frac{5 - 4}{2 - (-3)} = \frac{1}{5}$ slope of $\overline{DC} = \frac{0 - 3}{-1 - 3} = \frac{-3}{-4}$ or $\frac{3}{4}$

Since the slopes of $\overline{AB}$ and $\overline{DC}$ are *not* equal, $\overline{BC} \nparallel \overline{AD}$. Since quadrilateral $ABCD$ has only one pair of opposite sides that are parallel, quadrilateral $ABCD$ is a trapezoid.

ReadingMath

Symbols Recall that the symbol $\nparallel$ means *is not parallel to.*

Step 2 Use the Distance Formula to compare the lengths of legs $\overline{AB}$ and $\overline{DC}$. A trapezoid is isosceles if its legs are congruent.

$AB = \sqrt{(-3 - 2)^2 + (4 - 5)^2}$ or $\sqrt{26}$

$DC = \sqrt{(-1 - 3)^2 + (0 - 3)^2} = \sqrt{25}$ or 5

Since $AB \neq DC$, legs $\overline{AB}$ abd $\overline{DC}$ are *not* congruent. Therefore, trapezoid $ABCD$ is not isosceles.

GuidedPractice

2. Quadrilateral $QRST$ has vertices $Q(-8, -4)$, $R(0, 8)$, $S(6, 8)$, and $T(-6, -10)$. Show that $QRST$ is a trapezoid and determine whether $QRST$ is an isosceles trapezoid. **$\overline{RQ} \parallel \overline{ST}$, $\overline{RS} \nparallel \overline{QT}$; not isosceles, $RS = 6$, $QT = \sqrt{40}$**

ReadingMath

Midsegment A midsegment of a trapezoid can also be called a *median.*

The **midsegment of a trapezoid** is the segment that connects the midpoints of the legs of the trapezoid.

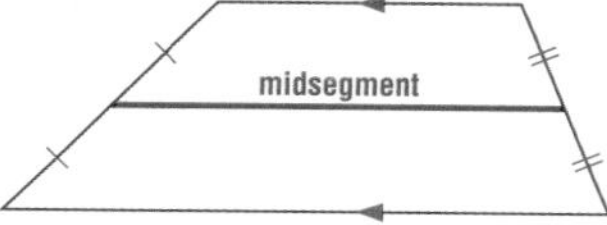

The theorem below relates the midsegment and the bases of a trapezoid.

Theorem 6.24 Trapezoid Midsegment Theorem

The midsegment of a trapezoid is parallel to each base and its measure is one half the sum of the lengths of the bases.

Example If $\overline{BE}$ is the midsegment of trapezoid $ACDF$, then $\overline{AF} \parallel \overline{BE}$, $\overline{CD} \parallel \overline{BE}$, and $BE = \frac{1}{2}(AF + CD)$.

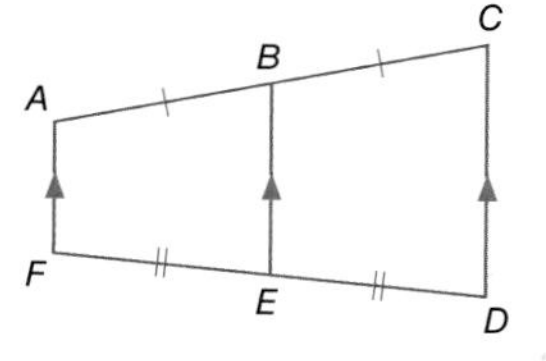

You will prove Theorem 6.24 in Exercise 33.

Additional Example

2 Quadrilateral $ABCD$ has vertices $A(5, 1)$, $B(-3, -1)$, $C(-2, 3)$, and $D(2, 4)$. Show that $ABCD$ is a trapezoid and determine whether it is an isosceles trapezoid.

Step 1 slope of $\overline{AB} = \frac{1}{4}$;
slope of $\overline{CD} = \frac{1}{4}$;
slope of $\overline{AD} = -1$;
slope of $\overline{BC} = 4$.

Because $\overline{AB}$ and $\overline{CD}$ have the same slope, $\overline{AB} \parallel \overline{CD}$. Exactly one pair of opposite sides is parallel. Therefore, $ABCD$ is a trapezoid.

Step 2. $BC = \sqrt{17}$, and $AD = \sqrt{18}$; because the legs are not congruent, $ABCD$ is not an isosceles trapezoid.

WatchOut!

Coordinate Geometry When using the Slope or Distance Formulas, be careful with the signs of the numbers. Also be sure to use x and y values in the correct order.

DifferentiatedInstruction OL BL

Extension There are several words that have multiple meanings within mathematics. The word median can be applied to geometry or statistics. Have the students compare and contrast the meanings of median when applied to a triangle and a trapezoid. Also have them state the meaning of median of a data set. The comparison is that a median of a triangle and of a trapezoid connects the midpoint of a line segment to another location on that figure. The contrast is that a median of a triangle connects to a vertex while a trapezoid median joins the midpoints of the legs. The median of a data set is the middle value in a set of ordered data.

Additional Example

3 STANDARDIZED TEST EXAMPLE In the figure, $\overline{MN}$ is the midsegment of trapezoid *FGJK*. What is the value of *x*?

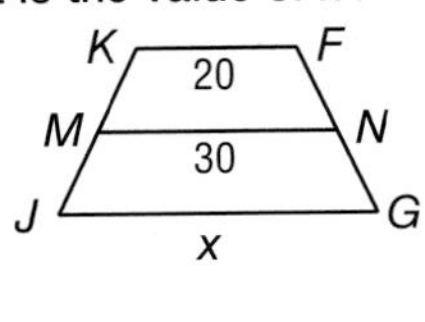

40

Tips for New Teachers

Trapezoids An alternate definition of a trapezoid is to have *at least* one pair of parallel sides. In this definition, a parallelogram is a special case of a trapezoid.

Standardized Test Example 3 Midsegment of a Trapezoid

GRIDDED RESPONSE In the figure, $\overline{LH}$ is the midsegment of trapezoid *FGJK*. What is the value of *x*?

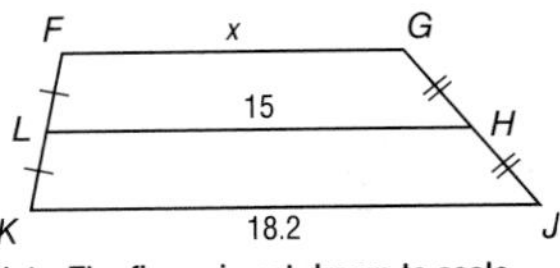

Note: The figure is not drawn to scale.

Read the Test Item

You are given the measure of the midsegment of a trapezoid and the measure of one of its bases. You are asked to find the measure of the other base.

Solve the Test Item

$LH = \frac{1}{2}(FG + KJ)$	Trapezoid Midsegment Theorem
$5 = \frac{1}{2}(x + \mathbf{18.2})$	Substitution
$30 = x + 18.2$	Multiply each side by 2.
$11.8 = x$	Subtract 18.2 from each side.

Grid In Your Answer

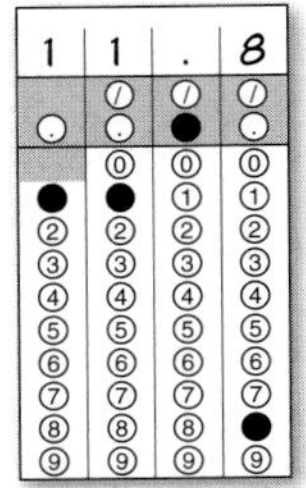

- You can align the numerical answer by placing the first digit in the left answer box or by putting the last digit in the right answer box.
- Do not leave blank boxes in the middle of an answer.
- Fill in **one** bubble for each filled answer box. Do not fill more than one bubble for an answer box. Do not fill in a bubble for blank answer boxes.

Test-TakingTip

Gridded Responses
Rational answers can often be gridded in more than one way. An answer such as $\frac{8}{5}$ could be gridded as 8/5 or 1.6, but not as 1 3/5.

GuidedPractice

3. **GRIDDED RESPONSE** Trapezoid *ABCD* is shown below. If $\overline{FG}$ is parallel to $\overline{AD}$, what is the *x*-coordinate of point *G*? **10.5**

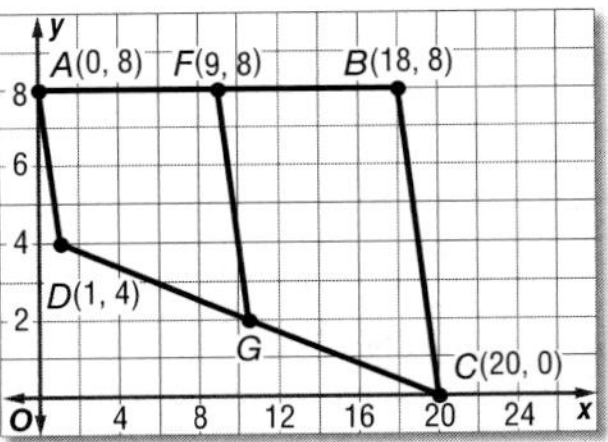

2 Properties of Kites A **kite** is a quadrilateral with exactly two pairs of consecutive congruent sides. Unlike a parallelogram, the opposite sides of a kite are not congruent or parallel.

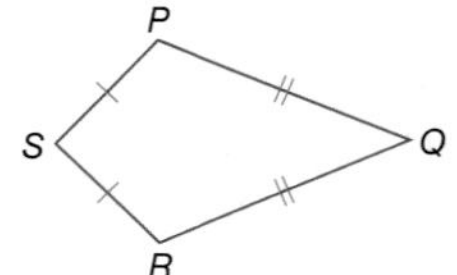

Teach with Tech

Interactive Whiteboard Draw a table with 7 columns, labeled as quadrilateral, parallelogram, rectangle, rhombus, square, kite, and trapezoid. Display several examples of each on the board and choose students to drag each shape to the column with the most specific name that identifies it. If students believe the shape could be classified in more than one way, help students identify the most *specific* name.

StudyTip

Kites The congruent angles of a kite are included by the non-congruent adjacent sides.

Theorems Kites

6.25 If a quadrilateral is a kite, then its diagonals are perpendicular.

Example If quadrilateral *ABCD* is a kite, then $\overline{AC} \perp \overline{BD}$.

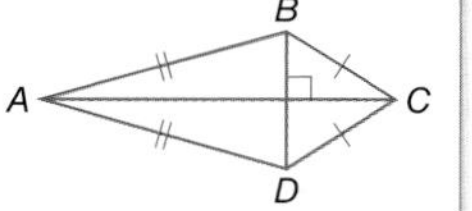

6.26 If a quadrilateral is a kite, then exactly one pair of opposite angles is congruent.

Example If quadrilateral *JKLM* is a kite, $\overline{JK} \cong \overline{KL}$, and $\overline{JM} \cong \overline{LM}$, then $\angle J \cong \angle L$ and $\angle K \ncong \angle M$.

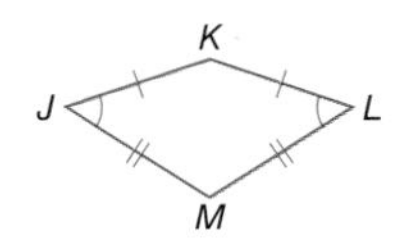

You will prove Theorems 6.25 and 6.26 in Exercises 31 and 32, respectively.

You can use the theorems above, the Pythagorean Theorem, and the Polygon Interior Angles Sum Theorem to find missing measures in kites.

Example 4 Use Properties of Kites

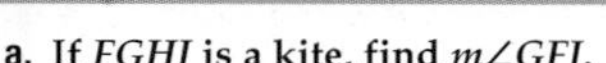

a. If *FGHJ* is a kite, find $m\angle GFJ$.

Since a kite can only have one pair of opposite congruent angles and $\angle G \ncong \angle J$, then $\angle F \cong \angle H$. So, $m\angle F = m\angle H$. Write and solve an equation to find $m\angle F$.

G, F, H, J; 128°, 72°

$m\angle F + m\angle G + m\angle H + m\angle J = 360$	Polygon Interior Angles Sum Theorem
$m\angle F + 128 + m\angle F + 72 = 360$	Substitution
$2m\angle F + 200 = 360$	Simplify.
$2m\angle F = 160$	Subtract 200 from each side.
$m\angle F = 80$	Divide each side by 2.

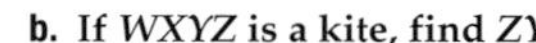

b. If *WXYZ* is a kite, find *ZY*.

Since the diagonals of a kite are perpendicular, they divide *WXYZ* into four right triangles. Use the Pythagorean Theorem to find *ZY*, the length of the hypotenuse of right $\triangle YPZ$.

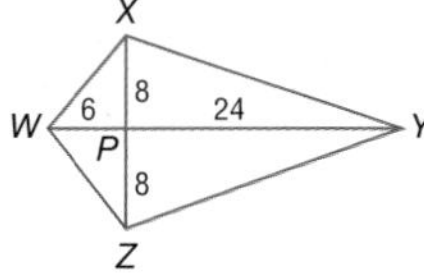

$PZ^2 + PY^2 = ZY^2$	Pythagorean Theorem
$8^2 + 24^2 = ZY^2$	Substitution
$640 = ZY^2$	Simplify.
$\sqrt{640} = ZY$	Take the square root of each side.
$8\sqrt{10} = ZY$	Simplify.

GuidedPractice

4A. If $m\angle BAD = 38$ and $m\angle BCD = 50$, find $m\angle ADC$. **136**

4B. If $BT = 5$ and $TC = 8$, find CD. $\sqrt{89}$

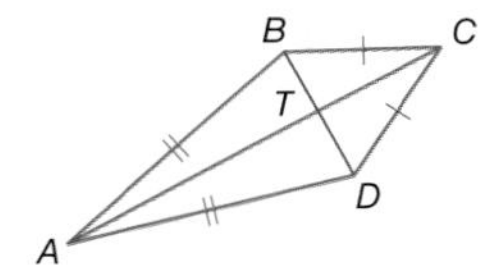

Real-WorldLink

The fastest recorded speed of a kite is over 120 miles per hour. The record for the highest single kite flown is 12,471 feet.

Source: Borealis Kites

2 Properties of Kites

Example 4 shows how to use theorems and properties to prove or identify that a figure is a kite.

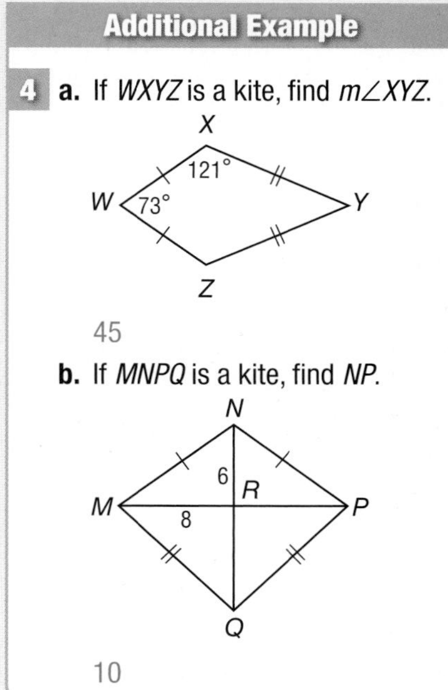

Additional Example

4 a. If *WXYZ* is a kite, find $m\angle XYZ$.

45

b. If *MNPQ* is a kite, find *NP*.

10

Focus on Mathematical Content

Kites There are three additional properties of kites. 1) The angles between the noncongruent sides of a kite are always congruent. 2) The diagonal of the noncongruent angles is always the perpendicular bisector of the diagonal of the congruent angles. 3) The noncongruent angles are bisected by the diagonal.

DifferentiatedInstruction AL OL

Visual/Spatial Learners Students can demonstrate congruent sides as well as congruent and noncongruent angles of kites. Have students fold a sheet of paper in half. Then instruct them to make a diagonal cut of any length, starting at the fold. Have them repeat the process starting at the other end of the fold and cutting until the two diagonal cuts meet. Students can then compare the congruent and noncongruent angles and sides. Have students cut out several different sized kites to demonstrate that these characteristics are always true.

3 Practice

Formative Assessment

Use Exercises 1–7 to check for understanding.

Then use the chart at the bottom of this page to customize assignments for your students.

Follow-up

Students have explored characteristics of quadrilaterals.

Ask:

- Why is it helpful to have different names for quadrilaterals? Sample answer: Different quadrilaterals have different associated characteristics. For example, it may be helpful to describe a quadrilateral as a square instead of a rectangle, because a square has congruent side lengths.

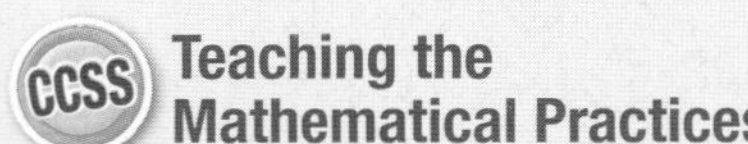

Teaching the Mathematical Practices

Sense-Making Mathematically proficient students start by explaining the meaning of a problem to themselves and looking for entry points to its solution. In Exercises 6–7 and 24–27, encourage students to review the properties of a kite before starting on the exercises.

Additional Answers

12. $\overline{BC} \parallel \overline{AD}$, $\overline{AB} \nparallel \overline{CD}$; $ABCD$ is a trapezoid, but not isosceles since $AB = \sqrt{17}$ and $CD = 5$.

13. $\overline{JK} \parallel \overline{LM}$, $\overline{KL} \nparallel \overline{JM}$; $JKLM$ is a trapezoid, but not isosceles since $KL = \sqrt{26}$ and $JM = 5$.

14. $\overline{QR} \parallel \overline{ST}$, $\overline{RS} \nparallel \overline{QT}$; $QRST$ is a trapezoid. Isosceles since $RS = \sqrt{50} = QT$.

15. $\overline{XY} \parallel \overline{WZ}$, $\overline{WX} \nparallel \overline{YZ}$; $WXYZ$ is a trapezoid, but not isosceles since $XZ = \sqrt{74}$ and $WY = \sqrt{68}$.

34a. $\overline{BC} \parallel \overline{AD}$, $\overline{AB} \nparallel \overline{CD}$; $ABCD$ is a trapezoid, but not isosceles, because $AB = \sqrt{17}$ and $CD = 4$.

34b. No; it is not $\parallel$ to the bases which have slopes of $-\frac{3}{4}$, while $y = -x + 1$ has a slope of -1.

Check Your Understanding

= Step-by-Step Solutions begin on page R14.

Example 1 Find each measure.

1. $m\angle D$ 101

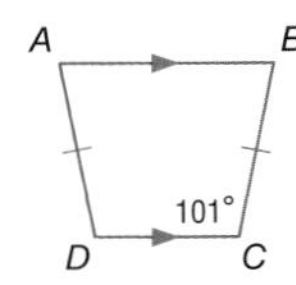

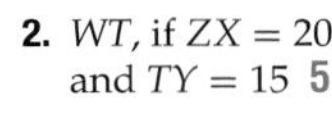

2. WT, if $ZX = 20$ and $TY = 15$ 5

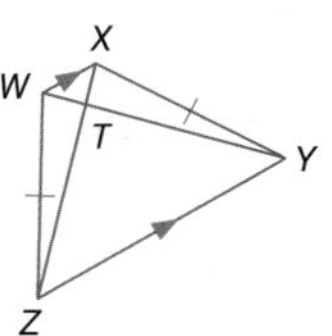

Example 2 COORDINATE GEOMETRY **Quadrilateral $ABCD$ has vertices $A(-4, -1)$, $B(-2, 3)$, $C(3, 3)$, and $D(5, -1)$.**

3. Verify that $ABCD$ is a trapezoid. $\overline{BC} \parallel \overline{AD}$, $\overline{AB} \nparallel \overline{CD}$; $ABCD$ is a trapezoid.

4. Determine whether $ABCD$ is an isosceles trapezoid. Explain. isosceles; $AB = \sqrt{20} = CD$

Example 3

5. **GRIDDED RESPONSE** In the figure at the right, $\overline{YZ}$ is the midsegment of trapezoid $TWRV$. Determine the value of x. 1.2

T 14.8 W, Y 8 Z, x, V R

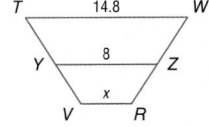

Example 4 CCSS SENSE-MAKING **If $ABCD$ is a kite, find each measure.**

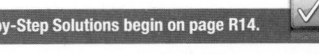

6. AB 5

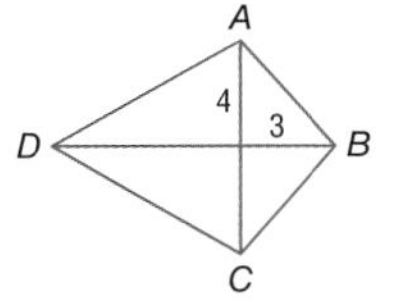

7. $m\angle C$ 70

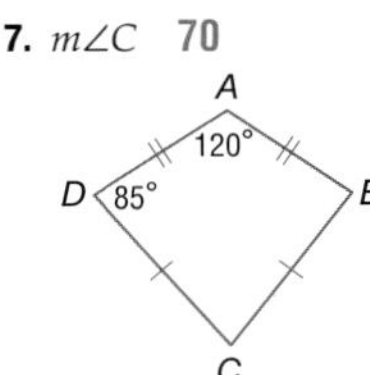

Practice and Problem Solving

Extra Practice is on page R6.

Example 1 Find each measure.

8. $m\angle K$ 100

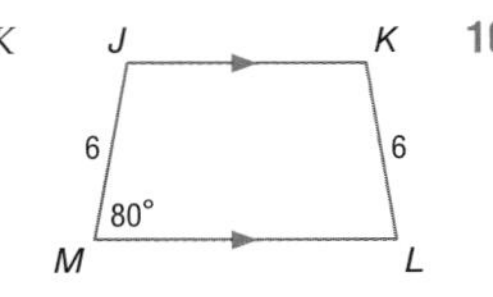

9. $m\angle Q$ 70

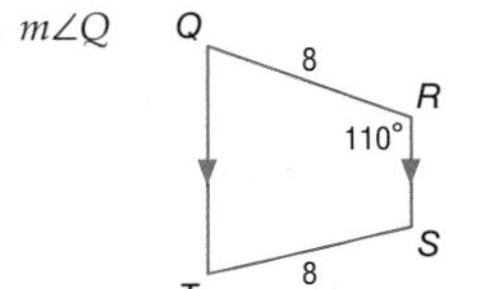

10. JL, if $KP = 4$ and $PM = 7$ 11

K, J, P, L, M

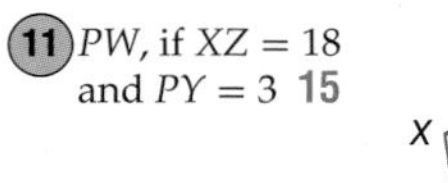

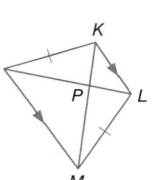

11. PW, if $XZ = 18$ and $PY = 3$ 15

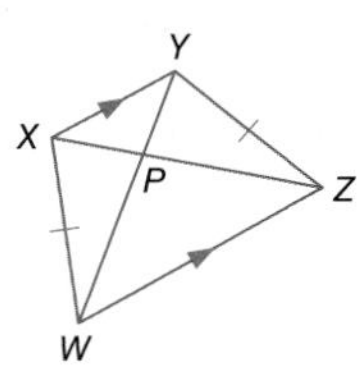

Example 2 COORDINATE GEOMETRY **For each quadrilateral with the given vertices, verify that the quadrilateral is a trapezoid and determine whether the figure is an isosceles trapezoid.** 12–15. See margin.

12. $A(-2, 5)$, $B(-3, 1)$, $C(6, 1)$, $D(3, 5)$

13. $J(-4, -6)$, $K(6, 2)$, $L(1, 3)$, $M(-4, -1)$

14. $Q(2, 5)$, $R(-2, 1)$, $S(-1, -6)$, $T(9, 4)$

15. $W(-5, -1)$, $X(-2, 2)$, $Y(3, 1)$, $Z(5, -3)$

444 | Lesson 6-6 | Trapezoids and Kites

Differentiated Homework Options

Level	Assignment	Two-Day Option	
AL Basic	8–27, 65, 67–84	9–27 odd, 70–73	8–26 even, 65, 67–69, 74–84
OL Core	9–27 odd, 29–63 odd, 65, 67–84	8–27, 70–73	28–65, 67–69, 74–84
BL Advanced	28–81, (optional: 82–84)		

Example 3 For trapezoid *QRTU*, *V* and *S* are midpoints of the legs.

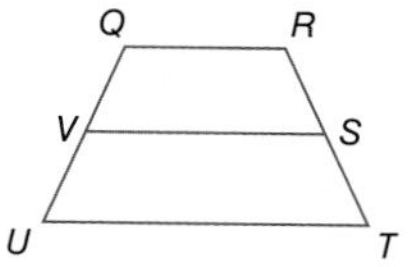

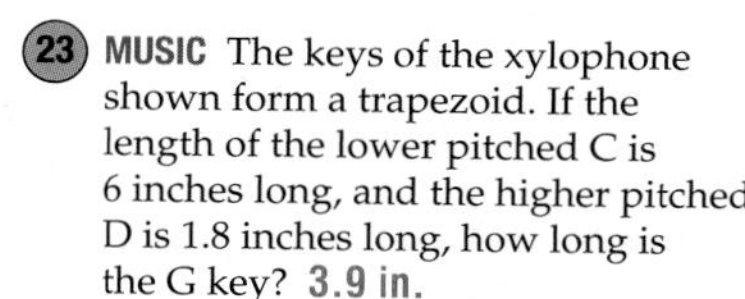

16. If $QR = 12$ and $UT = 22$, find VS. **17**
17. If $QR = 4$ and $UT = 16$, find VS. **10**
18. If $VS = 9$ and $UT = 12$, find QR. **6**
19. If $TU = 26$ and $SV = 17$, find QR. **8**
20. If $QR = 2$ and $VS = 7$, find UT. **12**
21. If $RQ = 5$ and $VS = 11$, find UT. **17**

22. **DESIGN** Juana is designing a window box. She wants the end of the box to be a trapezoid with the dimensions shown. If she wants to put a shelf in the middle for the plants to rest on, about how wide should she make the shelf? **17 in.**

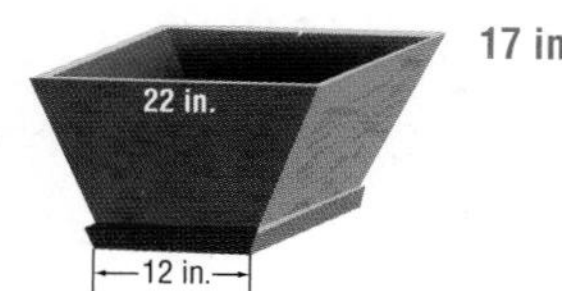

23. **MUSIC** The keys of the xylophone shown form a trapezoid. If the length of the lower pitched C is 6 inches long, and the higher pitched D is 1.8 inches long, how long is the G key? **3.9 in.**

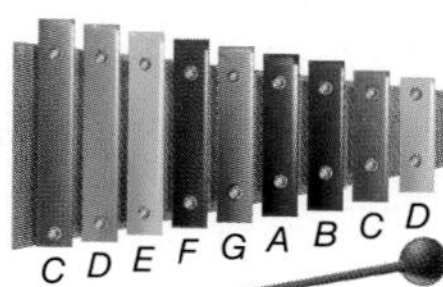

Example 4 **CCSS SENSE-MAKING** If *WXYZ* is a kite, find each measure.

24. YZ $\sqrt{89}$

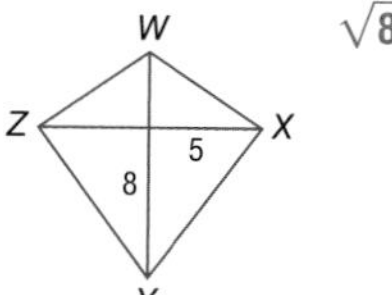

25. WP $\sqrt{20}$

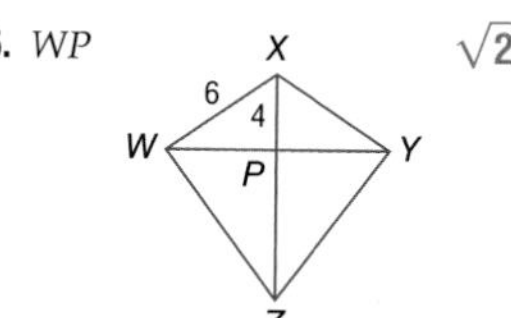

26. $m\angle X$ **117**

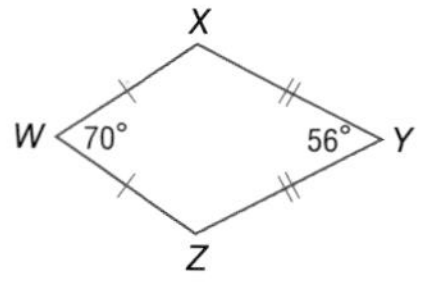

27. $m\angle Z$ **75**

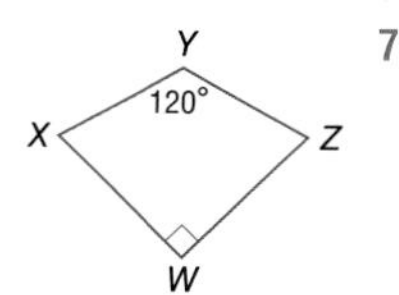

B **PROOF** Write a paragraph proof for each theorem. **28–33. See Ch. 6 Answer Appendix.**

28. Theorem 6.21
29. Theorem 6.22
30. Theorem 6.23
31. Theorem 6.25
32. Theorem 6.26
33. **PROOF** Write a coordinate proof for Theorem 6.24.

34. **COORDINATE GEOMETRY** Refer to quadrilateral *ABCD*.
   a. Determine whether the figure is a trapezoid. If so, is it isosceles? Explain. **a, b. See margin.**
   b. Is the midsegment contained in the line with equation $y = -x + 1$? Justify your answer.
   c. Find the length of the midsegment. **7.5 units**

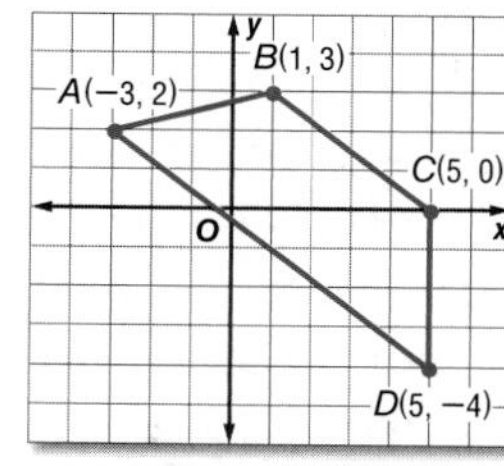

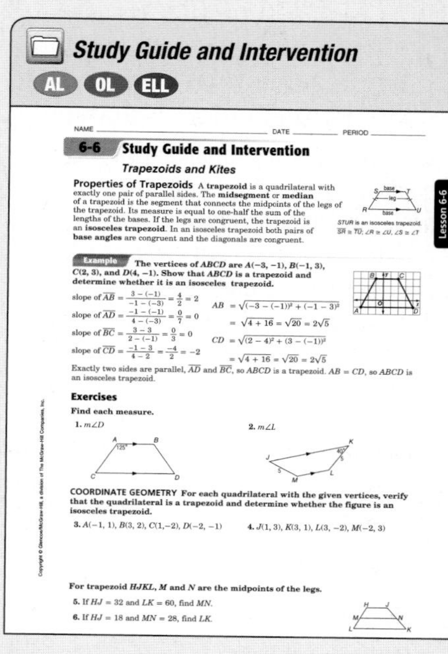
Study Guide and Intervention
AL OL ELL

6-6 Study Guide and Intervention
Trapezoids and Kites

Properties of Trapezoids A trapezoid is a quadrilateral with exactly one pair of parallel sides. The midsegment or median of a trapezoid is the segment that connects the midpoints of the legs of the trapezoid. Its measure is equal to one-half the sum of the lengths of the bases. If the legs are congruent, the trapezoid is an isosceles trapezoid. In an isosceles trapezoid both pairs of base angles are congruent and the diagonals are congruent.

Example The vertices of *ABCD* are $A(-3, -1)$, $B(-1, 3)$, $C(2, 3)$, and $D(4, -1)$. Show that *ABCD* is a trapezoid and determine whether it is an isosceles trapezoid.

Exactly two sides are parallel, $\overline{AD}$ and $\overline{BC}$, so *ABCD* is a trapezoid. $AB = CD$, so *ABCD* is an isosceles trapezoid.

Exercises
Find each measure.
1. $m\angle D$
2. $m\angle L$

COORDINATE GEOMETRY For each quadrilateral with the given vertices, verify that the quadrilateral is a trapezoid and determine whether the figure is an isosceles trapezoid.
3. $A(-1, 1)$, $B(3, 2)$, $C(1, -2)$, $D(-2, -1)$
4. $J(1, 3)$, $K(3, 1)$, $L(3, -2)$, $M(-2, 3)$

For trapezoid *HJKL*, *M* and *N* are the midpoints of the legs.
5. If $HJ = 32$ and $LK = 60$, find MN.
6. If $HJ = 18$ and $MN = 28$, find LK.

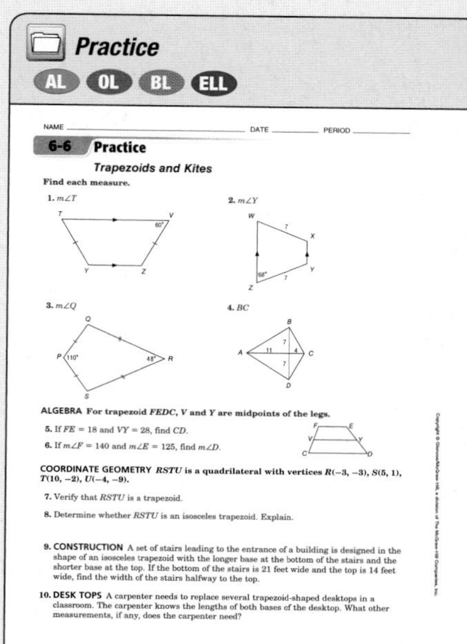
Practice
AL OL BL ELL

6-6 Practice
Trapezoids and Kites
Find each measure.
1. $m\angle T$
2. $m\angle Y$
3. $m\angle Q$
4. BC

ALGEBRA For trapezoid *FEDC*, *V* and *Y* are midpoints of the legs.
5. If $FE = 18$ and $VY = 28$, find CD.
6. If $m\angle F = 140$ and $m\angle E = 125$, find $m\angle D$.

COORDINATE GEOMETRY *RSTU* is a quadrilateral with vertices $R(-3, -3)$, $S(5, 1)$, $T(10, -2)$, $U(-4, -9)$.
7. Verify that *RSTU* is a trapezoid.
8. Determine whether *RSTU* is an isosceles trapezoid. Explain.

9. CONSTRUCTION A set of stairs leading to the entrance of a building is designed in the shape of an isosceles trapezoid with the longer base at the bottom of the stairs and the shorter base at the top. If the bottom of the stairs is 21 feet wide and the top is 14 feet wide, find the width of the stairs halfway to the top.

10. DESK TOPS A carpenter needs to replace several trapezoid-shaped desktops in a classroom. The carpenter knows the lengths of both bases of the desktop. What other measurements, if any, does the carpenter need?

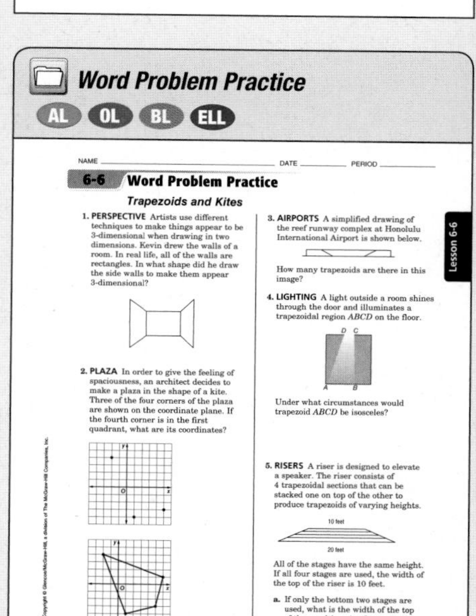
Word Problem Practice
AL OL BL ELL

6-6 Word Problem Practice
Trapezoids and Kites

1. PERSPECTIVE Artists use different techniques to make things appear to be 3-dimensional when drawing in two dimensions. Kevin drew the walls of a room. In real life, all of the walls are rectangles. In what shape did he draw the side walls to make them appear 3-dimensional?

2. PLAZA In order to give the feeling of spaciousness, an architect decides to make a plaza in the shape of a kite. Three of the four corners of the plaza are shown on the coordinate plane. If the fourth corner is in the first quadrant, what are its coordinates?

3. AIRPORTS A simplified drawing of the reef runway complex at Honolulu International Airport is shown below. How many trapezoids are there in this image?

4. LIGHTING A light outside a room shines through the door and illuminates a trapezoidal region *ABCD* on the floor. Under what circumstances would trapezoid *ABCD* be isosceles?

5. RISERS A riser is designed to elevate a speaker. The riser consists of 4 trapezoidal sections that can be stacked one on top of the other to produce trapezoids of varying heights. All of the stages have the same height. If all four stages are used, the width of the top of the riser is 10 feet.
   a. If only the bottom two stages are used, what is the width of the top of the resulting riser?
   b. What would be the width of the riser if the bottom three stages are used?

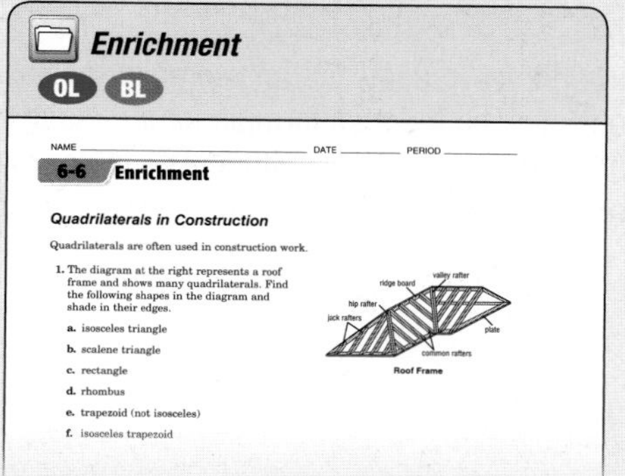
Enrichment
OL BL

6-6 Enrichment
Quadrilaterals in Construction
Quadrilaterals are often used in construction work.
1. The diagram at the right represents a roof frame and shows many quadrilaterals. Find the following shapes in the diagram and shade in their edges.
   a. isosceles triangle
   b. scalene triangle
   c. rectangle
   d. rhombus
   e. trapezoid (not isosceles)
   f. isosceles trapezoid

connectED.mcgraw-hill.com

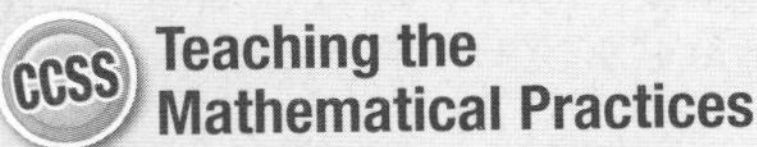

Teaching the Mathematical Practices

Arguments Mathematically proficient students understand and use stated assumptions and definitions in constructing arguments. They make conjectures and build a logical progression of statements to explore the truth of their conjectures. In Exercises 51–52, encourage students to review their notes on triangle congruence.

Additional Answers

51. Given: *ABCD* is an isosceles trapezoid.

Prove: $\angle DAC \cong \angle CBD$

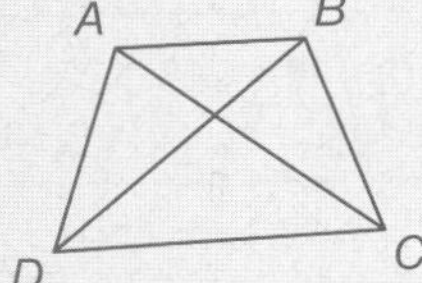

Statements (Reasons)

1. *ABCD* is an isosceles trapezoid. (Given)
2. $\overline{AD} \cong \overline{BC}$ (Def. of isos. trap.)
3. $\overline{DC} \cong \overline{DC}$ (Refl. Prop.)
4. $\overline{AC} \cong \overline{BD}$ (Diags. of isos. trap. are $\cong$.)
5. $\triangle ADC \cong \triangle BCD$ (SSS)
6. $\angle DAC \cong \angle CBD$ (CPCTC)

52. Given: $\overline{WZ} \cong \overline{ZV}$, $\overline{XY}$ bisects $\overline{WZ}$ and $\overline{ZV}$, and $\angle W \cong \angle ZXY$.

Prove: *WXYV* is an isosceles trapezoid.

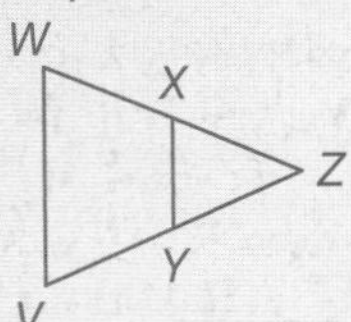

Statements (Reasons)

1. $\overline{WZ} \cong \overline{ZV}$, $\overline{XY}$ bisects $\overline{WZ}$ and $\overline{ZV}$. (Given)
2. $\frac{1}{2}WZ = \frac{1}{2}ZV$ (Mult. Prop.)
3. $WX = VY$ (Def. of midpt.)
4. $\overline{WX} \cong \overline{VY}$ (Def. of $\cong$ segs.)
5. $\angle W \cong \angle ZXY$ (Given)
6. $\overline{XY} \parallel \overline{WV}$ (If corr. $\angle$s are $\cong$, lines are $\parallel$.)
7. *WXYV* is an isosceles trapezoid. (Def. of isos. trap.)

ALGEBRA ***ABCD*** **is a trapezoid.**

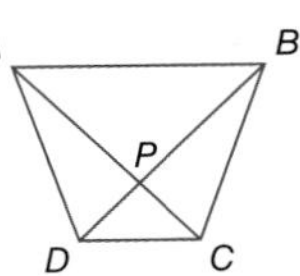
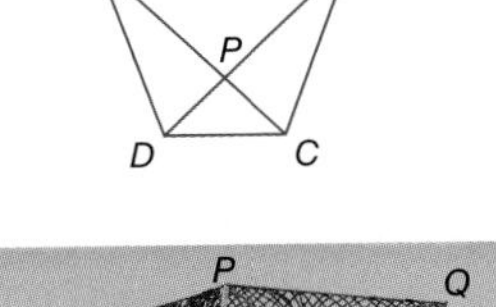
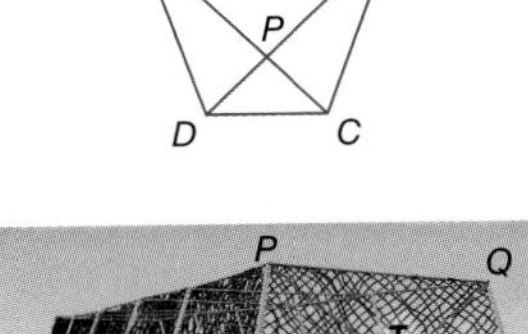

35. If $AC = 3x - 7$ and $BD = 2x + 8$, find the value of x so that *ABCD* is isosceles. **15**

36. If $m\angle ABC = 4x + 11$ and $m\angle DAB = 2x + 33$, find the value of x so that *ABCD* is isosceles. **11**

SPORTS **The end of the batting cage shown is an isosceles trapezoid. If $PT = 12$ feet, $ST = 28$ feet, and $m\angle PQR = 110$, find each measure.**

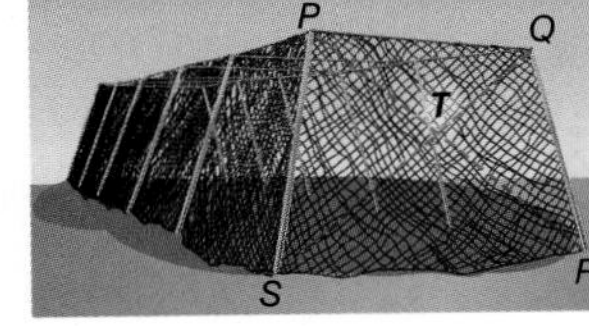

37. *TR* **28 ft**

38. *SQ* **40 ft**

39. $m\angle QRS$ **70**

40. $m\angle QPS$ **110**

ALGEBRA **For trapezoid** ***QRST***, ***M*** **and** ***P*** **are midpoints of the legs.**

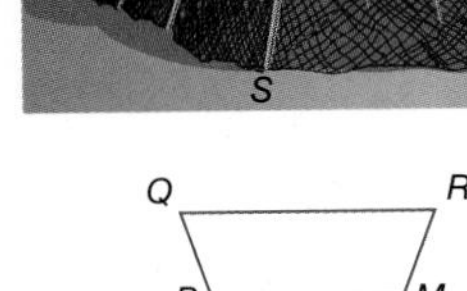
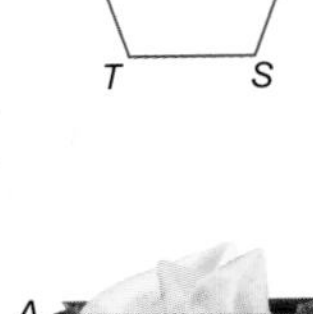

41. If $QR = 16$, $PM = 12$, and $TS = 4x$, find x. **2**

42. If $TS = 2x$, $PM = 20$, and $QR = 6x$, find x. **5**

43. If $PM = 2x$, $QR = 3x$, and $TS = 10$, find PM. **20**

44. If $TS = 2x + 2$, $QR = 5x + 3$, and $PM = 13$, find TS. **8**

SHOPPING **The side of the shopping bag shown is an isosceles trapezoid. If $EC = 9$ inches, $DB = 19$ inches, $m\angle ABE = 40$, and $m\angle EBC = 35$, find each measure.**

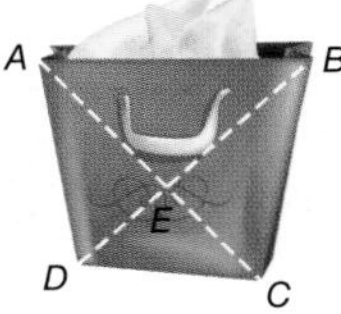

45. *AE* **10 in.**

46. *AC* **19 in.**

47. $m\angle BCD$ **105**

48. $m\angle EDC$ **40**

ALGEBRA ***WXYZ*** **is a kite.**

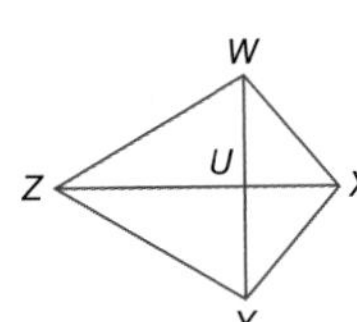

49. If $m\angle WXY = 120$, $m\angle WZY = 4x$, and $m\angle ZWX = 10x$, find $m\angle ZYX$. **100**

50. If $m\angle WXY = 13x + 24$, $m\angle WZY = 35$, and $m\angle ZWX = 13x + 14$, find $m\angle ZYX$. **105**

CCSS ARGUMENTS **Write a two-column proof.** **51, 52. See margin.**

51. Given: *ABCD* is an isosceles trapezoid.

Prove: $\angle DAC \cong \angle CBD$

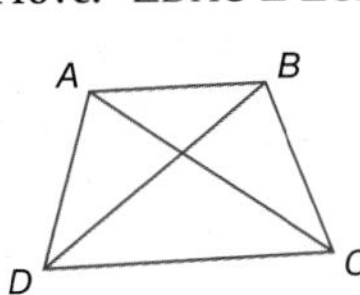

52. Given: $\overline{WZ} \cong \overline{ZV}$, $\overline{XY}$ bisects $\overline{WZ}$ and $\overline{ZV}$, and $\angle W \cong \angle ZXY$.

Prove: *WXYV* is an isosceles trapezoid.

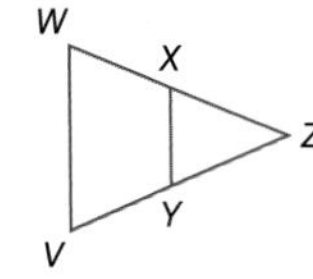

Determine whether each statement is *always*, *sometimes*, or *never* true. Explain.

53. The opposite angles of a trapezoid are supplementary.

54. One pair of opposite sides are parallel in a kite.

55. A square is a rhombus.

56. A rectangle is a square.

57. A parallelogram is a rectangle.

53. Sometimes; opp $\angle$s are supplementary in an isosceles trapezoid.
54. Never; exactly two pairs of adjacent sides are congruent.
55. Always; by def., a square is a quadrilateral with 4 rt. $\angle$s and 4 $\cong$ sides. Since by def., a rhombus is a quadrilateral with 4 $\cong$ sides, a square is always a rhombus.
56. Sometimes; if the rectangle has 4 $\cong$ sides, then it is a square. Otherwise, it is not a square.
57. Sometimes; only if the parallelogram has 4 rt. $\angle$s and/or congruent diagonals, is it a rectangle.

Differentiated Instruction OL BL

Extension Students learned some of the basic formulas for area in Chapter 1. Have students describe how knowing the area formula for a rectangle is sufficient for deriving the area formulas of triangles and other quadrilaterals. Students can use examples to demonstrate the decomposition of polygons and other methods used to find corresponding areas and total areas.

58. **KITES** Refer to the kite at the right. Using the properties of kites, write a two-column proof to show that $\triangle MNR$ is congruent to $\triangle PNR$. See Ch. 6 Answer Appendix.

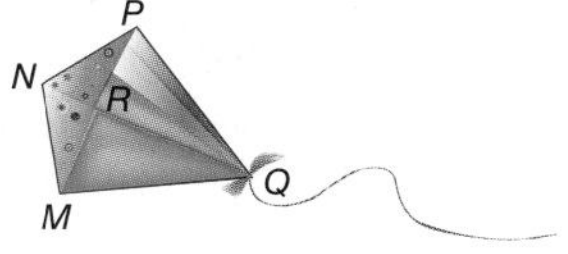

59. **VENN DIAGRAM** Create a Venn diagram that incorporates all quadrilaterals, including trapezoids, isosceles trapezoids, kites, and quadrilaterals that cannot be classified as anything other than quadrilaterals. See Ch. 6 Answer Appendix.

COORDINATE GEOMETRY Determine whether each figure is a *trapezoid*, a *parallelogram*, a *square*, a *rhombus*, or a *quadrilateral* given the coordinates of the vertices. Choose the most specific term. Explain.

60. $A(-1, 4)$, $B(2, 6)$, $C(3, 3)$, $D(0, 1)$ **Parallelogram; opp. sides $\parallel$, no rt. $\angle$s, no consecutive sides $\cong$.**

61. $W(-3, 4)$, $X(3, 4)$, $Y(5, 3)$, $Z(-5, 1)$ **quadrilateral; no parallel sides**

62. **MULTIPLE REPRESENTATIONS** In this problem, you will explore proportions in kites.

a. **Geometric** Draw a segment. Construct a noncongruent segment that perpendicularly bisects the first segment. Connect the endpoints of the segments to form a quadrilateral *ABCD*. Repeat the process two times. Name the additional quadrilaterals *PQRS* and *WXYZ*. See margin.

b. **Tabular** Copy and complete the table below.

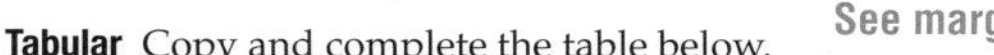

Figure	Side	Length	Side	Length	Side	Length	Side	Length
ABCD	AB	0.8 cm	BC	0.8 cm	CD	1.6 cm	DA	1.6 cm
PQRS	PQ	1.4 cm	QR	1.4 cm	RS	1.8 cm	SP	1.8 cm
WXYZ	WX	0.4 cm	XY	0.4 cm	YZ	1.5 cm	ZW	1.5 cm

c. **Verbal** Make a conjecture about a quadrilateral in which the diagonals are perpendicular, exactly one diagonal is bisected, and the diagonals are not congruent. See margin.

PROOF Write a coordinate proof of each statement.

63. The diagonals of an isosceles trapezoid are congruent. See margin.

64. The median of an isosceles trapezoid is parallel to the bases. See Ch. 6 Answer Appendix.

65. Belinda; $m\angle D = m\angle B$. So, $m\angle A + m\angle B + m\angle C + m\angle D = 360$ or $m\angle A + 100 + 45 + 100 = 360$. So, $m\angle A = 115$.

H.O.T. Problems Use Higher-Order Thinking Skills

65. **ERROR ANALYSIS** Bedagi and Belinda are trying to determine $m\angle A$ in kite *ABCD* shown. Is either of them correct? Explain.

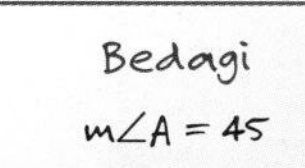

Belinda
m∠A = 115

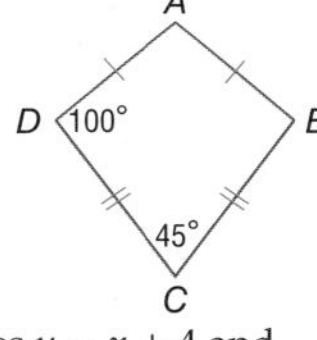

67. Never; a square has all 4 sides $\cong$, while a kite does not have any opposite sides congruent.

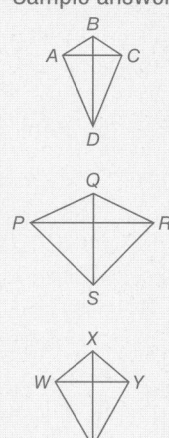

66. **CHALLENGE** If the parallel sides of a trapezoid are contained by the lines $y = x + 4$ and $y = x - 8$, what equation represents the line contained by the midsegment? $y = x - 2$

67. **ARGUMENTS** Is it *sometimes*, *always*, or *never* true that a square is also a kite? Explain.

68. **OPEN ENDED** Sketch two noncongruent trapezoids *ABCD* and *FGHJ* in which $\overline{AC} \cong \overline{FH}$ and $\overline{BD} \cong \overline{GJ}$. See Ch. 6 Answer Appendix.

69. **WRITING IN MATH** Describe the properties a quadrilateral must possess in order for the quadrilateral to be classified as a trapezoid, an isosceles trapezoid, or a kite. Compare the properties of all three quadrilaterals. See Ch. 6 Answer Appendix.

Multiple Representations

In Exercise 62, students use geometric sketches, a table, and verbal description to explore proportions in kites.

Exercise Alert

Straightedge and Compass
Exercise 62 requires the use of a straightedge and a compass.

WatchOut!

Error Analysis In Exercise 65, students should recognize that a kite contains only one pair of congruent angles. Since $\overline{AB} \cong \overline{AD}$ and $\overline{CB} \cong \overline{CD}$, $\angle B \cong \angle D$ and $m\angle A = 115$. Belinda is correct.

Teaching the Mathematical Practices

Arguments Mathematically proficient students understand and use stated assumptions and definitions in constructing arguments. In Exercise 67, encourage students to review the definitions of *square* and *kite*.

Additional Answers

62a. Sample answer:

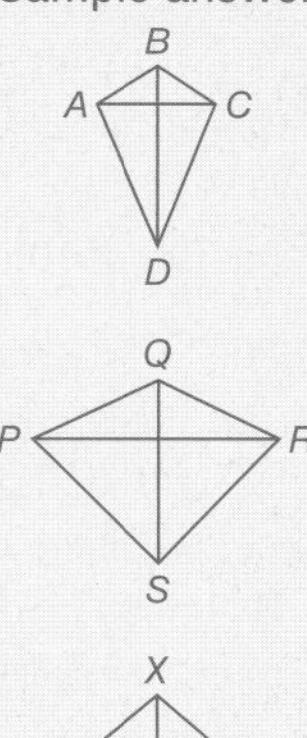

62c. If the diagonals of a quadrilateral are perpendicular, exactly one is bisected, and the diagonals are not congruent, then the quadrilateral is a kite.

63. Given: isosceles trapezoid *ABCD* with $\overline{AD} \cong \overline{BC}$

Prove: $\overline{BD} \cong \overline{AC}$

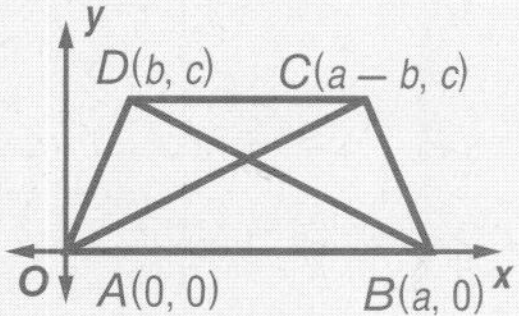

Proof:

$DB = \sqrt{(a - b)^2 + (0 - c)^2}$ or $\sqrt{(a - b)^2 + c^2}$

$AC = \sqrt{((a - b) - 0)^2 + (c - 0)^2}$ or $\sqrt{(a - b)^2 + c^2}$

$BD = AC$ and $\overline{BD} \cong \overline{AC}$

4 Assess

Name the Math Have students describe each type of quadrilateral. They should write a paragraph explaining the difference between parallelograms, trapezoids, and kites. Also ask them to differentiate rectangles, rhombi, and squares.

Formative Assessment

Check for understanding of concepts in Lesson 6-6.

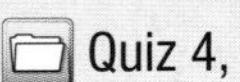 Quiz 4, p. 46

Additional Answers

78. No; $AB = \sqrt{65} = CD$, $BC = \sqrt{37} = DA$, so $ABCD$ is a parallelogram. $BD = \sqrt{106}$; $AC = \sqrt{98}$. $BD \neq AC$, so the diagonals are not congruent. Thus, $ABCD$ is not a rectangle.

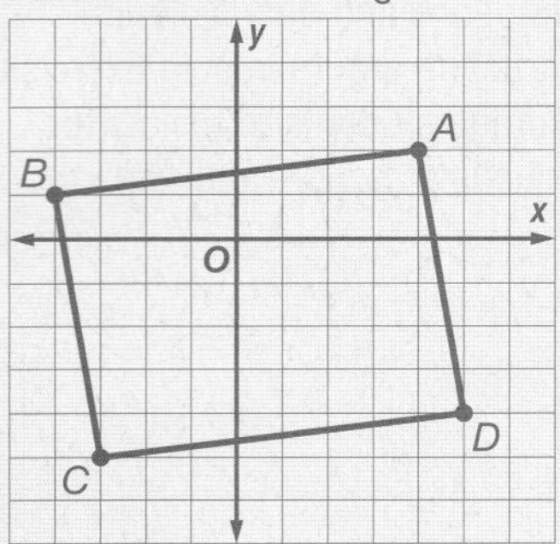

79. No; slope of $\overline{JK} = \frac{1}{8}$ = slope of $\overline{LM}$ and slope of $\overline{KL} = -6$ = slope of $\overline{MJ}$. So, $JKLM$ is a parallelogram. The product of the slopes of consecutive sides $\neq -1$, so the consecutive sides are not perpendicular. Thus, $JKLM$ is not a rectangle.

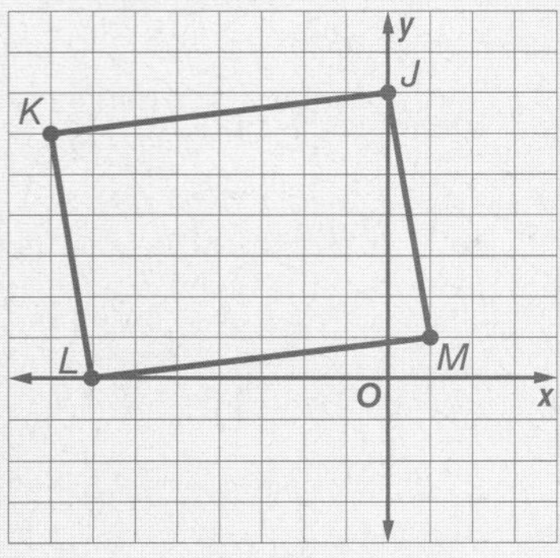

Standardized Test Practice

70. ALGEBRA All of the items on a breakfast menu cost the same whether ordered with something else or alone. Two pancakes and one order of bacon costs \$4.92. If two orders of bacon cost \$3.96, what does one pancake cost? B

A \$0.96 C \$1.98
B \$1.47 D \$2.94

71. GRIDDED RESPONSE If quadrilateral $ABCD$ is a kite, what is $m\angle C$? 76

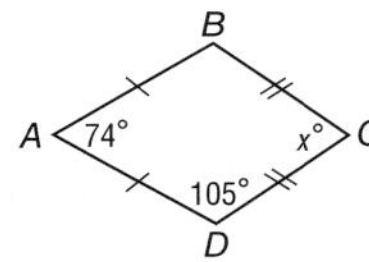

72. Which figure can serve as a counterexample to the conjecture below? J

If the diagonals of a quadrilateral are congruent, then the quadrilateral is a rectangle.

F square H parallelogram
G rhombus J isosceles trapezoid

73. SAT/ACT In the figure below, what is the value of x? B

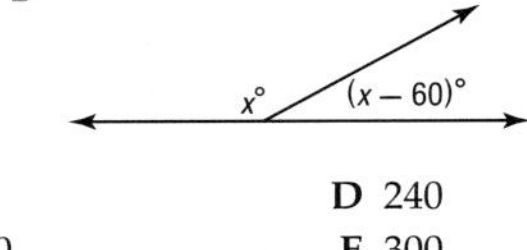

A 60 D 240
B 120 E 300
C 180

Spiral Review

ALGEBRA Quadrilateral *DFGH* is a rhombus. Find each value or measure. (Lesson 6-5)

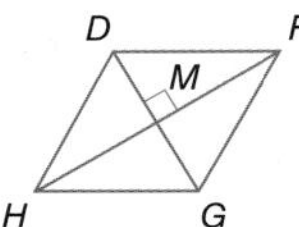

74. If $m\angle FGH = 118$, find $m\angle MHG$. 31

75. If $DM = 4x - 3$ and $MG = x + 6$, find DG. 18

76. If $DF = 10$, find FG. 10

77. If $HM = 12$ and $HD = 15$, find MG. 9

COORDINATE GEOMETRY Graph each quadrilateral with the given vertices. Determine whether the figure is a rectangle. Justify your answer using the indicated formula. (Lesson 6-4)

78. $A(4, 2)$, $B(-4, 1)$, $C(-3, -5)$, $D(5, -4)$; Distance Formula 78, 79. See margin

79. $J(0, 7)$, $K(-8, 6)$, $L(-7, 0)$, $M(1, 1)$; Slope Formula

80. BASEBALL A batter hits the ball to the third baseman and begins to run toward first base. At the same time, the runner on first base runs toward second base. If the third baseman wants to throw the ball to the nearest base, to which base should he throw? Explain. (Lesson 5-3)

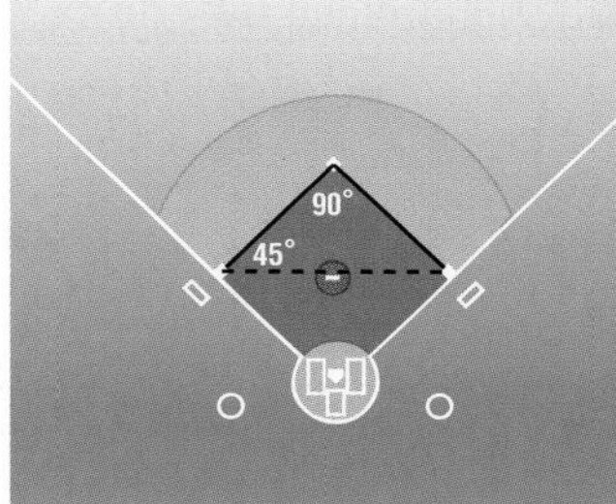

81. PROOF Write a two-column proof. (Lesson 4-5) 80, 81. See margin.

Given: $\angle CMF \cong \angle EMF$,
$\angle CFM \cong \angle EFM$
Prove: $\triangle DMC \cong \triangle DME$

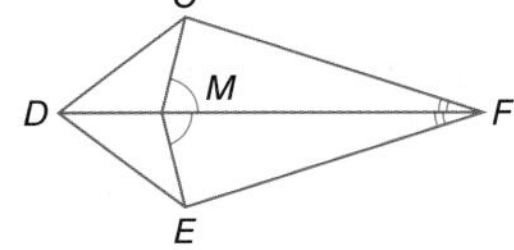

Skills Review

Write an expression for the slope of each segment given the coordinates and endpoints.

82. $(x, 4y)$, $(-x, 4y)$ 0

83. $(-x, 5x)$, $(0, 6x)$ 1

84. (y, x), (y, y) undefined

80. Second base; the angle opposite the side from third base to second base is smaller than the angle opposite the side from third to first. Therefore, the distance from third to second is shorter than the distance from third to first.

CHAPTER 6 Study Guide and Review

Study Guide

KeyConcepts

Angles of Polygons (Lesson 6-1)

- The sum of the measures of the interior angles of a polygon is given by the formula $S = (n - 2)180$.
- The sum of the measures of the exterior angles of a convex polygon is 360.

Properties of Parallelograms (Lessons 6-2 and 6-3)

- Opposite sides are congruent and parallel.
- Opposite angles are congruent.
- Consecutive angles are supplementary.
- If a parallelogram has one right angle, it has four right angles.
- Diagonals bisect each other.

Properties of Rectangles, Rhombi, Squares, and Trapezoids (Lesson 6-4 through 6-6)

- A rectangle has all the properties of a parallelogram. Diagonals are congruent and bisect each other. All four angles are right angles.
- A rhombus has all the properties of a parallelogram. All sides are congruent. Diagonals are perpendicular. Each diagonal bisects a pair of opposite angles.
- A square has all the properties of a parallelogram, a rectangle, and a rhombus.
- In an isosceles trapezoid, both pairs of base angles are congruent and the diagonals are congruent.

FOLDABLES StudyOrganizer

Be sure the Key Concepts are noted in your Foldable.

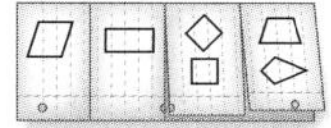

KeyVocabulary 

- base (p. 439)
- base angle (p. 439)
- diagonal (p. 393)
- isosceles trapezoid (p. 439)
- kite (p. 442)
- legs (p. 439)
- midsegment of a trapezoid (p. 441)
- parallelogram (p. 403)
- rectangle (p. 423)
- rhombus (p. 430)
- square (p. 431)
- trapezoid (p. 439)

VocabularyCheck

State whether each sentence is *true* or *false*. If *false*, replace the underlined word or phrase to make a true sentence.

1. No angles in an isosceles trapezoid are congruent. false, both pairs of base angles
2. If a parallelogram is a rectangle, then the diagonals are congruent. true
3. A midsegment of a trapezoid is a segment that connects any two nonconsecutive vertices. false, diagonal
4. The base of a trapezoid is one of the parallel sides. true
5. The diagonals of a rhombus are perpendicular. true
6. The diagonal of a trapezoid is the segment that connects the midpoints of the legs. false, midsegment
7. A rectangle is not always a parallelogram. false, is always
8. A quadrilateral with only one set of parallel sides is a parallelogram. false, trapezoid
9. A rectangle that is also a rhombus is a square. true
10. The leg of a trapezoid is one of the parallel sides. false, nonparallel

FOLDABLES StudyOrganizer

Dinah Zike's Foldables®

Have students look through the chapter to make sure they have included examples in their Foldables for each tab. Suggest that students keep their Foldables handy while completing the Study Guide and Review pages. Point out that their Foldables can serve as a quick review tool for studying for the Chapter Test.

Formative Assessment

KeyVocabulary The page references after each word denote where that term was first introduced. If students have difficulty answering questions 1–10, remind them that they can use these page references to refresh their memories about the vocabulary terms.

Summative Assessment

Vocabulary Test, p. 48

Vocabulary Review

Vocabulary Review provides students the opportunity to check their understanding of important concepts and terminology in an online game format.

Additional Answers (p. 448)

81. **Given:** $\angle CMF \cong \angle EMF$, $\angle CFM \cong \angle EFM$
Prove: $\triangle DMC \cong \triangle DME$

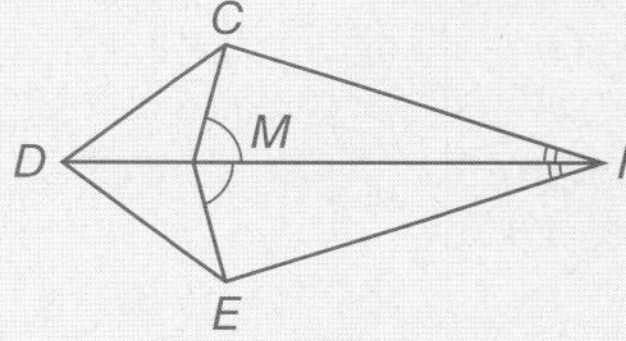

Proof:

Statements (Reasons)

1. $\angle CMF \cong \angle EMF$, $\angle CFM \cong \angle EFM$ (Given)
2. $\overline{MF} \cong \overline{MF}$, $\overline{DM} \cong \overline{DM}$ (Reflexive Property)
3. $\triangle CMF \cong \triangle EMF$ (ASA)
4. $\overline{CM} \cong \overline{EM}$ (CPCTC)
5. $\angle DMC$ and $\angle CMF$ are supplementary and $\angle DME$ and $\angle EMF$ are supplementary. (Supplement Th.)
6. $\angle DMC \cong \angle DME$ (⦞ suppl. to ≅ ⦞ are ≅.)
7. $\triangle DMC \cong \triangle DME$ (SAS)

Lesson-by-Lesson Review

Intervention If the given examples are not sufficient to review the topics covered by the questions, remind students that the lesson references tell them where to review that topic in their textbook.

Two-Day Option Have students complete the Lesson-by-Lesson Review. Then you can use eAssessment to customize another review worksheet that practices all the objectives of this chapter or only the objectives on which your students need more help.

Additional Answers

20. $x = 5, y = 12$
21. $x = 37, y = 6$
22. Sample answer: If both pairs of opposite sides are the same length or if one pair of opposite sides is congruent and parallel, then the shapes are parallelograms. The shapes can also be parallelograms if both pairs of opposite angles are congruent or if the diagonals bisect each other.

CHAPTER 6 Study Guide and Review *Continued*

Lesson-by-Lesson Review

6-1 Angles of Polygons

Find the sum of the measures of the interior angles of each convex polygon.

11. decagon 1440
12. 15-gon 2340
13. **SNOWFLAKES** The snowflake decoration at the right suggests a regular hexagon. Find the sum of the measures of the interior angles of the hexagon. 720

The measure of an interior angle of a regular polygon is given. Find the number of sides in the polygon.

14. 135 8
15. ≈166.15 26

Example 1

Find the sum of the measures of the interior angles of a convex 22-gon.

$m = (n - 2)180$	Write an equation.
$= (22 - 2)180$	Substitution
$= 20 \cdot 180$	Subtract.
$= 3600$	Multiply.

Example 2

The measure of an interior angle of a regular polygon is 157.5. Find the number of sides in the polygon.

$157.5n = (n - 2)180$	Write an equation.
$157.5n = 180n - 360$	Distributive Property
$-22.5n = -360$	Subtract.
$n = 16$	Divide.

The polygon has 16 sides.

6-2 Parallelograms

Use ▱*ABCD* to find each measure.

16. $m\angle ADC$ 65°
17. *AD* 18
18. *AB* 12
19. $m\angle BCD$ 115°

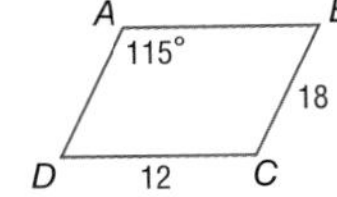

ALGEBRA Find the value of each variable in each parallelogram. 20, 21. See margin.

20.

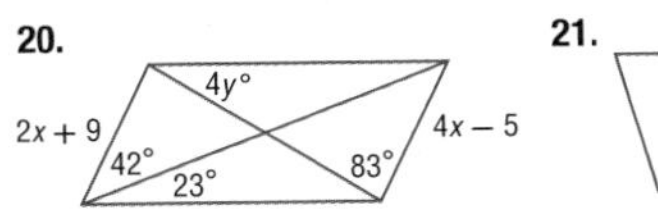

21.

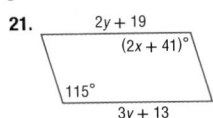

22. **DESIGN** What type of information is needed to determine whether the shapes that make up the stained glass window below are parallelograms? See margin.

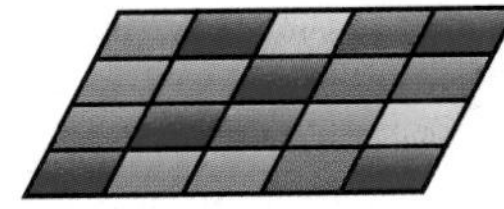

Example 3

ALGEBRA If *KLMN* is a parallelogram, find the value of the indicated variable.

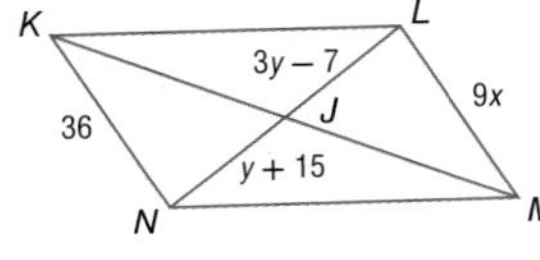

a. *x*

$\overline{KN} \cong \overline{LM}$	Opp. sides of a ▱ are ≅.
$KN = LM$	Definition of congruence
$36 = 9x$	Substitution
$4 = x$	Divide.

b. *y*

$\overline{NJ} \cong \overline{JL}$	Diag. of a ▱ bisect each other.
$NJ = JL$	Definition of congruence
$y + 15 = 3y - 7$	Substitution
$-2y = -22$	Subtract.
$y = 11$	Divide.

6-3 Tests for Parallelograms

Determine whether each quadrilateral is a parallelogram. Justify your answer. 23, 24. See margin.

23.

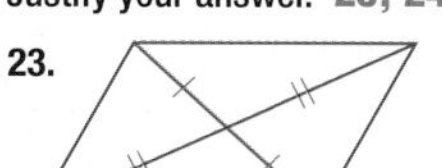

24.

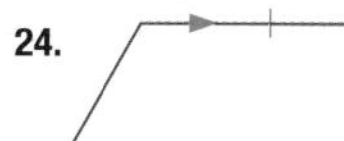

25. PROOF Write a two-column proof. See margin.

Given: ▱$ABCD$, $\overline{AE} \cong \overline{CF}$

Prove: Quadrilateral $EBFD$ is a parallelogram.

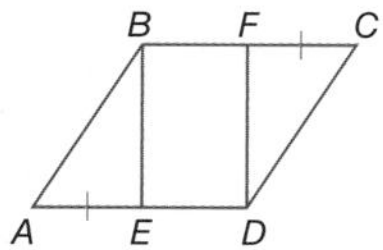

ALGEBRA Find x and y so that the quadrilateral is a parallelogram. 26, 27. See margin.

26.

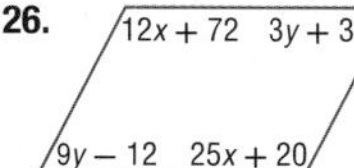

27.

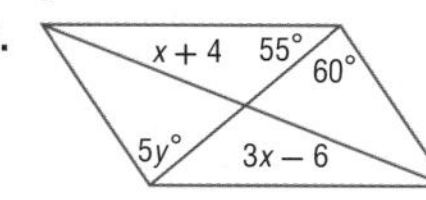

Example 4

If $TP = 4x + 2$, $QP = 2y - 6$, $PS = 5y - 12$, and $PR = 6x - 4$, find x and y so that the quadrilateral is a parallelogram.

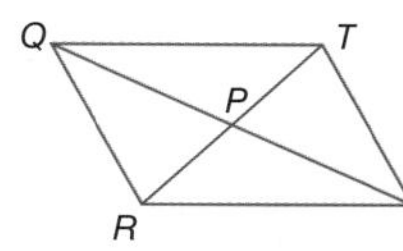

Find x such that $\overline{TP} \cong \overline{PR}$ and y such that $\overline{QP} \cong \overline{PS}$.

$TP = PR$	Definition of $\cong$
$4x + 2 = 6x - 4$	Substitution
$-2x = -6$	Subtract.
$x = 3$	Divide.
$QP = PS$	Definition of $\cong$
$2y - 6 = 5y - 12$	Substitution
$-3y = -6$	Subtract.
$y = 2$	Divide.

6-4 Rectangles

28. PARKING The lines of the parking space shown below are parallel. How wide is the space (in inches)? 60 in.

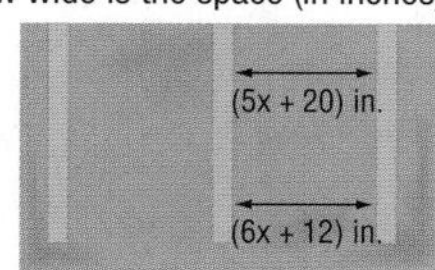

ALGEBRA Quadrilateral $EFGH$ is a rectangle.

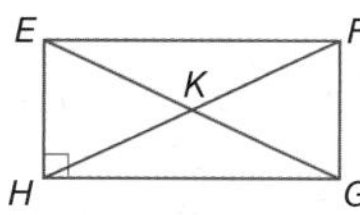

29. If $m\angle FEG = 57$, find $m\angle GEH$. 33

30. If $m\angle HGE = 13$, find $m\angle FGE$. 77

31. If $FK = 32$ feet, find EG. 64

32. Find $m\angle HEF + m\angle EFG$. 180

33. If $EF = 4x - 6$ and $HG = x + 3$, find EF. 6

Example 5

ALGEBRA Quadrilateral $ABCD$ is a rectangle. If $m\angle ADB = 4x + 8$ and $m\angle DBA = 6x + 12$, find x.

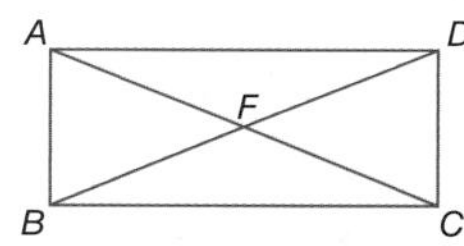

$ABCD$ is a rectangle, so $m\angle ABC = 90$. Since the opposite sides of a rectangle are parallel, and the alternate interior angles of parallel lines are congruent, $\angle DBC \cong \angle ADB$ and $m\angle DBC = m\angle ADB$.

$m\angle DBC + m\angle DBA = 90$	Angle Addition
$m\angle ADB + m\angle DBA = 90$	Substitution
$4x + 8 + 6x + 12 = 90$	Substitution
$10x + 20 = 90$	Add.
$10x = 70$	Subtract.
$x = 7$	Divide.

Additional Answers

23. yes, Theorem 6.11

24. yes, Theorem 6.12

25. Given: ▱$ABCD$, $\overline{AE} \cong \overline{CF}$

Prove: Quadrilateral $EBFD$ is a parallelogram.

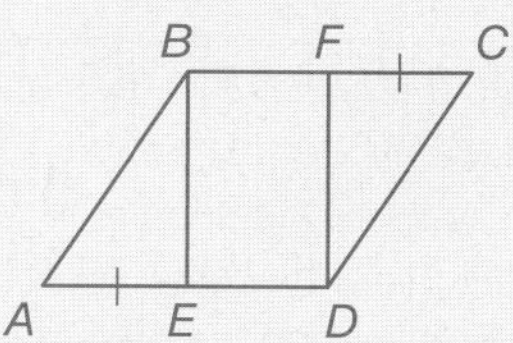

1. $ABCD$ is a parallelogram, $\overline{AE} \cong \overline{CF}$ (Given)
2. $AE = CF$ (Def. of $\cong$ segs)
3. $\overline{BC} \cong \overline{AD}$ (Opp. sides of a ▱ are $\cong$)
4. $BC = AD$ (Def. of $\cong$ segs)
5. $BC = BF + CF$, $AD = AE + ED$ (Seg. Add. Post.)
6. $BF + CF = AE + ED$ (Subst.)
7. $BF + AE = AE + ED$ (Subst.)
8. $BF = ED$ (Subt. Prop.)
9. $\overline{BF} \cong \overline{ED}$ (Def. of $\cong$ segs)
10. $\overline{BF} \parallel \overline{ED}$ (Def. of ▱)
11. Quadrilateral $EBFD$ is a parallelogram. (If one pair of opposite sides is parallel and congruent then it is a parallelogram.)

26. $x = 4$, $y = 8$

27. $x = 5$, $y = 12$

connectED.mcgraw-hill.com 451

Anticipation Guide

Have students complete the Chapter 6 Anticipation Guide and discuss how their responses have changed now that they have completed Chapter 6.

Additional Answers

43a. Sample answer: The legs of the trapezoids are part of the diagonals of the square. The diagonals of a square bisect opposite angles, so each base angle of a trapezoid measures 45°. One pair of sides is parallel and the base angles are congruent.

43b. $16 + 8\sqrt{2} \approx 27.3$ in.

CHAPTER 6 Study Guide and Review *Continued*

6-5 Rhombi and Squares

ALGEBRA *ABCD* is a rhombus. If $EB = 9$, $AB = 12$ and $m\angle ABD = 55$, find each measure.

34. AE 7.9

35. $m\angle BDA$ 55

36. CE 7.9

37. $m\angle ACB$ 35

38. LOGOS A car company uses the symbol shown at the right for their logo. If the inside space of the logo is a rhombus, what is the length of FJ? 2.5 cm

F, G, H, J, 2.5 cm

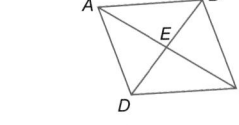

39. Rectangle, rhombus, square; all sides are ≅, consecutive are ⊥.

COORDINATE GEOMETRY Given each set of vertices, determine whether ▱*QRST* is a *rhombus*, a *rectangle*, or a *square*. List all that apply. Explain.

39. $Q(12, 0)$, $R(6, -6)$, $S(0, 0)$, $T(6, 6)$

40. $Q(-2, 4)$, $R(5, 6)$, $S(12, 4)$, $T(5, 2)$

40. Rhombus; all sides are ≅, diagonals are ⊥.

Example 6

The diagonals of rhombus *QRST* intersect at *P*. Use the information to find each measure or value.

a. ALGEBRA If $QT = x + 7$ and $TS = 2x - 9$, find x.

$\overline{QT} \cong \overline{TS}$	Def. of rhombus
$QT = TS$	Def. of congruence
$x + 7 = 2x - 9$	Substitution
$-x = -16$	Subtract.
$x = 16$	Divide.

b. If $m\angle QTS = 76$, find $m\angle TSP$.

$\overline{TR}$ bisects $\angle QTS$. Therefore, $m\angle PTS = \frac{1}{2}m\angle QTS$. So $m\angle PTS = \frac{1}{2}(76)$ or 38. Since the diagonals of a rhombus are perpendicular, $m\angle TPS = 90$.

$m\angle PTS + m\angle TPS + m\angle TSP = 180$	△ Sum Thm.
$38 + 90 + m\angle TSP = 180$	Substitution
$128 + m\angle TSP = 180$	Add.
$m\angle TSP = 52$	Subtract.

6-6 Trapezoids and Kites

Find each measure.

41. GH 19.2

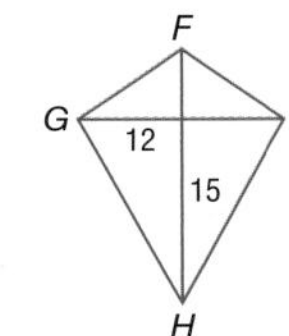

42. $m\angle Z$ 68

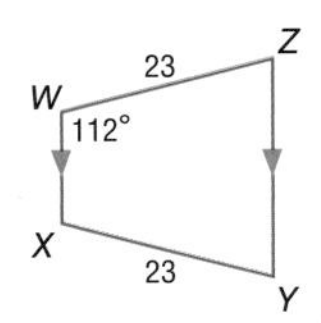

43. DESIGN Renee designed the square tile as an art project.

a. Describe a way to determine if the trapezoids in the design are isosceles. See margin.

b. If the perimeter of the tile is 48 inches and the perimeter of the red square is 16 inches, what is the perimeter of one of the trapezoids? See margin.

Example 7

If *QRST* is a kite, find $m\angle RST$.

Since $\angle Q \cong \angle S$, $m\angle Q = m\angle S$. Write and solve an equation to find $m\angle S$.

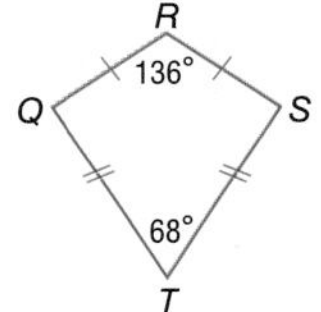

$m\angle Q + m\angle R + m\angle S + m\angle T = 360$	Polygon Int. ∠s Sum Thm
$m\angle Q + 136 + m\angle S + 68 = 360$	Substitution
$2m\angle S + 204 = 360$	Simplify.
$2m\angle S = 156$	Subtract.
$m\angle S = 78$	Divide.

Additional Answers (Practice Test)

3a. Sample answer: She should measure the angles at the vertices to see if they are 90 or she can check to see if the diagonals are congruent and perpendicular.

17. Sample answer: Yes. If it is a rectangle, the diagonals are congruent.

CHAPTER 6 Practice Test

Find the sum of the measures of the interior angles of each convex polygon.

1. hexagon **720**
2. 16-gon **2520**

3. **ART** Jen is making a frame to stretch a canvas over for a painting. She nailed four pieces of wood together at what she believes will be the four vertices of a square.

   a. How can she be sure that the canvas will be a square? **See margin.**

   b. If the canvas has the dimensions shown below, what are the missing measures? **$x = 2$ ft, $y = 90$**

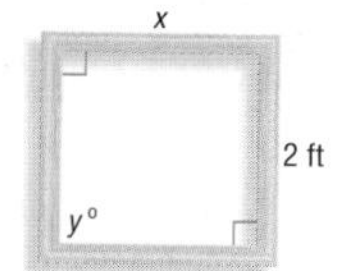

Quadrilateral *ABCD* is an isosceles trapezoid.

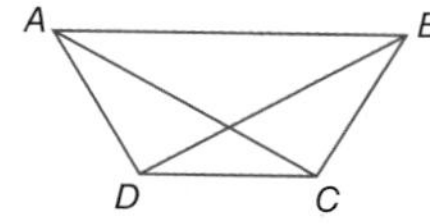

4. Which angle is congruent to $\angle C$? **$\angle D$**
5. Which side is parallel to $\overline{AB}$? **$\overline{DC}$**
6. Which segment is congruent to $\overline{AC}$? **$\overline{BD}$**

The measure of the interior angles of a regular polygon is given. Find the number of sides in the polygon.

7. 900 **7**
8. 1980 **13**
9. 2880 **18**
10. 5400 **32**

11. **MULTIPLE CHOICE** If *QRST* is a parallelogram, what is the value of x? **C**

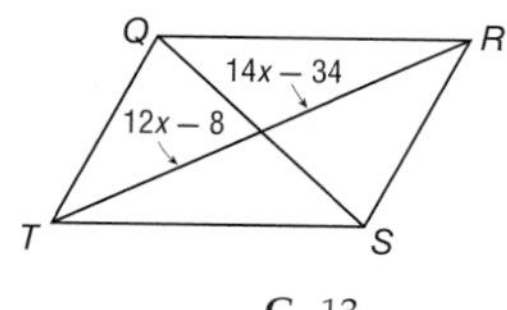

A 11
B 12
C 13
D 14

If *CDFG* is a kite, find each measure.

12. *GF* **5**
13. $m\angle D$ **122**

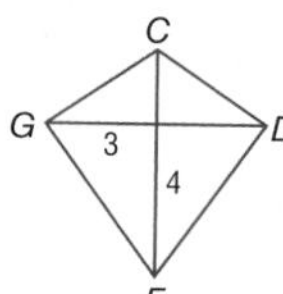

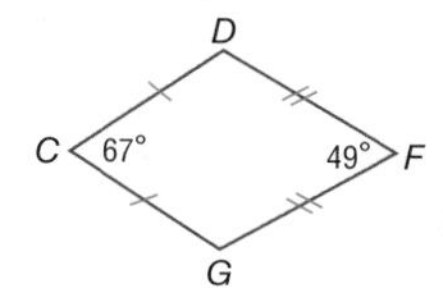

ALGEBRA Quadrilateral *MNOP* is a rhombus. Find each value or measure.

14. $m\angle MRN$ **90**
15. If $PR = 12$, find RN. **12**
16. If $m\angle PON = 124$, find $m\angle POM$. **62**

M N R P O

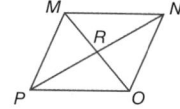

17. **CONSTRUCTION** The Smiths are building an addition to their house. Mrs. Smith is cutting an opening for a new window. If she measures to see that the opposite sides are congruent and that the diagonal measures are congruent, can Mrs. Smith be sure that the window opening is rectangular? Explain. **See margin.**

Use ▱*JKLM* to find each measure.

18. $m\angle JML$ **109**
19. *JK* **6**
20. $m\angle KLM$ **71**

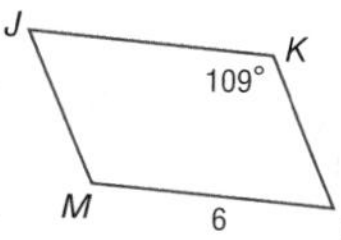

ALGEBRA Quadrilateral *DEFG* is a rectangle.

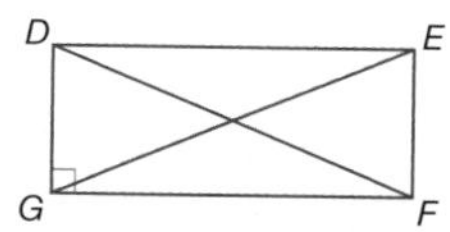

21. If $DF = 2(x + 5) - 7$ and $EG = 3(x - 2)$, find *EG*. **21**
22. If $m\angle EDF = 5x - 3$ and $m\angle DFG = 3x + 7$, find $m\angle EDF$. **22**
23. If $DE = 14 + 2x$ and $GF = 4(x - 3) + 6$, find *GF*. **34**

Determine whether each quadrilateral is a parallelogram. Justify your answer. **24, 25. See margin.**

24.

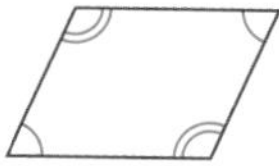

25.

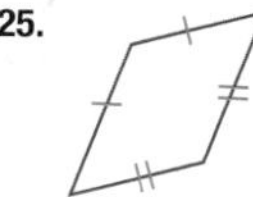

Summative Assessment

Use these alternate leveled chapter tests to differentiate assessment for your students.

Leveled Chapter 6 Tests

Form	Type	Level	Page(s)
1	MC	AL	49–50
2A	MC	OL	51–52
2B	MC	OL	53–54
2C	FR	OL	55–56
2D	FR	OL	57–58
3	FR	BL	59–60
Vocabulary Test			48
Extended-Response Test			61

MC = multiple-choice questions
FR = free-response questions

eAssessment Customize and create multiple versions of your chapter test and their answer keys. All of the questions from the leveled chapter tests in the *Chapter 6 Resource Masters* are also available in eAssessment.

Additional Answers

24. Yes, opposite angles are congruent.
25. No, opposite sides are not congruent.

InterventionPlanner

TIER 1 On Level OL

If students miss about 25% of the exercises or less,

Then choose a resource:

SE Lessons 6-4, 6-5 and 6-6

Skills Practice, pp. 25, 33, and 39

connectED.mcgraw-hill.com Self-Check Quiz

TIER 2 Strategic Intervention AL approaching grade level

If students miss about 50% of the exercises,

Then choose a resource:

Study Guide and Intervention, Chapter 6

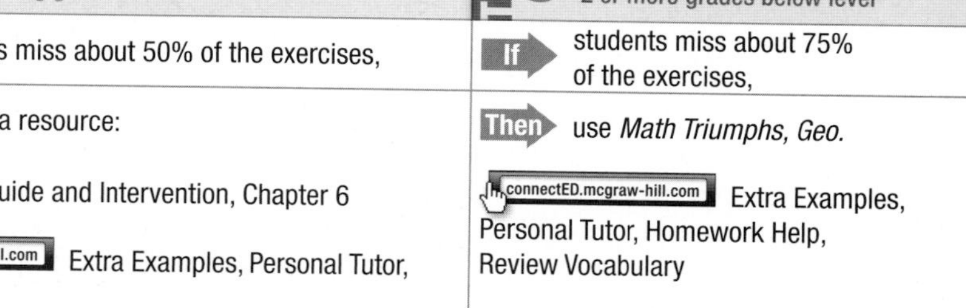
connectED.mcgraw-hill.com Extra Examples, Personal Tutor, Homework Help

TIER 3 Intensive Intervention 2 or more grades below level

If students miss about 75% of the exercises,

Then use *Math Triumphs, Geo.*

connectED.mcgraw-hill.com Extra Examples, Personal Tutor, Homework Help, Review Vocabulary

1 Focus

Objective Learn how to apply geometric definitions and properties to solve problems.

2 Teach

Scaffolding Questions

Ask:

- How can using definitions and properties of geometry help you to solve problems? Sample answer: Definitions and properties can be used to solve for unknowns in a problem.
- How can you identify what definitions and properties to use from the question? Sample answer: You can look for key words such as "sum", "perimeter", "angle measure", or "quadrilateral" to determine whether a definition or property can be used to help solve the problem.
- What other information should you collect when you begin to solve a problem? Sample answer: When solving a problem, you should write down any values, angle measures, or equations that are given in the problem.

CHAPTER 6 Preparing for Standardized Tests

Apply Definitions and Properties

Many geometry problems on standardized tests require the application of definitions and properties in order to solve them. Use this section to practice applying definitions to help you solve extended-response test items.

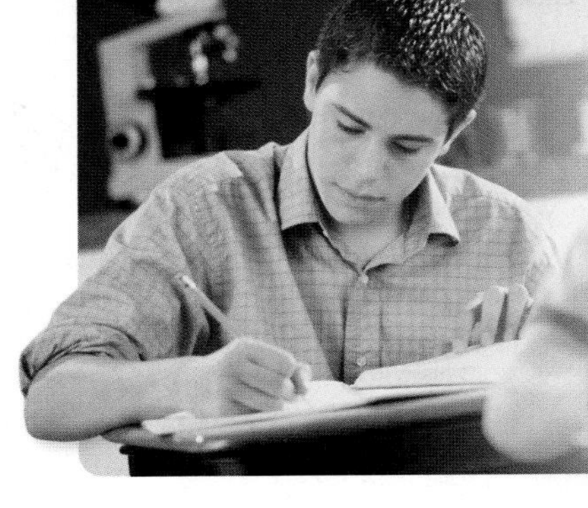

Strategies for Applying Definitions and Properties

Step 1

Read the problem statement carefully.

- Determine what you are being asked to solve.
- Study any figures given in the problem.
- **Ask yourself:** What principles or properties of this figure can I apply to solve the problem?

Step 2

Solve the problem.

- Identify any definitions or geometric concepts you can use to help you find the unknowns in the problem.
- Use definitions and properties of figures to set up and solve an equation.

Step 3

- Check your answer.

Standardized Test Example

Read the problem. Identify what you need to know. Then use the information in the problem to solve. Show your work.

A performing arts group is building a theater in the round for upcoming productions. The stage will be a regular octagon with a perimeter of 76 feet.

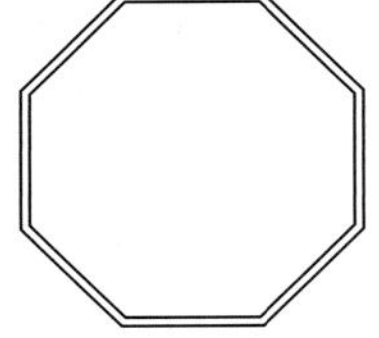

a. What length should each board be to form the sides of the stage?

b. What angle should the end of each board be cut so that they will fit together properly to form the stage? Explain.

Read the problem carefully. You are told that the boards form a regular octagon with a perimeter of 76 feet. You need to find the length of each board and the angle that they should be cut to fit together properly.

To find the length of each board, divide the perimeter by the number of boards.

$76 \div 8 = 9.5$

So, each board should be 9.5 feet, or 9 feet 6 inches, long.

Use the property of the interior angle sum of convex polygons to find the measure of an interior angle of a regular octagon. First find the sum S of the interior angles.

$$S = (n - 2) \cdot 180$$
$$= (8 - 2) \cdot 180$$
$$= 1080$$

So, the measure of an interior angle of a regular octagon is $1080 \div 8$, or 135°. Since two boards are used to form each vertex of the stage, the end of each board should be cut at an angle of $135 \div 2$, or 67.5°.

Exercises

Read each problem. Identify what you need to know. Then use the information in the problem to solve. Show your work.

1. $\overline{RS}$ is the midsegment of trapezoid $MNOP$. What is the length of $\overline{RS}$? **D**

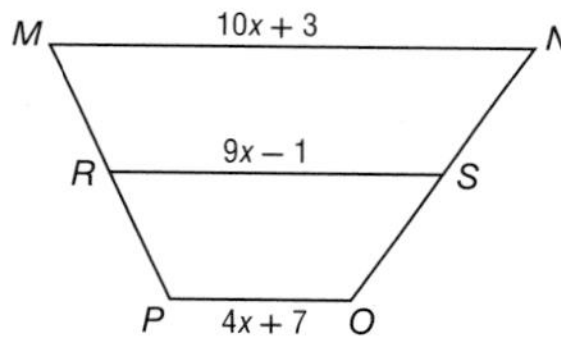

A 14 units
B 19 units
C 23 units
D 26 units

2. If $\overline{AB} \parallel \overline{DC}$, find x. **J**

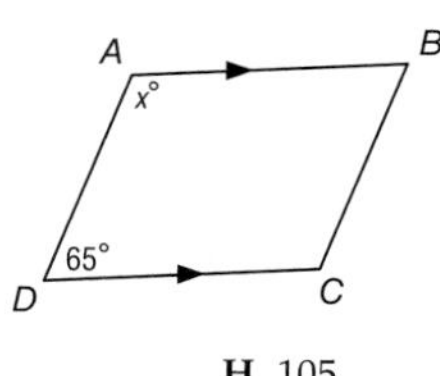

F 32.5
G 65
H 105
J 115

3. Use the graph shown below to answer each question. **a, b. See margin.**

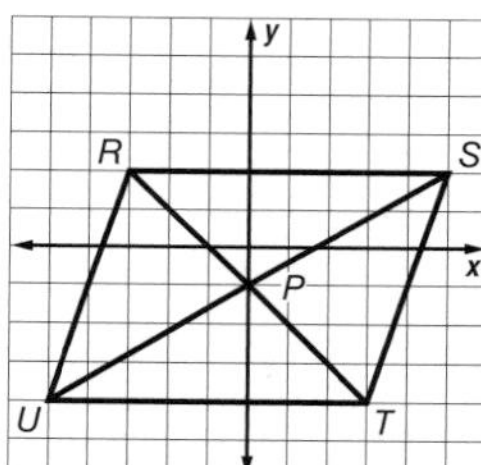

a. Do the diagonals of quadrilateral $RSTU$ bisect each other? Use the Distance Formula to verify your answer.

b. What type of quadrilateral is $RSTU$? Explain using the properties and/or definitions of this type of quadrilateral.

4. What is the sum of the measures of the exterior angles of a regular octagon? **C**

A 45
B 135
C 360
D 1080

Additional Example

A trampoline is designed in the shape of a regular hexagon. The perimeter of the trampoline is 35 feet.

a. What is the length of each side of the trampoline? $5\frac{5}{6}$ feet

b. What is the measure of the angle formed in by each corner of the trampoline? 120

3 Assess

Use Exercises 1–4 to assess students' understanding.

Additional Answers

3a. Sample answer: Yes; because $PS = \sqrt{34}$, $UP = \sqrt{34}$, $RP = 3\sqrt{2}$, and $PT = 3\sqrt{2}$, the diagonals bisect each other.

3b. Sample answer: Parallelogram; if the diagonals of a quadrilateral bisect each other, the figure is a parallelogram.

connectED.mcgraw-hill.com 455

Diagnose Student Errors

Survey student responses for each item. Class trends may indicate common errors and misconceptions.

1. A chose the first *true* statement
B statement is true
C applied definition incorrectly
D correct

2. F did not choose *most appropriate* term
G correct
H incorrect use of definition
J guess

3. A arithmetic error
B arithmetic error
C arithmetic error
D correct

4. F incorrect formula used
G correct
H incorrect formula used
J incorrect formula used

5. A difference between angle measure and 90
B correct
C guess
D identifies angles as congruent

6. F arithmetic error
G correct
H arithmetic error
J arithmetic error

7. A misunderstanding of definition
B misunderstanding of definition
C correct
D misunderstanding of definition

CHAPTER 6 Standardized Test Practice

Cumulative, Chapters 1 through 6

Multiple Choice

Read each question. Then fill in the correct answer on the answer document provided by your teacher or on a sheet of paper.

1. If $a \parallel b$, which of the following might not be true? D

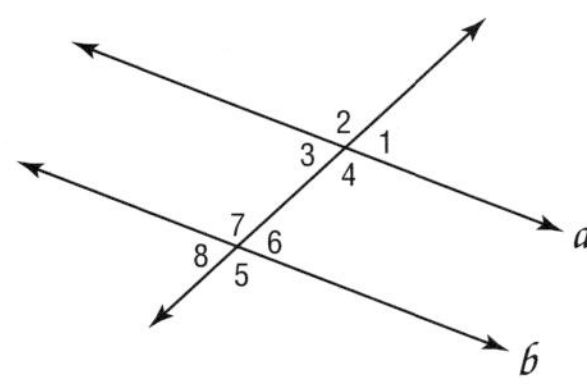

A $\angle 1 \cong \angle 3$
B $\angle 4 \cong \angle 7$
C $\angle 2 \cong \angle 5$
D $\angle 8 \cong \angle 2$

2. Classify the triangle below according to its angle measures. Choose the most appropriate term. G

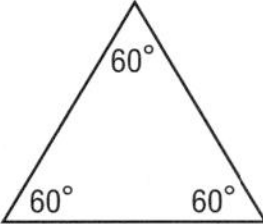

F acute
G equiangular
H obtuse
J right

3. Solve for x in parallelogram $RSTU$. D

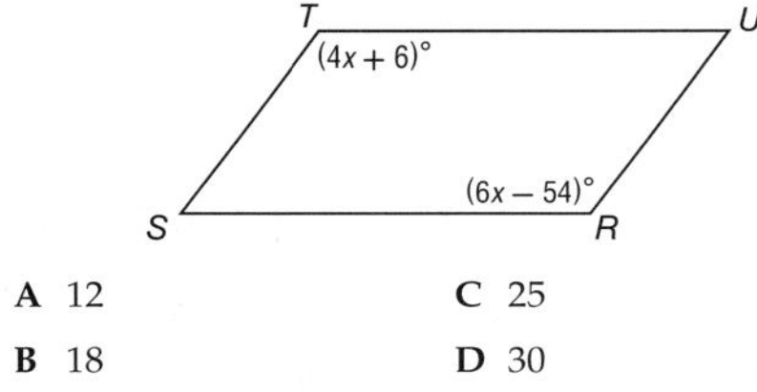

A 12
B 18
C 25
D 30

Test-Taking Tip

Question 3 Use the properties of parallelograms to solve the problem. Opposite angles are congruent.

4. What is the measure of an interior angle of a regular pentagon? G

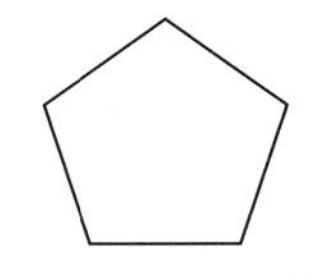

F 96
G 108
H 120
J 135

5. Quadrilateral $ABCD$ is a rhombus. If $m\angle BCD = 120$, find $m\angle DAC$. B

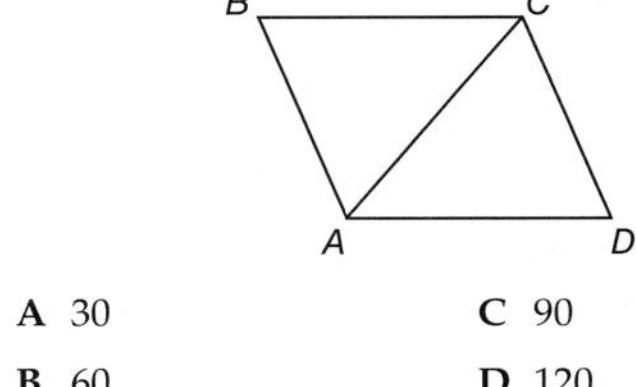

A 30
B 60
C 90
D 120

6. What is the value of x in the figure below? G

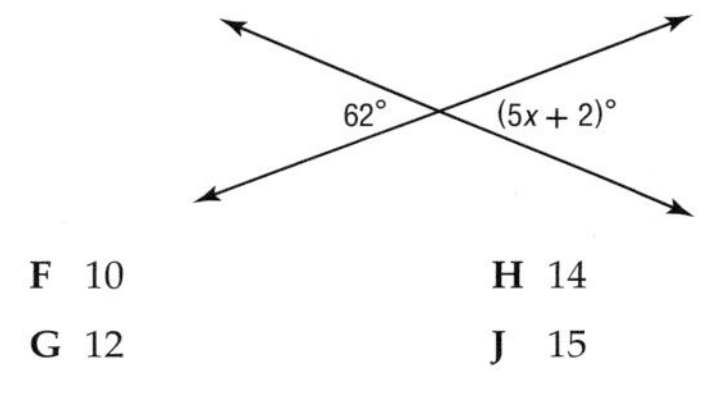

F 10
G 12
H 14
J 15

7. Which of the following statements is true? C

A All rectangles are squares.
B All rhombi are squares.
C All rectangles are parallelograms.
D All parallelograms are rectangles.

Short Response/Gridded Response

Record your answers on the answer sheet provided by your teacher or a sheet of paper.

8. **GRIDDED RESPONSE** The posts for Nancy's gazebo form a regular hexagon. What is the measure of the angle formed at each corner of the gazebo? 120

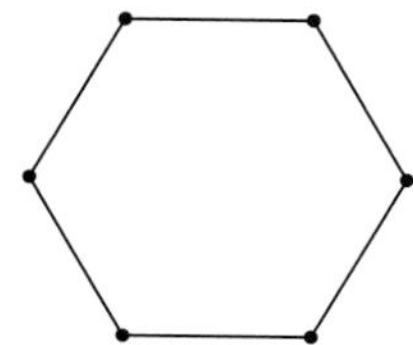

9. What are the coordinates of point P, the fourth vertex of an isosceles trapezoid? Show your work. (6, −3)

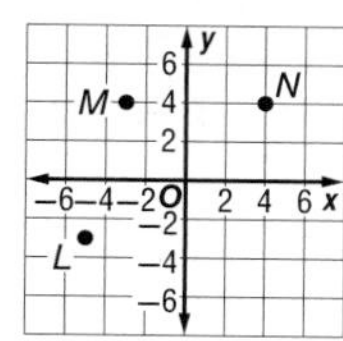

10. What do you know about a parallelogram if its diagonals are perpendicular? Explain. Sample answer: The parallelogram is a square or a rhombus.

11. Determine whether the stated conclusion is valid based on the given information below. If not, write *invalid*. Explain your reasoning. Sample answer: The conclusion is valid; Law of Detachment.

Given: If a number is divisible by 9, then the number is divisible by 3. The number 144 is divisible by 9.

Conclusion: The number 144 is divisible by 3.

12. **GRIDDED RESPONSE** Solve for x in the figure below. Round to the nearest tenth if necessary. 3

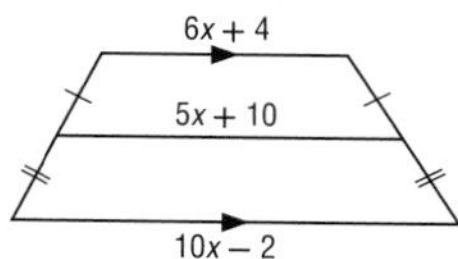

13. What are the coordinates of the circumcenter of the triangle below? (1, 2)

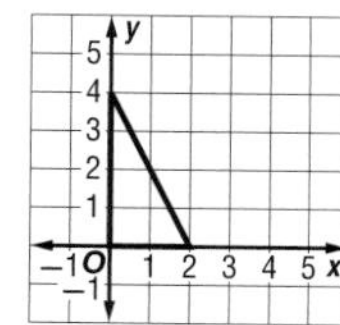

Extended Response

Record your answers on a sheet of paper. Show your work.

14. Determine whether you can prove each figure is a parallelogram. If not, tell what additional information would be needed to prove that it is a parallelogram. Explain your reasoning.

a. 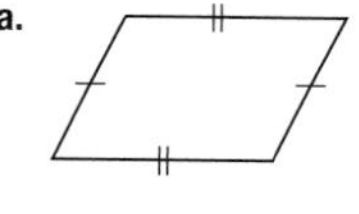

a–c. See margin.

b. 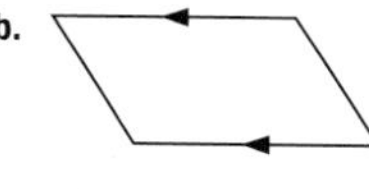

c. 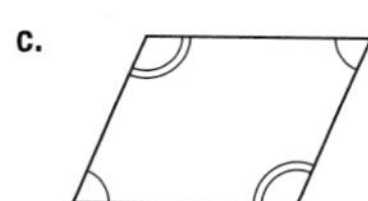

Need ExtraHelp?

If you missed Question...	1	2	3	4	5	6	7	8	9	10	11	12	13	14
Go to Lesson...	3-2	4-1	6-2	6-1	6-5	2-8	6-5	6-1	6-6	6-5	2-4	6-6	5-1	6-3

Formative Assessment

You can use these pages to benchmark student progress.

Standardized Test Practice, pp. 62–64

Answer Sheet Practice

Have students simulate taking a standardized test by recording their answers on a practice recording sheet.

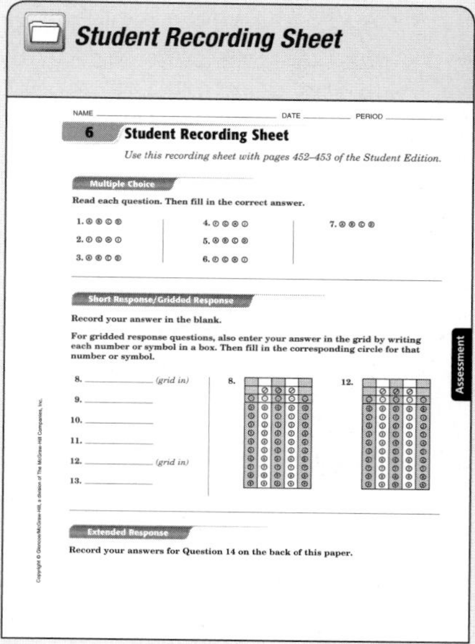

Homework Option

Get Ready for Chapter 7 Assign students the exercises on page 459 as homework to assess whether they possess the prerequisite skills needed for the next chapter.

eAssessment Create practice tests that align to your state standards, the Common Core State Standards, and other national standards such as TIMSS and NAEP.

Additional Answers

14a. Yes, opposite sides are congruent, so the figure is a parallelogram.

14b. No, only one pair of opposite sides is parallel. You would have to show that either 1) the parallel sides are also congruent, or 2) the other pair of opposite sides is parallel.

14c. Yes, opposite angles are congruent, so the figure is a parallelogram.

Lesson 6-1

50. 30, 90, 60; By the Interior Angle Sum Theorem, the sum of the interior angles is 720. Since polygon *QRSTVX* is regular, there are 6 congruent angles. Each angle has a measure of 120. So, $m\angle XQR$ and $m\angle XVT = 120$. Since polygon *QRSTVX* is regular, $XQ = QR$. By the Isosceles $\triangle$ Theorem, $m\angle QXR \cong m\angle QRX$. The interior angles of a triangle add up to 180, so $m\angle QXR + m\angle QRX + m\angle XQR = 180$. By substitution, $a + a + 120 = 180$. So, $2a = 60$ and $a = 30$.

The $m\angle QRS = m\angle QRX + m\angle XRS$, by angle addition. By substitution, $120 = 30 + m\angle XRS$. From subtraction,

$m\angle XRS = 90$. So, $b = 90$. By SAS, $\triangle XVT \cong \triangle XQR$ and $\triangle XTS \cong \triangle XRS$. By angle addition, $m\angle VXQ = m\angle VXT + m\angle TXS + m\angle SXR + m\angle RXQ$. By substitution, $120 = 30 + m\angle TXS + m\angle SXR + 30$. So, $m\angle TXS + m\angle SXR = 60$ and since $m\angle TXS \cong m\angle SXR$ by CPCTC, $m\angle TXS = m\angle SXR = 30$. In $\triangle XTS$, $m\angle XTS + m\angle TSX + m\angle SXT = 180$. By substitution, $90 + c + 30 = 180$. So $c = 60$.

Lesson 6-2

25. Proof:

Statements (Reasons):

1. $\triangle ACD \cong \triangle CAB$ (Given)
2. $\angle ACD \cong \angle CAB$ (CPCTC)
3. $\angle DPC \cong \angle BPA$ (Vert. $\angle$s are $\cong$.)
4. $\overline{AB} \cong \overline{CD}$ (CPCTC)
5. $\triangle ABP \cong \triangle CDP$ (AAS)
6. $\overline{DP} \cong \overline{PB}$(CPCTC)

26. Proof:

Statements (Reasons)

1. ▱*GKLM* (Given)
2. $\overline{GK} \parallel \overline{ML}$, $\overline{GM} \parallel \overline{KL}$ (Opp. sides of a ▱ are $\parallel$.)
3. $\angle G$ and $\angle K$ are supplementary, $\angle K$ and $\angle L$ are supplementary, $\angle L$ and $\angle M$ are supplementary, and $\angle M$ and $\angle G$ are supplementary. (Cons. int. $\angle$s are suppl.)

27. Proof:

Statements (Reasons)

1. ▱*WXYZ* (Given)
2. $\overline{WX} \cong \overline{ZY}$, $\overline{WZ} \cong \overline{XY}$ (Opp. sides of a ▱ are $\cong$.)
3. $\angle ZWX \cong \angle XYZ$ (Opp. $\angle$s of a ▱ are $\cong$.)
4. $\triangle WXZ \cong \triangle YZX$ (SAS)

28. Proof:

Statements (Reasons)

1. ▱*PQRS* (Given)
2. Draw an auxiliary segment $\overline{PR}$ and label angles 1, 2, 3, and 4 as shown. (Diagonal of *PQRS*)
3. $\overline{PQ} \parallel \overline{SR}$, $\overline{PS} \parallel \overline{QR}$ (Opp. sides of a ▱ are $\parallel$.)
4. $\angle 1 \cong \angle 2$, and $\angle 3 \cong \angle 4$ (Alt. int. $\angle$s Thm.)
5. $\overline{PR} \cong \overline{RP}$ (Refl. Prop.)
6. $\triangle QPR \cong \triangle SRP$ (ASA)
7. $\overline{PQ} \cong \overline{RS}$, $\overline{QR} \cong \overline{SP}$ (CPCTC)

29. Proof: It is given that *ACDE* is a parallelogram. Since opposite sides of a parallelogram are congruent, $\overline{EA} \cong \overline{DC}$. By definition of a parallelogram, $\overline{EA} \parallel \overline{DC}$. $\angle AEB \cong \angle DCB$ and $\angle EAB \cong \angle CDB$ because alternate interior angles are congruent. $\triangle EBA \cong \triangle CBD$ by ASA. $\overline{EB} \cong \overline{BC}$ and $\overline{AB} \cong \overline{BD}$ by CPCTC. By the definition of segment bisector, $\overline{EC}$ bisects $\overline{AD}$ and $\overline{AD}$ bisects $\overline{EC}$.

Lesson 6-3 (Guided Practice)

2.

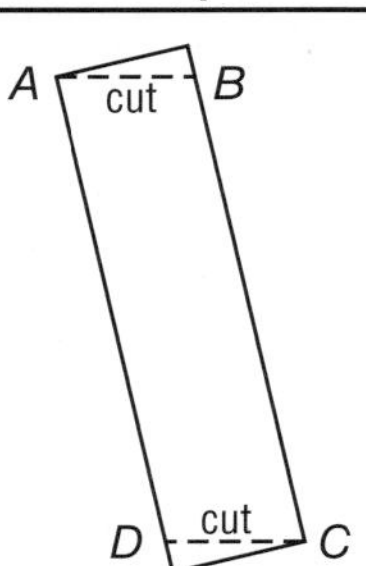

Since $AD = BC$, $\overline{AD} \cong \overline{BC}$. We are given that the sides of the bulletin board paper are parallel, so $\overline{AD} \parallel \overline{BC}$. So by Theorem 6.12, quadrilateral *ABCD* is a parallelogram. Since by definition opposite sides of a parallelogram are parallel, we know that $\overline{AB} \parallel \overline{DC}$.

Lesson 6-3

8. Given: *ABCD* is a parallelogram.
Prove: $\overline{AC}$ and $\overline{DB}$ bisect each other.

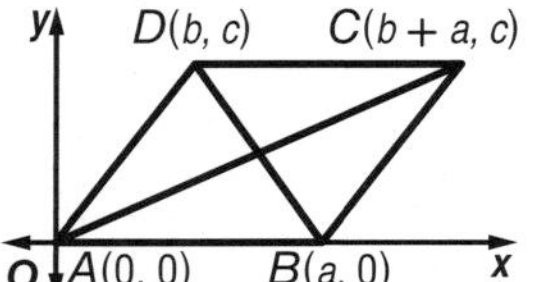

Proof:
midpoint of $\overline{AC}$

$$= \left(\frac{0 + (a + b)}{2}, \frac{0 + c}{2}\right)$$
$$= \left(\frac{a + b}{2}, \frac{c}{2}\right)$$

midpoint of $\overline{DB}$

$$= \left(\frac{a + b}{2}, \frac{0 + c}{2}\right)$$
$$= \left(\frac{a + b}{2}, \frac{c}{2}\right)$$

$\overline{AM} \cong \overline{MC}$ and $\overline{DM} \cong \overline{MB}$ by definition of midpoint so $\overline{AC}$ and $\overline{DB}$ bisect each other.

15.

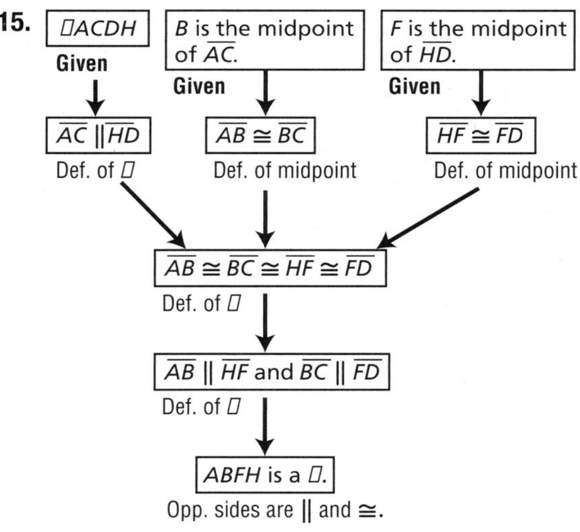

16. Given: *WXYZ* is a parallelogram, $\angle W \cong \angle X$, and *M* is the midpoint of $\overline{WX}$.

Prove: *ZMY* is an isosceles triangle.

Proof: Since *WXYZ* is a parallelogram, $\overline{WZ} \cong \overline{XY}$. *M* is the midpoint of $\overline{WX}$, so $\overline{WM} \cong \overline{MX}$. It is given that $\angle W \cong \angle X$, so by SAS $\triangle ZWM \cong \triangle YXM$. By CPCTC, $\overline{ZM} \cong \overline{YM}$. So, *ZMY* is an isosceles triangle, by the definition of an isosceles triangle.

17. Given: *ABEF* is a parallelogram; *BCDE* is a parallelogram.
Prove: *ACDF* is a parallelogram.

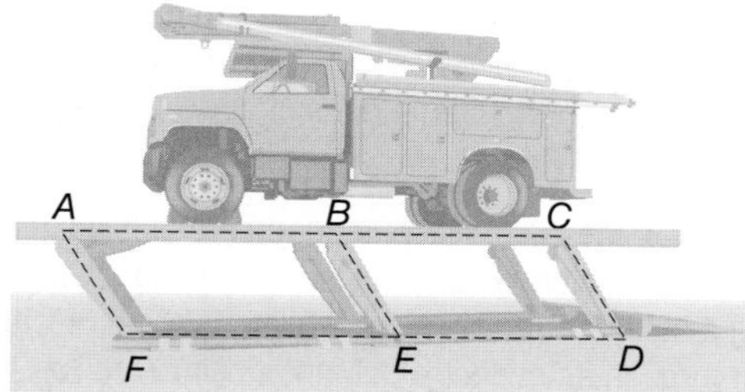

Proof:

Statements (Reasons)

1. *ABEF* is a parallelogram; *BCDE* is a parallelogram. (Given)
2. $\overline{AF} \cong \overline{BE}$, $\overline{BE} \cong \overline{CD}$, $\overline{AF} \parallel \overline{BE}$, $\overline{BE} \parallel \overline{CD}$ (Def. of ▱)
3. $\overline{AF} \cong \overline{CD}$, $\overline{AF} \parallel \overline{CD}$ (Trans. Prop.)
4. *ACDF* is a parallelogram. (If one pair of opp. sides is $\cong$ and $\parallel$, then the quad. is a ▱.)

24. Yes; slope of $\overline{AB} = \frac{1}{7}$ = slope of $\overline{CD}$. So, $\overline{AB} \parallel \overline{CD}$. Slope of $\overline{BC} = -6$ = slope of $\overline{AD}$. So, $\overline{BC} \parallel \overline{AD}$. Since both pairs of opposite sides are parallel, *ABCD* is a parallelogram.

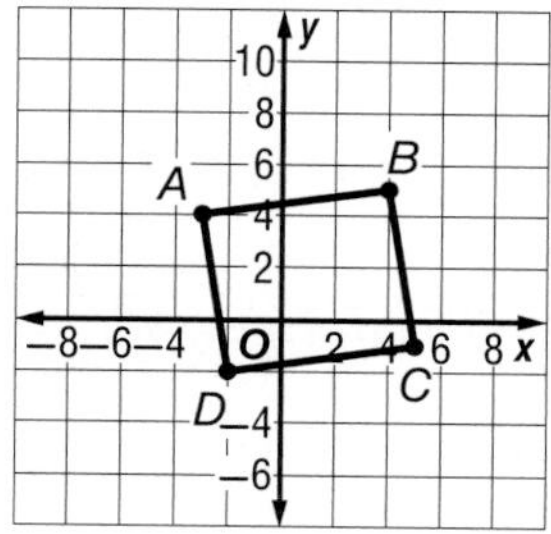

25. No; both pairs of opposite sides must be congruent. The distance between *K* and *L* is $\sqrt{53}$. The distance between *L* and *M* is $\sqrt{37}$. The distance between *M* and *J* is $\sqrt{50}$. The distance between *J* and *K* is $\sqrt{26}$. Since, both pairs of opposite sides are not congruent, *JKLM* is not a parallelogram.

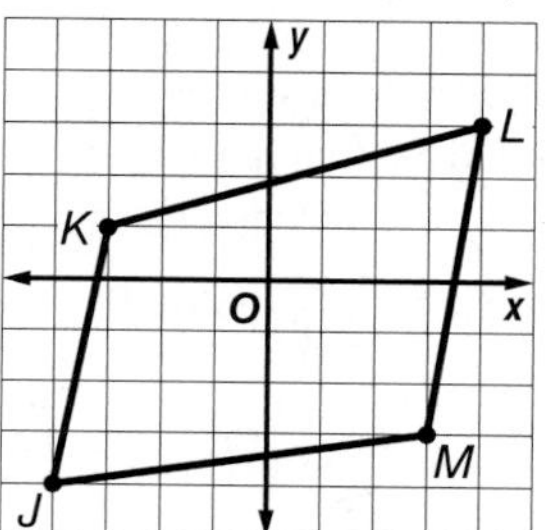

26. No; a pair of opposite sides must be parallel and congruent. Slope of $\overline{YV} = -\frac{2}{7}$, slope of $\overline{XW} - \frac{4}{7}$, slope of $\overline{YX} = \frac{5}{2}$, and slope of $\overline{VW} = \frac{7}{2}$. Since the slope of $\overline{YV} \neq$ slope of $\overline{XW}$ and the slope of $\overline{YX} \neq$ slope of $\overline{VW}$, *VWXY* is not a parallelogram.

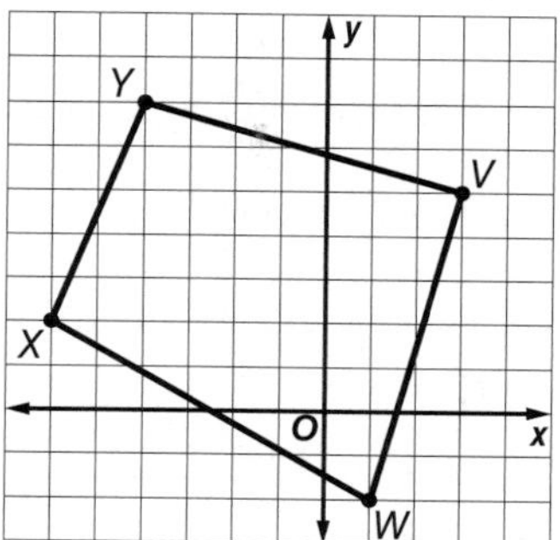

27. Yes; a pair of opposite sides must be parallel and congruent. Slope of $\overline{QR} = \frac{7}{2}$ = slope of $\overline{ST}$, so $\overline{QR} \parallel \overline{ST}$. $QR = ST = \sqrt{53}$, so $\overline{QR} \cong \overline{ST}$. So, *QRST* is a parallelogram.

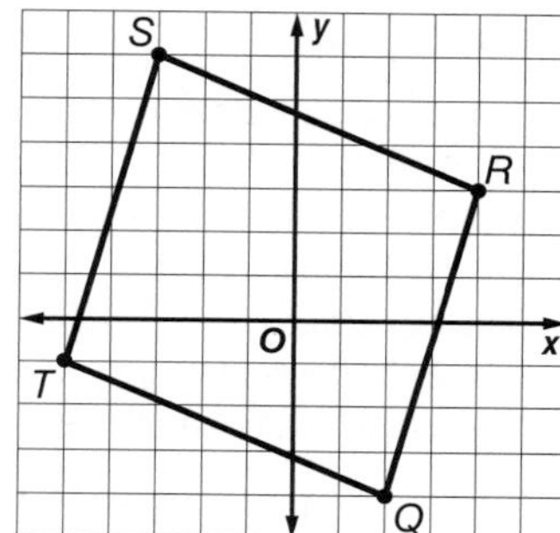

28. Given: $\overline{AB} \cong \overline{CD}$, $\overline{AD} \cong \overline{BC}$
Prove: *ABCD* is a parallelogram.

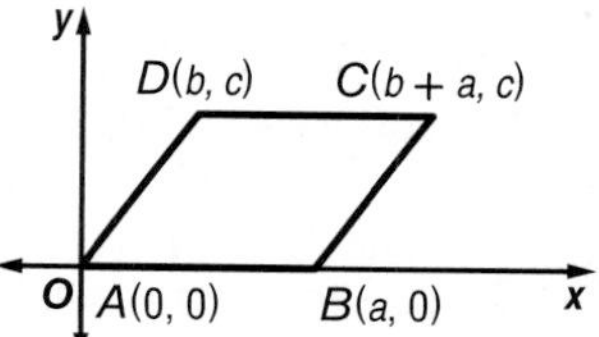

Proof:

slope of $\overline{AD} = \frac{c-0}{b-0} = \frac{c}{b}$

The slope of $\overline{AB}$ is 0.

slope of $\overline{BC} = \frac{c-0}{b+a-a} = \frac{c}{b}$

The slope of $\overline{CD}$ is 0.

Therefore, $\overline{AD} \parallel \overline{BC}$ and $\overline{AB} \parallel \overline{CD}$. So by definition of a parallelogram, *ABCD* is a parallelogram.

29. Given: *ABCD* is a parallelogram.
$\angle A$ is a right angle.

Prove: $\angle B$, $\angle C$, and $\angle D$ are right angles.

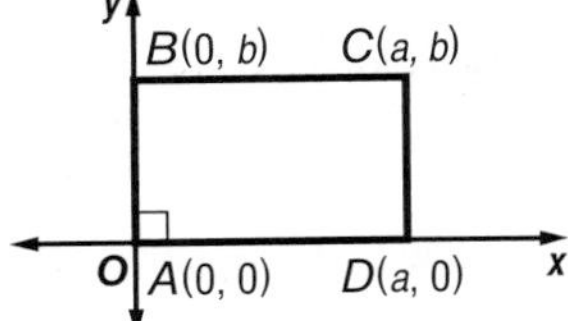

Proof:

slope of $\overline{BC} = \left(\frac{b-b}{a-0}\right)$ or 0 The slope of $\overline{CD}$ is undefined.

slope of $\overline{AD} = \left(\frac{0-0}{a-0}\right)$ or 0 The slope of $\overline{AB}$ is undefined.

Therefore, $\overline{BC} \perp \overline{CD}$, $\overline{CD} \perp \overline{AD}$, and $\overline{AB} \perp \overline{BC}$. So, $\angle B$, $\angle C$, and $\angle D$ are right angles.

30. Given: $\angle A \cong \angle C$, $\angle B \cong \angle D$

Prove: *ABCD* is a parallelogram.

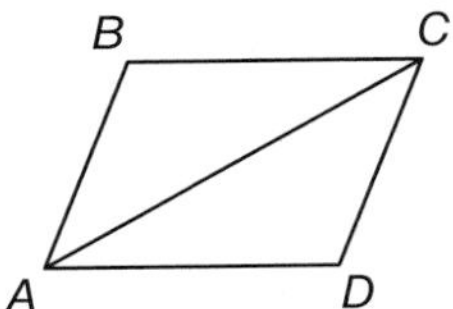

Proof: Draw $\overline{AC}$ to form two triangles. The sum of the angles of one triangle is 180, so the sum of the angles for two triangles is 360. So, $m\angle A + m\angle B + m\angle C + m\angle D = 360$. Since $\angle A \cong \angle C$ and $\angle B \cong \angle D$, $m\angle A = m\angle C$ and $m\angle B = m\angle D$. By substitution, $m\angle A + m\angle A + m\angle B + m\angle B = 360$. So, $2(m\angle A) + 2(m\angle B) = 360$. Dividing each side by 2 yields $m\angle A + m\angle B = 180$. So, the consecutive angles are supplementary and $\overline{AD} \parallel \overline{BC}$. Likewise, $2(m\angle A) + 2(m\angle D) = 360$ or $m\angle A + m\angle D = 180$. So, these consecutive angles are supplementary and $\overline{AB} \parallel \overline{DC}$. Opposite sides are parallel, so *ABCD* is a parallelogram.

31a. Given: $\overline{AC} \cong \overline{CF}$, $\overline{AB} \cong \overline{CD} \cong \overline{BE}$, and $\overline{DF} \cong \overline{DE}$

Prove: $\overline{BE} \parallel \overline{CD}$.

Proof: We are given that $\overline{AC} \cong \overline{CF}$, $\overline{AB} \cong \overline{CD} \cong \overline{BE}$, and $\overline{DF} \cong \overline{DE}$. $AC = CF$ by the definition of congruence. $AC = AB + BC$ and $CF = CD + DF$ by the Segment Addition Postulate and $AB + BC = CD + DF$ by substitution. Using substitution again, $AB + BC = AB + DF$, and $BC = DF$ by the Subtraction Property. $\overline{BC} \cong \overline{DF}$ by the definition of congruence, and $\overline{BC} \cong \overline{DE}$ by the Transitive Property. If both pairs of opposite sides of a quadrilateral are congruent, then the quadrilateral is a parallelogram, so *BCDE* is a parallelogram. By the definition of a parallelogram, $\overline{BE} \parallel \overline{CD}$.

32. Given: $\overline{AE} \cong \overline{EC}$, $\overline{DE} \cong \overline{EB}$

Prove: *ABCD* is a parallelogram.

Proof:

Statements (Reasons)

1. $\overline{AE} \cong \overline{EC}$, $\overline{DE} \cong \overline{EB}$ (Given)
2. $\angle 1 \cong \angle 2$, $\angle 3 \cong \angle 4$ (Vertical $\angle$s are $\cong$.)
3. $\triangle ABE \cong \triangle CDE$, $\triangle ADE \cong \triangle CBE$ (SAS)
4. $\overline{AB} \cong \overline{DC}$, $\overline{AD} \cong \overline{BC}$ (CPCTC)
5. *ABCD* is a parallelogram. (If both pairs of opp. sides are $\cong$, then quad is a ▱.)

33. Given: $\overline{AB} \cong \overline{DC}$, $\overline{AB} \parallel \overline{DC}$

Prove: *ABCD* is a parallelogram.

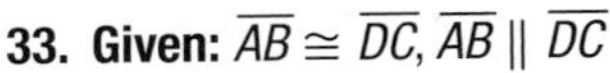

Proof:

Statements (Reasons)

1. $\overline{AB} \cong \overline{DC}$, $\overline{AB} \parallel \overline{DC}$ (Given)
2. Draw $\overline{AC}$. (Two points determine a line.)
3. $\angle 1 \cong \angle 2$ (If two lines are $\parallel$, then alt. int. $\angle$s are $\cong$.)
4. $\overline{AC} \cong \overline{AC}$ (Refl. Prop.)
5. $\triangle ABC \cong \triangle CDA$ (SAS)
6. $\overline{AD} \cong \overline{BC}$ (CPCTC)
7. *ABCD* is a parallelogram. (If both pairs of opp. sides are $\cong$, then the quad. is ▱.)

34. By Theorem 6.11, if the diagonals of a quadrilateral bisect each other, then the quadrilateral is a parallelogram. Begin by drawing and bisecting a segment $\overline{AB}$. Then draw a line that intersects the first segment through its midpoint *D*. Mark a point *C* on one side of this line and then construct a segment $\overline{DE}$ congruent to $\overline{CD}$ on the other side of *D*. You now have intersecting segments which bisect each other. Connect point *A* to point *C*, point *C* to point *B*, point *B* to point *E*, and point *E* to point *A* to form ▱*ACBE*.

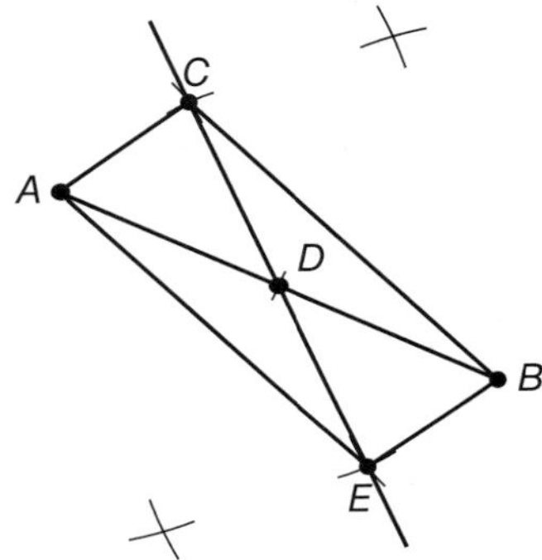

38. Given: *RSTV* is a quadrilateral.
A, *B*, *C*, and *D* are midpoints of sides $\overline{RS}$, $\overline{ST}$, $\overline{TV}$, and $\overline{VR}$, respectively.

Prove: *ABCD* is a parallelogram.

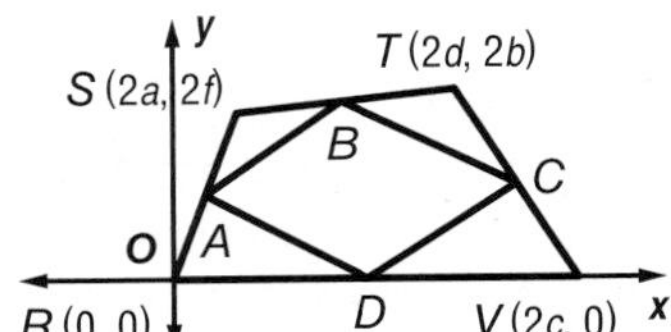

Proof:

Place quadrilateral *RSTV* on the coordinate plane and label coordinates as shown. (Using coordinates that are multiples of 2 will make the computation easier.) By the Midpoint Formula, the coordinates of *A*, *B*, *C*, and *D* are $A\left(\frac{2a}{2}, \frac{2f}{2}\right) = (a, f)$;

$B\left(\frac{2d+2a}{2}, \frac{2f+2b}{2}\right) = (d+a, f+b)$; $C\left(\frac{2d+2c}{2}, \frac{2b}{2}\right) = (d+c, b)$; and $D\left(\frac{2c}{2}, \frac{0}{2}\right) = (c, 0)$.

Find the slopes of $\overline{AB}$ and $\overline{DC}$.

Slope of $\overline{AB}$

$$m = \frac{y_2 - y_1}{x_2 - x_1} = \frac{(f+b) - f}{(d+a) - a} = \frac{b}{d}$$

Slope of $\overline{DC}$

$$m = \frac{y_2 - y_1}{x_2 - x_1} = \frac{0 - b}{c - (d+c)} = \frac{-b}{-d} \text{ or } \frac{b}{d}$$

The slopes of $\overline{AB}$ and $\overline{DC}$ are the same so the segments are parallel. Use the Distance Formula to find AB and DC.

$$AB = \sqrt{(d+a-a)^2 + (f+b-f)^2} = \sqrt{d^2 + b^2}$$

$$DC = \sqrt{(d+c-c)^2 + (b-0)^2} = \sqrt{d^2 + b^2}$$

Thus, $AB = DC$ and $\overline{AB} \cong \overline{DC}$. Therefore, $ABCD$ is a parallelogram because if one pair of opposite sides of a quadrilateral are both parallel and congruent, then the quadrilateral is a parallelogram.

44. **Given:** $ABCD$ is a parallelogram and $\overline{AJ} \cong \overline{KC}$.
Prove: Quadrilateral $JBKD$ is a parallelogram.

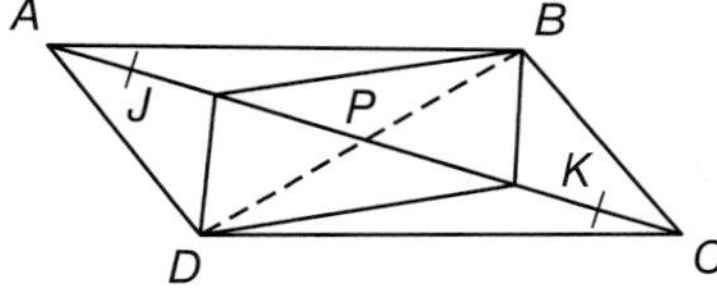

Proof:

Draw in segment $\overline{DB}$. Since $ABCD$ is a parallelogram, then by Theorem 6.3, diagonals $\overline{DB}$ and $\overline{AC}$ bisect each other. Label their point of intersection P. By the definition of bisect, $\overline{AP} \cong \overline{PC}$, so $AP = PC$. By Segment Addition, $AP = AJ + JP$ and $PC = PK + KC$. So $AJ + JP = PK + KC$ by Substitution. Since $\overline{AJ} \cong \overline{KC}$, $AJ = KC$ by the definition of congruence. Substituting yields $KC + JP = PK + KC$. By the Subtraction Property, $JP = KC$. So by the definition of congruence, $\overline{JP} \cong \overline{PK}$. Thus, P is the midpoint of $\overline{JK}$. Since $\overline{JK}$ and $\overline{DB}$ bisect each other and are diagonals of quadrilateral $JBKD$, by Theorem 6.11, quadrilateral $JBKD$ is a parallelogram.

45. Sample answer: You can show that: both pairs of opposite sides are congruent or parallel, both pairs of opposite angles are congruent, diagonals bisect each other, or one pair of opposite sides is both congruent and parallel.

56. Proof:

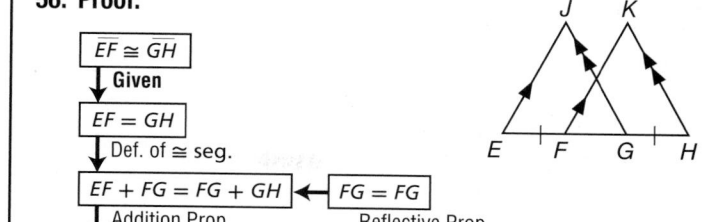

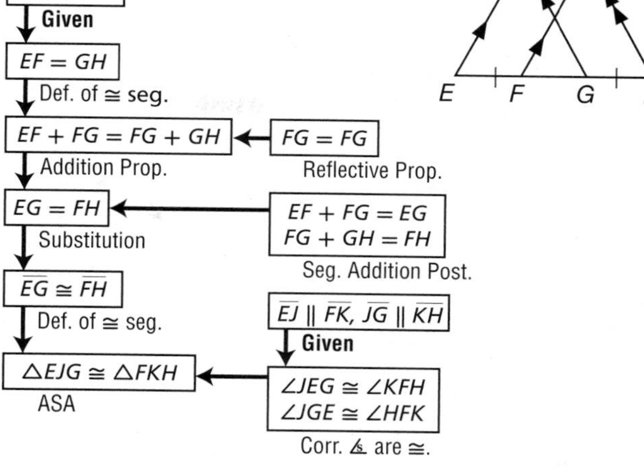

57. Proof:

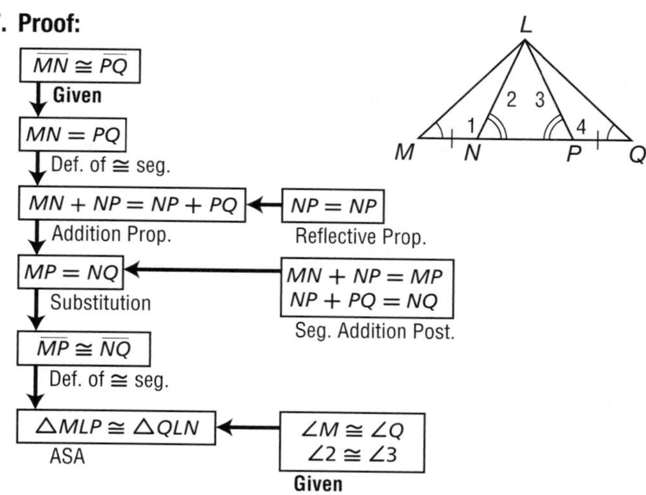

Mid-Chapter Quiz

19. Proof:

Statements (Reasons)

1. ▱$GFBA$ and ▱$HACD$ (Given)
2. $\angle F \cong \angle A$, $\angle A \cong \angle D$ (Opp. ∡ of a ▱ are ≅)
3. $\angle F \cong \angle D$ (Transitive Prop.)

22. Sample answer: The legs are made so that they will bisect each other, so the quadrilateral formed by the ends of the legs is always a parallelogram. Therefore, the top of the stand is parallel to the floor.

24. Yes; both pairs of opposite sides must be congruent. The distance between A and B is $\sqrt{26}$. The distance between B and C is $\sqrt{10}$. The distance between C and D is $\sqrt{26}$. The distance between D and A is $\sqrt{10}$. Since both pairs of opposite sides are congruent, $ABCD$ is a parallelogram.

25. No; both pairs of opposite sides must be parallel; since the slope of $\overline{QR} \neq$ slope of $\overline{TS}$, $QRST$ is not a parallelogram.

Lesson 6-4

8. No; slope of $\overline{WX} = \frac{2}{5}$, slope of $\overline{XY} = -2$, slope of $\overline{YZ} = \frac{3}{5}$, and slope of $\overline{ZW} = -\frac{5}{2}$. Slope of $\overline{WX} \neq$ slope of $\overline{YZ}$, and slope of $\overline{XY} \neq$ slope of $\overline{ZW}$, so $WXYZ$ is not a parallelogram. Therefore, $WXYZ$ is not a rectangle.

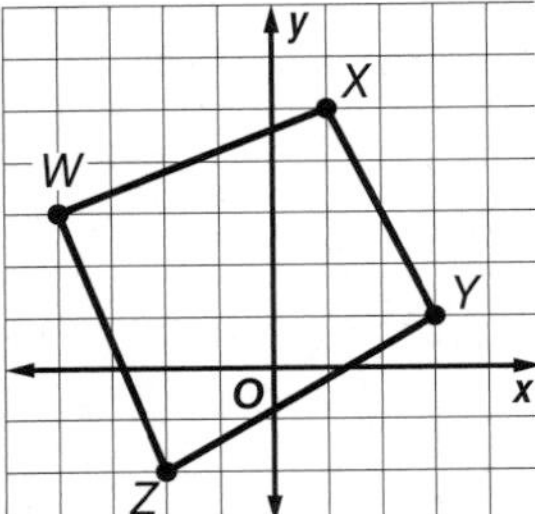

9. Yes; $AB = 5 = CD$ and $BC = 8 = AD$. So, $ABCD$ is a parallelogram. $BD = \sqrt{89} = AC$, so the diagonals are congruent. Thus, $ABCD$ is a rectangle.

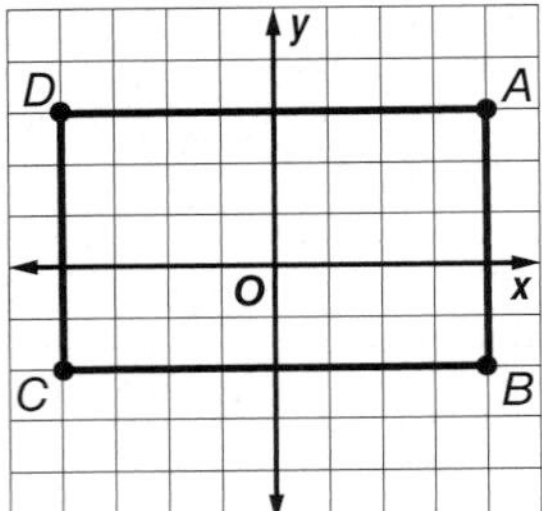

20. Proof:

Statements (Reasons)

1. $ABCD$ is a rectangle. (Given)
2. $ABCD$ is a parallelogram. (Def. of rectangle)
3. $\overline{AD} \cong \overline{BC}$ (Opp. sides of a ▱ are ≅.)
4. $\overline{DC} \cong \overline{CD}$ (Refl. Prop.)
5. $\overline{AC} \cong \overline{BD}$ (Diagonals of a rectangle are ≅.)
6. $\triangle ADC \cong \triangle BCD$ (SSS)

21. Proof:

Statements (Reasons)

1. $QTVW$ is a rectangle; $\overline{QR} \cong \overline{ST}$. (Given)
2. $QTVW$ is a parallelogram. (Def. of rectangle)
3. $\overline{WQ} \cong \overline{VT}$ (Opp sides of a ▱ are ≅.)
4. $\angle Q$ and $\angle T$ are right angles. (Def. of rectangle)
5. $\angle Q \cong \angle T$ (All rt ∠s are ≅.)
6. $QR = ST$ (Def. of ≅ segs.)
7. $\overline{RS} \cong \overline{RS}$ (Refl. Prop.)
8. $RS = RS$ (Def. of ≅ segs.)
9. $QR + RS = RS + ST$ (Add. prop.)
10. $QS = QR + RS$, $RT = RS + ST$ (Seg. Add. Post.)
11. $QS = RT$ (Subst.)
12. $\overline{QS} \cong \overline{RT}$ (Def. of ≅ segs.)
13. $\triangle SWQ \cong \triangle RVT$ (SAS)

22. Yes; slope of $\overline{WX} = \frac{1}{7}$ = slope of $\overline{YZ}$, slope of $\overline{XY} = -7$ = slope of $\overline{ZW}$. So $WXYZ$ is a parallelogram. The product of the slopes of consecutive sides is -1, so the consecutive sides are perpendicular and form right angles. Thus, $WXYZ$ is a rectangle.

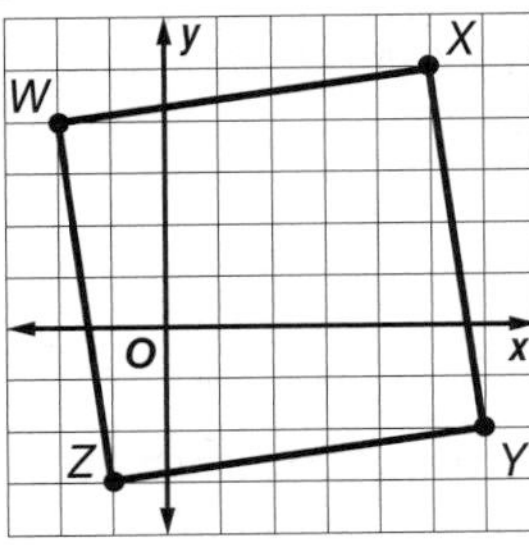

23. No; $JK = \sqrt{65} = LM$, $KL = \sqrt{37} = MJ$, so $JKLM$ is a parallelogram. $KM = \sqrt{106}$; $JL = \sqrt{98}$. $KM \neq JL$, so the diagonals are not congruent. Thus, $JKLM$ is not a rectangle.

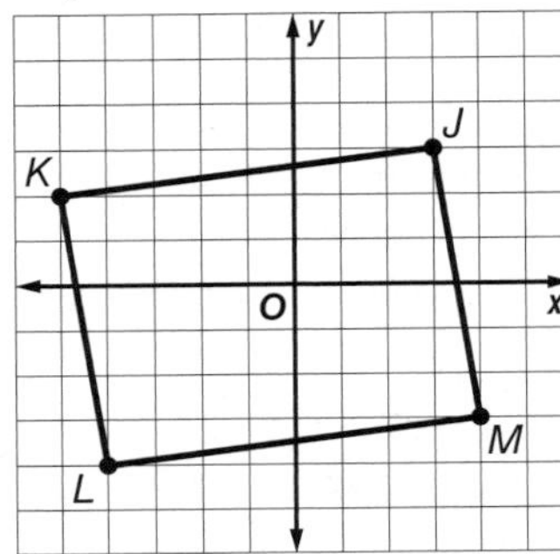

24. Yes; $QR = \sqrt{20} = ST$, $RS = \sqrt{45} = TQ$, so $QRST$ is a parallelogram. $QS = \sqrt{65} = RT$, so the diagonals are congruent. $QRST$ is a rectangle.

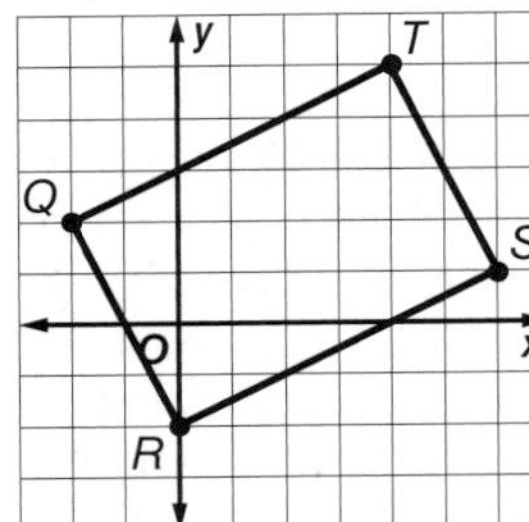

25. No; slope of $\overline{GH} = \frac{1}{8}$ = slope of $\overline{JK}$ and slope of $\overline{HJ} = -6$ = slope of $\overline{KG}$. So, $GHJK$ is a parallelogram. The product of the slopes of consecutive sides $\neq -1$, so the consecutive sides are not perpendicular. Thus, $GHJK$ is not a rectangle.

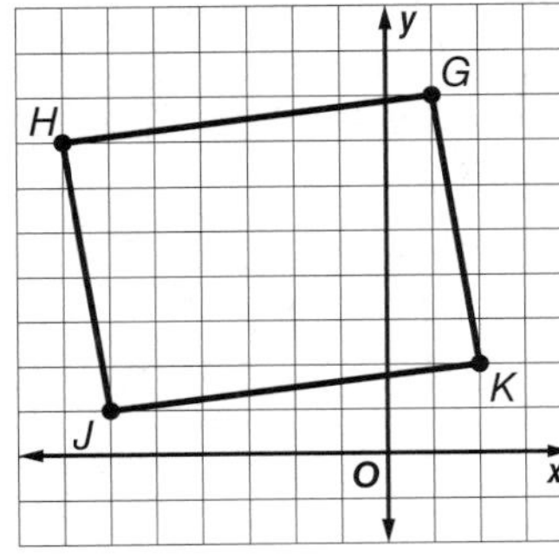

33. Given: *WXYZ* is a rectangle with diagonals $\overline{WY}$ and $\overline{XZ}$.

Prove: $\overline{WY} \cong \overline{XZ}$

Proof:

1. *WXYZ* is a rectangle with diagonals $\overline{WY}$ and $\overline{XZ}$. (Given)
2. $\overline{WX} \cong \overline{ZY}$ (Opp. sides of a ▱ are $\cong$.)
3. $\overline{WZ} \cong \overline{WZ}$ (Refl. Prop.)
4. $\angle XWZ$ and $\angle YZW$ are right angles. (Def. of rectangle)
5. $\angle XWZ \cong \angle YZW$ (All right $\angle$s are $\cong$.)
6. $\triangle XWZ \cong \triangle YZW$ (SAS)
7. $\overline{WY} \cong \overline{XZ}$ (CPCTC)

34. Given: $\overline{WX} \cong \overline{YZ}$, $\overline{XY} \cong \overline{WZ}$, and $\overline{WY} \cong \overline{XZ}$

Prove: *WXYZ* is a rectangle.

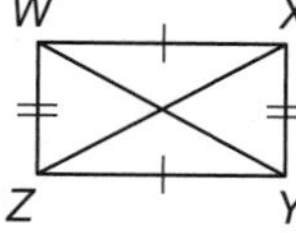

Proof:

1. $\overline{WX} \cong \overline{YZ}$, $\overline{XY} \cong \overline{WZ}$, and $\overline{WY} \cong \overline{XZ}$ (Given)
2. $\triangle WZX \cong \triangle XYW$ (SSS)
3. $\angle ZWX \cong \angle YXW$ (CPCTC)
4. $m\angle ZWX = m\angle YXW$ (Def. of $\cong$ $\angle$s)
5. *WXYZ* is a parallelogram. (If both pairs of opp. sides are $\cong$, then quad. is ▱.)
6. $\angle ZWX$ and $\angle YXW$ are supplementary. (Cons. $\angle$s of ▱ are suppl.)
7. $m\angle ZWX + m\angle YXW = 180$ (Def of suppl.)
8. $\angle ZWX$ and $\angle YXW$ are right angles. (If 2 $\angle$ are $\cong$ and suppl., each $\angle$ is a rt. $\angle$.)
9. $\angle WZY$ and $\angle XYZ$ are right angles. (If a ▱ has 1 rt. $\angle$, it has 4 rt. $\angle$s.)
10. *WXYZ* is a rectangle. (Def. of rectangle)

35.

ABCD is a parallelogram, and $\angle B$ is a right angle. Since *ABCD* is a parallelogram and has one right angle, then it has four right angles. So by the definition of a rectangle, *ABCD* is a rectangle.

36.

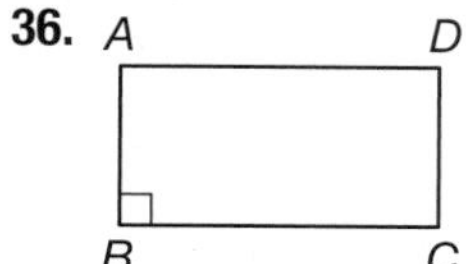

ABCD is a quadrilateral with four right angles. *ABCD* is a parallelogram because both pairs of opposite angles are congruent. By definition of a rectangle, *ABCD* is a rectangle.

37. Sample answer: Since $\overline{RP} \perp \overline{PQ}$ and $\overline{SQ} \perp \overline{PQ}$. $m\angle P = m\angle Q = 90$. Lines that are perpendicular to the same line are parallel, so $\overline{RP} \parallel \overline{SQ}$. The same compass setting was used to locate points *R* and *S*, so $\overline{RP} \cong \overline{SQ}$. If one pair of opposite sides of a quadrilateral is both parallel and congruent, then the quadrilateral is a parallelogram. A parallelogram with right angles is a rectangle. Thus, *PRSQ* is a rectangle.

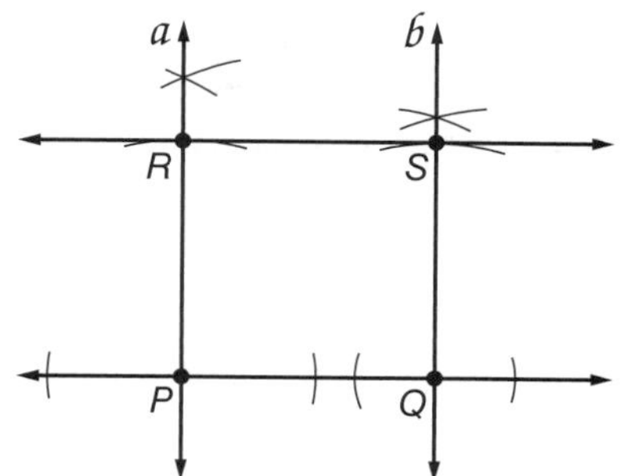

38. Sample answer: He should measure the diagonals of the end zone and both pairs of opposite sides. If the diagonals and a pair of opposite sides are congruent, then the end zone is a rectangle.

Lesson 6-5

14. Proof:

Statements (Reasons)

1. *QRST* is a parallelogram; $\overline{TR} \cong \overline{QS}$; $m\angle QPR = 90$. (Given)
2. *QRST* is a rectangle. (If the diags of a ▱ are $\cong$, the ▱ is a rectangle.)
3. $\angle QPR$ is a right angle. (Def of rt. $\angle$)
4. $\overline{QS} \perp \overline{TR}$ (Def. of perpendicular)
5. *QRST* is a rhombus. (If the diags of a ▱ are $\perp$, ▱ is a rhombus.)
6. *QRST* is a square. (Thm.6.2, if a quadrilateral is both a rectangle and a rhombus, then it is a square.)

15. Proof:

Statements (Reasons)

1. *JKQP* is a square. $\overline{ML}$ bisects $\overline{JP}$ and $\overline{KQ}$. (Given)
2. *JKQP* is a parallelogram. (All squares are parallelograms.)
3. $\overline{JM} \parallel \overline{KL}$ (Def. of ▱)
4. $\overline{JP} \cong \overline{KQ}$ (Opp. Sides of ▱ are $\cong$.)
5. $JP = KQ$ (Def of $\cong$ segs.)
6. $JM = MP$, $KL = LQ$ (Def. of bisects)
7. $JP = JM + MP$, $KQ = KL + LQ$ (Seg. Add Post.)
8. $JP = 2JM$, $KQ = 2KL$ (Subst.)
9. $2JM = 2KL$ (Subst.)
10. $JM = KL$ (Division Prop.)
11. $\overline{KL} \cong \overline{JM}$ (Def. of $\cong$ segs.)
12. *JKLM* is a parallelogram. (If one pair of opp. sides is $\cong$ and $\parallel$, then the quad. is a ▱.)

16. Proof:

Statements (Reasons)

1. $ACDH$ and $BCDF$ are parallelograms; $\overline{BF} \cong \overline{AB}$. (Given)
2. $\overline{CD} \cong \overline{BF}$, $\overline{CD} \cong \overline{AH}$ (Def. of ▱)
3. $\overline{BF} \cong \overline{AH}$ (Trans. Prop)
3. $\overline{BC} \cong \overline{FD}$, $\overline{AC} \cong \overline{HD}$ (Def. of ▱)
4. $AC = HD$ (Def of $\cong$ segs.)
5. $AC = AB + BC$, $HD = HF + FD$ (Seg. Add. Post.)
6. $AC - HD = AB + BC - HF - FD$ (Subt. Prop.)
7. $AB = HF$ (Subst.)
8. $\overline{AB} \cong \overline{HF}$ (Def. of $\cong$ segs.)
9. $\overline{AH} \cong \overline{BF} \cong \overline{AB} \cong \overline{HF}$ (Subst.)
10. $ABFH$ is a rhombus. (Def. of rhombus)

34. Given: $ABCD$ is a rhombus.

Prove: Each diagonal bisects a pair of opposite angles.

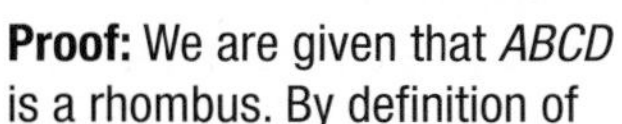

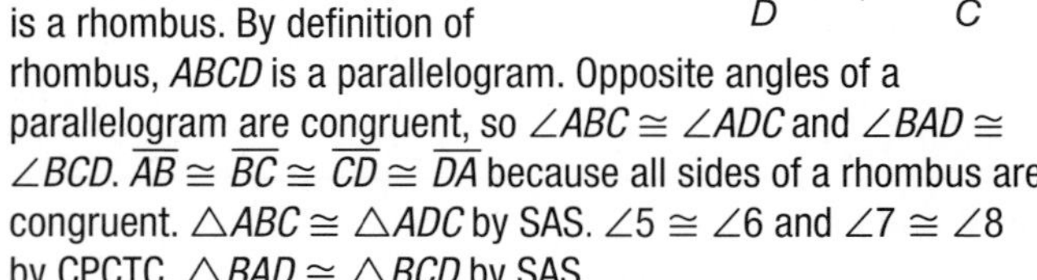

Proof: We are given that $ABCD$ is a rhombus. By definition of rhombus, $ABCD$ is a parallelogram. Opposite angles of a parallelogram are congruent, so $\angle ABC \cong \angle ADC$ and $\angle BAD \cong \angle BCD$. $\overline{AB} \cong \overline{BC} \cong \overline{CD} \cong \overline{DA}$ because all sides of a rhombus are congruent. $\triangle ABC \cong \triangle ADC$ by SAS. $\angle 5 \cong \angle 6$ and $\angle 7 \cong \angle 8$ by CPCTC. $\triangle BAD \cong \triangle BCD$ by SAS.

$\angle 1 \cong \angle 2$ and $\angle 3 \cong \angle 4$ by CPCTC. By definition of angle bisector, each diagonal bisects a pair of opposite angles.

35. Given: $ABCD$ is a parallelogram; $\overline{AC} \perp \overline{BD}$.

Prove: $ABCD$ is a rhombus.

Proof: We are given that $ABCD$ is a parallelogram. The diagonals of a parallelogram bisect each other, so $\overline{AE} \cong \overline{EC}$. $\overline{BE} \cong \overline{BE}$ because congruence of segments is reflexive. We are also given that $\overline{AC} \perp \overline{BD}$. Thus, $\angle AEB$ and $\angle BEC$ are right angles by the definition of perpendicular lines. Then $\angle AEB \cong \angle BEC$ because all right angles are congruent. Therefore, $\triangle AEB \cong \triangle CEB$ by SAS. $\overline{AB} \cong \overline{CB}$ by CPCTC. Opposite sides of parallelograms are congruent, so $\overline{AB} \cong \overline{CD}$ and $\overline{BC} \cong \overline{AD}$. Then since congruence of segments is transitive, $\overline{AB} \cong \overline{CD} \cong \overline{BC} \cong \overline{AD}$. All four sides of $ABCD$ are congruent, so $ABCD$ is a rhombus by definition.

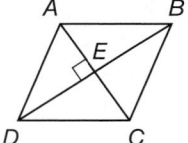

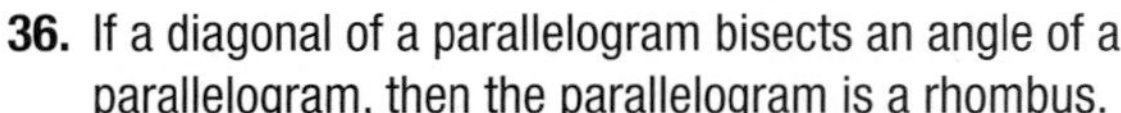

36. If a diagonal of a parallelogram bisects an angle of a parallelogram, then the parallelogram is a rhombus.

Given: $ABCD$ is a parallelogram; diagonal $\overline{AC}$ bisects $\angle DAB$ and $\angle BCD$.

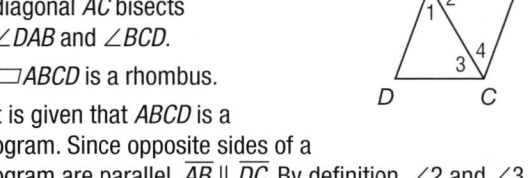

Prove: ▱$ABCD$ is a rhombus.

Proof: It is given that $ABCD$ is a parallelogram. Since opposite sides of a parallelogram are parallel, $\overline{AB} \parallel \overline{DC}$. By definition, $\angle 2$ and $\angle 3$ are alternate interior angles of parallel sides $\overline{AB}$ and $\overline{DC}$. Since alternate interior angles are congruent, $\angle 2 \cong \angle 3$. Congruence of angles is symmetric, therefore $\angle 3 \cong \angle 2$. it is given that $\overline{AC}$ bisects $\angle DAB$ and $\angle BCD$, so $\angle 1 \cong \angle 2$ and $\angle 3 \cong \angle 4$ by definition. By the Transitive Property, $\angle 1 \cong \angle 3$ and $\angle 2 \cong \angle 4$. The sides opposite congruent angles in a triangle are congruent, therefore, $\overline{AD} \cong \overline{DC}$ and $\overline{AB} \cong \overline{BC}$. So, since a pair of consecutive sides of the parallelogram are congruent, $ABCD$ is a rhombus.

37. Given: $ABCD$ is a parallelogram; $\overline{AB} \cong \overline{BC}$.

Prove: $ABCD$ is a rhombus.

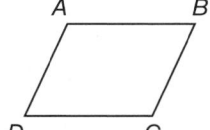

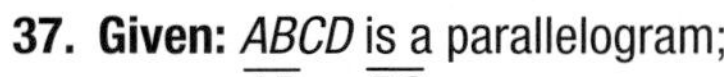

Proof: Opposite sides of a parallelogram are congruent, so $\overline{BC} \cong \overline{AD}$ and $\overline{AB} \cong \overline{CD}$. We are given that $\overline{AB} \cong \overline{BC}$. So, by the Transitive Property, $\overline{BC} \cong \overline{CD}$. So, $\overline{BC} \cong \overline{CD} \cong \overline{AB} \cong \overline{AD}$. Thus, $ABCD$ is a rhombus by definition.

38. Given: $ABCD$ is a rectangle and a rhombus.

Prove: $ABCD$ is a square.

Proof: We know that $ABCD$ is a rectangle and a rhombus. $ABCD$ is a parallelogram, since all rectangles and rhombi are parallelograms. By the definition of a rectangle, $\angle A$, $\angle B$, $\angle C$, and $\angle D$ are right angles. By the definition of a rhombus, all of the sides are congruent. Therefore, $ABCD$ is a square since $ABCD$ is a parallelogram with all four sides congruent and all the angles are right.

39.

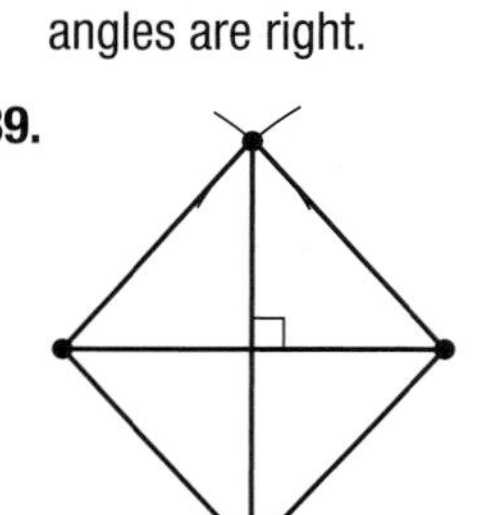

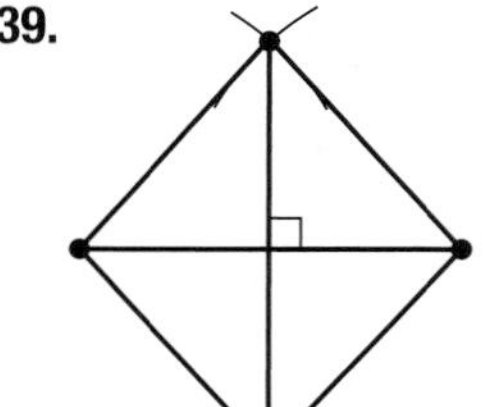

Sample answer: The diagonals bisect each other, so the quadrilateral is a parallelogram. Since the diagonals of the parallelogram are perpendicular to each other, the parallelogram is a rhombus.

40.

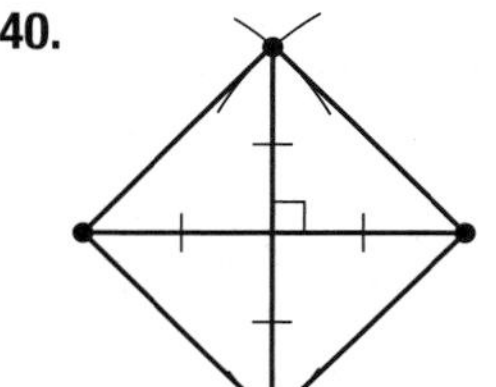

Sample answer: The diagonals bisect each other, so the quadrilateral is a parallelogram. Since the diagonals of the parallelogram are congruent and perpendicular, the parallelogram is a square.

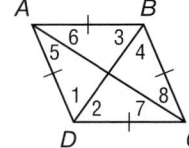

41. Given: *ABCD* is a square.

Prove: $\overline{AC} \perp \overline{DB}$

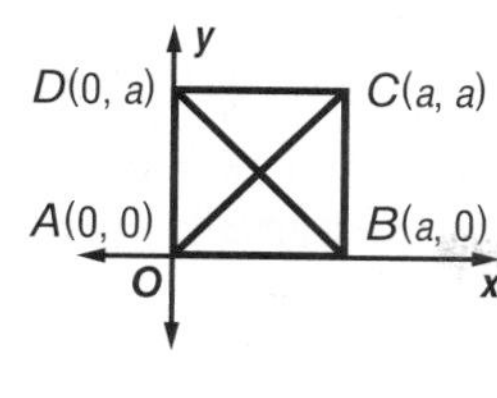

Proof:

slope of $\overline{DB} = \frac{0 - a}{a - 0}$ or -1

slope of $\overline{AC} = \frac{0 - a}{0 - a}$ or 1

The slope of $\overline{AC}$ is the negative reciprocal of the slope of $\overline{DB}$, so they are perpendicular.

42. Given: *ABCD* is a rectangle. *Q, R, S,* and *T* are midpoints of their respective sides.

Prove: *QRST* is a rhombus.

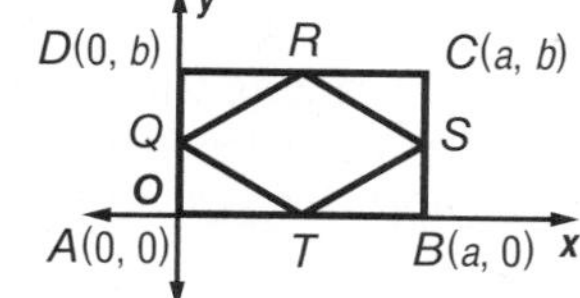

Proof:

Midpoint *Q* is $\left(\frac{0+0}{2}, \frac{b+0}{2}\right)$ or $\left(0, \frac{b}{2}\right)$.

Midpoint *R* is $\left(\frac{a+0}{2}, \frac{b+b}{2}\right)$ or $\left(\frac{a}{2}, \frac{2b}{2}\right)$ or $\left(\frac{a}{2}, b\right)$.

Midpoint *S* is $\left(\frac{a+a}{2}, \frac{b+0}{2}\right)$ or $\left(\frac{2a}{2}, \frac{b}{2}\right)$ or $\left(a, \frac{b}{2}\right)$.

Midpoint *T* is $\left(\frac{a+0}{2}, \frac{0+0}{2}\right)$ or $\left(\frac{a}{2}, 0\right)$.

$$QR = \sqrt{\left(\frac{a}{2} - 0\right)^2 + \left(b - \frac{b}{2}\right)^2} = \sqrt{\left(\frac{a}{2}\right)^2 + \left(\frac{b}{2}\right)^2}$$

$$RS = \sqrt{\left(a - \frac{a}{2}\right)^2 + \left(\frac{b}{2} - b\right)^2} = \sqrt{\left(\frac{a}{2}\right)^2 + \left(-\frac{b}{2}\right)^2}$$

or $\sqrt{\left(\frac{a}{2}\right)^2 + \left(\frac{b}{2}\right)^2}$

$$ST = \sqrt{\left(a - \frac{a}{2}\right)^2 + \left(\frac{b}{2} - 0\right)^2} = \sqrt{\left(\frac{a}{2}\right)^2 + \left(\frac{b}{2}\right)^2}$$

$$QT = \sqrt{\left(\frac{a}{2} - 0\right)^2 + \left(0 - \frac{b}{2}\right)^2} = \sqrt{\left(\frac{a}{2}\right)^2 + \left(-\frac{b}{2}\right)^2}$$

or $\sqrt{\left(\frac{a}{2}\right)^2 + \left(\frac{b}{2}\right)^2}$

$QR = RS = ST = QT$

$\overline{QR} \cong \overline{RS} \cong \overline{ST} \cong \overline{QT}$

QRST is a rhombus.

43. Squares; sample answer: Since the octagons are regular each side is congruent, and the quadrilaterals share common sides with the octagons, so the quadrilaterals are either rhombuses or squares. The vertices of the quadrilaterals are formed by the exterior angles of the sides of the octagons adjacent to the vertices. The sum of the measures of the exterior angles of a polygon is always 360 and since a regular octagon has 8 congruent exterior angles, each one measures 45. As shown in the diagram, each angle of the quadrilaterals in the pattern measures 45 + 45 or 90. Therefore, the quadrilateral is a square.

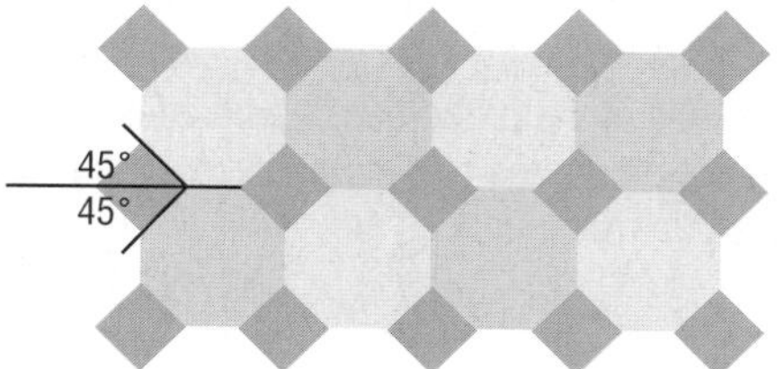

45a. Sample answer:

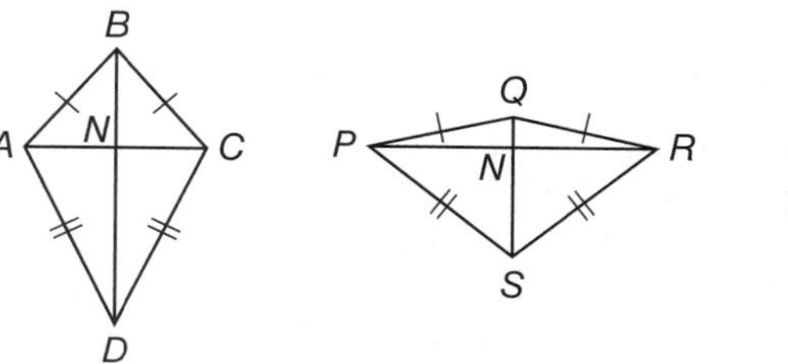

47. True; sample answer: A rectangle is a quadrilateral with four right angles and a square is both a rectangle and a rhombus, so a square is always a rectangle.

Converse: If a quadrilateral is a rectangle then it is a square. False; sample answer: A rectangle is a quadrilateral with four right angles. It is not necessarily a rhombus, so it is not necessarily a square.

Inverse: If a quadrilateral is not a square, then it is not a rectangle. False; sample answer: A quadrilateral that has four right angles and two pairs of congruent sides is not a square, but it is a rectangle.

Contrapositive: If a quadrilateral is not a rectangle, then it is not a square. True; sample answer: If a quadrilateral is not a rectangle, it is also not a square by definition.

50. Sample Answer:

Parallelogram: Opposite sides of a parallelogram are parallel and congruent. Opposite angles of a parallelogram are congruent. The diagonals of a parallelogram bisect each other and each diagonal separates a parallelogram into two congruent triangles.

Rectangle: A rectangle has all the properties of a parallelogram. A rectangle has four right angles. The diagonals of a rectangle are congruent.

Rhombus: A rhombus has all of the properties of a parallelogram. All sides of a rhombus are congruent. The diagonals of a rhombus are perpendicular and bisect the angles of the rhombus.

Square: A square has all of the properties of a parallelogram. A square has all of the properties of a rectangle. A square has all of the properties of a rhombus.

Lesson 6-6

28. Given: *ABCD* is an isosceles trapezoid.
$\overline{BC} \parallel \overline{AD}$, $\overline{AB} \cong \overline{CD}$

Prove: $\angle A \cong \angle D$,
$\angle ABC \cong \angle DCB$

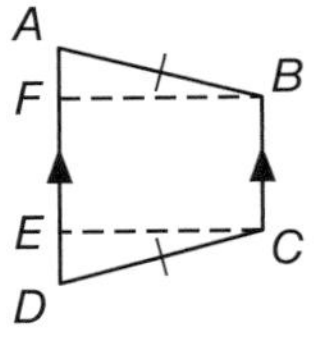

Proof: Draw auxiliary segments so that $\overline{BF} \perp \overline{AD}$ and $\overline{CE} \perp \overline{AD}$. Since $\overline{BC} \parallel \overline{AD}$ and parallel lines are everywhere equidistant, $\overline{BF} \cong \overline{CE}$. Perpendicular lines form right angles, so $\angle BFA$ and $\angle CED$ are right angles. $\angle BFA$ and $\angle CED$ are right triangles by definition. Therefore, $\triangle BFA \cong \triangle CED$ by HL. $\angle A \cong \angle D$ by CPCTC. Since $\angle CBF$ and $\angle BCE$ are right angles and all right angles are congruent, $\angle CBF \cong \angle BCE$. $\angle ABF \cong \angle DCE$ by CPCTC. So, $\angle ABC \cong \angle DCB$ by angle addition.

29. Given: *ABCD* is a trapezoid;
$\angle D \cong \angle C$.

Prove: Trapezoid *ABCD* is isosceles.

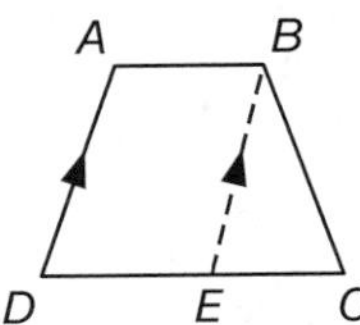

Proof: By the Parallel Postulate, we can draw the auxillary line $\overline{EB} \parallel \overline{AD}$. $\angle D \cong \angle BEC$, by the Corr. $\angle$s Thm. We are given that $\angle D \cong \angle C$, so by the Trans. Prop, $\angle BEC \cong \angle C$. So, $\triangle EBC$ is isosceles and $\overline{EB} \cong \overline{BC}$. From the def. of a trapezoid, $\overline{AB} \parallel \overline{DE}$. Since both pairs of opposite sides are parallel, *ABED* is a parallelogram. So, $\overline{AD} \cong \overline{EB}$. By the Transitive Property, $\overline{BC} \cong \overline{AD}$. Thus, *ABCD* is an isosceles trapezoid.

30. Given: *ABCD* is a trapezoid;
$\overline{AC} \cong \overline{BD}$.

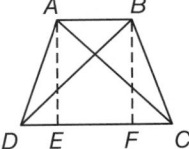

Prove: trapezoid *ABCD* is isosceles.

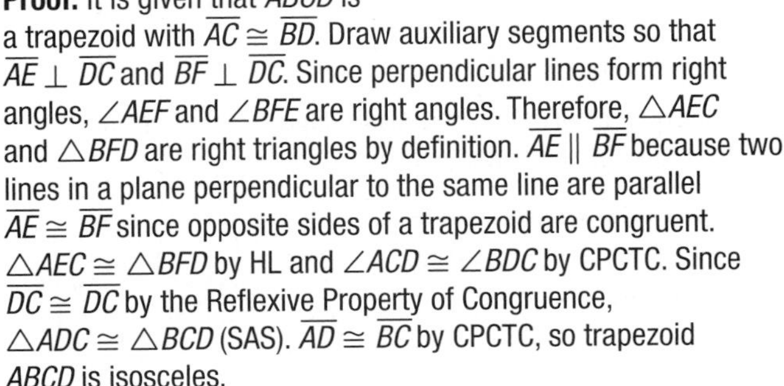

Proof: It is given that *ABCD* is a trapezoid with $\overline{AC} \cong \overline{BD}$. Draw auxiliary segments so that $\overline{AE} \perp \overline{DC}$ and $\overline{BF} \perp \overline{DC}$. Since perpendicular lines form right angles, $\angle AEF$ and $\angle BFE$ are right angles. Therefore, $\triangle AEC$ and $\triangle BFD$ are right triangles by definition. $\overline{AE} \parallel \overline{BF}$ because two lines in a plane perpendicular to the same line are parallel $\overline{AE} \cong \overline{BF}$ since opposite sides of a trapezoid are congruent. $\triangle AEC \cong \triangle BFD$ by HL and $\angle ACD \cong \angle BDC$ by CPCTC. Since $\overline{DC} \cong \overline{DC}$ by the Reflexive Property of Congruence, $\triangle ADC \cong \triangle BCD$ (SAS). $\overline{AD} \cong \overline{BC}$ by CPCTC, so trapezoid *ABCD* is isosceles.

31. Given: *ABCD* is a kite with
$\overline{AB} \cong \overline{BC}$ and $\overline{AD} \cong \overline{DC}$.

Prove: $\overline{BD} \perp \overline{AC}$

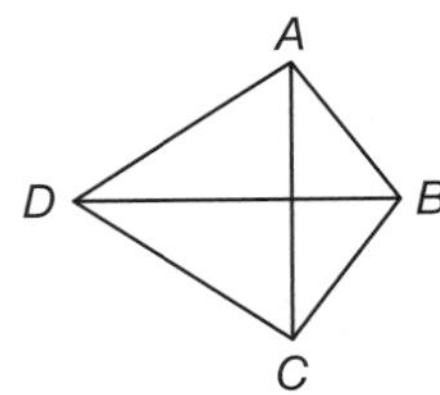

Proof: We know that $\overline{AB} \cong \overline{BC}$ and $\overline{AD} \cong \overline{DC}$. So, *B* and *D* are both equidistant from *A* and *C*. If a point is equidistant from the endpoints of a segment, then it is on the perpendicular bisector of the segment. The line that contains *B* and *D* is the perpendicular bisector of $\overline{AC}$, since only one line exists through two points. Thus, $\overline{BD} \perp \overline{AC}$.

32. Given: *ABCD* is a kite

Prove: $\angle B \cong \angle D$,
$\angle BAD \not\cong \angle BCD$

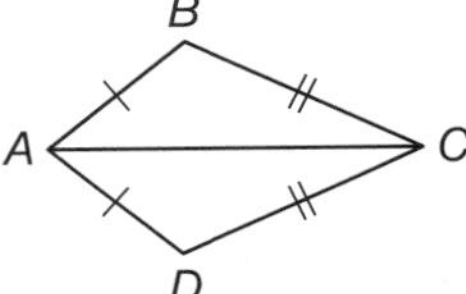

Proof:

We know that $\overline{AB} \cong \overline{AD}$ and $\overline{BC} \cong \overline{CD}$ by the definition of a kite. $\overline{AC} \cong \overline{AC}$ by the Reflexive Property. Therefore, $\triangle ABC \cong \triangle ADC$ by SSS. $\angle B \cong \angle D$ by CPCTC. If $\angle BAD \cong \angle BCD$, then *ABCD* is a parallelogram by definition, which cannot be true because we are given that *ABCD* is a kite. Therefore, $\angle BAD \not\cong \angle BCD$.

33. Given: $ABCD$ is a trapezoid with median $\overline{EF}$.

Prove: $\overline{EF} \parallel \overline{AB}$ and $\overline{EF} \parallel \overline{DC}$ and $EF = \frac{1}{2}(AB + DC)$

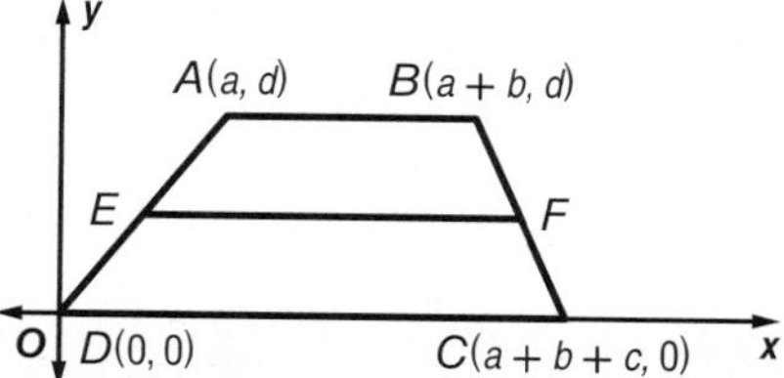

Proof:

By the definition of the median of a trapezoid, E is the midpoint of $\overline{AD}$ and F is the midpoint of $\overline{BC}$.

Midpoint E is $\left(\frac{a+0}{2}, \frac{d+0}{2}\right)$ or $\left(\frac{a}{2}, \frac{d}{2}\right)$.

Midpoint F is $\left(\frac{a+b+a+b+c}{2}, \frac{d+0}{2}\right)$

or $\left(\frac{2a+2b+c}{2}, \frac{d}{2}\right)$.

The slope of $\overline{AB} = 0$, the slope of $\overline{EF} = 0$, and the slope of $\overline{DC} = 0$. Thus, $\overline{EF} \parallel \overline{AB}$ and $\overline{EF} \parallel \overline{DC}$.

$AB = \sqrt{[(a+b) - a]^2 + (d-d)^2} = \sqrt{b^2}$ or b

$DC = \sqrt{[(a+b+c) - 0]^2 + (0-0)^2}$

$= \sqrt{(a+b+c)^2}$ or $a+b+c$

$EF = \sqrt{\left(\frac{2a+2b+c-a}{2}\right) + \left(\frac{d}{2} - \frac{d}{2}\right)^2}$

$= \sqrt{\left(\frac{a+2b+c}{2}\right)^2}$ or $\frac{a+2b+c}{2}$

$\frac{1}{2}(AB + DC) = \frac{1}{2}[b + (a+b+c)]$

$= \frac{1}{2}(a+2b+c)$

$= \frac{a+2b+c}{2}$

$= EF$

Thus, $\frac{1}{2}(AB + DC) = EF$.

58. Sample answer:

Given: Kite $MNPQ$

Prove: $\triangle MNR \cong \triangle PNR$

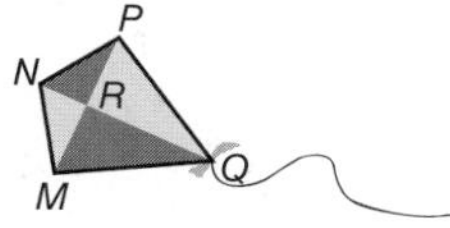

Proof:

Statements (Reasons)

1. $MNPQ$ is a kite. (Given)
2. $\overline{NM} \cong \overline{NP}$, $\overline{MQ} \cong \overline{PQ}$ (Def. of a kite)
3. $\overline{QN} \cong \overline{QN}$ (Refl. Prop.)
4. $\triangle NMQ \cong \triangle NPQ$ (SSS)
5. $\angle MNR \cong \angle PNR$ (CPCTC)
6. $\overline{NR} \cong \overline{NR}$ (Refl. Prop.)
7. $\triangle MNR \cong \triangle PNR$ (SAS)

59.

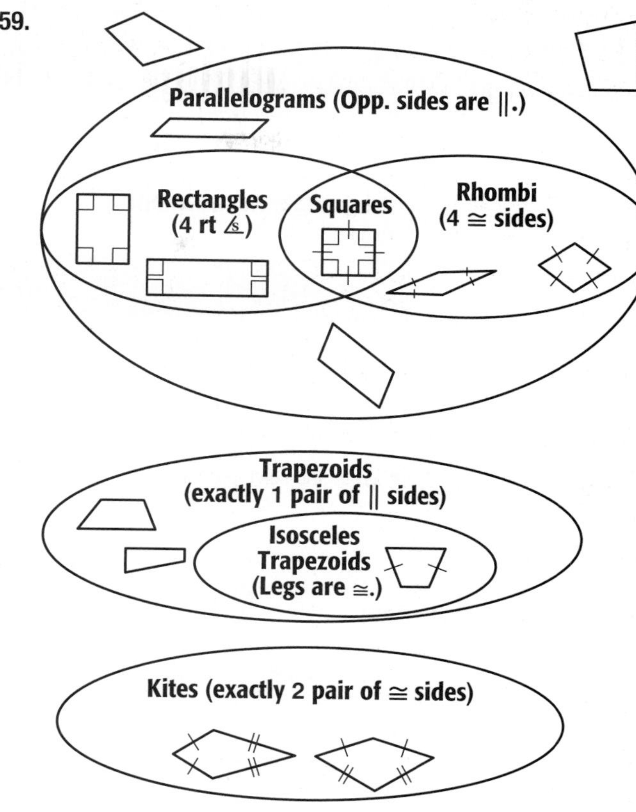

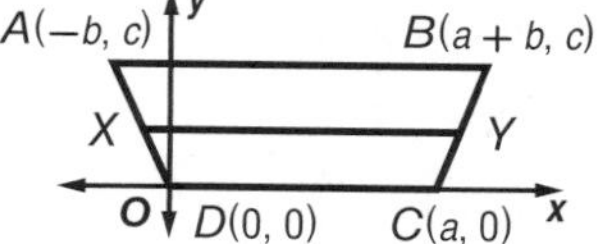

64. Given: $ABCD$ is an isosceles trapezoid with median $\overline{XY}$.

Prove: $\overline{XY} \parallel \overline{AB}$ and $\overline{XY} \parallel \overline{DC}$

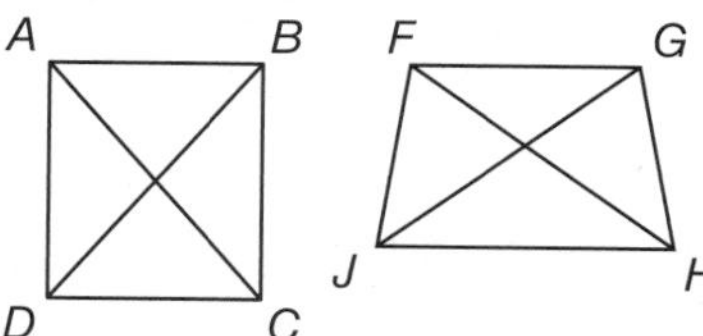

Proof:

The midpoint of $\overline{AD}$ is X. The coordinates are $\left(\frac{-b}{2}, \frac{c}{2}\right)$.

The midpoint of $\overline{BC}$ is $Y\left(\frac{2a+b}{2}, \frac{c}{2}\right)$.

The slope of $\overline{AB} = 0$, the slope of $\overline{XY} = 0$, and the slope of $\overline{DC} = 0$. Thus, $\overline{XY} \parallel \overline{AB}$ and $\overline{XY} \parallel \overline{DC}$.

68. Sample answer:

A B F G

J H

D C

69. A quadrilateral must have exactly one pair of sides parallel to be a trapezoid. If the legs are congruent, then the trapezoid is an isosceles trapezoid. If a quadrilateral has exactly two pairs of consecutive congruent sides with the opposite sides not congruent, the quadrilateral is a kite. A trapezoid and a kite both have four sides. In a trapezoid and isosceles trapezoid, both have exactly one pair of parallel sides.

Chapter Planner

	Diagnostic Assessment Quick Check LESSON 7-1 **45 min:** 0.5 day **90 min:** 0.25 day	EXTEND 7-1 **45 min:** 0.5 day **90 min:** 0.5 day	LESSON 7-2 **45 min:** 1 day **90 min:** 0.5 day
Title	**Ratios and Proportions**	**Graphing Technology Lab: Fibonacci Sequence and Ratios**	**Similar Polygons**
Objectives	▪ Write ratios. ▪ Write and solve proportions.	▪ Compare each term in the Fibonacci sequence with its preceding term using a spreadsheet.	▪ Use proportions to identify similar polygons. ▪ Solve problems using the properties of similar polygons.
Key Vocabulary	ratio proportion cross products		similar polygons similar ratio scale factor
CCSS	G.MG.3		G.SRT.2
Multiple Representations	✓		✓
Lesson Resources	connectED.mcgraw-hill.com Leveled Worksheets Vocabulary Personal Tutor Self-Check Quiz ▪ *5-Minute Check* ▪ *Study Notebook*	connectED.mcgraw-hill.com Personal Tutor **Materials:** ▪ TI-83/84 Plus or other graphing calculator ▪ spreadsheet program	connectED.mcgraw-hill.com Leveled Worksheets Quiz 1 Vocabulary Animations Personal Tutor Self-Check Quiz ▪ *5-Minute Check* ▪ *Study Notebook*
Resources for Every Lesson	IWB eStudent Edition IWB Interactive Classroom	▪ eTeacher Edition ▪ eSolutions Manual ▪ eAssessment	
Differentiated Instruction	pp. 462, 463		pp. 470, 477

IWB All digital assets are Interactive Whiteboard ready.

Suggested Pacing			
Time Periods	Instruction	Review & Assess	Total
45-minute	8 days	2 days	10 days
90-minute	5 days	1 day	6 days

LESSON 7-3 45 min: 1 day 90 min: 0.5 day	EXTEND 7-3 45 min: 0.5 day 90 min: 0.25 day	LESSON 7-4 45 min: 1 day 90 min: 0.5 day	LESSON 7-5 45 min: 1 day 90 min: 0.5 day
Similar Triangles	**Geometry Lab: Slopes of Perpendicular and Parallel Lines**	**Parallel Lines and Proportional Parts**	**Parts of Similar Triangles**
■ Identify similar triangles using the AA Similarity Postulate and the SSS and SAS Similarity Theorems. ■ Use similar triangles to solve problems.	■ Use similar triangles to prove the slope criteria for perpendicular and parallel lines.	■ Use proportional parts within triangles. ■ Use proportional parts with parallel lines.	■ Recognize and use proportional relationships of corresponding segments of similar triangles. ■ Use the Triangle Angle Bisector Theorem.
		midsegment of a triangle	
G.SRT.4, G.SRT.5	G.GPE.5	G.SRT.4, G.SRT.5	G.SRT.4, G.SRT.5
connectED.mcgraw-hill.com Leveled Worksheets Animations Personal Tutor Self-Check Quiz ■ *5-Minute Check* ■ *Study Notebook* ■ *Teaching Geometry with Manipulatives*	connectED.mcgraw-hill.com **Materials:** ■ compass ■ straightedge	connectED.mcgraw-hill.com Leveled Worksheets Quiz 2 Vocabulary Animations Personal Tutor Virtual Manipulatives Self-Check Quiz ■ *5-Minute Check* ■ *Study Notebook* ■ *Teaching Geometry with Manipulatives*	connectED.mcgraw-hill.com Leveled Worksheets Personal Tutor Self-Check Quiz ■ *5-Minute Check* ■ *Study Notebook*
IWB eStudent Edition IWB Interactive Classroom	■ eTeacher Edition ■ eSolutions Manual ■ eAssessment		
pp. 480, 486		pp. 493, 494, 499	pp. 503, 506

Formative Assessment
Mid-Chapter Quiz

Chapter Planner

	EXTEND 7-5 (45 min: 0.5 day; 90 min: 0.5 day)	LESSON 7-6 (45 min: 1 day; 90 min: 0.75 day)	LESSON 7-7 (45 min: 1 day; 90 min: 0.75 day)
Title	**Geometry Lab: Fractals**	**Similarity Transformations**	**Scale Drawings and Models**
Objectives	■ Investigate iteration and draw fractals. ■ Write recursive formulas.	■ Identify similarity transformations. ■ Verify similarity after a similarity transformation.	■ Interpret scale models. ■ Use scale factors to solve problems.
Key Vocabulary	fractal iteration self-similar	dilation similarity transformation scale factor of a dilation	scale model scale drawing scale
CCSS		G.SRT.2, G.SRT.5	G.MG.3
Multiple Representations			
Lesson Resources	connectED.mcgraw-hill.com Vocabulary Virtual Manipulatives ■ *Teaching Geometry with Manipulatives* **Materials:** ■ isometric dot paper	connectED.mcgraw-hill.com Leveled Worksheets Quiz 3 Vocabulary Personal Tutor Virtual Manipulatives Self-Check Quiz ■ *5-Minute Check* ■ *Study Notebook*	connectED.mcgraw-hill.com Leveled Worksheets Quiz 4 Vocabulary Animations Personal Tutor Self-Check Quiz ■ *5-Minute Check* ■ *Study Notebook*
Resources for Every Lesson	IWB eStudent Edition IWB Interactive Classroom	■ eTeacher Edition ■ eSolutions Manual ■ eAssessment	
Differentiated Instruction		p. 516	pp. 519, 522

Summative Assessment
Study Guide and Review
Practice Test

What the Research Says...

An instructional approach that moves teachers and students away from dependence on teacher-directed talk and questioning toward student-generated talk and questioning. After students read the text, they highlight the text by noting their likes, dislikes, puzzles (things they wonder about), and patterns they discovered (Chambers, 1996).

- Ask students to read the lessons, instruct them to place question marks where they are unsure, stars where they make connections, and check marks where they disagree. Afterward, have a discussion about their remarks.
- Ask students to summarize their interpretation of the theorems presented in this chapter, providing examples when applicable.

Teacher to Teacher

Mike Patterson
Advanced Technologies Academy
Las Vegas, NV

Use With Lesson 7-1

"I use currency exchange as a way to teach ratios. Every year I have students bring in currency from foreign countries, and we determine its value compared to the U.S. dollar. I am always amazed at how well students handle ratios when it involves money. The students really enjoy this lesson because they are able to see many different forms of money and discuss where they have traveled or lived around the world. I use this every year. It's a big hit!"

Reading and Writing in Mathematics

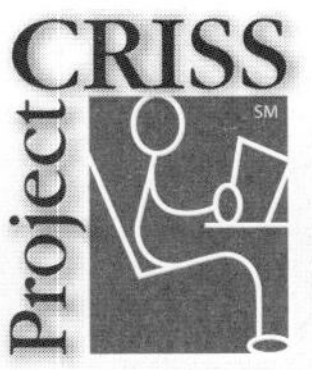

STUDY SKILL

Encourage students to write process notes as they study new concepts and algorithms. Process notes help students work through the steps of problem solving by writing the steps in the left column and the solution of a problem in the right column. The process notes to the right determine whether a pair of figures is similar. Students study this in Lesson 7-2.

Process	Example
Determine whether the △'s are similar.	Triangle ABC with AB = 5, BC = 10, AC = 12.5; triangle EDF with ED = 2, DF = 4, EF = 5
Step 1 Identify corresponding angles and corresponding sides.	Corresponding angles: $\angle A$ and $\angle E$, $\angle C$ and $\angle F$, and $\angle B$ and $\angle D$ Corresponding sides: $\overline{AB}$ and $\overline{DE}$, $\overline{BC}$ and $\overline{DF}$, and $\overline{AC}$ and $\overline{EF}$
Step 2 Determine whether corresponding angles are all congruent.	$\angle A \cong \angle E$; $\angle C \cong \angle F \rightarrow$ given $\angle B \cong \angle D \rightarrow$ Third Angles Theorem
Step 3 Determine whether corresponding sides are proportional.	$\frac{5}{2} = \frac{10}{4} = \frac{12.5}{5} = 2\frac{1}{2}$ ✓
Step 4 If the corresponding angles and corresponding sides are all proportional, the two polygons are similar.	$\triangle ABC \sim \triangle EDF$

Creating Independence through Student-owned Strategies

Assessment and Intervention

SE = Student Edition, **TE** = Teacher Edition, **CRM** = Chapter Resource Masters

	Diagnosis	Prescription
DIAGNOSTIC ASSESSMENT	**Beginning Chapter 7**	
	Get Ready for Chapter 7 **SE**	Response to Intervention **TE**
	Beginning Every Lesson	
	Then, Now, Why? **SE** 5-Minute Checks	Chapter 0 **SE**
FORMATIVE ASSESSMENT	**During/After Every Lesson**	
	Guided Practice **SE**, every example Check Your Understanding **SE** H.O.T. Problems **SE** Spiral Review **SE** Additional Examples **TE** Watch Out! **TE** Step 4, Assess **TE** Chapter 7 Quizzes **CRM**, pp. 51–52 Self-Check Quizzes connectED.mcgraw-hill.com	TIER 1 Intervention Skills Practice **CRM**, Ch. 1–7 connectED.mcgraw-hill.com TIER 2 Intervention Differentiated Instruction **TE** Differentiated Homework Options **TE** Study Guide and Intervention **CRM**, Ch. 1–7 TIER 3 Intervention *Math Triumphs, Geometry,* Ch. 2 and 5
	Mid-Chapter	
	Mid-Chapter Quiz **SE** Mid-Chapter Test **CRM**, p. 53 eAssessment	TIER 1 Intervention Skills Practice **CRM**, Ch. 1–7 connectED.mcgraw-hill.com TIER 2 Intervention Study Guide and Intervention **CRM**, Ch. 1–7 TIER 3 Intervention *Math Triumphs, Geometry,* Ch. 2 and 5
	Before Chapter Test	
	Chapter Study Guide and Review **SE** Practice Test **SE** Standardized Test Practice **SE** Chapter Test connectED.mcgraw-hill.com Standardized Test Practice connectED.mcgraw-hill.com Vocabulary Review connectED.mcgraw-hill.com eAssessment	TIER 1 Intervention Skills Practice **CRM**, Ch. 1–7 connectED.mcgraw-hill.com TIER 2 Intervention Study Guide and Intervention **CRM**, Ch. 1–7 TIER 3 Intervention *Math Triumphs, Geometry,* Ch. 2 and 5
SUMMATIVE ASSESSMENT	**After Chapter 7**	
	Multiple-Choice Tests, Forms 1, 2A, 2B **CRM**, pp. 55–60 Free-Response Tests, Forms 2C, 2D, 3 **CRM**, pp. 61–65 Vocabulary Test **CRM**, p. 54 Extended Response Test **CRM**, p. 67 Standardized Test Practice **CRM**, pp. 68–70 eAssessment	Study Guide and Intervention **CRM**, Ch. 1–7 connectED.mcgraw-hill.com

Differentiated Instruction

Option 1 Reaching All Learners

Intrapersonal Have students use the Internet to explore the Golden Ratio. Have them prepare an explanation about what it is and why it was named this. Ask them to identify sculptures, buildings or artworks that contain rectangles with the golden ratio. They can create a poster or multimedia presentation on their discoveries.

Visual/Spatial Photocopy several polygons for each student. Make a transparency of each polygon. Have students measure the printed polygons that were distributed to them and measure the projected polygons to figure out the factor of proportionality in their perimeters and areas.

Option 2 Approaching Level AL

Ask students to explain the answer to the following question using words and examples.
If you know the price of five gallons of something, how can you use proportions to find out the price of 32 gallons?

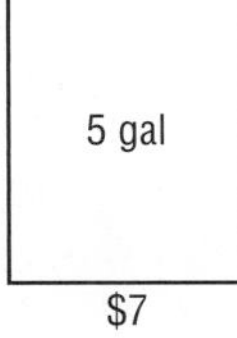

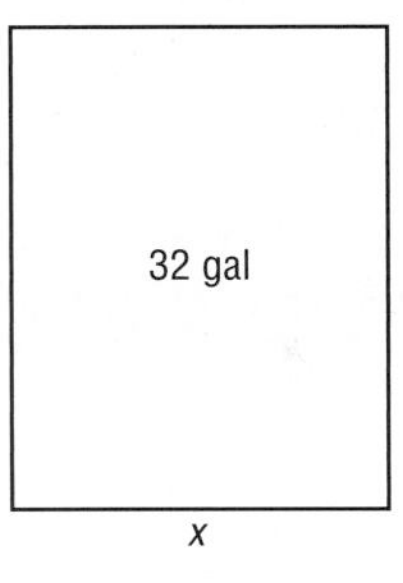

Option 3 English Learners

Have students bring in foreign currency. Have students convert the foreign currency to U.S. currency using proportions. If students are bringing in currency from their native country, allow them time to share stories of the country they came from.

Option 4 Beyond Level BL

Have students use Geometer's Sketch Pad or graph paper to draw and label the cafeteria or library. Have them measure the perimeter of the room and all objects within the perimeter, identifying a scale and key on their sketch.

Chapter 7 discusses the use of the Golden Ratio specifically in art. Challenge students to find more information related to the ratio. Which artists used the ratio in creating their work? Further, can students develop a means of testing the visual appeal of rectangles that exhibit the Golden Ratio in their dimensions?

Focus on Mathematical Content

Vertical Alignment

Before Chapter 7

Related Topics from Grade 8

- Solve real-life problems including those involving proportional relationships.
- Describe effects when dimensions change proportionally.

Related Topics from Algebra 1

- Use symbols to represent unknowns and variables.
- Look for patterns and represent generalizations algebraically.

Chapter 7

Related Topics from Geometry

- Use ratios to solve problems involving similar figures.
- Formulate and test conjectures about the properties and attributes of polygons and their component parts based on explorations and concrete models.

After Chapter 7

Preparation for Precalculus

- Represent patterns using arithmetic and geometric sequences and series.
- Use properties of functions to analyze, solve problems, and make predictions.

Lesson-by-Lesson Preview

7-1 Ratios and Proportions

A *ratio* is a comparison of two quantities. The ratio of a to b can be expressed $\frac{a}{b}$, where b is not zero, or as $a : b$. The ratio of two corresponding quantities is called a *scale factor.* For example, a model might be $\frac{1}{8}$ the size of the actual object. An equation stating that two ratios are equal is a *proportion.* Equivalent fractions are set equal to each other to form a proportion. Every proportion has two cross products. To find the cross products, multiply the numerator of the first fraction by the denominator of the second fraction, and the numerator of the second fraction by the denominator of the first fraction. One cross product forms the *extremes*, the other the *means*. The product of the means equals the product of the extremes. In other words, for any numbers a and c and any nonzero numbers b and d, $\frac{a}{b} = \frac{c}{d}$ if and only if $ad = bc$.

7-2 Similar Polygons

When figures have the same shape but may be different in size, they are similar figures. Two polygons are similar if and only if their corresponding angles are congruent and the measures of their corresponding sides are proportional. The order of the vertices is important because it identifies the corresponding angles and sides.

similarity statement	congruent angles	corresponding sides
$ABCD \sim EFGH$	$\angle A \cong \angle E$ $\angle B \cong \angle F$ $\angle C \cong \angle G$ $\angle D \cong \angle H$	$\frac{AB}{EF} = \frac{BC}{FG} = \frac{CD}{GH} = \frac{DA}{HE}$

The ratio of the lengths of two corresponding sides of two similar polygons is the scale factor. The use of scale factors will produce similar figures.

7-3 Similar Triangles

For triangles to be similar, their corresponding angles must be congruent and the measures of their corresponding sides must be proportional. However, triangles can be proved similar without knowing the measures of every angle and side. The Angle-Angle Similarity Postulate states that if two angles of one triangle are congruent to two angles of another triangle, then the triangles are similar.

If the measures of the corresponding sides of two triangles are proportional, then the triangles are similar (Side-Side-Side Similarity Theorem). If the measures of two sides of a triangle are proportional to the measures of two corresponding sides of another triangle and the included angles are congruent, then the triangles are similar (Side-Angle-Side Similarity Theorem).

Similarity of triangles is reflexive, symmetric, and transitive. Properties of similar triangles can be used to solve real-world problems by using indirect measurement.

7-4 Parallel Lines and Proportional Parts

The Triangle Proportionality Theorem states that if a line is parallel to one side of a triangle and intersects the other two sides in two distinct points, then it separates these sides into segments of proportional lengths. The converse of this theorem also holds true. If a line intersects two sides of a triangle and separates the sides into corresponding segments of proportional lengths, then the line is parallel to the third side. These theorems can be extended to three or more parallel lines. If three or more parallel lines intersect two transversals, then they cut off the transversals proportionally. If three or more parallel lines cut off congruent segments on one transversal, then they cut off congruent segments on every transversal.

One notable case of a line parallel to one side of a triangle is the *midsegment*. A midsegment is a segment with endpoints that are the midpoints of two sides of the triangle. A midsegment is parallel to one side of the triangle, and its length is one-half the length of that side.

7-5 Parts of Similar Triangles

If two triangles are similar, then the perimeters are proportional to the measures of corresponding sides. This proportionality relationship is also seen in the altitudes of similar triangles. If two triangles are similar, then the measures of the corresponding altitudes are proportional to the measures of the corresponding sides. In fact, this relationship holds true for angle bisectors and medians as well.

There is also a relationship between an angle bisector and the side of the triangle opposite the angle. An angle bisector in a triangle separates the opposite side into segments that have the same ratio as the other two sides.

7-6 Similarity Transformations

A similarity transformation is an operation that maps an original figure, the preimage, onto a new similar figure, the image. Dilations are one type of similarity factor. A *dilation* is an enlargement if the scale factor is greater than 1, or a reduction if the scale factor is between 0 and 1. Similarity transformations can be verified by using coordinate geometry.

7-7 Scale Drawings and Models

A *scale model* or a *scale drawing* is an object or drawing with lengths proportional to the object it represents. The scale is the ratio of a length on the object or drawing to the actual length of the object it represents.

Professional Development

Targeted professional development has been articulated throughout Geometry. More quality, customized professional development is available from McGraw-Hill Professional Development. Visit connectED.mcgraw-hill.com for details on each product.

- Online Lessons emphasize the strategies and techniques used to teach Geometry. Includes streaming video, interactive pages, and online tools.
- Video Workshops allow mentors, coaches, or leadership personnel to facilitate on-site workshops on educational strategies in mathematics and mathematical concepts.
- MHPD Online (www.mhpdonline.com) offers online professional development with video clips of instructional strategies, links, student activities, and news and issues in education.
- Teaching Today (teachingtoday.glencoe.com) gives secondary teachers practical strategies and materials that inspire excellence and innovation in teaching.

Chapter Project

Model Makers

Students use what they have learned about ratios, proportions, and scale drawings to complete a project.

This chapter project addresses business literacy, as well as several specific skills identified as being essential to student success by the Framework for 21st Century Learning.

Visit connectED.mcgraw-hill.com for student and teacher handouts.

KeyVocabulary Introduce the key vocabulary in the chapter using the routine below.

Define: The scale factor is the ratio of the lengths of the corresponding sides of two similar polygons.

Example: In the diagram, $\triangle DFG \sim \triangle JHK$.

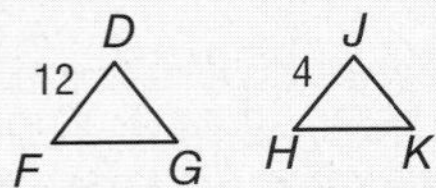

Ask: What is the scale factor of $\triangle DFG$ to $\triangle JHK$? $\frac{12}{4}$ or 3

What is the scale factor of $\triangle JHK$ to $\triangle DFG$?
$\frac{4}{12}$ or $\frac{1}{3}$

CHAPTER 7 Proportions and Similarity

Then

You learned about ratios and proportions and applied them to real-world applications.

Now

In this chapter, you will:

- Identify similar polygons and use ratios and proportions to solve problems.
- Identify and apply similarity transformations.
- Use scale models and drawings to solve problems.

Why?

SPORTS Similar triangles can be used in sports to describe the path of a ball, such as a bounce pass from one person to another.

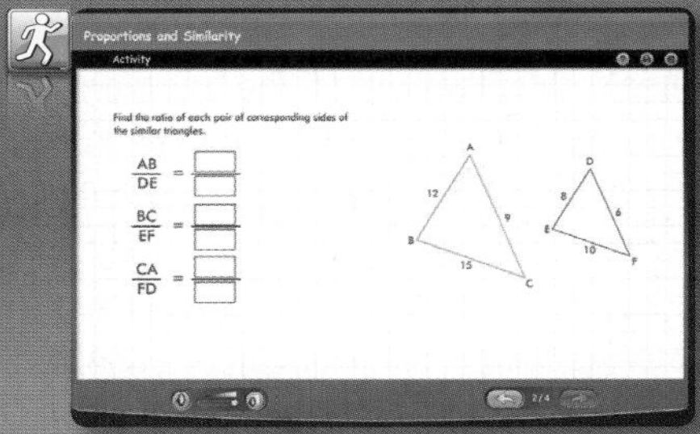

connectED.mcgraw-hill.com Your Digital Math Portal

Animation | Vocabulary | eGlossary | Personal Tutor | Virtual Manipulatives | Graphing Calculator | Audio | Foldables | Self-Check Practice | Worksheets

Get Ready for the Chapter

Diagnose Readiness | You have two options for checking prerequisite skills.

1 Textbook Option

Take the Quick Check below. Refer to the Quick Review for help.

QuickCheck

Solve each equation.

1. $\frac{3x}{8} = \frac{6}{x}$ 4 or −4
2. $\frac{7}{3} = \frac{x-4}{6}$ 18
3. $\frac{x+9}{2} = \frac{3x-1}{8}$ −37
4. $\frac{3}{2x} = \frac{3x}{8}$ 2 or −2
5. **EDUCATION** The student to teacher ratio at Elder High School is 17 to 1. If there are 1088 students in the school, how many teachers are there? 64

QuickReview

Example 1 (Used in Lessons 7-1 through 7-7)

Solve $\frac{4x-3}{5} = \frac{2x+11}{3}$.

$\frac{4x-3}{5} = \frac{2x+11}{3}$	Original equation
$3(4x - 3) = 5(2x + 11)$	Cross multiplication
$12x - 9 = 10x + 55$	Distributive Property
$2x = 64$	Add.
$x = 32$	Simplify.

ALGEBRA In the figure, $\overrightarrow{BA}$ and $\overrightarrow{BC}$ are opposite rays and $\overrightarrow{BD}$ bisects $\angle ABF$.

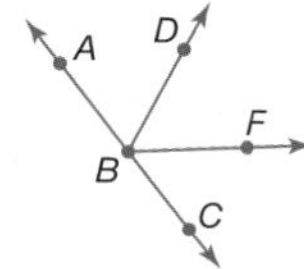

6. If $m\angle ABF = 3x - 8$ and $m\angle ABD = x + 14$, find $m\angle ABD$. 50
7. If $m\angle FBC = 2x + 25$ and $m\angle ABF = 10x - 1$, find $m\angle DBF$. 64.5
8. **LANDSCAPING** A landscape architect is planning to add sidewalks around a fountain as shown below. If $\overrightarrow{BA}$ and $\overrightarrow{BC}$ are opposite rays and $\overrightarrow{BD}$ bisects $\angle ABF$, find $m\angle FBC$. 64

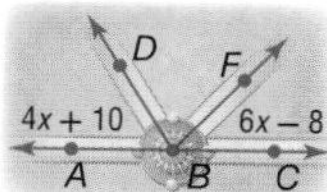

Example 2 (Used in Lesson 7-5)

In the figure, $\overrightarrow{QP}$ and $\overrightarrow{QR}$ are opposite rays, and $\overrightarrow{QT}$ bisects $\angle SQR$. If $m\angle SQR = 6x + 8$ and $m\angle TQR = 4x - 14$, find $m\angle SQT$.

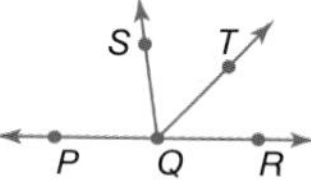

Since $\overrightarrow{TQ}$ bisects $\angle SQR$, $m\angle SQR = 2(m\angle TQR)$.

$m\angle SQR = 2(m\angle TQR)$	Def. of ∠ bisector
$6x + 8 = 2(4x - 14)$	Substitution
$6x + 8 = 8x - 28$	Distributive Property
$-2x = -36$	Subtract.
$x = 18$	Simplify.

Since $\overrightarrow{TQ}$ bisects $\angle SQR$, $m\angle SQT = m\angle TQR$.

$m\angle SQT = m\angle TQR$	Def. of ∠ bisector
$m\angle SQT = 4x - 14$	Substitution
$m\angle SQT = 58$	$x = 18$

2 Online Option

Take an online self-check Chapter Readiness Quiz at connectED.mcgraw-hill.com.

459

Essential Questions

- How can two objects be similar? Sample answers: Two objects could have similar designs, patterns, shapes, sizes, or colors.
- How does similarity in mathematics compare to similarity in everyday life? Sample answer: In mathematics, similarity has a more specific definition: objects or figures can only be similar if they have the same shape.

Get Ready for the Chapter

Response to Intervention (RtI)

Use the *Quick Check* results and the Intervention Planner chart to help you determine your Response to Intervention. The If-Then statements in the chart help you decide the appropriate tier of RtI and suggest intervention resources for each tier.

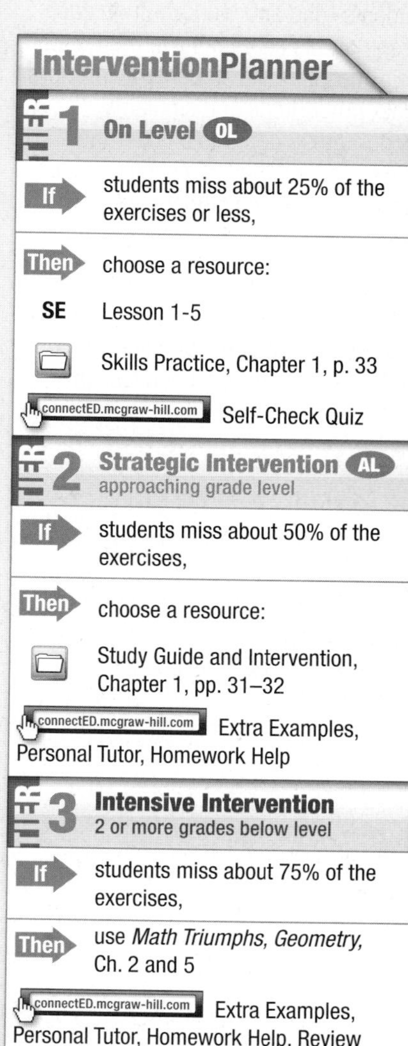

InterventionPlanner

TIER 1 On Level OL

If students miss about 25% of the exercises or less,

Then choose a resource:

SE Lesson 1-5

Skills Practice, Chapter 1, p. 33

connectED.mcgraw-hill.com Self-Check Quiz

TIER 2 Strategic Intervention AL approaching grade level

If students miss about 50% of the exercises,

Then choose a resource:

Study Guide and Intervention, Chapter 1, pp. 31–32

connectED.mcgraw-hill.com Extra Examples, Personal Tutor, Homework Help

TIER 3 Intensive Intervention 2 or more grades below level

If students miss about 75% of the exercises,

Then use *Math Triumphs, Geometry,* Ch. 2 and 5

connectED.mcgraw-hill.com Extra Examples, Personal Tutor, Homework Help, Review Vocabulary

FOLDABLES StudyOrganizer

Dinah Zike's Foldables®

Focus Students write notes about each lesson in this chapter.

Teach Have students make and label the Foldable as illustrated.

Students use their Foldables for notes, problem solving, and descriptions. As students read and work through each lesson of this chapter, have them record their questions. As students learn more about proportions and similarity, encourage students to answer their own questions. Self-questioning is a strategy that helps students stay focused during reading.

When to use it Use the appropriate tabs as students cover each lesson in this chapter. Students can add to the vocabulary tab during each lesson.

Differentiated Instruction

Student-Built Glossary, p. 1

Students complete the chart by providing the definition of each term and an example as they progress through Chapter 7. This study tool can also be used to review for the chapter test.

Get Started on the Chapter

You will learn several new concepts, skills, and vocabulary terms as you study Chapter 7. To get ready, identify important terms and organize your resources. You may wish to refer to Chapter 0 to review prerequisite skills.

FOLDABLES StudyOrganizer

Proportions and Similarity Make this Foldable to help you organize your Chapter 7 notes about proportions, similar polygons, and similarity transformations. Begin with four sheets of notebook paper.

1 **Fold** the four sheets of paper in half.

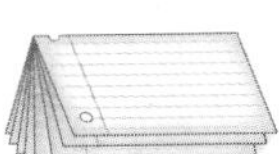

2 **Cut** along the top fold of the papers. Staple along the side to form a book.

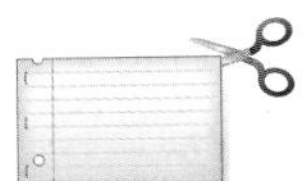

3 **Cut** the right sides of each paper to create a tab for each lesson.

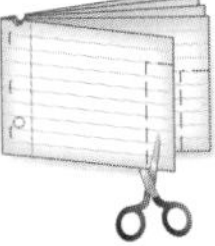

4 **Label** each tab with a lesson number, as shown.

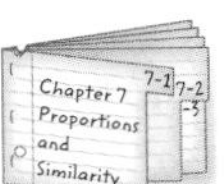

NewVocabulary

English		Español
ratio	p. 461	razón
proportion	p. 462	proporción
extremes	p. 462	extremos
means	p. 462	medias
cross products	p. 462	productos cruzados
similar polygons	p. 469	polígonos semejantes
scale factor	p. 470	factor de escala
dilation	p. 511	homotecia
similarity transformation	p. 511	transformación de semejanza
enlargement	p. 511	ampliación
reduction	p. 511	reducción
scale model	p. 518	modelo a escala
scale drawing	p. 518	dibujo a escala

ReviewVocabulary

altitude altura a segment drawn from a vertex of a triangle perpendicular to the line containing the other side

angle bisector bisectriz de un ángulo a ray that divides an angle into two congruent angles

median mediana a segment drawn from a vertex of a triangle to the midpoint of the opposite side

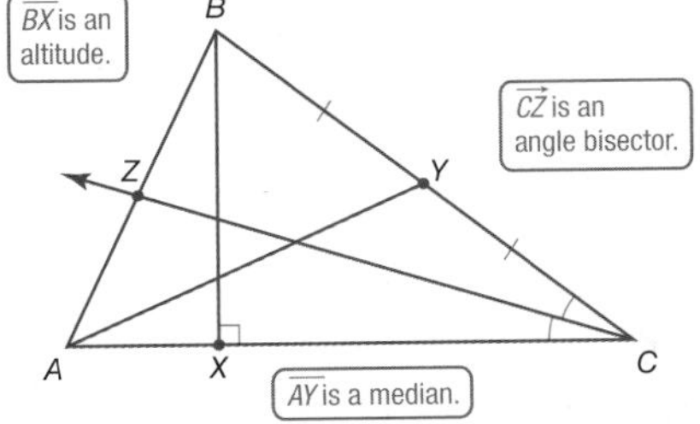

460 | Chapter 7 | Proportions and Similarity

LESSON 7-1 Ratios and Proportions

Then

- You solved problems by writing and solving equations.

Now

1. Write ratios.
2. Write and solve proportions.

Why?

- The aspect ratio of a television or computer screen is the screen's width divided by its height. A standard television screen has an aspect ratio of $\frac{4}{3}$ or 4:3, while a high definition television screen (HDTV) has an aspect ratio of 16:9.

NewVocabulary
ratio
extended ratios
proportion
extremes
means
cross products

Common Core State Standards

Content Standards
G.MG.3 Apply geometric methods to solve problems (e.g., designing an object or structure to satisfy physical constraints or minimize cost; working with typographic grid systems based on ratios). ★

Mathematical Practices
7 Look for and make use of structure.
8 Look for and express regularity in repeated reasoning.

1 Write and Use Ratios

A **ratio** is a comparison of two quantities using division. The ratio of quantities a and b can be expressed as a to b, $a:b$, or $\frac{a}{b}$, where $b \neq 0$. Ratios are usually expressed in simplest form.

The aspect ratios 32:18 and 16:9 are equivalent.

$$\frac{\text{width of screen}}{\text{height of screen}} = \frac{32 \text{ in.}}{18 \text{ in.}}$$ Divide out units.

$$= \frac{32 \div 2}{18 \div 2} \text{ or } \frac{16}{9}$$ Divide out common factors.

Real-World Example 1 Write and Simplify Ratios

SPORTS A baseball player's batting average is the ratio of the number of base hits to the number of at-bats, not including walks. Minnesota Twins' Joe Mauer had the highest batting average in Major League Baseball in 2006. If he had 521 official at-bats and 181 hits, find his batting average.

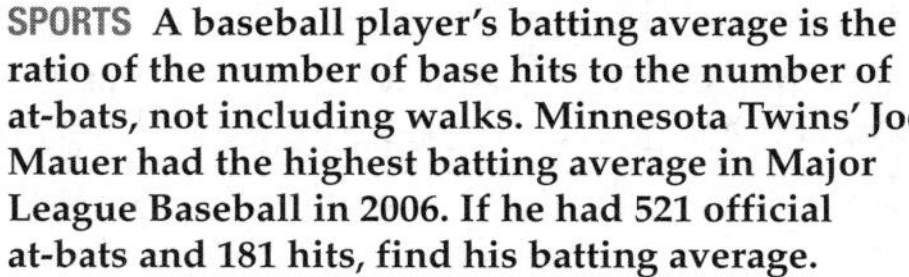

Divide the number of hits by the number of at-bats.

$$\frac{\text{number of hits}}{\text{number of at-bats}} = \frac{181}{521}$$

$$\approx \frac{0.347}{1}$$ A ratio in which the denominator is 1 is called a *unit ratio.*

Joe Mauer's batting average was 0.347.

GuidedPractice

1. SCHOOL In Logan's high school, there are 190 teachers and 2650 students. What is the approximate student-teacher ratio at his school? **about 14:1**

Extended ratios can be used to compare three or more quantities. The expression $a:b:c$ means that the ratio of the first two quantities is $a:b$, the ratio of the last two quantities is $b:c$, and the ratio of the first and last quantities is $a:c$.

1 Focus

VerticalAlignment

Before Lesson 7-1 Solve problems by writing and solving equations.

Lesson 7-1 Write ratios. Write and solve proportions.

After Lesson 7-1 Use and extend similarity properties to explore and justify conjectures about geometric figures.

2 Teach

Scaffolding Questions

Have students read the **Why?** section of the lesson.

Ask:

- If the dimensions of the screen shown are 32 inches by 18 inches, is the screen standard or high definition? high definition
- Would a standard television have a narrower or wider screen? narrower
- What is the height of a high definition television that is 48 inches wide? 27 inches

Lesson 7-1 Resources

Resource	Approaching Level AL	On Level OL	Beyond Level BL	English Learners ELL
Teacher Edition	▪ Differentiated Instruction, p. 462	▪ Differentiated Instruction, pp. 462, 463	▪ Differentiated Instruction, pp. 462, 463	
Chapter Resource Masters	▪ Study Guide and Intervention, pp. 5–6 ▪ Skills Practice, p. 7 ▪ Practice, p. 8 ▪ Word Problem Practice, p. 9	▪ Study Guide and Intervention, pp. 5–6 ▪ Skills Practice, p. 7 ▪ Practice, p. 8 ▪ Word Problem Practice, p. 9 ▪ Enrichment, p. 10 ▪ Graphing Calculator Activity, p. 11	▪ Practice, p. 8 ▪ Word Problem Practice, p. 9 ▪ Enrichment, p. 10	▪ Study Guide and Intervention, pp. 5–6 ▪ Skills Practice, p. 7 ▪ Practice, p. 8 ▪ Word Problem Practice, p. 9
Other	▪ 5-Minute Check 7-1 ▪ Study Notebook	▪ 5-Minute Check 7-1 ▪ Study Notebook	▪ 5-Minute Check 7-1 ▪ Study Notebook	▪ 5-Minute Check 7-1 ▪ Study Notebook

1 Write and Use Ratios

Examples 1 and 2 show how to use comparable quantities to write ratios.

Formative Assessment

Use the Guided Practice exercises after each example to determine students' understanding of concepts.

Additional Examples

1 **SCHOOL** The number of students that participate in sports programs at Central High School is 520. The total number of students in the school is 1850. Find the athlete-to-student ratio to the nearest tenth. 0.3

2 In $\triangle EFG$, the ratio of the measures of the angles is 5:12:13, and the perimeter is 90 centimeters. Find the measures of the angles. 30, 72, 78

Additional Examples also in Interactive Classroom PowerPoint® Presentations

Tips for New Teachers

Reasoning Remind students that while ratios often appear as fractions, a ratio is a comparison of two quantities. This means that if the quantities have units, the numerator and denominator should have the same units and in some cases a conversion factor may be needed.

WatchOut!

Undefined Ratios The equations $ab = cd$ and $\frac{a}{b} = \frac{c}{d}$ are equivalent only when b and d are nonzero.

Example 2 Use Extended Ratios

The ratio of the measures of the angles in a triangle is 3:4:5. Find the measures of the angles.

Just as the ratio $\frac{3}{4}$ or 3:4 is equivalent to $\frac{3x}{4x}$ or $3x:4x$, the extended ratio 3:4:5 can be written as $3x:4x:5x$.

Sketch and label the angle measures of the triangle. Then write and solve an equation to find the value of x.

$3x + 4x + 5x = 180$ Triangle Sum Theorem

$12x = 180$ Combine like terms.

$x = 15$ Divide each side by 12.

So the measures of the angles are 3(15) or 45, 4(15) or 60, and 5(15) or 75.

CHECK The sum of the angle measures should be 180.

$45 + 60 + 75 = 180$ ✓

GuidedPractice

2. In a triangle, the ratio of the measures of the sides is 2:2:3 and the perimeter is 392 inches. Find the length of the longest side of the triangle. 168 in.

ReadingMath

Proportion When a proportion is written using colons, it is read using the word *to* for the colon. For example, 2:3 is read *2 to 3*. The means are the inside numbers, and the extremes are the outside numbers.

extremes
2:3 = 6:9
means

2 Use Properties of Proportions

An equation stating that two ratios are equal is called a **proportion**. In the proportion $\frac{a}{b} = \frac{c}{d}$, the numbers a and d are called the **extremes** of the proportion, while the numbers b and c are called the **means** of the proportion.

extreme → $\frac{a}{b} = \frac{c}{d}$ ← mean
mean → ← extreme

The product of the extremes ad and the product of the means bc are called **cross products**.

KeyConcept Cross Products Property

Words	In a proportion, the product of the extremes equals the product of the means.
Symbols	If $\frac{a}{b} = \frac{c}{d}$ when $b \neq 0$ and $d \neq 0$, then $ad = bc$.
Example	If $\frac{4}{10} = \frac{6}{15}$, then $4 \cdot 15 = 10 \cdot 6$.

You will prove the Cross Products Property in Exercise 41.

The converse of the Cross Products Property is also true. If $ad = bc$ and $b \neq 0$ and $d \neq 0$, then $\frac{a}{b} = \frac{c}{d}$. That is, $\frac{a}{b}$ and $\frac{c}{d}$ form a proportion. You can use the Cross Products Property to solve a proportion.

DifferentiatedInstruction AL OL BL

Logical/Mathematical Learners Stress that the proportion $\frac{a}{b} = \frac{c}{d}$ can also be written as $\frac{c}{d} = \frac{a}{b}$. Ask students to find the product of the means and the product of the extremes for each proportion. Then use the Commutative Property of Multiplication to verify that in each case, $ad = bc$.

Example 3 Use Cross Products to Solve Proportions

Solve each proportion.

a. $\frac{6}{x} = \frac{21}{31.5}$

$\frac{6}{x} = \frac{21}{31.5}$	Original proportion
$6(31.5) = x(21)$	Cross Products Property
$189 = 21x$	Simplify.
$9 = x$	Solve for *x*.

b. $\frac{x+3}{2} = \frac{4x}{5}$

$$\frac{x+3}{2} = \frac{4x}{5}$$
$$(x+3)5 = 2(4x)$$
$$5x + 15 = 8x$$
$$15 = 3x$$
$$5 = x$$

StudyTip

CCSS Perseverance Example 3b could also be solved by multiplying each side of the equation by 10, the least common denominator.

$$10\left(\frac{x+3}{2}\right) = \frac{4x}{5}(10)$$
$$5(x+3) = 2(4x)$$
$$5x + 15 = 8x$$
$$15 = 3x$$
$$5 = x$$

GuidedPractice

3A. $\frac{x}{4} = \frac{11}{-6}$ $-\frac{22}{3}$

3B. $\frac{-4}{7} = \frac{6}{2y+5}$ $-\frac{31}{4}$

3C. $\frac{7}{z-1} = \frac{9}{z+4}$ $\frac{37}{2}$

Proportions can be used to make predictions.

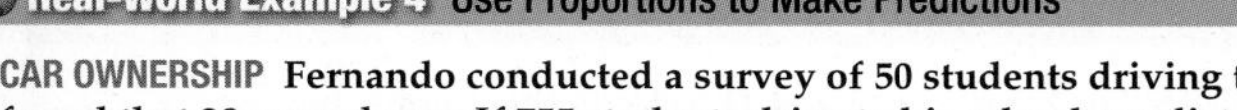

Real-World Example 4 Use Proportions to Make Predictions

CAR OWNERSHIP **Fernando conducted a survey of 50 students driving to school and found that 28 owned cars. If 755 students drive to his school, predict the total number of students who own cars.**

Write and solve a proportion that compares the number of students who own cars to the number who drive to school.

$$\frac{28}{50} = \frac{x}{755}$$ ← students owning cars / ← students driving to school

$28 \cdot 755 = 50 \cdot x$	Cross Products Property
$21{,}140 = 50x$	Simplify.
$422.8 = x$	Divide each side by 50.

Based on Fernando's survey, about 423 students at his school own cars.

Real-WorldLink

The percent of driving-age teens (ages 15 to 20) with their own vehicles nearly doubled nationwide from 22 percent in 1985 to 42 percent in 2003.

Source: CNW Marketing Research

GuidedPractice

4. **BIOLOGY** In an experiment, students netted butterflies, recorded the number with tags on their wings, and then released them. The students netted 48 butterflies and 3 of those had tagged wings. Predict the number of butterflies that would have tagged wings out of 100 netted. **about 6 butterflies**

The proportion shown in Example 4 is not the only correct proportion for that situation. Equivalent forms of a proportion all have identical cross products.

KeyConcept Equivalent Proportions

Symbols The following proportions are equivalent.

$$\frac{a}{b} = \frac{c}{d}, \quad \frac{b}{a} = \frac{d}{c}, \quad \frac{a}{c} = \frac{b}{d}, \quad \frac{c}{a} = \frac{d}{b}$$

Examples $\frac{28}{50} = \frac{x}{755}, \frac{50}{28} = \frac{755}{x}, \frac{28}{x} = \frac{50}{755}, \frac{x}{28} = \frac{755}{50}.$

DifferentiatedInstruction OL BL

Extension A rate is a ratio that compares two quantities, one of which can be an amount of time. Have students name a commonly used rate. A unit rate uses one as a denominator. Have students make up word problems using a proportion with a unit rate. Sample answer: Miles per hour; problems will vary.

2 Use Properties of Proportions

Examples 3 and 4 show how to use the Cross Products Property to solve proportions.

Additional Examples

3 Solve each proportion.

a. $\frac{6}{18.2} = \frac{9}{y}$ 27.3

b. $\frac{4x-5}{3} = \frac{-26}{6}$ -2

4 **PETS** Monique randomly surveyed 30 students from her class and found that 18 had a dog or a cat for a pet. If there are 870 students in Monique's school, predict the total number of students with a dog or a cat. 522

CCSS Teaching the Mathematical Practices

Perseverance Mathematically proficient students check their answers to problems using a different method, and they continually ask themselves, "does this make sense?" Encourage students to use alternative methods of problem solving.

Teach with Tech

Interactive Whiteboard Write two ratios on the board and show students how to determine if they form a proportion. Drag the numerators and denominators to show how to form the cross products and then simplify.

Focus on Mathematical Content

Intervention Students may have previous experience with solving equations by cross-multiplying. Emphasize that a proportion is a statement of equality between ratios. Because the product of the means equals the product of extremes, cross multiplying can be used to solve a proportion.

3 Practice

Formative Assessment
Use Exercises 1–9 to check for understanding.

Use the chart at the bottom of this page to customize assignments for your students.

Teaching the Mathematical Practices

Modeling Mathematically proficient students can apply the mathematics they know to solve problems arising in everyday life. In Exercises 9 and 39, encourage students to read the exercises carefully to identify the ratios needed to solve the problems.

Additional Answers

38a. Decreased; 60.2% of teens had jobs in 2000 and 51.6% had jobs in 2006.

38b. About 361 teens or 51.6% of 700.

Check Your Understanding

= Step-by-Step Solutions begin on page R14.

Example 1

1. **PETS** Out of a survey of 1000 households, 460 had at least one dog or cat as a pet. What is the ratio of pet owners to households? **23:50**

2. **SPORTS** Thirty girls tried out for 15 spots on the basketball team. What is the ratio of open spots to the number of girls competing? **1:2**

Example 2

3. The ratio of the measures of three sides of a triangle is 2:5:4, and its perimeter is 165 units. Find the measure of each side of the triangle. **30, 75, 60**

4. The ratios of the measures of three angles of a triangle are 4:6:8. Find the measure of each angle of the triangle. **40, 60, 80**

Example 3

Solve each proportion.

5. $\frac{2}{3} = \frac{x}{24}$ **16**
6. $\frac{x}{5} = \frac{28}{100}$ **1.4**
7. $\frac{2.2}{x} = \frac{26.4}{96}$ **8**
8. $\frac{x-3}{3} = \frac{5}{8}$ **4.875**

Example 4

9. CCSS **MODELING** Ella is baking apple muffins for the Student Council bake sale. The recipe that she is using calls for 2 eggs per dozen muffins, and she needs to make 108 muffins. How many eggs will she need? **18**

Practice and Problem Solving

Extra Practice is on page R7.

Example 1

MOVIES For Exercises 10 and 11, refer to the graphic below.

10. Of the films listed, which had the greatest ratio of Academy Awards to number of nominations? **Movie B; 1:1**

11. Which film listed had the lowest ratio of awards to nominations? **Movie A; 1:2**

Example 2

12. **GAMES** A video game store has 60 games to choose from, including 40 sports games. What is the ratio of sports games to video games? **2:3**

13. The ratio of the measures of the three sides of a triangle is 9 : 7 : 5. Its perimeter is 191.1 inches. Find the measure of each side. **81.9 in., 63.7 in., 45.5 in.**

14. The ratio of the measures of the three sides of a triangle is 3:7:5, and its perimeter is 156.8 meters. Find the measure of each side. **31.4 m, 73.2 m, 52.3 m**

15. The ratio of the measures of the three sides of a triangle is $\frac{1}{4}:\frac{1}{8}:\frac{1}{6}$. Its perimeter is 4.75 feet. Find the length of the longest side. **2.2 ft**

16. The ratio of the measures of the three sides of a triangle is $\frac{1}{4}:\frac{1}{3}:\frac{1}{6}$, and its perimeter is 31.5 centimeters. Find the length of the shortest side. **7 cm**

Differentiated Homework Options

Level	Assignment	Two-Day Option	
AL Basic	10–30, 44, 46–65	11–29 odd, 50–53	10–30 even, 38–44, 46–49, 54–65
OL Core	11–37 odd, 38–44, 46–65	10–30, 50–53	31–44, 46–49, 54–65
BL Advanced	31–64, (65 optional)		

Find the measures of the angles of each triangle.

17. The ratio of the measures of the three angles is 3:6:1. **54, 108, 18**

18. The ratio of the measures of the three angles is 7:5:8. **63, 45, 72**

19. The ratio of the measures of the three angles is 10:8:6. **75, 60, 45**

20. The ratio of the measures of the three angles is 5:4:7. **56.25, 45, 78.75**

Example 3 **Solve each proportion.**

21. $\frac{5}{8} = \frac{y}{3}$ $\frac{15}{8}$ 22. $\frac{w}{6.4} = \frac{1}{2}$ **3.2** 23. $\frac{4x}{24} = \frac{56}{112}$ **3** 24. $\frac{11}{20} = \frac{55}{20x}$ **5**

25. $\frac{2x+5}{10} = \frac{42}{20}$ **8** 26. $\frac{a+2}{a-2} = \frac{3}{2}$ **10** 27. $\frac{3x-1}{4} = \frac{2x+4}{5}$ **3** 28. $\frac{3x-6}{2} = \frac{4x-2}{4}$ **5**

Example 4 29. **NUTRITION** According to a recent study, 7 out of every 500 Americans aged 13 to 17 years are vegetarian. In a group of 350 13- to 17-year-olds, about how many would you expect to be vegetarian? **about 5**

30. **CURRENCY** Your family is traveling to Mexico on vacation. You have saved \$500 to use for spending money. If 269 Mexican pesos is equivalent to 25 United States dollars, how much money will you get when you exchange your \$500 for pesos? **5380 pesos**

ALGEBRA **Solve each proportion. Round to the nearest tenth.**

31. $\frac{2x+3}{3} = \frac{6}{x-1}$ **3, −3.5** 32. $\frac{x^2+4x+4}{40} = \frac{x+2}{10}$ **2, −2** 33. $\frac{9x+6}{18} = \frac{20x+4}{3x}$ **12.9, −0.2**

34. The perimeter of a rectangle is 98 feet. The ratio of its length to its width is 5:2. Find the area of the rectangle. **490 ft²**

35. The perimeter of a rectangle is 220 inches. The ratio of its length to its width is 7:3. Find the area of the rectangle. **2541 in²**

36. The ratio of the measures of the side lengths of a quadrilateral is 2:3:5:4. Its perimeter is 154 feet. Find the length of the shortest side. **22 ft**

37. The ratio of the measures of the angles of a quadrilateral is 2:4:6:3. Find the measures of the angles of the quadrilateral. **48, 96, 144, 72**

38. **SUMMER JOBS** In June of 2000, 60.2% of American teens 16 to 19 years old had summer jobs. By June of 2006, 51.6% of teens in that age group were a part of the summer work force.

a. Has the number of 16- to 19-year-olds with summer jobs increased or decreased since 2000? Explain your reasoning. **See margin.**

b. In June 2006, how many 16- to 19-year-olds would you expect to have jobs out of 700 in that age group? Explain your reasoning. **See margin.**

39. **CCSS MODELING** In a golden rectangle, the ratio of the length to the width is about 1.618. This is known as the *golden ratio*.

a. Recall from page 461 that a standard television screen has an aspect ratio of 4:3, while a high-definition television screen has an aspect ratio of 16:9. Is either type of screen a golden rectangle? Explain.

b. The golden ratio can also be used to determine column layouts for Web pages. Consider a site with two columns, the left for content and the right as a sidebar. The ratio of the left to right column widths is the golden ratio. Determine the width of each column if the page is 960 pixels wide.

39a. No; the HDTV aspect ratio is 1.77778 and the standard aspect ratio is 1.33333. Neither television set is a golden rectangle since the ratios of the lengths to the widths are not the golden ratio.

39b. 593 pixels and 367 pixels

40. **SCHOOL ACTIVITIES** A survey of club involvement showed that, of the 36 students surveyed, the ratio of French Club members to Spanish Club members to Drama Club members was 2:3:7. How many of those surveyed participate in Spanish Club? Assume that each student is active in only one club. **9 students**

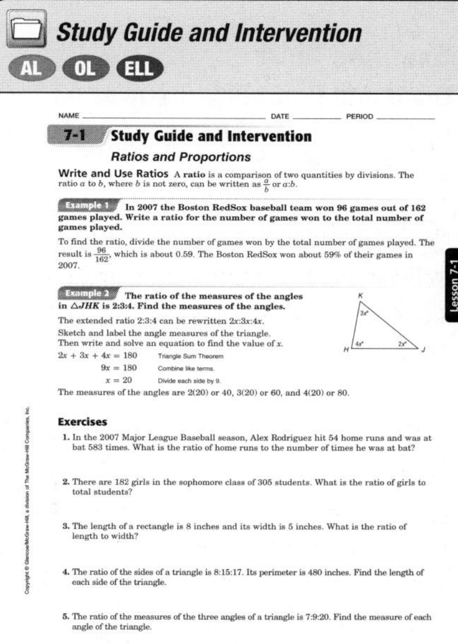

Study Guide and Intervention AL OL ELL

7-1 Study Guide and Intervention

Ratios and Proportions

Write and Use Ratios A **ratio** is a comparison of two quantities by divisions. The ratio a to b, where b is not zero, can be written as $\frac{a}{b}$ or $a:b$.

Example 1 In 2007 the Boston RedSox baseball team won 96 games out of 162 games played. Write a ratio for the number of games won to the total number of games played.

To find the ratio, divide the number of games won by the total number of games played. The result is $\frac{96}{162}$, which is about 0.59. The Boston RedSox won about 59% of their games in 2007.

Example 2 The ratio of the measures of the angles in △JHK is 2:3:4. Find the measures of the angles.

The extended ratio 2:3:4 can be rewritten 2x:3x:4x. Sketch and label the angle measures of the triangle. Then write and solve an equation to find the value of x.

2x + 3x + 4x = 180 Triangle Sum Theorem
9x = 180 Combine like terms.
x = 20 Divide each side by 9.

The measures of the angles are 2(20) or 40, 3(20) or 60, and 4(20) or 80.

Exercises

1. In the 2007 Major League Baseball season, Alex Rodriguez hit 54 home runs and was at bat 583 times. What is the ratio of home runs to the number of times he was at bat?

2. There are 182 girls in the sophomore class of 305 students. What is the ratio of girls to total students?

3. The length of a rectangle is 8 inches and its width is 5 inches. What is the ratio of length to width?

4. The ratio of the sides of a triangle is 8:15:17. Its perimeter is 480 inches. Find the length of each side of the triangle.

5. The ratio of the measures of the three angles of a triangle is 7:9:20. Find the measure of each angle of the triangle.

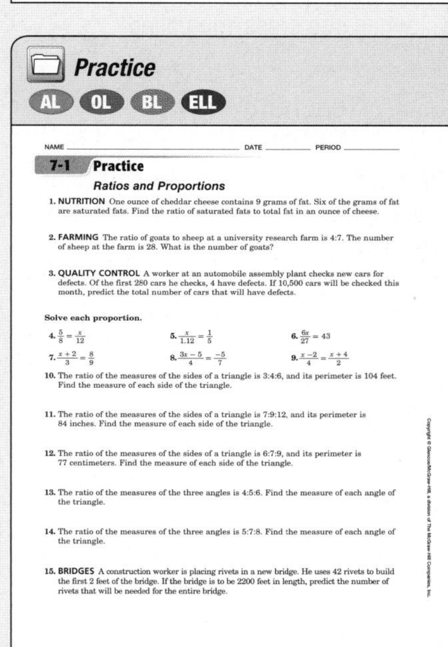

Practice AL OL BL ELL

7-1 Practice

Ratios and Proportions

1. **NUTRITION** One ounce of cheddar cheese contains 9 grams of fat. Six of the grams of fat are saturated fats. Find the ratio of saturated fats to total fat in an ounce of cheese.

2. **FARMING** The ratio of goats to sheep at a university research farm is 4:7. The number of sheep at the farm is 28. What is the number of goats?

3. **QUALITY CONTROL** A worker at an automobile assembly plant checks new cars for defects. Of the first 280 cars he checks, 4 have defects. If 10,500 cars will be checked this month, predict the total number of cars that will have defects.

Solve each proportion.

10. The ratio of the measures of the sides of a triangle is 3:4:6, and its perimeter is 104 feet. Find the measure of each side of the triangle.

11. The ratio of the measures of the sides of a triangle is 7:9:12, and its perimeter is 84 inches. Find the measure of each side of the triangle.

12. The ratio of the measures of the sides of a triangle is 6:7:9, and its perimeter is 77 centimeters. Find the measure of each side of the triangle.

13. The ratio of the measures of the three angles is 4:5:6. Find the measure of each angle of the triangle.

14. The ratio of the measures of the three angles is 5:7:8. Find the measure of each angle of the triangle.

15. **BRIDGES** A construction worker is placing rivets in a new bridge. He uses 42 rivets to build the first 2 feet of the bridge. If the bridge is to be 2200 feet in length, predict the number of rivets that will be needed for the entire bridge.

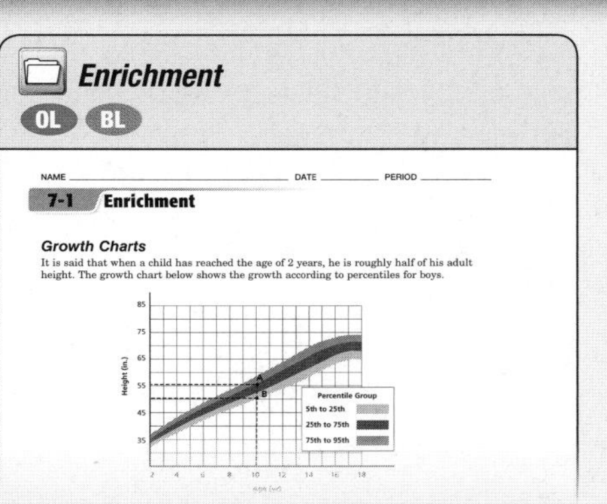

Enrichment OL BL

7-1 Enrichment

Growth Charts

It is said that when a child has reached the age of 2 years, he is roughly half of his adult height. The growth chart below shows the growth according to percentiles for boys.

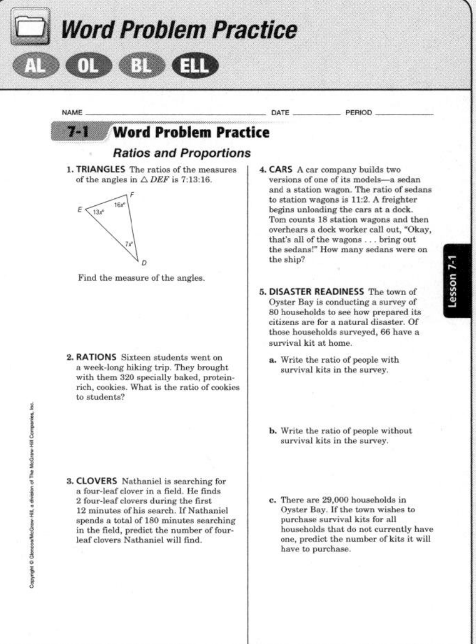

Word Problem Practice AL OL BL ELL

7-1 Word Problem Practice

Ratios and Proportions

1. **TRIANGLES** The ratios of the measures of the angles in △DEF is 7:13:16.

Find the measure of the angles.

2. **RATIONS** Sixteen students went on a week-long hiking trip. They brought with them 320 specially baked, protein-rich, cookies. What is the ratio of cookies to students?

3. **CLOVERS** Nathaniel is searching for a four-leaf clover in a field. He finds 2 four-leaf clovers during the first 12 minutes of his search. If Nathaniel spends a total of 180 minutes searching in the field, predict the number of four-leaf clovers Nathaniel will find.

4. **CARS** A car company builds two versions of one of its models—a sedan and a station wagon. The ratio of sedans to station wagons is 11:2. A freighter begins unloading the cars at a dock. Tom counts 18 station wagons and then overhears a dock worker call out, "Okay, that's all of the wagons . . . bring out the sedans!" How many sedans were on the ship?

5. **DISASTER READINESS** The town of Oyster Bay is conducting a survey of 80 households to see how prepared its citizens are for a natural disaster. Of those households surveyed, 66 have a survival kit at home.

a. Write the ratio of people with survival kits in the survey.

b. Write the ratio of people without survival kits in the survey.

c. There are 29,000 households in Oyster Bay. If the town wishes to purchase survival kits for all households that do not currently have one, predict the number of kits it will have to purchase.

Exercise Alert

Ruler and Protractor Exercise 43 requires the use of a protractor and a straightedge.

Multiple Representations

In Exercise 43, students use geometric sketches, a table, and a verbal description to explore proportional relationships in triangles.

WatchOut!

Error Analysis Students should remember all of the rules for solving equations. In Exercise 44, Eva did not distribute correctly when she cross-multiplied.

Teaching the Mathematical Practices

Reasoning Mathematically proficient students make sense of quantities and their relationships in problem situations. In Exercise 46, encourage students to draw two quadrilaterals that match the description in the problem.

Additional Answers

41. Given: $\frac{a}{b} = \frac{c}{d}$, $b \neq 0$, $d \neq 0$

Prove: $ad = bc$

Proof:

Statement (Reasons)

1. $\frac{a}{b} = \frac{c}{d}$, $b \neq 0$, $d \neq 0$ (Given)
2. $(bd)\frac{a}{b} = (bd)\frac{c}{d}$ (Mult. Prop.)
3. $da = bc$ (Simplify.)
4. $ad = bc$ (Comm. Prop.)

43a.

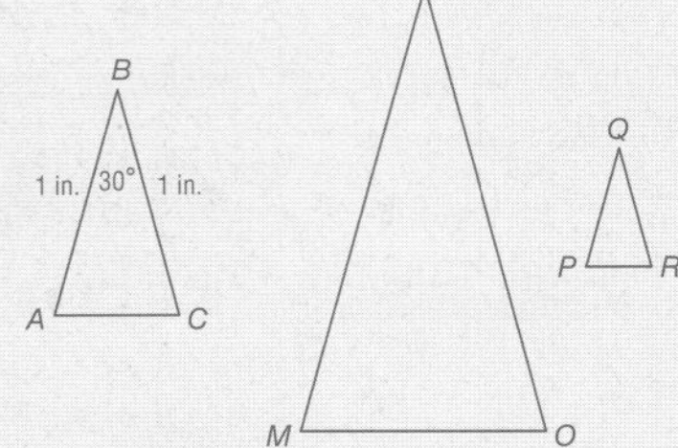

41. PROOF Write an algebraic proof of the Cross Products Property. **See margin.**

42. SPORTS Jane jogs the same path every day in the winter to stay in shape for track season. She runs at a constant rate, and she spends a total of 39 minutes jogging. If the ratio of the times of the four legs of the jog is 3:5:1:4, how long does the second leg of the jog take her? **15 min**

43. MULTIPLE REPRESENTATIONS In this problem, you will explore proportional relationships in triangles.

a. **Geometric** Draw an isosceles triangle *ABC*. Measure and label the legs and the vertex angle. Draw a second triangle *MNO* with a congruent vertex angle and legs twice as long as *ABC*. Draw a third triangle *PQR* with a congruent vertex angle and legs half as long as *ABC*. **See margin.**

b. **Tabular** Copy and complete the table below using the appropriate measures.

Triangle	*ABC*	*MNO*	*PQR*
Leg length	1 in.	2 in.	0.5 in.
Perimeter	2.5 in.	5 in.	1.25 in.

c. **Verbal** Make a conjecture about the change in the perimeter of an isosceles triangle if the vertex angle is held constant and the leg length is increased or decreased by a factor. **Sample answer: When the vertex angle of an isosceles triangle is held constant and the leg length is increased or decreased by a factor, the perimeter of the triangle increases or decreases by the same factor.**

H.O.T. Problems Use Higher-Order Thinking Skills

44. ERROR ANALYSIS Mollie and Eva have solved the proportion $\frac{x-3}{4} = \frac{1}{2}$. Is either of them correct? Explain your reasoning.

Neither; Mollie did not cross multiply and Eva did not distribute the 2.

Mollie	Eva
$(x-3)1 = 4(2)$	$x - 3(2) = 4(1)$
$x - 3 = 8$	$x - 3 = 4$
$x = 11$	$x = 7$

45. CHALLENGE The dimensions of a rectangle are y and $y^2 + 1$ and the perimeter of the rectangle is 14 units. Find the ratio of the longer side of the rectangle to the shorter side of the rectangle. **5:2**

46. REASONING The ratio of the lengths of the diagonals of a quadrilateral is 1:1. The ratio of the lengths of the consecutive sides of the quadrilateral is 3:4:3:5. Classify the quadrilateral. Explain. **See margin.**

47. WHICH ONE DOESN'T BELONG? Identify the proportion that does not belong with the other three. Explain your reasoning. **See margin.**

$\frac{3}{8} = \frac{8.4}{22.4}$ $\frac{2}{3} = \frac{5}{7.5}$ $\frac{5}{6} = \frac{14}{16.8}$ $\frac{7}{9} = \frac{19.6}{25.2}$

48. OPEN ENDED Write four ratios that are equivalent to the ratio 2:5. Explain why all of the ratios are equivalent. **Sample answer: 6:15, 8:20, 10:25, 12:30; All of the ratios simplify to 2:5.**

49. WRITING IN MATH Compare and contrast a ratio and a proportion. Explain how you use both to solve a problem. **See margin.**

46. Isosceles trapezoid; sample answer: Both pairs of opposite sides cannot be congruent since the ratios are not congruent, so the quadrilateral is not a parallelogram. The diagonals of an isosceles trapezoid are also congruent, and two of the sides are congruent based on the ratio of the sides. Therefore, the quadrilateral is an isosceles trapezoid.

47. $\frac{2}{3} = \frac{5}{7.5}$; You need to multiply $\frac{2}{3}$ by a factor of 2.5 to get $\frac{5}{7.5}$. The factor of the other three proportions is 2.8.

49. Both are written with fractions. A ratio compares two quantities with division, while a proportion equates two ratios. First, ratios are used to write proportions. Then the cross product is used to solve the proportion.

Standardized Test Practice

50. Solve the following proportion. **C**

$$\frac{x}{-8} = \frac{12}{6}$$

A −12 **C** −16
B −14 **D** −18

51. What is the area of rectangle *WXYZ*? **F**

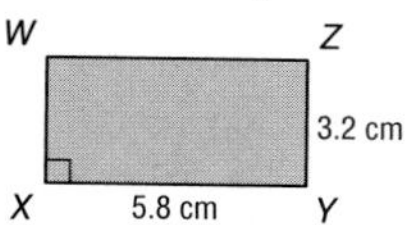

F 18.6 cm^2 **H** 21.2 cm^2
G 20.4 cm^2 **J** 22.8 cm^2

52. GRIDDED RESPONSE Mrs. Sullivan's rectangular bedroom measures 12 feet by 10 feet. She wants to purchase carpet for the bedroom that costs $2.56 per square foot, including tax. How much will it cost in dollars to carpet her bedroom? **307.20**

53. SAT/ACT Kamilah has 5 more than 4 times the number of DVDs that Mercedes has. If Mercedes has *x* DVDs, then in terms of *x*, how many DVDs does Kamilah have? **D**

A $4(x + 5)$ **D** $4x + 5$
B $4(x + 3)$ **E** $5x + 4$
C $9x$

Spiral Review

For trapezoid *ABCD*, *S* and *T* are midpoints of the legs. (Lesson 6-6)

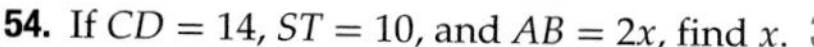

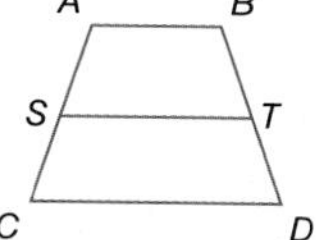

54. If $CD = 14$, $ST = 10$, and $AB = 2x$, find x. **3**

55. If $AB = 3x$, $ST = 15$, and $CD = 9x$, find x. **2.5**

56. If $AB = x + 4$, $CD = 3x + 2$, and $ST = 9$, find AB. **7**

57. SPORTS The infield of a baseball diamond is a square, as shown at the right. Is the pitcher's mound located in the center of the infield? Explain. (Lesson 6-5) **See margin.**

2nd
90 ft
3rd
Pitcher
1st
127 ft $3\frac{3}{8}$ in.
60 ft 6 in.
Home

Write an inequality for the range of values for *x*. (Lesson 5-6)

58. $x > 4$

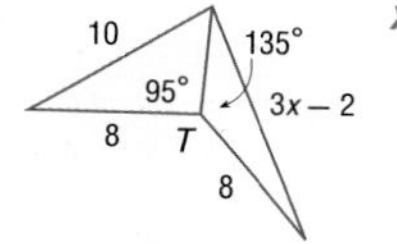

59. $-\frac{4}{7} < x < \frac{136}{7}$

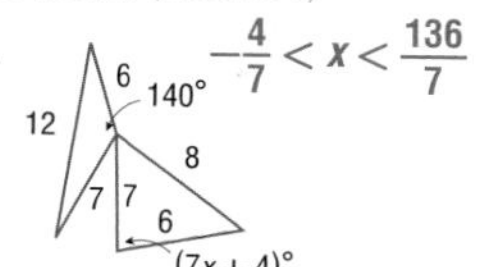

Use the Exterior Angle Inequality Theorem to list all of the angles that satisfy the stated condition. (Lesson 5-3) **60.** **∠2, ∠7, ∠8, ∠10** **61.** **∠1, ∠4, ∠11**

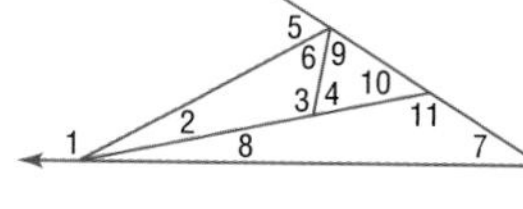

60. measures less than $m\angle 5$

61. measures greater than $m\angle 6$

62. measures greater than $m\angle 10$ **∠3, ∠5**

63. measures less than $m\angle 11$ **∠2, ∠6, ∠9, ∠4**

64. REASONING Find a counterexample for the following statement. (Lesson 3-5)
If lines p and m are cut by transversal t so that consecutive interior angles are congruent, then lines p and m are parallel and t is perpendicular to both lines. **See margin.**

Skills Review

Write a paragraph proof. **See margin.**

65. Given: $\triangle ABC \cong \triangle DEF$; $\triangle DEF \cong \triangle GHI$
Prove: $\triangle ABC \cong \triangle GHI$

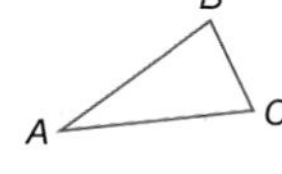

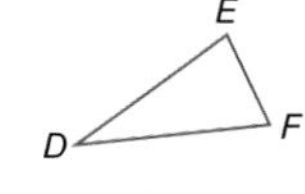

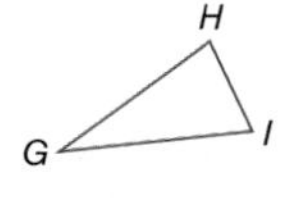

4 Assess

Name the Math Have students write a paragraph that summarizes how to solve a proportion.

Additional Answers

57. Since a square is a parallelogram, the diagonals bisect each other. Since a square is a rhombus, the diagonals are congruent. Therefore, the distance from first base to third base is equal to the distance between home plate and second base. Thus, the distance from home plate to the center of the infield is 127 ft $3\frac{3}{8}$ in. divided by 2 or 63 ft $7\frac{11}{16}$ in. This distance is longer than the distance from home plate to the pitcher's mound so the pitcher's mound is not located in the center of the field. It is about 3 ft closer to home.

64.

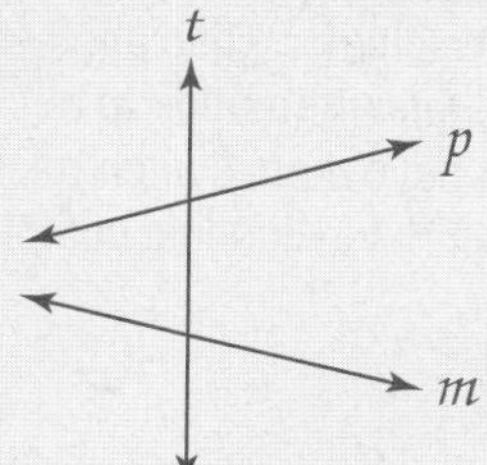

65. Given: $\triangle ABC \cong \triangle DEF$
$\triangle DEF \cong \triangle GHI$
Prove: $\triangle ABC \cong \triangle GHI$

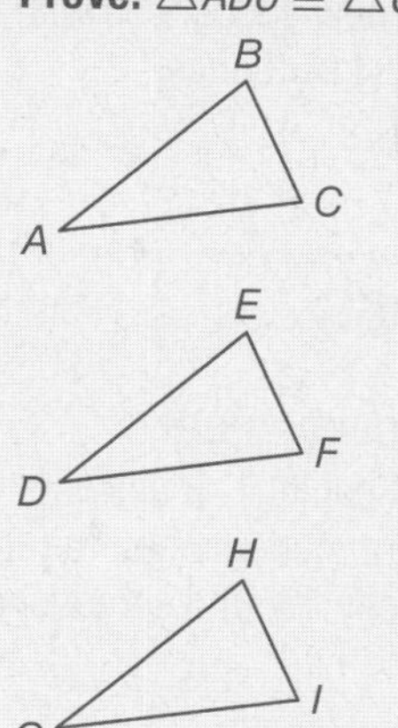

Proof:

You are given that $\triangle ABC \cong \triangle DEF$. Because corresponding parts of congruent triangles are congruent, $\angle A \cong \angle D$, $\angle B \cong \angle E$, $\angle C \cong \angle F$, $\overline{AB} \cong \overline{DE}$, $\overline{BC} \cong \overline{EF}$, and $\overline{AC} \cong \overline{DF}$. You are also given that $\triangle DEF \cong \triangle GHI$. So $\angle D \cong \angle G$, $\angle E \cong \angle H$, $\angle F \cong \angle I$, $\overline{DE} \cong \overline{GH}$, $\overline{EF} \cong \overline{HI}$, and $\overline{DF} \cong \overline{GI}$ by CPCTC.

Therefore, $\angle A \cong \angle G$, $\angle B \cong \angle H$, $\angle C \cong \angle I$, $\overline{AB} \cong \overline{GH}$, $\overline{BC} \cong \overline{HI}$, and $\overline{AC} \cong \overline{GI}$ because congruence of angles and segments is transitive. Thus, $\triangle ABC \cong \triangle GHI$ by the definition of congruent triangles.

1 Focus

Objective Compare each term in the Fibonacci sequence with its preceding term using a spreadsheet.

Materials

- graphing calculator
- spreadsheet program

Teaching Tip

Show students how they can move around the screen by using the arrows. The **CellSheet** program on the calculator works just like a computer spreadsheet.

2 Teach

Working in Cooperative Pairs

Arrange students in pairs, mixing abilities. Ask one student to enter the data into the calculator while another student reads the information to be entered. Then have them switch roles and take turns. Have students complete Exercises 1–4.

Ask:

When students have completed the activity, have each group create a new sequence by setting **A1** as a different single-digit integer. Have the students compare these new sequences with the original Fibonacci sequence.

3 Assess

Formative Assessment

In Analyze the Results 1–5 answers will be correct only if students entered their formulas correctly into the spreadsheet.

EXTEND 7-1 Graphing Technology Lab
Fibonacci Sequence and Ratios

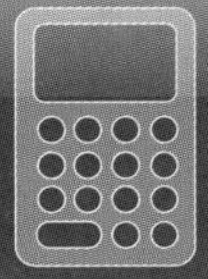

Leonardo Pisano (c. 1170–c. 1250), or Fibonacci, was born in Italy but educated in North Africa. As a result, his work is similar to that of other North African authors of that time. His book *Liber abaci*, published in 1202, introduced what is now called the Fibonacci sequence, in which each term after the first two terms is the sum of the two numbers before it.

Term	1	2	3	4	5	6	7
Fibonacci Number	1	1	2	3	5	8	13
			↑ 1 + 1	↑ 1 + 2	↑ 2 + 3	↑ 3 + 5	↑ 5 + 8

Activity

You can use CellSheet on a TI-83/84 Plus graphing calculator to calculate terms of the Fibonacci sequence. Then compare each term with its preceding term.

Step 1 Access the **CellSheet** application by pressing the APPS key. Choose the number for **CellSheet** and press ENTER.

Step 2 Enter the column headings in row 1. Use the **ALPHA** key to enter letters and press ["] at the beginning of each label.

Step 3 Enter **1** into cell **A2**. Then insert the formula **=A2+1** in cell **A3**. Press STO to insert the = in the formula. Then use F3 to copy this formula and use F4 to paste it in each cell in the column. This will automatically calculate the number of the term.

Step 4 In **column B**, we will record the Fibonacci numbers. Enter 1 in cells **B2** and **B3** since you do not have two previous terms to add. Then insert the formula **=B2+B3** in cell **B4**. Copy this formula down the column.

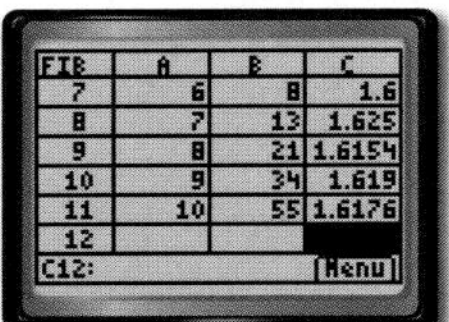

Step 5 In **column C**, we will find the ratio of each term to its preceding term. Enter 1 in cell **C2** since there is no preceding term. Then enter B3/B2 in cell **C3**. Copy this formula down the column. *The screens show the results for terms 1 through 11.*

4. The increase in terms confirms the original observations.
5. As the number of terms increases, the ratio of each term to its preceding term approaches the golden ratio.

Analyze the Results

1. What happens to the Fibonacci number as the number of the term increases? **It increases also.**
2. What pattern of odd and even numbers do you notice in the Fibonacci sequence? **odd-odd-even**
3. As the number of terms gets greater, what pattern do you notice in the ratio column? **It approaches 1.618.**
4. Extend the spreadsheet to calculate fifty terms of the Fibonacci sequence. Describe any differences in the patterns you described in Exercises 1–3.
5. **MAKE A CONJECTURE** How might the Fibonacci sequence relate to the golden ratio?

From Concrete to Abstract

Have students research on the Internet other sequences. Hand out dried sunflowers or pinecones and determine how the Fibonacci sequence is found in nature.

Additional Answer (Guided Practice)

1. Congruent angles: $\angle N \cong \angle U$, $\angle P \cong \angle V$, $\angle Q \cong \angle S$, $\angle R \cong \angle T$
Proportion: $\frac{NP}{UV} = \frac{PQ}{VS} = \frac{QR}{ST} = \frac{RN}{TU}$

LESSON 7-2 Similar Polygons

Then

- You used proportions to solve problems.

Now

1. Use proportions to identify similar polygons.
2. Solve problems using the properties of similar polygons.

Why?

- People often customize their computer desktops using photos, centering the images at their original size or stretching them to fit the screen. This second method distorts the image, because the original and new images are not geometrically similar.

NewVocabulary
similar polygons
scale factor

Common Core State Standards

Content Standards
G.SRT.2 Given two figures, use the definition of similarity in terms of similarity transformations to decide if they are similar; explain using similarity transformations the meaning of similarity for triangles as the equality of all corresponding pairs of angles and the proportionality of all corresponding pairs of sides.

Mathematical Practices
7 Look for and make use of structure.
3 Construct viable arguments and critique the reasoning of others.

1 Identify Similar Polygons

Similar polygons have the same shape but not necessarily the same size.

KeyConcept Similar Polygons

Two polygons are similar if and only if their corresponding angles are congruent and corresponding side lengths are proportional.

Example In the diagram below, *ABCD* is similar to *WXYZ*.

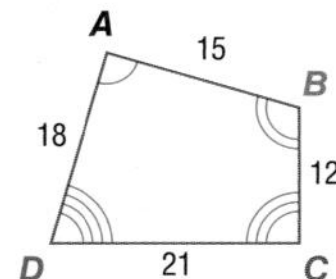

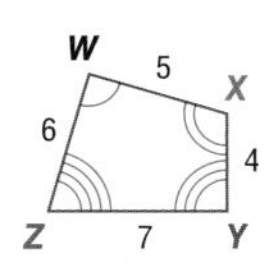

Corresponding angles

$\angle A \cong \angle W$, $\angle B \cong \angle X$, $\angle C \cong \angle Y$, and $\angle D \cong \angle Z$

Corresponding sides

$$\frac{AB}{WX} = \frac{BC}{XY} = \frac{CD}{YZ} = \frac{DA}{ZW} = \frac{3}{1}$$

Symbols $ABCD \sim WXYZ$

As with congruence statements, the order of vertices in a similarity statement like $ABCD \sim WXYZ$ is important. It identifies the corresponding angles and sides.

Example 1 Use a Similarity Statement

If $\triangle FGH \sim \triangle JKL$, list all pairs of congruent angles, and write a proportion that relates the corresponding sides.

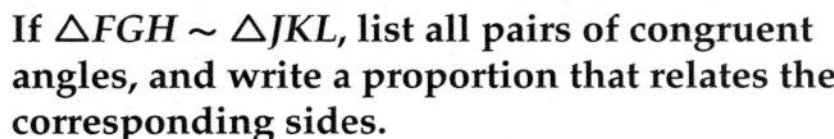

Use the similarity statement.

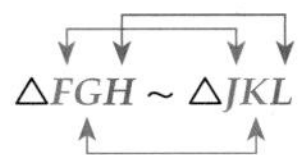

Congruent angles: $\angle F \cong \angle J$, $\angle G \cong \angle K$, $\angle H \cong \angle L$

Proportion: $\frac{FG}{JK} = \frac{GH}{KL} = \frac{HF}{LJ}$

GuidedPractice

1. In the diagram, $NPQR \sim UVST$. List all pairs of congruent angles, and write a proportion that relates the corresponding sides. See margin.

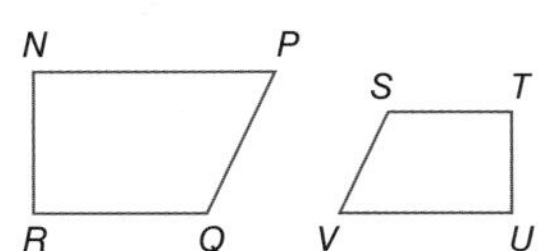

1 Focus

VerticalAlignment

Before Lesson 7-2 Use proportions to solve problems.

Lesson 7-2 Use proportions to identify similar polygons. Solve problems using the properties of similar polygons.

After Lesson 7-2 Use numeric patterns to make generalizations about ratios in similar figures.

2 Teach

Scaffolding Questions

Have students read the **Why?** section of the lesson.

Ask:

- In what direction has the picture been stretched? lengthwise
- Why is the photo distorted when it is made to fit the screen? The screen is wider than it is tall.
- What other ways could the picture be used to fit the screen without distorting it? Sample answer: Multiple copies of the picture could be tiled.

Lesson 7-2 Resources

Resource	Approaching Level AL	On Level OL	Beyond Level BL	English Learners ELL
Teacher Edition	▪ Differentiated Instruction, p. 470	▪ Differentiated Instruction, pp. 470, 477	▪ Differentiated Instruction, pp. 470, 477	
Chapter Resource Masters	▪ Study Guide and Intervention, pp. 12–13 ▪ Skills Practice, p. 14 ▪ Practice, p. 15 ▪ Word Problem Practice, p. 16	▪ Study Guide and Intervention, pp. 12–13 ▪ Skills Practice, p. 14 ▪ Practice, p. 15 ▪ Word Problem Practice, p. 16 ▪ Enrichment, p. 17	▪ Practice, p. 15 ▪ Word Problem Practice, p. 16 ▪ Enrichment, p. 17	▪ Study Guide and Intervention, pp. 12–13 ▪ Skills Practice, p. 14 ▪ Practice, p. 15 ▪ Word Problem Practice, p. 16
Other	▪ 5-Minute Check 7-2 ▪ Study Notebook	▪ 5-Minute Check 7-2 ▪ Study Notebook	▪ 5-Minute Check 7-2 ▪ Study Notebook	▪ 5-Minute Check 7-2 ▪ Study Notebook

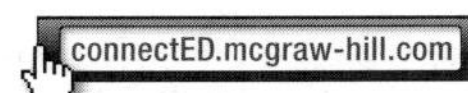

1 Identify Similar Polygons

Examples 1 and 2 show how to use key concepts to identify similar figures.

Formative Assessment

Use the Guided Practice exercises after each example to determine students' understanding of concepts.

Additional Example

1 If $\triangle ABC \sim \triangle RST$, list all pairs of congruent angles and write a proportion that relates the corresponding sides.

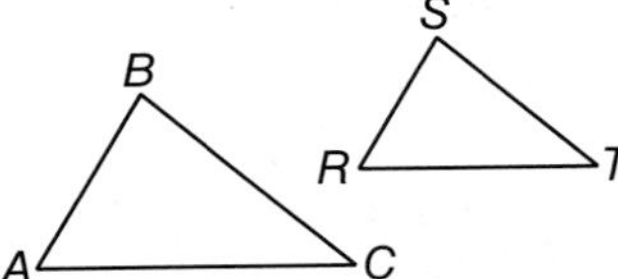

Congruent angles: $\angle A \cong \angle R$, $\angle B \cong \angle S$, $\angle C \cong \angle T$;

Proportion: $\frac{AB}{RS} = \frac{BC}{ST} = \frac{AC}{RT}$

Additional Examples also in Interactive Classroom PowerPoint® Presentations

Teach with Tech

Digital Camera Have students take a picture and have several different size prints created (3″ × 5″, 4″ × 6″, 6″ × 9″, and 8″ × 10″). Have students measure the photos and use proportions to determine which of the photos are similar rectangles. Have students present their photos to the class, showing that similar and non-similar photos look different.

StudyTip

Similarity Ratio The scale factor between two similar polygons is sometimes called the *similarity ratio.*

The ratio of the lengths of the corresponding sides of two similar polygons is called the **scale factor**. The scale factor depends on the order of comparison.

In the diagram, $\triangle ABC \sim \triangle XYZ$.

The scale factor of $\triangle ABC$ to $\triangle XYZ$ is $\frac{6}{3}$ or 2.

The scale factor of $\triangle XYZ$ to $\triangle ABC$ is $\frac{3}{6}$ or $\frac{1}{2}$.

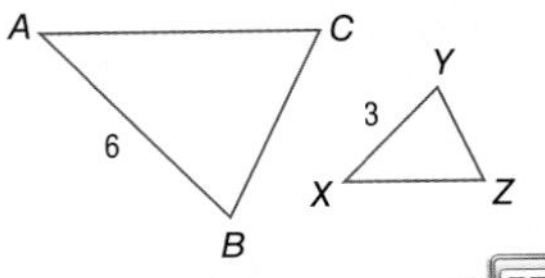

Real-World Example 2 Identify Similar Polygons

PHOTO EDITING **Kuma wants to use the rectangular photo shown as the background for her computer's desktop, but she needs to resize it. Determine whether the following rectangular images are similar. If so, write the similarity statement and scale factor. Explain your reasoning.**

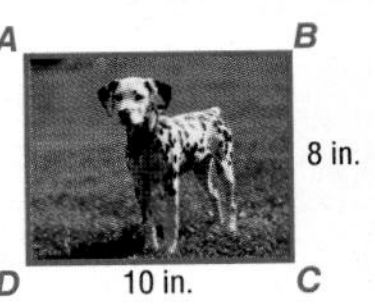

a.

b.

a. Step 1 Compare corresponding angles.

Since all angles of a rectangle are right angles and right angles are congruent, corresponding angles are congruent.

Step 2 Compare corresponding sides.

$\frac{DC}{HG} = \frac{10}{14}$ or $\frac{5}{7}$ $\qquad$ $\frac{BC}{FG} = \frac{8}{12}$ or $\frac{2}{3}$ $\qquad$ $\frac{5}{7} \neq \frac{2}{3}$

Since corresponding sides are not proportional, $ABCD \nsim EFGH$. So the photos are not similar.

ReadingMath

Similarity Symbol The symbol $\nsim$ is read as *is not similar to.*

b. Step 1 Since *ABCD* and *JKLM* are both rectangles, corresponding angles are congruent.

Step 2 Compare corresponding sides.

$\frac{DC}{ML} = \frac{10}{15}$ or $\frac{2}{3}$ $\qquad$ $\frac{BC}{KL} = \frac{8}{12}$ or $\frac{2}{3}$ $\qquad$ $\frac{2}{3} = \frac{2}{3}$

Since corresponding sides are proportional, $ABCD \sim JKLM$. So the rectangles are similar with a scale factor of $\frac{2}{3}$.

GuidedPractice

2. Determine whether the triangles shown are similar. If so, write the similarity statement and scale factor. Explain your reasoning.

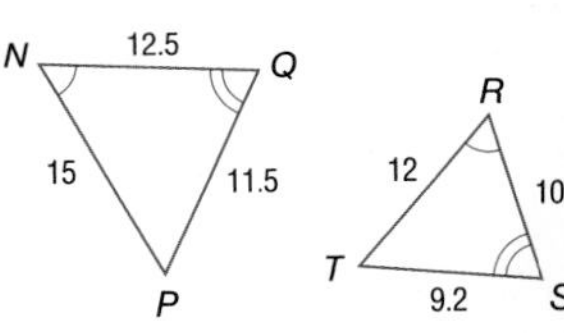

2. Yes; $\triangle NQP \sim \triangle RST$, since $\angle N \cong \angle R$, $\angle Q \cong \angle S$, and $\angle P \cong \angle T$ by the Third Angles Theorem, and $\frac{NQ}{RS} = \frac{QP}{ST} = \frac{PN}{TR}$. The scale factor is $\frac{5}{4}$.

DifferentiatedInstruction AL OL BL

Visual/Spatial Learners Show students how to be consistent when analyzing figures for similarity. For example, they may choose to always compare the figure on the left to the figure on the right. Show students ways to organize their work so that they reference corresponding vertices in the correct order.

> **StudyTip**
> **Similarity and Congruence** If two polygons are congruent, they are also similar. All of the corresponding angles are congruent, and the lengths of the corresponding sides have a ratio of 1:1.

2 Use Similar Figures

You can use scale factors and proportions to solve problems involving similar figures.

Example 3 Use Similar Figures to Find Missing Measures

In the diagram, $ACDF \sim VWYZ$.

a. Find x.

Use the corresponding side lengths to write a proportion.

$\frac{CD}{WY} = \frac{DF}{YZ}$	Similarity proportion
$\frac{9}{6} = \frac{x}{10}$	$CD = 9$, $WY = 6$, $DF = x$, $YZ = 10$
$9(10) = 6(x)$	Cross Products Property
$90 = 6x$	Multiply.
$15 = x$	Divide each side by 6.

b. Find y.

$\frac{CD}{WY} = \frac{FA}{ZV}$	Similarity proportion
$\frac{9}{6} = \frac{12}{3y-1}$	$CD = 9$, $WY = 6$, $FA = 12$, $ZV = 3y - 1$
$9(3y - 1) = 6(12)$	Cross Products Property
$27y - 9 = 72$	Multiply.
$27y = 81$	Add 9 to each side.
$y = 3$	Divide each side by 27.

GuidedPractice

Find the value of each variable if $\triangle JLM \sim \triangle QST$.

3A. x 1.5

3B. y 4

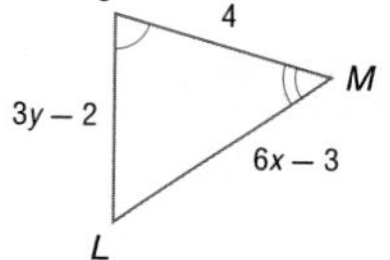

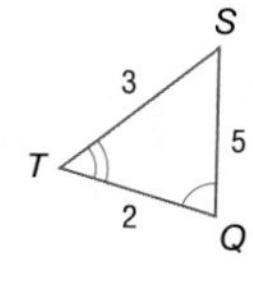

> **StudyTip**
> **Identifying Similar Triangles** When only two congruent angles of a triangle are given, remember that you can use the Third Angles Theorem to establish that the remaining corresponding angles are also congruent.

In similar polygons, the ratio of any two corresponding lengths is proportional to the scale factor between them. This leads to the following theorem about the perimeters of two similar polygons.

Theorem 7.1 Perimeters of Similar Polygons

If two polygons are similar, then their perimeters are proportional to the scale factor between them.

Example If $ABCD \sim JKLM$, then

$$\frac{AB + BC + CD + DA}{JK + KL + LM + MJ} = \frac{AB}{JK} = \frac{BC}{KL} = \frac{CD}{LM} = \frac{DA}{MJ}.$$

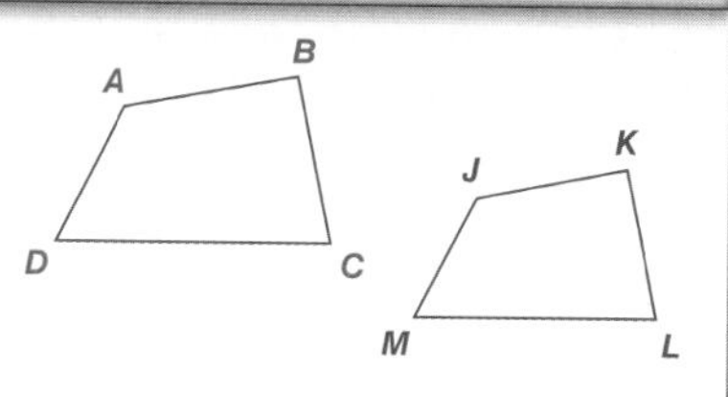

Additional Example

2 MENUS Tan is designing a new menu for the restaurant where he works. Determine whether the following sizes for the new menu are similar to the original menu. If so, write the similarity statement and scale factor. Explain your reasoning.

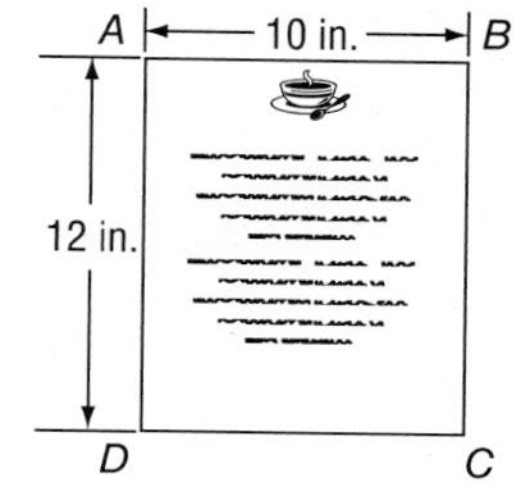

a.

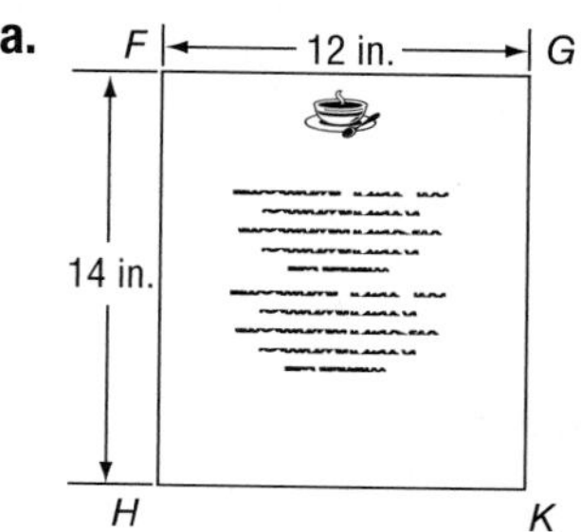

No, because $\frac{AB}{FG} \neq \frac{AD}{FH}$.

b.

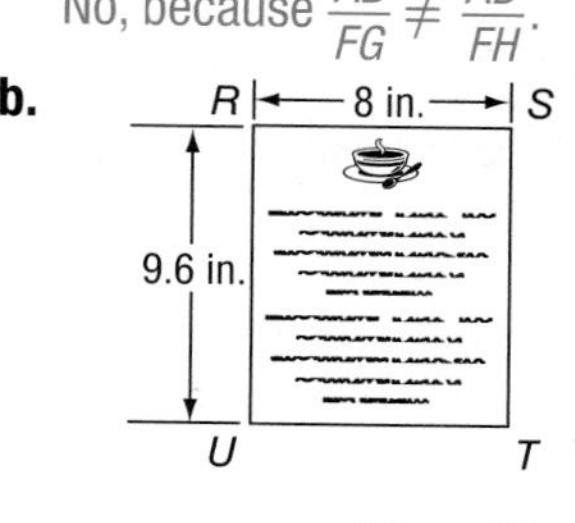

Yes, because $\frac{AB}{RS} = \frac{AD}{RU} = \frac{5}{4}$.

Tips for New Teachers

Vary Colors When identifying corresponding parts, use different colors to circle letters of congruent angles.

Follow-up

Students have explored proportions, similar triangles, and Similarity Theorems.

Ask:

- How can you determine whether two objects are similar? Sample answer: You can compare corresponding angle measures to see if they are congruent and corresponding side lengths to see if they are proportional.

Focus on Mathematical Content

Prior Knowledge In Chapter 4, students learned that congruent triangles have corresponding angles and sides congruent. In this lesson, emphasize that if two figures are congruent, their scale factor is 1.

2 Use Similar Figures

Examples 3 and 4 show how to use scale factors to find unknown quantities.

Additional Examples

3 The two polygons are similar.

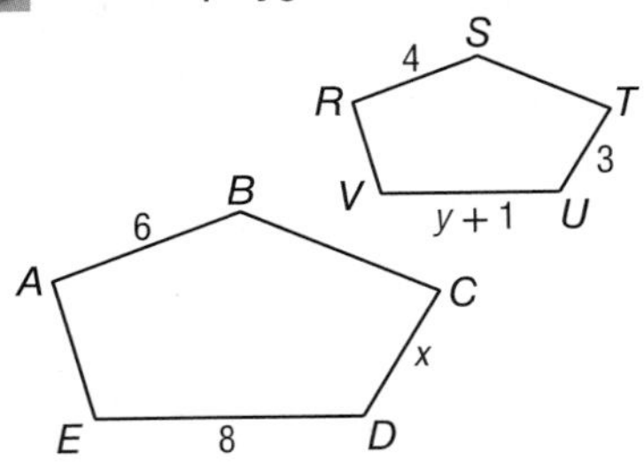

a. Find x. $\frac{9}{2}$

b. Find y. $\frac{13}{3}$

4 If $ABCDE \sim RSTUV$, find the scale factor of $ABCDE$ to $RSTUV$ and the perimeter of each polygon.

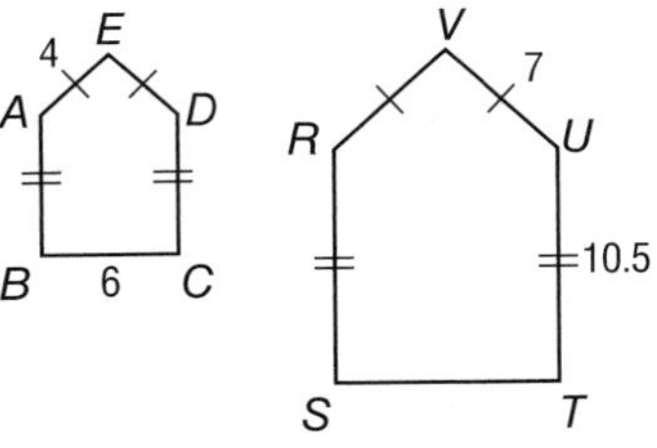

scale factor: $\frac{4}{7}$; perimeter of $ABCDE$: 26; perimeter of $RSTUV$: 45.5

Example 4 Use a Scale Factor to Find Perimeter

If $ABCDE \sim PQRST$, find the scale factor of $ABCDE$ to $PQRST$ and the perimeter of each polygon.

The scale factor of $ABCDE$ to $PQRST$ is $\frac{CD}{RS}$ or $\frac{4}{3}$.

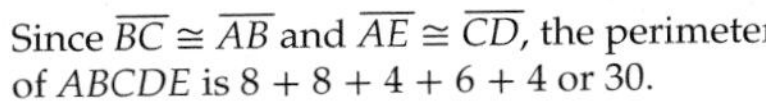

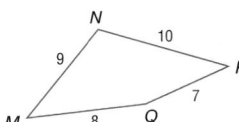

Since $\overline{BC} \cong \overline{AB}$ and $\overline{AE} \cong \overline{CD}$, the perimeter of $ABCDE$ is $8 + 8 + 4 + 6 + 4$ or 30.

Use the perimeter of $ABCDE$ and the scale factor to write a proportion. Let x represent the perimeter of $PQRST$.

$\frac{4}{3} = \frac{\text{perimeter of } ABCDE}{\text{perimeter of } PQRST}$ Theorem 7.1

$\frac{4}{3} = \frac{30}{x}$ Substitution

$(3)(30) = 4x$ Cross Products Property

$22.5 = x$ Solve.

So, the perimeter of $PQRST$ is 22.5.

WatchOut!

Perimeter Remember that perimeter is the distance around a figure. Be sure to find the sum of all side lengths when finding the perimeter of a polygon. You may need to use other markings or geometric principles to find the length of unmarked sides.

Guided Practice

4. If $MNPQ \sim XYZW$, find the scale factor of $MNPQ$ to $XYZW$ and the perimeter of each polygon.

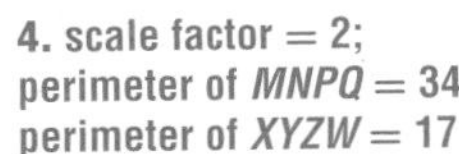

4. scale factor = 2; perimeter of $MNPQ = 34$, perimeter of $XYZW = 17$

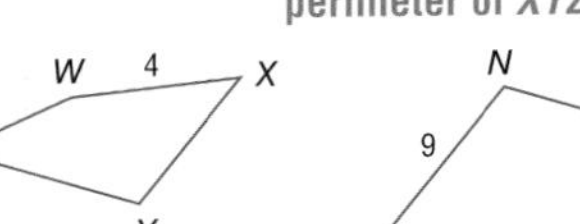

1. $\angle A \cong \angle Z$, $\angle B \cong \angle Y$, $\angle C \cong \angle X$; $\frac{AC}{ZX} = \frac{BC}{YX} = \frac{AB}{ZY}$

2. $\angle J \cong \angle T$, $\angle K \cong \angle S$, $\angle M \cong \angle Q$; $\angle L \cong \angle R$; $\frac{JM}{TQ} = \frac{ML}{QR} = \frac{KL}{SR} = \frac{JK}{TS}$

Check Your Understanding

= Step-by-Step Solutions begin on page R14.

Example 1 List all pairs of congruent angles, and write a proportion that relates the corresponding sides for each pair of similar polygons.

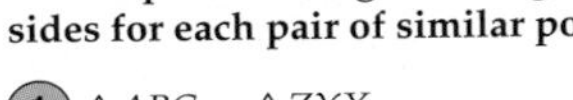

1. $\triangle ABC \sim \triangle ZYX$

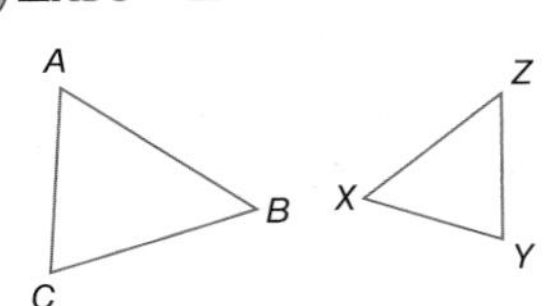

2. $JKLM \sim TSRQ$

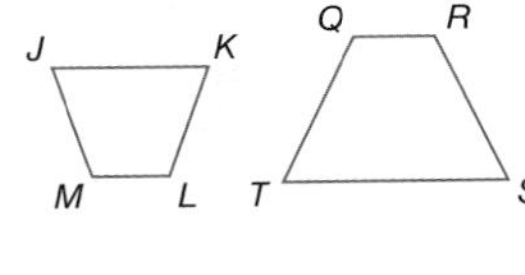

4. Yes; $\triangle ABC \sim \triangle HFJ$ since $\angle A \cong \angle H$, $\angle B \cong \angle F$, $\angle C \cong \angle J$ and $\frac{AB}{HF} = \frac{BC}{FJ} = \frac{CA}{JH}$; scale factor: $\frac{2}{1}$.

Example 2 Determine whether each pair of figures is similar. If so, write the similarity statement and scale factor. If not, explain your reasoning.

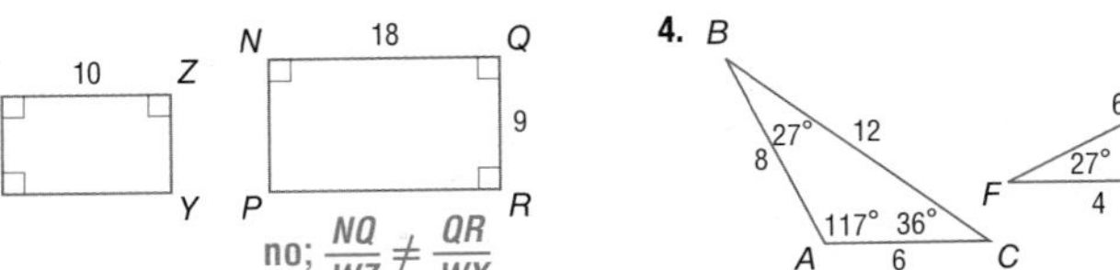

no; $\frac{NQ}{WZ} \neq \frac{QR}{WX}$

Example 3 **Each pair of polygons is similar. Find the value of x.**

5. 6

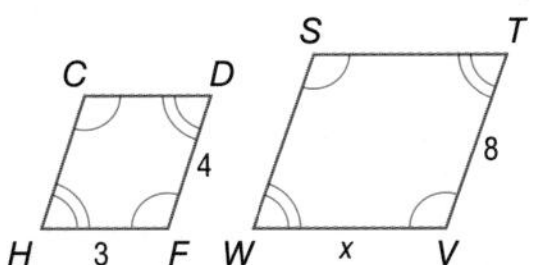

6. 16

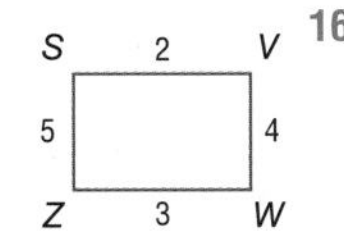

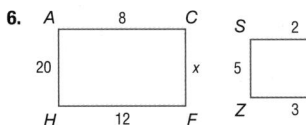

Example 4 **7. DESIGN** On the blueprint of the apartment shown, the balcony measures 1 inch wide by 1.75 inches long. If the actual length of the balcony is 7 feet, what is the perimeter of the balcony? 22 ft

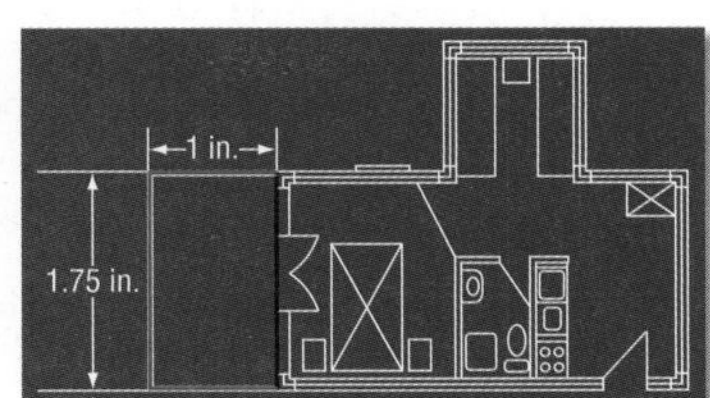

Practice and Problem Solving

Extra Practice is on page R7.

Example 1 **List all pairs of congruent angles, and write a proportion that relates the corresponding sides for each pair of similar polygons.**

8. $\triangle CHF \sim \triangle YWS$

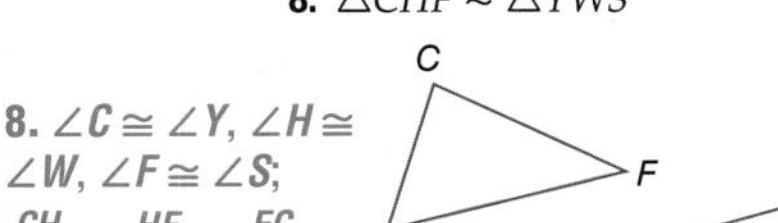

8. $\angle C \cong \angle Y$, $\angle H \cong \angle W$, $\angle F \cong \angle S$; $\frac{CH}{YW} = \frac{HF}{WS} = \frac{FC}{SY}$

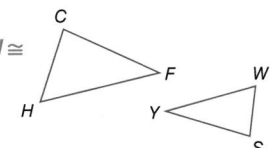

9. $JHFM \sim PQST$

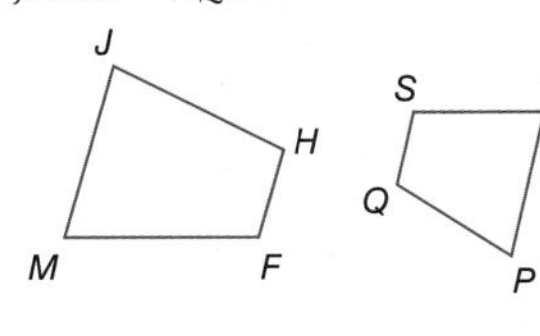

9. $\angle J \cong \angle P$, $\angle F \cong \angle S$, $\angle M \cong \angle T$, $\angle H \cong \angle Q$; $\frac{PQ}{JH} = \frac{TS}{MF} = \frac{SQ}{FH} = \frac{TP}{MJ}$

10. $ABDF \sim VXZT$

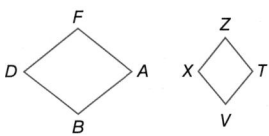

11. $\triangle DFG \sim \triangle KMJ$

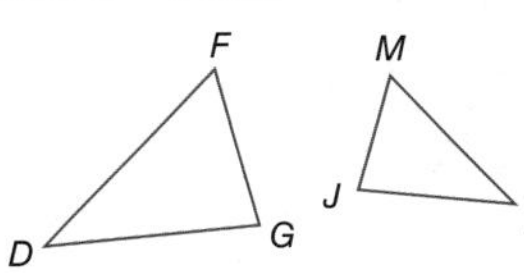

10. $\angle A \cong \angle V$, $\angle B \cong \angle X$, $\angle D \cong \angle Z$, $\angle F \cong \angle T$; $\frac{AB}{VX} = \frac{BD}{XZ} = \frac{DF}{ZT} = \frac{FA}{TV}$

11. $\angle D \cong \angle K$, $\angle F \cong \angle M$, $\angle G \cong \angle J$; $\frac{DF}{KM} = \frac{FG}{MJ} = \frac{GD}{JK}$

Example 2 **CCSS ARGUMENTS** **Determine whether each pair of figures is similar. If so, write the similarity statement and scale factor. If not, explain your reasoning.**

12.

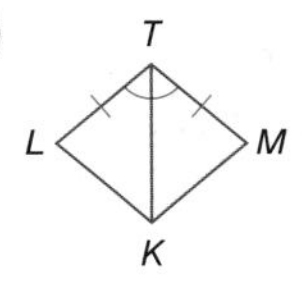

no; $\angle L \not\cong \angle W$

13.

Yes; $\triangle LTK \sim \triangle MTK$ because $\triangle LTK \cong \triangle MTK$; scale factor: 1.

14.

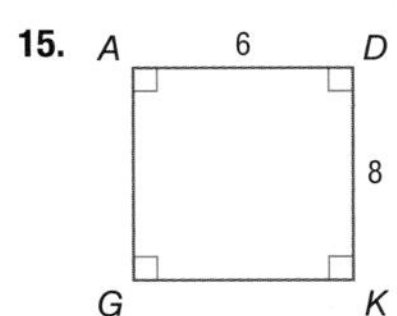

14. Yes; $\triangle BDC \sim \triangle FGC$ because $\angle B \cong \angle F$, $\angle D \cong \angle G$, $\angle BCD \cong \angle FCG$, $\frac{BD}{FG} = \frac{DC}{GC} = \frac{CB}{CF}$; scale factor: $\frac{3}{4}$.

15.

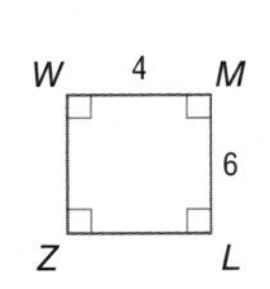

no; $\frac{AD}{WM} \neq \frac{DK}{ML}$

Differentiated Homework Options

Level	Assignment	Two-Day Option	
AL Basic	8–26, 52–72	9–25 odd, 56–59	8–26 even, 52–55, 60–72
OL Core	9–29 odd, 31–34, 35–45 odd, 47–50, 52–72	8–26, 56–59	27–50, 52–55, 60–72
BL Advanced	27–69, (optional: 70–72)		

3 Practice

Formative Assessment

Use Exercises 1–7 to check for understanding.

Use the chart at the bottom of this page to customize assignments for your students.

CCSS Teaching the Mathematical Practices

Arguments Mathematically proficient students understand and use stated assumptions and definitions in constructing arguments. In Exercises 12–15, encourage students to redraw the figures so the orientation of each is the same.

Study Guide and Intervention

AL OL ELL

NAME ______ DATE ______ PERIOD ______

7-2 Study Guide and Intervention

Similar Polygons

Identify Similar Polygons Similar polygons have the same shape but not necessarily the same size.

Example 1 If $\triangle ABC \sim \triangle XYZ$, list all pairs of congruent angles and write a proportion that relates the corresponding sides.

Use the similarity statement.

Congruent angles: $\angle A \cong \angle X$, $\angle B \cong \angle Y$, $\angle C \cong \angle Z$

Proportion: $\frac{AB}{XY} = \frac{BC}{YZ} = \frac{CA}{ZX}$

Example 2 Determine whether the pair of figures is similar. If so, write the similarity statement and scale factor. Explain your reasoning.

Step 1 Compare corresponding angles.
$\angle W \cong \angle P$, $\angle X \cong \angle Q$, $\angle Y \cong \angle R$, $\angle Z \cong \angle S$
Corresponding angles are congruent.

Step 2 Compare corresponding sides.
$\frac{WX}{PQ} = \frac{12}{8} = \frac{3}{2}$, $\frac{XY}{QR} = \frac{18}{12} = \frac{3}{2}$, $\frac{YZ}{RS} = \frac{15}{10} = \frac{3}{2}$, and
$\frac{ZW}{SP} = \frac{9}{6} = \frac{3}{2}$. Since corresponding sides are proportional,
$WXYZ \sim PQRS$. The polygons are similar with a scale factor of $\frac{3}{2}$.

Exercises

List all pairs of congruent angles, and write a proportion that relates the corresponding sides for each pair of similar polygons.

1. $\triangle DEF \sim \triangle GHJ$

2. $PQRS \sim TUWX$

Determine whether each pair of figures is similar. If so, write the similarity statement and scale factor. If not, explain your reasoning.

3. 4.

Practice

AL OL BL ELL

NAME ______ DATE ______ PERIOD ______

7-2 Practice

Similar Polygons

Determine whether each pair of figures is similar. If so, write the similarity statement and scale factor. If not, explain your reasoning.

1. 2.

Each pair of polygons is similar. Find the value of x.

3. 4.

5. **PENTAGONS** If $ABCDE \sim PQRST$, find the scale factor of $ABCDE$ to $PQRST$ and the perimeter of each polygon.

6. **SWIMMING POOLS** The Minnitte family and the neighboring Gaudet family both have in-ground swimming pools. The Minnitte family pool, $PQRS$, measures 48 feet by 84 feet. The Gaudet family pool, $WXYZ$, measures 40 feet by 70 feet. Are the two pools similar? If so, write the similarity statement and scale factor.

Lesson 7-2

Word Problem Practice

AL OL BL ELL

NAME ______ DATE ______ PERIOD ______

7-2 Word Problem Practice

Similar Polygons

1. **PANELS** When closed, an entertainment center is made of four square panels. The three smaller panels are congruent squares.

What is the scale factor of the larger square to one of the smaller squares?

2. **WIDESCREEN TELEVISIONS** An electronics company manufactures widescreen television sets in several different sizes. The rectangular viewing area of each television size is similar to the viewing areas of the other sizes. The company's 42-inch widescreen television has a viewing area perimeter of approximately 144.4 inches. What is the viewing area perimeter of the company's 46-inch widescreen television?

3. **ICE HOCKEY** An official Olympic-sized ice hockey rink measures 30 meters by 60 meters. The ice hockey rink at the local community college measures 25.5 meters by 51 meters. Are the ice hockey rinks similar? Explain your reasoning.

4. **ENLARGING** Camille wants to make a pattern for a four-pointed star with dimensions twice as long as the one shown. Help her by drawing a star with dimensions twice as long on the grid below.

5. **BIOLOGY** A paramecium is a small single-cell organism. The paramecium magnified below is actually one tenth of a millimeter long.

a. If you want to make a photograph of the original paramecium so that its image is 1 centimeter long, by what scale factor should you magnify it?

b. If you want to make a photograph of the original paramecium so that its image is 15 centimeters long, by what scale factor should you magnify it?

c. By approximately what scale factor has the paramecium been enlarged to make the image shown?

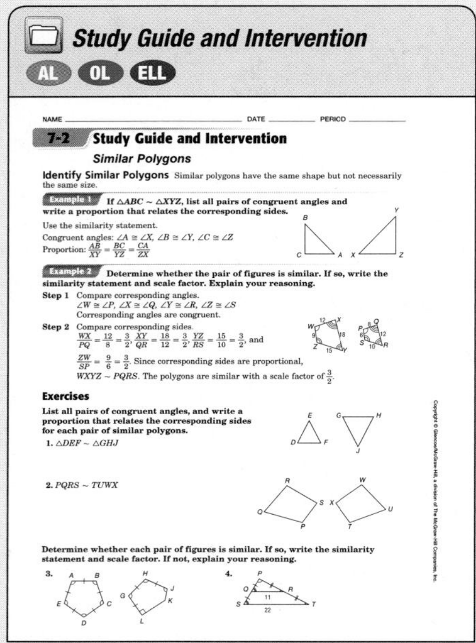

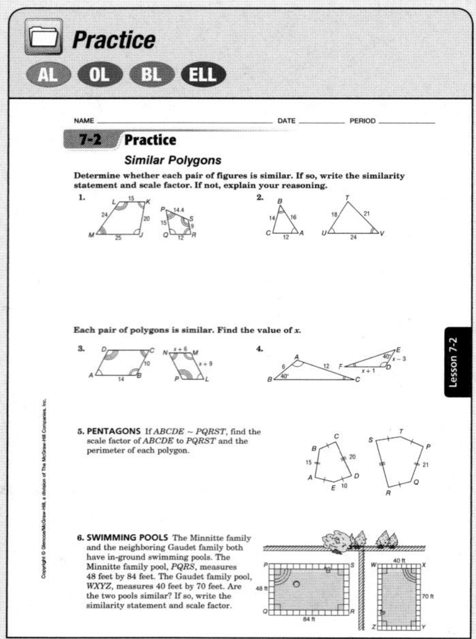

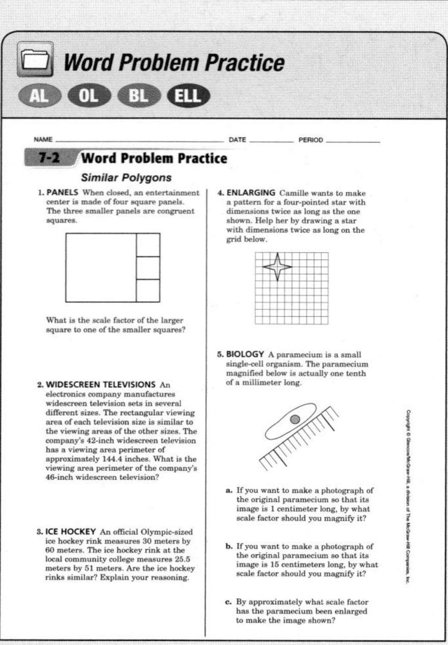

16. **GAMES** The dimensions of a hockey rink are 200 feet by 85 feet. Are the hockey rink and the air hockey table shown similar? Explain your reasoning.
No; sample answer: The ratio of the lengths of the hockey rink and air hockey table is about 2 and the ratio of the widths is about 1.7.

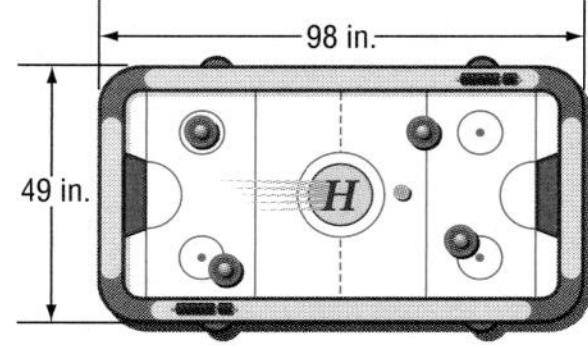

17. **COMPUTERS** The dimensions of a 17-inch flat panel computer screen are approximately $13\frac{1}{4}$ by $10\frac{3}{4}$ inches. The dimensions of a 19-inch flat panel computer screen are approximately $14\frac{1}{2}$ by 12 inches. To the nearest tenth, are the computer screens similar? Explain your reasoning. **Yes; sample answer: The ratio of the longer dimensions of the screens is approximately 1.1 and the ratio of the shorter dimensions of the screens is approximately 1.1.**

Example 3 **CCSS REGULARITY** **Each pair of polygons is similar. Find the value of x.**

18. **7**

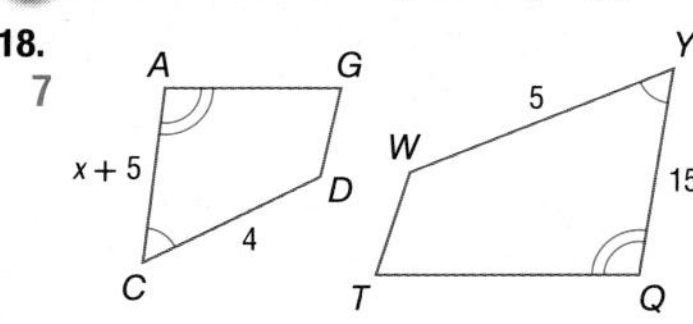

19. **5**

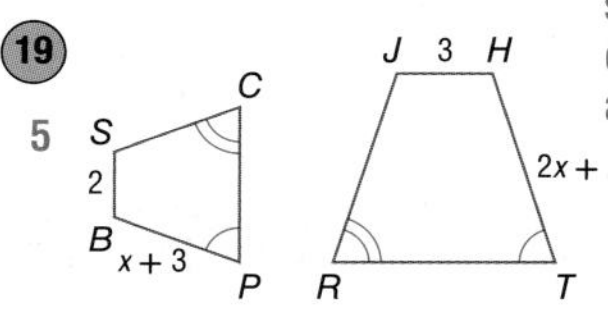

20. **2**

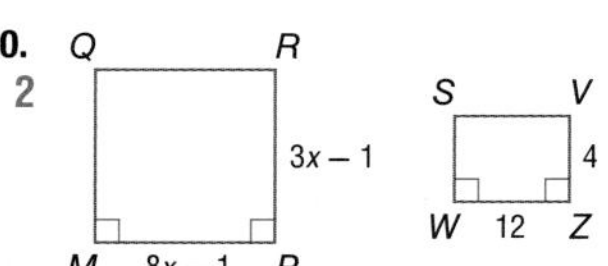

21. **3**

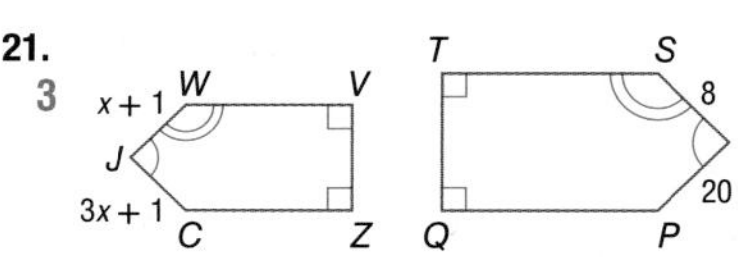

Example 4

22. Rectangle $ABCD$ has a width of 8 yards and a length of 20 yards. Rectangle $QRST$, which is similar to rectangle $ABCD$, has a length of 40 yards. Find the scale factor of rectangle $ABCD$ to rectangle $QRST$ and the perimeter of each rectangle. **1:2; perimeter of $ABCD$ = 56 yd, perimeter of $QRST$ = 112 yd**

Find the perimeter of the given triangle.

23. $\triangle DEF$, if $\triangle ABC \sim \triangle DEF$, $AB = 5$, $BC = 6$, $AC = 7$, and and $DE = 3$ **10.8**

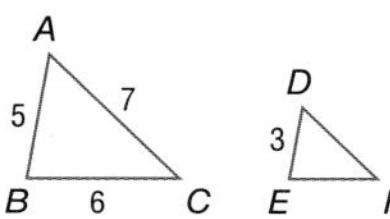

24. $\triangle WZX$, if $\triangle WZX \sim \triangle SRT$, $ST = 6$, $WX = 5$, and the perimeter of $\triangle SRT = 15$ **12.5**

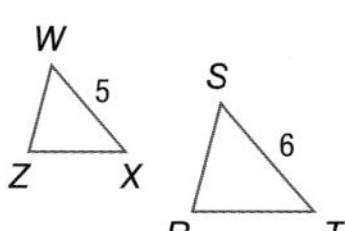

25. $\triangle CBH$, if $\triangle CBH \sim \triangle FEH$, $ADEG$ is a parallelogram, $CH = 7$, $FH = 10$, $FE = 11$, and $EH = 6$ **18.9**

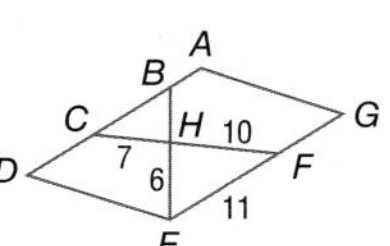

26. $\triangle DEF$, if $\triangle DEF \sim \triangle CBF$, perimeter of $\triangle CBF = 27$, $DF = 6$, $FC = 8$ **20.25**

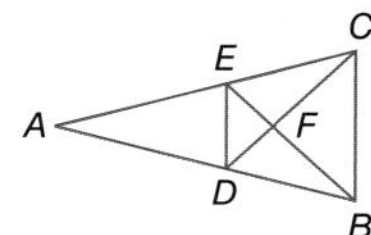

B 27. Two similar rectangles have a scale factor of 2:4. The perimeter of the large rectangle is 80 meters. Find the perimeter of the small rectangle. **40 m**

28. Two similar rectangles have a scale factor of 3:2. The perimeter of the small rectangle is 50 feet. Find the perimeter of the large rectangle. **75 ft**

Enrichment

OL BL

NAME ______ DATE ______ PERIOD ______

7-2 Enrichment

Constructing Similar Polygons

Here are four steps for constructing a polygon that is similar to and with sides twice as long as those of an existing polygon.

Step 1 Choose any point either inside or outside the polygon and label it O.

Step 2 Draw rays from O through each vertex of the polygon.

Step 3 For vertex V, set the compass to length OV. Then locate a new point V' on ray OV such that $VV' = OV$. Thus, $OV' = 2(OV)$.

Step 4 Repeat Step 3 for each vertex. Connect points V', W', X' and Y' to form the new polygon.

Two constructions of polygons similar to and with sides twice those of $VWXY$ are shown below. Notice that the placement of point O does not affect the size or shape of $V'W'X'Y'$, only its location.

Lesson 7-2

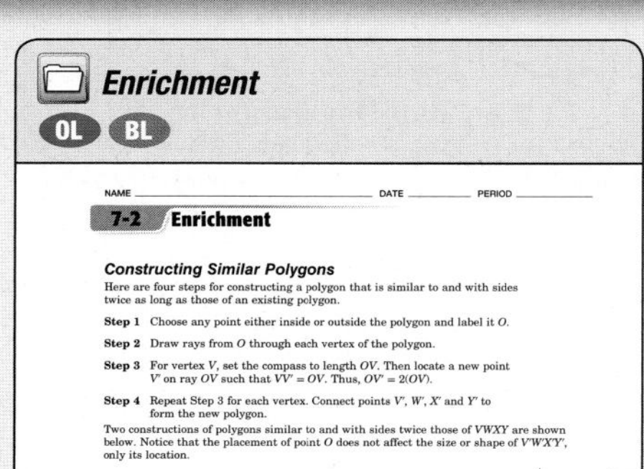

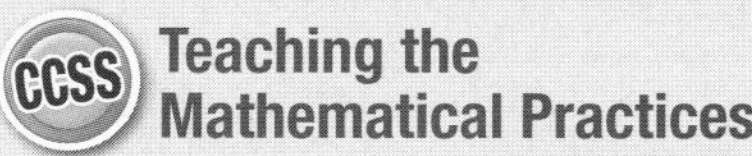

CCSS Teaching the Mathematical Practices

Regularity Mathematically proficient students maintain oversight of the process, while attending to the details. They continually evaluate the reasonableness of their intermediate results. Encourage students to write a similarity statement for each exercise.

List all pairs of congruent angles, and write a proportion that relates the corresponding sides. 29–30. See margin.

29.

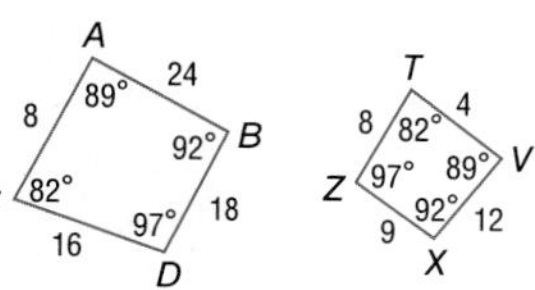

30.

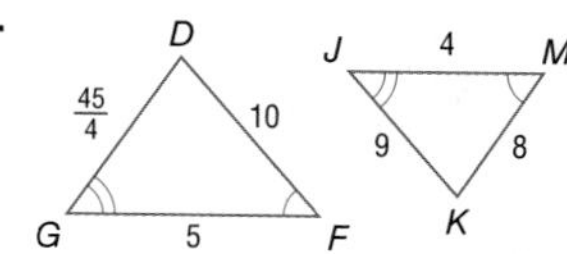

J 4 M, 9, 8, K

SHUFFLEBOARD **A shuffleboard court forms three similar triangles in which $\angle AHB \cong \angle AGC \cong \angle AFD$. For the given sides or angles, find the corresponding side(s) or angle(s) that are congruent.**

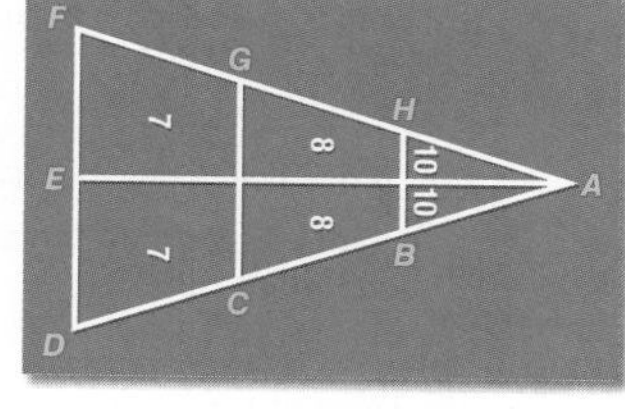

31. $\overline{AB}$  $\overline{AC}$, $\overline{AD}$

32. $\overline{FD}$ $\overline{HB}$, $\overline{GC}$

33. $\angle ACG$ $\angle ABH$, $\angle ADF$

34. $\angle A$

34. $\angle A$ is included in all of the triangles.

Find the value of each variable.

35 $ABCD \sim QSRP$ $x = 63$, $y = 32$

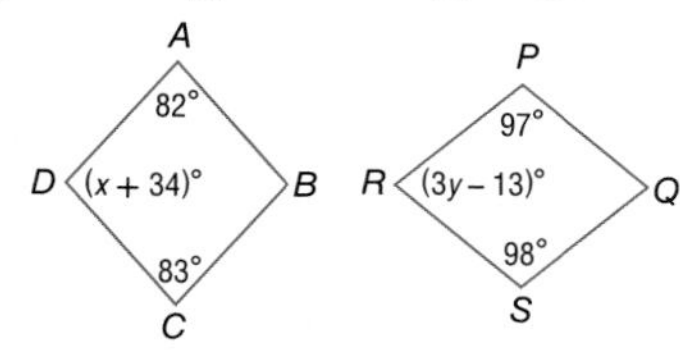

36. $\triangle JKL \sim \triangle WYZ$ $x = 21$, $y = 65$

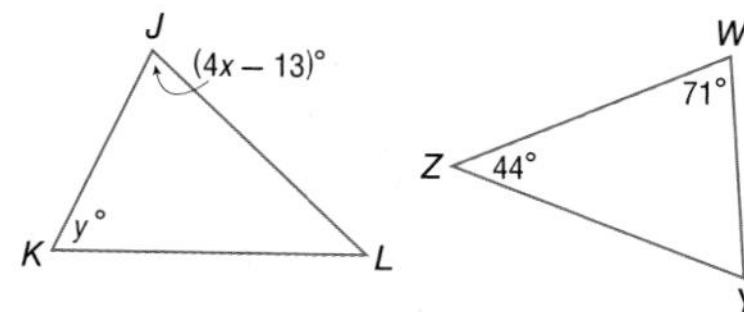

37. SLIDE SHOW You are using a digital projector for a slide show. The photos are 13 inches by $9\frac{1}{4}$ inches on the computer screen, and the scale factor of the computer image to the projected image is 1:4. What are the dimensions of the projected image? 52 in. by 37 in.

COORDINATE GEOMETRY **For the given vertices, determine whether rectangle *ABCD* is similar to rectangle *WXYZ*. Justify your answer.**

38. $A(-1, 5)$, $B(7, 5)$, $C(7, -1)$, $D(-1, -1)$;
$W(-2, 10)$, $X(14, 10)$, $Y(14, -2)$, $Z(-2, -2)$

39. $A(5, 5)$, $B(0, 0)$, $C(5, -5)$, $D(10, 0)$;
$W(1, 6)$, $X(-3, 2)$, $Y(2, -3)$, $Z(6, 1)$ no; $\frac{BC}{XY} \neq \frac{AB}{WX}$

38. $ABCD \sim WXYZ$ because $\angle A \cong \angle W$, $\angle B \cong \angle X$, $\angle C \cong \angle Y$, $\angle D \cong \angle Z$, $\frac{AB}{WX} = \frac{BC}{XY} = \frac{CD}{YZ} = \frac{DA}{ZW} = \frac{1}{2}$

CCSS ARGUMENTS **Determine whether the polygons are *always*, *sometimes*, or *never* similar. Explain your reasoning.** 40–45. See margin.

40. two obtuse triangles

41. a trapezoid and a parallelogram

42. two right triangles

43. two isosceles triangles

44. a scalene triangle and an isosceles triangle

45. two equilateral triangles

46. PROOF Write a paragraph proof of Theorem 7.1.

Given: $\triangle ABC \sim \triangle DEF$ and $\frac{AB}{DE} = \frac{m}{n}$

Prove: $\frac{\text{perimeter of } \triangle ABC}{\text{perimeter of } \triangle DEF} = \frac{m}{n}$ See Ch. 7 Answer Appendix.

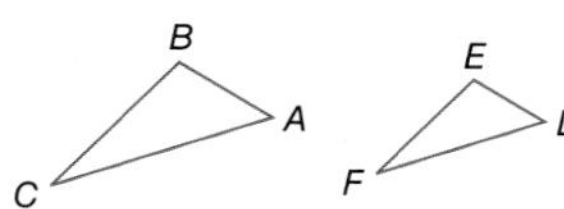

Additional Answers

29. $\angle A \cong \angle V$, $\angle B \cong \angle X$, $\angle D \cong \angle Z$, $\angle F \cong \angle T$; $\frac{AB}{VX} = \frac{BD}{XZ} = \frac{DF}{ZT} = \frac{FA}{TV} = 2$

30. $\angle D \cong \angle K$, $\angle F \cong \angle M$, $\angle G \cong \angle J$; $\frac{DF}{KM} = \frac{FG}{MJ} = \frac{GD}{JK} = 1.25$

40. Sometimes; sample answer: If corresponding angles are congruent and corresponding sides are proportional, two obtuse triangles are similar.

41. Never; sample answer: Parallelograms have both pairs of opposite sides parallel. Trapezoids have exactly one pair of parallel legs. Therefore, the two figures cannot be similar because they can never be the same type of figure.

42. Sometimes; sample answer: If corresponding angles are congruent and corresponding sides are proportional, two right triangles are similar.

43. Sometimes; sample answer: If corresponding angles are congruent and corresponding sides are proportional, two isosceles triangles are similar.

44. Never; sample answer: Since an isosceles triangle has two congruent sides and a scalene triangle has three non-congruent sides, the ratios of the three pairs of sides can never be equal. Therefore, an isosceles triangle and a scalene triangle can never be similar.

45. Always; sample answer: Equilateral triangles always have three 60° angles, so the angles of one equilateral triangle are always congruent to the angles of a second equilateral triangle. The three sides of an equilateral triangle are always congruent, so the ratio of each pair of legs of one triangle to a second triangle will always be the same. Therefore, a pair of equilateral triangles is always similar.

CCSS Teaching the Mathematical Practices

Arguments Mathematically proficient students understand and use stated assumptions and definitions in constructing arguments. In Exercises 40–45, encourage students to use dynamic geometry software to explore their conjectures.

Exercise Alert

Ruler Exercise 50 requires the use of a ruler.

Multiple Representations

In Exercise 50, students use geometric sketches, a table, and verbal description to investigate similarity in squares.

CCSS Teaching the Mathematical Practices

Reasoning Mathematically proficient students make sense of quantities and their relationships in problem situations. Encourage students to use the definition of *regular polygon*.

Additional Answers

53. Sample answer:

54.

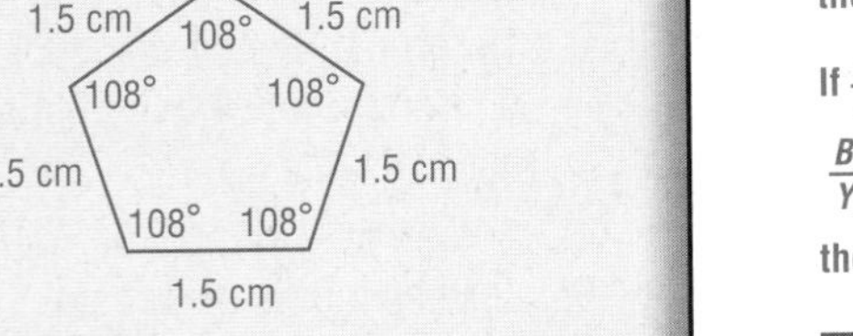

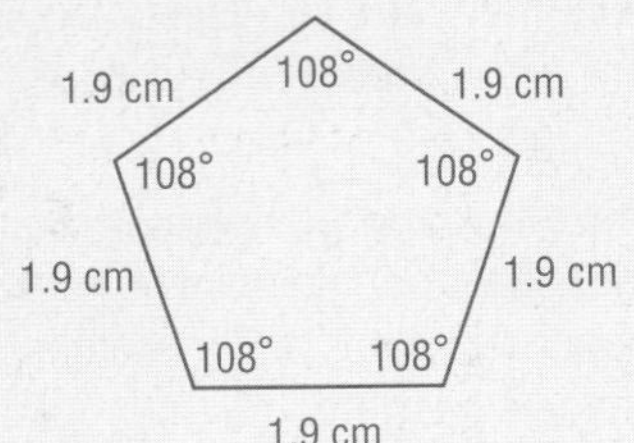

Yes; yes; sample answer: The pentagons are similar because their corresponding angles are congruent and their corresponding sides are proportional. All of the angles and sides in a regular polygon are congruent. The angles will be congruent regardless of the size of the figure, and since all of the sides are congruent the ratios of the sides of one regular figure to a second regular figure with the same number of sides will all be the same. Therefore, all regular polygons with the same number of sides are congruent.

47. **PHOTOS** You are enlarging the photo shown at the right for your school yearbook. If the dimensions of the original photo are $2\frac{1}{3}$ inches by $1\frac{2}{3}$ inches and the scale factor of the old photo to the new photo is 2:3, what are the dimensions of the new photo? **$3\frac{1}{2}$ in. by $2\frac{1}{2}$ in.**

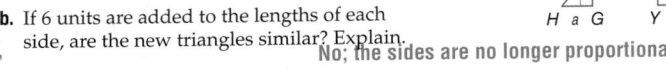

48. **CHANGING DIMENSIONS** Rectangle *QRST* is similar to rectangle *JKLM* with sides in a ratio of 4:1.

a. What is the ratio of the areas of the two rectangles? **16:1**

b. Suppose the dimension of each rectangle is tripled. What is the new ratio of the sides of the rectangles? **4:1**

c. What is the ratio of the areas of these larger rectangles? **16:1**

49. **CHANGING DIMENSIONS** In the figure shown, $\triangle FGH \sim \triangle XYZ$.

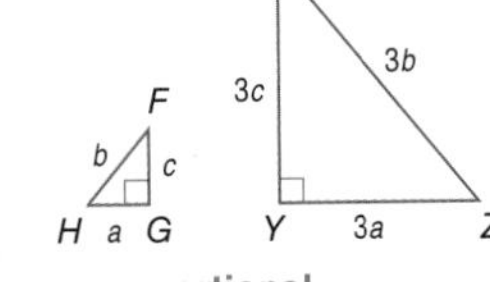

a. Show that the perimeters of $\triangle FGH$ and $\triangle XYZ$ have the same ratio as their corresponding sides.

49a. $\frac{a}{3a} = \frac{b}{3b} = \frac{c}{3c} = \frac{a+b+c}{3(a+b+c)} = \frac{1}{3}$

b. If 6 units are added to the lengths of each side, are the new triangles similar? Explain. **No; the sides are no longer proportional.**

50. **MULTIPLE REPRESENTATIONS** In this problem, you will investigate similarity in squares.

a. **Geometric** Draw three different-sized squares. Label them *ABCD*, *PQRS*, and *WXYZ*. Measure and label each square with its side length. **See Ch. 7 Answer Appendix.**

b. **Tabular** Calculate and record in a table the ratios of corresponding sides for each pair of squares: *ABCD* and *PQRS*, *PQRS* and *WXYZ*, and *WXYZ* and *ABCD*. Is each pair of squares similar? **See Ch. 7 Answer Appendix.**

c. **Verbal** Make a conjecture about the similarity of all squares. **Sample answer: All squares are similar.**

52. Yes; sample answer: Similarity is reflexive, symmetric, and transitive. If $\triangle ABC \sim \triangle XYZ$, then $\frac{AB}{XY} = \frac{AB}{XY}$. If $\frac{AB}{XY} = \frac{BC}{YZ}$, then $\frac{BC}{YZ} = \frac{AB}{XY}$. If $\frac{AB}{XY} = \frac{BC}{YZ}$ and $\frac{BC}{YZ} = \frac{CA}{ZX}$, then $\frac{AB}{XY} = \frac{CA}{ZX}$.

H.O.T. Problems Use Higher-Order Thinking Skills

51. **CHALLENGE** For what value(s) of *x* is $BEFA \sim EDCB$? **4**

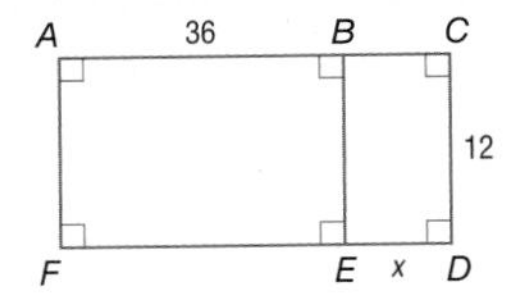

52. **REASONING** Recall that an *equivalence relation* is any relationship that satisfies the Reflexive, Symmetric, and Transitive Properties. Is similarity an equivalence relation? Explain.

53. **OPEN ENDED** Find a counterexample for the following statement. **See margin.**

All rectangles are similar.

54. **CCSS REASONING** Draw two regular pentagons of different sizes. Are the pentagons similar? Will any two regular polygons with the same number of sides be similar? Explain. **See margin.**

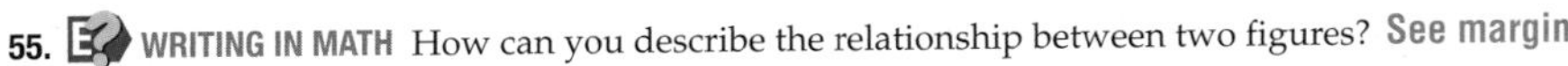

55. **WRITING IN MATH** How can you describe the relationship between two figures? **See margin.**

55. Sample answer: The figures could be described as congruent if they are the same size and shape, similar if their corresponding angles are congruent and their corresponding sides are proportional, and equal if they are the same exact figure.

Standardized Test Practice

56. ALGEBRA If the arithmetic mean of $4x$, $3x$, and 12 is 18, then what is the value of x? A

A 6 C 4
B 5 D 3

57. Two similar rectangles have a scale factor of 3:5. The perimeter of the large rectangle is 65 meters. What is the perimeter of the small rectangle? G

F 29 m H 49 m
G 39 m J 59 m

58. SHORT RESPONSE If a jar contains 25 dimes and 7 quarters, what is the probability that a coin selected from the jar at random will be a dime? 0.78

59. SAT/ACT If the side of a square is $x + 3$, then what is the diagonal of the square? E

A $x^2 + 3$ D $x\sqrt{3} + 3\sqrt{3}$
B $3x + 3$ E $x\sqrt{2} + 3\sqrt{2}$
C $2x + 6$

Spiral Review

60. COMPUTERS In a survey of 5000 households, 4200 had at least one computer. What is the ratio of computers to households? (Lesson 7-1) 21:25

61. PROOF Write a flow proof. (Lesson 6-6) See margin.

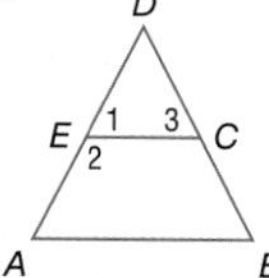

Given: E and C are midpoints of $\overline{AD}$ and $\overline{DB}$, $\overline{AD} \cong \overline{DB}$, $\angle A \cong \angle 1$.
Prove: $ABCE$ is an isosceles trapezoid.

62. COORDINATE GEOMETRY Determine the coordinates of the intersection of the diagonals of $\square JKLM$ with vertices $J(2, 5)$, $K(6, 6)$, $L(4, 0)$, and $M(0, -1)$. (Lesson 6-2) (3, 2.5)

State the assumption you would make to start an indirect proof of each statement. (Lesson 5-4)

63. If $3x > 12$, then $x > 4$. $x \leq 4$

64. $\overline{PQ} \cong \overline{ST}$ $\overline{PQ} \not\cong \overline{ST}$

65. The angle bisector of the vertex angle of an isosceles triangle is also an altitude of the triangle. The angle bisector of the vertex angle of an isosceles triangle is not an altitude of the triangle.

66. If a rational number is any number that can be expressed as $\frac{a}{b}$, where a and b are integers and $b \neq 0$, then 6 is a rational number. 6 cannot be expressed as $\frac{a}{b}$, where a and b are integers and $b \neq 0$.

Find the measures of each numbered angle. (Lesson 4-2)

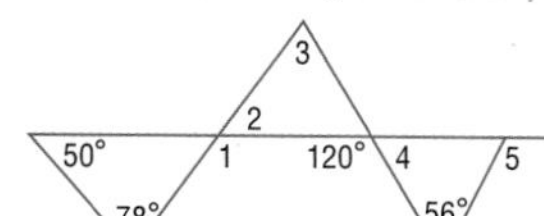

67. $m\angle 1$ 128

68. $m\angle 2$ 52

69. $m\angle 3$ 68

Skills Review

ALGEBRA Find x and the unknown side measures of each triangle.

70.

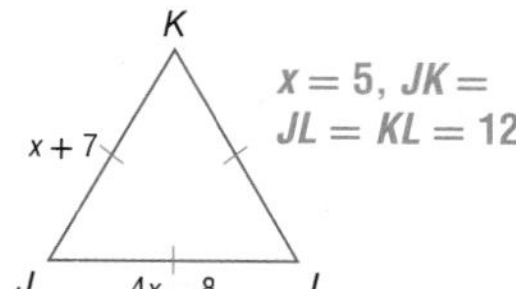

$x = 5$, $JK = JL = KL = 12$

71.

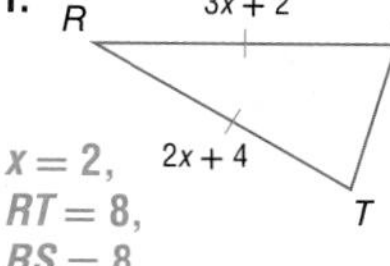

$x = 2$, $RT = 8$, $RS = 8$

72.

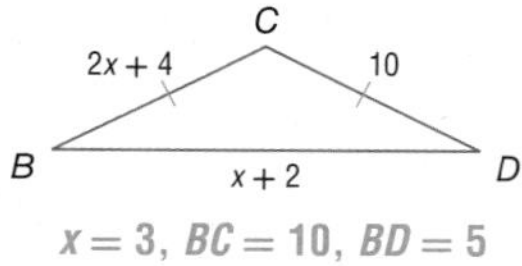

$x = 3$, $BC = 10$, $BD = 5$

DifferentiatedInstruction OL BL

Extension Have students use a word processing program and experiment with different polygons that the program provides. After they choose a shape, have them generate a figure that is similar. They can copy the original figure then change the figure's scale, which will make the second figure similar. A way to check for similarity is to superimpose the two polygons at any vertex. The angles should be identical.

4 Assess

Crystal Ball Ask students to predict how today's lesson about similar polygons helped them prepare for tomorrow's lesson about similar triangles. What may be the same? What may be different?

Formative Assessment

Check for student understanding of Lessons 7-1 and 7-2.

 Quiz 1, p. 51

Additional Answer

61. Given: E and C are midpoints of $\overline{AD}$ and $\overline{AB}$, $\overline{AD} \cong \overline{DB}$, $\angle A \cong \angle 1$
Prove: $ABCE$ is an isosceles trapezoid.
Proof:

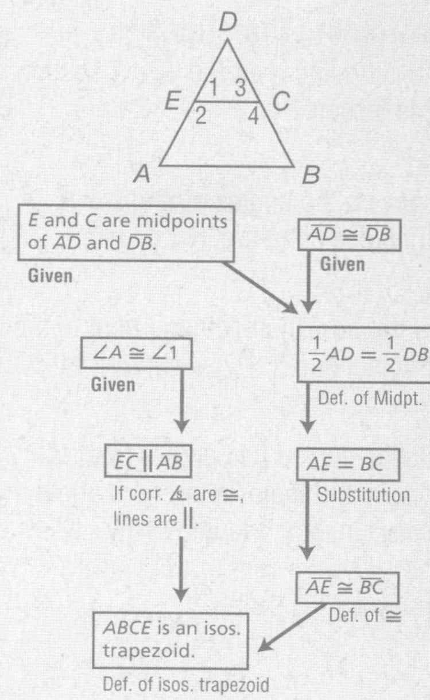

1 Focus

Vertical Alignment

Before Lesson 7-3 Use the AAS, SSS, and SAS Congruence Theorems to prove triangles congruent.

Lesson 7-3 Identify similar triangles, using the AA Similarity Postulate and SSS and SAS Similarity Theorems. Use similar triangles to solve problems.

After Lesson 7-3 Justify triangle similarity relationships.

2 Teach

Scaffolding Questions

Have students read the **Why?** section of the lesson.

Ask:

- How do the angles of the two triangles compare? They are congruent.
- Is the new triangle congruent to the original one? No, the side lengths are not the same.
- Julian copied two angles from the original triangle. Is the third angle the same in each triangle? Why? Yes, because the sum of the angle measures is 180.

LESSON 7-3 Similar Triangles

Then	Now	Why?
You used the AAS, SSS, and SAS Congruence Theorems to prove triangles congruent.	1 Identify similar triangles using the AA Similarity Postulate and the SSS and SAS Similarity Theorems. 2 Use similar triangles to solve problems.	Julian wants to draw a similar version of his skate club's logo on a poster. He first draws a line at the bottom of the poster. Next, he uses a cutout of the original triangle to copy the two bottom angles. Finally, he extends the noncommon sides of the two angles.

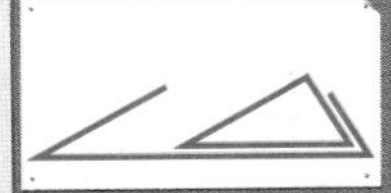

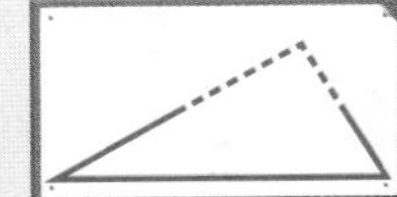

CCSS Common Core State Standards

Content Standards

G.SRT.4 Prove theorems about triangles.

G.SRT.5 Use congruence and similarity criteria for triangles to solve problems and to prove relationships in geometric figures.

Mathematical Practices

4 Model with mathematics.

7 Look for and make use of structure.

1 Identify Similar Triangles

The example suggests that two triangles are similar if two pairs of corresponding angles are congruent.

Postulate 7.1 Angle-Angle (AA) Similarity

If two angles of one triangle are congruent to two angles of another triangle, then the triangles are similar.

Example If $\angle A \cong \angle F$ and $\angle B \cong \angle G$, then $\triangle ABC \sim \triangle FGH$.

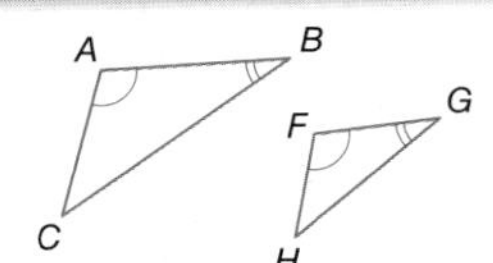

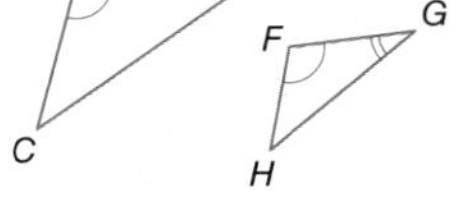

Example 1 Use the AA Similarity Postulate

Determine whether the triangles are similar. If so, write a similarity statement. Explain your reasoning.

a.

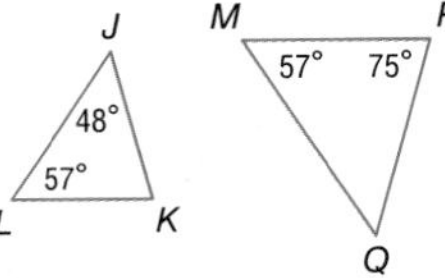

b.

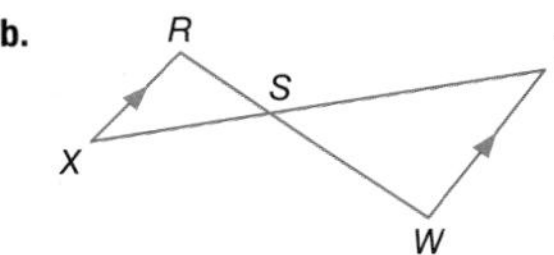

a. Since $m\angle L = m\angle M$, $\angle L \cong \angle M$. By the Triangle Sum Theorem, $57 + 48 + m\angle K = 180$, so $m\angle K = 75$. Since $m\angle P = 75$, $\angle K \cong \angle P$. So, $\triangle LJK \sim \triangle MQP$ by AA Similarity.

b. $\angle RSX \cong \angle WST$ by the Vertical Angles Theorem. Since $\overline{RX} \parallel \overline{TW}$, $\angle R \cong \angle W$. So, $\triangle RSX \sim \triangle WST$ by AA Similarity.

Guided Practice

1A. A, C, B, 44°; D, F, G, 47°

No; no 2 pairs of ∡ ≅.

1B.

Yes; $\angle LJK \cong \angle LPQ$ and $\angle L \cong \angle L$, so $\triangle KLJ \sim \triangle QLP$.

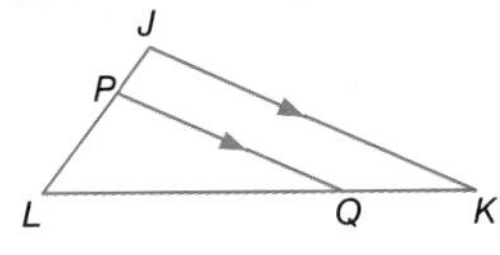

478 | Lesson 7-3

Lesson 7-3 Resources

Resource	Approaching Level AL	On Level OL	Beyond Level BL	English Learners ELL
Teacher Edition	▪ Differentiated Instruction, p. 480	▪ Differentiated Instruction, pp. 480, 486	▪ Differentiated Instruction, pp. 480, 486	▪ Differentiated Instruction, p. 480
Chapter Resource Masters	▪ Study Guide and Intervention, pp. 18–19 ▪ Skills Practice, p. 20 ▪ Practice, p. 21 ▪ Word Problem Practice, p. 22	▪ Study Guide and Intervention, pp. 18–19 ▪ Skills Practice, p. 20 ▪ Practice, p. 21 ▪ Word Problem Practice, p. 22 ▪ Enrichment, p. 23	▪ Practice, p. 21 ▪ Word Problem Practice, p. 22 ▪ Enrichment, p. 23	▪ Study Guide and Intervention, pp. 18–19 ▪ Skills Practice, p. 20 ▪ Practice, p. 21 ▪ Word Problem Practice, p. 22
Other	▪ 5-Minute Check 7-3 ▪ Study Notebook ▪ Teaching Geometry with Manipulatives	▪ 5-Minute Check 7-3 ▪ Study Notebook ▪ Teaching Geometry with Manipulatives	▪ 5-Minute Check 7-3 ▪ Study Notebook	▪ 5-Minute Check 7-3 ▪ Study Notebook ▪ Teaching Geometry with Manipulatives

You can use the AA Similarity Postulate to prove the following two theorems.

Theorems Triangle Similarity

7.2 Side-Side-Side (SSS) Similarity
If the corresponding side lengths of two triangles are proportional, then the triangles are similar.

Example If $\frac{JK}{MP} = \frac{KL}{PQ} = \frac{LJ}{QM}$, then $\triangle JKL \sim \triangle MPQ$.

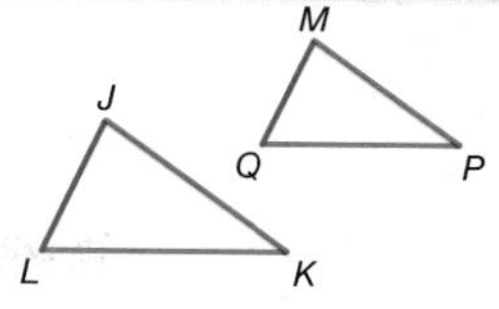

7.3 Side-Angle-Side (SAS) Similarity
If the lengths of two sides of one triangle are proportional to the lengths of two corresponding sides of another triangle and the included angles are congruent, then the triangles are similar.

Example If $\frac{RS}{XY} = \frac{ST}{YZ}$ and $\angle S \cong \angle Y$, then $\triangle RST \sim \triangle XYZ$.

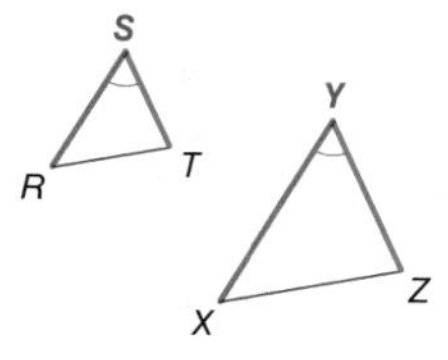

You will prove Theorem 7.3 in Exercise 25.

Proof Theorem 7.2

Given: $\frac{AB}{FG} = \frac{BC}{GH} = \frac{AC}{FH}$
Prove: $\triangle ABC \sim \triangle FGH$

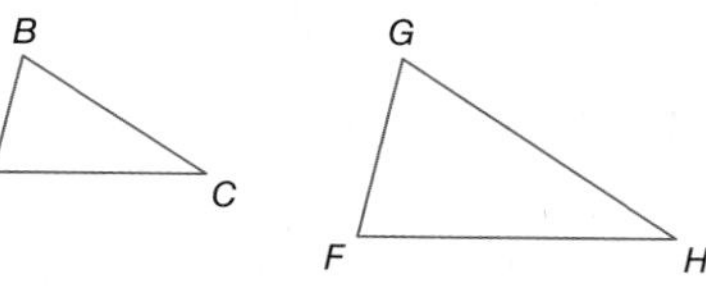

StudyTip

Corresponding Sides To determine which sides of two triangles correspond, begin by comparing the longest sides, then the next longest sides, and finish by comparing the shortest sides.

Paragraph Proof:

Locate J on $\overline{FG}$ so that $JG = AB$. Draw $\overline{JK}$ so that $\overline{JK} \parallel \overline{FH}$. Label $\angle GJK$ as $\angle 1$.

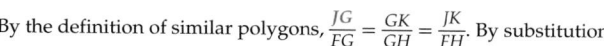

Since $\angle G \cong \angle G$ by the Reflexive Property and $\angle 1 \cong \angle F$ by the Corresponding Angles Postulate, $\triangle GJK \sim \triangle GFH$ by the AA Similarity Postulate.

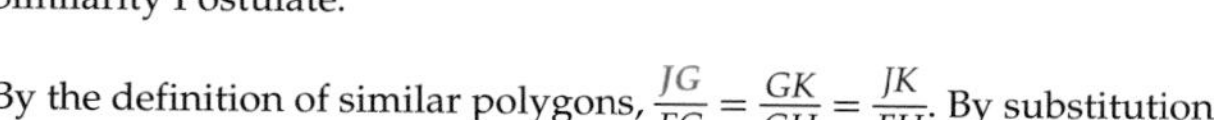

By the definition of similar polygons, $\frac{JG}{FG} = \frac{GK}{GH} = \frac{JK}{FH}$. By substitution, $\frac{AB}{FG} = \frac{GK}{GH} = \frac{JK}{FH}$.

Since we are also given that $\frac{AB}{FG} = \frac{BC}{GH} = \frac{AC}{FH}$, we can say that $\frac{GK}{GH} = \frac{BC}{GH}$ and $\frac{JK}{FH} = \frac{AC}{FH}$. This means that $GK = BC$ and $JK = AC$, so $\overline{GK} \cong \overline{BC}$ and $\overline{JK} \cong \overline{AC}$.

By SSS, $\triangle ABC \cong \triangle JGK$.

By CPCTC, $\angle B \cong \angle G$ and $\angle A \cong \angle 1$. Since $\angle 1 \cong \angle F$, $\angle A \cong \angle F$ by the Transitive Property. By AA Similarity, $\triangle ABC \sim \triangle FGH$.

1 Identify Similar Triangles

Examples 1–3 shows how to use new theorems and postulates to prove triangles are similar. **Examples 4 and 5** show how to use properties of similar triangles to find unknown lengths.

Formative Assessment

Use the Guided Practice exercises after each example to determine students' understanding of concepts.

Additional Example

1 Determine whether the triangles are similar. If so, write a similarity statement. Explain your reasoning.

a.

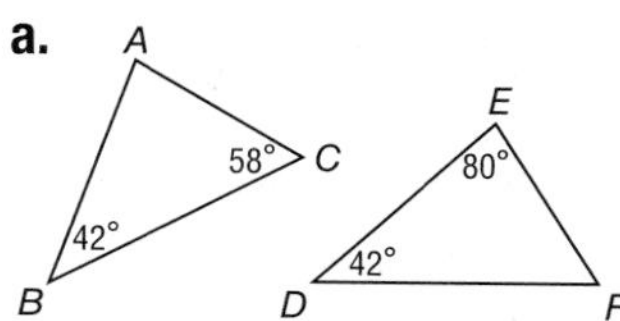

By the Triangle Sum Theorem, $m\angle A = 80$. Since $\angle A \cong \angle E$ and $\angle B \cong \angle D$, $\triangle ABC \sim \triangle EDF$ by AA Similarity.

b.

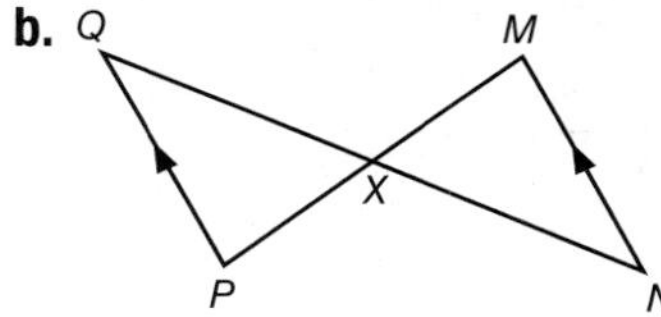

By the Vertical Angles Theorem, $\angle QXP \cong \angle NXM$, and since $\overline{PQ} \parallel \overline{MN}$, $\angle Q \cong \angle N$. Therefore, $\triangle QXP \sim \triangle NXM$ by AA Similarity.

Additional Examples also in Interactive Classroom PowerPoint® Presentations

Focus on Mathematical Content

Comparing Point out the similarities and differences between the triangle congruence postulates and theorems in Chapter 4 and the similarity postulates and theorems in this chapter. Emphasize that although only two pairs of corresponding angles need to be congruent for two triangles to be similar, all three pairs of corresponding sides must be proportional.

Additional Examples

2 Determine whether the triangles are similar. If so, write a similarity statement. Explain your reasoning.

a.

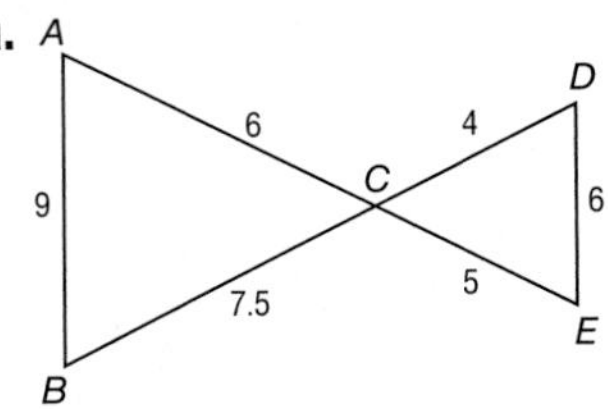

$\triangle ABC \sim \triangle DEC$ by the SSS Similarity Theorem.

b.

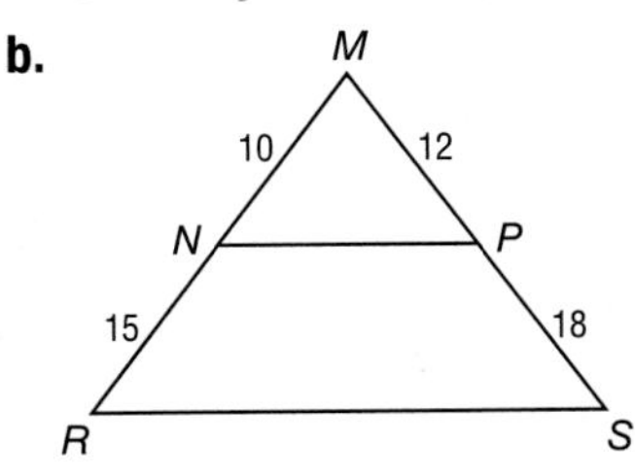

$\triangle MNP \sim \triangle MRS$ by the SAS Similarity Theorem

3 STANDARDIZED TEST PRACTICE If $\triangle RST$ and $\triangle XYZ$ are two triangles such that $\frac{RS}{XY} = \frac{2}{3}$ which of the following would be sufficient to prove that the triangles are similar? B

A $\frac{RT}{XZ} = \frac{ST}{YZ}$ **C** $\angle R \cong \angle S$

B $\frac{RS}{XY} = \frac{RT}{XZ} = \frac{ST}{YZ}$ **D** $\frac{RS}{RT} = \frac{XY}{XZ}$

WatchOut!

Congruent Angles The SAS Similarity Theorem can be used only if the angle is between the two corresponding sides of each triangle.

Teach with Tech

Interactive Whiteboard Use geometry software to draw a triangle and measure its side lengths. Project the figure on the screen and tell students they can measure only one side of the triangle. Have them use a proportion to find the lengths of the other sides. Repeat with different triangles.

PT

Example 2 Use the SSS and SAS Similarity Theorems

Determine whether the triangles are similar. If so, write a similarity statement. Explain your reasoning.

a.

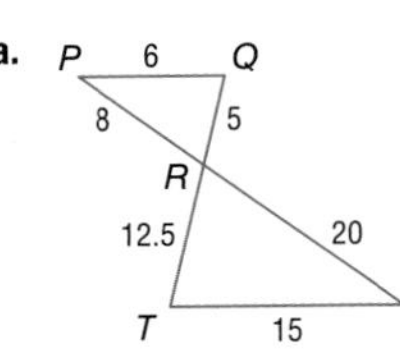

$\frac{PR}{SR} = \frac{8}{20}$ or $\frac{2}{5}$, $\frac{PQ}{ST} = \frac{6}{15}$ or $\frac{2}{5}$, and $\frac{QR}{TR} = \frac{5}{12.5} = \frac{50}{125}$ or $\frac{2}{5}$. So, $\triangle PQR \sim \triangle STR$ by the SSS Similarity Theorem.

b.

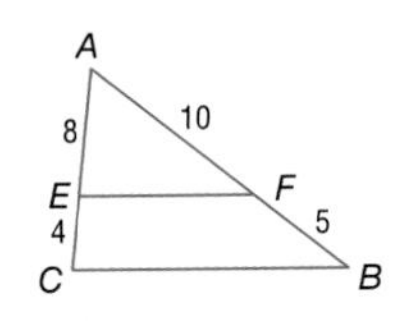

By the Reflexive Property, $\angle A \cong \angle A$.

$\frac{AF}{AB} = \frac{10}{10+5} = \frac{10}{15}$ or $\frac{2}{3}$ and $\frac{AE}{AC} = \frac{8}{8+4} = \frac{8}{12}$ or $\frac{2}{3}$.

Since the lengths of the sides that include $\angle A$ are proportional, $\triangle AEF \sim \triangle ACB$ by the SAS Similarity Theorem.

StudyTip

Draw Diagrams It is helpful to redraw similar triangles so that the corresponding side lengths have the same orientation.

GuidedPractice

2A.

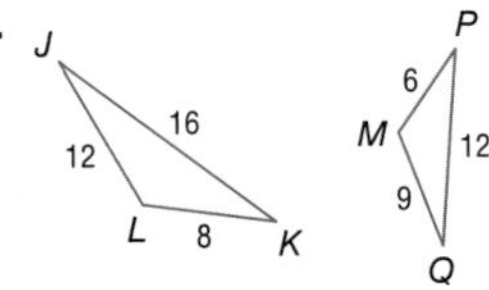

2B.

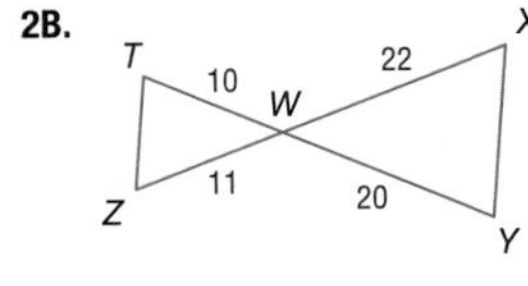

2A. Yes; $\triangle JLK \sim \triangle QMP$ by SSS Similarity since $\frac{JL}{QM} = \frac{LK}{MP} = \frac{JK}{QP} = \frac{4}{3}$.

2B. Yes; $\triangle TWZ \sim \triangle YWX$ by SAS Similarity since $\angle W \cong \angle W$ and $\frac{TW}{YW} = \frac{WZ}{WX} = \frac{1}{2}$.

You can decide what is sufficient to prove that two triangles are similar.

PT

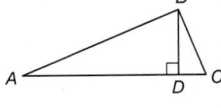

Standardized Test Example 3 Sufficient Conditions

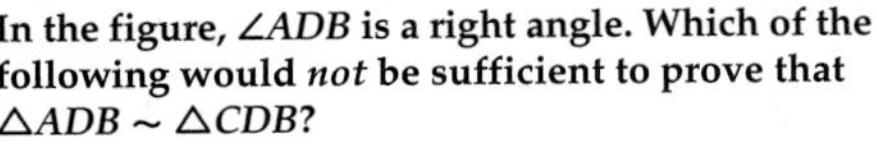

In the figure, $\angle ADB$ is a right angle. Which of the following would *not* be sufficient to prove that $\triangle ADB \sim \triangle CDB$?

B, A, D, C

A $\frac{AD}{BD} = \frac{BD}{CD}$ **C** $\angle ABD \cong \angle C$

B $\frac{AB}{BC} = \frac{BD}{CD}$ **D** $\frac{AD}{BD} = \frac{BD}{CD} = \frac{AB}{BC}$

Read the Test Item

You are given that $\angle ADB$ is a right angle and asked to identify which additional information would not be enough to prove that $\triangle ADB \sim \triangle CDB$.

Solve the Test Item

Since $\angle ADB$ is a right angle, $\angle CDB$ is also a right angle. Since all right angles are congruent, $\angle ADB \cong \angle CDB$. Check each answer choice until you find one that does not supply a sufficient additional condition to prove that $\triangle ADB \sim \triangle CDB$.

Test-TakingTip

Identifying Nonexamples Sometimes test questions require you to find a nonexample, as in this case. You must check each option until you find a valid nonexample. If you would like to check your answer, confirm that each additional option is correct.

Choice A: If $\frac{AD}{BD} = \frac{BD}{CD}$ and $\angle ADB \cong \angle CDB$, then $\triangle ADB \sim \triangle CDB$ by SAS Similarity.

Choice B: If $\frac{AB}{BC} = \frac{BD}{CD}$ and $\angle ADB \cong \angle CDB$, then we cannot conclude that $\triangle ADB \sim \triangle CDB$ because the included angle of side $\overline{AB}$ and $\overline{BD}$ is not $\angle ADB$. So the answer is B.

DifferentiatedInstruction AL OL BL ELL

Interpersonal Learners Have students choose a partner. Ask each pair of students to measure the height of the school building by using their own shadows and similar triangles.

GuidedPractice

3. If $\triangle JKL$ and $\triangle FGH$ are two triangles such that $\angle J \cong \angle F$, which of the following would be sufficient to prove that the triangles are similar? G

F $\frac{KL}{GH} = \frac{JL}{FH}$ **G** $\frac{JL}{JK} = \frac{FH}{FG}$ **H** $\frac{JK}{FG} = \frac{KL}{GH}$ **J** $\frac{JL}{JK} = \frac{GH}{FG}$

2 Use Similar Triangles

Like the congruence of triangles, similarity of triangles is reflexive, symmetric, and transitive.

Theorem 7.4 Properties of Similarity

Reflexive Property of Similarity	$\triangle ABC \sim \triangle ABC$
Symmetric Property of Similarity	If $\triangle ABC \sim \triangle DEF$, then $\triangle DEF \sim \triangle ABC$.
Transitive Property of Similarity	If $\triangle ABC \sim \triangle DEF$, and $\triangle DEF \sim \triangle XYZ$, then $\triangle ABC \sim \triangle XYZ$.

You will prove Theorem 7.4 in Exercise 26.

Example 4 Parts of Similar Triangles

Find BE and AD.

Since $\overline{BE} \parallel \overline{CD}$, $\angle ABE \cong \angle BCD$, and $\angle AEB \cong \angle EDC$ because they are corresponding angles. By AA Similarity, $\triangle ABE \sim \triangle ACD$.

$\frac{AB}{AC} = \frac{BE}{CD}$ Definition of Similar Polygons

$\frac{3}{5} = \frac{x}{3.5}$ $AC = 5$, $CD = 3.5$, $AB = 3$, $BE = x$

$3.5 \cdot 3 = 5 \cdot x$ Cross Products Property

$2.1 = x$ BE is 2.1.

$\frac{AC}{AB} = \frac{AD}{AE}$ Definition of Similar Polygons

$\frac{5}{3} = \frac{y+3}{y}$ $AC = 5$, $AB = 3$, $AD = y + 3$, $AE = y$

$5 \cdot y = 3(y + 3)$ Cross Products Property

$5y = 3y + 9$ Distributive Property

$2y = 9$ Subtract $3y$ from each side.

$y = 4.5$ AD is $y + 3$ or 7.5.

StudyTip

Proportions An additional proportion that is true for Example 4 is $\frac{AC}{CD} = \frac{AB}{BE}$.

GuidedPractice

Find each measure.

4A. QP and MP 3; 8

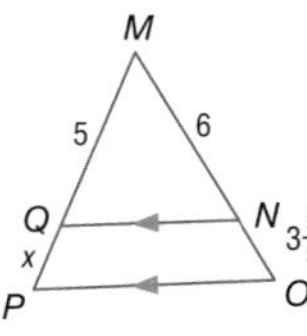

4B. WR and RT 8; 10

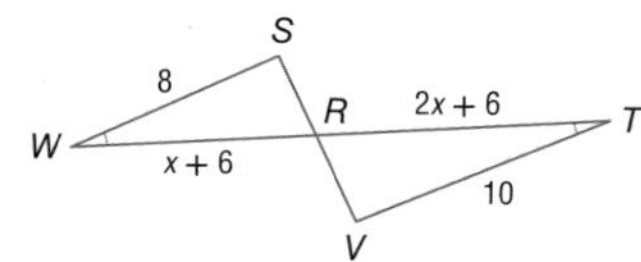

Additional Example

4 ALGEBRA Given $\overline{RS} \parallel \overline{UT}$, $RS = 4$, $RQ = x + 3$, $QT = 2x + 10$, $UT = 10$. Find RQ and QT. 8; 20

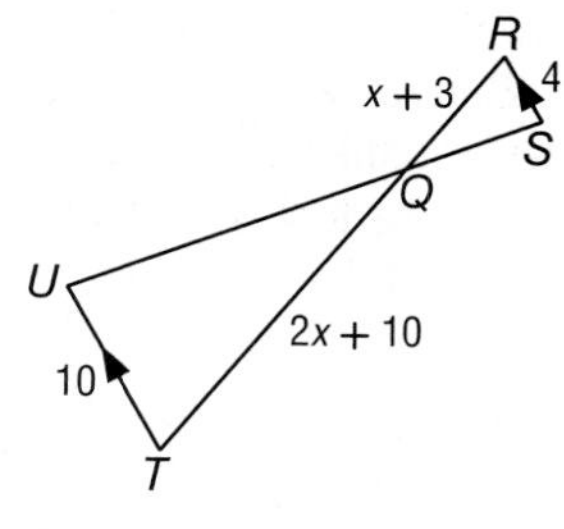

connectED.mcgraw-hill.com 481

Additional Example

5 SKYSCRAPERS Josh wanted to measure the height of the Sears Tower in Chicago. He used a 12-foot light pole and measured its shadow at 1 P.M. The length of the shadow was 2 feet. Then he measured the length of Sears Tower's shadow and it was 242 feet at the same time. What is the height of the Sears Tower?

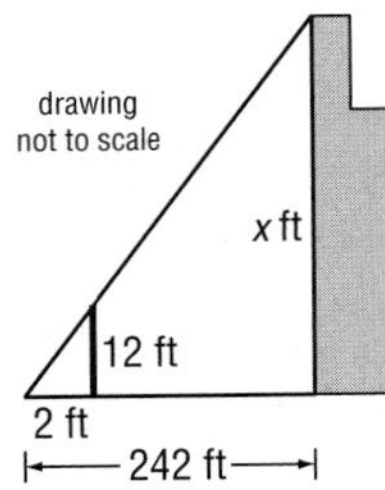

1452 ft (actual height: 1450 feet)

Real-World Example 5 Indirect Measurement

ROLLER COASTERS Hallie is estimating the height of the Superman roller coaster in Mitchellville, Maryland. She is 5 feet 3 inches tall and her shadow is 3 feet long. If the length of the shadow of the roller coaster is 40 feet, how tall is the roller coaster?

Understand Make a sketch of the situation. 5 feet 3 inches is equivalent to 5.25 feet.

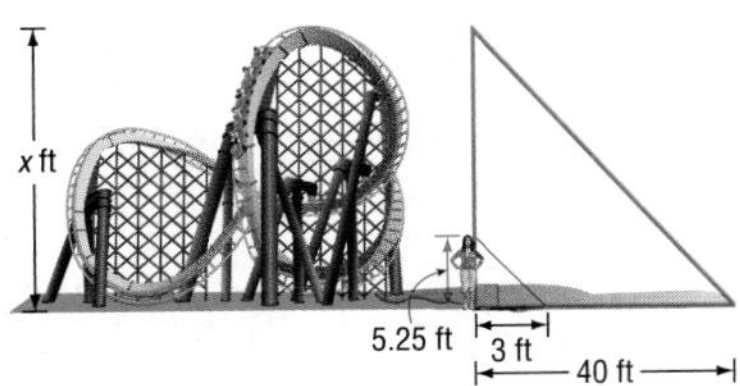

Plan In shadow problems, you can assume that the angles formed by the Sun's rays with any two objects are congruent and that the two objects form the sides of two right triangles.

Since two pairs of angles are congruent, the right triangles are similar by the AA Similarity Postulate. So, the following proportion can be written.

$$\frac{\text{Hallie's height}}{\text{coaster's height}} = \frac{\text{Hallie's shadow length}}{\text{coaster's shadow length}}$$

Solve Substitute the known values and let x = roller coaster's height.

$\frac{5.25}{x} = \frac{3}{40}$	Substitution
$3 \cdot x = 40(5.25)$	Cross Products Property
$3x = 210$	Simplify.
$x = 70$	Divide each side by 3.

The roller coaster is 70 feet tall.

Check The roller coaster's shadow length is $\frac{40 \text{ ft}}{3 \text{ ft}}$ or about 13.3 times Hallie's shadow length. Check to see that the roller coaster's height is about 13.3 times Hallie's height. $\frac{70 \text{ ft}}{5.25 \text{ ft}} \approx 13.3$ ✓

Problem-Solving Tip

Reasonable Answers When you have solved a problem, check your answer for reasonableness. In this example, Hallie's shadow is a little more than half her height. The coaster's shadow is also a little more than half of the height you calculated. Therefore, the answer is reasonable.

Guided Practice

5. BUILDINGS Adam is standing next to the Palmetto Building in Columbia, South Carolina. He is 6 feet tall and the length of his shadow is 9 feet. If the length of the shadow of the building is 322.5 feet, how tall is the building? 215 ft

Concept Summary Triangle Similarity

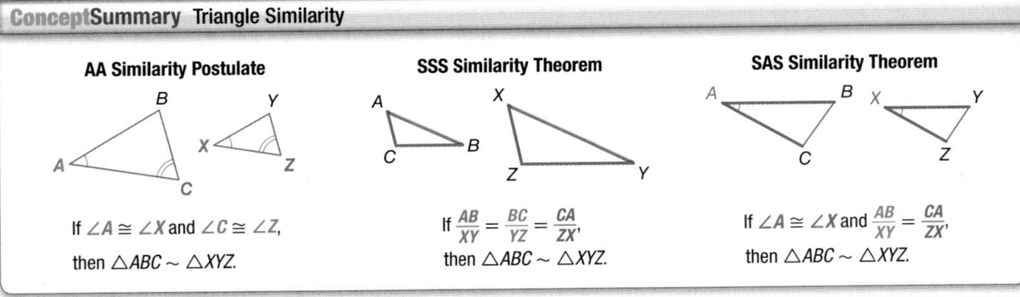

AA Similarity Postulate	SSS Similarity Theorem	SAS Similarity Theorem
If $\angle A \cong \angle X$ and $\angle C \cong \angle Z$, then $\triangle ABC \sim \triangle XYZ$.	If $\frac{AB}{XY} = \frac{BC}{YZ} = \frac{CA}{ZX}$, then $\triangle ABC \sim \triangle XYZ$.	If $\angle A \cong \angle X$ and $\frac{AB}{XY} = \frac{CA}{ZX}$, then $\triangle ABC \sim \triangle XYZ$.

Check Your Understanding

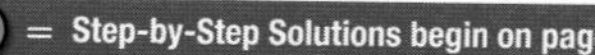
● = Step-by-Step Solutions begin on page R14.

Examples 1–2 **Determine whether the triangles are similar. If so, write a similarity statement. Explain your reasoning.**

1.

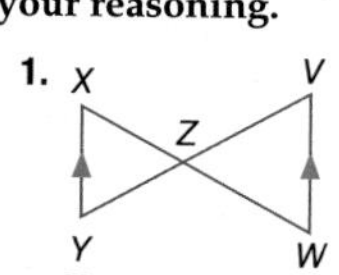

Yes; $\triangle YXZ \sim \triangle VWZ$ by AA Similarity.

2.

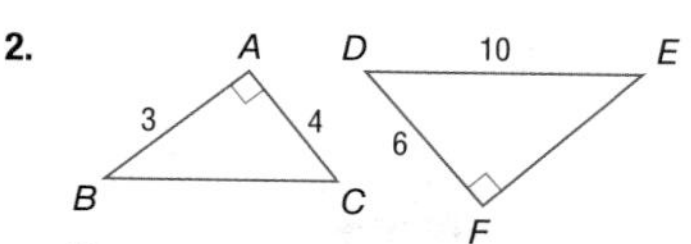

Yes; $\triangle BAC \sim \triangle DFE$ by SAS Similarity.

3. No; corresponding sides are not proportional.

3.

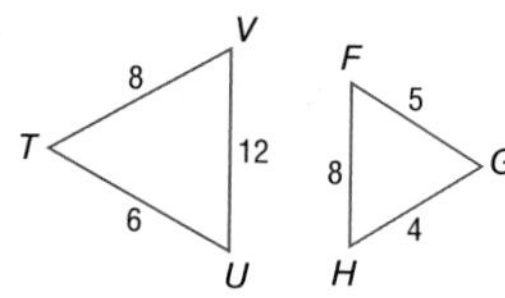

4.

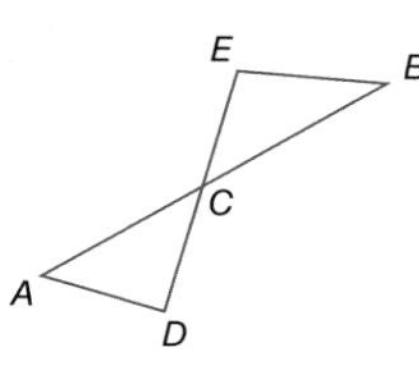

Yes; $\triangle JLK \sim \triangle SRQ$ by SSS Similarity.

Example 3

5. MULTIPLE CHOICE In the figure, $\overline{AB}$ intersects $\overline{DE}$ at point *C*. Which additional information would be enough to prove that $\triangle ADC \sim \triangle BEC$? **C**

A $\angle DAC$ and $\angle ECB$ are congruent.

B $\overline{AC}$ and $\overline{BC}$ are congruent.

C $\overline{AD}$ and $\overline{EB}$ are parallel.

D $\angle CBE$ is a right angle.

Example 4

CCSS STRUCTURE **Identify the similar triangles. Find each measure.**

6. *KL* $\triangle XYZ \sim \triangle JKL$; 12

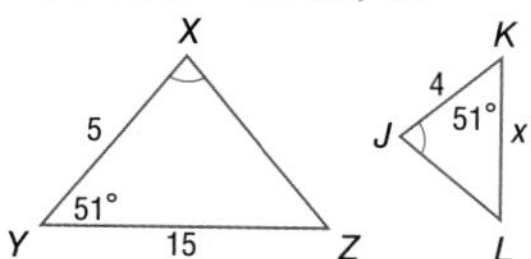

7. *VS* $\triangle QVS \sim \triangle RTS$; 20

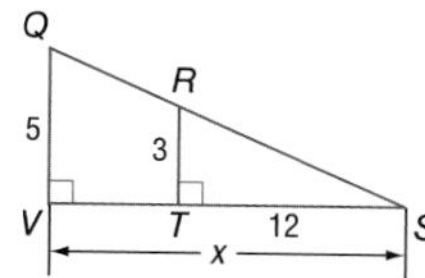

Example 5

8. COMMUNICATION A cell phone tower casts a 100-foot shadow. At the same time, a 4-foot 6-inch post near the tower casts a shadow of 3 feet 4 inches. Find the height of the tower. 135 ft

Practice and Problem Solving

Extra Practice is on page R7.

Examples 1–3 **Determine whether the triangles are similar. If so, write a similarity statement. If not, what would be sufficient to prove the triangles similar? Explain your reasoning.**

9. Yes; $\triangle XUZ \sim \triangle WUY$ by SSS Similarity.
10. See margin.
11. Yes; $\triangle CBA \sim \triangle DBF$ by SAS Similarity.

9.

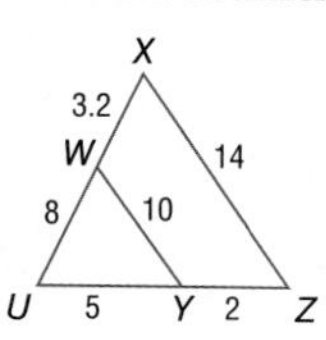

10.

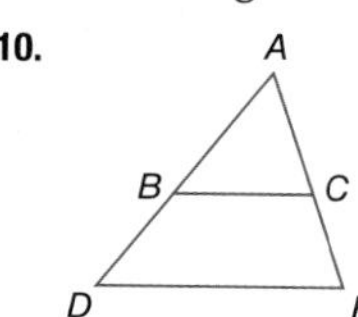

11

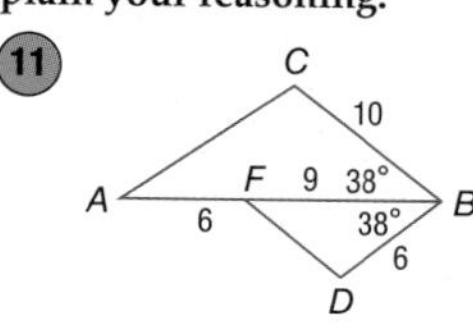

3 Practice

Formative Assessment

Use Exercises 1–8 to check for understanding.

Use the chart at the bottom of this page to customize assignments for your students.

CCSS Teaching the Mathematical Practices

Structure Mathematically proficient students look closely to discern a pattern or structure. They also can step back for an overview and shift perspective. In Exercises 6–7, it may be helpful to some students to draw the similar triangles in the same orientation.

Additional Answer

10. No; $\overline{BC}$ needs to be parallel to $\overline{DF}$ for $\triangle DAF \sim \triangle BAC$ by AA Similarity.

Differentiated Homework Options

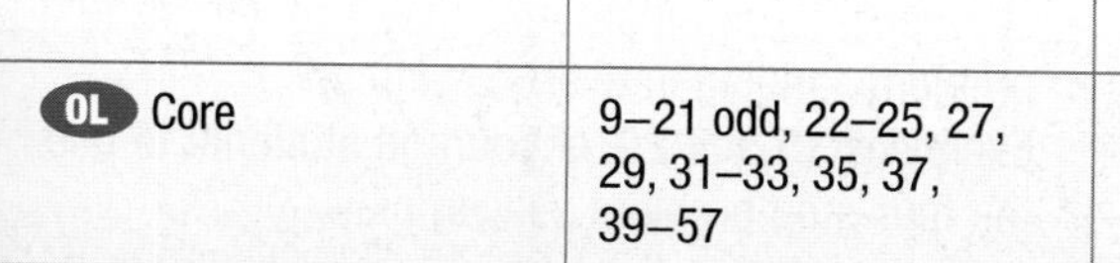

Level	Assignment	Two-Day Option	
AL Basic	9–24, 37, 39–57	9–23 odd, 42–45	10–24 even, 37, 39–41, 46–57
OL Core	9–21 odd, 22–25, 27, 29, 31–33, 35, 37, 39–57	9–24, 42–45	25–37, 39–41, 46–57
BL Advanced	25–56, (optional: 57)		

Study Guide and Intervention

AL OL ELL

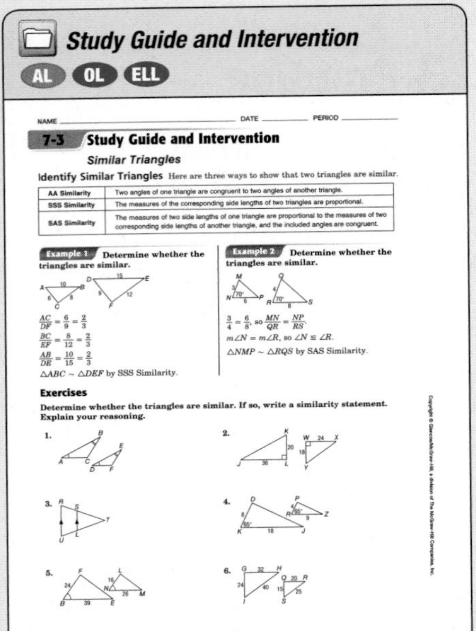

NAME ______ DATE ______ PERIOD ______

7-3 Study Guide and Intervention

Similar Triangles

Identify Similar Triangles Here are three ways to show that two triangles are similar.

AA Similarity	Two angles of one triangle are congruent to two angles of another triangle.
SSS Similarity	The measures of the corresponding side lengths of two triangles are proportional.
SAS Similarity	The measures of two side lengths of one triangle are proportional to the measures of two corresponding side lengths of another triangle, and the included angles are congruent.

Example 1 Determine whether the triangles are similar.

$\frac{AC}{DF} = \frac{6}{9} = \frac{2}{3}$

$\frac{BC}{EF} = \frac{8}{12} = \frac{2}{3}$

$\frac{AB}{DE} = \frac{10}{15} = \frac{2}{3}$

$\triangle ABC \sim \triangle DEF$ by SSS Similarity.

Example 2 Determine whether the triangles are similar.

$\frac{3}{4} = \frac{6}{8}$, so $\frac{MN}{QR} = \frac{NP}{RS}$

$m\angle N = m\angle R$, so $\angle N \cong \angle R$.

$\triangle NMP \sim \triangle RQS$ by SAS Similarity.

Exercises

Determine whether the triangles are similar. If so, write a similarity statement. Explain your reasoning.

Practice

AL OL BL ELL

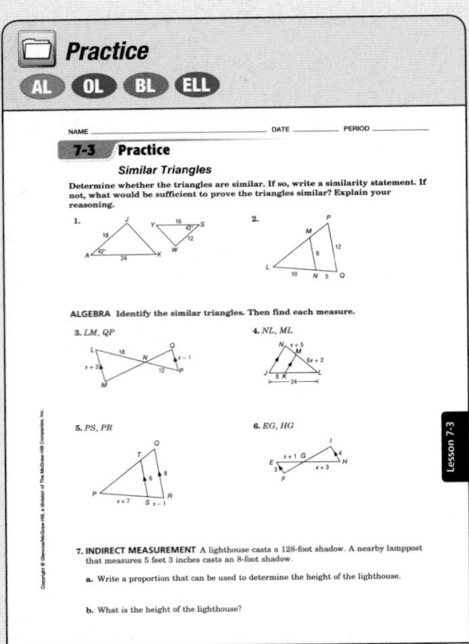

NAME ______ DATE ______ PERIOD ______

7-3 Practice

Similar Triangles

Determine whether the triangles are similar. If so, write a similarity statement. If not, what would be sufficient to prove the triangles similar? Explain your reasoning.

ALGEBRA Identify the similar triangles. Then find each measure.

3. LM, QP

4. NL, ML

5. PS, PR

6. EG, HG

7. INDIRECT MEASUREMENT A lighthouse casts a 128-foot shadow. A nearby lamppost that measures 5 feet 3 inches casts an 8-foot shadow.

a. Write a proportion that can be used to determine the height of the lighthouse.

b. What is the height of the lighthouse?

Word Problem Practice

AL OL BL ELL

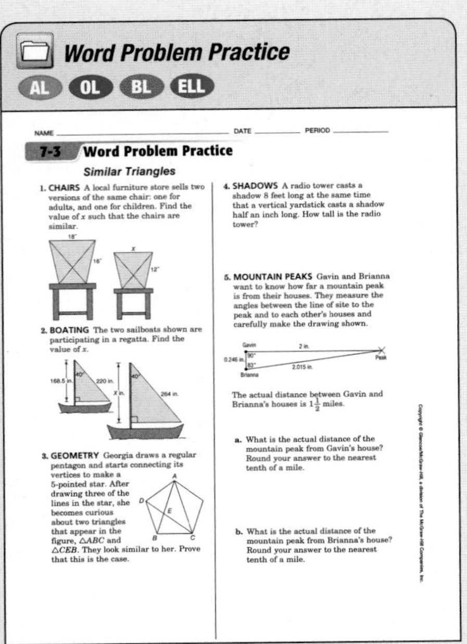

NAME ______ DATE ______ PERIOD ______

7-3 Word Problem Practice

Similar Triangles

1. CHAIRS A local furniture store sells two versions of the same chair: one for adults, and one for children. Find the value of x such that the chairs are similar.

2. BOATING The two sailboats shown are participating in a regatta. Find the value of x.

3. GEOMETRY Georgia draws a regular pentagon and starts connecting its vertices to make a 5-pointed star. After drawing three of the lines in the star, she becomes curious about two triangles that appear in the figure, $\triangle ABC$ and $\triangle CEB$. They look similar to her. Prove that this is the case.

4. SHADOWS A radio tower casts a shadow 8 feet long at the same time that a vertical yardstick casts a shadow half an inch long. How tall is the radio tower?

5. MOUNTAIN PEAKS Gavin and Brianna want to know how far a mountain peak is from their houses. They measure the angles between the line of site to the peak and to each other's houses and carefully make the drawing shown.

The actual distance between Gavin and Brianna's houses is $1\frac{1}{2}$ miles.

a. What is the actual distance of the mountain peak from Gavin's house? Round your answer to the nearest tenth of a mile.

b. What is the actual distance of the mountain peak from Brianna's house? Round your answer to the nearest tenth of a mile.

Examples 1–3 **Determine whether the triangles are similar. If so, write a similarity statement. If not, what would be sufficient to prove the triangles similar? Explain your reasoning.**

12. **13.** **14.**

12. Yes; $\triangle MLJ \sim \triangle PKJ$ by AA Similarity. 13–14. See Ch. 6 Answer Appendix.

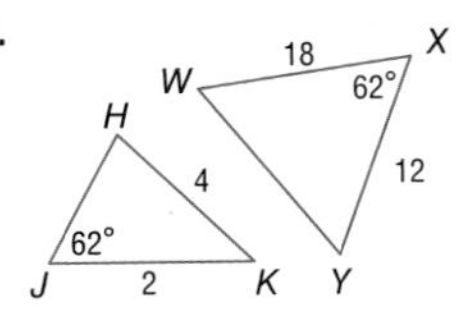

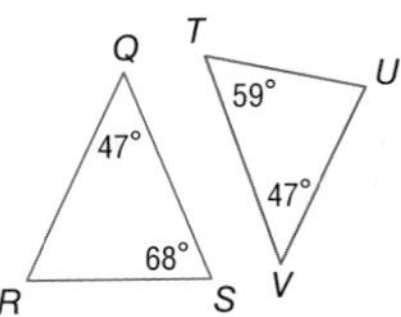

15. **CCSS MODELING** When we look at an object, it is projected on the retina through the pupil. The distances from the pupil to the top and bottom of the object are congruent and the distances from the pupil to the top and bottom of the image on the retina are congruent. Are the triangles formed between the object and the pupil and the object and the image similar? Explain your reasoning.

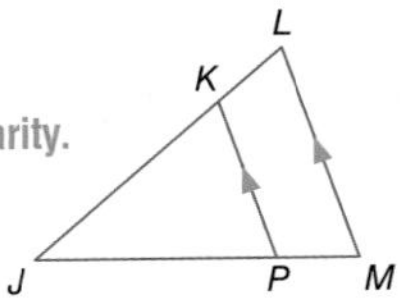

15. Yes; sample answer: $\overline{AB} \cong \overline{EB}$ and $\overline{CB} \cong \overline{DB}$, so $\frac{AB}{CB} = \frac{EB}{DB}$. $\angle ABE \cong \angle CBD$ because vertical angles are congruent. Therefore, $\triangle ABE \sim \triangle CBD$ by SAS Similarity.

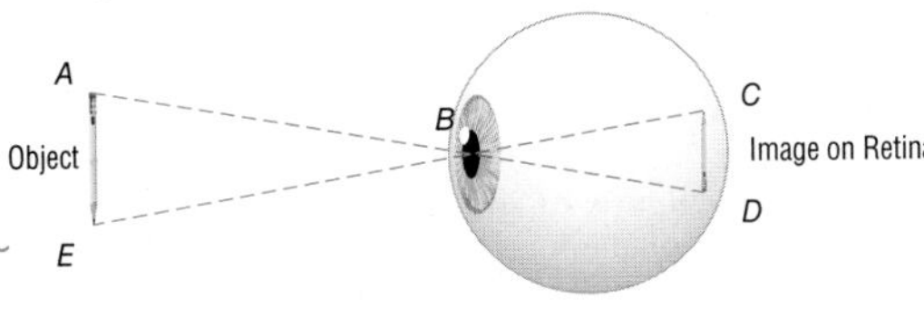

Example 4 **ALGEBRA Identify the similar triangles. Then find each measure.**

16. *JK*

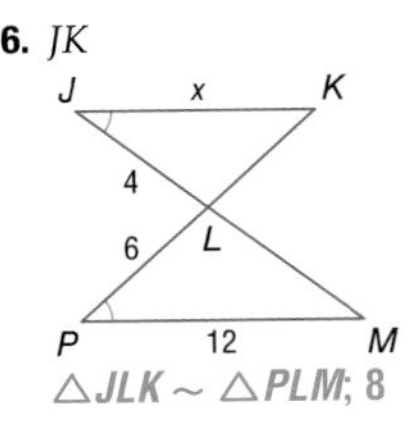

$\triangle JLK \sim \triangle PLM$; 8

17 *ST*

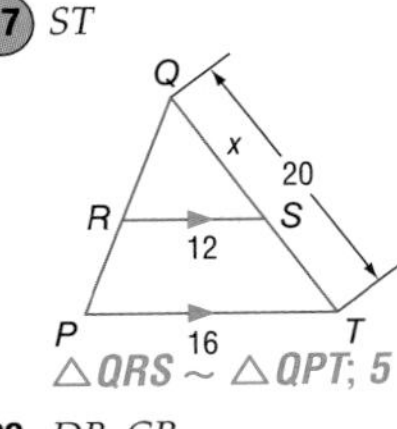

$\triangle QRS \sim \triangle QPT$; 5

18. *WZ, UZ*

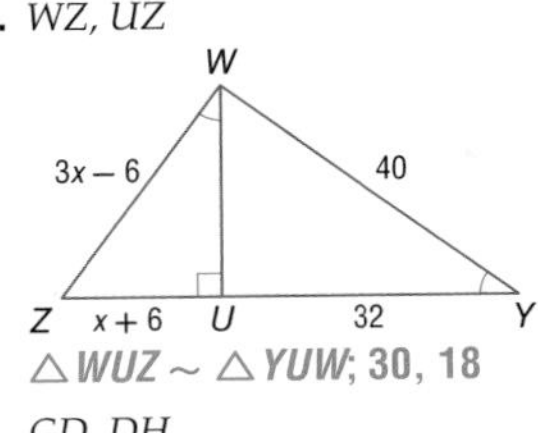

$\triangle WUZ \sim \triangle YUW$; 30, 18

19. *HJ, HK*

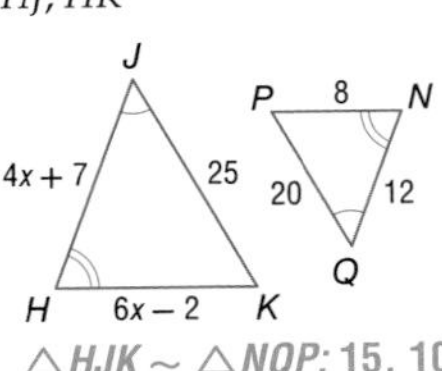

$\triangle HJK \sim \triangle NQP$; 15, 10

20. *DB, CB*

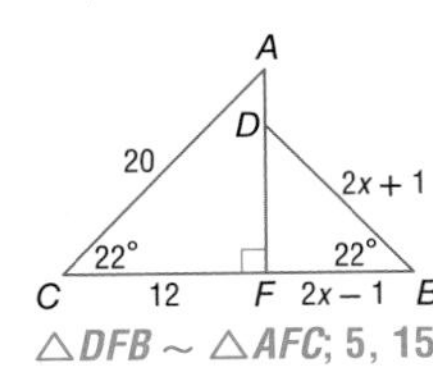

$\triangle DFB \sim \triangle AFC$; 5, 15

21. *GD, DH*

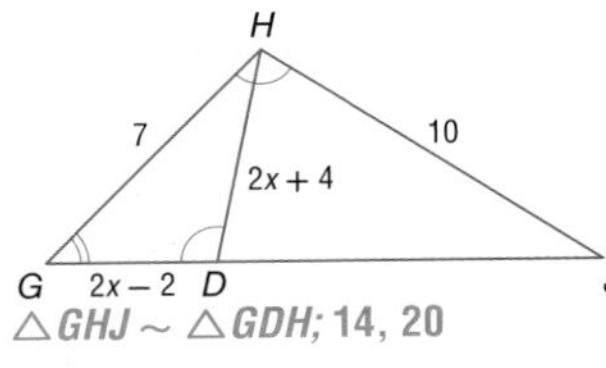

$\triangle GHJ \sim \triangle GDH$; 14, 20

Example 5 **22. STATUES** Mei is standing next to a statue in the park. If Mei is 5 feet tall, her shadow is 3 feet long, and the statue's shadow is $10\frac{1}{2}$ feet long, how tall is the statue? $17\frac{1}{2}$ ft

23. SPORTS When Alonzo, who is 5′11″ tall, stands next to a basketball goal, his shadow is 2′ long, and the basketball goal's shadow is 4′4″ long. About how tall is the basketball goal? about 12.8 ft

24. FORESTRY A hypsometer, as shown, can be used to estimate the height of a tree. Bartolo looks through the straw to the top of the tree and obtains the readings given. Find the height of the tree. 10.75

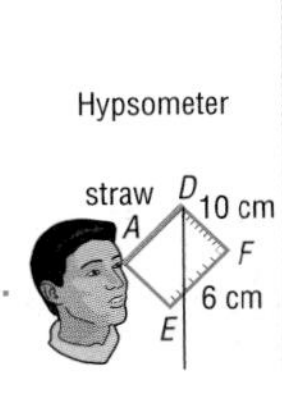

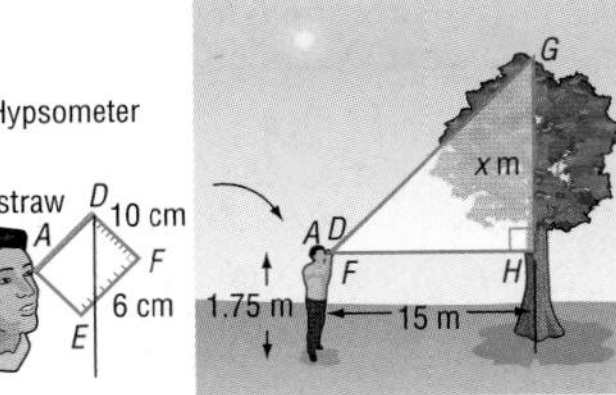

B **PROOF Write a two-column proof.** 25–26. See margin.

25. Theorem 7.3 **26.** Theorem 7.4

484 | Lesson 7-3 | Similar Triangles

Enrichment

OL BL

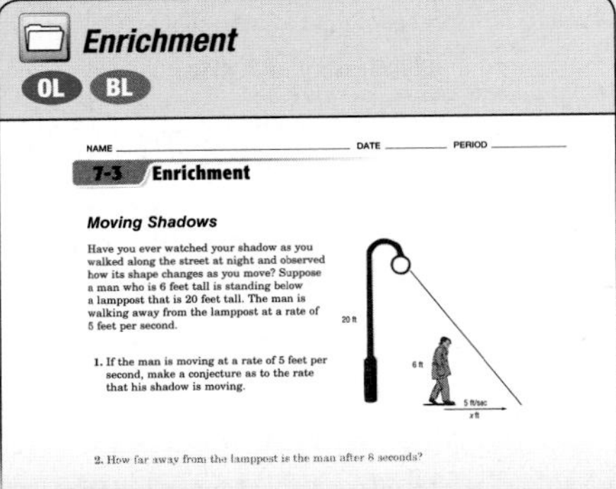

NAME ______ DATE ______ PERIOD ______

7-3 Enrichment

Moving Shadows

Have you ever watched your shadow as you walked along the street at night and observed how its shape changes as you move? Suppose a man who is 6 feet tall is standing below a lamppost that is 20 feet tall. The man is walking away from the lamppost at a rate of 5 feet per second.

1. If the man is moving at a rate of 5 feet per second, make a conjecture as to the rate that his shadow is moving.

2. How far away from the lamppost is the man after 6 seconds?

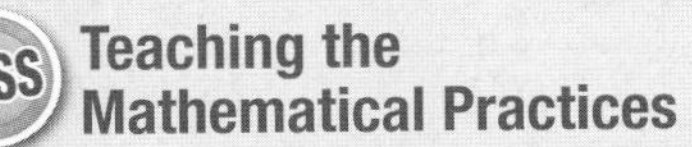

CCSS Teaching the Mathematical Practices

Modeling Mathematically proficient students can apply the mathematics they know to solve problems arising in everyday life. In Exercises 15 and 29, encourage students to use the four-step problem solving plan.

PROOF **Write a two-column proof.** 27–28. See Ch. 7 Answer Appendix.

27. Given: $\triangle XYZ$ and $\triangle ABC$ are right triangles; $\frac{XY}{AB} = \frac{YZ}{BC}$.
Prove: $\triangle YXZ \sim \triangle BAC$

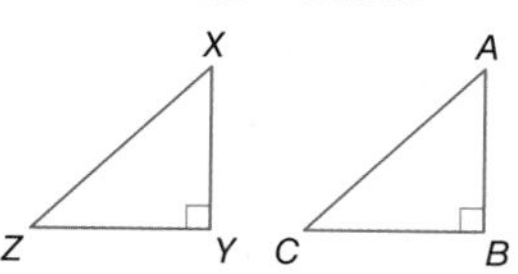

28. Given: $ABCD$ is a trapezoid.
Prove: $\frac{DP}{PB} = \frac{CP}{PA}$

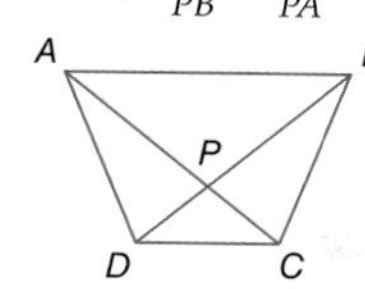

29. **CCSS MODELING** When Luis's dad threw a bounce pass to him, the angles formed by the basketball's path were congruent. The ball landed $\frac{2}{3}$ of the way between them before it bounced back up. If Luis's dad released the ball 40 inches above the floor, at what height did Luis catch the ball? 20 in.

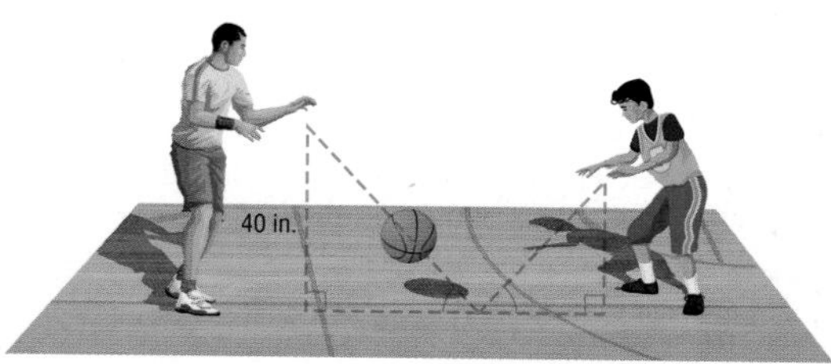

COORDINATE GEOMETRY **$\triangle XYZ$ and $\triangle WYV$ have vertices $X(-1, -9)$, $Y(5, 3)$, $Z(-1, 6)$, $W(1, -5)$, and $V(1, 5)$.**

30. Graph the triangles, and prove that $\triangle XYZ \sim \triangle WYV$. See Ch. 7 Answer Appendix.

31. Find the ratio of the perimeters of the two triangles. $\frac{3}{2}$

32. **BILLIARDS** When a ball is deflected off a smooth surface, the angles formed by the path are congruent. Booker hit the orange ball and it followed the path from A to B to C as shown below. What was the total distance traveled by the ball from the time Booker hit it until it came to rest at the end of the table? about 61 in.

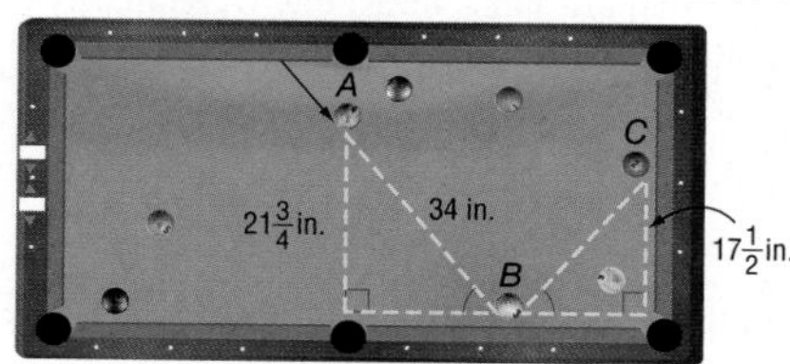

33. **PROOF** Use similar triangles to show that the slope of the line through any two points on that line is constant. That is, if points A, B, A' and B' are on line ℓ, use similar triangles to show that the slope of the line from A to B is equal to the slope of the line from A' to B'.

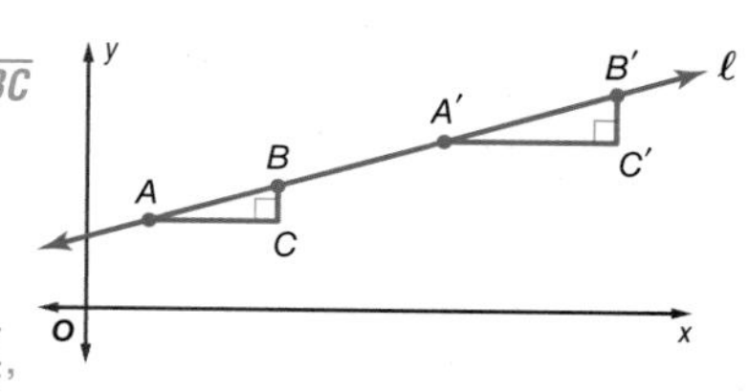

33. $\angle C \cong \angle C'$, since all rt. ∠s are ≅. Line ℓ is a transversal of ∥ segments $\overline{BC}$ and $\overline{B'C'}$, so $\angle ABC \cong \angle A'B'C'$ since corresponding ∠s of ∥ lines are ≅. Therefore, by AA Similarity, $\triangle ABC \sim \triangle A'B'C'$. So $\frac{BC}{AC}$, the slope of line ℓ through points A and B, is equal to $\frac{B'C'}{A'C'}$, the slope of line ℓ through points A' and B'.

Additional Answers

25. Given: $\angle B \cong \angle E$, $\overline{QP} \parallel \overline{BC}$, $\overline{QP} \cong \overline{EF}$, $\frac{AB}{DE} = \frac{BC}{EF}$
Prove: $\triangle ABC \sim \triangle DEF$

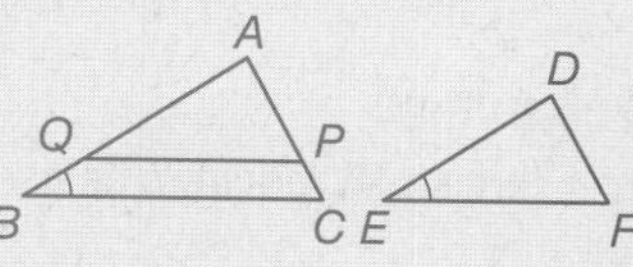

Proof:

Statements (Reasons)

1. $\angle B \cong \angle E$, $\overline{QP} \parallel \overline{BC}$, $\overline{QP} \cong \overline{EF}$, $\frac{AB}{DE} = \frac{BC}{EF}$ (Given)
2. $\angle APQ \cong \angle C$, $\angle AQP \cong \angle B$ (Corr. ∠s Post.)
3. $\angle AQP \cong \angle E$ (Trans. Prop.)
4. $\triangle ABC \sim \triangle AQP$ (AA Similarity)
5. $\frac{AB}{AQ} = \frac{BC}{QP}$ (Def. of ∼ △s)
6. $AB \cdot QP = AQ \cdot BC$; $AB \cdot EF = DE \cdot BC$ (Cross products)
7. $QP = EF$ (Def. of ≅ segs.)
8. $AB \cdot EF = AQ \cdot BC$ (Subst.)
9. $AQ \cdot BC = DE \cdot BC$ (Subst.)
10. $AQ = DE$ (Div. Prop.)
11. $\overline{AQ} \cong \overline{DE}$ (Def. of ≅ segs.)
12. $\triangle AQP \cong \triangle DEF$ (SAS)
13. $\angle APQ \cong \angle F$ (CPCTC)
14. $\angle C \cong \angle F$ (Trans. Prop.)
15. $\triangle ABC \sim \triangle DEF$ (AA Similarity)

26.

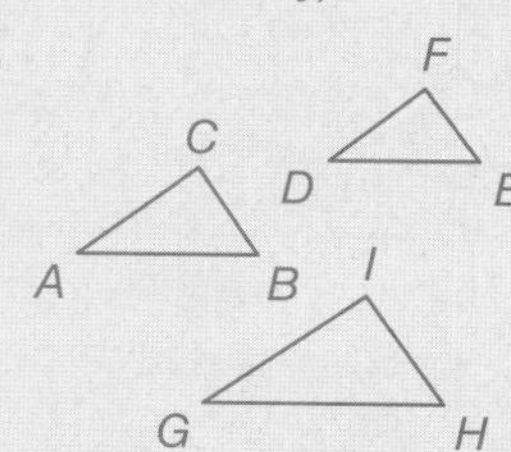

Reflexive Property of Similarity

Given: $\triangle ABC$
Prove: $\triangle ABC \sim \triangle ABC$
Proof:

Statements (Reasons)

1. $\triangle ABC$ (Given)
2. $\angle A \cong \angle A$, $\angle B \cong \angle B$ (Refl. Prop.)
3. $\triangle ABC \sim \triangle ABC$ (AA Similarity)

Symmetric Property of Similarity

Given: $\triangle ABC \sim \triangle DEF$
Prove: $\triangle DEF \sim \triangle ABC$

Statements (Reasons)

1. $\triangle ABC \sim \triangle DEF$ (Given)
2. $\angle A \cong \angle D$, $\angle B \cong \angle E$ (Def. of ∼ polygons)
3. $\angle D \cong \angle A$, $\angle E \cong \angle B$ (Symm. Prop.)
4. $\triangle DEF \sim \triangle ABC$ (AA Similarity)

Transitive Property of Similarity

Given: $\triangle ABC \sim \triangle DEF$ and $\triangle DEF \sim \triangle GHI$
Prove: $\triangle ABC \sim \triangle GHI$

Statements (Reasons)

1. $\triangle ABC \sim \triangle DEF$, $\triangle DEF \sim \triangle GHI$ (Given)
2. $\angle A \cong \angle D$, $\angle B \cong \angle E$, $\angle D \cong \angle G$, $\angle E \cong \angle H$ (Def. of ∼ polygons)
3. $\angle A \cong \angle G$, $\angle B \cong \angle H$ (Trans. Prop.)
4. $\triangle ABC \sim \triangle GHI$ (AA Similarity)

Multiple Representations

In Exercise 36, students use geometric sketches, a table, and verbal descriptions to explore proportional parts of triangles.

Exercise Alert

Ruler Exercise 36 requires the use of a ruler.

Protractor and Ruler Exercise 40 requires the use of a protractor and a ruler.

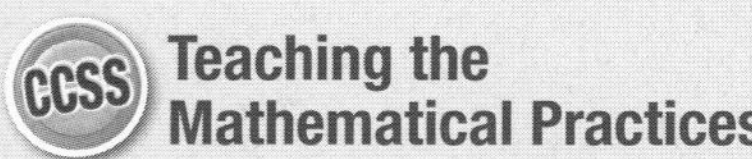

Teaching the Mathematical Practices

Reasoning Mathematically proficient students make sense of quantities and their relationships in problem situations. In Exercise 39, encourage students to draw a diagram representing the similar triangles described in the exercise.

Additional Answers

36a. Sample answer:

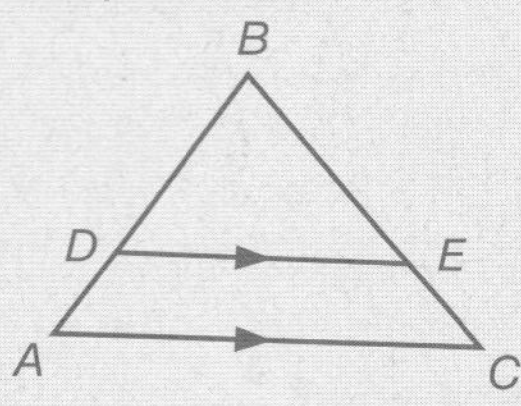

36b. Sample answer:

Lengths		Ratios	
AD	0.9 cm	$\frac{AD}{DB}$	$\frac{1}{2}$
DB	1.8 cm		
CE	1.1 cm	$\frac{CE}{EB}$	$\frac{1}{2}$
EB	2.2 cm		

37. Sample answer: The AA Similarity Postulate, SSS Similarity Theorem, and SAS Similarity Theorem are all tests that can be used to determine whether two triangles are similar. The AA Similarity Postulate is used when two pairs of congruent angles on two triangles are given. The SSS Similarity Theorem is used when the corresponding side lengths of two triangles are given. The SAS Similarity Theorem is used when two proportional side lengths and the included angle on two triangles are given.

34a. 10 in^2; The ratio of the areas is the square of the scale factor.

34b. 7 in^2; The ratio of the areas is the square of the scale factor.

34. CHANGING DIMENSIONS Assume that $\triangle ABC \sim \triangle JKL$.

a. If the lengths of the sides of $\triangle JKL$ are half the length of the sides of $\triangle ABC$, and the area of $\triangle ABC$ is 40 square inches, what is the area of $\triangle JKL$? How is the area related to the scale factor of $\triangle ABC$ to $\triangle JKL$?

b. If the lengths of the sides of $\triangle ABC$ are three times the length of the sides of $\triangle JKL$, and the area of $\triangle ABC$ is 63 square inches, what is the area of $\triangle JKL$? How is the area related to the scale factor of $\triangle ABC$ to $\triangle JKL$?

35. MEDICINE Certain medical treatments involve laser beams that contact and penetrate the skin, forming similar triangles. Refer to the diagram at the right. How far apart should the laser sources be placed to ensure that the areas treated by each source do not overlap? **31.5 cm**

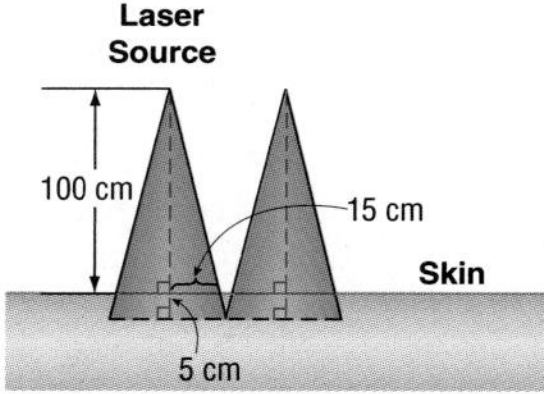

36. MULTIPLE REPRESENTATIONS In this problem, you will explore proportional parts of triangles.

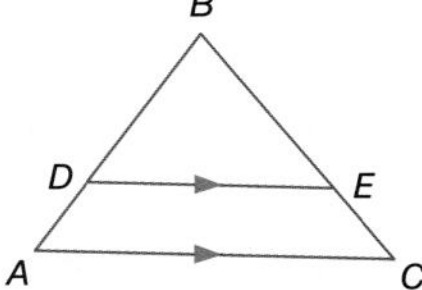

a. **Geometric** Draw $\triangle ABC$ with $\overline{DE}$ parallel to $\overline{AC}$ as shown at the right. **See margin.**

b. **Tabular** Measure and record the lengths AD, DB, CD, and EB and the ratios $\frac{AD}{DB}$ and $\frac{CE}{EB}$ in a table. **See margin.**

c. **Verbal** Make a conjecture about the segments created by a line parallel to one side of a triangle and intersecting the other two sides. **Sample answer: The segments created by a line || to one side of a $\triangle$ and intersecting the other two sides are proportional.**

H.O.T. Problems Use Higher-Order Thinking Skills

37. WRITING IN MATH Compare and contrast the AA Similarity Postulate, the SSS Similarity Theorem, and the SAS similarity theorem. **See margin.**

38. CHALLENGE $\overline{YW}$ is an altitude of $\triangle XYZ$. Find YW. $\frac{5\sqrt{2}}{2}$

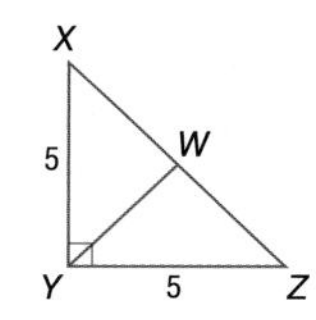

39. CCSS REASONING A pair of similar triangles has angle measures of 50°, 85°, and 45°. The sides of one triangle measure 3, 3.25, and 4.23 units, and the sides of the second triangle measure $x - 0.46$, x, and $x + 1.81$ units. Find the value of x. **6**

40. OPEN ENDED Draw a triangle that is similar to $\triangle ABC$ shown. Explain how you know that it is similar. **See margin.**

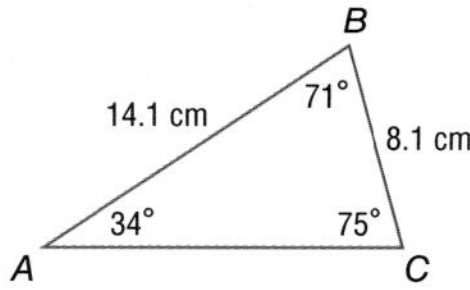

41. WRITING IN MATH How can you choose an appropriate scale? **See margin.**

Differentiated Instruction OL BL

Extension Have students draw a right triangle on a coordinate plane and label each vertex with an ordered pair. Then have them draw another right triangle that is larger and proportional to it. Students should write a paragraph proof to show that the two right triangles are similar. Sample answer: Because the measures of two sides of a triangle are proportional to the measures of two corresponding sides of another triangle and the included angles are congruent, the triangles are similar.

486 | Lesson 7-3 | Similar Triangles

Standardized Test Practice

42. PROBABILITY $\frac{x!}{(x-3)!} =$ D

A 3.0
B 0.33
C $x^2 - 3x + 2$
D $x^3 - 3x^2 + 2x$

43. EXTENDED RESPONSE In the figure below, $\overline{EB} \parallel \overline{DC}$.

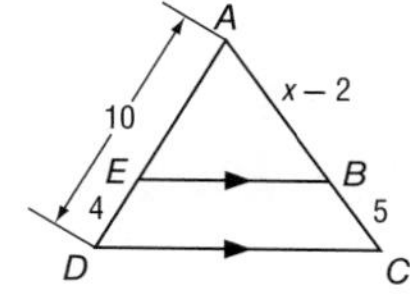

a. Write a proportion that could be used to find x. $\frac{6}{x-2} = \frac{4}{5}$

b. Find the value of x and the measure of $\overline{AB}$. 9.5, 7.5

44. ALGEBRA Which polynomial represents the area of the shaded region? J

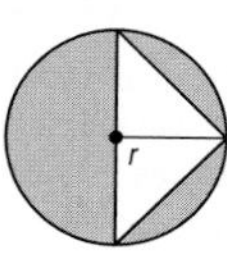

F πr^2
G $\pi r^2 + r^2$
H $\pi r^2 + r$
J $\pi r^2 - r^2$

45. SAT/ACT The volume of a certain rectangular solid is $16x$ cubic units. If the dimensions of the solid are integers x, y, and z units, what is the greatest possible value of z? B

A 32
B 16
C 8
D 4
E 2

Spiral Review

List all pairs of congruent angles, and write a proportion that relates the corresponding sides for each pair of similar polygons. (Lesson 7-2) 46–48. See margin.

46. $\triangle JKL \sim \triangle CDE$

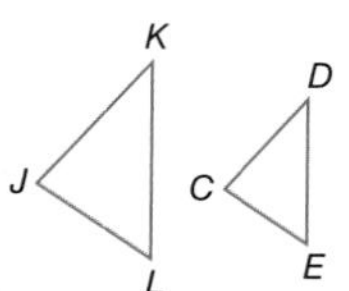

47. $WXYZ \sim QRST$

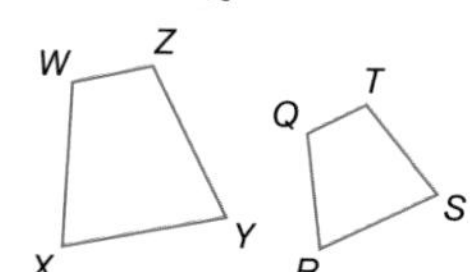

48. $FGHJ \sim MPQS$

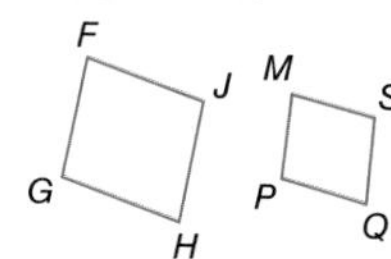

Solve each proportion. (Lesson 7-1)

49. $\frac{3}{4} = \frac{x}{16}$ 12

50. $\frac{x}{10} = \frac{22}{50}$ 4.4

51. $\frac{20.2}{88} = \frac{12}{x}$ 52.3

52. $\frac{x-2}{2} = \frac{3}{8}$ 2.8

53. TANGRAMS A tangram set consists of seven pieces: a small square, two small congruent right triangles, two large congruent right triangles, a medium-sized right triangle, and a quadrilateral. How can you determine the shape of the quadrilateral? Explain. (Lesson 6-3) See margin.

Determine which postulate can be used to prove that the triangles are congruent. If it is not possible to prove congruence, write *not possible*. (Lesson 4-4)

54.  not possible

55.  not possible

56. 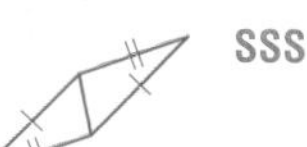 SSS

Skills Review

Write a two-column proof. See margin.

57. Given: $r \parallel t$; $\angle 5 \cong \angle 6$

Prove: $\ell \parallel m$

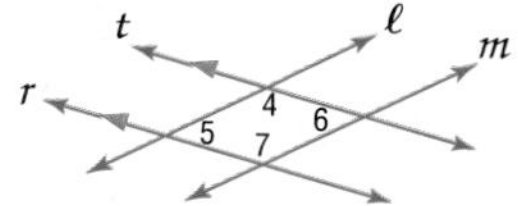

4 Assess

Ticket Out the Door Ask students to explain how similar triangles can be used to find the height of a tall tree. Have them tell you on their way out the door.

Additional Answers

40. Sample answer:

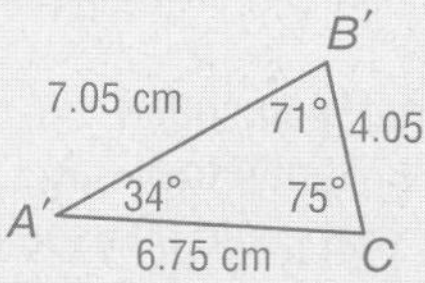

$\triangle A'B'C' \sim \triangle ABC$ because the measures of each side are half the measure of the corresponding side and the measures of corresponding angles are equal.

41. Sample answer: You could consider the amount of space that the actual object occupies and compare it to the amount of space that is available for the scale model or drawing. Then, you could determine the amount of detail that you want the scale model or drawing to have, and you could use these factors to choose an appropriate scale.

46. $\angle L \cong \angle E$, $\angle K \cong \angle D$, $\angle J \cong \angle C$; $\frac{KL}{DE} = \frac{JK}{CD} = \frac{JL}{CE}$

47. $\angle X \cong \angle R$, $\angle W \cong \angle Q$, $\angle Y \cong \angle S$, $\angle Z \cong \angle T$; $\frac{WX}{QR} = \frac{ZY}{TS} = \frac{WZ}{QT} = \frac{XY}{RS}$

48. $\angle G \cong \angle P$, $\angle F \cong \angle M$, $\angle J \cong \angle S$, $\angle H \cong \angle Q$; $\frac{JH}{SQ} = \frac{GH}{PQ} = \frac{GF}{PM} = \frac{FJ}{MS}$

53. Sample answer: If one pair of opposite sides are congruent and parallel, the quadrilateral is a parallelogram.

57. Given: $r \parallel t$; $\angle 5 \cong \angle 6$

Prove: $\ell \parallel m$

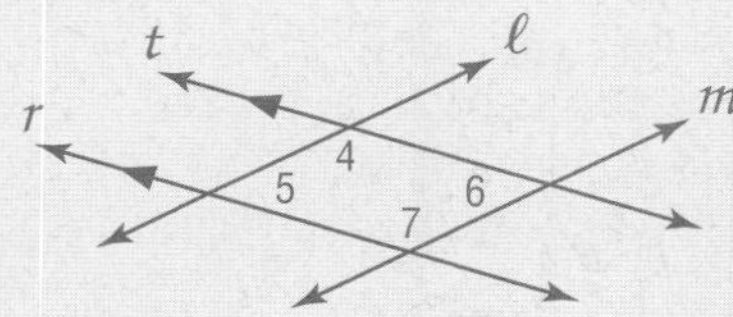

Proof:

Statements (Reasons)

1. $r \parallel t$; $\angle 5 \cong \angle 6$ (Given)
2. $\angle 4$ and $\angle 5$ are supplementary. (Consecutive Interior Angle Theorem)
3. $m\angle 4 + m\angle 5 = 180$ (Definition of supplementary angles)
4. $m\angle 5 = m\angle 6$ (Definition of congruent angles)
5. $m\angle 4 + m\angle 6 = 180$ (Substitution)
6. $\angle 4$ and $\angle 6$ are supplementary. (Definition of supplementary)
7. $\ell \parallel m$ (If cons. int. $\angle$s are suppl., then lines are $\parallel$)

1 Focus

Objective Use similar triangles to prove the slope criteria for perpendicular and parallel lines.

Materials for Each Group

- compass
- straightedge

Teaching Tip

Ask students what techniques (AA, SSS, SAS Similarity) they have learned thus far that could be used to prove that two triangles are similar.

2 Teach

Working in Cooperative Groups

Arrange students in groups of 2, mixing abilities. Then have students complete the activity.

Practice Have students complete Exercises 1 and 2.

Focus on Mathematical Content

Finding Slope In Activity 1, the slope of $\overleftrightarrow{AC}$ is negative because it is the *rise* from *A* to *B* in the *negative* direction over the *run* from *B* to *C* in the *positive* direction.

EXTEND 7-3

Geometry Lab: Proofs of Perpendicular and Parallel Lines

You have learned that two straight lines that are neither horizontal nor vertical are perpendicular if and only if the product of their slopes is –1. In this activity, you will use similar triangles to prove the first half of this theorem: if two straight lines are perpendicular, then the product of their slopes is –1.

Common Core State Standards
Content Standards
G.GPE.5 Prove the slope criteria for parallel and perpendicular lines and use them to solve geometric problems (e.g., find the equation of a line parallel or perpendicular to a given line that passes through a given point).
Mathematical Practices 3

Activity 1 Perpendicular Lines

Given: Slope of $\overleftrightarrow{AC} = m_1$, slope of $\overleftrightarrow{CE} = m_2$, and $\overleftrightarrow{AC} \perp \overleftrightarrow{CE}$.
Prove: $m_1 m_2 = -1$

Step 1 On a coordinate plane, construct $\overleftrightarrow{AC} \perp \overleftrightarrow{CE}$ and transversal $\overleftrightarrow{BD}$ parallel to the *x*-axis through *C*. Then construct right $\triangle ABC$ such that $\overline{AC}$ is the hypotenuse and right $\triangle EDC$ such that $\overline{CE}$ is the hypotenuse. The legs of both triangles should be parallel to the *x*-and *y*-axes, as shown.

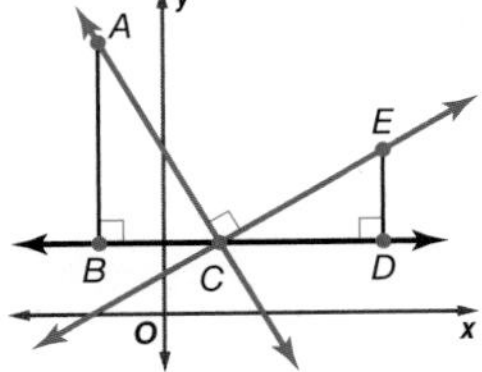

Step 2 Find the slopes of $\overleftrightarrow{AC}$ and $\overleftrightarrow{CE}$.

Slope of $\overleftrightarrow{AC}$

$m_1 = \frac{\text{rise}}{\text{run}}$ Slope Formula

$= \frac{-AB}{BC}$ or $-\frac{AB}{BC}$ rise = –*AB*, run = *BC*

Slope of $\overleftrightarrow{CE}$

$m_2 = \frac{\text{rise}}{\text{run}}$ Slope Formula

$= \frac{DE}{CD}$ rise = *DE*, run = *CD*

Step 3 Show that $\triangle ABC \sim \triangle CDE$.

Since $\triangle ACB$ is a right triangle with right angle *B*, $\angle BAC$ is complementary to $\angle ACB$. It is given that $\overleftrightarrow{AC} \perp \overleftrightarrow{CE}$, so we know that $\triangle ACE$ is a right angle. By construction, $\angle BCD$ is a straight angle. So, $\angle ECD$ is complementary to $\angle ACB$. Since angles complementary to the same angle are congruent, $\angle BAC \cong \angle ECD$. Since right angles are congruent, $\angle B \cong \angle D$. Therefore, by AA Similarity, $\triangle ABC \sim \triangle CDE$.

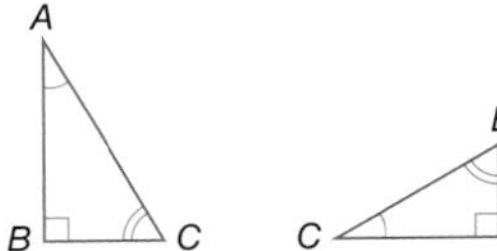

Step 4 Use the fact that $\triangle ABC \sim \triangle CDE$ to show that $m_1 m_2 = -1$.

Since $m_1 = -\frac{AB}{BC}$ and $m_2 = \frac{DE}{CD}$, $m_1 m_2 = \left(-\frac{AB}{BC}\right)\left(\frac{DE}{CD}\right)$. Since two similar polygons have proportional sides, $\frac{AB}{BC} = \frac{CD}{DE}$. Therefore, by substitution, $m_1 m_2 = \left(-\frac{CD}{DE}\right)\left(\frac{DE}{CD}\right)$ or –1.

Additional Answer

1. The slope of $\overleftrightarrow{CE} = m_1 = \frac{DE}{CD}$, and the slope of $\overleftrightarrow{AC} = m_2 = -\frac{AB}{BC}$.

$m_1 m_2 = -1$ Given

$\left(\frac{DE}{CD}\right)\left(-\frac{AB}{BC}\right) = -1$ Substitution

$\left(\frac{DE}{CD}\right)\left(-\frac{AB}{BC}\right)\left(-\frac{BC}{AB}\right) = -1\left(-\frac{BC}{AB}\right)$ Multiply.

$\frac{DE}{CD} = \frac{BC}{AB}$ Simplify.

Since $\angle B$ and $\angle D$ are right angles, $\angle B \cong \angle D$. By SAS Similarity, $\triangle ABC \sim \triangle CDE$. Since $\angle B$ is a right angle, $\angle BAC$ and $\angle BCA$ are complementary. Since $\triangle ABC \sim \triangle CDE$, $\angle BAC \cong \angle DCE$. By substitution, $\angle DCE$ and $\angle BCA$ are complementary. By definition of complementary, $m\angle DCE + m\angle BCA = 90$. Since $\angle BCD$ is a straight angle, by angle addition $m\angle DCE + m\angle ACE + m\angle BCA = 180$ or $(m\angle DCE + m\angle BCA) + m\angle ACE = 180$. By substitution, $90 + m\angle ACE = 180$, so $m\angle ACE = 90$. By definition, $\angle ACE$ is a right angle. Since $\overleftrightarrow{CE}$ and $\overleftrightarrow{AC}$ intersect to form right $\angle ACE$, $\overleftrightarrow{CE} \perp \overleftrightarrow{AC}$.

Model

1. **PROOF** Use the diagram from Activity 1 to prove the second half of the theorem.

Given: Slope of $\overleftrightarrow{CE} = m_1$, slope of $\overleftrightarrow{AC} = m_2$, and $m_1m_2 = -1$. $\triangle ABC$ is a right triangle with right angle B. $\triangle CDE$ is a right triangle with right angle D.

Prove: $\overleftrightarrow{CE} \perp \overleftrightarrow{AC}$ See margin.

You can also use similar triangles to prove statements about parallel lines.

Activity 2 Parallel Lines

Given: Slope of $\overleftrightarrow{FG} = m_1$, slope of $\overleftrightarrow{JK} = m_2$, and $m_1 = m_2$. $\triangle FHG$ is a right triangle with right angle H. $\triangle JLK$ is a right triangle with right angle L.

Prove: $\overleftrightarrow{FG} \parallel \overleftrightarrow{JK}$

Step 1 On a coordinate plane, construct $\overleftrightarrow{FG}$ and $\overleftrightarrow{JK}$, right $\triangle FHG$, and right $\triangle JLK$. Then draw horizontal transversal $\overleftrightarrow{FL}$, as shown.

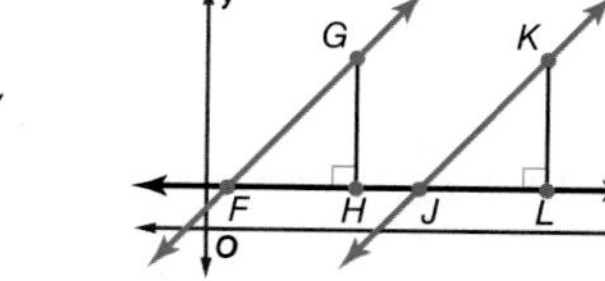

Step 2 Find the slopes of $\overleftrightarrow{FG}$ and $\overleftrightarrow{JK}$.

Slope of $\overleftrightarrow{FG}$		Slope of $\overleftrightarrow{JK}$	
$m_1 = \frac{\text{rise}}{\text{run}}$	Slope Formula	$m_2 = \frac{\text{rise}}{\text{run}}$	Slope Formula
$= \frac{GH}{HF}$	rise = GH, run = HF	$= \frac{KL}{LJ}$	rise = KL, run = LJ

Step 3 Show that $\triangle FHG \sim \triangle JLK$.

It is given that $m_1 = m_2$. By substitution, $\frac{GH}{HF} = \frac{KL}{LJ}$. This ratio can be rewritten as $\frac{GH}{KL} = \frac{HF}{LJ}$. Since $\angle H$ and $\angle L$ are right angles, $\angle H \cong \angle L$. Therefore, by SAS similarity, $\triangle FHG \sim \triangle JLK$.

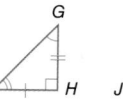

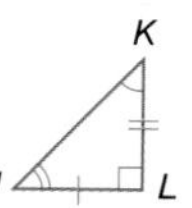

Step 4 Use the fact that $\triangle FHG \sim \triangle JLK$ to prove that $\overleftrightarrow{FG} \parallel \overleftrightarrow{JK}$.

Corresponding angles in similar triangles are congruent, so $\angle GFH \cong \angle KJL$. From the definition of congruent angles, $m\angle GFH = m\angle KJL$ (or $\angle GFH \cong \angle KJL$). By definition, $\angle KJH$ and $\angle KJL$ form a linear pair. Since linear pairs are supplementary, $m\angle KJH + m\angle KJL = 180$. So, by substitution, $m\angle KJH + m\angle GFH = 180$. By definition, $\angle KJH$ and $\angle GFH$ are supplementary. Since $\angle KJH$ and $\angle GFH$ are supplementary and are consecutive interior angles, $\overleftrightarrow{FG} \parallel \overleftrightarrow{JK}$.

Model

2. **PROOF** Use the diagram from Activity 2 to prove the following statement.

Given: Slope of $\overleftrightarrow{FG} = m_1$, slope of $\overleftrightarrow{JK} = m_2$, and $\overleftrightarrow{FG} \parallel \overleftrightarrow{JK}$.

Prove: $m_1 = m_2$ See margin.

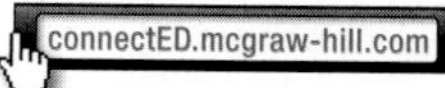

3 Assess

Formative Assessment

Use Exercises 1 and 2 to assess whether students understand how to prove the slope criteria for perpendicular and parallel lines.

Additional Answer

2. The slope of $\overleftrightarrow{FG} = m_1 = \frac{GH}{HF}$, and the slope of $\overleftrightarrow{JK} = m_2 = \frac{KL}{LJ}$. Since $\overleftrightarrow{FG} \parallel \overleftrightarrow{JK}$, $\overleftrightarrow{FG}$ and $\overleftrightarrow{JK}$ are cut by transversal $\overleftrightarrow{FL}$, $\angle GFH$ and $\angle KJH$ are supplementary consecutive interior angles. From the definition of supplementary, $m\angle KJH = 180 - m\angle GFH$. By definition, $\angle KJH$ and $\angle KJL$ form a linear pair. Since linear pairs are supplementary, $m\angle KJH = 180 - m\angle KJL$. Therefore, by substitution, $180 - m\angle GFH = 180 - m\angle KJL$ and $m\angle GFH = m\angle KJL$. Since right angles are congruent, $\angle GHF \cong \angle KLJ$. Therefore, by AA Similarity, $\triangle FGH \sim \triangle JKL$. Since similar triangles have proportional sides, $\frac{GH}{HF} = \frac{KL}{LJ}$. Since $m_1 = \frac{GH}{HF}$ and $m_2 = \frac{KL}{LJ}$, by substitution, $m_1 = m_2$.

1 Focus

Vertical Alignment

Before Lesson 7-4 Use proportions to solve problems between similar triangles.

Lesson 7-4 Use proportional parts within triangles and with parallel lines.

After Lesson 7-4 Justify triangle similarity relationships, such as right triangle ratios, using a variety of methods.

2 Teach

Scaffolding Questions

Have students read the **Why?** section of the lesson.

Ask:

- Describe the distance between two parallel lines. It is always the same.
- Why does the distance between the train tracks appear to get smaller? Sample answer: The lines in the picture get closer together.
- Are the lines in the picture formed by the train tracks parallel? yes

LESSON 7-4 Parallel Lines and Proportional Parts

Then

- You used proportions to solve problems between similar triangles.

Now

1. Use proportional parts within triangles.
2. Use proportional parts with parallel lines.

Why?

- Photographers have many techniques at their disposal that can be used to add interest to a photograph. One such technique is the use of a vanishing point perspective, in which an image with parallel lines, such as train tracks, is photographed so that the lines appear to converge at a point on the horizon.

New Vocabulary
midsegment of a triangle

Common Core State Standards

Content Standards
G.SRT.4 Prove theorems about triangles.
G.SRT.5 Use congruence and similarity criteria for triangles to solve problems and to prove relationships in geometric figures.

Mathematical Practices
1 Make sense of problems and persevere in solving them.
3 Construct viable arguments and critique the reasoning of others.

1 Proportional Parts Within Triangles

When a triangle contains a line that is parallel to one of its sides, the two triangles formed can be proved similar using the Angle-Angle Similarity Postulate. Since the triangles are similar, their sides are proportional.

Theorem 7.5 Triangle Proportionality Theorem

If a line is parallel to one side of a triangle and intersects the other two sides, then it divides the sides into segments of proportional lengths.

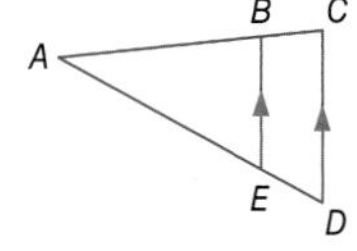

Example If $\overline{BE} \parallel \overline{CD}$, then $\frac{AB}{BC} = \frac{AE}{ED}$.

You will prove Theorem 7.5 in Exercise 30.

Example 1 Find the Length of a Side

In $\triangle PQR$, $\overline{ST} \parallel \overline{RQ}$. If $PT = 7.5$, $TQ = 3$, and $SR = 2.5$, find PS.

Use the Triangle Proportionality Theorem.

$\frac{PS}{SR} = \frac{PT}{TQ}$ Triangle Proportionality Theorem

$\frac{PS}{2.5} = \frac{7.5}{3}$ Substitute.

$PS \cdot 3 = (2.5)(7.5)$ Cross Products Property

$3PS = 18.75$ Multiply.

$PS = 6.25$ Divide each side by 3.

Guided Practice

1. If $PS = 12.5$, $SR = 5$, and $PT = 15$, find TQ. 6

Lesson 7-4 Resources

Resource	Approaching Level AL	On Level OL	Beyond Level BL	English Learners ELL
Teacher Edition	▪ Differentiated Instruction, p. 494	▪ Differentiated Instruction, pp. 493, 494, 499	▪ Differentiated Instruction, pp. 493, 494, 499	
Chapter Resource Masters	▪ Study Guide and Intervention, pp. 24–25 ▪ Skills Practice, p. 26 ▪ Practice, p. 27 ▪ Word Problem Practice, p. 28	▪ Study Guide and Intervention, pp. 24–25 ▪ Skills Practice, p. 26 ▪ Practice, p. 27 ▪ Word Problem Practice, p. 28 ▪ Enrichment, p. 29	▪ Practice, p. 27 ▪ Word Problem Practice, p. 28 ▪ Enrichment, p. 29	▪ Study Guide and Intervention, pp. 24–25 ▪ Skills Practice, p. 26 ▪ Practice, p. 27 ▪ Word Problem Practice, p. 28
Other	▪ 5-Minute Check 7-4 ▪ Study Notebook ▪ Teaching Geometry with Manipulatives	▪ 5-Minute Check 7-4 ▪ Study Notebook ▪ Teaching Geometry with Manipulatives	▪ 5-Minute Check 7-4 ▪ Study Notebook	▪ 5-Minute Check 7-4 ▪ Study Notebook ▪ Teaching Geometry with Manipulatives

The converse of Theorem 7.5 is also true and can be proved using the proportional parts of a triangle.

Math HistoryLink

Galileo Galilei **(1564–1642)** Galileo was born in Pisa, Italy. He studied philosophy, astronomy, and mathematics. Galileo made essential contributions to all three disciplines. Refer to Exercise 39.

Source: *Encyclopaedia Britannica*

Theorem 7.6 Converse of Triangle Proportionality Theorem

If a line intersects two sides of a triangle and separates the sides into proportional corresponding segments, then the line is parallel to the third side of the triangle.

Example If $\frac{AE}{EB} = \frac{CD}{DB}$, then $\overline{AC} \parallel \overline{ED}$.

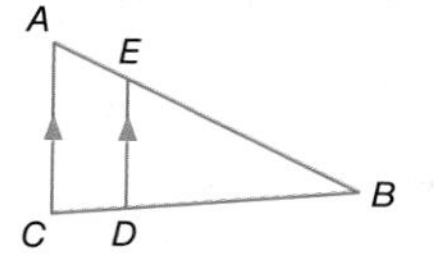

You will prove Theorem 7.6 in Exercise 31.

Example 2 Determine if Lines are Parallel

In $\triangle DEF$, $EH = 3$, $HF = 9$, and DG is one-third the length of $\overline{GF}$. Is $\overline{DE} \parallel \overline{GH}$?

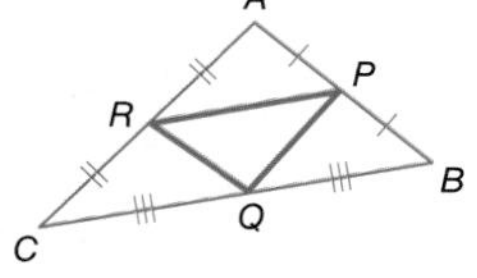

Using the converse of the Triangle Proportionality Theorem, in order to show that $\overline{DE} \parallel \overline{GH}$, we must show that $\frac{DG}{GF} = \frac{EH}{HF}$.

Find and simplify each ratio. Let $DG = x$.
Since DG is one-third of GF, $GF = 3x$.

$\frac{DG}{GF} = \frac{x}{3x}$ or $\frac{1}{3}$ $\qquad$ $\frac{EH}{HF} = \frac{3}{9}$ or $\frac{1}{3}$

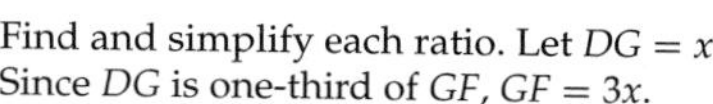

Since $\frac{1}{3} = \frac{1}{3}$, the sides are proportional, so $\overline{DE} \parallel \overline{GH}$.

GuidedPractice

2. DG is half the length of $\overline{GF}$, $EH = 6$, and $HF = 10$. Is $\overline{DE} \parallel \overline{GH}$? no

StudyTip

Midsegment Triangle The three midsegments of a triangle form the *midsegment triangle.*

A **midsegment of a triangle** is a segment with endpoints that are the midpoints of two sides of the triangle. Every triangle has three midsegments. The midsegments of $\triangle ABC$ are $\overline{RP}$, $\overline{PQ}$, $\overline{RQ}$.

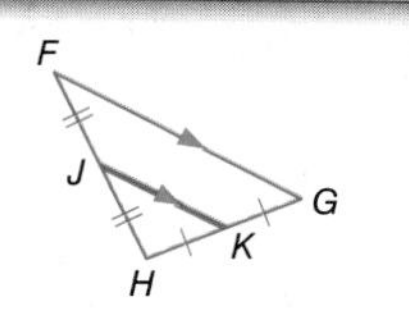

A special case of the Triangle Proportionality Theorem is the Triangle Midsegment Theorem.

Theorem 7.7 Triangle Midsegment Theorem

A midsegment of a triangle is parallel to one side of the triangle, and its length is one half the length of that side.

Example If J and K are midpoints of $\overline{FH}$ and $\overline{HG}$, respectively, then $\overline{JK} \parallel \overline{FG}$ and $JK = \frac{1}{2}FG$.

F J G K H

You will prove Theorem 7.7 in Exercise 32.

1 Proportional Parts Within Triangles

Examples 1–3 show how to use theorems involving proportional parts of triangles to find unknown measures.

Formative Assessment

Use the Guided Practice exercises after each example to determine students' understanding of concepts.

Additional Examples

1 In $\triangle RST$, $\overline{RT} \parallel \overline{VU}$, $SV = 3$, $VR = 8$, and $UT = 12$. Find SU.

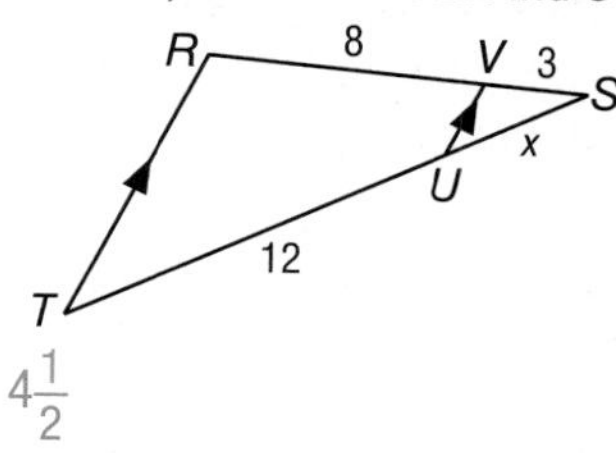

$4\frac{1}{2}$

2 In $\triangle DEF$, $DH = 18$, $HE = 36$, and $DG = \frac{1}{2}GF$. Is $\overline{GH} \parallel \overline{FE}$?

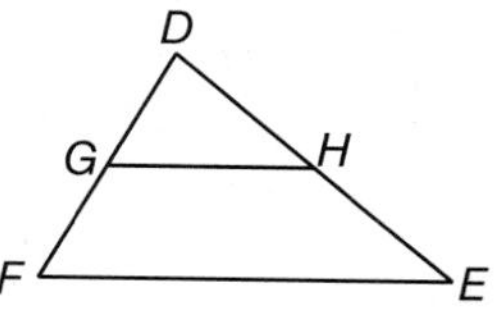

Yes; from the given information, $\frac{DG}{GH} = \frac{DH}{HE}$. Because the segments have proportional lengths, $\overline{GH} \parallel \overline{FE}$.

Additional Examples also in Interactive Classroom PowerPoint® Presentations

Teach with Tech

Interactive Whiteboard Draw two similar triangles on the board. Drag the smaller triangle on top of the larger triangle to show that the triangles have a pair of sides that are parallel. Use this diagram and the idea of similar triangles to help explain why a line parallel to a side of a triangle splits the sides into proportional segments.

WatchOut!

Proportional Lengths When students use the Triangle Proportionality Theorem, direct them to write a proportion. Remind them that if they are finding the length of an entire side of a triangle, that they must use the entire side of the similar triangle.

Additional Example

3 In the figure, $\overline{DE}$ and $\overline{EF}$ are midsegments of $\triangle ABC$. Find each measure.

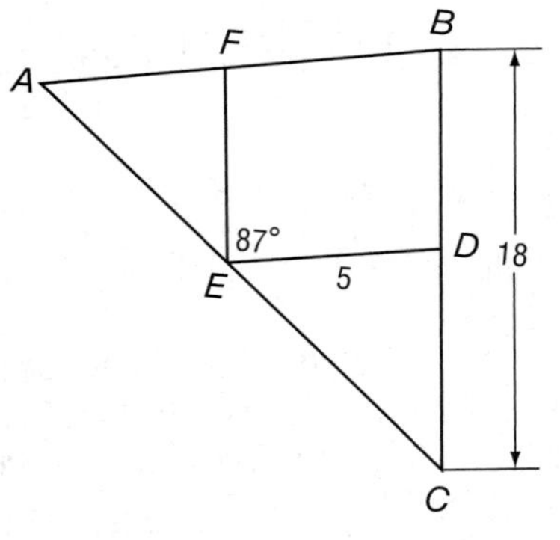

a. AB 10

b. FE 9

c. $m\angle AFE$ 87

StudyTip

Midsegment The Triangle Midsegment Theorem is similar to the Trapezoid Midsegment Theorem, which states that the midsegment of a trapezoid is parallel to the bases and its length is one half the sum of the measures of the bases. (Lesson 6-6)

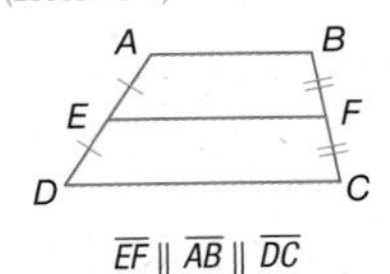

$\overline{EF} \parallel \overline{AB} \parallel \overline{DC}$

$EF = \frac{1}{2}(AB + DC)$

Example 3 Use the Triangle Midsegment Theorem

In the figure, $\overline{XY}$ and $\overline{XZ}$ are midsegments of $\triangle RST$. Find each measure.

a. XZ

$XZ = \frac{1}{2}RT$ Triangle Midsegment Theorem

$XZ = \frac{1}{2}(13)$ Substitution

$XZ = 6.5$ Simplify.

b. ST

$XY = \frac{1}{2}ST$ Triangle Midsegment Theorem

$7 = \frac{1}{2}ST$ Substitution

$14 = ST$ Multiply each side by 2.

c. $m\angle RYX$

By the Triangle Midsegment Theorem, $\overline{XZ} \parallel \overline{RT}$.

$\angle RYX \cong \angle YXZ$ Alternate Interior Angles Theorem

$m\angle RYX = m\angle YXZ$ Definition of congruence

$m\angle RYX = 124$ Substitution

GuidedPractice

Find each measure.

3A. DE 7.5

3B. DB 9.2

3C. $m\angle FED$ 82

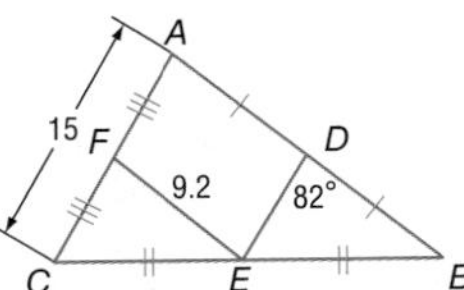

2 Proportional Parts with Parallel Lines

Another special case of the Triangle Proportionality Theorem involves three or more parallel lines cut by two transversals. Notice that if transversals a and b are extended, they form triangles with the parallel lines.

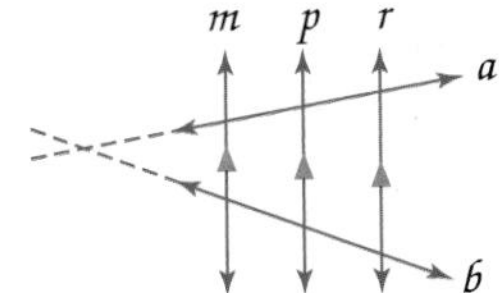

StudyTip

Other Proportions Two other proportions can be written for the example in Corollary 7.1.

$\frac{AB}{EF} = \frac{BC}{FG}$ and $\frac{AC}{BC} = \frac{EG}{FG}$

Corollary 7.1 Proportional Parts of Parallel Lines

If three or more parallel lines intersect two transversals, then they cut off the transversals proportionally.

Example If $\overline{AE} \parallel \overline{BF} \parallel \overline{CG}$, then $\frac{AB}{BC} = \frac{EF}{FG}$.

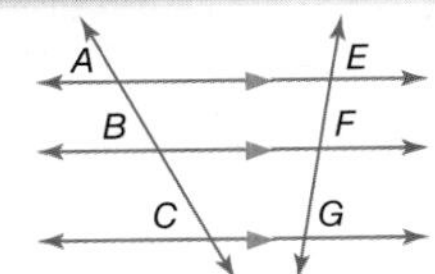

You will prove Corollary 7.1 in Exercise 28.

492 | Lesson 7-4 | Parallel Lines and Proportional Parts

Real-WorldLink

To make a two-dimensional drawing appear three-dimensional, an artist provides several perceptual cues.

- *size* - faraway items look smaller
- *clarity* - closer objects appear more in focus
- *detail* - nearby objects have texture, while distant ones are roughly outlined

Source: Center for Media Literacy

Real-World Example 4 Use Proportional Segments of Transversals

ART Megan is drawing a hallway in one-point perspective. She uses the guidelines shown to draw two windows on the left wall. If segments $\overline{AD}$, $\overline{BC}$, $\overline{WZ}$, and $\overline{XY}$ are all parallel, $AB = 8$ centimeters, $DC = 9$ centimeters, and $ZY = 5$ centimeters, find WX.

By Corollary 7.1, if $\overline{AD} \parallel \overline{BC} \parallel \overline{WZ} \parallel \overline{XY}$,

then $\frac{AB}{WX} = \frac{DC}{ZY}$.

$\frac{AB}{WX} = \frac{DC}{ZY}$ Corollary 7.1

$\frac{8}{WX} = \frac{9}{5}$ Substitute.

$WX \cdot 9 = 8 \cdot 5$ Cross Products Property

$9WX = 40$ Simplify.

$WX = \frac{40}{9}$ Divide each side by 4.

The distance between W and X should be $\frac{40}{9}$ or about 4.4 centimeters.

CHECK The ratio of DC to ZY is 9 to 5, which is about 10 to 5 or 2 to 1. The ratio of AB to WX is 8 to 4.4 or about 8 to 4 or 2 to 1 as well, so the answer is reasonable. ✓

GuidedPractice

4. REAL ESTATE *Frontage* is the measurement of a property's boundary that runs along the side of a particular feature such as a street, lake, ocean, or river. Find the ocean frontage for Lot A to the nearest tenth of a yard. **82.9 yd**

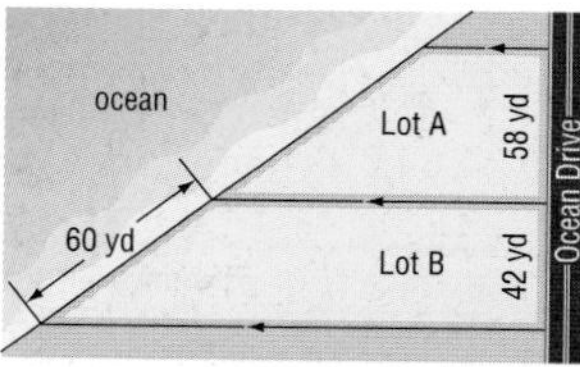

If the scale factor of the proportional segments is 1, they separate the transversals into congruent parts.

Corollary 7.2 Congruent Parts of Parallel Lines

If three or more parallel lines cut off congruent segments on one transversal, then they cut off congruent segments on every transversal.

Example If $\overline{AE} \parallel \overline{BF} \parallel \overline{CG}$, and $\overline{AB} \cong \overline{BC}$, then $\overline{EF} \cong \overline{FG}$.

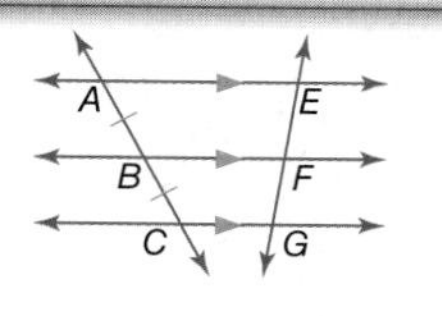

You will prove Corollary 7.2 in Exercise 29.

2 Proportional Parts with Parallel Lines

Examples 4 and 5 show how to find proportional and congruent segments by using the theorems in this lesson.

Additional Example

4 MAPS In the figure, Larch, Maple, and Nuthatch Streets are all parallel. The figure shows the distances in between city blocks. Find x.

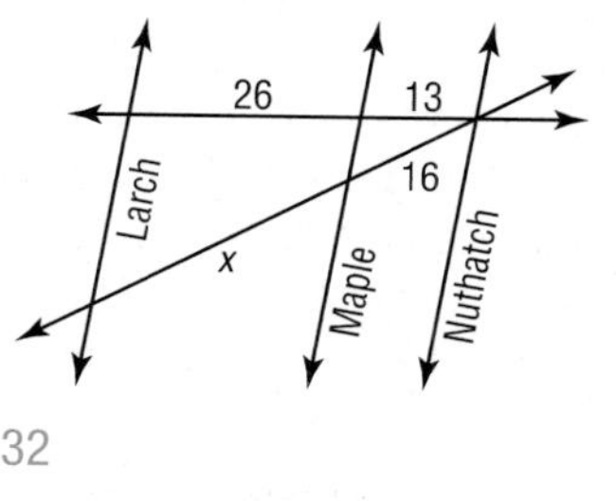

32

Focus on Mathematical Content

Parallel Lines The converse of Corollary 7.2 is true as well. If three lines cut off congruent segments on every transversal, then they cut off congruent segments on any line perpendicular to each of the respective lines. This shows the three lines are the same distance apart and hence parallel.

DifferentiatedInstruction OL BL

Visual Learners Artistically talented students can further investigate the mathematics of vanishing points (see p. 493, Example 4). Have students create a drawing that uses a vanishing point and discuss the mathematics involved.

Additional Example

5 Find x and y.

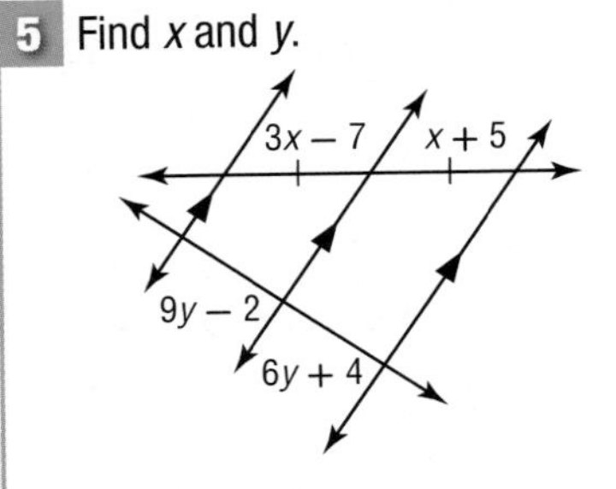

$x = 6$; $y = 2$

WatchOut!

Answering Questions Be careful to answer the question that is asked. In Example 5, you find the values of x and y, not the lengths of the line segments.

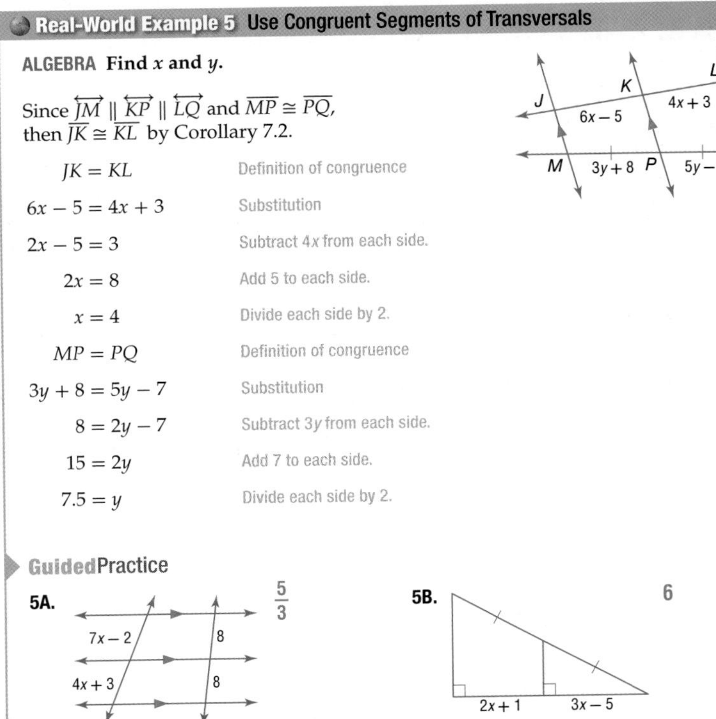

Real-World Example 5 Use Congruent Segments of Transversals

ALGEBRA **Find x and y.**

Since $\overleftrightarrow{JM} \parallel \overleftrightarrow{KP} \parallel \overleftrightarrow{LQ}$ and $\overline{MP} \cong \overline{PQ}$, then $\overline{JK} \cong \overline{KL}$ by Corollary 7.2.

$JK = KL$	Definition of congruence
$6x - 5 = 4x + 3$	Substitution
$2x - 5 = 3$	Subtract $4x$ from each side.
$2x = 8$	Add 5 to each side.
$x = 4$	Divide each side by 2.
$MP = PQ$	Definition of congruence
$3y + 8 = 5y - 7$	Substitution
$8 = 2y - 7$	Subtract $3y$ from each side.
$15 = 2y$	Add 7 to each side.
$7.5 = y$	Divide each side by 2.

GuidedPractice

5A. $\frac{5}{3}$

5B. 6

It is possible to separate a segment into two congruent parts by constructing the perpendicular bisector of a segment. However, a segment cannot be separated into three congruent parts by constructing perpendicular bisectors. To do this, you must use parallel lines and Corollary 7.2.

Construction Trisect a Segment

Draw a segment $\overline{AB}$. Then use Corollary 7.2 to trisect $\overline{AB}$.

Step 1 Draw $\overline{AC}$. Then with the compass at A, mark off an arc that intersects $\overline{AC}$ at X.

Step 2 Use the same compass setting to mark off Y and Z such that $\overline{AX} \cong \overline{XY} \cong \overline{YZ}$. Then draw ZB.

Step 3 Construct lines through Y and X that are parallel to $\overline{ZB}$. Label the intersection points on $\overline{AB}$ as J and K.

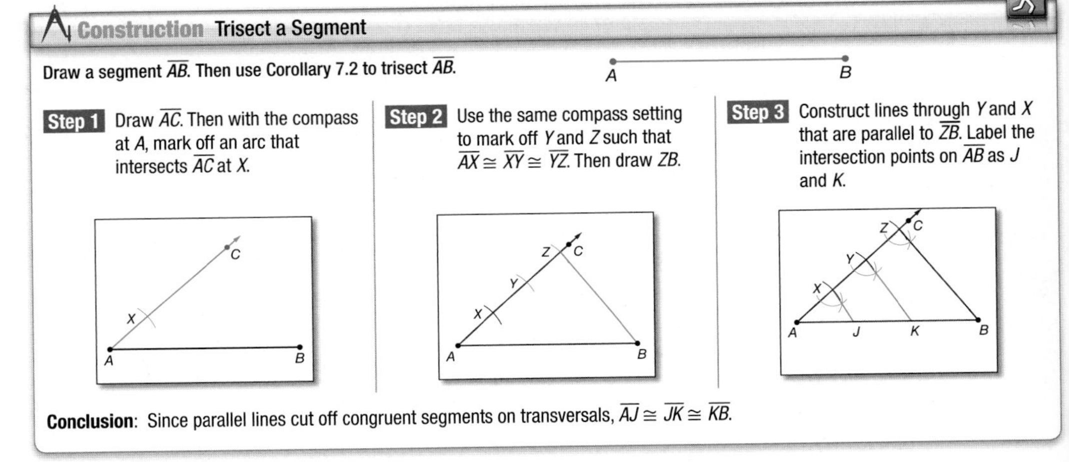

Conclusion: Since parallel lines cut off congruent segments on transversals, $\overline{AJ} \cong \overline{JK} \cong \overline{KB}$.

DifferentiatedInstruction AL OL BL

Kinesthetic Learners Have students use string, masking tape, and a tiled floor to mark off congruent segments on parallel lines made with masking tape on the floor. Use the string to show that if three or more parallel lines form congruent segments on one transversal, they form congruent segments on another transversal.

Check Your Understanding

 = Step-by-Step Solutions begin on page R14. 

Example 1

1. If $XM = 4$, $XN = 6$, and $NZ = 9$, find XY. **10**
2. If $XN = 6$, $XM = 2$, and $XY = 10$, find NZ. **24**

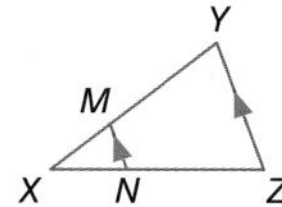

Example 2

3. In $\triangle ABC$, $BC = 15$, $BE = 6$, $DC = 12$, and $AD = 8$. Determine whether $\overline{DE} \parallel \overline{AB}$. Justify your answer.

3. Yes; $\frac{AD}{DC} = \frac{BE}{EC} = \frac{2}{3}$, so $\overline{DE} \parallel \overline{AB}$.

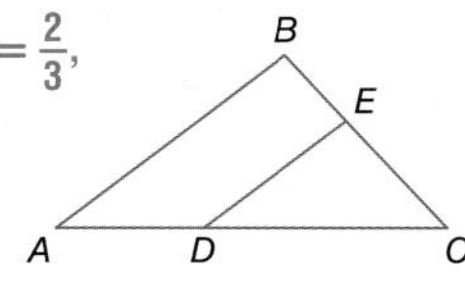

4. In $\triangle JKL$, $JK = 15$, $JM = 5$, $LK = 13$, and $PK = 9$. Determine whether $\overline{JL} \parallel \overline{MP}$. Justify your answer. **no; $\frac{5}{10} \neq \frac{4}{9}$**

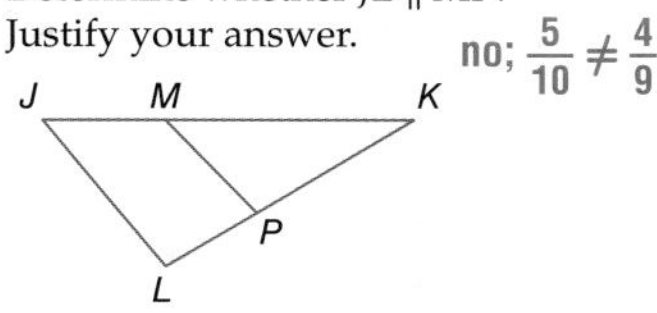

Example 3 $\overline{JH}$ **is a midsegment of $\triangle KLM$. Find the value of x.**

5. **11**

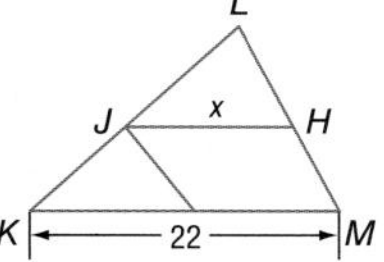

6. **10**

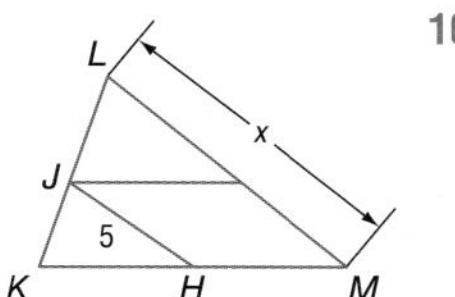

Example 4

7. **MAPS** Refer to the map at the right. 3rd Avenue and 5th Avenue are parallel. If the distance from 3rd Avenue to City Mall along State Street is 3201 feet, find the distance between 5th Avenue and City Mall along Union Street. Round to the nearest tenth. **2360.3 ft**

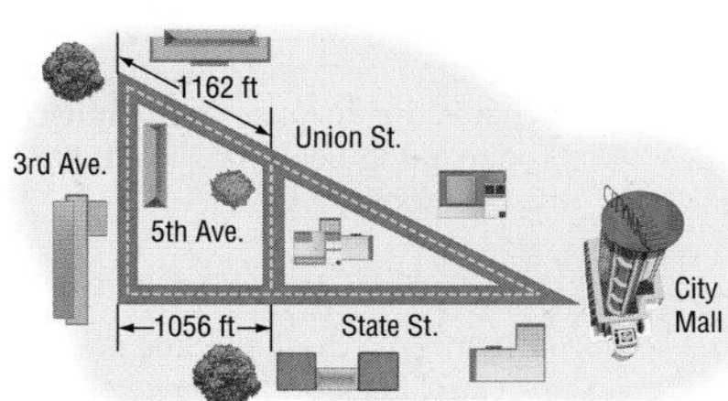

Example 5 **ALGEBRA** **Find x and y.**

8. **$x = 5$; $y = 8$**

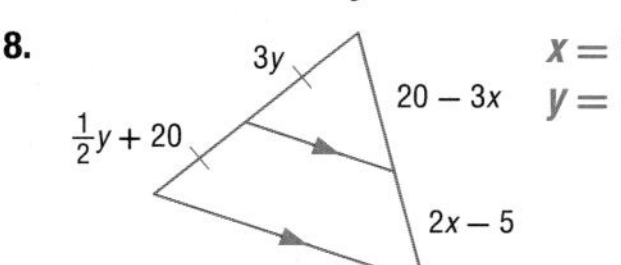

9. **$x = 20$; $y = 2$**

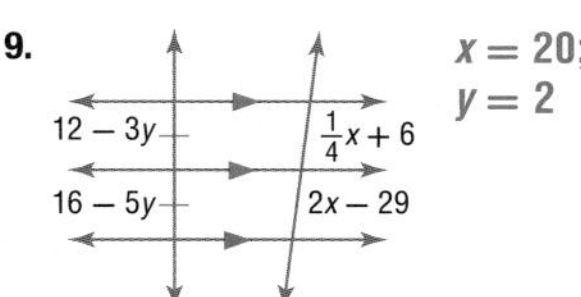

Practice and Problem Solving

Extra Practice is on page R7.

Example 1

10. If $AB = 6$, $BC = 4$, and $AE = 9$, find ED. **6**
11. If $AB = 12$, $AC = 16$, and $ED = 5$, find AE. **15**
12. If $AC = 14$, $BC = 8$, and $AD = 21$, find ED. **12**
13. If $AD = 27$, $AB = 8$, and $AE = 12$, find BC. **10**

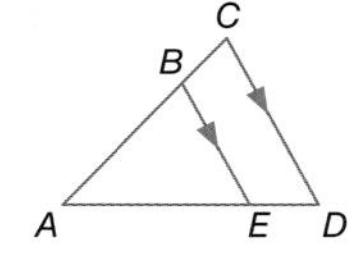

Differentiated Homework Options

Level	Assignment	Two-Day Option	
AL Basic	10–25, 48, 49, 51–71	11–25 odd, 53–56	10–24 even, 48, 49, 51, 52, 57–71
OL Core	11–47 odd, 48, 49, 51–71	10–25, 53–56	26–49, 51, 52, 57–71
BL Advanced	26–66, (optional: 67–71)		

3 Practice

Formative Assessment

Use Exercises 1–9 to check for understanding.

Use the chart at the bottom of this page to customize assignments for your students.

Study Guide and Intervention

AL OL ELL

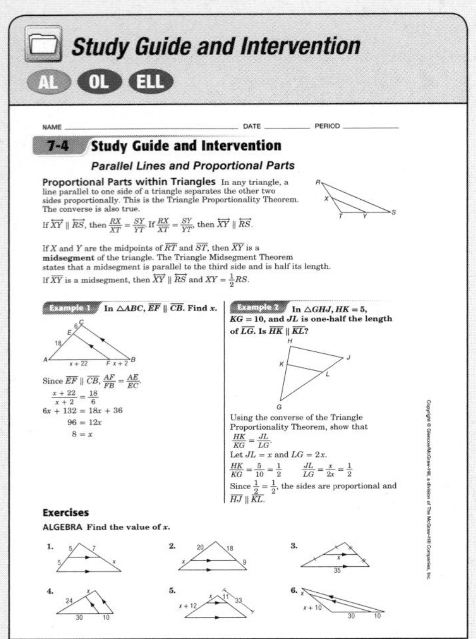
NAME ______ DATE ______ PERIOD ______

7-4 Study Guide and Intervention

Parallel Lines and Proportional Parts

Proportional Parts within Triangles In any triangle, a line parallel to one side of a triangle separates the other two sides proportionally. This is the Triangle Proportionality Theorem. The converse is also true.

If $\overline{XY} \parallel \overline{RS}$, then $\frac{RX}{XT} = \frac{SY}{YT}$. If $\frac{RX}{XT} = \frac{SY}{YT}$, then $\overline{XY} \parallel \overline{RS}$.

If X and Y are the midpoints of $\overline{RT}$ and $\overline{ST}$, then $\overline{XY}$ is a **midsegment** of the triangle. The Triangle Midsegment Theorem states that a midsegment is parallel to the third side and is half its length.

If $\overline{XY}$ is a midsegment, then $\overline{XY} \parallel \overline{RS}$ and $XY = \frac{1}{2}RS$.

Example 1 In $\triangle ABC$, $\overline{EF} \parallel \overline{CB}$. Find x.

Since $\overline{EF} \parallel \overline{CB}$, $\frac{AF}{FB} = \frac{AE}{EC}$.

$\frac{x + 22}{x + 2} = \frac{18}{6}$

$6x + 132 = 18x + 36$

$96 = 12x$

$8 = x$

Example 2 In $\triangle GHJ$, $HK = 5$, $KG = 10$, and JL is one-half the length of $\overline{LG}$. Is $\overline{HJ} \parallel \overline{KL}$?

Using the converse of the Triangle Proportionality Theorem, show that $\frac{HK}{KG} = \frac{JL}{LG}$.

Let $JL = x$ and $LG = 2x$.

$\frac{HK}{KG} = \frac{5}{10} = \frac{1}{2}$ $\quad \frac{JL}{LG} = \frac{x}{2x} = \frac{1}{2}$

Since $\frac{1}{2} = \frac{1}{2}$, the sides are proportional and $\overline{HJ} \parallel \overline{KL}$.

Exercises

ALGEBRA Find the value of x.

1. 2. 3. 4. 5. 6.

Practice

AL OL BL ELL

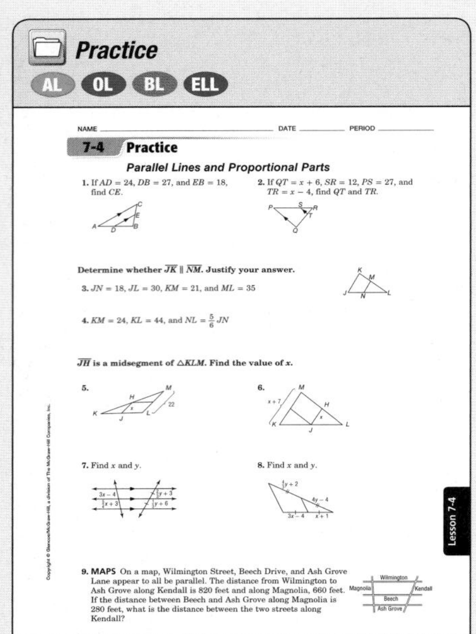
NAME ______ DATE ______ PERIOD ______

7-4 Practice

Parallel Lines and Proportional Parts

1. If $AD = 24$, $DB = 27$, and $EB = 18$, find CE.

2. If $QT = x + 6$, $SR = 12$, $PS = 27$, and $TR = x - 4$, find QT and TR.

Determine whether $\overline{JK} \parallel \overline{NM}$. Justify your answer.

3. $JN = 18$, $JL = 30$, $KM = 21$, and $ML = 35$

4. $KM = 24$, $KL = 44$, and $NL = \frac{5}{6}JN$

$\overline{JH}$ is a midsegment of $\triangle KLM$. Find the value of x.

5. 6.

7. Find x and y.

8. Find x and y.

9. **MAPS** On a map, Wilmington Street, Beech Drive, and Ash Grove Lane appear to all be parallel. The distance from Wilmington to Ash Grove along Kendall is 820 feet and along Magnolia, 660 feet. If the distance between Beech and Ash Grove along Magnolia is 280 feet, what is the distance between the two streets along Kendall?

Word Problem Practice

AL OL BL ELL

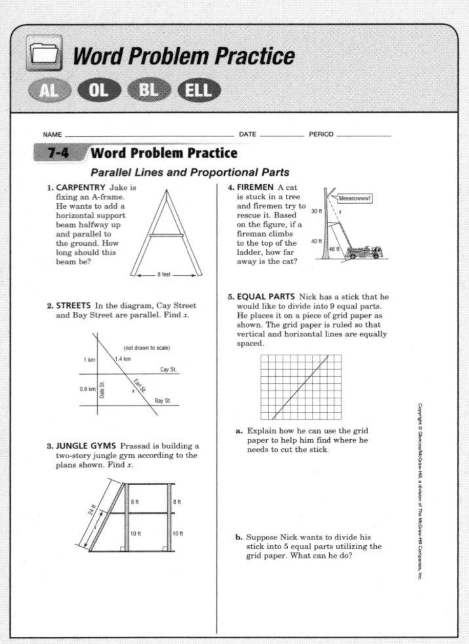
NAME ______ DATE ______ PERIOD ______

7-4 Word Problem Practice

Parallel Lines and Proportional Parts

1. **CARPENTRY** Jake is fixing an A-frame. He wants to add a horizontal support beam halfway up and parallel to the ground. How long should this beam be?

2. **STREETS** In the diagram, Cay Street and Bay Street are parallel. Find x.

3. **JUNGLE GYMS** Prassad is building a two-story jungle gym according to the plans shown. Find x.

4. **FIREMEN** A cat is stuck in a tree and firemen try to rescue it. Based on the figure, if a fireman climbs to the top of the ladder, how far away is the cat?

5. **EQUAL PARTS** Nick has a stick that he would like to divide into 9 equal parts. He places it on a piece of grid paper as shown. The grid paper is ruled so that vertical and horizontal lines are equally spaced.

a. Explain how he can use the grid paper to help him find where he needs to cut the stick.

b. Suppose Nick wants to divide his stick into 5 equal parts utilizing the grid paper. What can he do?

Example 2 Determine whether $\overline{VY} \parallel \overline{ZW}$. Justify your answer.

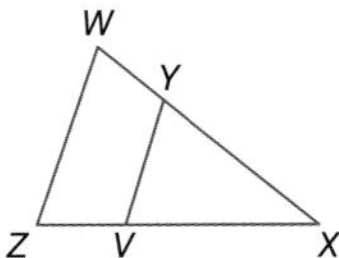

14. $ZX = 18$, $ZV = 6$, $WX = 24$, and $YX = 16$ **yes; $\frac{ZV}{VX} = \frac{WY}{YX} = \frac{1}{2}$**

15. $VX = 7.5$, $ZX = 24$, $WY = 27.5$, and $WX = 40$ **yes; $\frac{ZV}{VX} = \frac{WY}{YX} = \frac{11}{5}$**

16. $ZV = 8$, $VX = 2$, and $YX = \frac{1}{2}WY$ **no; $\frac{ZV}{VX} \neq \frac{WY}{YX}$**

17. $WX = 31$, $YX = 21$, and $ZX = 4ZV$ **no; $\frac{ZV}{VX} \neq \frac{WY}{YX}$**

Example 3 $\overline{JH}$, $\overline{JP}$, and $\overline{PH}$ are midsegments of $\triangle KLM$. Find the value of x.

18. **57**

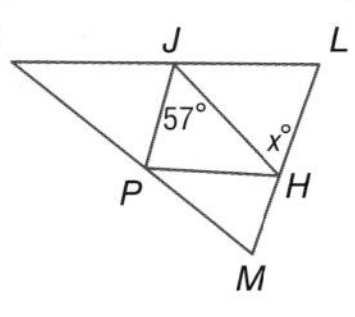

19. **60**

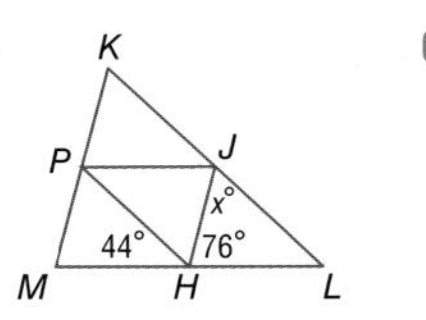

20. **50**

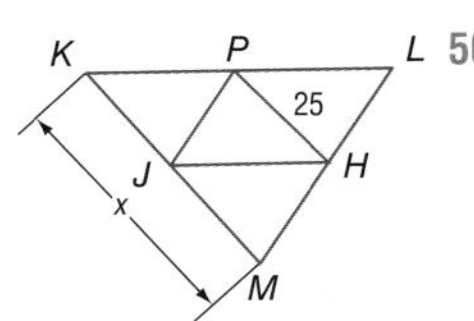

21. **1.35**

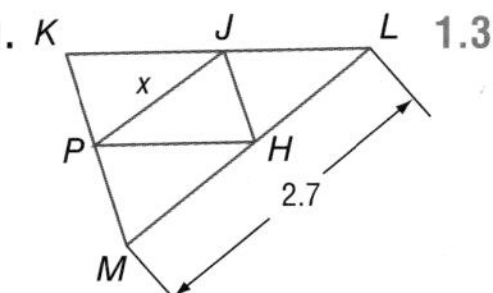

Example 4

22. **CCSS MODELING** In Charleston, South Carolina, Logan Street is parallel to both King Street and Smith Street between Beaufain Street and Queen Street. What is the distance from Smith to Logan along Beaufain? Round to the nearest foot. **about 891 ft**

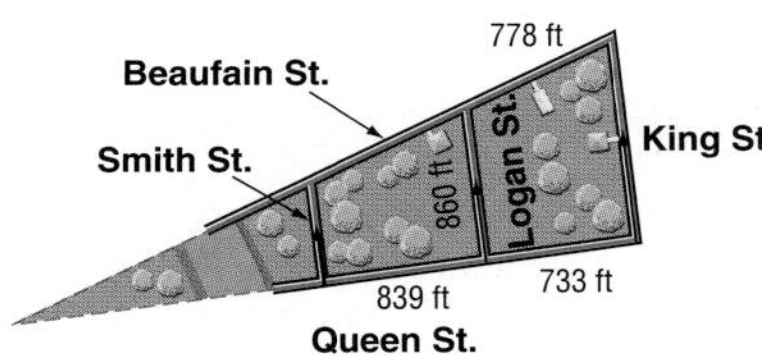

23. **ART** Tonisha drew the line of dancers shown below for her perspective project in art class. Each of the dancers is parallel. Find the lower distance between the first two dancers. **1.2 in.**

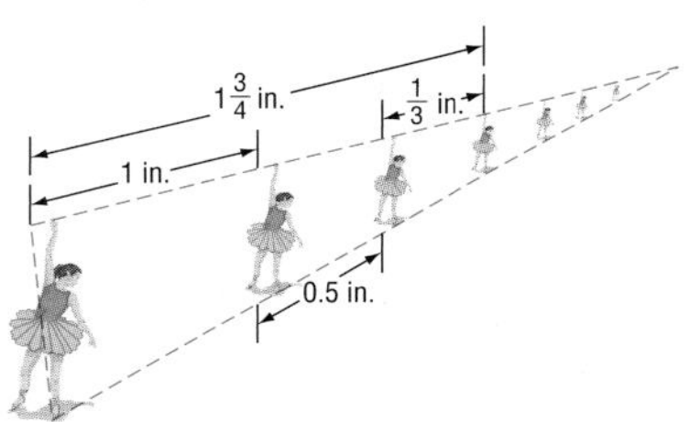

Example 5 **ALGEBRA** Find x and y.

24. **x = 2; y = 5**

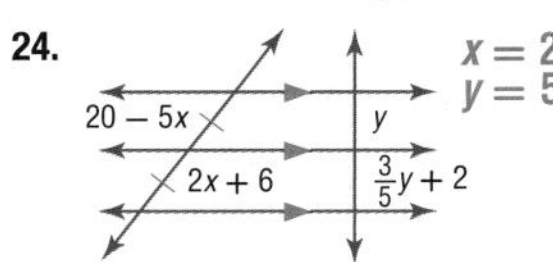

25. **x = 18; y = 3**

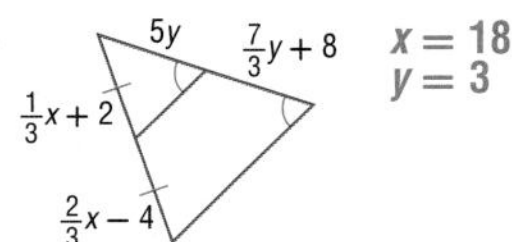

Enrichment

OL BL

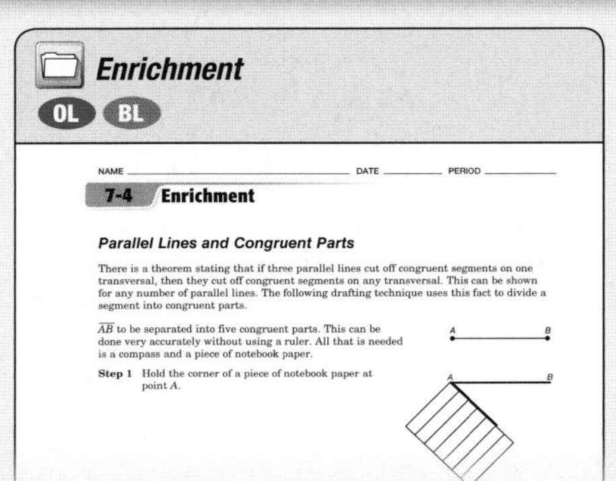
NAME ______ DATE ______ PERIOD ______

7-4 Enrichment

Parallel Lines and Congruent Parts

There is a theorem stating that if three parallel lines cut off congruent segments on one transversal, then they cut off congruent segments on any transversal. This can be shown for any number of parallel lines. The following drafting technique uses this fact to divide a segment into congruent parts.

$\overline{AB}$ to be separated into five congruent parts. This can be done very accurately without using a ruler. All that is needed is a compass and a piece of notebook paper.

Step 1 Hold the corner of a piece of notebook paper at point A.

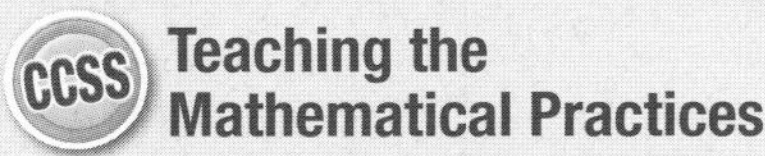

Teaching the Mathematical Practices

Modeling Mathematically proficient students can apply the mathematics they know to solve problems arising in everyday life. In Exercise 22, encourage students to analyze the given diagram to identify information important to solving the problem.

B **ALGEBRA** Find x and y.

26. $x = 10$; $y = 3$

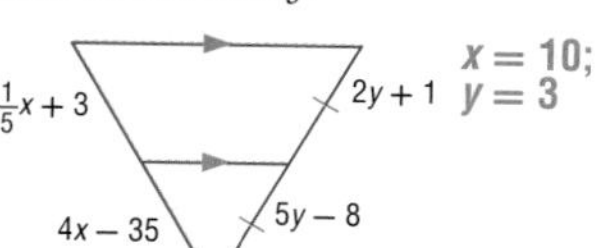

27. $x = 48$; $y = 72$

CCSS ARGUMENTS Write a paragraph proof. **28–30. See margin.**

28. Corollary 7.1 **29.** Corollary 7.2 **30.** Theorem 7.5

CCSS ARGUMENTS Write a two-column proof. **31–32. See Ch. 7 Answer Appendix.**

31. Theorem 7.6 **32.** Theorem 7.7

Refer to $\triangle QRS$.

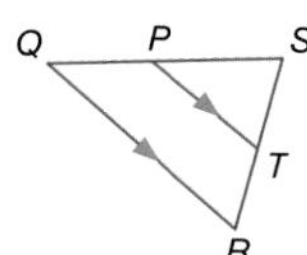

33. If $ST = 8$, $TR = 4$, and $PT = 6$, find QR. **9**

34. If $SP = 4$, $PT = 6$, and $QR = 12$, find SQ. **8**

35 If $CE = t - 2$, $EB = t + 1$, $CD = 2$, and $CA = 10$, find t and CE. **3, 1**

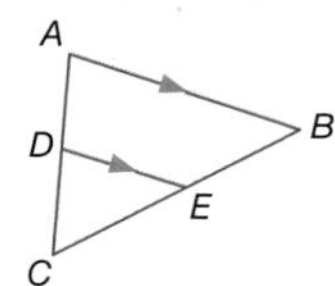

36. If $WX = 7$, $WY = a$, $WV = 6$, and $VZ = a - 9$, find WY. **21**

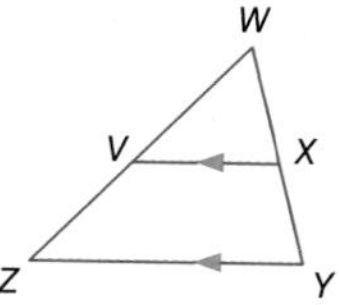

37. If $QR = 2$, $XW = 12$, $QW = 15$, and $ST = 5$, find RS and WV. **8, 7.5**

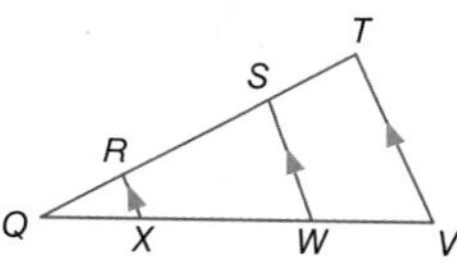

38. If $LK = 4$, $MP = 3$, $PQ = 6$, $KJ = 2$, $RS = 6$, and $LP = 2$, find ML, QR, QK, and JH. **2, 3, 6, 4**

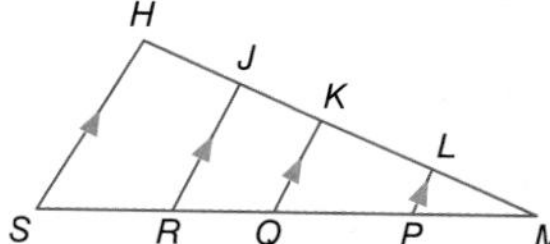

39. MATH HISTORY The sector compass was a tool perfected by Galileo in the sixteenth century for measurement. To draw a segment two-fifths the length of a given segment, align the ends of the arms with the given segment. Then draw a segment at the 40 mark. Write a justification that explains why the sector compass works for proportional measurement. **See Ch. 7 Answer Appendix.**

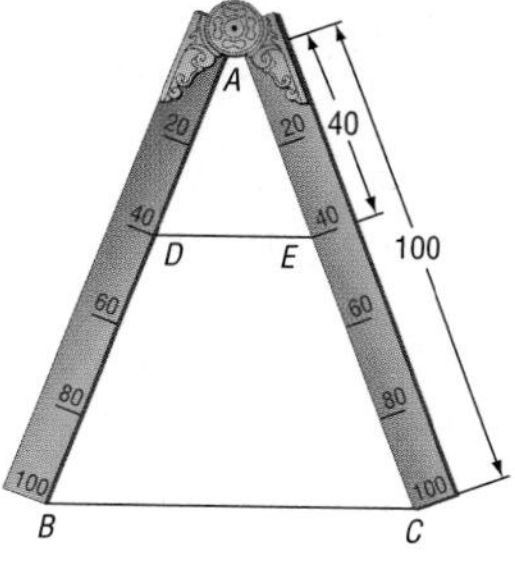

Determine the value of x so that $\overline{BC} \parallel \overline{DF}$.

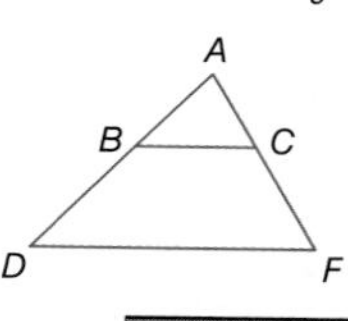

40. $AB = x + 5$, $BD = 12$, $AC = 3x + 1$, and $CF = 15$ **3**

41. $AC = 15$, $BD = 3x - 2$, $CF = 3x + 2$, and $AB = 12$ **6**

Additional Answers

28–30. Sample answers given.

28. Given: $\overleftrightarrow{AD} \parallel \overleftrightarrow{BE} \parallel \overleftrightarrow{CF}$

Prove: $\frac{AB}{BC} = \frac{DE}{EF}$

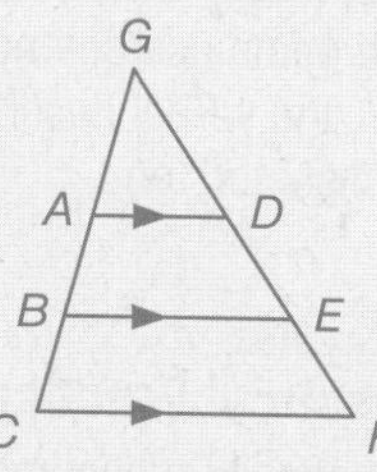

Proof:

In $\triangle GBE$, $\overline{AD} \parallel \overline{BE}$. By the Triangle Proportionality Theorem, AB and DE are proportional. In $\triangle GCF$, $\overline{BE} \parallel \overline{CF}$. By the Triangle Proportionality Theorem, BC and EF are proportional. Therefore, $\frac{AB}{BC} = \frac{DE}{EF}$.

29. Given: $\overleftrightarrow{AD} \parallel \overleftrightarrow{BE} \parallel \overleftrightarrow{CF}$, $\overline{AB} \cong \overline{BC}$

Prove: $\overline{DE} \cong \overline{EF}$

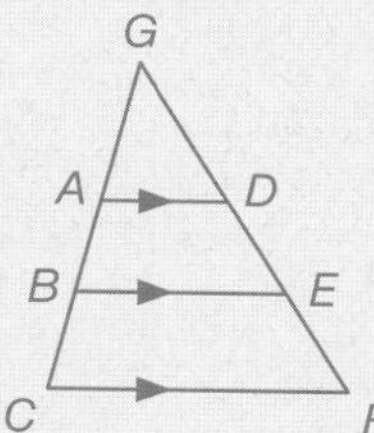

Proof:

From Corollary 7.1, $\frac{AB}{BC} = \frac{DE}{EF}$. Since $\overline{AB} \cong \overline{BC}$, $AB = BC$ by definition of congruence. Therefore, $\frac{AB}{BC} = 1$. By substitution, $1 = \frac{DE}{EF}$. Thus, $DE = EF$. By definition of congruence, $\overline{DE} \cong \overline{EF}$.

30. Given: $\overline{BD} \parallel \overline{AE}$

Prove: $\frac{BA}{CB} = \frac{DE}{CD}$

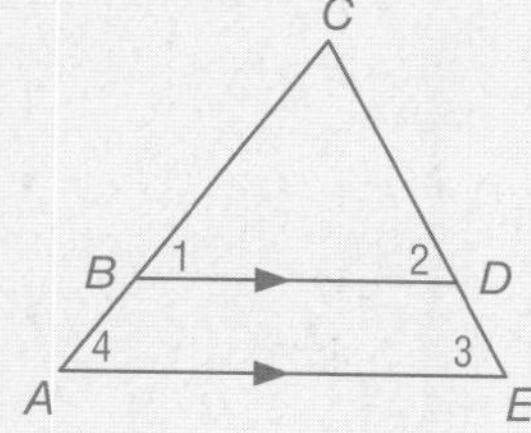

Proof: $\overline{BD} \parallel \overline{AE}$, $\angle 4 \cong \angle 1$ and $\angle 3 \cong \angle 2$ because they are corresponding angles. By AA Similarity, $\triangle ACE \sim \triangle BCD$. From the definition of similar polygons, $\frac{CA}{CB} = \frac{CE}{CD}$. By the Segment Addition Postulate, $CA = BA + CB$ and $CE = DE + CD$. By substitution, $\frac{BA + CB}{CB} = \frac{DE + CD}{CD}$. Rewriting as a sum, $\frac{BA}{CB} + \frac{CB}{CB} = \frac{DE}{CD} + \frac{CD}{CD}$. From simplifying, $\frac{BA}{CB} + 1 = \frac{DE}{CD} + 1$. Thus, $\frac{BA}{CB} = \frac{DE}{CD}$ by subtracting one from each side.

Exercise Alert

Straightedge and Compass Exercises 44–47 require the use of a straightedge and a compass.

 **Multiple Representations** In Exercise 47, students use geometric sketches, a table, and verbal description to explore angle bisectors and proportions.

CCSS Teaching the Mathematical Practices

Critique Mathematically proficient students can distinguish correct logic from flawed reasoning. In Exercise 48, students should use the figure to judge the reasonableness of their answers. Sebastian reversed the role of the two parallel segments from Theorem 7.7, and he should see that $\overline{JL}$ is longer than $\overline{MP}$.

42. **COORDINATE GEOMETRY** $\triangle ABC$ has vertices $A(-8, 7)$, $B(0, 1)$, and $C(7, 5)$. Draw $\triangle ABC$. Determine the coordinates of the midsegment of $\triangle ABC$ that is parallel to $\overline{BC}$. Justify your answer. See margin.

 43. **HOUSES** Refer to the diagram of the gable at the right. Each piece of siding is a uniform width. Find the lengths of $\overline{FG}$, $\overline{EH}$, and $\overline{DJ}$. 8.75 in., 17.5 in., 26.25 in.

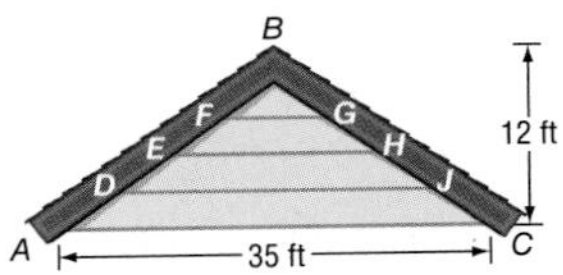

CONSTRUCTIONS Construct each segment as directed. 44–46. See margin.

44. a segment separated into five congruent segments
45. a segment separated into two segments in which their lengths have a ratio of 1 to 3
46. a segment 3 inches long, separated into four congruent segments

47. **MULTIPLE REPRESENTATIONS** In this problem, you will explore angle bisectors and proportions.

a. **Geometric** Draw three triangles, one acute, one right, and one obtuse. Label one triangle ABC and draw angle bisector $\overrightarrow{BD}$. Label the second MNP with angle bisector $\overrightarrow{NQ}$ and the third WXY with angle bisector $\overrightarrow{XZ}$. See margin.

b. **Tabular** Copy and complete the table at the right with the appropriate values.

c. **Verbal** Make a conjecture about the segments of a triangle created by an angle bisector.

47c. Sample answer: The proportion of the segments created by the angle bisector of a triangle is equal to the proportion of their respective consecutive sides.

Triangle	Length		Ratio	
ABC	AD	1.1 cm	$\frac{AD}{CD}$	1.0
	CD	1.1 cm		
	AB	2.0 cm	$\frac{AB}{CB}$	1.0
	CB	2.0 cm		
MNP	MQ	1.4 cm	$\frac{MQ}{PQ}$	0.8
	PQ	1.7 cm		
	MN	1.6 cm	$\frac{MN}{PN}$	0.8
	PN	2.0 cm		
WXY	WZ	0.8 cm	$\frac{WZ}{YZ}$	0.7
	YZ	1.2 cm		
	WX	2.0 cm	$\frac{WX}{YX}$	0.7
	YX	2.9 cm		

H.O.T. Problems Use Higher-Order Thinking Skills

48. **CCSS CRITIQUE** Jacob and Sebastian are finding the value of x in $\triangle JHL$. Jacob says that MP is one half of JL, so x is 4.5. Sebastian says that JL is one half of MP, so x is 18. Is either of them correct? Explain.

48. Jacob; sample answer: $\overline{MP}$ is the midsegment, so $MP = \frac{1}{2}JL$.

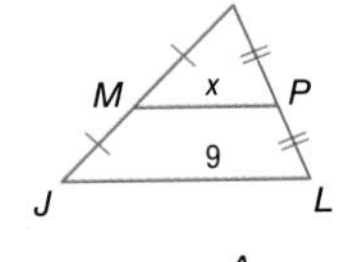

49. **REASONING** In $\triangle ABC$, $AF = FB$ and $AH = HC$. If D is $\frac{3}{4}$ of the way from A to B and E is $\frac{3}{4}$ of the way from A to C, is DE *always*, *sometimes*, or *never* $\frac{3}{4}$ of BC? Explain. See margin.

A F H D E B C

50. **CHALLENGE** Write a two-column proof.

Given: $AB = 4$, $BC = 4$, and $CD = DE$

Prove: $\overline{BD} \parallel \overline{AE}$ See Ch. 7 Answer Appendix.

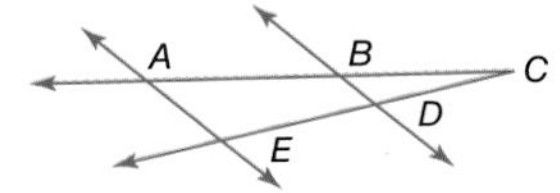

51. **OPEN ENDED** Draw three segments, a, b, and c, of all different lengths. Draw a fourth segment, d, such that $\frac{a}{b} = \frac{c}{d}$. See Ch. 7 Answer Appendix.

52. **WRITING IN MATH** Compare the Triangle Proportionality Theorem and the Triangle Midsegment Theorem.

52. Both theorems deal with a parallel line inside the triangle. The Midsegment Theorem is a special case of the Converse of the Proportionality Theorem.

Additional Answers

42.

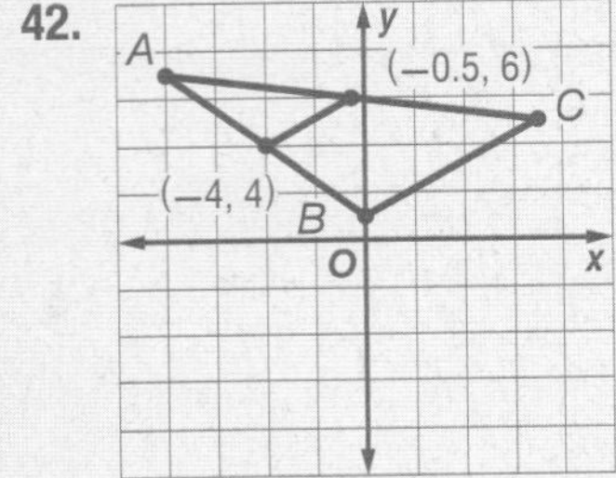

The endpoints of the midsegment are $(-4, 4)$ and $(-0.5, 6)$. Sample answer: The segment is parallel to $\overline{BC}$ because the slopes are both $\frac{4}{7}$ and the segment length is half of $\overline{BC}$. Thus, the segment is the midsegment of $\triangle ABC$.

44. Sample answer:

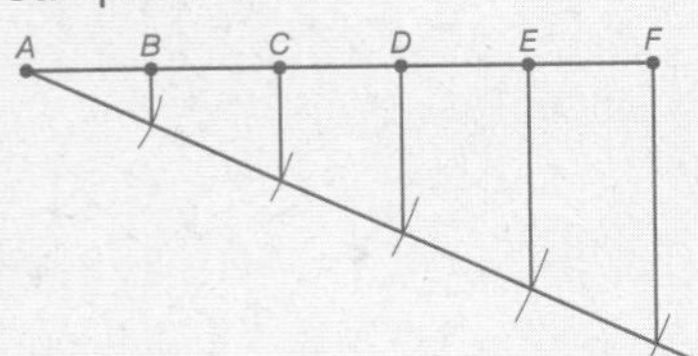

45. Sample answer:

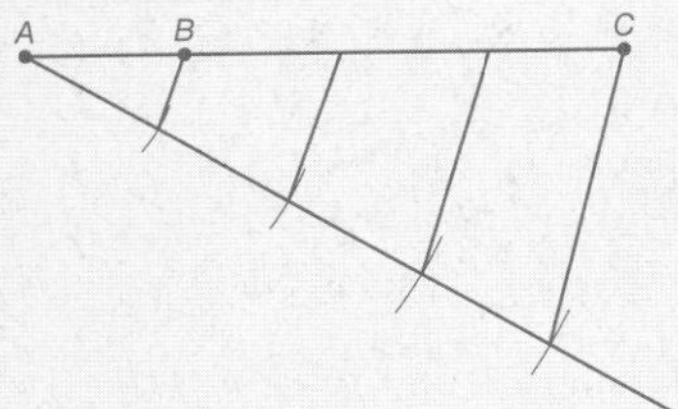

46. Sample answer:

A B C D E

Standardized Test Practice

53. SHORT RESPONSE What is the value of x? **8**

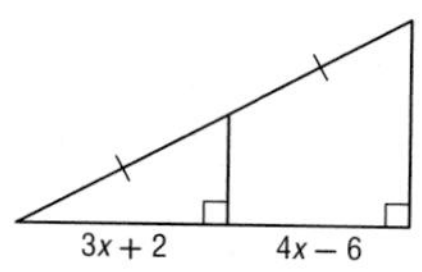

54. If the vertices of triangle JKL are (0, 0), (0, 10) and (10, 10), then the area of triangle JKL is **D**

A 20 units^2 C 40 units^2
B 30 units^2 D 50 units^2

55. ALGEBRA A breakfast cereal contains wheat, rice, and oats in the ratio 2:4:1. If the manufacturer makes a mixture using 110 pounds of wheat, how many pounds of rice will be used? **G**

F 120 lb H 240 lb
G 220 lb J 440 lb

56. SAT/ACT If the area of a circle is 16 square meters, what is its radius in meters? **A**

A $\frac{4\sqrt{\pi}}{\pi}$ D 12π
B $\frac{8}{\pi}$ E 16π
C $\frac{16}{\pi}$

57. $\triangle ABE \sim \triangle CDE$ **by AA Similarity; 6.25** **58.** $\triangle RSW \sim \triangle TRW$ **by SAS Similarity; 15, 20**

Spiral Review

ALGEBRA Identify the similar triangles. Then find the measure(s) of the indicated segment(s). (Lesson 7-3)

57. $\overline{AB}$

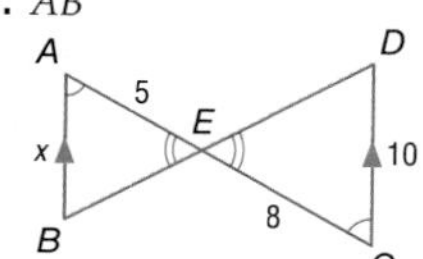

58. $\overline{RT}, \overline{RS}$

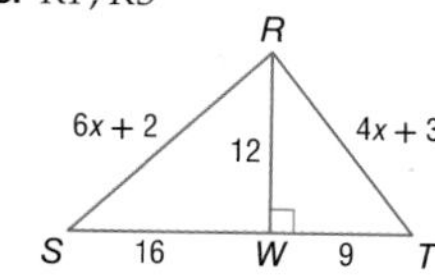

$\triangle WZT \sim \triangle WXY$ **by AA Similarity; 7.5**

59. $\overline{TY}$

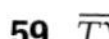
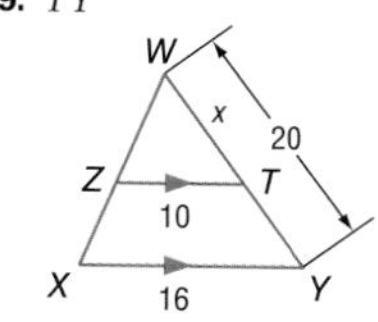

60. SURVEYING Mr. Turner uses a carpenter's square to find the distance across a stream. The carpenter's square models right angle NOL. He puts the square on top of a pole that is high enough to sight along $\overline{OL}$ to point P across the river. Then he sights along $\overline{ON}$ to point M. If MK is 1.5 feet and OK is 4.5 feet, find the distance KP across the stream. (Lesson 7-2) **13.5 ft**

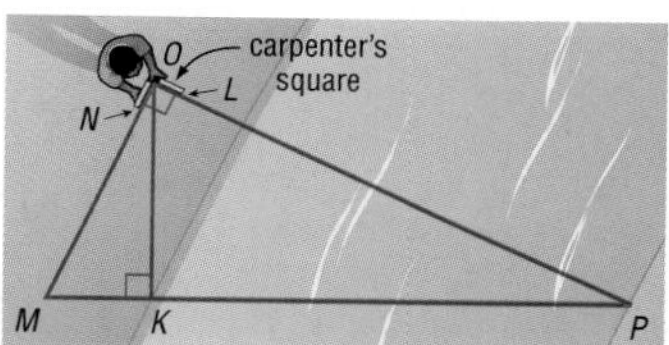

COORDINATE GEOMETRY For each quadrilateral with the given vertices, verify that the quadrilateral is a trapezoid and determine whether the figure is an isosceles trapezoid. (Lesson 6-6) **61–62. See margin.**

61. $Q(-12, 1), R(-9, 4), S(-4, 3), T(-11, -4)$

62. $A(-3, 3), B(-4, -1), C(5, -1), D(2, 3)$

Point S is the incenter of $\triangle JPL$. Find each measure. (Lesson 5-1)

63. SQ **6**

64. QJ **8**

65. $m\angle MPQ$ **56**

66. $m\angle SJP$ **37.5**

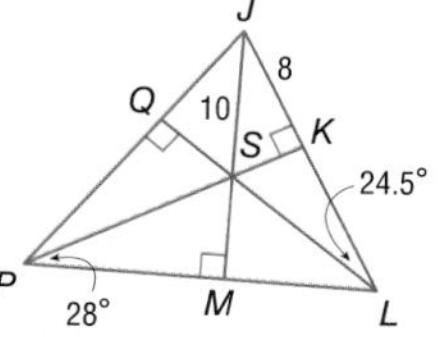

Skills Review

Solve each proportion.

67. $\frac{1}{3} = \frac{x}{2}$ $\frac{2}{3}$

68. $\frac{3}{4} = \frac{5}{x}$ **6.7**

69. $\frac{2.3}{4} = \frac{x}{3.7}$ **2.1**

70. $\frac{x-2}{2} = \frac{4}{5}$ **3.6**

71. $\frac{x}{12-x} = \frac{8}{3}$ **8.7**

Differentiated Instruction OL BL

Extension A town's water tower is at location A. The borders of the town form a triangle using points B, C, and the water tower. Point D is halfway between the water tower and point B. Point E is halfway between the water tower and point C. The distance from D to E is 18.9 miles. What is the distance from point C to point B? 37.8 miles

4 Assess

Name The Math Have students explain the Triangle Proportionality Theorem using triangle similarity properties.

Formative Assessment

Check for student understanding of Lessons 7-3 and 7-4.

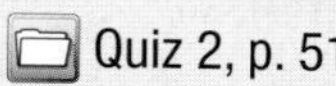

Quiz 2, p. 51

Additional Answers

47a. Sample answer:

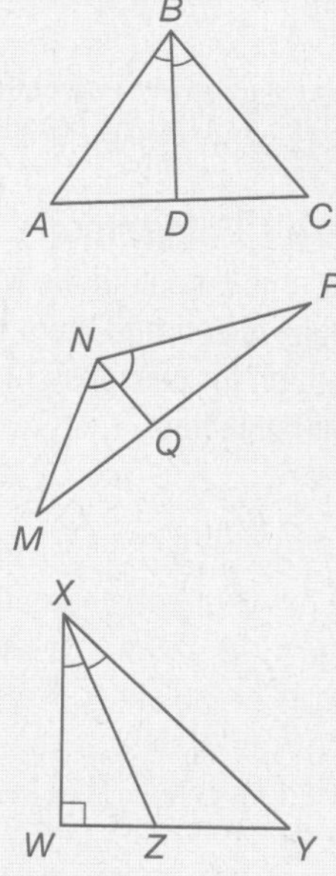

49. Always; sample answer: FH is a midsegment. Let $BC = x$, then $FH = \frac{1}{2}x$. $FHCB$ is a trapezoid, so $DE = \frac{1}{2}(BC + FH) = \frac{1}{2}\left(x + \frac{1}{2}x\right) = \frac{1}{2}x + \frac{1}{4}x = \frac{3}{4}x$. Therefore, $DE = \frac{3}{4}BC$.

61. $\overline{QR} \parallel \overline{TS}$, $\overline{QT} \nparallel \overline{RS}$; $QRST$ is an isosceles trapezoid since $RS = \sqrt{26} = QT$.

62. $\overline{AD} \parallel \overline{BC}$, $\overline{CD} \nparallel \overline{AB}$; $ABCD$ is a trapezoid, but not isosceles since $AB = \sqrt{17}$ and $CD = 5$.

Formative Assessment

Use the Mid-Chapter Quiz to assess students' progress in the first half of the chapter.

Have students review the lesson indicated for the problems that they answered incorrectly.

Summative Assessment

Mid-Chapter Test, p. 53

eAssessment Customize and create multiple versions of your Mid-Chapter Test and their answer keys.

FOLDABLES® StudyOrganizer

Dinah Zike's Foldables®

Before students complete the Mid-Chapter Quiz, encourage them to review the information for Lessons 7-1 through 7-4 in their Foldables.

Additional Answer

13a. The bar connects the midpoints of each leg of the letter and it is parallel to the base. Therefore, the length of the bar is one-half the length of the base because a midsegment of a triangle is parallel to one side of the triangle, and its length is one-half the length of that side.

CHAPTER 7 Mid-Chapter Quiz

Lessons 7-1 through 7-4

Solve each proportion. (Lesson 7-1)

1. $\frac{2}{5} = \frac{x}{25}$ **10**

2. $\frac{10}{3} = \frac{7}{x}$ **2.1**

3. $\frac{y+4}{11} = \frac{y-2}{9}$ **29**

4. $\frac{z-1}{3} = \frac{8}{z+1}$ **5 or −5**

5. **BASEBALL** A pitcher's earned run average, or ERA, is the product of 9 and the ratio of earned runs the pitcher has allowed to the number of innings pitched. During the 2007 season, Johan Santana of the Minnesota Twins allowed 81 earned runs in 219 innings pitched. Find his ERA to the nearest hundredth. (Lesson 7-1) **3.33**

Each pair of polygons is similar. Find the value of *x*. (Lesson 7-2)

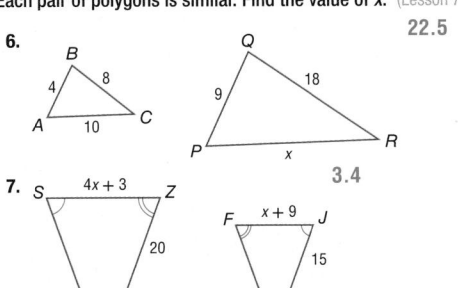

6. **22.5**

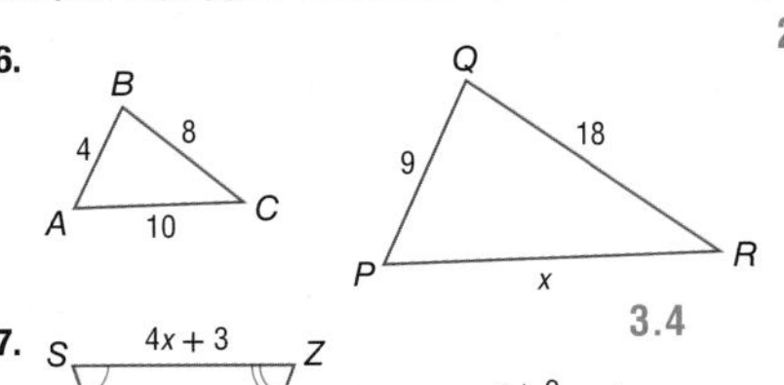

7. **3.4**

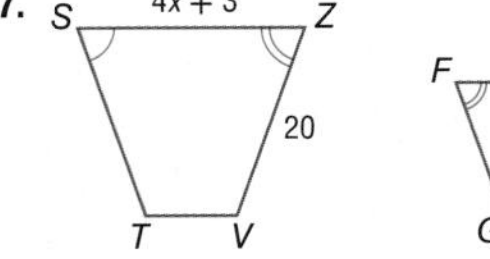

F, $x + 9$, J, 15, G, H

8. **MULTIPLE CHOICE** Two similar polygons have a scale factor of 3:5. The perimeter of the larger polygon is 120 feet. Find the perimeter of the smaller polygon. (Lesson 7-2) **B**

   A 68 ft **C** 192 ft

   B 72 ft **D** 200 ft

9. Yes; $\triangle YXZ \sim \triangle QRZ$ by AA Similarity.

10. No; the missing ∠s of the △s can never be ≅, so the △s can never be ~.

Determine whether the triangles are similar. If so, write a similarity statement. If not, what would be sufficient to prove the triangles similar? Explain your reasoning. (Lesson 7-3)

9. X, R, Y, Q, Z

10. B, 53°, A, 61°, C

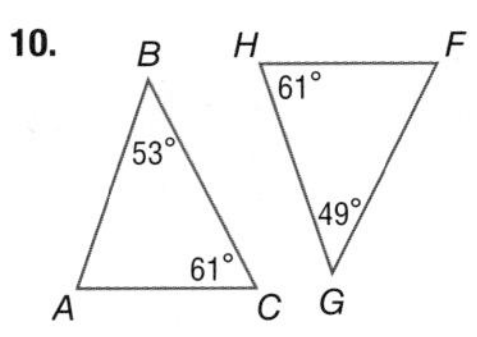

ALGEBRA Identify the similar triangles. Find each measure. (Lesson 7-3)

11. *SR* **$\triangle JKL \sim \triangle RST$; 4**

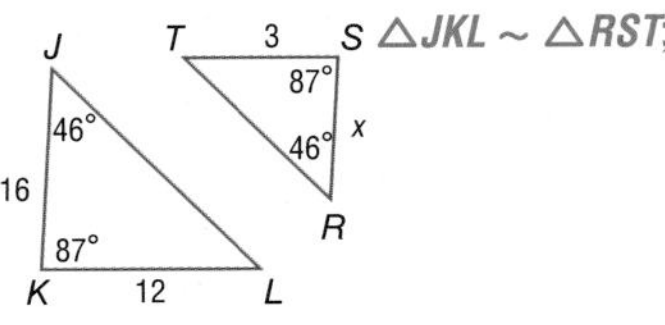

12. *AF* **$\triangle ABC \sim \triangle AFD$; 10.8**

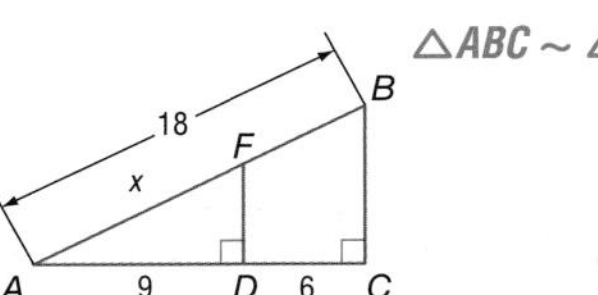

13. **HISTORY** In the fifteenth century, mathematicians and artists tried to construct the perfect letter. A square was used as a frame to design the letter "A," as shown below. The thickness of the major stroke of the letter was $\frac{1}{12}$ the height of the letter. (Lesson 7-4)

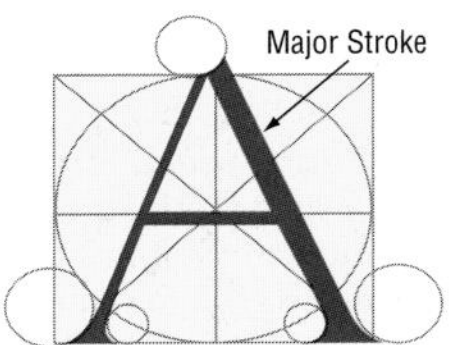

   a. Explain why the bar through the middle of the A is half the length of the space between the outside bottom corners of the sides of the letter. **See margin.**

   b. If the letter were 3 centimeters tall, how wide would the major stroke be? **0.25 cm**

ALGEBRA Find *x* and *y*. (Lesson 7-4)

14. **$x = 13$, $y = 4$**

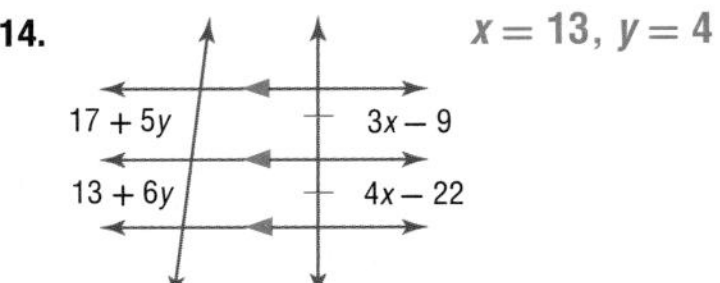

15. **$x = 3$, $y = 8$**

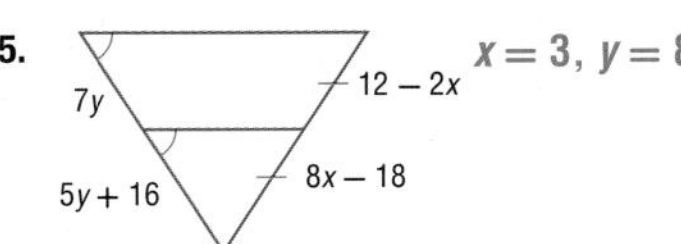

InterventionPlanner

TIER 1 On Level OL

 **If** students miss about 25% of the exercises or less,

 **Then** choose a resource:

SE Lessons 7-1, 7-2, 7-3, and 7-4

 Skills Practice, pp. 7, 14, 20, and 26

 Self-Check Quiz

TIER 2 Strategic Intervention AL approaching grade level

 **If** students miss about 50% of the exercises,

 **Then** choose a resource:

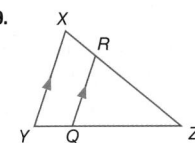 Study Guide and Intervention, pp. 5, 12, 18, 24

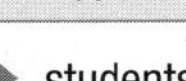   Extra Examples, Personal Tutor

TIER 3 Intensive Intervention 2 or more grades below level

 **If** students miss about 75% of the exercises,

 **Then** use *Math Triumphs, Geometry*, Chs. 2 and 5

connectED.mcgraw-hill.com Extra Examples, Personal Tutor, Homework Help, Review Vocabulary

LESSON 7-5 Parts of Similar Triangles

Then

- You learned that corresponding sides of similar polygons are proportional.

Now

1. Recognize and use proportional relationships of corresponding angle bisectors, altitudes, and medians of similar triangles.
2. Use the Triangle Bisector Theorem.

Why?

- The "Rule of Thumb" uses the average ratio of a person's arm length to the distance between his or her eyes and the altitudes of similar triangles to estimate the distance between a person and an object of approximately known width.

CCSS Common Core State Standards

Content Standards

G.SRT.4 Prove theorems about triangles.

G.SRT.5 Use congruence and similarity criteria for triangles to solve problems and to prove relationships in geometric figures.

Mathematical Practices

1. Make sense of problems and persevere in solving them.
3. Construct viable arguments and critique the reasoning of others.

1 Special Segments of Similar Triangles

You learned in Lesson 7-2 that the corresponding side lengths of similar polygons, such as triangles, are proportional. This concept can be extended to other segments in triangles.

Theorems Special Segments of Similar Triangles

7.8 If two triangles are similar, the lengths of corresponding altitudes are proportional to the lengths of corresponding sides.

Abbreviation *~△s have corr. altitudes proportional to corr. sides.*

Example If $\triangle ABC \sim \triangle FGH$, then $\frac{AD}{FJ} = \frac{AB}{FG}$.

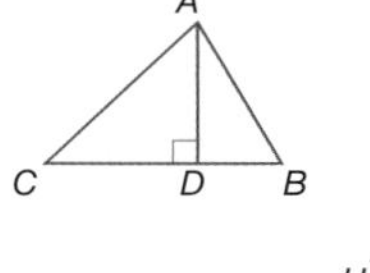

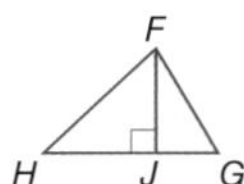

7.9 If two triangles are similar, the lengths of corresponding angle bisectors are proportional to the lengths of corresponding sides.

Abbreviation *~△s have corr. ∠ bisectors proportional to corr. sides.*

Example If $\triangle KLM \sim \triangle QRS$, then $\frac{LP}{RT} = \frac{LM}{RS}$.

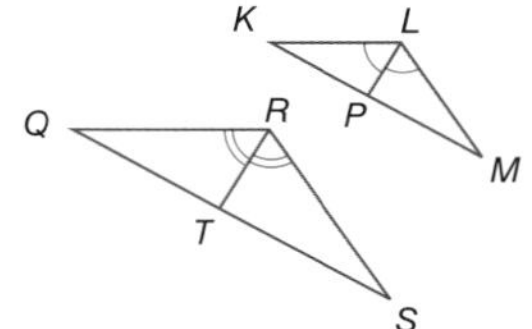

7.10 If two triangles are similar, the lengths of corresponding medians are proportional to the lengths of corresponding sides.

Abbreviation *~△s have corr. medians proportional to corr. sides.*

Example If $\triangle ABC \sim \triangle WXY$, then $\frac{CD}{YZ} = \frac{AB}{WX}$.

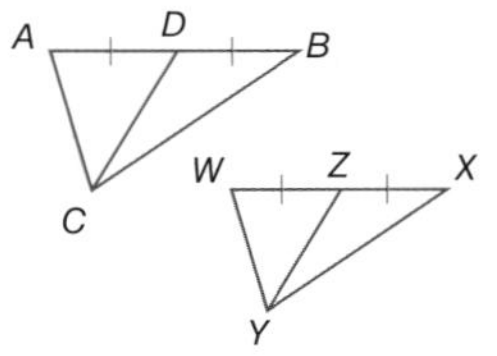

You will prove Theorems 7.9 and 7.10 in Exercises 18 and 19, respectively.

1 Focus

VerticalAlignment

Before Lesson 7-5 Learn that corresponding sides of similar polygons are proportional.

Lesson 7-5 Recognize and use proportional relationships of corresponding angle bisectors, altitudes, and medians in similar triangles. Use the Triangle Angle Bisector Theorem.

After Lesson 7-5 Use and extend similarity properties to explore and justify conjectures about geometric figures.

2 Teach

Scaffolding Questions

Have students read the **Why?** section of the lesson.

Ask:

- What is the "Rule of Thumb" used to measure? It estimates distance to an object.
- What are some other ways to approximate distances? Sample answer: Count the number of steps.
- Would the ratio of a person's arm length to the distance between the person's eyes be less than or greater than 1? greater than

Lesson 7-5 Resources

Resource	Approaching Level AL	On Level OL	Beyond Level BL	English Learners ELL
Teacher Edition	▪ Differentiated Instruction, p. 503	▪ Differentiated Instruction, pp. 503, 506	▪ Differentiated Instruction, pp. 503, 506	
Chapter Resource Masters	▪ Study Guide and Intervention, pp. 30–31 ▪ Skills Practice, p. 32 ▪ Practice, p. 33 ▪ Word Problem Practice, p. 34	▪ Study Guide and Intervention, pp. 30–31 ▪ Skills Practice, p. 32 ▪ Practice, p. 33 ▪ Word Problem Practice, p. 34 ▪ Enrichment, p. 35 ▪ Spreadsheet Activity, p. 36	▪ Practice, p. 33 ▪ Word Problem Practice, p. 34 ▪ Enrichment, p. 35	▪ Study Guide and Intervention, pp. 30–31 ▪ Skills Practice, p. 32 ▪ Practice, p. 33 ▪ Word Problem Practice, p. 34
Other	▪ 5-Minute Check 7-5 ▪ Study Notebook	▪ 5-Minute Check 7-5 ▪ Study Notebook	▪ 5-Minute Check 7-5 ▪ Study Notebook	▪ 5-Minute Check 7-5 ▪ Study Notebook

1 Special Segments of Similar Triangles

Examples 1 and 2 show how to use special segments in similar triangles to find missing measures and solve problems.

Formative Assessment

Use the Guided Practice exercises after each example to determine students' understanding of concepts.

Additional Example

1 In the figure, $\triangle LJK \sim \triangle SQR$. Find the value of x.

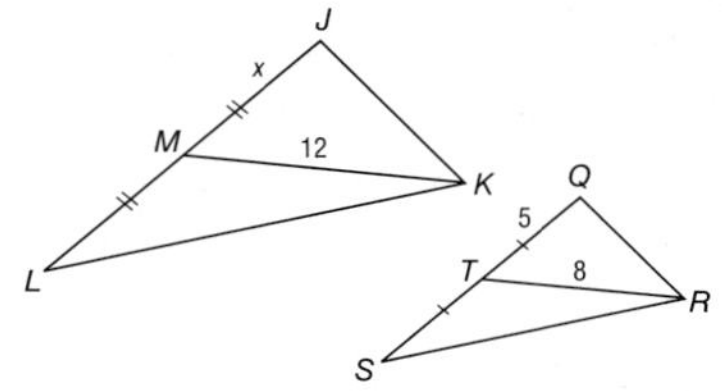

7.5

Additional Examples also in Interactive Classroom PowerPoint® Presentations

Interactive White Board READY

WatchOut!

Rotate Similar triangles may be orientated differently. Be sure to carefully look at markings on the figures to determine congruent angles and corresponding sides.

Real-World Career

Athletic Trainer Athletic trainers help prevent and treat sports injuries. They ensure that protective equipment is used properly and that people understand safe practices that prevent injury. An athletic trainer must have a bachelor's degree to be certified. Most also have master's degrees. Refer to Exercise 29.

Proof Theorem 7.8

Given: $\triangle FGH \sim \triangle KLM$
$\overline{FJ}$ and $\overline{KP}$ are altitudes.

Prove: $\frac{FJ}{KP} = \frac{HF}{MK}$

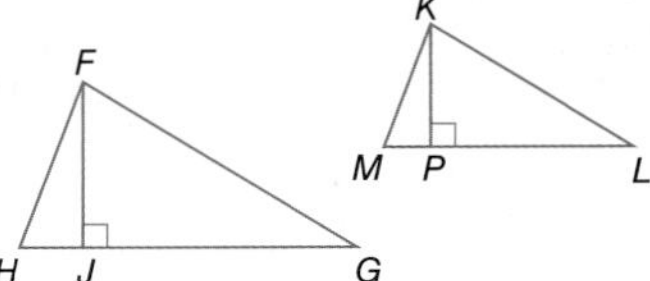

Paragraph Proof:
Since $\triangle FGH \sim \triangle KLM$, $\angle H \cong \angle M$. $\angle FJH \cong \angle KPM$ because they are both right angles created by the altitudes drawn to the opposite side and all right angles are congruent.

Thus $\triangle HFJ \sim \triangle MKP$ by AA Similarity. So $\frac{FJ}{KP} = \frac{HF}{MK}$ by the definition of similar polygons.

Since the corresponding altitudes are chosen at random, we need not prove Theorem 7.8 for every pair of altitudes.

You can use special segments in similar triangles to find missing measures.

Example 1 Use Special Segments in Similar Triangles

In the figure, $\triangle ABC \sim \triangle FDG$. Find the value of x.

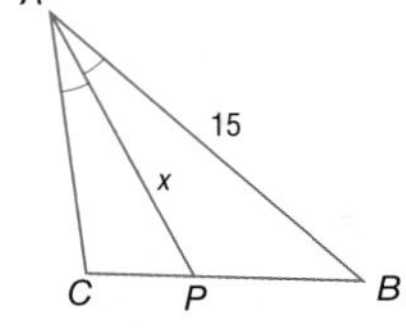

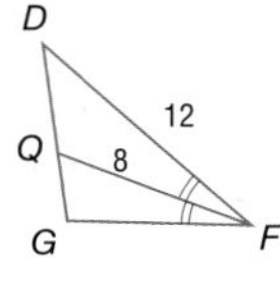

$\overline{AP}$ and $\overline{FQ}$ are corresponding angle bisectors and $\overline{AB}$ and $\overline{FD}$ are corresponding sides of similar triangles ABC and FDG.

$\frac{AP}{FQ} = \frac{AB}{FD}$ ~△s have corr. ∠ bisectors proportional to the corr. sides.

$\frac{x}{8} = \frac{15}{12}$ Substitution

$8 \cdot 15 = x \cdot 12$ Cross Products Property

$120 = 12x$ Simplify.

$10 = x$ Divide each side by 12.

StudyTip

Use Scale Factor Example 1 could also have been solved by first finding the scale factor between $\triangle ABC$ and $\triangle FDG$. The ratio of the angle bisector in $\triangle ABC$ to the angle bisector in $\triangle FDG$ would then be equal to this scale factor.

Guided Practice

Find the value of x.

1A.

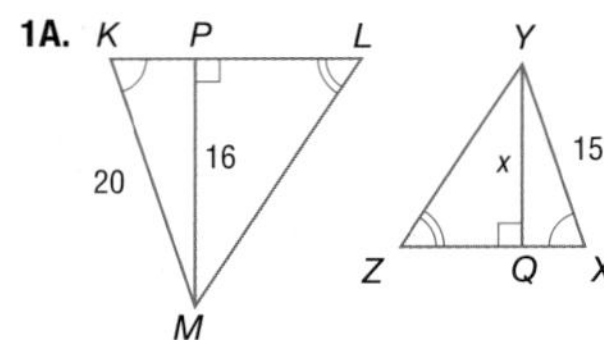

12

1B.

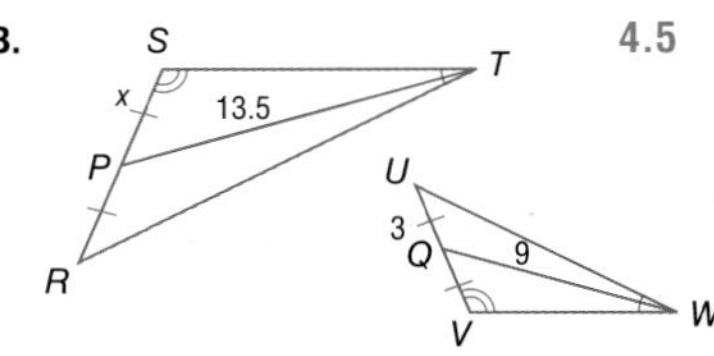

4.5

502 | Lesson 7-5 | Parts of Similar Triangles

You can use special segments in similar triangles to solve real-world problems.

Real-WorldLink

Hold your outstretched hand horizontal at arm's length with your palm facing you; for each hand width the sun is above the horizon, there is one remaining hour of sunlight.

Source: Sail Island Channels

Real-World Example 2 Use Similar Triangles to Solve Problems

ESTIMATING DISTANCES Liliana holds her arm straight out in front of her with her elbow straight and her thumb pointing up. Closing one eye, she aligns one edge of her thumb with a car she is sighting. Next she switches eyes without moving her head or her arm. The car appears to jump 4 car widths. If Liliana's arm is about 10 times longer than the distance between her eyes, and the car is about 5.5 feet wide, estimate the distance from Liliana's thumb to the car.

Understand Make a diagram of the situation labeling the given distances and the distance you need to find as x. Also, label the vertices of the triangles formed.

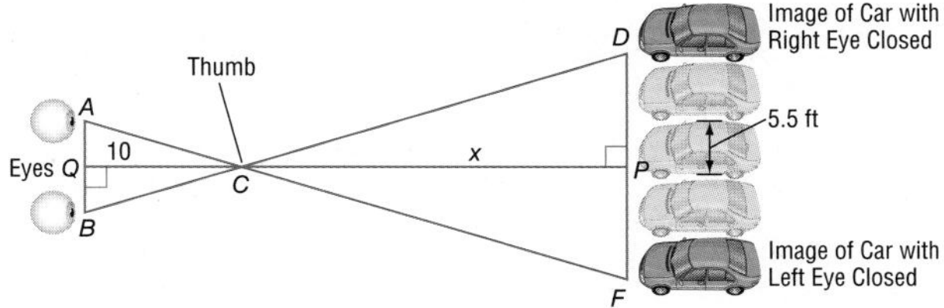

Note: Not drawn to scale.

We assume that if Liliana's thumb is straight out in front of her, then $\overline{PC}$ is an altitude of $\triangle ABC$. Likewise, $\overline{QC}$ is the corresponding altitude. We assume that $\overline{AB} \parallel \overline{DF}$.

Plan Since $\overline{AB} \parallel \overline{DF}$, $\angle BAC \cong \angle DFC$ and $\angle CBA \cong \angle CDF$ by the Alternate Interior Angles Theorem. Therefore $\triangle ABC \sim \triangle FDC$ by AA Similarity. Write a proportion and solve for x.

Solve

$\frac{PC}{QC} = \frac{AB}{DF}$ Theorem 7.8

$\frac{10}{x} = \frac{1}{5.5 \cdot 4}$ Substitution

$\frac{10}{x} = \frac{1}{22}$ Simplify.

$10 \cdot 22 = x \cdot 1$ Cross Products Property

$220 = x$ Simplify.

So the estimated distance to the car is 220 feet.

Check The ratio of Liliana's arm length to the width between her eyes is 10 to 1. The ratio of the distance to the car to the distance the image of the car jumped is 22 to 220 or 10 to 1. ✓

GuidedPractice

2. Suppose Liliana stands at the back of her classroom and sights a clock on the wall at the front of the room. If the clock is 30 centimeters wide and appears to move 3 clock widths when she switches eyes, estimate the distance from Liliana's thumb to the clock. 900 cm or 9 m

Additional Example

2 ESTIMATING DISTANCE Sanjay's arm is about 9 times longer than the distance between his eyes. He sights a statue across the park that is 10 feet wide. If the statue appears to move 4 widths when he switches eyes, estimate the distance from Sanjay's thumb to the statue. 360 feet

Teach with Tech

Blog On your secure class blog, have students explain why the perimeter of two similar triangles has the same proportion as the side lengths. Have them explain in terms of adding side lengths and using properties of addition and multiplication.

DifferentiatedInstruction AL OL BL

Visual Learners A common error is to believe that the corresponding angles of two similar triangles have the same ratio as the corresponding sides. Emphasize that the corresponding angles of two similar triangles must be congruent.

2 Triangle Angle Bisector

Example 3 shows how to use the Triangle Angle Bisector Theorem to find missing links.

Additional Example

3 Find *x*.

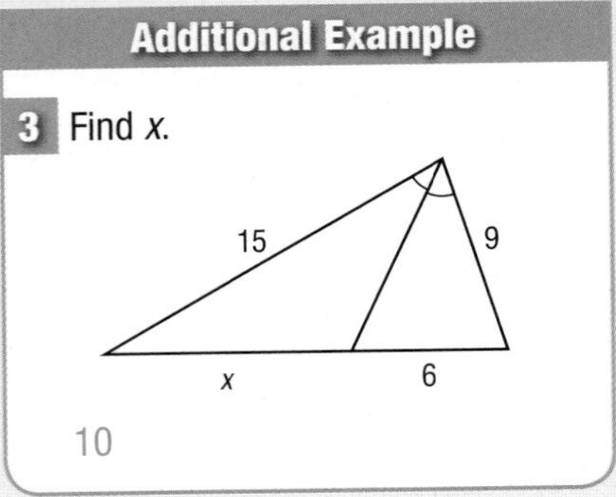

10

Focus on Mathematical Content

More Proportions in Similar Triangles You may want to ask students to make a conjecture about what other related segments may have the same proportions as the corresponding sides of the triangles. Then ask them to test their conjectures.

2 Triangle Angle Bisector Theorem An angle bisector of a triangle also divides the side opposite the angle proportionally.

StudyTip

Proportions Another proportion that could be written using the Triangle Angle Bisector Theorem is $\frac{KM}{KJ} = \frac{LM}{LJ}$.

Theorem 7.11 Triangle Angle Bisector

An angle bisector in a triangle separates the opposite side into two segments that are proportional to the lengths of the other two sides.

Example If $\overline{JM}$ is an angle bisector of $\triangle JKL$, then $\frac{KM}{LM} = \frac{KJ}{LJ}$. ← segments with vertex *K* ← segments with vertex *L*

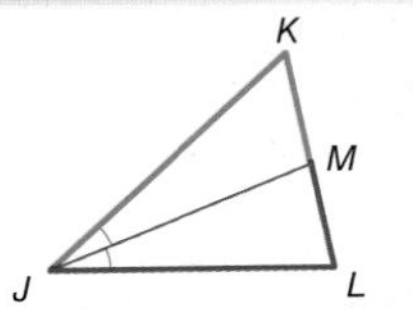

You will prove Theorem 7.11 in Exercise 25.

Example 3 Use the Triangle Angle Bisector Theorem

Find *x*.

Since $\overline{RT}$ is an angle bisector of $\triangle QRS$, you can use the Triangle Angle Bisector Theorem to write a proportion.

$\frac{QT}{ST} = \frac{QR}{SR}$	Triangle Angle Bisector Theorem
$\frac{x}{18 - x} = \frac{6}{14}$	Substitution
$(18 - x)(6) = x \cdot 14$	Cross Products Property
$108 - 6x = 14x$	Simplify.
$108 = 20x$	Add 6*x* to each side.
$5.4 = x$	Divide each side by 20.

Q, x, 18, T, 6, R, 14, S

GuidedPractice

Find the value of *x*.

3A.

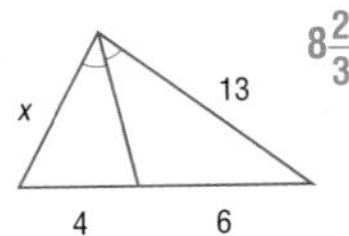

$8\frac{2}{3}$

3B.

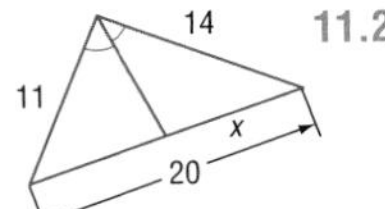

11.2

Check Your Understanding

● = Step-by-Step Solutions begin on page R14.

Example 1 **Find *x*.**

1.

x, 12, 10, 15

8

2.

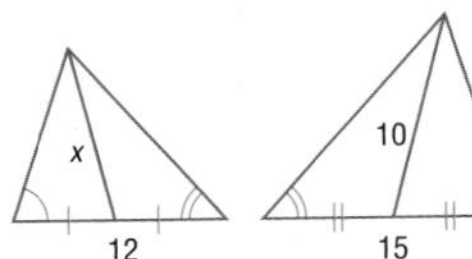

x, 8, 6, 9

12

Example 2 **3. VISION** A cat that is 10 inches tall forms a retinal image that is 7 millimeters tall. If $\triangle ABE \sim \triangle DBC$ and the distance from the pupil to the retina is 25 millimeters, how far away from your pupil is the cat? 35.7 ft

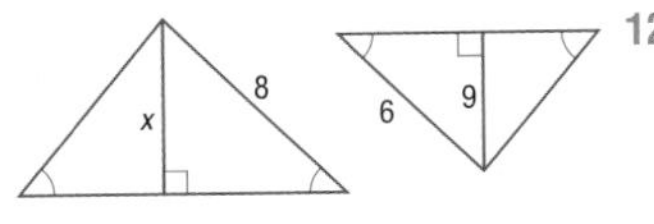

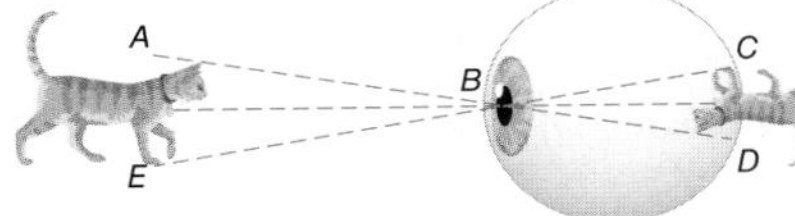

Example 3 Find the value of each variable.

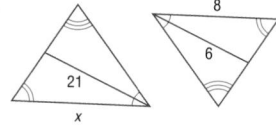

4. 6

5. 20

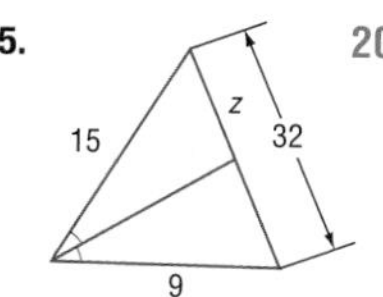

Practice and Problem Solving

Extra Practice is on page R7.

Example 1 Find x.

6. 28

7. 8.5

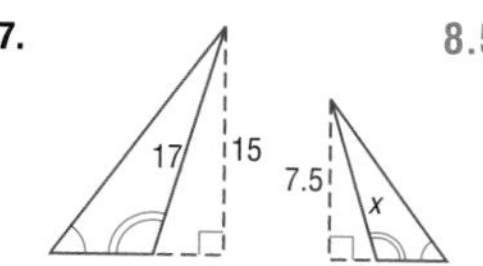

8. 9

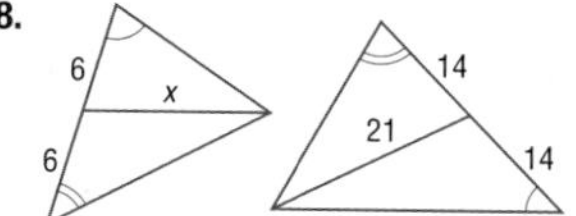

9. 18

Example 2 **10. ROADWAYS** The intersection of the two roads shown forms two similar triangles. If AC is 382 feet, MP is 248 feet, and the gas station is 50 feet from the intersection, how far from the intersection is the bank? about 77 ft

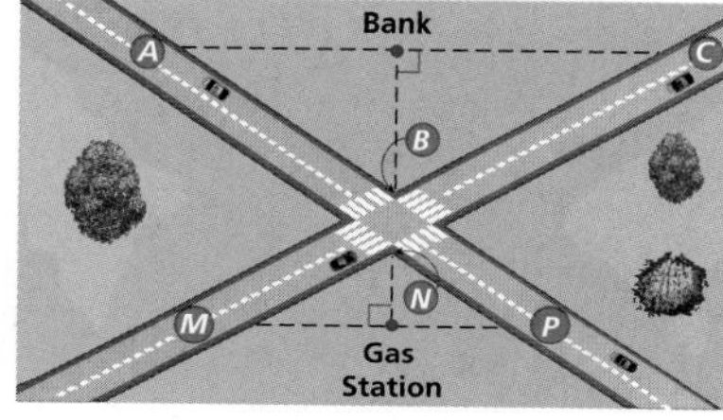

Example 3 **SENSE-MAKING** Find the value of each variable.

11 18

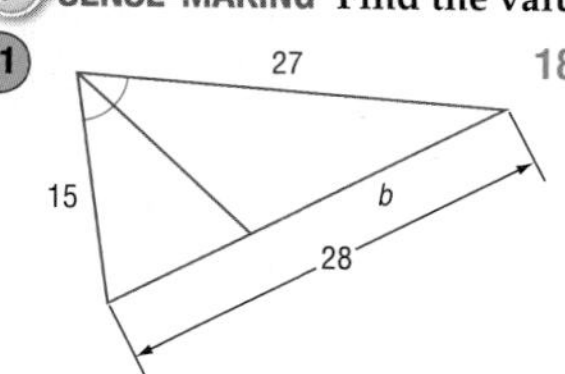

12. 12

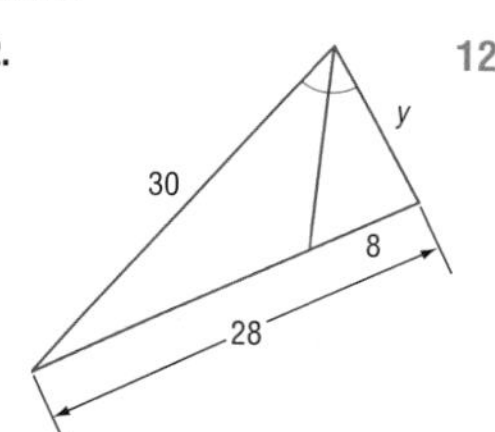

13. 15

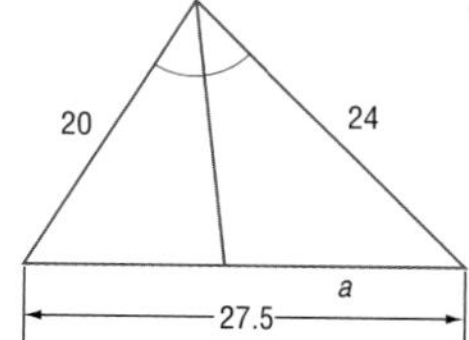

14. 11

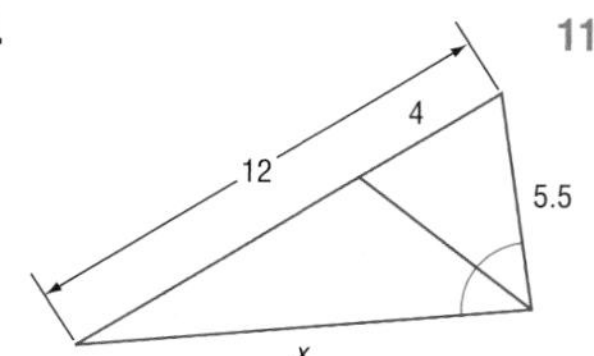

Differentiated Homework Options

Level	Assignment	Two-Day Option	
AL Basic	6–16, 31, 32, 34–51	7–15 odd, 36–39	6–16 even, 31, 32, 34, 35, 40–51
OL Core	7–23 odd, 24, 25, 27, 29–32, 34–51	6–16, 36–39	17–32, 34, 35, 40–51
BL Advanced	17–45, (optional: 46–51)		

3 Practice

Formative Assessment

Use Exercises 1–5 to check for understanding.

Use the chart at the bottom of this page to customize assignments for your students.

Teaching the Mathematical Practices

Sense-Making Mathematically proficient students start by explaining the meaning of a problem to themselves and looking for entry points to its solution. They plan a solution pathway rather than simply jumping into a solution attempt. In Exercises 11–14, encourage students to make a plan to solve each problem first.

WatchOut!

Error Analysis In Exercise 31, students should remember that in the Angle Bisector Theorem, each ratio compares the corresponding sides of the two triangles. Traci wrote each ratio to compare the two sides of one triangle at a time.

Teaching the Mathematical Practices

Arguments Mathematically proficient students understand and use stated assumptions and definitions in constructing arguments. They make conjectures and build a logical progression of statements to explore the truth of their conjectures. In Exercises 25–26, encourage students to plan their proofs first.

Exercise Alert

Ruler Exercise 34 requires the use of a ruler.

Additional Answers

18. Given: $\triangle RTS \sim \triangle EGF$, $\overline{TA}$ and $\overline{GB}$ are angle bisectors.

Prove: $\frac{TA}{GB} = \frac{RT}{EG}$

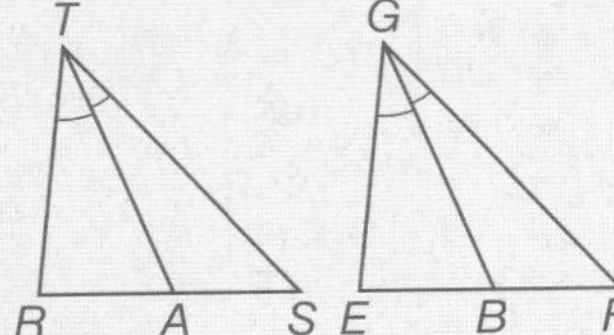

Proof: Because corresponding angles of similar triangles are congruent, $\angle R \cong \angle E$ and $\angle RTS \cong \angle EGF$. Since $\angle RTS$ and $\angle EGF$ are bisected, we know that $\frac{1}{2}m\angle RTS = \frac{1}{2}m\angle EGF$ or $m\angle RTS = m\angle EGF$. This makes $\angle RTA \cong \angle EGB$ and $\triangle RTA \sim \triangle EGB$ by AA Similarity. Thus, $\frac{TA}{GB} = \frac{RT}{EG}$.

32.

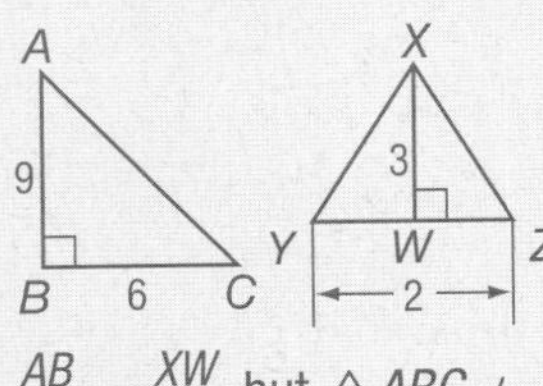

$\frac{AB}{BC} = \frac{XW}{YZ}$, but $\triangle ABC \nsim \triangle XYZ$.

15. ALGEBRA If $\overline{AB}$ and $\overline{JK}$ are altitudes, $\triangle DAC \sim \triangle MJL$, $AB = 9$, $AD = 4x - 8$, $JK = 21$, and $JM = 5x + 3$, find x. **5**

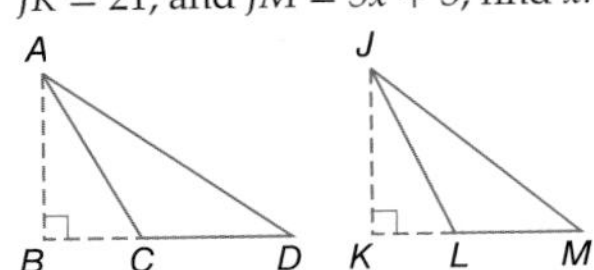

16. ALGEBRA If $\overline{NQ}$ and $\overline{VX}$ are medians, $\triangle PNR \sim \triangle WVY$, $NQ = 8$, $PR = 12$, $WY = 7x - 1$, and $VX = 4x + 2$, find x. **4**

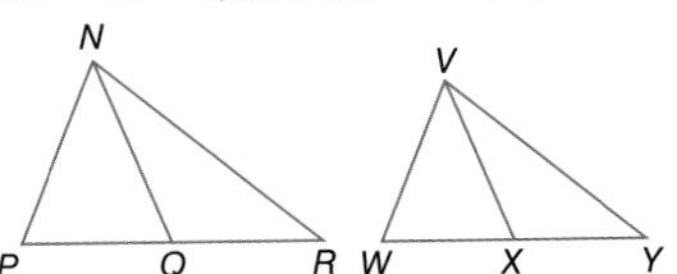

B

17. If $\triangle SRY \sim \triangle WXQ$, $\overline{RT}$ is an altitude of $\triangle SRY$, $\overline{XV}$ is an altitude of $\triangle WXQ$, $RT = 5$, $RQ = 4$, $QY = 6$, and $YX = 2$, find XV. **4**

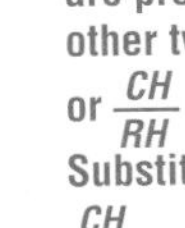

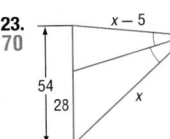

18. PROOF Write a paragraph proof of Theorem 7.9. **See margin.**

19. PROOF Write a two-column proof of Theorem 7.10. **See Ch. 7 Answer Appendix.**

ALGEBRA Find x.

20. **7**

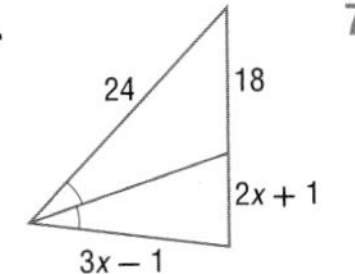

21. **3**

6x + 2
8
10
9x − 2

22. **3.1**

21
2x + 6
16

23. **70**

x − 5
54
28
x

24. SPORTS Consider the triangle formed by the path between a batter, center fielder, and right fielder as shown. If the batter gets a hit that bisects the triangle at $\angle B$, is the center fielder or the right fielder closer to the ball? Explain your reasoning.

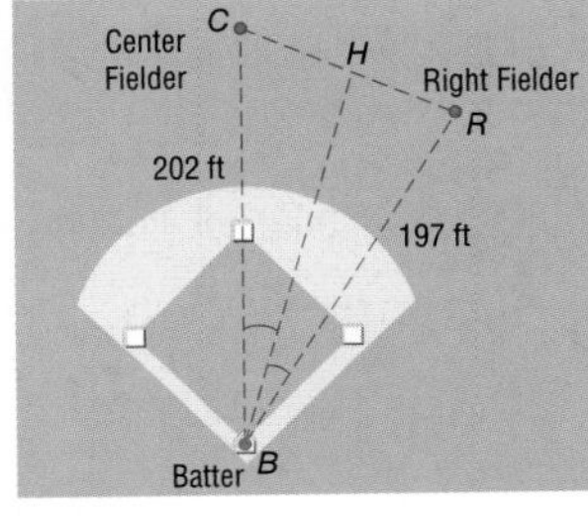

24. Right fielder; sample answer: Since the hit bisects the triangle, the sides opposite the angle are proportional to the other two sides, or $\frac{CH}{RH} = \frac{BC}{BR}$. Substituting, $\frac{CH}{RH} = \frac{202}{197} = 1.03$. Since $\frac{CH}{RH}$ is slightly greater than 1, $\overline{CH}$ is slightly longer than $\overline{RH}$. Therefore, the right fielder is closer to the hit.

ARGUMENTS **Write a two-column proof.** **25–26. See Ch. 7 Answer Appendix.**

25. Theorem 7.11

Given: $\overline{CD}$ bisects $\angle ACB$.
By construction, $\overline{AE} \parallel \overline{CD}$.

Prove: $\frac{AD}{DB} = \frac{AC}{BC}$

E
C
3
1
2
A
D
B

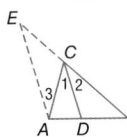

26. Given: $\angle H$ is a right angle.
L, K, and M are midpoints.

Prove: $\angle LKM$ is a right angle.

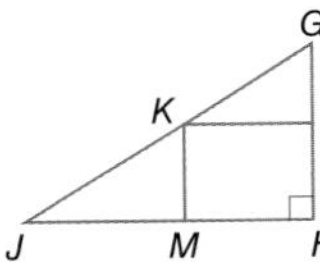

Differentiated Instruction OL BL

Extension Arrange students in groups of 3 or 4, mixing abilities. Students should make a scale drawing of the perimeter of their school. Have the groups measure the perimeter of the school by counting how many paces it takes to walk the perimeter. Next, have them use a ratio of the number of paces to the number of units that they will be using for their drawing.

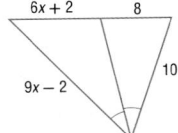

PROOF Write a two-column proof. **27–28. See Ch. 7 Answer Appendix.**

27. Given: $\triangle QTS \sim \triangle XWZ$, $\overline{TR}$ and $\overline{WY}$ are angle bisectors.

Prove: $\frac{TR}{WY} = \frac{QT}{XW}$

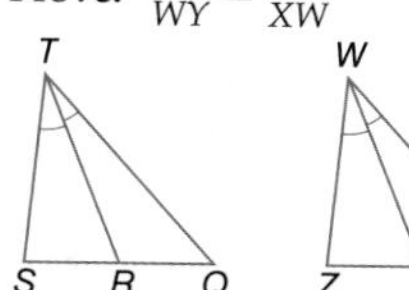

28. Given: $\overline{FD} \parallel \overline{BC}$, $\overline{BF} \parallel \overline{CD}$, $\overline{AC}$ bisects $\angle C$.

Prove: $\frac{DE}{EC} = \frac{BA}{AC}$

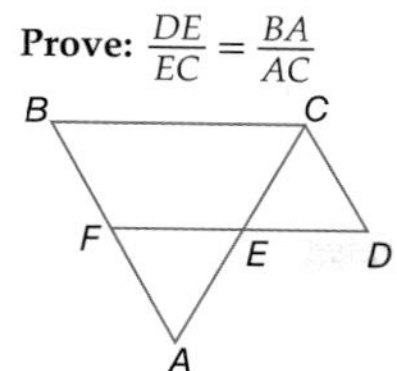

B **29.** **SPORTS** During football practice, Trevor threw a pass to Ricardo as shown below. If Eli is farther from Trevor when he completes the pass to Ricardo and Craig and Eli move at the same speed, who will reach Ricardo to tackle him first? **Craig**

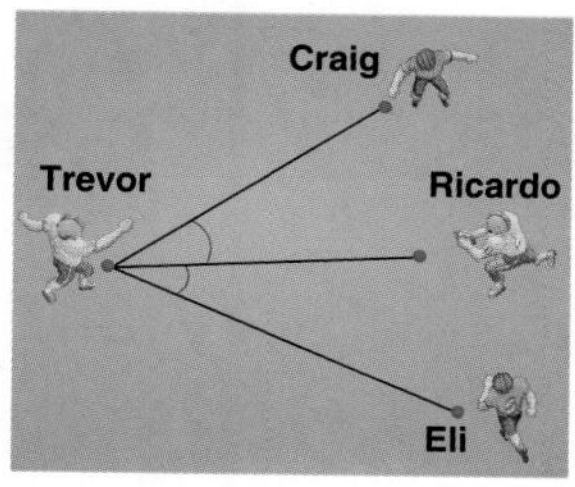

30. **SHELVING** In the bookshelf shown, the distance between each shelf is 13 inches and $\overline{AK}$ is a median of $\triangle ABC$. If EF is $3\frac{1}{3}$ inches, what is BK? **10 in.**

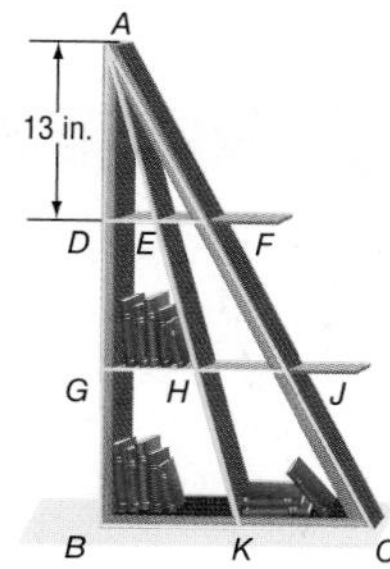

H.O.T. Problems Use Higher-Order Thinking Skills

31. **ERROR ANALYSIS** Chun and Traci are determining the value of x in the figure. Chun says to find x, solve the proportion $\frac{5}{8} = \frac{15}{x}$, but Traci says to find x, the proportion $\frac{5}{x} = \frac{8}{15}$ should be solved. Is either of them correct? Explain.
Chun; by the Angle Bisector Theorem, the correct proportion is $\frac{5}{8} = \frac{15}{x}$.

32. **CCSS ARGUMENTS** Find a counterexample to the following statement. Explain.

If the measure of an altitude and side of a triangle are proportional to the corresponding altitude and corresponding side of another triangle, then the triangles are similar. **See margin.**

33. **CHALLENGE** The perimeter of $\triangle PQR$ is 94 units. $\overline{QS}$ bisects $\angle PQR$. Find PS and RS. **$PS = 18.4$, $RS = 24$**

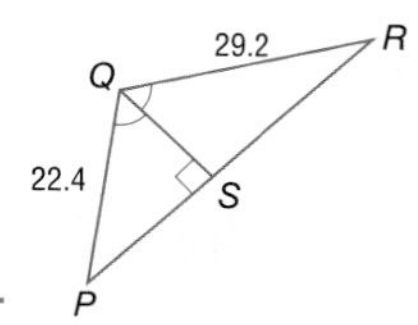

34. **OPEN ENDED** Draw two triangles so that the measures of corresponding medians and a corresponding side are proportional, but the triangles are not similar. **See margin.**

35. **WRITING IN MATH** Compare and contrast Theorem 7.9 and the Triangle Angle Bisector Theorem. **See Ch. 7 Answer Appendix.**

Additional Answer

34. Sample answer:

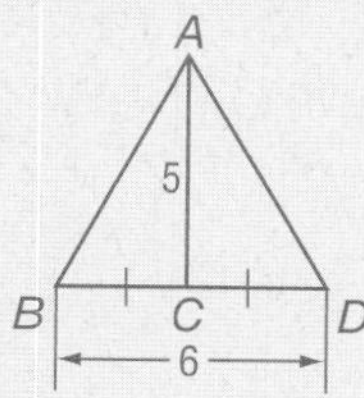

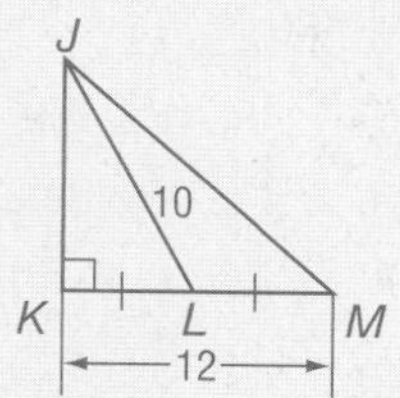

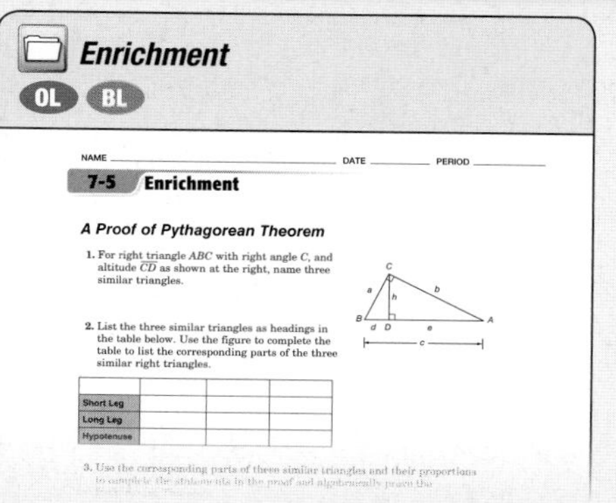

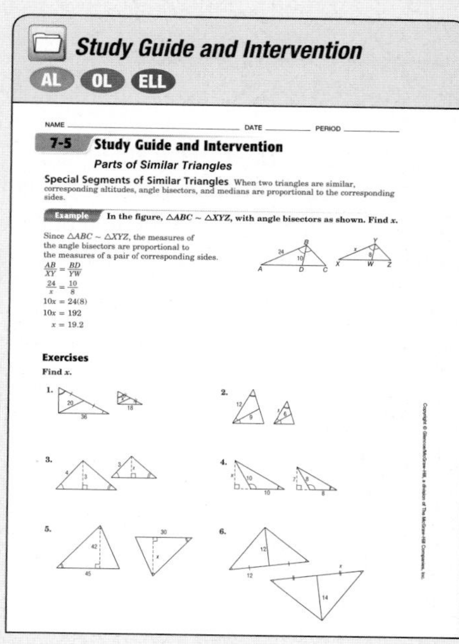

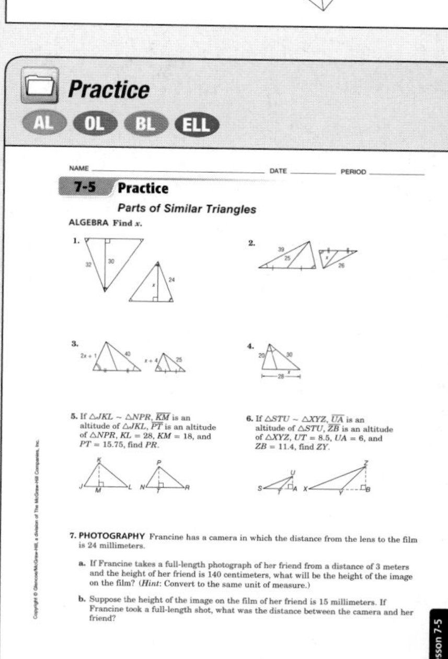

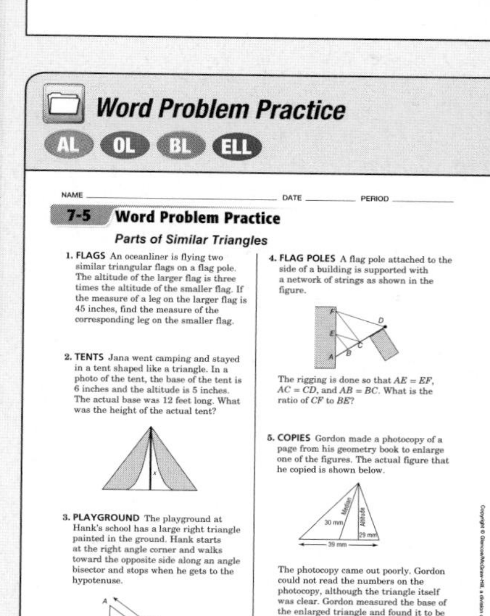

Lesson 7-5

4 Assess

Ticket Out the Door Have students draw and label a triangle with perimeter 24 centimeters. Then ask them to draw and label a similar triangle with a scale factor of $\frac{2}{3}$. Ask them to find the perimeter. Have them tell the perimeter on the way out of the classroom. 16 cm

Additional Answers

45. **Given:** $\overline{EF} \cong \overline{HF}$
G is the midpoint of $\overline{EH}$.
Prove: $\triangle EFG \cong \triangle HFG$

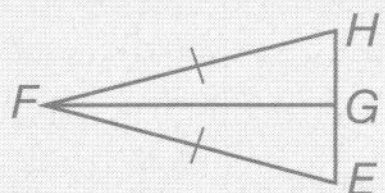

Proof:

Statements (Reasons)

1. $\overline{EF} \cong \overline{HF}$; G is the midpoint of $\overline{EH}$ (Given)
2. $\overline{EG} \cong \overline{GH}$ (Def. of midpoint)
3. $\overline{FG} \cong \overline{FG}$ (Reflexive Prop.)
4. $\triangle EFG \cong \triangle HFG$ (SSS)

Additional Answers (p. 508, Extend 7-5)

3. The perimeter will approach zero.
4. **Given:** $\triangle KAP$ is equilateral. $D, F, M, B, C,$ and E are midpoints of $\overline{KA}, \overline{AP}, \overline{PK}, \overline{DA}, \overline{AF},$ and $\overline{FD}$, respectively.
Prove: $\triangle BAC \sim \triangle KAP$

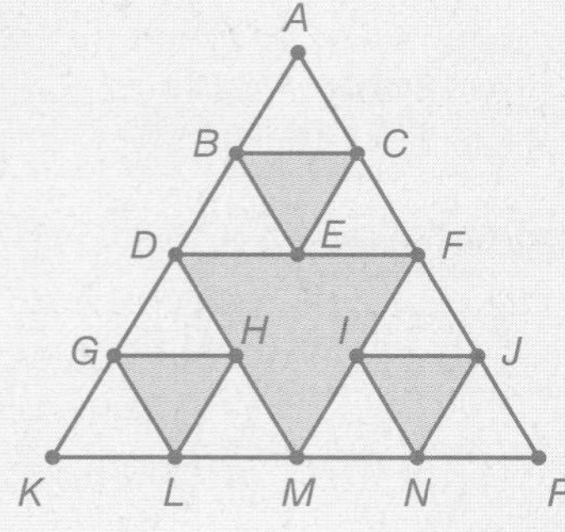

Standardized Test Practice

36. ALGEBRA Which shows 0.00234 written in scientific notation? D

A 2.34×10^5
B 2.34×10^3
C 2.34×10^{-2}
D 2.34×10^{-3}

37. SHORT RESPONSE In the figures below, $\overline{AB} \perp \overline{DC}$ and $\overline{GH} \perp \overline{FE}$.

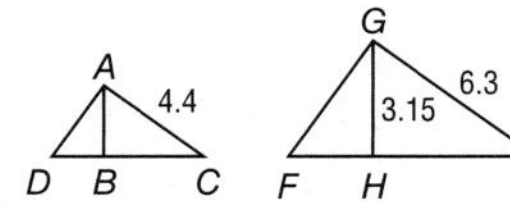

If $\triangle ACD \sim \triangle GEF$, find AB. 2.2

38. Quadrilateral $HJKL$ is a parallelogram. If the diagonals are perpendicular, which statement must be true? H

F Quadrilateral $HJKL$ is a square.
G Quadrilateral $HJKL$ is a rectangle.
H Quadrilateral $HJKL$ is a rhombus.
J Quadrilateral $HJKL$ is an isosceles trapezoid.

39. SAT/ACT The sum of three numbers is 180. Two of the numbers are the same, and each of them is one third of the greatest number. What is the least number? C

A 15
B 30
C 36
D 45
E 60

Spiral Review

ALGEBRA **Find x and y.** (Lesson 7-4)

40.

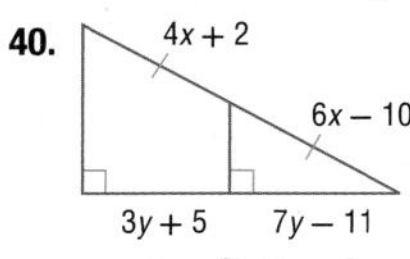

$x = 6$; $y = 4$

41. $x = 2$; $y = 3$

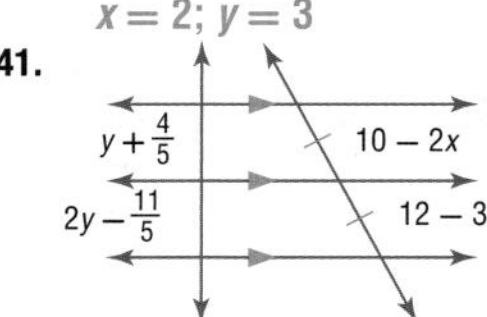

42. $x = 4$; $y = 10$

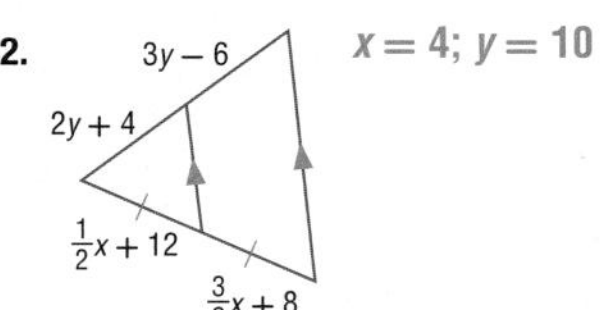

Find the indicated measure(s). (Lesson 7-3)

43. If $\overline{PR} \parallel \overline{KL}$, $KN = 9$, $LN = 16$, and $PM = 2(KP)$, find KP, KM, MR, ML, MN, and PR.

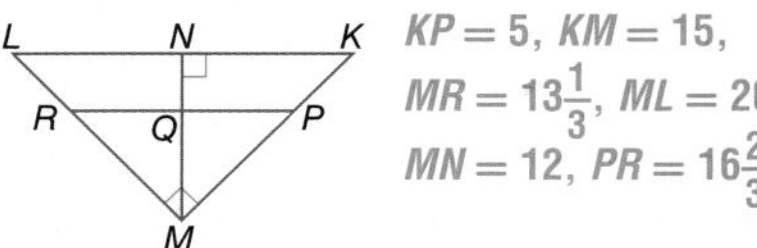

$KP = 5$, $KM = 15$, $MR = 13\frac{1}{3}$, $ML = 20$, $MN = 12$, $PR = 16\frac{2}{3}$

44. If $\overline{PR} \parallel \overline{WX}$, $WX = 10$, $XY = 6$, $WY = 8$, $RY = 5$, and $PS = 3$, find PY, SY, and PQ.

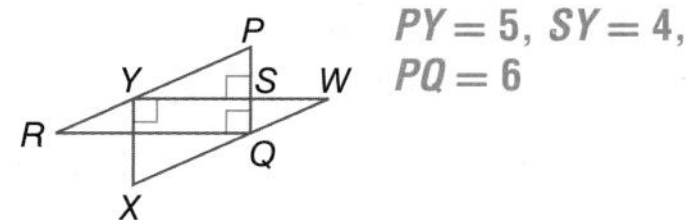

$PY = 5$, $SY = 4$, $PQ = 6$

45. GEESE A flock of geese flies in formation. Prove that $\triangle EFG \cong \triangle HFG$ if $\overline{EF} \cong \overline{HF}$ and that G is the midpoint of $\overline{EH}$. (Lesson 4-4) See margin.

46. $\sqrt{164} \approx 12.8$
49. $\sqrt{137} \approx 11.7$
50. $\sqrt{232} \approx 15.2$

Skills Review

Find the distance between each pair of points.

46. $E(-3, -2)$, $F(5, 8)$
47. $A(2, 3)$, $B(5, 7)$ 5
48. $C(-2, 0)$, $D(6, 4)$ $\sqrt{80} \approx 8.9$
49. $W(7, 3)$, $Z(-4, -1)$
50. $J(-4, -5)$, $K(2, 9)$
51. $R(-6, 10)$, $S(8, -2)$ $\sqrt{340} \approx 18.4$

Proof:

Statements (Reasons)

1. $\triangle KAP$ is equilateral. $D, F, M, B, C,$ and E are midpoints of $\overline{KA}, \overline{AP}, \overline{PK}, \overline{DA}, \overline{AF},$ and $\overline{FD}$, respectively. (Given)
2. $\overline{DF}$ is a midsegment of $\triangle KAP$; $\overline{BC}$ is a midsegment of $\triangle BAC$ (Def. of $\triangle$ midsegment)
3. $\overline{DF} \parallel \overline{KP}$, $\overline{BC} \parallel \overline{DF}$ ($\triangle$ Midsegment Thm.)
4. $\overline{KP} \parallel \overline{BC}$ (Two segs. $\parallel$ to the same seg. are $\parallel$.)
5. $\angle ABC \cong \angle AKP$ (Corr. $\angle$s Post.)
6. $\angle A \cong \angle A$ (Refl. Prop.)
7. $\triangle BAC \sim \triangle KAP$ (AA Similarity)

508 | Lesson 7-5 | Parts of Similar Triangles

EXTEND 7-5 Geometry Lab: Fractals

A **fractal** is a geometric figure that is created using iteration. **Iteration** is a process of repeating the same operation over and over again. Fractals are **self-similar**, which means that the smaller details of the shape have the same geometric characteristics as the original form.

Activity 1

Stage 0 Draw an equilateral triangle on isometric dot paper in which each side is 8 units long.

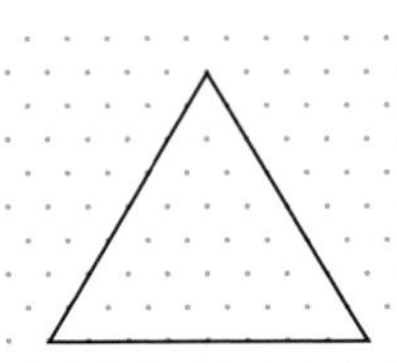

Stage 1 Connect the midpoints of the sides to form another triangle. Shade the center triangle.

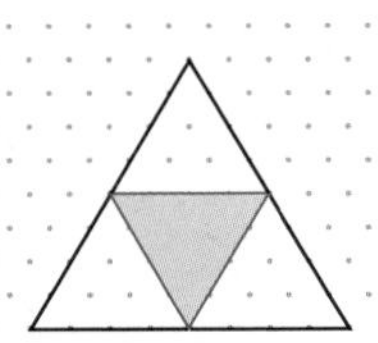

Stage 2 Repeat the process using the three unshaded triangles. Connect the midpoints of the sides to form three other triangles.

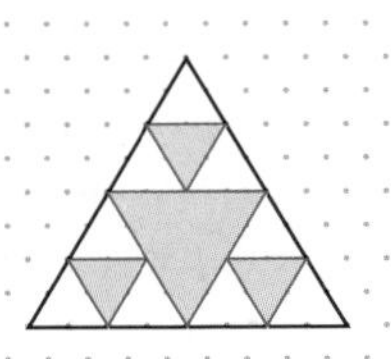

If you repeat this process indefinitely, the figure that results is called the Sierpinski Triangle.

Analyze the Results

1. If you continue the process, how many unshaded triangles will you have at Stage 3? **27**
2. What is the perimeter of an unshaded triangle in Stage 4? **1.5 units**
3. If you continue the process indefinitely, what will happen to the perimeters of the unshaded triangles? **See margin.**
4. **CHALLENGE** Complete the proof below. **See margin.**

   Given: $\triangle KAP$ is equilateral. $D, F, M, B, C,$ and E are midpoints of $\overline{KA}, \overline{AP}, \overline{PK}, \overline{DA}, \overline{AF},$ and $\overline{FD}$, respectively.

   Prove: $\triangle BAC \sim \triangle KAP$

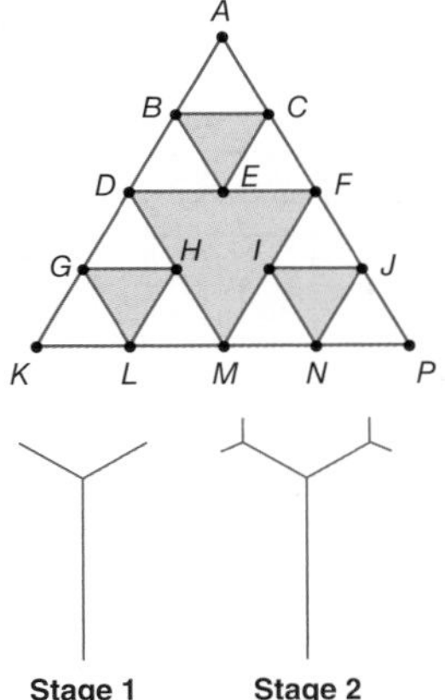

5. A *fractal tree* can be drawn by making two new branches from the endpoint of each original branch, each one-third as long as the previous branch. **a–b. See margin.**
   a. Draw Stages 3 and 4 of a fractal tree. How many total branches do you have in Stages 1 through 4? (Do not count the stems.)
   b. Write an expression to predict the number of branches at each stage.

(continued on the next page)

Additional Answers

5a. Stage 1: 2, Stage 2: 6, Stage 3: 14, Stage 4: 30

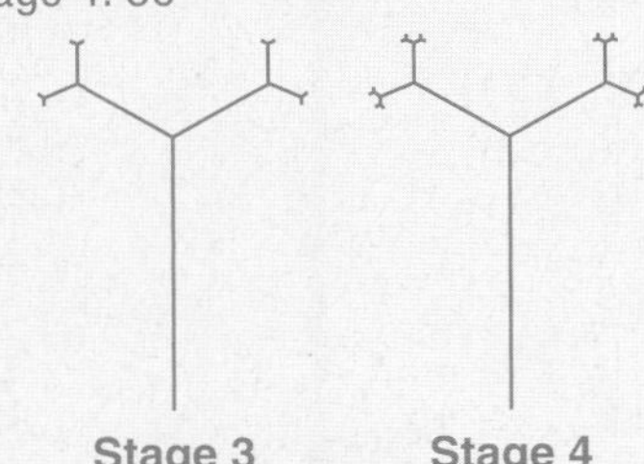

5b. At Stage n, the total number of branches is $2(2^n - 1)$.

1 Focus

Objectives

- Investigate iteration and draw fractals.
- Write recursive formulas.

Materials

- isometric dot paper

Easy to Make Manipulatives

Teaching Geometry with Manipulatives, template for:

- isometric dot paper, p. 7

Teaching Tip

Discuss with students how each stage is determined so that students understand the process. Every time each triangle is bisected to form one or more other triangles, it is one stage. Ask students to record the number of triangles at each stage so they can analyze the pattern in the numbers.

2 Teach

Working in Cooperative Groups

Arrange students in groups of 4, mixing abilities. Tell one student in each group to collect the data by drawing the triangles while another student analyzes the data by counting the triangles and forming a sequence from the count. Tell a third student to find the perimeters of the triangles as the activity continues, and the fourth student to generate a sequence of numbers representing the perimeters of the triangles. This sequence should help them see that the perimeter approaches zero as the number of triangles increases. Have students complete Exercise 1.

Ask:

- Combine three copies of the Stage 4 Sierpinski Triangle. What stage of the Sierpinski Triangle is this? Stage 5

Practice Have students complete Analyze the Results 2–7.

3 Assess

Formative Assessment

Use Analyze the Results 1–7 to assess whether students understand the meaning of fractals, iterations, self-similarity, and fractal trees.

Extending the Concept

Ask:

- Is a fractal tree self-similar? yes

From Concrete to Abstract

Use Exercise 12 to extend what the students have observed algebraically.

Geometry Lab
Fractals *Continued*

Not all iterative processes involve manipulation of geometric shapes. Some iterative processes can be translated into formulas or algebraic equations, similar to the expression you wrote in Exercise 5 on the previous page.

Activity 2

Pascal's Triangle is a numerical pattern in which each row begins and ends with 1 and all other terms in the row are the sum of the two numbers above it. Find a formula in terms of the row number for any row in Pascal's Triangle.

Step 1 Draw rows 1 through 5 in Pascal's Triangle.

Step 2 Find the sum of values in each row.

Step 3 Find a pattern using the row number that can be used to determine the sum of any row.

Row	Pascal's Triangle	Sum	Pattern
1	1	1	$2^0 = 2^{1-1}$
2	1 1	2	$2^1 = 2^{2-1}$
3	1 2 1	4	$2^2 = 2^{3-1}$
4	1 3 3 1	8	$2^3 = 2^{4-1}$
5	1 4 6 4 1	16	$2^4 = 2^{5-1}$

Analyze the Results

6. Write a formula for the sum S of any row n in the Pascal Triangle. $S = 2^{n-1}$
7. What is the sum of the values in the eighth row of Pascal's Triangle? 128

Exercises

Write a formula for $F(x)$.

8.

x	2	4	6	8	10
$F(x)$	3	7	11	15	19

$F(x) = 2x - 1$

9.

x	0	5	10	15	20
$F(x)$	0	20	90	210	380

$F(x) = x^2 - x$

10.

x	1	2	4	8	10
$F(x)$	1	0.5	0.25	0.125	0.1

$F(x) = \frac{1}{x}$

11.

x	4	9	16	25	36
$F(x)$	5	6	7	8	9

$F(x) = \sqrt{x} + 3$

12. **CHALLENGE** The figural pattern below represents a sequence of figural numbers called *triangular numbers*. How many dots will be in the 8th term in the sequence? Is it possible to write a formula that can be used to determine the number of dots in the nth triangular number in the series? If so, write the formula. If not, explain why not. 36; $F(n) = \frac{n(n+1)}{2}$

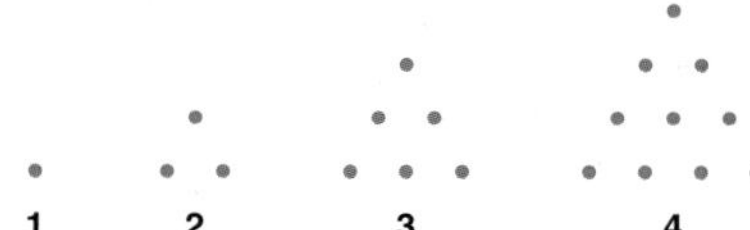

LESSON 7-6 Similarity Transformations

Then

- You identified congruence transformations.

Now

1. Identify similarity transformations.
2. Verify similarity after a similarity transformation.

Why?

- Adriana uses a copier to enlarge a movie ticket to use as the background for a page in her movie ticket scrapbook. She places the ticket on the glass of the copier. Then she must decide what percentage to input in order to create an image that is three times as big as her original ticket.

Polaris Center 14 Presenting
BEST MOVIE EVER
4:00 PM Sat 1/17/09
MATINEE 11:50
Auditorium 8
00912300050027
01/17/09 2:20 PM

5 cm
6.4 cm

NewVocabulary
dilation
similarity transformation
center of dilation
scale factor of a dilation
enlargement
reduction

Common Core State Standards

Content Standards

G.SRT.2 Given two figures, use the definition of similarity in terms of similarity transformations to decide if they are similar; explain using similarity transformations the meaning of similarity for triangles as the equality of all corresponding pairs of angles and the proportionality of all corresponding pairs of sides.

G.SRT.5 Use congruence and similarity criteria for triangles to solve problems and to prove relationships in geometric figures.

Mathematical Practices

6 Attend to precision.
4 Model with mathematics.

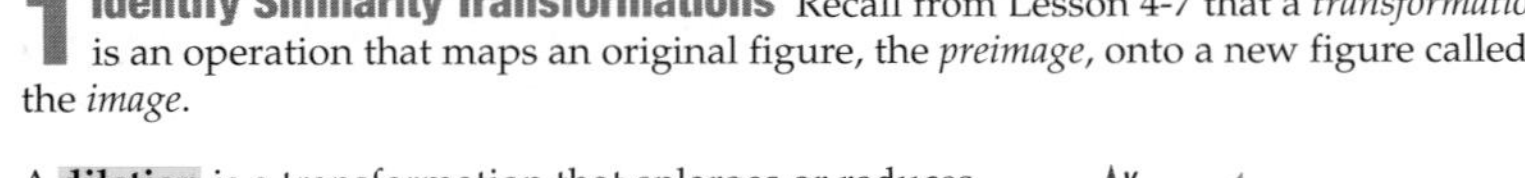

1 Identify Similarity Transformations

Recall from Lesson 4-7 that a *transformation* is an operation that maps an original figure, the *preimage*, onto a new figure called the *image*.

A **dilation** is a transformation that enlarges or reduces the original figure proportionally. Since a dilation produces a similar figure, a dilation is a type of **similarity transformation**.

Dilations are performed with respect to a fixed point called the **center of dilation**.

The **scale factor of a dilation** describes the extent of the dilation. The scale factor is the ratio of a length on the image to a corresponding length on the preimage.

The letter k usually represents the scale factor of a dilation. The value of k determines whether the dilation is an enlargement or a reduction.

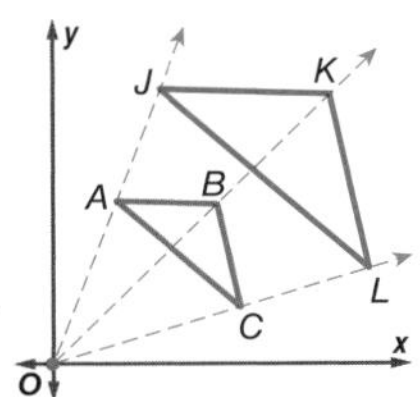

$\triangle JKL$ is a dilation of $\triangle ABC$.
Center of dilation: (0, 0)
Scale factor: $\frac{JK}{AB}$

ConceptSummary Types of Dilations

A dilation with a scale factor greater than 1 produces an **enlargement**, or an image that is larger than the original figure.

Symbols If $k > 1$, the dilation is an enlargement.

Example $\triangle FGH$ is dilated by a scale factor of 3 to produce $\triangle RST$. Since $3 > 1$, $\triangle RST$ is an enlargement of $\triangle FGH$.

$k < 1$

A dilation with a scale factor between 0 and 1 produces a **reduction**, an image that is smaller than the original figure.

Symbols If $0 < k < 1$, the dilation is a reduction.

Example $ABCD$ is dilated by a scale factor of $\frac{1}{4}$ to produce $WXYZ$. Since $0 < \frac{1}{4} < 1$, $WXYZ$ is a reduction of $ABCD$.

$0 < k < 1$

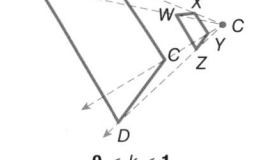

1 Focus

VerticalAlignment

Before Lesson 7-6 Identify congruence transformations.

Lesson 7-6 Identify similarity transformations, and verify similarity after transformations.

After Lesson 7-6 Apply the properties of similar figures to scale models.

2 Teach

Scaffolding Questions

Have students read the **Why?** section of the lesson.

Ask:

- How much larger does Adriana want to make the image? 3 times larger
- Are the ticket and its copy congruent or similar? similar
- If the length and width of the ticket are three times as long, how much greater will the area be? 27 times greater

Lesson 7-6 Resources

Resource	Approaching Level AL	On Level OL	Beyond Level BL	English Learners ELL
Teacher Edition	▪ Differentiated Instruction, p. 516	▪ Differentiated Instruction, p. 516	▪ Differentiated Instruction, p. 516	
Chapter Resource Masters	▪ Study Guide and Intervention, pp. 37–38 ▪ Skills Practice, p. 39 ▪ Practice, p. 40 ▪ Word Problem Practice, p. 41	▪ Study Guide and Intervention, pp. 37–38 ▪ Skills Practice, p. 39 ▪ Practice, p. 40 ▪ Word Problem Practice, p. 41 ▪ Enrichment, p. 42	▪ Practice, p. 40 ▪ Word Problem Practice, p. 41 ▪ Enrichment, p. 42	▪ Study Guide and Intervention, pp. 37–38 ▪ Skills Practice, p. 39 ▪ Practice, p. 40 ▪ Word Problem Practice, p. 41
Other	▪ 5-Minute Check 7-6 ▪ Study Notebook	▪ 5-Minute Check 7-6 ▪ Study Notebook	▪ 5-Minute Check 7-6 ▪ Study Notebook	▪ 5-Minute Check 7-6 ▪ Study Notebook

1 Identify Similarity Transformations

Examples 1 and 2 show how to find and use the scale factor of a similarity transformation.

Formative Assessment

Use the Guided Practice exercises after each example to determine students' understanding of concepts.

Additional Examples

1 Determine whether the dilation from Figure *A* to Figure *B* is an *enlargement* or a *reduction*. Then find the scale factor of the dilation.

a.

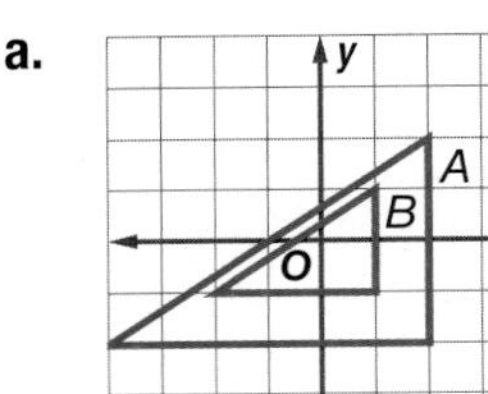

reduction; $\frac{1}{2}$

b.

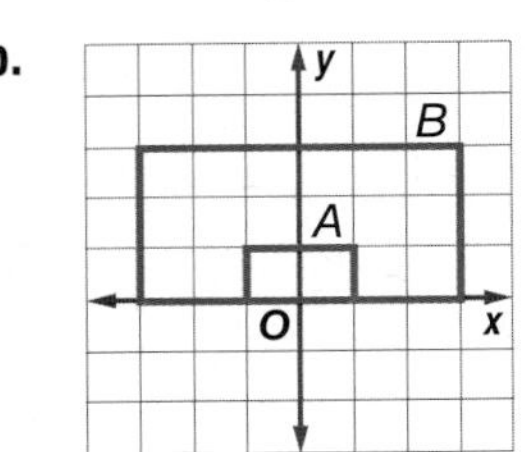

englargement; 3

2 **PHOTOCOPYING** A photocopy of a receipt is 1.5 inches wide and 4 inches long. By what percent should the receipt be enlarged so that its image is 2 times the original? What will be the dimensions of the enlarged image? 200%; 3 in. wide, 8 in. long

Additional Examples also in Interactive Classroom PowerPoint® Presentations

IWB Interactive White Board READY

StudyTip

Multiple Representations The scale factor of a dilation can be represented as a fraction, a decimal, or as a percent. For example, a scale factor of $\frac{2}{5}$ can also be written as 0.4 or as 40%.

Example 1 Identify a Dilation and Find Its Scale Factor

Determine whether the dilation from *A* to *B* is an *enlargement* or a *reduction*. Then find the scale factor of the dilation.

a.

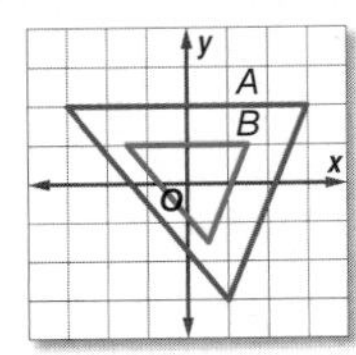

B is smaller than *A*, so the dilation is a reduction.

The distance between the vertices at (−3, 2) and (3, 2) for *A* is 6 and from the vertices at (−1.5, 1) and (1.5, 1) for *B* is 3. So the scale factor is $\frac{3}{6}$ or $\frac{1}{2}$.

b.

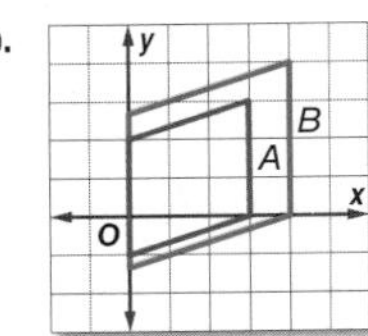

B is larger than *A*, so the dilation is an enlargement.

The distance between the vertices at (3, 3) and (3, 0) for *A* is 3 and between the vertices at (4, 4) and (4, 0) for *B* is 4. So the scale factor is $\frac{4}{3}$.

GuidedPractice

1A.

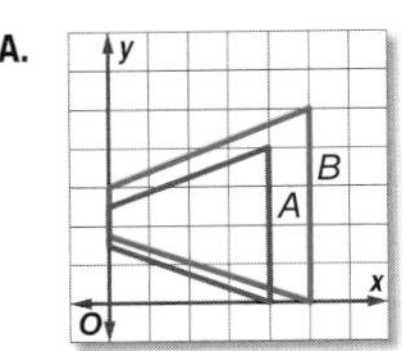

enlargement; $\frac{5}{4}$

1B.

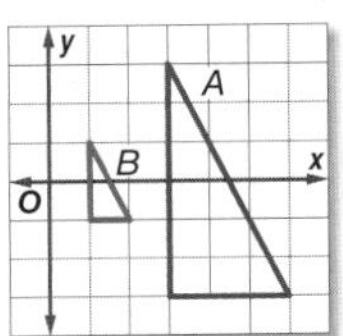

reduction; $\frac{1}{3}$

Dilations and their scale factors are used in many real-world situations.

Real-World Example 2 Find and Use a Scale Factor

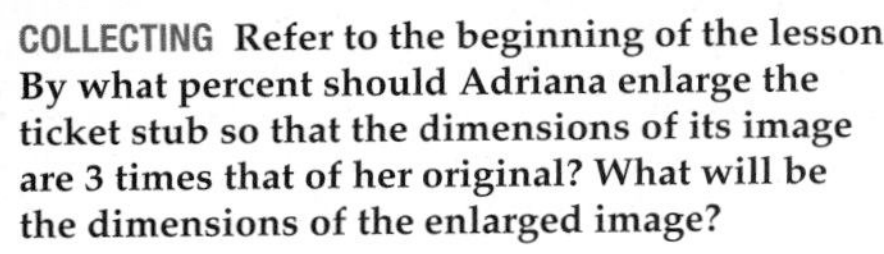

Real-WorldLink

Hew Weng Fatt accepted a contest challenge to collect the most movie stubs from a certain popular fantasy movie. He collected 6561 movie stubs in 38 days!

Source: *Youth2, Star Publications*

COLLECTING **Refer to the beginning of the lesson. By what percent should Adriana enlarge the ticket stub so that the dimensions of its image are 3 times that of her original? What will be the dimensions of the enlarged image?**

Adriana wants to create a dilated image of her ticket stub using the copier. The scale factor of her enlargement is 3. Written as a percent, the scale factor is (3 • 100)% or 300%. Now find the dimension of the enlarged image using the scale factor.

width: 5 cm • 300% = 15 cm   length: 6.4 cm • 300% = 19.2 cm

The enlarged ticket stub image will be 15 centimeters by 19.2 centimeters.

GuidedPractice 30%; The scale factor of the dilation is $\frac{1.5 \text{ cm}}{5 \text{ cm}}$ or 0.3, which is 30%.

2. If the resulting ticket stub image was 1.5 centimeters wide by about 1.9 centimeters long instead, what percent did Adriana mistakenly use to dilate the original image? Explain your reasoning.

WatchOut!

Decimal or Percent When working with scale factors, be careful to know whether the scale factor is given as a decimal or as a percentage.

Teach with Tech

Photo Editing Software Give students digital photos of different objects from the classroom. Then have them use a photo editing program to change the size of the photo. Have them try multiplying the length and width by factors greater than 1 and factors between 0 and 1. Make sure students realize that all of the enlargements and reductions are similar because the ratio of length to width was not changed.

2 Verify Similarity

Verify Similarity You can verify that a dilation produces a similar figure by comparing corresponding sides and angles. For triangles, you can also use SAS Similarity.

Example 3 Verify Similarity after a Dilation

Graph the original figure and its dilated image. Then verify that the dilation is a similarity transformation.

> **StudyTip**
> **Center of Dilation** Unless otherwise stated, all dilations on the coordinate plane use the origin as their center of dilation.

a. original: $A(-6, -3)$, $B(3, 3)$, $C(3, -3)$; image: $X(-4, -2)$, $Y(2, 2)$, $Z(2, -2)$

Graph each figure. Since $\angle C$ and $\angle Z$ are both right angles, $\angle C \cong \angle Z$. Show that the lengths of the sides that include $\angle C$ and $\angle Z$ are proportional.

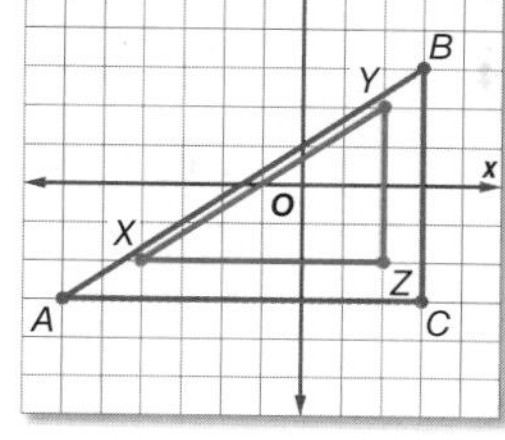

Use the coordinate grid to find the side lengths.

$\frac{XZ}{AC} = \frac{6}{9}$ or $\frac{2}{3}$, and $\frac{YZ}{BC} = \frac{4}{6}$ or $\frac{2}{3}$, so $\frac{XZ}{AC} = \frac{YZ}{BC}$.

Since the lengths of the sides that include $\angle C$ and $\angle Z$ are proportional, $\triangle XYZ \sim \triangle ABC$ by SAS Similarity.

b. original: $J(-6, 4)$, $K(6, 8)$, $L(8, 2)$, $M(-4, -2)$; image: $P(-3, 2)$, $Q(3, 4)$, $R(4, 1)$, $S(-2, -1)$

Use the Distance Formula to find the length of each side.

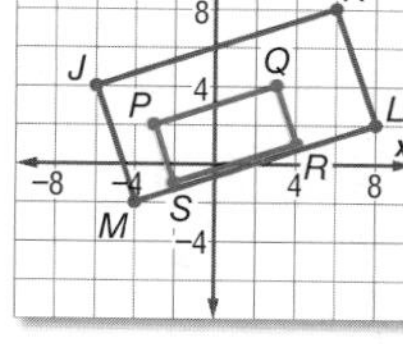

$JK = \sqrt{[6-(-6)]^2 + (8-4)^2} = \sqrt{160}$ or $4\sqrt{10}$

$PQ = \sqrt{[3-(-3)]^2 + (4-2)^2} = \sqrt{40}$ or $2\sqrt{10}$

$KL = \sqrt{(8-6)^2 + (2-8)^2} = \sqrt{40}$ or $2\sqrt{10}$

$QR = \sqrt{(4-3)^2 + (1-4)^2} = \sqrt{10}$

$LM = \sqrt{(-4-8)^2 + (-2-2)^2} = \sqrt{160}$ or $4\sqrt{10}$

$RS = \sqrt{(-2-4)^2 + (-1-1)^2} = \sqrt{40}$ or $2\sqrt{10}$

$MJ = \sqrt{[-6-(-4)]^2 + [4-(-2)]^2} = \sqrt{40}$ or $2\sqrt{10}$

$SP = \sqrt{[-3-(-2)]^2 + [2-(-1)]^2} = \sqrt{10}$

Find and compare the ratios of corresponding sides.

$\frac{PQ}{JK} = \frac{2\sqrt{10}}{4\sqrt{10}}$ or $\frac{1}{2}$ $\quad \frac{QR}{KL} = \frac{\sqrt{10}}{2\sqrt{10}}$ or $\frac{1}{2}$ $\quad \frac{RS}{LM} = \frac{2\sqrt{10}}{4\sqrt{10}}$ or $\frac{1}{2}$ $\quad \frac{SP}{MJ} = \frac{\sqrt{10}}{2\sqrt{10}}$ or $\frac{1}{2}$

$PQRS$ and $JKLM$ are both rectangles. This can be proved by showing that diagonals $\overline{PR} \cong \overline{SQ}$ and $\overline{JL} \cong \overline{KM}$ are congruent using the Distance Formula. Since they are both rectangles, their corresponding angles are congruent.

Since $\frac{PQ}{JK} = \frac{QR}{KL} = \frac{RS}{LM} = \frac{SP}{MJ}$ and corresponding angles are congruent, $PQRS \sim JKLM$.

GuidedPractice **3A, 3B. See margin.**

3A. original: $A(2, 3)$, $B(0, 1)$, $C(3, 0)$
image: $D(4, 6)$, $F(0, 2)$, $G(6, 0)$

3B. original: $H(0, 0)$, $J(6, 0)$, $K(6, 4)$, $L(0, 4)$
image: $W(0, 0)$, $X(3, 0)$, $Y(3, 2)$, $Z(0, 2)$

Additional Answers (Guided Practice)

3A.

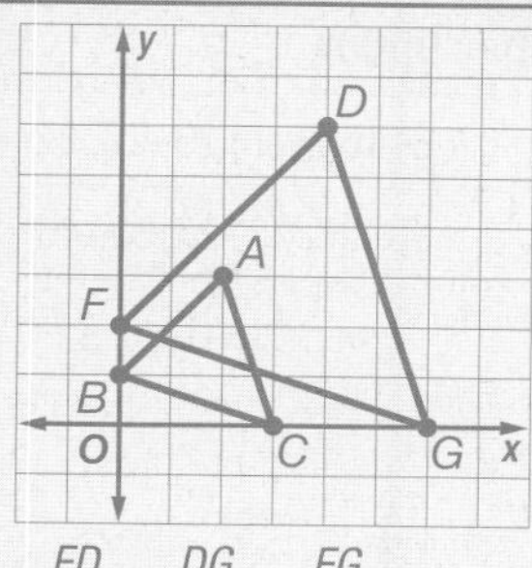

$\frac{FD}{AB} = \frac{DG}{AC} = \frac{FG}{BC} = 2$, so $\triangle DFG \sim \triangle ABC$ by SSS Similarity.

3B.

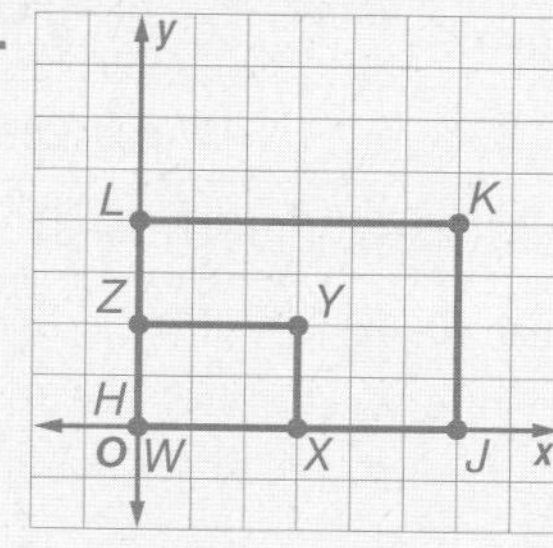

$\angle H$, $\angle J$, $\angle K$, $\angle L$, $\angle W$, $\angle X$, $\angle Y$, and $\angle Z$ are rt $\angle$s. Therefore $\angle H \cong \angle W$, $\angle J \cong \angle X$, $\angle K \cong \angle Y$, and $\angle L \cong \angle Z$ since rt $\angle$s are $\cong$. $\frac{WX}{HJ} = \frac{XY}{JK} = \frac{KL}{YZ} = \frac{ZW}{LH} = \frac{1}{2}$. So by the definition of similar polygons, $WXYZ \sim HJKL$.

2 Verify Similarity

Example 3 shows how to verify that a dilation is a similarity transformation of the original figure.

Additional Example

3 Graph the original figure and its dilated image. Then verify that the dilation is a similarity transformation.

a. original: $A(-6, -3)$, $B(6, -3)$, $C(-6, 6)$; image: $D(-2, -1)$, $E(2, -1)$, $F(-2, 2)$

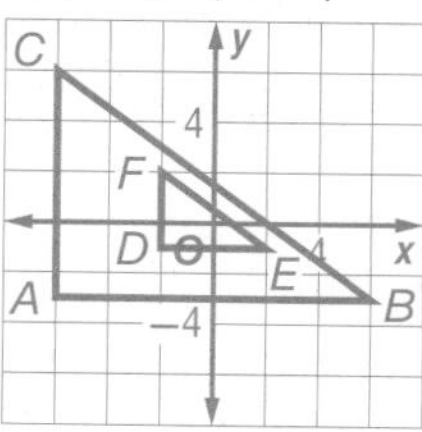

$\frac{FD}{CA} = \frac{DE}{AB} = \frac{FE}{CB} = \frac{1}{3}$, so $\triangle CAB \sim \triangle FDE$ by SSS similarity.

b. original: $P(2, 1)$, $Q(4, 1)$, $R(2, 0)$, $S(4, 0)$; image: $W(4, 2)$, $X(8, 2)$, $Y(8, 0)$, $R(4, 0)$

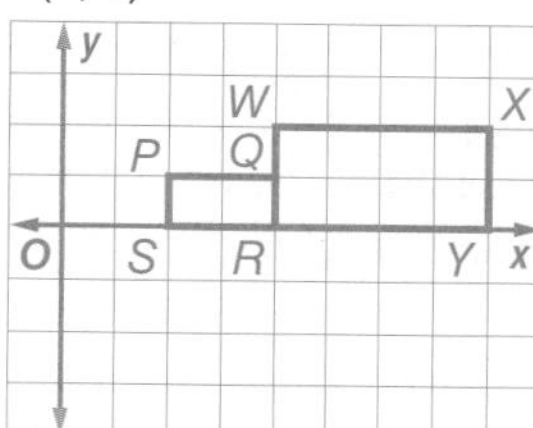

$\angle P$, $\angle Q$, $\angle R$, $\angle S$, $\angle W$, $\angle X$, and $\angle Y$ are rt. $\angle$s. Therefore $\angle P \cong \angle W$, $\angle Q \cong \angle X$, $\angle R \cong \angle Y$, and $\angle S \cong \angle R$, since rt. $\angle$s are $\cong$. $\frac{WX}{PQ} = \frac{XY}{QR} = \frac{RY}{SR} = \frac{WR}{PS} = 2$. So by the definition of similar polygons, $PQRS \sim WXYR$.

Focus on Mathematical Content

Center of Dilation A similarity transformation must have a center of dilation. On the coordinate plane, the center of dilation is often assumed to be the origin.

3 Practice

Formative Assessment

Use Exercises 1–5 to check for understanding.

Use the chart at the bottom of this page to customize assignments for your students.

Follow-up

Students have explored similar triangles and Similarity Theorems.

Ask:

- Why is similarity useful? Sample answer: Similarity can be used to create scale drawings and models and to solve problems involving indirect measurement.

Teaching the Mathematical Practices

Arguments Mathematically proficient students understand and use stated assumptions and definitions in constructing arguments. In Exercises 4–5, encourage students to review triangle similarity theorems and postulates.

Additional Answers

4. $\frac{AC}{AE} = \frac{AB}{AD} = 2$ and $\angle A \cong \angle A$ by the Reflexive Property, so $\triangle ADE \sim \triangle ABC$ by SAS Similarity.

5. $\frac{RJ}{KJ} = \frac{SJ}{LJ} = \frac{RS}{KL} = \frac{1}{2}$, so $\triangle RSJ \sim \triangle KLJ$ by SSS Similarity.

12. Yes; $\frac{3}{2}$; sample answer: Since $\frac{4}{6} = \frac{6\frac{2}{3}}{10} = \frac{2}{3}$, the photo in the yearbook is a dilation of the original photo. The scale factor is $\frac{6}{4}$, or $\frac{3}{2}$.

Check Your Understanding

 = Step-by-Step Solutions begin on page R14.

Example 1 **Determine whether the dilation from A to B is an *enlargement* or a *reduction*. Then find the scale factor of the dilation.**

1. 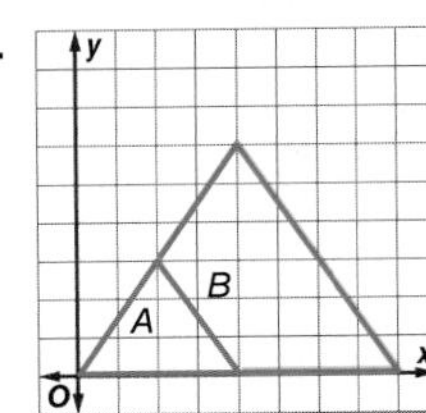

enlargement; 2

2. 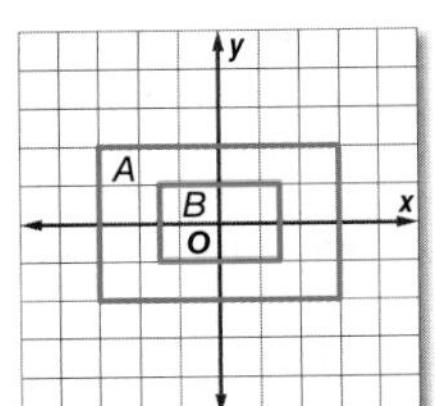

reduction; $\frac{1}{2}$

Example 2

3. **GAMES** The dimensions of a regulation tennis court are 27 feet by 78 feet. The dimensions of a table tennis table are 152.5 centimeters by 274 centimeters. Is a table tennis table a dilation of a tennis court? If so, what is the scale factor? Explain.
No; sample answer: Since $\frac{152.5}{27} \neq \frac{274}{78}$, a table tennis table is not a dilation of a tennis court.

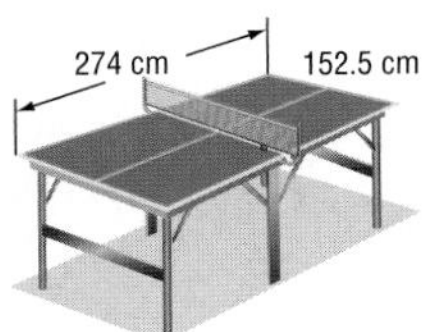

Example 3 **CCSS ARGUMENTS** **Verify that the dilation is a similarity transformation.** 4–5. See margin.

4. 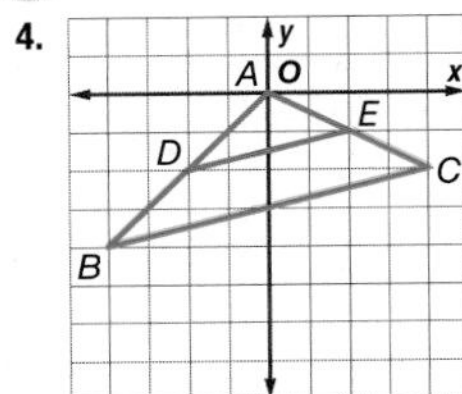

5.
L
S
K
R
O
J
x
y

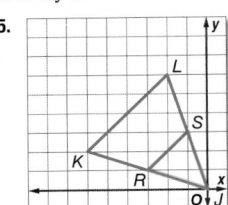

Practice and Problem Solving

Extra Practice is on page R7.

Example 1 **Determine whether the dilation from A to B is an *enlargement* or a *reduction*. Then find the scale factor of the dilation.**

6. 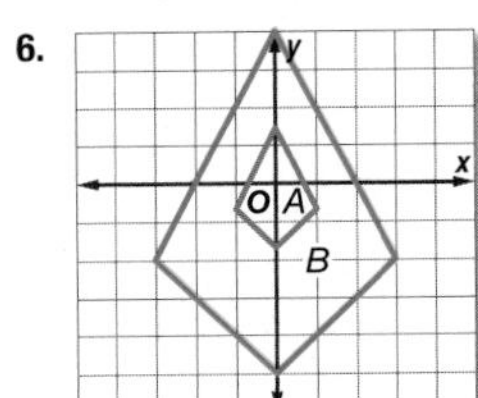

enlargement; 3

7. 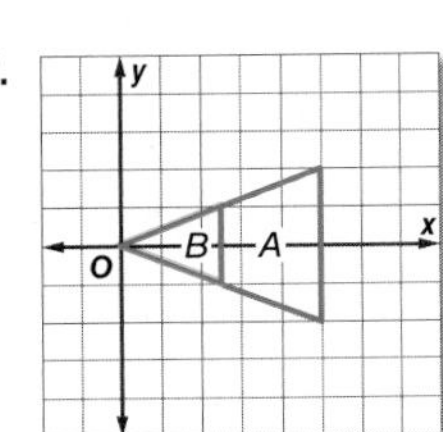

reduction; $\frac{1}{2}$

8. 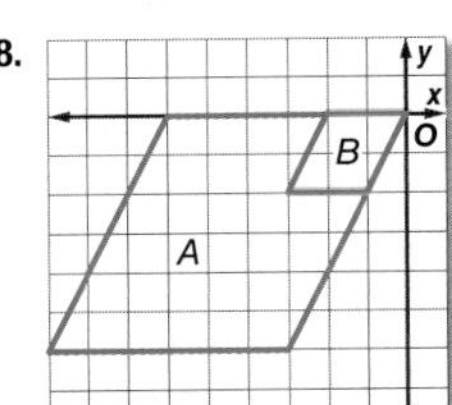

reduction; $\frac{1}{3}$

9. 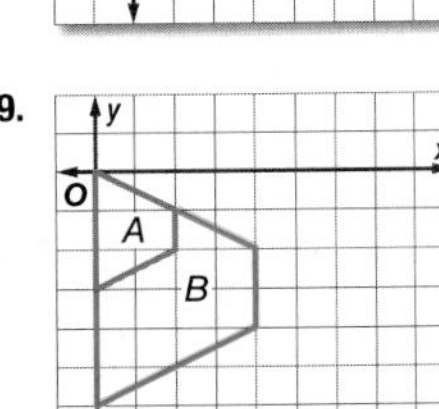

enlargement; 2

Differentiated Homework Options

Level	Assignment	Two-Day Option	
AL Basic	6–17, 23–45	7–17 odd, 28–31	6–16 even, 23–27, 32–45
OL Core	7–19 odd, 20, 21, 23–45	6–17, 28–31	18–21, 23–27, 32–45
BL Advanced	18–39, (optional: 40–45)		

Determine whether each dilation is an *enlargement* or *reduction*.

10. Before 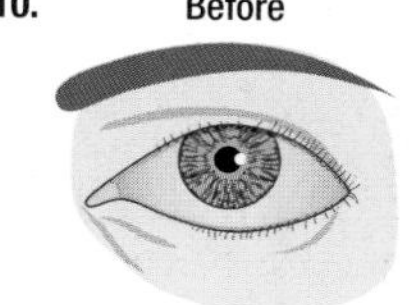 After 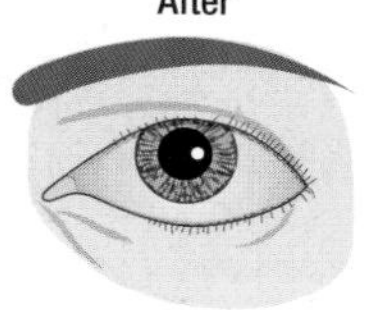 enlargement

11. Painting  Postcard  reduction

Example 2 **12. YEARBOOK** Jordan is putting a photo of the lacrosse team in a full-page layout in the yearbook. The original photo is 4 inches by 6 inches. If the photo in the yearbook is $6\frac{2}{3}$ inches by 10 inches, is the yearbook photo a dilation of the original photo? If so, what is the scale factor? Explain. See margin.

13. CCSS **MODELING** Candace created a design to be made into temporary tattoos for a homecoming game as shown. Is the temporary tattoo a dilation of the original design? If so, what is the scale factor? Explain.

13. No; sample answer: Since $\frac{1.2}{2.5} \neq \frac{1.25}{3}$, the design and the actual tattoo are not proportional. Therefore, the tattoo is not a dilation of the design.

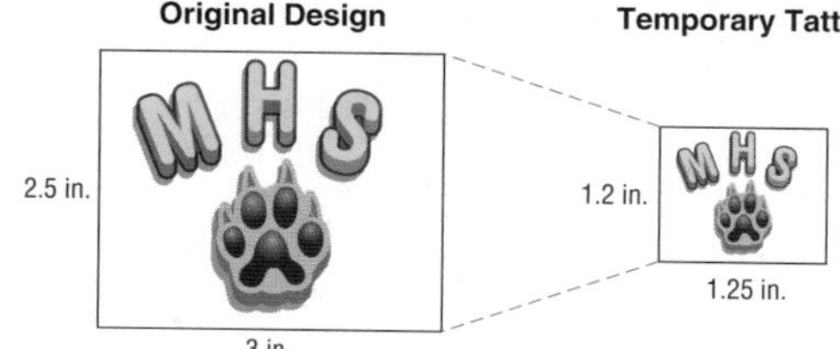

Example 3 **Graph the original figure and its dilated image. Then verify that the dilation is a similarity transformation.** 14–17. See Ch. 7 Answer Appendix.

14. $M(1, 4), P(2, 2), Q(5, 5); S(-3, 6), T(0, 0), U(9, 9)$

15. $A(1, 3), B(-1, 2), C(1, 1); D(-7, -1), E(1, -5)$

16. $V(-3, 4), W(-5, 0), X(1, 2); Y(-6, -2), Z(3, 1)$

17. $J(-6, 8), K(6, 6), L(-2, 4); D(-12, 16), G(12, 12), H(-4, 8)$

B **If $\triangle ABC \sim \triangle AYZ$, find the missing coordinate.**

18. (12, 0)

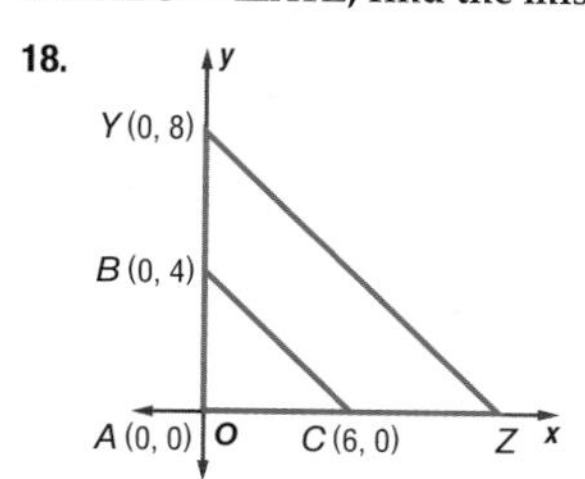

19 (0, –2)

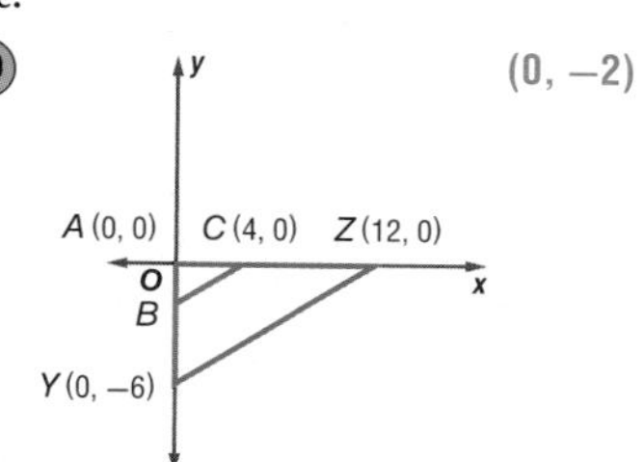

CCSS Teaching the Mathematical Practices

Modeling Mathematically proficient students can apply the mathematics they know to solve problems arising in everyday life. In Exercise 13, point out to students that they should divide the corresponding measures to find the scale factor.

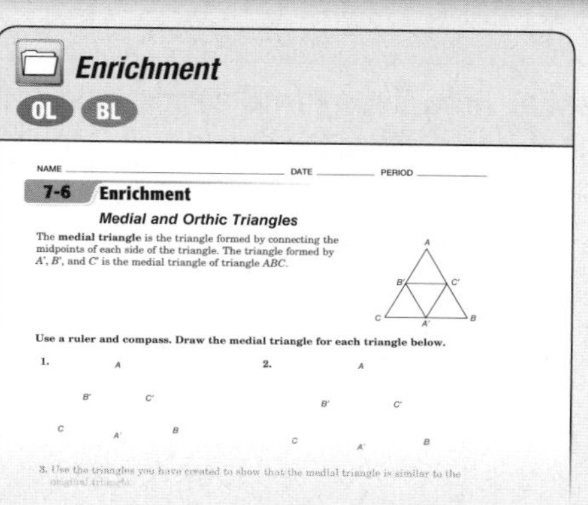

Enrichment
OL BL

NAME ______ DATE ______ PERIOD ______

7-6 Enrichment

Medial and Orthic Triangles

The **medial triangle** is the triangle formed by connecting the midpoints of each side of the triangle. The triangle formed by A', B', and C' is the medial triangle of triangle ABC.

Use a ruler and compass. Draw the medial triangle for each triangle below.

1. 2.

3. Use the triangles you have created to show that the medial triangle is similar to the original triangle.

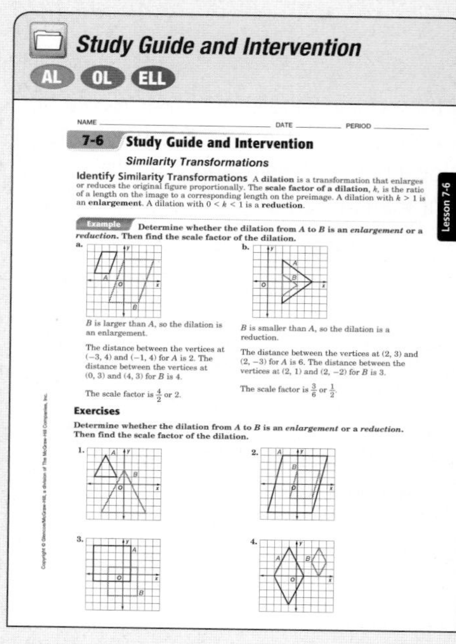

Study Guide and Intervention
AL OL ELL

NAME ______ DATE ______ PERIOD ______

7-6 Study Guide and Intervention

Similarity Transformations

Identify Similarity Transformations A **dilation** is a transformation that enlarges or reduces the original figure proportionally. The **scale factor of a dilation**, k, is the ratio of a length on the image to a corresponding length on the preimage. A dilation with $k > 1$ is an **enlargement**. A dilation with $0 < k < 1$ is a **reduction**.

Example **Determine whether the dilation from A to B is an *enlargement* or a *reduction*. Then find the scale factor of the dilation.**

a. B is larger than A, so the dilation is an enlargement.

The distance between the vertices at $(-3, 4)$ and $(-1, 4)$ for A is 2. The distance between the vertices at $(0, 3)$ and $(4, 3)$ for B is 4.

The scale factor is $\frac{4}{2}$ or 2.

b. B is smaller than A, so the dilation is a reduction.

The distance between the vertices at $(2, 3)$ and $(2, -3)$ for A is 6. The distance between the vertices at $(2, 1)$ and $(2, -2)$ for B is 3.

The scale factor is $\frac{3}{6}$ or $\frac{1}{2}$.

Exercises

Determine whether the dilation from A to B is an *enlargement* or a *reduction*. Then find the scale factor of the dilation.

1. 2. 3. 4.

Lesson 7-6

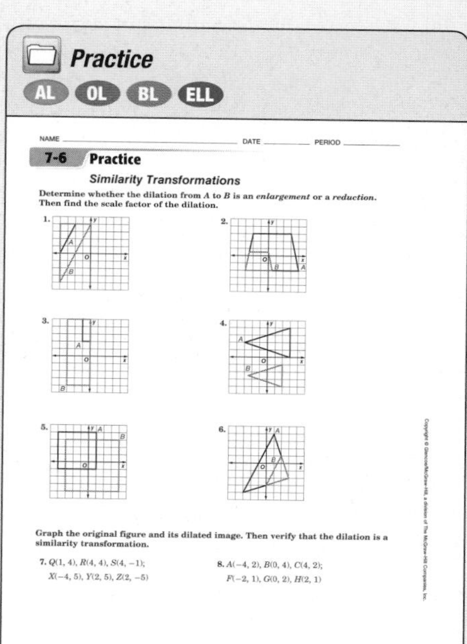

Practice
AL OL BL ELL

NAME ______ DATE ______ PERIOD ______

7-6 Practice

Similarity Transformations

Determine whether the dilation from A to B is an *enlargement* or a *reduction*. Then find the scale factor of the dilation.

1. 2. 3. 4. 5. 6.

Graph the original figure and its dilated image. Then verify that the dilation is a similarity transformation.

7. $Q(1, 4), R(4, 4), S(4, -1); X(-4, 5), Y(2, 5), Z(2, -5)$

8. $A(-4, 2), B(0, 4), C(4, 2); F(-2, 1), G(0, 2), H(2, 1)$

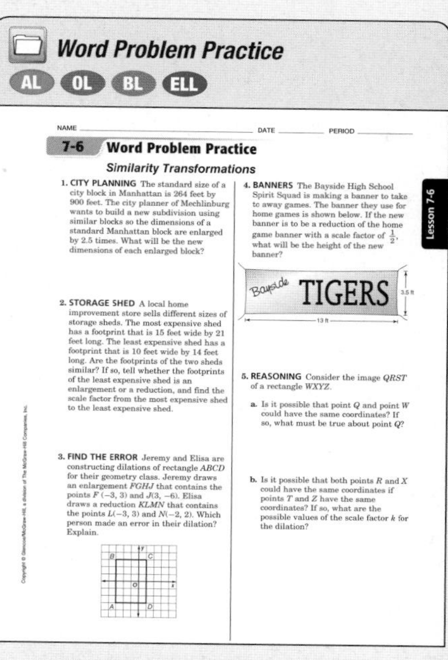

Word Problem Practice
AL OL BL ELL

NAME ______ DATE ______ PERIOD ______

7-6 Word Problem Practice

Similarity Transformations

1. **CITY PLANNING** The standard size of a city block in Manhattan is 264 feet by 900 feet. The city planner of Mechlinburg wants to build a new subdivision using similar blocks so the dimensions of a standard Manhattan block are enlarged by 2.5 times. What will be the new dimensions of each enlarged block?

2. **STORAGE SHED** A local home improvement store sells different sizes of storage sheds. The most expensive shed has a footprint that is 15 feet wide by 21 feet long. The least expensive shed has a footprint that is 10 feet wide by 14 feet long. Are the footprints of the two sheds similar? If so, tell whether the footprints of the least expensive shed is an enlargement or a reduction, and find the scale factor from the most expensive shed to the least expensive shed.

3. **FIND THE ERROR** Jeremy and Elisa are constructing dilations of rectangle $ABCD$ for their geometry class. Jeremy draws an enlargement $FGHJ$ that contains the points $F(-3, 3)$ and $J(3, -6)$. Elisa draws a reduction $KLMN$ that contains the points $L(-3, 3)$ and $N(-2, 2)$. Which person made an error in their dilation? Explain.

4. **BANNERS** The Bayside High School Spirit Squad is making a banner to take to away games. The banner they use for home games is shown below. If the new banner is to be a reduction of the home game banner with a scale factor of $\frac{1}{2}$, what will be the height of the new banner?

Bayside TIGERS
3.5 ft
13 ft

5. **REASONING** Consider the image $QRST$ of a rectangle $WXYZ$.

a. Is it possible that point Q and point W could have the same coordinates? If so, what must be true about point Q?

b. Is it possible that both points R and X could have the same coordinates if points T and Z have the same coordinates? If so, what are the possible values of the scale factor k for the dilation?

Lesson 7-6

Multiple Representations

In Exercise 21, students use geometric sketches, a table, and a verbal description to investigate similarity of triangles on the coordinate plane.

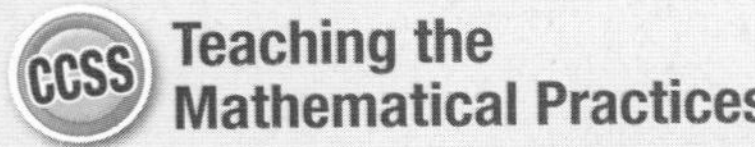

Teaching the Mathematical Practices

Reasoning Mathematically proficient students make sense of quantities and their relationships in problem situations. In Exercise 23, encourage students to analyze the relationship between each set of ordered pairs.

Additional Answers

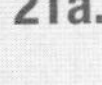

21a.

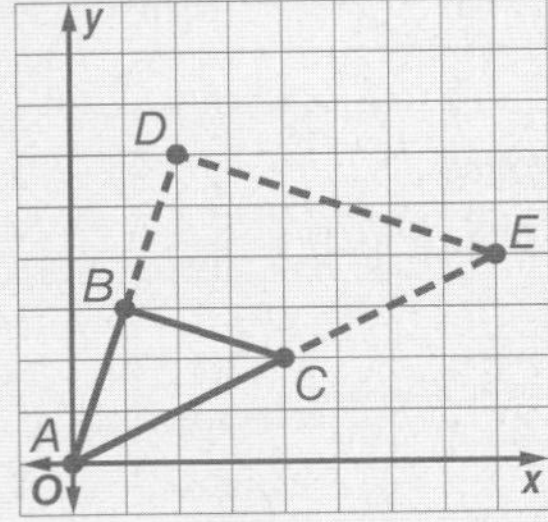

21b.

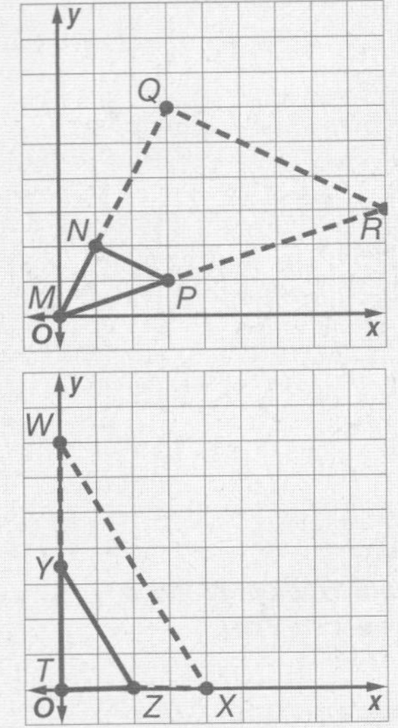

23. No; sample answer: Since the *x*-coordinates are multiplied by 3 and the *y*-coordinates are multiplied by 2, $\triangle XYZ$ is 3 times as wide and only 2 times as tall as $\triangle PQR$. Therefore, the transformation is not a dilation.

20. GRAPHIC ART Aimee painted the sample sign shown using $\frac{1}{2}$ bottle of glass paint. The actual sign she will paint in a shop window is to be 3 feet by $7\frac{1}{2}$ feet.

a. $\frac{6 \text{ in.}}{15 \text{ in.}} = \frac{3 \text{ ft}}{7.5 \text{ ft}}$ is a true proportion.
b. 18 bottles

a. Explain why the actual sign is a dilation of her sample.

b. How many bottles of paint will Aimee need to complete the actual sign?

21. MULTIPLE REPRESENTATIONS In this problem, you will investigate similarity of triangles on the coordinate plane. **a–b. See margin.**

a. Geometric Draw a triangle with vertex *A* at the origin. Make sure that the two additional vertices *B* and *C* have whole-number coordinates. Draw a similar triangle that is twice as large as $\triangle ABC$ with its vertex also located at the origin. Label the triangle *ADE*.

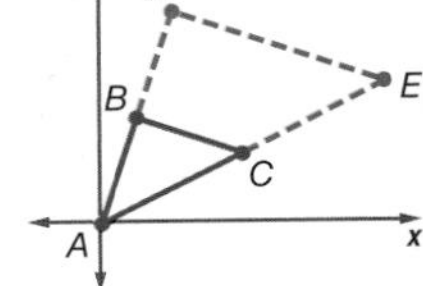

b. Geometric Repeat the process in part **a** two times. Label the second pair of triangles *MNP* and *MQR* and the third pair *TWX* and *TYZ*. Use different scale factors than part **a**.

c. Tabular Copy and complete the table below with the appropriate values.

Coordinates											
$\triangle ABC$		$\triangle ADE$		$\triangle MNP$		$\triangle MQR$		$\triangle TWX$		$\triangle TYZ$	
A	(0, 0)	A	(0, 0)	M	(0, 0)	M	(0, 0)	T	(0, 0)	T	(0, 0)
B	(1, 3)	D	(2, 6)	N	(1, 2)	Q	(3, 6)	W	(0, 7)	Y	(0, 3.5)
C	(4, 2)	E	(8, 4)	P	(3, 1)	R	(9, 3)	X	(4, 0)	Z	(2, 0)

d. Verbal Make a conjecture about how you could predict the coordinates of a dilated triangle with a scale factor of *n* if the two similar triangles share a corresponding vertex at the origin. **Sample answer: Multiply the coordinates of the given triangle by the scale factor to get the coordinates of the dilated triangle.**

H.O.T. Problems Use Higher-Order Thinking Skills

22. CHALLENGE *MNOP* is a dilation of *ABCD*. How is the scale factor of the dilation related to the similarity ratio of *ABCD* to *MNOP*? Explain your reasoning. **See Ch. 6 Answer Appendix.**

23. REASONING The coordinates of two triangles are provided in the table at the right. Is $\triangle XYZ$ a dilation of $\triangle PQR$? Explain. **See margin.**

$\triangle PQR$		$\triangle XYZ$	
P	(a, b)	X	(3a, 2b)
Q	(c, d)	Y	(3c, 2d)
R	(e, f)	Z	(3e, 2f)

24. Sample answer: An image formed using a digital projector is an enlargement.

OPEN ENDED Describe a real-world example of each transformation other than those given in this lesson. **25. Sample answer: Architectural plans are reductions.**

24. enlargement **25.** reduction **26.** congruence transformation

26. Sample answer: Stamps are congruence transformations.

27. WRITING IN MATH Explain how you can use scale factor to determine whether a transformation is an enlargement, a reduction, or a congruence transformation. **See margin.**

Differentiated Instruction AL OL BL

Spatial Have students make paper cutouts of triangles and quadrilaterals labeled with a scale factor. The students should then trade their cutouts with a classmate and make a similar figure using the scale factor.

Standardized Test Practice

28. ALGEBRA Which equation describes the line that passes through $(-3, 4)$ and is perpendicular to $3x - y = 6$? **B**

A $y = -\frac{1}{3}x + 4$ C $y = 3x + 4$

B $y = -\frac{1}{3}x + 3$ D $y = 3x + 3$

29. SHORT RESPONSE What is the scale factor of the dilation shown below? $\frac{1}{2}$

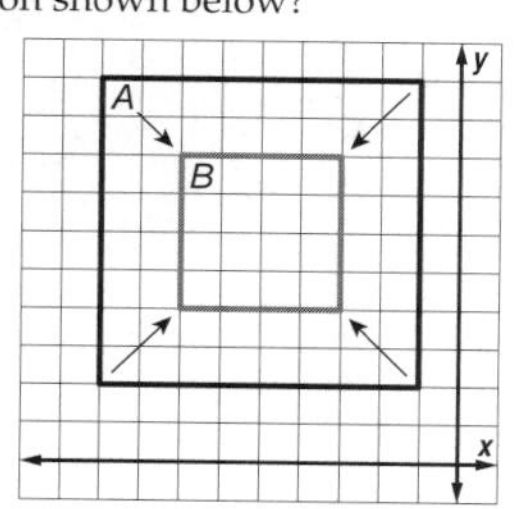

30. In the figure below, $\angle A \cong \angle C$.

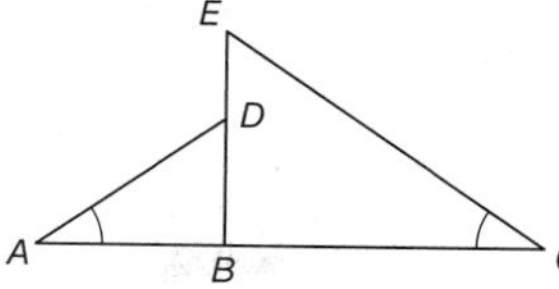

Which additional information would *not* be enough to prove that $\triangle ADB \sim \triangle CEB$? **H**

F $\frac{AB}{DB} = \frac{CB}{EB}$ H $\overline{ED} \cong \overline{DB}$

G $\angle ADB \cong \angle CEB$ J $\overline{EB} \perp \overline{AC}$

31. SAT/ACT $x = \frac{6}{4p + 3}$ and $xy = \frac{3}{4p + 3}$. $y =$ **E**

A 4 C 1 E $\frac{1}{2}$

B 2 D $\frac{3}{4}$

Spiral Review

32. LANDSCAPING Shea is designing two gardens shaped like similar triangles. One garden has a perimeter of 53.5 feet, and the longest side is 25 feet. She wants the second garden to have a perimeter of 32.1 feet. Find the length of the longest side of this garden. (Lesson 7-5) **15 ft**

Determine whether $\overline{AB} \parallel \overline{CD}$. Justify your answer. (Lesson 7-4)

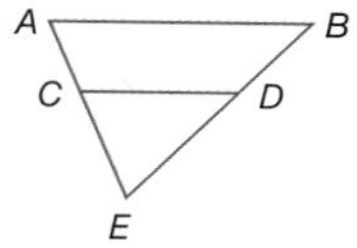

A B C D E

33. $AC = 8.4$, $BD = 6.3$, $DE = 4.5$, and $CE = 6$ **33. yes; $\frac{AC}{BD} = \frac{DE}{CE} = \frac{4}{3}$**

34. $AC = 7$, $BD = 10.5$, $BE = 22.5$, and $AE = 15$ **34. yes; $\frac{AC}{BD} = \frac{AE}{BE} = \frac{2}{3}$**

35. $AB = 8$, $AE = 9$, $CD = 4$, and $CE = 4$ **no; $\frac{AB}{CD} \neq \frac{AE}{CE}$**

If each figure is a kite, find each measure. (Lesson 6-6)

36. QR **10**

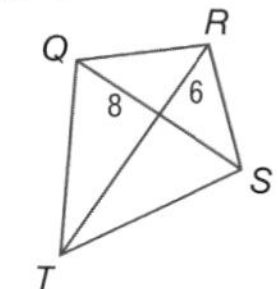

37. $m\angle K$ **117**

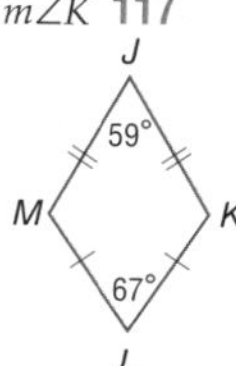

38. BC **13**

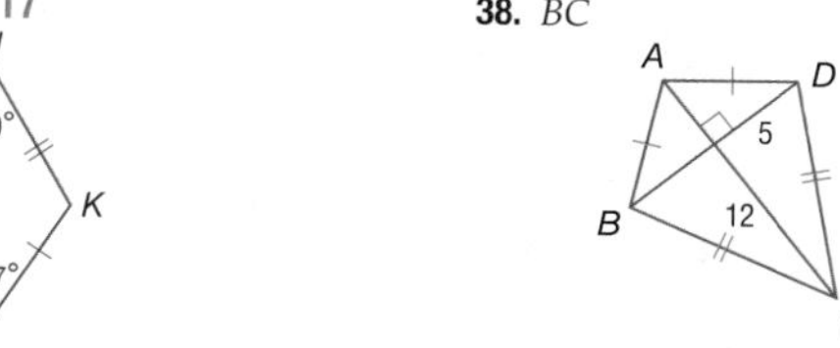

39. PROOF Write a coordinate proof for the following statement. (Lesson 4-8) **See margin.**
If a line segment joins the midpoints of two sides of a triangle, then it is parallel to the third side.

Skills Review

Solve each equation.

40. $145 = 29 \cdot t$ **5**

41. $216 = d \cdot 27$ **8**

42. $2r = 67 \cdot 5$ **167.5**

43. $100t = \frac{70}{240}$ **0.003**

44. $\frac{80}{4} = 14d$ **1.43**

45. $\frac{2t + 15}{t} = 92$ **0.17**

27. Sample answer: If a transformation is an enlargement, the lengths of the transformed object will be greater than the original object, so the scale factor will be greater than 1. If a transformation is a reduction, the lengths of the transformed object will be less than the original object, so the scale factor will be less than 1, but greater than 0. If the transformation is a congruence transformation, the scale factor is 1, because the lengths of the transformed object are equal to the lengths of the original object.

4 Assess

Crystal Ball Have students discuss how learning about similarity transformations could help them understand the meaning of scale on a map.

Formative Assessment

Check for student understanding of Lessons 7-5 and 7-6.

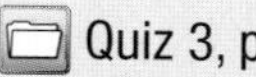
Quiz 3, p. 52

Additional Answers

39.

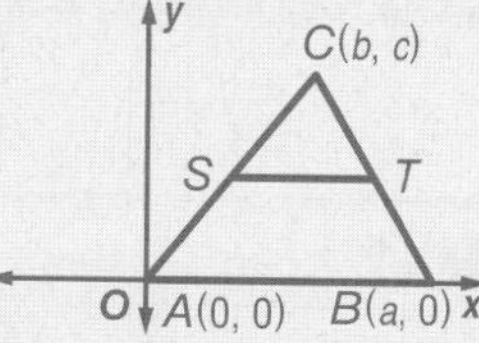

Given: $\triangle ABC$
S is the midpoint of $\overline{AC}$.
T is the midpoint of $\overline{BC}$.

Prove: $\overline{ST} \parallel \overline{AB}$

Proof:

Midpoint S is $\left(\frac{b+0}{2}, \frac{c+0}{2}\right)$ or $\left(\frac{b}{2}, \frac{c}{2}\right)$.

Midpoint T is $\left(\frac{a+b}{2}, \frac{0+c}{2}\right)$ or $\left(\frac{a+b}{2}, \frac{c}{2}\right)$.

Slope of $\overline{ST} = \dfrac{\frac{c}{2} - \frac{c}{2}}{\frac{a+b}{2} - \frac{b}{2}} = \dfrac{0}{\frac{a}{2}}$ or 0.

Slope of $\overline{AB} = \frac{0-0}{a-0} = \frac{0}{a}$ or 0.

$\overline{ST}$ and $\overline{AB}$ have the same slope so $\overline{ST} \parallel \overline{AB}$.

1 Focus

VerticalAlignment

Before Lesson 7-7 Use scale factors to solve problems with similar polygons.

Lesson 7-7 Interpret scale models and use scale factor to solve problems.

After Lesson 7-7 Understand and use transformations and symmetry in the coordinate plane.

2 Teach

Scaffolding Questions

Have students read the **Why?** section of the lesson.

Ask:

- How are the proportions for the planet models determined? They are based on the real planets.
- What is the ratio of the diameter of the real planet to the diameter of the model of the planet? $\approx 1{,}000{,}000{,}000$

LESSON 7-7 Scale Drawings and Models

Then	Now	Why?
You used scale factors to solve problems with similar polygons.	1 Interpret scale models. 2 Use scale factors to solve problems.	In Saint-Luc, Switzerland, Le Chemin des planetes, has constructed a scale model of each planet in the solar system. It is one of the largest complete three-dimensional scale models of the solar system. The diameter of the center of the model of Saturn shown is 121 millimeters; the diameter of the real planet is about 121,000 kilometers.

NewVocabulary
scale model
scale drawing
scale

Common Core State Standards

Content Standards
G.MG.3 Apply geometric methods to solve problems (e.g., designing an object or structure to satisfy physical constraints or minimize cost; working with typographic grid systems based on ratios). ★

Mathematical Practices
4 Model with mathematics.
7 Look for and make use of structure.

1 Scale Models A **scale model** or a **scale drawing** is an object or drawing with lengths proportional to the object it represents. The **scale** of a model or drawing is the ratio of a length on the model or drawing to the actual length of the object being modeled or drawn.

Example 1 Use a Scale Drawing

MAPS The scale on the map shown is 0.4 inch : 40 miles. Find the actual distance from Nashville to Memphis.

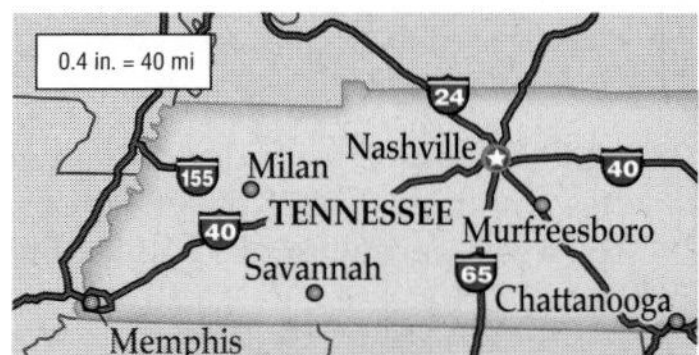

Use a ruler. The distance between Nashville and Memphis is about 1.5 inches.

Method 1 Write and solve a proportion.

Let x represent the distance between Nashville and Memphis.

Scale — Nashville to Memphis

$$\frac{0.4 \text{ in.}}{40 \text{ mi}} = \frac{1.5 \text{ in.}}{x \text{ mi}}$$ (map → numerator; actual → denominator)

$0.4 \cdot x = 40 \cdot 1.5$ Cross Products Property

$x = 150$ Simplify.

Method 2 Write and solve an equation.

Let a = actual distance in miles between Nashville and Memphis and m = map distance in inches. Write the scale as $\frac{40 \text{ mi}}{0.4 \text{ in.}}$, which is $40 \div 0.4$ or 100 miles per inch. So for every inch on the map, the actual distance is 100 miles.

$a = 100 \cdot m$ Write an equation.

$= 100 \cdot 1.5$ $m = 1.5$ in.

$= 150$ Solve.

CHECK Use dimensional analysis.

$$\text{mi} = \frac{\text{mi}}{\text{in.}} \cdot \text{in.} \Rightarrow \text{mi} = \text{mi} \checkmark$$

The distance between Nashville and Memphis is 150 miles.

GuidedPractice

1. **MAPS** Find the actual distance between Nashville and Chattanooga. 87.5 mi

Lesson 7-7 Resources

Resource	Approaching Level AL	On Level OL	Beyond Level BL	English Learners ELL
Teacher Edition	▪ Differentiated Instruction, p. 522	▪ Differentiated Instruction, pp. 519, 522	▪ Differentiated Instruction, pp. 519, 522	▪ Differentiated Instruction, p. 522
Chapter Resource Masters	▪ Study Guide and Intervention, pp. 43–44 ▪ Skills Practice, p. 45 ▪ Practice, p. 46 ▪ Word Problem Practice, p. 47	▪ Study Guide and Intervention, pp. 43–44 ▪ Skills Practice, p. 45 ▪ Practice, p. 46 ▪ Word Problem Practice, p. 47 ▪ Enrichment, p. 48	▪ Practice, p. 46 ▪ Word Problem Practice, p. 47 ▪ Enrichment, p. 48	▪ Study Guide and Intervention, pp. 43–44 ▪ Skills Practice, p. 45 ▪ Practice, p. 46 ▪ Word Problem Practice, p. 47
Other	▪ 5-Minute Check 7-7 ▪ Study Notebook	▪ 5-Minute Check 7-7 ▪ Study Notebook	▪ 5-Minute Check 7-7 ▪ Study Notebook	▪ 5-Minute Check 7-7 ▪ Study Notebook

2 Use Scale Factors The scale factor of a drawing or scale model is written as a unitless ratio in simplest form. Scale factors are always written so that the model length in the ratio comes first.

Example 2 Find the Scale

SCALE MODEL **This is a miniature replica of a 1923 Checker Cab. The length of the model is 6.5 inches. The actual length of the car was 13 feet.**

a. What is the scale of the model?

To find the scale, write the ratio of a model length to an actual length.

$$\frac{\text{model length}}{\text{actual length}} = \frac{6.5 \text{ in.}}{13 \text{ ft}} \text{ or } \frac{1 \text{ in.}}{2 \text{ ft}}$$

The scale of the model is 1 in.:2 ft.

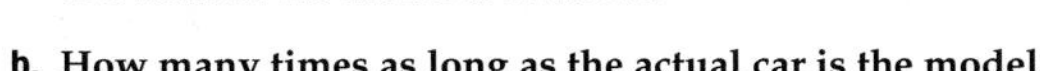

b. How many times as long as the actual car is the model?

To answer this question, find the scale factor of the model. Multiply by a conversion factor that relates inches to feet to obtain a unitless ratio.

$$\frac{1 \text{ in.}}{2 \text{ ft}} = \frac{1 \text{ in.}}{2 \text{ ft}} \cdot \frac{1 \text{ ft}}{12 \text{ in.}} = \frac{1}{24}$$

The scale factor is 1:24. That is, the model is $\frac{1}{24}$ as long as the actual car.

StudyTip

CCSS Regularity The scale factor of a model that is smaller than the original object is between 0 and 1 and the scale factor for a model that is larger than the original object is greater than 1.

GuidedPractice

2. SCALE MODEL Mrs. Alejandro's history class made a scale model of the Alamo that is 3 feet tall. The actual height of the building is 33 feet 6 inches.
   A. What is the scale of the model? $\frac{1 \text{ ft}}{11 \text{ ft } 2 \text{ in.}}$
   B. How many times as tall as the actual building is the model? How many times as tall as the model is the actual building? $\frac{1}{11.2}$; 11.2

Real-World Example 3 Construct a Scale Model

SCALE MODEL **Suppose you want to build a model of the St. Louis Gateway Arch that is no more than 11 inches tall. Choose an appropriate scale and use it to determine the height of the model. Use the information at the left.**

The actual monument is 630 feet tall. Since 630 feet ÷ 11 inches = 57.3 feet per inch, a scale of 1 inch = 60 feet is an appropriate scale. So, for every inch on the model m, let the actual measure a be 60 feet. Write this as an equation.

$a = 60 \cdot m$	Write an equation.
$630 = 60 \cdot m$	$a = 630$
$10.5 = m$	So the height of the model would be 10.5 inches.

Real-WorldLink

The St. Louis Gateway Arch is the tallest national monument in the United States at 630 feet. The span of the base is also 630 feet. The arch weighs 17,246 tons and can sway a maximum of 9 inches in each direction during high winds.

Source: Gateway Arch Facts

GuidedPractice Sample answer: 1 in. = 1.5 ft; 8 in. × $9\frac{1}{3}$ in.

3. SCALE DRAWING Sonya is making a scale drawing of her room on an 8.5-by-11-inch sheet of paper. If her room is 14 feet by 12 feet, find an appropriate scale for the drawing and determine the dimensions of the drawing.

1 Scale Models

Examples 1–3 show how to use scale models to find real and scale measurements.

Formative Assessment

Use the Guided Practice exercises after each example to determine students' understanding of concepts.

Additional Examples

1. **MAPS** The distance between Boston and Chicago on a map is 9 inches. If the scale of the map is 1 inch : 95 miles, what is the actual distance from Boston to Chicago? 855 miles
2. **SCALE MODEL** A miniature replica of a fighter jet is 4 inches long. The actual length of the jet is 12.8 yards.
   a. What is the scale of the model? 1 inch: 3.2 yards
   b. How many times as long as the model is the actual jet? 115.2
3. **SCALE DRAWING** Gerrard is making a scale model of his classroom on an 11-by-17 inch sheet of paper. If the classroom is 20 feet by 32 feet, choose an appropriate scale for the drawing and determine the drawing's dimensions. 1 in.: 2 ft; 10 in. wide, 16 in. long

Additional Examples also in Interactive Classroom PowerPoint® Presentations

DifferentiatedInstruction OL BL

Extension Special effects have relied on miniature models to produce movie scenes. Students interested in this aspect of scale factor can be asked to create a movie scene by developing and using a scale model.

CCSS Teaching the Mathematical Practices

Regularity Mathematically proficient students maintain oversight of the process, while attending to the details. They continually evaluate the reasonableness of their intermediate results. Encourage students to check the reasonableness of their results.

Teach with Tech

Document Camera Give students an object and have them create scale drawings and models. Have several students present their drawings to the class, and discuss how different scales change the appearance of the drawing.

3 Practice

Formative Assessment

Use Exercises 1–4 to check for understanding.

Use the chart at the bottom of this page to customize assignments for your students.

Exercise Alert

Ruler Exercises 1, 2, 4, 10–14, and 24 require the use of a ruler marked in inches. Exercises 5–8 require the use of a ruler marked in centimeters.

Additional Answers

4. Sample answer: 1 in. = 4 m

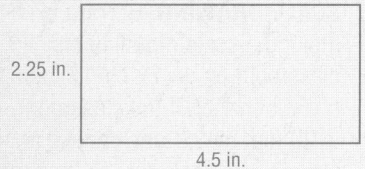

10b. $\frac{1}{15{,}840}$; Sample answer: The map distance is $\frac{1}{15{,}840}$ of the actual distance; the actual distance is 15,840 times as long as the map distance.

11. Sample answer: 1 in. = 12 ft

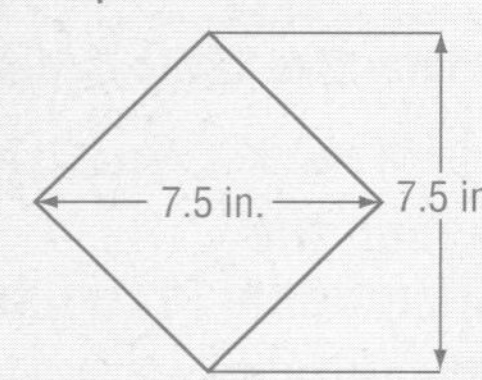

Figure not shown actual size.

Check Your Understanding

= Step-by-Step Solutions begin on page R14.

Example 1 **MAPS Use the map of Maine shown and a customary ruler to find the actual distance between each pair of cities. Measure to the nearest sixteenth of an inch.**

1. Bangor and Portland about 117 mi
2. Augusta and Houlton about 156 mi

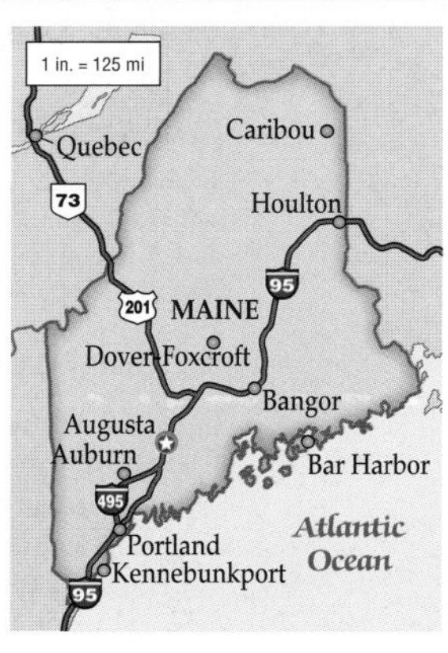

Example 2 3. **SCALE MODELS** Carlos made a scale model of a local bridge. The model spans 6 inches; the actual bridge spans 50 feet.

a. What is the scale of the model? 6 in. : 50 ft

b. What scale factor did Carlos use to build his model? $\frac{1}{100}$

Example 3 4. **SPORTS** A volleyball court is 9 meters wide and 18 meters long. Choose an appropriate scale and construct a scale drawing of the court to fit on a 3-inch by 5-inch index card. See margin.

Practice and Problem Solving

Extra Practice is on page R7.

Example 1 CCSS **MODELING Use the map of Oklahoma shown and a metric ruler to find the actual distance between each pair of cities. Measure to the nearest centimeter.**

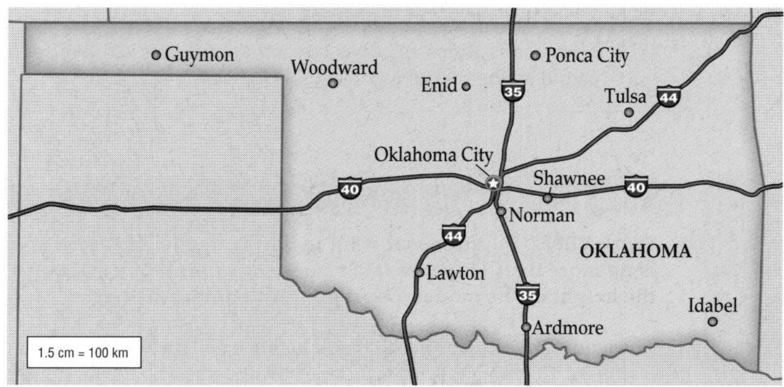

5. Guymon and Oklahoma City 380 km
6. Lawton and Tulsa 280 km
7. Enid and Tulsa 173 km
8. Ponca City and Shawnee 153 km

Example 2 9. **SCULPTURE** A replica of *The Thinker* is 10 inches tall. A statue of *The Thinker* at the University of Louisville is 10 feet tall.

a. What is the scale of the replica? 1 in. : 1 ft

b. How many times as tall as the actual sculpture is the replica? $\frac{1}{12}$ times

Differentiated Homework Options

Level	Assignment	Two-Day Option	
AL Basic	5–12, 21, 23–49	5–11 odd, 26–29	6–12 even, 21, 23–25, 30–49
OL Core	5–11 odd, 13–21, 23–49	5–12, 26–29	13–21, 23–25, 30–49
BL Advanced	13–44, (optional: 45–49)		

10. **MAPS** The map below shows a portion of Frankfort, Kentucky.

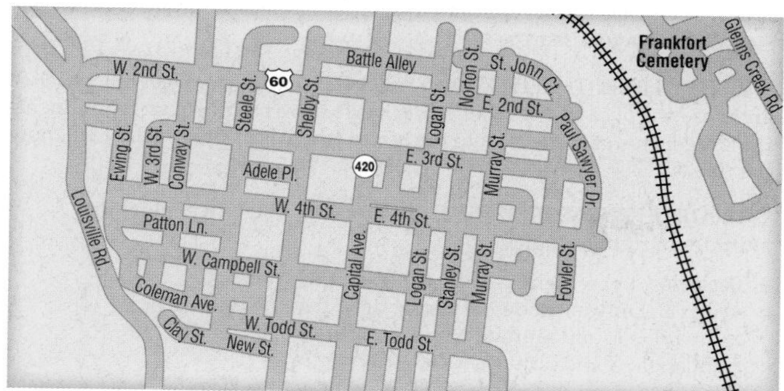

a. If the actual distance from the intersection of Conway Street and 4th Street to the intersection of Murray Street and 4th Street is 0.47 mile, use a customary ruler to estimate the scale of the map. **1 in.:0.25 mi**

b. What is the approximate scale factor of the map? Interpret its meaning. **See margin.**

Example 3 **SPORTS** **Choose an appropriate scale and construct a scale drawing of each playing area so that it would fit on an 8.5-by-11-inch sheet of paper.** **11. See margin.**

11. A baseball diamond is a square 90 feet on each side with about a 128-foot diagonal.

12. A high school basketball court is a rectangle with length 84 feet and width 50 feet. **See Ch. 7 Answer Appendix.**

B **CCSS MODELING** **Use the map shown and an inch ruler to answer each question. Measure to the nearest sixteenth of an inch and assume that you can travel along any straight line.**

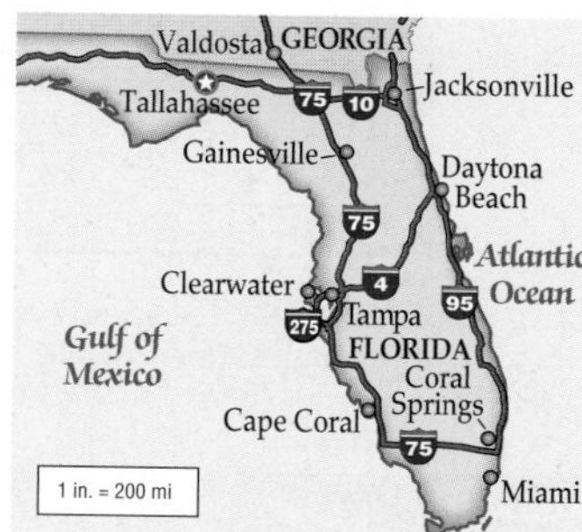

13. About how long would it take to drive from Valdosta, Georgia, to Daytona Beach, Florida, traveling at 65 miles per hour? **about 2.7 h or 2 h and 42 min**

14. How long would it take to drive from Gainesville to Miami, Florida, traveling at 70 miles per hour? **about 4.1 h or 4 h and 6 min**

15. **SCALE MODELS** If the distance between Earth and the Sun is actually 150,000,000 kilometers, how far apart are Earth and the Sun when using the 1:93,000,000 scale model? **1.61 km**

16. **LITERATURE** In the book, *Alice's Adventures in Wonderland*, Alice's size changes from her normal height of about 50 inches. Suppose Alice came across a door about 15 inches high and her height changed to 10 inches.

a. Find the ratio of the height of the door to Alice's height in Wonderland. $\frac{3}{2}$

b. How tall would the door have been in Alice's normal world? **about 75 in.**

17. **ROCKETS** Peter bought a $\frac{1 \text{ in.}}{12 \text{ ft}}$ scale model of the Mercury-Redstone rocket.

a. If the height of the model is 7 inches, what is the approximate height of the rocket? **84 ft**

b. If the diameter of the rocket is 70 inches, what is the diameter of the model? Round to the nearest half inch. **0.5 in.**

CCSS Teaching the Mathematical Practices

Modeling Mathematically proficient students can apply the mathematics they know to solve problems arising in everyday life. In Exercises 5–8 and 13–14, encourage students to check their answers using online mapping programs.

Enrichment
OL BL

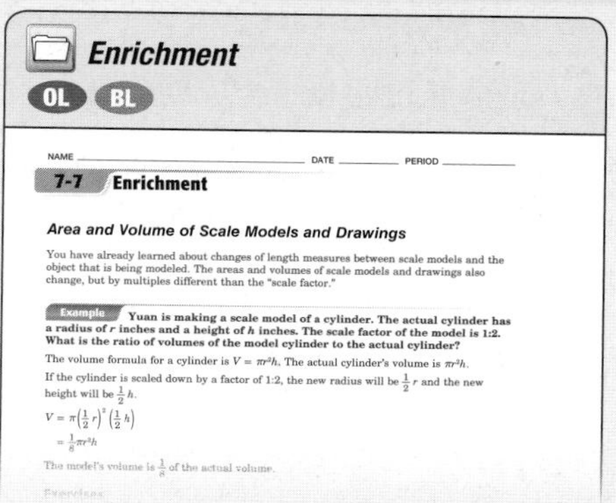

NAME ______ DATE ______ PERIOD ______

7-7 Enrichment

Area and Volume of Scale Models and Drawings

You have already learned about changes of length measures between scale models and the object that is being modeled. The areas and volumes of scale models and drawings also change, but by multiples different than the "scale factor."

Example **Yuan is making a scale model of a cylinder. The actual cylinder has a radius of *r* inches and a height of *h* inches. The scale factor of the model is 1:2. What is the ratio of volumes of the model cylinder to the actual cylinder?**

The volume formula for a cylinder is $V = \pi r^2 h$. The actual cylinder's volume is $\pi r^2 h$.

If the cylinder is scaled down by a factor of 1:2, the new radius will be $\frac{1}{2}r$ and the new height will be $\frac{1}{2}h$.

$V = \pi\left(\frac{1}{2}r\right)^2\left(\frac{1}{2}h\right)$

$= \frac{1}{8}\pi r^2 h$

The model's volume is $\frac{1}{8}$ of the actual volume.

Study Guide and Intervention
AL OL ELL

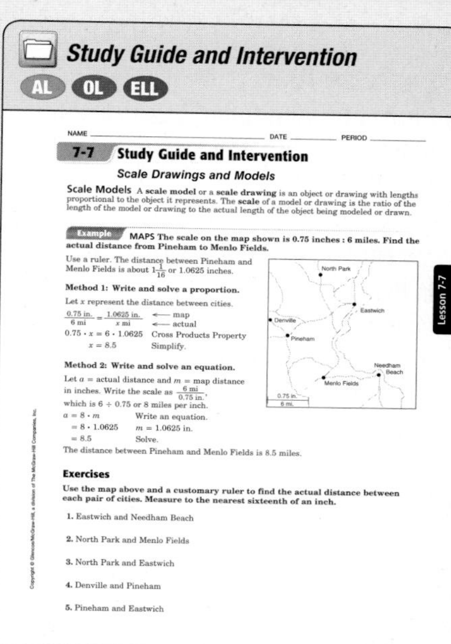

NAME ______ DATE ______ PERIOD ______

7-7 Study Guide and Intervention

Scale Drawings and Models

Scale Models A **scale model** or a **scale drawing** is an object or drawing with lengths proportional to the object it represents. The **scale** of a model or drawing is the ratio of the length of the model or drawing to the actual length of the object being modeled or drawn.

Example **MAPS The scale on the map shown is 0.75 inches : 6 miles. Find the actual distance from Pineham to Menlo Fields.**

Use a ruler. The distance between Pineham and Menlo Fields is about $1\frac{1}{16}$ or 1.0625 inches.

Method 1: Write and solve a proportion.

Let *x* represent the distance between cities.

$\frac{0.75 \text{ in.}}{6 \text{ mi}} = \frac{1.0625 \text{ in.}}{x \text{ mi}}$ ← map, ← actual

$0.75 \cdot x = 6 \cdot 1.0625$ Cross Products Property

$x = 8.5$ Simplify.

Method 2: Write and solve an equation.

Let *a* = actual distance and *m* = map distance in inches. Write the scale as $\frac{6 \text{ mi}}{0.75 \text{ in.}}$ which is 6 ÷ 0.75 or 8 miles per inch.

$a = 8 \cdot m$ Write an equation.

$= 8 \cdot 1.0625$ $m = 1.0625$ in.

$= 8.5$ Solve.

The distance between Pineham and Menlo Fields is 8.5 miles.

Exercises

Use the map above and a customary ruler to find the actual distance between each pair of cities. Measure to the nearest sixteenth of an inch.

1. Eastwich and Needham Beach
2. North Park and Menlo Fields
3. North Park and Eastwich
4. Denville and Pineham
5. Pineham and Eastwich

Lesson 7-7

Practice
AL OL BL ELL

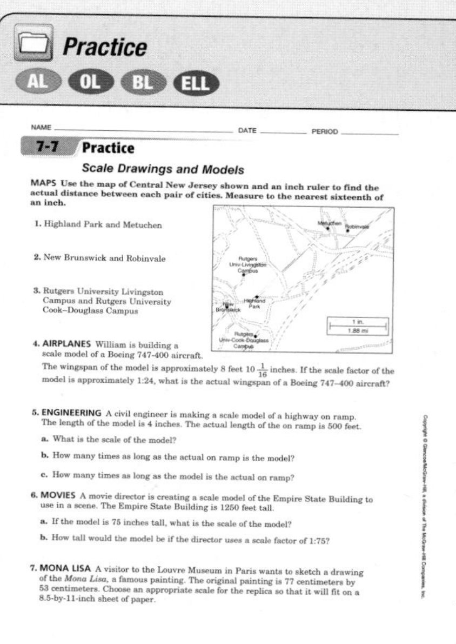

NAME ______ DATE ______ PERIOD ______

7-7 Practice

Scale Drawings and Models

MAPS Use the map of Central New Jersey shown and an inch ruler to find the actual distance between each pair of cities. Measure to the nearest sixteenth of an inch.

1. Highland Park and Metuchen
2. New Brunswick and Robinvale
3. Rutgers University Livingston Campus and Rutgers University Cook–Douglass Campus

4. **AIRPLANES** William is building a scale model of a Boeing 747-400 aircraft. The wingspan of the model is approximately 8 feet $10\frac{1}{16}$ inches. If the scale factor of the model is approximately 1:24, what is the actual wingspan of a Boeing 747-400 aircraft?

5. **ENGINEERING** A civil engineer is making a scale model of a highway on ramp. The length of the model is 4 inches. The actual length of the on ramp is 500 feet.
a. What is the scale of the model?
b. How many times as long as the actual on ramp is the model?
c. How many times as long as the model is the actual on ramp?

6. **MOVIES** A movie director is creating a scale model of the Empire State Building to use in a scene. The Empire State Building is 1250 feet tall.
a. If the model is 75 inches tall, what is the scale of the model?
b. How tall would the model be if the director uses a scale factor of 1:75?

7. **MONA LISA** A visitor to the Louvre Museum in Paris wants to sketch a drawing of the *Mona Lisa*, a famous painting. The original painting is 77 centimeters by 53 centimeters. Choose an appropriate scale for the replica so that it will fit on a 8.5-by-11-inch sheet of paper.

Word Problem Practice
AL OL BL ELL

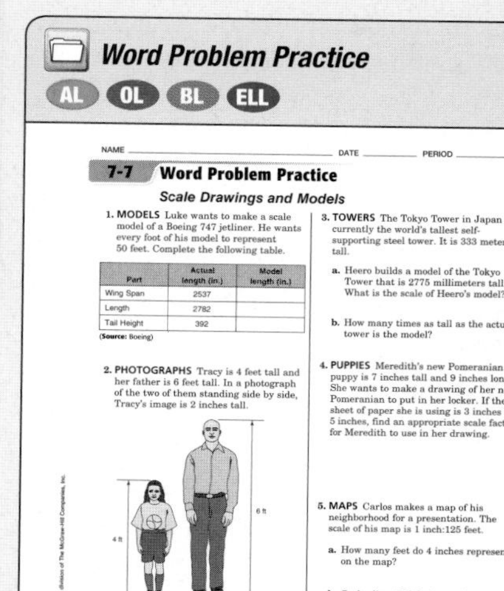

NAME ______ DATE ______ PERIOD ______

7-7 Word Problem Practice

Scale Drawings and Models

1. **MODELS** Luke wants to make a scale model of a Boeing 747 jetliner. He wants every foot of his model to represent 50 feet. Complete the following table.

Part	Actual length (in.)	Model length (in.)
Wing Span	2537	
Length	2782	
Tail Height	392	

(Source: Boeing)

2. **PHOTOGRAPHS** Tracy is 4 feet tall and her father is 6 feet tall. In a photograph of the two of them standing side by side, Tracy's image is 2 inches tall.

Although their images are much smaller, the ratio of their heights remains the same. How tall is Tracy's father's image in the photo? What is the scale of the photo?

3. **TOWERS** The Tokyo Tower in Japan is currently the world's tallest self-supporting steel tower. It is 333 meters tall.
a. Heero builds a model of the Tokyo Tower that is 2775 millimeters tall. What is the scale of Heero's model?
b. How many times as tall as the actual tower is the model?

4. **PUPPIES** Meredith's new Pomeranian puppy is 7 inches tall and 9 inches long. She wants to make a drawing of her new Pomeranian to put in her locker. If the sheet of paper she is using is 3 inches by 5 inches, find an appropriate scale factor for Meredith to use in her drawing.

5. **MAPS** Carlos makes a map of his neighborhood for a presentation. The scale of his map is 1 inch:125 feet.
a. How many feet do 4 inches represent on the map?
b. Carlos lives 250 feet away from Andrew. How many inches separate Carlos' home from Andrew's on the map?
c. During a practice run in front of his parents, Carlos realizes that his map is far too small. He decides to make his map 5 times as large. What would be the scale of the larger map?

Lesson 7-7

connectED.mcgraw-hill.com

Exercise Alert

Protractor and Ruler Exercise 20 requires the use of a protractor and a ruler.

Multiple Representations

In Exercise 20, students use geometric sketches, a table, and verbal description to explore the altitudes of right triangles.

WatchOut!

Error Analysis In Exercise 21, students should pay careful attention to the wording. To find the scale factor of the actual high school to the replica, write a ratio of the height of the high school to the height of the replica. Divide to find the scale factor. Tamara found the scale factor of the replica to the school.

Tips for New Teachers

Sense-Making Show students that they can solve Exercise 22 by considering a particular case. Demonstrate this idea by extending each dimension of a regular and an irregular polygon by a constant. Then write and solve proportions for each figure to show that the extended regular polygon is a scale model of the original.

Additional Answer

20a. Sample answer:

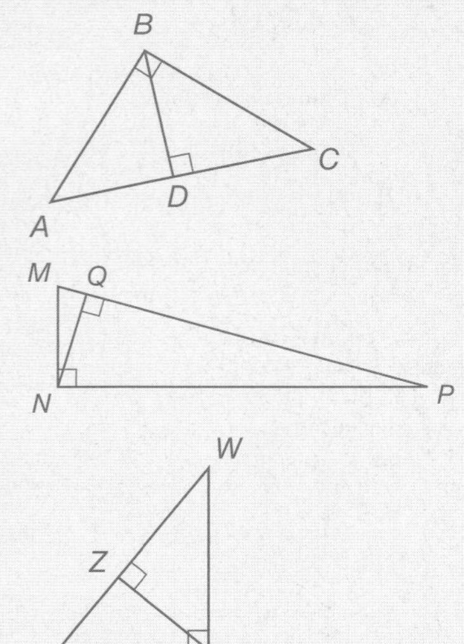

18. **ARCHITECTURE** A replica of the Statue of Liberty in Austin, Texas, is $16\frac{3}{4}$ feet tall. If the scale factor of the replica to the actual statue is 1:9, how tall is the actual statue in New York Harbor? **151 ft**

19 **AMUSEMENT PARK** The Eiffel Tower in Paris, France, is 986 feet tall, not including its antenna. A replica of the Eiffel Tower was built as a ride in an amusement park. If the scale factor of the replica to the actual tower is approximately 1:3, how tall is the ride? **329 ft**

20. **MULTIPLE REPRESENTATIONS** In this problem, you will explore the altitudes of right triangles.

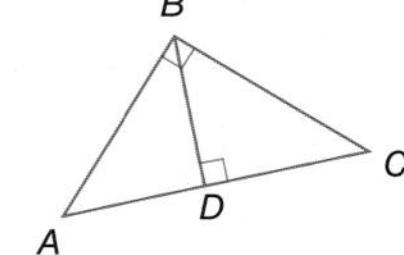

a. Geometric Draw right $\triangle ABC$ with the right angle at vertex B. Draw altitude $\overline{BD}$. Draw right $\triangle MNP$, with right angle N and altitude $\overline{NQ}$, and right $\triangle WXY$, with right angle X and altitude $\overline{XZ}$. **See margin.**

b. Tabular Measure and record indicated angles in the table below. **Sample answers are given.**

	Angle Measure					
△ABC	△ABC		△BDC		△ADB	
	ABC	90°	BDC	90°	ADB	90°
	A	47°	CBD	47°	BAD	47°
	C	43°	DCB	43°	DBA	43°
△MNP	△MNP		△NQP		△MQN	
	MNP	90°	NQP	90°	MQN	90°
	M	74°	PNQ	74°	NMQ	74°
	P	16°	QPN	16°	QNM	16°
△WXY	△WXY		△WZX		△XZY	
	WXY	90°	WZX	90°	XZY	90°
	W	38°	XWZ	38°	YXZ	38°
	Y	52°	ZXW	52°	ZYX	52°

c. Verbal Make a conjecture about the altitude of a right triangle originating at the right angle of the triangle. **Sample answer: The altitude originating at the right vertex of a right triangle divides the triangle into three similar triangles.**

21. Felix; sample answer: The ratio of the actual high school to the replica is $\frac{75}{1.5}$ or 50:1.

22. Sample answer: The figure must be regular so that when each dimension is increased by a constant value, the proportion remains the same.

23. The first drawing will be larger. The second drawing will be $\frac{1}{6}$ the size of the first drawing, so the scale factor is 1:6.

25. Both can be written as ratios comparing lengths. A scale factor must have the same unit of measure for both measurements.

H.O.T. Problems Use Higher-Order Thinking Skills

21. **ERROR ANALYSIS** Felix and Tamara are building a replica of their high school. The high school is 75 feet tall and the replica is 1.5 feet tall. Felix says the scale factor of the actual high school to the replica is 50:1, while Tamara says the scale factor is 1:50. Is either of them correct? Explain your reasoning.

22. **CHALLENGE** You can produce a scale model of a certain object by extending each dimension by a constant. What must be true of the shape of the object? Explain your reasoning.

23. CCSS **SENSE-MAKING** Sofia is making two scale drawings of the lunchroom. In the first drawing, Sofia used a scale of 1 inch = 1 foot, and in the second drawing she used a scale of 1 inch = 6 feet. Which scale will produce a larger drawing? What is the scale factor of the first drawing to the second drawing? Explain.

24. **OPEN ENDED** Draw a scale model of your classroom using any scale. **See students' work.**

25. **WRITING IN MATH** Compare and contrast scale and scale factor.

Differentiated Instruction AL OL BL ELL

If students have trouble understanding the concept of scale,

Then have them make simple models with building blocks in a scale of 1 to 3, or a similar scale. The students should see that for every block in the smaller model, there are three blocks in the larger one.

Standardized Test Practice

26. SHORT RESPONSE If $3^x = 27^{(x-4)}$, then what is the value of x? **6**

27. In $\triangle ABC$, $\overline{BD}$ is a median. If $AD = 3x + 5$ and $CD = 5x - 1$, find AC. **D**

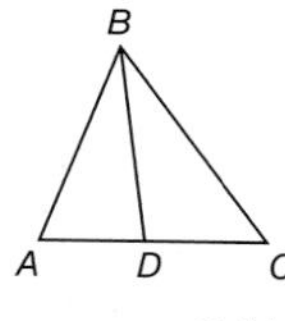

A 6
B 12
C 14
D 28

28. In a triangle, the ratio of the measures of the sides is 4 : 7 : 10, and its longest side is 40 centimeters. Find the perimeter of the triangle in centimeters. **H**

F 37 cm
G 43 cm
H 84 cm
J 168 cm

29. SAT/ACT If Lydia can type 80 words in two minutes, how long will it take Lydia to type 600 words? **C**

A 30 min
B 20 min
C 15 min
D 10 min
E 5 min

Spiral Review

30. PAINTING Aaron is painting a portrait of a friend for an art class. Since his friend doesn't have time to model, he uses a photo that is 6 inches by 8 inches. If the canvas is 24 inches by 32 inches, is the painting a dilation of the original photo? If so, what is the scale factor? Explain. (Lesson 7-6) **Yes; 4; sample answer: Since $\frac{24}{6} = \frac{32}{8} = \frac{4}{1}$, the portrait is an enlargement of the photo. The scale factor is 4.**

Find x. (Lesson 7-5)

31. **12**

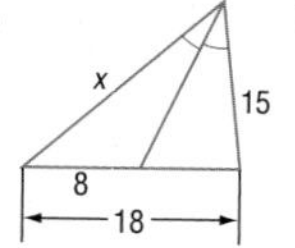

32. **22**

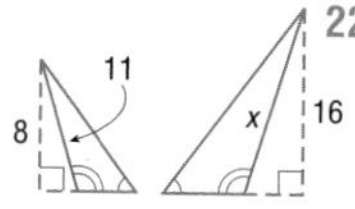

33. **17.5**

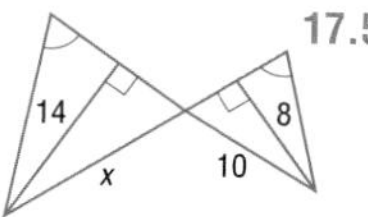

ALGEBRA Quadrilateral $JKMN$ is a rectangle. (Lesson 6-4)

34. If $NQ = 2x + 3$ and $QK = 5x - 9$, find JQ. **11**

35. If $m\angle NJM = 2x - 3$ and $m\angle KJM = x + 5$, find x. **29.3**

36. If $NM = 8x - 14$ and $JK = x^2 + 1$, find JK. **10 or 26**

J K Q N M

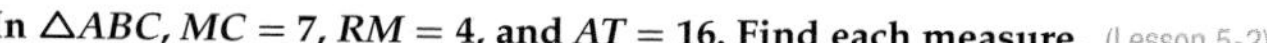

In $\triangle ABC$, $MC = 7$, $RM = 4$, and $AT = 16$. Find each measure. (Lesson 5-2)

37. MS **3.5**
38. AM **10.7**
39. SC **10.5**
40. RB **12**
41. MB **8**
42. TM **5.3**

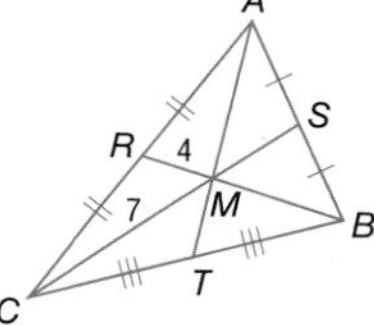

Determine whether $\triangle JKL \cong \triangle XYZ$. Explain. (Lesson 4-4) **43–44. See margin.**

43. $J(3, 9)$, $K(4, 6)$, $L(1, 5)$, $X(1, 7)$, $Y(2, 4)$, $Z(-1, 3)$

44. $J(-1, -1)$, $K(0, 6)$, $L(2, 3)$, $X(3, 1)$, $Y(5, 3)$, $Z(8, 1)$

Skills Review

Simplify each expression.

45. $\sqrt{4 \cdot 16}$ **8**
46. $\sqrt{3 \cdot 27}$ **9**
47. $\sqrt{32 \cdot 72}$ **48**
48. $\sqrt{15 \cdot 16}$ **$4\sqrt{15}$**
49. $\sqrt{33 \cdot 21}$ **$3\sqrt{77}$**

4 Assess

Name the Math Have students discuss how the information they have learned about similar figures applies to scale models.

Formative Assessment

Check for student understanding of Lesson 7-7.

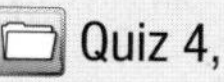

Quiz 4, p. 52

Additional Answers

43. $JK = \sqrt{10}$, $KL = \sqrt{10}$, $JL = \sqrt{20}$, $XY = \sqrt{10}$, $YZ = \sqrt{10}$, and $XZ = \sqrt{20}$. Each pair of corresponding sides has the same measure so they are congruent. $\triangle JKL \cong \triangle XYZ$ by SSS.

44. $JK = \sqrt{50}$, $KL = \sqrt{13}$, $JL = 5$, $XY = \sqrt{8}$, $YZ = \sqrt{13}$, and $XZ = 5$. The corresponding sides are not congruent so $\triangle JKL$ is not congruent to $\triangle XYZ$.

Formative Assessment

KeyVocabulary The page references after each word denote where that term was first introduced. If students have difficulty answering questions 1–8, remind them that they can use these page references to refresh their memories about the vocabulary terms.

Summative Assessment

Vocabulary Test, p. 54

Vocabulary Review

Vocabulary Review provides students the opportunity to check their understanding of important concepts and terminology in an online game format.

FOLDABLES StudyOrganizer

Dinah Zike's Foldables®

Have students look through the chapter to make sure they have included examples in their Foldables for each lesson of the chapter. Suggest that students keep their Foldables handy while completing the Study Guide and Review pages. Point out that their Foldables can serve as a quick review when studying for the chapter test.

CHAPTER 7 Study Guide and Review

Study Guide

KeyConcepts

Proportions (Lesson 7-1)

- For any numbers a and c and any nonzero numbers b and d, $\frac{a}{b} = \frac{c}{d}$ if and only if $ad = bc$.

Similar Polygons and Triangles (Lessons 7-2 and 7-3)

- Two polygons are similar if and only if their corresponding angles are congruent and the measures of their corresponding sides are proportional.
- Two triangles are similar if:

  AA: Two angles of one triangle are congruent to two angles of the other triangle.

  SSS: The measures of the corresponding sides of the two triangles are proportional.

  SAS: The measures of two sides of one triangle are proportional to the measures of two corresponding sides of another triangle and their included angles are congruent.

Proportional Parts (Lessons 7-4 and 7-5)

- If a line is parallel to one side of a triangle and intersects the other two sides in two distinct points, then it separates these sides into segments of proportional length.
- A midsegment of a triangle is parallel to one side of the triangle and its length is one-half the length of that side.
- Two triangles are similar when each of the following are proportional in measure: their perimeters, their corresponding altitudes, their corresponding angle bisectors, and their corresponding medians.

Similarity Transformations and Scale Drawings and Models (Lessons 7-6 and 7-7)

- A scale model or scale drawing has lengths that are proportional to the corresponding lengths in the object it represents.

FOLDABLES StudyOrganizer

Be sure the Key Concepts are noted in your Foldable.

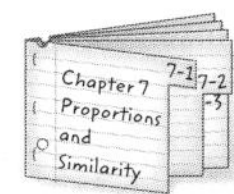

KeyVocabulary

cross products (p. 462)	reduction (p. 511)
dilation (p. 511)	scale (p. 518)
enlargement (p. 511)	scale drawing (p. 518)
extremes (p. 462)	scale factor (p. 470)
means (p. 462)	scale model (p. 518)
midsegment of a triangle (p. 491)	similar polygons (p. 469)
proportion (p. 462)	similarity transformation (p. 511)
ratio (p. 461)	

VocabularyCheck

Choose the letter of the word or phrase that best completes each statement.

a. ratio	**h.** SSS Similarity Theorem
b. proportion	**i.** SAS Similarity Theorem
c. means	**j.** midsegment
d. extremes	**k.** dilation
e. similar	**l.** enlargement
f. scale factor	**m.** reduction
g. AA Similarity Post.	

1. A(n) __?__ of a triangle has endpoints that are the midpoints of two sides of the triangle. j
2. A(n) __?__ is a comparison of two quantities using division. a
3. If $\angle A \cong \angle X$ and $\angle C \cong \angle Z$, then $\triangle ABC \sim \triangle XYZ$ by the __?__. g
4. A(n) __?__ is an example of a similarity transformation. k
5. If $\frac{a}{b} = \frac{c}{d}$, then a and d are the __?__. d
6. The ratio of the lengths of two corresponding sides of two similar polygons is the __?__. f
7. A(n) __?__ is an equation stating that two ratios are equivalent. b
8. A dilation with a scale factor of $\frac{2}{5}$ will result in a(n) __?__. m

Lesson-by-Lesson Review

7-1 Ratios and Proportions

Solve each proportion.

9. $\frac{x+8}{6} = \frac{2x-3}{10}$ **49**

10. $\frac{3x+9}{x} = \frac{12}{5}$ **−15**

11. $\frac{x}{12} = \frac{50}{6x}$ **10 or −10**

12. $\frac{7}{x} = \frac{14}{9}$ **4.5**

13. The ratio of the lengths of the three sides of a triangle is 5 : 8 : 10. If its perimeter is 276 inches, find the length of the longest side of the triangle. **120 in.**

14. CARPENTRY A board that is 12 feet long must be cut into two pieces that have lengths in a ratio of 3 to 2. Find the lengths of the two pieces. **7.2 ft and 4.8 ft**

Example 1

Solve $\frac{2x-3}{4} = \frac{x+9}{3}$.

$\frac{2x-3}{4} = \frac{x+9}{3}$	Original proportion
$3(2x-3) = 4(x+9)$	Cross Products Property
$6x - 9 = 4x + 36$	Simplify.
$2x - 9 = 36$	Subtract.
$2x = 45$	Add 9 to each side.
$x = 22.5$	Divide each side by 2.

7-2 Similar Polygons

Determine whether each pair of figures is similar. If so, write the similarity statement and scale factor. If not, explain your reasoning. **15–16. See margin.**

15.

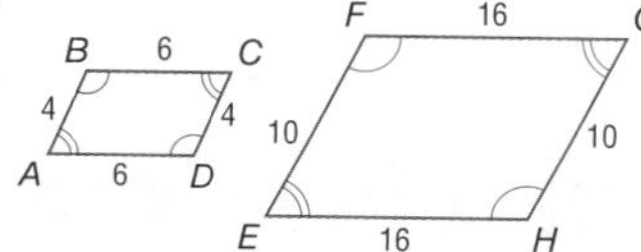

16.

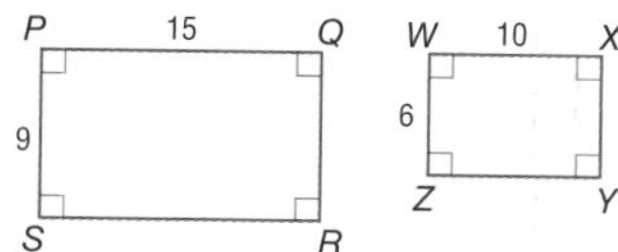

17. The two triangles in the figure below are similar. Find the value of *x*. **16.5**

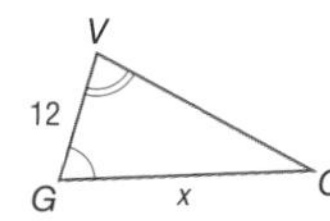

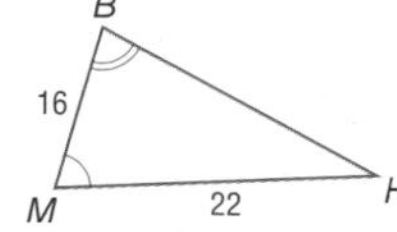

18. PHOTOS If the dimensions of a photo are 2 inches by 3 inches and the dimensions of a poster are 8 inches by 12 inches, are the photo and poster similar? Explain. **Yes; the ratios are the same.**

Example 2

Determine whether the pair of triangles is similar. If so, write the similarity statement and scale factor. If not, explain your reasoning.

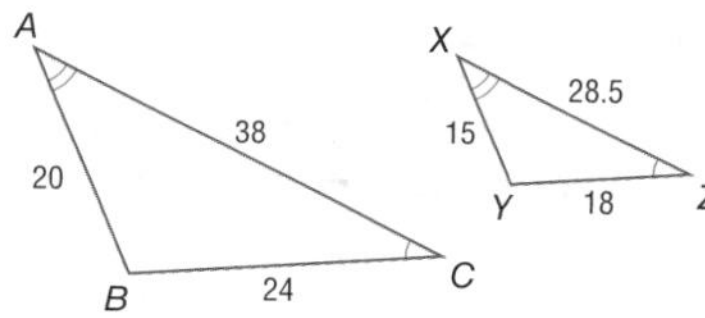

$\angle A \cong \angle X$ and $\angle C \cong \angle Z$, so by the Third Angle Theorem, $\angle B \cong \angle Y$. All of the corresponding angles are therefore congruent.

Similar polygons must also have proportional side lengths. Check the ratios of corresponding side lengths.

$\frac{AB}{XY} = \frac{20}{15}$ or $\frac{4}{3}$ $\quad \frac{BC}{YZ} = \frac{24}{18}$ or $\frac{4}{3}$ $\quad \frac{AC}{XZ} = \frac{38}{28.5}$ or $\frac{4}{3}$

Since corresponding sides are proportional, $\triangle ABC \sim \triangle XYZ$. So, the triangles are similar with a scale factor of $\frac{4}{3}$.

Lesson-by-Lesson Review

Intervention If the given examples are not sufficient to review the topics covered by the questions, remind students that the lesson references tell them where to review that topic in their textbooks.

Two-Day Option Have students complete the Lesson-by-Lesson Review. Then you can use eAssessment to customize another review worksheet that practices all the objectives of this chapter or only the objectives on which your students need more help.

Additional Answers

15. No, the polygons are not similar because the corresponding sides are not proportional.

16. Yes, the rectangles are similar because all of the corresponding angles are congruent and the corresponding sides are proportional in a 3:2 ratio.

connectED.mcgraw-hill.com 525

CHAPTER 7 Study Guide and Review *Continued*

7-3 Similar Triangles

Determine whether the triangles are similar. If so, write a similarity statement. Explain your reasoning.

19.

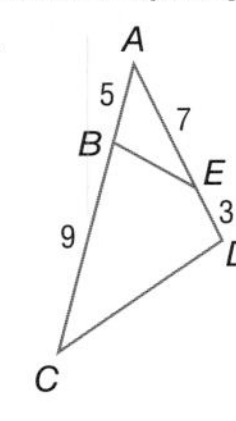

20.

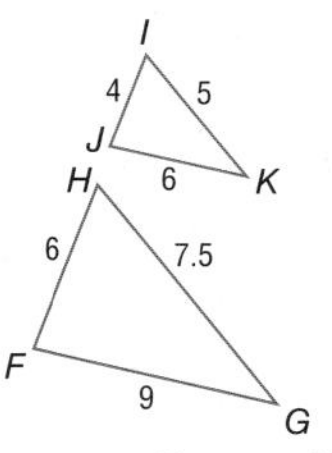

21.

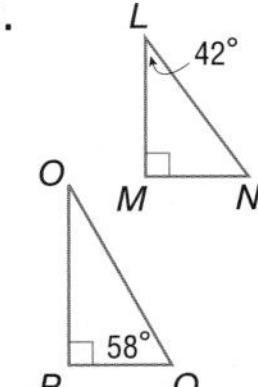

22.

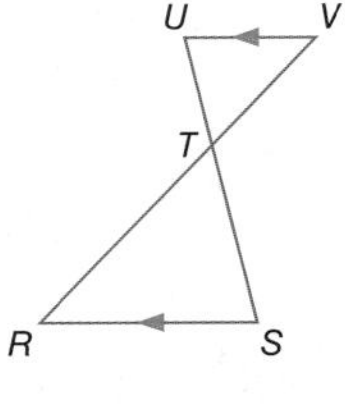

23. TREES To estimate the height of a tree, Dave stands in the shadow of the tree so that his shadow and the tree's shadow end at the same point. Dave is 6 feet 4 inches tall and his shadow is 15 feet long. If he is standing 66 feet away from the tree, what is the height of the tree? 34.2 ft

Example 3

Determine whether the triangles are similar. If so, write a similarity statement. Explain your reasoning.

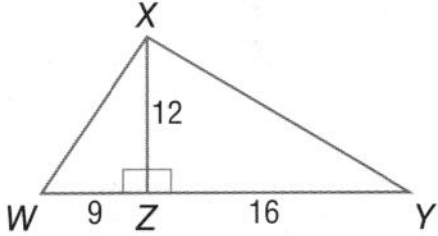

$\angle WZX \cong \angle XZY$ because they are both right angles. Now compare the ratios of the legs of the right triangles.

$$\frac{WZ}{XZ} = \frac{9}{12} = \frac{3}{4} \qquad \frac{XZ}{YZ} = \frac{12}{16} = \frac{3}{4}$$

Since two pairs of sides are proportional with the included angles congruent, $\triangle WZX \sim \triangle XZY$ by SAS Similarity.

19. Yes, $\triangle ABE \sim \triangle ADC$ by the SAS ~ Thm.
20. Yes, $\triangle IJK \sim \triangle HFG$ by the SSS ~ Thm.
21. No, the triangles are not similar because not all corresponding angles are congruent.
22. Yes, $\triangle TUV \sim \triangle TSR$ by the AA ~ Post.

7-4 Parallel Lines and Proportional Parts

Find *x*.

24. 9.6

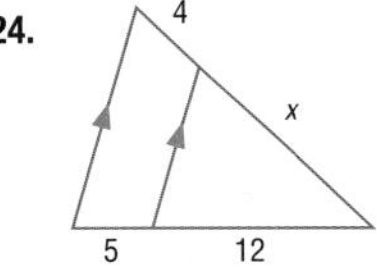

25. 22.5

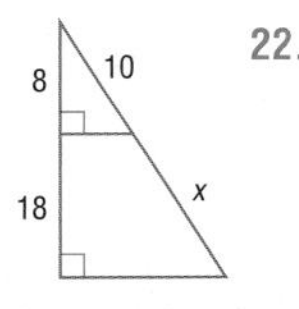

26. STREETS Find the distance along Broadway between 37th Street and 36th Street. 275 ft

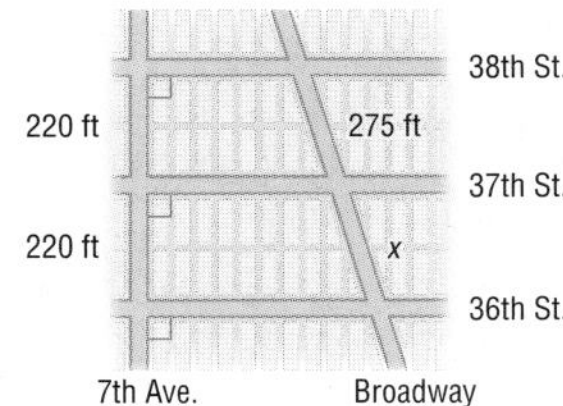

Example 4

ALGEBRA Find *x* and *y*.

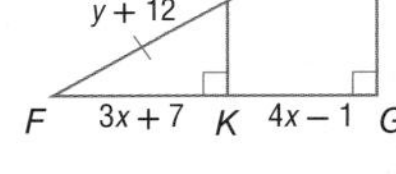

$FK = KG$

$3x + 7 = 4x - 1$

$-x = -8$

$x = 8$

$FJ = JH$	Definition of congruence
$y + 12 = 2y - 5$	Substitution
$-y = -17$	Subtract.
$y = 17$	Simplify.

526 | Chapter 7 | Study Guide and Review

7-5 Parts of Similar Triangles

Find the value of each variable.

27.

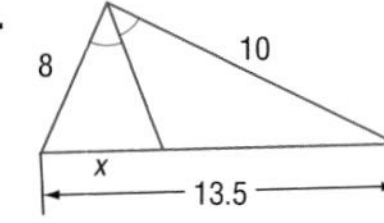

6

28.

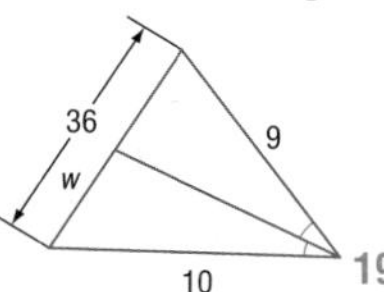

19

29. MAPS The scale given on a map of the state of Missouri indicates that 3 inches represents 50 miles. The cities of St. Louis, Springfield, and Kansas City form a triangle. If the measurements of the lengths of the sides of this triangle on the map are 15 inches, 10 inches, and 13 inches, find the perimeter of the actual triangle formed by these cities to the nearest mile. 633 mi

Example 5

Find x.

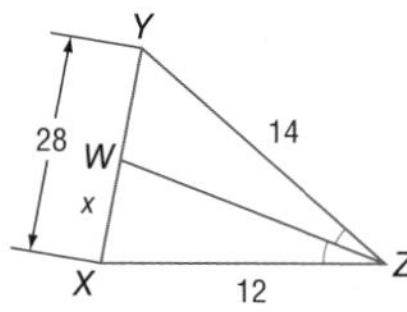

Use the Triangle Angle Bisector Theorem to write a proportion.

$\frac{WX}{YW} = \frac{XZ}{YZ}$ Triangle Angle Bisector Thm.

$\frac{x}{28 - x} = \frac{12}{14}$ Substitution

$(28 - x)(12) = x \cdot 14$ Cross Products Property

$336 - 12x = 14x$ Simplify.

$336 = 26x$ Add.

$12.9 = x$ Simplify.

30. reduction; $\frac{1}{3}$
31. enlargement; 2

7-6 Similarity Transformations

Determine whether the dilation from A to B is an *enlargement* or a *reduction*. Then find the scale factor of the dilation.

30.

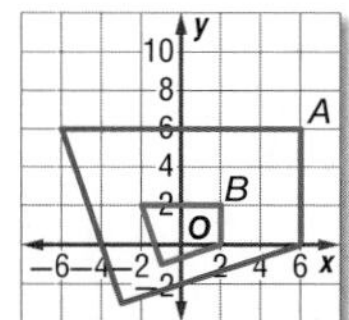

31.

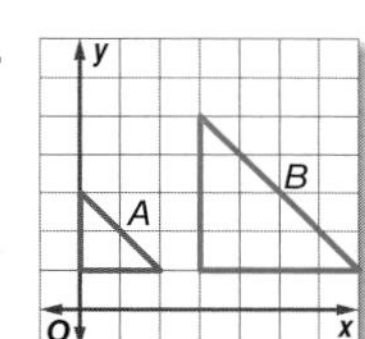

32. GRAPHIC DESIGN Jamie wants to use a photocopier to enlarge her design for the Honors Program at her school. She sets the copier to 250%. If the original drawing was 6 inches by 9 inches, find the dimensions of the enlargement. 15 in. by 22.5 in.

Example 6

Determine whether the dilation from A to B is an *enlargement* or a *reduction*. Then find the scale factor of the dilation.

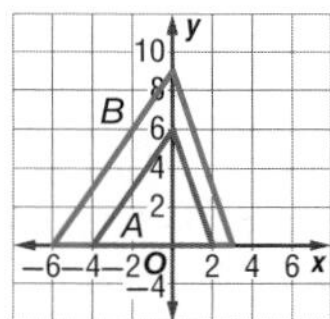

B is larger than A, so the dilation is an enlargement. The distance between the vertices at $(-4, 0)$ and $(2, 0)$ for A is 6 and the distance between the vertices at $(-6, 0)$ and $(3, 0)$ for B is 9. So the scale factor is $\frac{9}{6}$ or $\frac{3}{2}$.

connectED.mcgraw-hill.com 527

Anticipation Guide

Have students complete the Chapter 7 Anticipation Guide and discuss how their responses have changed now that they have completed Chapter 7.

Anticipation Guide, p. 3

CHAPTER 7 Study Guide and Review *Continued*

7-7 Scale Drawings and Models

33. **BUILDING PLANS** In a scale drawing of a school's floor plan, 6 inches represents 100 feet. If the distance from one end of the main hallway to the other is 175 feet, find the corresponding length in the scale drawing. 10.5 in.

34. **MODEL TRAINS** A popular scale for model trains is the 1 : 48 scale. If the actual train car had a length of 72 feet, find the corresponding length of the model in inches. 18 in.

35. **MAPS** A map of the eastern United States has a scale where 3 inches = 25 miles. If the distance on the map between Columbia, South Carolina, and Charlotte, North Carolina, is 11.5 inches what is the actual distance between the cities? 95.8 mi

Example 7

In the scale of a map of the Pacific Northwest 1 inch = 20 miles. The distance on the map between Portland, Oregon, and Seattle, Washington, is 8.75 inches. Find the distance between the two cities.

$\frac{1}{20} = \frac{8.75}{x}$ Write a proportion.

$x = 20(8.75)$ Cross Products Property

$x = 175$ Simplify.

The distance between the two cities is 175 miles.

CHAPTER 7 Practice Test

Solve each proportion.

1. $\frac{3}{7} = \frac{12}{x}$ 28
2. $\frac{2x}{5} = \frac{x+3}{3}$ 15
3. $\frac{4x}{15} = \frac{60}{x}$ 15 or −15
4. $\frac{5x-4}{4x+7} = \frac{13}{11}$ 45

Determine whether each pair of figures is similar. If so, write the similarity statement and scale factor. If not, explain your reasoning.

5. 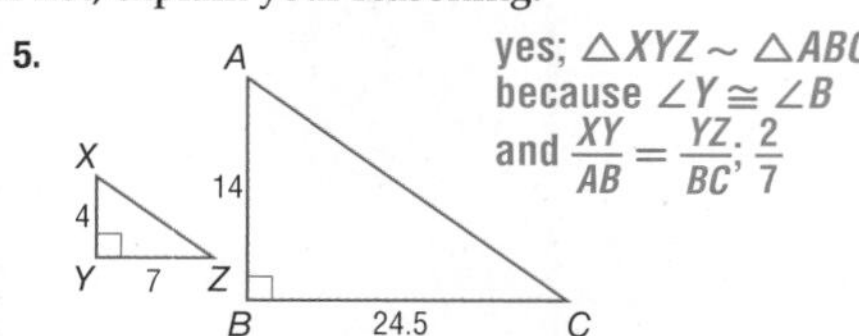

yes; $\triangle XYZ \sim \triangle ABC$ because $\angle Y \cong \angle B$ and $\frac{XY}{AB} = \frac{YZ}{BC}$; $\frac{2}{7}$

6. 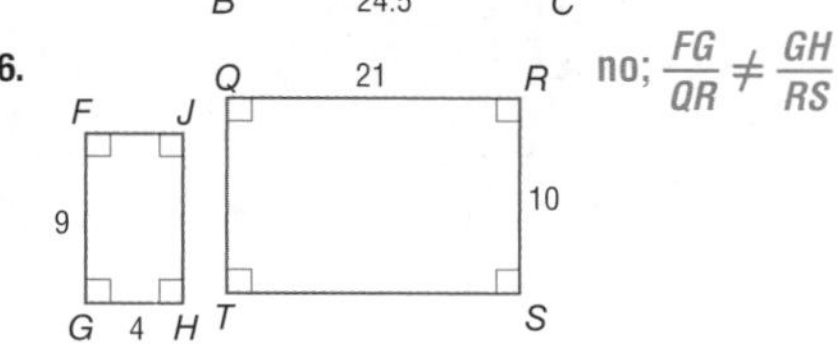

no; $\frac{FG}{QR} \neq \frac{GH}{RS}$

7. **CURRENCY** Jane is traveling to Europe this summer with the French Club. She plans to bring \$300 to spend while she is there. If \$90 in U.S. currency is equivalent to 63 euros, how many euros will she receive when she exchanges her money? 210

ALGEBRA **Find x and y. Round to the nearest tenth if necessary.**

8. 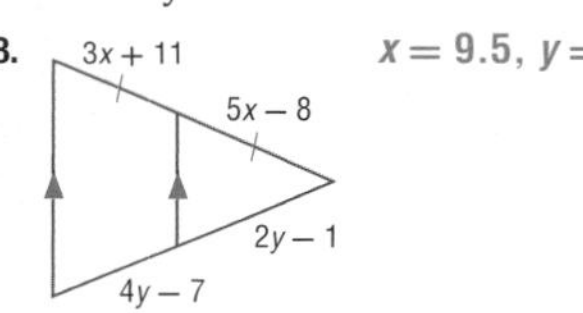

$x = 9.5$, $y = 3$

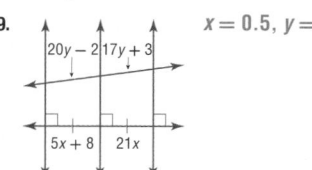

9. $x = 0.5$, $y = 1.7$

20y − 2, 17y + 3, 5x + 8, 21x

10. **ALGEBRA** Equilateral $\triangle MNP$ has perimeter $12a + 18b$. $\overline{QR}$ is a midsegment. What is QR? $2a + 3b$

11. **ALGEBRA** Right isosceles $\triangle ABC$ has hypotenuse length h. $\overline{DE}$ is a midsegment with length $4x$ that is not parallel to the hypotenuse. What is the perimeter of $\triangle ABC$? $16x + h$

12. **SHORT RESPONSE** Jimmy has a diecast metal car that is a scale model of an actual race car. If the actual length of the car is 10 feet and 6 inches and the model has a length of 7 inches, what is the scale factor of model to actual car? 1:18

Find x.

13. 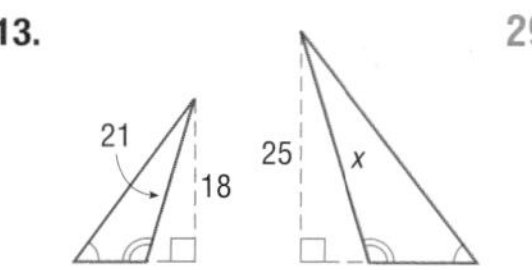

29.2

14. 34.7

26, 30, x, 40

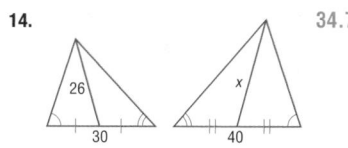

Determine whether the dilation from A to B is an *enlargement* or a *reduction*. Then find the scale factor of the dilation.

15. 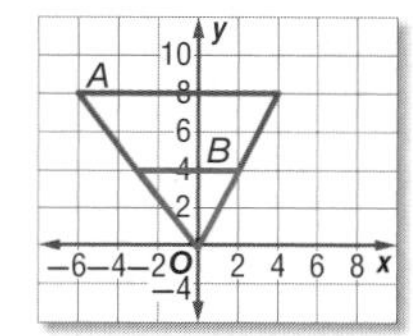

reduction; $\frac{1}{2}$

16. 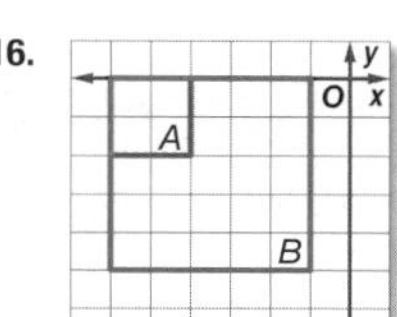

enlargement; $\frac{5}{2}$

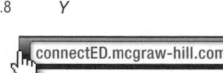

17. **ALGEBRA** Identify the similar triangles. Find WZ and UZ.
$\triangle WUZ \sim \triangle YUW$ by AA Similarity; 12, 7.2

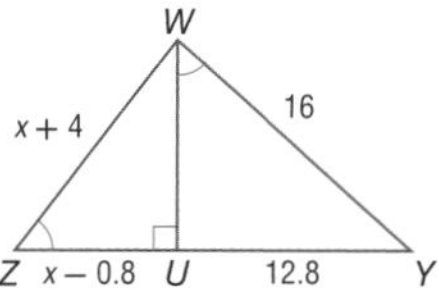

Summative Assessment

Use these alternate leveled chapter tests to differentiate assessment for your students.

Leveled Chapter 7 Tests

Form	Type	Level	Page(s)
1	MC	AL	55–56
2A	MC	OL	57–58
2B	MC	OL	59–60
2C	FR	OL	61–62
2D	FR	OL	63–64
3	FR	BL	65–66
Vocabulary Test			54
Extended-Response Test			67

MC = multiple-choice questions
FR = free-response questions

eAssessment Customize and create multiple versions of your chapter test and their answer keys. All of the questions from the leveled chapter tests in the *Chapter 7 Resource Masters* are also available on eAssessment.

InterventionPlanner

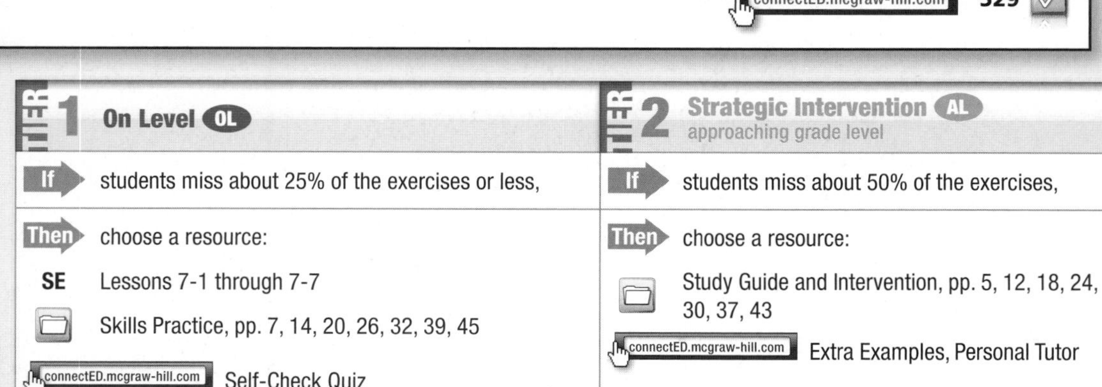

Tier 1 On Level OL

If students miss about 25% of the exercises or less,

Then choose a resource:

SE Lessons 7-1 through 7-7

Skills Practice, pp. 7, 14, 20, 26, 32, 39, 45

connectED.mcgraw-hill.com Self-Check Quiz

Tier 2 Strategic Intervention AL approaching grade level

If students miss about 50% of the exercises,

Then choose a resource:

Study Guide and Intervention, pp. 5, 12, 18, 24, 30, 37, 43

connectED.mcgraw-hill.com Extra Examples, Personal Tutor

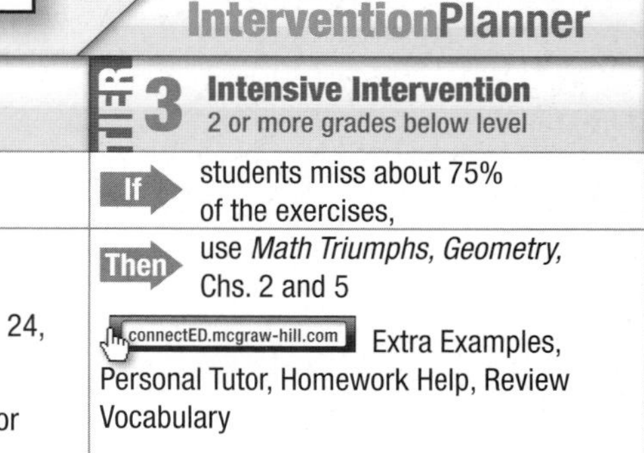

Tier 3 Intensive Intervention 2 or more grades below level

If students miss about 75% of the exercises,

Then use *Math Triumphs, Geometry,* Chs. 2 and 5

connectED.mcgraw-hill.com Extra Examples, Personal Tutor, Homework Help, Review Vocabulary

1 Focus

Objective Identify the answer choices that are incorrect in a standardized test problem.

2 Teach

Scaffolding Questions

Ask:

- Have you ever wondered when you stretch a picture why the new image doesn't look like the original? Answers will vary.
- What is your favorite baseball player's batting average? Answers will vary.
- What is the student-teacher ratio at your school? Answers will vary.

CHAPTER 7 Preparing for Standardized Tests

Identifying Nonexamples

Multiple choice items sometimes ask you to determine which of the given answer choices is a nonexample. These types of problems require a different approach when solving them.

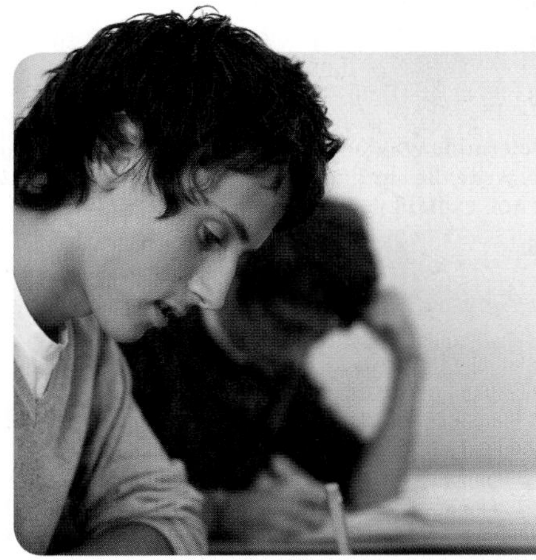

Strategies for Identifying Nonexamples

Step 1

Read and understand the problem statement.

- **Nonexample:** A nonexample is an answer choice that does not satisfy the conditions of the problem statement.
- **Keywords:** Look for the word *not* (usually bold, all capital letters, or italicized) to indicate that you need to find a nonexample.

Step 2

Follow the concepts and steps below to help you identify nonexamples. Identify any answer choices that are clearly incorrect and eliminate them.

- Eliminate any answer choices that are not in the proper format.
- Eliminate any answer choices that do not have the correct units.

Standardized Test Example

Read the problem. Identify what you need to know. Then use the information in the problem to solve.

In the adjacent triangle, you know that $\angle MQN \cong \angle RQS$. Which of the following would *not* be sufficient to prove that $\triangle QMN \sim \triangle QRS$?

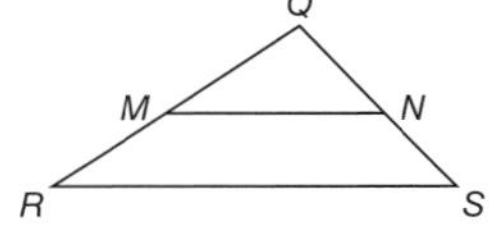

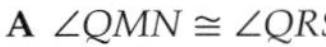

A $\angle QMN \cong \angle QRS$

B $\overline{MN} \parallel \overline{RS}$

C $\overline{QN} \cong \overline{NS}$

D $\dfrac{QM}{QR} = \dfrac{QN}{QS}$

530 | Chapter 7 | Preparing for Standardized Tests

The italicized *not* indicates that you need to find a nonexample. Test each answer choice using the principles of triangle similarity to see which one would not prove $\triangle QMN \cong \triangle QRS$.

Choice A: $\angle QMN \cong \angle QRS$

If $\angle QMN \cong \angle QRS$, then $\triangle QMN \sim \triangle QRS$ by AA Similarity.

Choice B: $\overline{MN} \parallel \overline{RS}$

If $\overline{MN} \parallel \overline{RS}$, then $\angle QMN \cong \angle QRS$, because they are corresponding angles of two parallel lines cut by transversal $\overline{QR}$. Therefore, $\triangle QMN \sim \triangle QRS$ by AA Similarity.

Choice C: $\overline{QN} \cong \overline{NS}$

If $\overline{QN} \cong \overline{NS}$, we cannot conclude that $\triangle QMN \sim \triangle QRS$ because we do not know anything about $\overline{QM}$ and $\overline{MR}$. So, answer choice C is a nonexample.

The correct answer is C. You should also check answer choice D to make sure it is a valid example if you have time.

Exercises

Read each problem. Identify what you need to know. Then use the information in the problem to solve.

1. The ratio of the measures of the angles of the quadrilateral below is 6:5:4:3. Which of the following is *not* an angle measure of the figure? D

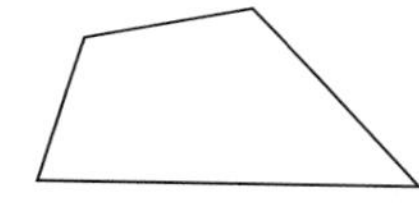

A 60°
B 80°
C 120°
D 140°

2. Which figure can serve as a counterexample to the conjecture below? G

> If all angles of a quadrilateral are right angles, then the quadrilateral is a square.

F parallelogram
G rectangle
H rhombus
J trapezoid

3. Consider the figure below. Which of the following is *not* sufficient to prove that $\triangle GIK \sim \triangle HIG$? C

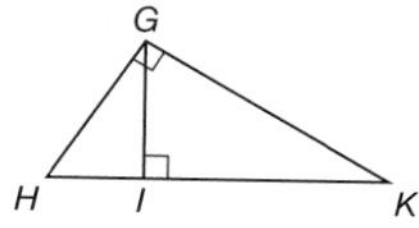

A $\angle GKI \cong \angle HGI$

B $\frac{HI}{GI} = \frac{GI}{IK}$

C $\frac{GH}{GI} = \frac{GK}{IK}$

D $\angle IGK \cong \angle IHG$

4. Which triangles are *not* necessarily similar? H

F two right triangles with one angle measuring 30°
G two right triangles with one angle measuring 45°
H two isosceles triangles
J two equilateral triangles

Additional Example

In the triangle below, you know that $\angle EBF \cong \angle ABC$. Which of the following would *not* be sufficient to prove that $\triangle BFE \sim \triangle BCA$? C

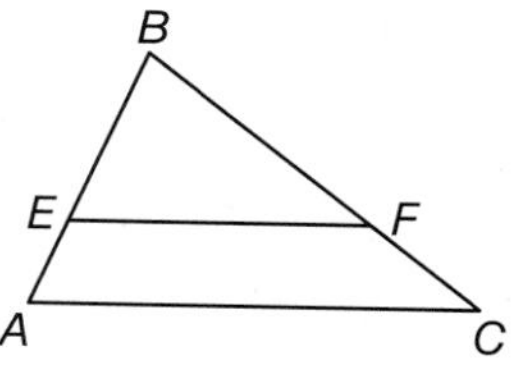

A $\angle BFE \cong \angle BCA$

B $\overline{EF} \parallel \overline{AC}$

C $\overline{BE} \cong \overline{EA}$

D $\frac{BF}{BC} = \frac{BE}{BA}$

3 Assess

Use Exercises 1–4 to assess students' understanding.

connectED.mcgraw-hill.com 531

Diagnose Student Errors

Survey student responses for each item. Class trends may indicate common errors and misconceptions.

1. A guess
B error in calculation
C error in calculation
D correct

2. F error in calculation
G correct
H error in calculation
J guess

3. A guess
B seen as a flip
C correct
D seen as a slide

4. F misunderstanding definition
G correct
H viewed arrow going the other way
J guess

5. A guess
B error in calculation
C correct
D error in calculation

6. F error in calculation
G error in calculation
H correct
J guess

7. A correct
B error in calculation
C multiplied answer by 2
D used 21 yd for smaller trapezoid

CHAPTER 7

Standardized Test Practice

Cumulative, Chapters 1 through 7

Multiple Choice

Read each question. Then fill in the correct answer on the answer document provided by your teacher or on a sheet of paper.

1. Adrian wants to measure the width of a ravine. He marks distances as shown in the diagram.

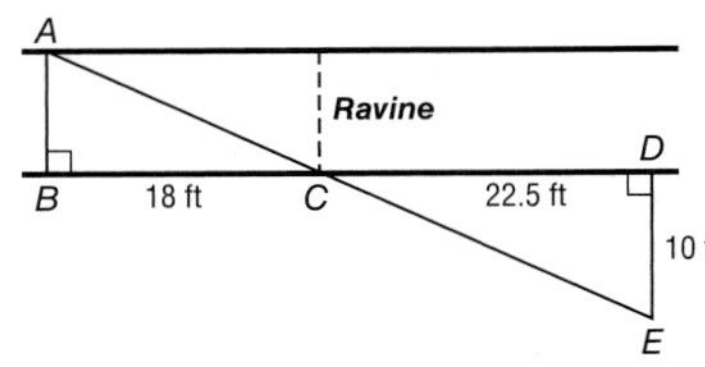

Using this information, what is the *approximate* width of the ravine? D

A 5 ft
B 6 ft
C 7 ft
D 8 ft

2. Kyle and his family are planning a vacation in Cancun, Mexico. Kyle wants to convert 200 US dollars to Mexican pesos for spending money. If 278 Mexican pesos are equivalent to \$25, how many pesos will Kyle get for \$200? G

F 2178
G 2224
H 2396
J 2504

3. Which of the following terms *best* describes the transformation below? C

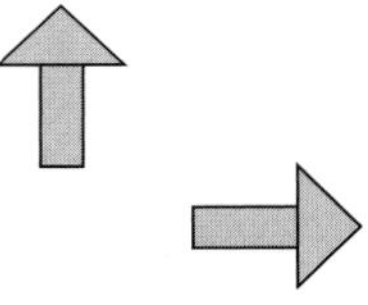

A dilation
B reflection
C rotation
D translation

Test-Taking Tip

Question 2 Set up and solve the proportion for the number of pesos. Use the ratio pesos : dollars.

4. Refer to the figures below. Which of the following terms *best* describes the transformation? G

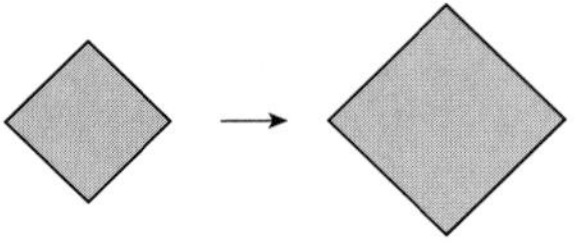

F congruent
G enlargement
H reduction
J scale

5. The ratio of North Carolina residents to Americans is about 295 to 10,000. If there are approximately 300,000,000 Americans, how many of them are North Carolina residents? C

A 7,950,000
B 8,400,000
C 8,850,000
D 9,125,000

6. Solve for x. H

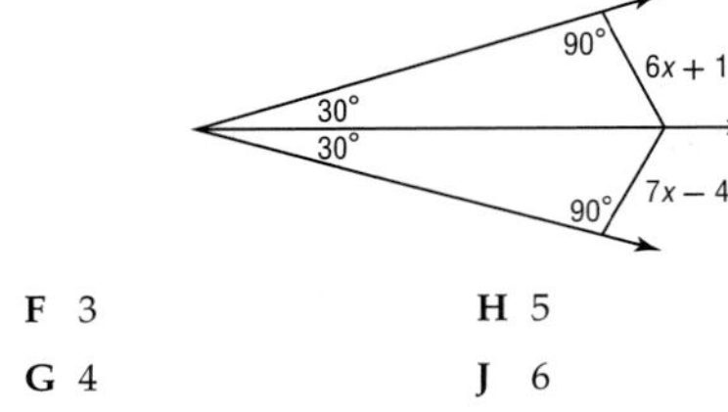

F 3
G 4
H 5
J 6

7. Two similar trapezoids have a scale factor of 3:2. The perimeter of the larger trapezoid is 21 yards. What is the perimeter of the smaller trapezoid? A

A 14 yd
B 17.5 yd
C 28 yd
D 31.5 yd

Short Response/Gridded Response

Record your answers on the answer sheet provided by your teacher or on a sheet of paper.

8. **GRIDDED RESPONSE** Colleen surveyed 50 students in her school and found that 35 of them have homework at least four nights a week. If there are 290 students in the school altogether, how many of them would you expect to have homework at least four nights a week? **203**

9. **GRIDDED RESPONSE** In the triangle below, $\overline{MN} \parallel \overline{BC}$. Solve for x. **9**

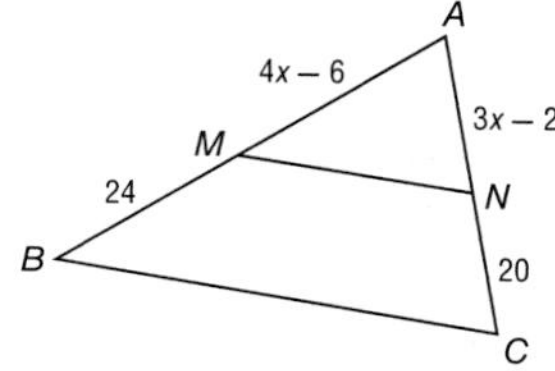

10. Quadrilateral $WXYZ$ is a rhombus. If $m\angle XYZ = 110°$, find $m\angle ZWY$. **55°**

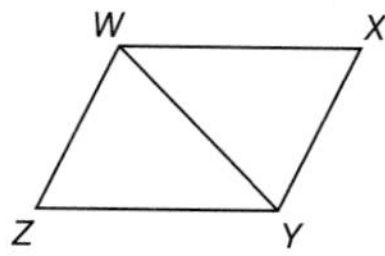

11. What is the contrapositive of the statement below?

If Tom was born in Louisville, then he was born in Kentucky.

See margin.

12. **GRIDDED RESPONSE** In the triangle below, $\overline{RS}$ bisects $\angle VRU$. Solve for x. **10**

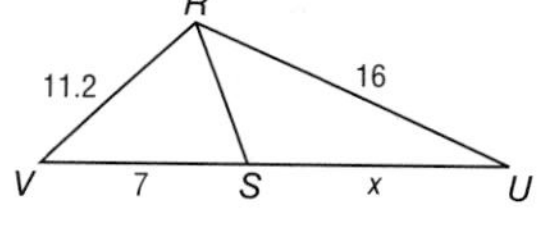

13. **GRIDDED RESPONSE** The scale of a map is 1 inch = 2.5 miles. What is the distance between two cities that are 3.3 inches apart on the map? Round to the nearest tenth, if necessary. **8.3**

14. What is the value of x in the figure? **12**

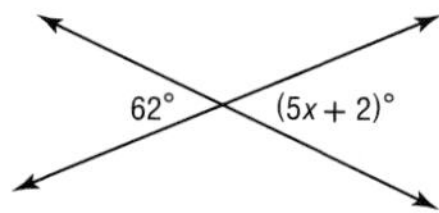

Extended Response

Record your answers on a sheet of paper. Show your work.

15. Refer to triangle XYZ to answer each question.

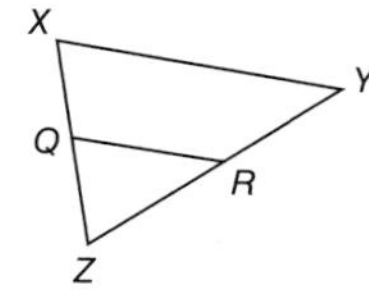

a. Suppose $\overline{QR} \parallel \overline{XY}$. What do you know about the relationship between segments XQ, QZ, YR, and RZ? $\frac{XQ}{QZ} = \frac{YR}{RZ}$

b. If $\overline{QR} \parallel \overline{XY}$, $XQ = 15$, $QZ = 12$, and $YR = 20$, what is the length of $\overline{RZ}$? **16 units**

c. Suppose $\overline{QR} \parallel \overline{XY}$, $\overline{XQ} \cong \overline{QZ}$, and $QR = 9.5$ units. What is the length of $\overline{XY}$? **19 units**

Need ExtraHelp?

If you missed Question...	1	2	3	4	5	6	7	8	9	10	11	12	13	14	15
Go to Lesson...	7-3	7-1	4-7	7-6	7-1	5-1	7-2	7-1	7-6	6-5	2-3	7-5	7-7	1-5	7-4

Additional Answer

11. If Tom was not born in Kentucky, then he was not born in Louisville.

Formative Assessment

You can use these two pages to benchmark student progress.

Standardized Test Practice, pp. 68–70

Answer Sheet Practice

Have students simulate taking a standardized test by recording their answers on a practice recording sheet.

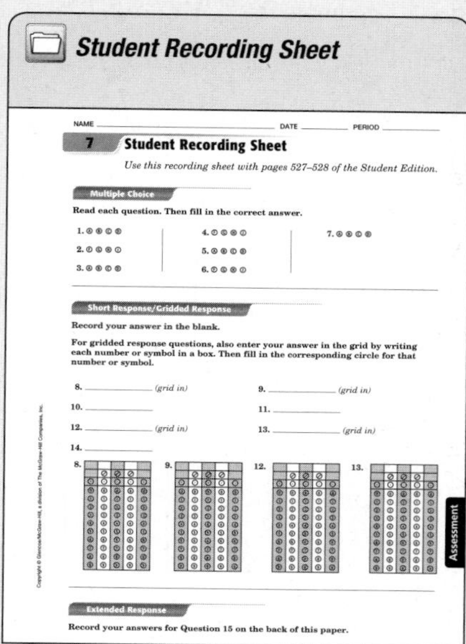

Student Recording Sheet

NAME ______ DATE ______ PERIOD ______

7 **Student Recording Sheet**

Use this recording sheet with pages 527–528 of the Student Edition.

Multiple Choice

Read each question. Then fill in the correct answer.

1. Ⓐ Ⓑ Ⓒ Ⓓ 2. Ⓐ Ⓑ Ⓒ Ⓓ 3. Ⓐ Ⓑ Ⓒ Ⓓ 4. Ⓐ Ⓑ Ⓒ Ⓓ 5. Ⓐ Ⓑ Ⓒ Ⓓ 6. Ⓐ Ⓑ Ⓒ Ⓓ 7. Ⓐ Ⓑ Ⓒ Ⓓ

Short Response/Gridded Response

Record your answer in the blank.

For gridded response questions, also enter your answer in the grid by writing each number or symbol in a box. Then fill in the corresponding circle for that number or symbol.

8. ______ *(grid in)* 9. ______ *(grid in)*
10. ______ 11. ______
12. ______ *(grid in)* 13. ______ *(grid in)*
14. ______

8. 9. 12. 13.

Assessment

Extended Response

Record your answers for Question 15 on the back of this paper.

eAssessment Create practice tests that align to your state standards, the Common Core State Standards, and other national standards such as TIMSS and NAEP.

Homework Option

Get Ready for Chapter 8 Assign students the exercises on p. 535 as homework to assess whether they possess the prerequisite skills needed for the next chapter.

Lesson 7-2

46. Given: $\triangle ABC \sim \triangle DEF$ and $\frac{AB}{DE} = \frac{m}{n}$

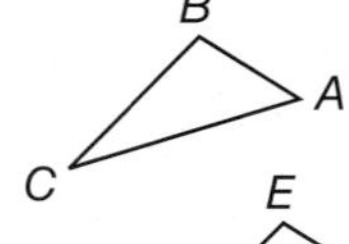

Prove: $\frac{\text{perimeter of } \triangle ABC}{\text{perimeter of } \triangle DEF} = \frac{m}{n}$

Proof: Because $\triangle ABC \sim \triangle DEF$, $\frac{AB}{DE} = \frac{BC}{EF} = \frac{AC}{DF}$. So $\frac{AB}{DE} = \frac{BC}{EF} = \frac{AC}{DF} = \frac{m}{n}$. Cross products yield $AB = DE\left(\frac{m}{n}\right)$, $BC = EF\left(\frac{m}{n}\right)$, and $AC = DF\left(\frac{m}{n}\right)$. Using substitution, the perimeter of $\triangle ABC = DE\left(\frac{m}{n}\right) + EF\left(\frac{m}{n}\right) + DF\left(\frac{m}{n}\right)$, or $\frac{m}{n}(DE + EF + DF)$. The ratio of the two perimeters = $\frac{\frac{m}{n}(DE + EF + DF)}{DE + EF + DF}$ or $\frac{m}{n}$.

50a. Sample answer:

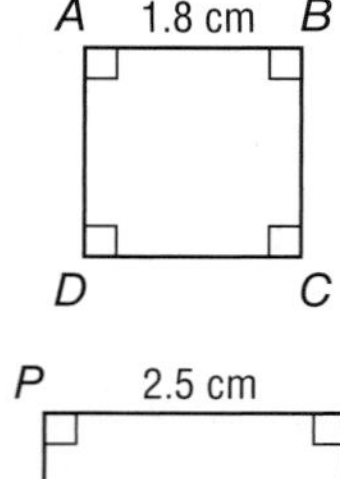

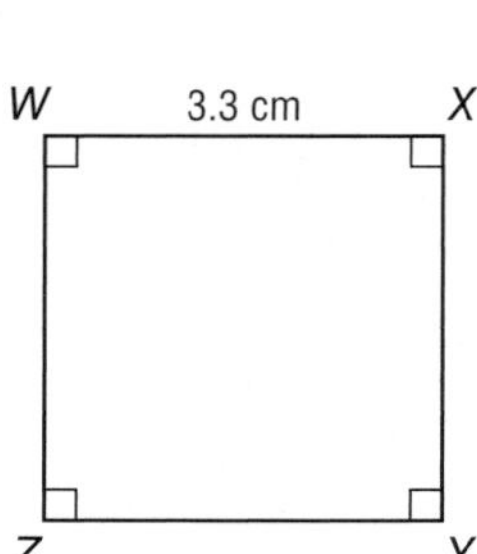

P 2.5 cm Q

S R

50b.

ABCD* and *PQRS		***PQRS* and *WXYZ***		***WXYZ* and *ABCD***	
AB:*PQ*	0.72	*PQ*:*WX*	0.76	*WX*:*AB*	1.8
BC:*QR*	0.72	*QR*:*XY*	0.76	*XY*:*BC*	1.8
CD:*RS*	0.72	*RS*:*YZ*	0.76	*YZ*:*CD*	1.8
AD:*SP*	0.72	*SP*:*ZW*	0.76	*ZW*:*DA*	1.8

ABCD is similar to *PQRS; PQRS* is similar to *WXYZ*; *WXYZ* is similar to *ABCD*.

Lesson 7-3

13. No; not enough information to determine. If $JH = 3$ or $WY = 24$, then $\triangle JHK \sim \triangle XWY$ by SSS Similarity.

14. No; the angles of the triangles can never be congruent, so the triangles can never be similar.

27. Proof:

Statements (Reasons)

1. $\triangle XYZ$ and $\triangle ABC$ are right triangles. (Given)
2. $\angle XYZ$ and $\angle ABC$ are right angles. (Def. of rt. $\triangle$)
3. $\angle XYZ \cong \angle ABC$ (All rt. $\angle$s are $\cong$.)
4. $\frac{XY}{AB} = \frac{YZ}{BC}$ (Given)
5. $\triangle YXZ \sim \triangle BAC$ (SAS Similarity)

28. Proof:

Statements (Reasons)

1. *ABCD* is a trapezoid. (Given)
2. $\overline{AB} \parallel \overline{DC}$ (Def. of trap.)
3. $\angle BDC \cong \angle ABD$, $\angle BAC \cong \angle DCA$ (Alt. Int. $\angle$ Thm.)
4. $\triangle DCP \sim \triangle BAP$ (AA Similarity)
5. $\frac{DP}{PB} = \frac{CP}{PA}$ (Corr. sides of $\sim$ $\triangle$s are proportional.)

30.

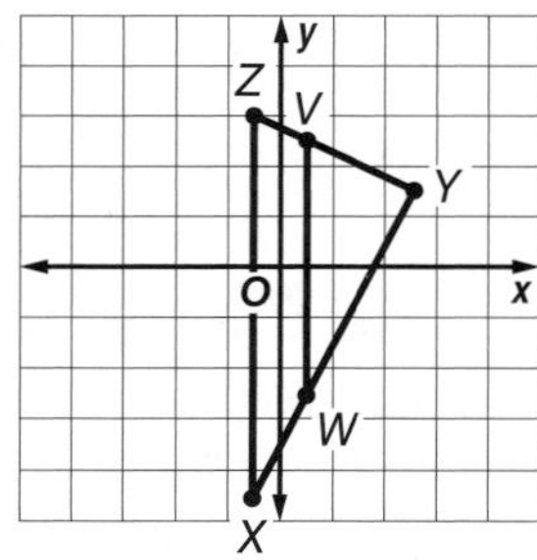

$XY = \sqrt{12^2 + 6^2} = \sqrt{180}$ or $6\sqrt{5}$; $YZ = \sqrt{3^2 + (-6)^2} = \sqrt{45}$ or $3\sqrt{5}$; $ZX = 6 - (-9) = 15$; $VW = 5 - (-5) = 10$; $WY = \sqrt{8^2 + 4^2} = \sqrt{80}$ or $4\sqrt{5}$; $YV = \sqrt{2^2 + (-4)^2} = \sqrt{20} = 2\sqrt{5}$. $\frac{XY}{WY} = \frac{6\sqrt{5}}{4\sqrt{5}}$ or $\frac{3}{2}$, $\frac{YZ}{YV} = \frac{3\sqrt{5}}{2\sqrt{5}}$ or $\frac{3}{2}$, $\frac{ZX}{VW} = \frac{15}{10}$ or $\frac{3}{2}$.

Since $\frac{XY}{WY} = \frac{YZ}{YV} = \frac{ZX}{VW} = \frac{3}{2}$, $\triangle XYZ \sim \triangle WYV$ by SSS Similarity.

Lesson 7-4

31. Given: $\frac{DB}{AD} = \frac{EC}{AE}$

Prove: $\overline{DE} \parallel \overline{BC}$

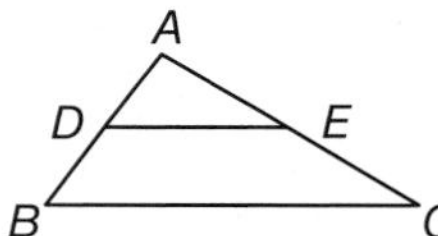

Proof:

Statements (Reasons)

1. $\frac{DB}{AD} = \frac{EC}{AE}$ (Given)
2. $\frac{AD}{AD} + \frac{DB}{AD} = \frac{AE}{AE} + \frac{EC}{AE}$ (Add. Prop.)
3. $\frac{AD + DB}{AD} = \frac{AE + EC}{AE}$ (Subst.)
4. $AB = AD + DB$, $AC = AE + EC$ (Seg. Add. Post.)
5. $\frac{AB}{AD} = \frac{AC}{AE}$ (Subst.)
6. $\angle A \cong \angle A$ (Refl. Prop.)
7. $\triangle ADE \sim \triangle ABC$ (SAS Similarity)
8. $\angle ADE \cong \angle ABC$ (Def. of $\sim$ polygons)
9. $\overline{DE} \parallel \overline{BC}$ (If corr. $\angle$s are $\cong$, then the lines are $\parallel$.)

32. Given: D is the midpoint of $\overline{AB}$.
E is the midpoint of $\overline{AC}$.

Prove: $\overline{DE} \parallel \overline{BC}$; $DE = \frac{1}{2}BC$

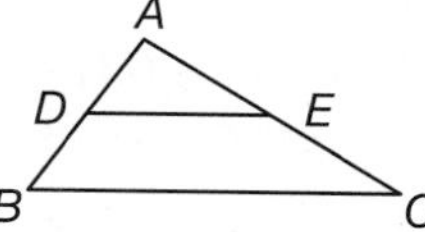

Proof:

Statements (Reasons)

1. D is the midpoint of $\overline{AB}$; E is the midpoint of $\overline{AC}$. (Given)
2. $\overline{AD} \cong \overline{DB}$, $\overline{AE} \cong \overline{EC}$ (Midpoint Thm.)
3. $AD = DB$, $AE = EC$ (Def. of $\cong$ segs.)
4. $AB = AD + DB$, $AC = AE + EC$ (Seg. Add. Post.)
5. $AB = AD + AD$, $AC = AE + AE$ (Subst.)
6. $AB = 2AD$, $AC = 2AE$ (Subst.)
7. $\frac{AB}{AD} = 2$, $\frac{AC}{AE} = 2$ (Div. Prop.)
8. $\frac{AB}{AD} = \frac{AC}{AE}$ (Trans. Prop.)
9. $\angle A \cong \angle A$ (Refl. Prop.)
10. $\triangle ADE \sim \triangle ABC$ (SAS Similarity)
11. $\angle ADE \cong \angle ABC$ (Def. of $\sim$ polygons)
12. $\overline{DE} \parallel \overline{BC}$ (If corr. ∠s are $\cong$, the lines are parallel.)
13. $\frac{BC}{DE} = \frac{AB}{AD}$ (Def. of $\sim$ polygons)
14. $\frac{BC}{DE} = 2$ (Substitution Prop.)
15. $2DE = BC$ (Mult. Prop.)
16. $DE = \frac{1}{2}BC$ (Division Prop.)

39.

$\triangle ABC \sim \triangle ADE$	SAS Similarity
$\frac{AD}{AB} = \frac{DE}{BC}$	Def. of $\sim$ △s
$\frac{40}{100} = \frac{DE}{BC}$	Substitution
$\frac{2}{5} = \frac{DE}{BC}$	Simplify.
$\frac{2}{5}BC = DE$	Multiply.

50. Proof:

Statements (Reasons)

1. $AB = 4$, $BC = 4$ (Given)
2. $AB = BC$ (Subst.)
3. $AB + BC = AC$ (Seg. Add. Post.)
4. $BC + BC = AC$ (Subst.)
5. $2BC = AC$ (Subst.)
6. $AC = 2BC$ (Symm. Prop).
7. $\frac{AC}{BC} = 2$ (Div. Prop.)
8. $ED = DC$ (Given)
9. $ED + DC = EC$ (Seg. Add. Post.)
10. $DC + DC = EC$ (Subst.)
11. $2DC = EC$ (Subst.)
12. $2 = \frac{EC}{DC}$ (Div. Prop.)
13. $\frac{AC}{BC} = \frac{EC}{DC}$ (Trans. Prop.)
14. $\angle C \cong \angle C$ (Reflexive Prop.)
15. $\triangle ACE \sim \triangle BCD$ (SAS Similarity)
16. $\angle CAE \cong \angle CBD$ (Def. of $\sim$ polygons)
17. $\overline{BD} \parallel \overline{AE}$ (If corr. ∠s are $\cong$, lines are $\parallel$.)

51.

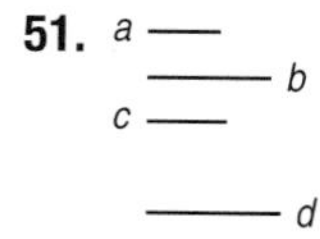

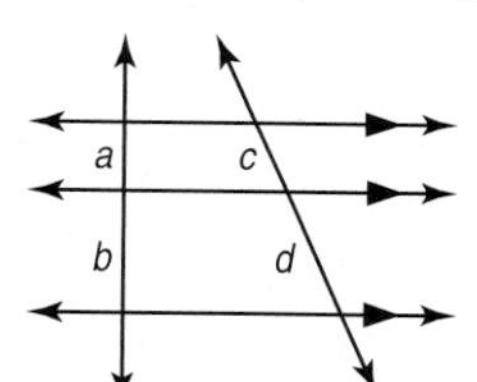

By Corollary 7.1, $\frac{a}{b} = \frac{c}{d}$.

Lesson 7-5

19. Given: $\triangle ABC \sim \triangle RST$
$\overline{AD}$ is a median of $\triangle ABC$.
$\overline{RU}$ is a median of $\triangle RST$.

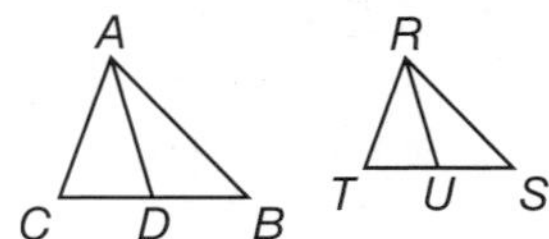

Prove: $\frac{AD}{RU} = \frac{AB}{RS}$

Proof:

Statements (Reasons)

1. $\triangle ABC \sim \triangle RST$; $\overline{AD}$ is a median of $\triangle ABC$; $\overline{RU}$ is a median of $\triangle RST$. (Given)
2. $CD = DB$; $TU = US$ (Def. of median)
3. $\frac{AB}{RS} = \frac{CB}{TS}$ (Def. of $\sim$ ⚠s)
4. $CB = CD + DB$; $TS = TU + US$ (Seg. Add. Post.)
5. $\frac{AB}{RS} = \frac{CD + DB}{TU + US}$ (Subst.)
6. $\frac{AB}{RS} = \frac{DB + DB}{US + US}$ or $\frac{2(DB)}{2(US)}$ (Subst.)
7. $\frac{AB}{RS} = \frac{DB}{US}$ (Subst.)
8. $\angle B \cong \angle S$ (Def. of $\sim$ ⚠s)
9. $\triangle ABD \sim \triangle RSU$ (SAS Similarity)
10. $\frac{AD}{RU} = \frac{AB}{RS}$ (Def. of $\sim$ ⚠s)

25. Proof:

Statements (Reasons)

1. $\overline{CD}$ bisects $\angle ACB$; By construction, $\overline{AE} \parallel \overline{CD}$. (Given)
2. $\frac{AD}{DB} = \frac{EC}{BC}$ ($\triangle$ Prop. Thm.)
3. $\angle 1 \cong \angle 2$ (Def. of $\angle$ Bisector)
4. $\angle 3 \cong \angle 1$ (Alt. Int. $\angle$ Thm.)
5. $\angle 2 \cong \angle E$ (Corr. $\angle$ Post.)
6. $\angle 3 \cong \angle E$ (Trans. Prop.)
7. $\overline{EC} \cong \overline{AC}$ (Conv. of Isos. $\triangle$ Thm.)
8. $EC = AC$ (Def. of $\cong$ segs.)
9. $\frac{AD}{DB} = \frac{AC}{BC}$ (Subst.)

26. Proof:

Statements (Reasons)

1. $\angle H$ is a right angle. L, K, and M are midpoints. (Given)
2. $\overline{JH} \parallel \overline{LK}$, $\overline{GH} \parallel \overline{KM}$ (Midsegment Thm.)
3. $\angle H \cong \angle GLK$ (Corr. ∠s Post.)
4. $\angle GLK \cong \angle LKM$ (Alt. Int. ∠s Thm.)
5. $\angle GLK$ is a right angle. (Subst.)
6. $\angle LKM$ is a right angle. (Subst.)

27. Proof:

Statements (Reasons)

1. $\triangle STQ \sim \triangle ZWX$, $\overline{TR}$ and $\overline{WY}$ are angle bisectors. (Given)
2. $\angle STQ \cong \angle ZWX$, $\angle Q \cong \angle X$ (Def of $\sim$ ⚠s)
3. $\angle STR \cong \angle QTR$, $\angle ZWY \cong \angle XWY$ (Def. $\angle$ bisector)
4. $m\angle STQ = m\angle STR + m\angle QTR$, $m\angle ZWX = m\angle ZWY \not\equiv m\angle XWY$ ($\angle$ Add. Post.)
5. $m\angle STQ = 2m\angle QTR$, $m\angle ZWX = 2m\angle XWY$ (Subst.)
6. $2m\angle QTR = 2m\angle XWY$ (Subst.)
7. $m\angle QTR = m\angle XWY$ (Div.)
8. $\angle QTR \cong \angle XWY$
9. $\triangle QTR \sim \triangle XWY$ (AA Similarity)
10. $\frac{TR}{WY} = \frac{QT}{XW}$ (Def of $\sim$ ⚠s)

28. Proof:

Statements (Reasons)

1. $\overline{FD} \parallel \overline{BC}$, $\overline{BF} \parallel \overline{CD}$, $\overline{AC}$ bisects $\angle BCD$. (Given)
2. $\angle BCE \cong \angle DCE$ (Def. $\angle$ bisector)
3. $\angle BCE \cong \angle AEF$ (Corr. ∠s Post.)
4. $\angle AEF \cong \angle DEC$ (Vert. ∠s are $\cong$)
5. $\angle BCE \cong \angle DEC$ (Trans. Prop.)
6. $\angle BAC \cong \angle DCE$ (Alt. Int ∠s Thm.)
7. $\triangle DEC \sim \triangle BAC$ (AA Similarity)
8. $\frac{DE}{EC} = \frac{BA}{AC}$ (Def of $\sim$ ⚠s)

35. Both theorems have a segment that bisects an angle and have proportionate ratios. The Triangle Angle Bisector Theorem pertains to one triangle, while Theorem 7.9 pertains to similar triangles. Unlike the Triangle Angle Bisector Theorem, which separates the opposite side into segments that have the same ratio as the other two sides, Theorem 7.9 relates the angle bisector to the measures of the sides.

Lesson 7-6

14.

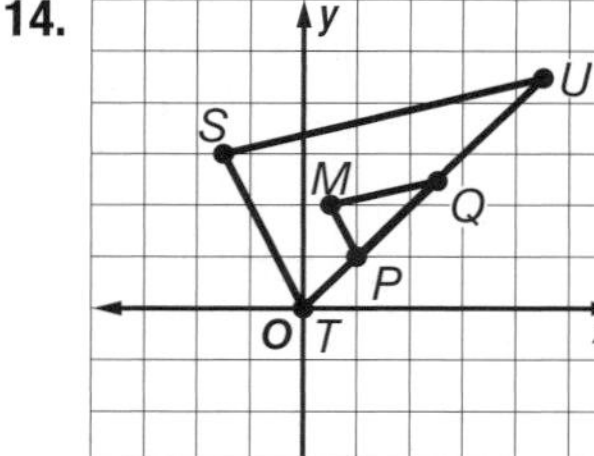

$\frac{MP}{ST} = \frac{PQ}{TU} = \frac{MQ}{SU} = \frac{1}{3}$, so $\triangle MPQ \sim \triangle STU$ by SSS Similarity.

15. $\angle A \cong \angle A$ and $\frac{AB}{AD} = \frac{AC}{AE} = \frac{1}{4}$, so $\triangle ABC \sim \triangle ADE$ by SAS Similarity.

16. 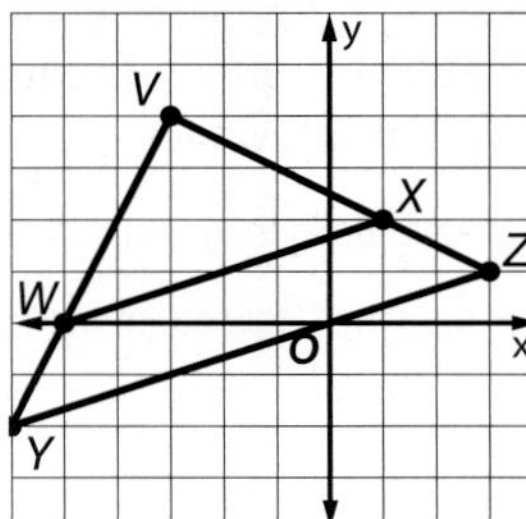

$\frac{VW}{VY} = \frac{VX}{VZ} = \frac{2}{3}$ and $\angle V \cong \angle V$ by the Reflexive Property, so $\triangle VWX \sim \triangle VYZ$ by SAS Similarity.

17. 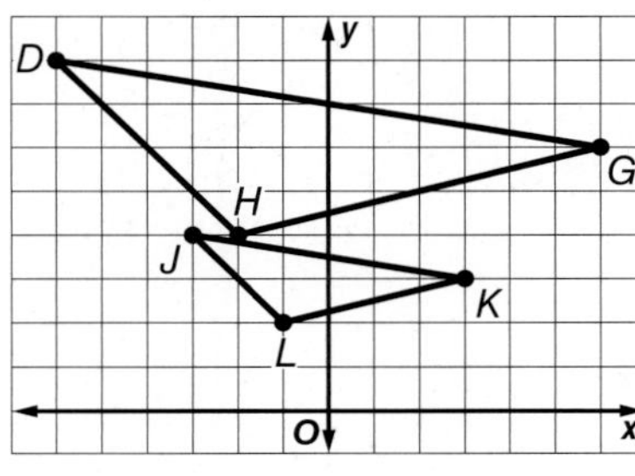

$\frac{JK}{DG} = \frac{KL}{GH} = \frac{JL}{DH} = \frac{1}{2}$, so $\triangle JKL \sim \triangle DGH$ by SSS Similarity.

22. Reciprocals; sample answer: The similarity ratio of *ABCD* to *MNOP* can be expressed using the ratio $\frac{AB}{MN}$. The scale factor is the ratio $\frac{MN}{AB}$. Therefore, the similarity ratio of *ABCD* to *MNOP* and the scale factor are reciprocals.

Lesson 7-7

12. Sample answer: 1 in. = 8 ft

6.25 in.

10.5 in.

Chapter Planner

	Diagnostic Assessment Quick Check		
	LESSON 8-1 45 min: 1 day 90 min: 0.5 day	EXPLORE 8-2 45 min: 0.5 day 90 min: 0.25 day	LESSON 8-2 45 min: 1.5 days 90 min: 0.5 day
Title	**Geometric Mean**	**Geometry Lab: Proofs Without Words**	**The Pythagorean Theorem and Its Converse**
Objectives	■ Find the geometric mean between two numbers. ■ Solve problems involving relationships between parts of a right triangle and the altitude to its hypotenuse.	■ Prove the Pythagorean Theorem by using diagrams without words.	■ Use the Pythagorean Theorem. ■ Use the Converse of the Pythagorean Theorem.
Key Vocabulary	geometric mean		Pythagorean triple
CCSS	G.SRT.4, G.SRT.5	G.CO.10	G.SRT.8, G.MG.3
Multiple Representations			
Lesson Resources	connectED.mcgraw-hill.com Leveled Worksheets Vocabulary Personal Tutor Self-Check Quiz ■ *5-Minute Check* ■ *Study Notebook*	connectED.mcgraw-hill.com Animations ■ *Teaching Geometry with Manipulatives* **Materials:** ■ patty paper ■ ruler	connectED.mcgraw-hill.com Leveled Worksheets Quiz 1 Vocabulary Personal Tutor Self-Check Quiz ■ *5-Minute Check* ■ *Study Notebook* ■ *Teaching Geometry with Manipulatives*
Resources for Every Lesson	IWB eStudent Edition IWB Interactive Classroom	■ eTeacher Edition ■ eSolutions Manual ■ eAssessment	
Differentiated Instruction	pp. 539, 543		pp. 549, 550

IWB All digital assets are Interactive Whiteboard ready.

Suggested Pacing			
Time Periods	Instruction	Review & Assess	Total
45-minute	12 days	2 days	14 days
90-minute	5 days	1 day	6 days

EXTEND 8-2 **45 min:** 1 day **90 min:** 0.25 day	LESSON 8-3 **45 min:** 1 day **90 min:** 0.5 day	EXPLORE 8-4 **45 min:** 0.5 day **90 min:** 0.25 day	LESSON 8-4 **45 min:** 1 day **90 min:** 0.5 day
Geometry Lab: Coordinates in Space	**Special Right Triangles**	**Graphing Technology Lab: Trigonometry**	**Trigonometry**
▪ Graph points in space. ▪ Use the distance and midpoint formulas in space.	▪ Use the properties of 45°-45°-90° triangles. ▪ Use the properties of 30°-60°-90° triangles.	▪ Use Cabri Jr. to explore trigonometry, the study of patterns in right triangles.	▪ Find trigonometric ratios using right triangles. ▪ Use trigonometric ratios to find angle measures in right triangles.
ordered triple			trigonometry trigonometric ratio sine cosine tangent inverse sine inverse cosine inverse tangent
	G.SRT.6	G.SRT.6	G.SRT.6, G.SRT.7
connectED.mcgraw-hill.com Animations Vocabulary Virtual Manipulatives **Materials:** ▪ ruler	connectED.mcgraw-hill.com Leveled Worksheets Personal Tutor Self-Check Quiz ▪ *5-Minute Check* ▪ *Study Notebook*	connectED.mcgraw-hill.com Personal Tutor **Materials:** ▪ TI-83/84 Plus or other graphing calculator	connectED.mcgraw-hill.com Leveled Worksheets Quiz 2 Vocabulary Personal Tutor Self-Check Quiz ▪ *5-Minute Check* ▪ *Study Notebook* ▪ *Teaching Geometry with Manipulatives*
IWB eStudent Edition IWB Interactive Classroom	▪ eTeacher Edition ▪ eSolutions Manual ▪ eAssessment		
	pp. 559, 566		pp. 570, 572

Chapter Planner

	EXTEND 8-4 (45 min: 0.5 day; 90 min: 0.25 day)	LESSON 8-5 (45 min: 1 day; 90 min: 0.5 day)	LESSON 8-6 (45 min: 1.5 days; 90 min: 0.5 day)
Title	**Graphing Technology Lab: Secant, Cosecant, and Cotangent**	**Angles of Elevation and Depression**	**The Law of Sines and Law of Cosines**
Objectives	▪ Explore the trigonometric functions secant, cosecant, and cotangent.	▪ Solve problems involving angles of elevation and depression. ▪ Use angles of elevation and depression to find the distance between two objects.	▪ Use the Law of Sines to solve triangles. ▪ Use the Law of Cosines to solve triangles.
Key Vocabulary	cosecant secant cotangent	angle of elevation angle of depression	Law of Sines Law of Cosines
CCSS	G.SRT.6	G.SRT.8	G.SRT.9, G.SRT.10
Multiple Representations			
Lesson Resources	connectED.mcgraw-hill.com Vocabulary Personal Tutor **Materials:** ▪ TI-83/84 Plus or other graphing calculator ▪ ruler	connectED.mcgraw-hill.com Leveled Worksheets Vocabulary Personal Tutor Virtual Manipulatives Self-Check Quiz ▪ *5-Minute Check* ▪ *Study Notebook*	connectED.mcgraw-hill.com Leveled Worksheets Quiz 3 Vocabulary Animations Personal Tutor Self-Check Quiz ▪ *5-Minute Check* ▪ *Study Notebook* ▪ *Teaching Geometry with Manipulatives*
Resources for Every Lesson	IWB eStudent Edition IWB Interactive Classroom	▪ eTeacher Edition ▪ eSolutions Manual ▪ eAssessment	
Differentiated Instruction		pp. 581, 582	pp. 589, 591

Formative Assessment
Mid-Chapter Quiz

IWB All digital assets are Interactive Whiteboard ready.

EXTEND 8-6 (45 min: 0.5 day; 90 min: 0.25 day)	LESSON 8-7 (45 min: 1.5 days; 90 min: 0.5 day)	EXTEND 8-7 (45 min: 0.5 day; 90 min: 0.25 day)
Geometry Lab: The Ambiguous Case	**Vectors**	**Geometry Lab: Adding Vectors**
■ Determine whether three given measures define 0, 1, 2 or infinitely many triangles.	■ Find the magnitudes and directions of vectors. ■ Add and subtract vectors.	■ Use scale drawings and direct measurement to find the resultant of two vectors.
ambiguous case	vector magnitude direction standard position component form resultant	
G.SRT.11	G.GPE.6	
connectED.mcgraw-hill.com Vocabulary Animations **Materials:** ■ 5″ × 8″ notecard ■ $\frac{1}{2}$-inch strip of cardstock that is about 6 inches long ■ brass fasteners ■ colored pencils or markers	connectED.mcgraw-hill.com Leveled Worksheets Quiz 4 Vocabulary Animations Personal Tutor Virtual Manipulatives Self-Check Quiz ■ *5-Minute Check* ■ *Study Notebook* ■ *Teaching Geometry with Manipulatives*	connectED.mcgraw-hill.com Virtual Manipulatives **Materials:** ■ ruler ■ protractor
IWB eStudent Edition IWB Interactive Classroom	■ eTeacher Edition ■ eSolutions Manual ■ eAssessment	
	pp. 601, 603	

Summative Assessment
Study Guide and Review
Practice Test

Assessment and Intervention

SE = Student Edition, **TE** = Teacher Edition, **CRM** = Chapter Resource Masters

	Diagnosis	Prescription
DIAGNOSTIC ASSESSMENT	**Beginning Chapter 8**	
	Get Ready for Chapter 8 **SE**	Response to Intervention **TE**
	Beginning Every Lesson	
	Then, Now, Why? **SE** 5-Minute Checks	Chapter 0 **SE**
FORMATIVE ASSESSMENT	**During/After Every Lesson**	
	Guided Practice **SE**, every example Check Your Understanding **SE** H.O.T. Problems **SE** Spiral Review **SE** Additional Examples **TE** Watch Out! **TE** Step 4, Assess **TE** Chapter 8 Quizzes **CRM**, pp. 51–52 Self-Check Quizzes connectED.mcgraw-hill.com	TIER 1 Intervention Skills Practice **CRM**, Ch. 1–8 connectED.mcgraw-hill.com TIER 2 Intervention Differentiated Instruction **TE** Differentiated Homework Options **TE** Study Guide and Intervention **CRM**, Ch. 1–8 TIER 3 Intervention *Math Triumphs, Geo.,* Ch. 6
	Mid-Chapter	
	Mid-Chapter Quiz **SE** Mid-Chapter Test **CRM**, p. 53 eAssessment	TIER 1 Intervention Skills Practice **CRM**, Ch. 1–8 connectED.mcgraw-hill.com TIER 2 Intervention Study Guide and Intervention **CRM**, Ch. 1–8 TIER 3 Intervention *Math Triumphs, Geo.,* Ch. 6
	Before Chapter Test	
	Chapter Study Guide and Review **SE** Practice Test **SE** Standardized Test Practice **SE** Chapter Test connectED.mcgraw-hill.com Standardized Test Practice connectED.mcgraw-hill.com Vocabulary Review connectED.mcgraw-hill.com eAssessment	TIER 1 Intervention Skills Practice **CRM**, Ch. 1–8 connectED.mcgraw-hill.com TIER 2 Intervention Study Guide and Intervention **CRM**, Ch. 1–8 TIER 3 Intervention *Math Triumphs, Geo.,* Ch. 6
SUMMATIVE ASSESSMENT	**After Chapter 8**	
	Multiple-Choice Tests, Forms 1, 2A, 2B **CRM**, pp. 55–60 Free-Response Tests, Forms 2C, 2D, 3 **CRM**, pp. 61–66 Vocabulary Test **CRM**, p. 54 Extended Response Test **CRM**, p. 67 Standardized Test Practice **CRM**, pp. 68–70 eAssessment	Study Guide and Intervention **CRM**, Ch. 1–8 *Quick Review Math Handbook* connectED.mcgraw-hill.com

Differentiated Instruction

Option 1 Reaching All Learners

Verbal/Linguistic Have students rewrite the equations for the Law of Cosines in their own words without using variables. Then they can describe scenarios for which the Law of Cosines is the most useful. Finally, have them close their books and draw and label a triangular figure, attempting to reproduce the equation for the Law of Cosines using their written explanations and descriptions.

Naturalist Have students research how to make a clinometer using the Internet. If time permits, have them discuss the historical and current uses for this instrument. Then, go outside and have them find the heights of trees or other tall objects on the school's campus.

Option 2 Approaching Level AL

Give students the following problem for additional practice:
A hill slopes upward at a 5-degree angle. Trevor traveled a horizontal distance of about 200 feet. What is the change in Trevor's vertical position? What distance has Trevor traveled along the path? 17.5 ft; 200.8 ft

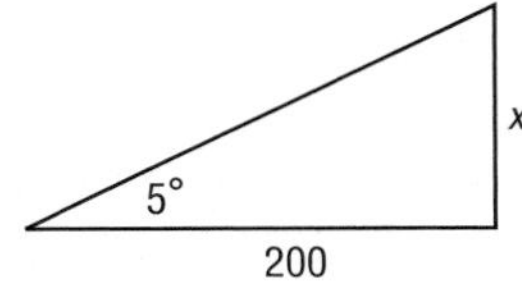

Option 3 English Learners ELL

Working in small groups, have students create a poster of terms from the chapter. Have them illustrate the term with an example and the formula related to the term. They can use this poster to study and review as they learn the material in this chapter.

Option 4 Beyond Level BL

Have students use the Internet and additional resources to investigate the life of Pythagoras. Have them research the proofs of the Pythagorean Theorem. Additionally, have them arrive at their own proof. Students should compile their research into a presentable form—either a poster, report, or PowerPoint. Then, have them share their findings with the class.

Focus on Mathematical Content

VerticalAlignment

Before Chapter 8

Related Topics from Grade 8

- Find solutions to application problems involving proportional relationships.
- Use geometric concepts to solve problems.

Chapter 8

Related Topics from Geometry

- Use and extend similarity properties to explore and justify conjectures about geometric figures.
- Derive, extend, and use the Pythagorean Theorem.
- Identify and apply patterns from right triangles to solve meaningful problems, including special right triangles (45°-45°-90° and 30°-60°-90°) and triangles with sides that are Pythagorean triples.
- Develop, apply, and justify triangle similarity relationships, such as trigonometric ratios using a variety of methods.

After Chapter 8

Preparation for Precalculus

- Solve problems from physical situations using trigonometry, including the use of Law of Sines, Law of Cosines, and area formulas.

Lesson-by-Lesson Preview

8-1 Geometric Mean

The geometric mean between two numbers is the square root of their product. For two positive numbers a and b, the geometric mean is the positive number x for which the proportion $a : x = x : b$ is true. This proportion is equivalent to $x = \sqrt{ab}$.

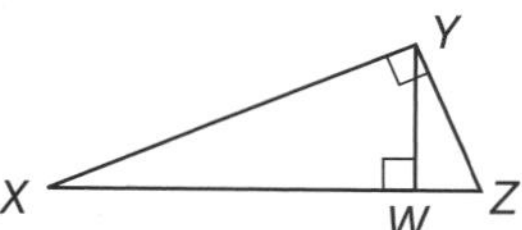

The *geometric mean* has a particular application for a right triangle. If an altitude is drawn from the vertex of the right angle of a right triangle to its hypotenuse, then the two triangles formed are similar to the given triangle and to each other. The measure of this altitude is the geometric mean between the measures of the two segments of the hypotenuse. Moreover, the measure of a leg of the triangle is the geometric mean between the measures of the hypotenuse and the segment of the hypotenuse adjacent to that leg. Altitude YW is the geometric mean of XW and ZW.

8-2 The Pythagorean Theorem and Its Converse

The Pythagorean Theorem states that in a right triangle, the sum of the squares of the measures of the legs equals the square of the measure of the hypotenuse. The converse of the Pythagorean Theorem is useful in determining whether given measures are those of a right triangle. If the sum of the squares of the measures of two sides of a triangle equals the square of the measure of the longest side, then the triangle is a right triangle. A Pythagorean triple is a group of three whole numbers that satisfy the equation $a^2 + b^2 = c^2$, where c is the greatest number.

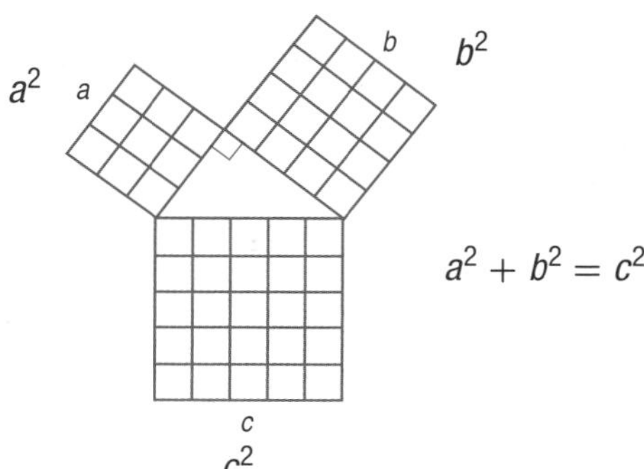

8-3 Special Right Triangles

A 45°-45°-90° triangle is the only type of isosceles right triangle. One of its special properties is that the hypotenuse is $\sqrt{2}$ times as long as a leg, so the ratio of the sides is 1:1: $\sqrt{2}$. A 30°-60°-90° triangle also has special properties. The measures of the sides are x, $x\sqrt{3}$, and $2x$, giving the sides a ratio of 1:$\sqrt{3}$: 2. Knowing these properties can save you valuable time when you are solving problems involving special right triangles.

8-4 Trigonometry

A ratio of the lengths of the sides of a right triangle is called a *trigonometric ratio*. The three most common trigonometric ratios are sine, cosine, and tangent, abbreviated sin, cos, and tan. *Sine* of $\angle A$ is the measure of the leg opposite $\angle A$ divided by the measure of the hypotenuse. *Cosine* of $\angle A$ is the measure of the leg adjacent $\angle A$ divided by the measure of the hypotenuse. *Tangent* of $\angle A$ is the measure of the leg opposite the angle divided by the measure of the leg adjacent the angle. The value of this ratio does not depend on the size of the triangle or the measures of the sides.

Trigonometric ratios are used to find missing measures of a right triangle. You only need to know the measures of two sides or the measure of one side and one acute angle. The inverse of each trigonometric ratio yields the angle measure. The inverses are written $\sin^{-1}$, $\cos^{-1}$, and $\tan^{-1}$.

8-5 Angles of Elevation and Depression

An *angle of elevation* is the angle between the line of sight and the horizontal when an observer looks upward. An *angle of depression* is the angle between the line of sight and the horizontal when an observer looks downward. Trigonometric ratios can be used to solve problems involving angles of elevation and depression. Angles of elevation and depression to two different objects can be used to find the distance between those objects.

8-6 The Law of Sines and the Law of Cosines

In trigonometry, the Law of Sines can be used to find missing measures of triangles that are not right triangles. Let $\triangle ABC$ be any triangle with a, b, and c representing the measures of the sides opposite the angles with measures A, B, and C, respectively. Then, $\frac{\sin A}{a} = \frac{\sin B}{b} = \frac{\sin C}{c}$.

The Law of Sines can be used to solve a triangle. This means finding the measure of every side and angle. The Law of Sines can be used to solve a triangle if you know the measures of two angles and any side of a triangle, or if you know the measures of two sides and an angle opposite one of these sides of the triangle.

The Law of Cosines allows you to solve a triangle in some situations when the Law of Sines cannot be used. This occurs when you know the measures of two sides and the included angle (SAS) or three sides (SSS). Let $\triangle ABC$ be any triangle with a, b, and c representing the measures of sides opposite angles with measures A, B, and C, respectively. Then the following equations are true.

$a^2 = b^2 + c^2 - 2bc \cos A$

$b^2 = a^2 + c^2 - 2ac \cos B$

$c^2 = a^2 + b^2 - 2ab \cos C$

8-7 Vectors

A *vector* is a quantity that has magnitude, or length, and direction. They can be represented by directed line segments. Two vectors are equal if and only if they have the same magnitude and direction, parallel if and only if they have the same or opposite direction, and opposite if and only if they have the same magnitude and opposite direction. The sum of two vectors is the resultant and can be found by two different geometric methods: the parallelogram method and the triangle method.

Mc Graw Hill Professional Development

Targeted professional development has been articulated throughout Geometry. More quality, customized professional development is available from McGraw-Hill Professional Development. Visit connectED.mcgraw-hill.com for details on each product.

- Online Lessons emphasize the strategies and techniques used to teach Geometry. Includes streaming video, interactive pages, and online tools.
- Video Workshops allow mentors, coaches, or leadership personnel to facilitate on-site workshops on educational strategies in mathematics and mathematical concepts.
- MHPD Online (www.mhpdonline.com) offers online professional development with video clips of instructional strategies, links, student activities, and news and issues in education.
- Teaching Today (teachingtoday.glencoe.com) gives secondary teachers practical strategies and materials that inspire excellence and innovation in teaching.

Chapter Project

Surveyors

Students use what they have learned about right triangles and trigonometry to complete a project.

This chapter project addresses business literacy, as well as several specific skills identified as being essential to student success by the Framework for 21st Century Learning.

Visit connectED.mcgraw-hill.com for student and teacher handouts.

KeyVocabulary Introduce the key vocabulary in the chapter using the method below.

Define: The geometric mean of two positive real numbers a and b is the number x such that $\frac{a}{x} = \frac{x}{b}$.

Example: The geometric mean of 1 and 16 is 4, as $\frac{1}{4} = \frac{4}{16}$.

Ask: Is the geometric mean the average of the two numbers? What are equivalent ways to show the relationship given by the geometric mean? No; $\frac{a}{x} = \frac{x}{b}$, $x^2 = ab$, $x = \sqrt{ab}$.

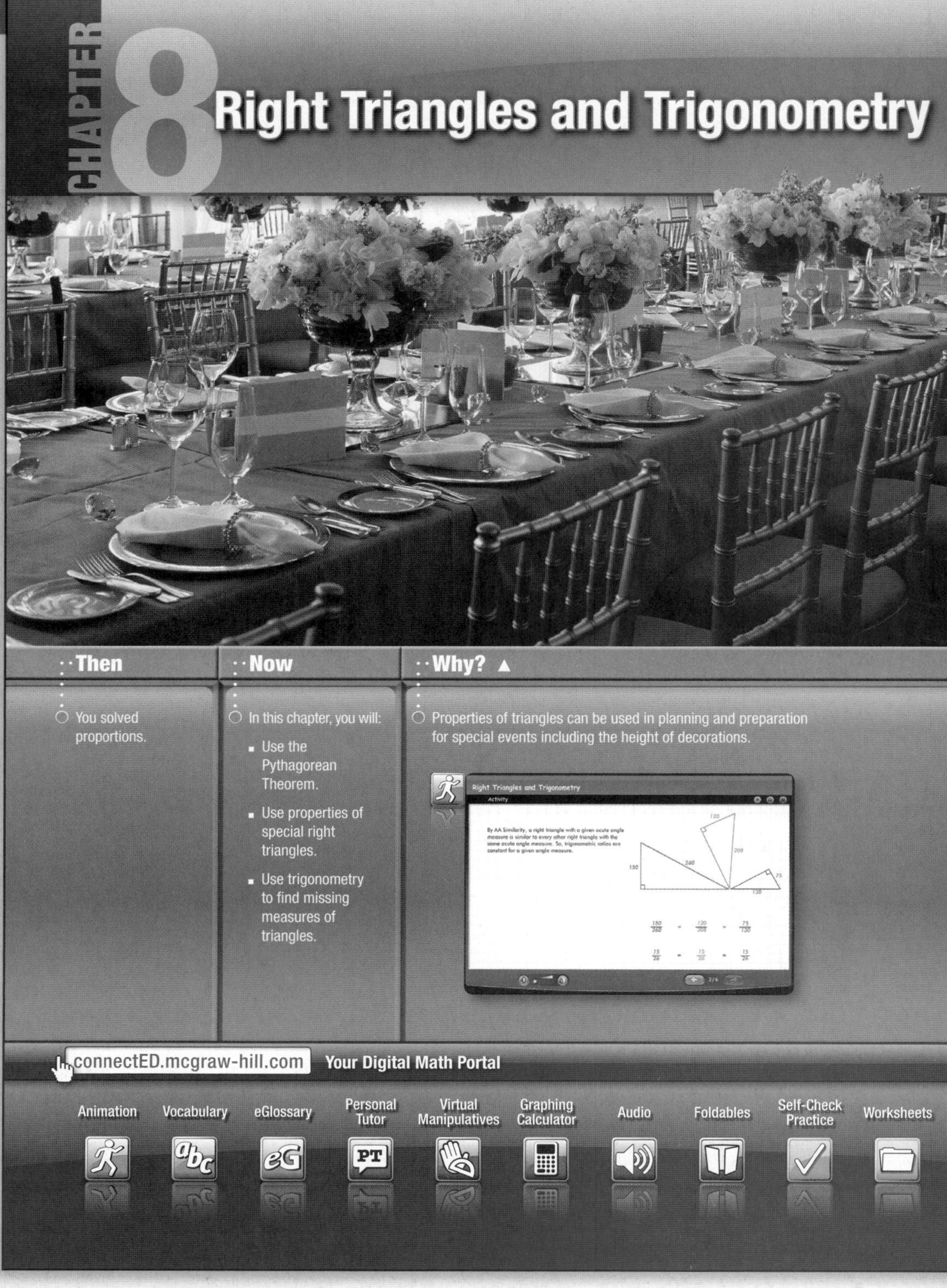

CHAPTER 8
Right Triangles and Trigonometry
Then
You solved proportions.
Now
In this chapter, you will:
Use the Pythagorean Theorem.
Use properties of special right triangles.
Use trigonometry to find missing measures of triangles.
Why?
Properties of triangles can be used in planning and preparation for special events including the height of decorations.
Right Triangles and Trigonometry
connectED.mcgraw-hill.com
Your Digital Math Portal
Animation
Vocabulary
eGlossary
Personal Tutor
Virtual Manipulatives
Graphing Calculator
Audio
Foldables
Self-Check Practice
Worksheets

Get Ready for the Chapter

Diagnose Readiness | You have two options for checking prerequisite skills.

1 Textbook Option Take the Quick Check below. Refer to the Quick Review for help.

QuickCheck

Simplify.

1. $\sqrt{112}$ $4\sqrt{7}$
2. $\frac{\sqrt{24}}{2\sqrt{3}}$ $\sqrt{2}$
3. $\sqrt{15 \cdot 20}$ $10\sqrt{3}$
4. $\frac{\sqrt{6}}{\sqrt{3}} \cdot \frac{\sqrt{18}}{\sqrt{3}}$ $2\sqrt{3}$
5. $\sqrt{\frac{45}{80}}$ $\frac{3}{4}$
6. $\frac{8\sqrt{2}}{6 - 3\sqrt{8}}$ $-\frac{4\sqrt{2}+8}{3}$

Find *x*.

7. 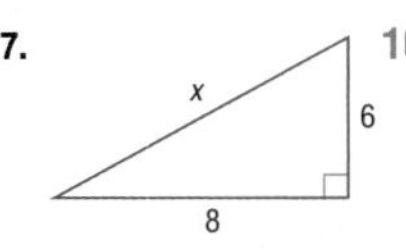

10

8. 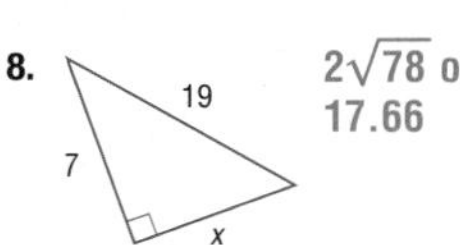

$2\sqrt{78}$ or 17.66

9. **BANNERS** Anna is making a banner out of 4 congruent triangles as shown below. How much blue trim will she need for each side?

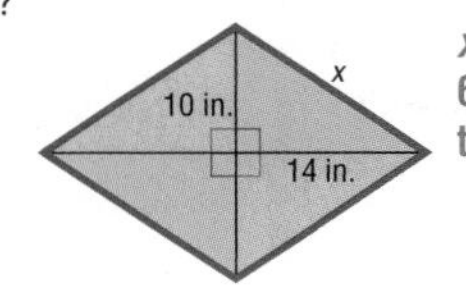

$x = 17.2$ in., 68.8 in. of trim

Graph the line segment with the given endpoints.

10. $G(3, -4)$ and $H(3, 4)$ **10–12. See margin.**
11. $E(-3, 5)$ and $F(4, -3)$
12. **COLLEGES** Quinn is visiting a college campus. He notices from his map that several important buildings are located around a grassy area the students call the Quad. If the library is represented on the map by $L(6, 8)$ and the cafeteria is represented by $C(0, 0)$, graph the line segment that represents the shortest path between the two buildings.

QuickReview

Example 1 (Used in Lessons 8-1 through 8-7)

Simplify $\frac{6}{\sqrt{3}}$.

$\frac{6}{\sqrt{3}} = \frac{6}{\sqrt{3}} \cdot \frac{\sqrt{3}}{\sqrt{3}}$ Multiply by $\frac{\sqrt{3}}{\sqrt{3}}$.

$= \frac{6\sqrt{3}}{3}$ or $2\sqrt{3}$ Simplify.

Example 2 (Used in Lessons 8-2 through 8-6)

Find *x*.

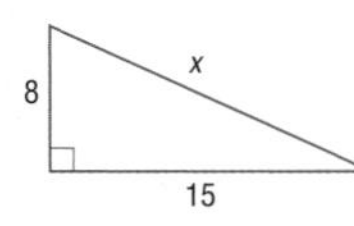

$a^2 + b^2 = c^2$	Pythagorean Theorem
$8^2 + 15^2 = x^2$	$a = 8$ and $b = 15$
$289 = x^2$	Simplify.
$\sqrt{289} = \sqrt{x^2}$	Take the positive square root of each side.
$17 = x$	Simplify.

Example 3 (Used in Lesson 8-7)

Graph the line segment with endpoints $A(-4, 2)$ and $B(3, -2)$.

Plot points *A* and *B*.

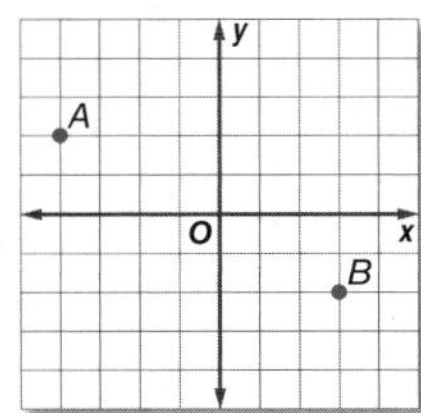

Connect the points.

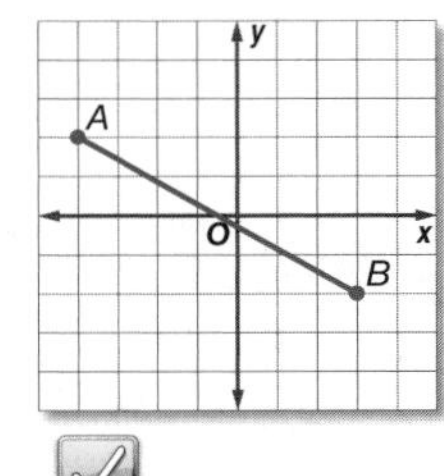

2 Online Option Take an online self-check Chapter Readiness Quiz at connectED.mcgraw-hill.com.

Essential Question

- Why do we use mathematics to model real-world situations? Sample answers: to solve problems, understand phenomena, look for trends

Additional Answers

10–12. See p. 536.

Get Ready for the Chapter

Response to Intervention (RtI)

Use the *Quick Check* results and the Intervention Planner chart to help you determine your Response to Intervention. The If-Then statements in the chart help you decide the appropriate tier of RtI and suggest intervention resources for each tier.

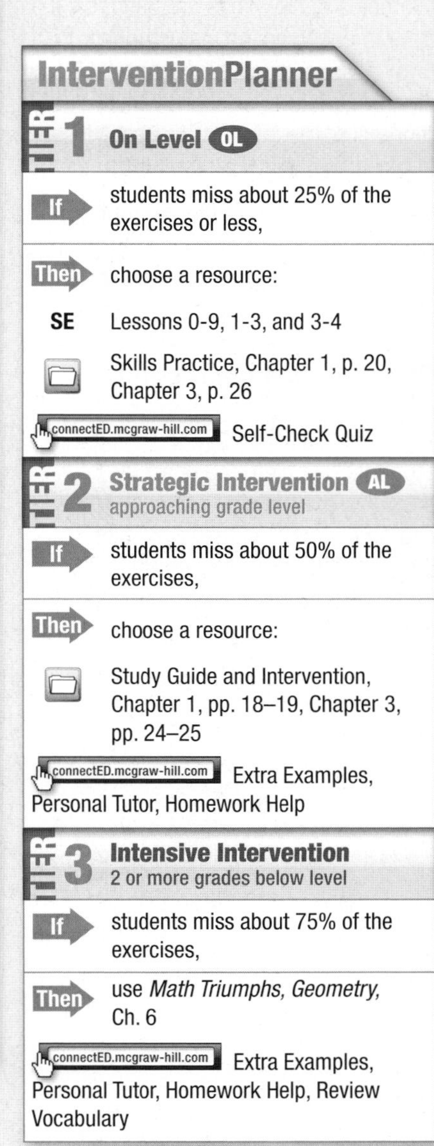

InterventionPlanner

TIER 1 On Level OL

If students miss about 25% of the exercises or less,

Then choose a resource:

SE Lessons 0-9, 1-3, and 3-4

Skills Practice, Chapter 1, p. 20, Chapter 3, p. 26

connectED.mcgraw-hill.com Self-Check Quiz

TIER 2 Strategic Intervention AL approaching grade level

If students miss about 50% of the exercises,

Then choose a resource:

Study Guide and Intervention, Chapter 1, pp. 18–19, Chapter 3, pp. 24–25

connectED.mcgraw-hill.com Extra Examples, Personal Tutor, Homework Help

TIER 3 Intensive Intervention 2 or more grades below level

If students miss about 75% of the exercises,

Then use *Math Triumphs, Geometry,* Ch. 6

connectED.mcgraw-hill.com Extra Examples, Personal Tutor, Homework Help, Review Vocabulary

FOLDABLES® StudyOrganizer

Dinah Zike's Foldables®

Focus Students use the Foldable journal to write about right triangles and trigonometry.

Teach Under the tabs of their Foldables, students take notes, define terms, solve problems, and write examples of how laws are used. On the front of each section, ask students to draw a visual, such as a graph, diagram, picture, or chart, which represents the information in the lesson in a concise, easy-to-study format.

When to Use It Use the appropriate tabs as students cover each lesson in this chapter. Students can add to the vocabulary tab during each lesson.

Differentiated Instruction

Student-Built Glossary, pp. 1–2

Students complete the chart by providing the definition of each term and an example as they progress through Chapter 8. This study tool can also be used to review for the chapter test.

Get Started on the Chapter

You will learn several new concepts, skills, and vocabulary terms as you study Chapter 8. To get ready, identify important terms and organize your resources. You may wish to refer to Chapter 0 to review prerequisite skills.

FOLDABLES StudyOrganizer

Right Angles and Trigonometry Make this Foldable to help you organize your Chapter 8 notes about right angles and trigonometry. Begin with three sheets of notebook paper and one sheet of construction paper.

1. **Stack** the notebook paper on the construction paper.

2. **Fold** the paper diagonally to form a triangle and cut off the excess.

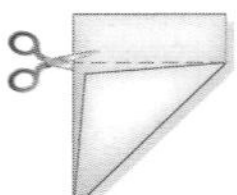

3. **Open** the paper and staple the inside fold to form a booklet.

4. **Label** each page with a lesson number and title.

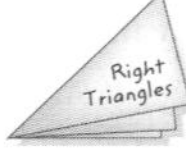

NewVocabulary

English		Español
geometric mean	p. 537	media geométrica
Pythagorean triple	p. 548	triplete pitágorico
trigonometry	p. 568	trigonométria
trigonometric ratio	p. 568	razón trigonométrica
sine	p. 568	seno
cosine	p. 568	coseno
tangent	p. 568	tangente
angle of elevation	p. 580	ángulo de elevación
angle of depression	p. 580	ángulo de depresión
Law of Sines	p. 588	ley de los senos
Law of Cosines	p. 589	ley do los cosenos
vector	p. 600	vector
magnitude	p. 600	magnitud
resultant	p. 601	resultante
component form	p. 602	componente

ReviewVocabulary

altitude altura a segment drawn from a vertex of a triangle perpendicular to the line containing the other side

Pythagorean Theorem Teorema de Pitágoras If a and b are the measures of the legs of a right triangle and c is the measure of the hypotenuse, then $a^2 + b^2 = c^2$.

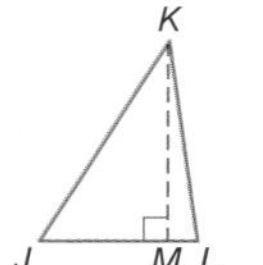

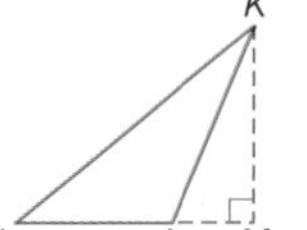

$\overline{KM}$ is an altitude of $\triangle JKL$.

Additional Answers (Get Ready p. 535)

10.

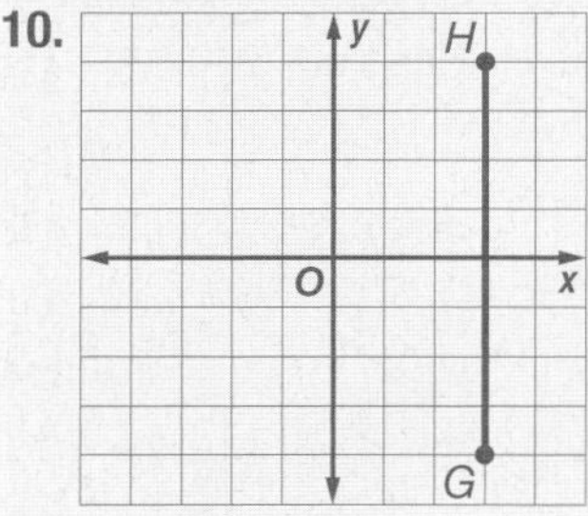

11.

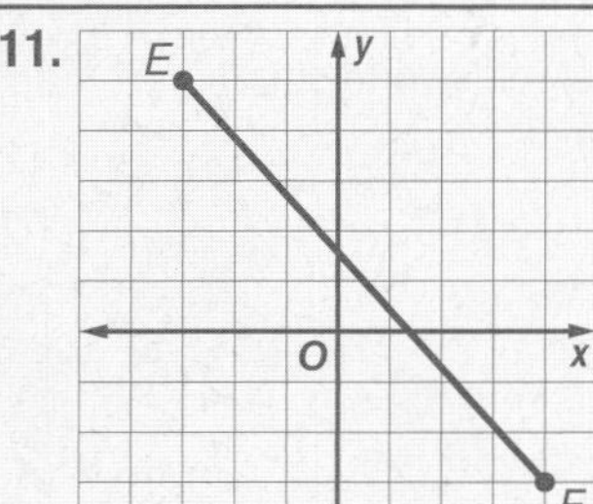

12.

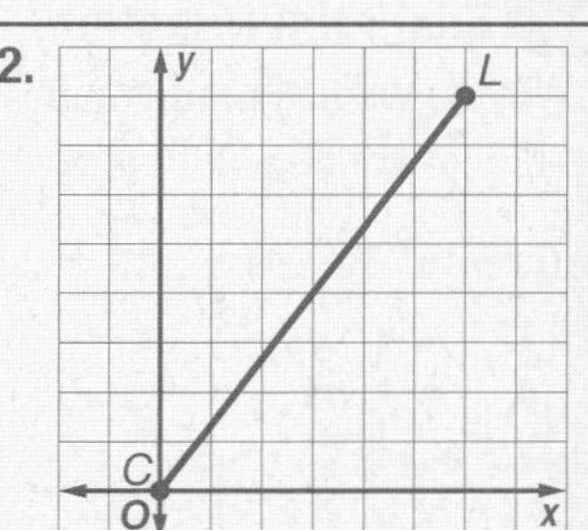

LESSON 8-1 Geometric Mean

Then

- You used proportional relationships of corresponding angle bisectors, altitudes, and medians of similar triangles.

Now

1. Find the geometric mean between two numbers.
2. Solve problems involving relationships between parts of a right triangle and the altitude to its hypotenuse.

Why?

- Photographing very tall or very wide objects can be challenging. It can be difficult to include the entire object in your shot without distorting the image. If your camera is set for a vertical viewing angle of 90° and you know the height of the object you wish to photograph, you can use the geometric mean of the distance from the top of the object to your camera level and the distance from the bottom of the object to camera level.

NewVocabulary
geometric mean

Common Core State Standards

Content Standards
G.SRT.4 Prove theorems about triangles.
G.SRT.5 Use congruence and similarity criteria for triangles to solve problems and to prove relationships in geometric figures.

Mathematical Practices
7 Look for and make use of structure.
3 Construct viable arguments and critique the reasoning of others.

1 Geometric Mean

When the means of a proportion are the same number, that number is called the geometric mean of the extremes. The **geometric mean** between two numbers is the positive square root of their product.

$$\text{extreme} \rightarrow \frac{a}{x} = \frac{x}{b} \leftarrow \text{mean}$$
$$\text{mean} \rightarrow \quad\quad \leftarrow \text{extreme}$$

KeyConcept Geometric Mean

Words	The geometric mean of two positive numbers a and b is the number x such that $\frac{a}{x} = \frac{x}{b}$. So, $x^2 = ab$ and $x = \sqrt{ab}$.
Example	The geometric mean of $a = 9$ and $b = 4$ is 6, because $6 = \sqrt{9 \cdot 4}$.

Example 1 Geometric Mean

Find the geometric mean between 8 and 10.

$x = \sqrt{ab}$ — Definition of geometric mean
$= \sqrt{8 \cdot 10}$ — $a = 8$ and $b = 10$
$= \sqrt{(4 \cdot 2) \cdot (2 \cdot 5)}$ — Factor.
$= \sqrt{16 \cdot 5}$ — Associative Property
$= 4\sqrt{5}$ — Simplify.

The geometric mean between 8 and 10 is $4\sqrt{5}$ or about 8.9.

GuidedPractice

Find the geometric mean between each pair of numbers.

1A. 5 and 45 **15**

1B. 12 and 15 **$6\sqrt{5}$ or about 13.4**

2 Geometric Means in Right Triangles

In a right triangle, an altitude drawn from the vertex of the right angle to the hypotenuse forms two additional right triangles. These three right triangles share a special relationship.

1 Focus

VerticalAlignment

Before Lesson 8-1 Use proportional relationships of corresponding angle bisectors, altitudes, and medians of similar triangles.

Lesson 8-1 Find the geometric mean between two numbers. Solve problems involving relationships between parts of a right triangle and the altitude to its hypotenuse.

After Lesson 8-1 Develop, apply, and justify triangle similarity relationships, such as trigonometric ratios and Pythagorean triples using a variety of methods.

2 Teach

Scaffolding Questions

Have students read the **Why?** section of the lesson.

Ask:

- What is one possible problem when taking a picture of a very tall object? Sample statement: The image can be distorted.
- At what vertical viewing angle should the camera be set to use the geometric mean to photograph an object? 90°

(continued on the next page)

Lesson 8-1 Resources

Resource	Approaching Level AL	On Level OL	Beyond Level BL	English Learners ELL
Teacher Edition	▪ Differentiated Instruction, p. 539	▪ Differentiated Instruction, pp. 539, 543	▪ Differentiated Instruction, pp. 539, 543	
Chapter Resource Masters	▪ Study Guide and Intervention, pp. 5–6 ▪ Skills Practice, p. 7 ▪ Practice, p. 8 ▪ Word Problem Practice, p. 9	▪ Study Guide and Intervention, pp. 5–6 ▪ Skills Practice, p. 7 ▪ Practice, p. 8 ▪ Word Problem Practice, p. 9 ▪ Enrichment, p. 10	▪ Practice, p. 8 ▪ Word Problem Practice, p. 9 ▪ Enrichment, p. 10	▪ Study Guide and Intervention, pp. 5–6 ▪ Skills Practice, p. 7 ▪ Practice, p. 8 ▪ Word Problem Practice, p. 9
Other	▪ 5-Minute Check 8-1 ▪ Study Notebook	▪ 5-Minute Check 8-1 ▪ Study Notebook	▪ 5-Minute Check 8-1 ▪ Study Notebook	▪ 5-Minute Check 8-1 ▪ Study Notebook

- What measure do you need when using the geometric mean to photograph a very tall object? the height of the object

1 Geometric Mean

Example 1 shows how to find the geometric mean between two numbers.

Formative Assessment

Use the Guided Practice exercises after each Example to determine students' understanding of concepts.

Additional Example

1 Find the geometric mean between 2 and 50. 10

Additional Examples also in Interactive Classroom PowerPoint® Presentations

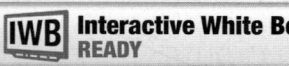

Interactive White Board READY

2 Geometric Means in Right Triangles

Example 2 shows how to use Theorem 8.1. **Examples 3 and 4** show how to use the geometric mean to find unknown values in a triangle.

Additional Example

2 Write a similarity statement identifying the three similar triangles in the figure.

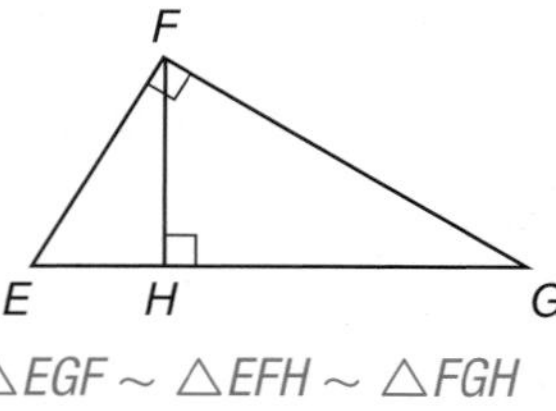

$\triangle EGF \sim \triangle EFH \sim \triangle FGH$

ReviewVocabulary

altitude (of a triangle)
a segment from a vertex to the line containing the opposite side and perpendicular to the line containing that side

Theorem 8.1

If the altitude is drawn to the hypotenuse of a right triangle, then the two triangles formed are similar to the original triangle and to each other.

Example If $\overline{CD}$ is the altitude to hypotenuse $\overline{AB}$ of right $\triangle ABC$, then $\triangle ACD \sim \triangle ABC$, $\triangle CBD \sim \triangle ABC$, and $\triangle ACD \sim \triangle CBD$.

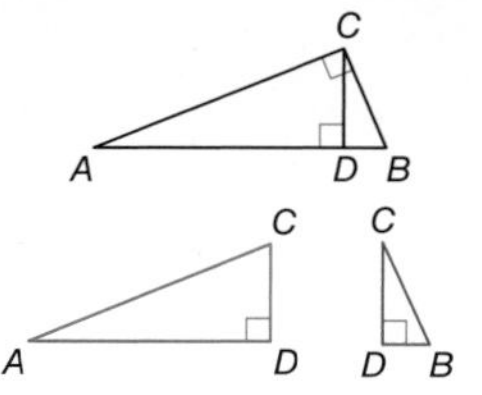

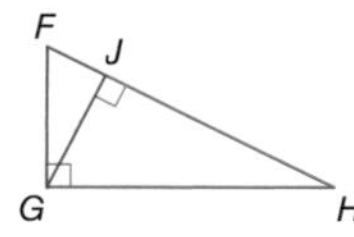

You will prove Theorem 8.1 in Exercise 39.

PT

Example 2 Identify Similar Right Triangles

Write a similarity statement identifying the three similar right triangles in the figure.

Separate the triangle into two triangles along the altitude. Then sketch the three triangles, reorienting the smaller ones so that their corresponding angles and sides are in the same positions as the original triangle.

F J G H

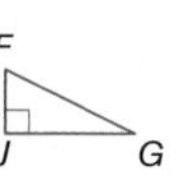

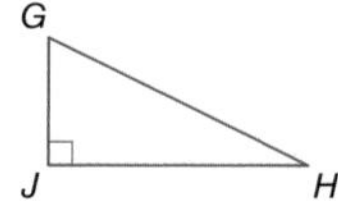

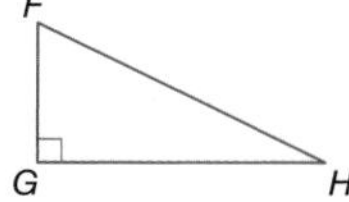

So by Theorem 8.1, $\triangle FJG \sim \triangle GJH \sim \triangle FGH$.

StudyTip

Reorienting Triangles
To reorient the right triangles in Example 2, first match up the right angles. Then match up the shorter sides.

GuidedPractice

2A.

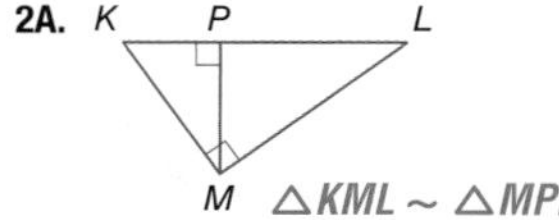

$\triangle KML \sim \triangle MPL \sim \triangle KPM$

2B.

$\triangle STR \sim \triangle QTS \sim \triangle QSR$

From Theorem 8.1, you know that altitude $\overline{CD}$ drawn to the hypotenuse of right triangle ABC forms three similar triangles: $\triangle ACB \sim \triangle ADC \sim \triangle CDB$. By the definition of similar polygons, you can write the following proportions comparing the side lengths of these triangles.

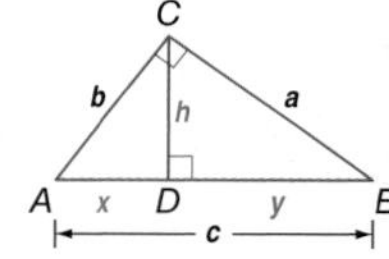

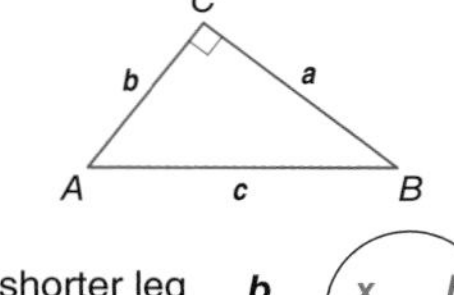

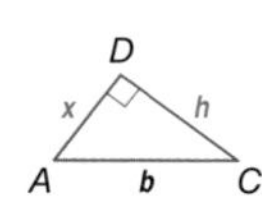

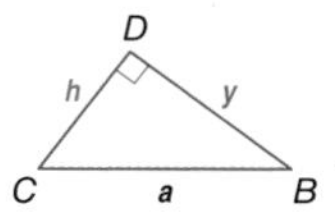

$$\frac{\text{shorter leg}}{\text{longer leg}} = \frac{b}{a} = \frac{x}{h} = \frac{h}{y} \qquad \frac{\text{hypotenuse}}{\text{shorter leg}} = \frac{c}{b} = \frac{b}{x} = \frac{a}{h}$$

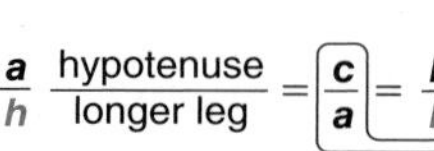

$$\frac{\text{hypotenuse}}{\text{longer leg}} = \frac{c}{a} = \frac{b}{h} = \frac{a}{y}$$

Notice that the circled relationships involve geometric means. This leads to the theorems at the top of the next page.

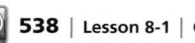

WatchOut!

Naming Triangles When writing similarity statements for triangles, be sure to name the vertices in the corresponding order in each triangle.

Teach with Tech

Interactive Whiteboard Draw a right triangle on the board and draw its altitude. Then draw the two triangle formed by the altitude. Use transformations to illustrate the side and angle relationships among the first triangle and its two component triangles.

Theorems Right Triangle Geometric Mean Theorems

8.2 Geometric Mean (Altitude) Theorem The altitude drawn to the hypotenuse of a right triangle separates the hypotenuse into two segments. The length of this altitude is the geometric mean between the lengths of these two segments.

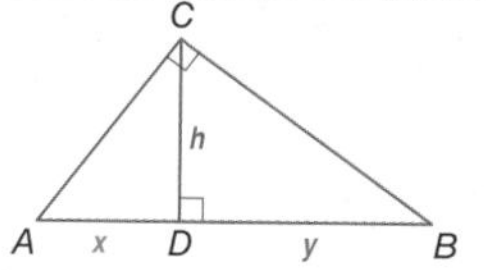

Example If $\overline{CD}$ is the altitude to hypotenuse $\overline{AB}$ of right $\triangle ABC$, then $\frac{x}{h} = \frac{h}{y}$ or $h = \sqrt{xy}$.

8.3 Geometric Mean (Leg) Theorem The altitude drawn to the hypotenuse of a right triangle separates the hypotenuse into two segments. The length of a leg of this triangle is the geometric mean between the length of the hypotenuse and the segment of the hypotenuse adjacent to that leg.

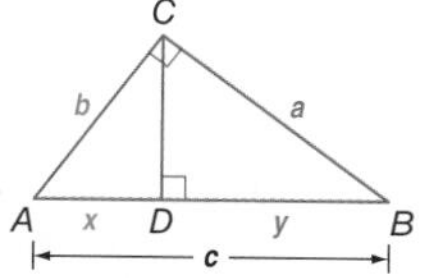

Example If $\overline{CD}$ is the altitude to hypotenuse $\overline{AB}$ of right $\triangle ABC$, then $\frac{c}{b} = \frac{b}{x}$ or $b = \sqrt{xc}$ and $\frac{c}{a} = \frac{a}{y}$ or $a = \sqrt{yc}$.

You will prove Theorems 8.2 and 8.3 in Exercises 40 and 41, respectively.

Example 3 Use Geometric Mean with Right Triangles

Find x, y, and z.

Since x is the measure of the altitude drawn to the hypotenuse of right $\triangle JKL$, x is the geometric mean of the lengths of the two segments that make up the hypotenuse, JM and MK.

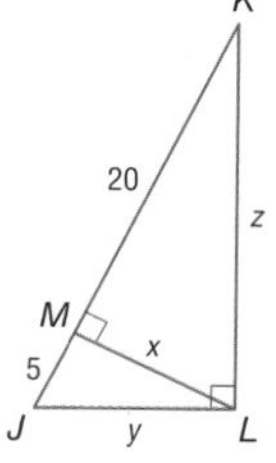

$x = \sqrt{JM \cdot MK}$	Geometric Mean (Altitude) Theorem
$= \sqrt{5 \cdot 20}$	Substitution
$= \sqrt{100}$ or 10	Simplify.

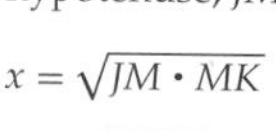

StudyTip

Use a Proportion In Example 3, the value of x could also be found by solving the proportion $\frac{5}{x} = \frac{x}{20}$.

Since y is the measure of leg $\overline{JL}$, y is the geometric mean of $\overline{JM}$, the measure of the segment adjacent to this leg, and the measure of the hypotenuse JK.

$y = \sqrt{JM \cdot JK}$	Geometric Mean (Leg) Theorem
$= \sqrt{5 \cdot (20 + 5)}$	Substitution
$= \sqrt{125}$ or about 11.2	Use a calculator to simplify.

Since z is the measure of leg $\overline{KL}$, z is the geometric mean of $\overline{MK}$, the measure of the segment adjacent to $\overline{KL}$, and the measure of the hypotenuse JK.

$z = \sqrt{MK \cdot JK}$	Geometric Mean (Leg) Theorem
$= \sqrt{20 \cdot (20 + 5)}$	Substitution
$= \sqrt{500}$ or about 22.4	Use a calculator to simplify.

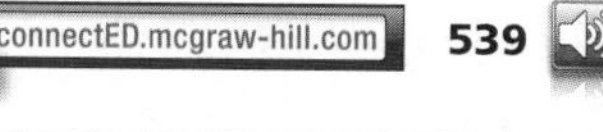

DifferentiatedInstruction AL OL BL

Intrapersonal Learners Allow students to sit quietly and explore similarities and differences between Theorem 8.2 and 8.3. Encourage students to use the examples in the book or create their own to reinforce the concepts outlined in these two theorems. Ask students to think and write about why the formulas for geometric mean work for a right triangle with an altitude drawn to its hypotenuse.

Focus on Mathematical Content

Length Remind students that they automatically discard the negative root when finding the altitude or geometric mean because these values represent lengths and lengths cannot be a negative value.

Additional Example

3 Find c, d, and e.

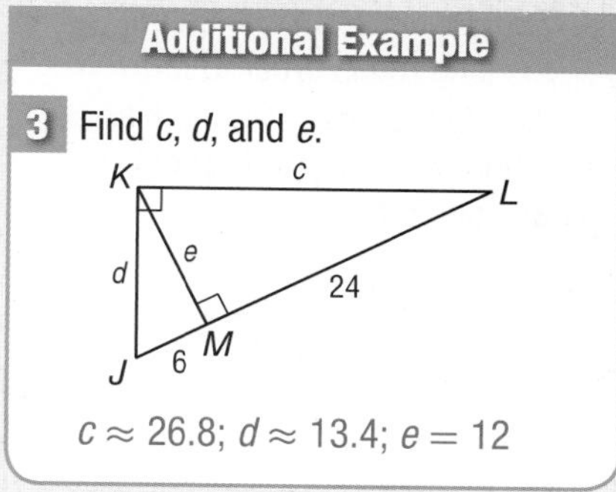

$c \approx 26.8$; $d \approx 13.4$; $e = 12$

Tips for New Teachers

Altitude The altitude drawn to the hypotenuse originates from the right angle. The other two altitudes of a right triangle are the legs.

Additional Example

4 KITES Mrs. Alspach is making a kite for her son. She has to arrange two support rods so that they are perpendicular. The shorter rod is 27 inches long. If she places the short rod 7.25 inches from one end of the long rod in order to form two right angles with the kite fabric, what is the length of the long rod?

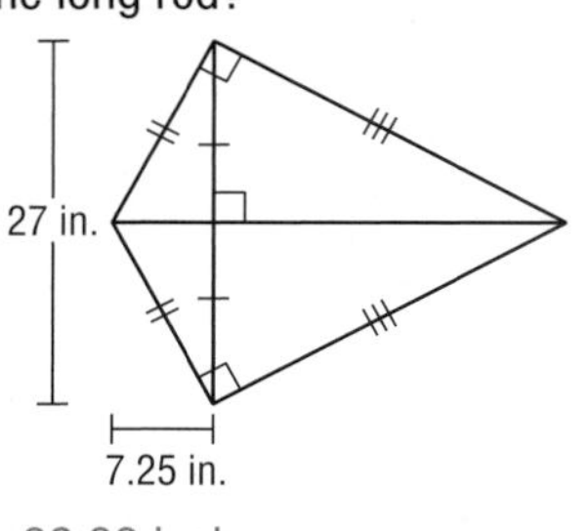

$\approx$32.39 inches

3A. $x = 2\sqrt{66}$ or about 16.2, $y = 5\sqrt{33}$ or about 28.7, $z = 10\sqrt{2}$ or about 14.1

3B. $x = 16$, $y = 20$, $z = 15$

Guided Practice

Find x, y, and z.

3A.

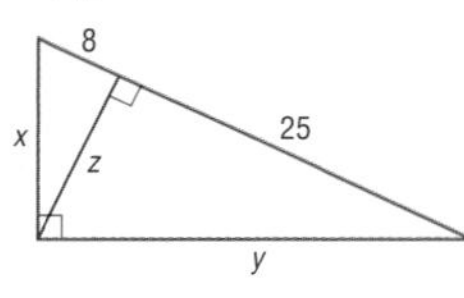

3B.

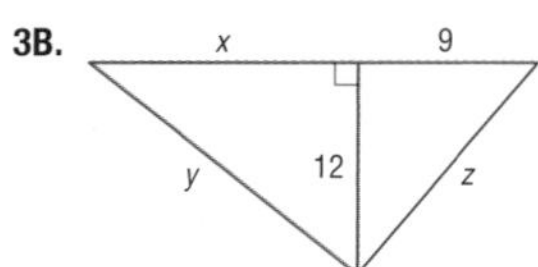

You can use geometric mean to measure height indirectly.

Real-World Career
Event Planner
Event planners organize events including choosing a location, arranging for food, and scheduling entertainment. They also coordinate services like transportation and photography.
Most of the skills required for event planning are acquired through on-the-job experience.

Real-World Example 4 Indirect Measurement

ADVERTISING Zach wants to order a banner that will hang over the side of his high school baseball stadium grandstand and reach the ground.

To find this height, he uses a cardboard square to line up the top and bottom of the grandstand. He measures his distance from the grandstand and from the ground to his eye level. Find the height of the grandstand to the nearest foot.

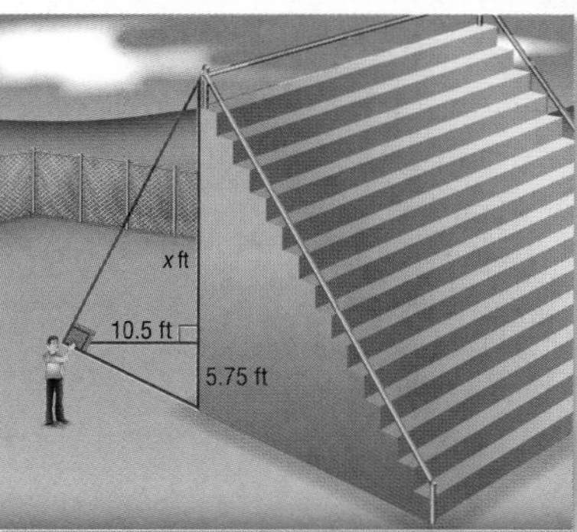

Note: Not drawn to scale

The distance from Zach to the grandstand is the altitude to the hypotenuse of a right triangle. The length of this altitude is the geometric mean of the two segments that make up the hypotenuse. The shorter segment has the measure of 5.75 feet. Let the unknown measure be x feet.

$10.5 = \sqrt{5.75 \cdot x}$	Geometric Mean (Altitude) Theorem
$110.25 = 5.75x$	Square each side.
$19.17 \approx x$	Divide each side by 5.75.

The height of the grandstand is the total length of the hypotenuse, $5.75 + 19.17$, or about 25 feet.

Guided Practice

4. **SPORTS** A community center needs to estimate the cost of installing a rock climbing wall by estimating the height of the wall. Sue holds a book up to her eyes so that the top and bottom of the wall are in line with the bottom edge and binding of the cover. If her eye level is 5 feet above the ground and she stands 11 feet from the wall, how high is the wall? Draw a diagram and explain your reasoning. **29.2 ft**

540 | Lesson 8-1 | Geometric Mean

Check Your Understanding

= Step-by-Step Solutions begin on page R14.

Example 1 **Find the geometric mean between each pair of numbers.**

1. 5 and 20 **10** **2.** 36 and 4 **12** **3.** 40 and 15 **$10\sqrt{6}$ or 24.5**

Example 2 **4.** Write a similarity statement identifying the three similar triangles in the figure. **$\triangle CFD \sim \triangle ECD \sim \triangle EFC$**

Example 3 **Find x, y, and z.**

5. **$x = 6$; $y = 3\sqrt{5} \approx 6.7$; $z = 6\sqrt{5} \approx 13.4$**

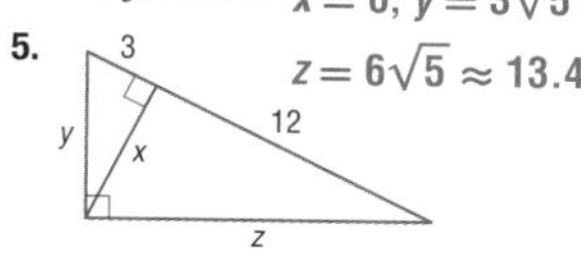

6. **$x = 32$; $y = 16\sqrt{5} \approx 35.8$; $z = 8\sqrt{5} \approx 17.9$**

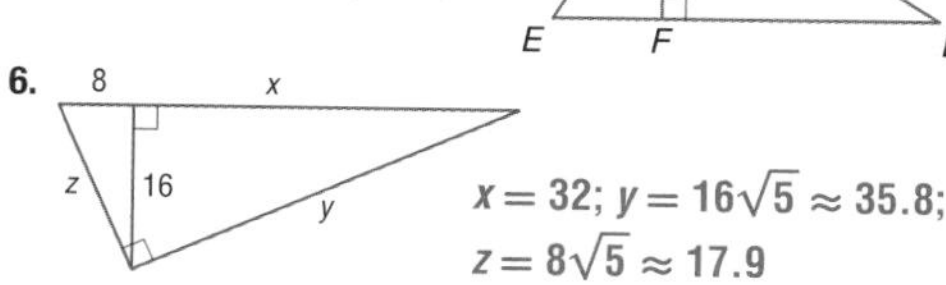

Example 4 **7.**  **MODELING** Corey is visiting the Jefferson Memorial with his family. He wants to estimate the height of the statue of Thomas Jefferson. Corey stands so that his line of vision to the top and base of the statue form a right angle as shown in the diagram. About how tall is the statue? **18 ft 11 in.**

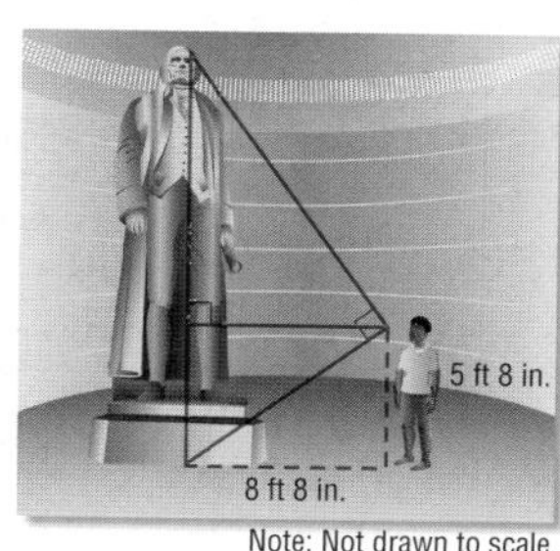

Note: Not drawn to scale.

Practice and Problem Solving

Extra Practice is on page R8.

Example 1 **Find the geometric mean between each pair of numbers.**

8. 81 and 4 **18**  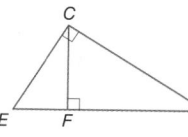 **9.** 25 and 16 **20** **10.** 20 and 25 **$10\sqrt{5} \approx 22.4$**

11. 36 and 24 **$12\sqrt{6} \approx 29.4$** **12.** 12 and 2.4 **$\frac{12\sqrt{5}}{5} \approx 5.4$** **13.** 18 and 1.5 **$3\sqrt{3} \approx 5.2$**

Example 2 **Write a similarity statement identifying the three similar triangles in the figure.**

14.

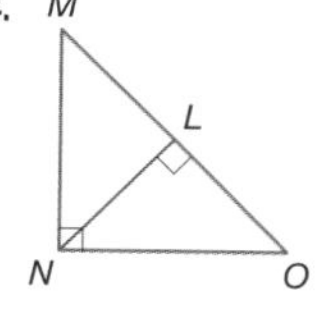

15.

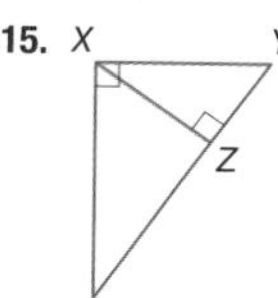

14. **$\triangle MNO \sim \triangle NLO \sim \triangle MLN$**
15. **$\triangle WXY \sim \triangle XZY \sim \triangle WZX$**
16. **$\triangle QRS \sim \triangle RTS \sim \triangle QTR$**
17. **$\triangle HGF \sim \triangle HIG \sim \triangle GIF$**

16.

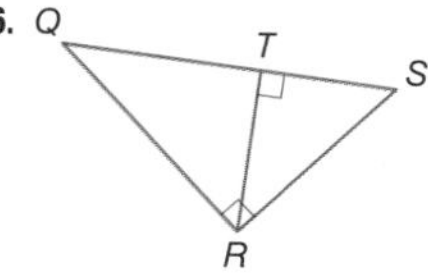

17.

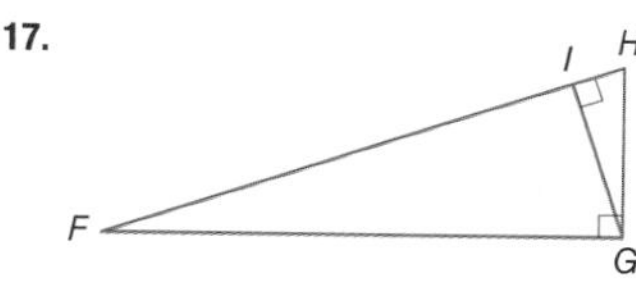

Differentiated Homework Options

Level	Assignment	Two-Day Option	
AL Basic	8–25, 49, 51–74	9–25 odd, 54–57	8–24 even, 49, 51–53, 58–74
OL Core	9–37 odd, 38, 39, 41, 42, 43–47 odd, 48, 49, 51–74	8–25, 54–57	26–49, 51–53, 58–74
BL Advanced	26–69, (optional: 70–74)		

3 Practice

Formative Assessment

Use Exercises 1–7 to check for understanding.

Use the chart at the bottom of this page to customize assignments for your students.

Teaching the Mathematical Practices

Modeling Mathematically proficient students can apply the mathematics they know to solve problems arising in everyday life. In Exercise 7, encourage students to use the diagrams given to identify information important to solving each problem.

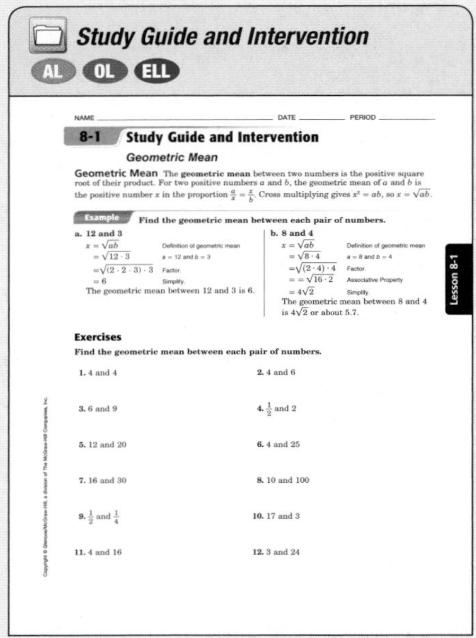

Study Guide and Intervention

AL OL ELL

NAME ______ DATE ______ PERIOD ______

8-1 Study Guide and Intervention

Geometric Mean

Geometric Mean The **geometric mean** between two numbers is the positive square root of their product. For two positive numbers a and b, the geometric mean of a and b is the positive number x in the proportion $\frac{a}{x} = \frac{x}{b}$. Cross multiplying gives $x^2 = ab$, so $x = \sqrt{ab}$.

Example Find the geometric mean between each pair of numbers.

a. 12 and 3
$x = \sqrt{ab}$ Definition of geometric mean
$= \sqrt{12 \cdot 3}$ $a = 12$ and $b = 3$
$= \sqrt{(2 \cdot 2 \cdot 3) \cdot 3}$ Factor.
$= 6$ Simplify.
The geometric mean between 12 and 3 is 6.

b. 8 and 4
$x = \sqrt{ab}$ Definition of geometric mean
$= \sqrt{8 \cdot 4}$ $a = 8$ and $b = 4$
$= \sqrt{(2 \cdot 4) \cdot 4}$ Factor.
$= \sqrt{16 \cdot 2}$ Associative Property
$= 4\sqrt{2}$ Simplify.
The geometric mean between 8 and 4 is $4\sqrt{2}$ or about 5.7.

Exercises

Find the geometric mean between each pair of numbers.

1. 4 and 4
2. 4 and 6
3. 6 and 9
4. $\frac{1}{2}$ and 2
5. 12 and 20
6. 4 and 25
7. 16 and 30
8. 10 and 100
9. $\frac{1}{2}$ and $\frac{1}{4}$
10. 17 and 3
11. 4 and 16
12. 3 and 24

Lesson 8-1

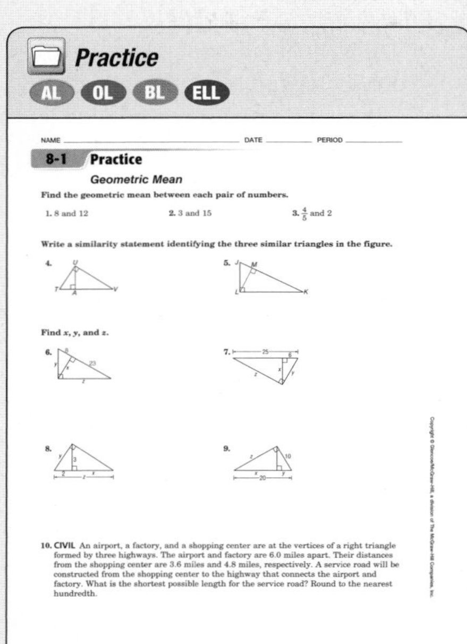

Practice

AL OL BL ELL

NAME ______ DATE ______ PERIOD ______

8-1 Practice

Geometric Mean

Find the geometric mean between each pair of numbers.

1. 8 and 12
2. 3 and 15
3. $\frac{4}{5}$ and 2

Write a similarity statement identifying the three similar triangles in the figure.

4.
5.

Find x, y, and z.

6.
7.
8.
9.

10. CIVIL An airport, a factory, and a shopping center are at the vertices of a right triangle formed by three highways. The airport and factory are 6.0 miles apart. Their distances from the shopping center are 3.6 miles and 4.8 miles, respectively. A service road will be constructed from the shopping center to the highway that connects the airport and factory. What is the shortest possible length for the service road? Round to the nearest hundredth.

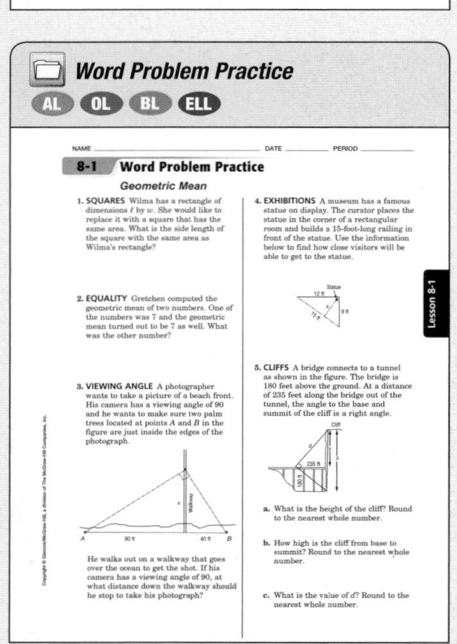

Word Problem Practice

AL OL BL ELL

NAME ______ DATE ______ PERIOD ______

8-1 Word Problem Practice

Geometric Mean

1. SQUARES Wilma has a rectangle of dimensions ℓ by w. She would like to replace it with a square that has the same area. What is the side length of the square with the same area as Wilma's rectangle?

2. EQUALITY Gretchen computed the geometric mean of two numbers. One of the numbers was 7 and the geometric mean turned out to be 7 as well. What was the other number?

3. VIEWING ANGLE A photographer wants to take a picture of a beach front. His camera has a viewing angle of 90 and he wants to make sure two palm trees located at points A and B in the figure are just inside the edges of the photograph.

He walks out on a walkway that goes over the ocean to get the shot. If his camera has a viewing angle of 90, at what distance down the walkway should he stop to take his photograph?

4. EXHIBITIONS A museum has a famous statue on display. The curator places the statue in the corner of a rectangular room and builds a 15-foot-long railing in front of the statue. Use the information below to find how close visitors will be able to get to the statue.

5. CLIFFS A bridge connects to a tunnel as shown in the figure. The bridge is 180 feet above the ground. At a distance of 235 feet along the bridge out of the tunnel, the angle to the base and summit of the cliff is a right angle.

a. What is the height of the cliff? Round to the nearest whole number.

b. How high is the cliff from base to summit? Round to the nearest whole number.

c. What is the value of d? Round to the nearest whole number.

Lesson 8-1

Example 3 Find x, y, and z.

18. $x = 6$; $y = 3\sqrt{13} \approx 10.8$; $z = 2\sqrt{13} \approx 7.2$

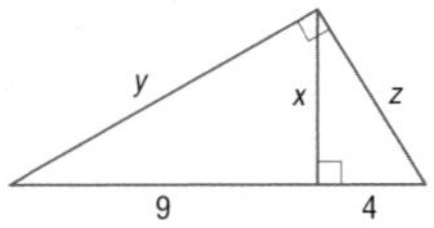

19.
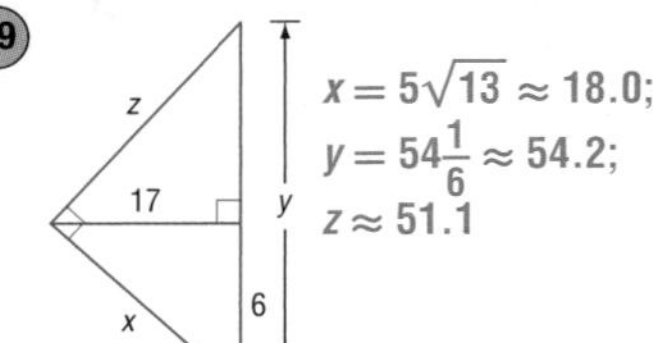

$x = 5\sqrt{13} \approx 18.0$; $y = 54\frac{1}{6} \approx 54.2$; $z \approx 51.1$

20.
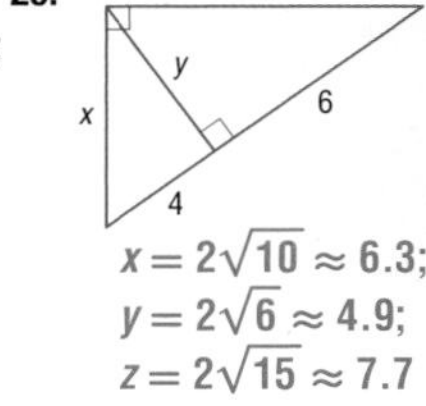

$x = 2\sqrt{10} \approx 6.3$; $y = 2\sqrt{6} \approx 4.9$; $z = 2\sqrt{15} \approx 7.7$

21. $x \approx 4.7$; $y \approx 1.8$; $z \approx 13.1$

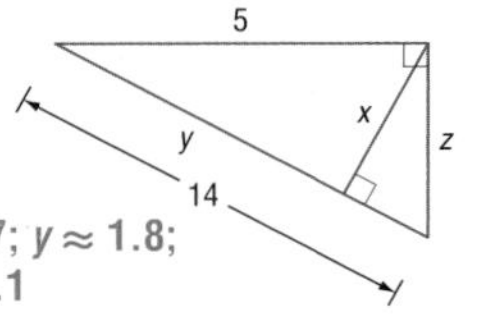

22.
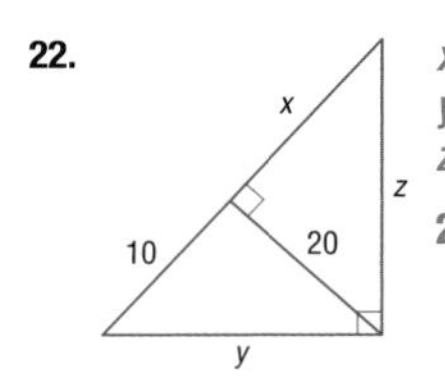

$x = 40$; $y = 10\sqrt{5} \approx 4$; $z = 20\sqrt{5} \approx 44.7$

23.
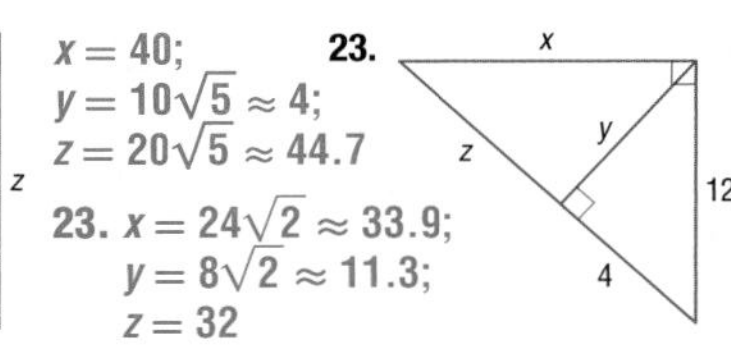

23. $x = 24\sqrt{2} \approx 33.9$; $y = 8\sqrt{2} \approx 11.3$; $z = 32$

Example 4

24. CCSS **MODELING** Evelina is hanging silver stars from the gym ceiling using string for the homecoming dance. She wants the ends of the strings where the stars will be attached to be 7 feet from the floor. Use the diagram to determine how long she should make the strings. **18 ft**

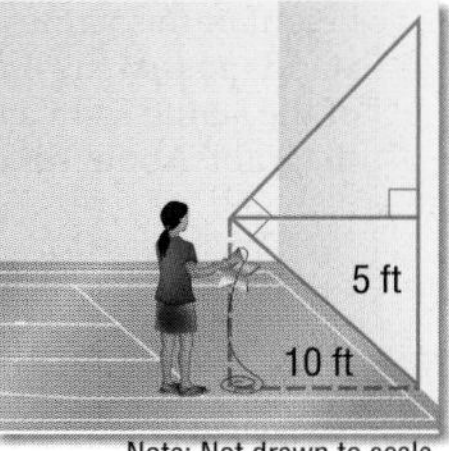

Note: Not drawn to scale.

25. CCSS **MODELING** Makayla is using a book to sight the top of a waterfall. Her eye level is 5 feet from the ground and she is a horizontal distance of 28 feet from the waterfall. Find the height of the waterfall to the nearest tenth of a foot. **161.8 ft**

Note: Not drawn to scale

B Find the geometric mean between each pair of numbers.

26. $\frac{1}{5}$ and 60 $2\sqrt{3}$ or 3.5

27. $\frac{3\sqrt{2}}{7}$ and $\frac{5\sqrt{2}}{7}$ $\frac{\sqrt{30}}{7}$ or 0.8

28. $\frac{3\sqrt{5}}{4}$ and $\frac{5\sqrt{5}}{4}$ $\frac{5\sqrt{3}}{4}$ or 2.2

Find x, y, and z.

29.
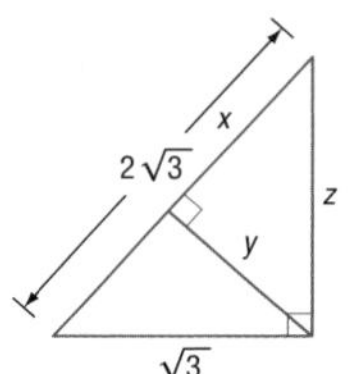

$x = \frac{3\sqrt{3}}{2} \approx 2.6$; $y = \frac{3}{2}$; $z = 3$

30.
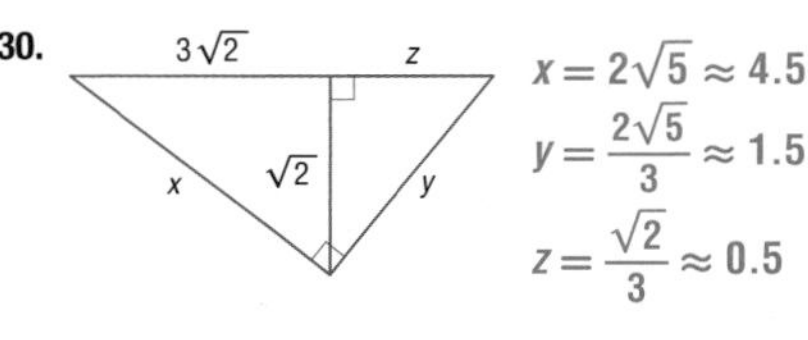

$x = 2\sqrt{5} \approx 4.5$; $y = \frac{2\sqrt{5}}{3} \approx 1.5$; $z = \frac{\sqrt{2}}{3} \approx 0.5$

31. **ALGEBRA** The geometric mean of a number and four times the number is 22. What is the number? **11**

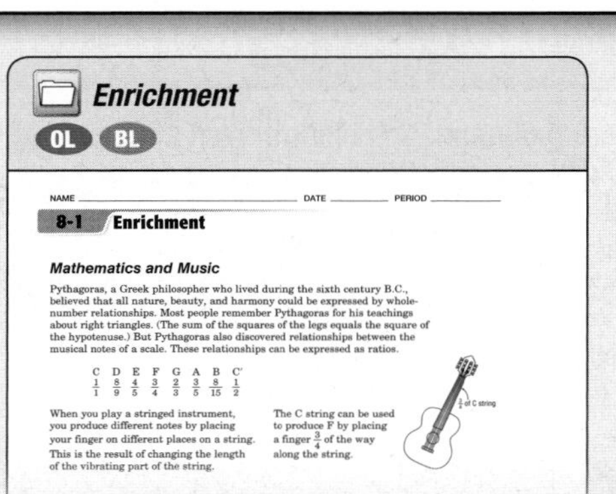

Enrichment

OL BL

NAME ______ DATE ______ PERIOD ______

8-1 Enrichment

Mathematics and Music

Pythagoras, a Greek philosopher who lived during the sixth century B.C., believed that all nature, beauty, and harmony could be expressed by whole-number relationships. Most people remember Pythagoras for his teachings about right triangles. (The sum of the squares of the legs equals the square of the hypotenuse.) But Pythagoras also discovered relationships between the musical notes of a scale. These relationships can be expressed as ratios.

C	D	E	F	G	A	B	C'
$\frac{1}{1}$	$\frac{8}{9}$	$\frac{4}{5}$	$\frac{3}{4}$	$\frac{2}{3}$	$\frac{3}{5}$	$\frac{8}{15}$	$\frac{1}{2}$

When you play a stringed instrument, you produce different notes by placing your finger on different places on a string. This is the result of changing the length of the vibrating part of the string.

The C string can be used to produce F by placing a finger $\frac{3}{4}$ of the way along the string.

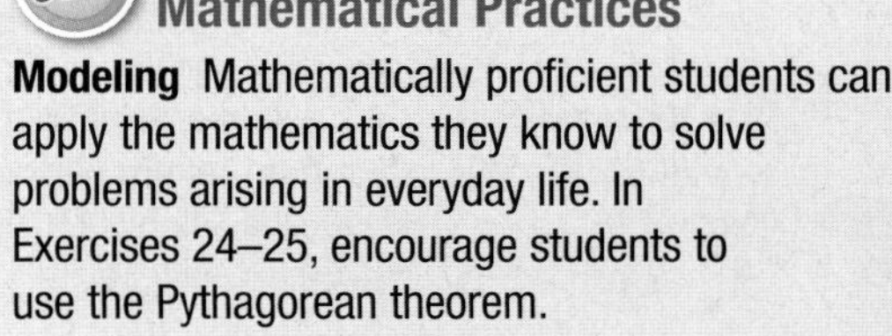

Teaching the Mathematical Practices

Modeling Mathematically proficient students can apply the mathematics they know to solve problems arising in everyday life. In Exercises 24–25, encourage students to use the Pythagorean theorem.

Use similar triangles to find the value of x.

32.

6.4 ft

33.

3.5 ft

34.

15.6 ft
29.3 ft
x
33.2 ft

13.75 ft

ALGEBRA Find the value of the variable.

35.

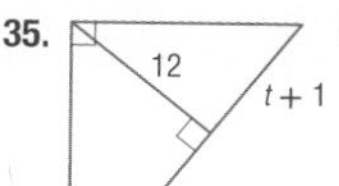

5

36.

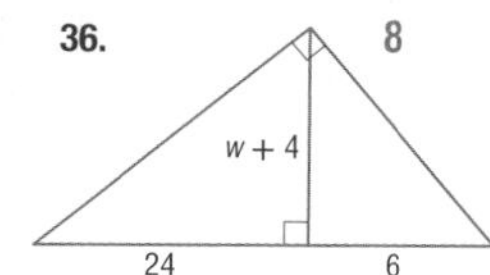

8

37.

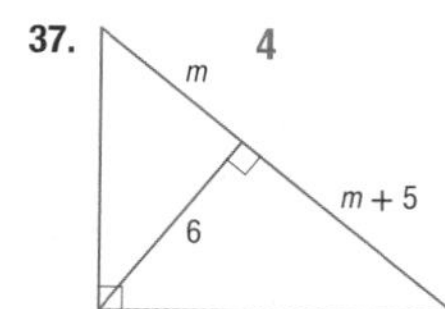

4

38. CONSTRUCTION A room-in-attic truss is a truss design that provides support while leaving area that can be enclosed as living space. In the diagram, $\angle BCA$ and $\angle EGB$ are right angles, $\triangle BEF$ is isosceles, $\overline{CD}$ is an altitude of $\triangle ABC$, and $\overline{EG}$ is an altitude of $\triangle BEF$. If $DB = 5$ feet, $CD = 6$ feet 4 inches, $BF = 10$ feet 10 inches, and $EG = 4$ feet 6 inches, what is AE? **about 20.07 ft**

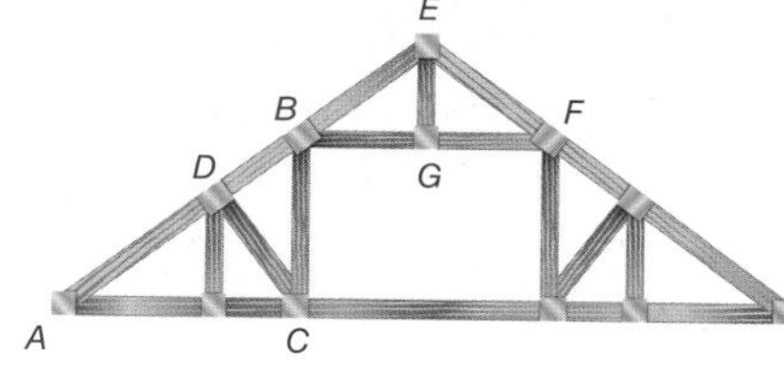

CCSS ARGUMENTS Write a proof for each theorem. **39–41. See Ch. 8 Answer Appendix.**

39. Theorem 8.1 **40.** Theorem 8.2 **41.** Theorem 8.3

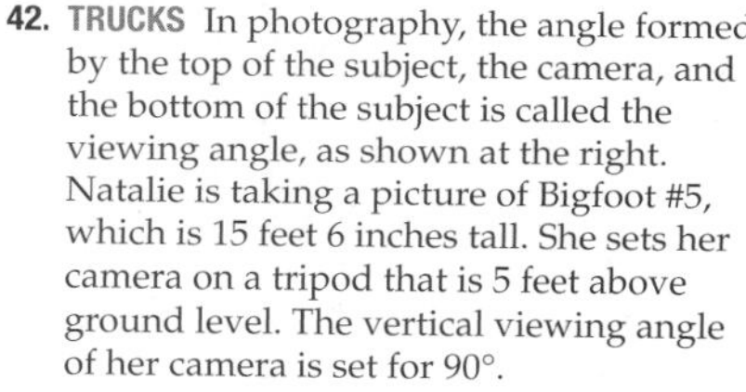

42. TRUCKS In photography, the angle formed by the top of the subject, the camera, and the bottom of the subject is called the viewing angle, as shown at the right. Natalie is taking a picture of Bigfoot #5, which is 15 feet 6 inches tall. She sets her camera on a tripod that is 5 feet above ground level. The vertical viewing angle of her camera is set for 90°.

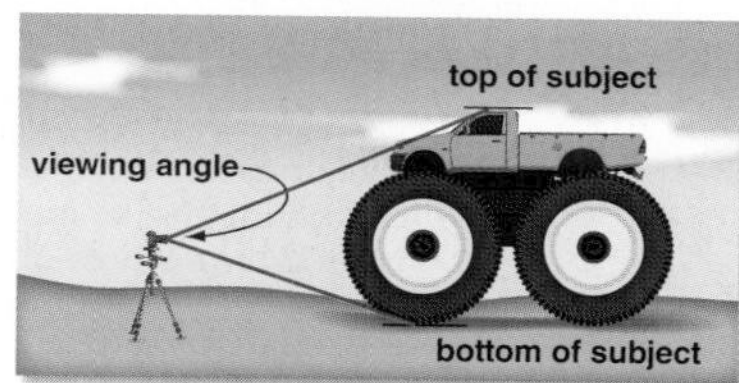

a. Sketch a diagram of this situation. **See Ch. 8 Answer Appendix.**

b. How far away from the truck should Natalie stand so that she perfectly frames the entire height of the truck in her shot? **about 7.2 ft**

43 FINANCE The average rate of return on an investment over two years is the geometric mean of the two annual returns. If an investment returns 12% one year and 7% the next year, what is the average rate of return on this investment over the two-year period? **about 9%**

Tips for New Teachers

Similar Triangles If students are uncertain about applying the geometric mean theorems, point out that they can write a similarity statement and a proportion of corresponding sides to find missing lengths.

CCSS Teaching the Mathematical Practices

Arguments Mathematically proficient students understand and use stated assumptions and definitions in constructing arguments. They make conjectures and build a logical progression of statements to explore the truth of their conjectures. In Exercises 39–41, encourage students to draw diagrams of each theorem first.

Differentiated Instruction OL BL

Extension In Chapter 7, a comparison was made between words that have multiple meanings within mathematics. The word *mean* can be applied to geometry or statistics. In their own words, have the students compare and contrast the meaning of *mean* when applied to a triangle.

Sample answer: The comparison is that the geometrical mean of a triangle and the statistical mean are comparing two or more numbers. The contrast is that the geometrical mean of a triangle uses different mathematical applications than the statistical mean.

Multiple Representations

In Exercise 48, students use a table, a graph, and verbal description to investigate geometric mean.

WatchOut!

Error Analysis Students should remember that proportions should compare similar parts of different triangles. In Exercise 49, Aiden uses segment lengths from only the smaller triangle.

Teaching the Mathematical Practices

Reasoning Mathematically proficient students make sense of quantities and their relationships in problem situations. In Exercise 52, encourage students to review the definition of *orthocenter.*

Additional Answers

44. Using the Geometric Mean (Leg) Theorem, $a = \sqrt{yc}$ and $b = \sqrt{xc}$. Squaring both values, $a^2 = yc$ and $b^2 = xc$. The sum of the squares is $a^2 + b^2 = yc + xc$. Factoring the c on the right side of the equation, $a^2 + b^2 = c(y + x)$. By the Segment Addition Postulate, $c = y + x$. Substituting, $a^2 + b^2 = c(c)$ or $a^2 + b^2 = c^2$.

45. Never; sample answer: The geometric mean of two consecutive integers is $\sqrt{x(x+1)}$, and the average of two consecutive integers is $\frac{x + (x+1)}{2}$. If you set the two expressions equal to each other, the equation has no solution.

48b.

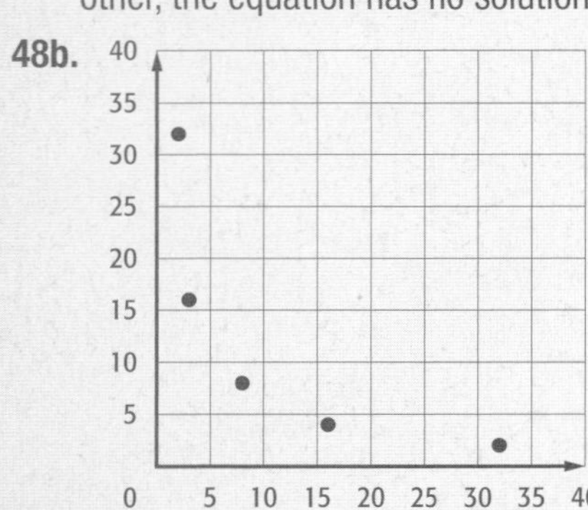

48c. hyperbola; yes; As x increases, y decreases, and as x decreases, y increases.

44. PROOF Derive the Pythagorean Theorem using the figure at the right and the Geometric Mean (Leg) Theorem. **See margin.**

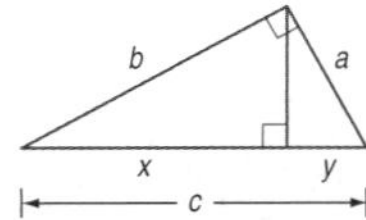

46. Always; sample answer: Since $\sqrt{ab}$ is equal to $\sqrt{a} \cdot \sqrt{b}$, the geometric mean for two perfect squares will always be the product of two positive integers, which is a positive integer.

47. Sometimes; sample answer: When the product of the two integers is a perfect square, the geometric mean will be a positive integer.

Determine whether each statement is *always*, *sometimes*, or *never* true. Explain your reasoning.

45. The geometric mean for consecutive positive integers is the mean of the two numbers. **See margin.**

46. The geometric mean for two perfect squares is a positive integer.

47. The geometric mean for two positive integers is another integer.

48. MULTIPLE REPRESENTATIONS In this problem, you will investigate geometric mean.

a. **Tabular** Copy and complete the table of five ordered pairs (x, y) such that $\sqrt{xy} = 8$.

x	y	$\sqrt{xy}$
2	32	8
4	16	8
8	8	8
16	4	8
32	2	8

b. **Graphical** Graph the ordered pairs from your table in a scatter plot.

c. **Verbal** Make a conjecture as to the type of graph that would be formed if you connected the points from your scatter plot. Do you think the graph of any set of ordered pairs that results in the same geometric mean would have the same general shape? Explain your reasoning. **b–c. See margin.**

H.O.T. Problems Use Higher-Order Thinking Skills

49. Neither; sample answer: On the similar triangles created by the altitude, the leg that is x units long on the smaller triangle corresponds with the leg that is 8 units long on the larger triangle, so the correct proportion is $\frac{4}{x} = \frac{x}{8}$ and x is about 5.7.

51. Sample answer: 9 and 4, 8 and 8; In order for two whole numbers to result in a whole-number geometric mean, their product must be a perfect square.

49. ERROR ANALYSIS Aiden and Tia are finding the value x in the triangle shown. Is either of them correct? Explain your reasoning.

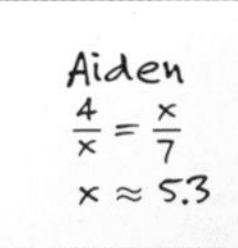

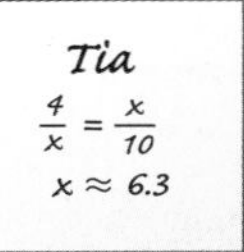

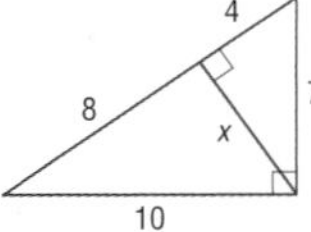

50. CHALLENGE Refer to the figure at the right. Find x, y, and z. **$x = 5.2$, $y = 6.8$, $z = 11$**

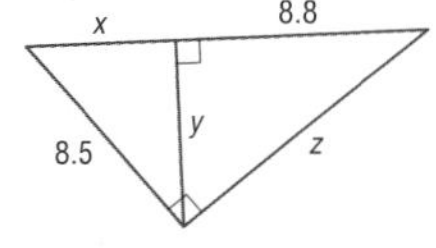

51. OPEN ENDED Find two pairs of whole numbers with a geometric mean that is also a whole number. What condition must be met in order for a pair of numbers to produce a whole-number geometric mean?

52.  **REASONING** Refer to the figure at the right. The orthocenter of $\triangle ABC$ is located 6.4 units from point D. Find BC. **10.0**

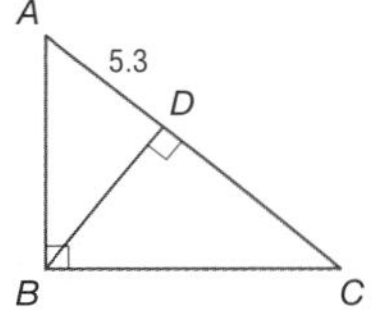

53. WRITING IN MATH Compare and contrast the arithmetic and geometric means of two numbers. When will the two means be equal? Justify your reasoning. **See Ch. 8 Answer Appendix.**

544 | Lesson 8-1 | Geometric Mean

Standardized Test Practice

54. What is the geometric mean of 8 and 22 in simplest form? **A**

A $4\sqrt{11}$ C $16\sqrt{11}$
B 15 D 176

55. SHORT RESPONSE If $\overline{MN} \parallel \overline{PQ}$, use a proportion to find the value of x. Show your work. **10**

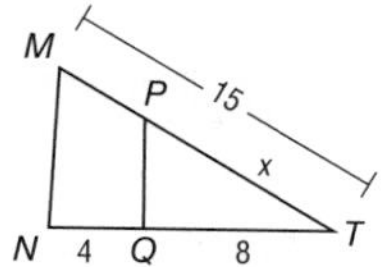

56. ALGEBRA What are the solutions of the quadratic equation $x^2 - 20 = 8x$? **J**

F 2, 10 H −1, 20
G 20, 1 J −2, 10

57. SAT/ACT In the figure, $\overline{AD}$ is perpendicular to $\overline{BC}$, and $\overline{AB}$ is perpendicular to $\overline{AC}$. What is BC? **C**

A $5\sqrt{2}$
B $5\sqrt{3}$
C 20
D 25
E 75

Spiral Review

58. MAPS Use the map to estimate how long it would take to drive from Chicago to Springfield if you averaged 65 miles per hour. (Lesson 7-7) **about 3 h**

Graph the original figure and its dilated image. Then verify that the dilation is a similarity transformation. (Lesson 7-6) **59–61. See margin.**

59. $A(-3, 1), B(9, 7), C(3, -2); D(-1, 1), E(3, 3), F(1, 0)$

60. $G(-4, -4), H(-1, 2), J(2, -1); K(-3, -2), L(1, 0)$

61. $M(7, -4), N(5, -4), P(7, -1); Q(2, -8), R(6, -8), S(2, -2)$

The interior angle measure of a regular polygon is given. Identify the polygon. (Lesson 6-1)

62. 108 **pentagon** **63.** 135 **octagon**

Find x and y in each figure. (Lesson 3-2) **64–66. See margin.**

64.

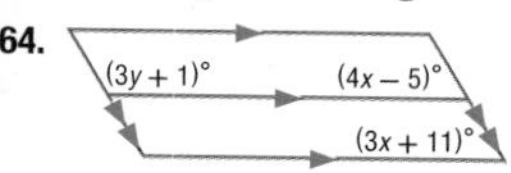

65.

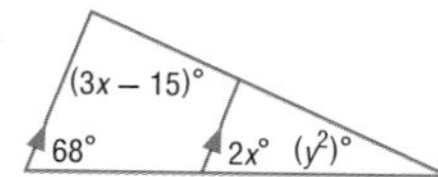

66.

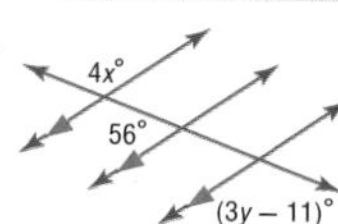

Identify each solid. Name the bases, faces, edges, and vertices. (Lesson 1-7) **67–69. See margin.**

67.

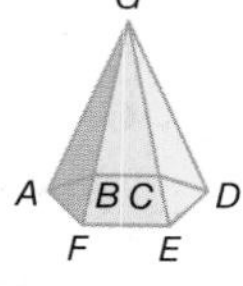

68.

69.

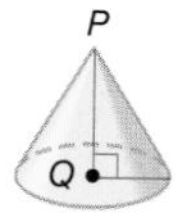

Skills Review

Simplify each expression by rationalizing the denominator.

70. $\frac{2}{\sqrt{2}}$ $\sqrt{2}$

71. $\frac{16}{\sqrt{3}}$ $\frac{16\sqrt{3}}{3}$

72. $\frac{\sqrt{6}}{\sqrt{4}}$ $\frac{\sqrt{6}}{2}$

73. $\frac{3\sqrt{5}}{\sqrt{11}}$ $\frac{3\sqrt{55}}{11}$

74. $\frac{21}{\sqrt{3}}$ $7\sqrt{3}$

67. hexagonal pyramid; base: *ABCDEF*, faces: *ABCDEF, AGF, FGE, EGD, DGC, CGB, BGA*; edges: $\overline{AF}, \overline{FE}, \overline{ED}, \overline{DC}, \overline{CB}, \overline{BA}, \overline{AG}, \overline{FG}, \overline{EG}, \overline{DG}, \overline{CG}$, and $\overline{BG}$; vertices: *A, B, C, D, E, F*, and *G*

68. cylinder; bases: circles *P* and *Q*

69. cone; bases: circle *Q*; vertex: *P*

4 Assess

Crystal Ball Have students describe how to find the geometric mean between numbers and how this helps to find the altitude of a triangle. Then explain how this process may connect to the next lesson on the Pythagorean Theorem.

Additional Answers

59.

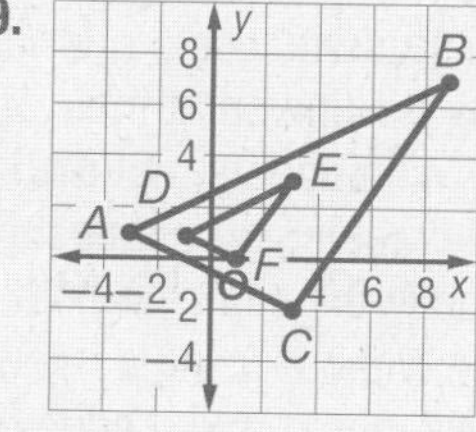

$\frac{AB}{DE} = \frac{BC}{EF} = \frac{AC}{DF} = 3$, so $\triangle ABC \sim \triangle DEF$ by SSS Similarity.

60.

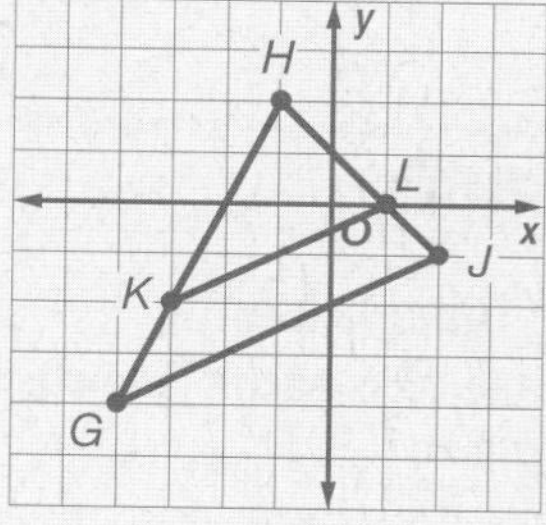

$\angle H \cong \angle H$ and $\frac{HK}{HG} = \frac{HL}{HJ} = \frac{2}{3}$, so $\triangle GHJ \sim \triangle KHL$ by SAS Similarity.

61.

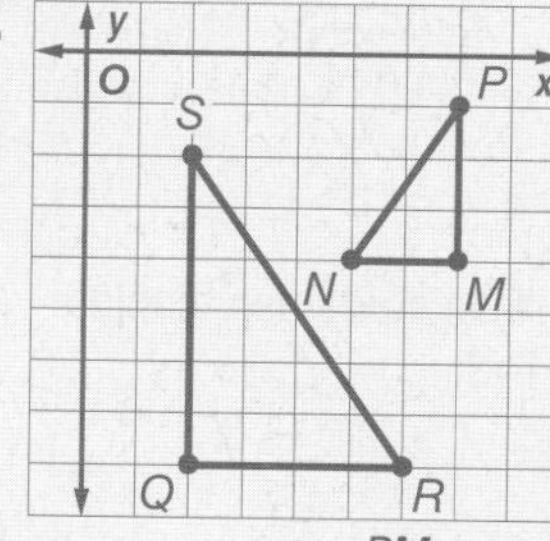

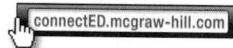

$\angle M \cong \angle Q$ and $\frac{PM}{SQ} = \frac{MN}{QR} = \frac{1}{2}$, so $\triangle MNP \sim \triangle QRS$ by SAS Similarity.

64. $x = 16, y = 40$

65. $x = 34, y = \pm 5$

66. $x = 31, y = 45$

1 Focus

Objective Prove the Pythagorean Theorem by using diagrams without words.

Materials

- tracing paper
- ruler

Teaching Tip

In **Step 3**, have students use a ruler and a pencil to draw the lines that the creases make. Tell students that the key to this activity is making sure measures *a* and *b* are exactly the same on both sheets of paper. Without using a ruler, students may use one marked edge of the first paper to mark accurate lengths on the second paper.

2 Teach

Working Independently

Model for the class each of the steps as they follow along.

Ask:

- How can you verify that the two pieces of paper have the same area? Answers will vary: suggest that you could cut out the shaded triangles from the second piece of paper and arrange them over the shaded areas of the first piece of paper.

Practice Have students complete Exercises 1–3.

3 Assess

Formative Assessment

Ask students to summarize what they have learned about the Pythagorean Theorem.

EXPLORE 8-2 Geometry Lab Proofs Without Words

In Chapter 1, you learned that the Pythagorean Theorem relates the measures of the legs and the hypotenuse of a right triangle. You can prove the Pythagorean Theorem by using diagrams without words.

Common Core State Standards
Content Standards
G.CO.10 Prove theorems about triangles.
Mathematical Practices 4

Activity

Prove the Pythagorean Theorem by using paper and algebra.

Step 1

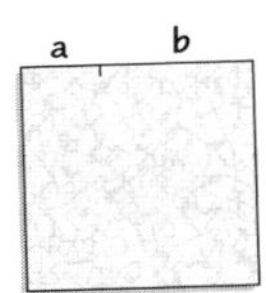

On a piece of tracing paper, mark one side *a* and *b* as shown above.

Step 2

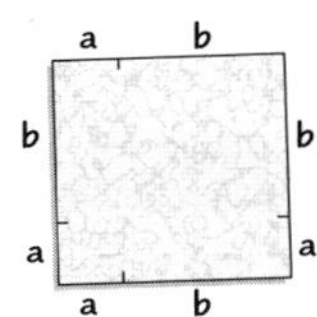

Copy these measures on each of the other sides.

Step 3

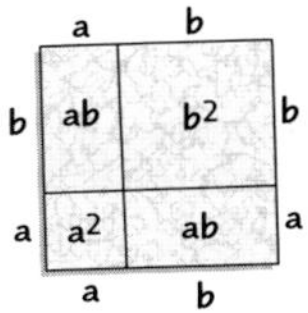

Fold the paper into four sections and label the area of each section.

Step 4

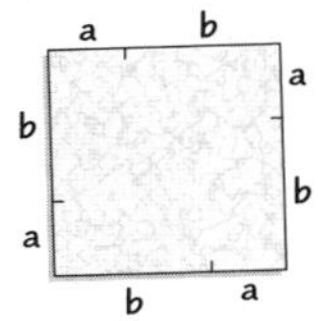

On another piece of tracing paper, mark each side *a* and *b* as shown above.

Step 5

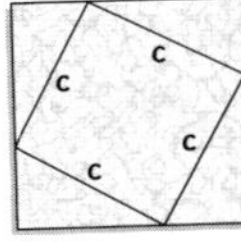

Connect the marks using a straightedge. Let *c* represent the length of each hypotenuse.

Step 6

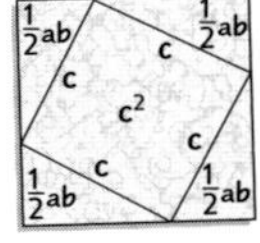

Label the area of each triangle $\frac{1}{2}ab$ and the area of each square c^2.

Step 7 Place the squares side by side and color the corresponding regions that have the same area. For example, $ab = \frac{1}{2}ab + \frac{1}{2}ab$. The parts that are not shaded tell us that $a^2 + b^2 = c^2$.

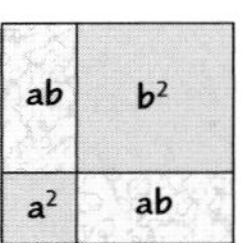

=

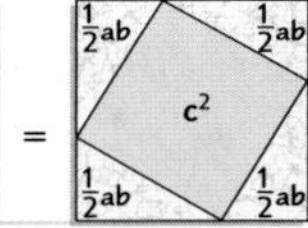

Analyze the Results

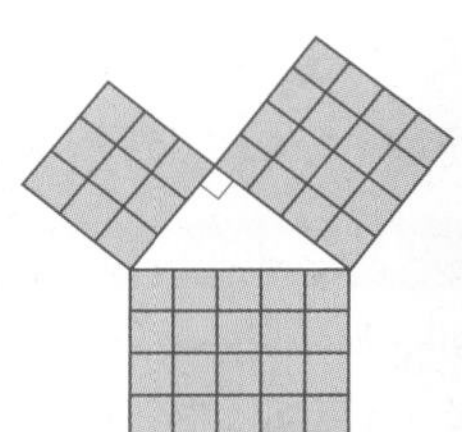

1. Use a ruler to measure *a*, *b*, and *c*. Do these measures confirm that $a^2 + b^2 = c^2$? **yes**
2. Repeat the activity with different *a* and *b* values. What do you notice? $a^2 + b^2 = c^2$
3. **WRITING IN MATH** Explain why the diagram at the right is an illustration of the Pythagorean Theorem. **3–4. See margin.**
4. **CHALLENGE** Draw a geometric diagram to show that for any positive numbers *a* and *b*, $a + b > \sqrt{a^2 + b^2}$. Explain.

From Concrete to Abstract

Have students draw a right triangle on paper and then trade with another student. Tell students to measure two of the sides, and then find the unknown side length. Ask them to check their answers by measuring the third side.

Additional Answers

3. Sample answer: The sum of the areas of the two smaller squares is equal to the area of the largest square.

4. 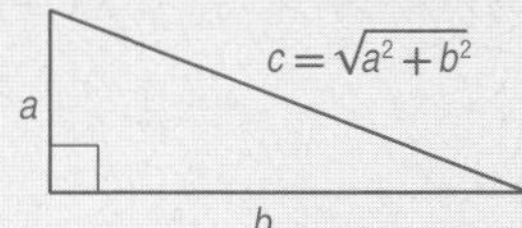

By the Triangle Inequality Theorem, $a + b > c$. Since $c = \sqrt{a^2 + b^2}$, by substitution, $a + b > \sqrt{a^2 + b^2}$.

LESSON 8-2 The Pythagorean Theorem and Its Converse

Then

- You used the Pythagorean Theorem to develop the Distance Formula.

Now

1. Use the Pythagorean Theorem.
2. Use the Converse of the Pythagorean Theorem.

Why?

- Tether lines are used to steady an inflatable snowman. Suppose you know the height at which the tether lines are attached to the snowman and how far away you want to anchor the tether in the ground. You can use the converse of the Pythagorean Theorem to adjust the lengths of the tethers to keep the snowman perpendicular to the ground.

NewVocabulary
Pythagorean triple

Common Core State Standards

Content Standards
G.SRT.8 Use trigonometric ratios and the Pythagorean Theorem to solve right triangles in applied problems. ★
G.MG.3 Apply geometric methods to solve problems (e.g., designing an object or structure to satisfy physical constraints or minimize cost; working with typographic grid systems based on ratios). ★

Mathematical Practices
1 Make sense of problems and persevere in solving them.
4 Model with mathematics.

1 The Pythagorean Theorem

The Pythagorean Theorem is perhaps one of the most famous theorems in mathematics. It relates the lengths of the hypotenuse (side opposite the right angle) and legs (sides adjacent to the right angle) of a right triangle.

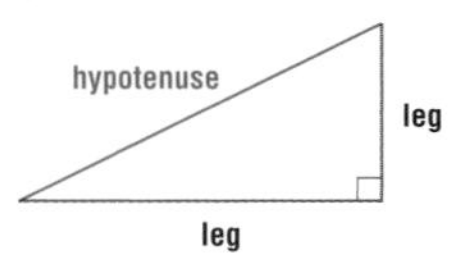

Theorem 8.4 Pythagorean Theorem

Words In a right triangle, the sum of the squares of the lengths of the legs is equal to the square of the length of the hypotenuse.

Symbols If $\triangle ABC$ is a right triangle with right angle C, then $a^2 + b^2 = c^2$.

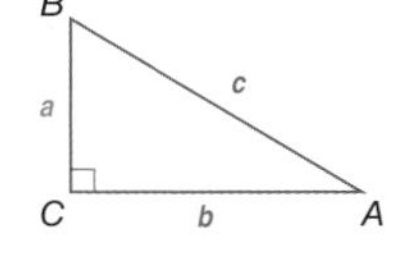

The geometric mean can be used to prove the Pythagorean Theorem.

Proof Pythagorean Theorem

Given: $\triangle ABC$ with right angle at C

Prove: $a^2 + b^2 = c^2$

Proof:

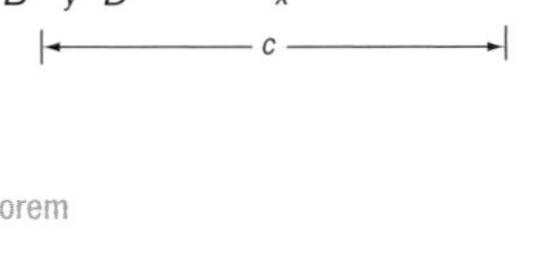

Draw right triangle ABC so C is the right angle. Then draw the altitude from C to $\overline{AB}$. Let $AB = c$, $AC = b$, $BC = a$, $AD = x$, $DB = y$, and $CD = h$. Two geometric means now exist.

$\frac{c}{a} = \frac{a}{y}$ and	$\frac{c}{b} = \frac{b}{x}$	Geometric Mean (Leg) Theorem
$a^2 = cy$	$b^2 = cx$	Cross products
$a^2 + b^2 = cy + cx$		Add the equations.
$a^2 + b^2 = c(y + x)$		Factor.
$a^2 + b^2 = c \cdot c$		Since $c = y + x$, substitute c for $(y + x)$.
$a^2 + b^2 = c^2$		Simplify.

1 Focus

VerticalAlignment

Before Lesson 8-2 Use the Pythagorean Theorem to develop the Distance Formula.

Lesson 8-2 Use the Pythagorean Theorem. Use the Converse of the Pythagorean Theorem.

After Lesson 8-2 Use the properties of special right triangles.

2 Teach

Scaffolding Questions

Have students read the **Why?** section of the lesson.

Ask:

- What are tether lines used for? to steady a large object such as an inflatable snowman
- What type of triangle is formed by the snowman, the tether, and the ground? a right triangle
- What measurements do you need to find the length of the tether? the height at which it is attached and the placement of the anchor

Lesson 8-2 Resources

Resource	Approaching Level AL	On Level OL	Beyond Level BL	English Learners ELL
Teacher Edition	▪ Differentiated Instruction, p. 549	▪ Differentiated Instruction, pp. 549, 550	▪ Differentiated Instruction, p. 550	
Chapter Resource Masters	▪ Study Guide and Intervention, pp. 11–12 ▪ Skills Practice, p. 13 ▪ Practice, p. 14 ▪ Word Problem Practice, p. 15 ▪ Spreadsheet Activity, p. 17	▪ Study Guide and Intervention, pp. 11–12 ▪ Skills Practice, p. 13 ▪ Practice, p. 14 ▪ Word Problem Practice, p. 15 ▪ Enrichment, p. 16 ▪ Spreadsheet Activity, p. 17	▪ Practice, p. 14 ▪ Word Problem Practice, p. 15 ▪ Enrichment, p. 16 ▪ Spreadsheet Activity, p. 17	▪ Study Guide and Intervention, pp. 11–12 ▪ Skills Practice, p. 13 ▪ Practice, p. 14 ▪ Word Problem Practice, p. 15 ▪ Spreadsheet Activity, p. 17
Other	▪ 5-Minute Check 8-2 ▪ Study Notebook ▪ Teaching Geometry with Manipulatives	▪ 5-Minute Check 8-2 ▪ Study Notebook ▪ Teaching Geometry with Manipulatives	▪ 5-Minute Check 8-2 ▪ Study Notebook	▪ 5-Minute Check 8-2 ▪ Study Notebook ▪ Teaching Geometry with Manipulatives

1 The Pythagorean Theorem

Examples 1–3 shows how to use the Pythagorean Theorem to find any unknowns of a right triangle.

Formative Assessment

Use the Guided Practice exercises after each example to determine students' understanding of concepts.

Additional Example

1 Find x.

a.

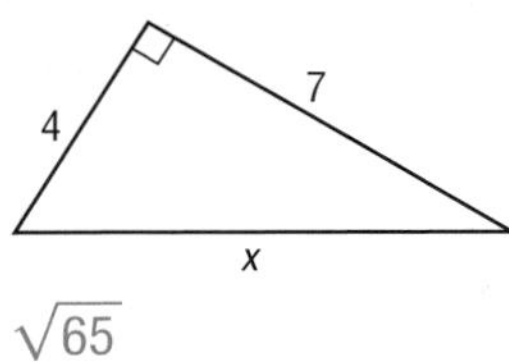

$\sqrt{65}$

b.

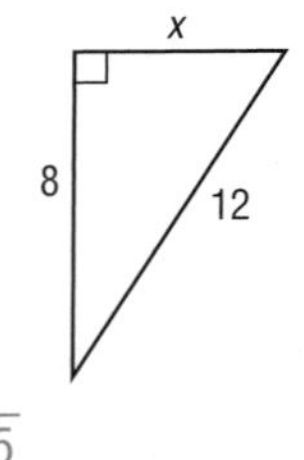

$4\sqrt{5}$

Additional Examples also in Interactive Classroom PowerPoint® Presentations

IWB Interactive White Board READY

WatchOut!

Side Lengths Pythagorean Triples are not the only possible side lengths for a right triangle; they give the triangles where all the lengths are whole numbers, but the side lengths could be any real numbers.

You can use the Pythagorean Theorem to find the measure of any side of a right triangle given the lengths of the other two sides.

Example 1 Find Missing Measures Using the Pythagorean Theorem

Find x.

a.

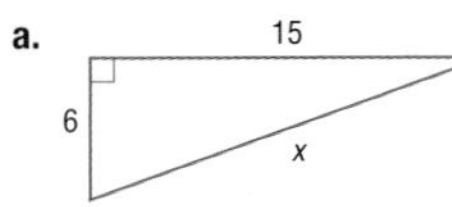

The side opposite the right angle is the hypotenuse, so $c = x$.

$a^2 + b^2 = c^2$	Pythagorean Theorem
$6^2 + 15^2 = x^2$	$a = 6$ and $b = 15$
$261 = x^2$	Simplify.
$\sqrt{261} = x$	Take the positive square root of each side.
$3\sqrt{29} = x$	Simplify.

StudyTip
Positive Square Root When finding the length of a side using the Pythagorean Theorem, use only the positive and not the negative square root, since length cannot be negative.

b.

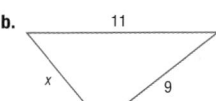

The hypotenuse is 11, so $c = 11$.

$a^2 + b^2 = c^2$	Pythagorean Theorem
$x^2 + 9^2 = 11^2$	$a = x$ and $b = 9$
$x^2 + 81 = 121$	Simplify.
$x^2 = 40$	Subtract 81 from each side.
$x = \sqrt{40}$ or $2\sqrt{10}$	Take the positive square root of each side and simplify.

GuidedPractice

1A.

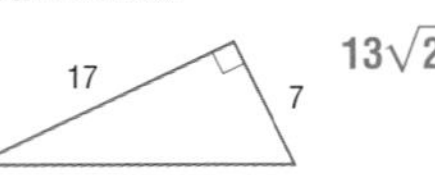

$13\sqrt{2}$

1B.

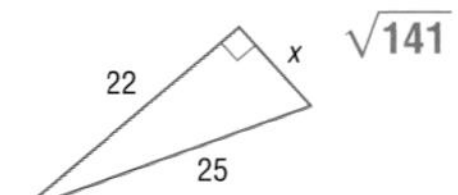

$\sqrt{141}$

A **Pythagorean triple** is a set of three nonzero whole numbers a, b, and c, such that $a^2 + b^2 = c^2$. One common Pythagorean triple is 3, 4, 5; that is, the sides of a right triangle are in the ratio 3:4:5. The most common Pythagorean triples are shown below in the first row. The triples below these are found by multiplying each number in the triple by the same factor.

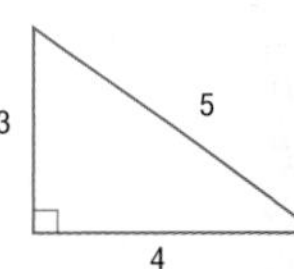

StudyTip
Pythagorean Triples If the measures of the sides of any right triangle are *not* whole numbers, the measures do not form a Pythagorean triple.

KeyConcept Common Pythagorean Triples

3, 4, 5	5, 12, 13	8, 15, 17	7, 24, 25
6, 8, 10	10, 24, 26	16, 30, 34	14, 48, 50
9, 12, 15	15, 36, 39	24, 45, 51	21, 72, 75
$3x$, $4x$, $5x$	$5x$, $12x$, $13x$	$8x$, $15x$, $17x$	$7x$, $24x$, $25x$

The largest number in each triple is the length of the hypotenuse.

548 | Lesson 8-2 | The Pythagorean Theorem and Its Converse

Example 2 Use a Pythagorean Triple

Use a Pythagorean triple to find x. Explain your reasoning.

Notice that 15 and 12 are both multiples of 3, because $15 = 3 \cdot 5$ and $12 = 3 \cdot 4$. Since 3, 4, 5 is a Pythagorean triple, the missing leg length x is $3 \cdot 3$ or 9.

CHECK $12^2 + 9^2 \stackrel{?}{=} 15^2$ Pythagorean Theorem

$225 = 225$ ✓ Simplify.

Reading Math

3-4-5 A right triangle with side lengths 3, 4, and 5 is called a *3-4-5 right triangle.*

Guided Practice

2A.

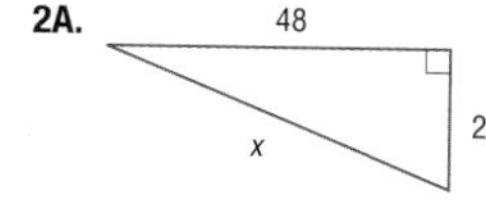

2B.

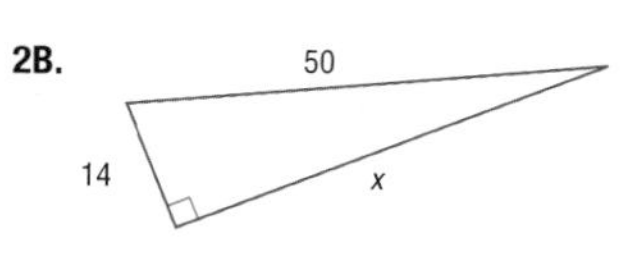

2A. 52; $20 = 4 \cdot 5$ and $48 = 4 \cdot 12$. Since 5, 12, 13 is a Pythagorean triple, $x = 4 \cdot 13$ or 52.
2B. 48; $50 = 2 \cdot 25$ and $14 = 2 \cdot 7$. Since 7, 24, 25 is a Pythagorean triple, $x = 2 \cdot 24$ or 48.

The Pythagorean Theorem can be used to solve many real-world problems.

Standardized Test Example 3 Use the Pythagorean Theorem

Damon is locked out of his house. The only open window is on the second floor, which is 12 feet above the ground. He needs to borrow a ladder from his neighbor. If he must place the ladder 5 feet from the house to avoid some bushes, what length of ladder does Damon need?

A 7 feet C 13 feet

B 11 feet D 17 feet

12 ft
5 ft

Note: Not drawn to scale

Read the Test Item

The distance the ladder is from the house, the height the ladder reaches, and the length of the ladder itself make up the lengths of the sides of a right triangle. You need to find the length of the ladder, which is the hypotenuse.

Solve the Test Item

Method 1 Use a Pythagorean triple.

The lengths of the legs are 5 and 12. 5, 12, 13 is a Pythagorean triple, so the length of the ladder is 13 feet.

Method 2 Use the Pythagorean Theorem.

Let x represent the length of the ladder.

$5^2 + 12^2 = x^2$ Pythagorean Theorem

$169 = x^2$ Simplify.

$\sqrt{169} = x$ Take the positive square root of each side.

$13 = x$ Simplify.

So, the answer is choice C.

Test-Taking Tip

CCSS Sense-Making

Since the hypotenuse of a right triangle is always the longest side, the length of the ladder in Example 3 must be greater than 5 or 12 feet. Since 7 and 11 feet are both less than 12 feet, choices A and B can be eliminated.

Differentiated Instruction AL OL

Visual/Spatial Learners Explain that many artists use right triangles in their works because they are so appealing to the eye. Right triangles can serve as guidelines to draw mountains in the background or to create vanishing points and perspective. Ask the students to construct one or more right triangles on a blank sheet of paper, find the lengths of the sides and then try to compose a picture using the triangles in an image or as a guide for an image. Examples could be a picture of a road vanishing in the distance or a house with right triangles as part of its roof.

Additional Examples

2 Use a Pythagorean triple to find x. Explain your reasoning.

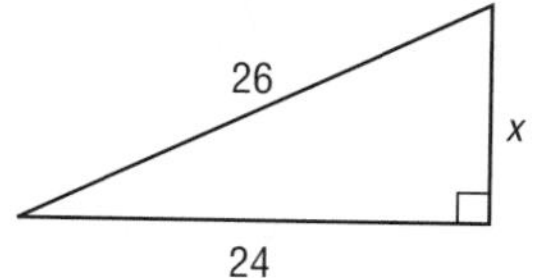

10; Because 24 and 26 are multiples of 2, $24 = 2 \cdot 12$ and $26 = 2 \cdot 13$. The missing leg is $2 \cdot 5 = 10$.

3 STANDARDIZED TEST EXAMPLE A 20-foot ladder is placed against a building to reach a window that is 16 feet above the ground. How many feet away from the building is the bottom of the ladder? C

A 3 **C** 12

B 4 **D** 15

Focus on Mathematical Content

Pythagorean Inequalities You may want to introduce the following Pythagorean inequalities to your students.

$a^2 + b^2 < c^2$ for obtuse triangles

$a^2 + b^2 > c^2$ for acute triangles

These inequalities, along with the Triangle Inequality Theorem, help students to further understand the relationships between the sides and angles of triangles.

CCSS Teaching the Mathematical Practices

Sense-Making Mathematically proficient students start by explaining the meaning of a problem to themselves and looking for entry points to its solution. Encourage students to analyze the answer choices and eliminate any unreasonable choices.

2 Converse of the Pythagorean Theorem

Example 4 shows how to use the converse of the Pythagorean Theorem to prove that a triangle is or is not a right triangle.

GuidedPractice

3. According to your company's safety regulations, the distance from the base of a ladder to a wall that it leans against should be at least one fourth of the ladder's total length. You are given a 20-foot ladder to place against a wall at a job site. If you follow the company's safety regulations, what is the maximum distance x up the wall the ladder will reach, to the nearest tenth? G

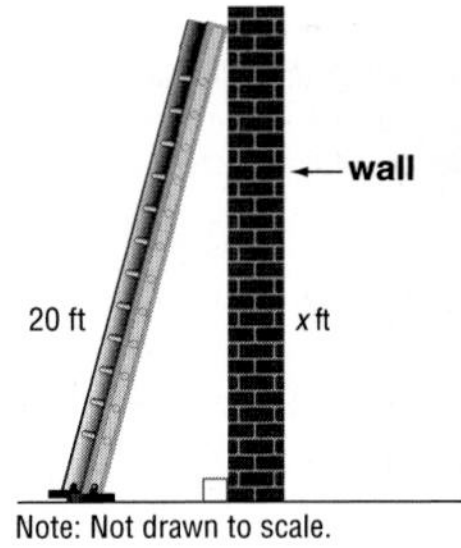

F 12 feet   H 20.6 feet

G 19.4 feet   J 30.6 feet

2 Converse of the Pythagorean Theorem The converse of the Pythagorean Theorem also holds. You can use this theorem to help you determine whether a triangle is a right triangle given the measures of all three sides.

Theorem 8.5 Converse of the Pythagorean Theorem

Words If the sum of the squares of the lengths of the shortest sides of a triangle is equal to the square of the length of the longest side, then the triangle is a right triangle.

Symbols If $a^2 + b^2 = c^2$, then $\triangle ABC$ is a right triangle.

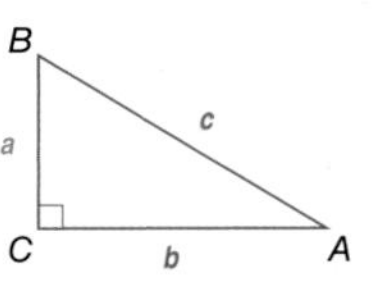

You will prove Theorem 8.5 in Exercise 35.

StudyTip

Determining the Longest Side If the measures of any of the sides of a triangle are expressed as radicals, you may wish to use a calculator to determine which length is the longest.

You can also use side lengths to classify a triangle as acute or obtuse.

Theorems Pythagorean Inequality Theorems

8.6 If the square of the length of the longest side of a triangle is less than the sum of the squares of the lengths of the other two sides, then the triangle is an acute triangle.

Symbols If $c^2 < a^2 + b^2$, then $\triangle ABC$ is acute.

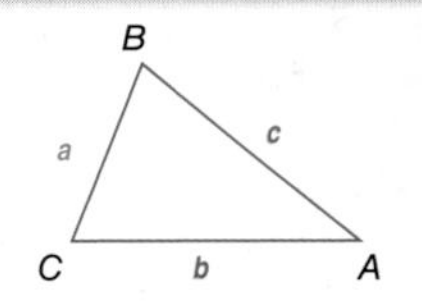

8.7 If the square of the length of the longest side of a triangle is greater than the sum of the squares of the lengths of the other two sides, then the triangle is an obtuse triangle.

Symbols If $c^2 > a^2 + b^2$, then $\triangle ABC$ is obtuse.

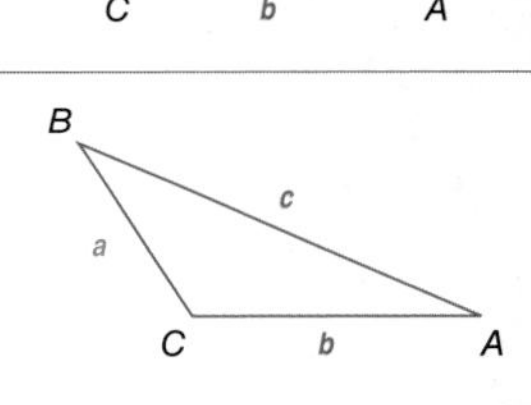

You will prove Theorems 8.6 and 8.7 in Exercises 36 and 37, respectively.

DifferentiatedInstruction OL BL

Extension A baseball diamond is a square with 90-foot sides. What is the approximate distance the catcher must throw from home to second base? 127.3 ft

Example 4 Classify Triangles

Determine whether each set of numbers can be the measures of the sides of a triangle. If so, classify the triangle as *acute*, *right*, or *obtuse*. Justify your answer.

a. **7, 14, 16**

Step 1 Determine whether the measures can form a triangle using the Triangle Inequality Theorem.

$7 + 14 > 16$ ✓ $14 + 16 > 7$ ✓ $7 + 16 > 14$ ✓

The side lengths 7, 14, and 16 can form a triangle.

Step 2 Classify the triangle by comparing the square of the longest side to the sum of the squares of the other two sides.

$c^2 \stackrel{?}{=} a^2 + b^2$ Compare c^2 and $a^2 + b^2$.

$16^2 \stackrel{?}{=} 7^2 + 14^2$ Substitution

$256 > 245$ Simplify and compare.

Since $c^2 > a^2 + b^2$, the triangle is obtuse.

b. **9, 40, 41**

Step 1 Determine whether the measures can form a triangle.

$9 + 40 > 41$ ✓ $40 + 41 > 9$ ✓ $9 + 41 > 40$ ✓

The side lengths 9, 40, and 41 can form a triangle.

Step 2 Classify the triangle.

$c^2 \stackrel{?}{=} a^2 + b^2$ Compare c^2 and $a^2 + b^2$.

$41^2 \stackrel{?}{=} 9^2 + 40^2$ Substitution

$1681 = 1681$ Simplify and compare.

Since $c^2 = a^2 + b^2$, the triangle is a right triangle.

Review Vocabulary

Triangle Inequality Theorem The sum of the lengths of any two sides of a triangle must be greater than the length of the third side.

Guided Practice

4A. 11, 60, 61 **4B.** $2\sqrt{3}, 4\sqrt{2}, 3\sqrt{5}$ **4C.** 6.2, 13.8, 20

4A. Yes; since $11 + 60 > 61$, $60 + 61 > 11$, and $11 + 61 > 60$; right, since $11^2 + 60^2 = 61^2$.

4B. Yes; since $2\sqrt{3} + 4\sqrt{2} > 3\sqrt{5}$, $2\sqrt{3} + 3\sqrt{5} > 4\sqrt{2}$, and $4\sqrt{2} + 3\sqrt{5} > 2\sqrt{3}$. Obtuse, since $(3\sqrt{5})^2 > (2\sqrt{3})^2 + (4\sqrt{2})^2$.

4C. No; since $6.2 + 13.8 \not> 20$, the side lengths cannot form a triangle.

Check Your Understanding

 = Step-by-Step Solutions begin on page R14.

Example 1 Find x.

1. 12

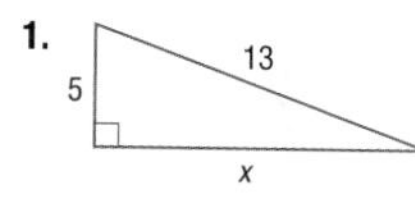

2. $4\sqrt{13} \approx 14.4$

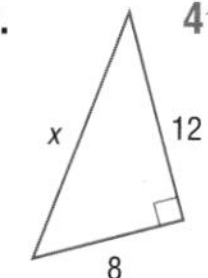
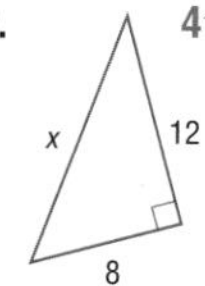

3. $4\sqrt{15} \approx 15.5$

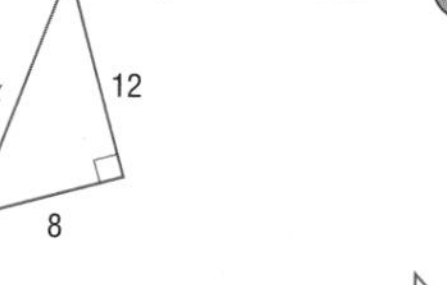
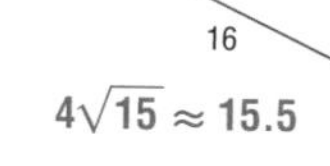

Example 2

4. Use a Pythagorean triple to find x. Explain your reasoning. **28; Since $35 = 7 \cdot 5$ and $21 = 7 \cdot 3$ and 3-4-5 is a Pythagorean triple, $x = 7 \cdot 4$ or 28.**

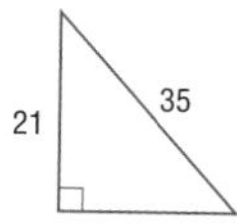

Additional Example

4 Determine whether each set of numbers can be the measures of the sides of a triangle. If so, classify the triangle as *acute*, *right*, or *obtuse*. Justify your answer.

a. 9, 12, and 15 The segments form the sides of a right triangle, because the measures form a Pythagorean triple.

b. 10, 11, and 13 The segments form the sides of an acute triangle because $13^2 < 10^2 + 11^2$.

Teach with Tech

Student Response System Create a presentation that shows students a set of three numbers. Ask them if the numbers could be the side lengths of a right triangle. Have students work independently, and respond with A for yes and B for no.

3 Practice

Formative Assessment

Use Exercises 1–8 to check for understanding.

Use the chart at the bottom of this page to customize assignments for your students.

Teaching the Mathematical Practices

Perseverance Mathematically proficient students check their answers to problems using a different method, and they continually ask themselves, "does this make sense?" In Exercises 15–18, encourage students to check their work.

Additional Answers

6. yes; right
$39^2 \stackrel{?}{=} 15^2 + 36^2$
$1521 = 225 + 1296$

7. yes; obtuse
$26^2 \stackrel{?}{=} 16^2 + 18^2$
$676 > 256 + 324$

8. yes; acute
$24^2 \stackrel{?}{=} 15^2 + 20^2$
$576 < 225 + 400$

21. yes; obtuse
$21^2 \stackrel{?}{=} 7^2 + 15^2$
$441 > 49 + 225$

22. no; $23 > 10 + 12$

23. yes; right
$20.5^2 \stackrel{?}{=} 4.5^2 + 20^2$
$420.25 = 20.25 + 400$

24. no; $91 > 44 + 46$

25. yes; acute
$7.6^2 \stackrel{?}{=} 4.2^2 + 6.4^2$
$57.76 < 17.64 + 40.96$

26. yes; obtuse
$14^2 \stackrel{?}{=} 4^2 + 12^2$
$196 > 16 + 144$

Example 3

5. MULTIPLE CHOICE The mainsail of a boat is shown. What is the length, in feet, of $\overline{LN}$? **D**

A 52.5 C 72.5

B 65 D 75

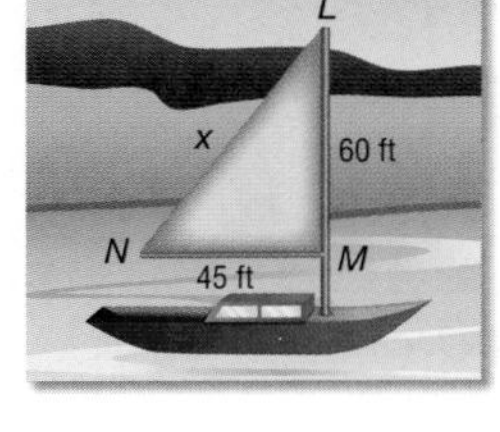

Example 4

Determine whether each set of numbers can be the measures of the sides of a triangle. If so, classify the triangle as *acute*, *obtuse*, or *right*. Justify your answer.

6. 15, 36, 39 **7.** 16, 18, 26 **8.** 15, 20, 24

6–8. See margin.

Practice and Problem Solving

Extra Practice is on page R8.

Example 1

Find x.

9. 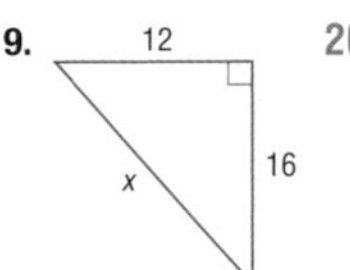

20

10. 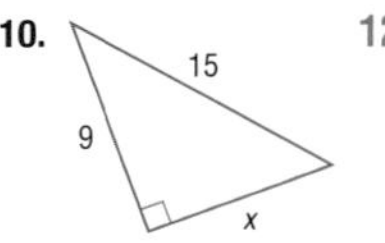

12

11.  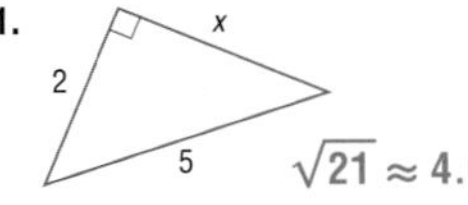

$\sqrt{21} \approx 4.6$

12. 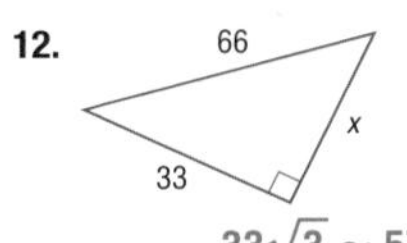

$33\sqrt{3} \approx 57.2$

13. 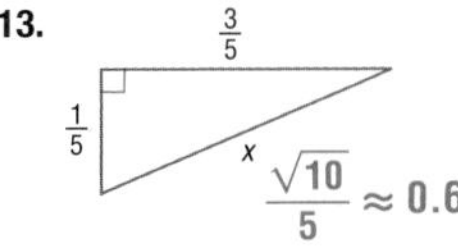

$\frac{\sqrt{10}}{5} \approx 0.6$

14. 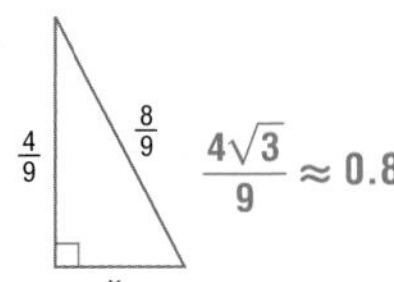

$\frac{4\sqrt{3}}{9} \approx 0.8$

Example 2

CCSS PERSEVERANCE **Use a Pythagorean Triple to find x.**

15. 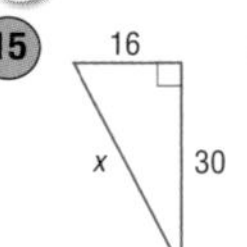

34

16. 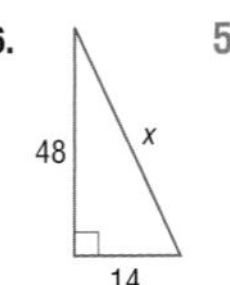

50

17. 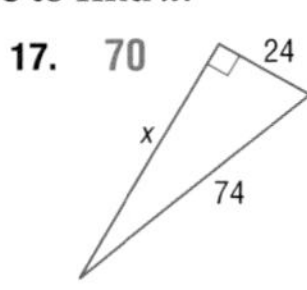

70

18. 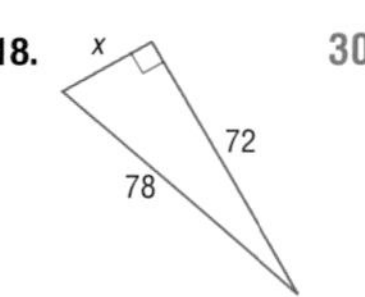

30

Example 3

19. BASKETBALL The support for a basketball goal forms a right triangle as shown. What is the length x of the horizontal portion of the support? **about 3 ft**

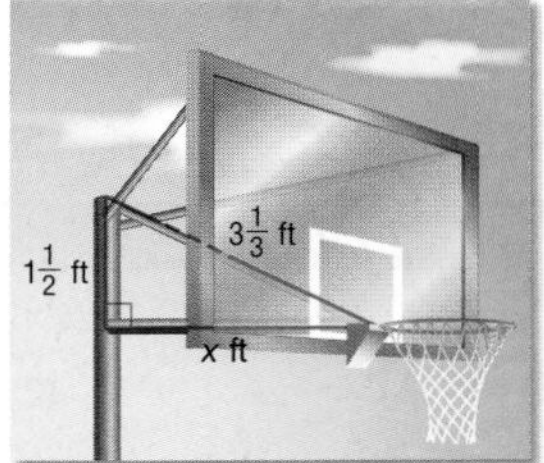

20. DRIVING The street that Khaliah usually uses to get to school is under construction. She has been taking the detour shown. If the construction starts at the point where Khaliah leaves her normal route and ends at the point where she re-enters her normal route, about how long is the stretch of road under construction? **about 2 mi**

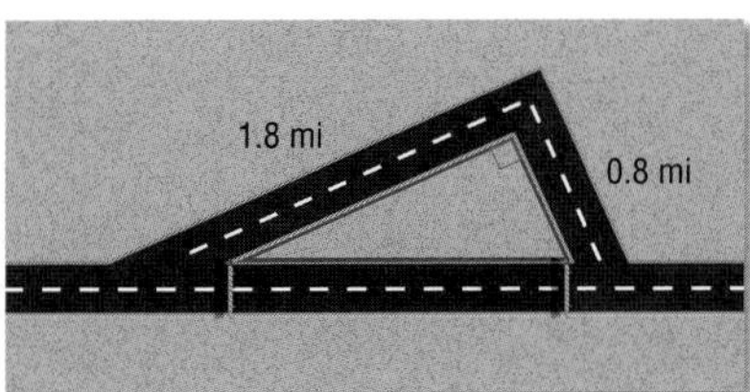

Differentiated Homework Options

Level	Assignment	Two-Day Option	
AL Basic	9–26, 50–76	9–25 odd, 53–56	10–26 even, 50–52, 57–76
OL Core	9–33 odd, 34, 35–41 odd, 42–45, 47, 48, 50–76	9–26, 53–56	27–52, 57–76
BL Advanced	27–72, (optional: 73–76)		

Example 4 Determine whether each set of numbers can be the measures of the sides of a triangle. If so, classify the triangle as *acute*, *obtuse*, or *right*. Justify your answer. **21–26. See margin.**

21. 7, 15, 21 **22.** 10, 12, 23 **23.** 4.5, 20, 20.5

24. 44, 46, 91 **25.** 4.2, 6.4, 7.6 **26.** 4, 12, 14

B Find x.

27. 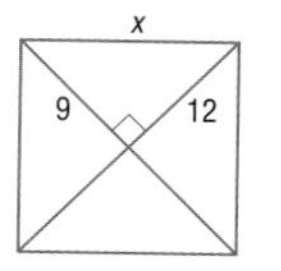

15

28. 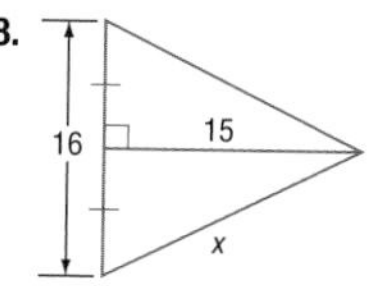

17

29. 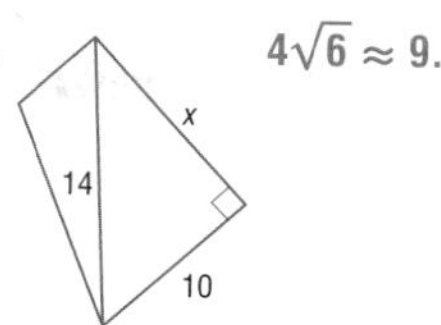

$4\sqrt{6} \approx 9.8$

COORDINATE GEOMETRY Determine whether $\triangle XYZ$ is an *acute*, *right*, or *obtuse* triangle for the given vertices. Explain. **30–33. See Ch. 8 Answer Appendix.**

30. $X(-3, -2), Y(-1, 0), Z(0, -1)$ **31.** $X(-7, -3), Y(-2, -5), Z(-4, -1)$

32. $X(1, 2), Y(4, 6), Z(6, 6)$ **33.** $X(3, 1), Y(3, 7), Z(11, 1)$

34. JOGGING Brett jogs in the park three times a week. Usually, he takes a $\frac{3}{4}$-mile path that cuts through the park. Today, the path is closed, so he is taking the orange route shown. How much farther will he jog on his alternate route than he would have if he had followed his normal path? **0.3 mi**

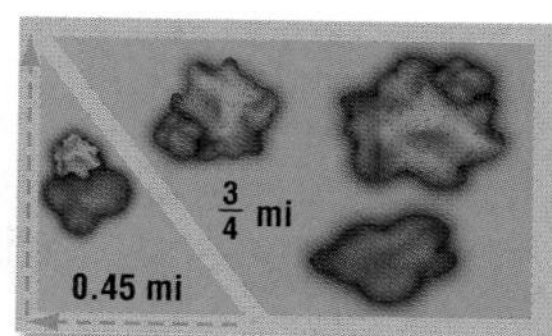

C 35. PROOF Write a paragraph proof of Theorem 8.5. **35–37. See Ch. 8 Answer Appendix.**

PROOF Write a two-column proof for each theorem.

36. Theorem 8.6 **37.** Theorem 8.7

CCSS SENSE-MAKING Find the perimeter and area of each figure.

38. 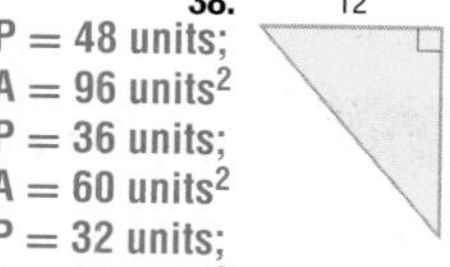

39. 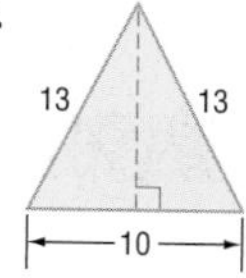

40. 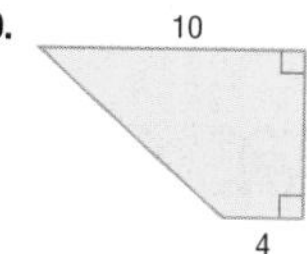

38. P = 48 units; A = 96 units^2
39. P = 36 units; A = 60 units^2
40. P = 32 units; A = 56 units^2

41. ALGEBRA The sides of a triangle have lengths x, $x + 5$, and 25. If the length of the longest side is 25, what value of x makes the triangle a right triangle? **15**

42. ALGEBRA The sides of a triangle have lengths $2x$, 8, and 12. If the length of the longest side is $2x$, what values of x make the triangle acute? $6 < x < 2\sqrt{13}$

43 TELEVISION The screen aspect ratio, or the ratio of the width to the height, of a high-definition television is 16:9. The size of a television is given by the diagonal distance across the screen. If an HDTV is 41 inches wide, what is its screen size? **47 in.**

CCSS Teaching the Mathematical Practices

Sense-Making Mathematically proficient students start by explaining the meaning of a problem to themselves and looking for entry points to its solution. They plan a solution pathway rather than simply jumping into a solution attempt. In Exercises 38–40, encourage students to use the Pythagorean theorem to find the measures of the missing sides.

Enrichment
OL BL

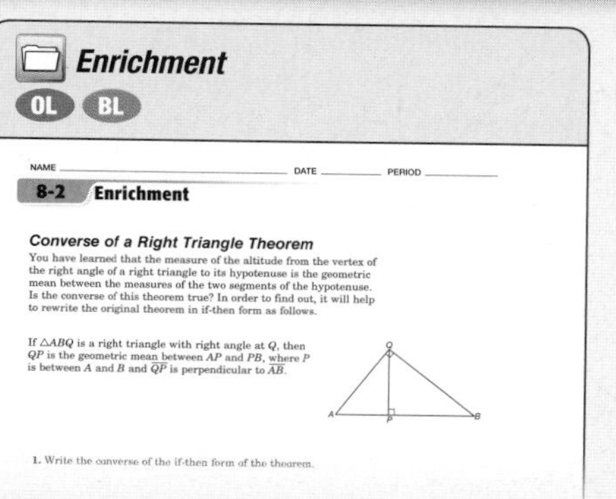

Study Guide and Intervention
AL OL ELL

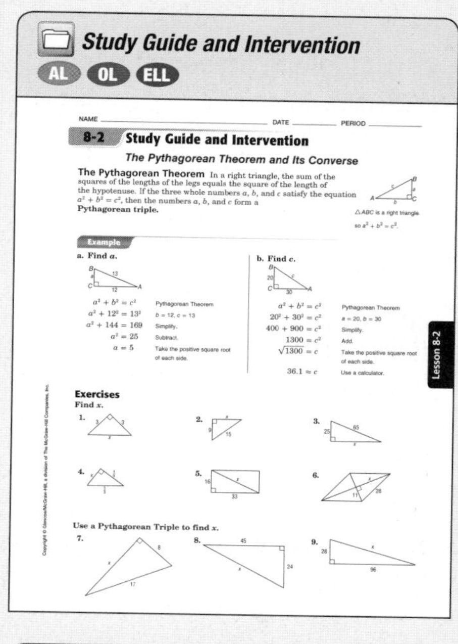

Practice
AL OL BL ELL

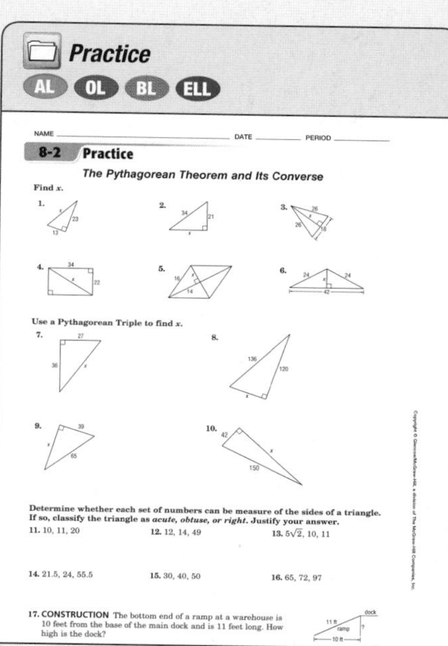

Word Problem Practice
AL OL BL ELL

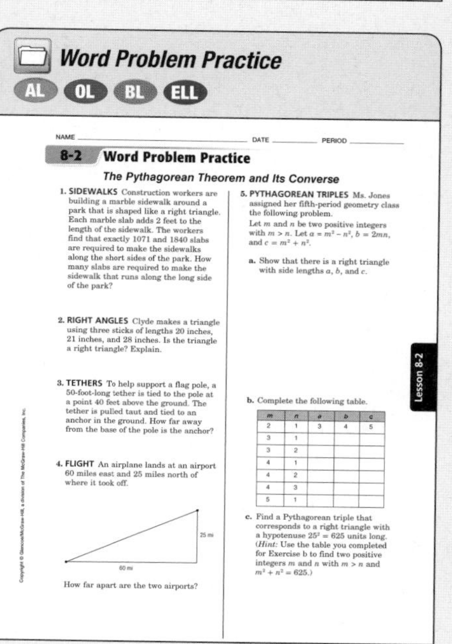

Multiple Representations

In Exercise 48, students use geometric sketches, a table, and verbal description to investigate special right triangles.

CCSS Teaching the Mathematical Practices

Arguments Mathematically proficient students understand and use stated assumptions and definitions in constructing arguments. They make conjectures and build a logical progression of statements to explore the truth of their conjectures. In Exercise 50, encourage students to start by finding examples or counterexamples.

Additional Answers

48a.

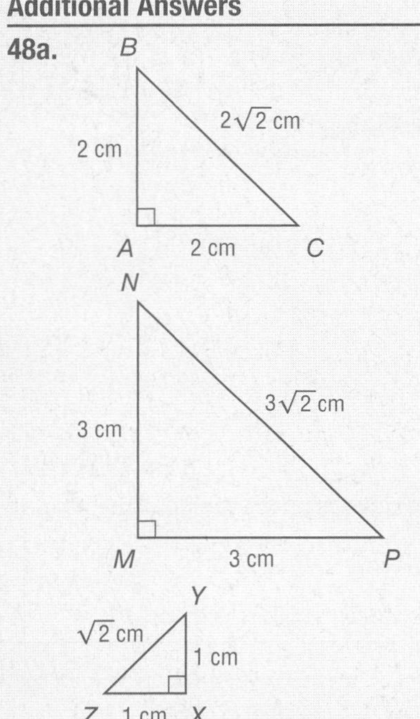

50. False; sample answer: A right triangle with legs measuring 3 in. and 4 in. has a hypotenuse of 5 in. and an area of $\frac{1}{2} \times 3 \times 4$ or 6 in^2. A right triangle with legs measuring 2 in. and $\sqrt{21}$ in. also has a hypotenuse of 5 in., but its area is $\frac{1}{2} \times 2 \times \sqrt{21}$ or $\sqrt{21}$ in^2, which is not equivalent to 6 in^2.

51.

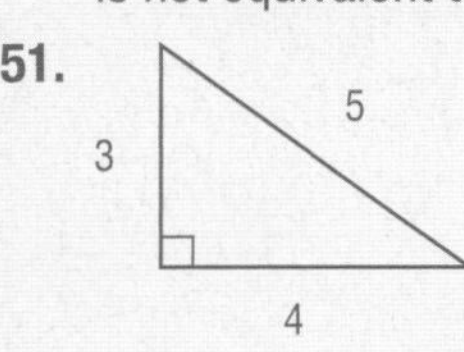

Right; sample answer: If you double or halve the side lengths, all three sides of the new triangles are proportional to the sides of the original triangle. Using the Side-Side-Side Similarity Theorem, you know that both of the new triangles are similar to the original triangle, so they are both right.

52. Sample answer: Incommensurable magnitudes are magnitudes of the same kind that do not have a common unit of measure. Irrational numbers were invented to describe geometric relationships, such as ratios of incommensurable magnitudes that cannot be described using rational numbers. For example, to express the measures of the sides of a square with an area of 2 square units, the irrational number $\sqrt{2}$ is needed.

---

44. PLAYGROUND According to the *Handbook for Public Playground Safety,* the ratio of the vertical distance to the horizontal distance covered by a slide should not be more than about 4 to 7. If the horizontal distance allotted in a slide design is 14 feet, approximately how long should the slide be? **about 16 ft**

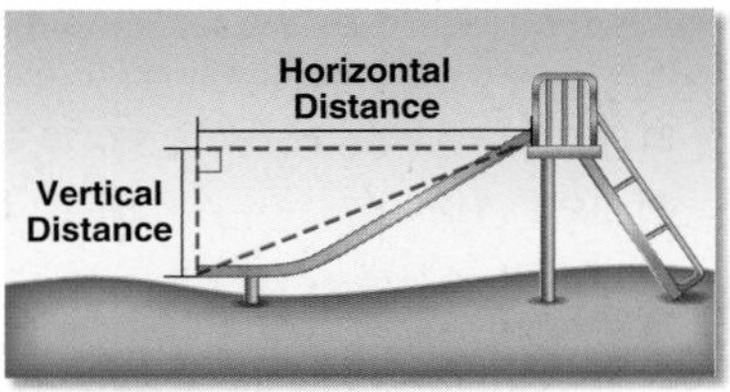

Find *x*.

45. **10**

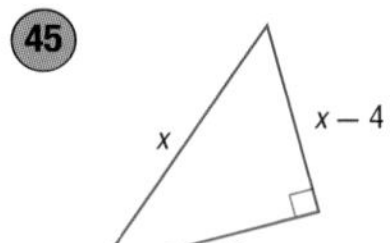

46. **15**

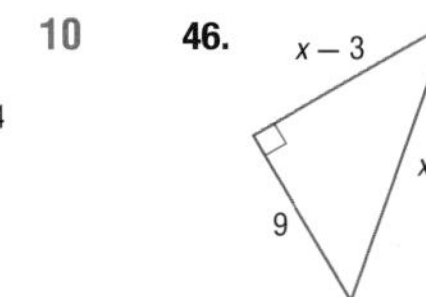

47. $\frac{1}{2}$

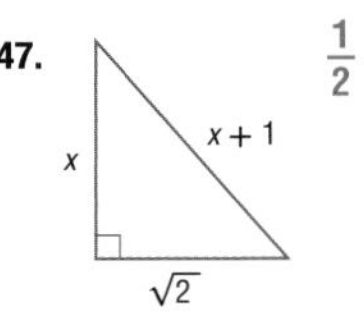

48. MULTIPLE REPRESENTATIONS In this problem, you will investigate special right triangles.

a. Geometric Draw three different isosceles right triangles that have whole-number side lengths. Label the triangles *ABC*, *MNP*, and *XYZ* with the right angle located at vertex *A*, *M*, and *X*, respectively. Label the leg lengths of each side, and find the exact length of the hypotenuse. **See margin.**

b. Tabular Copy and complete the table below.

Triangle	Length				Ratio	
ABC	*BC*	$2\sqrt{2}$	*AB*	2	$\frac{BC}{AB}$	$\sqrt{2}$
MNP	*NP*	$3\sqrt{2}$	*MN*	3	$\frac{NP}{MN}$	$\sqrt{2}$
XYZ	*YZ*	$\sqrt{2}$	*XY*	1	$\frac{YZ}{XY}$	$\sqrt{2}$

c. Verbal Make a conjecture about the ratio of the hypotenuse to a leg of an isosceles right triangle. **Sample answer: The ratio of the hypotenuse to a leg of an isosceles right triangle is $\sqrt{2}$.**

H.O.T. Problems Use Higher-Order Thinking Skills

49. CHALLENGE Find the value of *x* in the figure at the right. **5.4**

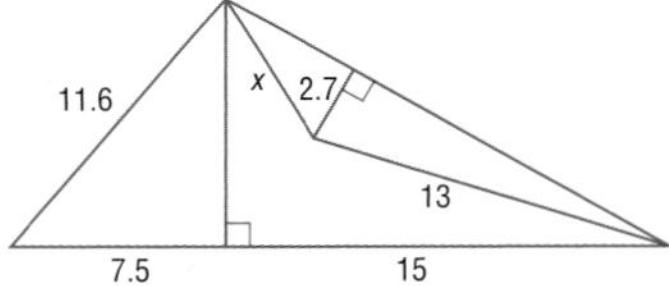

50. CCSS ARGUMENTS *True* or *false*? Any two right triangles with the same hypotenuse have the same area. Explain your reasoning. **See margin.**

51. OPEN ENDED Draw a right triangle with side lengths that form a Pythagorean triple. If you double the length of each side, is the resulting triangle *acute*, *right*, or *obtuse*? if you halve the length of each side? Explain. **See margin.**

52. WRITING IN MATH Research *incommensurable magnitudes*, and describe how this phrase relates to the use of irrational numbers in geometry. Include one example of an irrational number used in geometry. **See margin.**

Standardized Test Practice

53. Which set of numbers cannot be the measures of the sides of a triangle? **D**

A 10, 11, 20	**C** 35, 45, 75
B 14, 16, 28	**D** 41, 55, 98

54. A square park has a diagonal walkway from one corner to another. If the walkway is 120 meters long, what is the approximate length of each side of the park? **G**

F 60 m	**H** 170 m
G 85 m	**J** 240 m

55. SHORT RESPONSE If the perimeter of square 2 is 200 units and the perimeter of square 1 is 150 units, what is the perimeter of square 3? **250 units**

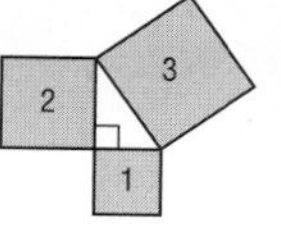

56. SAT/ACT In $\triangle ABC$, $\angle B$ is a right angle and $\angle A$ is 20° greater than $\angle C$. What is the measure of $\angle C$? **B**

A 30	**C** 40	**E** 70
B 35	**D** 45	

Spiral Review

Find the geometric mean between each pair of numbers. (Lesson 8-1)

57. 9 and 4 **6**
58. 45 and 5 **15**
59. 12 and 15 $6\sqrt{5} \approx 13.4$
60. 36 and 48 $24\sqrt{3} \approx 41.6$

61. SCALE DRAWING Teodoro is creating a scale model of a skateboarding ramp on a 10-by-8-inch sheet of graph paper. If the real ramp is going to be 12 feet by 8 feet, find an appropriate scale for the drawing and determine the ramp's dimensions. (Lesson 7-7) **1 in. = 2 ft; 6 in. × 4 in.**

Determine whether the triangles are similar. If so, write a similarity statement. If not, what would be sufficient to prove the triangles similar? Explain your reasoning. (Lesson 7-3)

62.

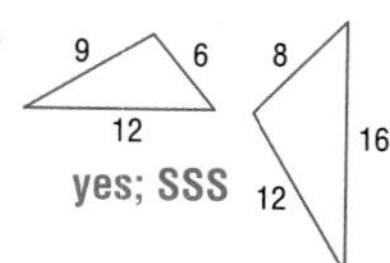

yes; SSS

63.

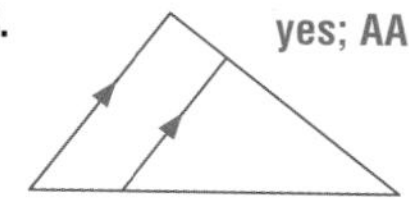

yes; AA

64.

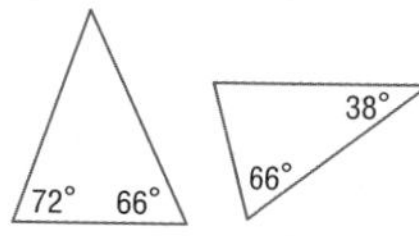

No; corresponding angles are not congruent.

65. PROOF Write a two-column proof. (Lesson 5-3) **See margin.**

Given: $\overline{FG} \perp \ell$
$\overline{FH}$ is any nonperpendicular segment from F to ℓ.

Prove: $FH > FG$

Find each measure if $m\angle DGF = 53$ and $m\angle AGC = 40$. (Lesson 4-2)

66. $m\angle 1$ **37**
67. $m\angle 2$ **50**
68. $m\angle 3$ **50**
69. $m\angle 4$ **40**

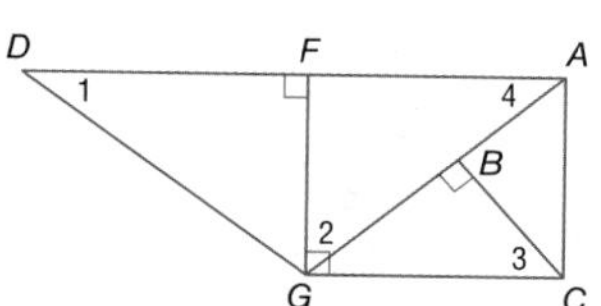

Find the distance between each pair of parallel lines with the given equations. (Lesson 3-6)

70. $y = 4x$
$y = 4x - 17$ $\sqrt{17}$

71. $y = 2x - 3$
$2x - y = -4$ $\frac{7\sqrt{5}}{5}$

72. $y = -0.75x - 1$
$3x + 4y = 20$ $\frac{24}{5}$

Skills Review

Find the value of x.

73. $18 = 3x\sqrt{3}$ $2\sqrt{3}$
74. $24 = 2x\sqrt{2}$ $6\sqrt{2}$
75. $9\sqrt{2} \cdot x = 18\sqrt{2}$ **2**
76. $2 = x \cdot \frac{4}{\sqrt{3}}$ $\frac{\sqrt{3}}{2}$

4 Assess

Name the Math Ask students to recall how right triangles are modeled in suspension bridges, and have them demonstrate how a right triangle could model real-world objects.

Formative Assessment

Check for student understanding of Lessons 8-1 and 8-2.

 Quiz 1, p. 51

Additional Answer

65. Given: $\overline{FG} \perp \ell$
$\overline{FH}$ is any nonperpendicular segment from F to ℓ.

Prove: $FH > FG$

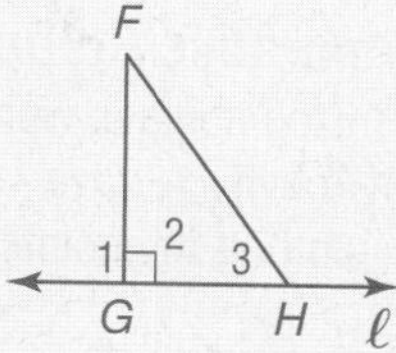

Proof:

Statements (Reasons)

1. $\overline{FG} \perp \ell$ (Given)
2. $\angle 1$ and $\angle 2$ are right angles. ($\perp$ lines form right angles.)
3. $\angle 1 \cong \angle 2$ (All right angles are congruent.)
4. $m\angle 1 = m\angle 2$ (Definition of congruent angles)
5. $m\angle 1 > m\angle 3$ (Exterior Angle Inequality Theorem)
6. $m\angle 2 > m\angle 3$ (Substitution Property)
7. $FH > FG$ (If an angle of a triangle is greater than a second angle, then the side opposite the greater angle is longer than the side opposite the lesser angle.)

1 Focus

Objective Graph points in space and use the distance and midpoint formulas in space.

Materials for Each Student

- ruler

Teaching Tip

Explain to students that three-dimensional space is based on two copies of the coordinate plane: the *xy*-plane and the *yz*-plane.

2 Teach

Working in Cooperative Groups

Have students of mixed abilities work in groups of three. In Activity 1, have students rotate in plotting the points in space.

If students have difficulty plotting points with the appropriate perspective, have them use a ruler to align each coordinate with the respective axis.

Practice Have students complete Exercises 1–5 and 10–14.

EXTEND 8-2 Geometry Lab: Coordinates in Space

You have used ordered pairs of two coordinates to describe the location of a point on the coordinate plane. Because space has three dimensions, a point requires three numbers, or coordinates, to describe its location in space.

A point in space is represented by an **ordered triple** of real numbers (x, y, z). In the figure at the right, the ordered triple (2, 3, 6) locates point *P*. Notice that a rectangular prism is used to show perspective.

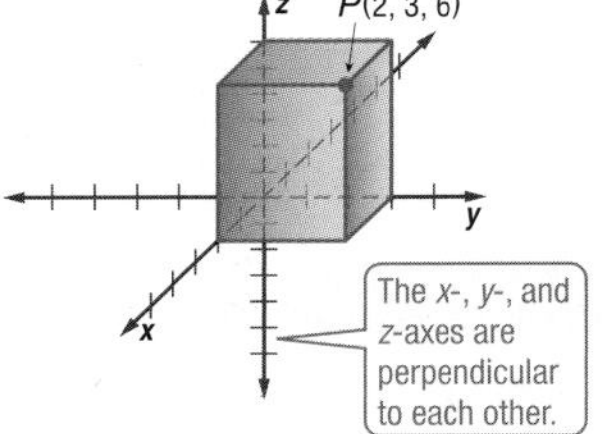

Activity 1 Graph a Rectangular Solid

Graph a rectangular solid that has two vertices, *L*(4, −5, 2) and the origin. Label the coordinates of each vertex.

Step 1 Plot the *x*-coordinate first. Draw a segment from the origin 4 units in the positive direction.

Step 2 To plot the *y*-coordinate, draw a segment five units in the negative direction.

Step 3 Next, to plot the *z*-coordinate, draw a segment two units long in the positive direction.

Step 4 Label the coordinate *L*.

Step 5 Draw the rectangular prism and label each vertex: *L*(4, −5, 2), *K*(0, −5, 2), *J*(0, 0, 2), *M*(4, 0, 2) *Q*(4, −5, 0), *P*(0, −5, 0), *N*(0, 0, 0), and *R*(4, 0, 0).

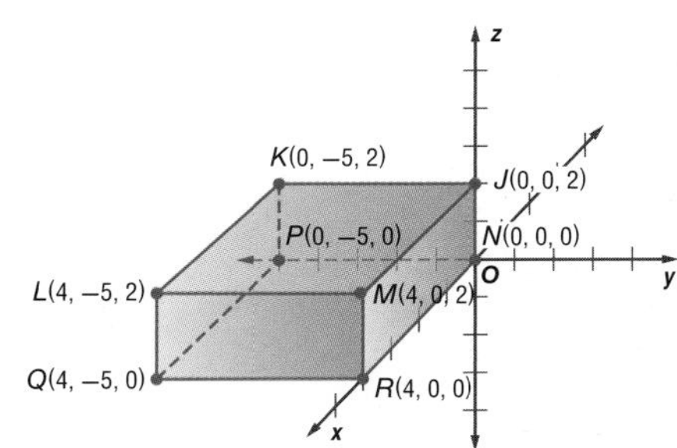

Finding the distance between points and the midpoint of a segment in space is similar to finding distance and a midpoint in the coordinate plane.

KeyConcept Distance and Midpoint Formulas in Space

If *A* has coordinates $A(x_1, y_1, z_1)$ and *B* has coordinates $B(x_2, y_2, z_2)$, then

$$AB = \sqrt{(x_2 - x_1)^2 + (y_2 - y_1)^2 + (z_2 - z_1)^2}.$$

The midpoint *M* of $\overline{AB}$ has coordinates

$$M\left(\frac{x_1 + x_2}{2}, \frac{y_1 + y_2}{2}, \frac{z_1 + z_2}{2}\right).$$

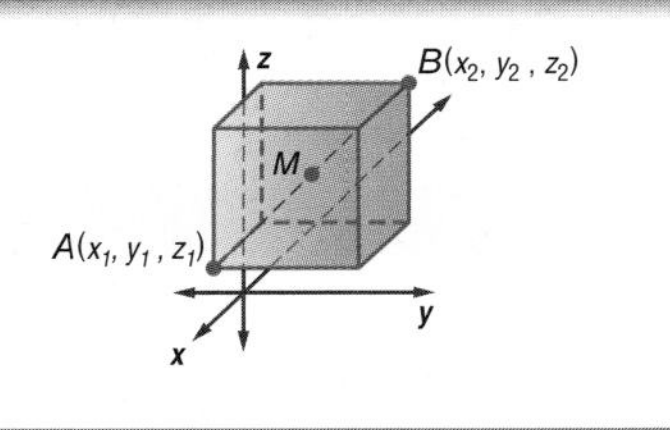

Activity 2 Distance and Midpoint Formulas in Space

Consider $J(2, 4, 9)$ and $K(-4, -5, 11)$.

a. Find JK.

$JK = \sqrt{(x_2 - x_1)^2 + (y_2 - y_1)^2 + (z_2 - z_1)^2}$ Distance Formula in Space

$= \sqrt{(-4 - 2)^2 + (-5 - 4)^2 + (11 - 9)^2}$ Substitution

$= \sqrt{121}$ Simplify.

$= 11$ Use a calculator.

b. Determine the coordinates of the midpoint M of $\overline{JK}$.

$M = \left(\frac{x_1 + x_2}{2}, \frac{y_1 + y_2}{2}, \frac{z_1 + z_2}{2}\right)$ Midpoint Formula in Space

$= \left(\frac{2 + (-4)}{2}, \frac{4 + (-5)}{2}, \frac{9 + 11}{2}\right)$ Substitution

$= \left(-1, -\frac{1}{2}, 10\right)$ Simplify.

Exercises

Graph a rectangular solid that contains the given point and the origin as vertices. Label the coordinates of each vertex. **1–9. See Ch. 8 Answer Appendix.**

1. $A(2, 1, 5)$
2. $P(-1, 4, 2)$
3. $C(-2, 2, 2)$
4. $R(3, -4, 1)$
5. $P(4, 6, -3)$
6. $G(4, 1, -3)$
7. $K(-2, -4, -4)$
8. $W(-1, -3, -6)$
9. $W(3, 3, 4)$

Determine the distance between each pair of points. Then determine the coordinates of the midpoint M of the segment joining the pair of points. **10–19. See margin.**

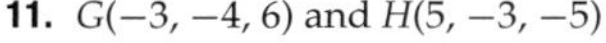

10. $D(0, 0, 0)$ and $E(1, 5, 7)$
11. $G(-3, -4, 6)$ and $H(5, -3, -5)$
12. $K(2, 2, 0)$ and $L(-2, -2, 0)$
13. $P(-2, -5, 8)$ and $Q(3, -2, -1)$
14. $A(4, 7, 9)$ and $B(-3, 8, -8)$
15. $W(-12, 8, 10)$ and $Z(-4, 1, -2)$
16. $F\left(\frac{3}{5}, 0, \frac{4}{5}\right)$ and $G(0, 3, 0)$
17. $G(1, -1, 6)$ and $H\left(\frac{1}{5}, -\frac{2}{5}, 2\right)$
18. $B(\sqrt{3}, 2, 2\sqrt{2})$ and $C(-2\sqrt{3}, 4, 4\sqrt{2})$
19. $S(6\sqrt{3}, 4, 4\sqrt{2})$ and $T(4\sqrt{3}, 5, \sqrt{2})$

20. **PROOF** Write a coordinate proof of the Distance Formula in Space. **See margin.**

Given: A has coordinates $A(x_1, y_1, z_1)$, and B has coordinates $B(x_2, y_2, z_2)$.

Prove: $AB = \sqrt{(x_2 - x_1)^2 + (y_2 - y_1)^2 + (z_2 - z_1)^2}$

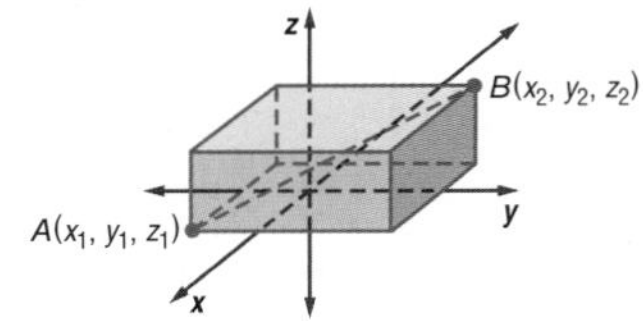

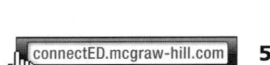

21. **WRITING IN MATH** Compare and contrast the Distance and Midpoint Formulas on the coordinate plane and in three-dimensional coordinate space. **See margin.**

3 Assess

Formative Assessment

Use Exercises 6–9 and 15–21 to assess students' understanding of working in three dimensions.

From Concrete to Abstract

Have students compare the distance and midpoint formulas to the same formulas in the coordinate plane when the points have z-values equal to zero.

Extending the Concept

Have students explore how to use the coordinates of a rectangular solid to determine its volume.

Additional Answers

10. $DE = 5\sqrt{3}; \left(\frac{1}{2}, \frac{5}{2}, \frac{7}{2}\right)$

11. $GH = \sqrt{186}; \left(1, -\frac{7}{2}, \frac{1}{2}\right)$

12. $KL = 4\sqrt{2}; (0, 0, 0)$

13. $PQ = \sqrt{115}; \left(\frac{1}{2}, -\frac{7}{2}, \frac{7}{2}\right)$

14. $AB = \sqrt{339}; \left(\frac{1}{2}, \frac{15}{2}, \frac{1}{2}\right)$

15. $WZ = \sqrt{257}; \left(-8, \frac{9}{2}, 4\right)$

16. $FG = \sqrt{10}; \left(\frac{3}{10}, \frac{3}{2}, \frac{2}{5}\right)$

17. $GH = \sqrt{17}; \left(\frac{3}{5}, -\frac{7}{10}, 4\right)$

18. $BC = \sqrt{39}; \left(-\frac{\sqrt{3}}{2}, 3, 3\sqrt{2}\right)$

19. $ST = \sqrt{31}; \left(5\sqrt{3}, \frac{9}{2}, \frac{5\sqrt{2}}{2}\right)$

20.

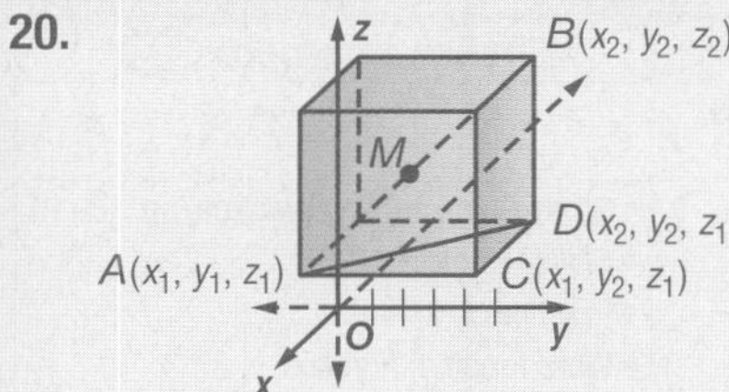

In $\triangle ACD$, $DC = (x_2 - x_1)$ and $AC = (y_2 - y_1)$. By the Pythagorean Theorem $(AD)^2 = (DC)^2 + (AC)^2$. Thus, $(AD)^2 = (x_2 - x_1)^2 + (y_2 - y_1)^2$. In $\triangle ADB$, $BD = (z_2 - z_1)$. By the Pythagorean Theorem, $(AB)^2 = (AD)^2 + (BD)^2$. Thus, $(AB)^2 = [(x_2 - x_1)^2 + (y_2 - y_1)^2] + (z_2 - z_1)^2$. Therefore, $AB = \sqrt{(x_2 - x_1)^2 + (y_2 - y_1)^2 + (z_2 - z_1)^2}$.

21. The formulas for the coordinate plane involve two coordinates and the formulas for three-dimensional space involve three coordinates. Both distance formulas involve the square root of the squares of the differences of the coordinates. Both midpoint formulas involve the averages of the coordinates.

1 Focus

VerticalAlignment

Before Lesson 8-3 Use properties of isosceles and equilateral triangles.

Lesson 8-3 Use the properties 45°-45°-90° triangles. Use properties of 30°-60°-90° triangles.

After Lesson 8-3 Develop, apply, and justify triangle similarity relationships, such as right triangle ratios using a variety of methods.

2 Teach

Scaffolding Questions

Have students read the **Why?** section of the lesson.

Ask:

- What type of triangle is the highlighter? equilateral
- Describe the height of the triangle. It is the length of the segment that bisects the top angle and the bottom side of the triangle.
- What are the measures of the angles in the two triangles formed by the altitude of the triangle? 30, 60, 90

LESSON 8-3 Special Right Triangles

Then

- You used properties of isosceles and equilateral triangles.

Now

1. Use the properties of 45°-45°-90° triangles.
2. Use the properties of 30°-60°-90° triangles.

Why?

- As part of a packet for students attending a regional student council meeting, Lyndsay orders triangular highlighters. She wants to buy rectangular boxes for the highlighters and other items, but she is concerned that the highlighters will not fit in the box she has chosen. If she knows the length of a side of the highlighter, Lyndsay can use the properties of special right triangles to determine if it will fit in the box.

CCSS Common Core State Standards

Content Standards

G.SRT.6 Understand that by similarity, side ratios in right triangles are properties of the angles in the triangle, leading to definitions of trigonometric ratios for acute angles.

Mathematical Practices

1. Make sense of problems and persevere in solving them.
7. Look for and make use of structure.

1 Properties of 45°-45°-90° Triangles

The diagonal of a square forms two congruent isosceles right triangles. Since the base angles of an isosceles triangle are congruent, the measure of each acute angle is 90 ÷ 2 or 45. Such a triangle is also known as a 45°-45°-90° triangle.

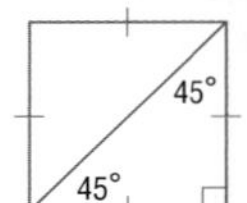

You can use the Pythagorean Theorem to find a relationship among the side lengths of a 45°-45°-90° right triangle.

$\ell^2 + \ell^2 = h^2$	Pythagorean Theorem
$2\ell^2 = h^2$	Simplify.
$\sqrt{2\ell^2} = \sqrt{h^2}$	Take the positive square root of each side.
$\ell\sqrt{2} = h$	Simplify.

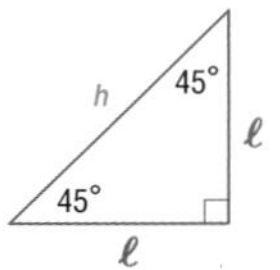

This algebraic proof verifies the following theorem.

Theorem 8.8 45°-45°-90° Triangle Theorem

In a 45°-45°-90° triangle, the legs ℓ are congruent and the length of the hypotenuse h is $\sqrt{2}$ times the length of a leg.

Symbols In a 45°-45°-90° triangle, $\ell = \ell$ and $h = \ell\sqrt{2}$.

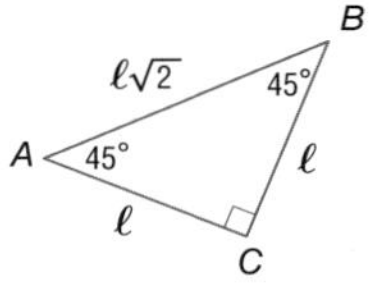

Example 1 Find the Hypotenuse Length in a 45°-45°-90° Triangle

Find x.

a.

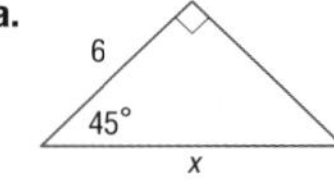

The acute angles of a right triangle are complementary, so the measure of the third angle is 90 − 45 or 45. Since this is a 45°-45°-90° triangle, use Theorem 8.8.

$h = \ell\sqrt{2}$	Theorem 8.8
$x = 6\sqrt{2}$	Substitution

b.

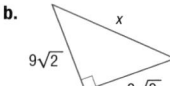

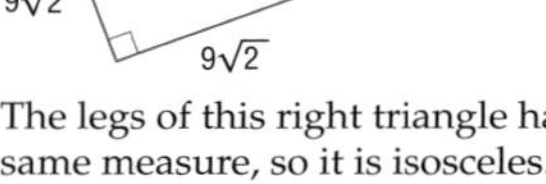

The legs of this right triangle have the same measure, so it is isosceles. Since this is a 45°-45°-90° triangle, use Theorem 8.8.

$h = \ell\sqrt{2}$	Theorem 8.8
$x = 9\sqrt{2} \cdot \sqrt{2}$	Substitution
$x = 9 \cdot 2$ or 18	$\sqrt{2} \cdot \sqrt{2} = 2$

Lesson 8-3 Resources

Resource	Approaching Level AL	On Level OL	Beyond Level BL	English Learners ELL
Teacher Edition		▪ Differentiated Instruction, pp. 559, 566	▪ Differentiated Instruction, pp. 559, 566	
Chapter Resource Masters	▪ Study Guide and Intervention, pp. 18–19 ▪ Skills Practice, p. 20 ▪ Practice, p. 21 ▪ Word Problem Practice, p. 22	▪ Study Guide and Intervention, pp. 18–19 ▪ Skills Practice, p. 20 ▪ Practice, p. 21 ▪ Word Problem Practice, p. 22 ▪ Enrichment, p. 23	▪ Practice, p. 21 ▪ Word Problem Practice, p. 22 ▪ Enrichment, p. 23	▪ Study Guide and Intervention, pp. 18–19 ▪ Skills Practice, p. 20 ▪ Practice, p. 21 ▪ Word Problem Practice, p. 22
Other	▪ 5-Minute Check 8-3 ▪ Study Notebook	▪ 5-Minute Check 8-3 ▪ Study Notebook	▪ 5-Minute Check 8-3 ▪ Study Notebook	▪ 5-Minute Check 8-3 ▪ Study Notebook

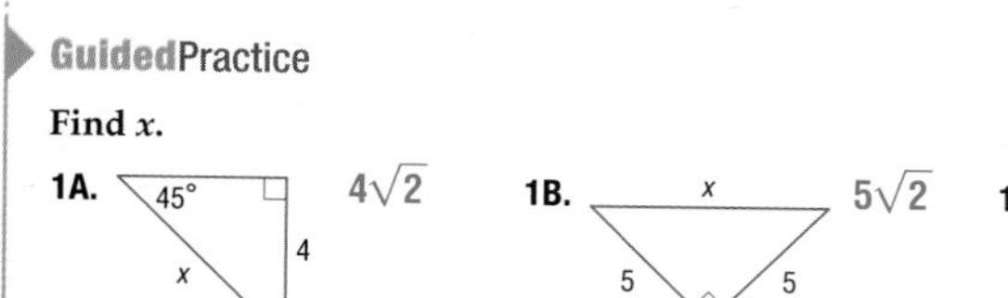

Guided Practice

Find x.

1A. $4\sqrt{2}$ **1B.** $5\sqrt{2}$ **1C.** 14

You can also work backward using Theorem 8.8 to find the lengths of the legs of a 45°-45°-90° triangle given the length of its hypotenuse.

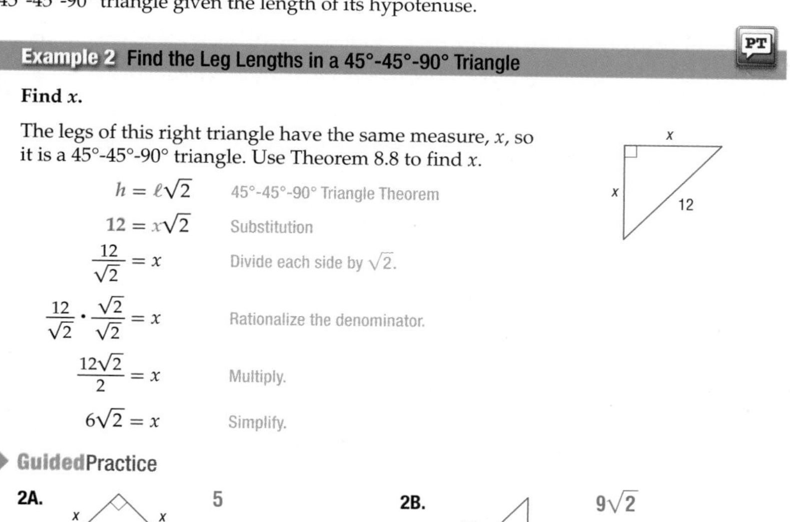

Example 2 Find the Leg Lengths in a 45°-45°-90° Triangle

Find x.

The legs of this right triangle have the same measure, x, so it is a 45°-45°-90° triangle. Use Theorem 8.8 to find x.

$h = \ell\sqrt{2}$ — 45°-45°-90° Triangle Theorem

$12 = x\sqrt{2}$ — Substitution

$\frac{12}{\sqrt{2}} = x$ — Divide each side by $\sqrt{2}$.

$\frac{12}{\sqrt{2}} \cdot \frac{\sqrt{2}}{\sqrt{2}} = x$ — Rationalize the denominator.

$\frac{12\sqrt{2}}{2} = x$ — Multiply.

$6\sqrt{2} = x$ — Simplify.

Review Vocabulary

rationalizing the denominator a method used to eliminate radicals from the denominator of a fraction

Guided Practice

2A. 5 **2B.** $9\sqrt{2}$

2 Properties of 30°-60°-90° Triangles

A 30°-60°-90° triangle is another *special* right triangle or right triangle with side lengths that share a special relationship. You can use an equilateral triangle to find this relationship.

Study Tip

Altitudes of Isosceles Triangles Notice that an altitude of an isosceles triangle is also a median of the triangle. In the figure at the right, $\overline{BD}$ bisects $\overline{AC}$.

When an altitude is drawn from any vertex of an equilateral triangle, two congruent 30°-60°-90° triangles are formed. In the figure shown, $\triangle ABD \cong \triangle CBD$, so $\overline{AD} \cong \overline{CD}$. If $AD = x$, then $CD = x$ and $AC = 2x$. Since $\triangle ABC$ is equilateral, $AB = 2x$ and $BC = 2x$.

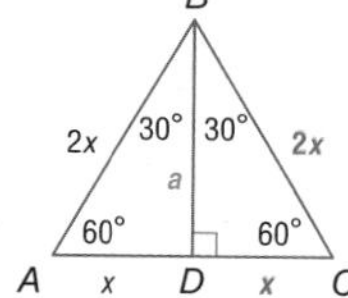

Use the Pythagorean Theorem to find a, the length of the altitude $\overline{BD}$, which is also the longer leg of $\triangle BDC$.

$a^2 + x^2 = (2x)^2$ — Pythagorean Theorem

$a^2 + x^2 = 4x^2$ — Simplify.

$a^2 = 3x^2$ — Subtract x^2 from each side.

$a = \sqrt{3x^2}$ — Take the positive square root of each side.

$a = x\sqrt{3}$ — Simplify.

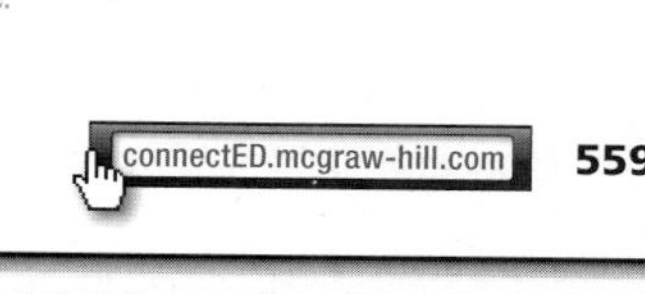

1 Properties of 45°-45°-90° Triangles

Examples 1 and 2 show how to use the 45°-45°-90° triangle theorem to find the length of the legs or hypotenuse of a right triangle.

Formative Assessment

Use the Guided Practice exercises after each example to determine students' understanding of concepts.

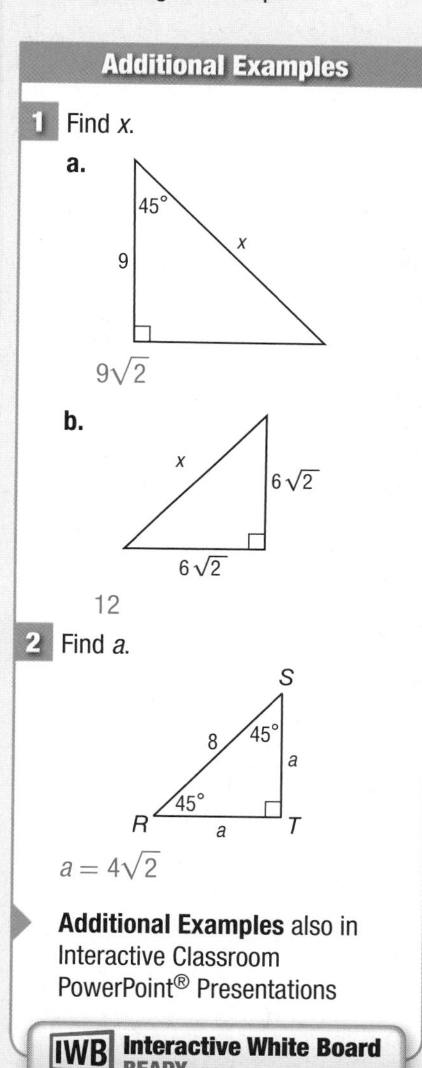

Additional Examples

1 Find x.

a. $9\sqrt{2}$

b. 12

2 Find a.

$a = 4\sqrt{2}$

Additional Examples also in Interactive Classroom PowerPoint® Presentations

IWB Interactive White Board READY

Differentiated Instruction OL BL

Logical/Mathematical Learners Suggest that students close their books and divide a piece of paper into two columns. At the top of one column, ask them to draw a square with diagonal d and side x. At the top of the other column, ask students to draw an equilateral triangle with one altitude and tell them to label the segment that the altitude divides with two xs. Then have students systematically use the Pythagorean Theorem to determine the side relationships of the 45°-45°-90° and 30°-60°-90° triangles in these two figures.

2 Properties of 30°-60°-90° Triangles

Examples 3 and 4 show how to use the 30°-60°-90° triangle theorem to find the length of the legs or hypotenuse of a right triangle.

Additional Example

3 Find x and y.

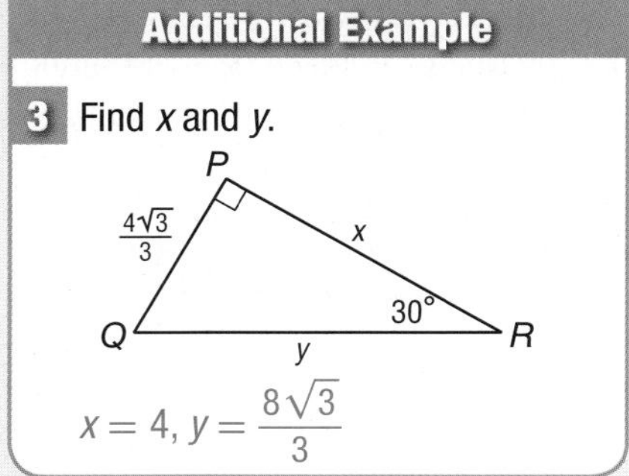

$x = 4,\ y = \frac{8\sqrt{3}}{3}$

Focus on Mathematical Content

Intervention Some students may have difficulty keeping the properties of 45°-45°-90° and 30°-60°-90° triangles straight. Suggest that they periodically reproduce the figures in Theorems 8.8 and 8.9 to keep these relationships fresh in their minds. Advise them, however, that they have the intuitive knowledge to derive either of these two figures by using the Pythagorean Theorem with a square or an equilateral triangle.

WatchOut!

Fractions When giving side lengths of special triangles, be sure to rationalize the denominator.

StudyTip

Use Ratios The lengths of the sides of a 30°-60°-90° triangle are in a ratio of 1 to $\sqrt{3}$ to 2 or $1 : \sqrt{3} : 2$.

This algebraic proof verifies the following theorem.

Theorem 8.9 30°-60°-90° Triangle Theorem

In a 30°-60°-90° triangle, the length of the hypotenuse h is 2 times the length of the shorter leg s, and the length of the longer leg ℓ is $\sqrt{3}$ times the length of the shorter leg.

Symbols In a 30°-60°-90° triangle, $h = 2s$ and $\ell = s\sqrt{3}$.

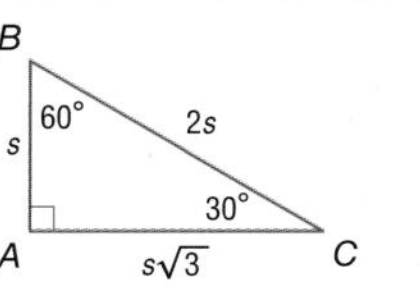

Remember, the shortest side of a triangle is opposite the smallest angle. So the shorter leg in a 30°-60°-90° triangle is opposite the 30° angle, and the longer leg is opposite the 60° angle.

Example 3 Find Lengths in a 30°-60°-90° Triangle

Find x and y.

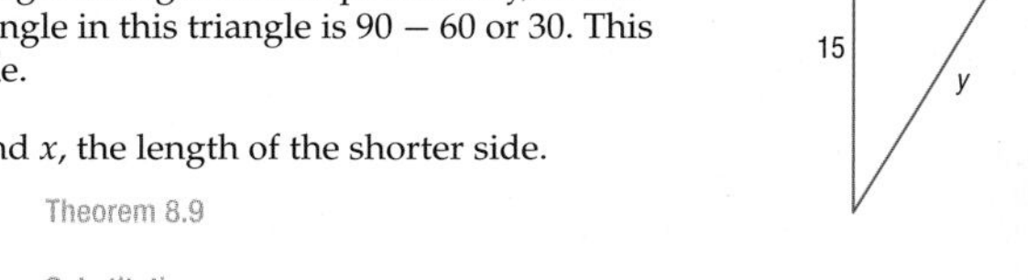

The acute angles of a right triangle are complementary, so the measure of the third angle in this triangle is 90 − 60 or 30. This is a 30°-60°-90° triangle.

Use Theorem 8.9 to find x, the length of the shorter side.

$\ell = s\sqrt{3}$	Theorem 8.9
$15 = x\sqrt{3}$	Substitution
$\frac{15}{\sqrt{3}} = x$	Divide each side by $\sqrt{3}$.
$\frac{15}{\sqrt{3}} \cdot \frac{\sqrt{3}}{\sqrt{3}} = x$	Rationalize the denominator.
$\frac{15\sqrt{3}}{\sqrt{3} \cdot \sqrt{3}} = x$	Multiply.
$\frac{15\sqrt{3}}{3} = x$	$\sqrt{3} \cdot \sqrt{3} = 3$
$5\sqrt{3} = x$	Simplify.

Now use Theorem 8.9 to find y, the length of the hypotenuse.

$h = 2s$	Theorem 8.9
$y = 2(5\sqrt{3})$ or $10\sqrt{3}$	Substitution

GuidedPractice

Find x and y.

3A.

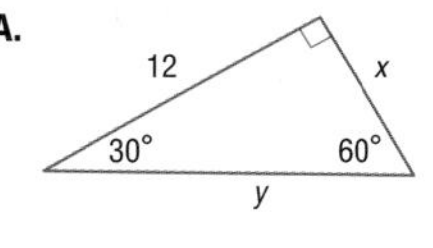

3B.

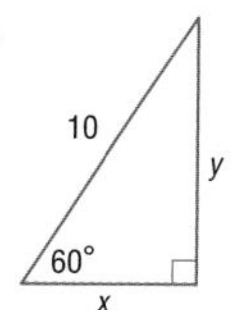

3C.

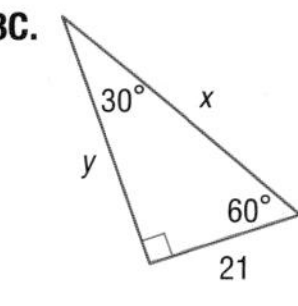

3A. $x = 4\sqrt{3};\ y = 8\sqrt{3}$
3B. $x = 5;\ y = 5\sqrt{3}$
3C. $x = 42;\ y = 21\sqrt{3}$

Teach with Tech

Interactive Whiteboard Use the whiteboard to work through finding the side lengths of a 45°-45°-90° and 30°-60°-90° triangle. Save your work and distribute it to students at the end of class.

You can use the properties of 30°-60°-90° and 45°-45°-90° triangles to solve real-world problems.

Real-World Example 4 Use Properties of Special Right Triangles

INVENTIONS **A company makes crayons that "do not roll off tables" by shaping them as triangular prisms with equilateral bases. Sixteen of these crayons fit into a box shaped like a triangular prism that is $1\frac{1}{2}$ inches wide. The crayons stand on end in the box and the base of the box is equilateral. What are the dimensions of each crayon?**

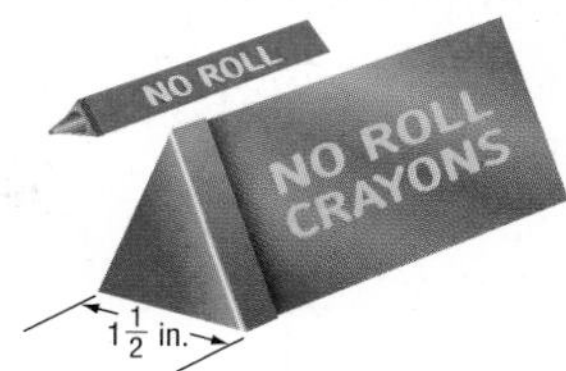

Understand You know that 16 crayons with equilateral triangular bases fit into a prism. You need to find the base length and height of each crayon.

Plan Guess and check to determine the arrangement of 16 crayons that would stack to fill the box. Find the width of one crayon and use the 30°-60°-90° Triangle Theorem to find its altitude.

Solve Make a guess that 4 equilateral crayons will fit across the base of the box. A sketch shows that the total number of crayons it takes to fill the box using 4 crayons across the base is 16. ✓

The width of the box is $1\frac{1}{2}$ inches, so the width of one crayon is $1\frac{1}{2} \div 4$ or $\frac{3}{8}$ inch.

Draw an equilateral triangle representing one crayon. Its altitude forms the longer leg of two 30°-60°-90° triangles. Use Theorem 8.9 to find the approximate length of the altitude a.

longer leg length = shorter leg length $\cdot \sqrt{3}$

$$a = \frac{3}{16} \cdot \sqrt{3} \text{ or about } 0.3$$

Each crayon is $\frac{3}{8}$ or about 0.4 inch by about 0.3 inch.

Check Find the height of the box using the 30°-60°-90° Triangle Theorem. Then divide by four, since the box is four crayons high. The result is a crayon height of about 0.3 inch. ✓

Problem-Solving Tip

Guess and Check When using the guess and check strategy, it can be helpful to keep a list of those guesses that you have already tried and know do not work.

In Example 4, suppose your first guess had been that the box was 5 crayons wide.

The sketch of this possibility reveals that this leads to a stack of 25, not 16 crayons.

Guided Practice

4. FURNITURE The top of the aquarium coffee table shown is an isosceles right triangle. The table's longest side, $\overline{AC}$, measures 107 centimeters. What is the distance from vertex B to side $\overline{AC}$? What are the lengths of the other two sides?
53.5 cm; 75.7 cm

Additional Example

4 QUILTING A quilt has the design shown in the figure, in which a square is divided into 8 isosceles right triangles. If the length of one side of the square is 3 inches, what are the dimensions of each triangle?

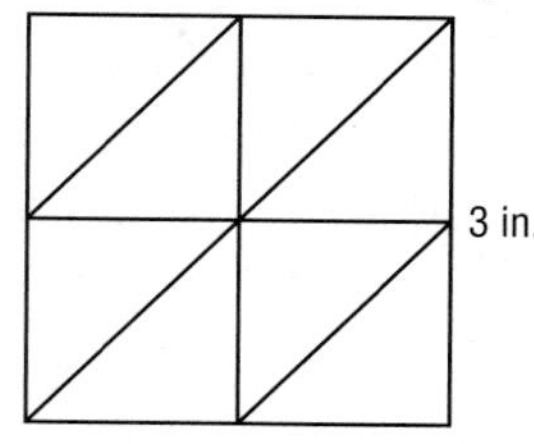

side length = 1.5 in.; hypotenuse = $1.5\sqrt{2}$

Tips for New Teachers

Common Misconceptions Advise students that a common mistake that can be made is to assume that the longer leg of a 30°-60°-90° triangle is twice the length of the shorter leg. Demonstrate that this cannot be true by providing one or more counterexamples.

connectED.mcgraw-hill.com 561

3 Practice

Formative Assessment

Use Exercises 1–7 to check for understanding.

Use the chart at the bottom of this page to customize assignments for your students.

Teaching the Mathematical Practices

Sense-Making Mathematically proficient students start by explaining the meaning of a problem to themselves and looking for entry points to its solution. They plan a solution pathway rather than simply jumping into a solution attempt. In Exercises 8–17, encourage students to analyze each figure to determine which special right triangle to use.

Additional Answer

7. Yes; sample answer: The height of the triangle is about $3\frac{1}{2}$ in., so since the height of the plaque is less than the diameter of the opening, it will fit.

Check Your Understanding

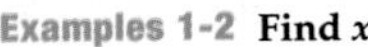 = Step-by-Step Solutions begin on page R14.

Examples 1-2 Find x.

1. 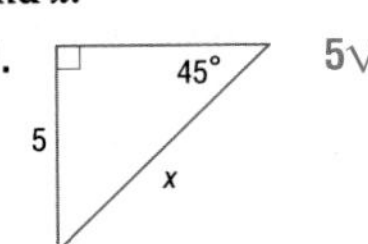

$5\sqrt{2}$

2. 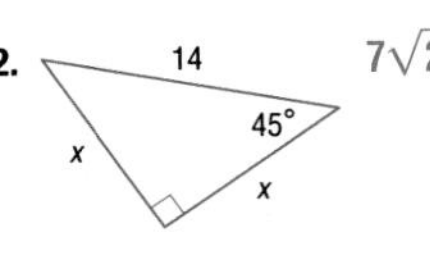

$7\sqrt{2}$

3. 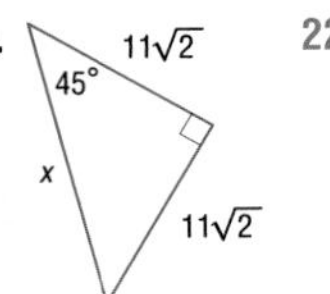

22

Example 3 Find x and y.

4. 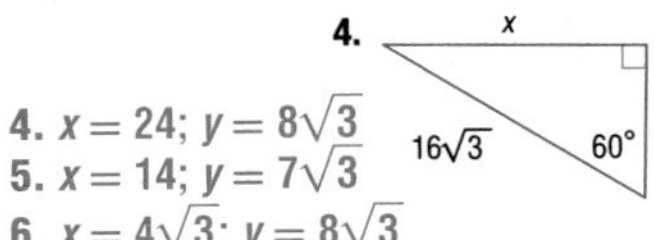

5. 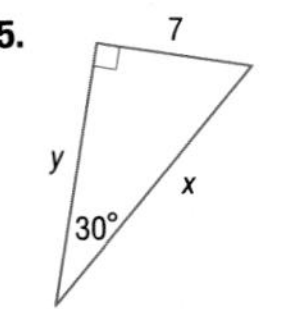

6. 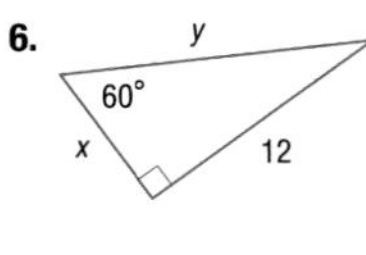

4. $x = 24$; $y = 8\sqrt{3}$
5. $x = 14$; $y = 7\sqrt{3}$
6. $x = 4\sqrt{3}$; $y = 8\sqrt{3}$

Example 4

7. **ART** Paulo is mailing an engraved plaque that is $3\frac{1}{4}$ inches high to the winner of a chess tournament. He has a mailer that is a triangular prism with 4-inch equilateral triangle bases as shown in the diagram. Will the plaque fit through the opening of the mailer? Explain. See margin.

Practice and Problem Solving

Extra Practice is on page R8.

Examples 1-2  **SENSE-MAKING** Find x.

8. 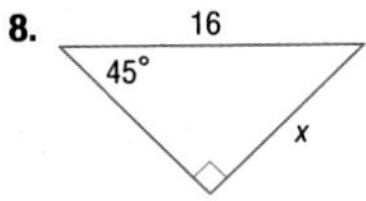

$8\sqrt{2}$

9. 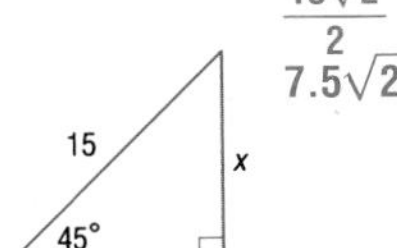

$\frac{15\sqrt{2}}{2}$ or $7.5\sqrt{2}$

10. 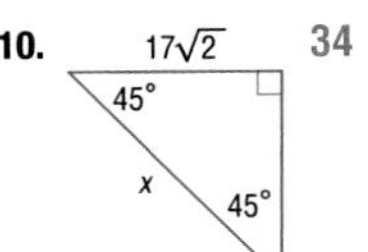

34

11. 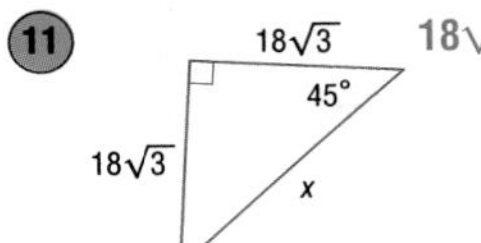

$18\sqrt{6}$

12. 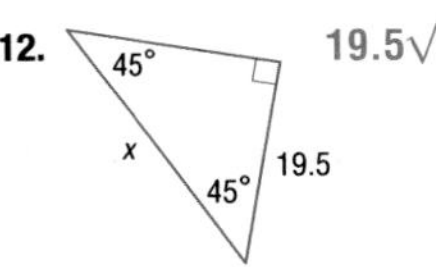

$19.5\sqrt{2}$

13. 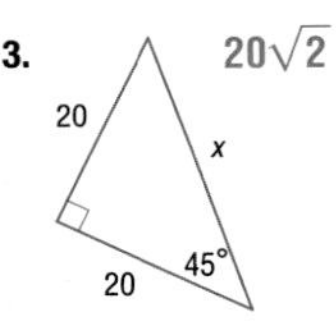

$20\sqrt{2}$

14. If a 45°-45°-90° triangle has a hypotenuse length of 9, find the leg length. $\frac{9\sqrt{2}}{2}$

15. Determine the length of the leg of a 45°-45°-90° triangle with a hypotenuse length of 11. $\frac{11\sqrt{2}}{2}$

16. What is the length of the hypotenuse of a 45°-45°-90° triangle if the leg length is 6 centimeters? $6\sqrt{2}$ or 8.5 cm

17. Find the length of the hypotenuse of a 45°-45°-90° triangle with a leg length of 8 centimeters. $8\sqrt{2}$ or 11.3 cm

Differentiated Homework Options

Level	Assignment	Two-Day Option	
AL Basic	8–27, 46, 47, 49–68	9–27 odd, 51–54	8–26 even, 46, 47, 49, 50, 55–68
OL Core	9–33 odd, 34–37, 39–43 odd, 44–47, 49–68	8–27, 51–54	28–47, 49, 50, 55–68
BL Advanced	28–65, (optional: 66–68)		

Example 3 Find x and y.

18.
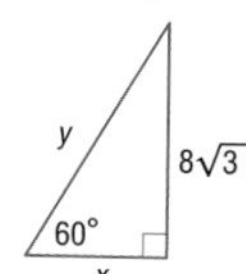

19. (triangle with sides y, x, $10\sqrt{3}$ and angle 30°)

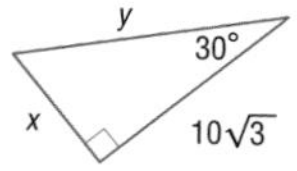

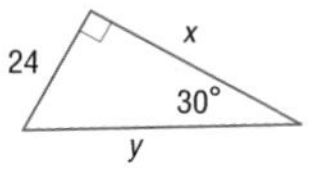

20.
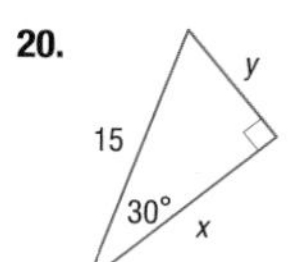

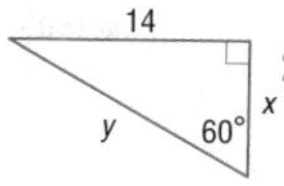

18. $x = 8$; $y = 16$
19. $x = 10$; $y = 20$
20. $x = \frac{15\sqrt{3}}{2}$; $y = \frac{15}{2}$
21. $x = \frac{17\sqrt{3}}{2}$; $y = \frac{17}{2}$
22. $x = 24\sqrt{3}$; $y = 48$
23. $x = \frac{14\sqrt{3}}{3}$; $y = \frac{28\sqrt{3}}{3}$

21.
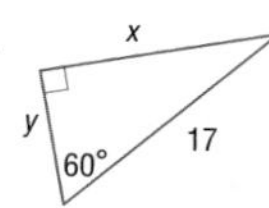

22. (triangle with sides 24, x, y and angle 30°)

23. (triangle with sides 14, x, y and angle 60°)

24. An equilateral triangle has an altitude length of 18 feet. Determine the length of a side of the triangle. $12\sqrt{3}$ **or 20.8 ft**

25. Find the length of the side of an equilateral triangle that has an altitude length of 24 feet. $16\sqrt{3}$ **or 27.7 ft**

Example 4

26. **CCSS MODELING** Refer to the beginning of the lesson. Each highlighter is an equilateral triangle with 9-centimeter sides. Will the highlighter fit in a 10-centimeter by 7-centimeter rectangular box? Explain.
No; sample answer: The height of the box is only 7 cm. and the height of the highlighter is about 7.8 cm., so it will not fit.

27. **EVENT PLANNING** Grace is having a party, and she wants to decorate the gable of the house as shown. The gable is an isosceles right triangle and she knows that the height of the gable is 8 feet. What length of lights will she need to cover the gable below the roof line? **22.6 ft**

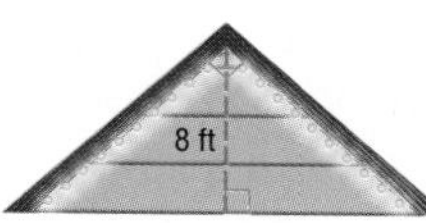

B Find x and y.

28.
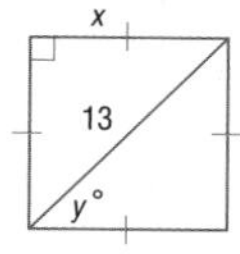

29.
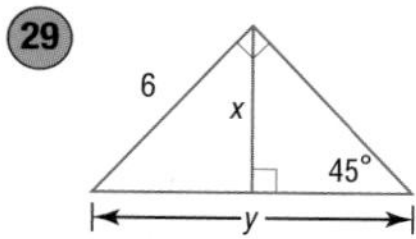

30.
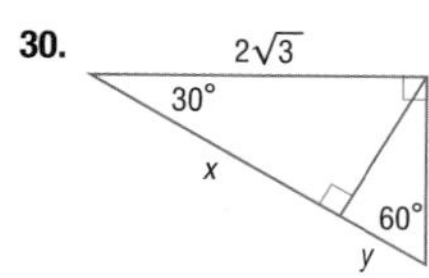

31.
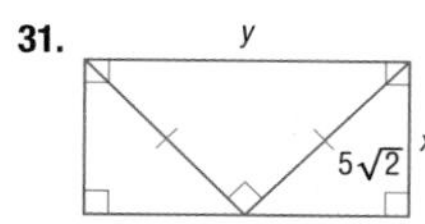

32.
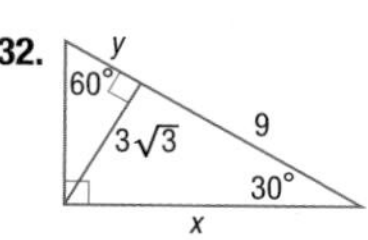

33.
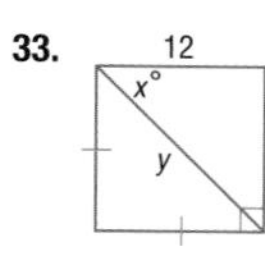

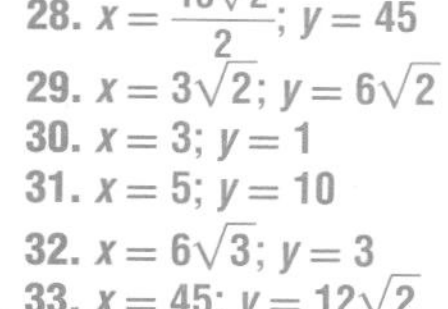

28. $x = \frac{13\sqrt{2}}{2}$; $y = 45$
29. $x = 3\sqrt{2}$; $y = 6\sqrt{2}$
30. $x = 3$; $y = 1$
31. $x = 5$; $y = 10$
32. $x = 6\sqrt{3}$; $y = 3$
33. $x = 45$; $y = 12\sqrt{2}$

34. **QUILTS** The quilt block shown is made up of a square and four isosceles right triangles. What is the value of x? What is the side length of the entire quilt block? **6 in.; 12 in.**

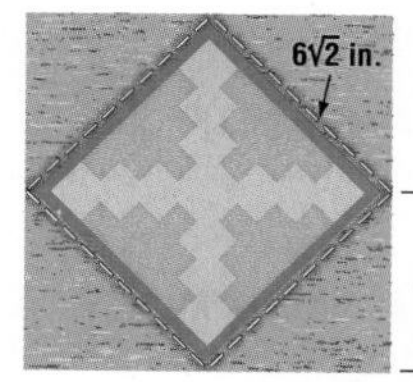

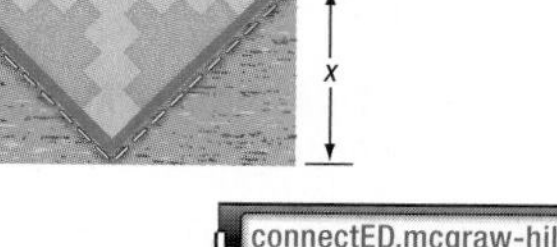

CCSS Teaching the Mathematical Practices

Modeling Mathematically proficient students can apply the mathematics they know to solve problems arising in everyday life. In Exercise 26, encourage students to make models of the highlighter and packing box.

Enrichment

OL BL

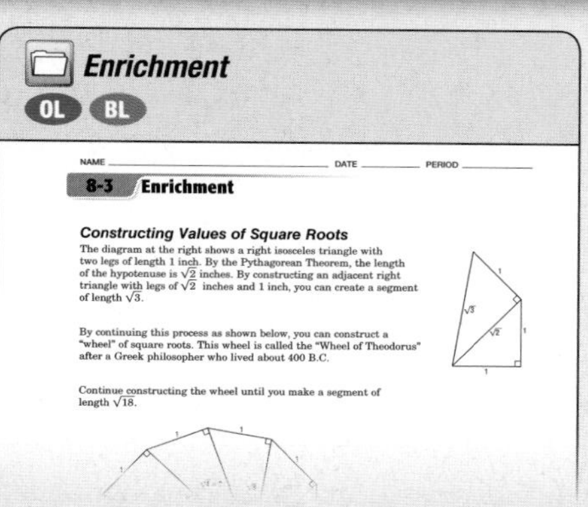

NAME ______ DATE ______ PERIOD ______

8-3 Enrichment

Constructing Values of Square Roots

The diagram at the right shows a right isosceles triangle with two legs of length 1 inch. By the Pythagorean Theorem, the length of the hypotenuse is $\sqrt{2}$ inches. By constructing an adjacent right triangle with legs of $\sqrt{2}$ inches and 1 inch, you can create a segment of length $\sqrt{3}$.

By continuing this process as shown below, you can construct a "wheel" of square roots. This wheel is called the "Wheel of Theodorus" after a Greek philosopher who lived about 400 B.C.

Continue constructing the wheel until you make a segment of length $\sqrt{18}$.

Study Guide and Intervention

AL OL ELL

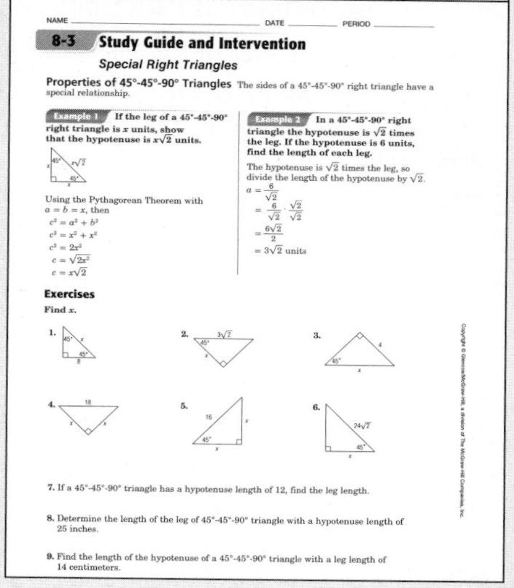

NAME ______ DATE ______ PERIOD ______

8-3 Study Guide and Intervention

Special Right Triangles

Properties of 45°-45°-90° Triangles The sides of a 45°-45°-90° right triangle have a special relationship.

Example 1 If the leg of a 45°-45°-90° right triangle is x units, show that the hypotenuse is $x\sqrt{2}$ units.

Using the Pythagorean Theorem with $a = b = x$, then
$c^2 = a^2 + b^2$
$c^2 = x^2 + x^2$
$c^2 = 2x^2$
$c = \sqrt{2x^2}$
$c = x\sqrt{2}$

Example 2 In a 45°-45°-90° right triangle the hypotenuse is $\sqrt{2}$ times the leg. If the hypotenuse is 6 units, find the length of each leg.

The hypotenuse is $\sqrt{2}$ times the leg, so divide the length of the hypotenuse by $\sqrt{2}$.
$a = \frac{6}{\sqrt{2}}$
$= \frac{6}{\sqrt{2}} \cdot \frac{\sqrt{2}}{\sqrt{2}}$
$= \frac{6\sqrt{2}}{2}$
$= 3\sqrt{2}$ units

Exercises

Find x.

1. 2. 3. 4. 5. 6.

7. If a 45°-45°-90° triangle has a hypotenuse length of 12, find the leg length.

8. Determine the length of the leg of 45°-45°-90° triangle with a hypotenuse length of 25 inches.

9. Find the length of the hypotenuse of a 45°-45°-90° triangle with a leg length of 14 centimeters.

Practice

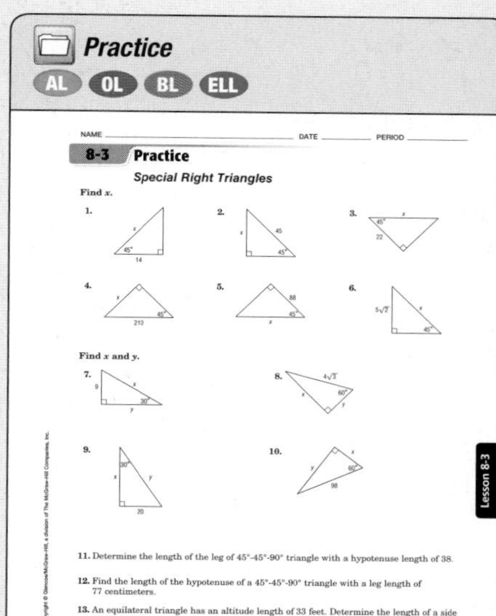

AL OL BL ELL

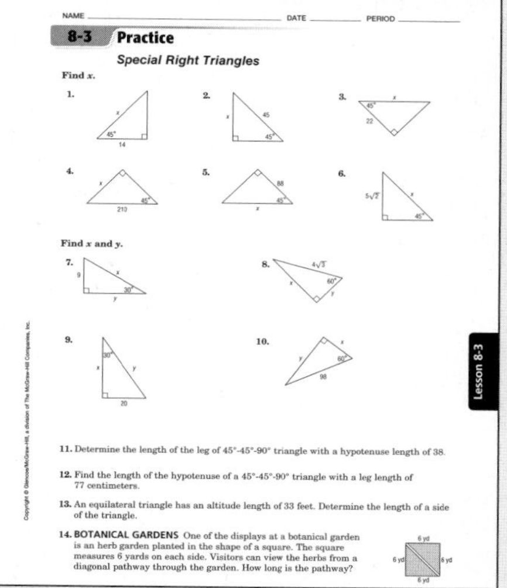

NAME ______ DATE ______ PERIOD ______

8-3 Practice

Special Right Triangles

Find x.

1. 2. 3. 4. 5. 6.

Find x and y.

7. 8. 9. 10.

11. Determine the length of the leg of 45°-45°-90° triangle with a hypotenuse length of 38.

12. Find the length of the hypotenuse of a 45°-45°-90° triangle with a leg length of 77 centimeters.

13. An equilateral triangle has an altitude length of 33 feet. Determine the length of a side of the triangle.

14. **BOTANICAL GARDENS** One of the displays at a botanical garden is an herb garden planted in the shape of a square. The square measures 6 yards on each side. Visitors can view the herbs from a diagonal pathway through the garden. How long is the pathway?

Lesson 8-3

Word Problem Practice

AL OL BL ELL

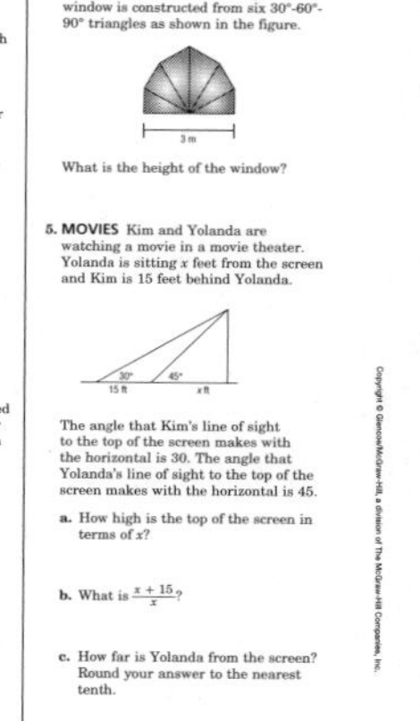

NAME ______ DATE ______ PERIOD ______

8-3 Word Problem Practice

Special Right Triangles

1. **ORIGAMI** A square piece of paper 150 millimeters on a side is folded in half along a diagonal. The result is a 45°-45°-90° triangle. What is the length of the hypotenuse of this triangle?

2. **ESCALATORS** A 40-foot-long escalator rises from the first floor to the second floor of a shopping mall. The escalator makes a 30° angle with the horizontal.

How high above the first floor is the second floor?

3. **HEXAGONS** A box of chocolates shaped like a regular hexagon is placed snugly inside of a rectangular box as shown in the figure.

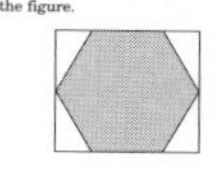

If the side length of the hexagon is 3 inches, what are the dimensions of the rectangular box?

4. **WINDOWS** A large stained glass window is constructed from six 30°-60°-90° triangles as shown in the figure.

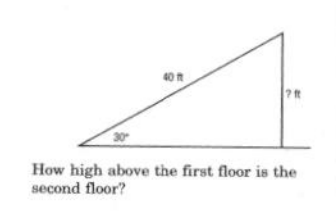

What is the height of the window?

5. **MOVIES** Kim and Yolanda are watching a movie in a movie theater. Yolanda is sitting x feet from the screen and Kim is 15 feet behind Yolanda.

The angle that Kim's line of sight to the top of the screen makes with the horizontal is 30. The angle that Yolanda's line of sight to the top of the screen makes with the horizontal is 45.

a. How high is the top of the screen in terms of x?

b. What is $\frac{x + 15}{x}$?

c. How far is Yolanda from the screen? Round your answer to the nearest tenth.

CCSS Teaching the Mathematical Practices

Modeling Mathematically proficient students can apply the mathematics they know to solve problems arising in everyday life. In Exercise 39, encourage students to make a model of the dump truck that shows how the height changes as the angle increases.

Additional Answers

45a.

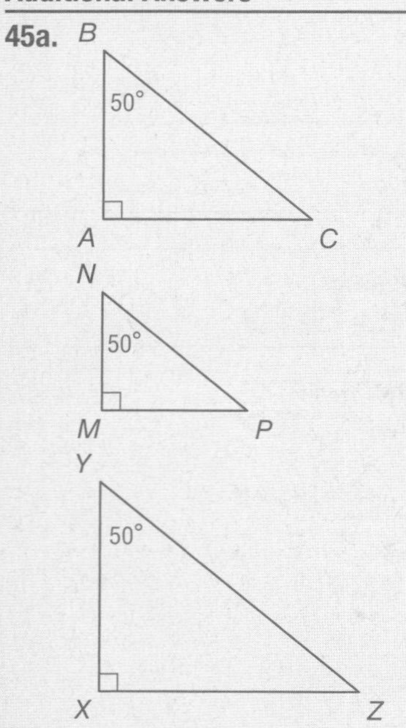

45c. The ratios will always be the same.

35. **ZIP LINE** Suppose a zip line is anchored in one corner of a course shaped like a rectangular prism. The other end is anchored in the opposite corner as shown. If the zip line makes a 60° angle with post $\overline{AF}$, find the zip line's length, AD. **50 ft**

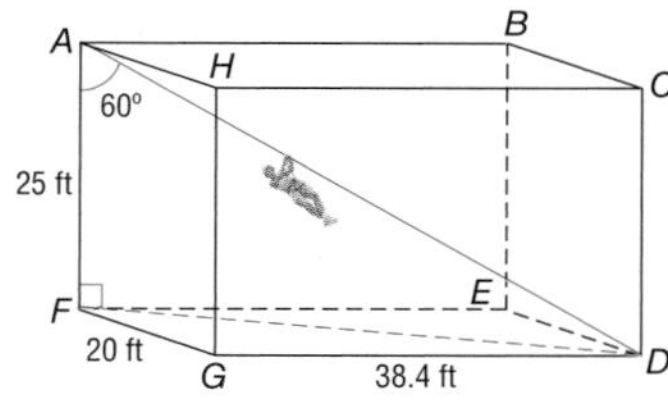

36. **GAMES** Kei is building a bean bag toss for the school carnival. He is using a 2-foot back support that is perpendicular to the ground 2 feet from the front of the board. He also wants to use a support that is perpendicular to the board as shown in the diagram. How long should he make the support? **1.4 ft**

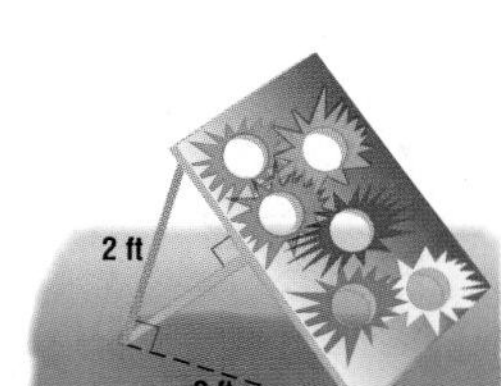

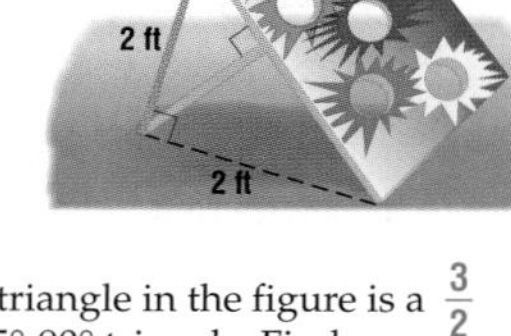

37. Find x, y, and z. $x = 9\sqrt{2}$; $y = 6\sqrt{3}$; $z = 12\sqrt{3}$

38. Each triangle in the figure is a 45°-45°-90° triangle. Find x. $\frac{3}{2}$

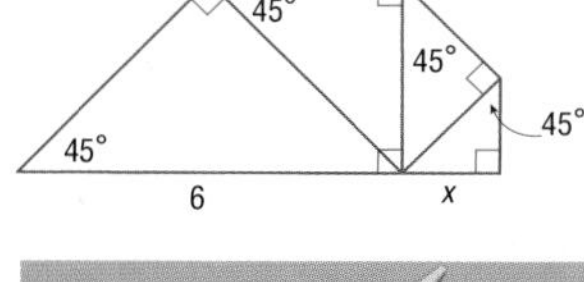

39. **CCSS MODELING** The dump truck shown has a 15-foot bed length. What is the height of the bed h when angle x is 30°? 45°? 60°?
7.5 ft; 10.6 ft; 13.0 ft

40. Find x, y, and z, and the perimeter of trapezoid $PQRS$. $x = 6$; $y = 10$; $z = 6\sqrt{3}$; $38 + 6\sqrt{2} + 6\sqrt{3}$ or ≈ 56.9 units

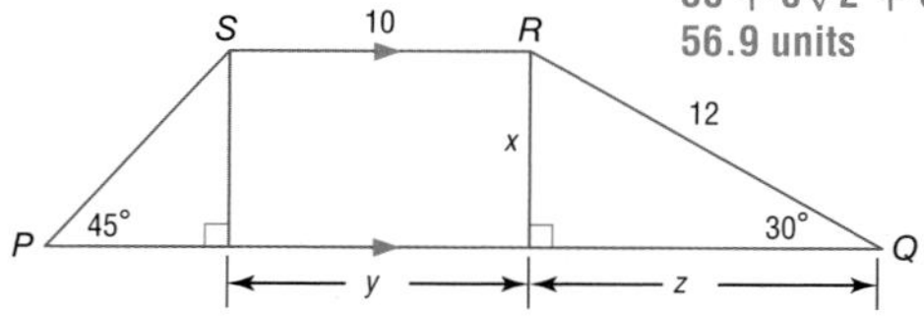

41. **COORDINATE GEOMETRY** $\triangle XYZ$ is a 45°-45°-90° triangle with right angle Z. Find the coordinates of X in Quadrant I for $Y(-1, 2)$ and $Z(6, 2)$. **(6, 9)**

42. **COORDINATE GEOMETRY** $\triangle EFG$ is a 30°-60°-90° triangle with $m\angle F = 90$. Find the coordinates of E in Quadrant III for $F(-3, -4)$ and $G(-3, 2)$. $\overline{FG}$ is the longer leg. $(-3 - 2\sqrt{3}, -4)$

43. **COORDINATE GEOMETRY** $\triangle JKL$ is a 45°-45°-90° triangle with right angle K. Find the coordinates of L in Quadrant IV for $J(-3, 5)$ and $K(-3, -2)$. **(4, −2)**

564 | Lesson 8-3 | Special Right Triangles

; sample
: The
is about
which will
nodate 16
With Eva
friends,
e a total of
e party, so
l all fit.

44. EVENT PLANNING Eva has reserved a gazebo at a local park for a party. She wants to be sure that there will be enough space for her 12 guests to be in the gazebo at the same time. She wants to allow 8 square feet of area for each guest. If the floor of the gazebo is a regular hexagon and each side is 7 feet, will there be enough room for Eva and her friends? Explain. (*Hint:* Use the Polygon Interior Angle Sum Theorem and the properties of special right triangles.)

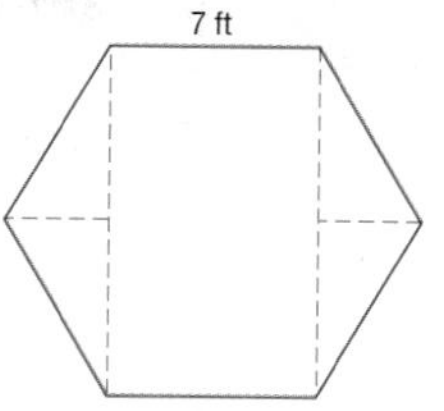

45 **MULTIPLE REPRESENTATIONS** In this problem, you will investigate ratios in right triangles.

a. Geometric Draw three similar right triangles with a 50° angle. Label one triangle *ABC* where angle *A* is the right angle and *B* is the 50° angle. Label a second triangle *MNP* where *M* is the right angle and *N* is the 50° angle. Label the third triangle *XYZ* where *X* is the right angle and *Y* is the 50° angle. See margin.

b. Tabular Copy and complete the table below. Sample answers given.

Triangle	Length				Ratio	
ABC	*AC*	2.4 cm	*BC*	3.2 cm	$\frac{AC}{BC}$	1.3
MNP	*MP*	1.7 cm	*NP*	2.2 cm	$\frac{MP}{NP}$	1.3
XYZ	*XZ*	3.0 cm	*YZ*	3.9 cm	$\frac{XZ}{YZ}$	1.3

c. Verbal Make a conjecture about the ratio of the leg opposite the 50° angle to the hypotenuse in any right triangle with an angle measuring 50°. See margin.

H.O.T. Problems Use Higher-Order Thinking Skills

46. CCSS CRITIQUE Carmen and Audrey want to find *x* in the triangle shown. Is either of them correct? Explain. See margin.

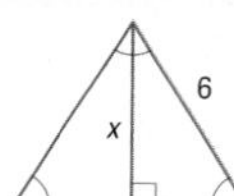

Carmen	Audrey
$x = \frac{6\sqrt{3}}{2}$	$x = \frac{6\sqrt{2}}{2}$
$x = 3\sqrt{3}$	$x = 3\sqrt{2}$

47. OPEN ENDED Draw a rectangle that has a diagonal twice as long as its width. Then write an equation to find the length of the rectangle. See margin.

48. CHALLENGE Find the perimeter of quadrilateral *ABCD*. 59.8

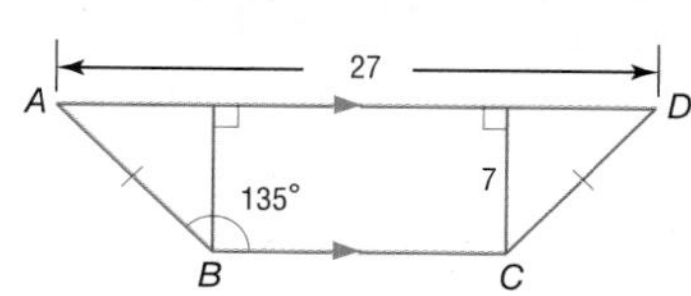

49. REASONING The ratio of the measure of the angles of a triangle is 1:2:3. The length of the shortest side is 8. What is the perimeter of the triangle? 37.9

50. WRITING IN MATH Why are some right triangles considered *special*? See margin.

Multiple Representations

In Exercise 45, students use geometric sketches, a table, and verbal description to investigate ratios in right triangles.

Exercise Alert

Protractor and Ruler Exercise 45 requires the use of a protractor and ruler.

Teaching the Mathematical Practices

Critique Mathematically proficient students can distinguish correct logic from flawed reasoning. In Exercise 46, Audrey wrote the expression for the side length incorrectly. Students may confuse the ratios of the lengths of the legs of a 45°-45°-90° triangle with those of a 30°-60°-90° triangle.

Additional Answers

46. Carmen; Sample answer: Since the three angles of the larger triangle are congruent, it is an equilateral triangle and the right triangles formed by the altitude are 30°-60°-90° triangles. The hypotenuse is 6, so the shorter leg is 3 and the longer leg *x* is $3\sqrt{3}$.

47. Sample answer:

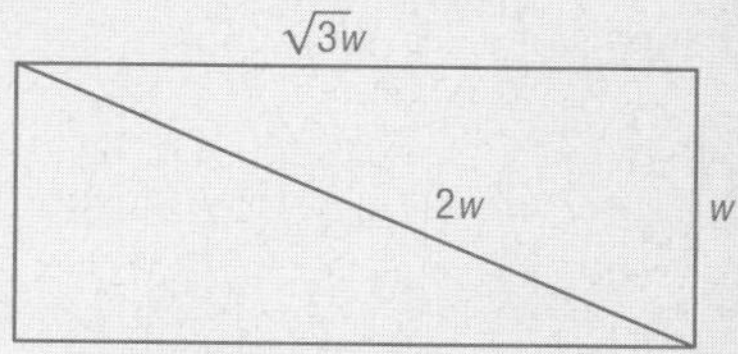

Let ℓ represent the length.
$\ell^2 + w^2 = (2w)^2$; $\ell^2 = 3w^2$;
$\ell = w\sqrt{3}$.

50. Sample answer: Once you identify that a right triangle is *special* or has a 30°, 60°, or 45° angle measure, you can solve the triangle without the use of a calculator.

4 Assess

Ticket Out the Door Have students write the side relationships for 45°-45°-90° triangles and 30°-60°-90° triangles. Have students turn in their papers as they exit the class.

Additional Answers

56. $x \approx 2\sqrt{11}$ or 6.6, $y \approx 8.0$, $z = 4.4$

57. $x \approx 16.9$, $y \approx 22.6$, $z \approx 25.0$

58. $x \approx 13.9$, $y \approx 6.9$, $z = 8$

Standardized Test Practice

51. If the length of the longer leg in a 30°-60°-90° triangle is $5\sqrt{3}$, what is the length of the shorter leg? **B**

A 3   **C** $5\sqrt{2}$

B 5   **D** 10

52. ALGEBRA Solve $\sqrt{5 - 4x} - 6 = 7$. **G**

F −44   **H** 41

G −41   **J** 44

53. SHORT RESPONSE $\triangle XYZ$ is a 45°-45°-90° triangle with right angle Y. Find the coordinates of X in Quadrant III for $Y(-3, -3)$ and $Z(-3, 7)$. **(−13, −3)**

54. SAT/ACT In the figure, below, square $ABCD$ is attached to $\triangle ADE$ as shown. If $m\angle EAD$ is 30° and AE is equal to $4\sqrt{3}$, then what is the area of square $ABCD$? **C**

A $8\sqrt{3}$

B 16

C 64

D 72

E $64\sqrt{2}$

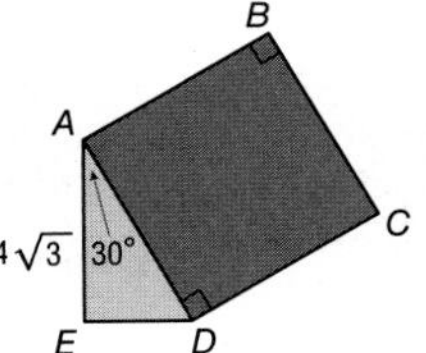

Spiral Review

55. SPORTS Dylan is making a ramp for bike jumps. The ramp support forms a right angle. The base is 12 feet long, and the height is 9 feet. What length of plywood does Dylan need for the ramp? (Lesson 8-2) **15 ft**

Find x, y, and z. (Lesson 8-1) **56–58. See margin.**

56.

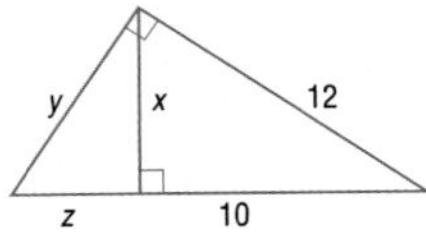

57.

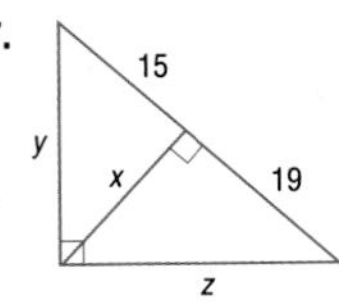

58.

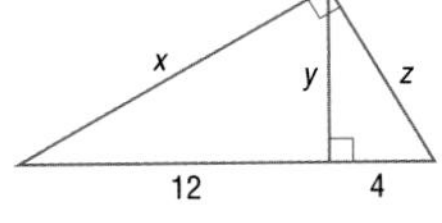

Find the measures of the angles of each triangle. (Lesson 7-1)

59. The ratio of the measures of the three angles is 2:5:3. **36, 90, 54**

60. The ratio of the measures of the three angles is 6:9:10. **43.2, 64.8, 72**

61. The ratio of the measures of the three angles is 5:7:8. **45, 63, 72**

Use the Exterior Angle Inequality Theorem to list all of the angles that satisfy the stated condition. (Lesson 5-3)

62. measures less than $m\angle 5$ **∠2, ∠7, ∠8, ∠10**

63. measures greater than $m\angle 6$ **∠1, ∠4, ∠11**

64. measures greater than $m\angle 10$ **∠1, ∠3, ∠5**

65. measures less than $m\angle 11$ **∠2, ∠6, ∠9, ∠8, ∠7**

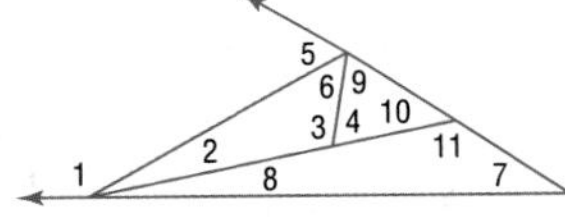

Skills Review

Find x.

66. **17.7**

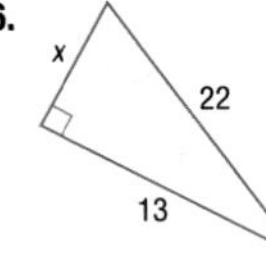

67. **12.0**

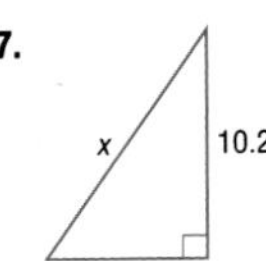

68. $\sqrt{7}$

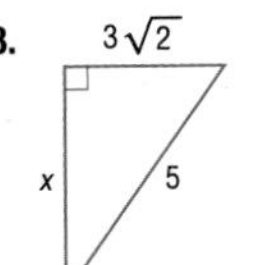

Differentiated Instruction OL BL

Extension Have students draw a 45°-45°-90° triangle and a 30°-60°-90° triangle and label each side length. Have the students use their drawings to choose one of the acute angles and find the ratio of the measure of the opposite leg to the measure of the adjacent leg. Explain that this ratio is called the tangent ratio. Discuss their findings.
Answers may vary. Tangent is the measure of the opposite leg divided by the measure of the adjacent leg.

566 | Lesson 8-3 | Special Right Triangles

EXPLORE 8-4

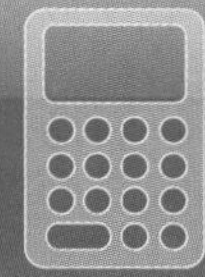

Graphing Technology Lab Trigonometry

You have investigated patterns in the measures of special right triangles. *Trigonometry* is the study of the patterns in all right triangles. You can use the Cabri™ Jr. application on a graphing calculator to investigate these patterns.

CCSS Common Core State Standards
Content Standards
G.SRT.6 Understand that by similarity, side ratios in right triangles are properties of the angles in the triangle, leading to definitions of trigonometric ratios for acute angles.
Mathematical Practices 5

Activity Investigate Trigonometric Ratios

Step 1 Use the line tool on the **F2** menu to draw a horizontal line. Label the points on the line A and B.

Step 2 Press **F2** and choose the **Perpendicular** tool to create a perpendicular line through point B. Draw and label a point C on the perpendicular line.

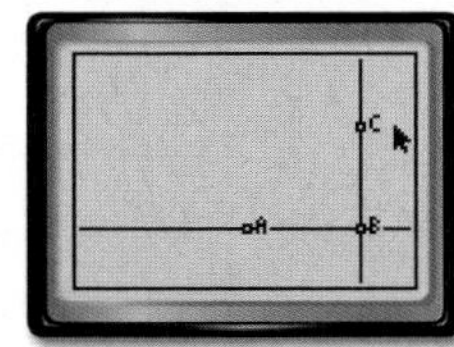

Steps 1 and 2

Step 3 Use the **Segment** tool on the **F2** menu to draw $\overline{AC}$.

Step 4 Find and label the measures of $\overline{BC}$ and $\overline{AC}$ using the **Distance** and **Length** tool under **Measure** on the **F5** menu. Use the **Angle** tool to find the measure of $\angle A$.

Step 5 Calculate and display the ratio $\frac{BC}{AC}$ using the **Calculate** tool on the **F5** menu. Label the ratio as A/B.

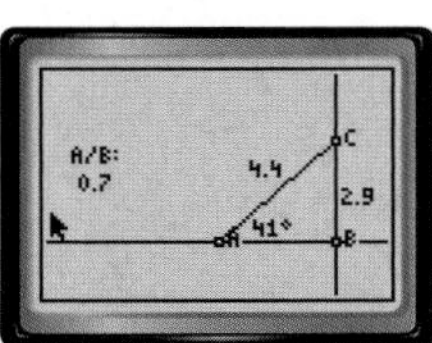

Steps 3 through 5

Step 6 Press CLEAR. Then use the arrow keys to move the cursor close to point B. When the arrow is clear, press and hold the ALPHA key. Drag B and observe the ratio.

Analyze the Results

1. Discuss the effect on $\frac{BC}{AC}$ by dragging point B on $\overline{BC}$, $\overline{AC}$, and $\angle A$. **1–3. See margin.**
2. Use the calculate tool to find the ratios $\frac{AB}{AC}$ and $\frac{BC}{AB}$. Then drag B and observe the ratios.
3. **MAKE A CONJECTURE** The *sine*, *cosine*, and *tangent* functions are trigonometric functions based on angle measures. Make a note of $m\angle A$. Exit Cabri Jr. and use SIN, COS, and TAN on the calculator to find *sine*, *cosine* and *tangent* for $m\angle A$. Compare the results to the ratios you found in the activity. Make a conjecture about the definitions of sine, cosine, and tangent.

Additional Answers

1. BC and AC change, but $m\angle A$ and $\frac{BC}{AC}$ are unchanged.
2. $\frac{AB}{AC}$ and $\frac{BC}{AB}$ are unchanged as B moves.
3. Sample answer: sine $A = \frac{BC}{AC}$; cosine $A = \frac{AB}{AC}$; and tangent $A = \frac{BC}{AB}$

1 Focus

Objective Use Cabri Jr. to explore trigonometry, the study of the patterns in right triangles.

Materials

- TI-83/84 Plus graphing calculator

2 Teach

Working in Pairs

Arrange students in pairs, mixing abilities. Tell students to go through the steps of the activity.

Ask:

- What do you predict will happen to the ratio as B is moved?

Practice Have students complete Exercises 1–3.

3 Assess

Formative Assessment

Use Exercises 1–3 to assess whether students understand the concept of special right triangles.

From Concrete to Abstract

Tell students to fold a paper diagonally to form a right triangle. Ask them to measure the length of the side opposite the right angle and one leg. What is the ratio of the length of the hypotenuse to the length of the leg? How does this compare to the ratio A/B in the activity? The ratio should be the same.

Extending the Concept

Ask:

- How can you use what you have learned about the relationships between the trigonometric functions *sine*, *cosine*, and *tangent*, and the ratios between the side lengths in a right triangle? Find missing measures in a right triangle.

1 Focus

VerticalAlignment

Before Lesson 8-4 Use the Pythagorean Theorem to find missing lengths in right triangles.

Lesson 8-4 Find trigonometric ratios by using right triangles. Use trigonometric ratios to find angle measures in right triangles.

After Lesson 8-4 Use functions such as trigonometric to model real-life data.

2 Teach

Scaffolding Questions

Have students read the **Why?** section of the lesson.

Ask:

- What does percent of grade measure? the steepness of an incline
- What ratio determines the percent of grade? the vertical distance over the horizontal distance
- What is the percent of grade of a trail that falls 8.5 feet over a horizontal distance of 100 feet? 8.5%

LESSON 8-4 Trigonometry

Then

- You used the Pythagorean Theorem to find missing lengths in right triangles.

Now

1. Find trigonometric ratios using right triangles.
2. Use trigonometric ratios to find angle measures in right triangles.

Why?

- The steepness of a hiking trail is often expressed as a *percent of grade*. The steepest part of Bright Angel Trail in the Grand Canyon National Park has about a 15.7% grade. This means that the trail rises or falls 15.7 feet over a horizontal distance of 100 feet. You can use trigonometric ratios to determine that this steepness is equivalent to an angle of about 9°.

NewVocabulary

trigonometry
trigonometric ratio
sine
cosine
tangent
inverse sine
inverse cosine
inverse tangent

Common Core State Standards

Content Standards

G.SRT.6 Understand that by similarity, side ratios in right triangles are properties of the angles in the triangle, leading to definitions of trigonometric ratios for acute angles.

G.SRT.7 Explain and use the relationship between the sine and cosine of complementary angles.

Mathematical Practices

1 Make sense of problems and persevere in solving them.

5 Use appropriate tools strategically.

1 Trigonometric Ratios The word **trigonometry** comes from two Greek terms, *trigon*, meaning triangle, and *metron*, meaning measure. The study of trigonometry involves triangle measurement. A **trigonometric ratio** is a ratio of the lengths of two sides of a right triangle. One trigonometric ratio of $\triangle ABC$ is $\frac{AC}{AB}$.

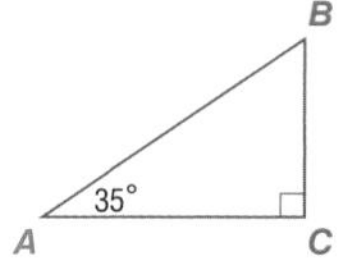

By AA Similarity, a right triangle with a given acute angle measure is similar to every other right triangle with the same acute angle measure. So, trigonometric ratios are constant for a given angle measure.

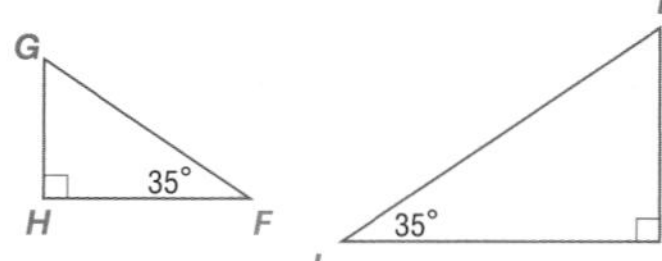

$\triangle ABC \sim \triangle FGH \sim \triangle JKL$, so $\frac{AC}{AB} = \frac{FH}{FG} = \frac{JL}{JK}$

The names of the three most common trigonometric ratios are given below.

KeyConcept Trigonometric Ratios

Words	Symbols
If $\triangle ABC$ is a right triangle with acute $\angle A$, then the **sine** of $\angle A$ (written sin A) is the ratio of the length of the leg opposite $\angle A$ (opp) to the length of the hypotenuse (hyp).	$\sin A = \frac{\text{opp}}{\text{hyp}}$ or $\frac{a}{c}$ $\sin B = \frac{\text{opp}}{\text{hyp}}$ or $\frac{b}{c}$
If $\triangle ABC$ is a right triangle with acute $\angle A$, then the **cosine** of $\angle A$ (written cos A) is the ratio of the length of the leg adjacent $\angle A$ (adj) to the length of the hypotenuse (hyp).	$\cos A = \frac{\text{adj}}{\text{hyp}}$ or $\frac{b}{c}$ $\cos B = \frac{\text{adj}}{\text{hyp}}$ or $\frac{a}{c}$
If $\triangle ABC$ is a right triangle with acute $\angle A$, then the **tangent** of $\angle A$ (written tan A) is the ratio of the length of the leg opposite $\angle A$ (opp) to the length of the leg adjacent $\angle A$ (adj).	$\tan A = \frac{\text{opp}}{\text{adj}}$ or $\frac{a}{b}$ $\tan B = \frac{\text{opp}}{\text{adj}}$ or $\frac{b}{a}$

Lesson 8-4 Resources

Resource	Approaching Level AL	On Level OL	Beyond Level BL	English Learners ELL
Teacher Edition	▪ Differentiated Instruction, p. 570	▪ Differentiated Instruction, pp. 570, 572	▪ Differentiated Instruction, p. 572	
Chapter Resource Masters	▪ Study Guide and Intervention, pp. 24–25 ▪ Skills Practice, p. 26 ▪ Practice, p. 27 ▪ Word Problem Practice, p. 28	▪ Study Guide and Intervention, pp. 24–25 ▪ Skills Practice, p. 26 ▪ Practice, p. 27 ▪ Word Problem Practice, p. 28 ▪ Enrichment, p. 29	▪ Practice, p. 27 ▪ Word Problem Practice, p. 28 ▪ Enrichment, p. 29	▪ Study Guide and Intervention, pp. 24–25 ▪ Skills Practice, p. 26 ▪ Practice, p. 27 ▪ Word Problem Practice, p. 28
Other	▪ 5-Minute Check 8-4 ▪ Study Notebook ▪ Teaching Geometry with Manipulatives	▪ 5-Minute Check 8-4 ▪ Study Notebook ▪ Teaching Geometry with Manipulatives	▪ 5-Minute Check 8-4 ▪ Study Notebook	▪ 5-Minute Check 8-4 ▪ Study Notebook ▪ Teaching Geometry with Manipulatives

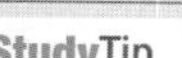

StudyTip

Memorizing Trigonometric Ratios SOH-CAH-TOA is a mnemonic device for learning the ratios for sine, cosine, and tangent using the first letter of each word in the ratios.

$\sin A = \frac{\text{opp}}{\text{hyp}}$

$\cos A = \frac{\text{adj}}{\text{hyp}}$

$\tan A = \frac{\text{opp}}{\text{adj}}$

Example 1 Find Sine, Cosine, and Tangent Ratios

Express each ratio as a fraction and as a decimal to the nearest hundredth.

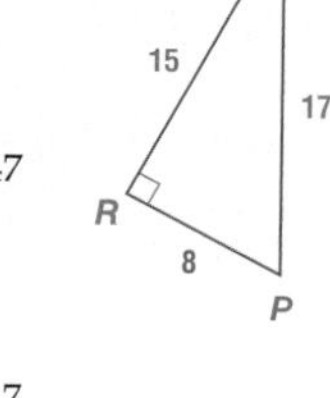

a. sin *P*

$\sin P = \frac{\text{opp}}{\text{hyp}}$

$= \frac{15}{17}$ or about 0.88

b. cos *P*

$\cos P = \frac{\text{adj}}{\text{hyp}}$

$= \frac{8}{17}$ or about 0.47

c. tan *P*

$\tan P = \frac{\text{opp}}{\text{adj}}$

$= \frac{15}{8}$ or about 1.88

d. sin *Q*

$\sin Q = \frac{\text{opp}}{\text{hyp}}$

$= \frac{8}{17}$ or about 0.47

e. cos *Q*

$\cos Q = \frac{\text{adj}}{\text{hyp}}$

$= \frac{15}{17}$ or about 0.88

f. tan *Q*

$\tan Q = \frac{\text{opp}}{\text{adj}}$

$= \frac{8}{15}$ or about 0.53

Guided Practice

1. Find sin *J*, cos *J*, tan *J*, sin *K*, cos *K*, and tan *K*. Express each ratio as a fraction and as a decimal to the nearest hundredth.

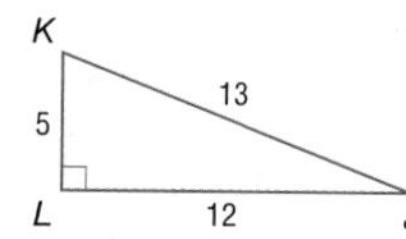

1. $\sin J = \frac{5}{13} \approx 0.38$, $\cos J = \frac{12}{13} \approx 0.92$, $\tan J = \frac{5}{12} \approx 0.42$, $\sin K = \frac{12}{13} \approx 0.92$, $\cos K = \frac{5}{13} \approx 0.38$, $\tan K = \frac{12}{5} \approx 2.4$

Special right triangles can be used to find the sine, cosine, and tangent of 30°, 60°, and 45° angles.

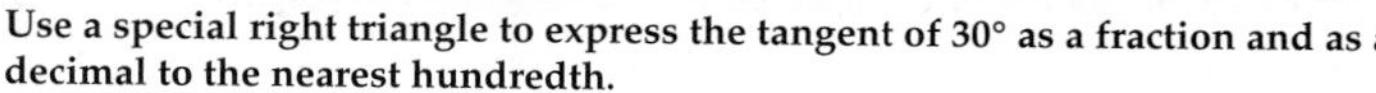

Example 2 Use Special Right Triangles to Find Trigonometric Ratios

Use a special right triangle to express the tangent of 30° as a fraction and as a decimal to the nearest hundredth.

Draw and label the side lengths of a 30°-60°-90° right triangle, with *x* as the length of the shorter leg.

The side opposite the 30° angle has a measure of *x*.

The side adjacent to the 30° angle has a measure of $x\sqrt{3}$.

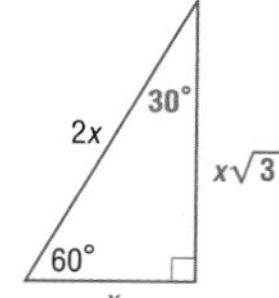

$\tan 30° = \frac{\text{opp}}{\text{adj}}$	Definition of tangent ratio
$= \frac{x}{x\sqrt{3}}$	Substitution
$= \frac{1}{\sqrt{3}} \cdot \frac{\sqrt{3}}{\sqrt{3}}$	Simplify and rationalize the denominator.
$= \frac{\sqrt{3}}{3}$ or about 0.58	Simplify and use a calculator.

Guided Practice

2. Use a special right triangle to express the cosine of 45° as a fraction and as a decimal to the nearest hundredth. $\frac{\sqrt{2}}{2} \approx 0.71$

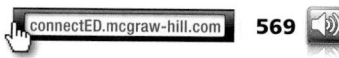

1 Trigonometric Ratios

Examples 1 and 2 show how to find trigonometric ratios by using the lengths of sides of a right triangle. **Example 3** shows how to use a trigonometric ratio to find unknown lengths in a right triangle.

Formative Assessment

Use the Guided Practice exercises after each example to determine students' understanding of concepts.

Additional Examples

1 Express each ratio as a fraction and as a decimal to the nearest hundredth.

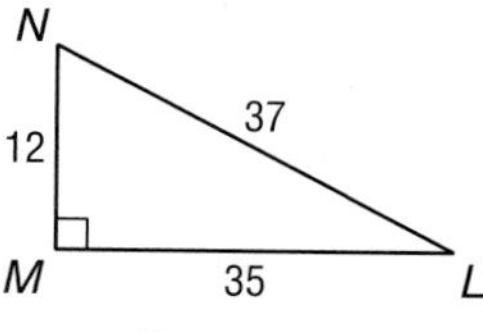

a. sin *L* $\frac{12}{37}$ or 0.32

b. cos *L* $\frac{35}{37}$ or 0.95

c. tan *L* $\frac{12}{35}$ or 0.34

d. sin *N* $\frac{35}{37}$ or 0.95

e. cos *N* $\frac{12}{37}$ or 0.32

f. tan *N* $\frac{35}{12}$ or 2.92

2 Use a special right triangle to express the cosine of 60° as a fraction and as a decimal to the nearest hundredth. $\frac{1}{2}$, 0.5

Additional Examples also in Interactive Classroom PowerPoint® Presentations

IWB Interactive White Board READY

Teach with Tech

Interactive Whiteboard Draw a right triangle on the board and label each of the side lengths. To write the trigonometric ratios, drag the measurement from the side of the triangle to the ratio.

Tips for New Teachers

Trigonometry The trigonometric ratios are only defined for nonnegative values. These definitions can be extended to give the familiar trigonometric functions defined on all real numbers.

Focus on Mathematical Content

Right Triangles The definitions of the trigonometric functions as ratios apply only to right triangles. The Law of Sines and the Law of Cosines from Lesson 8-6 can be used to solve similar problems when the triangle is not a right triangle.

Additional Example

3 EXERCISE A fitness trainer sets the incline on a treadmill to 7°. The walking surface is 5 feet long. Approximately how many inches did the trainer raise the end of the treadmill from the floor?

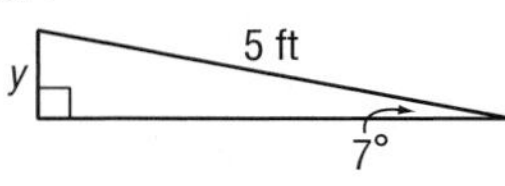

≈7.3 in.

Real-World Example 3 Estimate Measures Using Trigonometry

HIKING A certain part of a hiking trail slopes upward at about a 5° angle. After traveling a horizontal distance of 100 feet along this part of the trail, what would be the change in a hiker's vertical position? What distance has the hiker traveled along the path?

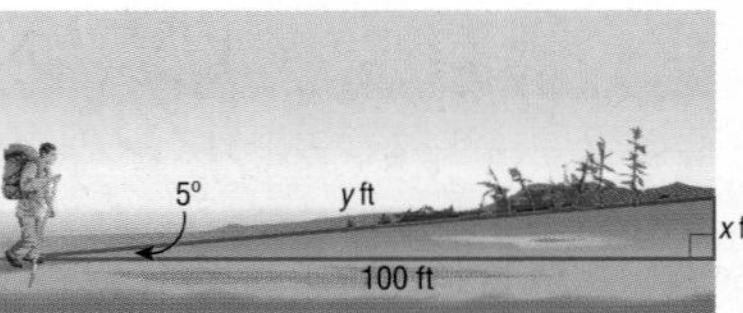

Let $m\angle A = 5$. The vertical change in the hiker's position is x, the measure of the leg opposite $\angle A$. The horizontal distance traveled is 100 feet, the measure of the leg adjacent to $\angle A$. Since the length of the leg opposite and the leg adjacent to a given angle are involved, write an equation using a tangent ratio.

$\tan A = \frac{\text{opp}}{\text{adj}}$ Definition of tangent ratio

$\tan 5° = \frac{x}{100}$ Substitution

$100 \cdot \tan 5° = x$ Multiply each side by 100.

Use a calculator to find x.

100 [TAN] 5 [ENTER] **8.748866353**

The hiker is about 8.75 feet higher than when he started walking.

The distance y traveled along the path is the length of the hypotenuse, so you can use a cosine ratio to find this distance.

$\cos A = \frac{\text{adj}}{\text{hyp}}$ Definition of cosine ratio

$\cos 5° = \frac{100}{y}$ Substitution

$y \cdot \cos 5° = 100$ Multiply each side by y.

$y = \frac{100}{\cos 5°}$ Divide each side by cos 5°.

Use a calculator to find y.

100 [÷] [COS] 5 [ENTER] **100.3819838**

The hiker has traveled a distance of about 100.38 feet along the path.

Real-WorldLink

The grade of a trail often changes many times. Average grade is the average of several consecutive running grades of a trail. Maximum grade is the smaller section of a trail that exceeds the trail's typical running grade. Trails often have maximum grades that are much steeper than a trail's average running grade.

Source: Federal Highway Administration

StudyTip

Graphing Calculator Be sure your graphing calculator is in degree mode rather than radian mode.

GuidedPractice

Find x to the nearest hundredth.

3A. 18, 25°, x — 8.39

3B. 43.86

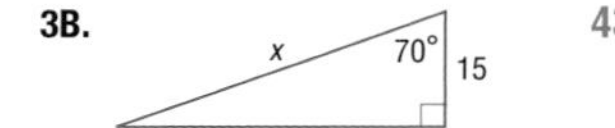

3C. ARCHITECTURE The front of the vacation cottage shown is an isosceles triangle. What is the height x of the cottage above its foundation? What is the length y of the roof? Explain your reasoning.
$x \approx 56$ ft because $x = 32.5 \tan 60°$; since all the angles of the cottage are 60° this is an equilateral triangle, so $y = 65$ ft.

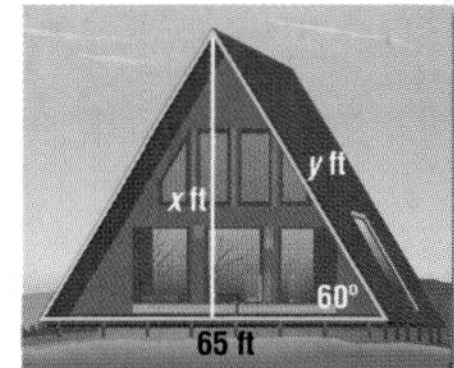

DifferentiatedInstruction AL OL

Auditory/Musical Learners The easiest way for auditory learners to remember the ratios for sine, cosine, and tangent is for them to chant SOH-CAH-TOA. When introducing this mnemonic device to students, have them repeat it as a class a few times in rhythm. Point out that SOH and CAH each have one syllable because the "H" is silent, so students can remember that one "silent" hypotenuse is involved for the sine and cosine ratios. TOA has two syllables and involves the two legs for the tangent ratio.

2 Use Inverse Trigonometric Ratios

In Example 2, you found that $\tan 30° \approx 0.58$. It follows that if the tangent of an acute angle is 0.58, then the angle measures approximately 30.

If you know the sine, cosine, or tangent of an acute angle, you can use a calculator to find the measure of the angle, which is the inverse of the trigonometric ratio.

ReadingMath

Inverse Trigonometric Ratios The expression $\sin^{-1} x$ is read *the inverse sine of x* and is interpreted as the angle with sine x. Be careful not to confuse this notation with the notation for negative exponents—

$\sin^{-1} x \neq \frac{1}{\sin x}$.

Instead, this notation is similar to the notation for an inverse function, $f^{-1}(x)$.

KeyConcept Inverse Trigonometric Ratios

Words	If $\angle A$ is an acute angle and the sine of A is x, then the **inverse sine** of x is the measure of $\angle A$.
Symbols	If $\sin A = x$, then $\sin^{-1} x = m\angle A$.
Words	If $\angle A$ is an acute angle and the cosine of A is x, then the **inverse cosine** of x is the measure of $\angle A$.
Symbols	If $\cos A = x$, then $\cos^{-1} x = m\angle A$.
Words	If $\angle A$ is an acute angle and the tangent of A is x, then the **inverse tangent** of x is the measure of $\angle A$.
Symbols	If $\tan A = x$, then $\tan^{-1} x = m\angle A$.

So if $\tan 30° \approx 0.58$, then $\tan^{-1} 0.58 \approx 30°$.

Example 4 Find Angle Measures Using Inverse Trigonometric Ratios

Use a calculator to find the measure of $\angle A$ to the nearest tenth.

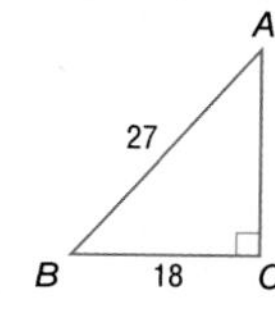

The measures given are those of the leg opposite $\angle A$ and the hypotenuse, so write an equation using the sine ratio.

$\sin A = \frac{18}{27}$ or $\frac{2}{3}$ $\quad \sin A = \frac{\text{opp}}{\text{hyp}}$

If $\sin A = \frac{2}{3}$, then $\sin^{-1} \frac{2}{3} = m\angle A$. Use a calculator.

KEYSTROKES: [2nd] [SIN^{-1}] [(] 2 [÷] 3 [)] [ENTER] 41.8103149

So, $m\angle A \approx 41.8°$.

StudyTip

CCSS Tools Use a graphing calculator. The second functions of the [SIN], [COS], and [TAN] keys are usually the inverses.

GuidedPractice

Use a calculator to find the measure of $\angle A$ to the nearest tenth.

4A. 16.7° **4B.** 78.5°

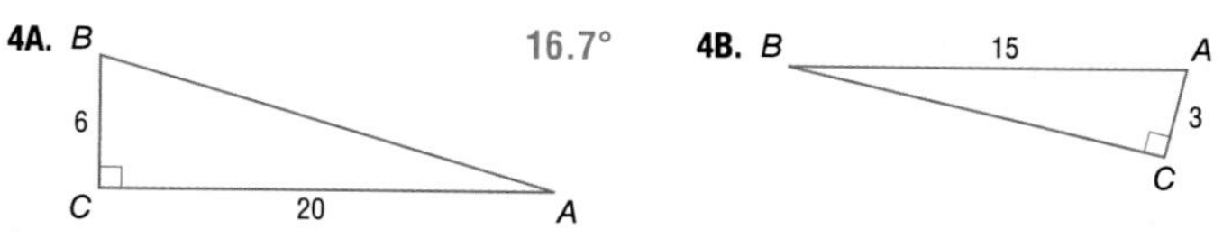

2 Using Inverse Trigonometric Ratios

Examples 4 and 5 show how to use inverse trigonometric ratios to find unknown measures in a right triangle.

Additional Example

4 Use a calculator to find the measure of $\angle P$ to the nearest tenth.

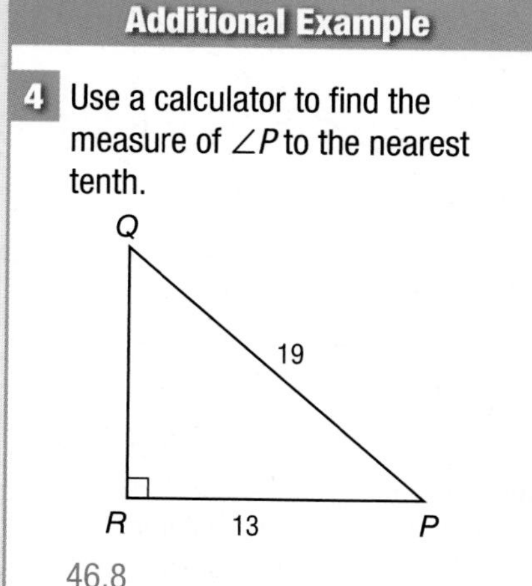

46.8

WatchOut!

Rounding When finding missing measures of a triangle, the angles may not add to 180° because of rounding errors.

CCSS Teaching the Mathematical Practices

Tools Mathematically proficient students consider the available tools when solving a mathematical problem. Encourage students to use their graphing calculators to explore trigonometric concepts.

Additional Example

5 Solve the right triangle. Round side measures to the nearest hundredth and angle measures to the nearest degree.

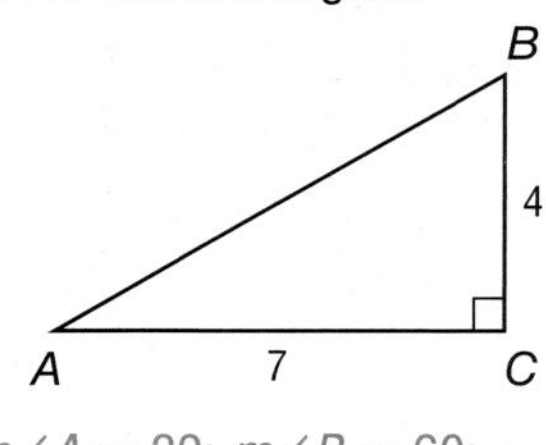

$m\angle A \approx 30$; $m\angle B \approx 60$; $AB \approx 8.06$

CCSS Teaching the Mathematical Practices

Tools Mathematically proficient students consider the available tools when solving a mathematical problem. In Exercises 12–14, encourage students to use a graphing calculator to find the measure.

Additional Answers (Guided Practice)

5A. $m\angle F \approx 23$; $m\angle G \approx 67$; $FH = 12$

5B. $m\angle C = 28$; $AB \approx 4.7$; $BC \approx 8.8$

5C. $m\angle P = 57$; $QR \approx 24.6$; $PR \approx 29.4$

When you use given measures to find the unknown angle and side measures of a right triangle, this is known as *solving a right triangle*. To solve a right triangle, you need to know

- two side lengths or
- one side length and the measure of one acute angle.

Example 5 Solve a Right Triangle

Solve the right triangle. Round side measures to the nearest tenth and angle measures to the nearest degree.

X
5
Z
9
Y

Step 1 Find $m\angle X$ by using a tangent ratio.

$\tan X = \frac{9}{5}$	$\tan X = \frac{\text{opp}}{\text{adj}}$
$\tan^{-1}\frac{9}{5} = m\angle X$	Definition of inverse tangent
$60.9453959 \approx m\angle X$	Use a calculator.

So, $m\angle X \approx 61$.

Step 2 Find $m\angle Y$ using Corollary 4.1, which states that the acute angles of a right triangle are complementary.

$m\angle X + m\angle Y = 90$	Corollary 4.1
$61 + m\angle Y \approx 90$	$m\angle X \approx 61$
$m\angle Y \approx 29$	Subtract 61 from each side.

So, $m\angle Y \approx 29$.

Step 3 Find XY by using the Pythagorean Theorem.

$(XZ)^2 + (ZY)^2 = (XY)^2$	Pythagorean Theorem
$5^2 + 9^2 = (XY)^2$	Substitution
$106 = (XY)^2$	Simplify.
$\sqrt{106} = XY$	Take the positive square root of each side.
$10.3 \approx XY$	Use a calculator.

So $XY \approx 10.3$.

StudyTip

Alternative Methods Right triangles can often be solved using different methods. In Example 5, $m\angle Y$ could have been found using a tangent ratio, and $m\angle X$ and a sine ratio could have been used to find XY.

WatchOut!

Approximation If using calculated measures to find other measures in a right triangle, be careful not to round values until the last step. So in the following equation, use $\tan^{-1}\frac{9}{5}$ instead of its approximate value, 61°.

$$XY = \frac{9}{\sin X} = \frac{9}{\sin\left(\tan^{-1}\frac{9}{5}\right)} \approx 10.3$$

GuidedPractice

Solve each right triangle. Round side measures to the nearest tenth and angle measures to the nearest degree. **5A–5C. See margin.**

5A.

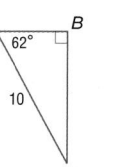

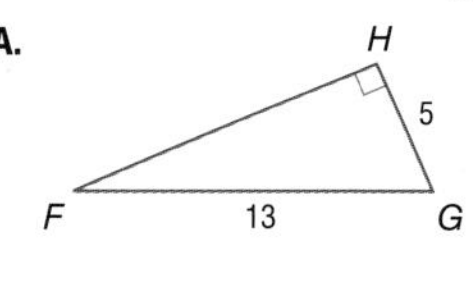

5B.

A
B
62°
10
C

5C.

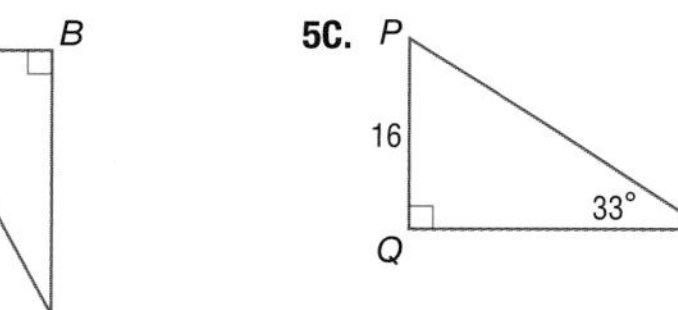

DifferentiatedInstruction OL BL

Extension Give students the length of one side of a right triangle and the measure of one of its acute angles. Ask students which trigonometric ratio to use if you want to find the length of the hypotenuse. If the side you give them is adjacent to the angle you give them, then use the cosine ratio. If the side you give them is opposite the angle you give them, then use the sine ratio.

572 | Lesson 8-4 | Trigonometry

Check Your Understanding

 = Step-by-Step Solutions begin on page R14. 

Example 1 **Express each ratio as a fraction and as a decimal to the nearest hundredth.**

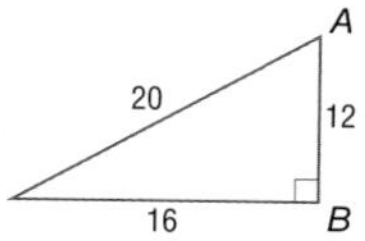

1. $\sin A$ $\frac{16}{20} = 0.80$
2. $\tan C$ $\frac{12}{16} = 0.75$
3. $\cos A$ $\frac{12}{20} = 0.60$
4. $\tan A$
5. $\cos C$
6. $\sin C$

(Triangle ABC: $AC = 20$, $AB = 12$, $CB = 16$, right angle at B.)

Example 2

7. Use a special right triangle to express $\sin 60°$ as a fraction and as a decimal to the nearest hundredth. See margin.

Example 3 **Find x. Round to the nearest hundredth.**

4. $\frac{16}{12} \approx 1.33$
5. $\frac{16}{20} = 0.80$
6. $\frac{12}{20} = 0.60$

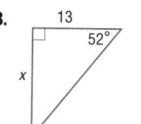

8. 16.64 (13, 52°, x)

9. 27.44

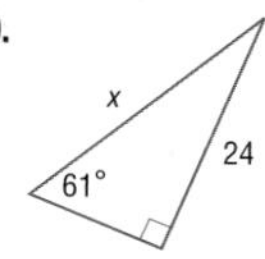

10. 16.93

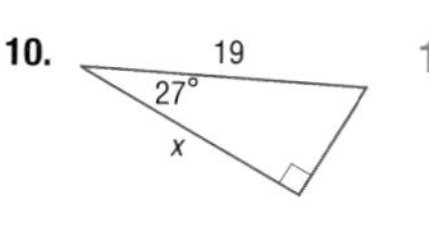

11. **SPORTS** David is building a bike ramp. He wants the angle that the ramp makes with the ground to be 20°. If the board he wants to use for his ramp is $3\frac{1}{2}$ feet long, about how tall will the ramp need to be at the highest point? about 1.2 ft

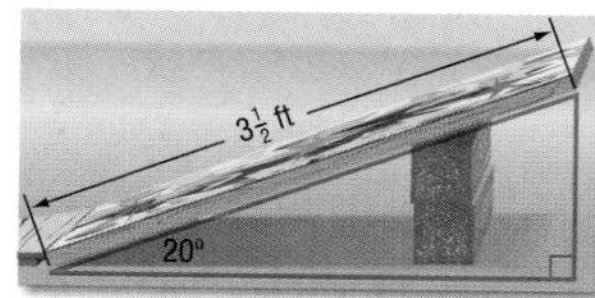

Example 4 **CCSS TOOLS** **Use a calculator to find the measure of $\angle Z$ to the nearest tenth.**

12. 33.7

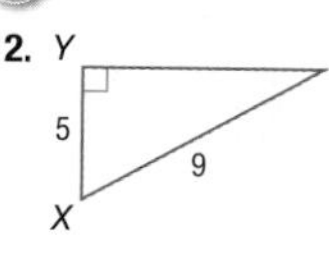

13. 44.4

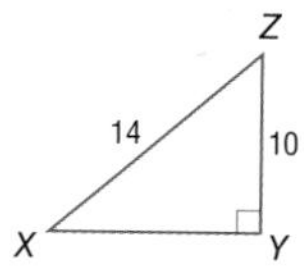

14. 36.9

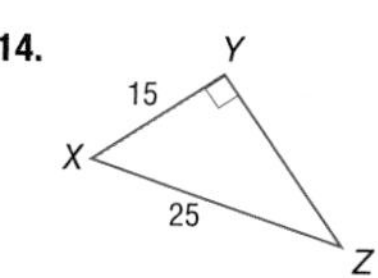

Example 5

15. Solve the right triangle. Round side measures to the nearest tenth and angle measures to the nearest degree. See margin.

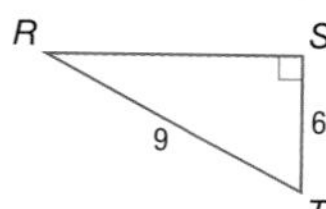

Practice and Problem Solving

Extra Practice is on page R8.

Example 1 **Find $\sin J$, $\cos J$, $\tan J$, $\sin L$, $\cos L$, and $\tan L$. Express each ratio as a fraction and as a decimal to the nearest hundredth.** 16–21. See margin.

16.

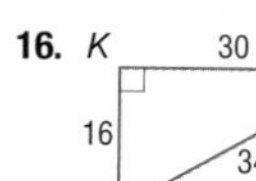
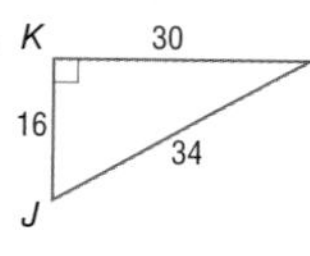

 17.

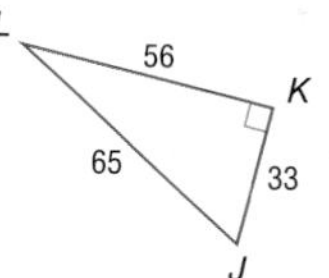

18.

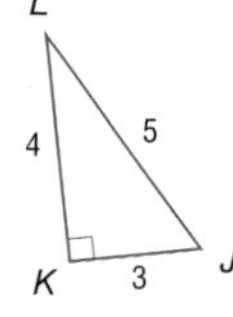

19.

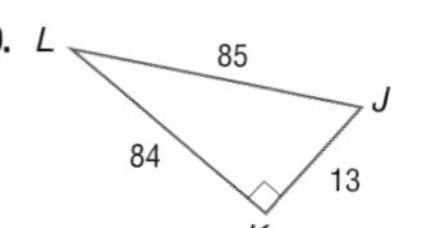

20.

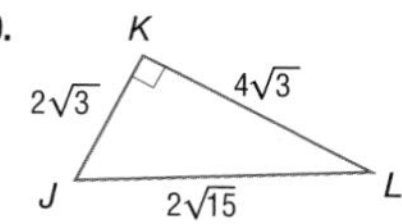

21.

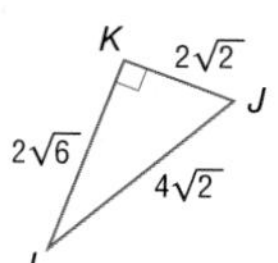

Differentiated Homework Options

Level	Assignment	Two-Day Option	
AL Basic	16–46, 63–87	17–45 odd, 66–69	16–46 even, 63–65, 70–87
OL Core	17–45 odd, 46, 47, 49, 50, 51–55 odd, 56, 57, 59, 60, 61, 63–87	16–46, 66–69	47–61, 63–65, 70–87
BL Advanced	47–81, (optional: 82–87)		

3 Practice

Formative Assessment

Use Exercises 1–15 to check for understanding.

Use the chart at the bottom of this page to customize assignments for your students.

Additional Answers

7. $\frac{\sqrt{3}}{2} \approx 0.87$

15. $RS \approx 6.7$; $m\angle R \approx 42$; $m\angle T \approx 48$

16. $\frac{30}{34} \approx 0.88$; $\frac{16}{34} \approx 0.47$; $\frac{30}{16} \approx 1.88$; $\frac{16}{34} \approx 0.47$; $\frac{30}{34} \approx 0.88$; $\frac{16}{30} \approx 0.53$

17. $\frac{56}{65} \approx 0.86$; $\frac{33}{65} \approx 0.51$; $\frac{56}{33} \approx 1.70$; $\frac{33}{65} \approx 0.51$; $\frac{56}{65} \approx 0.86$; $\frac{33}{56} \approx 0.59$

18. $\frac{4}{5} = 0.80$; $\frac{3}{5} = 0.60$; $\frac{4}{3} \approx 1.33$; $\frac{3}{5} = 0.60$; $\frac{4}{5} = 0.80$; $\frac{3}{4} = 0.75$

19. $\frac{84}{85} \approx 0.99$; $\frac{13}{85} \approx 0.15$; $\frac{84}{13} \approx 6.46$; $\frac{13}{85} \approx 0.15$; $\frac{84}{85} \approx 0.99$; $\frac{13}{84} \approx 0.15$

20. $\frac{2\sqrt{5}}{5} \approx 0.89$; $\frac{\sqrt{5}}{5} \approx 0.45$; $\frac{4\sqrt{3}}{2\sqrt{3}} = 2$; $\frac{\sqrt{5}}{5} \approx 0.45$; $\frac{2\sqrt{5}}{5} \approx 0.89$; $\frac{2\sqrt{3}}{4\sqrt{3}} = 0.50$

21. $\frac{\sqrt{3}}{2} \approx 0.87$; $\frac{2\sqrt{2}}{4\sqrt{2}} = 0.50$; $\frac{2\sqrt{6}}{2\sqrt{2}} = \sqrt{3} \approx 1.73$; $\frac{2\sqrt{2}}{4\sqrt{2}} = 0.50$; $\frac{\sqrt{3}}{2} \approx 0.87$; $\frac{\sqrt{3}}{3} \approx 0.58$

Study Guide and Intervention

AL OL ELL

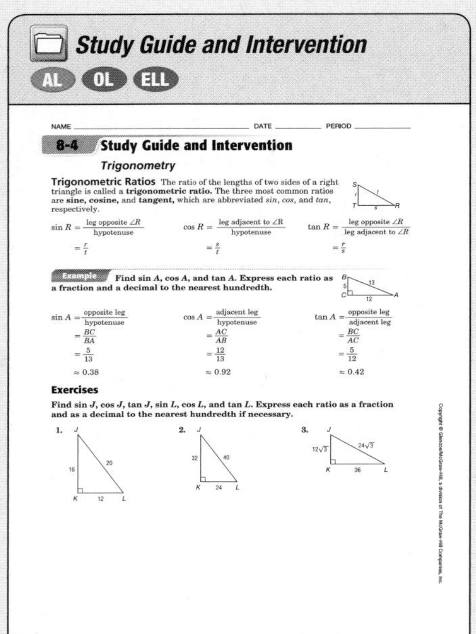
NAME ____ DATE ____ PERIOD ____

8-4 Study Guide and Intervention

Trigonometry

Trigonometric Ratios The ratio of the lengths of two sides of a right triangle is called a **trigonometric ratio.** The three most common ratios are **sine, cosine,** and **tangent,** which are abbreviated *sin, cos,* and *tan,* respectively.

$\sin R = \frac{\text{leg opposite } \angle R}{\text{hypotenuse}} = \frac{r}{t}$ $\cos R = \frac{\text{leg adjacent to } \angle R}{\text{hypotenuse}} = \frac{s}{t}$ $\tan R = \frac{\text{leg opposite } \angle R}{\text{leg adjacent to } \angle R} = \frac{r}{s}$

Example Find sin *A*, cos *A*, and tan *A*. Express each ratio as a fraction and a decimal to the nearest hundredth.

$\sin A = \frac{\text{opposite leg}}{\text{hypotenuse}} = \frac{BC}{BA} = \frac{5}{13} \approx 0.38$ $\cos A = \frac{\text{adjacent leg}}{\text{hypotenuse}} = \frac{AC}{AB} = \frac{12}{13} \approx 0.92$ $\tan A = \frac{\text{opposite leg}}{\text{adjacent leg}} = \frac{BC}{AC} = \frac{5}{12} \approx 0.42$

Exercises

Find sin *J*, cos *J*, tan *J*, sin *L*, cos *L*, and tan *L*. Express each ratio as a fraction and as a decimal to the nearest hundredth if necessary.

1. 2. 3.

Practice

AL OL BL ELL

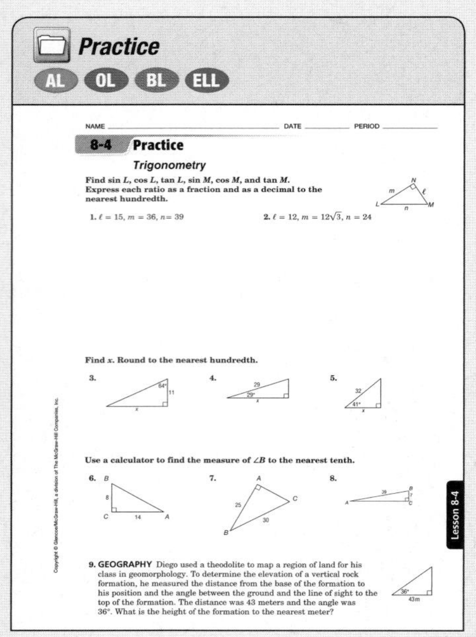
NAME ____ DATE ____ PERIOD ____

8-4 Practice

Trigonometry

Find sin *L*, cos *L*, tan *L*, sin *M*, cos *M*, and tan *M*. Express each ratio as a fraction and as a decimal to the nearest hundredth.

1. $\ell = 15, m = 36, n = 39$
2. $\ell = 12, m = 12\sqrt{3}, n = 24$

Find *x*. Round to the nearest hundredth.

3. 4. 5.

Use a calculator to find the measure of ∠*B* to the nearest tenth.

6. 7. 8.

9. **GEOGRAPHY** Diego used a theodolite to map a region of land for his class in geomorphology. To determine the elevation of a vertical rock formation, he measured the distance from the base of the formation to his position and the angle between the ground and the line of sight to the top of the formation. The distance was 43 meters and the angle was 36°. What is the height of the formation to the nearest meter?

Word Problem Practice

AL OL BL ELL

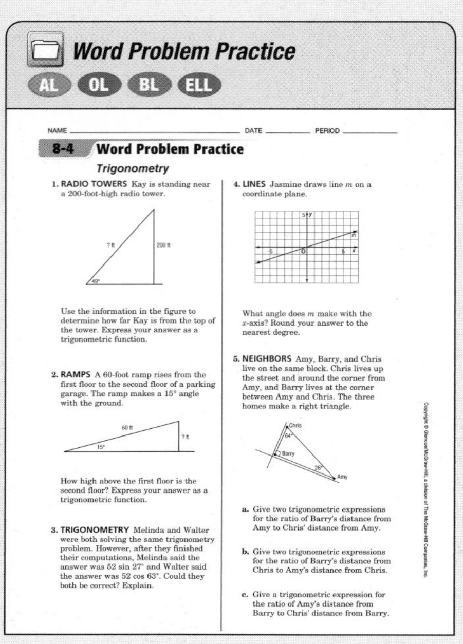
NAME ____ DATE ____ PERIOD ____

8-4 Word Problem Practice

Trigonometry

1. **RADIO TOWERS** Kay is standing near a 200-foot-high radio tower.

Use the information in the figure to determine how far Kay is from the top of the tower. Express your answer as a trigonometric function.

2. **RAMPS** A 60-foot ramp rises from the first floor to the second floor of a parking garage. The ramp makes a 15° angle with the ground.

How high above the first floor is the second floor? Express your answer as a trigonometric function.

3. **TRIGONOMETRY** Melinda and Walter were both solving the same trigonometry problem. However, after they finished their computations, Melinda said the answer was 52 sin 27° and Walter said the answer was 52 cos 63°. Could they both be correct? Explain.

4. **LINES** Jasmine draws line *m* on a coordinate plane.

What angle does *m* make with the *x*-axis? Round your answer to the nearest degree.

5. **NEIGHBORS** Amy, Barry, and Chris live on the same block. Chris lives up the street and around the corner from Amy, and Barry lives at the corner between Amy and Chris. The three homes make a right triangle.

a. Give two trigonometric expressions for the ratio of Barry's distance from Amy to Chris' distance from Amy.

b. Give two trigonometric expressions for the ratio of Barry's distance from Chris to Amy's distance from Chris.

c. Give a trigonometric expression for the ratio of Amy's distance from Barry to Chris' distance from Barry.

Example 2 Use a special right triangle to express each trigonometric ratio as a fraction and as a decimal to the nearest hundredth.

22. tan 60° $\sqrt{3} \approx 1.73$
23. cos 30° $\frac{\sqrt{3}}{2} \approx 0.87$
24. sin 45° $\frac{\sqrt{2}}{2} \approx 0.71$
25. sin 30° $\frac{1}{2}$ or 0.5
26. tan 45° 1
27. cos 60° $\frac{1}{2}$ or 0.5

Example 3 Find *x*. Round to the nearest tenth.

28. 30.7

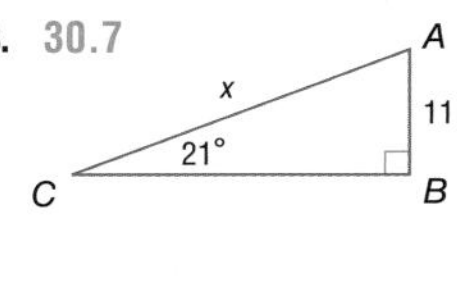

29. 28.7

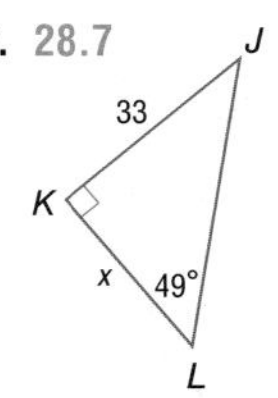

30. 23.2

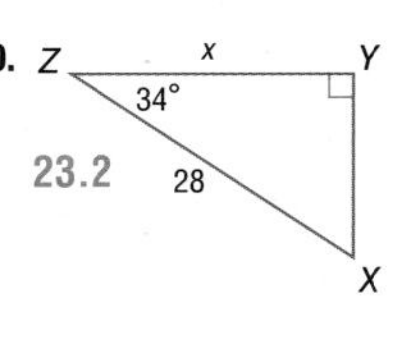

31. 57.2

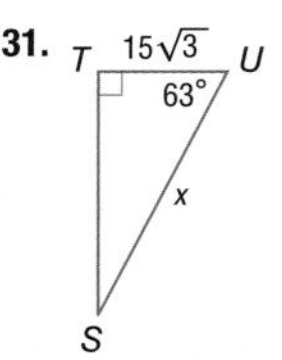

32. 17.7

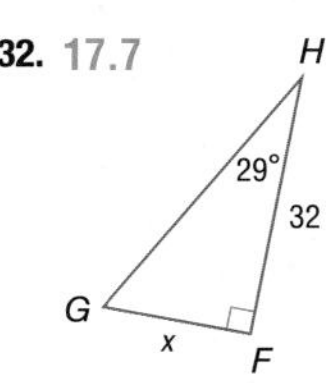

33. 17.4

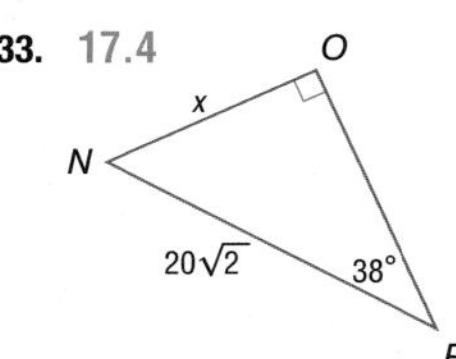

34. **GYMNASTICS** The springboard that Eric uses in his gymnastics class has 6-inch coils and forms an angle of 14.5° with the base. About how long is the springboard? about 24 in.

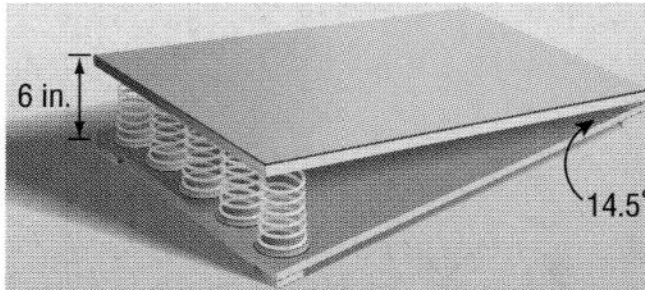

35. **ROLLER COASTERS** The angle of ascent of the first hill of a roller coaster is 55°. If the length of the track from the beginning of the ascent to the highest point is 98 feet, what is the height of the roller coaster when it reaches the top of the first hill? 80 ft

Example 4 CCSS **TOOLS** Use a calculator to find the measure of ∠*T* to the nearest tenth.

36. 33.7

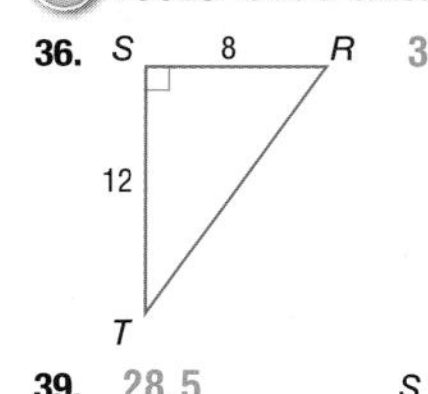

37. 61.4

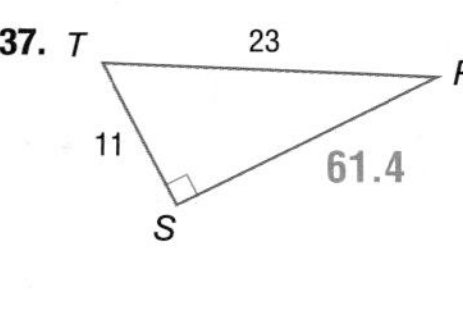

38. 56.4

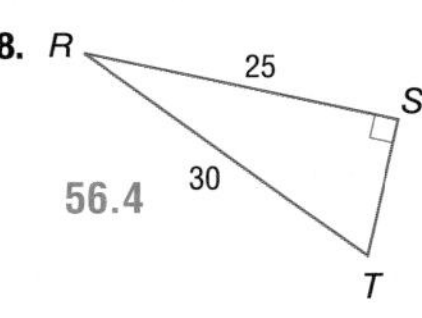

39. 28.5

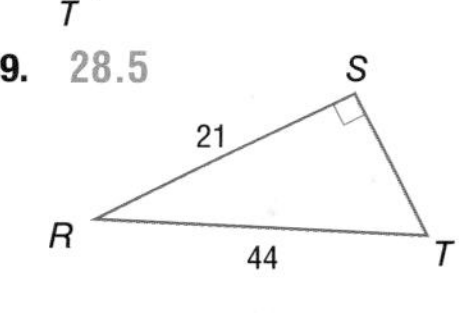

40. 64.6

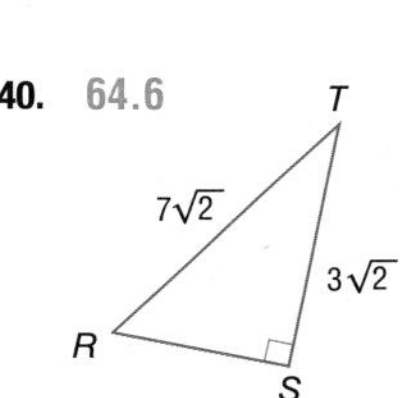

41. 21.8

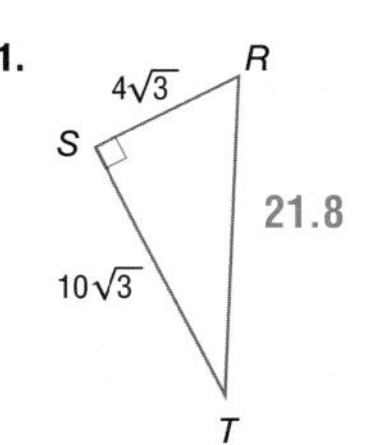

Enrichment

OL BL

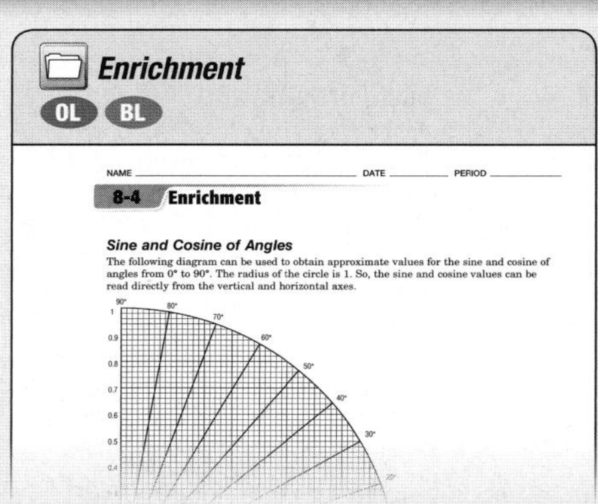
NAME ____ DATE ____ PERIOD ____

8-4 Enrichment

Sine and Cosine of Angles

The following diagram can be used to obtain approximate values for the sine and cosine of angles from 0° to 90°. The radius of the circle is 1. So, the sine and cosine values can be read directly from the vertical and horizontal axes.

Teaching the Mathematical Practices

Tools Mathematically proficient students consider the available tools when solving a mathematical problem. In Exercises 36–41, encourage students to use a graphing calculator to find the measure.

Example 5 **Solve each right triangle. Round side measures to the nearest tenth and angle measures to the nearest degree.**

42. $HF = 17.6$; $GH = 20.8$; $m\angle G = 58$
43. $WX = 15.1$; $XZ = 9.8$; $m\angle W = 33$
44. $LK = 20.5$; $m\angle J = 69$; $m\angle K = 21$
45. $ST = 30.6$; $m\angle R = 58$; $m\angle T = 32$

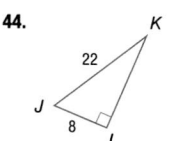

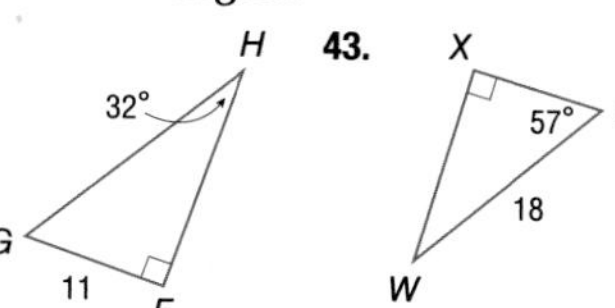

46. BACKPACKS Ramón has a rolling backpack that is $3\frac{3}{4}$ feet tall when the handle is extended. When he is pulling the backpack, Ramon's hand is 3 feet from the ground. What angle does his backpack make with the floor? Round to the nearest degree. 53°

B **COORDINATE GEOMETRY** **Find the measure of each angle to the nearest tenth of a degree using the Distance Formula and an inverse trigonometric ratio.**

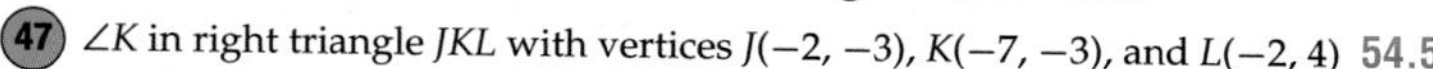

47. $\angle K$ in right triangle JKL with vertices $J(-2, -3)$, $K(-7, -3)$, and $L(-2, 4)$ 54.5

48. $\angle Y$ in right triangle XYZ with vertices $X(4, 1)$, $Y(-6, 3)$, and $Z(-2, 7)$ 56.3

49. $\angle A$ in right triangle ABC with vertices $A(3, 1)$, $B(3, -3)$, and $C(8, -3)$ 51.3

50. SCHOOL SPIRIT Hana is making a pennant for each of the 18 girls on her basketball team. She will use $\frac{1}{2}$-inch seam binding to finish the edges of the pennants.

a. What is the total length of seam binding needed to finish all of the pennants? about 494 in.

b. If seam binding is sold in 3-yard packages at a cost of \$1.79, how much will it cost? \$8.95

51. 13.83 in.; 7.50 in^2
52. 28.53 cm; 23.46 cm^2
53. 8.74 ft; 3.41 ft^2

CCSS SENSE-MAKING **Find the perimeter and area of each triangle. Round to the nearest hundredth.**

51.

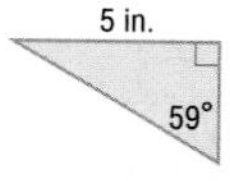

52.

53.

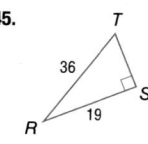

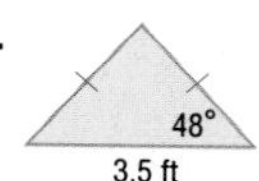

54. Find the tangent of the greater acute angle in a triangle with side lengths of 3, 4, and 5 centimeters. 1.33

55. Find the cosine of the smaller acute angle in a triangle with side lengths of 10, 24, and 26 inches. 0.92

56. ESTIMATION Ethan and Tariq want to estimate the area of the field that their team will use for soccer practice. They know that the field is rectangular, and they have paced off the width of the field as shown. They used the fence posts at the corners of the field to estimate that the angle between the length of the field and the diagonal is about 40°. If they assume that each of their steps is about 18 inches, what is the area of the practice field in square feet? Round to the nearest square foot. 210, 227 ft^2

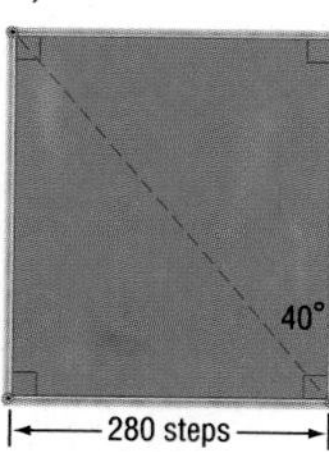

Follow-up

Students have explored trigonometry.

Ask:

- Why is trigonometry useful? Sample answer: It allows us to solve problems modeled by triangles that cannot be solved using the Pythagorean Theorem.

Teaching the Mathematical Practices

Sense-Making Mathematically proficient students start by explaining the meaning of a problem to themselves and looking for entry points to its solution. They plan a solution pathway rather than simply jumping into a solution attempt. In Exercises 51–53, encourage students to use the Pythagorean theorem to find the measures of missing sides.

Multiple Representations

In Exercise 61, students use geometric sketches, a table, algebraic conjecture and algebraic proof to investigate the algebraic relationship between sine and cosine.

Exercise Alert

Ruler Exercises 61 and 64 require the use of a ruler.

Additional Answers

60. Sample answer:

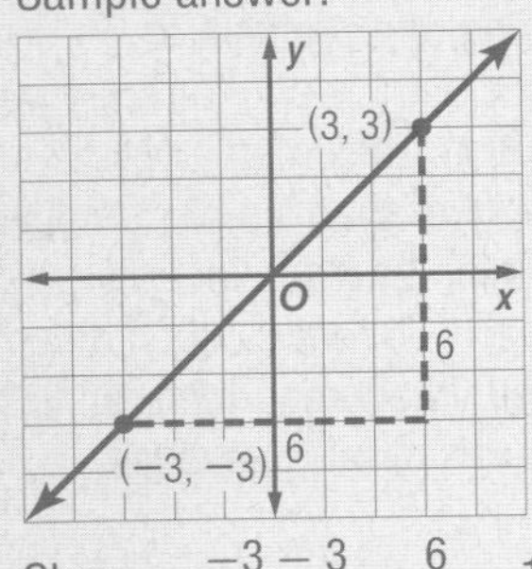

$\text{Slope} = \frac{-3-3}{-3-3} = \frac{6}{6} = 1$

Since the slope is 1 and slope is rise over run, which is tan 45° or tan 225°. From a calculator both equal 1.

61a. Sample Answer:

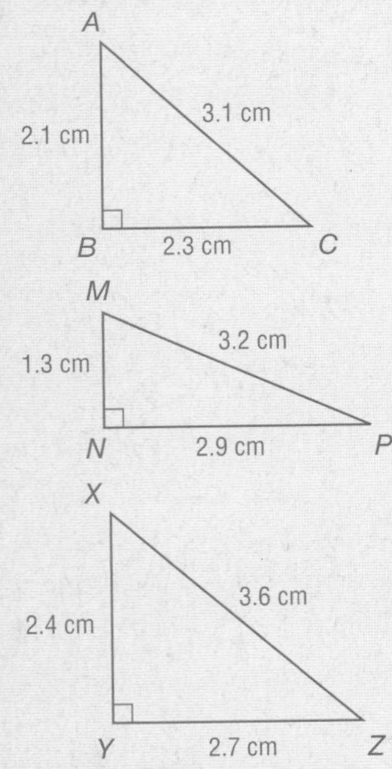

61c. Sample answer: The sum of the cosine squared and the sine squared of an acute angle of a right triangle is 1.

C Find x and y. Round to the nearest tenth. 58. $x = 37.2$; $y = 33.4$

57.

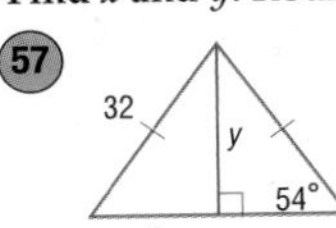

$x = 18.8$; $y = 25.9$

58.

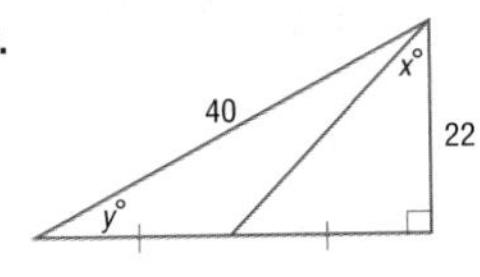

59.

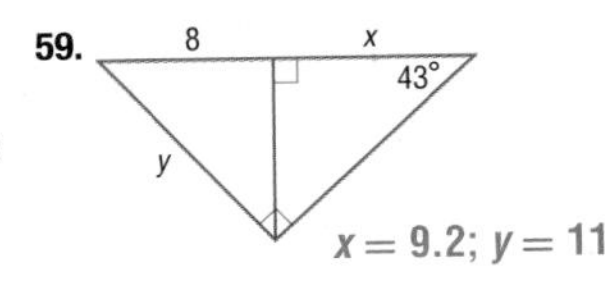

$x = 9.2$; $y = 11.7$

60. **COORDINATE GEOMETRY** Show that the slope of a line at 225° from the x-axis is equal to the tangent of 225°. See margin.

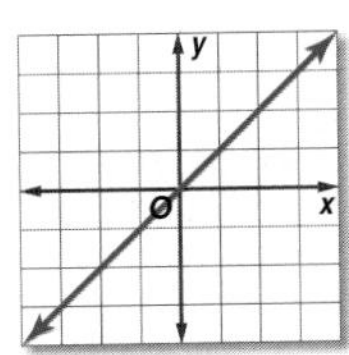

62. $m\angle A = 53$, $m\angle B = 90$, $m\angle C = 37$, $AB = 12$, $BC = 16$, $AC = 20$

63. Sample answer: Yes; since the values of sine and cosine are both calculated by dividing one of the legs of a right triangle by the hypotenuse, and the hypotenuse is always the longest side of a right triangle, the values will always be less than 1. You will always be dividing the smaller number by the larger number.

61. **MULTIPLE REPRESENTATIONS** In this problem, you will investigate an algebraic relationship between the sine and cosine ratios.

a. **Geometric** Draw three right triangles that are not similar to each other. Label the triangles ABC, MNP, and XYZ, with the right angles located at vertices B, N, and Y, respectively. Measure and label each side of the three triangles. See margin.

b. **Tabular** Copy and complete the table below. Sample answers given.

Triangle	Trigonometric Ratios				Sum of Ratios Squared	
ABC	cos A	0.677	sin A	0.742	$(\cos A)^2 + (\sin A)^2 =$	1
	cos C	0.742	sin C	0.677	$(\cos C)^2 + (\sin C)^2 =$	1
MNP	cos M	0.406	sin M	0.906	$(\cos M)^2 + (\sin M)^2 =$	1
	cos P	0.906	sin P	0.406	$(\cos P)^2 + (\sin P)^2 =$	1
XYZ	cos X	0.667	sin X	0.75	$(\cos X)^2 + (\sin X)^2 =$	1
	cos Z	0.75	sin Z	0.667	$(\cos Z)^2 + (\sin Z)^2 =$	1

c. **Verbal** Make a conjecture about the sum of the squares of the cosine and sine of an acute angle of a right triangle. See margin.

d. **Algebraic** Express your conjecture algebraically for an angle X. $(\sin X)^2 + (\cos X)^2 = 1$

e. **Analytical** Show that your conjecture is valid for angle A in the figure at the right using the trigonometric functions and the Pythagorean Theorem. See margin.

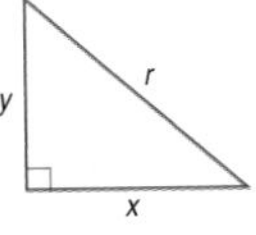

H.O.T. Problems Use Higher-Order Thinking Skills

62. **CHALLENGE** Solve $\triangle ABC$. Round to the nearest whole number.

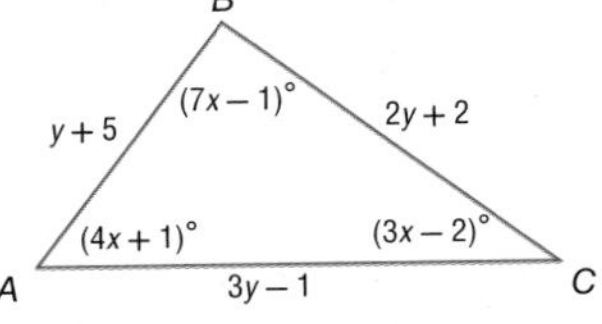

63. **REASONING** Are the values of sine and cosine for an acute angle of a right triangle always less than 1? Explain.

64. **CCSS REASONING** What is the relationship between the sine and cosine of complementary angles? Explain your reasoning and use the relationship to find cos 50 if sin 40 ≈ 0.64. See margin.

65. **WRITING IN MATH** Explain how you can use ratios of the side lengths to find the angle measures of the acute angles in a right triangle. See margin.

61e. Sample answer:

$(\sin A)^2 + (\cos A)^2 \stackrel{?}{=} 1$ (Conjecture)

$\left(\frac{y}{r}\right)^2 + \left(\frac{x}{r}\right)^2 \stackrel{?}{=} 1$ $\left(\sin A = \frac{y}{r}, \cos A = \frac{x}{r}\right)$

$\frac{y^2}{r^2} + \frac{x^2}{r^2} \stackrel{?}{=} 1$ (Simplify.)

$\frac{y^2 + x^2}{r^2} \stackrel{?}{=} 1$ (Combine fractions with like denominators.)

$\frac{r^2}{r^2} \stackrel{?}{=} 1$ (Pythagorean Theorem)

$1 = 1$ (Simplify.)

CCSS Teaching the Mathematical Practices

Reasoning Mathematically proficient students make sense of quantities and their relationships in problem situations. In Exercise 64, encourage students to analyze the relationship between sine and cosine.

Standardized Test Practice

66. What is the value of tan x? **D**

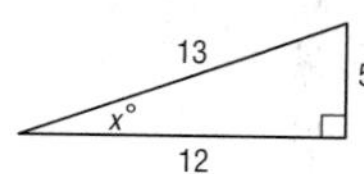

A $\tan x = \frac{13}{5}$

B $\tan x = \frac{12}{5}$

C $\tan x = \frac{5}{13}$

D $\tan x = \frac{5}{12}$

67. ALGEBRA Which of the following has the same value as $2^{-12} \times 2^3$? **H**

F 2^{-36}

G 4^{-9}

H 2^{-9}

J 2^{-4}

68. GRIDDED RESPONSE If $AC = 12$ and $AB = 25$, what is the measure of $\angle B$ to the nearest tenth? **28.7**

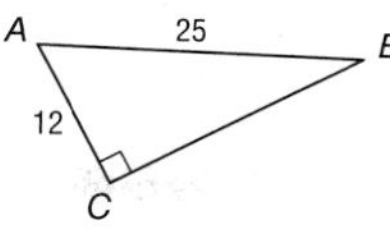

69. SAT/ACT The area of a right triangle is 240 square inches. If the base is 30 inches long, how many inches long is the hypotenuse? **E**

A 5

B 8

C 16

D $2\sqrt{241}$

E 34

Spiral Review

Find x and y. (Lesson 8-3)

70. $x = 6$; $y = 12$

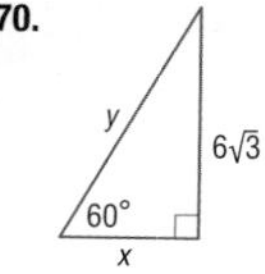

71. $x = 7\sqrt{2}$; $y = 14$

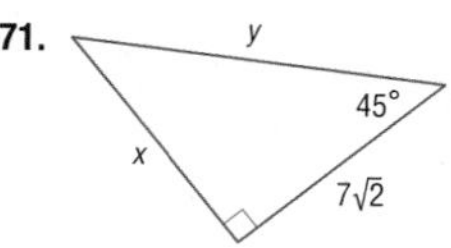

72. $x = 7\sqrt{3}$; $y = 7$

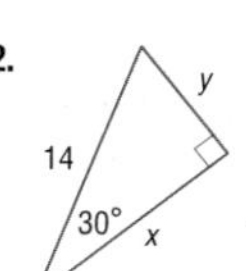

Determine whether each set of numbers can be the measures of the sides of a triangle. If so, classify the triangle as *acute*, *obtuse*, or *right*. Justify your answer. (Lesson 8-2) **73–78. See margin.**

73. 8, 15, 17

74. 11, 12, 24

75. 13, 30, 35

76. 18, 24, 30

77. 3.2, 5.3, 8.6

78. $6\sqrt{3}$, 14, 17

79. MAPS The scale on the map of New Mexico is 2 centimeters = 160 miles. The width of New Mexico through Albuquerque on the map is 4.1 centimeters. How long would it take to drive across New Mexico if you drove at an average of 60 miles per hour? (Lesson 7-7) **See margin.**

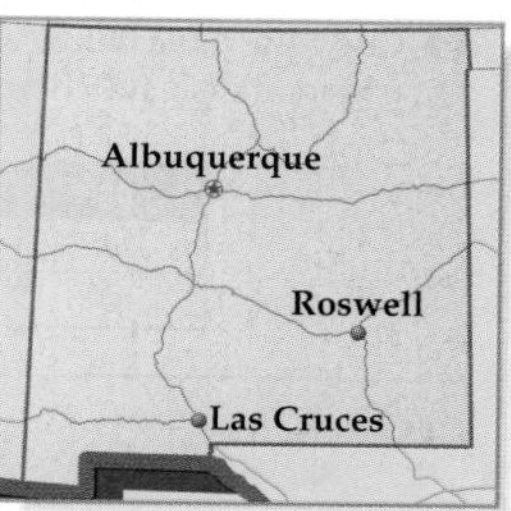

ALGEBRA Find x and y. (Lesson 7-4)

80. $x = 14$, $y = 15$

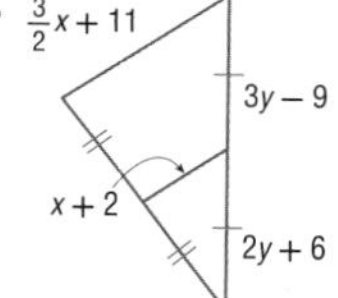

81. $x = 1$, $y = \frac{3}{2}$

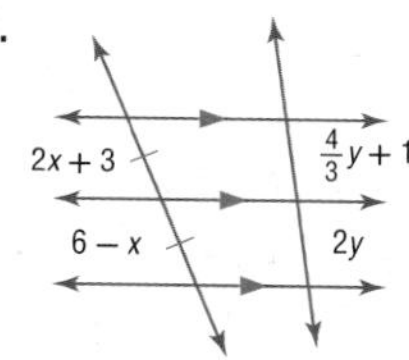

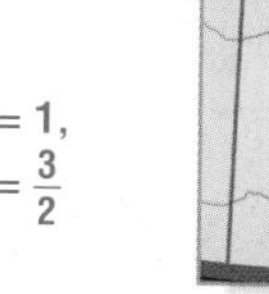

Skills Review

Solve each proportion. Round to the nearest tenth if necessary.

82. $2.14 = \frac{x}{12}$ **25.7**

83. $0.05x = 13$ **260**

84. $0.37 = \frac{32}{x}$ **86.5**

85. $0.74 = \frac{14}{x}$ **18.9**

86. $1.66 = \frac{x}{23}$ **38.2**

87. $0.21 = \frac{33}{x}$ **157.1**

64. In the diagram, $\sin A = x$ and $\cos B = x$; therefore $\sin A = \cos B$.

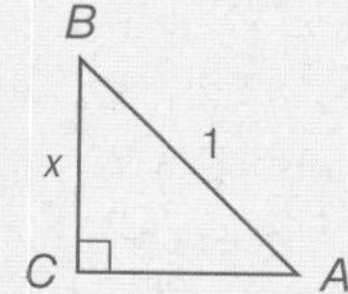

Since the acute angles of a right triangle are complementary, $m\angle B = 90 - m\angle A$. By substitution, $\sin A = \cos(90 - A)$. Since $\sin A = x$, $\cos(90 - A) = x$ by substitution. Applying this relationship, if $\sin 40 \approx 0.64$, then $\cos(90 - 40) \approx 0.64$. Since $90 - 40 = 50$, $\cos 50 \approx 0.64$.

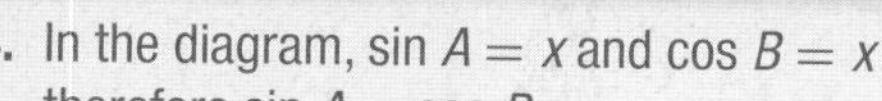

4 Assess

Yesterday's News Have students write how the properties of special right triangles helped in learning trigonometry.

Formative Assessment

Check for student understanding of Lessons 8-3 and 8-4.

Quiz 2, p. 51

Additional Answers

65. Sample answer: To find the measure of an acute angle of a right triangle, you can find the ratio of the leg opposite the angle to the hypotenuse and use a calculator to find the inverse sine of the ratio, you can find the ratio of the leg adjacent to the angle to the hypotenuse and use a calculator to find the inverse cosine of the ratio, or you can find the ratio of the leg opposite the angle to the leg adjacent to the angle and use a calculator to find the inverse tangent of the ratio.

73. yes; right
$17^2 \stackrel{?}{=} 8^2 + 15^2$
$289 = 64 + 225$

74. no; $24 > 12 + 11$

75. yes; obtuse
$35^2 \stackrel{?}{=} 30^2 + 13^2$
$1225 > 900 + 169$

76. yes; right
$30^2 \stackrel{?}{=} 18^2 + 24^2$
$900 = 324 + 576$

77. no; $8.6 > 3.2 + 5.3$

78. yes; acute
$17^2 \stackrel{?}{=} 6\sqrt{3}^2 + 14^2$
$289 < 108 + 196$

79. $5\frac{7}{15}$ hours or 5 hours 28 min

1 Focus

Objective Explore the trigonometric functions, secant, cosecant, and cotangent.

Materials for Each Group

- TI-83/84 Plus or other graphing calculator
- ruler

Teaching Tip

As a variation, have students complete the activity with a 30°-60°-90° triangle and find all of the trigonometric values algebraically, instead of using a calculator.

2 Teach

Working in Cooperative Groups

Have students of mixed abilities work in groups of three. Have students rotate finding each trigonometric function in Step 2 and Step 3.

Show students the equivalence of the two new definitions in symbols of each function by using complex fractions.

Practice Have students complete Exercises 1 and 2.

3 Assess

Formative Assessment

Use Exercise 3 to assess whether students understand the concepts of secant, cosecant, and cotangent.

From Concrete to Abstract

Give students a table such as that in Step 4 with half of the values filled in, and have them use reciprocals to find the missing values.

EXTEND 8-4 Graphing Technology Lab Secant, Cosecant, and Cotangent

In the previous lesson, you used the trigonometric functions sine, cosine, and tangent to find angle relationships in right angles. In this activity, you will use the reciprocals of those functions, cosecant, secant, and cotangent, to explore angle and side relationships in right triangles.

CCSS Common Core State Standards
Content Standards
G.SRT.6 Understand that by similarity, side ratios in right triangles are properties of the angles in the triangle, leading to definitions of trigonometric ratios for acute angles.
Mathematical Practices 5

KeyConcept Reciprocal Trigonometric Ratios

Words	Symbols
The **cosecant** of $\angle A$ (written csc A) is the reciprocal of sin A.	$\csc A = \frac{1}{\sin A}$ or $\frac{c}{a}$
The **secant** of $\angle A$ (written sec A) is the reciprocal of cos A.	$\sec A = \frac{1}{\cos A}$ or $\frac{c}{b}$
The **cotangent** of $\angle A$ (written cot A) is the reciprocal of tan A.	$\cot A = \frac{1}{\tan A}$ or $\frac{b}{a}$

Activity Find Trigonometric Values

Step 1 Draw and label a right triangle with the dimensions shown at the right.

Step 2 Use your graphing calculator to find the values for sin A, cos A, and tan A.

Step 3 Next, find the value for csc A by dividing 1 by [SIN] A. Repeat step 3 to find sec A and cot A .

Step 4 Copy the table below and record your results. Next, find the value of each trigonometric function for angle C.

Angle	sin	cos	tan	csc	sec	cot
A						
C						

Exercises

1. Find the values of the six trigonometric functions for a 45° angle in a 45°-45°-90° triangle with legs that are 4 cm. **1–3. See margin.**
2. In $\triangle FGH$, $\tan F = \frac{5}{12}$. Find cot F and sin F if $\angle G$ is a right angle.
3. Find the values of the six trigonometric functions for angle T in $\triangle RST$ if $m\angle R = 36°$. Round to the nearest hundredth.

Extending the Concept

Have students determine under what conditions sine, cosine, and tangent could be equal to their reciprocals.

Additional Answers

1. $\sin 45° = \frac{1}{\sqrt{2}} = \frac{\sqrt{2}}{2}$; $\cos 45° = \frac{1}{\sqrt{2}} = \frac{\sqrt{2}}{2}$; $\tan 45° = 1$; $\csc 45° = \sqrt{2}$; $\sec 45° = \sqrt{2}$; $\cot 45° = 1$
2. $\cot F = \frac{12}{5}$ or 2.4; $\sin F = \frac{5}{13}$
3. $\sin T = 0.81$; $\cos T = 0.59$; $\tan T = 1.38$; $\csc T = 1.24$; $\sec T = 1.70$; $\cot T = 0.73$

CHAPTER 8 Mid-Chapter Quiz
Lessons 8-1 through 8-4

Find the geometric mean between each pair of numbers. (Lesson 8-1)

1. 12 and 3 6
2. 63 and 7 21
3. 45 and 20 30
4. 50 and 10 $10\sqrt{5}$

Write a similarity statement identifying the three similar triangles in each figure. (Lesson 8-1)

5.

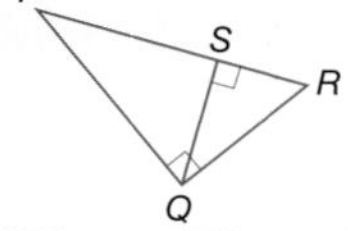

$\triangle PRQ \sim \triangle QRS \sim \triangle PQS$

6.

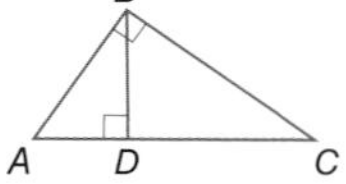

$\triangle ABD \sim \triangle BDC \sim \triangle ACB$

7. Find *x*, *y*, and *z*. (Lesson 8-1) $x = 12,\ y = 15,\ z = 20$

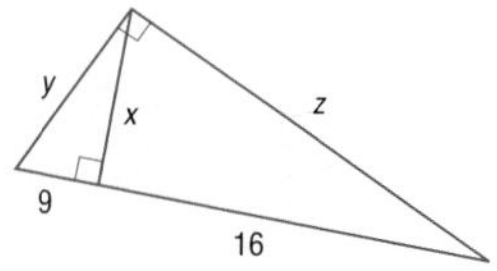

8. PARKS There is a small park in a corner made by two perpendicular streets. The park is 100 ft by 150 ft, with a diagonal path, as shown below. What is the length of path $\overline{AC}$? (Lesson 8-2) 180.3 ft

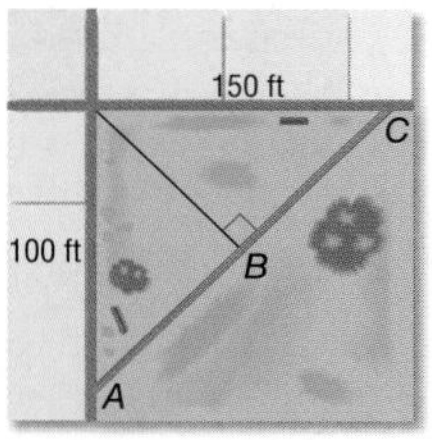

Find *x*. Round to the nearest hundredth. (Lesson 8-2)

9.

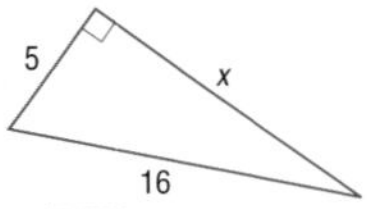

$\sqrt{231} \approx 15.20$

10.

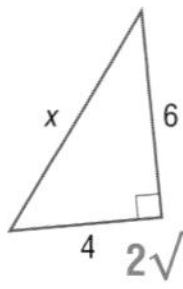

$2\sqrt{13} \approx 7.21$

11. MULTIPLE CHOICE Which of the following sets of numbers is not a Pythagorean triple? (Lesson 8-2) D

A 9, 12, 15
B 21, 72, 75
C 15, 36, 39
D 8, 13, 15

Find *x*. (Lesson 8-3)

12.

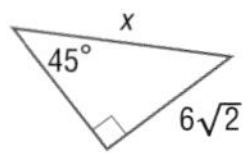

12

13.

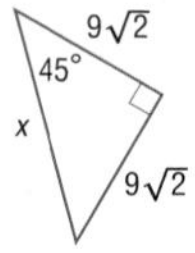

18

14. DESIGN Jamie designed a pinwheel to put in her garden. In the pinwheel, the blue triangles are congruent equilateral triangles, each with an altitude of 4 inches. The red triangles are congruent isosceles right triangles. The hypotenuse of a red triangle is congruent to a side of the blue triangle. (Lesson 8-3)

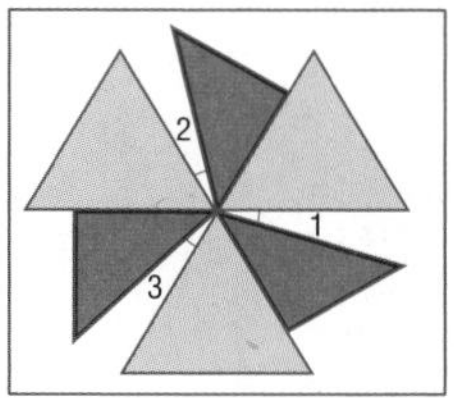

a. If angles 1, 2, and 3 are congruent, find the measure of each angle. 15

b. Find the perimeter of the pinwheel. 55 in.

Find *x* and *y*. (Lesson 8-3)

15.

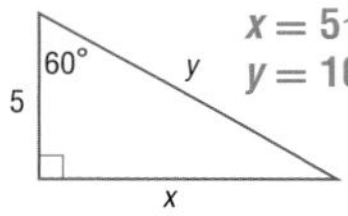

$x = 5\sqrt{3};\ y = 10$

16.

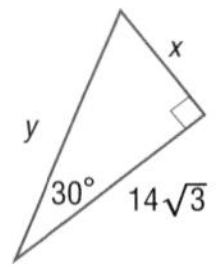

$x = 14;\ y = 28$

Express each ratio as a fraction and as a decimal to the nearest hundredth. (Lesson 8-4)

17. tan *M* $\frac{15}{36} = 0.42$
18. cos *M* $\frac{36}{39} = 0.92$
19. cos *N* $\frac{15}{39} = 0.38$
20. sin *N* $\frac{36}{39} = 0.92$

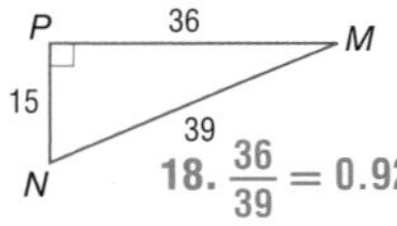

21. Solve the right triangle. Round angle measures to the nearest degree and side measures to the nearest tenth. (Lesson 8-4) $JG = 41.7;\ m\angle G = 30;\ m\angle J = 60$

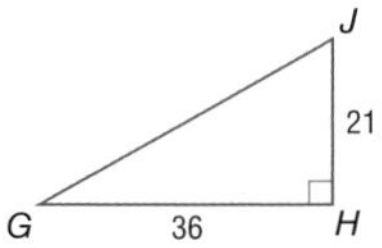

Formative Assessment

Use the Mid-Chapter Quiz to assess students' progress in the first half of the chapter.

Have students review the lessons indicated for the problems that they answered incorrectly.

Summative Assessment

Mid-Chapter Test, p. 53

eAssessment Customize and create multiple versions of your Mid-Chapter Test and their answer keys.

FOLDABLES® StudyOrganizer

Dinah Zike's Foldables®

Before students complete the Mid-Chapter Quiz, encourage them to review the information they have recorded for Lessons 8-1 through 8-4 in their Foldables.

InterventionPlanner

TIER 1 On Level OL	TIER 2 Strategic Intervention AL approaching grade level	TIER 3 Intensive Intervention 2 or more grades below level
If students miss about 25% of the exercises or less,	**If** students miss about 50% of the exercises,	**If** students miss about 75% of the exercises,
Then choose a resource: SE Lessons 8-1 through 8-4 Skills Practice, pp. 7, 13, 20 and 26 connectED.mcgraw-hill.com Self-Check Quiz	**Then** choose a resource: Study Guide and Intervention, pp. 5, 11, 18, 24 connectED.mcgraw-hill.com Extra Examples, Personal Tutor, Homework Help	**Then** use *Math Triumphs, Geo.*, Ch. 6 connectED.mcgraw-hill.com Extra Examples, Personal Tutor, Homework Help, Review Vocabulary

1 Focus

Vertical Alignment

Before Lesson 8-5 Use similar triangles to measure distances indirectly.

Lesson 8-5 Solve problems involving angles of elevation and depression. Use angles of elevation and depression to find the distance between two objects.

After Lesson 8-5 Use functions such as trigonometric to model real-life data.

2 Teach

Scaffolding Questions

Have students read the **Why?** section of the lesson.

Ask:

- What two rays form the angle of elevation? One ray is from the ball to the base of the goal post, and the other is from the ball to the horizontal bar.
- What values could you reasonably expect the angle of elevation to be? Sample answer: 30° to 60°
- Would the angle of elevation be greater if the ball were placed closer to or farther away from the goalpost? closer

LESSON 8-5 Angles of Elevation and Depression

Then

- You used similar triangles to measure distances indirectly.

Now

1. Solve problems involving angles of elevation and depression.
2. Use angles of elevation and depression to find the distance between two objects.

Why?

- To make a field goal, a kicker must kick the ball with enough force and at an appropriate angle of elevation to ensure that the ball will reach the goal post at a level high enough to make it over the horizontal bar. This angle must change depending on the initial placement of the ball away from the base of the goalpost.

NewVocabulary
angle of elevation
angle of depression

Common Core State Standards

Content Standards
G.SRT.8 Use trigonometric ratios and the Pythagorean Theorem to solve right triangles in applied problems. ★

Mathematical Practices
4 Model with mathematics.
1 Make sense of problems and persevere in solving them.

1 Angles of Elevation and Depression

An **angle of elevation** is the angle formed by a horizontal line and an observer's line of sight to an object above the horizontal line. An **angle of depression** is the angle formed by a horizontal line and an observer's line of sight to an object below the horizontal line.

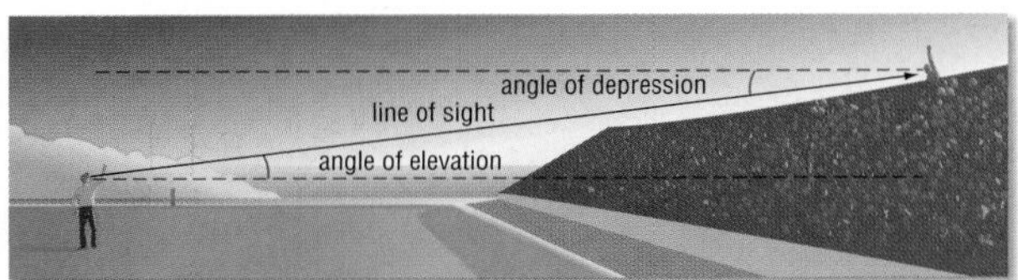

Horizontal lines are parallel, so the angle of elevation and the angle of depression in the diagram are congruent by the Alternate Interior Angles Theorem.

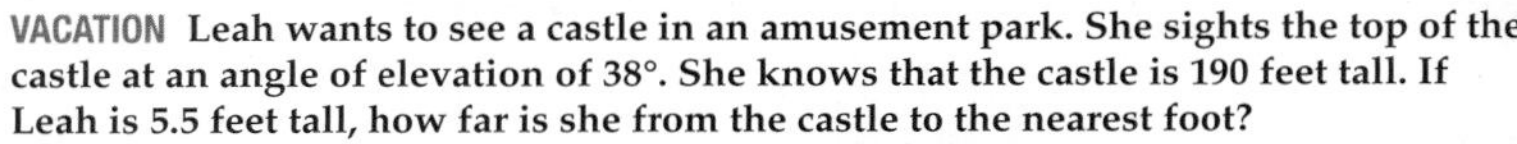

Example 1 Angle of Elevation

VACATION Leah wants to see a castle in an amusement park. She sights the top of the castle at an angle of elevation of 38°. She knows that the castle is 190 feet tall. If Leah is 5.5 feet tall, how far is she from the castle to the nearest foot?

Make a sketch to represent the situation.

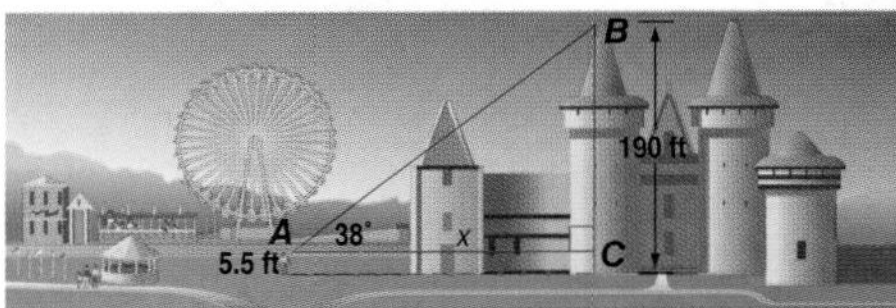

Since Leah is 5.5 feet tall, $BC = 190 - 5.5$ or 184.5 feet. Let x represent the distance from Leah to the castle, AC.

$\tan A = \frac{BC}{AC}$ — $\tan = \frac{\text{opposite}}{\text{adjacent}}$

$\tan 38° = \frac{184.5}{x}$ — $m\angle A = 38$, $BC = 184.5$, $AC = x$

$x = \frac{184.5}{\tan 38°}$ — Solve for x.

$x \approx 236.1$ — Use a calculator.

Leah is about 236 feet from the castle.

Lesson 8-5 Resources

Resource	Approaching Level AL	On Level OL	Beyond Level BL	English Learners ELL
Teacher Edition	▪ Differentiated Instruction, p. 582	▪ Differentiated Instruction, pp. 581, 582	▪ Differentiated Instruction, pp. 581, 582	
Chapter Resource Masters	▪ Study Guide and Intervention, pp. 30–31 ▪ Skills Practice, p. 32 ▪ Practice, p. 33 ▪ Word Problem Practice, p. 34	▪ Study Guide and Intervention, pp. 30–31 ▪ Skills Practice, p. 32 ▪ Practice, p. 33 ▪ Word Problem Practice, p. 34 ▪ Enrichment, p. 35	▪ Practice, p. 33 ▪ Word Problem Practice, p. 34 ▪ Enrichment, p. 35	▪ Study Guide and Intervention, pp. 30–31 ▪ Skills Practice, p. 32 ▪ Practice, p. 33 ▪ Word Problem Practice, p. 34
Other	▪ 5-Minute Check 8-5 ▪ Study Notebook	▪ 5-Minute Check 8-5 ▪ Study Notebook	▪ 5-Minute Check 8-5 ▪ Study Notebook	▪ 5-Minute Check 8-5 ▪ Study Notebook

GuidedPractice

1. **FOOTBALL** The cross bar of a goalpost is 10 feet high. If a field goal attempt is made 25 yards from the base of the goalpost that clears the goal by 1 foot, what is the smallest angle of elevation at which the ball could have been kicked to the nearest degree? **8°**

Example 2 Angle of Depression

EMERGENCY A search and rescue team is airlifting people from the scene of a boating accident when they observe another person in need of help. If the angle of depression to this other person is 42° and the helicopter is 18 feet above the water, what is the horizontal distance from the rescuers to this person to the nearest foot?

Make a sketch of the situation.

Since $\overrightarrow{AB}$ and $\overline{DC}$ are parallel, $m\angle BAC = m\angle ACD$ by the Alternate Interior Angles Theorem.

Let x represent the horizontal distance from the rescuers to the person DC.

Note: Art not drawn to scale.

$\tan C = \frac{AD}{DC}$ — $\tan = \frac{\text{opposite}}{\text{adjacent}}$

$\tan 42° = \frac{18}{x}$ — $C = 42$, $AD = 18$, and $DC = x$

$x \tan 42° = 18$ — Multiply each side by x.

$x = \frac{18}{\tan 42°}$ — Divide each side by tan 42°.

$x \approx 20.0$ — Use a calculator.

The horizontal distance from the rescuers to the person is 20.0 feet.

GuidedPractice

2. **LIFEGUARDING** A lifeguard is watching a beach from a line of sight 6 feet above the ground. She sees a swimmer at an angle of depression of 8°. How far away from the tower is the swimmer? **about 43 ft**

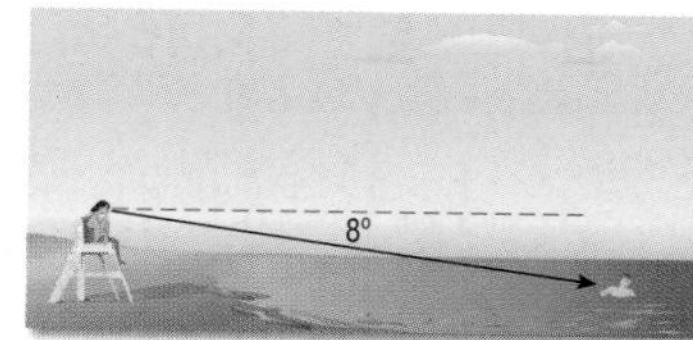

WatchOut!

Angles of Elevation and Depression To avoid mislabeling, remember that angles of elevation and depression are always formed with a horizontal line and never with a vertical line.

Math HistoryLink

Eratosthenes (276–194 B.C.) Eratosthenes was a mathematician and astronomer who was born in Cyrene, which is now Libya. He used the angle of elevation of the Sun at noon in the cities of Alexandria and Syene (now Egypt) to measure the circumference of Earth.

Source: *Encyclopaedia Britannica*

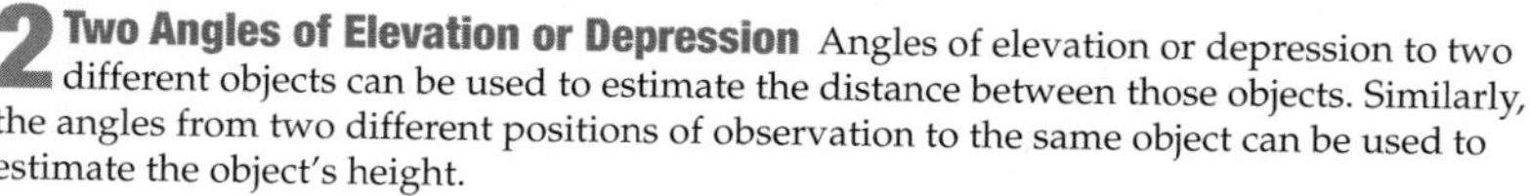

2 Two Angles of Elevation or Depression Angles of elevation or depression to two different objects can be used to estimate the distance between those objects. Similarly, the angles from two different positions of observation to the same object can be used to estimate the object's height.

DifferentiatedInstruction OL BL

Extension A 14-foot ladder is used to scale a 13-foot wall. At what angle of elevation must the ladder be situated in order to reach the top of the wall? The ladder must be situated with about a 68.2° angle of elevation in order to reach the top of the wall.

1 Angles of Elevation and Depression

Examples 1 and 2 shows how to find the angles of elevation and depression in a real-world scenario.

Teach with Tech

Computer Projector Use the computer projector as an example to find an angle of depression. Measure the distance from the ceiling to the bottom of the screen, and the horizontal distance from the projector to the screen. Then show your class how to use trigonometry to find the angle of depression.

Formative Assessment

Use the Guided Practice exercises after each example to determine students' understanding of concepts.

Additional Examples

1. **CIRCUS ACTS** At the circus, a person in the audience at ground level watches the high-wire routine. A 5-foot-6-inch tall acrobat is standing on a platform that is 25 feet off the ground. How far is the audience member from the base of the platform, if the angle of elevation from the audience member's line of sight to the top of the acrobat's head is 27°? about 60 ft

2. **DISTANCE** Maria is at the top of a cliff and sees a seal in the water. If the cliff is 40 feet above the water and the angle of depression is 52°, what is the horizontal distance from the seal to the cliff, to the nearest foot? 31 ft

Additional Examples also in Interactive Classroom PowerPoint® Presentations

2 Two Angles of Elevation or Depression

Example 3 shows how to use two angles of depression to find the distance between two objects.

Additional Example

3 DISTANCE Vernon is on the top deck of a cruise ship and observes two dolphins following each other directly away from the ship in a straight line. Vernon's position is 154 meters above sea level, and the angles of depression to the two dolphins are 35° and 36°. Find the distance between the two dolphins to the nearest meter. about 8 m

Focus on Mathematical Content

Intervention Remind students to draw upon their previous knowledge of angle relationships formed by two parallel lines cut by a transversal. Students should review these relationships.

Real-WorldLink

In the United States, lumber volume is measured in board-feet, which is defined as a piece of wood containing 144 cubic inches. Woodland owners often estimate the lumber volume of trees they own to determine how many to cut and sell.

Source: The Ohio State University School of Natural Resources

Example 3 Use Two Angles of Elevation or Depression

TREE REMOVAL **To estimate the height of a tree she wants removed, Mrs. Long sights the tree's top at a 70° angle of elevation. She then steps back 10 meters and sights the top at a 26° angle. If Mrs. Long's line of sight is 1.7 meters above the ground, how tall is the tree to the nearest meter?**

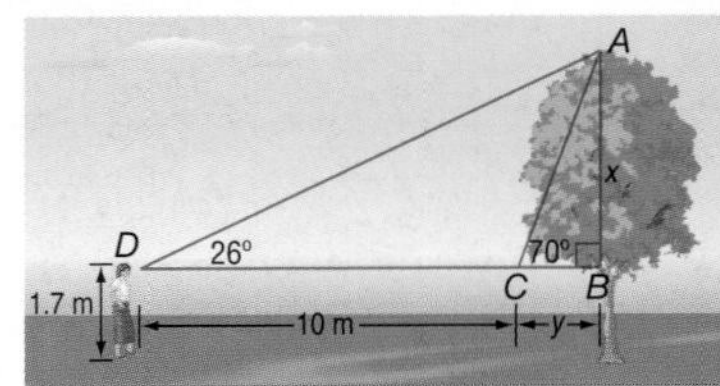

Understand $\triangle ABC$ and $\triangle ABD$ are right triangles. The height of the tree is the sum of Mrs. Long's height and AB.

Plan Since her initial distance from the tree is not given, write and solve a system of equations using both triangles. Let $AB = x$ and $CB = y$. So $DB = y + 10$ and the height of the tree is $x + 1.7$.

Solve Use $\triangle ABC$.

$$\tan 70° = \frac{x}{y} \qquad \tan = \frac{\text{opposite}}{\text{adjacent}};\ m\angle ACB = 70$$

$$y \tan 70° = x \qquad \text{Multiply each side by } y.$$

Use $\triangle ABD$.

$$\tan 26° = \frac{x}{y + 10} \qquad \tan = \frac{\text{opposite}}{\text{adjacent}};\ m\angle D = 26$$

$$(y + 10) \tan 26° = x \qquad \text{Multiply each side by } y + 10.$$

Substitute the value for x from $\triangle ABD$ in the equation for $\triangle ABC$ and solve for y.

$$y \tan 70° = x$$

$$y \tan 70° = (y + 10) \tan 26°$$

$$y \tan 70° = y \tan 26° + 10 \tan 26°$$

$$y \tan 70° - y \tan 26° = 10 \tan 26°$$

$$y(\tan 70° - \tan 26°) = 10 \tan 26°$$

$$y = \frac{10 \tan 26°}{\tan 70° - \tan 26°}$$

Use a calculator to find that $y \approx 2.16$. Using the equation from $\triangle ABC$, $x = 2.16 \tan 70°$ or about 5.9.

The height of the tree is 5.9 + 1.7 or 7.6, which is about 8 meters.

Check Substitute the value for y in the equation from $\triangle ABD$.

$x = (2.16 + 10) \tan 26°$ or about 5.9. This is the same value found using the equation from $\triangle ABC$. ✓

StudyTip

Indirect Measurement When using the angles of depression to two different objects to calculate the distance between them, it is important to remember that the two objects must lie in the same horizontal plane. In other words, one object cannot be higher or lower than the other.

GuidedPractice

3. **SKYSCRAPERS** Two buildings are sited from atop a 200-meter skyscraper. Building A is sited at a 35° angle of depression, while Building B is sighted at a 36° angle of depression. How far apart are the two buildings to the nearest meter? 10 m

DifferentiatedInstruction AL OL BL

Kinesthetic Learners Using a meterstick and a calculator, groups of students can find angles of elevation and depression for different objects in the classroom. Groups can measure one person's eye level from the floor, and the topmost height of a wall clock from the floor. The person stands 5 feet away from the clock, and the group calculates the angle of elevation from the person's line of sight to the top of the object. Repeat for items placed on the floor, and include variations like having the person stand on a platform, or placing two objects on the floor a certain distance from each other.

Check Your Understanding 

= Step-by-Step Solutions begin on page R14.

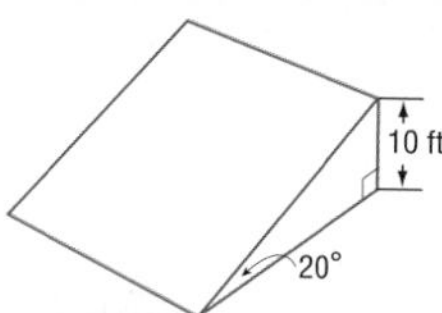

Example 1

1. **BIKING** Lenora wants to build the bike ramp shown. Find the length of the base of the ramp. **27.5 ft**

Example 2

2. **BASEBALL** A fan is seated in the upper deck of a stadium 200 feet away from home plate. If the angle of depression to the field is 62°, at what height is the fan sitting? **176.6 ft**

Example 3

3. CCSS **MODELING** Annabelle and Rich are setting up decorations for their school dance. Rich is standing 5 feet directly in front of Annabelle under a disco ball. If the angle of elevation from Annabelle to the ball is 40° and Rich to the ball is 50°, how high is the disco ball? **14.2 ft**

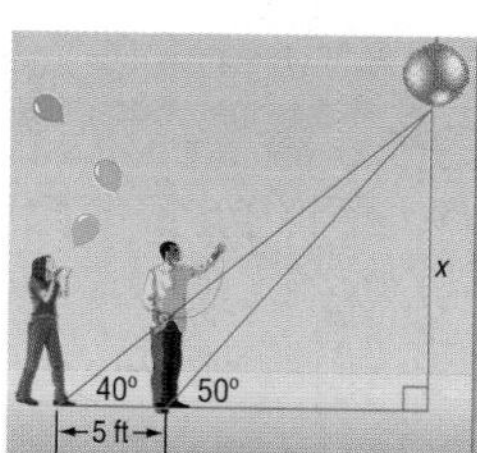

Practice and Problem Solving

Extra Practice is on page R8.

Example 1

4. **HOCKEY** A hockey player takes a shot 20 feet away from a 5-foot goal. If the puck travels at a 15° angle of elevation toward the center of the goal, will the player score? **no; 5.4 > 5**

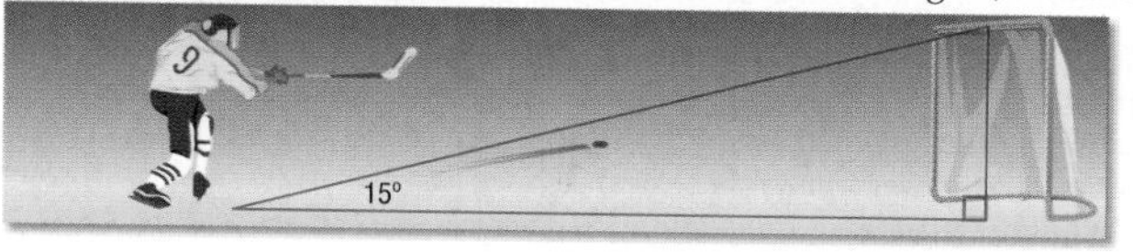

5. **MOUNTAINS** Find the angle of elevation to the peak of a mountain for an observer who is 155 meters from the mountain if the observer's eye is 1.5 meters above the ground and the mountain is 350 meters tall. **66°**

Example 2

6. **WATERPARK** Two water slides are 50 meters apart on level ground. From the top of the taller slide, you can see the top of the shorter slide at an angle of depression of 15°. If you know that the top of the other slide is approximately 15 meters above the ground, about how far above the ground are you? Round to the nearest tenth of a meter. **28.4 m**

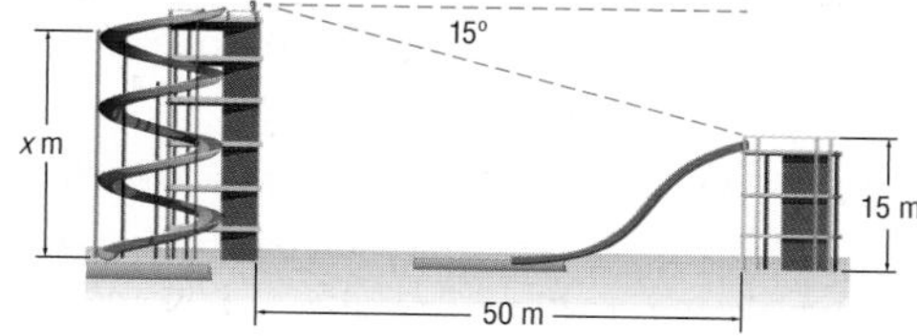

7. **AVIATION** Due to a storm, a pilot flying at an altitude of 528 feet has to land. If he has a horizontal distance of 2000 feet to land, at what angle of depression should he land? **14.8°**

Example 3

8. **PYRAMIDS** Miko and Tyler are visiting the Great Pyramid in Egypt. From where Miko is standing, the angle of elevation to the top of the pyramid is 48.6°. From Tyler's position, the angle of elevation is 50°. If they are standing 20 feet apart, and they are each 5 feet 6 inches tall, how tall is the pyramid? **about 475.5 ft**

Differentiated Homework Options

Level	Assignment	Two-Day Option	
AL Basic	4–11, 23, 25–48	5–11 odd, 28–31	4–10 even, 23, 25–27, 32–48
OL Core	5–11 odd, 12–23, 25–48	4–11, 28–31	12–23, 25–27, 32–48
BL Advanced	12–44, (optional: 45–48)		

3 Practice

Formative Assessment

Use Exercises 1–3 to check for understanding.

Then use the chart at the bottom of this page to customize assignments for your students.

Teaching the Mathematical Practices

Modeling Mathematically proficient students can apply the mathematics they know to solve problems arising in everyday life. In Exercise 3, encourage students to analyze the figure given to see which trigonometric functions can be used.

Study Guide and Intervention

AL OL ELL

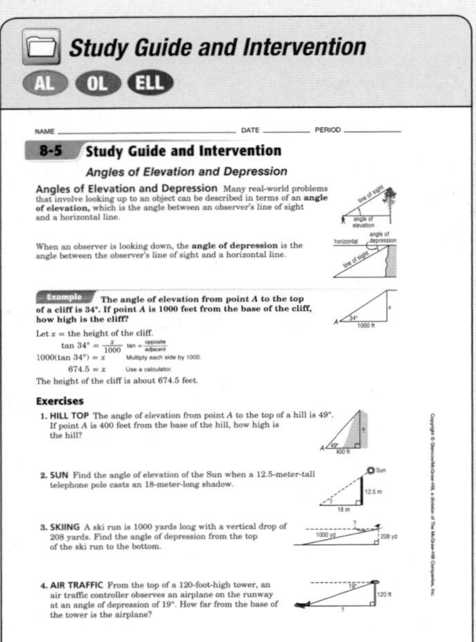

NAME ______ DATE ______ PERIOD ______

8-5 Study Guide and Intervention

Angles of Elevation and Depression

Angles of Elevation and Depression Many real-world problems that involve looking up to an object can be described in terms of an **angle of elevation**, which is the angle between an observer's line of sight and a horizontal line.

When an observer is looking down, the **angle of depression** is the angle between the observer's line of sight and a horizontal line.

Example The angle of elevation from point *A* to the top of a cliff is 34°. If point *A* is 1000 feet from the base of the cliff, how high is the cliff?

Let x = the height of the cliff.

$\tan 34° = \frac{x}{1000}$ $\tan = \frac{\text{opposite}}{\text{adjacent}}$

$1000(\tan 34°) = x$ Multiply each side by 1000.

$674.5 = x$ Use a calculator.

The height of the cliff is about 674.5 feet.

Exercises

1. **HILL TOP** The angle of elevation from point *A* to the top of a hill is 49°. If point *A* is 400 feet from the base of the hill, how high is the hill?
2. **SUN** Find the angle of elevation of the Sun when a 12.5-meter-tall telephone pole casts an 18-meter-long shadow.
3. **SKIING** A ski run is 1000 yards long with a vertical drop of 208 yards. Find the angle of depression from the top of the ski run to the bottom.
4. **AIR TRAFFIC** From the top of a 120-foot-high tower, an air traffic controller observes an airplane on the runway at an angle of depression of 19°. How far from the base of the tower is the airplane?

Practice

AL OL BL ELL

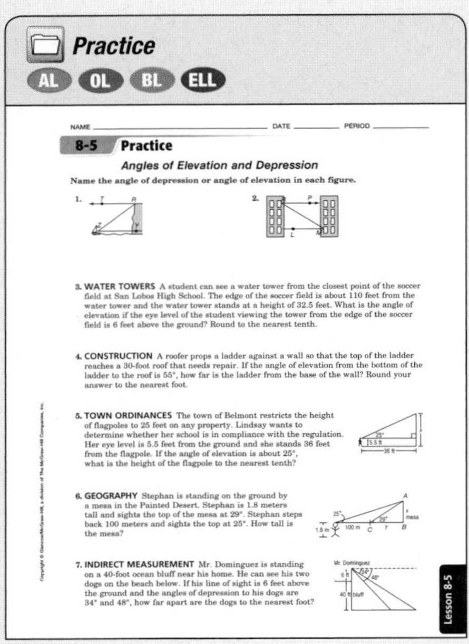

NAME ______ DATE ______ PERIOD ______

8-5 Practice

Angles of Elevation and Depression

Name the angle of depression or angle of elevation in each figure.

1. 2.

3. **WATER TOWERS** A student can see a water tower from the closest point of the soccer field at San Lobos High School. The edge of the soccer field is about 110 feet from the water tower and the water tower stands at a height of 32.5 feet. What is the angle of elevation if the eye level of the student viewing the tower from the edge of the soccer field is 6 feet above the ground? Round to the nearest tenth.
4. **CONSTRUCTION** A roofer props a ladder against a wall so that the top of the ladder reaches a 30-foot roof that needs repair. If the angle of elevation from the bottom of the ladder to the roof is 55°, how far is the ladder from the base of the wall? Round your answer to the nearest foot.
5. **TOWN ORDINANCES** The town of Belmont restricts the height of flagpoles to 25 feet on any property. Lindsay wants to determine whether her school is in compliance with the regulation. Her eye level is 5.5 feet from the ground and she stands 36 feet from the flagpole. If the angle of elevation is about 25°, what is the height of the flagpole to the nearest tenth?
6. **GEOGRAPHY** Stephan is standing on the ground by a mesa in the Painted Desert. Stephan is 1.8 meters tall and sights the top of the mesa at 29°. Stephan steps back 100 meters and sights the top at 25°. How tall is the mesa?
7. **INDIRECT MEASUREMENT** Mr. Dominguez is standing on a 40-foot ocean bluff near his home. He can see his two dogs on the beach below. If his line of sight is 6 feet above the ground and the angles of depression to his dogs are 34° and 48°, how far apart are the dogs to the nearest foot?

Word Problem Practice

AL OL BL ELL

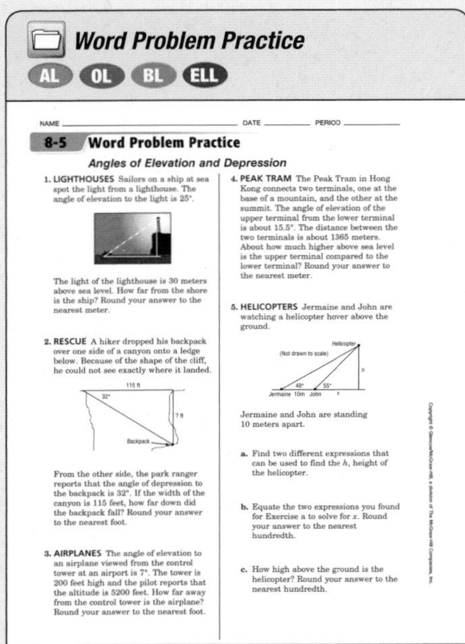

NAME ______ DATE ______ PERIOD ______

8-5 Word Problem Practice

Angles of Elevation and Depression

1. **LIGHTHOUSES** Sailors on a ship at sea spot the light from a lighthouse. The angle of elevation to the light is 25°.

   The light of the lighthouse is 30 meters above sea level. How far from the shore is the ship? Round your answer to the nearest meter.
2. **RESCUE** A hiker dropped his backpack over one side of a canyon onto a ledge below. Because of the shape of the cliff, he could not see exactly where it landed.

   From the other side, the park ranger reports that the angle of depression to the backpack is 32°. If the width of the canyon is 115 feet, how far down did the backpack fall? Round your answer to the nearest foot.
3. **AIRPLANES** The angle of elevation to an airplane viewed from the control tower at an airport is 7°. The tower is 200 feet high and the pilot reports that the altitude is 5200 feet. How far away from the control tower is the airplane? Round your answer to the nearest foot.
4. **PEAK TRAM** The Peak Tram in Hong Kong connects two terminals, one at the base of a mountain, and the other at the summit. The angle of elevation of the upper terminal from the lower terminal is about 15.5°. The distance between the two terminals is about 1365 meters. About how much higher above sea level is the upper terminal compared to the lower terminal? Round your answer to the nearest meter.
5. **HELICOPTERS** Jermaine and John are watching a helicopter hover above the ground.

   Jermaine and John are standing 10 meters apart.

   a. Find two different expressions that can be used to find the *h*, height of the helicopter.

   b. Equate the two expressions you found for Exercise a to solve for *x*. Round your answer to the nearest hundredth.

   c. How high above the ground is the helicopter? Round your answer to the nearest hundredth.

9. **DIVING** Austin is standing on the high dive at the local pool. Two of his friends are in the water as shown. If the angle of depression to one of his friends is 40°, and 30° to his other friend who is 5 feet beyond the first, how tall is the platform? **9.3 ft**

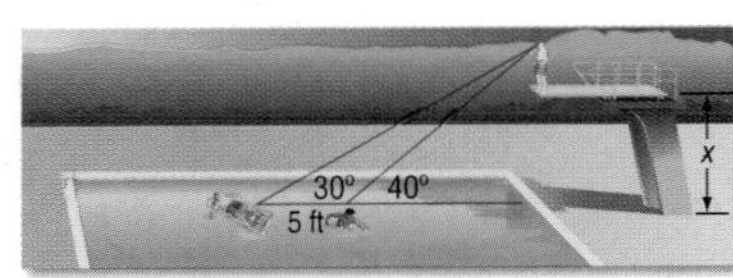

10. **BASKETBALL** Claire and Marisa are both waiting to get a rebound during a basketball game. If the height of the basketball hoop is 10 feet, the angle of elevation between Claire and the goal is 35°, and the angle of elevation between Marisa and the goal is 25°, how far apart are they standing? **7.2 ft**

11. **RIVERS** Hugo is standing in the top of St. Louis' Gateway Arch, looking down on the Mississippi River. The angle of depression to the closer bank is 45° and the angle of depression to the farther bank is 18°. The arch is 630 feet tall. Estimate the width of the river at that point. **about 1309 ft**

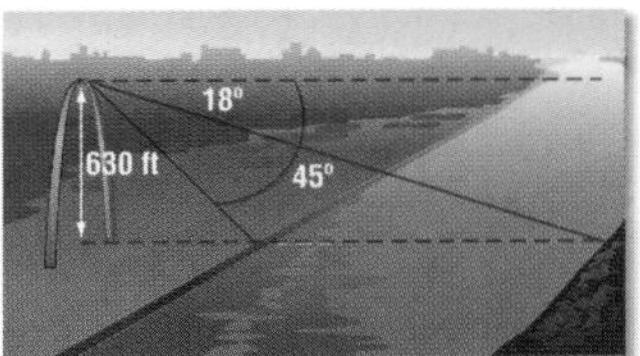

B 12. **CCSS MODELING** The Unzen Volcano in Japan has a magma reservoir located 15 kilometers beneath the Chijiwa Bay, located east of the volcano. A magma channel, which connects the reservoir to the volcano, rises at a 40° angle of elevation toward the volcano. What length of magma channel is below sea level? **23.3 km**

13. **BRIDGES** Suppose you are standing in the middle of the platform of the world's longest suspension bridge, the Akashi Kaikyo Bridge. If the height from the top of the platform holding the suspension cables is 297 meters, and the length from the platform to the center of the bridge is 995 meters, what is the angle of depression from the center of the bridge to the platform? **16.6°**

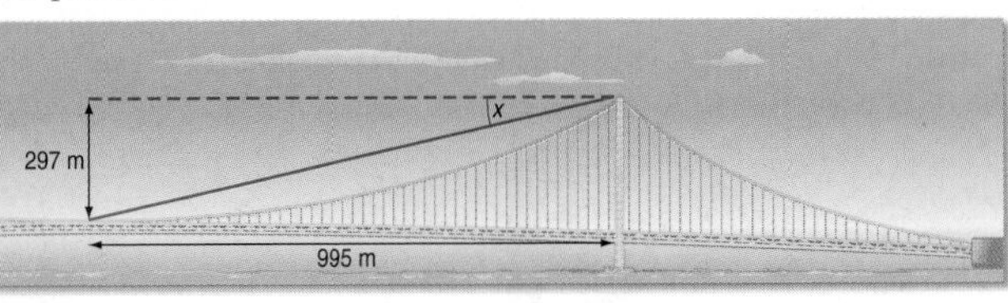

14. Little Gull Island Lighthouse has a span of 866 ft, and Plum Island Lighthouse has a span of 974 ft. So, the light from Plum Island Lighthouse would reach the boat.

14. **LIGHTHOUSES** Little Gull Island Lighthouse shines a light from a height of 91 feet with a 6° angle of depression. Plum Island Lighthouse, 1800 feet away, shines a light from a height of 34 feet with a 2° angle of depression. Which light will reach a boat that sits exactly between Little Gull Island Lighthouse and Plum Island Lighthouse?

15. **TOURISM** From the position of the bus on the street, the L'arc de Triomphe is at an angle of 34°. If the arc is 162 feet tall, how far away is the bus? Round to the nearest tenth. **240.2 ft**

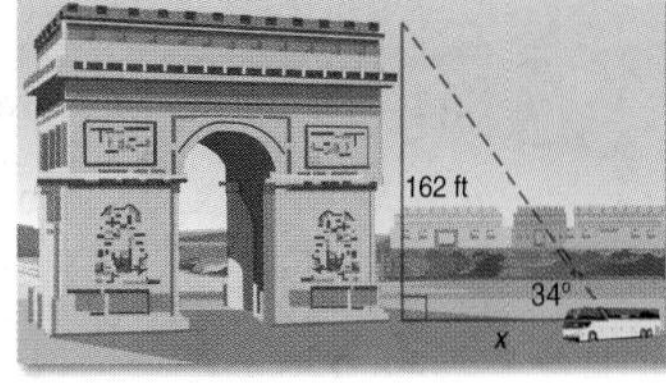

Enrichment

OL BL

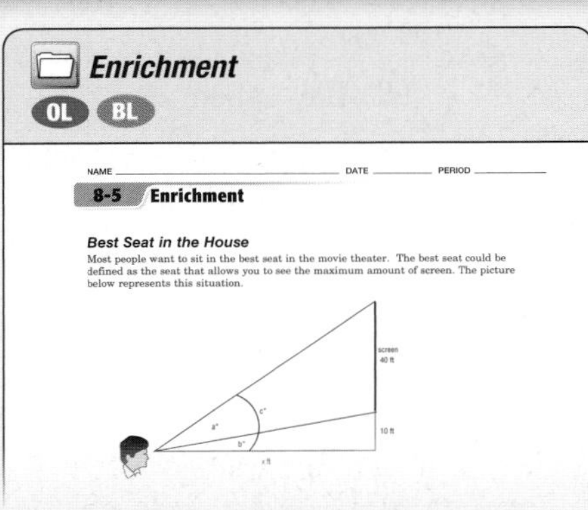

NAME ______ DATE ______ PERIOD ______

8-5 Enrichment

Best Seat in the House

Most people want to sit in the best seat in the movie theater. The best seat could be defined as the seat that allows you to see the maximum amount of screen. The picture below represents this situation.

584 | Lesson 8-5 | Angles of Elevation and Depression

16. MAINTENANCE Two telephone repair workers arrive at a location to restore electricity after a power outage. One of the workers climbs up the telephone pole while the other worker stands 10 feet to left of the pole. If the terminal box is located 30 feet above ground on the pole and the angle of elevation from the truck to the repair worker is 70°, how far is the worker on the ground standing from the truck? **20.9 ft**

17. PHOTOGRAPHY A digital camera with a panoramic lens is described as having a view with an angle of elevation of 38°. If the camera is on a 3-foot tripod aimed directly at a 124-foot-tall monument, how far from the monument should you place the tripod to see the entire monument in your photograph? **154.9 ft**

18. CCSS MODELING As a part of their weather unit, Anoki's science class took a hot air balloon ride. As they passed over a fenced field, the angle of depression of the closer side of the fence was 32°, and the angle of depression of the farther side of the fence was 27°. If the height of the balloon was 800 feet, estimate the width of the field. **289.8 ft**

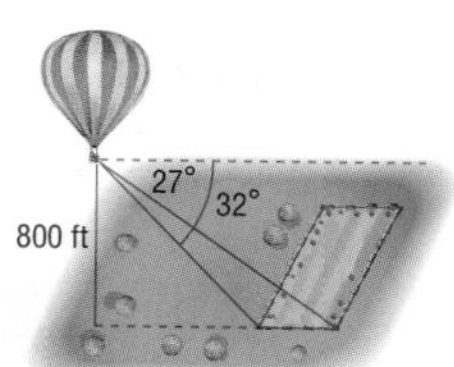

19. MARATHONS The Badwater Ultramarathon is a race that begins at the lowest point in California, Death Valley, and ends at the highest point of the state, Mount Whitney. The race starts at a depth of 86 meters below sea level and ends 2530 meters above sea level.

a. Determine the angle of elevation to Mount Whitney if the horizontal distance from the base to the peak is 1200 meters. **≈64.6°**

b. If the angle of depression to Death Valley is 38°, what is the horizontal distance from sea level? **≈110.1 m**

C 20. AMUSEMENT PARKS India, Enrique, and Trina went to an amusement park while visiting Japan. They went on a Ferris wheel that was 100 meters in diameter and on an 80-meter cliff-dropping slide.

a. When Enrique and Trina are at the topmost point on the Ferris wheel shown below, how far are they from India? **119.2 m**

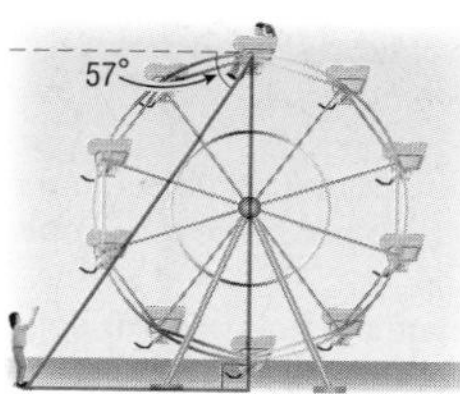

b. If the cliff-dropping ride has an angle of depression of 46°, how long is the slide? **111.2 m**

CCSS Teaching the Mathematical Practices

Modeling Mathematically proficient students can apply the mathematics they know to solve problems arising in everyday life. In Exercises 12 and 18, encourage students to analyze the figure given to see which trigonometric functions can be used.

connectED.mcgraw-hill.com 585

Exercise Alert

Ruler and Protractor Exercise 22 requires the use of a ruler and a protractor.

Multiple Representations

In Exercise 22, students use geometric sketches, a table, and verbal description to investigate the relationships between the sides and angles of a triangle.

WatchOut!

Error Analysis In Exercise 23, Terrence does not explain the angle of depression correctly. Students should remember that the angle of elevation and the angle of depression are congruent.

Additional Answers

22a. Sample answer:

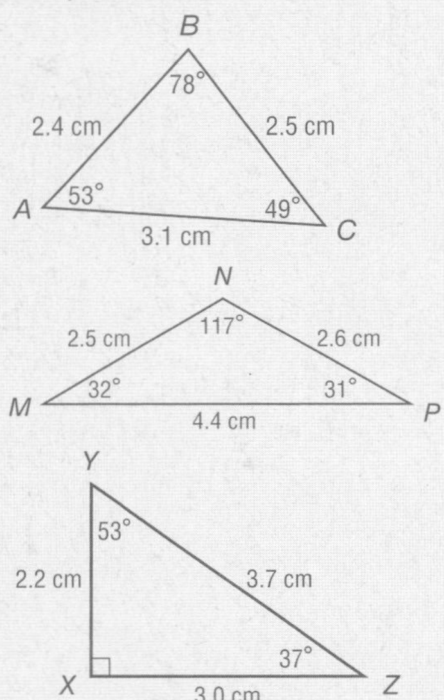

22c. Sample answer: The ratio of the sine of an angle to the length of the leg opposite that angle is approximately equal for all three angles of a triangle.

23. Rodrigo; sample answer: Since your horizontal line of sight is parallel to the other person's horizontal line of sight, the angles of elevation and depression are congruent according to the Alternate Interior Angles Theorem.

21. **DARTS** Kelsey and José are throwing darts from a distance of 8.5 feet. The center of the bull's-eye on the dartboard is 5.7 feet from the floor. José throws from a height of 6 feet, and Kelsey throws from a height of 5 feet. What are the angles of elevation or depression from which each must throw to get a bull's-eye? Ignore other factors such as air resistance, velocity, and gravity.

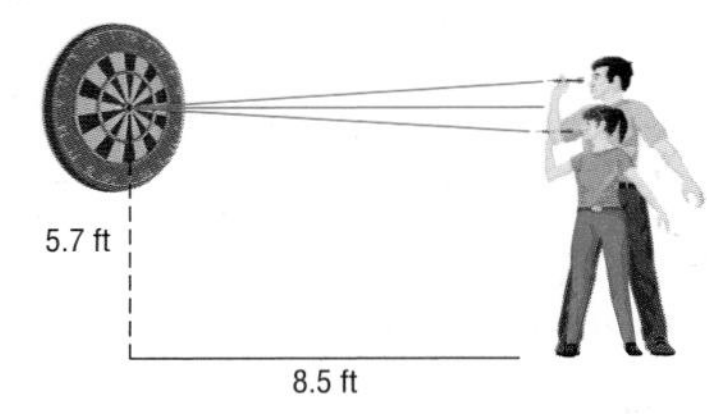

José throws at an angle of depression of 2.02°. Kelsey throws at an angle of elevation of 4.71°.

22. **MULTIPLE REPRESENTATIONS** In this problem, you will investigate relationships between the sides and angles of triangles.

a. **Geometric** Draw three triangles. Make one acute, one obtuse, and one right. Label one triangle *ABC*, a second *MNP*, and the third *XYZ*. Label the side lengths and angle measures of each triangle. See margin.

b. **Tabular** Copy and complete the table below. Sample answers given.

Triangle	Ratios		
ABC	$\frac{\sin A}{BC} = 0.3$	$\frac{\sin B}{CA} = 0.3$	$\frac{\sin C}{AB} = 0.3$
MNP	$\frac{\sin M}{NP} = 0.2$	$\frac{\sin N}{PM} = 0.2$	$\frac{\sin P}{MN} = 0.2$
XYZ	$\frac{\sin X}{YZ} = 0.3$	$\frac{\sin Y}{ZX} = 0.3$	$\frac{\sin Z}{XY} = 0.3$

c. **Verbal** Make a conjecture about the ratio of the sine of an angle to the length of the leg opposite that angle for a given triangle. See margin.

H.O.T. Problems Use Higher-Order Thinking Skills

23. **ERROR ANALYSIS** Terrence and Rodrigo are trying to determine the relationship between angles of elevation and depression. Terrence says that if you are looking up at someone with an angle of elevation of 35°, then they are looking down at you with an angle of depression of 55°, which is the complement of 35°. Rodrigo disagrees and says that the other person would be looking down at you with an angle of depression equal to your angle of elevation, or 35°. Is either of them correct? Explain. See margin.

24. **CHALLENGE** Find the value of *x*. Round to the nearest tenth. 7.9

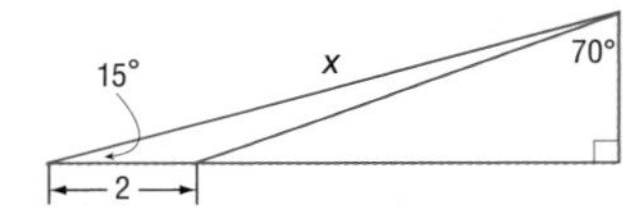

25. **CCSS REASONING** Classify the statement below as *true* or *false*. Explain. See margin.

As a person moves closer to an object he or she is sighting, the angle of elevation increases.

26. **WRITE A QUESTION** A classmate finds the angle of elevation of an object, but she is trying to find the angle of depression. Write a question to help her solve the problem.

26. Sample answer: What is the relationship between the angle of elevation and angle of depression?

27. **WRITING IN MATH** Describe a way that you can estimate the height of an object without using trigonometry by choosing your angle of elevation. Explain your reasoning. See margin.

25. True; sample answer: As a person moves closer to an object, the horizontal distance decreases, but the height of the object is constant. The tangent ratio will increase, and therefore the measure of the angle also increases.

27. Sample answer: If you sight something with a 45° angle of elevation, you don't have to use trigonometry to determine the height of the object. Since the legs of a 45°-45°-90° are congruent, the height of the object will be the same as your horizontal distance from the object.

Standardized Test Practice

28. Ryan wanted to know the height of a cell-phone tower neighboring his property. He walked 80 feet from the base of the tower and measured the angle of elevation to the top of the tower at 54°. If Ryan is 5 feet tall, what is the height of the cell-phone tower? **D**

A 52 ft
B 63 ft
C 110 ft
D 115 ft

29. SHORT RESPONSE A searchlight is 6500 feet from a weather station. If the angle of elevation to the spot of light on the clouds above the station is 45°, how high is the cloud ceiling? **6500 ft**

30. ALGEBRA What is the solution of this system of equations? **G**

$$2x - 4y = -12$$
$$-x + 4y = 8$$

F (4, 4)
G (−4, 1)
H (−4, −4)
J (1, −4)

31. SAT/ACT A triangle has sides in the ratio of 5:12:13. What is the measure of the triangle's smallest angle in degrees? **B**

A 13.34
B 22.62
C 34.14
D 42.71
E 67.83

Spiral Review

Express each ratio as a fraction and as a decimal to the nearest hundredth. (Lesson 8-4)

32. $\sin C$ $\frac{15}{25} = 0.60$
33. $\tan A$ $\frac{20}{15} = 1.33$
34. $\cos C$ $\frac{20}{25} = 0.80$
35. $\tan C$ $\frac{15}{20} = 0.75$
36. $\cos A$ $\frac{15}{25} = 0.60$
37. $\sin A$ $\frac{20}{25} = 0.80$

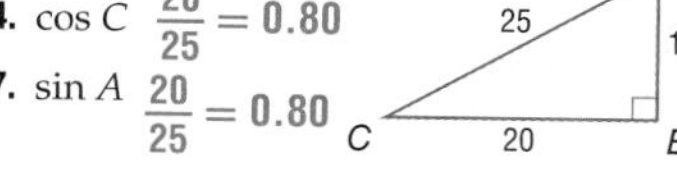

38. LANDSCAPING Imani needs to determine the height of a tree. Holding a drafter's 45° triangle so that one leg is horizontal, she sights the top of the tree along the hypotenuse, as shown at the right. If she is 6 yards from the tree and her eyes are 5 feet from the ground, find the height of the tree. (Lesson 8-3) **23 ft**

PROOF **Write a two-column proof.** (Lesson 7-5) **39–40. See margin.**

39. Given: $\overline{CD}$ bisects $\angle ACB$.
By construction, $\overline{AE} \parallel \overline{CD}$.
Prove: $\frac{AD}{DB} = \frac{AC}{BC}$

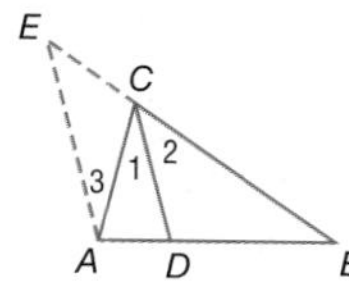

40. Given: $\overline{JF}$ bisects $\angle EFG$.
$\overline{EH} \parallel \overline{FG}$, $\overline{EF} \parallel \overline{HG}$
Prove: $\frac{EK}{KF} = \frac{GJ}{JF}$

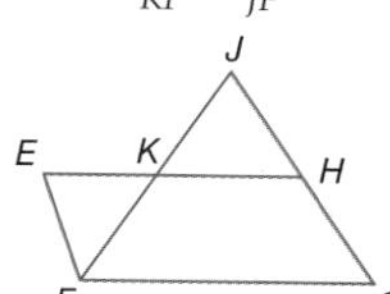

COORDINATE GEOMETRY **Find the coordinates of the centroid of each triangle.** (Lesson 5-2)

41. $A(2, 2)$, $B(7, 8)$, $C(12, 2)$ **(7, 4)**
42. $X(-3, -2)$, $Y(1, -12)$, $Z(-7, -7)$ **(−3, −7)**
43. $A(-1, 11)$, $B(-5, 1)$, $C(-9, 6)$ **(−5, 6)**
44. $X(4, 0)$, $Y(-2, 4)$, $Z(0, 6)$ $\left(\frac{2}{3}, 3\frac{1}{3}\right)$

Skills Review

Solve each proportion.

45. $\frac{1}{5} = \frac{x}{10}$ **2**
46. $\frac{2x}{11} = \frac{3}{8}$ **2.1**
47. $\frac{4x}{16} = \frac{62}{118}$ **2.1**
48. $\frac{12}{21} = \frac{45}{10x}$ **7.9**

Teaching the Mathematical Practices

Reasoning Mathematically proficient students make sense of quantities and their relationships in problem situations. In Exercise 25, encourage students to analyze the relationship between the angle of elevation and the sight line of a person watching an object.

4 Assess

Ticket Out the Door Have students create questions about either angles of elevation or depression that involve real-world situations. Each student will then pick another student's question to solve step by step to turn in.

Additional Answers

39. Proof:

Statements (Reasons)

1. $\overline{CD}$ bisects $\angle ACB$. By construction, $\overline{AE} \parallel \overline{CD}$. (Given)
2. $\frac{AD}{DB} = \frac{EC}{BC}$ (Triangle Proportionality Thm.)
3. $\angle 1 \cong \angle 2$ (Def. of ∠ Bisector)
4. $\angle 3 \cong \angle 1$ (Alt. Int. ∠s Thm.)
5. $\angle 2 \cong \angle E$ (Corr. ∠s Post.)
6. $\angle 3 \cong \angle E$ (Transitive Prop.)
7. $\overline{EC} \cong \overline{AC}$ (Isosceles △ Thm.)
8. $EC = AC$ (Def. of ≅ segments)
9. $\frac{AD}{DB} = \frac{AC}{BC}$ (Substitution)

40. Proof:

Statements (Reasons)

1. $\overline{JF}$ bisects $\angle EFG$.; $\overline{EH} \parallel \overline{FG}$, $\overline{EF} \parallel \overline{HG}$ (Given)
2. $\angle EFK \cong \angle KFG$ (Def. of ∠ bisector)
3. $\angle KFG \cong \angle JKH$ (Corr. ∠s Post.)
4. $\angle JKH \cong \angle EKF$ (Vertical ∠s are ≅.)
5. $\angle EFK \cong \angle EKF$ (Transitive Prop.)
6. $\angle FJH \cong \angle EKF$ (Alt. Int. ∠s Thm.)
7. $\angle FJH \cong \angle EFK$ (Transitive Prop.)
8. $\triangle EKF \sim \triangle GJF$ (AA Similarity)
9. $\frac{EK}{KF} = \frac{GJ}{JF}$ (Def. of ~△s)

1 Focus

Vertical Alignment

Before Lesson 8-6 Use trigonometric ratios to solve right triangles.

Lesson 8-6 Use the Law of Sines and Law of Cosines to solve a triangle.

After Lesson 8-6 Use trigonometric functions to solve problems with vectors.

2 Teach

Scaffolding Questions

Have students read the **Why?** section of the lesson.

Ask:

- What method can be used to find the height of a tree? right triangle trigonometry
- What measurements do you need to find the height of a tree? the angle of elevation and the distance to the tree
- If the tree is leaning at an angle, why can you not use right triangle trigonometry? The tree does not form a right angle with the ground.

LESSON 8-6 The Law of Sines and Law of Cosines

Then
- You used trigonometric ratios to solve right triangles.

Now
1. Use the Law of Sines to solve triangles.
2. Use the Law of Cosines to solve triangles.

Why?
- You have learned that the height or length of a tree can be calculated using *right triangle trigonometry* if you know the angle of elevation to the top of the tree and your distance from the tree. Some trees, however, grow at an angle or lean due to weather damage. To calculate the length of such trees, you must use other forms of trigonometry.

New Vocabulary
Law of Sines
Law of Cosines

Common Core State Standards

Content Standards

G.SRT.9 Derive the formula $A = \frac{1}{2}ab \sin(C)$ for the area of a triangle by drawing an auxiliary line from a vertex perpendicular to the opposite side.

G.SRT.10 Prove the Laws of Sines and Cosines and use them to solve problems.

Mathematical Practices
4 Model with mathematics.
1 Make sense of problems and persevere in solving them.

1 Law of Sines

In Lesson 8-4, you used trigonometric ratios to find side lengths and acute angle measures in *right* triangles. To find measures for nonright triangles, the definitions of sine and cosine can be extended to obtuse angles.

The **Law of Sines** can be used to find side lengths and angle measures for any triangle.

Theorem 8.10 Law of Sines

If $\triangle ABC$ has lengths a, b, and c, representing the lengths of the sides opposite the angles with measures A, B, and C, then

$$\frac{\sin A}{a} = \frac{\sin B}{b} = \frac{\sin C}{c}.$$

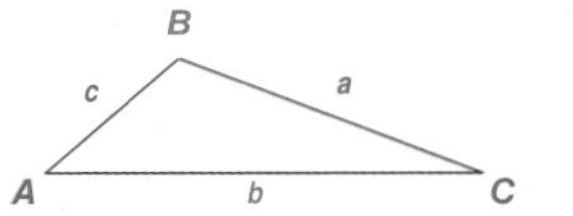

You will prove one of the proportions for Theorem 8.10 in Exercise 45.

You can use the Law of Sines to solve a triangle if you know the measures of two angles and any side (AAS or ASA).

Example 1 Law of Sines (AAS)

Find x. Round to the nearest tenth.

We are given the measures of two angles and a nonincluded side, so use the Law of Sines to write a proportion.

$\frac{\sin A}{a} = \frac{\sin C}{c}$ Law of Sines

$\frac{\sin 97°}{16} = \frac{\sin 21°}{x}$ $m\angle A = 97$, $a = 16$, $m\angle C = 21$, $c = x$

$x \sin 97° = 16 \sin 21°$ Cross Products Property

$x = \frac{16 \sin 21°}{\sin 97°}$ Divide each side by sin 97°.

$x \approx 5.8$ Use a calculator.

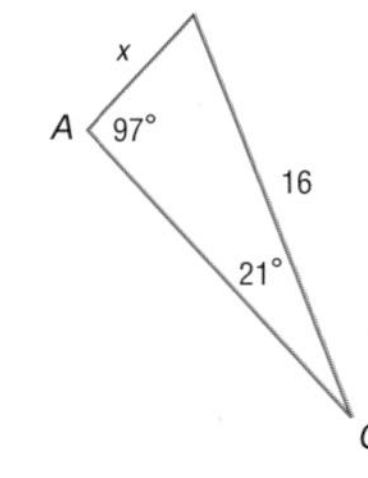

Guided Practice

1A. 7.1

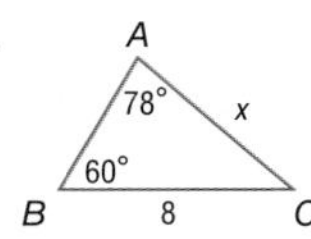

1B. 9.9

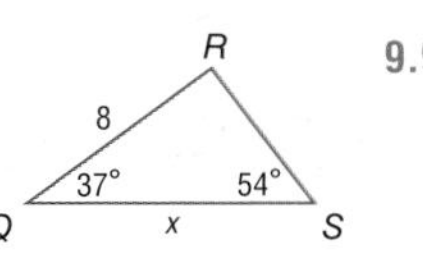

Lesson 8-5 Resources

Resource	Approaching Level AL	On Level OL	Beyond Level BL	English Learners ELL
Teacher Edition	▪ Differentiated Instruction, p. 589	▪ Differentiated Instruction, pp. 589, 591	▪ Differentiated Instruction, p. 591	
Chapter Resource Masters	▪ Study Guide and Intervention, pp. 36–37 ▪ Skills Practice, p. 38 ▪ Practice, p. 39 ▪ Word Problem Practice, p. 40	▪ Study Guide and Intervention, pp. 36–37 ▪ Skills Practice, p. 38 ▪ Practice, p. 39 ▪ Word Problem Practice, p. 40 ▪ Enrichment, p. 41 ▪ Graphing Calculator Activity, p. 42	▪ Practice, p. 39 ▪ Word Problem Practice, p. 40 ▪ Enrichment, p. 41	▪ Study Guide and Intervention, pp. 36–37 ▪ Skills Practice, p. 38 ▪ Practice, p. 39 ▪ Word Problem Practice, p. 40
Other	▪ 5-Minute Check 8-6 ▪ Study Notebook	▪ 5-Minute Check 8-6 ▪ Study Notebook	▪ 5-Minute Check 8-6 ▪ Study Notebook	▪ 5-Minute Check 8-6 ▪ Study Notebook ▪ Teaching Geometry with Manipulatives

StudyTip

Ambiguous Case You can sometimes use the Law of Sines to solve a triangle if you know the measures of two sides and a nonincluded angle (SSA). However, these three measures do not always determine exactly one triangle. You will learn more about this *ambiguous case* in Extend 8-6.

If given ASA, use the Triangle Angle Sum Theorem to first find the measure of the third angle.

Example 2 Law of Sines (ASA)

Find x. Round to the nearest tenth.

By the Triangle Angle Sum Theorem, $m\angle K = 180 - (45 + 73)$ or 62.

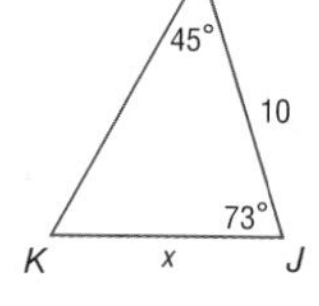

$\frac{\sin H}{h} = \frac{\sin K}{k}$	Law of Sines
$\frac{\sin 45°}{x} = \frac{\sin 62°}{10}$	$m\angle H = 45$, $h = x$, $m\angle K = 62$, $k = 10$
$10 \sin 45° = x \sin 62°$	Cross Products Property
$\frac{10 \sin 45°}{\sin 62°} = x$	Divide each side by sin 62°.
$x \approx 8.0$	Use a calculator.

GuidedPractice

2A. 7.2

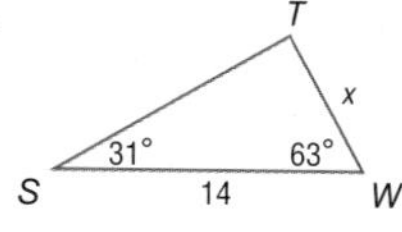

2B. 10.8

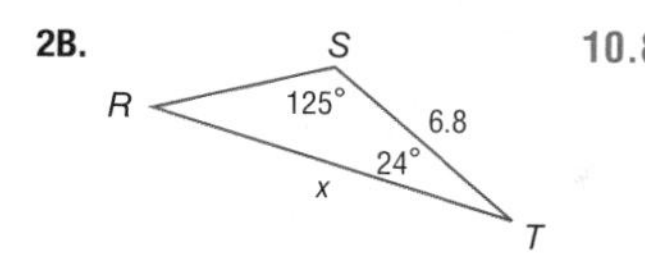

2 Law of Cosines

When the Law of Sines cannot be used to solve a triangle, the Law of Cosines may apply.

Theorem 8.11 Law of Cosines

If $\triangle ABC$ has lengths a, b, and c, representing the lengths of the sides opposite the angles with measures A, B, and C, then

$a^2 = b^2 + c^2 - 2bc \cos A$,

$b^2 = a^2 + c^2 - 2ac \cos B$, and

$c^2 = a^2 + b^2 - 2ab \cos C$.

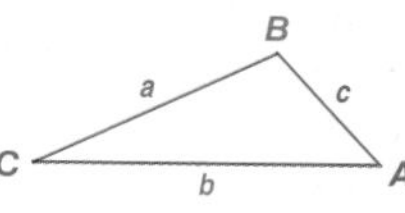

You will prove one of the equations for Theorem 8.11 in Exercise 46.

You can use the **Law of Cosines** to solve a triangle if you know the measures of two sides and the included angle (SAS).

Example 3 Law of Cosines (SAS)

Find x. Round to the nearest tenth.

We are given the measures of two sides and their included angle, so use the Law of Cosines.

$c^2 = a^2 + b^2 - 2ab \cos C$	Law of Cosines
$x^2 = 9^2 + 11^2 - 2(9)(11) \cos 28°$	Substitution
$x^2 = 202 - 198 \cos 28°$	Simplify.
$x = \sqrt{202 - 198 \cos 28°}$	Take the square root of each side.
$x \approx 5.2$	Use a calculator.

WatchOut!

Order of operations Remember to follow the order of operations when simplifying expressions. Multiplication or division must be performed before addition or subtraction. So, $202 - 198 \cos 28°$ *cannot* be simplified to $4 \cos 28°$.

DifferentiatedInstruction AL OL

Interpersonal Learners Organize students into groups of three students to work through exercises. One group member can select the exercise. The second member sets up the equation for the Law of Sines and fills in the values. The third member uses a calculator to solve the problem. Group members rotate tasks so each member participates in each responsibility.

1 The Law of Sines

Examples 1 and 2 show how to use the Law of Sines to find the missing measures of a triangle.

Formative Assessment

Use the Guided Practice exercises after each example to determine students' understanding of concepts.

Tips for New Teachers

Time-Saver In Example 2, students can also write $k \sin H = h \sin K$ and then substitute values to solve.

Additional Examples

1 Find p. Round to the nearest tenth.

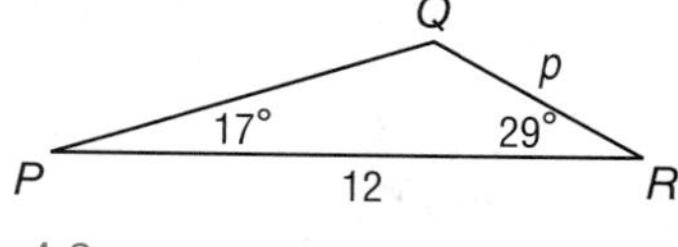

4.9

2 Find x. Round to the nearest tenth.

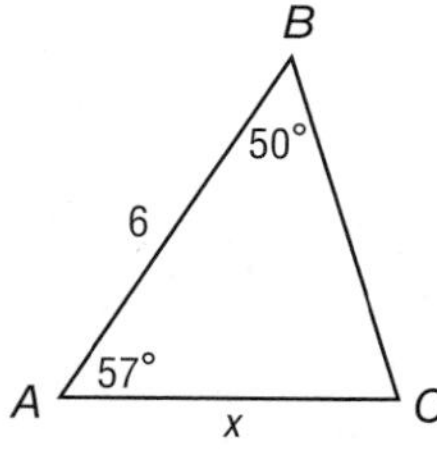

4.8

Additional Examples also in Interactive Classroom PowerPoint® Presentations

2 Law of Cosines

Examples 3 and 4 show how to use the Law of Cosines to find the missing measures of a triangle. **Examples 5 and 6** show how to use the Law of Sines and Law of Cosines to solve a triangle.

Additional Examples

3 Find x. Round to the nearest tenth.

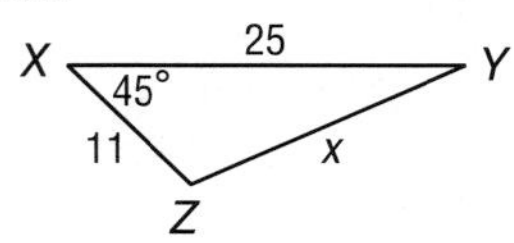

≈18.9

4 Find $m\angle L$. Round to the nearest degree.

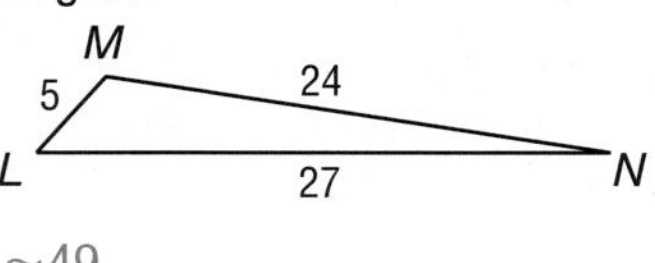

≈49

5 **AIRCRAFT** From the diagram of the airplane shown, determine the approximate width of each wing. Round to the nearest tenth meter. 16.9 m

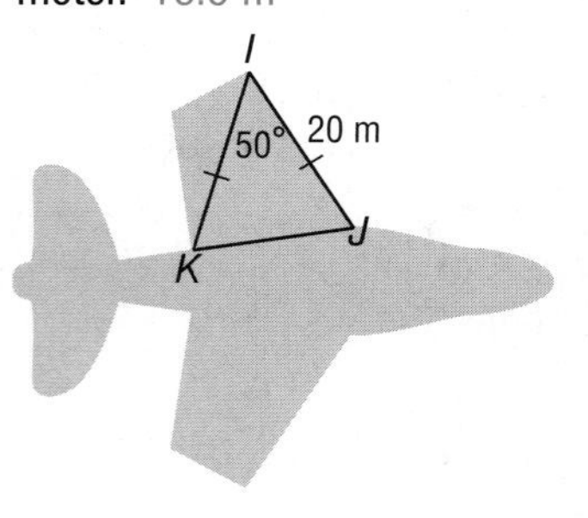

Tips for New Teachers

Reasoning Encourage students to recognize a pattern in the equations for the Law of Cosines. Show them that they can memorize one equation and obtain the other two equations by changing the letters. For example, in $a^2 = b^2 + c^2 - 2bc \cos A$, if a and b are reversed, the equation becomes $b^2 = a^2 + c^2 - 2ac \cos B$.

StudyTip

Obtuse Angles There are also values for sin A, cos A, and tan A when $A \geq 90°$. Values of the ratios for these angles can be found using the trigonometric functions on your calculator.

GuidedPractice

Find x. Round to the nearest tenth.

3A. 30.2

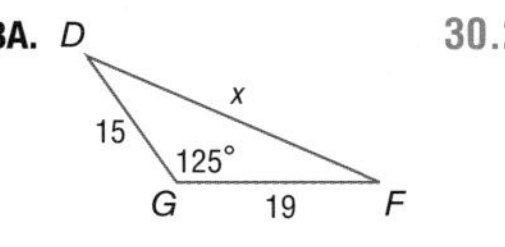

3B. 6.2

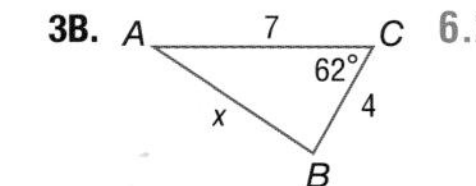

You can also use the Law of Cosines if you know three side measures (SSS).

Example 4 Law of Cosines (SSS)

Find x. Round to the nearest degree.

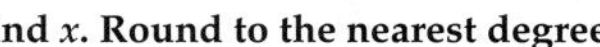

$m^2 = p^2 + q^2 - 2pq \cos M$	Law of Cosines
$8^2 = 6^2 + 3^2 - 2(6)(3) \cos x°$	Substitution
$64 = 45 - 36 \cos x°$	Simplify.
$19 = -36 \cos x°$	Subtract 45 from each side.
$\frac{19}{-36} = \cos x°$	Divide each side by −36.
$x = \cos^{-1}\left(-\frac{19}{36}\right)$	Use the inverse cosine ratio.
$x \approx 122$	Use a calculator.

GuidedPractice

4A. 63

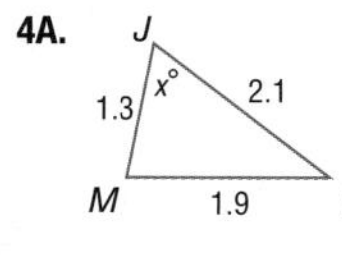

4B. 28

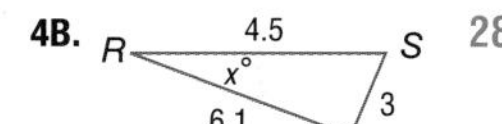

You can use the Law of Sines and Law of Cosines to solve direct and indirect measurement problems.

Real-World Example 5 Indirect Measurement

BASKETBALL Drew and Hunter are playing basketball. Drew passes the ball to Hunter when he is 26 feet from the goal and 24 feet from Hunter. How far is Hunter from the goal if the angle from the goal to Drew and then to Hunter is 34°?

Draw a diagram. Since we know two sides of a triangle and the included angle, use the Law of Cosines.

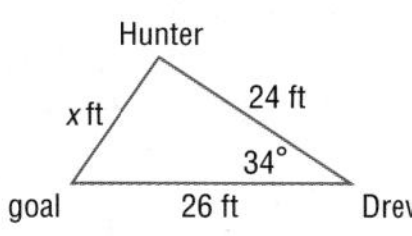

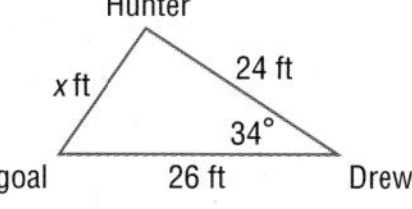

$x^2 = 24^2 + 26^2 - 2(24)(26) \cos 34°$	Law of Cosines
$x = \sqrt{1252 - 1248 \cos 34°}$	Simplify and take the positive square root of each side.
$x \approx 15$	Use a calculator.

Hunter is about 15 feet from the goal when he takes his shot.

Real-WorldLink

The first game of basketball was played at a YMCA in Springfield, Massachusetts, on December 1, 1891. James Naismith, a physical education instructor, invented the sport using a soccer ball and two half-bushel peach baskets, which is how the name *basketball* came about.

Source: *Encyclopaedia Britannica.*

Focus on Mathematical Content

Check for Reasonableness Consider $\triangle ABC$ with $m\angle A = 25$, $BC = 8$, and $AC = 16$. To find $m\angle B$, we apply the Law of Sines. Thus, $\frac{\sin 25}{8} = \frac{\sin B}{16}$. Solving for B, we get $\sin^{-1} 0.845 = B$. A calculator returns a value of 57.7 for $m\angle B$, but this answer is not reasonable, since $\angle B$ is an obtuse angle. Point out that the sine of an angle x is also equal to the sine of its supplement; that is, $\sin x = \sin (180 - x)$. When finding the measure of this obtuse angle, students will need to find the supplement of their answer. Thus, $m\angle B = 180 - 57.7$ or 122.3.

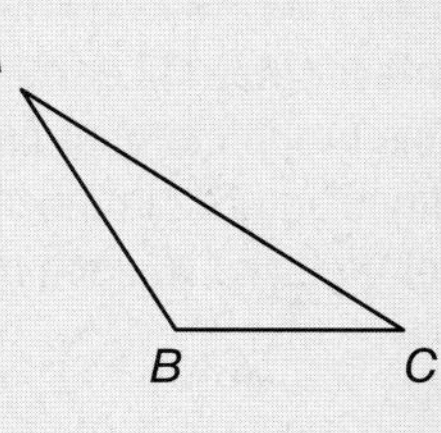

GuidedPractice

5. **LANDSCAPING** At 10 feet away from the base of a tree, the angle the top of a tree makes with the ground is 61°. If the tree grows at an angle of 78° with respect to the ground, how tall is the tree to the nearest foot? **about 13 ft**

When solving right triangles, you can use sine, cosine, or tangent. When solving other triangles, you can use the Law of Sines or the Law of Cosines, depending on what information is given.

ReadingMath

Solve a Triangle Remember that to *solve* a triangle means to find all of the missing side measures and/or angle measures.

Example 6 Solve a Triangle

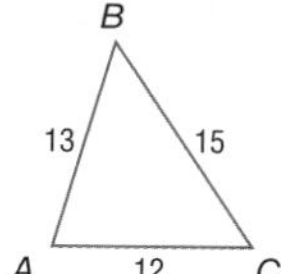

Solve triangle *ABC*. Round to the nearest degree.

Since $13^2 + 12^2 \neq 15^2$, this is not a right triangle. Since the measures of all three sides are given (SSS), begin by using the Law of Cosines to find $m\angle A$.

$a^2 = b^2 + c^2 - 2bc \cos A$	Law of Cosines
$15^2 = 12^2 + 13^2 - 2(12)(13) \cos A$	$a = 15$, $b = 12$, and $c = 13$
$225 = 313 - 312 \cos A$	Simplify.
$-88 = -312 \cos A$	Subtract 313 from each side.
$\frac{-88}{-312} = \cos A$	Divide each side by −312.
$m\angle A = \cos^{-1} \frac{88}{312}$	Use the inverse cosine ratio.
$m\angle A \approx 74$	Use a calculator.

Use the Law of Sines to find $m\angle B$.

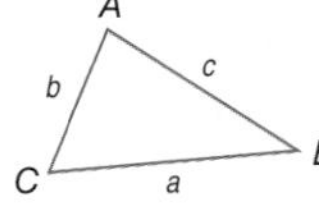

$\frac{\sin A}{a} = \frac{\sin B}{b}$	Law of Sines
$\frac{\sin 74°}{15} \approx \frac{\sin B}{12}$	$m\angle A \approx 74$, $a = 15$, and $b = 12$
$12 \sin 74° = 15 \sin B$	Cross Products Property
$\frac{12 \sin 74°}{15} = \sin B$	Divide each side by 15.
$m\angle B = \sin^{-1} \frac{12 \sin 74°}{15}$	Use the inverse sine ratio.
$m\angle B \approx 50$	Use a calculator.

By the Triangle Angle Sum Theorem, $m\angle C \approx 180 - (74 + 50)$ or 56. Therefore $m\angle A \approx 74$, $m\angle B \approx 50$, and $m\angle C \approx 56$.

WatchOut

Rounding When you round a numerical solution and then use it in later calculations, your answers may be inaccurate. Wait until after you have completed all of your calculations to round.

GuidedPractice

Solve triangle *ABC* using the given information. Round angle measures to the nearest degree and side measures to the nearest tenth.

A
b c
C a B

6A. $b = 10.2$, $c = 9.3$, $m\angle A = 26$

6B. $a = 6.4$, $m\angle B = 81$, $m\angle C = 46$

6A. $a = 4.5$, $m\angle B = 84$, $m\angle C = 70$
6B. $b = 7.9$, $c = 5.8$, $m\angle A = 53$

Additional Example

6 Solve triangle *PQR*. Round to the nearest degree.

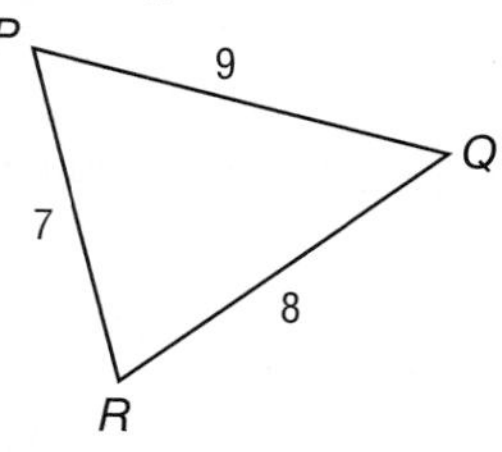

$m\angle P = 58$; $m\angle Q = 48$; $m\angle R = 74$

Teach with Tech

Document Camera Assign several word problems to the class, giving students sufficient time to work through the problems. Then choose several students to share and explain their work to the class. Be sure the students sketch a diagram and explain how they decided whether to use the Law of Sines or the Law of Cosines to solve the problem.

DifferentiatedInstruction OL BL

Extension Have the students draw right triangles. Then have them use rulers and protractors to find the length of the hypotenuse and the measure of an acute angle. The students should use sine and cosine ratios to find the lengths of the legs of the triangles. Have them check their answers by measuring the legs directly. Answers will vary.

3 Practice

Formative Assessment
Use Exercises 1–11 to check for understanding.

Then use the chart at the bottom of this page to customize assignments for your students.

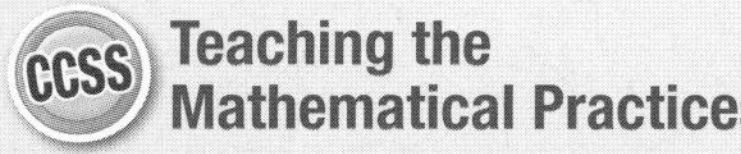

Teaching the Mathematical Practices

Structure Mathematically proficient students look closely to discern a pattern or structure. They also can step back for an overview and shift perspective. In Exercises 8–10, point out to students that none of these triangles are right triangles therefore the Pythagorean theorem and special right triangles will not apply.

ConceptSummary Solving a Triangle

To solve . . .	Given	Begin by using . . .
a right triangle	leg-leg (LL) hypotenuse-leg (HL) acute angle-hypotenuse (AH) acute angle-leg (AL)	tangent ratio sine or cosine ratio sine or cosine ratio sine, cosine, or tangent ratios
any triangle	angle-angle-side (AAS) angle-side-angle (ASA) side-angle-side (SAS) side-side-side (SSS)	Law of Sines Law of Sines Law of Cosines Law of Cosines

Check Your Understanding

= Step-by-Step Solutions begin on page R14.

Examples 1–2 Find x. Round angle measures to the nearest degree and side measures to the nearest tenth.

1. 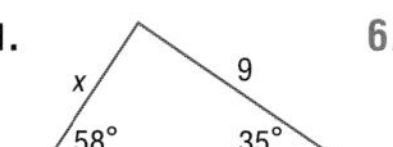

6.1

2. 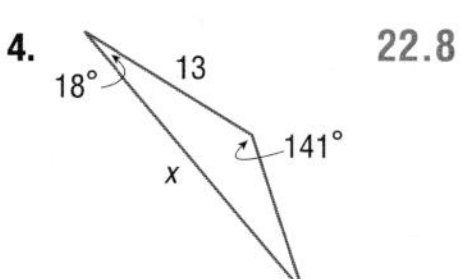

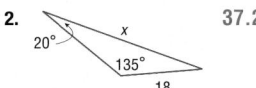

37.2

3. 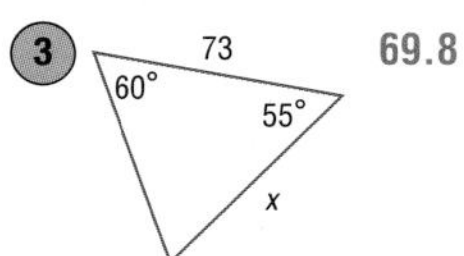

69.8

4. 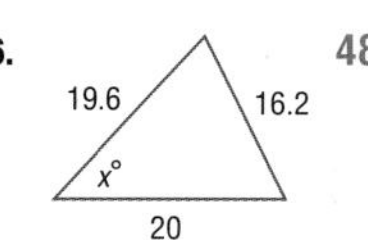

22.8

Examples 3–4 **5.** 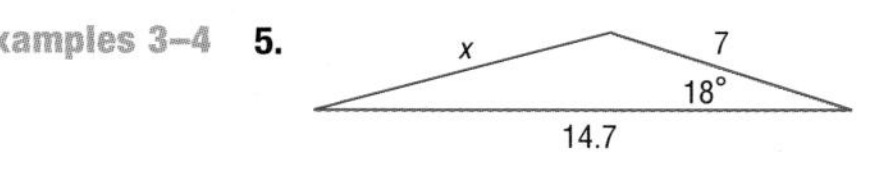

8.3

6.
19.6 16.2 $x°$ 20
48

Example 5 **7. SAILING** Determine the length of the bottom edge, or foot, of the sail. 47.1 ft

47° 55 ft 62 ft foot

8. $m\angle B = 77$, $AB \approx 7.8$, $BC \approx 4.4$

9. $m\angle N = 42$, $MP \approx 35.8$, $NP \approx 24.3$

10. $m\angle X \approx 63$, $m\angle Y \approx 54$, $XY \approx 9.9$

Example 6  **STRUCTURE** Solve each triangle. Round angle measures to the nearest degree and side measures to the nearest tenth.

8. 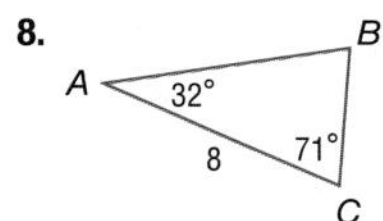

9. 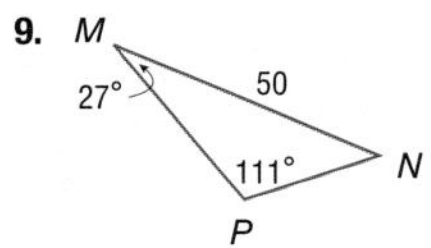

10. 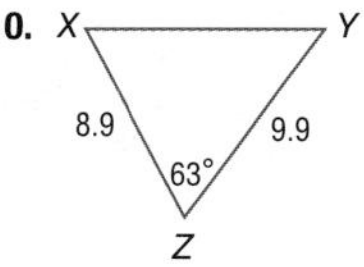

11. Solve $\triangle DEF$ if $DE = 16$, $EF = 21.6$, $FD = 20$. $m\angle D \approx 73$, $m\angle E \approx 62$, $m\angle F \approx 45$

Differentiated Homework Options

Level	Assignment	Two-Day Option	
AL Basic	12–42, 54, 56–73	13–41 odd, 59–62	12–42 even, 54, 56–58, 63–73
OL Core	11–49 odd, 51–54, 56–74	12–42, 59–62	43–54, 56–58, 63–73
BL Advanced	43–70, (71–73 optional)		

Practice and Problem Solving

Extra Practice is on page R8.

Examples 1–2 Find x. Round side measures to the nearest tenth.

12. 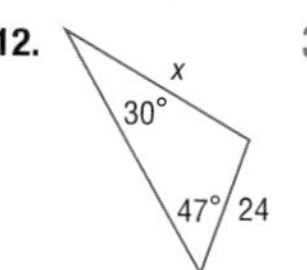

35.1

13. 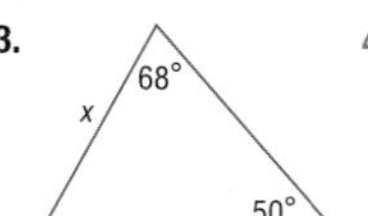

4.1

14. 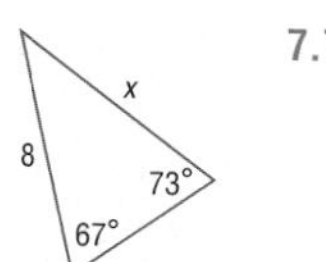

7.7

15. 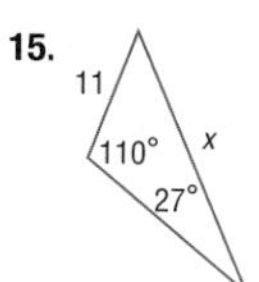

22.8

16. 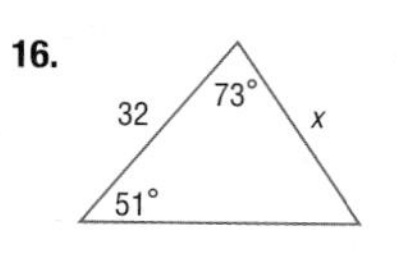

30.0

17. 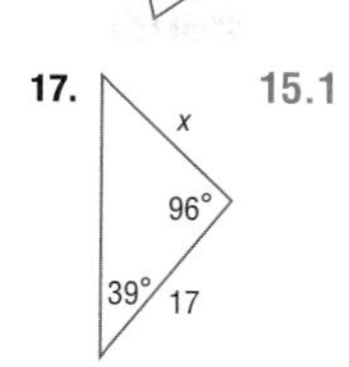

15.1

18. 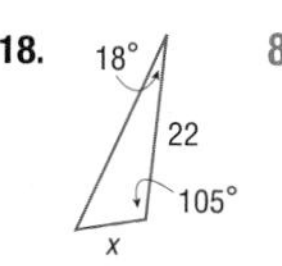

8.1

19. 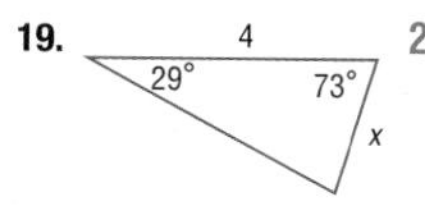

2.0

20. 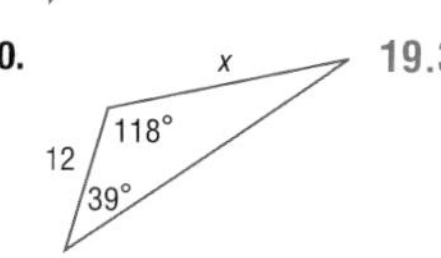

19.3

21. **CCSS MODELING** Angelina is looking at the Big Dipper through a telescope. From her view, the cup of the constellation forms a triangle that has measurements shown on the diagram at the right. Use the Law of Sines to determine distance between A and C. 2.8 in.

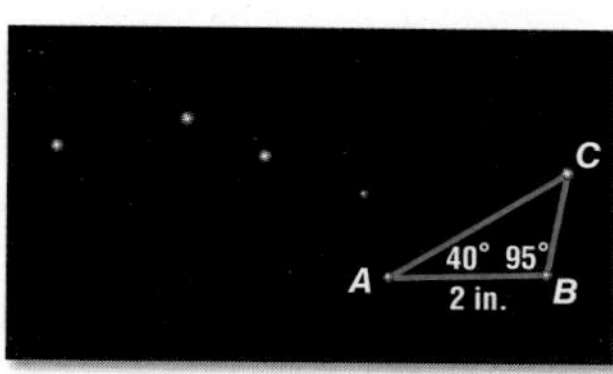

Examples 3–4 Find x. Round angle measures to the nearest degree and side measures to the nearest tenth.

22. 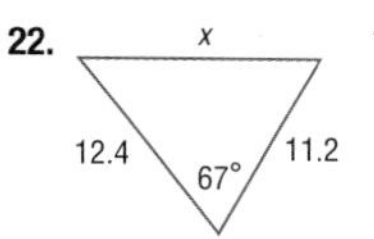

13.1

23. 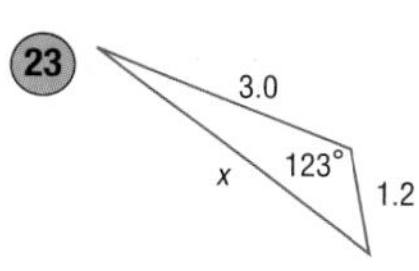

3.8

24. 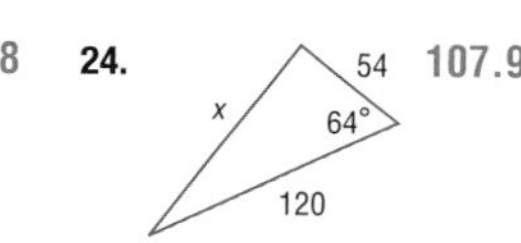

107.9

25. 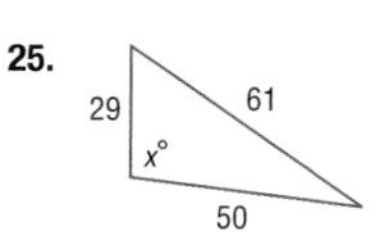

98

26. 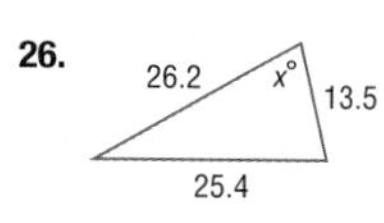

72

27. 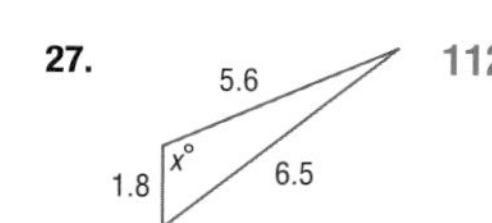

112

28. **HIKING** A group of friends who are camping decide to go on a hike. According to the map shown at the right, what is the measure of the angle between Trail 1 and Trail 2? 104

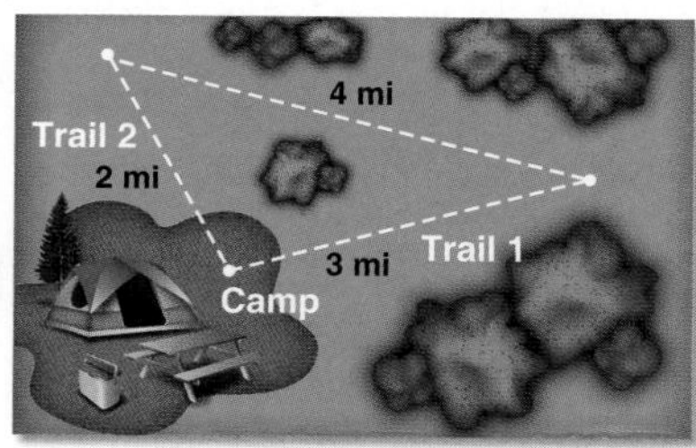

CCSS Teaching the Mathematical Practices

Modeling Mathematically proficient students can apply the mathematics they know to solve problems arising in everyday life. In Exercise 21, encourage students to use the diagram given to identify information important to solving the problem.

Enrichment
OL BL

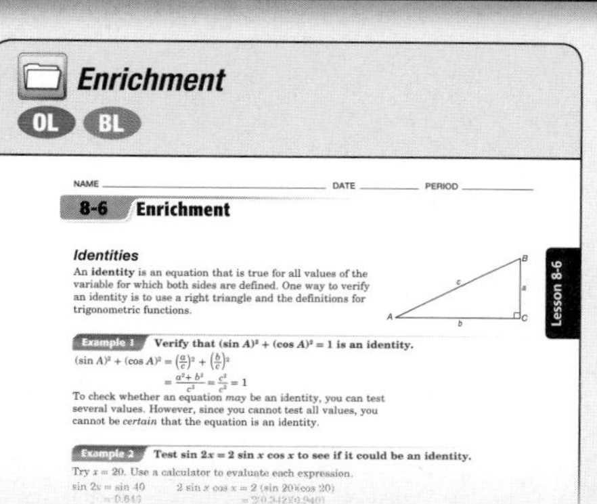
NAME ________ DATE ________ PERIOD ________

8-6 Enrichment

Identities

An **identity** is an equation that is true for all values of the variable for which both sides are defined. One way to verify an identity is to use a right triangle and the definitions for trigonometric functions.

Example 1 Verify that $(\sin A)^2 + (\cos A)^2 = 1$ is an identity.

$(\sin A)^2 + (\cos A)^2 = \left(\frac{a}{c}\right)^2 + \left(\frac{b}{c}\right)^2$

$= \frac{a^2 + b^2}{c^2} = \frac{c^2}{c^2} = 1$

To check whether an equation *may* be an identity, you can test several values. However, since you cannot test all values, you cannot be *certain* that the equation is an identity.

Example 2 Test $\sin 2x = 2 \sin x \cos x$ to see if it could be an identity.

Try $x = 20$. Use a calculator to evaluate each expression.

$\sin 2x = \sin 40$ $\quad 2 \sin x \cos x = 2 (\sin 20)(\cos 20)$

Lesson 8-6

Study Guide and Intervention
AL OL ELL

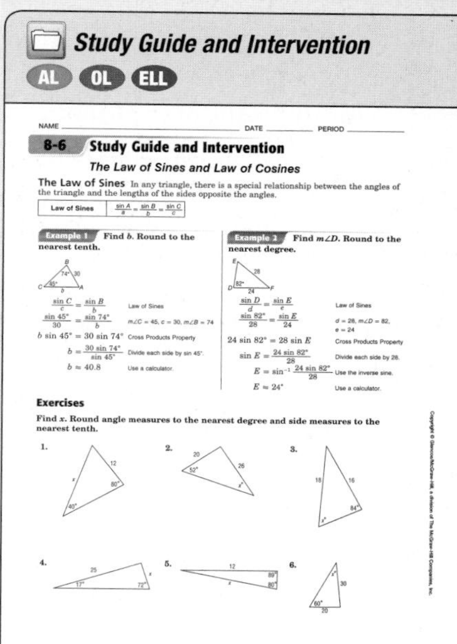
NAME ________ DATE ________ PERIOD ________

8-6 Study Guide and Intervention

The Law of Sines and Law of Cosines

The Law of Sines In any triangle, there is a special relationship between the angles of the triangle and the lengths of the sides opposite the angles.

Law of Sines	$\frac{\sin A}{a} = \frac{\sin B}{b} = \frac{\sin C}{c}$

Example 1 Find b. Round to the nearest tenth.

$\frac{\sin C}{c} = \frac{\sin B}{b}$ Law of Sines

$\frac{\sin 45°}{30} = \frac{\sin 74°}{b}$ $m\angle C = 45$, $c = 30$, $m\angle B = 74$

$b \sin 45° = 30 \sin 74°$ Cross Products Property

$b = \frac{30 \sin 74°}{\sin 45°}$ Divide each side by sin 45°.

$b \approx 40.8$ Use a calculator.

Example 2 Find $m\angle D$. Round to the nearest degree.

$\frac{\sin D}{d} = \frac{\sin E}{e}$ Law of Sines

$\frac{\sin 82°}{28} = \frac{\sin E}{24}$ $d = 28$, $m\angle D = 82$, $e = 24$

$24 \sin 82° = 28 \sin E$ Cross Products Property

$\sin E = \frac{24 \sin 82°}{28}$ Divide each side by 28.

$E = \sin^{-1} \frac{24 \sin 82°}{28}$ Use the inverse sine.

$E \approx 58°$ Use a calculator.

Exercises

Find x. Round angle measures to the nearest degree and side measures to the nearest tenth.

1. 2. 3. 4. 5. 6.

Practice
AL OL BL ELL

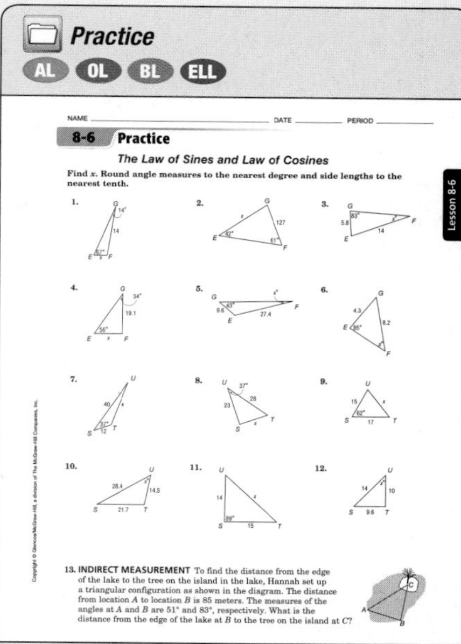
NAME ________ DATE ________ PERIOD ________

8-6 Practice

The Law of Sines and Law of Cosines

Find x. Round angle measures to the nearest degree and side lengths to the nearest tenth.

1. 2. 3. 4. 5. 6. 7. 8. 9. 10. 11. 12.

13. **INDIRECT MEASUREMENT** To find the distance from the edge of the lake to the tree on the island in the lake, Hannah set up a triangular configuration as shown in the diagram. The distance from location A to location B is 85 meters. The measures of the angles at A and B are 51° and 83°, respectively. What is the distance from the edge of the lake at B to the tree on the island at C?

Lesson 8-6

Word Problem Practice
AL OL BL ELL

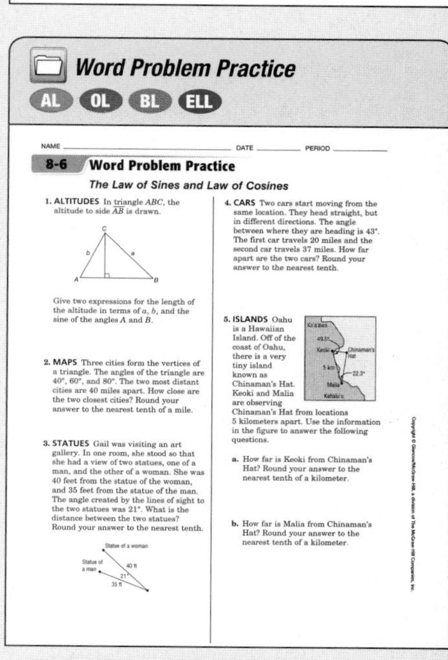
NAME ________ DATE ________ PERIOD ________

8-6 Word Problem Practice

The Law of Sines and Law of Cosines

1. **ALTITUDES** In triangle ABC, the altitude to side $\overline{AB}$ is drawn.

Give two expressions for the length of the altitude in terms of a, b, and the sine of the angles A and B.

2. **MAPS** Three cities form the vertices of a triangle. The angles of the triangle are 40°, 60°, and 80°. The two most distant cities are 40 miles apart. How close are the two closest cities? Round your answer to the nearest tenth of a mile.

3. **STATUES** Gail was visiting an art gallery. In one room, she stood so that she had a view of two statues, one of a man, and the other of a woman. She was 40 feet from the statue of the woman, and 35 feet from the statue of the man. The angle created by the lines of sight to the two statues was 21°. What is the distance between the two statues? Round your answer to the nearest tenth.

4. **CARS** Two cars start moving from the same location. They head straight, but in different directions. The angle between where they are heading is 43°. The first car travels 20 miles and the second car travels 37 miles. How far apart are the two cars? Round your answer to the nearest tenth.

5. **ISLANDS** Oahu is a Hawaiian Island. Off of the coast of Oahu, there is a very tiny island known as Chinaman's Hat. Keoki and Malia are observing Chinaman's Hat from locations 5 kilometers apart. Use the information in the figure to answer the following questions.

a. How far is Keoki from Chinaman's Hat? Round your answer to the nearest tenth of a kilometer.

b. How far is Malia from Chinaman's Hat? Round your answer to the nearest tenth of a kilometer.

Teaching the Mathematical Practices

Structure Mathematically proficient students look closely to discern a pattern or structure. They also can step back for an overview and shift perspective. In Exercises 8–10, point out to students that none of these triangles are right triangles therefore the Law of Sines or the Law of Cosines will be used.

Example 5

29. **TORNADOES** Find the width of the mouth of the tornado shown below. **126.2 ft**

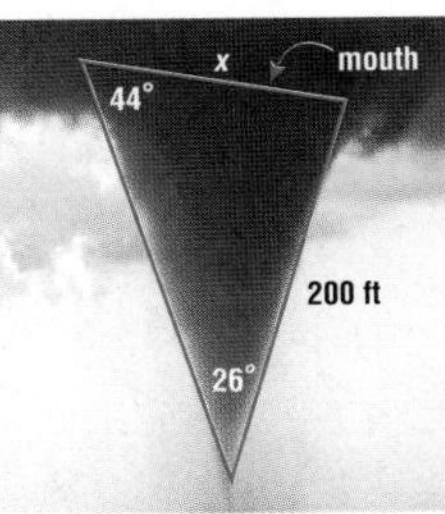

30. **TRAVEL** A pilot flies 90 miles from Memphis, Tennessee, to Tupelo, Mississippi, to Huntsville, Alabama, and finally back to Memphis. How far is Memphis from Huntsville? **207 mi**

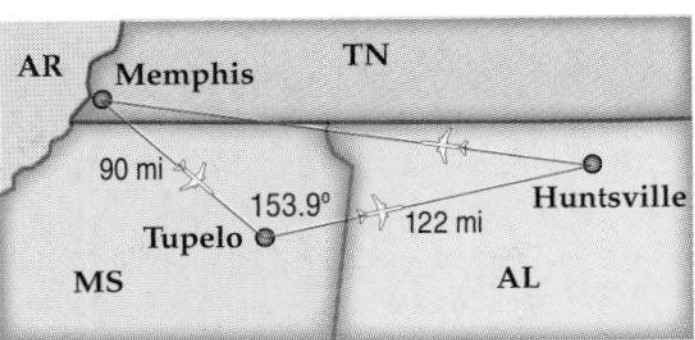

Example 6

CCSS STRUCTURE **Solve each triangle. Round angle measures to the nearest degree and side measures to the nearest tenth.**

31. 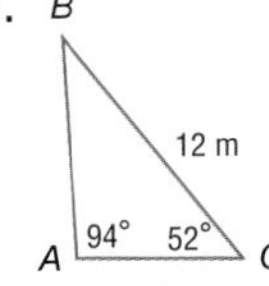

32. 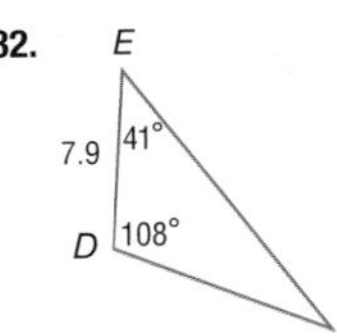

33. 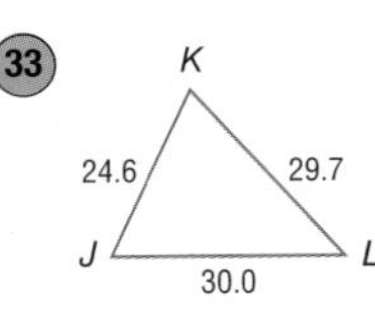

34. 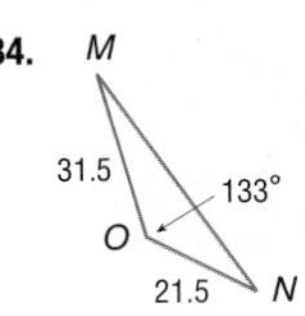

35. 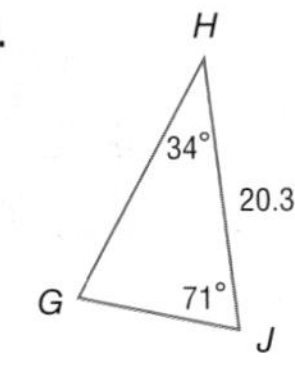

36. 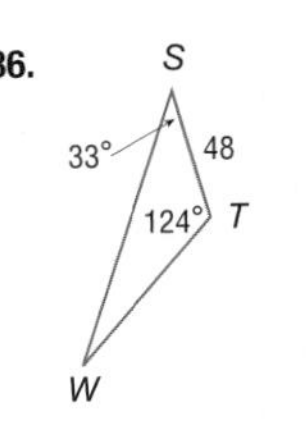

37. 38. 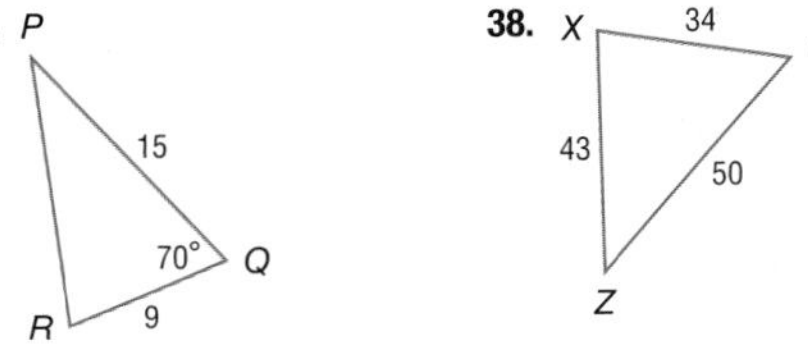

39. 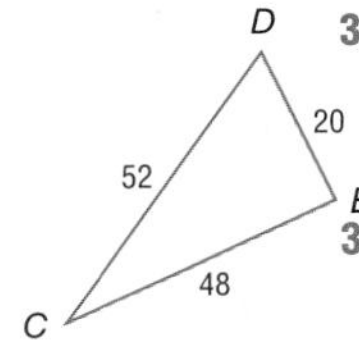

40. Solve $\triangle JKL$ if $JK = 33$, $KL = 56$, $LJ = 65$.

41. Solve $\triangle ABC$ if $m\angle B = 119$, $m\angle C = 26$, $CA = 15$.

42. Solve $\triangle XYZ$ if $XY = 190$, $YZ = 184$, $ZX = 75$.

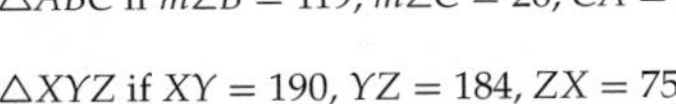

B 43. **GARDENING** Crystal has an organic vegetable garden. She wants to add another triangular section so that she can start growing tomatoes. If the garden and neighboring space have the dimensions shown, find the perimeter of the new garden to the nearest foot. **≈96.2 ft**

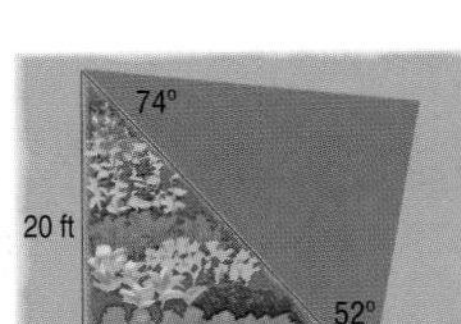
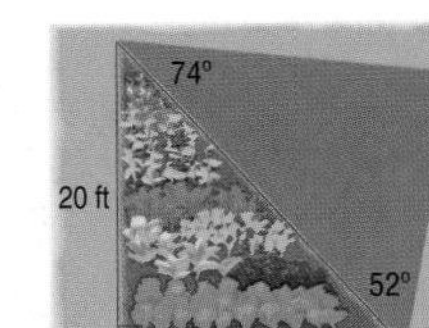

31. $m\angle B = 34$, $AB \approx 9.5$, $CA \approx 6.7$
32. $m\angle F = 31$, $DF \approx 10.1$, $EF \approx 14.6$
33. $m\angle J \approx 65$, $m\angle K \approx 66$, $m\angle L \approx 49$
34. $m\angle M \approx 19$, $m\angle N \approx 28$, $MN \approx 48.8$
35. $m\angle G = 75$, $GH \approx 19.9$, $GJ \approx 11.8$
36. $m\angle W \approx 23$, $WS \approx 101.8$, $TW \approx 66.9$
37. $m\angle P \approx 35$, $m\angle R \approx 75$, $RP \approx 14.6$
38. $m\angle X \approx 80$, $m\angle Y \approx 58$, $m\angle Z \approx 42$
39. $m\angle C \approx 23$, $m\angle D \approx 67$, $m\angle E \approx 90$
40. $m\angle L \approx 31$, $m\angle K \approx 90$, $m\angle J \approx 59$
41. $m\angle A = 35$, $AB \approx 7.5$, $BC \approx 9.8$
42. $m\angle X \approx 74$, $m\angle Y \approx 23$, $m\angle Z \approx 83$

44. FIELD HOCKEY Alyssa and Nari are playing field hockey. Alyssa is standing 20 feet from one goal post and 25 feet from the opposite post. Nari is standing 45 feet from one goal post and 38 feet from the other post. If the goal is 12 feet wide, which player has a greater chance to make a shot? What is the measure of the player's angle? **Alyssa; 28.2**

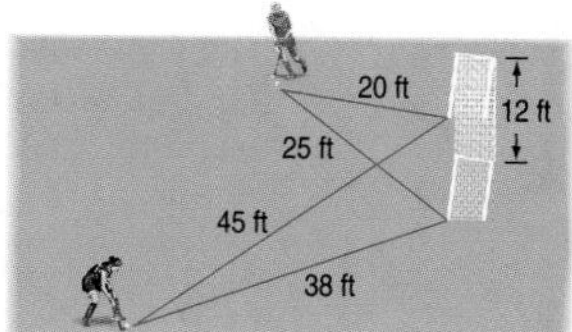

45. PROOF Justify each statement for the derivation of the Law of Sines.

Given: $\overline{CD}$ is an altitude of $\triangle ABC$.

Prove: $\frac{\sin A}{a} = \frac{\sin B}{b}$

Proof:

Statements	Reasons
$\overline{CD}$ is an altitude of $\triangle ABC$	Given
$\triangle ACD$ and $\triangle CBD$ are right	Def. of altitude
a. $\sin A = \frac{h}{b}$, $\sin B = \frac{h}{a}$	**a.** ___?___
b. $b \sin A = h$, $a \sin B = h$	**b.** ___?___
c. $b \sin A = a \sin B$	**c.** ___?___
d. $\frac{\sin A}{a} = \frac{\sin B}{b}$	**d.** ___?___

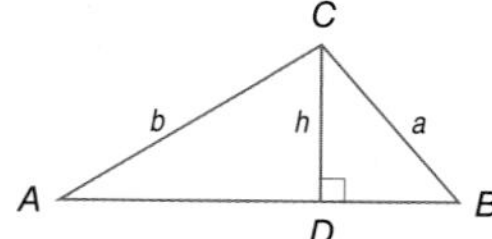

45a. Def. of sine
45b. Mult. Prop.
45c. Subs.
45d. Div. Prop.

46. PROOF Justify each statement for the derivation of the Law of Cosines.

Given: h is an altitude of $\triangle ABC$.

Prove: $c^2 = a^2 + b^2 - 2ab \cos C$

Proof:

Statements	Reasons
h is an altitude of $\triangle ABC$	Given
Altitude h separates $\triangle ABC$ into two right triangles	Def. of altitude
a. $c^2 = (a - x)^2 + h^2$	**a.** ___?___
b. $c^2 = a^2 - 2ax + x^2 + h^2$	**b.** ___?___
c. $x^2 + h^2 = b^2$	**c.** ___?___
d. $c^2 = a^2 - 2ax + b^2$	**d.** ___?___
e. $\cos C = \frac{x}{b}$	**e.** ___?___
f. $b \cos C = x$	**f.** ___?___
g. $c^2 = a^2 - 2a(b \cos C) + b^2$	**g.** ___?___
h. $c^2 = a^2 + b^2 - 2ab \cos C$	**h.** ___?___

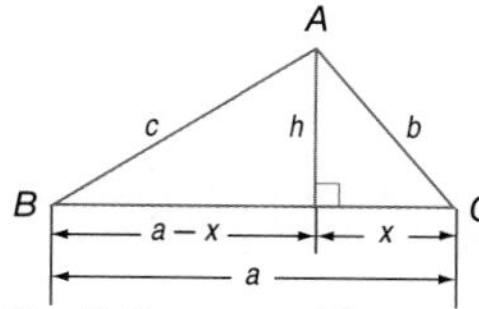

46a. Pythagorean Thm.
46b. Subs.
46c. Pythagorean Thm.
46d. Subs.
46e. Def. of cosine
46f. Mult. Prop
46g. Subs.
46h. Comm. Prop.

CCSS SENSE-MAKING **Find the perimeter of each figure. Round to the nearest tenth.**

47. **24.3**

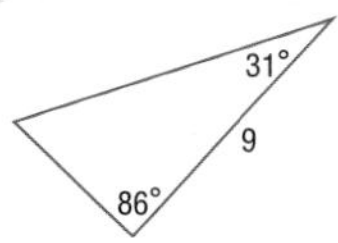

48. **14.7**

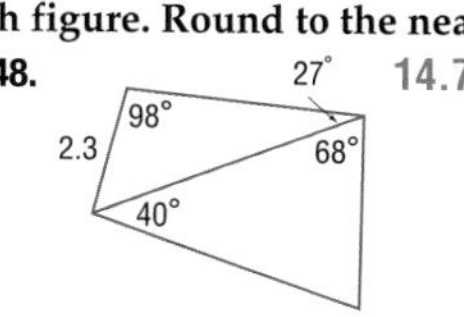

49 **275.1**

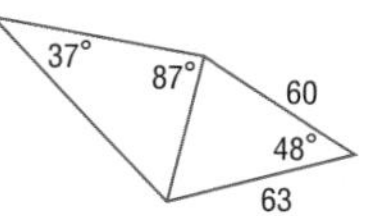

50. **340.3**

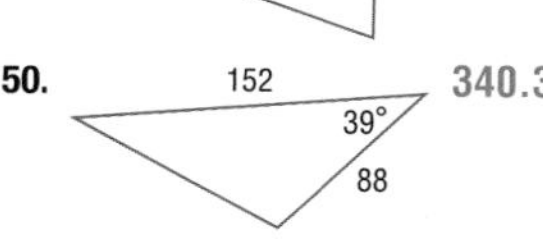

CCSS Teaching the Mathematical Practices

Sense-Making Mathematically proficient students start by explaining the meaning of a problem to themselves and looking for entry points to its solution. They plan a solution pathway rather than simply jumping into a solution attempt. In Exercises 47–50, encourage students to make a plan to solve each problem first.

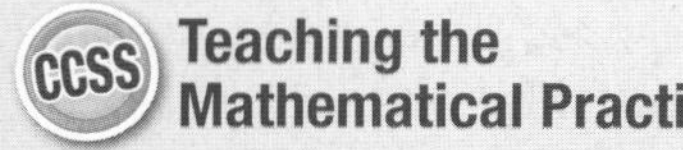

Multiple Representations

In Exercise 53, students use geometric sketches, algebraic equations, and numeric calculations to investigate the areas of triangles.

Teaching the Mathematical Practices

Critique Mathematically proficient students can distinguish correct logic from flawed reasoning. In Exercise 54, Mike did not apply the Law of Sines correctly. It is important to be careful that the correct proportions are used to compare the angles and side lengths.

Additional Answers

52. 82; Sample answer: Find the lengths of each segment of the triangle.

$AB = \sqrt{(4-(-3))^2 + (2-6)^2} \approx 8.1$

$BC = \sqrt{(-5-4)^2 + (1-2)^2} \approx 9.1$

$AC = \sqrt{(-5-(-3))^2 + (1-6)^2} \approx 5.4$

$9.1 > 8.1 > 5.4$, so $BC > AB > AC$.

Using the Triangle Inequality Theorem, the angle opposite the longest side, or $\angle A$, is the largest angle.

To find the measure of $\angle A$, use the Law of Cosines.

$BC^2 = AB^2 + AC^2 - 2(AB)(AC)\cos A$

$(9.1)^2 = (8.1)^2 + (5.4)^2 - 2(8.1)(5.4)\cos A$

$m\angle A = 82$

53a.

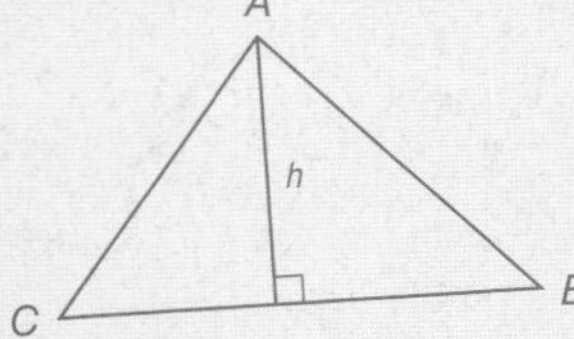

56. The Law of Cosines relates the measures of two sides a and b of any triangle to the measure of the third side c given the measure of the angle C between those two sides using the equation $a^2 + b^2 - 2ab \cos C = c^2$. When $m\angle C = 90$, we have $a^2 + b^2 - 2ab \cos 90° = c^2$. Since $\cos 90°$ is 0, this equation simplifies to $a^2 + b^2 - 2ab(0) = c^2$ or $a^2 + b^2 = c^2$, which is the same as the Pythagorean Theorem. Therefore, the Pythagorean Theorem is a specific case of the Law of Cosines.

57a. Sample answer:

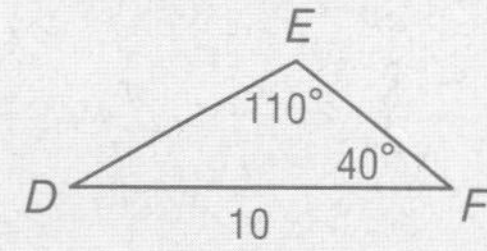

57b. Sample answer:

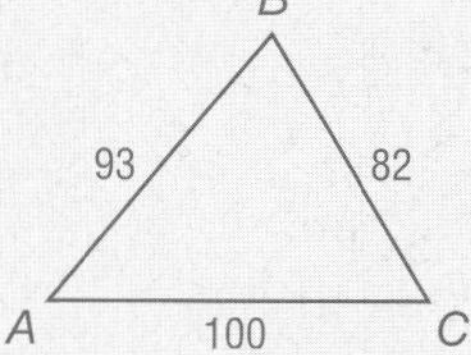

51 **MODELS** Vito is working on a model castle. Find the length of the missing side (in inches) using the diagram at the right. **8.4 in.**

52. **COORDINATE GEOMETRY** Find the measure of the largest angle in $\triangle ABC$ with coordinates $A(-3, 6)$, $B(4, 2)$, and $C(-5, 1)$. Explain your reasoning. **See margin.**

53. **MULTIPLE REPRESENTATIONS** In this problem, you will use trigonometry to find the area of a triangle.

a. **Geometric** Draw an acute, scalene $\triangle ABC$ including an altitude of length h originating at vertex A. **See margin.**

b. **Algebraic** Use trigonometry to represent h in terms of $m\angle B$. $h = AB \sin B$

c. **Algebraic** Write an equation to find the area of $\triangle ABC$ using trigonometry. $A = \frac{1}{2}(BC)(AB \sin B)$

d. **Numerical** If $m\angle B$ is 47, $AB = 11.1$, $BC = 14.1$, and $CA = 10.4$, find the area of $\triangle ABC$. Round to the nearest tenth. **57.2 units²**

e. **Analytical** Write an equation to find the area of $\triangle ABC$ using trigonometry in terms of a different angle measure. $A = \frac{1}{2}(BC)(CA \sin C)$

H.O.T. Problems Use Higher-Order Thinking Skills

54. **CCSS CRITIQUE** Colleen and Mike are planning a party. Colleen wants to sew triangular decorations and needs to know the perimeter of one of the triangles to buy enough trim. The triangles are isosceles with angle measurements of 64° at the base and side lengths of 5 inches. Colleen thinks the perimeter is 15.7 inches and Mike thinks it is 15 inches. Is either of them correct? **Neither; 5 + 5 + 4.4 = 14.4 in.**

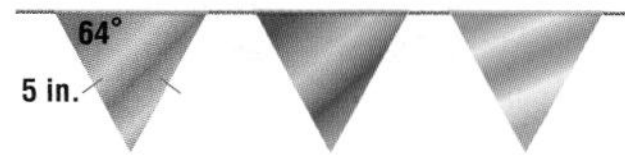

55. **CHALLENGE** Find the value of x in the figure at the right. **5.6**

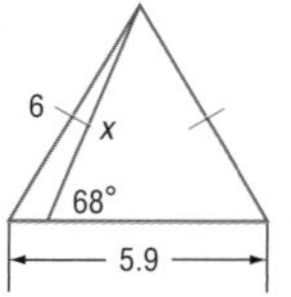

56. **REASONING** Explain why the Pythagorean Theorem is a specific case of the Law of Cosines. **See margin.**

57. **OPEN ENDED** Draw and label a triangle that can be solved: **a–b. See margin.**

a. using only the Law of Sines.

b. using only the Law of Cosines.

58.  **WRITING IN MATH** What methods can you use to solve a triangle? **See margin.**

Standardized Test Practice

59. For $\triangle ABC$, $m\angle A = 42$, $m\angle B = 74$, and $a = 3$, what is the value of b? **A**

A 4.3 C 2.1
B 3.8 D 1.5

60. ALGEBRA Which inequality *best* describes the graph below? **G**

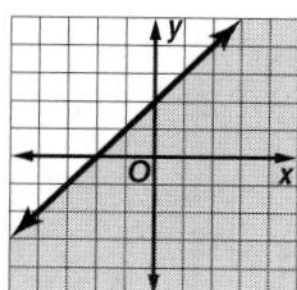

F $y \geq -x + 2$ H $y \geq -3x + 2$
G $y \leq x + 2$ J $y \leq 3x + 2$

61. SHORT RESPONSE What is the perimeter of the triangle shown below? Round to the nearest tenth. **325.6**

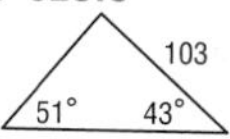

62. SAT/ACT If $\sin x = 0.6$ and $AB = 12$, what is the area of $\triangle ABC$? **D**

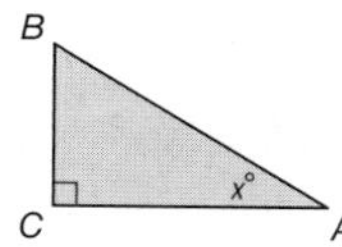

A 9.6 units^2 D 34.6 units^2
B 28.8 units^2 E 42.3 units^2
C 31.2 units^2

Spiral Review

63. HIKING A hiker is on top of a mountain 250 feet above sea level with a 68° angle of depression. She can see her camp from where she is standing. How far is her camp from the top of the mountain? (Lesson 8-5) **269.6 ft**

68°
250 ft

Use a calculator to find the measure of $\angle J$ to the nearest degree. (Lesson 8-4)

64.

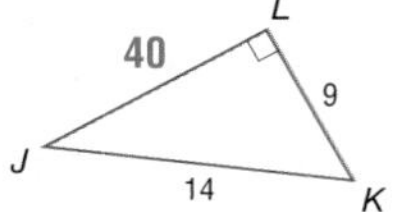

65.

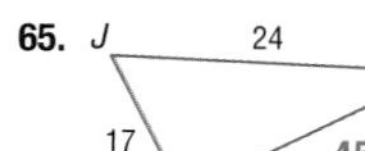
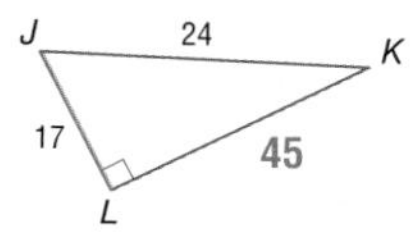

Determine whether the polygons are *always, sometimes,* or *never* similar. Explain your reasoning. (Lesson 7-2) **66–67. See margin.**

66. a right triangle and an isosceles triangle

67. an equilateral triangle and a scalene triangle

Name the missing coordinates of each triangle. (Lesson 4-8)

68.

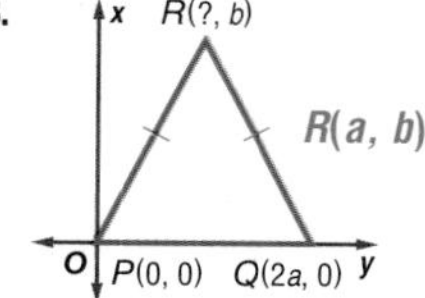

$R(a, b)$

69.

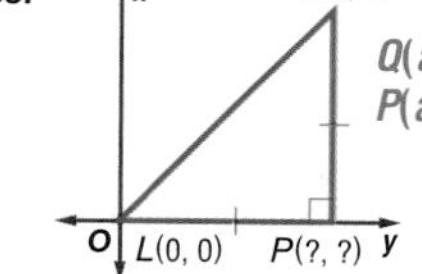

$Q(a, a)$
$P(a, 0)$

70.

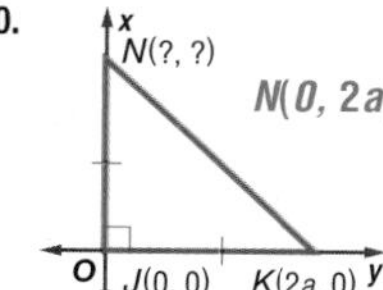

$N(0, 2a)$

Skills Review

Find the distance between each pair of points. Round to the nearest tenth.

71. $A(5, 1)$ and $C(-3, -3)$ $\sqrt{80} \approx 8.9$

72. $J(7, 11)$ and $K(-1, 5)$ **10.0**

73. $W(2, 0)$ and $X(8, 6)$ $\sqrt{72} \approx 8.5$

4 Assess

Crystal Ball Students know that there are three types of triangles that can be solved using the Law of Sines (AAS, ASA and SSA). Have students list the other types of triangles that may be solved using the Law of Cosines.

Formative Assessment

Check for student understanding of Lessons 8-5 and 8-6.

 Quiz 3, p. 52

Additional Answers

58. Sample answer: When solving a right triangle, you can use the Pythagorean Theorem to find missing side lengths and trigonometric ratios to find missing side lengths or angle measures. To solve any triangle, you can use the Law of Sines or the Law of Cosines, depending on what measures you are given.

66. Sometimes; sample answer: If corresponding angles are congruent and corresponding sides are proportional, a right triangle and an isosceles triangle are similar.

67. Never; sample answer: Since an equilateral triangle has three congruent sides and a scalene triangle has three non-congruent sides, the ratios of the three pairs of sides can never be equal. Therefore, an equilateral triangle and a scalene triangle can never be similar.

Follow-up

Students have explored the Law of Sines and Law of Cosines.

Ask:

- What are the strengths and weakness of the Law of Sines and Law of Cosines? Sample answer: strengths: only three measurements are needed to solve a triangle, they can be used to solve *any* triangle; weaknesses: approximated values that are substituted back into the formulas may result in accuracy issues, technology must be used to calculate missing values

1 Focus

Objective

- Determine whether three given measures (angles or sides) define 0, 1, 2, or infinitely many triangles.

Materials for Each Group

- $5'' \times 8''$ notecard
- $\frac{1}{2}$-inch strip of cardstock that is about 6 inches long
- brass fasteners
- colored pencils or markers

Teaching Tips

- To refresh students memories about SSS, SAS, ASA, and AAS each determining a unique triangle, you may wish to review triangle congruence constructions using these measures.
- In Exercise 5, many students will see only one triangle that can be formed. Encourage students to rotate side *a* in each Exercise to be sure they have found all possible triangles.

2 Teach

Working in Cooperative Groups

Organize students into groups of 2 or 3, mixing abilities. Then have groups complete Activities 1 and 2 and Exercises 1–6, 13, and 17.

Ask:

- Before calculating any measures, what is the first thing you should note for each problem in Exercises 18–23? whether $\angle A$ is acute or obtuse

Practice Have students complete Exercises 7–12, 14–16, and 18–23.

2. If side *a* is perpendicular to the third side of the triangle, the triangle is a right triangle. By the sine ratio we know that $\sin A = \frac{a}{b}$, which implies that $a = b \sin A$.

EXTEND 8-6 Geometry Lab The Ambiguous Case

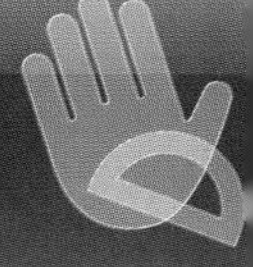

From your work with congruent triangles, you know that three measures determine a unique triangle when the measures are

- three sides (SSS),
- two sides and an included angle (SAS),
- two angles and an included side (ASA), or
- two angles and a nonincluded side (AAS).

A unique triangle is not necessarily determined by three angles (AAA) or by two sides and a nonincluded angle. In this lab, you will investigate how many triangles are determined by this last case (SSA), called the **ambiguous case**.

CCSS Common Core State Standards
Content Standards
G.SRT.11 Understand and apply the Law of Sines and the Law of Cosines to find unknown measurements in right and non-right triangles (e.g., surveying problems, resultant forces).
Mathematical Practices 2

Activity 1 The Ambiguous Case (SSA): $\angle A$ is Acute

Step 1 On a $5'' \times 8''$ notecard, draw and label $\overline{AC}$ and a ray extending from *A* to form an acute angle. Label side $\overline{AC}$ as *b*.

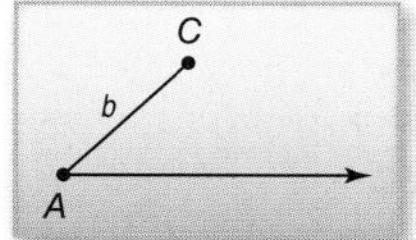

Step 2 Using a brass fastener, attach one end of a half-inch strip of cardstock to the notecard at *C*. The strip should be longer than *b*. This represents side *a*.

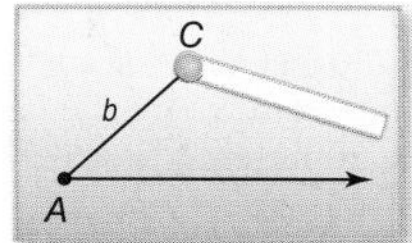

Step 3 Position side *a* so that it is perpendicular to the ray. Make a black mark on the strip at the point where it touches the ray.

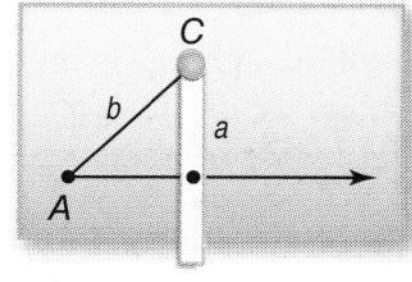

Model and Analyze

1. If *a* has the given length, how many triangles can be formed? (*Hint*: Rotate the strip to see if the mark can intersect the ray at any other locations to form a different triangle.) 1
2. Show that if side *a* is perpendicular to the third side of the triangle, then $a = b \sin A$. See margin.

Determine the number of triangles that can be formed given each of the modifications to *a* in Activity 1.

3. $a < b \sin A$ (*Hint*: Make a green mark above the black mark on the strip, and try to form triangle(s) using this new length for *a*.) 0
4. $a = b$ (*Hint*: Rotate the strip so that it lies on top of $\overline{AC}$ and mark off this length in red. Then rotate the strip to try to form triangle(s) using this new length for *a*.) 1
5. $a < b$ and $a > b \sin A$ (*Hint*: Make a blue mark between the black and the red marks. Then rotate the strip to try to form triangle(s) using this new length for *a*.) 2
6. $a > b$ (*Hint*: Rotate the strip to try to form triangle(s) using the entire length of the strip as the length for *a*.) 1

Use your results from Exercises 1–6 to determine whether the given measures define *0*, *1*, *2*, or *infinitely many* acute triangles. Justify your answers. 7–12. See margin for justifications.

7. $a = 14, b = 16, m\angle A = 55$ 2
8. $a = 7, b = 11, m\angle A = 68$ 0
9. $a = 22, b = 25, m\angle A = 39$ 2
10. $a = 13, b = 12, m\angle A = 81$ 1
11. $a = 10, b = 10, m\angle A = 45$ 1
12. $a = 6, b = 9, m\angle A = 24$ 2

Additional Answers

7. $b \sin A = 16 \sin 55°$ or about 13.1. Since $\angle A$ is acute, $14 < 16$, and $14 > 13.1$, the measures define 2 triangles.
8. $b \sin A = 11 \sin 68°$ or about 10.2. Since $\angle A$ is acute, and $7 < 10.2$, the measures define 0 triangles.
9. $b \sin A = 25 \sin 39°$ or about 15.7. Since $\angle A$ is acute, $22 < 25$, and $25 > 15.7$, the measures define 2 triangles.
10. Since $\angle A$ is acute and $13 > 12$, the measures define 1 triangle.
11. Since $\angle A$ is acute and $a = b = 10$, the measures define 1 triangle.
12. $b \sin A = 9 \sin 24°$ or about 3.6. Since $\angle A$ is acute, $6 < 9$, and $6 > 3.6$, the measures define 2 triangles.

In the next activity, you will investigate how many triangles are determined for the ambiguous case when the angle given is obtuse.

Activity 2 The Ambiguous Case (SSA): $\angle A$ is Obtuse

Step 1 On a 5″ × 8″ notecard, draw and label $\overline{AC}$ and a ray extending from A to form an obtuse angle. Label side $\overline{AC}$ as b.

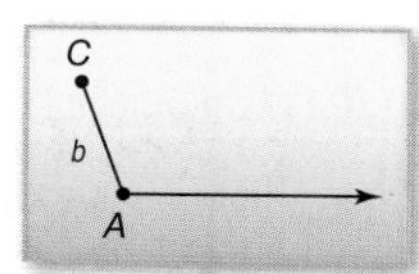

Step 2 Using a brass fastener, attach one end of a half-inch strip of cardstock to the notecard at C. The strip should be longer than b. This represents side a.

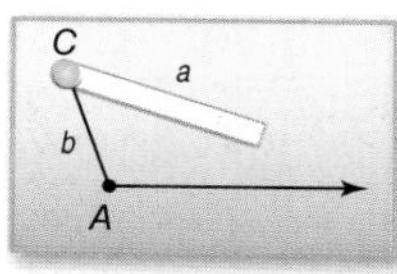

Model and Analyze

13. How many triangles can be formed if $a = b$? if $a < b$? if $a > b$? **0; 0; 1**

Use your results from Exercise 13 to determine whether the given measures define *0, 1, 2,* or *infinitely many* obtuse triangles. Justify your answers. **14–16. See margin for justifications.**

14. $a = 10, b = 8, m\angle A = 95$ **1**

15. $a = 13, b = 17, m\angle A = 100$ **0**

16. $a = 15, b = 15, m\angle A = 125$ **0**

17. Explain why three angle measures do not determine a unique triangle. How many triangles are determined by three angles measures? **See margin.**

Determine whether the given measures define *0, 1, 2,* or *infinitely many* triangles. Justify your answers. **18–23. See margin for justifications.**

18. $a = 25, b = 21, m\angle A = 39$ **1**

19. $m\angle A = 41, m\angle B = 68, m\angle C = 71$ **infinitely many**

20. $a = 17, b = 15, m\angle A = 128$ **1**

21. $a = 13, b = 17, m\angle A = 52$ **0**

22. $a = 5, b = 9, c = 6$ **1**

23. $a = 10, b = 15, m\angle A = 33$ **2**

24. OPEN ENDED Give measures for a, b, and an acute $\angle A$ that define **Sample answers given.**

a. 0 triangles. **$a = 22, b = 25, m\angle A = 70$**

b. exactly one triangle. **$a = 25, b = 22, m\angle A = 95$**

c. two triangles. **$a = 22, b = 30, m\angle A = 43$**

25. CHALLENGE Find both solutions for $\triangle ABC$ if $a = 15$, $b = 21$, $m\angle A = 42$. Round angle measures to the nearest degree and side measures to the nearest tenth.

- For Solution 1, assume that $\angle B$ is acute, and use the Law of Sines to find $m\angle B$. Then find $m\angle C$. Finally, use the Law of Sines again to find c.
- For Solution 2, assume that $\angle B$ is obtuse. Let this obtuse angle be $\angle B'$. Use $m\angle B$ you found in Solution 1 and the diagram shown to find $m\angle B'$. Then find $m\angle C$. Finally, use the Law of Sines to find c.

25. Solution 1: $m\angle B \approx 70$, $m\angle C \approx 68$, $c \approx 20.9$ Solution 2: $m\angle B \approx 110$, $m\angle C \approx 28$, $c \approx 10.4$

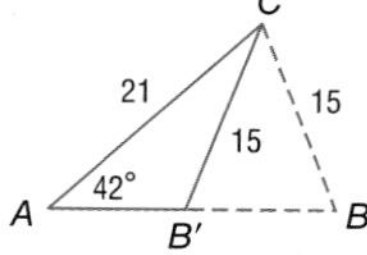

3 Assess

Formative Assessment

Use Exercise 24 to assess whether students understand how to determine whether three given measures (angles or sides) define 0, 1, 2, or infinitely many triangles.

From Concrete to Abstract

Ask students to summarize what they have learned about the ambiguous case for triangle measures.

Additional Answers

14. Since $\angle A$ is obtuse and $10 > 8$, the measures define 1 triangle.

15. Since $\angle A$ is obtuse and $13 < 17$, the measures define 0 triangles.

16. Since $\angle A$ is obtuse and $a = b = 15$, the measures define 0 triangles.

17. Sample answer: By AA Similarity, a triangle with two given angle measures is similar to infinitely many triangles with the same angle measures. Therefore, when given three angles, the solution is an infinite set of similar triangles.

18. Since $\angle A$ is acute and $25 > 21$, the measures define 1 triangle.

19. There are infinitely many similar triangles that have the same three angle measures.

20. Since $\angle A$ is obtuse and $17 > 15$, the measures define 1 triangle.

21. $b \sin A = 17 \sin 52°$ or about 13.4. Since $\angle A$ is acute and $13 < 13.4$, the measures define 0 triangles.

22. Three side measures (SSS) determine exactly 1 triangle.

23. $b \sin A = 15 \sin 33°$ or about 8.2. Since $\angle A$ is acute, $10 < 15$, and $10 > 8.2$, the measures define 2 triangles.

25. Solution 1: $m\angle B = 70°$, $m\angle C = 68°$, $c \approx 20.9$ Solution 2: $m\angle B = 110°$, $m\angle C = 28°$, $c \approx 10.4$

1 Focus

VerticalAlignment

Before Lesson 8-7 Use trigonometry to find side lengths and angle measures of right triangles.

Lesson 8-7 Perform vector operations geometrically and on the coordinate plane.

After Lesson 8-7 Use and extend similarity properties and transformations.

2 Teach

Scaffolding Questions

Have students read the **Why?** section of the lesson.

Ask:

- Why do you think that vectors are used to represent wind direction and speed? Sample answer: Using a vector is a convenient way to show both the size and direction of the wind.
- What types of quantities do you think that vectors could be used to represent? Sample answer: quantities that need to be described using both size and direction

LESSON 8-7 Vectors

Then

- You used trigonometry to find side lengths and angle measures of right triangles.

Now

1. Perform vector operations geometrically.
2. Perform vector operations on the coordinate plane.

Why?

- Meteorologists use vectors to represent weather patterns. For example, *wind vectors* are used to indicate wind direction and speed.

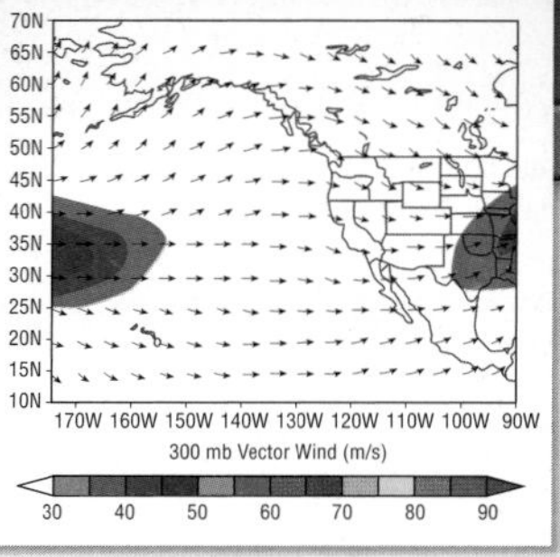

NewVocabulary
vector
magnitude
direction
resultant
parallelogram method
triangle method
standard position
component form

Common Core State Standards

Content Standards
G.GPE.6 Find the point on a directed line segment between two given points that partitions the segment in a given ratio.

Mathematical Practices
1 Make sense of problems and persevere in solving them.
4 Model with mathematics.

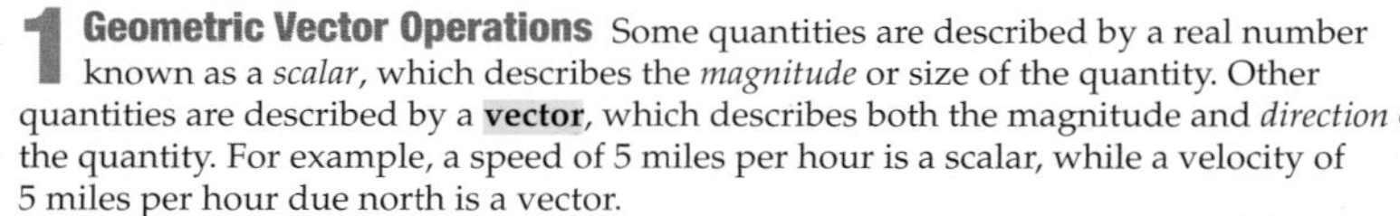

1 Geometric Vector Operations

Some quantities are described by a real number known as a *scalar*, which describes the *magnitude* or size of the quantity. Other quantities are described by a **vector**, which describes both the magnitude and *direction* of the quantity. For example, a speed of 5 miles per hour is a scalar, while a velocity of 5 miles per hour due north is a vector.

A vector can be represented by a directed line segment with an initial point and a terminal point. The vector shown, with initial point A and terminal point B, can be called $\overrightarrow{AB}$, $\vec{a}$, or **a**.

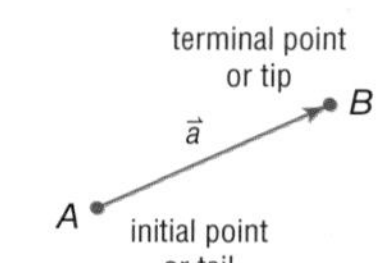

The **magnitude** of $\overrightarrow{AB}$, denoted $|\overrightarrow{AB}|$, is the length of the vector from its initial point to its terminal point. The **direction** of a vector can be expressed as the angle that it forms with the horizontal or as a measurement between 0° and 90° east or west of the north-south line.

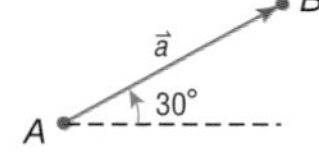

The direction of $\vec{a}$ is 30° relative to the horizontal.

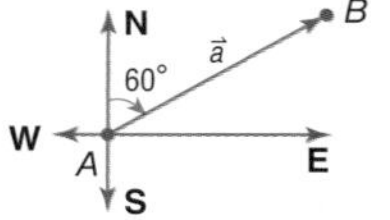

The direction of $\vec{a}$ is 60° east of north.

Example 1 Represent Vectors Geometrically

Use a ruler and a protractor to draw each vector. Include a scale on each diagram.

a. $\vec{m}$ **= 15 miles per hour at 140° to the horizontal**

Using a scale of 1 cm : 5 mi/h, draw and label a 15 ÷ 5 or 3-centimeter arrow at a 140° angle to the horizontal.

b. $\vec{c}$ **= 55 pounds of force 55° west of south**

Using a scale of 1 in: 25 lbs, draw and label a 55 ÷ 25 or 2.2-inch arrow 55° west of the north-south line on the south side.

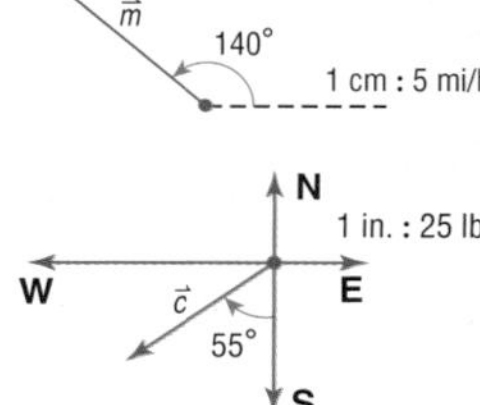

GuidedPractice 1A–1B. See margin.

1A. $\vec{b}$ = 40 feet per second at 35° to the horizontal

1B. $\vec{t}$ = 12 kilometers per hour at 85° east of north

Lesson 8-7 Resources

Resource	Approaching Level AL	On Level OL	Beyond Level BL	English Learners ELL
Teacher Edition	▪ Differentiated Instruction, p. 603	▪ Differentiated Instruction, pp. 601, 603	▪ Differentiated Instruction, p. 601	
Chapter Resource Masters	▪ Study Guide and Intervention, pp. 43–44 ▪ Skills Practice, p. 45 ▪ Practice, p. 46 ▪ Word Problem Practice, p. 47	▪ Study Guide and Intervention, pp. 43–44 ▪ Skills Practice, p. 45 ▪ Practice, p. 46 ▪ Word Problem Practice, p. 47 ▪ Enrichment, p. 48	▪ Practice, p. 46 ▪ Word Problem Practice, p. 47 ▪ Enrichment, p. 48	▪ Study Guide and Intervention, pp. 43–44 ▪ Skills Practice, p. 45 ▪ Practice, p. 46 ▪ Word Problem Practice, p. 47
Other	▪ 5-Minute Check 8-7 ▪ Study Notebook ▪ Teaching Geometry with Manipulatives	▪ 5-Minute Check 8-7 ▪ Study Notebook ▪ Teaching Geometry with Manipulatives	▪ 5-Minute Check 8-7 ▪ Study Notebook	▪ 5-Minute Check 8-7 ▪ Study Notebook ▪ Teaching Geometry with Manipulatives

The sum of two or more vectors is a single vector called the **resultant**.

KeyConcept Vector Addition

To find the resultant of $\vec{a}$ and $\vec{b}$, use one of the following methods.

Parallelogram Method	Triangle Method
Step 1 Translate $\vec{b}$ so that the tail of $\vec{b}$ touches the tail of $\vec{a}$.	**Step 1** Translate $\vec{b}$ so that the tail of $\vec{b}$ touches the tip of $\vec{a}$.
Step 2 Complete the parallelogram. The resultant is the indicated diagonal of the parallelogram. 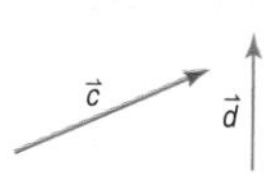	**Step 2** Draw the resultant vector from the tail of $\vec{a}$ to the tip of $\vec{b}$.

StudyTip

Types of Vectors
Parallel vectors have the same or opposite direction but not necessarily the same magnitude.

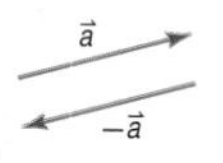

Opposite vectors have the same magnitude but *opposite* direction.

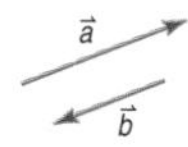

Equivalent vectors have the same magnitude and direction.

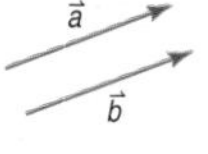

Example 2 Find the Resultant of Two Vectors

Copy the vectors. Then find $\vec{c} - \vec{d}$.

Subtracting a vector is equivalent to adding its opposite vector.

Parallelogram Method	Triangle Method
Step 1 Copy $\vec{c}$ and $\vec{d}$. Draw $-\vec{d}$, and translate it so that its tail touches the tail of $\vec{c}$. 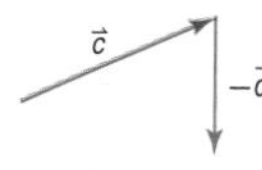	**Step 1** Copy $\vec{c}$ and $\vec{d}$. Draw $-\vec{d}$, and translate it so that its tail touches the tip of $\vec{c}$.
Step 2 Complete the parallelogram. Then draw the diagonal. 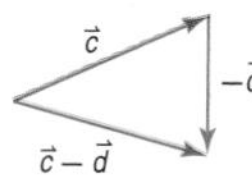	**Step 2** Draw the resultant vector from the tail of $\vec{c}$ to the tip of $-\vec{d}$.

Both methods produce the same resultant vector $\vec{c} - \vec{d}$. You can use a ruler and a protractor to measure the magnitude and direction of each vector to verify your results.

GuidedPractice

2A. Find $\vec{c} + \vec{d}$.

2B. Find $\vec{d} - \vec{c}$.

2A.

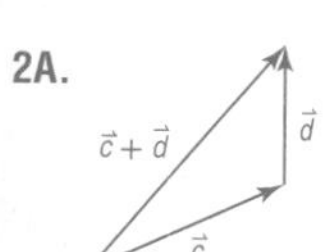

2B.

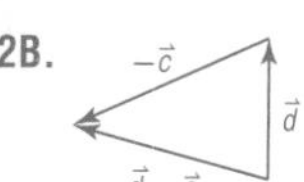

DifferentiatedInstruction OL BL

Extension The vector $k\vec{v}$ is a dilation of the vector $\vec{v}$ with scale factor k. What is the direction of $k\vec{v}$ when $k > 0$? $k < 0$? When $k > 0$, $k\vec{v}$ has the same direction as $\vec{v}$. When $k < 0$, $k\vec{v}$ has the opposite direction as $\vec{v}$.

Geometric Vector Operations

Example 1 shows how to represent a vector geometrically. **Example 2** shows how to find the resultant of two vectors.

Formative Assessment

Use the Guided Practice exercises after each example to determine students' understanding of concepts.

Additional Examples

1 Use a ruler and a protractor to draw each vector. Include a scale on each diagram.

a. $\vec{s} = 80$ meters at 24° west of north

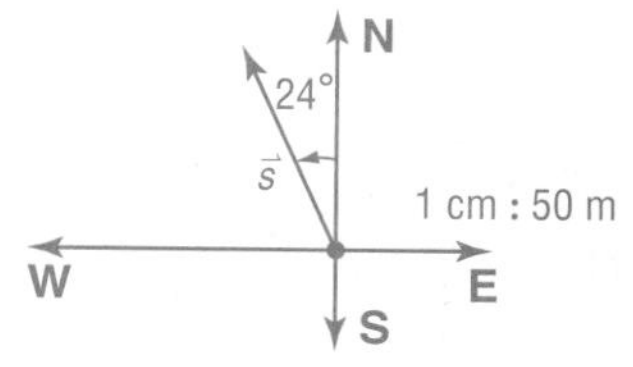

b. $\vec{d} = 16$ yards per second at 165° to the horizontal

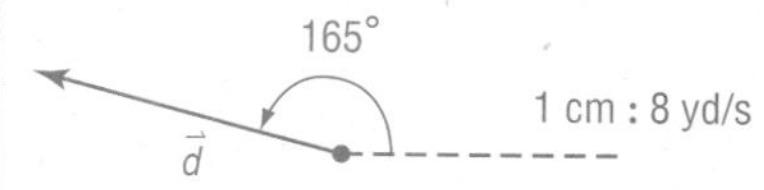

2 Copy the vectors. Then find $\vec{a} - \vec{b}$.

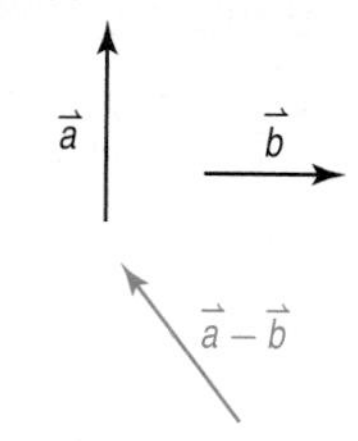

Additional Answers

1A.

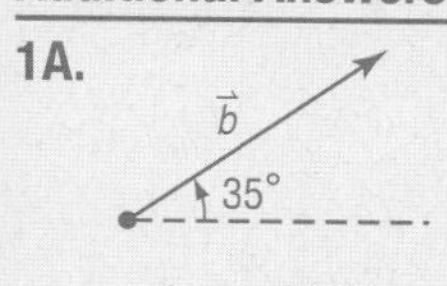

1B.

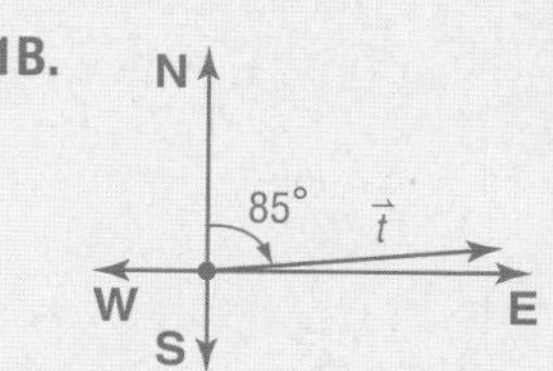

Vectors on the Coordinate Plane

Example 3 shows how to write a vector in component form. **Example 4** shows how to find the magnitude and direction of a vector. **Example 5** shows how to operate with vectors in the coordinate plane.

Additional Examples

3 Write the component form of $\overrightarrow{AB}$.

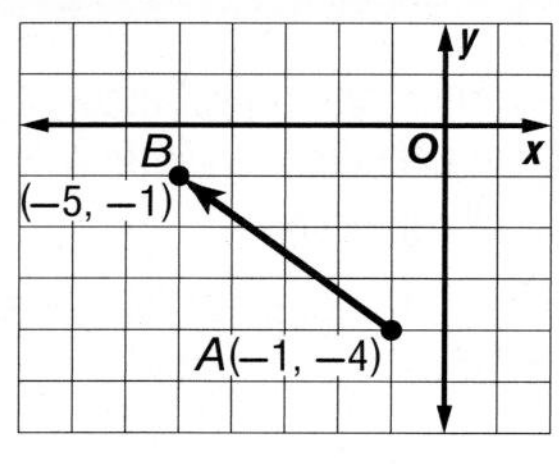

$\langle -4, 3\rangle$

4 Find the magnitude and direction of $\vec{t} = \langle 7, -5\rangle$.
$\sqrt{74}$; ≈324.5°

WatchOut!

Vector Notation Remind students that the notation $\langle a, b\rangle$ is used to represent the component form of a vector, while the notation (a, b) is used to represent a point such as the initial or terminal point of the vector.

2 Vectors on the Coordinate Plane

Vectors can also be represented on the coordinate plane.

A vector is in **standard position** if its initial point is at the origin. In this position, a vector can be uniquely described by its terminal point $P(x, y)$.

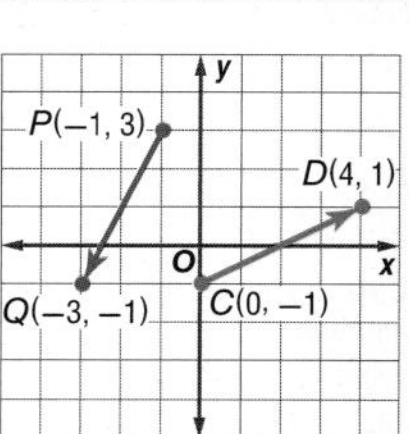

To describe a vector with any initial point, you can use the **component form** $\langle x, y\rangle$, which describes the vector in terms of its horizontal component x and vertical component y.

To write the component form of a vector with initial point (x_1, y_1) and terminal point (x_2, y_2), find $\langle x_2 - x_1, y_2 - y_1\rangle$.

Example 3 Write a Vector in Component Form

Write the component form of $\overrightarrow{CD}$.

$\overrightarrow{CD} = \langle x_2 - x_1, y_2 - y_1\rangle$ — Component form of a vector

$= \langle 4 - 0, 1 - (-1)\rangle$ — $(x_1, y_1) = (0, -1)$ and $(x_2, y_2) = (4, 1)$

$= \langle 4, 2\rangle$ — Simplify.

GuidedPractice

3. Write the component form of $\overrightarrow{PQ}$. $\langle -2, -4\rangle$

The magnitude of a vector on the coordinate plane can be found by using the Distance Formula, and the direction can be found by using trigonometric ratios.

Example 4 Find the Magnitude and Direction of a Vector

Find the magnitude and direction of $\vec{r} = \langle -4, -5\rangle$.

Step 1 Use the Distance Formula to find the magnitude.

$|\vec{r}| = \sqrt{(x_2 - x_1)^2 + (y_2 - y_1)^2}$ — Distance Formula

$= \sqrt{(-4 - 0)^2 + (-5 - 0)^2}$ — $(x_1, y_1) = (0, 0)$ and $(x_2, y_2) = (-4, -5)$

$= \sqrt{41}$ or about 6.4 — Simplify.

StudyTip

Direction Angles Vectors in standard position that lie in the third or fourth quadrants will have direction angles greater than 180°.

Step 2 Use trigonometry to find the direction.

Graph $\vec{r}$, its horizontal component, and its vertical component. Then use the inverse tangent function to find θ.

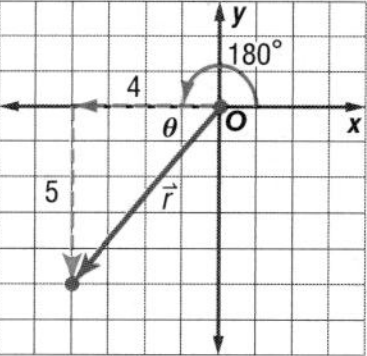

$\tan \theta = \frac{5}{4}$ — $\tan \theta = \frac{\text{opp}}{\text{adj}}$

$\theta = \tan^{-1} \frac{5}{4}$ — Def. of inverse tangent

$\theta \approx 51.3°$ — Use a calculator.

The direction of $\vec{r}$ is the angle that it makes with the positive x-axis, which is about 180° + 51.3° or 231.3°.

So, the magnitude of $\vec{r}$ is about 6.4 units and the direction is at an angle of about 231.3° to the horizontal.

GuidedPractice

4. Find the magnitude and direction of $\vec{p} = \langle -1, 4\rangle$. $\sqrt{17}$ or about 4.1; 104.0°

Teach with Tech

Interactive Whiteboard Display a coordinate plane on the board. Draw a vector in standard position and show students how to find its magnitude and direction. Then drag the vector to other locations on the plane and find the magnitude and direction of the vector again. Explain to students that the location of the vector on the coordinate plane does not change its magnitude or direction.

You can use the properties of real numbers to add vectors, subtract vectors, and multiply vectors by scalars.

KeyConcept Vector Operations

If $\langle a, b\rangle$ and $\langle c, d\rangle$ are vectors and k is a scalar, then the following are true.

Vector Addition	$\langle a, b\rangle + \langle c, d\rangle = \langle a + c, b + d\rangle$
Vector Subtraction	$\langle a, b\rangle - \langle c, d\rangle = \langle a - c, b - d\rangle$
Scalar Multiplication	$k\langle a, b\rangle = \langle ka, kb\rangle$

Example 5 Operations with Vectors

Find each of the following for $\vec{r} = \langle 3, 4\rangle$, $\vec{s} = \langle 5, -1\rangle$, and $\vec{t} = \langle 1, -2\rangle$. Check your answers graphically.

a. $\vec{r} + \vec{t}$

Solve Algebraically

$\vec{r} + \vec{t} = \langle 3, 4\rangle + \langle 1, -2\rangle$

$= \langle 3 + 1, 4 + (-2)\rangle$

$= \langle 4, 2\rangle$

Check Graphically

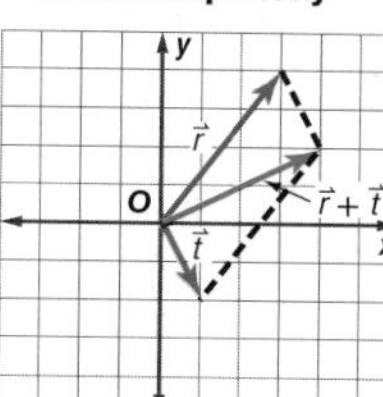

b. $\vec{s} - \vec{r}$

$\vec{s} - \vec{r} = \vec{s} + (-\vec{r})$

$= \langle 5, -1\rangle + \langle -3, -4\rangle$

$= \langle 5 + (-3), -1 + (-4)\rangle$

$= \langle 2, -5\rangle$

StudyTip

Vector Subtraction To represent vector subtraction graphically, graph the opposite of the vector that is being subtracted. For instance, in Example 5b, the opposite of $\vec{r} = \langle 3, 4\rangle$ is $-\vec{r} = \langle -3, -4\rangle$.

c. $2\vec{t} - \vec{s}$

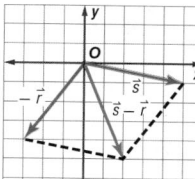

$2\vec{t} - \vec{s} = 2\vec{t} + (-\vec{s})$

$= 2\langle 1, -2\rangle + \langle -5, 1\rangle$

$= \langle 2, -4\rangle + \langle -5, 1\rangle$

$= \langle 2 + (-5), -4 + 1\rangle$

$= \langle -3, -3\rangle$

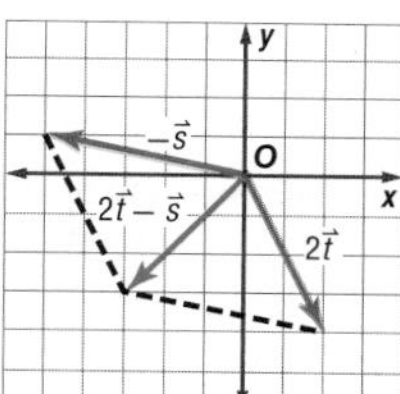

StudyTip

Scalar Multiplication The graph of a vector $k\langle a, b\rangle$ is a dilation of the vector $\langle a, b\rangle$ with scale factor k. For instance, in Example 5c, $2\vec{t} = \langle 2, -4\rangle$ is a dilation of $\vec{t} = \langle 1, -2\rangle$ with scale factor 2.

GuidedPractice 5A–5C. See margin.

5A. $\vec{t} - \vec{r}$ **5B.** $\vec{s} + 2\vec{t}$ **5C.** $\vec{s} - \vec{t}$

Additional Example

5 Find each of the following for $\vec{x} = \langle -1, 4\rangle$, $\vec{y} = \langle 3, 1\rangle$, and $\vec{z} = \langle -2, -4\rangle$.

a. $\vec{x} + \vec{y}$

$\langle 2, 5\rangle$

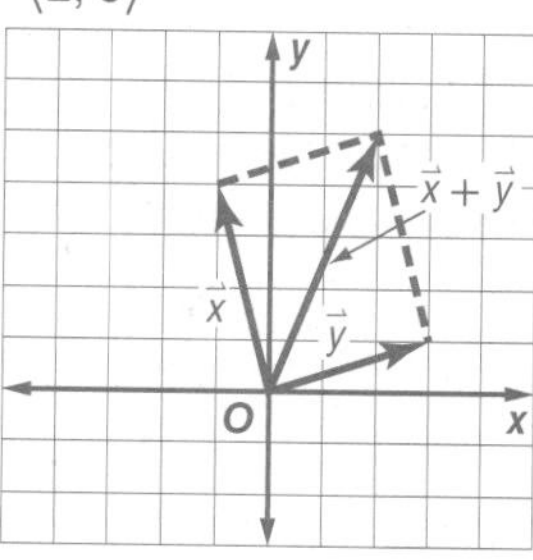

b. $\vec{z} - \vec{x}$

$\langle -1, -8\rangle$

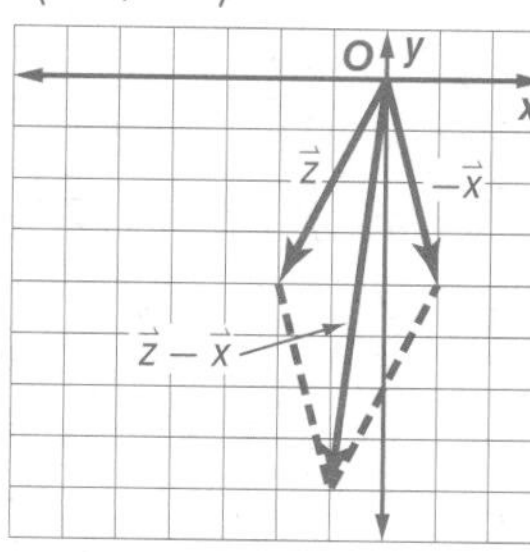

c. $2\vec{y} + \vec{z}$

$\langle 4, -2\rangle$

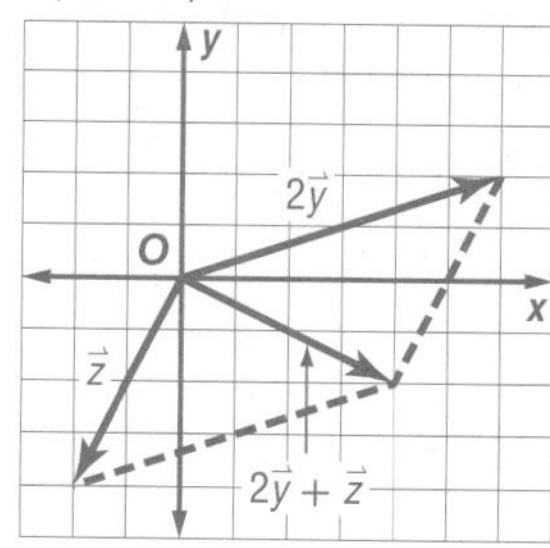

Additional Answers

5A–5C. See p. 604.

DifferentiatedInstruction AL OL

Intrapersonal Learners Have students create and plot their own examples of a pair of equivalent vectors, a pair of parallel vectors, and a vector that is multiplied by a constant. Tell students to label the magnitude and direction of each vector and find the component form of each vector. Students can then create an example of a translation with vectors and vector addition on another sheet of paper.

Example 6 shows how to use vectors to solve real-world problems.

Additional Example

6 CANOEING Suppose a person is canoeing due east across a river at 4 miles per hour. If the river is flowing south at 3 miles per hour, what is the resultant velocity of the canoe?

5 mi/h; ≈53.1° east of south

Additional Answers (Guided Practice)

5A. $\langle -2, -6 \rangle$

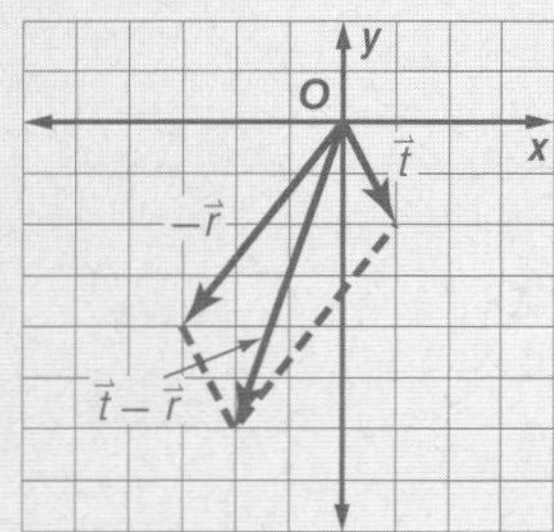

5B. $\langle 7, -5 \rangle$

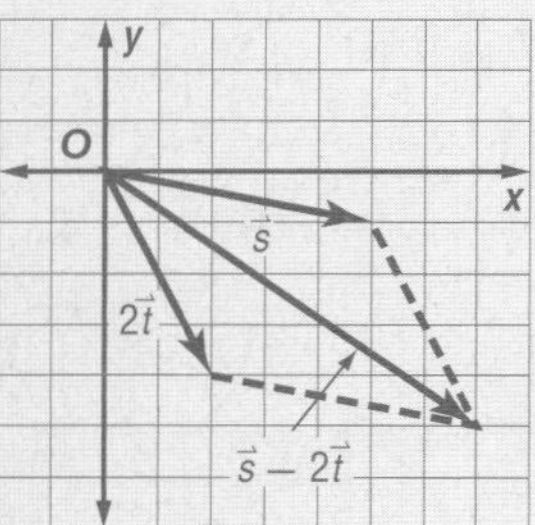

5C. $\langle 4, 1 \rangle$

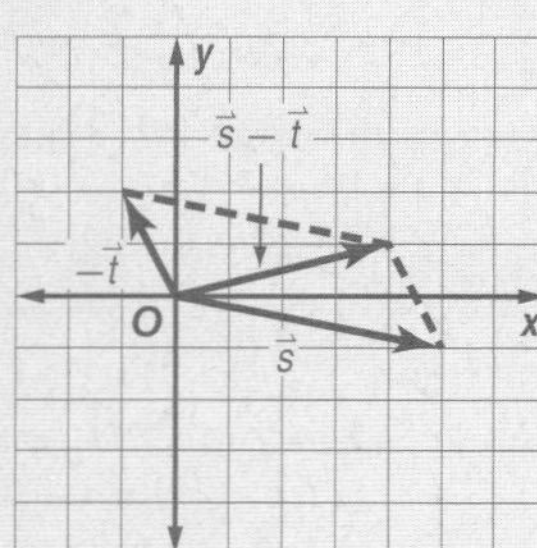

You can use vectors to solve real-world problems.

Real-WorldLink

Approximately 47% of kayakers participate in the sport one to three times per year.

Source: Outdoor Industry Association

Real-World Example 6 Vector Applications

KAYAKING Trey is paddling due north in a kayak at 7 feet per second. The river is moving with a velocity of 3 feet per second due west. What is the resultant speed and direction of the kayak to an observer on shore?

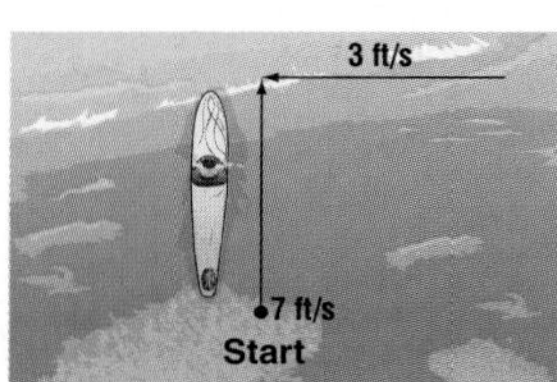

Step 1 Draw a diagram. Let $\vec{r}$ represent the resultant vector.

The component form of the vector representing the paddling velocity is $\langle 0, 7 \rangle$, and the component form of the vector representing the velocity of the river is $\langle -3, 0 \rangle$.

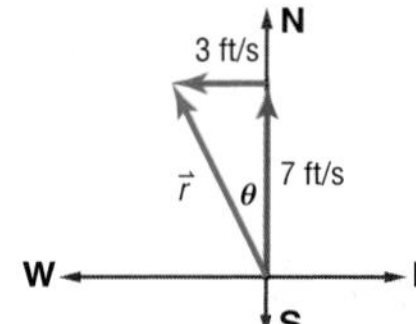

The resultant vector is $\langle 0, 7 \rangle + \langle -3, 0 \rangle$ or $\langle -3, 7 \rangle$. This vector represents the resultant velocity of the kayak, and its magnitude represents the resultant speed.

Step 2 Use the Distance Formula to find the resultant speed.

$|\vec{r}| = \sqrt{(x_2 - x_1)^2 + (y_2 - y_1)^2}$ Distance Formula

$= \sqrt{(-3 - 0)^2 + (7 - 0)^2}$ $(x_1, y_1) = (0, 0)$ and $(x_2, y_2) = (-3, 7)$

$= \sqrt{58}$ or about 7.6 Simplify.

Step 3 Use trigonometry to find the resultant direction.

$\tan \theta = \frac{3}{7}$ $\tan \theta = \frac{\text{opp}}{\text{adj}}$

$\theta = \tan^{-1} \frac{3}{7}$ Def. of inverse tangent

$\theta \approx 23.2°$ Use a calculator.

The direction of $\vec{r}$ is about 23.2° west of north.

Therefore, the resultant speed of the kayak is about 7.6 feet per second at an angle of about 23.2° west of north.

GuidedPractice

6. KAYAKING Suppose Trey starts paddling due south at a speed of 8 feet per second. If the river is flowing at a velocity of 2 feet per second due west, what is the resultant speed and direction of the kayak? $\sqrt{68}$ **or about 8.2 ft/s; 14.0° west of south**

Teaching the Mathematical Practices

Modeling Mathematically proficient students can apply the mathematics they know to solve problems arising in everyday life. In Exercise 11, encourage students to graph the resultant vector.

Check Your Understanding

= Step-by-Step Solutions begin on page R14.

Example 1 **Use a ruler and a protractor to draw each vector. Include a scale on each diagram.** 1–2. See margin.

1. $\vec{w}$ = 75 miles per hour 40° east of south
2. $\vec{h}$ = 46 feet per second 170° to the horizontal

Example 2 **Copy the vectors. Then find each sum or difference.** 3–4. See margin.

3. $\vec{c} + \vec{d}$

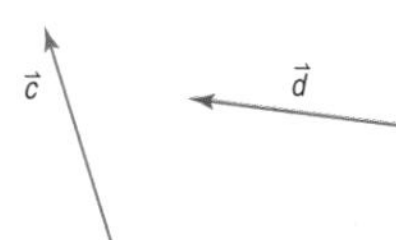

4. $\vec{y} - \vec{z}$

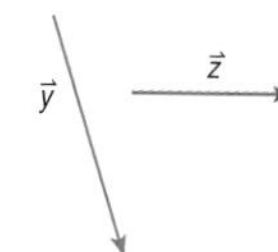

Example 3 **Write the component form of each vector.**

5. ⟨5, 5⟩

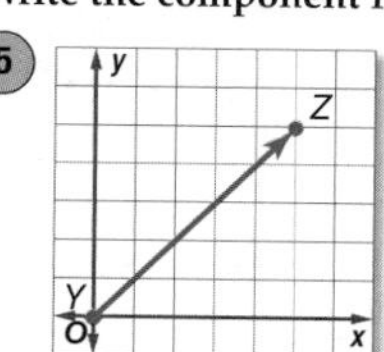

6. ⟨−6, 0⟩

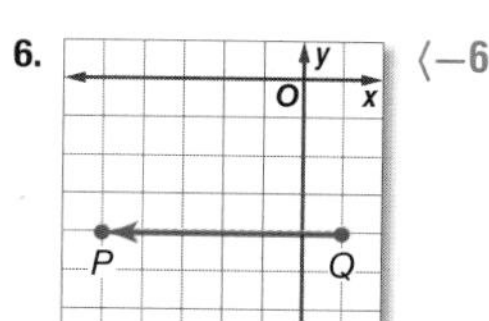

Example 4 **Find the magnitude and direction of each vector.**

7. $\vec{t} = \langle 2, -4 \rangle$ $\sqrt{20}$; ≈ 296.6°
8. $\vec{f} = \langle -6, -5 \rangle$ $\sqrt{61}$; ≈ 219.8°

Example 5 **Find each of the following for $\vec{a} = \langle -4, 1 \rangle$, $\vec{b} = \langle -1, -3 \rangle$, and $\vec{c} = \langle 3, 5 \rangle$. Check your answers graphically.** 9–10. See margin.

9. $\vec{c} + \vec{a}$
10. $2\vec{b} - \vec{a}$

Example 6 11. CCSS **MODELING** A plane is traveling due north at a speed of 350 miles per hour. If the wind is blowing from the west at a speed of 55 miles per hour, what is the resultant speed and direction that the airplane is traveling? ≈ 354.3 mi/h at angle of 8.9° east of north

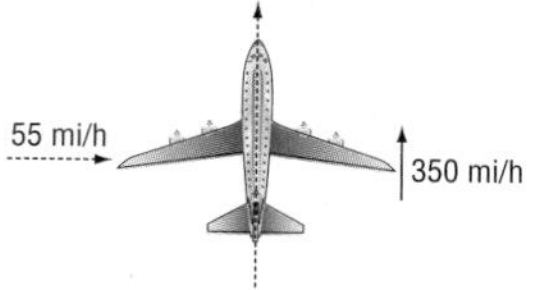

Practice and Problem Solving

Extra Practice is on page R8.

Example 1 **Use a ruler and a protractor to draw each vector. Include a scale on each diagram.**

12. $\vec{g}$ = 60 inches per second at 145° to the horizontal 12–15. See Chapter 8 Answer Appendix
13. $\vec{n}$ = 8 meters at an angle of 24° west of south
14. $\vec{a}$ = 32 yards per minute at 78° to the horizontal
15. $\vec{k}$ = 95 kilometers per hour at angle of 65° east of north

Differentiated Homework Options

Level	Assignment	Two-Day Option	
AL Basic	12–42, 49–56, 58–70	13–41 odd, 54–57	12–45 even, 49–56, 58–70
OL Core	13–45 odd, 46–47, 58–70	12–42, 54–57	43–53, 58–70
BL Advanced	43–67, (optional: 68–70)		

3 Practice

Formative Assessment

Use Exercises 1–11 to check for understanding.

Use the chart at the bottom of this page to customize assignments for your students.

Additional Answers

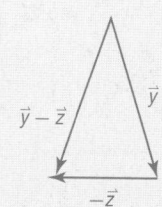

1.

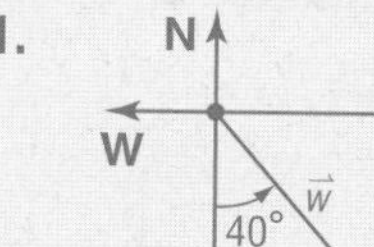

1 in. : 60 mi/h

2.

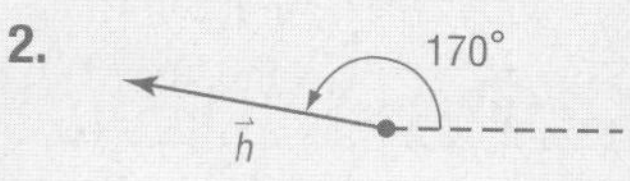

1 cm : 20 ft/s

3.

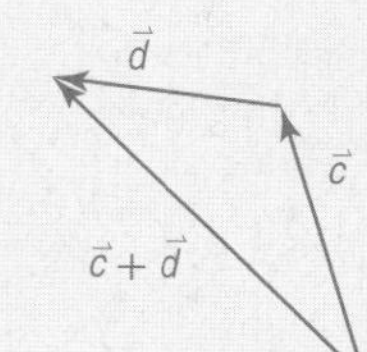

4.

9. ⟨−1, 6⟩

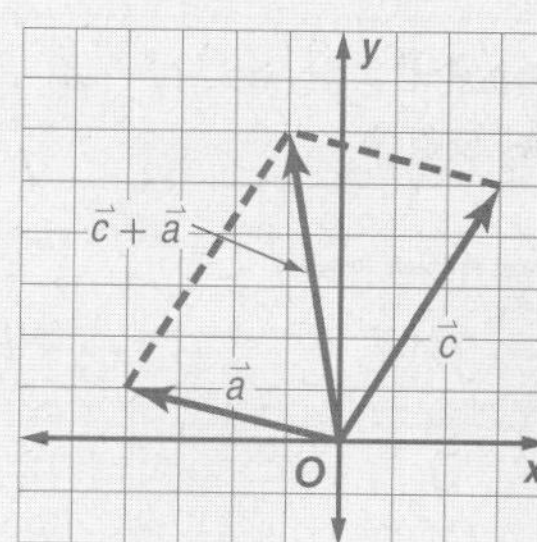

10. ⟨2, −7⟩

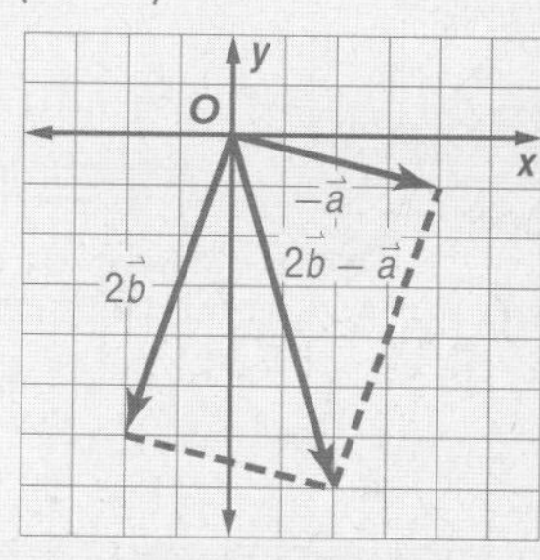

Study Guide and Intervention
AL OL ELL

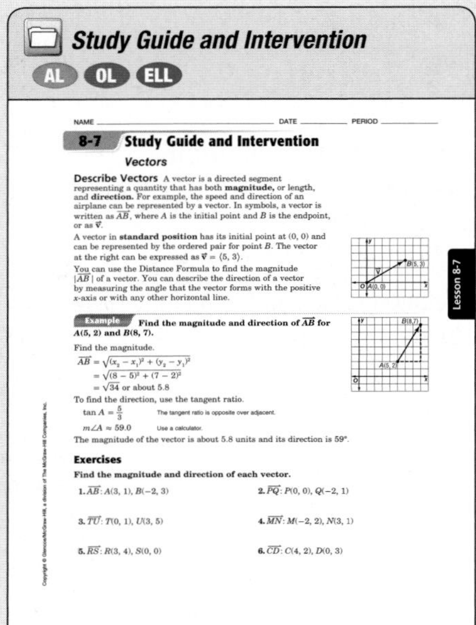
NAME ______ DATE ______ PERIOD ______

8-7 Study Guide and Intervention

Vectors

Describe Vectors A vector is a directed segment representing a quantity that has both **magnitude,** or length, and **direction.** For example, the speed and direction of an airplane can be represented by a vector. In symbols, a vector is written as $\overrightarrow{AB}$, where A is the initial point and B is the endpoint, or as $\vec{v}$.

A vector in **standard position** has its initial point at (0, 0) and can be represented by the ordered pair for point B. The vector at the right can be expressed as $\vec{v} = \langle 5, 3 \rangle$.

You can use the Distance Formula to find the magnitude $|\overrightarrow{AB}|$ of a vector. You can describe the direction of a vector by measuring the angle that the vector forms with the positive x-axis or with any other horizontal line.

Example Find the magnitude and direction of $\overrightarrow{AB}$ for $A(5, 2)$ and $B(8, 7)$.

Find the magnitude.

$\overrightarrow{AB} = \sqrt{(x_2 - x_1)^2 + (y_2 - y_1)^2}$

$= \sqrt{(8-5)^2 + (7-2)^2}$

$= \sqrt{34}$ or about 5.8

To find the direction, use the tangent ratio.

$\tan A = \frac{5}{3}$ The tangent ratio is opposite over adjacent.

$m\angle A \approx 59.0$ Use a calculator.

The magnitude of the vector is about 5.8 units and its direction is 59°.

Exercises

Find the magnitude and direction of each vector.

1. $\overrightarrow{AB}$: $A(3, 1)$, $B(-2, 3)$
2. $\overrightarrow{PQ}$: $P(0, 0)$, $Q(-2, 1)$
3. $\overrightarrow{TU}$: $T(0, 1)$, $U(3, 5)$
4. $\overrightarrow{MN}$: $M(-2, 2)$, $N(3, 1)$
5. $\overrightarrow{RS}$: $R(3, 4)$, $S(0, 0)$
6. $\overrightarrow{CD}$: $C(4, 2)$, $D(0, 3)$

Practice
AL OL BL ELL

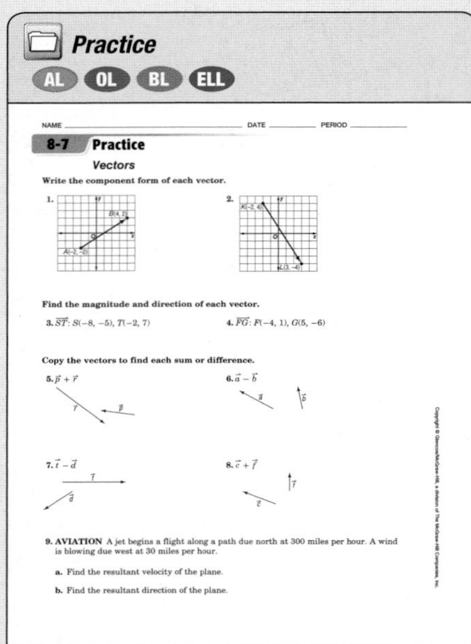
NAME ______ DATE ______ PERIOD ______

8-7 Practice

Vectors

Write the component form of each vector.

1. 2.

Find the magnitude and direction of each vector.

3. $\overrightarrow{ST}$: $S(-8, -5)$, $T(-2, 7)$
4. $\overrightarrow{FG}$: $F(-4, 1)$, $G(5, -6)$

Copy the vectors to find each sum or difference.

5. $\vec{p} + \vec{r}$
6. $\vec{a} - \vec{b}$
7. $\vec{t} - \vec{d}$
8. $\vec{c} + \vec{f}$

9. **AVIATION** A jet begins a flight along a path due north at 300 miles per hour. A wind is blowing due west at 30 miles per hour.

a. Find the resultant velocity of the plane.

b. Find the resultant direction of the plane.

Word Problem Practice
AL OL BL ELL

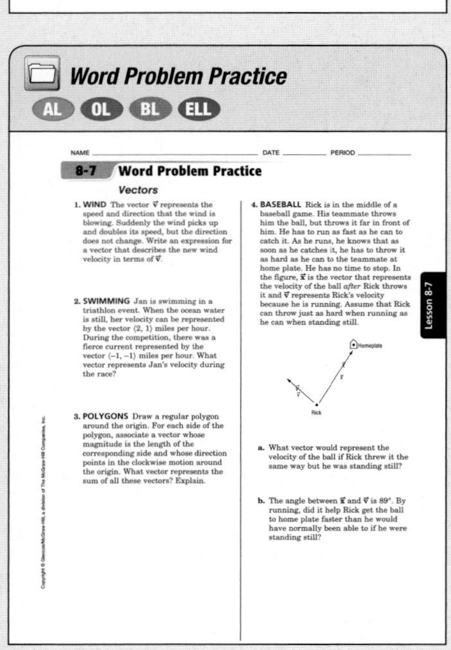
NAME ______ DATE ______ PERIOD ______

8-7 Word Problem Practice

Vectors

1. **WIND** The vector $\vec{v}$ represents the speed and direction that the wind is blowing. Suddenly the wind picks up and doubles its speed, but the direction does not change. Write an expression for a vector that describes the new wind velocity in terms of $\vec{v}$.

2. **SWIMMING** Jan is swimming in a triathlon event. When the ocean water is still, her velocity can be represented by the vector ⟨2, 1⟩ miles per hour. During the competition, there was a fierce current represented by the vector ⟨−1, −1⟩ miles per hour. What vector represents Jan's velocity during the race?

3. **POLYGONS** Draw a regular polygon around the origin. For each side of the polygon, associate a vector whose magnitude is the length of the corresponding side and whose direction points in the clockwise motion around the origin. What vector represents the sum of all these vectors? Explain.

4. **BASEBALL** Rick is in the middle of a baseball game. His teammate throws him the ball, but throws it far in front of him. He has to run as fast as he can to catch it. As he runs, he knows that as soon as he catches it, he has to throw it as hard as he can to the teammate at home plate. He has no time to stop. In the figure, $\vec{x}$ is the vector that represents the velocity of the ball *after* Rick throws it and $\vec{v}$ represents Rick's velocity because he is running. Assume that Rick can throw just as hard when running as he can when standing still.

a. What vector would represent the velocity of the ball if Rick threw it the same way but he was standing still?

b. The angle between $\vec{x}$ and $\vec{v}$ is 89°. By running, did it help Rick get the ball to home plate faster than he would have normally been able to if he were standing still?

Example 2 **Copy the vectors. Then find each sum or difference.** 16–21. See Ch. 8 Answer Appendix.

16. $\vec{t} - \vec{m}$

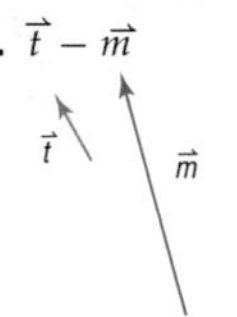

17. $\vec{j} - \vec{k}$

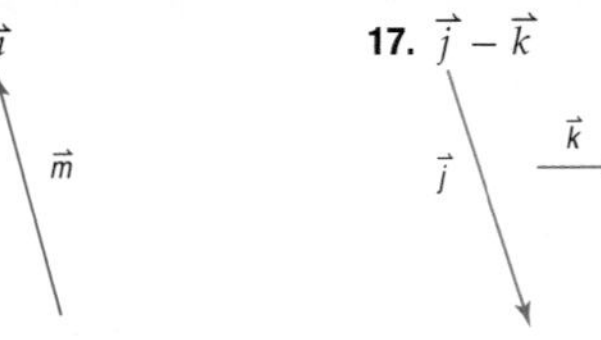

18. $\vec{w} + \vec{z}$

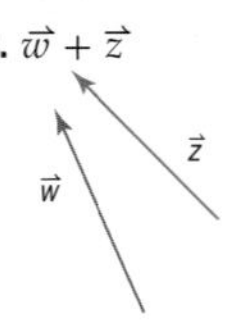

19. $\vec{c} + \vec{a}$

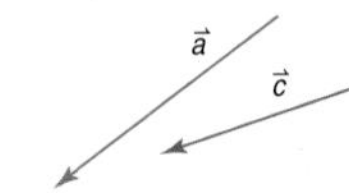

20. $\vec{d} - \vec{f}$

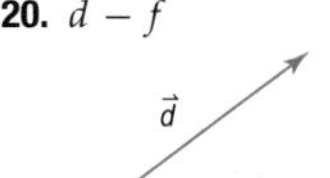

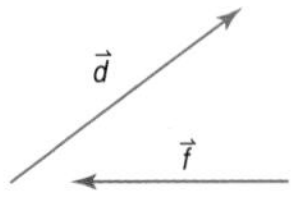

21. $\vec{t} - \vec{m}$

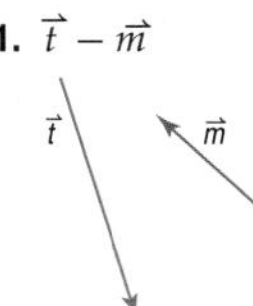

Example 3 **Write the component form of each vector.**

22. ⟨0, 4⟩

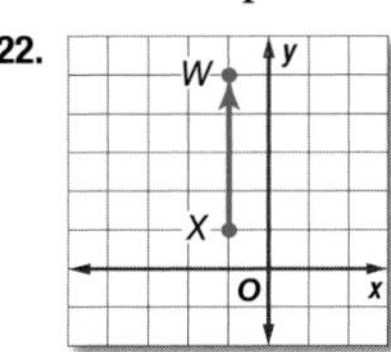

23. ⟨5, 0⟩

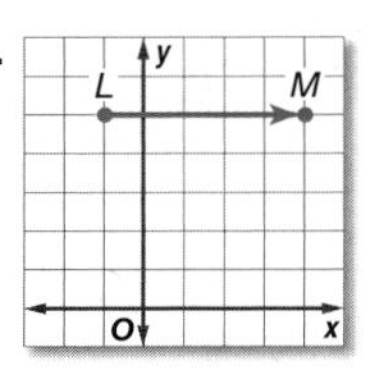

24. ⟨2, 5⟩

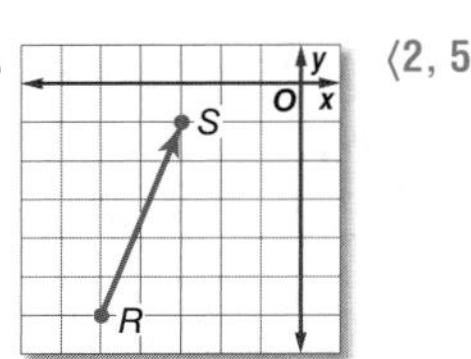

25. 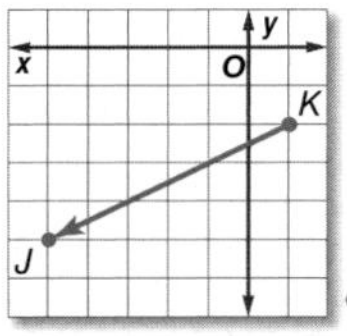 ⟨−6, −3⟩

26. ⟨−5, 4⟩

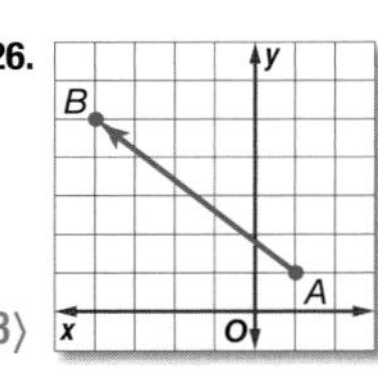

27. ⟨−3, −6⟩

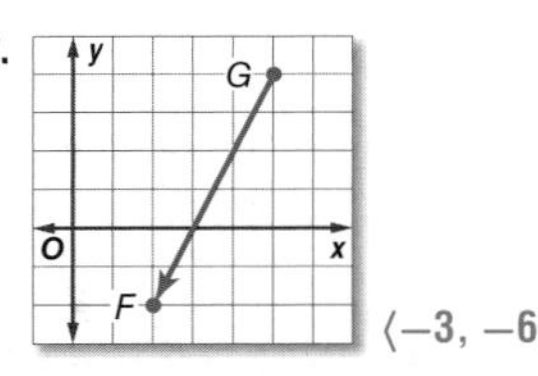

28. **FIREWORKS** The ascent of a firework shell can be modeled using a vector. Write a vector in component form that can be used to describe the path of the firework shown. ⟨70, 350⟩

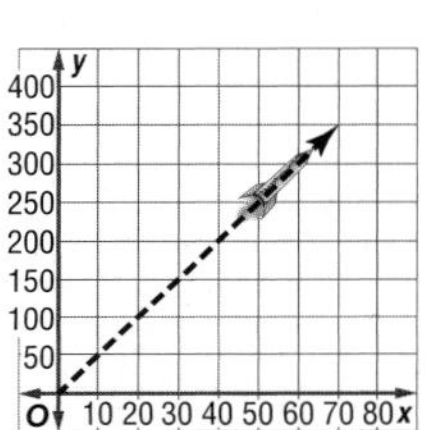

Example 4 **CCSS SENSE-MAKING Find the magnitude and direction of each vector.**

29. $\vec{c} = \langle 5, 3 \rangle$ $\sqrt{34}$; ≈ 31.0°
30. $\vec{m} = \langle 2, 9 \rangle$ $\sqrt{85}$; ≈ 77.5°
31. $\vec{z} = \langle -7, 1 \rangle$ $\sqrt{50}$; ≈ 171.9°
32. $\vec{d} = \langle 4, -8 \rangle$ $\sqrt{80}$; ≈ 296.6°
33. $\vec{k} = \langle -3, -6 \rangle$ $\sqrt{45}$; ≈ 243.4°
34. $\vec{q} = \langle -9, -4 \rangle$ $\sqrt{97}$; ≈ 204.0°

Example 5 **Find each of the following for $\vec{a} = \langle -3, -5 \rangle$, $\vec{b} = \langle 2, 4 \rangle$, and $\vec{c} = \langle 3, -1 \rangle$. Check your answers graphically.** 35–40. See Ch. 8 Answer Appendix.

35. $\vec{b} + \vec{c}$
36. $\vec{c} + \vec{a}$
37. $\vec{b} - \vec{c}$
38. $\vec{a} - \vec{c}$
39. $2\vec{c} - \vec{a}$
40. $2\vec{b} + \vec{c}$

Enrichment
OL BL

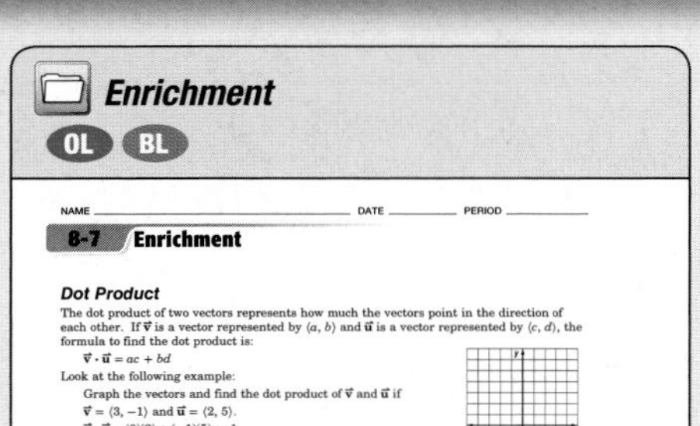
NAME ______ DATE ______ PERIOD ______

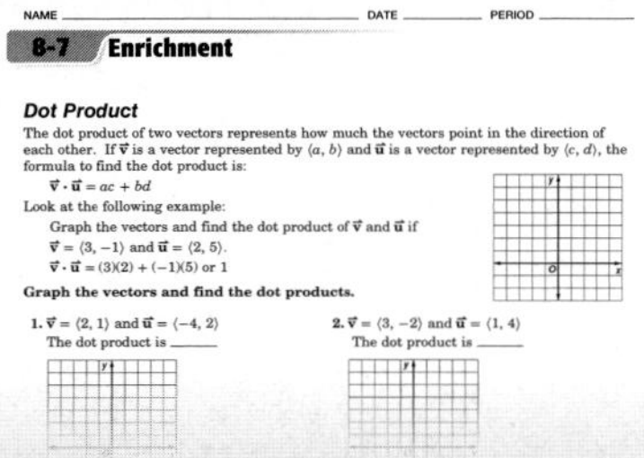

8-7 Enrichment

Dot Product

The dot product of two vectors represents how much the vectors point in the direction of each other. If $\vec{v}$ is a vector represented by (a, b) and $\vec{u}$ is a vector represented by (c, d), the formula to find the dot product is:

$\vec{v} \cdot \vec{u} = ac + bd$

Look at the following example:

Graph the vectors and find the dot product of $\vec{v}$ and $\vec{u}$ if $\vec{v} = (3, -1)$ and $\vec{u} = (2, 5)$.

$\vec{v} \cdot \vec{u} = (3)(2) + (-1)(5)$ or 1

Graph the vectors and find the dot products.

1. $\vec{v} = (2, 1)$ and $\vec{u} = (-4, 2)$ The dot product is ______
2. $\vec{v} = (3, -2)$ and $\vec{u} = (1, 4)$ The dot product is ______

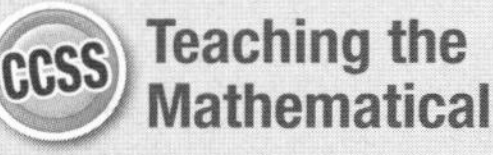

Teaching the Mathematical Practices

Sense-Making Mathematically proficient students start by explaining the meaning of a problem to themselves and looking for entry points to its solution. They plan a solution pathway rather than simply jumping into a solution attempt. In Exercises 29–34, encourage students to make a plan to solve each problem first.

41. **HIKING** Amy hiked due east for 2 miles and then hiked due south for 3 miles.

a. Draw a diagram to represent the situation, where $\vec{r}$ is the resultant vector. **See margin.**

b. How far and in what direction is Amy from her starting position? **3.6 mi at an angle of 33.7° east of south**

42. **EXERCISE** A runner's velocity is 6 miles per hour due east, with the wind blowing 2 miles per hour due north.

a. Draw a diagram to represent the situation, where $\vec{r}$ is the resultant vector. **See margin.**

b. What is the resultant velocity of the runner? **6.3 mi/h at an angle of 71.6° east of north**

Find each of the following for $\vec{f} = \langle -4, -2 \rangle$, $\vec{g} = \langle 6, 1 \rangle$, and $\vec{h} = \langle 2, -3 \rangle$.

43. $\vec{f} + \vec{g} + \vec{h}$ **$\langle 4, -4 \rangle$**

44. $\vec{h} - 2\vec{f} + \vec{g}$ **$\langle 16, 2 \rangle$**

45. $2\vec{g} - 3\vec{f} + \vec{h}$ **$\langle 26, 5 \rangle$**

46. **HOMECOMING** Nikki is on a committee to help plan her school's homecoming parade. The parade starts at the high school and continues as shown.

a. Find the magnitude and direction of the vector formed with an initial point at the school and terminal point at the end of the parade. **$\sqrt{26} \approx 5.1$; $\approx 348.7°$**

b. Find the length of the parade if 1 unit = 0.25 mile. **≈ 2.1 mi**

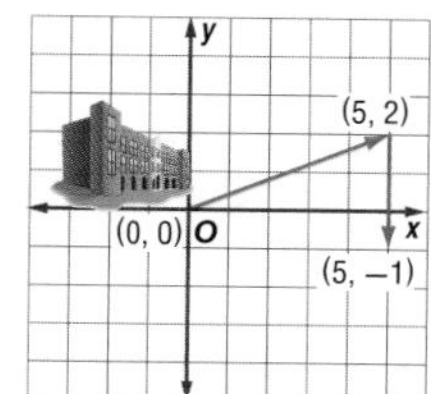

47. **SWIMMING** Jonas is swimming from the east bank to the west bank of a stream at a speed of 3.3 feet per second. The stream is 80 feet wide and flows south. If Jonas crosses the stream in 20 seconds, what is the speed of the current? **2.3 ft/s**

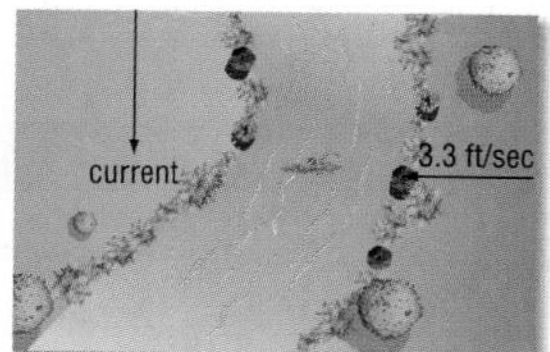

H.O.T. Problems Use Higher-Order Thinking Skills

48. **CHALLENGE** Find the coordinates of point P on $\overline{AB}$ that partitions the segment into the given ratio AP to PB.

a. $A(0, 0)$, $B(0, 6)$, 2 to 1 **(0, 4)**

b. $A(0, 0)$, $B(-15, 0)$, 2 to 3 **(−6, 0)**

49. **CCSS PRECISION** Are parallel vectors *sometimes*, *always*, or *never* opposite vectors? Explain. **See margin.**

PROOF **Prove each vector property. Let $\vec{a} = \langle x_1, y_1 \rangle$ and $\vec{b} = \langle x_2, y_2 \rangle$.**

50. commutative: $\vec{a} + \vec{b} = \vec{b} + \vec{a}$

51. scalar multiplication: $k(\vec{a} + \vec{b}) = k\vec{a} + k\vec{b}$, where k is a scalar
50–51. See margin.

52. **OPEN ENDED** Draw a set of parallel vectors.

a. Find the sum of the two vectors. What is true of the direction of the vector representing the sum?

b. Find the difference of the two vectors. What is true of the direction of the vector representing the difference?
52a–52b. See Ch. 8 Answer Appendix.

53. **WRITING IN MATH** Compare and contrast the parallelogram and triangle methods of adding vectors. **See margin.**

CCSS Teaching the Mathematical Practices

Precision Mathematically proficient students use clear definitions in discussion with others and in their own reasoning. In Exercise 49, encourage students to analyze the definitions of parallel vectors and opposite vectors.

Additional Answers

41a.

N, S, W, E, 2 mi, 3 mi, θ, $\vec{r}$

42a.

N, S, W, E, 6 mi/h, 2 mi/h, θ, $\vec{r}$

48. $\sqrt{20} \approx 4.5$ m/s; $\approx 26.6°$

49. Sometimes; sample answer: Parallel vectors can either have the same or opposite direction.

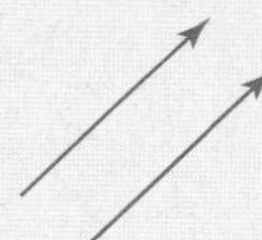

50.
$$\begin{aligned} \vec{a} + \vec{b} &= \langle x_1, y_1 \rangle + \langle x_2, y_2 \rangle \\ &= \langle x_1 + x_2, y_1 + y_2 \rangle \\ &= \langle x_2 + x_1, y_2 + y_1 \rangle \\ &= \langle x_2, y_2 \rangle + \langle x_1, y_1 \rangle \\ &= \vec{b} + \vec{a} \end{aligned}$$

51.
$$\begin{aligned} k(\vec{a} + \vec{b}) &= k(\langle x_1, y_1 \rangle + \langle x_2, y_2 \rangle) \\ &= k\langle x_1 + x_2, y_1 + y_2 \rangle \\ &= \langle k(x_1 + x_2), k(y_1 + y_2) \rangle \\ &= \langle kx_1 + kx_2, ky_1 + ky_2 \rangle \\ &= \langle kx_1, ky_1 \rangle + \langle kx_2, ky_2 \rangle \\ &= k\langle x_1, y_1 \rangle + k\langle x_2, y_2 \rangle \\ &= k\vec{a} + k\vec{b} \end{aligned}$$

53. The initial point of the resultant starts at the initial point of the first vector in both methods. However, in the parallelogram method, both vectors start at the same initial point, whereas, in the triangle method, the resultant connects the initial point of the first vector and the terminal point of the second. The resultant is the diagonal of the parallelogram formed using the parallelogram method.

4 Assess

Name the Math Students can practice naming vector parts and explaining how vectors apply to real-world situations. Select examples or create examples, and select students to use the vocabulary terms and concepts of this lesson to analyze the problems aloud in class.

Formative Assessment

Check for student understanding of Lesson 8-7.

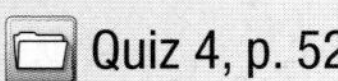 Quiz 4, p. 52

Additional Answers

68. $\triangle 1 \cong \triangle 10$, $\triangle 2 \cong \triangle 9$, $\triangle 3 \cong \triangle 8$, $\triangle 4 \cong \triangle 7$, $\triangle 5 \cong \triangle 6$

69. $\triangle$s 1–4, $\triangle$s 5–12, $\triangle$s 13–20

70. $\triangle$s 1, 5, 6, and 11, $\triangle$s 3, 8, 10, and 12, $\triangle$s 2, 4, 7, and 9

Standardized Test Practice

54. **EXTENDED RESPONSE** Sydney parked her car and hiked along two paths described by the vectors (2, 3) and (5, −1).
    a. What vector represents her hike along both paths? $\langle 2, 3\rangle + \langle 5, -1\rangle = \langle 7, 2\rangle$
    b. When she got to the end of the second path, how far is she from her car if the numbers represent miles? $\sqrt{7^2 + 2^2} = \sqrt{53}$ or ≈ 7.3 mi

55. In right triangle ABC shown below, what is the measure of $\angle A$ to the nearest tenth of a degree? **B**

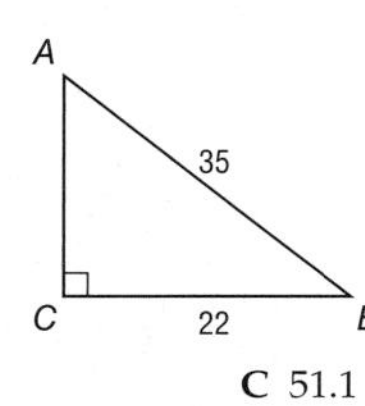

A 32.2   C 51.1
B 38.9   D 57.8

56. **PROBABILITY** A die is rolled. Find the probability of rolling a number greater than 4. **G**

F 0.17   G 0.33   H 0.5   J 0.67

57. **SAT/ACT** Caleb followed the two paths shown below to get to his house C from a store S. What is the total distance of the two paths, in meters, from C to S? **D**

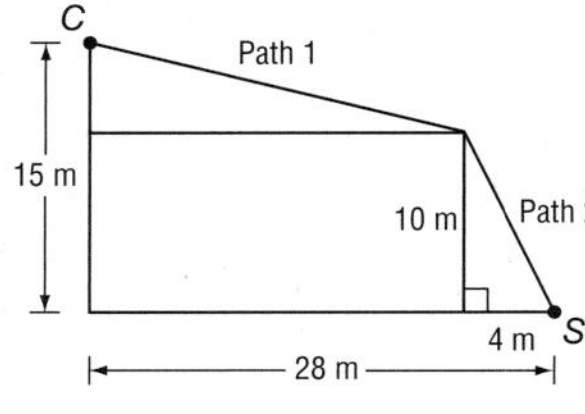

A 10.8 m   D 35.3 m
B 24.5 m   E 38.4 m
C 31.8 m

Spiral Review

Find x. Round angle measures to the nearest degree and side measures to the nearest tenth. (Lesson 8-6)

58. 50.6   59. 72.0

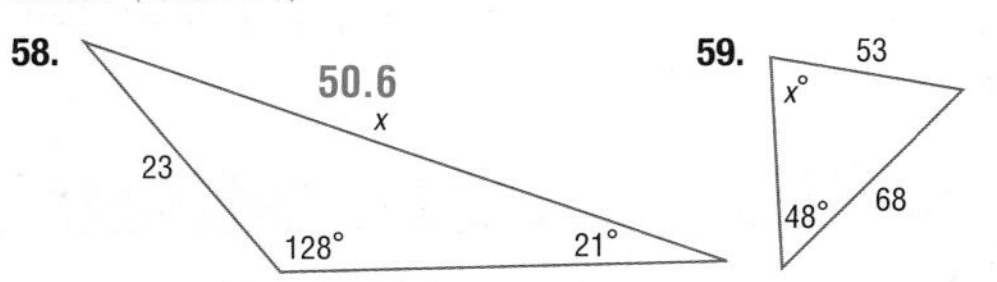

60. 117.6

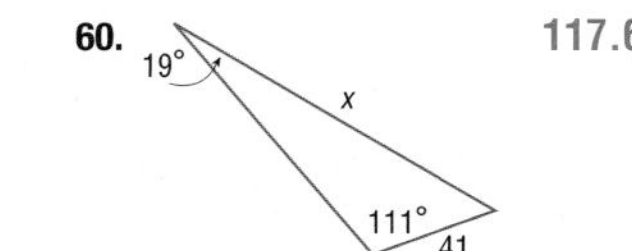

61. **SOCCER** Adelina is in a soccer stadium 80 feet above the field. The angle of depression to the field is 12°. What is the horizontal distance between Adelina and the soccer field? (Lesson 8-5) **376.4**

Quadrilateral $WXYZ$ is a rectangle. Find each measure if $m\angle 1 = 30$. (Lesson 6-4)

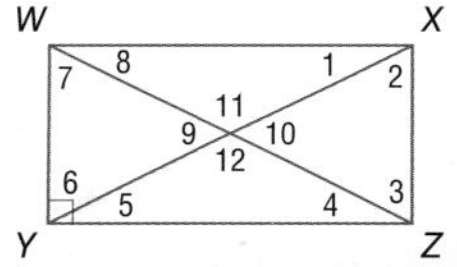

62. $m\angle 2$ **60**   63. $m\angle 8$ **30**   64. $m\angle 12$ **120**

65. $m\angle 5$ **30**   66. $m\angle 6$ **60**   67. $m\angle 3$ **60**

Skills Review

Assume that segments and angles that appear to be congruent in each figure are congruent. Indicate which triangles are congruent. **68–70. See margin.**

68.

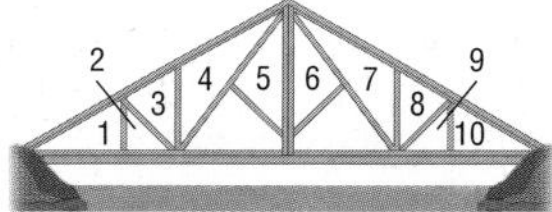

69.

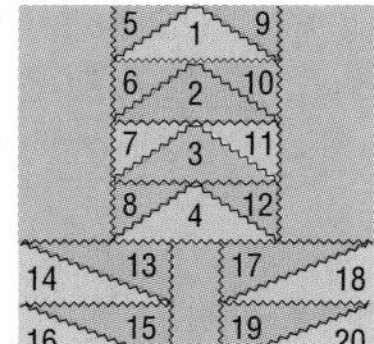

70.

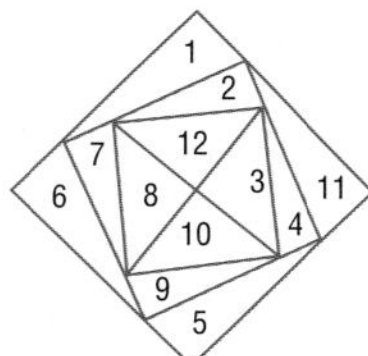

608 | Lesson 8-7 | Vectors

8-7 Geometry Lab: Adding Vectors

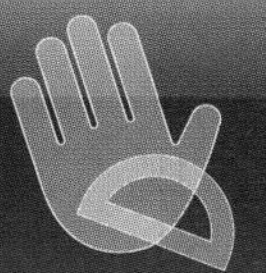

You can use scale drawings to represent vectors and solve problems.

Activity

A small aircraft flies due south at an average speed of 175 miles per hour. The wind is blowing 30° south of west at 25 miles per hour. What is the resultant velocity and direction of the plane?

Step 1 **Choose a scale.**

Since it is not reasonable to represent the vectors using their actual sizes, you can use a scale drawing. For this activity, let 2 inches represent 100 miles.

Step 2 **Make a scale drawing.**

Use a ruler and protractor to make a scale drawing of the two vectors.

Step 3 **Find the resultant.**

Find the resultant of the two vectors by using the triangle method or the parallelogram method.

Step 4 **Measure the resultant.**

Measure the length and angle of the resultant. The resultant length is $3\frac{3}{4}$ inches, and it makes a 7° angle with the vector representing the velocity of the plane.

Step 5 **Find the magnitude and direction of the resultant.**

Use the scale with the length that you measured in Step 4 to calculate the magnitude of the plane's resultant velocity.

$$3\frac{3}{4}\ \cancel{\text{in.}} \times \frac{100 \text{ mph}}{2\ \cancel{\text{in.}}} = 187.5 \text{ mph}$$

2 in. = 100 mph

Velocity of plane 3.5 in.

wind velocity 0.5 in.

The resultant velocity of the plane is 187.5 miles per hour 7° west of south.

Exercises

Make a scale drawing to solve each problem.

1. **BIKING** Lance is riding his bike west at a velocity of 10 miles per hour. The wind is blowing 5 miles per hour 20° north of east. What is Lance's resultant velocity and direction? **See margin.**

2. **CANOEING** Bianca is traveling due north across a river in a canoe with a current of 3 miles per hour due west. If Bianca can canoe at a rate of 7 miles per hour, what is her resultant velocity and direction? **7.6 mph 23° west of north**

Additional Answer

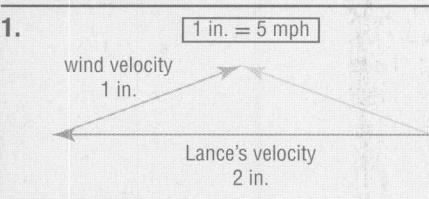

1. 1 in. = 5 mph

wind velocity 1 in.

Lance's velocity 2 in.

5.6 mph 18° north of west

1 Focus

Objective Use scale drawings and direct measurement to find the resultant of two vectors.

Materials for Each Group

- ruler
- protractor

Teaching Tip

Explain to students that, although the scale of the drawing is arbitrary, it should be chosen to make the work convenient and meaningful.

2 Teach

Working in Cooperative Groups

Have students work in mixed ability pairs. Have students alternate the steps of the activity.

Remind students that to answer the original question, they must be sure to use the conversion factor to get an answer in the original units, as in Step 4.

Practice Have students complete Exercises 1 and 2.

3 Assess

Formative Assessment

Use Exercises 1 and 2 to assess students' understanding of using scale drawings to represent vectors.

From Concrete to Abstract

Have students determine the resultant velocity when two wind speeds are blowing in opposite directions.

Formative Assessment

KeyVocabulary The page references after each word denote where that term was first introduced. If students have difficulty answering questions 1–10, remind them that they can use these page references to refresh their memories about the vocabulary terms.

Summative Assessment

Vocabulary Test, p. 54

Vocabulary Review

Vocabulary Review provides students the opportunity to check their understanding of important concepts and terminology in an online game format.

FOLDABLES StudyOrganizer

Dinah Zike's Foldables®

Have students look through the chapter to make sure they have included examples in their Foldables for each tab. Suggest that students keep their Foldables handy while completing the Study Guide and Review pages. Point out that their Foldables can serve as a quick review tool for studying for the chapter test.

CHAPTER 8 Study Guide and Review

Study Guide

KeyConcepts

Geometric Mean (Lesson 8-1)

- For two positive numbers a and b, the geometric mean is the positive number x where $a : x = x : b$ is true.

Pythagorean Theorem (Lesson 8-2)

- Let $\triangle ABC$ be a right triangle with right angle C. Then $a^2 + b^2 = c^2$.

Special Right Triangles (Lesson 8-3)

- The measures of the sides of a 45°-45°-90° triangle are x, x, and $x\sqrt{2}$.
- The measures of the sides of a 30°-60°-90° triangle are x, $2x$, and $x\sqrt{3}$.

Trigonometry (Lesson 8-4)

- $\sin A = \dfrac{\text{opposite leg}}{\text{hypotenuse}}$
- $\cos A = \dfrac{\text{adjacent leg}}{\text{hypotenuse}}$
- $\tan A = \dfrac{\text{opposite leg}}{\text{adjacent leg}}$

Angles of Elevation and Depression (Lesson 8-5)

- An angle of elevation is the angle formed by a horizontal line and the line of sight to an object above.
- An angle of depression is the angle formed by a horizontal line and the line of sight to an object below.

Laws of Sines and Cosines (Lesson 8-6)

Let $\triangle ABC$ be any triangle.

- Law of Sines: $\dfrac{\sin A}{a} = \dfrac{\sin B}{b} = \dfrac{\sin C}{c}$
- Law of Cosines: $a^2 = b^2 + c^2 - 2bc \cos A$
  $b^2 = a^2 + c^2 - 2ac \cos B$
  $c^2 = a^2 + b^2 - 2ab \cos C$

Vectors (Lesson 8-7)

- A vector is a quantity with both magnitude and direction.

FOLDABLES StudyOrganizer

Be sure the Key Concepts are noted in your Foldable.

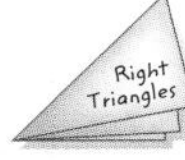

KeyVocabulary

angle of depression (p. 580)	Law of Sines (p. 588)
angle of elevation (p. 580)	magnitude (p. 600)
component form (p. 602)	Pythagorean triple (p. 548)
cosine (p. 568)	resultant (p. 601)
direction (p. 600)	sine (p. 568)
geometric mean (p. 537)	standard position (p. 602)
inverse cosine (p. 571)	tangent (p. 568)
inverse sine (p. 571)	trigonometric ratio (p. 568)
inverse tangent (p. 571)	trigonometry (p. 568)
Law of Cosines (p. 589)	vector (p. 600)

VocabularyCheck

State whether each sentence is *true* or *false.* If *false,* replace the underlined word or phrase to make a true sentence.

1. The arithmetic mean of two numbers is the positive square root of the product of the numbers. **false, geometric**
2. Extended ratios can be used to compare three or more quantities. **true**
3. To find the length of the hypotenuse of a right triangle, take the square root of the difference of the squares of the legs. **false, sum**
4. An angle of elevation is the angle formed by a horizontal line and an observer's line of sight to an object below the horizon. **false, depression**
5. The sum of two vectors is the resultant. **true**
6. Magnitude is the angle a vector makes with the x-axis. **false, length of the vector**
7. A vector is in standard position when the initial point is at the origin. **true**
8. The component form of a vector describes the vector in terms of change in x and change in y. **true**
9. The Law of Sines can be used to find an angle measure when given three side lengths. **false, Law of Cosines**
10. A trigonometric ratio is a ratio of the lengths of two sides of a right triangle. **true**

Lesson-by-Lesson Review

8-1 Geometric Mean

Find the geometric mean between each pair of numbers.

11. 9 and 4 6

12. $\sqrt{20}$ and $\sqrt{80}$ $\sqrt{40}$

13. $\frac{8\sqrt{2}}{3}$ and $\frac{4\sqrt{2}}{3}$ $\frac{8}{3}$

14. Find *x*, *y*, and *z*.
$x = 2\sqrt{13}$,
$y = 3\sqrt{13}$, $z = 6$

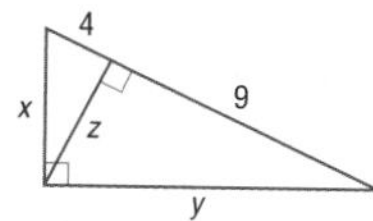

15. DANCES Mike is hanging a string of lights on his barn for a square dance. Using a book to sight the top and bottom of the barn, he can see he is 15 feet from the barn. If his eye level is 5 feet from the ground, how tall is the barn? 50 ft

Example 1

Find the geometric mean between 10 and 15.

$x = \sqrt{ab}$	Definition of geometric mean
$= \sqrt{10 \cdot 15}$	$a = 10$ and $b = 15$
$= \sqrt{(5 \cdot 2) \cdot (3 \cdot 5)}$	Factor.
$= \sqrt{25 \cdot 6}$	Associative Property
$= 5\sqrt{6}$	Simplify.

18. yes; right
$25^2 \stackrel{?}{=} 7^2 + 24^2$
$625 = 49 + 576$

19. yes; acute
$16^2 \stackrel{?}{=} 13^2 + 15^2$
$256 < 169 + 225$

20. yes; acute
$88^2 \stackrel{?}{=} 65^2 + 72^2$
$7744 < 4225 + 5184$

8-2 The Pythagorean Theorem and Its Converse

Find *x*.

16. $2\sqrt{221} \approx 29.7$

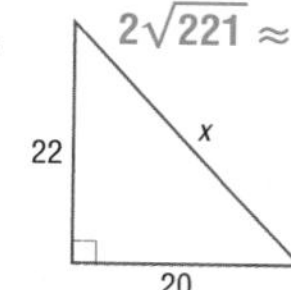

17.

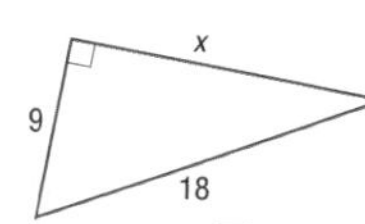

$9\sqrt{3} \approx 15.6$

Determine whether each set of numbers can be the measures of the sides of a triangle. If so, classify the triangle as *acute*, *obtuse*, or *right*. Justify your answer.

18. 7, 24, 25

19. 13, 15, 16

20. 65, 72, 88

21. SWIMMING Alexi walks 27 meters south and 38 meters east to get around a lake. Her sister swims directly across the lake. How many meters to the nearest tenth did Alexi's sister save by swimming? 18.4 m

Example 2

Find *x*.

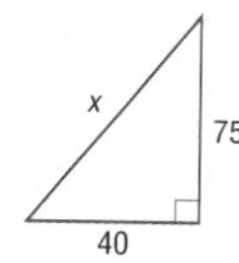

The side opposite the right angle is the hypotenuse, so $c = x$.

$a^2 + b^2 = c^2$	Pythagorean Theorem
$40^2 + 75^2 = x^2$	$a = 40$ and $b = 75$
$7225 = x^2$	Simplify.
$\sqrt{7225} = x$	Take the positive square root of each side.
$85 = x$	Simplify.

Lesson-by-Lesson Review

Intervention If the given examples are not sufficient to review the topics covered by the questions, remind students that the lesson references tell them where to review that topic in their textbooks.

Two-Day Option Have students complete the Lesson-by-Lesson Review. Then you can use eAssessment to customize another review worksheet that practices all the objectives of this chapter or only the objectives on which your students need more help.

Additional Answer

24. 10 ft. sample answer: since the ground and the side of the play structure make a 90° angle, this is a 30°-60°-90° triangle. The short side is 5 feet. The climbing wall will be the hypotenuse, so it is 10 feet.

CHAPTER 8 Study Guide and Review *Continued*

8-3 Special Right Triangles

Find x and y.

22.

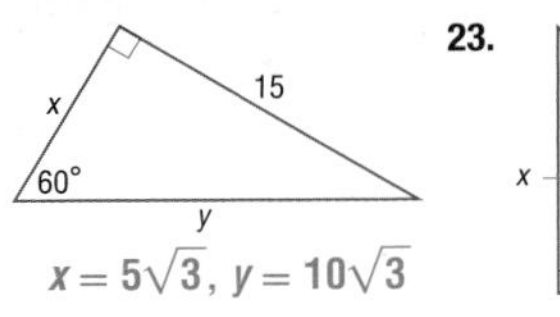

$x = 5\sqrt{3},\ y = 10\sqrt{3}$

23.

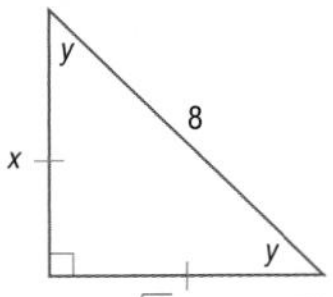

$x = 4\sqrt{2},\ y = 45°$

24. CLIMBING Jason is adding a climbing wall to his little brother's swing-set. If he starts building 5 feet out from the existing structure, and wants it to have a 60° angle, how long should the wall be? **See margin.**

Example 3

Find x and y.

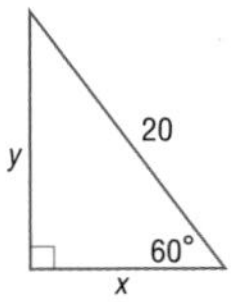

The measure of the third angle in this triangle is 90 – 60 or 30. This is a 30°-60°-90° triangle.

$h = 2s$	30°-60°-90° Triangle Theorem
$20 = 2x$	Substitute.
$10 = x$	Divide.

Now find y, the length of the longer leg.

$\ell = s\sqrt{3}$	30°-60°-90° Triangle Theorem
$y = 10\sqrt{3}$	Substitute.

8-4 Trigonometry

Express each ratio as a fraction and as a decimal to the nearest hundredth.

25. sin A **26.** tan B
27. sin B **28.** cos A
29. tan A **30.** cos B

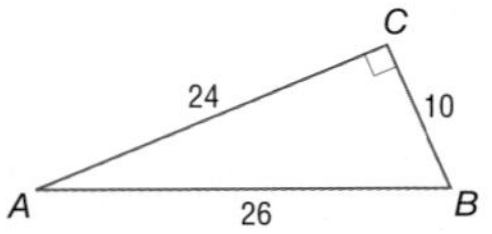

Find x.

31. **32.**

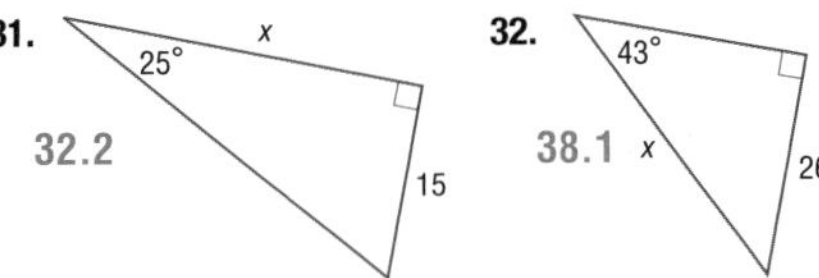

33. GARDENING Sofia wants to put a flower bed in the corner of her yard by laying a stone border that starts 3 feet from the corner of one fence and ends 6 feet from the corner of the other fence. Find the angles, x and y, the fence make with the border. **63.4° and 26.6°**

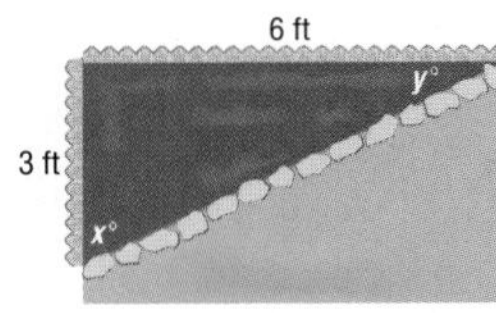

Example 4

Express each ratio as a fraction and as a decimal to the nearest hundredth.

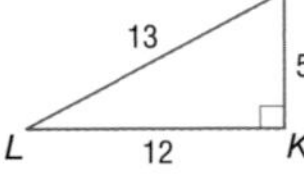

a. sin L

$\sin L = \frac{5}{13}$ or about 0.38 $\qquad \sin L = \frac{\text{opp}}{\text{hyp}}$

b. cos L

$\cos L = \frac{12}{13}$ or about 0.92 $\qquad \cos L = \frac{\text{adj}}{\text{hyp}}$

c. tan L

$\tan L = \frac{5}{12}$ or 0.42 $\qquad \tan L = \frac{\text{opp}}{\text{adj}}$

25. $\frac{5}{13}$, 0.38
26. $\frac{12}{5}$, 2.40
27. $\frac{12}{13}$, 0.92
28. $\frac{12}{13}$, 0.92
29. $\frac{5}{12}$, 0.42
30. $\frac{5}{13}$, 0.38

612 | Chapter 8 | Study Guide and Review

8-5 Angles of Elevation and Depression

34. **JOBS** Tom delivers papers on a rural route from his car. If he throws a paper from a height of 4 feet, and it lands 15 feet from the car, at what angle of depression did he throw the paper to the nearest degree? **15°**

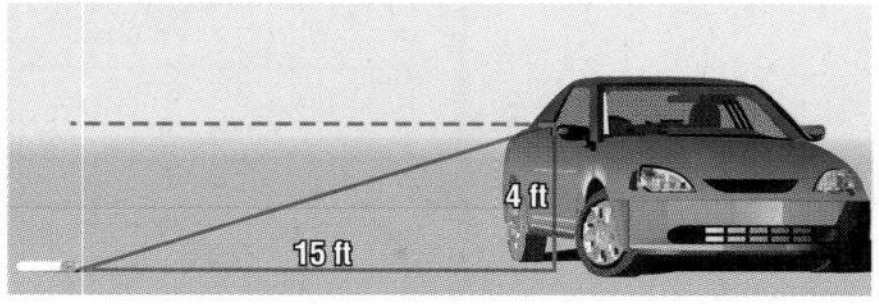

35. **TOWER** There is a cell phone tower in the field across from Jen's house. If Jen walks 50 feet from the tower, and finds the angle of elevation from her position to the top of the tower to be 60°, how tall is the tower? **86.6 ft**

Example 5

Sarah's cat climbed up a tree. If she sights her cat at an angle of elevation of 40°, and her eyes are 5 feet off the ground, how high up from the ground is her cat?

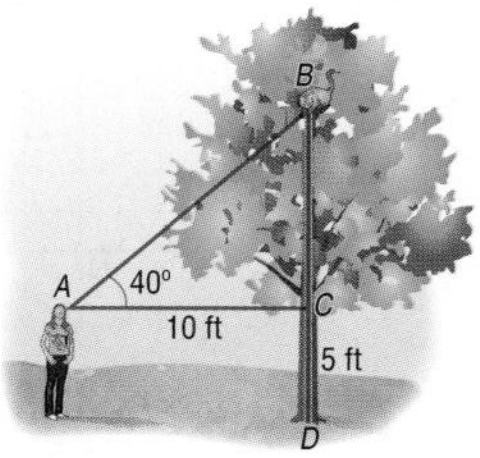

To find the how high the cat is up the tree, find *CB*.

$\tan 40 = \frac{CB}{10}$ — $\tan = \frac{\text{opposite}}{\text{adjacent}}$

$10(\tan 40) = CB$ — Multiply each side by 10.

$8.4 = CB$ — Simplify.

Since Sarah's eyes are 5 feet from the ground, add 5 to 8.4. Sarah's cat is 13.4 feet up.

8-6 The Law of Sines and Law of Cosines

Find *x*. Round angle measures to the nearest degree and side measures to the nearest tenth.

36. **15.0**

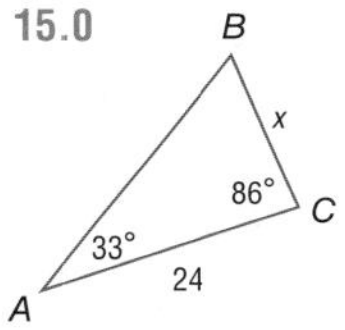

37. **15.2**

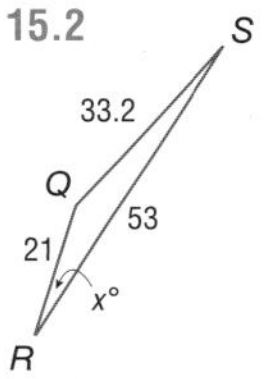

38. **SKIING** At Crazy Ed's Ski resort, Ed wants to put in another ski lift for the skiers to ride from the base to the summit of the mountain. The run over which the ski lift will go is represented by the figure below. The length of the lift is represented by *SB*. If Ed needs twice as much cable as the length of $\overline{SB}$, how much cable does he need? **3601.7 ft**

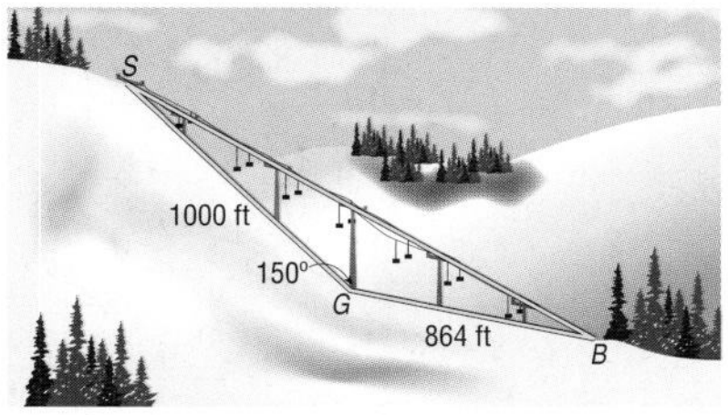

Example 6

Find *x*. Round to the nearest tenth.

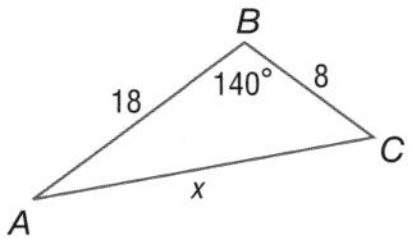

We are given the measures of two sides and their included angle, so use the Law of Cosines.

$b^2 = a^2 + c^2 - 2ac\cos B$ — Law of Cosines

$x^2 = 8^2 + 18^2 - 2(8)(18)\cos 140°$ — Substitution

$x^2 = 388 - 288\cos 140°$ — Simplify.

$x = \sqrt{388 - 288\cos 140°} \approx 24.7$ — Take the square root of each side.

Example 7

Find *x*. Round to the nearest tenth.

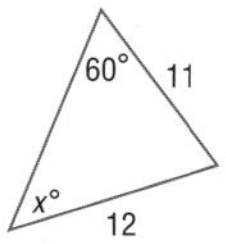

$\frac{\sin A}{a} = \frac{\sin C}{c}$ — Law of Sines

$\frac{\sin 60}{12} = \frac{\sin x}{11}$ — Substitution

$11\sin 60° = 12\sin x$ — Cross Products Property

$\frac{11\sin 60}{12} = \sin x$ — Divide each side by 12.

$x = \sin^{-1}\frac{11\sin 60}{12}$ or about 52.5°

connectED.mcgraw-hill.com 613

Anticipation Guide

Have students complete the Chapter 8 Anticipation Guide and discuss how their responses have changed now that they have completed Chapter 8.

Anticipation Guide, p. 3

8-7 Vectors

39. Write the component form of the vector shown. **⟨−6, −5⟩**

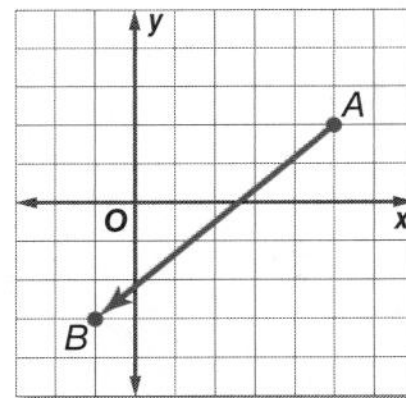

40. Copy the vectors to find $\vec{a} + \vec{b}$.

41. Given that $\vec{s}$ is $\langle 2, -6\rangle$ and $\vec{t}$ is $\langle -10, 7\rangle$, find the component form of $\vec{s} + \vec{t}$. **⟨−8, 1⟩**

40.

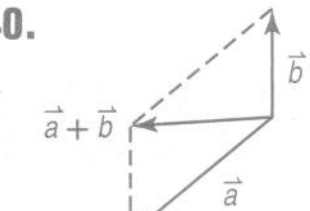

Example 8

Find the magnitude and direction of $\overrightarrow{AB}$ for $A(1, 2)$ and $B(-1, 5)$.

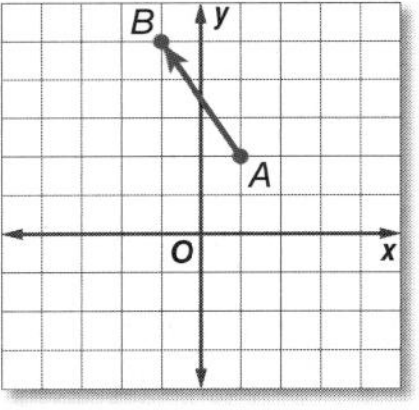

Use the Distance Formula to find the magnitude.

$|\overrightarrow{AB}| = \sqrt{(x_2 - x_1)^2 + (y_2 - y_1)^2}$ Distance Formula

$= \sqrt{(-1 - 1)^2 + (5 - 2)^2}$ Substitute.

$= \sqrt{13}$ or about 3.6 Simplify.

Draw a right triangle with hypotenuse $\overrightarrow{AB}$ and acute angle A.

$\tan A = \left|\frac{5 - 2}{-1 - 1}\right|$ or $\frac{3}{2}$ $\tan = \frac{\text{opp}}{\text{adj}}$; length cannot be negative.

$m\angle A = \tan^{-1}\left(-\frac{3}{2}\right)$ Def. of inverse tangent

≈ -56.3 Use a calculator.

The direction of $\overrightarrow{AB}$ is 180 − 56.3 or 123.7°.

CHAPTER 8 Practice Test

Find the geometric mean between each pair of numbers.

1. 7 and 11 $\sqrt{77} \approx 8.8$
2. 12 and 9 $6\sqrt{3} \approx 10.4$
3. 14 and 21 $7\sqrt{6} \approx 17.1$
4. $4\sqrt{3}$ and $10\sqrt{3}$ $2\sqrt{30} \approx 11.0$
5. Find x, y, and z. $x = 6$, $y = 2\sqrt{13}$, $z = 3\sqrt{13}$

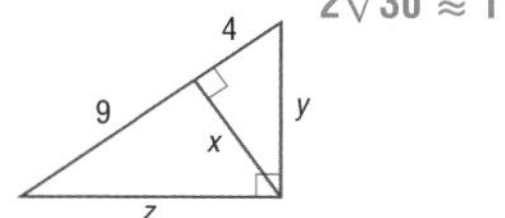

6. **FAIRS** Blake is setting up his tent at a renaissance fair. If the tent is 8 feet tall, and the tether can be staked no more than two feet from the tent, how long should the tether be? 8.2 ft

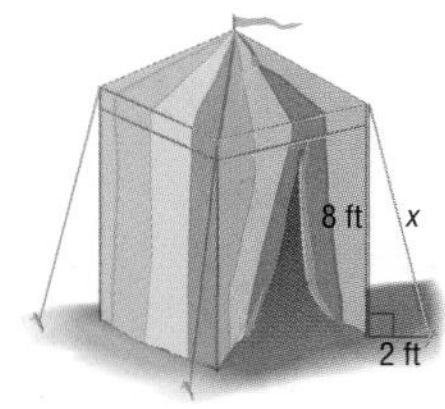

Use a calculator to find the measure of $\angle R$ to the nearest tenth.

7. 70.9
8. 39.6

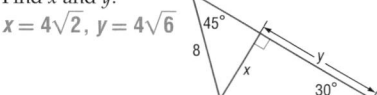

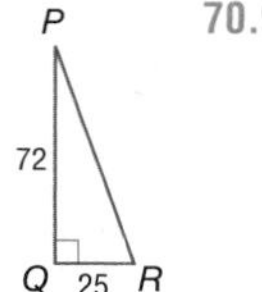

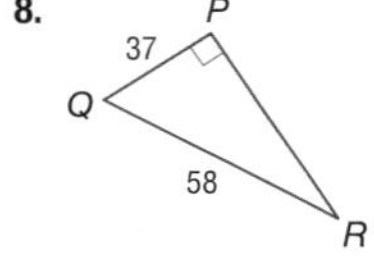

9. Find x and y. $x = 4\sqrt{2}$, $y = 4\sqrt{6}$

Express each ratio as a fraction and as a decimal to the nearest hundredth.

10. $\cos X$ 10–13. See margin.
11. $\tan X$
12. $\tan V$
13. $\sin V$

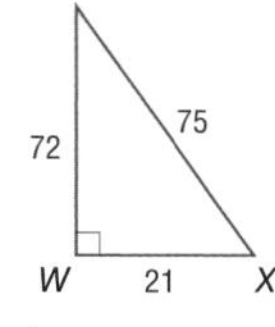

Find the magnitude and direction of each vector.

14. $\overrightarrow{JK}$: $J(-6, -4)$ and $K(-10, -4)$ 4 units; 180°
15. $\overrightarrow{RS}$: $R(1, 0)$ and $S(-2, 3)$ $3\sqrt{2}$; 135°

16. **SPACE** Anna is watching a space shuttle launch 6 miles from Cape Canaveral in Florida. When the angle of elevation from her viewing point to the shuttle is 80°, how high is the shuttle, if it is going straight up? 34 mi

Find x. Round angle measures to the nearest degree and side measures to the nearest tenth.

17. 34.8
18. 40

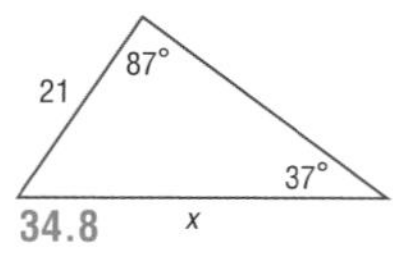

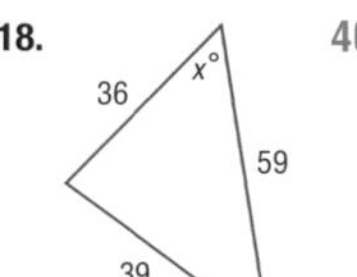

19. **MULTIPLE CHOICE** Which of the following is the length of the leg of a 45°-45°-90° triangle with a hypotenuse of 20? B
   - A 10
   - B $10\sqrt{2}$
   - C 20
   - D $20\sqrt{2}$

Find x.

20. 26
21. $\sqrt{320} \approx 17.9$

22. **WHALE WATCHING** Isaac is looking through binoculars on a whale watching trip when he notices a sea otter in the distance. If he is 20 feet above sea level in the boat, and the angle of depression is 30°, how far away from the boat is the otter to the nearest foot? 35 ft

Write the component form of each vector.

23. $\langle 6, 3\rangle$
24. $\langle 2, 2\rangle$

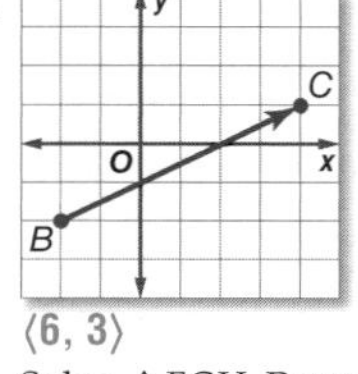

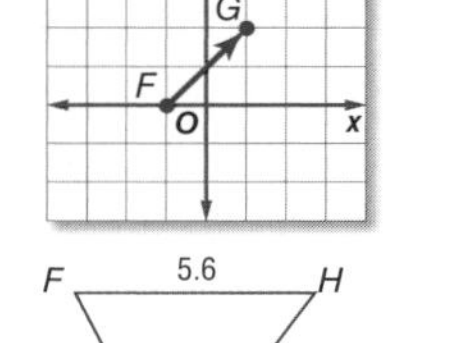

25. Solve $\triangle FGH$. Round to the nearest degree. $m\angle H = 58$, $m\angle G = 55$, $m\angle F = 67$

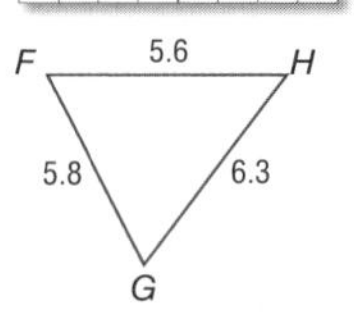

Summative Assessment

Use these alternate leveled chapter tests to differentiate assessment for your students.

Leveled Chapter 8 Tests

Form	Type	Level	Page(s)
1	MC	AL	55–56
2A	MC	OL	57–58
2B	MC	OL	59–60
2C	FR	OL	61–62
2D	FR	OL	63–64
3	FR	BL	65–66
Vocabulary Test			54
Extended-Response Test			67

MC = multiple-choice questions
FR = free-response questions

eAssessment Customize and create multiple versions of your chapter test and their answer keys. All of the questions from the leveled chapter tests in the *Chapter 8 Resource Masters* are also available on eAssessment.

Additional Answers

10. $\frac{21}{75} = 0.28$
11. $\frac{72}{21} \approx 3.43$
12. $\frac{21}{72} \approx 0.29$
13. $\frac{21}{75} = 0.28$

InterventionPlanner

Tier 1 On Level OL

If students miss about 25% of the exercises or less,

Then choose a resource:

SE Lessons 8-1, 8-2, 8-3, 8-4, 8-5, 8-6, and 8-7

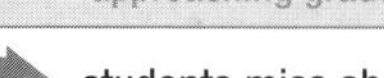 Skills Practice, pp. 7, 13, 20, 26, 32, 38, and 45

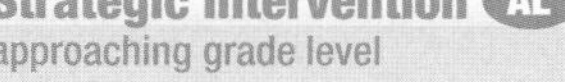 connectED.mcgraw-hill.com Self-Check Quiz

Tier 2 Strategic Intervention AL approaching grade level

If students miss about 50% of the exercises,

Then choose a resource:

 Study Guide and Intervention, pp. 5, 11, 18, 24, 30, 36, 43

 connectED.mcgraw-hill.com Extra Examples, Personal Tutor, Homework Help

Tier 3 Intensive Intervention 2 or more grades below level

If students miss about 75% of the exercises,

Then use *Math Triumphs, Geo.*, Ch. 6

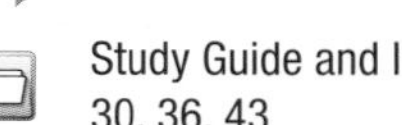 connectED.mcgraw-hill.com Extra Examples, Personal Tutor, Homework Help, Review Vocabulary

1 Focus

Objective Learn to use formulas to solve problems on standardized tests.

2 Teach

Scaffolding Questions

Ask:

- When have you used formulas to solve problems in other classes? Answers will vary.
- What are some ways to remember formulas from this chapter? Sample answer: The mnemonic device SOH-CAH-TOA can be used to remember the trigonometric ratios sine, cosine, and tangent.
- What formulas do you know how to derive if you cannot remember them exactly? Sample answer: The Pythagorean Theorem can be used to derive the 45°-45°-90° and 30°-60°-90° Triangle Theorems.

CHAPTER 8 Preparing for Standardized Tests

Use a Formula

Sometimes it is necessary to use a formula to solve problems on standardized tests. In some cases you may even be given a sheet of formulas that you are permitted to reference while taking the test.

Formulas

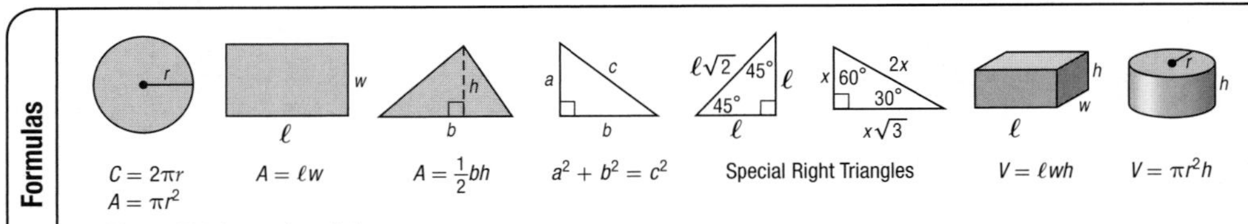

The are 360 degrees in a circle.
The sum of the measures of the angles of a triangle is 180.

Strategies for Using a Formula

Step 1

Read the problem statement carefully.

Ask yourself:

- What am I being asked to solve?
- What information is given in the problem?
- Are there any formulas that I can use to help me solve the problem?

Step 2

Solve the problem.

- Substitute the known quantities that are given in the problem statement into the formula.
- Simplify to solve for the unknown values in the formula.

Step 3

Check your solution.

- Determine a reasonable range of values for the answer.
- Check to make sure that your answer makes sense.
- If time permits, check your answer.

616 | Chapter 8 | Preparing for Standardized Tests

Standardized Test Example

Read the problem. Identify what you need to know. Then use the information in the problem to solve.

The ratio of the width to the height of a high-definition television is 16:9. This is also called the *aspect ratio* of the television. The size of a television is given in terms of the diagonal distance across the screen. If an HD television is 25.5 inches tall, what is its screen size?

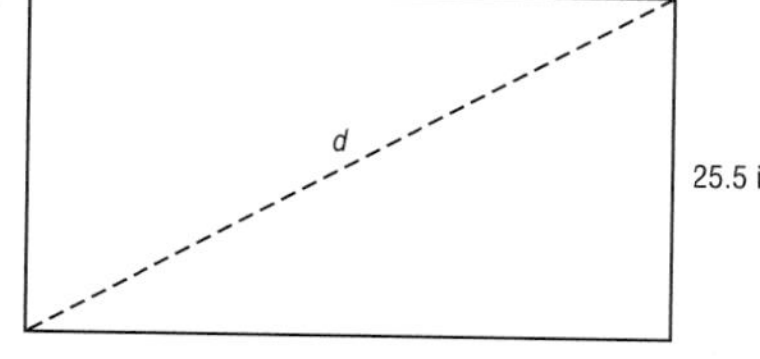

A 48 inches
B 50 inches
C 51 inches
D 52 inches

Read the problem statement carefully. You are given the height of the screen and the ratio of the width to the height. You are asked to find the diagonal distance of the screen. You can use the **Pythagorean Theorem** to solve the problem.

Find the width of the screen. Set up and solve a proportion using the aspect ratio 16:9.

$\frac{16}{9} = \frac{w}{25.5}$ ← width of the screen / ← height of the screen

$9w = 408$ Cross Products Property

$w = 45\frac{1}{3}$ Divide each side by 9.

So, the width of the screen is $45\frac{1}{3}$ inches. Use the Pythagorean Theorem to solve for the diagonal distance.

$c^2 = a^2 + b^2$ Pythagorean Theorem

$c^2 = (25.5)^2 + \left(45\frac{1}{3}\right)^2$ Substitute for a and b.

$c \approx 52.01$ Simplify. Take the square root of both sides to solve for c.

The diagonal distance of the screen is about 52 inches. So, the answer is D.

Exercises

Read each problem. Identify what you need to know. Then use the information in the problem to solve.

1. Christine is flying a kite on the end of a taut string. The kite is 175 feet above the ground and is a horizontal distance of 130 feet from where Christine is standing. How much kite string has Christine let out? Round to the nearest foot. B

A 204 ft
B 218 ft
C 225 ft
D 236

2. What is the value of x below to the nearest tenth? F

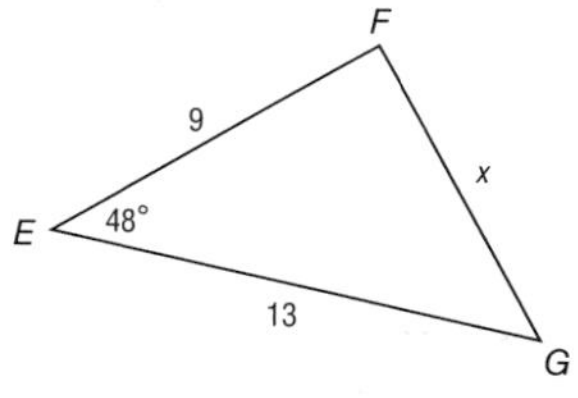

F 9.7 **G** 10.2 **H** 10.5 **J** 11.1

Additional Example

The ratio of the width and height of a standard television is 4 : 3. This is also called the *aspect ratio* of the television. The size of the television is given in terms of the diagonal across the screen. If a standard television is 21.6 inches wide, what is the screen size? B

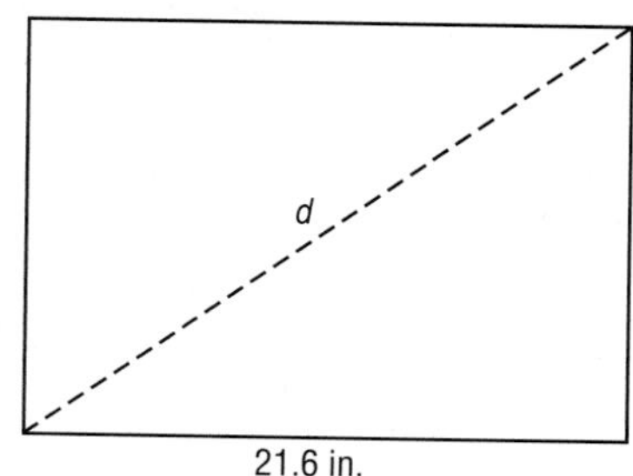

A 16.2 inches
B 27 inches
C 37.8 inches
D 42 inches

3 Assess

Use Exercises 1 and 2 to assess students' understanding.

Diagnose Student Errors

Survey student responses for each item. Class trends may indicate common errors and misconceptions.

1. A correct
B arithmetic error
C arithmetic error
D arithmetic error

2. F multiplied 90 by $\sqrt{3}$ instead of $\sqrt{2}$
G arithmetic error
H correct
J arithmetic error

3. A correct
B arithmetic error
C arithmetic error
D arithmetic error

4. F incorrect ratio used
G correct
H incorrect ratio used
J used formula for sine

5. A incorrect definition
B incorrect definition
C correct
D added angles incorrectly

6. F correct
G incorrect ratio used
H incorrect ratio used
J used formula for cosine

CHAPTER 8

Standardized Test Practice

Cumulative, Chapters 1 through 8

Multiple Choice

Read each question. Then fill in the correct answer on the answer document provided by your teacher or on a sheet of paper.

1. What is the value of x in the figure below? A

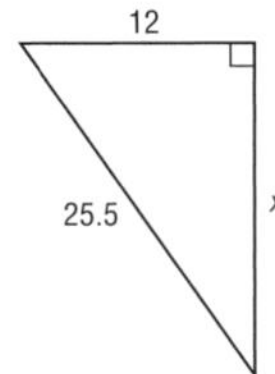

A 22.5

B 23

C 23.5

D 24

2. A baseball diamond is a square with 90-ft sides. What is the length from 3rd base to 1st base? Round to the nearest tenth. H

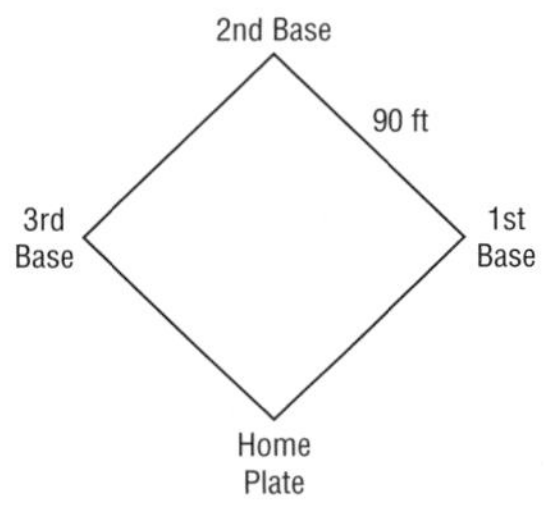

F 155.9 ft

G 141.6 ft

H 127.3 ft

J 118.2 ft

Test-TakingTip

Question 1 Some test items require the use of a formula to solve them. Use the Pythagorean Theorem to find x.

3. The scale of a map is 1 inch = 4.5 kilometers. What is the distance between two cities that are 2.4 inches apart on the map? A

A 10.8 kilometers

B 11.1 kilometers

C 11.4 kilometers

D 11.5 kilometers

4. What is the value of x in the figure below? Round to the nearest tenth. G

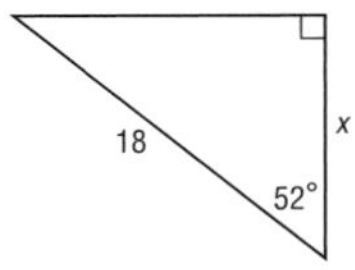

F 10.5

G 11.1

H 13.6

J 14.2

5. What type of triangle is formed by the locations of Lexington, Somerset, and Bowling Green? C

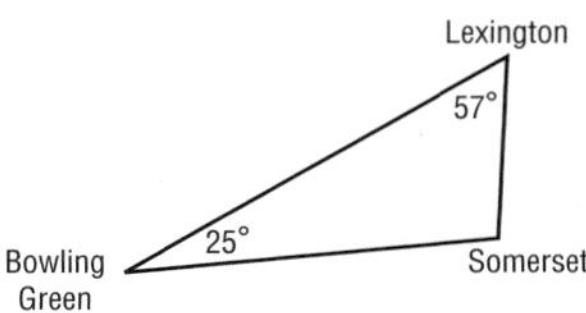

A acute

B equiangular

C obtuse

D right

6. Grant is flying a kite on the end of a string that is 350 feet long. The angle elevation from Grant to the kite is 74°. How high above the ground is the kite? Round your answer to the nearest tenth if necessary. F

F 336.4 ft

G 295.6 ft

H 141.2 ft

J 96.5 ft

Short Response/Gridded Response

Record your answers on the answer sheet provided by your teacher or on a sheet of paper.

7. **GRIDDED RESPONSE** Find x in the figure below. Round your answer to the nearest tenth if necessary. **93.9**

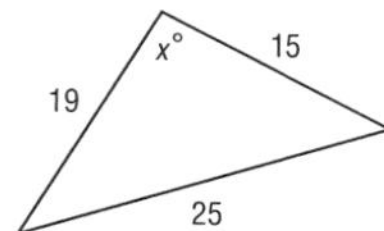

8. Amy is paddling her canoe across a lake at a speed of 10 feet per second headed due north. The wind is blowing 40° east of north with a velocity of 2.8 feet per second. What is Amy's resultant velocity? Express your answer as a vector. Show your work. **about 12.3 feet per second at a heading of 8.4° east of north, $\langle 1.8, 12.1 \rangle$**

9. Janice used a 16-inch dowel and a 21-inch dowel to build a kite as shown below. What is the perimeter of her kite? **54 in.**

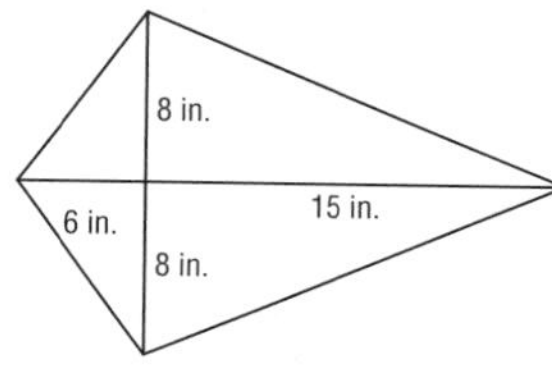

10. **GRIDDED RESPONSE** A model airplane takes off at an angle of elevation of 30°. How high will the plane be after traveling 100 feet horizontally? Round to the nearest tenth. Show your work. **57.7 ft**

11. According to the Perpendicular Bisector Theorem, what is the length of segment AB below? **2.5 cm**

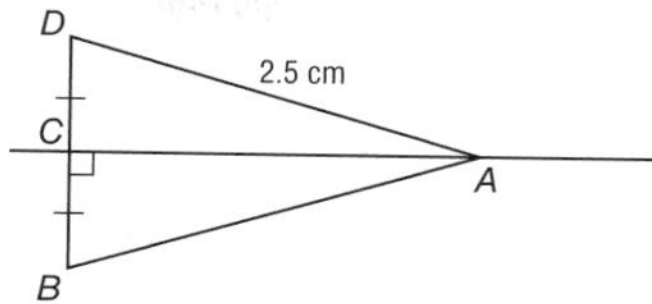

12. Find the slope of the line that contains the points (7, 2) and (3, 4). $-\frac{1}{2}$

13. If $EG = 15$ meters, what is the length of segment FG? **6 m**

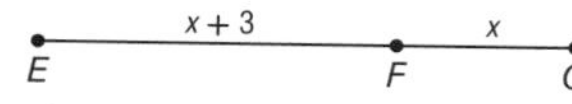

14. What is the contrapositive of the statement below?

If a quadrilateral is a rectangle, then it is a parallelogram. **If a quadrilateral is not a parallelogram, then it is not a rectangle.**

Extended Response

Record your answers on a sheet of paper. Show your work.

15. Refer to the triangle shown below.

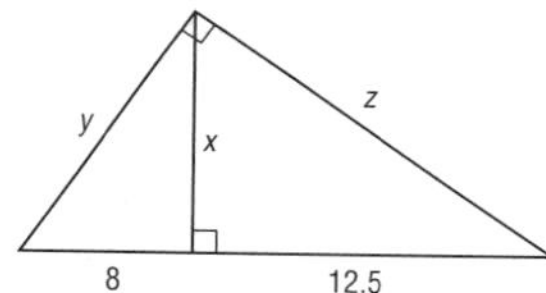

a. Find x to the nearest tenth. **10**

b. Find y to the nearest tenth. **12.8**

c. Find z to the nearest tenth. **16.0**

Need ExtraHelp?

If you missed Question...	1	2	3	4	5	6	7	8	9	10	11	12	13	14	15
Go to Lesson...	8-2	8-3	7-7	8-4	4-1	8-5	8-6	8-7	6-6	8-5	5-1	3-3	1-2	2-3	8-1

Formative Assessment

You can use these pages to benchmark student progress.

Standardized Test Practice, pp. 68–70

Answer Sheet Practice

Have students simulate taking a standardized test by recording their answers on a practice recording sheet.

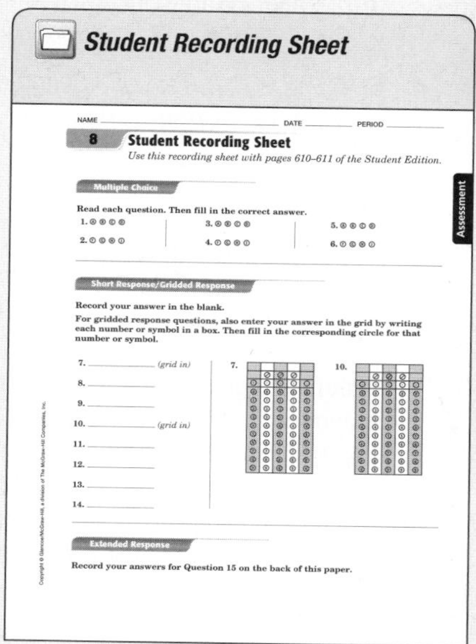

Student Recording Sheet

NAME ____________ DATE ________ PERIOD ________

8 Student Recording Sheet

Use this recording sheet with pages 610–611 of the Student Edition.

Multiple Choice

Read each question. Then fill in the correct answer.

1. Ⓐ Ⓑ Ⓒ Ⓓ
2. Ⓕ Ⓖ Ⓗ Ⓙ
3. Ⓐ Ⓑ Ⓒ Ⓓ
4. Ⓕ Ⓖ Ⓗ Ⓙ
5. Ⓐ Ⓑ Ⓒ Ⓓ
6. Ⓕ Ⓖ Ⓗ Ⓙ

Short Response/Gridded Response

Record your answer in the blank.

For gridded response questions, also enter your answer in the grid by writing each number or symbol in a box. Then fill in the corresponding circle for that number or symbol.

7. ________ *(grid in)*
8. ________
9. ________
10. ________ *(grid in)*
11. ________
12. ________
13. ________
14. ________

Extended Response

Record your answers for Question 15 on the back of this paper.

Assessment

eAssessment Create practice tests that align to your state standards, the Common Core State Standards, and other national standards such as TIMSS and NAEP.

Homework Option

Get Ready for Chapter 9 Assign students the exercises on page 621 as homework to assess whether they possess the prerequisite skills needed for the next chapter.

Lesson 8-1

39. Given: $\angle PQR$ is a right angle.
$\overline{QS}$ is an altitude of $\triangle PQR$.

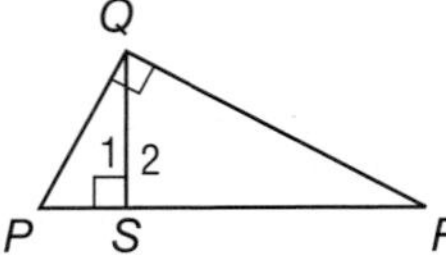

Prove: $\triangle PSQ \sim \triangle PQR$
$\triangle PQR \sim \triangle QSR$
$\triangle PSQ \sim \triangle QSR$

Proof:

Statements (Reasons)

1. $\angle PQR$ is a right angle. $\overline{QS}$ is an altitude of $\triangle PQR$. (Given)
2. $\overline{QS} \perp \overline{RP}$ (Definition of altitude)
3. $\angle 1$ and $\angle 2$ are right $\angle$s. (Definition of $\perp$ lines)
4. $\angle 1 \cong \angle PQR$; $\angle 2 \cong \angle PQR$ (All right $\angle$s are $\cong$.)
5. $\angle P \cong \angle P$; $\angle R \cong \angle R$ (Congruence of angles is reflexive.)
6. $\triangle PSQ \sim \triangle PQR$; $\triangle PQR \sim \triangle QSR$ (AA Similarity Statements 4 and 5)
7. $\triangle PSQ \sim \triangle QSR$ (Similarity of triangles is transitive.)

40. Given: $\triangle ADC$ is a right triangle.
$\overline{DB}$ is an altitude of $\triangle ADC$.

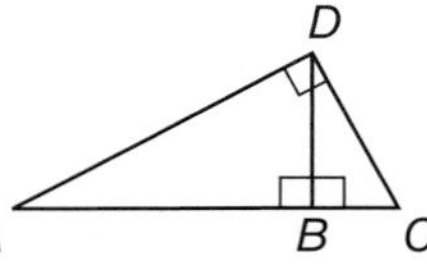

Prove: $\dfrac{AB}{DB} = \dfrac{DB}{CB}$

Proof: It is given that $\triangle ADC$ is a right triangle and $\overline{DB}$ is an altitude of $\triangle ADC$. $\angle ADC$ is a right angle by the definition of a right triangle. Therefore, $\triangle ADB \sim \triangle DCB$, because if the altitude is drawn from the vertex of the right angle to the hypotenuse of a right triangle, then the two triangles formed are similar to the given triangle and to each other. So $\dfrac{AB}{DB} = \dfrac{DB}{CB}$ by definition of similar triangles.

41. Given: $\angle ADC$ is a right angle.
$\overline{DB}$ is an altitude of $\triangle ADC$.

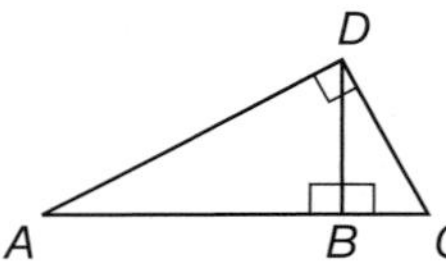

Prove: 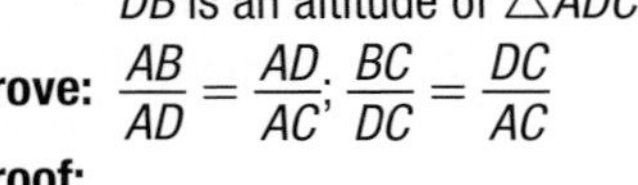 $\dfrac{AB}{AD} = \dfrac{AD}{AC}$; $\dfrac{BC}{DC} = \dfrac{DC}{AC}$

Proof:

Statements (Reasons)

1. $\angle ADC$ is a right angle. $\overline{DB}$ is an altitude of $\triangle ADC$ (Given)
2. $\triangle ADC$ is a right triangle. (Definition of right triangle)
3. $\triangle ABD \sim \triangle ADC$; $\triangle DBC \sim \triangle ADC$ (If the altitude is drawn from the vertex of the rt. $\angle$ to the hypotenuse of a rt. $\triangle$, then the 2 $\triangle$s formed are similar to the given $\triangle$ and to each other.)
4. $\dfrac{AB}{AD} = \dfrac{AD}{AC}$; $\dfrac{BC}{DC} = \dfrac{DC}{AC}$ (Definition of similar triangles)

42a.

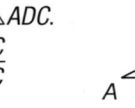

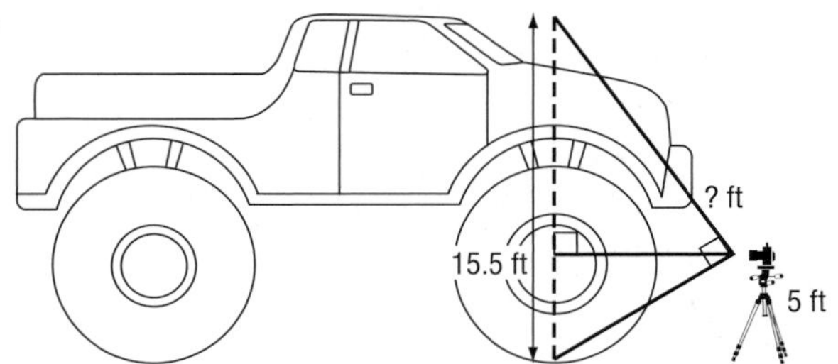

53. Sample answer: Both the arithmetic and the geometric mean calculate a value between two given numbers. The arithmetic mean of two numbers a and b is $\dfrac{a+b}{2}$, and the geometric mean of two numbers a and b is $\sqrt{ab}$. The two means will be equal when $a = b$.

Justification:

$$\frac{a+b}{2} = \sqrt{ab}$$
$$\left(\frac{a+b}{2}\right)^2 = ab$$
$$\frac{(a+b)^2}{4} = ab$$
$$(a+b)^2 = 4ab$$
$$a^2 + 2ab + b^2 = 4ab$$
$$a^2 - 2ab + b^2 = 0$$
$$(a-b)^2 = 0$$
$$a - b = 0$$
$$a = b$$

Lesson 8-2

35. Given: $\triangle ABC$ with sides of measure a, b, and c, where $c^2 = a^2 + b^2$

Prove: $\triangle ABC$ is a right triangle.

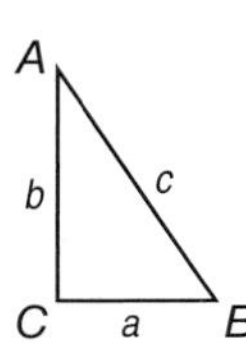

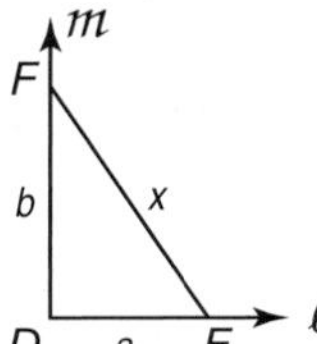

Proof: Draw $\overline{DE}$ on line ℓ with measure equal to a. At D, draw line $m \perp \overline{DE}$. Locate point F on m so that $DF = b$. Draw $\overline{FE}$ and call its measure x. Because $\triangle FED$ is a right triangle, $a^2 + b^2 = x^2$. But $a^2 + b^2 = c^2$, so $x^2 = c^2$ or $x = c$. Thus, $\triangle ABC \cong \triangle FED$ by SSS. This means $\angle C \cong \angle D$. Therefore, $\angle C$ must be a right angle, making $\triangle ABC$ a right triangle.

36. Given: In $\triangle ABC$, $c^2 < a^2 + b^2$ where c is the length of the longest side. In $\triangle PQR$, $\angle R$ is a right angle.

Prove: $\triangle ABC$ is an acute triangle.

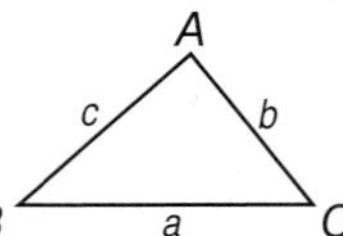

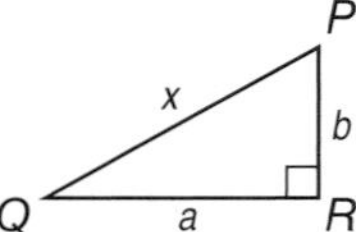

Proof:

Statements (Reasons)

1. In $\triangle ABC$, $c^2 < a^2 + b^2$ where c is the length of the longest side. In $\triangle PQR$, $\angle R$ is a right angle. (Given)
2. $a^2 + b^2 = x^2$ (Pythagorean Theorem)
3. $c^2 < x^2$ (Substitution Property)
4. $c < x$ (A property of square roots)
5. $m\angle R = 90°$ (Definition of a right angle)
6. $m\angle C < m\angle R$ (Converse of the Hinge Theorem)
7. $m\angle C < 90°$ (Substitution Property)

8. $\angle C$ is an acute angle. (Definition of an acute angle)
9. $\triangle ABC$ is an acute triangle. (Definition of an acute triangle)

37. Given: In $\triangle ABC$, $c^2 > a^2 + b^2$, where c is the length of the longest side.

Prove: $\triangle ABC$ is an obtuse triangle.

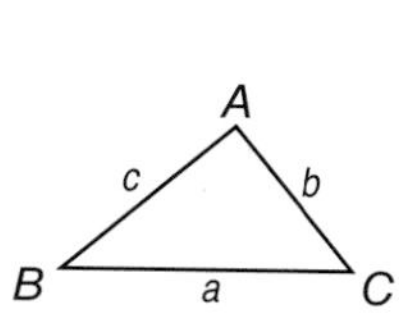

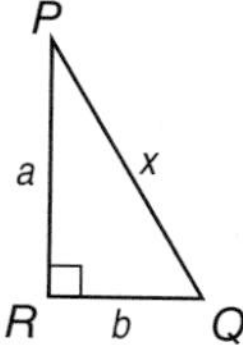

Proof:

Statements (Reasons)

1. In $\triangle ABC$, $c^2 > a^2 + b^2$, where c is the length of the longest side. In $\triangle PQR$, $\angle R$ is a right angle. (Given)
2. $a^2 + b^2 = x^2$ (Pythagorean Theorem)
3. $c^2 > x^2$ (Substitution Property)
4. $c > x$ (A property of square roots)
5. $m\angle R = 90$ (Definition of a right angle)
6. $m\angle C > m\angle R$ (Converse of the Hinge Theorem)
7. $m\angle C > 90$ (Substitution Property of Equality)
8. $\angle C$ is an obtuse angle. (Definition of an obtuse angle)
9. $\triangle ABC$ is an obtuse triangle. (Definition of an obtuse triangle)

Extend 8-2

1.

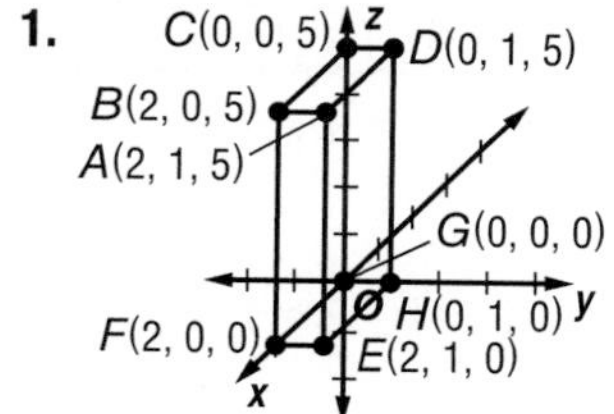

2.

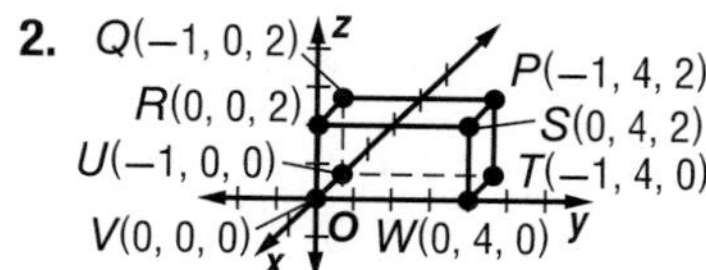

3.

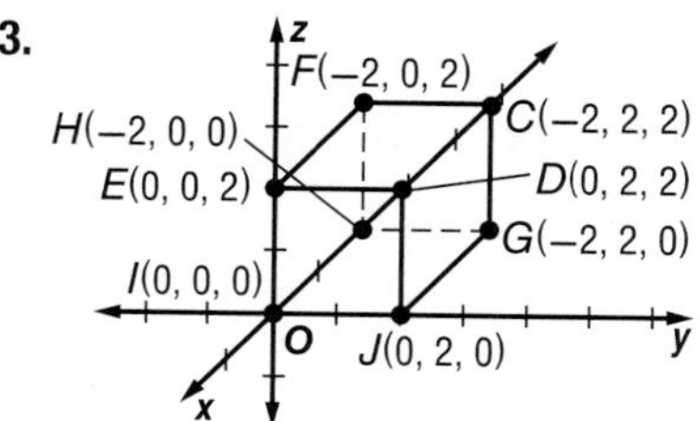

4.

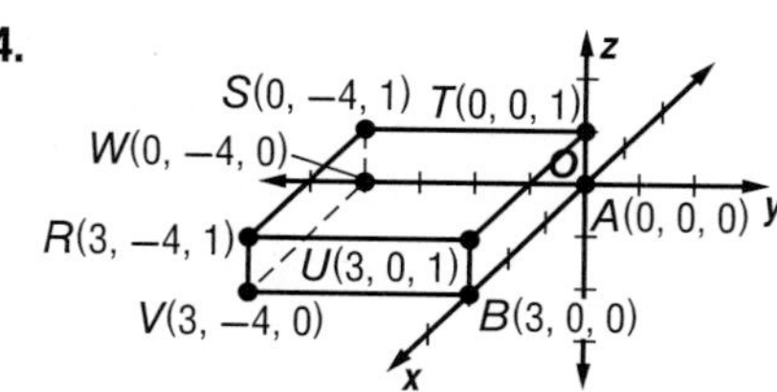

5.

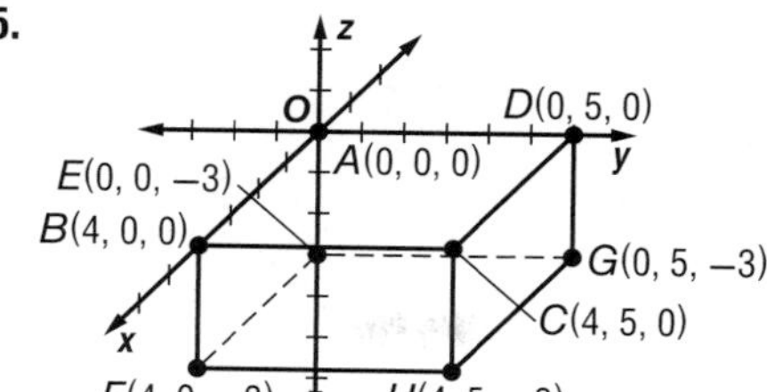

6.

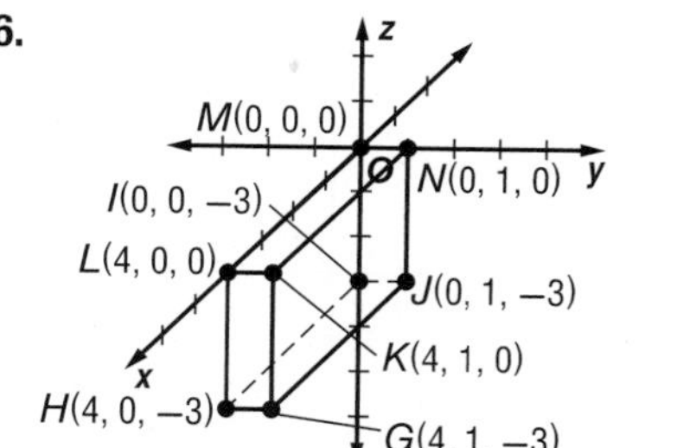

7.

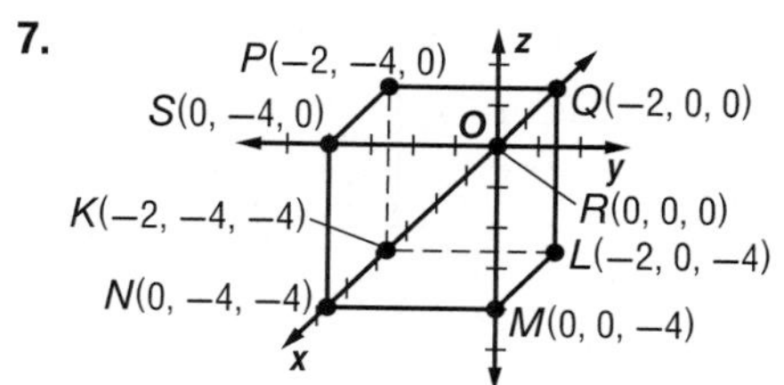

8.

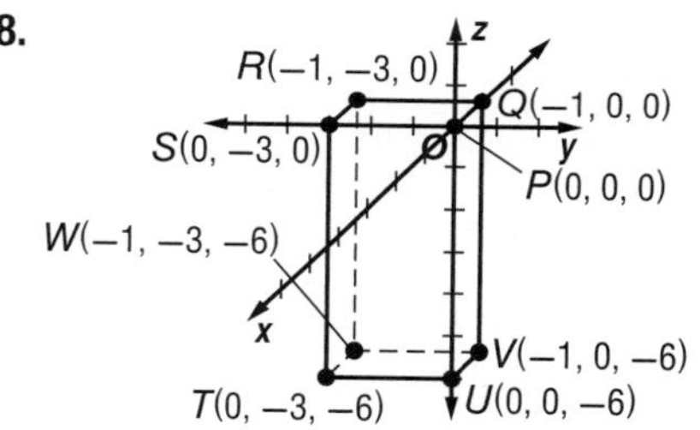

9.

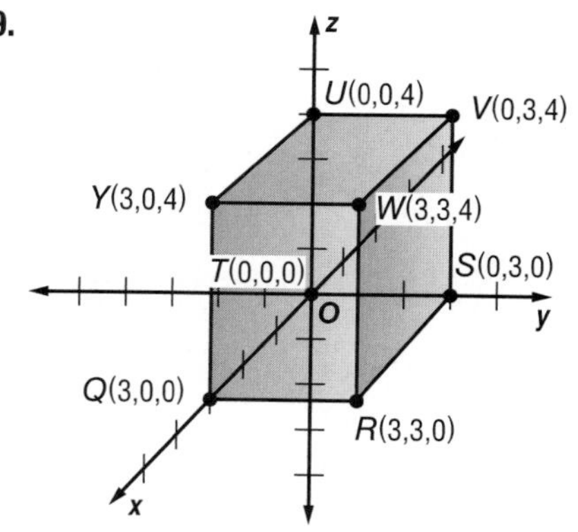

Lesson 8-2

30. right; $XY = \sqrt{8}$, $YZ = \sqrt{2}$, $XZ = \sqrt{10}$

31. acute; $XY = \sqrt{29}$, $YZ = \sqrt{20}$, $XZ = \sqrt{13}$; $(\sqrt{29})^2 < (\sqrt{20})^2 + (\sqrt{13})^2$

32. obtuse; $XY = 5$, $YZ = 2$, $XZ = \sqrt{41}$; $(\sqrt{41})^2 > 5^2 + 2^2$

33. right; $XY = 6$, $YZ = 10$, $XZ = 8$; $6^2 + 8^2 = 10^2$

Lesson 8-7

12.

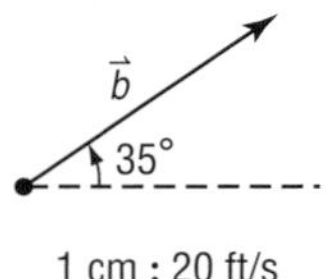

13.

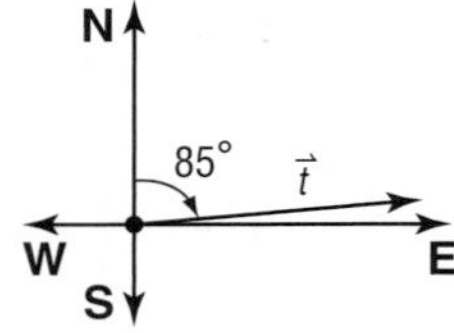

14.

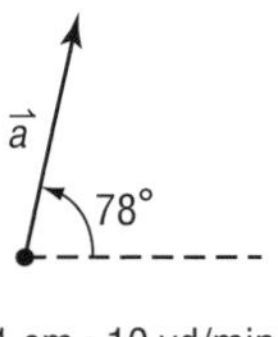

15.

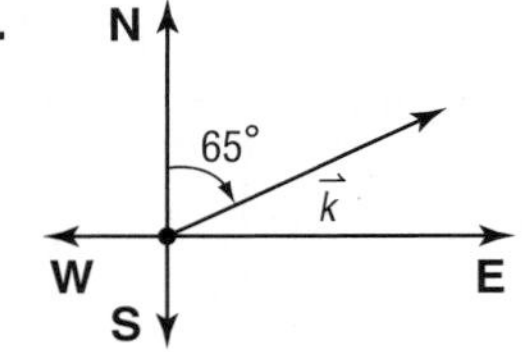

16.

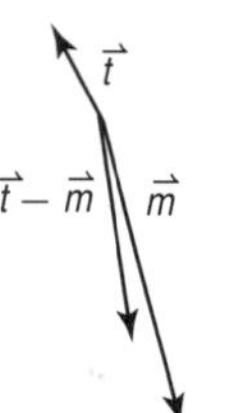

17.

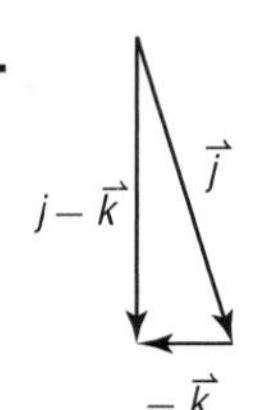

18.

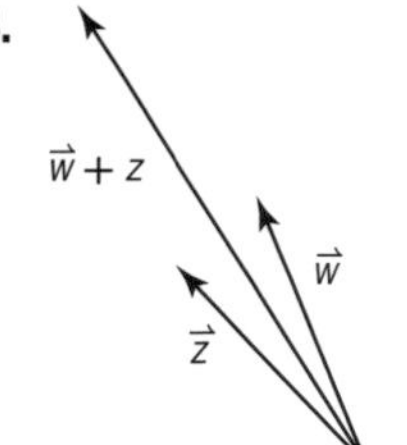

19.

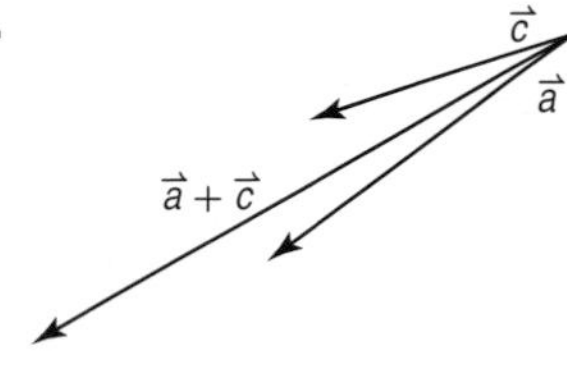

20.

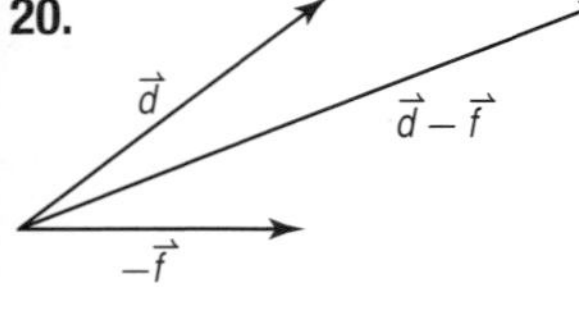

21.

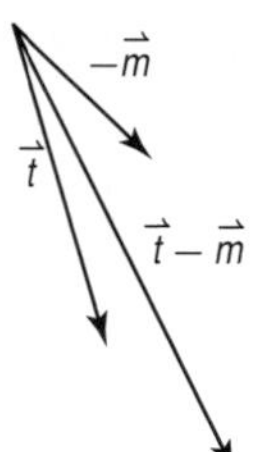

35. $\langle 5, 3 \rangle$

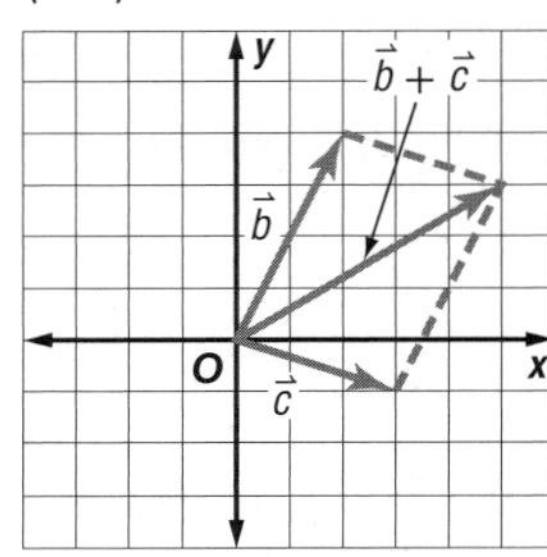

36. $\langle 0, -6 \rangle$

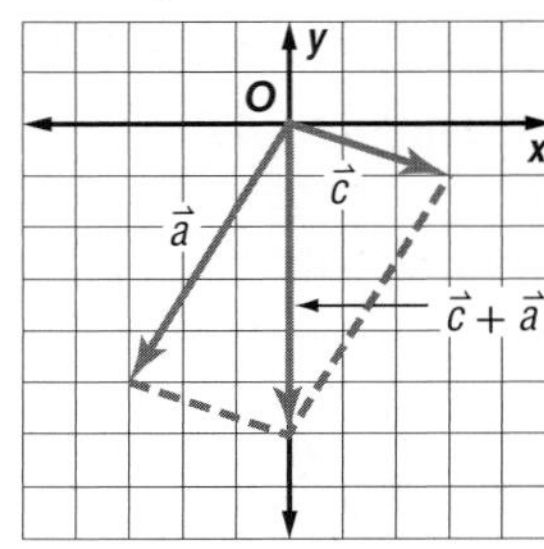

37. $\langle -1, 5 \rangle$

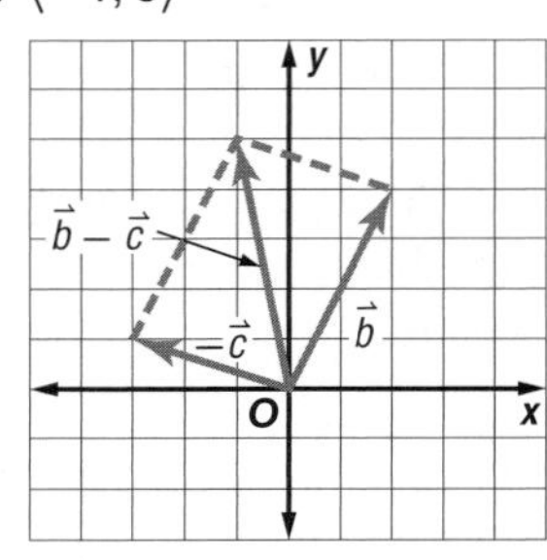

38. $\langle -6, -4 \rangle$

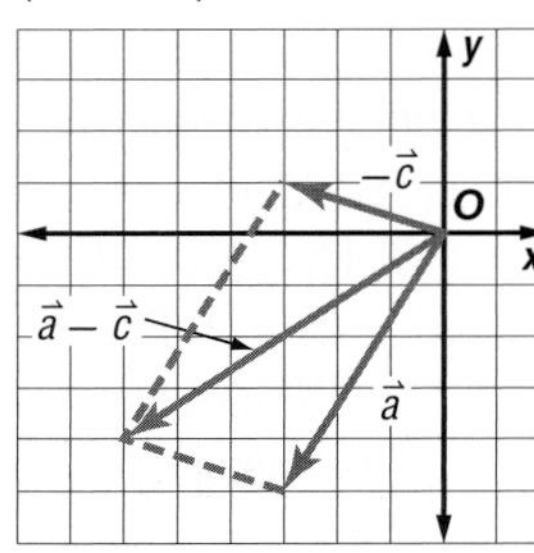

39. $\langle 9, 3 \rangle$

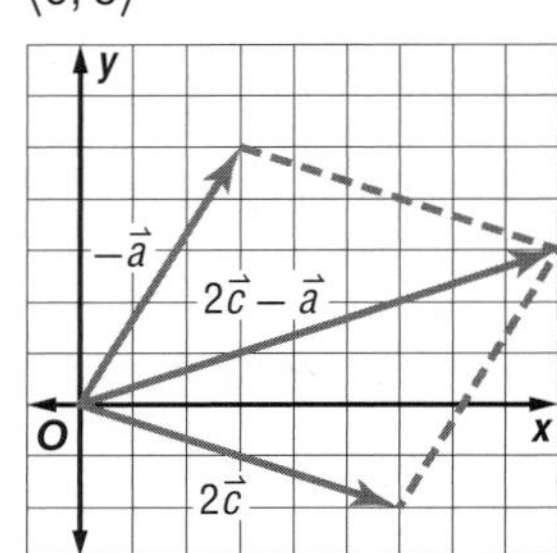

40. $\langle 7, 7 \rangle$

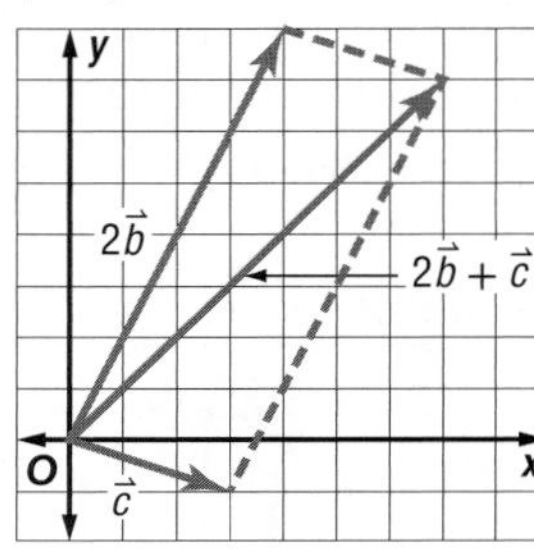

52a.

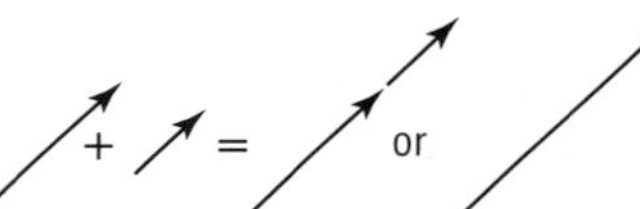

Sample answer: The sum of the two vectors is parallel to both of the original vectors.

52b.

Sample answer: The difference of the two vectors is parallel to both of the original vectors.

Chapter Planner

	Diagnostic Assessment Quick Check			
	LESSON 9-1 **45 min:** 1 day **90 min:** 0.5 day	**LESSON 9-2** **45 min:** 1 day **90 min:** 0.5 day	**EXPLORE 9-3** **45 min:** 0.5 day **90 min:** 0.25 day	**LESSON 9-3** **45 min:** 1 day **90 min:** 0.5 day
Title	**Reflections**	**Translations**	**Geometry Lab: Rotations**	**Rotations**
Objectives	▪ Draw reflections. ▪ Draw reflections in the coordinate plane.	▪ Draw translations. ▪ Draw translations in the coordinate plane.	▪ Explore the properties of rotations.	▪ Draw rotations. ▪ Draw rotations in the coordinate plane.
Key Vocabulary	line of reflection	translation vector		center of rotation angle of rotation
CCSS	G.CO.4, G.CO.5	G.CO.4, G.CO.5	G.CO.2, G.CO.5	G.CO.4, G.CO.5
Multiple Representations				
Lesson Resources	connectED.mcgraw-hill.com Leveled Worksheets Vocabulary Personal Tutor Virtual Manipulatives Self-Check Quiz ▪ *5-Minute Check* ▪ *Study Notebook* ▪ *Teaching Geometry with Manipulatives*	connectED.mcgraw-hill.com Leveled Worksheets Quiz 1 Vocabulary Personal Tutor Virtual Manipulatives Self-Check Quiz ▪ *5-Minute Check* ▪ *Study Notebook* ▪ *Teaching Geometry with Manipulatives*	connectED.mcgraw-hill.com Animations Virtual Manipulatives ▪ *Teaching Geometry with Manipulatives* **Materials:** ▪ patty paper ▪ straightedge ▪ protractor	connectED.mcgraw-hill.com Leveled Worksheets Quiz 2 Vocabulary Personal Tutor Virtual Manipulatives Self-Check Quiz ▪ *5-Minute Check* ▪ *Study Notebook* ▪ *Teaching Geometry with Manipulatives*
Resources for Every Lesson	IWB eStudent Edition IWB Interactive Classroom	▪ eTeacher Edition ▪ eSolutions Manual ▪ eAssessment		
Differentiated Instruction	pp. 625, 629	pp. 633, 638		pp. 641, 642

IWB All digital assets are Interactive Whiteboard ready.

Suggested Pacing			
Time Periods	Instruction	Review & Assess	Total
45-minute	10 days	2 days	12 days
90-minute	5 days	1 day	6 days

EXTEND 9-3 (45 min: 0.5 day; 90 min: 0.25 day)	EXPLORE 9-4 (45 min: 0.5 day; 90 min: 0.25 day)	LESSON 9-4 (45 min: 1.5 days; 90 min: 0.75 day)	EXTEND 9-4 (45 min: 0.5 day; 90 min: 0.25 day)
Geometry Lab: Solids of Revolution	**Geometry Software Lab: Compositions of Transformations**	**Compositions of Transformations**	**Geometry Lab: Tessellations**
▪ Identify and sketch solids formed by revolving two-dimensional figures about lines.	▪ Explore the effects of performing multiple transformations on a figure.	▪ Draw glide reflections and other compositions of isometries in the coordinate plane. ▪ Draw compositions of reflections in parallel and intersecting lines.	▪ Identify regular tessellations. ▪ Create tessellations with and without using technology.
solids of revolution		composition of transformations glide reflections	tessellation regular tessellation uniform tessellation
G.GMD.4	G.CO.2, G.CO.5	G.CO.2, G.CO.5	
connectED.mcgraw-hill.com Vocabulary Animations **Materials:** ▪ straws or dowel rods ▪ card stock or heavy construction paper ▪ graphing paper	connectED.mcgraw-hill.com Personal Tutor **Materials:** ▪ computers with Geometer's Sketchpad software	connectED.mcgraw-hill.com Leveled Worksheets Vocabulary Personal Tutor Virtual Manipulatives Self-Check Quiz ▪ *5-Minute Check* ▪ *Study Notebook*	connectED.mcgraw-hill.com Vocabulary Animations ▪ *Teaching Geometry with Manipulatives* **Materials:** ▪ computers with Geometer's Sketchpad software ▪ straightedge
IWB eStudent Edition IWB Interactive Classroom	▪ eTeacher Edition ▪ eSolutions Manual ▪ eAssessment		
		pp. 654, 657	

Formative Assessment
Mid-Chapter Quiz

Chapter Planner

	LESSON 9-5 (45 min: 1 day; 90 min: 0.5 day)	EXTEND 9-5 (45 min: 0.5 day; 90 min: 0.25 day)	EXPLORE 9-6 (45 min: 0.5 day; 90 min: 0.25 day)
Title	**Symmetry**	**Geometry Lab: Exploring Constructions with a Reflective Device**	**Graphing Technology Lab: Dilations**
Objectives	▪ Identify line and rotational symmetries in two-dimensional figures. ▪ Identify plane and axis symmetries in three-dimensional figures.	▪ Use a reflective device for geometric constructions.	▪ Use graphing technology to explore the properties of dilations.
Key Vocabulary	symmetry line symmetry line of symmetry rotational symmetry center of symmetry order of symmetry		
CCSS	G.CO.3	G.CO.12	G.SRT.1
Multiple Representations			
Lesson Resources	connectED.mcgraw-hill.com Leveled Worksheets Quiz 3 Vocabulary Personal Tutor Self-Check Quiz ▪ *5-Minute Check* ▪ *Study Notebook*	connectED.mcgraw-hill.com **Materials:** ▪ reflective device ▪ straightedge	connectED.mcgraw-hill.com Personal Tutor **Materials:** ▪ TI-Nspire technology
Resources for Every Lesson	IWB eStudent Edition IWB Interactive Classroom	▪ eTeacher Edition ▪ eSolutions Manual ▪ eAssessment	
Differentiated Instruction	p. 665		

IWB All digital assets are Interactive Whiteboard ready.

LESSON 9-6 (45 min: 1 day; 90 min: 0.5 day)	EXTEND 9-6 (45 min: 0.5 day; 90 min: 0.25 day)
Dilations	**Geometry Lab: Establishing Triangle Congruence and Similarity**
▪ Draw dilations. ▪ Draw dilations in the coordinate plane.	▪ Explore how triangle congruence and similarity follow from an understanding of transformations.
	principle of superposition
G.CO.2, G.SRT.1	G.CO.8, G.SRT.3
connectED.mcgraw-hill.com Leveled Worksheets Quiz 4 Animations Personal Tutor Virtual Manipulatives Self-Check Quiz ▪ *5-Minute Check* ▪ *Study Notebook*	connectED.mcgraw-hill.com Vocabulary
IWB eStudent Edition IWB Interactive Classroom	▪ eTeacher Edition ▪ eSolutions Manual ▪ eAssessment
pp. 675, 676	
	Summative Assessment Study Guide and Review Practice Test

What the Research Says...

In a meta-analysis of 60 research studies, Sowell (1989) found that for students of all ages, mathematics achievement is increased and students' attitudes toward mathematics are improved with the long-term use of manipulative materials. (Sowell, 1989)

- Use the differentiated instruction activities provided to give students opportunities to use manipulatives with each concept.
- Explore Lessons 9-3 and 9-4 and Extend Lessons 9-4 and 9-6 allow students to practice the concepts by performing them first-hand.

Teacher to Teacher

Liza Allen
Conway High School West
Conway, AR

Use With Lesson 9-4

"*Bring a quilt or have students bring quilts to class to find the transformations described in this chapter in the quilt patterns. Quilt patterns often use rotations, translations, and dilations as well as being examples of tessellating a plane.*"

Assessment and Intervention

SE = Student Edition, **TE** = Teacher Edition, **CRM** = Chapter Resource Masters

	Diagnosis	Prescription
DIAGNOSTIC ASSESSMENT	**Beginning Chapter 9**	
	Get Ready for Chapter 9 **SE**	Response to Intervention **TE**
	Beginning Every Lesson	
	Then, Now, Why? **SE** 5-Minute Checks	Chapter 0 **SE**
FORMATIVE ASSESSMENT	**During/After Every Lesson**	
	Guided Practice **SE**, every example Check Your Understanding **SE** H.O.T. Problems **SE** Spiral Review **SE** Additional Examples **TE** Watch Out! **TE** Step 4, Assess **TE** Chapter 9 Quizzes **CRM**, pp. 45–46 Self-Check Quizzes connectED.mcgraw-hill.com	TIER 1 Intervention Skills Practice **CRM**, Ch. 1–9 connectED.mcgraw-hill.com TIER 2 Intervention Differentiated Instruction **TE** Differentiated Homework Options **TE** Study Guide and Intervention **CRM**, Ch. 1–9 TIER 3 Intervention *Math Triumphs, Geometry,* Ch. 5
	Mid-Chapter	
	Mid-Chapter Quiz **SE** Mid-Chapter Test **CRM**, p. 47 eAssessment	TIER 1 Intervention Skills Practice **CRM**, Ch. 1–9 connectED.mcgraw-hill.com TIER 2 Intervention Study Guide and Intervention **CRM**, Ch. 1–9 TIER 3 Intervention *Math Triumphs, Geometry,* Ch. 5
	Before Chapter Test	
	Chapter Study Guide and Review **SE** Practice Test **SE** Standardized Test Practice **SE** Chapter Test connectED.mcgraw-hill.com Standardized Test Practice connectED.mcgraw-hill.com Vocabulary Review connectED.mcgraw-hill.com eAssessment	TIER 1 Intervention Skills Practice **CRM**, Ch. 1–9 connectED.mcgraw-hill.com TIER 2 Intervention Study Guide and Intervention **CRM**, Ch. 1–9 TIER 3 Intervention *Math Triumphs, Geometry,* Ch. 5
SUMMATIVE ASSESSMENT	**After Chapter 9**	
	Multiple-Choice Tests, Forms 1, 2A, 2B **CRM**, pp. 49–54 Free-Response Tests, Forms 2C, 2D, 3 **CRM**, pp. 55–60 Vocabulary Test **CRM**, p. 48 Extended Response Test **CRM**, p. 61 Standardized Test Practice **CRM**, pp. 62–64 eAssessment	Study Guide and Intervention **CRM**, Ch. 1–9 connectED.mcgraw-hill.com

Differentiated Instruction

Option 1 Reaching All Learners AL OL BL ELL

Visual/Spatial Use digital or disposable cameras to capture examples of symmetry or reflections. If desired, have students bring small hand mirrors with them to create and then photograph reflections. Print and mount the pictures your students take. Hang them in the hall or on a plain wall to create a gallery collection.

Naturalist Take a nature walk with your students. Have them bring a notebook and pencil in which to record their observations. Walk around campus and have them draw the items they see in nature that are symmetrical. Have them label their drawings and ask them to write what the purpose of symmetry is in nature, in their opinions.

Option 2 Approaching Level AL

Have students use a cork board marked as a grid, pushpins, laminated shapes, and string or yarn to model rotations. They can start by placing a shape on the board and affixing lengths of yarn to each vertex. Then, they can choose a center of rotation and use a pushpin to secure the loose ends of each string to this point. Finally, they can determine an angle of rotation, use a protractor to measure the angle, and slide the shape to its new rotation.

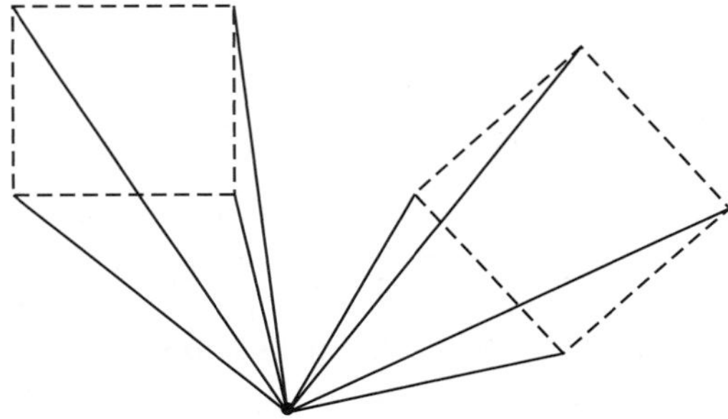

Option 3 English Learners ELL

Have students work in small groups and create a poster-sized display of one figure and its image under each type of transformation. Have groups exchange their posters and then write the name of each type of transformation and a brief description of how the image compares to the original figure.

Option 4 Beyond Level BL

Either using Geometer's Sketchpad or paper and pencil, have students create tessellations—one by reflection, another with rotation, and the last using translation. If using Geometer's Sketchpad, students can use the Transform menu of the program. Tell students to hide all the points by using the Edit and Display menus when they are finished manipulating the piece. The completed tessellations can be colored in or left as an outline.

Focus on Mathematical Content

VerticalAlignment

Before Chapter 9

Related Topics from Grade 8

- Graph dilations, reflections, and translations on a coordinate plane.

Previous Topics from Algebra 1

- Represent relationships using tables and graphs.
- Solve linear equations.

Chapter 9

Related Topics from Geometry

- Use congruence transformations to make conjectures and justify properties of geometric figures.

After Chapter 9

Preparation for Precalculus

- Apply basic transformations, including $a \cdot f(x)$, $f(x) + d$, $f(x - c)$, $f(b \cdot x)$, $|f(x)|$, $f(|x|)$ to the parent functions.
- Perform operations including composition of functions, find inverses, and describe these procedures and results verbally, numerically, symbolically, and graphically.

Lesson-by-LessonPreview

9-1 Reflections

A reflection is a transformation representing a flip of a figure.

Reflection

A figure can be flipped over a line.

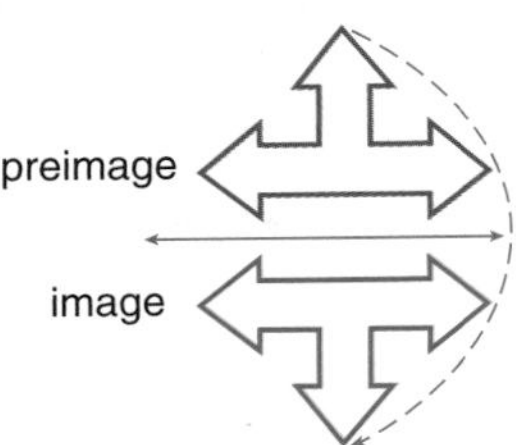

Figures may be reflected in a point, a line, or a plane. A reflected image is always congruent to its preimage. In other words, a reflection is a congruence transformation or an isometry. Reflections can occur in the coordinate plane, allowing you to assign coordinates to each point in the image and preimage.

9-2 Translations

A translation is a transformation that moves all points of a figure the same distance in the same direction.

Translation

A figure can be slid in any direction.

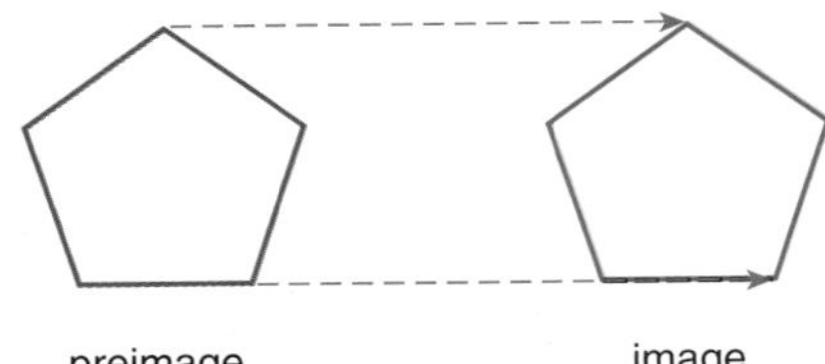

Translations on the coordinate plane can be drawn if you know the direction and how far the figure is moving horizontally and/or vertically. One way to translate a figure in the coordinate plane is simply to count units on the *x*-axis and on the *y*-axis, much as you count for slope.

9-3 Rotations

A rotation is a transformation that turns every point of a preimage through a specified angle and direction about a fixed point.

Rotation
A figure can be turned around a point.

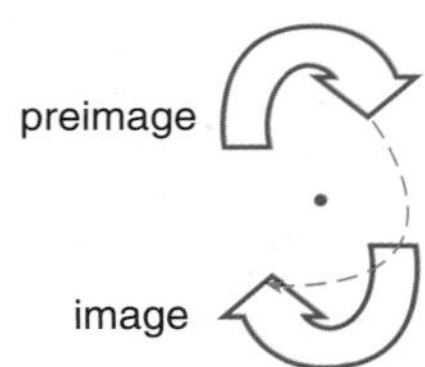

The fixed point is called the *center of rotation*. The angle of rotation is the angle formed by a point on the preimage, the center of rotation, and the corresponding point on the rotated image. A rotation exhibits all the properties of isometries, including preservation of distance and angle measure.

A rotation can be performed using a protractor to measure the angle of rotation and a compass to mark the new points.

9-4 Compositions of Transformations

When a transformation is applied to a figure, and then another transformation is applied to its image, the resulting transformation is called a *composition of transformations*. A *glide translation* is a translation followed by a reflection in a line parallel to the translation vector. Theorem 9.2 states that a translation is equivalent to two reflections in parallel lines. Theorem 9.3 states that a rotation is equivalent to two reflections in intersecting lines.

9-5 Symmetry

A figure has *symmetry* if there is a rigid motion—reflection, translation, rotation, or glide reflection—that maps the figure onto itself. A figure has *line symmetry* if it can mapped onto itself by a reflection in a line. A figure has rotational symmetry if it can be mapped onto itself by a rotation between 0° and 360° about the center of the figure. Similarly, three-dimensional figures can have *plane* or *axis* symmetry.

9-6 Dilations

A dilation is a transformation that changes the size of a figure.

Dilation
A figure can be enlarged or reduced.

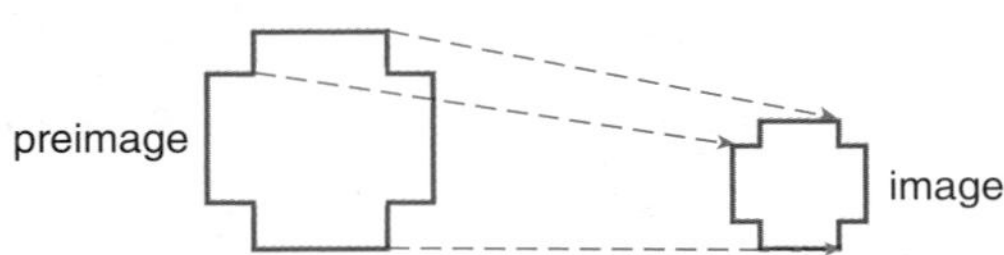

The new figure may be smaller or larger than the original by a scale factor. If the scale factor is 1, then the dilation is a congruence transformation. If the scale factor is not 1, then the dilation is a similarity transformation. This means that the new figure and the original are similar. It is important to note that a negative scale factor does not result in a negative measure. It simply means that the new image falls on the opposite side of the center than the preimage. The center of a dilation is always its own image.

In the coordinate plane, you can use the scale factor to determine the coordinate of the image of dilations centered at the origin. If $P(x, y)$ is the preimage of a dilation centered at the origin with a scale factor r, then the image is $P'(rx, ry)$. To determine the scale factor of a dilation on the coordinate plane, divide the image length by the preimage length.

McGraw Hill Professional Development

Targeted professional development has been articulated throughout Geometry. More quality, customized professional development is available from McGraw-Hill Professional Development. Visit connectED.mcgraw-hill.com for details on each product.

- Online Lessons emphasize the strategies and techniques used to teach Geometry. Includes streaming video, interactive pages, and online tools.
- Video Workshops allow mentors, coaches, or leadership personnel to facilitate on-site workshops on educational strategies in mathematics and mathematical concepts.
- MHPD Online (www.mhpdonline.com) offers online professional development with video clips of instructional strategies, links, student activities, and news and issues in education.
- Teaching Today (teachingtoday.glencoe.com) gives secondary teachers practical strategies and materials that inspire excellence and innovation in teaching.

Chapter Project

Graphic Design

Students use what they have learned about transformations of polygons to complete a project.

This chapter project addresses entrepreneurial literacy, as well as several specific skills identified as being essential to student success by the Framework for 21st Century Learning.

Visit connectED.mcgraw-hill.com for student and teacher handouts.

KeyVocabulary Introduce the key vocabulary in the chapter using the method below.

Define: The center of rotation is the fixed point about which an angle of $x°$ maps a point to its image.

Example:

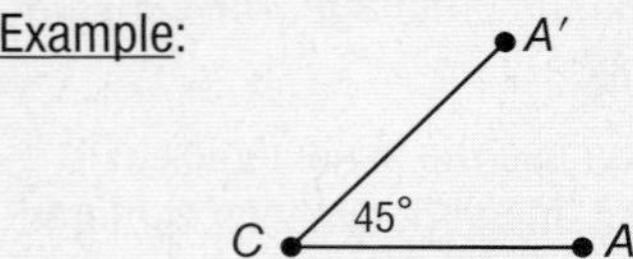

Ask: What point is the center of rotation? In what direction is the rotation? Point *C*; counterclockwise

CHAPTER 9 Transformations and Symmetry

Then

You identified reflections, translations, and rotations.

Now

In this chapter, you will:

- Name and draw figures that have been reflected, translated, rotated, or dilated.
- Recognize and draw compositions of transformations.
- Identify symmetry in two- and three-dimensional figures.

Why?

PHOTOGRAPHY Photographers use reflections, rotations, and symmetry to make photographs interesting and visually appealing.

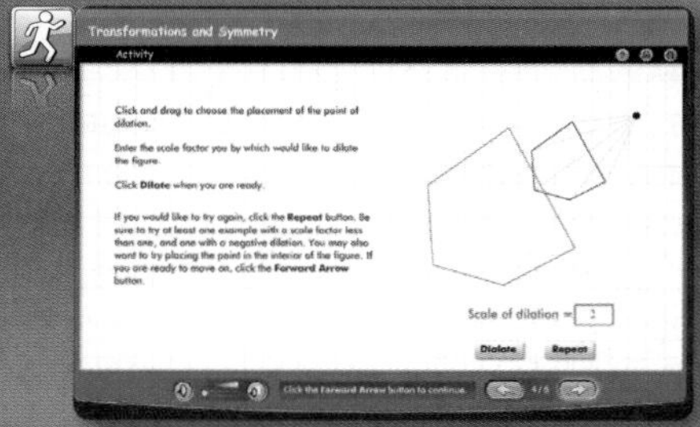

connectED.mcgraw-hill.com Your Digital Math Portal

Animation | Vocabulary | eGlossary | Personal Tutor | Virtual Manipulatives | Graphing Calculator | Audio | Foldables | Self-Check Practice | Worksheets

Get Ready for the Chapter

Diagnose Readiness | You have two options for checking prerequisite skills.

1 Textbook Option Take the Quick Check below. Refer to the Quick Review for help.

QuickCheck

Identify the type of congruence transformation shown as a *reflection*, *translation*, or *rotation*.

1. *A* to *B* rotation
2. *D* to *A*

translation or reflection
3. *A* to *C* translation

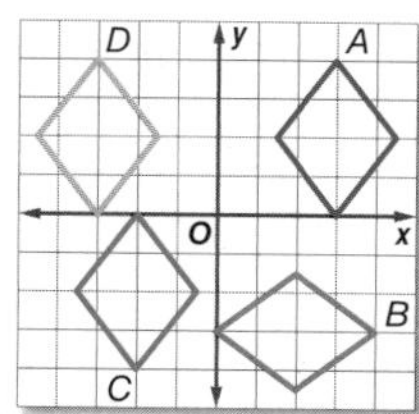

Find the sum of each pair of vectors.

4. $\langle 13, -4\rangle + \langle -11, 9\rangle$ $\langle 2, 5\rangle$
5. $\langle 6, -31\rangle + \langle -22, 3\rangle$ $\langle -16, -28\rangle$
6. **BAND** During part of a song, the drummer in a marching band moves from (1, 4) to (5, 1). Write the component form of the vector that describes his movement. $\langle 4, -3\rangle$

7. Determine whether the dilation from *A* to *B* is an *enlargement* or a *reduction*. Then find the scale factor of the dilation. reduction; $\frac{1}{2}$

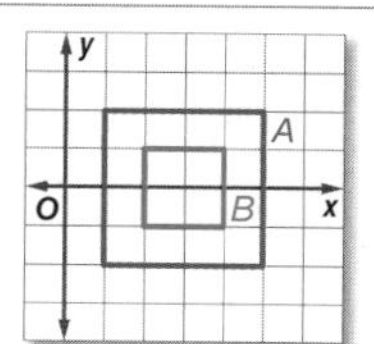

8. **PLAYS** Bob is making a model of an ant for a play. Find the scale factor of the model if the ant is $\frac{1}{2}$ inch long and the model is 1 foot long. 24

QuickReview

Example 1 (Used in Lessons 9-1 through 9-4)

Identify the type of congruence transformation shown as a *reflection*, *translation*, or *rotation*.

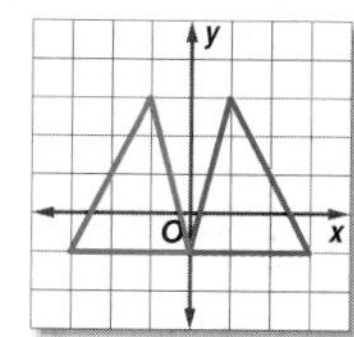

Each vertex and its image are the same distance from the *y*-axis. This is a reflection.

Example 2 (Used in Lesson 9-2)

Write the component form of $\overrightarrow{AB}$ for $A(-1, 1)$ and $B(4, -3)$.

$\overrightarrow{AB} = \langle x_2 - x_1, y_2 - y_1\rangle$ Component form of vector

$= \langle 4 - (-1), -3 - 1\rangle$ Substitute.

$= \langle 5, -4\rangle$ Simplify.

Example 3 (Used in Lesson 9-6)

Determine whether the dilation from *A* to *B* is an *enlargement* or a *reduction*. Then find the scale factor of the dilation.

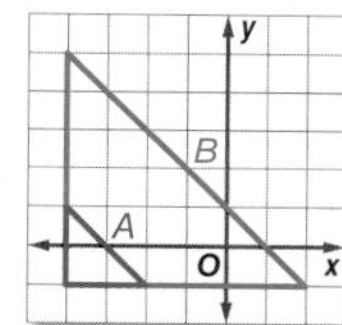

B is larger than *A*, so it is an enlargement.

The distance between the vertices of *A* is 2 and the corresponding distance for *B* is 6.

The scale factor is $\frac{6}{2}$ or 3.

2 Online Option Take an online self-check Chapter Readiness Quiz at connectED.mcgraw-hill.com.

Essential Questions

- Where can transformations be found? Sample answer: in architectural designs, in art, in clothing patterns, in animations
- Why is symmetry desirable? Sample answer: Symmetry may be desirable in some cases, such as fashion or architecture, as a design element for visual appeal. In other cases, such as carpentry or engineering, it may be used for its structural benefits to stabilize objects.

Get Ready for the Chapter

Response to Intervention (RtI)

Use the *Quick Check* results and the Intervention Planner chart to help you determine your Response to Intervention. The If-Then statements in the chart help you decide the appropriate tier of RtI and suggest intervention resources for each tier.

InterventionPlanner

TIER 1 On Level OL

If students miss about 25% of the exercises or less,

Then choose a resource:

SE Lessons 4-7, 7-6, and 8-7

Skills Practice, Chapter 4, p. 45, Chapter 7 p. 39, Chapter 8 p. 45

connectED.mcgraw-hill.com Self-Check Quiz

TIER 2 Strategic Intervention AL
approaching grade level

If students miss about 50% of the exercises,

Then choose a resource:

Study Guide and Intervention, Chapter 4, pp. 43–44, Chapter 7 pp. 37–38, Chapter 8 pp. 43–44

connectED.mcgraw-hill.com Extra Examples, Personal Tutor, Homework Help

TIER 3 Intensive Intervention
2 or more grades below level

If students miss about 75% of the exercises,

Then use *Math Triumphs, Geometry*, Ch. 5

connectED.mcgraw-hill.com Extra Examples, Personal Tutor, Homework Help, Review Vocabulary

FOLDABLES® StudyOrganizer

Dinah Zike's Foldables®

Focus Students write notes and draw sketches of transformations.

Teach Have students make and label the Foldable as illustrated.

Students use their Foldables to take notes, define terms, and write examples. At the end of each lesson, ask students to write a definition for each vocabulary word in their own words.

When to Use It Use the appropriate pockets as students cover each lesson in this chapter. Students can add to the vocabulary tab during each lesson.

Differentiated Instruction

Student-Built Glossary, pp. 1–2

Students should complete the chart by providing the definition of each term and an example as they progress through Chapter 9. This study tool can also be used to review for the chapter test.

Get Started on the Chapter

You will learn several new concepts, skills, and vocabulary terms as you study Chapter 9. To get ready, identify important terms and organize your resources. You may refer to Chapter 0 to review prerequisite skills.

FOLDABLES StudyOrganizer

Transformations and Symmetry Make this Foldable to help you organize your Chapter 9 notes about transformations and symmetry. Begin with three sheets of notebook paper.

1 **Fold** each sheet of paper in half.

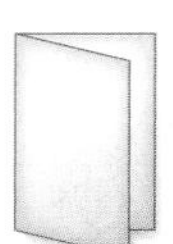

2 **Open** the folded papers and fold each paper lengthwise two inches, to form a pocket.

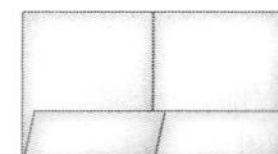

3 **Glue** the sheets side-by-side to create a booklet.

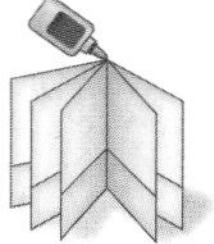

4 **Label** each of the pockets as shown.

NewVocabulary

English		Español
line of reflection	p. 623	línea de reflexión
center of rotation	p. 640	centro de rotación
angle of rotation	p. 640	ángulo de rotación
composition of transformations	p. 651	composición de transformaciones
symmetry	p. 663	símetria
line symmetry	p. 663	símetria lineal
line of symmetry	p. 663	eje de símetria

ReviewVocabulary

reflection reflexión a transformation representing a flip of the figure over a point, line or plane

rotation rotación a transformation that turns every point of a preimage through a specified angle and direction about a fixed point

translation traslación a transformation that moves all points of a figure the same distance in the same direction

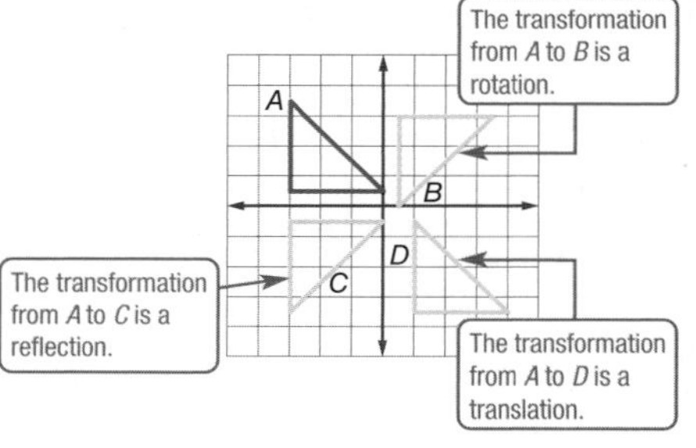

Additional Answers (Lesson 9-1, Guided Practice)

1A.

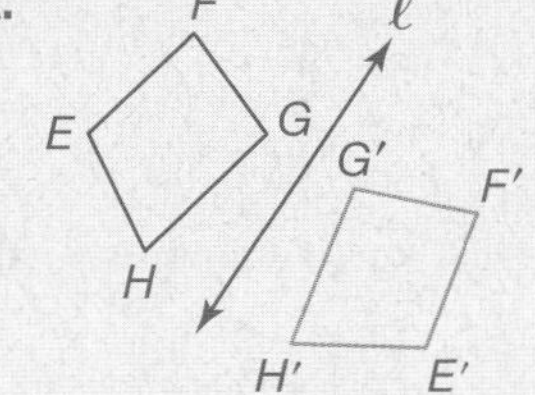

1B.

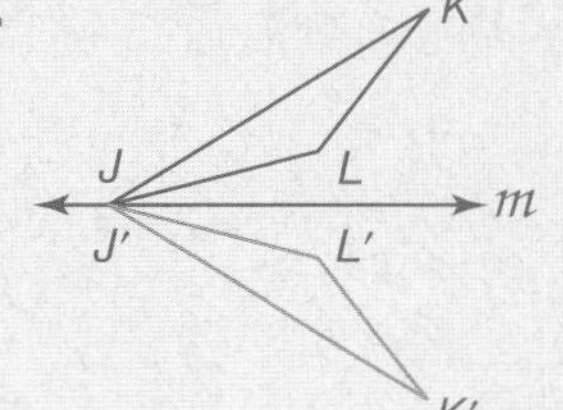

1C.

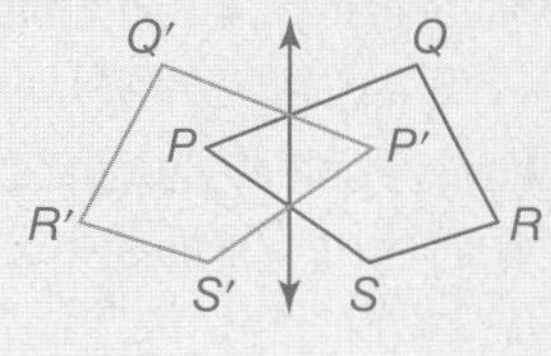

LESSON 9-1 Reflections

:: Then	:: Now	:: Why?
You identified reflections and verified them as congruence transformations.	1 Draw reflections. 2 Draw reflections in the coordinate plane.	Notice in this water reflection that the distance a point lies above the water line appears the same as the distance its image lies below the water.

NewVocabulary
line of reflection

Common Core State Standards

Content Standards
G.CO.4 Develop definitions of rotations, reflections, and translations in terms of angles, circles, perpendicular lines, parallel lines, and line segments.
G.CO.5 Given a geometric figure and a rotation, reflection, or translation, draw the transformed figure using, e.g., graph paper, tracing paper, or geometry software. Specify a sequence of transformations that will carry a given figure onto another.

Mathematical Practices
5 Use appropriate tools strategically.
7 Look for and make use of structure.

1 Draw Reflections In Lesson 4-7, you learned that a reflection or *flip* is a transformation in a line called the **line of reflection**. Each point of the preimage and its corresponding point on the image are the same distance from this line.

KeyConcept Reflection in a Line

A reflection in a line is a function that maps a point to its image such that
- if the point is on the line, then the image and preimage are the same point, or
- if the point is not on the line, the line is the perpendicular bisector of the segment joining the two points.

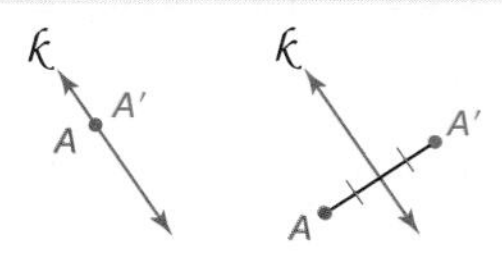

A′, A″, A‴, and so on, name corresponding points for one or more transformations.

To reflect a polygon in a line, reflect each of the polygon's vertices. Then connect these vertices to form the reflected image.

Example 1 Reflect a Figure in a Line

Copy the figure and the given line of reflection. Then draw the reflected image in this line using a ruler.

Step 1 Draw a line through each vertex that is perpendicular to line k.

Step 2 Measure the distance from point A to line k. Then locate A' the same distance from line k on the opposite side

Step 3 Repeat Step 2 to locate points B' and C'. Then connect vertices A', B', and C' to form the reflected image.

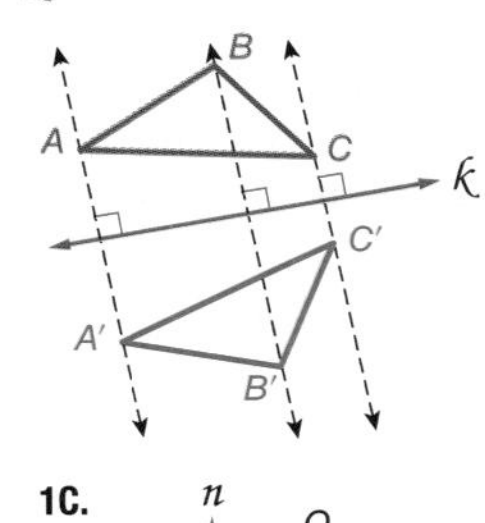

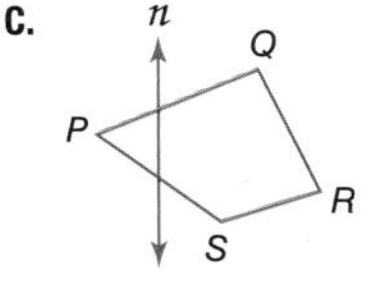

GuidedPractice 1A–1C. See margin.

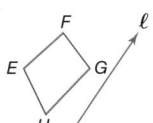

1A.

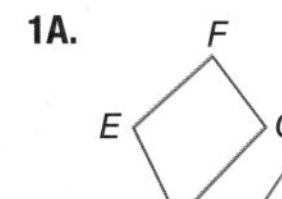

1B.

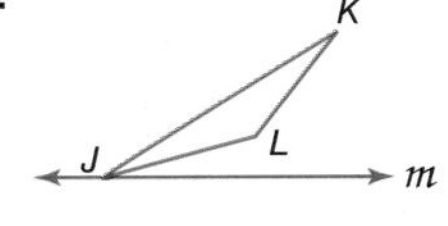

1C.

1 Focus

VerticalAlignment

Before Lesson 9-1 Identify reflections and verify them as congruence transformations.

Lesson 9-1 Draw a reflection in a line of reflection and in the coordinate plane.

After Lesson 9-1 Use and extend similarity properties and transformations to explore and justify conjectures about geometric figures.

2 Teach

Scaffolding Questions

Have students read the **Why?** section of the lesson.

Ask:
- What type of transformation does this picture represent? reflection
- What is another term used for reflection? mirror image or flip
- Would you say that the image has horizontal or vertical symmetry? Why? Horizontal; it is reflected across a horizontal line.

Lesson 9-1 Resources

Resource	Approaching Level AL	On Level OL	Beyond Level BL	English Learners ELL
Teacher Edition		▪ Differentiated Instruction, pp. 625, 629	▪ Differentiated Instruction, pp. 625, 629	▪ Differentiated Instruction, p. 625
Chapter Resource Masters	▪ Study Guide and Intervention, pp. 5–6 ▪ Skills Practice, p. 7 ▪ Practice, p. 8 ▪ Word Problem Practice, p. 9	▪ Study Guide and Intervention, pp. 5–6 ▪ Skills Practice, p. 7 ▪ Practice, p. 8 ▪ Word Problem Practice, p. 9 ▪ Enrichment, p. 10	▪ Practice, p. 8 ▪ Word Problem Practice, p. 9 ▪ Enrichment, p. 10	▪ Study Guide and Intervention, pp. 5–6 ▪ Skills Practice, p. 7 ▪ Practice, p. 8 ▪ Word Problem Practice, p. 9
Other	▪ 5-Minute Check 9-1 ▪ Study Notebook ▪ Teaching Geometry with Manipulatives	▪ 5-Minute Check 9-1 ▪ Study Notebook ▪ Teaching Geometry with Manipulatives	▪ 5-Minute Check 9-1 ▪ Study Notebook	▪ 5-Minute Check 9-1 ▪ Study Notebook ▪ Teaching Geometry with Manipulatives

1 Draw Reflections

Examples 1 and 2 show how to draw reflections and use reflections to minimize distance.

Formative Assessment

Use the Guided Practice exercises after each example to determine students' understanding of concepts.

Additional Examples

1 Draw the reflected image of quadrilateral *WXYZ* in line *p* using a ruler.

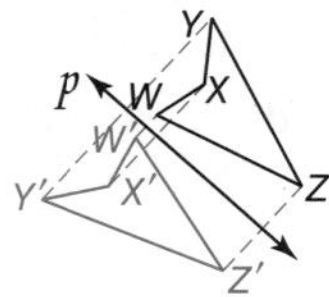

2 **BILLIARDS** Suppose that you must bounce the cue ball off side *A* before it rolls into the pocket at *B*. Locate the point *C* along side *A* that the ball must hit to ensure that it will roll directly toward the pocket.

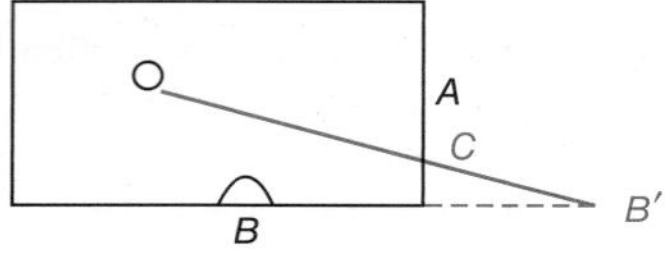

Additional Examples also in Interactive Classroom PowerPoint® Presentations

2 Draw Reflections in the Coordinate Plane

Examples 3–5 show how to draw reflections in the coordinate plane.

Additional Example

3 Quadrilateral *JKLM* has vertices *J*(2, 3), *K*(3, 2), *L*(2, −1), and *M*(0, 1). Graph *JKLM* and its image in the given line.

a. $x = 1$

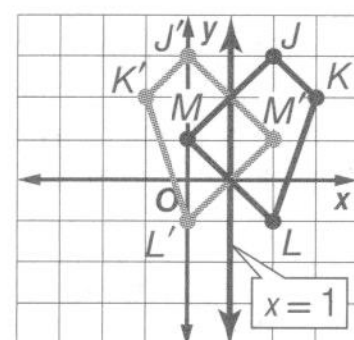

Recall that a reflection is a *congruence transformation* or *isometry*. In the figure in Example 1, $\triangle ABC \cong \triangle A'B'C'$.

Real-WorldCareer

Photographer Photographers take photos for a variety of reasons such as journalism, art, to record an event, or for scientific purposes. In some photography fields such as photojournalism and scientific photography, a bachelor's degree is required. For others, such as portrait photography, technical proficiency is the only requirement.

Real-World Example 2 Minimize Distance by Using a Reflection

SHOPPING Suppose you are going to buy clothes in Store B, return to your car, and then buy shoes at Store G. Where along line *s* of parking spaces should you park to minimize the distance you will walk?

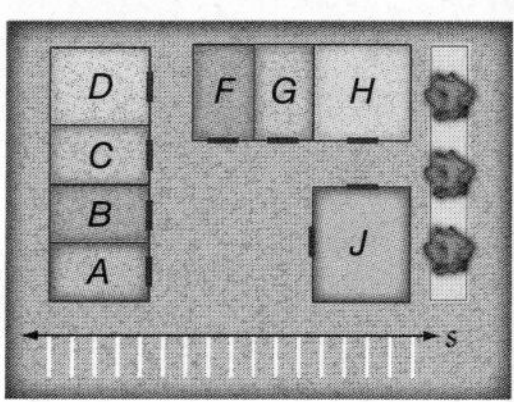

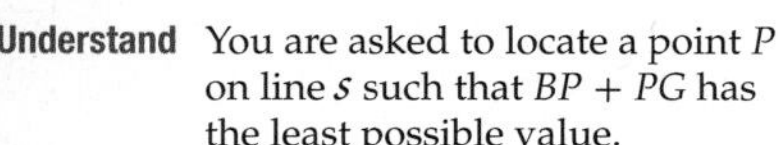

Understand You are asked to locate a point *P* on line *s* such that $BP + PG$ has the least possible value.

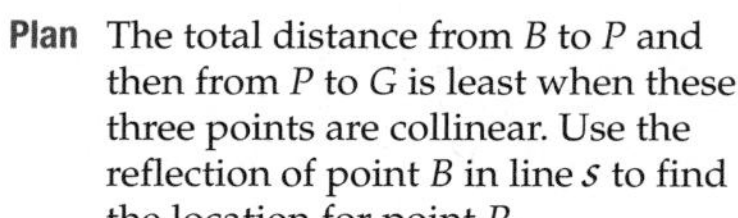

Plan The total distance from *B* to *P* and then from *P* to *G* is least when these three points are collinear. Use the reflection of point *B* in line *s* to find the location for point *P*.

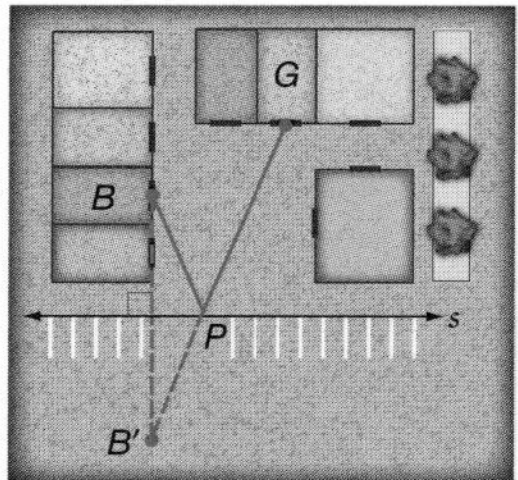

Solve Draw $\overline{B'G}$. Locate *P* at the intersection of line *s* and $\overline{B'G}$.

Check Compare the sum $BP + PG$ for each case to verify that the location found for *P* minimizes this sum.

GuidedPractice

2. TICKET SALES Joy wants to select a good location to sell tickets for a dance. Locate point *P* such that the distance someone would have to walk from Hallway *A*, to point *P* on the wall, and then to their next class in Hallway *B* is minimized. **See margin.**

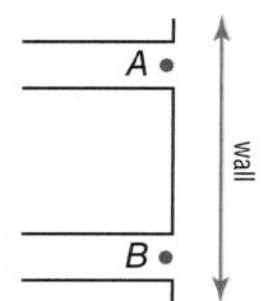

2 Draw Reflections in the Coordinate Plane

Reflections can also be performed in the coordinate plane by using the techniques presented in Example 3.

StudyTip

Characteristics of a Reflection Reflections, like all isometries, preserve distance, angle measure, betweenness of points, and collinearity. The orientation of a preimage and its image, however, are reversed.

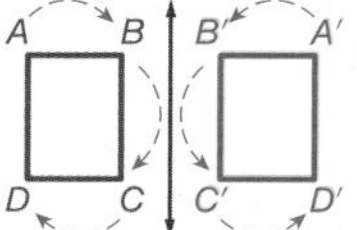

Example 3 Reflect a Figure in a Horizontal or Vertical Line

Triangle *JKL* has vertices *J*(0, 3), *K*(−2, −1), and *L*(−6, 1). Graph $\triangle JKL$ and its image in the given line.

a. $x = -4$

Find a corresponding point for each vertex so that a vertex and its image are equidistant from the line $x = -4$.

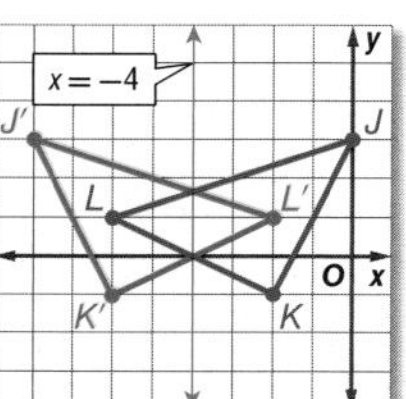

b. $y = 2$

Find a corresponding point for each vertex so that a vertex and its image are equidistant from the line $y = 2$.

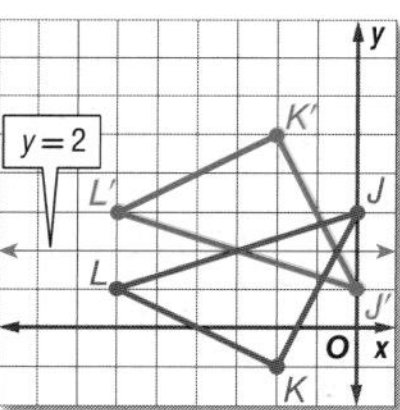

Teach with Tech

Interactive Whiteboard Draw a triangle on a the board. Demonstrate reflections using horizontal and vertical flips. Have students identify the relationship between the figures.

Additional Answer (Guided Practice)

2.

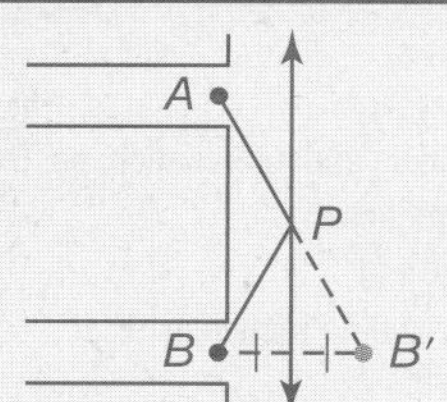

GuidedPractice

Trapezoid *RSTV* has vertices $R(-1, 1)$, $S(4, 1)$, $T(4, -1)$, and $V(-1, -3)$. Graph trapezoid *RSTV* and its image in the given line. **3A–B. See Ch. 9 Answer Appendix.**

3A. $y = -3$ **3B.** $x = 2$

When the line of reflection is the x- or y-axis, you can use the following rule.

KeyConcept Reflection in the x- or y-axis

	Reflection in the x-axis		Reflection in the y-axis
Words	To reflect a point in the x-axis, multiply its y-coordinate by -1.	**Words**	To reflect a point in the y-axis, multiply its x-coordinate by -1.
Symbols	$(x, y) \rightarrow (x, -y)$	**Symbols**	$(x, y) \rightarrow (-x, y)$
Example	A(4, 1), B(7, 3), A′(4, −1), B′(7, −3)	**Example**	A′(−2, 3), A(2, 3), B′(−6, −4), B(6, −4)

ReadingMath

Coordinate Function Notation The expression $P(a, b) \rightarrow P'(a, -b)$ can be read as *point P with coordinates a and b is mapped to new location P prime with coordinates a and negative b.*

Example 4 Reflect a Figure in the x- or y-axis

Graph each figure and its image under the given reflection.

a. $\triangle ABC$ with vertices $A(-5, 3)$, $B(2, 0)$, and $C(1, 2)$ in the x-axis

Multiply the y-coordinate of each vertex by -1.

$(x, y) \rightarrow (x, -y)$

$A(-5, 3) \rightarrow A'(-5, -3)$

$B(2, 0) \rightarrow B'(2, 0)$

$C(1, 2) \rightarrow C'(1, -2)$

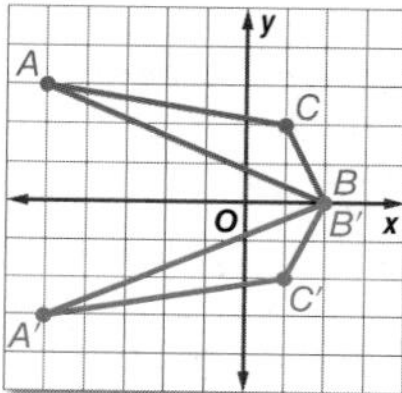
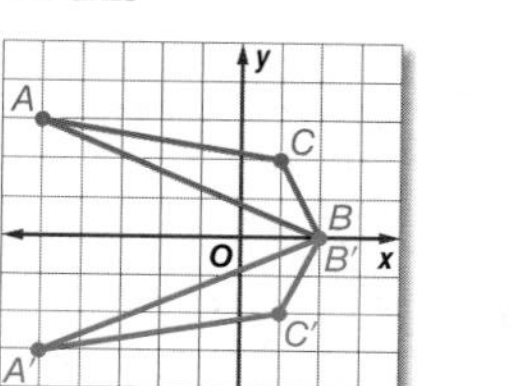

StudyTip

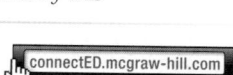

Invariant Points In Example 4a, point *B* is called an *invariant point* because it maps onto itself. Only points that lie on the line of reflection are invariant under a reflection.

b. parallelogram *PQRS* with vertices $P(-4, 1)$, $Q(2, 3)$, $R(2, -1)$, and $S(-4, -3)$ in the y-axis

Multiply the x-coordinate of each vertex by -1.

$(x, y) \rightarrow (-x, y)$

$P(-4, 1) \rightarrow P'(4, 1)$

$Q(2, 3) \rightarrow Q'(-2, 3)$

$R(2, -1) \rightarrow R'(-2, -1)$

$S(-4, -3) \rightarrow S'(4, -3)$

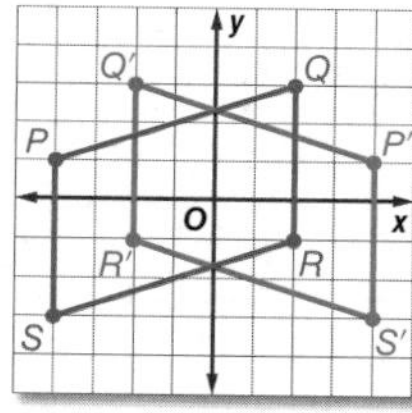

GuidedPractice **4A–B. See Ch. 9 Answer Appendix.**

4A. rectangle with vertices $E(-4, -1)$, $F(2, 2)$, $G(3, 0)$, and $H(-3, -3)$ in the x-axis

4B. $\triangle JKL$ with vertices $J(3, 2)$, $K(2, -2)$, and $L(4, -5)$ in the y-axis

Additional Examples

3 b. $y = -2$

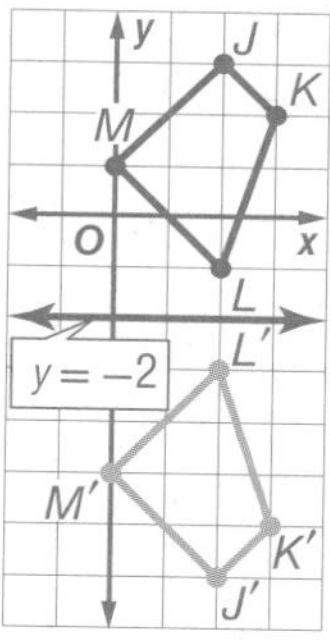

4 Graph each figure and its image under the given reflection.

a. quadrilateral *ABCD* with vertices $A(1, 1)$, $B(3, 2)$, $C(4, -1)$, and $D(2, -3)$ in the x-axis.

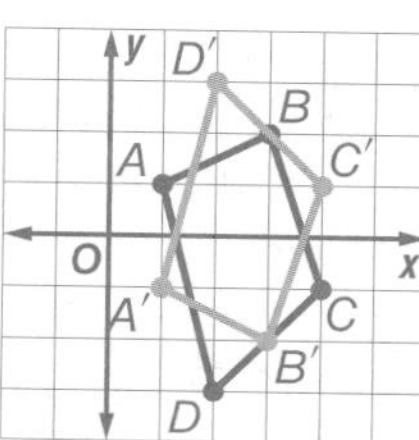

b. quadrilateral *ABCD* and its image under reflection in the y-axis.

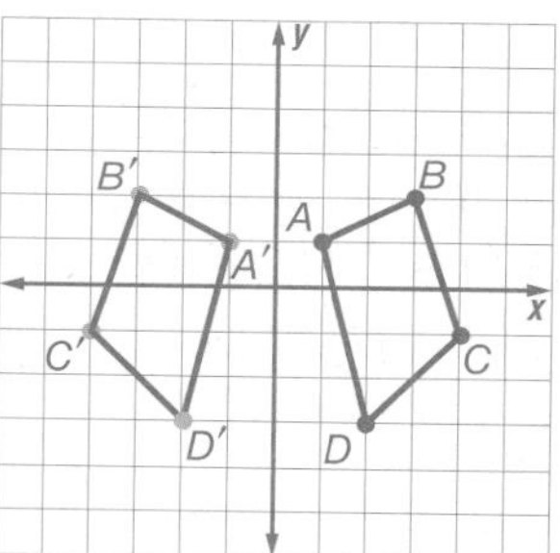

$A(1, 1) \longrightarrow A'(-1, 1)$,
$B(3, 2) \longrightarrow B'(-3, 2)$,
$C(4, -1) \longrightarrow C'(-4, -1)$,
$D(2, -3) \longrightarrow D'(-2, -3)$

DifferentiatedInstruction OL BL ELL

Naturalist Learners Allow the class to discuss examples of reflections in nature and in everyday objects that they use. Students can explain where lines of reflection and lines of symmetry are in objects and decide whether they have point symmetry. Natural examples could be leaves, flowers, fruits, vegetables, animals, eggs, etc. Everyday objects could be pencils, paper, cars, compact discs, clothing, etc.

ReviewVocabulary

Perpendicular Lines Two nonvertical lines are perpendicular if and only if the product of their slopes is −1.

You can also reflect an image in the line $y = x$.

The slope of $y = x$ is 1. In the graph shown, $\overline{CC'}$ is perpendicular to $y = x$, so its slope is −1. From $C(-3, 2)$, move right 2.5 units and down 2.5 units to reach $y = x$. From this point on $y = x$, move right 2.5 units and down 2.5 units to locate $C'(2, -3)$. Using a similar method, the image of $D(-3, -1)$ is found to be $D'(-1, -3)$.

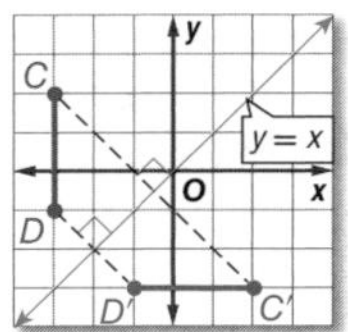

Comparing the coordinates of these and other examples leads to the following rule for reflections in the line $y = x$.

KeyConcept Reflection in Line $y = x$

Words To reflect a point in the line $y = x$, interchange the x- and y-coordinates.

Symbols $(x, y) \rightarrow (y, x)$

Example

B(−1, 4)
A(−5, 2)
y = x
O
B′(4, −1)
A′(2, −5)

Example 5 Reflect a Figure in the Line $y = x$

StudyTip

Preimage and Image In this book, the preimage will always be blue and the image will always be green.

Quadrilateral $JKLM$ has vertices $J(2, 2)$, $K(4, 1)$, $L(3, -3)$, and $M(0, -4)$. Graph $JKLM$ and its image $J'K'L'M'$ in the line $y = x$.

Interchange the x- and y-coordinates of each vertex.

$(x, y) \rightarrow (y, x)$

$J(2, 2) \rightarrow J'(2, 2)$

$K(4, 1) \rightarrow K'(1, 4)$

$L(3, -3) \rightarrow L'(-3, 3)$

$M(0, -4) \rightarrow M'(-4, 0)$

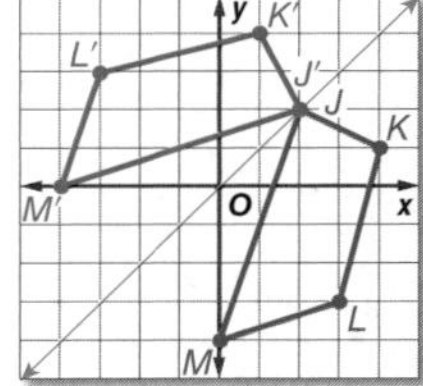

GuidedPractice

5. $\triangle BCD$ has vertices $B(-3, 3)$, $C(1, 4)$, and $D(-2, -4)$. Graph $\triangle BCD$ and its image in the line $y = x$. **See margin.**

ConceptSummary Reflection in the Coordinate Plane

Reflection in the x-axis	Reflection in the y-axis	Reflection in the line $y = x$
P(x, y); P′(x, −y)	P(x, y); P′(−x, y)	P(x, y); P′(y, x); y = x
$(x, y) \rightarrow (x, -y)$	$(x, y) \rightarrow (-x, y)$	$(x, y) \rightarrow (y, x)$

Additional Example

5 Quadrilateral $ABCD$ has vertices $A(1, 1)$, $B(3, 2)$, $C(4, -1)$, and $D(2, -3)$. Graph $ABCD$ and its image under reflection in the line $y = x$.

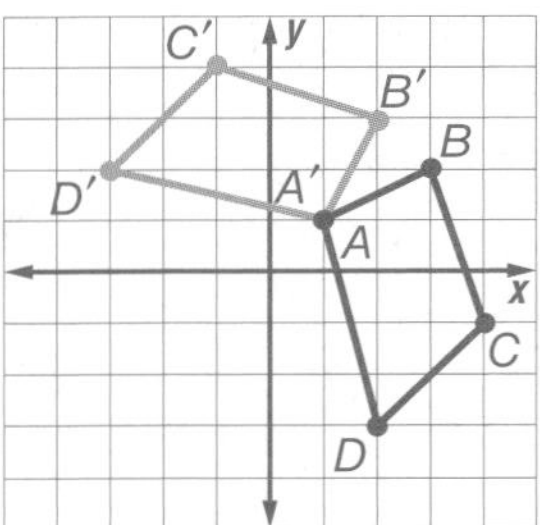

$A(1, 1) \longrightarrow A'(1, 1)$, $B(3, 2) \longrightarrow B'(2, 3)$, $C(4, -1) \longrightarrow C'(-1, 4)$, $D(2, -3) \longrightarrow D'(-3, 2)$

Focus on Mathematical Content

Common Misconceptions A common mistake is to multiply the x-coordinate by −1 to reflect in the x-axis, and multiply the y-coordinate by −1 to reflect in the y-axis. Remind students that reflecting in the x-axis means that the x-coordinate stays the same but the y-coordinate changes. Reflecting in the y-axis means that the y-coordinate stays the same but the x-coordinate changes. Also point out that a reflection in the x-axis flips a figure up or down, affecting the y-coordinate, and a reflection in the y-axis flips a figure left or right, affecting the x-coordinate.

WatchOut!

Vertices When drawing a reflection, keep careful track of the vertices and their images. This is particularly important for symmetrical figures such as a square, where the labeling is needed to determine a unique transformation.

Tips for New Teachers

Reflections In different texts, the terms *reflect in a line*, *reflect over a line*, and *reflect across a line* are all used to mean the same thing.

CCSS Teaching the Mathematical Practices

Tools Mathematically proficient students consider the available tools when solving a mathematical problem. In Exercises 10–15, encourage students to use a straightedge and tracing paper.

Additional Answer (Guided Practice)

5.

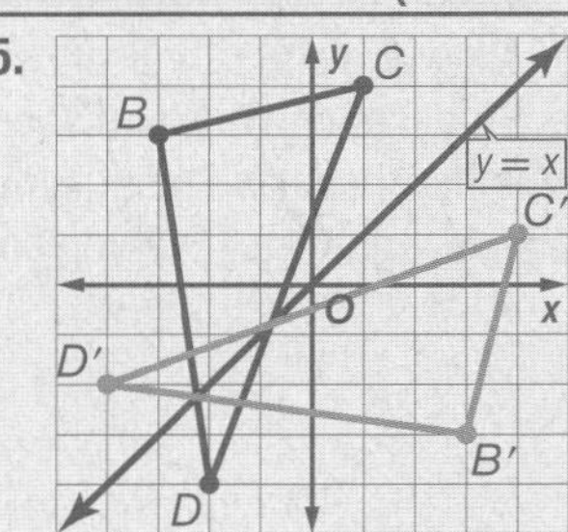

Check Your Understanding

 = Step-by-Step Solutions begin on page R14. 

Example 1 **Copy the figure and the given line of reflection. Then draw the reflected image in this line using a ruler.** 1–3. See margin.

1. 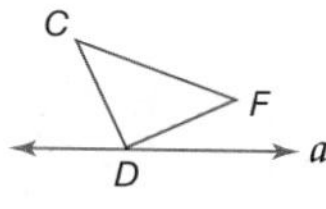

2. 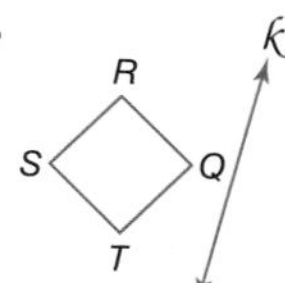

3. 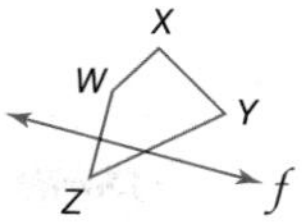 X W Y Z f

Example 2 4. **SPORTING EVENTS** Toru is waiting at a café for a friend to bring him a ticket to a sold-out sporting event. At what point P along the street should the friend try to stop his car to minimize the distance Toru will have to walk from the café, to the car, and then to the arena entrance? Draw a diagram. See Ch. 9 Answer Appendix.

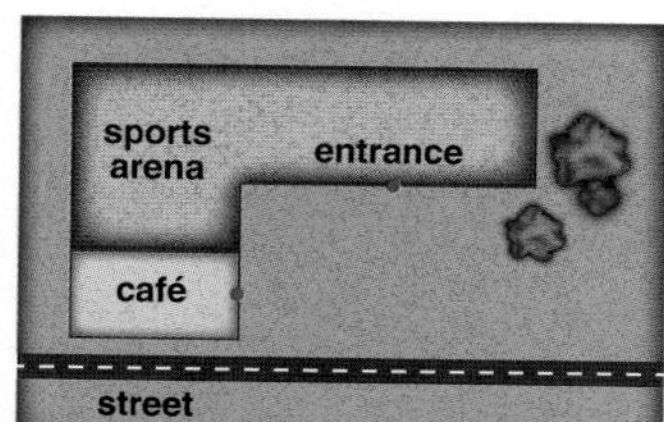

Example 3 **Graph $\triangle ABC$ and its image in the given line.** 5–6. See margin.

5. $y = -2$

6. $x = 3$

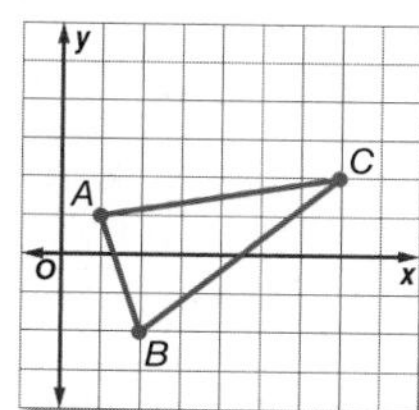

Examples 4–5 **Graph each figure and its image under the given reflection.** 7–9. See Ch. 9 Answer Appendix.

7. $\triangle XYZ$ with vertices $X(0, 4)$, $Y(-3, 4)$, and $Z(-4, -1)$ in the y-axis

8. $\square QRST$ with vertices $Q(-1, 4)$, $R(4, 4)$, $S(3, 1)$, and $T(-2, 1)$ in the x-axis

9. quadrilateral $JKLM$ with vertices $J(-3, 1)$, $K(-1, 3)$, $L(1, 3)$, and $M(-3, -1)$ in the line $y = x$

Practice and Problem Solving

Extra Practice is on page R9.

Example 1 CCSS **TOOLS** **Copy the figure and the given line of reflection. Then draw the reflected image in this line using a ruler.** 10–15. See Ch. 9 Answer Appendix.

10. 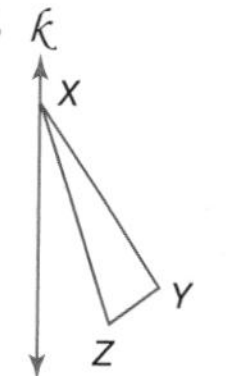

11. 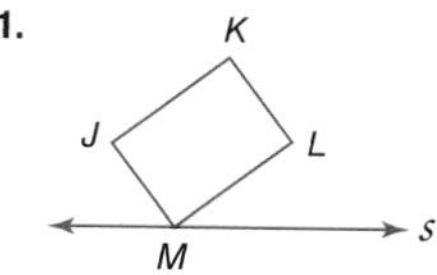

12. 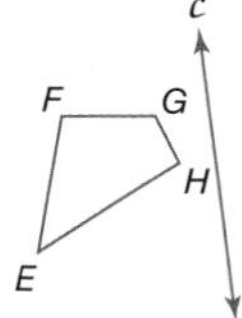

13. 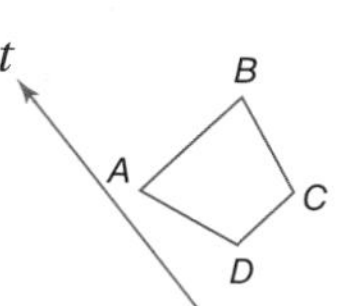

14. 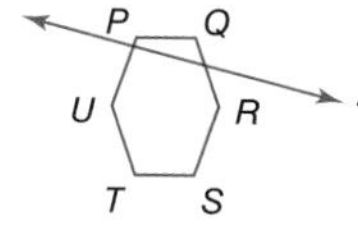

15. 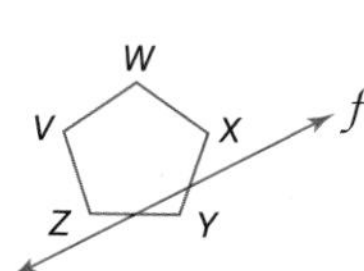

3 Practice

Formative Assessment

Use Exercises 1–9 to check for understanding.

Then use the chart at the bottom of this page to customize assignments for your students.

Additional Answers

1. 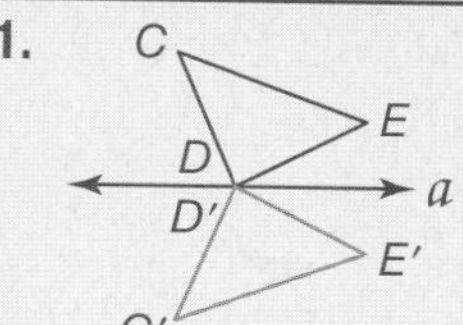

2. 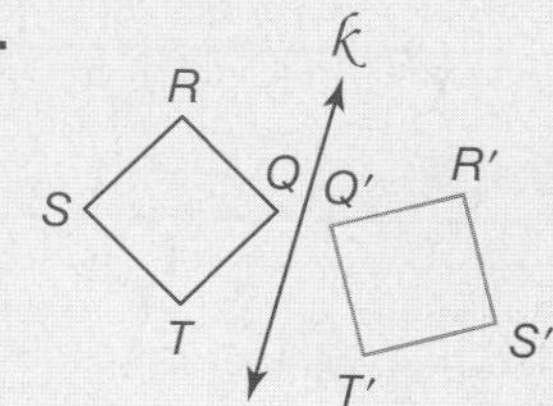

3. 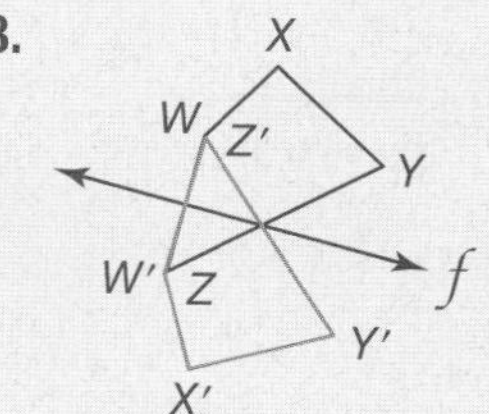

5. 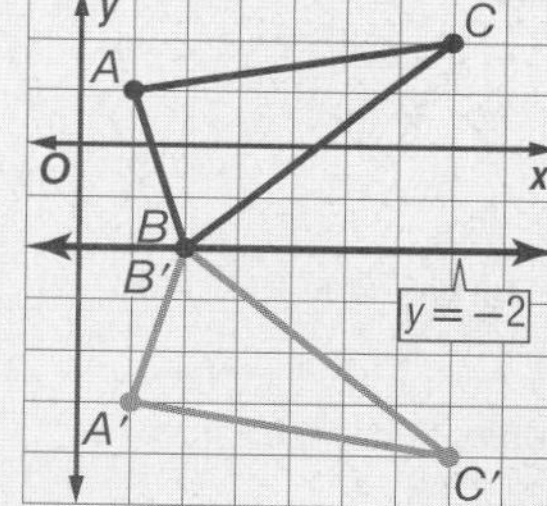

6. 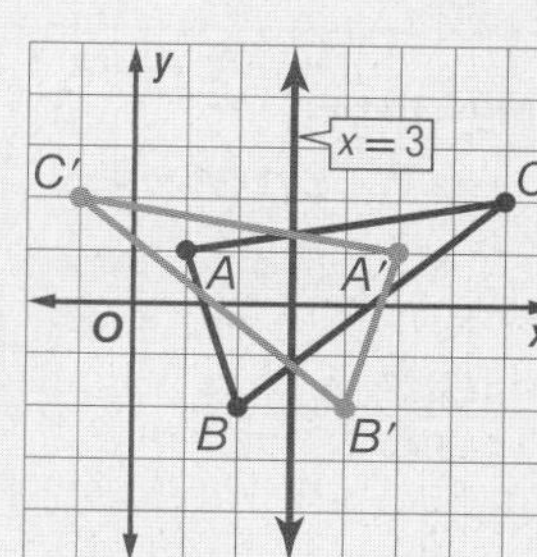

Differentiated Homework Options

Level	Assignment	Two-Day Option	
AL Basic	10–29, 45, 46, 48, 50–67	11–29 odd, 52–55	10–28 even, 45, 46, 48, 50, 51, 56–67
OL Core	11–45 odd, 46, 48, 50, 51, 56–67	10–29, 52–55	30–46, 48, 50, 51, 56–67
BL Advanced	30–63 (optional: 64–67)		

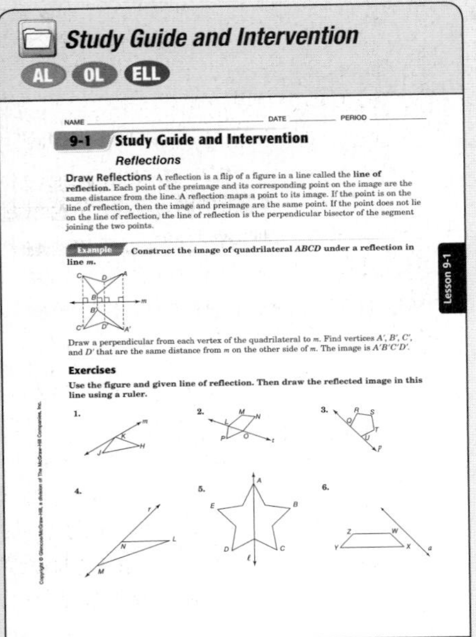

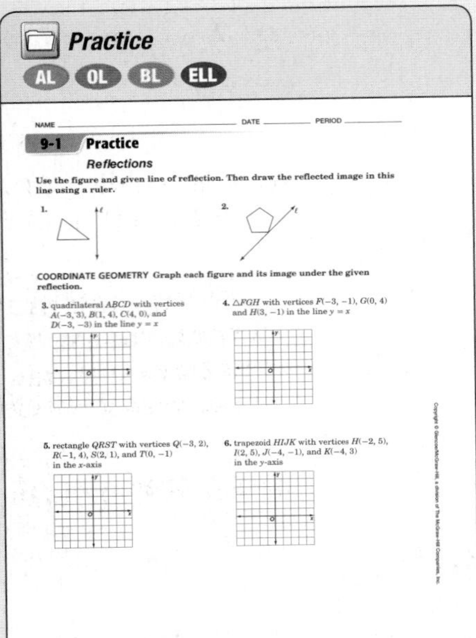

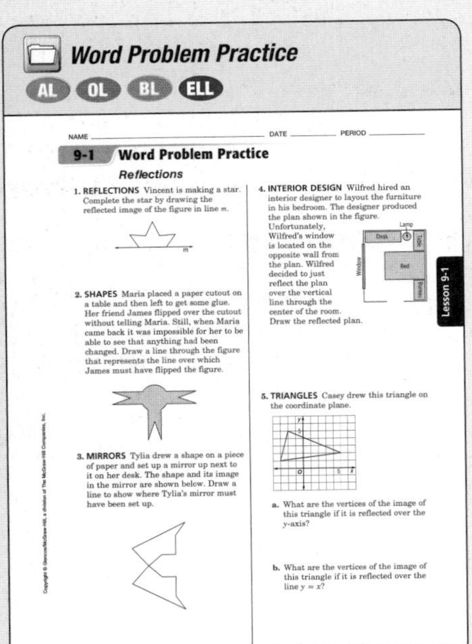

Example 2 **SPORTS** When a ball is rolled or struck without spin against a wall, it bounces off the wall and travels in a ray that is the reflected image of the path of the ball if it had gone straight through the wall. Use this information in Exercises 16 and 17.

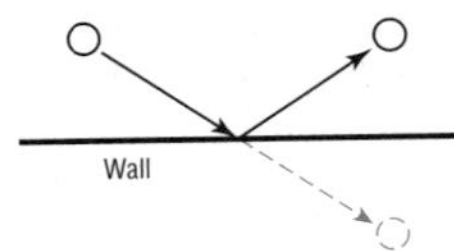

16. **BILLIARDS** Tadeo is playing billiards. He wants to strike the eight ball with the cue ball so that the eight ball bounces off the rail and rolls into the indicated pocket. If the eight ball moves with no spin, draw a diagram showing the exact point P along the right rail where the eight ball should hit after being struck by the cue ball. **16–17. See Ch. 9 Answer Appendix.**

17. **INDOOR SOCCER** Abby is playing indoor soccer, and she wants to hit the ball to point C, but must avoid an opposing player at point B. She decides to hit the ball at point A so that it bounces off the side wall. Draw a diagram that shows the exact point along the top wall for which Abby should aim.

Example 3 **Graph each figure and its image in the given line.** **18–23. See Ch. 9 Answer Appendix.**

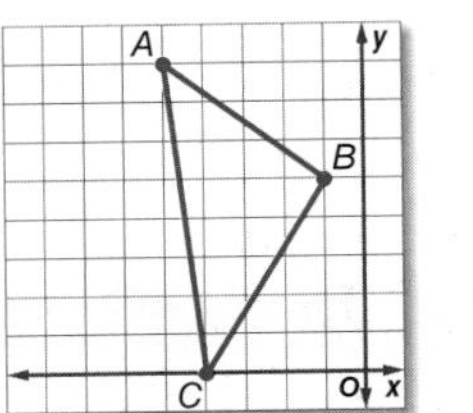

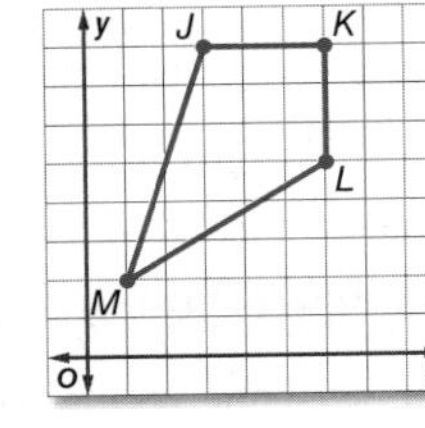

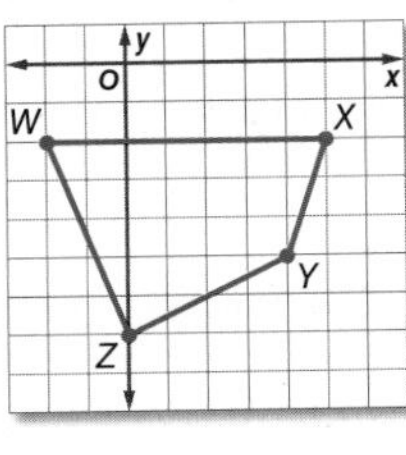

18. $\triangle ABC$; $y = 3$

19. $\triangle ABC$; $x = -1$

20. $JKLM$; $x = 1$

21. $JKLM$; $y = 4$

22. $WXYZ$; $y = -4$

23. $WXYZ$; $x = -2$

Examples 4–5  **STRUCTURE** **Graph each figure and its image under the given reflection.** **24–29. See Ch. 9 Answer Appendix.**

24. rectangle $ABCD$ with vertices $A(-5, 2)$, $B(1, 2)$, $C(1, -1)$, and $D(-5, -1)$ in the line $y = -2$

25 square $JKLM$ with vertices $J(-4, 6)$, $K(0, 6)$, $L(0, 2)$, and $M(-4, 2)$ in the y-axis

26. $\triangle FGH$ with vertices $F(-3, 2)$, $G(-4, -1)$, and $H(-6, -1)$ in the line $y = x$

27. $\square WXYZ$ with vertices $W(2, 3)$, $X(7, 3)$, $Y(6, -1)$, and $Z(1, -1)$ in the x-axis

28. trapezoid $PQRS$ with vertices $P(-1, 4)$, $Q(2, 4)$, $R(1, -1)$, and $S(-1, -1)$ in the y-axis

29. $\triangle STU$ with vertices $S(-3, -2)$, $T(-2, 3)$, and $U(2, 2)$ in the line $y = x$

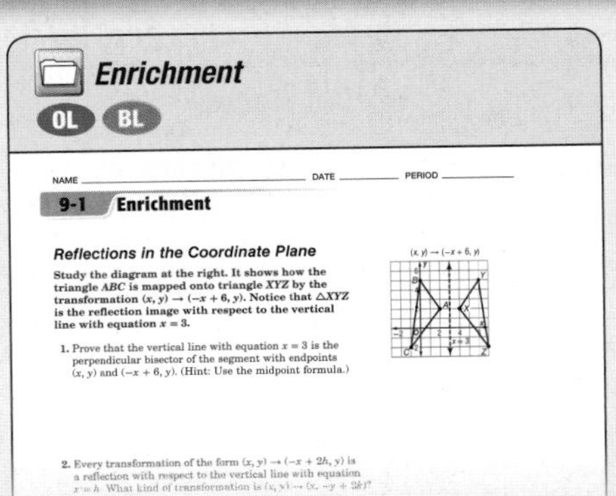

Teaching the Mathematical Practices

Structure Mathematically proficient students look closely to discern a pattern or structure. They also can step back for an overview and shift perspective. In Exercises 24–29, encourage students to find a pattern to their problem solving strategy used here.

B **Each figure shows a preimage and its reflected image in some line. Copy each figure and draw the line of reflection.** 30–32. See margin.

30. 

31. 

32. 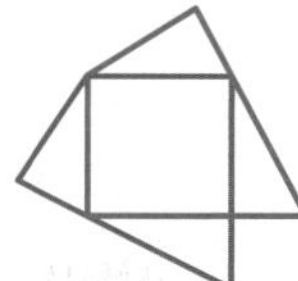

CONSTRUCTION To construct the reflection of a figure in a line using only a compass and a straightedge, you can use:

- the construction of a line perpendicular to a given line through a point not on the line (p. 55), and
- the construction of a segment congruent to a given segment (p. 17).

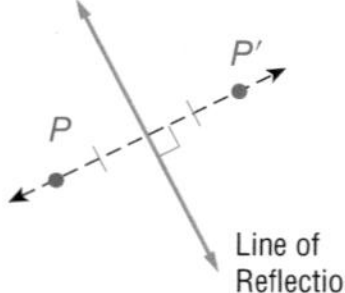

CCSS TOOLS Copy each figure and the given line of reflection. Then construct the reflected image. 33–34. See Ch. 9 Answer Appendix.

33. 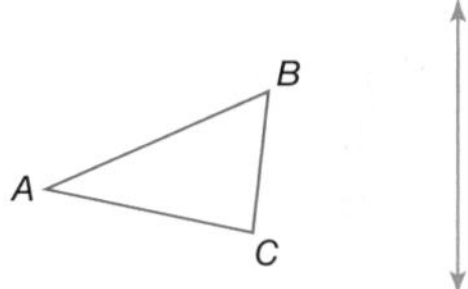

34. 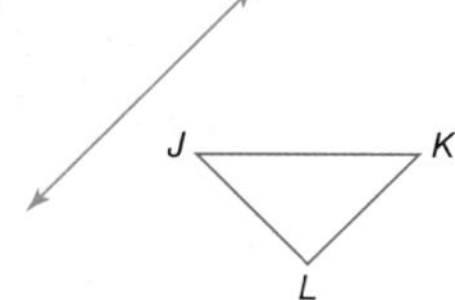

35 **PHOTOGRAPHY** Refer to the photo at the right.

a. What object separates the zebras and their reflections? the water

b. What geometric term can be used to describe this object? finite plane

ALGEBRA Graph the line $y = 2x - 3$ and its reflected image in the given line. What is the equation of the reflected image? 36–38. See Ch. 9 Answer Appendix.

36. x-axis **37.** y-axis **38.** $y = x$

39. Reflect $\triangle CDE$ shown below in the line $y = 3x$. See margin.

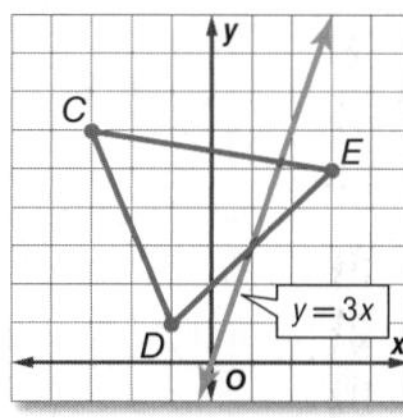

40. Relocate vertex C so that $ABCDE$ is convex, and all sides remain the same length. See margin.

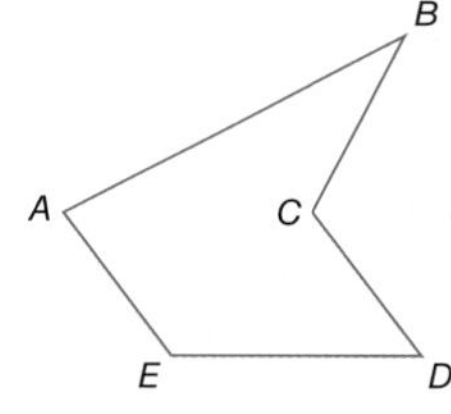

Differentiated Instruction OL BL

Extension Geometric reflections play an important role in many sports, such as golf, billiards, tennis, table tennis, and hockey. Refer to Exercises 16 and 17 to discuss how reflections can be used to construct the perfect miniature golf shot. Have students design a 9-hole miniature golf course. Students must include the shape of the green for each hole, the point at which the golf ball must begin, and the location of the hole. Then students can construct the perfect shots for each hole of their golf course or of the course of a peer.

Exercise Alert

Compass and Straightedge Exercises 33 and 34 require the use of a compass and a straightedge.

Teaching the Mathematical Practices

Tools Mathematically proficient students consider the available tools when solving a mathematical problem. In Exercises 10–15, encourage students to use a compass and straightedge.

Additional Answers

30. 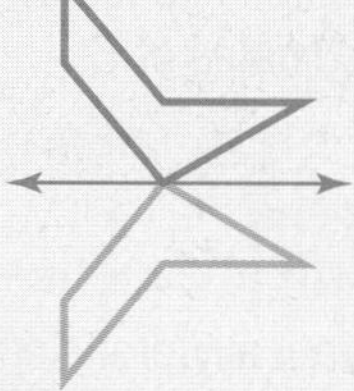

31. 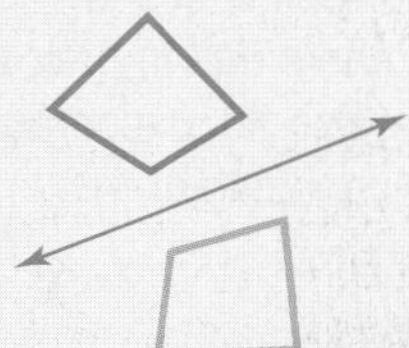

32. 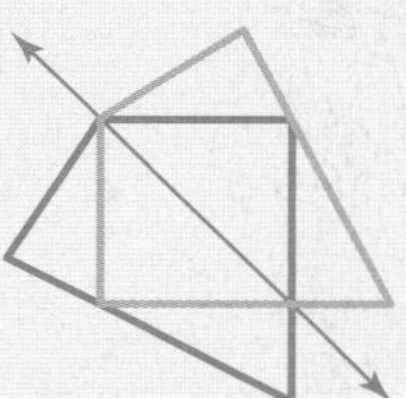

39. 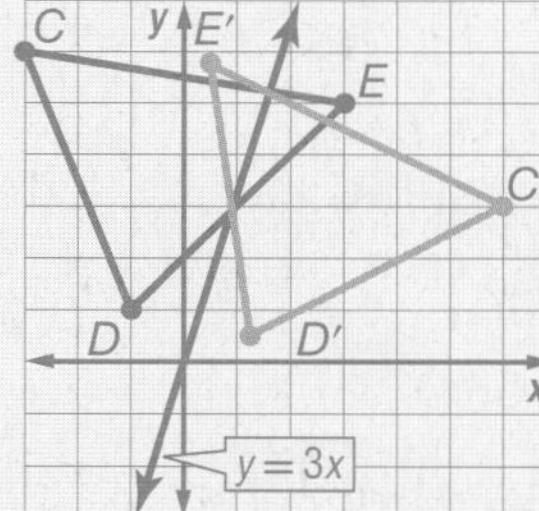

40. 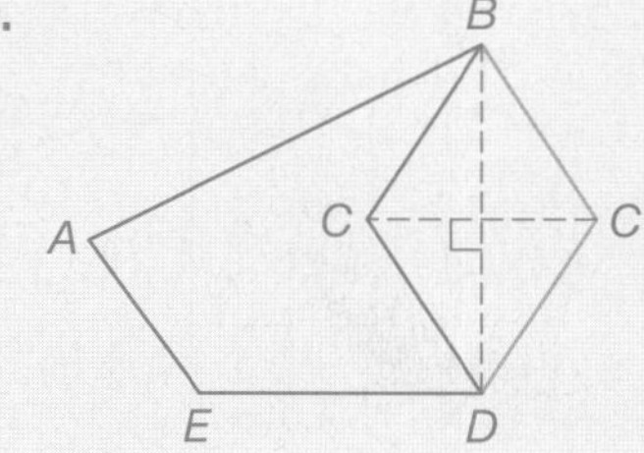

Multiple Representations

In Exercise 44, students use geometric sketches, a graph, a table and verbal descriptions to investigate reflections in the origin.

WatchOut!

Error Analysis In Exercise 45, students should recognize that Ashley made the common mistake of changing the x-coordinate when an object is reflected in the x-axis. Remind students that this is a very common error. Jamil has found the correct coordinates of C'.

CCSS Teaching the Mathematical Practices

Precision Mathematically proficient students use clear definitions in discussion with others and in their own reasoning. In Exercise 50, encourage students to draw a sketch of the situation described.

Additional Answers

41.

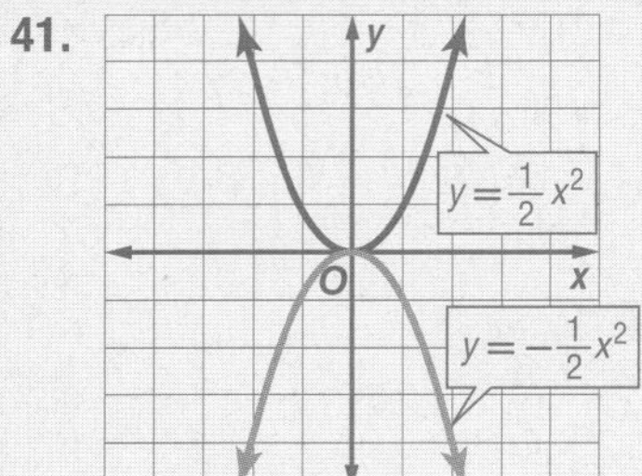

42.

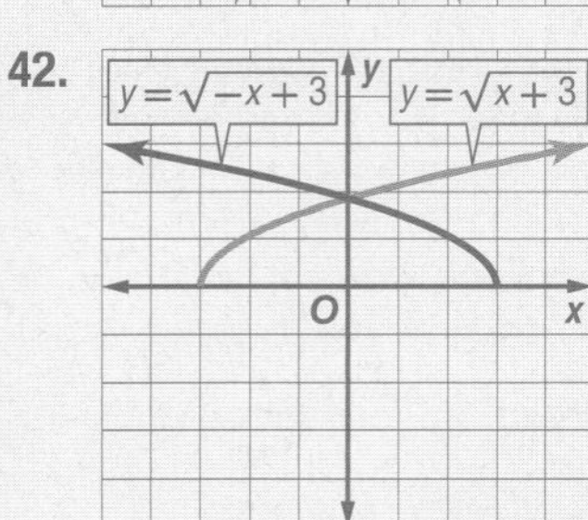

43.

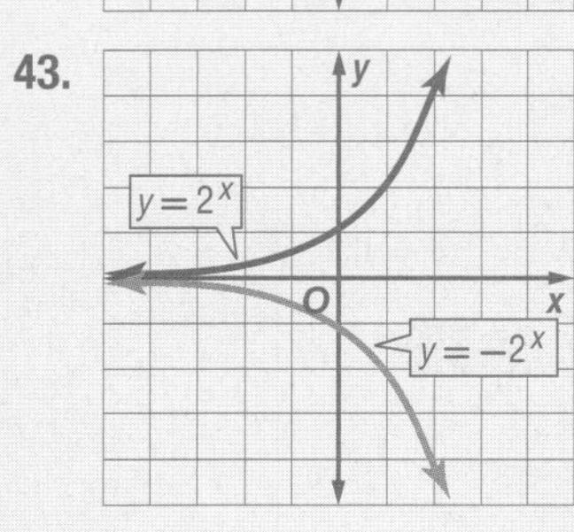

C **ALGEBRA** **Graph the reflection of each function in the given line. Then write the equation of the reflected image.** 41–43. See margin.

41. x-axis

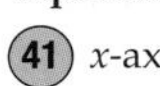

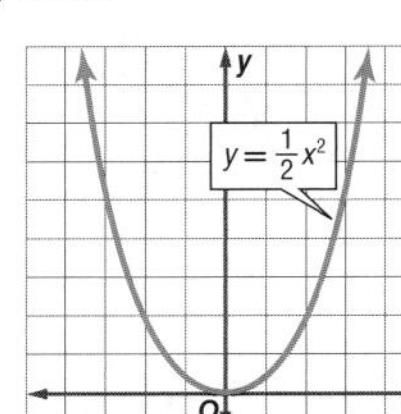

42. y-axis

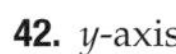

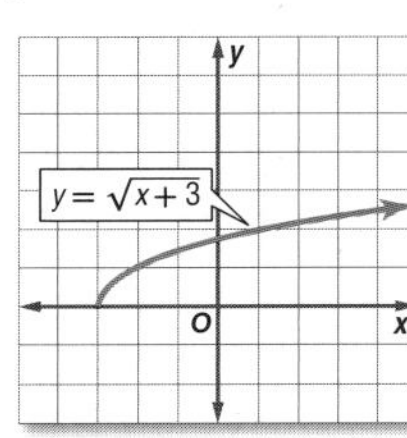

43. x-axis

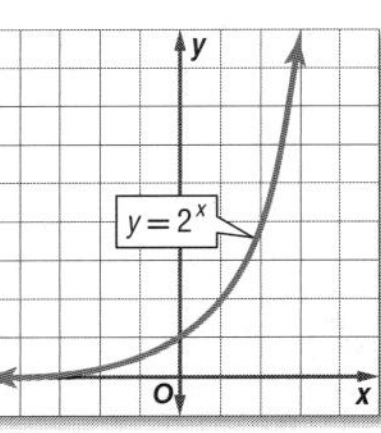

44. **MULTIPLE REPRESENTATIONS** In this problem, you will investigate a reflection in the origin. a, b, d. See margin.

   a. **Geometric** Draw $\triangle ABC$ in the coordinate plane so that each vertex is a whole-number ordered pair.

   b. **Graphical** Locate each reflected point A', B', and C' so that the reflected point, the original point, and the origin are collinear, and both the original point and the reflected point are equidistant from the origin.

   c. **Tabular** Copy and complete the table below. Sample answers given.

	$\triangle ABC$		$\triangle A'B'C'$	
Coordinates	A	(2, 4)	A'	(−2, −4)
	B	(4, 5)	B'	(−4, −5)
	C	(3, 1)	C'	(−3, −1)

   d. **Verbal** Make a conjecture about the relationship between corresponding vertices of a figure reflected in the origin.

H.O.T. Problems Use Higher-Order Thinking Skills

45. **ERROR ANALYSIS** Jamil and Ashley are finding the coordinates of the image of (2, 3) after a reflection in the x-axis. Is either of them correct? Explain. See margin.

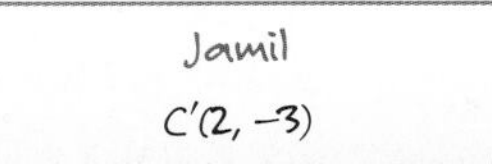

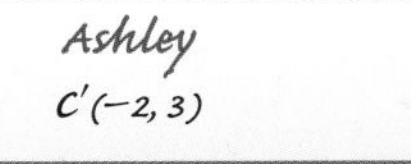

46. **WRITING IN MATH** Describe how to reflect a figure not on the coordinate plane across a line. See margin.

47. **CHALLENGE** A point in the second quadrant with coordinates $(-a, b)$ is reflected in the x-axis. If the reflected point is then reflected in the line $y = -x$, what are the final coordinates of the image? (a, b)

48. **OPEN ENDED** Draw a polygon on the coordinate plane that when reflected in the x-axis looks exactly like the original figure. See margin.

49. **CHALLENGE** When $A(4, 3)$ is reflected in a line, its image is $A'(-1, 0)$. Find the equation of the line of reflection. Explain your reasoning. See margin.

50. **CCSS PRECISION** The image of a point reflected in a line is *always, sometimes,* or *never* located on the other side of the line of reflection. See margin.

51. **WRITING IN MATH** Suppose points P, Q, and R are collinear, with point Q between points P and R. Describe a plan for a proof that the reflection of points P, Q, and R in a line preserves collinearity and betweenness of points. See margin.

44a. Sample answer:

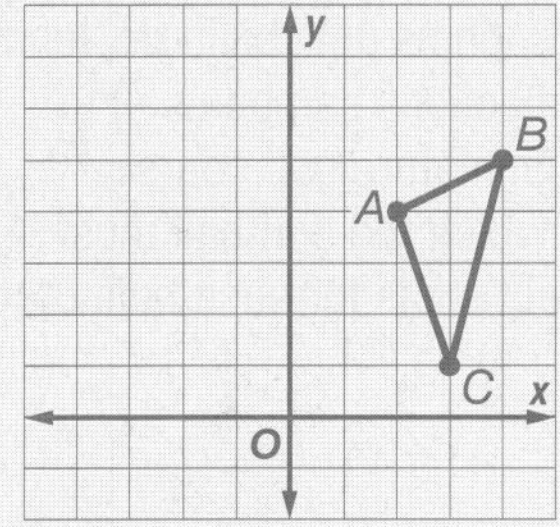

44b.

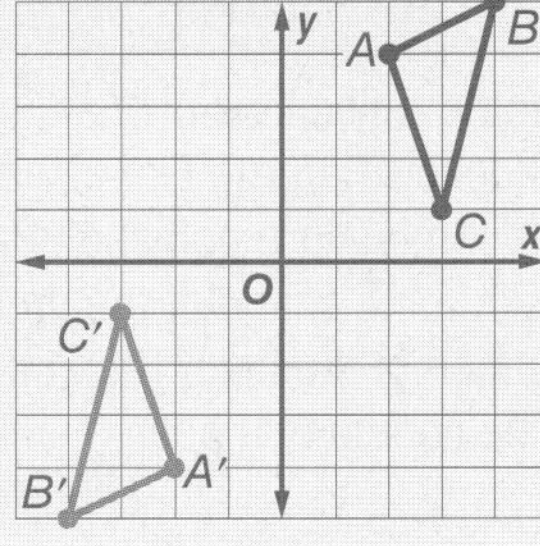

Standardized Test Practice

52. SHORT RESPONSE If quadrilateral *WXYZ* is reflected across the *y*-axis to become quadrilateral *W′X′Y′Z′*, what are the coordinates of *X′*? **(0, 3)**

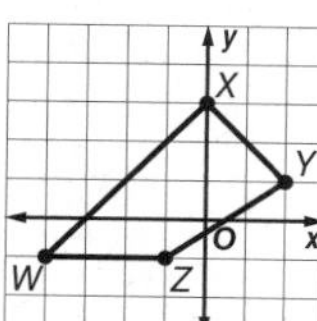

53. ALGEBRA If the arithmetic mean of $6x$, $3x$, and 27 is 18, then what is the value of x? **B**

A 2   C 5
B 3   D 6

54. In $\triangle DEF$, $m\angle E = 108$, $m\angle F = 26$, and $f = 20$. Find d to the nearest whole number. **G**

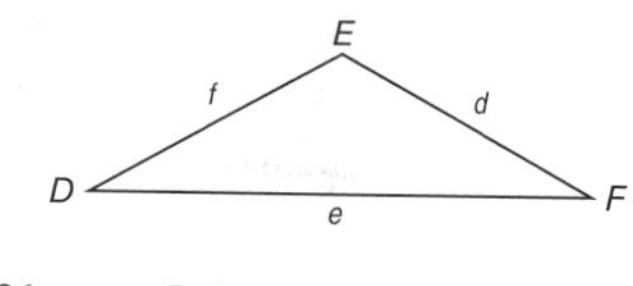

F 26   G 33   H 60   J 65

55. SAT/ACT In a coordinate plane, points *A* and *B* have coordinates $(-2, 4)$ and $(3, 3)$, respectively. What is the value of *AB*? **E**

A $\sqrt{50}$ D $(1, -1)$
B $(1, 7)$ E $\sqrt{26}$
C $(5, -1)$

Spiral Review

Write the component form of each vector. (Lesson 8-7)

56. $\langle -5, 0 \rangle$

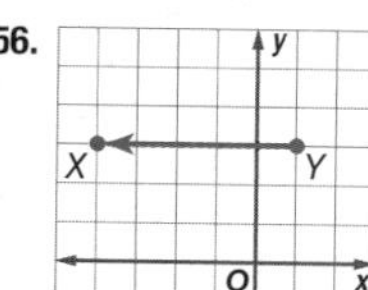

57. $\langle 3, 2 \rangle$

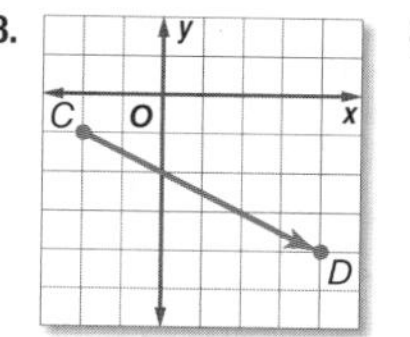

58. $\langle 6, -3 \rangle$

59. REAL ESTATE A house is built on a triangular plot of land. Two sides of the plot are 160 feet long, and they meet at an angle of 85°. If a fence is to be placed along the perimeter of the property, how much fencing material is needed? (Lesson 8-6) **about 536 ft**

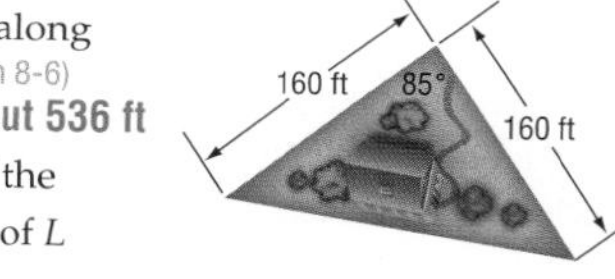

60. COORDINATE GEOMETRY In $\triangle LMN$, $\overline{PR}$ divides $\overline{NL}$ and $\overline{MN}$ proportionally. If the vertices are $N(8, 20)$, $P(11, 16)$, and $R(3, 8)$ and $\frac{LP}{PN} = \frac{2}{1}$, find the coordinates of *L* and *M*. (Lesson 7-4) **$L(17, 8)$; $M(-7, -16)$**

Use the figure at the right to write an inequality relating the given pair of angle or segment measures. (Lesson 5-6)

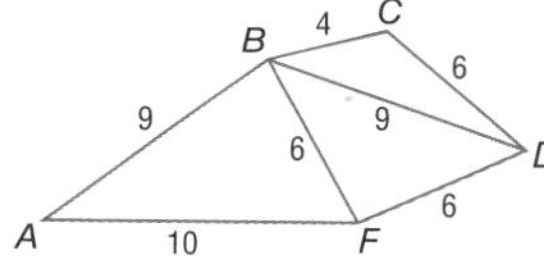

61. *AB*, *FD* **$AB > FD$**

62. $m\angle BDC$, $m\angle FDB$ **$m\angle BDC < m\angle FDB$**

63. $m\angle FBA$, $m\angle DBF$ **$m\angle FBA > m\angle DBF$**

Skills Review

Find the magnitude and direction of each vector.

64. $\overrightarrow{RS}$: $R(-3, 3)$ and $S(-9, 9)$ **$6\sqrt{2} \approx 8.5$, 135°**

65. $\overrightarrow{JK}$: $J(8, 1)$ and $K(2, 5)$ **$2\sqrt{13} \approx 7.2$, 146.3°**

66. $\overrightarrow{FG}$: $F(-4, 0)$ and $G(-6, -4)$ **$2\sqrt{5} \approx 4.5$, 243.4°**

67. $\overrightarrow{AB}$: $A(-1, 10)$ and $B(1, -12)$ **$2\sqrt{122} \approx 22.1$, 275.2°**

49. The slope of the line connecting the two points is $\frac{3}{5}$. The Midpoint Formula can be used to find the midpoint between the two points, which is $\left(\frac{3}{2}, \frac{3}{2}\right)$. Using the point-slope form, the equation of the line is $y = -\frac{5}{3}x + 4$. (The slope of the bisector is $-\frac{5}{3}$ because it is the negative reciprocal of the slope $\frac{3}{5}$.)

50. Sometimes; if the point in located on the line of reflection, then the point will remain in its same location.

51. Construct *P*, *Q*, *R* collinear with *Q* between *P* and *R*. Draw line ℓ, then construct perpendicular lines from *P*, *Q*, and *R* to line ℓ. Show equidistance or similarity of slope.

4 Assess

Ticket Out the Door Have students work in pairs and use grid paper to plot and draw figures and reflections. One student can plot a simple figure with three vertices and draw and label the point or line in which the other student will draw the reflection. Students will hand in their papers as they exit the classroom.

Additional Answers

44d. Sample answer: The coordinates of the reflective image are the additive inverses of the coordinates of the original image.

45. Jamil; sample answer: When you reflect a point across the *x*-axis, the reflected point is in the same place horizontally, but not vertically. When (2, 3) is reflected across the *x*-axis, the coordinates of the reflected point are (2, −3) since it is in the same location horizontally, but the other side of the *x*-axis vertically.

46. Draw a line through each vertex of the image that is perpendicular to the line you are reflecting in. Next, measure the distance from each vertex to the line of reflection. Locate each vertex the same perpendicular distance from the opposite side of the line. Connect each of the vertices to form the reflected image.

48. Sample answer:

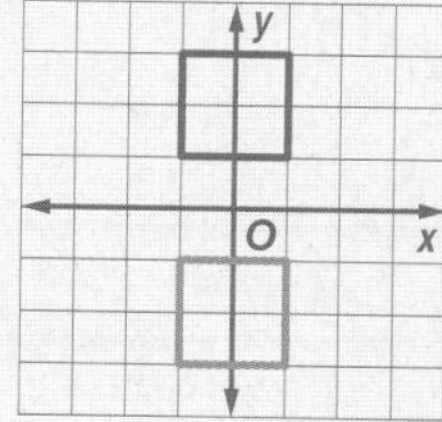

1 Focus

VerticalAlignment

Before Lesson 9-2 Find the magnitude and direction of vectors.

Lesson 9-2 Draw translations in a plane and in a coordinate plane.

After Lesson 9-2 Use and extend similarity properties and transformations to explore and justify conjectures about geometric figures.

2 Teach

Scaffolding Questions

Have students read the **Why?** section of the lesson.

Ask:

- Why is it important that the figure be moved by very small amounts? It is important to create the illusion of movement. Otherwise, the frames would not mimic movement, but rather would resemble still shots of something in a different position.
- In order to trick the eye into believing that the object is moving, what must be true of the figure itself? The components must maintain the same size, shape, and proximate relationship with the entire figure in order to appear as though they are moving rather than morphing.

LESSON 9-2 Translations

Then

- You found the magnitude and direction of vectors.

Now

1. Draw translations.
2. Draw translations in the coordinate plane.

Why?

- Stop-motion animation is a technique in which an object is moved by very small amounts between individually photographed frames. When the series of frames is played as a continuous sequence, the result is the illusion of movement.

NewVocabulary
translation vector

Common Core State Standards

Content Standards

G.CO.4 Develop definitions of rotations, reflections, and translations in terms of angles, circles, perpendicular lines, parallel lines, and line segments.

G.CO.5 Given a geometric figure and a rotation, reflection, or translation, draw the transformed figure using, e.g., graph paper, tracing paper, or geometry software. Specify a sequence of transformations that will carry a given figure onto another.

Mathematical Practices

5 Use appropriate tools strategically.

4 Model with mathematics.

1 Draw Translations

In Lesson 4-7, you learned that a translation or *slide* is a transformation that moves all points of a figure the same distance in the same direction. Since vectors can be used to describe both distance and direction, vectors can be used to define translations.

KeyConcept Translation

A translation is a function that maps each point to its image along a vector, called the **translation vector**, such that

- each segment joining a point and its image has the same length as the vector, and
- this segment is also parallel to the vector.

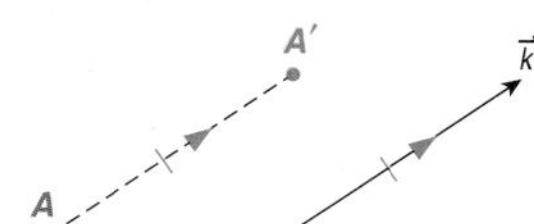

Point A' is a translation of point A along translation vector $\vec{k}$.

Example 1 Draw a Translation

Copy the figure and the given translation vector. Then draw the translation of the figure along the translation vector.

Step 1 Draw a line through each vertex parallel to vector $\vec{w}$

Step 2 Measure the length of vector $\vec{w}$. Locate point X' by marking off this distance along the line through vertex X, starting at X and in the same direction as the vector.

Step 3 Repeat Step 2 to locate points Y' and Z'. Then connect vertices X', Y', and Z' to form the translated image.

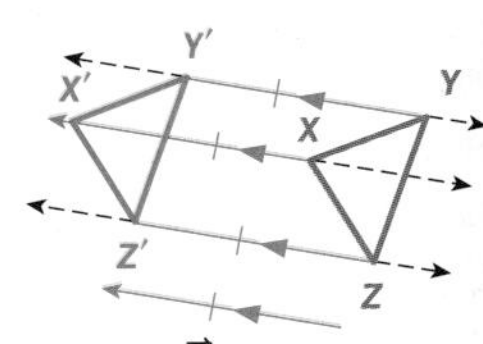

GuidedPractice 1A–B. See Ch. 9 Answer Appendix.

1A.

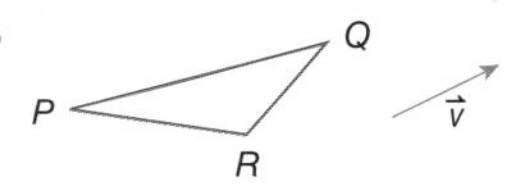

1B.

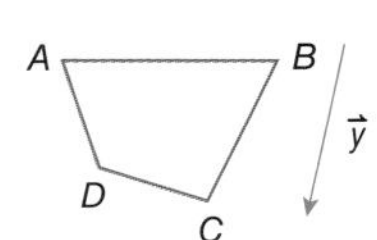

632 | Lesson 9-2

Lesson 9-2 Resources

Resource	Approaching Level AL	On Level OL	Beyond Level BL	English Learners ELL
Teacher Edition	▪ Differentiated Instruction, p. 633	▪ Differentiated Instruction, p. 638	▪ Differentiated Instruction, p. 638	▪ Differentiated Instruction, p. 633
Chapter Resource Masters	▪ Study Guide and Intervention, pp. 11–12 ▪ Skills Practice, p. 13 ▪ Practice, p. 14 ▪ Word Problem Practice, p. 15	▪ Study Guide and Intervention, pp. 11–12 ▪ Skills Practice, p. 13 ▪ Practice, p. 14 ▪ Word Problem Practice, p. 15 ▪ Enrichment, p. 16 ▪ Computer Activities, pp. 17, 18	▪ Practice, p. 14 ▪ Word Problem Practice, p. 15 ▪ Enrichment, p. 16	▪ Study Guide and Intervention, pp. 11–12 ▪ Skills Practice, p. 13 ▪ Practice, p. 14 ▪ Word Problem Practice, p. 15
Other	▪ 5-Minute Check 9-2 ▪ Study Notebook ▪ Teaching Geometry with Manipulatives	▪ 5-Minute Check 9-2 ▪ Study Notebook ▪ Teaching Geometry with Manipulatives	▪ 5-Minute Check 9-2 ▪ Study Notebook	▪ 5-Minute Check 9-2 ▪ Study Notebook ▪ Teaching Geometry with Manipulatives

2 Draw Translations in the Coordinate Plane

Recall that a vector in the coordinate plane can be written as $\langle a, b\rangle$, where a represents the horizontal change and b is the vertical change from the vector's tip to its tail. $\overline{CD}$ is represented by the ordered pair $\langle 2, -4\rangle$.

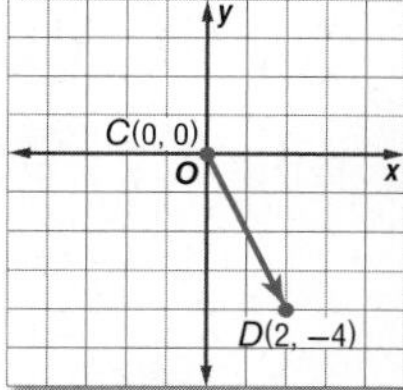

Written in this form, called the component form, a vector can be used to translate a figure in the coordinate plane.

ReadingMath

Horizontal and Vertical Translations When the translation vector is of the form $\langle a, 0\rangle$, the translation is horizontal only. When the translation vector is of the form $\langle 0, b\rangle$, the translation is vertical only.

KeyConcept Translation in the Coordinate Plane

Words	To translate a point along vector $\langle a, b\rangle$, add a to the x-coordinate and b to the y-coordinate.
Symbols	$(x, y) \rightarrow (x + a, y + b)$
Example	The image of $P(-2, 3)$ translated along vector $\langle 7, 4\rangle$ is $P'(5, 7)$.

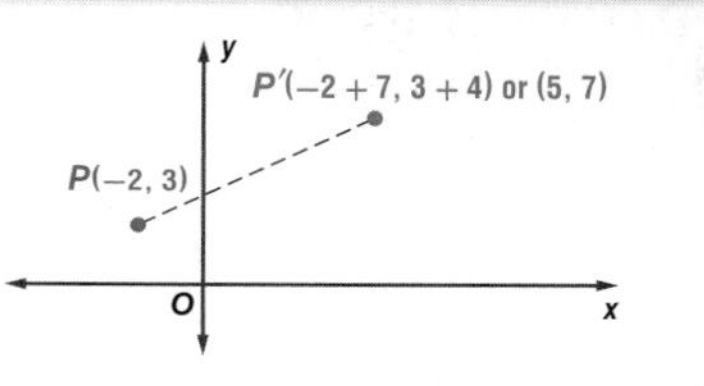

A translation is another type of congruence transformation or isometry.

Example 2 Translations in the Coordinate Plane

Graph each figure and its image along the given vector.

a. **$\triangle EFG$ with vertices $E(-7, -1)$, $F(-4, -4)$, and $G(-3, -1)$; $\langle 2, 5\rangle$**

The vector indicates a translation 2 units right and 5 units up.

$(x, y) \rightarrow (x + 2, y + 5)$

$E(-7, -1) \rightarrow E'(-5, 4)$

$F(-4, -4) \rightarrow F'(-2, 1)$

$G(-3, -1) \rightarrow G'(-1, 4)$

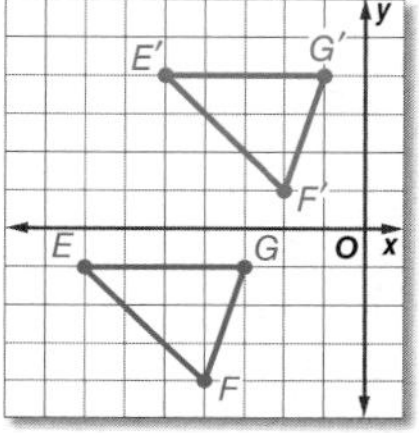

b. **square $JKLM$ with vertices $J(3, 4)$, $K(5, 2)$, $L(7, 4)$, and $M(5, 6)$; $\langle -3, -4\rangle$**

The vector indicates a translation 3 units left and 4 units down.

$(x, y) \rightarrow (x + (-3), y + (-4))$

$J(3, 4) \rightarrow J'(0, 0)$

$K(5, 2) \rightarrow K'(2, -2)$

$L(7, 4) \rightarrow L'(4, 0)$

$M(5, 6) \rightarrow M'(2, 2)$

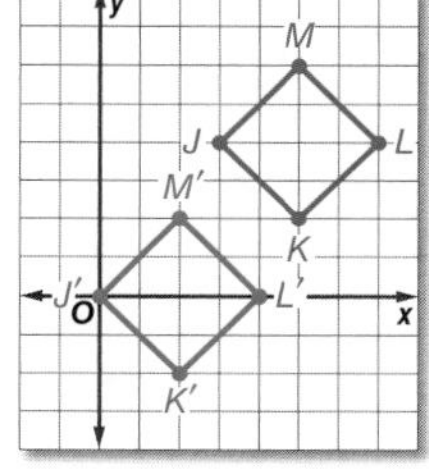

GuidedPractice 2A–2B. See Ch. 9 Answer Appendix.

2A. $\triangle ABC$ with vertices $A(2, 6)$, $B(1, 1)$, and $C(7, 5)$; $\langle -4, -1\rangle$

2B. quadrilateral $QRST$ with vertices $Q(-8, -2)$, $R(-9, -5)$, $S(-4, -7)$, and $T(-4, -2)$; $\langle 7, 1\rangle$

Math HistoryLink

Felix Klein (1849–1925) Klein's definition of geometry as the study of the properties of a space that remain invariant under a group of transformations allowed for the inclusion of both Euclidean and non-Euclidean geometry.

1 Draw Translations

Example 1 shows how to draw a translation, given a translation vector.

Formative Assessment

Use the Guided Practice exercises after each Example to determine students' understanding of concepts.

Additional Example

1 Copy the figure and given translation vector. Then draw the translation of the figure along the translation vector.

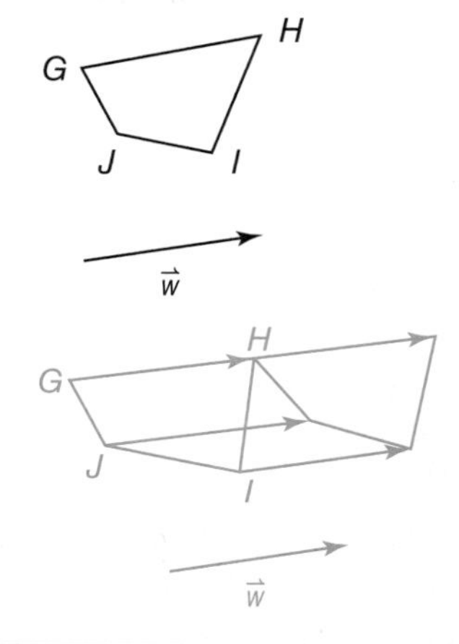

2 Draw Translations in the Coordinate Plane

Examples 2 and 3 show how to translate a figure on a coordinate plane by moving the figure horizontally, vertically, or in both directions.

DifferentiatedInstruction AL ELL

Kinesthetic Learners Create three or four large coordinate grids using poster board. Provide several laminated shapes, such as rectangles, hexagons, pentagons, and trapezoids. Students can practice physically translating shapes on the grids. Students can use examples of translations in the lesson or create their own.

Additional Examples

2 Graph each figure and its image along the given vector.

a. $\triangle TUV$ with vertices $T(-1, -4)$, $U(6, 2)$, and $V(5, -5)$; $\langle -3, 2\rangle$

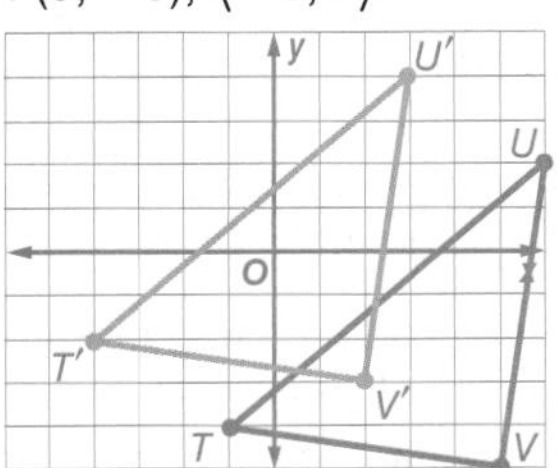

b. pentagon *PENTA* with vertices $P(1, 0)$, $E(2, 2)$, $N(4, 1)$, $T(4, -1)$, $A(2, -2)$; $\langle -5, -1\rangle$

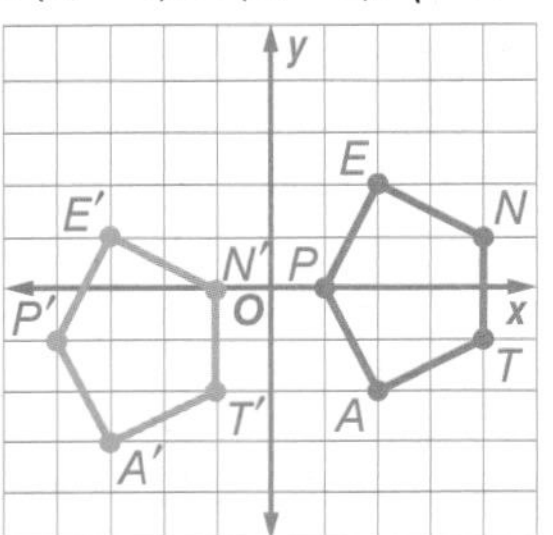

3 **ANIMATION** The graph shows repeated translations that result in the animation of the raindrop.

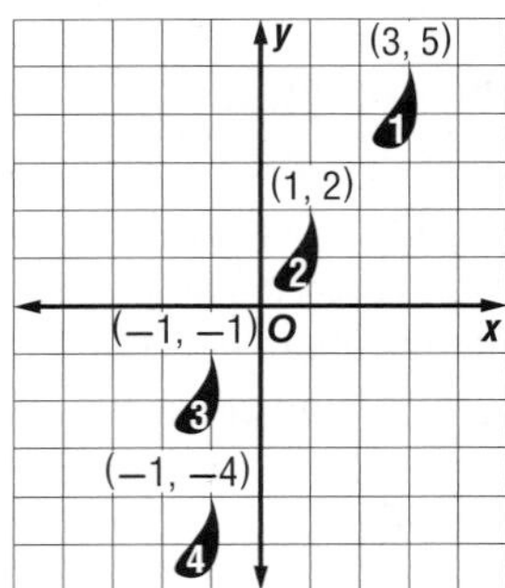

a. Describe the translation of the raindrop from position 2 to position 3 in function notation and in words. The point (1, 2) moves to position (−1, −1); $(x, y) \to (x - 2, x - 3)$

b. Describe the translation of the raindrop from position 3 to position 4 using a translation vector. $\langle 0, -3\rangle$

Real-WorldLink

Marching bands often make use of a series of formations that can include geometric shapes. Usually, each band member has an assigned position in each formation. *Floating* is the movement of a group of members together without changing the shape or size of their formation.

Real-World Example 3 Describing Translations

MARCHING BAND In one part of a marching band's performance, a line of trumpet players starts at position 1, marches to position 2, and then to position 3. Each unit on the graph represents one step.

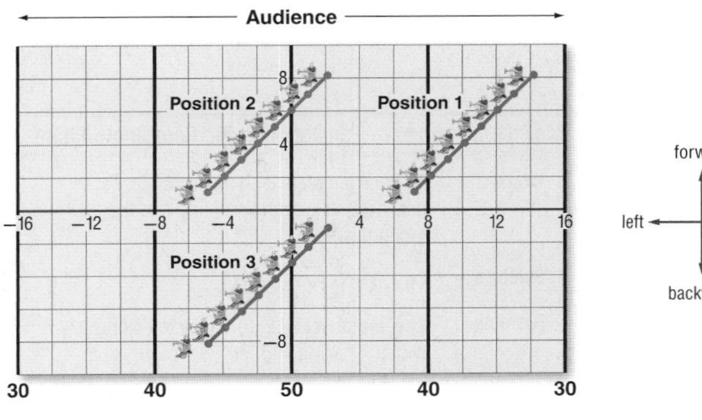

a. Describe the translation of the trumpet line from position 1 to position 2 in function notation and in words.

One point on the line in position 1 is (14, 8). In position 2, this point moves to (2, 8). Use the translations function $(x, y) \to (x + a, y + b)$ to write and solve equations to find a and b.

$(14 + a, 8 + b)$ or $(2, 8)$

$14 + a = 2$ $\qquad$ $8 + b = 8$

$a = -12$ $\qquad$ $b = 0$

function notation: $(x, y) \to (x + (-12), y + 0)$

So, the trumpet line is translated 12 steps *left* but no steps forward or backward from position 1 to position 2.

b. Describe the translation of the line from position 1 to position 3 using a translation vector.

$(14 + a, 8 + b)$ or $(2, -1)$

$14 + a = 2$ $\qquad$ $8 + b = -1$

$a = -12$ $\qquad$ $b = -9$

translation vector: $\langle -12, -9\rangle$

GuidedPractice **3A.** $(x, y) \to (x + 3, y + 2)$; **The coin is translated 3 units right and 2 units up.**

3. ANIMATION A coin is filmed using stop-motion animation so that it appears to move.

A. Describe the translation from *A* to *B* in function notation and in words.

B. Describe the translation from *A* to *C* using a translation vector. $\langle 7, 3\rangle$

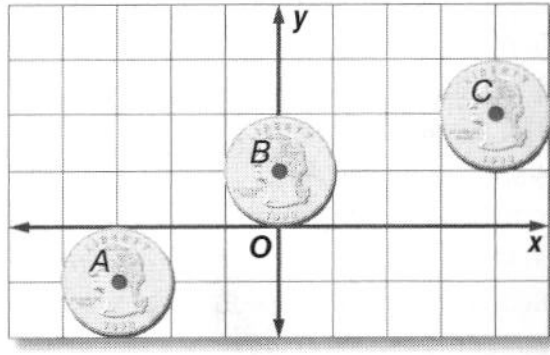

WatchOut!

Translations When translating a point along a vector, be careful of the signs of the coordinate of the point and the vector.

Teach with Tech

Interactive Whiteboard Draw a polygon on a coordinate plane. Demonstrate a translation by dragging the polygon to another location on the coordinate plane. Have students find the vertices of the image of the polygon and use these to describe the translation.

Check Your Understanding

 = Step-by-Step Solutions begin on page R14. 

Example 1 Copy the figure and the given translation vector. Then draw the translation of the figure along the translation vector. **1–3. See margin.**

1. 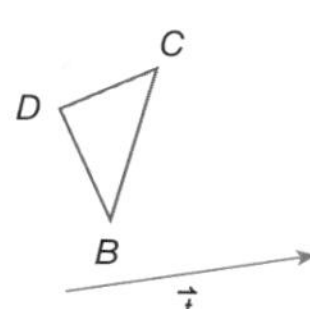
2. 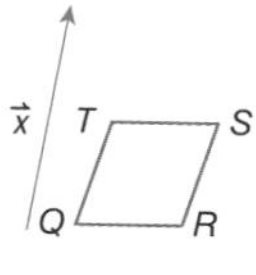
3. 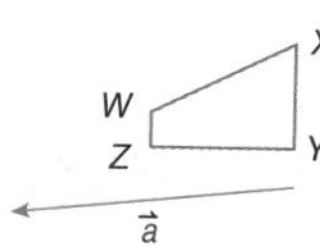

Example 2 Graph each figure and its image along the given vector. **4–6. See Ch. 9 Answer Appendix.**

4. trapezoid $JKLM$ with vertices $J(2, 4)$, $K(1, 1)$, $L(5, 1)$ and $M(4, 4)$; $\langle 7, 1\rangle$
5. $\triangle DFG$ with vertices $D(-8, 8)$, $F(-10, 4)$, and $G(-7, 6)$; $\langle 5, -2\rangle$
6. parallelogram $WXYZ$ with vertices $W(-6, -5)$, $X(-2, -5)$, $Y(-1, -8)$, and $Z(-5, -8)$; $\langle -1, 4\rangle$

Example 3

7. **VIDEO GAMES** The object of the video game shown is to manipulate the colored tiles left or right as they fall from the top of the screen to completely fill each row without leaving empty spaces. If the starting position of the tile piece at the top of the screen is (x, y), use function notation to describe the translation that will fill the indicated row. $(x, y) \rightarrow (x + 3, y - 5)$

Practice and Problem Solving

Extra Practice is on page R9.

Example 1 **CCSS TOOLS** Copy the figure and the given translation vector. Then draw the translation of the figure along the translation vector. **8–13. See Ch. 9 Answer Appendix.**

8. 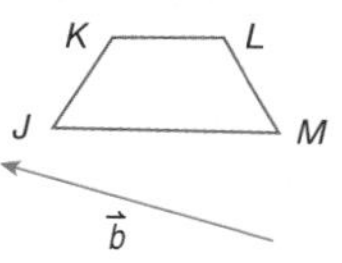
9. 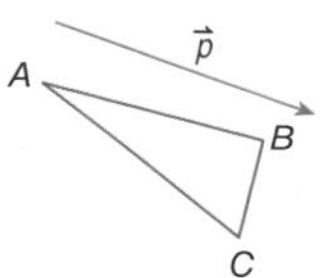
10. 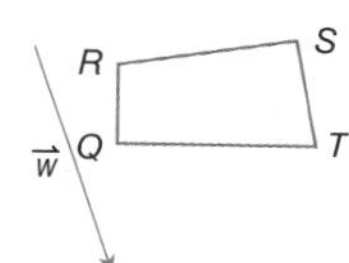
11. 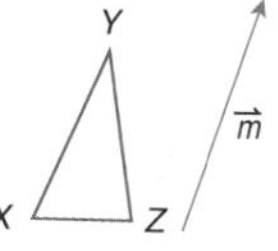
12. 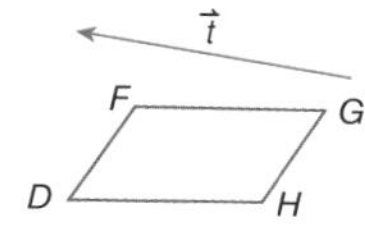
13. 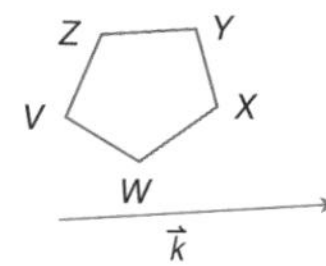

Example 2 Graph each figure and its image along the given vector. **14–19. See Ch. 9 Answer Appendix.**

14. $\triangle ABC$ with vertices $A(1, 6)$, $B(3, 2)$, and $C(4, 7)$; $\langle 4, -1\rangle$
15. $\triangle MNP$ with vertices $M(4, -5)$, $N(5, -8)$, and $P(8, -6)$; $\langle -2, 5\rangle$
16. rectangle $QRST$ with vertices $Q(-8, 4)$, $R(-8, 2)$, $S(-3, 2)$, and $T(-3, 4)$; $\langle 2, 3\rangle$
17. quadrilateral $FGHJ$ with vertices $F(-4, -2)$, $G(-1, -1)$, $H(0, -4)$, and $J(-3, -6)$; $\langle -5, -2\rangle$
18. ▱$WXYZ$ with vertices $W(-3, -1)$, $X(1, -1)$, $Y(2, -4)$, and $Z(-2, -4)$; $\langle -3, 4\rangle$
19. trapezoid $JKLM$ with vertices $J(-4, -2)$, $K(-1, -2)$, $L(0, -5)$, and $M(-5, -5)$; $\langle 6, 5\rangle$

Differentiated Homework Options

Level	Assignment	Two-Day Option	
AL Basic	8–21, 30, 32–54	9–21 odd, 35–38	8–20 even, 22–30, 32–34, 39–54
OL Core	9–21 odd, 22, 23, 25, 26, 28–30, 32–54	8–21, 35–38	22–30, 32–34, 39–54
BL Advanced	22–50, (optional: 51–54)		

3 Practice

Formative Assessment

Use Exercises 1–7 to check for understanding.

Then use the chart at the bottom of this page to customize assignments for your students.

Teaching the Mathematical Practices

Tools Mathematically proficient students consider the available tools when solving a mathematical problem. In Exercises 8–13, encourage students to use tracing paper.

Additional Answers

1. 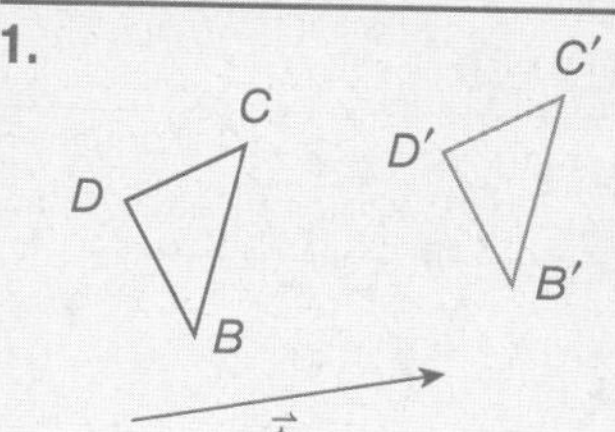
2. 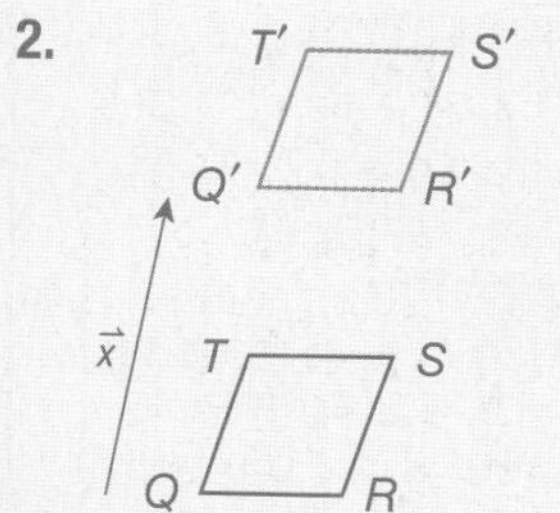
3. 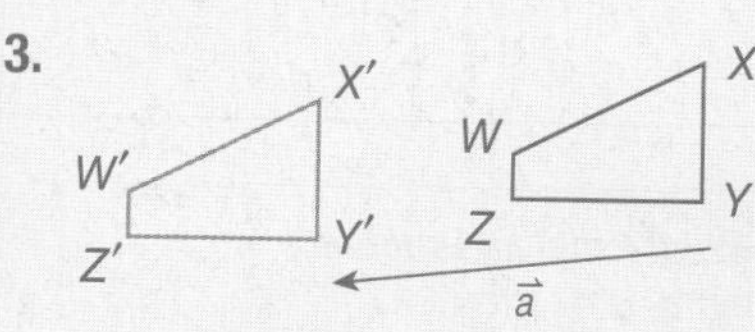

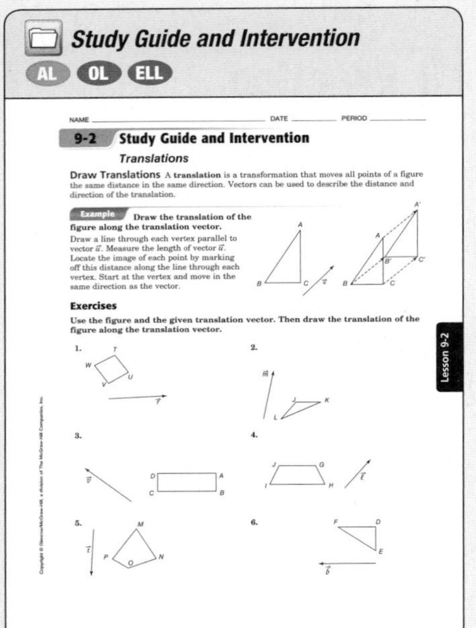

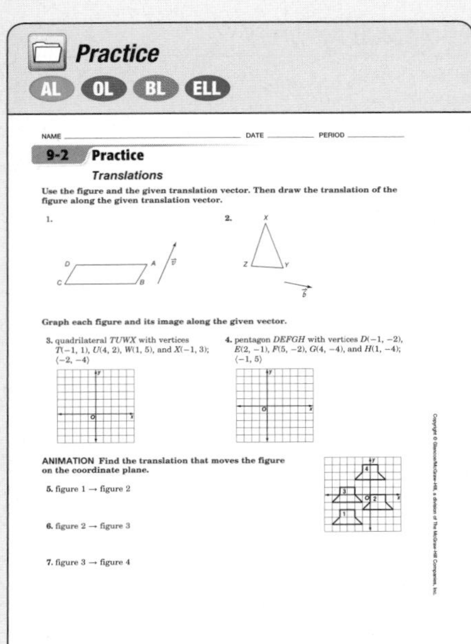

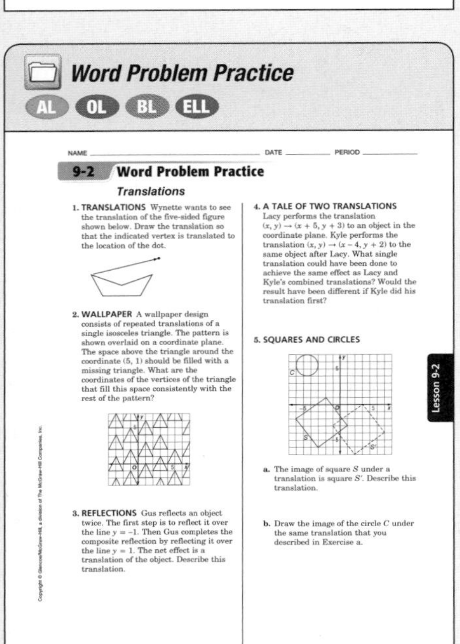

Example 3

20. CCSS MODELING Brittany's neighborhood is shown on the grid at the right.

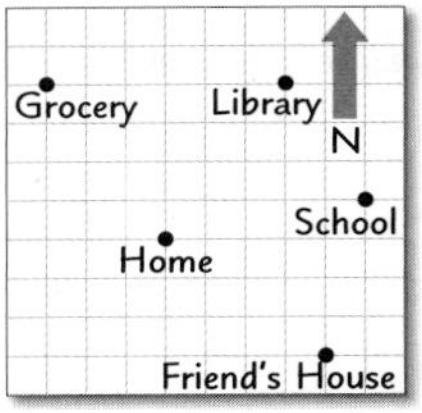

a. If she leaves home and travels 4 blocks north and 3 blocks east, what is her new location? **Library**

b. Use words to describe two possible translations that will take Brittany home from school. **See Ch. 9 Answer Appendix.**

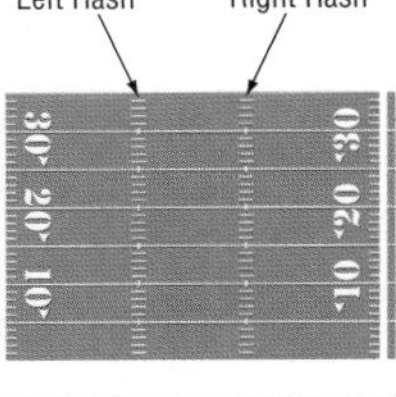

21. FOOTBALL A wide receiver starts from his 15-yard line on the right hash mark and runs a route that takes him 12 yards to the left and down field for a gain of 17 yards. Write a translation vector to describe the receiver's route. **$\langle -12, 17\rangle$**

B 22. CHESS Each chess piece has a path that it can follow to move. The rook, which begins in square a8, can only move vertically or horizontally. The knight, which begins in square b8, can move two squares horizontally and then one square vertically, or two squares vertically and one square horizontally. The bishop, which begins in square f8, can only move diagonally.

a. The knight moves 2 squares vertically and 1 square horizontally on its first move, then two squares horizontally and 1 square vertically on its second move. What are the possible locations for the knight after two moves? **a7, a5, c7, c5, e7, or e5**

b. After two moves, the rook is in square d3. Describe a possible translation to describe the two moves. **22b–c. See Ch. 9 Answer Appendix.**

c. Describe a translation that can take the bishop to square a1. What is the minimum number of moves that can be used to accomplish this translation?

Write each translation vector.

23. 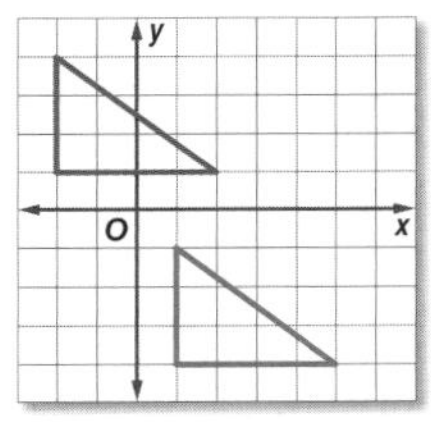 **$\langle 3, -5\rangle$**

24. 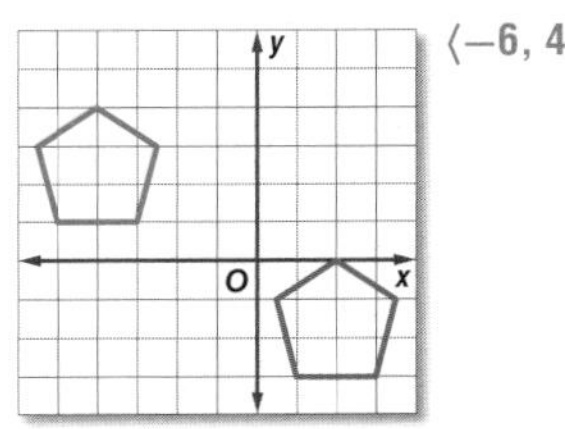 **$\langle -6, 4\rangle$**

25. CONCERTS Dexter's family buys tickets every year for a concert. Last year they were in seats C3, C4, C5, and C6. This year, they will be in seats D16, D17, D18, and D19. Write a translation in words and using vector notation that can be used to describe the change in their seating. **They move to the right 13 seats and back one row; $\langle 13, -1\rangle$.**

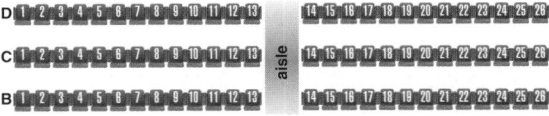

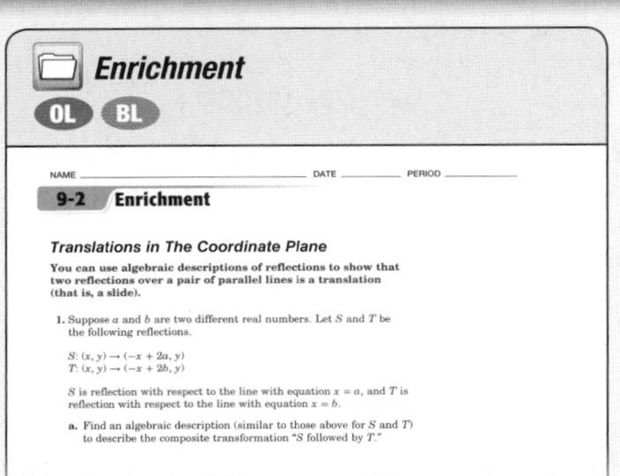

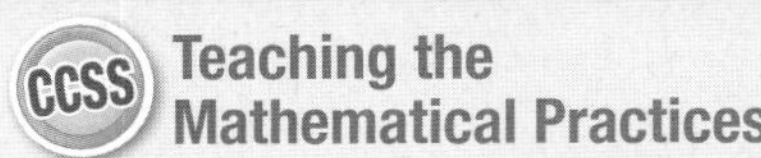

Teaching the Mathematical Practices

Modeling Mathematically proficient students can apply the mathematics they know to solve problems arising in everyday life. In Exercise 20, remind students that when heading north, east is to the right.

SENSE-MAKING Graph the translation of each function along the given vector. Then write the equation of the translated image. 26–27. See margin.

26. $\langle 4, 1 \rangle$

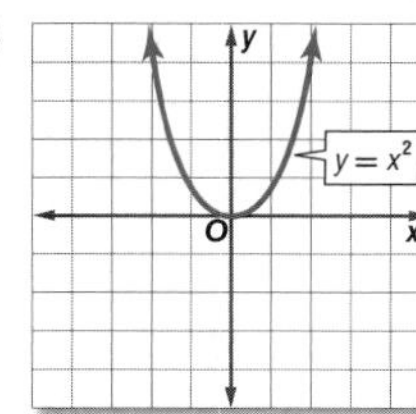

27. $\langle -2, 0 \rangle$

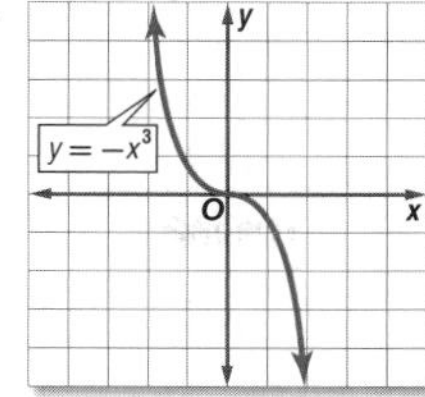

28. **ROLLER COASTERS** The length of the roller coaster track from the top of a hill to the bottom of the hill is 125 feet at a 53° angle with the vertical. If the position at the top of the hill is (x, y), use function notation to describe the translation to the bottom of the hill. Round to the nearest foot. $(x, y) \to (x + 75, y - 100)$

29. **MULTIPLE REPRESENTATIONS** In this problem, you will investigate reflections over a pair of parallel lines. a–b. See Ch. 9 Answer Appendix.

a. **Geometric** On patty paper, draw $\triangle ABC$ and a pair of vertical lines ℓ and m. Reflect $\triangle ABC$ in line ℓ by folding the patty paper. Then reflect $\triangle A'B'C'$, in line m. Label the final image $\triangle A''B''C''$.

A C B ℓ m

b. **Geometric** Repeat the process in part **a** for $\triangle DEF$ reflected in vertical lines n and p and $\triangle JKL$ reflected in vertical lines q and r.

c. **Tabular** Copy and complete the table below. Sample answers given.

Distance Between Corresponding Points (cm)		Distance Between Vertical Lines (cm)	
A and A'', B and B'', C and C''	4.4	ℓ and m	2.2
D and D'', E and E'', F and F''	5.6	n and p	2.8
J and J'', K and K'', L and L''	2.8	q and r	1.4

d. **Verbal** Describe the result of two reflections in two vertical lines using one transformation.
Sample answer: The composition of two reflections in vertical lines can be described by a horizontal translation that is twice the distance between the two vertical lines.

H.O.T. Problems Use Higher-Order Thinking Skills

30. **REASONING** Determine a rule to find the final image of a point that is translated along $\langle x + a, y + b \rangle$ and then $\langle x + c, y + d \rangle$. $\langle x + a + c, y + b + d \rangle$

31. **CHALLENGE** A line $y = mx + b$ is translated using the vector $\langle a, b \rangle$. Write the equation of the translated line. What is the value of the y-intercept? $y = m(x - a) + 2b$; $2b - ma$

32. **OPEN ENDED** Draw a figure on the coordinate plane so that the figure has the same orientation after it is reflected in the line $y = 1$. Explain what must be true in order for this to occur. See Ch. 9 Answer Appendix.

33. **WRITING IN MATH** Compare and contrast function notation and vector notation for translations. See margin.

34. **WRITING IN MATH** Recall from Lesson 9-1 that an invariant point maps onto itself. Can invariant points occur with translations? Explain why or why not. See margin.

Exercise Alert

Patty Paper Exercise 29 requires the use of patty paper or tracing paper.

Multiple Representations

In Exercise 29, students use geometric sketches, a table and verbal descriptions to investigate reflections over a pair of parallel lines.

Additional Answers

26.

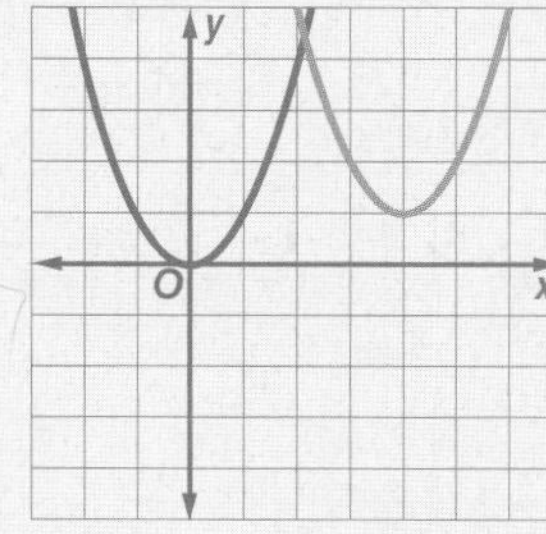

$y = (x - 4)^2 + 1$

27.

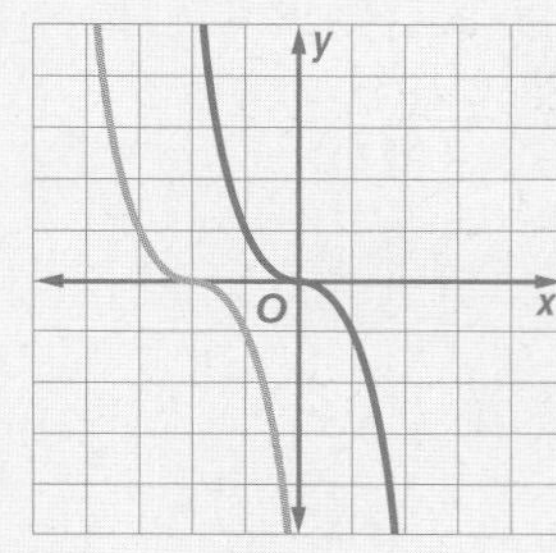

$y = -(x + 2)^3$

33. Sample answer: Both vector notation and function notation describe the distance a figure is translated in the horizontal and vertical directions. Vector notation does not give a rule in terms of initial location, but function notation does. For example, the translation a units to the right and b units up from the point (x, y) would be written $\langle a, b \rangle$ in vector notation and $(x, y) \to (x + a, y + b)$ in function notation.

34. Sample answer: No; since an image must move in order for a translation to have taken place, and the orientation of the figure must remain the same, no point can be invariant in a translation. If any of the points remain invariant, the resulting figure is the original figure.

Tips for New Teachers

Translations of Continuous Functions When a continuous function is transformed as in Exercises 26 and 27, remind students that shape is preserved as it is in congruence transformations.

Teaching the Mathematical Practices

Sense-Making Mathematically proficient students start by explaining the meaning of a problem to themselves and looking for entry points to its solution. They plan a solution pathway rather than simply jumping into a solution attempt. In Exercises 26–27, encourage students to make a plan to solve each problem first.

4 Assess

Name the Math Create or draw selected translations from the book on the board and call on students to describe the transformations aloud.

Formative Assessment

Check for student understanding of concepts of Lessons 9-1 and 9-2.

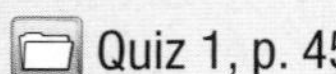 Quiz 1, p. 45

Additional Answers

39.
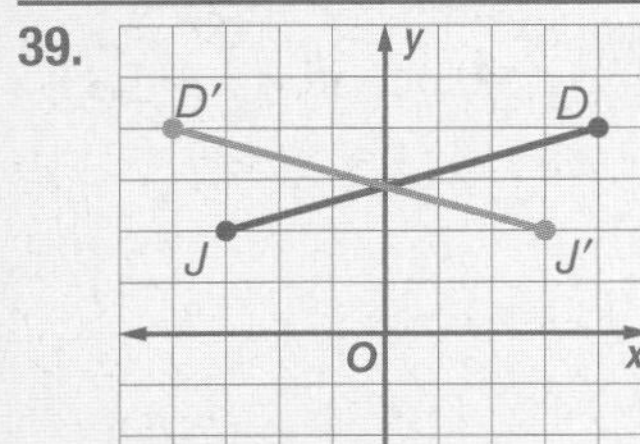

40.
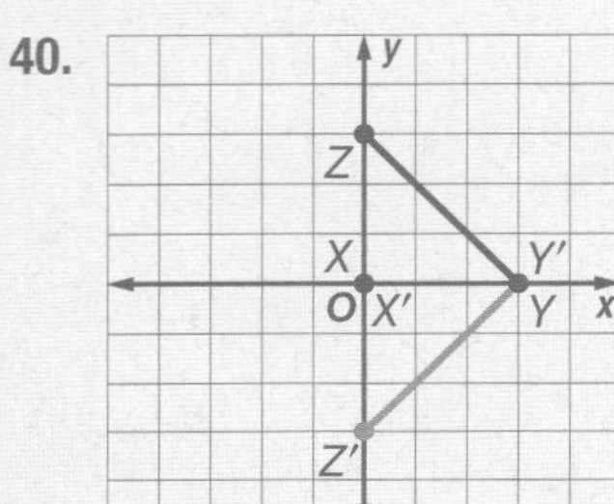

41.
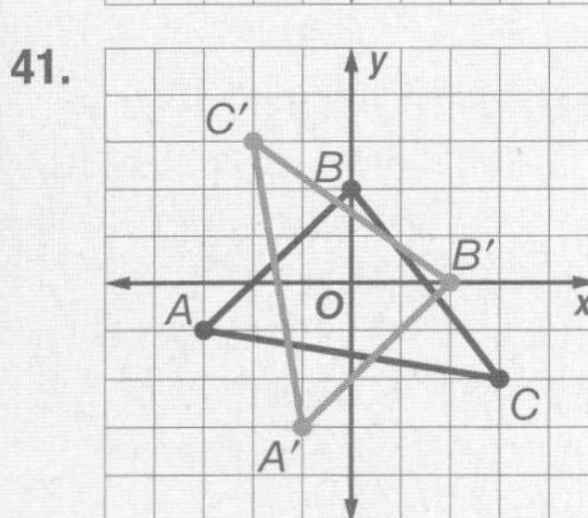

42.
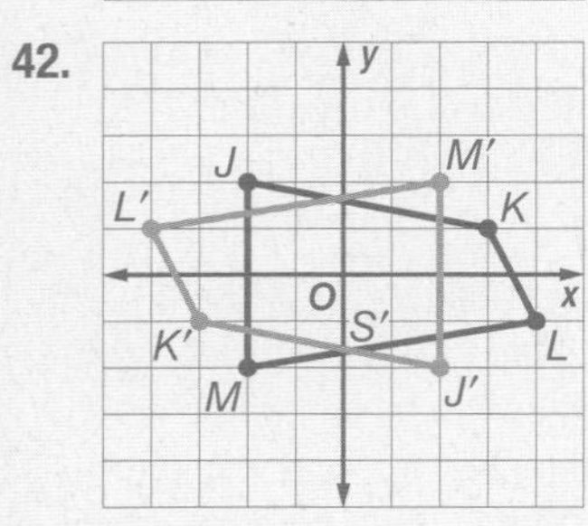

Standardized Test Practice

35. Identify the location of point P under translation $(x + 3, y + 1)$. **D**

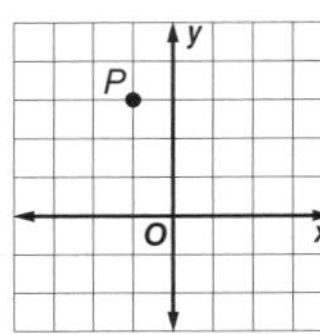

A (0, 6) C (2, −4)
B (0, 3) D (2, 4)

36. **SHORT RESPONSE** Which vector best describes the translation of $A(3, -5)$ to $A'(-2, -8)$? **⟨−5, −3⟩**

37. **ALGEBRA** Over the next four days, Amanda plans to drive 160 miles, 235 miles, 185 miles, and 220 miles. If her car gets an average of 32 miles per gallon of gas, how many gallons of gas should she expect to use in all? **F**

F 25 G 30 H 35 J 40

38. **SAT/ACT** A bag contains 5 red marbles, 2 blue marbles, 4 white marbles, and 1 yellow marble. If two marbles are chosen in a row, without replacement, what is the probability of getting 2 white marbles? **B**

A $\frac{1}{66}$ C $\frac{1}{9}$ E $\frac{2}{5}$
B $\frac{1}{11}$ D $\frac{5}{33}$

Spiral Review

Graph each figure and its image under the given reflection. (Lesson 9-1) **39–42. See margin.**

39. $\overline{DJ}$ with endpoints $D(4, 4)$, $J(-3, 2)$ in the y-axis
40. $\triangle XYZ$ with vertices $X(0, 0)$, $Y(3, 0)$, and $Z(0, 3)$ in the x-axis
41. $\triangle ABC$ with vertices $A(-3, -1)$, $B(0, 2)$, and $C(3, -2)$, in the line $y = x$
42. quadrilateral $JKLM$ with vertices $J(-2, 2)$, $K(3, 1)$, $L(4, -1)$, and $M(-2, -2)$ in the origin

Copy the vectors to find each sum or difference. (Lesson 8-7) **43–45. See Ch. 9 Answer Appendix.**

43. $\vec{c} + \vec{d}$

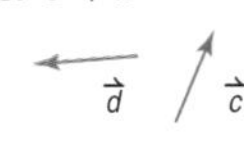

44. $\vec{w} + \vec{x}$

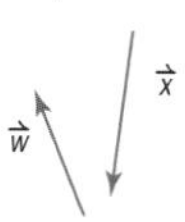

45. $\vec{n} - \vec{p}$

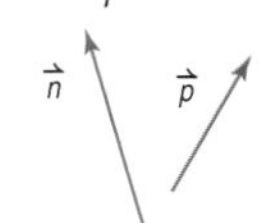

46. **NAVIGATION** An airplane is three miles above sea level when it begins to climb at a 3.5° angle. If this angle is constant, how far above sea level is the airplane after flying 50 miles? (Lesson 8-4) **6.1 mi**

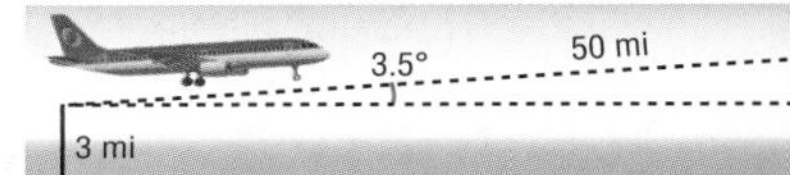

Use ▱$JKLM$ to find each measure. (Lesson 6-2)

47. $m\angle MJK$ **100**
48. $m\angle JML$ **80**
49. $m\angle JKL$ **80**
50. $m\angle KJL$ **30**

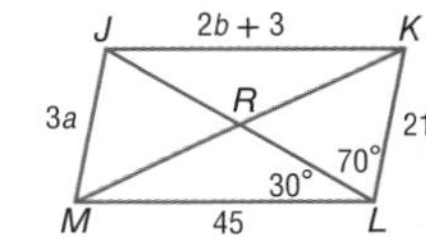

Skills Review

Copy the diagram shown, and extend each ray. Classify each angle as *right*, *acute*, or *obtuse*. Then use a protractor to measure the angle to the nearest degree.

51. $\angle AMC$ **obtuse; 110**
52. $\angle FMD$ **acute; 20**
53. $\angle BMD$ **obtuse; 140**
54. $\angle CMB$ **right; 90**

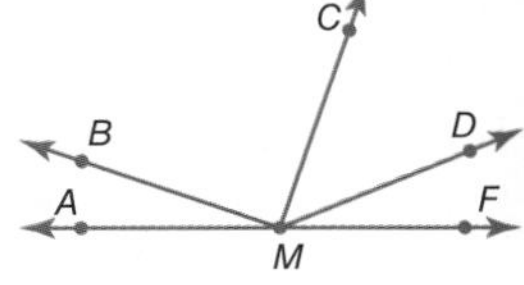

Differentiated Instruction OL BL

Extension What kind of transformation is a reflection over two intersecting lines? Use a coordinate plane to illustrate your answer. rotation

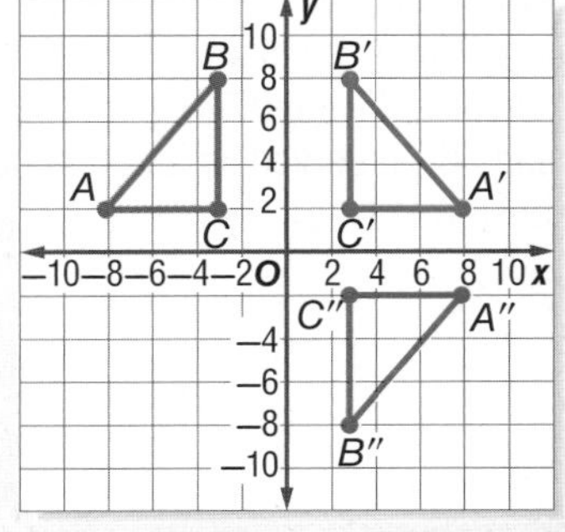

EXPLORE 9-3 Geometry Lab Rotations

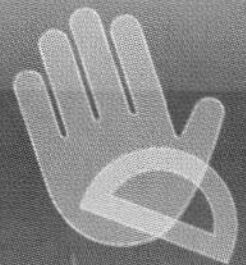

In Chapter 4, you learned that a rotation is a type of transformation that moves a figure about a fixed point, or center of rotation, through a specific angle and in a specific direction. In this activity you will use tracing paper to explore the properties of rotations.

CCSS Common Core State Standards
Content Standards
G.CO.2 Represent transformations in the plane using, e.g., transparencies and geometry software; describe transformations as functions that take points in the plane as inputs and give other points as outputs. Compare transformations that preserve distance and angle to those that do not (e.g., translation versus horizontal stretch).
G.CO.5 Given a geometric figure and a rotation, reflection, or translation, draw the transformed figure using, e.g., graph paper, tracing paper, or geometry software. Specify a sequence of transformations that will carry a given figure onto another.
Mathematical Practices 5

Activity Explore Rotations by Using Patty Paper

Step 1 On a piece of tracing paper, draw quadrilateral *ABCD* and a point *P*.

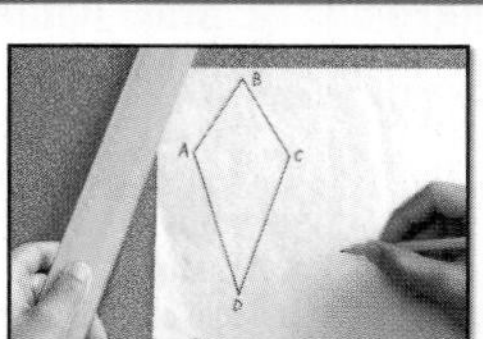

Step 1

Step 2 On another piece of tracing paper, trace quadrilateral *ABCD* and point *P*. Label the new quadrilateral *A′B′C′D′* and the new point *P*.

Step 3 Position the tracing paper so that both points *P* coincide. Rotate the paper so that *ABCD* and *A′B′C′D′* do not overlap. Tape the two pieces of tracing paper together.

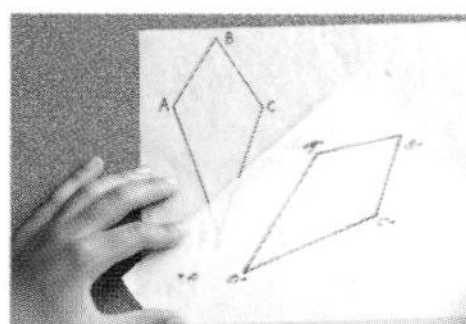

Steps 2 and 3

Step 4 Measure the distance between *A*, *B*, *C*, and *D* to point *P*. Repeat for quadrilateral *A′B′C′D′*. Then copy and complete the table below.

Quadrilateral	Length			
ABCD	AP	BP	CP	DP
A′B′C′D′	A′P	B′P	C′P	D′P

1a. $J'(-3, 1)$, $K'(-1, 2)$, and $L'(-4, 3)$

Exercises

1. Graph $\triangle JKL$ with vertices $J(1, 3)$, $K(2, 1)$, and $L(3, 4)$ on a coordinate plane, and then trace on tracing paper.
   a. Use a protractor to rotate each vertex 90° clockwise about the origin as shown in the figure at the right. What are the vertices of the rotated image?
   b. Rotate $\triangle JKL$ 180° about the origin. What are the vertices of the rotated image? **See margin.**
   c. Use the Distance Formula to find the distance from points *J*, *K*, and *L* to the origin. Repeat for *J′K′L′* and *J″K″L″*. $OJ = OJ' = OJ'' = \sqrt{10}$; $OK = OK' = OK'' = \sqrt{5}$; $OL = OL' = OL'' = 5$

2. **WRITING IN MATH** If you rotate point (4, 2) 90° and 180° about the origin, how do the *x*- and *y*-coordinates change? **See margin.**
3. **MAKE A PREDICTION** What are the new coordinates of a point (x, y) that is rotated 270°? $(y, -x)$
4. **MAKE A CONJECTURE** Make a conjecture about the distances from the center of rotation *P* to each corresponding vertex of *ABCD* and *A′B′C′D′*. **See margin.**

Additional Answers

1b. $J''(-1, -3)$, $K''(-2, -1)$, and $L''(-3, -4)$

2. After a 90° rotation the *x*- and *y*-coordinates interchange and the *x*-coordinate becomes negative; in a 180° rotation both coordinates become negative.

4. Each point of the original figure and its image are the same distance from the center.

From Concrete to Abstract

Have students write an algebraic representation for the changes of the *x*- and *y*-coordinates of a point rotated 90°, 180°, and 270° about the origin of a coordinate plane.

1 Focus

Objective Explore the properties of rotations.

Materials for Each Group

- tracing paper
- straightedge
- protractor

Teaching Tip

The objective of this Geometry Lab is to illustrate the properties of a rotation. In order for the properties to be obvious, advise students that the measurements in Step 4 and Exercise 1 must be precise.

2 Teach

Working in Cooperative Groups

Organize students in groups of 2, mixing abilities. Then have groups complete Exercises 1–2.

Ask:

- What do you notice about the lengths measured in Step 4? $AP = A'P$, $BP = B'P$, $CP = C'P$, $DP = D'P$
- Where do you place the vertex point on the protractor in order to measure the 90° angle of rotation in Exercise 1? Place the vertex point on the protractor at the origin on the coordinate plane.
- How do you determine the *x*- and *y*-coordinates for *J′K′L′* and *J″K″L″*? The coordinates must be found by placement on the coordinate plane.

Practice Have students complete Exercises 1–2.

3 Assess

Formative Assessment

Use Exercises 3–4 to assess whether students understand the properties of a rotation.

1 Focus

VerticalAlignment

Before Lesson 9-3 Draw reflections in a line and in a coordinate plane. Draw translations in a plane and in the coordinate plane. Verify reflections and translations as congruence transformations.

Lesson 9-3 Draw rotations in a plane and in the coordinate plane.

After Lesson 9-3 Use and extend similarity properties and transformations to explore and justify conjectures about geometric figures.

2 Teach

Scaffolding Questions

Have students read the **Why?** section of the lesson.

Ask:

- What things are rotating on the windmill? The blades of the windmill.
- What geometric term would you call the housing at the center of the blades? the center of rotation.
- If the angles between each of the blades are equal, what does each of the angles measure? 120

LESSON 9-3 Rotations

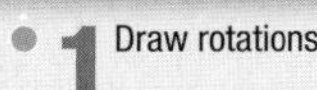

Then	Now	Why?
You identified rotations and verified them as congruence transformations.	1 Draw rotations. 2 Draw rotations in the coordinate plane.	Modern windmill technology may be an important alternative to fossil fuels. Windmills convert the wind's energy into electricity through the rotation of turbine blades.

NewVocabulary
center of rotation
angle of rotation

Common Core State Standards

Content Standards

G.CO.4 Develop definitions of rotations, reflections, and translations in terms of angles, circles, perpendicular lines, parallel lines, and line segments.

G.CO.5 Given a geometric figure and a rotation, reflection, or translation, draw the transformed figure using, e.g., graph paper, tracing paper, or geometry software. Specify a sequence of transformations that will carry a given figure onto another.

Mathematical Practices

2 Reason abstractly and quantitatively.

5 Use appropriate tools strategically.

1 Draw Rotations

In Lesson 4-7, you learned that a rotation or *turn* moves every point of a preimage through a specified angle and direction about a fixed point.

KeyConcept Rotation

A rotation about a fixed point, called the **center of rotation**, through an angle of $x°$ is a function that maps a point to its image such that

- if the point is the center of rotation, then the image and preimage are the same point, or
- if the point is not the center of rotation, then the image and preimage are the same distance from the center of rotation and the measure of the **angle of rotation** formed by the preimage, center of rotation, and image points is x.

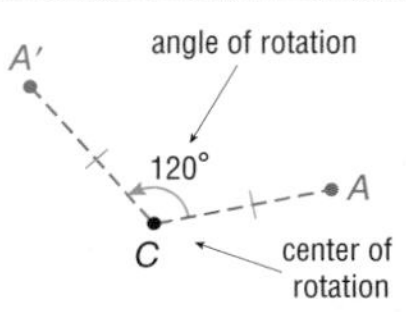

A' is the image of A after a 120° rotation about point C.

The direction of a rotation can be either clockwise or counterclockwise. Assume that all rotations are counterclockwise unless stated otherwise.

clockwise

counterclockwise

Example 1 Draw a Rotation

Copy $\triangle ABC$ and point K. Then use a protractor and ruler to draw a 140° rotation of $\triangle ABC$ about point K.

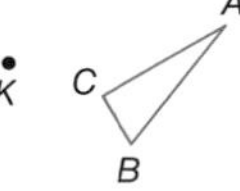

Step 1 Draw a segment from A to K.

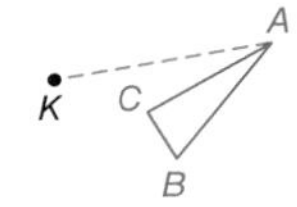

Step 2 Draw a 140° angle using $\overline{KA}$.

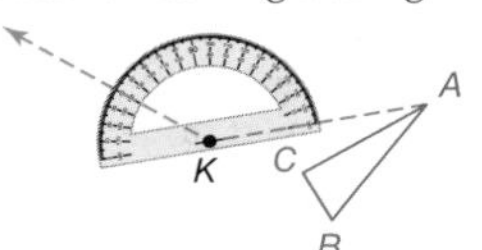

Step 3 Use a ruler to draw A' such that $KA' = KA$.

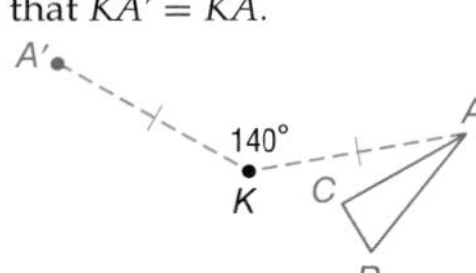

Step 4 Repeat Steps 1–3 for vertices B and C and draw $\triangle A'B'C'$.

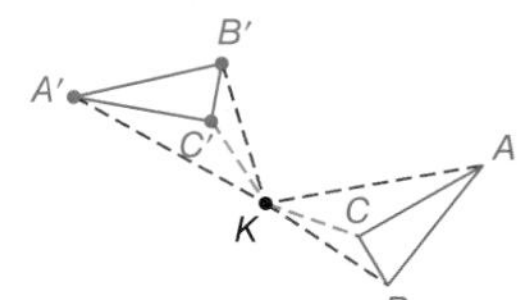

Lesson 9-3 Resources

Resource	Approaching Level AL	On Level OL	Beyond Level BL	English Learners ELL
Teacher Edition	▪ Differentiated Instruction, p. 641	▪ Differentiated Instruction, pp. 641, 642	▪ Differentiated Instruction, pp. 641, 642	
Chapter Resource Masters	▪ Study Guide and Intervention, pp. 19–20 ▪ Skills Practice, p. 21 ▪ Practice, p. 22 ▪ Word Problem Practice, p. 23	▪ Study Guide and Intervention, pp. 19–20 ▪ Skills Practice, p. 21 ▪ Practice, p. 22 ▪ Word Problem Practice, p. 23 ▪ Enrichment, p. 24	▪ Practice, p. 22 ▪ Word Problem Practice, p. 23 ▪ Enrichment, p. 24	▪ Study Guide and Intervention, pp. 19–20 ▪ Skills Practice, p. 21 ▪ Practice, p. 22 ▪ Word Problem Practice, p. 23
Other	▪ 5-Minute Check 9-3 ▪ Study Notebook ▪ Teaching Geometry with Manipulatives	▪ 5-Minute Check 9-3 ▪ Study Notebook ▪ Teaching Geometry with Manipulatives	▪ 5-Minute Check 9-3 ▪ Study Notebook	▪ 5-Minute Check 9-3 ▪ Study Notebook ▪ Teaching Geometry with Manipulatives

1A.

GuidedPractice

Copy each figure and point *K*. Then use a protractor and ruler to draw a rotation of the figure the given number of degrees about *K*.

1A. 65°

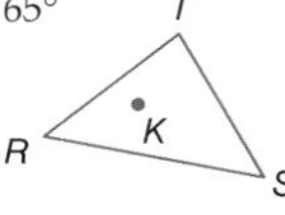

1B. 170°

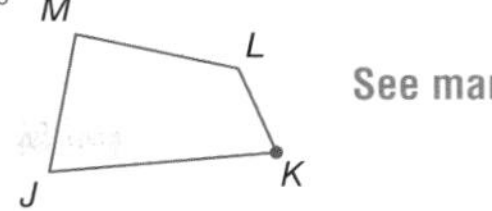

See margin.

StudyTip

Clockwise Rotation Clockwise rotation can be designated by a negative angle measure. For example a rotation of $-90°$ about the origin is a rotation 90° clockwise about the origin.

2 Draw Rotations in the Coordinate Plane

When a point is rotated 90°, 180°, or 270° counterclockwise about the origin, you can use the following rules.

KeyConcept Rotations in the Coordinate Plane

90° Rotation To rotate a point 90° counterclockwise about the origin, multiply the *y*-coordinate by -1 and then interchange the *x*- and *y*-coordinates. **Symbols** $(x, y) \rightarrow (-y, x)$	**Example** $P'(-2, 5)$, $P(5, 2)$, 90°
180° Rotation To rotate a point 180° counterclockwise about the origin, multiply the *x*- and *y*-coordinates by -1. **Symbols** $(x, y) \rightarrow (-x, -y)$	**Example** $P(5, 2)$, $P'(-5, -2)$, 180°
270° Rotation To rotate a point 270° counterclockwise about the origin, multiply the *x*-coordinate by -1 and then interchange the *x*- and *y*-coordinates. **Symbols** $(x, y) \rightarrow (y, -x)$	**Example** $P(5, 2)$, $P'(2, -5)$, 270°

StudyTip

360° Rotation A rotation of 360° about a point returns a figure to its original position. That is, the image under a 360° rotation is equal to the preimage.

Example 2 Rotations in the Coordinate Plane

Triangle *PQR* has vertices *P*(1, 1), *Q*(4, 5), and *R*(5, 1). Graph $\triangle PQR$ and its image after a rotation 90° about the origin.

Multiply the *y*-coordinate of each vertex by -1 and interchange.

$(x, y) \rightarrow (-y, x)$

$P(1, 1) \rightarrow P'(-1, 1)$

$Q(4, 5) \rightarrow Q'(-5, 4)$

$R(5, 1) \rightarrow R'(-1, 5)$

Graph $\triangle PQR$ and its image $\triangle P'Q'R'$.

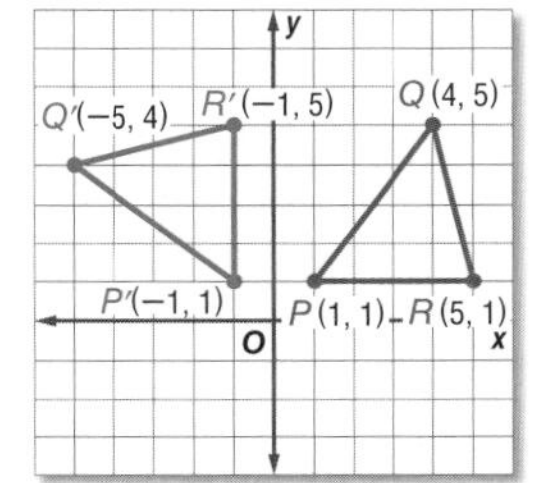

GuidedPractice

2. Parallelogram *FGHJ* has vertices *F*(2, 1), *G*(7, 1), *H*(6, −3), and *J*(1, −3). Graph *FGHJ* and its image after a rotation 180° about the origin.

2.

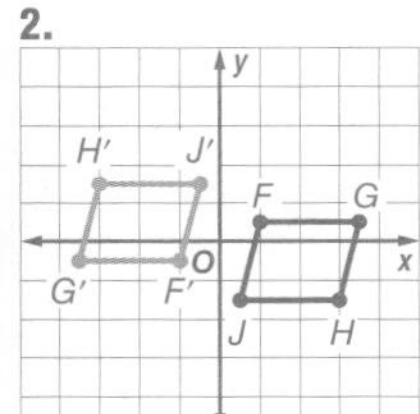

DifferentiatedInstruction AL OL BL

Logical/Mathematical Learners Tell students to develop a system for rotating images. First, they should read the problem and locate or plot the figure for visual recognition. They should also carefully note the specifications, especially the direction of the rotation. Finally, they can apply the rotation. Students can use a system similar to this, or they can create their own.

1 Draw Rotations

Example 1 shows how to draw a rotation in a plane.

Formative Assessment

Use the Guided Practice exercises after each example to determine students' understanding of concepts.

Teach with Tech

Photo Editing Software Give students several digital pictures that were taken while holding a camera at different angles. Have them use a photo editing program to rotate the image until it appears right-side up. Have them make connections between the image they see and the angle and direction of rotation they used.

Additional Example

1 Copy quadrilateral *RSTV* and point *A*. Then use a protractor and ruler to draw a 45° rotation of *RSTV* about point *A*.

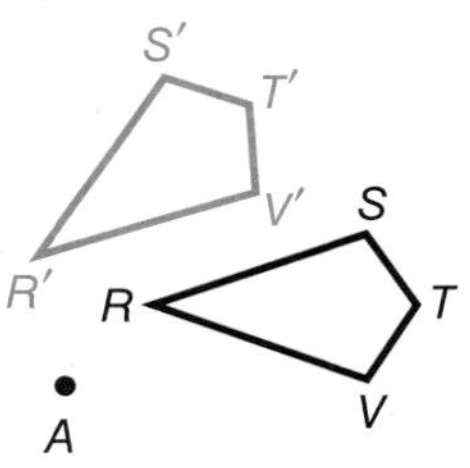

Additional Examples also in Interactive Classroom PowerPoint® Presentations

Interactive White Board READY

Additional Answer (Guided Practice)

1B.

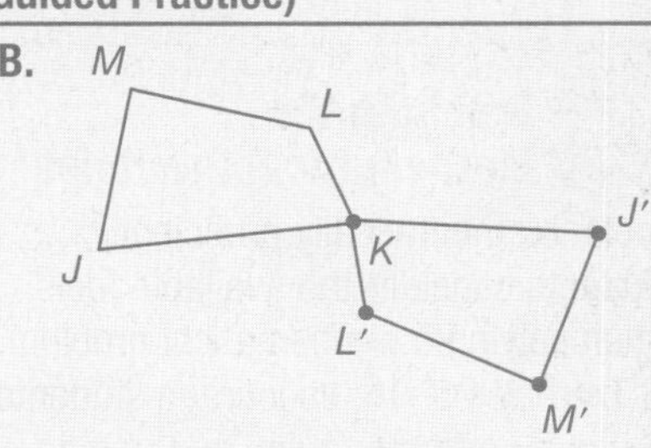

Tips for New Teachers

Direction and Center of Rotations Emphasize that unless otherwise noted, rotations are counterclockwise about the origin.

2 Draw Rotations in the Coordinate Plane

Examples 2 and 3 show how to draw rotations in the coordinate plane.

Additional Examples

2 Triangle DEF has vertices $D(-2, -1)$, $E(-1, 1)$, and $F(1, -1)$. Graph $\triangle DEF$ and its image after a rotation of 115° clockwise about the point $G(-4, -2)$.

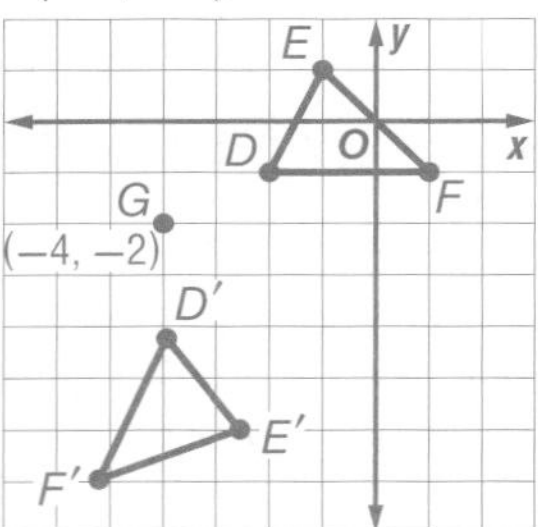

3 **STANDARDIZED TEST PRACTICE** Hexagon $DGJTSR$ is shown below. What is the image of point T after a 90° counterclockwise rotation about the origin? C

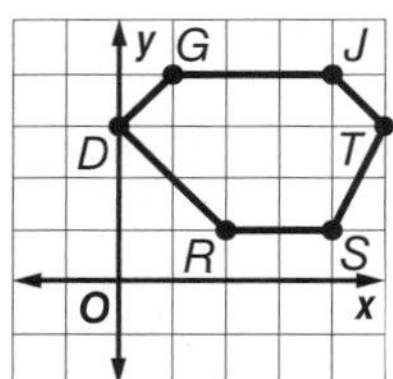

A (5, −3)
B (−5, −3)
C (−3, 5)
D (3, −5)

Teaching the Mathematical Practices

Tools Mathematically proficient students consider the available tools when solving a mathematical problem. In Exercises 5–10, encourage students to use a protractor, ruler, and tracing paper.

Standardized Test Example 3 Rotations in the Coordinate Plane

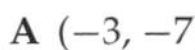

Triangle JKL is shown at the right. What is the image of point J after a rotation 270° counterclockwise about the origin?

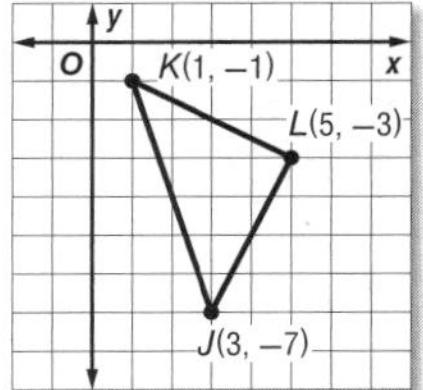

A (−3, −7)
B (−7, 3)
C (−7, −3)
D (7, −3)

Read the Test Item

You are given that $\triangle JKL$ has coordinates $J(3, -7)$, $K(1, -1)$, and $L(5, -3)$ and are then asked to identify the coordinates of the image of point J after a 270° counterclockwise rotation about the origin.

StudyTip

270° Rotation You can complete a 270° rotation by performing a 90° rotation and a 180° rotation in sequence.

Solve the Test Item

To find the coordinates of point J after a 270° counterclockwise rotation about the origin, multiply the x-coordinate by −1 and then interchange the x- and y-coordinates.

$(x, y) \rightarrow (y, -x)$ $\quad\quad$ $(3, -7) \rightarrow (-7, -3)$

The answer is choice C.

GuidedPractice

3. Parallelogram $WXYZ$ is rotated 180° counterclockwise about the origin. Which of these graphs represents the resulting image? H

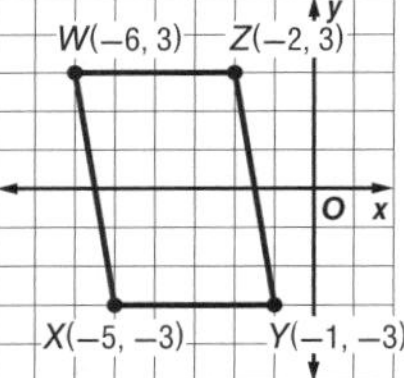

Test-TakingTip

Sense-Making Instead of checking all four vertices of parallelogram $WXYZ$ in each graph, check just one vertex, such as X.

F

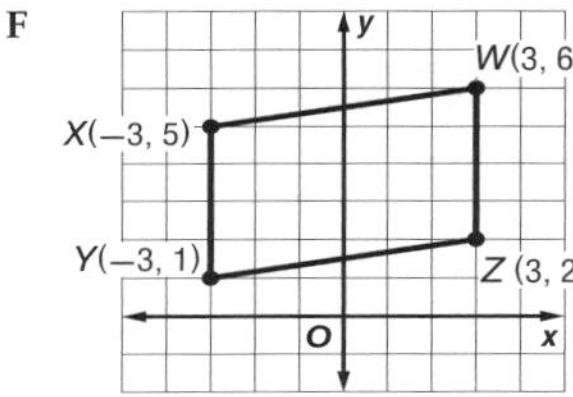

H

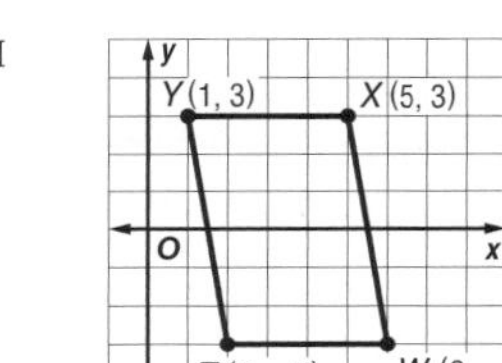

G

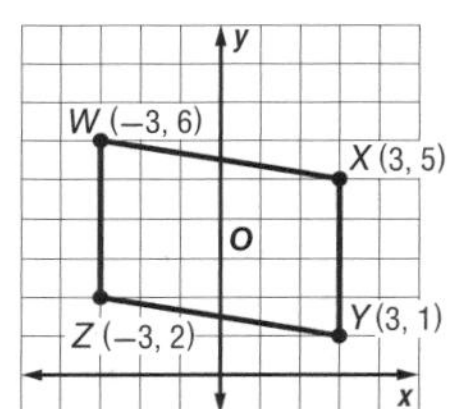

J

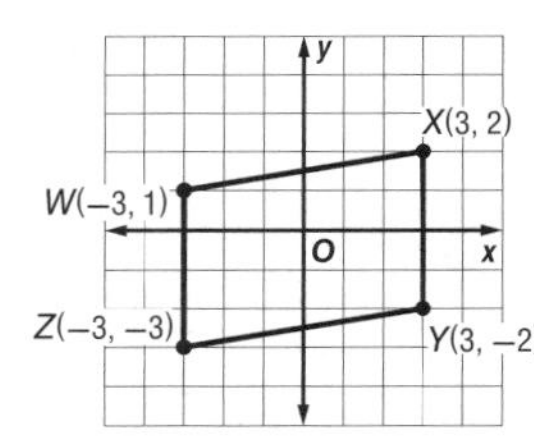

DifferentiatedInstruction OL BL

Extension What is the angle of rotation for the images? 72°

Check Your Understanding

○ = Step-by-Step Solutions begin on page R14.

Example 1 Copy each polygon and point K. Then use a protractor and ruler to draw the specified rotation of each figure about point K.

1. 45° See margin.

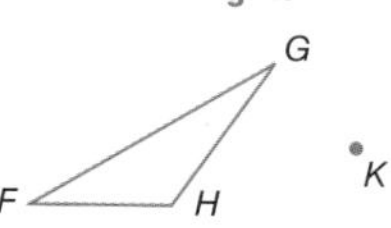

2. 120° See margin.

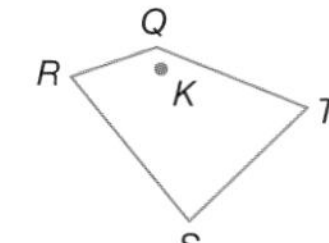

Example 2  **3.** Triangle DFG has vertices $D(-2, 6)$, $F(2, 8)$, and $G(2, 3)$. Graph $\triangle DFG$ and its image after a rotation 180° about the origin. See margin.

Example 3 **4. MULTIPLE CHOICE** For the transformation shown, what is the measure of the angle of rotation of $ABCD$ about the origin? B

A 90°

B 180°

C 270°

D 360°

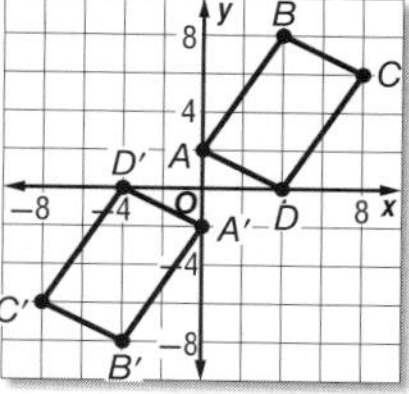

Practice and Problem Solving

Extra Practice is on page R9.

Example 1 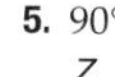 **TOOLS** Copy each polygon and point K. Then use a protractor and ruler to draw the specified rotation of each figure about point K. 5–10. See Ch. 9 Answer Appendix.

5. 90°

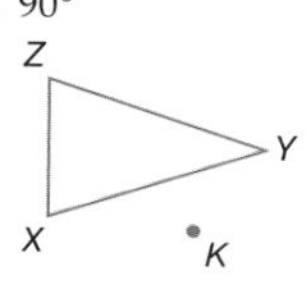

6. 15°

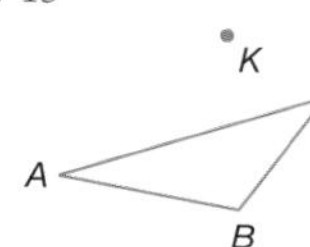

7. 145°

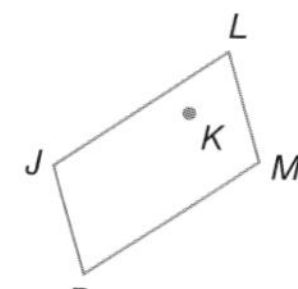

8. 30°

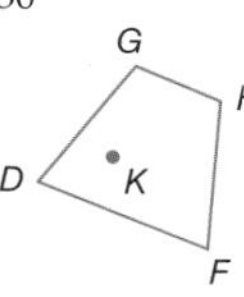

9. 260°

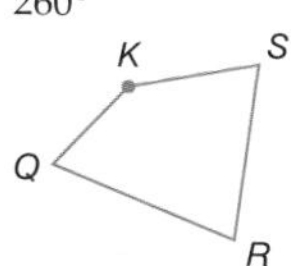

10. 50°

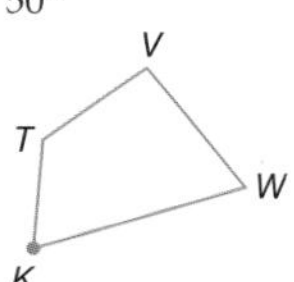

PINWHEELS Find the angle of rotation to the nearest tenth of a degree that maps P onto P'. Explain your reasoning. 11–13. See margin.

11.

12.

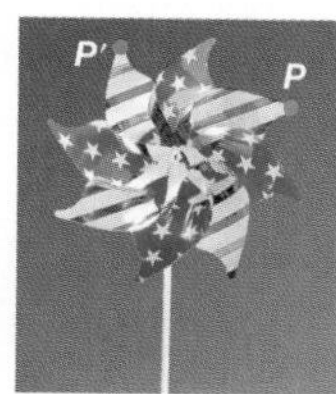

13.

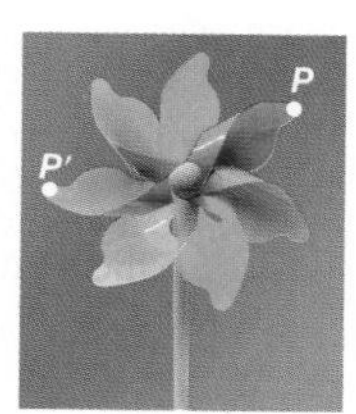

Differentiated Homework Options

Level	Assignment	Two-Day Option	
AL Basic	5–19, 34, 36–49	5–19 odd, 39–42	6–18 even, 34, 36–38, 43–49
OL Core	5–19 odd, 20, 21, 23–29 odd, 31–34, 36–49	5–19, 39–42	20–34, 36–38, 43–49
BL Advanced	20–46, (optional: 47–49)		

3 Practice

Formative Assessment

Use Exercises 1–4 to check for understanding.

Then use the chart at the bottom of this page to customize assignments for your students.

Additional Answers

1.

2.

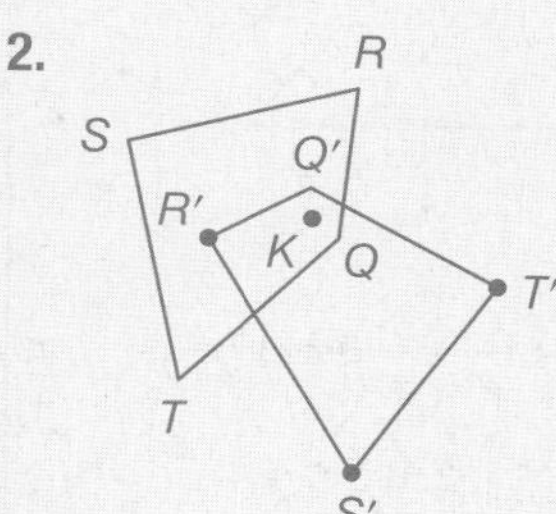

3.

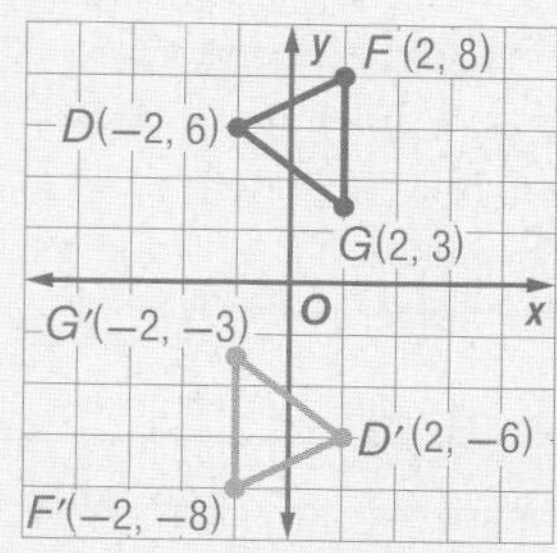

11. 120°; 360° ÷ 6 petals = 60° per petal. Two petal turns is 2 • 60° or 120°.

12. 90°; 360° ÷ 8 petals = 45° per petal. Two petal turns is 2 • 45° or 90°.

13. 154.2°; 360° ÷ 7 petals = 51.4° per petal. Three petal turns is 3 • 51.4° or 154.2°.

Study Guide and Intervention

AL OL ELL

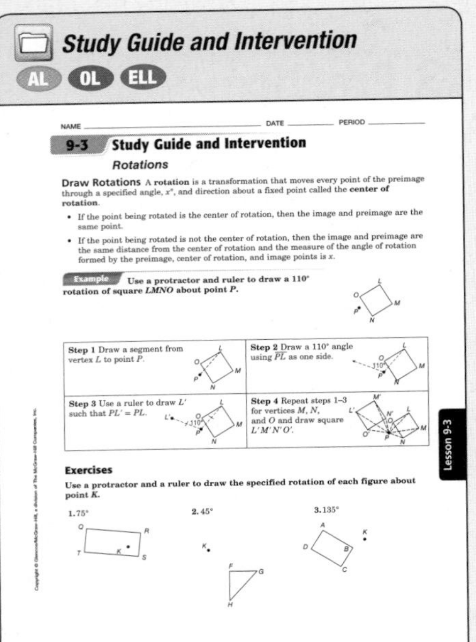
NAME ______ DATE ______ PERIOD ______

9-3 Study Guide and Intervention

Rotations

Draw Rotations A **rotation** is a transformation that moves every point of the preimage through a specified angle, $x°$, and direction about a fixed point called the **center of rotation**.

- If the point being rotated is the center of rotation, then the image and preimage are the same point.
- If the point being rotated is not the center of rotation, then the image and preimage are the same distance from the center of rotation and the measure of the angle of rotation formed by the preimage, center of rotation, and image points is x.

Example Use a protractor and ruler to draw a 110° rotation of square *LMNO* about point *P*.

Step 1 Draw a segment from vertex *L* to point *P*.	Step 2 Draw a 110° angle using $\overline{PL}$ as one side.
Step 3 Use a ruler to draw *L′* such that *PL′* = *PL*.	Step 4 Repeat steps 1–3 for vertices *M*, *N*, and *O* and draw square *L′M′N′O′*.

Exercises

Use a protractor and a ruler to draw the specified rotation of each figure about point *K*.

1. 75° 2. 45° 3. 135°

Practice

AL OL BL ELL

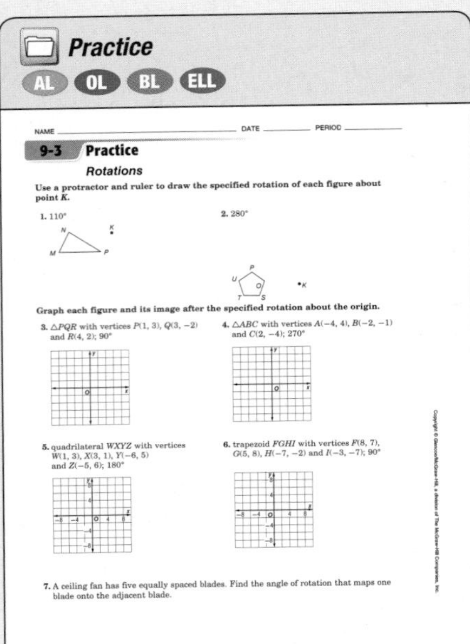
NAME ______ DATE ______ PERIOD ______

9-3 Practice

Rotations

Use a protractor and ruler to draw the specified rotation of each figure about point *K*.

1. 110° 2. 280°

Graph each figure and its image after the specified rotation about the origin.

3. △*PQR* with vertices *P*(1, 3), *Q*(3, −2) and *R*(4, 2); 90°
4. △*ABC* with vertices *A*(−4, 4), *B*(−2, −1) and *C*(2, −4); 270°
5. quadrilateral *WXYZ* with vertices *W*(1, 3), *X*(3, 1), *Y*(−6, 5) and *Z*(−5, 6); 180°
6. trapezoid *FGHI* with vertices *F*(8, 7), *G*(5, 8), *H*(−7, −2) and *I*(−3, −7); 90°
7. A ceiling fan has five equally spaced blades. Find the angle of rotation that maps one blade onto the adjacent blade.

Word Problem Practice

AL OL BL ELL

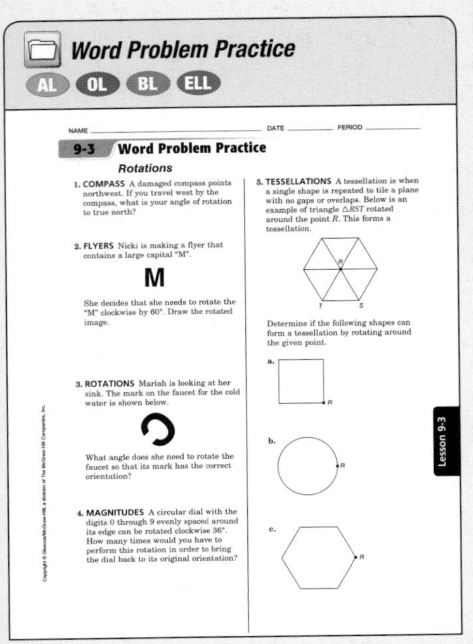
NAME ______ DATE ______ PERIOD ______

9-3 Word Problem Practice

Rotations

1. COMPASS A damaged compass points northwest. If you travel west by the compass, what is your angle of rotation to true north?
2. FLYERS Nicki is making a flyer that contains a large capital "M". She decides that she needs to rotate the "M" clockwise by 60°. Draw the rotated image.
3. ROTATIONS Mariah is looking at her sink. The mark on the faucet for the cold water is shown below. What angle does she need to rotate the faucet so that its mark has the correct orientation?
4. MAGNITUDES A circular dial with the digits 0 through 9 evenly spaced around its edge can be rotated clockwise 36°. How many times would you have to perform this rotation in order to bring the dial back to its original orientation?
5. TESSELLATIONS A tessellation is when a single shape is repeated to tile a plane with no gaps or overlaps. Below is an example of triangle △*RST* rotated around the point *R*. This forms a tessellation. Determine if the following shapes can form a tessellation by rotating around the given point.

Examples 2–3 **Graph each figure and its image after the specified rotation about the origin.** 14–19. See Ch. 9 Answer Appendix.

14. △*JKL* has vertices *J*(2, 6), *K*(5, 2), and *L*(7, 5); 90°
15. rhombus *WXYZ* has vertices *W*(−3, 4), *X*(0, 7), *Y*(3, 4), and *Z*(0, 1); 90°
16. △*FGH* has vertices *F*(2, 4), *G*(5, 6), and *H*(7, 2); 180°
17. trapezoid *ABCD* has vertices *A*(−7, −2), *B*(−6, −6), *C*(−1, −1), and *D*(−5, 0); 180°
18. △*RST* has vertices *R*(−6, −1), *S*(−4, −5), and *T*(−2, −1); 270°
19. parallelogram *MPQV* has vertices *M*(−6, 3), *P*(−2, 3), *Q*(−3, −2), and *V*(−7, −2); 270°

B

20. **WEATHER** A weathervane is used to indicate the direction of the wind. If the vane is pointing northeast and rotates 270°, what is the new wind direction? southeast

21. **CCSS MODELING** The photograph of the Grande Roue, or Big Wheel, at the right appears blurred because of the camera's shutter speed—the length of time the camera's shutter was open. The diameter of the wheel is 60 meters.
    a. Estimate the angle of rotation in the photo. (*Hint:* Use points *A* and *A′*.) 10°
    b. If the Ferris wheel makes one revolution per minute, use your estimate from part **a** to estimate the camera's shutter speed. about 1.7 seconds

Each figure shows a preimage and its image after a rotation about point *P*. Copy each figure, locate point *P*, and find the angle of rotation. 22–23. See Ch. 9 Answer Appendix.

22. 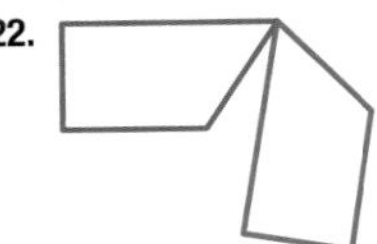

23. 

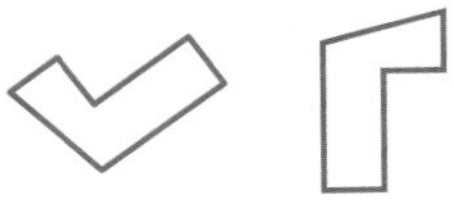

C

ALGEBRA **Give the equation of the line $y = -x - 2$ after a rotation about the origin through the given angle. Then describe the relationship between the equations of the image and preimage.**

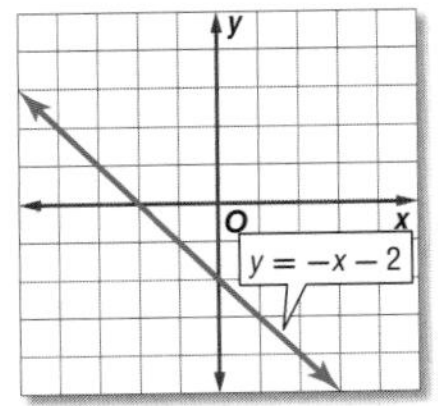

24. 90° 25. 180°

26. 270° 27. 360°

24. $y = x - 2$; perpendicular
25. $y = -x + 2$; parallel
26. $y = x + 2$; perpendicular
27. $y = -x - 2$; collinear

ALGEBRA **Rotate the line the specified number of degrees about the *x*- and *y*-intercepts and find the equation of the resulting image.** 28–30. See Ch. 9 Answer Appendix.

28. $y = x - 5$; 90°
29. $y = 2x + 4$; 180°
30. $y = 3x - 2$; 270°

31. **RIDES** An amusement park ride consists of four circular cars. The ride rotates at a rate of 0.25 revolution per second. In addition, each car rotates 0.5 revolution per second. If Jane is positioned at point *P* when the ride begins, what coordinates describe her position after 31 seconds? (2, −4)

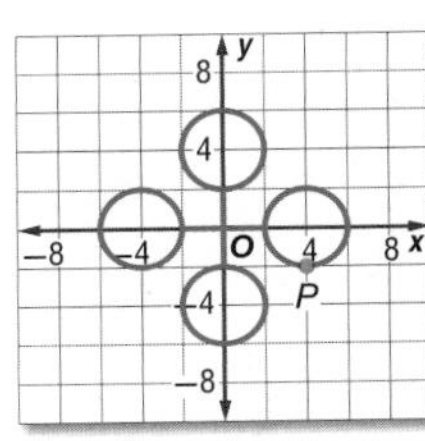

Enrichment

OL BL

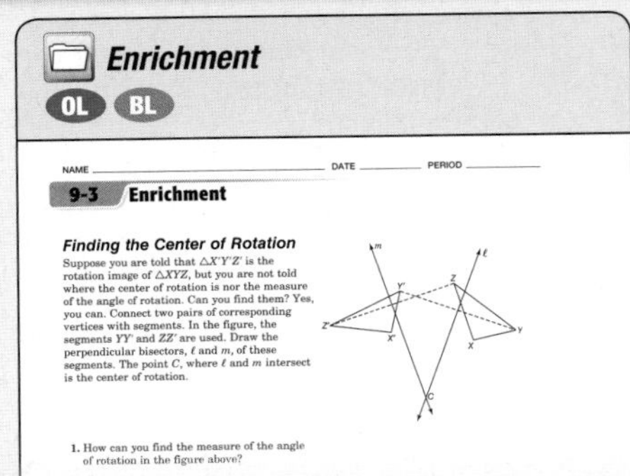
NAME ______ DATE ______ PERIOD ______

9-3 Enrichment

Finding the Center of Rotation

Suppose you are told that △*X′Y′Z′* is the rotation image of △*XYZ*, but you are not told where the center of rotation is nor the measure of the angle of rotation. Can you find them? Yes, you can. Connect two pairs of corresponding vertices with segments. In the figure, the segments *YY′* and *ZZ′* are used. Draw the perpendicular bisectors, ℓ and *m*, of these segments. The point *C*, where ℓ and *m* intersect is the center of rotation.

1. How can you find the measure of the angle of rotation in the figure above?

CCSS Teaching the Mathematical Practices

Modeling Mathematically proficient students can apply the mathematics they know to solve problems arising in everyday life. In Exercise 21, encourage students to use a protractor to check their estimate in part **a**.

32. BICYCLE RACING Brandon and Nestor are participating in a bicycle race on a circular track with a radius of 200 feet.

a. If the race starts at (200, 0) and both complete one rotation in 30 seconds, what are their coordinates after 5 seconds? **(100, 173.2)**

b. Suppose the length of race is 50 laps and Brandon continues the race at the same rate. If Nestor finishes in 26.2 minutes, who is the winner? **Brandon; 25 min < 26.2 min**

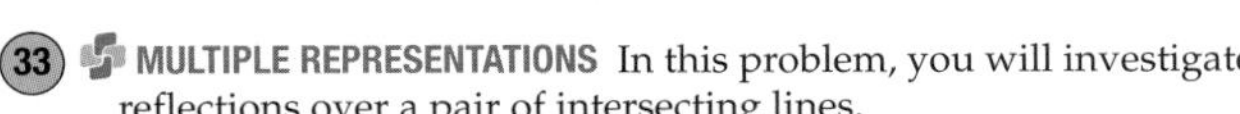

33. MULTIPLE REPRESENTATIONS In this problem, you will investigate reflections over a pair of intersecting lines.

a. Geometric On a coordinate plane, draw a triangle and a pair of intersecting lines. Label the triangle *ABC* and the lines ℓ and m. Reflect $\triangle ABC$ in the line ℓ. Then reflect $\triangle A'B'C'$ in the line m. Label the final image $A''B''C''$. **See Ch. 9 Answer Appendix.**

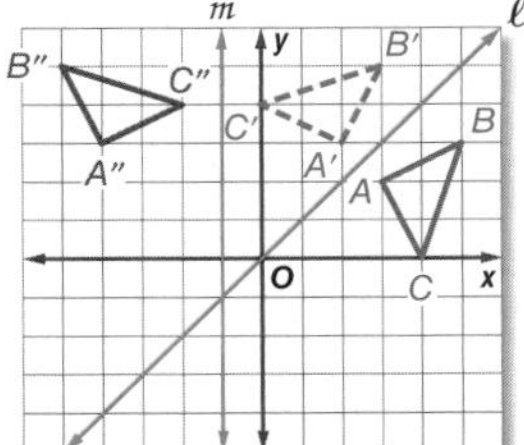

b. Geometric Repeat the process in part a two more times in two different quadrants. Label the second triangle *DEF* and reflect it in intersecting lines n and p. Label the third triangle *MNP* and reflect it in intersecting lines q and r. **See Ch. 9 Answer Appendix.**

c. Tabular Measure the angle of rotation of each triangle about the point of intersection of the two lines. Copy and complete the table below.

Angle of Rotation Between Figures		Angle Between Intersecting Lines	
$\triangle ABC$ and $\triangle A''B''C''$	90°	ℓ and m	45°
$\triangle DEF$ and $\triangle D''E''F''$	180°	n and p	90°
$\triangle MNP$ and $\triangle M''N''P''$	90°	q and r	45°

d. Verbal Make a conjecture about the angle of rotation of a figure about the intersection of two lines after the figure is reflected in both lines.

33d. Sample answer: The measure of the angle of rotation about the point where the lines intersect is twice the measure of the angle between the two intersecting lines.

H.O.T. Problems Use Higher-Order Thinking Skills

34. WRITING IN MATH Are collinearity and betweenness of points maintained under rotation? Explain. **34. Yes; sample answer: A rotation is a transformation which may change the orientation of the points but maintains congruence of the original figure and its image. So, the preimage can be mapped onto the image and corresponding segments will be congruent. Therefore, collinearity and betweenness of points are maintained in rotation.**

35. CHALLENGE Point C has coordinates C(5, 5). The image of this point after a rotation of 100° about a certain point is C′(−5, 7.5). Use construction to estimate the coordinates of the center of this rotation. Explain. **See margin.**

36. OPEN ENDED Draw a figure on the coordinate plane. Describe a nonzero rotation that maps the image onto the preimage with no change in orientation. **See margin.**

37. CCSS ARGUMENTS Is the reflection of a figure in the x-axis equivalent to the rotation of that same figure 180° about the origin? Explain. **See margin.**

38. WRITING IN MATH Do invariant points *sometimes*, *always*, or *never* occur in a rotation? Explain your reasoning. **See margin.**

Multiple Representations

In Exercise 33, students use geometric sketches, a graph, a table and verbal descriptions to investigate reflections over a pair of intersecting lines.

CCSS Teaching the Mathematical Practices

Arguments Mathematically proficient students understand and use stated assumptions and definitions in constructing arguments. They are able to analyze situations by breaking them into cases, and can recognize and use counterexamples. In Exercise 37, encourage students to draw each transformation described in the problem.

Additional Answers

35. Sample answer: (−1, 2); Since $\triangle CC'P$ is isosceles and the vertex angle of the triangle is formed by the angle of rotation, both $m\angle PCC'$ and $m\angle PC'C$ are 40° because the base angles of isosceles triangles are congruent. When you construct a 40° angle with a vertex at C and a 40° angle with a vertex at C', the intersection of the rays forming the two angles intersect at the point of rotation, or (−1, 2).

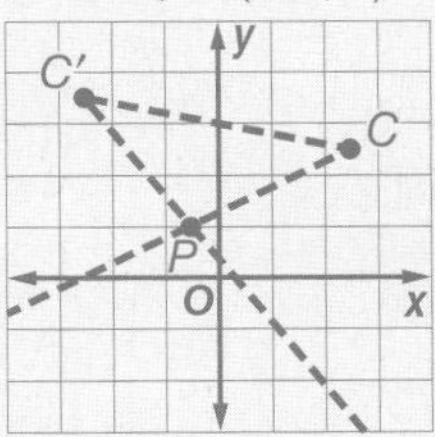

36. Sample answer:

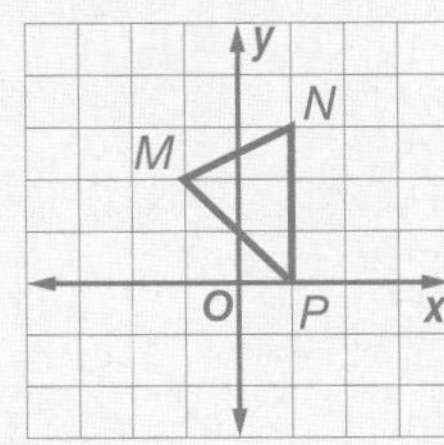

a 360° rotation

37. No; sample answer: When a figure is reflected about the x-axis, the x-coordinates of the transformed figure remain the same, and the y-coordinates are negated. When a figure is rotated 180° about the origin, both the x- and y-coordinates are negated. Therefore, the transformations are not equivalent.

38. Sometimes; sample answer: When a figure is rotated about a point on the figure, then the point of rotation is invariant. If a figure is rotated about a point not on the figure, then there are no invariant points in the rotation.

4 Assess

Yesterday's News Ask students to write how the lesson on transformations helped them understand the concept of rotations.

Formative Assessment

Check for student understanding of Lesson 9-3.

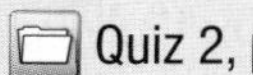 Quiz 2, p. 45

Additional Answers

43. 50 mi;

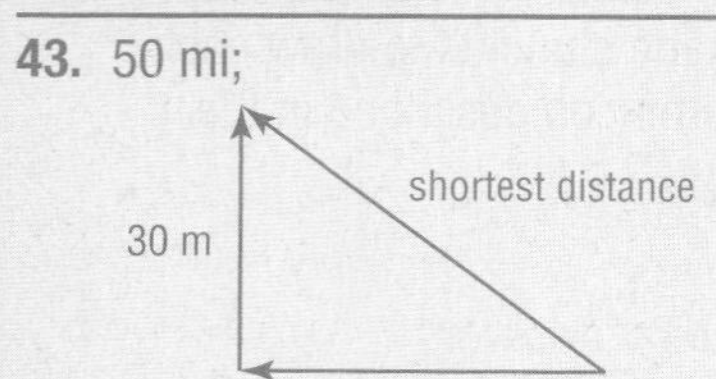

44.

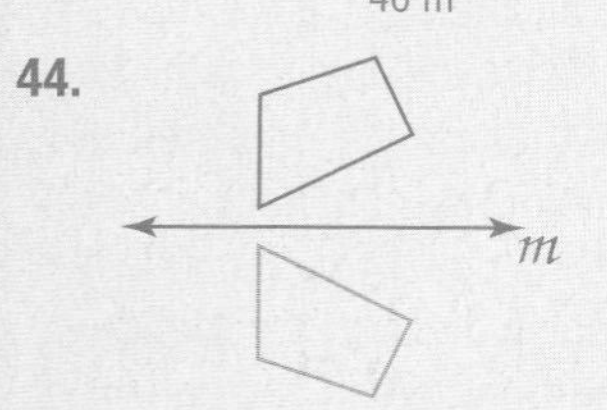

45.

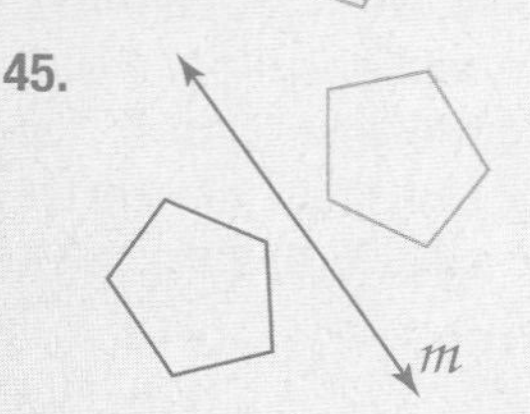

46.

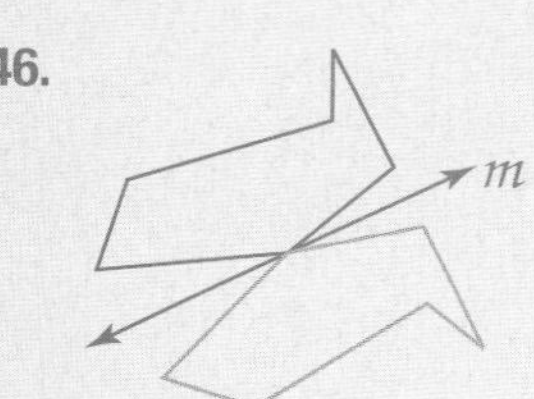

Standardized Test Practice

39. What rotation of trapezoid $QRST$ creates an image with point R' at (4, 3)? D

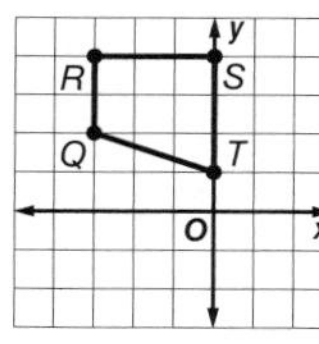

A 270° counterclockwise about point T
B 185° counterclockwise about point T
C 180° clockwise about the origin
D 90° clockwise about the origin

40. SHORT RESPONSE $\triangle XYZ$ has vertices $X(1, 7)$, $Y(0, 2)$, and $Z(-5, -2)$. What are the coordinates of X' after a rotation 270° counterclockwise about the origin? (7, −1)

41. ALGEBRA The population of the United States in July of 2007 was estimated to have surpassed 301,000,000. At the same time the world population was estimated to be over 6,602,000,000. What percent of the world population, to the nearest tenth, lived in the United States at this time? J

F 3.1% **H** 4.2%
G 3.5% **J** 4.6%

42. SAT/ACT An 18-foot ladder is placed against the side of a house. The base of the ladder is positioned 8 feet from the house. How high up on the side of the house, to the nearest tenth of a foot, does the ladder reach? B

A 10.0 ft **D** 22.5 ft
B 16.1 ft **E** 26.0 ft
C 19.7 ft

Spiral Review

43. VOLCANOES A cloud of dense gas and dust from a volcano blows 40 miles west and then 30 miles north. Make a sketch to show the translation of the dust particles. Then find the distance of the shortest path that would take the particles to the same position. (Lesson 9-2) See margin.

Copy the figure and the given line of reflection. Then draw the reflected image in this line using a ruler. (Lesson 9-1) 44–46. See margin.

44.

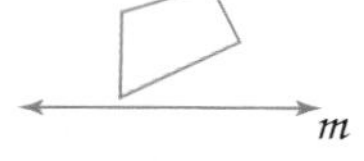

45.

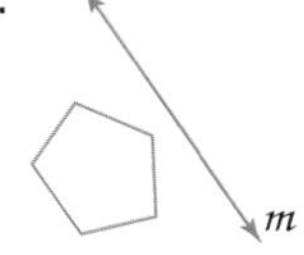

46.

Skills Review

Identify the type of congruence transformation shown as a *reflection*, *translation*, or *rotation*.

47. reflection

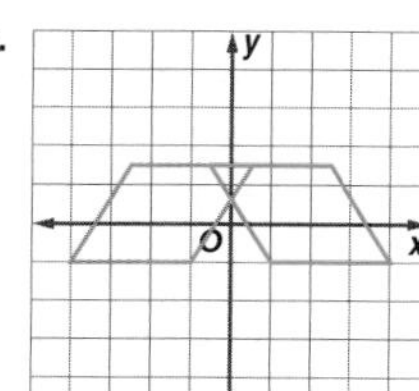

48. translation

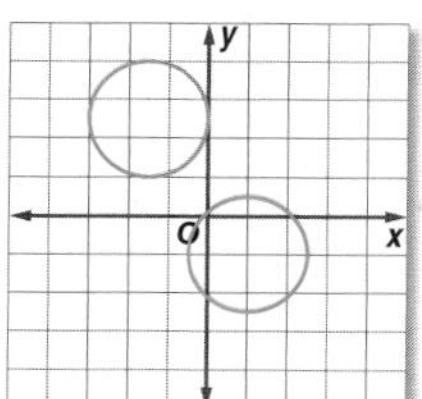

49. rotation or reflection

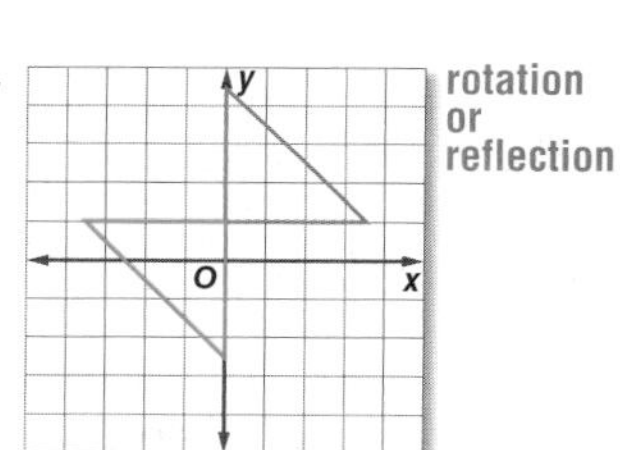

646 | Lesson 9-3 | Rotations

EXTEND 9-3 Geometry Lab: Solids of Revolution

A **solid of revolution** is a three-dimensional figure obtained by rotating a plane figure or curve about a line.

CCSS Common Core State Standards
Content Standards
G.GMD.4 Identify the shapes of two-dimensional cross-sections of three-dimensional objects, and identify three-dimensional objects generated by rotations of two-dimensional objects.
Mathematical Practices 5

Activity 1

Identify and sketch the solid formed by rotating the right triangle shown about line ℓ.

Step 1 Copy the triangle onto card stock or heavy construction paper and cut it out.

Step 2 Use tape to attach the triangle to a dowel rod or straw.

Step 3 Rotate the end of the straw quickly between your hands and observe the result.

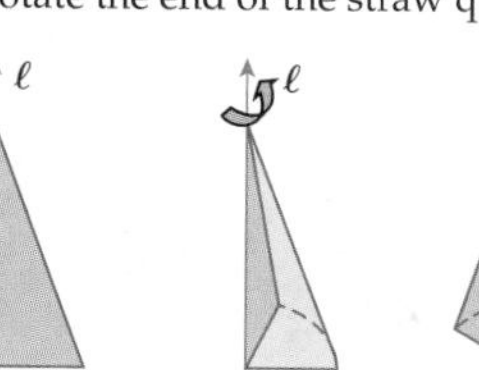

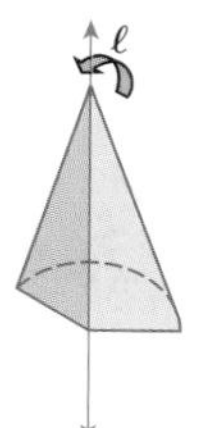

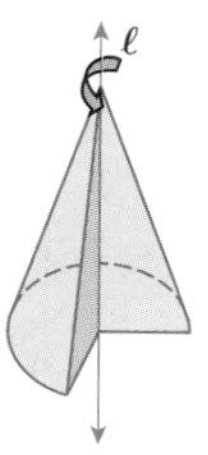

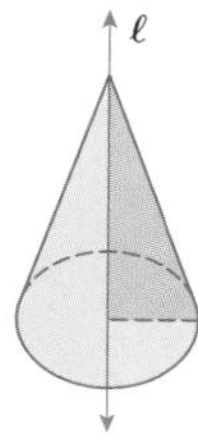

The blurred image you observe is that of a cone.

Model and Analyze 1–3. See margin for drawings.

Identify and sketch the solid formed by rotating the two-dimensional shape about line ℓ.

1. 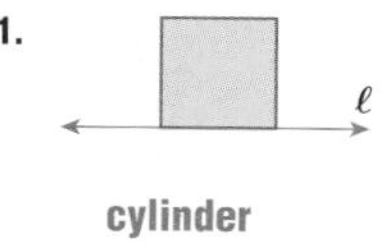 cylinder

2. 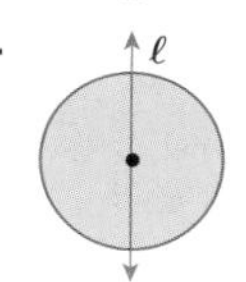 sphere

3. 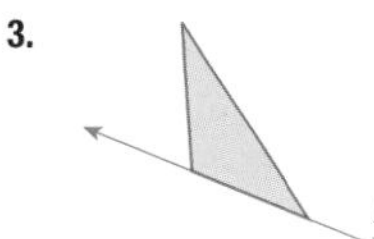 cone with a smaller cone removed from base

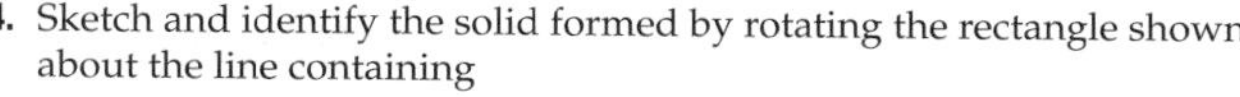

4. Sketch and identify the solid formed by rotating the rectangle shown about the line containing
   a. side $\overline{AB}$.
   b. side $\overline{AD}$.
   c. the midpoints of sides $\overline{AB}$ and $\overline{AD}$. See margin.

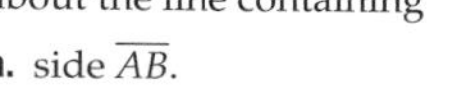

5. **DESIGN** Draw a two-dimensional figure that could be rotated to form the vase shown, including the line in which it should be rotated. See margin.

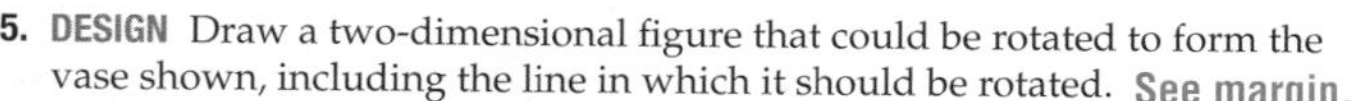

6. **REASONING** *True* or *false:* All solids can be formed by rotating a two-dimensional figure. Explain your reasoning. See margin.

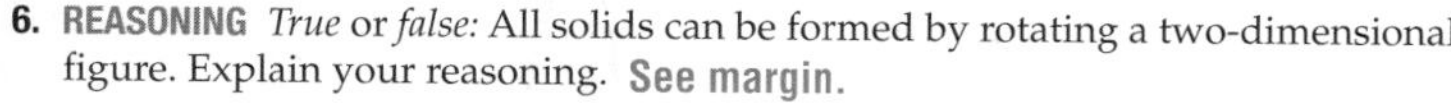

1 Focus

Objective Identify and sketch solids formed by revolving two-dimensional figures about lines.

Materials
- straws or dowel rods
- card stock or heavy construction paper
- graphing paper

Teaching Tip
Have students predict what solid will result before doing each activity and exercise.

2 Teach

Working in Cooperative Groups
Have students work in mixed ability pairs, taking turns rotating the figure. Encourage students to draw, cut out, attach, and rotate shapes to verify the sketches they generate for each exercise.

Additional Answers

1.

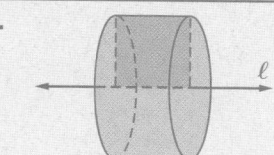

2.

3.

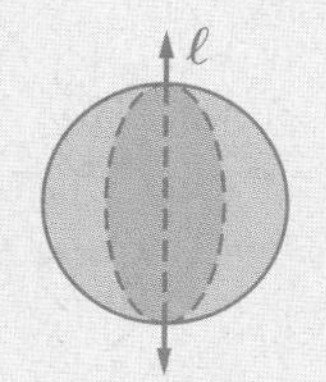

4a.

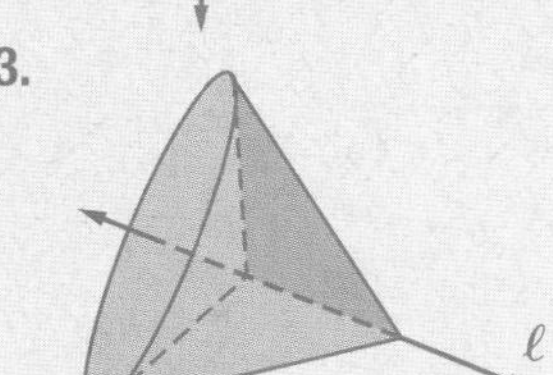

4b.

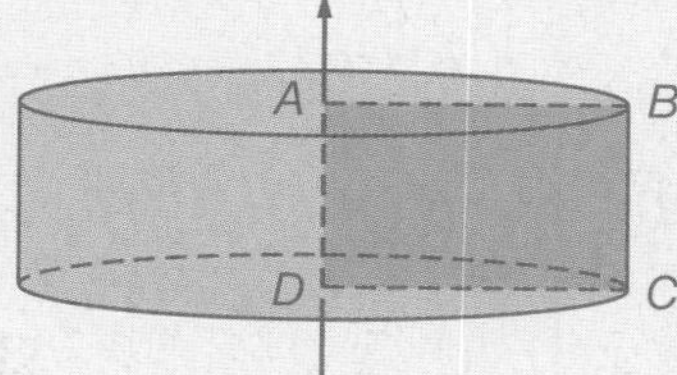

4c.

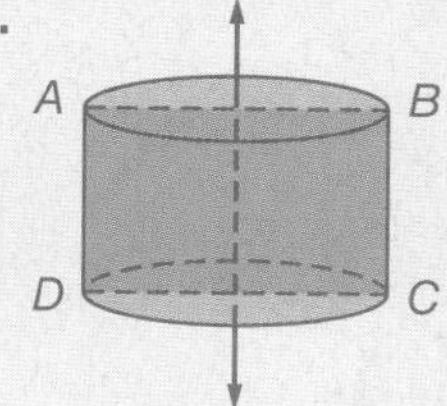

5. Sample answer:

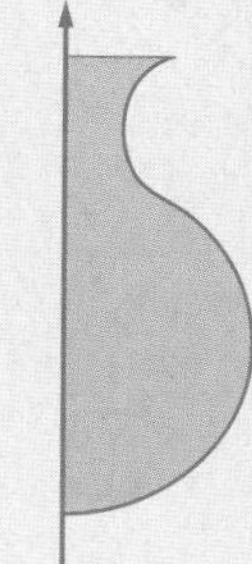

6. False; prisms and pyramids cannot be formed in this way. Only solids that have curved sides can be formed by rotating a two-dimensional figure.

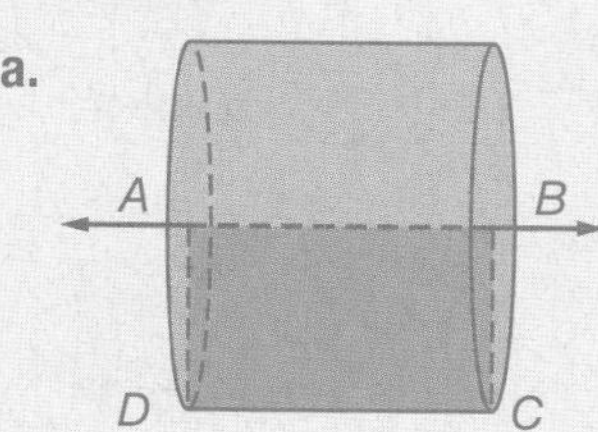

connectED.mcgraw-hill.com 647

Practice Have students complete Activities 1 and 2 and Exercises 1–5, 7–12, and 14.

3 Assess

Formative Assessment

Use Exercises 6 and 13 to assess each student's understanding of solids of revolution.

From Concrete to Abstract

Ask students to summarize what they learned about solids of revolution and to suggest ways in which they might be used in the real world.

Additional Answers

7.
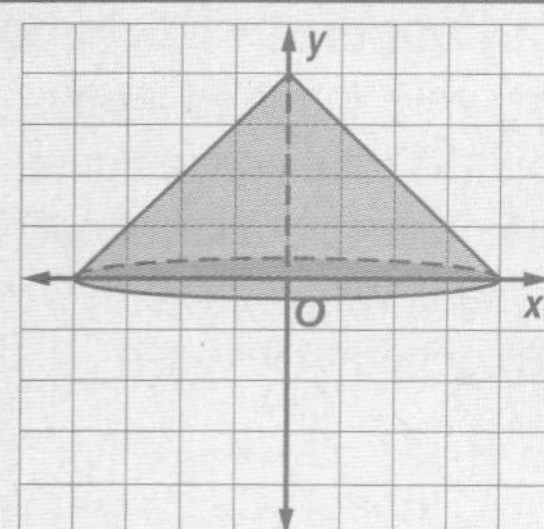

8.
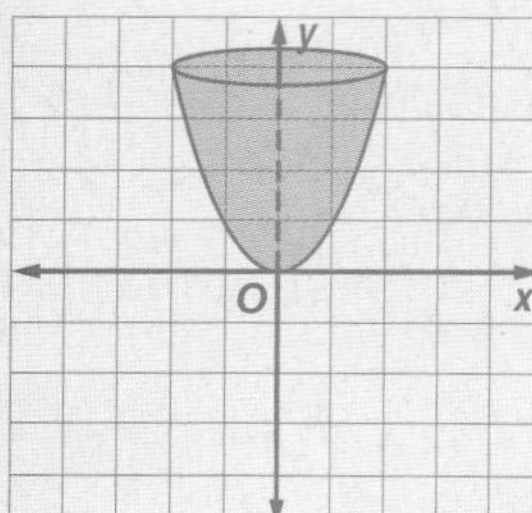

9.
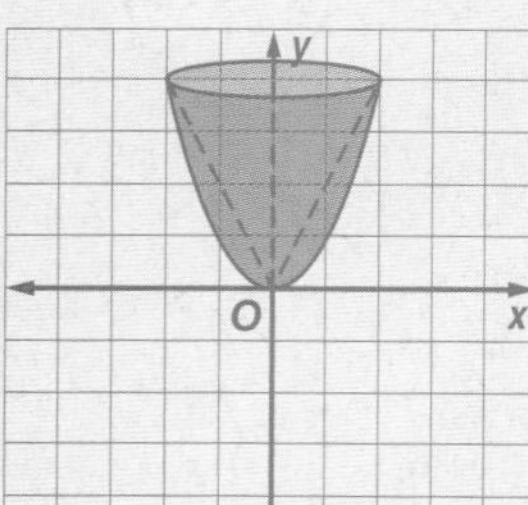

10.
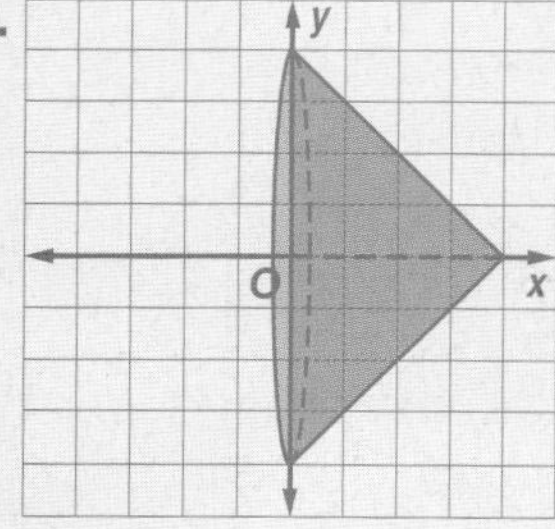

Geometry Lab
Solids of Revolution *Continued*

In calculus, you will be asked to find the volumes of solids generated by revolving a region on the coordinate plane about the *x*- or *y*-axis. An important first step in solving these problems is visualizing the solids formed.

Activity 2

Sketch the solid that results when the region enclosed by $y = x$, $x = 4$, and $y = 0$ is revolved about the y-axis.

Step 1 Graph each equation to find the region to be rotated.

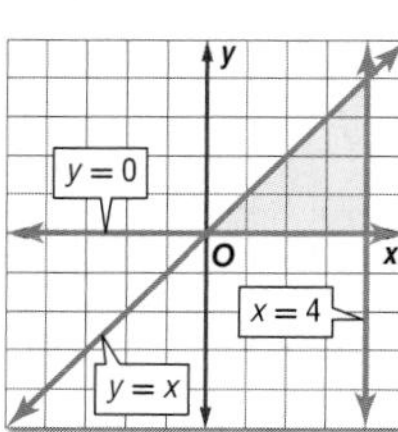

Step 2 Reflect the region about the *y*-axis.

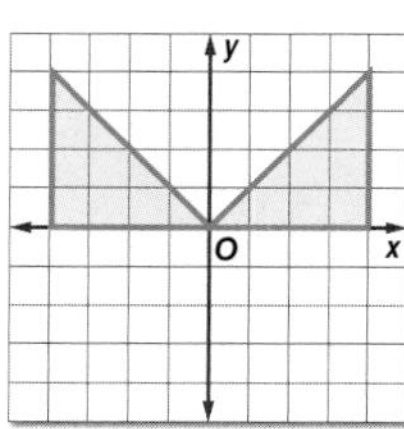

Step 3 Connect the vertices of the right triangles using curved lines.

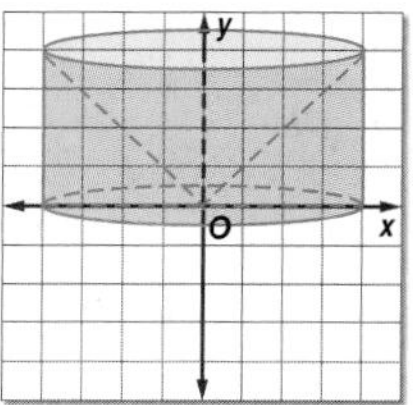

The solid is a cylinder with a cone cut out of its center.

Model and Analyze 7–9. See margin.

Sketch the solid that results when the region enclosed by the given equations is revolved about the y-axis.

7. $y = -x + 4$
$x = 0$
$y = 0$

8. $y = x^2$
$y = 4$

9. $y = x^2$
$y = 2x$

Sketch the solid that results when the region enclosed by the given equations is revolved about the x-axis. 10–12. See margin.

10. $y = -x + 4$
$x = 0$
$y = 0$

11. $y = x^2$
$y = 0$
$x = 2$

12. $y = x^2$
$y = 2x$

13. **OPEN ENDED** Graph a region in the first quadrant of the coordinate plane.
   a. Sketch the graph of the region when revolved about the y-axis.
   b. Sketch the graph of the region when revolved about the x-axis. a–b. See Chapter 9 Answer Appendix.

14. **CHALLENGE** Find equations that enclose a region such that when rotated about the x-axis, a solid is produced with a volume of 18π cubic units. Sample answer: $x = 0$, $x = 2$, $y = 0$, $y = 3$

11.
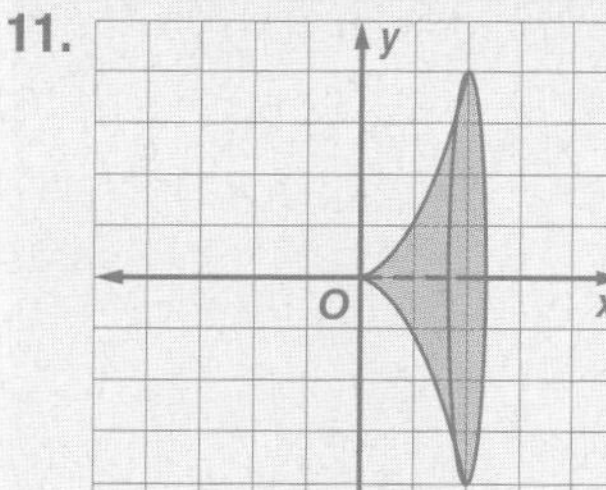

12.
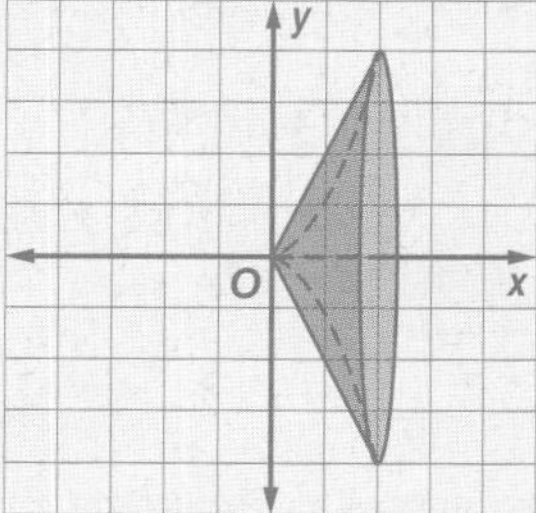

CHAPTER 9

Mid-Chapter Quiz

Lessons 9-1 through 9-3

Copy the figure and the given line of reflection. Then draw the reflected image in this line using a ruler. (Lesson 9-1)

1.

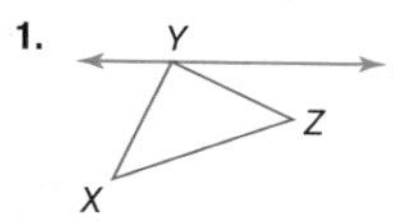

2.

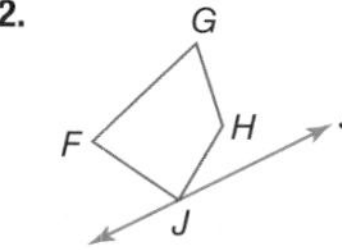

1–2. See Ch. 9 Answer Appendix.

Graph each figure and its image after the specified reflection. (Lesson 9-1) **3–5. See Ch. 9 Answer Appendix.**

3. $\triangle FGH$ has vertices $F(-4, 3)$, $G(-2, 0)$, and $H(-1, 4)$; in the y-axis

4. rhombus $QRST$ has vertices $Q(2, 1)$, $R(4, 3)$, $S(6, 1)$, and $T(4, -1)$; in the x-axis

5. CLUBS The drama club is selling candy during the intermission of a school play. Locate point P along the wall to represent the candy table so that people coming from either door A or door B would walk the same distance to the table. (Lesson 9-1)

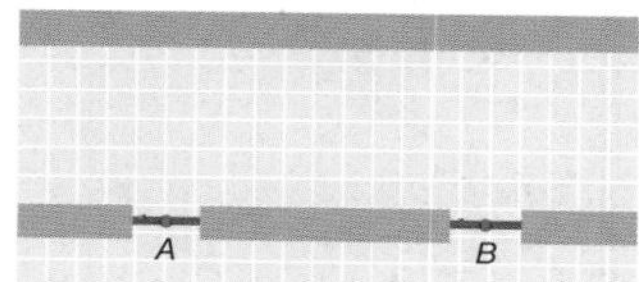

Graph each figure and its image after the specified translation. (Lesson 9-2) **6–7. See Ch. 9 Answer Appendix.**

6. $\triangle ABC$ with vertices $A(0, 0)$, $B(2, 1)$, $C(1, -3)$; $\langle 3, -1 \rangle$

7. rectangle $JKLM$ has vertices $J(-4, 2)$, $K(-4, -2)$, $L(-1, -2)$, and $M(-1, 2)$; $\langle 5, -3 \rangle$

Copy the figure and the given translation vector. Then draw the translation of the figure along the translation vector. (Lesson 9-2)

8.

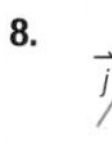

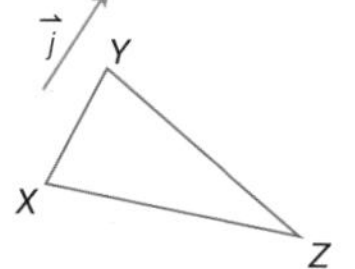

9.

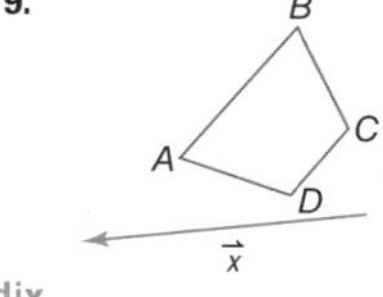

8–9. See Ch. 9 Answer Appendix.

10. COMICS Alex is making a comic. He uses graph paper to make sure the dimensions of his drawings are accurate. If he draws a coordinate plane with two flies as shown below, what vector represents the movement from fly 1 to fly 2? (Lesson 9-2) **⟨6, 1⟩**

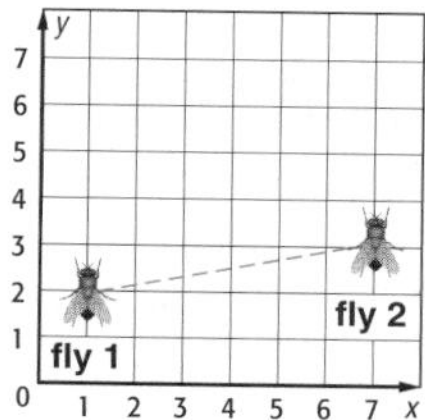

Copy each polygon and point R. Then use a protractor and ruler to draw the specified rotation of each figure about point R. (Lesson 9-3) **11–12. See Ch. 9 Answer Appendix.**

11. 45°

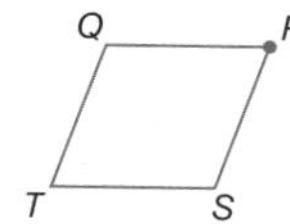

12. 60°

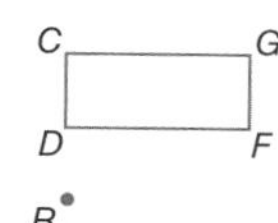

13. MULTIPLE CHOICE What is the image of point M after a rotation of 90° about the origin? (Lesson 9-3) **A**

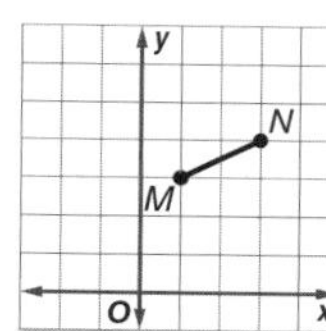

A $(-3, 1)$

B $(-3, -1)$

C $(-1, -3)$

D $(3, 1)$

Graph each figure and its image after the specified rotation. (Lesson 9-3) **14–15. See Ch. 9 Answer Appendix.**

14. $\triangle RST$ has vertices $R(-3, 0)$, $S(-1, -4)$, and $T(0, -1)$; 90°

15. square $JKLM$ has vertices $J(-1, 2)$, $K(-1, -2)$, $L(3, -2)$, and $M(3, 2)$; 180°

Formative Assessment

Use the Mid-Chapter Quiz to assess students' progress in the first half of the chapter.

For the problems that they answered incorrectly have students review the lessons indicated in parentheses.

Summative Assessment

Mid-Chapter Test, p. 47

eAssessment Customize and create multiple versions of your Mid-Chapter Test and their answer keys.

FOLDABLES® StudyOrganizer

Dinah Zike's Foldables®

Before students take the Mid-Chapter Quiz, encourage them to review the information for Lessons 9-1 through 9-3 in their Foldables.

InterventionPlanner

TIER 1 On Level OL

If students miss about 25% of the exercises or less,

Then choose a resource:

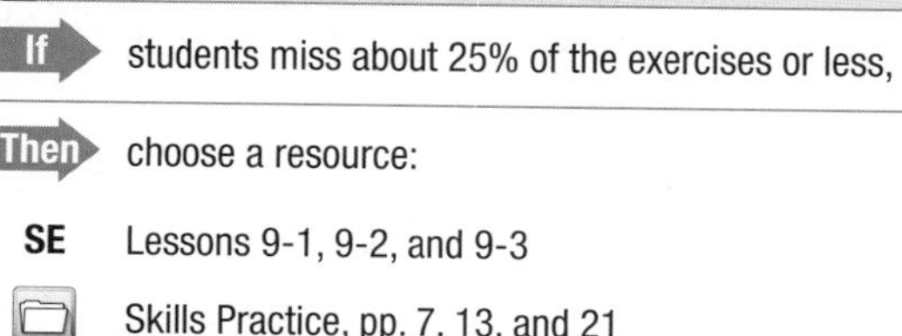

SE Lessons 9-1, 9-2, and 9-3

Skills Practice, pp. 7, 13, and 21

connectED.mcgraw-hill.com Self-Check Quiz

TIER 2 Strategic Intervention AL approaching grade level

If students miss about 50% of the exercises,

Then choose a resource:

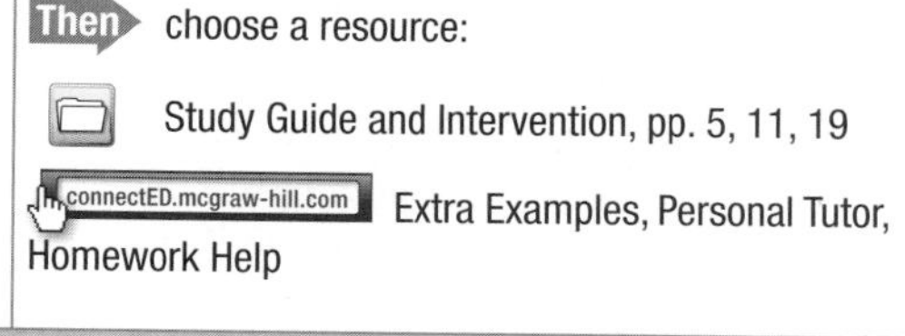

Study Guide and Intervention, pp. 5, 11, 19

connectED.mcgraw-hill.com Extra Examples, Personal Tutor, Homework Help

TIER 3 Intensive Intervention 2 or more grades below level

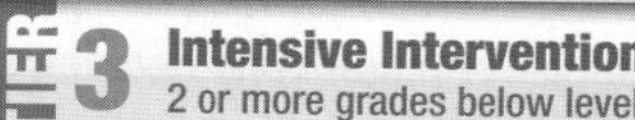

If students miss about 75% of the exercises,

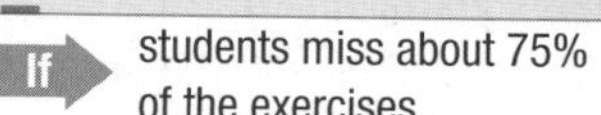

Then use *Math Triumphs, Geo.*, Ch. 5

connectED.mcgraw-hill.com Extra Examples, Personal Tutor, Homework Help, Review Vocabulary

1 Focus

Objective Explore the effects of performing multiple transformations on a figure.

Materials for Each Group

- Geometer's Sketchpad Software

Teaching Tip

Students should be familiar with the basic tools of the Geometer's Sketchpad. Allow time for students to explore and practice with the software. Remind students that all of the correct components must be collected in order for the software to perform the intended transformation.

2 Teach

Working in Cooperative Groups

Have students work individually to complete the Activity. Then organize students in groups of 2 or 3, mixing abilities to complete Exercises 1–6.

Practice Have students complete Exercises 1–6.

3 Assess

Formative Assessment

Have students describe how a composite of reflections results in either a translation or a rotation to assess whether students understand composite reflections.

From Concrete to Abstract

Have students use coordinate geometry to verify that a composite of reflections over parallel lines results in the same transformation as a translation.

EXPLORE 9-4 Geometry Software Lab Compositions of Transformations

In this lab, you will use Geometer's Sketchpad to explore the effects of performing multiple transformations on a figure.

CCSS Common Core State Standards
Content Standards
G.CO.2 Represent transformations in the plane using, e.g., transparencies and geometry software; describe transformations as functions that take points in the plane as inputs and give other points as outputs. Compare transformations that preserve distance and angle to those that do not (e.g., translation versus horizontal stretch).
G.CO.5 Given a geometric figure and a rotation, reflection, or translation, draw the transformed figure using, e.g., graph paper, tracing paper, or geometry software. Specify a sequence of transformations that will carry a given figure onto another.
Mathematical Practices 5

Activity

Reflect a figure in two vertical lines.

Step 1 Use the line segment tool to construct a triangle with one vertex pointing to the left so that you can easily see changes as you perform transformations. Label the triangle *ABC*.

Step 2 Insert and label a line *m* to the right of $\triangle ABC$. Insert a point so that the distance from the point to line *m* is greater than the width of $\triangle ABC$. Draw the line parallel to line *m* through the point and label the new line *r*.

Step 3 Select line *m* and choose **Mark Mirror** from the **Transform** menu. Select all sides and vertices of $\triangle ABC$ and choose **Reflect** from the **Transform** menu.

Step 4 Repeat the process you used in Step 3 to reflect the new image in line *r*.

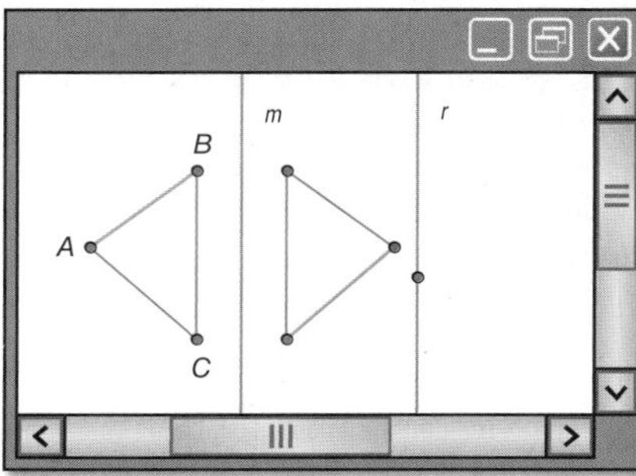

Steps 1–3

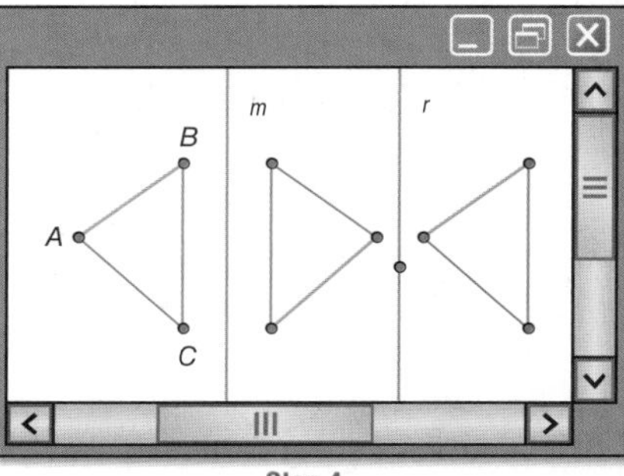

Step 4

Analyze the Results

1. How are the original figure and the final figure related? **Sample answer: The figures are congruent, and they are facing the same way.**
2. What single transformation could be used to produce the final figure? **translation**
3. If you move line *m*, what happens? if you move line *r*? **3–6. See margin.**
4. **MAKE A CONJECTURE** If you reflected the figure in a third line, what single transformation do you think could be used to produce the final figure? Explain your reasoning.
5. Repeat the activity for a pair of perpendicular lines. What single transformation could be used to produce the same final figure?
6. **MAKE A CONJECTURE** If you reflected the figure from Exercise 5 in a third line perpendicular to the second line, what single transformation do you think could be used to produce the final figure? Explain your reasoning.

Additional Answers

3. Sample answer: If you move line *m*, both of the reflected figures move. If you move line *p*, only the second reflected figure moves.
4. Sample answer: Since the figure would be facing the opposite direction, you would have to use a reflection or rotation to produce the figure in a single transformation.
5. You would have to use a 180° rotation to produce the figure in a single transformation.
6. Sample answer: You would still have to use rotation to produce the figure in a single transformation, because the orientation of the figure reflected across an additional line would not have the same orientation as the original figure.

LESSON 9-4 Compositions of Transformations

Then
- You drew reflections, translations, and rotations.

Now
1. Draw glide reflections and other compositions of isometries in the coordinate plane.
2. Draw compositions of reflections in parallel and intersecting lines.

Why?
- The pattern of footprints left in the sand after a person walks along the edge of a beach illustrates the composition of two different transformations—translations and reflections.

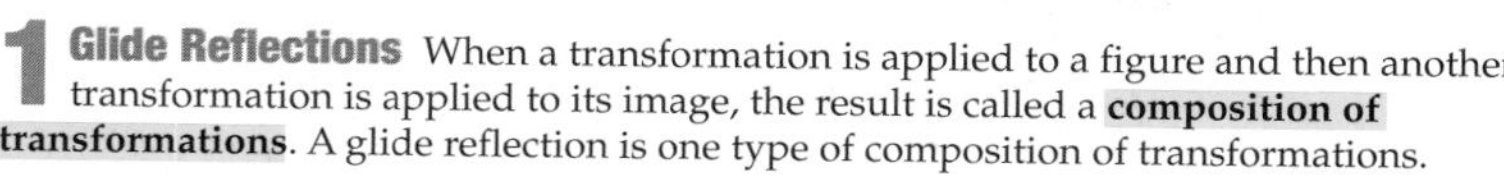

NewVocabulary
composition of transformations
glide reflection

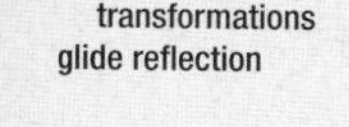

Common Core State Standards

Content Standards
G.CO.2 Represent transformations in the plane using, e.g., transparencies and geometry software; describe transformations as functions that take points in the plane as inputs and give other points as outputs. Compare transformations that preserve distance and angle to those that do not (e.g., translation versus horizontal stretch).
G.CO.5 Given a geometric figure and a rotation, reflection, or translation, draw the transformed figure using, e.g., graph paper, tracing paper, or geometry software. Specify a sequence of transformations that will carry a given figure onto another.

Mathematical Practices
1 Make sense of problems and persevere in solving them.
4 Model with mathematics.

1 Glide Reflections

When a transformation is applied to a figure and then another transformation is applied to its image, the result is called a **composition of transformations**. A glide reflection is one type of composition of transformations.

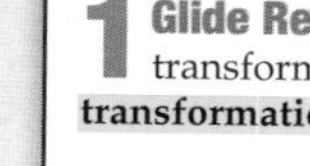

KeyConcept Glide Reflection

A **glide reflection** is the composition of a translation followed by a reflection in a line parallel to the translation vector.

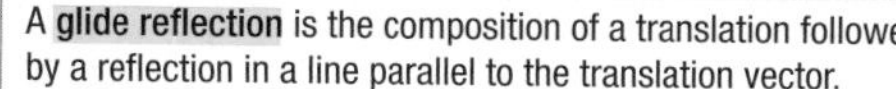

Example
The glide reflection shown is the composition of a translation along $\vec{w}$ followed by a reflection in line ℓ.

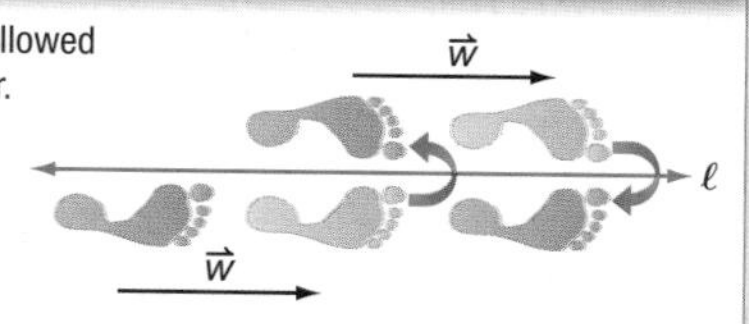

Example 1 Graph a Glide Reflection

Triangle JKL has vertices $J(6, -1)$, $K(10, -2)$, and $L(5, -3)$. Graph $\triangle JKL$ and its image after a translation along $\langle 0, 4\rangle$ and a reflection in the y-axis.

Step 1 translation along $\langle 0, 4\rangle$

(x, y)	$\rightarrow$	$(x, y + 4)$
$J(6, -1)$	$\rightarrow$	$J'(6, 3)$
$K(10, -2)$	$\rightarrow$	$K'(10, 2)$
$L(5, -3)$	$\rightarrow$	$L'(5, 1)$

Step 2 reflection in the y-axis

(x, y)	$\rightarrow$	$(-x, y)$
$J'(6, 3)$	$\rightarrow$	$J''(-6, 3)$
$K'(10, 2)$	$\rightarrow$	$K''(-10, 2)$
$L'(5, 1)$	$\rightarrow$	$L''(-5, 1)$

Step 3 Graph $\triangle JKL$ and its image $\triangle J''K''L''$.

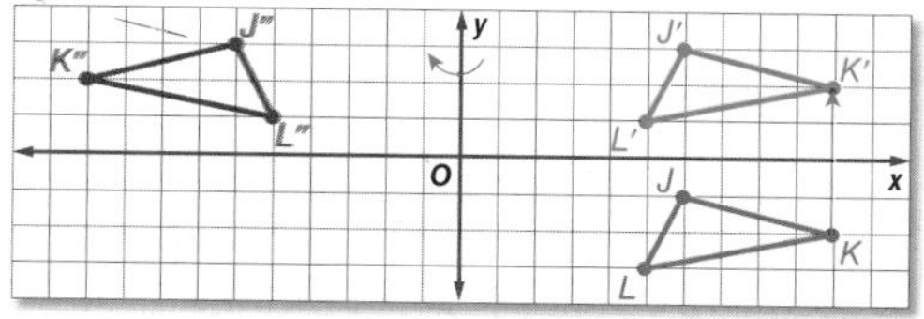

GuidedPractice

Triangle PQR has vertices $P(1, 1)$, $Q(2, 5)$, and $R(4, 2)$. Graph $\triangle PQR$ and its image after the indicated glide reflection. 1A–1B. See Ch. 9 Answer Appendix.

1A. Translation: along $\langle -2, 0\rangle$
Reflection: in x-axis

1B. Translation: along $\langle -3, -3\rangle$
Reflection: in $y = x$

1 Focus

VerticalAlignment

Before Lesson 9-4 Draw reflections, translations, and rotations.

Lesson 9-4 Draw compositions of transformations, including glide reflections and reflections over parallel and intersecting lines.

After Lesson 9-4 Apply properties of transformations to analyze symmetry of figures.

2 Teach

Scaffold Questioning

Have students read the **Why?** section of the lesson.

Ask:
- Why can the consecutive footprints not be classified as a simple translation? The consecutive footprints do not have the same orientation.
- Describe what composition of transformations results in the pattern shown by the footprints. The consecutive footprint pattern could result from a slide and then a reflection. This is called a glide reflection.

(*continued on the next page*)

Lesson 9-4 Resources

Resource	Approaching Level AL	On Level OL	Beyond Level BL	English Learners ELL
Teacher Edition	▪ Differentiated Instruction, p. 654	▪ Differentiated Instruction, pp. 654, 657	▪ Differentiated Instruction, p. 657	▪ Differentiated Instruction, p. 654
Chapter Resource Masters	▪ Study Guide and Intervention, pp. 25–26 ▪ Skills Practice, p. 27 ▪ Practice, p. 28 ▪ Word Problem Practice, p. 29	▪ Study Guide and Intervention, pp. 25–26 ▪ Skills Practice, p. 27 ▪ Practice, p. 28 ▪ Word Problem Practice, p. 29 ▪ Enrichment, p. 30	▪ Practice, p. 28 ▪ Word Problem Practice, p. 29 ▪ Enrichment, p. 30	▪ Study Guide and Intervention, pp. 25–26 ▪ Skills Practice, p. 27 ▪ Practice, p. 28 ▪ Word Problem Practice, p. 29
Other	▪ 5-Minute Check 9-4 ▪ Study Notebook	▪ 5-Minute Check 9-4 ▪ Study Notebook	▪ 5-Minute Check 9-4 ▪ Study Notebook	▪ 5-Minute Check 9-4 ▪ Study Notebook

- What other type of pattern could result from the same composite transformation? the pattern made by someone walking on his or her hands through sand

1 Glide Reflections

Examples 1 and 2 show how to graph the composition of transformations on a coordinate plane.

Formative Assessment

Use the Guided Practice exercises after each Example to determine students' understanding of concepts.

Additional Examples

1 Quadrilateral *BGTS* has vertices $B(-3, 4)$, $G(-1, 3)$, $T(-1, 1)$, and $S(-4, 2)$. Graph *BGTS* and its image after a translation along $\langle 5, 0\rangle$ and a reflection in the *x*-axis.

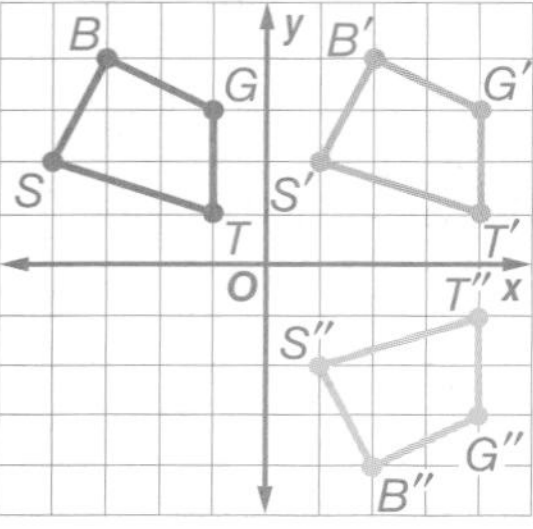

2 $\triangle TUV$ has vertices $T(2, -1)$, $U(5, -2)$, and $V(3, -4)$. Graph $\triangle TUV$ and its image after a translation along $\langle -1, 5\rangle$ and a rotation 180° about the origin.

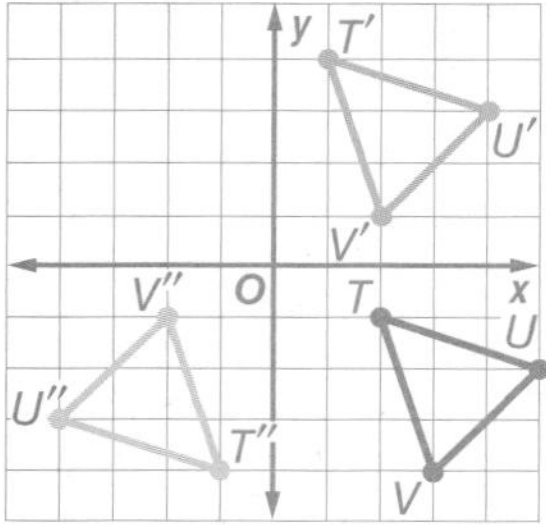

Additional Examples also in Interactive Classroom PowerPoint® Presentations

In Example 1, $\triangle JKL \cong \triangle J'K'L'$ and $\triangle J'K'L' \cong \triangle J''K''L''$. By the Transitive Property of Congruence, $\triangle JKL \cong \triangle J''K''L''$. This suggests the following theorem.

Theorem 9.1 Composition of Isometries

The composition of two (or more) isometries is an isometry.

You will prove one case of Theorem 9.1 in Exercise 30.

> **StudyTip**
> **Rigid Motions** Glide reflections, reflections, translations, and rotations are the only four *rigid motions* or isometries in a plane.

So, the composition of two or more isometries—reflections, translations, or rotations—results in an image that is congruent to its preimage.

Example 2 Graph Other Compositions of Isometries

The endpoints of $\overline{CD}$ are $C(-7, 1)$ and $D(-3, 2)$. Graph $\overline{CD}$ and its image after a reflection in the *x*-axis and a rotation 90° about the origin.

Step 1 reflection in the *x*-axis

(x, y)	$\rightarrow$	$(x, -y)$
$C(-7, 1)$	$\rightarrow$	$C'(-7, -1)$
$D(-3, 2)$	$\rightarrow$	$D'(-3, -2)$

Step 2 rotation 90° about origin

(x, y)	$\rightarrow$	$(-y, x)$
$C'(-7, -1)$	$\rightarrow$	$C''(1, -7)$
$D'(-3, -2)$	$\rightarrow$	$D''(2, -3)$

Step 3 Graph $\overline{CD}$ and its image $\overline{C''D''}$.

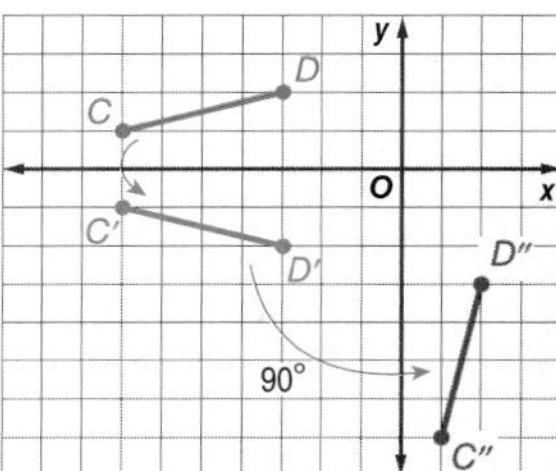

> **ReadingMath**
> **Double Primes** Double primes are used to indicate that a vertex is the image of a second transformation.

GuidedPractice

Triangle *ABC* has vertices $A(-6, -2)$, $B(-5, -5)$, and $C(-2, -1)$. Graph $\triangle ABC$ and its image after the composition of transformations in the order listed.

2A. Translation: along $\langle 3, -1\rangle$
Reflection: in *y*-axis

2B. Rotation: 180° about origin
Translation: along $\langle -2, 4\rangle$

2A.

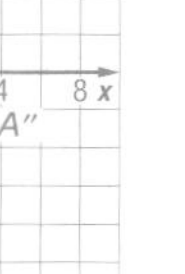

2B.

2 Compositions of Two Reflections

The composition of two reflections in parallel lines is the same as a translation.

Theorem 9.2 Reflections in Parallel Lines

The composition of two reflections in parallel lines can be described by a translation vector that is
- perpendicular to the two lines, and
- twice the distance between the two lines.

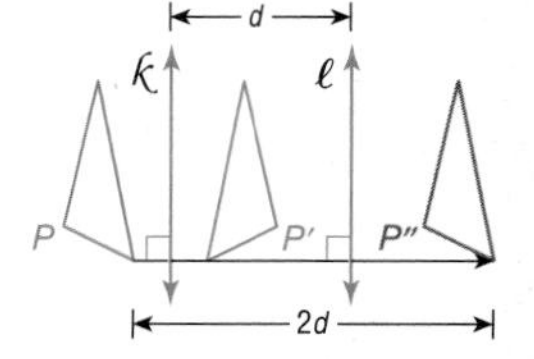

You will prove Theorem 9.2 in Exercise 36.

Tips for New Teachers

Reasoning Demonstrate to students that a composition of two reflections in two parallel lines can also be described as a 360° rotation.

The composition of two reflections in intersecting lines is the same as a rotation.

Theorem 9.3 Reflections in Intersecting Lines

The composition of two reflections in intersecting lines can be described by a rotation

- about the point where the lines intersect and
- through an angle that is twice the measure of the acute or right angle formed by the lines.

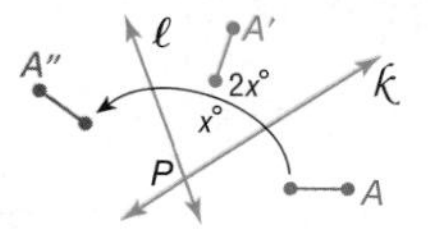

You will prove Theorem 9.3 in Exercise 37.

Example 3 Reflect a Figure in Two Lines

Copy and reflect figure A in line m and then line p. Then describe a single transformation that maps A onto A''.

a.

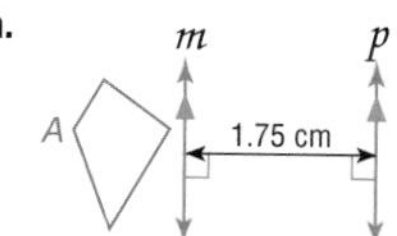

Step 1 Reflect A in line m.

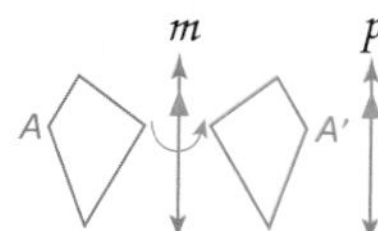

Step 2 Reflect A' in line p.

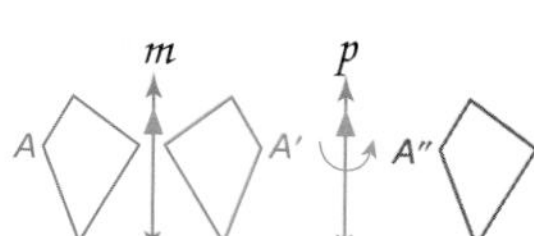

By Theorem 9.2, the composition of two reflections in parallel vertical lines m and p is equivalent to a horizontal translation right 2 • 1.75 or 3.5 centimeters.

b.

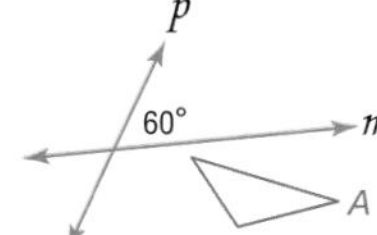

Step 1

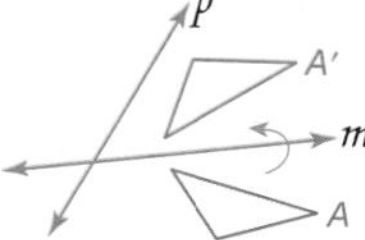

Step 2

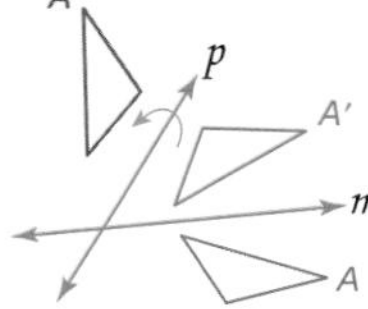

By Theorem 9.3, the composition of two reflections in intersecting lines m and p is equivalent to a 2 • 60° or 120° counterclockwise rotation about the point where lines m and p intersect.

Guided Practice

Copy and reflect figure B in line n and then line q. Then describe a single transformation that maps B onto B''.

3A.

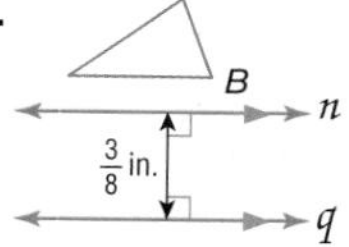

3B.

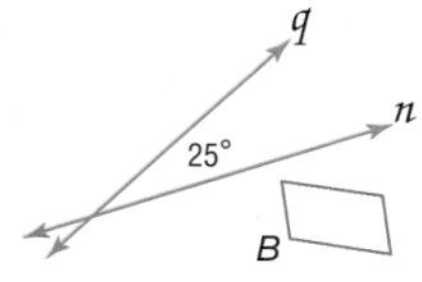

WatchOut!

Order of Composition Be sure to compose two transformations according to the order in which they are given.

3A. vertical translation down $\frac{3}{4}$ in.

3B. 50° counterclockwise rotation about the point where lines q and n intersect

2 Compositions of Two Reflections

Example 3 shows how to reflect a figure in two parallel or two intersecting lines. **Example 4** shows how to identify transformations in real-world patterns.

Additional Example

3 Copy and reflect figure *EFGH* in line p and then line q. Then describe a single transformation that maps *EFGH* onto $E''F''G''H''$.

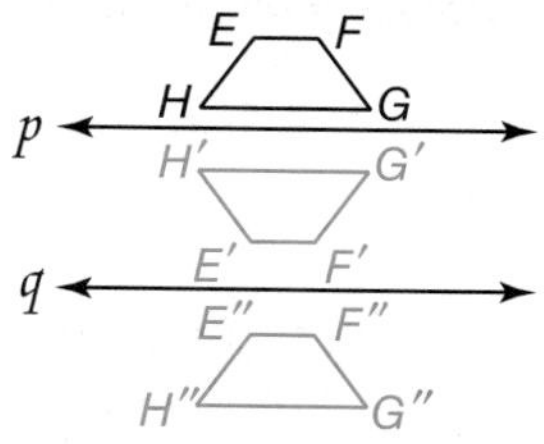

Sample answer: a translation down

Focus on Mathematical Content

Conditions Explain that a translation by a composition of reflections only works with an even number of parallel lines.

Teach with Tech

Interactive Whiteboard Draw a square on a coordinate plane, and write 3 different transformations on the board (for example: reflect in the x-axis, translate 3 units up, and rotate 90° clockwise about the origin). Have students choose two of these transformations and apply one and then the other to find the image of the square. Choose students to come to the board to draw and explain their transformations. Discuss with students whether the order in which the transformations are applied affects the image.

Additional Example

4 LANDSCAPING Describe the transformations that are combined to create each brick pattern shown.

a.

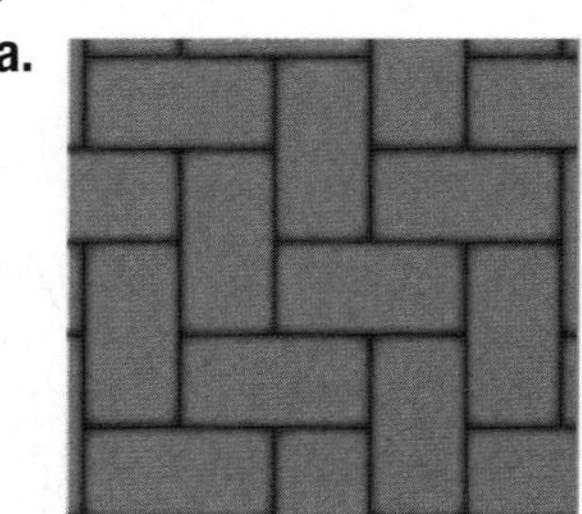

The pattern is created by successive translations and rotations.

b.

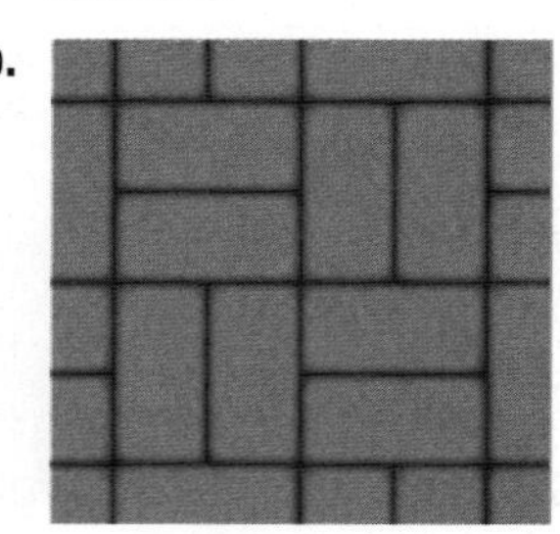

The pattern is created by successive rotations of two bricks or by alternating translations then rotations.

Real-WorldLink

In carpets, border patterns result when any of several basic transformations are repeated in one direction. There are seven possible combinations: translations, horizontal reflections, vertical reflections, vertical followed by horizontal reflections, glide reflections, rotations, and reflections followed by glide reflections.

Source: The Textile Museum

Many patterns in the real world are created using compositions of transformations.

Real-World Example 4 Describe Transformations

STATIONERY BORDERS Describe the transformations that are combined to create each stationery border shown.

a.

The pattern is created by successive translations of the first four potted plants. So this pattern can be created by combining two reflections in lines m and p as shown. Notice that line m goes through the center of the preimage.

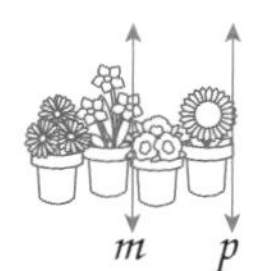

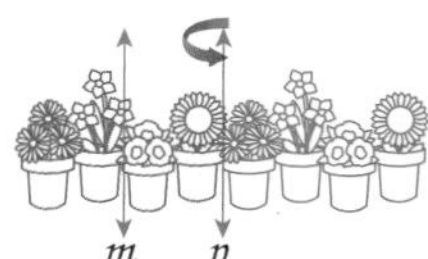

b.

The pattern is created by glide reflection. So this pattern can be created by combining a translation along translation vector $\vec{v}$ followed by a reflection over horizontal line n as shown.

GuidedPractice

4. CARPET PATTERNS Describe the transformations that are combined to create each carpet pattern shown.

A.

rotation

B.

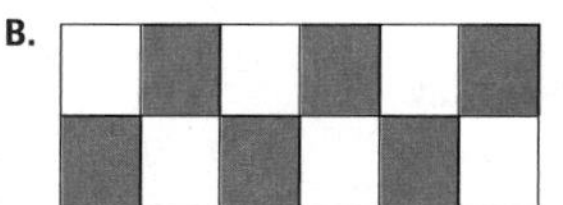

glide reflection

ConceptSummary Compositions of Translations

Glide Reflection	Translation	Rotation
the composition of a reflection and a translation	the composition of two reflections in parallel lines	the composition of two reflections in intersecting lines

DifferentiatedInstruction AL OL ELL

Visual/Spatial Learners Have students connect the beauty of art with geometry by designing a figure and then applying transformations, including composite transformations, to the figure over a large sheet of paper. Then, have students complete the art project by adding color and decoration as they choose.

Check Your Understanding 

= Step-by-Step Solutions begin on page R14.

Example 1 **Triangle *CDE* has vertices $C(-5, -1)$, $D(-2, -5)$, and $E(-1, -1)$. Graph $\triangle CDE$ and its image after the indicated glide reflection.** 1–3. See margin.

1. Translation: along $\langle 4, 0\rangle$
   Reflection: in x-axis

2. Translation: along $\langle 0, 6\rangle$
   Reflection: in y-axis

Example 2 3. The endpoints of $\overline{JK}$ are $J(2, 5)$ and $K(6, 5)$. Graph $\overline{JK}$ and its image after a reflection in the x-axis and a rotation 90° about the origin.

Example 3 **Copy and reflect figure *S* in line *m* and then line *p*. Then describe a single transformation that maps *S* onto *S″*.** 4–5. See Ch. 9 Answer Appendix.

4.

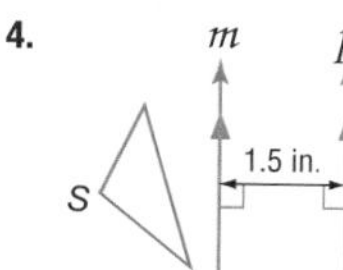

5.

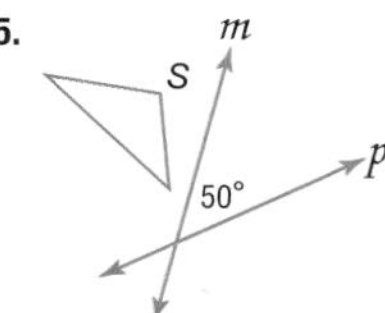

Example 4 6. **TILE PATTERNS** Viviana is creating a pattern for the top of a table with tiles in the shape of isosceles triangles. Describe the transformation combination that was used to transform the white triangle to the blue triangle.
reflection and translation (glide reflection)

Practice and Problem Solving

Extra Practice is on page R9.

Example 1 **Graph each figure with the given vertices and its image after the indicated glide reflection.** 7–12. See Ch. 9 Answer Appendix.

7. $\triangle RST$: $R(1, -4)$, $S(6, -4)$, $T(5, -1)$
   Translation: along $\langle 2, 0\rangle$
   Reflection: in x-axis

8. $\triangle JKL$: $J(1, 3)$, $K(5, 0)$, $L(7, 4)$
   Translation: along $\langle -3, 0\rangle$
   Reflection: in x-axis

9. $\triangle XYZ$: $X(-7, 2)$, $Y(-5, 6)$, $Z(-2, 4)$
   Translation: along $\langle 0, -1\rangle$
   Reflection: in y-axis

10. $\triangle ABC$: $A(2, 3)$, $B(4, 7)$, $C(7, 2)$
    Translation: along $\langle 0, 4\rangle$
    Reflection: in y-axis

11. $\triangle DFG$: $D(2, 8)$, $F(1, 2)$, $G(4, 6)$
    Translation: along $\langle 3, 3\rangle$
    Reflection: in $y = x$

12. $\triangle MPQ$: $M(-4, 3)$, $P(-5, 8)$, $Q(-1, 6)$
    Translation: along $\langle -4, -4\rangle$
    Reflection: in $y = x$

Example 2 CCSS **SENSE-MAKING** **Graph each figure with the given vertices and its image after the indicated composition of transformations.** 13–16. See Ch. 9 Answer Appendix.

13. $\overline{WX}$: $W(-4, 6)$ and $X(-4, 1)$
    Reflection: in x-axis
    Rotation: 90° about origin

14. $\overline{AB}$: $A(-3, 2)$ and $B(3, 8)$
    Rotation: 90° about origin
    Translation: along $\langle 4, 4\rangle$

15. $\overline{FG}$: $F(1, 1)$ and $G(6, 7)$
    Reflection: in x-axis
    Rotation: 180° about origin

16. $\overline{RS}$: $R(2, -1)$ and $S(6, -5)$
    Translation: along $\langle -2, -2\rangle$
    Reflection: in y-axis

Differentiated Homework Options

Level	Assignment	Two-Day Option	
AL Basic	7–24, 38, 39, 41–57	7–23 odd, 45–48	8–24 even, 38, 39, 41–44, 49–57
OL Core	7–27 odd, 28–33, 35, 37, 38, 39, 41–57	7–24, 45–48	25–39, 41–44, 49–57
BL Advanced	25–54 (optional: 55–57)		

3 Practice

Formative Assessment

Use Exercises 1–6 to check for understanding.

Then use the chart at the bottom of this page to customize assignments for your students.

Exercise Alert

Tracing or Patty Paper It may be helpful for students to have tracing paper or patty paper when completing Exercises 4 and 5.

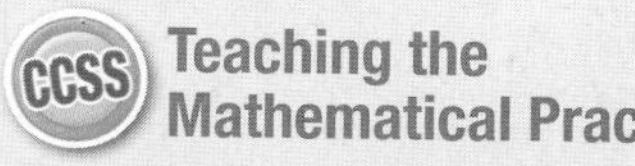

Teaching the Mathematical Practices

Sense-Making Mathematically proficient students start by explaining the meaning of a problem to themselves and looking for entry points to its solution. In Exercises 13–16, encourage students to graph each figure first and then develop a plan for solving the problem.

Additional Answers

1.

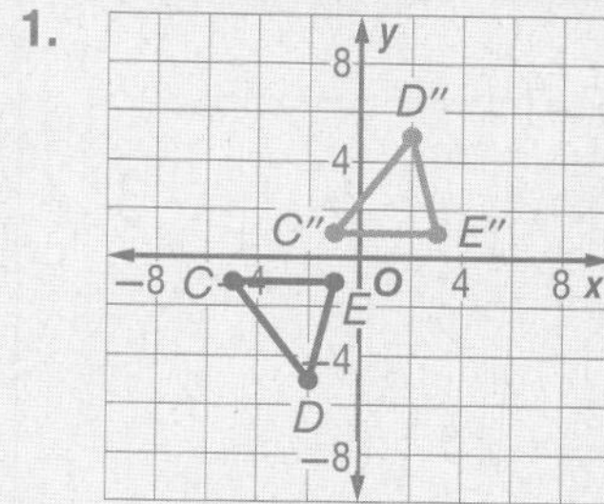

2.

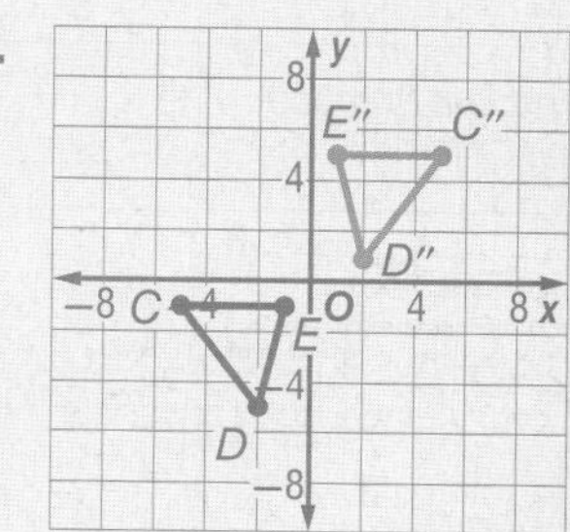

3.

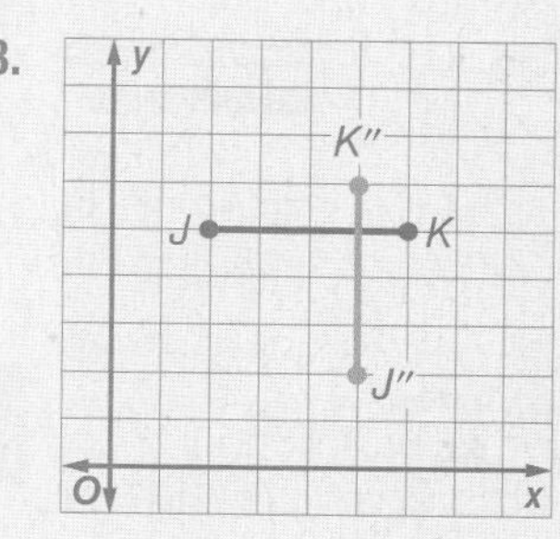

Study Guide and Intervention

AL OL ELL

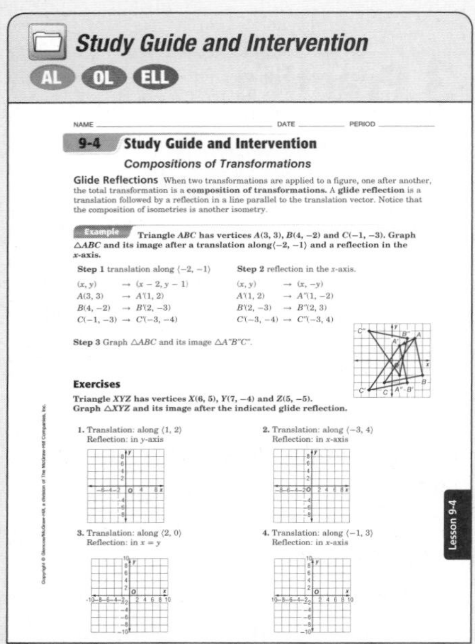

NAME ______ DATE ______ PERIOD ______

9-4 Study Guide and Intervention

Compositions of Transformations

Glide Reflections When two transformations are applied to a figure, one after another, the total transformation is a **composition of transformations**. A **glide reflection** is a translation followed by a reflection in a line parallel to the translation vector. Notice that the composition of isometries is another isometry.

Example Triangle *ABC* has vertices *A*(3, 3), *B*(4, −2) and *C*(−1, −3). Graph △*ABC* and its image after a translation along ⟨−2, −1⟩ and a reflection in the *x*-axis.

Step 1 translation along ⟨−2, −1⟩
(x, y) → (x − 2, y − 1)
A(3, 3) → A′(1, 2)
B(4, −2) → B′(2, −3)
C(−1, −3) → C′(−3, −4)

Step 2 reflection in the *x*-axis.
(x, y) → (x, −y)
A′(1, 2) → A″(1, −2)
B′(2, −3) → B″(2, 3)
C′(−3, −4) → C″(−3, 4)

Step 3 Graph △*ABC* and its image △*A″B″C″*.

Exercises

Triangle *XYZ* has vertices *X*(6, 5), *Y*(7, −4) and *Z*(5, −5). Graph △*XYZ* and its image after the indicated glide reflection.

1. Translation: along ⟨1, 2⟩ Reflection: in *y*-axis
2. Translation: along ⟨−3, 4⟩ Reflection: in *x*-axis
3. Translation: along ⟨2, 0⟩ Reflection: in *x* = *y*
4. Translation: along ⟨−1, 3⟩ Reflection: in *x*-axis

Lesson 9-4

Practice

AL OL BL ELL

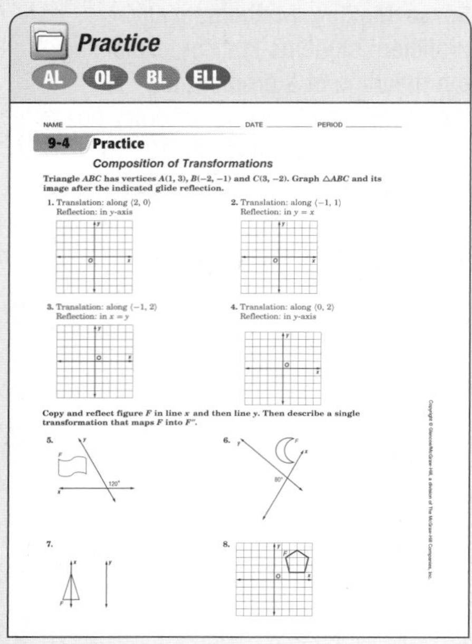

NAME ______ DATE ______ PERIOD ______

9-4 Practice

Composition of Transformations

Triangle *ABC* has vertices *A*(1, 3), *B*(−2, −1) and *C*(3, −2). Graph △*ABC* and its image after the indicated glide reflection.

1. Translation: along ⟨2, 0⟩ Reflection: in *y*-axis
2. Translation: along ⟨−1, 1⟩ Reflection: in *y* = *x*
3. Translation: along ⟨−1, 2⟩ Reflection: in *x* = *y*
4. Translation: along ⟨0, 2⟩ Reflection: in *y*-axis

Copy and reflect figure *F* in line *x* and then line *y*. Then describe a single transformation that maps *F* into *F″*.

5.
6.
7.
8.

Word Problem Practice

AL OL BL ELL

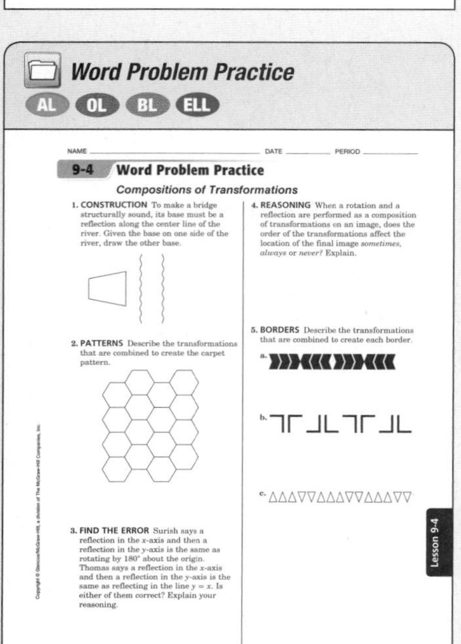

NAME ______ DATE ______ PERIOD ______

9-4 Word Problem Practice

Compositions of Transformations

1. **CONSTRUCTION** To make a bridge structurally sound, its base must be a reflection along the center line of the river. Given the base on one side of the river, draw the other base.

2. **PATTERNS** Describe the transformations that are combined to create the carpet pattern.

3. **FIND THE ERROR** Surish says a reflection in the *x*-axis and then a reflection in the *y*-axis is the same as rotating by 180° about the origin. Thomas says a reflection in the *x*-axis and then a reflection in the *y*-axis is the same as reflecting in the line *y* = *x*. Is either of them correct? Explain your reasoning.

4. **REASONING** When a rotation and a reflection are performed as a composition of transformations on an image, does the order of the transformations affect the location of the final image *sometimes, always* or *never*? Explain.

5. **BORDERS** Describe the transformations that are combined to create each border.

Lesson 9-4

Example 3 Copy and reflect figure *D* in line *m* and then line *p*. Then describe a single transformation that maps *D* onto *D″*. **17–20. See margin.**

17. m p D 2 cm

18.

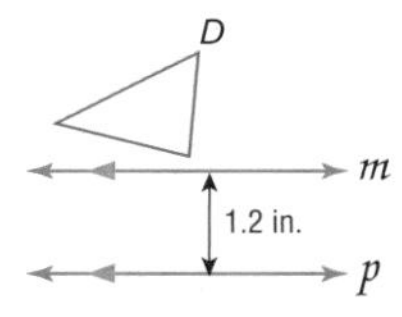

19. m D 35° p

20.

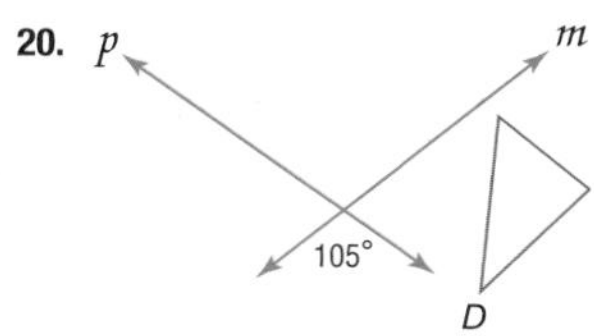

Example 4 **CCSS MODELING** Describe the transformations combined to create the outlined kimono fabric pattern.

21. **22.**

23.

translation rotation, then translation reflection

24. SKATEBOARDS Elizabeth has airbrushed the pattern shown onto her skateboard. What combination of transformations did she use to create the pattern? **glide reflection or two translations**

25.

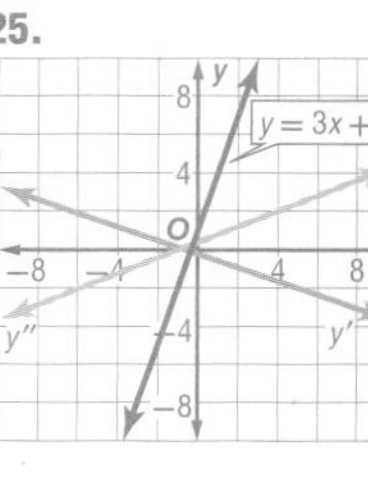

B **ALGEBRA** Graph each figure and its image after the indicated transformations.

25 Rotation: 90° about the origin
Reflection: in *x*-axis

26. Reflection: in *x*-axis
Reflection: in *y*-axis

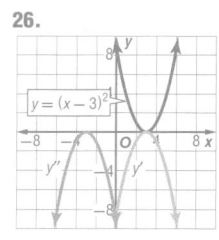

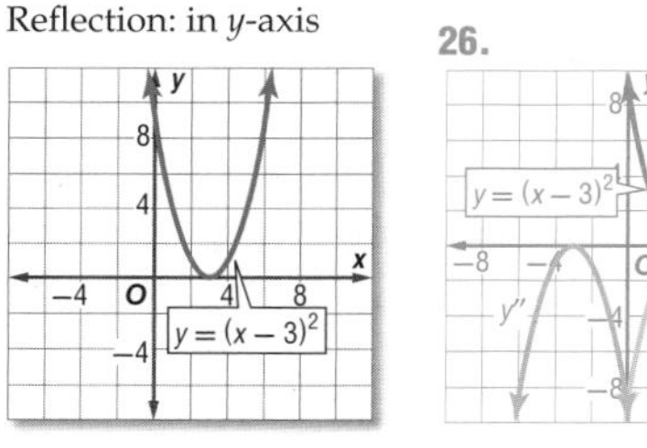

27. Find the coordinates of △*A″B″C″* after a reflection in the *x*-axis and a rotation of 180° about the origin if △*ABC* has vertices *A*(−3, 1), *B*(−2, 3), and *C*(−1, 0). ***A″*(3, 1), *B″*(2, 3), *C″*(1, 0)**

Enrichment

OL BL

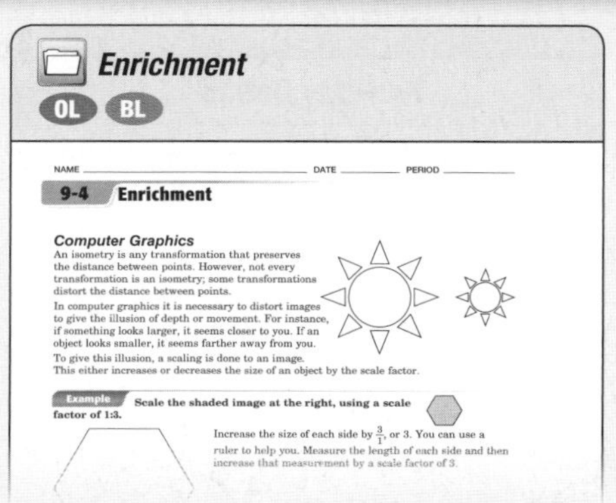

NAME ______ DATE ______ PERIOD ______

9-4 Enrichment

Computer Graphics

An isometry is any transformation that preserves the distance between points. However, not every transformation is an isometry; some transformations distort the distance between points.

In computer graphics it is necessary to distort images to give the illusion of depth or movement. For instance, if something looks larger, it seems closer to you. If an object looks smaller, it seems farther away from you.

To give this illusion, a scaling is done to an image. This either increases or decreases the size of an object by the scale factor.

Example Scale the shaded image at the right, using a scale factor of 1:3.

Increase the size of each side by $\frac{3}{1}$, or 3. You can use a ruler to help you. Measure the length of each side and then increase that measurement by a scale factor of 3.

Additional Answer

17.

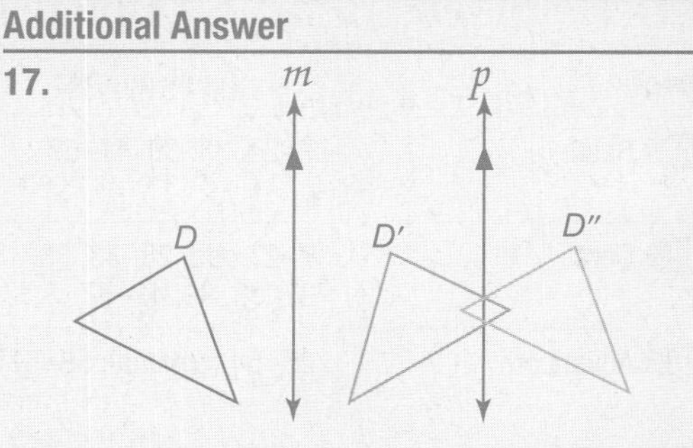

horizontal translation 4 cm to the right

28. FIGURE SKATING Kayla is practicing her figure skating routine. What combination of transformations is needed for Kayla to start at A, skate to A', and end up at A''?

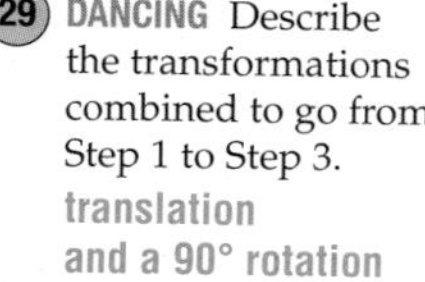

Sample answer: translation and a 450° rotation

29. DANCING Describe the transformations combined to go from Step 1 to Step 3. translation and a 90° rotation

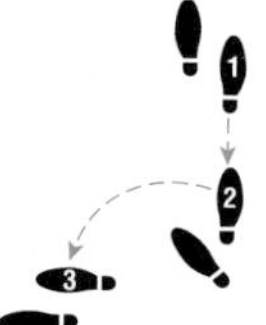

30. PROOF Write a paragraph proof for one case of the Composition of Isometries Theorem.

Given: A translation along $\langle a, b\rangle$ maps X to X' and Y to Y'. A reflection in z maps X' to X'' and Y' to Y''.

Prove: $\overline{XY} \cong \overline{X''Y''}$

See Ch. 9 Answer Appendix.

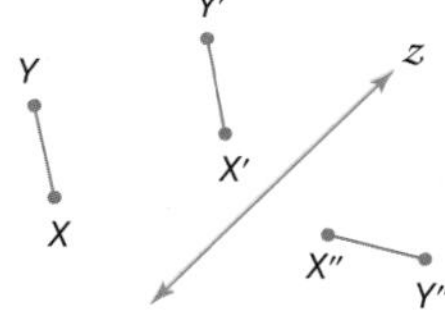

CCSS MODELING **The length of an animal's stride is the distance between two consecutive tracks. The average stride length of a turkey is about 11 inches, and the average stride length of a duck is about 5 inches. Write a glide reflection that can be used to predict the location of the next track for each set of animal tracks.**

31. turkey $(x + 5.5, y)$ reflected in the line that separates the left prints from the right prints

32. duck $(x + 2.5, y)$ reflected in the line that separates the left prints from the right prints

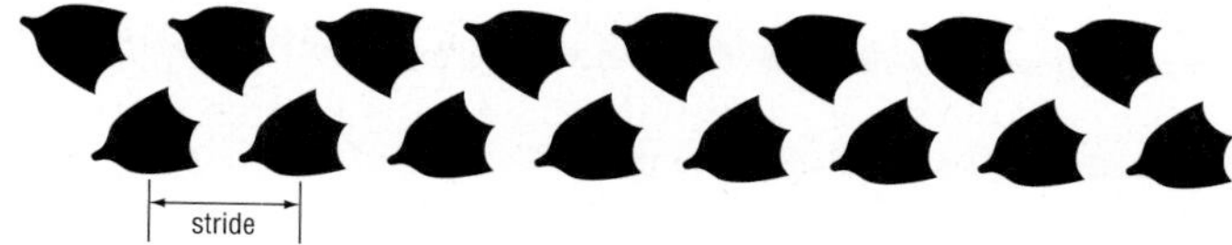

33. KNITTING Tonisha is knitting a scarf using the tumbling blocks pattern shown at the right. Describe the transformations combined to transform the red figure to the blue figure. double reflection

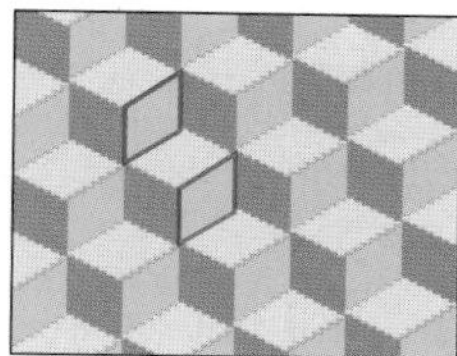

Describe the transformations that combined to map each figure.

34.

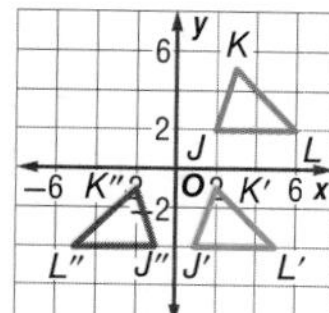

35.

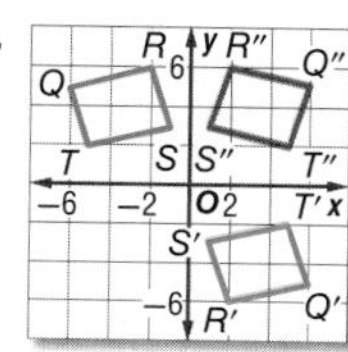

34. translation along $\langle -1, -6\rangle$ and reflection in the y-axis
35. rotation 180° about the origin and reflection in the x-axis

Differentiated Instruction OL BL

Extension Find the image of parallelogram $WXYZ$ under reflections in line p and then line q.

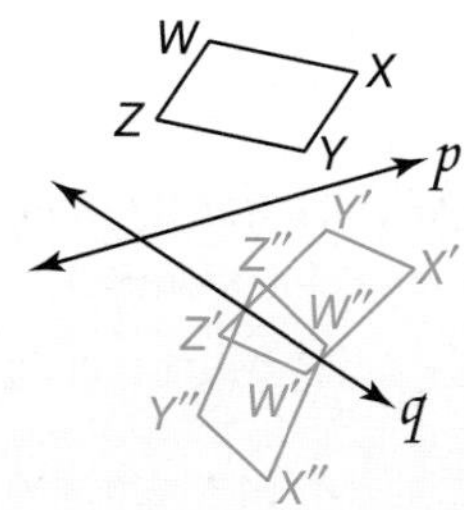

Exercise Alert

Tracing or Patty Paper It may be helpful for students to have tracing paper or patty paper when completing Exercises 17–20.

CCSS Teaching the Mathematical Practices

Modeling Mathematically proficient students can apply the mathematics they know to solve problems arising in everyday life. In Exercises 21–23 and 31–32, encourage students to copy the patterns onto tracing paper and then use these models to solve the problems.

Additional Answers

18.

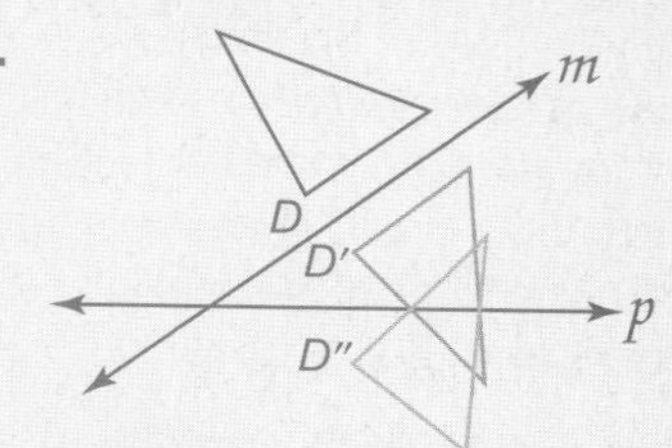

vertical translation 2.4 in. down

19.

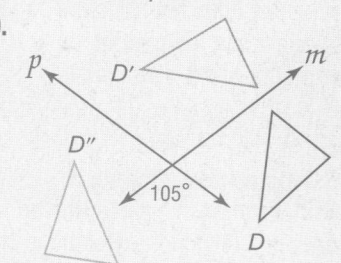

70° rotation about the point where lines m and p intersect

20.

210° rotation about the point where lines m and p intersect

WatchOut!

Error Analysis In Exercise 38, Lolita is correct. Tell students that although a glide reflection is a composite transformation, it does not produce the composite transformation described. The translation must be in a path parallel to the line of reflection, and in this case, the translation along ⟨2, 2⟩ is not parallel to $y = 2$.

Additional Answers

41. Yes; sample answer: If a segment with endpoints (a, b) and (c, d) is to be reflected about the x-axis, the coordinates of the endpoints of the reflected image are $(a, -b)$ and $(c, -d)$. If the segment is then reflected about the line $y = x$, the coordinates of the endpoints of the final image are $(-b, a)$ and $(-d, c)$. If the original image is first reflected about $y = x$, the coordinates of the endpoints of the reflected image are (b, a) and (d, c). If the segment is then reflected about the x-axis, the coordinates of the endpoints of the final image are $(b, -a)$ and $(d, -c)$.

43. Sometimes; sample answer: When two rotations are performed on a single image, the order of the rotations does not affect the final image when the two rotations are centered at the same point.

44. Sample answer: Glide reflections are compositions of transformations. But not all compositions of transformations are glide reflections. Rotations can be included in compositions of transformations but not glide reflections. Translations and reflections can both be used in compositions of transformations, but only make up a glide reflection when a figure is translated along a vector and then reflected in a line parallel to that vector.

36. PROOF Write a two-column proof of Theorem 9.2.

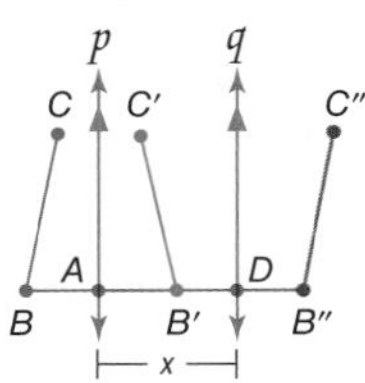

Given: A reflection in line p maps $\overline{BC}$ to $\overline{B'C'}$.
A reflection in line q maps $\overline{B'C'}$ to $\overline{B''C''}$.
$p \parallel q$, $AD = x$

Prove: **a.** $\overline{BB''} \perp p$, $\overline{BB''} \perp q$

b. $BB'' = 2x$

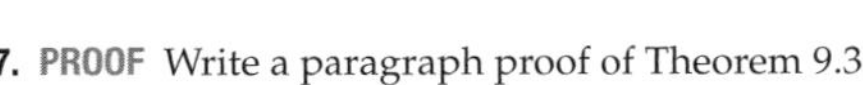
36–37. See Ch. 9 Answer Appendix.

37. PROOF Write a paragraph proof of Theorem 9.3.

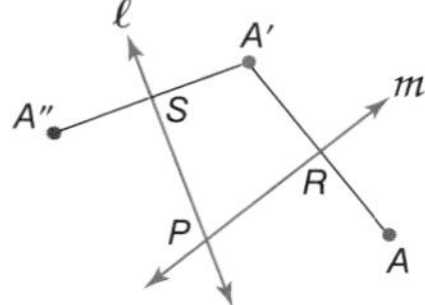

Given: Lines ℓ and m intersect at point P.
A is any point not on ℓ or m.

Prove: **a.** If you reflect point A in m, and then reflect its image A' in ℓ, A'' is the image of A after a rotation about point P.

b. $m\angle APA'' = 2(m\angle SPR)$

38. Lolita; sample answer: Since the line $y = 2$ is not parallel to the vector ⟨2, 2⟩, the transformation cannot be a glide reflection. It is a composition of a translation and a reflection, so it is a composition of transformations.

H.O.T. Problems Use Higher-Order Thinking Skills

38. ERROR ANALYSIS Daniel and Lolita are translating $\triangle XYZ$ along ⟨2, 2⟩ and reflecting it in the line $y = 2$. Daniel says that the transformation is a glide reflection. Lolita disagrees and says that the transformation is a composition of transformations. Is either of them correct? Explain your reasoning.

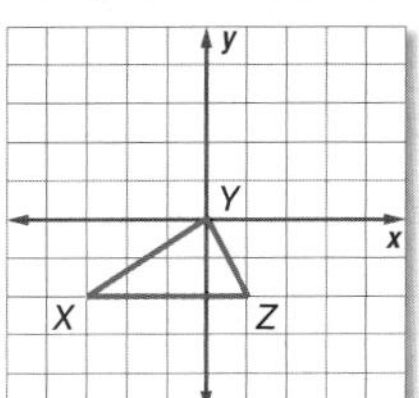

39. WRITING IN MATH Do any points remain invariant under glide reflections? under compositions of transformations? Explain. **See Ch. 9 Answer Appendix.**

40. CHALLENGE If $PQRS$ is translated along ⟨3, −2⟩, reflected in $y = -1$, and rotated 90° about the origin, what are the coordinates of $P'''Q'''R'''S'''$?
$P'''(1, -2)$, $Q'''(2, 1)$, $R'''(-1, 3)$, $S'''(-2, 0)$

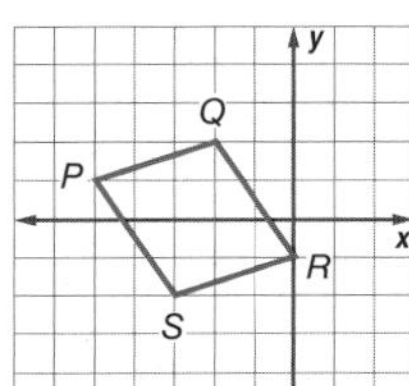

41. CCSS ARGUMENTS If an image is to be reflected in the line $y = x$ and the x-axis, does the order of the reflections affect the final image? Explain. **See margin.**

42. OPEN ENDED Write a glide reflection or composition of transformations that can be used to transform $\triangle ABC$ to $\triangle DEF$.

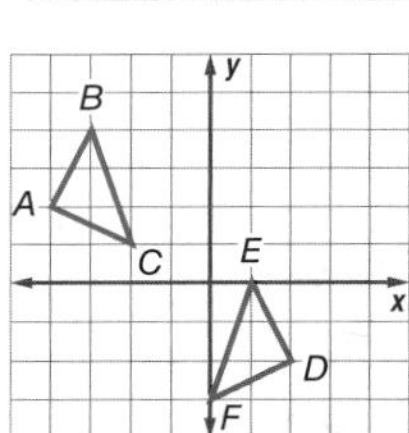

42. Sample answer: $\triangle ABC$ can be translated along ⟨0, −4⟩ and reflected in $x = -1$ to form $\triangle DEF$.

43. REASONING When two rotations are performed on a single image, does the order of the rotations *sometimes*, *always*, or *never* affect the location of the final image? Explain. **See margin.**

44. WRITING IN MATH Compare and contrast glide reflections and compositions of transformations. **See margin.**

Follow-up

Students have explored reflections, translations, rotations, and compositions of transformations.

Ask:

- How are all congruence transformations related? Sample answer: Rotations and translations can be defined in terms of compositions of two or more reflections.

Standardized Test Practice

45. $\triangle ABC$ is translated along the vector $\langle -2, 3\rangle$ and then reflected in the x-axis. What are the coordinates of A' after the transformation? **A**

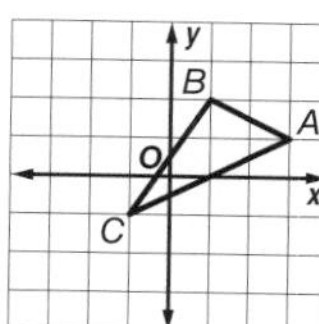

A $(1, -4)$
B $(1, 4)$
C $(-1, 4)$
D $(-1, -4)$

46. SHORT RESPONSE What are the coordinates of D'' if $\overline{CD}$ with vertices $C(2, 4)$ and $D(8, 7)$ is translated along $\langle -6, 2\rangle$ and then reflected over the y-axis? **(−2, 9)**

47. ALGEBRA Write $\dfrac{18x^2 - 2}{3x^2 - 5x - 2}$ in simplest terms. **H**

F $\dfrac{18}{3x + 1}$
G $\dfrac{2(3x + 1)}{x - 2}$
H $\dfrac{2(3x - 1)}{x - 2}$
J $2(3x - 1)$

48. SAT/ACT If $f(x) = x^3 - x^2 - x$, what is the value of $f(-3)$? **B**

A −39
B −33
C −21
D −15
E −12

Spiral Review

Copy each polygon and point X. Then use a protractor and ruler to draw the specified rotation of each figure about point X. (Lesson 9-3) **49–51. See margin.**

49. 60°

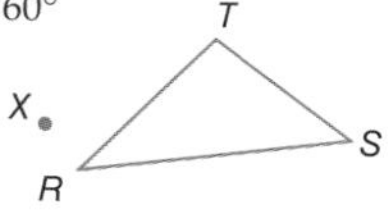

50. 120°

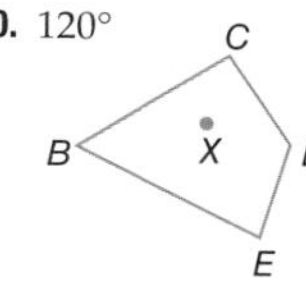

51. 180°

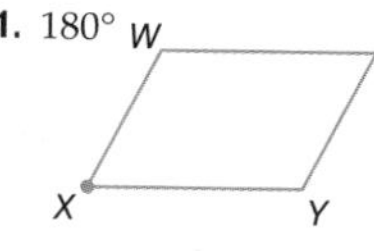

Graph each figure and its image along the given vector. (Lesson 9-2) **52–53. See margin.**

52. $\triangle FGH$ with vertices $F(1, -4)$, $G(3, -1)$, and $H(7, -1)$; $\langle 2, 6\rangle$

53. quadrilateral $ABCD$ with vertices $A(-2, 7)$, $B(-1, 4)$, $C(2, 3)$, and $D(2, 7)$; $\langle -3, -5\rangle$

54. AVIATION A jet is flying northwest, and its velocity is represented by $\langle -450, 450\rangle$ miles per hour. The wind is from the west, and its velocity is represented by $\langle 100, 0\rangle$ miles per hour. (Lesson 8-7)

a. Find the resultant vector for the jet in component form. **⟨−350, 450⟩ mph**

b. Find the magnitude of the resultant. **about 570 mph**

c. Find the direction of the resultant. **52.1° north of west**

Skills Review

Each figure shows a preimage and its reflected image in some line. Copy each figure and draw the line of reflection. **55–57. See margin.**

55.

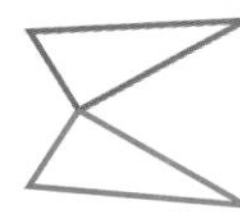

56.

57.

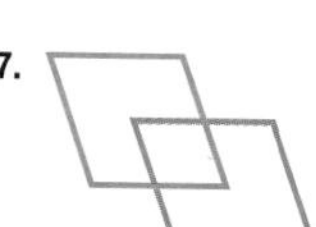

55.

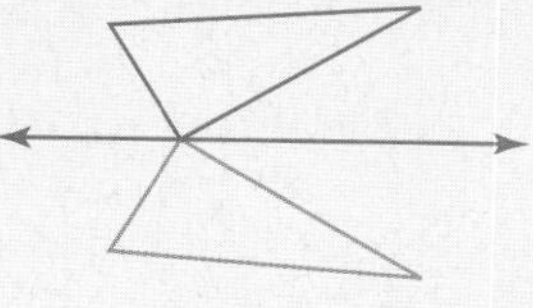

56.

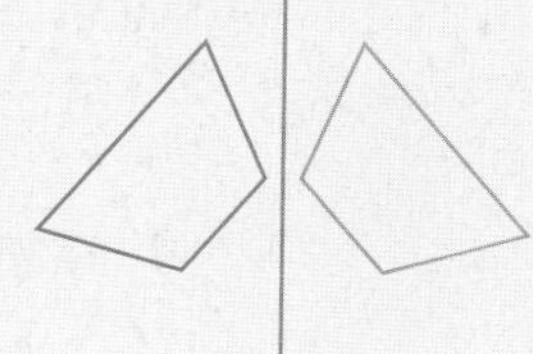

57.

CCSS Teaching the Mathematical Practices

Arguments Mathematically proficient students understand and use stated assumptions and definitions in constructing arguments. They are able to analyze situations by breaking them into cases, and can recognize and use counterexamples. In Exercise 41, encourage students to perform the composition of transformations on a figure twice, reversing the order the second time.

4 Assess

Yesterday's News Have students write about how what they learned about single transformations has helped them with composite transformations.

Additional Answers

49.

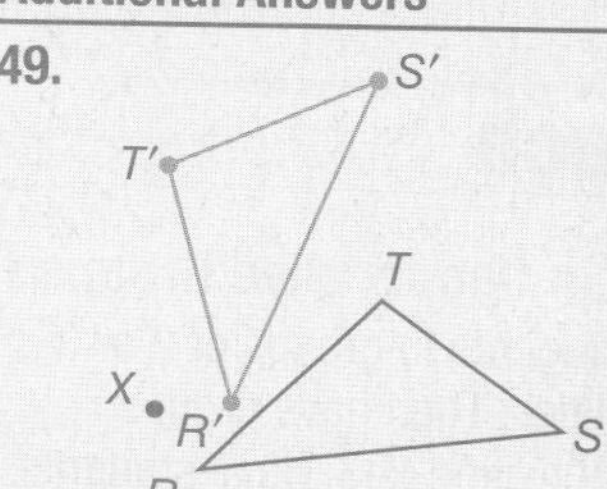
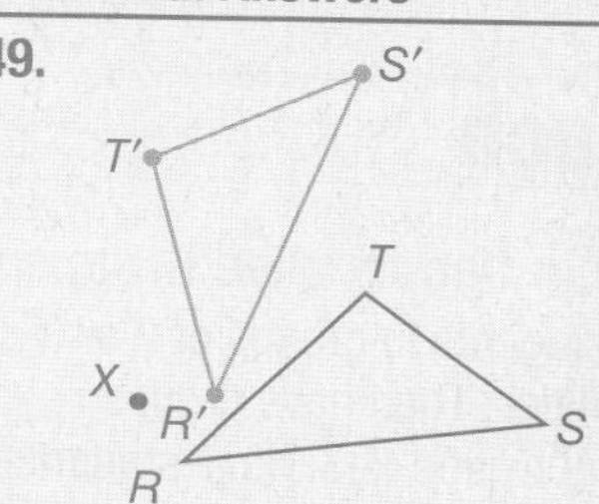
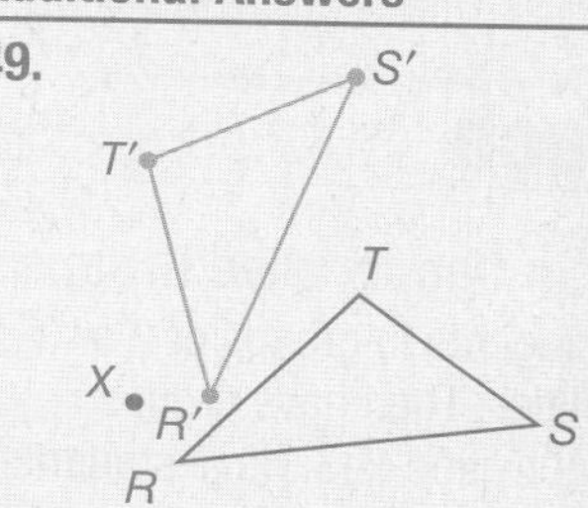

50.

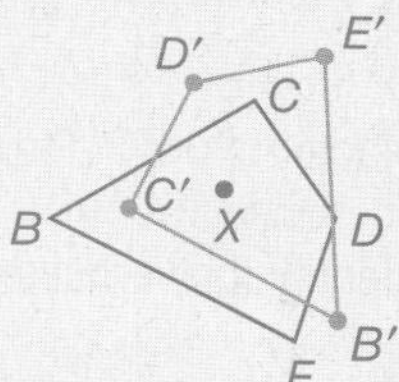
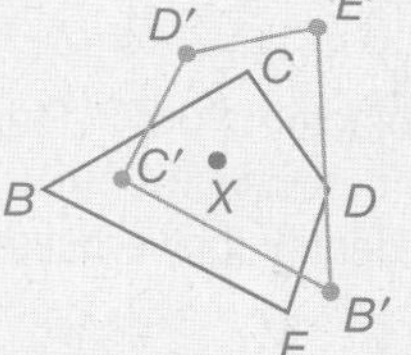
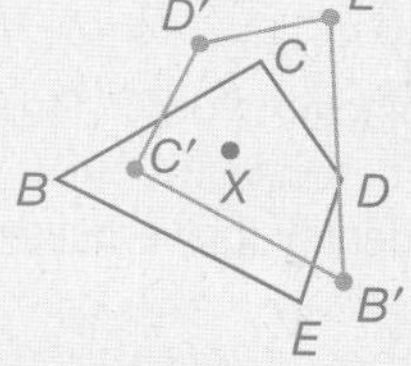

51.

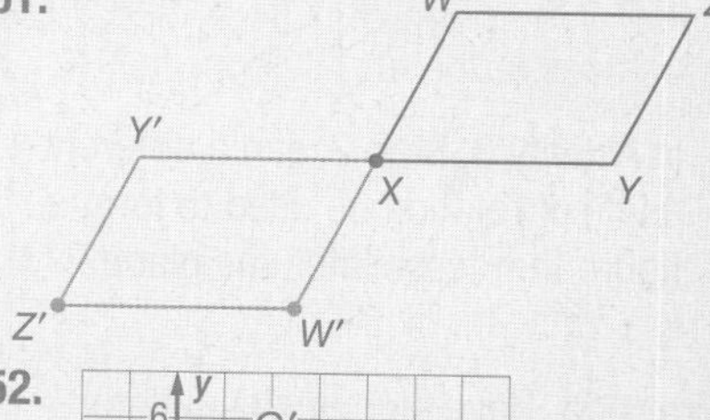

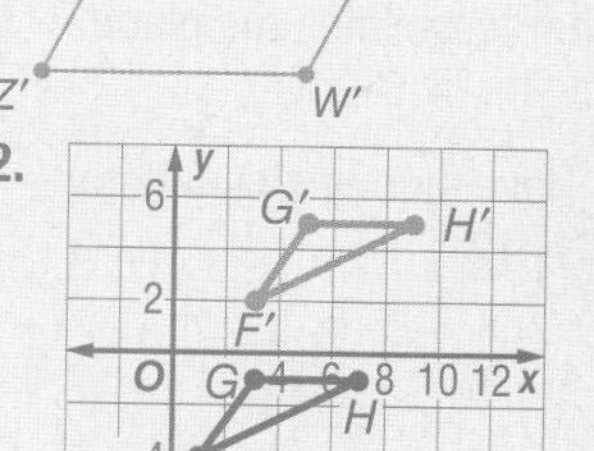
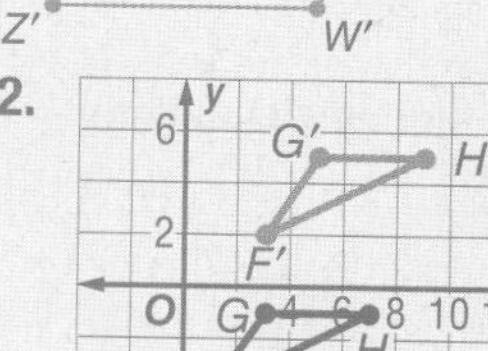

52.

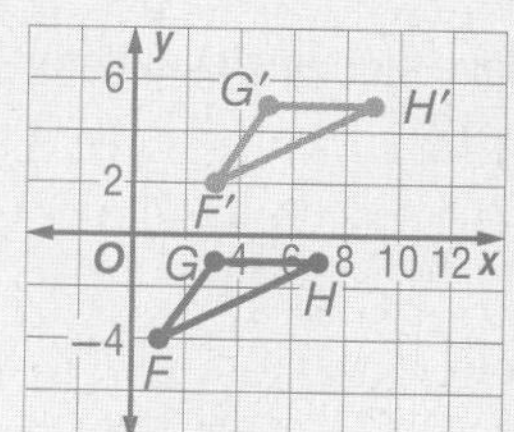

53.

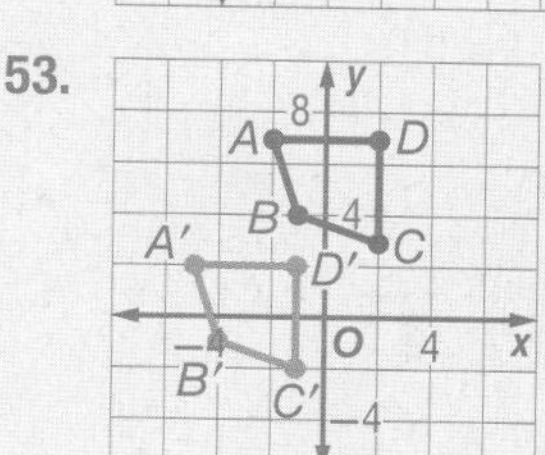
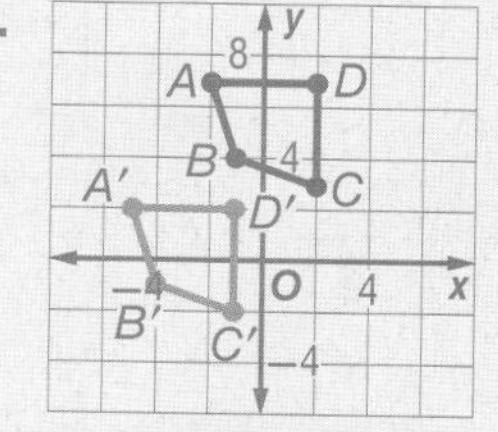

1 Focus

Objectives

- Identify regular tessellations.
- Create tessellations with and without technology.

Materials for Each Group

- Geometer's Sketchpad Software
- straightedge

Teaching Tip

Students may have difficulty completing this lab in one class session, particularly if they are not familiar with Geometer's Sketchpad. Consider devoting two class sessions to this Geometry Lab.

2 Teach

Working in Cooperative Groups

Organize students in groups of 2 or 3, mixing abilities. Then have groups complete Activities 1–3. Have students complete Activity 4 individually.

Ask:

- Why is 120 a factor of 360? 120 is a factor of 360 because 120(3) = 360.
- How do you identify the vertices of a tessellation? Identify the polygon being tessellated; the vertices of each of the individual polygons are also vertices of the tessellation.
- In Activity 3, Step 2, can a different angle of rotation be used to form a figure that tessellates the plane? No; the triangles would overlap.

Practice Have students complete Exercises 1–12.

EXTEND 9-4

Geometry Lab: Tessellations

A **tessellation** is a pattern of one or more figures that covers a plane so that there are no overlapping or empty spaces. The sum of the angles around the vertex of a tessellation is 360°.

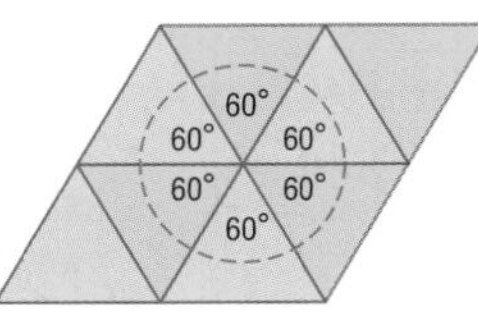
60°
60°
60°
60°
60°
60°

A **regular tessellation** is formed by only one type of regular polygon. A regular polygon will tessellate if it has an interior angle measure that is a factor of 360. A **semi-regular tessellation** is formed by two or more regular polygons.

Activity 1 Regular Tessellation

Determine whether each regular polygon will tessellate in the plane. Explain.

a. hexagon

Let x represent the measure of an interior angle of a regular hexagon.

$$x = \frac{180(n-2)}{n} \quad \text{Interior Angle Formula}$$
$$= \frac{180(6-2)}{6} \quad n = 6$$
$$= 120 \quad \text{Simplify.}$$

Since 120 is a factor of 360, a regular hexagon will tessellate in the plane.

b. decagon

Let x represent the measure of an interior angle of a regular decagon.

$$x = \frac{180(n-2)}{n} \quad \text{Interior Angle Formula}$$
$$= \frac{180(10-2)}{10} \quad n = 10$$
$$= 144 \quad \text{Simplify.}$$

Since 144 is not a factor of 360, a regular decagon will not tessellate in the plane.

A tessellation is **uniform** if it contains the same arrangement of shapes and angles at each vertex.

Uniform

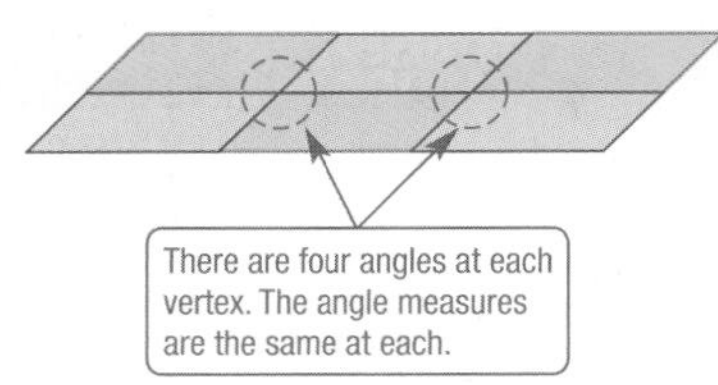
There are four angles at each vertex. The angle measures are the same at each.

Not Uniform

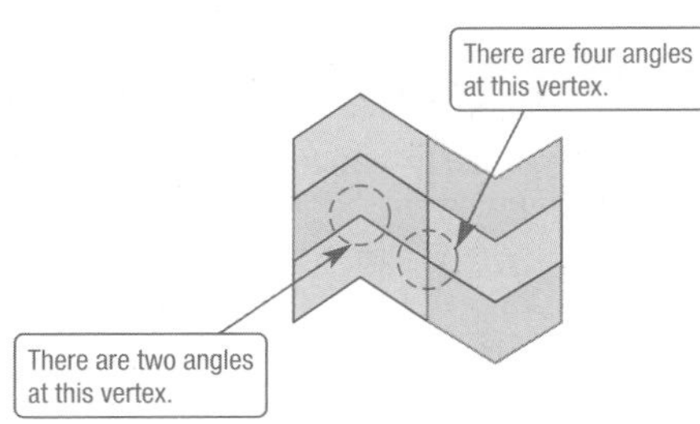
There are four angles at this vertex.
There are two angles at this vertex.

Activity 2 Classify Tessellations

Determine whether each pattern is a tessellation. If so, describe it as *regular*, *semi-regular*, or *neither* and *uniform* or *not uniform*.

a. 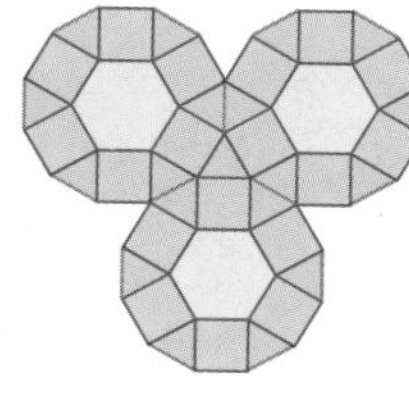

There is no unfilled space, and none of the figures overlap, so the pattern is a **tessellation**.

The tessellation consists of regular hexagons, squares and equilateral triangles, so it is **semi-regular**.

There are four angles around some of the vertices and five around others, so it is **not uniform**.

b. 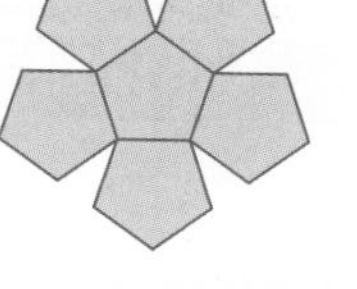

There is unfilled space, so the pattern is a **not a tessellation**.

c.

There is no unfilled space, and none of the figures overlap, so the pattern is a **tessellation**.

The tessellation consists of trapezoids, which are not regular polygons, so it is **neither** regular nor semi-regular.

There are four angles around each of the vertices and the angle measures are the same at each vertex, so it is **uniform**.

You can use the properties of tessellations to design and create tessellations.

Activity 3 Draw a Tessellation

Draw a triangle and use it to create a tessellation.

Step 1 Draw a triangle and find the midpoint of one side.

Step 2 Rotate the triangle 180° about the point.

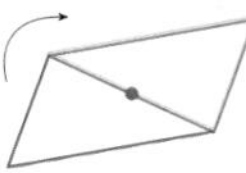

Step 3 Translate the pair of triangles to make a row.

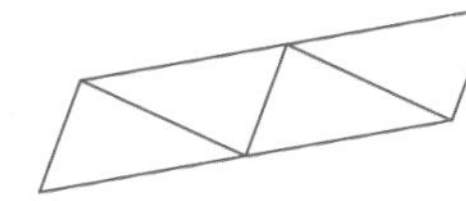

Step 4 Translate the row to make a tessellation.

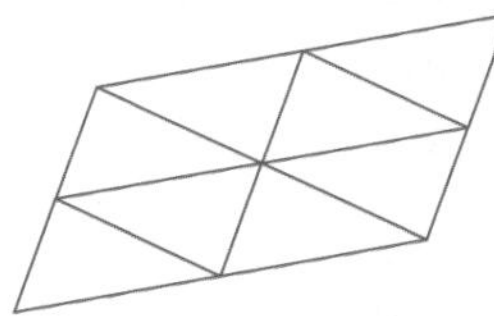

Focus on Mathematical Content

Irregular Figures It is possible for nonregular figures to tessellate. These figures are classified as neither regular nor semiregulr.

connectED.mcgraw-hill.com 661

3 Assess

Formative Assessment

Use Exercises 1–6 to assess whether students comprehend the properties of tessellations.

From Concrete to Abstract

Have students write an algebraic equation that uses n, the number of sides of a polygon, to explicitly determine whether a polygon tessellates a plane. For example, $\dfrac{360}{\dfrac{180(n-2)}{n}} = \dfrac{2n}{n-2}$, so if x is a whole number and $x = \dfrac{2n}{n-2}$, then the polygon with n sides tessellates the plane.

Additional Answers

1. Yes; sample answer: The interior angle measure of an equilateral triangle is 60°, which is a factor of 360.
2. No; sample answer: The interior angle measure of a regular pentagon is 108°, which is not a factor of 360.
3. No; sample answer: The interior angle measure of a regular 16-gon is 157.5°, which is not a factor of 360.
7. Sample answer:

8. Sample answer:

Geometry Lab
Tessellations *Continued*

Activity 4 Tessellations using Technology

Use Geometer's Sketchpad to create a tessellation.

Step 1 Insert three points and construct a line through two of the points. Then construct the line parallel to the first line through the third point using the **Parallel Line** option from the **Construct** menu. Complete the parallelogram and label the points A, B, C, and D. Hide the lines.

Step 2 Insert another point E on the exterior of the parallelogram. Draw the segments between A and B, B and E, E and C, and C and D.

Step 3 Highlight B and then A. From the **Transform** menu, choose **Mark Vector**. Select the $\overline{BE}$, $\overline{EC}$, and point E. From the **Transform** menu, choose **Translate**.

Step 4 Starting with A, select all of the vertices around the perimeter of the polygon. Choose **Hexagon Interior** from the **Construct** menu.

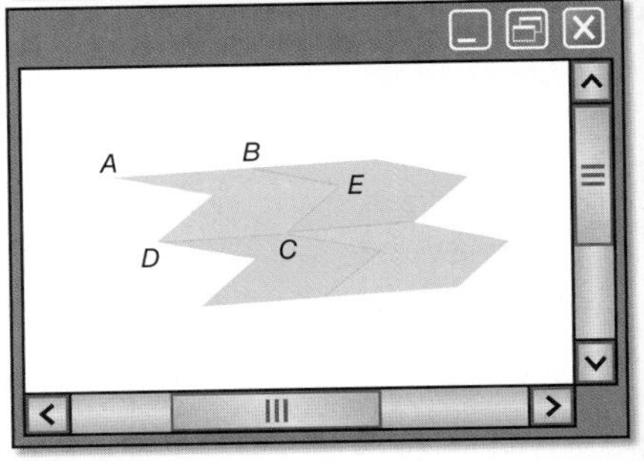

Step 5 Choose point A and then point B and mark the vector as you did in Step 3. Select the interior of the polygon and choose **Translate** from the **Transform** menu. Continue the tessellation by marking vectors and translating the polygon. You can choose **Color** from the **Display** menu to create a color pattern.

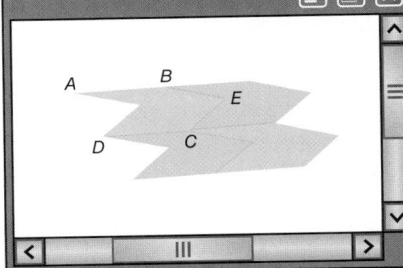

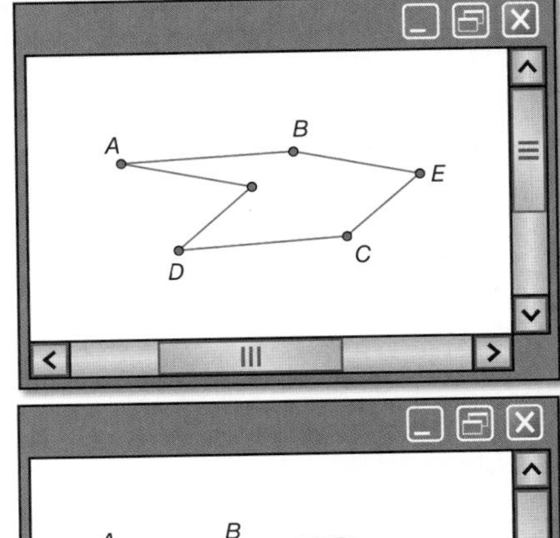

Exercises

Determine whether each regular polygon will tessellate in the plane. Write *yes* or *no*. Explain. 1–3. See margin.

1. triangle
2. pentagon
3. 16-gon

Determine whether each pattern is a tessellation. Write *yes* or *no*. If so, describe it as *regular*, *semi-regular*, or *neither* and *uniform* or *not uniform*.

4. 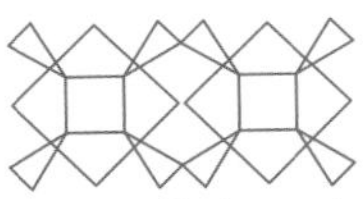 no
5. 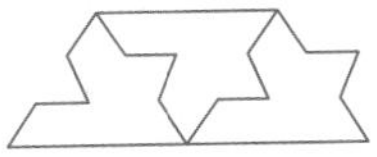 yes; neither; not uniform
6. yes; regular; uniform

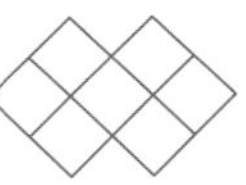

Draw a tessellation using the following shape(s). 7–10. See margin.

7. octagon and square
8. hexagon and triangle
9. right triangle
10. trapezoid and a parallelogram
11. **WRITING IN MATH** Find examples of the use of tessellations in architecture, mosaics, and artwork. For each example, explain how tessellations were used. See students' work.
12. **MAKE A CONJECTURE** Describe a figure that you think will tessellate in three-dimensional space. Explain your reasoning. See margin.

9. Sample answer:

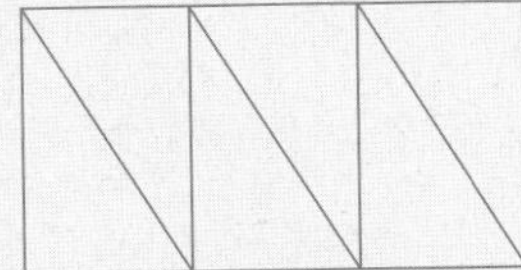

10. Sample answer:

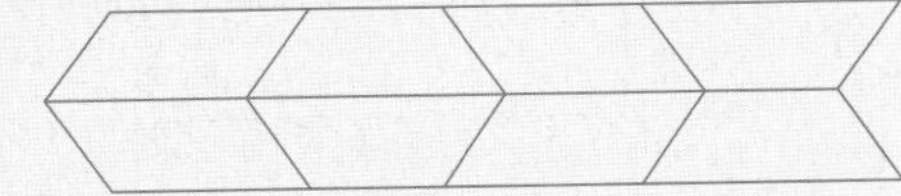

12. Sample answer: I think an equilateral triangular prism will tessellate because equilateral triangles tessellate in the plane and stacking prisms will not leave unfilled space.

LESSON 9-5 Symmetry

Then
- You drew reflections and rotations of figures.

Now
1. Identify line and rotational symmetries in two-dimensional figures.
2. Identify plane and axis symmetries in three-dimensional figures.

Why?
- In the animal kingdom, the symmetry of an animal's body is often an indication of the animal's complexity. Animals displaying line symmetry, such as insects, are usually more complex life forms than those displaying rotational symmetry, like a jellyfish.

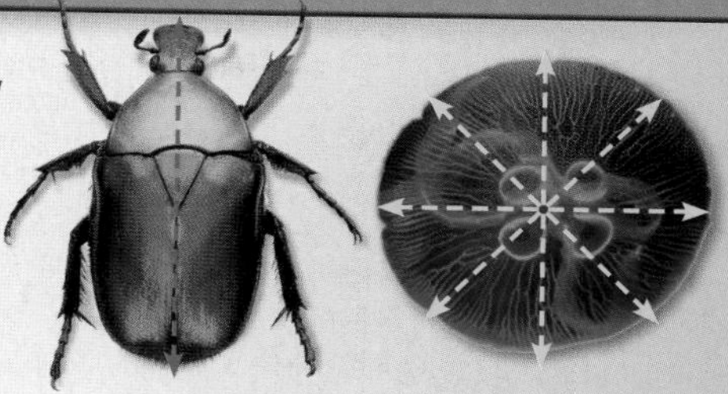

NewVocabulary
symmetry
line symmetry
line of symmetry
rotational symmetry
center of symmetry
order of symmetry
magnitude of symmetry
plane symmetry
axis symmetry

Common Core State Standards

Content Standards
G.CO.3 Given a rectangle, parallelogram, trapezoid, or regular polygon, describe the rotations and reflections that carry it onto itself.

Mathematical Practices
4 Model with mathematics.
8 Look for and express regularity in repeated reasoning.

1 Symmetry in Two-Dimensional Figures

A figure has **symmetry** if there exists a rigid motion—reflection, translation, rotation, or glide reflection—that maps the figure onto itself. One type of symmetry is line symmetry.

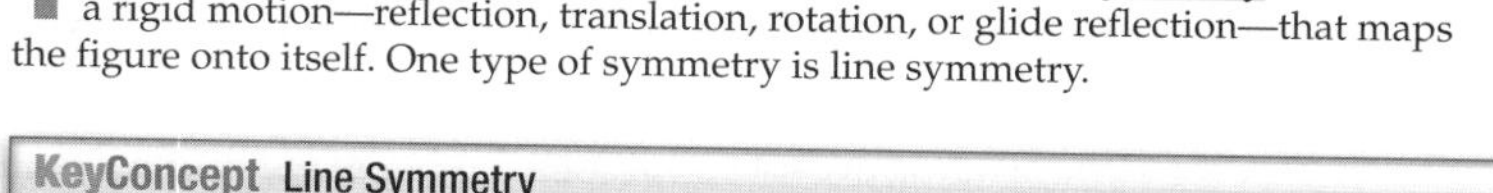

KeyConcept Line Symmetry

A figure in the plane has **line symmetry** (or *reflection symmetry*) if the figure can be mapped onto itself by a reflection in a line, called a **line of symmetry** (or *axis of symmetry*).

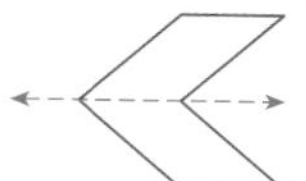

Real-World Example 1 Identify Line Symmetry

BEACHES State whether the object appears to have line symmetry. Write *yes* or *no*. If so, copy the figure, draw all lines of symmetry, and state their number.

a. 

Yes; the crab has one line of symmetry.

b. 

Yes; the starfish has five lines of symmetry.

c. 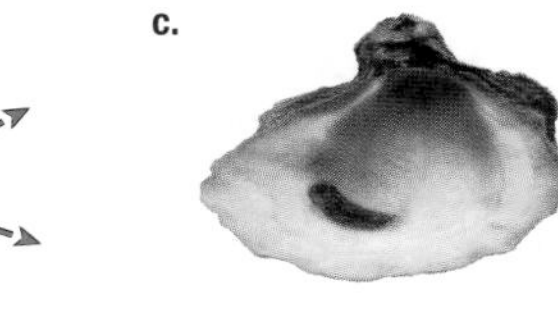

No; there is no line in which the oyster shell can be reflected so that it maps onto itself.

GuidedPractice 1B–C. See Ch. 9 Answer Appendix.

State whether the figure has line symmetry. Write *yes* or *no*. If so, copy the figure, draw all lines of symmetry, and state their number.

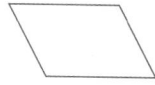

1A.  no

1B. 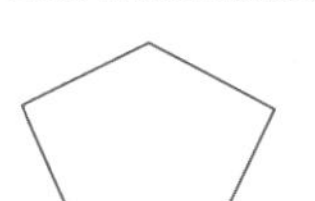

1C. 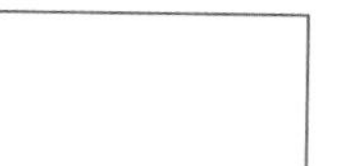

1 Focus

VerticalAlignment

Before Lesson 9-5 Draw reflections and rotations of figures.

Lesson 9-5 Identify line and rotational symmetries in two-dimensional and three-dimensional figures.

After Lesson 9-5 Use congruence transformations to make conjectures and justify properties of geometric figures including figures on a coordinate plane.

2 Teach

Scaffold Questioning

Have students read the **Why?** section of the lesson.

Ask:
- Use the picture of the beetle to conjecture about what bilateral symmetry means. Check students' responses.
- Use the picture of the jellyfish to conjecture about what radial symmetry means. Check students' responses.
- Human beings have what type of symmetry? bilateral symmetry

Lesson 9-5 Resources

Resource	Approaching Level AL	On Level OL	Beyond Level BL	English Learners ELL
Teacher Edition	▪ Differentiated Instruction, p. 665	▪ Differentiated Instruction, p. 665		▪ Differentiated Instruction, p. 665
Chapter Resource Masters	▪ Study Guide and Intervention, pp. 31–32 ▪ Skills Practice, p. 33 ▪ Practice, p. 34 ▪ Word Problem Practice, p. 35	▪ Study Guide and Intervention, pp. 31–32 ▪ Skills Practice, p. 33 ▪ Practice, p. 34 ▪ Word Problem Practice, p. 35 ▪ Enrichment, p. 36	▪ Practice, p. 34 ▪ Word Problem Practice, p. 35 ▪ Enrichment, p. 36	▪ Study Guide and Intervention, pp. 31–32 ▪ Skills Practice, p. 33 ▪ Practice, p. 34 ▪ Word Problem Practice, p. 35
Other	▪ 5-Minute Check 9-5 ▪ Study Notebook	▪ 5-Minute Check 9-5 ▪ Study Notebook	▪ 5-Minute Check 9-5 ▪ Study Notebook	▪ 5-Minute Check 9-5 ▪ Study Notebook

1 Symmetry in Two-Dimensional Figures

Examples 1 and 2 show how to determine whether a figure has line symmetry and/or rotational symmetry.

Formative Assessment

Use the Guided Practice exercises after each Example to determine students' understanding of concepts.

Additional Example

1 **KALEIDOSCOPES** State whether the object appears to have line symmetry. Write yes or no. If so, copy the figure, draw all lines of symmetry, and state their number.

a.

yes

b.

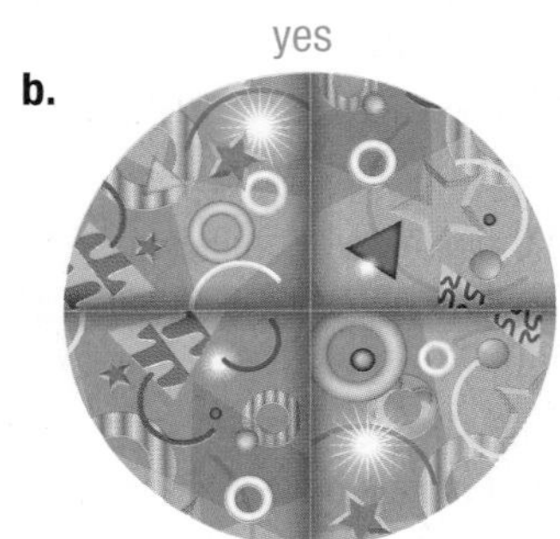

no

c.

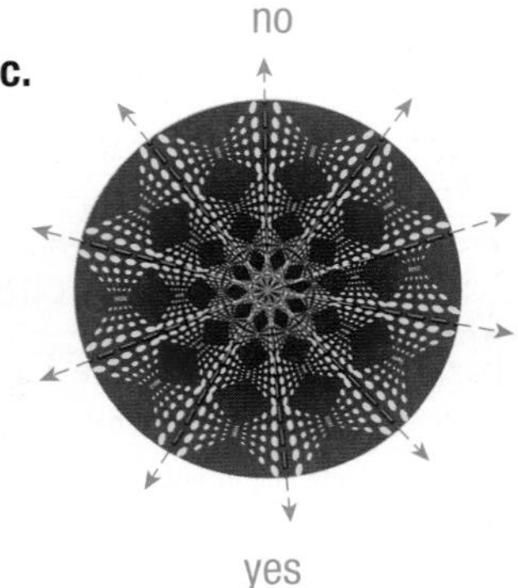

yes

Additional Examples also in Interactive Classroom PowerPoint® Presentations

IWB Interactive White Board READY

Another type of symmetry is rotational symmetry.

KeyConcept Rotational Symmetry

A figure in the plane has **rotational symmetry** (or *radial symmetry*) if the figure can be mapped onto itself by a rotation between 0° and 360° about the center of the figure, called the **center of symmetry** (or *point of symmetry*).

Examples The figure below has rotational symmetry because a rotation of 90°, 180°, or 270° maps the figure onto itself.

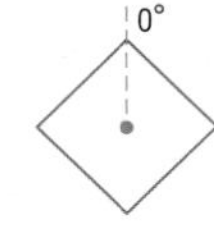

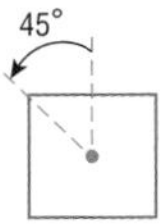

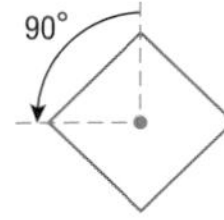

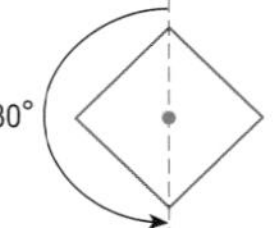

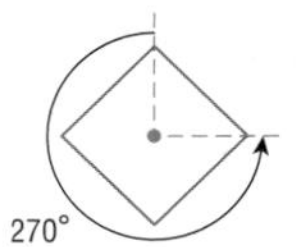

The number of times a figure maps onto itself as it rotates from 0° to 360° is called the **order of symmetry**. The **magnitude of symmetry** (or angle of rotation) is the smallest angle through which a figure can be rotated so that it maps onto itself. The order and magnitude of a rotation are related by the following equation.

$$\text{magnitude} = 360° \div \text{order}$$

The figure above has rotational symmetry of order 4 and magnitude 90°.

Example 2 Identify Rotational Symmetry

State whether the figure has rotational symmetry. Write *yes* or *no*. If so, copy the figure, locate the center of symmetry, and state the order and magnitude of symmetry.

a.

Yes; the regular hexagon has order 6 rotational symmetry and magnitude 360° ÷ 6 or 60°. The center is the intersection of the diagonals.

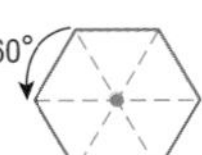

b.

No; no rotation between 0° and 360° maps the right triangle onto itself.

c.

Yes; the figure has order 2 rotational symmetry and magnitude 360° ÷ 2 or 180°. The center is the intersection of the diagonals.

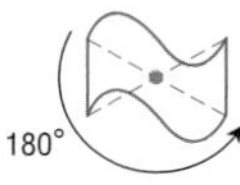

StudyTip

Point Symmetry A figure has *point symmetry* if the figure can be mapped onto itself by a rotation of 180°. A playing card exhibits point symmetry. It looks the same right-side up as upside down.

GuidedPractice

FLOWERS **State whether the flower appears to have rotational symmetry. Write *yes* or *no*. If so, copy the flower, locate the center of symmetry, and state the order and magnitude of symmetry.** 2A–C. See Ch. 9 Answer Appendix.

2A.

2B.

2C.

Tips for New Teachers

Sense-Making Alert students that they are asked whether a figure "appears to have symmetry" because many objects that seem to have symmetry, like a human face, are not actually symmetric when the strict mathematical definition is applied.

Follow-up

Students have explored reflections, translations, rotations, compositions of transformations, and symmetry.

Ask:

- How are transformations and symmetry related? Sample answer: The symmetry of a figure can be confirmed using congruence transformations.

2 Symmetry in Three-Dimensional Figures

Three-dimensional figures can also have symmetry.

KeyConcept Three-Dimensional Symmetries

Plane Symmetry

A three-dimensional figure has **plane symmetry** if the figure can be mapped onto itself by a reflection in a plane.

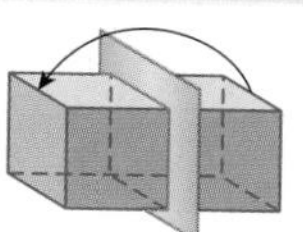

Axis Symmetry

A three-dimensional figure has **axis symmetry** if the figure can be mapped onto itself by a rotation between 0° and 360° in a line.

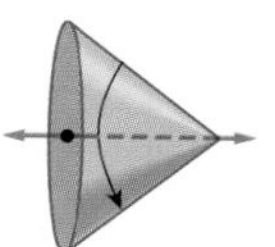

Example 3 Three-Dimensional Symmetry

State whether the figure has *plane* symmetry, *axis* symmetry, *both*, or *neither*.

a. L-shaped prism

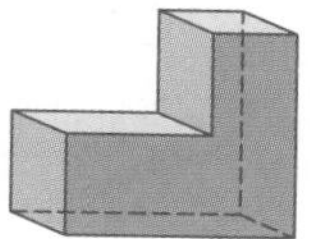

plane symmetry

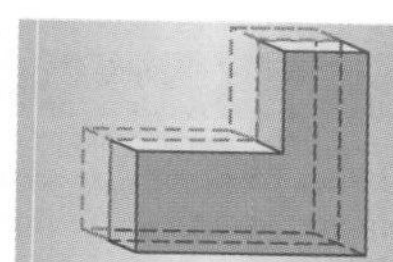

b. regular pentagonal prism

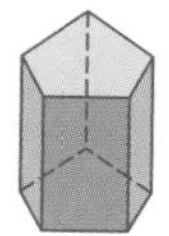

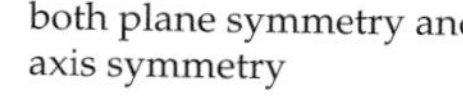

both plane symmetry and axis symmetry

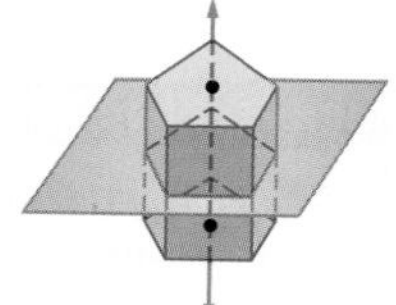

ReviewVocabulary

prism a polyhedron with two parallel congruent bases connected by parallelogram faces

GuidedPractice

SPORTS **State whether each piece of sports equipment appears to have *plane* symmetry, *axis* symmetry, *both*, or *neither* (ignoring the equipment's stitching or markings).**

3A.  both

3B.  neither

3C.  plane

3D.  both

Real-WorldLink

Aerodynamically designed to spin after it is thrown, a football's shape is that of a prolate spheroid. This means that one axis of symmetry is longer than its other axes.

Source: *Complete Idiot's Guide to Football*

Additional Example

2 State whether the figure has rotational symmetry. Write yes or no. If so, copy the figure, locate the center of symmetry, and state the order and magnitude of symmetry.

a.

The center of the star is the center of rotation. The order is 5 and the magnitude is 72°.

b.

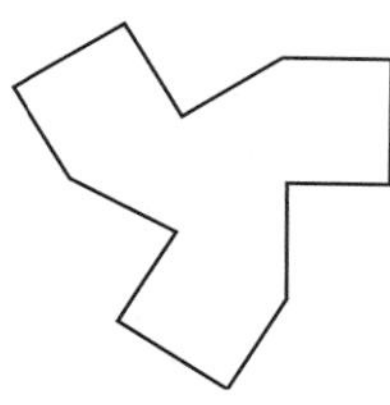

The center of the propeller is the center of rotation. The order is 3 and the magnitude is 120°.

c.

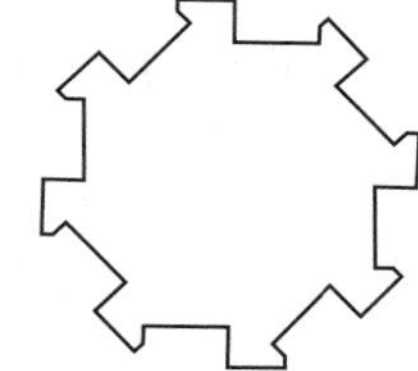

The center of the gear is the center of rotation. The order is 8 and the magnitude is 45°.

DifferentiatedInstruction

Naturalist Learners There are many examples of objects in nature that have symmetry. Have students draw or gather examples of objects in nature for each of the types of symmetry discussed in this lesson.

2 Symmetry in Three-Dimensional Figures

Example 3 shows how to determine whether a figure has plane symmetry or axis symmetry.

Additional Example

3 State whether the figure has *plane* symmetry, *axis* symmetry, *both*, or *neither*.

a.

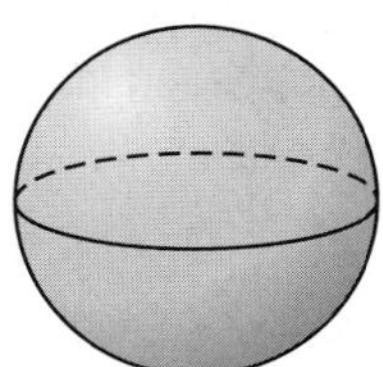

both plane and axis symmetry

b.

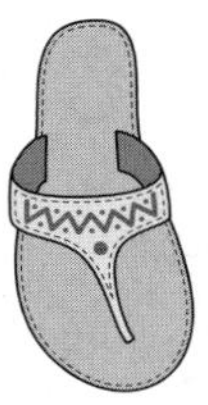

neither plane or axis symmetry

3 Practice

Formative Assessment

Use Exercises 1–8 to check for understanding.

Then use the chart at the bottom of this page to customize assignments for your students.

Exercise Alert

Patty Paper It may be helpful for students to have tracing paper or patty paper for Exercises 9–14, 18–23.

Additional Answers

1. yes; 4

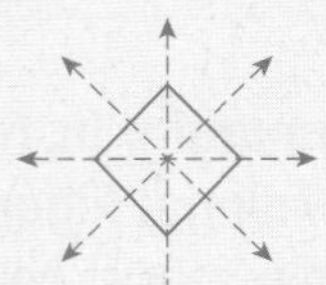

3. yes; 1

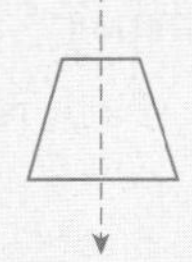

5. yes; 2; 180°

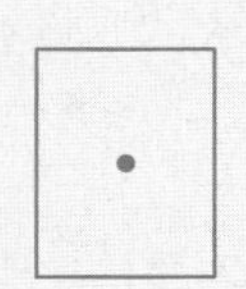

Check Your Understanding

 = Step-by-Step Solutions begin on page R14.

Example 1

State whether the figure appears to have line symmetry. Write *yes* or *no*. If so, copy the figure, draw all lines of symmetry, and state their number.

1. 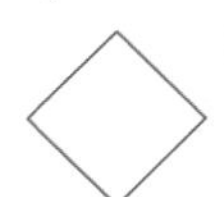 See margin.

2. 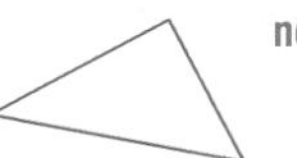 no

3. 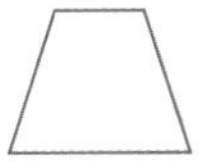 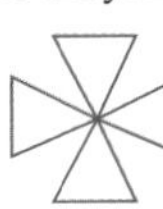 See margin.

Example 2

State whether the figure has rotational symmetry. Write *yes* or *no*. If so, copy the figure, locate the center of symmetry, and state the order and magnitude of symmetry.

4. 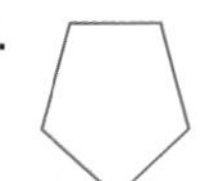 no

5.  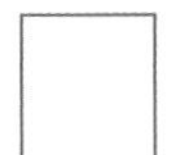 See margin.

6. See Ch. 9 Answer Appendix.

Examples 2–3

7. **U.S. CAPITOL** Completed in 1863, the dome is one of the most recent additions to the United States Capitol. It is supported by 36 iron ribs and has 108 windows, divided equally among three levels.

a. Excluding the spire of the dome, how many horizontal and vertical planes of symmetry does the dome appear to have? no horizontal; 36 vertical

b. Does the dome have axis symmetry? If so, state the order and magnitude of symmetry. yes; 36; 10°

Example 3

8. State whether the figure has *plane* symmetry, *axis* symmetry, *both*, or *neither*. both

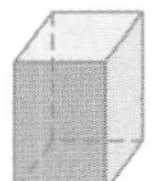

Practice and Problem Solving

Extra Practice is on page R9.

Example 1

CCSS REGULARITY State whether the figure appears to have line symmetry. Write *yes* or *no*. If so, copy the figure, draw all lines of symmetry, and state their number.

10–13. See Ch. 9 Answer Appendix.

9. 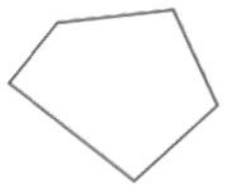 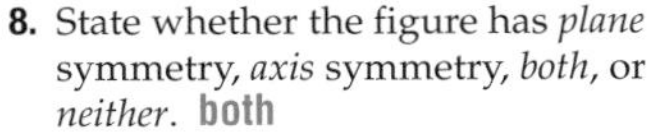 no

10. 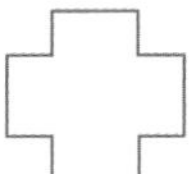

11. 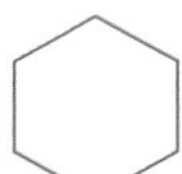

12. 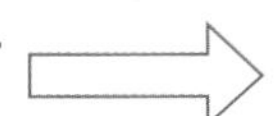

13. 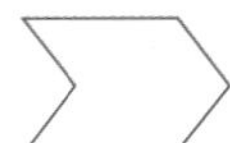

14. 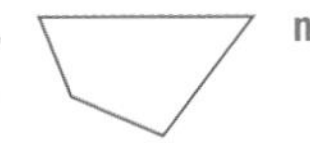 no

15. no

16–17. See Ch. 9 Answer Appendix.

FLAGS State whether each flag design appears to have line symmetry. Write *yes* or *no*. If so, copy the flag, draw all lines of symmetry, and state their number.

15. 

16. 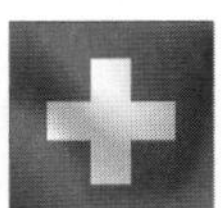

17. 

Differentiated Homework Options

Level	Assignment	Two-Day Option	
AL Basic	9–30, 46, 48–61	9–29 odd, 51–54	10–30 even, 46, 48–50, 55–61
OL Core	9–33 odd, 34, 35–45 odd, 46, 48–61	9–30, 51–54	31–46, 48–50, 55–61
BL Advanced	31–58, (optional: 59–61)		

Example 2 State whether the figure has rotational symmetry. Write *yes* or *no*. If so, copy the figure, locate the center of symmetry, and state the order and magnitude of symmetry.

18, 19, 22, 23. See Ch. 9 Answer Appendix.

18.

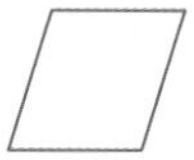

19.

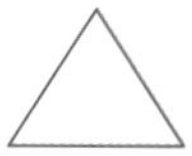

20. no

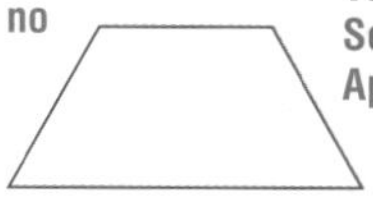

21.  no

22.

23.

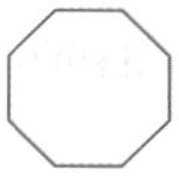

Example 2 **WHEELS** State whether each wheel cover appears to have rotational symmetry. Write *yes* or *no*. If so, state the order and magnitude of symmetry.

24.

25.

26.

24. yes; 5; 72°
25. yes; 8; 45°
26. yes; 10; 36°

Example 3 State whether the figure has *plane* symmetry, *axis* symmetry, *both*, or *neither*.

27. 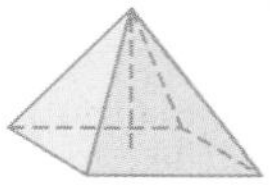 both

28. 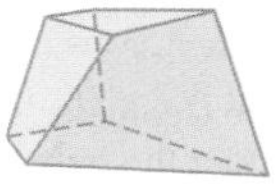 neither

29. 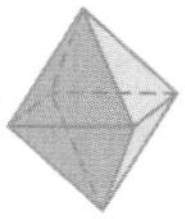 both

30. 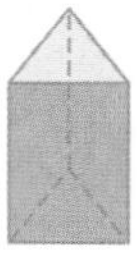 both

B **CONTAINERS** Determine the number of horizontal and vertical planes of symmetry for each container shown below.

31.  no horizontal, infinitely many vertical

32. 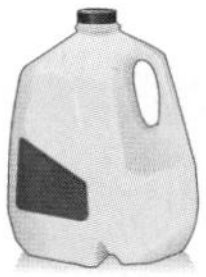 no horizontal, 1 vertical

33.  1 horizontal, infinitely many vertical

34. **CCSS MODELING** Symmetry is an important component of photography. Photographers often use reflection in water to create symmetry in photos. The photo at the right is a long exposure shot of the Eiffel tower reflected in a pool. **a–b. See Ch. 9 Answer Appendix.**

a. Describe the two-dimensional symmetry created by the photo.

b. Is three-dimensional symmetry applicable? Explain your reasoning.

CCSS Teaching the Mathematical Practices

Regularity Mathematically proficient students maintain oversight of the process, while attending to the details. They continually evaluate the reasonableness of their intermediate results. In Exercises 9–14, encourage students to check the reasonableness of their results.

Enrichment

OL BL

NAME ______ DATE ______ PERIOD ______

9-5 Enrichment

Symmetry in Quadrilaterals

Different types of quadrilaterals have different numbers of lines of symmetry. Did you know that the only quadrilateral with exactly four lines of symmetry is a square? You can define quadrilaterals by the number of lines of symmetry they contain.

All rectangles that are not squares have exactly two lines of symmetry.

All isosceles trapezoids have exactly one line of symmetry.

Study Guide and Intervention

AL OL ELL

NAME ______ DATE ______ PERIOD ______

9-5 Study Guide and Intervention

Symmetry

Symmetry In Two-Dimensional Figures A two-dimensional figure has **line symmetry** if the figure can be mapped onto itself by a reflection in a line called the **line of symmetry**. A figure in a plane has **rotational symmetry** if the figure can be mapped onto itself by a rotation between 0° and 360° about the center of the figure, called the **center of symmetry**.

Example 1 State whether the figure appears to have line symmetry. If so, draw all lines of symmetry, and state their number.

The heart has line symmetry. It has one line of symmetry.

Example 2 State whether the figure appears to have rotational symmetry. If so, locate the center of symmetry and state the order and magnitude of symmetry.

The figure has rotational symmetry. The figure has order 4 symmetry and magnitude of 360 ÷ 4 or 90°. The center of symmetry is the intersection of the diagonals.

Exercises

State whether the figure appears to have line symmetry. Write *yes* or *no*. If so, draw all lines of symmetry and state their number.

1.

2.

3.

State whether the figure has rotational symmetry. Write *yes* or *no*. If so, locate the center of symmetry, and state the order and magnitude of symmetry.

4.

5.

6.

Lesson 9-5

Practice

AL OL BL ELL

NAME ______ DATE ______ PERIOD ______

9-5 Practice

Symmetry

State whether the figure has line symmetry. Write *yes* or *no*. If so, draw all lines of symmetry and state their number.

1.

2.

3.

State whether the figure has rotational symmetry. Write *yes* or *no*. If so, locate the center of symmetry and state the order and magnitude of symmetry.

4.

5.

6.

State whether the figure has *plane* symmetry, *axis* symmetry, *both*, or *neither*.

7.

8.

9. **STEAMBOATS** A paddle wheel on a steamboat is driven by a steam engine that rotates the paddles attached to the wheel to propel the boat through the water. If a paddle wheel consists of 18 evenly spaced paddles, identify the order and magnitude of its rotational symmetry.

Word Problem Practice

AL OL BL ELL

NAME ______ DATE ______ PERIOD ______

9-5 Word Problem Practice

Symmetry

1. **LETTERS** Examine each capital letter in the alphabet. Determine which letters have 180° rotational symmetry about a point in the center of the letter.

2. **POLYGONS** A regular polygon has rotational symmetry with an order of 5 and a magnitude of 72°. What is the figure?

3. **HUBCAPS** Steve found the hubcaps shown below at his local junkyard. Does each hubcap appear to have line symmetry?

4. **SYMMETRY** Martha made the figure shown. How many lines of symmetry does the figure have?

5. **PLACE SETTINGS** Kelly is designing how she wants to put the place settings for her party. She wants the tables to be set up symmetrically with the design that is on the table. First she places plates shown.

a. What is the order and magnitude of the rotational symmetry of the figure?

b. Make the least possible number of the additions of plates to the figure so that the table has rotational symmetry of order 4 around its center.

c. Is it possible to rearrange the locations of the 4 plates in the original figure so that (1) their distance from the center of the table does not change,(2) their centers remain somewhere on the rectangle design, and (3) the resulting figure has a rotational symmetry of order 4? If so, draw the figure. If not, explain why.

Lesson 9-5

Multiple Representations

Exercise 45 students use a table of values to investigate how the order of symmetry of a regular polygon relates to the number of sides of the polygon.

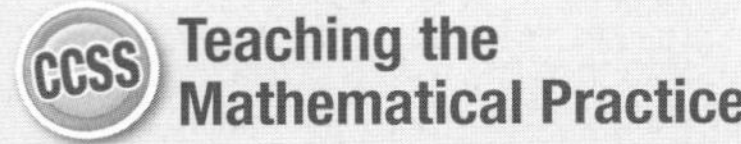

Teaching the Mathematical Practices

Critique Mathematically proficient students can distinguish correct logic from flawed reasoning. In Exercise 46, neither Jaime nor Jewel is correct. Students should recognize that Figure A has both line symmetry and rotational symmetry.

Additional Answers

39. rotational; 2; 180°; line symmetry; $y = -x$

$y = x$

40. line; $x = 0$

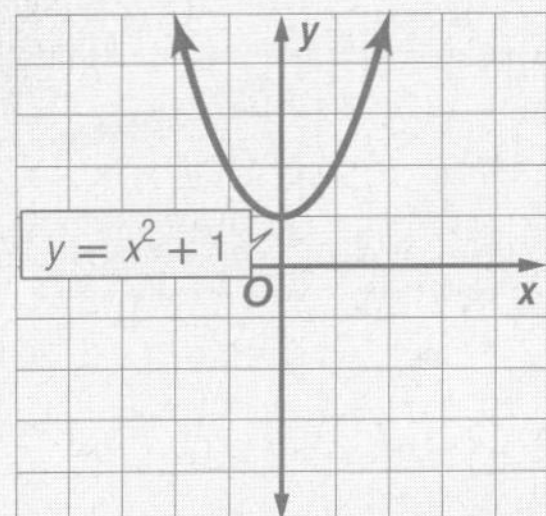

41. rotational; 2; 180°

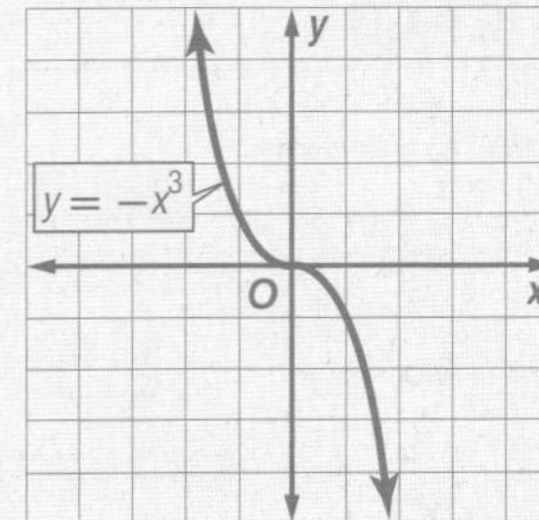

COORDINATE GEOMETRY **Determine whether the figure with the given vertices has *line* symmetry and/or *rotational* symmetry.**

35. $A(-4, 0)$, $B(0, 4)$, $C(4, 0)$, $D(0, -4)$ line and rotational

36. $R(-3, 3)$, $S(-3, -3)$, $T(3, 3)$ line

37. $F(0, -4)$, $G(-3, -2)$, $H(-3, 2)$, $J(0, 4)$, $K(3, 2)$, $L(3, -2)$ line and rotational

38. $W(-2, 3)$, $X(-3, -3)$, $Y(3, -3)$, $Z(2, 3)$ line

ALGEBRA **Graph the function and determine whether the graph has *line* and/or *rotational* symmetry. If so, state the order and magnitude of symmetry, and write the equations of any lines of symmetry.** 39–41. See margin.

39. $y = x$

40. $y = x^2 + 1$

41. $y = -x^3$

CRYSTALLOGRAPHY **Determine whether the crystals below have *plane* symmetry and/or *axis* symmetry. If so, state the magnitude of symmetry.**

42. 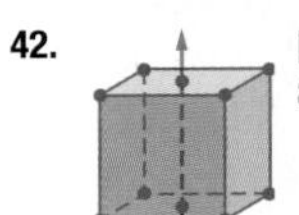 plane and axis; 90

43.  plane and axis; 180

44. 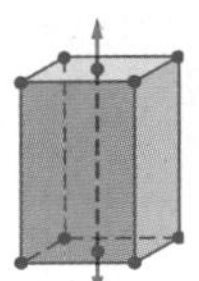 plane and axis; 180

45. **MULTIPLE REPRESENTATIONS** In this problem, you will use dynamic geometric software to investigate line and rotational symmetry in regular polygons.

a. **Geometric** Use The Geometer's Sketchpad to draw an equilateral triangle. Use the reflection tool under the transformation menu to investigate and determine all possible lines of symmetry. Then record their number. 3

b. **Geometric** Use the rotation tool under the transformation menu to investigate the rotational symmetry of the figure in part **a**. Then record its order of symmetry. 3

c. **Tabular** Repeat the process in parts **a** and **b** for a square, regular pentagon, and regular hexagon. Record the number of lines of symmetry and the order of symmetry for each polygon. See margin.

d. **Verbal** Make a conjecture about the number of lines of symmetry and the order of symmetry for a regular polygon with n sides.
Sample answer: A regular polygon with n sides has n lines of symmetry and order of symmetry n.

H.O.T. Problems Use Higher-Order Thinking Skills

46. **CCSS CRITIQUE** Jaime says that Figure A has only line symmetry, and Jewel says that Figure A has only rotational symmetry. Is either of them correct? Explain your reasoning. See margin.

Figure A

47. **CHALLENGE** A quadrilateral in the coordinate plane has exactly two lines of symmetry, $y = x - 1$ and $y = -x + 2$. Find possible vertices for the figure. Graph the figure and the lines of symmetry.
Sample answer: (−1, 0), (2, 3), (4, 1), and (1, −2); see margin for graph.

48. **REASONING** A regular polyhedron has axis symmetry of order 3, but does not have plane symmetry. What is the figure? Explain. See margin.

49. **OPEN ENDED** Draw a figure with line symmetry but not rotational symmetry. Explain. See margin.

50. **WRITING IN MATH** How are line symmetry and rotational symmetry related?
See Ch. 9 Answer Appendix.

45c.

Polygon	Lines of Symmetry	Order of Symmetry
equilateral triangle	3	3
square	4	4
regular pentagon	5	5
regular hexagon	6	6

Standardized Test Practice

51. How many lines of symmetry can be drawn on the picture of the Canadian flag below? B

A 0 C 2

B 1 D 4

52. GRIDDED RESPONSE What is the order of symmetry for the figure below? 8

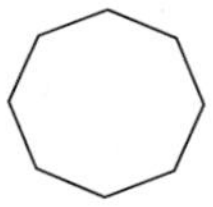

53. ALGEBRA A computer company ships computers in wooden crates that each weigh 45 pounds when empty. If each computer weighs no more than 13 pounds, which inequality *best* describes the total weight in pounds w of a crate of computers that contains c computers? H

F $c \leq 13 + 45w$ H $w \leq 13c + 45$

G $c \geq 13 + 45w$ J $w \geq 13c + 45$

54. SAT/ACT What is the slope of the line determined by the linear equation $5x - 2y = 10$? E

A -5 D $\frac{2}{5}$

B $-\frac{5}{2}$ E $\frac{5}{2}$

C $-\frac{2}{5}$

Spiral Review

Triangle JKL has vertices $J(1, 5)$, $K(3, 1)$, and $L(5, 7)$. Graph $\triangle JKL$ and its image after the indicated transformation. (Lesson 9-4) 55–56. See margin.

55. Translation: along $\langle -7, -1 \rangle$
Reflection: in x-axis

56. Translation: along $\langle 1, 2 \rangle$
Reflection: in y-axis

57. Quadrilateral $QRST$ is shown at the right. What is the image of point R after a rotation 180° counterclockwise about the origin? (Lesson 9-3) (7, −7)

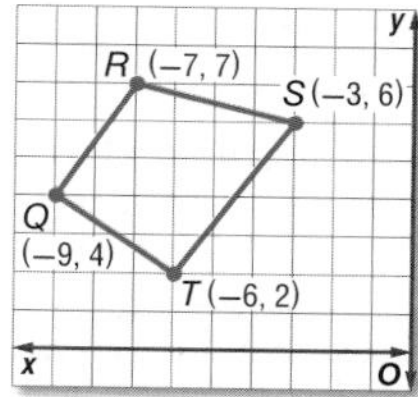

58. AMUSEMENT PARKS From the top of a roller coaster, 60 yards above the ground, a rider looks down and sees the merry-go-round and the Ferris wheel. If the angles of depression are 11° and 8° respectively, how far apart are the merry-go-round and the Ferris wheel? (Lesson 8-5) about 118.2 yd

Skills Review

Determine whether the dilation from Figure A to Figure B is an *enlargement* or a *reduction*. Then find the scale factor of the dilation. 59–61. See margin.

59.

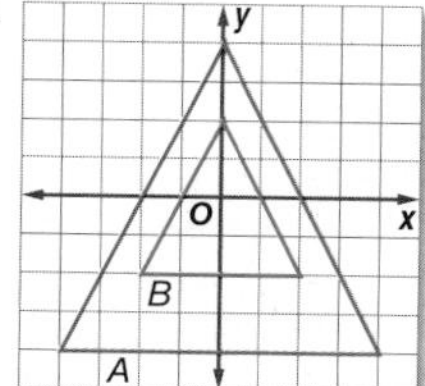

60.

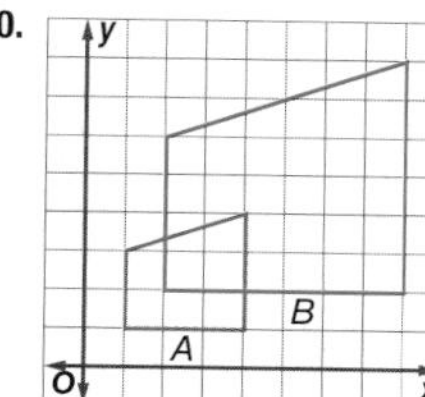

61.

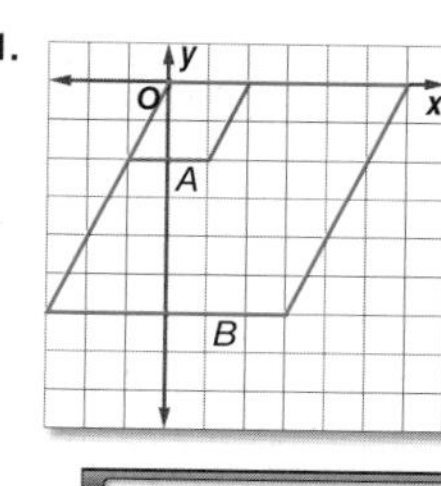

55.

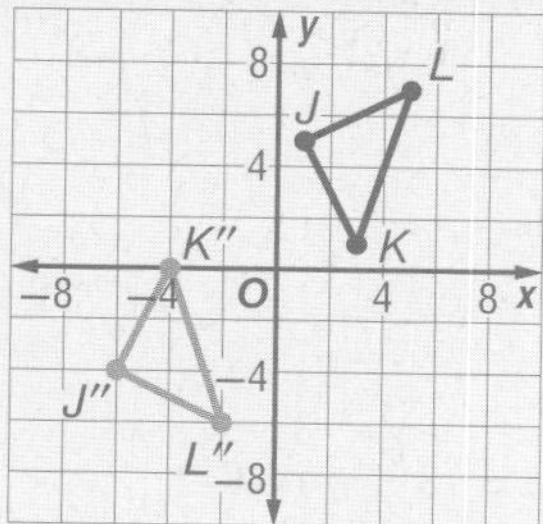

56.

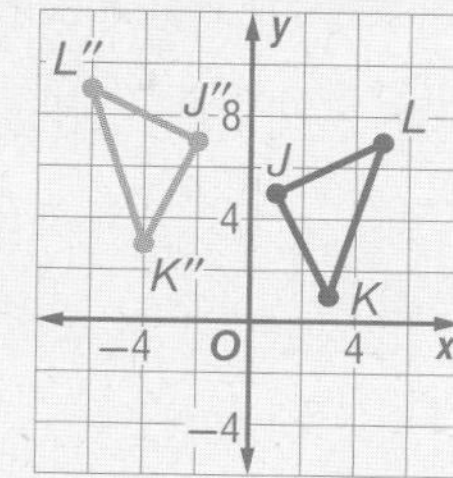

59. reduction; $\frac{1}{2}$

60. enlargement; 2

61. enlargement; 3

4 Assess

Yesterday's News Have students write how what they have learned about congruence transformations has helped them with the lesson on symmetry.

Formative Assessment

Check for student understanding of Lessons 9-4 and 9-5.

Quiz 3, p. 46

Additional Answers

46. Neither; Figure A has both rotational and line symmetry.

47.

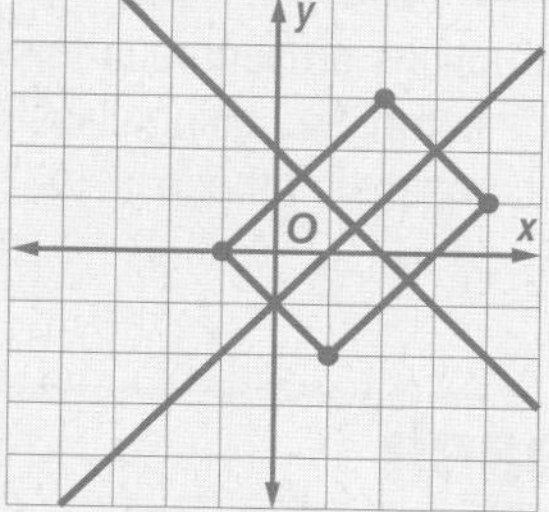

48. Equilateral triangular pyramid; sample answer: Since the figure has axis symmetry of order 3, the base has to be an equilateral triangle. Because it does not have plane symmetry, you know that it is a pyramid instead of a prism. Therefore, the figure must be an equilateral triangular pyramid.

49. Sample answer:

An isosceles triangle has line symmetry from the vertex angle to the base of the triangle, but it does not have rotational symmetry because it cannot be rotated from 0° to 360° and map onto itself.

1 Focus

Objective Use a reflective device for geometric constructions.

Materials

- reflective device
- straightedge

Teaching Tip

Reflective devices work best when used in a well-lit room on a flat surface. Students can use the edge of the reflective device as a straightedge.

Alternative Method

The constructions presented in this lab can also be completed using classic ruler and compass methods.

2 Teach

Working in Cooperative Groups

Divide the class into pairs. Work through Activity 1 and Activity 2 as a class. Then ask students to work with their partners to complete Activity 3 and Activity 4.

Practice Have students complete Exercise 1.

EXTEND 9-5 Geometry Lab Exploring Constructions with a Reflective Device

A reflective device is a tool made of semitransparent plastic that reflects objects. It works best if you lay it on a flat service in a well-lit room. You can use a reflective device to transform geometric objects.

CCSS Common Core State Standards
Content Standards
G.CO.12 Make formal geometric constructions with a variety of tools and methods (compass and straightedge, string, reflective devices, paper folding, dynamic geometric software, etc.).
Mathematical Practices 5

Activity 1 Reflect a Triangle

Use a reflective device to reflect $\triangle ABC$ in w. Label the reflection $\triangle A'B'C'$.

Step 1 Draw $\triangle ABC$ and the line of reflection w.

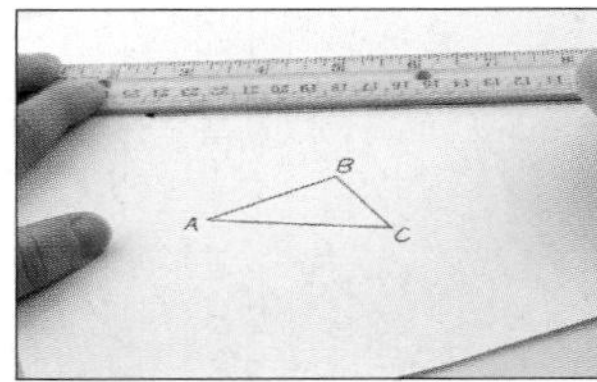

Step 2 With the reflective device on line w, draw points for the vertices of the reflection.

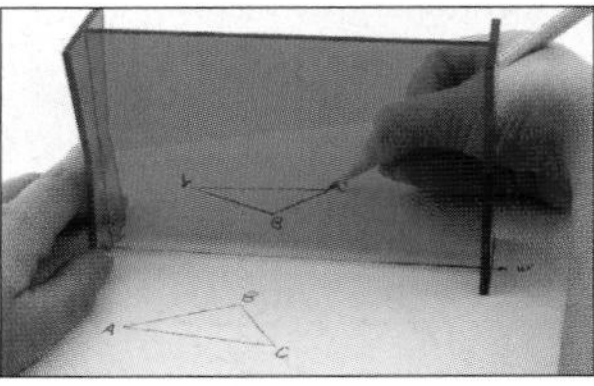

Step 3 Use a straightedge to connect the points to form $\triangle A'B'C'$.

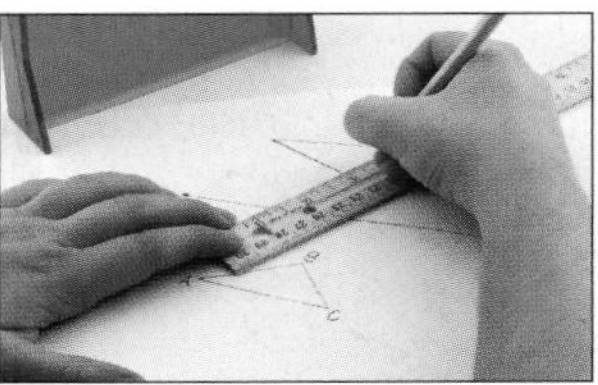

We have used a compass, straightedge, string, and paper folding to make geometric constructions. You can also use a reflective device for constructions.

Activity 2 Construct Lines of Symmetry

Use a reflective device to construct the lines of symmetry for a regular hexagon.

Step 1 Draw a regular hexagon. Place the reflective device on the shape and move it until one half of the shape matches the reflection of the other half. Draw the line of symmetry.

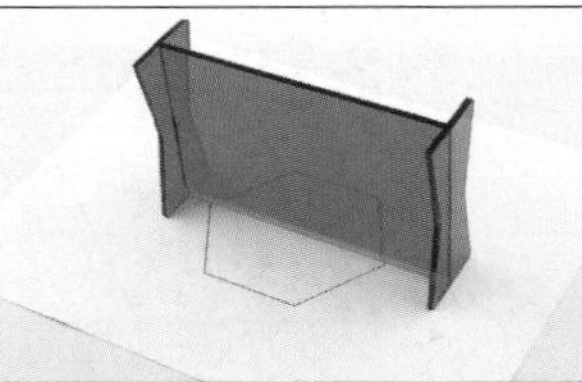

Step 2 Repeat Step 1 until you have found all the lines of symmetry.

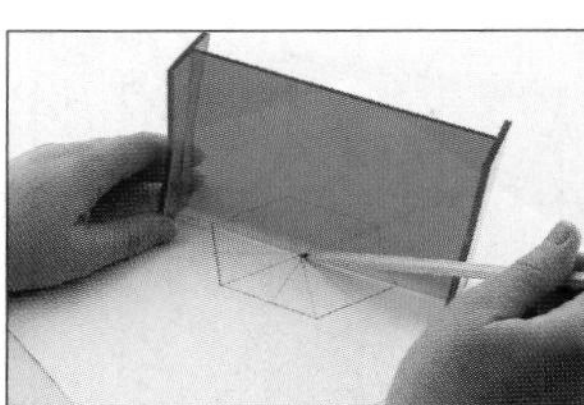

670 | Extend 9-5 | Geometry Lab: Exploring Constructions with a Reflective Device

Activity 3 Construct a Parallel line

Use a reflective device to reflect line ℓ to line m that is parallel and passes through point P.

Step 1

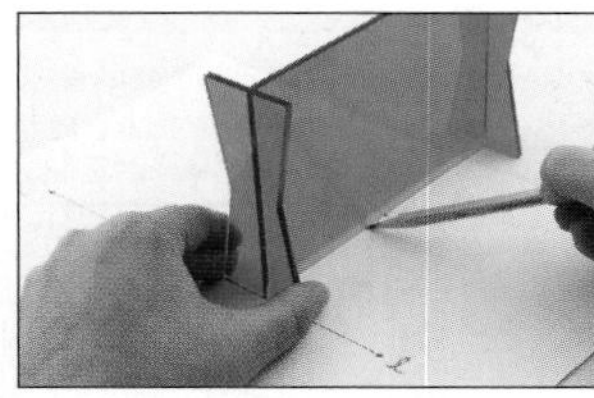

Draw line ℓ and point P. Place a short side of the reflective device on line ℓ and the long side on point P. Draw a line. This line is perpendicular to ℓ through P.

Step 2

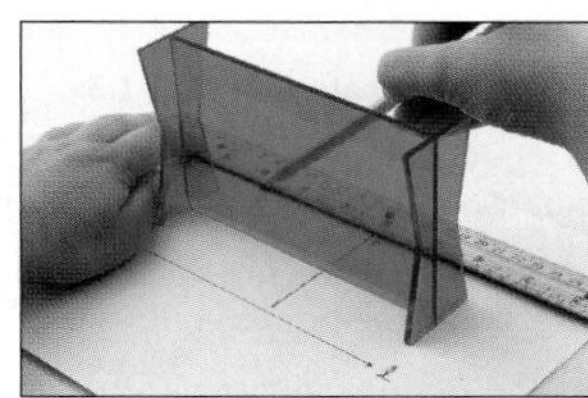

Place the reflective device so that the perpendicular line coincides with itself and the reflection of line ℓ passes through point P. Use a straightedge to draw the parallel line m through P.

In Explore Lesson 5-1, we constructed perpendicular bisectors with paper folding. You can also use a reflective device to construct perpendicular bisectors of a triangle.

Activity 4 Construct Perpendicular Bisectors

Use a reflective device to find the circumcenter of $\triangle ABC$.

Step 1 Draw $\triangle ABC$. Place the reflective device between A and B and adjust it until A and B coincide. Draw the line of symmetry.

Step 2 Repeat Step 1 for sides $\overline{AC}$ and $\overline{BC}$. Then place a point at the intersection of the three perpendicular bisectors. This is the circumcenter of the triangle.

Model and Analyze 1–2. See margin.

1. How do you know that the steps in Activity 4 give the actual perpendicular bisector and the circumcenter of $\triangle ABC$?

2. Construct the angle bisectors and find the incenter of $\triangle XYZ$. Describe how you used the reflective device for the construction.

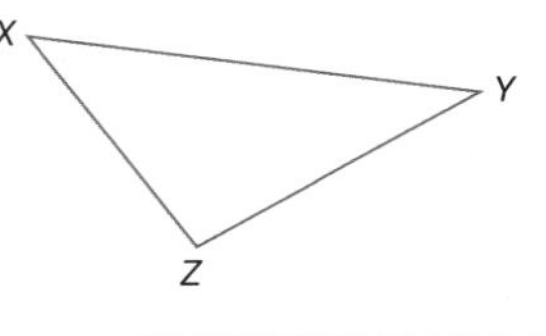

3 Assess

Formative Assessment

Use Exercise 2 to assess each student's ability to complete a construction with a reflective device.

From Concrete to Abstract

Ask students to summarize how they can utilize a reflective device for geometric constructions.

Additional Answers

1. When you find the reflection of vertex A on B, you are finding the bisector of $\overline{AB}$ with the reflective device being the line of reflection. We know that the line of reflection is always perpendicular to the segment connecting the points. By definition, the circumcenter is located at the intersection of the three perpendicular bisectors for a triangle. Therefore in Activity 3, the circumcenter is located in the correct location.

2. 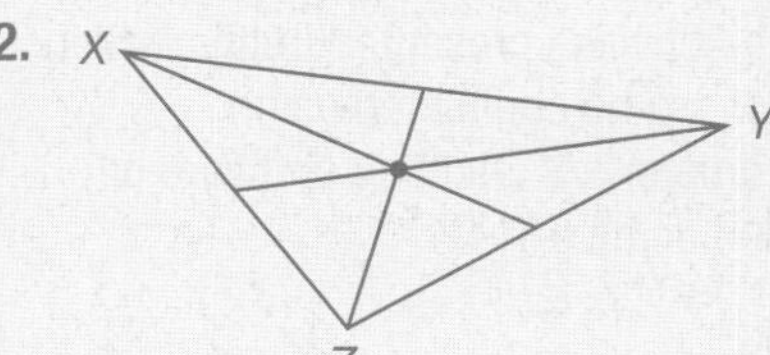

Place the reflective device at X and adjust it until $\overline{XZ}$ coincides with $\overline{XY}$. Draw the line of symmetry. Repeat for vertex Y and Z. Place a point at the intersection of the three angle bisectors. This is the incenter.

1 Focus

Objective Use graphing technology to explore the properties of dilations.

Materials

- TI-Nspire technology

Teaching Tip

- Explain to students that their measurements will not be the same as the measurements on the screen.
- When dilating the figures, it is important that the display confirms the selection prior to pressing **ENTER**.
- If the transformation causes the figure to move off the screen, move the cursor to a blank place on the screen and hold down on the center of the touchpad until the hand closes. Drag until the figure is on the screen.
- To use the **Slope** tool on the **Measurement** menu, students will need to place a line segment on top of the side of the triangle.

Alternative Method

The activities presented in this lesson can also be completed using Geometer's Sketchpad software or Cabri Jr. on a TI-84.

2 Teach

Working in Cooperative Groups

Divide the class into pairs. Work through Activity 1 as a class. Then ask students to work with their partners to complete Activities 2 and 3.

Practice Have students complete Exercises 7–9.

EXPLORE 9-6 Graphing Technology Lab Dilations

You can use TI-Nspire Technology to explore properties of dilations.

CCSS Common Core State Standards
Content Standards
G.SRT.1 Understand similarity in terms of similarity transformations. Verify experimentally the properties of dilations given by a center and a scale factor:
a. A dilation takes a line not passing through the center of the dilation to a parallel line, and leaves a line passing through the center unchanged.
b. The dilation of a line segment is longer or shorter in the ratio given by the scale factor.
Mathematical Practices 5

Activity 1 Dilation of a Triangle

Dilate a triangle by a scale factor of 1.5.

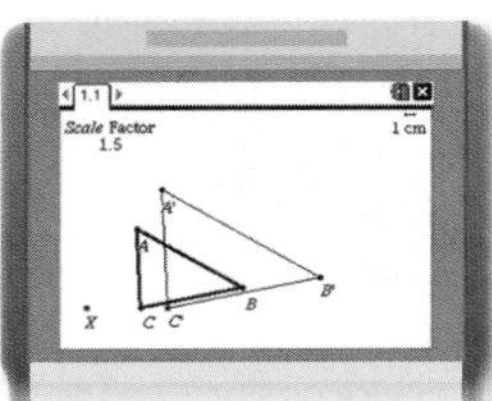

Step 1 Add a new **Geometry** page. Then, from the **Points & Lines** menu, use the **Point** tool to add a point and label it *X*.

Step 2 From the **Shapes** menu, select **Triangle** and specify three points. Label the points *A*, *B*, and *C*.

Step 3 From the **Actions** menu, use the **Text** tool to separately add the text *Scale Factor* and *1.5* to the page.

Step 4 From the **Transformation** menu, select **Dilation**. Then select point *X*, $\triangle ABC$, and the text *1.5*.

Step 5 Label the points on the image A', B', and C'.

Analyze the Results 1–3. See margin.

1. Using the **Slope** tool on the **Measurement** menu, describe the effect of the dilation on $\overline{AB}$. That is, how are the lines through $\overline{AB}$ and $\overline{A'B'}$ related?
2. What is the effect of the dilation on the line passing through side $\overline{CA}$?
3. What is the effect of the dilation on the line passing through side $\overline{CB}$?

Activity 2 Dilation of a Polygon

Dilate a polygon by a scale factor of −0.5.

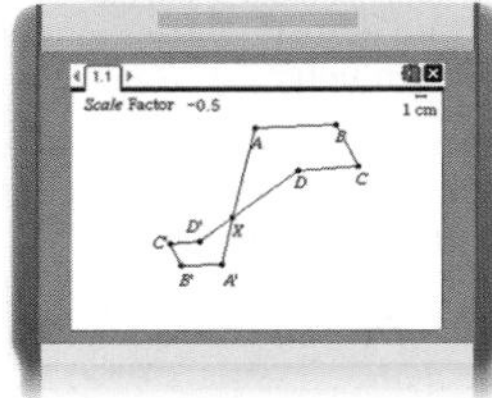

Step 1 Add a new **Geometry** page and draw polygon *ABCDX* as shown. Add the text *Scale Factor* and -0.5 to the page.

Step 2 From the **Transformation** menu, select **Dilation**. Then select point *X*, polygon *ABCDX*, and the text -0.5.

Step 3 Label the points on the image A', B', C', and D'.

Model and Analyze 4–6. See margin.

4. Analyze the effect of the dilation in Activity 2 on sides that contain the center of the dilation.
5. Analyze the effect of a dilation of trapezoid *ABCD* shown with a scale factor of 0.75 and the center of the dilation at *A*.
6. **MAKE A CONJECTURE** Describe the effect of a dilation on segments that pass through the center of a dilation and segments that do not pass through the center of a dilation.

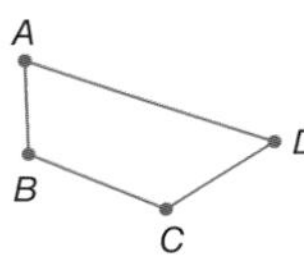

Activity 3 Dilation of a Segment

Dilate a segment $\overline{AB}$ by the indicated scale factor.

a. scale factor: 0.75

Step 1 On a new **Geometry** page, draw a line segment using the **Points & Lines** menu. Label the endpoints *A* and *B*. Then add and label a point *X*.

Step 2 Add the text *Scale Factor* and *0.75* to the page.

Step 3 From the **Transformation** menu, select **Dilation**. Then select point *X*, $\overline{AB}$, and the text *0.75*.

Step 4 Label the dilated segment $\overline{A'B'}$.

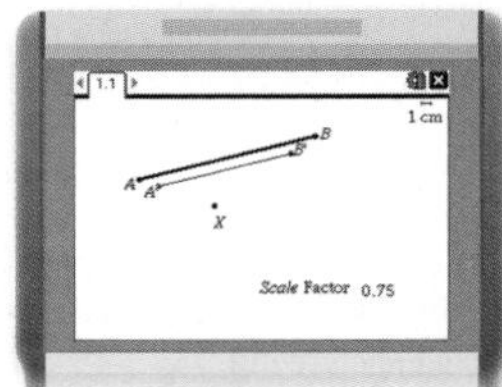

b. scale factor: 1.25

Step 1 Add the text *1.25* to the page.

Step 2 From the **Transformation** menu, select **Dilation**. Then select point *X*, $\overline{AB}$, and the text 1.25.

Step 3 Label the dilated segment $\overline{A''B''}$.

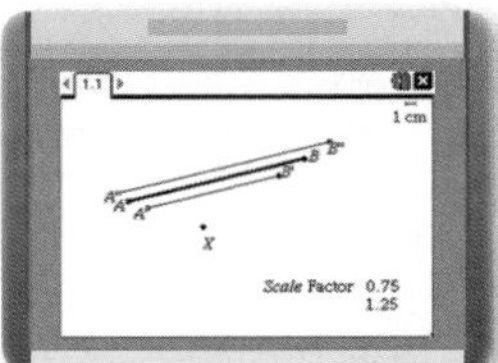

Model and Analyze 7–12. See margin.

7. Using the **Length** tool on the **Measurement** menu, find the measures of $\overline{AB}$, $\overline{A'B'}$, and $\overline{A''B''}$.

8. What is the ratio of $A'B'$ to AB? What is the ratio of $A''B''$ to AB?

9. What is the effect of the dilation with scale factor 0.75 on segment $\overline{AB}$? What is the effect of the dilation with scale factor 1.25 on segment $\overline{AB}$?

10. Dilate segment $\overline{AB}$ in Activity 3 by scale factors of −0.75 and −1.25. Describe the effect on the length of each dilated segment.

11. **MAKE A CONJECTURE** Describe the effect of a dilation on the length of a line segment.

12. Describe the dilation from $\overline{AB}$ to $\overline{A'B'}$ and $\overline{A'B'}$ to $\overline{A''B''}$ in the triangles shown.

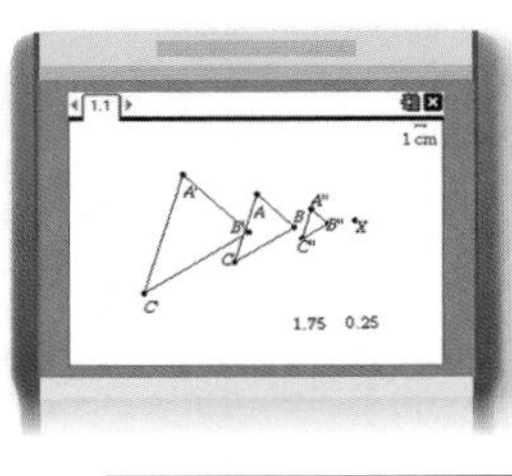

11. If the absolute value of the scale factor is between 0 and 1, the segment is mapped onto a parallel segment that is shorter in length. If the absolute value of the scale factor is greater than 1, the segment is mapped onto a parallel segment that is longer in length.

12. $\overline{AB}$ is dilated by 1.75 to $\overline{A'B'}$. Then $\overline{A'B'}$ is dilated by 0.25 to $\overline{A''B''}$.

3 Assess

Formative Assessment

Use Exercises 10–12 to assess each student's knowledge of the effects of dilating figures.

From Concrete to Abstract

Ask students to summarize the effects of dilations on line segments and on figures.

Additional Answers

1. The dilation maps $\overline{AB}$ to $\overline{A'B'}$, which are parallel segments.
2. The dilation maps $\overline{CA}$ to $\overline{C'A'}$, which are parallel segments.
3. The dilation maps $\overline{CB}$ to $\overline{C'B'}$, which are parallel segments.
4. The original line segment and dilated segment are part of the same line.
5. The new trapezoid $A'B'C'D'$ is 75% the size of trapezoid $ABCD$ and is oriented so that A and A' coincide.
6. Sample answer: Segments that do not pass through the center of the dilation are mapped onto parallel segments. Segments that pass through the center of a dilation are mapped onto segments that are part of the same line.
7. Sample answer: AB is 15.7 units, $A'B'$ is 11.8 units, and $A''B''$ is 19.6 units.
8. The ratio of $A'B'$ to AB is 0.75, and the ratio of $A''B''$ to AB is 1.25.
9. With a scale factor of 0.75, $\overline{AB}$ is mapped onto a parallel segment that is 75% the length of $\overline{AB}$. With a scale factor of 1.25, $\overline{AB}$ *is* mapped onto a parallel segment that is 125% the length of $\overline{AB}$.
10. With a scale factor of −0.75, $\overline{AB}$ is mapped onto a parallel segment that is 75% the length of $\overline{AB}$ and is reflected in the center of dilation. With a scale factor of 1.25, $\overline{AB}$ is mapped onto a parallel segment that is 125% the length of $\overline{AB}$ and is reflected in the center of dilation.

1 Focus

VerticalAlignment

Before Lesson 9-6 Identify dilations and verify them as similarity transformations.

Lesson 9-6 Draw dilations.

After Lesson 9-6 Use congruence transformations to make conjectures and justify properties of geometric figures including figures on a coordinate plane.

2 Teach

Scaffolding Questions

Have students read the **Why?** section of the lesson.

Ask:

- If you enlarge the entire photo shown, will it decrease the empty space at the top of the photo? No, because the entire photo is enlarged by the same amount.
- What is the relationship between the original photo and the enlarged photo? They are similar.
- How can you prove that a dilated figure is similar? Prove that their corresponding angles are congruent and the measures of their corresponding sides are proportional.

LESSON 9-6 Dilations

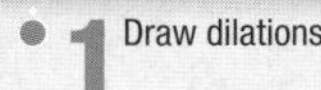

Then	Now	Why?
You identified dilations and verified them as similarity transformations.	1 Draw dilations. 2 Draw dilations in the coordinate plane.	Some photographers still prefer traditional cameras and film to produce negatives. From these negatives, photographers can create scaled reproductions.

Common Core State Standards

Content Standards

G.CO.2 Represent transformations in the plane using, e.g., transparencies and geometry software; describe transformations as functions that take points in the plane as inputs and give other points as outputs. Compare transformations that preserve distance and angle to those that do not (e.g., translation versus horizontal stretch).

G.SRT.1 Understand similarity in terms of similarity transformations. Verify experimentally the properties of dilations given by a center and a scale factor:

a. A dilation takes a line not passing through the center of the dilation to a parallel line, and leaves a line passing through the center unchanged.

b. The dilation of a line segment is longer or shorter in the ratio given by the scale factor.

Mathematical Practices

1 Make sense of problems and persevere in solving them.

5 Use appropriate tools strategically.

1 Draw Dilations A dilation or *scaling* is a similarity transformation that enlarges or reduces a figure proportionally with respect to a *center* point and a *scale* factor.

KeyConcept Dilation

A dilation with center C and positive scale factor k, $k \neq 1$, is a function that maps a point P in a figure to its image such that

- if point P and C coincide, then the image and preimage are the same point, or
- if point P is not the center of dilation, then P' lies on $\overrightarrow{CP}$ and $CP' = k(CP)$.

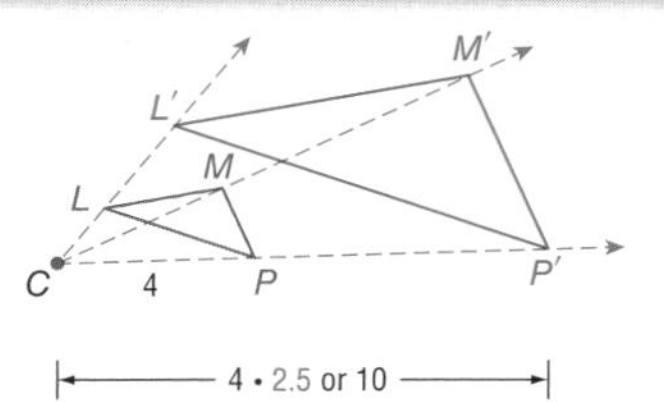

$\triangle L'M'P'$ is the image of $\triangle LMP$ under a dilation with center C and scale factor 2.5.

Example 1 Draw a Dilation

Copy $\triangle ABC$ and point D. Then use a ruler to draw the image of $\triangle ABC$ under a dilation with center D and scale factor $\frac{1}{2}$.

Step 1 Draw rays from D though each vertex.

Step 2 Locate A' on $\overrightarrow{DA}$ such that $DA' = \frac{1}{2}DA$.

Step 3 Locate B' on $\overrightarrow{DB}$ and C' on $\overrightarrow{DC}$ in the same way. Then draw $\triangle A'B'C'$.

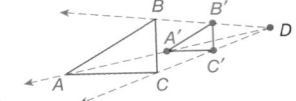

GuidedPractice 1A, 1B. See Ch. 9 Answer Appendix.

Copy the figure and point J. Then use a ruler to draw the image of the figure under a dilation with center J and the scale factor k indicated.

1A. $k = \frac{3}{2}$

1B. $k = 0.75$

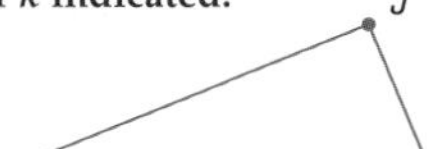

674 | Lesson 9-6

Lesson 9-6 Resources

Resource	Approaching Level AL	On Level OL	Beyond Level BL	English Learners ELL
Teacher Edition	▪ Differentiated Instruction, p. 675	▪ Differentiated Instruction, pp. 675, 676	▪ Differentiated Instruction, pp. 675, 676	▪ Differentiated Instruction, p. 675
Chapter Resource Masters	▪ Study Guide and Intervention, pp. 37–38 ▪ Skills Practice, p. 39 ▪ Practice, p. 40 ▪ Word Problem Practice, p. 41	▪ Study Guide and Intervention, pp. 37–38 ▪ Skills Practice, p. 39 ▪ Practice, p. 40 ▪ Word Problem Practice, p. 41 ▪ Enrichment, p. 42	▪ Practice, p. 40 ▪ Word Problem Practice, p. 41 ▪ Enrichment, p. 42	▪ Study Guide and Intervention, pp. 37–38 ▪ Skills Practice, p. 39 ▪ Practice, p. 40 ▪ Word Problem Practice, p. 41
Other	▪ 5-Minute Check 9-6 ▪ Study Notebook	▪ 5-Minute Check 9-6 ▪ Study Notebook	▪ 5-Minute Check 9-6 ▪ Study Notebook	▪ 5-Minute Check 9-6 ▪ Study Notebook

In Lesson 7-6, you also learned that if $k > 1$, then the dilation is an *enlargement*. If $0 < k < 1$, then the dilation is a *reduction*. Since $\frac{1}{2}$ is between 0 and 1, the dilation in Example 1 is a reduction.

A dilation with a scale factor of 1 is called an *isometry dilation*. It produces an image that coincides with the preimage. The two figures are congruent.

Real-World Example 2 Find the Scale Factor of a Dilation

PT

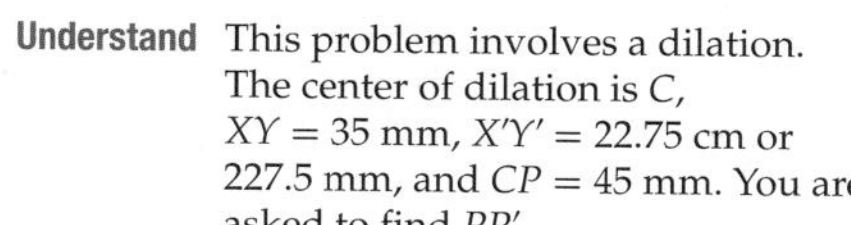

PHOTOGRAPHY To create different-sized prints, you can adjust the distance between a film negative and the enlarged print by using a photographic enlarger. Suppose the distance between the light source *C* and the negative is 45 millimeters (*CP*). To what distance *PP′* should you adjust the enlarger to create a 22.75-centimeter wide print (*X′Y′*) from a 35-millimeter wide negative (*XY*)?

Understand This problem involves a dilation. The center of dilation is *C*, $XY = 35$ mm, $X'Y' = 22.75$ cm or 227.5 mm, and $CP = 45$ mm. You are asked to find *PP′*.

Plan Find the scale factor of the dilation from the preimage *XY* to the image *X′Y′*. Use the scale factor to find *CP′* and then use *CP* and *CP′* to find *PP′*.

Solve The scale factor *k* of the enlargement is the ratio of a length on the image to a corresponding length on the preimage.

$k = \frac{\text{image length}}{\text{preimage length}}$ Scale factor of image

$= \frac{X'Y'}{XY}$ image = $X'Y'$, preimage = XY

$= \frac{227.5}{35}$ or 6.5 Divide.

Use this scale factor of 6.5 to find *CP′*.

$CP' = k(CP)$ Definition of dilation

$= 6.5(45)$ $k = 6.5$ and $CP = 45$

$= 292.5$ Multiply.

Use *CP′* and *CP* to find *PP′*.

$CP + PP' = CP'$ Segment Addition

$45 + PP' = 292.5$ $CP = 45$ and $CP' = 292.5$

$PP' = 247.5$ Subtract 45 from each side.

So the enlarger should be adjusted so that the distance from the negative to the enlarged print (*PP′*) is 247.5 millimeters or 24.75 centimeters.

Check Since the dilation is an enlargement, the scale factor should be greater than 1. Since $6.5 > 1$, the scale factor found is reasonable. ✓

Problem-Solving Tip

CCSS Perseverance

To prevent careless errors in your calculations, estimate the answer to a problem before solving. In Example 2, you can estimate the scale factor of the dilation to be about $\frac{240}{40}$ or 6. Then *CP′* would be about 6 • 50 or 300 and *PP′* about 300 − 50 or 250 millimeters, which is 25 centimeters. A measure of 24.75 centimeters is close to this estimate, so the answer is reasonable.

1 Draw Dilations

Example 1 shows how to draw a dilation. **Example 2** shows how to find the scale factor of a dilation.

Formative Assessment

Use the Guided Practice exercises after each example to determine students' understanding of concepts.

Additional Examples

1 Copy trapezoid *PQRS* and point *C*. Then use a ruler to draw the image of trapezoid *PQRS* under a dilation with center *C* and scale factor 3.

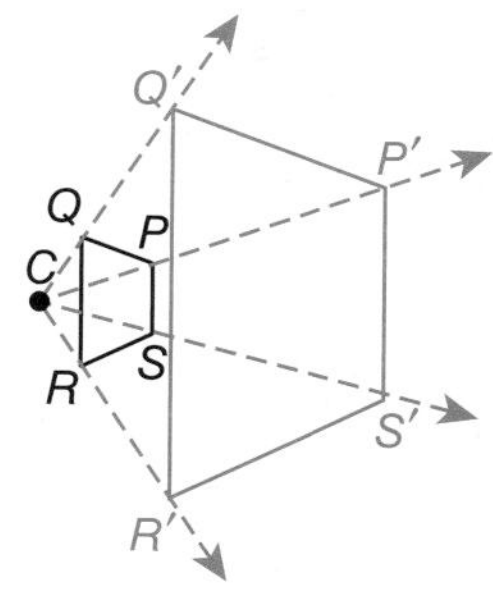

2 PUPPETS To create the illusion of a "life-sized" image, puppeteers sometimes use a light source to show an enlarged image of a puppet projected on a screen or wall. Suppose that the distance between a light source *L* and the puppet is 24 inches (*LP*). To what distance *PP′* should you place the puppet from the screen to create a 49.5-inch tall shadow (*I′M′*) from a 9 inch puppet?

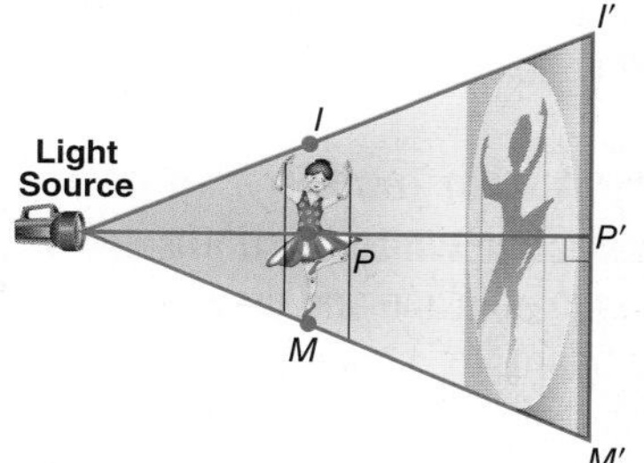

9 feet or 108 inches

Additional Examples also in Interactive Classroom PowerPoint® Presentations

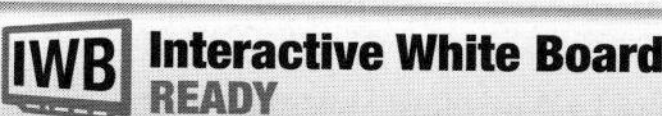

Differentiated Instruction AL OL BL ELL

Auditory/Musical Learners Students can relate dilations to music by how loud or soft a sound is. A harmonica's sound is magnified or dilated with a scale factor of *r* greater than 1 when a great force is used to create a musical note. The sound is much softer when the same note is produced with half the force. They can also correlate drawing a breath through the harmonica with a negative scale factor and exhaling into the harmonica with a positive scale factor.

2 Dilations in the Coordinate Plane

Example 3 shows how to find the image of a dilation in the coordinate plane.

Additional Example

3 Trapezoid *EFGH* has vertices $E(-8, 4)$, $F(-4, 8)$, $G(8, 4)$, and $H(-4, -8)$. Graph the image of *EFGH* after a dilation centered at the origin with a scale factor of $\frac{1}{4}$.

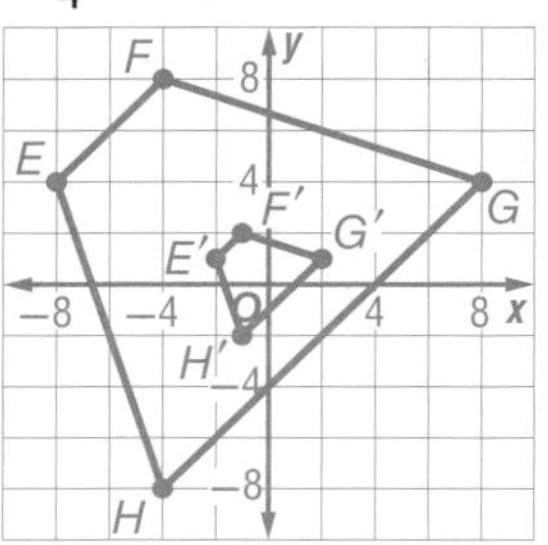

WatchOut!

Center of Dilation Watch for students who begin their dilation at a point on the figure and measure beyond the center of dilation. Reinforce that the scale factor is to be measured beginning at the center of dilation.

Focus on Mathematical Content

Orientation Point out to students that a dilation preserves angle measure and orientation, but not size.

Teach with Tech

Interactive Whiteboard Display a coordinate plane and draw a figure on the board. Tell students the scale factor for a dilation and have them name the vertices of the dilated figure. Plot these points and draw the image of the figure.

GuidedPractice

2. Determine whether the dilation from Figure Q to Q' is an *enlargement* or a *reduction*. Then find the scale factor of the dilation and x. **enlargement; 3; 10**

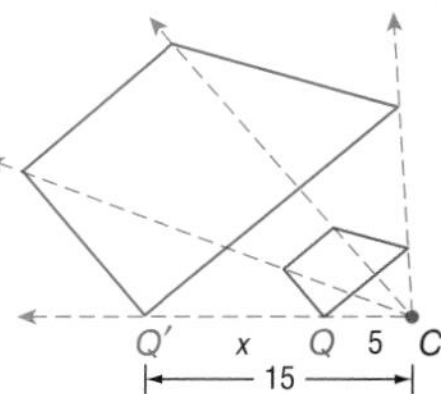

2 Dilations in the Coordinate Plane

You can use the following rules to find the image of a figure after a dilation centered at the origin.

StudyTip

Negative Scale Factors Dilations can also have negative scale factors. You will investigate this type of dilation in Exercise 36.

KeyConcept Dilations in the Coordinate Plane

Words To find the coordinates of an image after a dilation centered at the origin, multiply the *x*- and *y*-coordinates of each point on the preimage by the scale factor of the dilation, *k*.

Symbols $(x, y) \rightarrow (kx, ky)$

Example

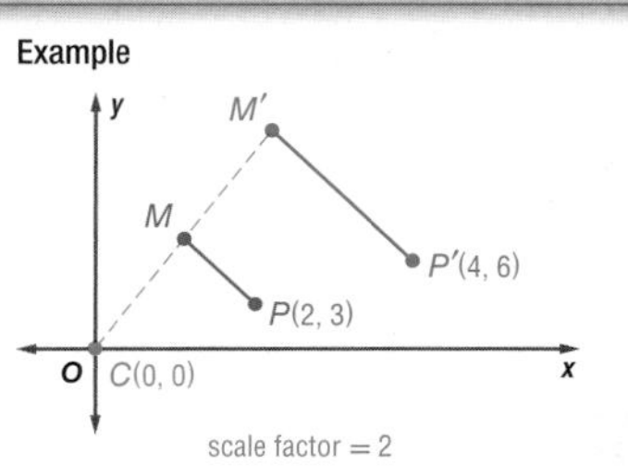

Example 3 Dilations in the Coordinate Plane

Quadrilateral *JKLM* has vertices $J(-2, 4)$, $K(-2, -2)$, $L(-4, -2)$, and $M(-4, 2)$. Graph the image of *JKLM* after a dilation centered at the origin with a scale factor of 2.5.

Multiply the *x*- and *y*-coordinates of each vertex by the scale factor, 2.5.

(x, y)	$\rightarrow$	$(2.5x, 2.5y)$
$J(-2, 4)$	$\rightarrow$	$J'(-5, 10)$
$K(-2, -2)$	$\rightarrow$	$K'(-5, -5)$
$L(-4, -2)$	$\rightarrow$	$L'(-10, -5)$
$M(-4, 2)$	$\rightarrow$	$M'(-10, 5)$

Graph *JKLM* and its image $J'K'L'M'$.

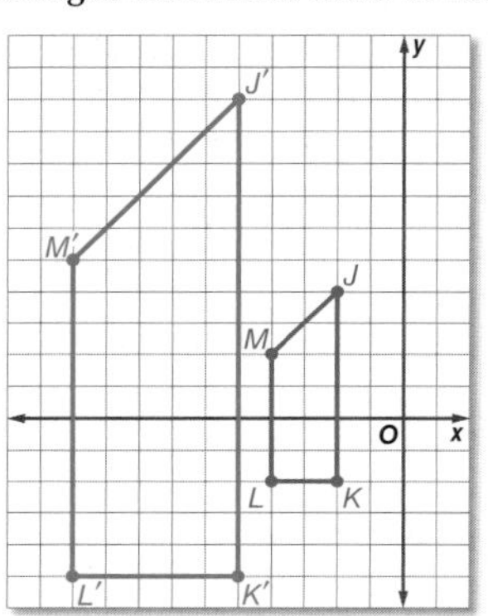

GuidedPractice

Find the image of each polygon with the given vertices after a dilation centered at the origin with the given scale factor. **3A, 3B. See margin.**

3A. $Q(0, 6)$, $R(-6, -3)$, $S(6, -3)$; $k = \frac{1}{3}$

3B. $A(2, 1)$, $B(0, 3)$, $C(-1, 2)$, $D(0, 1)$; $k = 2$

DifferentiatedInstruction OL BL

Extension Ask students to list the steps in constructing a dilation. Students should include examples that illustrate the steps and list the properties of a dilation. Accept all reasonable answers.

Check Your Understanding

 = Step-by-Step Solutions begin on page R14.

Example 1 **Copy the figure and point M. Then use a ruler to draw the image of the figure under a dilation with center M and the scale factor k indicated.** 1–2. See margin.

1. $k = \frac{1}{4}$

2. $k = 2$

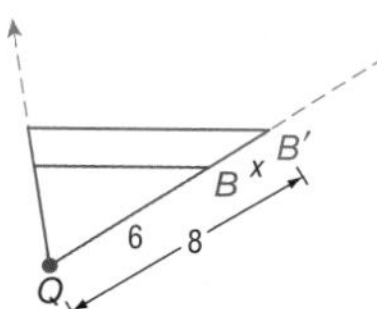

Example 2

3. Determine whether the dilation from Figure B to B' is an *enlargement* or a *reduction*. Then find the scale factor of the dilation and x. enlargement; $\frac{4}{3}$; 2

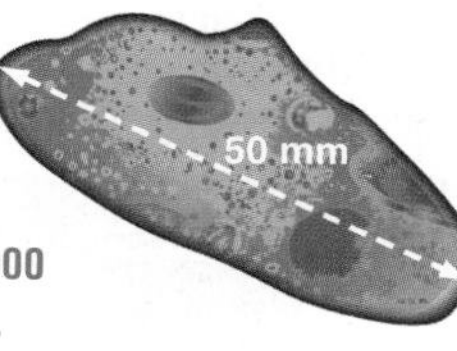

4. **BIOLOGY** Under a microscope, a single-celled organism 200 microns in length appears to be 50 millimeters long. If 1 millimeter = 1000 microns, what magnification setting (scale factor) was used? Explain your reasoning.
250×; The organism's length in millimeters is 200 ÷ 1000 or 0.2 mm. The scale factor of the dilation is $\frac{50}{0.2}$ or 250.

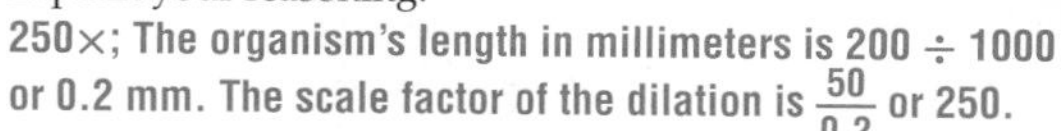

Example 3 **Graph the image of each polygon with the given vertices after a dilation centered at the origin with the given scale factor.** 5–8. See Ch. 9 Answer Appendix.

5. $W(0, 0), X(6, 6), Y(6, 0); k = 1.5$
6. $Q(-4, 4), R(-4, -4), S(4, -4), T(4, 4); k = \frac{1}{2}$
7. $A(-1, 4), B(2, 4), C(3, 2), D(-2, 2); k = 2$
8. $J(-2, 0), K(2, 4), L(8, 0), M(2, -4); k = \frac{3}{4}$

Practice and Problem Solving

Extra Practice is on page R9.

Example 1 CCSS **TOOLS** **Copy the figure and point S. Then use a ruler to draw the image of the figure under a dilation with center S and the scale factor k indicated.** 9–14. See Ch. 9 Answer Appendix.

9. $k = \frac{5}{2}$

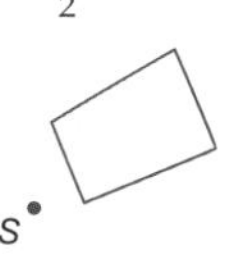

10. $k = 3$

11. $k = 0.8$

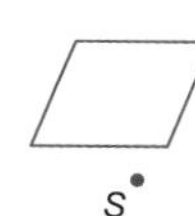

12. $k = \frac{1}{3}$

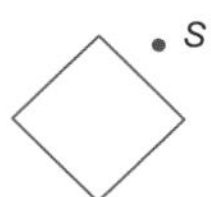

13. $k = 2.25$

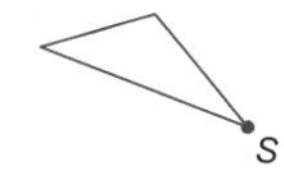

14. $k = \frac{7}{4}$

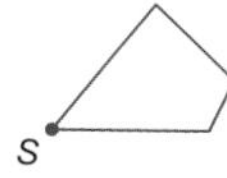

Differentiated Homework Options

Level	Assignment	Two-Day Option	
AL Basic	9–26, 38–55	9–25 odd, 42–45	10–26 even, 38–41, 46–55
OL Core	9–27 odd, 28, 29–35 odd, 36, 38–55	9–26, 42–45	27–36, 38–41, 46–55
BL Advanced	27–51, (optional: 52–55)		

3 Practice

Formative Assessment

Use Exercises 1–8 to check for understanding.

Then use the chart at the bottom of this page to customize assignments for your students.

CCSS Teaching the Mathematical Practices

Tools Mathematically proficient students consider the available tools when solving a mathematical problem. In Exercises 9–14, encourage students to use tracing paper or patty paper and a ruler.

Additional Answers (Guided Practice)

3A.

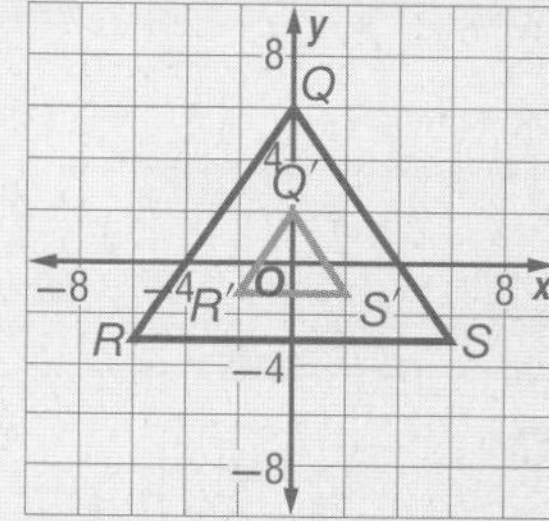

3B.

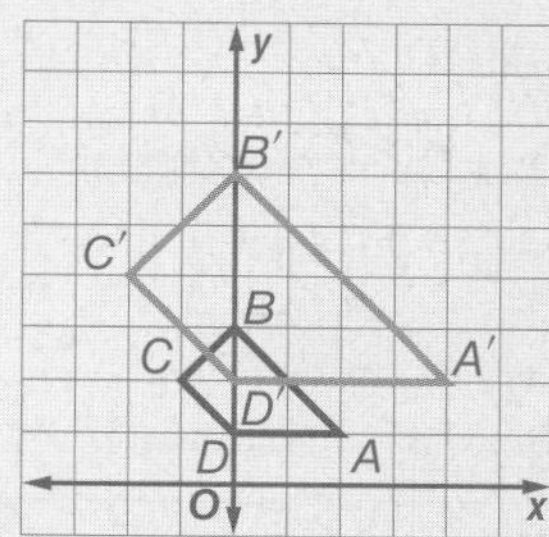

Additional Answers

1.

2.

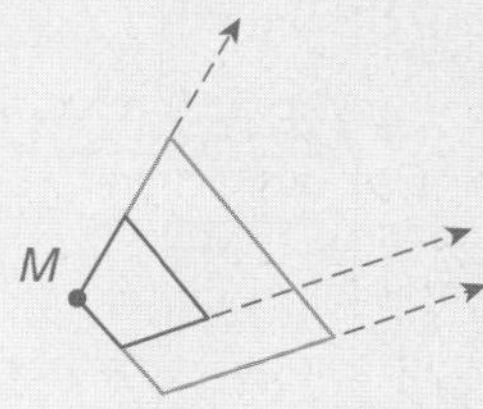

Study Guide and Intervention

AL OL ELL

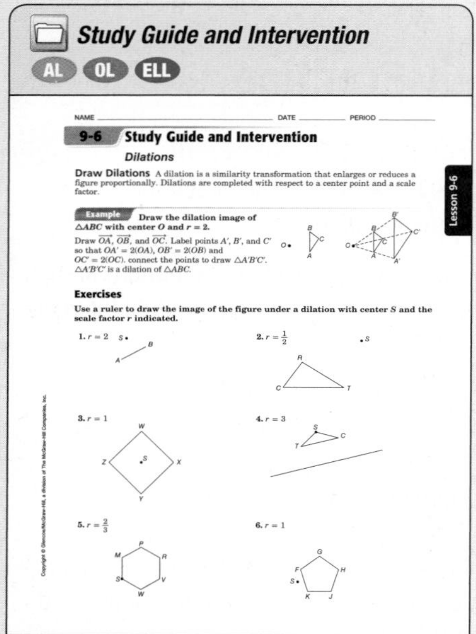
NAME ______ DATE ______ PERIOD ______

9-6 Study Guide and Intervention

Dilations

Draw Dilations A dilation is a similarity transformation that enlarges or reduces a figure proportionally. Dilations are completed with respect to a center point and a scale factor.

Example Draw the dilation image of $\triangle ABC$ with center O and $r = 2$.

Draw $\overline{OA}$, $\overline{OB}$, and $\overline{OC}$. Label points A', B', and C' so that $OA' = 2(OA)$, $OB' = 2(OB)$ and $OC' = 2(OC)$. connect the points to draw $\triangle A'B'C'$. $\triangle A'B'C'$ is a dilation of $\triangle ABC$.

Exercises

Use a ruler to draw the image of the figure under a dilation with center S and the scale factor r indicated.

1. $r = 2$
2. $r = \frac{1}{2}$
3. $r = 1$
4. $r = 3$
5. $r = \frac{2}{3}$
6. $r = 1$

Practice

AL OL BL ELL

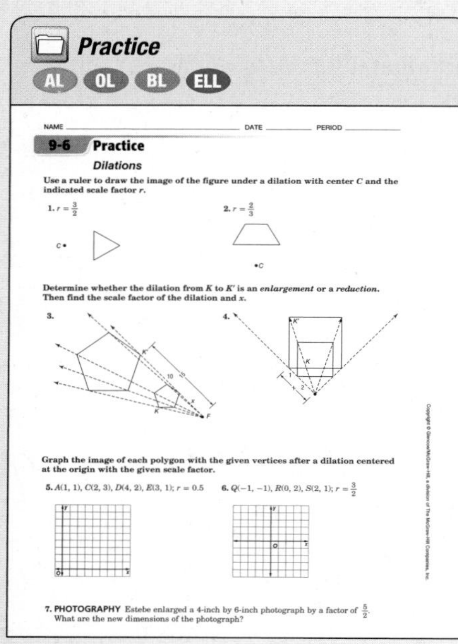
NAME ______ DATE ______ PERIOD ______

9-6 Practice

Dilations

Use a ruler to draw the image of the figure under a dilation with center C and the indicated scale factor r.

1. $r = \frac{3}{2}$
2. $r = \frac{2}{3}$

Determine whether the dilation from K to K′ is an *enlargement* or a *reduction*. Then find the scale factor of the dilation and x.

3.
4.

Graph the image of each polygon with the given vertices after a dilation centered at the origin with the given scale factor.

5. $A(1, 1), C(2, 3), D(4, 2), E(3, 1); r = 0.5$
6. $Q(-1, -1), R(0, 2), S(2, 1); r = \frac{3}{2}$

7. **PHOTOGRAPHY** Estebe enlarged a 4-inch by 6-inch photograph by a factor of $\frac{5}{2}$. What are the new dimensions of the photograph?

Word Problem Practice

AL OL BL ELL

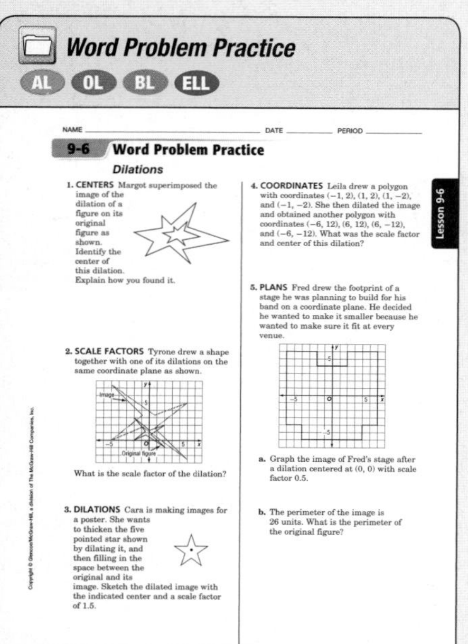
NAME ______ DATE ______ PERIOD ______

9-6 Word Problem Practice

Dilations

1. **CENTERS** Margot superimposed the image of the dilation of a figure on its original figure as shown. Identify the center of this dilation. Explain how you found it.

2. **SCALE FACTORS** Tyrone drew a shape together with one of its dilations on the same coordinate plane as shown.

   What is the scale factor of the dilation?

3. **DILATIONS** Cara is making images for a poster. She wants to thicken the five pointed star shown by dilating it, and then filling in the space between the original and its image. Sketch the dilated image with the indicated center and a scale factor of 1.5.

4. **COORDINATES** Leila drew a polygon with coordinates (−1, 2), (1, 2), (1, −2), and (−1, −2). She then dilated the image and obtained another polygon with coordinates (−6, 12), (6, 12), (6, −12), and (−6, −12). What was the scale factor and center of this dilation?

5. **PLANS** Fred drew the footprint of a stage he was planning to build for his band on a coordinate plane. He decided he wanted to make it smaller because he wanted to make sure it fit at every venue.

   a. Graph the image of Fred's stage after a dilation centered at (0, 0) with scale factor 0.5.

   b. The perimeter of the image is 26 units. What is the perimeter of the original figure?

Example 2 **Determine whether the dilation from figure *W* to *W′* is an *enlargement* or a *reduction*. Then find the scale factor of the dilation and *x*.**

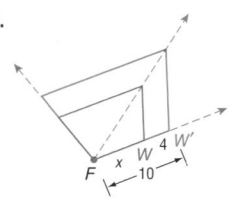

15. W′ 4.5 W x F; 9 — enlargement; 2; 4.5

16. F x W 4 W′; 10 — enlargement; $\frac{5}{3}$; 6

17. W x W′ 10.5 F; 14 — reduction; $\frac{3}{4}$; 3.5

18. F x W′ 8 W; 12 — reduction; $\frac{1}{3}$; 4

INSECTS **When viewed under a microscope, each insect has the measurement given on the picture. Given the actual measure of each insect, what magnification was used? Explain your reasoning.**

19. 3.75 cm

Cat Flea
Actual Length: 2.5 mm

20. 4.8 cm

Spider Mite
Actual Length: 0.5 mm

Example 3 **CCSS SENSE-MAKING** **Find the image of each polygon with the given vertices after a dilation centered at the origin with the given scale factor.** **21–26. See Ch. 9 Answer Appendix.**

21. $J(-8, 0), K(-4, 4), L(-2, 0); k = 0.5$

22. $S(0, 0), T(-4, 0), V(-8, -8); k = 1.25$

23. $A(9, 9), B(3, 3), C(6, 0); k = \frac{1}{3}$

24. $D(4, 4), F(0, 0), G(8, 0); k = 0.75$

25. $M(-2, 0), P(0, 2), Q(2, 0), R(0, -2); k = 2.5$

26. $W(2, 2), X(2, 0), Y(0, 1), Z(1, 2); k = 3$

19. 15×; The insect's image length in millimeters is 3.75 • 10 or 37.5 mm. The scale factor of the dilation is $\frac{37.5}{2.5}$ or 15.

20. 96×; The insect's image length in millimeters is 4.8 • 10 or 48 mm. The scale factor of the dilation is $\frac{48}{0.5}$ or 96.

B **27.** **COORDINATE GEOMETRY** Refer to the graph of *FGHJ*. **a, b, d. See Ch. 9 Answer Appendix.**

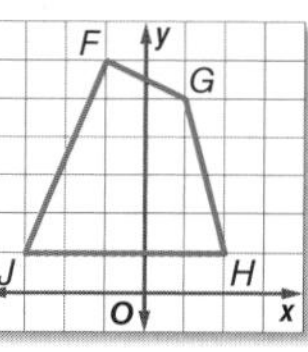

a. Dilate *FGHJ* by a scale factor of $\frac{1}{2}$ centered at the origin, and then reflect the dilated image in the *y*-axis.

b. Complete the composition of transformations in part **a** in reverse order.

c. Does the order of the transformations affect the final image? **no**

d. Will the order of a composition of a dilation and a reflection *always*, *sometimes*, or *never* affect the dilated image? Explain your reasoning.

Enrichment

OL BL

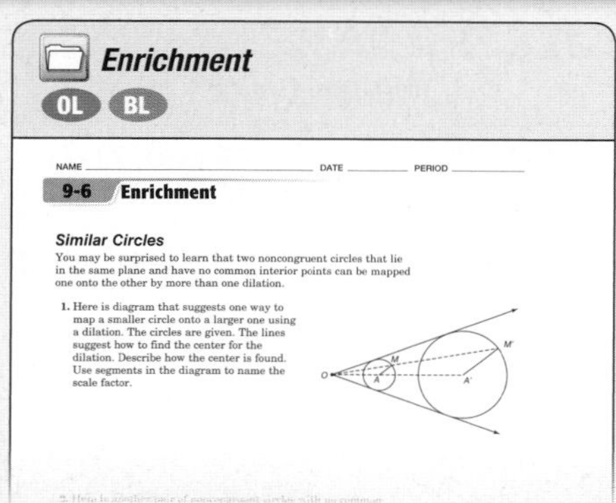
NAME ______ DATE ______ PERIOD ______

9-6 Enrichment

Similar Circles

You may be surprised to learn that two noncongruent circles that lie in the same plane and have no common interior points can be mapped one onto the other by more than one dilation.

1. Here is diagram that suggests one way to map a smaller circle onto a larger one using a dilation. The circles are given. The lines suggest how to find the center for the dilation. Describe how the center is found. Use segments in the diagram to name the scale factor.

CCSS Teaching the Mathematical Practices

Sense-Making Mathematically proficient students start by explaining the meaning of a problem to themselves and looking for entry points to its solution. They plan a solution pathway rather than simply jumping into a solution attempt. In Exercises 21–26, encourage students to make a plan to solve each problem first.

28. **PHOTOGRAPHY AND ART** To make a scale drawing of a photograph, students overlay a $\frac{1}{4}$-inch grid on a 5-inch by 7-inch high contrast photo, overlay a $\frac{1}{2}$-inch grid on a 10-inch by 14-inch piece of drawing paper, and then sketch the image in each square of the photo to the corresponding square on the drawing paper.

a. What is the scale factor of the dilation? **2:1**

b. To create an image that is 10 times as large as the original, what size grids are needed? **2.5 in.**

c. What would be the area of a grid drawing of a 5-inch by 7-inch photo that used 2-inch grids? **2240 in^2**

29. **MEASUREMENT** Determine whether the image shown is a dilation of *ABCD*. Explain your reasoning.

29. No; sample answer: The measures of the sides of the rectangles are not proportional, so they are not similar and cannot be a dilation.

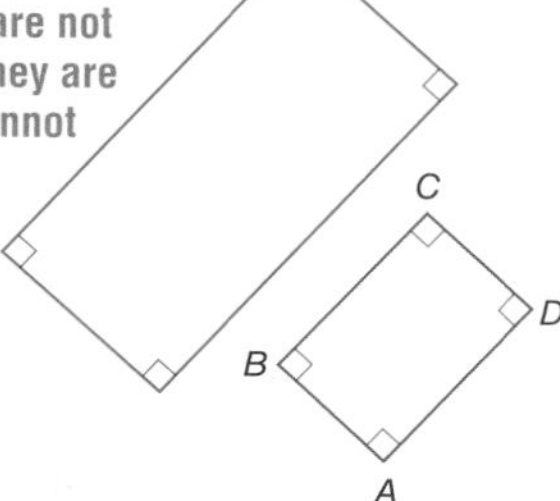

30. **COORDINATE GEOMETRY** *WXYZ* has vertices $W(6, 2)$, $X(3, 7)$, $Y(-1, 4)$, and $Z(4, -2)$. **a–b. See margin.**

a. Graph *WXYZ* and find the perimeter of the figure. Round to the nearest tenth.

b. Graph the image of *WXYZ* after a dilation of $\frac{1}{2}$ centered at the origin.

c. Find the perimeter of the dilated image. Round to the nearest tenth. How is the perimeter of the dilated image related to the perimeter of *WXYZ*?

30c. 11.6; The perimeter of the dilated figure is half of the perimeter of *WXYZ*.

31. **CHANGING DIMENSIONS** A three-dimensional figure can also undergo a dilation. Consider the rectangular prism shown.

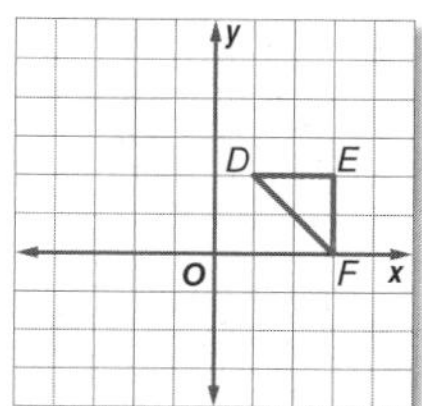

a. Find the surface area and volume of the prism.

b. Find the surface area and volume of the prism after a dilation with a scale factor of 2.

c. Find the surface area and volume of the prism after a dilation with a scale factor of $\frac{1}{2}$. **surface area: 22 cm^2; volume: 6 cm^3**

d. How many times as great is the surface area and volume of the image as the preimage after each dilation? **See margin.**

e. Make a conjecture as to the effect a dilation with a positive scale factor *r* would have on the surface area and volume of a prism. **See margin.**

31a. surface area: 88 cm^2; volume: 48 cm^3

31b. surface area: 352 cm^2; volume: 384 cm^3

32. **CCSS PERSEVERANCE** Refer to the graph of $\triangle DEF$. **a–c. See margin.**

a. Graph the dilation of $\triangle DEF$ centered at point *D* with a scale factor of 3.

b. Describe the dilation as a composition of transformations including a dilation with a scale factor of 3 centered at the origin.

c. If a figure is dilated by a scale factor of 3 with a center of dilation (x, y), what composition of transformations, including a dilation with a scale factor of 3 centered at the origin, will produce the same final image?

CCSS Teaching the Mathematical Practices

Perseverance Mathematically proficient students check their answers to problems using a different method, and they continually ask themselves, "does this make sense?" Encourage students to use alternative methods of problem solving.

Additional Answers

30a. 23.1

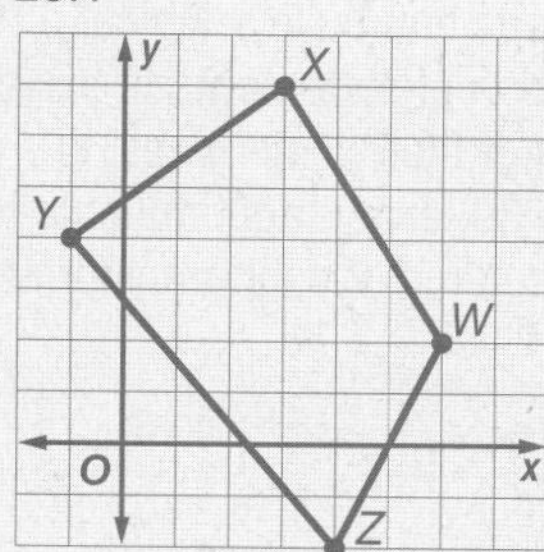

30b.

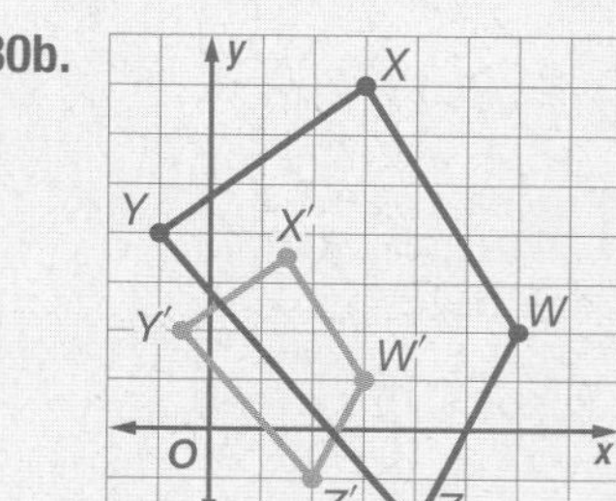

31d. surface area: 4 times greater after dilation with scale factor 2; $\frac{1}{4}$ as great after dilation with scale factor $\frac{1}{2}$. Volume: 8 times greater after dilation with scale factor 2; $\frac{1}{8}$ as great after dilation with scale factor $\frac{1}{2}$.

31e. The surface area of the preimage would be multiplied by r^2. The volume of the preimage would be multiplied by r^3.

32a.

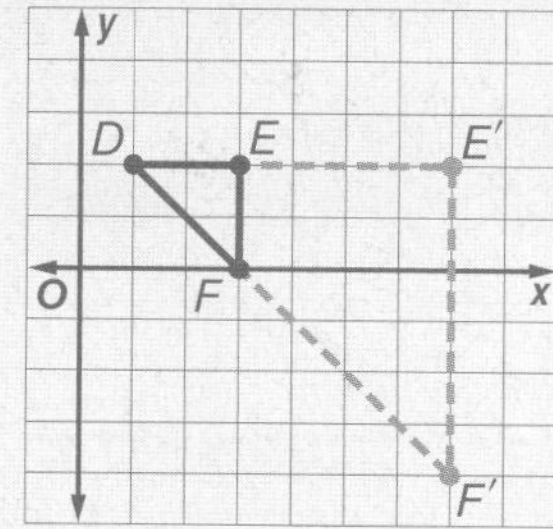

32b. the composition of a dilation with scale factor 3 centered at the origin and a translation along $\langle -2, -4 \rangle$

32c. the composition of a dilation with a scale factor of 3 centered at the origin and a translation along $\langle -2x, -2y \rangle$

Multiple Representations

In Exercise 36, students use geometric sketches, a table, algebraic expressions, and verbal description to investigate dilations centered at the origin with negative scale factors.

Teaching the Mathematical Practices

Arguments Mathematically proficient students understand and use stated assumptions and definitions in constructing arguments. They make conjectures and build a logical progression of statements to explore the truth of their conjectures. In Exercise 39, encourage students to draw diagrams of each transformation.

Additional Answers

34.

$\frac{4}{5}$

35.

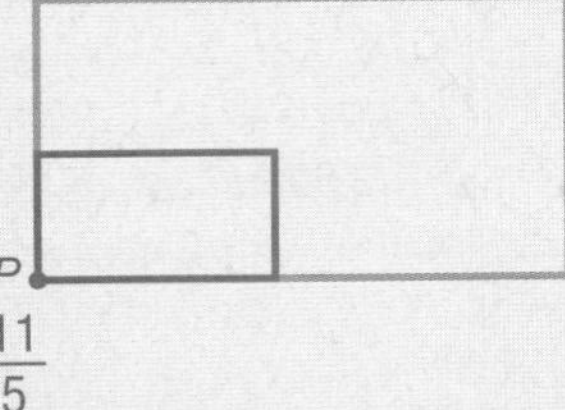

$\frac{11}{5}$

36a.

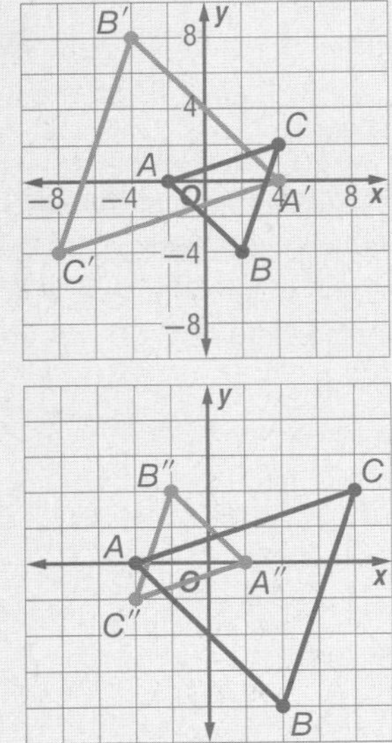

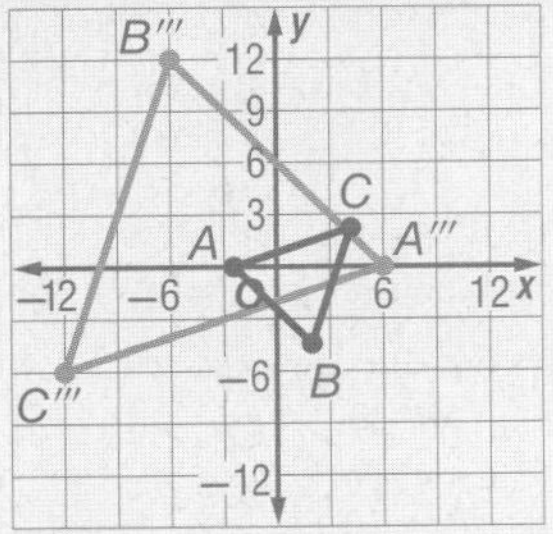

Scale Factor	Coordinates		
	A	B	C
−2	(4, 0)	(−4, 8)	(−8, −4)
$-\frac{1}{2}$	(1, 0)	(−1, 2)	(−2, −1)
−3	(6, 0)	(−6, 12)	(−12, −6)

33. HEALTH A coronary artery may be dilated with a balloon catheter as shown. The cross section of the middle of the balloon is a circle.

a. A surgeon inflates a balloon catheter in a patient's coronary artery, dilating the balloon from a diameter of 1.5 millimeters to 2 millimeters. Find the scale factor of this dilation. $1\frac{1}{3}$

b. Find the cross-sectional area of the balloon before and after the dilation. 1.77 mm²; 3.14 mm²

Each figure shows a preimage and its image after a dilation centered at point *P*. Copy each figure, locate point *P*, and estimate the scale factor. 34–35. See margin.

34.

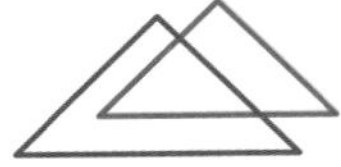

35.

36. MULTIPLE REPRESENTATIONS In this problem, you will investigate dilations centered at the origin with negative scale factors. a. See margin.

a. Geometric Draw $\triangle ABC$ with points $A(-2, 0)$, $B(2, -4)$, and $C(4, 2)$. Then draw the image of $\triangle ABC$ after a dilation centered at the origin with a scale factor of −2. Repeat the dilation with scale factors of $-\frac{1}{2}$ and −3. Record the coordinates for each dilation.

b. Verbal Make a conjecture about the function relationship for a dilation centered at the origin with a negative scale factor.

36b. Sample answer: Each of the coordinates is multiplied by the negative scale factor.

c. Analytical Write the function rule for a dilation centered at the origin with a scale factor of $-k$. $(x, y) \rightarrow (-kx, -ky)$

d. Verbal Describe a dilation centered at the origin with a negative scale factor as a composition of transformations.

36d. Sample answer: A dilation centered at the origin with a scale factor of $-k$ can be described as a dilation centered at the origin with a scale factor of k and a rotation 180° about the origin.

H.O.T. Problems Use Higher-Order Thinking Skills

37. CHALLENGE Find the equation for the dilated image of the line $y = 4x - 2$ if the dilation is centered at the origin with a scale factor of 1.5. $y = 4x - 3$

38. WRITING IN MATH Are parallel lines (parallelism) and collinear points (collinearity) preserved under all transformations? Explain. See Ch. 9 Answer Appendix.

39. CCSS ARGUMENTS Determine whether invariant points are *sometimes*, *always*, or *never* maintained for the transformations described below. If so, describe the invariant point(s). If not, explain why invariant points are not possible. a–e. See margin.

a. dilation of *ABCD* with scale factor 1

b. rotation of $\overline{AB}$ 74° about *B*

c. reflection of $\triangle MNP$ in the *x*-axis

d. translation of *PQRS* along $\langle 7, 3 \rangle$

e. dilation of $\triangle XYZ$ centered at the origin with scale factor 2

40. OPEN ENDED Graph a triangle. Dilate the triangle so that its area is four times the area of the original triangle. State the scale factor and center of your dilation. See margin.

41. WRITING IN MATH Can you use transformations to create congruent figures, similar figures, and equal figures? Explain. See margin.

Standardized Test Practice

42. EXTENDED RESPONSE Quadrilateral *PQRS* was dilated to form quadrilateral *WXYZ*.

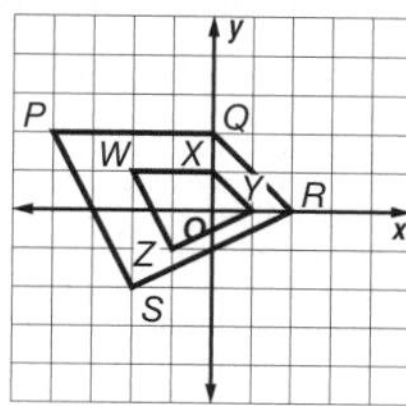

a. Is the dilation from *PQRS* to *WXYZ* an enlargement or reduction? **reduction**

b. Which number *best* represents the scale factor for this dilation? $\frac{1}{2}$

43. ALGEBRA How many ounces of pure water must a pharmacist add to 50 ounces of a 15% saline solution to make a solution that is 10% saline? **A**

A 25   C 15

B 20   D 5

44. Tionna wants to replicate a painting in an art museum. The painting is 3 feet wide and 6 feet long. She decides on a dilation reduction factor of 0.25. What size paper should she use? **J**

F 4 in. × 8 in.   H 8 in. × 16 in.

G 6 in. × 12 in.   J 10 in. × 20 in.

45. SAT/ACT For all x, $(x - 7)^2 = ?$ **D**

A $x^2 - 49$ D $x^2 - 14x + 49$

B $x^2 + 49$ E $x^2 + 14x - 49$

C $x^2 - 14x - 49$

Spiral Review

State whether the figure appears to have line symmetry. Write *yes* or *no*. If so, copy the figure, draw all lines of symmetry, and state their number. (Lesson 9-5)

46. 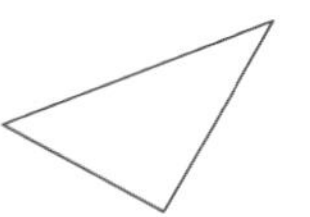 **no**

47. 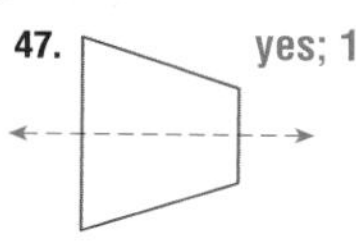 **yes; 1**

48. 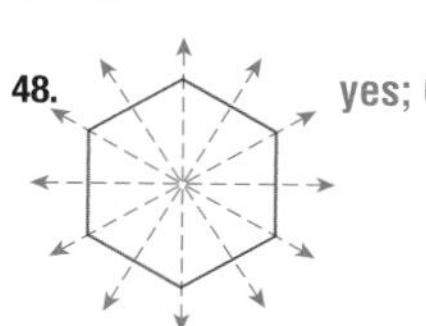 **yes; 6**

Describe the transformations that combined to map each figure. (Lesson 9-4)

49. 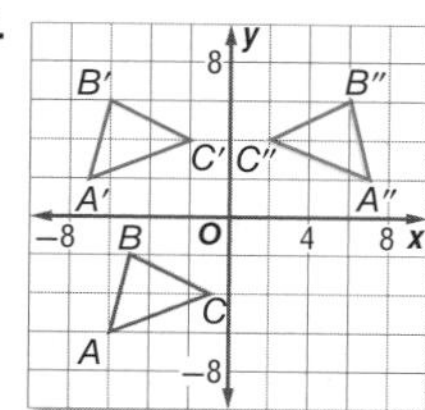

translation along ⟨−1, 8⟩ and reflection in the *y*-axis

50. 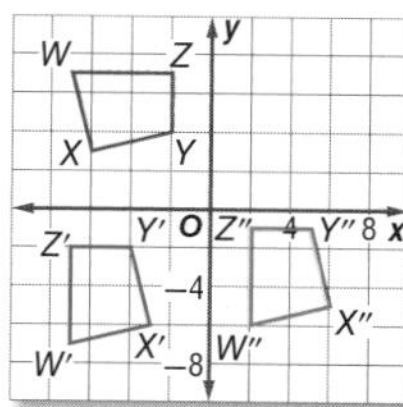

rotation 90° about the origin and translation along ⟨9, 1⟩

51. PAINTING A painter sets a ladder up to reach the bottom of a second-story window 16 feet above the ground. The base of the ladder is 12 feet from the house. While the painter mixes the paint, a neighbor's dog bumps the ladder, which moves the base 2 feet farther away from the house. How far up the side of the house does the ladder reach? (Lesson 8-2) **$2\sqrt{51}$ ft ≈ 14.3 ft**

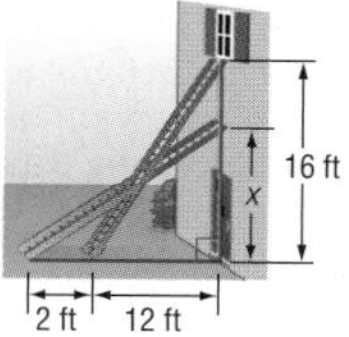

Skills Review

Find the value of x to the nearest tenth.

52. $58.9 = 2x$ **29.5**

53. $\frac{108.6}{\pi} = x$ **34.6**

54. $228.4 = \pi x$ **72.7**

55. $\frac{336.4}{x} = \pi$ **107.1**

40. 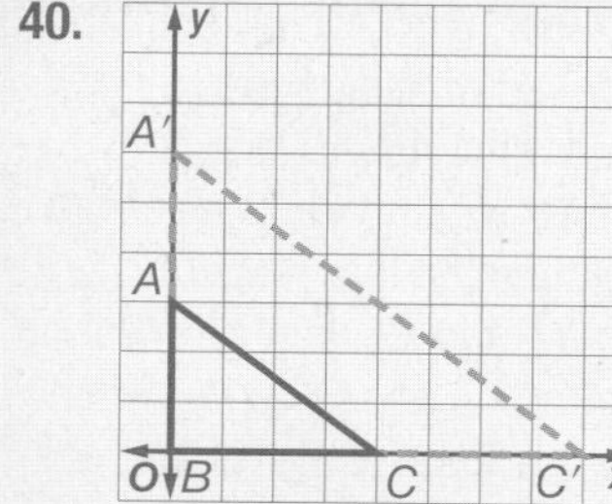

$k = 2$, center of dilation is B.

41. Sample answer: Translations, reflections, and rotations produce congruent figures because the sides and angles of the preimage are congruent to the corresponding sides and angles of the image. Dilations produce similar figures, because the angles of the preimage and the image are congruent and the sides of the preimage are proportional to the corresponding sides of the image. A dilation with a scale factor of 1 produces an equal figure because the image is mapped onto its corresponding parts in the preimage.

4 Assess

Ticket Out the Door Students should measure an object in the room and apply a dilation to reduce the object and make a model with poster board and/or construction paper. Have students turn in their models before they leave the classroom.

Formative Assessment

Check for students understanding of Lesson 9-6.

Quiz 4, p. 46

Additional Answers

39a. Always; sample answer: Since a dilation of 1 maps an image onto itself, all four vertices will remain invariant under the dilation.

39b. Always; sample answer: Since the rotation is centered at B, point B will always remain invariant under the rotation.

39c. Sometimes: sample answer: If one of the vertices is on the *x*-axis, then that point will remain invariant under reflection. If two vertices are on the *x*-axis, then the two vertices located on the *x*-axis will remain invariant under reflection.

39d. Never; when a figure is translated, all points move an equal distance. Therefore, no points can remain invariant under translation.

39e. Sometimes; sample answer: If one of the vertices of the triangle is located at the origin, then that vertex would remain invariant under the dilation. If none of the points on $\triangle XYZ$ are located at the origin, then no points will remain invariant under the dilation.

1 Focus

Objective

- Explore how triangle congruence and similarity follow from an understanding of transformations.

2 Teach

Working in Cooperative Groups

Divide the class into pairs. Work through Activity 1 as a class. Then ask students to work with their partners to complete Exercises 1–3.

Practice Have students complete Exercise 4.

3 Assess

Formative Assessment

Use Exercises 5–9 to assess whether students comprehend how to use rigid motions and dilations to establish triangle congruence and similarity.

From Concrete to Abstract

Have students describe the transformation(s) and/or dilation necessary to map $\triangle ABC$ onto $\triangle XYZ$ in Exercises 7–9 or explain how they know that $\triangle ABC$ cannot be mapped onto $\triangle XYZ$.

Additional Answers

1. Sample answer: The activity establishes a rigid motion that maps $\overline{AB}$ onto $\overline{XY}$, $\angle A$ onto $\angle X$, and $\overline{AC}$ onto $\overline{XZ}$, ensuring that $\overline{AB} \cong \overline{XY}$, $\angle A \cong \angle X$, and $\overline{AC} \cong \overline{XZ}$, which is our given when using the SAS congruence criterion. From these statements we know that A is mapped onto X, B is mapped onto Y, and C is mapped onto Z. Since distances between points are preserved in a rigid motion, we know that $\overline{BC} \cong \overline{YZ}$. Since angle measures are preserved in a rigid motion, we know that $\angle B \cong \angle Y$ and $\angle C \cong \angle Z$. Therefore, $\triangle ABC$ is mapped exactly onto $\triangle XYZ$, so $\triangle ABC \cong \triangle XYZ$.

EXTEND 9-6 Geometry Lab: Establishing Triangle Congruence and Similarity

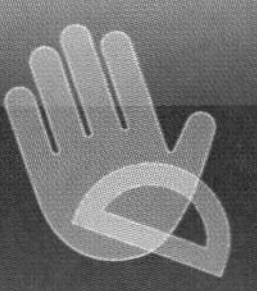

In Chapter 4, two triangles were defined to be congruent if all of their corresponding parts were congruent and the criteria for proving triangle congruence (SAS, SSS, and ASA) were presented as postulates. Triangle congruence can also be defined in terms of rigid motions (reflections, translations, rotations).

Common Core State Standards
Content Standards
G.CO.8 Explain how the criteria for triangle congruence (ASA, SAS, and SSS) follow from the definition of congruence in terms of rigid motions.
G.SRT.3 Use the properties of similarity transformations to establish the AA criterion for two triangles to be similar.
Mathematical Practices 5

The **principle of superposition** states that two figures are congruent if and only if there is a rigid motion or a series of rigid motions that maps one figure exactly onto the other. We can use the following assumed properties of rigid motions to establish the SAS, SSS, and ASA criteria for triangle congruence.

- The distance between points is preserved. Sides are mapped to sides of the same length.
- Angle measures are preserved. Angles are mapped to angles of the same measure.

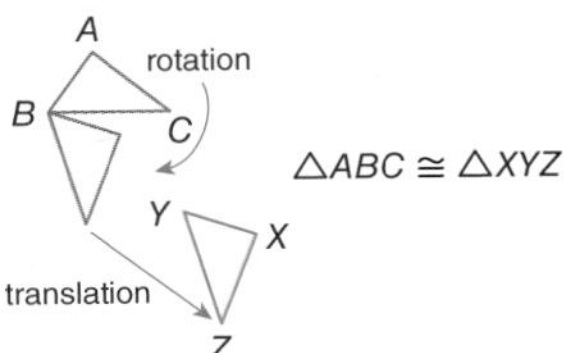

Activity 1 Establish Congruence

Use a rigid motion to map side $\overline{AB}$ of $\triangle ABC$ onto side $\overline{XY}$ of $\triangle XYZ$, $\angle A$ onto $\angle X$, and side $\overline{AC}$ onto side $\overline{XZ}$.

Step 1 Copy the triangles below onto a sheet of paper.

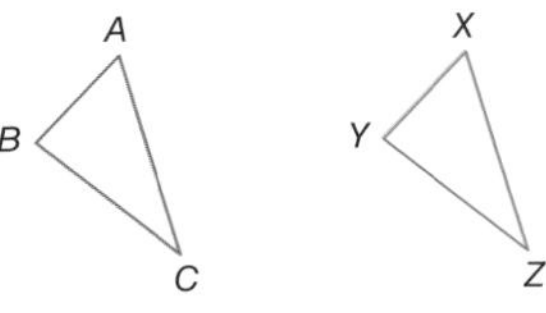

Step 2 Copy $\triangle ABC$ onto a sheet of tracing paper and label. Translate the paper until $\overline{AB}$, $\angle A$, and $\overline{AC}$ lie exactly on top of $\overline{XY}$, $\angle X$, and $\overline{XZ}$.

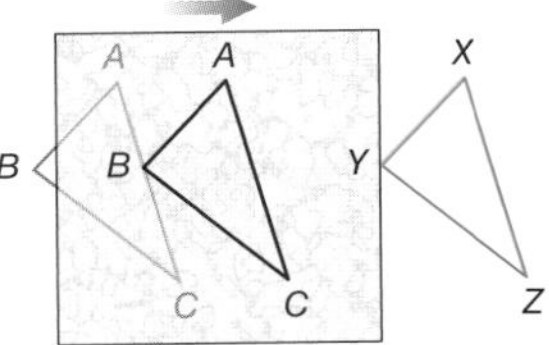

Analyze the Results 1–2. See margin.

1. Use this activity to explain how the SAS criterion for triangle congruence follows from the definition of congruence in terms of rigid motions. (*Hint*: Extend lines on the tracing paper.)

2. Use the principle of superposition to explain why two triangles are congruent if and only if corresponding pairs of sides and corresponding pairs of angles are congruent.

Using the same triangles shown above, describe the steps in an activity to illustrate the indicated criterion for triangle congruence. Then explain how this criterion follows from the principle of superposition. 3–4. See margin.

3. SSS
4. ASA

2. Sample answer: By superposition, two triangles are congruent if and only if there is a rigid motion or a series of rigid motions that map one triangle exactly onto the other. One triangle will map exactly onto another triangle if and only if corresponding pairs of sides and corresponding pairs of angles are congruent. Thus, two triangles are congruent if and only if corresponding pairs of sides and corresponding pairs of angles are congruent.
3. Sample answer: Step 1, copy the triangles onto a sheet of paper; Step 2, copy and label $\triangle ABC$ onto a sheet of tracing paper. Step 3, translate the paper until $\overline{AB}$, $\overline{AC}$, and $\overline{BC}$ lie exactly on top of $\overline{XY}$, $\overline{XZ}$, and $\overline{YZ}$. The activity establishes a rigid motion that maps $\overline{AB}$ onto $\overline{XY}$, $\overline{AC}$ onto $\overline{XZ}$, and $\overline{BC}$ onto $\overline{YZ}$ ensuring that $\overline{AB} \cong \overline{XY}$, $\overline{AC} \cong \overline{XZ}$, and $\overline{BC} \cong \overline{YZ}$. From these statements we know that A is mapped onto X, B is mapped onto Y, and C is mapped onto Z. Since angle measures are preserved in a rigid motion, we know that $\angle A \cong \angle X$,

Two figures are similar if there is a rigid motion, or a series of rigid motions, followed by a dilation, or vice versa, that map one figure exactly onto the other. We can use the following assumed properties of dilations to establish the AA criteria for triangle similarity.

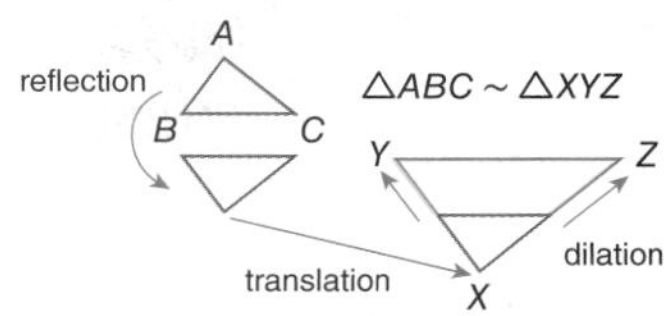

- Angle measures are preserved. Angles are mapped to angles of the same measure.
- Lines are mapped to parallel lines and sides are mapped to parallel sides that are longer or shorter in the ratio given by the scale factor.

Activity 2 Establish Similarity

Use a rigid motion followed by a dilation to map $\angle B$ onto $\angle Y$ and $\angle A$ onto $\angle X$.

Step 1 Copy the triangles below onto a sheet of paper.

Step 2 Copy $\triangle ABC$ onto tracing paper and label.

Step 3 Translate the paper until $\angle B$ lies exactly on top of $\angle Y$. Tape this paper down so that it will not move.

Step 4 On another sheet of tracing paper, copy and label $\angle A$.

Step 5 Translate this second sheet of tracing paper along the line from A to Y on the first sheet, until this second $\angle A$ lies exactly on top of $\angle X$.

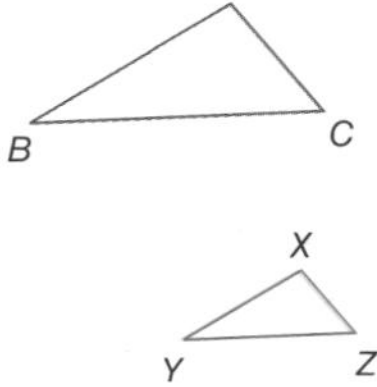

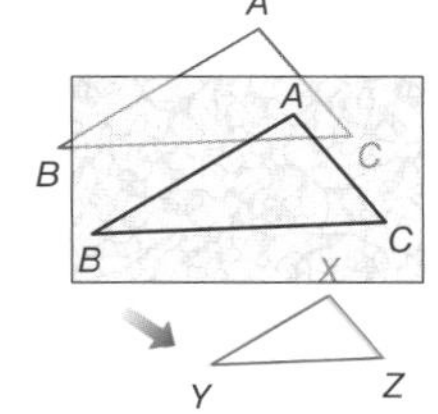

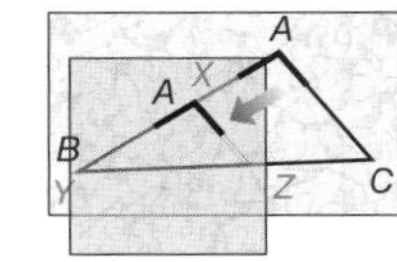

Analyze the Results **5–6. See margin.**

5. Use this activity to explain how the AA criterion for triangle similarity follows from the definition of similarity in terms of dilations. (*Hint*: Use parallel lines.)
6. Use the definition of similarity in terms of transformations to explain why two triangles are similar if all corresponding pairs of angles are congruent and all corresponding pairs of sides are proportional.

Use a series of rigid motions and/or dilations to determine whether $\triangle ABC$ and $\triangle XYZ$ are *congruent, similar,* or *neither.*

7. **congruent**

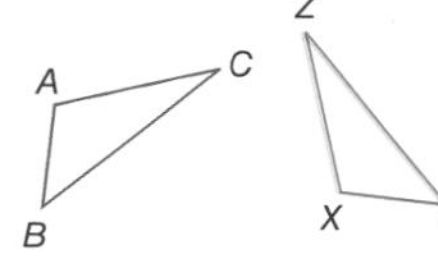

8. **similar**

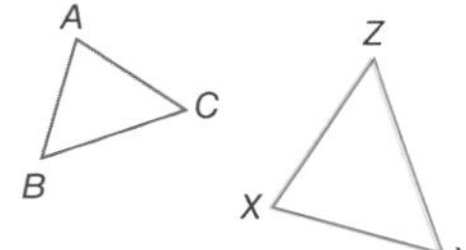

9. **neither**

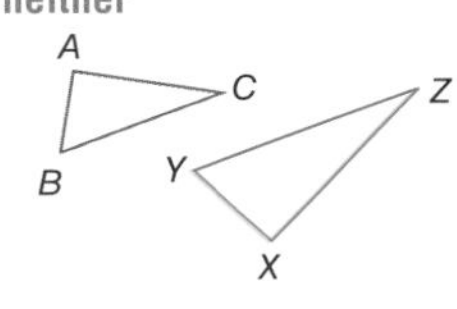

6. Sample answer: Two triangles are similar if there is a dilation followed by a rigid motion or a series of rigid motions that map one triangle exactly onto the other. Both the dilation and the rigid motion or series of rigid motions preserve angle measure, so the corresponding angles mapped to each other are congruent. The dilation followed by the rigid motion or series of rigid motions maps the sides of the first triangle to corresponding sides longer or shorter in the ratio given by the scale factor k of the dilation, so the corresponding sides of the two triangles are proportional with a constant of proportionality k. Thus, two triangles are similar if corresponding pairs of angles are congruent and all corresponding pairs of sides are proportional.

Additional Answers

$\angle B \cong \angle Y$, and $\angle C \cong \angle Z$. Therefore, $\triangle ABC$ is mapped exactly onto $\triangle XYZ$, so $\triangle ABC \cong \triangle XYZ$.

4. Sample answer: Step 1, copy the triangles onto a sheet of paper; Step 2, copy and label $\triangle ABC$ onto a sheet of tracing paper. Step 3, translate the paper until $\angle A$, $\overline{AB}$, and $\angle B$ lie exactly on top of $\angle X$, $\overline{XY}$, and $\angle Y$. The activity establishes a rigid motion that maps $\angle A$ onto $\angle X$, $\overline{AB}$ onto $\overline{XY}$, and $\angle B$ onto $\angle Y$ ensuring that $\angle A \cong \angle X$, $\overline{AB} \cong \overline{XY}$, and $\angle B \cong \angle Y$. From these statements we know that A is mapped onto X, B is mapped onto Y, and C is mapped onto Z. Since distances between points are preserved in a rigid motion, we know that $\overline{BC} \cong \overline{YZ}$. Since angle measures are preserved in a rigid motion, we know that $\angle A \cong \angle X$ and $\angle C \cong \angle Z$. Therefore, $\triangle ABC$ is mapped exactly onto $\triangle XYZ$, so $\triangle ABC \cong \triangle XYZ$.
5. The activity establishes a rigid motion followed by a dilation that maps $\angle A$ onto $\angle X$ and $\angle B$ onto $\angle Y$, ensuring that $\angle A \cong \angle X$ and $\angle B \cong \angle Y$, which is our given when using the AA similarity criterion. If we extend the sides of $\angle A$ on the second sheet, call this $\angle A'$, one side intersects side $\overleftrightarrow{BC}$ at exactly point Z. Since sides in a dilation are mapped to parallel lines, the lines through $\overline{A'Z}$ and $\overline{AC}$ are parallel. Since parallel lines $\overleftrightarrow{A'Z}$ and $\overleftrightarrow{AC}$ are cut by transversal $\overleftrightarrow{BC}$, $\angle A'ZB \cong \angle ACB$ since corresponding angles of parallel lines cut by a transversal are congruent. Since $\angle A' \cong \angle A$ and $\angle A \cong \angle X$, $\angle A' \cong \angle X$, and $\angle B \cong \angle Y$, we can say that $\angle Z \cong \angle C$. Since a dilation maps sides onto parallel sides longer or shorter in the ratio given by the scale factor, $\frac{A'Z}{AC} = \frac{A'Y}{AB} = \frac{YZ}{BC}$ and by substitution, $\frac{XZ}{AC} = \frac{XY}{AB} = \frac{YZ}{BC}$. Therefore, since all corresponding pairs of angles are congruent and all corresponding pairs of sides are proportional, $\triangle ABC \sim \triangle XYZ$.

Formative Assessment

KeyVocabulary The page references after each word denote where that term was first introduced. If students have difficulty answering questions 1–10, remind them that they can use these page references to refresh their memories about the vocabulary terms.

Summative Assessment

Vocabulary Test, p. 48

Vocabulary Review

Vocabulary Review provides students the opportunity to check their understanding of important concepts and terminology in an online game format.

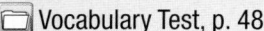

FOLDABLES StudyOrganizer

Dinah Zike's Foldables®

Have students look through the chapter to make sure they have included examples in their Foldables for each lesson of the chapter. Suggest that students keep their Foldables handy while completing the Study Guide and Review pages. Point out that their Foldables can serve as a quick review tool for studying for the chapter test.

Additional Answers

11.

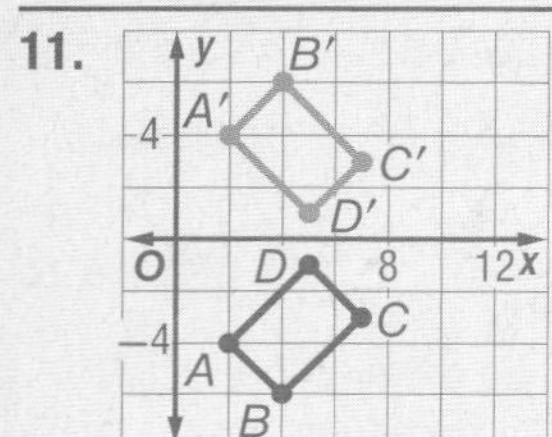

12.

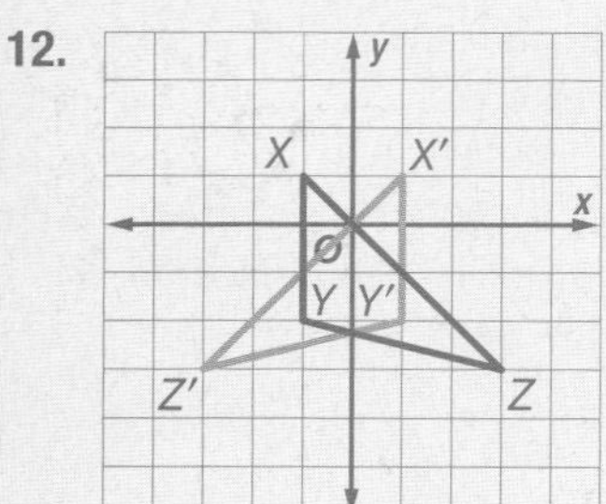

13.

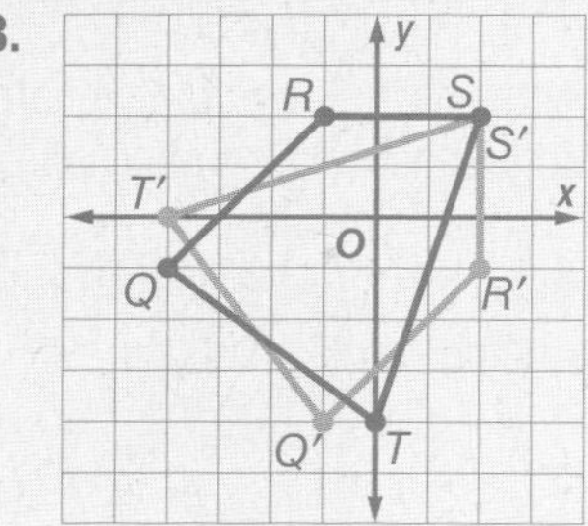

Chapter 9 Study Guide and Review

Study Guide

KeyConcepts

Reflections (Lesson 9-1)

- A reflection is a transformation representing a flip of a figure over a point, line, or plane.

Translations (Lesson 9-2)

- A translation is a transformation that moves all points of a figure the same distance in the same direction.
- A translation maps each point to its image along a translation vector.

Rotations (Lesson 9-3)

- A rotation turns each point in a figure through the same angle about a fixed point.

Compositions of Transformations (Lesson 9-4)

- A translation can be represented as a composition of reflections in parallel lines and a rotation can be represented as a composition of reflections in intersecting lines.

Symmetry (Lesson 9-5)

- The line of symmetry in a figure is a line where the figure could be folded in half so that the two halves match exactly.
- The number of times a figure maps onto itself as it rotates from 0° to 360° is called the order of symmetry.
- The magnitude of symmetry is the smallest angle through which a figure can be rotated so that it maps onto itself.

Dilations (Lesson 9-6)

- Dilations enlarge or reduce figures proportionally.

FOLDABLES StudyOrganizer

Be sure the Key Concepts are noted in your Foldable.

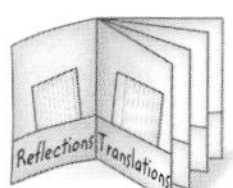

KeyVocabulary

- angle of rotation (p. 640)
- axis symmetry (p. 665)
- center of rotation (p. 640)
- composition of transformations (p. 651)
- glide reflection (p. 651)
- line of reflection (p. 623)
- line of symmetry (p. 663)
- line symmetry (p. 663)
- magnitude of symmetry (p. 664)
- order of symmetry (p. 664)
- plane symmetry (p. 665)
- rotational symmetry (p. 664)
- symmetry (p. 663)
- translation vector (p. 632)

VocabularyCheck

Choose the term that best completes each sentence.

1. When a transformation is applied to a figure, and then another transformation is applied to its image, this is a(n) (composition of transformations, order of symmetries).
2. If a figure is folded across a straight line and the halves match exactly, the fold line is called the (line of reflection, line of symmetry).
3. A (dilation, glide reflection) enlarges or reduces a figure proportionally.
4. The number of times a figure maps onto itself as it rotates from 0° to 360° is called the (magnitude of symmetry, order of symmetry).
5. A (line of reflection, translation vector) is the same distance from each point of a figure and its image.
6. A figure has (a center of rotation, symmetry) if it can be mapped onto itself by a rigid motion.
7. A glide reflection includes both a reflection and a (rotation, translation).
8. To rotate a point (90°, 180°) counterclockwise about the origin, multiply the y-coordinate by -1 and then interchange the x- and y-coordinates.
9. A (vector, reflection) is a congruence transformation.
10. A figure has (plane symmetry, rotational symmetry) if the figure can be mapped onto itself by a rotation between 0° and 360° about the center of the figure.

Lesson-by-Lesson Review

9-1 Reflections

Graph each figure and its image under the given reflection. 11–14. See margin.

11. rectangle $ABCD$ with $A(2, -4)$, $B(4, -6)$, $C(7, -3)$, and $D(5, -1)$ in the x-axis
12. triangle XYZ with $X(-1, 1)$, $Y(-1, -2)$, and $Z(3, -3)$ in the y-axis
13. quadrilateral $QRST$ with $Q(-4, -1)$, $R(-1, 2)$, $S(2, 2)$, and $T(0, -4)$ in the line $y = x$
14. **ART** Anita is making the two-piece sculpture shown for a memorial garden. In her design, one piece of the sculpture is a reflection of the other, to be placed beside a sidewalk that would be located along the line of reflection. Copy the figures and draw the line of reflection.

Example 1

Graph $\triangle JKL$ with vertices $J(1, 4)$, $K(2, 1)$, and $L(6, 2)$ and its reflected image in the x-axis.

Multiply the y-coordinate of each vertex by -1.

$(x, y) \rightarrow (x, -y)$

$J(1, 4) \rightarrow J'(1, -4)$

$K(2, 1) \rightarrow K'(2, -1)$

$L(6, 2) \rightarrow L'(6, -2)$

Graph $\triangle JKL$ and its image $\triangle J'K'L'$.

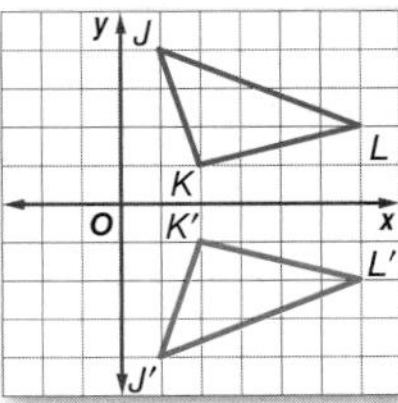

9-2 Translations

15. Graph $\triangle ABC$ with vertices $A(0, -1)$, $B(2, 0)$, $C(3, -3)$ and its image along $\langle -5, 4 \rangle$. 15–17. See margin.
16. Copy the figure and the given translation vector. Then draw the translation of the figure along the translation vector.

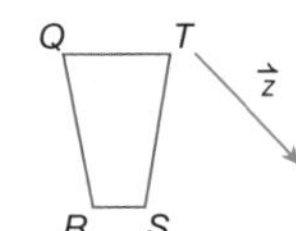

17. **DANCE** Five dancers are positioned onstage as shown. Dancers B, F, and C move along $\langle 0, -2 \rangle$, while dancer A moves along $\langle 5, -1 \rangle$. Draw the dancers' final positions.

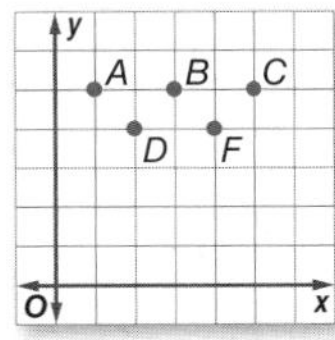

Example 2

Graph $\triangle XYZ$ with vertices $X(2, 2)$, $Y(5, 5)$, $Z(5, 3)$ and its image along $\langle -3, -5 \rangle$.

The vector indicates a translation 3 units left and 5 units down.

$(x, y) \rightarrow (x - 3, y - 5)$

$X(2, 2) \rightarrow X'(-1, -3)$

$Y(5, 5) \rightarrow Y'(2, 0)$

$Z(5, 3) \rightarrow Z'(2, -2)$

Graph $\triangle XYZ$ and its image $\triangle X'Y'Z'$.

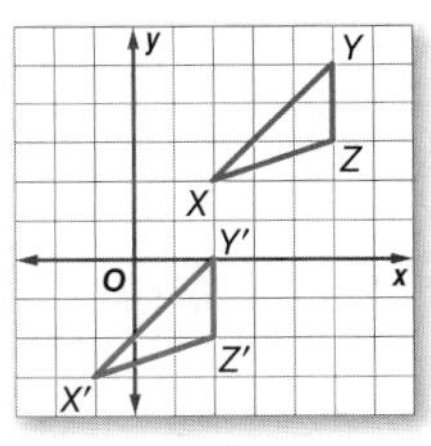

Lesson-by-Lesson Review

Intervention If the given examples are not sufficient to review the topics covered by the questions, remind students that the lesson references tell them where to review that topic in their textbooks.

Two-Day Option Have students complete the Lesson-by-Lesson Review. Then you can use eAssessment to customize another review worksheet that practices all the objectives of this chapter or only the objectives on which your students need more help.

Additional Answers

14.

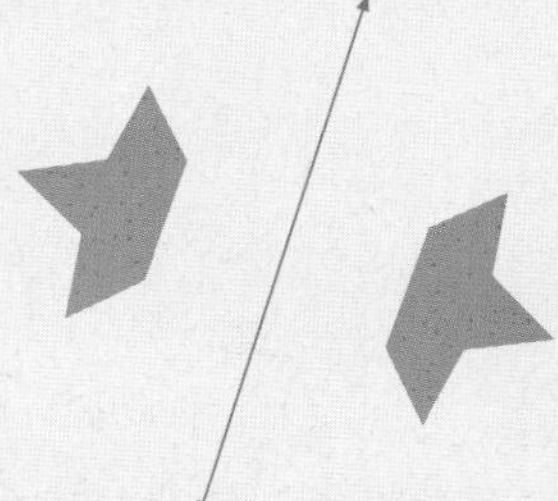

15.

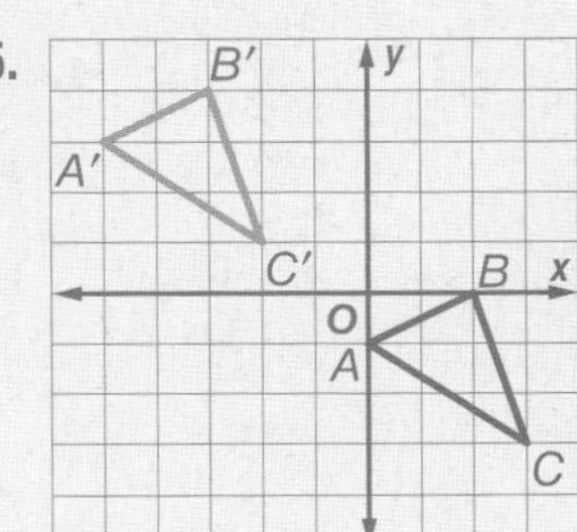

16.

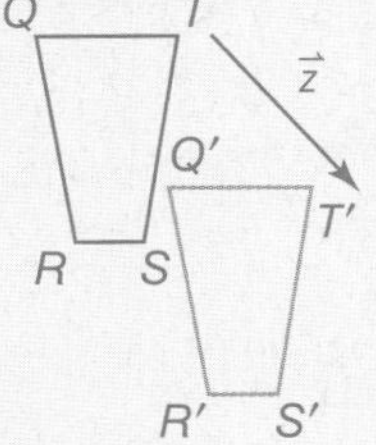

17.

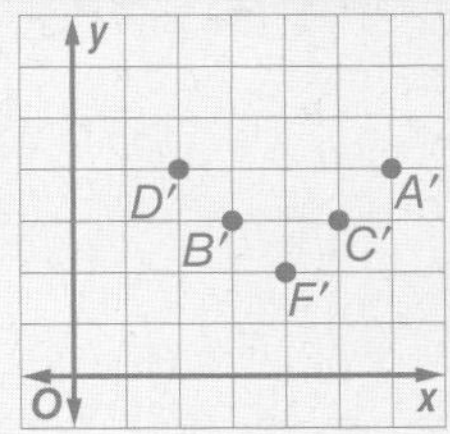

Additional Answers

18.

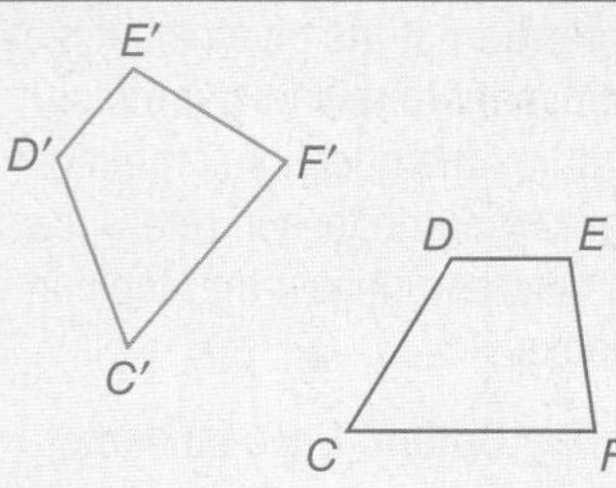

19.

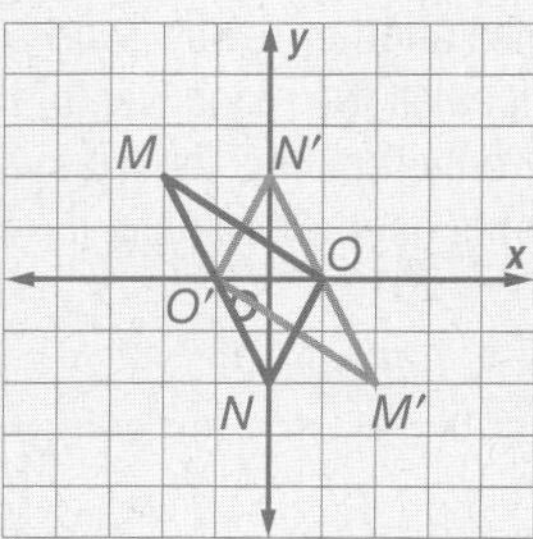

20.

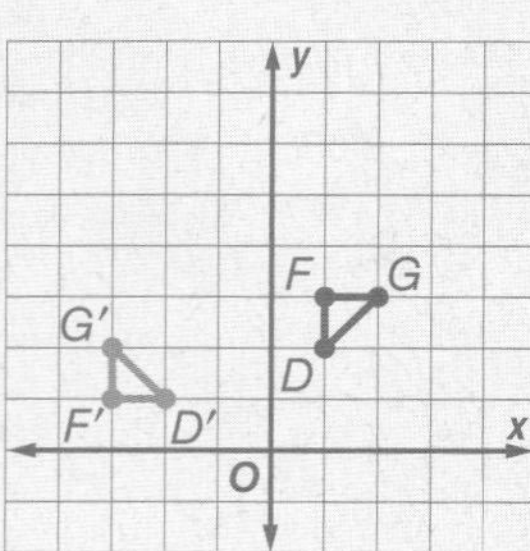

21.

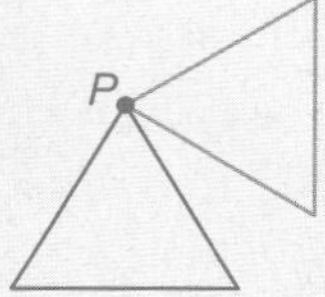

90°

22.

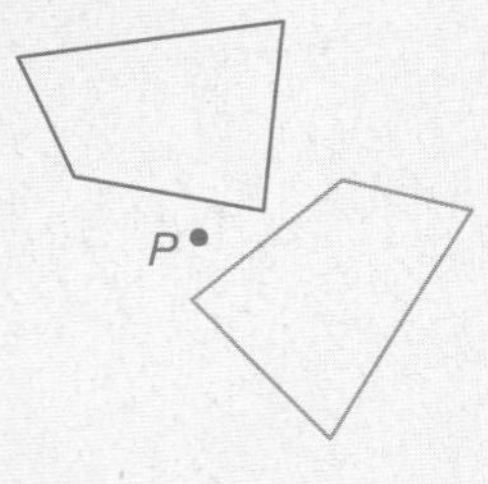

130°

CHAPTER 9 Study Guide and Review *Continued*

9-3 Rotations

18. Copy trapezoid *CDEF* and point *P*. Then use a protractor and ruler to draw a 50° rotation of *CDEF* about point *P*. **18–22. See margin.**

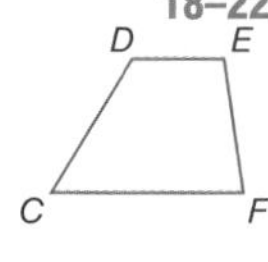

Graph each figure and its image after the specified rotation about the origin.

19. $\triangle MNO$ with vertices $M(-2, 2)$, $N(0, -2)$, $O(1, 0)$; 180°

20. $\triangle DGF$ with vertices $D(1, 2)$, $G(2, 3)$, $F(1, 3)$; 90°

Each figure shows a preimage and its image after a rotation about a point *P*. Copy each figure, locate point *P*, and find the angle of rotation.

21.

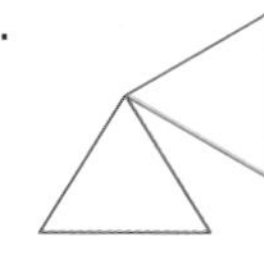

22.

Example 3

Triangle *ABC* has vertices $A(-4, 0)$, $B(-3, 4)$, and $C(-1, 1)$. Graph $\triangle ABC$ and its image after a rotation 270° about the origin.

One method to solve this is to combine a 180° rotation with a 90° rotation. Multiply the *x*- and *y*-coordinates of each vertex by −1.

$(x, y) \rightarrow (-x, -y)$
$A(-4, 0) \rightarrow A'(4, 0)$
$B(-3, 4) \rightarrow B'(3, -4)$
$C(-1, 1) \rightarrow C'(1, -1)$

Multiply the *y*-coordinate of each vertex by −1 and interchange.

$(-x, -y) \rightarrow (y, -x)$
$A'(4, 0) \rightarrow A''(0, 4)$
$B'(3, -4) \rightarrow B''(4, 3)$
$C'(1, -1) \rightarrow C''(1, 1)$

Graph $\triangle ABC$ and its image $\triangle A''B''C''$.

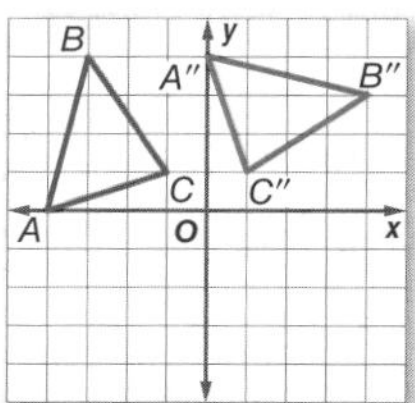

9-4 Compositions of Transformations

Graph each figure with the given vertices and its image after the indicated transformation. **23–25. See margin.**

23. $\overline{CD}$: $C(3, 2)$ and $D(1, 4)$
Reflection: in $y = x$
Rotation: 270° about the origin.

24. $\overline{GH}$: $G(-2, -3)$ and $H(1, 1)$
Translation: along $\langle 4, 2 \rangle$
Reflection: in the *x*-axis

25. PATTERNS Jeremy is creating a pattern for the border of a poster using a stencil. Describe the transformation combination that he used to create the pattern below.

Example 4

The endpoints of $\overline{RS}$ are $R(4, 3)$ and $S(1, 1)$. Graph $\overline{RS}$ and its image after a translation along $\langle -5, -1 \rangle$ and a rotation 180° about the origin.

Step 1 translation along $\langle -5, -1 \rangle$

$(x, y) \rightarrow (x - 5, y - 1)$
$R(4, 3) \rightarrow R'(-1, 2)$
$S(1, 1) \rightarrow S'(-4, 0)$

Step 2 rotation 180° about origin

$(x, y) \rightarrow (-x, -y)$
$R'(-1, 2) \rightarrow R''(1, -2)$
$S'(-4, 0) \rightarrow S''(4, 0)$

23.

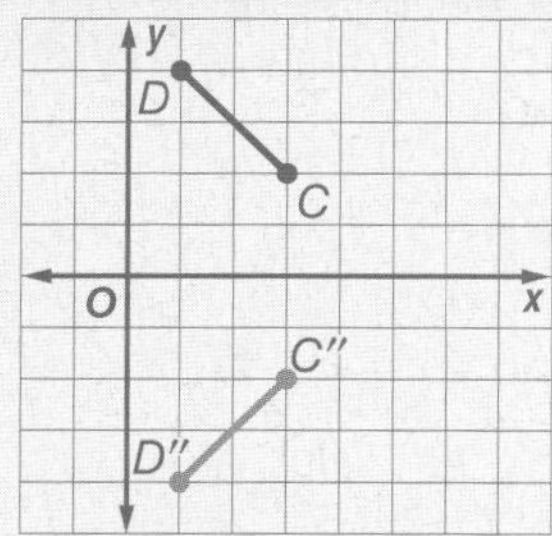

24.

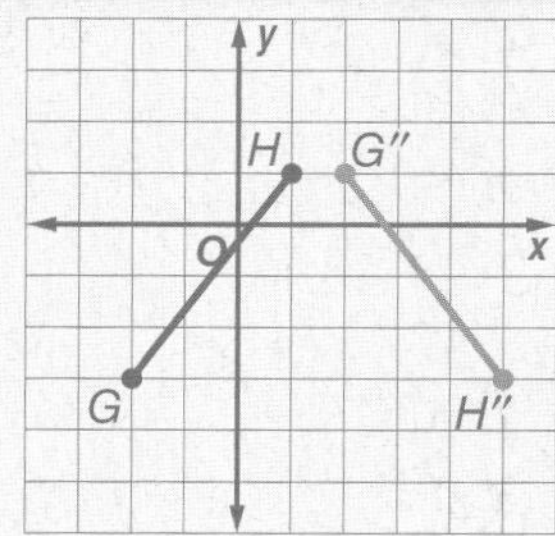

26. Copy and reflect figure T in line ℓ and then line m. Then describe a single transformation that maps T onto T''. See margin.

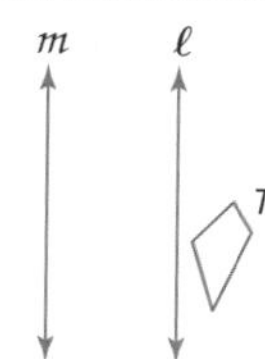

Step 3 Graph $\overline{RS}$ and its image $\overline{R''S''}$.

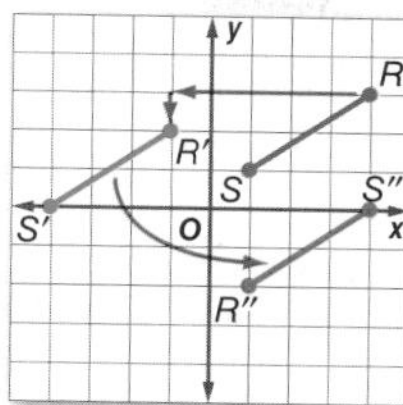

9-5 Symmetry

State whether each figure appears to have line symmetry. Write *yes* or *no*. If so, copy the figure, draw all lines of symmetry, and state their number. 27–28. See margin.

27. 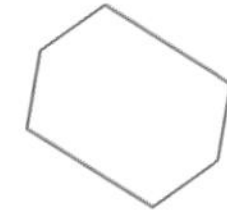

28. 

State whether each figure has rotational symmetry. Write *yes* or *no*. If so, copy the figure, locate the center of symmetry, and state the order and magnitude of symmetry.

29.  See margin.

30.  no

31. **KNITTING** Amy is creating a pattern for a scarf she is knitting for her friend. How many lines of symmetry are there in the pattern? 4

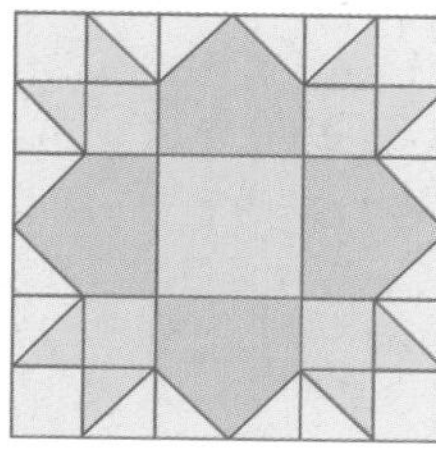

Example 5

State whether each figure has *plane* symmetry, *axis* symmetry, *both*, or *neither*.

a. 

The light bulb has both plane and axis symmetry.

b. The prism has plane symmetry.

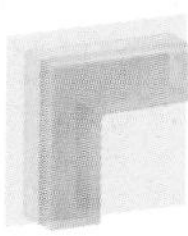

Additional Answers

25. Sample answer: translation right and down, translation of result right and up

26. 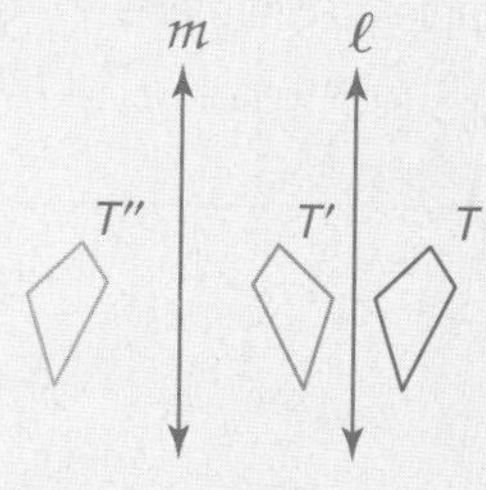

translate left

27. yes; 2

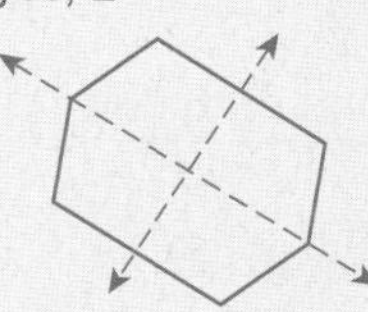

28. yes; 1

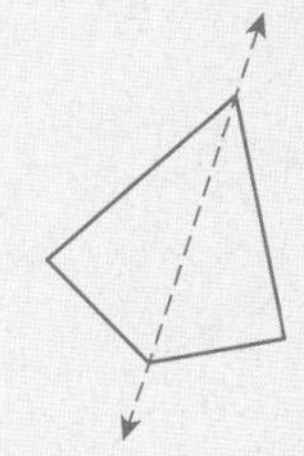

29. yes; 4; 90°

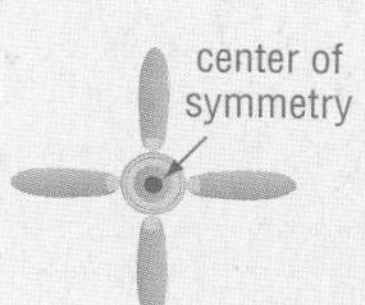

connectED.mcgraw-hill.com 687

Anticipation Guide

Have students complete the Chapter 9 Anticipation Guide and discuss how their responses have changed now that they have completed Chapter 9.

Additional Answer

32.

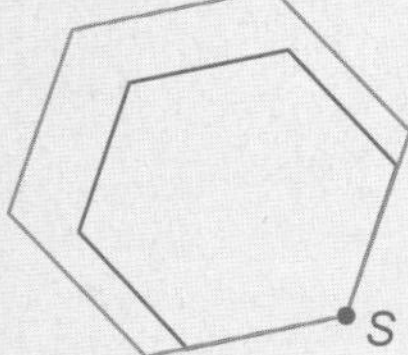

Additional Answers (Practice Test)

1.

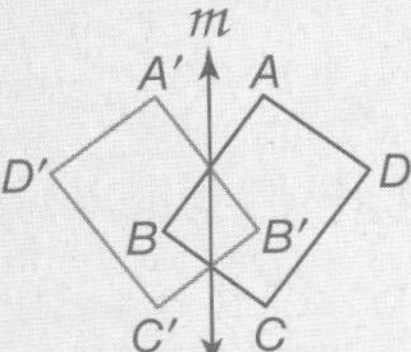

2.

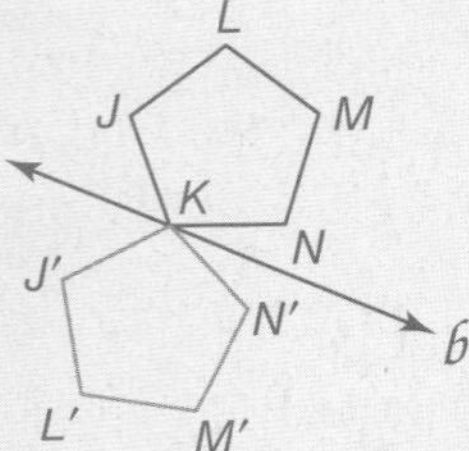

4.

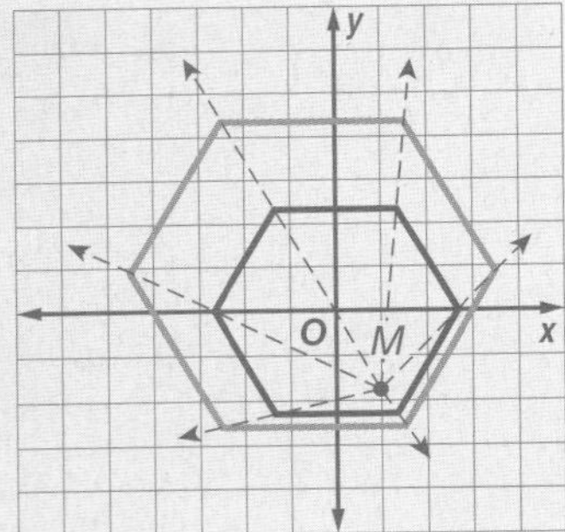

5.

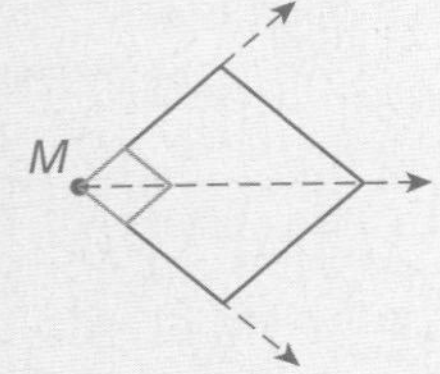

9-6 Dilations

32. Copy the figure and point *S*. Then use a ruler to draw the image of the figure under a dilation with center *S* and scale factor $r = 1.25$. **See margin.**

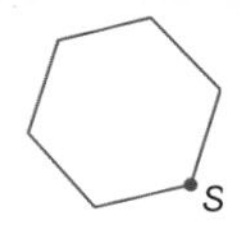

33. Determine whether the dilation from figure *W* to *W′* is an *enlargement* or a *reduction*. Then find the scale factor of the dilation and *x*. **reduction; 8.25, 0.45**

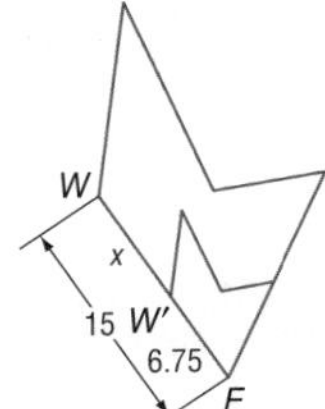

34. CLUBS The members of the Math Club use an overhead projector to make a poster. If the original image was 6 inches wide, and the image on the poster is 4 feet wide, what is the scale factor of the enlargement? **8**

Example 6

Square *ABCD* has vertices *A*(0, 0), *B*(0, 8), *C*(8, 8), and *D*(8, 0). Find the image of *ABCD* after a dilation centered at the origin with a scale factor of 0.5.

Multiply the *x*- and *y*-coordinates of each vertex by the scale factor, 0.5.

(x, y)	$\rightarrow$	$(0.5x, 0.5y)$
$A(0, 0)$	$\rightarrow$	$A'(0, 0)$
$B(0, 8)$	$\rightarrow$	$B'(0, 4)$
$C(8, 8)$	$\rightarrow$	$C'(4, 4)$
$D(8, 0)$	$\rightarrow$	$D'(4, 0)$

Graph *ABCD* and its image *A′B′C′D′*.

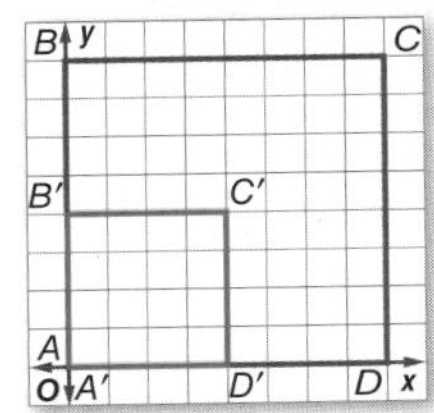

9.

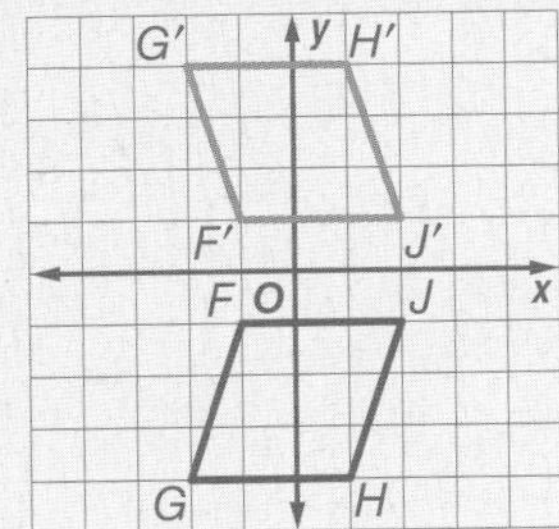

10.

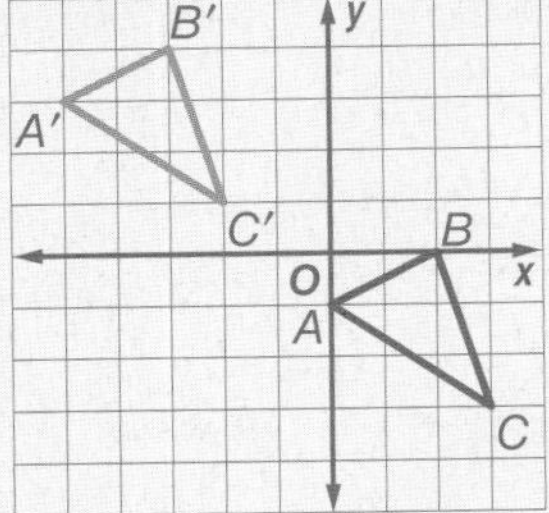

CHAPTER 9 Practice Test

Copy the figure and the given line of reflection. Then draw the reflected image in this line using a ruler.

1. 

2. 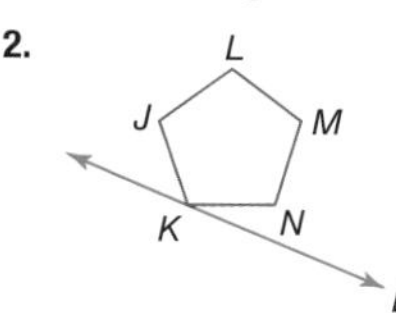

1–2. See margin.

3. **PROJECTS** Eduardo wants to enlarge the picture below to 4 inches by 6 inches for a school project. If his school's copy machine can only enlarge up to 150% by whole number percents, find two whole number percents by which he can enlarge the piece and get as close to 4 inches by 6 inches or less.

3 in.
2 in.

150% and 133%

Copy the figure and point M. Then use a ruler to draw the image of the figure under a dilation with center M and the scale factor r indicated. 4–5. See margin.

4. $r = 1.5$ 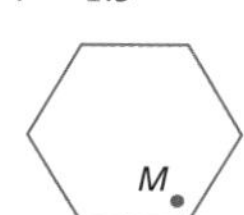

5. $r = \frac{1}{3}$ 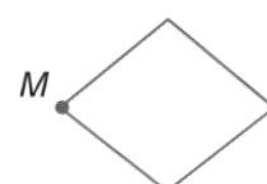

6. **PARKS** Isabel is on a ride at an amusement park that slides the rider to the right, and then rotates counterclockwise about its own center 60° every 2 seconds. How many seconds pass before Isabel completes one full rotation? 12 s

State whether each figure has *plane* symmetry, *axis* symmetry, *both*, or *neither*.

7. 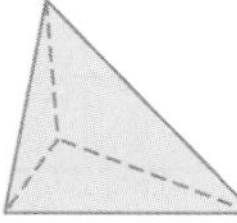 neither

8. 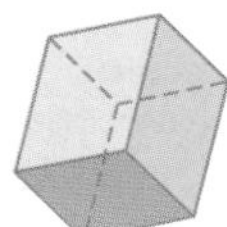 both

Graph each figure and its image under the given transformation. 9–11. See margin.

9. ▱$FGHJ$ with vertices $F(-1, -1)$, $G(-2, -4)$, $H(1, -4)$, and $J(2, -1)$ in the x-axis

10. $\triangle ABC$ with vertices $A(0, -1)$, $B(2, 0)$, $C(3, -3)$; $\langle -5, 4\rangle$

11. quadrilateral $WXYZ$ with vertices $W(2, 3)$, $X(1, 1)$, $Y(3, 0)$, $Z(5, 2)$; 180° about the origin

Copy the figure and the given translation vector. Then draw the translation of the figure along the translation vector. 12–13. See Ch. 9 Answer Appendix.

12. 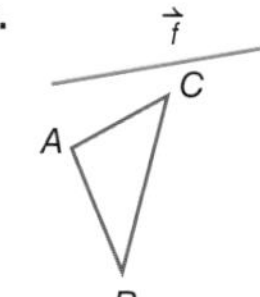

13. 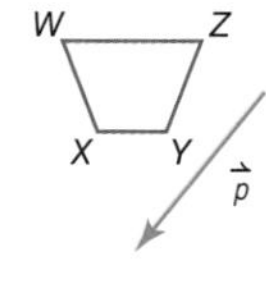

14. **ART** An artist's rendition of what Stonehenge, a famous archeological site in England, would have looked like before the stones fell or were removed, is shown below. What is the order and magnitude of symmetry for the outer ring? 30; 12°

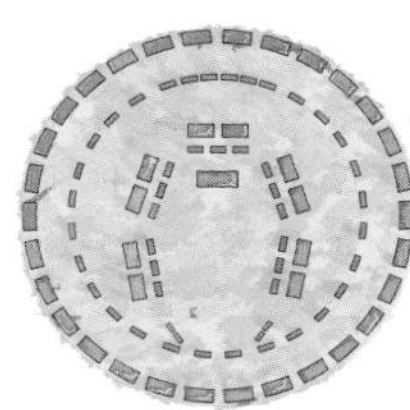

15. **MULTPLE CHOICE** What transformation or combination of transformations does the figure below represent? B

A dilation
B glide reflection
C rotation
D translation

Summative Assessment

Use these alternate leveled chapter tests to differentiate assessment for your students.

Leveled Chapter 9 Tests

Form	Type	Level	Page(s)
1	MC	AL	49–50
2A	MC	OL	51–52
2B	MC	OL	53–54
2C	FR	OL	55–56
2D	FR	OL	57–58
3	FR	BL	59–60
Vocabulary Test			48
Extended-Response Test			61

MC = multiple-choice questions
FR = free-response questions

eAssessment Customize and create multiple versions of your chapter tests and their answer keys. All of the questions from the leveled chapter tests in the *Chapter 9 Resource Masters* are also available on eAssessment.

Additional Answer

11. 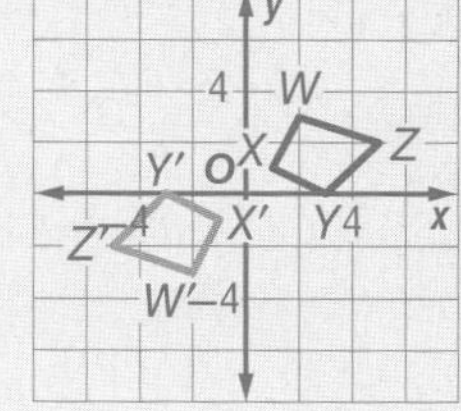

InterventionPlanner

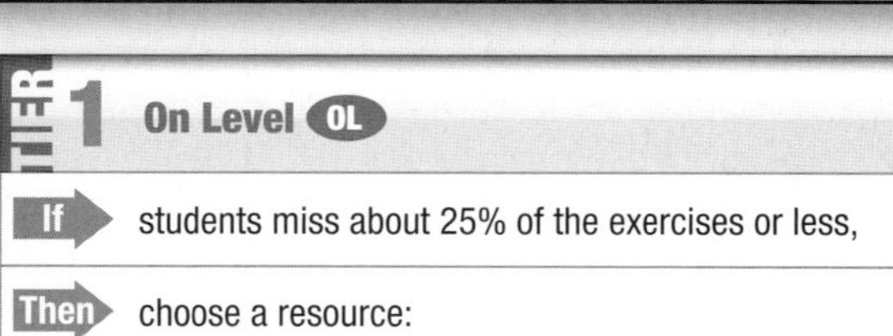

TIER 1 On Level OL

If students miss about 25% of the exercises or less,

Then choose a resource:

SE Lessons 9-1, 9-2, 9-3, 9-4, 9–5 and 9-6

Skills Practice, pp. 7, 13, 21, 27, 33, and 39

connectED.mcgraw-hill.com Self-Check Quiz

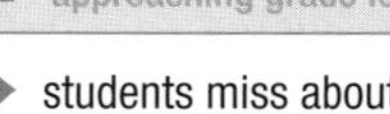

TIER 2 Strategic Intervention AL approaching grade level

If students miss about 50% of the exercises,

Then choose a resource:

Study Guide and Intervention, pp. 5, 11, 19, 25, 31 and 37

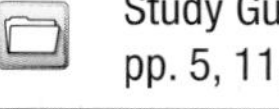

connectED.mcgraw-hill.com Extra Examples, Personal Tutor, Homework Help

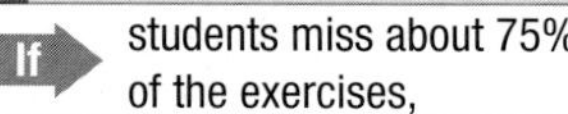

TIER 3 Intensive Intervention 2 or more grades below level

If students miss about 75% of the exercises,

Then use *Math Triumphs, Geo.*, Ch. 5

connectED.mcgraw-hill.com Extra Examples, Personal Tutor, Homework Help, Review Vocabulary

1 Focus

Objective Learn to work backward to solve a problem when the end result is given.

2 Teach

Scaffolding Questions

Ask:

- What are some words in a question that indicate you may want to work backwards? Sample answer: Words such as "before", "original", and "beginning" indicate that you may need to work backwards to solve a problem.
- What is a question from this chapter that could be solved by working backwards? Sample answer: In Question #33 part **b**, you are asked to find the cross-sectional area of a balloon *before* and after a dilation.
- How is this process similar to strategies for writing formal proofs? Sample answer: When writing a proof, you can begin by writing what you want to prove as the last step or statement, and then work backwards until you arrive at the first step or given information.

CHAPTER 9 Preparing for Standardized Tests

Work Backward

In most problems, a set of conditions or facts is given and you must find the end result. However, some problems give you the end result and ask you to find something that happened earlier in the process. To solve problems like this, you must work backward.

Strategies for Working Backward

Step 1

Look for keywords that indicate you will need to work backward to solve the problem.

Sample Keywords:

- What was the **original**...?
- What was the value **before**...?
- Where was the **starting** or **beginning**...?

Step 2

Undo the steps given in the problem statement to solve.

- List the sequence of steps from the beginning to the end result.
- Begin with the end result. Retrace the steps in reverse order.
- "Undo" each step using inverses to get back to the original value.

Step 3

Check your solution if time permits.

- Make sure your answer makes sense.
- Begin with your answer and follow the steps in the problem statement forward to see if you get the same end result.

Standardized Test Example

Solve the problem below. Responses will be graded using the short-response scoring rubric shown.

Kelly is using a geometry software program to experiment with transformations on the coordinate grid. She began with a point and translated it 4 units up and 8 units left. Then she reflected the image in the x-axis. Finally, she dilated this new image by a scale factor of 0.5 with respect to the origin to arrive at $(-1, -4)$. What were the original coordinates of the point?

Scoring Rubric

Criteria	Score
Full Credit: The answer is correct and a full explanation is provided that shows each step.	2
Partial Credit: • The answer is correct, but the explanation is incomplete. • The answer is incorrect, but the explanation is correct.	1
No Credit: Either an answer is not provided or the answer does not make sense.	0

690 | Chapter 9 | Preparing for Standardized Tests

Read the problem statement carefully. You are given a sequence of transformations of a point on a coordinate grid. You know the coordinates of the final image and are asked to find the original coordinates. Undo each transformation in reverse order to work backward and solve the problem.

Example of a 2-point response:

original point → translation → reflection → dilation → end result

Begin with the coordinates of the end result and work backward.

Dilate by 2 to undo the dilation by 0.5:

$(-1, -4) \rightarrow (-1 \times 2, -4 \times 2) = (-2, -8)$

Reflect back across the x-axis to undo the reflection:

$(-2, -8) \rightarrow (-2, 8)$

Translate 4 units down and 8 units right to undo the translation:

$(-2, 8) \rightarrow (-2 + 8, 8 - 4) = (6, 4)$

The original coordinates of the point were (6, 4).

The steps, calculations, and reasoning are clearly stated. The student also arrives at the correct answer. So, this response is worth the full 2 points.

Exercises

Solve each problem. Show your work. Responses will be graded using the short-response scoring rubric given at the beginning of the lesson.

1. A flea landed on a coordinate grid. The flea hopped across the x-axis and then across the y-axis in the form of two consecutive reflections. Then it walked 9 units to the right and 4 units down. If the flea's final position was at (4, −1), what point did it originally land on? (5, −3)

2. The coordinate grid below shows the final image when a point was rotated 90° clockwise about the origin, dilated by a scale factor of 2, and shifted 7 units right. What were the original coordinates? (−1, −3)

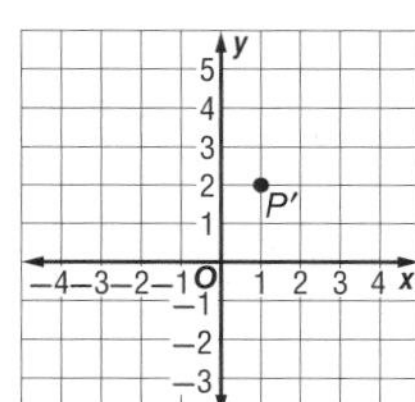

3. Figure $ABCD$ is an isosceles trapezoid.

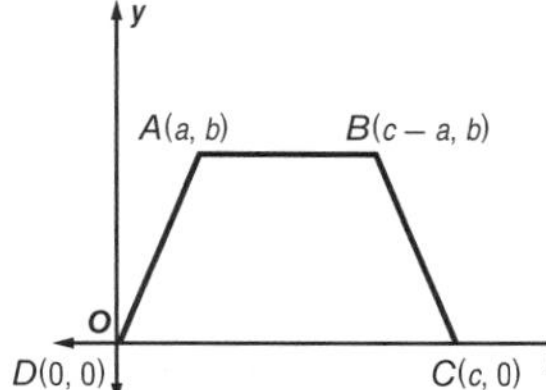

Which of the following are the coordinates of an endpoint of the median of $ABCD$? B

A $\left(\frac{a+b}{2}, \frac{a+b}{2}\right)$

B $\left(\frac{2c-a}{2}, \frac{b}{2}\right)$

C $\left(\frac{c}{2}, 0\right)$

D $\left(\frac{c}{2}, b\right)$

4. If the measure of an interior angle of a regular polygon is 108, what type of polygon is it? H

F octagon

G hexagon

H pentagon

J triangle

Additional Example

1 Xavier is using a geometry software program to experiment with transformations on the coordinate grid. He began with a point and translated it 3 units down and 5 units right. Then he reflected the image across the y-axis. Finally he dilated this new image by a scale factor of 3 to arrive at (6, 6). What were the original coordinates of the point? (−7, 5)

3 Assess

Use Exercises 1–4 to assess students' understanding.

Diagnose Student Errors

Survey student responses for each item. Class trends may indicate common errors and misconceptions.

1. A reflects across line $y = x$
   B guess
   C reflects over x-axis
   D correct
2. F correct
   G translation is down
   H contains a rotation
   J contains a rotation
3. A visual guess
   B arithmetic error
   C correct
   D arithmetic error
4. F wrong definition used
   G wrong definition used
   H correct
   J wrong definition used
5. A guess
   B guess
   C guess
   D correct
6. F found value of x
   G arithmetic error
   H arithmetic error
   J correct
7. A correct
   B did not consider that congruent sides must be consecutive
   C did not consider that congruent sides must be consecutive
   D guess

CHAPTER 9 Standardized Test Practice

Cumulative, Chapters 1 through 9

Multiple Choice

Read each question. Then fill in the correct answer on the answer document provided by your teacher or on a sheet of paper.

1. Point N has coordinates (4, −3). What will the coordinates of its image be after a reflection across the y-axis? D

   A N′(−3, 4)
   B $N'(-4, 3)$
   C N′(4, 3)
   D $N'(-4, -3)$

2. Which pair of figures shows a reflection across the line followed by a translation up? F

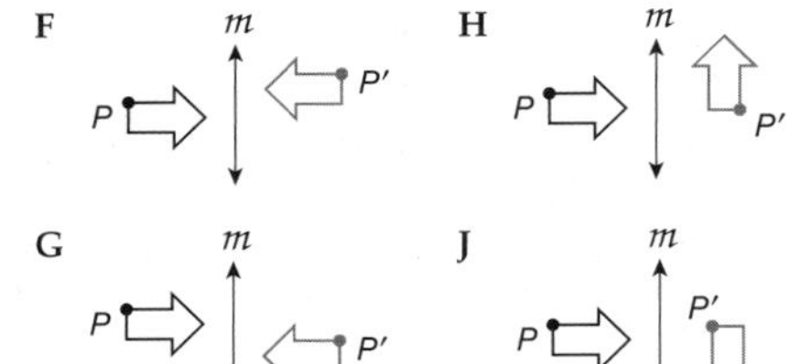

3. What is the angle of clockwise rotation that maps point T onto T' in the figure below? C

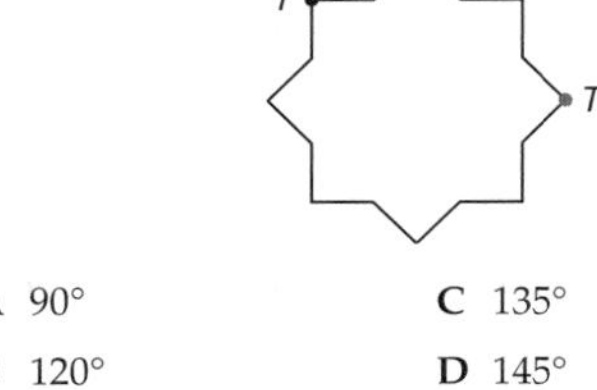

   A 90°
   B 120°
   C 135°
   D 145°

Test-Taking Tip

Question 3 How many points are there on the star? Divide 360° by this number to find the angle of rotation from one point to the next.

4. Given: $a \parallel b$

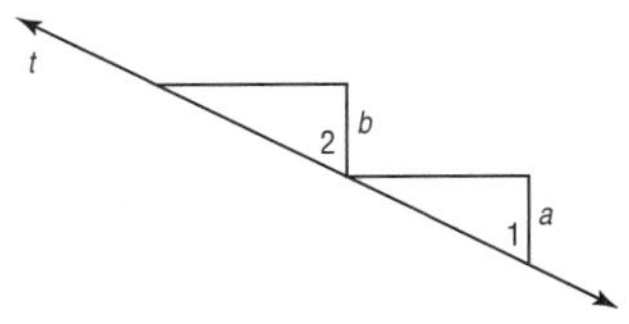

   Which statement below justifies the conclusion that $\angle 1 \cong \angle 2$? H

   F If $a \parallel b$ and are cut by transversal t, then alternate exterior angles are congruent.
   G If $a \parallel b$ and are cut by transversal t, then alternate interior angles are congruent.
   H If $a \parallel b$ and are cut by transversal t, then corresponding angles are congruent.
   J If $a \parallel b$ and are cut by transversal t, then vertical angles are congruent.

5. What is the geometric mean of 8 and 18? D

   A 9
   B 10
   C 11
   D 12

6. Which of the following is a side length in isosceles triangle DEF? J

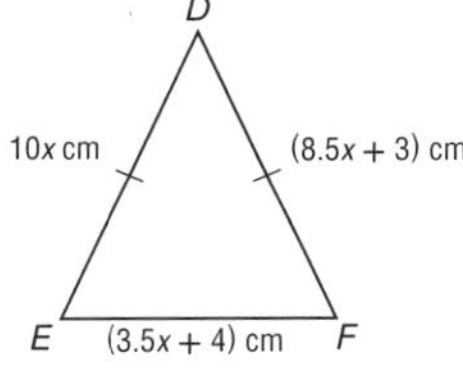

   F 2 cm
   G 8 cm
   H 9 cm
   J 11 cm

7. Which of the following has exactly two pairs of consecutive congruent sides? A

   A kite
   B parallelogram
   C rhombus
   D trapezoid

Short Response/Gridded Response

Record your answers on the answer sheet provided by your teacher or on a sheet of paper.

8. State whether the figure has rotational symmetry. If so, copy the figure, locate the center, and state the order and magnitude of symmetry.

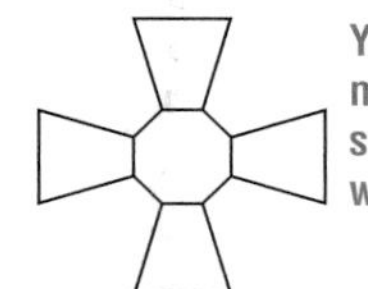

Yes, order 4, magnitude 90°; see students' work.

9. Dilate the figure shown on the coordinate grid by a scale factor of 1.5 centered at the origin. See margin.

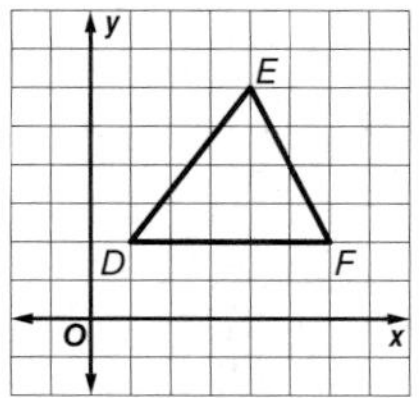

10. Complete the following statement. See margin.

According to the Angle Bisector Theorem, if a point is on the bisector of an angle, then it is _______.

11. Regina left her office downtown and traveled 3 blocks west and 5 blocks north. Write a translation vector to describe her route. ⟨−3, 5⟩

12. What is the interior angle measure of the regular pentagon? 108°

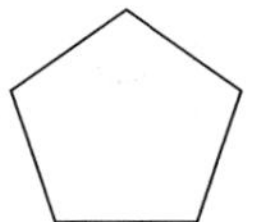

13. **GRIDDED RESPONSE** A group of 75 students were asked what types of movies they like to watch. The results are shown in the Venn diagram.

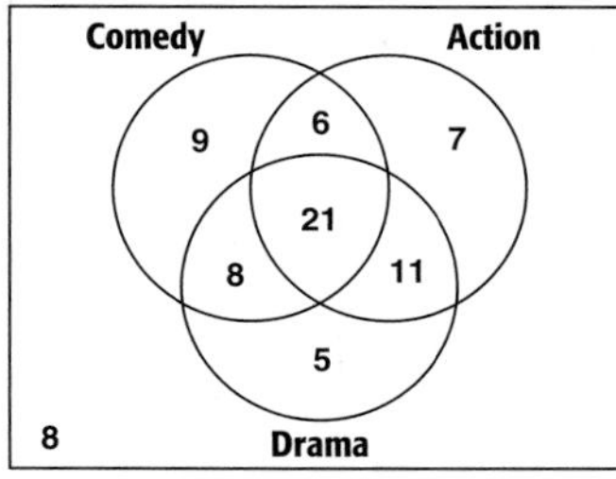

How many students said that they like to watch action and drama movies, but not comedy? 11

Extended Response

Record your answers on a sheet of paper. Show your work.

14. Rodrigo is making a scale model.

a. The actual length of the Golden Gate Bridge is about 9000 feet. If Rodrigo's model is 45 inches, what is the scale of his model? 1 in. : 200 ft

b. How wide will Rodrigo's model of the bridge be if the actual width is 90 feet? 0.45 in.

c. In Rodrigo's model, the tower will be 2.5 inches above the roadway. How high above the roadway is the actual tower? 500 ft

Need ExtraHelp?

If you missed Question...	1	2	3	4	5	6	7	8	9	10	11	12	13	14
Go to Lesson...	9-1	9-4	9-3	3-2	8-1	4-6	6-6	9-5	9-6	5-1	9-2	6-1	2-2	7-7

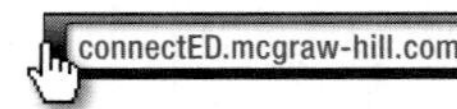

Formative Assessment

You can use these pages to benchmark student progress.

Standardized Test Practice, pp. 62–64

Answer Sheet Practice

Have students simulate taking a standardized test by recording their answers on a practice recording sheet.

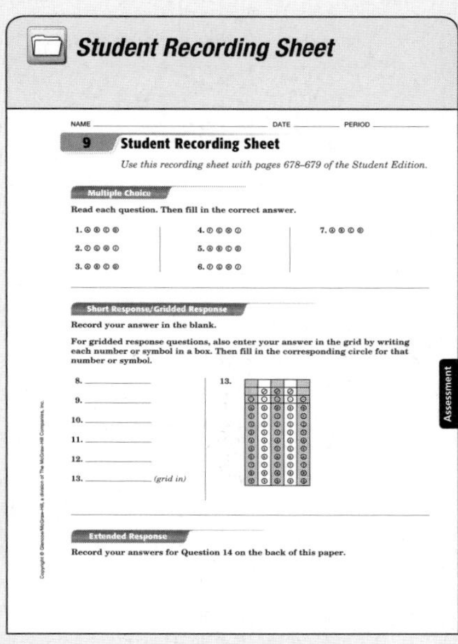

eAssessment Create practice tests that align to your state standards, the Common Core State Standards, and other national standards such as TIMSS and NAEP.

Homework Option

Get Ready for Chapter 10 Assign students the exercises on p. 695 as homework to assess whether they possess the prerequisite skills needed for the next chapter.

Additional Answers

9.

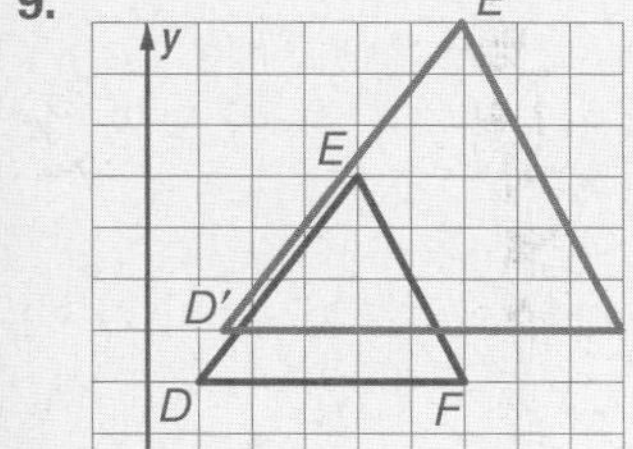

10. Sample answer: equidistant from the sides of the angle.

Lesson 9-1 (Guided Practice)

3A.

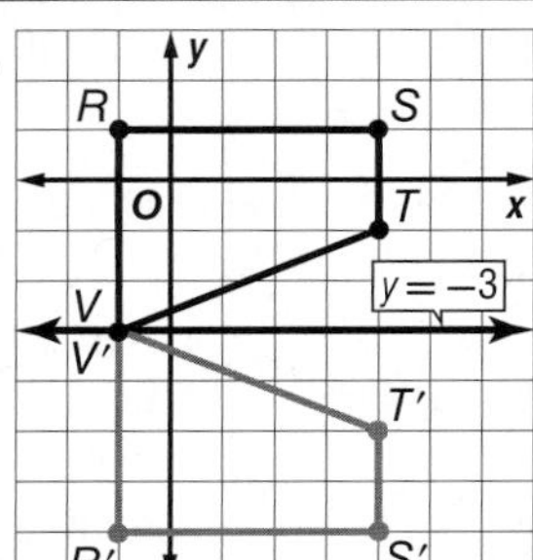

3B.

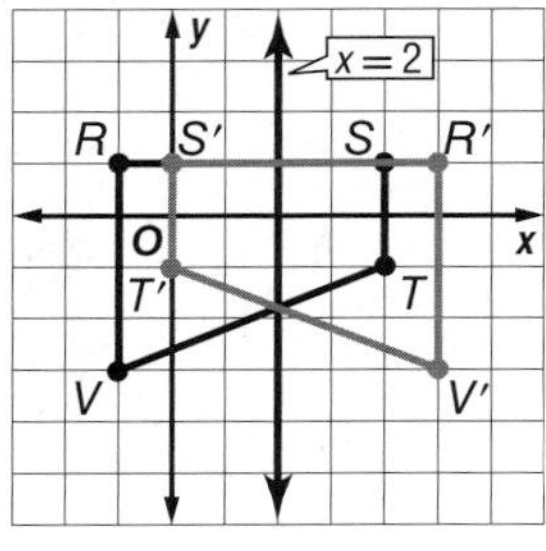

4A.

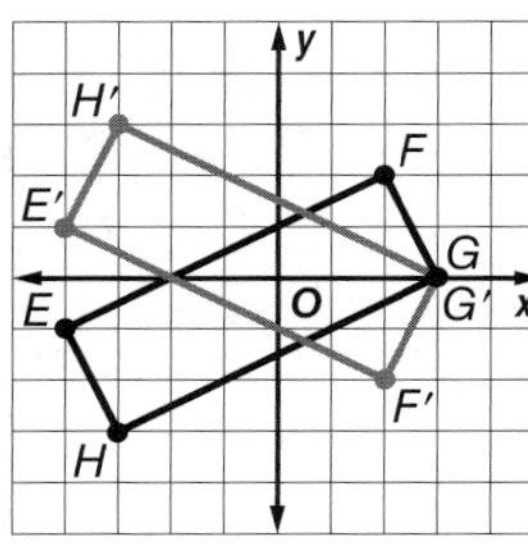

4B.

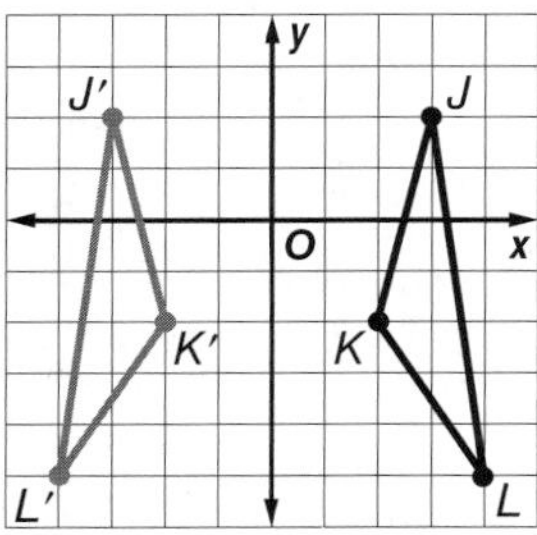

Lesson 9-1

4. Sample answer:

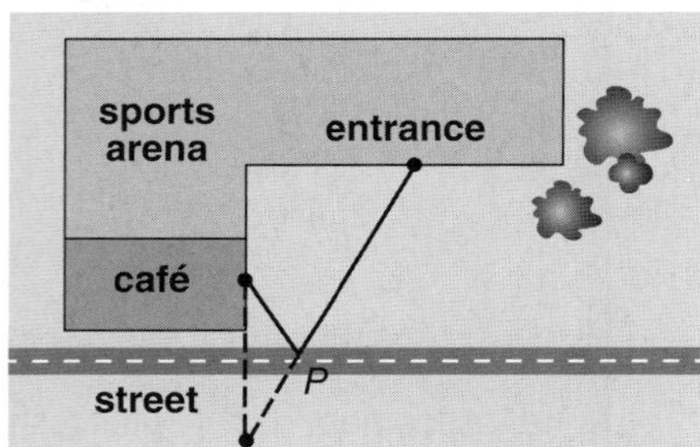

7.

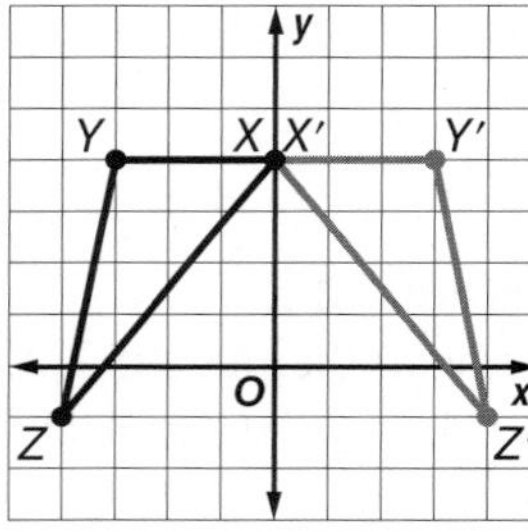

8.

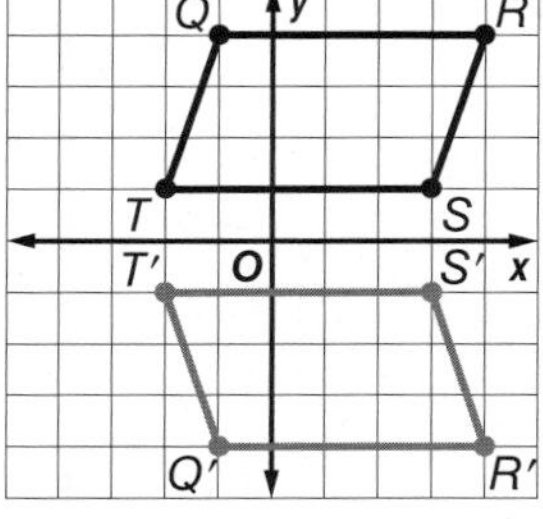

9.

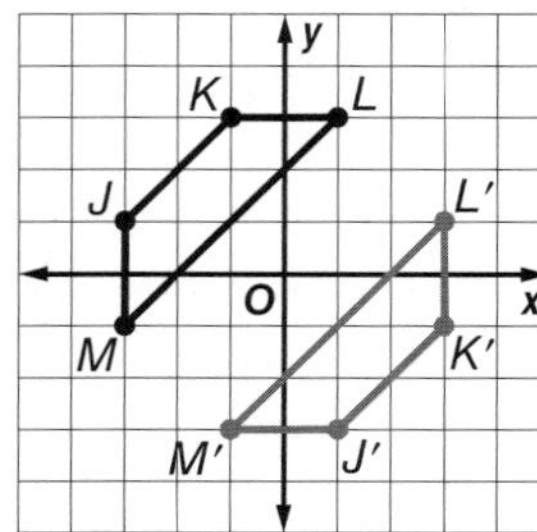

10.

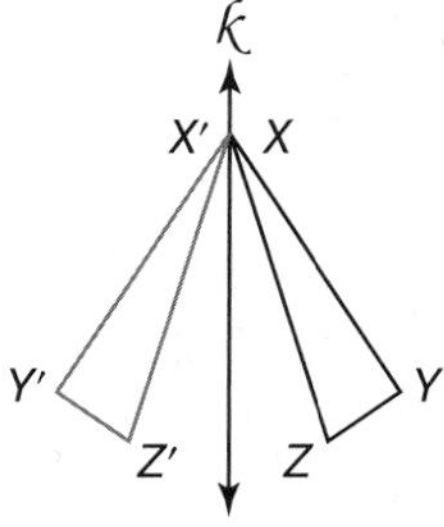

11.

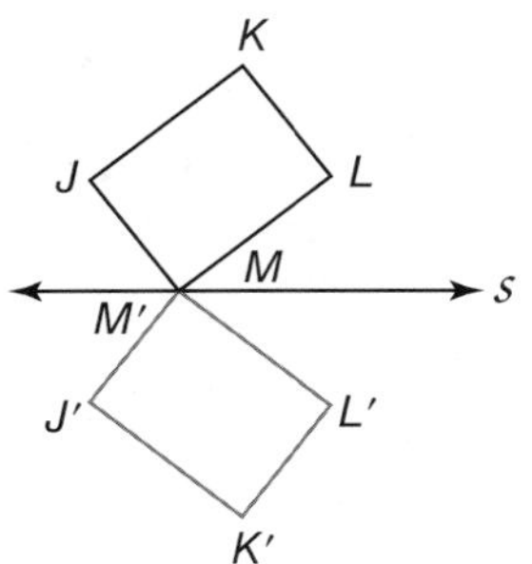

12.

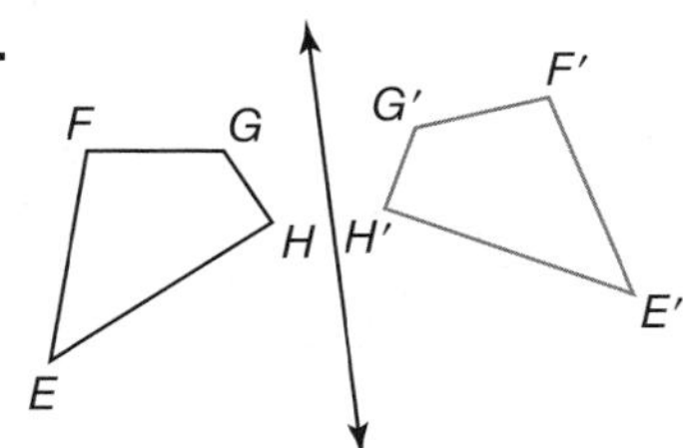

13.

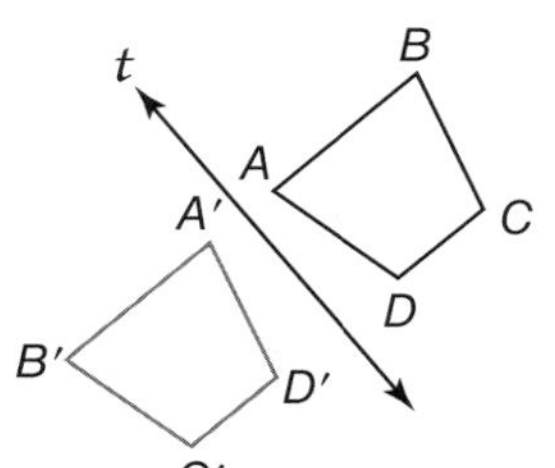

14.

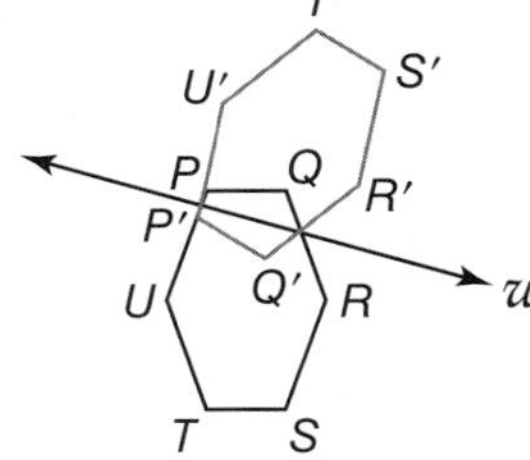

15.

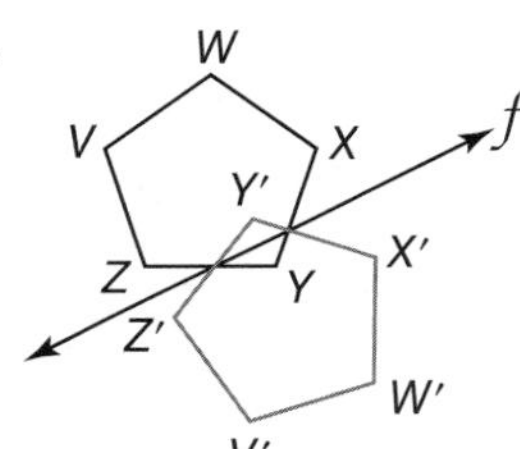

16.

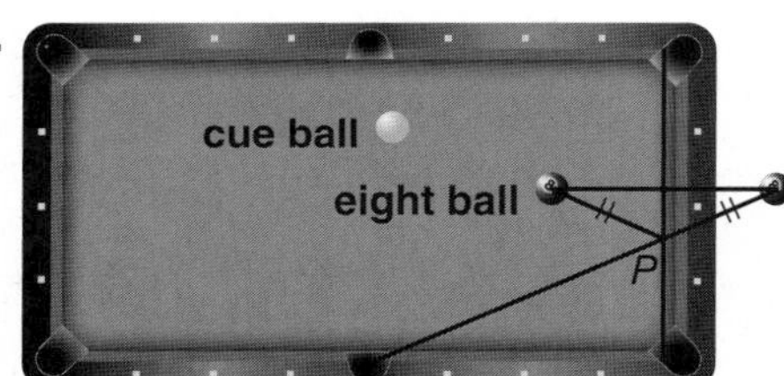

17.

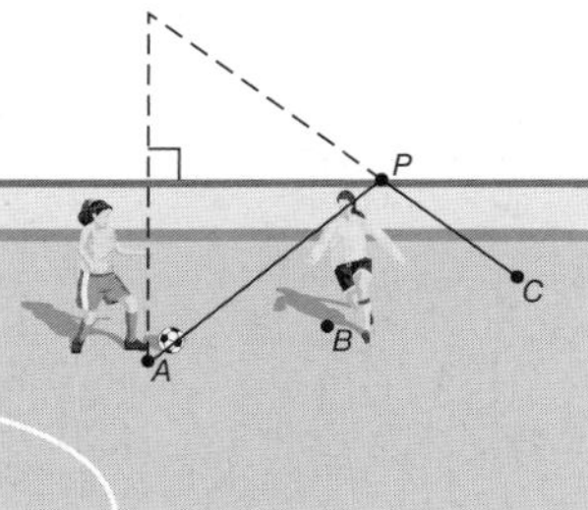

18.
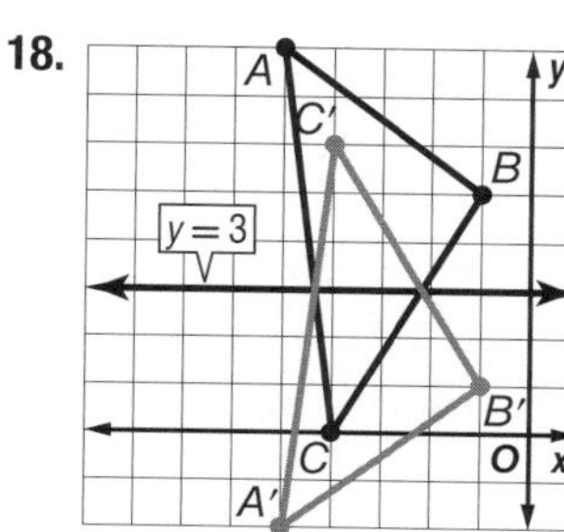

19.
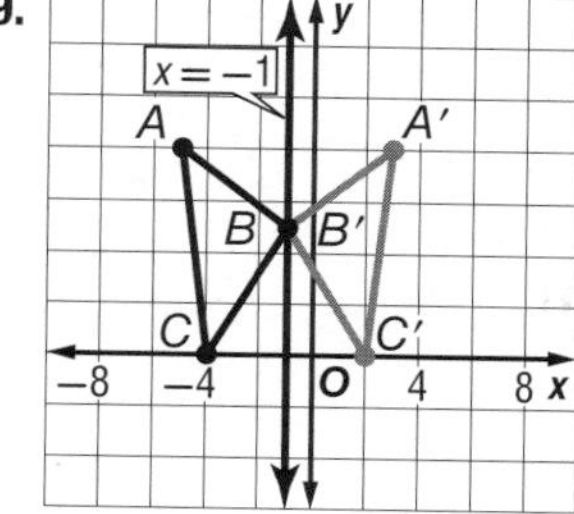

20.
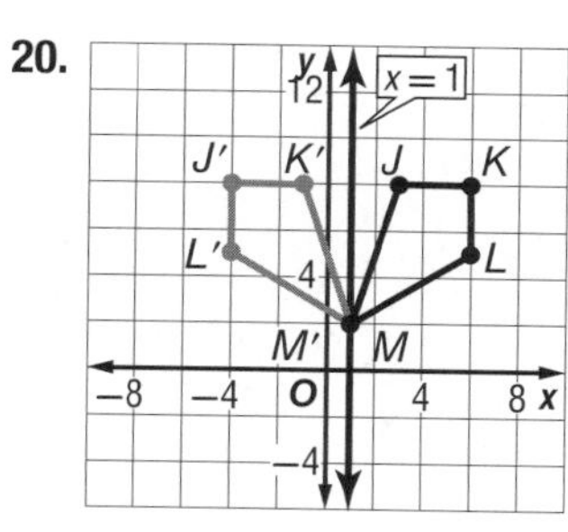

21.
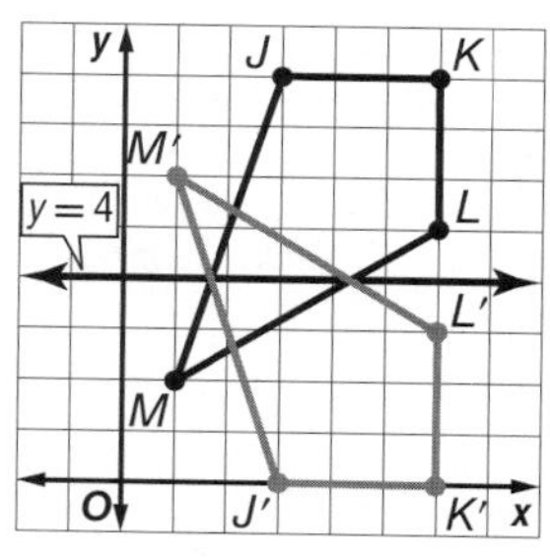

22.
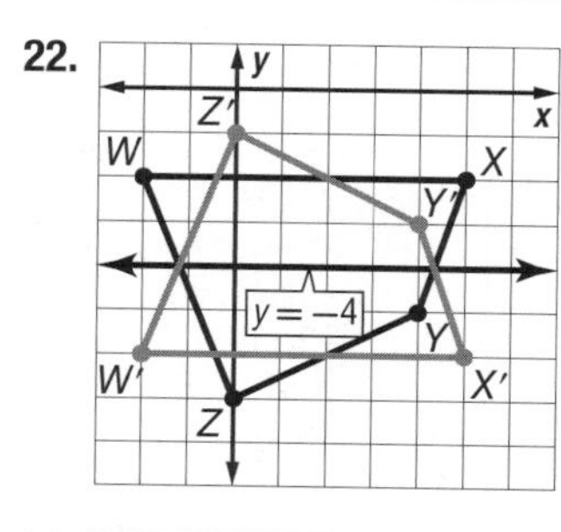

23.
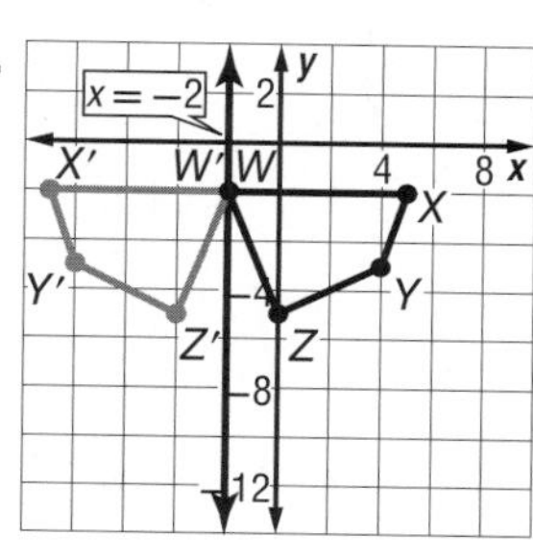

24.
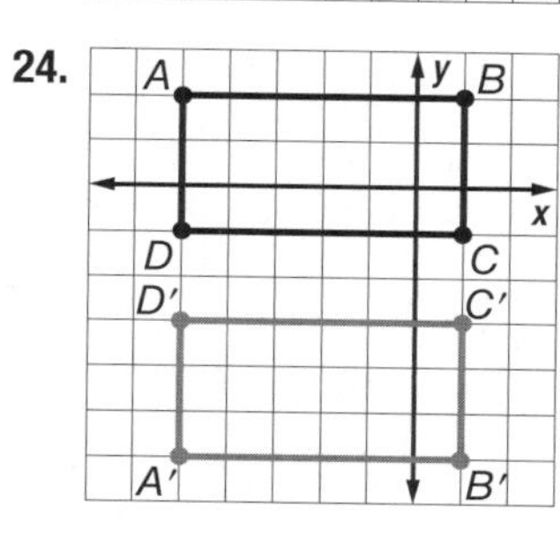

25.
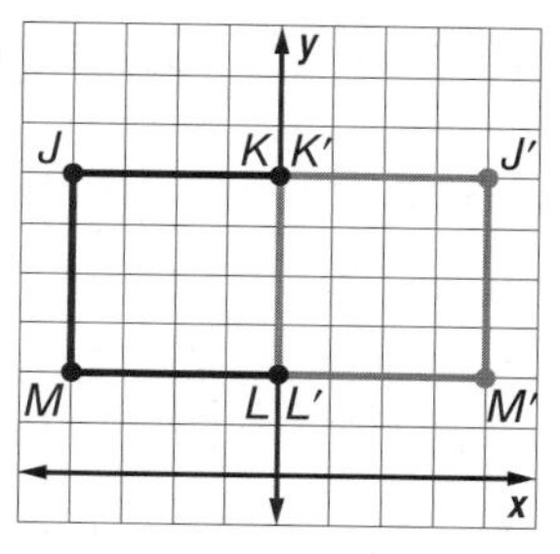

26.
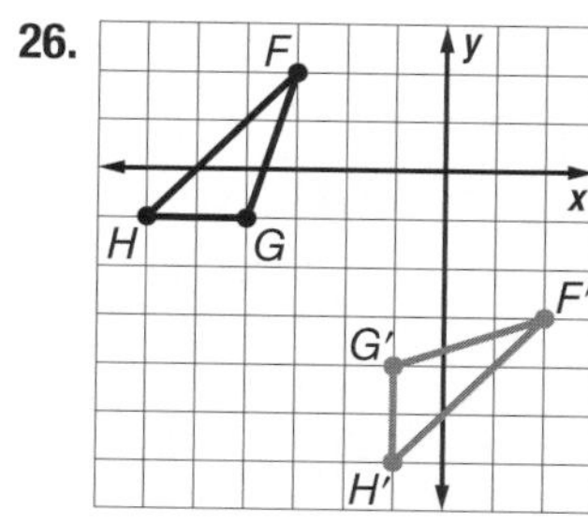

27.
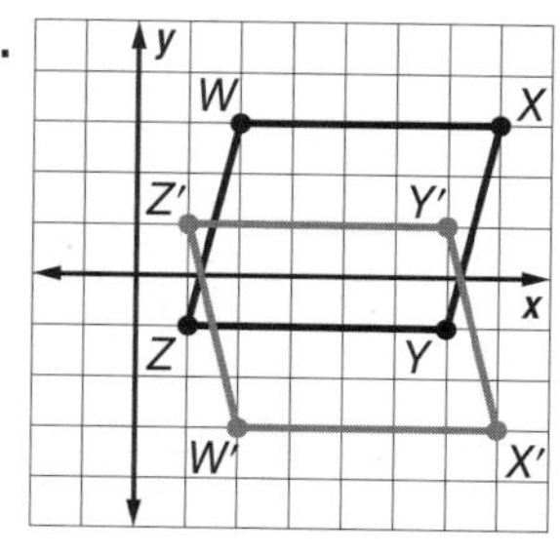

28.
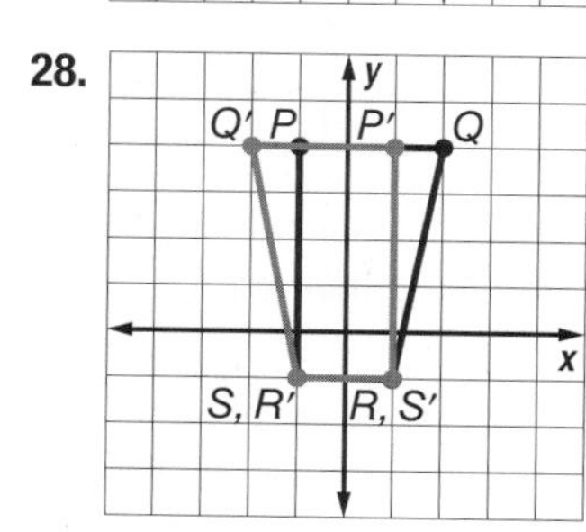

29.
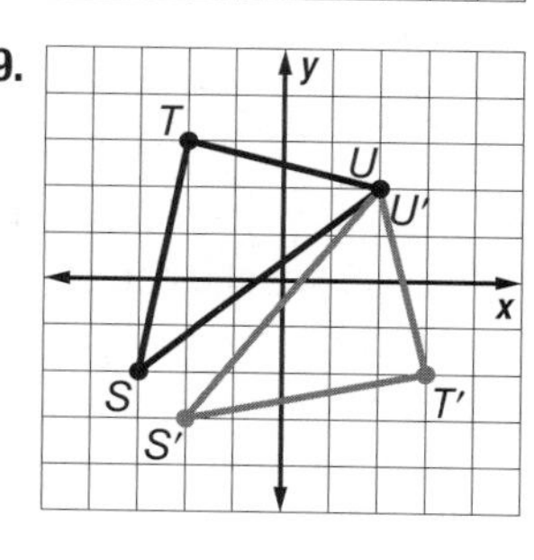

33.
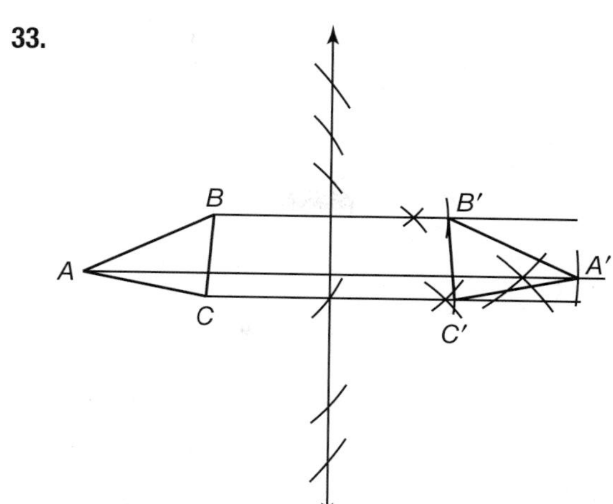

34.
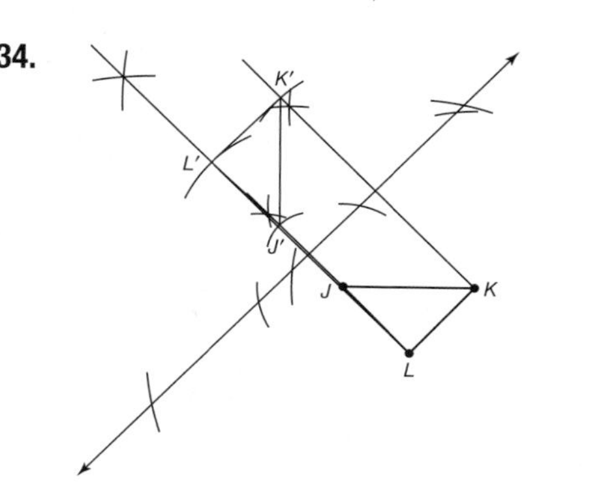

36.
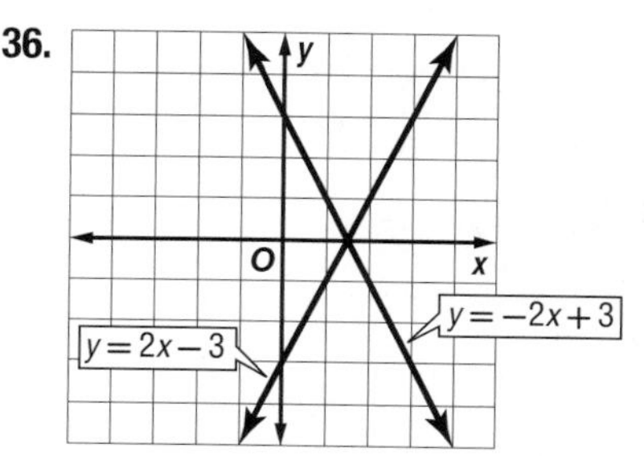

37.
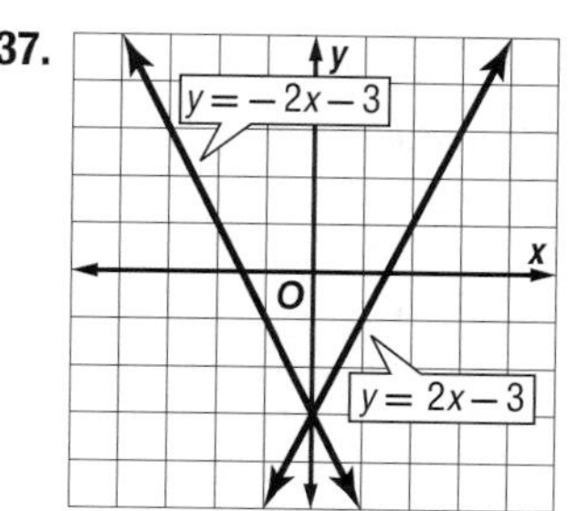

38.
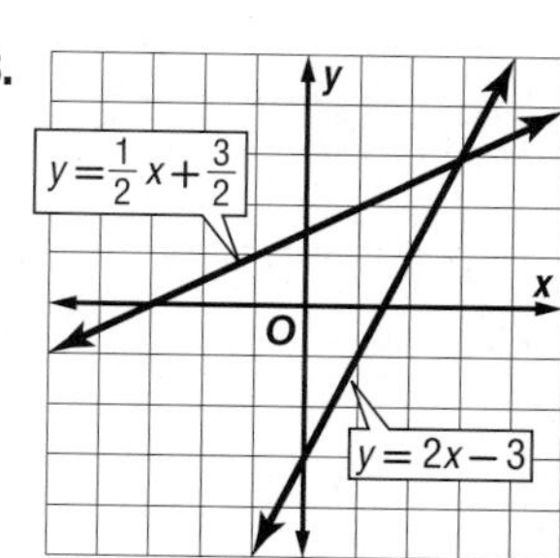

Lesson 9-2 (Guided Practice)

1A.
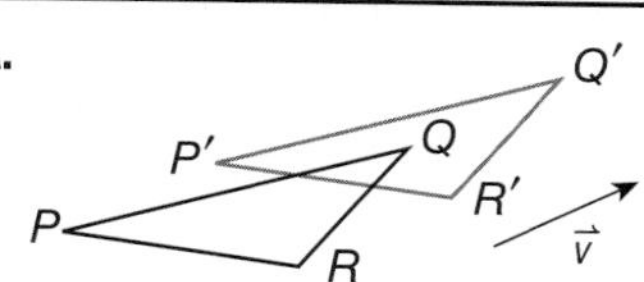

1B.

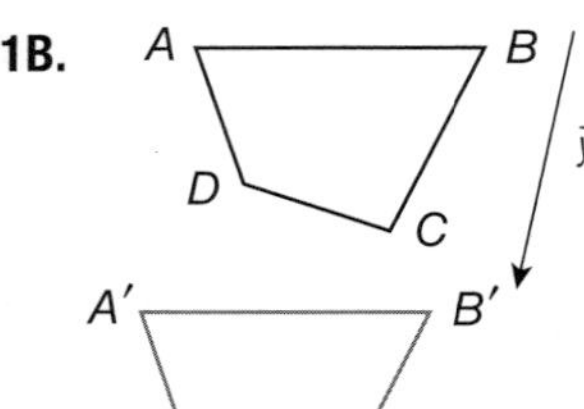

2A.

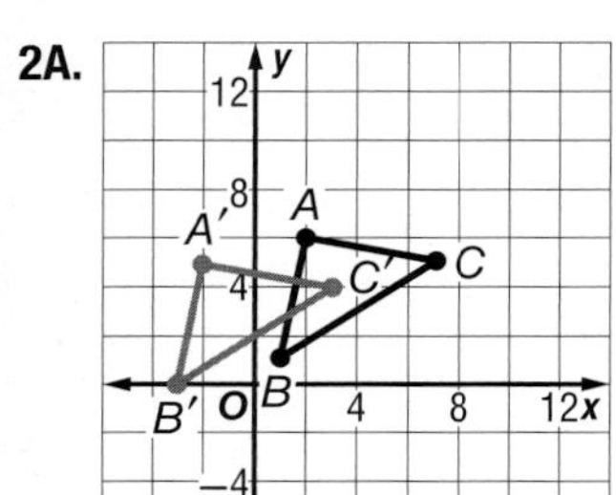

2B.

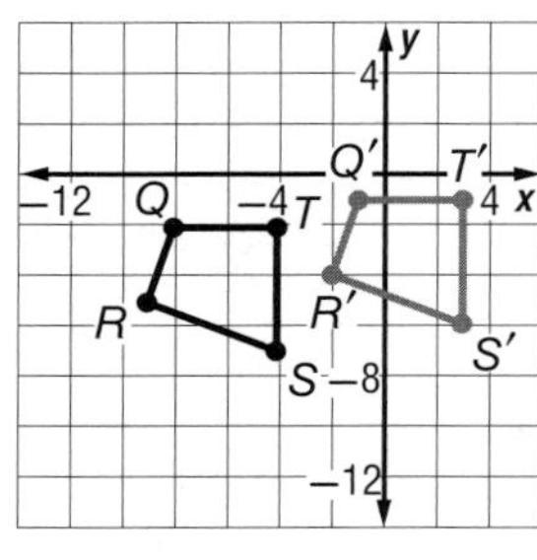

Lesson 9-2

4.

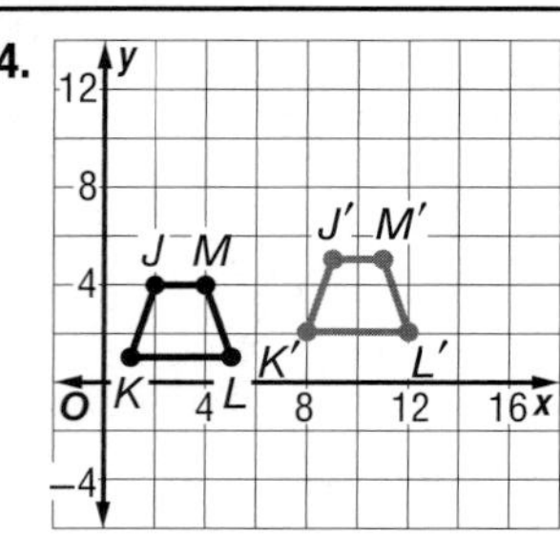

5.

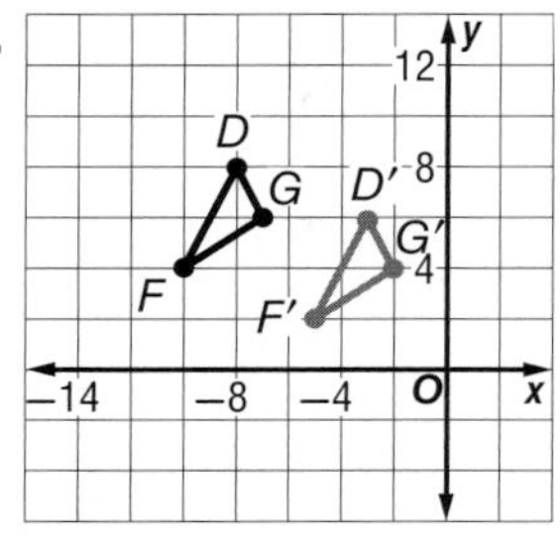

6.

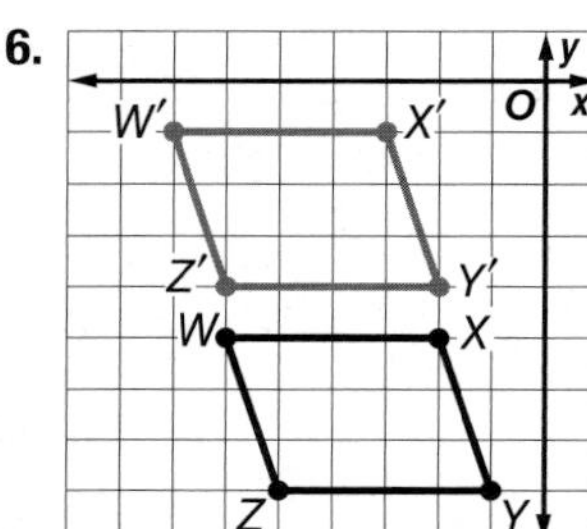

8.

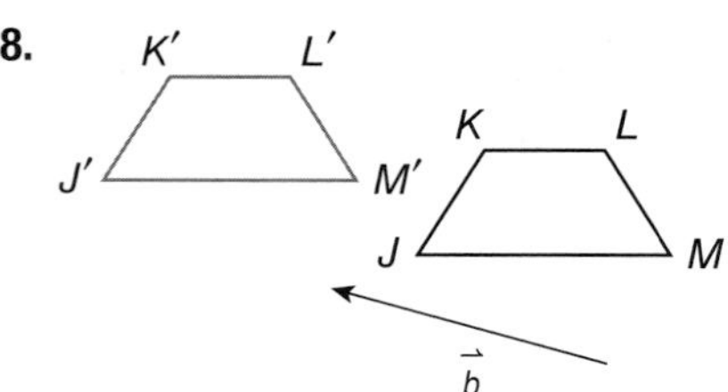

9.

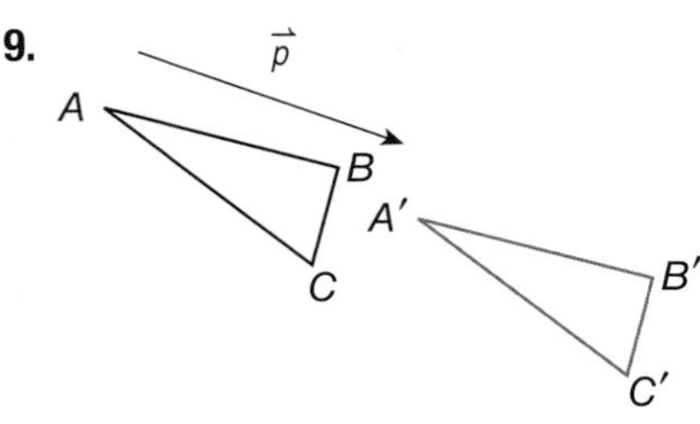

10. **11.**

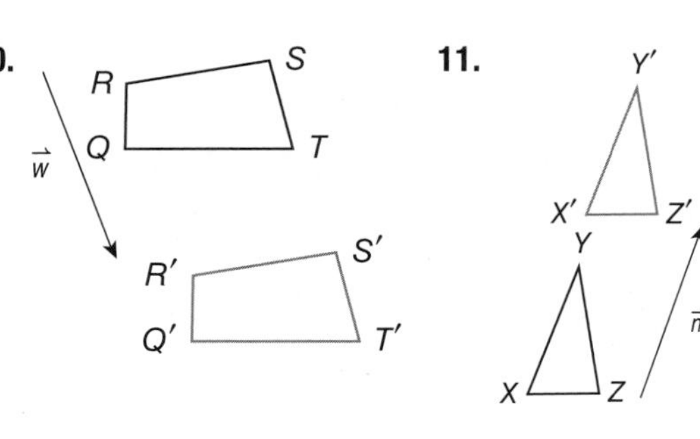

12.

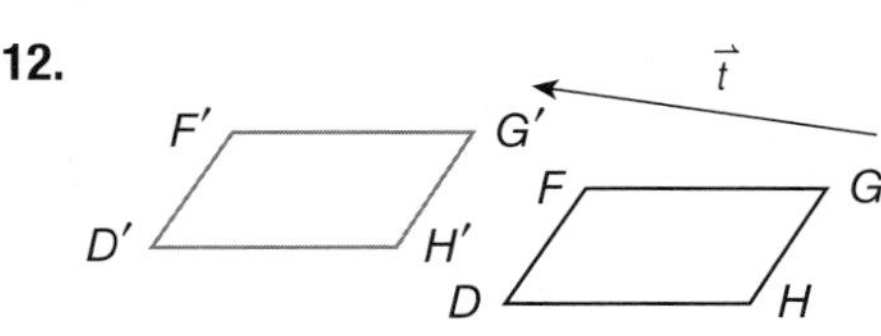

13.

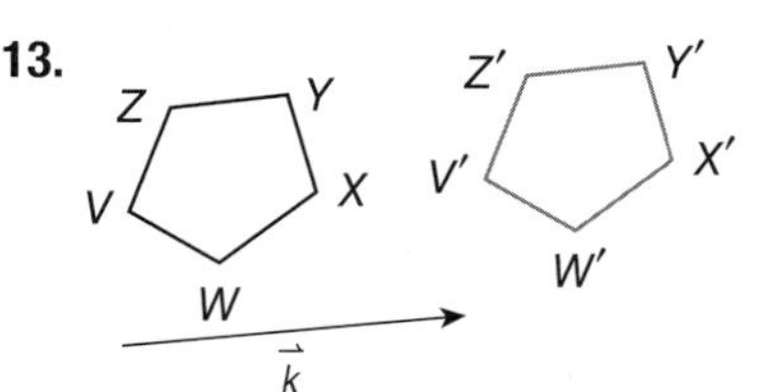

14.

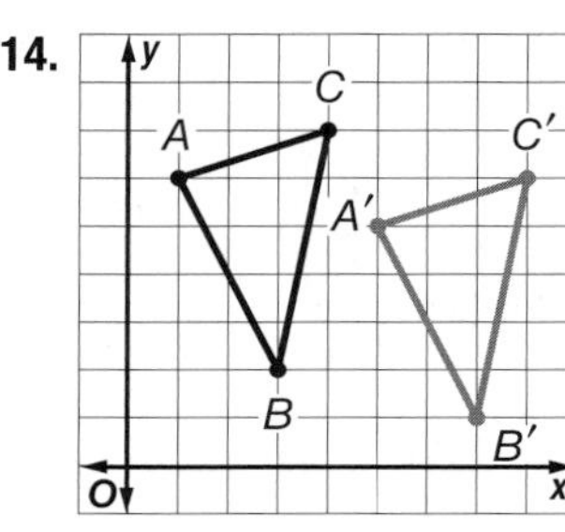

15.

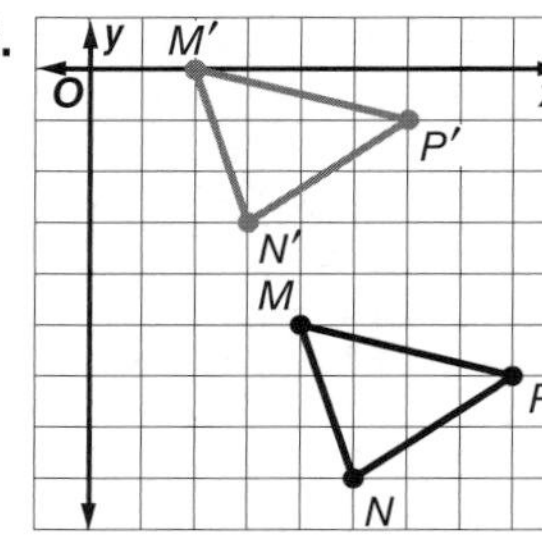

16.

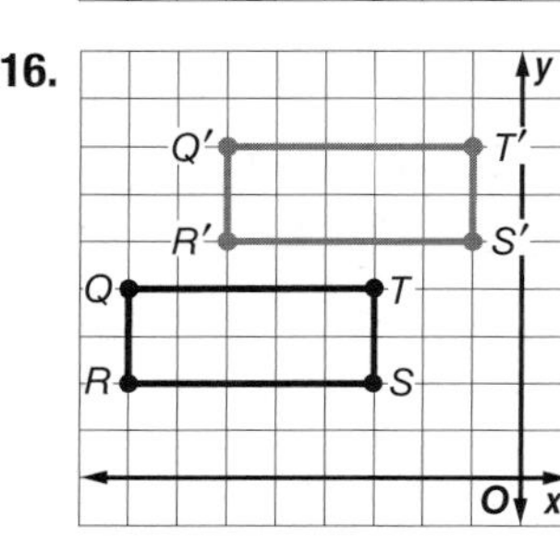

17.

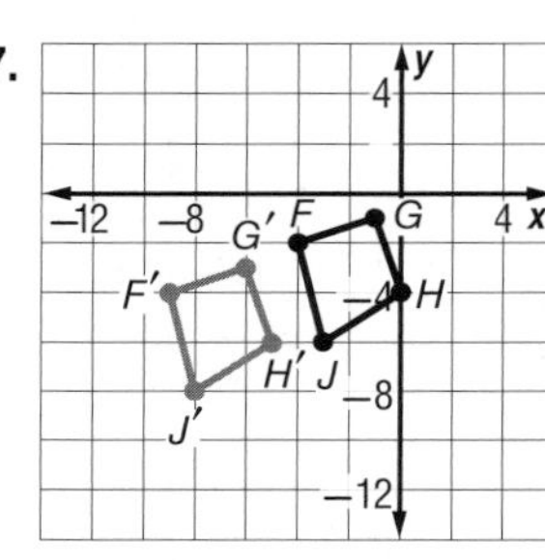

18.

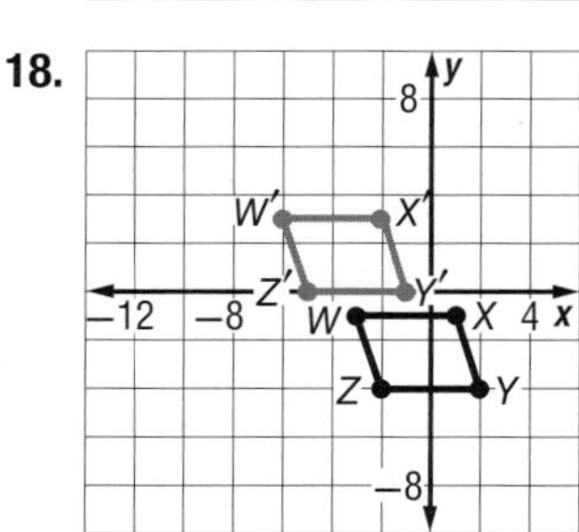

19.

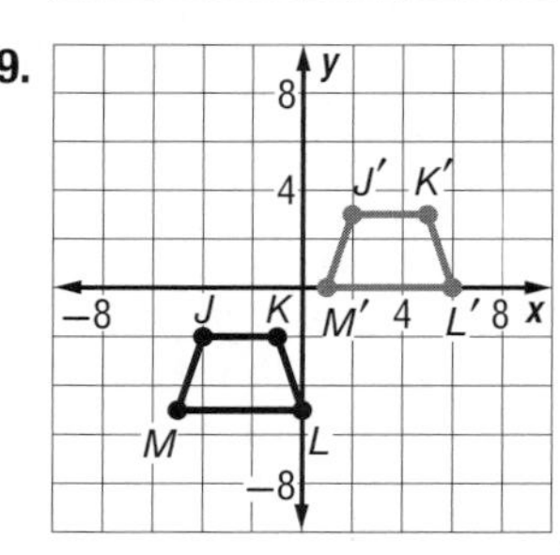

20b. Sample answer: She can go west 5 blocks and then south 1 block, or she can go south 1 block and then west 5 blocks.

22b. Sample answer: The rook could have moved vertically 5 squares down on the first move and then horizontally three squares right on the second turn.

22c. Sample answer: The bishop could move to g7, then g7 to a1. The minimum number of moves is 2.

29a. A, B, C; ℓ; A′, B′, C′; m; A″, B″, C″

29b.

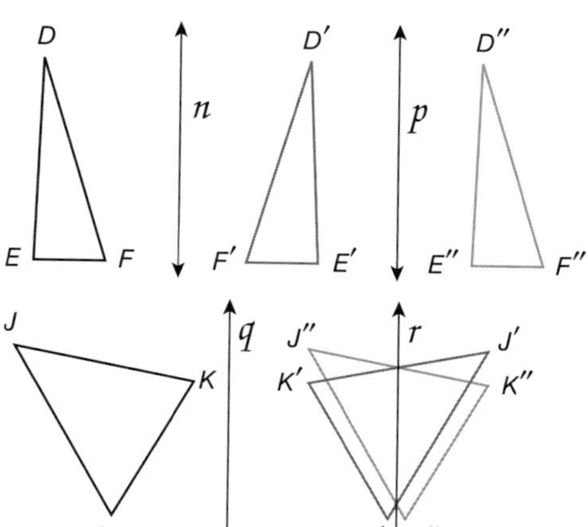

32.

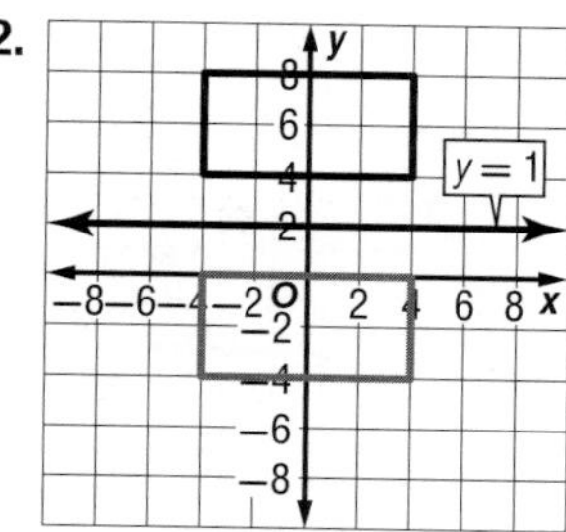

Sample answer: In order for the figure to be the same, it must match up when you fold it in half horizontally at the $y = 1$ line.

43. **44.**

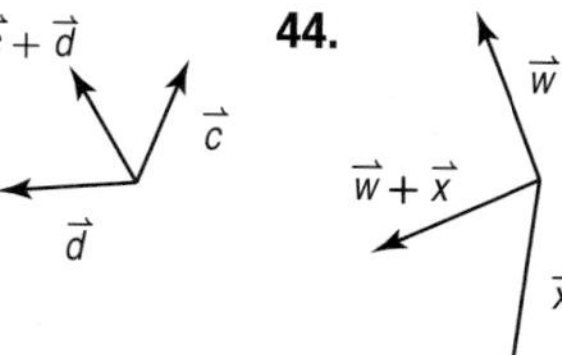

45.

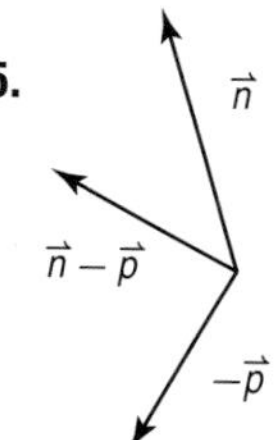

Lesson 9-3

5.

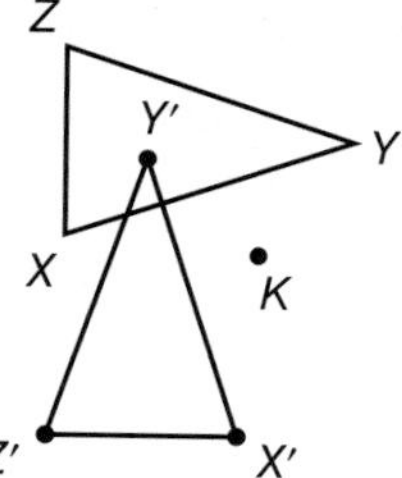

6.

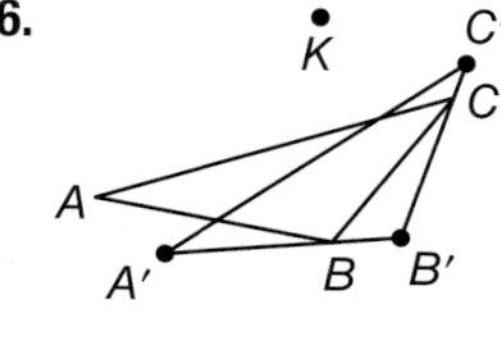

7.

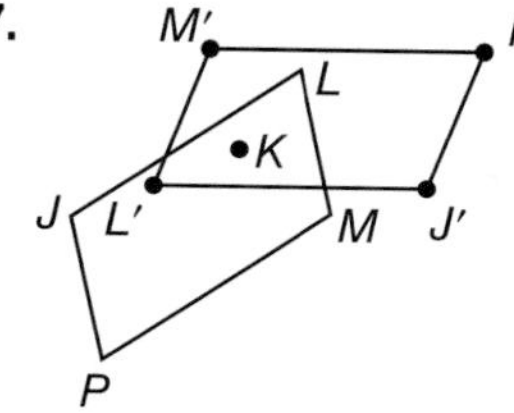

8.

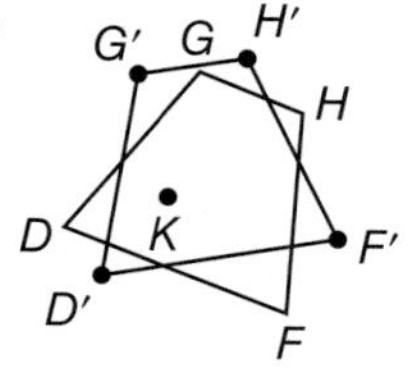

9.

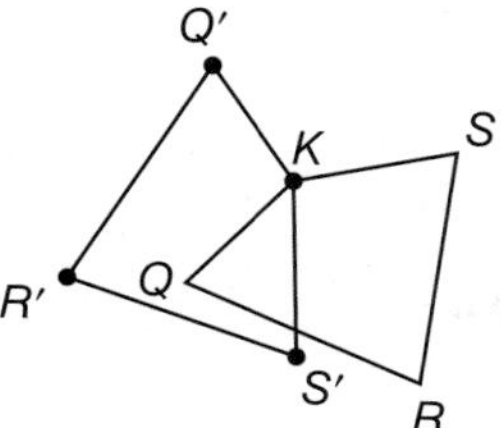

10.

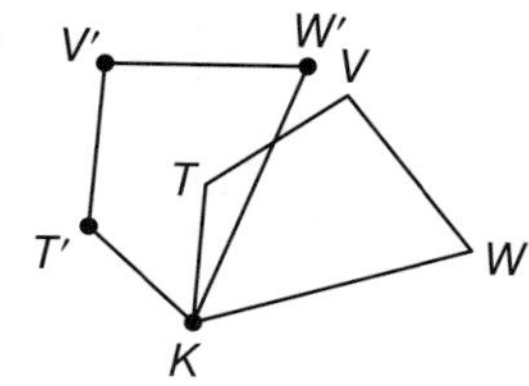

14.

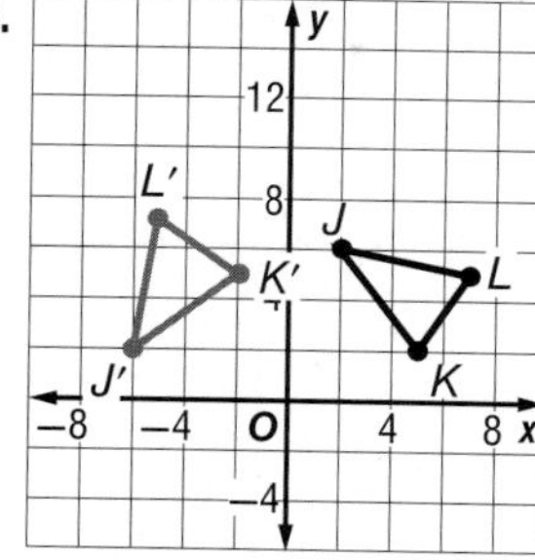

15.

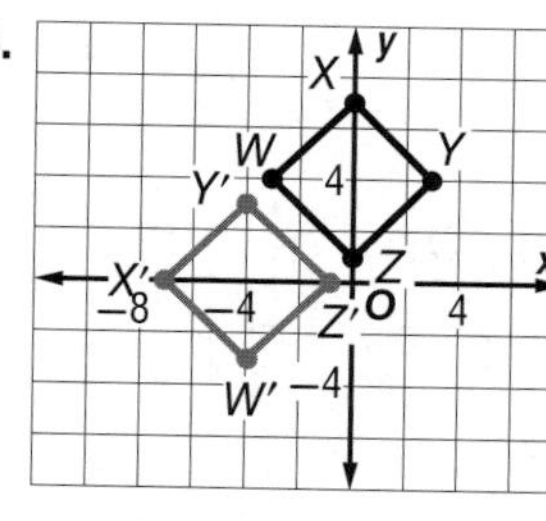

16.

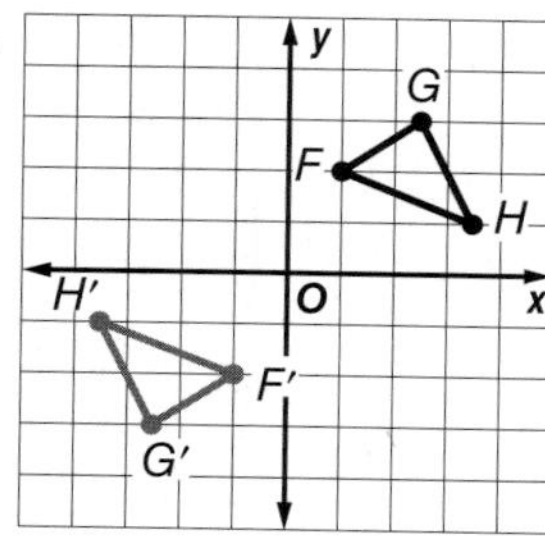

17.

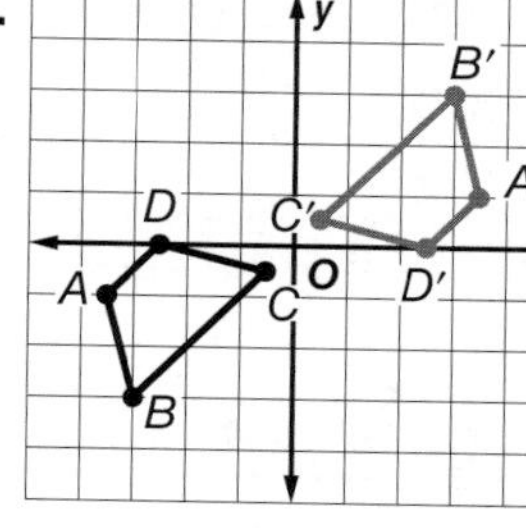

18.

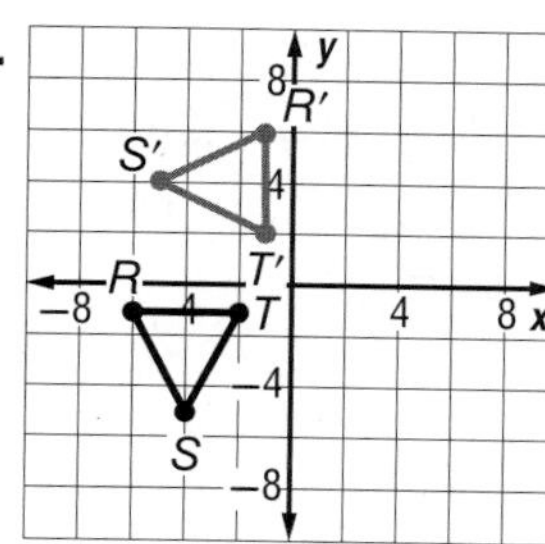

19.

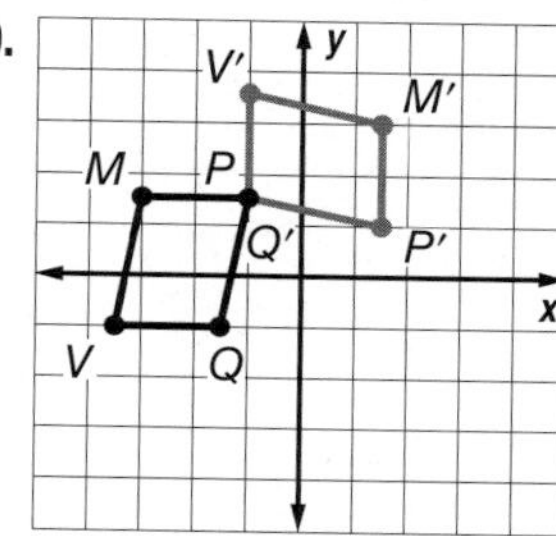

22.

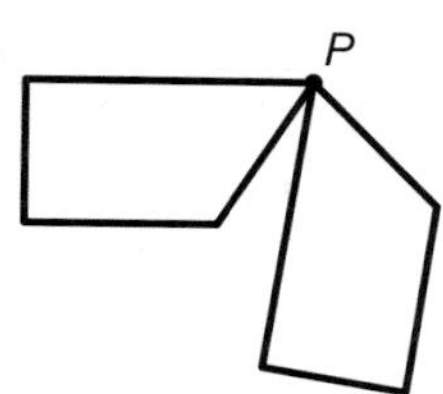

80°

23.

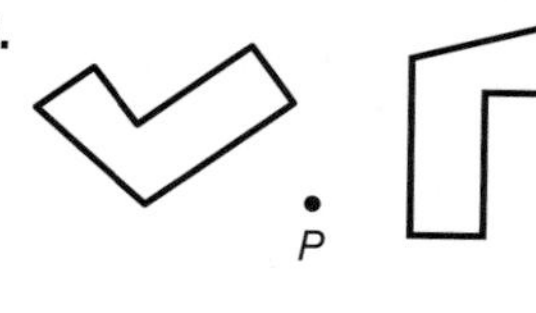

125°

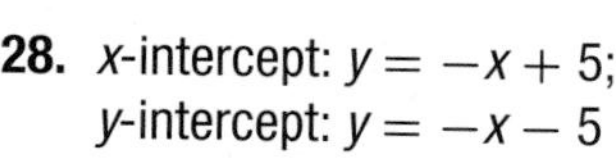

28. x-intercept: $y = -x + 5$; y-intercept: $y = -x - 5$

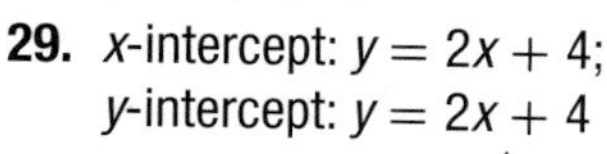

29. x-intercept: $y = 2x + 4$; y-intercept: $y = 2x + 4$

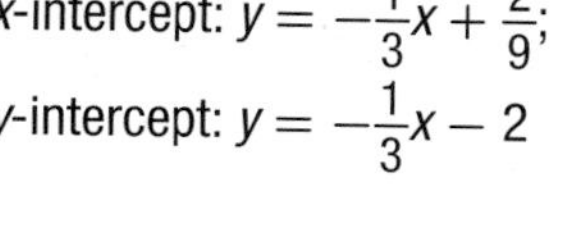

30. x-intercept: $y = -\frac{1}{3}x + \frac{2}{9}$; y-intercept: $y = -\frac{1}{3}x - 2$

33a.

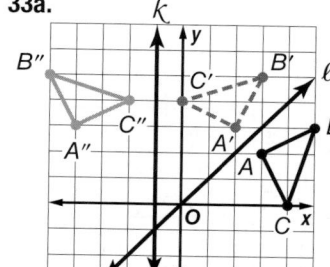

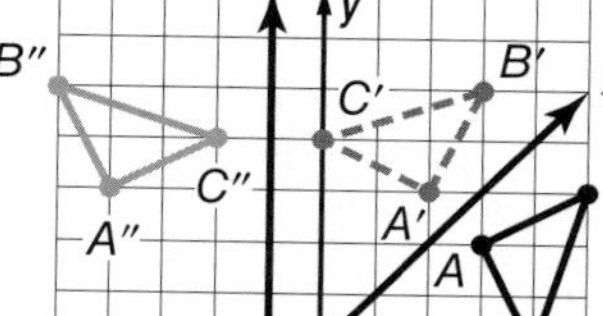

33b.

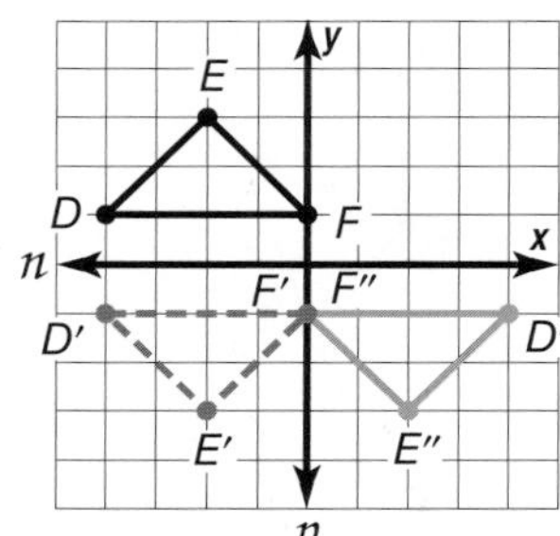

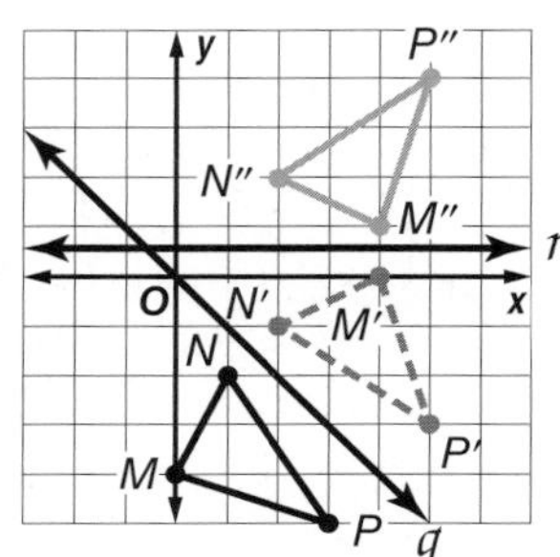

Extend 9-3

13. Sample answer:

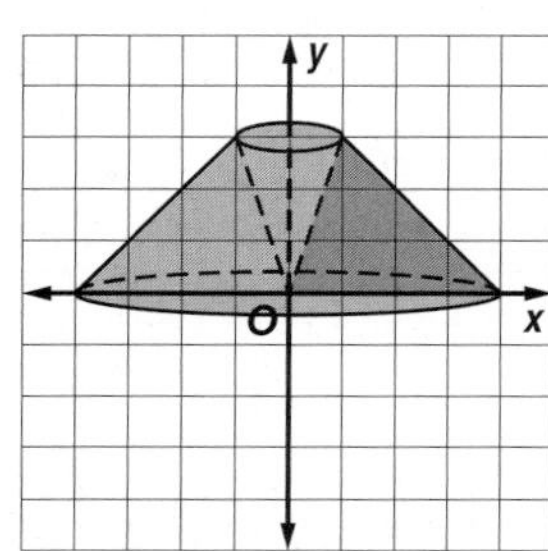

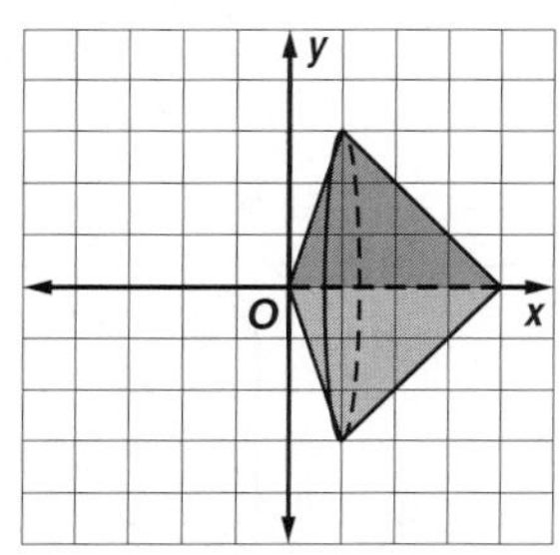

Mid-Chapter Quiz

1.

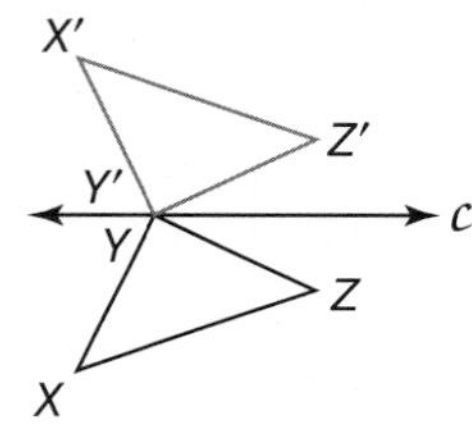

2.

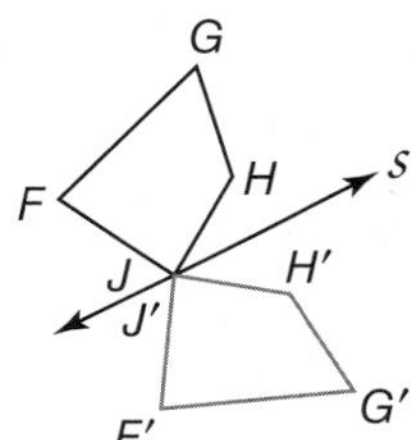

3.

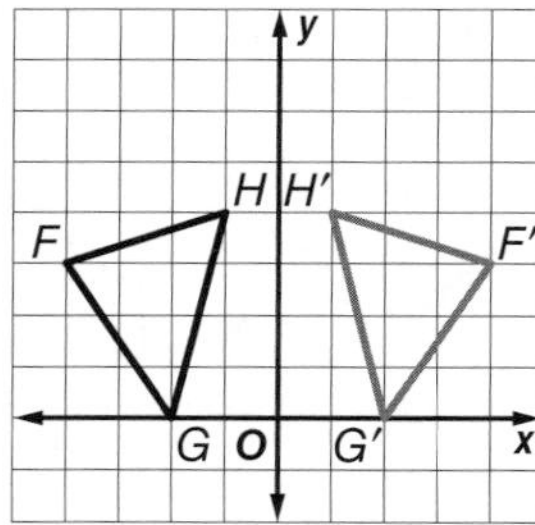

4.

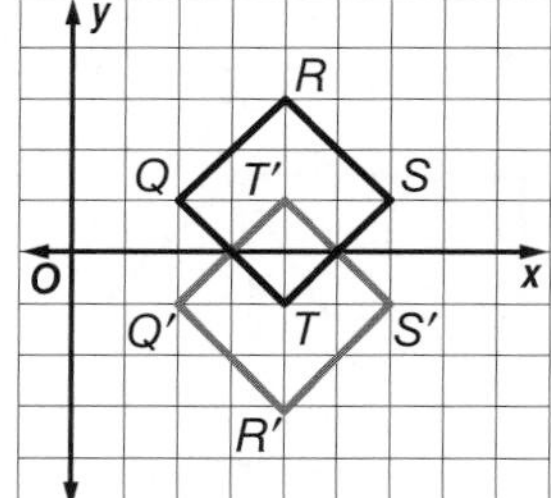

5.

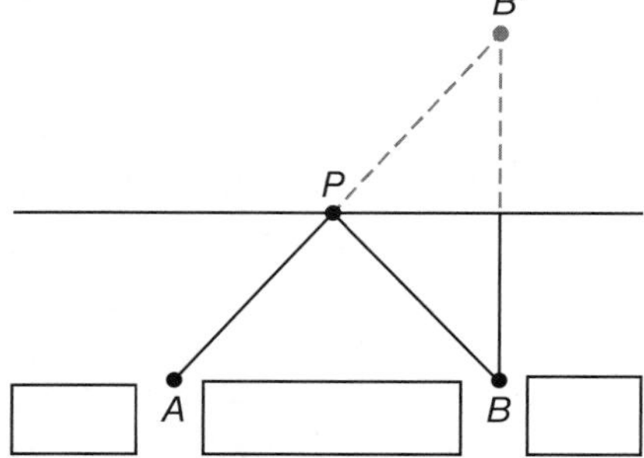

6.

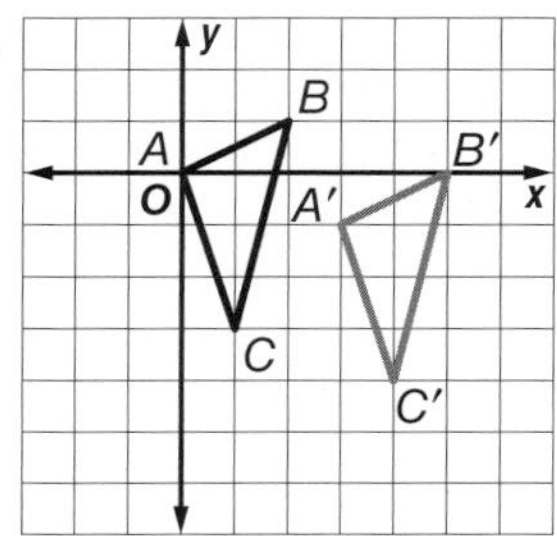

7.

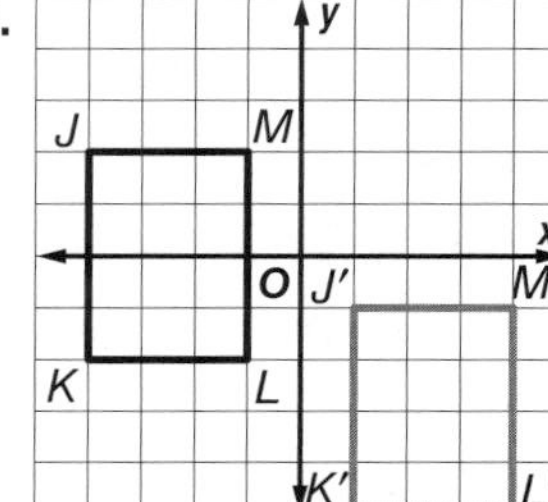

8.

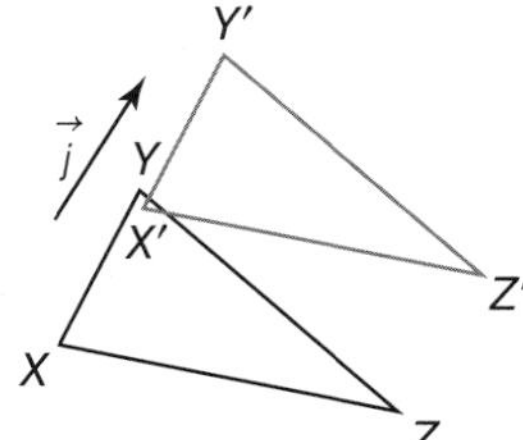

9.

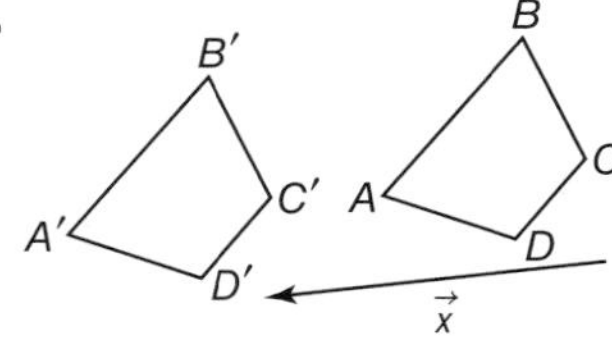

11.

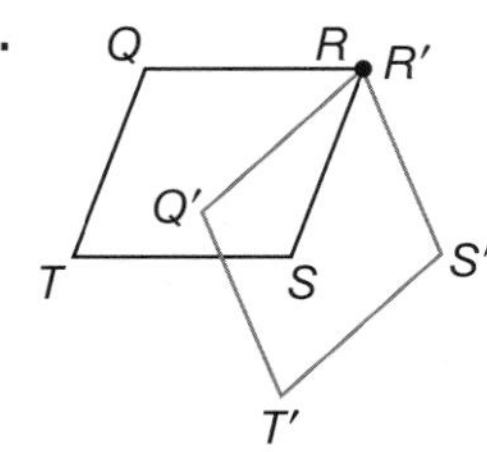

12.

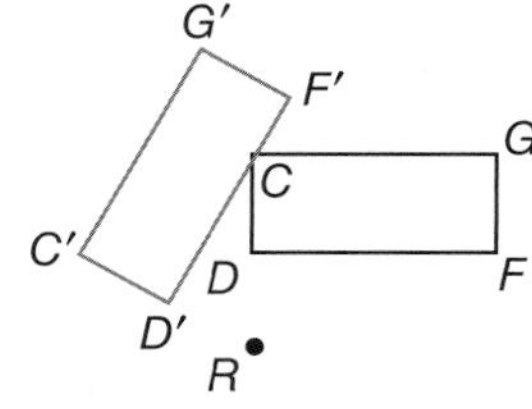

14.

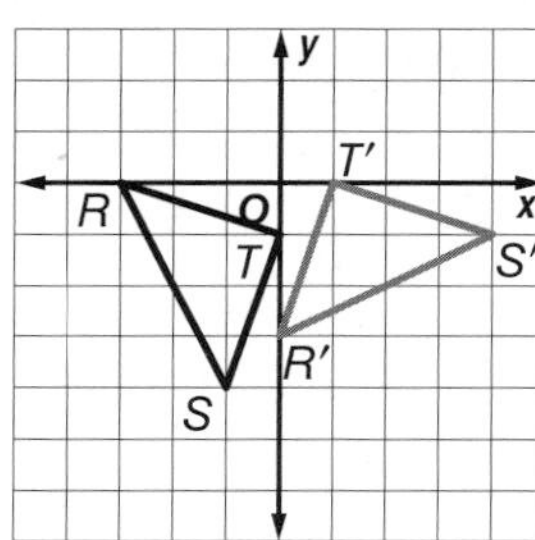

15.

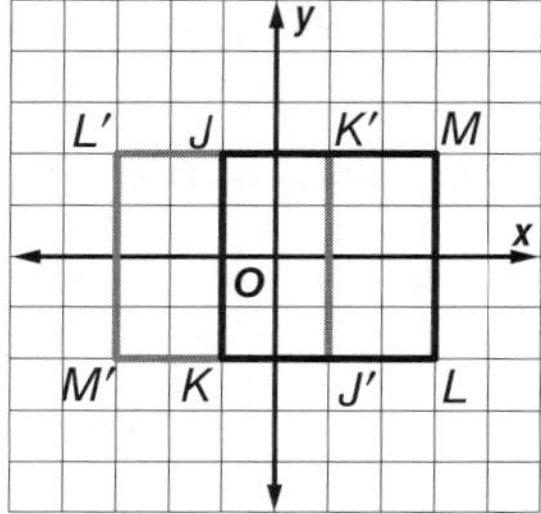

Lesson 9-4 (Guided Practice)

1A.

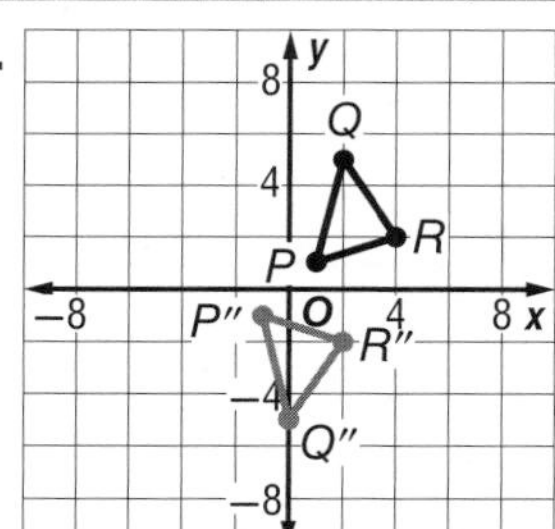

1B.

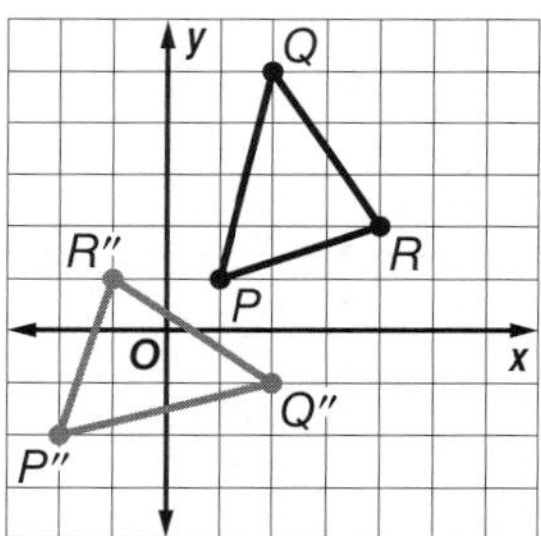

Lesson 9-4

4. 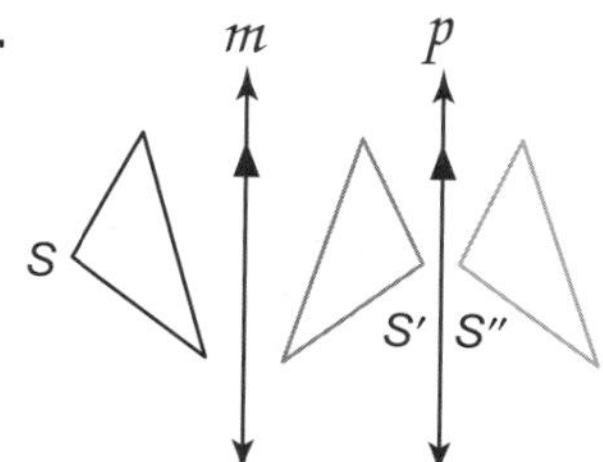

horizontal translation 3 in. to the right

5. 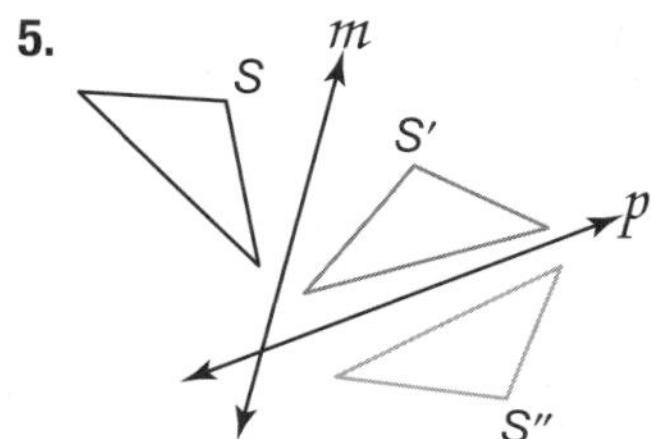

rotation clockwise 100° about point where lines m and p intersect

7. 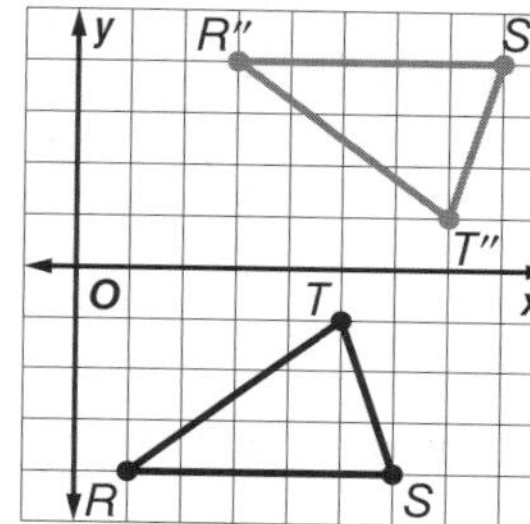

8. 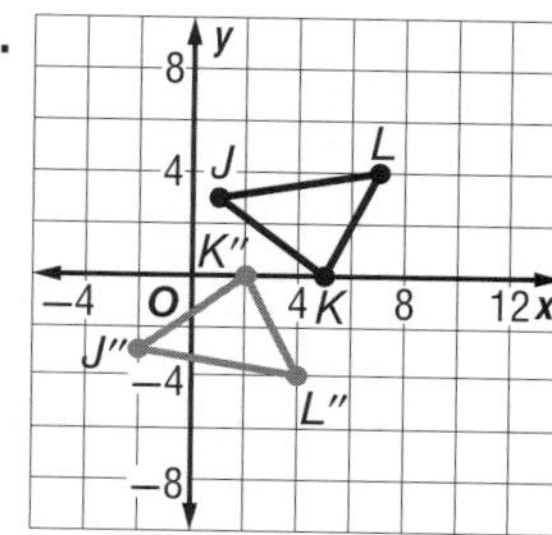

9. 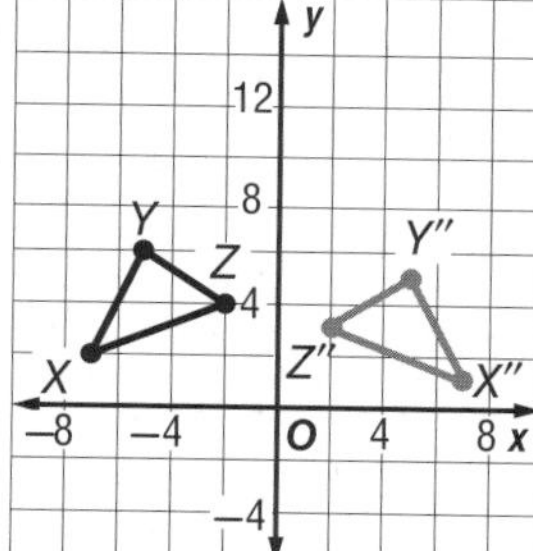

10. 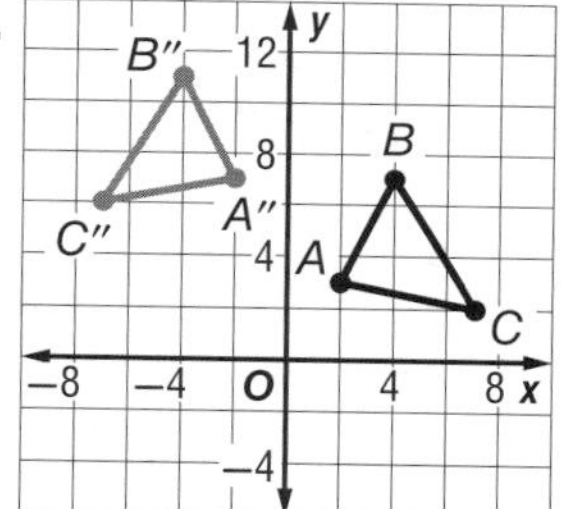

11. 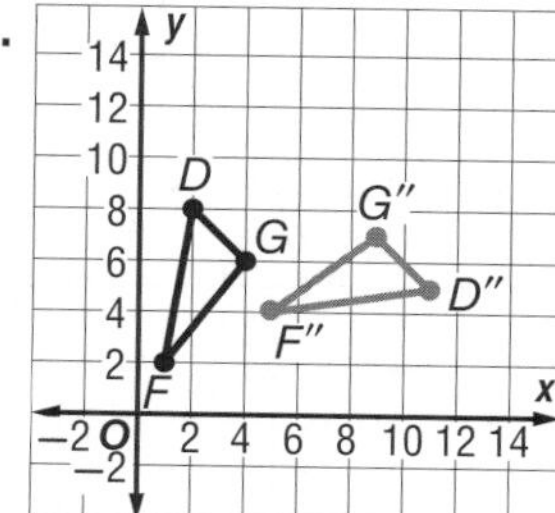

12. 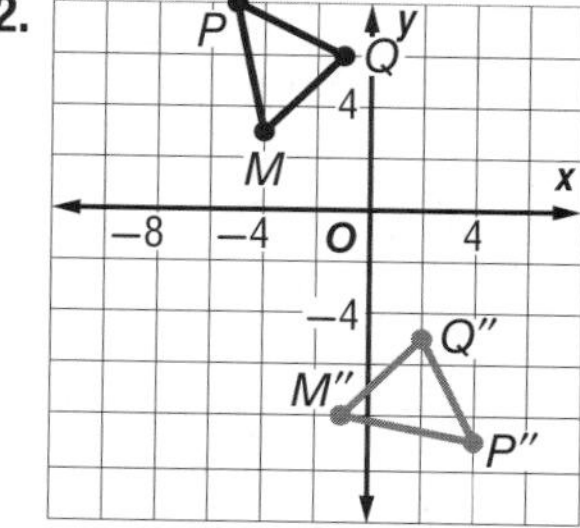

13. 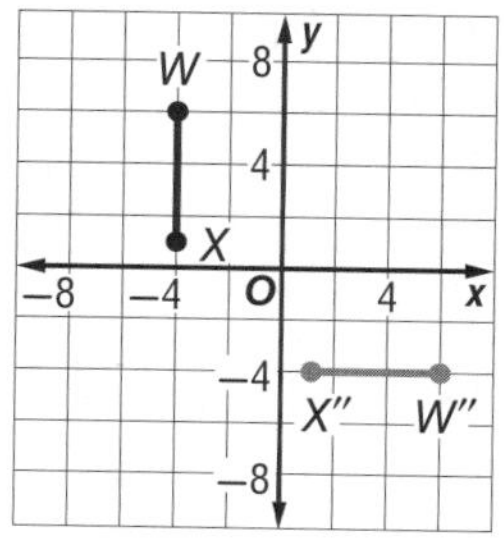

14. 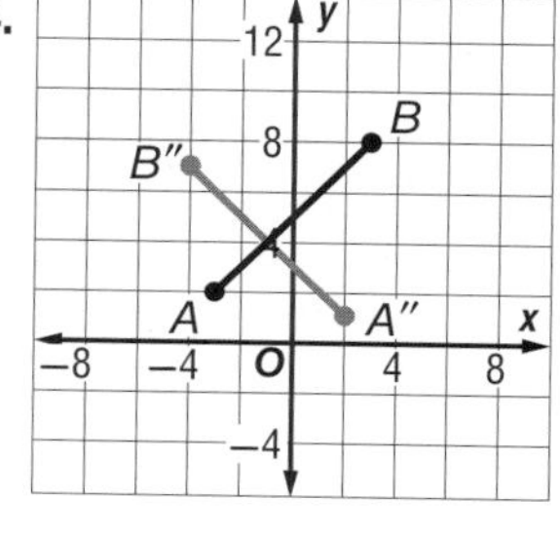

15. 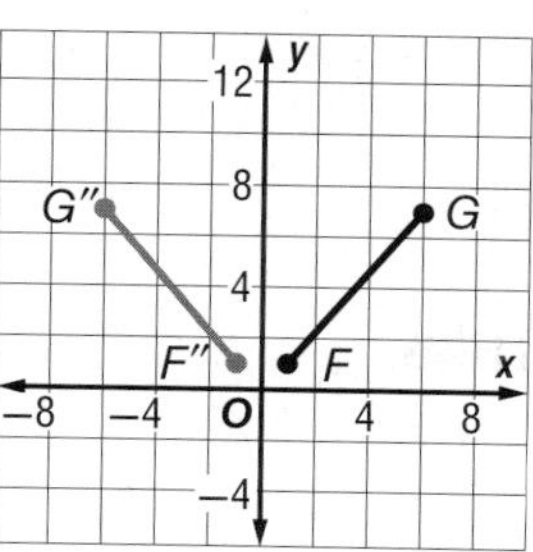

16. 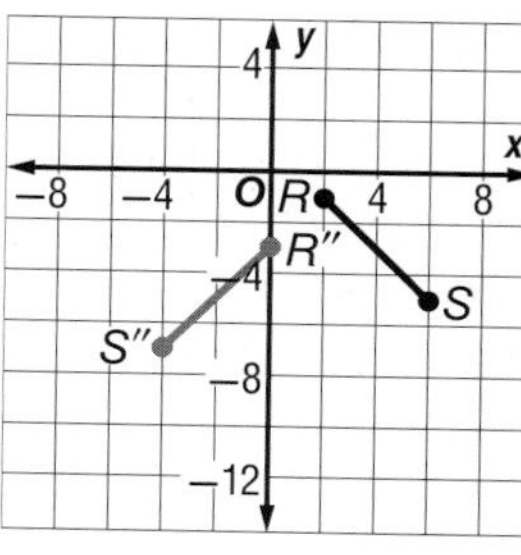

30. Proof: It is given that a translation along $\langle a, b\rangle$ maps X to X' and Y to Y'. Using the definition of a translation, points X and Y move the same distance in the same direction, therefore $\overline{XY} \cong \overline{X'Y'}$. It is also given that a reflection in z maps X' to X'' and Y' to Y''. Using the definition of a reflection, points X and Y are the same distance from line z, so $\overline{X'Y'} \cong \overline{X''Y''}$. By the Transitive Property of Congruence, $\overline{XY} \cong \overline{X''Y''}$.

36. **Proof:**

Statements (Reasons):

1. A reflection in line p maps $\overline{BC}$ to $\overline{B'C'}$; a reflection in line q maps $\overline{B'C'}$ to $\overline{B''C''}$.; $p \parallel q$; x is the distance between p and q. (Given)
2. p is the perpendicular bisector of $\overline{BB'}$, and q is the perpendicular bisector of $\overline{B'B''}$. (Def. of $\perp$ bisector)
3. $BB' + B'B'' = BB''$ (Seg. Add. Post.)
4. $\overline{BB''} \perp p$, $\overline{BB''} \perp q$ (A line perpendicular to a portion of a segment is perpendicular to the whole segment.)
5. $\overline{BA} \cong \overline{AB'}$; $\overline{B'D} \cong \overline{DB''}$ (Def. of refl.)
6. $BA = AB'$; $B'D = DB''$ (Def. of $\cong$)
7. $BA + AB' + B'D + DB' = BB''$ (Seg. Add. Post.)
8. $AB' + AB' + B'D + B'D = BB''$ (Subs.)
9. $2AB' + 2\,B'D = BB''$ (Add. Prop.)
10. $2(AB' + B'D) = BB''$ (Dist. Prop.)
11. $AB' + B'D = AD$ (Seg. Add. Post.)
12. $2AD = BB''$ (Subs.)
13. $2x = BB''$ (Subs.)

37. **Proof:** We are given that ℓ and m intersect at point P and that A is not on ℓ or m. Reflect A over m to A' and reflect A' over ℓ to A''. By the definition of reflection, m is the perpendicular bisector of $\overline{AA'}$ at R, and ℓ is the perpendicular bisector of $\overline{A'A''}$ at S. $\overline{AR} \cong \overline{A'R}$ and $\overline{A'S} \cong \overline{A''S}$ by the definition of a perpendicular bisector. Through any two points there is exactly one line, so we can draw auxiliary segments $\overline{AP}$, $\overline{A'P}$, and $\overline{A''P}$. $\angle ARP$, $\angle A'RP$, $\angle A'SP$ and $\angle A''SP$ are right angles by the definition of perpendicular bisectors. $\overline{RP} \cong \overline{RP}$ and $\overline{SP} \cong \overline{SP}$ by the Reflexive Property. $\triangle ARP \cong \triangle A'RP$ and $\triangle A'SP \cong \triangle A''SP$ by the SAS Congruence Postulate. Using CPCTC, $\overline{AP} \cong \overline{A'P}$ and $\overline{A'P} \cong \overline{A''P}$, and $\overline{AP} \cong \overline{A''P}$ by the Transitive Property. By the definition of a rotation, A'' is the image of A after a rotation about point P. Also using CPCTC, $\angle APR \cong \angle A'PR$ and $\angle A'PS \cong \angle A''PS$. By the definition of congruence, $m\angle APR = m\angle A'PR$ and $m\angle A'PS = m\angle A''PS$. $m\angle APR + m\angle A'PR + m\angle A'PS + m\angle A''PS = m\angle APA''$ and $m\angle A'PS + m\angle A'PR = m\angle SPR$ by the Angle

Addition Postulate. $m\angle A'PR + m\angle A'PR + m\angle A'PS + m\angle A'PS = m\angle APA''$ by Substitution, which simplifies to $2(m\angle A'PR + m\angle A'PS) = m\angle APA''$. By Substitution, $2(m\angle SPR) = m\angle APA''$.

39. Sample answer: No; there are no invariant points in a glide reflection because all of the points are translated along a vector. Perhaps for compositions of transformations, there may be invariant points when a figure is rotated and reflected, rotated twice, or reflected twice.

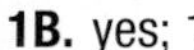

Lesson 9-5 (Guided Practice)

1B. yes; 1

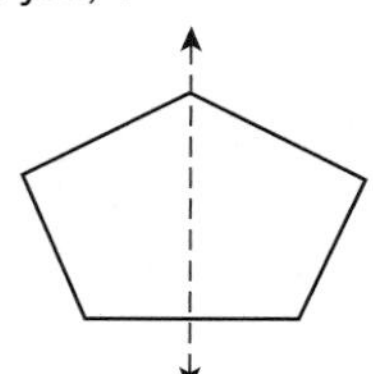

1C. yes; 2

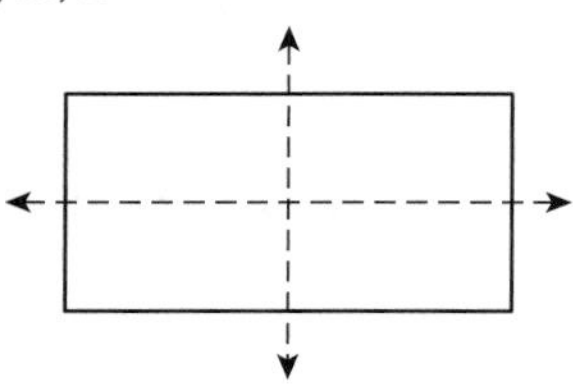

2A. yes; 5; 360° ÷ 5 or 72°

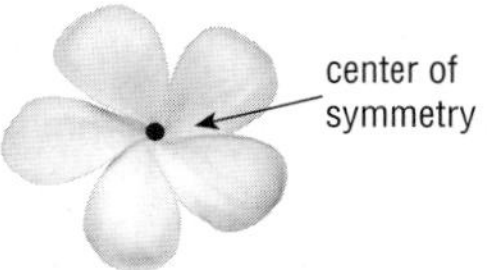

2B. yes; 3; 360° ÷ 3 or 120°

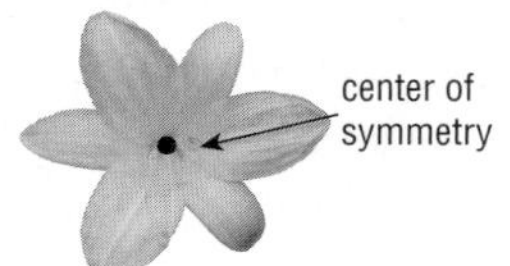

2C. no

Lesson 9-5

6. yes; 4; 90°

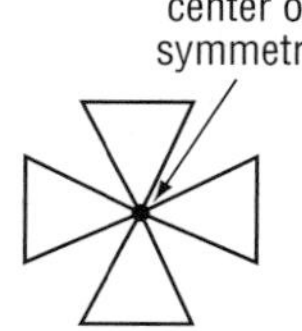

10. yes; 4

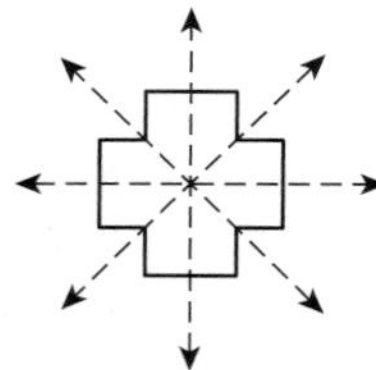

11. yes; 6

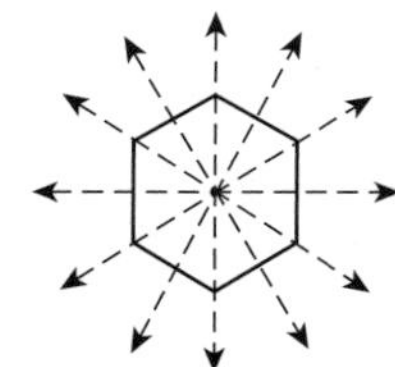

12. yes; 1

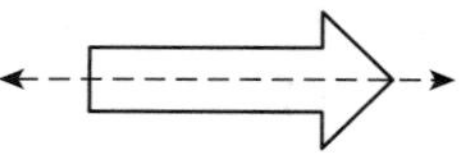

13. yes; 1

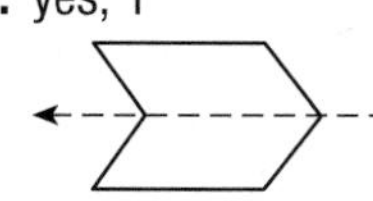

16. yes; 4

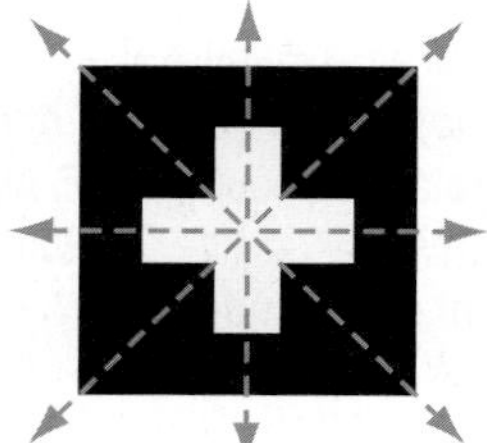

17. yes; 1

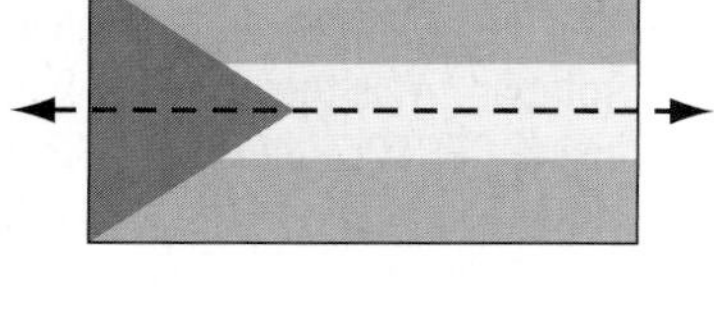

18. yes; 2; 180°

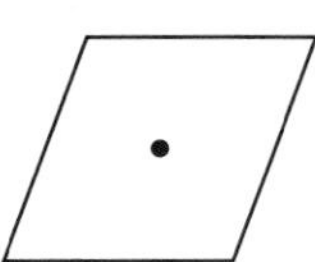

19. yes; 3; 120°

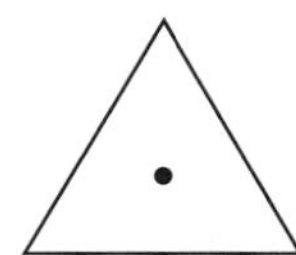

22. yes; 8; 45°

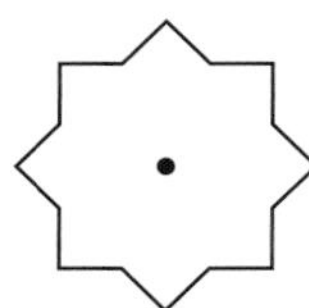

23. yes; 8; 45°

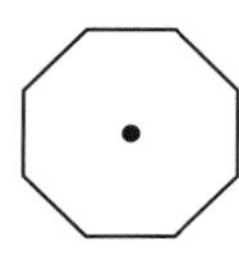

34a. Sample answer: There is a horizontal line of symmetry between the tower and its reflection. There is a vertical line of symmetry through the center of the photo.

34b. No; sample answer: Since the tower itself is three-dimensional and the reflection is two-dimensional, three-dimensional symmetry does not apply.

50. Sample answer: In both rotational and line symmetry a figure is mapped onto itself. However, in line symmetry the figure is mapped onto itself by a reflection, and in rotational symmetry a figure is mapped onto itself by a rotation. A figure can have line symmetry and rotational symmetry.

Lesson 9-6 (Guided Practice)

1A.

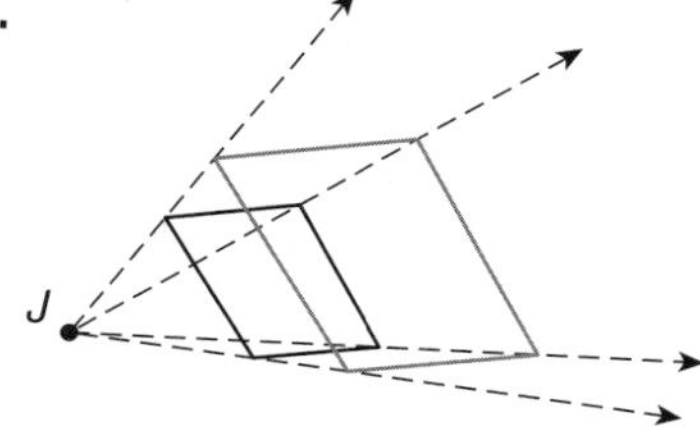

1B.

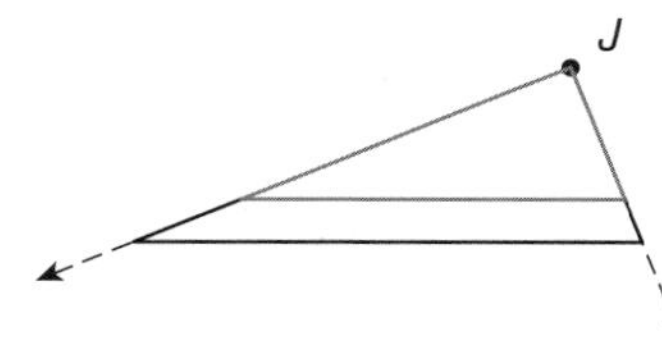

Lesson 9-6

5.

6.

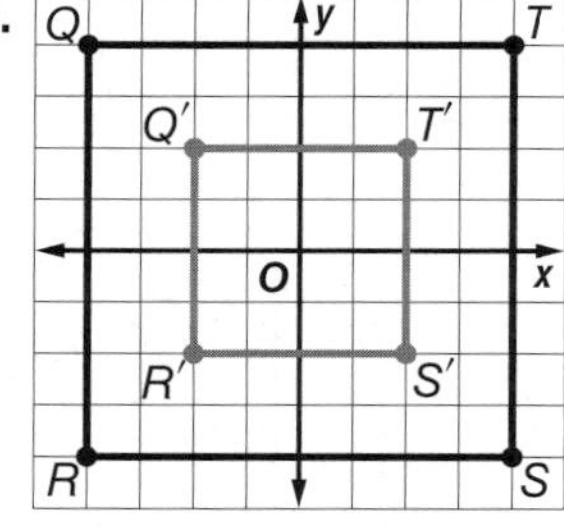

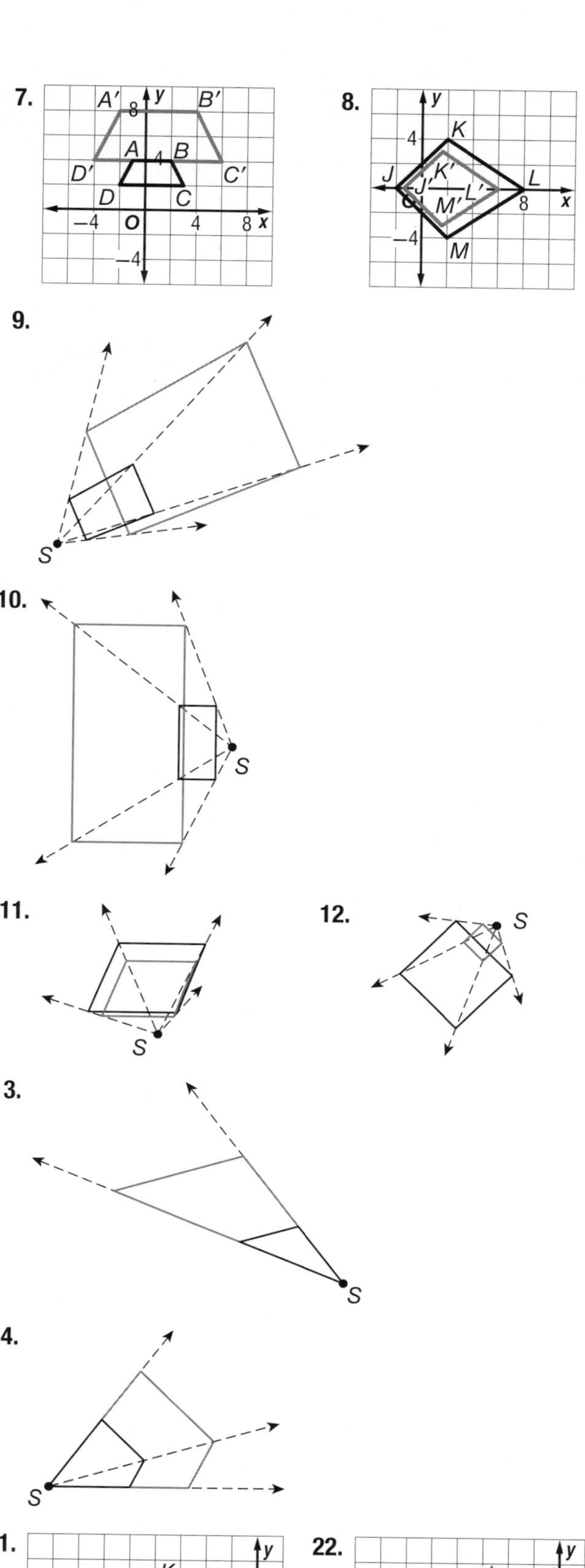

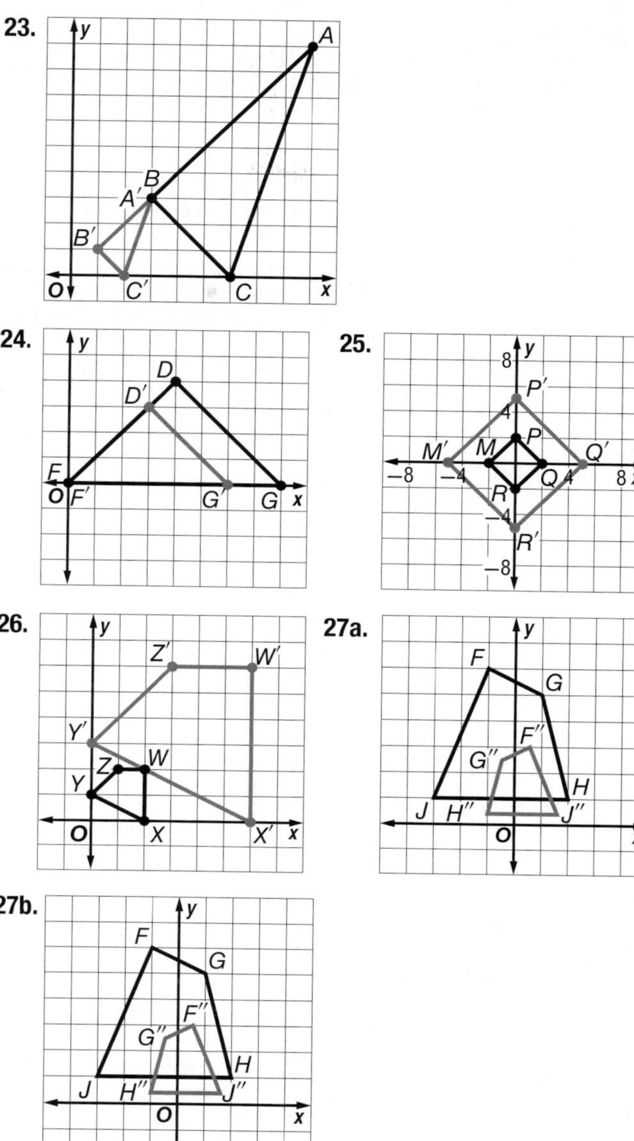

38. Sample answer: Yes; in translations, reflections, and rotations, congruent figures are formed, which means that sides that were parallel before transformation will be parallel after transformation and points that were collinear before transformation will still be collinear after transformation. Both parallel sides and collinear points are also preserved under dilations because a similar figure is formed, which has the same shape, but in a different proportion.

Practice Test

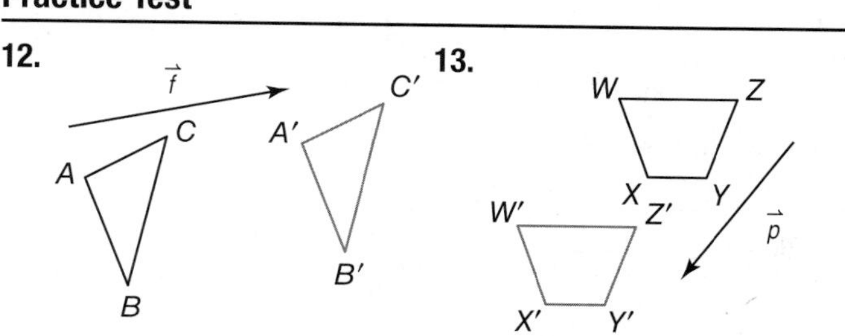

Chapter Planner

	Diagnostic Assessment Quick Check		
	LESSON 10-1 **45 min:** 1 day **90 min:** 0.5 day	**LESSON 10-2** **45 min:** 1 day **90 min:** 0.5 day	**LESSON 10-3** **45 min:** 1 day **90 min:** 0.5 day
Title	**Circles and Circumference**	**Measuring Angles and Arcs**	**Arcs and Chords**
Objectives	▪ Identify and use parts of circles. ▪ Solve problems involving the circumference of a circle.	▪ Identify central angles, major arcs, minor arcs, and semicircles, and find their measures. ▪ Find arc lengths.	▪ Recognize and use relationships between arcs and chords. ▪ Recognize and use relationships between arcs, chords, and diameters.
Key Vocabulary	center circle chord diameter radius concentric circles circumference pi (π) inscribed circumscribed	central angle arc minor arc major arc semicircle congruent arcs adjacent arcs arc length	
CCSS	G.CO.1, G.C.1	G.C.2, G.C.5	G.C.2, G.MG.3
Multiple Representations			
Lesson Resources	connectED.mcgraw-hill.com Leveled Worksheets Vocabulary Personal Tutor Self-Check Quiz ▪ *5-Minute Check* ▪ *Study Notebook*	connectED.mcgraw-hill.com Leveled Worksheets Vocabulary Quiz 1 Personal Tutor Self-Check Quiz ▪ *5-Minute Check* ▪ *Study Notebook*	connectED.mcgraw-hill.com Leveled Worksheets Personal Tutor Self-Check Quiz ▪ *5-Minute Check* ▪ *Study Notebook* ▪ *Teaching Geometry with Manipulatives*
Resources for Every Lesson	IWB eStudent Edition IWB Interactive Classroom	▪ eTeacher Edition ▪ eSolutions Manual ▪ eAssessment	
Differentiated Instruction	pp. 699, 700	pp. 708, 709, 712	pp. 718, 722

IWB All digital assets are Interactive Whiteboard ready.

Suggested Pacing			
Time Periods	Instruction	Review & Assess	Total
45-minute	9 days	2 days	11 days
90-minute	5 days	1 day	6 days

LESSON 10-4 (45 min: 1 day; 90 min: 0.5 day)	LESSON 10-5 (45 min: 1 day; 90 min: 0.5 day)	EXTEND 10-5 (45 min: 0.5 day; 90 min: 0.5 day)	LESSON 10-6 (45 min: 1 day; 90 min: 0.5 day)
Inscribed Angles	**Tangents**	**Geometry Lab: Inscribed and Circumscribed Circles**	**Secants, Tangents, and Angle Measures**
▪ Find measures of inscribed angles. ▪ Find measures of angles of inscribed polygons.	▪ Use properties of tangents. ▪ Solve problems involving circumscribed polygons.	▪ Construct inscribed circles and circumscribed triangles.	▪ Find measures of angles formed by lines intersecting on or inside a circle. ▪ Find measures of angles formed by lines intersecting outside the circle.
inscribed angle intercepted arc	tangent point of tangency common tangent		secant
G.C.2, G.C.3	G.CO.12, G.C.4	G.CO.13, G.C.3	
connectED.mcgraw-hill.com Leveled Worksheets Quiz 2 Vocabulary Personal Tutor Self-Check Quiz ▪ *5-Minute Check* ▪ *Study Notebook* ▪ *Teaching Geometry with Manipulatives*	connectED.mcgraw-hill.com Leveled Worksheets Vocabulary Animations Personal Tutor Self-Check Quiz ▪ *5-Minute Check* ▪ *Study Notebook* ▪ *Teaching Geometry with Manipulatives*	connectED.mcgraw-hill.com Animations Virtual Manipulatives ▪ *Teaching Geometry with Manipulatives* **Materials:** ▪ straightedge ▪ compass	connectED.mcgraw-hill.com Leveled Worksheets Quiz 3 Vocabulary Personal Tutor Self-Check Quiz ▪ *5-Minute Check* ▪ *Study Notebook*
pp. 724, 725, 730	pp. 734, 735		pp. 742, 743, 749

IWB eStudent Edition
IWB Interactive Classroom

- eTeacher Edition
- eSolutions Manual
- eAssessment

Formative Assessment
Mid-Chapter Quiz

Chapter Planner

	LESSON 10-7 (45 min: 1 day; 90 min: 0.5 day)	LESSON 10-8 (45 min: 1 day; 90 min: 0.5 day)	EXTEND 10-8 (45 min: 0.5 day; 90 min: 0.5 day)
Title	**Special Segments in a Circle**	**Equations of Circles**	**Geometry Lab: Parabolas**
Objectives	▪ Find measures of segments that intersect in the interior of a circle. ▪ Find measures of segments that intersect in the exterior of a circle.	▪ Write the equation of a circle ▪ Graph a circle on the coordinate plane.	▪ Identify conic sections. ▪ Translate between the geometric description and the equation for a parabola. ▪ Determine intersections between lines and parabolas.
Key Vocabulary	chord segment secant segment external secant segment tangent segment	compound locus	conic sections conics parabola focus directrix
CCSS		G.GPE.1, G.GPE.6	G.GPE.2
Multiple Representations			
Lesson Resources	connectED.mcgraw-hill.com Leveled Worksheets Vocabulary Personal Tutor Self-Check Quiz ▪ *5-Minute Check* ▪ *Study Notebook*	connectED.mcgraw-hill.com Leveled Worksheets Quiz 4 Vocabulary Personal Tutor Virtual Manipulatives Self-Check Quiz ▪ *5-Minute Check* ▪ *Study Notebook*	connectED.mcgraw-hill.com Vocabulary Animations **Materials:** ▪ modeling clay ▪ wax paper ▪ graph paper
Resources for Every Lesson	IWB eStudent Edition IWB Interactive Classroom	▪ eTeacher Edition ▪ eSolutions Manual ▪ eAssessment	
Differentiated Instruction	pp. 751, 752	pp. 759, 763	

Summative Assessment
Study Guide and Review
Practice Test

IWB All digital assets are Interactive Whiteboard ready.

What the Research Says...

Students are able to learn new skills and concepts while they are solving challenging problems. They found it is not necessary for teachers to focus first on skill development and then move to problem solving. Both can be done together. In fact, students who develop conceptual understanding through problem solving early perform best on procedural knowledge later. (Grouws and Cebulla, 2000)

- Arrange students in small groups and allow them to work on the geometry activities in the lessons first, before pre-teaching the concepts.
- Use the lesson opener, Get Ready for the Lesson, and the scaffolding questions to initiate a dialogue on the concepts to come. Have students work through the lesson examples together and then discuss their findings.

Teacher to Teacher

Kim A. Halvorson
DeSoto County High School
Arcadia, FL

Use With Lesson 10-1

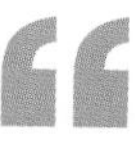

My students are asked to decorate a T-shirt with a "pi" theme. Then they wear them on March 14 (3.14). The rest of the school (via morning announcements) is encouraged to ask the geometry students to discuss their shirts. ”

Reading and Writing in Mathematics

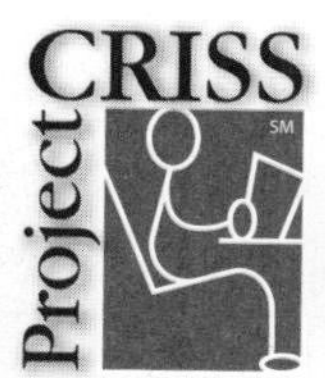

STUDY SKILL

As you begin studying a new lesson or chapter, it may be helpful for students to complete a K-W-L frame. Have students quickly skim through the lesson looking at the list of new vocabulary and the illustrations so they have an idea of what is included. Next have them record what they think they know and what they want (or expect) to learn. After completing the lesson, they should make corrections to the Know column and complete the Learned column-including the answers to their Want to know questions. The completed sample frame at the right shows information that a student recorded before and after studying Lesson 10-1 on circles and circumference.

What I Know	What I Want to Know	What I Learned
I know a circle has a center. The distance from the center to a point on the circle is the radius (r). The diameter (distance across, through center) $= 2r$. Circumference $= \pi D^2$, $\pi = 3.14$. I think a chord is a section of the circle. A circle has 360°.	What is the difference between circumscribed and inscribed?	• I found out that $C = \pi D$ not πD^2. A chord is a line segment with endpoints on the circle, not a section of the circle. • Concentric circles are in the same plane and have the same center. • The triangle is <u>inscribed</u> in a circle. The circle <u>circumscribes</u> the triangle.

Creating Independence through Student-owned Strategies

Assessment and Intervention

SE = Student Edition, **TE** = Teacher Edition, **CRM** = Chapter Resource Masters

	Diagnosis	Prescription
DIAGNOSTIC ASSESSMENT	**Beginning Chapter 10**	
	Get Ready for Chapter 10 **SE**	Response to Intervention **TE**
	Beginning Every Lesson	
	Then, Now, Why? **SE** 5-Minute Checks	Chapter 0 **SE**
FORMATIVE ASSESSMENT	**During/After Every Lesson**	
	Guided Practice **SE**, every example Check Your Understanding **SE** H.O.T. Problems **SE** Spiral Review **SE** Additional Examples **TE** Watch Out! **TE** Step 4, Assess **TE** Chapter 10 Quizzes **CRM**, pp. 57–58 Self-Check Quizzes connectED.mcgraw-hill.com	TIER 1 Intervention Skills Practice **CRM**, Ch. 1–10 connectED.mcgraw-hill.com TIER 2 Intervention Differentiated Instruction **TE**; Differentiated Homework Options **TE**; Study Guide and Intervention **CRM**, Ch. 1–10 TIER 3 Intervention *Math Triumphs, Geometry,* Ch. 2 and 6
	Mid-Chapter	
	Mid-Chapter Quiz **SE** Mid-Chapter Test **CRM**, p. 59 eAssessment	TIER 1 Intervention Skills Practice **CRM**, Ch. 1–10 connectED.mcgraw-hill.com TIER 2 Intervention Study Guide and Intervention **CRM**, Ch. 1–10 TIER 3 Intervention *Math Triumphs, Geometry,* Ch. 2 and 6
	Before Chapter Test	
	Chapter Study Guide and Review **SE** Practice Test **SE** Standardized Test Practice **SE** Chapter Test connectED.mcgraw-hill.com Standardized Test Practice connectED.mcgraw-hill.com Vocabulary Review connectED.mcgraw-hill.com eAssessment	TIER 1 Intervention Skills Practice **CRM**, Ch. 1–10 connectED.mcgraw-hill.com TIER 2 Intervention Study Guide and Intervention **CRM**, Ch. 1–10 TIER 3 Intervention *Math Triumphs, Geometry,* Ch. 2 and 6
SUMMATIVE ASSESSMENT	**After Chapter 10**	
	Multiple-Choice Tests, Forms 1, 2A, 2B **CRM**, pp. 61–66 Free-Response Tests, Forms 2C, 2D, 3 **CRM**, pp. 67–72 Vocabulary Test **CRM**, p. 60 Extended Response Test **CRM**, p. 73 Standardized Test Practice **CRM**, pp. 74–76 eAssessment	Study Guide and Intervention **CRM**, Ch. 1–10 connectED.mcgraw-hill.com

Differentiated Instruction

Option 1 Reaching All Learners 

Kinesthetic/Interpersonal Draw several large circles on the parking lot or other black top area on your school's campus. To draw a perfect circle, attach a large piece of chalk (sidewalk chalk works well) to a string. Have one student hold one end of the string tightly to a point (the center) while another pulls the string taut holding the chalk end, and walk in a circle while drawing with the chalk. It is important to keep the line very taut as you draw.

If possible, cover a large area with many circles, labeling them (A, B, C, D, etc.). Have students work together to find the circumference of each circle. They should walk from circle to circle and, using a clipboard report their measurements and findings. Have them share their problem-solving strategies with the class when they get back to the room.

Kinesthetic/Logical Provide students with the opportunity not only to use compasses to create circles but to understand the definition of circle through such uses. Ask students to be creative and think of other materials that can be used to create perfect circles in the absence of compasses. Have students use these techniques prior to beginning the chapter and create their own definition for the term *circle*.

Option 2 Approaching Level AL

Arrange students in small mixed ability groups. Use a cork board, pushpins, a cutout circle and a flexible rubber band to model inscribed angles. Place the circle on the cork board and put two pushpins on the circle to represent the points of an intercepted arc. Wrap the rubber band around the pins and use a pencil to drag the rubber band to the opposite end of the circle to represent the vertex of the inscribed angle. Students can move the pencil along the circle and use a protractor to note that the measure of the angle stays the same.

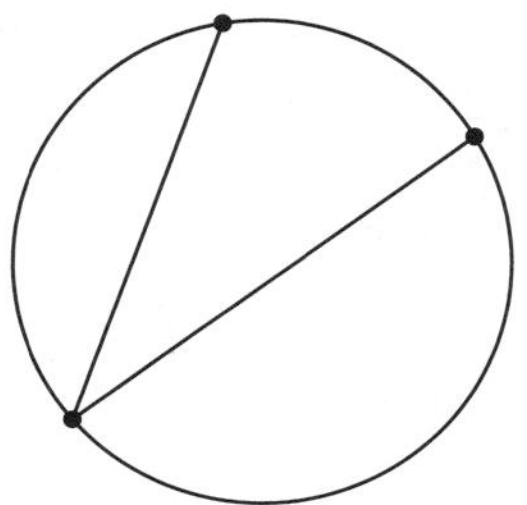

Option 3 English Learners ELL

Have students write about the parts of a circle and its circumference in their own words. They can write a paragraph that explains each vocabulary term and the relationship of the terms to each other, or they can list the terms and write a brief explanation and provide an example for each. Students can then be arranged in pairs to quiz each other by giving a definition and asking for the word and an example, or giving the word, and asking for the definition and example.

Option 4 Beyond Level BL

Using a compact disc as a template, have students trace a circle onto a piece of paper. Then, have students place two metric rulers beside the disc to model two tangents. Have students arrange the rulers so that they form two tangents that intersect on the sheet. Then have students lightly draw the two tangents from the circle to the point of intersection and measure the distance from the circle to the point of intersection to confirm that the measures are equal.

Focus on Mathematical Content

Vertical Alignment

Before Chapter 10

Related Topics from Grade 8

- Approximate the value of irrational numbers as they arrive from situations (such as π, $\sqrt{2}$).
- Communicate mathematical ideas using language, efficient tools, appropriate units, and graphical, numerical, physical, or algebraic mathematical models.

Chapter 10

Related Topics from Geometry

- Find areas of sectors and arc lengths of circles using proportional reasoning.
- Use numeric and geometric patterns to make generalizations about geometric properties including properties of angle relationships in circles.

After Chapter 10

Preparation for Algebra 2

- Use characteristics of the quadratic parent function to sketch the related graphs and connect between the $y = ax^2 + bx + c$ and the $y = a(x - h)^2 + k$ symbolic representations of quadratic functions.
- Use the parent function to investigate, describe, and predict the effects of changes in a, h, and k on the graphs of $y = a(x - h)^2 + k$ form of a function in applied and purely mathematics situations.

Lesson-by-Lesson Preview

10-1 Circles and Circumference

A circle is the locus of all points in a plane equidistant from a given point, which is the center of the circle. A circle is usually named by its center point. Any segment with endpoints on the circle is a chord of the circle. A chord that contains the center of the circle is the diameter of the circle. Any segment with endpoints that are the center and a point on the circle is a radius. All radii of a circle are congruent and all diameters are congruent.

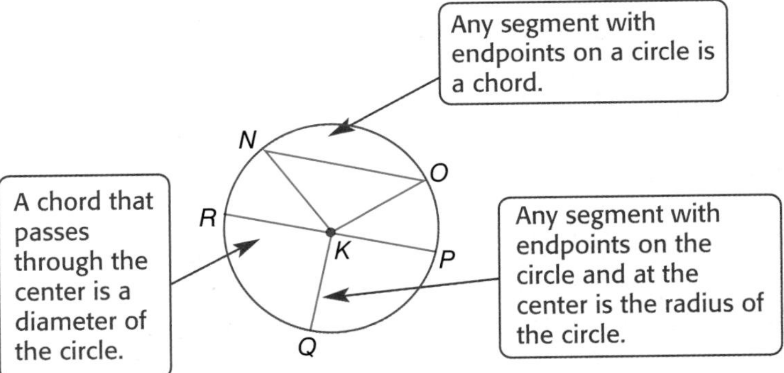

The circumference of a circle is the distance around the circle. The ratio of the circumference to the diameter of a circle is always equal to π. For a circumference of C units and a diameter of d units or a radius of r units, $C = \pi d$ or $C = 2\pi r$.

10-2 Measuring Angles and Arcs

A central angle of a circle has the center of the circle as its vertex, and its sides are two radii of the circle. A central angle separates the circle into two parts, each of which is an arc.

The measure of each arc is related to the measure of its central angle. A minor arc degree measure equals the measure of the central angle and is less than 180. A semicircle is also considered an arc and has a measure of 180.

Another way to measure an arc is by its length. An arc is part of the circle, so the length of an arc is part of the circumference. The ratio of the arc degree measure to 360 is equal to the ratio of the arc length to the circumference. You can use these ratios to solve for arc length.

10-3 Arcs and Chords

The endpoints of a chord are also endpoints of an arc. Arcs and chords have a special relationship. In a circle or in congruent circles, two minor arcs are congruent if and only if their corresponding chords are congruent. In a circle or congruent circles, two chords are congruent if and only if they are equidistant from the center of the circle.

The chords of adjacent arcs can form a polygon. Such a polygon is said to be *inscribed* in the circle because all its vertices lie on the circle. The circle circumscribes the polygon.

10-4 Inscribed Angles

An inscribed angle is an angle that has its vertex on the circle and its sides contained in chords of the circle. If an angle is inscribed in a circle, then the measure of the angle equals one-half of the measure of its intercepted arc (or the measure of the intercepted arc is twice the measure of the inscribed angle). If two inscribed angles of a circle (or congruent circles) intercept congruent arcs or the same arc, then the angles are congruent.

Inscribed polygons also have special properties. An inscribed triangle with a side that is a diameter is a special type of triangle. If an inscribed angle intercepts a semicircle, the angle is a right angle. If a quadrilateral is inscribed in a circle, then its opposite angles are supplementary.

10-5 Tangents

A tangent intersects a circle in exactly one point. This point is called the point of tangency. A line is tangent to a circle if and only if it is perpendicular to the radius drawn to the point of tangency.

More than one line can be tangent to the same circle. If two segments from the same exterior point are tangent to a circle, then they are congruent.

Circles can be inscribed in polygons, just as polygons can be inscribed in circles. If a circle is inscribed in a polygon, then every side of the polygon is tangent to the circle.

10-6 Secants, Tangents, and Angle Measures

A line that intersects a circle in exactly two points is called a *secant*. If two secants intersect in the interior of a circle, then the measure of an angle formed is one-half the sum of the measure of the arcs intercepted by the angle and its vertical angle.

A secant can also intersect a tangent at the point of tangency. If this occurs, then the measure of each angle formed is one-half the measure of its intercepted arc. Secants and tangents can intersect outside a circle as well. If two secants, a tangent and a secant, or two tangents intersect in the exterior of a circle, then the measure of the angle formed is one-half the positive difference of the measures of the intercepted arcs.

10-7 Special Segments in a Circle

If two chords intersect in a circle, then the products of the measures of the segments of the chords are equal. You can also use intersecting chords to measure arcs.

If two secant segments are drawn to a circle from an exterior point, then the product of the measures of one secant segment and its external secant segment is equal to the product of the measures of the other secant segment and its external secant segment. This product can also be used if a tangent segment and a secant segment are drawn to a circle from an exterior point. In this case, the square of the measure of the tangent segment is equal to the product of the measures of the secant segment and its external secant segment.

10-8 Equations of Circles

An equation for a circle with center at (h, k) and radius of r units is $(x - h)^2 + (y - k)^2 = r^2$. You can analyze the equation of a circle to find information that will help you graph the circle on a coordinate plane. Once you know the coordinates of the center and the radius of a circle, you can graph the circle. In fact, if you know just three points on a circle, you can graph it and write its equation. By graphing the points as a triangle and constructing two perpendicular bisectors, you can locate the center of the circle. Then you can use the Distance Formula to calculate the radius. Finally, write an equation for the circle.

Mc Graw Hill Professional Development

Targeted professional development has been articulated throughout Geometry. More quality, customized professional development is available from McGraw-Hill Professional Development. Visit connectED.mcgraw-hill.com for details on each product.

- Online Lessons emphasize the strategies and techniques used to teach Geometry. Includes streaming video, interactive pages, and online tools.
- Video Workshops allow mentors, coaches, or leadership personnel to facilitate on-site workshops on educational strategies in mathematics and mathematical concepts.
- MHPD Online (www.mhpdonline.com) offers online professional development with video clips of instructional strategies, links, student activities, and news and issues in education.
- Teaching Today (teachingtoday.glencoe.com) gives secondary teachers practical strategies and materials that inspire excellence and innovation in teaching.

Chapter Project

Olympic Games

Students use what they have learned about circles to complete a project.

This chapter project addresses global awareness, as well as several specific skills identified as being essential to student success by the Framework for 21st Century Learning.

Visit connectED.mcgraw-hill.com for student and teacher handouts.

KeyVocabulary Introduce the key vocabulary in the chapter using the example below.

Define: Concentric circles are coplanar circles that share the same center.

Example:

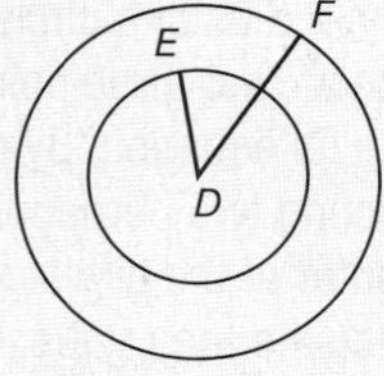

Ask: Are coplanar circles similar or congruent? Explain. The circles are similar because they have the same shape. The circles are not congruent because that have different radii.

CHAPTER 10 Circles

Then

You learned about special segments and angle relationships in triangles.

Now

In this chapter, you will:

- Learn the relationships between central angles, arcs, and inscribed angles in a circle.
- Define and use secants and tangents.
- Use an equation to identify or describe a circle.

Why?

SCIENCE The actual shape of a rainbow is a complete circle. The portion of the circle that can be seen above the horizon is a special segment of a circle called an arc.

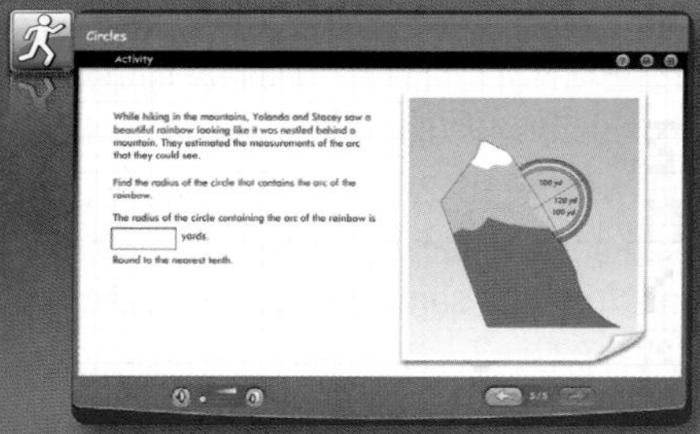

connectED.mcgraw-hill.com Your Digital Math Portal

Animation | Vocabulary | eGlossary | Personal Tutor | Virtual Manipulatives | Graphing Calculator | Audio | Foldables | Self-Check Practice | Worksheets

Get Ready for the Chapter

Diagnose Readiness | You have two options for checking prerequisite skills.

1 Textbook Option Take the Quick Check below. Refer to the Quick Review for help.

QuickCheck

Find the percent of the given number.

1. 26% of 500 130
2. 79% of 623 492.17
3. 19% of 82 15.58
4. 10% of 180 18
5. 92% of 90 82.8
6. 65% of 360 234
7. **TIPPING** A couple ate dinner at an Italian restaurant where their bill was $32.50. If they want to leave an 18% tip, how much tip money should they leave? $5.85

8. Find x. Round to the nearest tenth. 14.1

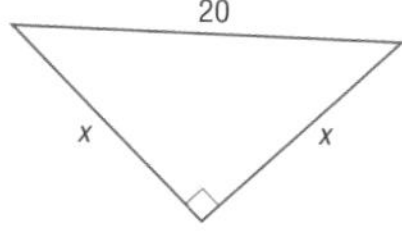

9. **CONSTRUCTION** Jennifer is putting a brace in a board, as shown at the right. Find the length of the board used for a brace. 8.5 ft

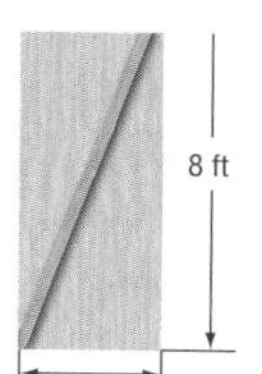

Solve each equation by using the Quadratic Formula. Round to the nearest tenth if necessary.

10. $5x^2 + 4x - 20 = 0$ −2.4, 1.6
11. $x^2 = x + 12$ −3, 4
12. **FIREWORKS** The Patriot Squad, a professional fireworks company, performed a show during a July 4th celebration. One of the rockets in the show failed to explode at a distance of $d = 80t - 16t^2$ from the ground. What length of time t did it take the rocket dud to hit the ground? 5 seconds

QuickReview

Example 1 (Used in Lesson 10-2)

Find the percent of the given number.

15% of $35 = (0.15)(35)$ Change the percent to a decimal.

$= 5.25$ Multiply.

So, 15% of 35 is 5.25.

Example 2 (Used in Lesson 10-5)

Find x. Round to the nearest tenth.

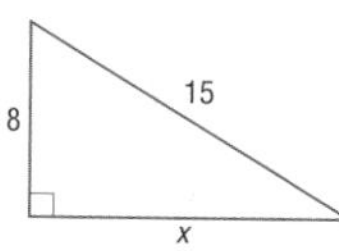

$a^2 + b^2 = c^2$ Pythagorean Theorem

$x^2 + 8^2 = 15^2$ Substitution

$x^2 + 64 = 225$ Simplify.

$x^2 = 161$ Subtract.

$x = \sqrt{161}$ or about 12.7

Example 3 (Used in Lesson 10-7)

Solve $x^2 + 3x - 40 = 0$ by using the Quadratic Formula. Round to the nearest tenth.

$x = \frac{-b \pm \sqrt{b^2 - 4ac}}{2a}$ Quadratic Formula

$= \frac{-3 \pm \sqrt{3^2 - 4(1)(-40)}}{2(1)}$ Substitution

$= \frac{-3 \pm \sqrt{169}}{2}$ Simplify.

$= 5$ or -8 Simplify.

2 Online Option Take an online self-check Chapter Readiness Quiz at connectED.mcgraw-hill.com.

695

Essential Questions

- How can circles be used? Sample answer: Circles can be used for their shape, to model a circular object, or for their properties, or to model an equal distance around a certain point.

Get Ready for the Chapter

Response to Intervention (RtI)

Use the *Quick Check* results and the Intervention Planner chart to help you determine your Response to Intervention. The If-Then statements in the chart help you decide the appropriate tier of RtI and suggest intervention resources for each tier.

TIER 1 On Level OL

 students miss about 25% of the exercises or less,

 choose a resource:

SE Lesson 8-2

 Skills Practice, Chapter 8, p. 13

 Self-Check Quiz

TIER 2 Strategic Intervention AL approaching grade level

If students miss about 50% of the exercises,

Then choose a resource:

Study Guide and Intervention, Chapter 8, pp. 11–12

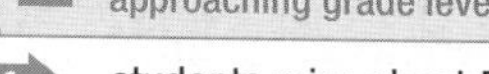

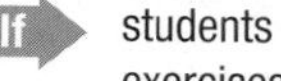 Extra Examples, Personal Tutor, Homework Help

TIER 3 Intensive Intervention 2 or more grades below level

 students miss about 75% of the exercises,

 use *Math Triumphs, Geometry,* Ch. 2 and 6

connectED.mcgraw-hill.com Extra Examples, Personal Tutor, Homework Help, Review Vocabulary

FOLDABLES StudyOrganizer

Dinah Zike's Foldables®

Focus Students write about circles and angles, and the lines that are related to them.

Teach After students make their Foldable, have them label the flaps to correspond with the eight lessons in this chapter.

Have students take notes about circles and about angles, arcs, chords, tangents, secants, and segments of circles. Encourage students to apply these concepts by drawing examples and applying the mathematical concepts associated with them.

When to Use It Instruct students to take notes while reading each lesson and listening to instruction. They should include definitions of terms and key concepts, as well as diagrams to illustrate each term.

Differentiated Instruction

Student-Built Glossary, pp. 1–2

Students should complete the chart by providing the definition of each term and an example as they progress through Chapter 10. This study tool can also be used to review for the chapter test.

Get Started on the Chapter

You will learn several new concepts, skills, and vocabulary terms as you study Chapter 10. To get ready, identify important terms and organize your resources. You may wish to refer to Chapter 0 to review prerequisite skills.

FOLDABLES StudyOrganizer

Circles Make this Foldable to help you organize your Chapter 10 notes on circles. Begin with nine sheets of paper.

1 **Trace** an 8-inch circle on each paper using a compass.

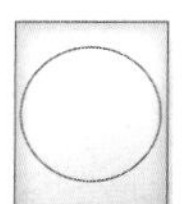

2 **Cut** out each of the circles.

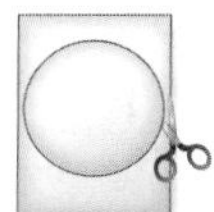

3 **Staple** an inch from the left side of the papers.

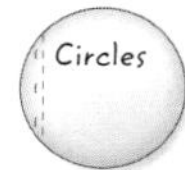
Circles

4 **Label** as shown.

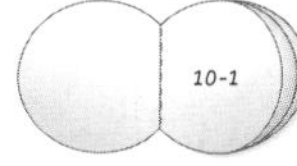
10-1

NewVocabulary

English		Español
circle	p. 697	círculo
center	p. 697	centro
radius	p. 697	radio
chord	p. 697	cuerda
diameter	p. 697	diámetro
circumference	p. 699	circunferencia
pi (π)	p. 699	pi (π)
inscribed	p. 700	inscrito
circumscribed	p. 700	circunscrito
central angle	p. 706	ángulo central
arc	p. 706	arco
tangent	p. 732	tangente
secant	p. 741	secante
chord segment	p. 750	segmento de cuerda

ReviewVocabulary

coplanar coplanar points that lie in the same plane

degree grado $\frac{1}{360}$ of the circular rotation about a point

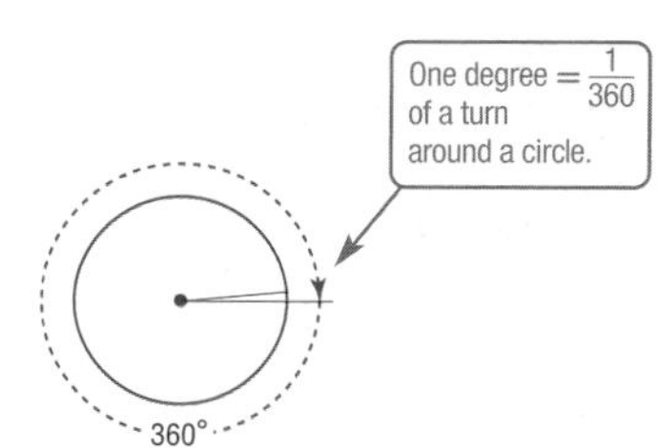
One degree = $\frac{1}{360}$ of a turn around a circle.
360°

LESSON 10-1 Circles and Circumference

Then

- You identified and used parts of parallelograms.

Now

1. Identify and use parts of circles.
2. Solve problems involving the circumference of a circle.

Why?

- The maxAir ride shown speeds back and forth and rotates counterclockwise. At times, the riders are upside down 140 feet above the ground experiencing "airtime"—a feeling of weightlessness. The ride's width, or *diameter*, is 44 feet. You can find the distance that a rider travels in one rotation by using this measure.

NewVocabulary
circle
center
radius
chord
diameter
concentric circles
circumference
pi (π)
inscribed
circumscribed

Common Core State Standards

Content Standards
G.CO.1 Know precise definitions of angle, circle, perpendicular line, parallel line, and line segment, based on the undefined notions of point, line, distance along a line, and distance around a circular arc.
G.C.1 Prove that all circles are similar.

Mathematical Practices
4 Model with mathematics.
1 Make sense of problems and persevere in solving them.

1 Segments in Circles

A **circle** is the locus or set of all points in a plane equidistant from a given point called the **center** of the circle.

Segments that intersect a circle have special names.

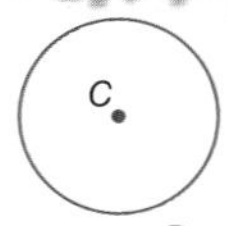

Circle C or $\odot C$

KeyConcept Special Segments in a Circle

A **radius** (plural radii) is a segment with endpoints at the center and on the circle.
Examples $\overline{CD}$, $\overline{CE}$, and $\overline{CF}$ are radii of $\odot C$.

A **chord** is a segment with endpoints on the circle.
Examples $\overline{AB}$ and $\overline{DE}$ are chords of $\odot C$.

A **diameter** of a circle is a chord that passes through the center and is made up of collinear radii.
Example $\overline{DE}$ is a diameter of $\odot C$. Diameter $\overline{DE}$ is made up of collinear radii $\overline{CD}$ and $\overline{CE}$.

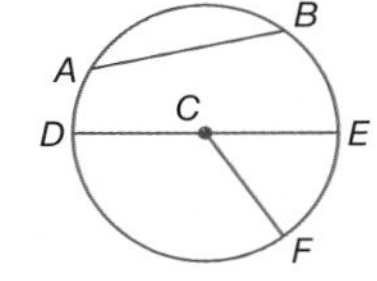

Example 1 Identify Segments in a Circle

a. Name the circle and identify a radius.

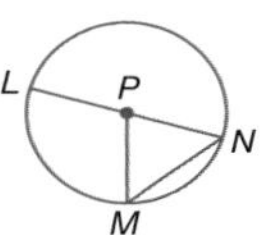

The circle has a center at P, so it is named circle P, or $\odot P$. Three radii are shown: $\overline{PL}$, $\overline{PN}$, and $\overline{PM}$.

b. Identify a chord and a diameter of the circle.

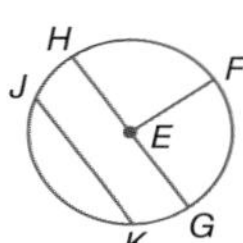

Two chords are shown: $\overline{JK}$ and $\overline{HG}$. $\overline{HG}$ goes through the center, so $\overline{HG}$ is a diameter.

GuidedPractice

1. Name the circle, a radius, a chord, and a diameter of the circle.
circle X; radius $\overline{XV}$, $\overline{XT}$, $\overline{XU}$, or $\overline{XZ}$; chord $\overline{RS}$, $\overline{TZ}$; diameter $\overline{TZ}$

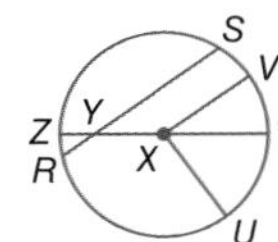

697

1 Focus

VerticalAlignment

Before Lesson 10-1 Identify and use parts of parallelograms.

Lesson 10-1 Identify and use parts of circles. Solve problems involving the circumference of a circle.

After Lesson 10-1 Identify angles and arcs of circles and find their measures.

2 Teach

Scaffolding Questions

Have students read the **Why?** section of the lesson.

Ask:

- What does the distance a rider travels in one rotation represent? the circumference of the circular ride
- How could a wheel be used to measure distance? Find the circumference of the wheel and multiply by the number of rotations made in the distance to be measured.
- How is the concept of measuring distance with a wheel applied in real life? Sample answer: Odometers use wheel rotation to record mileage, surveyors use a wheel to measure distance, and so on.

(continued on the next page)

Lesson 10-1 Resources

Resource	Approaching Level AL	On Level OL	Beyond Level BL	English Learners ELL
Teacher Edition	▪ Differentiated Instruction, p. 700	▪ Differentiated Instruction, pp. 699, 700	▪ Differentiated Instruction, p. 699	
Chapter Resource Masters	▪ Study Guide and Intervention, pp. 5–6 ▪ Skills Practice, p. 7 ▪ Practice, p. 8 ▪ Word Problem Practice, p. 9	▪ Study Guide and Intervention, pp. 5–6 ▪ Skills Practice, p. 7 ▪ Practice, p. 8 ▪ Word Problem Practice, p. 9 ▪ Enrichment, p. 10	▪ Practice, p. 8 ▪ Word Problem Practice, p. 9 ▪ Enrichment, p. 10	▪ Study Guide and Intervention, pp. 5–6 ▪ Skills Practice, p. 7 ▪ Practice, p. 8 ▪ Word Problem Practice, p. 9
Other	▪ 5-Minute Check 10-1 ▪ Study Notebook	▪ 5-Minute Check 10-1 ▪ Study Notebook	▪ 5-Minute Check 10-1 ▪ Study Notebook	▪ 5-Minute Check 10-1 ▪ Study Notebook

- Why might measuring with a wheel be better than measuring with a meter stick or a tape measure? Sample answer: A wheel measurement is continuous, but a meter stick or tape measure has to be picked up and moved. Also, a wheel can measure around curves, but a meter stick or tape measure is not as accurate around curves.

1 Segments in Circles

Examples 1–3 show how to identify and find the measures of segments in circles.

Formative Assessment

Use the Guided Practice exercises after each example to determine students' understanding of concepts.

Additional Example

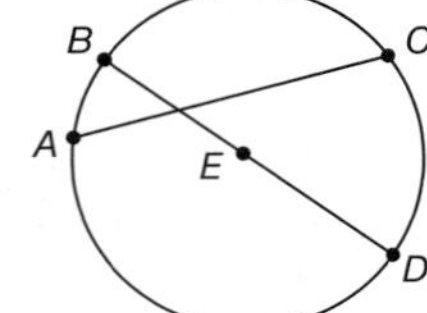

a. Name the circle and identify a radius. Name: Circle E or $\odot E$ Two radii shown: $\overline{EB}$ and $\overline{ED}$

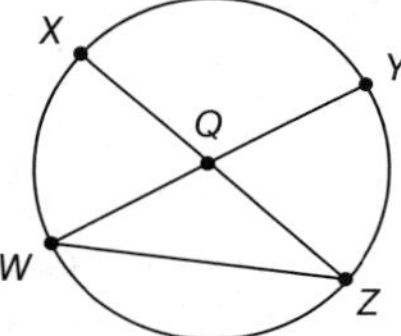

b. Identify a chord and a diameter of the circle.
Three chords: $\overline{WY}$, $\overline{XZ}$, and $\overline{WZ}$
Two diameters: $\overline{WY}$ and $\overline{XZ}$

Additional Examples also in Interactive Classroom PowerPoint® Presentations

Interactive White Board READY

ReadingMath

CCSS Precision The words *radius* and *diameter* are used to describe lengths as well as segments. Since a circle has many different radii and diameters, the phrases *the radius* and *the diameter* refer to lengths rather than segments.

By definition, the distance from the center of a circle to any point on the circle is always the same. Therefore, all radii r of a circle are congruent. Since a diameter d is composed of two radii, all diameters of a circle are also congruent.

KeyConcept Radius and Diameter Relationships

If a circle has radius r and diameter d, the following relationships are true.

Radius Formula $r = \frac{d}{2}$ or $r = \frac{1}{2}d$ **Diameter Formula** $d = 2r$

Example 2 Find Radius and Diameter

If $QV = 8$ inches, what is the diameter of $\odot Q$?

$d = 2r$ Diameter Formula

$= 2(8)$ or 16 Substitute and simplify.

The diameter of $\odot Q$ is 16 inches.

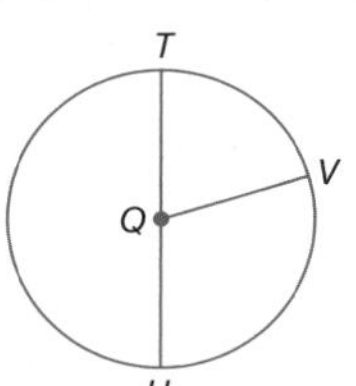

GuidedPractice

2A. If $TU = 14$ feet, what is the radius of $\odot Q$? 7 ft

2B. If $QT = 11$ meters, what is QU? 11 m

As with other figures, pairs of circles can be congruent, similar, or share other special relationships.

ReviewVocabulary

coplanar points that lie in the same plane

KeyConcept Circle Pairs

Two circles are congruent if and only if they have congruent radii.	All circles are similar.	**Concentric circles** are coplanar circles that have the same center.
Example $\overline{GH} \cong \overline{JK}$, so $\odot G \cong \odot J$.	Example $\odot X \sim \odot Y$	Example $\odot A$ with radius $\overline{AB}$ and $\odot A$ with radius $\overline{AC}$ are concentric.

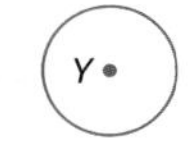

You will prove that all circles are similar in Exercise 52.

Two circles can intersect in two different ways.

2 Points of Intersection	1 Point of Intersection	No Points of Intersection

Teach with Tech

Video In the photo in the Real-World Link, the tennis court appears to be elliptical. You may want to go to your favorite video-sharing site and search for "Andre Agassi vs. Roger Federer–Dubai." Once the students watch the video, they should be able to affirm that the court is round. Then discuss the advantages and disadvantages of playing on a round court.

CCSS Teaching the Mathematical Practices

Precision Mathematically proficient students use clear definitions in discussion with others and in their own reasoning. Encourage students to use mathematical vocabulary properly, both spoken in class and in writing assignments.

The segment connecting the centers of the two intersecting circles contains the radii of the two circles.

Example 3 Find Measures in Intersecting Circles

The diameter of $\odot S$ is 30 units, the diameter of $\odot R$ is 20 units, and $DS = 9$ units. Find CD.

Since the diameter of $\odot S$ is 30, $CS = 15$.
$\overline{CD}$ is part of radius $\overline{CS}$.

$CD + DS = CS$	Segment Addition Postulate
$CD + 9 = 15$	Substitution
$CD = 6$	Subtract 9 from each side.

GuidedPractice

3. Use the diagram above to find RC. 4 units

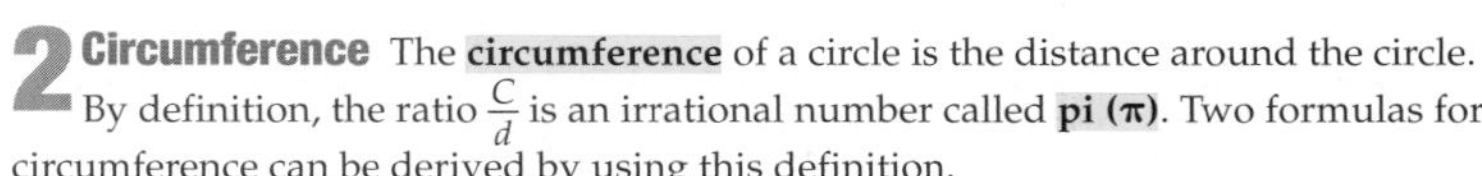

2 Circumference

The **circumference** of a circle is the distance around the circle. By definition, the ratio $\frac{C}{d}$ is an irrational number called **pi (π)**. Two formulas for circumference can be derived by using this definition.

$\frac{C}{d} = \pi$	Definition of pi
$C = \pi d$	Multiply each side by d.
$C = \pi(2r)$	$d = 2r$
$C = 2\pi r$	Simplify.

KeyConcept Circumference

Words	If a circle has diameter d or radius r, the circumference C equals the diameter times pi or twice the radius times pi.
Symbols	$C = \pi d$ or $C = 2\pi r$

Real-WorldLink

In 2005, Roger Federer and Andre Agassi played tennis on the helipad of the Burj Al Arab hotel in the United Arab Emirates. The helipad has a diameter of 79 feet and is nearly 700 feet high.

Source: Burj Al Arab, Emporis Buildings

Real-World Example 4 Find Circumference

TENNIS Find the circumference of the helipad described at the left.

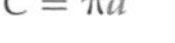

$C = \pi d$	Circumference formula
$= \pi(79)$	Substitution
$= 79\pi$	Simplify.
≈ 248.19	Use a calculator.

The circumference of the helipad is 79π feet or about 248.19 feet.

GuidedPractice

Find the circumference of each circle described. Round to the nearest hundredth.

4A. radius = 2.5 centimeters 15.71 cm **4B.** diameter = 16 feet 50.27 ft

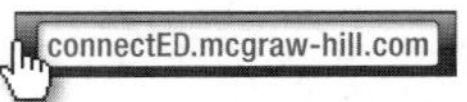

Additional Examples

2 If $RT = 21$ cm, what is the length of $\overline{QV}$?

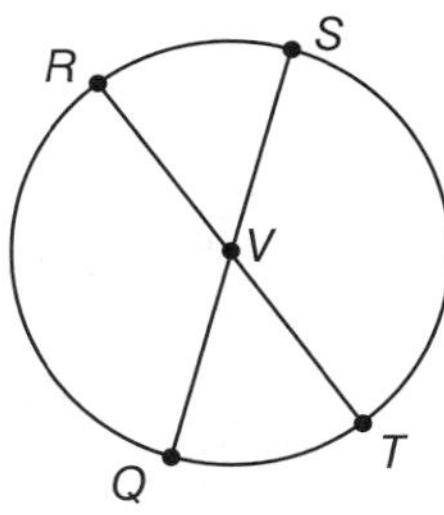

10.5 cm

3 The diameter of $\odot X$ is 22 units, the diameter of $\odot Y$ is 16 units, and $WZ = 5$ units. Find XY. 14 units

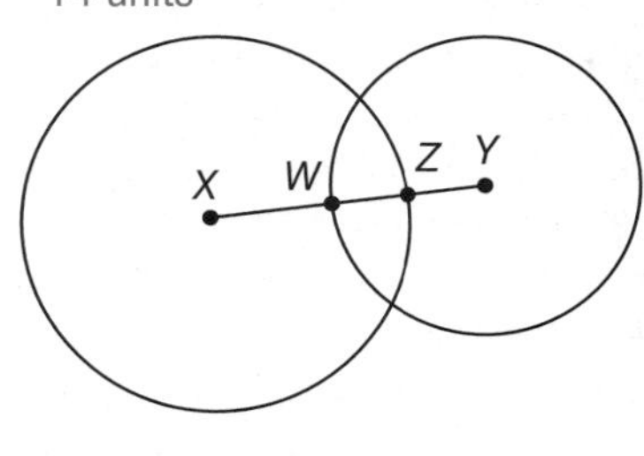

2 Circumference

The circumference of a circle is the distance around the circle. **Examples 4–6** show how to find and use circumference.

Additional Example

4 CROP CIRCLES A series of crop circles was discovered in Alberta, Canada on September 4, 1999. The largest of the three circles had a radius of 30 feet. Find its circumference. ≈ 188.50

WatchOut!

Radius or Diameter In problems involving circles, be careful to check if information is given about the radius or the diameter.

DifferentiatedInstruction OL BL

Extension Have students answer the following question. An asteroid hit Earth and created a huge round crater. Scientists measured the distance around the crater as 78.5 miles. What was the diameter of the crater? ≈ 25 miles

Additional Examples

5 Find the diameter and radius of a circle to the nearest hundredth if the circumference of the circle is 65.4 feet. $d \approx 20.82$ ft; $r \approx 10.41$ ft

6 Find the exact circumference of $\odot K$. 6π units

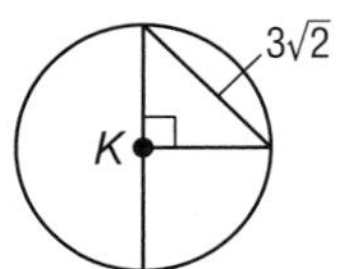

Focus on Mathematical Content

Circumcircle and Incircle Every triangle can be circumscribed by a circumcircle and inscribed by an incircle. Quadrilaterals (with the exception of convex kites) can be circumscribed and inscribed by circles only if the opposite angles of the quadrilateral are supplementary. All convex kites can be inscribed by a circle, although they cannot be circumscribed by a circle. All other polygons must be regular polygons to be circumscribed and inscribed by circles.

These circumference formulas can also be used to determine the diameter and radius of a circle when the circumference is given.

Example 5 Find Diameter and Radius

Find the diameter and radius of a circle to the nearest hundredth if the circumference of the circle is 106.4 millimeters.

$C = \pi d$	Circumference Formula	$r = \frac{1}{2}d$	Radius Formula
$106.4 = \pi d$	Substitution	$\approx \frac{1}{2}(33.87)$	$d \approx 33.87$
$\frac{106.4}{\pi} = d$	Divide each side by π.	≈ 16.94 mm	Use a calculator.
$33.87 \text{ mm} \approx d$	Use a calculator.		

StudyTip

Levels of Accuracy Since π is irrational, its value cannot be given as a terminating decimal. Using a value of 3 for π provides a quick estimate in calculations. Using a value of 3.14 or $\frac{22}{7}$ provides a closer approximation. For the most accurate approximation, use the π key on a calculator. Unless stated otherwise, assume that in this text, a calculator with a π key was used to generate answers.

GuidedPractice

5. Find the diameter and radius of a circle to the nearest hundredth if the circumference of the circle is 77.8 centimeters. **24.76 cm; 12.38 cm**

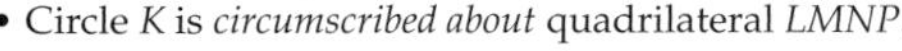

A polygon is **inscribed** in a circle if all of its vertices lie on the circle. A circle is **circumscribed** about a polygon if it contains all the vertices of the polygon.

- Quadrilateral *LMNP* is *inscribed in* $\odot K$.
- Circle *K* is *circumscribed about* quadrilateral *LMNP*.

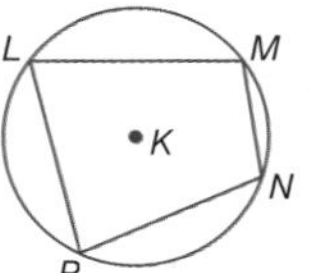

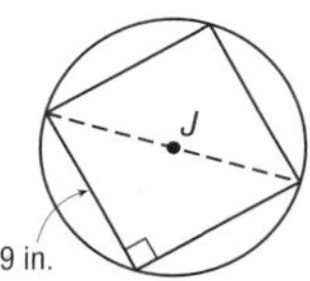

Standardized Test Example 6 Circumference of Circumscribed Polygon

SHORT RESPONSE A square with side length of 9 inches is inscribed in $\odot J$. Find the exact circumference of $\odot J$.

Read the Test Item

You need to find the diameter of the circle and use it to calculate the circumference.

Solve the Test Item

First, draw a diagram. The diagonal of the square is the diameter of the circle and the hypotenuse of a right triangle.

$a^2 + b^2 = c^2$	Pythagorean Theorem
$9^2 + 9^2 = c^2$	Substitution
$162 = c^2$	Simplify.
$9\sqrt{2} = c$	Take the positive square root of each side.

The diameter of the circle is $9\sqrt{2}$ inches.

Find the circumference in terms of π by substituting $9\sqrt{2}$ for d in $C = \pi d$. The exact circumference is $9\pi\sqrt{2}$ inches.

StudyTip

Circumcircle A *circumcircle* is a circle that passes through all of the vertices of a polygon.

GuidedPractice

Find the exact circumference of each circle by using the given polygon.

6A. inscribed right triangle with legs 7 meters and 3 meters long $\pi\sqrt{58}$ **m**

6B. circumscribed square with side 10 feet long $10\pi\sqrt{2}$ **ft**

DifferentiatedInstruction AL OL

Visual/Spatial Learners Instruct students to use a piece of string to estimate the circumference of discs or cylinders. Then have students measure the diameter of the object. Review the formulas for finding circumference by using the diameter and the radius. Have students find the circumference mathematically, using the diameter and then the radius. Have students compare their calculations with the estimate they found by using the string.

Check Your Understanding

= Step-by-Step Solutions begin on page R14.

Examples 1–2 **For Exercises 1–4, refer to ⊙*N*.**

1. Name the circle. **⊙*N***
2. Identify each.
   a. a chord **$\overline{EF}$, $\overline{DF}$** b. a diameter **$\overline{DF}$** c. a radius **$\overline{NC}$, $\overline{ND}$, $\overline{NE}$, or $\overline{NF}$**
3. If $CN = 8$ centimeters, find DN. **8 cm**
4. If $EN = 13$ feet, what is the diameter of the circle? **26 ft**

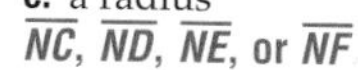

Example 3 **The diameters of ⊙*A*, ⊙*B*, and ⊙*C* are 8 inches, 18 inches, and 11 inches, respectively. Find each measure.**

5. FG **14 in.**
6. FB **5 in.**

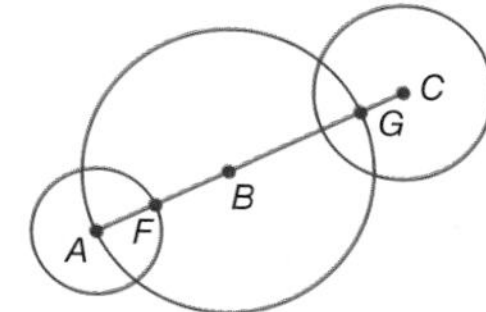

Example 4 7. **RIDES** The circular ride described at the beginning of the lesson has a diameter of 44 feet. What are the radius and circumference of the ride? Round to the nearest hundredth, if necessary. **22 ft; 138.23 ft**

Example 5 8. **CCSS MODELING** The circumference of the circular swimming pool shown is about 56.5 feet. What are the diameter and radius of the pool? Round to the nearest hundredth. **17.98 ft; 8.99 ft**

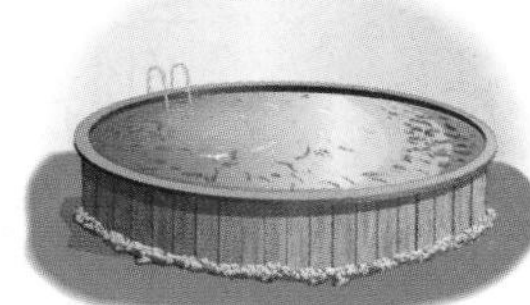

Example 6 9. **SHORT RESPONSE** The right triangle shown is inscribed in ⊙*D*. Find the exact circumference of ⊙*D*. **$4\pi\sqrt{13}$ cm**

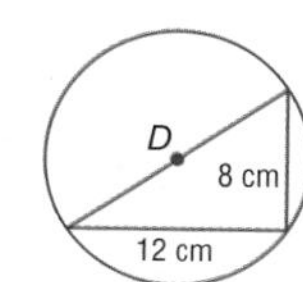

Practice and Problem Solving

Extra Practice is on page R10.

Examples 1–2 **For Exercises 10–13, refer to ⊙*R*.**

10. Name the center of the circle. ***R***
11. Identify a chord that is also a diameter. **$\overline{SU}$**
12. Is $\overline{VU}$ a radius? Explain. **No; it is a chord.**
13. If $SU = 16.2$ centimeters, what is RT? **8.1 cm**

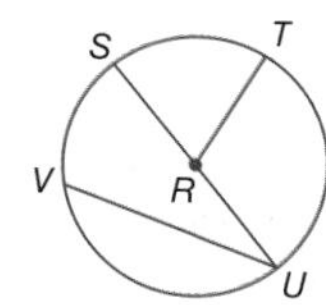

For Exercises 14–17, refer to ⊙*F*.

14. Identify a chord that is not a diameter. **$\overline{DE}$ or $\overline{AE}$**
15. If $CF = 14$ inches, what is the diameter of the circle? **28 in.**
16. Is $\overline{AF} \cong \overline{EF}$? Explain. **Yes; they are both radii of ⊙*F*.**
17. If $DA = 7.4$ centimeters, what is EF? **3.7 cm**

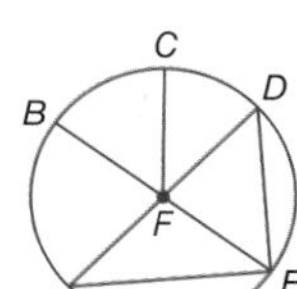

3 Practice

Formative Assessment

Use Exercises 1–9 to check for understanding.

Use the chart at the bottom of this page to customize assignments for your students.

CCSS Teaching the Mathematical Practices

Modeling Mathematically proficient students can apply the mathematics they know to solve problems arising in everyday life. In Exercise 8, point out to students that they are calculating the radius and diameter of the surface of the water in the pool.

Differentiated Homework Options

Level	Assignment	Two-Day Option	
AL Basic	10–35, 48, 49, 51, 52, 54–72	11–35 odd, 55–58	10–34 even, 48, 49, 51, 52, 54, 59–72
OL Core	11–41 odd, 43–49, 51, 52, 54–72	10–35, 55–58	36–49, 51, 52, 54, 59–72
BL Advanced	36–68, (optional: 69–72)		

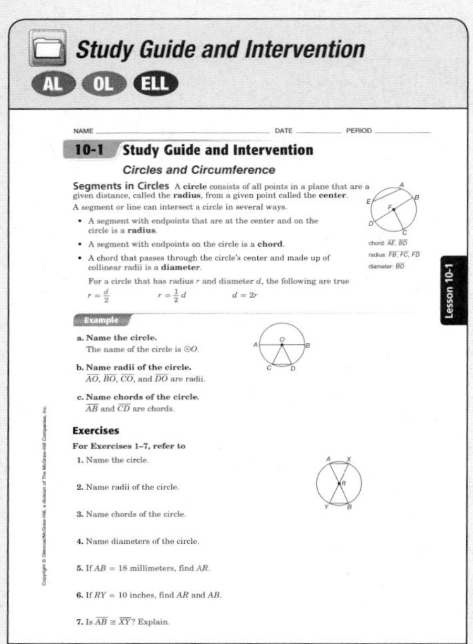
Study Guide and Intervention
AL OL ELL

NAME ______ DATE ______ PERIOD ______

10-1 Study Guide and Intervention

Circles and Circumference

Segments in Circles A **circle** consists of all points in a plane that are a given distance, called the **radius**, from a given point called the **center**.

A segment or line can intersect a circle in several ways.

- A segment with endpoints that are at the center and on the circle is a **radius**.
- A segment with endpoints on the circle is a **chord**.
- A chord that passes through the circle's center and made up of collinear radii is a **diameter**.

chord: $\overline{AE}$, $\overline{BD}$
radius: $\overline{FB}$, $\overline{FC}$, $\overline{FD}$
diameter: $\overline{BD}$

For a circle that has radius r and diameter d, the following are true

$r = \frac{d}{2}$ $r = \frac{1}{2}d$ $d = 2r$

Example

a. Name the circle.
The name of the circle is ⊙O.

b. Name radii of the circle.
$\overline{AO}$, $\overline{BO}$, $\overline{CO}$, and $\overline{DO}$ are radii.

c. Name chords of the circle.
$\overline{AB}$ and $\overline{CD}$ are chords.

Exercises

For Exercises 1–7, refer to

1. Name the circle.
2. Name radii of the circle.
3. Name chords of the circle.
4. Name diameters of the circle.
5. If AB = 18 millimeters, find AR.
6. If RY = 10 inches, find AR and AB.
7. Is $\overline{AB} \cong \overline{XY}$? Explain.

Lesson 10-1

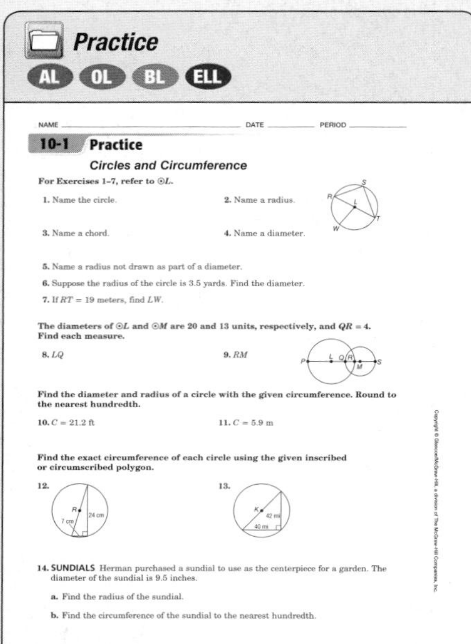
Practice
AL OL BL ELL

NAME ______ DATE ______ PERIOD ______

10-1 Practice

Circles and Circumference

For Exercises 1–7, refer to ⊙L.

1. Name the circle.
2. Name a radius.
3. Name a chord.
4. Name a diameter.
5. Name a radius not drawn as part of a diameter.
6. Suppose the radius of the circle is 3.5 yards. Find the diameter.
7. If RT = 19 meters, find LW.

The diameters of ⊙L and ⊙M are 20 and 13 units, respectively, and QR = 4. Find each measure.

8. LQ
9. RM

Find the diameter and radius of a circle with the given circumference. Round to the nearest hundredth.

10. C = 21.2 ft
11. C = 5.9 m

Find the exact circumference of each circle using the given inscribed or circumscribed polygon.

12.
13.

14. **SUNDIALS** Herman purchased a sundial to use as the centerpiece for a garden. The diameter of the sundial is 9.5 inches.
a. Find the radius of the sundial.
b. Find the circumference of the sundial to the nearest hundredth.

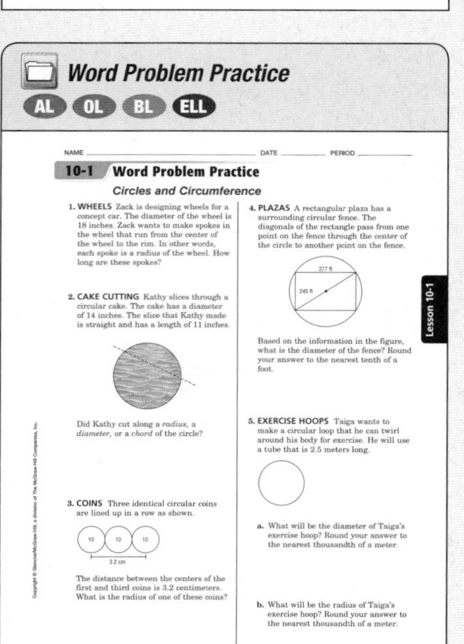
Word Problem Practice
AL OL BL ELL

NAME ______ DATE ______ PERIOD ______

10-1 Word Problem Practice

Circles and Circumference

1. **WHEELS** Zack is designing wheels for a concept car. The diameter of the wheel is 18 inches. Zack wants to make spokes in the wheel that run from the center of the wheel to the rim. In other words, each spoke is a radius of the wheel. How long are these spokes?

2. **CAKE CUTTING** Kathy slices through a circular cake. The cake has a diameter of 14 inches. The slice that Kathy made is straight and has a length of 11 inches.

Did Kathy cut along a *radius*, a *diameter*, or a *chord* of the circle?

3. **COINS** Three identical circular coins are lined up in a row as shown.

The distance between the centers of the first and third coins is 3.2 centimeters. What is the radius of one of these coins?

4. **PLAZAS** A rectangular plaza has a surrounding circular fence. The diagonals of the rectangle pass from one point on the fence through the center of the circle to another point on the fence.

Based on the information in the figure, what is the diameter of the fence? Round your answer to the nearest tenth of a foot.

5. **EXERCISE HOOPS** Taiga wants to make a circular loop that he can twirl around his body for exercise. He will use a tube that is 2.5 meters long.

a. What will be the diameter of Taiga's exercise hoop? Round your answer to the nearest thousandth of a meter.

b. What will be the radius of Taiga's exercise hoop? Round your answer to the nearest thousandth of a meter.

Lesson 10-1

Example 3 Circle J has a radius of 10 units, ⊙K has a radius of 8 units, and BC = 5.4 units. Find each measure.

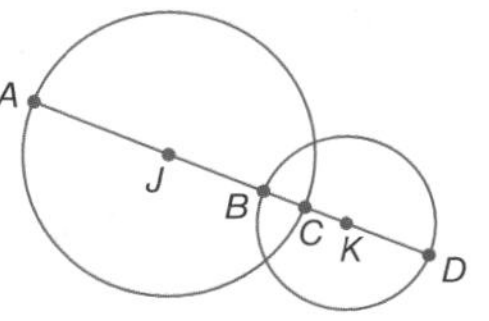

18. CK **2.6**
19. AB **14.6**
20. JK **12.6**
21. AD **30.6**

Example 4

22. **PIZZA** Find the radius and circumference of the pizza shown. Round to the nearest hundredth, if necessary. **8 in.; 50.27 in.**

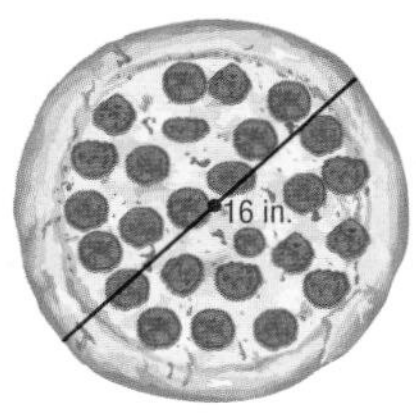

23. **BICYCLES** A bicycle has tires with a diameter of 26 inches. Find the radius and circumference of a tire. Round to the nearest hundredth, if necessary. **13 in.; 81.68 in.**

Example 5 **Find the diameter and radius of a circle with the given circumference. Round to the nearest hundredth.**

24. C = 18 in. **5.73 in.; 2.86 in.**
25. C = 124 ft **39.47 ft; 19.74 ft**
26. C = 375.3 cm **119.46 cm; 59.73 cm**
27. C = 2608.25 m **830.23 m; 415.12 m**

Example 6 **CCSS SENSE-MAKING** **Find the exact circumference of each circle by using the given inscribed or circumscribed polygon.**

28.

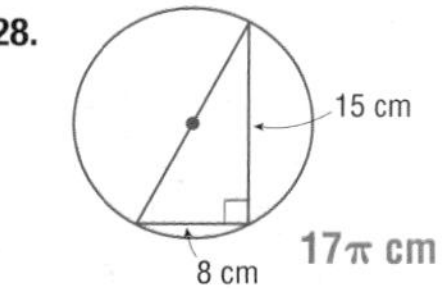

17π cm

29. $6\sqrt{2}$ ft **12π ft**

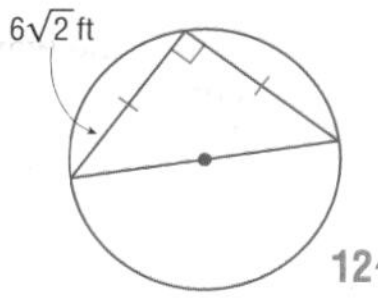

30.

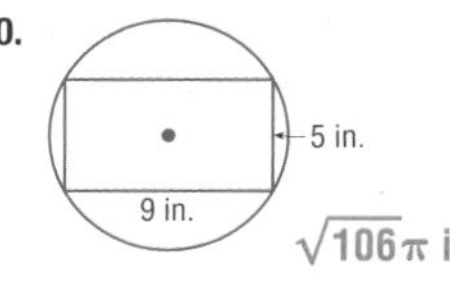

$\sqrt{106}\pi$ **in.**

31.

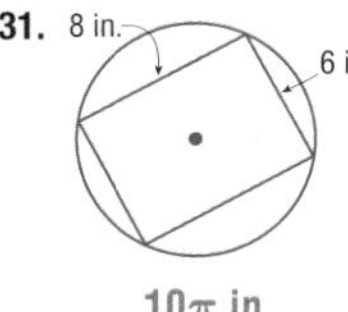

10π in.

32.

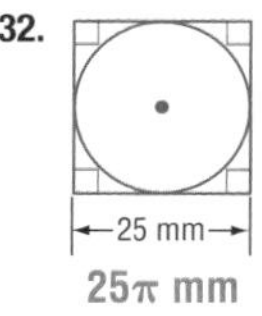

25π mm

33.

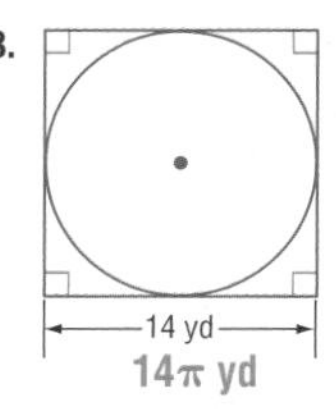

14π yd

34. **DISC GOLF** Disc golf is similar to regular golf, except that a flying disc is used instead of a ball and clubs. For professional competitions, the maximum weight of a disc in grams is 8.3 times the diameter in centimeters. What is the maximum allowable weight for a disc with circumference 66.92 centimeters? Round to the nearest tenth. **176.8 g**

35. **PATIOS** Mr. Martinez is going to build the patio shown.

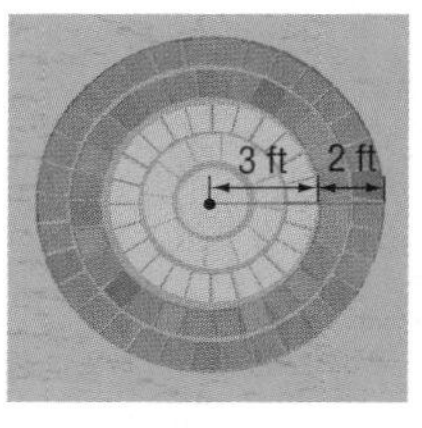

a. What is the patio's approximate circumference? **31.42 ft**

b. If Mr. Martinez changes the plans so that the inner circle has a circumference of approximately 25 feet, what should the radius of the circle be to the nearest foot? **4 ft**

36. 4.25 in.; 26.70 in.
37. 22.80 ft; 71.63 ft
38. 11.14x cm; 5.57x cm
39. 0.25x; 0.79x

B **The radius, diameter, or circumference of a circle is given. Find each missing measure to the nearest hundredth.**

36. $d = 8\frac{1}{2}$ in., r = __?__, C = __?__
37. $r = 11\frac{2}{5}$ ft, d = __?__, C = __?__
38. $C = 35x$ cm, d = __?__, r = __?__
39. $r = \frac{x}{8}$, d = ____, C = __?__

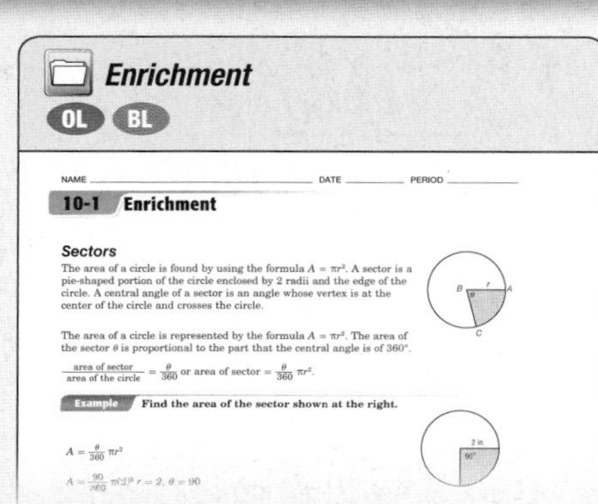
Enrichment
OL BL

NAME ______ DATE ______ PERIOD ______

10-1 Enrichment

Sectors

The area of a circle is found by using the formula $A = \pi r^2$. A sector is a pie-shaped portion of the circle enclosed by 2 radii and the edge of the circle. A central angle of a sector is an angle whose vertex is at the center of the circle and crosses the circle.

The area of a circle is represented by the formula $A = \pi r^2$. The area of the sector θ is proportional to the part that the central angle is of 360°.

$\frac{\text{area of sector}}{\text{area of the circle}} = \frac{\theta}{360}$ or area of sector $= \frac{\theta}{360}\pi r^2$.

Example Find the area of the sector shown at the right.

$A = \frac{\theta}{360}\pi r^2$

$A = \frac{90}{360}\pi(2)^2$ $r = 2$, $\theta = 90$

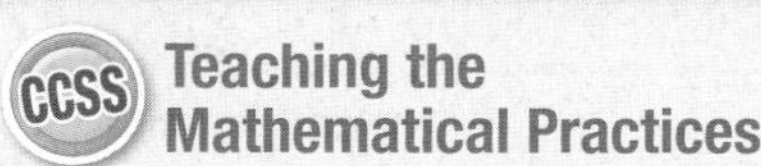
Teaching the Mathematical Practices

Sense-Making Mathematically proficient students start by explaining the meaning of a problem to themselves and looking for entry points to its solution. They plan a solution pathway rather than simply jumping into a solution attempt. In Exercises 28–33, encourage students to apply their knowledge of triangles and rectangles to find the radius of each circle.

Determine whether the circles in the figures below appear to be *congruent, concentric,* or *neither.*

40.

concentric

41.

neither

42.

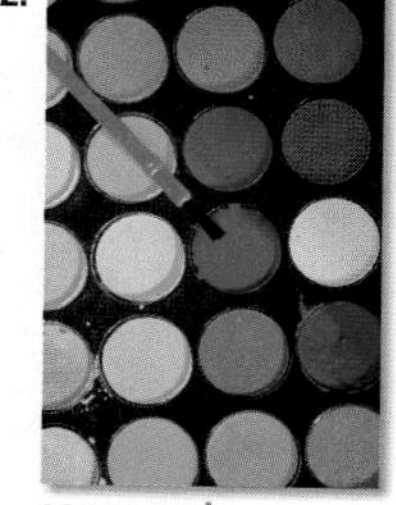

congruent

43. **HISTORY** The *Indian Shell Ring* on Hilton Head Island approximates a circle. If each unit on the coordinate grid represents 25 feet, how far would someone have to walk to go completely around the ring? Round to the nearest tenth. 471.2 ft

44. **CCSS MODELING** A brick path is being installed around a circular pond. The pond has a circumference of 68 feet. The outer edge of the path is going to be 4 feet from the pond all the way around. What is the approximate circumference of the path? Round to the nearest hundredth. 93.13 ft

45. **MULTIPLE REPRESENTATIONS** In this problem, you will explore changing dimensions in circles.

a. **Geometric** Use a compass to draw three circles in which the scale factor from each circle to the next larger circle is 1 : 2. See margin.

b. **Tabular** Calculate the radius (to the nearest tenth) and circumference (to the nearest hundredth) of each circle. Record your results in a table. See margin.

c. **Verbal** Explain why these three circles are geometrically similar. They all have the same shape—circular.

d. **Verbal** Make a conjecture about the ratio between the circumferences of two circles when the ratio between their radii is 2. The ratio of their circumferences is also 2.

e. **Analytical** The scale factor from $\odot A$ to $\odot B$ is $\frac{b}{a}$. Write an equation relating the circumference (C_A) of $\odot A$ to the circumference (C_B) of $\odot B$. $(C_B) = \frac{b}{a}(C_A)$

f. **Numerical** If the scale factor from $\odot A$ to $\odot B$ is $\frac{1}{3}$, and the circumference of $\odot A$ is 12 inches, what is the circumference of $\odot B$? 4 in.

46. **BUFFON'S NEEDLE** Measure the length ℓ of a needle (or toothpick) in centimeters. Next, draw a set of horizontal lines that are ℓ centimeters apart on a sheet of plain white paper.

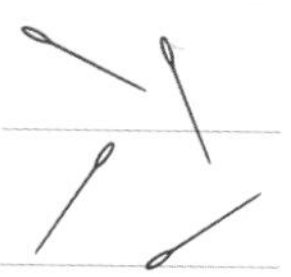

a. Drop the needle onto the paper. When the needle lands, record whether it touches one of the lines as a hit. Record the number of hits after 25, 50, and 100 drops. a–b. See students' work.

b. Calculate the ratio of two times the total number of drops to the number of hits after 25, 50, and 100 drops.

c. How are the values you found in part **b** related to π? Sample answer: The values are approaching 3.14, which is approximately equal to π.

CCSS Teaching the Mathematical Practices

Modeling Mathematically proficient students can apply the mathematics they know to solve problems arising in everyday life. In Exercise 44, encourage students to draw a diagram of the situation that shows the pond and brick path.

Exercise Alerts

Compass Exercise 45 requires the use of a compass.

Centimeter Ruler and Toothpicks Exercise 46 requires the use of a centimeter ruler and toothpicks.

Multiple Representations

In Exercise 45, students use geometry, a table, verbal descriptions, and numeric calculations to investigate the relationship between scale factor and other dimensions of circles.

Additional Answers

45a. Sample answer:

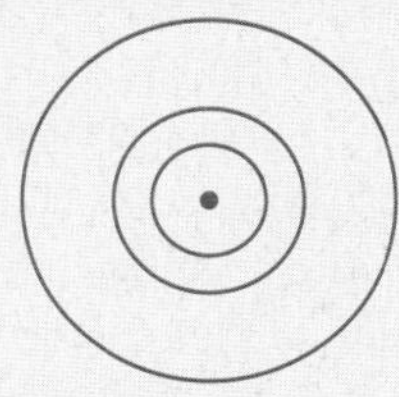

45b. Sample answer:

Circle Radius (cm)	Circumference (cm)
0.5	3.14
1	6.28
2	12.57

Exercise Alert

Compass Exercise 48 requires the use of a compass.

Additional Answers

48. Sample answer: A line that intersects a circle in one point can be described as a tangent. A line that intersects a circle in exactly two points can be described as a secant. A line segment with endpoints on a circle can be described as a chord. If the chord passes through the center of the circle, it can be described as a diameter. A line segment with endpoints at the center and on the circle can be described as a radius.

49a. $8r$ and $6r$; Twice the radius of the circle, $2r$ is the side length of the square, so the perimeter of the square is $4(2r)$ or $8r$. The regular hexagon is made up of six equilateral triangles with side length r, so the perimeter of the hexagon is $6(r)$ or $6r$.

49b. less; greater; $6r < C < 8r$

49c. $3d < C < 4d$; The circumference of the circle is between 3 and 4 times its diameter.

49d. These limits will approach a value of πd, implying that $C = \pi d$.

52. A circle is a locus of points in a plane equidistant from a given point. For any two circles $\odot A$ and $\odot B$, there exists a translation that maps center A onto center B, moving $\odot A$ so that it is concentric with $\odot B$. There also exists a dilation with scale factor k such that each point that makes up $\odot A$ is moved to be the same distance from center A as the points that make up $\odot B$ are from center B. Therefore, $\odot A$ is mapped onto $\odot B$. Since there exists a rigid motion followed by a scaling that maps $\odot A$ onto $\odot B$, the circles are similar. Thus, all circles are similar.

47 **MAPS** The concentric circles on the map below show the areas that are 5, 10, 15, 20, 25, and 30 miles from downtown Phoenix.

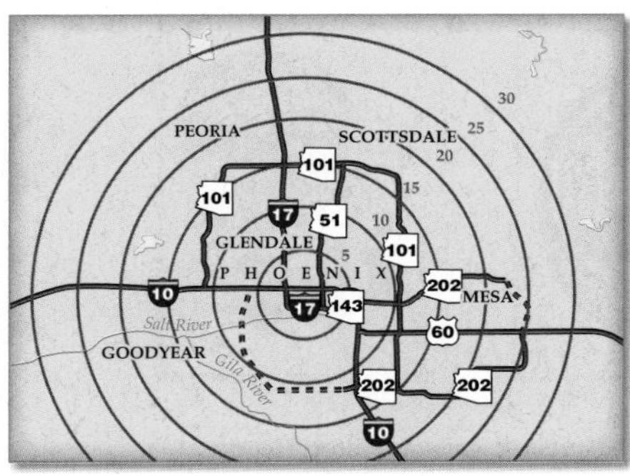

a. How much greater is the circumference of the outermost circle than the circumference of the center circle? **157.1 mi**

b. As the radii of the circles increase by 5 miles, by how much does the circumference increase? **≈31.4 mi**

51. Always; a radius is a segment drawn between the center of the circle and a point on the circle. A segment drawn from the center to a point inside the circle will always have a length less than the radius of the circle.

H.O.T. Problems Use Higher-Order Thinking Skills

48. **WRITING IN MATH** How can we describe the relationships that exist between circles and lines? **See margin.**

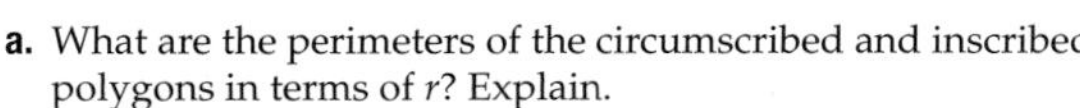

49. **REASONING** In the figure, a circle with radius r is inscribed in a regular polygon and circumscribed about another. **a–d. See margin.**

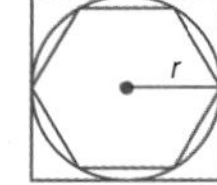

a. What are the perimeters of the circumscribed and inscribed polygons in terms of r? Explain.

b. Is the circumference C of the circle greater or less than the perimeter of the circumscribed polygon? the inscribed polygon? Write a compound inequality comparing C to these perimeters.

c. Rewrite the inequality from part **b** in terms of the diameter d of the circle and interpret its meaning.

d. As the number of sides of both the circumscribed and inscribed polygons increase, what will happen to the upper and lower limits of the inequality from part **c**, and what does this imply?

50. **CHALLENGE** The sum of the circumferences of circles H, J, and K shown at the right is 56π units. Find KJ. **24 units**

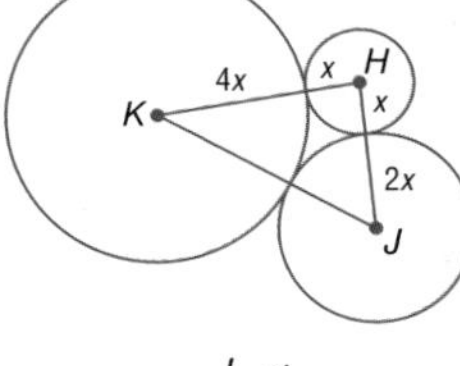

51. **REASONING** Is the distance from the center of a circle to a point in the interior of a circle *sometimes*, *always*, or *never* less than the radius of the circle? Explain.

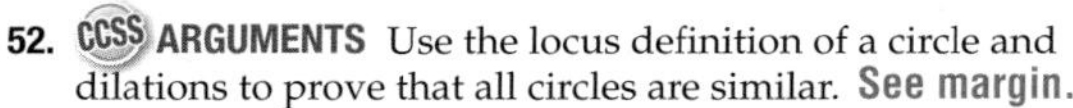

52. **CCSS ARGUMENTS** Use the locus definition of a circle and dilations to prove that all circles are similar. **See margin.**

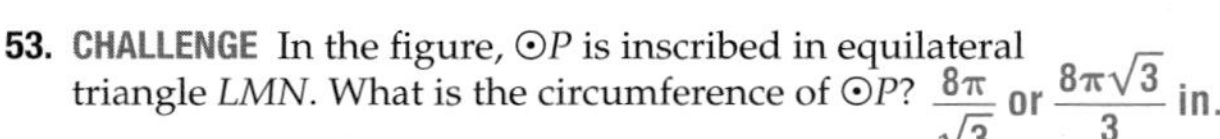

53. **CHALLENGE** In the figure, $\odot P$ is inscribed in equilateral triangle LMN. What is the circumference of $\odot P$? **$\frac{8\pi}{\sqrt{3}}$ or $\frac{8\pi\sqrt{3}}{3}$ in.**

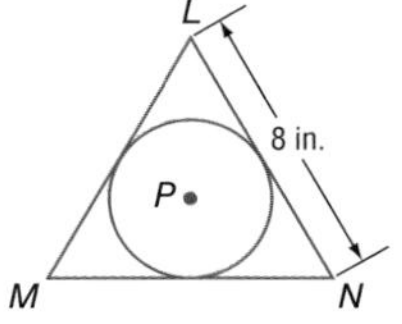

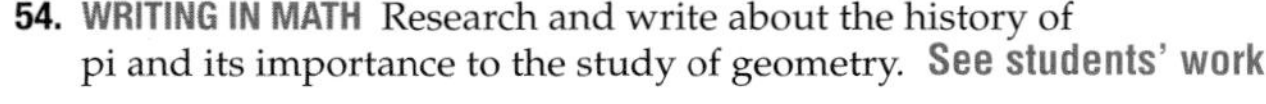

54. **WRITING IN MATH** Research and write about the history of pi and its importance to the study of geometry. **See students' work.**

Teaching the Mathematical Practices

Arguments Mathematically proficient students reason inductively about data, making plausible arguments that take into account context from which the data arose. In Exercise 52, encourage students to review the tests for similarity.

Standardized Test Practice

55. GRIDDED RESPONSE What is the circumference of ⊙T? Round to the nearest tenth. **40.8**

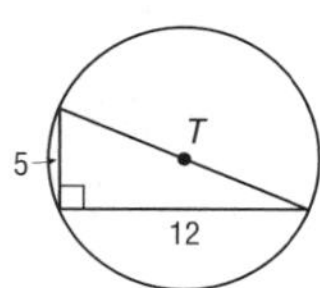

56. What is the radius of a table with a circumference of 10 feet? **A**

A 1.6 ft
B 2.5 ft
C 3.2 ft
D 5 ft

57. ALGEBRA Bill is planning a circular vegetable garden with a fence around the border. If he can use up to 50 feet of fence, what radius can he use for the garden? **J**

F 10 G 9 H 8 J 7

58. SAT/ACT What is the radius of a circle with an area of $\frac{\pi}{4}$ square units? **B**

A 0.4 units
B 0.5 units
C 2 units
D 4 units
E 16 units

Spiral Review

Copy each figure and point B. Then use a ruler to draw the image of the figure under a dilation with center B and the scale factor r indicated. (Lesson 9-6) **59–62. See margin.**

59. $r = \frac{1}{5}$

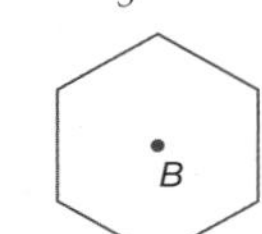

60. $r = \frac{2}{5}$

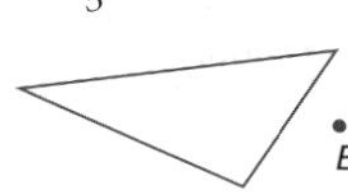

61. $r = 2$

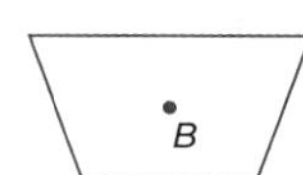

62. $r = 3$

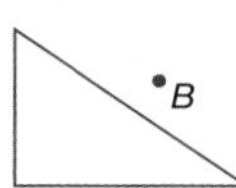

State whether each figure has rotational symmetry. If so, copy the figure, locate the center of symmetry, and state the order and magnitude of symmetry. (Lesson 9-5)

63.

no

64.

yes; 4, 90

65.

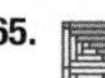

no

66.

no

Determine the truth value of the following statement for each set of conditions. Explain your reasoning. (Lesson 2-2)

If you are over 18 years old, then you vote in all elections. **67, 68. See margin.**

67. You are 19 years old and you vote.

68. You are 21 years old and do not vote.

Skills Review

Find x.

69. **90**

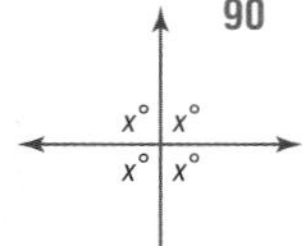

70. **60**

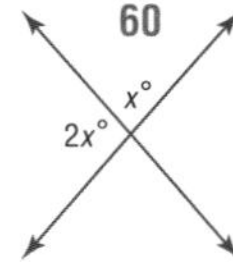

71. **20**

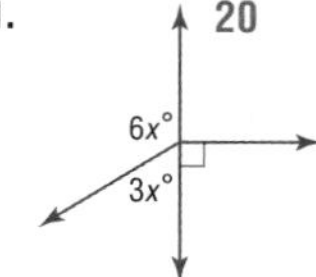

72. **45**

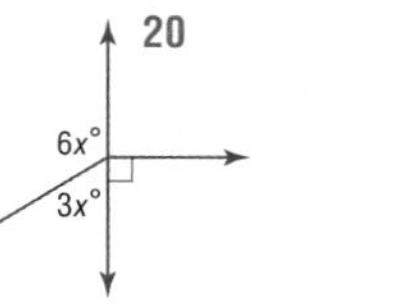

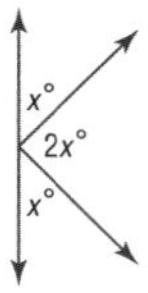

4 Assess

Name the Math Students can practice vocabulary terms in this lesson by describing selected circles and defining terms aloud.

Additional Answers

59. B

60. B

61.

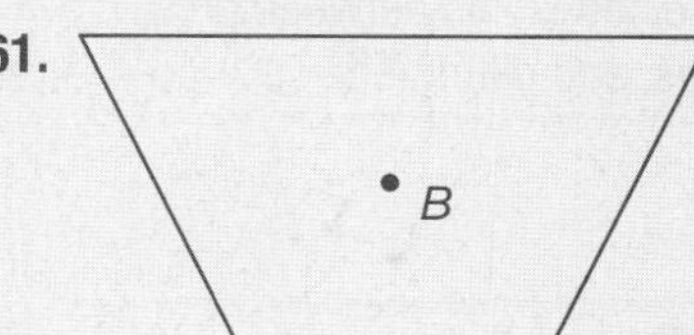

62.

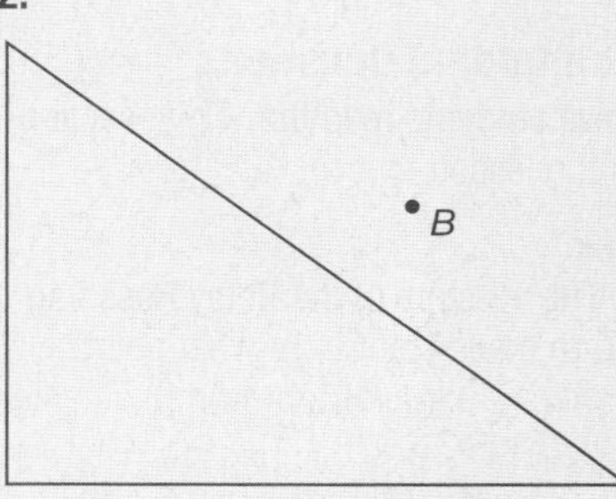

67. True; sample answer: Since the hypothesis is true and the conclusion is true, then the statement is true for the conditions.

68. False; sample answer: Since the hypothesis is true and the conclusion is false, then the statement is false for the conditions.

Follow-up

- How are circles and polygons similar? different? Sample answer: Circles and polygons are similar in that they have shapes that can be used to model real-world objects, and you can find the distance around each figure or the area that the figure takes up. They are different in that polygons are closed figures composed of straight line segments, whereas a circle is made up of a locus of points equidistant from one point. Also, all circles are similar, but all polygons are not similar.

1 Focus

Vertical Alignment

Before Lesson 10-2 Measure and identify congruent angles.

Lesson 10-2 Identify and measure central angles, arcs, and semicircles. Find arc length.

After Lesson 10-2 Recognize and use relationships between arcs, chords, and diameters.

2 Teach

Scaffolding Questions

Have students read the **Why?** section of the lesson.

Ask:

- The 13 stars of the Betsy Ross flag are equidistant from what point? The stars are equidistant from the center of the circle.
- Assume that the circumference of the circle of stars is 44 inches. Approximately how far is each star from the center of the circle? about 7 in.
- Make a conjecture about why the central angle in the circle of stars remains constant regardless of the size of the circle. The distance between any two stars and the center of the circle changes proportionally when the circle of stars increases or decreases in circumference.

LESSON 10-2 Measuring Angles and Arcs

Then	Now	Why?
You measured angles and identified congruent angles.	1 Identify central angles, major arcs, minor arcs, and semicircles, and find their measures. 2 Find arc lengths.	The thirteen stars of the Betsy Ross flag are arranged equidistant from each other and from a fixed point. The distance between consecutive stars varies depending on the size of the flag, but the measure of the central angle formed by the center of the circle and any two consecutive stars is always the same.

New Vocabulary
central angle
arc
minor arc
major arc
semicircle
congruent arcs
adjacent arcs
arc length

Common Core State Standards

Content Standards

G.C.2 Identify and describe relationships among inscribed angles, radii, and chords.

G.C.5 Derive using similarity the fact that the length of the arc intercepted by an angle is proportional to the radius, and define the radian measure of the angle as the constant of proportionality; derive the formula for the area of a sector.

Mathematical Practices

6 Attend to precision.
4 Model with mathematics.

1 Angles and Arcs A **central angle** of a circle is an angle with a vertex in the center of the circle. Its sides contain two radii of the circle. $\angle ABC$ is a central angle of $\odot B$.

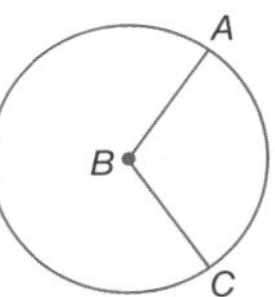

Recall from Lesson 1-4 that a *degree* is $\frac{1}{360}$ of the circular rotation about a point. This leads to the following relationship.

Key Concept Sum of Central Angles

Words The sum of the measures of the central angles of a circle with no interior points in common is 360.

Example $m\angle 1 + m\angle 2 + m\angle 3 = 360$

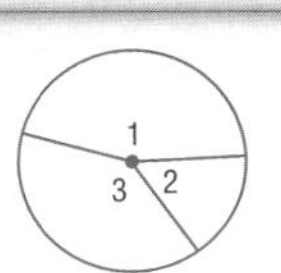

Example 1 Find Measures of Central Angles

Find the value of *x*.

$m\angle GFH + m\angle HFJ + m\angle GFJ = 360$	Sum of Central Angles
$130 + 90 + m\angle GFJ = 360$	Substitution
$220 + m\angle GFJ = 360$	Simplify.
$m\angle GFJ = 140$	Subtract 220 from each side.

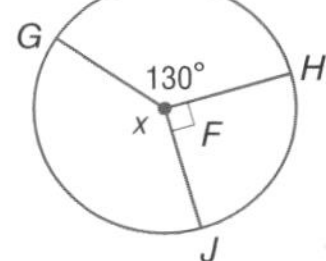

Guided Practice

1A.

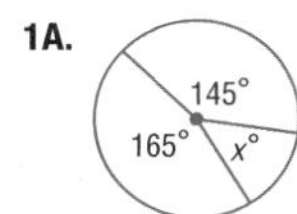

50

1B.

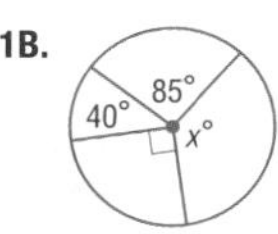

145

An **arc** is a portion of a circle defined by two endpoints. A central angle separates the circle into two arcs with measures related to the measure of the central angle.

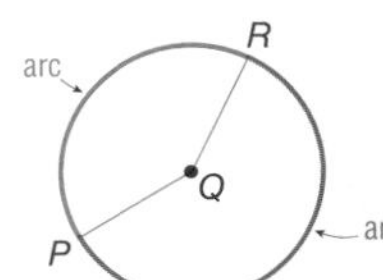

Lesson 10-2 Resources

Resource	Approaching Level AL	On Level OL	Beyond Level BL	English Learners ELL
Teacher Edition	▪ Differentiated Instruction, p. 712	▪ Differentiated Instruction, pp. 708, 709, 712	▪ Differentiated Instruction, pp. 708, 709, 712	
Chapter Resource Masters	▪ Study Guide and Intervention, pp. 11–12 ▪ Skills Practice, p. 13 ▪ Practice, p. 14 ▪ Word Problem Practice, p. 15	▪ Study Guide and Intervention, pp. 11–12 ▪ Skills Practice, p. 13 ▪ Practice, p. 14 ▪ Word Problem Practice, p. 15 ▪ Enrichment, p. 16	▪ Practice, p. 14 ▪ Word Problem Practice, p. 15 ▪ Enrichment, p. 16	▪ Study Guide and Intervention, pp. 11–12 ▪ Skills Practice, p. 13 ▪ Practice, p. 14 ▪ Word Problem Practice, p. 15
Other	▪ 5-Minute Check 10-2 ▪ Study Notebook	▪ 5-Minute Check 10-2 ▪ Study Notebook	▪ 5-Minute Check 10-2 ▪ Study Notebook	▪ 5-Minute Check 10-2 ▪ Study Notebook

StudyTip

Naming Arcs Minor arcs are named by their endpoints. Major arcs and semicircles are named by their endpoints and another point on the arc that lies between these endpoints.

KeyConcept Arcs and Arc Measure

Arc	Measure
A **minor arc** is the shortest arc connecting two endpoints on a circle.	The measure of a minor arc is less than 180 and equal to the measure of its related central angle. $m\widehat{AB} = m\angle ACB = x$
A **major arc** is the longest arc connecting two endpoints on a circle.	The measure of a major arc is greater than 180, and equal to 360 minus the measure of the minor arc with the same endpoints. $m\widehat{ADB} = 360 - m\widehat{AB} = 360 - x$
A **semicircle** is an arc with endpoints that lie on a diameter.	The measure of a semicircle is 180. $m\widehat{ADB} = 180$

Real-WorldCareer

Historical Researcher Research in museums includes authentication, verification, and description of artifacts. Employment as a historical researcher requires a minimum of a bachelor's degree in history. Refer to Exercises 42–43.

Example 2 Classify Arcs and Find Arc Measures

$\overline{GJ}$ is a diameter of $\odot K$. Identify each arc as a *major arc*, *minor arc*, or *semicircle*. Then find its measure.

a. $m\widehat{GH}$

$\widehat{GH}$ is a minor arc, so $m\widehat{GH} = m\angle GKH$ or 122.

b. $m\widehat{GLH}$

$\widehat{GLH}$ is a major arc that shares the same endpoints as minor arc $\widehat{GH}$.

$m\widehat{GHL} = 360 - m\widehat{GH}$

$= 360 - 122$ or 238

c. $m\widehat{GLJ}$

$\widehat{GLJ}$ is a semicircle, so $m\widehat{GLJ} = 180$.

GuidedPractice

$\overline{PM}$ is a diameter of $\odot R$. Identify each arc as a *major arc*, *minor arc*, or *semicircle*. Then find its measure.

2A. $\widehat{MQ}$ minor arc; 65 **2B.** $\widehat{MNP}$ semicircle; 180 **2C.** $\widehat{MNQ}$ major arc; 295

Congruent arcs are arcs in the same or congruent circles that have the same measure.

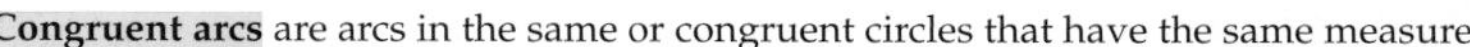

Theorem 10.1

Words In the same circle or in congruent circles, two minor arcs are congruent if and only if their central angles are congruent.

Example If $\angle 1 \cong \angle 2$, then $\widehat{FG} \cong \widehat{HJ}$.
If $\widehat{FG} \cong \widehat{HJ}$, then $\angle 1 \cong \angle 2$.

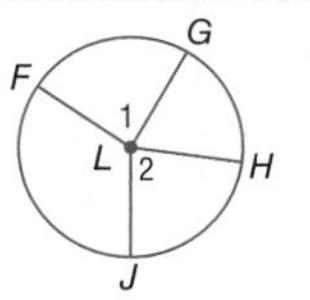

You will prove Theorem 10.1 in Exercise 52.

1 Angles and Arcs

Examples 1–4 show how to use the theorems and postulates to find the measures of arcs and angles of a circle.

Formative Assessment

Use the Guided Practice exercises after each example to determine students' understanding of concepts.

Additional Example

1 Find the value of x. 7

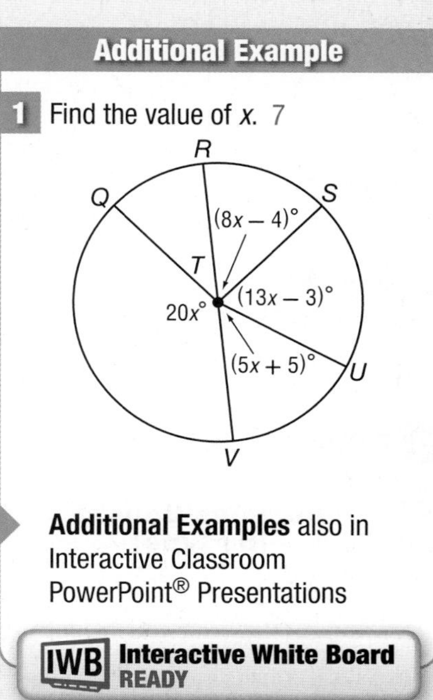

Additional Examples also in Interactive Classroom PowerPoint® Presentations

IWB Interactive White Board READY

Focus on Mathematical Content

Terminology The terms arc measure and arc length are not interchangeable. Like angles, arcs have degree measure, denoted $m\widehat{AC}$. Just as with segment length, arc length is a distance along a curve.

Teach with Tech

Interactive Whiteboard On the board, draw a circle with a diameter, several radii, and given angle measures. Choose a student to show how to find the measure of one of the minor arcs. Then choose a different student to find the measure of each of the remaining minor arcs.

Additional Examples

2 $\overline{WC}$ is a radius of $\odot C$.

Identify each arc as a *major arc, minor arc,* or *semicircle.*

Then find its measure.

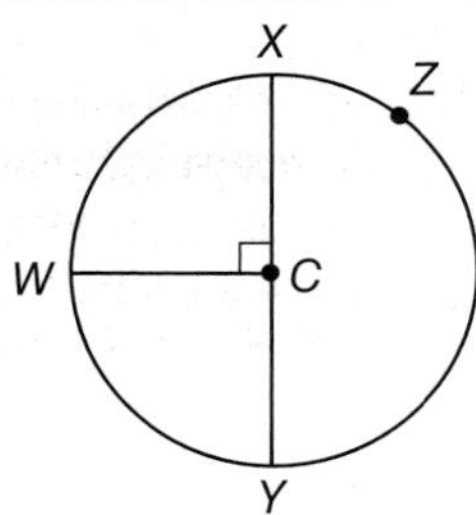

a. $m\widehat{XZY}$

semicircle; $m\widehat{XZY} = 180$

b. $m\widehat{WZX}$

major arc; $m\widehat{WZX} = 270$

c. $m\widehat{XW}$

minor arc; $m\widehat{XW} = 90$

3 **BICYCLES** Refer to the circle graph.

Bicycles Bought (by type)

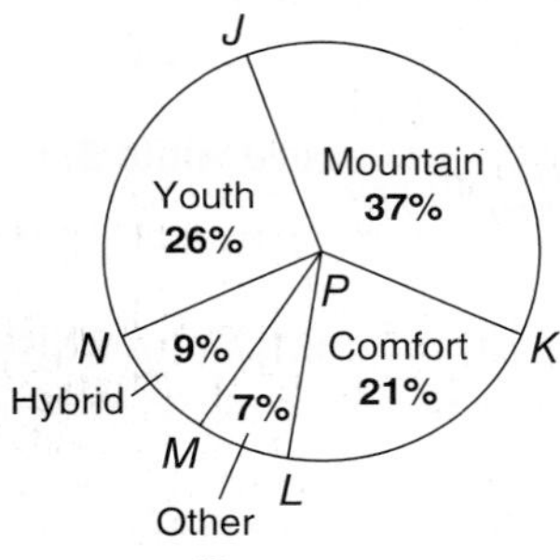

a. Find $m\widehat{KL}$. 75.6

b. Find $m\widehat{NJL}$. 302.4

4 Find each measure in $\odot M$.

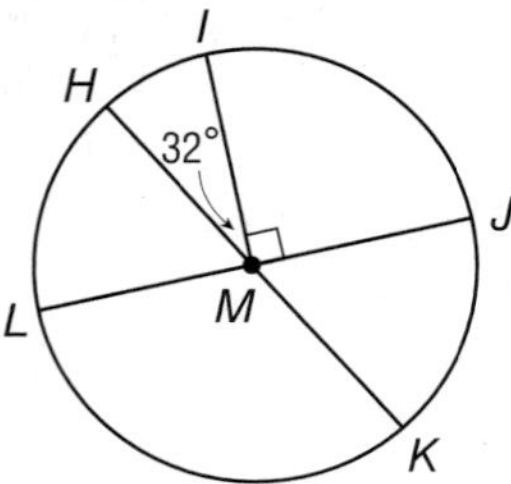

a. $m\widehat{LHI}$ 90

b. $m\widehat{IJK}$ 148

Real-World Example 3 Find Arc Measures in Circle Graphs

SPORTS Refer to the circle graph. Find each measure.

Female Participation in Sports

a. $m\widehat{CD}$

$\widehat{CD}$ is a minor arc. $m\widehat{CD} = m\angle CSD$

$\angle CSD$ represents 18% of the whole, or 18% of the circle.

$m\angle CSD = 0.18(360)$ Find 18% of 360.

$= 64.8$ Simplify.

b. $m\widehat{BC}$

The percents for volleyball and track and field are equal, so the central angles are congruent and the corresponding arcs are congruent.

$m\widehat{BC} = m\widehat{CD} = 64.8$

Guided Practice

3A. $m\widehat{EF}$ **50.4** **3B.** $m\widehat{FA}$ **50.4**

Adjacent arcs are arcs in a circle that have exactly one point in common. In $\odot M$, $\widehat{HJ}$ and $\widehat{JK}$ are adjacent arcs. As with adjacent angles, you can add the measures of adjacent arcs.

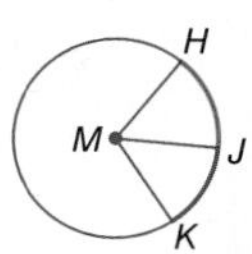

Postulate 10.1 Arc Addition Postulate

Words The measure of an arc formed by two adjacent arcs is the sum of the measures of the two arcs.

Example $m\widehat{XYZ} = m\widehat{XY} + m\widehat{YZ}$

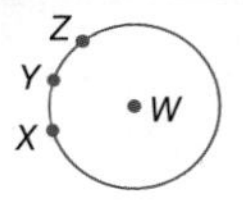

Math History Link

Euclid (c. 325–265 B.C.) The 13 books of Euclid's *Elements* are influential works of science. In them, geometry and other branches of mathematics are logically developed. Book 3 of *Elements* is devoted to circles, arcs, and angles.

Example 4 Use Arc Addition to Find Measures of Arcs

Find each measure in $\odot F$.

a. $m\widehat{AED}$

$m\widehat{AED} = m\widehat{AE} + m\widehat{ED}$ Arc Addition Postulate

$= m\angle AFE + m\angle EFD$ $m\widehat{AE} = m\angle AFE$, $m\widehat{ED} = m\angle EFD$

$= 63 + 90$ or 153 Substitution

b. $m\widehat{ADB}$

$m\widehat{ADB} = m\widehat{AE} + m\widehat{EDB}$ Arc Addition Postulate

$= 63 + 180$ or 243 $\widehat{EDB}$ is a semicircle, so $m\widehat{EDB} = 180$.

Guided Practice

4A. $m\widehat{CE}$ **117** **4B.** $m\widehat{ABD}$ **207**

Differentiated Instruction OL BL

Interpersonal Learners Draw a circle segmented with different sizes of central angles. Shade each portion of the circle with a different color. Repeat for two other circles the same size, but with different central angles. Laminate the paper, cut out the circles, and separate each portion. Provide the cutouts to groups of students who can fit the pieces together to form the three circles, find the central angle measures, arc measures, circumferences and arc lengths. Groups can compare to check results and/or determine which group is the most efficient at finding all the correct information.

WatchOut!

Arc Length The length of an arc is given in linear units, such as centimeters. The measure of an arc is given in degrees.

2 Arc Length

Arc length is the distance between the endpoints along an arc measured in linear units. Since an arc is a portion of a circle, its length is a fraction of the circumference.

KeyConcept Arc Length

Words The ratio of the length of an arc ℓ to the circumference of the circle is equal to the ratio of the degree measure of the arc to 360.

Proportion $\frac{\ell}{2\pi r} = \frac{x}{360}$ or

Equation $\ell = \frac{x}{360} \cdot 2\pi r$

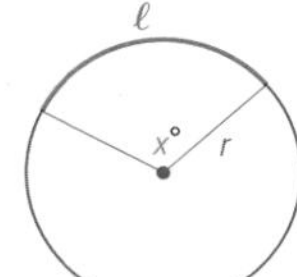

Example 5 Find Arc Length

Find the length of $\widehat{ZY}$. Round to the nearest hundredth.

a.

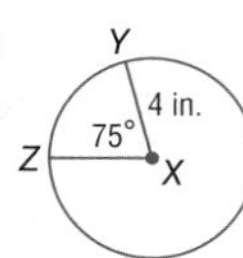

$\ell = \frac{x}{360} \cdot 2\pi r$ — Arc Length Equation

$= \frac{75}{360} \cdot 2\pi(4)$ — Substitution

≈ 5.24 in. — Use a calculator.

b.

$\ell = \frac{x}{360} \cdot 2\pi r$ — Arc Length Equation

$= \frac{130}{360} \cdot 2\pi(5)$ — Substitution

≈ 11.34 cm — Use a calculator.

c.

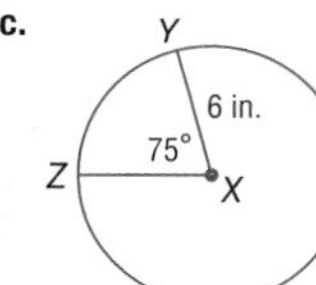

$\ell = \frac{x}{360} \cdot 2\pi r$ — Arc Length Equation

$= \frac{75}{360} \cdot 2\pi(6)$ — Substitution

≈ 7.85 in. — Use a calculator.

StudyTip

Alternate Method The arc lengths in Examples 5a, 5b, and 5c could also have been calculated using the arc length proportion $\frac{\ell}{2\pi r} = \frac{x}{360}$.

Notice that $\widehat{ZY}$ has the same measure, 75, in both Examples 5a and 5c. The arc lengths, however, are different. This is because they are in circles that have different radii.

GuidedPractice

Find the length of $\widehat{AB}$. Round to the nearest hundredth.

5A. 2.36 cm

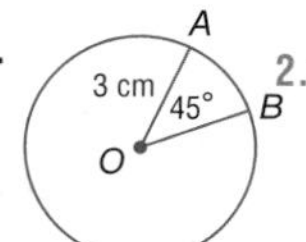

5B. 9.77 m

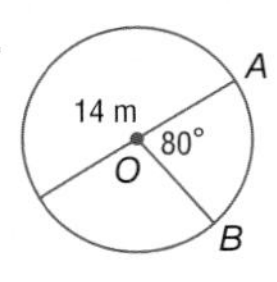

5C. 16.76 ft

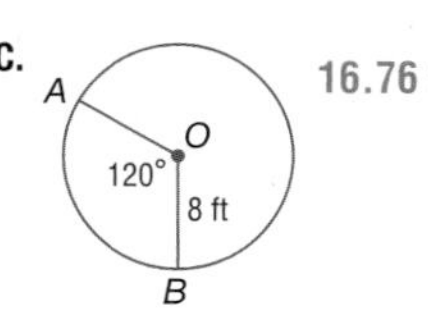

DifferentiatedInstruction OL BL

Extension Have students find the arc length of a circle by using the University of Texas clock tower as a model of a circle. The University of Texas clock face is 14 feet 8 inches in diameter. Find the measure of the central angle of the hands of the clock tower at 5 o'clock. Find the arc length of the hands of the clock tower at 5 o'clock. The measure of the central angle is 150. The measure of the arc length is ≈ 230 inches or 19 feet 2 inches.

2 Arc Length

Since the arc is part of the circle, the length of an arc is part of the circumference. **Example 5** shows how to find the arc length proportionally.

Tips for New Teachers

Sense-Making Advise students that two arcs can have equivalent measures, but different arc lengths. Explain using the formula for the length of an arc and show students that the length of the arc depends on the radius of the circle.

Additional Example

5 Find the length of $\widehat{DA}$. Round to the nearest hundredth.

a.

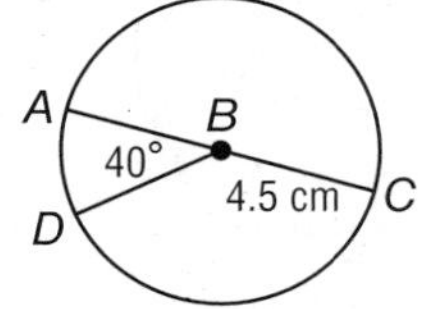

π or about 3.14 cm

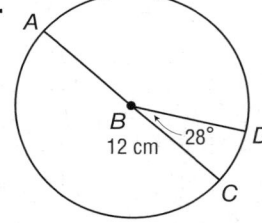

b. 15.92 cm

c. 14.66 cm

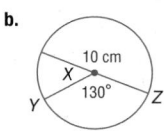

3 Practice

Formative Assessment

Use Exercises 1–11 to check for understanding.

Use the chart at the bottom of this page to customize assignments for your students.

Follow-up

Students have explored circles, circumference, angle measure, and arc measure.

Ask:

- What about circles makes them useful? Sample answers: They have a well-known shape; all circles are similar; they can be used to create graphical displays.

Additional Answer

24c. Yes; the arcs associated with the online and none of these categories have the same arc measure since each category accounts for the same percentage of the circle, 9%.

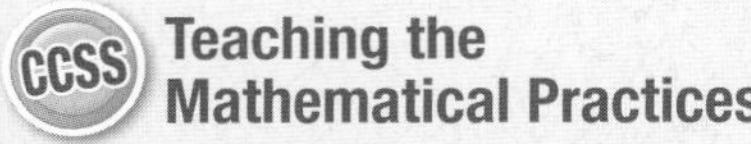

Teaching the Mathematical Practices

Precision Mathematically proficient students use clear definitions in discussion with others and in their own reasoning. In Exercises 3–5, encourage students to choose the best term for each arc.

Check Your Understanding

 = Step-by-Step Solutions begin on page R14.

Example 1 Find the value of x.

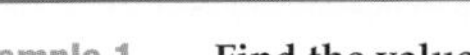

1. 170

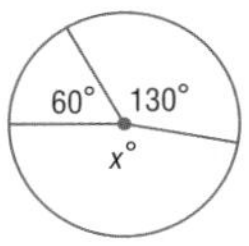

2. 150

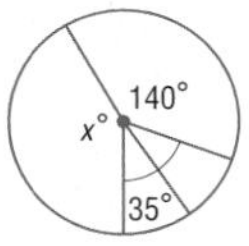

Example 2 CCSS **PRECISION** $\overline{HK}$ and $\overline{IG}$ are diameters of $\odot L$. Identify each arc as a *major arc, minor arc,* or *semicircle.* Then find its measure.

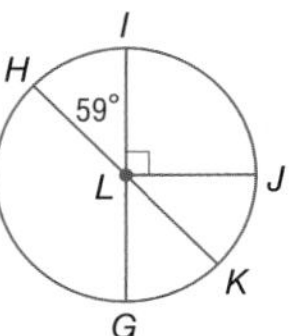

3. $m\widehat{IHJ}$ major arc; 270

4. $m\widehat{HI}$ minor arc; 59

5. $m\widehat{HGK}$ semicircle; 180

Example 3 **6. RESTAURANTS** The graph shows the results of a survey taken by diners relating what is most important about the restaurants where they eat.

a. Find $m\widehat{AB}$. 79.2

b. Find $m\widehat{BC}$. 28.8

c. Describe the type of arc that the category Great Food represents. major arc

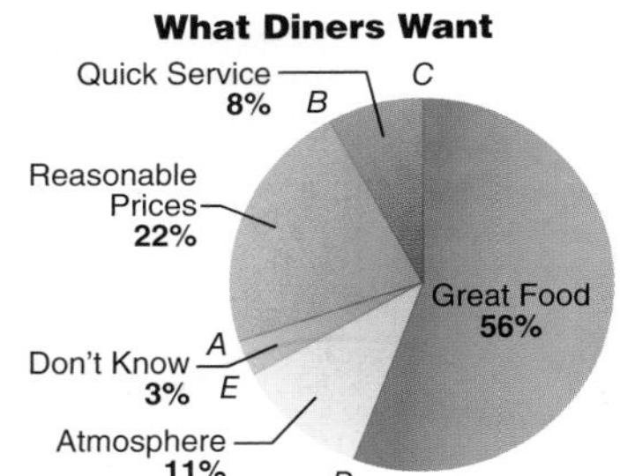

Example 4 $\overline{QS}$ is a diameter of $\odot V$. Find each measure.

7. $m\widehat{STP}$ 147

8. $m\widehat{QRT}$ 255

9. $m\widehat{PQR}$ 123

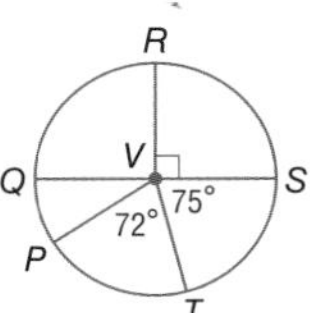

Example 5 Find the length of $\widehat{JK}$. Round to the nearest hundredth.

10. 1.05 ft

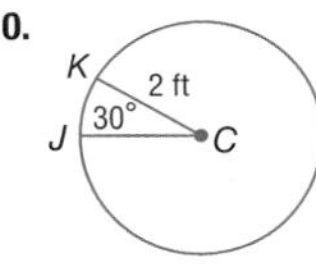

11. 13.74 cm

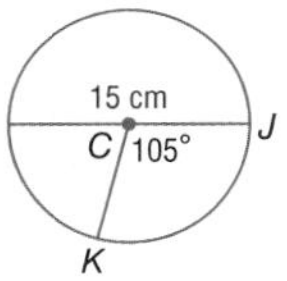

Practice and Problem Solving

Extra Practice is on page R10.

Example 1 Find the value of x.

12. 80

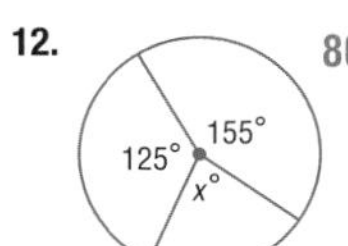

13. 225

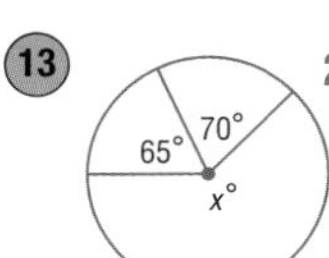

14. 35

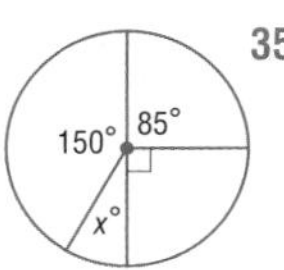

15. 40

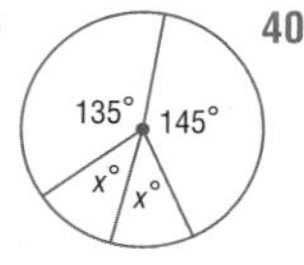

Differentiated Homework Options

Level	Assignment	Two-Day Option	
AL Basic	12–41, 55–58, 60, 62–77	13–41 odd, 63–66	12–40 even, 55–58, 60, 62, 67–77
OL Core	13–43 odd, 44, 45–51 odd, 52–58, 60, 62–77	12–41, 63–66	42–58, 60, 62, 67–77
BL Advanced	42–74, (optional: 75–77)		

Example 2 $\overline{AD}$ **and** $\overline{CG}$ **are diameters of** $\odot B$**. Identify each arc as a *major arc, minor arc,* or *semicircle*. Then find its measure.**

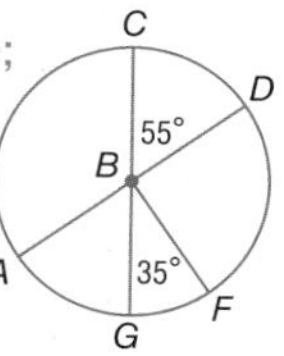

16. $m\widehat{CD}$ minor arc; 55 **17.** $m\widehat{AC}$ minor arc; 125 **18.** $m\widehat{CFG}$ **18.** semicircle; 180

19. $m\widehat{CGD}$ major arc; 305 **20.** $m\widehat{GCF}$ major arc; 325 **21.** $m\widehat{ACD}$ semicircle; 180

22. $m\widehat{AG}$ minor arc; 55 **23.** $m\widehat{ACF}$ major arc; 270

Example 3 **24. SHOPPING** The graph shows the results of a survey in which teens were asked where the best place was to shop for clothes.

Best Places to Clothes Shop

None of these 9%
Online 9%
Vintage stores 4%
Flea markets 2%
Mall 76%

a. What would be the arc measures associated with the mall and vintage stores categories? 273.6, 14.4

b. Describe the kinds of arcs associated with the category "Mall" and the category "None of these." major arc; minor arc

c. Are there any congruent arcs in this graph? Explain. See margin.

25. CCSS **MODELING** The table shows the results of a survey in which Americans were asked how long food could be on the floor and still be safe to eat.

Dropped Food	
Do you eat food dropped on the floor?	
Not safe to eat	78%
Three-second rule*	10%
Five-second rule*	8%
Ten-second rule*	4%

Source: American Diabetic Association
* The length of time the food is on the floor.

a. If you were to construct a circle graph of this information, what would be the arc measures associated with the first two categories? 280.8; 36

b. Describe the kind of arcs associated with the first category and the last category.

c. Are there any congruent arcs in this graph? Explain. No; no categories share the same percentage of the circle.

25b. major arc; minor arc

Examples 2, 4 **ENTERTAINMENT** **Use the Ferris wheel shown to find each measure.**

26. $m\widehat{FG}$ 40 **27.** $m\widehat{JH}$ 60

28. $m\widehat{JKF}$ 180 **29.** $m\widehat{JFH}$ 300

30. $m\widehat{GHF}$ 320 **31.** $m\widehat{GHK}$ 180

32. $m\widehat{HK}$ 100 **33.** $m\widehat{JKG}$ 220

34. $m\widehat{KFH}$ 260 **35.** $m\widehat{HGF}$ 120

Example 5 **Use** $\odot P$ **to find the length of each arc. Round to the nearest hundredth.**

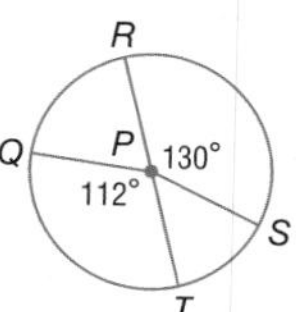

36. $\widehat{RS}$, if the radius is 2 inches 4.54 in.

37. $\widehat{QT}$, if the diameter is 9 centimeters 8.80 cm

38. $\widehat{QR}$, if $PS = 4$ millimeters 4.75 mm

39. $\widehat{RS}$, if $RT = 15$ inches 17.02 in.

40. $\widehat{QRS}$, if $RT = 11$ feet 19.01 ft

41. $\widehat{RTS}$, if $PQ = 3$ meters 12.04 m

CCSS Teaching the Mathematical Practices

Modeling Mathematically proficient students can apply the mathematics they know to solve problems arising in everyday life. They identify important quantities in a practical situation and map their relationships using graphs. In Exercise 25, encourage students to use the information given to construct a circle graph.

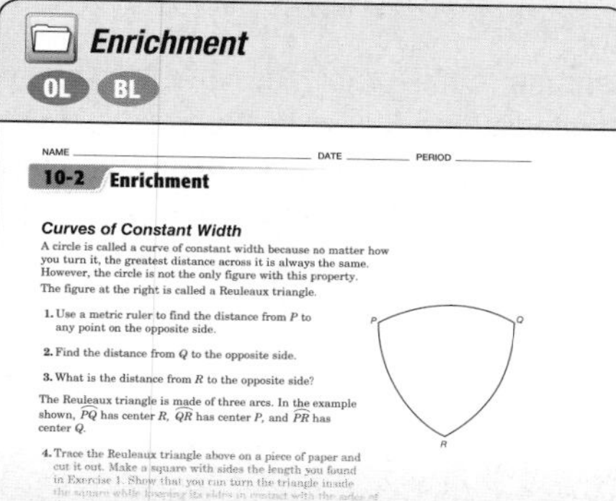

Enrichment

OL BL

NAME ________ DATE ________ PERIOD ________

10-2 Enrichment

Curves of Constant Width

A circle is called a curve of constant width because no matter how you turn it, the greatest distance across it is always the same. However, the circle is not the only figure with this property. The figure at the right is called a Reuleaux triangle.

1. Use a metric ruler to find the distance from P to any point on the opposite side.
2. Find the distance from Q to the opposite side.
3. What is the distance from R to the opposite side?

The Reuleaux triangle is made of three arcs. In the example shown, $\widehat{PQ}$ has center R, $\widehat{QR}$ has center P, and $\widehat{PR}$ has center Q.

4. Trace the Reuleaux triangle above on a piece of paper and cut it out. Make a square with sides the length you found in Exercise 1. Show that you can turn the triangle inside

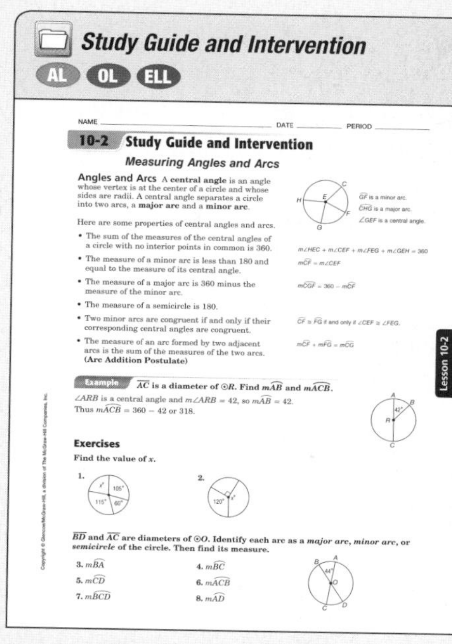

Study Guide and Intervention

AL OL ELL

NAME ________ DATE ________ PERIOD ________

10-2 Study Guide and Intervention

Measuring Angles and Arcs

Angles and Arcs A **central angle** is an angle whose vertex is at the center of a circle and whose sides are radii. A central angle separates a circle into two arcs, a **major arc** and a **minor arc**.

$\widehat{GF}$ is a minor arc. $\widehat{CHG}$ is a major arc. $\angle GEF$ is a central angle.

Here are some properties of central angles and arcs.

- The sum of the measures of the central angles of a circle with no interior points in common is 360. $m\angle HEC + m\angle CEF + m\angle FEG + m\angle GEH = 360$
- The measure of a minor arc is less than 180 and equal to the measure of its central angle. $m\widehat{CF} = m\angle CEF$
- The measure of a major arc is 360 minus the measure of the minor arc. $m\widehat{CGF} = 360 - m\widehat{CF}$
- The measure of a semicircle is 180.
- Two minor arcs are congruent if and only if their corresponding central angles are congruent. $\widehat{CF} \cong \widehat{FG}$ if and only if $\angle CEF \cong \angle FEG$.
- The measure of an arc formed by two adjacent arcs is the sum of the measures of the two arcs. **(Arc Addition Postulate)** $m\widehat{CF} + m\widehat{FG} = m\widehat{CG}$

Example $\overline{AC}$ **is a diameter of** $\odot R$**. Find** $m\widehat{AB}$ **and** $m\widehat{ACB}$**.**

$\angle ARB$ is a central angle and $m\angle ARB = 42$, so $m\widehat{AB} = 42$.
Thus $m\widehat{ACB} = 360 - 42$ or 318.

Exercises

Find the value of x.

1. 2.

$\overline{BD}$ **and** $\overline{AC}$ **are diameters of** $\odot O$**. Identify each arc as a *major arc*, *minor arc*, or *semicircle* of the circle. Then find its measure.**

3. $m\widehat{BA}$ 4. $m\widehat{BC}$
5. $m\widehat{CD}$ 6. $m\widehat{ACB}$
7. $m\widehat{BCD}$ 8. $m\widehat{AD}$

Lesson 10-2

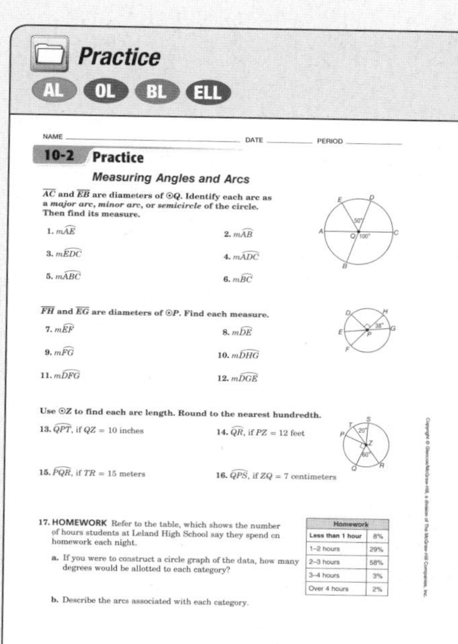

Practice

AL OL BL ELL

NAME ________ DATE ________ PERIOD ________

10-2 Practice

Measuring Angles and Arcs

$\overline{AC}$ **and** $\overline{EB}$ **are diameters of** $\odot Q$**. Identify each arc as a *major arc*, *minor arc*, or *semicircle* of the circle. Then find its measure.**

1. $m\widehat{AE}$ 2. $m\widehat{AB}$
3. $m\widehat{EDC}$ 4. $m\widehat{ADC}$
5. $m\widehat{ABC}$ 6. $m\widehat{BC}$

$\overline{FH}$ **and** $\overline{EG}$ **are diameters of** $\odot P$**. Find each measure.**

7. $m\widehat{EF}$ 8. $m\widehat{DE}$
9. $m\widehat{FG}$ 10. $m\widehat{DHG}$
11. $m\widehat{DFG}$ 12. $m\widehat{DGE}$

Use $\odot Z$ **to find each arc length. Round to the nearest hundredth.**

13. $\widehat{QPT}$, if $QZ = 10$ inches 14. $\widehat{QR}$, if $PZ = 12$ feet
15. $\widehat{PQR}$, if $TR = 15$ meters 16. $\widehat{QPS}$, if $ZQ = 7$ centimeters

17. **HOMEWORK** Refer to the table, which shows the number of hours students at Leland High School say they spend on homework each night.

Homework	
Less than 1 hour	8%
1–2 hours	29%
2–3 hours	58%
3–4 hours	3%
Over 4 hours	2%

a. If you were to construct a circle graph of the data, how many degrees would be allotted to each category?

b. Describe the arcs associated with each category.

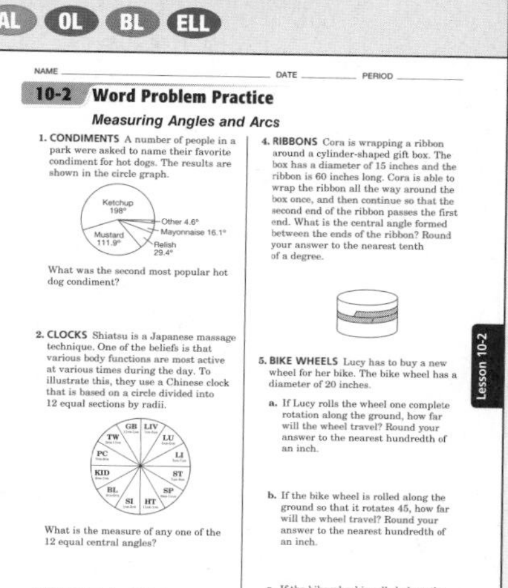

Word Problem Practice

AL OL BL ELL

NAME ________ DATE ________ PERIOD ________

10-2 Word Problem Practice

Measuring Angles and Arcs

1. **CONDIMENTS** A number of people in a park were asked to name their favorite condiment for hot dogs. The results are shown in the circle graph.

Ketchup 198°, Mustard 111.9°, Other 4.6°, Mayonnaise 16.1°, Relish 29.4°

What was the second most popular hot dog condiment?

2. **CLOCKS** Shiatsu is a Japanese massage technique. One of the beliefs is that various body functions are most active at various times during the day. To illustrate this, they use a Chinese clock that is based on a circle divided into 12 equal sections by radii.

What is the measure of any one of the 12 equal central angles?

3. **PIES** Yolanda has divided a circular apple pie into 4 slices by cutting the pie along 4 radii. The central angles of the 4 slices are $3x$, $6x - 10$, $4x + 10$, and $5x$ degrees. What exactly are the numerical measures of the central angles?

4. **RIBBONS** Cora is wrapping a ribbon around a cylinder-shaped gift box. The box has a diameter of 15 inches and the ribbon is 60 inches long. Cora is able to wrap the ribbon all the way around the box once, and then continue so that the second end of the ribbon passes the first end. What is the central angle formed between the ends of the ribbon? Round your answer to the nearest tenth of a degree.

5. **BIKE WHEELS** Lucy has to buy a new wheel for her bike. The bike wheel has a diameter of 20 inches.

a. If Lucy rolls the wheel one complete rotation along the ground, how far will the wheel travel? Round your answer to the nearest hundredth of an inch.

b. If the bike wheel is rolled along the ground so that it rotates 45, how far will the wheel travel? Round your answer to the nearest hundredth of an inch.

c. If the bike wheel is rolled along the ground for 10 inches, through what angle does the wheel rotate? Round your answer to the nearest tenth of a degree.

Lesson 10-2

Teaching the Mathematical Practices

Reasoning Mathematically proficient students make sense of quantities and their relationships in problem situations. In Exercises 45–47, encourage students to use the relationship between arc length and radius.

Additional Answers

42. $360 \div 13$ stars ≈ 27.7 between each star

43. The length of the arc would double.

54a. $m\widehat{\ell_1} = m\ell_2$; $\ell_1 < \ell_2$; these comparisons suggest that arc measure is not affected by the size of the circle, but arc length is affected.

54b. Since all circles are similar, the larger circle is a dilation of the smaller by some factor k, so $r_2 = kr_1$ or $k = \frac{r_2}{r_1}$. Likewise, the arc intercepted on the larger circle is a dilation of the arc intercepted on the smaller circle, so $\ell_2 = k\ell_1$ or $k = \frac{\ell_2}{\ell_1}$. Thus $\frac{r_2}{r_1} = \frac{\ell_2}{\ell_1}$ or $\frac{\ell_1}{r_1} = \frac{\ell_2}{r_2}$.

54c. $\ell_1 = \frac{\pi r_1 x}{180}$ and $\ell_2 = \frac{\pi r_2 x}{180}$; $k = \frac{\pi x}{180}$

B **HISTORY** The figure shows the stars in the Betsy Ross flag referenced at the beginning of the lesson.

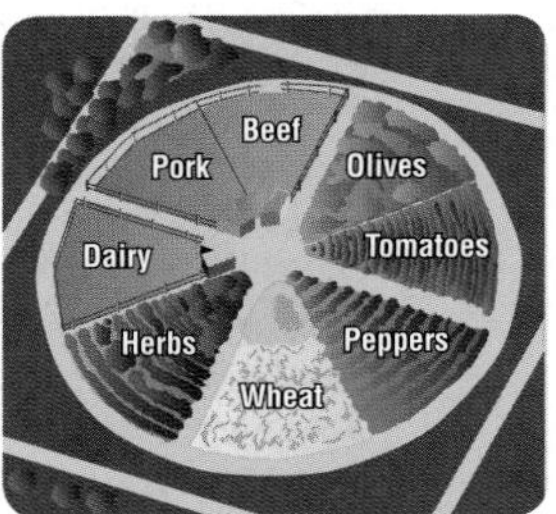

42. What is the measure of central angle A? Explain how you determined your answer. **See margin.**

43. If the diameter of the circle were doubled, what would be the effect on the arc length from the center of one star B to the next star C? **See margin.**

44. **FARMS** The *Pizza Farm* in Madera, California, is a circle divided into eight equal slices, as shown at the right. Each "slice" is used for growing or grazing pizza ingredients.

a. What is the total arc measure of the slices containing olives, tomatoes, and peppers? **135**

b. The circle is 125 feet in diameter. What is the arc length of one slice? Round to the nearest hundredth. **49.09 ft**

CCSS REASONING **Find each measure. Round each linear measure to the nearest hundredth and each arc measure to the nearest degree.**

45. circumference of $\odot S$ **40.83 in.**

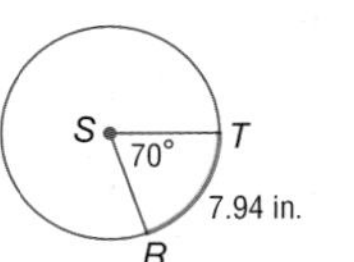

46. $m\widehat{CD}$ **150°**

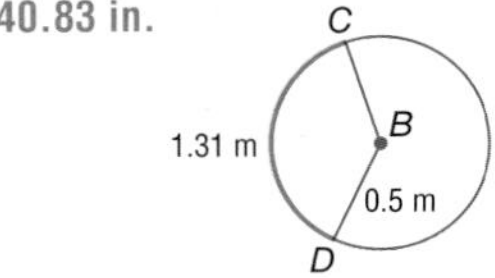

47. radius of $\odot K$ **9.50 ft**

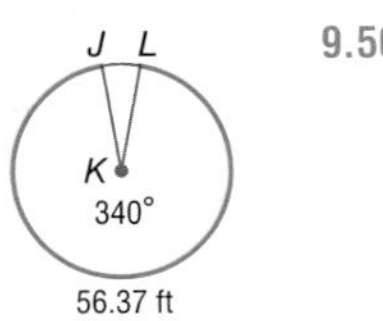

ALGEBRA **In $\odot C$, $m\angle HCG = 2x$ and $m\angle HCD = 6x + 28$. Find each measure.**

48. $m\widehat{EF}$ **52**

49. $m\widehat{HD}$ **142**

50. $m\widehat{HGF}$ **128**

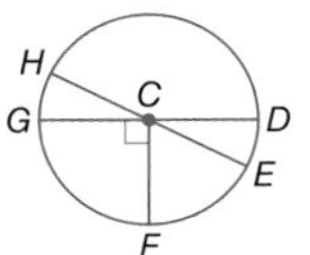

51 **RIDES** A pirate ship ride follows a semicircular path, as shown in the diagram.

a. What is $m\widehat{AB}$? **136**

b. If $CD = 62$ feet, what is the length of $\widehat{AB}$? Round to the nearest hundredth. **147.17 ft**

52. Proof:
Statements (Reasons)
1. $\angle BAC \cong \angle DAE$ (Given)
2. $m\angle BAC = m\angle DAE$ (Definition of $\cong$ ∠s)
3. $m\angle BAC = m\widehat{BC}$, $m\angle DAE = m\widehat{DE}$ (Definition of arc measure)
4. $m\widehat{BC} = m\widehat{DE}$ (Substitution)
5. $\widehat{BC} \cong \widehat{DE}$ (Definition of $\cong$ arcs)

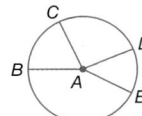

52. **PROOF** Write a two-column proof of Theorem 10.1.

Given: $\angle BAC \cong \angle DAE$

Prove: $\widehat{BC} \cong \widehat{DE}$

Differentiated Instruction AL OL BL

Extension Circle graphs are a very simple yet effective way of displaying data. Since many gifted students compromise our future researchers in a variety of fields, allow students the opportunity to develop and answer a research question related to an area of interest. Ask students to display the results using a circle graph with accurate arc measurements to represent their data.

53 **COORDINATE GEOMETRY** In the graph, point M is located at the origin. Find each measure in $\odot M$. Round each linear measure to the nearest hundredth and each arc measure to the nearest tenth degree.

y, J(5, 12), K(12, 5), M, L(13, 0) x

a. $m\widehat{JL}$ 67.4 **b.** $m\widehat{KL}$ 22.6 **c.** $m\widehat{JK}$ 44.8

d. length of $\widehat{JL}$ 15.29 units **e.** length of $\widehat{JK}$ 10.16 units

54. **ARC LENGTH AND RADIAN MEASURE** In this problem, you will use concentric circles to show that the length of the arc intercepted by a central angle of a circle is dependent on the circle's radius.

r_2, r_1, $x°$, ℓ_1, ℓ_2

a. Compare the measures of arc ℓ_1 and arc ℓ_2. Then compare the lengths of arc ℓ_1 and arc ℓ_2. What do these two comparisons suggest? a–c. See margin.

b. Use similarity transformations (dilations) to explain why the length of an arc ℓ intercepted by a central angle of a circle is proportional to the circle's radius r. That is, explain why we can say that for this diagram, $\frac{\ell_1}{r_1} = \frac{\ell_2}{r_2}$.

c. Write expressions for the lengths of arcs ℓ_1 and ℓ_2. Use these expressions to identify the constant of proportionality k in $\ell = kr$.

d. The expression that you wrote for k in part c gives the *radian measure* of an angle. Use it to find the radian measure of an angle measuring 90°. $\frac{\pi}{2}$

H.O.T. Problems Use Higher-Order Thinking Skills

55. **ERROR ANALYSIS** Brody says that $\widehat{WX}$ and $\widehat{YZ}$ are congruent since their central angles have the same measure. Selena says they are not congruent. Is either of them correct? Explain your reasoning.
Selena; the circles are not congruent because they do not have congruent radii. So, the arcs are not congruent.

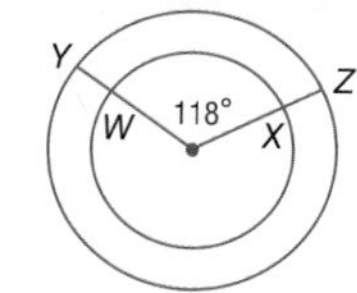

CCSS ARGUMENTS **Determine whether each statement is *sometimes*, *always*, or *never* true. Explain your reasoning.**

56. The measure of a minor arc is less than 180.

56. Always; by definition, an arc that measures less than 180 is a minor arc.

57. If a central angle is obtuse, its corresponding arc is a major arc.

57. Never; obtuse angles intersect arcs that measure between 90° and 180°.

58. The sum of the measures of adjacent arcs of a circle depends on the measure of the radius.

58. Never; the sum of the measures of adjacent arcs depends on the measures of the arcs.

59. **CHALLENGE** The measures of $\widehat{LM}$, $\widehat{MN}$, and $\widehat{NL}$ are in the ratio 5:3:4. Find the measure of each arc.
$m\widehat{LM} = 150$, $m\widehat{MN} = 90$, $m\widehat{NL} = 120$

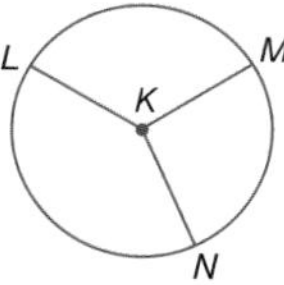

60. **OPEN ENDED** Draw a circle and locate three points on the circle. Estimate the measures of the three nonoverlapping arcs that are formed. Then use a protractor to find the measure of each arc. Label your circle with the arc measures. See margin.

61. **CHALLENGE** The time shown on an analog clock is 8:10. What is the measure of the angle formed by the hands of the clock? 175

62. **WRITING IN MATH** Describe the three different types of arcs in a circle and the method for finding the measure of each one. See margin.

Exercise Alerts

Compass, Straightedge, and Scissors Exercises 54 and 60 require the use of a compass, a straightedge, and scissors.

WatchOut!

Error Analysis In Exercise 55, students should realize that concentric circles that share a central angle will always have the same arc measure. However, the larger the circle, the greater the distance between the angle endpoints. Therefore, the arc length increases in direct proportion to the diameter of the circle. Selena is correct.

Proportions For Exercise 59, remind students that the order of the factors matters in proportions. For example, if the ratio of A to B to C is 1 to 2 to 3, $A : B : C = 1 : 2 : 3$.

CCSS Teaching the Mathematical Practices

Arguments Mathematically proficient students understand and use stated assumptions and definitions in constructing arguments. They make conjectures and build a logical progression of statements to explore the truth of their conjectures. In Exercises 56–58, encourage students to draw a diagram of the situation described.

Additional Answers

60. Sample answer:

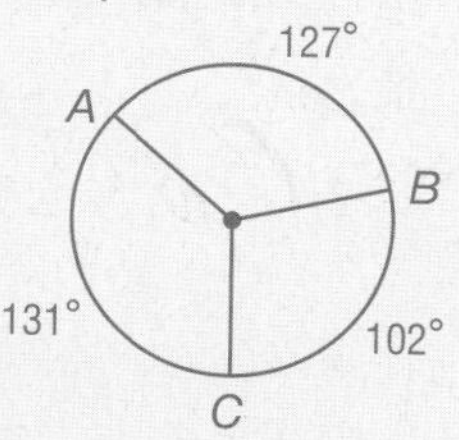

62. Sample answer: Minor arc, major arc, semicircle; the measure of a minor arc equals the measure of the corresponding central angle. The measure of a major arc equals 360 minus the measure of the minor arc with the same endpoints. The measure of a semicircle is 180.

4 Assess

Ticket Out the Door Ask students to sketch a circle with a central angle. Have them identify the length of the radius and then draw and label the degrees of a central angle. Instruct students to find the arc length for either the major or the minor arc. Have students turn in their work before they leave the classroom.

Formative Assessment

Check for student understanding of Lessons 10-1 and 10-2.

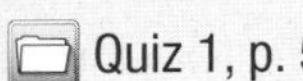 Quiz 1, p. 57

Additional Answers

70.

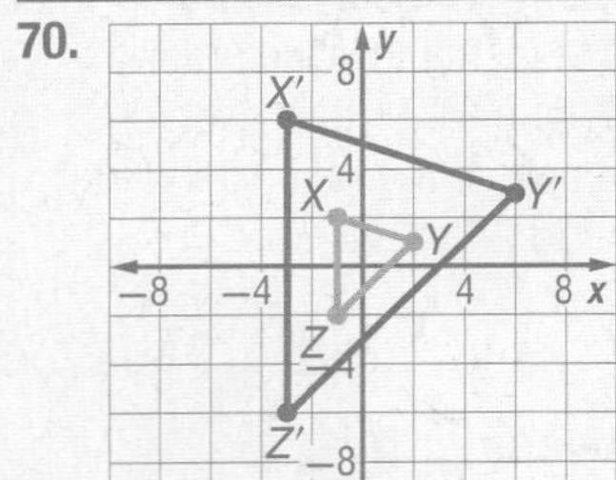

71.

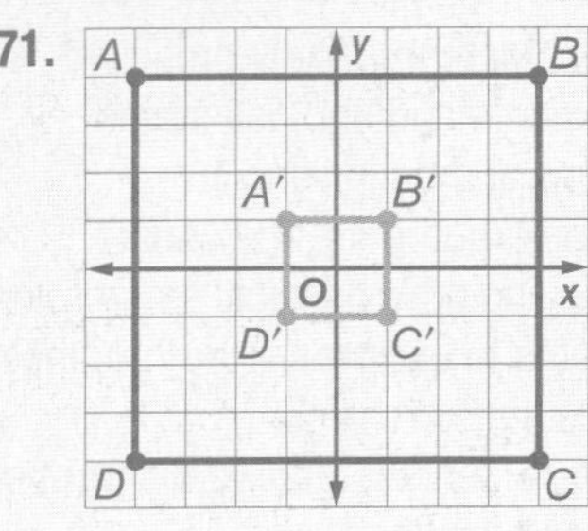

Standardized Test Practice

63. What is the value of x? **B**

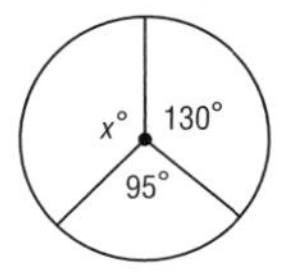

A 120
B 135
C 145
D 160

64. **GRIDDED RESPONSE** In $\odot B$, $m\angle LBM = 3x$ and $m\angle LBQ = 4x + 61$. What is the measure of $\angle PBQ$? **51**

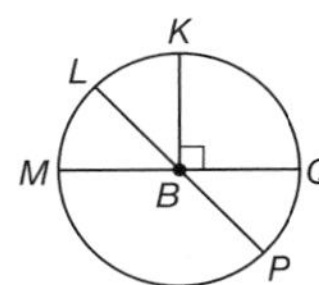

65. **ALGEBRA** A rectangle's width is represented by x and its length by y. Which expression best represents the area of the rectangle if the length and width are tripled? **H**

F $3xy$
G $3(xy)^2$
H $9xy$
J $(xy)^3$

66. **SAT/ACT** What is the area of the shaded region if $r = 4$? **A**

A $64 - 16\pi$
B $16 - 16\pi$
C $16 - 8\pi$
D $64 - 8\pi$
E $64\pi - 16$

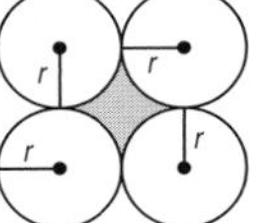

Spiral Review

Refer to $\odot J$. (Lesson 10-1)

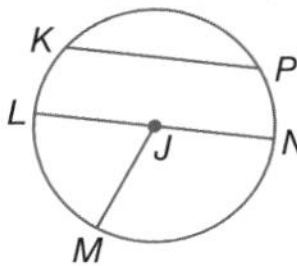

67. Name the center of the circle. **J**

68. Identify a chord that is also a diameter. **$\overline{LN}$**

69. If $LN = 12.4$, what is JM? **6.2**

Graph the image of each polygon with the given vertices after a dilation centered at the origin with the given scale factor. (Lesson 9-6) **70, 71. See margin.**

70. $X(-1, 2)$, $Y(2, 1)$, $Z(-1, -2)$; $r = 3$

71. $A(-4, 4)$, $B(4, 4)$, $C(4, -4)$, $D(-4, -4)$; $r = 0.25$

72. **BASEBALL** The diagram shows some dimensions of Comiskey Park in Chicago, Illinois. $\overline{BD}$ is a segment from home plate to dead center field, and $\overline{AE}$ is a segment from the left field foul pole to the right field foul pole. If the center fielder is standing at C, how far is he from home plate? (Lesson 8-3) **$\frac{347\sqrt{2}}{2} \approx 245.4$ ft**

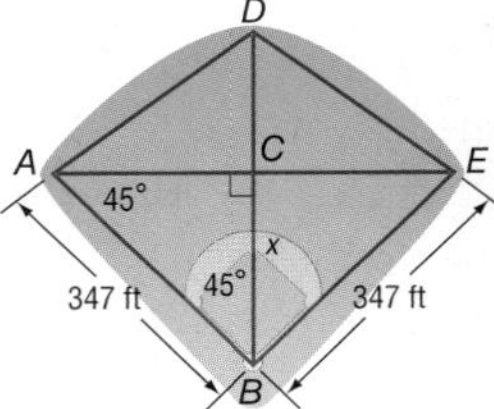

Find x, y, and z. (Lesson 8-1)

73.

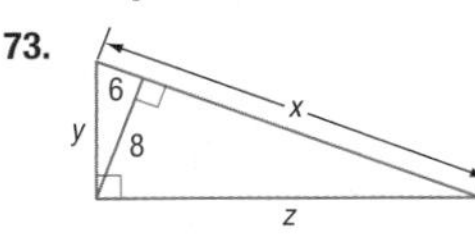

$x = \frac{50}{3}$; $y = 10$; $z = \frac{40}{3}$

74.

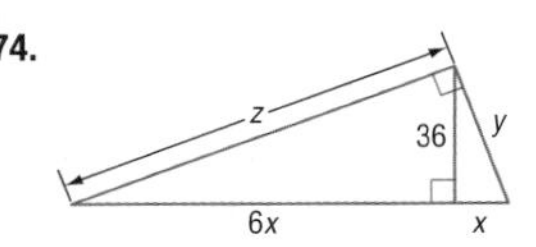

$x = 6\sqrt{6} \approx 14.7$; $y = 6\sqrt{42} \approx 38.9$; $z = 36\sqrt{7} \approx 95.2$

Skills Review

Find x.

75. $24^2 + x^2 = 26^2$ **10, −10**

76. $x^2 + 5^2 = 13^2$ **12, −12**

77. $30^2 + 35^2 = x^2$ **46.1, −46.1**

714 | Lesson 10-2 | Measuring Angles and Arcs

LESSON 10-3 Arcs and Chords

Then	Now	Why?
You used the relationships between arcs and angles to find measures.	**1** Recognize and use relationships between arcs and chords. **2** Recognize and use relationships between arcs, chords, and diameters.	Embroidery hoops are used in sewing, quilting, and cross-stitching, as well as for embroidering. The endpoints of the snowflake shown are both the endpoints of a chord and the endpoints of an arc.

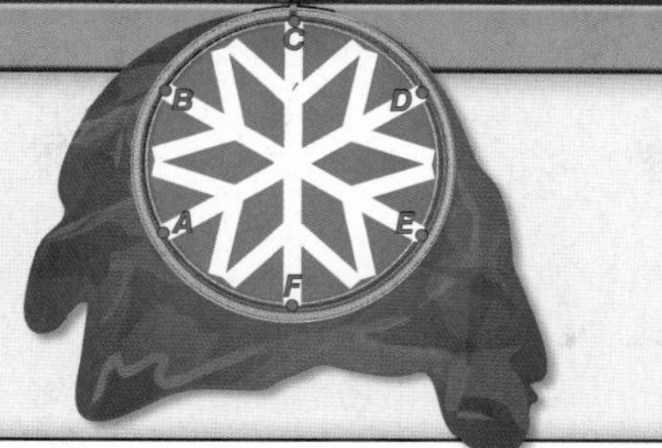

Common Core State Standards

Content Standards

G.C.2 Identify and describe relationships among inscribed angles, radii, and chords.

G.MG.3 Apply geometric methods to solve problems (e.g., designing an object or structure to satisfy physical constraints or minimize cost; working with typographic grid systems based on ratios). ★

Mathematical Practices

4 Model with mathematics.

3 Construct viable arguments and critique the reasoning of others.

1 Arcs and Chords

A *chord* is a segment with endpoints on a circle. If a chord is not a diameter, then its endpoints divide the circle into a major and a minor arc.

Theorem 10.2

Words In the same circle or in congruent circles, two minor arcs are congruent if and only if their corresponding chords are congruent.

Example $\widehat{FG} \cong \widehat{HJ}$ if and only if $\overline{FG} \cong \overline{HJ}$.

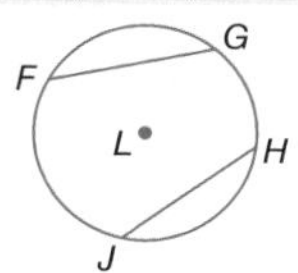

Proof Theorem 10.2 (part 1)

Given: $\odot P$; $\widehat{QR} \cong \widehat{ST}$

Prove: $\overline{QR} \cong \overline{ST}$

Proof:

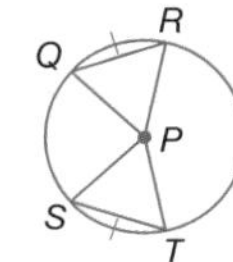

Statements	Reasons
1. $\odot P$, $\widehat{QR} \cong \widehat{ST}$	1. Given
2. $\angle QPR \cong \angle SPT$	2. If arcs are ≅, their corresponding central ∡ are ≅.
3. $\overline{QP} \cong \overline{PR} \cong \overline{SP} \cong \overline{PT}$	3. All radii of a circle are ≅.
4. $\triangle PQR \cong \triangle PST$	4. SAS
5. $\overline{QR} \cong \overline{ST}$	5. CPCTC

You will prove part 2 of Theorem 10.2 in Exercise 25.

Real-World Example 1 Use Congruent Chords to Find Arc Measure

CRAFTS **In the embroidery hoop, $\overline{AB} \cong \overline{CD}$ and $m\widehat{AB} = 60$. Find $m\widehat{CD}$.**

$\overline{AB}$ and $\overline{CD}$ are congruent chords, so the corresponding arcs $\widehat{AB}$ and $\widehat{CD}$ are congruent. $m\widehat{AB} = m\widehat{CD} = 60$

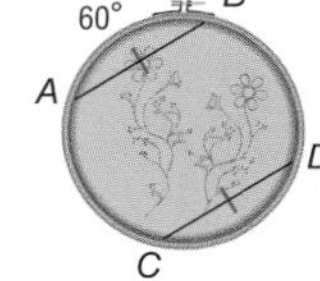

GuidedPractice

1. If $m\widehat{AB} = 78$ in the embroidery hoop, find $m\widehat{CD}$. 78

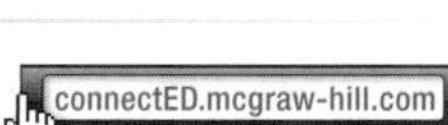

1 Focus

VerticalAlignment

Before Lesson 10-3 Use the relationship between arcs and angles to find measures.

Lesson 10-3 Recognize and use relationships between arcs and chords. Recognize and use relationships between arcs, chords, and diameters.

After Lesson 10-3 Find measures of inscribed angles, including angles of inscribed polygons.

2 Teach

Scaffolding Questions

Have students read the **Why?** section of the lesson.

Ask:

- What is the measure of one central angle of the embroidered snowflake? 60
- Assume that the embroidery hoop is 12 inches in diameter. What is the arc length of one central angle? Round to the nearest hundredth. 6.28 inches
- Assume that the size of the embroidery hoop is increased by 125%. Make a conjecture about the new length of a chord and an arc. Both lengths will also increase by 125%.

Lesson 10-3 Resources

Resource	Approaching Level AL	On Level OL	Beyond Level BL	English Learners ELL
Teacher Edition	▪ Differentiated Instruction, p. 718	▪ Differentiated Instruction, pp. 718, 722	▪ Differentiated Instruction, p. 722	▪ Differentiated Instruction, p. 718
Chapter Resource Masters	▪ Study Guide and Intervention, pp. 17–18 ▪ Skills Practice, p. 19 ▪ Practice, p. 20 ▪ Word Problem Practice, p. 21	▪ Study Guide and Intervention, pp. 17–18 ▪ Skills Practice, p. 19 ▪ Practice, p. 20 ▪ Word Problem Practice, p. 21 ▪ Enrichment, p. 22	▪ Practice, p. 20 ▪ Word Problem Practice, p. 21 ▪ Enrichment, p. 22	▪ Study Guide and Intervention, pp. 17–18 ▪ Skills Practice, p. 19 ▪ Practice, p. 20 ▪ Word Problem Practice, p. 21
Other	▪ 5-Minute Check 10-3 ▪ Study Notebook ▪ Teaching Geometry with Manipulatives	▪ 5-Minute Check 10-3 ▪ Study Notebook ▪ Teaching Geometry with Manipulatives	▪ 5-Minute Check 10-3 ▪ Study Notebook	▪ 5-Minute Check 10-3 ▪ Study Notebook ▪ Teaching Geometry with Manipulatives

1 Arcs and Chords

Examples 1 and 2 show how to use congruent arcs and chords to find the measure of arcs and length of chords.

Formative Assessment

Use the Guided Practice exercises after each example to determine students' understanding of concepts.

Additional Examples

1 **JEWELRY** A circular piece of jade is hung from a chain by two wires wrapped around the stone. $\overline{JM} \cong \overline{KL}$ and $m\widehat{KL} = 90$ Find $m\widehat{JM}$.

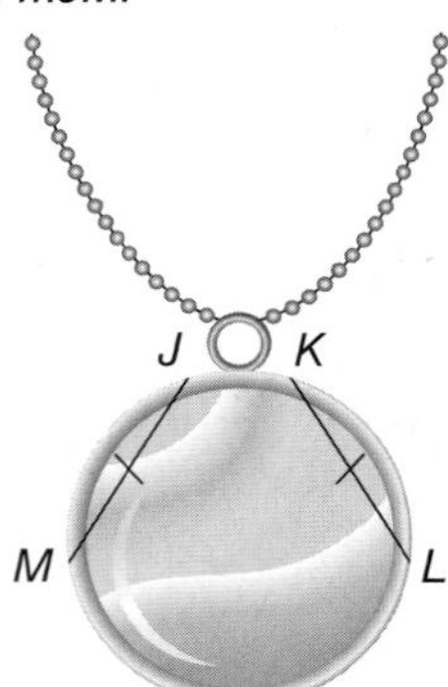

$m\widehat{KL} = m\widehat{JM} = 90$

2 **ALGEBRA** In the figure, $\odot A \cong \odot B$ and $\widehat{WX} \cong \widehat{YZ}$. Find WX.

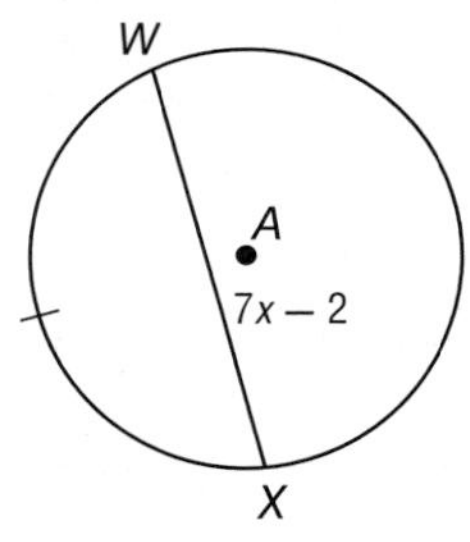

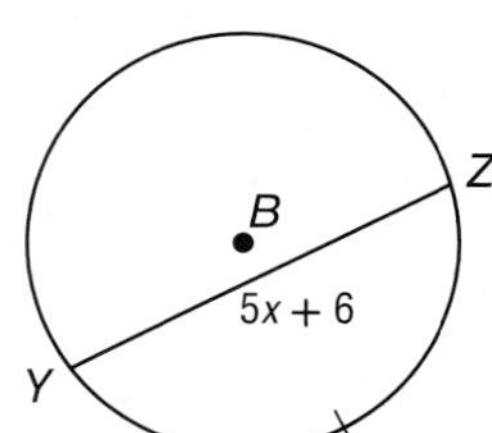

$WX = 26$

Additional Examples also in Interactive Classroom PowerPoint® Presentations

Example 2 Use Congruent Arcs to Find Chord Lengths

ALGEBRA In the figures, $\odot J \cong \odot K$ and $\widehat{MN} \cong \widehat{PQ}$. Find PQ.

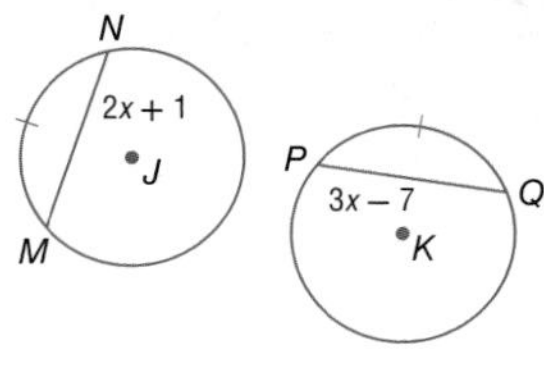

$\widehat{MN}$ and $\widehat{PQ}$ are congruent arcs in congruent circles, so the corresponding chords $\overline{MN}$ and $\overline{PQ}$ are congruent.

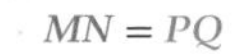

$MN = PQ$	Definition of congruent segments
$2x + 1 = 3x - 7$	Substitution
$8 = x$	Simplify.

So, $PQ = 3(8) - 7$ or 17.

GuidedPractice

2. In $\odot W$, $\widehat{RS} \cong \widehat{TV}$. Find RS. **11**

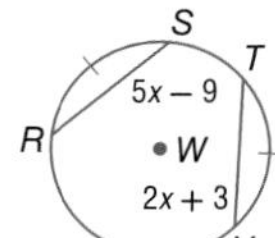

StudyTip

Arc Bisectors In the figure below, $\overline{FH}$ is an arc bisector of $\widehat{JG}$.

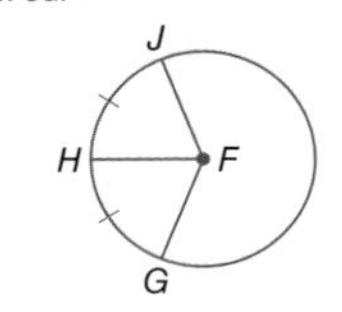

2 Bisecting Arcs and Chords

If a line, segment, or ray divides an arc into two congruent arcs, then it *bisects* the arc.

Theorems

10.3 If a diameter (or radius) of a circle is perpendicular to a chord, then it bisects the chord and its arc.

Example If diameter $\overline{AB}$ is perpendicular to chord $\overline{XY}$, then $\overline{XZ} \cong \overline{ZY}$ and $\widehat{XB} \cong \widehat{BY}$.

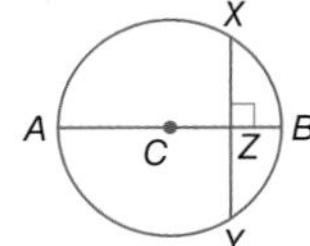

10.4 The perpendicular bisector of a chord is a diameter (or radius) of the circle.

Example If $\overline{AB}$ is a perpendicular bisector of chord $\overline{XY}$, then $\overline{AB}$ is a diameter of $\odot C$.

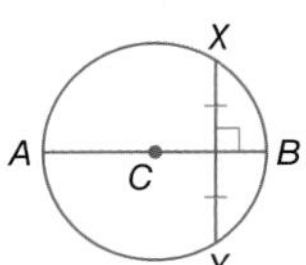

You will prove Theorems 10.3 and 10.4 in Exercises 26 and 28, respectively.

Example 3 Use a Radius Perpendicular to a Chord

In $\odot S$, $m\widehat{PQR} = 98$. Find $m\widehat{PQ}$.

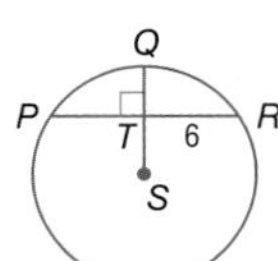

Radius $\overline{SQ}$ is perpendicular to chord $\overline{PR}$. So by Theorem 10.3, $\overline{SQ}$ bisects $\widehat{PQR}$. Therefore, $m\widehat{PQ} = m\widehat{QR}$. By substitution, $m\widehat{PQ} = \frac{98}{2}$ or 49.

GuidedPractice

3. In $\odot S$, find PR. **12 units**

Teach with Tech

Interactive Whiteboard Use a drawing program on your computer and project it on the board. This could help you save time and create more accurate sketches.

Real-WorldLink

To make stained glass windows, glass is heated to a temperature of 2000 degrees, until it is the consistency of taffy. The colors are caused by the addition of metallic oxides.

Source: *Artistic Stained Glass by Regg*

Real-World Example 4 Use a Diameter Perpendicular to a Chord

STAINED GLASS In the stained glass window, diameter $\overline{GH}$ is 30 inches long and chord $\overline{KM}$ is 22 inches long. Find JL.

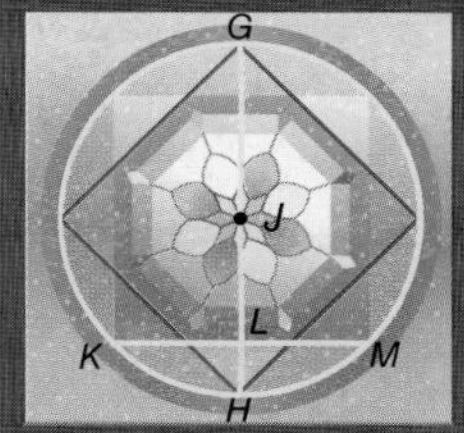

Step 1 Draw radius $\overline{JK}$.

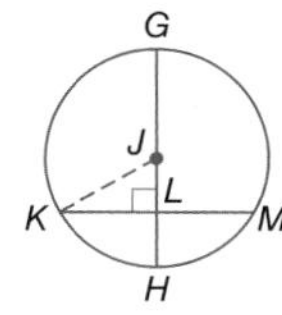

This forms right $\triangle JKL$.

Step 2 Find JK and KL.

Since $GH = 30$ inches, $JH = 15$ inches. All radii of a circle are congruent, so $JK = 15$ inches.

Since diameter $\overline{GH}$ is perpendicular to $\overline{KM}$, $\overline{GH}$ bisects chord $\overline{KM}$ by Theorem 10.3. So, $KL = \frac{1}{2}(22)$ or 11 inches.

Step 3 Use the Pythagorean Theorem to find JL.

$KL^2 + JL^2 = JK^2$	Pythagorean Theorem
$11^2 + JL^2 = 15^2$	$KL = 11$ and $JK = 15$
$121 + JL^2 = 225$	Simplify.
$JL^2 = 104$	Subtract 121 from each side.
$JL = \sqrt{104}$	Take the positive square root of each side.

So, JL is $\sqrt{104}$ or about 10.20 inches long.

StudyTip

Drawing Segments You can add any known information to a figure to help you solve the problem. In Example 4, radius $\overline{JK}$ was drawn.

GuidedPractice

4. In $\odot R$, find TV. Round to the nearest hundredth. **18.44 units**

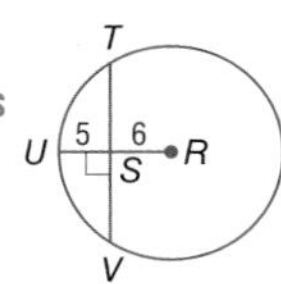

In addition to Theorem 10.2, you can use the following theorem to determine whether two chords in a circle are congruent.

Theorem 10.5

Words In the same circle or in congruent circles, two chords are congruent if and only if they are equidistant from the center.

Example $\overline{FG} \cong \overline{JH}$ if and only if $LX = LY$.

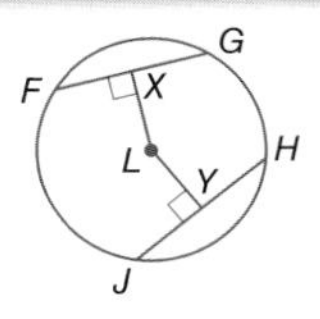

You will prove Theorem 10.5 in Exercises 29 and 30.

2 Bisecting Arcs and Chords

Perpendicular bisectors of chords create special segment and arc relationships. **Examples 3–5** show how to use theorems to find measures of parts of a circle.

Additional Examples

3 In $\odot G$, $m\widehat{DEF} = 150$. Find $m\widehat{DE}$.

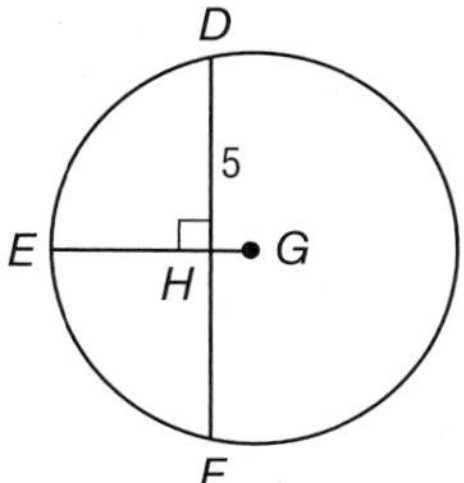

$m\widehat{DE} = 75$

4 **CERAMIC TILE** In the ceramic stepping stone below, diameter $\overline{AB}$ is 18 inches long, and chord $\overline{EF}$ is 8 inches long. Find CD.

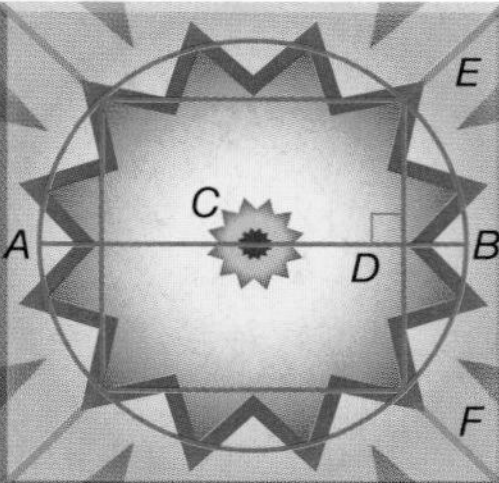

$CD = \sqrt{65} \approx 8.06$

Tips for New Teachers

Mark What is Known Any known information can be added to a figure to help solve problems. Angles, segment lengths, arcs, radii, and diameters all exist even if they are not drawn. Remind students to be careful to follow geometric conditions and definitions when they add elements to a figure.

Focus on Mathematical Content

Sectors and Segments Any central angle and the arc that connects the endpoints of that angle enclose a sector of a circle. Any chord and the arc that connects the endpoints of that chord enclose a segment of a circle. An isosceles triangle is formed any time a chord connects the endpoints of a central angle.

Additional Example

5 **ALGEBRA** In ⊙P, $EF = GH = 24$. Find PQ.

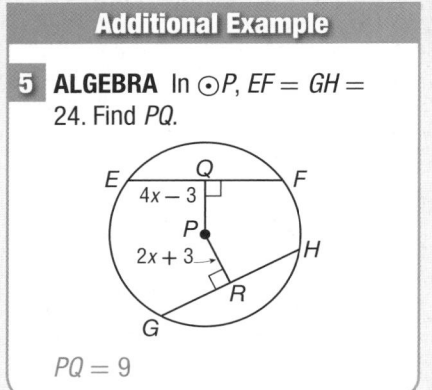

$PQ = 9$

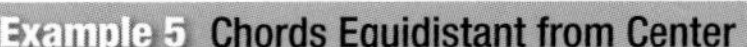

Example 5 Chords Equidistant from Center

ALGEBRA In ⊙A, $WX = XY = 22$. Find AB.

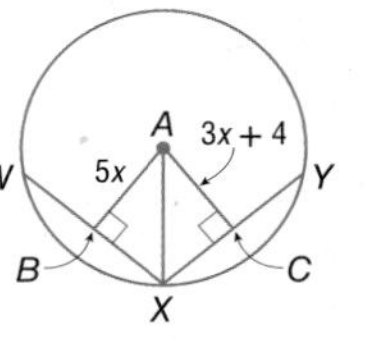

Since chords $\overline{WX}$ and $\overline{XY}$ are congruent, they are equidistant from A. So, $AB = AC$.

$AB = AC$

$5x = 3x + 4$ Substitution

$x = 2$ Simplify.

So, $AB = 5(2)$ or 10.

GuidedPractice

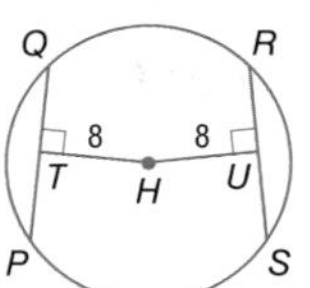

5. In ⊙H, $PQ = 3x - 4$ and $RS = 14$. Find x. 6

You can use Theorem 10.5 to find the point equidistant from three noncollinear points.

Construction Circle Through Three Noncollinear Points

Step 1

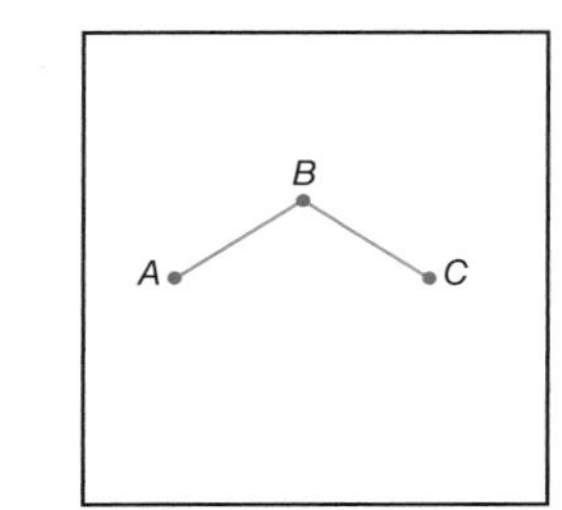

Draw three noncollinear points A, B, and C. Then draw segments $\overline{AB}$ and $\overline{BC}$.

Step 2

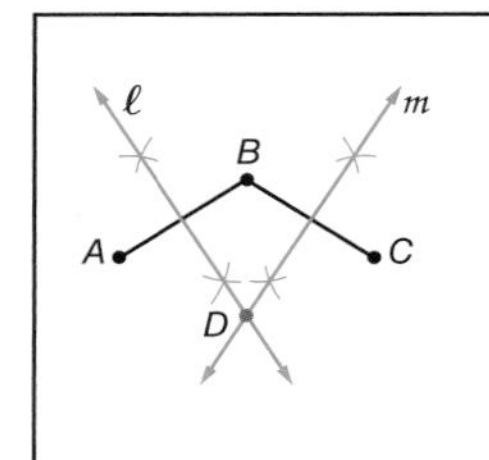

Construct the perpendicular bisectors ℓ and m of $\overline{AB}$ and $\overline{BC}$. Label the point of intersection D.

Step 3

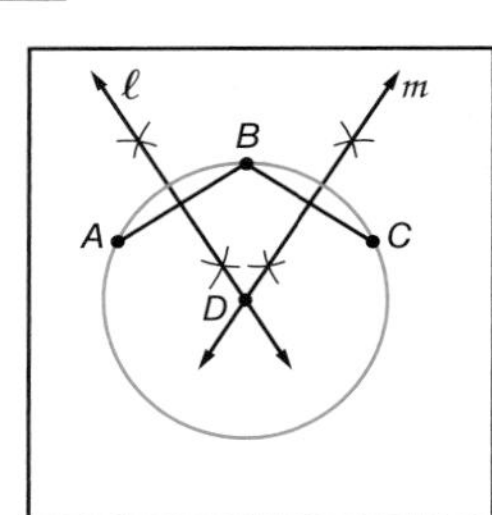

By Theorem 10.4, lines ℓ and m contain diameters of ⊙D. With the compass at point D, draw a circle through points A, B, and C.

Check Your Understanding

 = Step-by-Step Solutions begin on page R14.

Examples 1–2 ALGEBRA Find the value of x.

1 93

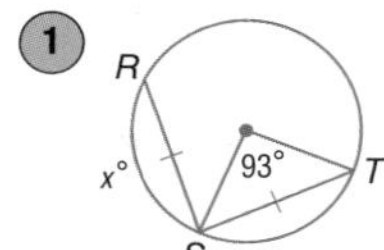

2. 70

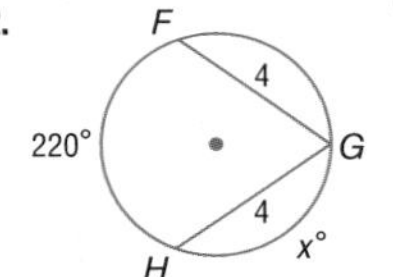

3. 3

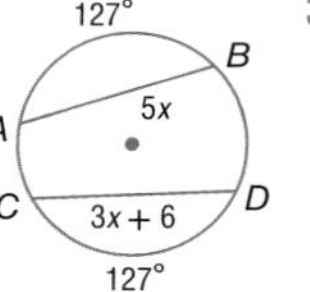

Examples 3–4 In ⊙P, $JK = 10$ and $m\widehat{JLK} = 134$. Find each measure. Round to the nearest hundredth.

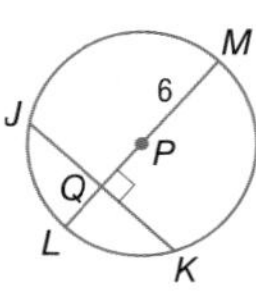

4. $m\widehat{JL}$ 67

5. PQ 3.32

Differentiated Instruction AL OL ELL

Verbal/Linguistic Learners Have students construct a circle with two congruent chords and the perpendicular bisectors. Then have them write a proof supporting the congruency of their construction.

Example 5 **6.** In ⊙J, $GH = 9$, $KL = 4x + 1$. Find x. **2**

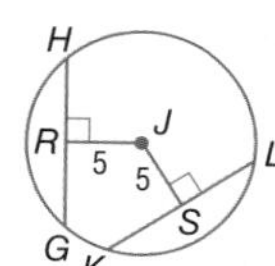

Practice and Problem Solving

Extra Practice is on page R10.

Examples 1–2 ALGEBRA Find the value of x.

7. **21**

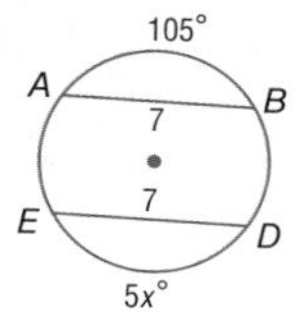

8. **70**

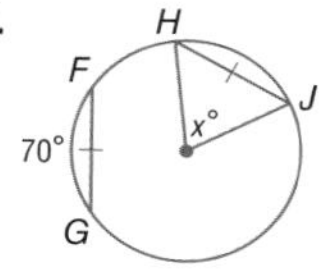

9. **127**

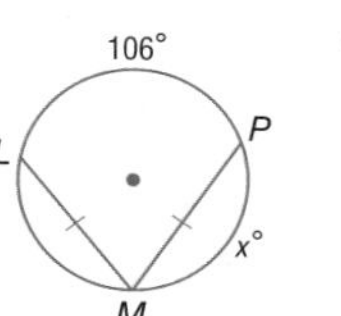

10. **72**

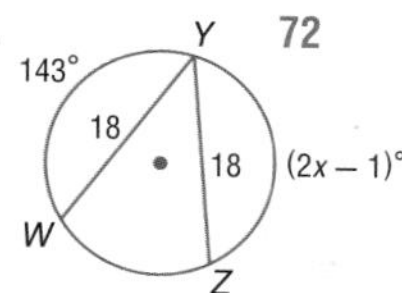

11. **7**

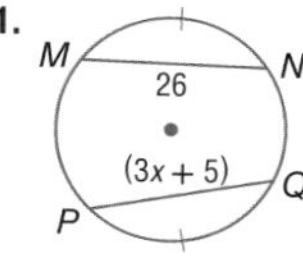

12. **4**

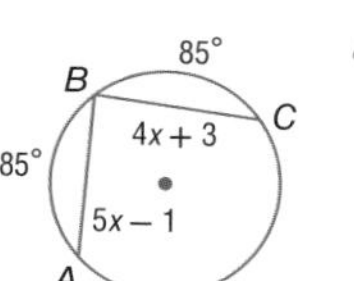

13. ⊙C ≅ ⊙D **27**

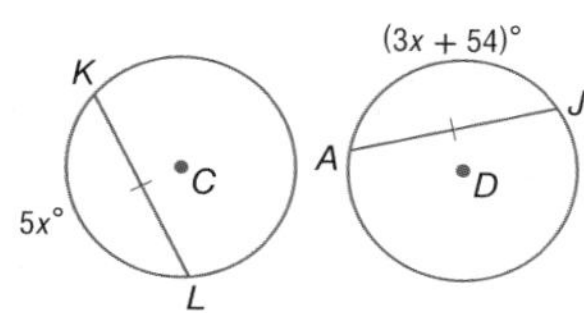

14. ⊙P ≅ ⊙Q **11**

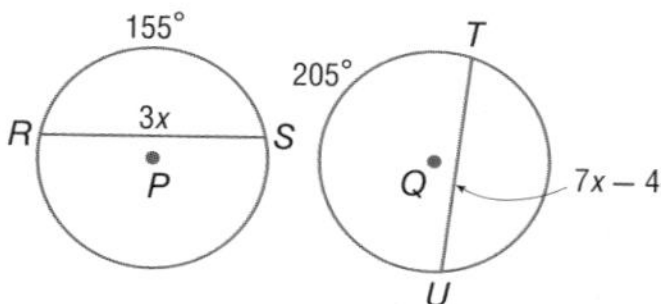

15. **CCSS MODELING** Angie is in a jewelry making class at her local arts center. She wants to make a pair of triangular earrings from a metal circle. She knows that $\widehat{AC}$ is 115°. If she wants to cut two equal parts off so that $\widehat{AB} = \widehat{BC}$, what is x? **122.5°**

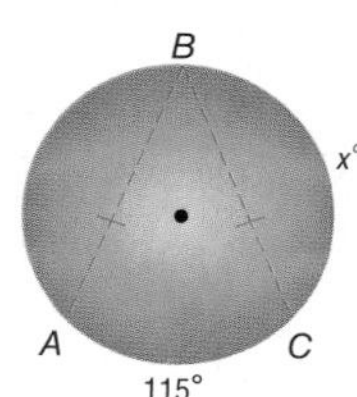

Examples 3–4 **In ⊙A, the radius is 14 and $CD = 22$. Find each measure. Round to the nearest hundredth, if necessary.**

16. CE **11**

17. EB **5.34**

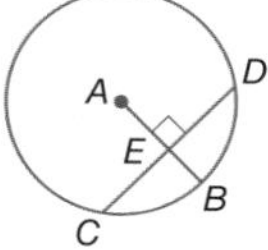

In ⊙H, the diameter is 18, $LM = 12$, and $m\widehat{LM} = 84$. Find each measure. Round to the nearest hundredth, if necessary.

18. $m\widehat{LK}$ **42**

19. HP **6.71**

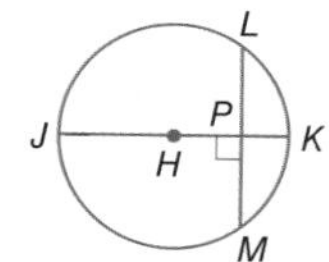

3 Practice

Formative Assessment

Use Exercises 1–6 to check for understanding.

Use the chart at the bottom of this page to customize assignments for your students.

CCSS Teaching the Mathematical Practices

Modeling Mathematically proficient students can apply the mathematics they know to solve problems arising in everyday life. In Exercise 15, point out to students that $m\widehat{AB} + m\widehat{BC} + m\widehat{AC} = 360$.

Differentiated Homework Options

Level	Assignment	Two-Day Option	
AL Basic	7–23, 32, 38–52	7–23 odd, 40–43	8–22 even, 36, 38–39, 44–52
OL Core	7–23 odd, 24–34, 38–52	7–23, 40–43	24–34, 36, 38–39, 44–52
BL Advanced	24–50, (optional: 51–52)		

Study Guide and Intervention
AL OL ELL

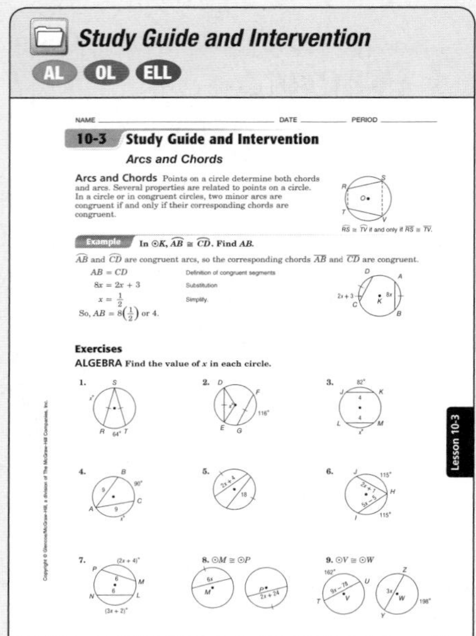

Practice
AL OL BL ELL

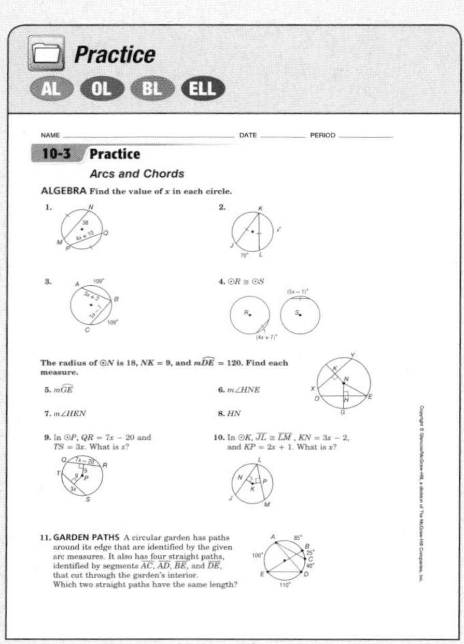

Word Problem Practice
AL OL BL ELL

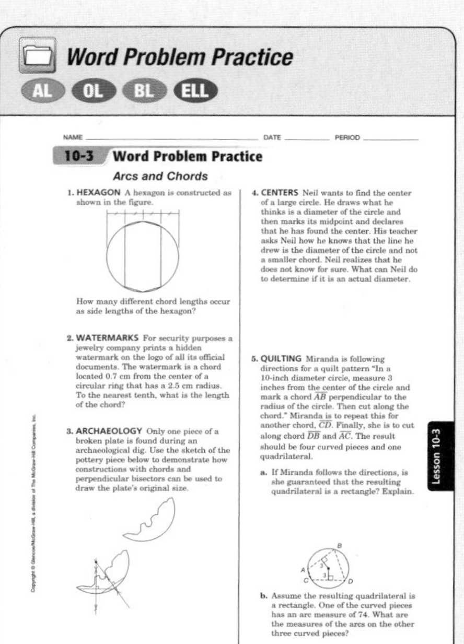

20. **SNOWBOARDING** The snowboarding rail shown is an arc of a circle in which $\overline{BD}$ is part of the diameter. If $\widehat{ABC}$ is about 32% of a complete circle, what is $m\widehat{AB}$? **57.6**

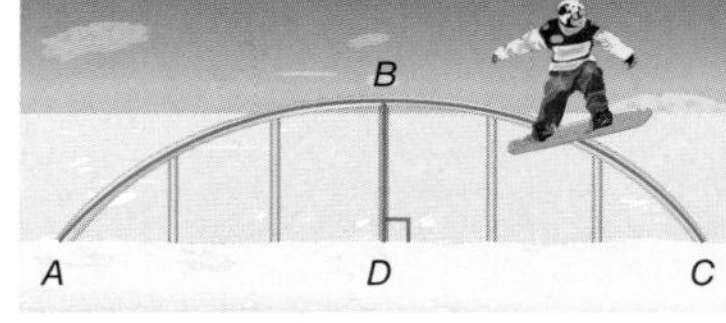

21. **ROADS** The curved road at the right is part of ⊙C, which has a radius of 88 feet. What is AB? Round to the nearest tenth. **98.3 ft**

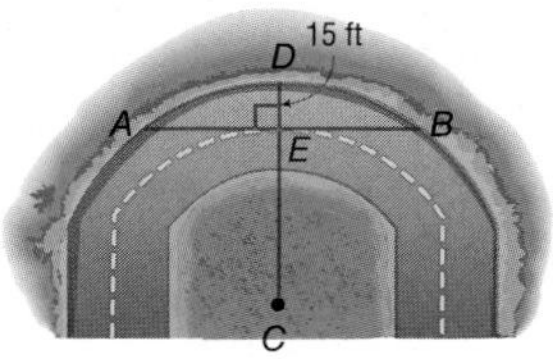

Example 5

22. **ALGEBRA** In ⊙F, $\overline{AB} \cong \overline{BC}$, $DF = 3x - 7$, and $FE = x + 9$. What is x? **8**

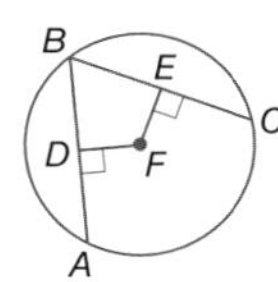

23. **ALGEBRA** In ⊙S, $LM = 16$ and $PN = 4x$. What is x? **4**

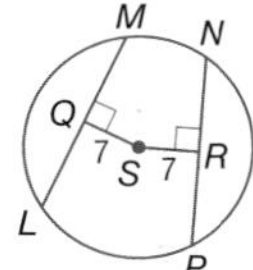

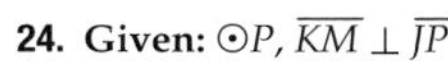

B **PROOF** Write a two-column proof.

24. **Given:** ⊙P, $\overline{KM} \perp \overline{JP}$

Prove: $\overline{JP}$ bisects $\overline{KM}$ and $\widehat{KM}$. **See margin.**

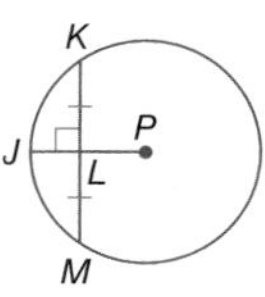

PROOF Write the specified type of proof. **25, 26. See margin.**

25. paragraph proof of Theorem 10.2, part 2

Given: ⊙P, $\overline{QR} \cong \overline{ST}$

Prove: $\widehat{QR} \cong \widehat{ST}$

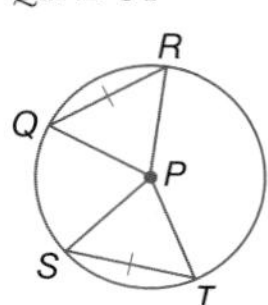

26. two-column proof of Theorem 10.3

Given: ⊙C, $\overline{AB} \perp \overline{XY}$

Prove: $\overline{XZ} \cong \overline{YZ}$, $\widehat{XB} \cong \widehat{YB}$

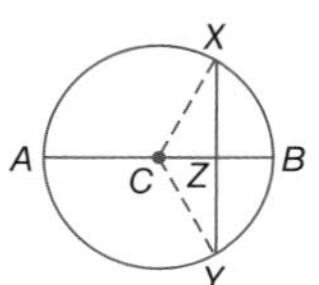

27. **DESIGN** Roberto is designing a logo for a friend's coffee shop according to the design at the right, where each chord is equal in length. What is the measure of each arc and the length of each chord?
Each arc is 90° and each chord is 2.12 ft.

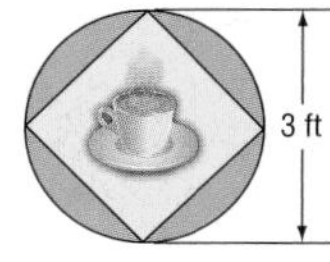

28. CCSS **ARGUMENTS** Write a two-column proof of Theorem 10.4. **See Ch. 10 Answer Appendix.**

Enrichment
OL BL

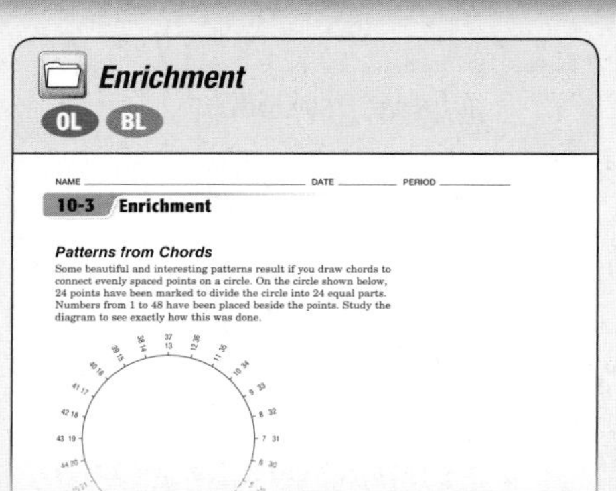

CCSS Teaching the Mathematical Practices

Arguments Mathematically proficient students understand and use stated assumptions and definitions in constructing arguments. They make conjectures and build a logical progression of statements to explore the truth of their conjectures. In Exercises 28, 29, and 30, encourage students to use the examples of each theorem in the text to begin each proof.

ARGUMENTS Write a two-column proof of the indicated part of Theorem 10.5.

29. In a circle, if two chords are equidistant from the center, then they are congruent.

30. In a circle, if two chords are congruent, then they are equidistant from the center.

29, 30. See Ch. 10 Answer Appendix.

ALGEBRA Find the value of x.

31. $\overline{AB} \cong \overline{DF}$ **2**

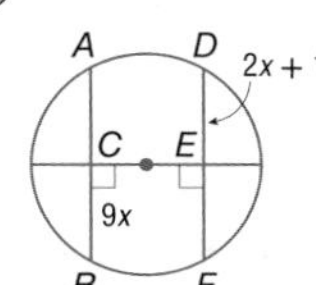

32. $\overline{GH} \cong \overline{KJ}$ **55**

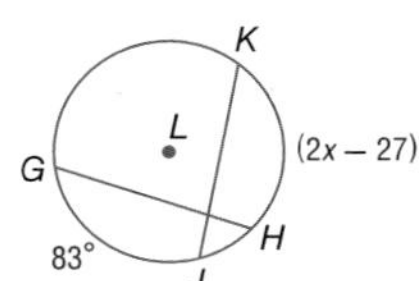

33. $\widehat{WTY} \cong \widehat{TWY}$ **5**

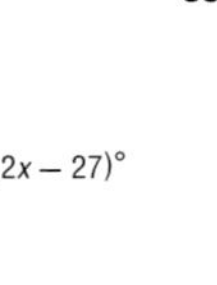

34. ADVERTISING A bookstore clerk wants to set up a display of new books. If there are three entrances into the store as shown in the figure at the right, where should the display be to get maximum exposure? **See Ch. 10 Answer Appendix.**

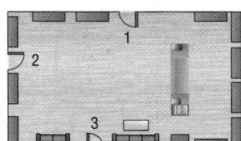

H.O.T. Problems Use Higher-Order Thinking Skills

35. CHALLENGE The common chord $\overline{AB}$ between $\odot P$ and $\odot Q$ is perpendicular to the segment connecting the centers of the circles. If $AB = 10$, what is the length of $\overline{PQ}$? Explain your reasoning. **See Ch. 10 Answer Appendix.**

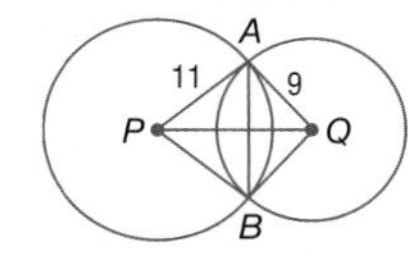

36. REASONING In a circle, $\overline{AB}$ is a diameter and $\overline{HG}$ is a chord that intersects $\overline{AB}$ at point X. Is it *sometimes*, *always*, or *never* true that $HX = GX$? Explain. **Sometimes; if the diameter is perpendicular to the chord, then it bisects the chord.**

37. CHALLENGE Use a compass to draw a circle with chord $\overline{AB}$. Refer to this construction for the following problem. **See Ch. 10 Answer Appendix.**

Step 1 Construct $\overline{CD}$, the perpendicular bisector of $\overline{AB}$.

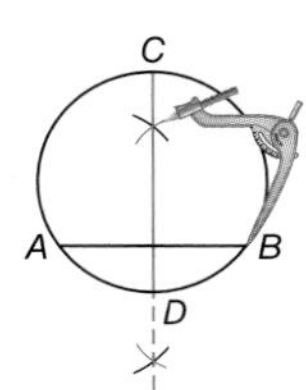

Step 2 Construct $\overline{FG}$, the perpendicular bisector of $\overline{CD}$. Label the point of intersection O.

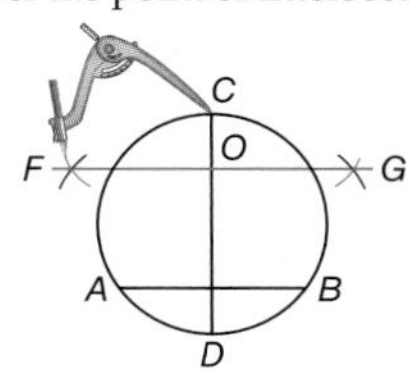

a. Use an indirect proof to show that $\overline{CD}$ passes through the center of the circle by assuming that the center of the circle is *not* on $\overline{CD}$.

b. Prove that O is the center of the circle.

38. OPEN ENDED Construct a circle and draw a chord. Measure the chord and the distance that the chord is from the center. Find the length of the radius. **See Ch. 10 Answer Appendix.**

39. WRITING IN MATH If the measure of an arc in a circle is tripled, will the chord of the new arc be three times as long as the chord of the original arc? Explain your reasoning. **See Ch. 10 Answer Appendix.**

Exercise Alert

Compass and Straightedge Exercise 38 requires the use of a compass and a straightedge.

Additional Answers

24. Given: $\odot P$, $\overline{KM} \perp \overline{JP}$

Prove: $\overline{JP}$ bisects $\overline{KM}$ and $\widehat{KM}$.

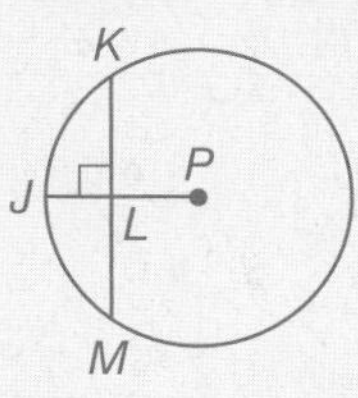

Proof:

Statements (Reasons)

1. $\overline{KM} \perp \overline{JP}$ (Given)
2. Draw radii $\overline{PK}$ and $\overline{PM}$. (2 points determine a line.)
3. $\overline{PK} \cong \overline{PM}$ (All radii of a $\odot$ are $\cong$.)
4. $\overline{PL} \cong \overline{PL}$ (Reflex. Prop. of $\cong$)
5. $\angle PLM$ and $\angle PLK$ are right $\angle$s. (Def. of $\perp$)
6. $\angle PLM \cong \angle PLK$ (All right $\angle$s are $\cong$.)
7. $\triangle PLM \cong \triangle PLK$ (SAS)
8. $\overline{ML} \cong \overline{KL}$ (CPCTC)
9. $\overline{PJ}$ bisects $\overline{KM}$. (Def. of bisect)
10. $\angle MPJ \cong \angle KPJ$ (CPCTC)
11. $\widehat{MJ} \cong \widehat{KJ}$ (In the same circle, two arcs are congruent if their corresponding central angles are congruent.)
12. $\overline{JP}$ bisects $\widehat{KM}$. (Def. of bisect)

25. Proof:
Because all radii are congruent, $\overline{QP} \cong \overline{PR} \cong \overline{SP} \cong \overline{PT}$. You are given that $\overline{QR} \cong \overline{ST}$, so $\triangle PQR \cong \triangle PST$ by SSS. Thus, $\angle QPR \cong \angle SPT$ by CPCTC. Since the central angles have the same measure, their intercepted arcs have the same measure and are therefore congruent. Thus, $\widehat{QR} \cong \widehat{ST}$.

26. Proof:

Statements (Reasons)

1. $\odot C$, $\overline{AB} \perp \overline{XY}$ (Given)
2. $\overline{CX} \cong \overline{CY}$ (All radii of a $\odot$ are $\cong$.)
3. $\overline{CZ} \cong \overline{CZ}$ (Reflexive Prop.)
4. $\angle XZC$ and $\angle YZC$ are rt. $\angle$s. (Definition of $\perp$ lines)
5. $\triangle XZC \cong \triangle YZC$ (HL)
6. $\overline{XZ} \cong \overline{YZ}$, $\angle XCZ \cong \angle YCZ$ (CPCTC)
7. $\widehat{XB} \cong \widehat{YB}$ (If central $\angle$s are $\cong$, intercepted arcs are $\cong$.)

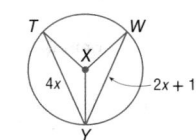

4 Assess

Yesterday's News Have students write a paragraph that explains how the lesson about angles and arcs helped them in the lesson about arcs and chords.

Additional Answers

48. yes; right
$17^2 \stackrel{?}{=} 8^2 + 15^2$
$289 = 64 + 225$

49. yes; obtuse
$31^2 \stackrel{?}{=} 20^2 + 21^2$
$961 > 400 + 441$

50. yes; acute
$18^2 \stackrel{?}{=} 10^2 + 16^2$
$324 < 100 + 256$

Standardized Test Practice

40. If $CW = WF$ and $ED = 30$, what is DF? D

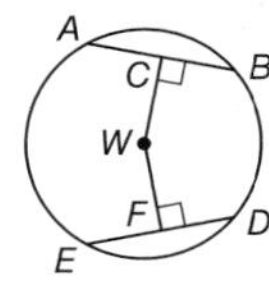

A 60
B 45
C 30
D 15

41. ALGEBRA Write the ratio of the area of the circle to the area of the square in simplest form. F

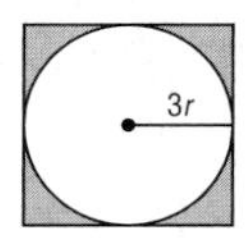

F $\frac{\pi}{4}$
G $\frac{\pi}{2}$
H $\frac{3\pi}{4}$
J π

42. SHORT RESPONSE The pipe shown is divided into five equal sections. How long is the pipe in feet (ft) and inches (in.)? 6 ft 3 in.

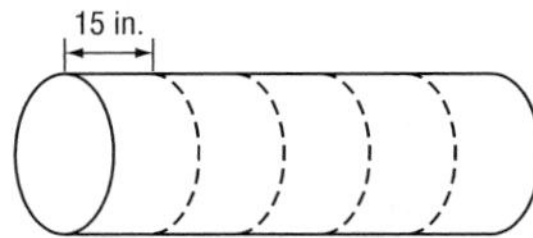

43. SAT/ACT Point B is the center of a circle, tangent to the y-axis, and the coordinates of Point B are (3, 1). What is the area of the circle? E

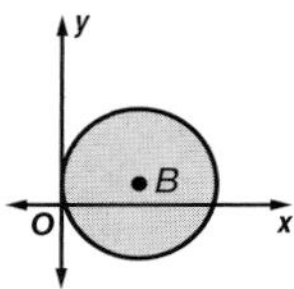

A π units^2
B 3π units^2
C 4π units^2
D 6π units^2
E 9π units^2

Spiral Review

Find x. (Lesson 10-2)

44. 114

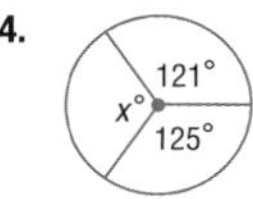

45. 170

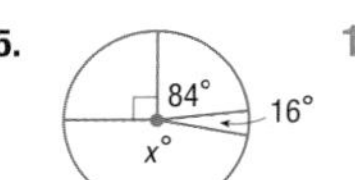

46. 152

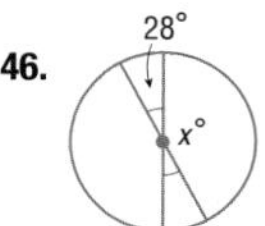

47. CRAFTS Ruby created a pattern to sew flowers onto a quilt by first drawing a regular pentagon that was 3.5 inches long on each side. Then she added a semicircle onto each side of the pentagon to create the appearance of five petals. How many inches of gold trim does she need to edge 10 flowers? Round to the nearest inch. (Lesson 10-1) 275 in.

Determine whether each set of numbers can be the measures of the sides of a triangle. If so, classify the triangle as *acute, obtuse,* or *right*. Justify your answer. (Lesson 8-2) 48–50. See margin.

48. 8, 15, 17
49. 20, 21, 31
50. 10, 16, 18

Skills Review

ALGEBRA Quadrilateral *WXZY* is a rhombus. Find each value or measure.

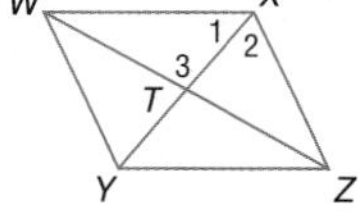

51. If $m\angle 3 = y^2 - 31$, find y. ± 11

52. If $m\angle XZY = 56$, find $m\angle YWZ$. 28

Differentiated Instruction OL BL

Extension Have students draw two circles on a sheet of paper. Tell students to draw a chord anywhere on the first circle, and then construct and label a perpendicular bisector for this chord. For the second circle, have students draw two segments extending from the center of the circle so that the chords perpendicular to these segments are congruent. Check students' work.

LESSON 10-4 Inscribed Angles

Then	Now	Why?
• You found measures of interior angles of polygons.	1 Find measures of inscribed angles. 2 Find measures of angles of inscribed polygons.	• The entrance to a school prom has a semicircular arch. Streamers are attached with one end at point *A* and the other end at point *B*. The middle of each streamer can then be attached to a different point *P* along the arch.

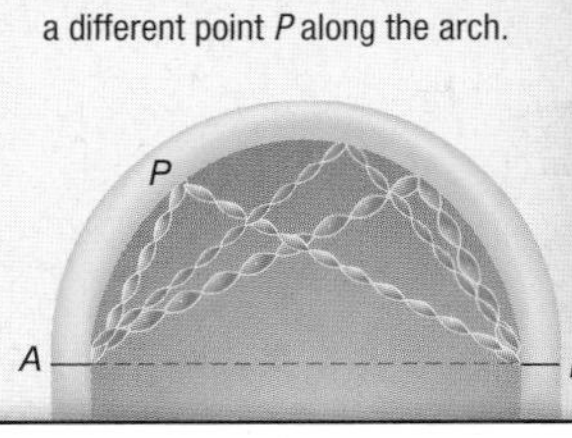

NewVocabulary
inscribed angle
intercepted arc

Common Core State Standards

Content Standards

G.C.2 Identify and describe relationships among inscribed angles, radii, and chords.

G.C.3 Construct the inscribed and circumscribed circles of a triangle, and prove properties of angles for a quadrilateral inscribed in a circle.

Mathematical Practices

7 Look for and make use of structure.

3 Construct viable arguments and critique the reasoning of others.

1 Inscribed Angles

Notice that the angle formed by each streamer appears to be congruent, no matter where point *P* is placed along the arch. An **inscribed angle** has a vertex on a circle and sides that contain chords of the circle. In $\odot C$, $\angle QRS$ is an inscribed angle.

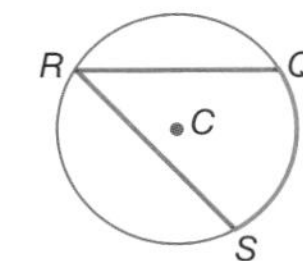

An **intercepted arc** has endpoints on the sides of an inscribed angle and lies in the interior of the inscribed angle. In $\odot C$, minor arc $\widehat{QS}$ is intercepted by $\angle QRS$.

There are three ways that an angle can be inscribed in a circle.

Case 1	Case 2	Case 3
Center *P* is on a side of the inscribed angle.	Center *P* is inside the inscribed angle.	The center *P* is in the exterior of the inscribed angle.

In Case 1, the side of the angle is a diameter of the circle.

For each of these cases, the following theorem holds true.

Theorem 10.6 Inscribed Angle Theorem

Words If an angle is inscribed in a circle, then the measure of the angle equals one half the measure of its intercepted arc.

Example $m\angle 1 = \frac{1}{2}m\widehat{AB}$ and $m\widehat{AB} = 2m\angle 1$

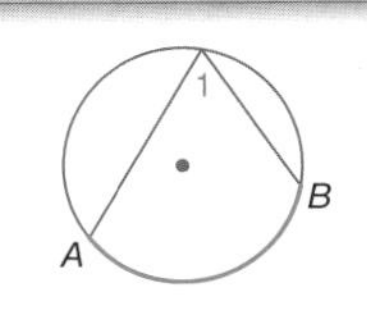

You will prove Cases 2 and 3 of the Inscribed Angle Theorem in Exercises 37 and 38.

1 Focus

VerticalAlignment

Before Lesson 10-4 Find measures of interior angles of polygons.

Lesson 10-4 Find measures of inscribed angles.
Find measures of angles of inscribed polygons.

After Lesson 10-4 Use properties of tangents to solve problems involving circumscribed polygons.

2 Teach

Scaffolding Questions

Have students read the **Why?** section of the lesson.

Ask:

- What kind of arc would the top of the doorway and a horizontal streamer form? semicircle
- Assume that the measure of the arc from point *B* to the point where the streamer attaches to the arch is 60°. What would be the measure of the arc from point *A* to the point where the streamer is attached to the arch? 120

(continued on the next page)

Lesson 10-4 Resources

Resource	Approaching Level AL	On Level OL	Beyond Level BL	English Learners ELL
Teacher Edition	▪ Differentiated Instruction, p. 725	▪ Differentiated Instruction, pp. 724, 725, 730	▪ Differentiated Instruction, pp. 724, 730	
Chapter Resource Masters	▪ Study Guide and Intervention, pp. 23–24 ▪ Skills Practice, p. 25 ▪ Practice, p. 26 ▪ Word Problem Practice, p. 27	▪ Study Guide and Intervention, pp. 23–24 ▪ Skills Practice, p. 25 ▪ Practice, p. 26 ▪ Word Problem Practice, p. 27 ▪ Enrichment, p. 28	▪ Practice, p. 26 ▪ Word Problem Practice, p. 27 ▪ Enrichment, p. 28	▪ Study Guide and Intervention, pp. 23–24 ▪ Skills Practice, p. 25 ▪ Practice, p. 26 ▪ Word Problem Practice, p. 27
Other	▪ 5-Minute Check 10-4 ▪ Study Notebook ▪ Teaching Geometry with Manipulatives	▪ 5-Minute Check 10-4 ▪ Study Notebook ▪ Teaching Geometry with Manipulatives	▪ 5-Minute Check 10-4 ▪ Study Notebook	▪ 5-Minute Check 10-4 ▪ Study Notebook ▪ Teaching Geometry with Manipulatives

- Assume that the doorway is three feet wide. How could you find the arc length of the doorway? The radius is half the width of the doorway, or 18 inches. Because the arch is a semicircle, the measure of the arc is 180°. Substitute the radius and the measure of the arc in the formula for arc length. $\ell = \frac{180}{360} \cdot 2\pi(18)$.

1 Inscribed Angles

Examples 1–3 show how to measure and prove inscribed angles using theorems of inscribed angles.

Formative Assessment

Use the Guided Practice exercises after each example to determine students' understanding of concepts.

Additional Examples

1 Find each measure.

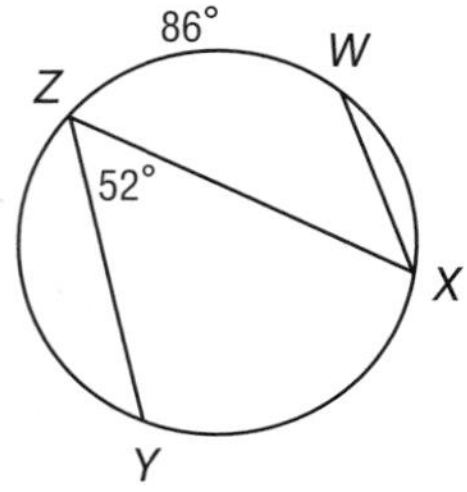

a. $m\angle X$ 43

b. $m\widehat{YX}$ 104

2 **ALGEBRA** Find $m\angle R$.

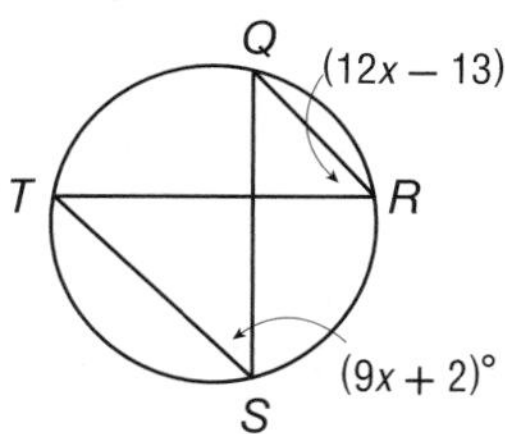

47

Additional Examples also in Interactive Classroom PowerPoint® Presentations

IWB **Interactive White Board READY**

VocabularyLink

Inscribed

Everyday Use: written on or in a surface, such as inscribing the inside of a ring with an inscription

Math Use: touching only the sides (or interior) of another figure

Proof Inscribed Angle Theorem (Case 1)

Given: $\angle B$ is inscribed in $\odot P$.

Prove: $m\angle B = \frac{1}{2}m\widehat{AC}$

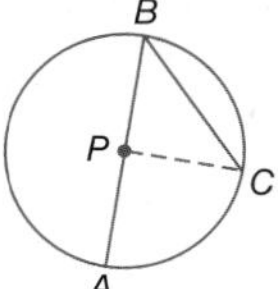

Proof:

Statements	Reasons
1. Draw an auxiliary radius $\overline{PC}$.	**1.** Two points determine a line.
2. $\overline{PB} \cong \overline{PC}$	**2.** All radii of a circle are $\cong$.
3. $\triangle PBC$ is isosceles.	**3.** Definition of isosceles triangle
4. $m\angle B = m\angle C$	**4.** Isosceles Triangle Theorem
5. $m\angle APC = m\angle B + m\angle C$	**5.** Exterior Angle Theorem
6. $m\angle APC = 2m\angle B$	**6.** Substitution (Steps 4, 5)
7. $m\widehat{AC} = m\angle APC$	**7.** Definition of arc measure
8. $m\widehat{AC} = 2m\angle B$	**8.** Substitution (Steps 6, 7)
9. $2m\angle B = m\widehat{AC}$	**9.** Symmetric Property of Equality
10. $m\angle B = \frac{1}{2}m\widehat{AC}$	**10.** Division Property of Equality

PT

Example 1 Use Inscribed Angles to Find Measures

Find each measure.

a. $m\angle P$

$m\angle P = \frac{1}{2}m\widehat{MN}$

$= \frac{1}{2}(70)$ or 35

b. $m\widehat{PO}$

$m\widehat{PO} = 2m\angle N$

$= 2(56)$ or 112

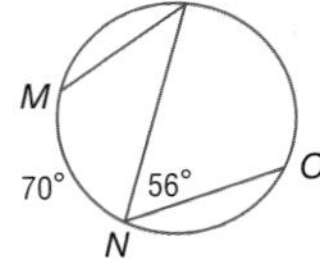

GuidedPractice

1A. $m\widehat{CF}$ 80

1B. $m\angle C$ 49

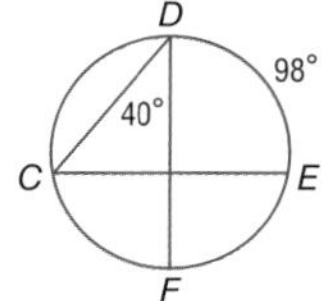

Two inscribed angles that intercept the same arc of a circle are related.

Theorem 10.7

Words If two inscribed angles of a circle intercept the same arc or congruent arcs, then the angles are congruent.

Example $\angle B$ and $\angle C$ both intercept $\widehat{AD}$. So, $\angle B \cong \angle C$.

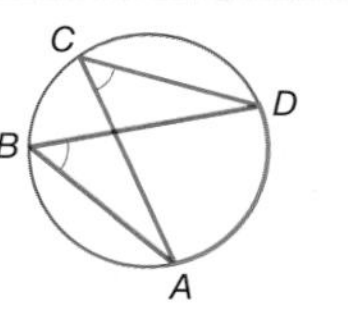

You will prove Theorem 10.7 in Exercise 39.

DifferentiatedInstruction OL BL

Logical Learners Lesson 10-4 includes a proof using multiple cases. Locate some other examples using a college geometry text or the internet that involve this type of proof to allow mathematically talented students to develop an understanding of why certain proofs require the consideration of multiple cases.

StudyTip

Inscribed Polygons Remember that for a polygon to be an inscribed polygon, *all* of its vertices must lie on the circle.

Example 2 Use Inscribed Angles to Find Measures

ALGEBRA Find $m\angle T$.

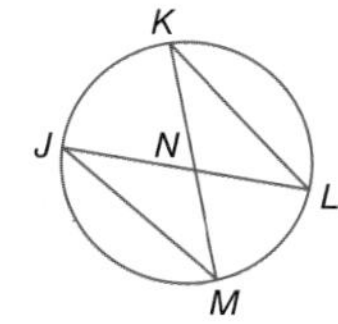

$\angle T \cong \angle U$	$\angle T$ and $\angle U$ both intercept $\widehat{SV}$.
$m\angle T = m\angle U$	Definition of congruent angles
$3x - 5 = 2x + 15$	Substitution
$x = 20$	Simplify.

So, $m\angle T = 3(20) - 5$ or 55.

GuidedPractice

2. If $m\angle S = 3x$ and $m\angle V = (x + 16)$, find $m\angle S$. **24**

Example 3 Use Inscribed Angles in Proofs

Write a two-column proof.

Given: $\widehat{JM} \cong \widehat{KL}$

Prove: $\triangle JMN \cong \triangle KLN$

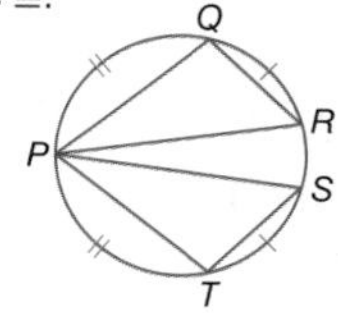

Proof:

Statements	Reasons
1. $\widehat{JM} \cong \widehat{KL}$	1. Given
2. $\overline{JM} \cong \overline{KL}$	2. If minor arcs are $\cong$, their corresponding chords are $\cong$.
3. $\angle M$ intercepts $\widehat{JK}$. $\angle L$ intercepts $\widehat{JK}$.	3. Definition of intercepted arc
4. $\angle M \cong \angle L$	4. Inscribed $\angle$s of same arc are $\cong$.
5. $\angle JNM \cong \angle KNL$	5. Vertical $\angle$s are $\cong$.
6. $\triangle JMN \cong \triangle KLN$	6. AAS

GuidedPractice

3. **Given:** $\widehat{QR} \cong \widehat{ST}$, $\widehat{PQ} \cong \widehat{PT}$ **See margin.**

Prove: $\triangle PQR \cong \triangle PTS$

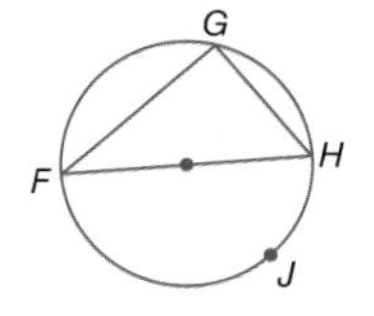

2 Angles of Inscribed Polygons

Triangles and quadrilaterals that are inscribed in circles have special properties.

Theorem 10.8

Words An inscribed angle of a triangle intercepts a diameter or semicircle if and only if the angle is a right angle.

Example If $\widehat{FJH}$ is a semicircle, then $m\angle G = 90$. If $m\angle G = 90$, then $\widehat{FJH}$ is a semicircle and $\overline{FH}$ is a diameter.

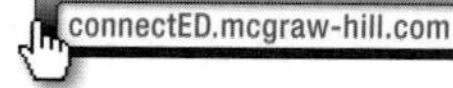

You will prove Theorem 10.8 in Exercise 40.

DifferentiatedInstruction AL OL

Intrapersonal Learners Select or provide examples that cover each concept in the lesson so that students can sit quietly and work at their desks. Ask students to make a note if a particular type of problem gives them difficulty. Encourage students to reread and use the examples and theorems to work and understand the problems.

Additional Example

3 Write a two-column proof.

Given: $\widehat{LO} \cong \widehat{MN}$

Prove: $\triangle MNP \cong \triangle LOP$

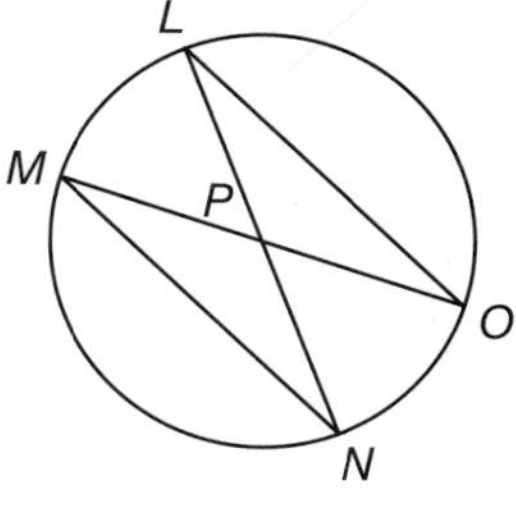

Statements (Reasons)

1. $\widehat{LO} \cong \widehat{MN}$ (Given)
2. $\overline{LO} \cong \overline{MN}$ (If minor arcs are $\cong$, then corr. chords are $\cong$.)
3. $\angle M$ intercepts $\widehat{NO}$ and $\angle L$ intercepts $\widehat{NO}$. (Def. of intercepted arc)
4. $\angle M \cong \angle L$ (Inscribed angles of same arc are $\cong$.)
5. $\angle MPN \cong \angle OPL$ (Vertical angles are congruent.)
6. $\triangle MNP \cong \triangle LOP$ (AAS)

Additional Answer (Guided Practice)

3. **Proof:**

Statements (Reasons)

1. $\widehat{QR} \cong \widehat{ST}$, $\widehat{PQ} \cong \widehat{PT}$ (Given)
2. $m\widehat{QR} = m\widehat{ST}$, $m\widehat{PQ} = m\widehat{PT}$ (Def. of $\cong$ arcs)
3. $\frac{1}{2}m\widehat{QR} = \frac{1}{2}m\widehat{ST}$, $\frac{1}{2}m\widehat{PQ} = \frac{1}{2}m\widehat{PT}$ (Mult. Prop.)
4. $m\angle QPR = \frac{1}{2}m\widehat{QR}$, $m\angle TPS = \frac{1}{2}m\widehat{ST}$, $m\angle QRP = \frac{1}{2}m\widehat{PQ}$, $m\angle TSP = \frac{1}{2}m\widehat{PT}$ (Inscribed $\angle$s Theorem)
5. $m\angle QPR = m\angle TPS$, $m\angle QRP = m\angle TSP$ (Substitution)
6. $\angle QPR \cong \angle TPS$, $\angle QRP \cong \angle TSP$ (Definition of $\cong$ $\angle$s)
7. $\overline{QR} \cong \overline{ST}$ ($\cong$ arcs have $\cong$ chords.)
8. $\triangle PQR \cong \triangle PTS$ (AAS)

2 Angles of Inscribed Polygons

Examples 4 and 5 show how to find angles of an inscribed polygon by using Theorems 10.7 and 10.8.

Additional Examples

4 **ALGEBRA** Find $m\angle B$.

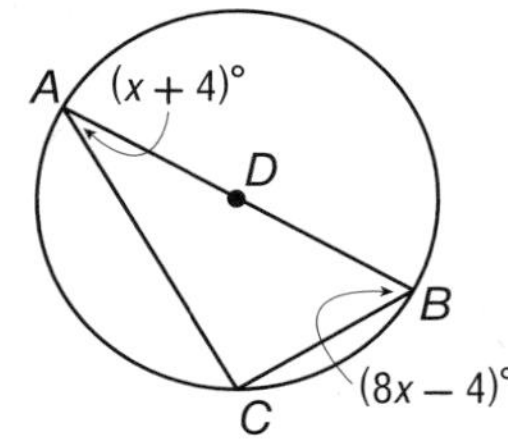

$m\angle B = 76$

5 **INSIGNIAS** An insignia is an emblem that signifies rank, achievement, membership, and so on. The insignia shown is a quadrilateral inscribed in a circle. Find $m\angle S$ and $m\angle T$.

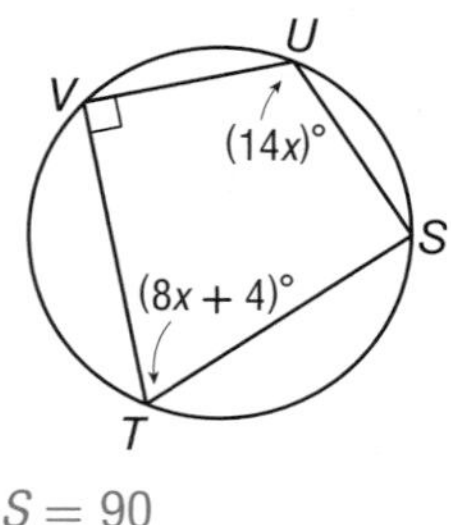

$m\angle S = 90$
$m\angle T = 68$

Teaching the Mathematical Practices

Arguments Mathematically proficient students understand and use stated assumptions and definitions in constructing arguments. They make conjectures and build a logical progression of statements to explore the truth of their conjectures. Encourage students to take notes on each theorem to reference while writing proofs.

Teach with Tech

Web Search Have students search the Web for an interactive applet for inscribed angles. Have students explore the concept by grabbing and dragging the angle to see how the measure of the arc changes.

Example 4 Find Angle Measures in Inscribed Triangles

ALGEBRA **Find $m\angle F$.**

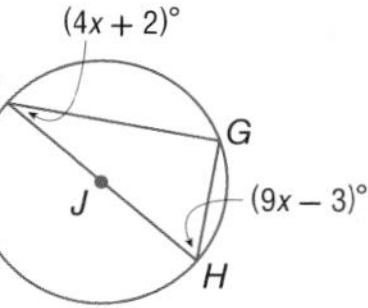

$\triangle FGH$ is a right triangle because $\angle G$ inscribes a semicircle.

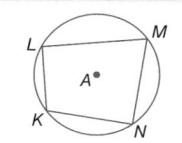

$m\angle F + m\angle G + m\angle H = 180$	Angle Sum Theorem
$(4x + 2) + 90 + (9x - 3) = 180$	Substitution
$13x + 89 = 180$	Simplify.
$13x = 91$	Subtract 89 from each side.
$x = 7$	Divide each side by 13.

So, $m\angle F = 4(7) + 2$ or 30.

GuidedPractice

4. If $m\angle F = 7x + 2$ and $m\angle H = 17x - 8$, find x. **4**

While many different types of triangles, including right triangles, can be inscribed in a circle, only certain quadrilaterals can be inscribed in a circle.

StudyTip

CCSS Arguments Theorem 10.9 can be verified by considering that the arcs intercepted by opposite angles of an inscribed quadrilateral form a circle.

Theorem 10.9

Words If a quadrilateral is inscribed in a circle, then its opposite angles are supplementary.

Example If quadrilateral $KLMN$ is inscribed in $\odot A$, then $\angle L$ and $\angle N$ are supplementary and $\angle K$ and $\angle M$ are supplementary.

You will prove Theorem 10.9 in Exercise 31.

Real-WorldLink

Charms for jewelry first became popular during the age of the Egyptian Pharaohs. They were repopularized by Queen Victoria in the early 20th century and by Louis Vuitton in 2001.

Source: *My Mother's Charms*

Real-World Example 5 Find Angle Measures

JEWELRY **The necklace charm shown uses a quadrilateral inscribed in a circle. Find $m\angle A$ and $m\angle B$.**

Since $ABCD$ is inscribed in a circle, opposite angles are supplementary.

$m\angle A + m\angle C = 180$	$m\angle B + m\angle D = 180$
$m\angle A + 90 = 180$	$(2x - 30) + x = 180$
$m\angle A = 90$	$3x - 30 = 180$
	$3x = 210$
	$x = 70$

So, $m\angle A = 90$ and $m\angle B = 2(70) - 30$ or 110.

GuidedPractice

5. Quadrilateral $WXYZ$ is inscribed in $\odot V$. Find $m\angle X$ and $m\angle Y$. **120; 85**

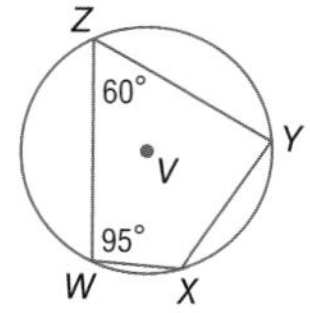

Focus on Mathematical Content

Concyclic Points Points that lie on the same circle are said to be concyclic. Three noncollinear points are always concyclic. There is always one unique circle that contains all three noncollinear points. A quadrilateral is said to be cyclic if there is a circle that passes through all four vertices. Opposite angles of a quadrilateral must be supplementary in order for the figure to be cyclic.

Check Your Understanding

 = Step-by-Step Solutions begin on page R14.

Example 1 Find each measure.

1. $m\angle B$ 30

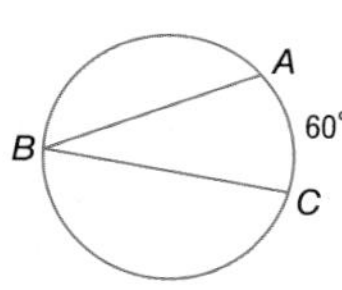

2. $m\widehat{RT}$ 126

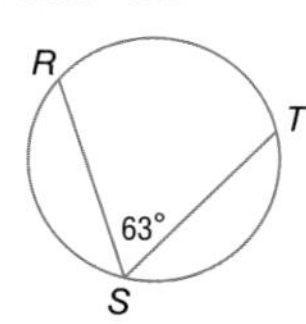

3. $m\widehat{WX}$ 66

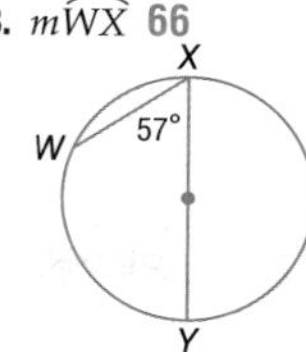

4. **SCIENCE** The diagram shows how light bends in a raindrop to make the colors of the rainbow. If $m\widehat{ST} = 144$, what is $m\angle R$? 72

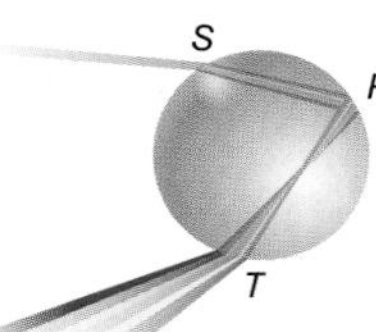

Example 2 **ALGEBRA** Find each measure.

5. $m\angle H$ 54

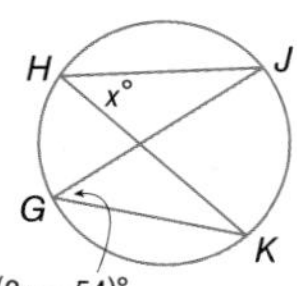

6. $m\angle B$ 36

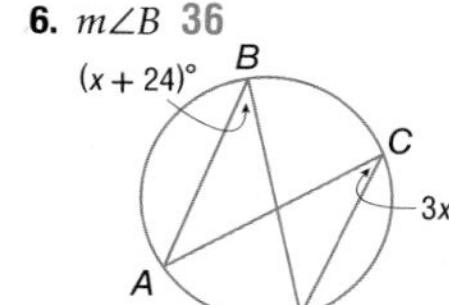

Example 3 7. **PROOF** Write a two-column proof. See margin.

Given: $\overline{RT}$ bisects $\overline{SU}$.

Prove: $\triangle RVS \cong \triangle UVT$

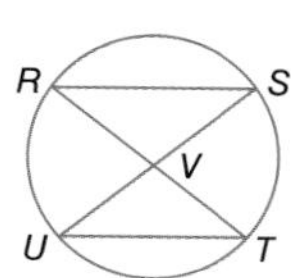

Examples 4–5 CCSS **STRUCTURE** Find each value.

8. $m\angle R$ 62

(3x + 1)°, P, Q, (7x – 1)°, R

9. x 25

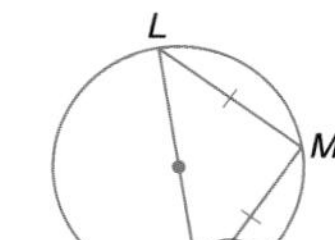

10. $m\angle C$ and $m\angle D$ 122; 80

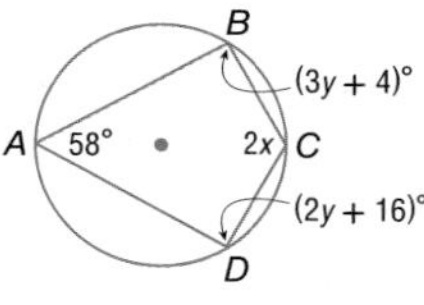

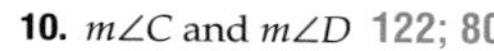

Practice and Problem Solving

Extra Practice is on page R10.

Example 1 Find each measure.

11. $m\widehat{DH}$ 162

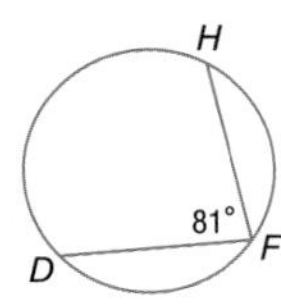

12. $m\angle K$ 46

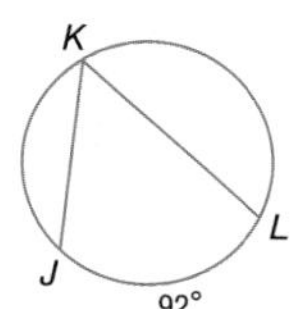

13. $m\angle P$ 70

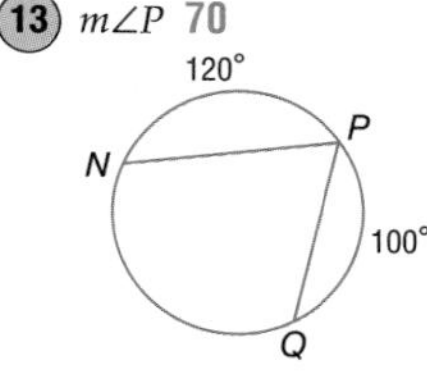

Differentiated Homework Options

Level	Assignment	Two-Day Option	
AL Basic	11–30, 42–46, 48–66	11–29 odd, 51–54	12–30 even, 42–46, 48–50, 55–66
OL Core	11–37 odd, 38–46, 48–66	11–30, 51–54	31–46, 48–50, 55–66
BL Advanced	31–62, (optional: 63–66)		

3 Practice

Formative Assessment

Use Exercises 1–10 to check for understanding.

Use the chart at the bottom of this page to customize assignments for your students.

Additional Answers

7. **Given:** $\overline{RT}$ bisects $\overline{SU}$.
Prove: $\triangle RVS \cong \triangle UVT$

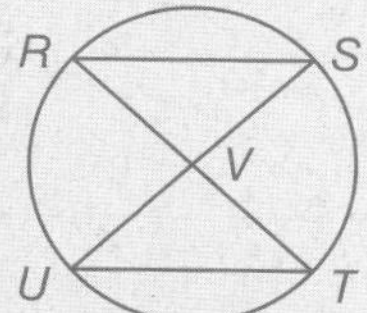

Proof:

Statements (Reasons)

1. $\overline{RT}$ bisects $\overline{SU}$. (Given)
2. $\overline{SV} \cong \overline{VU}$ (Def. of segment bisector)
3. $\angle SRT$ intercepts $\widehat{ST}$. $\angle SUT$ intercepts $\widehat{ST}$. (Def. of intercepted arc)
4. $\angle SRT \cong \angle SUT$ (Inscribed ∠s of same arc are ≅.)
5. $\angle RVS \cong \angle UVT$ (Vertical ∠s are ≅.)
6. $\triangle RVS \cong \triangle UVT$ (AAS)

CCSS Teaching the Mathematical Practices

Structure Mathematically proficient students look closely to discern a pattern or structure. They also can step back for an overview and shift perspective. In Exercises 8–10, encourage students to analyze each figure for right triangles.

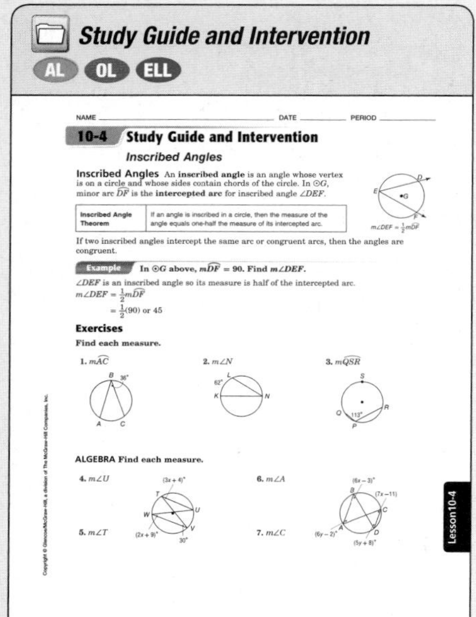

Study Guide and Intervention

AL OL ELL

NAME ______ DATE ______ PERIOD ______

10-4 Study Guide and Intervention

Inscribed Angles

Inscribed Angles An **inscribed angle** is an angle whose vertex is on a circle and whose sides contain chords of the circle. In ⊙G, minor arc $\widehat{DF}$ is the **intercepted arc** for inscribed angle ∠DEF.

Inscribed Angle Theorem	If an angle is inscribed in a circle, then the measure of the angle equals one-half the measure of its intercepted arc.

$m\angle DEF = \frac{1}{2}m\widehat{DF}$

If two inscribed angles intercept the same arc or congruent arcs, then the angles are congruent.

Example In ⊙G above, $m\widehat{DF} = 90$. Find $m\angle DEF$.

∠DEF is an inscribed angle so its measure is half of the intercepted arc.

$m\angle DEF = \frac{1}{2}m\widehat{DF}$

$= \frac{1}{2}(90)$ or 45

Exercises

Find each measure.

1. $m\widehat{AC}$ 2. $m\angle N$ 3. $m\widehat{QSR}$

ALGEBRA Find each measure.

4. $m\angle U$ 5. $m\angle T$ 6. $m\angle A$ 7. $m\angle C$

Lesson 10-4

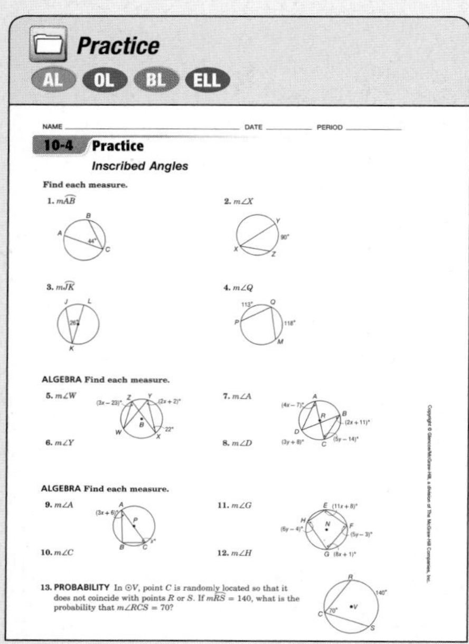

Practice

AL OL BL ELL

NAME ______ DATE ______ PERIOD ______

10-4 Practice

Inscribed Angles

Find each measure.

1. $m\widehat{AB}$ 2. $m\angle X$

3. $m\widehat{JK}$ 4. $m\angle Q$

ALGEBRA Find each measure.

5. $m\angle W$ 6. $m\angle Y$ 7. $m\angle A$ 8. $m\angle D$

ALGEBRA Find each measure.

9. $m\angle A$ 10. $m\angle C$ 11. $m\angle G$ 12. $m\angle H$

13. PROBABILITY In ⊙V, point C is randomly located so that it does not coincide with points R or S. If $m\widehat{RS} = 140$, what is the probability that $m\angle RCS = 70$?

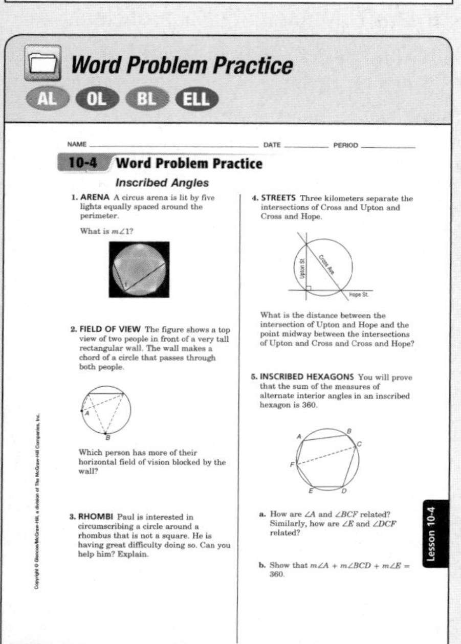

Word Problem Practice

AL OL BL ELL

NAME ______ DATE ______ PERIOD ______

10-4 Word Problem Practice

Inscribed Angles

1. ARENA A circus arena is lit by five lights equally spaced around the perimeter. What is $m\angle 1$?

2. FIELD OF VIEW The figure shows a top view of two people in front of a very tall rectangular wall. The wall makes a chord of a circle that passes through both people. Which person has more of their horizontal field of vision blocked by the wall?

3. RHOMBI Paul is interested in circumscribing a circle around a rhombus that is not a square. He is having great difficulty doing so. Can you help him? Explain.

4. STREETS Three kilometers separate the intersections of Cross and Upton and Cross and Hope. What is the distance between the intersection of Upton and Hope and the point midway between the intersections of Upton and Cross and Cross and Hope?

5. INSCRIBED HEXAGONS You will prove that the sum of the measures of alternate interior angles in an inscribed hexagon is 360.

a. How are ∠A and ∠BCF related? Similarly, how are ∠E and ∠DCF related?

b. Show that $m\angle A + m\angle BCD + m\angle E = 360$.

Lesson 10-4

14. $m\widehat{AC}$ 48 15. $m\widehat{GH}$ 140 16. $m\angle S$ 66

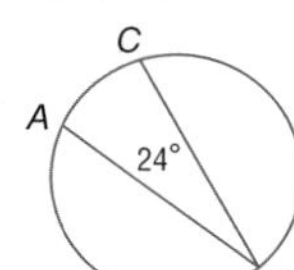
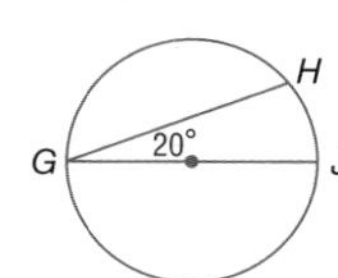
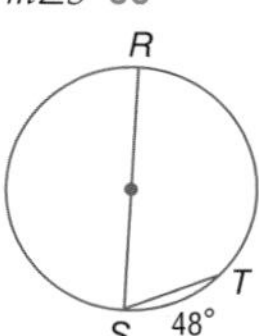

Example 2 **ALGEBRA** Find each measure.

17. $m\angle R$ 32
18. $m\angle S$ 34

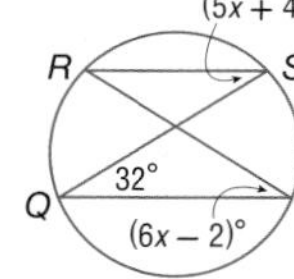

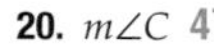

19. $m\angle A$ 20
20. $m\angle C$ 47

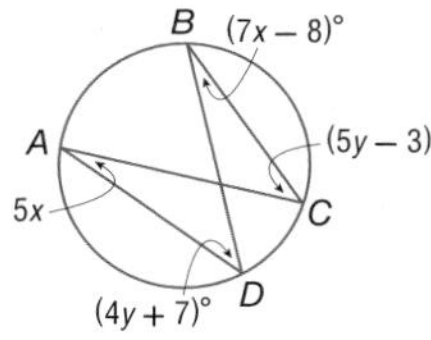

Example 3 **PROOF** Write the specified type of proof. 21, 22. See Ch. 10 Answer Appendix.

21. paragraph proof
Given: $m\angle T = \frac{1}{2}m\angle S$
Prove: $m\widehat{TUR} = 2m\widehat{URS}$

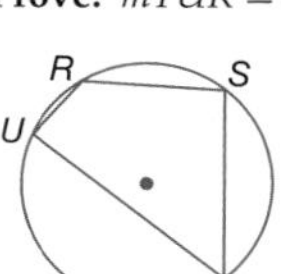

22. two-column proof
Given: ⊙C
Prove: △KML ~ △JMH

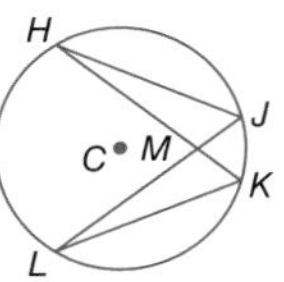

Example 4 **ALGEBRA** Find each value.

23. x 30
24. $m\angle T$ 60

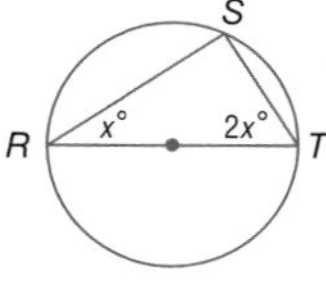

25. x 12.75
26. $m\angle C$ 51.75

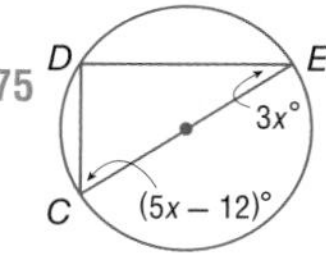

Example 5 **CCSS STRUCTURE** Find each measure.

27. $m\angle T$ 135
28. $m\angle Z$ 80

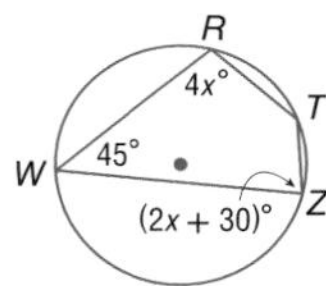

29. $m\angle H$ 106
30. $m\angle G$ 93

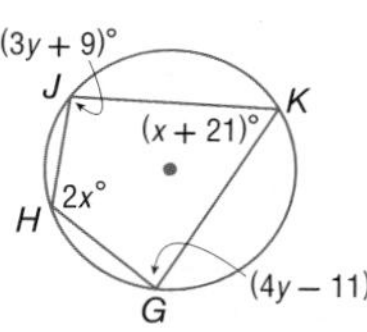

B 31. **PROOF** Write a paragraph proof for Theorem 10.9. See Ch. 10 Answer Appendix.

SIGNS A stop sign in the shape of a regular octagon is inscribed in a circle. Find each measure.

32. $m\widehat{NQ}$ 135
33. $m\angle RLQ$ 22.5
34. $m\angle LRQ$ 112.5
35. $m\angle LSR$ 135

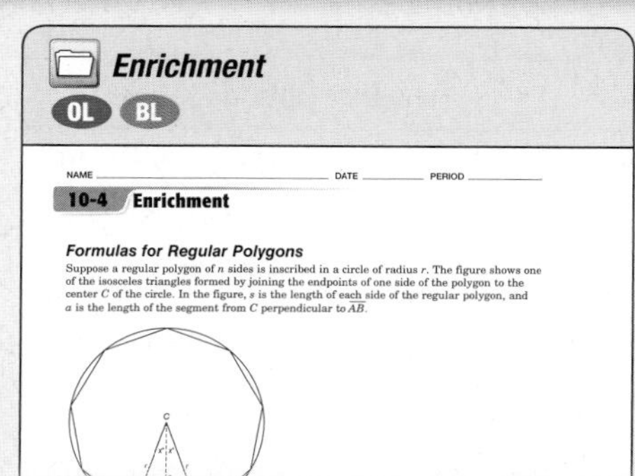

Enrichment

OL BL

NAME ______ DATE ______ PERIOD ______

10-4 Enrichment

Formulas for Regular Polygons

Suppose a regular polygon of n sides is inscribed in a circle of radius r. The figure shows one of the isosceles triangles formed by joining the endpoints of one side of the polygon to the center C of the circle. In the figure, s is the length of each side of the regular polygon, and a is the length of the segment from C perpendicular to $\overline{AB}$.

CCSS Teaching the Mathematical Practices

Structure Mathematically proficient students look closely to discern a pattern or structure. They also can step back for an overview and shift perspective. In Exercises 8–10, encourage students to analyze each figure for angles that are supplementary.

36. ART Four different string art star patterns are shown. If all of the inscribed angles of each star shown are congruent, find the measure of each inscribed angle.

a. 36 **b.** 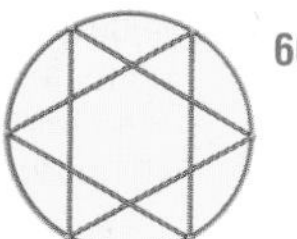 60 **c.**  **d.** 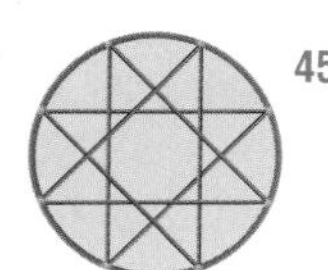 45

PROOF **Write a two-column proof for each case of Theorem 10.6.** **36c.** $\frac{180}{7}$ **or about 25.7**

37. **Case 2** **See margin.**

Given: P lies inside $\angle ABC$. $\overline{BD}$ is a diameter.

Prove: $m\angle ABC = \frac{1}{2}m\widehat{AC}$

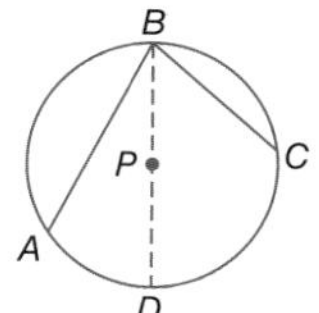

38. **Case 3** **See margin.**

Given: P lies outside $\angle ABC$. $\overline{BD}$ is a diameter.

Prove: $m\angle ABC = \frac{1}{2}m\widehat{AC}$

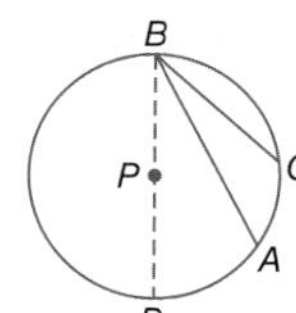

PROOF **Write the specified proof for each theorem.** **39, 40. See Ch. 10 Answer Appendix.**

 **39** Theorem 10.7, two-column proof

40. Theorem 10.8, paragraph proof

41. MULTIPLE REPRESENTATIONS In this problem, you will investigate the relationship between the arcs of a circle that are cut by two parallel chords.

a. Geometric Use a compass to draw a circle with parallel chords $\overline{AB}$ and $\overline{CD}$. Connect points A and D by drawing segment $\overline{AD}$. **See Ch. 10 Answer Appendix.**

b. Numerical Use a protractor to find $m\angle A$ and $m\angle D$. Then determine $m\widehat{AC}$ and $m\widehat{BD}$. What is true about these arcs? Explain. **See Ch. 10 Answer Appendix.**

c. Verbal Draw another circle and repeat parts **a** and **b**. Make a conjecture about arcs of a circle that are cut by two parallel chords.

d. Analytical Use your conjecture to find $m\widehat{PR}$ and $m\widehat{QS}$ in the figure at the right. Verify by using inscribed angles to find the measures of the arcs. **70; 70**

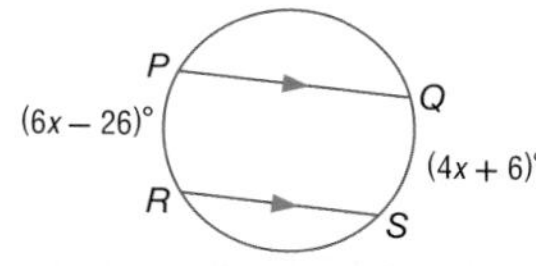

41c. Sample answer: In a circle, two parallel chords cut congruent arcs. See sudents work.

H.O.T. Problems Use Higher-Order Thinking Skills

CCSS ARGUMENTS **Determine whether the quadrilateral can *always*, *sometimes*, or *never* be inscribed in a circle. Explain your reasoning.** **42–46. See Ch. 10 Answer Appendix.**

42. square **43.** rectangle **44.** parallelogram **45.** rhombus **46.** kite

47. CHALLENGE A square is inscribed in a circle. What is the ratio of the area of the circle to the area of the square? $\frac{\pi}{2}$

48. WRITING IN MATH A 45°-45°-90° right triangle is inscribed in a circle. If the radius of the circle is given, explain how to find the lengths of the right triangle's legs. **See Ch. 10 Answer Appendix.**

49. OPEN ENDED Find and sketch a real-world logo with an inscribed polygon. **See students' work.**

50. WRITING IN MATH Compare and contrast inscribed angles and central angles of a circle. If they intercept the same arc, how are they related? **See Ch. 10 Answer Appendix.**

Exercise Alert

Compass, Protractor, and Straightedge Exercise 41 requires the use of a compass, a protractor, and a straightedge.

Multiple Representations

In Exercise 41, students use geometric sketches, measurements, and verbal descriptions to investigate arcs of a circle formed by parallel chords.

CCSS Teaching the Mathematical Practices

Arguments Mathematically proficient students understand and use stated assumptions and definitions in constructing arguments. They are able to analyze situations by breaking them into cases, and can recognize and use counterexamples. In Exercises 42–46, dynamic geometry software can help students visualize each situation.

Additional Answers

37. Proof:

Statements (Reasons)

1. $m\angle ABC = m\angle ABD + m\angle DBC$ ($\angle$ Addition Postulate)
2. $m\angle ABC = \frac{1}{2}m\widehat{AD}$
   $m\angle DBC = \frac{1}{2}m\widehat{DC}$
   (The measure of an inscribed $\angle$ whose side is a diameter is half the measure of the intercepted arc (Case 1).)
3. $m\angle ABC = \frac{1}{2}m\widehat{AD} + \frac{1}{2}m\widehat{DC}$ (Substitution)
4. $m\angle ABC = \frac{1}{2}(m\widehat{AD} + m\widehat{DC})$ (Factor)
5. $m\widehat{AD} + m\widehat{DC} = m\widehat{AC}$ (Arc Addition Postulate)
6. $m\angle ABC = \frac{1}{2}m\widehat{AC}$ (Substitution)

38. Proof:

Statements (Reasons)

1. $m\angle ABC = m\angle DBC - m\angle DBA$ ($\angle$ Addition Postulate, Subtraction Property of Equality)
2. $m\angle DBC = \frac{1}{2}m\widehat{DC}$
   $m\angle DBA = \frac{1}{2}m\widehat{DA}$
   (The measure of an inscribed $\angle$ whose side is a diameter is half the measure of the intercepted arc (Case 1).)
3. $m\angle ABC = \frac{1}{2}m\widehat{DC} - \frac{1}{2}m\widehat{DA}$ (Substitution)
4. $m\angle ABC = \frac{1}{2}(m\widehat{DC} - m\widehat{DA})$ (Factor).
5. $m\widehat{DA} + m\widehat{AC} = m\widehat{DC}$ (Arc Addition Postulate)
6. $m\widehat{AC} = m\widehat{DC} - m\widehat{DA}$ (Subtraction Property of Equality)
7. $m\angle ABC = \frac{1}{2}m\widehat{AC}$ (Substitution)

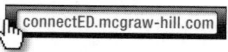

4 Assess

Crystal Ball Have students write how Lesson 10-4, Inscribed Angles, will help them understand tangents that occur outside the circle.

Formative Assessment

Check for student understanding of Lessons 10-3 and 10-4.

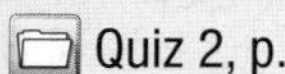 Quiz 2, p. 57

Standardized Test Practice

51. In the circle below, $m\widehat{AC} = 160$ and $m\angle BEC = 38$. What is $m\angle AEB$? **A**

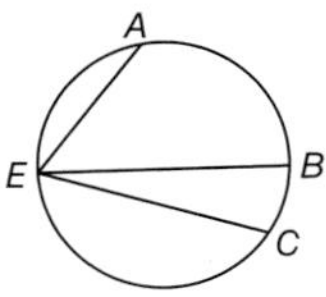

A 42 C 80
B 61 D 84

52. ALGEBRA Simplify $4(3x - 2)(2x + 4) + 3x^2 + 5x - 6$. **H**

F $9x^2 + 3x - 14$ H $27x^2 + 37x - 38$
G $9x^2 + 13x - 14$ J $27x^2 + 27x - 26$

53. SHORT RESPONSE In the circle below, $\overline{AB}$ is a diameter, $AC = 8$ inches, and $BC = 15$ inches. Find the diameter, the radius, and the circumference of the circle.

$d = 17$ in., $r = 8.5$ in., $C = 17\pi$ or about 53.4 in.

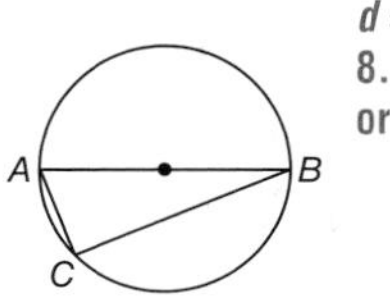

54. SAT/ACT The sum of three consecutive integers is −48. What is the least of the three integers? **C**

A −15 D −18
B −16 E −19
C −17

Spiral Review

In ⊙M, $FL = 24$, $HJ = 48$, and $m\widehat{HP} = 65$. Find each measure. (Lesson 10-3)

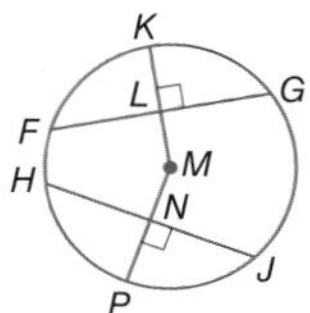

55. FG **48**

56. $m\widehat{PJ}$ **65**

57. NJ **24**

58. $m\widehat{HJ}$ **130**

Find x. (Lesson 10-2)

59. **107**

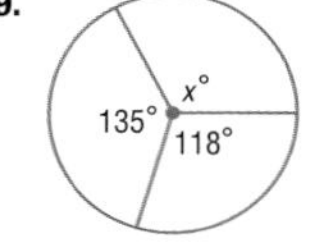

60. **162**

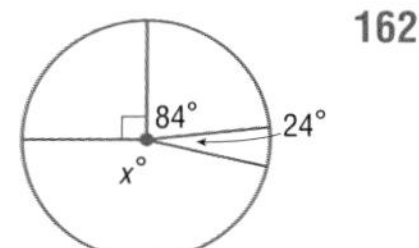

61. **144**

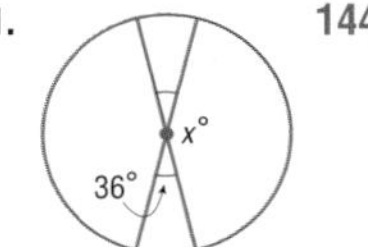

62. PHOTOGRAPHY In one of the first cameras invented, light entered an opening in the front. An image was reflected in the back of the camera, upside down, forming similar triangles. Suppose the image of the person on the back of the camera is 12 inches, the distance from the opening to the person is 7 feet, and the camera itself is 15 inches long. How tall is the person being photographed? (Lesson 7-3) **5.6 ft**

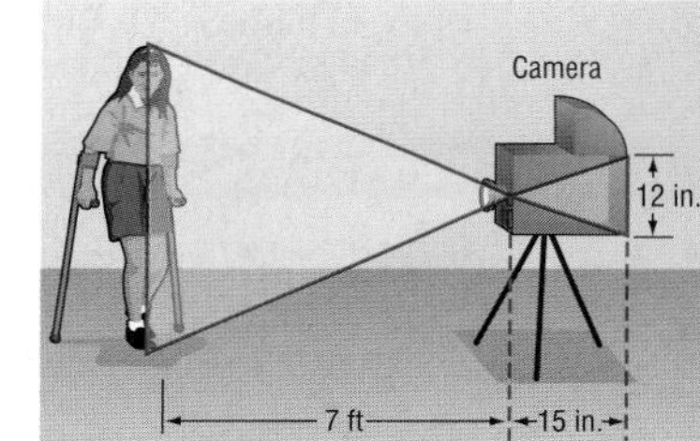

Skills Review

ALGEBRA Suppose B is the midpoint of $\overline{AC}$. Use the given information to find the missing measure.

63. $AB = 4x - 5$, $BC = 11 + 2x$, $AC = ?$ **54**

64. $AB = 6y - 14$, $BC = 10 - 2y$, $AC = ?$ **8**

65. $BC = 6 - 4m$, $AC = 8$, $m = ?$ $\frac{1}{2}$

66. $AB = 10s + 2$, $AC = 40$, $s = ?$ **1.8**

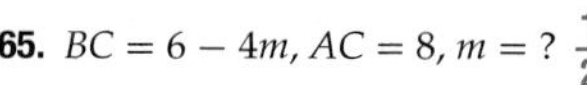

Differentiated Instruction OL BL

Extension Have students describe the difference between a central angle and an inscribed angle, and how their measures are related if they intercept the same arc. The vertex of the central angle is the center of the circle and its sides are radii of the circle. An inscribed angle has a vertex that is a point on the circle and its sides are chords of the circle. The measure of an inscribed angle is half the measure of a central angle that intercepts the same arc.

CHAPTER 10 Mid-Chapter Quiz
Lessons 10-1 through 10-4

For Exercises 1–3, refer to ⊙A. (Lesson 10-1)

1. Name the circle. ⊙A
2. Name a diameter. $\overline{EC}$
3. Name a chord that is not a diameter. $\overline{ED}$

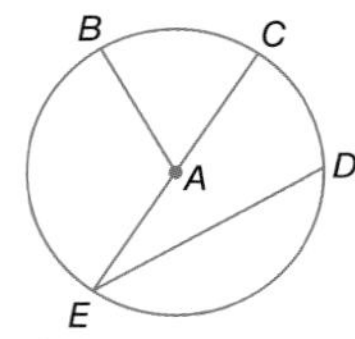

4. **BICYCLES** A bicycle has tires that are 24 inches in diameter. (Lesson 10-1)
   a. Find the circumference of one tire. **75.4 in.**
   b. How many inches does the tire travel after 100 rotations? **7540 in.**

Find the diameter and radius of a circle with the given circumference. Round to the nearest hundredth. (Lesson 10-1)

5. $C = 23$ cm **3.66 cm; 7.32 cm**
6. $C = 78$ ft **12.41 ft; 24.83 ft**
7. **MULTIPLE CHOICE** Find the length of $\widehat{BC}$. (Lesson 10-2) **B**

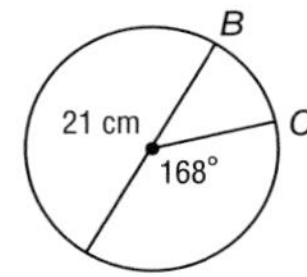

A 18°
B 2.20 cm
C 168°
D 30.79 cm

8. **MOVIES** The movie reel shown below has a diameter of 14.5 inches. (Lesson 10-2)

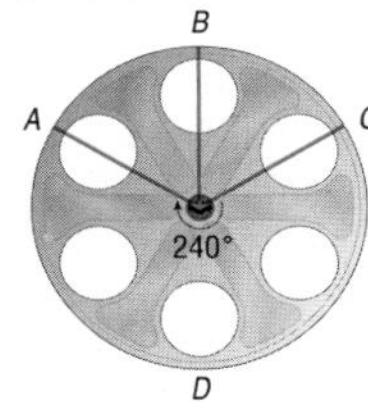

   a. Find $m\widehat{ADC}$. **240**
   b. Find the length of $\widehat{ADC}$. **30.4 in.**

9. Find the value of x. (Lesson 10-3) **70**

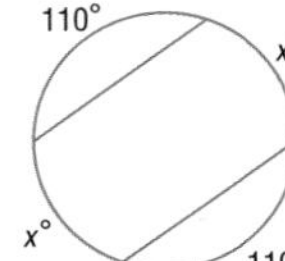

10. In ⊙B, $CE = 13.5$. Find BD. Round to the nearest hundredth. (Lesson 10-3) **4.29**

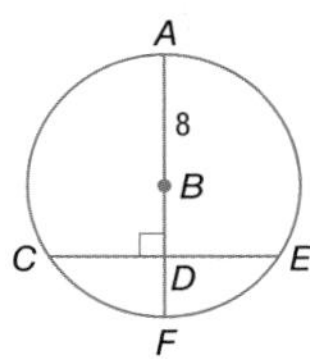

11. The two circles shown are congruent. Find x and the length of the chord. (Lesson 10-3) **$x = 16$; 41**

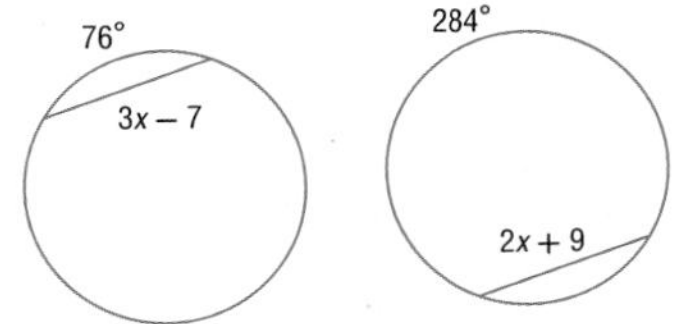

Find each measure. (Lesson 10-4)

12. $m\widehat{TU}$ **46**

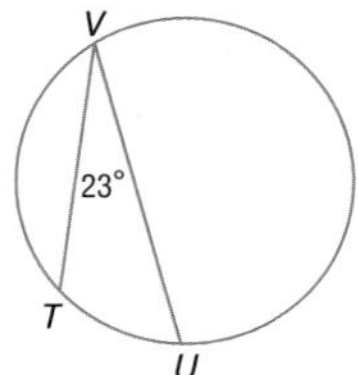

13. $m\angle A$ **85**

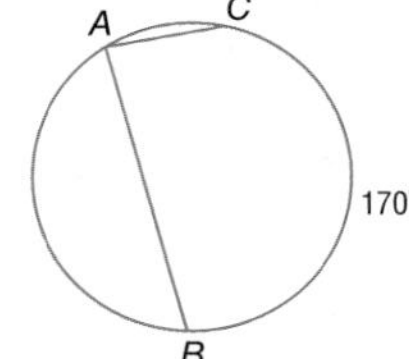

14. **MULTIPLE CHOICE** Find x. (Lesson 10-4) **G**

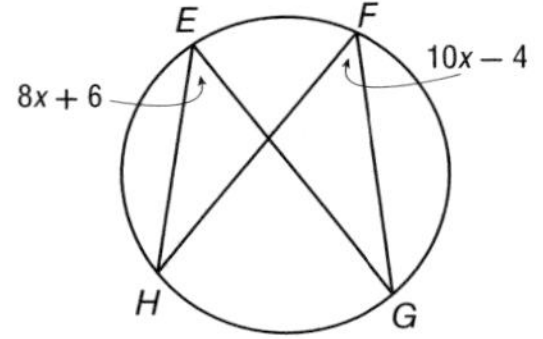

F 1.8
G 5
H 46
J 90

15. If a square with sides of 14 inches is inscribed in a circle, what is the diameter of the circle? (Lesson 10-4) **$14\sqrt{2}$ in.**

731

Formative Assessment

Use the Mid-Chapter Quiz to assess students' progress in the first half of the chapter.

Have students review the lessons indicated for the problems that they answered incorrectly.

Summative Assessment

Mid-Chapter Test, p. 59

eAssessment Customize and create multiple versions of your Mid-Chapter Test and their answer keys.

FOLDABLES® StudyOrganizer

Dinah Zike's Foldables®

Before students complete the Mid-Chapter Quiz, encourage them to review the information for Lessons 10-1 through 10-4 in their Foldables.

InterventionPlanner

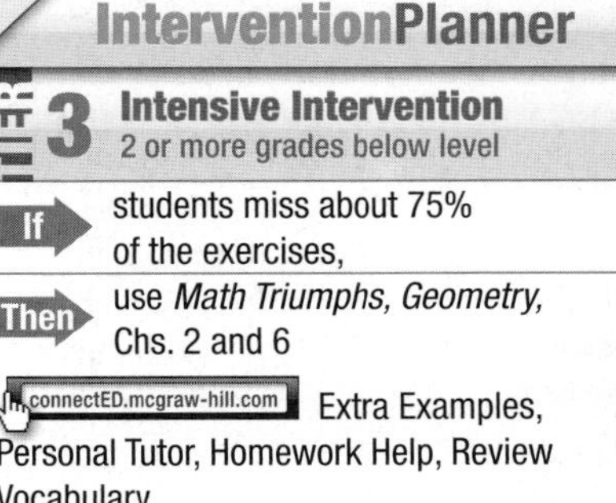

TIER 1 On Level OL	TIER 2 Strategic Intervention AL approaching grade level	TIER 3 Intensive Intervention 2 or more grades below level
If students miss about 25% of the exercises or less,	**If** students miss about 50% of the exercises,	**If** students miss about 75% of the exercises,
Then choose a resource: SE Lessons 10-1, 10-2, and 10-3, and 10-4 Skills Practice, pp. 7, 13, 19, and 25 connectED.mcgraw-hill.com Self-Check Quiz	**Then** choose a resource: Study Guide and Intervention, pp. 5, 11, 17, 23 connectED.mcgraw-hill.com Extra Examples, Personal Tutor, Homework Help	**Then** use *Math Triumphs, Geometry,* Chs. 2 and 6 connectED.mcgraw-hill.com Extra Examples, Personal Tutor, Homework Help, Review Vocabulary

1 Focus

Vertical Alignment

Before Lesson 10-5 Use the Pythagorean Theorem to find side lengths of right triangles.

Lesson 10-5 Use properties of tangents. Solve problems involving circumscribed polygons.

After Lesson 10-5 Find measures of angles formed by lines intersecting a circle.

2 Teach

Scaffolding Questions

Have students read the **Why?** section of the lesson.

Ask:

- What geometric figure does each gear represent? a circle
- How is the bike chain like a tangent? It connects the circles with a straight line.
- How is the bike chain not like a tangent? The chain touches the gear at more than one point. Tangents are straight lines that intersect a circle at exactly one point.

LESSON 10-5 Tangents

Then

- You used the Pythagorean Theorem to find side lengths of right triangles.

Now

1. Use properties of tangents.
2. Solve problems involving circumscribed polygons.

Why?

- The first bicycles were moved by pushing your feet on the ground. Modern bicycles use pedals, a chain, and gears. The chain loops around circular gears. The length of the chain between these gears is measured from the points of tangency.

NewVocabulary
tangent
point of tangency
common tangent

Common Core State Standards

Content Standards

G.CO.12 Make formal geometric constructions with a variety of tools and methods (compass and straightedge, string, reflective devices, paper folding, dynamic geometric software, etc.).

G.C.4 Construct a tangent line from a point outside a given circle to the circle.

Mathematical Practices

1. Make sense of problems and persevere in solving them.
2. Reason abstractly and quantitatively.

1 Tangents

A **tangent** is a line in the same plane as a circle that intersects the circle in exactly one point, called the **point of tangency**. $\overleftrightarrow{AB}$ is tangent to $\odot C$ at point A. $\overline{AB}$ and $\overrightarrow{AB}$ are also called tangents.

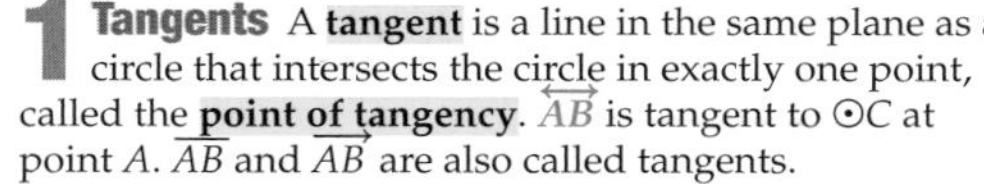

A **common tangent** is a line, ray, or segment that is tangent to two circles in the same plane. In each figure below, line ℓ is a common tangent of circles F and G.

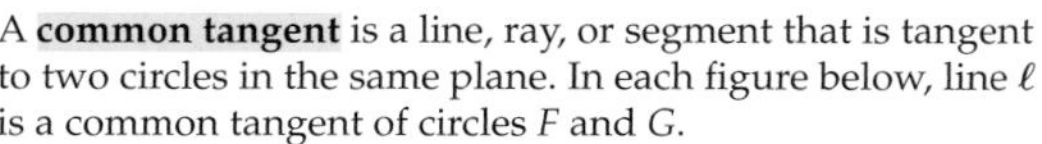

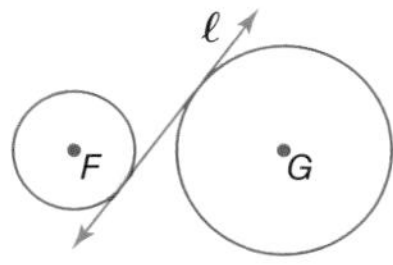

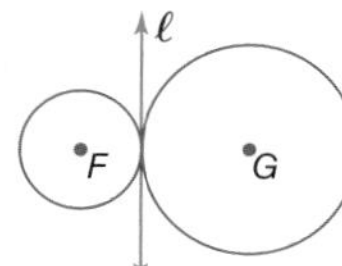

Example 1 Identify Common Tangents

Copy each figure and draw the common tangents. If no common tangent exists, state *no common tangent*.

a.

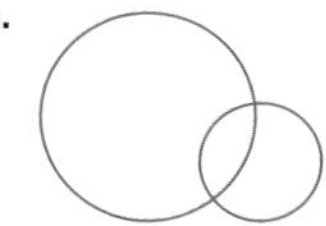

These circles have two common tangents.

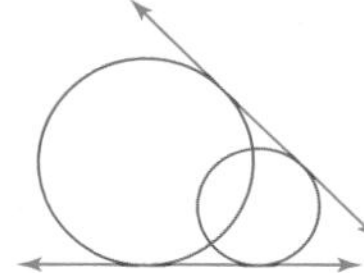

b.

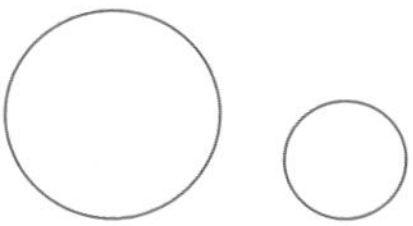

These circles have 4 common tangents.

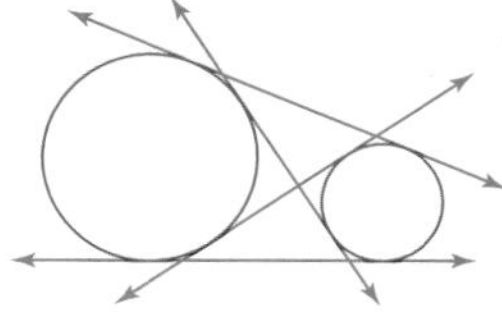

GuidedPractice 1A, 1B. See margin.

1A.

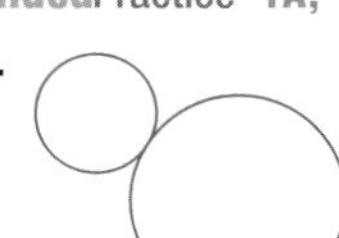

1B.

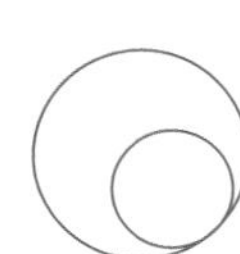

Lesson 10-5 Resources

Resource	Approaching Level AL	On Level OL	Beyond Level BL	English Learners ELL
Teacher Edition	▪ Differentiated Instruction, p. 734	▪ Differentiated Instruction, pp. 734, 735	▪ Differentiated Instruction, p. 735	
Chapter Resource Masters	▪ Study Guide and Intervention, pp. 29–30 ▪ Skills Practice, p. 31 ▪ Practice, p. 32 ▪ Word Problem Practice, p. 33	▪ Study Guide and Intervention, pp. 29–30 ▪ Skills Practice, p. 31 ▪ Practice, p. 32 ▪ Word Problem Practice, p. 33 ▪ Enrichment, p. 34 ▪ Computer Activity, p. 35 ▪ Computer Activity, p. 36	▪ Practice, p. 32 ▪ Word Problem Practice, p. 33 ▪ Enrichment, p. 34	▪ Study Guide and Intervention, pp. 29–30 ▪ Skills Practice, p. 31 ▪ Practice, p. 32 ▪ Word Problem Practice, p. 33
Other	▪ 5-Minute Check 10-5 ▪ Study Notebook ▪ Teaching Geometry with Manipulatives	▪ 5-Minute Check 10-5 ▪ Study Notebook ▪ Teaching Geometry with Manipulatives	▪ 5-Minute Check 10-5 ▪ Study Notebook	▪ 5-Minute Check 10-5 ▪ Study Notebook ▪ Teaching Geometry with Manipulatives

The shortest distance from a tangent to the center of a circle is the radius drawn to the point of tangency.

Theorem 10.10

Words In a plane, a line is tangent to a circle if and only if it is perpendicular to a radius drawn to the point of tangency.

Example Line ℓ is tangent to $\odot S$ if and only if $\ell \perp \overline{ST}$.

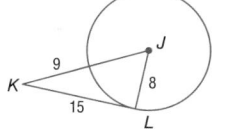

You will prove both parts of Theorem 10.10 in Exercises 32 and 33.

Example 2 Identify a Tangent

$\overline{JL}$ is a radius of $\odot J$. Determine whether $\overline{KL}$ is tangent to $\odot J$. Justify your answer.

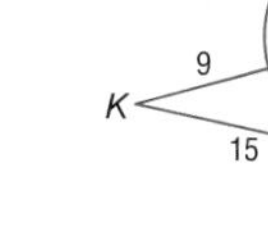

Test to see if $\triangle JKL$ is a right triangle.

$8^2 + 15^2 \stackrel{?}{=} (8 + 9)^2$ Pythagorean Theorem

$289 = 289$ ✓ Simplify.

$\triangle JKL$ is a right triangle with right angle JLK. So $\overline{KL}$ is perpendicular to radius $\overline{JL}$ at point L. Therefore, by Theorem 10.10, $\overline{KL}$ is tangent to $\odot J$.

Guided Practice

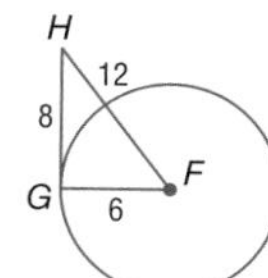

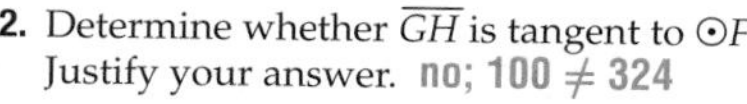

2. Determine whether $\overline{GH}$ is tangent to $\odot F$. Justify your answer. **no; $100 \neq 324$**

You can also use Theorem 10.10 to identify missing values.

Example 3 Use a Tangent to Find Missing Values

$\overline{JH}$ is tangent to $\odot G$ at J. Find the value of x.

By Theorem 10.10, $\overline{JH} \perp \overline{GJ}$. So, $\triangle GHJ$ is a right triangle.

$GJ^2 + JH^2 = GH^2$ Pythagorean Theorem

$x^2 + 12^2 = (x + 8)^2$ $GJ = x$, $JH = 12$, and $GH = x + 8$

$x^2 + 144 = x^2 + 16x + 64$ Multiply.

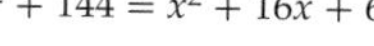

$80 = 16x$ Simplify.

$5 = x$ Divide each side by 16.

Problem-Solving Tip

CCSS Sense-Making You can use the *solve a simpler problem* strategy by sketching and labeling the right triangles without the circles. A drawing of the triangle in Example 3 is shown below.

Guided Practice

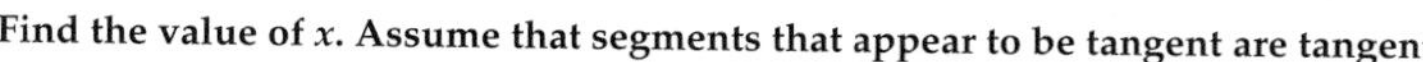

Find the value of x. Assume that segments that appear to be tangent are tangent.

3A.

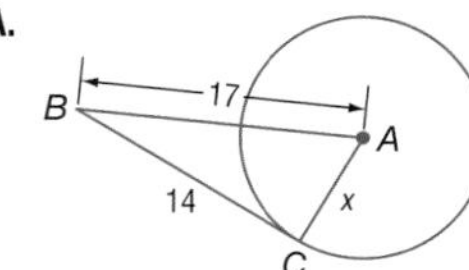

$\sqrt{93} \approx 9.64$

3B.

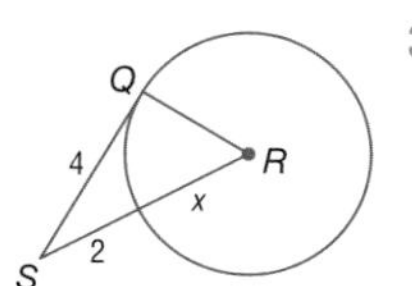

3

Additional Answer (Guided Practice)

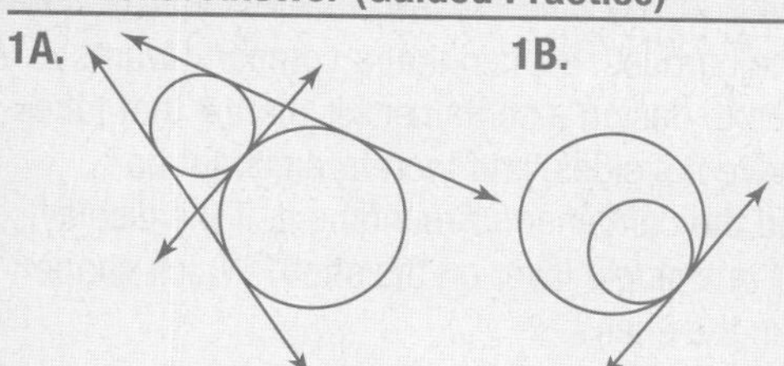

Teaching the Mathematical Practices

Sense-Making Mathematically proficient students consider analogous problems and try simpler forms of the original problem in order to gain insight into its solution. Encourage students to consider the Pythagorean theorem when a problem involves a right triangle.

1 Tangents

Examples 1–4 show how to use the theorems of tangents to solve problems involving tangents.

Formative Assessment

Use the Guided Practice exercises after each example to determine students' understanding of concepts.

Additional Examples

1 Copy each figure and draw the common tangents. If no common tangent exists, state *no common tangent.*

a.

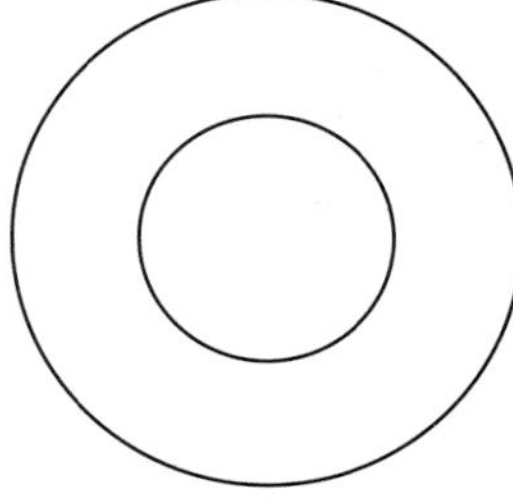

no common tangent

b.

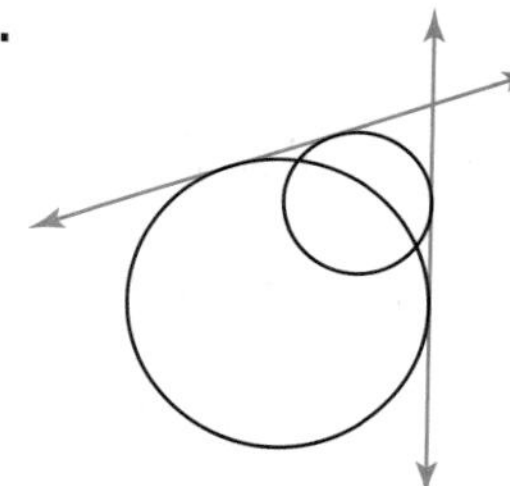

2 $\overline{KL}$ is a radius of $\odot K$. Determine whether $\overline{LM}$ is tangent to $\odot K$. Justify your answer.

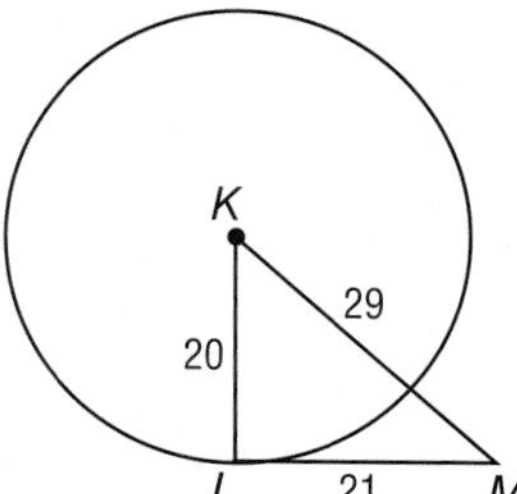

$\overline{LM}$ is tangent to $\odot K$ by the converse of the Pythagorean Theorem.

Additional Examples also in Interactive Classroom PowerPoint® Presentations

Interactive White Board READY

Additional Examples

3 In the figure, $\overline{WE}$ is tangent to $\odot D$ at W. Find the value of x. 10

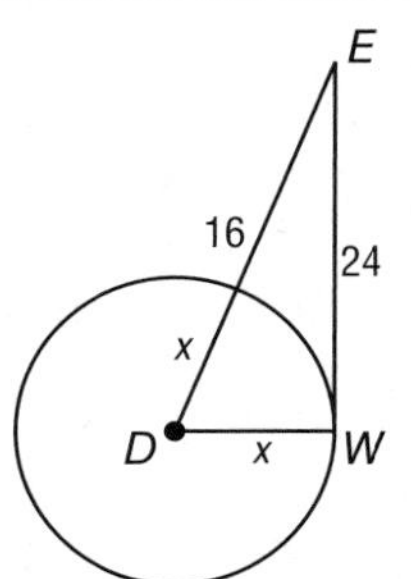

4 **ALGEBRA** $\overline{AC}$ and $\overline{BC}$ are tangent to $\odot Z$. Find the value of x. 5

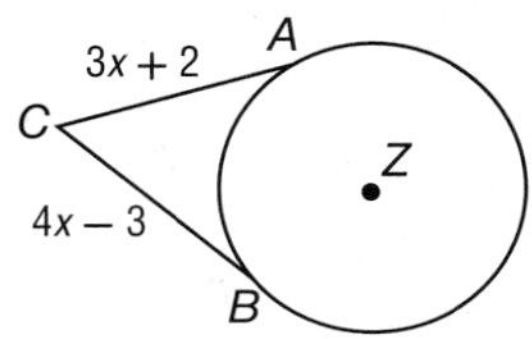

You can use Theorems 10.8 and 10.10 to construct a line tangent to a circle.

Construction Line Tangent to a Circle Through an External Point

Step 1 Use a compass to draw circle C and a point A outside of circle C. Then draw $\overline{CA}$.

Step 2 Construct line ℓ, the perpendicular bisector of $\overline{CA}$. Label the point of intersection X.

Step 3 Construct circle X with radius $\overline{XC}$. Label the points of intersection of the two circles D and E.

Step 4 Draw $\overleftrightarrow{AD}$ and $\overline{DC}$. $\triangle ADC$ is inscribed in a semicircle. So, $\angle ADC$ is a right angle and $\overleftrightarrow{AD}$ is tangent to $\odot C$.

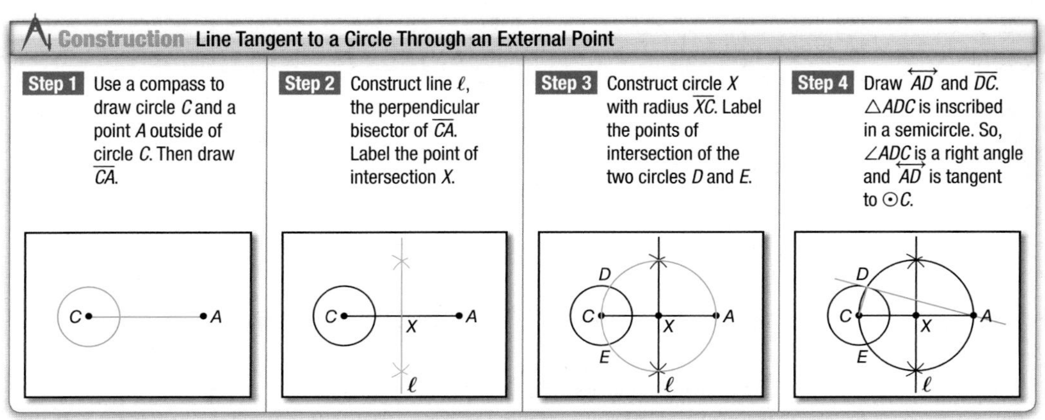

You will justify this construction in Exercise 36 and construct a line tangent to a circle through a point on the circle in Exercise 34.

More than one line can be tangent to the same circle.

Theorem 10.11

Words If two segments from the same exterior point are tangent to a circle, then they are congruent.

Example If $\overline{AB}$ and $\overline{CB}$ are tangent to $\odot D$, then $\overline{AB} \cong \overline{CB}$.

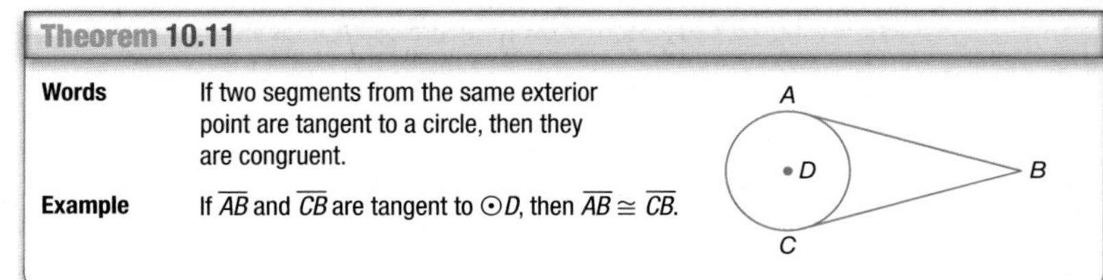

You will prove Theorem 10.11 in Exercise 28.

Example 4 Use Congruent Tangents to Find Measures

PT

ALGEBRA $\overline{AB}$ **and** $\overline{CB}$ **are tangent to** $\odot D$. **Find the value of** x.

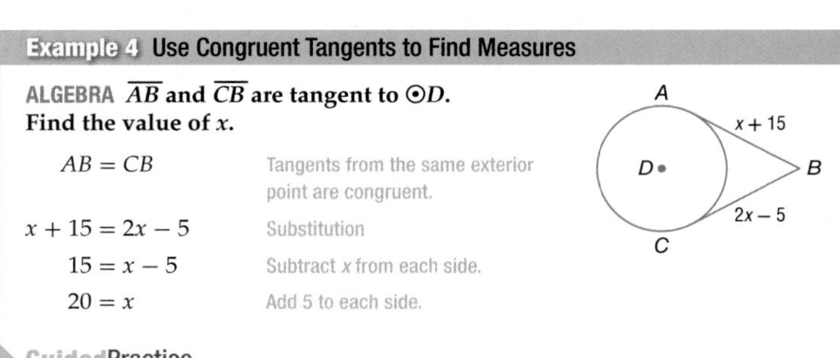

$AB = CB$	Tangents from the same exterior point are congruent.
$x + 15 = 2x - 5$	Substitution
$15 = x - 5$	Subtract x from each side.
$20 = x$	Add 5 to each side.

Guided Practice

ALGEBRA **Find the value of x. Assume that segments that appear to be tangent are tangent.**

4A. 6 **4B.** 3

Differentiated Instruction AL OL

Social/Interpersonal Learners Organize students in small groups. Explain that a company wants to market a new toy with a diameter of 5 inches. Their task is to design a container for the toy that takes up the least amount of shelf space. The container must have flat sides, and therefore cannot be circular. Have students draw and label the circular toy and the container surrounding it. If the display shelf is 3 feet by 10 feet, how many toy containers will fit in a single layer on the shelf? Which shape will allow the maximum number of toys to be displayed on the shelf?

2 Circumscribed Polygons

A polygon is circumscribed about a circle if every side of the polygon is tangent to the circle.

WatchOut!

Identifying Circumscribed Polygons Just because the circle is tangent to one or more of the sides of a polygon does not mean that the polygon is circumscribed about the circle, as shown in the second set of figures.

Circumscribed Polygons	Polygons Not Circumscribed
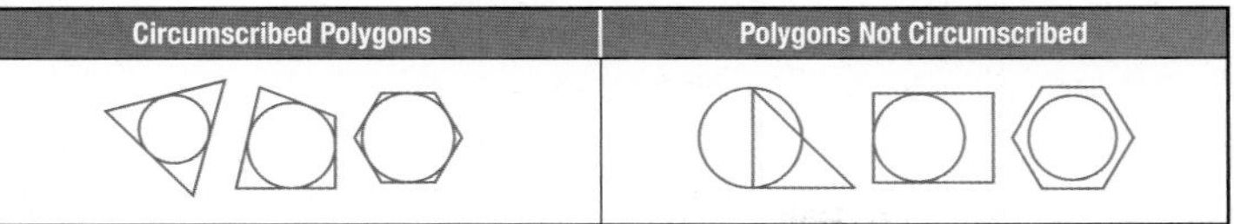	

You can use Theorem 10.11 to find missing measures in circumscribed polygons.

Real-World Example 5 Find Measures in Circumscribed Polygons

GRAPHIC DESIGN A graphic designer is giving directions to create a larger version of the triangular logo shown. If $\triangle ABC$ is circumscribed about $\odot G$, find the perimeter of $\triangle ABC$.

Step 1 Find the missing measures.

Since $\triangle ABC$ is circumscribed about $\odot G$, $\overline{AE}$ and $\overline{AD}$ are tangent to $\odot G$, as are $\overline{BE}$, $\overline{BF}$, $\overline{CF}$, and $\overline{CD}$. Therefore, $\overline{AE} \cong \overline{AD}$, $\overline{BF} \cong \overline{BE}$, and $\overline{CF} \cong \overline{CD}$.

So, $AE = AD = 8$ feet, $BF = BE = 7$ feet.

By Segment Addition, $CF + FB = CB$, so $CF = CB - FB = 10 - 7$ or 3 feet. So, $CD = CF = 3$ feet.

Step 2 Find the perimeter of $\triangle ABC$.

$$\text{perimeter} = AE + EB + BC + CD + DA$$
$$= 8 + 7 + 10 + 3 + 8 \text{ or } 36$$

So, the perimeter of $\triangle ABC$ is 36 feet.

GuidedPractice

5. Quadrilateral $RSTU$ is circumscribed about $\odot J$. If the perimeter is 18 units, find x. **1.5 units**

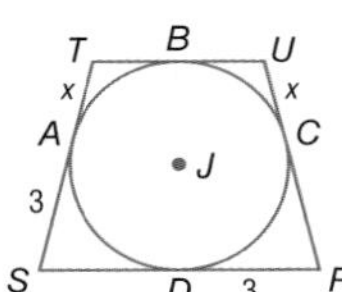

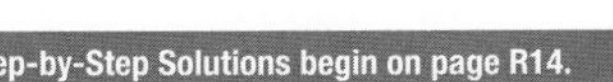

Check Your Understanding

 = Step-by-Step Solutions begin on page R14.

Example 1

1. Copy the figure shown, and draw the common tangents. If no common tangent exists, state *no common tangent*. **no common tangent**

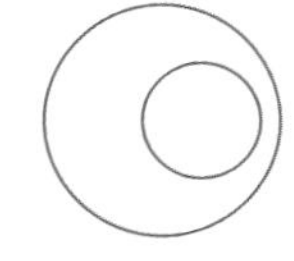

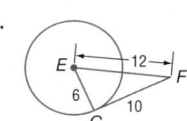

Example 2 **Determine whether $\overline{FG}$ is tangent to $\odot E$. Justify your answer.**

2. 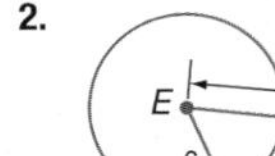

3. 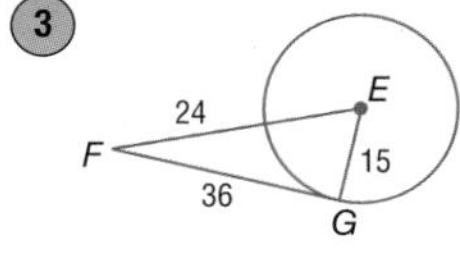

2. no; $136 \neq 144$
3. yes; $1521 = 1521$

2 Circumscribed Polygons

Polygons can also be circumscribed about a circle. **Example 5** shows how to find the perimeter of a triangle using theorems learned in this lesson.

Additional Example

5 **PACKAGING** The round cookies are marketed in a triangular package to pique the consumer's interest. If $\triangle QRS$ is circumscribed about $\odot T$, find the perimeter of $\triangle QRS$.

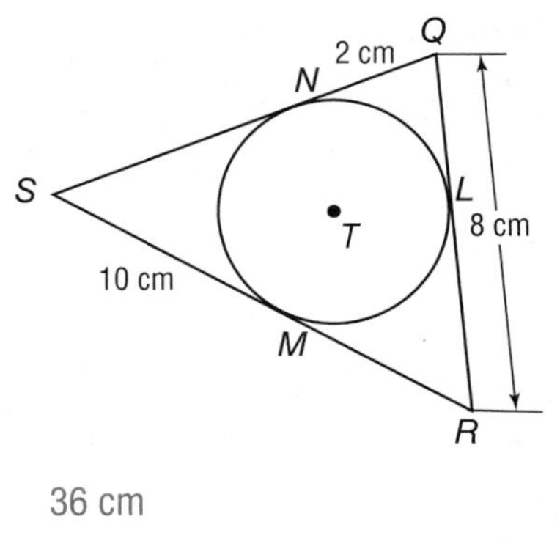

36 cm

Focus on Mathematical Content

Tangents Explain that even though a tangent intersects a circle, there is never any part of a tangent contained inside a circle. The only point that the tangent and the circle have in common is the point of tangency.

Teach with Tech

Blog On your secure class blog, have students write a blog entry to discuss why it is possible to draw any regular polygon as a circumscribed polygon. Students should realize that as the number of sides of the polygon increases, its shape becomes more circular.

DifferentiatedInstruction OL BL

Extension A circle is circumscribed about a square. The radius of the circle is r. Have the students write an expression for the perimeter of the square in terms of r. $4r\sqrt{2} \approx 5.66r$

3 Practice

Formative Assessment

Use Exercises 1–8 to check for understanding.

Use the chart at the bottom of this page to customize assignments for your students.

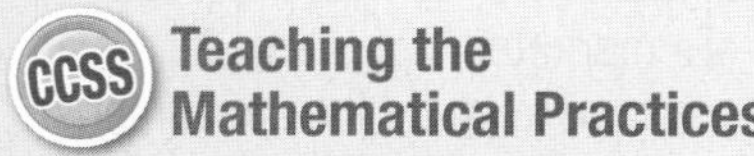

Teaching the Mathematical Practices

Sense-Making Mathematically proficient students start by explaining the meaning of a problem to themselves and looking for entry points to its solution. In Exercises 8, 24–25, encourage students to identify the segments tangent to the circle first.

Additional Answers

9.

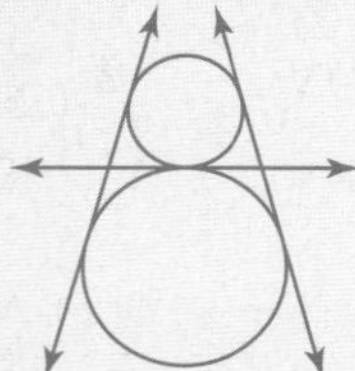

11.

12.

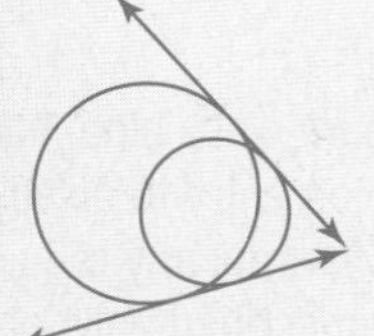

Examples 3–4 **Find x. Assume that segments that appear to be tangent are tangent.**

4. 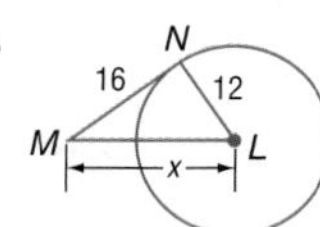

20

5. 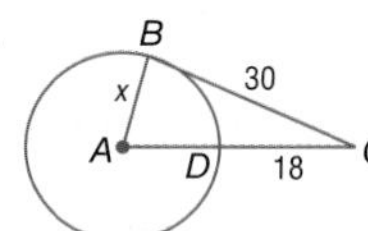

16

6. 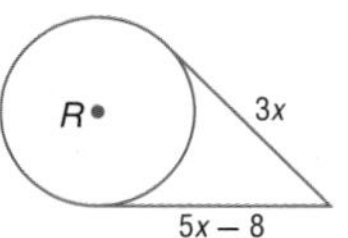

4

7. **LANDSCAPE ARCHITECT** A landscape architect is paving the two walking paths that are tangent to two approximately circular ponds as shown. The lengths given are in feet. Find the values of x and y. $x = 250$; $y = 275$

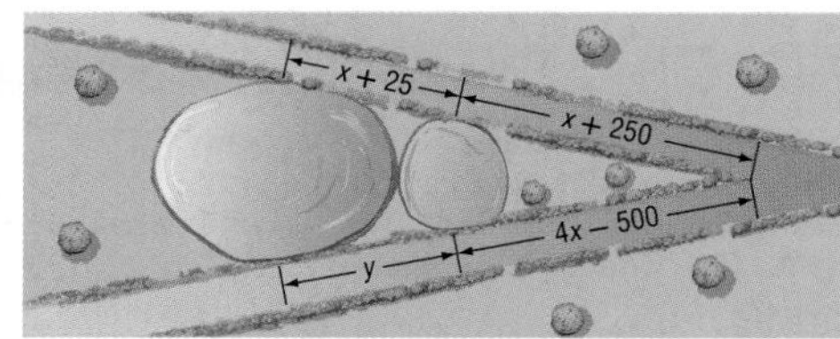

Example 5

8. **CCSS SENSE-MAKING** Triangle JKL is circumscribed about ⊙R.

 a. Find x. 4

 b. Find the perimeter of $\triangle JKL$. 52 units

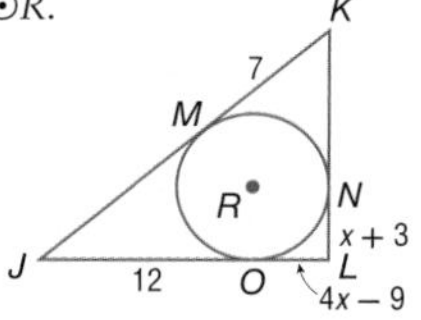

Practice and Problem Solving

Extra Practice is on page R10.

Example 1 **Copy each figure and draw the common tangents. If no common tangent exists, state *no common tangent*.** 9, 11, 12. See margin.

9. 

10. 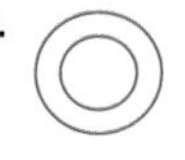
no common tangent

11. 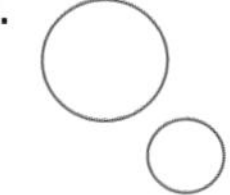

12. 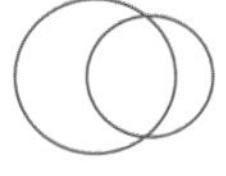

Example 2 **Determine whether each $\overline{XY}$ is tangent to the given circle. Justify your answer.**

13. 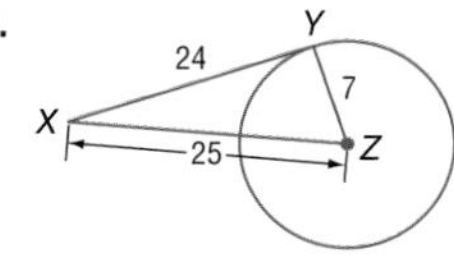

14. 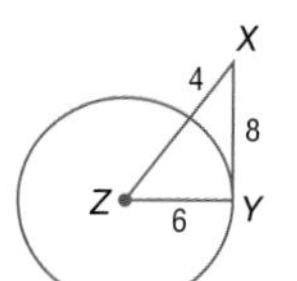

13. yes; 625 = 625
14. yes; 100 = 100
15. no; 89 ≠ 64
16. yes; 80 = 80

15. 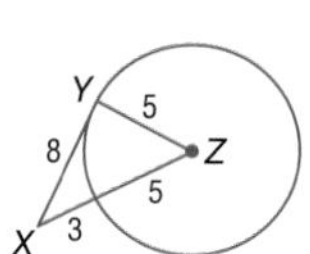

16. 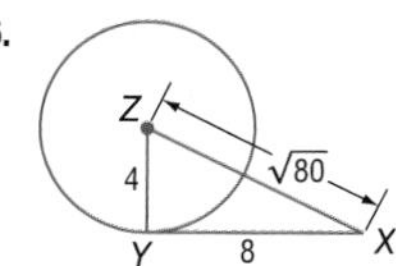

Differentiated Homework Options

Level	Assignment	Two-Day Option	
AL Basic	9–25, 36–55	9–25 odd, 40–43	10–24 even, 36–39, 44–55
OL Core	9–27 odd, 28–34, 36–55	9–25, 40–43	28–34, 36–39, 44–55
BL Advanced	26–52, (optional: 53–55)		

Examples 3–4 **Find x. Assume that segments that appear to be tangent are tangent. Round to the nearest tenth if necessary.**

17. 26
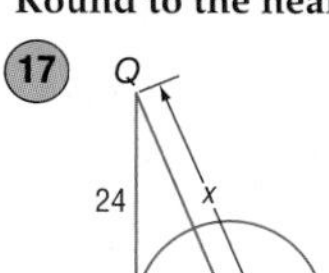

18. 8.5
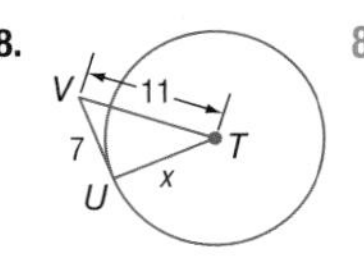

19. 9
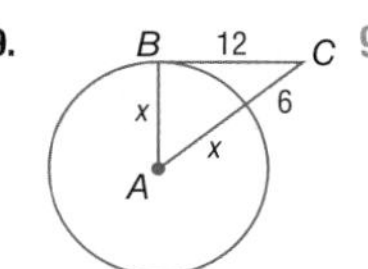

20. 10.7
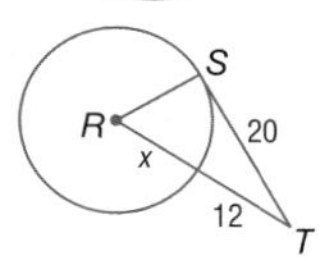

21. 4
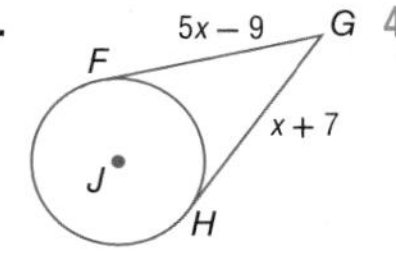

22. 1
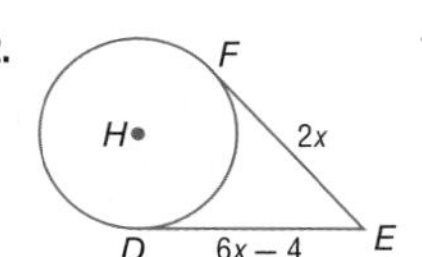

23. **ARBORS** In the arbor shown, $\overline{AC}$ and $\overline{BC}$ are tangents to ⊙D. The radius of the circle is 26 inches and $EC = 20$ inches. Find each measure to the nearest hundredth.

a. AC 37.95 in. b. BC 37.95 in.

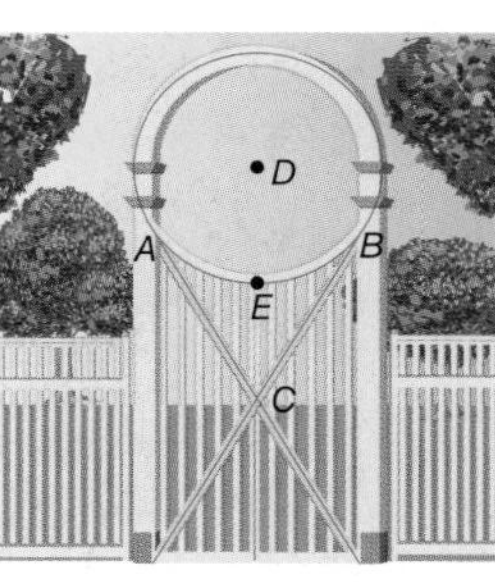

Example 5  **SENSE-MAKING** **Find the value of x. Then find the perimeter.**

24. 7; 82 in.
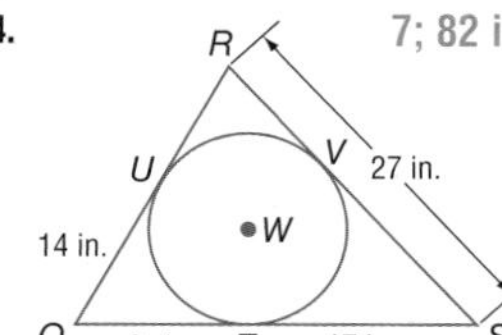

25. 8; 52 cm
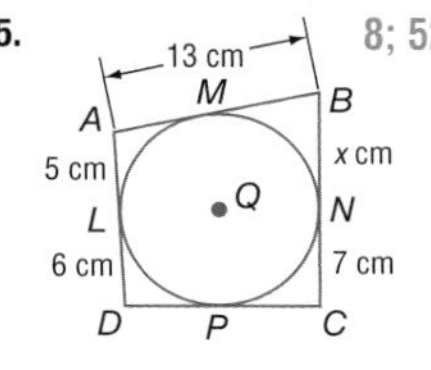

B **Find x to the nearest hundredth. Assume that segments that appear to be tangent are tangent.**

26. 9
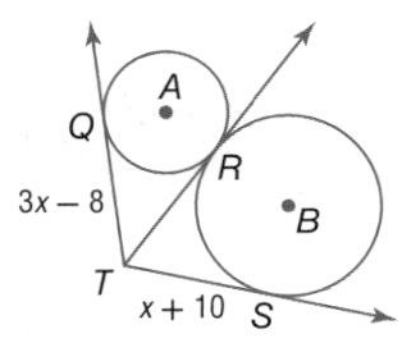

27. 8.06
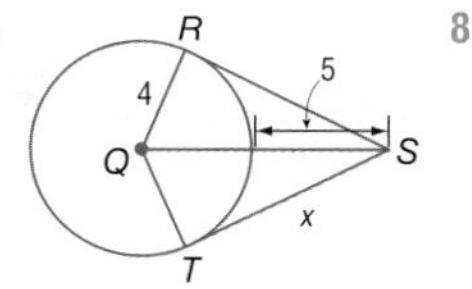

Write the specified type of proof. 28, 29. See Ch. 10 Answer Appendix.

28. two-column proof of Theorem 10.11

Given: $\overline{AC}$ is tangent to ⊙H at C.
$\overline{AB}$ is tangent to ⊙H at B.

Prove: $\overline{AC} \cong \overline{AB}$

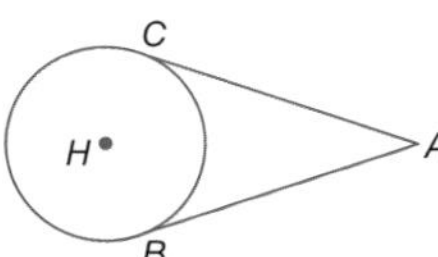

29. two-column proof

Given: Quadrilateral $ABCD$ is circumscribed about ⊙P.

Prove: $AB + CD = AD + BC$

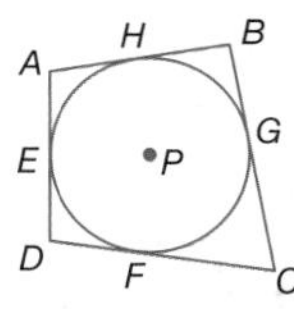

WatchOut!

Identifying Tangents Remind students that they should not assume that a segment that appears to be tangent to a circle is tangent, unless you are told to do so. The figure must either have a right angle symbol or include the measurements that confirm a right angle.

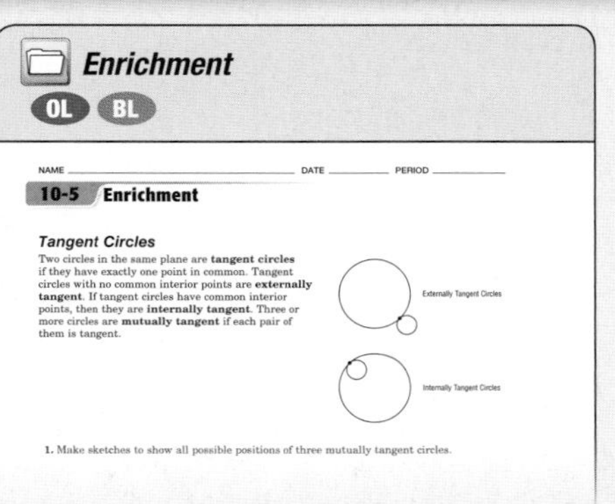

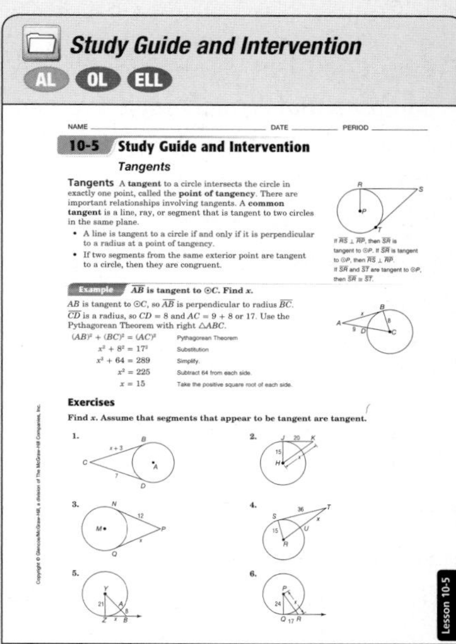

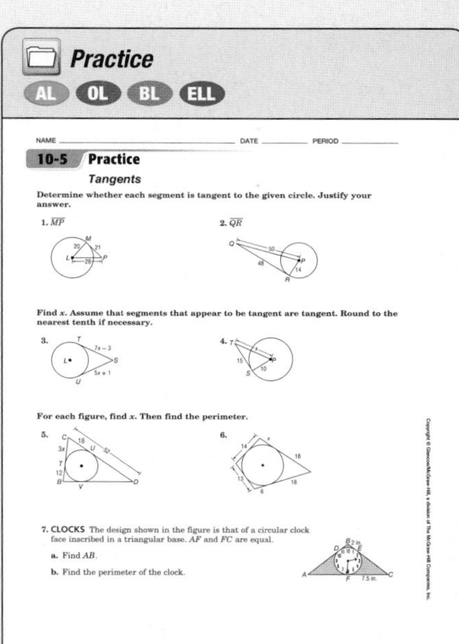

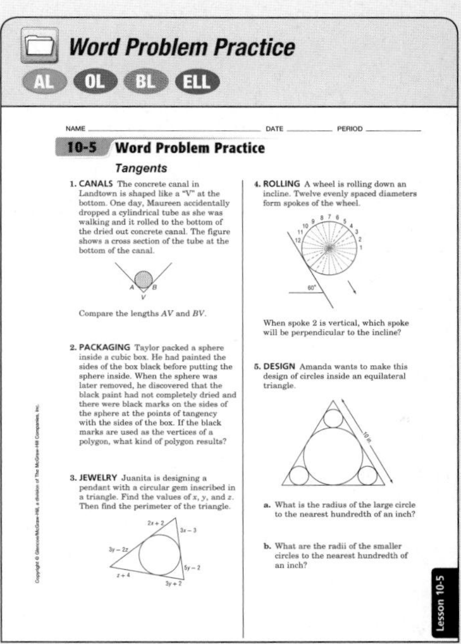

Exercise Alert

Compass and Straightedge Exercise 34 requires the use of a compass and a straightedge.

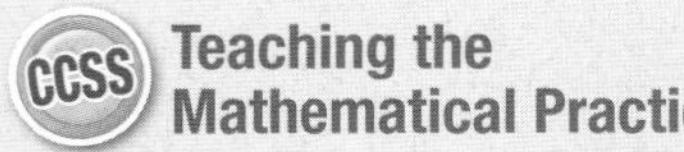

Teaching the Mathematical Practices

Tools Mathematically proficient students consider the available tools when solving a mathematical problem. In Exercise 34, students can use either a compass and straightedge or dynamic geometry software.

Additional Answers

31. 1916 mi;

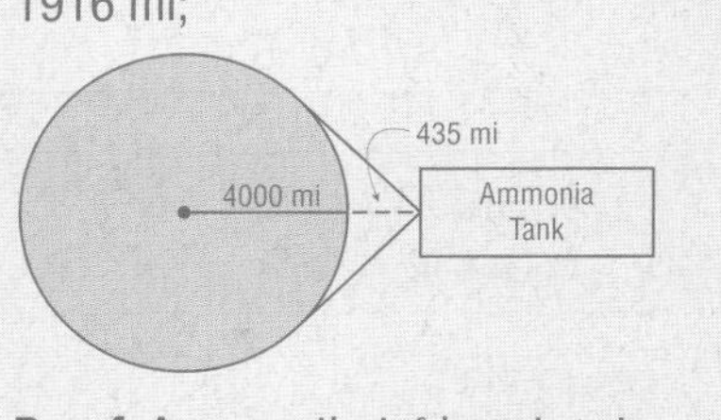

32. Proof: Assume that ℓ is not $\perp$ to $\overline{ST}$. If ℓ is not $\perp$ to $\overline{ST}$, some other segment $\overline{SQ}$ must be $\perp$ to ℓ. Also, there is a point R on $\overleftrightarrow{TR}$ as shown in the diagram such that $\overline{QT} \cong \overline{QR}$. $\angle SQT$ and $\angle SQR$ are right angles by the definition of perpendicular. $\angle SQT \cong \angle SQR$ and $\overline{SQ} \cong \overline{SQ}$. $\triangle SQT \cong \triangle SQR$ by SAS, so $\overline{ST} \cong \overline{SR}$ by CPCTC. Thus, both T and R are on $\odot S$. For two points of ℓ to also be on $\odot S$ contradicts the given fact that ℓ is tangent to $\odot S$ at T. Therefore, $\ell \perp \overline{ST}$ must be true.

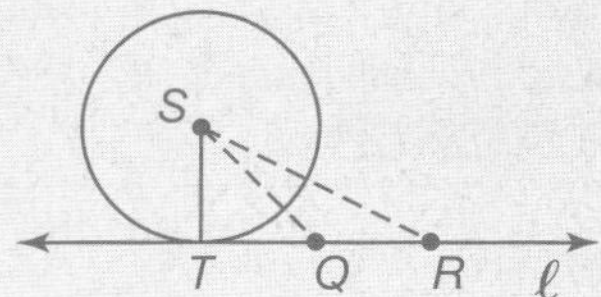

34. Sample answer:

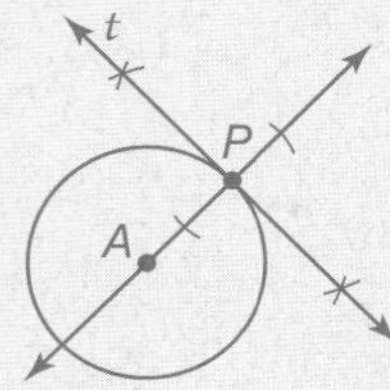

a. Draw $\overleftrightarrow{AP}$. (Two points determine a line.)

b. Construct a perpendicular at P. (The tangent is perpendicular to the radius at its endpoint.)

30. SATELLITES A satellite is 720 kilometers above Earth, which has a radius of 6360 kilometers. The region of Earth that is visible from the satellite is between the tangent lines $\overline{BA}$ and $\overline{BC}$. What is BA? Round to the nearest hundredth. **3110.76 km**

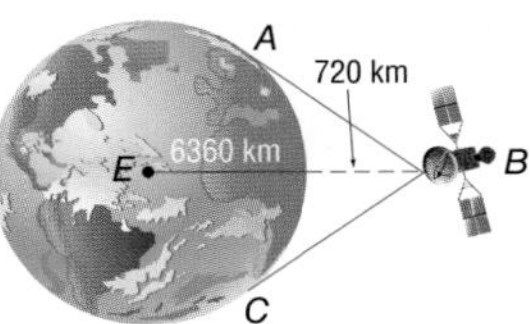

31. SPACE TRASH *Orbital debris* refers to materials from space missions that still orbit Earth. In 2007, a 1400-pound ammonia tank was discarded from a space mission. Suppose the tank has an altitude of 435 miles. What is the distance from the tank to the farthest point on Earth's surface from which the tank is visible? Assume that the radius of Earth is 4000 miles. Round to the nearest mile, and include a diagram of this situation with your answer. **See margin.**

32. PROOF Write an indirect proof to show that if a line is tangent to a circle, then it is perpendicular to a radius of the circle. (Part 1 of Theorem 10.10)

Given: ℓ is tangent to $\odot S$ at T; $\overline{ST}$ is a radius of $\odot S$.

Prove: $\ell \perp \overline{ST}$

(*Hint:* Assume ℓ is *not* $\perp$ to $\overline{ST}$.) **See margin.**

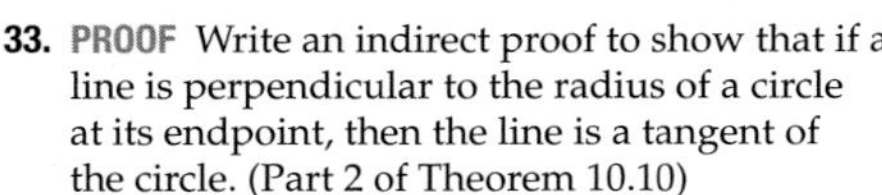

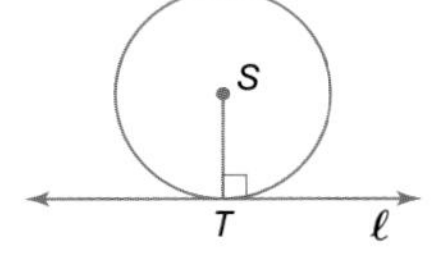

33. PROOF Write an indirect proof to show that if a line is perpendicular to the radius of a circle at its endpoint, then the line is a tangent of the circle. (Part 2 of Theorem 10.10)

Given: $\ell \perp \overline{ST}$; $\overline{ST}$ is a radius of $\odot S$.

Prove: ℓ is tangent to $\odot S$.

(*Hint:* Assume ℓ is *not* tangent to $\odot S$.)

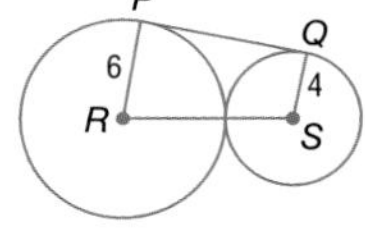

33. Proof: Assume that ℓ is not tangent to $\odot S$. Since ℓ intersects $\odot S$ at T, it must intersect the circle in another place. Call this point Q. Then $ST = SQ$. $\triangle STQ$ is isosceles, so $\angle T \cong \angle Q$. Since $\overline{ST} \perp \ell$, $\angle T$ and $\angle Q$ are right angles. This contradicts that a triangle can only have one right angle. Therefore, ℓ is tangent to $\odot S$.

34. CCSS TOOLS Construct a line tangent to a circle through a point on the circle.

Use a compass to draw $\odot A$. Choose a point P on the circle and draw $\overleftrightarrow{AP}$. Then construct a segment through point P perpendicular to $\overleftrightarrow{AP}$. Label the tangent line t. Explain and justify each step. **See margin.**

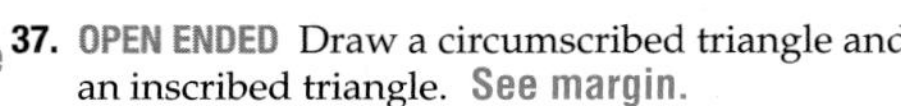

H.O.T. Problems Use Higher-Order Thinking Skills

35. CHALLENGE $\overline{PQ}$ is tangent to circles R and S. Find PQ. Explain your reasoning. **See margin.**

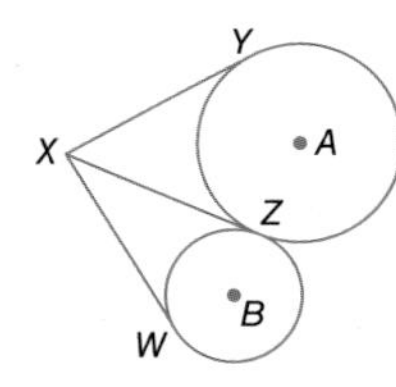

36. WRITING IN MATH Explain and justify each step in the construction on page 734. **See margin.**

37. OPEN ENDED Draw a circumscribed triangle and an inscribed triangle. **See margin.**

38. REASONING In the figure, $\overline{XY}$ and $\overline{XZ}$ are tangent to $\odot A$. $\overline{XZ}$ and $\overline{XW}$ are tangent to $\odot B$. Explain how segments $\overline{XY}$, $\overline{XZ}$, and $\overline{XW}$ can all be congruent if the circles have different radii.

38. By Theorem 10.11, if two segments from the same exterior point are tangent to a circle, then they are congruent. So, $\overline{XY} \cong \overline{XZ}$ and $\overline{XZ} \cong \overline{XW}$. Thus, $\overline{XY} \cong \overline{XZ} \cong \overline{XW}$.

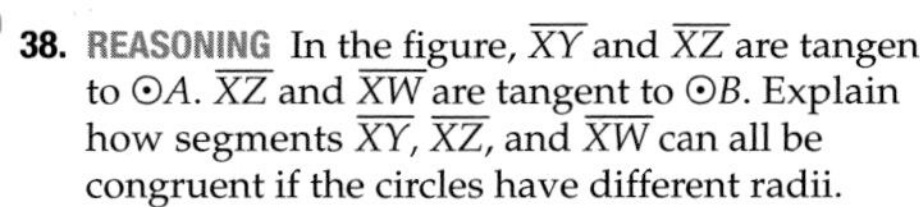

39.  **WRITING IN MATH** Is it possible to draw a tangent from a point that is located anywhere outside, on, or inside a circle? Explain. **See margin.**

35. Sample answer:

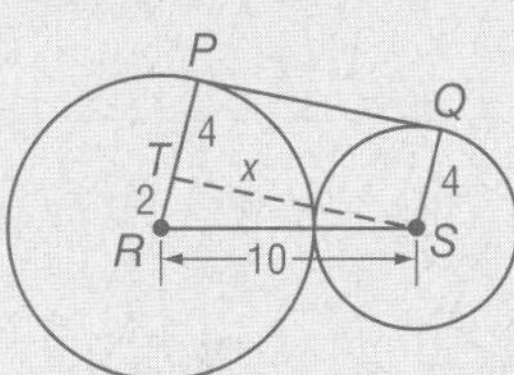

Using the Pythagorean Theorem, $2^2 + x^2 = 10^2$, so $x \approx 9.8$. Since $PQST$ is a rectangle, $PQ = x = 9.8$.

Standardized Test Practice

40. $\odot P$ has a radius of 10 centimeters, and $\overline{ED}$ is tangent to the circle at point D. F lies both on $\odot P$ and on segment $\overline{EP}$. If $ED = 24$ centimeters, what is the length of $\overline{EF}$? **B**

A 10 cm
C 21.8 cm
B 16 cm
D 26 cm

41. SHORT RESPONSE A square is inscribed in a circle having a radius of 6 inches. Find the length of each side of the square. **$6\sqrt{2}$ or about 8.5 in.**

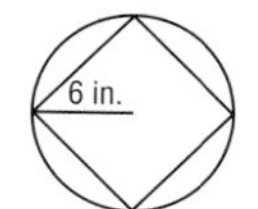

42. ALGEBRA Which of the following shows $25x^2 - 5x$ factored completely? **G**

F $5x(x)$
H $x(x - 5)$
G $5x(5x - 1)$
J $x(5x - 1)$

43. SAT/ACT What is the perimeter of the triangle shown below? **D**

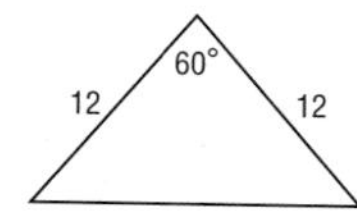

A 12 units
D 36 units
B 24 units
E 104 units
C 34.4 units

Spiral Review

Find each measure. (Lesson 10-4)

44. $m\widehat{JK}$ **56**

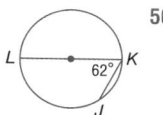

45. $m\angle B$ **61**

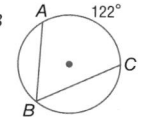

46. $m\widehat{VX}$ **152**

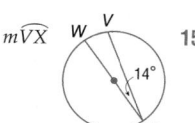

In $\odot F$, $GK = 14$ and $m\widehat{GHK} = 142$. Find each measure. Round to the nearest hundredth. (Lesson 10-3)

47. $m\widehat{GH}$ **71**

48. JK **7**

49. $m\widehat{KM}$ **109**

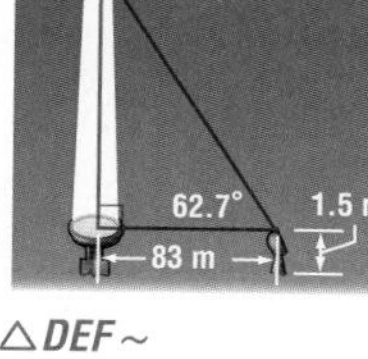

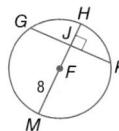

50. METEOROLOGY The altitude of the base of a cloud formation is called the *ceiling*. To find the ceiling one night, a meteorologist directed a spotlight vertically at the clouds. Using a theodolite, an optical instrument with a rotatable telescope, placed 83 meters from the spotlight and 1.5 meters above the ground, he found the angle of elevation to be 62.7°. How high was the ceiling? (Lesson 8-5) **about 162.3 m**

Determine whether the triangles are similar. If so, write a similarity statement. Explain your reasoning. (Lesson 7-3)

51.

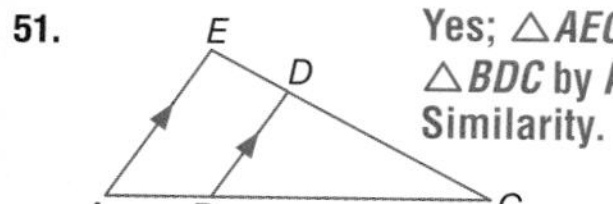

Yes; $\triangle AEC \sim \triangle BDC$ by AA Similarity.

52.

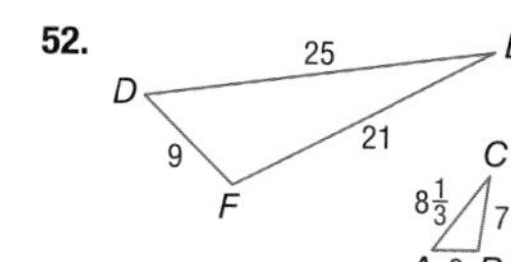

Yes; $\triangle DEF \sim \triangle ACB$ by SSS Similarity.

Skills Review

Solve each equation.

53. $15 = \frac{1}{2}[(360 - x) - 2x]$ **110**

54. $x + 12 = \frac{1}{2}[(180 - 120)]$ **18**

55. $x = \frac{1}{2}[(180 - 64)]$ **58**

4 Assess

Ticket Out the Door Provide an example on the board with a triangle formed by a tangent, a radius, and the line from the center of the circle to a point on the tangent. Assign lengths to the figure and ask students to write the equation necessary to solve the problem. Have them state the answer as they leave the classroom.

Additional Answers

36. First, a compass is used to draw circle C and a point A outside of circle C. Segment $\overline{CA}$ is drawn. There is exactly one line through points A and C. Next, a line ℓ is constructed bisecting $\overline{CA}$. According to the definition of a perpendicular bisector, point X is the midpoint of $\overline{AC}$. A second circle, X, is then drawn with a radius $\overline{XC}$ which intersects circle C at points D and E. Two circles can intersect at a maximum of two points. $\overleftrightarrow{AD}$ and $\overline{DC}$ are then drawn, and $\triangle ADC$ is inscribed in a semicircle. $\angle ADC$ is a right angle and $\overleftrightarrow{AD}$ is tangent to $\odot C$. $\overleftrightarrow{AD}$ is tangent to $\odot C$ at point D because it intersects the circle in exactly one point.

37. Sample answer:

circumscribed

inscribed

39. No; sample answer: Two tangents can be drawn from a point outside a circle and one tangent can be drawn from a point on a circle. However, no tangents can be drawn from a point inside the circle because a line would intersect the circle in two points.

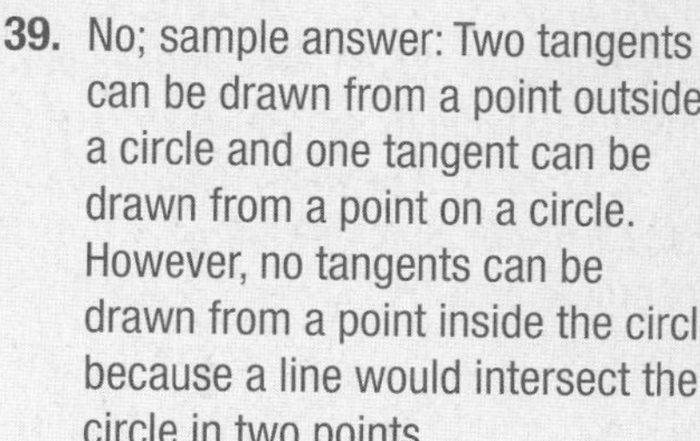

1 Focus

Objective Construct inscribed circles and circumscribed triangles.

Materials for Each Student

- straightedge
- compass

Teaching Tip

Explain that students will use the incenter of a triangle to construct a circle so that the triangle is circumscribed about the circle, and they will use the circumcenter of a triangle to construct a circle in which the triangle is circumscribed. They will also learn how to construct an equilateral triangle circumscribed about a circle.

2 Teach

Working in Cooperative Groups

Arrange students in groups of 3 or 4, mixing abilities. Then have groups complete Activities 1–2 and Exercises 1–2.

Practice Have students individually complete Exercises 3–4.

3 Assess

Formative Assessment

Use Exercises 3–4 to analyze the students' constructions and conjectures about the term *incenter*.

From Concrete to Abstract

Have students make conjectures about why the formula for circumference is $C = 2\pi r$ and not $6r$ when the radius is used to divide the circle into six congruent arcs.

EXTEND 10-5 Geometry Lab Inscribed and Circumscribed Circles

In this lab, you will perform constructions that involve inscribing or circumscribing a circle.

CCSS Common Core State Standards
Content Standards
G.CO.13 Construct an equilateral triangle, a square, and a regular hexagon inscribed in a circle.
G.C.3 Construct the inscribed and circumscribed circles of a triangle and prove properties of angles for a quadrilateral inscribed in a circle.
Mathematical Practices 5

Activity 1 Construct a Circle Inscribed in a Triangle

Step 1

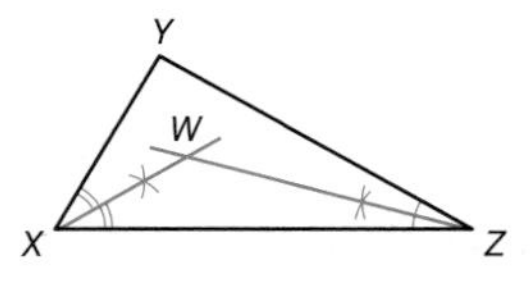

Draw a triangle *XYZ* and construct two angle bisectors of the triangle to locate the incenter *W*.

Step 2

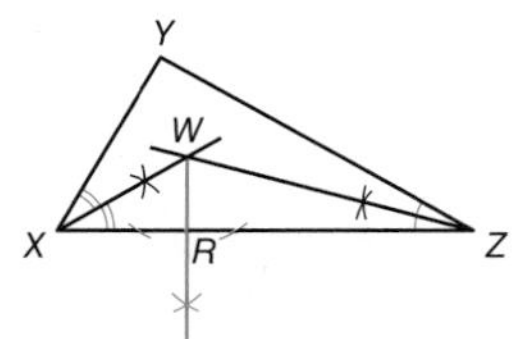

Construct a segment perpendicular to a side through the incenter. Label the intersection *R*.

Step 3

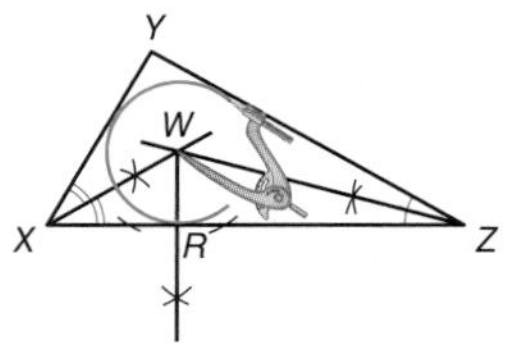

Set a compass of the length of $\overline{WR}$. Put the point of the compass on *W* and draw a circle with that radius.

Activity 2 Construct a Triangle Circumscribed About a Circle

Step 1

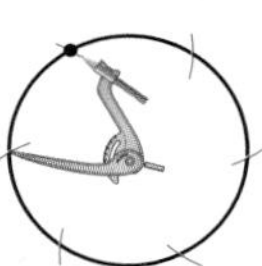

Construct a circle and draw a point. Use the same compass setting you used to construct the circle to construct an arc on the circle from the point. Continue as shown.

Step 2

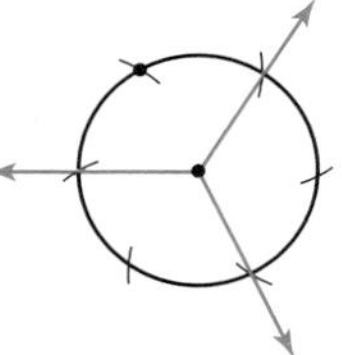

Draw rays from the center through every other arc.

Step 3

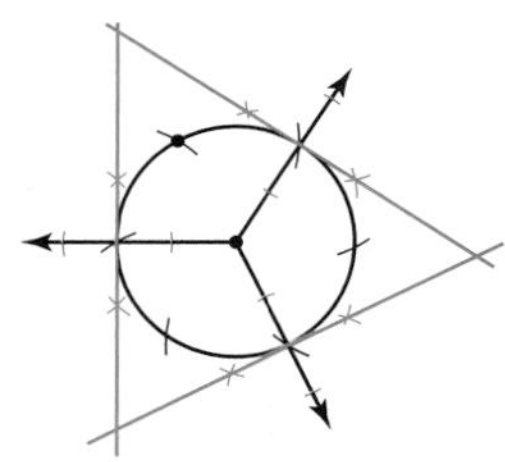

Construct a line perpendicular to each of the rays.

Model 2–4. See Ch. 10 Answer Appendix.

1. Draw a right triangle and inscribe a circle in it. See margin.
2. Inscribe a regular hexagon in a circle. Then inscribe an equilateral triangle in a circle. (*Hint:* The first step of each construction is identical to Step 1 in Activity 2.)
3. Inscribe a square in a circle. Then circumscribe a square about a circle.
4. **CHALLENGE** Circumscribe a regular hexagon about a circle.

Extending the Concept

Challenge students to repeat the activities for different types of polygons and practice the constructions.

Additional Answer

1. Sample answer:

LESSON 10-6 Secants, Tangents, and Angle Measures

Then

- You found measures of segments formed by tangents to a circle.

Now

1. Find measures of angles formed by lines intersecting on or inside a circle.
2. Find measures of angles formed by lines intersecting outside the circle.

Why?

- An average person's field of vision is about 180°. Most cameras have a much narrower viewing angle of between 20° and 50°. This viewing angle determines how much of a curved object a camera can capture on film.

NewVocabulary
secant

Common Core State Standards

Content Standards
Reinforcement of G.C.4
Construct a tangent line from a point outside a given circle to the circle.

Mathematical Practices
3 Construct viable arguments and critique the reasoning of others.
1 Make sense of problems and persevere in solving them.

1 Intersections On or Inside a Circle

A **secant** is a line that intersects a circle in exactly two points. Lines j and k are secants of $\odot C$.

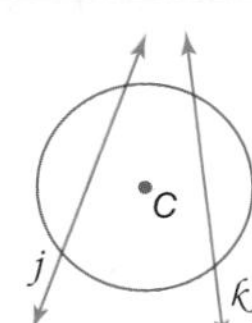

When two secants intersect inside a circle, the angles formed are related to the arcs they intercept.

Theorem 10.12

Words If two secants or chords intersect in the interior of a circle, then the measure of an angle formed is one half the *sum* of the measure of the arcs intercepted by the angle and its vertical angle.

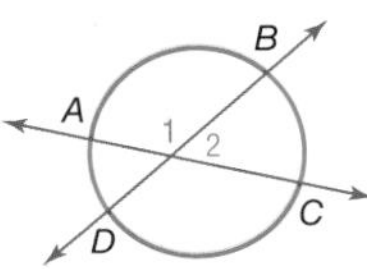

Example $m\angle 1 = \frac{1}{2}(m\widehat{AB} + m\widehat{CD})$ and $m\angle 2 = \frac{1}{2}(m\widehat{DA} + m\widehat{BC})$

Proof

Given: $\overleftrightarrow{HK}$ and $\overleftrightarrow{JL}$ intersect at M.

Prove: $m\angle 1 = \frac{1}{2}(m\widehat{JH} + m\widehat{LK})$

Proof:

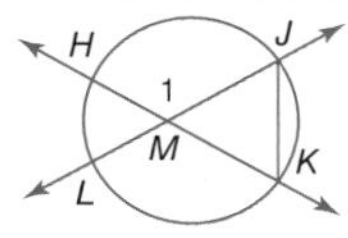

Statements	Reasons
1. $\overleftrightarrow{HK}$ and $\overleftrightarrow{JL}$ intersect at M.	1. Given
2. $m\angle 1 = m\angle MJK + m\angle MKJ$	2. Exterior Angle Theorem
3. $m\angle MJK = \frac{1}{2}m\angle\widehat{LK}$, $m\angle MKJ = \frac{1}{2}m\angle\widehat{JH}$	3. The measure of an inscribed $\angle$ equals half the measure of the intercepted arc.
4. $m\angle 1 = \frac{1}{2}m\angle\widehat{LK} + \frac{1}{2}m\angle\widehat{JH}$	4. Substitution
5. $m\angle 1 = \frac{1}{2}(m\widehat{JH} + m\widehat{LK})$	5. Distributive Property

1 Focus

VerticalAlignment

Before Lesson 10-6 Find measures of segments formed by tangents to a circle.

Lesson 10-6 Find measures of angles formed by lines intersecting on or inside a circle.
Find measures of angles formed by lines intersecting outside a circle.

After Lesson 10-6 Find measures of segments that intersect in the interior and exterior of a circle.

2 Teach

Scaffolding Questions

Have students read the **Why?** section of the lesson.

Ask:

- What percentage of the measure of a circle is 180°? 50%
- If a camera has a viewing angle of 50°, how much less of a viewing angle does the camera have compared to the average person's field of vision? 130°

Lesson 10-6 Resources

Resource	Approaching Level AL	On Level OL	Beyond Level BL	English Learners ELL
Teacher Edition	▪ Differentiated Instruction, pp. 742, 743	▪ Differentiated Instruction, pp. 742, 743, 749	▪ Differentiated Instruction, pp. 742, 743, 749	▪ Differentiated Instruction, pp. 742, 743
Chapter Resource Masters	▪ Study Guide and Intervention, pp. 37–38 ▪ Skills Practice, p. 39 ▪ Practice, p. 40 ▪ Word Problem Practice, p. 41	▪ Study Guide and Intervention, pp. 37–38 ▪ Skills Practice, p. 39 ▪ Practice, p. 40 ▪ Word Problem Practice, p. 41 ▪ Enrichment, p. 42	▪ Practice, p. 40 ▪ Word Problem Practice, p. 41 ▪ Enrichment, p. 42	▪ Study Guide and Intervention, pp. 37–38 ▪ Skills Practice, p. 39 ▪ Practice, p. 40 ▪ Word Problem Practice, p. 41
Other	▪ 5-Minute Check 10-6 ▪ Study Notebook	▪ 5-Minute Check 10-6 ▪ Study Notebook	▪ 5-Minute Check 10-6 ▪ Study Notebook	▪ 5-Minute Check 10-6 ▪ Study Notebook

1 Intersections On or Inside a Circle

Examples 1 and 2 show how to use the theorems in this lesson to find the measure of angles of secants or chords intersecting on or inside a circle.

Formative Assessment

Use the Guided Practice exercises after each example to determine students' understanding concepts.

Additional Example

1 Find x.

a.

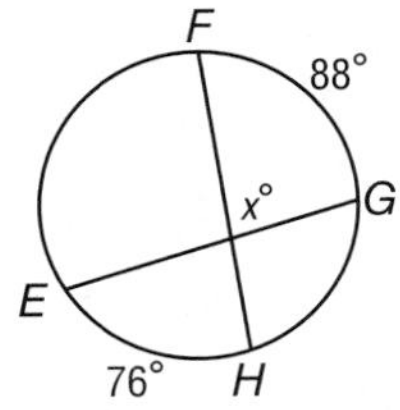

82

b.

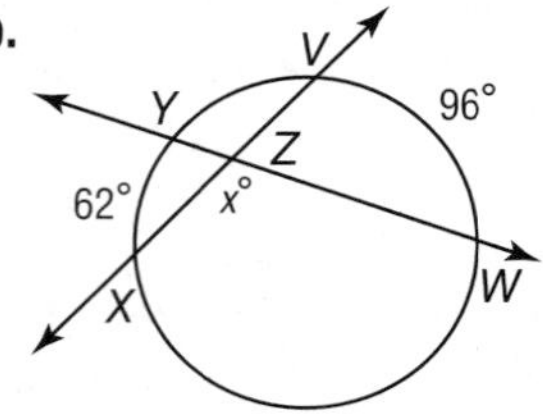

101

c.

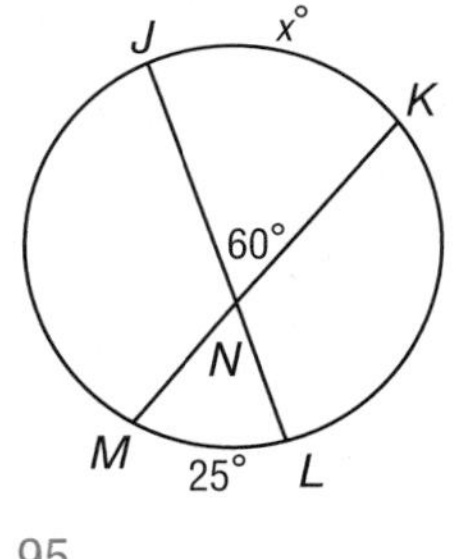

95

Additional Examples also in Interactive Classroom PowerPoint® Presentations

IWB Interactive White Board READY

Example 1 Use Intersecting Chords or Secants

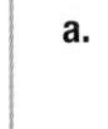

Find x.

a.

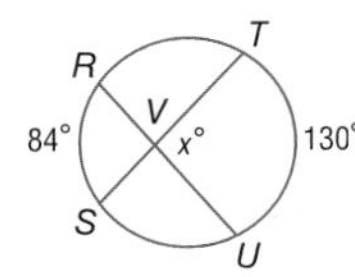

$m\angle TVU = \frac{1}{2}(m\widehat{RS} + m\widehat{TU})$ Theorem 10.12

$x = \frac{1}{2}(84 + 130)$ Substitution

$= \frac{1}{2}(214)$ or 107 Simplify.

StudyTip

Alternative Method
In Example 1b, $m\angle DEB$ can also be found by first finding the sum of the measures of $\widehat{AC}$ and $\widehat{BD}$.

$m\widehat{AC} + m\widehat{BD}$
$= 360 - (m\widehat{AC} + m\widehat{CD})$
$= 360 - (143 + 75)$
$= 142$

$m\angle DEB$
$= \frac{1}{2}(m\widehat{AC} + m\widehat{BD})$
$= \frac{1}{2}(142)$ or 71

b.

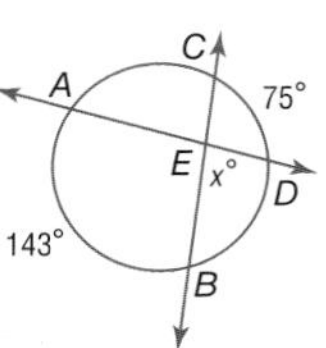

Step 1 Find $m\angle AEB$.

$m\angle AEB = \frac{1}{2}(m\widehat{AB} + m\widehat{CD})$ Theorem 10.12

$= \frac{1}{2}(143 + 75)$ Substitution

$= \frac{1}{2}(218)$ or 109 Simplify.

Step 2 Find x, the measure of $\angle DEB$.

$\angle AEB$ and $\angle DEB$ are supplementary angles.

So, $x = 180 - 109$ or 71.

c.

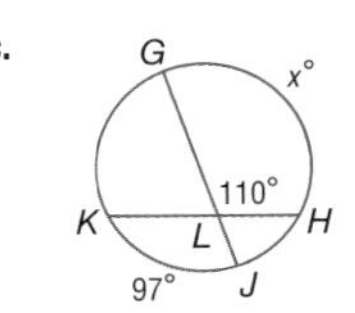

$m\angle GLH = \frac{1}{2}(m\widehat{GH} + m\widehat{KJ})$ Theorem 10.12

$110 = \frac{1}{2}(x + 97)$ Substitution

$220 = (x + 97)$ Multiply each side by 2.

$123 = x$ Subtract 97 from each side.

GuidedPractice

1A.

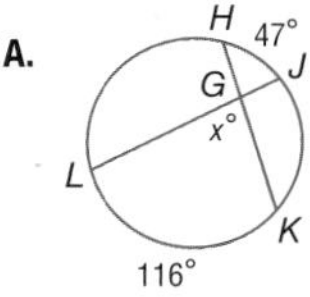

1B.

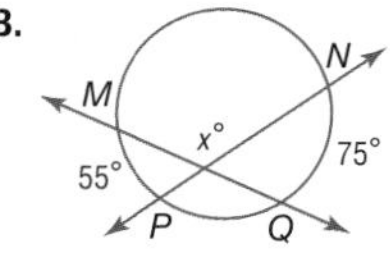

1C.

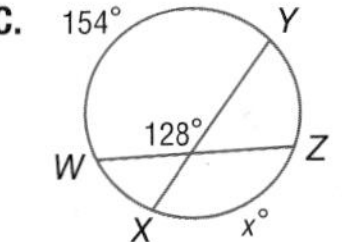

1A. 81.5
1B. 115
1C. 102

Recall that Theorem 10.6 states that the measure of an inscribed angle is half the measure of its intercepted arc. If one of the sides of this angle is tangent to the circle, this relationship still holds true.

Theorem 10.13

Words If a secant and a tangent intersect at the point of tangency, then the measure of each angle formed is one half the measure of its intercepted arc.

Example $m\angle 1 = \frac{1}{2}m\widehat{AB}$ and $m\angle 2 = \frac{1}{2}m\widehat{ACB}$

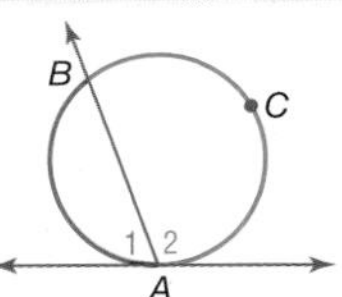

You will prove Theorem 10.13 in Exercise 33.

DifferentiatedInstruction

Naturalist Learners Explain that the relationships presented in this chapter are naturally occurring relationships that have been mathematically defined and explained. Tell students that scientists from all fields can use these relationships to examine everything from raindrops and soap bubbles to cells and microorganisms.

Example 2 Use Intersecting Secants and Tangents

Find each measure.

a. $m\angle QPR$

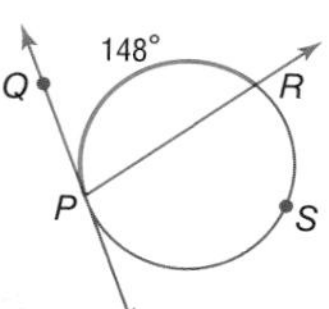

$m\angle QPR = \frac{1}{2}m\widehat{PR}$ — Theorem 10.13

$= \frac{1}{2}(148)$ or 74 — Substitute and simplify.

b. $m\widehat{DEF}$

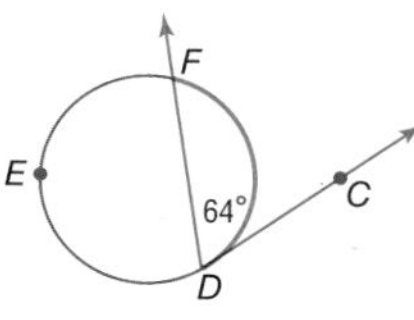

$m\angle CDF = \frac{1}{2}m\widehat{FD}$ — Theorem 10.13

$64 = \frac{1}{2}m\widehat{FD}$ — Substitution

$128 = m\widehat{FD}$ — Multiply each side by 2.

$m\widehat{DEF} = 360 - m\widehat{FD} = 360 - 128$ or 232

GuidedPractice

2A. Find $m\widehat{JLK}$. **232**

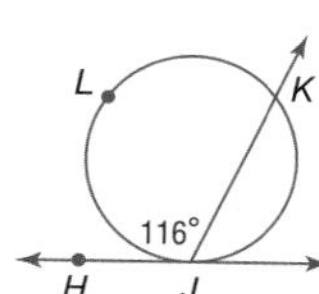

2B. Find $m\angle RQS$ if $m\widehat{QTS} = 238$. **61**

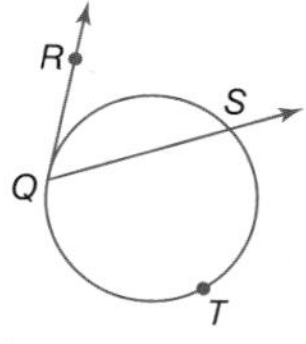

2 Intersections Outside a Circle

Secants and tangents can also meet outside a circle. The measure of the angle formed also involves half of the measures of the arcs they intercept.

Theorem 10.14

Words If two secants, a secant and a tangent, or two tangents intersect in the exterior of a circle, then the measure of the angle formed is one half the *difference* of the measures of the intercepted arcs.

Examples

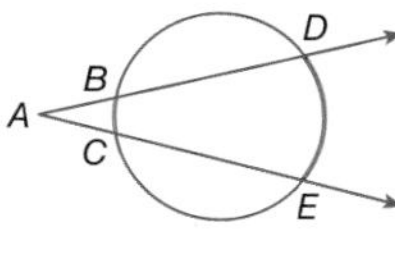

Two Secants

$m\angle A = \frac{1}{2}(m\widehat{DE} - m\widehat{BC})$

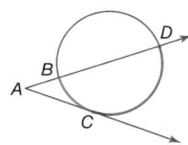

Secant-Tangent

$m\angle A = \frac{1}{2}(m\widehat{DC} - m\widehat{BC})$

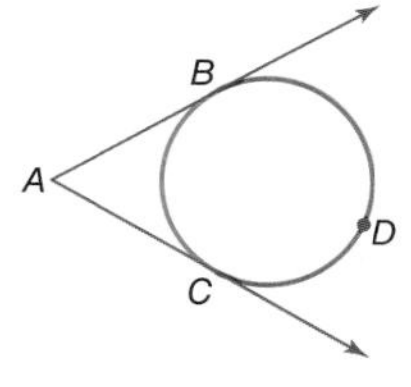

Two Tangents

$m\angle A = \frac{1}{2}(m\widehat{BDC} - m\widehat{BC})$

You will prove Theorem 10.14 in Exercises 30–32.

StudyTip

Absolute Value The measure of each $\angle A$ can also be expressed as half the absolute value of the difference of the arc measure. In this way, the order of the arc measures does not affect the outcome of the calculation.

Additional Example

2 Find each measure.

a. $m\angle QPS$ 125

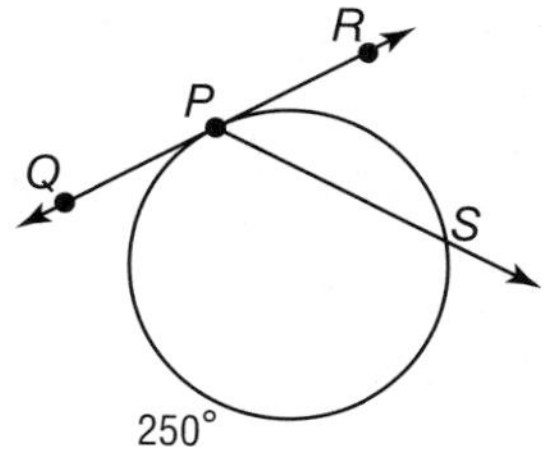

b. $m\widehat{BCD}$ 144

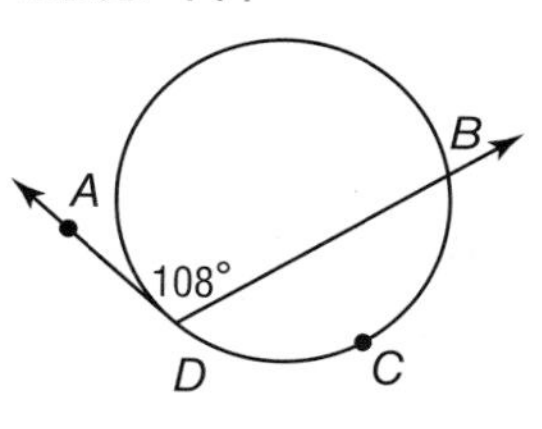

Focus on Mathematical Content

Chord vs. Secants Some students may ask you what the difference is between chords and secants and why there are two names for something that intersects a circle at two points. You may want to review how segments are parts of lines and explain that chords are segments of secants, which are lines that intersect circles. Tell students that every chord lies on a secant and that every secant contains a chord.

DifferentiatedInstruction AL OL BL ELL

Kinesthetic Learners Allow students time to create examples of Theorems like 10.14 for themselves. These theorems are difficult to remember, so drawing their own examples may help students to recall or derive the relationships later.

2 Intersections Outside a Circle

Examples 3 and 4 show how to use the theorem about secants and tangents to find the measure of an angle that intersects outside a circle.

Additional Examples

3 Find each measure.

a. $m\widehat{BC}$ 17

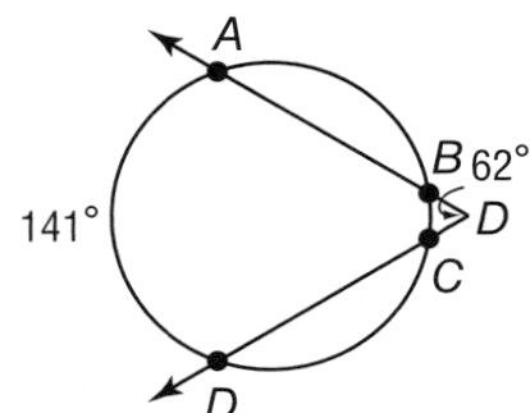

b. $m\widehat{XYZ}$ 220

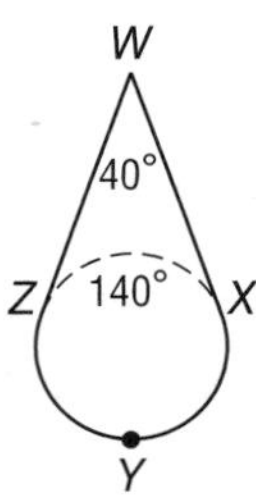

4 **PHYSICS** The diagram shows the path of a light ray as it hits a cut diamond. The ray is bent, or refracted, at points A, B, and C. If $m\widehat{AC} = 96$ and $m\angle S = 35$, what is $m\widehat{RBT}$? 26

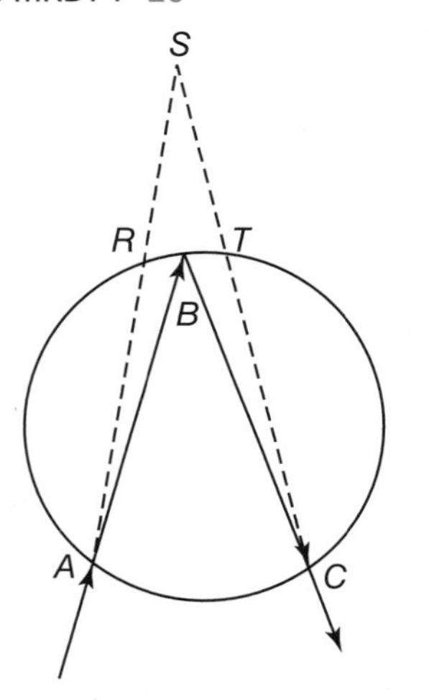

Example 3 Use Tangents and Secants that Intersect Outside a Circle

Find each measure.

a. $m\angle L$

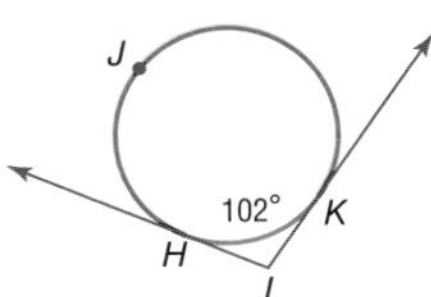

$m\angle L = \frac{1}{2}(m\widehat{HJK} - m\widehat{HK})$ Theorem 10.14

$= \frac{1}{2}(360 - 102) - 102$ Substitution

$= \frac{1}{2}(258 - 102)$ or 78 Simplify.

b. $m\widehat{CD}$

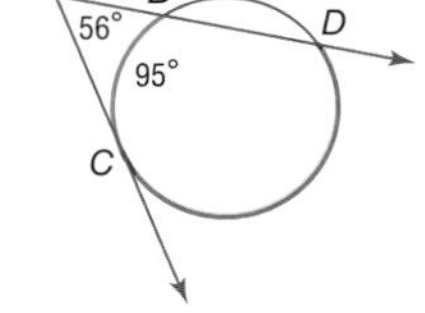

$m\angle A = \frac{1}{2}(m\widehat{CD} - m\widehat{BC})$ Theorem 10.14

$56 = \frac{1}{2}(m\widehat{CD} - 95)$ Substitution

$112 = m\widehat{CD} - 95$ Multiply each side by 2.

$207 = m\widehat{CD}$ Add 95 to each side.

GuidedPractice

3A. $m\angle S$ **54**

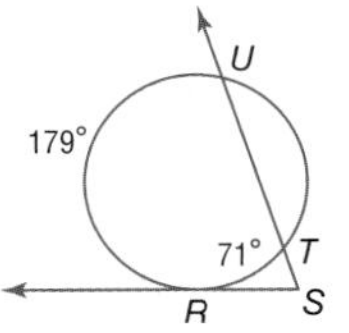

3B. $m\widehat{XZ}$ **88**

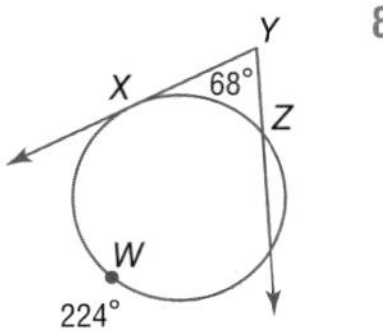

Real-WorldLink

There is a difference in the *index of refraction* between the two mediums such as air and glass. The index of refraction N is given by the equation $N = \frac{c}{V}$, where c is the speed of light and V is the velocity of light in that material.

Source: Microscopy Resource Center

You can apply the properties of intersecting secants to solve real-world problems.

Real-World Example 4 Apply Properties of Intersecting Secants

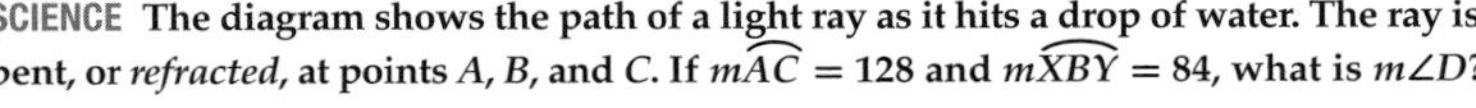

SCIENCE **The diagram shows the path of a light ray as it hits a drop of water. The ray is bent, or *refracted*, at points A, B, and C. If $m\widehat{AC} = 128$ and $m\widehat{XBY} = 84$, what is $m\angle D$?**

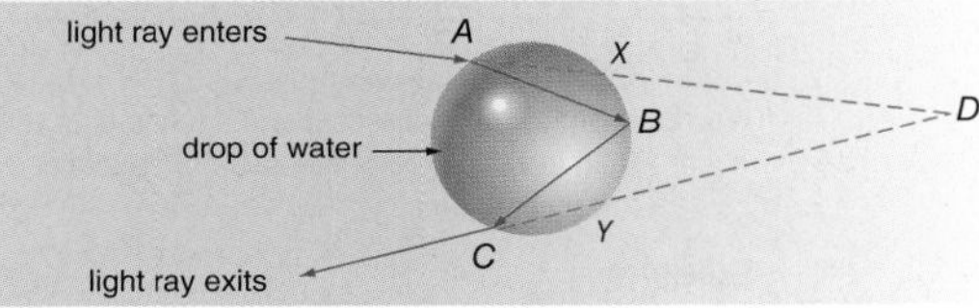

$m\angle D = \frac{1}{2}(m\widehat{AC} - m\widehat{XBY})$ Theorem 10.14

$= \frac{1}{2}(128 - 84)$ Substitution

$= \frac{1}{2}(44)$ or 22 Simplify.

GuidedPractice

4. Find the value of x. **60**

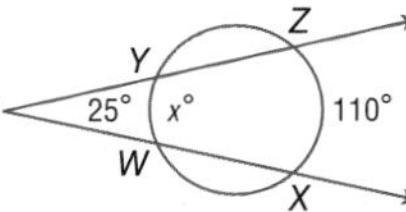

Teach with Tech

Video Recording Have students work in groups to create a video explaining the three theorems for when secants and tangents intersect outside of the circle. Have students explain how the theorems are similar and how they are different.

KeyConcept Circle and Angle Relationships

Vertex of Angle	Model(s)	Angle Measure
on the circle		one half the measure of the intercepted arc $m\angle 1 = \frac{1}{2}x$
inside the circle		one half the measure of the sum of the intercepted arc $m\angle 1 = \frac{1}{2}(x + y)$
outside the circle		one half the measure of the difference of the intercepted arcs $m\angle 1 = \frac{1}{2}(x - y)$

Check Your Understanding

Examples 1–2 Find each measure. Assume that segments that appear to be tangent are tangent.

1. $m\angle 1$ 110

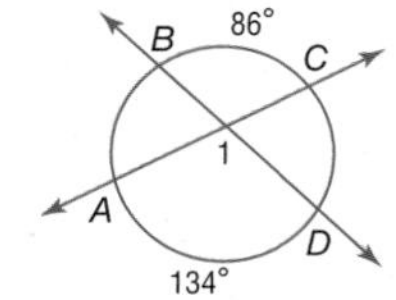

2. $m\widehat{TS}$ 144

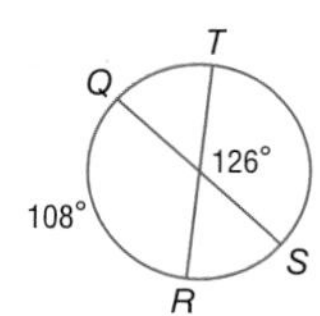

3. $m\angle 2$ 73

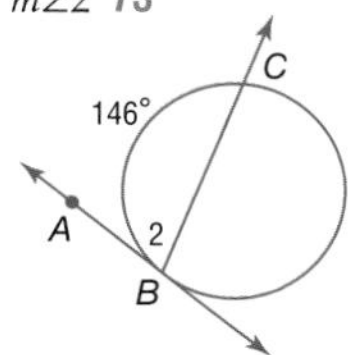

Examples 3–4 **4.** $m\angle H$ 31

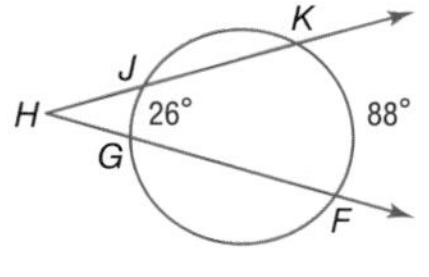

5. $m\widehat{QTS}$ 248

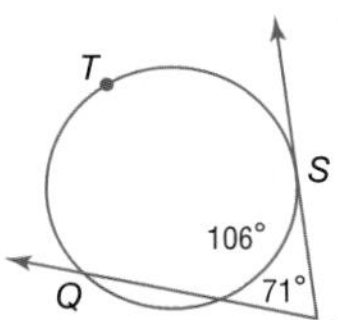

6. $m\widehat{LP}$ 150

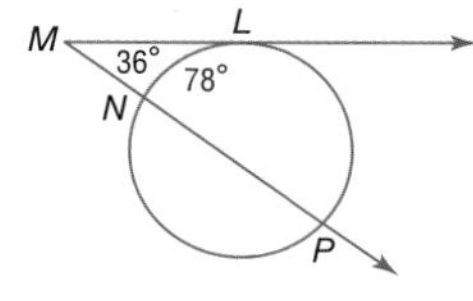

7. **STUNTS** A ramp is attached to the first of several barrels that have been strapped together for a circus motorcycle stunt as shown. What is the measure of the angle the ramp makes with the ground? 15

3 Practice

Formative Assessment

Use Exercises 1–7 to check for understanding.

Use the chart at the bottom of this page to customize assignments for your students.

Differentiated Homework Options

Level	Assignment	Two-Day Option	
AL Basic	8–25, 36, 38, 40–58	9–25 odd, 42–45	8–24 even, 36, 38, 40, 41, 46–58
OL Core	9–29 odd, 30–36, 38, 40–58	8–25, 42–45	26–36, 38, 40, 41, 46–58
BL Advanced	26–52, (optional: 53–58)		

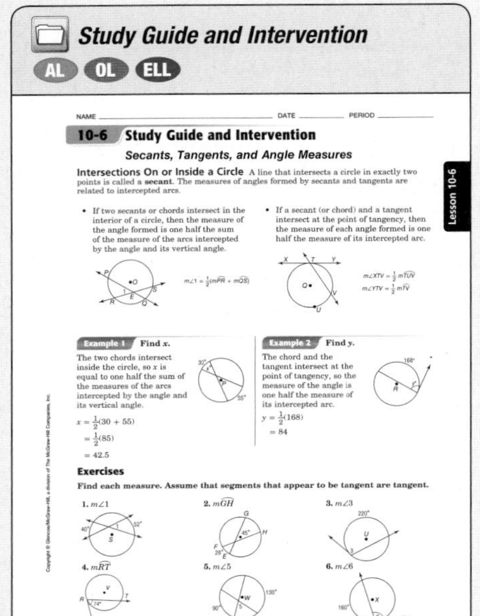

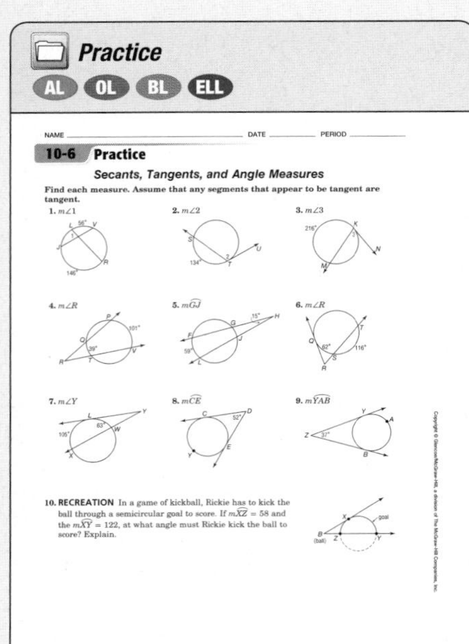

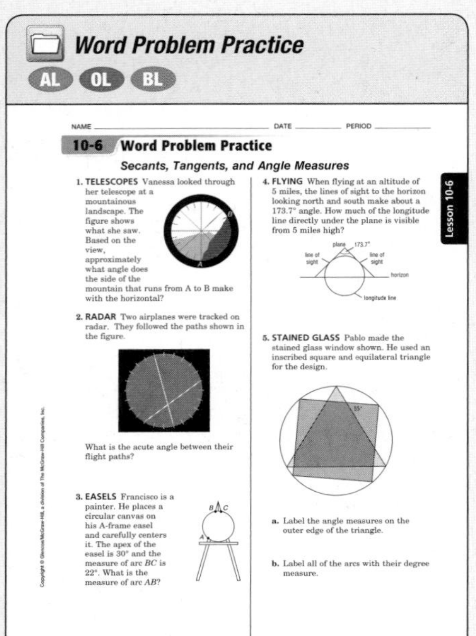

Practice and Problem Solving

Extra Practice is on page R10.

Examples 1–2 Find each measure. Assume that segments that appear to be tangent are tangent.

8. $m\angle 3$ **82**

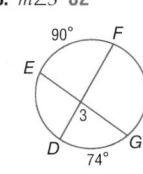

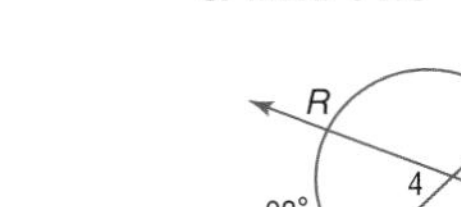

9. $m\angle 4$ **71.5**

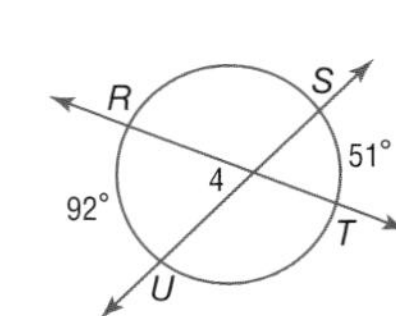

10. $m\angle JMK$ **102**

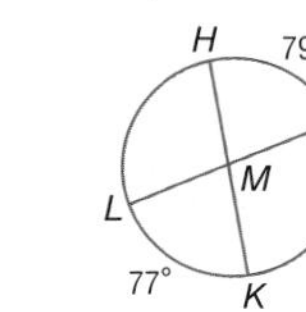

11 $m\widehat{RQ}$ **28**

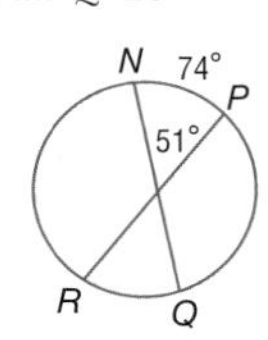

12. $m\angle K$ **97**

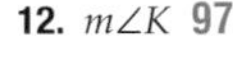

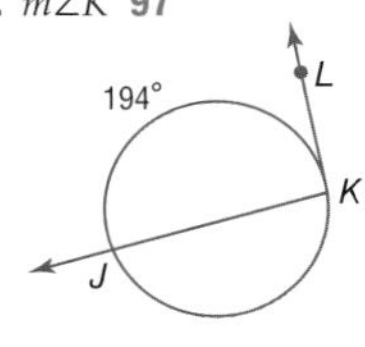

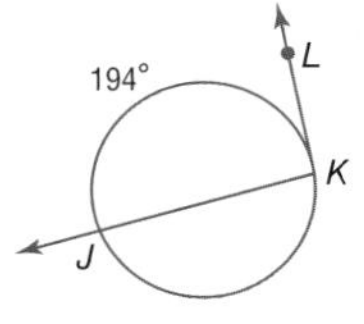

13. $m\widehat{PM}$ **144**

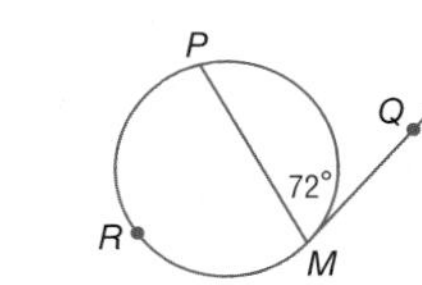

14. $m\angle ABD$ **103**

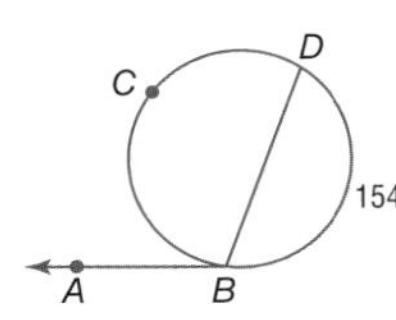

15. $m\angle DAB$ **125**

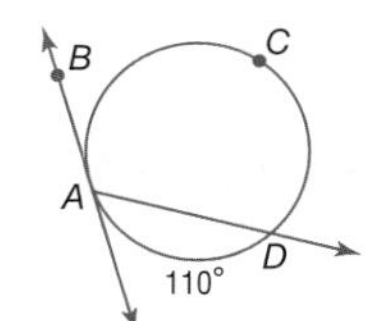

16. $m\widehat{GJF}$ **196**

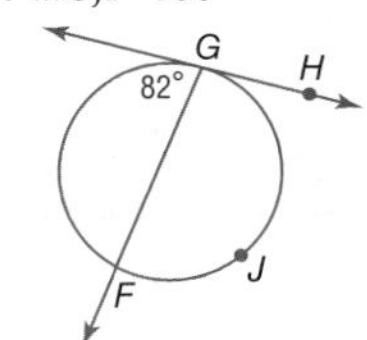

17. SPORTS The multi-sport field shown includes a softball field and a soccer field. If $m\widehat{ABC} = 200$, find each measure.

a. $m\angle ACE$ **100**

b. $m\angle ADC$ **20**

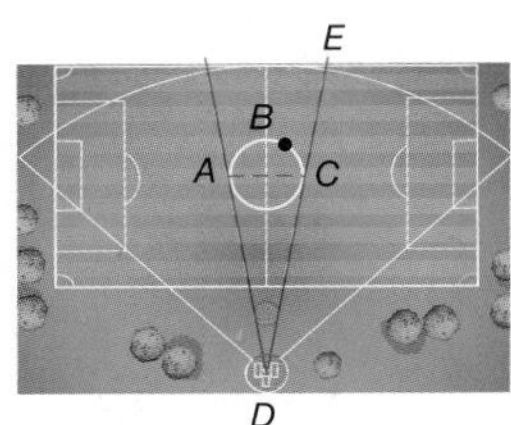

Examples 3–4 CCSS **STRUCTURE** Find each measure.

18. $m\angle A$ **81**

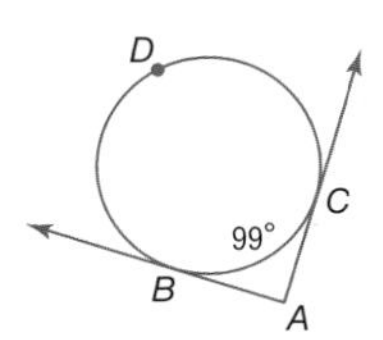

19. $m\angle W$ **74**

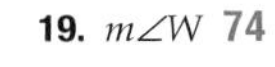

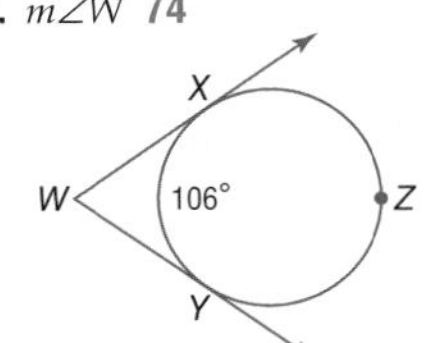

20. $m\widehat{JM}$ **205**

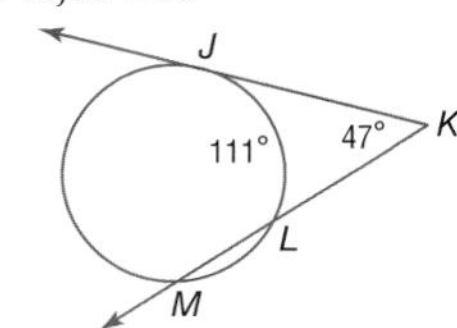

21. $m\widehat{XY}$ **185**

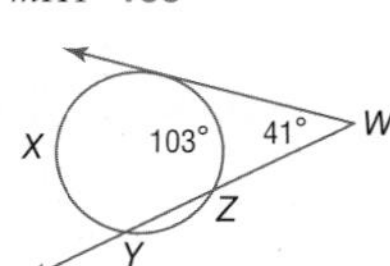

22. $m\angle R$ **30**

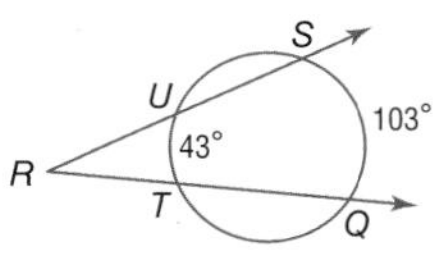

23. $m\widehat{SU}$ **22**

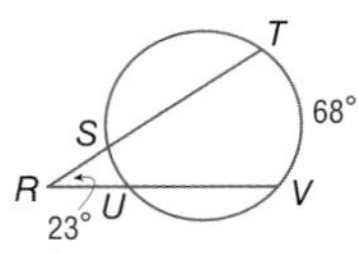

746 | Lesson 10-6 | Secants, Tangents, and Angle Measures

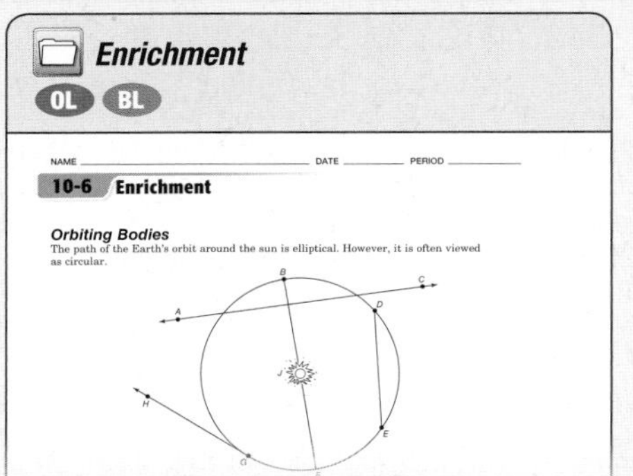

CCSS Teaching the Mathematical Practices

Structure Mathematically proficient students look closely to discern a pattern or structure. They also can step back for an overview and shift perspective. In Exercises 18–23, encourage students to identify the tangents and secants and use Theorem 10.14.

24. JEWELRY In the circular necklace shown, A and B are tangent points. If $x = 260$, what is y? **80**

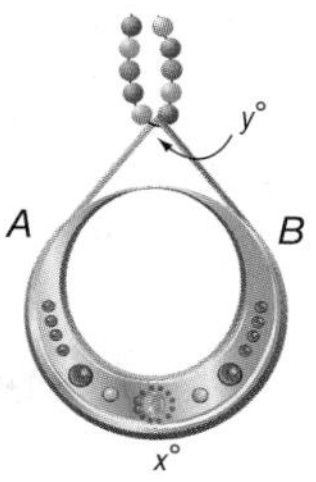

25. SPACE A satellite orbits above Earth's equator. Find x, the measure of the planet's arc, that is visible to the satellite. **168**

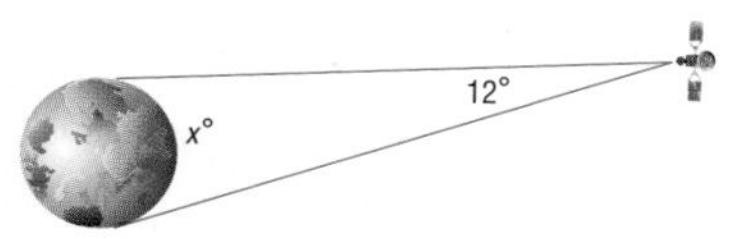

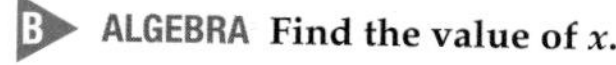

B ALGEBRA Find the value of x.

26.

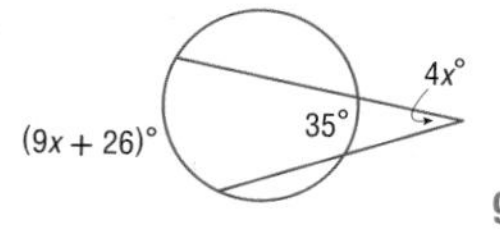

9

27

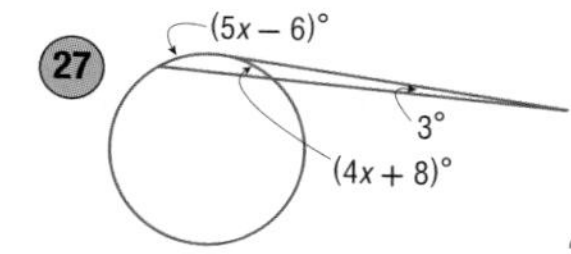

20

28.

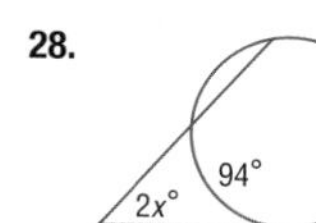

19

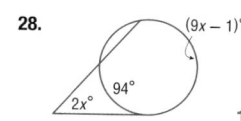

29. PHOTOGRAPHY A photographer frames a carousel in his camera shot as shown so that the lines of sight form tangents to the carousel.

a. If the camera's viewing angle is 35°, what is the arc measure of the carousel that appears in the shot? **145**

b. If you want to capture an arc measure of 150° in the photograph, what viewing angle should be used? **30**

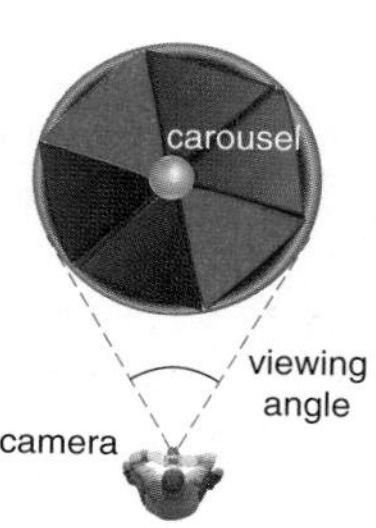

CCSS ARGUMENTS For each case of Theorem 10.14, write a two-column proof. 31–32. See margin.

30. Case 1 See Ch. 10 Answer Appendix.

Given: secants $\overrightarrow{AD}$ and $\overrightarrow{AE}$

Prove: $m\angle A = \frac{1}{2}(m\widehat{DE} - m\widehat{BC})$

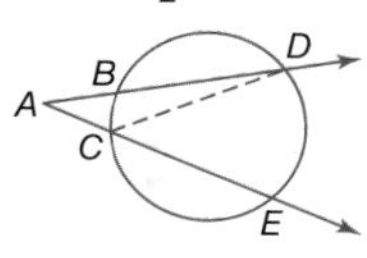

31. Case 2

Given: tangent $\overrightarrow{FM}$ and secant $\overrightarrow{FL}$

Prove: $m\angle F = \frac{1}{2}(m\widehat{LH} - m\widehat{GH})$

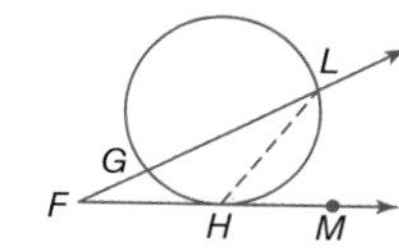

32. Case 3

Given: tangents $\overrightarrow{RS}$ and $\overrightarrow{RV}$

Prove: $m\angle R = \frac{1}{2}(m\widehat{SWT} - m\widehat{ST})$

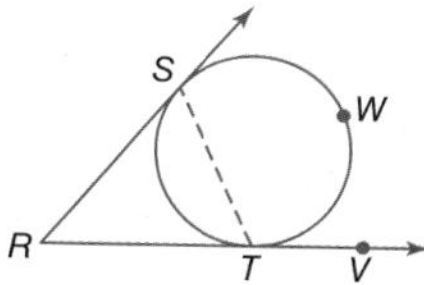

33. PROOF Write a paragraph proof of Theorem 10.13.

a. Given: $\overleftrightarrow{AB}$ is a tangent of $\odot O$.
$\overleftrightarrow{AC}$ is a secant of $\odot O$.
$\angle CAE$ is acute.

Prove: $m\angle CAE = \frac{1}{2}m\widehat{CA}$

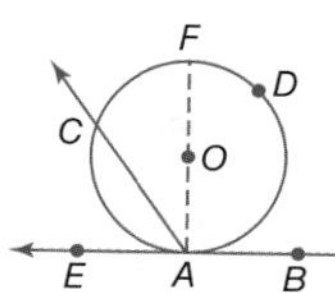

b. Prove that if $\angle CAB$ is obtuse, $m\angle CAB = \frac{1}{2}m\widehat{CDA}$. **See margin.**

CCSS Teaching the Mathematical Practices

Arguments Mathematically proficient students understand and use stated assumptions and definitions in constructing arguments. They make conjectures and build a logical progression of statements to explore the truth of their conjectures. In Exercises 30–32, encourage students to use the Exterior Angles Theorem in their proofs.

Additional Answers

31. Statements (Reasons)

1. $\overrightarrow{FM}$ is a tangent to the circle and $\overrightarrow{FL}$ is a secant to the circle. (Given)
2. $m\angle FLH = \frac{1}{2}m\widehat{HG}$, $m\angle LHM = \frac{1}{2}m\widehat{LH}$ (The meas. of an inscribed $\angle = \frac{1}{2}$ the measure of its intercepted arc.)
3. $m\angle LHM = m\angle FLH + m\angle F$ (Exterior ⦣ Theorem)
4. $\frac{1}{2}m\widehat{LH} = \frac{1}{2}m\widehat{HG} + m\angle F$ (Substitution)
5. $\frac{1}{2}m\widehat{LH} - \frac{1}{2}m\widehat{HG} = m\angle F$ (Subtraction Prop.)
6. $\frac{1}{2}(m\widehat{LH} - m\widehat{HG}) = m\angle F$ (Distributive Prop.)

32. Statements (Reasons)

1. $\overrightarrow{RS}$ and $\overrightarrow{RV}$ are tangents to the circle. (Given)
2. $m\angle STV = \frac{1}{2}m\widehat{SWT}$, $m\angle RST = \frac{1}{2}m\widehat{ST}$ (The meas. of an secant-tangent $\angle = \frac{1}{2}$ the measure of its intercepted arc.)
3. $m\angle STV = m\angle RST + m\angle R$ (Exterior ⦣ Theorem)
4. $\frac{1}{2}m\widehat{SWT} = \frac{1}{2}m\widehat{ST} + m\angle R$ (Substitution)
5. $\frac{1}{2}m\widehat{SWT} - \frac{1}{2}m\widehat{ST} = m\angle R$ (Subtraction Prop.)
6. $\frac{1}{2}(m\widehat{SWT} - m\widehat{ST}) = m\angle R$ (Distributive Prop.)

33a. Proof: By Theorem 10.10, $\overline{OA} \perp \overline{AB}$. So, $\angle FAE$ is a right $\angle$ with measure 90, and $\widehat{FCA}$ is a semicircle with measure of 180. Since $\angle CAE$ is acute, C is in the interior of $\angle FAE$. By the Angle and Arc Addition Postulates, $m\angle FAE = m\angle FAC + m\angle CAE$ and $m\widehat{FCA} = m\widehat{FC} + m\widehat{CA}$. By substitution, $90 = m\angle FAC + m\angle CAE$ and $180 = m\widehat{FC} + m\widehat{CA}$. So, $90 = \frac{1}{2}m\widehat{FC} + \frac{1}{2}m\widehat{CA}$ by Division Prop., and $m\angle FAC + m\angle CAE = \frac{1}{2}m\widehat{FC} + \frac{1}{2}m\widehat{CA}$ by substitution. $m\angle FAC = \frac{1}{2}m\widehat{FC}$ since $\angle FAC$ is inscribed, so substitution yields $\frac{1}{2}m\widehat{FC} + m\angle CAE = \frac{1}{2}m\widehat{FC} + \frac{1}{2}m\widehat{CA}$. By Subt. Prop., $m\angle CAE = \frac{1}{2}m\widehat{CA}$.

33b. Use same reasoning to prove $m\angle CAB = \frac{1}{2}m\widehat{CDA}$.

Multiple Representations

In Exercise 35, students use geometric sketches, a table, and verbal description to investigate the relationship between Theorems 10.11 and 10.5.

Exercise Alert

Compass, Straightedge, and Protractor Exercise 40 requires the use of a compass, a straightedge, and a protractor.

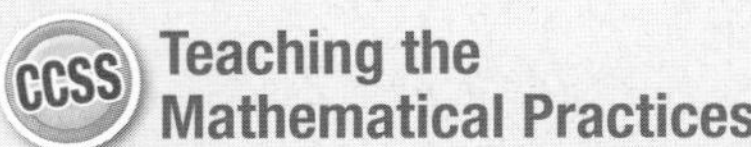

Teaching the Mathematical Practices

Arguments Mathematically proficient students understand and use stated assumptions, definitions, and previously established results in constructing arguments. In Exercise 39, encourage students to recognize the relationship between a diameter and its intercepted arc.

Additional Answers

35a. See bottom margin.

35b.

	Circle 1	Circle 2	Circle 3
$\widehat{CD}$	25	15	5
$\widehat{AB}$	50	50	50
x	37.5	32.5	27.5

38. Sample answer: $m\widehat{AB} = m\widehat{BC}$; $m\angle BAC = m\angle BCA$ because the triangle is isosceles. Since $\angle BAC$ and $\angle BCA$ are inscribed angles, by Theorem 10.6, $m\widehat{AB} = 2m\angle BCA$ and $m\widehat{BC} = 2m\angle BAC$. So, $m\widehat{AB} = m\widehat{BC}$.

39b. $m\widehat{KH} = 56$; $m\widehat{HJ} = 124$; Because a diameter is involved the intercepted arcs measure $(180 - x)$ and x degrees. Hence solving $\frac{180 - x - x}{2} = 34$ leads to the answer.

40. Sample answer:

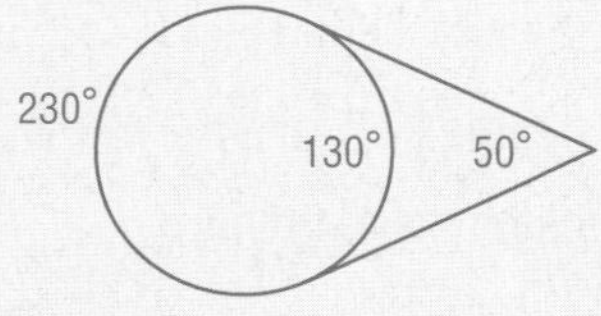

By Theorem 10.13, $m\angle 1 = \frac{1}{2}(x - y)$. So, $50 = \frac{1}{2}[(360 - x) - x]$. Therefore, x (minor arc) $= 130$, and y (major arc) $= 360 - 130$ or 230.

34. WALLPAPER In the wallpaper design shown, $\overline{BC}$ is a diameter of $\odot Q$. If $m\angle A = 26$ and $m\widehat{CE} = 67$, what is $m\widehat{DE}$? **98**

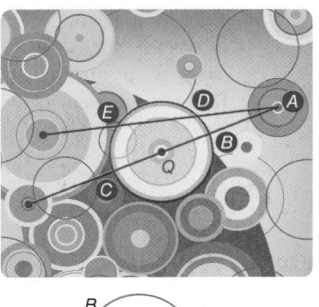

35. MULTIPLE REPRESENTATIONS In this problem, you will explore the relationship between Theorems 10.12 and 10.6.

a. **Geometric** Copy the figure shown. Then draw three successive figures in which the position of point D moves closer to point C, but points A, B, and C remain fixed. **See margin.**

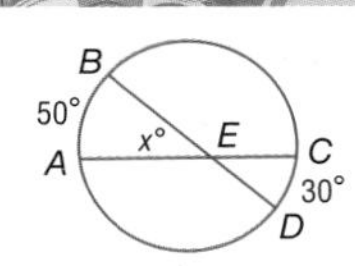

b. **Tabular** Estimate the measure of $\widehat{CD}$ for each successive circle, recording the measures of $\widehat{AB}$ and $\widehat{CD}$ in a table. Then calculate and record the value of x for each circle. **See margin.**

c. **Verbal** Describe the relationship between $m\widehat{AB}$ and the value of x as $m\widehat{CD}$ approaches zero. What type of angle does $\angle AEB$ become when $m\widehat{CD} = 0$?

35c. As the measure of $\widehat{CD}$ gets closer to 0, the measure of x approaches half of $m\widehat{AB}$; $\angle AEB$ becomes an inscribed angle.

d. **Analytical** Write an algebraic proof to show the relationship between Theorems 10.12 and 10.6 described in part **c**.
$x = \frac{1}{2}(m\widehat{AB} + m\widehat{CD})$; $x = \frac{1}{2}(m\widehat{AB} + 0)$; $x = \frac{1}{2}m\widehat{AB}$

H.O.T. Problems Use Higher-Order Thinking Skills

36. WRITING IN MATH Explain how to find the measure of an angle formed by a secant and a tangent that intersect outside a circle. **Find the difference of the two intercepted arcs and divide by 2**

37. CHALLENGE The circles below are concentric. What is x? **15**

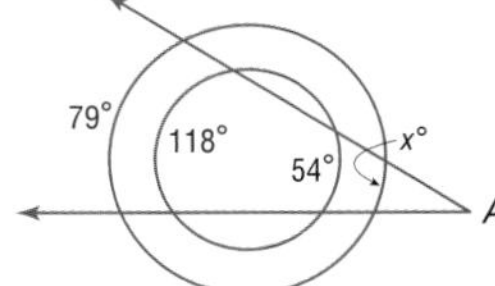
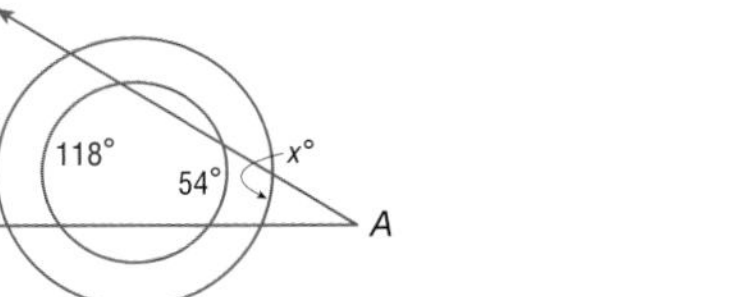

38. REASONING Isosceles $\triangle ABC$ is inscribed in $\odot D$. What can you conclude about $m\widehat{AB}$ and $m\widehat{BC}$? Explain. **See margin.**

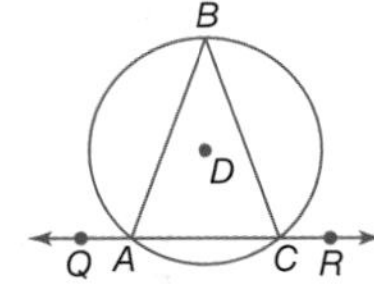

39a. $m\angle G \leq 90$; $m\angle G < 90$ for all values except when $\overrightarrow{JG} \perp \overrightarrow{GH}$ at G, then $m\angle G = 90$.

39. ARGUMENTS In the figure, $\overline{JK}$ is a diameter and $\overrightarrow{GH}$ is a tangent.

a. Describe the range of possible values for $m\angle G$. Explain.

b. If $m\angle G = 34$, find the measures of minor arcs HJ and KH. Explain. **See margin.**

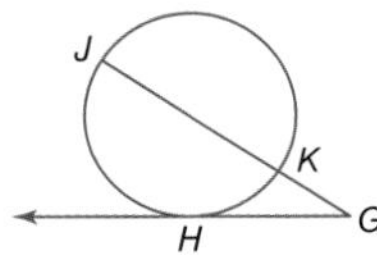

40. OPEN ENDED Draw a circle and two tangents that intersect outside the circle. Use a protractor to measure the angle that is formed. Find the measures of the minor and major arcs formed. Explain your reasoning. **See margin.**

41. WRITING IN MATH A circle is inscribed within $\triangle PQR$. If $m\angle P = 50$ and $m\angle Q = 60$, describe how to find the measures of the three minor arcs formed by the points of tangency.

41. Sample answer: Using Theorem 10.14, $60° = \frac{1}{2}[(360 - x) - x]$ or 120°; repeat for 50° to get 130°. The third arc can be found by adding 50° and 60° and subtracting from 360 to get 110°.

35a.

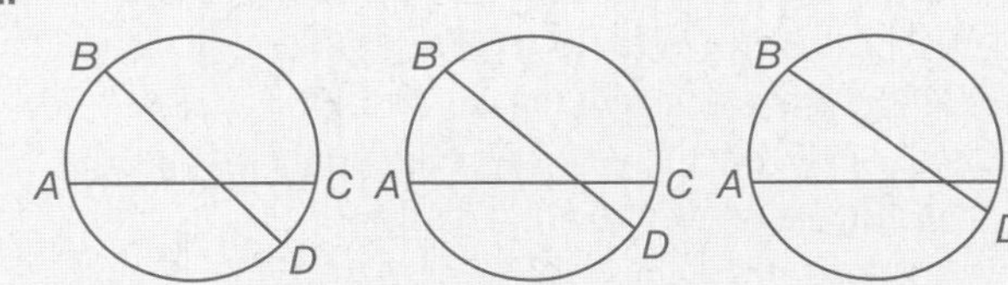

Standardized Test Practice

42. What is the value of x if $m\widehat{NR} = 62$ and $m\widehat{NP} = 108$? **C**

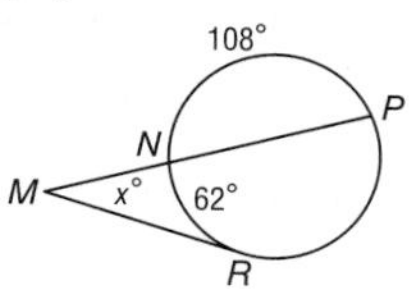

A 23°
B 31°
C 64°
D 128°

43. ALGEBRA Points $A(-4, 8)$ and $B(6, 2)$ are both on circle C, and $\overline{AB}$ is a diameter. What are the coordinates of C? **J**

F (2, 10)
G (10, −6)
H (5, −3)
J (1, 5)

44. GRIDDED RESPONSE If $m\angle AED = 95$ and $m\widehat{AD} = 120$, what is $m\angle BAC$? **35**

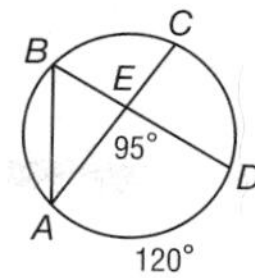

45. SAT/ACT If the circumference of the circle below is 16π units, what is the total area of the shaded regions? **B**

A 64π units^2
B 32π units^2
C 12π units^2
D 8π units^2
E 2π units^2

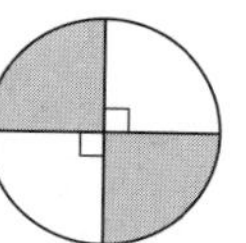

Spiral Review

Find x. Assume that segments that appear to be tangent are tangent. (Lesson 10-5)

46. 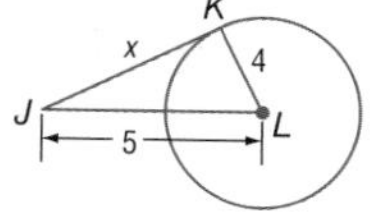

3

47. 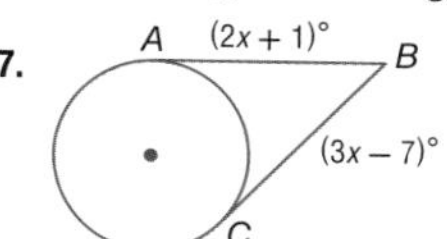

8

48. 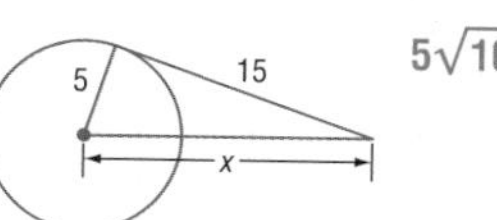

$5\sqrt{10}$

49. PROOF Write a two-column proof. (Lesson 10-4)

Given: $\widehat{MHT}$ is a semicircle; $\overline{RH} \perp \overline{TM}$.

Prove: $\frac{TR}{RH} = \frac{TH}{HM}$ **See margin.**

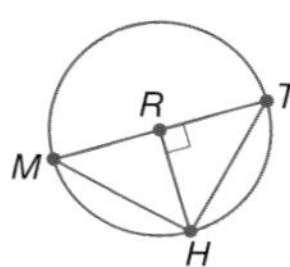

50. REMODELING The diagram at the right shows the floor plan of Trent's kitchen. Each square on the diagram represents a 3-foot by 3-foot area. While remodeling his kitchen, Trent moved his refrigerator from square A to square B. Describe one possible combination of transformations that could be used to make this move. (Lesson 9-4) **See margin.**

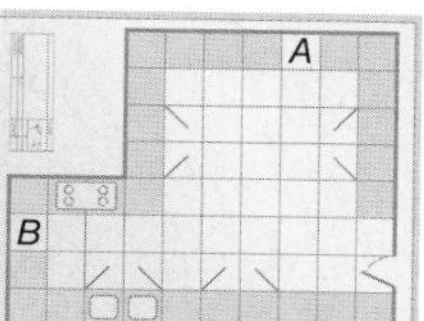

COORDINATE GEOMETRY Find the measure of each angle to the nearest tenth of a degree by using the Distance Formula and an inverse trigonometric ratio. (Lesson 8-4)

51. $\angle C$ in triangle BCD with vertices $B(-1, -5)$, $C(-6, -5)$, and $D(-1, 2)$ **54.5**

52. $\angle X$ in right triangle XYZ with vertices $X(2, 2)$, $Y(2, -2)$, and $Z(7, -2)$ **51.3**

Skills Review

Solve each equation.

53. $x^2 + 13x = -36$ **−4, −9**

54. $x^2 - 6x = -9$ **3**

55. $3x^2 + 15x = 0$ **0, −5**

56. $28 = x^2 + 3x$ **−7, 4**

57. $x^2 + 12x + 36 = 0$ **−6**

58. $x^2 + 5x = -\frac{25}{4}$ **$-\frac{5}{2}$**

Differentiated Instruction OL BL

Extension If two chords in the same circle cut two arcs of 75 degrees, what do you know about the chords? If the arcs have an endpoint on each chord, then the chords are parallel. If the arcs have both endpoints on the same chord, then the chords are congruent.

4 Assess

Name the Math Select examples and ask students to call out the names of the segments in the figure as they leave the classroom.

Formative Assessment

Check for student understanding of Lessons 10-5 and 10-6.

 Quiz 3, p. 58

Additional Answers

49. Given: $\widehat{MHT}$ is a semicircle. $\overline{RH} \perp \overline{TM}$.

Prove: $\frac{TR}{RH} = \frac{TH}{HM}$

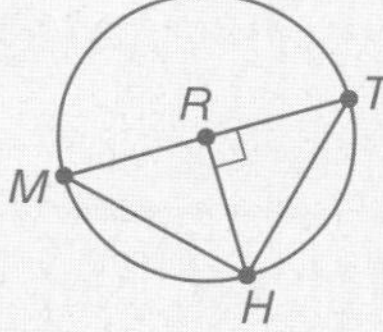

Proof:

Statements (Reasons)

1. $\widehat{MHT}$ is a semicircle; $\overline{RH} \perp \overline{TM}$. (Given)
2. $\angle THM$ is a right angle. (If an inscribed $\angle$ intercepts a semicircle, the $\angle$ is a rt. $\angle$.)
3. $\angle TRH$ is a right angle (Def. of $\perp$ lines)
4. $\angle THM \cong \angle TRH$ (All rt. angles are $\cong$.)
5. $\angle T \cong \angle T$ (Reflexive Prop.)
6. $\triangle TRH \sim \triangle THM$ (AA Sim.)
7. $\frac{TR}{RH} = \frac{TH}{HM}$ (Def. of $\sim \triangle$s)

50. The move is a translation 15 feet out from the wall and 21 feet to the left, then a rotation of 90° counterclockwise.

1 Focus

Vertical Alignment

Before Lesson 10-7 Find measures of diagonals that intersect in the interior of a parallelogram.

Lesson 10-7 Find measures of segments that intersect in the interior of a circle. Find measures of segments that intersect in the exterior of a circle.

After Lesson 10-7 Write the equation of a circle.
Graph a circle on the coordinate plane.

2 Teach

Scaffolding Questions

Have students read the **Why?** section of the lesson.

Ask:

- What geometric parts of a circle do the cut edge and the curved edge of the remaining cake represent with respect to the circular edge of the original cake? a chord and an arc, respectively
- Which measurements do you have to know to find the measure of the arc representing the curved edge of the remaining cake? the length of the chord (the cut edge of the cake) and the radius of the cake

LESSON 10-7 Special Segments in a Circle

Then

- You found measures of diagonals that intersect in the interior of a parallelogram.

Now

1. Find measures of segments that intersect in the interior of a circle.
2. Find measures of segments that intersect in the exterior of a circle.

Why?

- A large circular cake is cut lengthwise instead of into wedges to serve more people for a party. Only a small portion of the original cake remains. Using the geometry of circles, you can determine the diameter of the original cake.

New Vocabulary
chord segment
secant segment
external secant segment
tangent segment

Common Core State Standards

Content Standards
Reinforcement of G.C.4 Construct a tangent line from a point outside a given circle to the circle.

Mathematical Practices
1 Make sense of problems and persevere in solving them.
7 Look for and make use of structure.

1 Segments Intersecting Inside a Circle

When two chords intersect inside a circle, each chord is divided into two segments, called **chord segments**.

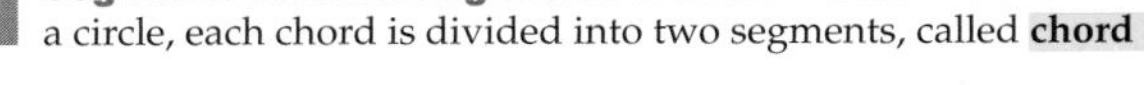

Theorem 10.15 Segments of Chords Theorem

Words If two chords intersect in a circle, then the products of the lengths of the chord segments are equal.

Example $AB \cdot BC = DB \cdot BE$

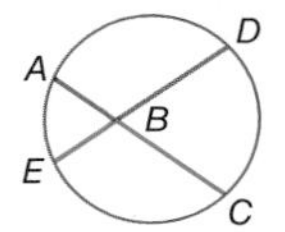

You will prove Theorem 10.15 in Exercise 23.

Example 1 Use the Intersection of Two Chords

Find x.

a.

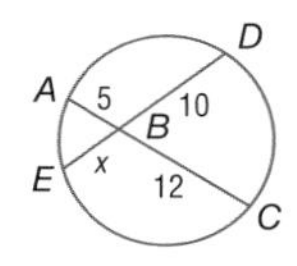

$AB \cdot BC = EB \cdot BD$ Theorem 10.15
$5 \cdot 12 = x \cdot 10$ Substitution
$60 = 10x$ Multiply.
$6 = x$ Divide each side by 10.

b.

P
x + 1
x + 10
L
K
x
J
x + 8
M

$JK \cdot KL = PK \cdot KM$ Theorem 10.15
$(x + 10) \cdot x = (x + 1)(x + 8)$ Substitution
$x^2 + 10x = x^2 + 9x + 8$ Multiply.
$10x = 9x + 8$ Subtract x^2 from each side.
$x = 8$ Subtract $9x$ from each side.

Guided Practice

1A. 10

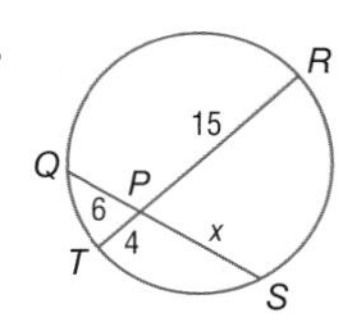

1B. 3

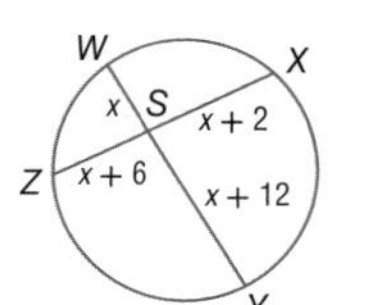

750 | Lesson 10-7

Lesson 10-7 Resources

Resource	Approaching Level AL	On Level OL	Beyond Level BL	English Learners ELL
Teacher Edition		▪ Differentiated Instruction, pp. 751, 752	▪ Differentiated Instruction, pp. 751, 752	
Chapter Resource Masters	▪ Study Guide and Intervention, pp. 43–44 ▪ Skills Practice, p. 45 ▪ Practice, p. 46 ▪ Word Problem Practice, p. 47	▪ Study Guide and Intervention, pp. 43–44 ▪ Skills Practice, p. 45 ▪ Practice, p. 46 ▪ Word Problem Practice, p. 47 ▪ Enrichment, p. 48	▪ Practice, p. 46 ▪ Word Problem Practice, p. 47 ▪ Enrichment, p. 48	▪ Study Guide and Intervention, pp. 43–44 ▪ Skills Practice, p. 45 ▪ Practice, p. 46 ▪ Word Problem Practice, p. 47
Other	▪ 5-Minute Check 10-7 ▪ Study Notebook	▪ 5-Minute Check 10-7 ▪ Study Notebook	▪ 5-Minute Check 10-7 ▪ Study Notebook	▪ 5-Minute Check 10-7 ▪ Study Notebook

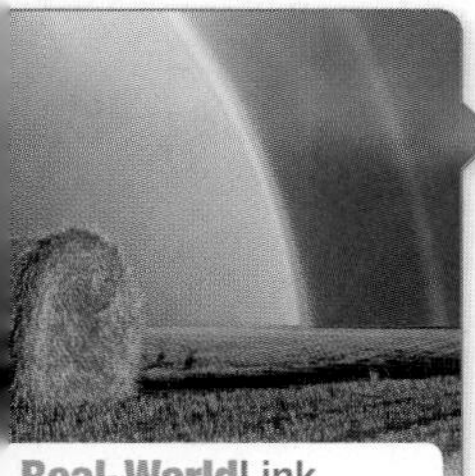

Real-WorldLink

The lower the Sun is to the horizon, the more of a rainbow you can see. At sunset, you could see a full semicircle of a rainbow with the top of the arch 42 degrees above the horizon.

Source: The National Center for Atmospheric Research

Real-World Example 2 Find Measures of Segments in Circles

SCIENCE **The true shape of a rainbow is a complete circle. However, we see only the arc of the circle that appears above Earth's horizon. What is the radius of the circle containing the arc of the rainbow shown?**

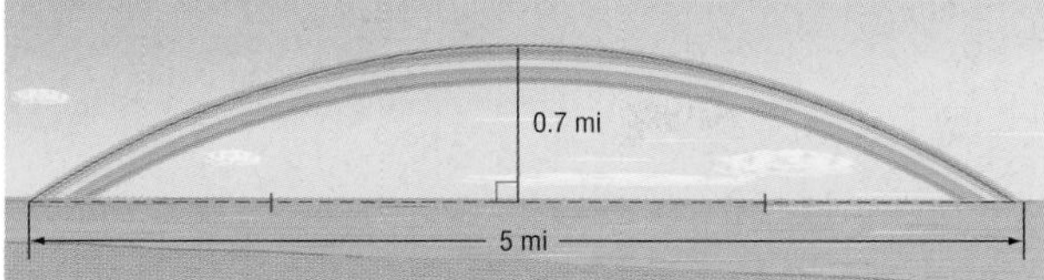

Understand You know that the rainbow's arc is part of a whole circle. $\overline{AC}$ is a chord of this circle, and $\overline{DB}$ is a perpendicular bisector of $\overline{AC}$.

Plan Draw a model. Since it bisects chord $\overline{AC}$, $\overline{DE}$ is a diameter of the circle. Use the products of the lengths of the intersecting chords to find the length of the diameter.

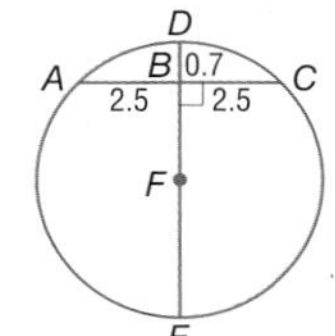

Solve

$AB \cdot BC = DB \cdot BE$	Theorem 10.15
$2.5 \cdot 2.5 = 0.7 \cdot BE$	Substitution
$6.25 = 0.7BE$	Multiply.
$8.9 \approx BE$	Divide each side by 0.7.
$DE = DB + BE$	Segment Addition Postulate
$= 0.7 + 8.9$	Substitution
$= 9.6$	Add.

Since the diameter of the circle is about 9.6 miles, the radius is about $9.6 \div 2$ or 4.8 miles.

Check Use the Pythagorean Theorem to check the triangle in the circle formed by the radius, the chord, and part of the diameter.

$DB + BF = DF$	Segment Addition Postulate
$0.7 + BF = 4.8$	Substitution
$BF = 4.1$	Subtract 0.7 from each side.
$BF^2 + BC^2 = CF^2$	Pythagorean Theorem
$4.1^2 + 2.5^2 \stackrel{?}{=} 4.8^2$	Substitution
$23.06 \approx 23.04$ ✓	Simplify.

Problem-SolvingTip

Make a Drawing When solving word problems involving circles, it is helpful to make a drawing and label all parts of the circle that are known. Use a variable to label the unknown measure.

GuidedPractice

2. ASTRODOME The highest point, or apex, of the Astrodome is 208 feet high, and the diameter of the circle containing the arc is 710 feet. How long is the stadium from one side to the other? **about 646 ft**

DifferentiatedInstruction OL BL

Logical Learners Direct students to revisit Example 1 on page 750. Have students draw chords connecting opposite endpoints of the intersecting lines. Have them write conjectures about the proportional relationship between the triangles they have created.

1 Segments Intersecting Inside a Circle

Examples 1 and 2 show how to use the Segments of Chords Theorem to find the measure of line segments that intersect inside a circle.

Formative Assessment

Use the Guided Practice exercises after each example to determine students' understanding of concepts.

Additional Examples

1 Find x.

a.

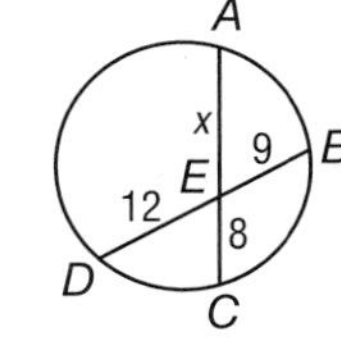

$x = 13.5$

b.

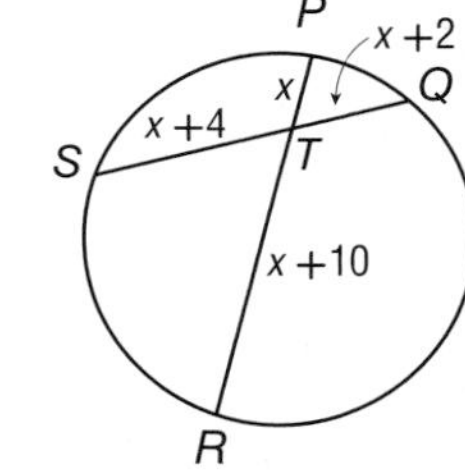

$x = 2$

2 **BIOLOGY** Biologists often examine organisms under microscopes. The circle represents the field of view under the microscope with a diameter of 2 mm. Determine the length of the organism if it is located 0.25 mm from the bottom of the field of view. Round to the nearest hundredth. 0.66 mm

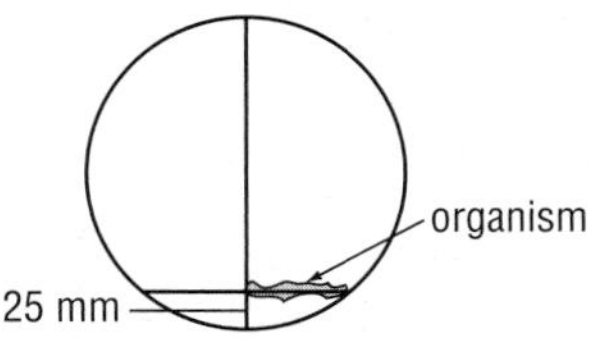

Additional Examples also in Interactive Classroom PowerPoint® Presentations

2 Segments Intersecting Outside a Circle

In **Examples 3 and 4** students use properties and theorems to find lengths of external secant segments.

Additional Example

3 Find *x*. 34.5

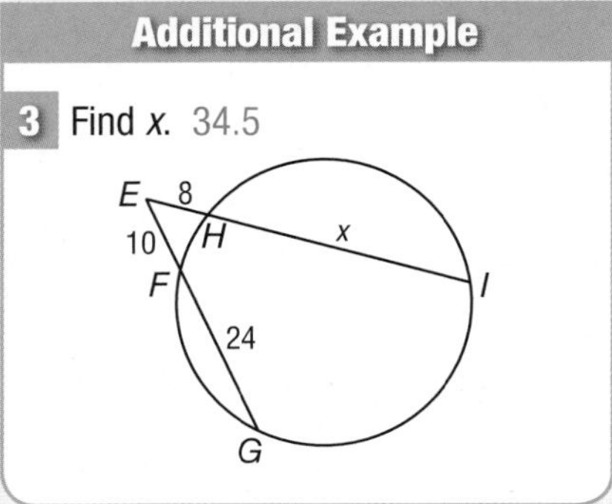

Focus on Mathematical Content

Chord Bisector Remind students that a diameter can be drawn to bisect any chord of a circle.

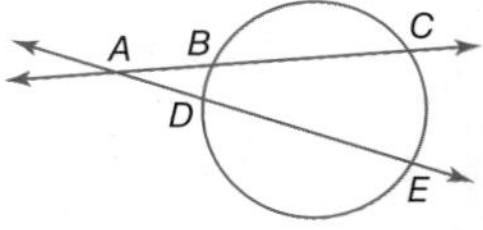

2 Segments Intersecting Outside a Circle A **secant segment** is a segment of a secant line that has exactly one endpoint on the circle. In the figure, $\overline{AC}$, $\overline{AB}$, $\overline{AE}$ and $\overline{AD}$ are secant segments.

A secant segment that lies in the exterior of the circle is called an **external secant segment**. In the figure, $\overline{AB}$ and $\overline{AD}$ are external secant segments.

A special relationship exists among secants and external secant segments.

StudyTip

Simplify the Theorem Each side of the equation in Theorem 10.16 is the product of the lengths of the exterior part and the whole segment.

Theorem 10.16 Secant Segments Theorem

Words If two secants intersect in the exterior of a circle, then the product of the measures of one secant segment and its external secant segment is equal to the product of the measures of the other secant and its external secant segment.

Example $AC \cdot AB = AE \cdot AD$

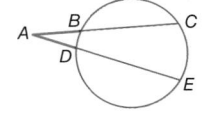

You will prove Theorem 10.16 in Exercise 24.

WatchOut!

Use the Correct Equation Be sure to multiply the length of the secant segment by the length of the external secant segment. Do not multiply the length of the internal secant segment, or chord, by the length of the external secant segment.

Example 3 Use the Intersection of Two Chords

Find *x*.

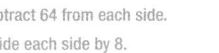

$JG \cdot JH = JL \cdot JK$	Theorem 10.16
$(x + 8)8 = (10 + 6)6$	Substitution
$8x + 64 = 96$	Multiply.
$8x = 32$	Subtract 64 from each side.
$x = 4$	Divide each side by 8.

GuidedPractice

3A. 3

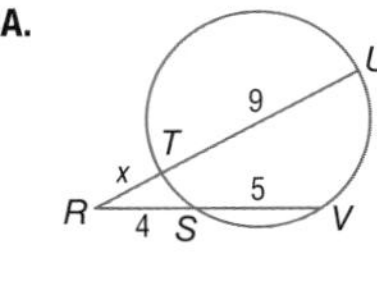

3B. $16\frac{1}{6}$

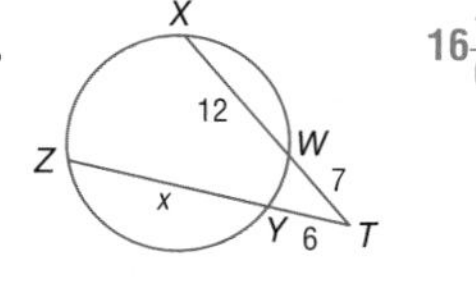

An equation similar to the one in Theorem 10.16 can be used when a secant and a tangent intersect outside a circle. In this case, the **tangent segment**, or segment of a tangent with one endpoint on the circle, is both the exterior and whole segment.

Theorem 10.17

Words If a tangent and a secant intersect in the exterior of a circle, then the square of the measure of the tangent is equal to the product of the measures of the secant and its external secant segment.

Example $JK^2 = JL \cdot JM$

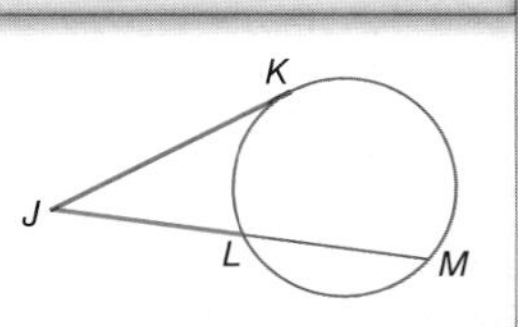

You will prove Theorem 10.17 in Exercise 25.

DifferentiatedInstruction OL BL

Extension Have each student find another real-life example of segments of circles in construction, nature, and so on. Instruct students to write a brief explanation of the example they found, construct a sketch of the example, insert accurate measurements if possible, and then write an equation on the information.

PT

Example 4 Use the Intersection of a Secant and a Tangent

$\overline{PQ}$ is tangent to the circle. Find x. Round to the nearest tenth.

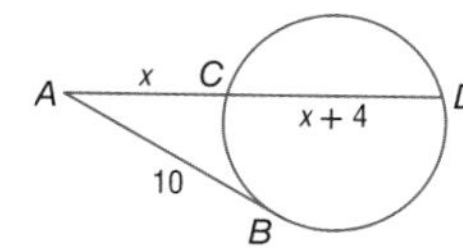

$PQ^2 = QR \cdot QS$	Theorem 10.17
$8^2 = x(x + 7)$	Substitution
$64 = x^2 + 7x$	Multiply.
$0 = x^2 + 7x - 64$	Subtract 64 from each side.

Since the expression is not factorable, use the Quadratic Formula.

$x = \frac{-b \pm \sqrt{b^2 - 4ac}}{2a}$	Quadratic Formula
$= \frac{-7 \pm \sqrt{7^2 - 4(1)(-64)}}{2(1)}$	$a = 1$, $b = 7$, and $c = -64$
$= \frac{-7 \pm \sqrt{305}}{2}$	Simplify.
≈ 5.2 or -12.2	Use a calculator.

Since lengths cannot be negative, the value of x is about 5.2.

GuidedPractice

4. $\overline{AB}$ is tangent to the circle. Find x. Round to the nearest tenth. **6.1**

Check Your Understanding

= Step-by-Step Solutions begin on page R14.

Examples 1, 3 and 4 **Find x. Assume that segments that appear to be tangent are tangent.**

1. 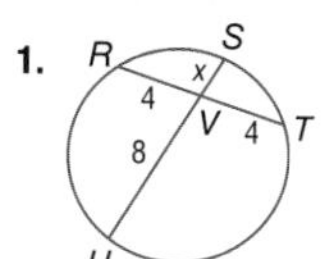 **2**

2. 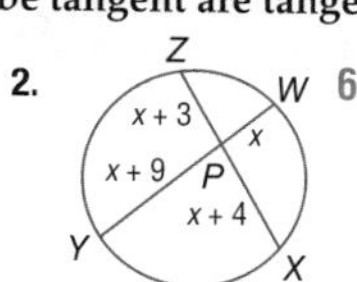 **6**

3. 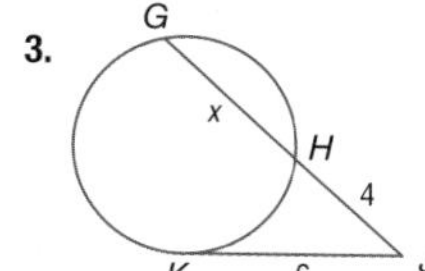 **5**

4.  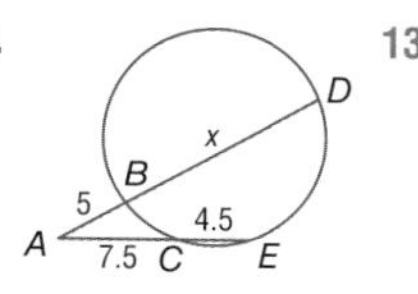 **13**

Example 2

5. **SCIENCE** A piece of broken pottery found at an archaeological site is shown. $\overline{QS}$ lies on a diameter of the circle. What was the circumference of the original pottery? Round to the nearest hundredth. **71.21 cm**

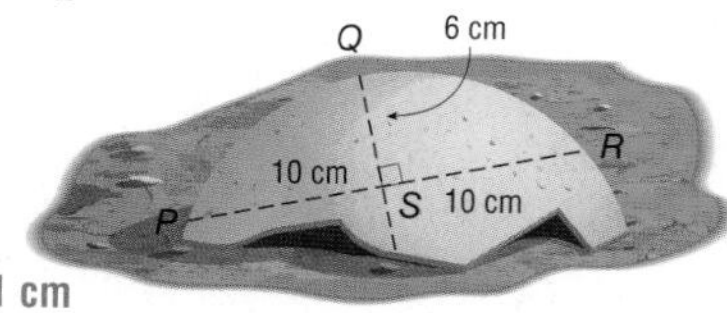

Additional Example

4 $\overline{LM}$ is tangent to the circle. Find x. Round the nearest tenth.

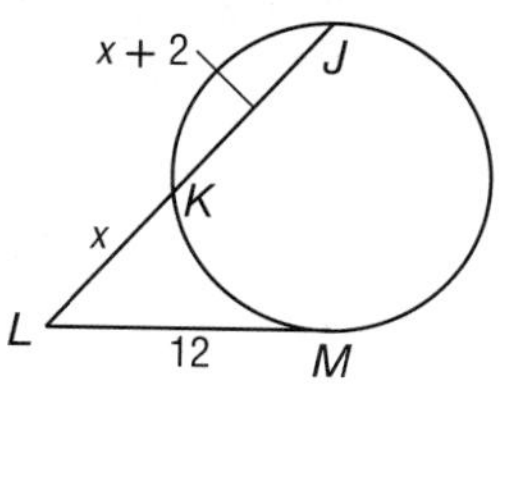

8

Teach with Tech

Web Page Post notes for this lesson on your class Web page. Cover the various theorems for tangents, secants, and chords in circles. Add links to the best student blog entries and the best class videos.

3 Practice

Formative Assessment

Use Exercises 1–5 to check for understanding.

Use the chart at the bottom of this page to customize assignments for your students.

Differentiated Homework Options

Level	Assignment	Two-Day Option	
AL Basic	6–21, 26, 27, 29–49	7–21 odd, 32–35	6–20 even, 26, 27, 29–31, 36–49
OL Core	7–21 odd, 22–27, 29–49	6–21, 32–35	22–27, 29–31, 36–49
BL Advanced	22–43, (optional: 44–49)		

Study Guide and Intervention

AL OL ELL

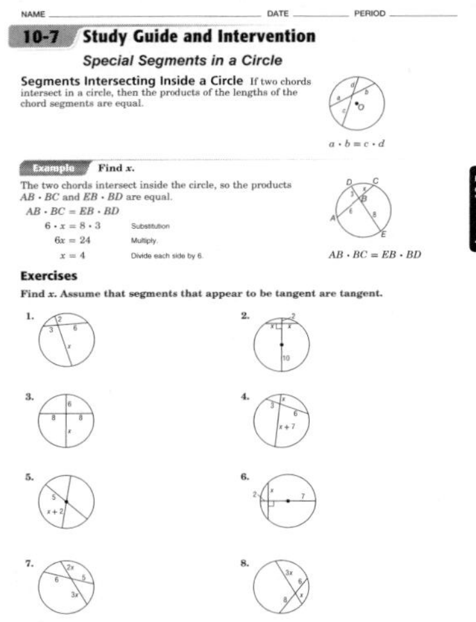

NAME ____________ DATE ________ PERIOD ________

10-7 Study Guide and Intervention

Special Segments in a Circle

Segments Intersecting Inside a Circle If two chords intersect in a circle, then the products of the lengths of the chord segments are equal.

$a \cdot b = c \cdot d$

Example Find x.

The two chords intersect inside the circle, so the products $AB \cdot BC$ and $EB \cdot BD$ are equal.

$AB \cdot BC = EB \cdot BD$

$6 \cdot x = 8 \cdot 3$ Substitution

$6x = 24$ Multiply.

$x = 4$ Divide each side by 6.

$AB \cdot BC = EB \cdot BD$

Exercises

Find x. Assume that segments that appear to be tangent are tangent.

1. 2. 3. 4. 5. 6. 7. 8.

Lesson 10-7

Practice

AL OL BL ELL

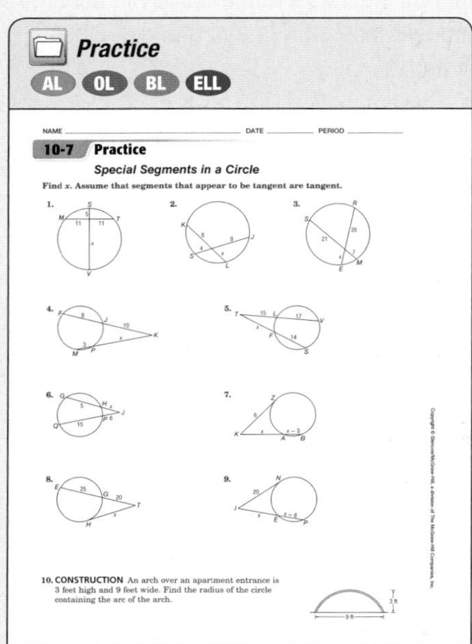

NAME ____________ DATE ________ PERIOD ________

10-7 Practice

Special Segments in a Circle

Find x. Assume that segments that appear to be tangent are tangent.

1. 2. 3. 4. 5. 6. 7. 8. 9.

10. CONSTRUCTION An arch over an apartment entrance is 3 feet high and 9 feet wide. Find the radius of the circle containing the arc of the arch.

Word Problem Practice

AL OL BL ELL

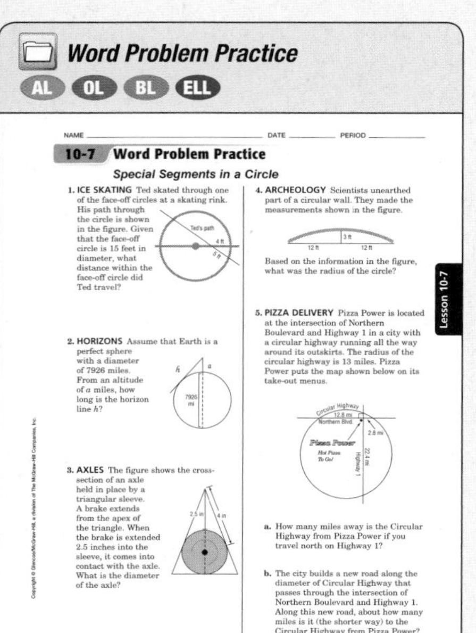

NAME ____________ DATE ________ PERIOD ________

10-7 Word Problem Practice

Special Segments in a Circle

1. ICE SKATING Ted skated through one of the face-off circles at a skating rink. His path through the circle is shown in the figure. Given that the face-off circle is 15 feet in diameter, what distance within the face-off circle did Ted travel?

2. HORIZONS Assume that Earth is a perfect sphere with a diameter of 7926 miles. From an altitude of a miles, how long is the horizon line h?

3. AXLES The figure shows the cross-section of an axle held in place by a triangular sleeve. A brake extends from the apex of the triangle. When the brake is extended 2.5 inches into the sleeve, it comes into contact with the axle. What is the diameter of the axle?

4. ARCHEOLOGY Scientists unearthed part of a circular wall. They made the measurements shown in the figure.

Based on the information in the figure, what was the radius of the circle?

5. PIZZA DELIVERY Pizza Power is located at the intersection of Northern Boulevard and Highway 1 in a city with a circular highway running all the way around its outskirts. The radius of the circular highway is 13 miles. Pizza Power puts the map shown below on its take-out menus.

a. How many miles away is the Circular Highway from Pizza Power if you travel north on Highway 1?

b. The city builds a new road along the diameter of Circular Highway that passes through the intersection of Northern Boulevard and Highway 1. Along this new road, about how many miles is it (the shorter way) to the Circular Highway from Pizza Power?

Practice and Problem Solving

Extra Practice is on page R10.

Examples 1, 3 and 4 **Find x to the nearest tenth. Assume that segments that appear to be tangent are tangent.**

6. 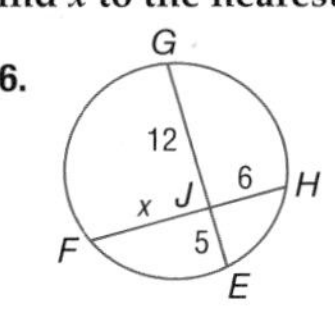 10

7. 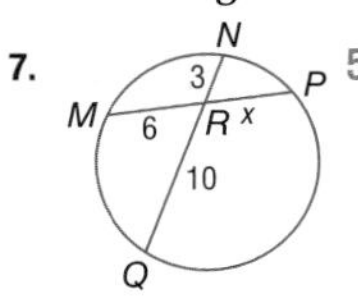 5

8. 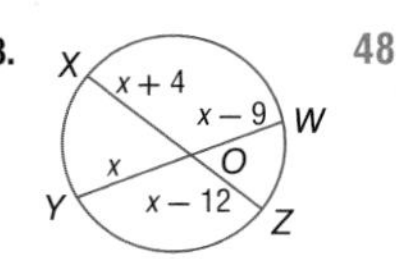 48

9. 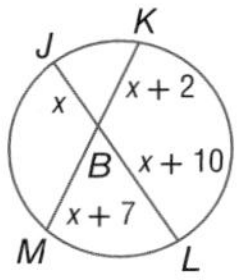 14

10. 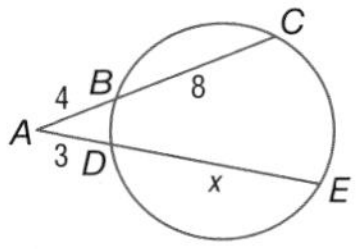 13

11. 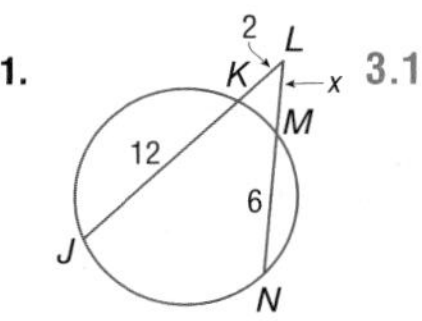 3.1

12. 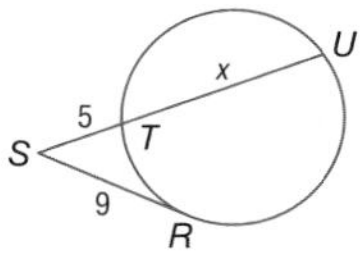 11.2

13. 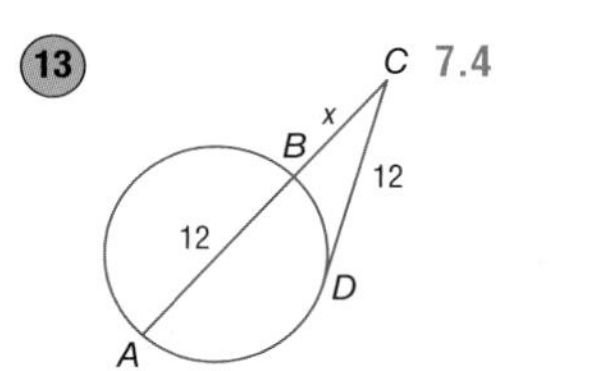 7.4

Example 2

14. **BRIDGES** What is the diameter of the circle containing the arc of the Sydney Harbour Bridge shown? Round to the nearest tenth. 588.1 m

15. **CAKES** Sierra is serving cake at a party. If the dimensions of the remaining cake are shown below, what was the original diameter of the cake? 13 in.

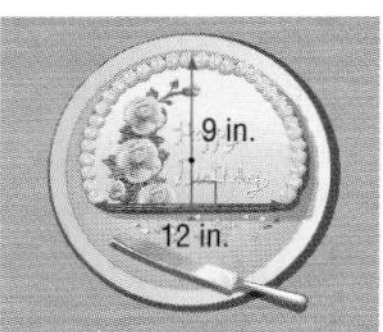

CCSS STRUCTURE Find each variable to the nearest tenth. Assume that segments that appear to be tangent are tangent. 20. $q = 9$; $r \approx 1.8$

16. 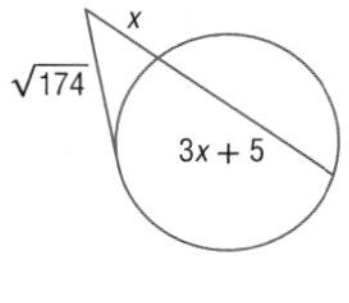 6

17. 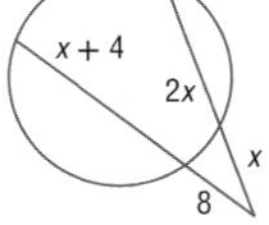 7.1

18. 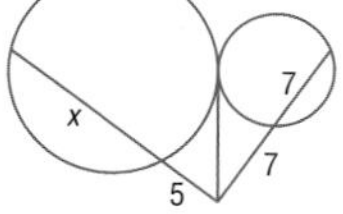 14.6

19. 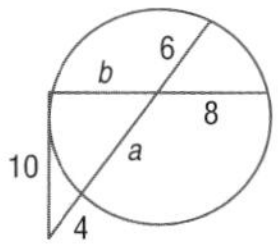 $a = 15$; $b \approx 11.3$

20.

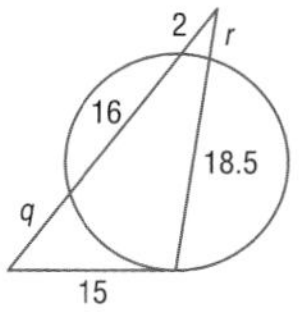

21. 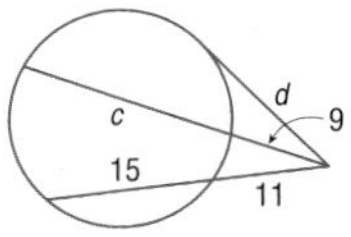 $c \approx 22.8$; $d \approx 16.9$

Enrichment

OL BL

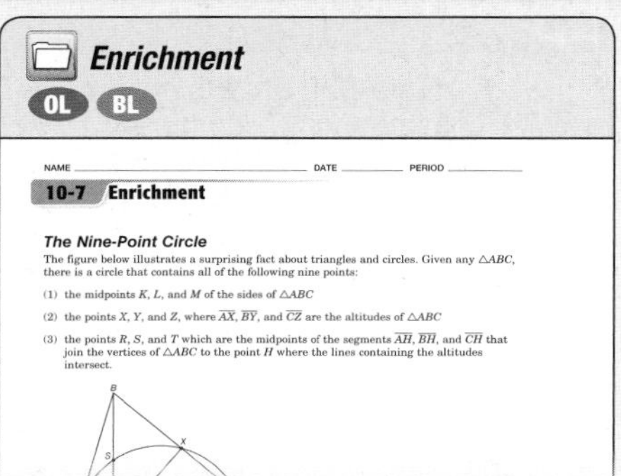

NAME ____________ DATE ________ PERIOD ________

10-7 Enrichment

The Nine-Point Circle

The figure below illustrates a surprising fact about triangles and circles. Given any $\triangle ABC$, there is a circle that contains all of the following nine points:

(1) the midpoints K, L, and M of the sides of $\triangle ABC$

(2) the points X, Y, and Z, where $\overline{AX}$, $\overline{BY}$, and $\overline{CZ}$ are the altitudes of $\triangle ABC$

(3) the points R, S, and T which are the midpoints of the segments $\overline{AH}$, $\overline{BH}$, and $\overline{CH}$ that join the vertices of $\triangle ABC$ to the point H where the lines containing the altitudes intersect.

CCSS Teaching the Mathematical Practices

Structure Mathematically proficient students look closely to discern a pattern or structure. They also can step back for an overview and shift perspective. In Exercises 16–21, encourage students to analyze each figure for chords, secants, and tangents before deciding which theorem applies.

22. INDIRECT MEASUREMENT Gwendolyn is standing 16 feet from a giant sequoia tree and Chet is standing next to the tree, as shown. The distance between Gwendolyn and Chet is 27 feet. Draw a diagram of this situation, and then find the diameter of the tree. **See Ch. 10 Answer Appendix.**

PROOF **Prove each theorem. 23–25. See margin.**

23. two-column proof of Theorem 10.15

Given: $\overline{AC}$ and $\overline{DE}$ intersect at B.

Prove: $AB \cdot BC = EB \cdot BD$

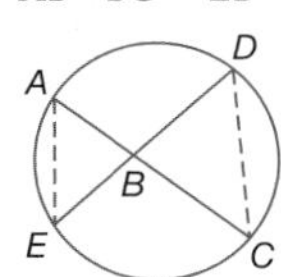

24. paragraph proof of Theorem 10.16

Given: Secants $\overline{AC}$ and $\overline{AE}$

Prove: $AB \cdot AC = AD \cdot AE$

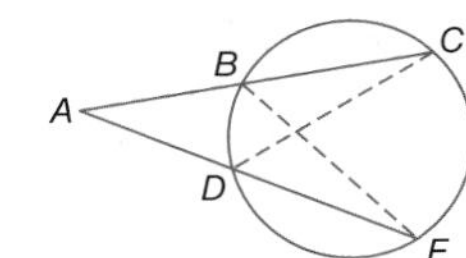

25. two-column proof of Theorem 10.17

Given: tangent $\overline{JK}$, secant $\overline{JM}$

Prove: $JK^2 = JL \cdot JM$

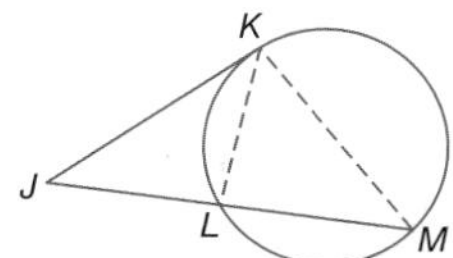

26. Jun; the segments intersect outside of the circle, so the correct equation involves the products of the measures of a secant and its external secant segment.

H.O.T. Problems Use Higher-Order Thinking Skills

26. CCSS CRITIQUE Tiffany and Jun are finding the value of x in the figure at the right. Tiffany wrote $3(5) = 2x$, and Jun wrote $3(8) = 2(2 + x)$. Is either of them correct? Explain your reasoning.

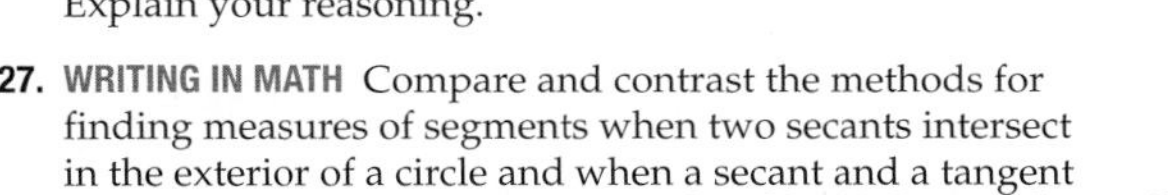

27. WRITING IN MATH Compare and contrast the methods for finding measures of segments when two secants intersect in the exterior of a circle and when a secant and a tangent intersect in the exterior of a circle. **See Ch. 10 Answer Appendix.**

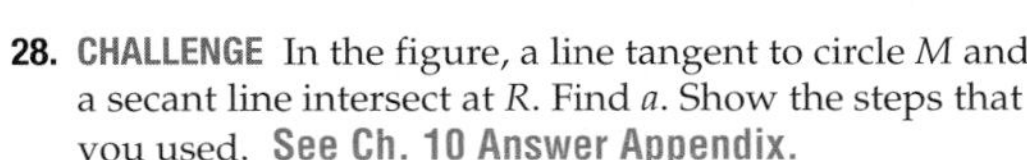

28. CHALLENGE In the figure, a line tangent to circle M and a secant line intersect at R. Find a. Show the steps that you used. **See Ch. 10 Answer Appendix.**

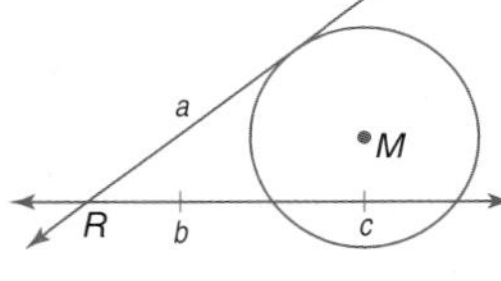

29. Sometimes; they are equal when the chords are perpendicular.

29. REASONING When two chords intersect at the center of a circle, are the measures of the intercepting arcs *sometimes, always,* or *never* equal to each other?

30. OPEN ENDED Investigate Theorem 10.17 by drawing and labeling a circle that has a secant and a tangent intersecting outside the circle. Measure and label the two parts of the secant segment to the nearest tenth of a centimeter. Use an equation to find the measure of the tangent segment. Verify your answer by measuring the segment. **See Ch. 10 Answer Appendix.**

31. WRITING IN MATH Describe the relationship among segments in a circle when two secants intersect inside a circle. **See Ch. 10 Answer Appendix.**

CCSS Teaching the Mathematical Practices

Critique Mathematically proficient students can distinguish correct logic from flawed reasoning. In Exercise 26, students should recognize that Tiffany's equation is used to find the length of chords that intersect in a circle. Jun's equation is correct because the two secants intersect outside the circle.

Exercise Alert

Compass and Ruler Exercise 30 requires the use of a compass and a ruler.

Additional Answers

23. Proof:

Statements (Reasons)

1. $\overline{AC}$ and $\overline{DE}$ intersect at B. (Given)
2. $\angle A \cong \angle D$, $\angle E \cong \angle C$ (Inscribed ∠s that intercept the same arc are ≅.)
3. $\triangle ABE \sim \triangle DBC$ (AA Similarity)
4. $\frac{AB}{BD} = \frac{EB}{BC}$ (Definition of similar △s)
5. $AB \cdot BC = EB \cdot BD$ (Cross products)

24. Proof:

$\overline{AC}$ and $\overline{AE}$ are secant segments. By the Reflexive Property, $\angle BAD \cong \angle DAB$. Inscribed angles that intercept the same arc are congruent. So, $\angle ACD \cong \angle AEB$. By AA Similarity, $\triangle AEB \sim \triangle ACD$. By the definition of similar triangles, $\frac{AB}{AD} = \frac{AE}{AC}$. Since the cross products of a proportion are equal, $AB \cdot AC = AD \cdot AE$.

25. Proof:

Statements (Reasons)

1. tangent $\overline{JK}$ and secant $\overline{JM}$ (Given)
2. $m\angle KML = \frac{1}{2}m\widehat{KL}$ (The measure of an inscribed ∠ equals half the measure of its intercept arc.)
3. $m\angle JKL = \frac{1}{2}m\widehat{KL}$ (The measure of an ∠ formed by a secant and a tangent = half the measure of its intercepted arc.)
4. $m\angle KML = m\angle JKL$ (Substitution)
5. $\angle KML \cong \angle JKL$ (Definition of ≅ ∠s)
6. $\angle J \cong \angle J$ (Reflexive Property)
7. $\triangle JMK \sim \triangle JKL$ (AA Similarity)
8. $\frac{JK}{JL} = \frac{JM}{JK}$ (Definition of ~ △s)
9. $JK^2 = JL \cdot JM$ (Cross products)

4 Assess

Yesterday's News Ask students to describe how the lesson on secants, tangents, and angles helped them better understand the lesson on special segments in a circle.

Additional Answers

34a. $x + y = 360$ and $y - x = 140$

34b. $x = 110°$, $y = 250°$

37.

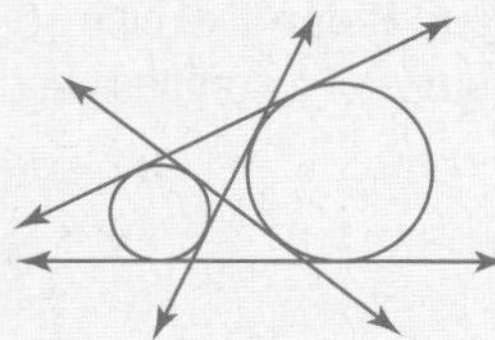

38. no common tangent

39.

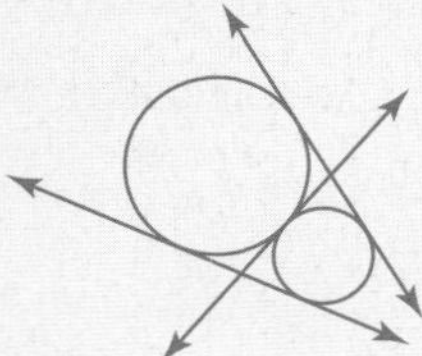

40.

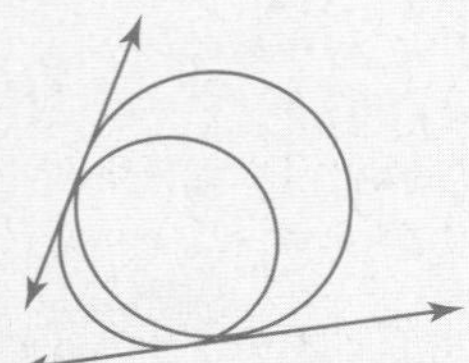

41.

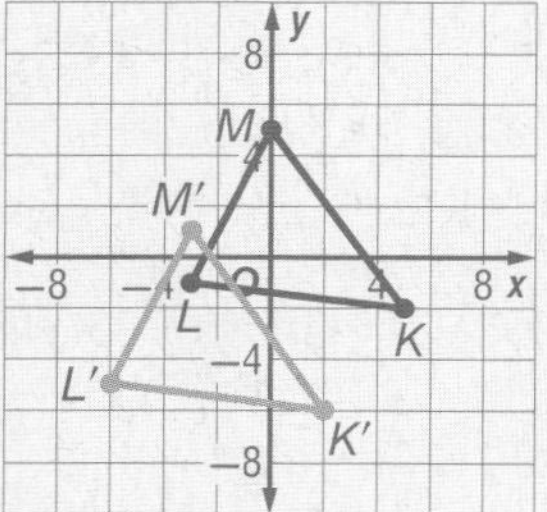

42.

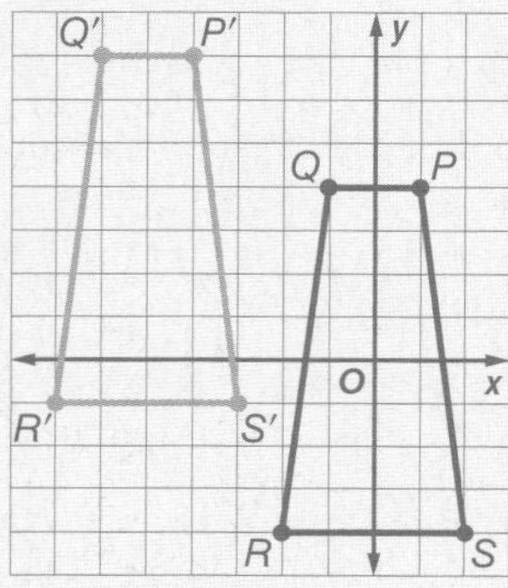

Standardized Test Practice

32. $\overline{TV}$ is tangent to the circle, and R and S are points on the circle. What is the value of x to the nearest tenth? **C**

A 7.6 **C** 5.7
B 6.4 **D** 4.8

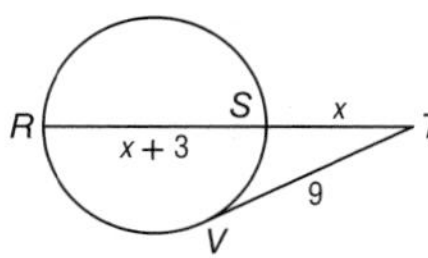

33. ALGEBRA A department store has all of its jewelry discounted 40%. It is having a sale that says you receive an additional 20% off the already discounted price. How much will you pay for a ring with an original price of $200? **G**

F $80 **H** $120
G $96 **J** $140

34. EXTENDED RESPONSE The degree measures of minor arc $\widehat{AC}$ and major arc $\widehat{ADC}$ are x and y, respectively. **See margin.**

a. If $m\angle ABC = 70°$, write two equations relating x and y.

b. Find x and y.

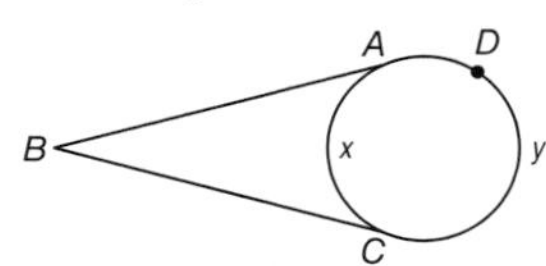

35. SAT/ACT During the first two weeks of summer vacation, Antonia earned $100 per week. During the next six weeks, she earned $150 per week. What was her average weekly pay? **E**

A $50 **D** $135
B $112.50 **E** $137.50
C $125

Spiral Review

36. WEAVING Once yarn is woven from wool fibers, it is often dyed and then threaded along a path of pulleys to dry. One set of pulleys is shown. Note that the yarn appears to intersect itself at C, but in reality it does not. Use the information from the diagram to find $m\widehat{BH}$. (Lesson 10-6) **141**

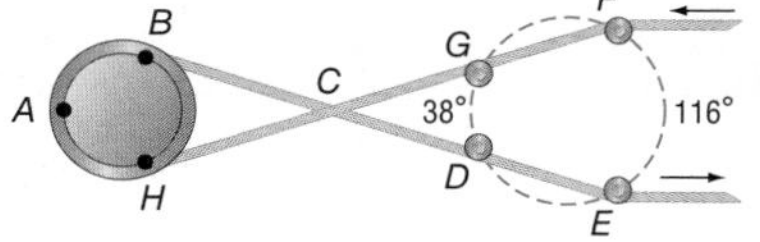

Copy the figure shown and draw the common tangents. If no common tangent exists, state *no common tangent*. (Lesson 10-5) **37–40. See margin.**

37.

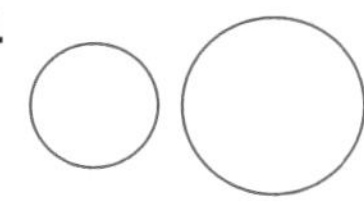

38.

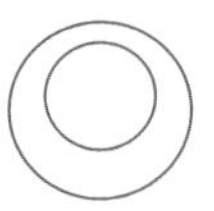

39.

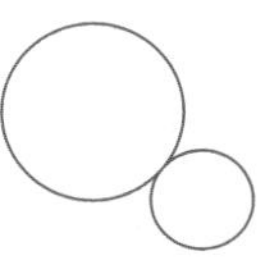

40.

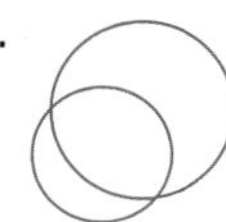

COORDINATE GEOMETRY Graph each figure and its image along the given vector. (Lesson 9-2) **41–43. See margin.**

41. $\triangle KLM$ with vertices $K(5, -2)$, $L(-3, -1)$, and $M(0, 5)$; $\langle -3, -4 \rangle$

42. quadrilateral $PQRS$ with vertices $P(1, 4)$, $Q(-1, 4)$, $R(-2, -4)$, and $S(2, -4)$; $\langle -5, 3 \rangle$

43. $\triangle EFG$ with vertices $E(0, -4)$, $F(-4, -4)$, and $G(0, 2)$; $\langle 2, -1 \rangle$

Skills Review

Write an equation in slope-intercept form of the line having the given slope and *y*-intercept.

44. m: 3, y-intercept: −4 $y = 3x - 4$

45. m: 2, (0, 8) $y = 2x + 8$

46. m: $\frac{5}{8}$, (0, −6) $y = \frac{5}{8}x - 6$

47. m: $\frac{2}{9}$, y-intercept: $\frac{1}{3}$ $y = \frac{2}{9}x + \frac{1}{3}$

48. m: −1, b: −3 $y = -x - 3$

49. m: $-\frac{1}{12}$, b: 1 $y = -\frac{1}{12}x + 1$

43.

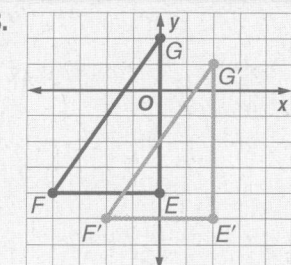

756 | Lesson 10-7 | Special Segments in a Circle

LESSON 10-8 Equations of Circles

Then	Now	Why?
You wrote equations of lines using information about their graphs.	1 Write the equation of a circle. 2 Graph a circle on the coordinate plane.	Telecommunications towers emit radio signals that are used to transmit cellular calls. Each tower covers a circular area, and towers are arranged so that a signal is available at any location in the coverage area.

NewVocabulary
compound locus

Common Core State Standards

Content Standards
G.GPE.1 Derive the equation of a circle of given center and radius using the Pythagorean Theorem; complete the square to find the center and radius of a circle given by an equation.
G.GPE.6 Find the point on a directed line segment between two given points that partitions the segment in a given ratio.

Mathematical Practices
2 Reason abstractly and quantitatively.
7 Look for and make use of structure.

1 Equation of a Circle

Since all points on a circle are equidistant from the center, you can find an equation of a circle by using the Distance Formula.

Let (x, y) represent a point on a circle centered at the origin. Using the Pythagorean Theorem, $x^2 + y^2 = r^2$.

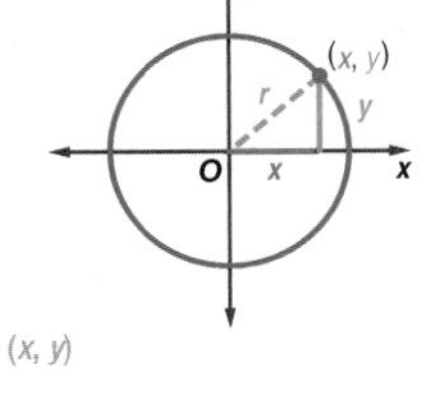

Now suppose that the center is not at the origin, but at the point (h, k). You can use the Distance Formula to develop an equation for the circle.

$$d = \sqrt{(x_2 - x_1)^2 + (y_2 - y_1)^2}$$ Distance Formula

$$r = \sqrt{(x - h)^2 + (y - k)^2}$$ $d = r, (x_1, y_1) = (h, k), (x_2, y_2) = (x, y)$

$$r^2 = (x - h)^2 + (y - k)^2$$ Square each side.

KeyConcept Equation of a Circle in Standard Form

The standard form of the equation of a circle with center at (h, k) and radius r is $(x - h)^2 + (y - k)^2 = r^2$.

The standard form of the equation of a circle is also called the *center-radius* form.

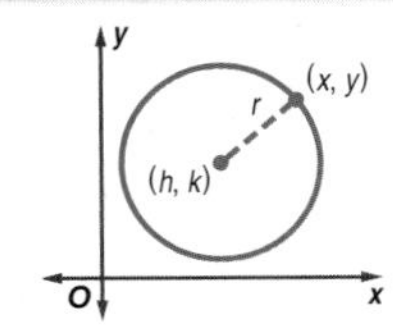

Example 1 Write an Equation Using the Center and Radius

Write the equation of each circle.

a. center at (1, −8), radius 7

$(x - h)^2 + (y - k)^2 = r^2$ Equation of a circle

$(x - 1)^2 + [y - (-8)]^2 = 7^2$ $(h, k) = (1, -8), r = 7$

$(x - 1)^2 + (y + 8)^2 = 49$ Simplify.

b. the circle graphed at the right

The center is at (0, 4) and the radius is 3.

$(x - h)^2 + (y - k)^2 = r^2$ Equation of a circle

$(x - 0)^2 + (y - 4)^2 = 3^2$ $(h, k) = (0, 4), r = 3$

$x^2 + (y - 4)^2 = 9$ Simplify.

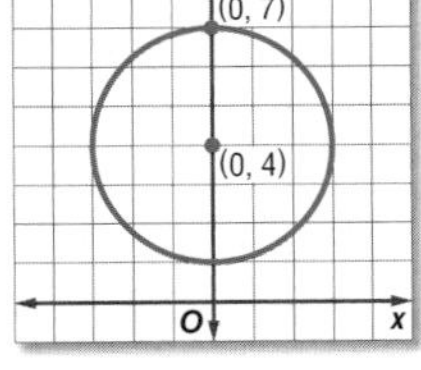

GuidedPractice **1A.** $x^2 + y^2 = 10$ **1B.** $(x - 4)^2 + (y + 1)^2 = 16$

1A. center at origin, radius $\sqrt{10}$

1B. center at (4, −1), diameter 8

1 Focus

VerticalAlignment

Before Lesson 10-8 Write equations of lines using information about their graphs.

Lesson 10-8 Write the equation of a circle. Graph a circle on the coordinate plane.

After Lesson 10-8 Extend similarity properties and transformations to explore and justify conjectures about geometric figures.

2 Teach

Scaffolding Questions

Have students read the **Why?** section of the lesson.

Ask:

- Where is the tower located in relationship to the area it covers? the center
- What does the distance from the tower to the farthest point of the service area represent? the radius
- A certain cellular tower sends out a signal with a 15-mile radius. To increase the service area by 50%, how many more miles does the signal from the tower have to reach? ≈3.37 miles

Lesson 10-8 Resources

Resource	Approaching Level AL	On Level OL	Beyond Level BL	English Learners ELL
Teacher Edition		▪ Differentiated Instruction, pp. 759, 763	▪ Differentiated Instruction, pp. 759, 763	
Chapter Resource Masters	▪ Study Guide and Intervention, pp. 49–50 ▪ Skills Practice, p. 51 ▪ Practice, p. 52 ▪ Word Problem Practice, p. 53	▪ Study Guide and Intervention, pp. 49–50 ▪ Skills Practice, p. 51 ▪ Practice, p. 52 ▪ Word Problem Practice, p. 53 ▪ Enrichment, p. 54	▪ Practice, p. 52 ▪ Word Problem Practice, p. 53 ▪ Enrichment, p. 54	▪ Study Guide and Intervention, pp. 49–50 ▪ Skills Practice, p. 51 ▪ Practice, p. 52 ▪ Word Problem Practice, p. 53
Other	▪ 5-Minute Check 10-8 ▪ Study Notebook ▪ Teaching Geometry with Manipulatives	▪ 5-Minute Check 10-8 ▪ Study Notebook ▪ Teaching Geometry with Manipulatives	▪ 5-Minute Check 10-8 ▪ Study Notebook	▪ 5-Minute Check 10-8 ▪ Study Notebook ▪ Teaching Geometry with Manipulatives

1 Equation of a Circle

Examples 1 and 2 show how to use information given about a circle to find the equation of a circle.

Formative Assessment

Use the Guided Practice exercises after each example to determine students' understanding of concepts.

Additional Examples

1 Write the equation of each circle.

a. center at (3, –3), radius 6
$(x-3)^2+(y+3)^2=36$

b. the circle graphed below

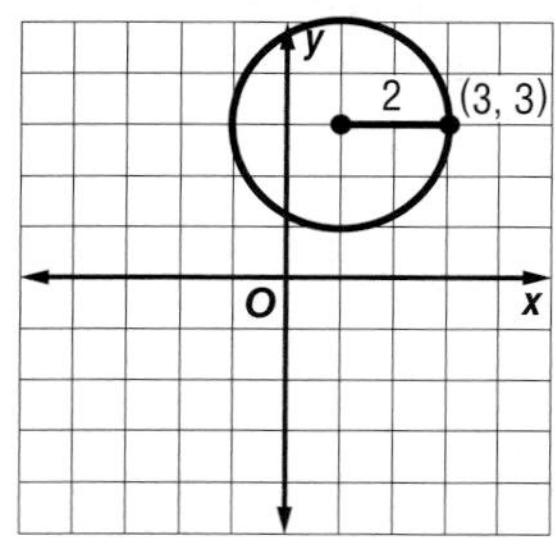

$(x-1)^2+(y-3)^2=4$

2 Write the equation of the circle with center at (–3, –2), that passes through (1, –2).
$(x+3)^2+(y+2)^2=16$

Additional Examples also in Interactive Classroom PowerPoint® Presentations

3A. (0, 0); 2

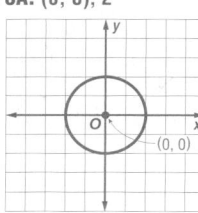

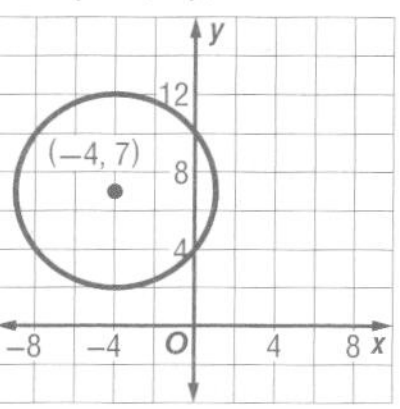

3B. (–4, 7); 5

(–4, 7)

StudyTip

Completing the Square To complete the square for any quadratic expression of the form $x^2 + bx$, follow these steps.

Step 1 Find one half of *b*.

Step 2 Square the result in Step 1.

Step 3 Add the result of Step 2 to $x^2 + bx$.

Example 2 Write an Equation Using the Center and a Point

Write the equation of the circle with center at (–2, 4), that passes through (–6, 7).

Step 1 Find the distance between the points to determine the radius.

$r=\sqrt{(x_2-x_1)^2+(y_2-y_1)^2}$	Distance Formula
$=\sqrt{[-6-(-2)]^2+(7-4)^2}$	$(x_1, y_1) = (-2, 4)$ and $(x_2, y_2) = (-6, 7)$
$=\sqrt{25}$ or 5	Simplify.

Step 2 Write the equation using $h = -2$, $k = 4$, and $r = 5$.

$(x-h)^2+(y-k)^2=r^2$	Equation of a circle
$[x-(-2)]^2+(y-4)^2=5^2$	$h=-2$, $k=4$, and $r=5$
$(x+2)^2+(y-4)^2=25$	Simplify.

GuidedPractice

2. Write the equation of the circle with center at (–3, –5) that passes through (0, 0). $(x+3)^2+(y+5)^2=34$

2 Graph Circles

You can use the equation of a circle to graph it on a coordinate plane. To do so, you may need to write the equation in standard form first.

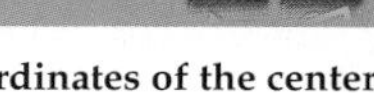

Example 3 Graph a Circle

The equation of a circle is $x^2 + y^2 - 8x + 2y = -8$. State the coordinates of the center and the measure of the radius. Then graph the equation.

Write the equation in standard form by completing the square.

$x^2+y^2-8x+2y=-8$	Original equation
$x^2-8x+y^2+2y=-8$	Isolate and group like terms.
$x^2-8x+16+y^2+2y+1=-8+16+1$	Complete the squares.
$(x-4)^2+(y+1)^2=9$	Factor and simplify.
$(x-4)^2+[y-(-1)]^2=3^2$	Write +1 as – (–1) and 9 as 3^2.

With the equation now in standard form, you can identify *h*, *k*, and *r*.

$$(x-4)^2+[y-(-1)]^2=3^2$$
$$(x-h)^2+(y-k)^2=r^2$$

So, $h = 4$, $k = -1$, and $r = 3$. The center is at (4, –1), and the radius is 3. Plot the center and four points that are 3 units from this point. Sketch the circle through these four points.

(4, –1)

GuidedPractice

For each circle with the given equation, state the coordinates of the center and the measure of the radius. Then graph the equation.

3A. $x^2+y^2-4=0$

3B. $x^2+y^2+8x-14y+40=0$

Teach with Tech

Interactive Whiteboard Display a coordinate plane on the board. Draw a circle centered at the origin. Display the coordinates of the center, the length of the radius, and the equation of the circle. Have students take turns moving the circle or changing the length of the radius. Save the results and distribute them to the class.

WatchOut!

Distance Formula When using the distance formula, remind students to be careful to keep the *x*- and *y*-coordinates in the correct order and to keep track of their signs.

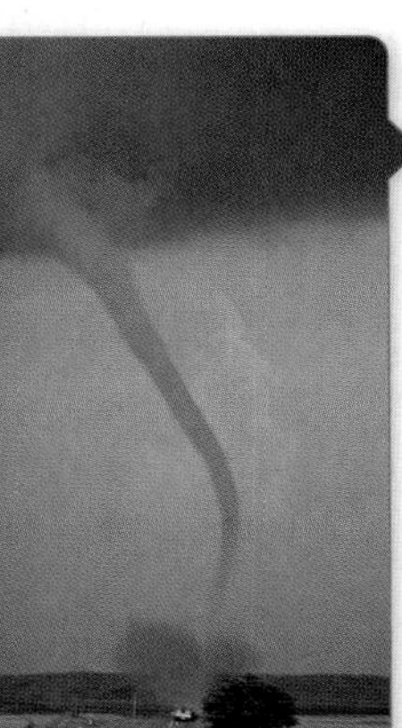

Real-World Example 4 Use Three Points to Write an Equation

TORNADOES Three tornado sirens are placed strategically on a circle around a town so they can be heard by all. Write the equation of the circle on which they are placed if the coordinates of the sirens are $A(-8, 3)$, $B(-4, 7)$, and $C(-4, -1)$.

Understand You are given three points that lie on a circle.

Plan Graph $\triangle ABC$. Construct the perpendicular bisectors of two sides to locate the center of the circle. Then find the radius.

Use the center and radius to write an equation.

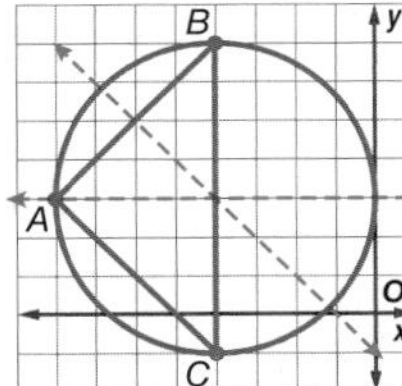

Solve The center appears to be at $(-4, 3)$. The radius is 4. Write an equation.

$$(x - h)^2 + (y - k)^2 = r^2$$
$$[x - (-4)]^2 + (y - 3)^2 = 4^2$$
$$(x + 4)^2 + (y - 3)^2 = 16$$

Check Verify the center by finding the equations of the two bisectors and solving the system of equations. Verify the radius by finding the distance between the center and another point on the circle. ✓

GuidedPractice $(x + 2)^2 + (y - 1)^2 = 10$

4. Write an equation of a circle that contains $R(1, 2)$, $S(-3, 4)$, and $T(-5, 0)$.

Real-WorldLink

About 1000 tornadoes are reported across the United States each year. The most violent tornadoes have wind speeds of 250 mph or more. Damage paths can be a mile wide and 50 miles long.

Source: National Oceanic & Atmospheric Administration

A line can intersect a circle in at most two points. You can find the point(s) of intersection between a circle and a line by applying techniques used to find the intersection between two lines and techniques used to solve quadratic equations.

Example 5 Intersections with Circles

Find the point(s) of intersection between $x^2 + y^2 = 4$ and $y = x$.

Graph these equations on the same coordinate plane. The points of intersection are solutions of both equations. You can estimate these points on the graph to be at about $(-1.4, -1.4)$ and $(1.4, 1.4)$. Use substitution to find the coordinates of these points algebraically.

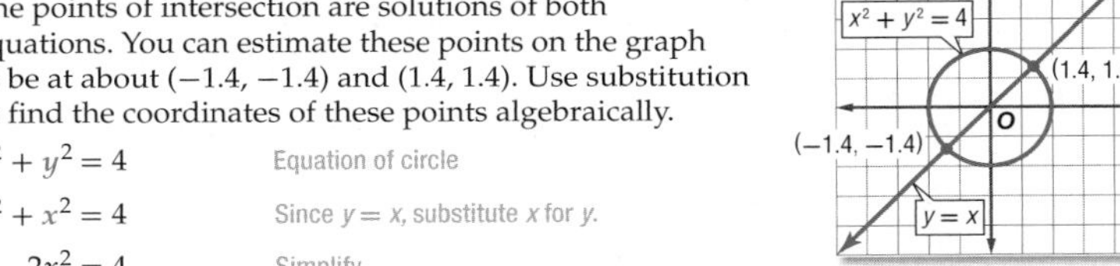

$x^2 + y^2 = 4$	Equation of circle
$x^2 + x^2 = 4$	Since $y = x$, substitute x for y.
$2x^2 = 4$	Simplify.
$x^2 = 2$	Divide each side by 2.
$x = \pm\sqrt{2}$	Take the square root of each side.

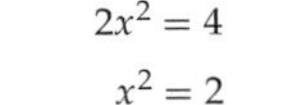

So $x = \sqrt{2}$ or $x = -\sqrt{2}$. Use the equation $y = x$ to find the corresponding y-values.

$y = x$	Equation of line	$y = x$
$y = \sqrt{2}$	$x = \sqrt{2}$ or $x = -\sqrt{2}$	$y = -\sqrt{2}$

The points of intersection are located at $(\sqrt{2}, \sqrt{2})$ and $(-\sqrt{2}, -\sqrt{2})$ or at about $(-1.4, -1.4)$ and $(1.4, 1.4)$. Check these solutions in both of the original equations.

GuidedPractice $(-2, 2)$ and $(2, -2)$

5. Find the point(s) of intersection between $x^2 + y^2 = 8$ and $y = -x$.

StudyTip

Quadratic Techniques In addition to taking square roots, other quadratic techniques that you may need to apply in order to solve equations of the form $ax^2 + bx + c = 0$ include completing the square, factoring, and the Quadratic Formula, $x = \frac{-b \pm \sqrt{b^2 - 4ac}}{2a}$.

2 Graph Circles

Examples 3 and 4 show how to analyze the equation of a circle that will help graph the circle on a coordinate plane. **Example 5** shows how to find the point(s) of intersection between a circle and a line.

Additional Examples

3 The equation of a circle is $x^2 - 4x + y^2 + 6y = -9$. State the coordinates of the center and the measure of the radius. Then graph the equation. $(2, -3)$; 2

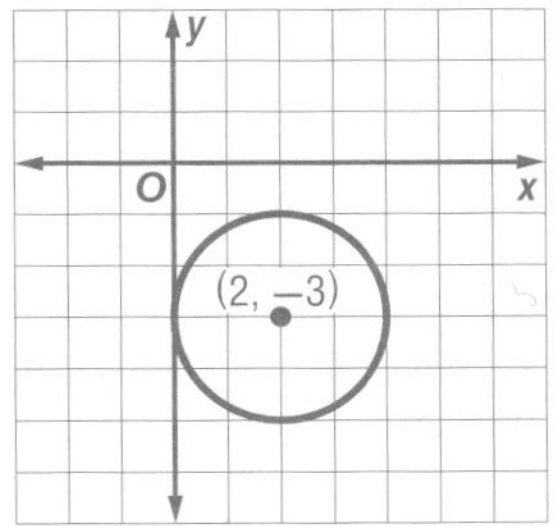

4 **ELECTRICITY** Strategically located substations are extremely important in the transmission and distribution of a power company's electric supply. Suppose three substations are modeled by the points $D(3, 6)$, $E(-1, 1)$, and $F(3, -4)$. Determine the location of a town equidistant from all three substations, and write an equation for the circle. $(4, 1)$; $(x - 4)^2 + (y - 1)^2 = 26$

5 Find the point(s) of intersection between $x^2 + y^2 = 32$ and $y = x + 8$. $(-4, 4)$

DifferentiatedInstruction OL BL

Logical Learners Explain that students will rely heavily on their geometric knowledge and reasoning skills to solve the problems in this lesson. Allow students to explain how to explore and collaborate as they work through examples and exercises. Students need to recall definitions, concepts, and theorems to help explain why they use certain methods to solve problems.

3 Practice

Formative Assessment

Use Exercises 1–12 to check for understanding.

Use the chart at the bottom of this page to customize assignments for your students.

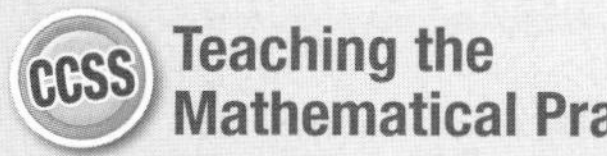

Teaching the Mathematical Practices

Structure Mathematically proficient students look closely to discern a pattern or structure. They also can step back for an overview and shift perspective. In Exercises 13–20, encourage students to identify h, k, and r.

Exercise Alert

Graph Paper Exercises 23–28, 39, 40, 42, and 46 require the use of graph paper.

Multiple Representations

In Exercise 42, students use a table, graphs, and verbal descriptions to investigate the compound locus of a pair of points.

Additional Answers

7. (3, −2); 4

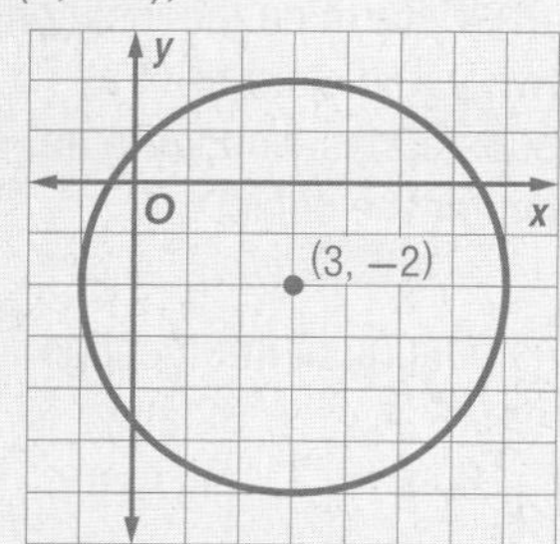

8. (0, −1); 2

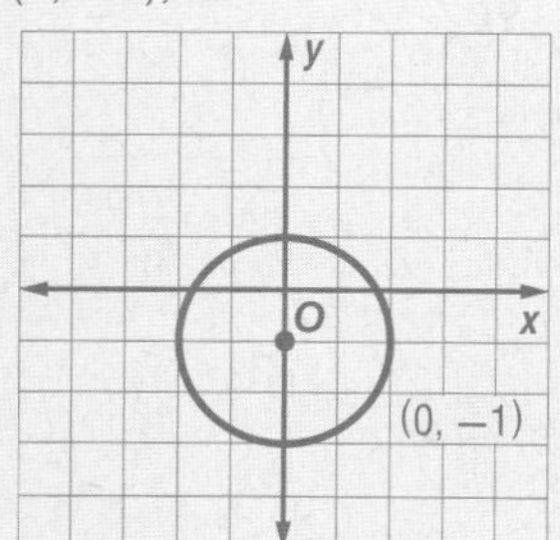

Check Your Understanding

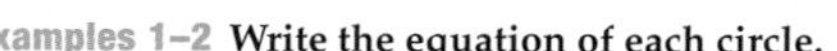

= Step-by-Step Solutions begin on page R14.

Examples 1–2 **Write the equation of each circle.**

1. center at (9, 0), radius 5
2. center at (3, 1), diameter 14
3. center at origin, passes through (2, 2)
4. center at (−5, 3), passes through (1, −4)

5.

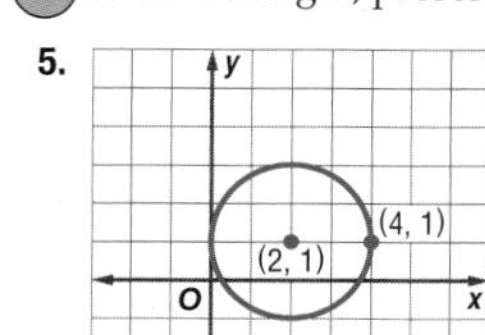

6.

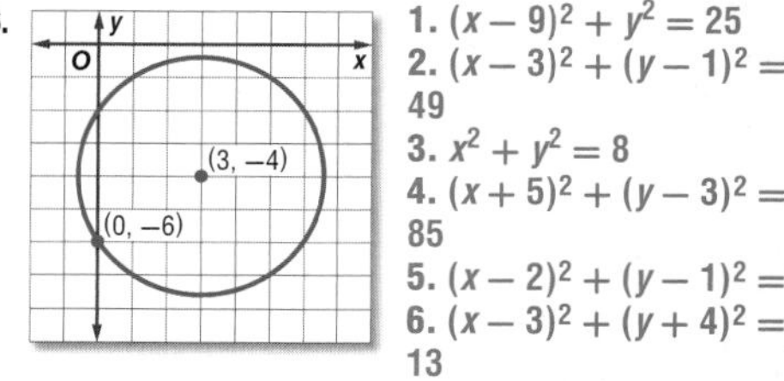

1. $(x-9)^2+y^2=25$
2. $(x-3)^2+(y-1)^2=49$
3. $x^2+y^2=8$
4. $(x+5)^2+(y-3)^2=85$
5. $(x-2)^2+(y-1)^2=4$
6. $(x-3)^2+(y+4)^2=13$

Example 3 **For each circle with the given equation, state the coordinates of the center and the measure of the radius. Then graph the equation.** **7, 8. See margin.**

7. $x^2-6x+y^2+4y=3$
8. $x^2+(y+1)^2=4$

Example 4

9. **RADIOS** Three radio towers are modeled by the points $R(4, 5)$, $S(8, 1)$, and $T(-4, 1)$. Determine the location of another tower equidistant from all three towers, and write an equation for the circle. **(2, −1); $(x-2)^2+(y+1)^2=40$**

10. **COMMUNICATION** Three cell phone towers can be modeled by the points $X(6, 0)$, $Y(8, 4)$, and $Z(3, 9)$. Determine the location of another cell phone tower equidistant from the other three, and write an equation for the circle. **(3, 4); $(x-3)^2+(y-4)^2=25$**

Example 5 **Find the point(s) of intersection, if any, between each circle and line with the equations given.**

11. $(x-1)^2+y^2=4$ **(1, 2), (−1, 0)**
$y=x+1$

12. $(x-2)^2+(y+3)^2=18$ **(−1, 0), $\left(2\frac{3}{5}, -7\frac{1}{5}\right)$**
$y=-2x-2$

Practice and Problem Solving

Extra Practice is on page R10.

Examples 1–2  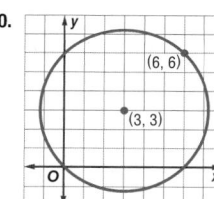 **STRUCTURE** **Write the equation of each circle.**

13. center at origin, radius 4
14. center at (6, 1), radius 7
15. center at (−2, 0), diameter 16
16. center at (8, −9), radius $\sqrt{11}$
17. center at (−3, 6), passes through (0, 6)
18. center at (1, −2), passes through (3, −4)

19.

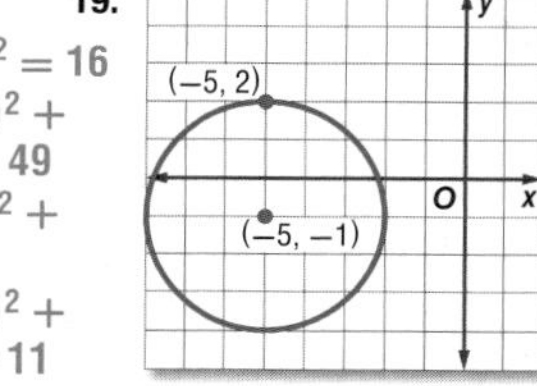

20.

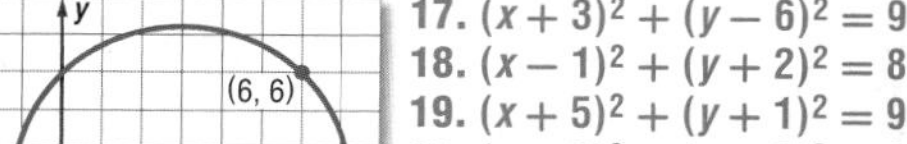

13. $x^2+y^2=16$
14. $(x-6)^2+(y-1)^2=49$
15. $(x+2)^2+y^2=64$
16. $(x-8)^2+(y+9)^2=11$
17. $(x+3)^2+(y-6)^2=9$
18. $(x-1)^2+(y+2)^2=8$
19. $(x+5)^2+(y+1)^2=9$
20. $(x-3)^2+(y-3)^2=18$

21. **WEATHER** A Doppler radar screen shows concentric rings around a storm. If the center of the radar screen is the origin and each ring is 15 miles farther from the center, what is the equation of the third ring? **$x^2+y^2=2025$**

22. **GARDENING** A sprinkler waters a circular area that has a diameter of 10 feet. The sprinkler is located 20 feet north of the house. If the house is located at the origin, what is the equation for the circle of area that is watered? **$x^2+(y-20)^2=25$**

Differentiated Homework Options

Level	Assignment	Two-Day Option	
AL Basic	13–34, 45–62	13–33, 49–52	14–44 even, 45–48, 53–62
OL Core	13–37 odd, 37–42, 44–62	13–34, 49–52	35–43, 45–48, 53–62
BL Advanced	35–59, (optional: 60–62)		

Example 3 For each circle with the given equation, state the coordinates of the center and the measure of the radius. Then graph the equation. 23–26. See margin.

23. $x^2 + y^2 = 36$

24. $x^2 + y^2 - 4x - 2y = -1$

25. $x^2 + y^2 + 8x - 4y = -4$

26. $x^2 + y^2 - 16x = 0$

Example 4 Write an equation of a circle that contains each set of points. Then graph the circle.

27. $A(1, 6), B(5, 6), C(5, 0)$ See Ch. 10 Answer Appendix.

28. $F(3, -3), G(3, 1), H(7, 1)$ See Ch. 10 Answer Appendix.

Example 5 Find the point(s) of intersection, if any, between each circle and line with the equations given.

29. $x^2 + y^2 = 5$, $y = \frac{1}{2}x$ (−2, −1), (2, 1)

30. $x^2 + y^2 = 2$, $y = -x + 2$ (1, 1)

31. $x^2 + (y + 2)^2 = 8$, $y = x - 2$ (−2, −4), (2, 0)

32. $(x + 3)^2 + y^2 = 25$, $y = -3x$ See margin.

33. $x^2 + y^2 = 5$, $y = 3x$ See margin.

34. $(x - 1)^2 + (y - 3)^2 = 4$, $y = -x$ no points of intersection

B Write the equation of each circle. 36. $(x + 13)^2 + (y - 6)^2 = 121$

35. a circle with a diameter having endpoints at (0, 4) and (6, −4) $(x - 3)^2 + y^2 = 25$

36. a circle with $d = 22$ and a center translated 13 units left and 6 units up from the origin

37. **CCSS MODELING** Different-sized engines will launch model rockets to different altitudes. The higher a rocket goes, the larger the circle of possible landing sites becomes. Under normal wind conditions, the landing radius is three times the altitude of the rocket. a. $x^2 + y^2 = 810{,}000$

a. Write the equation of the landing circle for a rocket that travels 300 feet in the air.

b. What would be the radius of the landing circle for a rocket that travels 1000 feet in the air? Assume the center of the circle is at the origin. 3000 ft

38. **SKYDIVING** Three of the skydivers in the circular formation shown have approximate coordinates of $G(13, -2)$, $H(-1, -2)$, and $J(6, -9)$.

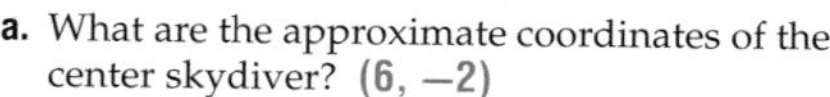
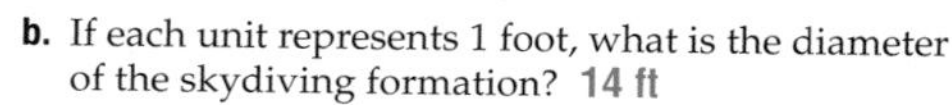

a. What are the approximate coordinates of the center skydiver? (6, −2)

b. If each unit represents 1 foot, what is the diameter of the skydiving formation? 14 ft

39b. All homes within the circle get free delivery. Consuela's home at (0, 0) is located outside the circle, so she cannot get free delivery.

39. **DELIVERY** Pizza and Subs offers free delivery within 6 miles of the restaurant. The restaurant is located 4 miles west and 5 miles north of Consuela's house.

a. Write and graph an equation to represent this situation if Consuela's house is at the origin of the coordinate system. See margin.

b. Can Consuela get free delivery if she orders pizza from Pizza and Subs? Explain.

C 40. **INTERSECTIONS OF CIRCLES** Graph $x^2 + y^2 = 4$ and $(x - 2)^2 + y^2 = 4$ on the same coordinate plane. e. $(1, \sqrt{3})$, $(1, -\sqrt{3})$; The coordinates are approximately the same.

a. Estimate the point(s) of intersection between the two circles. ≈(1, 1.7) and (1, −1.7)

b. Solve $x^2 + y^2 = 4$ for y. $y = \pm\sqrt{4 - x^2}$

c. Substitute the value you found in part **b** into $(x - 2)^2 + y^2 = 4$ and solve for x. $x = 1$

d. Substitute the value you found in part **c** into $x^2 + y^2 = 4$ and solve for y. $y = \pm\sqrt{3}$

e. Use your answers to parts **c** and **d** to write the coordinates of the points of intersection. Compare these coordinates to your estimate from part **a**.

f. Verify that the point(s) you found in part **d** lie on both circles. See margin.

39a. $(x + 4)^2 + (y - 5)^2 = 36$;

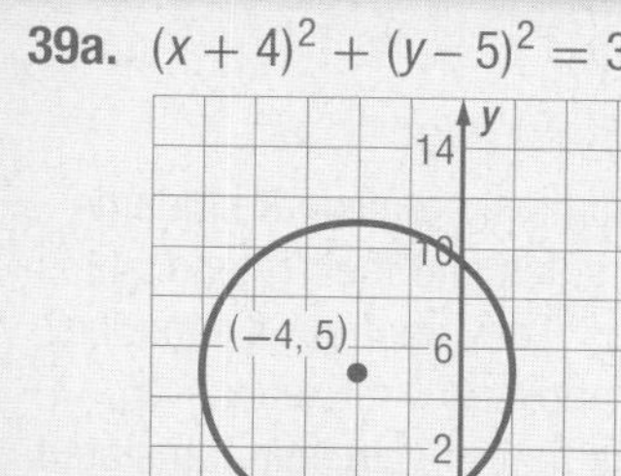

40f. Verify $(1, \sqrt{3})$.

$1^2 + (\sqrt{3})^2 = 4$

$1 + 3 = 4$ ✓

$(1 - 2)^2 + (\sqrt{3})^2 = 4$

$(-1)^2 + 3 = 4$

$1 + 3 = 4$ ✓

Verify $(1, -\sqrt{3})$.

$1^2 + (-\sqrt{3})^2 = 4$

$1 + 3 = 4$ ✓

$(1 - 2)^2 + (-\sqrt{3})^2 = 4$

$(-1)^2 + 3 = 4$

$1 + 3 = 4$ ✓

CCSS Teaching the Mathematical Practices

Modeling Mathematically proficient students can apply the mathematics they know to solve problems arising in everyday life. In Exercise 37, encourage students to interpret their results in the context of the situation.

Additional Answers

23. (0, 0); 6

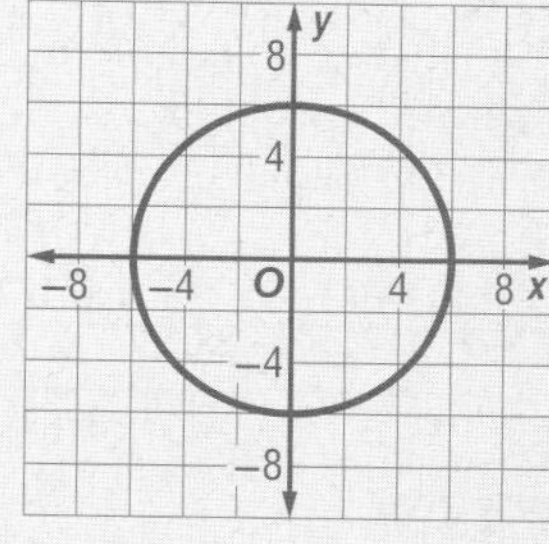

24. (2, 1); 2

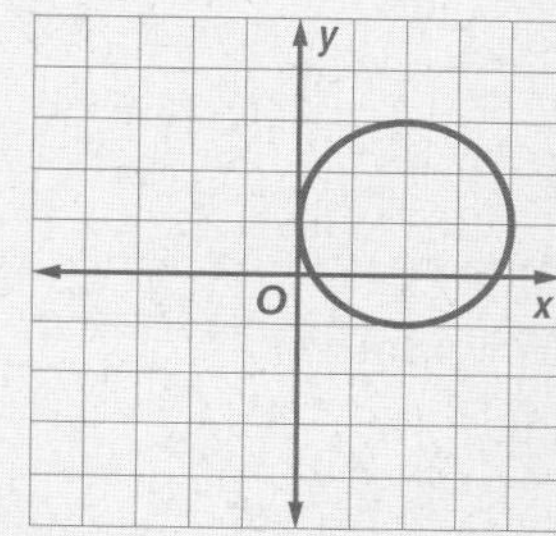

25. (−4, 2); 4

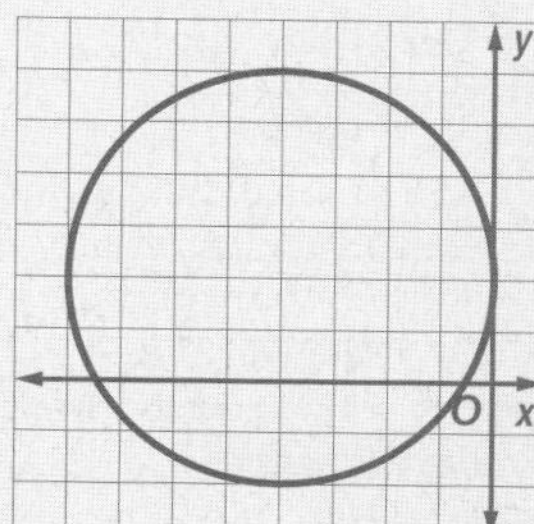

26. (8, 0); 8

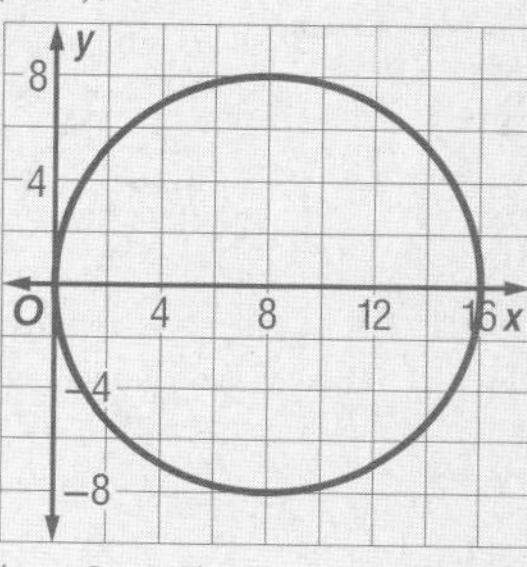

32. $\left(-1\frac{3}{5}, 4\frac{4}{5}\right)$, (1, −3)

33. $\left(\frac{\sqrt{2}}{2}, \frac{3\sqrt{2}}{2}\right)$, $\left(-\frac{\sqrt{2}}{2}, -\frac{3\sqrt{2}}{2}\right)$

Study Guide and Intervention

AL OL ELL

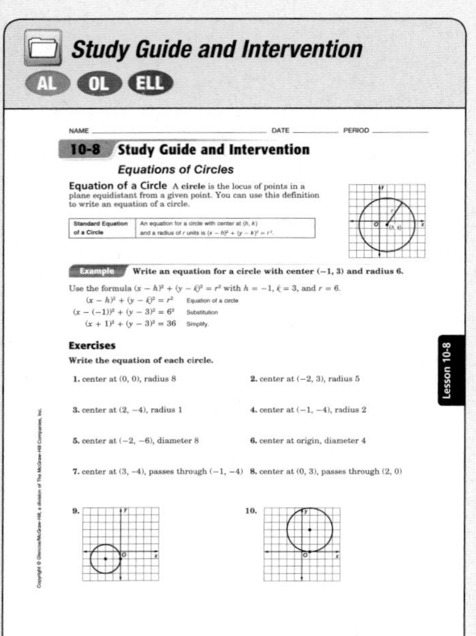
NAME _______ DATE _______ PERIOD _______

10-8 Study Guide and Intervention

Equations of Circles

Equation of a Circle A circle is the locus of points in a plane equidistant from a given point. You can use this definition to write an equation of a circle.

Standard Equation of a Circle	An equation for a circle with center at (h, k) and a radius of r units is $(x - h)^2 + (y - k)^2 = r^2$.

Example Write an equation for a circle with center $(-1, 3)$ and radius 6.

Use the formula $(x - h)^2 + (y - k)^2 = r^2$ with $h = -1$, $k = 3$, and $r = 6$.

$(x - h)^2 + (y - k)^2 = r^2$ Equation of a circle

$(x - (-1))^2 + (y - 3)^2 = 6^2$ Substitution

$(x + 1)^2 + (y - 3)^2 = 36$ Simplify.

Exercises

Write the equation of each circle.

1. center at (0, 0), radius 8
2. center at (−2, 3), radius 5
3. center at (2, −4), radius 1
4. center at (−1, −4), radius 2
5. center at (−2, −6), diameter 8
6. center at origin, diameter 4
7. center at (3, −4), passes through (−1, −4)
8. center at (0, 3), passes through (2, 0)
9.
10.

Practice

AL OL BL ELL

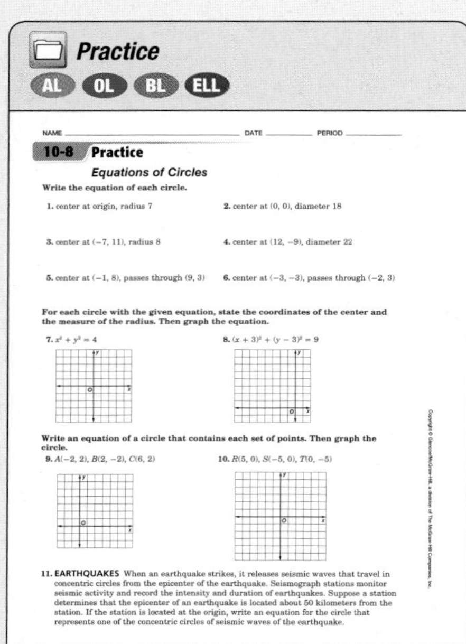
NAME _______ DATE _______ PERIOD _______

10-8 Practice

Equations of Circles

Write the equation of each circle.

1. center at origin, radius 7
2. center at (0, 0), diameter 18
3. center at (−7, 11), radius 8
4. center at (12, −9), diameter 22
5. center at (−1, 8), passes through (9, 3)
6. center at (−3, −3), passes through (−2, 3)

For each circle with the given equation, state the coordinates of the center and the measure of the radius. Then graph the equation.

7. $x^2 + y^2 = 4$
8. $(x + 3)^2 + (y - 3)^2 = 9$

Write an equation of a circle that contains each set of points. Then graph the circle.

9. A(−2, 2), B(2, −2), C(6, 2)
10. R(5, 0), S(−5, 0), T(0, −5)

11. EARTHQUAKES When an earthquake strikes, it releases seismic waves that travel in concentric circles from the epicenter of the earthquake. Seismograph stations monitor seismic activity and record the intensity and duration of earthquakes. Suppose a station determines that the epicenter of an earthquake is located about 50 kilometers from the station. If the station is located at the origin, write an equation for the circle that represents one of the concentric circles of seismic waves of the earthquake.

Word Problem Practice

AL OL BL

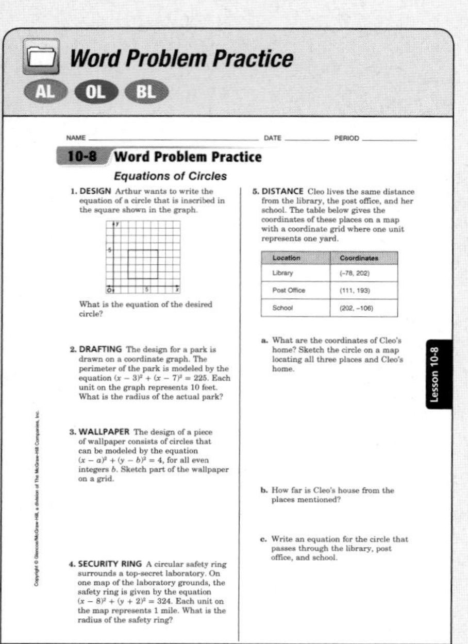
NAME _______ DATE _______ PERIOD _______

10-8 Word Problem Practice

Equations of Circles

1. DESIGN Arthur wants to write the equation of a circle that is inscribed in the square shown in the graph. What is the equation of the desired circle?

2. DRAFTING The design for a park is drawn on a coordinate graph. The perimeter of the park is modeled by the equation $(x - 3)^2 + (x - 7)^2 = 225$. Each unit on the graph represents 10 feet. What is the radius of the actual park?

3. WALLPAPER The design of a piece of wallpaper consists of circles that can be modeled by the equation $(x - a)^2 + (y - b)^2 = 4$, for all even integers b. Sketch part of the wallpaper on a grid.

4. SECURITY RING A circular safety ring surrounds a top-secret laboratory. On one map of the laboratory grounds, the safety ring is given by the equation $(x - 8)^2 + (y + 2)^2 = 324$. Each unit on the map represents 1 mile. What is the radius of the safety ring?

5. DISTANCE Cleo lives the same distance from the library, the post office, and her school. The table below gives the coordinates of these places on a map with a coordinate grid where one unit represents one yard.

Location	Coordinates
Library	(−78, 202)
Post Office	(111, 193)
School	(202, −106)

a. What are the coordinates of Cleo's home? Sketch the circle on a map locating all three places and Cleo's home.

b. How far is Cleo's house from the places mentioned?

c. Write an equation for the circle that passes through the library, post office, and school.

41. Prove or disprove that the point $(1, 2\sqrt{2})$ lies on a circle centered at the origin and containing the point $(0, -3)$. **See Ch. 10 Answer Appendix.**

42. **MULTIPLE REPRESENTATIONS** In this problem, you will investigate a compound locus for a pair of points. A **compound locus** satisfies more than one distinct set of conditions.

a. **Tabular** Choose two points A and B in the coordinate plane. Locate 5 coordinates from the locus of points equidistant from A and B.

b. **Graphical** Represent this same locus of points by using a graph.

c. **Verbal** Describe the locus of all points equidistant from a pair of points.

d. **Graphical** Using your graph from part **b**, determine and graph the locus of all points in a plane that are a distance of AB from B.

e. **Verbal** Describe the locus of all points in a plane equidistant from a single point. Then describe the locus of all points that are both equidistant from A and B and are a distance of AB from B. Describe the graph of the compound locus. **See margin.**

42b, 42d. See Ch.10 Answer Appendix.

42c. a line that is the perpendicular bisector of $\overline{AB}$

42a. Sample answer:

x	y
−1	−3
−1	−1
−1	0
−1	2
−1	4

43. A circle with a diameter of 12 has its center in the second quadrant. The lines $y = -4$ and $x = 1$ are tangent to the circle. Write an equation of the circle. $(x + 5)^2 + (y - 2)^2 = 36$

H.O.T. Problems Use Higher-Order Thinking Skills

44. **CHALLENGE** Write a coordinate proof to show that if an inscribed angle intercepts the diameter of a circle, as shown, the angle is a right angle. **See Ch. 10 Answer Appendix.**

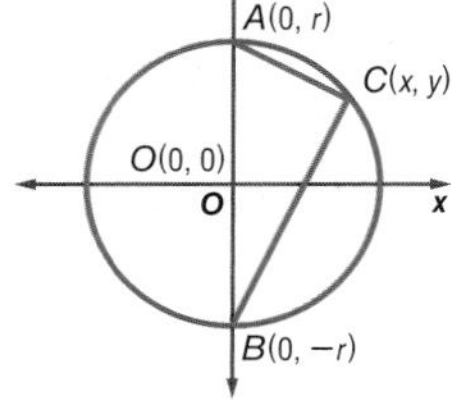

45. **CCSS REASONING** A circle has the equation $(x - 5)^2 + (y + 7)^2 = 16$. If the center of the circle is shifted 3 units right and 9 units up, what would be the equation of the new circle? Explain your reasoning. **See margin.**

46. **OPEN ENDED** Graph three noncollinear points and connect them to form a triangle. Then construct the circle that circumscribes it. **See Ch. 10 Answer Appendix.**

47. **WRITING IN MATH** Seven new radio stations must be assigned broadcast frequencies. The stations are located at $A(9, 2)$, $B(8, 4)$, $C(8, 1)$, $D(6, 3)$, $E(4, 0)$, $F(3, 6)$, and $G(4, 5)$, where 1 unit = 50 miles.

a. If stations that are more than 200 miles apart can share the same frequency, what is the least number of frequencies that can be assigned to these stations?

b. Describe two different beginning approaches to solving this problem.

c. Choose an approach, solve the problem, and explain your reasoning.

a–c. See Ch. 10 Answer Appendix.

CHALLENGE Find the coordinates of point P on $\overrightarrow{AB}$ that partitions the segment into the given ratio AP to PB.

48. $A(0, 0)$, $B(3, 4)$, 2 to 3 **(1.2, 1.6)**

49. $A(0, 0)$, $B(-8, 6)$, 4 to 1 **(−6.4, 4.8)**

50. **WRITING IN MATH** Describe how the equation for a circle changes if the circle is translated a units to the right and b units down. **See margin.**

Enrichment

OL BL

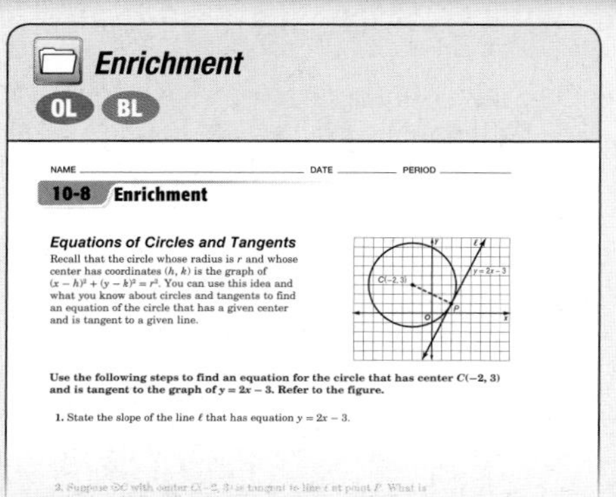
NAME _______ DATE _______ PERIOD _______

10-8 Enrichment

Equations of Circles and Tangents

Recall that the circle whose radius is r and whose center has coordinates (h, k) is the graph of $(x - h)^2 + (y - k)^2 = r^2$. You can use this idea and what you know about circles and tangents to find an equation of the circle that has a given center and is tangent to a given line.

Use the following steps to find an equation for the circle that has center $C(-2, 3)$ and is tangent to the graph of $y = 2x - 3$. Refer to the figure.

1. State the slope of the line ℓ that has equation $y = 2x - 3$.

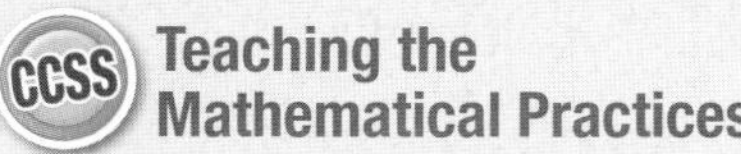

Reasoning Mathematically proficient students make sense of quantities and their relationships in problem situations. They abstract a situation and represent it symbolically. In Exercise 45, point out to students that the circle is translated so the radius is not changing.

Standardized Test Practice

51. Which of the following is the equation of a circle with center (6, 5) that passes through (2, 8)? **A**

A $(x - 6)^2 + (y - 5)^2 = 5^2$
B $(x - 5)^2 + (y - 6)^2 = 7^2$
C $(x + 6)^2 + (y + 5)^2 = 5^2$
D $(x - 2)^2 + (y - 8)^2 = 7^2$

52. ALGEBRA What are the solutions of $n^2 - 4n = 21$? **H**

F 3, 7
G 3, −7
H −3, 7
J −3, −7

53. SHORT RESPONSE Solve: $5(x - 4) = 16$.

Step 1: $5x - 4 = 16$
Step 2: $5x = 20$
Step 3: $x = 4$

Which is the first incorrect step in the solution shown above? **Step 1**

54. SAT/ACT The center of $\odot F$ is at (−4, 0) and has a radius of 4. Which point lies on $\odot F$? **D**

A (4, 0)
B (0, 4)
C (4, 3)
D (−4, 4)
E (0, 8)

Spiral Review

Find *x*. (Lesson 10-7)

55. 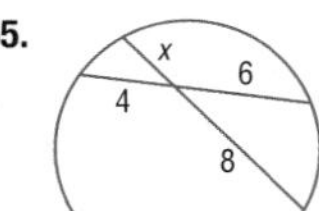

3

56. 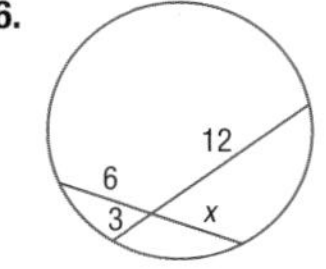

6

57. 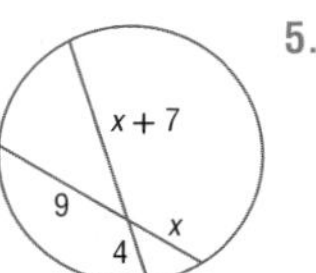

5.6

Find each measure. (Lesson 10-6)

58. $m\angle C$ **70**

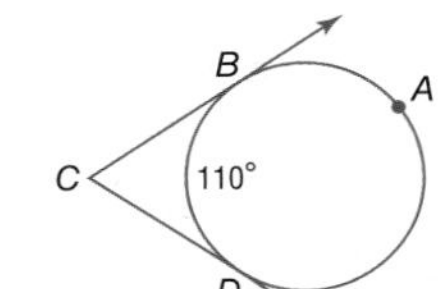

59. $m\angle K$ **53**

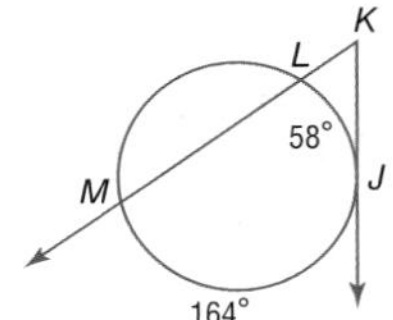

60. $m\widehat{YXZ}$ **194**

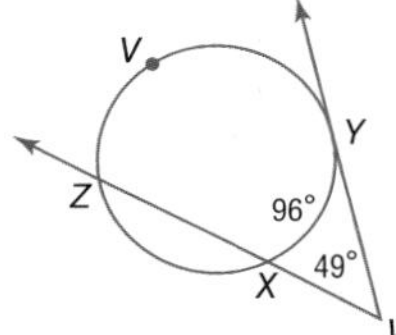

61. STREETS The neighborhood where Vincent lives has roundabouts where certain streets meet. If Vincent rides his bike once around the very edge of the grassy circle, how many feet will he have ridden? (Lesson 10-1) **28.3 ft**

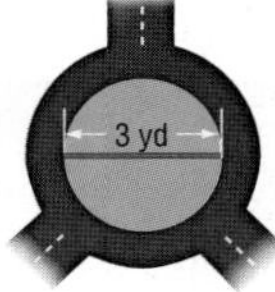

Skills Review

Find the perimeter and area of each figure.

62. 

50 in.; 144 in^2

63. 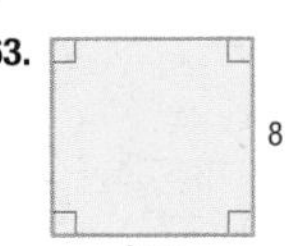

32 cm; 64 cm^2

64. 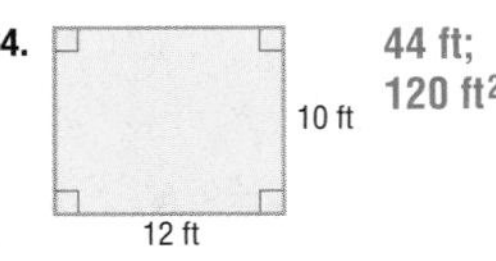

44 ft; 120 ft^2

Differentiated Instruction OL BL

Extension What is the relationship between concentric circles with the same radius? Explain. They are the same circle. A center and a radius are all it takes to define a circle. Two circles that share a center and have the same radius are identical.

4 Assess

Name the Math Let students take turns saying an equation of a circle. Then they should name the centers of the circles, and state the lengths of the radii.

Formative Assessment

Check for student understanding of Lessons 10-7 and 10-8.

 Quiz 4, p. 58

Additional Answers

42e. The locus of all points in a plane equidistant from a point is a circle. The locus of points that are both equidistant from *A* and *B* and are a distance of *AB* from *B* is the intersection of the locus of points equidistant from *A* and *B* and the locus of points that are a distance of *AB* from *B*. Graphically, the compound locus is represented as two points.

45. $(x - 8)^2 + (y - 2)^2 = 16$; the first circle has its center at (5, −7). If the circle is shifted 3 units right and 9 units up, the new center is at (8, 2), so the new equation becomes $(x - 8)^2 + (y - 2)^2 = 16$.

50. Sample answer: The equation for a circle is $(x - h)^2 + (y - k)^2 = r^2$. When the circle is shifted a units to the right, the new *x*-coordinate of the center is $x + a$. When the circle is translated b units down, the new *y*-coordinate of the center is $y - b$. The new equation for the circle is $[x - (h + a)]^2 + [y - (k - b)]^2 = r^2$ or is $(x - h - a)^2 + (y - k + b)^2 = r^2$.

1 Focus

Objectives

- Identify conic sections.
- Translate between the geometric description and the equation for a parabola.
- Determine intersections between lines and parabolas.

Materials for Each Group

- modeling clay
- wax paper
- graph paper

Teaching Tip

If time or materials is an issue, you may wish to complete Activity 1 as a class by finding and using an online conic section applet. Activity 2 can also be completed as a whole-class activity using a graphing calculator.

2 Teach

Working in Cooperative Groups

Organize students into groups of 2 or 3, mixing abilities. Then have groups complete Activities 1–3 and Exercises 1–8.

Ask:

- Will the graph of a parabola ever intersect its directrix? no
- In Algebra 1, you learned that a parabola is symmetric with respect to its axis of symmetry, which passes through its vertex. What is the relationship between the directrix and axis of symmetry? They are perpendicular.
- What is the relationship between the vertex and axis of symmetry? The vertex lies on the axis of symmetry.
- Where is the vertex located in relationship to the focus and the directrix? exactly halfway between the two along the axis of symmetry

EXTEND 10-8 Geometry Lab Parabolas

A circle is one type of cross-section of a right circular cone. Such cross-sections are called **conic sections** or **conics**. A circular cross-section is formed by the intersection of a cone with a plane that is perpendicular to the axis of the cone. You can find other conic sections using concrete models of cones.

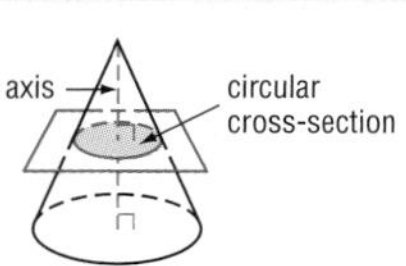

Common Core State Standards
Content Standards
G.GPE.2 Derive the equation of a parabola given a focus and directrix.
Mathematical Practices 5

Activity 1 Intersection of Cone and Plane

Sketch the intersection of a cone and a plane that lies at an angle to the axis of the cone but does not pass through its base.

Step 1 Fill a conical paper cup with modeling compound. Then peel away the cup.

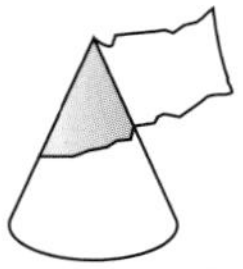

Step 2 Draw dental floss through the cone model at an angle to the axis that does not pass through the base.

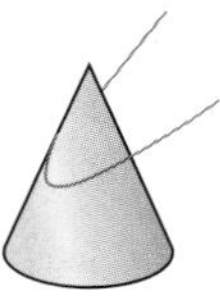

Step 3 Pull the pieces of the cone apart and trace the cross-section onto your paper.

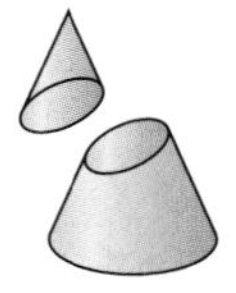

Model and Analyze

1. The conic section in Activity 1 is called an ellipse. What shape is an ellipse? an oval
2. Repeat Activity 1, drawing the dental floss through the model at an angle parallel to an imaginary line on the side of the cone through the cone's base. Describe the resulting shape. Sample answer: a U-shape or parabola

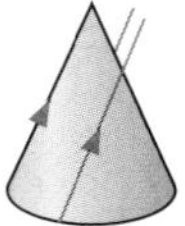

The conic section you found in Exercise 2 is called a **parabola**. In Algebra 1, a parabola was defined as the shape of the graph of a quadratic function, such as $y = x^2$. Like a circle and all conics, a parabola can also be defined as a locus of points. You can explore the loci definition of a parabola using paper folding.

Activity 2 Shape of Parabola

Use paper folding to approximate the shape of a parabola.

Step 1 Mark and label the bottom edge of a rectangular piece of wax paper *d*. Label a point *F* at the center.

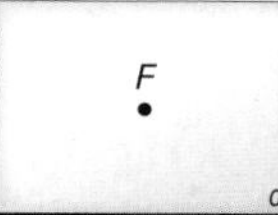

Step 2 Fold *d* up so that it touches *F*. Make a sharp crease. Then open the paper and smooth it flat.

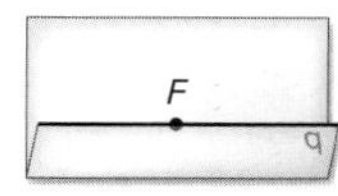

Step 3 Repeat Step 2 at least 20 times, folding the paper to a different point on *d* each time. Trace the curve formed.

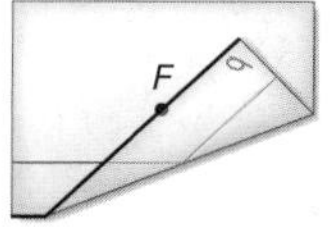

Focus on Mathematical Content

Double-Napped Cone In later courses, students will learn that conic sections are figures formed when a plane intersects a double-napped cone. Using this definition, students will explore another conic section called the *hyperbola*, which is formed by the intersection of a double-napped cone and a plane that is parallel to the axis of the cone.

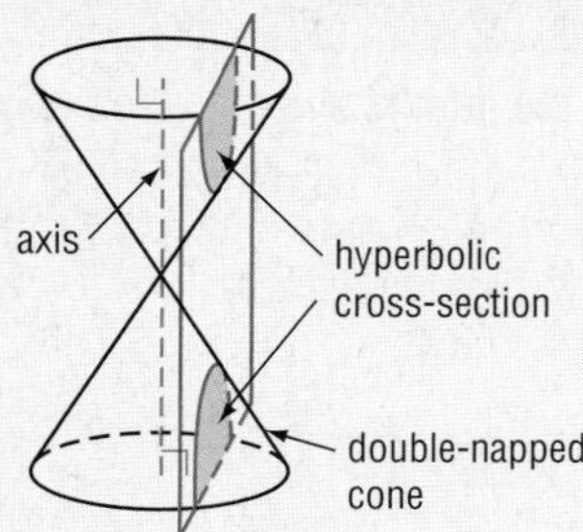

Model and Analyze

3. Label a point P on the parabola and draw $\overline{PF}$. Then use a protractor to find a point D on line d such that $\overline{PD} \perp d$. Describe the relationship between $\overline{PF}$ and $\overline{PD}$. **They are the same length.**

Repeat Activity 2, making the indicated change on a new piece of wax paper. Describe the effect on the parabola formed.

4. Place line d along the edge above point F.
5. Place line d along the edge to the right of point F.
6. Place line d along the edge to left of point F.
7. Place point F closer to line d.
8. Place point F farther away from line d. **4–8. See margin.**

Geometrically, a parabola is the locus of all points in a plane equidistant from a fixed point, called the **focus**, and a fixed line, called the **directrix**. Recall that the distance between a fixed point and a line is the length of the segment perpendicular to the line through that point. You can find an equation of a parabola on the coordinate plane using its locus definition and the Distance Formula.

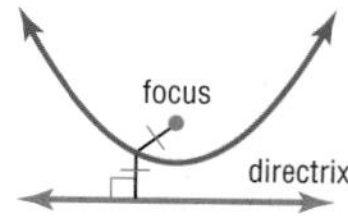

Activity 3 Equation of Parabola

Find an equation of the parabola with focus at (0, 1) and directrix $y = -1$.

Step 1 Graph $F(0, 1)$ and $y = -1$. Sketch a U-shaped curve for the parabola between the point and line as shown. Label a point $P(x, y)$ on the curve.

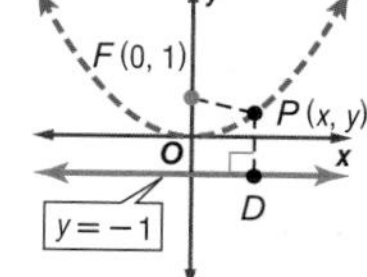

Step 2 Label a point D on $y = -1$ such that $\overline{PD}$ is perpendicular to the line $y = -1$. The coordinates of this point must therefore be $D(x, -1)$.

Step 3 Use the Distance Formula to find PD and PF.

$PD = \sqrt{(x - x)^2 + [y - (-1)]^2}$ — $D(x, -1), P(x, y), F(0, 1)$

$= \sqrt{(y + 1)^2}$ — Simplify.

$PF = \sqrt{(x - 0)^2 + (y - 1)^2}$

$= \sqrt{x^2 + (y - 1)^2}$

Step 4 Since $PD = PF$, set these expressions equal to each other.

$\sqrt{(y + 1)^2} = \sqrt{x^2 + (y - 1)^2}$ — $PD = PF$

$(y + 1)^2 = x^2 + (y - 1)^2$ — Square each side.

$y^2 + 2y + 1 = x^2 + y^2 - 2y + 1$ — Square each binomial.

$4y = x^2$ or $y = \frac{1}{4}x^2$ — Subtract $y^2 - 2y + 1$ from each side.

An equation of the parabola with focus at (0, 1) and directrix $y = -1$ is $y = \frac{1}{4}x^2$.

Model and Analyze

Find an equation of the parabola with the focus and directrix given. **9–16. See margin.**

9. $(0, -2), y = 2$
10. $\left(0, \frac{1}{2}\right), y = -\frac{1}{2}$
11. $(1, 0), x = -1$
12. $(-3, 0), x = 3$

A line can intersect a parabola in 0, 1, or 2 points. Find the point(s) of intersection, if any, between each parabola and line with the given equations.

13. $y = x^2, y = x + 2$
14. $y = 2x^2, y = 4x - 2$
15. $y = -3x^2, y = 6x$
16. $y = -(x + 1)^2, y = -x$

Differentiated Instruction BL

Extension Find a general equation for a parabola with focus $(0, a)$ and directrix $y = -a$. Then find the general equation of a parabola with focus $(a, 0)$ and directrix $x = -a$. What does a represent in each equation? $y = \frac{1}{4}ax^2$; $x = \frac{1}{4}ay^2$; Sample answer: half the distance between the focus and the directrix

Teaching Tips

- For Exercise 3, encourage students to use paper folding to compare $\overline{PF}$ to $\overline{PD}$.
- In Lesson 10-8, students used techniques for solving systems of equations and quadratic equations to find the intersection(s) between circles and lines. Tell students that these same techniques can be used to find the intersection(s) between parabolas and lines in Exercises 13–16.

Practice Have students complete Exercises 9–16.

3 Assess

Formative Assessment

Use Exercises 9 and 14 to assess whether students understand how to find the equation of a parabola given a focus and directrix and how to find the intersection(s) of a parabola and a line algebraically.

From Concrete to Abstract

Ask students to summarize what they have learned about the geometric definition of a parabola and how it relates to the algebraic definition they learned in Algebra 1.

Additional Answers

4. Sample answer: The parabola opens downward instead of upward.
5. Sample answer: The parabola opens to the left instead of upward.
6. Sample answer: The parabola opens to the right instead of upward.
7. Sample answer: The parabola does not open as widely.
8. Sample answer: The parabola opens more widely.
9. $y = -\frac{1}{8}x^2$
10. $y = \frac{1}{2}x^2$
11. $x = \frac{1}{4}y^2$
12. $x = -\frac{1}{12}y^2$
13. (−1, 1), (2, 4)
14. (1, 2)
15. (−2, −12), (0, 0)
16. no points of intersection

Formative Assessment

KeyVocabulary The page references after each word denote where that term was first introduced. If students have difficulty completing Exercises 1–9, remind them that they can use these page references to refresh their memories about the vocabulary terms.

Summative Assessment

Vocabulary Test, p. 60

Vocabulary Review

Vocabulary Review provides students the opportunity to check their understanding of important concepts and terminology in an online game format.

FOLDABLES StudyOrganizer

Dinah Zike's Foldables®

Have students look through the chapter to make sure they have included the key concepts under the proper lesson tabs in their Foldables. Suggest that students keep their Foldables handy while completing the Study Guide and Review pages. Point out that their Foldables can serve as a quick review tool for studying for the chapter test.

CHAPTER 10 Study Guide and Review

Study Guide

KeyConcepts

Circles and Circumference (Lesson 10-1)

- The circumference of a circle is equal to πd or $2\pi r$.

Angles, Arcs, Chords, and Inscribed Angles (Lessons 10-2 to 10-4)

- The sum of the measures of the central angles of a circle is 360°.
- The length of an arc is proportional to the length of the circumference.
- Diameters perpendicular to chords bisect chords and intercepted arcs.
- The measure of an inscribed angle is half the measure of its intercepted arc.

Tangents, Secants, and Angle Measures (Lessons 10-5 and 10-6)

- A line that is tangent to a circle intersects the circle in exactly one point and is perpendicular to a radius.
- Two segments tangent to a circle from the same exterior point are congruent.
- The measure of an angle formed by two secant lines is half the positive difference of its intercepted arcs.
- The measure of an angle formed by a secant and tangent line is half its intercepted arc.

Special Segments and Equation of a Circle (Lessons 10-7 and 10-8)

- The lengths of intersecting chords in a circle can be found by using the products of the measures of the segments.
- The equation of a circle with center (h, k) and radius r is $(x - h)^2 - (y - k)^2 = r^2$.

FOLDABLES StudyOrganizer

Be sure the Key Concepts are noted in your Foldable.

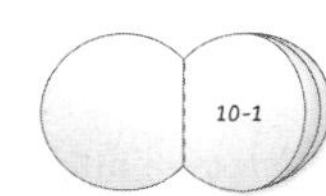

KeyVocabulary

adjacent arcs (p. 708)
arc (p. 706)
arc length (p. 709)
center (p. 697)
central angle (p. 706)
chord (p. 697)
chord segment (p. 750)
circle (p. 697)
circumference (p. 699)
circumscribed (p. 700)
common tangent (p. 732)
compound locus (p. 762)
concentric circles (p. 698)
congruent arcs (p. 707)
diameter (p. 697)
external secant segment (p. 752)
inscribed (p. 700)
inscribed angle (p. 723)
intercepted arc (p. 723)
major arc (p.707)
minor arc (p. 707)
pi (π) (p. 699)
point of tangency (p. 732)
radius (p. 697)
secant (p. 741)
secant segment (p. 752)
semicircle (p. 707)
tangent (p. 732)

VocabularyCheck

State whether each sentence is *true* or *false*. If *false*, replace the underlined word or phrase to make a true sentence.

1. Any segment with both endpoints on the circle is a <u>radius</u> of the circle. **false; chord**
2. A chord passing through the center of a circle is a <u>diameter</u>. **true**
3. A <u>central angle</u> has the center as its vertex and its sides contain two radii of the circle. **true**
4. An arc with a measure of less than 180° is a <u>major arc</u>. **false; minor arc**
5. An <u>intercepted arc</u> is an arc that has its endpoints on the sides of an inscribed angle and lies in the interior of the inscribed angle. **true**
6. A <u>common tangent</u> is the point at which a line in the same plane as a circle intersects the circle. **false; point of tangency**
7. A secant is a line that intersects a circle in exactly <u>one</u> point. **false; two**
8. A secant segment is a segment of a <u>diameter</u> that has exactly one endpoint on the circle. **false; secant line**
9. Two circles are <u>concentric</u> circles if and only if they have congruent radii. **false; congruent**

Lesson-by-Lesson Review

10-1 Circles and Circumference

For Exercises 10–12, refer to $\odot D$.

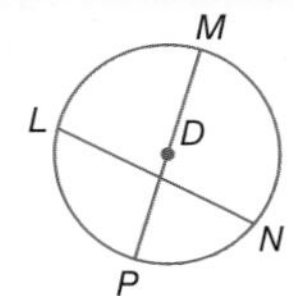

10. Name the circle. $\odot D$

11. Name a radius. $\overline{DM}$ or $\overline{DP}$

12. Name a chord that is not a diameter. $\overline{LN}$

Find the diameter and radius of a circle with the given circumference. Round to the nearest hundredth. **13–16. See margin.**

13. $C = 43$ cm **14.** $C = 26.7$ yd

15. $C = 108.5$ ft **16.** $C = 225.9$ mm

Example 1

Find the circumference of $\odot A$.

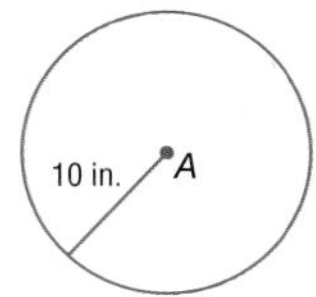

$C = 2\pi r$ Circumference formula

$= 2\pi(10)$ Substitution

≈ 62.83 Use a calculator.

The circumference of $\odot A$ is about 62.83 inches.

10-2 Measuring Angles and Arcs

Find the value of x.

17.

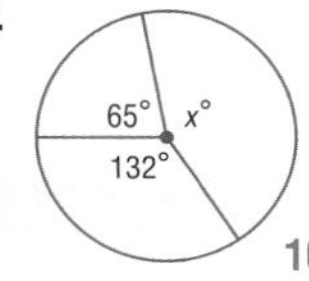

163

18.

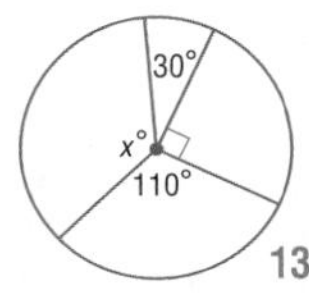

130

19. MOVIES The pie chart below represents the results of a survey taken by Mrs. Jameson regarding her students' favorite types of movies. Find each measure.

Mrs. Jameson's Students' Favorite Types of Movies

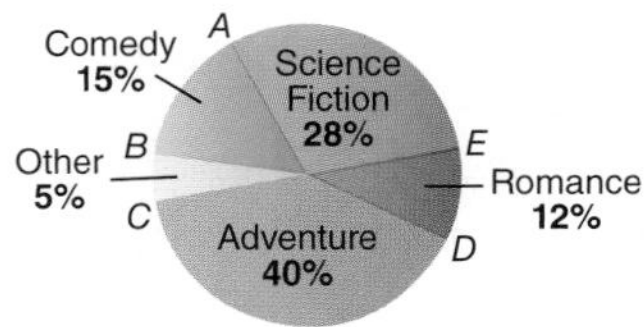

a. $m\widehat{AE}$ **100.8** **b.** $m\widehat{BC}$ **18**

c. Describe the type of arc that the category Adventure represents. **minor arc**

Example 2

Find the value of x.

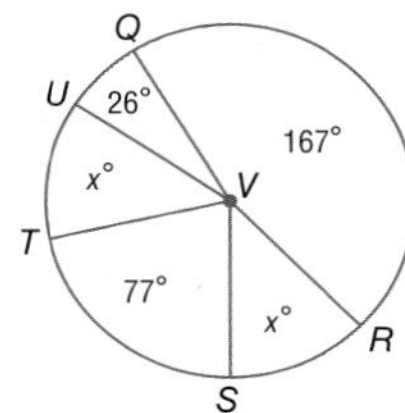

$m\angle QVR + m\angle RVS + m\angle SVT + m\angle TVU + m\angle UVQ = 360$ Sum of Central Angles

$167 + x + 77 + x + 26 = 360$ Substitution

$270 + 2x = 360$ Simplify.

$2x = 90$ Subtract.

$x = 45$ Divide.

Lesson-by-Lesson Review

Intervention If the given examples are not sufficient to review the topics covered by the questions, remind students that the lesson references tell them where to review that topic in their textbooks.

Two-Day Option Have students complete the Lesson-by-Lesson Review. Then you can use eAssessment to customize another review worksheet that practices all the objectives of this chapter or only the objectives on which your students need more help.

Additional Answers

13. 13.69 cm; 6.84 cm

14. 8.50 yd; 4.25 yd

15. 34.54 ft; 17.27 ft

16. 71.91 mm; 35.95 mm

connectED.mcgraw-hill.com 767

CHAPTER 10 Study Guide and Review *Continued*

10-3 Arcs and Chords

20. Find the value of x. **8**

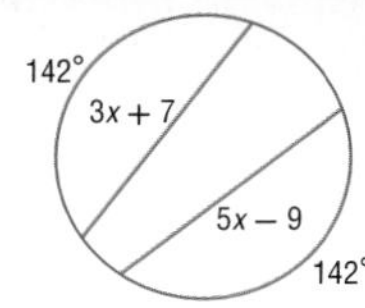

In $\odot K$, $MN = 16$ and $m\widehat{MN} = 98$. Find each measure. Round to the nearest hundredth.

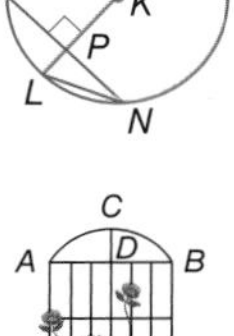

21. $m\widehat{NJ}$ **131** **22.** LN **8.94**

23. **GARDENING** The top of the trellis shown is an arc of a circle in which $\overline{CD}$ is part of the diameter and $\overline{CD} \perp \overline{AB}$. If $\widehat{ACB}$ is about 28% of a complete circle, what is $m\widehat{CB}$? **50.4**

Example 3

ALGEBRA In $\odot E$, $EG = EF$. Find AB.

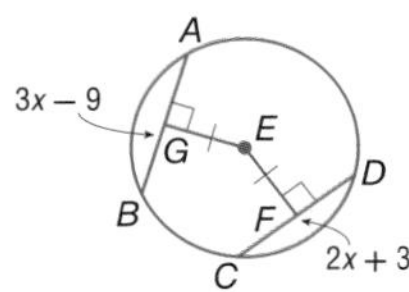

Since chords $\overline{EG}$ and $\overline{EF}$ are congruent, they are equidistant from E. So, $AB = CD$.

$AB = CD$	Theorem 10.5
$3x - 9 = 2x + 3$	Substitution
$3x = 2x + 12$	Add.
$x = 12$	Simplify.

So, $AB = 3(12) - 9$ or 27.

10-4 Inscribed Angles

Find each measure.

24. $m\angle 1$ **109**

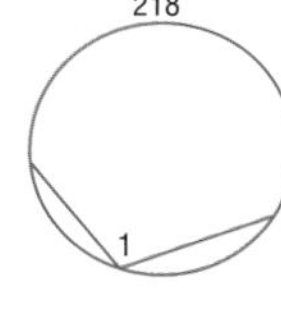

25. $m\widehat{GH}$ **56**

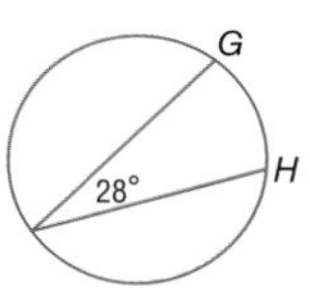

26. **MARKETING** In the logo at the right, $m\angle 1 = 42$. Find $m\angle 5$. **42**

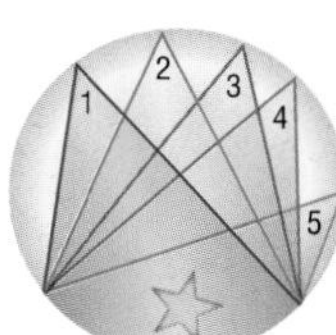

Example 4

Find $m\angle D$ and $m\angle B$.

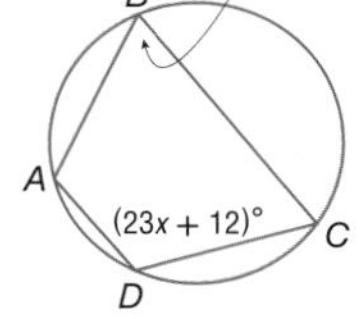

Since $ABCD$ is inscribed in a circle, opposite angles are supplementary.

$m\angle D + m\angle B = 180$	Definition of supplementary
$23x + 12 + 21x - 8 = 180$	Substitution
$44x + 4 = 180$	Simplify.
$44x = 176$	Subtract.
$x = 4$	Divide.

So, $m\angle D = 23(4) + 12$ or 104 and $m\angle B = 21(4) - 8$ or 76.

768 | Chapter 10 | Study Guide and Review

10-5 Tangents

27. SCIENCE FICTION In a story Todd is writing, instantaneous travel between a two-dimensional planet and its moon is possible when the time-traveler follows a tangent. Copy the figures below and draw all possible travel paths. **See margin.**

28. Find x and y. Assume that segments that appear to be tangent are tangent. Round to the nearest tenth if necessary. $x = 10$, $y = 12.6$

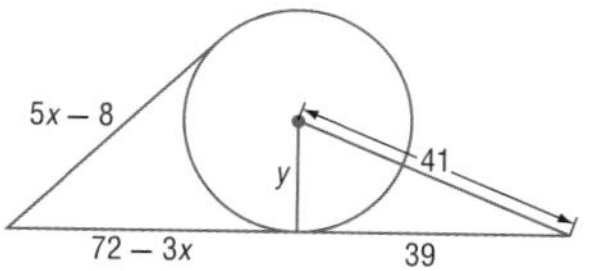

Example 5

In the figure, $\overline{KL}$ is tangent to $\odot M$ at K. Find the value of x.

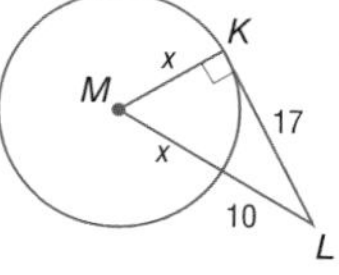

By Theorem 10.9, $\overline{MK} \perp \overline{KL}$. So, $\triangle MKL$ is a right triangle.

$KM^2 + KL^2 = ML^2$	Pythagorean Theorem
$x^2 + 17^2 = (x + 10)^2$	Substitution
$x^2 + 289 = x^2 + 20x + 100$	Multiply.
$289 = 20x + 100$	Simplify.
$189 = 20x$	Subtract.
$9.45 = x$	Divide.

10-6 Secants, Tangents, and Angle Measures

Find each measure. Assume that segments that appear to be tangent are tangent.

29. $m\angle 1$ 97

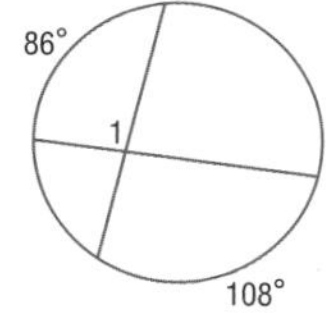

30. $m\widehat{AC}$ 56

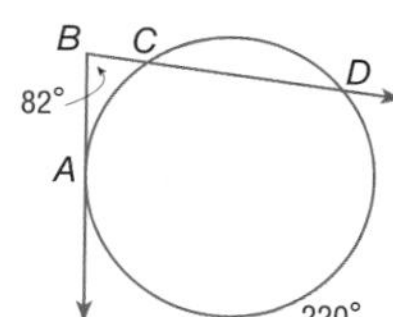

31. PHOTOGRAPHY Ahmed needs to take a close-up shot of an orange for his art class. He frames a shot of an orange as shown below, so that the lines of sight form tangents to the orange. If the measure of the camera's viewing angle is 34°, what is $m\widehat{ACB}$? 214

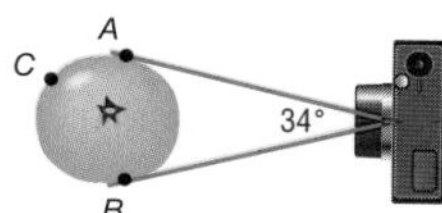

Example 6

Find the value of x.

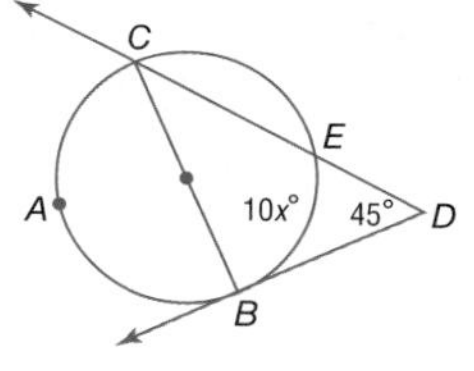

$\widehat{CAB}$ is a semicircle because $\overline{CB}$ is a diameter.

So, $m\widehat{CAB} = 180$.

$m\angle D = \frac{1}{2}(m\widehat{CB} - m\widehat{EB})$	Theorem 10.14
$45 = \frac{1}{2}(180 - 10x)$	Substitution
$90 = 180 - 10x$	Multiply.
$-90 = -10x$	Subtract.
$9 = x$	Divide.

Additional Answer

27.

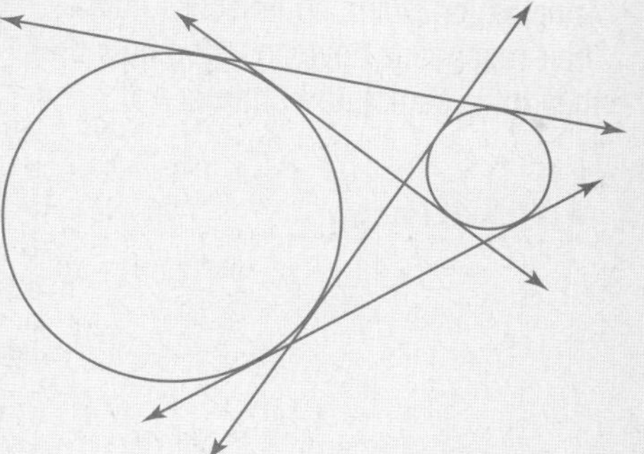

connectED.mcgraw-hill.com 769

Anticipation Guide

Have students complete the Chapter 10 Anticipation Guide and discuss how their responses have changed now that they have completed Chapter 10.

Additional Answer

37. $x^2 + y^2 = 1156$.

Chapter 10 Study Guide and Review *Continued*

10-7 Special Segments in a Circle

Find x. Assume that segments that appear to be tangent are tangent.

32. 9

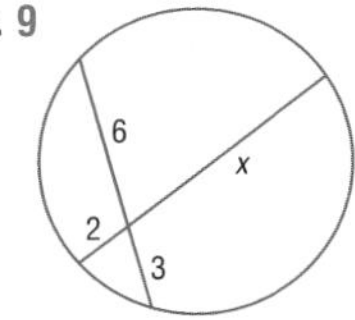

33. 4

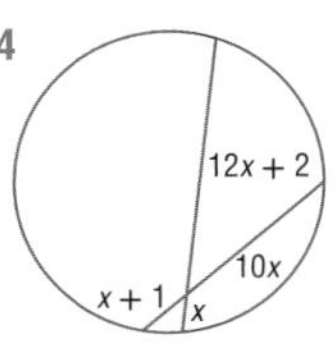

34. **ARCHAEOLOGY** While digging a hole to plant a tree, Henry found a piece of a broken saucer. What was the circumference of the original saucer? Round to the nearest hundredth. **19.1 in.**

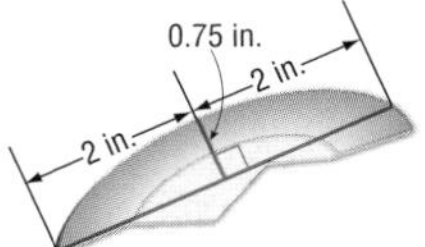

Example 7

Find the diameter of circle M.

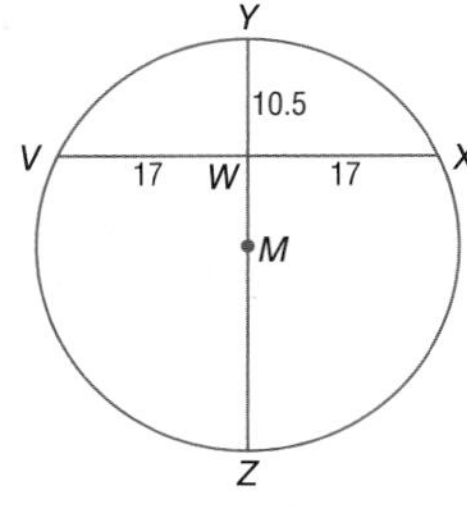

$VW \cdot WX = YW \cdot WZ$	Theorem 10.14
$17 \cdot 17 = 10.5 \cdot WZ$	Substitution
$289 = 10.5 \cdot WZ$	Simplify.
$27.5 \approx WZ$	Divide each side by 10.5.
$YZ = YW + WZ$	Segment Addition Postulate
$YZ = 10.5 + 27.5$	Substitution
$YZ = 38$	Simplify.

10-8 Equations of Circles

Write the equation of each circle.

35. center at (−2, 4), radius 5 $(x + 2)^2 + (y - 4)^2 = 25$

36. center at (1, 2), diameter 14 $(x - 1)^2 + (y - 2)^2 = 49$

37. **FIREWOOD** In an outdoor training course, Kat learns a wood-chopping safety check that involves making a circle with her arm extended, to ensure she will not hit anything overhead as she chops. If her reach is 19 inches, the hatchet handle is 15 inches, and her shoulder is located at the origin, what is the equation of Kat's safety circle? **See margin.**

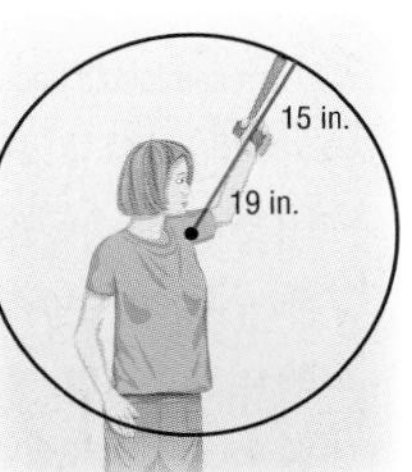

Example 8

Write the equation of the circle graphed below.

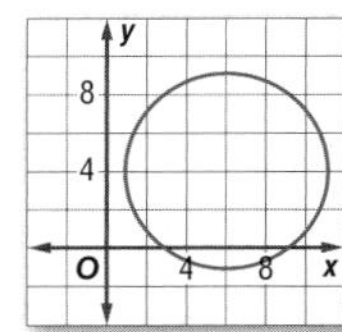

The center is at (6, 4) and the radius is 5.

$(x - h)^2 + (y - k)^2 = r^2$	Equation of a circle
$(x - 6)^2 + (y - 4)^2 = 5^2$	$(h, k) = (6, 4)$ and $r = 5$
$(x - 6)^2 + (y - 4)^2 = 25$	Simplify.

770 | Chapter 10 | Study Guide and Review

CHAPTER 10 Practice Test

1. **POOLS** Amanda's family has a swimming pool that is 4 feet deep in their backyard. If the diameter of the pool is 25 feet, what is the circumference of the pool to the nearest foot? **79 ft**

2. Find the exact circumference of the circle below. **32π**

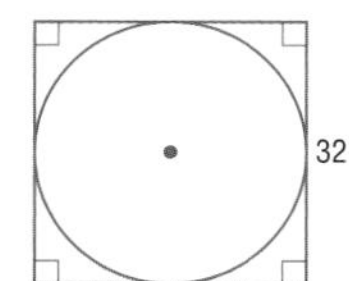

Find the value of x.

3. **23**

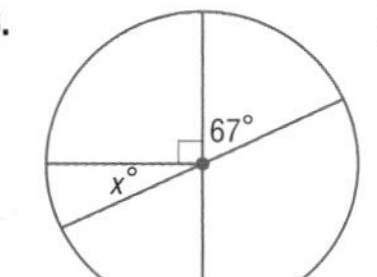

4. **95**

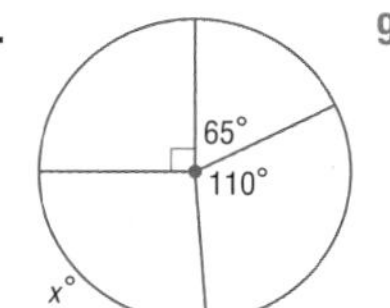

5. **4.1 in.**

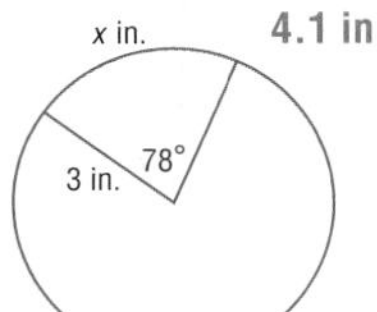

6. **3**

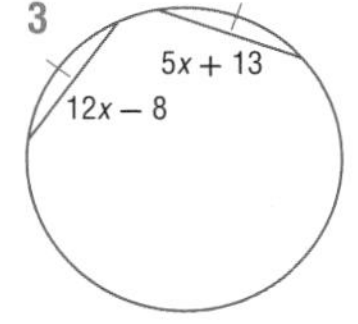

7. **MULTIPLE CHOICE** What is ED? **D**

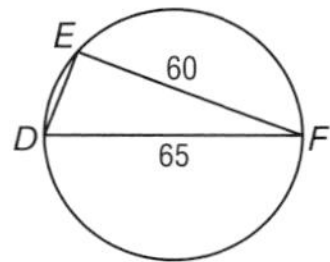

A 15
B 25
C 88.5
D not enough information

8. Find x if $\odot M \cong \odot N$. **9**

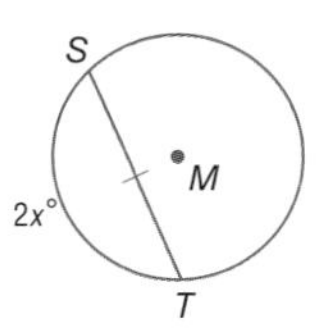

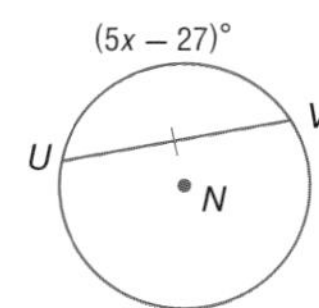

9. **MULTIPLE CHOICE** How many points are shared by concentric circles? **F**

F 0
G 1
H 2
J infinite points

10. Determine whether $\overline{FG}$ is tangent to $\odot E$. Justify your answer. **See margin.**

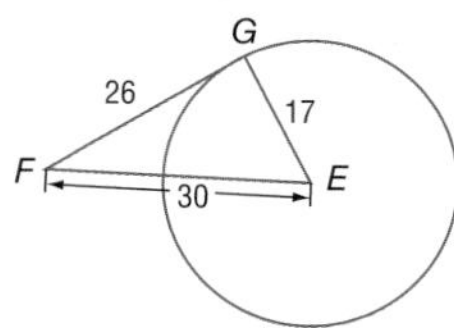

11. **MULTIPLE CHOICE** Which of the figures below shows a polygon circumscribed about a circle? **C**

A

C

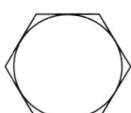

B

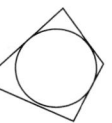

D

12. Find the perimeter of the triangle at the right. Assume that segments that appear to be tangent are tangent. **58**

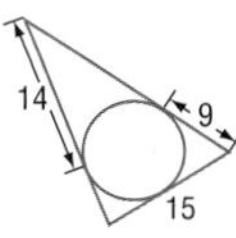

Find each measure.

13. $m\angle T$ **77**

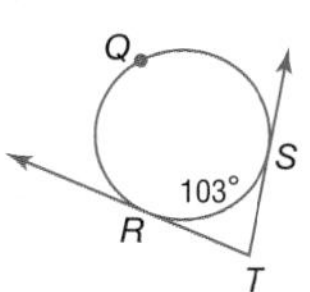

14. x **$\frac{1}{2}$**

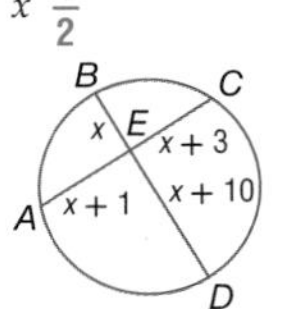

15. **FLOWERS** Hannah wants to encircle a tree trunk with a flower bed. If the center of the tree trunk is the origin and Hannah wants the flower bed to extend to 3 feet from the center of the tree, what is the equation that would represent the flower bed? **$x^2 + y^2 = 9$**

Summative Assessment

Use these alternate leveled chapter tests to differentiate assessment for your students.

Leveled Chapter 10 Tests

Form	Type	Level	Page(s)
1	MC	AL	61–62
2A	MC	OL	63–64
2B	MC	OL	65–66
2C	FR	OL	67–68
2D	FR	OL	69–70
3	FR	BL	71–72
Vocabulary Test			60
Extended-Response Test			73

MC = multiple-choice questions
FR = free-response questions

eAssessment Customize and create multiple versions of your chapter tests and their answer keys. All of the questions from the leveled chapter tests in the *Chapter 10 Resource Masters* are also available on eAssessment.

Additional Answer

10. No; $\triangle EFG$ is not a right triangle, so $\angle G$ is not a right angle and $\overline{FG}$ cannot be tangent.

InterventionPlanner

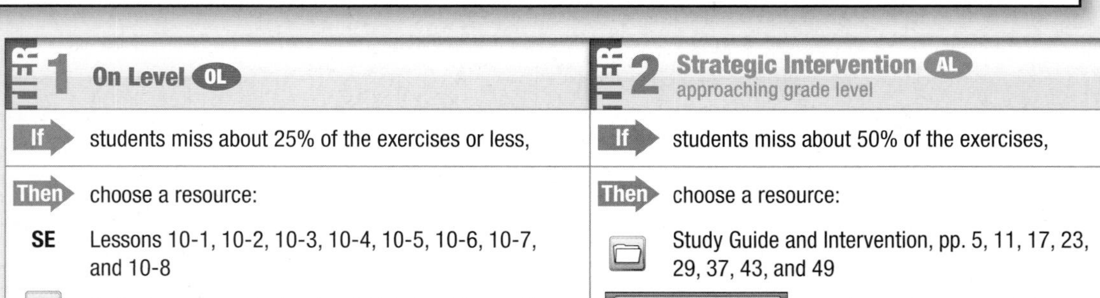

Tier 1 On Level OL

If students miss about 25% of the exercises or less,

Then choose a resource:

SE Lessons 10-1, 10-2, 10-3, 10-4, 10-5, 10-6, 10-7, and 10-8

Skills Practice, pp. 7, 13, 19, 25, 31, 39, 45, and 51

connectED.mcgraw-hill.com Self-Check Quiz

Tier 2 Strategic Intervention AL approaching grade level

If students miss about 50% of the exercises,

Then choose a resource:

Study Guide and Intervention, pp. 5, 11, 17, 23, 29, 37, 43, and 49

connectED.mcgraw-hill.com Extra Examples, Personal Tutor, Homework Help

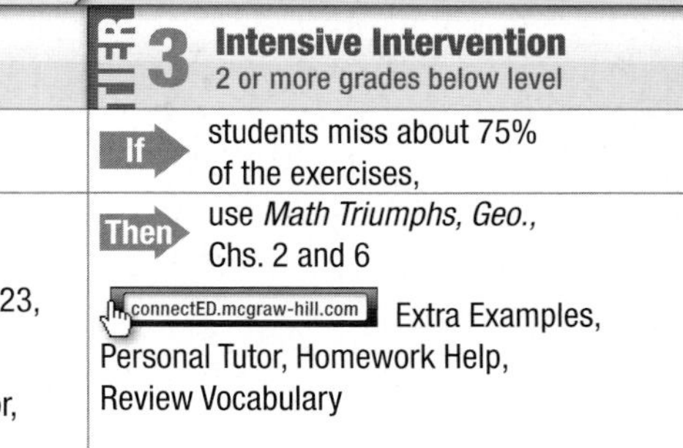

Tier 3 Intensive Intervention 2 or more grades below level

If students miss about 75% of the exercises,

Then use *Math Triumphs, Geo.*, Chs. 2 and 6

connectED.mcgraw-hill.com Extra Examples, Personal Tutor, Homework Help, Review Vocabulary

1 Focus

Objective Identify the parts of a circle, find arc, angle, and segment measures in a circle, and write the equation of a circle.

2 Teach

Scaffolding Questions

Ask:

- How do you find the circumference of a circle if you are given the radius? Double the radius and multiply by π.
- What is the difference between a chord, tangent, and secant? A secant intersects a circle at two points. A tangent intersects a circle at one point. A chord is a line inside a circle with endpoints on the circle.
- In the same circle or in congruent circles, if two chords are congruent then they are they are ___________ from the center? equidistant

Properties of Circles

A circle is a unique shape in which the angles, arcs, and segments intersecting the circle have special properties and relationships. You should be able to identify the parts of a circle, write the equation of a circle, and solve for arc, angle, and segment measures in a circle.

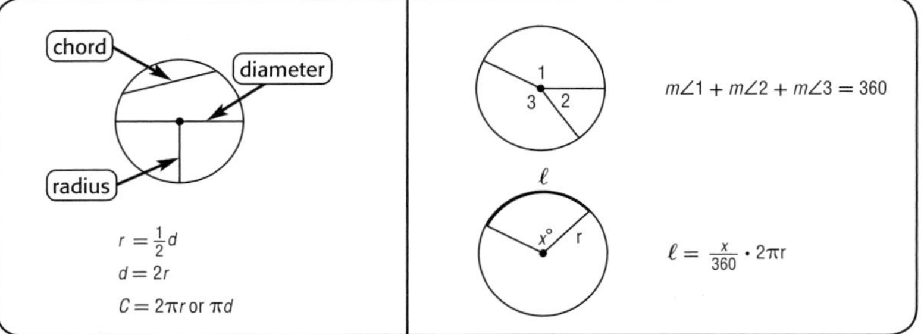

Strategies for Applying the Properties of Circles

Step 1

Review the parts of a circle and their relationships.

- Some key parts include: **radius, diameter, arc, chord, tangent, secant**
- Study the key theorems and the properties of circles as well as the relationships between the parts of a circle.

Step 2

Read the problem statement and study any figure you are given carefully.

- Determine what you are being asked to find.
- Fill in any information in the figure that you can.
- Determine which theorems or properties apply to the problem situation.

Step 3

Solve the problem and check your answer.

- Apply the theorems or properties to solve the problem.
- Check your answer to be sure it makes sense.

Standardized Test Example

Read the problem. Identify what you need to know. Then use the information in the problem to solve.

Solve for x in the figure.

A 2 **C** 4

B 3 **D** 6

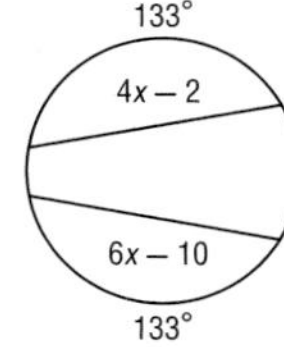

Read the problem statement and study the figure carefully. You are given a circle with two chords that correspond to congruent minor arcs. One important property of circles is that two chords are congruent if and only if their corresponding minor arcs are congruent. You can use this property to set up and solve an equation for x.

$4x - 2 = 6x - 10$	Definition of Congruent Segments
$4x - 6x = -10 + 2$	Subtract.
$-2x = -8$	Simplify.
$\frac{-2x}{-2} = \frac{-8}{-2}$	Divide each side by −2.
$x = 4$	Simplify.

So, the value of x is 4. The answer is C. You can check your answer by substituting 4 into each expression and making sure both chords have the same length.

Exercises

Read each problem. Identify what you need to know. Then use the information in the problem to solve.

1. Solve for x in the figure below. D

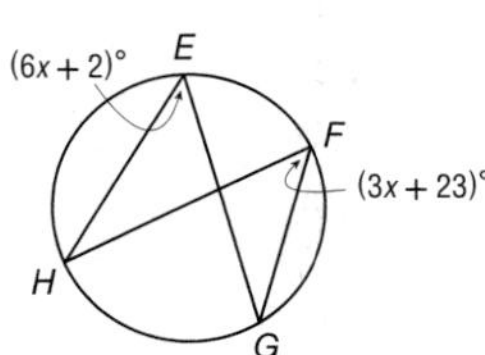

A 4 **C** 6

B 5 **D** 7

2. Triangle RST is circumscribed about the circle below. What is the perimeter of the triangle? G

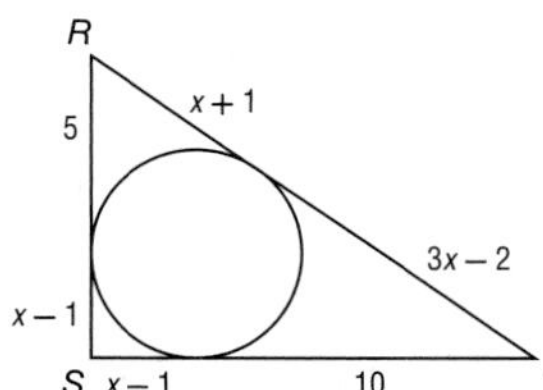

F 33 units **H** 37 units

G 36 units **J** 40 units

Additional Example

Read the problem. Identify what you need to know. Then use the information in the problem to solve for x.

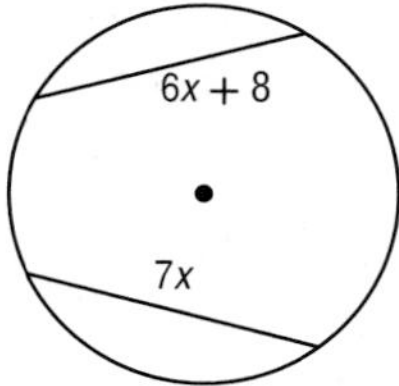

You need to know whether the segments are congruent. There is not enough information to solve for x.

3 Assess

Use Exercises 1 and 2 to assess students' understanding.

connectED.mcgraw-hill.com 773

Diagnose Student Errors

Survey student responses for each item. Class trends may indicate common errors and misconceptions.

1. A guess
B correct
C error in calculation
D error in calculation

2. F misunderstanding negation
G correct
H misunderstanding indirect proof
J guess

3. A used sum of 290° instead of 360°
B used sum of 330° instead of 360°
C correct
D used sum of 380° instead of 360°

4. F mistook corresponding angles for alternate exterior angles
G mistook corresponding angles for alternate interior angles
H correct
J misunderstands vertical angles definition

5. A guess
B guess
C guess
D correct

6. F misused ratio or Angle-Sum Theorem
G correct
H misused ratio or Angle-Sum Theorem
J misused ratio or Angle-Sum Theorem

CHAPTER 10

Standardized Test Practice

Cumulative, Chapters 1 through 10

Multiple Choice

Read each question. Then fill in the correct answer on the answer document provided by your teacher or on a sheet of paper.

1. If $ABCD$ is a rhombus, and $m\angle ABC = 70°$, what is $m\angle 1$? B

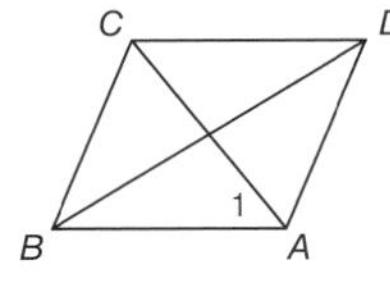

A 45°
B 55°
C 70°
D 125°

2. Karen argues that if you live in Greensboro, North Carolina, then you live in Guilford County. Which assumption would you need to make to form an indirect proof of this claim? G

F Suppose someone lives in Guilford County, but not in Greensboro.
G Suppose someone lives in Greensboro, but not in Guilford County.
H Suppose someone lives in Greensboro and in Guilford County.
J Suppose someone lives in Guilford County and in Greensboro.

3. What is the value of x in the figure? C

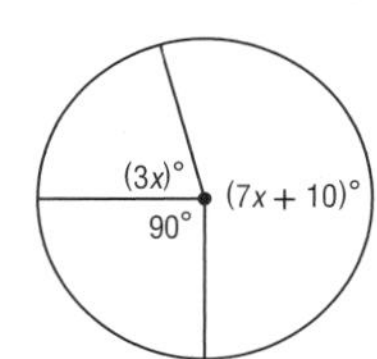

A 19
B 23
C 26
D 28

> **Test-Taking Tip**
> Question 3 Use the properties of circles to set up and solve an equation to find x.

4. Given $a \parallel b$, find $m\angle 1$. H

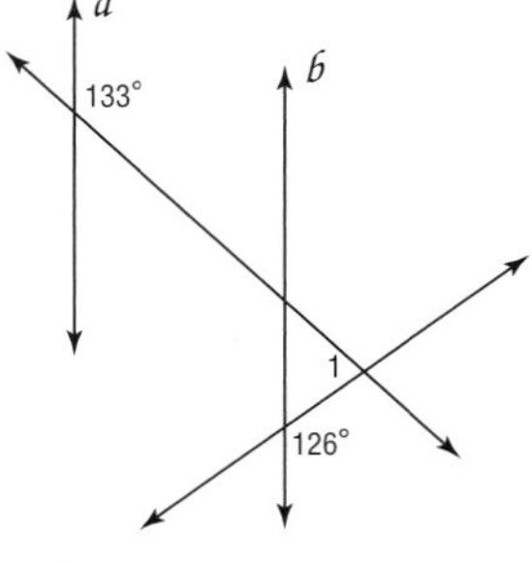

F 47°
G 54°
H 79°
J 101°

5. Which of the following conditions would *not* guarantee that a quadrilateral is a parallelogram? D

A both pairs of opposite sides congruent
B both pairs of opposite angles congruent
C diagonals bisect each other
D one pair of opposite sides parallel

6. The ratio of the measures of the angles of the triangle below is 3:2:1. Which of the following is *not* an angle measure of the triangle? G

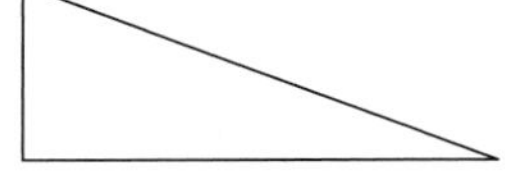

F 30°
G 45°
H 60°
J 90°

Short Response/Gridded Response

Record your answers on the answer sheet provided by your teacher or on a sheet of paper.

7. Does the figure shown have rotational symmetry? If so, give the order of symmetry. **yes; order 2**

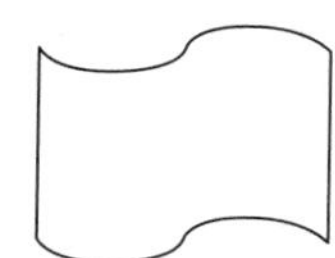

8. GRIDDED RESPONSE A square with 5-centimeter sides is inscribed in a circle. What is the circumference of the circle? Round your answer to the nearest tenth of a centimeter. **22.2**

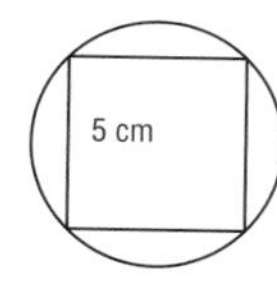

9. Solve for x in the figure. Show your work. **8**

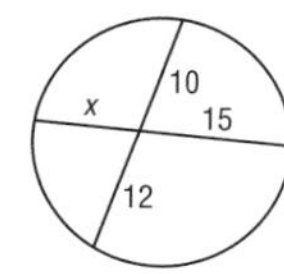

10. GRIDDED RESPONSE What is the perimeter of the right triangle below? Round your answer to the nearest tenth if necessary. **33.5**

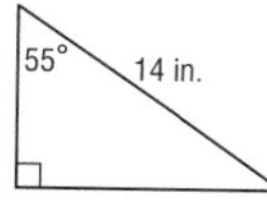

11. GRIDDED RESPONSE State the magnitude of rotational symmetry of the figure. Express your answer in degrees. **45**

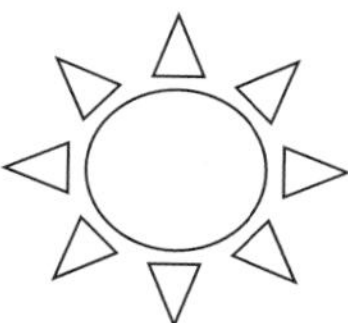

12. What is the length of $\overline{EF}$? **26**

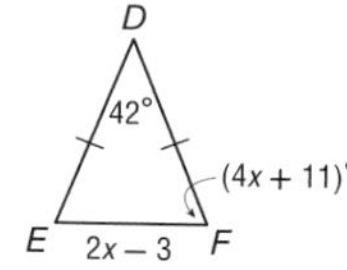

Extended Response

Record your answers on a sheet of paper. Show your work.

13. Use the circle shown to answer each question.

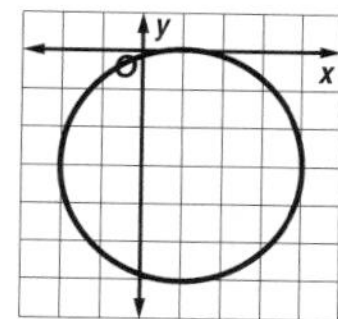

a. What is the center of the circle? **(1, −3)**

b. What is the radius of the circle? **3 units**

c. Write an equation for the circle.
$(x - 1)^2 + (y + 3)^2 = 3^2$

Need ExtraHelp?

If you missed Question...	1	2	3	4	5	6	7	8	9	10	11	12	13
Go to Lesson...	6-5	5-4	10-2	3-2	6-3	8-3	9-5	10-1	10-7	8-4	9-5	4-6	10-8

Formative Assessment

You can use these pages to benchmark student progress.

Standardized Test Practice, pp. 74–76

Answer Sheet Practice

Have students simulate taking a standardized test by recording their answers on a practice recording sheet.

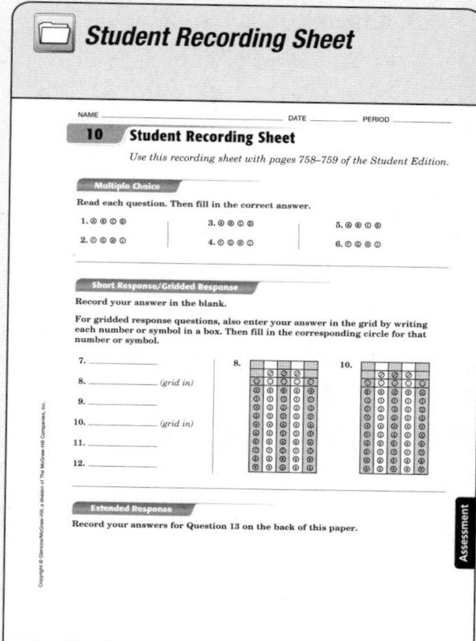

Student Recording Sheet

NAME ____________ DATE ________ PERIOD ________

10 Student Recording Sheet

Use this recording sheet with pages 758–759 of the Student Edition.

Multiple Choice

Read each question. Then fill in the correct answer.

1. Ⓐ Ⓑ Ⓒ Ⓓ
2. Ⓕ Ⓖ Ⓗ Ⓙ
3. Ⓐ Ⓑ Ⓒ Ⓓ
4. Ⓕ Ⓖ Ⓗ Ⓙ
5. Ⓐ Ⓑ Ⓒ Ⓓ
6. Ⓕ Ⓖ Ⓗ Ⓙ

Short Response/Gridded Response

Record your answer in the blank.

For gridded response questions, also enter your answer in the grid by writing each number or symbol in a box. Then fill in the corresponding circle for that number or symbol.

7. ____________
8. ____________ *(grid in)*
9. ____________
10. ____________ *(grid in)*
11. ____________
12. ____________

Extended Response

Record your answers for Question 13 on the back of this paper.

Assessment

eAssessment Create practice tests that align to your state standards, the Common Core State Standards, and other national standards such as TIMSS and NAEP.

Homework Option

Get Ready for Chapter 11 Assign students the exercises on p. 777 as homework to assess whether they possess the prerequisite skills needed for the next chapter.

Lesson 10-3

28. Given: $\odot A$, $\overline{ED}$ is the $\perp$ bisector of $\overline{BC}$.

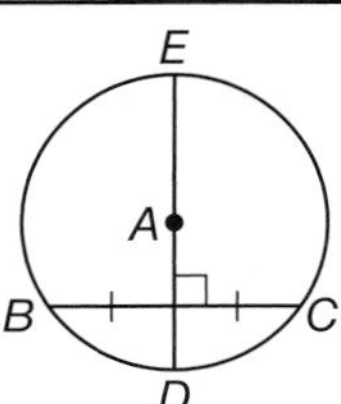

Prove: $\overline{ED}$ is a diameter of $\odot A$.

Proof:

Statements (Reasons):

1. $\overline{ED}$ is the $\perp$ bisector of $\overline{BC}$. (Given)
2. A is equidistant from B and C. (All radii of a $\odot$ are $\cong$.)
3. A lies on the $\perp$ bisector of $\overline{BC}$. (Conv. of the $\perp$ Bisector Thm.)
4. $\overline{ED}$ is a diameter of $\odot A$. (Def. of diameter)

29. Given: $\odot L$, $\overline{LX} \perp \overline{FG}$, $\overline{LY} \perp \overline{JH}$,

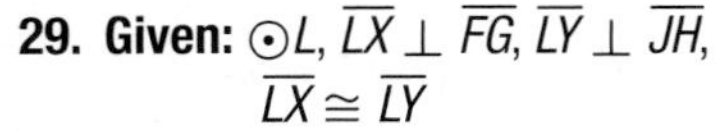
$\overline{LX} \cong \overline{LY}$

Prove: $\overline{FG} \cong \overline{JH}$

Proof:

Statements (Reasons):

1. $\overline{LG} \cong \overline{LH}$ (All radii of a $\odot$ are $\cong$.)
2. $\overline{LX} \perp \overline{FG}$, $\overline{LY} \perp \overline{JH}$, $\overline{LX} \cong \overline{LY}$ (Given)
3. $\angle LXG$ and $\angle LYH$ are right $\measuredangle$. (Definition of $\perp$ lines)
4. $\triangle XGL \cong \triangle YHL$ (HL)
5. $\overline{XG} \cong \overline{YH}$ (CPCTC)
6. $XG = YH$ (Definition of $\cong$ segments)
7. $2(XG) = 2(YH)$ (Multiplication Property)
8. $\overline{LX}$ bisects $\overline{FG}$; $\overline{LY}$ bisects $\overline{JH}$. (A radius $\perp$ to a chord bisects the chord.)
9. $FG = 2(XG)$, $JH = 2(YH)$ (Definition of segment bisector)
10. $FG = JH$ (Substitution)
11. $\overline{FG} \cong \overline{JH}$ (Definition of $\cong$ segments)

30. Given: $\odot L$, $\overline{FG} \cong \overline{JH}$

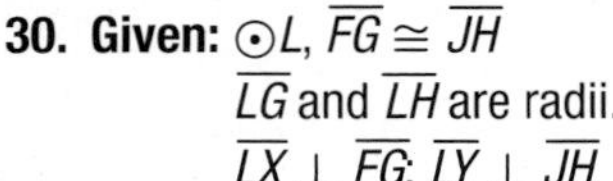
$\overline{LG}$ and $\overline{LH}$ are radii.
$\overline{LX} \perp \overline{FG}$; $\overline{LY} \perp \overline{JH}$

Prove: $\overline{LX} \cong \overline{LY}$

Proof:

Statements (Reasons):

1. $\odot L$, $\overline{FG} \cong \overline{JH}$ and $\overline{LG}$ and $\overline{LH}$ are radii. $\overline{LX} \perp \overline{FG}$; $\overline{LY} \perp \overline{JH}$ (Given)
2. $\overline{LX}$ bisects $\overline{FG}$; $\overline{LY}$ bisects $\overline{JH}$. ($\overline{LX}$ and $\overline{LY}$ are contained in radii. A radius $\perp$ to a chord bisects the chord.)
3. $XG = \frac{1}{2}FG$, $YH = \frac{1}{2}JH$ (Definition of bisector)
4. $FG = JH$ (Definition of $\cong$ segments)
5. $\frac{1}{2}FG = \frac{1}{2}JH$ (Multiplication Property)
6. $XG = YH$ (Substitution)
7. $\overline{XG} \cong \overline{YH}$ (Definition of $\cong$ segments)
8. $\overline{LG} \cong \overline{LH}$ (All radii of a circle are $\cong$.)
9. $\angle GXL$ and $\angle HYL$ are right $\measuredangle$ (Def. of $\perp$ lines)
10. $\triangle XLG \cong \triangle YLH$ (HL)
11. $\overline{LX} \cong \overline{LY}$ (CPCTC)

34.

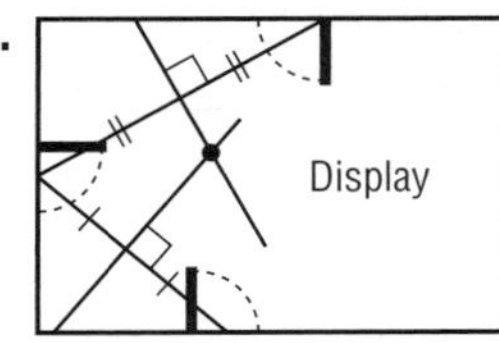

35. About 17.3; P and Q are equidistant from the endpoints of $\overline{AB}$ so they both lie on the perpendicular bisector of $\overline{AB}$, so $\overline{PQ}$ is the perpendicular bisector of $\overline{AB}$. Hence, both segments of $\overline{AB}$ are 5. Since $\overline{PS}$ is perpendicular to chord $\overline{AB}$, $\angle PSA$ is a right angle. So, $\triangle PSA$ is a right triangle. By the Pythagorean Theorem, $PS = \sqrt{(PA)^2 - (AS)^2}$. By substitution, $PS = \sqrt{11^2 - 5^2}$ or $\sqrt{96}$. Similarly, $\triangle ASQ$ is a right triangle with $SQ = \sqrt{(AQ)^2 - (AS)^2} = \sqrt{9^2 - 5^2}$ or $\sqrt{56}$. Since $PQ = PS + SQ$, $PQ = \sqrt{96} + \sqrt{56}$ or about 17.3.

37a. Given: $\overline{CD}$ is the perpendicular bisector of chord $\overline{AB}$ in $\odot X$.

Prove: $\overline{CD}$ contains point X.

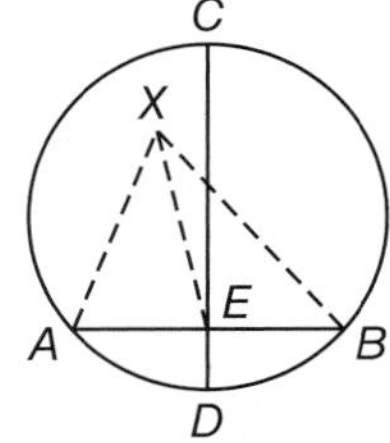

Proof:

Suppose X is not on $\overline{CD}$. Draw $\overline{XE}$ and radii $\overline{XA}$ and $\overline{XB}$. Since $\overline{CD}$ is the perpendicular bisector of $\overline{AB}$, E is the midpoint of $\overline{AB}$ and $\overline{AE} \cong \overline{EB}$. Also, $\overline{XA} \cong \overline{XB}$, since all radii of a $\odot$ are $\cong$. $\overline{XE} \cong \overline{XE}$ by the Reflexive Property. So, $\triangle AXE \cong \triangle BXE$ by SSS. By CPCTC, $\angle XEA \cong \angle XEB$. Since they also form a linear pair $\angle XEA$ and $\angle XEB$ are right angles. So $\overline{XE} \perp \overline{AB}$. By definition $\overline{XE}$ is the perpendicular bisector of $\overline{AB}$. But $\overline{CD}$ is also the perpendicular bisector of $\overline{AB}$. This contradicts the uniqueness of a perpendicular bisector of a segment. Thus, the assumption is false, and center X must be on $\overline{CD}$.

37b. Given: In $\odot X$, X is on $\overline{CD}$ and $\overline{FG}$ bisects $\overline{CD}$ at O.

Prove: Point O is point X.

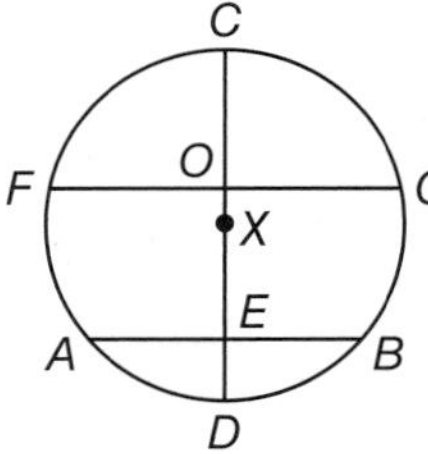

Proof:

Since point X is on $\overline{CD}$ and C and D are on $\odot X$, $\overline{CD}$ is a diameter of $\odot X$. Since $\overline{FG}$ bisects $\overline{CD}$ at O, O is the midpoint of $\overline{CD}$. Since the midpoint of a diameter is the center of a circle, O, is the center of the circle. Therefore, point O is point X.

38. Sample answer:

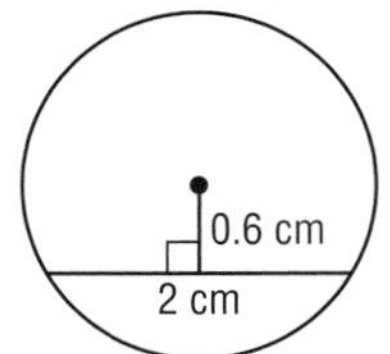

radius $\approx$ 1.2 cm

39. No; sample answer: In a circle with a radius of 12, an arc with a measure of 60 determines a chord of length 12. The triangle related to a central angle of 60 is equilateral. If the measure of the arc is tripled to 180, then the chord determined by the arc is a diameter and has a length of 2(12) or 24, which is not three times as long as the original chord.

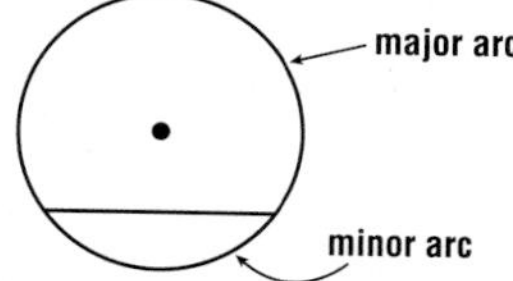

Lesson 10-4

21. Proof: Given $m\angle T = \frac{1}{2}m\angle S$ means that $m\angle S = 2m\angle T$. Since $m\angle S = \frac{1}{2}m\widehat{TUR}$ and $m\angle T = \frac{1}{2}m\widehat{URS}$, the equation becomes $\frac{1}{2}m\widehat{TUR} = 2\left(\frac{1}{2}m\widehat{URS}\right)$. Multiplying each side of the equation by 2 results in $m\widehat{TUR} = 2m\widehat{URS}$.

22. Statements (Reasons):

1. $\odot C$ (Given)
2. $\angle H \cong \angle L$ (Inscribed $\angle$s intercepting same arc are $\cong$.)
3. $\angle KML \cong \angle JMH$ (Vertical $\angle$s are $\cong$.)
4. $\triangle KML \sim \triangle JMH$ (AA Similarity)

31. Given: Quadrilateral *ABCD* is inscribed in $\odot O$.

Prove: $\angle A$ and $\angle C$ are supplementary. $\angle B$ and $\angle D$ are supplementary.

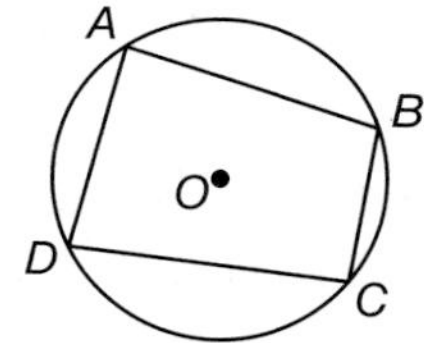

Proof: By arc addition and the definitions of arc measure and the sum of central angles, $m\widehat{DCB} + m\widehat{DAB} = 360$. Since by Theorem 10.6, $m\angle C = \frac{1}{2}m\widehat{DAB}$ and $m\angle A = \frac{1}{2}m\widehat{DCB}$, $m\angle C + m\angle A = \frac{1}{2}(m\widehat{DCB} + m\widehat{DAB})$, but $m\widehat{DCB} + m\widehat{DAB} = 360$, so $m\angle C + m\angle A = \frac{1}{2}(360)$ or 180. This makes $\angle C$ and $\angle A$ supplementary. Because the sum of the measures of the interior angles of a quadrilateral is 360, $m\angle A + m\angle C + m\angle B + m\angle D = 360$. But $m\angle A + m\angle C = 180$, so $m\angle B + m\angle D = 180$, making them supplementary also.

39. Given: $\angle FAE$ and $\angle CBD$ are inscribed; $\widehat{EF} \cong \widehat{DC}$

Prove: $\angle FAE \cong \angle CBD$

Proof:

Statements (Reasons)

1. $\angle FAE$ and $\angle CBD$ are inscribed; $\widehat{EF} \cong \widehat{DC}$ (Given)
2. $m\angle FAE = \frac{1}{2}m\widehat{EF}$; $m\angle CBD = \frac{1}{2}m\widehat{DC}$ (Measure of an inscribed $\angle$ = half measure of intercepted arc.)
3. $m\widehat{EF} = m\widehat{DC}$ (Def. of $\cong$ arcs)
4. $\frac{1}{2}m\widehat{EF} = \frac{1}{2}m\widehat{DC}$ (Mult. Prop.)
5. $m\angle FAE = m\angle CBD$ (Substitution)
6. $\angle FAE \cong \angle CBD$ (Def. of $\cong$ $\angle$s)

40. Part I: **Given:** $\widehat{ADC}$ is a semicircle.

Prove: $\angle ABC$ is a right angle.

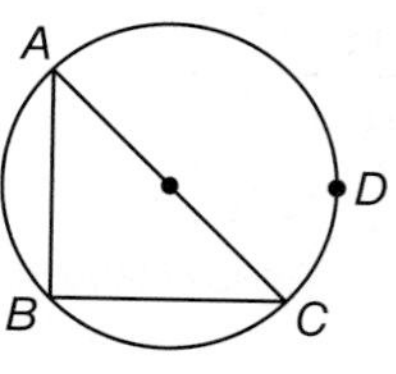

Proof: Since $\widehat{ADC}$ is a semicircle, then $m\widehat{ADC} = 180$. Since $\angle ABC$ is an inscribed angle, then $m\angle ABC = \frac{1}{2}m\widehat{ADC}$ or 90. So by definition $\angle ABC$ is a right angle.

Part II: **Given:** $\angle ABC$ a right angle.

Prove: $\widehat{ADC}$ is a semicircle.

Proof: Since $\angle ABC$ is an inscribed angle, then $m\angle ABC = \frac{1}{2}$ $m\widehat{ADC}$ and by the Multiplication Property of Equality, $m\widehat{ADC} = 2m\angle ABC$. Because $\angle ABC$ is a right angle, $m\angle ABC = 90$. Then $m\widehat{ADC} = 2(90)$ or 180. So by definition, $\widehat{ADC}$ is a semicircle.

41a.

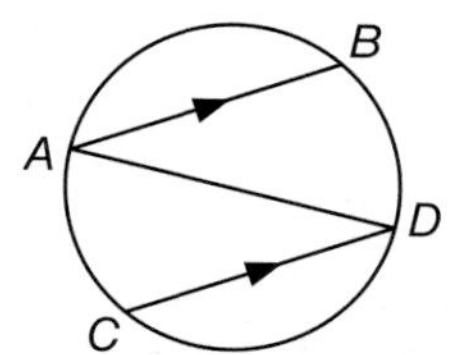

41b. Sample answer: $m\angle A = 30$, $m\angle D = 30$; $m\widehat{AC} = 60$, $m\widehat{BD} = 60$; The arcs are congruent because they have equal measures.

42. Always; squares have right angles at each vertex, therefore each pair of opposite angles will be supplementary and inscribed in a circle.

43. Always; rectangles have right angles at each vertex, therefore each pair of opposite angles will be supplementary and inscribed in a circle.

44. Sometimes; a parallelogram can be inscribed in a circle as long as it is a rectangle.

45. Sometimes; a rhombus can be inscribed in a cirlce as long as it is a square. Since the opposite angles of rhombi that are not squares are not supplementary, they can not be inscribed in a circle.

46. Sometimes; as long as the angles that compose the congruent pair of opposite angles are right angles.

48. Sample answer: According to Theorem 10.8, an inscribed angle of a triangle intercepts a diameter if the angle is a right angle. Therefore, the hypotenuse is a diameter and has a length of $2r$. Using trigonometry, each leg = sin 45° • $2r$ or $\sqrt{2}r$.

50. An inscribed angle has its vertex on the circle. A central angle has its vertex at the center of the circle. If an inscribed angle and a central angle intercept the same arc, then the measure of the inscribed angle is one-half the measure of the central angle.

Lesson 10-5

28. Proof:

Statements (Reasons)

1. $\overline{AC}$ is tangent to $\odot H$ at C; $\overline{AB}$ is tangent to $\odot H$ at B. (Given)
2. Draw $\overline{AH}$, $\overline{BH}$, and $\overline{CH}$. (Through any two points, there is one line.)
3. $\overline{AC} \perp \overline{CH}$, $\overline{AB} \perp \overline{BH}$ (Line tangent to a circle is $\perp$ to the radius at the pt. of tangency.)
4. $\angle ACH$ and $\angle ABH$ are right angles. (Def. of $\perp$ lines)
5. $\overline{CH} \cong \overline{BH}$ (All radii of a circle are $\cong$.)
6. $\overline{AH} \cong \overline{AH}$ (Reflexive Prop.)
7. $\triangle ACH \cong \triangle ABH$ (HL)
8. $\overline{AC} \cong \overline{AB}$ (CPCTC)

29. Statements (Reasons)

1. Quadrilateral $ABCD$ is circumscribed about $\odot P$. (Given)
2. Sides $\overline{AB}$, $\overline{BC}$, $\overline{CD}$, and $\overline{DA}$ are tangent to $\odot P$ at points H, G, F, and E, respectively. (Def. of circumscribed)
3. $\overline{EA} \cong \overline{AH}$; $\overline{HB} \cong \overline{BG}$; $\overline{GC} \cong \overline{CF}$; $\overline{FD} \cong \overline{DE}$ (Two segments tangent to a circle from the same exterior point are $\cong$.)
4. $AB = AH + HB$, $BC = BG + GC$, $CD = CF + FD$, $DA = DE + EA$ (Segment Addition)
5. $AB + CD = AH + HB + CF + FD$; $DA + BC = DE + EA + BG + GC$ (Substitution)
6. $AB + CD = AH + BG + GC + FD$; $DA + BC = FD + AH + BG + GC$ (Substitution)
7. $AB + CD = FD + AH + BG + GC$ (Comm. Prop. of Add.)
8. $AB + CD = DA + BC$ (Substitution)

Extend 10-5

2. Sample answers:

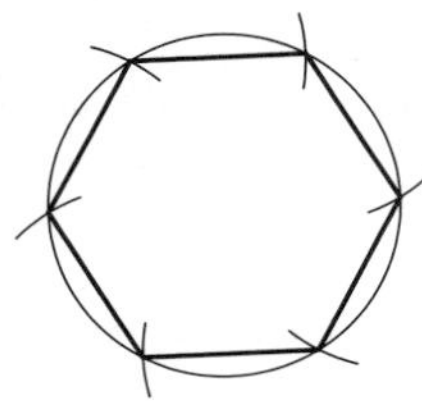
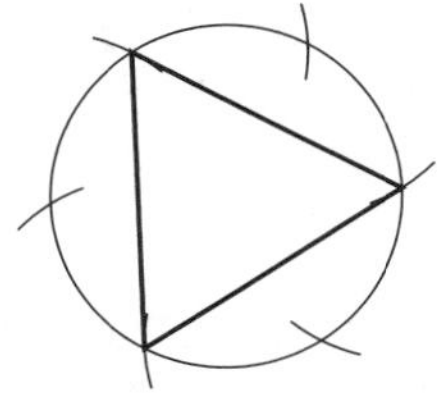

3. Sample answers:

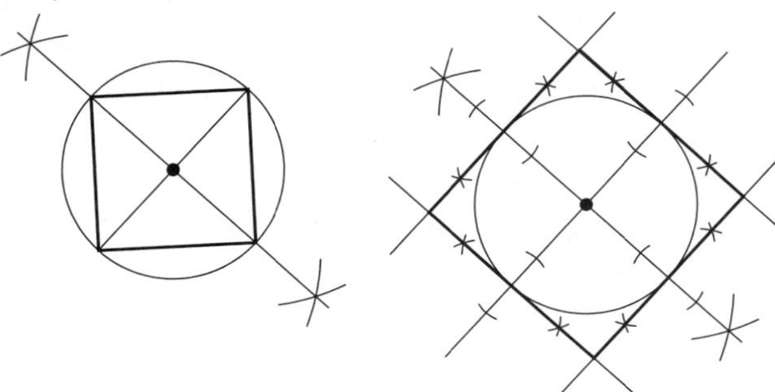

4. Sample answer:

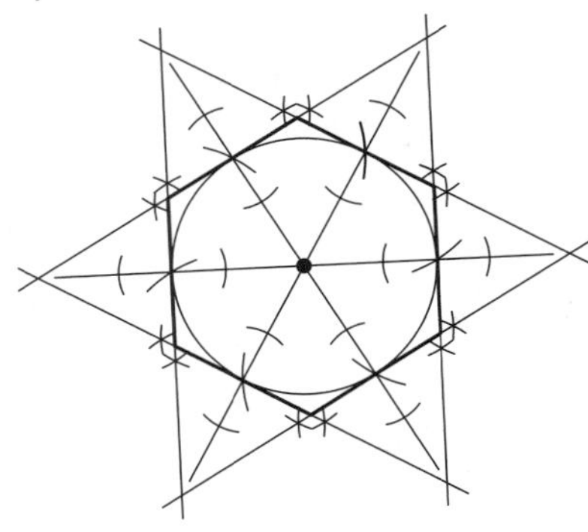

Lesson 10-6

30. Statements (Reasons)

1. AD and AE are secants to the circle. (Given)
2. $m\angle DCE = \frac{1}{2}m\widehat{DE}$, $m\angle ADC = \frac{1}{2}m\widehat{BC}$ (The measure of an inscribed $\angle = \frac{1}{2}$ the measure of its intercepted arc.)
3. $m\angle DCE = m\angle ADC + m\angle A$ (Exterior $\triangle$ Theorem)
4. $\frac{1}{2}m\widehat{DE} = \frac{1}{2}m\widehat{BC} + m\angle A$ (Substitution)
5. $\frac{1}{2}m\widehat{DE} - \frac{1}{2}m\widehat{BC} = m\angle A$ (Subtraction Prop.)
6. $\frac{1}{2}(m\widehat{DE} - m\widehat{BC}) = m\angle A$ (Distributive Prop.)

Lesson 10-7

22. 29.6 ft

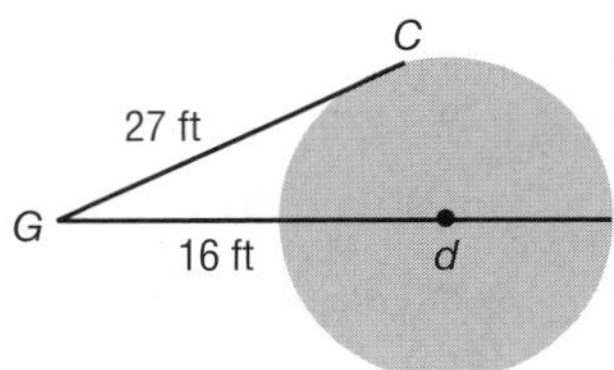

27. Sample answer: When two secants intersect in the exterior of a circle, the product of the measures of one secant segment and its external segment is equal to the product of the measures of the other secant segment and its external segment. When a secant and a tangent intersect at an exterior point, the product of the measures of the secant segment and its external segment equals the square of the measure of the tangent segment, because for the tangent the measures of the external segment and the whole segment are the same.

28. $b = c$

$a^2 = b(b + c)$

$a^2 = b(b + b)$

$a^2 = b(2b)$

$a^2 = 2b^2$

$a = \pm\sqrt{2b^2}$

$a = b\sqrt{2}$ Segments do not have negative length.

30. Sample answer:

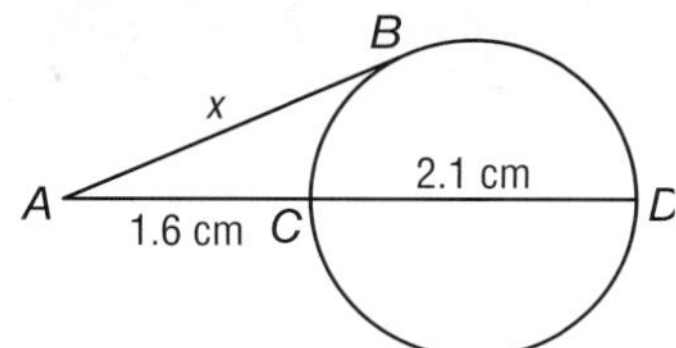

$x \approx 2.4$ cm

31. Sample answer: The product of the parts on one intersecting chord equals the product of the parts of the other chord.

Lesson 10-8

27. $(x - 3)^2 + (y - 3)^2 = 13$

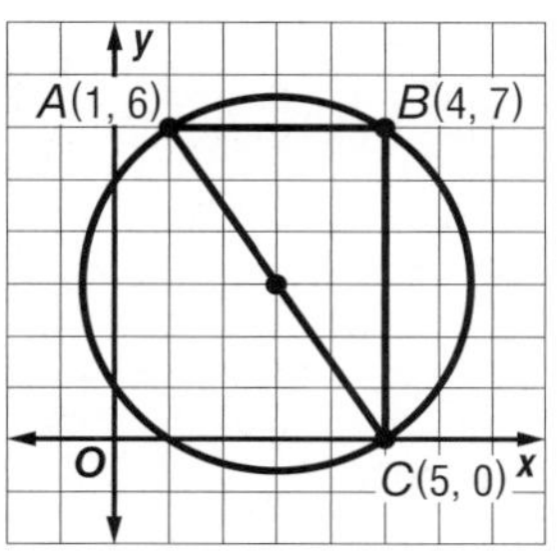

28. $(x - 5)^2 + (y + 1)^2 = 8$

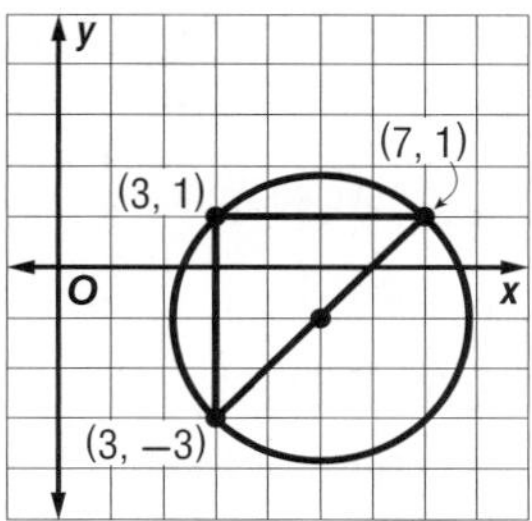

41. The equation of a circle centered at the origin and containing the point $(0, -3)$ is $x^2 + y^2 = 9$. The point $(1, 2\sqrt{2})$ lies on the circle, since evaluating $x^2 + y^2 = 9$ for $x = 1$ and $y = 2\sqrt{2}$ results in a true equation.

$$1^2 + (2\sqrt{2})^2 = 9$$
$$1 + 8 = 9$$
$$9 = 9 \checkmark$$

42b. Sample answer:

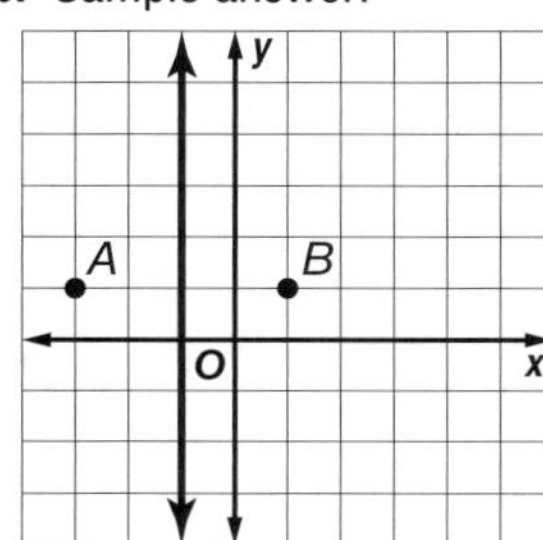

42d. Sample answer:

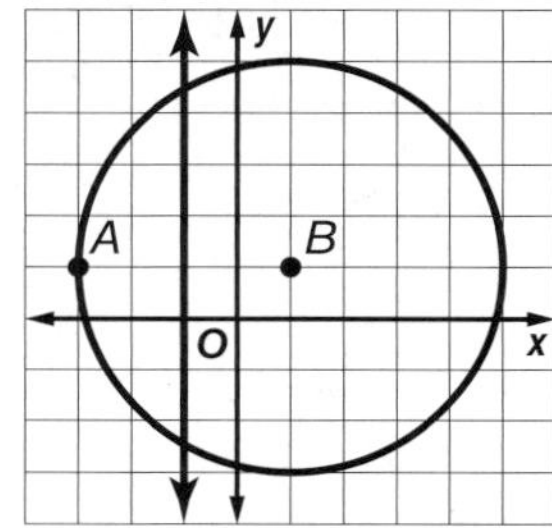

44. Given: $\overline{AB}$ is a diameter of $\odot O$, and C is a point on $\odot O$.

Prove: $\angle ACB$ is a right angle.

Proof:

$\overline{AC}$ has slope $\frac{y - r}{x}$, and $\overline{CB}$ has slope $\frac{y - (-r)}{x}$ or $\frac{y + r}{x}$.

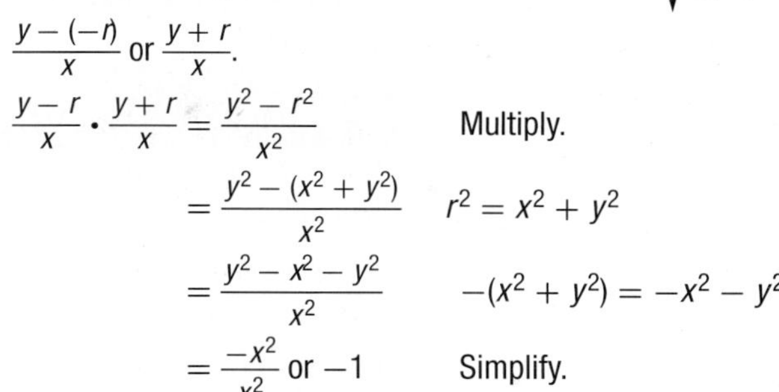

$$\frac{y - r}{x} \cdot \frac{y + r}{x} = \frac{y^2 - r^2}{x^2} \quad \text{Multiply.}$$
$$= \frac{y^2 - (x^2 + y^2)}{x^2} \quad r^2 = x^2 + y^2$$
$$= \frac{y^2 - x^2 - y^2}{x^2} \quad -(x^2 + y^2) = -x^2 - y^2$$
$$= \frac{-x^2}{x^2} \text{ or } -1 \quad \text{Simplify.}$$

Since the product of the slope of $\overline{AC}$ and $\overline{CB}$ is -1, $\overline{AC} \perp \overline{CB}$ and $\angle ACB$ is a right angle.

46. Sample answer:

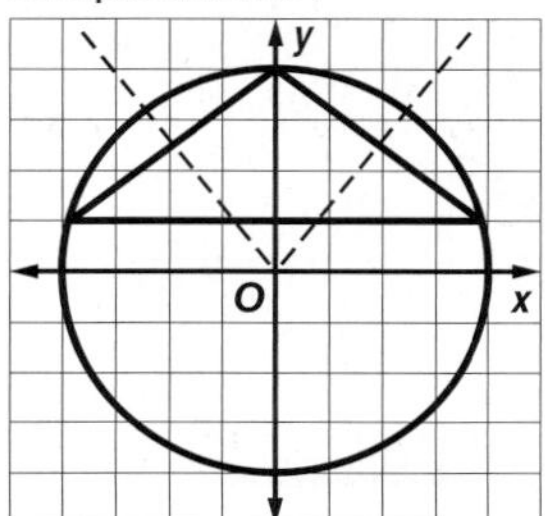

47a. 4

47b–c. Method 1: Draw circles centered on each station that have a radius of 4 units. Stations outside of a circle can have the same frequency as the station at the center of the circle. Method 2: Use the Pythagorean theorem to identify stations that are more than 200 miles apart. Using Method 2, plot the points representing the stations on a graph. Stations that are more than 4 units apart on the graph will be more than 200 miles apart and will thus be able to use the same frequency. Assign station A to the first frequency. Station B is within 4 units of station A, so it must be assigned the second frequency. Station C is within 4 units of both stations A and B, so it must be assigned a third frequency. Station D is also within 4 units of stations A, B, and C, so it must be assigned a fourth frequency, Station E is $\sqrt{29}$ or about 5.4 units away from station A, so it can share the first frequency. Station F is $\sqrt{29}$ or about 5.4 units away from station B, so it can share the second frequency. Station G is $\sqrt{32}$ or about 5.7 units away from station C, so it can share the third frequency. Therefore, the least number of frequencies that can be assigned is 4.

Chapter Planner

Diagnostic Assessment
Quick Check

	LESSON 11-1 (45 min: 1 day; 90 min: 0.5 day)	EXPLORE 11-2 (45 min: 1 day; 90 min: 0.5 day)	LESSON 11-2 (45 min: 1.5 days; 90 min: 0.75 day)
Title	**Areas of Parallelograms and Triangles**	**Graphing Technology Lab: Areas of Trapezoids, Rhombi, and Kites**	**Areas of Trapezoids, Rhombi, and Kites**
Objectives	▪ Find perimeters and areas of parallelograms. ▪ Find perimeters and areas of triangles.	▪ Investigate the areas of polygons using TI-Nspire Technology.	▪ Find areas of trapezoids. ▪ Find areas of rhombi and kites.
Key Vocabulary	base of a parallelogram height of a parallelogram base of a triangle height of a triangle		height of a trapezoid
CCSS	G.GPE.6		G.MG.3
Multiple Representations	✓		✓
Lesson Resources	connectED.mcgraw-hill.com Leveled Worksheets Vocabulary Personal Tutor Virtual Manipulatives Self-Check Quiz ▪ *5-Minute Check* ▪ *Study Notebook*	connectED.mcgraw-hill.com Personal Tutor **Materials:** ▪ TI-Nspire technology	connectED.mcgraw-hill.com Leveled Worksheets Quiz 1 Vocabulary Personal Tutor Virtual Manipulatives Self-Check Quiz ▪ *5-Minute Check* ▪ *Study Notebook* ▪ *Teaching Geometry with Manipulatives*
Resources for Every Lesson	IWB eStudent Edition IWB Interactive Classroom	▪ eTeacher Edition ▪ eSolutions Manual ▪ eAssessment	
Differentiated Instruction	pp. 781, 786		pp. 791, 792, 796

IWB All digital assets are Interactive Whiteboard ready.

Suggested Pacing			
Time Periods	**Instruction**	**Review & Assess**	**Total**
45-minute	9 days	2 days	11 days
90-minute	5 days	1 day	6 days

EXTEND 11-2 (45 min: 0.5 day; 90 min: 0.25 day)	LESSON 11-3 (45 min: 1 day; 90 min: 0.75 day)	EXPLORE 11-4 (45 min: 0.5 day; 90 min: 0.25 day)	LESSON 11-4 (45 min: 1.5 days; 90 min: 1 day)
Geometry Lab: Population Density	**Areas of Circles and Sectors**	**Geometry Lab: Investigating Areas of Regular Polygons**	**Areas of Regular Polygons and Composite Figures**
▪ Explore population density.	▪ Find areas of circles. ▪ Find areas of sectors of circles.	▪ Investigate the formula for the area of regular polygons.	▪ Find areas of regular polygons. ▪ Find areas of composite figures.
population density	sector of a circle	apothem	center of a regular polygon radius of a regular polygon apothem central angle of a regular polygon composite figure
G.MG.2	G.C.5, G.GMD.1		G.MG.3
connectED.mcgraw-hill.com Vocabulary	connectED.mcgraw-hill.com Leveled Worksheets Quiz 2 Vocabulary Personal Tutor Self-Check Quiz ▪ *5-Minute Check* ▪ *Study Notebook* ▪ *Teaching Geometry with Manipulatives*	connectED.mcgraw-hill.com Vocabulary Animations Virtual Manipulatives ▪ *Teaching Geometry with Manipulatives* **Materials:** ▪ straightedge ▪ compass	connectED.mcgraw-hill.com Leveled Worksheets Quiz 3 Vocabulary Animations Personal Tutor Virtual Manipulatives Self-Check Quiz ▪ *5-Minute Check* ▪ *Study Notebook* ▪ *Teaching Geometry with Manipulatives*
IWB eStudent Edition IWB Interactive Classroom	▪ eTeacher Edition ▪ eSolutions Manual ▪ eAssessment		
	p. 799		pp. 809, 810, 813
	Formative Assessment Mid-Chapter Quiz		

Chapter Planner

	EXTEND 11-4 (45 min: 1 day; 90 min: 0.5 day)	LESSON 11-5 (45 min: 1 day; 90 min: 0.5 day)
Title	**Geometry Lab: Regular Polygons on the Coordinate Plane**	**Areas of Similar Figures**
Objectives	■ Find areas and perimeters of regular polygons, including inscribed and circumscribed polygons, on the coordinate plane.	■ Find areas of similar figures by using scale factors. ■ Find scale factors or missing measures given the areas of similar figures.
Key Vocabulary		
CCSS		G.MG.1
Multiple Representations		
Lesson Resources	connectED.mcgraw-hill.com ■ *Teaching Geometry with Manipulatives* **Materials:** ■ grid paper	connectED.mcgraw-hill.com Leveled Worksheets Quiz 4 Personal Tutor Virtual Manipulatives Self-Check Quiz ■ *5-Minute Check* ■ *Study Notebook*
Resources for Every Lesson	IWB eStudent Edition IWB Interactive Classroom	■ eTeacher Edition ■ eSolutions Manual ■ eAssessment
Differentiated Instruction		pp. 820, 823, 824

Summative Assessment
Study Guide and Review
Practice Test

What the Research Says...

Teachers proactively modify curriculum, teaching methods, resources, learning activities, and student products to address the needs of individual students and small groups of students to maximize the learning opportunity for each student in the classroom. (Tomlinson et al, 2003)

- In Lessons 11-1 through 11-4, vary methods to help individual students grasp the concepts being taught. Besides direct instruction, include technology, manipulatives, and cooperative learning to reach all students.
- Use the differentiated instruction activities provided to modify the learning opportunities.

Teacher to Teacher

Sarah L. Waldrop
Forestview High School
Gastonia, NC

Use With Lesson 11-2

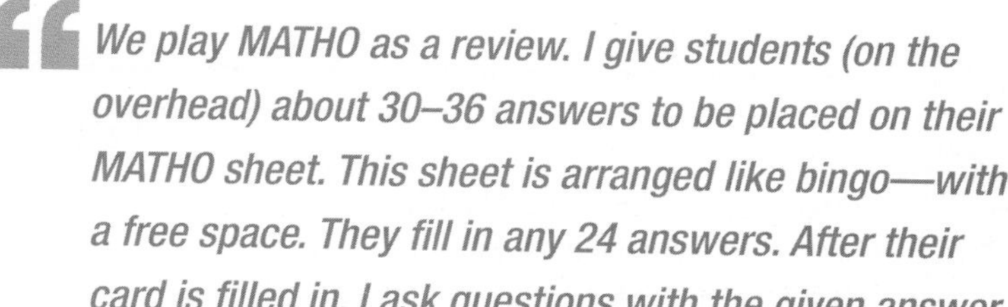

"We play MATHO as a review. I give students (on the overhead) about 30–36 answers to be placed on their MATHO sheet. This sheet is arranged like bingo—with a free space. They fill in any 24 answers. After their card is filled in, I ask questions with the given answer. When they have MATHO they get a prize (candy, points on a quiz, etc.)."

Reading and Writing in Mathematics

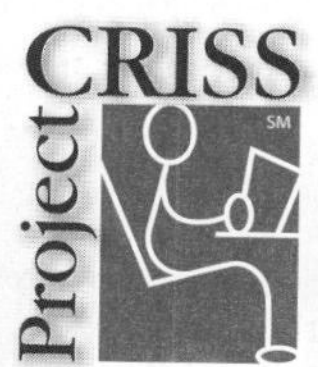

STUDY SKILL

Study cards can be a helpful study aid for students learning definitions and formulas. The cards at the right show some common shapes (front) and the formulas to find the areas (back) of each. Have students make study cards for other concepts in the chapter. They can use the cards to quiz themselves or to help each other prepare for tests.

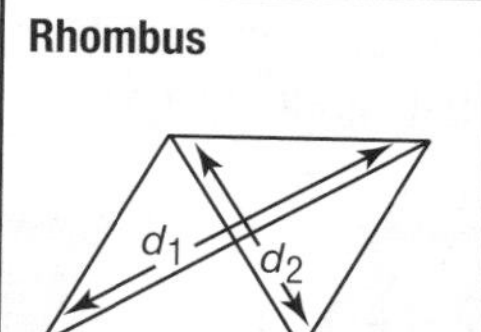
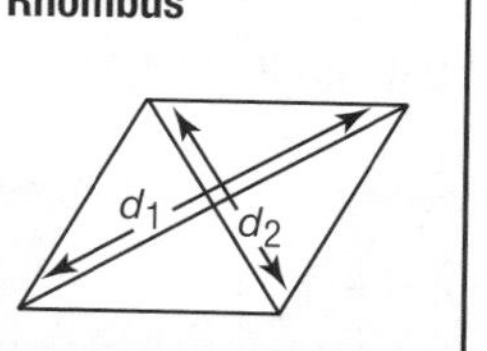

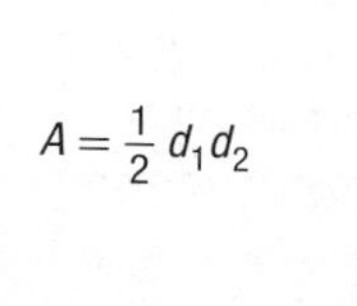

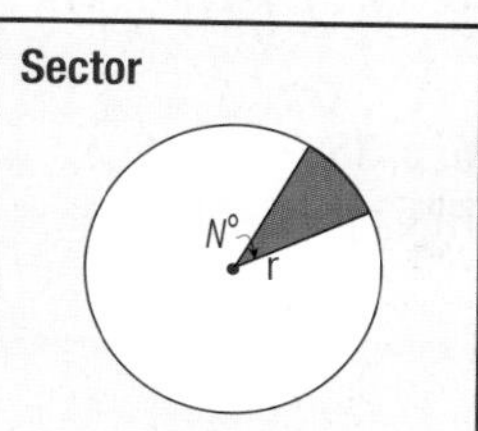

$$A = \frac{N}{360} \pi r^2$$

Creating Independence through Student-owned Strategies

CHAPTER 11

Areas of Polygons and Circles

Assessment and Intervention

SE = Student Edition, **TE** = Teacher Edition, **CRM** = Chapter Resource Masters

	Diagnosis	Prescription
DIAGNOSTIC ASSESSMENT	**Beginning Chapter 11**	
	Get Ready for Chapter 11 **SE**	Response to Intervention **TE**
	Beginning Every Lesson	
	Then, Now, Why? **SE** 5-Minute Checks	Chapter 0 **SE**
FORMATIVE ASSESSMENT	**During/After Every Lesson**	
	Guided Practice **SE**, every example Check Your Understanding **SE** H.O.T. Problems **SE** Spiral Review **SE** Additional Examples **TE** Watch Out! **TE** Step 4, Assess **TE** Chapter 11 Quizzes **CRM**, pp. 39–40 Self-Check Quizzes connectED.mcgraw-hill.com	TIER 1 Intervention Skills Practice **CRM**, Ch. 1–11 connectED.mcgraw-hill.com TIER 2 Intervention Differentiated Instruction **TE**; Differentiated Homework Options **TE**; Study Guide and Intervention **CRM**, Ch. 1–11 TIER 3 Intervention *Math Triumphs, Geometry,* Ch. 5
	Mid-Chapter	
	Mid-Chapter Quiz **SE** Mid-Chapter Test **CRM**, p. 41 eAssessment	TIER 1 Intervention Skills Practice **CRM**, Ch. 1–11 connectED.mcgraw-hill.com TIER 2 Intervention Study Guide and Intervention **CRM**, Ch. 1–11 TIER 3 Intervention *Math Triumphs, Geometry,* Ch. 5
	Before Chapter Test	
	Chapter Study Guide and Review **SE** Practice Test **SE** Standardized Test Practice **SE** Chapter Test connectED.mcgraw-hill.com Standardized Test Practice connectED.mcgraw-hill.com Vocabulary Review connectED.mcgraw-hill.com eAssessment	TIER 1 Intervention Skills Practice **CRM**, Ch. 1–11 connectED.mcgraw-hill.com TIER 2 Intervention Study Guide and Intervention **CRM**, Ch. 1–11 TIER 3 Intervention *Math Triumphs, Geometry,* Ch. 5
SUMMATIVE ASSESSMENT	**After Chapter 11**	
	Multiple-Choice Tests, Forms 1, 2A, 2B **CRM**, pp. 43–48 Free-Response Tests, Forms 2C, 2D, 3 **CRM**, pp. 49–54 Vocabulary Test **CRM**, p. 42 Extended Response Test **CRM**, p. 55 Standardized Test Practice **CRM**, pp. 56–58 eAssessment	Study Guide and Intervention **CRM**, Ch. 1–11 connectED.mcgraw-hill.com

Differentiated Instruction

Option 1 Reaching All Learners 

Visual/Spatial Have students design a new flag for the school or classroom. Explain that they must design it with either parallelograms or triangles, or both. Using scrap wallpaper (check your local stores for discontinued sample books), have students assemble the flags and list the areas of the various shapes on the back. Display the completed flags in the classroom. Have students find the areas of the shapes found on their classmates' flags. The areas can be turned in for teacher verification.

Verbal/Linguistic Have students research Euclid's Elements to find the meanings behind the variables and the formulas they are using in the classroom. Have them work either independently or in small groups to write a short composition on Euclid's contributions to geometry.

Visual/spatial The number of figures that can be created with exactly the same area is infinite. Challenge students to create as many triangles as they can with a given area. Engage mathematically talented students deeper in the task by relating the number of possible triangles to infinity. Ask these students to use successive drawings on graph paper to demonstrate the concept of infinite triangles with a given area.

Option 2 Approaching Level AL

Arrange students in pairs. Have one student draw a regular polygon and give the radius of the circumscribed circle. Then, have the other student find the area by first finding the apothem. Next, have them switch roles and repeat the activity. If students have difficulty finding the apothem of the polygon, ask them to discuss how right angle trigonometry may be used.

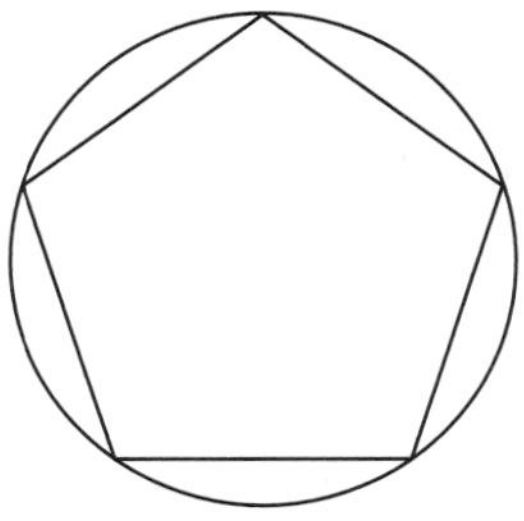

Option 3 English Learners ELL

Arrange students in pairs or small groups. Have them use string and masking tape to mark off composite shapes on a tiled floor. Ask students to estimate the area by counting squares and then verify the estimate mathematically, describing the figures and formulas used at each step. Have students repeat the process with another student or group's figure.

Option 4 Beyond Level BL

Using tangrams, have students create a parallelogram using all seven pieces. Have them write formulas for each piece that makes up the parallelogram. Have them create other irregular figures and find the area using the parts that make up the figure.

While the area of polygons can be easily explained using the rectangle as a base, understanding the formula for the area of a circle can be quite complex. Propose the task to mathematically talented students (prior to beginning Lesson 11-3 on area of circles) to develop a way to determine the area of a circle without relying on a formula. Give all students the same circle to demonstrate their methods, then compare and contrast different students' ideas comparing their estimated areas with the actual area.

Focus on Mathematical Content

Vertical Alignment

Before Chapter 11

Related Topics from Grade 8

- Use geometric concepts to solve problems.

Previous Topics from Geometry

- Make conjectures about polygons.
- Find area using proportional reasoning.

Chapter 11

Related Topics from Geometry

- Find areas of regular polygons, circles, and composite figures.
- Find areas of sectors and arc lengths of circles using proportional reasoning.

After Chapter 11

Preparation for Precalculus

- Use properties of conic sections to describe physical phenomena such as the reflective properties of light and sound.
- Use properties of functions to analyze and solve problems and make predictions.

Lesson-by-Lesson Preview

11-1 Areas of Parallelograms and Triangles

A parallelogram is a quadrilateral with both pairs of opposite sides parallel. Any side of a parallelogram can be called a base. For each base, there is a corresponding altitude that is perpendicular to the base. The altitude corresponds to the height of the parallelogram. If a parallelogram has an area of A square units, a base of b units, and a height of h units, then $A = bh$.

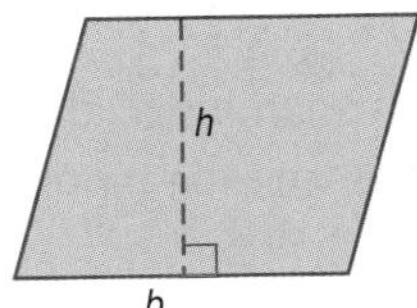

A parallelogram with an area of A square units, a base of b units, and a height of h units.

To find the area of a quadrilateral on the coordinate plane, you must first determine whether the figure is a parallelogram. You can use the formula for slope to determine whether opposite sides are parallel. Then you find the measures of the base and height and use those to calculate the area.

11-2 Areas of Trapezoids, Rhombi, and Kites

The formula for the area of a triangle is related to the formula for the area of a parallelogram or rectangle. It is $A = \frac{1}{2}bh$. This formula, in turn, yields the formulas for the areas of trapezoids, rhombi, and kites.

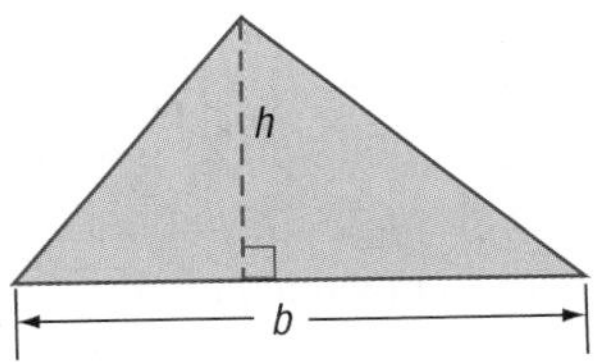

A triangle with an area of A square units, a base of b units, and a corresponding height of h units.

If a trapezoid has an area of A square units, bases of b_1 units and b_2 units, and a height of h units, then $A = \frac{1}{2}h(b_1 + b_2)$. If a rhombus or kite has an area of A square units and diagonals of d_1 and d_2 units, then $A = \frac{1}{2}d_1d_2$.

11-3 Areas of Circles and Sectors

The area of a circle cannot be found without the value known as π. If a circle has an area of A square units and a radius of r units, then $A = \pi r^2$. You can use the properties of circles and regular polygons to find the areas of inscribed and circumscribed polygons.

A sector of a circle is a region of a circle bounded by a central angle and its intercepted arc. The formula for the area of the sector of a circle is similar to the formula for arc length. If a sector of a circle has an area of A square units, a central angle measuring $N°$, and a radius of r units, then $A = \frac{N}{360}\pi r^2$.

11-4 Areas of Regular Polygons and Composite Figures

A regular polygon can be divided into congruent isosceles triangles by drawing a line from each vertex to the center of the polygon. The altitude of one of these triangles is called an *apothem*. The area of the polygon can be determined by adding the areas of the triangles. If a polygon has a side of s units and an apothem of a units, then the area of one of these triangles is $\frac{1}{2}sa$. By multiplying this formula by the number of sides and substituting P for the formula for perimeter contained in the result, you will find that the formula for the area of a regular polygon is $A = \frac{1}{2}Pa$.

A *composite figure* is a figure that cannot be classified into the specific shapes that the student has studied. A composite figure is also called an *irregular figure* or *irregular polygon*. To find the areas of composite figures, separate the figures into shapes for which you can find the area. The area of the composite figure is the sum of the areas of these separate shapes.

The formula for the area of a regular polygon does not apply to an irregular polygon. To find the area of an irregular polygon, separate the polygon into figures that have areas that can be calculated easily.

11-5 Areas of Similar Figures

If two polygons are similar, then the perimeters are proportional to the scale factor between them. There is also a relationship between the areas of two similar polygons. The areas of two similar polygons are proportional to the square of the scale factor between them. If the lengths of corresponding sides of two similar figures and the area of one of them are known, then the area of the second figure can be found. If the areas of each similar figure and one length are known, the corresponding length on the second figure can be found.

Professional Development

Targeted professional development has been articulated throughout Geometry. More quality, customized professional development is available from McGraw-Hill Professional Development. Visit connectED.mcgraw-hill.com for details on each product.

- Online Lessons emphasize the strategies and techniques used to teach Geometry. Includes streaming video, interactive pages, and online tools.
- Video Workshops allow mentors, coaches, or leadership personnel to facilitate on-site workshops on educational strategies in mathematics and mathematical concepts.
- MHPD Online (www.mhpdonline.com) offers online professional development with video clips of instructional strategies, links, student activities, and news and issues in education.
- Teaching Today (teachingtoday.glencoe.com) gives secondary teachers practical strategies and materials that inspire excellence and innovation in teaching.

Chapter Project

Real Estate

Students use what they have learned about areas of polygons and circles to complete a project.

This chapter project addresses business literacy, as well as several specific skills identified as being essential to student success by the Framework for 21st Century Learning.

Visit connectED.mcgraw-hill.com for student and teacher handouts.

KeyVocabulary Introduce the key vocabulary in the chapter using the example below.

Define: The apothem is a segment drawn perpendicular to a side of a regular polygon from the center point.

Example:

apothem = $\overline{PX}$

Ask:

- How does the apothem relate to the central angle of a regular polygon? The apothem bisects the central angle of a regular polygon.
- How does the radius of a circle circumscribed about a regular polygon relate to the apothem? The radius of a circle circumscribed about a regular polygon forms the hypotenuse of a right triangle with the apothem and half the length of the side of the polygon that is being bisected by the apothem.

CHAPTER 11

Areas of Polygons and Circles

Then

You learned about circles and angles within circles.

Now

In this chapter, you will:

- Find areas of polygons.
- Solve problems involving areas and sectors of circles.
- Find scale factors using similar figures.

Why?

ART Artisans and craftsmen use area to determine the amount of raw materials that they will need for a project.

connectED.mcgraw-hill.com Your Digital Math Portal

Animation | Vocabulary | eGlossary | Personal Tutor | Virtual Manipulatives | Graphing Calculator | Audio | Foldables | Self-Check Practice | Worksheets

Get Ready for the Chapter

Diagnose Readiness | You have two options for checking prerequisite skills.

1 Textbook Option Take the Quick Check below. Refer to the Quick Review for help.

QuickCheck

The area and width of a rectangle are given. Find the length of the rectangle.

1. $A = 25, w = 5$ 5
2. $A = 42, w = 6$ 7
3. $A = 280, w = 14$ 20
4. $A = 360, w = 60$ 6
5. **GARDENS** Molly planted a garden with a length of 72 feet. If she bought enough fertilizer to cover 792 square feet, what width should she make the garden? 11 ft

Evaluate each expression if $a = 9$, $b = 10$, $c = 12$, and $d = 13$.

6. $\frac{1}{2}a(b + c)$ 99
7. $\frac{1}{2}(ab + cd)$ 123
8. $\frac{1}{2}(a + bd)$ 69.5
9. $\frac{1}{2}cd$ 78
10. $\frac{1}{2}(ab + c)$ 51
11. $\frac{1}{2}(a + d)$ 11

Find h in each triangle.

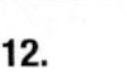

12. 8 in.

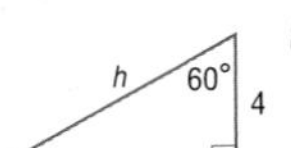

13. $3\sqrt{2}$ cm

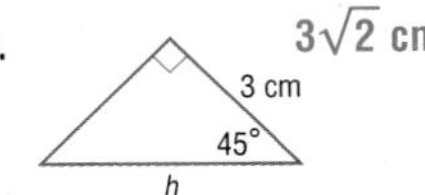

14. **LOOKOUT** The lookout on a pirate ship slides down a rope from the top of the mast 6 meters above the water. He can see the land at a 60° angle. How far does he slide? 12 m

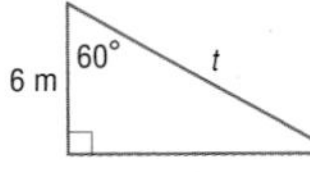

QuickReview

Example 1 (Used in Lesson 11-1)

The area of a rectangle is 64 square units and the width is 4 units. Find the length.

$A = \ell w$ Area of rectangle

$64 = \ell(4)$ Substitution

$16 = \ell$ Divide each side by 4.

The length is 16 units.

Example 2 (Used in Lessons 11-2 and 11-4)

Evaluate $\frac{1}{2}x(2x + 3y)$ for $x = 4$ and $y = 12$.

$\frac{1}{2}x(2x + 3y) = \frac{1}{2}(4)[2(4) + 3(12)]$ Substitution

$= 2(8 + 36)$ Multiply.

$= 2(44)$ Add.

$= 88$ Multiply.

Example 3 (Used in Lesson 11-4)

Find the value of h.

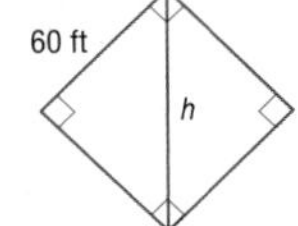

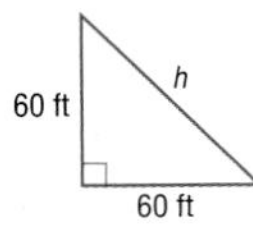

Since h is the hypotenuse of the triangle, the triangle can be redrawn as shown.

In a 45°-45°-90° triangle, the hypotenuse is $\sqrt{2}$ times the length of a leg.

$h = (\sqrt{2})60$

≈ 84.85

So, h is approximately 84.85 feet.

2 Online Option Take an online self-check Chapter Readiness Quiz at connectED.mcgraw-hill.com.

777

Essential Question

- How can decomposing and recomposing shapes help us build our understanding of mathematics?
  Sample answers: By doing so, you can visualize how different formulas are developed; you can solve problems involving composite figures.

Get Ready for the Chapter

Response to Intervention (RtI)

Use the *Quick Check* results and the Intervention Planner chart to help you determine your Response to Intervention. The If-Then statements in the chart help you decide the appropriate tier of RtI and suggest intervention resources for each tier.

TIER 1 On Level OL

If students miss about 25% of the exercises or less,

Then choose a resource:

SE Lesson 1-6, Lesson 8-3

Skills Practice, Chapter 1, p. 39, Chapter 8, p. 20

connectED.mcgraw-hill.com Self-Check Quiz

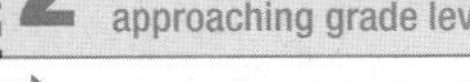

TIER 2 Strategic Intervention AL approaching grade level

If students miss about 50% of the exercises,

Then choose a resource:

Study Guide and Intervention, Chapter 1, pp. 37–38, Chapter 8, pp. 18–19

connectED.mcgraw-hill.com Extra Examples, Personal Tutor, Homework Help

TIER 3 Intensive Intervention 2 or more grades below level

If students miss about 75% of the exercises,

Then use *Math Triumphs, Geometry,* Ch. 5

connectED.mcgraw-hill.com Extra Examples, Personal Tutor, Homework Help, Review Vocabulary

FOLDABLES® StudyOrganizer

Dinah Zike's Foldables®

Focus Students write about polygons and circles.

Teach After students make their Foldables, have them label the tabs to correspond with the five lessons in this chapter. Instruct students to take notes while reading each lesson and listening to instruction. They should include definitions of terms and key concepts, as well as diagrams and examples related to each lesson.

When to Use It Use the appropriate tabs as students cover each lesson in this chapter. Students can add to the vocabulary tab during each lesson.

For a more durable Foldable, have students add a folded sheet of construction paper as a cover before stapling the paper.

Differentiated Instruction

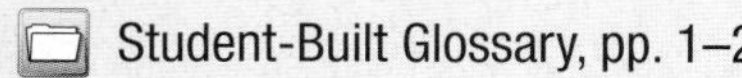

Students should complete the chart by providing the definition of each term and an example as they progress through Chapter 11. This study tool can also be used to review for the chapter test.

Get Started on the Chapter

You will learn several new concepts, skills, and vocabulary terms as you study Chapter 11. To get ready, identify important terms and organize your resources. You may wish to refer to Chapter 0 to review prerequisite skills.

FOLDABLES StudyOrganizer

Areas of Polygons and Circles Make this Foldable to help you organize your Chapter 11 notes about areas of polygons and circles. Begin with three sheets of notebook paper.

1 **Stack** three sheets of paper and fold them in half, lengthwise.

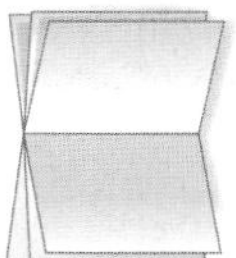

2 **Staple** the papers together one inch from the top fold.

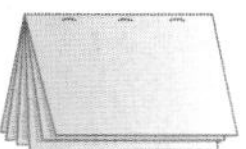

3 **Cut** the top sheet two inches from the top fold and each following sheet one inch longer than the previous sheet.

4 **Label** as shown.

NewVocabulary

English		Español
base of a parallelogram	p. 779	base de un paralelogramo
height of a parallelogram	p. 779	altura de un paralelogramo
base of a triangle	p. 781	base de un triángulo
height of a triangle	p. 781	altura de un triángulo
height of a trapezoid	p. 789	altura de un trapecio
sector of a circle	p. 799	sector circular
center of a regular polygon	p. 807	centro de un polígono regular
radius of a regular polygon	p. 807	radio de un polígono regular
apothem	p. 807	apotema
central angle of a regular polygon	p. 807	ángulo central de un polígono regular

ReviewVocabulary

arc arco **a part of a circle that is defined by two endpoints**

central angle ángulo central **an angle that intersects a circle in two points and has its vertex at the center of the circle**

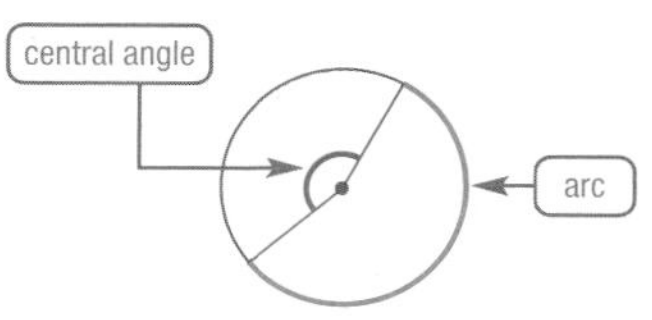

diagonal diagonal **a segment that connects nonconsecutive vertices of a polygon**

778 | Chapter 11 | Areas of Polygons and Circles

LESSON 11-1 Areas of Parallelograms and Triangles

Then

- You found areas of rectangles and squares.

Now

1. Find perimeters and areas of parallelograms.
2. Find perimeters and areas of triangles.

Why?

- A tangram is an ancient Chinese puzzle that can be rearranged to form different images, such as the animals shown. The area of the puzzle, before and after being rearranged, remains the same. It is the sum of all the areas of its pieces.

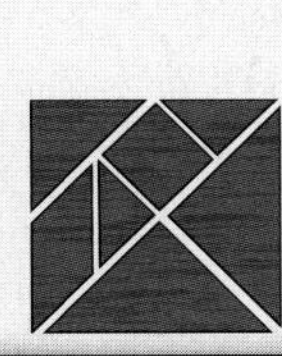

NewVocabulary
base of a parallelogram
height of a parallelogram
base of a triangle
height of a triangle

Common Core State Standards

Content Standards
G.GPE.7 Use coordinates to compute perimeters of polygons and areas of triangles and rectangles, e.g., using the distance formula.

Mathematical Practices
1 Make sense of problems and persevere in solving them.
7 Look for and make use of structure.

1 Areas of Parallelograms

In Lesson 6-2, you learned that a *parallelogram* is a quadrilateral with both pairs of opposite sides parallel. Any side of a parallelogram can be called the **base of a parallelogram**. The **height of a parallelogram** is the perpendicular distance between any two parallel bases.

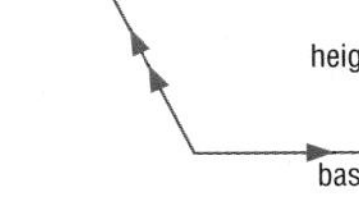

You can use the following postulate to develop the formula for the area of a parallelogram.

Postulate 11.1 Area Addition Postulate

The area of a region is the sum of the areas of its nonoverlapping parts.

In the figures below, a right triangle is cut off from one side of a parallelogram and translated to the other side as shown to form a rectangle with the same base and height.

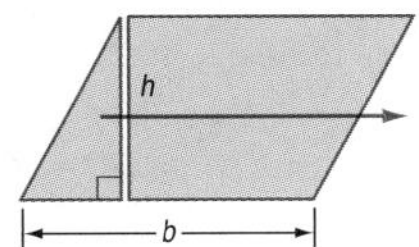

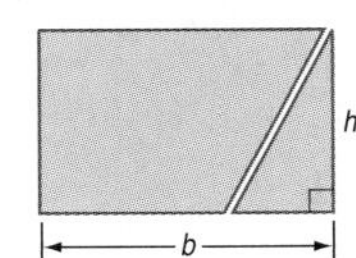

Recall from Lesson 1-6 that the area of a rectangle is the product of its base and height. By the Area Addition Postulate, a parallelogram with base b and height h has the same area as a rectangle with base b and height h.

KeyConcept Area of a Parallelogram

Words The area A of a parallelogram is the product of a base b and its corresponding height h.

Symbols $A = bh$

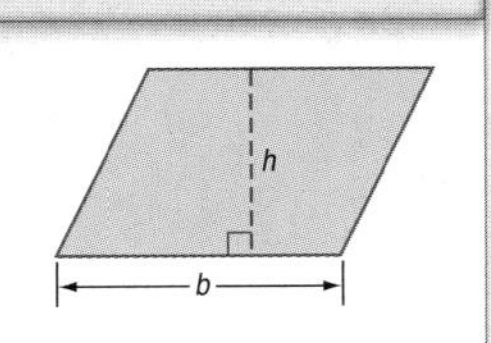

1 Focus

VerticalAlignment

Before Lesson 11-1 Find the area of rectangles and squares.

Lesson 11-1 Find the perimeter and area of parallelograms and triangles.

After Lesson 11-1 Find the area of trapezoids, rhombi, and kites.

2 Teach

Scaffolding Questions

Have students read the **Why?** section of the lesson.

Ask:

- What are some of the figures that can be made from the puzzle? Sample answer: a rabbit, a cat, and a duck
- Explain why the areas of the second and fourth figure are identical. The area of the pieces that make up each figure are the same.
- What is an easy way to find the area of one of the figures? Sample statement: Find the area of the square.

Lesson 11-1 Resources

Resource	Approaching Level AL	On Level OL	Beyond Level BL	English Learners ELL
Teacher Edition	▪ Differentiated Instruction, p. 781	▪ Differentiated Instruction, pp. 781, 786	▪ Differentiated Instruction, pp. 781, 786	▪ Differentiated Instruction, p. 781
Chapter Resource Masters	▪ Study Guide and Intervention, pp. 5–6 ▪ Skills Practice, p. 7 ▪ Practice, p. 8 ▪ Word Problem Practice, p. 9	▪ Study Guide and Intervention, pp. 5–6 ▪ Skills Practice, p. 7 ▪ Practice, p. 8 ▪ Word Problem Practice, p. 9 ▪ Enrichment, p. 10 ▪ Graphing Calculator Activity, pp. 11–12	▪ Practice, p. 8 ▪ Word Problem Practice, p. 9 ▪ Enrichment, p. 10	▪ Study Guide and Intervention, pp. 5–6 ▪ Skills Practice, p. 7 ▪ Practice, p. 8 ▪ Word Problem Practice, p. 9
Other	▪ 5-Minute Check 11-1 ▪ Study Notebook	▪ 5-Minute Check 11-1 ▪ Study Notebook	▪ 5-Minute Check 11-1 ▪ Study Notebook	▪ 5-Minute Check 11-1 ▪ Study Notebook

1 Areas of Parallelograms

Examples 1 and 2 show how to find the area of a parallelogram.

Formative Assessment

Use the Guided Practice exercises after each example to determine students' understanding of concepts.

Additional Examples

1 Find the perimeter and area of ▱RSTU.

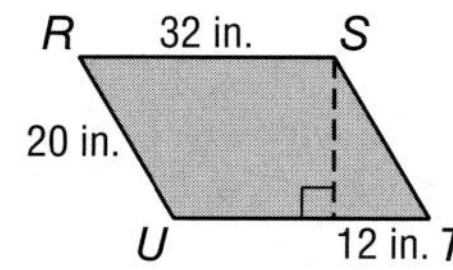

perimeter = 104 in.; area = 512 in^2

2 Find the area of ▱PQRS.

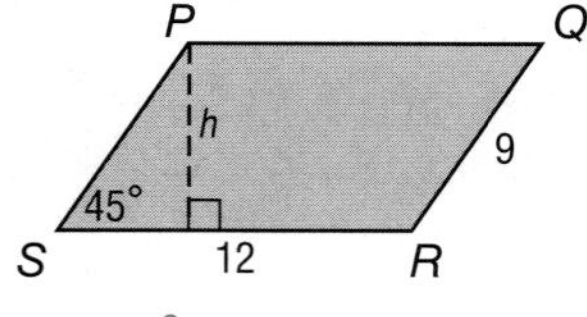

76.3 cm^2

Additional Examples also in Interactive Classroom PowerPoint® Presentations

Teaching the Mathematical Practices

Precision Mathematically proficient students are careful about specifying units of measure. They calculate accurately and efficiently. Encourage students to read each exercise carefully to determine the units of the result.

Example 1 Perimeter and Area of a Parallelogram

Find the perimeter and area of ▱ABCD.

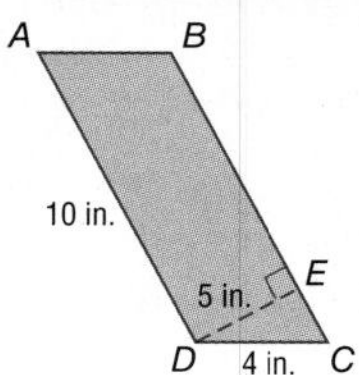

Perimeter

Since opposite sides of a parallelogram are congruent, $\overline{AB} \cong \overline{DC}$ and $\overline{BC} \cong \overline{AD}$. So $AB = 4$ inches and $BC = 10$ inches.

Perimeter of ▱$ABCD = AB + BC + DC + AD$
$= 4 + 10 + 4 + 10$ or 28 in.

Area

The height given, DE, is 5 inches. $\overline{BC}$ is the base, which measures 10 inches.

$A = bh$ — Area of a parallelogram

$= (10)(5)$ or 50 in^2 — $b = 10$ and $h = 5$

StudyTip

Heights of Figures The height of a figure can be measured by extending a base. In Example 1, the height of ▱ABCD that corresponds to base $\overline{DC}$ can be measured by extending $\overline{DC}$.

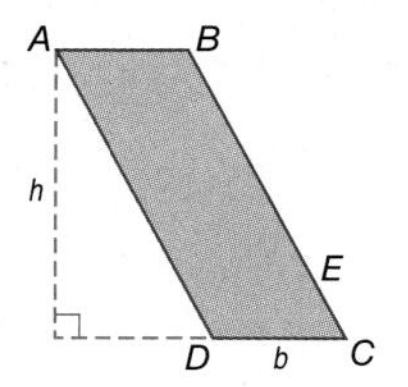

GuidedPractice

Find the perimeter and area of each parallelogram.

1A. 76 cm, 315 cm^2

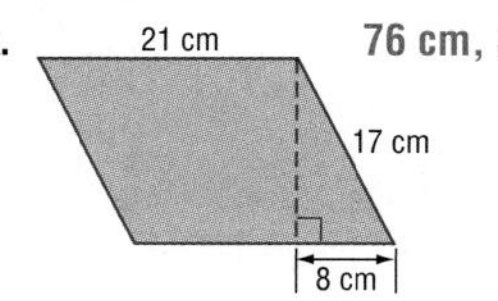

1B. 96 ft, 552 ft^2

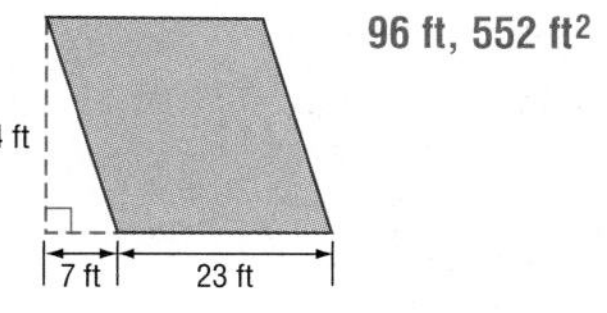

You may need to use trigonometry to find the area of a parallelogram.

Example 2 Area of a Parallelogram

Find the area of ▱EFGH.

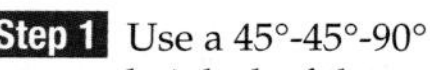

Step 1 Use a 45°-45°-90° triangle to find the height h of the parallelogram.

Recall that if the measure of the leg opposite the 45° angle is h, then the measure of the hypotenuse is $h\sqrt{2}$.

$h\sqrt{2} = 8.5$ — Substitute 8.5 for the measure of the hypotenuse.

$h = \frac{8.5}{\sqrt{2}}$ or about 6 mm — Divide each side by $\sqrt{2}$.

Step 2 Find the area.

$A = bh$ — Area of a parallelogram

$\approx (15)(6)$ or 90 mm^2 — $b = 15$ and $h \approx 6$

WatchOut!

Precision Remember that perimeter is measured in linear units such as inches and centimeters. Area is measured in square units such as square feet and square millimeters.

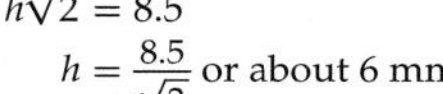

GuidedPractice

Find the area of each parallelogram. Round to the nearest tenth if necessary.

2A. 153 yd^2

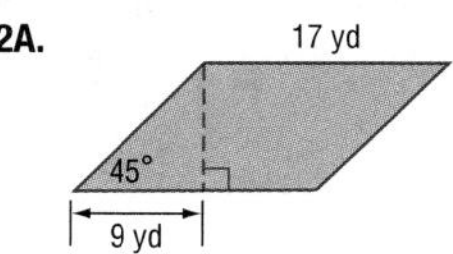

2B. 665.1 m^2

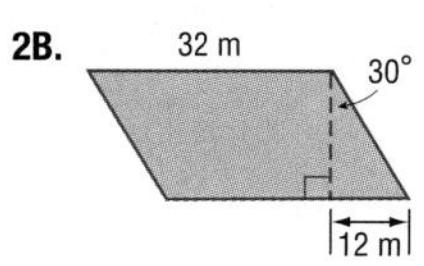

WatchOut!

Identifying Height The height of a parallelogram is the perpendicular distance between two parallel sides. Since parallelograms have two pairs of parallel sides, there are two heights. Depending on the orientation of the parallelogram, the given height does not have to be a vertical distance.

Review Vocabulary

altitude of a triangle a segment from a vertex of a triangle to the line containing the opposite side and perpendicular to the line containing that side

2 Areas of Triangles

Like the base of a parallelogram, the **base of a triangle** can be any side. The **height of a triangle** is the length of an altitude drawn to a given base.

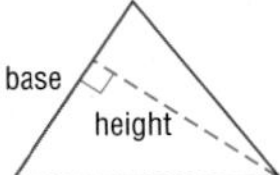

You can use the following postulate to develop the formula for the area of a triangle.

Postulate 11.2 Area Congruence Postulate

If two figures are congruent, then they have the same area.

In the figures below, a parallelogram is cut in half along a diagonal to form two congruent triangles with the same base and height.

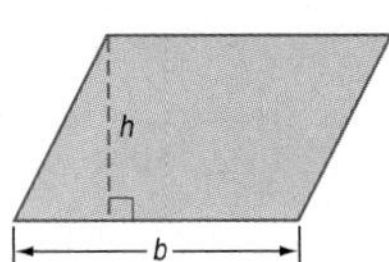

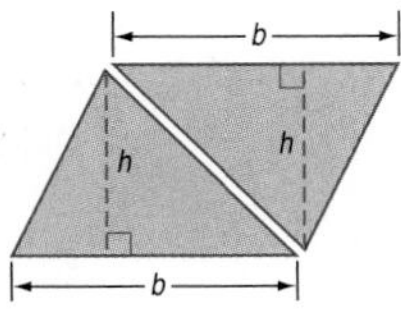

By the Area Congruence Postulate, the two congruent triangles have the same area. So, one triangle with base b and height h has half the area of a parallelogram with base b and height h.

KeyConcept Area of a Triangle

Words The area A of a triangle is one half the product of a base b and its corresponding height h.

Symbols $A = \frac{1}{2}bh$ or $A = \frac{bh}{2}$

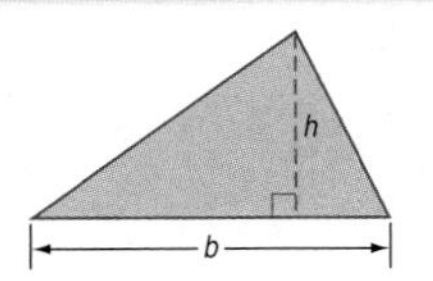

Real-WorldLink

Triangular gardens can serve as focal points in landscaping or simply result from intersecting walkways.

Real-World Example 3 Perimeter and Area of a Triangle

GARDENING D'Andre needs enough mulch to cover the triangular garden shown and enough paving stones to border it. If one bag of mulch covers 12 square feet and one paving stone provides a 4-inch border, how many bags of mulch and how many stones does he need to buy?

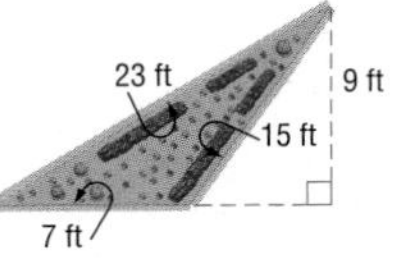

Step 1 Find the perimeter of the garden.

Perimeter of garden = 23 + 15 + 7 or 45 ft

Step 2 Find the area of the garden.

$A = \frac{1}{2}bh$ Area of a triangle

$= \frac{1}{2}(7)(9)$ or 31.5 ft^2 $b = 7$ and $h = 9$

Step 3 Use unit analysis to determine how many of each item are needed.

Bags of Mulch

$31.5 \cancel{\text{ft}^2} \cdot \frac{1 \text{ bag}}{12 \cancel{\text{ft}^2}} = 2.625 \text{ bags}$

Paving Stones

$45 \cancel{\text{ft}} \cdot \frac{12 \cancel{\text{in.}}}{1 \cancel{\text{ft}}} \cdot \frac{1 \text{ stone}}{4 \cancel{\text{in.}}} = 135 \text{ stones}$

Round the number of bags up so there is enough mulch. He will need 3 bags of mulch and 135 paving stones.

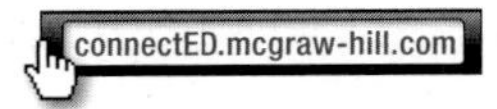

DifferentiatedInstruction

Visual/Spatial Learners Have students cut out two parallelograms of different sizes. First, have students cut a right triangle from the end of one of the parallelograms and rearrange the pieces to form a rectangle. Then, ask students to find the area of the rectangle. Next, have students cut the second parallelogram in half diagonally and determine the area of the resulting triangles.

Teach with Tech

Interactive Whiteboard Display a parallelogram on the board and draw one of its diagonals. Trace over the parallelogram to draw two triangles. Drag them apart and back together to show students that the area of the parallelogram is the sum of the areas of these two triangles.

2 Areas of Triangles

Examples 3 and 4 show how to use the areas of triangles to find unknown values.

Additional Example

3 SANDBOX You need to buy enough boards to make the frame of the triangular sandbox shown and enough sand to fill it. If one board is 3 feet long and one bag of sand fills 9 square feet of the sandbox, how many boards and bags do you need to buy?

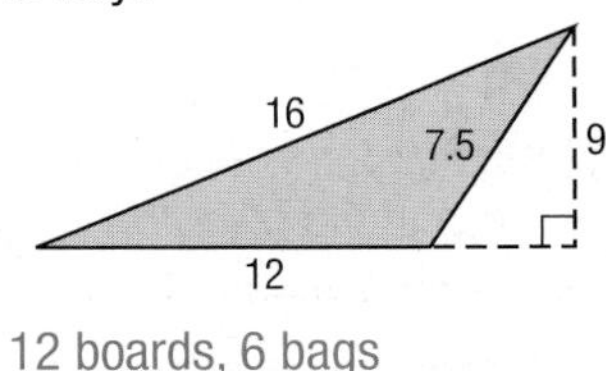

12 boards, 6 bags

Tips for New Teachers

Sense-Making You can have students create various figures on graph paper to verify the area formulas for parallelograms and triangles.

Additional Example

4 ALGEBRA The height of a triangle is 7 inches more than its base. The area of the triangle is 60 square inches. Find the base and height. base = 8 in., height = 15 in.

Focus on Mathematical Content

Area Point out that many different parallelograms can be drawn with the same altitude, with their bases congruent, and thus with the same area. Use a geoboard or similar modeling device to show different parallelograms with the same height and base. Ask students to explain how these parallelograms differ.

Tips for New Teachers

Modeling Help students understand the relationship between the area of a triangle and the area of a parallelogram or rectangle by showing them a model. Cut a piece of 8.5-inch × 11-inch paper in half along the diagonal to demonstrate that the area of a triangle is half the area of the rectangle that has the same base and height. Then cut a right triangle from an end of another sheet of 8.5-inch × 11-inch paper so that it has the same height as the original paper. Form a parallelogram from the sheet by sliding it to the other side of the sheet. Then cut it in half along the diagonal. The area of a triangle is half the area of this corresponding parallelogram.

GuidedPractice

Find the perimeter and area of each triangle.

3A. 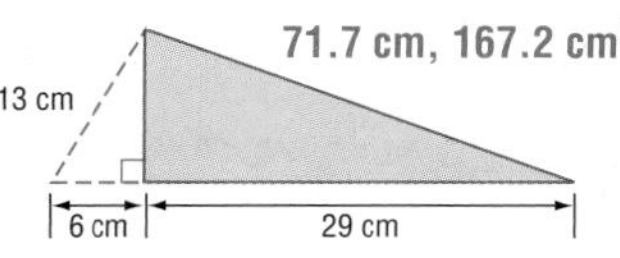

100.4 in., 285 in^2

3B. 13 cm, 6 cm, 29 cm — 71.7 cm, 167.2 cm^2

You can use algebra to solve for unknown measures in parallelograms and triangles.

Example 4 Use Area to Find Missing Measures

ALGEBRA The height of a triangle is 5 centimeters more than its base. The area of the triangle is 52 square centimeters. Find the base and height.

Step 1 Write expressions to represent each measure.

Let b represent the base of the triangle. Then the height is $b + 5$.

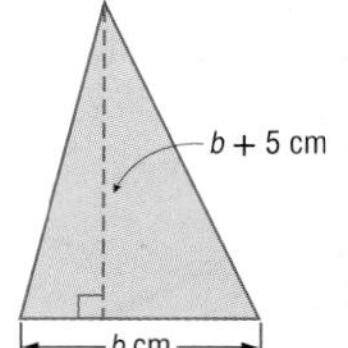

Step 2 Use the formula for the area of a triangle to find b.

$A = \frac{1}{2}bh$	Area of a triangle
$52 = \frac{1}{2}b(b + 5)$	Replace A with 52 and h with $b + 5$.
$104 = b(b + 5)$	Multiply each side by 2.
$104 = b^2 + 5b$	Distributive Property
$0 = b^2 + 5b - 104$	Subtract 104 from each side.
$0 = (b + 13)(b - 8)$	Factor.
$b + 13 = 0$ and $b - 8 = 0$	Zero Product Property
$b = -13$ $b = 8$	Solve for b.

StudyTip
Zero Product Property
If the product of two factors is 0, then at least one of the factors must be 0.

Step 3 Use the expressions from Step 1 to find each measure.

Since a length cannot be negative, the base measures 8 centimeters and the height measures 8 + 5 or 13 centimeters.

GuidedPractice

ALGEBRA Find x.

4A. $A = 148\text{ m}^2$ 18.5 m

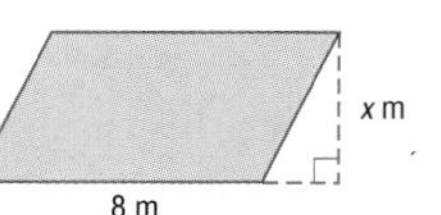

4B. $A = 357\text{ in}^2$ 21 in.

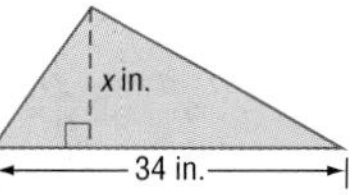

4C. ALGEBRA The base of a parallelogram is twice its height. If the area of the parallelogram is 72 square feet, find its base and height. $b = 12$ ft, $h = 6$ ft

782 | Lesson 11-1 | Areas of Parallelograms and Triangles

Check Your Understanding

 = Step-by-Step Solutions begin on page R14.

Examples 1–3 **Find the perimeter and area of each parallelogram or triangle. Round to the nearest tenth if necessary.**

1. 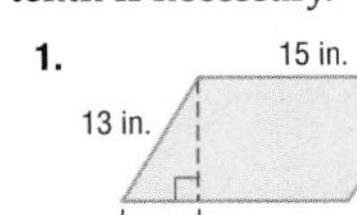

56 in., 180 in^2

2.  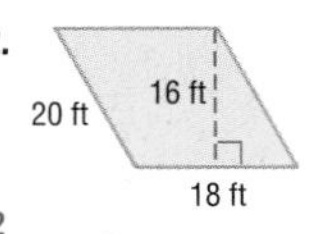

76 ft, 288 ft^2

3. 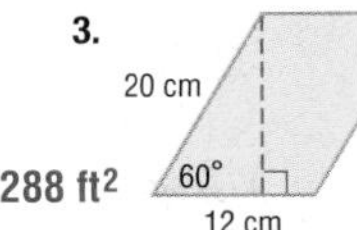

64 cm, 207.8 cm^2

4. 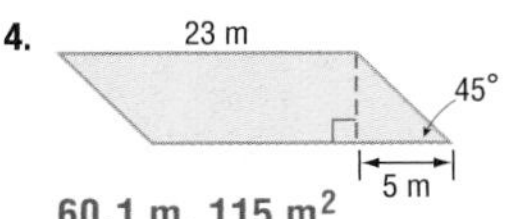

60.1 m, 115 m^2

5. 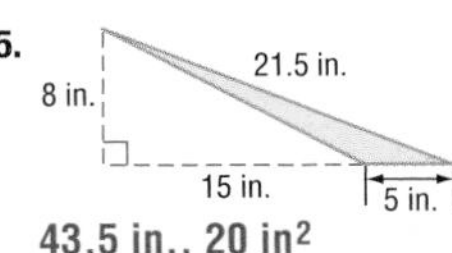

43.5 in., 20 in^2

6. 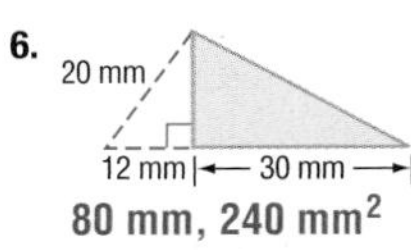

80 mm, 240 mm^2

7. **CRAFTS** Marquez and Victoria are making pinwheels. Each pinwheel is composed of 4 triangles with the dimensions shown. Find the perimeter and area of one triangle. **28.5 in., 33.8 in^2**

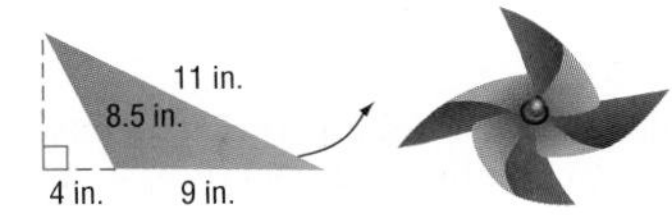

Example 4 **Find x.**

8. $A = 153$ in^2 **17 in.**
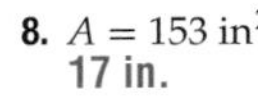 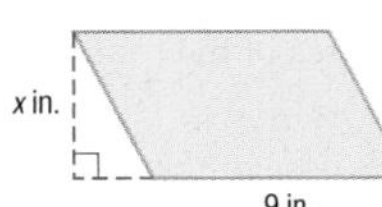

9. $A = 165$ cm^2 **11 cm**
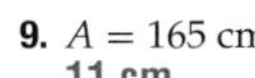 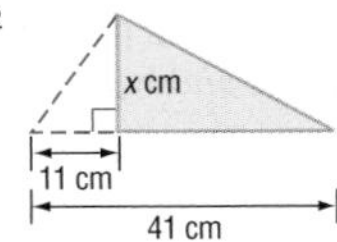

Practice and Problem Solving

Extra Practice is on page R11.

Examples 1–3 CCSS **STRUCTURE** **Find the perimeter and area of each parallelogram or triangle. Round to the nearest tenth if necessary.**

10. 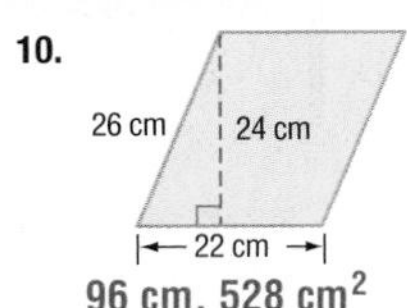

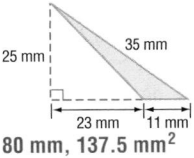

96 cm, 528 cm^2

11.  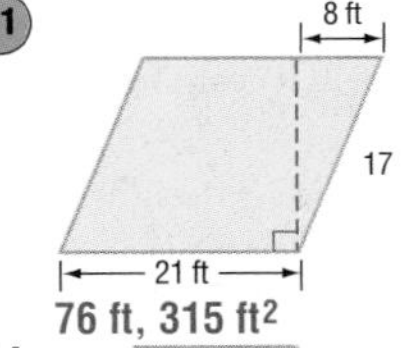 

76 ft, 315 ft^2

12. 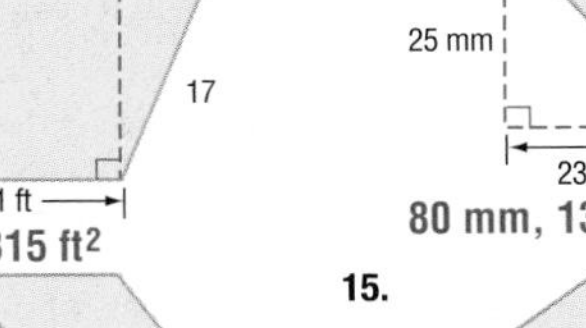

80 mm, 137.5 mm^2

13. 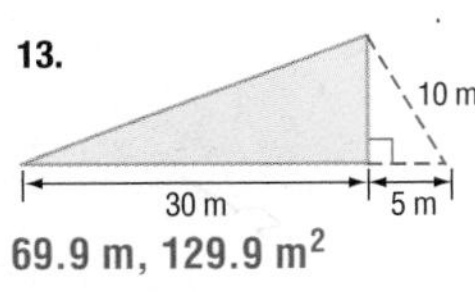

69.9 m, 129.9 m^2

14. 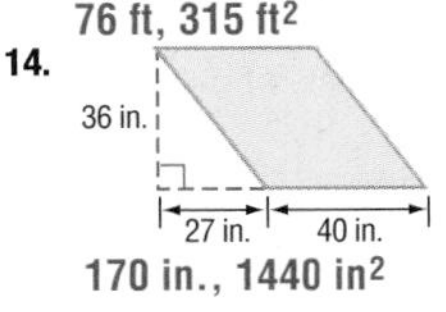

170 in., 1440 in^2

15. 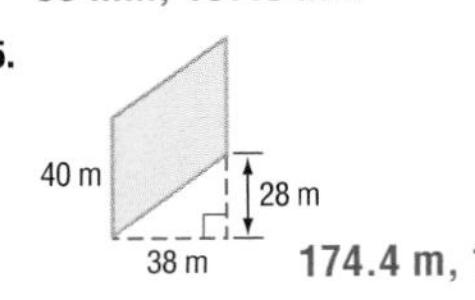

174.4 m, 1520 m^2

16. **TANGRAMS** The tangram shown is a 4-inch square.
    a. Find the perimeter and area of the purple triangle. Round to the nearest tenth. **9.7 in.; 4 in^2**
    b. Find the perimeter and area of the blue parallelogram. Round to the nearest tenth. **6.8 in.; 2 in^2**

4 in.
4 in.

3 Practice

Formative Assessment

Use Exercises 1–9 to check for understanding.

Use the chart at the bottom of this page to customize assignments for your students.

Teaching the Mathematical Practices

Structure Mathematically proficient students look closely to discern a pattern or structure. They also can step back for an overview and shift perspective. In Exercises 10–15, encourage students to make a plan for solving these problems.

Differentiated Homework Options

Level	Assignment	Two-Day Option	
AL Basic	10–27, 38–58	11–27 odd, 42–45	10–26 even, 38–41, 46–58
OL Core	11–27 odd, 28, 29–35 odd, 36, 38–58	10–27, 42–45	28–36, 38–41, 46–58
BL Advanced	28–53, (optional: 54–58)		

Study Guide and Intervention

AL OL ELL

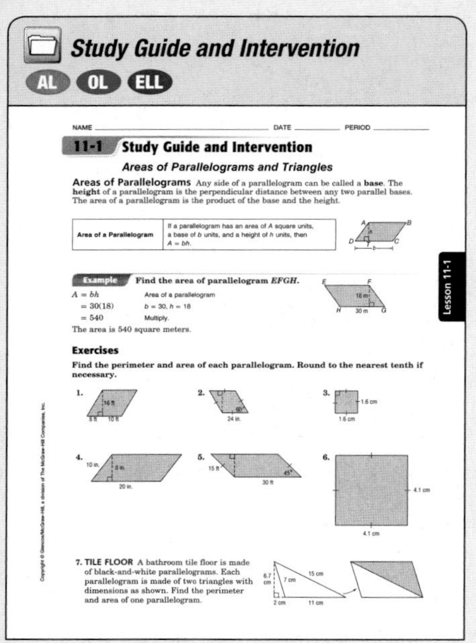

NAME ____________ DATE ________ PERIOD ________

11-1 Study Guide and Intervention

Areas of Parallelograms and Triangles

Areas of Parallelograms Any side of a parallelogram can be called a **base**. The **height** of a parallelogram is the perpendicular distance between any two parallel bases. The area of a parallelogram is the product of the base and the height.

Area of a Parallelogram	If a parallelogram has an area of A square units, a base of b units, and a height of h units, then $A = bh$.

Example Find the area of parallelogram $EFGH$.

$A = bh$ Area of a parallelogram
$= 30(18)$ $b = 30, h = 18$
$= 540$ Multiply.

The area is 540 square meters.

Exercises

Find the perimeter and area of each parallelogram. Round to the nearest tenth if necessary.

1. 2. 3. 4. 5. 6.

7. TILE FLOOR A bathroom tile floor is made of black-and-white parallelograms. Each parallelogram is made of two triangles with dimensions as shown. Find the perimeter and area of one parallelogram.

Practice

AL OL BL ELL

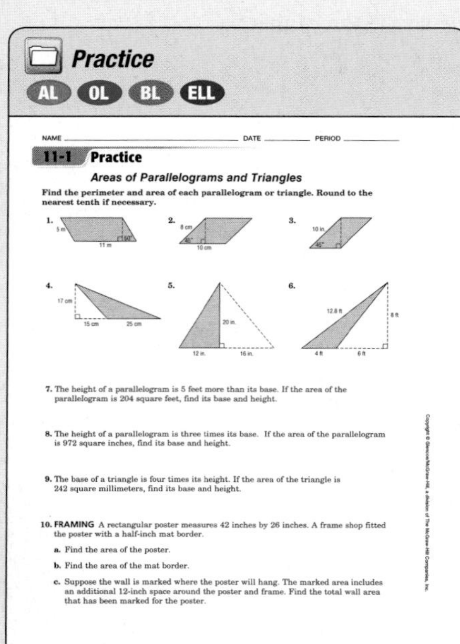

NAME ____________ DATE ________ PERIOD ________

11-1 Practice

Areas of Parallelograms and Triangles

Find the perimeter and area of each parallelogram or triangle. Round to the nearest tenth if necessary.

1. 2. 3. 4. 5. 6.

7. The height of a parallelogram is 5 feet more than its base. If the area of the parallelogram is 204 square feet, find its base and height.

8. The height of a parallelogram is three times its base. If the area of the parallelogram is 972 square inches, find its base and height.

9. The base of a triangle is four times its height. If the area of the triangle is 242 square millimeters, find its base and height.

10. FRAMING A rectangular poster measures 42 inches by 26 inches. A frame shop fitted the poster with a half-inch mat border.

a. Find the area of the poster.

b. Find the area of the mat border.

c. Suppose the wall is marked where the poster will hang. The marked area includes an additional 12-inch space around the poster and frame. Find the total wall area that has been marked for the poster.

Word Problem Practice

AL OL BL ELL

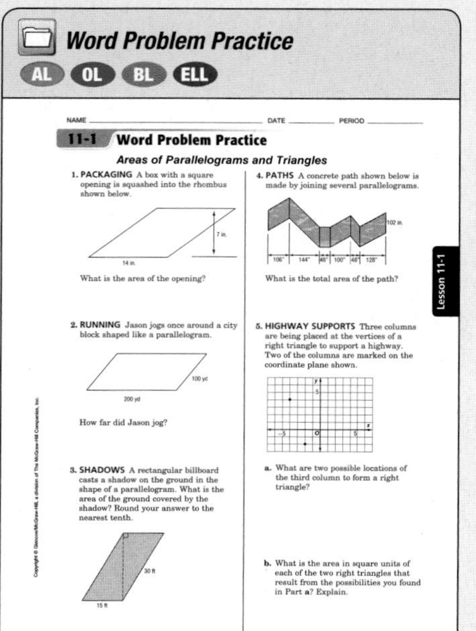

NAME ____________ DATE ________ PERIOD ________

11-1 Word Problem Practice

Areas of Parallelograms and Triangles

1. PACKAGING A box with a square opening is squashed into the rhombus shown below.

What is the area of the opening?

2. RUNNING Jason jogs once around a city block shaped like a parallelogram.

How far did Jason jog?

3. SHADOWS A rectangular billboard casts a shadow on the ground in the shape of a parallelogram. What is the area of the ground covered by the shadow? Round your answer to the nearest tenth.

4. PATHS A concrete path shown below is made by joining several parallelograms.

What is the total area of the path?

5. HIGHWAY SUPPORTS Three columns are being placed at the vertices of a right triangle to support a highway. Two of the columns are marked on the coordinate plane shown.

a. What are two possible locations of the third column to form a right triangle?

b. What is the area in square units of each of the two right triangles that result from the possibilities you found in Part a? Explain.

Example 2 CCSS STRUCTURE Find the area of each parallelogram. Round to the nearest tenth if necessary.

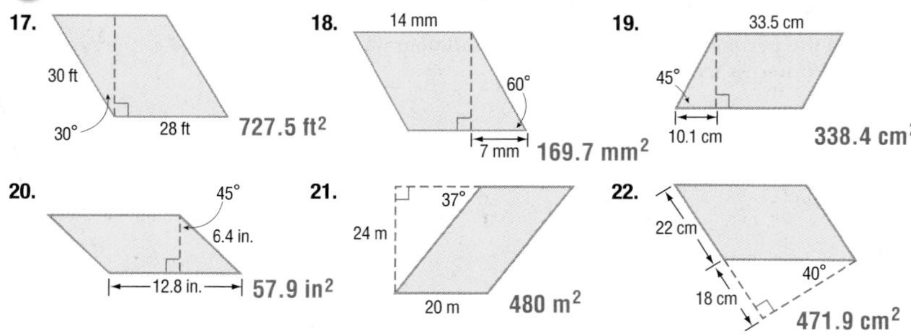

17. **727.5 ft²**
18. **169.7 mm²**
19. **338.4 cm²**
20. **57.9 in²**
21. **480 m²**

22. **471.9 cm²**

23. WEATHER Tornado watch areas are often shown on weather maps using parallelograms. What is the area of the region affected by the tornado watch shown? Round to the nearest square mile. **55,948 mi²**

Example 4

24. The height of a parallelogram is 4 millimeters more than its base. If the area of the parallelogram is 221 square millimeters, find its base and height. **b = 13 mm; h = 17 mm**

25. The height of a parallelogram is one fourth of its base. If the area of the parallelogram is 36 square centimeters, find its base and height. **b = 12 cm; h = 3 cm**

26. The base of a triangle is twice its height. If the area of the triangle is 49 square feet, find its base and height. **b = 14 ft; h = 7 ft**

27. The height of a triangle is 3 meters less than its base. If the area of the triangle is 44 square meters, find its base and height. **b = 11 m; h = 8 m**

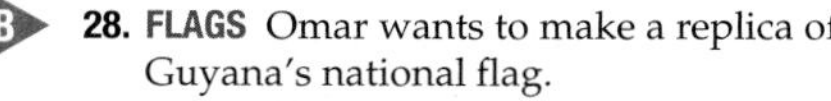

B 28. FLAGS Omar wants to make a replica of Guyana's national flag.

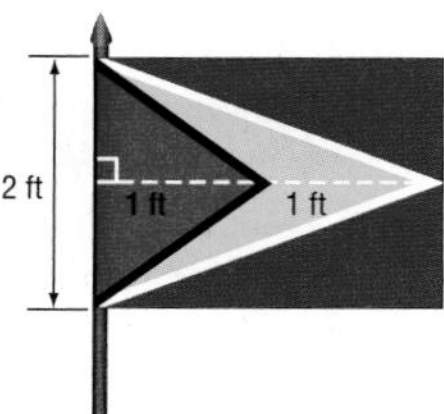

a. What is the area of the piece of fabric he will need for the red region? for the yellow region? **1 ft²; 1 ft²**

b. If the fabric costs $3.99 per square yard for each color and he buys exactly the amount of fabric he needs, how much will it cost to make the flag? **$1.77**

29. DRAMA Madison is in charge of the set design for her high school's rendition of *Romeo and Juliet*. One pint of paint covers 80 square feet. How many pints will she need of each color if the roof and tower each need 3 coats of paint? **1 pint of yellow, 3 pints of blue**

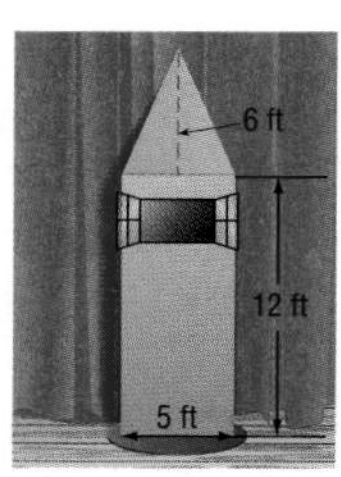

Find the perimeter and area of each figure. Round to the nearest hundredth, if necessary.

30. 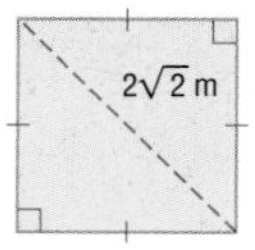 $2\sqrt{2}$ m **8 m; 4 m²**

31. 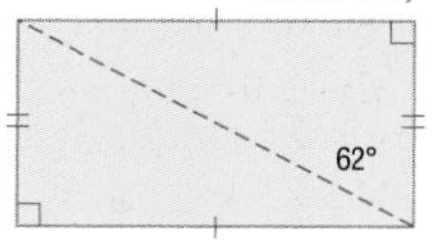 3 in. 62° **9.19 in.; 4.79 in²**

32. 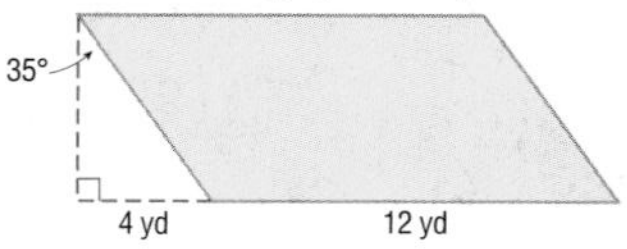 35° 4 yd 12 yd **37.95 yd; 68.55 yd²**

784 | Lesson 11-1 | Areas of Parallelograms and Triangles

Enrichment

OL BL

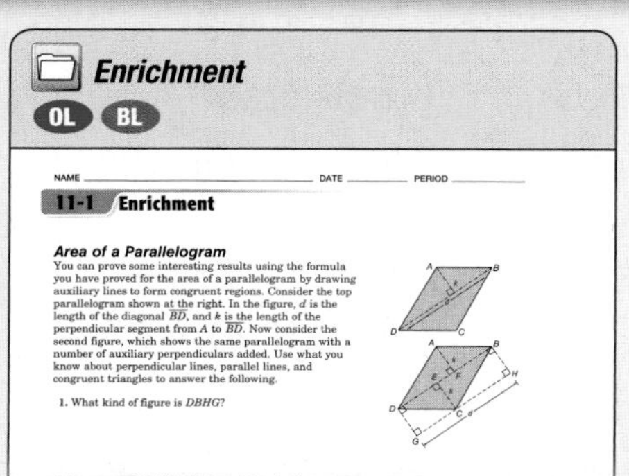

NAME ____________ DATE ________ PERIOD ________

11-1 Enrichment

Area of a Parallelogram

You can prove some interesting results using the formula you have proved for the area of a parallelogram by drawing auxiliary lines to form congruent regions. Consider the top parallelogram shown at the right. In the figure, d is the length of the diagonal $\overline{BD}$, and h is the length of the perpendicular segment from A to $\overline{BD}$. Now consider the second figure, which shows the same parallelogram with a number of auxiliary perpendiculars added. Use what you know about perpendicular lines, parallel lines, and congruent triangles to answer the following.

1. What kind of figure is $DBHG$?

2. If you moved $\triangle AFB$ to the lower-left end of figure $DBHG$, would it fit perfectly on top of $\triangle DGC$? Explain your answer.

CCSS Teaching the Mathematical Practices

Structure Mathematically proficient students look closely to discern a pattern or structure. They also can step back for an overview and shift perspective. In Exercises 17–22, encourage students to analyze each figure for special right triangles.

COORDINATE GEOMETRY **Find the area of each figure. Explain the method that you used.**

33. $\square ABCD$ with $A(4, 7)$, $B(2, 1)$, $C(8, 1)$, and $D(10, 7)$ **33. 36 units²; Graph the parallelogram, then measure the length of the base and the height and calculate the area.**

34. $\triangle RST$ with $R(-8, -2)$, $S(-2, -2)$, and $T(-3, -7)$ **34. 15 units²; Graph the triangle, then measure the length of the base and the height and calculate the area.**

35. **HERON'S FORMULA** Heron's Formula relates the lengths of the sides of a triangle to the area of the triangle. The formula is $A = \sqrt{s(s-a)(s-b)(s-c)}$, where s is the *semiperimeter*, or one half the perimeter, of the triangle and a, b, and c are the side lengths. **a–b. See Ch. 11 Answer Appendix.**

a. Use Heron's Formula to find the area of a triangle with side lengths 7, 10, and 4.

b. Show that the areas found for a 5-12-13 right triangle are the same using Heron's Formula and using the triangle area formula you learned earlier in this lesson.

36. **MULTIPLE REPRESENTATIONS** In this problem, you will investigate the relationship between the area and perimeter of a rectangle. **a–e. See margin.**

a. **Algebraic** A rectangle has a perimeter of 12 units. If the length of the rectangle is x and the width of the rectangle is y, write equations for the perimeter and area of the rectangle.

b. **Tabular** Tabulate all possible whole-number values for the length and width of the rectangle, and find the area for each pair.

c. **Graphical** Graph the area of the rectangle with respect to its length.

d. **Verbal** Describe how the area of the rectangle changes as its length changes.

e. **Analytical** For what whole-number values of length and width will the area be greatest? least? Explain your reasoning.

H.O.T. Problems Use Higher-Order Thinking Skills

37. **CHALLENGE** Find the area of $\triangle ABC$ graphed at the right. Explain your method. **See margin.**

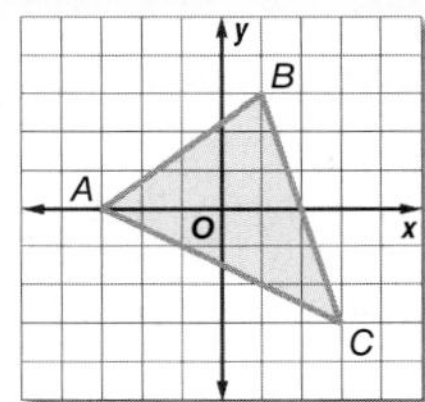

38. **ARGUMENTS** Will the perimeter of a nonrectangular parallelogram *always*, *sometimes*, or *never* be greater than the perimeter of a rectangle with the same area and the same height? Explain. **See Ch. 11 Answer Appendix.**

39–41. See Ch. 11 Answer Appendix.

39. **WRITING IN MATH** Points J and L lie on line m. Point K lies on line p. If lines m and p are parallel, describe how the area of $\triangle JKL$ will change as K moves along line p.

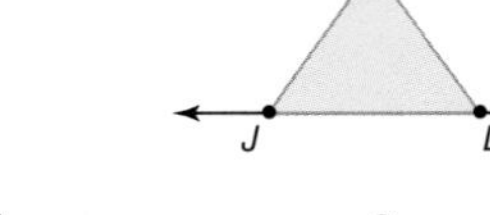

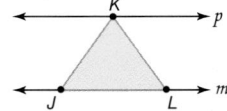

40. **OPEN ENDED** The area of a polygon is 35 square units. The height is 7 units. Draw three different triangles and three different parallelograms that meet these requirements. Label the base and height on each.

41. **WRITING IN MATH** Describe two different ways you could use measurement to find the area of parallelogram $PQRS$.

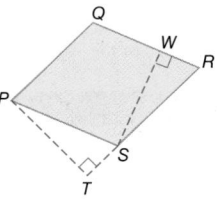

37. 15 units^2; Sample answer: I inscribed the triangle in a 6-by-6 square. I found the area of the square and subtracted the areas of the three right triangles inside the square that were positioned around the given triangle. The area of the given triangle is the difference, or 15 units^2.

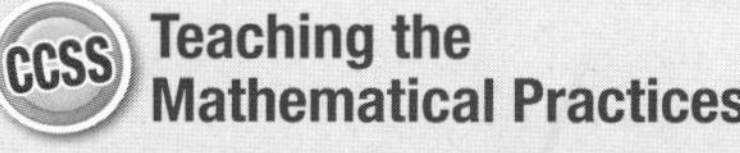

Multiple Representations

In Exercise 36 students use algebraic equations, a table, and a graph to investigate the relationship between the perimeter and the area of a rectangle.

CCSS Teaching the Mathematical Practices

Arguments Mathematically proficient students understand and use stated assumptions and definitions in constructing arguments. They make conjectures and build a logical progression of statements to explore the truth of their conjectures. In Exercise 38, encourage students to draw a diagram of the situation described.

Additional Answers

36a. $P = 2x + 2y$; $A = xy$

36b.

Length, x	Width, y	Area
1	5	5
2	4	8
3	3	9
4	2	8
5	1	5

36c.

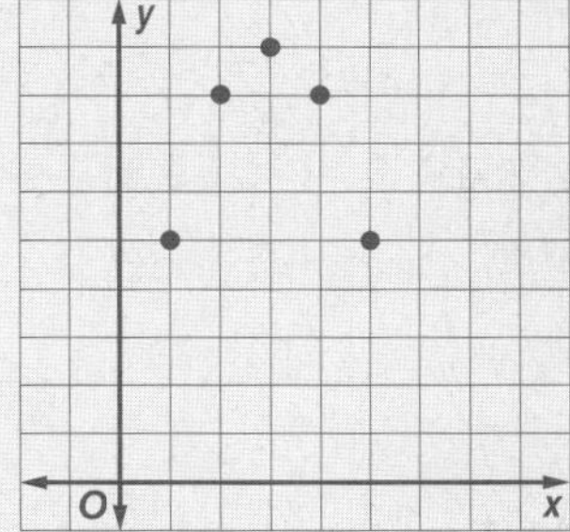

36d. Sample answer: The area increases as the length increases from 1 to 3, is highest at 3, then decreases as the length increases to 5.

36e. Sample answer: The graph reaches its highest point when $x = 3$, so the area of the rectangle will be greatest when the length is 3. The graph reaches its lowest points when $x = 1$ and 5, so the area of the rectangle will be the smallest when the length is 1 or 5.

4 Assess

Name the Math Have students describe how to find the area of a triangle.

Standardized Test Practice

42. What is the area, in square units, of the parallelogram shown? **C**

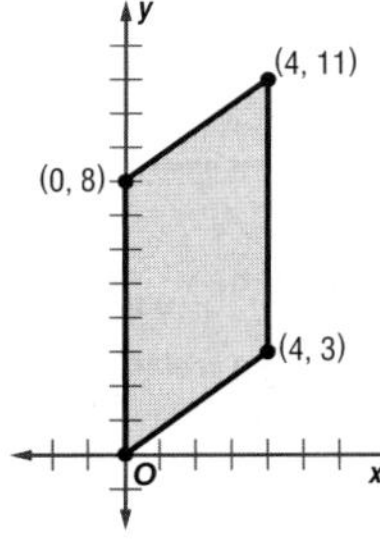

A 12
B 20
C 32
D 40

43. GRIDDED RESPONSE In parallelogram $ABCD$, $\overline{BD}$ and $\overline{AC}$ intersect at E. If $AE = 9$, $BE = 3x - 7$, and $DE = x + 5$, find x. **6**

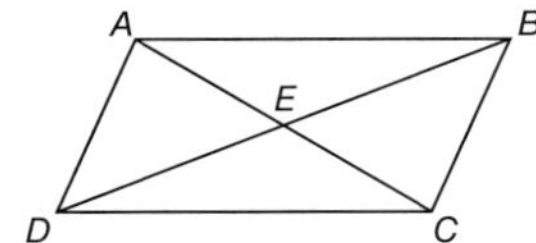

44. A wheelchair ramp is built that is 20 inches high and has a length of 12 feet as shown. What is the measure of the angle x that the ramp makes with the ground, to the *nearest* degree? **F**

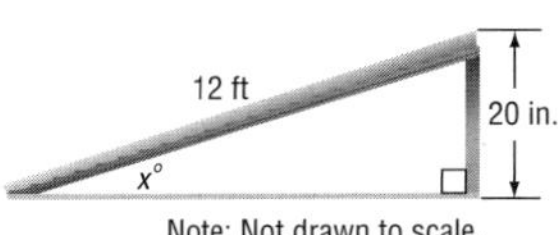

F 8
G 16
H 37
J 53

45. SAT/ACT The formula for converting a Celsius temperature to a Fahrenheit temperature is $F = \frac{9}{5}C + 32$, where F is the temperature in degrees Fahrenheit and C is the temperature in degrees Celsius. Which of the following is the Celsius equivalent to a temperature of 86° Fahrenheit? **B**

A 15.7° C
B 30° C
C 65.5° C
D 122.8° C
E 186.8° C

Spiral Review

Write the equation of each circle. (Lesson 10-8)

46. center at origin, $r = 3$ **$x^2 + y^2 = 9$**

47. center at origin, $d = 12$ **$x^2 + y^2 = 36$**

48. center at $(-3, -10)$, $d = 24$ **$(x + 3)^2 + (y + 10)^2 = 144$**

49. center at $(1, -4)$, $r = \sqrt{17}$ **$(x - 1)^2 + (y + 4)^2 = 17$**

Find x to the nearest tenth. Assume that segments that appear to be tangent are tangent. (Lesson 10-7)

50. **4**

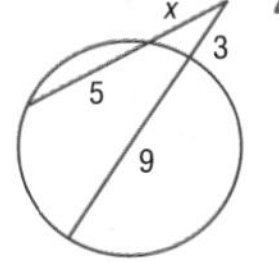

51. **5.6**

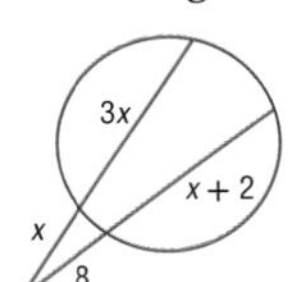

52. **6**

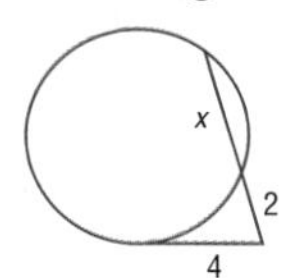

53. ARCHITECTURE The Louvre Pyramid is the main entrance to the Louvre Museum in Paris, France. The structure consists mainly of quadrilateral-shaped glass segments, as shown in the photo at the right. Describe one method that could be used to prove that the shapes of the segments are parallelograms. (Lesson 6-3)

53. Sample answer: If each pair of opposite sides is parallel, the quadrilateral is a parallelogram.

Skills Review

Evaluate each expression if $a = 2$, $b = 6$, and $c = 3$.

54. $\frac{1}{2}ac$ **3**

55. $\frac{1}{2}cb$ **9**

56. $\frac{1}{2}b(2a + c)$ **21**

57. $\frac{1}{2}c(b + a)$ **12**

58. $\frac{1}{2}a(2c + b)$ **12**

Differentiated Instruction OL BL

Extension Point out that each parallelogram has two altitudes. Ask each student to write a paragraph demonstrating why you do not use both altitudes to get the area of the parallelogram. Check students' work.

EXPLORE 11-2 Graphing Technology Lab: Areas of Trapezoids, Rhombi, and Kites

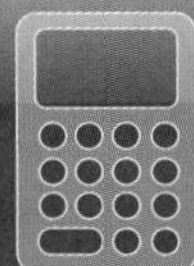

You can use the TI-Nspire Technology to explore special quadrilaterals.

CCSS Common Core State Standards
Content Standards
Preparation for G.MG.3 Apply geometric methods to solve problems (e.g., designing an object or structure to satisfy physical constraints or minimize cost; working with typographic grid systems based on ratios). ★
Mathematical Practices 5

PT

Activity 1

Step 1 Open a new **Graphs** page. Select **Show Grid** from the **View** menu so that points can be placed at integer coordinates.

Step 2 Select **Line** from the **Points & Lines** menu, and draw a horizontal line.

Step 3 Select **Parallel** from the **Construction** menu to draw a line parallel to your original line through a point with the same *x*-coordinate as a point in Step 2.

Step 4 Place an additional point on the parallel line you just constructed using **Point on** from the **Points & Lines** menu. Label the four points as shown.

Step 5 From the **Shapes** menu, select **Polygon**, and draw a polygon using the four points you created. From the **Actions** menu, select **Attributes**, select the polygon, and increase the line thickness of the polygon.

Step 6 Display the area of the polygon using the **Area** tool from the **Measurement** menu. Move each of the points and observe the effect on the area.

Step 1:

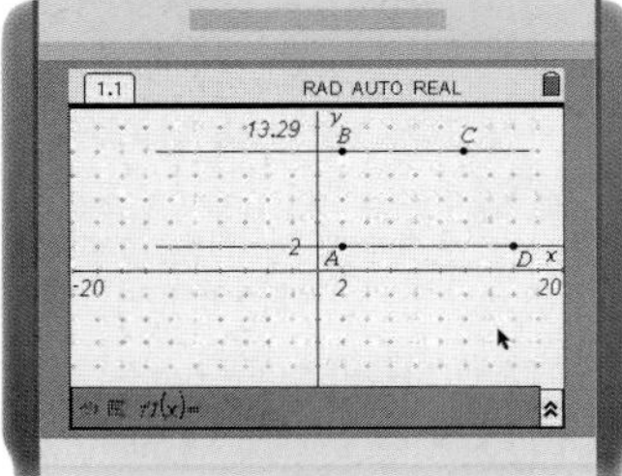

Step 5:

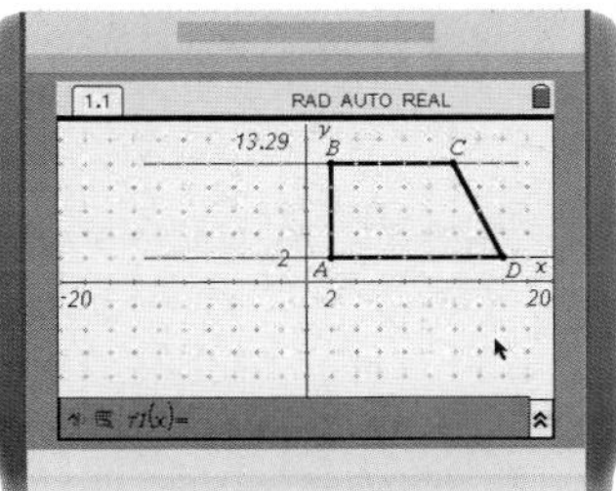

Step 6:

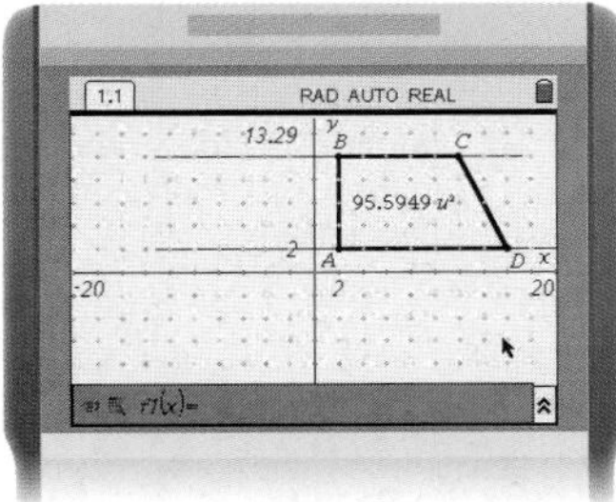

Analyze the Results

1. What type of quadrilateral is *ABCD*? Explain your reasoning. **1–2. See margin.**
2. **MAKE A CONJECTURE** Using the formulas you learned in Lesson 11-1, make a conjecture about the formula for the area of this type of quadrilateral if *BC* is b_1, *AD* is b_2, and *AB* is *h*. Explain.

(continued on the next page)

1 Focus

Objective Investigate the areas of polygons using the TI-Nspire Technology.

Materials
- TI-Nspire Technology

2 Teach

Students can work alone, or in pairs. Have them complete Activity 1 and Activity 2.

Activity 1

Ask:
- Into what two shapes can this quadrilateral as shown be divided? a right triangle and a parallelogram, which can be more precisely classified as a rectangle
- Move points *B* and *C* each the same number of units to the left along line *BC*. How are the two shapes that make up the figure affected? The right triangle becomes obtuse and the parallelogram can no longer be classified as a rectangle.
- What affect does this have on the area of the figure? Explain. The area remains constant. The base and height of the parallelogram and of the triangle that make up the figure, remain the same. Since these measures are used to calculate the areas of these figures, the total area of the figure will remain unchanged.

Additional Answers

1. Sample answer: Since exactly one pair of the sides of the quadrilateral is parallel, it is a trapezoid.
2. Sample answer: Divide the figure into a rectangle and a triangle and use the area formulas for each figure.

$$A = b_1h + \frac{1}{2}(b_2 - b_1)h$$
$$2A = 2b_1h + (b_2 - b_1)h$$
$$2A = 2b_1h + b_2h - b_1h$$
$$2A = h(2b_1 + b_2 - b_1)$$
$$2A = h(b_1 + b_2)$$
$$A = \frac{1}{2}h(b_1 + b_2)$$

Activity 2

Ask:

- In Activity 2, what happens when you drag *W* along the line? The area increases or decreases.
- Why does the area change? Moving *W* changes the length of a base. The area is determined by the altitude, which stays the same, and the length of the base, which can change.

Practice Have students complete Exercises 1–5.

3 Assess

Formative Assessment

Have students write responses to the questions in each activity to assess if students comprehend what they have learned about area.

From Concrete to Abstract

Allow students to verify the area formulas for a triangle, trapezoid, and rhombus by cutting the shapes out of paper. Encourage them to show how the formulas can be derived from other polygons.

Ask:

- If a rhombus has an area of 25 units^2 and one diagonal is 5 units long, what is the measure of the other diagonal? 10 units

Additional Answers

3. Sample answer: Since the diagonals are perpendicular, and pairs of adjacent sides are congruent, the quadrilateral is a kite.
4. Sample answer: Divide the figure into two triangles and use the area formula for a triangle. $\overline{WY}$ bisects $\overline{XZ}$.

$$A = \frac{1}{2}d_1\left(\frac{1}{2}d_2\right) + \frac{1}{2}d_1\left(\frac{1}{2}d_2\right)$$

$$A = \frac{1}{4}d_1 d_2 + \frac{1}{4}d_1 d_2$$

$$A = \frac{1}{2}d_1 d_2$$

Graphing Technology Lab
Areas of Trapezoids, Rhombi, and Kites *Continued*

Activity 2

Step 1 Open a new **Graphs** page. Select **Show Grid** from the **View** menu so that points can be placed at integer coordinates.

Step 2 Select **Line** from the **Points & Lines** menu, and draw a line.

Step 3 Place a point above the line by selecting **Point** from the **Points & Lines** menu.

Step 4 Reflect the point above the line by choosing **Reflection** from the **Transformation** menu, then select the point and then the line.

Step 1:

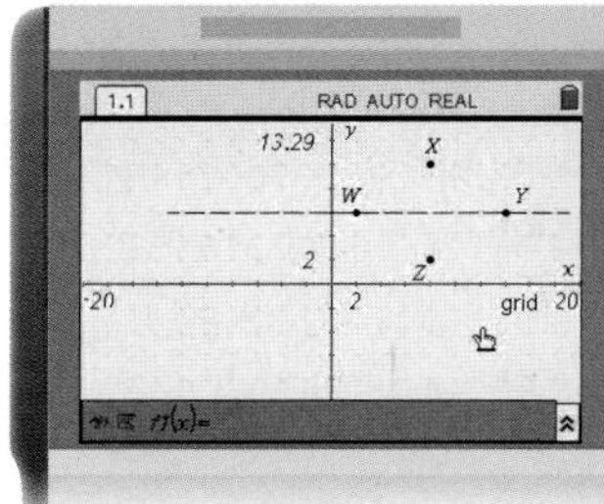

Step 5 Label the four points as shown.

Step 6 From the **Shapes** menu, select **Polygon**, and draw a polygon using points *W*, *X*, *Y*, and *Z*.

Step 7 Display the area of the polygon using the **Area** tool from the **Measurement** menu. Move points *W*, *X*, and *Y*, and observe the effect on the area.

Step 6:

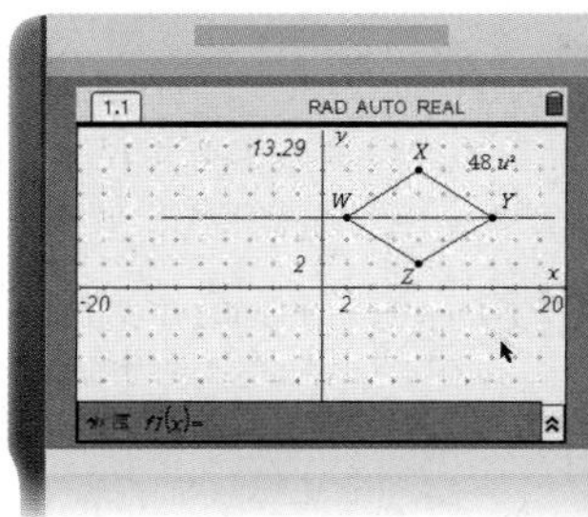

Step 8 Select **Segment** from the **Points & Lines** menu to draw the diagonals of *WXYZ*.

Step 9 Display the lengths of the diagonals using the **Length** tool from the **Measurement** menu, and display the angle between the diagonals using the **Angle** tool. Continue to move points *W*, *X*, and *Y*, and observe the effect on the area and the angle between the diagonals.

Step 8:

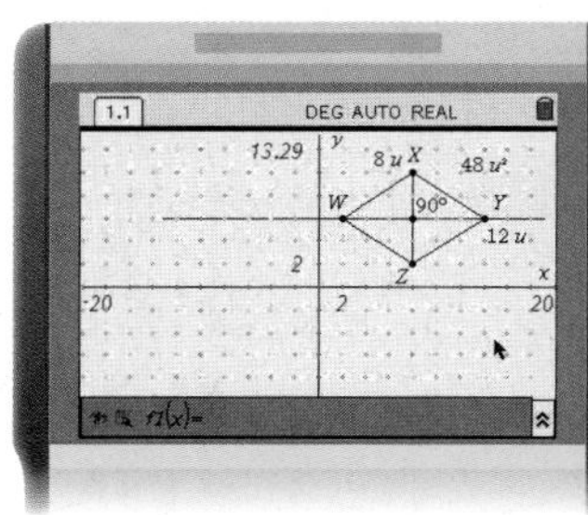

Analyze the Results

3. What type of quadrilateral is *WXYZ*? Explain your reasoning. **3–5. See margin.**
4. **MAKE A CONJECTURE** Using the formulas you learned in Lesson 11-1, develop a formula for the area of this type of quadrilateral. Let *WY* be d_1, and let *XZ* be d_2. Explain your reasoning.
5. **CHALLENGE** Construct a quadrilateral using two perpendicular lines and reflecting a point on each as you did in Step 4 of Activity 2. What type of quadrilateral is formed? Does the formula for the area you developed in Exercise 4 apply?

5. Sample answer:

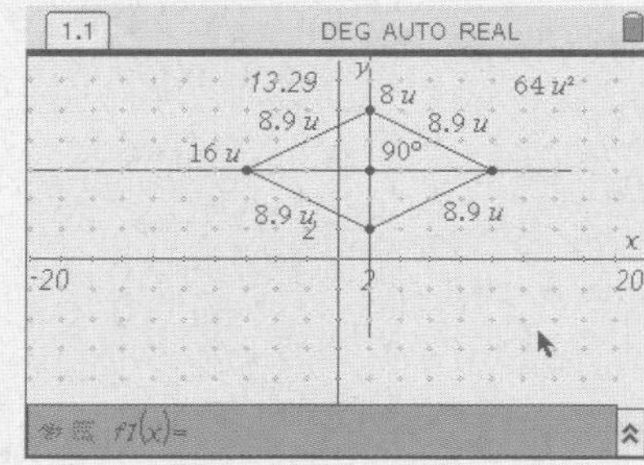

The quadrilateral is a rhombus since all four of the sides are congruent and the diagonals are perpendicular. The formula developed in Exercise 4 does apply, because $\frac{1}{2}d_1 d_2 = \frac{1}{2}(9.7996)(5.8505) \approx 28.67$, which is the area of the quadrilateral.

LESSON 11-2 Areas of Trapezoids, Rhombi, and Kites

Then

- You found areas of triangles and parallelograms.

Now

1. Find areas of trapezoids.
2. Find areas of rhombi and kites.

Why?

- Brianna has turned her hobby of making designer handbags and totes into a small business. Among her designs is a trapezoid-shaped handbag. To estimate the amount of material needed to produce each handbag, she needs to calculate the area of a trapezoid.

NewVocabulary
height of a trapezoid

Common Core State Standards

Content Standards
G.MG.3 Apply geometric methods to solve problems (e.g., designing an object or structure to satisfy physical constraints or minimize cost; working with typographic grid systems based on ratios). ★

Mathematical Practices
1 Make sense of problems and persevere in solving them.
7 Look for and make use of structure.

1 Areas of Trapezoids

In Lesson 6-6, you learned that a *trapezoid* is a quadrilateral with exactly one pair of parallel sides. These parallel sides are called *bases*. The **height of a trapezoid** is the perpendicular distance between its bases.

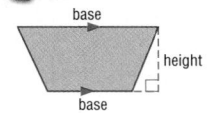

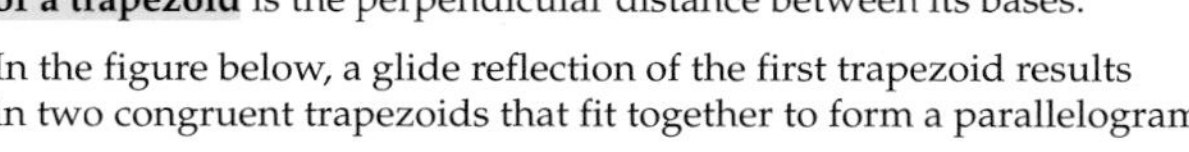

In the figure below, a glide reflection of the first trapezoid results in two congruent trapezoids that fit together to form a parallelogram.

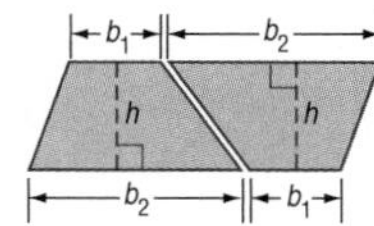

The area of the parallelogram is the product of the height h and the sum of the two bases, b_1 and b_2. The area of one trapezoid is one half the area of the parallelogram.

KeyConcept Area of a Trapezoid

Words The area A of a trapezoid is one half the product of the height h and the sum of its bases, b_1 and b_2.

Symbols $A = \frac{1}{2}h(b_1 + b_2)$

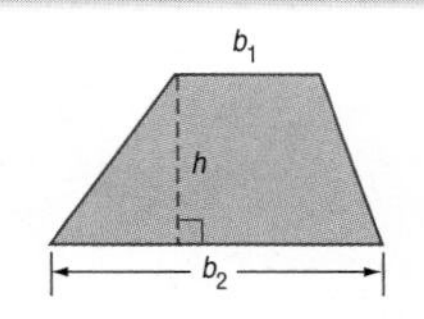

Real-World Example 1 Area of a Trapezoid

CRAFTS One of Brianna's trapezoid-shaped totes is shown. Find the amount of material used to make the side shown.

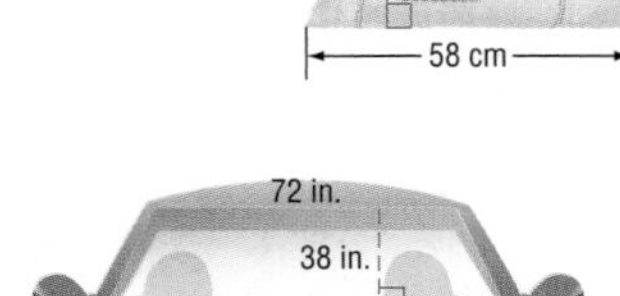

$A = \frac{1}{2}h(b_1 + b_2)$ Area of a trapezoid

$= \frac{1}{2}(30)(28 + 58)$ $h = 30, b_1 = 28, b_2 = 58$

$= 1290$ Simplify.

The tote requires 1290 square centimeters.

GuidedPractice

1. **AUTOMOBILES** Find the area of glass used to make the windshield of a van shown at the right. **2983 in²**

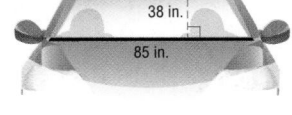

1 Focus

VerticalAlignment

Before Lesson 11-2 Find the areas of parallelograms and triangles.

Lesson 11-2 Find the areas of trapezoids, rhombi, and kites.

After Lesson 11-2 Find areas of regular polygons and circles.

2 Teach

Scaffolding Questions

Have students read the **Why?** section of the lesson.

Ask:

- What other shapes are common for handbags? Sample answers: squares, rectangles
- What could be an advantage of a trapezoid-shaped handbag? Sample statement: It has a wide opening.
- What would be a simple way to make an upper estimate for the area of the trapezoid? Sample statement: Find the area of a rectangle that has the same height and the width equal to the longer base of the trapezoid.

Lesson 11-2 Resources

Resource	Approaching Level AL	On Level OL	Beyond Level BL	English Learners ELL
Teacher Edition	▪ Differentiated Instruction, p. 791	▪ Differentiated Instruction, pp. 791, 792, 796	▪ Differentiated Instruction, pp. 791, 792, 796	▪ Differentiated Instruction, p. 791
Chapter Resource Masters	▪ Study Guide and Intervention, pp. 13–14 ▪ Skills Practice, p. 15 ▪ Practice, p. 16 ▪ Word Problem Practice, p. 17	▪ Study Guide and Intervention, pp. 13–14 ▪ Skills Practice, p. 15 ▪ Practice, p. 16 ▪ Word Problem Practice, p. 17 ▪ Enrichment, p. 18	▪ Practice, p. 16 ▪ Word Problem Practice, p. 17 ▪ Enrichment, p. 18	▪ Study Guide and Intervention, pp. 13–14 ▪ Skills Practice, p. 15 ▪ Practice, p. 16 ▪ Word Problem Practice, p. 17
Other	▪ 5-Minute Check 11-2 ▪ Study Notebook	▪ 5-Minute Check 11-2 ▪ Study Notebook	▪ 5-Minute Check 11-2 ▪ Study Notebook	▪ 5-Minute Check 11-2 ▪ Study Notebook

1 Areas of Trapezoids

Examples 1 and 2 show how to find the area of a trapezoid.

Formative Assessment

Use the Guided Practice exercises after each example to determine students' understanding of concepts.

Additional Examples

1 **SHAVING** Find the area of steel used to make the razor blade shown below.

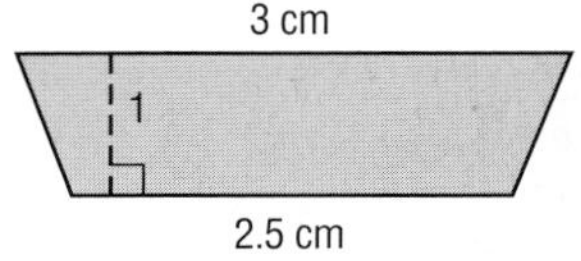

2.75 cm^2

2 **OPEN ENDED** Miguel designed a deck shaped like the trapezoid shown below. Find the area of the deck.

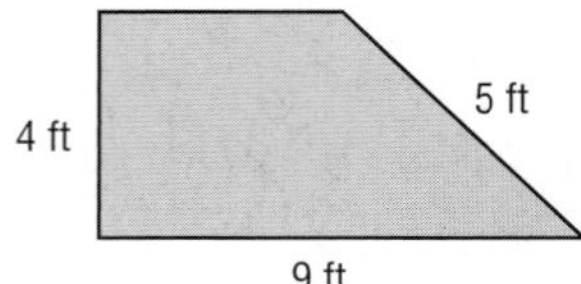

30 ft^2

Additional Examples also in Interactive Classroom PowerPoint® Presentations

Standardized Test Example 2 Area of a Trapezoid

SHORT RESPONSE Emelia designed the pennant shown for her team. Find the area of the shaded portion of her team's pennant.

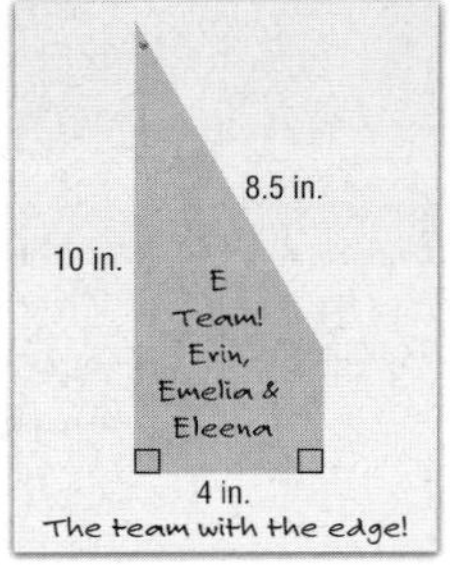

Read the Test Item

You are given a trapezoid with one base measuring 10 inches, a height of 4 inches, and a third side measuring 8.5 inches. To find the area of the trapezoid, first find the measure of the other base.

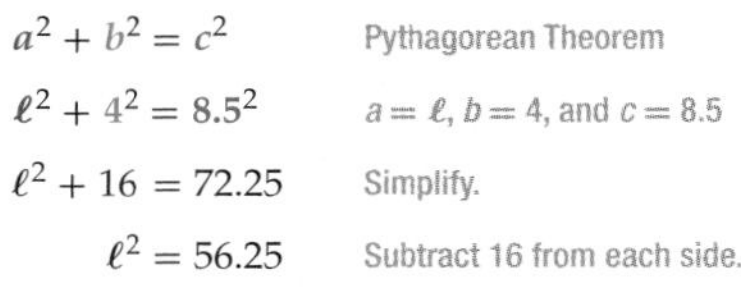

Solve the Test Item

Draw the segment shown to form a right triangle and a rectangle. The triangle has a hypotenuse of 8.5 inches and legs of 4 and ℓ inches. The rectangle has a length of 4 inches and a width of x inches.

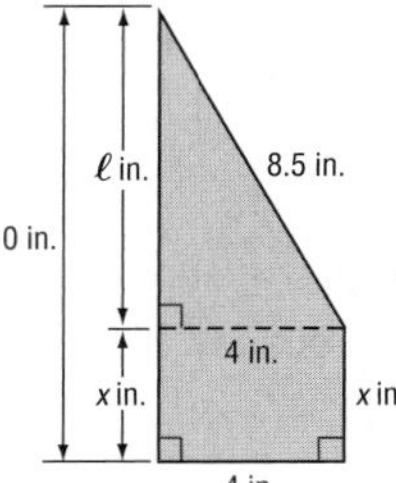

Use the Pythagorean Theorem to find ℓ.

$a^2 + b^2 = c^2$	Pythagorean Theorem
$\ell^2 + 4^2 = 8.5^2$	$a = \ell$, $b = 4$, and $c = 8.5$
$\ell^2 + 16 = 72.25$	Simplify.
$\ell^2 = 56.25$	Subtract 16 from each side.
$\ell = 7.5$	Take the positive square root of each side.

By Segment Addition, $\ell + x = 10$. So, $7.5 + x = 10$ and $x = 2.5$. The width of the rectangle is also the measure of the second base of the trapezoid.

$A = \frac{1}{2}h(b_1 + b_2)$	Area of a trapezoid
$= \frac{1}{2}(4)(10 + 2.5)$	$h = 4$, $b_1 = 10$, and $b_2 = 2.5$
$= 25$	Simplify.

So the pennant has an area of 25 square inches.

CHECK The area of the trapezoid is the sum of the areas of the right triangle and rectangle. The area of the triangle is $\frac{1}{2}(4)(7.5)$ or 15 square inches. The area of the rectangle is (4)(2.5) or 10 square inches. So the area of the trapezoid is 15 + 10 or 25 square inches. ✓

Real-WorldCareer

Craft Artist Craft artists create their art by hand to sell or exhibit. They work with a wide variety of materials including textiles, woods, metal, and ceramics.

Most artists receive some type of postsecondary training, and about 63% are self-employed. Craft artists make up about 3% of all artists.

GuidedPractice

2. SHORT RESPONSE Owen designed the silver earrings shown that are shaped like isosceles trapezoids. What is the area of each earring? **8.5 cm^2**

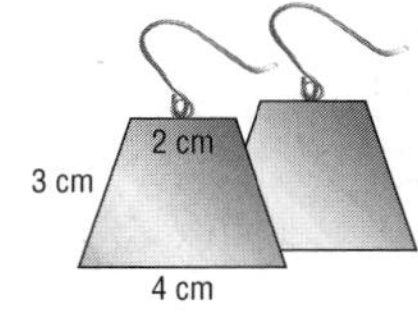

WatchOut!

Identifying Height The height of a trapezoid is the perpendicular between its bases. Depending on the orientation of the trapezoid, the height may not be a vertical distance.

2 Areas of Rhombi and Kites

Areas of Rhombi and Kites Recall from Lessons 6-5 and 6-6 that a *rhombus* is a parallelogram with all four sides congruent and a *kite* is a quadrilateral with exactly two pairs of consecutive congruent sides.

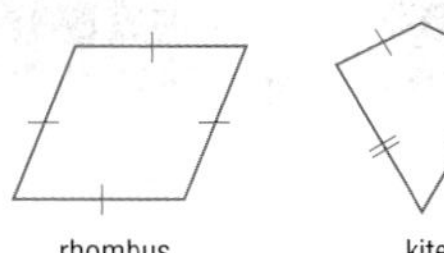

ReviewVocabulary

diagonal a segment that connects any two nonconsecutive vertices in a polygon

The areas of rhombi and kites are related to the lengths of their diagonals.

KeyConcept Area of a Rhombus or Kite

Words The area A of a rhombus or kite is one half the product of the lengths of its diagonals, d_1 and d_2.

Symbols $A = \frac{1}{2}d_1d_2$

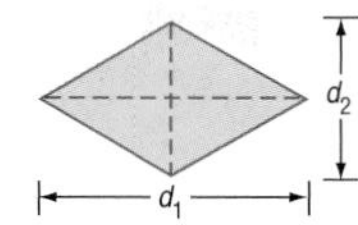
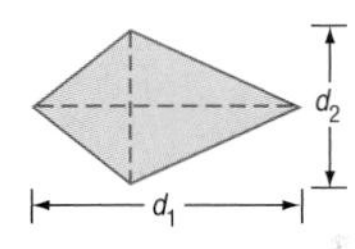

You will derive the formulas for the area of a kite and the area of a rhombus in Exercises 23 and 24.

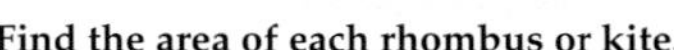

Example 3 Area of a Rhombus and a Kite

Find the area of each rhombus or kite.

a.

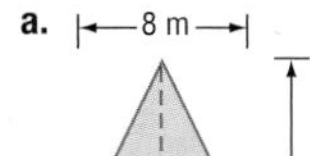

$A = \frac{1}{2}d_1d_2$ Area of a kite

$= \frac{1}{2}(8)(15)$ $d_1 = 8$ and $d_2 = 15$

$= 60 \text{ m}^2$ Simplify.

b.

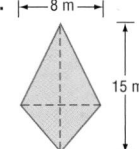

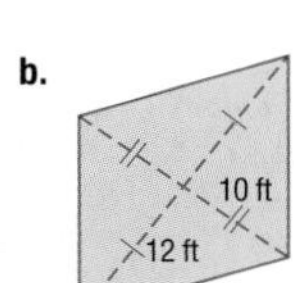

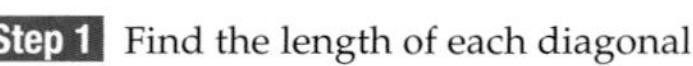

Step 1 Find the length of each diagonal.

Since the diagonals of a rhombus bisect each other, then lengths of the diagonals are 12 + 12 or 24 feet and 10 + 10 or 20 feet.

Step 2 Find the area of the rhombus.

$A = \frac{1}{2}d_1d_2$ Area of a rhombus

$= \frac{1}{2}(24)(20)$ $d_1 = 24$ and $d_2 = 20$

$= 240 \text{ ft}^2$ Simplify.

GuidedPractice

Find the area of each rhombus or kite.

3A. 84 mm²

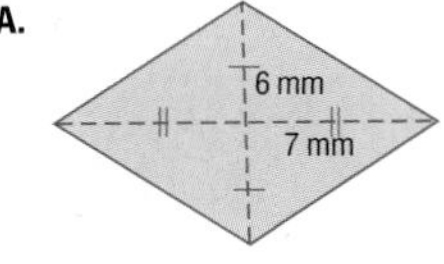

3B. 72 in²

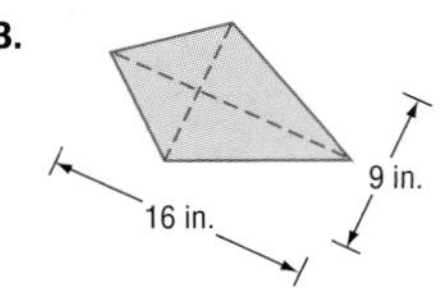

Math HistoryLink

Heron of Alexandria (c. 10–70 A.D.) Heron was a mathematician and engineer in Roman Egypt. He developed a formula for finding the area of a triangle if the lengths of the sides are known.

You can use algebra to solve for unknown measures in trapezoids, rhombi, and kites.

2 Areas of Rhombi and Kites

Example 3 shows how to find the areas of a rhombus and a kite. **Example 4** shows how to find a missing measure of a rhombus, given its area.

Additional Example

3 Find the area of each rhombus or kite.

a.

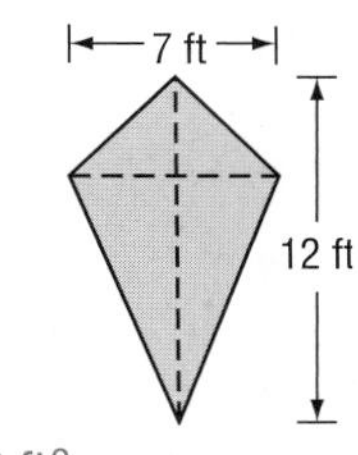

42 ft²

b.

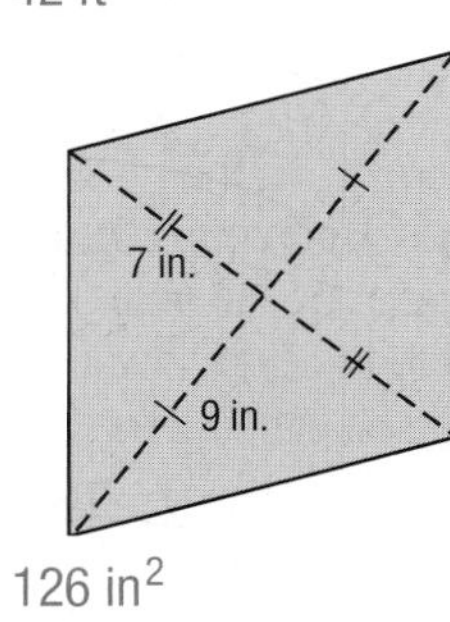

126 in²

Focus on Mathematical Content

Rhombi In Chapter 6, students learned that if a parallelogram has all sides congruent, it is a rhombus. In this lesson, emphasize that the diagonals—rather than the base and height—are used to find the area of a rhombus.

DifferentiatedInstruction AL OL BL ELL

Visual/Spatial Learners Stress that in some triangles, one side seems to be an altitude. This is not true unless the triangle is a right triangle, in which the legs are perpendicular. Students should not assume that angles are right angles unless they are clearly marked.

Additional Example

4 **ALGEBRA** One diagonal of a rhombus is half as long as the other diagonal. If the area of the rhombus is 64 square inches, what are the lengths of the diagonals? *US* = 16 in.; *RT* = 8

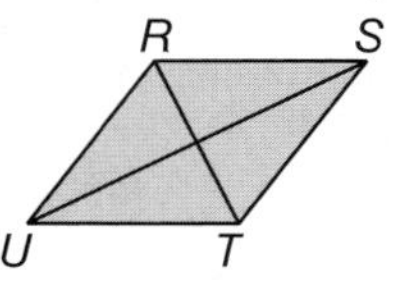

Teach with Tech

Portable Media Player Create image files of trapezoids, rhombi, and kites and the formulas for their volumes. Post the files on your class Web page for students to load onto their portable media players. Have them use these as "flashcards" to help them remember the formulas.

Follow-up

Students have explored the formulas for the areas of parallelograms, triangles, trapezoids, rhombi, and kites.

Ask:

- How are the area formulas for polygons related? Sample answer: The formula for the area of a parallelogram can be used to derive the formulas for the areas of other polygons.

Example 4 Use Area to Find Missing Measures

ALGEBRA **One diagonal of a rhombus is twice as long as the other diagonal. If the area of the rhombus is 169 square millimeters, what are the lengths of the diagonals?**

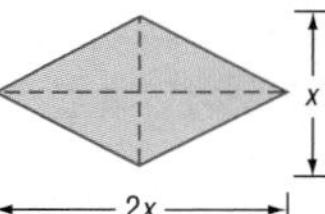

Step 1 Write an expression to represent each measure.

Let x represent the length of one diagonal. Then the length of the other diagonal is $2x$.

Step 2 Use the formula for the area of a rhombus to find x.

$A = \frac{1}{2}d_1d_2$ — Area of a rhombus

$169 = \frac{1}{2}(x)(2x)$ — $A = 169$, $d_1 = x$, and $d_2 = 2x$

$169 = x^2$ — Simplify.

$13 = x$ — Take the positive square root of each side.

So the lengths of the diagonals are 13 millimeters and 2(13) or 26 millimeters.

StudyTip
Kites Recall from Lesson 6-6 that the diagonals of kites are perpendicular.

GuidedPractice

ALGEBRA **Find x.**

4A. $A = 92 \text{ in}^2$ 8.4 in.

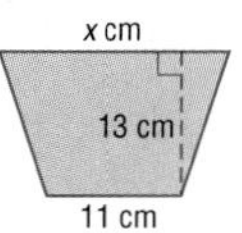

4B. $A = 177 \text{ cm}^2$ 16.2 cm

4C. **ALGEBRA** What is the area of the kite shown? 168 in^2

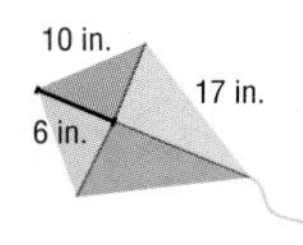

ConceptSummary Areas of Polygons

Parallelogram	Triangles	Trapezoids	Rhombi and Kites
$A = bh$	$A = \frac{1}{2}bh$	$A = \frac{1}{2}h(b_1 + b_2)$	$A = \frac{1}{2}d_1d_2$

DifferentiatedInstruction OL BL

Extension Draw on students' prior knowledge by having them create a blueprint of their kitchen including the bases of all structures. Ask students to include a scale. Use these drawings to have students estimate the number of tiles that would be needed to cover the floor. Varying the size of the tile is an easy way to differentiate this task for different ability levels. This task enables students to view area as something that is not always neat and formulaic.

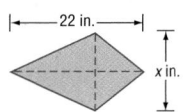

Check Your Understanding

= Step-by-Step Solutions begin on page R14.

Examples 1–3 Find the area of each trapezoid, rhombus, or kite.

1. 132 ft²

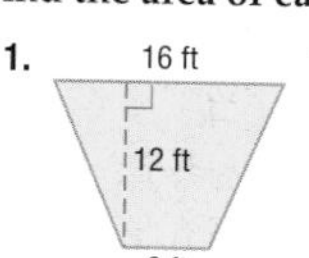

2. 90 m²

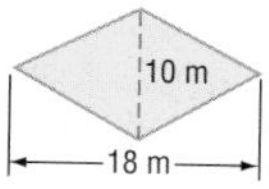

3. 178.5 m²

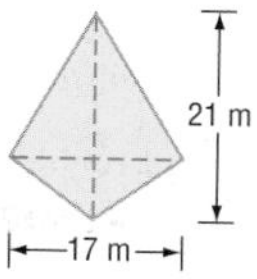

4. SHORT RESPONSE Suki is doing fashion design at 4-H Club. Her first project is to make a simple A-line skirt. How much fabric will she need according to the design at the right? $8\frac{3}{4}$ ft²

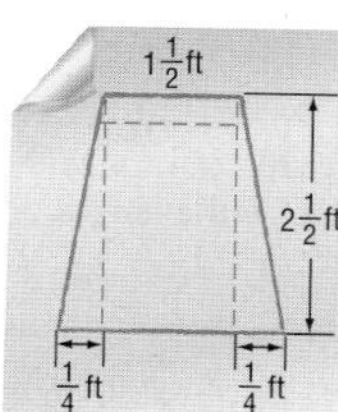

Example 4 ALGEBRA Find x.

5. $A = 78\text{ cm}^2$ 8 cm

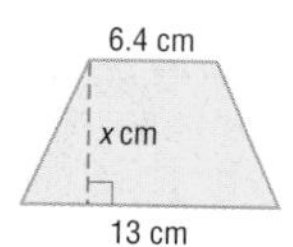

6. $A = 96\text{ in}^2$ 6.6 in.

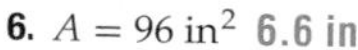
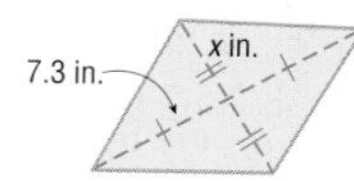

7. $A = 104\text{ ft}^2$ 6.3 ft

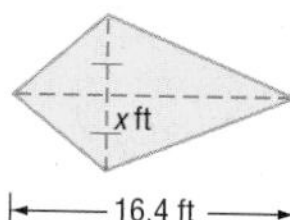

Practice and Problem Solving

Extra Practice is on page R11.

Examples 1–3 CCSS STRUCTURE Find the area of each trapezoid, rhombus, or kite. 8–13. See margin.

8.

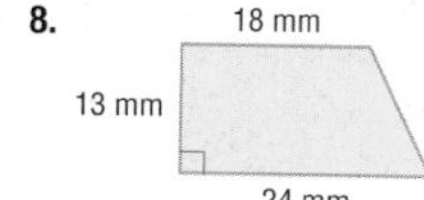

9.

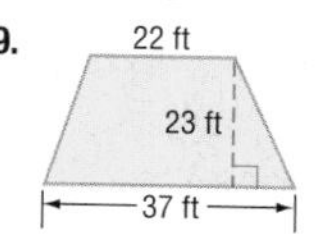

10.

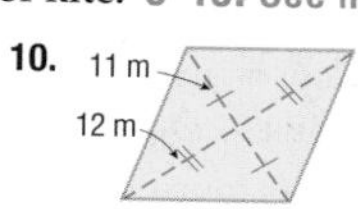

11.

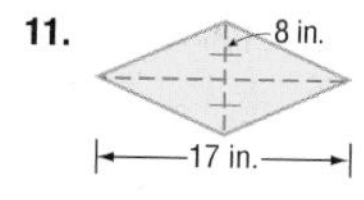

12.

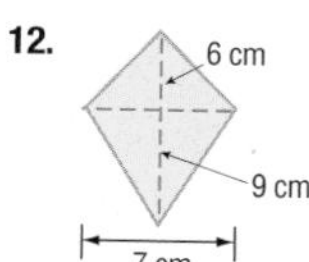

13.

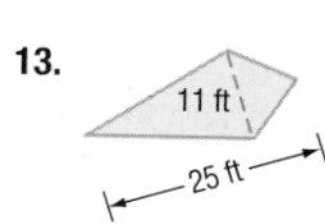

MICROSCOPES Find the area of the identified portion of each magnified image. Assume that the identified portion is either a trapezoid, rhombus, or kite. Measures are provided in microns. 14–16. See margin.

14. human skin

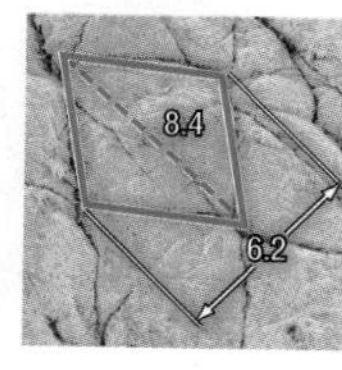

15 heartleaf plant

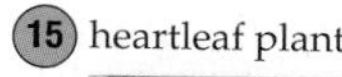
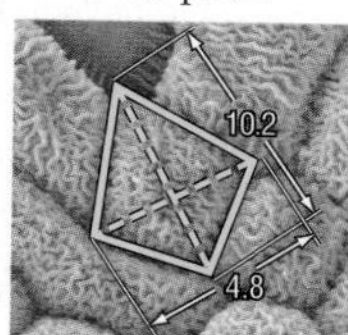

16. eye of a fly

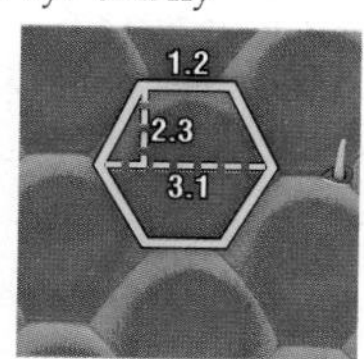

3 Practice

Formative Assessment

Use Exercises 1–7 to check for understanding.

Use the chart at the bottom of this page to customize assignments for your students.

CCSS Teaching the Mathematical Practices

Structure Mathematically proficient students look closely to discern a pattern or structure. They also can step back for an overview and shift perspective. In Exercises 8–13, encourage students to classify each figure first.

Additional Answers

8. 273 mm²
9. 678.5 ft²
10. 264 m²
11. 136 in²
12. 52.5 cm²
13. 137.5 ft²
14. 26 square microns
15. 24.5 square microns
16. 9.9 square microns

Differentiated Homework Options

Level	Assignment	Two-Day Option	
AL Basic	8–22, 34, 36–55	9–21 odd, 39–42	8–22 even, 34, 36–38, 43–55
OL Core	9–27 odd, 28, 29, 31, 33, 34, 36–55	8–22, 39–42	23–34, 36–38, 43–55
BL Advanced	23–52, (53–55 optional)		

Study Guide and Intervention

AL OL ELL

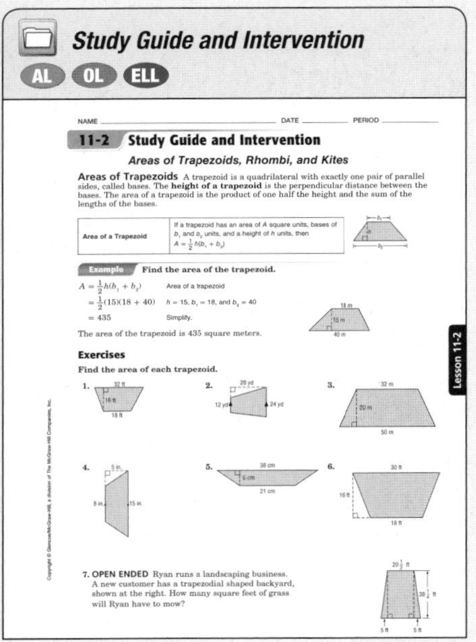
NAME _____ DATE _____ PERIOD _____

11-2 Study Guide and Intervention

Areas of Trapezoids, Rhombi, and Kites

Areas of Trapezoids A trapezoid is a quadrilateral with exactly one pair of parallel sides, called bases. The **height of a trapezoid** is the perpendicular distance between the bases. The area of a trapezoid is the product of one half the height and the sum of the lengths of the bases.

Area of a Trapezoid	If a trapezoid has an area of A square units, bases of b_1 and b_2 units, and a height of h units, then $A = \frac{1}{2}h(b_1 + b_2)$.

Example Find the area of the trapezoid.

$A = \frac{1}{2}h(b_1 + b_2)$ Area of a trapezoid

$= \frac{1}{2}(15)(18 + 40)$ $h = 15, b_1 = 18, \text{ and } b_2 = 40$

$= 435$ Simplify.

The area of the trapezoid is 435 square meters.

Exercises

Find the area of each trapezoid.

7. OPEN ENDED Ryan runs a landscaping business. A new customer has a trapezoidal shaped backyard, shown at the right. How many square feet of grass will Ryan have to mow?

Practice

AL OL BL ELL

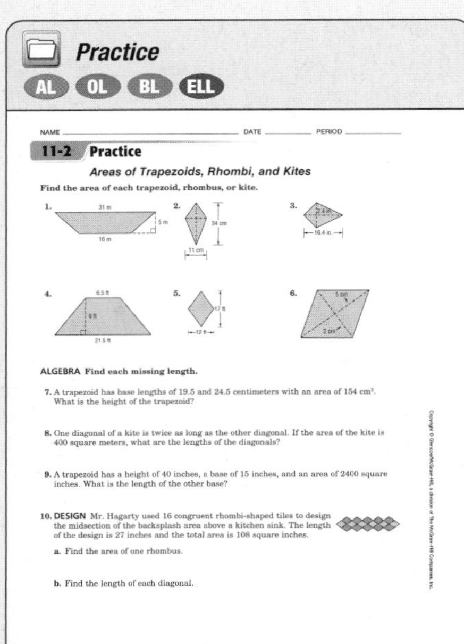
NAME _____ DATE _____ PERIOD _____

11-2 Practice

Areas of Trapezoids, Rhombi, and Kites

Find the area of each trapezoid, rhombus, or kite.

ALGEBRA Find each missing length.

7. A trapezoid has base lengths of 19.5 and 24.5 centimeters with an area of 154 cm². What is the height of the trapezoid?

8. One diagonal of a kite is twice as long as the other diagonal. If the area of the kite is 400 square meters, what are the lengths of the diagonals?

9. A trapezoid has a height of 40 inches, a base of 15 inches, and an area of 2400 square inches. What is the length of the other base?

10. DESIGN Mr. Hagarty used 16 congruent rhombi-shaped tiles to design the midsection of the backsplash area above a kitchen sink. The length of the design is 27 inches and the total area is 108 square inches.

a. Find the area of one rhombus.

b. Find the length of each diagonal.

Word Problem Practice

AL OL BL ELL

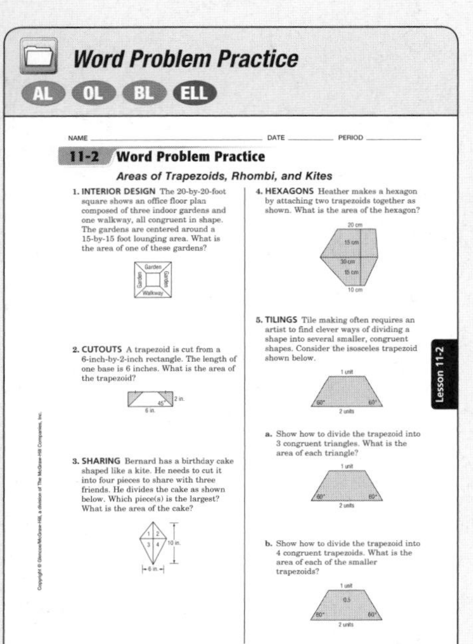
NAME _____ DATE _____ PERIOD _____

11-2 Word Problem Practice

Areas of Trapezoids, Rhombi, and Kites

1. INTERIOR DESIGN The 20-by-20-foot square shows an office floor plan composed of three indoor gardens and one walkway, all congruent in shape. The gardens are centered around a 15-by-15 foot lounging area. What is the area of one of these gardens?

2. CUTOUTS A trapezoid is cut from a 6-inch-by-2-inch rectangle. The length of one base is 6 inches. What is the area of the trapezoid?

3. SHARING Bernard has a birthday cake shaped like a kite. He needs to cut it into four pieces to share with three friends. He divides the cake as shown below. Which piece(s) is the largest? What is the area of the cake?

4. HEXAGONS Heather makes a hexagon by attaching two trapezoids together as shown. What is the area of the hexagon?

5. TILINGS Tile making often requires an artist to find clever ways of dividing a shape into several smaller, congruent shapes. Consider the isosceles trapezoid shown below.

a. Show how to divide the trapezoid into 3 congruent triangles. What is the area of each triangle?

b. Show how to divide the trapezoid into 4 congruent trapezoids. What is the area of each of the smaller trapezoids?

17. JOBS Jimmy works on his neighbors' yards after school to earn extra money to buy a car. He is going to plant grass seed in Mr. Troyer's yard. What is the area of the yard? **784 ft²**

Example 4 **ALGEBRA Find each missing length.**

18. One diagonal of a kite is twice as long as the other diagonal. If the area of the kite is 240 square inches, what are the lengths of the diagonals? **15.5 in., 31.0 in.**

19 The area of a rhombus is 168 square centimeters. If one diagonal is three times as long as the other, what are the lengths of the diagonals? **10.6 cm, 31.7 cm**

20. A trapezoid has base lengths of 12 and 14 feet with an area of 322 square feet. What is the height of the trapezoid? **24.8 ft**

21. A trapezoid has a height of 8 meters, a base length of 12 meters, and an area of 64 square meters. What is the length of the other base? **4 m**

22. HONORS Estella has been asked to join an honor society at school. Before the first meeting, new members are asked to sand and stain the front side of a piece of wood in the shape of an isosceles trapezoid. What is the surface area that Estella will need to sand and stain? **1.2 in²**

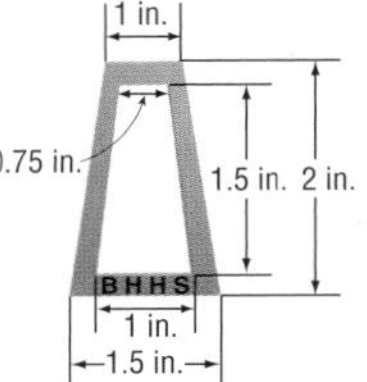

B **For each figure, provide a justification showing that $A = \frac{1}{2}d_1d_2$.**

23.

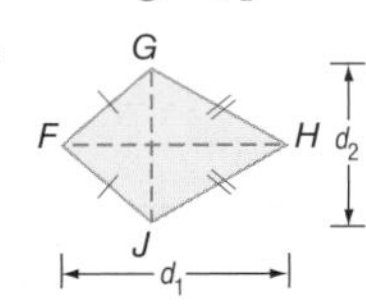

24.

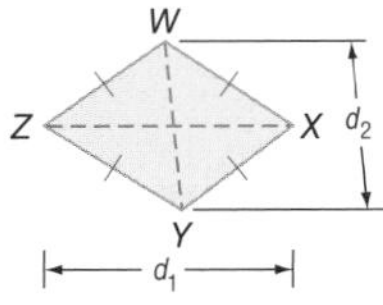

23–24. See margin.

25. CRAFTS Ashanti is in a kite competition. The yellow, red, orange, green, and blue pieces of her kite design shown are congruent rhombi.

a. How much fabric of each color does she need to buy?

b. Competition rules require that the total area of each kite be no greater than 200 square inches. Does Ashanti's kite meet this requirement? Explain. **Yes; her kite has an area of 140 in², which is less than 200 in².**

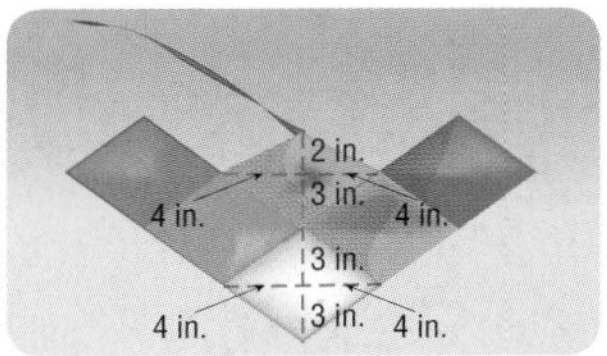

25a. 24 in² each of yellow, red, orange, green, and blue; 20 in² of purple

CCSS SENSE-MAKING Find the area of each quadrilateral with the given vertices.

26. $A(-8, 6), B(-5, 8), C(-2, 6)$, and $D(-5, 0)$ **24 sq. units**

27. $W(3, 0), X(0, 3), Y(-3, 0)$, and $Z(0, -3)$ **18 sq. units**

28. METALS When magnified in very powerful microscopes, some metals are composed of grains that have various polygonal shapes.

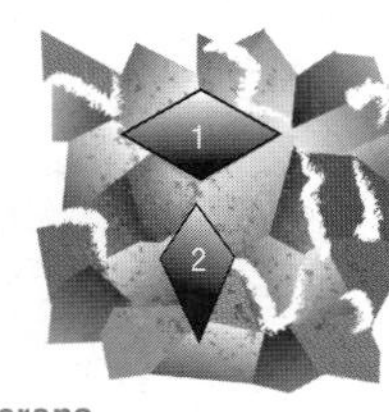

a. What is the area of figure 1 if the grain has a height of 4 microns and bases with lengths of 5 and 6 microns? **22 square microns**

b. If figure 2 has perpendicular diagonal lengths of 3.8 microns and 4.9 microns, what is the area of the grain? **9.3 square microns**

Enrichment

OL BL

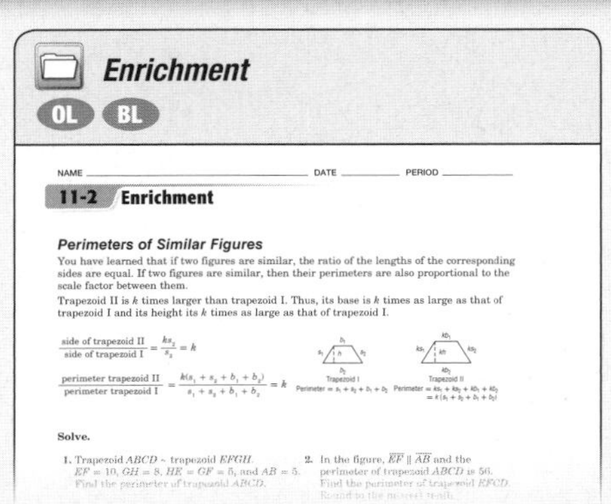
NAME _____ DATE _____ PERIOD _____

11-2 Enrichment

Perimeters of Similar Figures

You have learned that if two figures are similar, the ratio of the lengths of the corresponding sides are equal. If two figures are similar, then their perimeters are also proportional to the scale factor between them.

Trapezoid II is k times larger than trapezoid I. Thus, its base is k times as large as that of trapezoid I and its height its k times as large as that of trapezoid I.

Solve.

1. Trapezoid ABCD ~ trapezoid EFGH. EF = 10, GH = 8, HE = GF = 5, and AB = 5. Find the perimeter of trapezoid ABCD.

2. In the figure, $\overline{EF} \parallel \overline{AB}$ and the perimeter of trapezoid ABCD is 56. Find the perimeter of trapezoid EFCD.

Teaching the Mathematical Practices

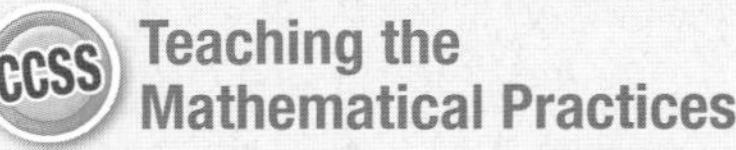

Sense-Making Mathematically proficient students start by explaining the meaning of a problem to themselves and looking for entry points to its solution. They plan a solution pathway rather than simply jumping into a solution attempt. In Exercises 26–27, encourage students to plot the vertices first and then classify the quadrilateral.

29. **PROOF** The figure at the right is a trapezoid that consists of two congruent right triangles and an isosceles triangle. In 1876, James A. Garfield, the 20th president of the United States, discovered a proof of the Pythagorean Theorem using this diagram. Prove that $x^2 + y^2 = z^2$. **See margin.**

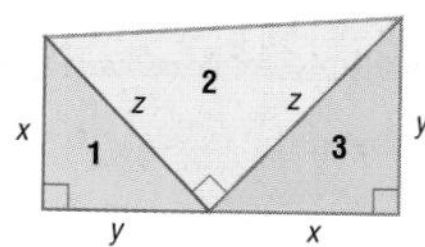

DIMENSIONAL ANALYSIS **Find the perimeter and area of each figure in feet. Round to the nearest tenth, if necessary.**

30. 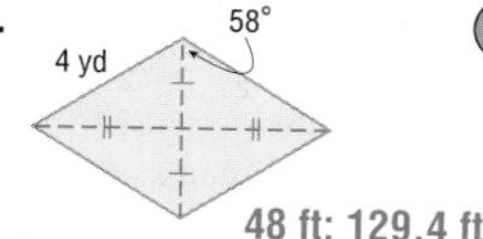

48 ft; 129.4 ft²

31. 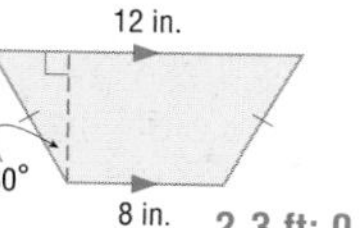

2.3 ft; 0.24 ft²

32. 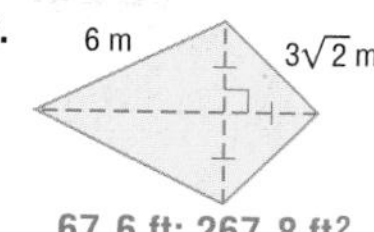

67.6 ft; 267.8 ft²

33. **MULTIPLE REPRESENTATIONS** In this problem, you will investigate perimeters of kites. **a–e. See Ch. 11 Answer Appendix.**

a. **Geometric** Draw a kite like the one shown if $x = 2$.

x cm
4 cm
12 cm

b. **Geometric** Repeat the process in part **a** for three x-values between 2 and 10 and for an x-value of 10.

c. **Tabular** Measure and record in a table the perimeter of each kite, along with the x-value.

d. **Graphical** Graph the perimeter versus the x-value using the data from your table.

e. **Analytical** Make a conjecture about the value of x that will minimize the perimeter of the kite. What is the significance of this value?

34. Madeline; sample answer: There is more than one trapezoid with a height of 4 units and an area of 18 square units. The sum of the bases of the trapezoid has to be 9, so one possibility is a trapezoid with bases of 4 and 5 units and a height of 4 units. Another is a trapezoid with bases of 3 and 6 units and a height of 4 units.

H.O.T. Problems Use Higher-Order Thinking Skills

34. **CCSS CRITIQUE** Antonio and Madeline want to draw a trapezoid that has a height of 4 units and an area of 18 square units. Antonio says that only one trapezoid will meet the criteria. Madeline disagrees and thinks that she can draw several different trapezoids with a height of 4 units and an area of 18 square units. Is either of them correct? Explain your reasoning.

35. **CHALLENGE** Find x in parallelogram $ABCD$. **7.2**

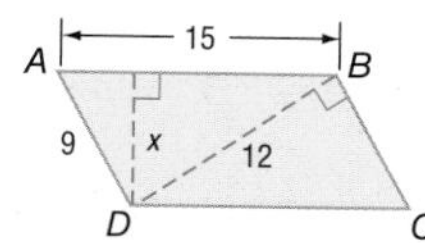

36. **OPEN ENDED** Draw a kite and a rhombus with an area of 6 square inches. Label and justify your drawings. **See Ch. 11 Answer Appendix.**

37. **REASONING** If the areas of two rhombi are equal, are the perimeters *sometimes*, *always*, or *never* equal? Explain. **Sometimes; sample answer: If the areas are equal, it means that the products of the diagonals are equal. The only time that the perimeters will be equal is when the diagonals are also equal, or when the two rhombi are congruent.**

38. **WRITING IN MATH** How can you use trigonometry to find the area of a figure? **See Ch. 11 Answer Appendix.**

29. The area of a trapezoid is $\frac{1}{2}h(b_1 + b_2)$. So, $A = \frac{1}{2}(x + y)(x + y)$ or $\frac{1}{2}(x^2 + 2xy + y^2)$. The area of $\triangle 1 = \frac{1}{2}(y)(x)$, $\triangle 2 = \frac{1}{2}(z)(z)$, and $\triangle 3 = \frac{1}{2}(x)(y)$. The area of $\triangle 1 + \triangle 2 + \triangle 3 = \frac{1}{2}xy + \frac{1}{2}z^2 + \frac{1}{2}xy$. Set the area of the trapezoid equal to the combined areas of the triangles to get $\frac{1}{2}(x^2 + 2xy + y^2) = \frac{1}{2}xy + \frac{1}{2}z^2 + \frac{1}{2}xy$. Multiply by 2 on each side: $x^2 + 2xy + y^2 = 2xy + z^2$. When simplified, $x^2 + y^2 = z^2$.

Exercise Alert

Ruler Exercises 33 and 36 require the use of a ruler.

Multiple Representations

In Exercise 33, students use sketches, a table, and a graph to investigate the perimeters of kites.

CCSS Teaching the Mathematical Practices

Critique Mathematically proficient students can distinguish correct logic from flawed reasoning. In Exercise 34, students should see that the sum of the bases of the trapezoid has to be 9; $\frac{1}{2} \cdot 4 \cdot 9 = 18$. Madeline is correct because there are many different trapezoids that have the sum of their bases equal to 9.

Additional Answers

23. The area of $\triangle HJF = \frac{1}{2}d_1\left(\frac{1}{2}d_2\right)$ and the area of $\triangle HGF = \frac{1}{2}d_1\left(\frac{1}{2}d_2\right)$. Therefore, the area of $\triangle HJF = \frac{1}{4}d_1d_2$, and the area of $\triangle HGF = \frac{1}{4}d_1d_2$. The area of kite $FGHJ$ is equal to the area of $\triangle HJF +$ the area of $\triangle HGF$ or $\frac{1}{4}d_1d_2 + \frac{1}{4}d_1d_2$. After simplification, the area of kite $FGHJ$ is equal to $\frac{1}{2}d_1d_2$.

24. The area of $\triangle ZWX = \frac{1}{2}d_1\left(\frac{1}{2}d_2\right)$ and the area of $\triangle ZYX = \frac{1}{2}d_1\left(\frac{1}{2}d_2\right)$. Therefore, the area of $\triangle ZWX = \frac{1}{4}d_1d_2$, and the area of $\triangle ZYX = \frac{1}{4}d_1d_2$. The area of rhombus $WXYZ$ is equal to the area of $\triangle ZWX +$ the area of $\triangle ZYX$ or $\frac{1}{4}d_1d_2 + \frac{1}{4}d_1d_2$. After simplification, the area of rhombus $WXYZ$ is equal to $\frac{1}{2}d_1d_2$.

4 Assess

Ticket Out the Door Ask students to list all the formulas for area they have learned so far in this chapter. Have them include a labeled diagram corresponding to each formula. Have students turn in their statements before they leave the classroom.

Formative Assessment

Check for student understanding of Lessons 11-1 and 11-2.

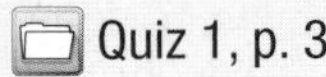 Quiz 1, p. 39

Standardized Test Practice

39. The lengths of the bases of an isosceles trapezoid are shown below.

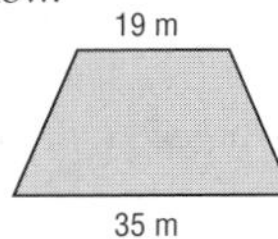

If the perimeter is 74 meters, what is its area? A

A 162 m^2 C 332.5 m^2
B 270 m^2 D 342.25 m^2

40. SHORT RESPONSE One diagonal of a rhombus is three times as long as the other diagonal. If the area of the rhombus is 54 square millimeters, what are the lengths of the diagonals? 6 mm, 18 mm

41. ALGEBRA What is the effect on the graph of the equation $y = \frac{1}{2}x$ when the equation is changed to $y = -2x$? J

F The graph is moved 1 unit down.
G The graph is moved 1 unit up.
H The graph is rotated 45° about the origin.
J The graph is rotated 90° about the origin.

42. A regular hexagon is divided into 6 congruent triangles. If the perimeter of the hexagon is 48 centimeters, what is the height of each triangle? B

A 4 cm C $6\sqrt{3}$ cm E $8\sqrt{3}$ cm
B $4\sqrt{3}$ cm D 8 cm

Spiral Review

COORDINATE GEOMETRY **Find the area of each figure.** (Lesson 11-1)

43. $\triangle JKL$ with $J(-4, 3)$, $K(-9, -1)$, and $L(-4, -4)$ 17.5 units²

44. ▱$RSTV$ with $R(-5, 7)$, $S(2, 7)$, $T(0, 2)$, and $V(-7, 2)$ 35 units²

45. WEATHER Meteorologists track severe storms using Doppler radar. A polar grid is used to measure distances as the storms progress. If the center of the radar screen is the origin and each ring is 10 miles farther from the center, what is the equation of the fourth ring? (Lesson 10-8) $x^2 + y^2 = 1600$

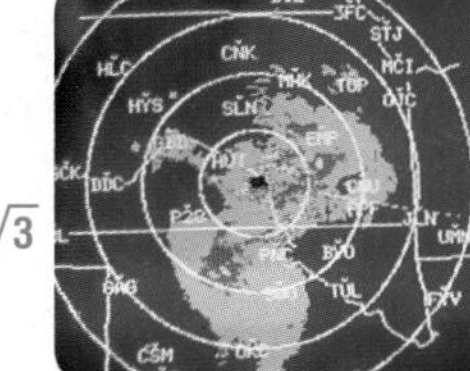

Find x and y. (Lesson 8-3)

46. $x = 8\sqrt{3}$; $y = 16$

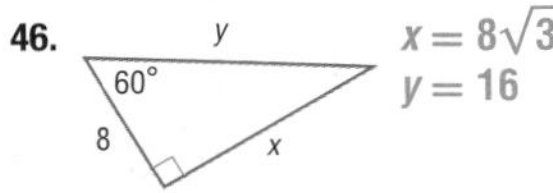

47. $x = 9$; $y = 9\sqrt{3}$

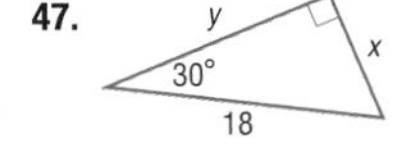

Use the Venn diagram to determine whether each statement is *always*, *sometimes*, or *never* true. (Lesson 6-5)

48. A parallelogram is a square. sometimes

49. A square is a rhombus. always

50. A rectangle is a parallelogram. always

51. A rhombus is a rectangle but not a square. never

52. A rhombus is a square. sometimes

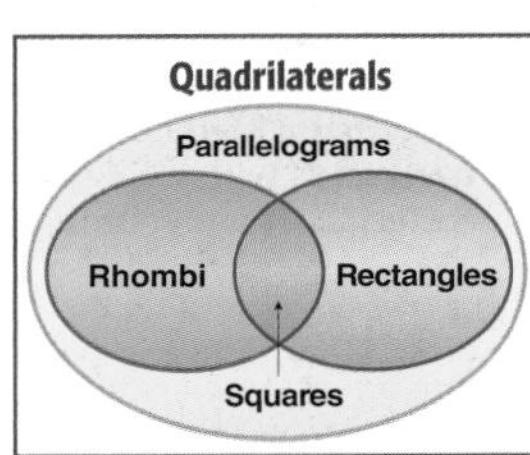

Skills Review

Find the circumference and area of each figure. Round to the nearest tenth.

53. 18.8 in.; 28.3 in²

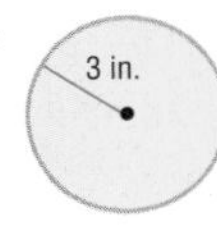

54. 19.5 cm; 30.2 cm²

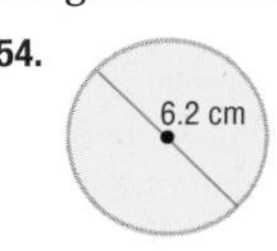

55. 36.4 ft; 105.7 ft²

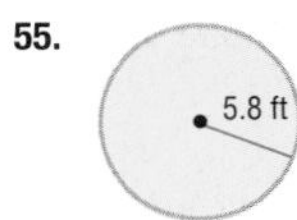

Differentiated Instruction OL BL

Extension Have students diagram the relationship between the area of a parallelogram and the area of a trapezoid. Answers will vary.

EXTEND 11-2

Geometry Lab
Population Density

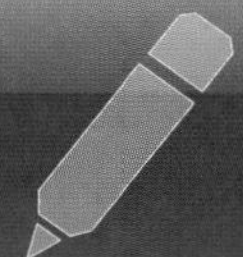

After data are collected for the U.S. census, the population density is calculated for states, major cities, and other areas. **Population density** is the measurement of population per unit of area.

CCSS Common Core State Standards
Content Standards
G.MG.2 Apply concepts of density based on area and volume in modeling situations (e.g., persons per square mile, BTUs per cubic foot). ★
Mathematical Practices 1

Activity 1 Calculate Population Density

Find the population density for the borough of Queens using the data in the table.

Calculate population density with the formula population density $= \frac{\text{population}}{\text{land area}}$.

The population density of Queens would be $\frac{2{,}229{,}379}{109.24}$ or about 20,408 people per square mile.

Borough	Population	Land Area (mi^2)
Brooklyn	2,465,326	70.61
Manhattan	1,537,195	22.96
Queens	2,229,379	109.24
Staten Island	443,728	58.48
The Bronx	1,332,650	42.03

Model and Analyze

1. Find the population densities for Brooklyn, Manhattan, Staten Island and the Bronx. Round to the nearest person. Of the five boroughs, which have the highest and the lowest population densities? See margin.

Activity 2 Use Population Density

PT

In a proposal to establish a new rustic campground at Yellowstone National Park, there is a concern about the number of wolves in the area. At last report, there were 98 wolves in the park. The new campground will be accepted if there are fewer than 2 wolves in the campground. Use the data in the table to determine if the new campground can be established.

Location	Size
Area of park	3472 mi^2
Area of new campground	10 acres

Step 1 Find the density of wolves in the park.
$98 \div 3472 = 0.028$ wolves per square mile

Step 2 Find the density of wolves in the proposed campground. First convert the size of the campground to square miles. If 1 acre is equivalent to 0.0015625 square mile, then 10 acres is 0.015625 square mile. The potential number of wolves in the proposed site is $0.015625 \cdot 0.028$ or 0.0004375 wolves.

Step 3 Since 0.0004375 is fewer than 2, the proposed campground can be accepted.

Exercises

2. Find the population density of gaming system owners if there are 436,000 systems in the United States and the area of the United States is 3,794,083 square miles. **about 0.115 owners/mi^2**

3. The population density of the burrowing owl in Cape Coral, Florida, is 8.3 pairs per square mile. A new golf club is planned for a 2.4-square-mile site where the owl population is estimated to be 17 pairs. Would Lee County approve the proposed club if their policy is to decline when the estimated population density of owls is below the average density? Explain. **No; the population density is about 7.08 pairs/mi^2.**

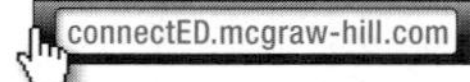

Additional Answer

1. 34,915; 66,951; 7,588; 31,707; Manhattan has the highest population density, and Staten Island has the lowest population density.

1 Focus

Objective Explore population density.

2 Teach

Working in Cooperative Groups

Divide the class into pairs. Work through Activities 1 and 2 as a class. Then ask students to work with their partners to complete Exercise 1.

Practice Have students complete Exercise 2.

3 Assess

Formative Assessment

Use Exercise 3 to assess each student's understanding of modeling with population density.

From Concrete to Abstract

Ask students to summarize how they can use population density to support a claim.

1 Focus

VerticalAlignment

Before Lesson 11-3 Find the circumference of a circle.

Lesson 11-3 Find the areas of circles and sectors of circles.

After Lesson 11-3 Find the area of regular polygons and composite figures.

2 Teach

Scaffolding Questions

Have students read the **Why?** section of the lesson.

Ask:

- How many degrees are in a circle? 360°
- If a pizza is cut into eight wedge-shaped pieces of equal size, how many degrees is the angle made by one slice? 45°
- If the slices are all of equal size, how does the area of one slice compare with the total area of the pizza? One slice is one-eighth the area of the entire pizza.

LESSON 11-3 Areas of Circles and Sectors

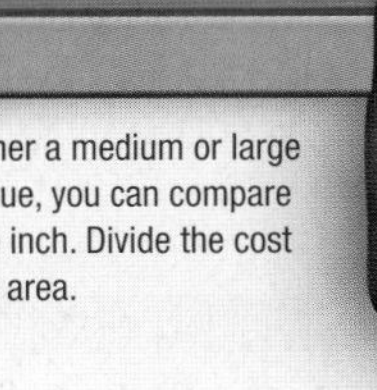

Then	Now	Why?
• You found the circumference of a circle.	• **1** Find areas of circles. **2** Find areas of sectors of circles.	• To determine whether a medium or large pizza is a better value, you can compare the cost per square inch. Divide the cost of each pizza by its area.

NewVocabulary

sector of a circle
segment of a circle

Common Core State Standards

Content Standards

G.C.5 Derive using similarity the fact that the length of the arc intercepted by an angle is proportional to the radius, and define the radian measure of the angle as the constant of proportionality; derive the formula for the area of a sector.

G.GMD.1 Give an informal argument for the formulas for the circumference of a circle, area of a circle, volume of a cylinder, pyramid, and cone.

Mathematical Practices

1 Make sense of problems and persevere in solving them.
6 Attend to precision.

1 Areas of Circles In Lesson 10-1, you learned that the formula for the circumference C of a circle with radius r is given by $C = 2\pi r$. You can use this formula to develop the formula for the area of a circle.

Below, a circle with radius r and circumference C has been divided into congruent pieces and then rearranged to form a figure that resembles a parallelogram.

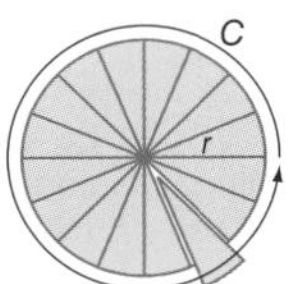

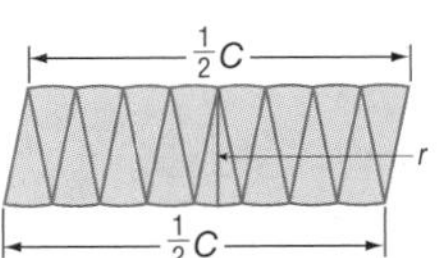

As the number of congruent pieces increases, the rearranged figure more closely approaches a parallelogram. The base of the parallelogram is $\frac{1}{2}C$ and the height is r, so its area is $\frac{1}{2}C \cdot r$. Since $C = 2\pi r$, the area of the parallelogram is also $\frac{1}{2}(2\pi r)r$ or πr^2.

KeyConcept Area of a Circle

Words	The area A of a circle is equal to π times the square of the radius r.
Symbols	$A = \pi r^2$

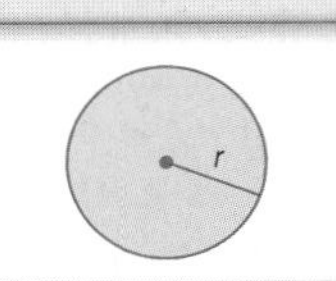

Real-World Example 1 Area of a Circle

SPORTS What is the area of the circular putting green shown to the nearest square foot?

20 ft

The diameter is 20 feet, so the radius is 10 feet.

$A = \pi r^2$ — Area of a circle
$= \pi(10)^2$ — $r = 10$
≈ 314 — Use a calculator.

So, the area is about 314 square feet.

GuidedPractice

1. SPORTS An archery target has a radius of 12 inches. What is the area of the target to the nearest square inch? **452 in²**

798 | Lesson 11-3

Lesson 11-3 Resources

Resource	Approaching Level AL	On Level OL	Beyond Level BL	English Learners ELL
Teacher Edition	▪ Differentiated Instruction, p. 799	▪ Differentiated Instruction, p. 799	▪ Differentiated Instruction, p. 799	▪ Differentiated Instruction, p. 799
Chapter Resource Masters	▪ Study Guide and Intervention, pp. 19–20 ▪ Skills Practice, p. 21 ▪ Practice, p. 22 ▪ Word Problem Practice, p. 23	▪ Study Guide and Intervention, pp. 19–20 ▪ Skills Practice, p. 21 ▪ Practice, p. 22 ▪ Word Problem Practice, p. 23 ▪ Enrichment, p. 24	▪ Practice, p. 22 ▪ Word Problem Practice, p. 23 ▪ Enrichment, p. 24	▪ Study Guide and Intervention, pp. 19–20 ▪ Skills Practice, p. 21 ▪ Practice, p. 22 ▪ Word Problem Practice, p. 23
Other	▪ 5-Minute Check 11-3 ▪ Study Notebook ▪ Teaching Geometry with Manipulatives	▪ 5-Minute Check 11-3 ▪ Study Notebook ▪ Teaching Geometry with Manipulatives	▪ 5-Minute Check 11-3 ▪ Study Notebook	▪ 5-Minute Check 11-3 ▪ Study Notebook ▪ Teaching Geometry with Manipulatives

Example 2 Use the Area of a Circle to Find a Missing Measure

ALGEBRA Find the radius of a circle with an area of 95 square centimeters.

$A = \pi r^2$ Area of a circle

$95 = \pi r^2$ $A = 95$

$\frac{95}{\pi} = r^2$ Divide each side by π.

$5.5 \approx r$ Use a calculator. Take the positive square root of each side.

The radius of the circle is about 5.5 centimeters.

GuidedPractice

2. ALGEBRA The area of a circle is 196π square yards. Find the diameter. 28 yd

ReviewVocabulary

central angle an angle with a vertex in the center of a circle and with sides that contain two radii of the circle

arc a portion of a circle defined by two endpoints

2 Areas of Sectors

A slice of a circular pizza is an example of a sector of a circle. A **sector of a circle** is a region of a circle bounded by a central angle and its intercepted major or minor arc. The formula for the area of a sector is similar to the formula for arc length.

KeyConcept Area of a Sector

The ratio of the **area A of a sector** to the **area of the whole circle, πr^2**, is equal to the ratio of the **degree measure of the intercepted arc x** to 360.

Proportion: $\frac{A}{\pi r^2} = \frac{x}{360}$

Equation: $A = \frac{x}{360} \cdot \pi r^2$

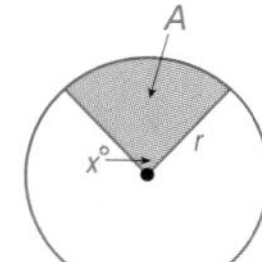

Real-WorldLink

About 3 billion pizzas are sold each year in the United States. That is equivalent to about 46 slices per person annually.

Source: ThinkQuest Library

Real-World Example 3 Area of a Sector

PIZZA A circular pizza has a diameter of 12 inches and is cut into 8 congruent slices. What is the area of one slice to the nearest hundredth?

Step 1 Find the arc measure of a pizza slice.

Since the pizza is equally divided into 8 slices, each slice will have an arc measure of $360 \div 8$ or 45.

Step 2 Find the radius of the pizza. Use this measure to find the area of the sector, or slice.

The diameter is 12 inches, so the radius is 6 inches.

$A = \frac{x}{360} \cdot \pi r^2$ Area of a sector

$= \frac{45}{360} \cdot \pi(6)^2$ $x = 45$ and $r = 6$

≈ 14.14 Use a calculator.

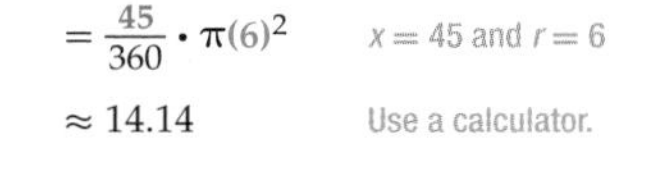

So, the area of one slice of this pizza is about 14.14 square inches.

DifferentiatedInstruction AL OL BL ELL

Verbal/Linguistic Learners Have students discuss how the area of a sector relates to the area of the entire circle. Have them write how the equation for a sector logically represents a portion of the circle.

1 Areas of Circles

Example 1 shows how to find the area of a circle. **Example 2** shows how to find the radius of a circle, given its area.

Formative Assessment

Use the Guided Practice exercises after each example to determine students' understanding of concepts.

Additional Examples

1 MANUFACTURING An outdoor accessories company manufactures circular covers for outdoor umbrellas. If the cover is 8 inches longer than the umbrella on each side, find the area of the cover in square inches. about 6082 in^2

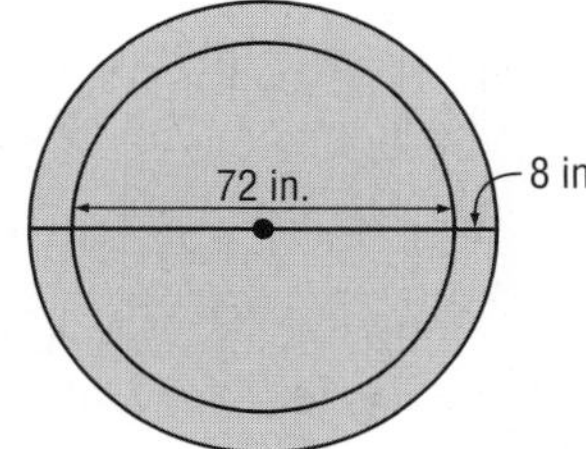

2 ALGEBRA Find the radius of a circle with an area of 58 square inches. 4.3 in.

Additional Examples also in Interactive Classroom PowerPoint® Presentations

2 Areas of Sectors

Example 3 shows how to find the area of a sector.

Additional Example

3 PIE A pie has a diameter of 9 inches and is cut into 10 congruent slices. What is the area of one slice to the nearest hundredth? 6.36 in^2

Focus on Mathematical Content

Radius of a Circle To find the area of the circle, it is enough to know the diameter, the circumference, or the radius; the radius can be determined from the diameter or circumference.

Teach with Tech

Audio Recording Have students create audio recordings explaining how to find the area of a sector of a circle. Listen to students' recordings to check for an understanding of the concept.

Guided Practice

Find the area of the shaded sector. Round to the nearest tenth.

3A. 7.4 ft^2

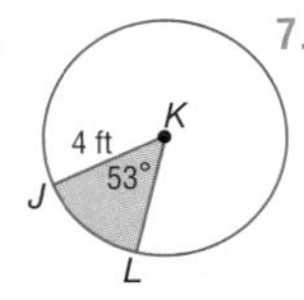

3B. 46.5 m^2

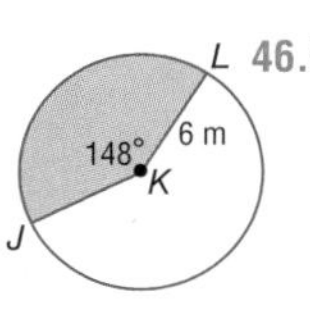

3C. 311.5 in^2

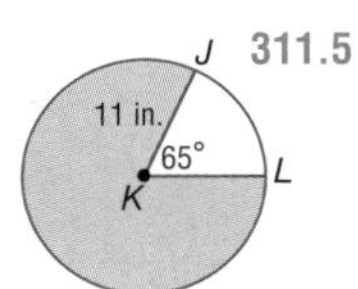

3D. CRAFTS The color wheel at the right is a tool that artists use to organize color schemes. If the diameter of the wheel is 10 inches and each of the 12 sections is congruent, find the approximate area covered by green hues. 19.6 in^2

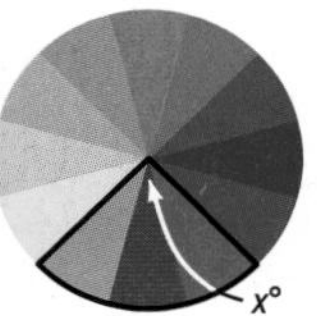

Check Your Understanding

 = Step-by-Step Solutions begin on page R14.

Example 1 **CONSTRUCTION** **Find the area of each circle. Round to the nearest tenth.**

1.  1385.4 yd^2

2. 0.1 km^2

Example 2 **Find the indicated measure. Round to the nearest tenth.**

3. Find the diameter of a circle with an area of 74 square millimeters. 9.7 mm

4. The area of a circle is 88 square inches. Find the radius. 5.3 in.

Example 3 **Find the area of each shaded sector. Round to the nearest tenth.**

5. 4.5 in^2

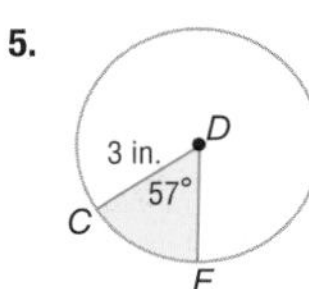

6. 39.3 cm^2

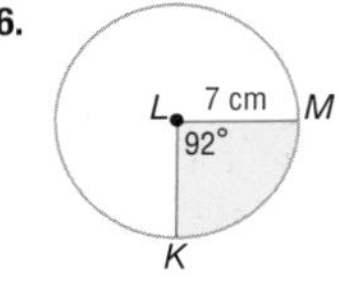

7. BAKING Chelsea is baking pies for a fundraiser at her school. She divides each 9-inch pie into 6 equal slices.

a. What is the area, in square inches, for each slice of pie? 10.6 in^2

b. If each slice costs \$0.25 to make and she sells 8 pies at \$1.25 for each slice, how much money will she raise? \$48

800 | Lesson 11-3 | Areas of Circles and Sectors

Practice and Problem Solving

Extra Practice is on page R11.

Example 1 CCSS **MODELING** **Find the area of each circle. Round to the nearest tenth.**

8. 28.3 ft^2
9. 78.5 yd^2
11. 14.2 in^2
12. 254.5 in^2

8.

9.

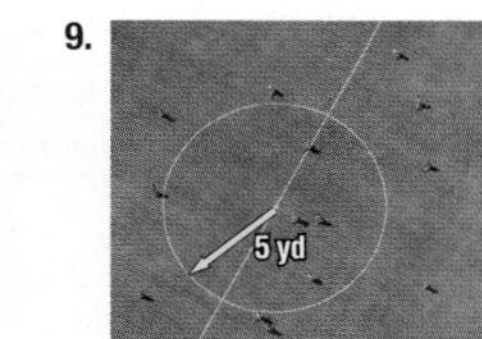

10. 50.3 ft^2

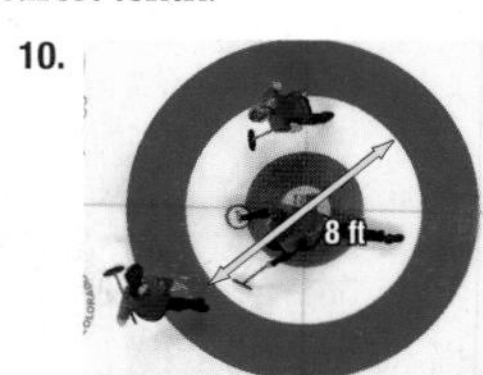

11. 4.25 in.

12.

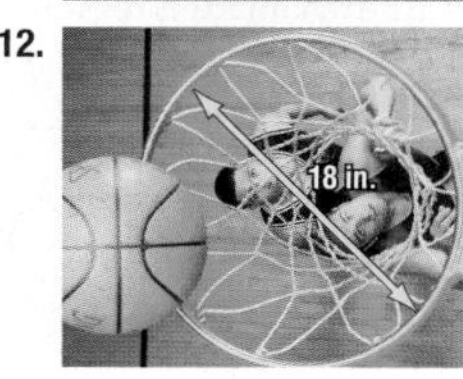

13. 78.5 ft^2

Example 2 **Find the indicated measure. Round to the nearest tenth, if necessary.**

14. The area of a circle is 68 square centimeters. Find the diameter. 9.3 cm
15. Find the diameter of a circle with an area of 94 square millimeters. 10.9 mm
16. The area of a circle is 112 square inches. Find the radius. 6 in.
17. Find the radius of a circle with an area of 206 square feet. 8.1 ft

Example 3 **Find the area of each shaded sector. Round to the nearest tenth, if necessary.**

18. 10 in^2 (circle B, radius 5 in., central angle ABC 46°)

19. 40.2 cm^2

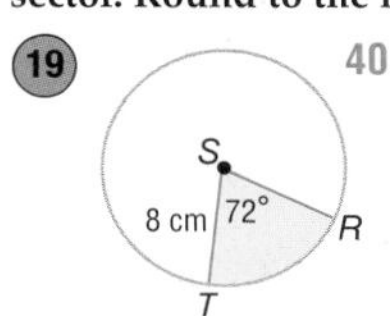

20. 167.1 ft^2

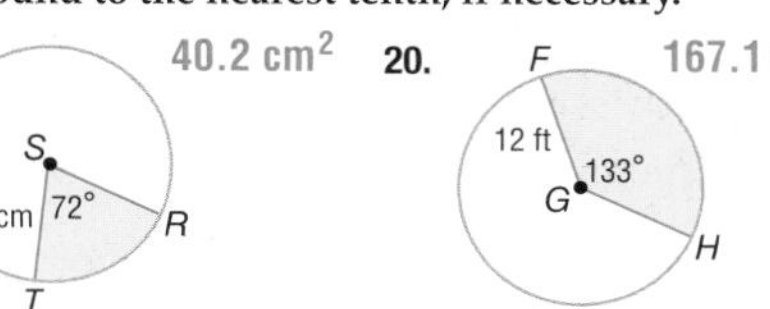

21. 322 m^2

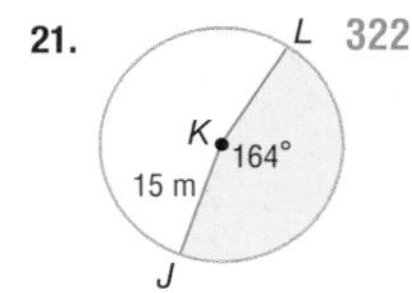

22. 333.9 mm^2

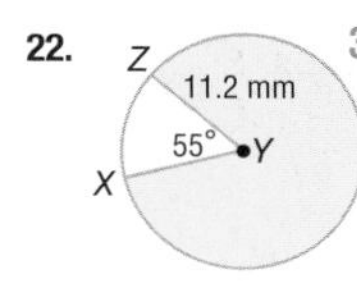

23. 284 in^2

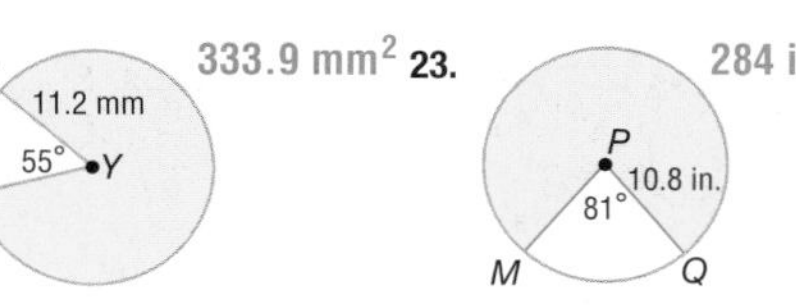

24. **MUSIC** The music preferences of students at Thomas Jefferson High are shown in the circle graph. Find the area of each sector and the degree measure of each intercepted arc if the radius of the circle is 1 unit. See margin.

Country 10%; Classical 2%; Alternative 14%; Rock & Roll 26%; Rap 48%

25. **JEWELRY** A jeweler makes a pair of earrings by cutting two 50° sectors from a silver disk.
    a. Find the area of each sector. 1.7 cm^2
    b. If the weight of the silver disk is 2.3 grams, how many milligrams does the silver wedge for each earring weigh? about 319.4 mg

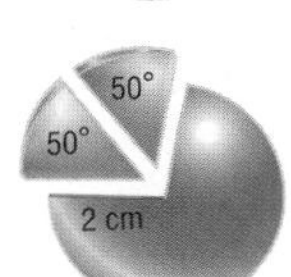

3 Practice

Formative Assessment

Use Exercises 1–7 to check for understanding.

Use the chart at the bottom of this page to customize assignments for your students.

Teaching the Mathematical Practices

Modeling Mathematically proficient students can apply the mathematics they know to solve problems arising in everyday life. In Exercises 8–13, encourage students to be careful about specifying the units of measure for each exercise.

Additional Answer

24. rap: 172.8°, 1.51 units^2; rock & roll: 93.6°, 0.82 units^2; alternative: 50.4°, 0.44 units^2; country: 36°, 0.31 units^2; classical: 7.2°, 0.06 units^2

Differentiated Homework Options

Level	Assignment	Two-Day Option	
AL Basic	8–25, 44, 46–61	9–25 odd, 50–53	8–24 even, 44, 46–49, 54–61
OL Core	9–25 odd, 26, 27, 29–31, 33–43 odd, 44, 46–61	8–25, 50–53	26–44, 46–49, 54–61
BL Advanced	26–58, (optional: 59–61)		

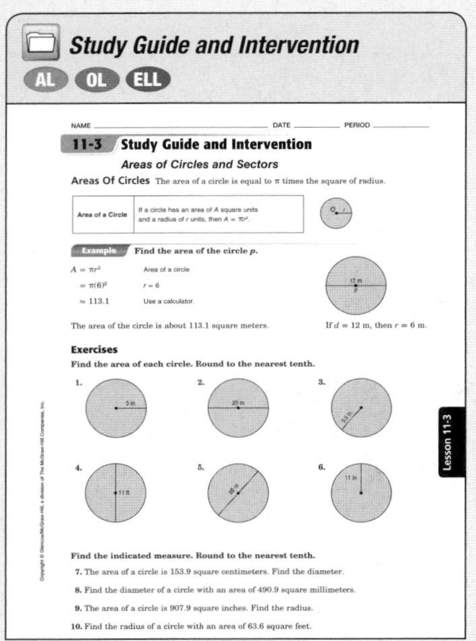

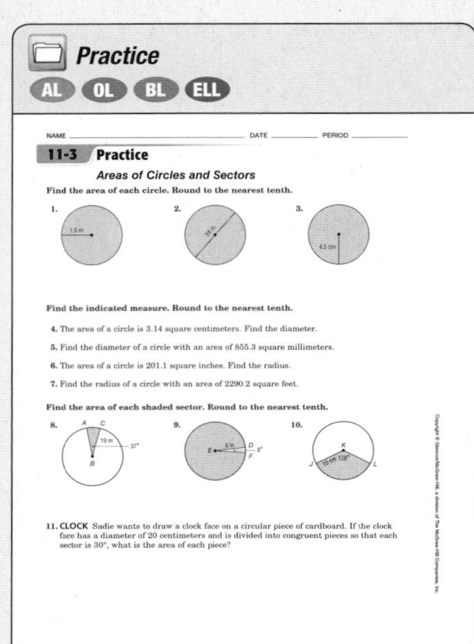

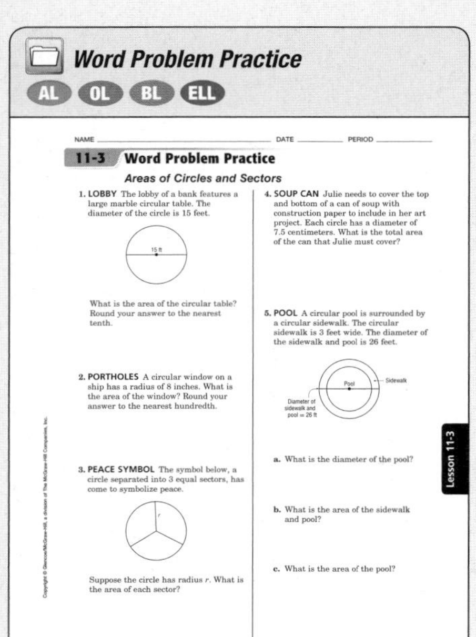

26. PROM The table shows the results of a survey of students to determine their preference for a prom theme.

Theme	Percent
An Evening of Stars	11
Mardi Gras	32
Springtime in Paris	8
Night in Times Square	47
Undecided	2

a. Create a circle graph with a diameter of 2 inches to represent these data. **a–b. See Ch. 11 Answer Appendix.**

b. Find the area of each theme's sector in your graph. Round to the nearest hundredth of an inch.

CCSS SENSE-MAKING **The area A of each shaded region is given. Find x.**

27. $A = 66 \text{ cm}^2$ **13**

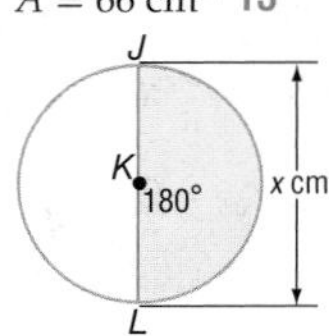

28. $A = 94 \text{ in}^2$ **55**

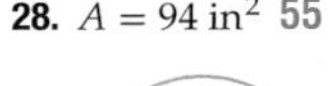

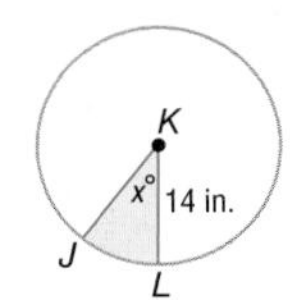

29. $A = 128 \text{ ft}^2$ **9.8**

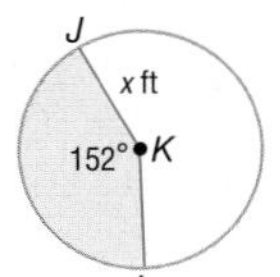

30. CRAFTS Luna is making tablecloths with the dimensions shown for a club banquet. Find the area of each tablecloth in square feet if each one is to just reach the floor. **about 107 ft²**

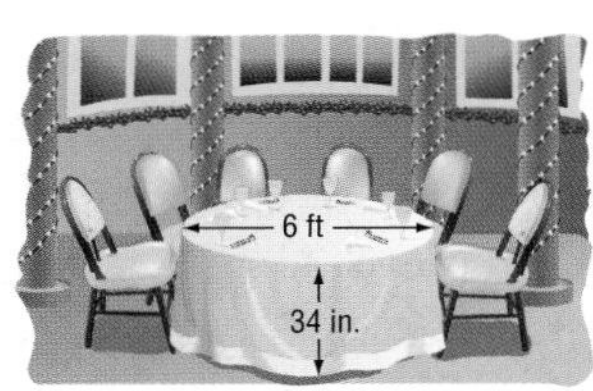

31 TREES The age of a living tree can be determined by multiplying the diameter of the tree by its growth factor, or rate of growth.

a. What is the diameter of a tree with a circumference of 2.5 feet? **0.8 ft**

b. If the growth factor of the tree is 4.5, what is the age of the tree? **3.6 yr**

Find the area of the shaded region. Round to the nearest tenth.

32. **69.5 ft²**

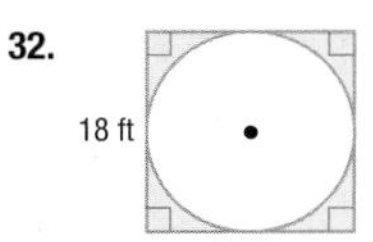

33. **53.5 m²**

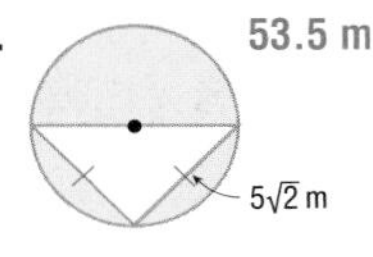

34. **77 mm²**

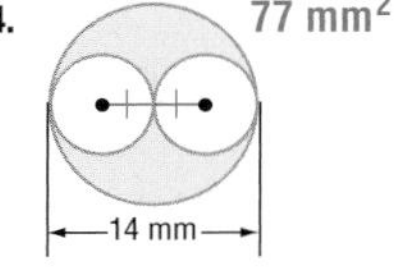

35. **10.7 cm²**

36. **7.9 m²**

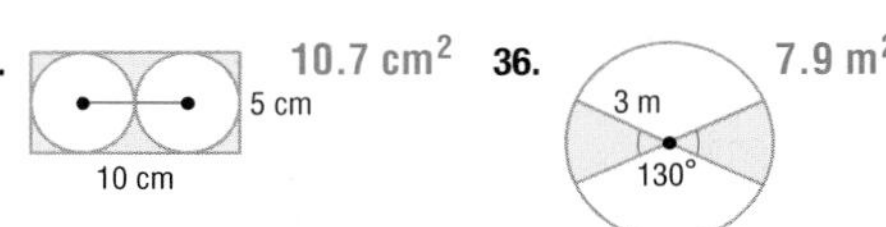

37. **7.9 in²**

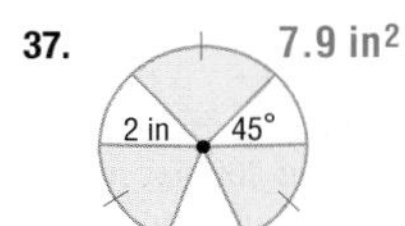

38. COORDINATE GEOMETRY What is the area of sector ABC shown on the graph? **28.3 square units**

39. ALGEBRA The figure shown below is a sector of a circle. If the perimeter of the figure is 22 millimeters, find its area in square millimeters. **30 mm²**

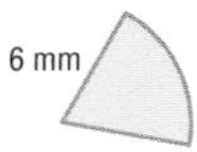

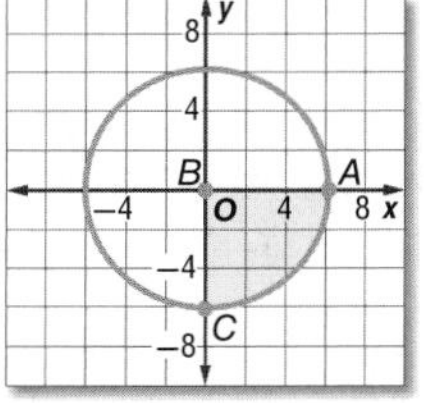

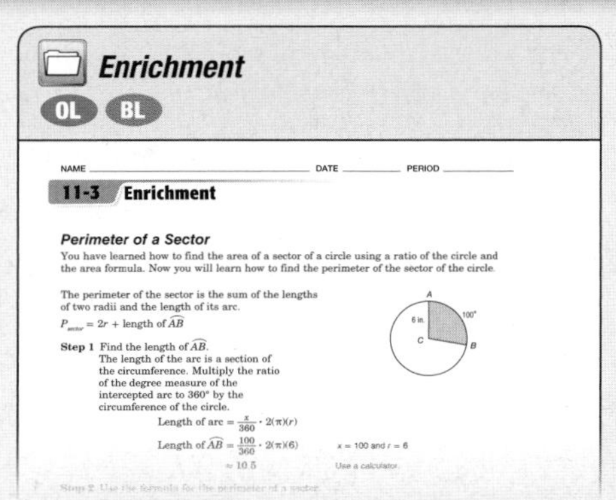

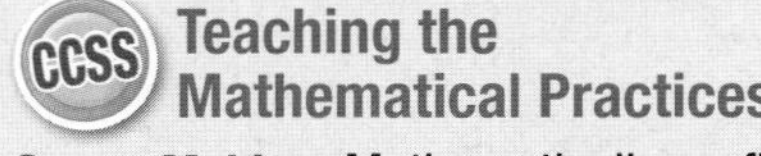

Teaching the Mathematical Practices

Sense-Making Mathematically proficient students start by explaining the meaning of a problem to themselves and looking for entry points to its solution. They plan a solution pathway rather than simply jumping into a solution attempt. In Exercises 27–29, encourage students to make a plan to solve each problem first.

Find the area of each shaded region.

40. 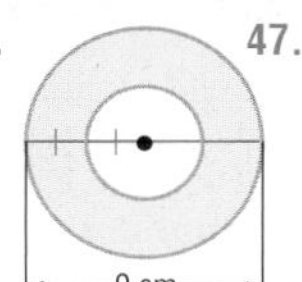

47.7 cm²

41 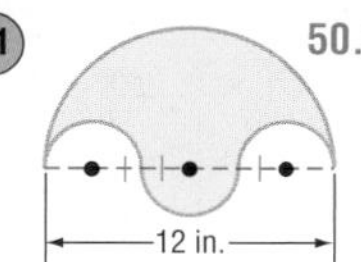

50.3 in²

42. 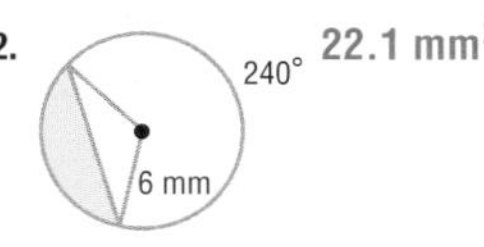

22.1 mm²

43. **MULTIPLE REPRESENTATIONS** In this problem, you will investigate segments of circles. A **segment of a circle** is the region bounded by an arc and a chord.

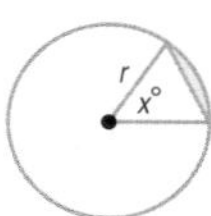

a. **Algebraic** Write an equation for the area A of a segment of a circle with a radius r and a central angle of $x°$. (*Hint*: Use trigonometry to find the base and height of the triangle.) **a–d. See margin.**

b. **Tabular** Calculate and record in a table ten values of A for x-values ranging from 10 to 90 if r is 12 inches. Round to the nearest tenth.

c. **Graphical** Graph the data from your table with the x-values on the horizontal axis and the A-values on the vertical axis.

d. **Analytical** Use your graph to predict the value of A when x is 63. Then use the formula you generated in part **a** to calculate the value of A when x is 63. How do the values compare?

H.O.T. Problems Use Higher-Order Thinking Skills

44. **ERROR ANALYSIS** Kristen and Chase want to find the area of the shaded region in the circle shown. Is either of them correct? Explain your reasoning.

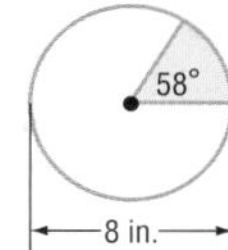

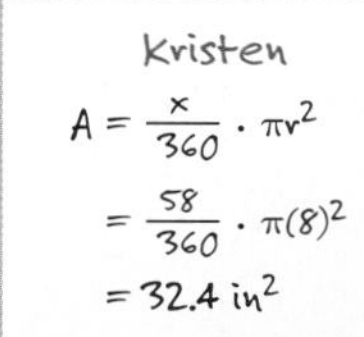
Kristen

$A = \frac{x}{360} \cdot \pi r^2$

$= \frac{58}{360} \cdot \pi(8)^2$

$= 32.4 \text{ in}^2$

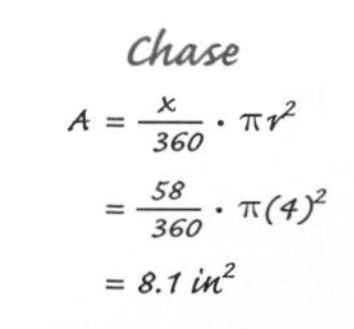
Chase

$A = \frac{x}{360} \cdot \pi r^2$

$= \frac{58}{360} \cdot \pi(4)^2$

$= 8.1 \text{ in}^2$

44. Chase; sample answer: Kristen used the diameter in the area formula instead of the radius.

45. **CHALLENGE** Find the area of the shaded region. Round to the nearest tenth. **449.0 cm²**

160°
10.5 cm
35 cm

46. **ARGUMENTS** Refer to Exercise 43. Is the area of a sector of a circle *sometimes*, *always*, or *never* greater than the area of its corresponding segment? **Sometimes; when the arc is a semicircle, the areas are the same.**

47. **WRITING IN MATH** Describe two methods you could use to find the area of the shaded region of the circle. Which method do you think is more efficient? Explain your reasoning. **See margin.**

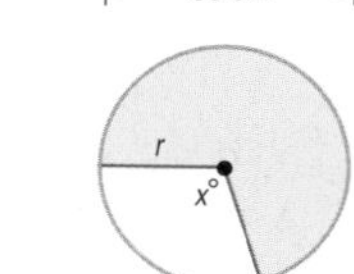

48. **CHALLENGE** Derive the formula for the area of a sector of a circle using the formula for arc length. **See Ch. 11 Answer Appendix.**

49. **WRITING IN MATH** If the radius of a circle doubles, will the measure of a sector of that circle double? Will it double if the arc measure of that sector doubles? **See Ch. 11 Answer Appendix.**

43d. Sample answer: From the graph, it looks like the area would be about 15.5 when x is 63°. Using the formula, the area is 15.0 when x is 63°. The values are very close because I used the formula to create the graph.

47. Sample answer: You can find the shaded area of the circle by subtracting x from 360° and using the resulting measure in the formula for the area of a sector. You could also find the shaded area by finding the area of the entire circle, finding the area of the unshaded sector using the formula for the area of a sector, and subtracting the area of the unshaded sector from the area of the entire circle. The method in which you find the ratio of the area of a sector to the area of the whole circle is more efficient. It requires less steps, is faster, and there is a lower probability for error.

Multiple Representations

In Exercise 43, students use algebraic equations, a table, and a graph to investigate segments of a circle.

WatchOut!

Error Analysis Students should remember that the formula for the area of a sector requires the radius of the circle. In Exercise 44, Kristen used the diameter instead of the radius.

Teaching the Mathematical Practices

Arguments Mathematically proficient students understand and use stated assumptions and definitions in constructing arguments. They are able to analyze situations by breaking them into cases, and can recognize and use counterexamples. In Exercise 46, dynamic geometry software can help students identify a counterexample.

Additional Answers

43a. $A = \frac{x\pi r^2}{360} - r^2\left[\sin\left(\frac{x}{2}\right)\cos\left(\frac{x}{2}\right)\right]$

43b.

x	A
10	0.1
20	0.5
30	1.7
40	4.0
45	5.6
50	7.7
60	13.0
70	20.3
80	29.6
90	41.1

43c.

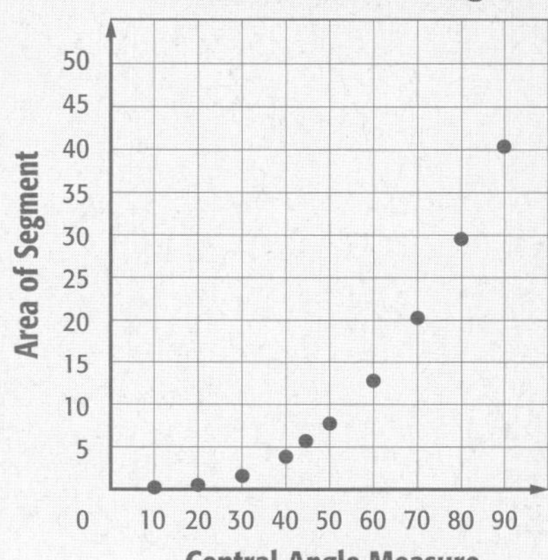

4 Assess

Ticket Out the Door Have students describe how to find the area of a circle, given its circumference.

Formative Assessment

Check for student understanding of Lesson 11-3.

Quiz 2, p. 39

Standardized Test Practice

50. What is the area of the sector? C

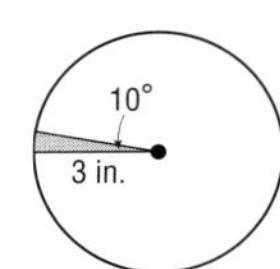

A $\frac{9\pi}{10}$ in^2 C $\frac{\pi}{4}$ in^2

B $\frac{3\pi}{5}$ in^2 D $\frac{\pi}{6}$ in^2

51. SHORT RESPONSE $\overleftrightarrow{MN}$ and $\overleftrightarrow{PQ}$ intersect at T. Find the value of x for which $m\angle MTQ = 2x + 5$ and $m\angle PTM = x + 7$. What are the degree measures of $\angle MTQ$ and $\angle PTM$? $x = 56$; $m\angle MTQ = 117$; $m\angle PTM = 63$

52. ALGEBRA Raphael bowled 4 games and had a mean score of 130. He then bowled two more games with scores of 180 and 230. What was his mean score for all 6 games? G

F 90 H 180

G 155 J 185

53. SAT/ACT The diagonals of rectangle $ABCD$ each have a length of 56 feet. If $m\angle BAC = 42°$, what is the length of $\overline{AB}$ to the nearest tenth of a foot? E

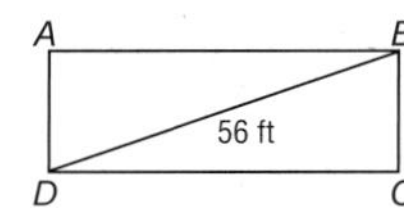

A 80.5 D 50.4

B 75.4 E 41.6

C 56.3

Spiral Review

Find each missing length. (Lesson 11-2)

54. One diagonal of a kite is half as long as the other diagonal. If the area of the kite is 188 square inches, what are the lengths of the diagonals? 27.4 in., 13.7 in.

55. The area of a rhombus is 175 square centimeters. If one diagonal is two times as long as the other, what are the lengths of the diagonals? 13.2 cm, 26.4 cm

Find the area of each parallelogram. Round to the nearest tenth if necessary. (Lesson 11-1)

56. 259.8 in^2

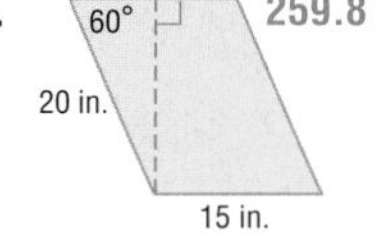

57.

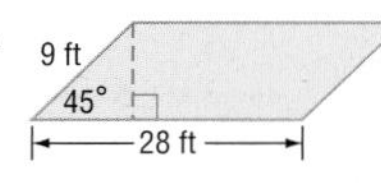

178.2 ft^2

58. 315.2 cm^2

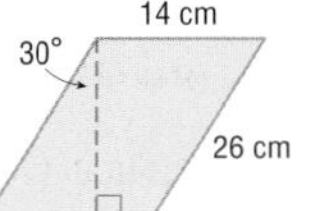

Skills Review

Find each measure.

59. XT 7

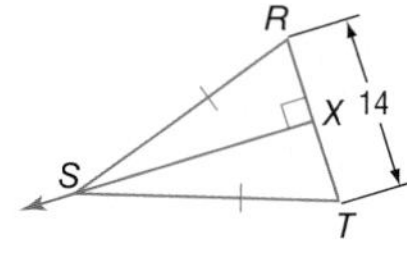

60. AC 38

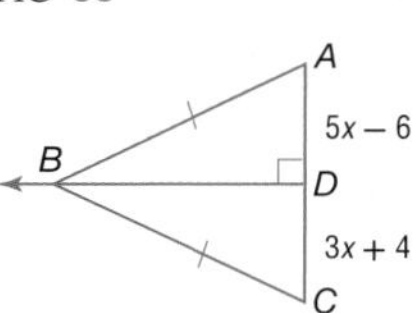

61. JK 31

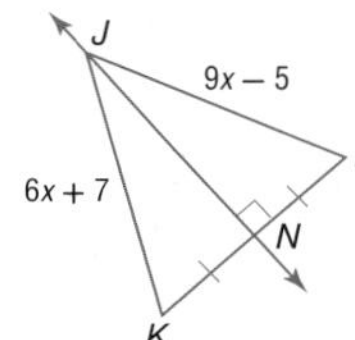

804 | Lesson 11-3 | Areas of Circles and Sectors

CHAPTER 11 Mid-Chapter Quiz

Lessons 11-1 through 11-3

Find the perimeter and area of each parallelogram or triangle. Round to the nearest tenth if necessary. (Lesson 11-1)

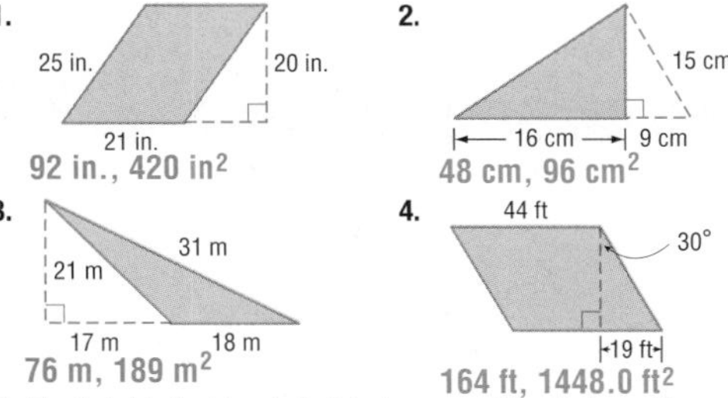

1. **92 in., 420 in^2**
2. **48 cm, 96 cm^2**
3. **76 m, 189 m^2**
4. **164 ft, 1448.0 ft^2**

5. The height of a triangle is 8 inches more than its base. The area of the triangle is 104.5 square inches. Find the base and height. (Lesson 11-1) **11 in., 19 in.**

6. **DESIGN** A plaque is made with a rhombus in the middle. If the diagonals of the rhombus measure 7 inches and 9 inches, how much space is available for engraving text onto the award? (Lesson 11-2) **31.5 in^2**

7. **MULTIPLE CHOICE** The area of a kite is 4 square feet. If the tail is to be 3 times longer than the kite's long diagonal, and the short diagonal measures 2 feet, how long should the kite's tail be? (Lesson 11-2) **D**

   A 4 feet **C** 7 feet

   B 6 feet **D** 12 feet

Find the area of each trapezoid, rhombus, or kite. (Lesson 11-2)

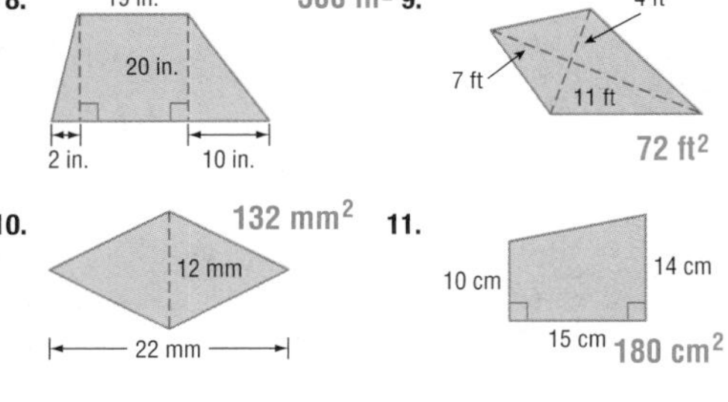

8. **500 in^2**
9. **72 ft^2**
10. **132 mm^2**
11. **180 cm^2**

12. **ARCHAEOLOGY** The most predominant shape in Incan architecture is the trapezoid. The doorway pictured below is 3 feet wide at the top and 4 feet wide at the bottom. A person who is 5 feet 8 inches tall can barely pass through the doorway. How much fabric would be necessary to make a curtain for the doorway? (Lesson 11-2) **19.8 ft^2**

13. **ALGEBRA** A sector of a circle has a central angle measure of 30° and radius r. Write an expression for the perimeter of the sector in terms of r. (Lesson 11-3) **$\frac{1}{6}\pi r + 2r$**

Find the area of each shaded sector. Round to the nearest tenth. (Lesson 11-3)

14. **1.8 cm^2**

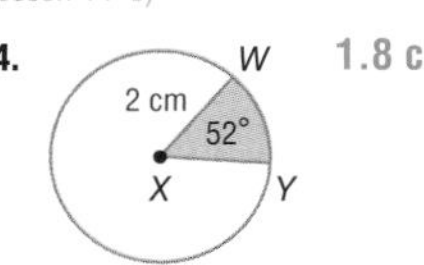

15. **207.6 in^2**

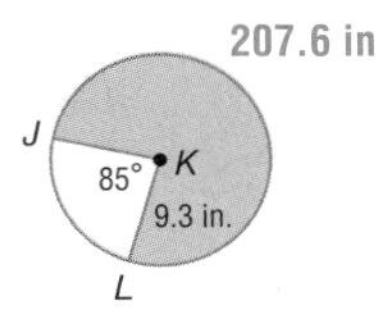

16. **10.0 ft^2**

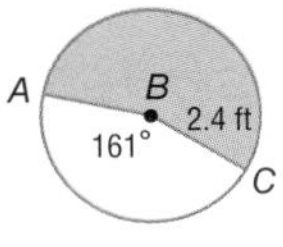

17. **182.6 mm^2**

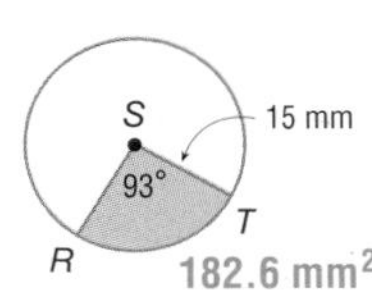

Find the indicated measure. Round to the nearest tenth. (Lesson 11-3)

18. The area of a circle is 52 square inches. Find the diameter. **8.1 in.**
19. Find the radius of a circle with an area of 104 square meters. **5.8 m**
20. **FRUIT** The diameter of the orange slice shown is 9 centimeters. If each of the orange's 10 sections are congruent, find the approximate area covered by 8 sections. (Lesson 11-3) **50.9 cm^2**

Formative Assessment

Use the Mid-Chapter Quiz to assess students' progress in the first half of the chapter.

Have students review the lesson indicated for the problems that they answered incorrectly.

Summative Assessment

Mid-Chapter Test, p. 41

eAssessment Customize and create multiple versions of your Mid-Chapter Test and their answer keys.

FOLDABLES® StudyOrganizer

Dinah Zike's Foldables®

Before students complete the Mid-Chapter Quiz, encourage them to review the information for Lessons 11-1 through 11-3 in their Foldables.

InterventionPlanner

TIER 1 On Level OL	TIER 2 Strategic Intervention AL approaching grade level	TIER 3 Intensive Intervention 2 or more grades below level
If students miss about 25% of the exercises or less,	**If** students miss about 50% of the exercises,	**If** students miss about 75% of the exercises,
Then choose a resource: SE Lessons 11-1, 11-2, and 11-3 Skills Practice, pp. 7, 15, and 21 connectED.mcgraw-hill.com Self-Check Quiz	**Then** choose a resource: Study Guide and Intervention, pp. 5, 13, and 19 connectED.mcgraw-hill.com Extra Examples, Personal Tutor, Homework Help	**Then** use *Math Triumphs, Geometry,* Ch. 5 connectED.mcgraw-hill.com Extra Examples, Personal Tutor, Homework Help, Review Vocabulary

1 Focus

Objective Investigate the formula for the area of regular polygons.

Materials

- straightedge
- compass

Teaching Tip

Discuss with students the characteristics of regular polygons. Every regular polygon can be divided into congruent triangles. The sum of the areas of each triangle (or the product of the area of one triangle and the number of sides of the polygon) equals the area of the polygon. The apothem bisects the central angle resulting in two congruent right triangles.

2 Teach

Working in Cooperative Groups

Arrange students in mixed-ability groups of 3 or 4. Direct students to discuss strategies for constructing a regular pentagon and the center point as they work through Steps 1–7 of the activity.

Ask:

- How do you know the five triangles inside the pentagon are congruent?

Practice Have students complete Analyze the Results 1 and 2.

3 Assess

Use Analyze the Results 2 to assess whether students understand the correlation between the area of a triangle and the area of the corresponding regular polygon.

EXPLORE 11-4

Geometry Lab
Investigating Areas of Regular Polygons

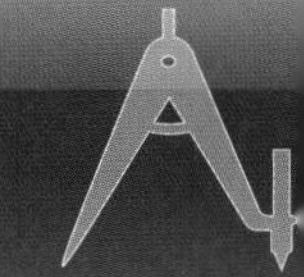

The point in the interior of a regular polygon that is equidistant from all of the vertices is the *center* of the polygon. A segment from the center that is perpendicular to a side of the polygon is an **apothem**.

Activity

Step 1 Copy regular pentagon *ABCDE* and its center *O*.

Step 2 Draw the apothem from *O* to side $\overline{AB}$ by constructing the perpendicular bisector of $\overline{AB}$. Label the apothem measure as *a*. Label the measure of $\overline{AB}$ as *s*.

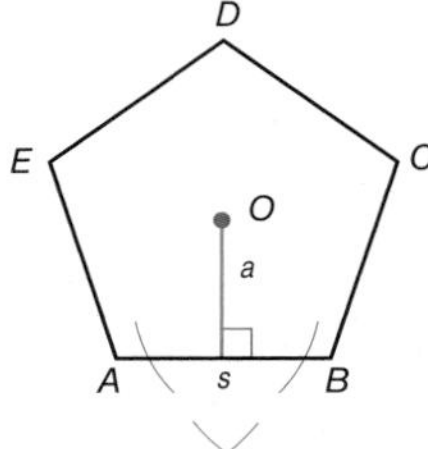

Step 3 Use a straightedge to draw $\overline{OA}$ and $\overline{OB}$.

Step 4 What measure in $\triangle AOB$ represents the base of the triangle? What measure represents the height? *s*; *a*

Step 5 Find the area of $\triangle AOB$ in terms of *s* and *a*. $\frac{1}{2}sa$

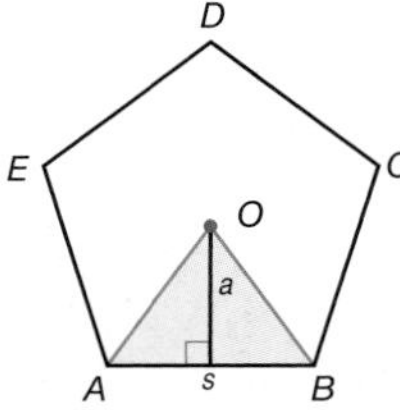

Step 6 Draw $\overline{OC}$, $\overline{OD}$, and $\overline{OE}$. What is true of the five small triangles formed? They are congruent.

Step 7 How do the areas of the five triangles compare? The areas are the same.

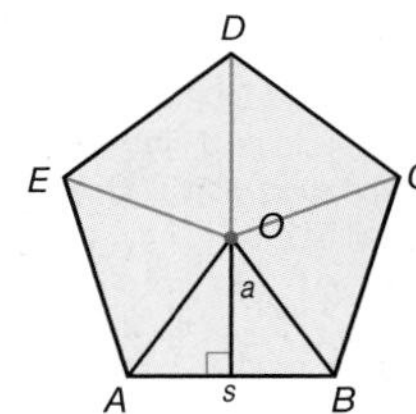

Analyze the Results

1. The area of a pentagon *ABCDE* can be found by adding the areas of the given triangles that make up the pentagonal region.
$A = \frac{1}{2}sa + \frac{1}{2}sa + \frac{1}{2}sa + \frac{1}{2}sa + \frac{1}{2}sa$
$A = \frac{1}{2}(sa + sa + sa + sa + sa)$ or $\frac{1}{2}(5sa)$
What does 5*s* represent? The perimeter of the pentagon
2. Write a formula for the area of a pentagon in terms of perimeter *P*. $A = \frac{1}{2}Pa$

Extending the Concept

Ask:

- Does this strategy for finding the area of a regular polygon apply to irregular polygons? Explain your reasoning. No; not all of the triangular areas would be the same.

From Concrete to Abstract

Ask:

- Could this strategy for finding the area of a regular polygon be used to the area of an irregular polygon if the irregular polygon were constructed from two or more regular polygons? Explain your reasoning. Yes; the sum of the two areas would equal the area of the irregular polygon.

LESSON 11-4 Areas of Regular Polygons and Composite Figures

Then	Now	Why?
You used inscribed and circumscribed figures and found the areas of circles.	1 Find areas of regular polygons. 2 Find areas of composite figures.	The top of the table shown is a regular hexagon. Notice that the top is composed of six congruent triangular sections. To find the area of the table top, you can find the sum of the areas of the sections.

NewVocabulary

center of a regular polygon
radius of a regular polygon
apothem
central angle of a regular polygon
composite figure

Common Core State Standards

Content Standards

G.MG.3 Apply geometric methods to solve problems (e.g., designing an object or structure to satisfy physical constraints or minimize cost; working with typographic grid systems based on ratios). ★

Mathematical Practices

1 Make sense of problems and persevere in solving them.
6 Attend to precision.

1 Areas of Regular Polygons

In the figure, a regular pentagon is *inscribed* in ⊙P, and ⊙P is *circumscribed* about the pentagon. The **center of a regular polygon** and the **radius of a regular polygon** are also the center and the radius of its circumscribed circle.

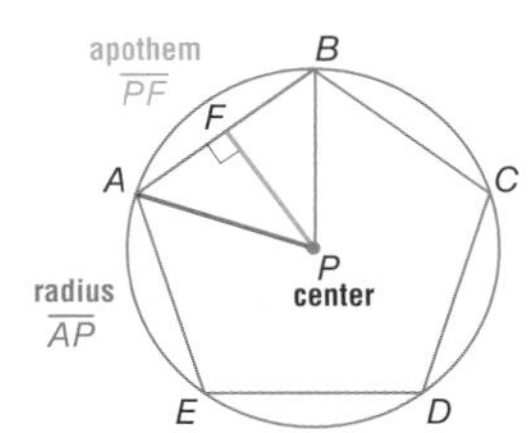

∠APB is a central angle of regular pentagon $ABCDE$.

A segment drawn from the center of a regular polygon perpendicular to a side of the polygon is called an **apothem**. Its length is the height of an isosceles triangle that has two radii as legs.

A **central angle of a regular polygon** has its vertex at the center of the polygon and its sides pass through consecutive vertices of the polygon. The measure of each central angle of a regular n-gon is $\frac{360}{n}$.

Example 1 Identify Segments and Angles in Regular Polygons

Square $FGHJ$ is inscribed in ⊙K. Identify the center, a radius, an apothem, and a central angle of the polygon. Then find the measure of a central angle.

center: point K radius: $\overline{KG}$ or $\overline{KH}$

apothem: $\overline{KL}$ central angle: ∠GKH

A square is a regular polygon with 4 sides. Thus, the measure of each central angle of square $FGHJ$ is $\frac{360}{4}$ or 90.

GuidedPractice

1. In the figure, regular hexagon $JKLMNP$ is inscribed in ⊙R. Identify the center, a radius, an apothem, and a central angle of the polygon. Then find the measure of a central angle. **center: point R, radius: $\overline{RK}$, apothem: $\overline{RS}$, central angle: $m∠KRL$, 60**

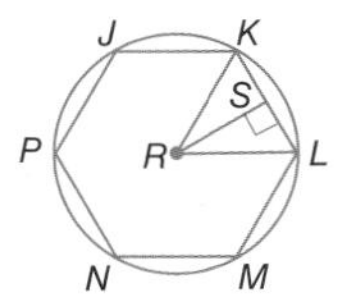

You can find the area of any regular n-gon by dividing the polygon into congruent isosceles triangles. This strategy is sometimes called *decomposing the polygon into triangles.*

1 Focus

VerticalAlignment

Before Lesson 11-4 Use inscribed and circumscribed figures and find the areas of circles.

Lesson 11-4 Find areas of regular polygons and composite figures.

After Lesson 11-4 Find the areas of similar figures.

2 Teach

Scaffolding Questions

Have students read the **Why?** section of the lesson.

Ask:

- How many sides does the table have? six
- If the area of one of the triangular sections of the table is 5 square feet, what is the area of the table? 30 ft²
- How can you find the area of a table that is composed of 10 triangular parts? Find the sum of the areas of the triangular sections.

Lesson 11-4 Resources

Resource	Approaching Level AL	On Level OL	Beyond Level BL	English Learners ELL
Teacher Edition	▪ Differentiated Instruction, p. 813	▪ Differentiated Instruction, pp. 809, 810, 813	▪ Differentiated Instruction, pp. 809, 810	▪ Differentiated Instruction, p. 813
Chapter Resource Masters	▪ Study Guide and Intervention, pp. 25–26 ▪ Skills Practice, p. 27 ▪ Practice, p. 28 ▪ Word Problem Practice, p. 29	▪ Study Guide and Intervention, pp. 25–26 ▪ Skills Practice, p. 27 ▪ Practice, p. 28 ▪ Word Problem Practice, p. 29 ▪ Enrichment, p. 30	▪ Practice, p. 28 ▪ Word Problem Practice, p. 29 ▪ Enrichment, p. 30	▪ Study Guide and Intervention, pp. 25–26 ▪ Skills Practice, p. 27 ▪ Practice, p. 28 ▪ Word Problem Practice, p. 29
Other	▪ 5-Minute Check 11-4 ▪ Study Notebook ▪ Teaching Geometry with Manipulatives	▪ 5-Minute Check 11-4 ▪ Study Notebook ▪ Teaching Geometry with Manipulatives	▪ 5-Minute Check 11-4 ▪ Study Notebook	▪ 5-Minute Check 11-4 ▪ Study Notebook ▪ Teaching Geometry with Manipulatives

1 Areas of Regular Polygons

Example 1 shows how to identify segments and angles in a regular polygon. **Examples 2 and 3** show how to find the area of a regular polygon.

Formative Assessment

Use the Guided Practice exercises after each example to determine students' understanding of concepts.

Additional Examples

1 In the figure, pentagon $PQRST$ is inscribed in $\odot X$. Identify the center, a radius, an apothem, and a central angle of the polygon. Then find the measure of a central angle.

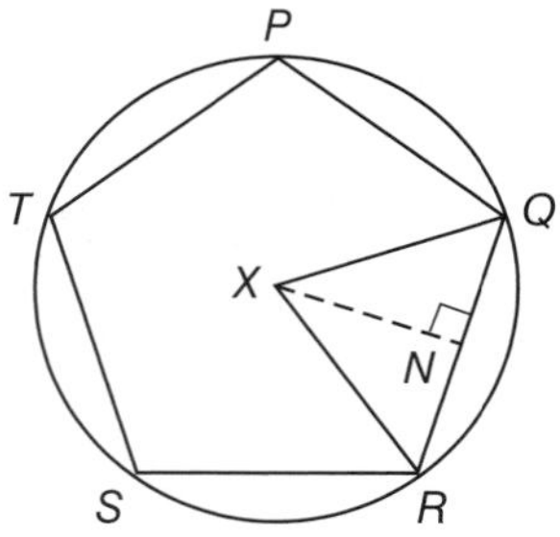

center: point X; radius: $\overline{XR}$ or $\overline{XQ}$; apothem: $\overline{XN}$; central angle: $\angle RXN$; $m\angle RXN = 72$

2 **FURNITURE** The top of the table shown is a regular hexagon with a side length of 3 feet and an apothem of 1.7 feet. What is the area of the tabletop to the nearest tenth?

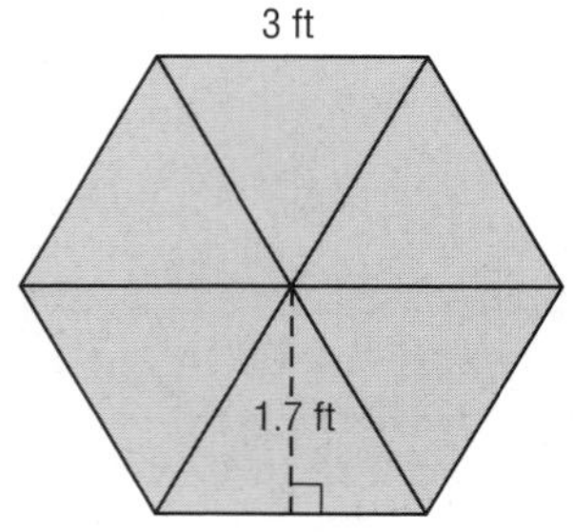

15.3 ft^2

Additional Examples also in Interactive Classroom PowerPoint® Presentations

ReadingMath

Apothem Like the *radius* of a circle, the *apothem* of a polygon refers to the length of any apothem of the polygon.

Real-World Example 2 Area of a Regular Polygon

ART **Kang created the stained glass window shown. The window is a regular octagon with a side length of 15 inches and an apothem of 18.1 inches. What is the area covered by the window?**

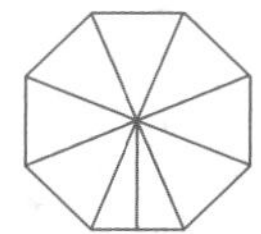

Step 1 Divide the polygon into congruent isosceles triangles.

Since the polygon has 8 sides, the polygon can be divided into 8 congruent isosceles triangles, each with a base of 15 inches and a height of 18.1 inches.

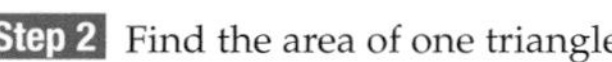

Step 2 Find the area of one triangle.

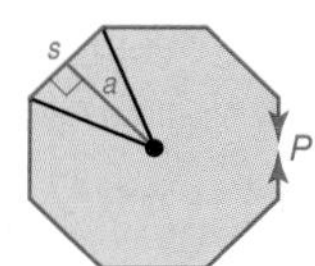

$A = \frac{1}{2}bh$ Area of a triangle

$= \frac{1}{2}(15)(18.1)$ $b = 15$ and $h = 18.1$

$= 135.75 \text{ in}^2$ Simplify.

Step 3 Multiply the area of one triangle by the total number of triangles.

Since there are 8 triangles, the area of the stained glass is 135.75 • 8 or 1086 square inches.

GuidedPractice

2. **HOT TUBS** The cover of the hot tub shown is a regular pentagon. If the side length is 2.5 feet and the apothem is 1.7 feet, find the area of the lid to the nearest tenth. **10.6 ft^2**

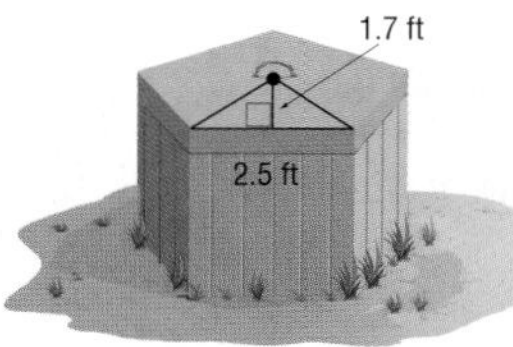

WatchOut!

Area of Regular Polygon this approach can only be applied to *regular* polygons.

From Example 2, we can develop a formula for the area of a regular n-gon with side length s and apothem a.

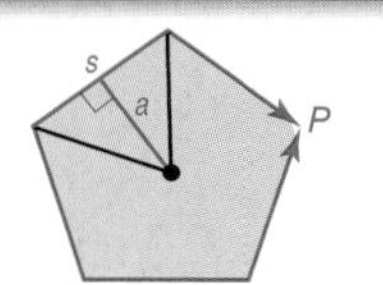

A = area of one triangle • number of triangles

$= \frac{1}{2}$ • base • height • number of triangles

$= \frac{1}{2} \cdot s \cdot a \cdot n$ Base of triangle is s and height is a. The number of triangles is n.

$= \frac{1}{2} \cdot a \cdot (n \cdot s)$ Commutative and Associative Properties

$= \frac{1}{2} \cdot a \cdot P$ The perimeter P of the polygon is $n \cdot s$.

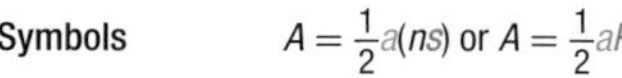

KeyConcept Area of a Regular Polygon

Words	The area A of a regular n-gon with side length s is one half the product of the apothem a and perimeter P.	
Symbols	$A = \frac{1}{2}a(ns)$ or $A = \frac{1}{2}aP$.	

Tips for New Teachers

Reasoning Remind students that the area of a regular polygon can be found using two different methods. Demonstrate to students that they can find the area of the component triangles or use the formula for the area of a regular polygon. Encourage students to use whichever method they are most comfortable with.

Example 3 Use the Formula for the Area of a Regular Polygon

Find the area of each regular polygon. Round to the nearest tenth.

a. regular hexagon

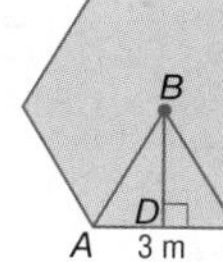

Step 1 Find the measure of a central angle.

A regular hexagon has 6 congruent central angles, so $m\angle ABC = \frac{360}{6}$ or 60.

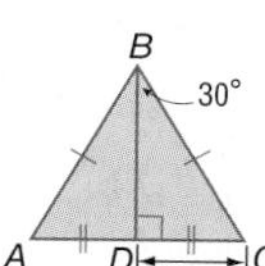

Step 2 Find the apothem.

Apothem $\overline{BD}$ is the height of isosceles $\triangle ABC$. It bisects $\angle ABC$, so $m\angle DBC = 30$. It also bisects $\overline{AC}$, so $DC = 1.5$ meters.

$\triangle BDC$ is a 30°-60°-90° triangle with a shorter leg that measures 1.5 meters, so $BD = 1.5\sqrt{3}$ meters.

> **StudyTip**
> **CCSS Precision** The altitude of an isosceles triangle from its vertex to its base is also an angle bisector and median of the triangle.

Step 3 Use the apothem and side length to find the area.

$A = \frac{1}{2}aP$ — Area of a regular polygon

$= \frac{1}{2}(1.5\sqrt{3})(18)$ — $a = 1.5\sqrt{3}$ and $P = 6(3)$ or 18

$\approx 23.4 \text{ m}^2$ — Use a calculator.

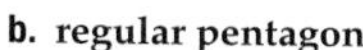

b. regular pentagon

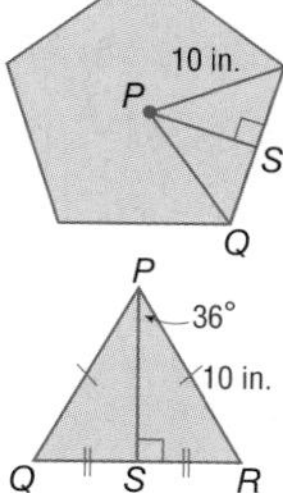

Step 1 A regular pentagon has 5 congruent central angles, so $m\angle QPR = \frac{360}{5}$ or 72.

Step 2 Apothem $\overline{PS}$ is the height of isosceles $\triangle RPQ$. It bisects $\angle RPQ$, so $m\angle RPS = 36$. Use trigonometric ratios to find the side length and apothem of the polygon.

$\sin 36° = \frac{SR}{10}$ $\qquad$ $\cos 36° = \frac{PS}{10}$

$10 \sin 36° = SR$ $\qquad$ $10 \cos 36° = PS$

$QR = 2SR$ or $2(10 \sin 36°)$. So the pentagon's perimeter is $5 \cdot 2(10 \sin 36°)$ or $10(10 \sin 36°)$. The length of the apothem $\overline{PS}$ is $10 \cos 36°$.

Step 3 $A = \frac{1}{2}aP$ — Area of a regular polygon

$= \frac{1}{2}(10 \cos 36°)[10(10 \sin 36°)]$ — $a = 10 \cos 36°$, $P = 10(10 \sin 36°)$

$\approx 237.8 \text{ in}^2$ — Use a calculator.

GuidedPractice

3A. **6.9 ft²**

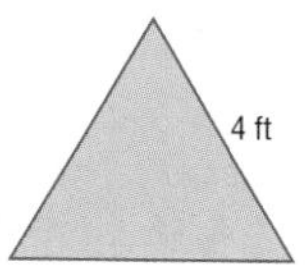

3B. **98 cm²**

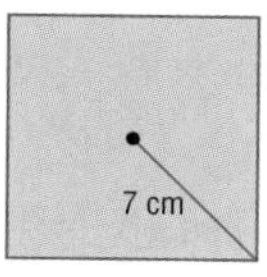

3C. **212.1 in²**

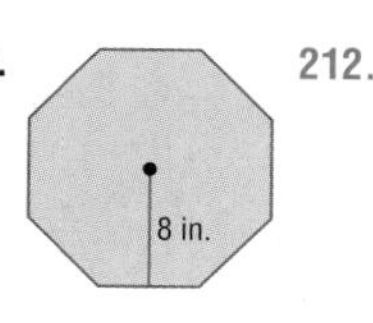

2 Areas of Composite Figures

A **composite figure** is a figure that can be separated into regions that are basic figures, such as triangles, rectangles, trapezoids, and circles. To find the area of a composite figure, find the area of each basic figure and then use the Area Addition Postulate.

DifferentiatedInstruction OL BL

Extension Have students describe how to find the area of an inscribed polygon. First, find the apothem, or the distance from the center of the polygon perpendicular to the midpoint of the opposite side. Then, find half the product of the perimeter and the apothem.

Additional Example

3 Find the area of each regular polygon. Round to the nearest tenth.

a. regular hexagon

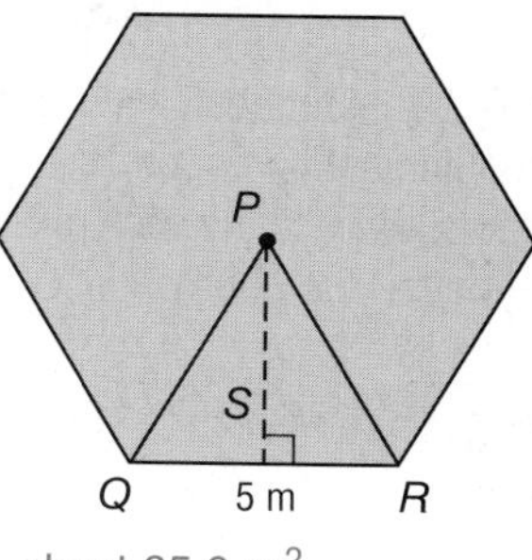

about 65.0 m²

b. regular pentagon

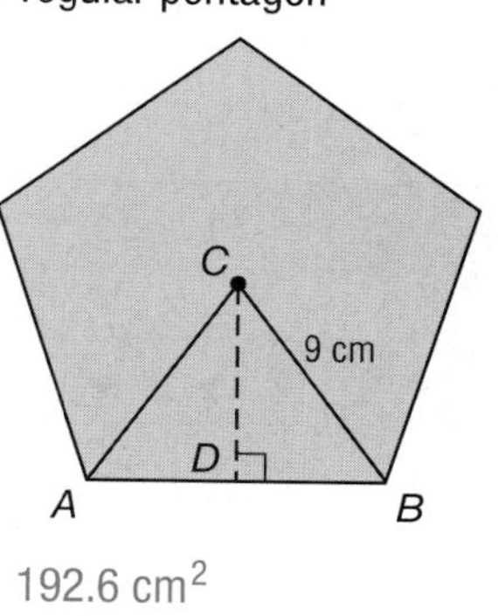

192.6 cm²

Focus on Mathematical Content

Area of Irregular Polygons Watch for students who think that the area formula for a regular polygon applies to any polygon. Stress that to find the area of a polygon that is not regular, you may need to divide the polygon into shapes with known area formulas.

Teaching the Mathematical Practices

Precision Mathematically proficient students use clear definitions in discussion with others and in their own reasoning. Encourage students to connect the altitude of a triangle to the altitude of a polygon.

2 Areas of Composite Figures

Examples 4 and 5 show how to find the area of an irregular figure by using known area formulas.

Additional Examples

4 **POOL** The dimensions of an irregularly shaped pool are shown. What is the area of the surface of the pool? 953.1 ft^2

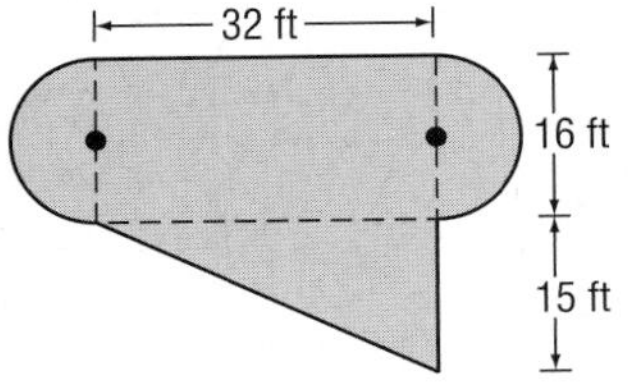

5 Find the area of the shaded figure. 8500 ft^2

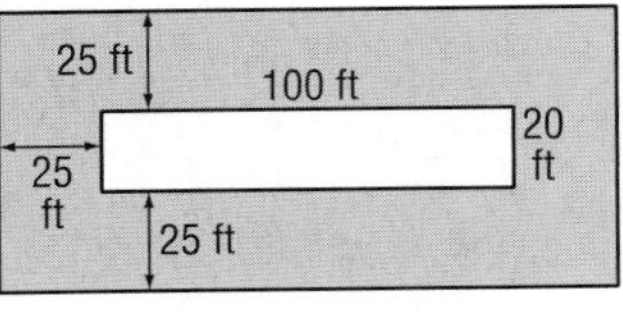

Teach with Tech

Video Recording Separate students into groups. Give each group the same composite figure and ask them to find the area. Have students explain the process they used to find the area. Record their explanations. Show the videos to the entire class to see if students had different approaches to solving the same problem.

Real-WorldLink

The first miniature golf course was built in Pinehurst, North Carolina, on a private estate owned by James Barber. There are currently between 5000 and 7500 miniature golf courses in the United States.

Source: Miniature Golf Association of the United States

Example 4 Find the Area of a Composite Figure by Adding

MINIATURE GOLF The dimensions of a putting green at a miniature golf course are shown. How many square feet of carpet are needed to cover this green?

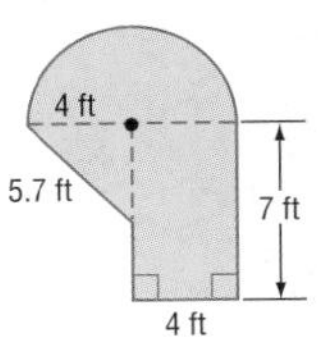

The area to be carpeted can be separated into a rectangle with a length of 4 feet and a width of 7 feet, a right triangle with a hypotenuse of 5.7 feet and a leg measuring 4 feet, and a semicircle with a radius of 4 feet.

Using the Pythagorean Theorem, the other leg of the right triangle is $\sqrt{5.7^2 - 4^2}$ or about 4.1 feet.

Area of green = area of rectangle + area of triangle + area of semicircle.

$$= \ell \cdot w + \frac{1}{2} \cdot b \cdot h + \frac{180}{360} \cdot \pi \cdot r^2$$

$$\approx 4 \cdot 7 + \frac{1}{2} \cdot 4 \cdot 4.1 + \frac{180}{360} \cdot \pi \cdot 4^2$$

$$\approx 28 + 8.2 + 8\pi \text{ or about } 61.3 \text{ ft}^2$$

So, about 62 square feet of carpet is needed.

GuidedPractice

Find the area of each figure. Round to the nearest tenth if necessary.

4A. 155.5 in^2 **4B.** 374.5 cm^2

The areas of some figures can be found by subtracting the areas of basic figures.

Example 5 Find the Area of a Composite Figure by Subtracting

Find the area of the figure. Round to the nearest tenth if necessary.

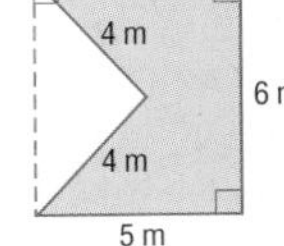

To find the area of the figure, subtract the area of the triangle from the area of the rectangle.

Using the Pythagorean Theorem, the height h of the triangle is $\sqrt{4^2 - 3^2}$ or $\sqrt{7}$ meters.

Area of figure = Area of rectangle − Area of triangle

$$= b \cdot h - \frac{1}{2}bh$$

$$= 5 \cdot 6 - \frac{1}{2}(6)(\sqrt{7})$$

$$\approx 30 - 7.9 \text{ or about } 22.1 \text{ m}^2$$

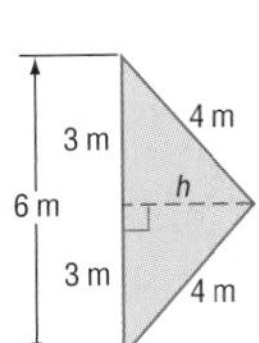

GuidedPractice

5A. 63.2 m^2

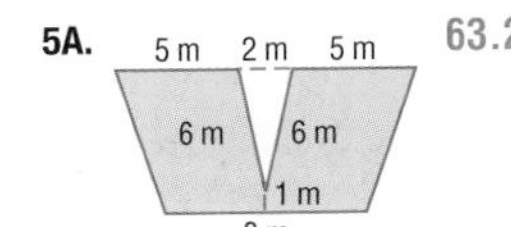

5B. 63 ft^2

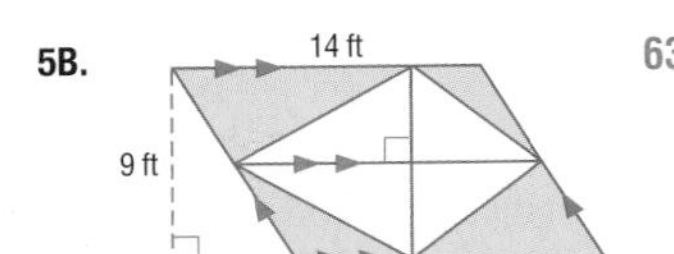

DifferentiatedInstruction OL BL

Extension Have the students find the area of the blue section of the United States flag. The regular pentagon in the center of the star has an apothem of 0.25 centimeter. The triangles of the star have bases of 1 centimeter and height of 1.5 centimeters. The area of each star is 4.375 cm^2. So the area of all the stars is 218.75 cm^2. The area of the blue section is 1321.92 cm^2. The difference is 1103.17 cm^2.

Check Your Understanding

= Step-by-Step Solutions begin on page R14.

Example 1 **1.** In the figure, square *ABDC* is inscribed in ⊙*F*. Identify the center, a radius, an apothem, and a central angle of the polygon. Then find the measure of a central angle. **See margin.**

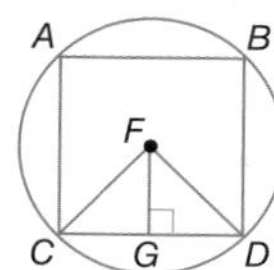

Examples 2–3 **Find the area of each regular polygon. Round to the nearest tenth.**

2. **15.6 m^2**

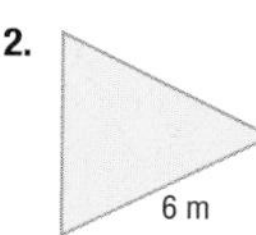

3. **162 in^2**

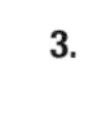

4. **POOLS** Kenton's job is to cover the community pool during fall and winter. Since the pool is in the shape of an octagon, he needs to find the area in order to have a custom cover made. If the pool has the dimensions shown at the right, what is the area of the pool? **120 ft^2**

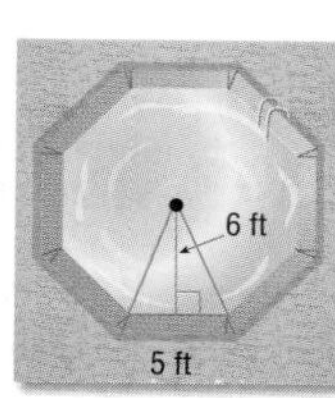

Examples 4–5 **CCSS SENSE-MAKING** **Find the area of each figure. Round to the nearest tenth if necessary.**

5. **239 ft^2**

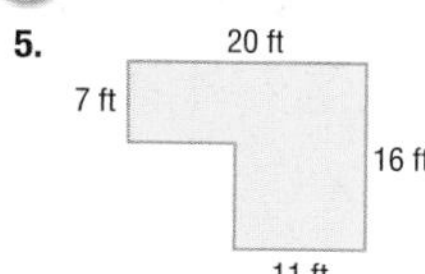

6. **71.8 in^2**

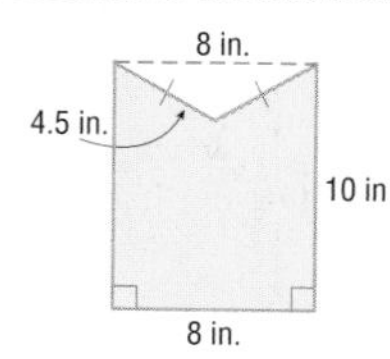

7 **BASKETBALL** The basketball court in Jeff's school is painted as shown.

a. What area of the court is blue? Round to the nearest square foot.

b. What area of the court is red? Round to the nearest square foot.

a. 371 ft^2 **b. 311 ft^2**

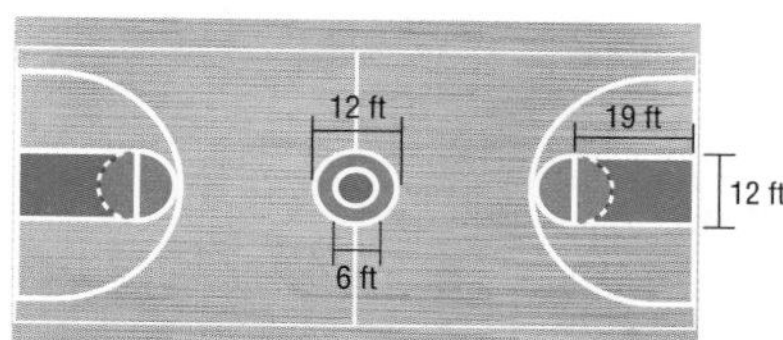

Note: Art not drawn to scale.

Practice and Problem Solving

Extra Practice is on page R11.

Example 1 **In each figure, a regular polygon is inscribed in a circle. Identify the center, a radius, an apothem, and a central angle of each polygon. Then find the measure of a central angle.**

8–9. See margin.

8.

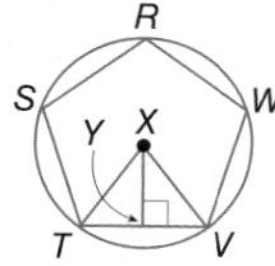

9.

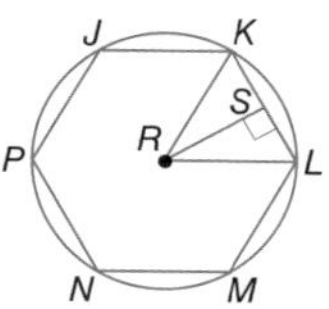

Differentiated Homework Options

Level	Assignment	Two-Day Option	
AL Basic	8–21, 35, 37–55	9–21 odd, 40–43	8–20 even, 35, 37–39, 44–55
OL Core	9–21 odd, 23–33 odd, 34, 35, 37–55	8–21, 40–43	22–35, 37–39, 44–55
BL Advanced	22–53, (54–55 optional)		

3 Practice

Formative Assessment

Use Exercises 1–7 to check for understanding.

Use the chart at the bottom of this page to customize assignments for your students.

CCSS Teaching the Mathematical Practices

Sense-Making Mathematically proficient students start by explaining the meaning of a problem to themselves and looking for entry points to its solution. They plan a solution pathway rather than simply jumping into a solution attempt. In Exercises 5–6, encourage students to make a plan to solve each problem first.

Additional Answers

1. center: point *F*, radius: $\overline{FD}$, apothem: $\overline{FG}$, central angle: $\angle CFD$, 90

8. center: point *X*, radius: $\overline{XV}$, apothem: $\overline{XY}$, central angle: $\angle VXT$, 72

9. center: point *R*, radius: $\overline{RL}$, apothem: $\overline{RS}$, central angle: $\angle KRL$, 60

Study Guide and Intervention

AL OL ELL

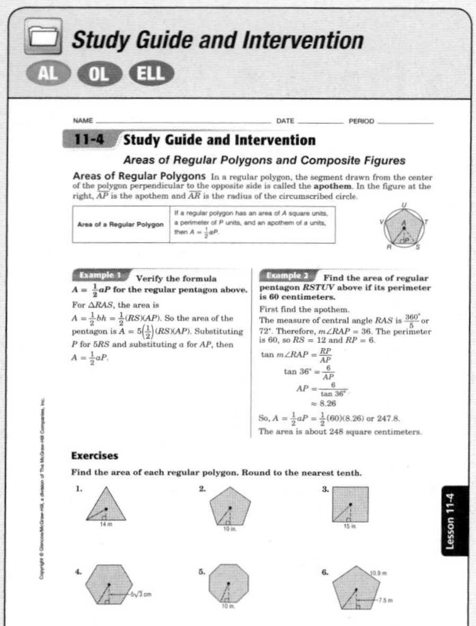

NAME ________ DATE ______ PERIOD ______

11-4 Study Guide and Intervention

Areas of Regular Polygons and Composite Figures

Areas of Regular Polygons In a regular polygon, the segment drawn from the center of the polygon perpendicular to the opposite side is called the **apothem**. In the figure at the right, $\overline{AP}$ is the apothem and $\overline{AR}$ is the radius of the circumscribed circle.

Area of a Regular Polygon	If a regular polygon has an area of A square units, a perimeter of P units, and an apothem of a units, then $A = \frac{1}{2}aP$.

Example 1 Verify the formula $A = \frac{1}{2}aP$ for the regular pentagon above.

For $\triangle RAS$, the area is $A = \frac{1}{2}bh = \frac{1}{2}(RS)(AP)$. So the area of the pentagon is $A = 5\left(\frac{1}{2}\right)(RS)(AP)$. Substituting P for 5RS and substituting a for AP, then $A = \frac{1}{2}aP$.

Example 2 Find the area of regular pentagon RSTUV above if its perimeter is 60 centimeters.

First find the apothem.

The measure of central angle RAS is $\frac{360°}{5}$ or 72°. Therefore, $m\angle RAP = 36$. The perimeter is 60, so $RS = 12$ and $RP = 6$.

$\tan m\angle RAP = \frac{RP}{AP}$

$\tan 36° = \frac{6}{AP}$

$AP = \frac{6}{\tan 36°}$

≈ 8.26

So, $A = \frac{1}{2}aP = \frac{1}{2}(60)(8.26)$ or 247.8.

The area is about 248 square centimeters.

Exercises

Find the area of each regular polygon. Round to the nearest tenth.

Practice

AL OL BL ELL

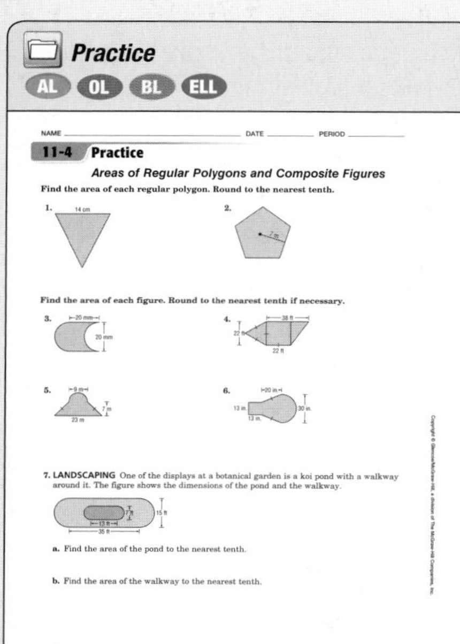

NAME ________ DATE ______ PERIOD ______

11-4 Practice

Areas of Regular Polygons and Composite Figures

Find the area of each regular polygon. Round to the nearest tenth.

Find the area of each figure. Round to the nearest tenth if necessary.

7. LANDSCAPING One of the displays at a botanical garden is a koi pond with a walkway around it. The figure shows the dimensions of the pond and the walkway.

a. Find the area of the pond to the nearest tenth.

b. Find the area of the walkway to the nearest tenth.

Word Problem Practice

AL OL BL ELL

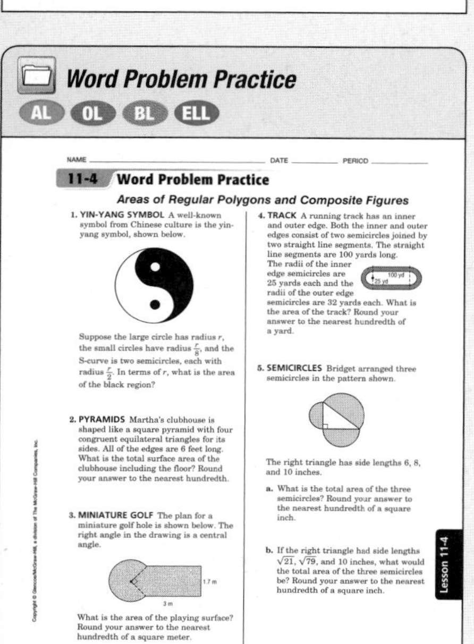

NAME ________ DATE ______ PERIOD ______

11-4 Word Problem Practice

Areas of Regular Polygons and Composite Figures

1. YIN-YANG SYMBOL A well-known symbol from Chinese culture is the yin-yang symbol, shown below.

Suppose the large circle has radius r, the small circles have radius $\frac{r}{5}$, and the S-curve is two semicircles, each with radius $\frac{r}{2}$. In terms of r, what is the area of the black region?

2. PYRAMIDS Martha's clubhouse is shaped like a square pyramid with four congruent equilateral triangles for its sides. All of the edges are 6 feet long. What is the total surface area of the clubhouse including the floor? Round your answer to the nearest hundredth.

3. MINIATURE GOLF The plan for a miniature golf hole is shown below. The right angle in the drawing is a central angle.

What is the area of the playing surface? Round your answer to the nearest hundredth of a square meter.

4. TRACK A running track has an inner and outer edge. Both the inner and outer edges consist of two semicircles joined by two straight line segments. The straight line segments are 100 yards long. The radii of the inner edge semicircles are 25 yards each and the radii of the outer edge semicircles are 32 yards each. What is the area of the track? Round your answer to the nearest hundredth of a yard.

5. SEMICIRCLES Bridget arranged three semicircles in the pattern shown.

The right triangle has side lengths 6, 8, and 10 inches.

a. What is the total area of the three semicircles? Round your answer to the nearest hundredth of a square inch.

b. If the right triangle had side lengths $\sqrt{21}$, $\sqrt{79}$, and 10 inches, what would the total area of the three semicircles be? Round your answer to the nearest hundredth of a square inch.

Examples 2–3 **Find the area of each regular polygon. Round to the nearest tenth.**

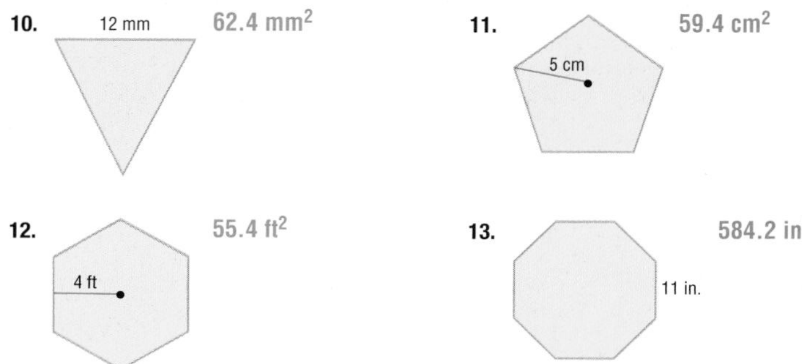

Example 4 **14. CARPETING** Ignacio's family is getting new carpet in their family room, and they want to determine how much the project will cost.

a. Use the floor plan shown to find the area to be carpeted. 363 ft^2

b. If the carpet costs \$4.86 per square yard, how much will the project cost? \$196.02

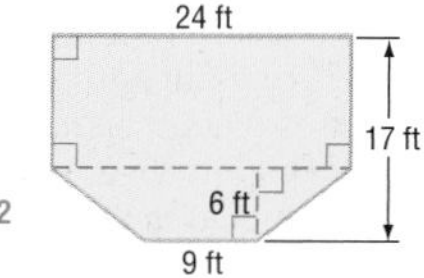

Examples 4–5 CCSS **SENSE-MAKING** **Find the area of each figure. Round to the nearest tenth if necessary.**

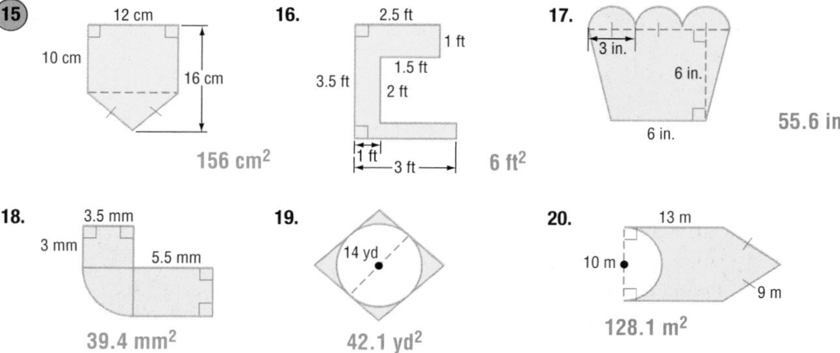

18. 3.5 mm, 3 mm, 5.5 mm — 39.4 mm^2

19.

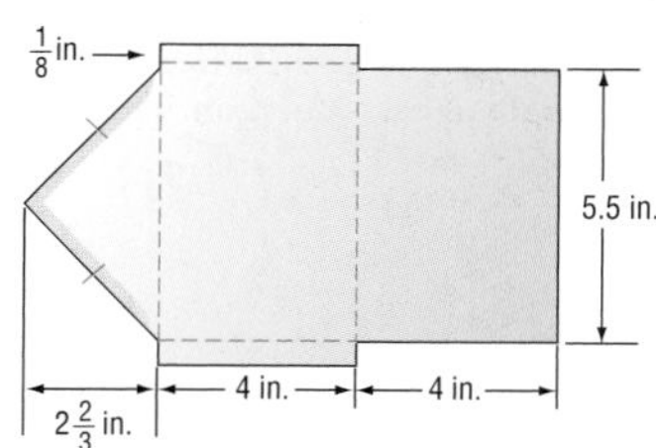

42.1 yd^2

20. 13 m, 10 m, 9 m — 128.1 m^2

21. CRAFTS Latoya's greeting card company is making envelopes for a card from the pattern shown. a. 29.7 in., 52.3 in^2

a. Find the perimeter and area of the pattern. Round to the nearest tenth.

b. If Latoya orders sheets of paper that are 2 feet by 4 feet, how many envelopes can she make per sheet? 16

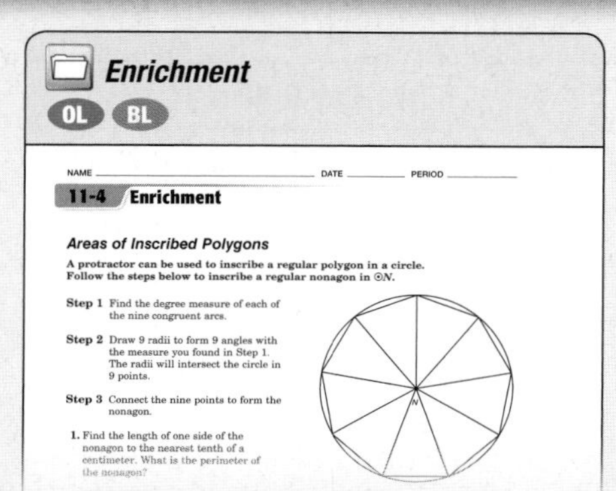

Enrichment

OL BL

NAME ________ DATE ______ PERIOD ______

11-4 Enrichment

Areas of Inscribed Polygons

A protractor can be used to inscribe a regular polygon in a circle. Follow the steps below to inscribe a regular nonagon in ⊙N.

Step 1 Find the degree measure of each of the nine congruent arcs.

Step 2 Draw 9 radii to form 9 angles with the measure you found in Step 1. The radii will intersect the circle in 9 points.

Step 3 Connect the nine points to form the nonagon.

1. Find the length of one side of the nonagon to the nearest tenth of a centimeter. What is the perimeter of the nonagon?

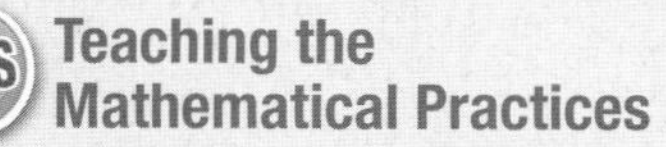

Teaching the Mathematical Practices

Sense-Making Mathematically proficient students start by explaining the meaning of a problem to themselves and looking for entry points to its solution. They plan a solution pathway rather than simply jumping into a solution attempt. In Exercises 5–6, encourage students to make a plan to solve each problem first.

B **Find the area of each shaded region formed by each circle and regular polygon. Round to the nearest tenth.**

22. 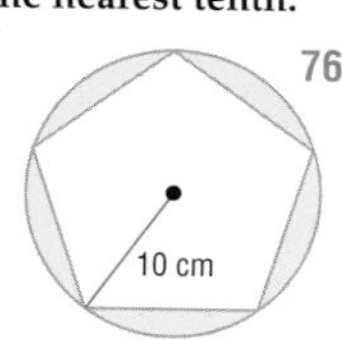

76.4 cm^2

23. 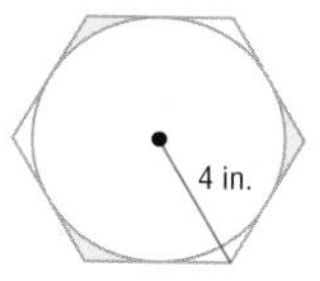

1.9 in^2

24. 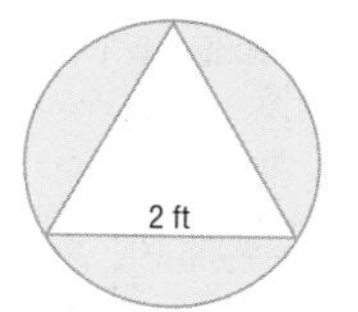

2.5 ft^2

25. FLOORING JoAnn wants to lay 12″ × 12″ tile on her bathroom floor.

a. Find the area of the bathroom floor in her apartment floor plan. 50.9 ft^2

b. If the tile comes in boxes of 15 and JoAnn buys no extra tile, how many boxes will she need? 4 boxes

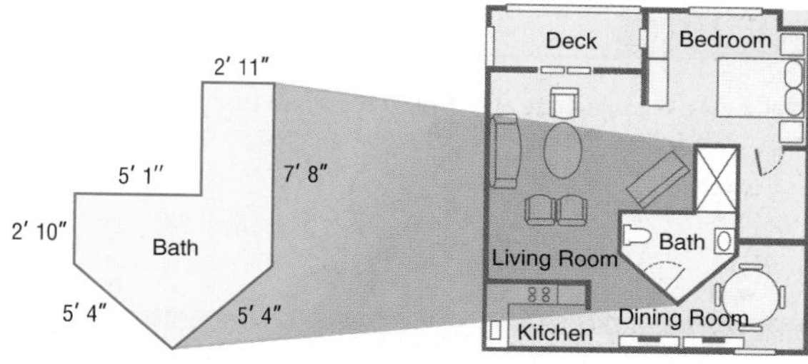

Find the perimeter and area of each figure. Round to the nearest tenth, if necessary.

26. a regular hexagon with a side length of 12 centimeters 72 cm; 374.1 cm^2

27. a regular pentagon circumscribed about a circle with a radius of 8 millimeters 58.1 mm; 232.4 mm^2

28. a regular octagon inscribed in a circle with a radius of 5 inches 30.6 in.; 70.7 in^2

CCSS **PERSEVERANCE** **Find the area of each shaded region. Round to the nearest tenth.**

29 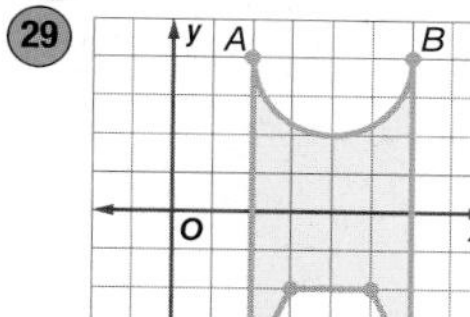

19.7 $units^2$

30. 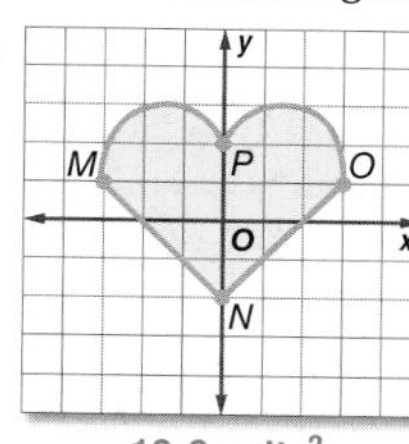

19.9 $units^2$

31. 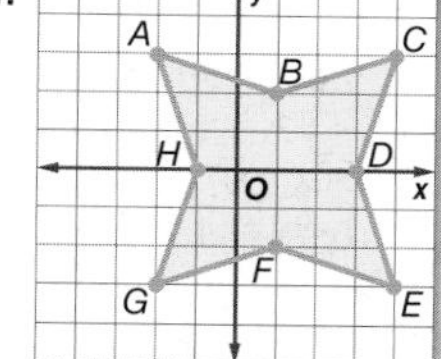

24 $units^2$

32. Find the total area of the shaded regions. Round to the nearest tenth. 52.0 in^2

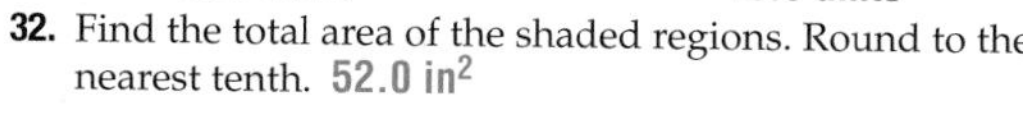

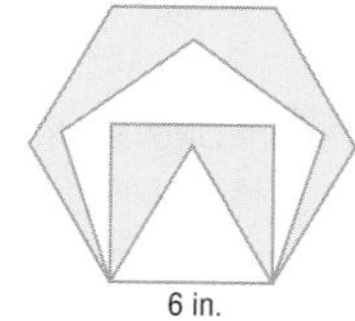

33. 0.43 in^2; 0.56 in^2; 0.62 in^2; 0.65 in^2; Sample answer: When the perimeter of a regular polygon is constant, as the number of sides increases, the area of the polygon increases.

33. CHANGING DIMENSIONS Calculate the area of an equilateral triangle with a perimeter of 3 inches. Calculate the areas of a square, a regular pentagon, and a regular hexagon with perimeters of 3 inches. How does the area of a regular polygon with a fixed perimeter change as the number of sides increases?

DifferentiatedInstruction AL OL ELL

Interpersonal Learners Have the students discuss how finding the area of a composite figure is similar to finding the area of a parallelogram, triangle, or trapezoid. Students should realize that throughout this chapter, they have separated figures into simpler regions to find area.

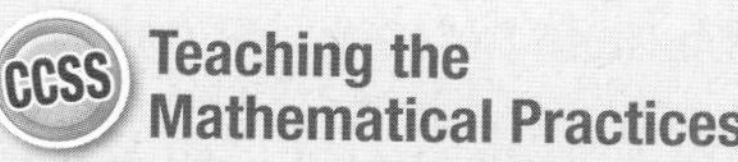

Teaching the Mathematical Practices

Perseverance Mathematically proficient students check their answers to problems using a different method, and they continually ask themselves, "does this make sense?" In Exercises 29–31, encourage students to check their answers.

Multiple Representations

In Exercise 34, students use geometric constructions, algebraic equations, and a table to investigate the areas of polygons inscribed in circles.

WatchOut!

Error Analysis Students should understand that a hexagon is composed of six equilateral triangles. In Exercise 35, the length of one side of the hexagon is 11 inches and its perimeter is 66 inches. Chloe calculated the perimeter correctly.

Teaching the Mathematical Practices

Sense-Making Mathematically proficient students consider analogous problems and try simpler forms of the original problem in order to gain insight into its solution. In Exercise 36, encourage students to divide the shape of the state into a triangle and rectangle.

Additional Answers

34a.

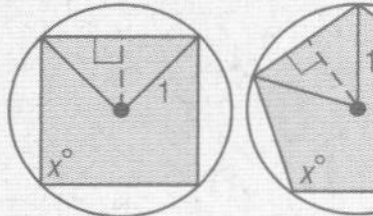

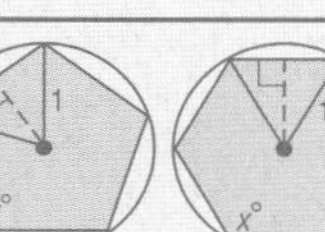

35. Chloe; sample answer: The measure of each angle of a regular hexagon is 120°, so the segments from the center to each vertex form 60° angles. The triangles formed by the segments from the center to each vertex are equilateral, so each side of the hexagon is 11 in. The perimeter of the hexagon is 66 in. Using trigonometry, the length of the apothem is about 9.5 in. Putting the values into the formula for the area of a regular polygon and simplifying, the area is about 313.5 in^2.

36. Sample answer: Divide Nevada into a rectangle that is about 315 miles by about 210 miles and a right triangle with a base of about 315 miles and a height of about 280 miles. Finding the areas of the two basic figures and adding to find the area of the composite figure, the area of Nevada is about 110,250 mi^2.

315 mi

NEVADA

210 mi

280 mi

0 140 mi

0.5 in: 140 mi

34. **MULTIPLE REPRESENTATIONS** In this problem, you will investigate the areas of regular polygons inscribed in circles.

a. Geometric Draw a circle with a radius of 1 unit and inscribe a square. Repeat twice, inscribing a regular pentagon and hexagon. See margin.

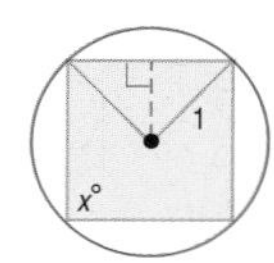

b. Algebraic Use the inscribed regular polygons from part **a** to develop a formula for the area of an inscribed regular polygon in terms of angle measure x and number of sides n. $A = n \cos\left(\frac{x}{2}\right) \sin\left(\frac{x}{2}\right)$

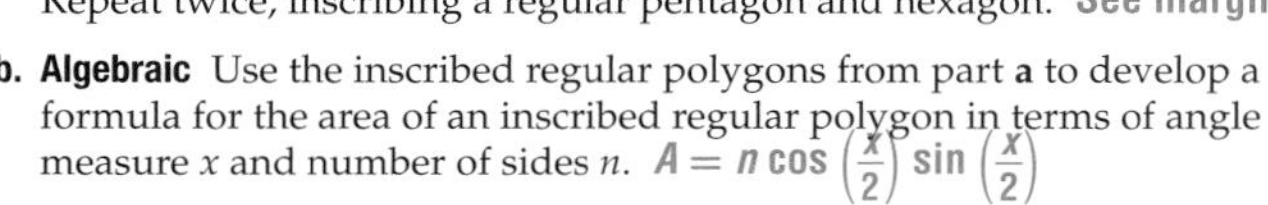

c. Tabular Use the formula you developed in part **b** to complete the table below. Round to the nearest hundredth.

Number of Sides, n	4	5	6	8	10	20	50	100
Interior Angle Measure, x	90°	108°	120°	135°	144°	162°	172.8°	176.4°
Area of Inscribed Regular Polygon	2.00	2.38	2.60	2.83	2.94	3.09	3.13	3.14

d. Verbal Make a conjecture about the area of an inscribed regular polygon with a radius of 1 unit as the number of sides increases.

34d. Sample answer: As the number of sides of the polygon increases, the area of a regular polygon inscribed in a circle approaches the area of the circle or π.

38b. Sample answer: $2ab = ab + ab$

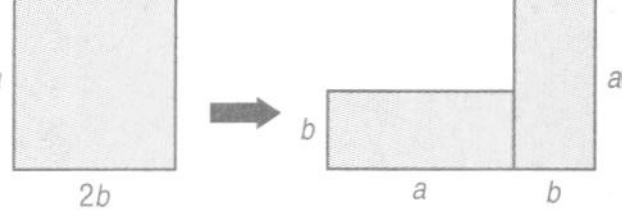

H.O.T. Problems Use Higher-Order Thinking Skills

35. **ERROR ANALYSIS** Chloe and Flavio want to find the area of the hexagon shown. Is either of them correct? Explain your reasoning. See margin.

Chloe

$A = \frac{1}{2}Pa$

$= \frac{1}{2}(66)(9.5)$

$= 313.5 \text{ in}^2$

Flavio

$A = \frac{1}{2}Pa$

$= \frac{1}{2}(33)(9.5)$

$= 156.8 \text{ in}^2$

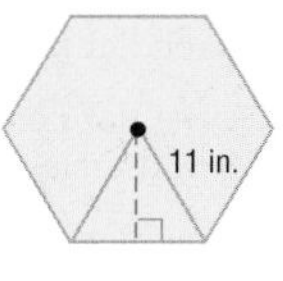

36. **CCSS SENSE-MAKING** Using the map of Nevada shown, estimate the area of the state. Explain your reasoning. See margin.

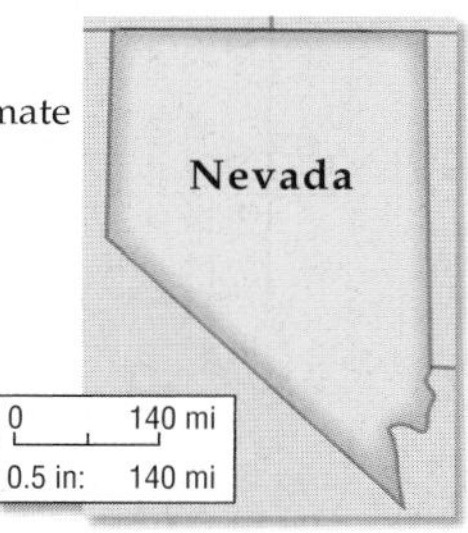

37. **OPEN ENDED** Draw a pair of composite figures that have the same area. Make one composite figure out of a rectangle and a trapezoid, and make the other composite figure out of a triangle and a rectangle. Show the area of each basic figure. See margin.

38. **WRITING IN MATH** Consider the sequence of area diagrams shown. a. See margin

a. What algebraic theorem do the diagrams prove? Explain your reasoning.

b. Create your own sequence of diagrams to prove a different algebraic theorem.

b
b
a
a
a − b
a
b

39. **WRITING IN MATH** How can you find the area of any figure? See margin.

37. Sample answer:

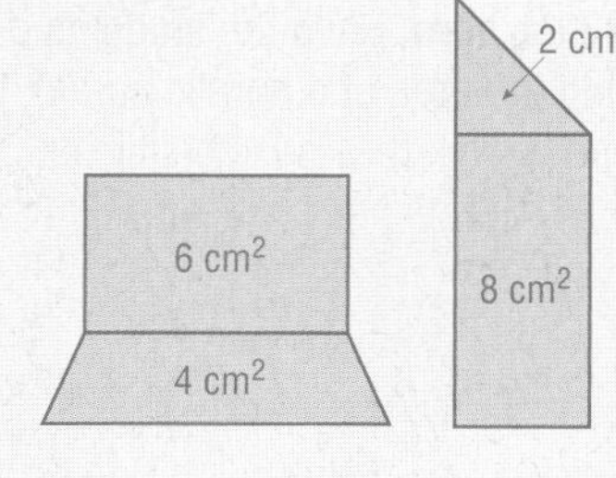

Standardized Test Practice

40. Which polynomial best represents the area of the regular pentagon shown below? D

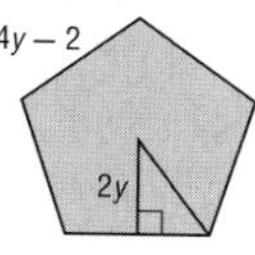

A $10y^2 - 5$
B $10y^2 + 5y$
C $20y^2 + 10$
D $20y^2 - 10y$

41. What is $27^{-\frac{2}{3}}$ in radical form? F

F $\frac{1}{(\sqrt[3]{27})^2}$
G $(\sqrt[3]{27})^2$
H $\frac{1}{(\sqrt{27})^2}$
J $(\sqrt{27})^3$

42. SHORT RESPONSE Find the area of the shaded figure in square inches. Round to the nearest tenth. 420 in²

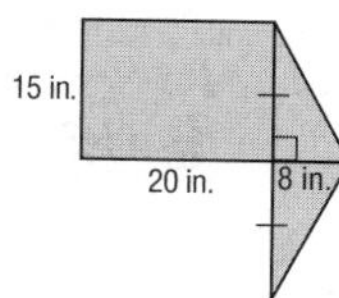

43. SAT/ACT If the $\cos \theta = \frac{12}{13}$ what is the value of $\tan \theta$? D

A $\frac{13}{5}$
B $\frac{12}{5}$
C $\frac{13}{12}$
D $\frac{5}{12}$
E $\frac{5}{13}$

Spiral Review

Find the indicated measure. Round to the nearest tenth. (Lesson 11-3)

44. The area of a circle is 95 square feet. Find the radius. 5.5 ft

45. Find the area of a circle whose radius is 9 centimeters. 254.5 cm²

46. The area of a circle is 256 square inches. Find the diameter. 18.1 in.

47. Find the area of a circle whose diameter is 25 millimeters. 490.9 mm²

Find the area of each trapezoid, rhombus, or kite. (Lesson 11-2)

48. 110 ft²

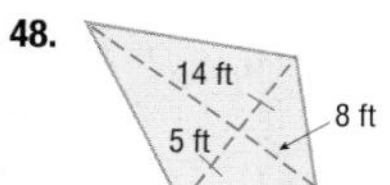

49. 272 in²

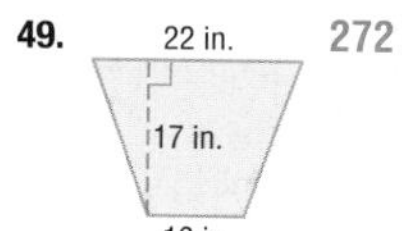

50. 540 m²

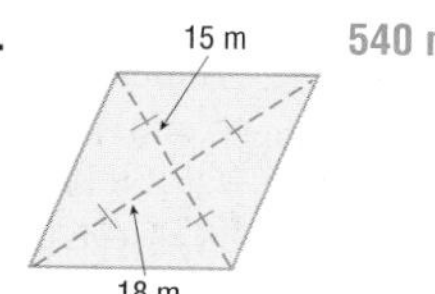

$\overline{EC}$ and $\overline{AB}$ are diameters of ⊙*O*. Identify each arc as a *major arc*, *minor arc*, or *semicircle* of the circle. Then find its measure. (Lesson 10-2)

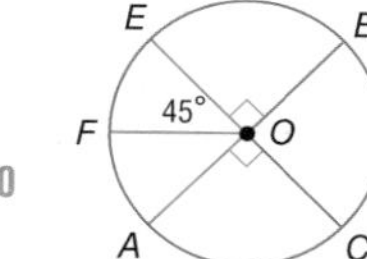

51. $m\widehat{ACB}$ semicircle; 180

52. $m\widehat{EB}$ minor arc; 90

53. $m\widehat{ACE}$ major arc; 270

Skills Review

Each pair of polygons is similar. Find *x*.

54. 91

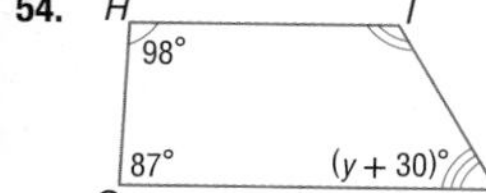

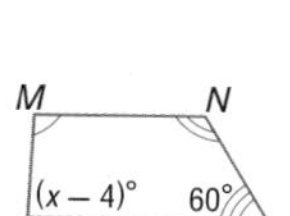

55. 30

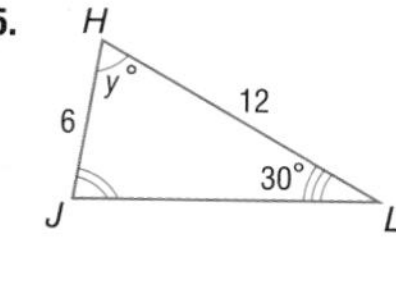

R, 8, 4, 80°, x°, Q, S

4 Assess

Name the Math Have students explain how to find the area of a composite figure.

Formative Assessment

Check for student understanding of Lesson 11-4.

Quiz 3, p. 40

Additional Answers

38a. $a^2 - b^2 = (a + b)(a - b)$; Sample answer: The area of the first figure is equal to the area of the larger square a^2 minus the area of the smaller square b^2 or $a^2 - b^2$. The area of the second figure is the area of a rectangle with side lengths $a + b$ and $a - b$ or $(a + b)(a - b)$. Since the figures are composed of congruent shapes, the areas are equal, so $a^2 - b^2 = (a + b)(a - b)$.

39. Sample answer: You can decompose the figure into shapes of which you know the area formulas. Then, you can sum all of the areas to find the total area of the figure.

Follow-Up

Students have explored the formula for the areas of regular polygons.

Ask:

- Is there more than one formula that can be used to find the area of a given polygon? Explain. Yes; sample answer: Every polygon can be decomposed into two or more figures. For example, a right trapezoid can be decomposed into a rectangle and a triangle. Therefore, another area formula that could be used is $A = r + t$, where r is the area of the rectangle and t is the area of the triangle.
- Why do we have specific formulas that we use to find the areas of certain polygons? Sample answer: The formulas typically represent the most efficient ways to calculate the areas.

1 Focus

Objective Find areas and perimeters of regular polygons, including inscribed and circumscribed polygons, on the coordinate plane.

Materials for Each Group

- grid paper

Easy to Make Manipulatives

Teaching Geometry with Manipulatives

- template for grid paper, p. 1

Teaching Tip

Encourage students to estimate the perimeter and area of each polygon before calculating each measure. One way to estimate the area of each polygon is to count the number of whole and partial squares inside the figure. An estimate of the figure's area is then $A \approx$ (whole squares) $+ \frac{1}{2}$ (partial squares). If the figure is inscribed in a circle, the area of the polygon is a little less than the area of the circle. If the figure is circumscribed about a circle, the area of the polygon is a little more than the area of the circle. The magnitude of the error will decrease as the number of sides increases.

2 Teach

Working in Cooperative Groups

Organize students into groups of 3 or 4, mixing abilities. Have groups complete the Activities 1 and 2.

EXTEND 11-4 Geometry Lab: Regular Polygons on the Coordinate Plane

If you know the coordinates of two consecutive vertices of a regular polygon, you can use the Distance Formula to find the length of each side. For example, in the figure shown, the length of $\overline{AB}$ is $\sqrt{(3-1)^2+(1-4)^2}$ or $\sqrt{13}$. Using this measure, you can then find the perimeter and area of the figure using the techniques presented in Lesson 11-4.

You can also use the Distance Formula to find the perimeter and area of a regular polygon inscribed in a circle given the coordinates of the endpoints of a radius.

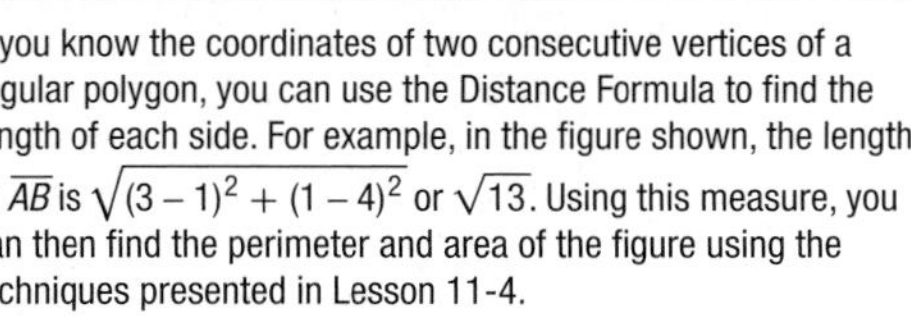

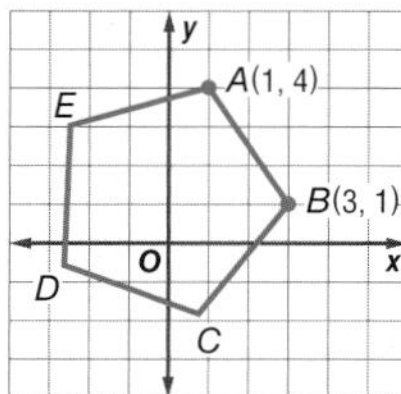

Activity 1 Inscribed Polygon

Find the perimeter and area of octagon *ABCDEFGH*, which is inscribed in ⊙*O*. Round to the nearest tenth, if necessary.

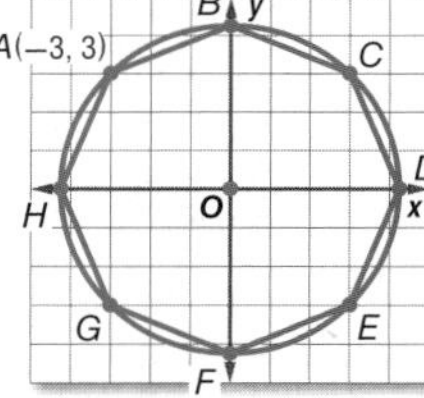

Step 1 Use the Distance Formula to find a radius of ⊙*O*.

$$OA = \sqrt{(-3-0)^2+(3-0)^2} \qquad x_2 = -3,\ x_1 = 0,\ y_2 = 3, \text{ and } y_1 = 0$$

$$= \sqrt{18} \text{ or } 3\sqrt{2} \qquad \text{Simplify.}$$

Step 2 Find the perimeter and area.

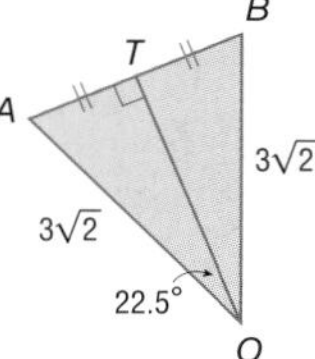

Because the octagon is inscribed in ⊙*O*, $\overline{OA}$ and $\overline{OB}$ are both radii of ⊙*O*. Therefore, $OA = OB = 3\sqrt{2}$. Let $\overline{OT}$ be an apothem of the octagon with length a. Then $\overline{OT}$ is also the height of isosceles $\triangle AOB$. Since the octagon is regular, $m\angle AOB$ is $360 \div 8$ or 45. Since $\overline{OT}$ bisects $\angle AOB$ and side $\overline{AB}$, $m\angle AOT = 45 \div 2$ or 22.5, and $AB = 2(AT)$.

Use trigonometric ratios to find a and AT.

$$\cos 22.5° = \frac{a}{3\sqrt{2}} \qquad \cos\theta = \frac{\text{adj}}{\text{hyp}}$$

$$a = 3\sqrt{2}\cos 22.5° \qquad \text{Solve for } a.$$

$$\sin 22.5° = \frac{AT}{3\sqrt{2}} \qquad \sin\theta = \frac{\text{opp}}{\text{hyp}}$$

$$AT = 3\sqrt{2}\sin 22.5° \qquad \text{Solve for } AT.$$

$AB = 2(AT)$, so $AB = 2(3\sqrt{2}\sin 22.5°)$ and the perimeter P of the octagon is $8(2)3\sqrt{2}\sin 22.5°$ or about 26.0 units. The area of the octagon is $\frac{1}{2}aP$, which is $\frac{1}{2}3\sqrt{2}\cos 22.5° \cdot 8(2)3\sqrt{2}\sin 22.5°$ or about 50.9 units^2.

816 | Extend 11-4 | Geometry Lab: Regular Polygons on the Coordinate Plane

You can also use the Distance Formula to find the perimeter and area of a regular polygon circumscribed about a circle given the coordinates of the endpoints of a radius.

Activity 2 Circumscribed Polygon

Find the perimeter and area of hexagon $ABCDEF$, which is circumscribed about $\odot Q$. Round to the nearest tenth, if necessary.

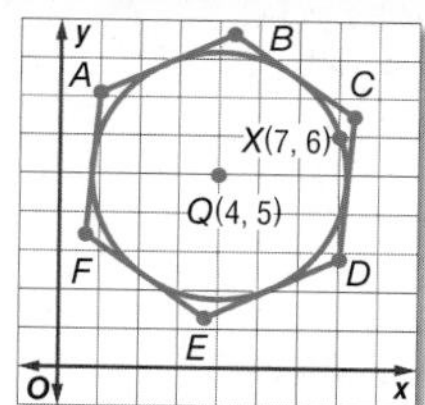

Step 1 Use the Distance Formula to find a radius of $\odot Q$.

$QX = \sqrt{(7-4)^2 + (6-5)^2}$ or $\sqrt{10}$ $\quad x_2 = 7, x_1 = 4, y_2 = 6$, and $y_1 = 5$

Step 2 Find the perimeter and area of hexagon $ABCDEF$.

Because the hexagon is circumscribed about $\odot Q$, $\overline{AB}$ is tangent to the circle. Let the point of tangency be T. Since all radii of a circle are congruent, radius $\overline{QT}$ also measures $\sqrt{10}$. $\overline{QT}$ is an apothem of the hexagon, so $a = \sqrt{10}$.

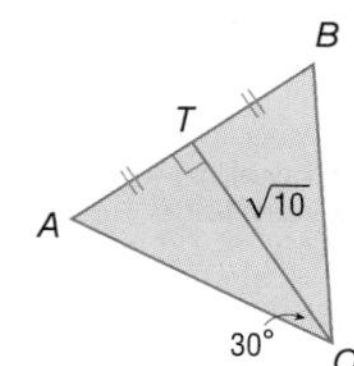

The apothem is also the height of isosceles $\triangle AQB$. Since the hexagon is regular, $m\angle AQB$ is $360 \div 6$ or 60. Since $\overline{QT}$ bisects $\angle AQB$ and side $\overline{AB}$ $m\angle AQT = 60 \div 2$ or 30, and $AB = 2(AT)$. Use trigonometric ratios to find AT. Then find AB.

$\tan 30° = \frac{AT}{\sqrt{10}}$ $\quad \tan\theta = \frac{\text{opp}}{\text{adj}}$

$AT = \sqrt{10}\tan 30°$ $\quad$ Solve for AT.

$AT = \sqrt{10}\left(\frac{\sqrt{3}}{3}\right)$ or $\frac{\sqrt{30}}{3}$ $\quad \tan 30° = \frac{\sqrt{3}}{3}$

$AB = 2(AT)$

$= 2\left(\frac{\sqrt{30}}{3}\right)$

$= \frac{2\sqrt{30}}{3}$

The perimeter P of the hexagon is $6 \cdot \frac{2\sqrt{30}}{3}$ or $4\sqrt{30}$, which is about 21.9 units. The area of the hexagon is $\frac{1}{2}aP$, which is $\frac{1}{2}\sqrt{10}(4\sqrt{30})$ or about 34.6 units^2.

Exercises

Find the perimeter and area of each regular polygon with the given consecutive vertices. Round to the nearest tenth, if necessary.

1. pentagon $ABCDE$; $A(1, 4)$, $B(3, 1)$ **18.0 units, 22.4 units^2**
2. hexagon $ABCDEF$; $A(-4, 2)$, $B(0, 5)$ **30 units, 65.0 units^2**

Find the perimeter and area of each regular polygon inscribed in $\odot O$, centered at the origin, and containing the given point. Round to the nearest tenth, if necessary.

3. pentagon $ABCDE$; $E(-4, -1)$ **24.2 units, 40.4 units^2**
4. hexagon $ABCDEF$; $D(4, -5)$ **38.4 units, 106.5 units^2**

Find the perimeter and area of each regular polygon circumscribed about $\odot Q$, with the given center and point X on the circle. Round to the nearest tenth, if necessary.

5. pentagon $ABCDE$; $Q(-2, 1)$; $X(-1, 3)$ **16.2 units, 18.2 units^2**
6. octagon $ABCDEFGH$; $Q(3, -1)$; $X(1, -3)$ **18.7 units, 26.5 units^2**

Practice Have students complete Exercises 1–6.

3 Assess

Formative Assessment

Use Exercises 1–6 to assess whether students understand how to find the areas and perimeters of regular polygons, including inscribed and circumscribed polygons, on the coordinate plane.

From Concrete to Abstract

In this lab, students are given the coordinates of two consecutive vertices in order to find the perimeter and area of a regular polygon. Have students write about whether or not the coordinates of two nonconsecutive vertices could be used to find the perimeter and area.

1 Focus

VerticalAlignment

Before Lesson 11-5 Use scale factors and proportions to solve problems involving the perimeters of similar figures.

Lesson 11-5 Find areas of similar figures by using scale factors. Find scale factors or missing measures given the areas of similar figures.

After Lesson 11-5 Find the volumes of similar solids.

2 Teach

Scaffolding Questioning

Have students read the **Why?** section of the lesson.

Ask:

- How tall is a building if the model is 2.5 feet tall and the scale factor is 12 feet to 1 inch? 360 feet
- If the side lengths of a rectangle are doubled, is the rectangle's area doubled? No, it quadruples.
- Are the proportions of the side lengths of similar figures and the proportions of the areas of similar figures always the same? No.

LESSON 11-5 Areas of Similar Figures

Then

- You used scale factors and proportions to solve problems involving the perimeters of similar figures.

Now

1. Find areas of similar figures by using scale factors.
2. Find scale factors or missing measures given the areas of similar figures.

Why?

- Architecture firms often hire model makers to make scale models of projects that are used to sell their designs. Since the base of a model is geometrically similar to the base of the actual building it represents, their areas are related.

CCSS Common Core State Standards

Content Standards

G.MG.1 Use geometric shapes, their measures, and their properties to describe objects (e.g., modeling a tree trunk or a human torso as a cylinder). ★

Mathematical Practices

1 Make sense of problems and persevere in solving them.

4 Model with mathematics.

1 Areas of Similar Figures

In Lesson 7-2, you learned that if two polygons are similar, then their perimeters are proportional to the scale factor between them. The areas of two similar polygons share a different relationship.

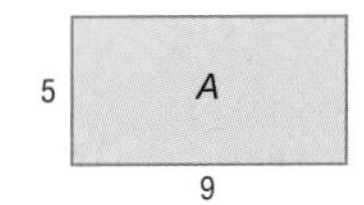

$$\frac{\text{perimeter of figure } B}{\text{perimeter of figure } A} = \frac{28k}{28} \text{ or } k$$

$$\frac{\text{area of figure } B}{\text{area of figure } A} = \frac{45k^2}{45} \text{ or } k^2$$

Theorem 11.1 Areas of Similar Polygons

Words If two polygons are similar, then their areas are proportional to the square of the scale factor between them.

Example If $ABCD \sim FGHJ$, then $\frac{\text{area of } FGHJ}{\text{area of } ABCD} = \left(\frac{FG}{AB}\right)^2$.

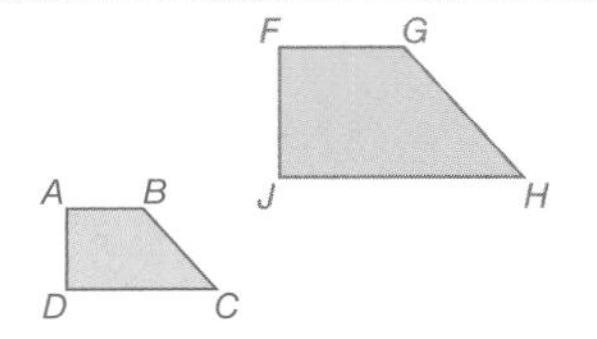

You will prove Theorem 11.1 for triangles in Exercise 22.

Example 1 Find Areas of Similar Polygons

If $\triangle JKL \sim \triangle PQR$ and the area of $\triangle JKL$ is 30 square inches, find the area of $\triangle PQR$.

The scale factor between $\triangle PQR$ and $\triangle JKL$ is $\frac{15}{12}$ or $\frac{5}{4}$, so the ratio of their areas is $\left(\frac{5}{4}\right)^2$.

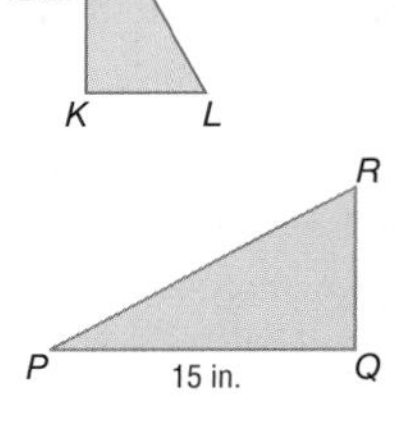

$\frac{\text{area of } \triangle PQR}{\text{area of } \triangle JKL} = \left(\frac{5}{4}\right)^2$ Write a proportion.

$\frac{\text{area of } \triangle PQR}{30} = \frac{25}{16}$ Area of $\triangle JKL = 30$ and $\left(\frac{5}{4}\right)^2 = \frac{25}{16}$

$\text{area of } \triangle PQR = \frac{25}{16} \cdot 30$ Multiply each side by 30.

$\text{area of } \triangle PQR = 46.875$ Simplify.

So the area of $\triangle PQR$ is about 46.9 square inches.

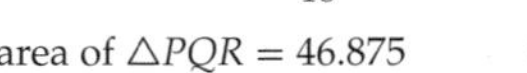

Lesson 11-5 Resources

Resource	Approaching Level AL	On Level OL	Beyond Level BL	English Learners ELL
Teacher Edition	▪ Differentiated Instruction, p. 820	▪ Differentiated Instruction, pp. 820, 823, 824	▪ Differentiated Instruction, pp. 820, 823, 824	▪ Differentiated Instruction, p. 823
Chapter Resource Masters	▪ Study Guide and Intervention, pp. 31–32 ▪ Skills Practice, p. 33 ▪ Practice, p. 34 ▪ Word Problem Practice, p. 35	▪ Study Guide and Intervention, pp. 31–32 ▪ Skills Practice, p. 33 ▪ Practice, p. 34 ▪ Word Problem Practice, p. 35 ▪ Enrichment, p. 36	▪ Practice, p. 34 ▪ Word Problem Practice, p. 35 ▪ Enrichment, p. 36	▪ Study Guide and Intervention, pp. 31–32 ▪ Skills Practice, p. 33 ▪ Practice, p. 34 ▪ Word Problem Practice, p. 35
Other	▪ 5-Minute Check 11-5 ▪ Study Notebook	▪ 5-Minute Check 11-5 ▪ Study Notebook	▪ 5-Minute Check 11-5 ▪ Study Notebook	▪ 5-Minute Check 11-5 ▪ Study Notebook

GuidedPractice

For each pair of similar figures, find the area of the green figure.

1A. 12.5 cm^2

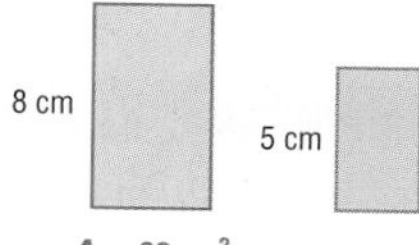

1B. 24 ft^2

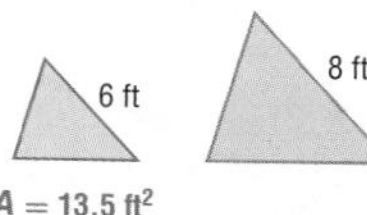

2 Scale Factors and Missing Measures in Similar Figures

You can use the areas of similar figures to find the scale factor between them or a missing measure.

Example 2 Use Areas of Similar Figures

The area of ▱$ABCD$ is 150 square meters. The area of ▱$FGHJ$ is 54 square meters. If ▱$ABCD \sim$ ▱$FGHJ$, find the scale factor of ▱$FGHJ$ to ▱$ABCD$ and the value of x.

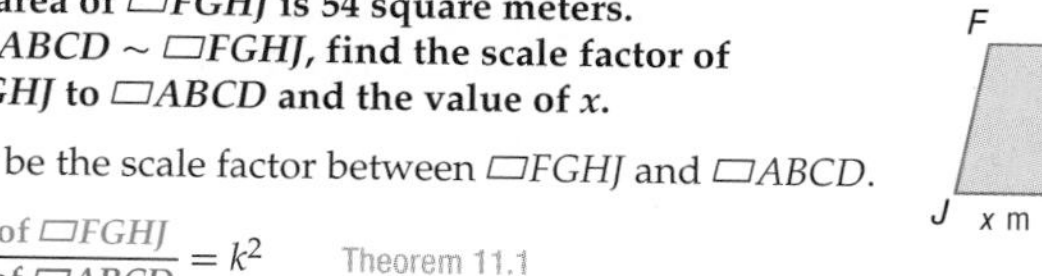

Let k be the scale factor between ▱$FGHJ$ and ▱$ABCD$.

F G J x m H — A B D 10 m C

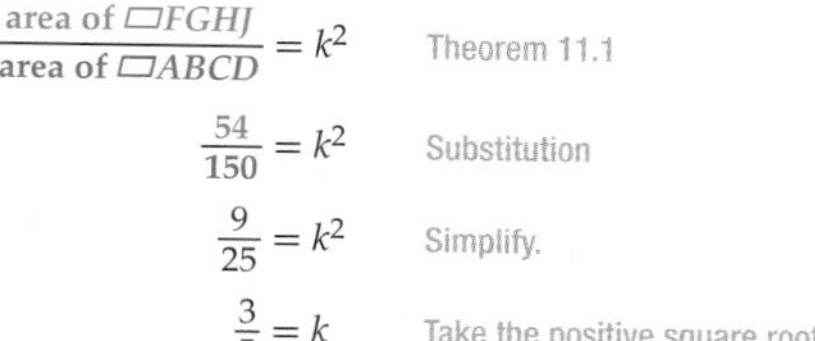

$\frac{\text{area of ▱}FGHJ}{\text{area of ▱}ABCD} = k^2$ Theorem 11.1

$\frac{54}{150} = k^2$ Substitution

$\frac{9}{25} = k^2$ Simplify.

$\frac{3}{5} = k$ Take the positive square root of each side.

So the scale factor of ▱$FGHJ$ to ▱$ABCD$ is $\frac{3}{5}$. Use this scale factor to find the value of x.

$\frac{JH}{DC} = k$ The ratio of corresponding lengths of similar polygons is equal to the scale factor between the polygons.

$\frac{x}{10} = \frac{3}{5}$ Substitution

$x = \frac{3}{5} \cdot 10$ or 6 Multiply each side by 10.

CHECK Confirm that $\frac{JH}{DC}$ is equal to the scale factor.

$\frac{JH}{DC} = \frac{6}{10} = \frac{3}{5}$ ✓

WatchOut!

Writing Ratios When finding the ratio of the area of Figure A to the area of Figure B, be sure to write your ratio as $\frac{\text{area of figure } A}{\text{area of figure } B}$.

ReadingMath

Ratios Ratios can be written in different ways. For example, x to y, $x : y$, and $\frac{x}{y}$ are all representations of the ratio of x and y.

GuidedPractice

For each pair of similar figures, use the given areas to find the scale factor of the blue to the green figure. Then find x.

2A. $\frac{5}{6}$; 5

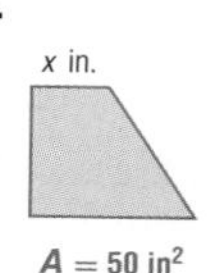

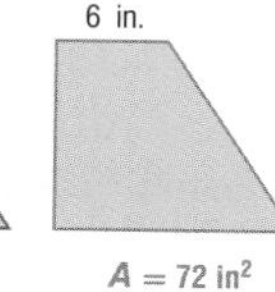

2B. $\frac{5}{2}$ or 2.5; 16

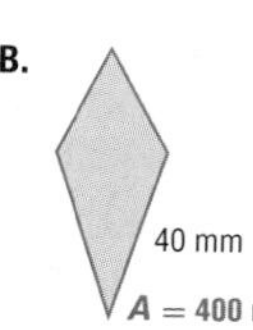

1 Areas of Similar Figures

Example 1 shows how to find the area of a figure, given the area of a similar figure.

Formative Assessment

Use the Guided Practice exercises after each example to determine students' understanding of concepts.

Additional Example

1 If $ABCD \sim PQRS$ and the area of $ABCD$ is 48 square inches, find the area of $PQRS$.

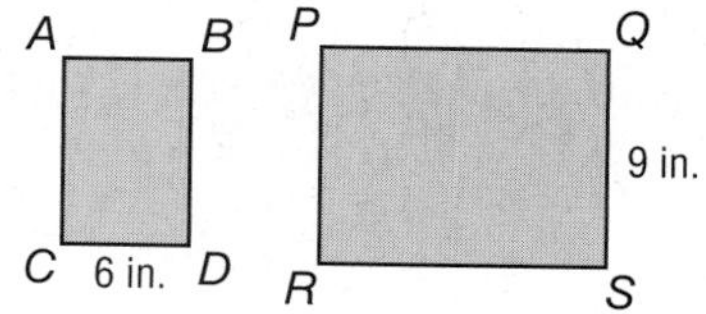

108 square inches

Additional Examples also in Interactive Classroom PowerPoint® Presentations

2 Scale Factors and Missing Measures in Similar Figures

Examples 2 and 3 show how to find the scale factor or a missing measure, given the areas of similar figures.

Additional Example

2 The area of $\triangle ABC$ is 98 square inches. The area of $\triangle RTS$ is 50 square inches. If $\triangle ABC \sim \triangle RTS$, find the scale factor from $\triangle ABC$ to $\triangle RTS$ and the value of x.

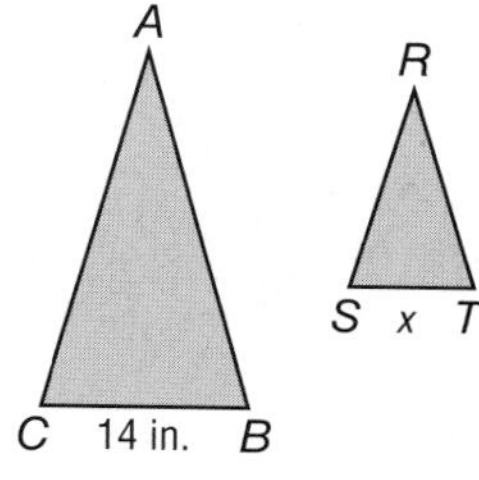

scale factor: $\frac{7}{5}$; 10

Teach with Tech

Interactive Whiteboard Show students a rectangle on the board and its image after a dilation with a scale factor of 3. To show that the area of the large rectangle is 9 times the area of the smaller rectangle, copy the small rectangle 9 times and drag it inside the large rectangle.

Additional Example

3 CRAFTS The area of one side of a skyscraper is 90,000 square feet. The area of the corresponding side of a scale model is 200 square inches. If the skyscraper is 720 feet tall, about how tall is the model? ≈ 34 in.

Focus on Mathematical Content

Scale Factors The ratio of areas of similar factors is the square of the scale factor because the area of the figure is based on length and width, each of which is multiplied by the scale factor.

In Lesson 7-2, you learned that if all corresponding angles are congruent and all corresponding sides are proportional, then two polygons are similar. For this reason, all regular polygons with the same number of sides are similar.

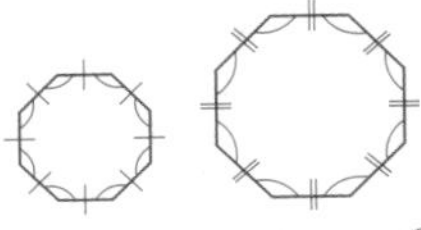

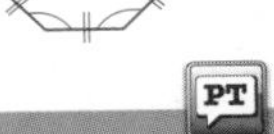

Real-World Example 3 Scale Models

Real-WorldLink

The Pentagon building, including its center courtyard, occupies approximately 34 acres or 1,481,000 square feet of land. Each outer wall of the regular pentagonal building is 921 feet in length.

Source: U.S. Department of Defense

CRAFTS Use the information at the left. Orlando and Mia are making a scale model of the Pentagon. If the area of the base of their model is approximately 50 square inches, about how many times the length of each outer wall of the Pentagon is the length of the outer wall of the model?

Understand All regular pentagons are similar, so the base of the model is similar to the base of the Pentagon. You need to find the scale factor from the Pentagon to their model.

Plan The ratio of the areas of the bases of the two figures is equal to the square of the scale factor between them. Before comparing the two areas, write them so that they have the same units.

Solve Convert the area of the model's base to square feet.

$$50 \text{ in}^2 \cdot \frac{1 \text{ ft}^2}{144 \text{ in}^2} \approx 0.3472 \text{ ft}^2$$

Next, write an equation using the ratio of the two areas in square feet. Let k represent the scale factor between the two bases.

$\frac{\text{area of model}}{\text{area of Pentagon}} = k^2$ Theorem 11.1

$\frac{0.3472 \text{ ft}^2}{1{,}481{,}000 \text{ ft}^2} \approx k^2$ Substitution

$2.34 \cdot 10^{-7} \approx k^2$ Simplify using a calculator.

$4.84 \cdot 10^{-4} \approx k$ Take the positive square root of each side.

$0.0005 \approx k$ Write in standard form.

$\frac{1}{2000} \approx k$ Write as a simplified fraction.

So the model's outer walls are about $\frac{1}{2000}$ the length of each outer wall of the Pentagon.

Check Multiply the area of the Pentagon's base by the square of this scale factor and compare to the given area of the model's base.

$$\frac{1{,}481{,}000 \text{ ft}^2}{1} \cdot \frac{144 \text{ in}^2}{1 \text{ ft}^2} \cdot \left(\frac{1}{2000}\right)^2 \approx 53 \text{ in}^2$$

This is close to the given area of 50 square inches, so our scale factor is reasonable. ✓

ReadingMath

Similar Circles Since all circles have the same shape, all circles are similar. Therefore, the areas of two circles are also related by the square of the scale factor between them.

GuidedPractice

3. CRAFTS Miyoki is crocheting two circles. The area of the larger circle is to be 2.5 times the size of the smaller. If the area of the smaller circle is about 50.2 square centimeters, what is the diameter of the larger circle? 12.6 cm

DifferentiatedInstruction AL OL BL

Logical Learners Have students write a proof of Theorem 11.1 for a rectangle. The area of rectangle $ABCD = AB \cdot BC$ and the area of similar rectangle $EFGH = EF \cdot FG$. The ratio of the area of $\frac{\text{rectangle } ABCD}{\text{rectangle } EFGH} = \frac{AB \cdot BC}{EF \cdot FG} = \left(\frac{AB}{EF}\right)^2$, which is the square or the ratio of the corresponding sides.

Check Your Understanding

○ = Step-by-Step Solutions begin on page R14.

Example 1 For each pair of similar figures, find the area of the green figure.

1. 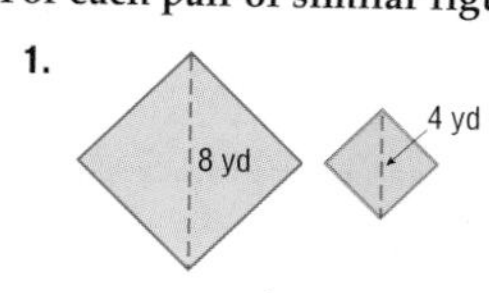

9 yd²

2. 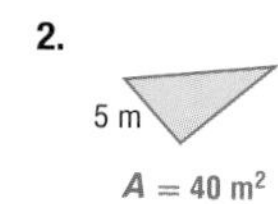 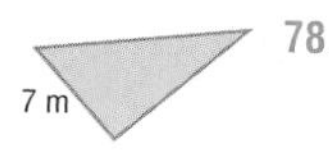

78.4 m²

Example 2 For each pair of similar figures, use the given areas to find the scale factor from the blue to the green figure. Then find x.

3. 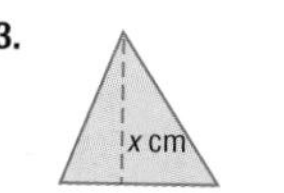 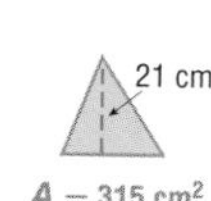

$\frac{5}{3}$; 35

4.  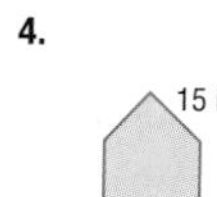

$\frac{3}{4}$; 20

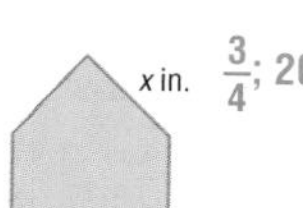

Example 3 5. **MEMORIES** Zola has a picture frame that holds all of her school pictures. Each small opening is similar to the large opening in the center. If the center opening has an area of 33 square inches, what is the area of each small opening? 5.28 in²

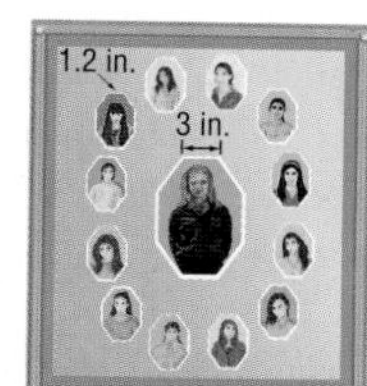

Practice and Problem Solving

Extra Practice is on page R11.

Example 1 For each pair of similar figures, find the area of the green figure.

6. 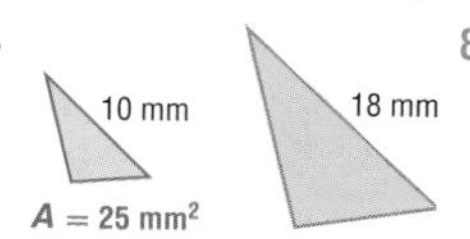

81 mm²

7. 

240 ft²

8. 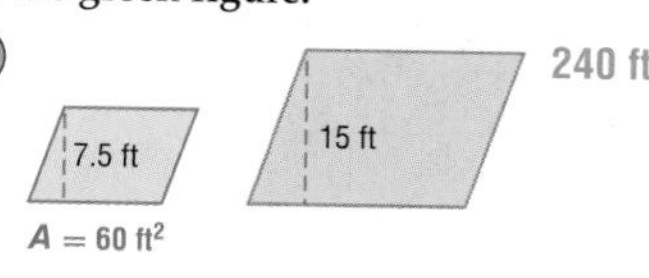

151.25 in²

9. 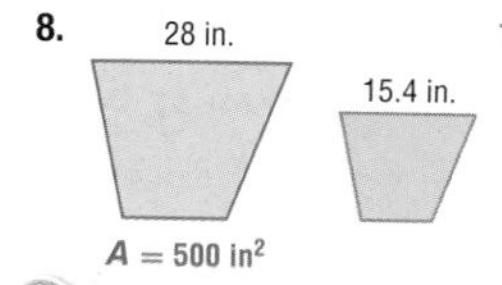

672 cm²

Example 2 CCSS **STRUCTURE** For each pair of similar figures, use the given areas to find the scale factor of the blue to the green figure. Then find x.

10. 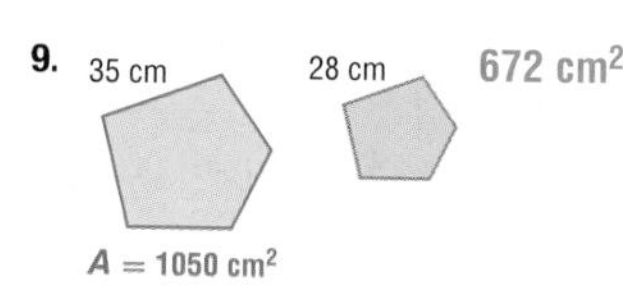

$\frac{6}{5}$; 10

11. 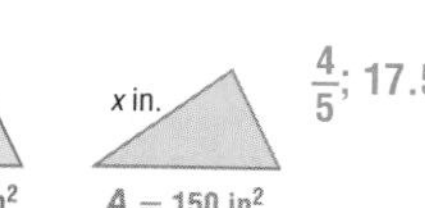

$\frac{4}{5}$; 17.5

12. 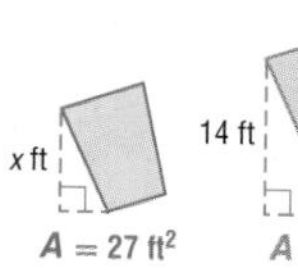

$\frac{3}{7}$; 6

13. 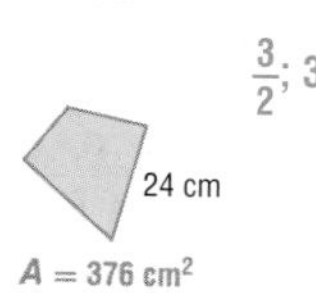

$\frac{3}{2}$; 36

3 Practice

Formative Assessment

Use Exercises 1–5 to check for understanding.

Use the chart at the bottom of this page to customize assignments for your students.

Teaching the Mathematical Practices

Structure Mathematically proficient students look closely to discern a pattern or structure. They also can step back for an overview and shift perspective. In Exercises 10–13, encourage students to write a proportion relating the areas of the similar figures.

Differentiated Homework Options

Level	Assignment	Two-Day Option	
AL Basic	6–15, 25, 27–45	7–15 odd, 30–33	6–14 even, 25, 27–29, 34–45
OL Core	7–15 odd, 17–18, 19–23 odd, 24, 25, 27–45	6–15, 30–33	16–25, 27–29, 34–45
BL Advanced	16–42, (optional: 43–45)		

Study Guide and Intervention

AL OL ELL

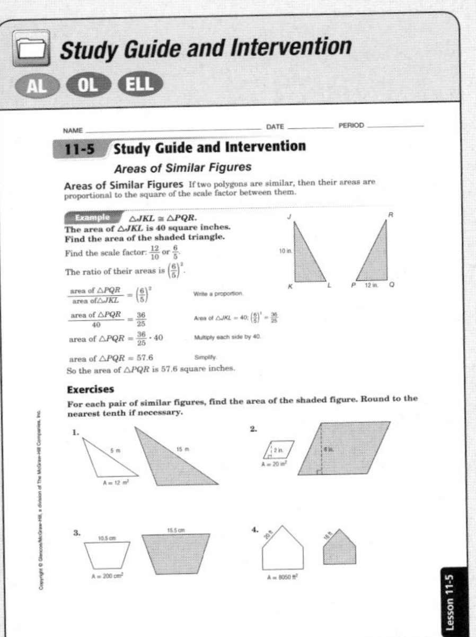
11-5 Study Guide and Intervention

Areas of Similar Figures

Practice

AL OL BL ELL

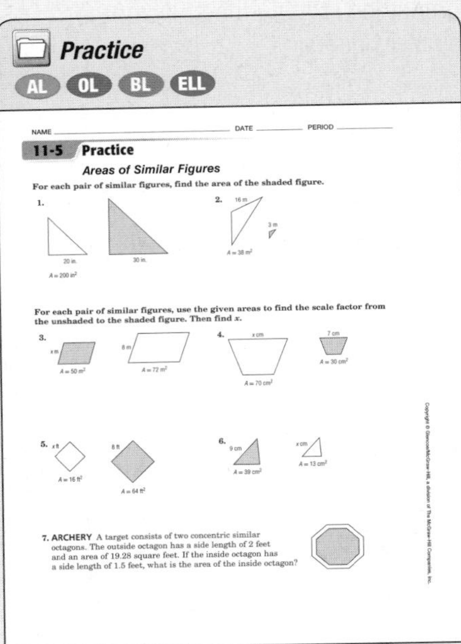
11-5 Practice

Areas of Similar Figures

Word Problem Practice

AL OL BL ELL

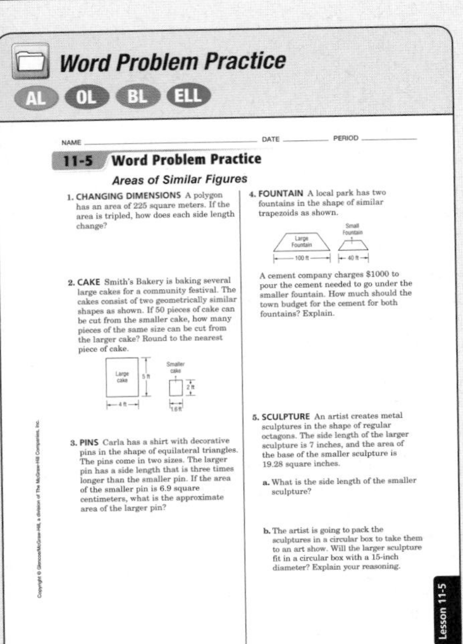
11-5 Word Problem Practice

Areas of Similar Figures

Example 3

14. **CRAFTS** Marina crafts unique trivets and other kitchenware. Each trivet is an equilateral triangle. The perimeter of the small trivet is 9 inches, and the perimeter of the large trivet is 12 inches. If the area of the small trivet is about 3.9 square inches, what is the approximate area of the large trivet? 6.9 in^2

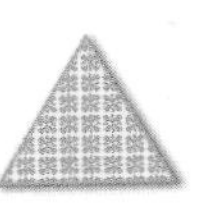
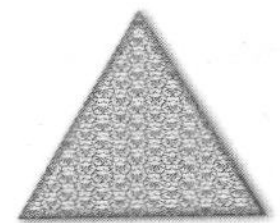

15. **BAKING** Kaitlyn wants to use one of two regular hexagonal cake pans for a recipe she is making. The side length of the larger pan is 4.5 inches, and the area of the base of the smaller pan is 41.6 square inches.
    a. What is the side length of the smaller pan? 4 in.
    b. The recipe that Kaitlyn is using calls for a circular cake pan with an 8-inch diameter. Which pan should she choose? Explain your reasoning. See Ch. 11 Answer Appendix.

B

16. **CHANGING DIMENSIONS** A polygon has an area of 144 square meters. a–c. See Ch. 11 Answer Appendix.
    a. If the area is doubled, how does each side length change?
    b. How does each side length change if the area is tripled?
    c. What is the change in each side length if the area is increased by a factor of x?

17. **CHANGING DIMENSIONS** A circle has a radius of 24 inches. a–c. See Ch. 11 Answer Appendix.
    a. If the area is doubled, how does the radius change?
    b. How does the radius change if the area is tripled?
    c. What is the change in the radius if the area is increased by a factor of x?

18. **CCSS MODELING** Federico's family is putting hardwood floors in the two geometrically similar rooms shown. If the cost of flooring is constant and the flooring for the kitchen cost \$2000, what will be the total flooring cost for the two rooms? Round to the nearest hundred dollars. \$7600

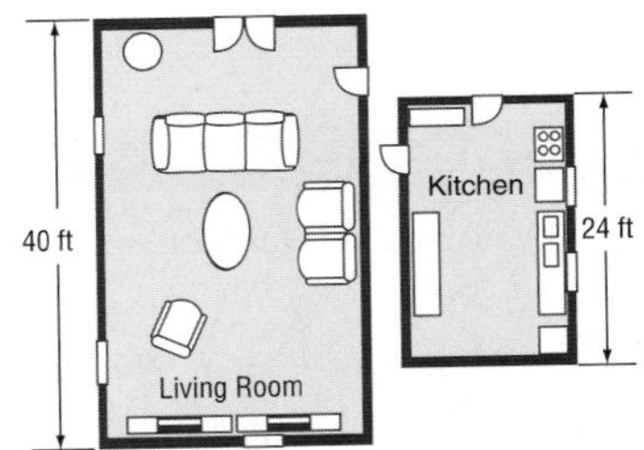

19. area of $\triangle JKL = 15$; area of $\triangle J'K'L' \approx 5.4$
20. area of $WXYZ = 30$; area of $W'X'Y'Z' \approx 53.3$

COORDINATE GEOMETRY Find the area of each figure. Use the segment length given to find the area of a similar polygon. 21. area of $ABCD = 18$; area of $A'B'C'D' \approx 56.2$

19. $J'L' = 3$

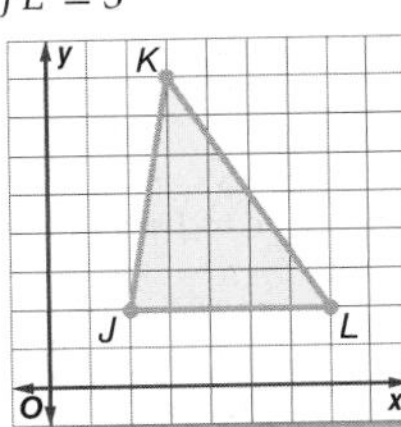

20. $W'X' = 8$

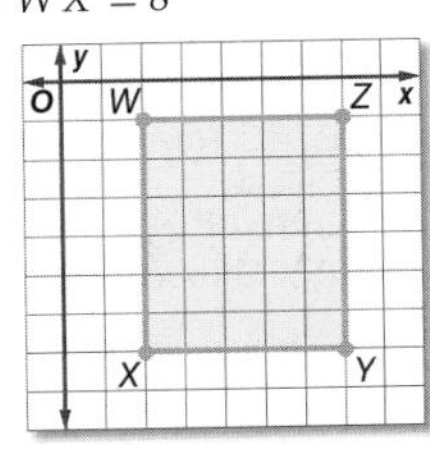

21. $B'C' = 5$

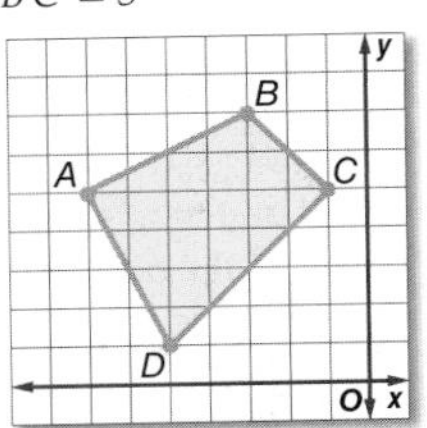

22. **PROOF** Write a paragraph proof. See Ch. 11 Answer Appendix.

Given: $\triangle ABC \sim \triangle XYZ$

Prove: $\frac{\text{area of } \triangle ABC}{\text{area of } \triangle XYZ} = \frac{a^2}{x^2}$

B, a, c, h_1, C, b, A

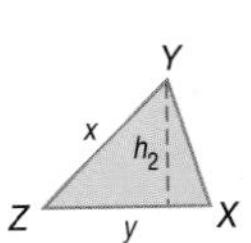

Enrichment

OL BL

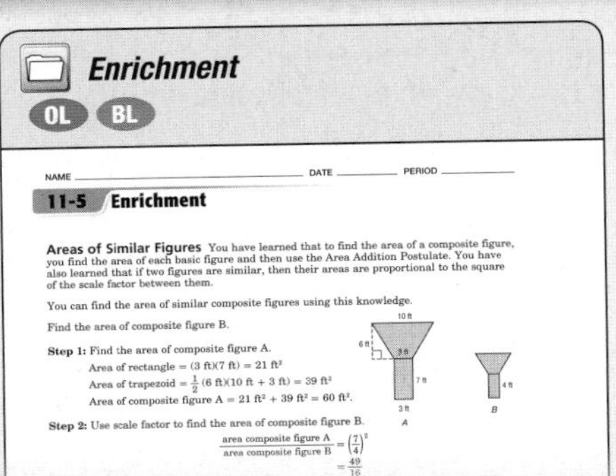
11-5 Enrichment

Areas of Similar Figures

CCSS Teaching the Mathematical Practices

Modeling Mathematically proficient students can apply the mathematics they know to solve problems arising in everyday life. In Exercise 18 encourage students to use the information given to write a proportion.

23. **STATISTICS** The graph shows the increase in high school tennis participation from 1995 to 2005.

a. Explain why the graph is misleading.

b. How could the graph be changed to more accurately represent the growth in high school tennis participation? **a–b. See margin.**

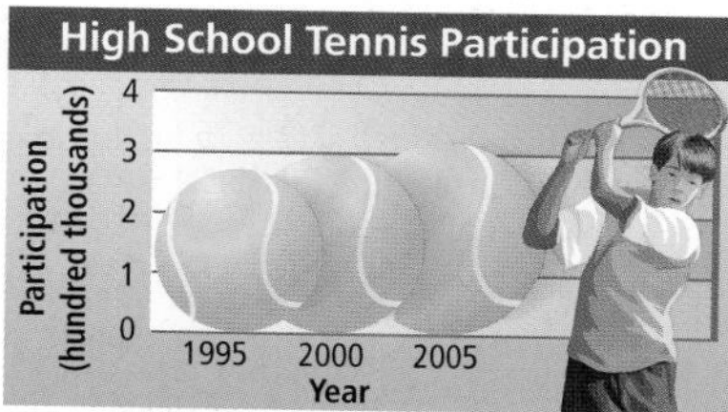

24.  **MULTIPLE REPRESENTATIONS** In this problem, you will investigate changing dimensions proportionally in three-dimensional figures.

a. **Tabular** Copy and complete the table below for each scale factor of a rectangular prism that is 2 inches by 3 inches by 5 inches.

Scale Factor	Length (in.)	Width (in.)	Height (in.)	Volume (in^3)	Ratio of Scaled Volume to Initial Volume
1	3	2	5	30	1
2	6	4	10	240	8
3	9	6	15	810	27
4	12	8	20	1920	64
5	15	10	25	3750	125
10	30	20	50	30,000	1000

b. **Verbal** Make a conjecture about the relationship between the scale factor and the ratio of the scaled volume to the initial volume. **b–c. See margin.**

c. **Graphical** Make a scatter plot of the scale factor and the ratio of the scaled volume to the initial volume using the **STAT PLOT** feature on your graphing calculator. Then use the **STAT CALC** feature to approximate the function represented by the graph.

d. **Algebraic** Write an algebraic expression for the ratio of the scaled volume to the initial volume in terms of scale factor k. k^3

25. Neither; sample answer: In order to find the area of the enlarged circle, you can multiply the radius by the scale factor and substitute it into the area formula, or you can multiply the area formula by the scale factor squared. The formula for the area of the enlargment is $A = \pi(kr)^2$ or $A = k^2\pi r^2$.

H.O.T. Problems Use Higher-Order Thinking Skills

25. **CCSS CRITIQUE** Violeta and Gavin are trying to come up with a formula that can be used to find the area of a circle with a radius r after it has been enlarged by a scale factor k. Is either of them correct? Explain your reasoning.

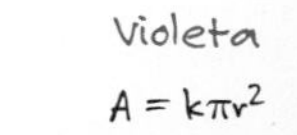

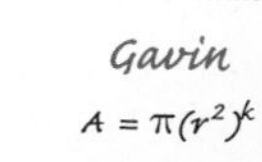

26. **CHALLENGE** If you want the area of a polygon to be x% of its original area, by what scale factor should you multiply each side length? **See margin.**

27. **REASONING** A regular n-gon is enlarged, and the ratio of the area of the enlarged figure to the area of the original figure is R. Write an equation relating the perimeter of the enlarged figure to the perimeter of the original figure Q. $P_{enlarged} = Q\sqrt{R}$

28. **OPEN ENDED** Draw a pair of similar figures with areas that have a ratio of 4:1. Explain. **28–29. See Ch. 11 Answer Appendix.**

29. **WRITING IN MATH** Explain how to find the area of an enlarged polygon if you know the area of the original polygon and the scale factor of the enlargement.

Differentiated Instruction AL OL BL ELL

Extension Have students describe the ratio between the areas of two similar composite figures.

Multiple Representations

In Exercise 24, students use a table, a graph, and an algebraic equation to investigate changing dimensions proportionally in three-dimensional figures.

CCSS Teaching the Mathematical Practices

Critique Mathematically proficient students can distinguish correct logic from flawed reasoning. In Exercise 25, students should understand that the area formula should include the square of the scale factor k. Neither Violeta nor Gavin is correct.

Additional Answers

23a. Sample answer: The graph is misleading because the tennis balls used to illustrate the number of participants are similar circles. When the diameter of the tennis ball increases, the area of the tennis ball also increases. Since the area of the tennis ball increases at a greater rate than the diameter of the tennis ball, it looks like the number of participants in high school tennis is increasing more than it actually is.

23b. Sample answer: If you use a figure with a constant width to represent the participation in each year and only change the height, the graph would not be misleading.

24b. Sample answer: The ratio increases at a greater rate than the scale factor, so the relationship is not linear.

24c.

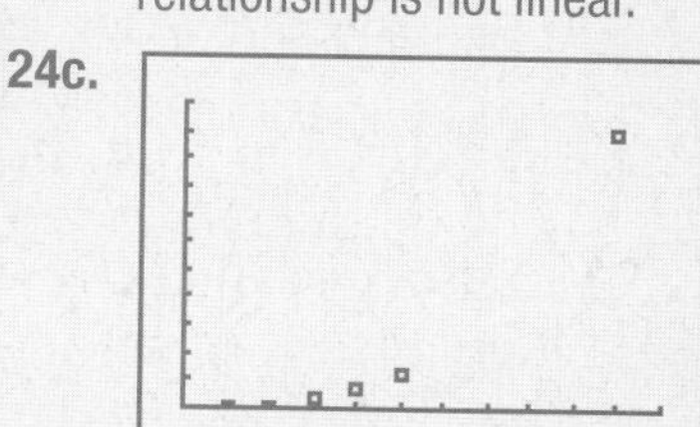

[0, 11] scl: 1 by [0, 1100] scl: 100; $y \approx x^3$

26. $\sqrt{\frac{x}{100}}$ or $\frac{1}{10}\sqrt{x}$

4 Assess

Crystal Ball Ask students how they think the volumes of similar objects are related.

Formative Assessment

Check for student understanding of Lesson 11-5.

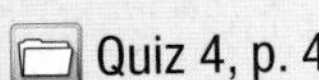 Quiz 4, p. 40

Additional Answers

32a. $(2x + 1) + (5x - 9) = 90$

32b. 61°; 29°

34. center: point R, radius: $\overline{RX}$, apothem: $\overline{RS}$, central angle: $\angle YRX$, 90

Standardized Test Practice

30. $\triangle ABC \sim \triangle PRT$, $AC = 15$ inches, $PT = 6$ inches, and the area of $\triangle PRT$ is 24 square inches. Find the area of $\triangle ABC$. **D**

A 9.6 in^2 C 66.7 in^2
B 60 in^2 D 150 in^2

31. ALGEBRA Which of the following shows $2x^2 - 18xy - 72y^2$ factored completely? **J**

F $(2x - 18y)(x + 4y)$ H $(2x - 9y)(x + 4y)$
G $2(x - 9y)(x + 4y)$ J $2(x - 12y)(x + 3y)$

32. EXTENDED RESPONSE The measures of two complementary angles are represented by $2x + 1$ and $5x - 9$. **See margin.**

a. Write an equation that represents the relationship between the two angles.
b. Find the degree measure of each angle.

33. SAT/ACT Which of the following are the values of x for which $(x + 5)(x - 4) = 10$? **E**

A −5 and 4 D 6 and −5
B 5 and 6 E −6 and 5
C −4 and 5

Spiral Review

34. In the figure, square $WXYZ$ is inscribed in $\odot R$. Identify the center, a radius, an apothem, and a central angle of the polygon. Then find the measure of a central angle. (Lesson 11-4) **See margin.**

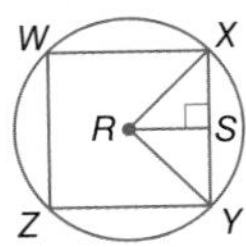

Find the area of the shaded region. Round to the nearest tenth. (Lesson 11-3)

35. **66.3 cm^2**

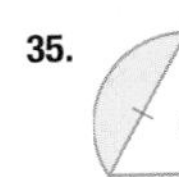

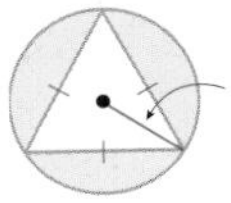

36.

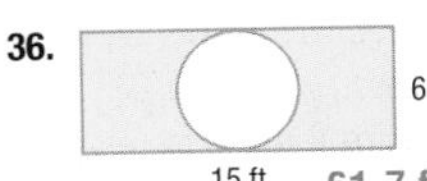

61.7 ft^2

37. **37.4 in^2**

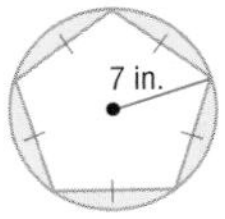

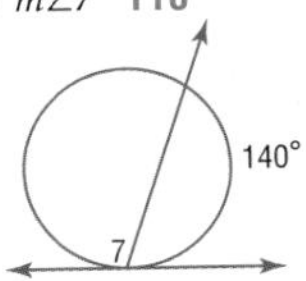

Find each measure. (Lesson 10-6)

38. $m\angle 5$ **75**

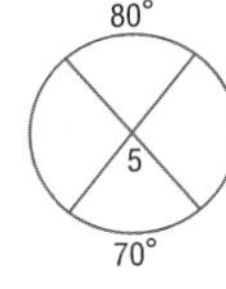

39. $m\angle 6$ **142.5**

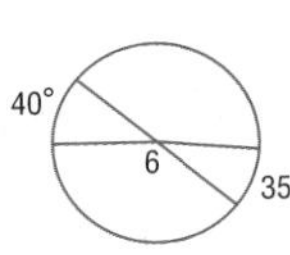

40. $m\angle 7$ **110**

41. State whether the figure has *plane* symmetry, *axis* symmetry, *both*, or *neither*. (Lesson 9-5) **both**

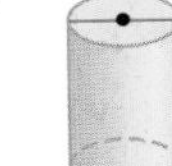

42. YEARBOOKS Tai resized a photograph that was 8 inches by 10 inches so that it would fit in a 4-inch by 4-inch area on a yearbook page. (Lesson 7-7)

a. Find the maximum dimensions of the reduced photograph. **3.2 in. by 4 in.**
b. What is the percent of reduction of the length? **60%**

Skills Review

Refer to the figure at the right to identify each of the following.

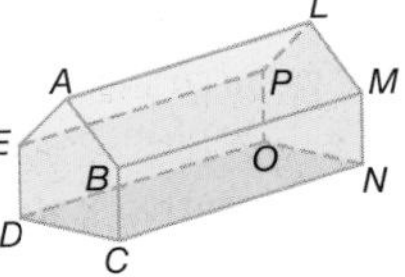

43. Name all segments parallel to $\overline{AE}$. $\overline{LP}$

44. Name all planes intersecting plane BCN. ***ABM, OCN, ABC, LMN***

45. Name all segements skew to $\overline{DC}$. $\overline{BM}, \overline{AL}, \overline{EP}, \overline{OP}, \overline{PL}, \overline{LM}, \overline{MN}$

Differentiated Instruction OL BL

Extension In many social studies classes, students learn about distortion on different types of maps. Challenge students to determine which parts of Earth are most distorted on a globe. Ask them to develop a mathematically sound presentation demonstrating how this distortion affects the scale area of a region. What should the scale area be based on the actual area of that region and the globe's scale?

CHAPTER 11 Study Guide and Review

Study Guide

KeyConcepts

Areas of Parallelograms and Triangles (Lesson 11-1)

- The area A of a parallelogram is the product of a base b and its corresponding height h. $A = bh$
- The area A of a triangle is one half the product of a base b and its corresponding height h. $A = \frac{1}{2}bh$ or $A = \frac{bh}{2}$

Areas of Trapezoids, Rhombi, and Kites (Lesson 11-2)

- The area A of a trapezoid is one half the product of the height h and the sum of its bases, b_1 and b_2. $A = \frac{1}{2}h(b_1 + b_2)$
- The area A of a rhombus or kite is one half the product of the lengths of its diagonals, d_1 and d_2. $A = \frac{1}{2}d_1d_2$

Areas of Circles and Sectors (Lesson 11-3)

- The area A of a circle is equal to π times the square of the radius r. $A = \pi r^2$
- The ratio of the area A of a sector to the area of the whole circle, πr^2, is equal to the ratio of the degree measure of the intercepted arc x to 360.
  Proportion: $\frac{A}{\pi r^2} = \frac{x}{360}$ Equation: $A = \frac{x}{360} \cdot \pi r^2$

Areas of Regular Polygons and Composite Figures (Lesson 11-4)

- The area A of a regular n-gon with side length s is one half the product of the apothem a and perimeter P. $A = \frac{1}{2}a(ns)$ or $A = \frac{1}{2}aP$

Areas of Similar Figures (Lesson 11-5)

- If two polygons are similar, then their areas are proportional to the square of the scale factor between them.
  If $ABCD \sim FGHJ$, then $\frac{\text{area of } FGHJ}{\text{area of } ABCD} = \left(\frac{FG}{AB}\right)^2$.

FOLDABLES StudyOrganizer

Be sure the Key Concepts are noted in your Foldable.

KeyVocabulary

- apothem (p. 807)
- base of a parallelogram (p. 779)
- base of a triangle (p. 781)
- center of a regular polygon (p. 807)
- central angle of a regular polygon (p. 807)
- composite figure (p. 809)
- height of a parallelogram (p. 779)
- height of a trapezoid (p. 789)
- height of a triangle (p. 781)
- radius of a regular polygon (p. 807)
- sector of a circle (p. 799)

VocabularyCheck

State whether each sentence is *true* or *false*. If *false*, replace the underlined term to make a true sentence.

1. The center of a trapezoid is the perpendicular distance between the bases. **false; height**
2. A slice of pizza is a sector of a circle. **true**
3. The center of a regular polygon is the distance from the middle to the circle circumscribed around the polygon. **false; radius**
4. The segment from the center of a square to the corner can be called the radius of the square. **true**
5. A segment drawn perpendicular to a side of a regular polygon is called an apothem of the polygon. **true**
6. The measure of each radial angle of a regular n-gon is $\frac{360}{n}$. **false; central**
7. The apothem of a polygon is the perpendicular distance between any two parallel bases. **false; height of a parallelogram**
8. The height of a triangle is the length of an altitude drawn to a given base. **true**
9. Any side of a parallelogram can be called the height of a parallelogram. **false; base**
10. The center of a regular polygon is also the center of its circumscribed circle. **true**

Formative Assessment

KeyVocabulary The page references after each word denote where that term was first introduced. If students have difficulty completing Exercises 1–10, remind them that they can use these page references to refresh their memories about the vocabulary terms.

Summative Assessment

Vocabulary Test, p. 42

Vocabulary Review

Vocabulary Review provides students the opportunity to check their understanding of important concepts and terminology in an online game format.

FOLDABLES StudyOrganizer

Dinah Zike's Foldables®

Have students look through the chapter to make sure they have included the key concepts for each lesson of the chapter under the proper lesson tab in their Foldables. Suggest that students keep their Foldables handy while completing the Study Guide and Review pages. Point out that their Foldables can serve as a quick review when studying for the chapter test.

Lesson-by-Lesson Review

Intervention If the given examples are not sufficient to review the topics covered by the questions, remind students that the lesson references tell them where to review that topic in their textbooks.

Two-Day Option Have students complete the Lesson-by-Lesson Review. Then you can use eAssessment to customize another review worksheet that practices all the objectives of this chapter or only the objectives on which your students need more help.

Additional Answers

11. $P = 50$ cm; $A = 60$ cm^2

12. $P = 38.4$ in.; $A = 70$ in^2

13. $P = 13.2$ mm; $A = 6$ mm^2

14. $P = 36$ ft; $A = 54$ ft^2

CHAPTER 11 Study Guide and Review *Continued*

Lesson-by-Lesson Review

11-1 Areas of Parallelograms and Triangles

Find the perimeter and area of each parallelogram or triangle. Round to the nearest tenth if necessary. **11–14. See margin.**

11.

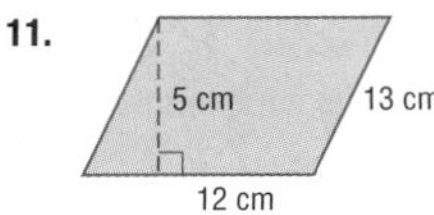

12.

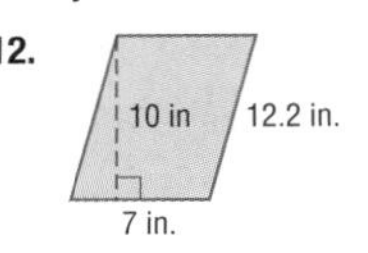

13.

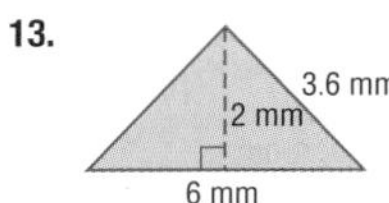

14.

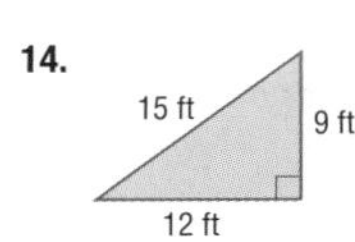

15. PAINTING Two of the walls of an attic in an A-frame house are triangular, each with a height of 12 feet and a width of 22 feet. How much paint is needed to paint one end of the attic? **132 ft^2**

Example 1

Find the perimeter and area of ▱*JKLM*.

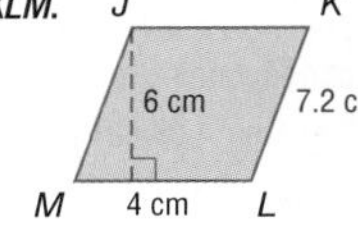

Perimeter

Perimeter of ▱$JKLM = JK + KL + LM + JM$

$= 4 + 7.2 + 4 + 7.2$ or 22.4 cm

Area

$A = bh$ — Area of a parallelogram

$= (4)(6)$ or 24 cm^2 — $b = 4$ and $h = 6$

11-2 Areas of Trapezoids, Rhombi, and Kites

Find the area of each trapezoid, rhombus, or kite.

16.

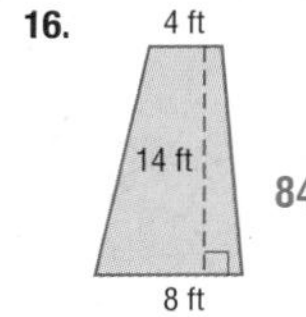

84 ft^2

17. 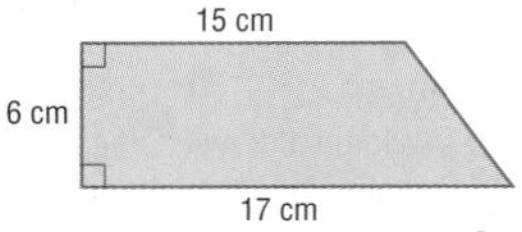 15 cm, 6 cm, 17 cm **96 cm^2**

18. **19.**

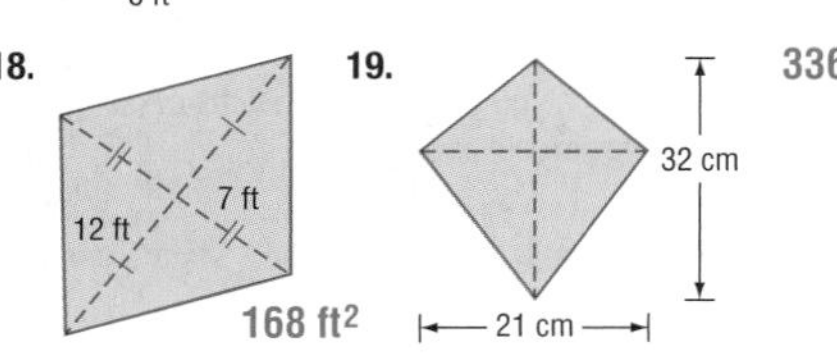

18. **168 ft^2** 19. **336 cm^2**

20. KITES Team Dragon's kite is 4 feet long and 3 feet across. How much fabric does it take to make their kite? **6 ft^2**

Example 2

Find the area of each rhombus or kite.

a.

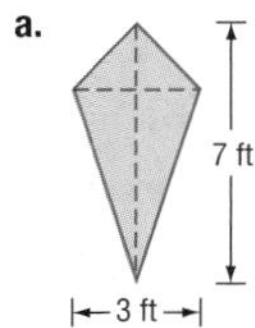

$A = \frac{1}{2}d_1d_2$ — Area of a kite

$= \frac{1}{2}(7)(3)$ — $d_1 = 7$ and $d_2 = 3$

$= 10.5$ ft^2 — Simplify.

b. 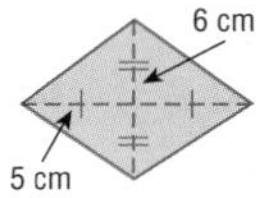 (6 cm, 5 cm) Since the diagonals of a rhombus bisect each other, the lengths of the diagonals are $6 + 6$ or 12 centimeters and $5 + 5$ or 10 centimeters.

$A = \frac{1}{2}d_1d_2$ — Area of a rhombus

$= \frac{1}{2}(10)(12)$ — $d_1 = 10$ and $d_2 = 12$

$= 60$ cm^2 — Simplify.

11-3 Areas of Circles and Sectors

Find the area of each shaded sector. Round to the nearest tenth.

21. 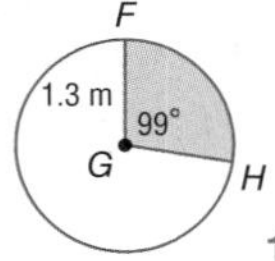

1.5 m^2

22. 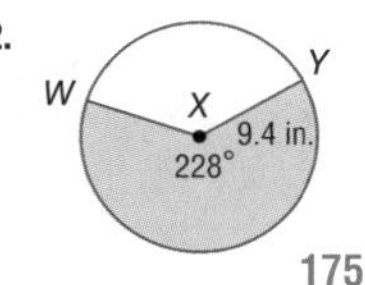

175.8 in^2

23. **BICYCLES** A bicycle tire decoration covers $\frac{1}{9}$ of the circle formed by the tire. If the tire has a diameter of 26 inches, what is the area of the decoration? 59 in^2

24. **PIZZA** Charlie and Kris ordered a 16-inch pizza and cut the pizza into 12 slices.

a. If Charlie ate 3 pieces, what area of the pizza did he eat? 50.27 in^2

b. If Kris ate 2 pieces, what area of the pizza did she eat? 33.51 in^2

c. What is the area of leftover pizza? 117.29 in^2

Example 3

Find the area of the shaded sector. Round to the nearest tenth.

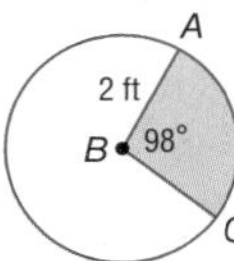

$A = \frac{x}{360} \cdot \pi r^2$	Area of a sector
$= \frac{98}{360} \cdot \pi(2)^2$	Substitution
$\approx 3.4\text{ ft}^2$	Simplify.

11-4 Areas of Regular Polygons and Composite Figures

Find the area of each regular polygon or composite figure. Round to the nearest tenth.

25. 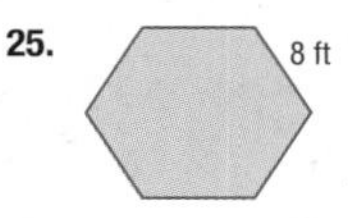

166.3 ft^2

26. 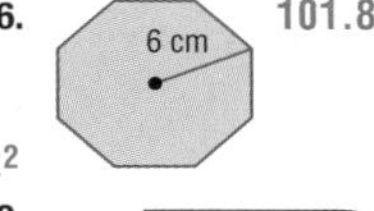

101.8 cm^2

27. 5 m

65.0 m^2

28. 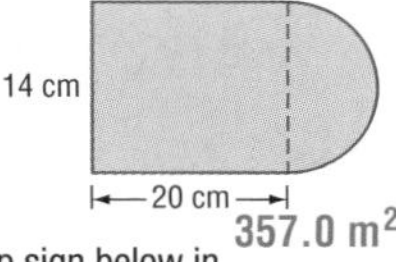

357.0 m^2

29. **SIGNS** Find the area of the stop sign below in square inches. $\approx 695\text{ in}^2$

Example 4

Find the area of the figure.

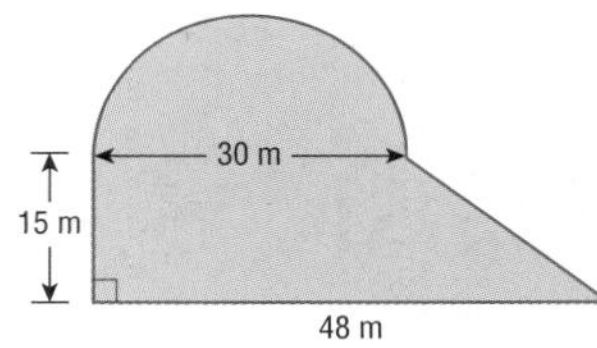

The composite shape is made up of a semicircle and a trapezoid.

Area = Area of semicircle + Area of trapezoid

$$= \frac{180}{360} \cdot \pi \cdot r^2 + \frac{1}{2} \cdot h \cdot (b_1 + b_1)$$

$$\approx \frac{180}{360} \cdot \pi \cdot 15^2 + \frac{1}{2} \cdot 15 \cdot (30 + 48)$$

$$\approx 112.5\pi + 585 \text{ or about } 938.4\text{ m}^2$$

connectED.mcgraw-hill.com 827

Anticipation Guide

Have students complete the Chapter 11 Anticipation Guide, and discuss how their responses have changed now that they have completed Chapter 11.

Additional Answers

30. $\frac{\sqrt{3}}{2}; \frac{5\sqrt{3}}{2}$

31. $\frac{1}{2}; 8$

32. $\frac{\sqrt{3}}{3}; 6\sqrt{3}$

33. area of $\triangle RST = 18$ square units; area of $\triangle R'S'T' = 4.5$ square units

34. area of $\triangle JKL = 25$ square units; area of $\triangle J'K'L' \approx 225$ square units

CHAPTER 11 Study Guide and Review *Continued*

11-5 Areas of Similar Figures

For each pair of similar figures, use the given areas to find the scale factor from the blue to the green figure. Then find x. **30–32. See margin.**

30. x m, $A = 30$ m^2; 5 m, $A = 40$ m^2

31.

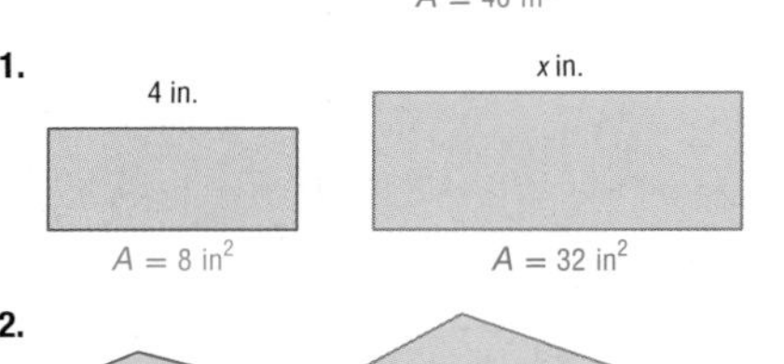

32. x, $A = 525$ cm^2; 18 cm, $A = 1575$ cm^2

COORDINATE GEOMETRY Find the area of each figure. Use the segment length given to find the area of a similar polygon. **33–34. See margin.**

33. $R'S' = 3$

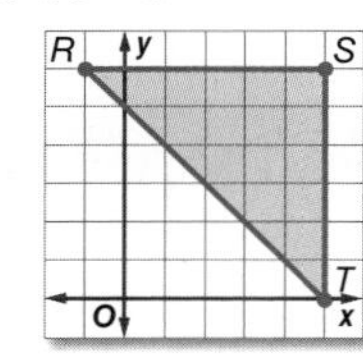

34. $K'L' = 15$

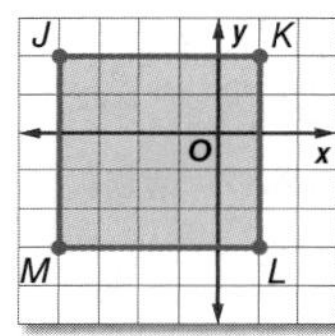

35. LAND OWNERSHIP Joshua's land is 600 square miles. A map of his land is 5 square feet. If one side of the map is 1.5 feet, how long is the corresponding side of the land? **16.4 mi**

Example 5

The area of trapezoid $JKLM$ is 138 square feet. The area of trapezoid $QRST$ is 5.52 square feet. If trapezoid $JKLM \sim$ trapezoid $QRST$, find the scale factor from trapezoid $JKLM$ to trapezoid $QRST$ and the value of x.

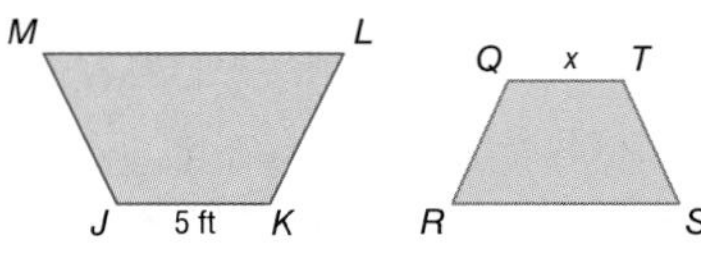

Let k be the scale factor between trapezoid $JKLM$ and trapezoid $QRST$.

$\frac{\text{Area of trapezoid } JKLM}{\text{Area of trapezoid } QRST} = k^2$ Theorem 11.1

$\frac{138}{5.52} = k^2$ Substitution

$5 = k$ Take the positive square root of each side.

So, the scale factor from trapezoid $JKLM$ to trapezoid $QRST$ is 5. Use this scale factor to find the value of x.

$\frac{JK}{QT} = k$ The ratio of corresponding lengths of similar polygons is equal to the scale factor between the polygons.

$\frac{5}{x} = 5$ Substitution

$1 = x$ Simplify.

CHAPTER 11 Practice Test

Find the area and perimeter of each figure. Round to the nearest tenth if necessary. **1–4. See margin.**

1.
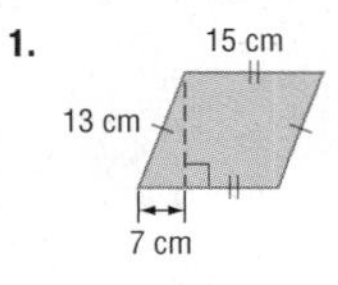

2.
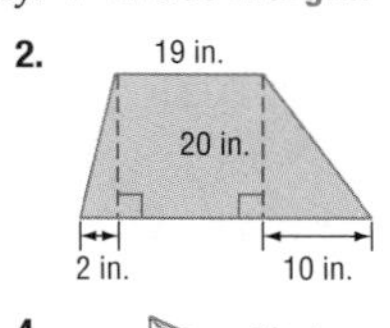

3.
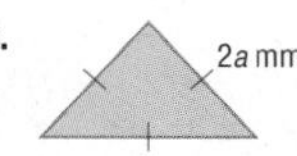

4.
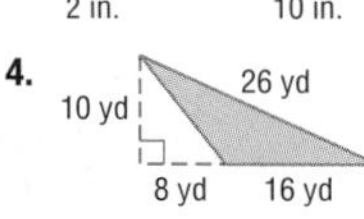

5. **ARCHAELOGY** The tile pattern shown was used in Pompeii for paving. If the diagonals of each rhombus are 2 and 3 inches, what area makes up each "cube" in the pattern? **9 in^2**

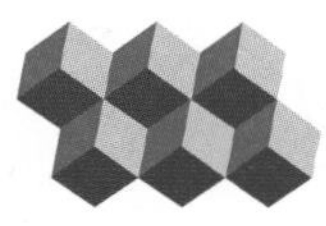

Find the area of each figure. Round to the nearest tenth if necessary.

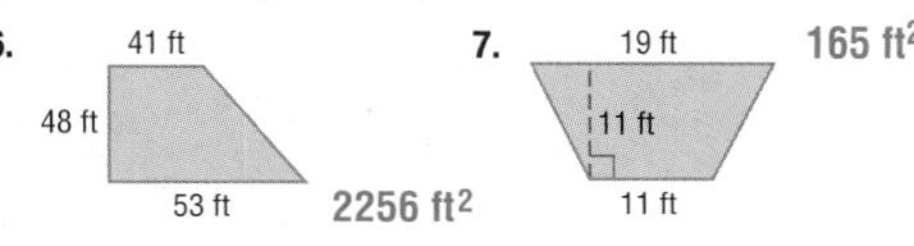

6. **2256 ft^2**

7. **165 ft^2**

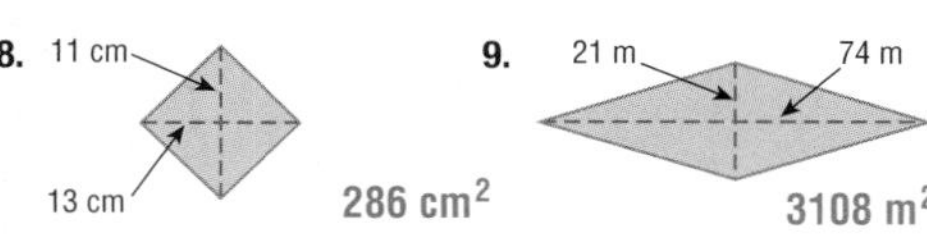

8. **286 cm^2**

9. **3108 m^2**

10. **GEMOLOGY** A gem is cut in a kite shape. It is 6.2 millimeters wide at its widest point and 5 millimeters long. What is the area? **15.5 mm^2**

11. **ALGEBRA** The area of a triangle is 16 square units. The base of the triangle is $x + 4$ and the height is x. Find x. **4**

12. **ASTRONOMY** A large planetarium in the shape of a dome is being built. When it is complete, the base of the dome will have a circumference of 870 meters. How many square meters of land were required for this planetarium? **60,232 m^2**

Find the area of each circle or sector. Round to the nearest tenth.

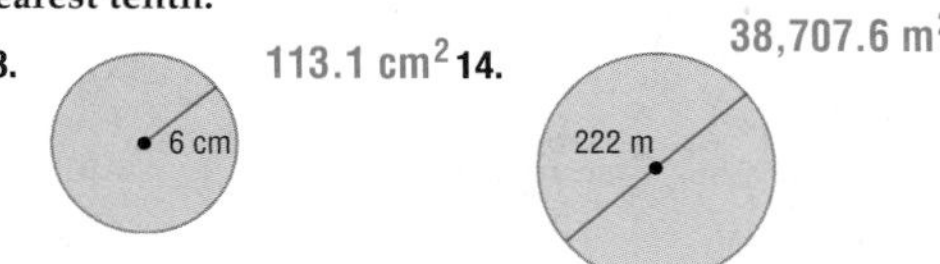

13. **113.1 cm^2**

14. **38,707.6 m^2**

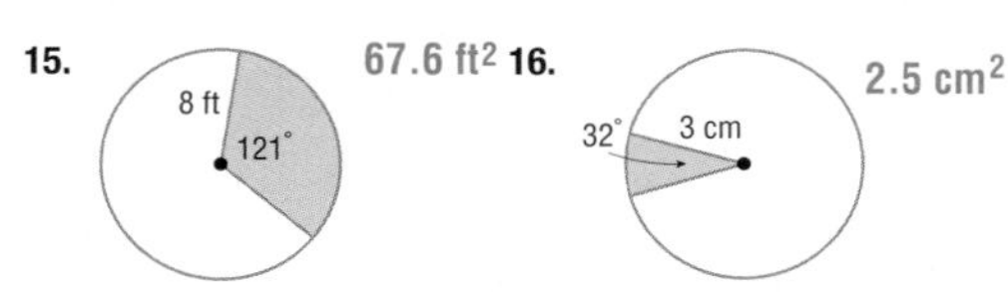

15. **67.6 ft^2**

16. **2.5 cm^2**

17. **MURALS** An artisan is creating a circular street mural for an art festival. The mural is going to be 50 feet wide.

 a. Find the area of the mural to the nearest square foot. **1963 ft^2**

 b. One sector of the mural spans 38°. What is the area of this sector to the nearest square foot? **207 ft^2**

Find the perimeter and area of each figure. Round to the nearest tenth if necessary.

18. **31.4; 54**

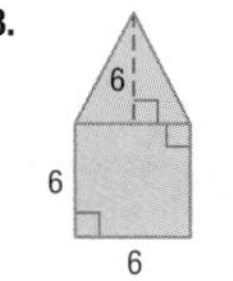

19. **24; 21**

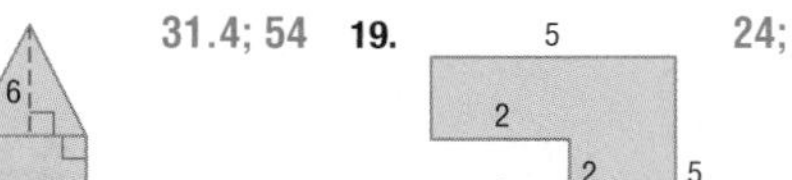

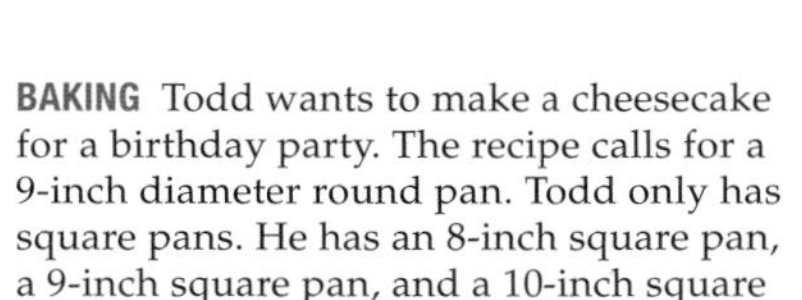

20. **BAKING** Todd wants to make a cheesecake for a birthday party. The recipe calls for a 9-inch diameter round pan. Todd only has square pans. He has an 8-inch square pan, a 9-inch square pan, and a 10-inch square pan. Which pan comes closest in area to the one that the recipe suggests? **8 in.**

Summative Assessment

Use these alternate leveled chapter tests to differentiate assessment for your students.

Leveled Chapter 11 Tests

Form	Type	Level	Page(s)
1	MC	AL	43–44
2A	MC	OL	45–46
2B	MC	OL	47–48
2C	FR	OL	49–50
2D	FR	OL	51–52
3	FR	BL	53–54
Vocabulary Test			42
Extended-Response Test			55

MC = multiple-choice questions
FR = free-response questions

eAssessment Customize and create multiple versions of your chapter tests and their answer keys. All of the questions from the leveled chapter tests in the *Chapter 11 Resource Masters* are also available on eAssessment.

Additional Answers

1. $P = 56$ cm, $A = 164.3$ cm^2
2. $P = 92.5$ in., $A = 500$ in^2
3. $P = 6a$ mm, $A = a^2\sqrt{3}$ mm^2
4. $P = 54.8$ yd, $A = 80$ yd^2

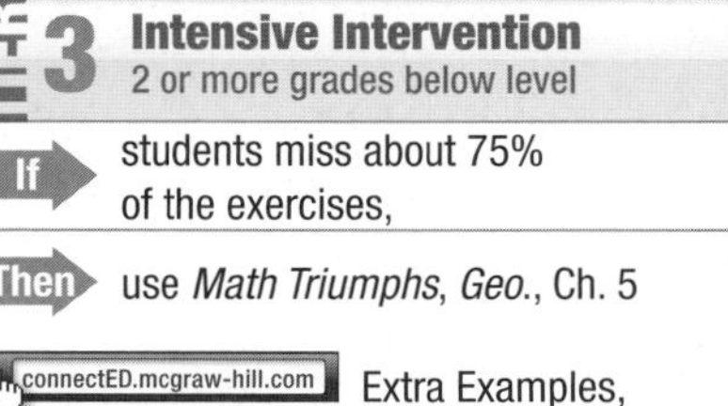

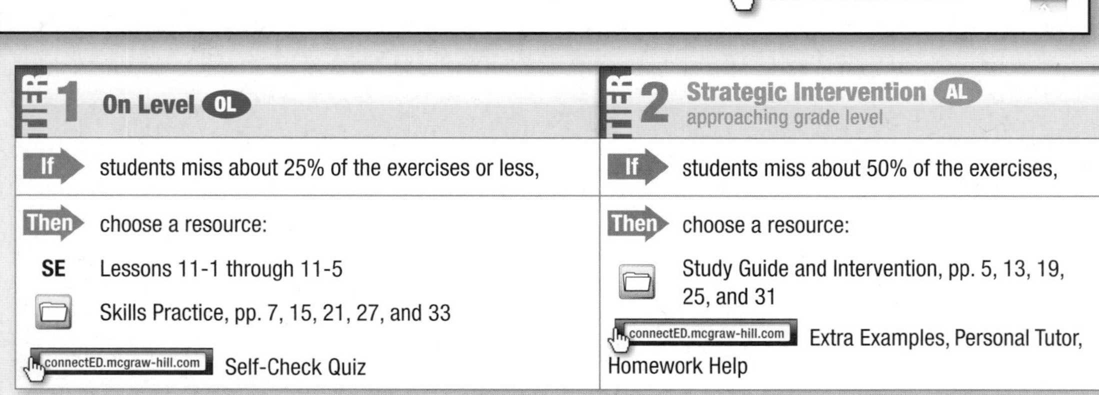

TIER 1 On Level OL	TIER 2 Strategic Intervention AL approaching grade level	TIER 3 Intensive Intervention 2 or more grades below level
If students miss about 25% of the exercises or less,	**If** students miss about 50% of the exercises,	**If** students miss about 75% of the exercises,
Then choose a resource:	**Then** choose a resource:	**Then** use *Math Triumphs, Geo.*, Ch. 5
SE Lessons 11-1 through 11-5 Skills Practice, pp. 7, 15, 21, 27, and 33 connectED.mcgraw-hill.com Self-Check Quiz	Study Guide and Intervention, pp. 5, 13, 19, 25, and 31 connectED.mcgraw-hill.com Extra Examples, Personal Tutor, Homework Help	connectED.mcgraw-hill.com Extra Examples, Personal Tutor, Homework Help, Review Vocabulary

1 Focus

Objective Identify strategies for solving multi-step problems on standardized tests.

2 Teach

Scaffolding Questions

Ask:

- What might be a good way to organize the information given in a multi-step problem? tables, lists, assigning variables to unknowns, labeling units and meanings of intermediate answers
- If there is more than one way to solve a problem, how will you decide which approach is best? the method that best utilizes the known information, the most familiar method, a combination of methods that result in more usable information
- What problem-solving strategies might make checking and correcting your work more efficient? showing the work of the intermediate steps so computational errors can be identified, organizing the work in a manner that is easily readable, keeping all work legible, labeling intermediate answers

CHAPTER 11 Preparing for Standardized Tests

Solve Multi-Step Problems

Some problems that you will encounter on standardized tests require you to solve multiple parts in order to come up with the final solution. Use this lesson to practice these types of problems.

Strategies for Solving Multi-Step Problems

Step 1

Read the problem statement carefully.

Ask yourself:

- What am I being asked to solve? What information is given?
- Are there any intermediate steps that need to be completed before I can solve the problem?

Step 2

Organize your approach.

- List the steps you will need to complete in order to solve the problem.
- Remember that there may be more than one possible way to solve the problem.

Step 3

Solve and check.

- Work as efficiently as possible to complete each step and solve.
- If time permits, check your answer.

Standardized Test Example

Read the problem. Identify what you need to know. Then use the information in the problem to solve.

What is the area of the triangle? Round your answer to the nearest tenth if necessary.

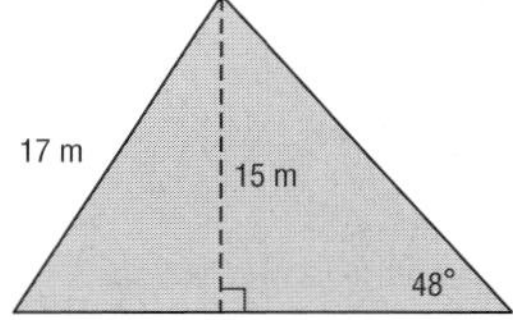

A 137.4 m^2 C 170.5 m^2

B 161.3 m^2 D 186.9 m^2

830 | Chapter 11 | Preparing for Standardized Tests

Read the problem statement and study the figure carefully. At first glance, the problem may appear fairly straightforward. Notice, however, that you must first find the base of the triangle before you can find its area. Organize an approach to solve the problem.

Step 1 Use the Pythagorean Theorem to find a.

Step 2 Use trigonometry to find b.

Step 3 Find the area of the triangle.

17 m, 15 m, 48°, a, b

Step 1 Find a.

$a^2 + 15^2 = 17^2$

$a^2 = 289 - 225$

$a^2 = 64$

$a = 8$

Step 2 Find b.

$\tan 48° = \frac{15}{b}$

$b = \frac{15}{\tan 48°}$

$b \approx 13.506$

Step 3 Find the area of the triangle.

The base of the triangle is $a + b$ or about 21.506 meters.

$A \approx \frac{1}{2}(21.506)(15)$

≈ 161.3

So, the area of the triangle is about 161.3 square meters. The answer is B.

Additional Example

What is the area of the kite?

Round your answer to the nearest tenth if necessary. D

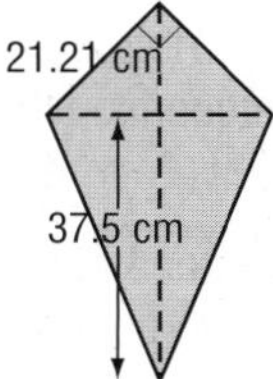

A 787.5 cm^2

B 850.1 cm^2

C 1125 cm^2

D 1245.2 cm^2

3 Assess

Use Exercises 1 and 2 to assess student's understanding.

Exercises

Read the problem. Identify what you need to know. Then use the information in the problem to solve.

1. What is the area of the figure? Round to the nearest tenth. A

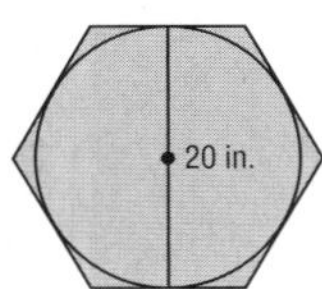

A 346.4 in^2

B 372.1 in^2

C 383.2 in^2

D 564.7 in^2

2. Kaleb is painting just the shaded part of the basketball key shown below. How much area will he need to cover? Round to the nearest tenth. J

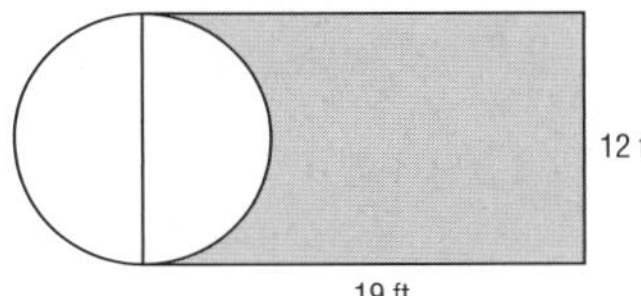

F 114.9 ft^2

G 142.4 ft^2

H 159.9 ft^2

J 171.5 ft^2

connectED.mcgraw-hill.com 831

Diagnose Student Errors

Survey student responses for each item. Class trends may indicate common errors and misconceptions.

1. A did not find geometric mean
B correct
C did not find geometric mean
D did not find geometric mean

2. F misunderstood definition
G misunderstood definition
H misunderstood definition
J correct

3. A used side measure instead of base
B used cosine instead of sine
C guess
D correct

4. F misunderstood definition of exterior angles
G misunderstood definition of vertical angles
H misunderstood correct order of proof
J correct

5. A found "run over rise"
B correct
C stated slope as positive rather than negative
D found "run over rise" and stated slope as positive

CHAPTER 11

Standardized Test Practice

Cumulative, Chapters 1 through 11

Multiple Choice

Read each question. Then fill in the correct answer on the answer document provided by your teacher or on a sheet of paper.

1. What is the value of x in the figure below? B

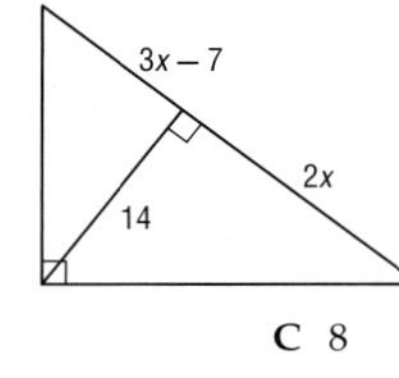

A 5 **C** 8

B 7 **D** 10

2. Which of the following is *not* a property of parallelograms? J

F The opposite angles of a parallelogram are congruent.

G The opposite sides of a parallelogram are congruent.

H The consecutive angles of a parallelogram are supplementary.

J The consecutive angles of a parallelogram are complementary.

3. What is the area of the triangle below? Round your answer to the nearest tenth if necessary. D

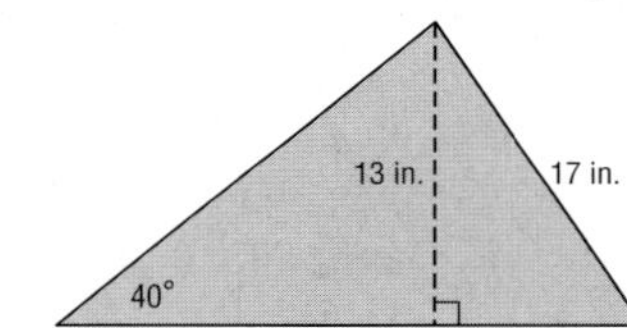

A 110.5 in^2

B 144.2 in^2

C 164.5 in^2

D 171.9 in^2

Test-Taking Tip

Question 3 Some problems require multiple steps to solve. You can use the Pythagorean Theorem and trigonometry to find the base of the triangle.

4. Given: $\overline{AC} \cong \overline{BD}$

$\overline{AC} \parallel \overline{BD}$

Prove: $\triangle ABC \cong \triangle DCB$

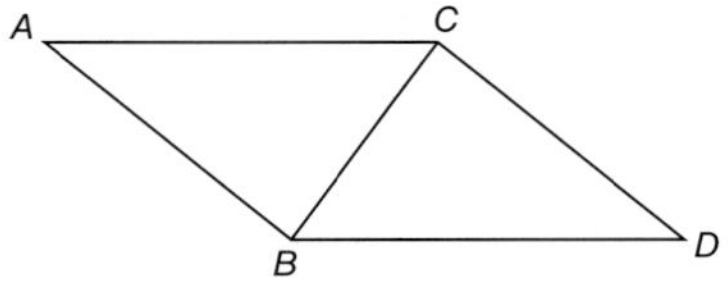

Statements	Reasons
1. $\overline{AC} \cong \overline{BD}$	1. Given
2. $\overline{AC} \parallel \overline{BD}$	2. Given
3. $\angle ACB \cong \angle DCB$	3. ___?___
4. $\overline{BC} \cong \overline{CB}$	4. Reflexive Property of Congruence
5. $\triangle ABC \cong \triangle DCB$	5. SAS

What is the missing line needed to complete the proof? J

F Same side exterior angles are congruent.

G Vertical angles are congruent.

H Corresponding parts of congruent triangles are congruent.

J Alternate interior angles are congruent.

5. What is the slope of the line? B

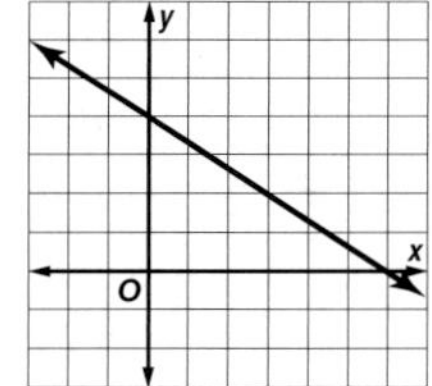

A $-\frac{3}{2}$ **C** $\frac{2}{3}$

B $-\frac{2}{3}$ **D** $\frac{3}{2}$

Additional Answer

7. There should be 4 common tangents.

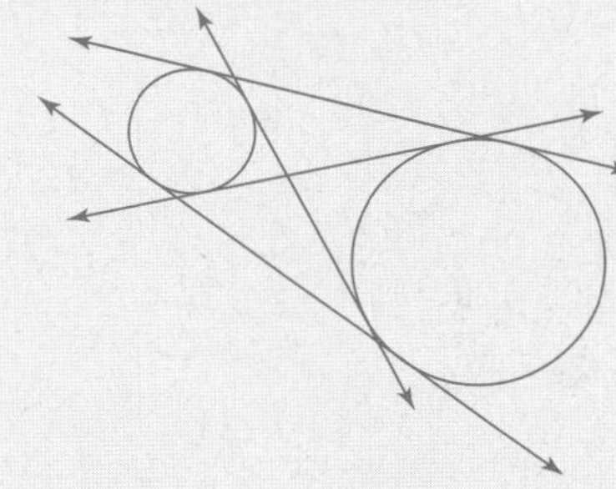

Short Response/Gridded Response

Record your answers on the answer sheet provided by your teacher or on a sheet of paper.

6. **GRIDDED RESPONSE** Suppose two similar rectangles have a scale factor of 3:5. The perimeter of the smaller rectangle is 21 millimeters. What is the perimeter of the larger rectangle? Express your answer in millimeters. 35

7. Copy the circles below on a sheet of paper and draw the common tangents, if any exist. See margin.

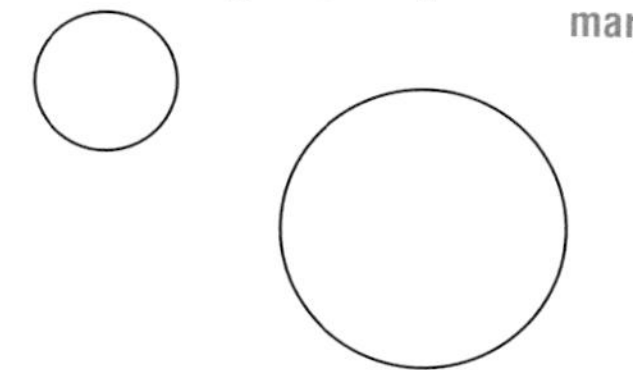

8. What is the contrapositive of the statement below? See margin.

If a chord contains the center of a circle, then the chord is a diameter.

9. Copy the figure and point D. Then use a ruler to draw the image of the figure under a dilation with center D and a scale factor of 2. See margin.

10. **GRIDDED RESPONSE** Solve for x in the figure below. 4.75

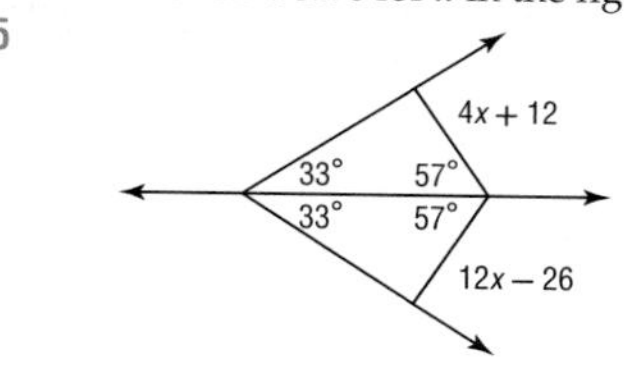

11. **GRIDDED RESPONSE** What is the area of the parallelogram below? Express your answer in square feet. Round to the nearest whole number if necessary. 106

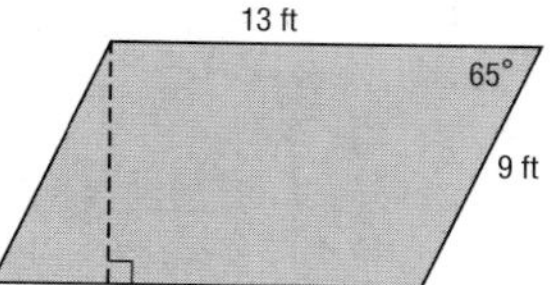

Extended Response

Record your answers on a sheet of paper. Show your work.

12. Use the figure below to answer each question.

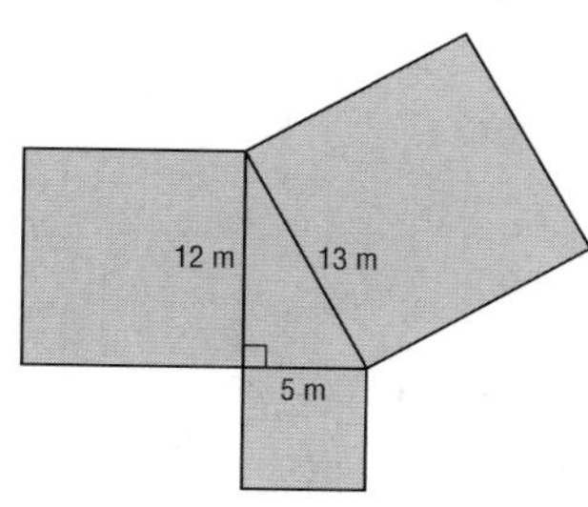

a. Find the area of each square and the area of the triangle. 144 m^2, 169 m^2, 25 m^2, 30 m^2

b. What is the total area of the figure? 368 m^2

c. Explain how the areas of the squares model the Pythagorean Theorem. See margin.

Need ExtraHelp?

If you missed Question...	1	2	3	4	5	6	7	8	9	10	11	12
Go to Lesson...	8-1	6-2	11-1	4-4	3-3	7-2	10-5	2-3	9-6	5-1	11-1	11-4

Formative Assessment

You can use these pages to benchmark student progress.

Standardized Test Practice, pp. 56–58

Answer Sheet Practice

Have students simulate taking a standardized test by recording their answers on a practice recording sheet.

Student Recording Sheet

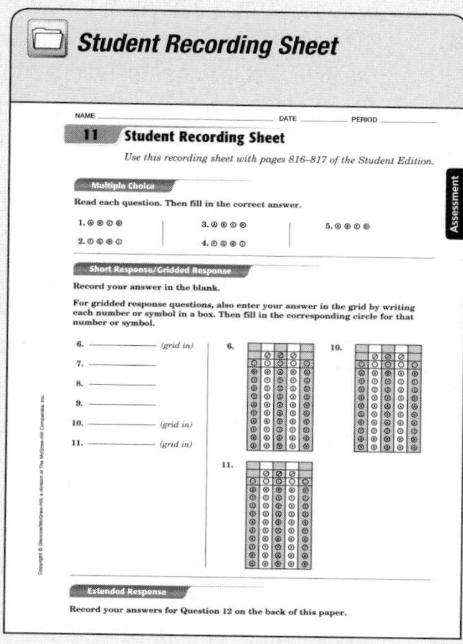

eAssessment Create practice tests that align to your state standards, the Common Core State Standards, and other national standards such as TIMSS and NAEP.

Homework Option

Get Ready for Chapter 12 Assign students the exercises on page 835 as homework to assess whether they possess the prerequisite skills needed for the next chapter.

Additional Answers

8. If the chord is not a diameter, then the chord does not contain the center of the circle.

9. 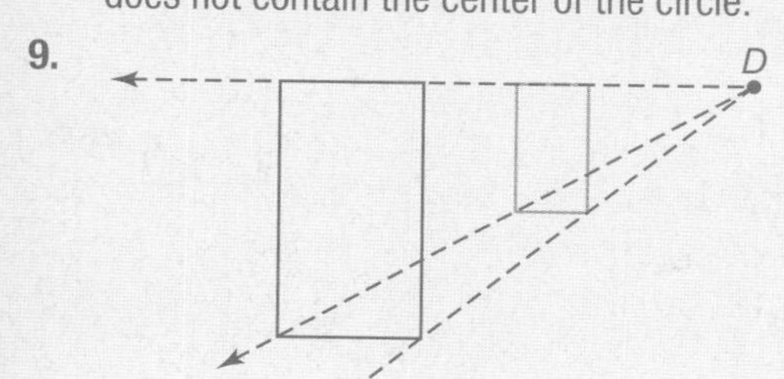

12c. Sample answer: The area of each square represents the square of a side of a right triangle. They show that $a^2 + b^2 = c^2$ since $25 + 144 = 169$.

Lesson 11-1

35a. 10.9 units^2

35b. $\sqrt{s(s-a)(s-b)(s-c)} \stackrel{?}{=} \frac{1}{2}bh$

$$\sqrt{15(15-5)(15-12)(15-13)} \stackrel{?}{=} \frac{1}{2}(5)(12)$$

$$\sqrt{15(10)(3)(2)} \stackrel{?}{=} 30$$

$$\sqrt{900} \stackrel{?}{=} 30$$

$$30 = 30$$

38. Always; sample answer: If the areas are equal, the perimeter of the nonrectangular parallelogram will always be greater because the side that is not perpendicular to the height forms a right triangle with the height. The height is a leg of the triangle and the side of the parallelogram is the hypotenuse of the triangle. Since the hypotenuse is always the longest side of a right triangle, the nonperpendicular side of the parallelogram is always greater than the height. The bases of the quadrilaterals have to be the same because the areas and the heights are the same. Since the bases are the same and the height of the rectangle is also the length of a side, the perimeter of the parallelogram will always be greater.

39. Sample answer: The area will not change as K moves along line p. Since lines m and p are parallel, the perpendicular distance between them is constant. That means that no matter where K is on line p, the perpendicular distance to line p, or the height of the triangle, is always the same. Since point J and L are not moving, the distance between them, or the length of the base, is constant. Since the height of the triangle and the base of the triangle are both constant, the area will always be the same.

40.

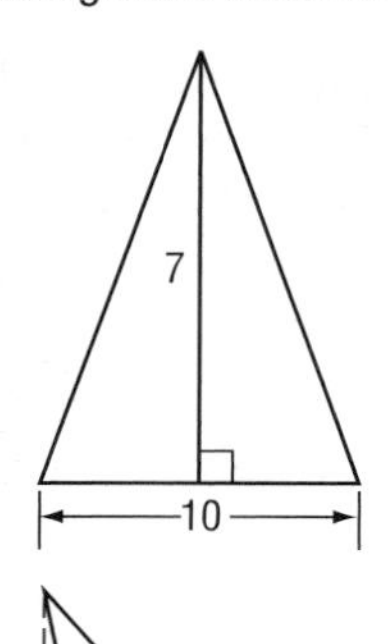

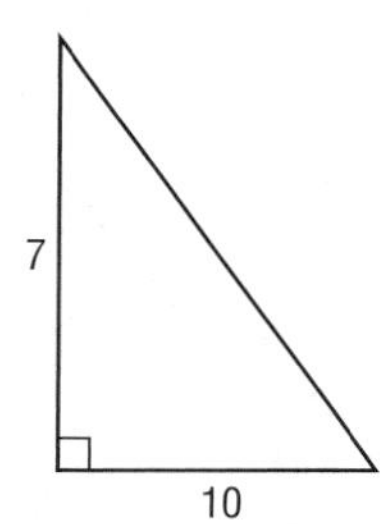

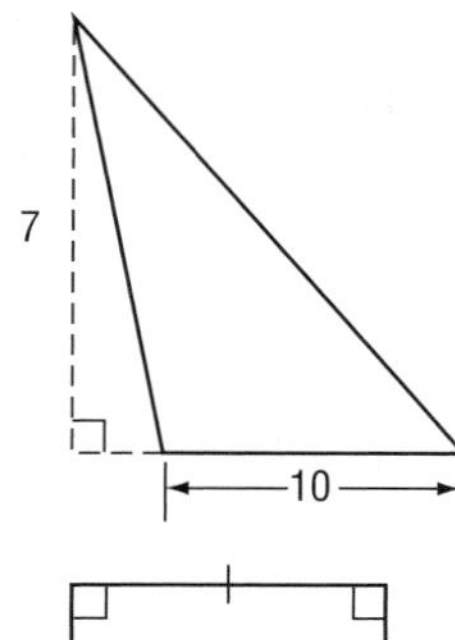

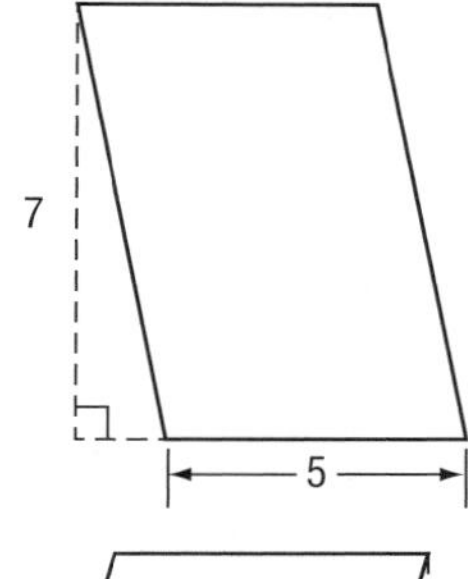

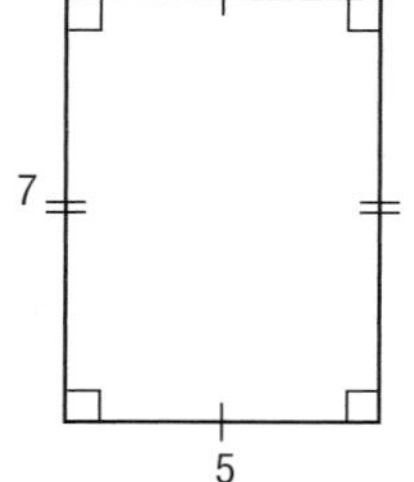

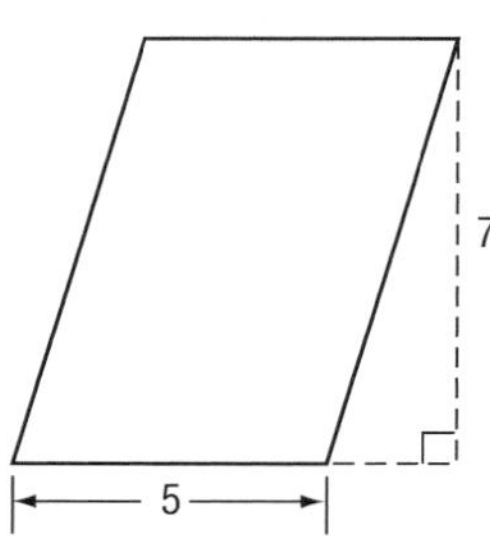

41. Sample answer: To find the area of the parallelogram, you can measure the height $\overline{PT}$ and then measure one of the bases $\overline{PQ}$ or $\overline{SR}$ and multiply the height by the base to get the area. You can also measure the height $\overline{SW}$ and measure one of the bases $\overline{QR}$ or $\overline{PS}$ and then multiply the height by the base to get the area. It doesn't matter which side you choose to use as the base, as long as you use the height that is perpendicular to that base to calculate the area.

Lesson 11-2

33a. 2 cm

4 cm

12 cm

33b.

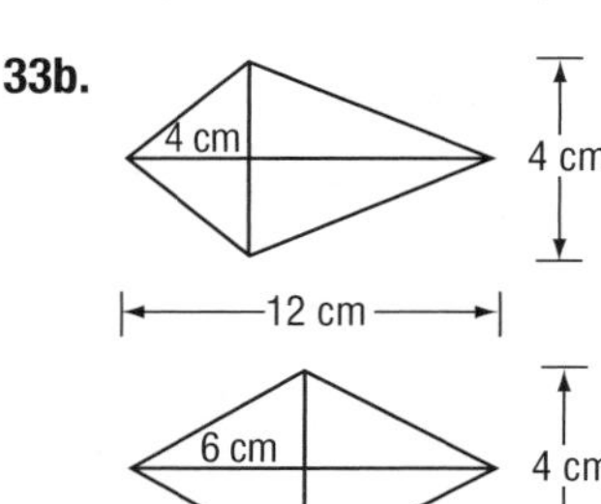

6 cm

4 cm

12 cm

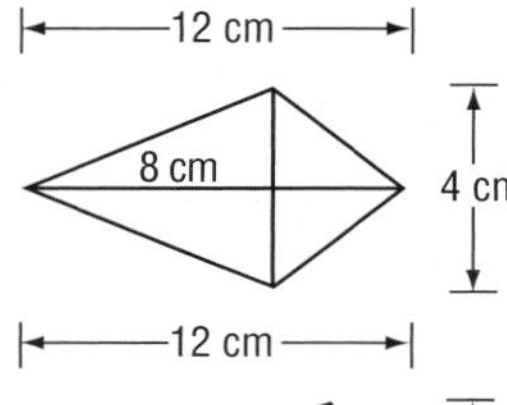

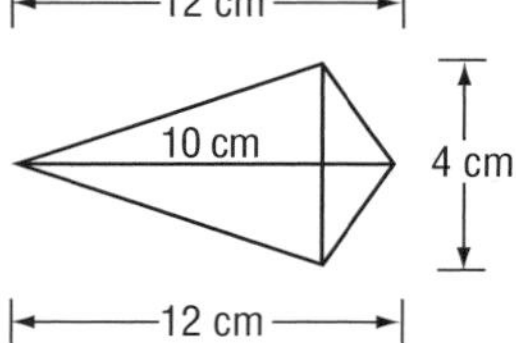

33c.

x	P
2 cm	26.1 cm
4 cm	25.4 cm
6 cm	25.3 cm
8 cm	25.4 cm
10 cm	26.1 cm

33d.

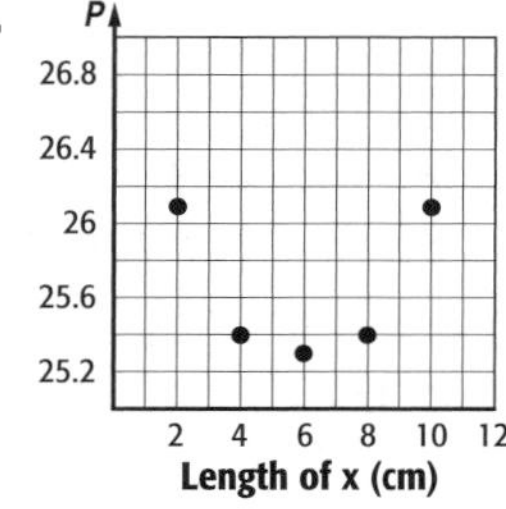

33e. Sample answer: Based on the graph, the perimeter will be minimized when $x = 6$. This value is significant because when $x = 6$, the figure is a rhombus.

36.

4 in.

3 in.

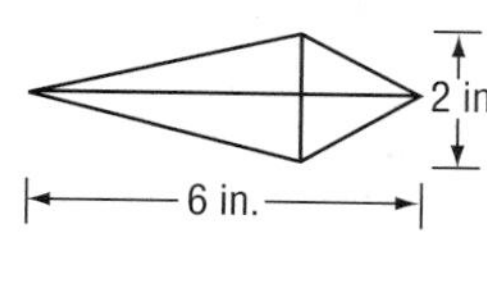

Sample answer: Since the area formula for both a rhombus and a kite is one half the product of the lengths of the two diagonals, if the area is 6 square inches, the product of the two diagonals must be 12. I used 3 and 4 inches for the diagonals of the rhombus and 2 and 6 inches for the diagonals of the kite.

38. Sample answer: You can use trigonometry and known angle and side measures to find unknown triangular measures that are required to calculate the area.

Lesson 11-3

26a.

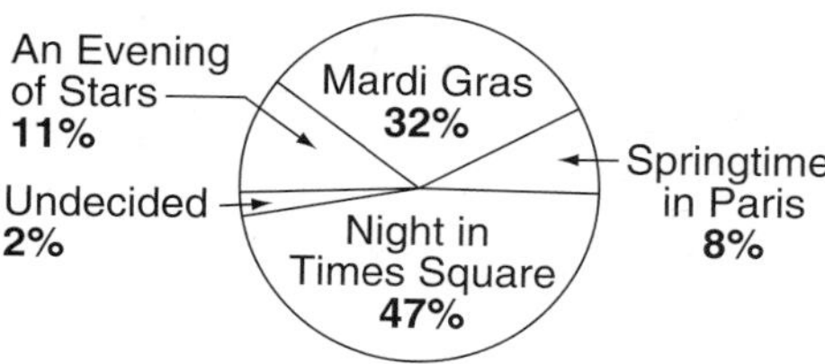

26b. An Evening of Stars: 0.35 in^2; Mardi Gras: 1.01 in^2; Springtime in Paris: 0.25 in^2; Night in Times Square: 1.48 in^2; Don't care: 0.06 in^2

48. The ratio of the area of a sector to the area of a whole circle is equal to the ratio of the corresponding arc length to the circumference of the circle. Let A represent the area of the sector.

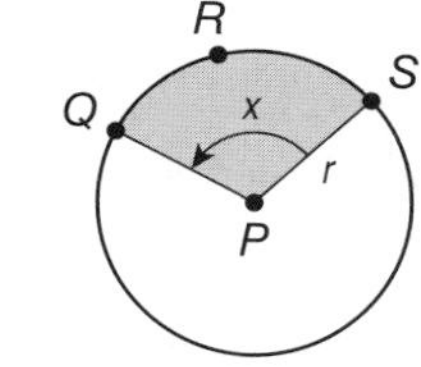

$$\frac{A}{\pi r^2} = \frac{\text{length of } \widehat{QRS}}{2\pi r} \qquad \frac{\text{area of sector}}{\text{area of circle}} = \frac{\text{arc length}}{\text{circumference of circle}}$$

$$\frac{A}{\pi r^2} = \frac{\frac{\pi r x}{180}}{2\pi r} \qquad \text{The length of } \widehat{QRS} \text{ is } \frac{\pi r x}{180}.$$

$$A = \frac{\pi r^2 x}{360} \qquad \text{Solve for } A.$$

49. Sample answer: If the radius of the circle doubles, the area will not double. If the radius of the circle doubles, the area will be four times as great. Since the radius is squared, if you multiply the radius by 2, you multiply the area by 2^2, or 4. If the arc length of a sector is doubled, the area of the sector is doubled. Since the arc length is not raised to a power, if the arc length is doubled, the area would also be twice as large.

Lesson 11–5

15b. Larger; sample answer: The area of a circular pie pan with an 8 in. diameter is about 50 in^2. The area of the larger pan is 52.6 in^2, and the area of the smaller pan is 41.6 in^2. The area of the larger pan is closer to the area of the circle, so Kaitlyn should choose the larger pan to make the recipe.

16a. If the area is doubled, each side length will increase by a factor of $\sqrt{2}$.

16b. If the area is tripled, each side length will increase by a factor of $\sqrt{3}$.

16c. If the area changes by a factor of x, then each side length will change by a factor of $\sqrt{x}$.

17a. If the area is doubled, the radius changes from 24 in. to 33.9 in.

17b. If the area is tripled, the radius changes from 24 in. to 41.6 in.

17c. If the area changes by a factor of x, then the radius changes from 24 in. to $24\sqrt{x}$ in.

22. The area of $\triangle ABC = \frac{1}{2}b \cdot h_1$ and the area of $\triangle XYZ = \frac{1}{2}y \cdot h_2$. The ratio of the area of $\frac{\triangle ABC}{\triangle XYZ} = \frac{h_1 b}{h_2 y}$ or $\frac{h_1}{h_2} \cdot \frac{b}{y}$. The ratio of the corresponding measures are $\frac{a}{x} = \frac{b}{y} = \frac{h_1}{h_2}$. Therefore, by substitution, $\frac{\triangle ABC}{\triangle XYZ} = \left(\frac{a}{x}\right)\left(\frac{a}{x}\right)$ or $\frac{a^2}{x^2}$.

28.

0.5 in. | $A = 0.5$ in.^{2} | 1 in.

1 in. | $A = 2$ in.^{2} | 2 in.

Sample answer: Since the ratio of the areas should be 4:1, the ratio of the lengths of the sides will be $\sqrt{4} : \sqrt{1}$ or 2:1. Thus a 0.5-inch by 1-inch rectangle and a 1-inch by 2-inch rectangle are similar, and the ratio of their areas is 4:1.

29. Sample answer: If you know the area of the original polygon and the scale factor of the enlargement, you can find the area of the enlarged polygon by multiplying the original area by the scale factor squared.

Chapter Planner

	Diagnostic Assessment Quick Check		
	EXPLORE 12-1 45 min: 0.5 day 90 min: 0.5 day	LESSON 12-1 45 min: 1 day 90 min: 0.5 day	EXTEND 12-1 45 min: 0.5 day 90 min: 0.25 day
Title	**Geometry Lab: Solids Formed by Translation**	**Representations of Three-Dimensional Figures**	**Geometry Lab: Topographic Maps**
Objectives	▪ Identify and sketch solids formed by translating two-dimensional figures along vectors.	▪ Draw isometric views of three-dimensional figures. ▪ Investigate cross sections of three-dimensional figures.	▪ Interpret and draw topographic maps.
Key Vocabulary	right solid oblique solid	isometric view cross section	topographic maps
CCSS		G.GMD.4	
Multiple Representations			
Lesson Resources	connectED.mcgraw-hill.com Vocabulary **Materials:** ▪ playing cards ▪ triangular tangram pieces ▪ rolls of quarters or other coins ▪ ruler	connectED.mcgraw-hill.com Leveled Worksheets Vocabulary Personal Tutor Virtual Manipulatives Self-Check Quiz ▪ *5-Minute Check* ▪ *Study Notebook*	connectED.mcgraw-hill.com Vocabulary ▪ *Teaching Geometry with Manipulatives* **Materials:** ▪ ruler
Resources for Every Lesson	IWB eStudent Edition IWB Interactive Classroom	▪ eTeacher Edition ▪ eSolutions Manual ▪ eAssessment	
Differentiated Instruction		pp. 840, 844	

IWB All digital assets are Interactive Whiteboard ready.

Suggested Pacing			
Time Periods	Instruction	Review & Assess	Total
45-minute	11 days	2 days	13 days
90-minute	6 days	1 day	7 days

LESSON 12-2 (45 min: 1 day, 90 min: 0.5 day)	LESSON 12-3 (45 min: 1 day, 90 min: 0.5 day)	LESSON 12-4 (45 min: 1 day, 90 min: 0.5 day)	EXTEND 12-4 (45 min: 1 day, 90 min: 0.5 day)
Surface Areas of Prisms and Cylinders	**Surface Areas of Pyramids and Cones**	**Volumes of Prisms and Cylinders**	**Graphing Technology Lab: Changing Dimensions**
▪ Find lateral areas and surface areas of prisms. ▪ Find lateral areas and surface areas of cylinders.	▪ Find lateral areas and surface areas of pyramids. ▪ Find lateral areas and surface areas of cones.	▪ Find volumes of prisms. ▪ Find volumes of cylinders.	▪ Explore how volume of a prism is affected by changing dimensions using the spreadsheet of the TI-Nspire Technology.
lateral face lateral edge base edge altitude height lateral area axis composite solid	regular pyramid slant height right cone oblique cone		
G.MG.3	G.MG.1	G.GMD.1, G.GMD.3	
connectED.mcgraw-hill.com Leveled Worksheets Quiz 1 Vocabulary Personal Tutor Virtual Manipulatives Self-Check Quiz ▪ *5-Minute Check* ▪ *Study Notebook* ▪ *Teaching Geometry with Manipulatives*	connectED.mcgraw-hill.com Leveled Worksheets Vocabulary Personal Tutor Virtual Manipulatives Self-Check Quiz ▪ *5-Minute Check* ▪ *Study Notebook* ▪ *Teaching Geometry with Manipulatives*	connectED.mcgraw-hill.com Leveled Worksheets Quiz 2 Personal Tutor Virtual Manipulatives Self-Check Quiz ▪ *5-Minute Check* ▪ *Study Notebook*	connectED.mcgraw-hill.com Personal Tutor **Materials:** ▪ TI-Nspire technology
IWB eStudent Edition IWB Interactive Classroom	▪ eTeacher Edition ▪ eSolutions Manual ▪ eAssessment		
pp. 848, 853	pp. 855, 862	pp. 865, 868, 870	

Formative Assessment
Mid-Chapter Quiz

Chapter Planner

	LESSON 12-5 (45 min: 1 day; 90 min: 0.5 day)	LESSON 12-6 (45 min: 1 day; 90 min: 0.5 day)	EXTEND 12-6 (45 min: 0.5 day; 90 min: 0.5 day)
Title	**Volumes of Pyramids and Cones**	**Surface Areas and Volumes of Spheres**	**Geometry Lab: Locus and Spheres**
Objectives	▪ Find volumes of pyramids. ▪ Find volumes of cones.	▪ Find surface areas of spheres. ▪ Find volumes of spheres.	▪ Find the locus of points a given distance from the endpoints of a segment
Key Vocabulary		great circle pole hemisphere	
CCSS	G.GMD.1, G.GMD.3	G.GMD.1, G.GMD.3	
Multiple Representations			
Lesson Resources	connectED.mcgraw-hill.com Leveled Worksheets Personal Tutor Virtual Manipulatives Self-Check Quiz ▪ *5-Minute Check* ▪ *Study Notebook*	connectED.mcgraw-hill.com Leveled Worksheets Quiz 3 Vocabulary Personal Tutor Virtual Manipulatives Self-Check Quiz ▪ *5-Minute Check* ▪ *Study Notebook*	connectED.mcgraw-hill.com Animations Virtual Manipulatives ▪ *Teaching Geometry with Manipulatives* **Materials:** ▪ ruler ▪ compass
Resources for Every Lesson	IWB eStudent Edition IWB Interactive Classroom	▪ eTeacher Edition ▪ eSolutions Manual ▪ eAssessment	
Differentiated Instruction	pp. 875, 879	pp. 883, 886	

IWB All digital assets are Interactive Whiteboard ready.

LESSON 12-7 (45 min: 1 day; 90 min: 0.5 day)	EXTEND 12-7 (45 min: 0.5 day; 90 min: 0.25 day)	LESSON 12-8 (45 min: 1 day; 90 min: 0.5 day)
Spherical Geometry	**Geometry Lab: Navigational Coordinates**	**Congruent and Similar Solids**
■ Describe sets of points on a sphere. ■ Compare and contrast Euclidean and spherical geometries.	■ Understand navigational coordinates. ■ Find distances by using measurements of navigational coordinates.	■ Identify congruent or similar solids. ■ Use properties of similar solids.
Euclidean geometry spherical geometry non-Euclidean geometry	meridian longitude latitude parallels	similar solids congruent solids
connectED.mcgraw-hill.com Leveled Worksheets Vocabulary Personal Tutor Self-Check Quiz ■ *5-Minute Check* ■ *Study Notebook* ■ *Teaching Geometry with Manipulatives*	connectED.mcgraw-hill.com Vocabulary **Materials:** ■ world globe or map	connectED.mcgraw-hill.com Leveled Worksheets Quiz 4 Vocabulary Personal Tutor Self-Check Quiz ■ *5-Minute Check* ■ *Study Notebook*
IWB eStudent Edition IWB Interactive Classroom	■ eTeacher Edition ■ eSolutions Manual ■ eAssessment	
pp. 890, 894		pp. 898, 902

Summative Assessment
Study Guide and Review
Practice Test

CHAPTER 12

Extending Surface Area and Volume

Assessment and Intervention

SE = Student Edition, **TE** = Teacher Edition, **CRM** = Chapter Resource Masters

	Diagnosis	Prescription
DIAGNOSTIC ASSESSMENT	**Beginning Chapter 12**	
	Get Ready for Chapter 12 **SE**	Response to Intervention **TE**
	Beginning Every Lesson	
	Then, Now, Why? **SE** 5-Minute Checks	Chapter 0 **SE**
FORMATIVE ASSESSMENT	**During/After Every Lesson**	
	Guided Practice **SE**, every example Check Your Understanding **SE** H.O.T. Problems **SE** Spiral Review **SE** Additional Examples **TE** Watch Out! **TE** Step 4, Assess **TE** Chapter 12 Quizzes **CRM**, pp. 57–58 Self-Check Quizzes connectED.mcgraw-hill.com	TIER 1 Intervention Skills Practice **CRM**, Ch. 1–12 connectED.mcgraw-hill.com TIER 2 Intervention Differentiated Instruction **TE**; Differentiated Homework Options **TE**; Study Guide and Intervention **CRM**, Ch. 1–12 TIER 3 Intervention *Math Triumphs, Geometry,* Ch. 5
	Mid-Chapter	
	Mid-Chapter Quiz **SE** Mid-Chapter Test **CRM**, p. 59 eAssessment	TIER 1 Intervention Skills Practice **CRM**, Ch. 1–12 connectED.mcgraw-hill.com TIER 2 Intervention Study Guide and Intervention **CRM**, Ch. 1–12 TIER 3 Intervention *Math Triumphs, Geometry*, Ch. 5
	Before Chapter Test	
	Chapter Study Guide and Review **SE** Practice Test **SE** Standardized Test Practice **SE** Chapter Test connectED.mcgraw-hill.com Standardized Test Practice connectED.mcgraw-hill.com Vocabulary Review connectED.mcgraw-hill.com eAssessment	TIER 1 Intervention Skills Practice **CRM**, Ch. 1–12 connectED.mcgraw-hill.com TIER 2 Intervention Study Guide and Intervention **CRM**, Ch. 1–12 TIER 3 Intervention *Math Triumphs, Geometry,* Ch. 5
SUMMATIVE ASSESSMENT	**After Chapter 12**	
	Multiple-Choice Tests, Forms 1, 2A, 2B **CRM**, pp. 61–66 Free-Response Tests, Forms 2C, 2D, 3 **CRM**, pp. 67–72 Vocabulary Test **CRM**, p. 60 Extended Response Test **CRM**, p. 73 Standardized Test Practice **CRM**, pp. 74–76 eAssessment	Study Guide and Intervention **CRM**, Ch. 1–12 connectED.mcgraw-hill.com

Differentiated Instruction

Option 1 Reaching All Learners

Kinesthetic Have students take a tour of the school to find prisms of various shapes and sizes. Have them work with a partner to classify the shapes they find, and then calculate the lateral area and surface area of each prism.

Visual/Spatial Have students use prisms to create a model of a famous building. Using grid paper, scissors, and tape, have students create various sized and shaped prisms. Then, have them glue or tape their prisms together to form the model. Have them find the lateral and surface areas of their building. Ask them to find the scale factor from their model to the real building.

Option 2 Approaching Level AL

Draw the faces for a number of figures including rectangular prisms, triangular prisms, and cylinders. Cut apart the faces for each figure, then shuffle all the pieces together. Have students either fit the pieces together again and recreate the figures or make nets for the figures. Finally, have students find the surface area for the figures they put together.

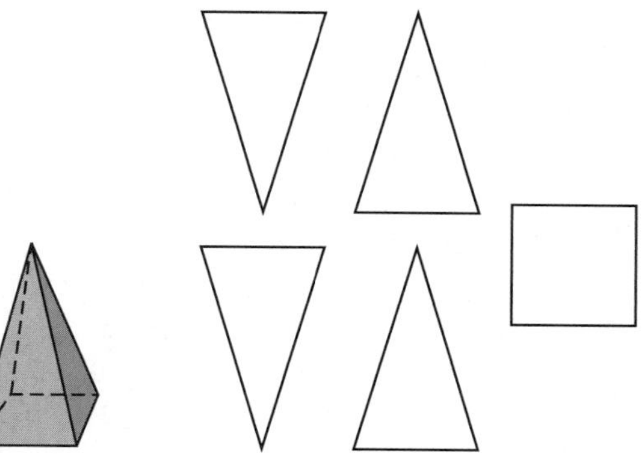

Option 3 English Learners ELL

While working with a partner, have students construct a prism by using grid paper, tape, and scissors. Then, have students find the lateral area and the surface area of that prism. They should label each face of their prism as a base or lateral face and have the type of prism labeled as well. Have them repeat this activity with several prisms of various sizes.

Option 4 Beyond Level BL

Arrange students in pairs. Have one student create a net of a figure studied in this chapter by using scissors and grid paper. After the first student makes the net, have the other student decide which figure it represents. Then, have students work together to find out how many nets can be created to represent the figure.

Focus on Mathematical Content

VerticalAlignment

Before Chapter 12

Related Topics from Grade 8

- Graph on a coordinate plane.

Previous Topics from Geometry

- Find areas of regular polygons and circles.
- Find areas by using proportional reasoning.
- Make conjectures about polygons.

Chapter 12

Related Topics from Geometry

- Find surface areas and volumes of prisms, pyramids, spheres, cones, cylinders, and composites of these figures.
- Describe the effect on area and volume when one or more dimensions of a figure are changed.

After Chapter 12

Preparation for Precalculus

- Use properties of functions to analyze and solve problems and make predictions.

Lesson-by-Lesson Preview

12-1 Representations of Three-Dimensional Figures

The view of a figure from a corner is called the *corner view* or *perspective view*. An orthographic drawing shows the top, left, front, and right sides of an object, giving you a complete picture of that object. An orthographic drawing can be used to render a corner view or the view of a figure from a corner. Isometric dot paper can be used to draw the corner view of a solid figure. The intersection of a solid with a plane is called a *cross section* of the solid.

12-2 Surface Areas of Prisms and Cylinders

The bases of a prism are congruent faces in parallel planes. The faces that are not bases are called *lateral faces*. A segment perpendicular to the bases, with an endpoint in each plane, is the altitude of the prism. The height of the prism is the length of the altitude. A prism with lateral edges that are also altitudes is a right prism. If the lateral edges of a prism are not perpendicular to the bases, it is an oblique prism.

The lateral area of a prism is the sum of the areas of the lateral faces. If a right prism has a lateral area of L square units, a height of h units, and each base has a perimeter of P units, then $L = Ph$.

The surface area is the lateral area plus the area of the bases. If the surface area of a right prism is T square units, its height is h units, and each base has an area of B square units and a perimeter of P units, then $T = Ph + 2B$.

A cylinder is a solid with bases that are congruent circles that lie in parallel planes. The axis of the cylinder is the segment with endpoints that are centers of those circles. If the axis is also the altitude, then the cylinder is called a *right cylinder*. Otherwise, it is an oblique cylinder. The net of a cylinder is composed of two congruent circles and a rectangle. The area of this rectangle is the lateral area of the cylinder. The length of the rectangle is the same as the circumference of the base, $2\pi r$. If a right cylinder has a lateral area of L square units, a height of h units, and the bases have radii of r units, then $L = 2\pi rh$. If a right cylinder has a surface area of T square units, a height of h units, and the bases have radii of r units, then $T = 2\pi rh + 2\pi r^2$.

12-3 Surface Areas of Pyramids and Cones

A pyramid is a solid with faces that, except the base, intersect at one point called the *vertex*. The faces that intersect at the vertex are called *lateral faces* and form triangles. The altitude is the segment from the vertex perpendicular to the base.

If the base of a pyramid is a regular polygon and the segment from the center of the base to the vertex is perpendicular to the base, then the pyramid is called a *regular pyramid.* The height of each lateral face is called the *slant height* of the pyramid. If a regular pyramid has a lateral area of L square units, a slant height of ℓ units, and its base has a perimeter of P units, then $L = \frac{1}{2}P\ell$. If a regular pyramid has a surface area of T square units, a slant height of ℓ units, and its base has a perimeter of P units and an area of B square units, then $T = \frac{1}{2}P\ell + B$.

A cone with an axis that is also an altitude is a right cone. The measure of any segment joining the vertex of a right cone to the edge of the circular base is called the slant height. If a right circular cone has a lateral area of L square units, a slant height of ℓ units, and the radius of the base is r units, then $L = 2\pi r\ell$. If a right circular cone has a surface area of T square units, a slant height of ℓ units, and the radius of the base is r units, then $T = \pi r\ell + \pi r^2$.

12-4 Volumes of Prisms and Cylinders

Volume is measured in cubic units. If a prism has a volume of V cubic units, a height of h units, and each base has an area of B units, then $V = Bh$.

Like the volume of a prism, the volume of a cylinder is a product of the area of the base and the height. If a cylinder has a volume of V cubic units, a height of h units, and the bases have radii of r units, then $V = \pi r^2 h$.

The formulas for prisms and cylinders apply to both right solids and oblique solids. Cavalieri's Principle, which applies to the volumes of all solids, states that if two solids have the same height and the same cross-sectional area at every level, then they have the same volume.

12-5 Volumes of Pyramids and Cones

The formulas for the volumes of pyramids and cones are also based on the product of the area of the base and the height. If a pyramid has a volume of V cubic units, a height of h units, and a base with an area of B units, then $V = \frac{1}{3}Bh$. Similarly, if a cone has a volume of V units, a height of h units, and the base has a radius of r units, then $V = \frac{1}{3}Bh$ or $V = \frac{1}{3}\pi r^2 h$.

12-6 Surface Areas and Volumes of Spheres

A sphere is the locus of all points that are a given distance from a given point called its *center.* If a sphere has a surface area of T square units and a radius of r units, then $T = 4\pi r^2$. If a sphere has a volume of V cubic units and a radius of r units, then $V = \frac{4}{3}\pi r^3$.

12-7 Spherical Geometry

In Euclidean geometry, a plane is a flat surface made up of points that extend infinitely in every direction. In *spherical geometry* a plane is the surface of a sphere. Lines in spherical geometry are great circles. Some, but not all, of the properties of Euclidean geometry apply to spherical geometry. For example, it is not true that for every line on a sphere and a point not on the line there is exactly one line containing the point that is parallel to the given line.

12-8 Congruent and Similar Solids

Similar solids are solids that have exactly the same shape but not necessarily the same size. You can determine if two solids are similar by comparing the ratios of corresponding linear measurements and verifying corresponding angles congruent. The ratio of the measures of two similar figures is called the *scale factor.*

Congruent solids are exactly the same shape and exactly the same size. Two solids are congruent when the corresponding angles, faces, and edges are congruent. The volumes of two congruent solids are equal.

Professional Development

Targeted professional development has been articulated throughout Geometry. More quality, customized professional development is available from McGraw-Hill Professional Development. Visit connectED.mcgraw-hill.com for details on each product.

- Online Lessons emphasize the strategies and techniques used to teach Geometry. Includes streaming video, interactive pages, and online tools.
- Video Workshops allow mentors, coaches, or leadership personnel to facilitate on-site workshops on educational strategies in mathematics and mathematical concepts.
- MHPD Online (www.mhpdonline.com) offers online professional development with video clips of instructional strategies, links, student activities, and news and issues in education.
- Teaching Today (teachingtoday.glencoe.com) gives secondary teachers practical strategies and materials that inspire excellence and innovation in teaching.

Chapter Project

Vacation Resorts

Students use what they have learned about surface areas and volumes to complete a project.

This chapter project addresses business literacy, as well as several specific skills identified as being essential to student success by the Framework for 21st Century Learning.

Visit connectED.mcgraw-hill.com for student and teacher handouts.

KeyVocabulary Introduce the key vocabulary in the chapter using the method below.

Define: A cross section is the intersection of a solid and a plane, and it depends on the angle of the plane.

Example: The horizontal cross section of a cube is a square.

Ask: What is the cross section of a sphere? What are the possible cross sections of a square prism? circle; square or rectangle

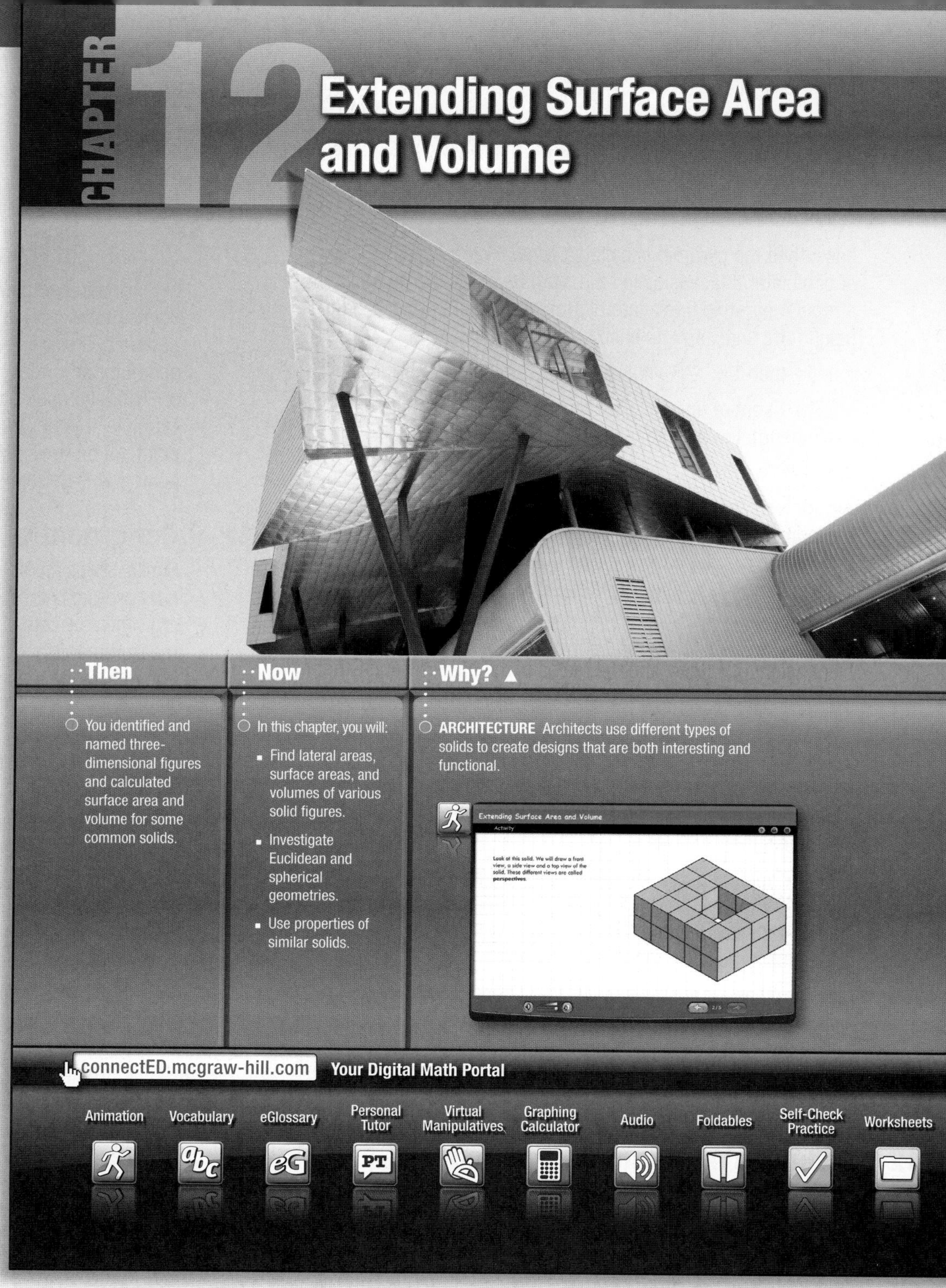

CHAPTER 12
Extending Surface Area and Volume
Then
You identified and named three-dimensional figures and calculated surface area and volume for some common solids.
Now
In this chapter, you will:
Find lateral areas, surface areas, and volumes of various solid figures.
Investigate Euclidean and spherical geometries.
Use properties of similar solids.
Why?
ARCHITECTURE Architects use different types of solids to create designs that are both interesting and functional.
Extending Surface Area and Volume
connectED.mcgraw-hill.com
Your Digital Math Portal
Animation
Vocabulary
eGlossary
Personal Tutor
Virtual Manipulatives
Graphing Calculator
Audio
Foldables
Self-Check Practice
Worksheets

Get Ready for the Chapter

Diagnose Readiness | You have two options for checking prerequisite skills.

1 Textbook Option Take the Quick Check below. Refer to the Quick Review for help.

QuickCheck

Determine whether each statement about the figure in Example 1 is *true, false*, or *cannot be determined.*

1. ▱*ABCD* lies in plane $\mathcal{M}$. true
2. ▱*CDHG* lies in plane $\mathcal{N}$. false
3. $\overline{AB}$ lies in plane $\mathcal{M}$. true
4. $\overline{HG}$ lies in plane $\mathcal{N}$. cannot be determined
5. $\overline{AE} \perp$ to plane $\mathcal{M}$. true
6. $\overline{DC} \parallel$ line ℓ. true

Find the area of each figure. Round to the nearest tenth if necessary.

7. 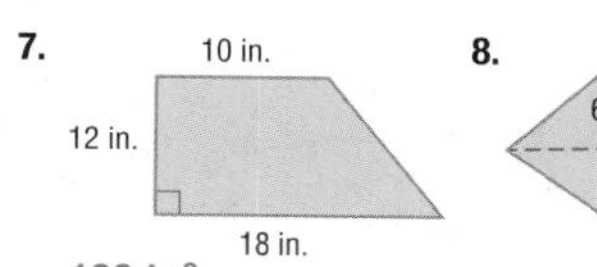

168 in^2

8. 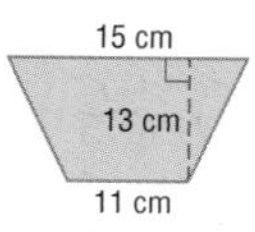

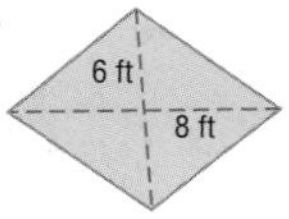

96 ft^2

9. **CRAFTS** A seamstress wants to cover a kite frame with cloth. If the length of one diagonal is 16 inches and the other diagonal is 22 inches, find the area of the surface of the kite. 176 in^2

Find the value of the variable in each equation.

10. $a^2 + 40^2 = 41^2$ ± 9
11. $8^2 + b^2 = 17^2$ ± 15
12. $a^2 + 6^2 = (7\sqrt{3})^2$ $\pm\sqrt{111}$

QuickReview

Example 1 (Used in Lesson 12-1)

In the figure, $\overline{AD} \perp \ell$ and *ABCDEFGH* is a cube. Determine whether plane $\mathcal{M} \perp$ plane $\mathcal{N}$.

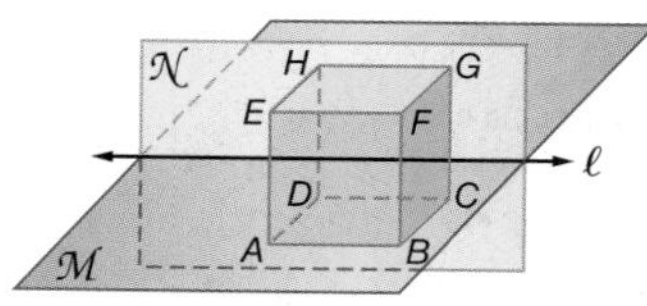

Plane $\mathcal{M} \perp$ plane $\mathcal{N}$ cannot be determined from the given information.

Example 2 (Used in Lessons 12-2 through 12-6)

Find the area of the figure. Round to the nearest tenth if necessary.

15 cm
13 cm
11 cm

$A = \frac{1}{2}h(b_1 + b_2)$ Area of a trapezoid

$= \frac{1}{2}(13)(15 + 11)$ Substitution

$= \frac{1}{2}(13)(26)$ Simplify.

$= 169$ Multiply.

The area of the trapezoid is 169 cm^2.

Example 3 (Used in Lessons 12-4 through 12-6)

Find the value of the variable in $8^2 + 7^2 = c^2$.

$c^2 = 8^2 + 7^2$ Original equation

$c^2 = 64 + 49$ Evaluate the exponents.

$c^2 = 113$ Simplify.

$c = \pm\sqrt{113}$ Take the square root of each side.

2 Online Option Take an online self-check Chapter Readiness Quiz at connectED.mcgraw-hill.com.

835

Essential Question

- How are two-dimensional and three-dimensional figures related? Sample answer: The faces and bases of three-dimensional figures are two-dimensional figures. For example, a pyramid has faces that are triangles and a base that is a polygon.

Get Ready for the Chapter

Response to Intervention (RtI)

Use the *Quick Check* results and the Intervention Planner chart to help you determine your Response to Intervention. The If-Then statements in the chart below help you decide the appropriate tier of RtI and suggest intervention resources for each tier.

InterventionPlanner

TIER 1 On Level OL

If students miss about 25% of the exercises or less,

Then choose a resource:

SE Lessons 0-9, 1-1, and 11-2

Skills Practice, Chapter 1, p. 7, Chapter 11, p. 15

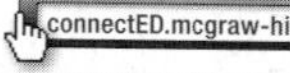
connectED.mcgraw-hill.com Self-Check Quiz

TIER 2 Strategic Intervention AL approaching grade level

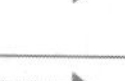
If students miss about 50% of the exercises,

Then choose a resource:

Study Guide and Intervention, Chapter 1, pp. 5–6, Chapter 11, pp. 13–14

connectED.mcgraw-hill.com Extra Examples, Personal Tutor, Homework Help

TIER 3 Intensive Intervention 2 or more grades below level

If students miss about 75% of the exercises,

Then use *Math Triumphs, Geometry*, Ch. 5

connectED.mcgraw-hill.com Extra Examples, Personal Tutor, Homework Help, Review Vocabulary

FOLDABLES StudyOrganizer

Dinah Zike's Foldables®

Focus Use this Foldable concept map for student writing about three-dimensional figures.

Teach Begin with the central chapter theme of *Surface Area and Volume* as the title. Have students list the five types of solids introduced in Lesson 1–7 on each half of their Foldables, leaving room between each to list related formulas and definitions. Students can use their Foldables to take notes, define terms, record concepts, and define basic concepts.

When to Use It Use the appropriate tabs as students cover each lesson in this chapter. Students can add to the vocabulary tab during each lesson.

Differentiated Instruction

Student-Built Glossary, pp. 1–2

Students complete the chart by providing the definition of each term and an example as they progress through Chapter 12. This study tool can also be used to review for the chapter test.

Get Started on the Chapter

You will learn several new concepts, skills, and vocabulary terms as you study Chapter 12. To get ready, identify important terms and organize your resources. You may refer to Chapter 0 to review prerequisite skills.

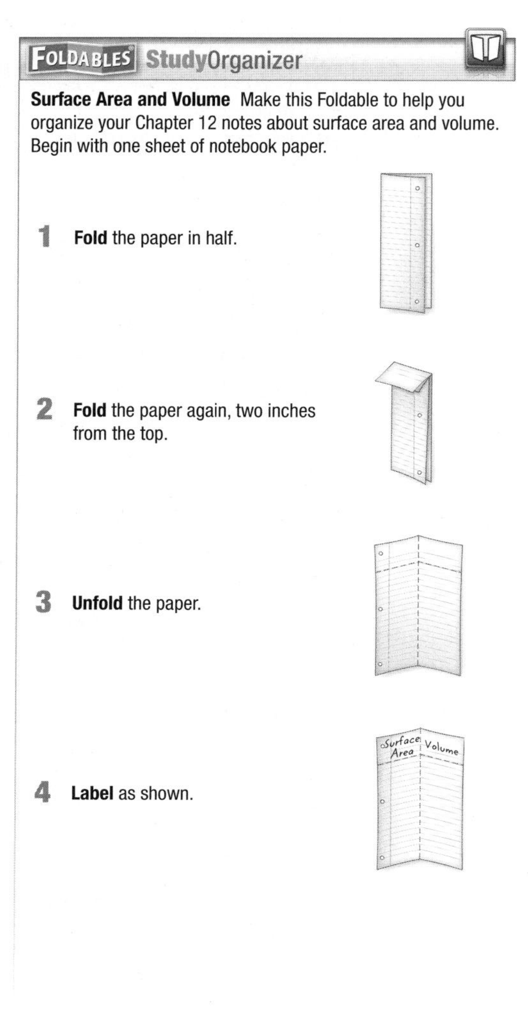

FOLDABLES StudyOrganizer

Surface Area and Volume Make this Foldable to help you organize your Chapter 12 notes about surface area and volume. Begin with one sheet of notebook paper.

1. **Fold** the paper in half.
2. **Fold** the paper again, two inches from the top.
3. **Unfold** the paper.
4. **Label** as shown.

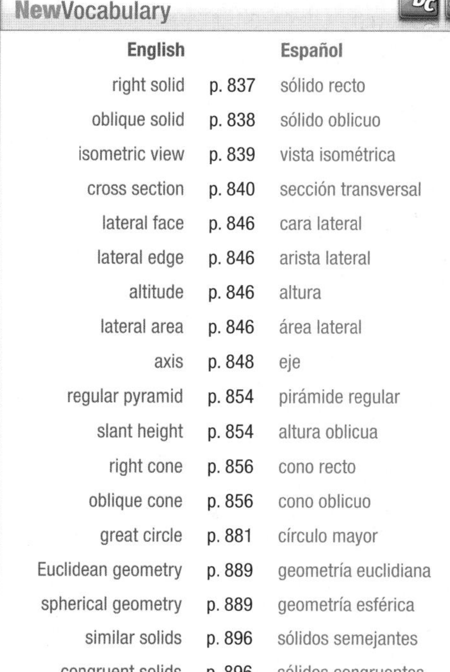

NewVocabulary

English		Español
right solid	p. 837	sólido recto
oblique solid	p. 838	sólido oblicuo
isometric view	p. 839	vista isométrica
cross section	p. 840	sección transversal
lateral face	p. 846	cara lateral
lateral edge	p. 846	arista lateral
altitude	p. 846	altura
lateral area	p. 846	área lateral
axis	p. 848	eje
regular pyramid	p. 854	pirámide regular
slant height	p. 854	altura oblicua
right cone	p. 856	cono recto
oblique cone	p. 856	cono oblicuo
great circle	p. 881	círculo mayor
Euclidean geometry	p. 889	geometría euclidiana
spherical geometry	p. 889	geometría esférica
similar solids	p. 896	sólidos semejantes
congruent solids	p. 896	sólidos congruentes

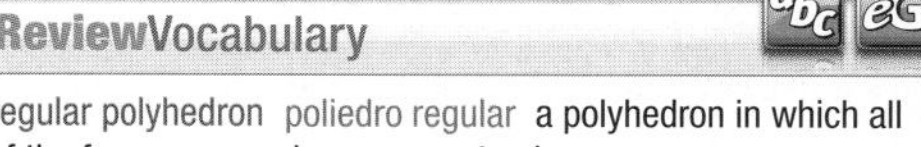

ReviewVocabulary

regular polyhedron poliedro regular a polyhedron in which all of the faces are regular congruent polygons

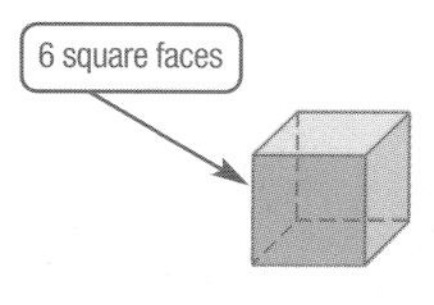

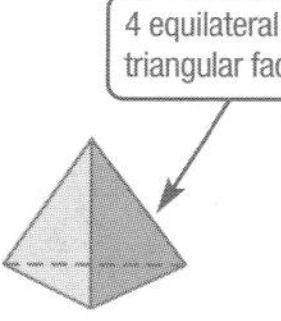

836 | Chapter 12 | Extending Surface Area and Volume

EXPLORE

12-1 Geometry Lab: Solids Formed by Translation

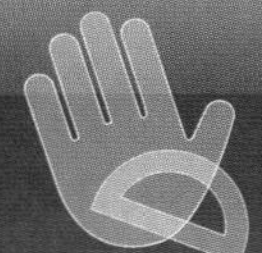

We can relate some three-dimensional solids to two-dimensional figures with which we are already familiar. Some three-dimensional solids can be formed by translating a two-dimensional figure along a vector.

A **right solid** has base(s) that are perpendicular to the edges connecting them or connecting the base and the vertex of the solid. Some right solids are formed by translating a two-dimensional figure along a vector that is perpendicular to the plane in which the figure lies.

Activity 1

Identify and sketch the solid formed by translating a horizontal rectangle vertically.

To help visualize the solid formed, let a playing card represent the rectangle, and lay it flat on a table so that it is horizontal. To show the translation of the rectangle vertically, stack other cards neatly, one by one, on top of the first.

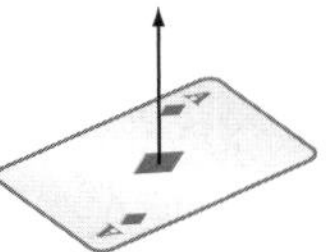

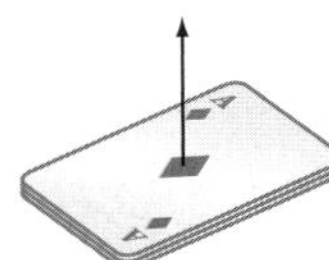

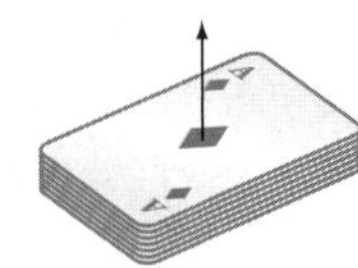

Notice that the solid formed is a right rectangular prism, which has a rectangular base, a translated copy of this base on the opposite side parallel to the base, and four congruent edges connecting the two congruent rectangles. These edges are parallel to each other but perpendicular to the bases. A sketch of the figure is shown.

Model and Analyze 1–2. See margin for drawings.

1. Use congruent triangular tangram pieces to identify and sketch the solid formed by translating a horizontal triangle vertically. right triangular prism

2. Use the coins from a roll of quarters to identify and sketch the solid formed by translating a horizontal circle vertically. right cylinder

Identify and sketch the solid formed by translating a vertical two-dimensional figure horizontally. 3–5. See margin for drawings.

3. rectangle

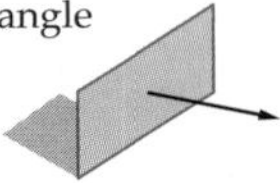

right rectangular prism

4. triangle

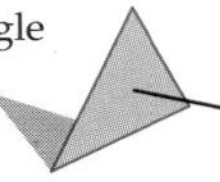

right triangular prism

5. circle

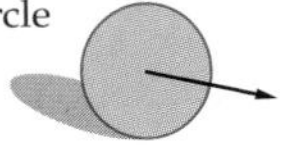

right cylinder

6. **REASONING** Are the solids formed in Exercises 3, 4, and 5 right solids? Explain your reasoning. Yes; the edges are perpendicular to the bases.

(continued on the next page)

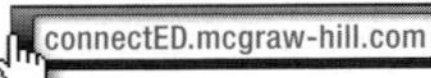

5.

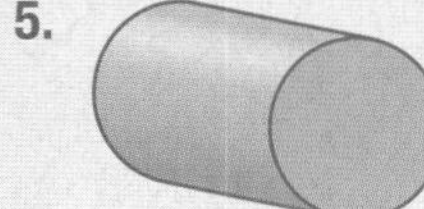

1 Focus

Objective Identify and sketch solids formed by translating two-dimensional figures along vectors.

Materials

- playing cards
- triangular tangram pieces
- rolls of quarters or other coins
- ruler

Teaching Tip

Have students predict what solid will result before doing each activity and exercise.

2 Teach

Working in Cooperative Groups

Have students work in mixed ability pairs, taking turns stacking each set of concrete models. Encourage students to use concrete models for Exercises 3–5 as well.

Additional Answers

1.

2.

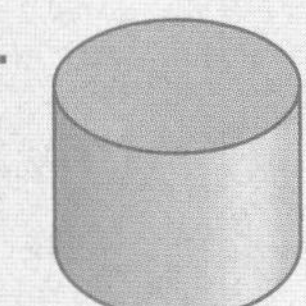

3.

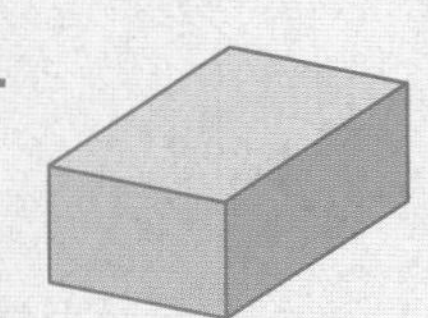

4.

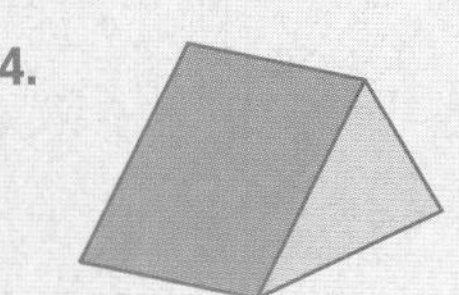

Practice Have students complete Activities 1 and 2 and Exercises 1–5 and 7–11.

3 Assess

Formative Assessment

Use Exercises 6 and 12 to assess each student's understanding of right and oblique solids.

From Concrete to Abstract

Ask students to summarize what they have learned about solids formed by translation and about the difference between right and oblique solids.

Additional Answers

7. 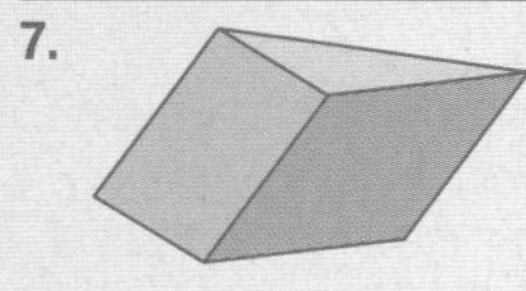

8. 

Geometry Lab

Solids Formed by Translation *Continued*

An **oblique solid** has base(s) that are not perpendicular to the edges connecting the two bases or vertex. An oblique solid can be formed by translating a two-dimensional figure along an oblique vector that is neither parallel nor perpendicular to the plane in which the two-dimensional figure lies.

Activity 2

Identify and sketch the solid formed by translating a horizontal rectangle along an oblique vector.

Let a playing card represent the rectangle. Lay it flat on a table so that it is horizontal. To show the translation of the rectangle along an oblique line, stack other cards one by one on top of the first so that the cards are shifted from the center of the previous card the same amount each time.

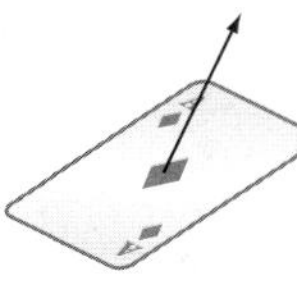
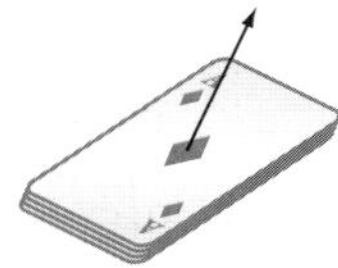
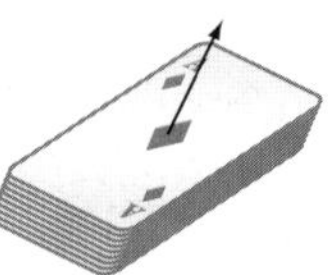

The solid formed is an oblique rectangular prism, which has a rectangular base, a translated copy of this base on the opposite side parallel to the base, and four congruent edges connecting the two congruent rectangles. These edges are parallel to each other but oblique to the bases. A sketch of the figure is shown.

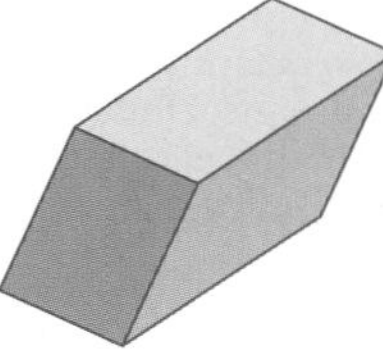

Model and Analyze

Identify and sketch the solid formed by translating each vertical two-dimensional figure along an oblique vector. Use concrete models if needed. 7–8. See margin for drawings.

7. triangle 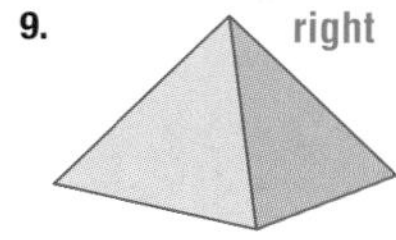 oblique triangular prism

8. circle oblique cylinder

Identify each solid as *right*, *oblique*, or *neither*.

9. right

10. neither

11. oblique

12. **REASONING** Can a pyramid with a square base be formed by translating the base vertically? Explain your reasoning. No; this translation would result in a square-based rectangular prism.

838 | Explore 12-1 | Geometry Lab: Solids Formed by Translation

Additional Answer (Lesson 12-1, Guided Practice)

1. Sample answer:

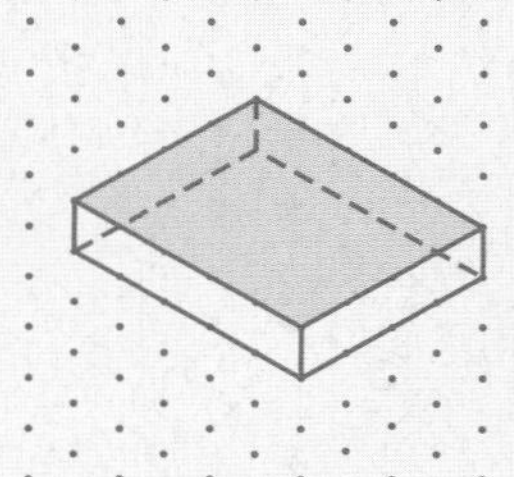

LESSON 12-1 Representations of Three-Dimensional Figures

Then	Now	Why?
You identified parallel planes and intersecting planes in three-dimensional figures.	1 Draw isometric views of three-dimensional figures. 2 Investigate cross sections of three-dimensional figures.	Video game programmers use technology to make the gaming environments appear three-dimensional. As players move in the various video game worlds, objects are realistically shown from different perspectives.

NewVocabulary
isometric view
cross section

Common Core State Standards

Content Standards
G.GMD.4 Identify the shapes of two-dimensional cross-sections of three-dimensional objects, and identify three-dimensional objects generated by rotations of two-dimensional objects.

Mathematical Practices
5 Use appropriate tools strategically.
1 Make sense of problems and persevere in solving them.

1 Draw Isometric Views

In video games, three-dimensional figures are represented on a two-dimensional screen. You can use isometric dot paper to draw **isometric views**, or corner views, of three-dimensional geometric solids on two-dimensional paper.

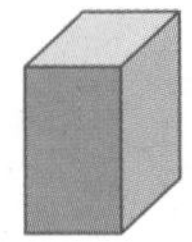
front view

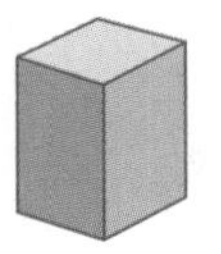
isometric view

Example 1 Use Dimensions of a Solid to Sketch a Solid

Use isometric dot paper to sketch a triangular prism 3 units high with two sides of the base that are 2 units long and 4 units long.

Step 1

Mark the corner of the solid. Draw 3 units down, 2 units to the left, and 4 units to the right. Then draw a triangle for the top of the solid.

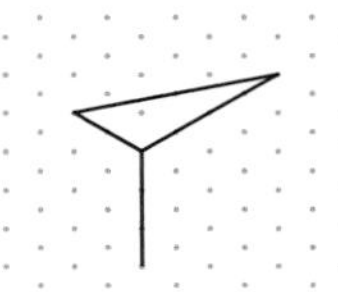

Step 2

Draw segments 3 units down from each vertex for the vertical edges. Connect the appropriate vertices using a dashed line for the hidden edge.

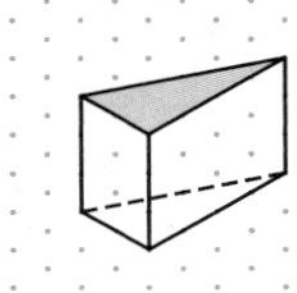

GuidedPractice

1. Use isometric dot paper to sketch a rectangular prism 1 unit high, 5 units long, and 4 units wide. See margin.

Recall that an *orthographic drawing* shows the top, left, front, and right views of a solid. You can use an orthographic drawing to draw an isometric view of a three-dimensional figure. The top, front, and right views of a cube are shown at the right.

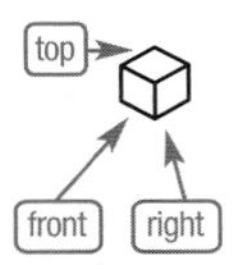

1 Focus

VerticalAlignment

Before Lesson 12-1 Identify parallel planes and intersecting planes in three-dimensional figures.

Lesson 12-1 Draw isometric views and investigate cross sections of three-dimensional figures.

After Lesson 12-1 Find surface areas and volumes of prisms, pyramids, spheres, cones, cylinders.

2 Teach

Scaffolding Questions

Have students read the **Why?** section of the lesson.

- What are some other ways to represent three-dimensional objects? Sample answer: paintings, television, figures in mathematics textbooks
- When an object on a video game is viewed from only one side, what are some ways that the object can be made to appear three-dimensional? Sample answer: the use of shadow
- How does movement help objects appear three-dimensional? Sample answer: As an object moves, you can see its different sides.

Lesson 12-1 Resources

Resource	Approaching Level AL	On Level OL	Beyond Level BL	English Learners ELL
Teacher Edition	▪ Differentiated Instruction, p. 840	▪ Differentiated Instruction, pp. 840, 844	▪ Differentiated Instruction, p. 844	
Chapter Resource Masters	▪ Study Guide and Intervention, pp. 5–6 ▪ Skills Practice, p. 7 ▪ Practice, p. 8 ▪ Word Problem Practice, p. 9	▪ Study Guide and Intervention, pp. 5–6 ▪ Skills Practice, p. 7 ▪ Practice, p. 8 ▪ Word Problem Practice, p. 9 ▪ Enrichment, p. 10 ▪ Graphing Calculator Activity, p. 11	▪ Practice, p. 8 ▪ Word Problem Practice, p. 9 ▪ Enrichment, p. 10	▪ Study Guide and Intervention, pp. 5–6 ▪ Skills Practice, p. 7 ▪ Practice, p. 8 ▪ Word Problem Practice, p. 9
Other	▪ 5-Minute Check 12-1 ▪ Study Notebook	▪ 5-Minute Check 12-1 ▪ Study Notebook	▪ 5-Minute Check 12-1 ▪ Study Notebook	▪ 5-Minute Check 12-1 ▪ Study Notebook

1 Draw Isometric Views

Examples 1 and 2 show how to draw two-dimensional views of a three-dimensional figure by using isometric dot paper and orthographic drawings.

Teach with Tech

Interactive Whiteboard Drag a dot grid onto the board, and use this to help you draw accurate isometric sketches for your class.

Additional Examples

1 Use isometric dot paper to sketch a triangular prism 6 units high, with bases that are right triangles with legs 6 units and 4 units long.

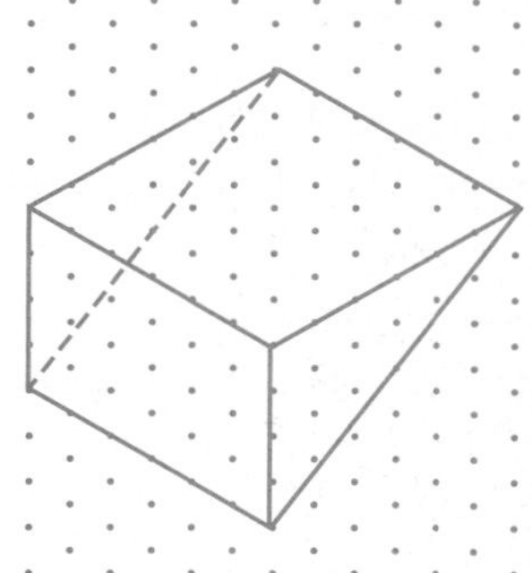

2 Use isometric dot paper and the orthographic drawing to sketch a solid.

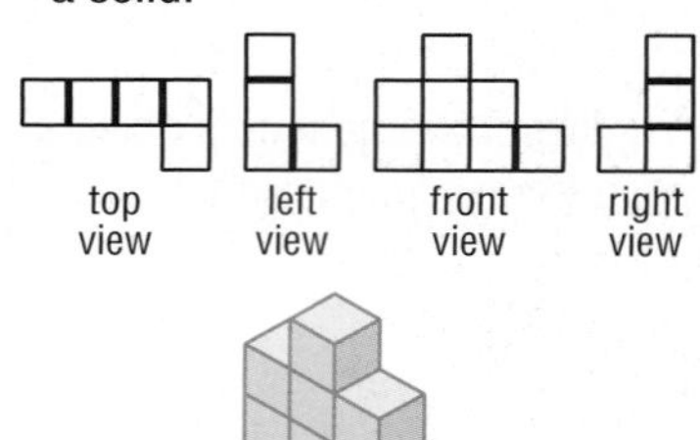

Additional Examples also in Interactive Classroom PowerPoint® Presentations

IWB Interactive White Board READY

Example 2 Use an Orthographic Drawing to Sketch a Solid

Use isometric dot paper and the orthographic drawing to sketch a solid.

- top view: There are two rows and two columns. The dark segments indicate that there are different heights.
- left view: The figure is 3 units high on the left.
- front view: The first column is 3 units high and the second column is 1 unit high.
- right view: The figure is 3 units high on the right. The dark segments indicate that there are breaks in the surface.

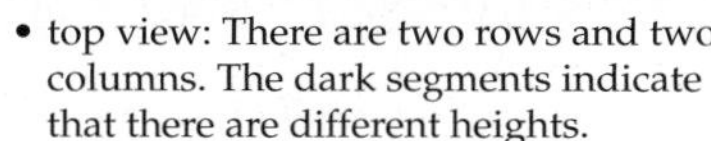

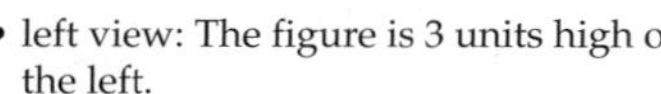

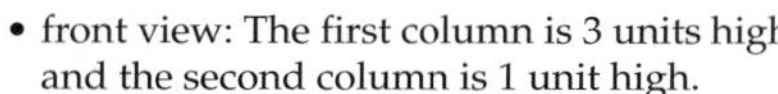

top view / left view / front view / right view

Connect the dots on the isometric dot paper to represent the edges of the solid. Shade the tops of each column.

2. Sample answer:

Guided Practice

2.

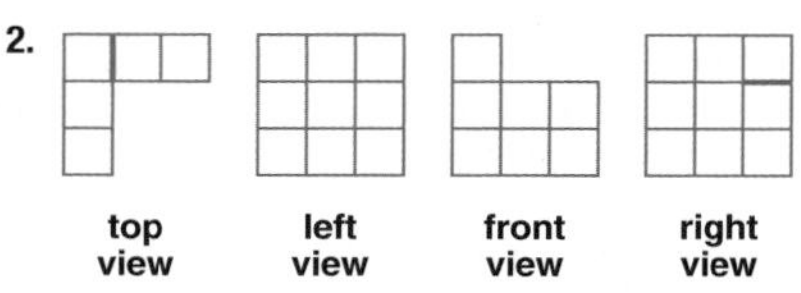

top view / left view / front view / right view

2 Investigate Cross Sections

A **cross section** is the intersection of a solid and a plane. The shape of the cross section formed by the intersection of a plane and a three-dimensional figure depends on the angle of the plane.

Real-World Example 3 Identify Cross Sections of Solids

PYRAMIDS Scientists are able to use computers to study cross sections of ancient artifacts and structures. Determine the shape of each cross section of the pyramid below.

The horizontal cross section is a square. The angled cross section is a trapezoid. The vertical cross section is a triangle.

Real-World Link

The largest pyramid ever constructed is about 63 miles from Mexico City. It is 177 feet tall and its base covers an area of nearly 45 acres.

Source: *Guinness World Records*

Guided Practice

3. **CAKES** Ramona has a cake pan shaped like half of a sphere, as shown at the right. Describe the shape of the cross sections of cakes baked in this pan if they are cut horizontally and vertically. **circle, semicircle**

Differentiated Instruction AL OL

Visual Learners To help students use an orthographic drawing to visualize a solid, have each student construct a model using blocks. Trade models and have the students check the top, left, front, and right views of the model. Then have them find the surface area.

Check Your Understanding

Example 1 **Use isometric dot paper to sketch each prism.**

1. triangular prism 2 units high, with two sides of the base that are 5 units long and 4 units long **See Ch. 12 Answer Appendix.**
2. rectangular prism 2 units high, 3 units wide, and 5 units long **See Ch. 12 Answer Appendix.**

Example 2 **Use isometric dot paper and each orthographic drawing to sketch a solid.** **3–4. See Ch. 12 Answer Appendix.**

3. 4.

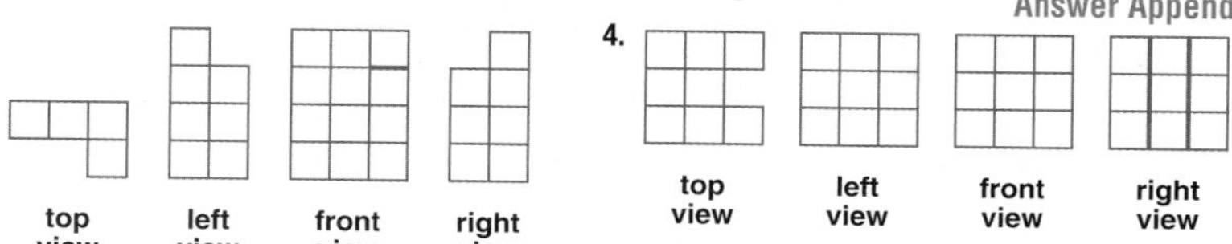

Example 3 5. **FOOD** Describe how the cheese at the right can be sliced so that the slices form each shape.

a. rectangle **slice vertically**
b. triangle **slice horizontally**
c. trapezoid **slice at an angle**

Describe each cross section.

6. **rectangle**

7. **triangle**

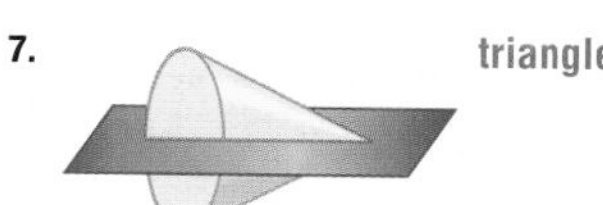

Practice and Problem Solving

Extra Practice is on page R12.

Example 1 **Use isometric dot paper to sketch each prism.** **8–10. See Ch. 12 Answer Appendix.**

8. cube 3 units on each edge
9. triangular prism 4 units high, with two sides of the base that are 1 unit long and 3 units long
10. triangular prism 4 units high, with two sides of the base that are 2 units long and 6 units long

Example 2 **CCSS TOOLS** **Use isometric dot paper and each orthographic drawing to sketch a solid.** **11–14. See Ch. 12 Answer Appendix.**

11. 12.

13. 14.

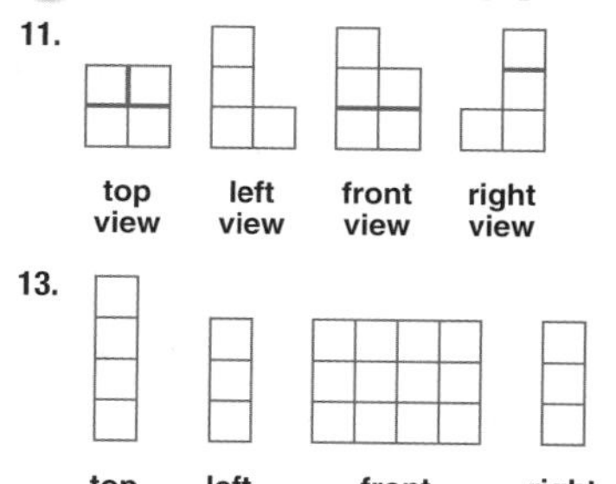

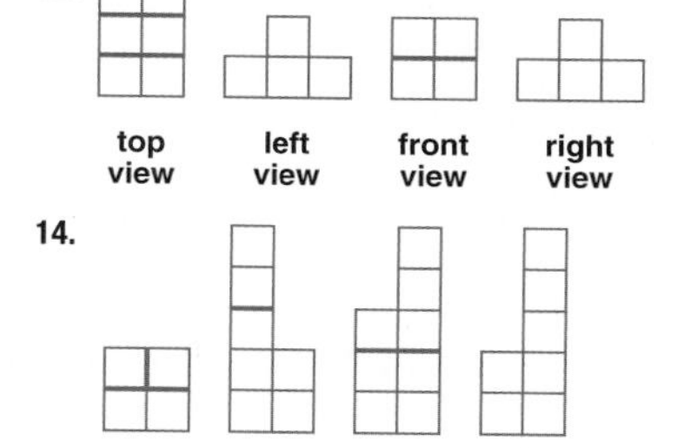

Differentiated Homework Options

Level	Assignment	Two-Day Option	
AL Basic	8–19, 36, 37, 39–50	9–19 odd, 40–43	8–18 even, 36, 37, 39, 44–50
OL Core	9–27 odd, 28, 29–33 odd, 34, 36, 37, 39–50	8–19, 40–43	20–34, 36, 37, 39, 44–50
BL Advanced	20–47, (optional: 48–50)		

2 Investigate Cross Sections

Example 3 uses cross sections to show different planes of three-dimensional objects.

Additional Example

3 BAKERY A customer ordered a two-layer sheet cake. Determine the shape of each cross section of the cake below.

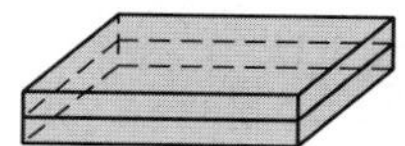

Sample answer: If the cake is cut horizontally, the cross section will be a rectangle. If the cake is cut vertically, the cross section will also be a rectangle.

Focus on Mathematical Content

Cross Sections Stress to students that cross sections are two-dimensional. When modeling cross sections, the thickness of the cut should be ignored.

3 Practice

Formative Assessment

Use Exercises 1–7 to check for understanding.

Use the chart at the bottom of this page to customize assignments for your students.

Exercise Alert

Isometric Dot Paper Exercises 1–4, 8–14, and 34 require the use of isometric dot paper.

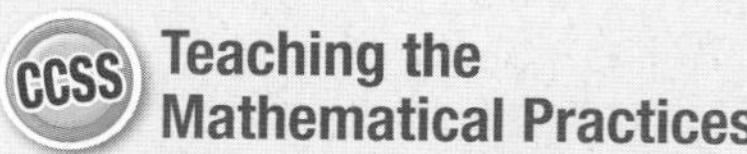

Teaching the Mathematical Practices

Tools Mathematically proficient students consider the available tools when solving a mathematical problem. In Exercises 11–14, encourage students to use blocks to make a model of each orthographic drawing.

Teaching the Mathematical Practices

Tools Mathematically proficient students consider the available tools when solving a mathematical problem. In Exercises 11–14, encourage students to make models of each figure with modeling clay.

Multiple Representations

In Exercise 34, students use a table and verbal descriptions to investigate isometric drawings.

Example 3

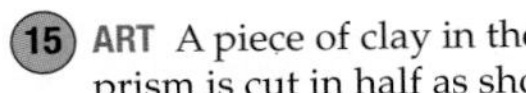
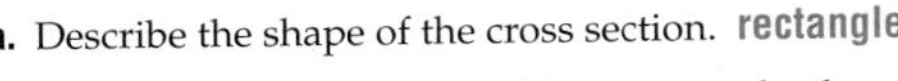

15. ART A piece of clay in the shape of a rectangular prism is cut in half as shown at the right.

a. Describe the shape of the cross section. **rectangle**

b. Describe how the clay could be cut to make the cross section a triangle. **Cut off a corner of the clay.**

Describe each cross section.

16. rectangle
17. hexagon
18. circle
19. trapezoid

16.

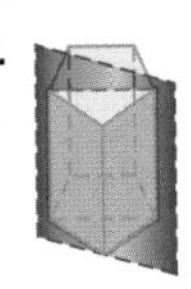

17.

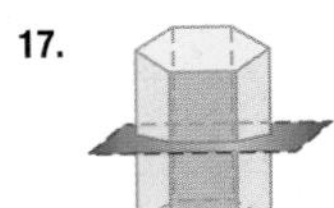

18.

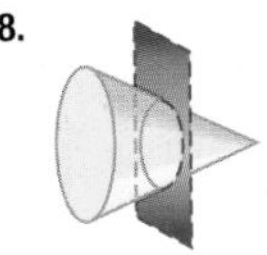

19.

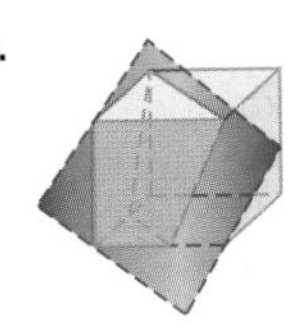

20. ARCHITECTURE Draw a top view, front view, and side view of the house at the right. **See margin.**

COOKIES Describe how to make a cut through a roll of cookie dough in the shape of a cylinder to make each shape. 21–24. See margin.

21. circle

22. longest rectangle

23. oval

24. shorter rectangle

TOOLS Sketch the cross section from a vertical slice of each figure. 25–27. See margin.

25.

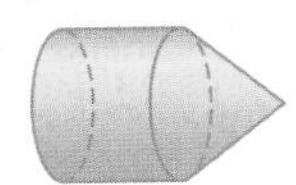

26.

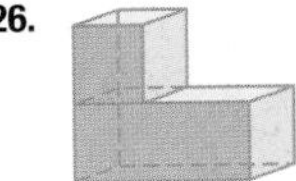

27.

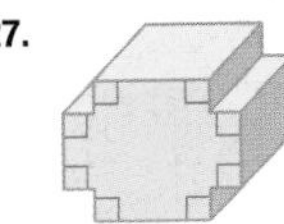

28. EARTH SCIENCE Crystals are solids in which the atoms are arranged in regular geometrical patterns. Sketch a cross section from a horizontal slice of each crystal. Then describe the rotational symmetry about the vertical axis. **a–c. See margin.**

a. tetragonal

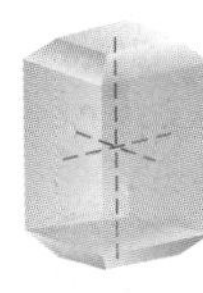

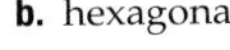

b. hexagonal

c. monoclinic

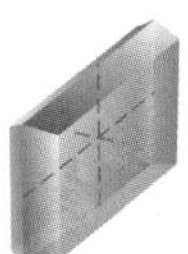

29. ART In a *perspective drawing*, a *vanishing point* is used to make the two-dimensional drawing appear three-dimensional. From one vanishing point, objects can be drawn from different points of view, as shown at the right. **a–c. See Ch. 12 Answer Appendix.**

vanishing point

a. Draw a horizontal line and a vanishing point on the line. Draw a rectangle somewhere above the line and use the vanishing point to make a perspective drawing.

b. On the same drawing, draw a rectangle somewhere below the line and use the vanishing point to make a perspective drawing.

c. Describe the different views of the two drawings.

Additional Answers

20.

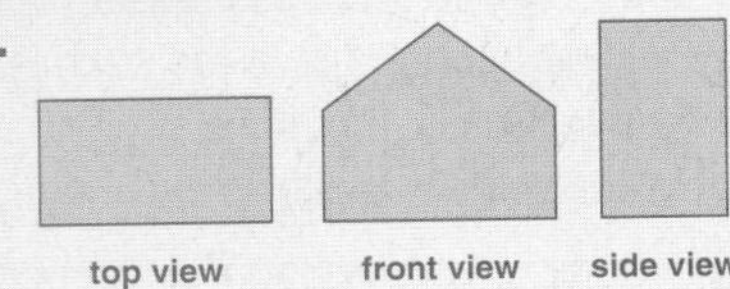

21. Make a vertical cut.

22. Make a horizontal cut through the center of the bases.

23. Make an angled cut.

24. Make a horizontal cut not through the center of the bases.

25. Sample answer:

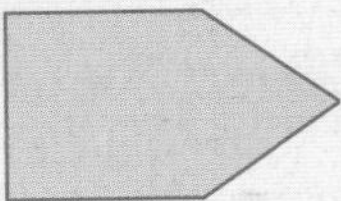

26. Sample answer:

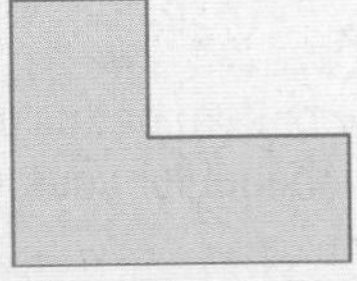

27. Sample answer:

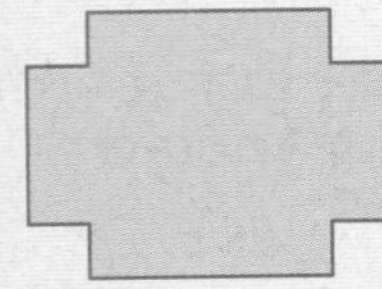

28a.

The crystal appears the same for every 90° rotation about the axis.

28b.

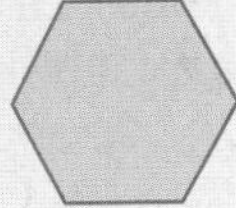

The crystal appears the same for every 60° rotation about the axis.

28c.

The crystal appears the same for every 180° rotation about the axis.

Draw the top, left, front, and right view of each solid. 30–32. See Ch. 12 Answer Appendix.

30. 

31. 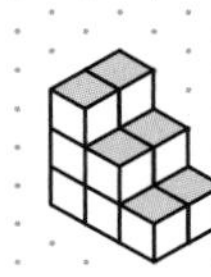

32. 

33. The top, front, and right views of a three-dimensional figure are shown at the right.

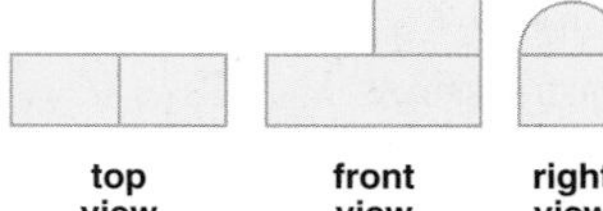

a. Make a sketch of the solid. a–c. See Ch. 12 Answer Appendix.

b. Describe two different ways that a rectangular cross section can be made.

c. Make a connection between the front and right views of the solid and cross sections of the solid.

34. MULTIPLE REPRESENTATIONS In this problem, you will investigate isometric drawings. a–c. See Ch. 12 Answer Appendix.

a. **Geometric** Create isometric drawings of three different solids.

b. **Tabular** Create a table that includes the number of cubes needed to construct the solid and the number of squares visible in the isometric drawing.

c. **Verbal** Is there a correlation between the number of cubes needed to construct a solid and the number of squares visible in the isometric drawing? Explain.

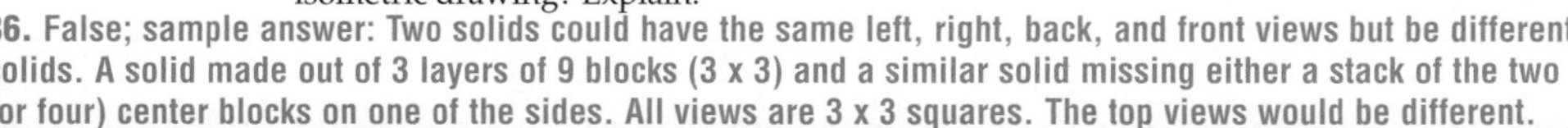

36. False; sample answer: Two solids could have the same left, right, back, and front views but be different solids. A solid made out of 3 layers of 9 blocks (3 x 3) and a similar solid missing either a stack of the two (or four) center blocks on one of the sides. All views are 3 x 3 squares. The top views would be different.

H.O.T. Problems Use Higher-Order Thinking Skills

35. CHALLENGE The figure at the right is a cross section of a geometric solid. Describe a solid and how the cross section was made. Sample answer: A cone is sliced at an angle through its lateral side and base.

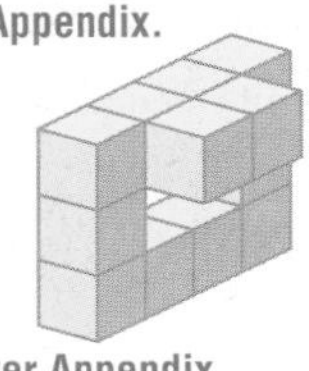

36.  ARGUMENTS Determine whether the following statement is *true* or *false*. Explain your reasoning.

If the left, right, front, and back orthographic views of two objects are the same, then the objects are the same figure.

37. OPEN ENDED Use isometric dot paper to draw a solid consisting of 12 cubic units. Then sketch the orthographic drawing for your solid. See Ch. 12 Answer Appendix.

38. CHALLENGE Draw the top view, front view, and left view of the solid figure at the right. See Ch. 12 Answer Appendix.

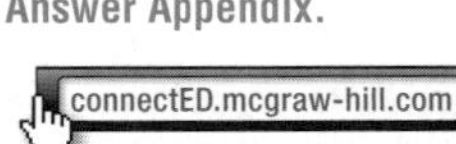

39. WRITING IN MATH A hexagonal pyramid is sliced through the vertex and the base so that the prism is separated into two congruent parts. Describe the cross section. Is there more than one way to separate the figure into two congruent parts? Will the shape of the cross section change? Explain. See Ch. 12 Answer Appendix.

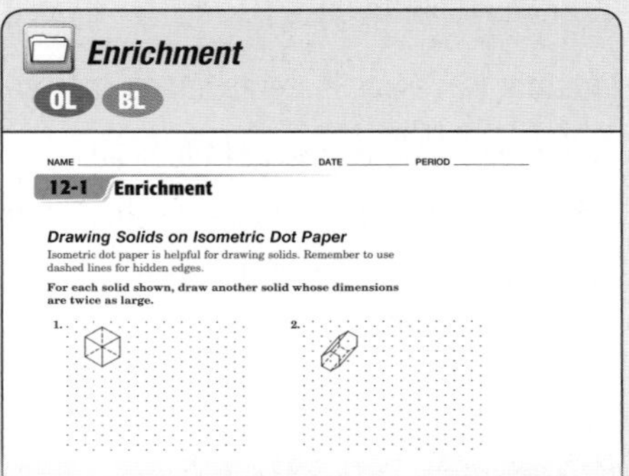

Teaching the Mathematical Practices

Arguments Mathematically proficient students understand and use stated assumptions and definitions in constructing arguments. They make conjectures and build a logical progression of statements to explore the truth of their conjectures. In Exercise 36 encourage students to use blocks to model the situation described.

Study Guide and Intervention
AL OL ELL

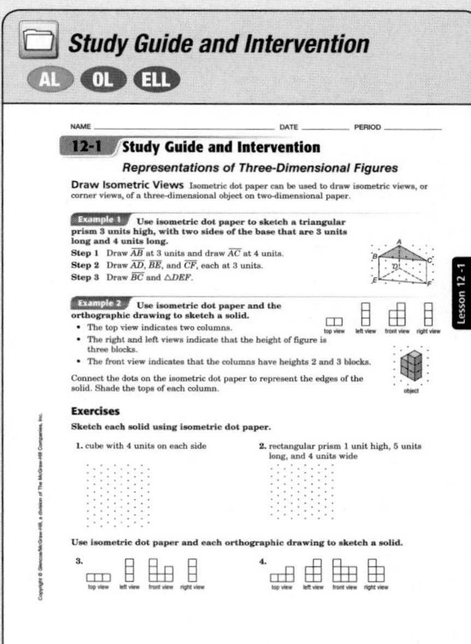

Practice
AL OL BL ELL

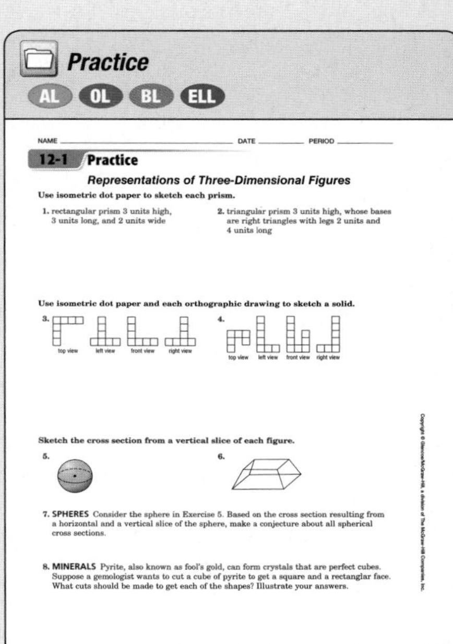

Word Problem Practice
AL OL BL ELL

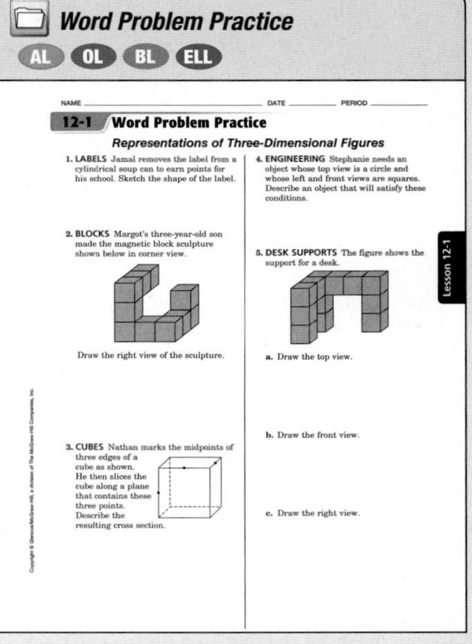

Enrichment
OL BL

12-1 Enrichment

Drawing Solids on Isometric Dot Paper

Isometric dot paper is helpful for drawing solids. Remember to use dashed lines for hidden edges.

For each solid shown, draw another solid whose dimensions are twice as large.

4 Assess

Name the Math Have students describe how to find the number of faces, edges, and vertices of a prism.

Additional Answers

41a. inner side of deck = circumference of pool = 81.64 ÷ $\pi \approx 26$ ft; outer side of deck = 26 + 3 + 3 = 32 ft; outer perimeter of deck = 4 × 32 = 128 ft

41b. area of deck = (2 × 3 × 32) + (2 × 3 × 26) = 348 square feet

Standardized Test Practice

40. Which polyhedron is represented by the net shown below? D

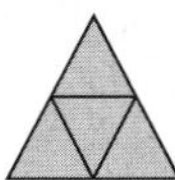

A cube
B octahedron
C triangular prism
D triangular pyramid

41. EXTENDED RESPONSE A homeowner wants to build a 3-foot-wide deck around his circular pool as shown below. See margin.

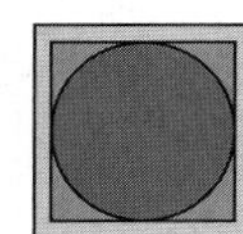

a. Find the outer perimeter of the deck to the nearest foot, if the circumference of the pool is about 81.64 feet.

b. What is the area of the top of the deck?

42. ALGEBRA Which inequality *best* describes the graph shown below? F

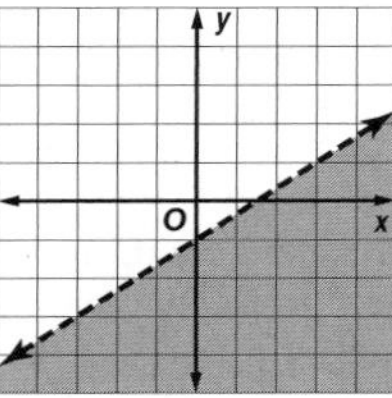

F $y < \frac{2}{3}x - 1$
G $y \leq \frac{2}{3}x - 1$
H $y > \frac{2}{3}x - 1$
J $y \geq \frac{2}{3}x - 1$

43. SAT/ACT Expand $(4\sqrt{5})^2$. E

A 20
B $8\sqrt{5}$
C $16\sqrt{5}$
D 40
E 80

Spiral Review

For each pair of similar figures, use the given areas to find the scale factor from the blue to the green figure. Then find x. (Lesson 11-5)

44. $\frac{5}{6}$; 10

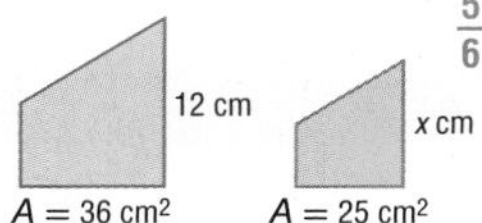

45. $\frac{3}{2}$; 9

6 in
A = 48 in²

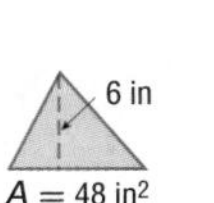

46. $\frac{7}{11}$; 14

22 m
A = 242 m²

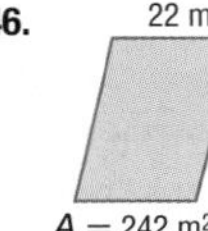

47. FURNITURE DESIGN Jenna wants to cover the cushions of her papasan chair with new fabric. There are seven congruent circular cushions with a diameter of 12 inches around a center cushion with a diameter of 20 inches. Find the area of fabric in square yards that she will need to cover both sides of the cushions. Allow an extra 3 inches of fabric around each cushion. (Lesson 11-4) about 3.6 yd²

Skills Review

Find the perimeter or circumference and area of each figure. Round to the nearest tenth.

48. 38 cm; 88 cm²

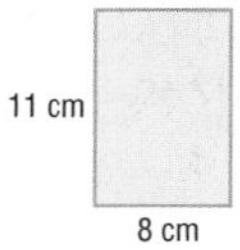

11 cm
8 cm

49. 28.9 in.; 66.5 in²

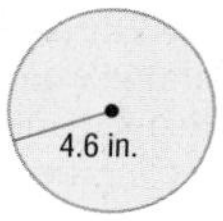

4.6 in.

50. 36 m; 54 m²

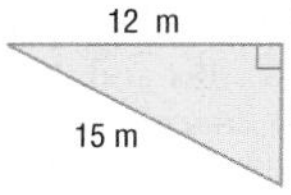

12 m
15 m
9 m

Differentiated Instruction

Extension Have the students choose any solid.

a. Draw the isometric view of the solid. See students' work.

b. Construct a model of the solid using the isometric view. See students' work.

c. Find the surface area of the solid. See students' work.

12-1 Geometry Lab: Topographic Maps

Maps are representations of Earth or some part of Earth. **Topographic maps** are representations of the three-dimensional surface of Earth on a two-dimensional piece of paper. In a topographic map, the *topography*, or shape of Earth's surface, is illustrated through the use of *contours*, which are imaginary lines that join locations with the same elevation.

Some topographic maps show more than contours. These maps may include symbols that represent vegetation, rivers, and other landforms, as well as streets and buildings.

Follow these steps to read a topographic map.

- Thin lines represent contours. Since each contour is a line of equal elevation, they never cross. The closer together the contour lines, the steeper the slope.
- Contour lines form V shapes in valleys or riverbeds. The Vs point uphill.
- Most often, closed loops indicate that the surface slopes uphill on the inside and downhill on the outside. The innermost loop is the highest area.
- Pay attention to the colors. Blue represents water; green represents vegetation; red represents urban areas; black represents roads, trails, and railroads.
- The scale on a 1:24,000 map indicates that 1 inch equals 2000 feet.

3. The contour lines for the peaks are closed curves or figures.

Explore the Model

Use the topographic map above to answer these questions.

1. According to the scale, what is the vertical distance between each contour line? **200 ft**
2. What is the difference in height between the lowest and highest points? **1600 ft**
3. What do you notice about the contour lines for the peaks of the hills?
4. Describe a steep slope on the topographic map. How do you know it is steep?
5. Explain how you would draw a topographic map given a side view of some hills.

4. On the 2200-foot hill, the contour lines for 2000 and 1800 are quite close, which would be a steep slope.

5. Sample answer: Make a rectangle for the topographic map and draw segment *AB* across in the middle horizontally. Then mark points at high and low points and some points in between for the hills. Connect the points on the hill diagram with points on the segment *AB*. Then draw contour lines corresponding to the height of the points.

Model and Analyze **6–7. See margin.**

6. Draw a topographic map similar to the map below for the side view of the hills from points A to B.

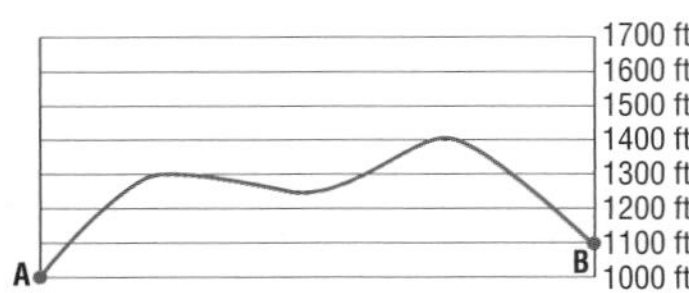

7. Draw a possible side view similar to the map below from points A to B of the hills from the topographic map. Measures are given in feet.

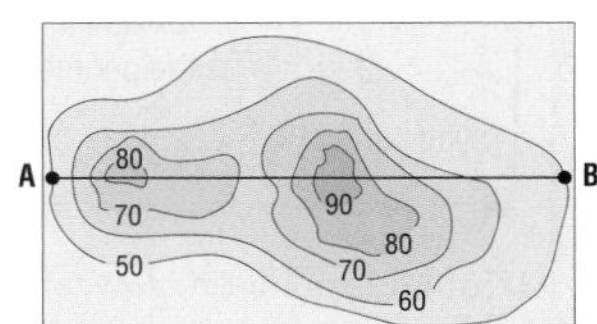

1 Focus

Objective Interpret and draw topographic maps.

Materials for Each Student

- ruler

Teaching Tips

Another common way to add emphasis in a topological map is to shade the area between each level line, with the lowest elevations being lightest and the highest elevations being darkest.

2 Teach

Working in Cooperative Groups

Organize students in pairs, mixing abilities. Have pairs help each other to complete the activity.

Practice Have students complete Model and Analyze 6 and 7.

3 Assess

Formative Assessment

Use Model and Analyze 6 and 7 to assess whether students understand topographical maps.

From Concrete to Abstract

Ask students what it would mean if the level lines on a topographical map were all equally spaced. Sample answer: The change in altitude would be uniform.

Additional Answers

6.

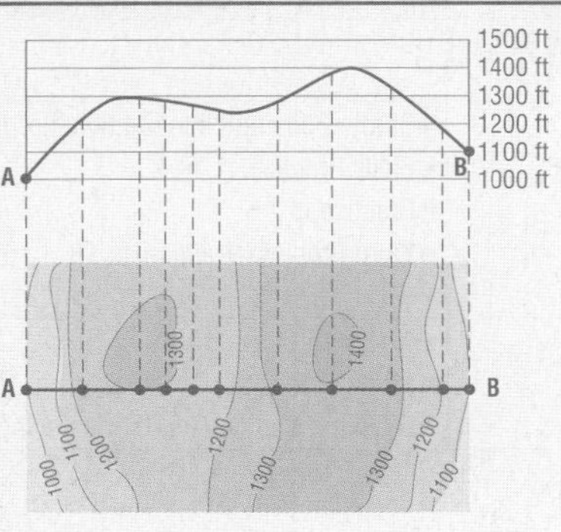

7.

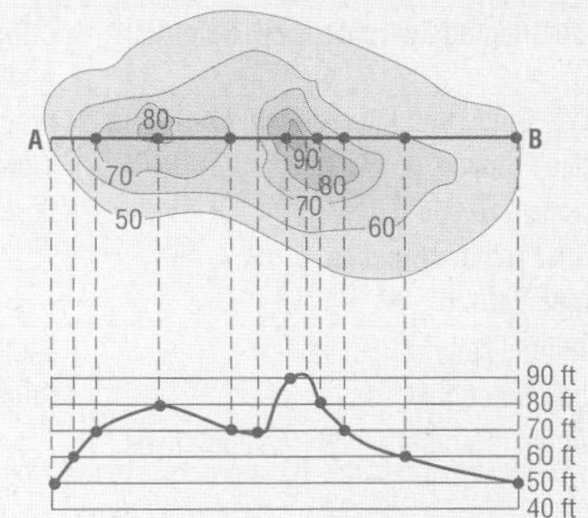

1 Focus

VerticalAlignment

Before Lesson 12-2 Find the areas of polygons.

Lesson 12-2 Find the lateral areas and surface areas of prisms. Find the lateral and surface areas of cylinders.

After Lesson 12-2 Find the volume of prisms and cylinders.

2 Teach

Scaffolding Questions

Have students read the **Why?** section of the lesson.

Ask:

- What is the shape of the underwater tunnel? a semicylinder, or half of a cylinder
- If you are given the area and length of a surface, how can you find its width? Divide the area by the length.
- How could you find the length of the semicircle that makes the tunnel? Divide 4574 by 100.

LESSON 12-2 Surface Areas of Prisms and Cylinders

Then

- You found areas of polygons.

Now

1. Find lateral areas and surface areas of prisms.
2. Find lateral areas and surface areas of cylinders.

Why?

- Atlanta's Georgia Aquarium is the largest aquarium in the world, with more than 8 million gallons of water and more than 500 species from around the world. The aquarium has an underwater tunnel that is 100 feet long with 4574 square feet of viewing windows.

NewVocabulary

lateral face
lateral edge
base edge
altitude
height
lateral area
axis
composite solid

Common Core State Standards

Content Standards

G.MG.3 Apply geometric methods to solve problems (e.g., designing an object or structure to satisfy physical constraints or minimize cost; working with typographic grid systems based on ratios). ★

Mathematical Practices

1 Make sense of problems and persevere in solving them.
6 Attend to precision.

1 Lateral Areas and Surface Areas of Prisms

In a solid figure, faces that are not bases are called **lateral faces**. Lateral faces intersect each other at the **lateral edges**, which are all parallel and congruent. The lateral faces intersect the base at the **base edges**. The **altitude** is a perpendicular segment that joins the planes of the bases. The **height** is the length of the altitude.

Recall that a prism is a polyhedron with two parallel congruent bases. In a right prism, the lateral edges are altitudes and the lateral faces are rectangles. In an oblique prism, the lateral edges are not perpendicular to the bases. At least one lateral face is not a rectangle.

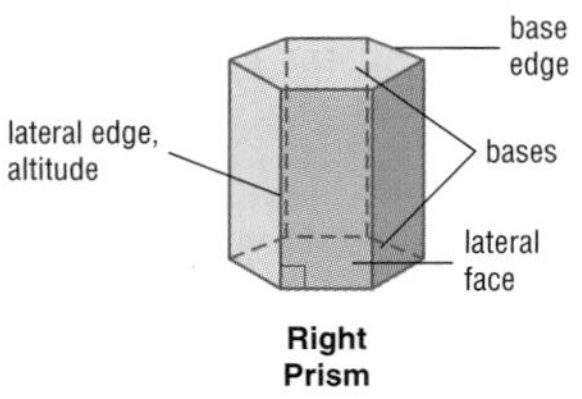

Right Prism

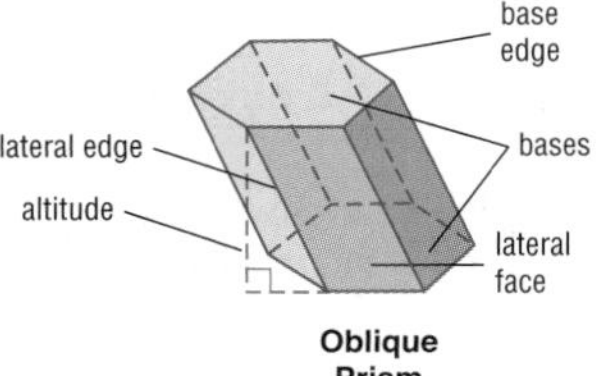

Oblique Prism

The **lateral area** L of a prism is the sum of the areas of the lateral faces. The net at the right shows how to find the lateral area of a prism.

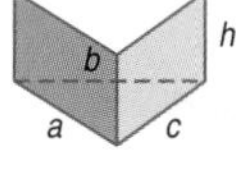

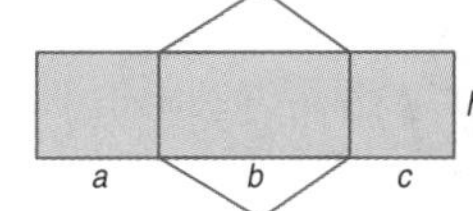

$L = a(h) + b(h) + c(h)$ Sum of areas of lateral faces

$= (a + b + c)h$ Distributive Property

$= Ph$ $P = a + b + c$

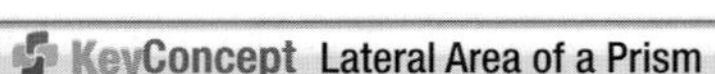

KeyConcept Lateral Area of a Prism

Words The lateral area L of a right prism is $L = Ph$, where h is the height of the prism and P is the perimeter of a base.

Symbols $L = Ph$

Model

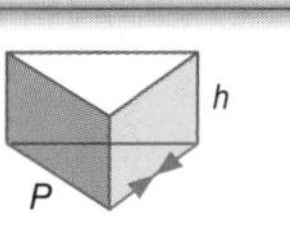

From this point on, you can assume that solids in the text are right solids. If a solid is oblique, it will be clearly stated.

846 | Lesson 12-2

Lesson 12-2 Resources

Resource	Approaching Level AL	On Level OL	Beyond Level BL	English Learners ELL
Teacher Edition		▪ Differentiated Instruction, pp. 848, 853	▪ Differentiated Instruction, pp. 848, 853	
Chapter Resource Masters	▪ Study Guide and Intervention, pp. 12–13 ▪ Skills Practice, p. 14 ▪ Practice, p. 15 ▪ Word Problem Practice, p. 16	▪ Study Guide and Intervention, pp. 12–13 ▪ Skills Practice, p. 14 ▪ Practice, p. 15 ▪ Word Problem Practice, p. 16 ▪ Enrichment, p. 17	▪ Practice, p. 15 ▪ Word Problem Practice, p. 16 ▪ Enrichment, p. 17	▪ Study Guide and Intervention, pp. 12–13 ▪ Skills Practice, p. 14 ▪ Practice, p. 15 ▪ Word Problem Practice, p. 16
Other	▪ 5-Minute Check 12-2 ▪ Study Notebook ▪ Teaching Geometry with Manipulatives	▪ 5-Minute Check 12-2 ▪ Study Notebook ▪ Teaching Geometry with Manipulatives	▪ 5-Minute Check 12-2 ▪ Study Notebook	▪ 5-Minute Check 12-2 ▪ Study Notebook ▪ Teaching Geometry with Manipulatives

Example 1 Lateral Area of a Prism

Find the lateral area of the prism. Round to the nearest tenth.

Step 1 Find the missing side length of the base.

$c^2 = 6^2 + 5^2$ Pythagorean Theorem

$c^2 = 61$ Simplify.

$c \approx 7.8$ Take the positive square root of each side.

Step 2 Find the lateral area.

$L = Ph$ Lateral area of a prism

$\approx (5 + 6 + 7.8)7$ Substitution

≈ 131.6 Simplify.

The lateral area is about 131.6 square centimeters.

WatchOut!

Right Prisms The bases of a right prism are congruent, but the faces are not always congruent.

GuidedPractice

1. The length of each side of the base of a regular octagonal prism is 6 inches, and the height is 11 inches. Find the lateral area. **528 in^2**

The surface area of a prism is the sum of the lateral area and the areas of the bases.

KeyConcept Surface Area of a Prism

Words The surface area S of a right prism is $S = L + 2B$, where L is its lateral area and B is the area of a base.

Symbols $S = L + 2B$ or $S = Ph + 2B$

Model

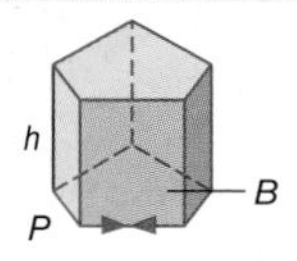

Example 2 Surface Area of a Prism

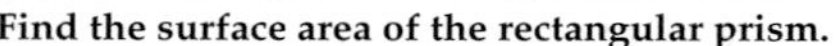

Find the surface area of the rectangular prism.

Use the 9-foot by 4-foot rectangle as the base.

$S = Ph + 2B$ Surface area of a prism

$= (2 \cdot 9 + 2 \cdot 4)(6) + 2(9 \cdot 4)$ Substitution

$= 228$ Simplify.

The surface area of the prism is 228 square feet.

StudyTip

Perseverance In Example 2, you can also use a 6-foot by 4-foot rectangle as the base. The height would be 9 feet. While choosing a different base does not affect the surface area, it will change the lateral area.

GuidedPractice

2. Find the surface area of the triangular prism. Round to the nearest tenth. **471.8 mm^2**

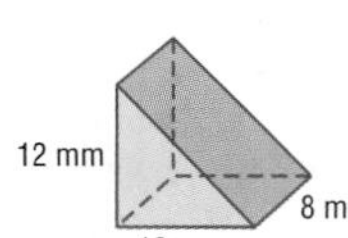

1 Lateral Areas and Surface Areas of Prisms

Example 1 shows how to find the lateral area of a right prism. **Example 2** shows how to find the surface area of a right prism.

Formative Assessment

Use the Guided Practice exercises after each Example to determine students' understanding of concepts.

Additional Examples

1 Find the lateral area of the regular hexagonal prism. 360 cm^2

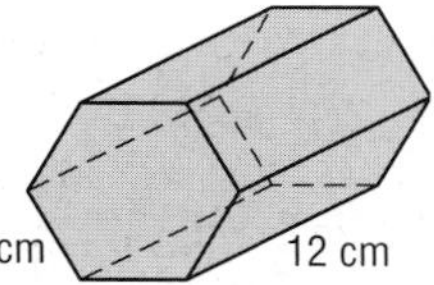

2 Find the surface area of the rectangular prism. 360 cm^2

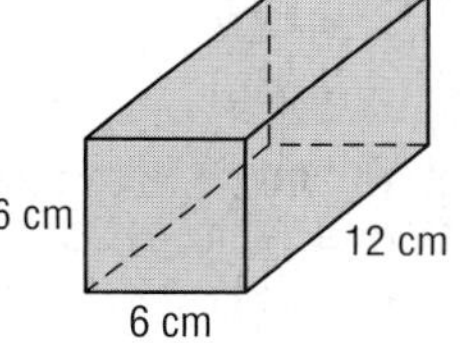

Additional Examples also in Interactive Classroom PowerPoint® Presentations

Focus on Mathematical Content

Lateral Edges The lateral edges of a prism are congruent and parallel. This is true for oblique prisms as well as right prisms.

Teaching the Mathematical Practices

Perseverance Mathematically proficient students check their answers to problems using a different method. They can identify correspondences between different approaches to problem solving. Encourage students to use alternative methods of problem solving.

Tips for New Teachers

Reasoning Ask students if they can derive an alternate formula for the surface area of a right rectangular prism. Have students write their derivations on the board, or show students that an alternate formula is $L = 2\ell w + 2\ell h + 2wh$.

WatchOut!

Lateral Area The formula $L = Ph$ is true for right prisms only. If a prism is oblique, find the sum of the areas of the lateral faces.

2 Lateral Areas and Surface Areas of Cylinders

Example 3 shows how to find the lateral area and surface area of a cylinder. **Example 4** shows how to find a missing dimension for a cylinder.

Additional Example

3 Find the lateral area and the surface area of the cylinder. Round to the nearest tenth.
$L = 1583.4 \text{ ft}^2$; $S = 2814.9 \text{ ft}^2$

14 ft
18 ft

Focus on Mathematical Content

Cylinders The formula for the surface area of a right cylinder can be written $S = L + 2B$ because the bases of a cylinder are congruent.

Teach with Tech

Blog On your secure class blog, have students write a blog entry explaining similarities and differences between finding surface areas of prisms and cylinders. Students should understand that in each case, they are adding the lateral area and the area of the bases.

2 Lateral Areas and Surface Areas of Cylinders The **axis** of a cylinder is the segment with endpoints that are centers of the circular bases. If the axis is also an altitude, then the cylinder is a right cylinder. If the axis is not an altitude, then the cylinder is an oblique cylinder.

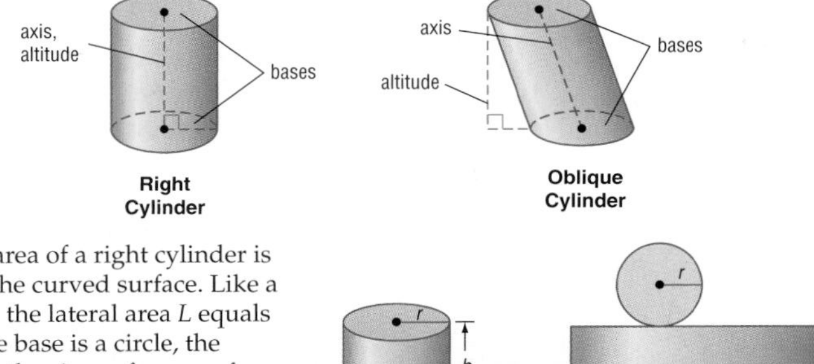

The lateral area of a right cylinder is the area of the curved surface. Like a right prism, the lateral area L equals Ph. Since the base is a circle, the perimeter is the circumference of the circle C. So, the lateral area is Ch or $2\pi rh$.

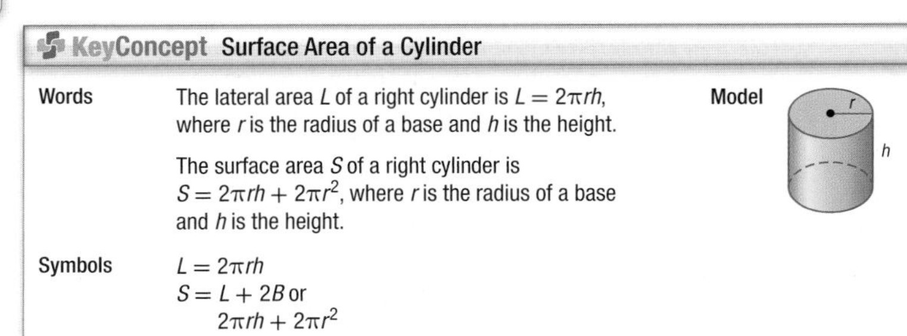

StudyTip
Formulas An alternate formula for the lateral area of a cylinder is $L = \pi dh$, with πd as the circumference of a circle.

The surface area of a cylinder is the lateral area plus the areas of the bases.

KeyConcept Surface Area of a Cylinder

Words The lateral area L of a right cylinder is $L = 2\pi rh$, where r is the radius of a base and h is the height.

The surface area S of a right cylinder is $S = 2\pi rh + 2\pi r^2$, where r is the radius of a base and h is the height.

Symbols $L = 2\pi rh$
$S = L + 2B$ or $2\pi rh + 2\pi r^2$

Model
r
h

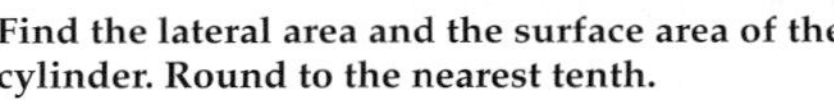

Example 3 Lateral Area and Surface Area of a Cylinder

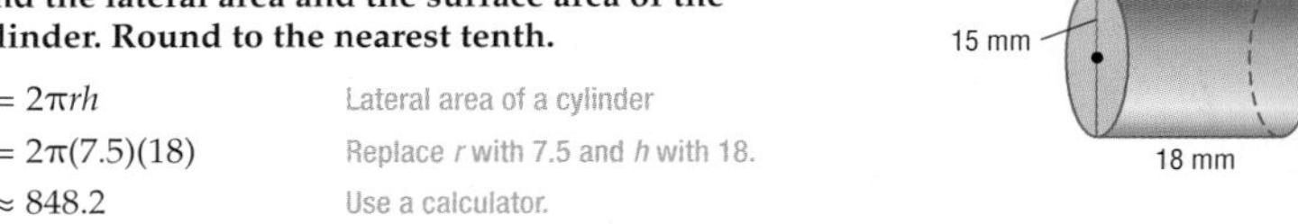

Find the lateral area and the surface area of the cylinder. Round to the nearest tenth.

$L = 2\pi rh$	Lateral area of a cylinder
$= 2\pi(7.5)(18)$	Replace r with 7.5 and h with 18.
≈ 848.2	Use a calculator.
$S = 2\pi rh + 2\pi r^2$	Surface area of a cylinder
$\approx 848.2 + 2\pi(7.5)^2$	Replace $2\pi rh$ with 848.2 and r with 7.5.
≈ 1201.6	Use a calculator.

The lateral area is about 848.2 square millimeters, and the surface area is about 1201.6 square millimeters.

StudyTip
Estimation Before finding the lateral area of a cylinder, use mental math to estimate. To estimate, multiply the diameter by 3 (to approximate π) and then by the height of the cylinder.

GuidedPractice

3A. $r = 5$ in., $h = 9$ in. $L \approx 282.7 \text{ in}^2$; $S \approx 439.8 \text{ in}^2$

3B. $d = 6$ cm, $h = 4.8$ cm $L \approx 90.5 \text{ cm}^2$; $S \approx 147.0 \text{ cm}^2$

DifferentiatedInstruction OL BL

Logical Learners Show students that the formula for the surface area of a cylinder is the lateral surface area plus the area of each circle at the ends of the cylinder.

Real-World Example 4 Find Missing Dimensions

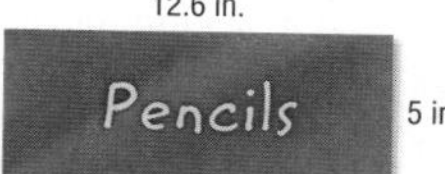

CRAFTS Sheree used the rectangular piece of felt shown at the right to cover the curved surface of her cylindrical pencil holder. What is the radius of the pencil holder?

12.6 in. Pencils 5 in.

$L = 2\pi rh$	Lateral area of a cylinder
$63 = 2\pi r(5)$	Replace L with 12.6 • 5 or 63 and h with 5.
$63 = 10\pi r$	Simplify.
$2.0 \approx r$	Divide each side by 10π.

The radius of the pencil holder is about 2 inches.

Guided Practice

4. Find the diameter of a base of a cylinder if the surface area is 464π square centimeters and the height is 21 centimeters. **16 cm**

Check Your Understanding

= Step-by-Step Solutions begin on page R14.

Example 1

1. Find the lateral area of the prism. **112.5 in^2**

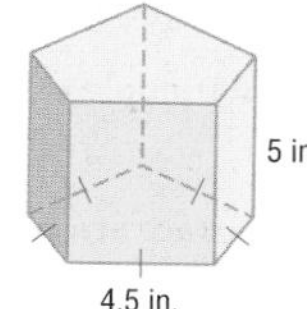

Examples 1–2 Find the lateral area and surface area of each prism.

2. 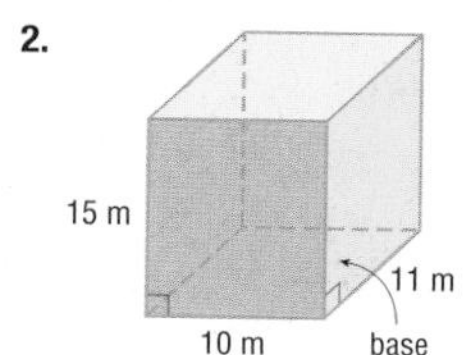

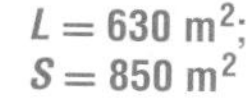

$L = 630$ m^2; $S = 850$ m^2

3. 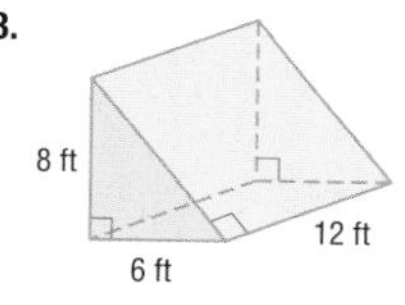

$L = 288$ ft^2; $S = 336$ ft^2

Example 3

4. **CARS** Evan is buying new tire rims that are 14 inches in diameter and 6 inches wide. Determine the lateral area of each rim. Round to the nearest tenth. **263.9 in^2**

Find the lateral area and surface area of each cylinder. Round to the nearest tenth.

5. 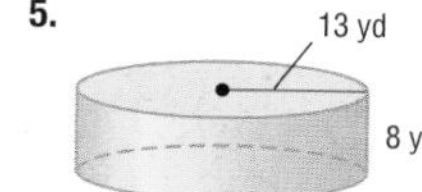

$L \approx 653.5$ yd^2; $S \approx 1715.3$ yd^2

6. 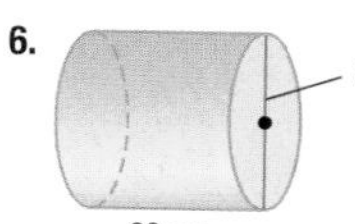

$L \approx 1409.9$ cm^2; $S \approx 2063.6$ cm^2

Example 4

7. **FOOD** The can of soup at the right has a surface area of 286.3 square centimeters. What is the height of the can? Round to the nearest tenth. **10.0 cm**

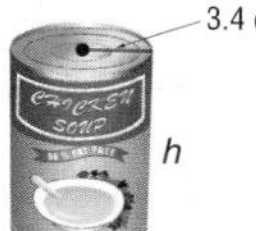

8. The surface area of a cube is 294 square inches. Find the length of a lateral edge. **7 in.**

Differentiated Homework Options

Level	Assignment	Two-Day Option	
AL Basic	9–27, 39–42, 44–56	9–27 odd, 45–48	10–26 even, 39–42, 44, 49–56
OL Core	9–27 odd, 28, 29, 31–42, 44–56	9–27, 45–48	28–42, 44, 49–56
BL Advanced	28–53, (optional: 54–56)		

Additional Example

4 **MANUFACTURING** A soup can is covered with the label shown. What is the radius of the soup can?

Tasty SOUP 8 in. 15.7 in.

2.5 in.

3 Practice

Formative Assessment

Use Exercises 1–8 to check for understanding.

Use the chart at the bottom of this page to customize assignments for your students.

Tips for New Teachers

Ask students if they can think of a more efficient way to find the radius in Example 4. Lead students to see that 12.6 inches represents the circumference of the pencil can. Since $C = 2\pi r$, students can solve the equation $12.6 = 2\pi r$ for r and find that $r \approx 2.0$ inches.

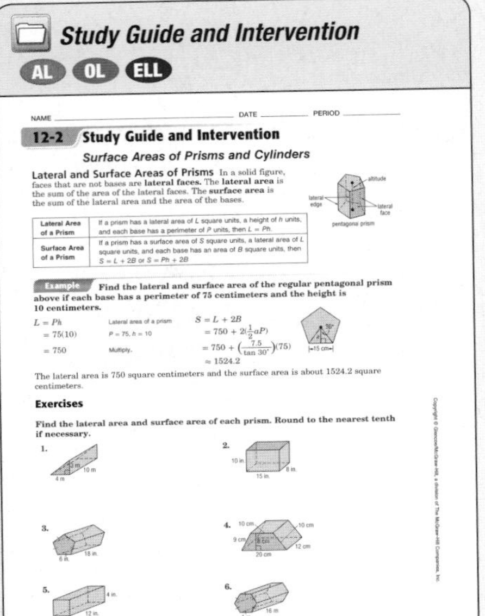

Study Guide and Intervention

AL OL ELL

NAME ____ DATE ____ PERIOD ____

12-2 Study Guide and Intervention

Surface Areas of Prisms and Cylinders

Lateral and Surface Areas of Prisms In a solid figure, faces that are not bases are **lateral faces**. The **lateral area** is the sum of the areas of the lateral faces. The **surface area** is the sum of the lateral area and the area of the bases.

Lateral Area of a Prism	If a prism has a lateral area of L square units, a height of h units, and each base has a perimeter of P units, then L = Ph.
Surface Area of a Prism	If a prism has a surface area of S square units, a lateral area of L square units, and each base has an area of B square units, then S = L + 2B or S = Ph + 2B

Example Find the lateral and surface area of the regular pentagonal prism above if each base has a perimeter of 75 centimeters and the height is 10 centimeters.

The lateral area is 750 square centimeters and the surface area is about 1524.2 square centimeters.

Exercises

Find the lateral area and surface area of each prism. Round to the nearest tenth if necessary.

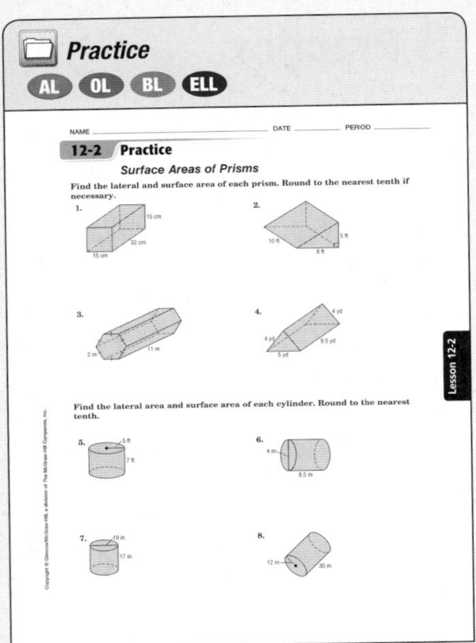

Practice

AL OL BL ELL

NAME ____ DATE ____ PERIOD ____

12-2 Practice

Surface Areas of Prisms

Find the lateral and surface area of each prism. Round to the nearest tenth if necessary.

Find the lateral area and surface area of each cylinder. Round to the nearest tenth.

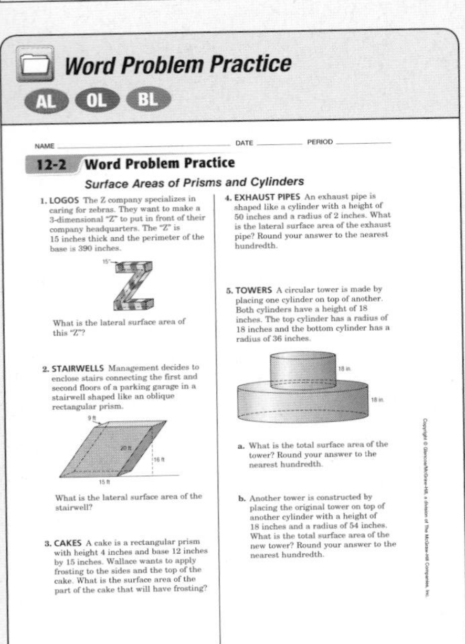

Word Problem Practice

AL OL BL

NAME ____ DATE ____ PERIOD ____

12-2 Word Problem Practice

Surface Areas of Prisms and Cylinders

1. LOGOS The Z company specializes in caring for zebras. They want to make a 3-dimensional "Z" to put in front of their company headquarters. The "Z" is 15 inches thick and the perimeter of the base is 390 inches.

What is the lateral surface area of this "Z"?

2. STAIRWELLS Management decides to enclose stairs connecting the first and second floors of a parking garage in a stairwell shaped like an oblique rectangular prism.

What is the lateral surface area of the stairwell?

3. CAKES A cake is a rectangular prism with height 4 inches and base 12 inches by 15 inches. Wallace wants to apply frosting to the sides and the top of the cake. What is the surface area of the part of the cake that will have frosting?

4. EXHAUST PIPES An exhaust pipe is shaped like a cylinder with a height of 50 inches and a radius of 2 inches. What is the lateral surface area of the exhaust pipe? Round your answer to the nearest hundredth.

5. TOWERS A circular tower is made by placing one cylinder on top of another. Both cylinders have a height of 18 inches. The top cylinder has a radius of 18 inches and the bottom cylinder has a radius of 36 inches.

a. What is the total surface area of the tower? Round your answer to the nearest hundredth.

b. Another tower is constructed by placing the original tower on top of another cylinder with a height of 18 inches and a radius of 54 inches. What is the total surface area of the new tower? Round your answer to the nearest hundredth.

Practice and Problem Solving

Extra Practice is on page R12.

Examples 1–2 Find the lateral area and surface area of each prism. Round to the nearest tenth if necessary.

9. 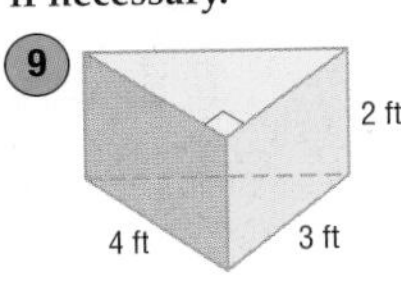

$L = 24$ ft^2; $S = 36$ ft^2

10. 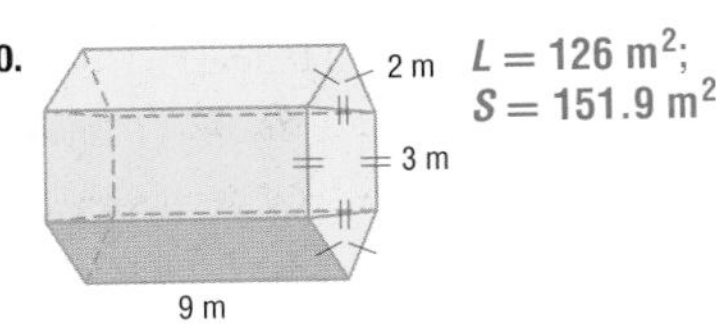

$L = 126$ m^2; $S = 151.9$ m^2

11. 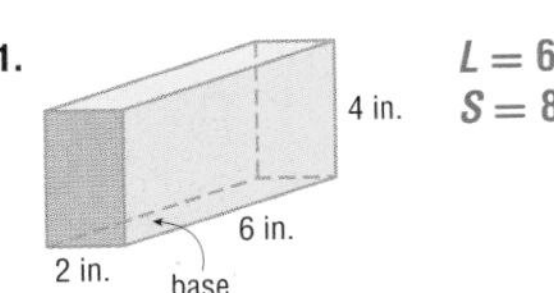

$L = 64$ in^2; $S = 88$ in^2

12. 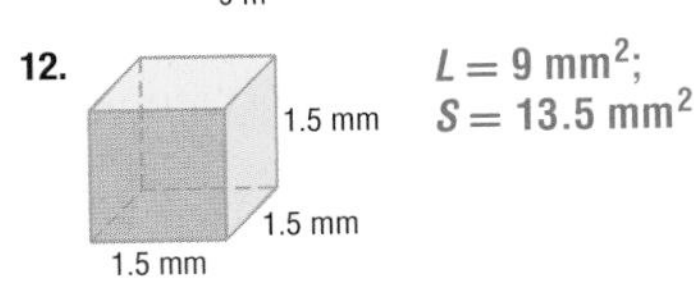

$L = 9$ mm^2; $S = 13.5$ mm^2

13. 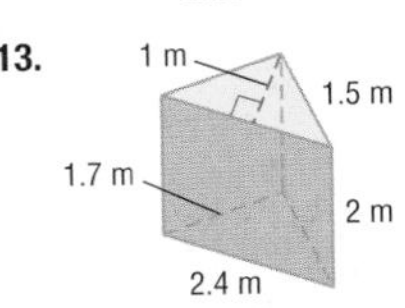

$L = 11.2$ m^2; $S = 13.6$ m^2

14. 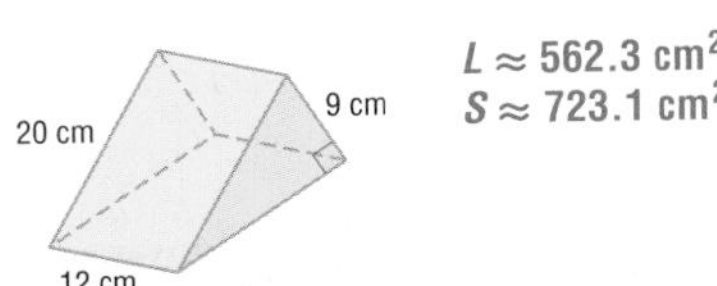

$L \approx 562.3$ cm^2; $S \approx 723.1$ cm^2

15. rectangular prism: $\ell = 25$ centimeters, $w = 18$ centimeters, $h = 12$ centimeters **See margin.**

16. triangular prism: $h = 6$ inches, right triangle base with legs 9 inches and 12 inches
$L = 216$ in^2; $S = 324$ in^2

Examples 1–3 **CEREAL** Find the lateral area and the surface area of each cereal container. Round to the nearest tenth if necessary.

17. 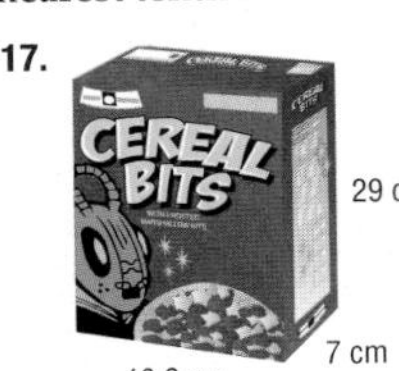

$L = 1484.8$ cm^2; $S = 1745.2$ cm^2

18. 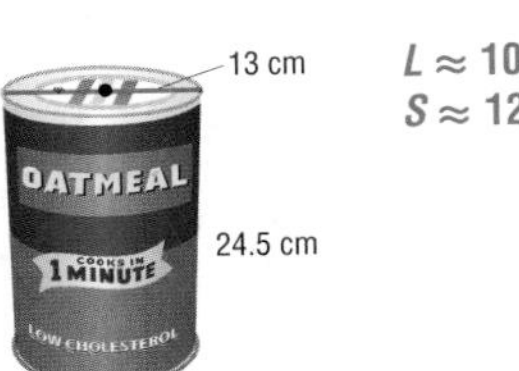

$L \approx 1000.6$ cm^2; $S \approx 1266.1$ cm^2

Example 3 **CCSS SENSE-MAKING** Find the lateral area and surface area of each cylinder. Round to the nearest tenth.

19. 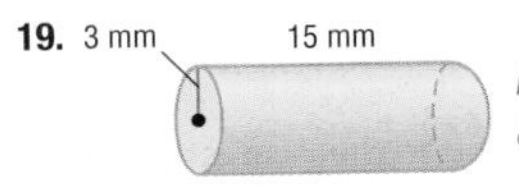

$L \approx 282.7$ mm^2; $S \approx 339.3$ mm^2

20. 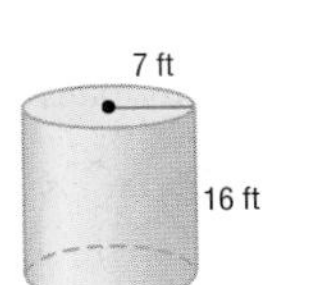

$L \approx 703.7$ ft^2; $S \approx 1011.6$ ft^2

21. 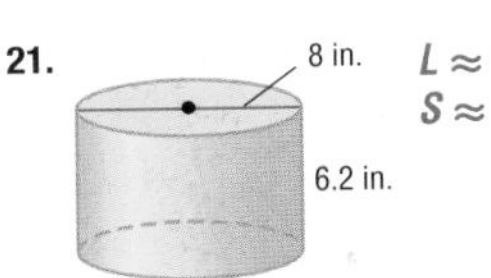

$L \approx 155.8$ in^2; $S \approx 256.4$ in^2

22. 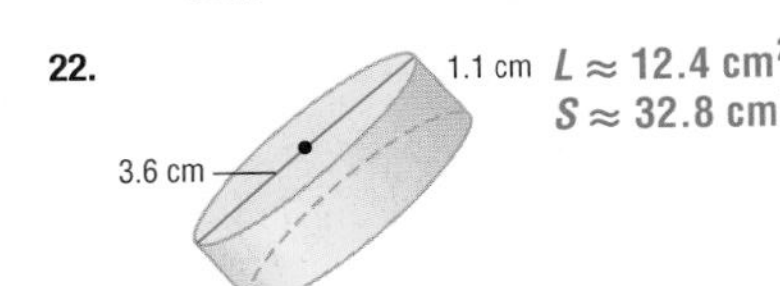

$L \approx 12.4$ cm^2; $S \approx 32.8$ cm^2

23. **WORLD RECORDS** The largest beverage can was a cylinder with height 4.67 meters and diameter 2.32 meters. What was the surface area of the can to the nearest tenth? 42.5 m^2

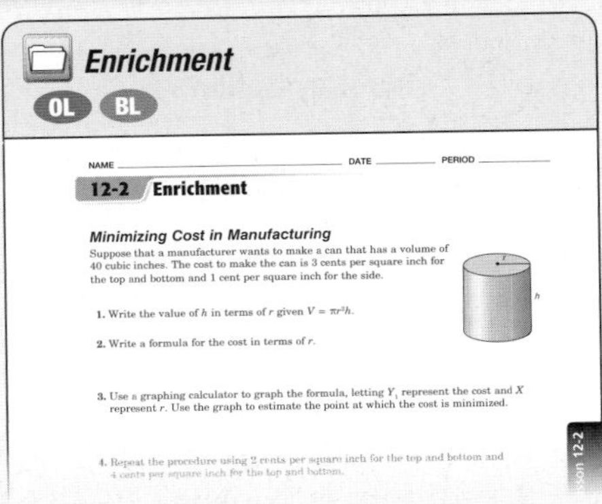

Enrichment

OL BL

NAME ____ DATE ____ PERIOD ____

12-2 Enrichment

Minimizing Cost in Manufacturing

Suppose that a manufacturer wants to make a can that has a volume of 40 cubic inches. The cost to make the can is 3 cents per square inch for the top and bottom and 1 cent per square inch for the side.

1. Write the value of h in terms of r given $V = \pi r^2 h$.

2. Write a formula for the cost in terms of r.

3. Use a graphing calculator to graph the formula, letting Y_1 represent the cost and X represent r. Use the graph to estimate the point at which the cost is minimized.

Additional Answer

15. $L = 1032$ cm^2; $S = 1932$ cm^2 (18 × 25 base); $L = 1332$ cm^2; $S = 1932$ cm^2 (25 × 12 base); $L = 1500$ cm^2; $S = 1932$ cm^2 (18 × 12 base)

Example 4 **Use the given lateral area and the diagram to find the missing measure of each solid. Round to the nearest tenth if necessary.**

24. $L = 48 \text{ in}^2$ **$h = 4$ in.**

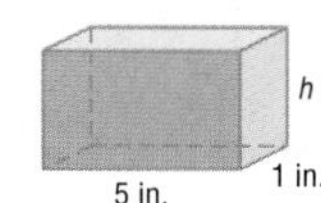

25. $L \approx 635.9 \text{ cm}^2$ **$r = 9.2$ cm**

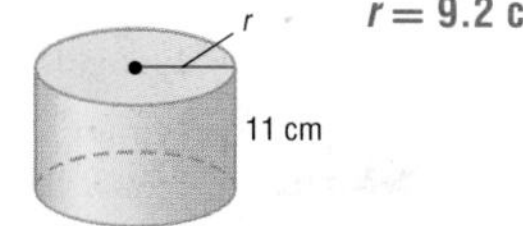

26. A right rectangular prism has a surface area of 1020 square inches, a length of 6 inches, and a width of 9 inches. Find the height. **30.4 in.**

27 A cylinder has a surface area of 256π square millimeters and a height of 8 millimeters. Find the diameter. **16 mm**

B **28. MONUMENTS** A *monolith* mysteriously appeared overnight at Seattle, Washington's Manguson Park. A hollow rectangular prism, the monolith was 9 feet tall, 4 feet wide, and 1 foot deep.

a. Find the area in square feet of the structure's surfaces that lie above the ground. **94 ft²**

b. Use dimensional analysis to find the area in square yards. **10.4 yd²**

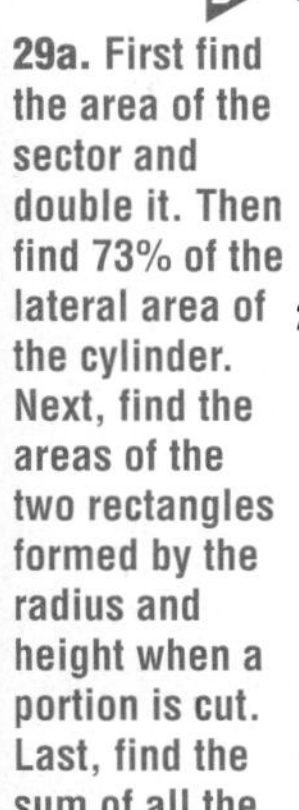

29a. First find the area of the sector and double it. Then find 73% of the lateral area of the cylinder. Next, find the areas of the two rectangles formed by the radius and height when a portion is cut. Last, find the sum of all the areas.

29. ENTERTAINMENT The graphic shows the results of a survey in which people were asked where they like to watch movies.

a. Suppose the film can is a cylinder 12 inches in diameter. Explain how to find the surface area of the portion that represents people who prefer to watch movies at home.

b. If the film can is 3 inches tall, find the surface area of the portion in part **a**. **283.7 in²**

CCSS SENSE-MAKING **Find the lateral area and surface area of each oblique solid. Round to the nearest tenth.**

30. **≈513.6 m²; ≈573.6 m²**

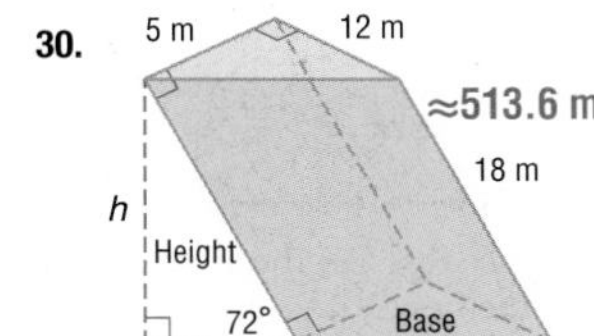

31. **1392.0 cm²; 2032 cm²**

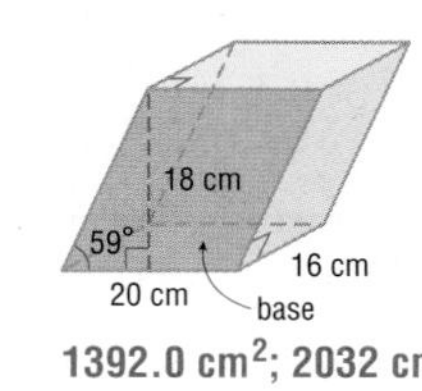

32. LAMPS The lamp shade is a cylinder of height 18 inches with a diameter of $6\frac{3}{4}$ inches.

a. What is the lateral area of the shade to the nearest tenth? **381.7 in²**

b. How does the lateral area change if the height is divided by 2? **The lateral area is divided by 2.**

33. Find the approximate surface area of a right hexagonal prism if the height is 9 centimeters and each base edge is 4 centimeters. (*Hint*: First, find the length of the apothem of the base.) **about 299.1 cm²**

CCSS Teaching the Mathematical Practices

Sense-Making Mathematically proficient students start by explaining the meaning of a problem to themselves and looking for entry points to its solution. They plan a solution pathway rather than simply jumping into a solution attempt. In Exercises 19–22 and 30–31, encourage students to make a plan to solve each problem first.

Multiple Representations

In Exercise 38, students use a table and verbal descriptions to investigate surface area of a cylinder.

WatchOut!

Error Analysis In Exercise 39, students should see that Montell used the incorrect formula. Each term in the formula for surface area has 2 as a coefficient.

Additional Answers

34a. Sample answer:

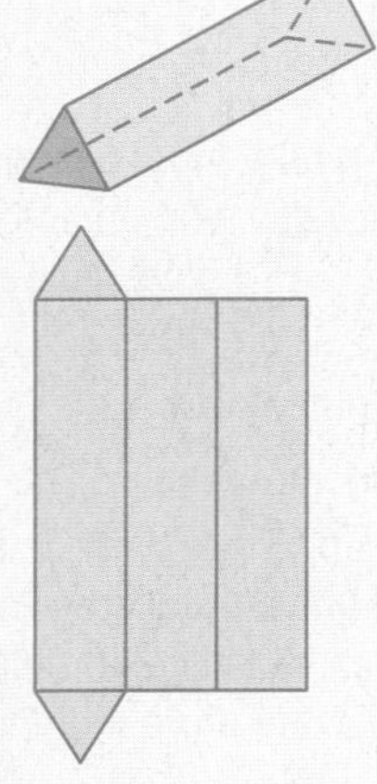

38a.

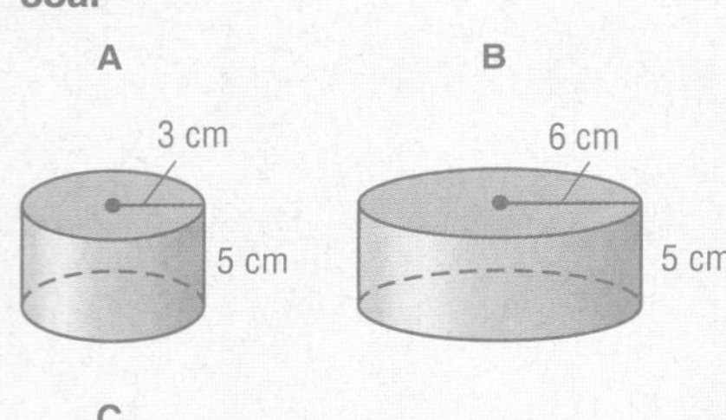

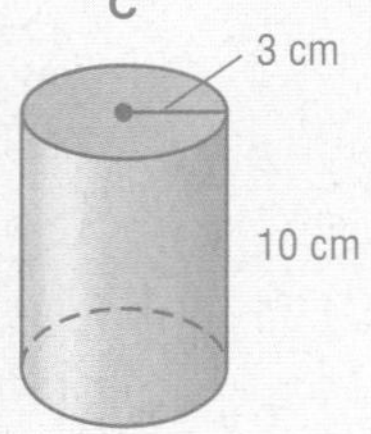

38b.

Cylinder	Radius	Height	Lateral Area	Surface Area
A	3	5	30π	48π
B	6	5	60π	132π
C	3	10	60π	78π

34b. side lengths of triangular bases, about 10.39 in. each; height, 38 in.; 1278 in^2

34. DESIGN A mailer needs to hold a poster that is almost 38 inches long and has a maximum rolled diameter of 6 inches.

a. Design a mailer that is a triangular prism. Sketch the mailer and its net. **See margin.**

b. Suppose you want to minimize the surface area of the mailer. What would be the dimensions of the mailer and its surface area?

C **A composite solid is a three-dimensional figure that is composed of simpler figures. Find the surface area of each composite solid. Round to the nearest tenth if necessary.**

35

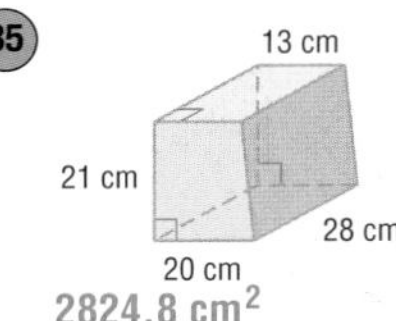

2824.8 cm^2

36.

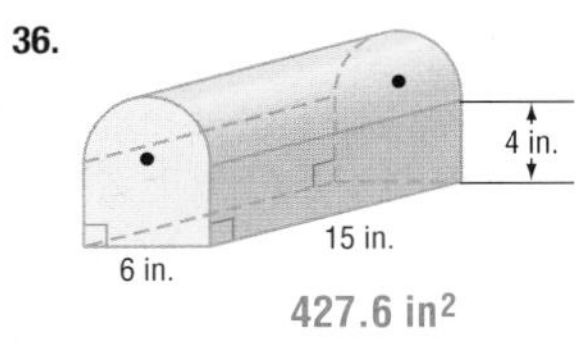

427.6 in^2

37.

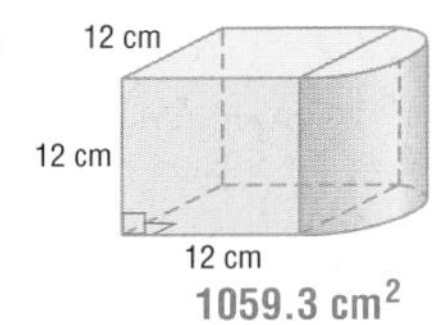

1059.3 cm^2

38c. Sample answer: If the radius is doubled, the lateral area is doubled and the surface area is more than doubled. If the height is doubled, the lateral area is doubled and the surface area is increased, but not doubled.

38. MULTIPLE REPRESENTATIONS In this problem, you will investigate the lateral area and surface area of a cylinder.

a. Geometric Sketch cylinder A with a radius of 3 centimeters and a height of 5 centimeters, cylinder B with a radius of 6 centimeters and a height of 5 centimeters, and cylinder C with a radius of 3 centimeters and a height of 10 centimeters. **See margin.**

b. Tabular Create a table of the radius, height, lateral area, and surface area of cylinders A, B, and C. Write the areas in terms of π. **See margin.**

c. Verbal If the radius is doubled, what effect does it have on the lateral area and the surface area of a cylinder? If the height is doubled, what effect does it have on the lateral area and the surface area of a cylinder?

41. To find the surface area of any solid figure, find the area of the base (or bases) and add to the area of the lateral faces of the figure. The lateral faces and bases of a rectangular prism are rectangles. Since the bases of a cylinder are circles, the "lateral faces" of a cylinder is a rectangle.

H.O.T. Problems Use Higher-Order Thinking Skills

39. ERROR ANALYSIS Montell and Derek are finding the surface area of a cylinder with height 5 centimeters and radius 6 centimeters. Is either of them correct? Explain.

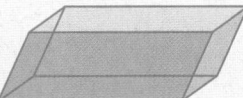

39. Derek; sample answer: $S = 2\pi r^2 + 2\pi rh$, so the surface area of the cylinder is $2\pi(6)^2 + 2\pi(6)(5)$ or 132π cm^2.

Montell	Derek
$S = \pi(6)^2 + \pi(6)(5)$	$S = 2\pi(6)^2 + 2\pi(6)(5)$
$= 36\pi + 30\pi$	$= 72\pi + 60\pi$
$= 66\pi$ cm^2	$= 132\pi$ cm^2

40. WRITING IN MATH Sketch an oblique rectangular prism, and describe the shapes that would be included in a net for the prism. Explain how the net is different from that of a right rectangular prism. **See margin.**

41. CCSS PRECISION Compare and contrast finding the surface area of a prism and finding the surface area of a cylinder.

42. OPEN ENDED Give an example of two cylinders that have the same lateral area and different surface areas. Describe the lateral area and surface areas of each. **See margin.**

43. CHALLENGE A right prism has a height of h units and a base that is an equilateral triangle of side ℓ units. Find the general formula for the total surface area of the prism. Explain your reasoning. **See margin.**

44. WRITING IN MATH A square based prism and a triangular prism are the same height. The base of the triangular prism is an equilateral triangle, with an altitude equal in length to the side of the square. Compare the lateral areas of the prisms. **See margin.**

852 | Lesson 12-2 | Surface Areas of Prisms and Cylinders

40. Sample answer:

Rectangles and parallelograms; the net for a right prism includes rectangles only.

42. Sample answer: A cylinder with height 8 units and radius 3 units has a lateral area of 48π square units and surface area of 66π square units; a cylinder with height 6 units and radius 4 units has a lateral area of 48π square units and surface area of 80π square units.

43. $\frac{\sqrt{3}}{2}\ell^2 + 3\ell h$; the area of an equilateral triangle of side ℓ is $\frac{\sqrt{3}}{4}\ell^2$ and the perimeter of the triangle is 3ℓ. So, the total surface area is $\frac{\sqrt{3}}{2}\ell^2 + 3\ell h$.

Standardized Test Practice

45. If the surface area of the right rectangular prism is 310 square centimeters, what is the measure of the height h of the prism? **A**

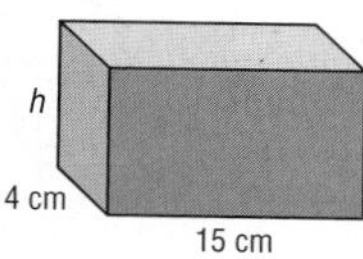

A 5 cm
B $5\frac{1}{6}$ cm
C 10
D $13\frac{3}{9}$ cm

46. **SHORT RESPONSE** A cylinder has a circumference of 16π inches and a height of 20 inches. What is the surface area of the cylinder in terms of π? **448π in^2**

47. Parker Flooring charges the following to install a hardwood floor in a new home.
Subflooring: $2.25 per square foot
Wood flooring : $4.59 per square foot
Baseboards: $1.95 per linear foot around room
Nail & other materials: $25.95 per job
Labor: $99 plus $0.99 square foot
What is the cost to install hardwood flooring in a room that is 18 by 15 feet? **H**

F $2169.75
G $2268.75
H $2367.75
J $2765.55

48. **SAT/ACT** What is the value of $f(-2)$ if $f(x) = x^3 + 4x^2 - 2x - 3$? **C**

A −31
B $-\frac{9}{2}$
C 9
D 25
E 28

Spiral Review

Use isometric dot paper to sketch each prism. (Lesson 12-1)

49. rectangular prism 2 units high, 3 units long, and 2 units wide **See margin.**

50. triangular prism 2 units high with bases that are right triangles with legs 3 units and 4 units long **See margin.**

51. **BAKING** A bakery sells single-layer mini-cakes that are 3 inches in diameter for $4 each. They also have a cake with the same thickness and a 9-inch diameter for $15. Compare the areas of the cake tops to determine, which option is a better buy, nine mini-cakes or one 9-inch cake. Explain. (Lesson 11-5) **See margin.**

The diameters of $\odot R$, $\odot S$, and $\odot T$ are 10 inches, 14 inches, and 9 inches, respectively. Find each measure. (Lesson 10-1)

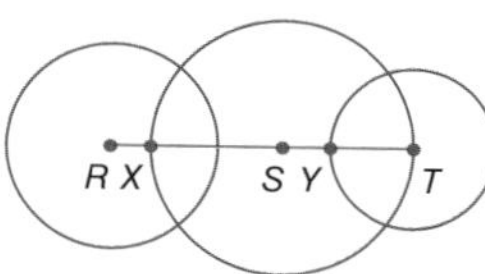

52. YX **9.5 in.**

53. SY **2.5 in.**

Skills Review

Find x. Round to the nearest tenth.

54. **8.1**

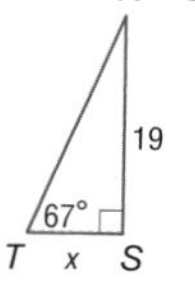

55. **20.5**

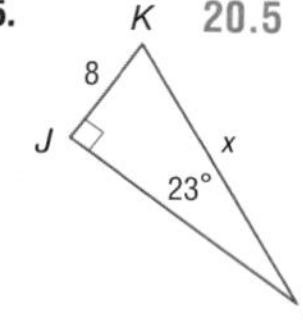

56. **42.3**

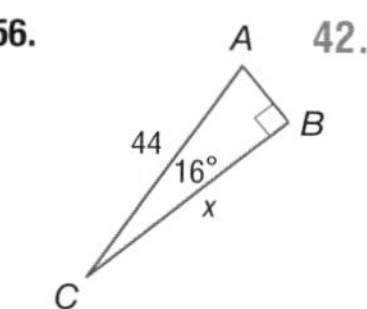

DifferentiatedInstruction OL BL

Extension Is a surface two-dimensional or three-dimensional? Explain your response. Sample answer: A surface itself is two-dimensional because it has no thickness. A surface can, however, span three dimensions. A polyhedron has three dimensions, but the surface itself is still two-dimensional.

Exercise Alert

Isometric Dot Paper Exercises 49 and 50 require the use of isometric dot paper.

4 Assess

Ticket Out the Door Ask students to use a rectangular prism shown on isometric dot paper to find surface area. Have students turn in their statements before they leave the classroom.

Formative Assessment

Check for student understanding of Lessons 12-1 and 12-2.

Quiz 1, p. 57

Additional Answers

44. The lateral area of the square-based prism is greater than that of the triangular prism. The square has a perimeter of $4s$ and the triangle has a perimeter of $2\sqrt{3}s$ and $4s > 2\sqrt{3}s$.

49.

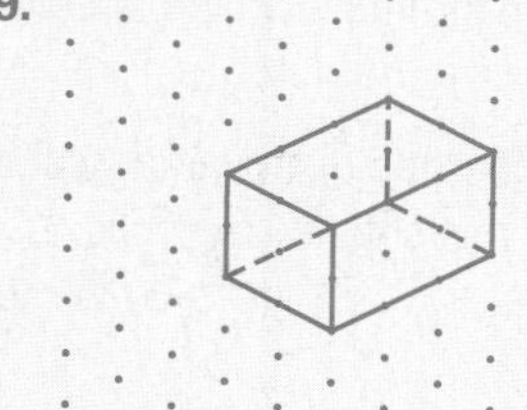

50.

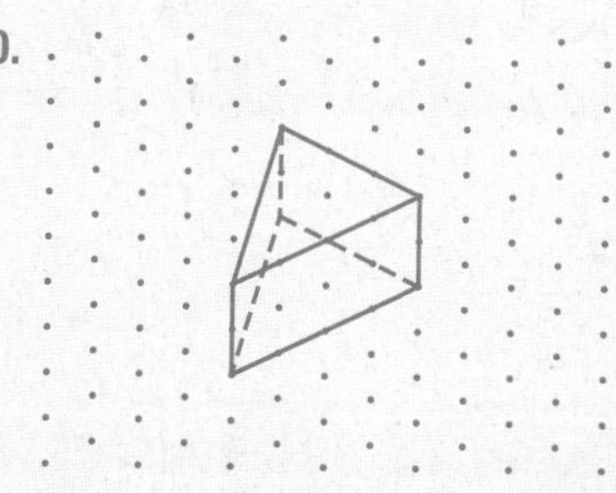

51. One 9-inch cake: Nine minicakes have the same top area as one 9-inch cake, but nine minicakes cost 9($4) or $36 while the 9-inch cake is only $15, so the 9-inch cake is a better buy.

1 Focus

VerticalAlignment

Before Lesson 12-3 Find the areas of regular polygons.

Lesson 12-3 Find lateral areas and surface areas of pyramids. Find lateral areas and surface areas of cones.

After Lesson 12-3 Find the volume of pyramids and cones.

2 Teach

Scaffolding Questions

Have students read the **Why?** section of the lesson.

Ask:

- What is the general shape of the building? a pyramid
- How does the design allow more light to reach the street? Sample answer: It is narrower at the top.
- What is a possible disadvantage of a building of this shape? Sample answer: There is less room on the top floors.

LESSON 12-3 Surface Areas of Pyramids and Cones

Then

- You found areas of regular polygons.

Now

1. Find lateral areas and surface areas of pyramids.
2. Find lateral areas and surface areas of cones.

Why?

- The Transamerica Pyramid in San Francisco, California, covers nearly one city block. Its unconventional design allows light and air to filter down to the streets around the building, unlike the more traditional rectangular prism skyscrapers.

NewVocabulary
regular pyramid
slant height
right cone
oblique cone

Common Core State Standards

Content Standards
G.MG.1 Use geometric shapes, their measures, and their properties to describe objects (e.g., modeling a tree trunk or a human torso as a cylinder). ★

Mathematical Practices
1 Make sense of problems and persevere in solving them.
6 Attend to precision.

1 Lateral Area and Surface Area of Pyramids

The *lateral faces* of a pyramid intersect at a common point called the *vertex*. Two lateral faces intersect at a *lateral edge*. A lateral face and the base intersect at a *base edge*. The *altitude* is the segment from the vertex perpendicular to the base.

A **regular pyramid** has a base that is a regular polygon and the altitude has an endpoint at the center of the base. All the lateral edges are congruent and all the lateral faces are congruent isosceles triangles. The height of each lateral face is called the **slant height** ℓ of the pyramid.

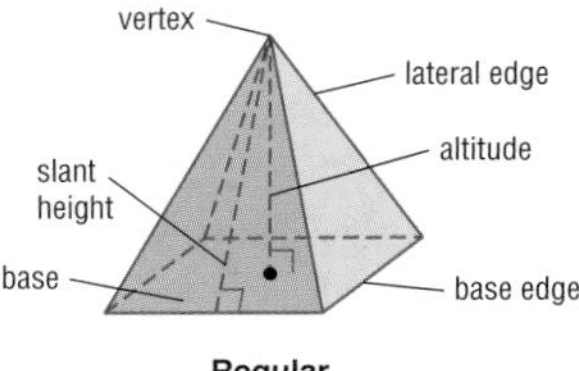

Regular Pyramid

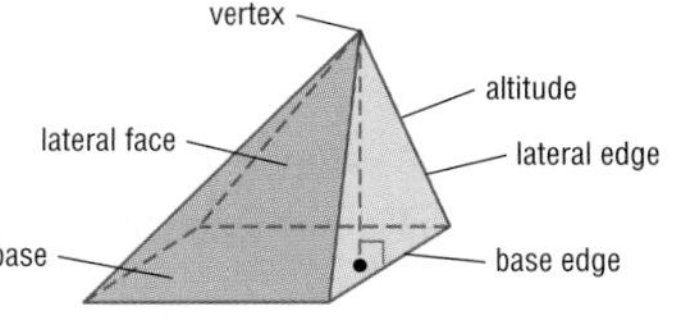

Nonregular Pyramid

The lateral area L of a regular pentagonal pyramid is the sum of the areas of all its congruent triangular faces as shown in the net at the right.

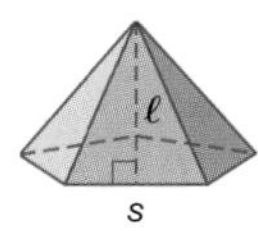

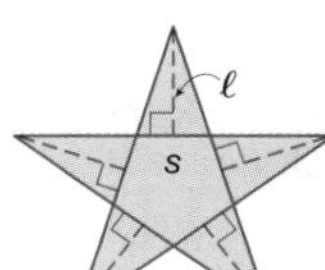

$L = \frac{1}{2}s\ell + \frac{1}{2}s\ell + \frac{1}{2}s\ell + \frac{1}{2}s\ell + \frac{1}{2}s\ell$ Sum of the areas of the lateral faces

$= \frac{1}{2}\ell(s + s + s + s + s)$ Distributive Property

$= \frac{1}{2}P\ell$ $P = s + s + s + s + s$

KeyConcept Lateral Area of a Regular Pyramid

Words The lateral area L of a regular pyramid is $L = \frac{1}{2}P\ell$, where ℓ is the slant height and P is the perimeter of the base.

Symbols $L = \frac{1}{2}P\ell$

Model

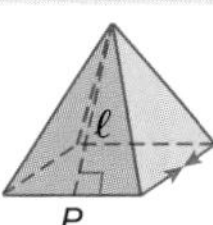

Lesson 12-3 Resources

Resource	Approaching Level AL	On Level OL	Beyond Level BL	English Learners ELL
Teacher Edition	▪ Differentiated Instruction, p. 855	▪ Differentiated Instruction, pp. 855, 862	▪ Differentiated Instruction, p. 862	
Chapter Resource Masters	▪ Study Guide and Intervention, pp. 18–19 ▪ Skills Practice, p. 20 ▪ Practice, p. 21 ▪ Word Problem Practice, p. 22	▪ Study Guide and Intervention, pp. 18–19 ▪ Skills Practice, p. 20 ▪ Practice, p. 21 ▪ Word Problem Practice, p. 22 ▪ Enrichment, p. 23 ▪ Spreadsheet Activity, p. 24	▪ Practice, p. 21 ▪ Word Problem Practice, p. 22 ▪ Enrichment, p. 23	▪ Study Guide and Intervention, pp. 18–19 ▪ Skills Practice, p. 20 ▪ Practice, p. 21 ▪ Word Problem Practice, p. 22
Other	▪ 5-Minute Check 12-3 ▪ Study Notebook ▪ Teaching Geometry with Manipulatives	▪ 5-Minute Check 12-3 ▪ Study Notebook ▪ Teaching Geometry with Manipulatives	▪ 5-Minute Check 12-3 ▪ Study Notebook	▪ 5-Minute Check 12-3 ▪ Study Notebook ▪ Teaching Geometry with Manipulatives

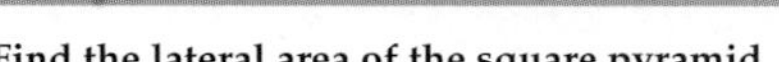

Example 1 Lateral Area of a Regular Pyramid

Find the lateral area of the square pyramid.

$L = \frac{1}{2}P\ell$ — Lateral area of a regular pyramid

$= \frac{1}{2}(16)(6)$ or 48 — $P = 4 \cdot 4$ or 16, $\ell = 6$

The lateral area is 48 square inches.

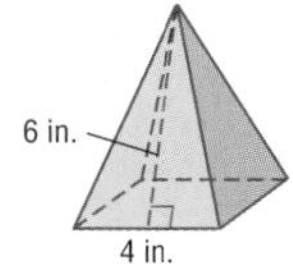

> **StudyTip**
> Alternative Method You can also find the lateral area of a pyramid by adding the areas of the congruent lateral faces.
> area of one face:
> $\frac{1}{2}(4)(6) = 12 \text{ in}^2$
> lateral area:
> $4 \cdot 12 = 48 \text{ in}^2$

GuidedPractice

1. Find the lateral area of a regular hexagonal pyramid with a base edge of 9 centimeters and a lateral height of 7 centimeters. **189 cm^2**

The surface area of a pyramid is the sum of the lateral area and the area of the base.

KeyConcept Surface Area of a Regular Pyramid

Words The surface area S of a regular pyramid is $S = \frac{1}{2}P\ell + B$, where P is the perimeter of the base, ℓ is the slant height, and B is the area of the base.

Model

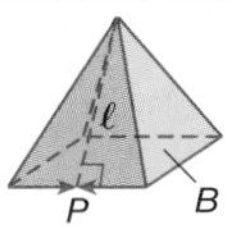

Symbols $S = \frac{1}{2}P\ell + B$

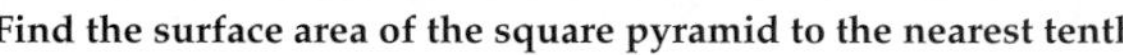

Example 2 Surface Area of a Square Pyramid

Find the surface area of the square pyramid to the nearest tenth.

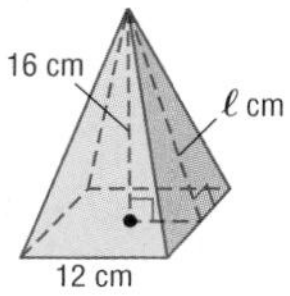

Step 1 Find the slant height.

$c^2 = a^2 + b^2$ — Pythagorean Theorem

$\ell^2 = 16^2 + 6^2$ — $a = 16$, $b = 6$, and $c = \ell$

$\ell = \sqrt{292}$ — Simplify.

Step 2 Find the perimeter and area of the base.

$P = 4 \cdot 12$ or 48 cm $\quad A = 12^2$ or 144 cm^2

Step 3 Find the surface area of the pyramid.

$S = \frac{1}{2}P\ell + B$ — Surface area of a regular pyramid

$= \frac{1}{2}(48)\sqrt{292} + 144$ — $P = 48$, $\ell = \sqrt{292}$, and $B = 144$

≈ 554.1 — Use a calculator.

The surface area of the pyramid is about 554.1 square centimeters.

> **StudyTip**
> Making Connections The surface area of a pyramid equals $L + B$, not $L + 2B$, because a pyramid has only one base.

GuidedPractice

2A.

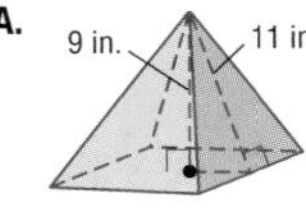

438.3 in^2

2B.

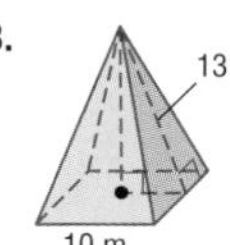

360 m^2

1 Lateral Area and Surface Area of Pyramids

Example 1 shows how to find the lateral area of a regular pyramid. **Examples 2 and 3** show how to find the surface area of a regular pyramid.

Formative Assessment

Use the Guided Practice exercises after each example to determine students' understanding of concepts.

Additional Examples

1 Find the lateral area of the square pyramid.

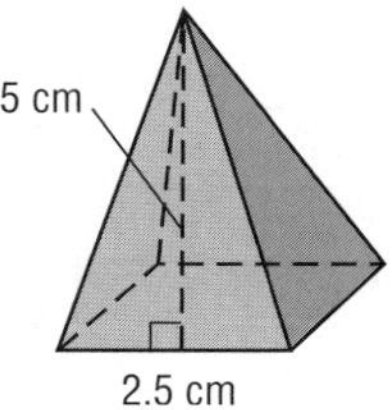

25 cm^2

2 Find the surface area of the square pyramid to the nearest tenth.

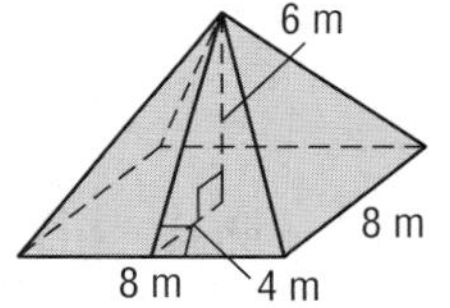

179.4 m^2

Additional Examples also in Interactive Classroom PowerPoint® Presentations

Focus on Mathematical Content

Altitude Recall that the altitude of a regular pyramid has an endpoint at the center of the base. So, the side length of the triangle in the interior of the pyramid in Example 2 equals $\frac{1}{2} \cdot 12$ cm or 6 cm.

DifferentiatedInstruction AL OL

Auditory/Musical Learners Ask students to name a similarity and a difference between finding the lateral area of a pyramid and the lateral area of a prism. The similarity is that both lateral areas use the perimeter of the base in their formulas. The difference is that the lateral area of a pyramid is one-half the perimeter of the base times its slant height, while the lateral area of a prism is the perimeter of the base times its regular height.

Additional Example

3 Find the surface area of the regular pyramid. Round to the nearest tenth.

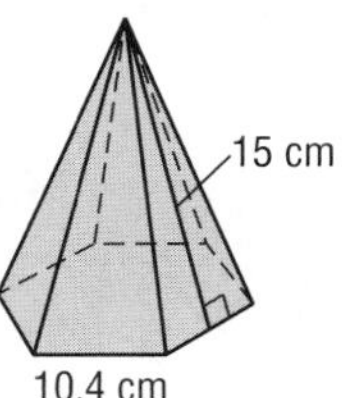

748.8 cm^2

Focus on Mathematical Content

Altitude The difference between the slant height and the height of a pyramid may be confusing for some students. Point out that the slant height is the height of a lateral face, while the height is the altitude of the pyramid.

Tips for New Teachers

To help students visualize the derivation of the lateral area of a cone, use a cone filter or conical water cup. Have students cut and measure the cone filter or water cup.

Example 3 Surface Area of a Regular Pyramid

Find the surface area of the regular pyramid. Round to the nearest tenth.

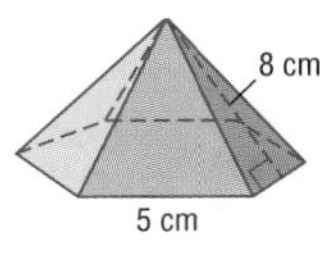

Step 1 Find the perimeter of the base.
$P = 6 \cdot 5$ or 30 cm

Step 2 Find the length of the apothem and the area of the base.

A central angle of the hexagon is $\frac{360°}{6}$ or 60°, so the angle formed in the triangle at the right is 30°.

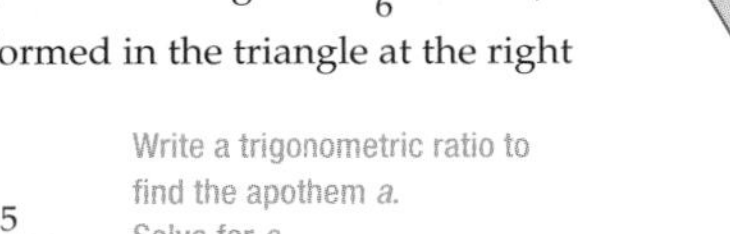

$\tan 30° = \frac{2.5}{a}$	Write a trigonometric ratio to find the apothem a.
$a = \frac{2.5}{\tan 30°}$	Solve for a.
≈ 4.3	Use a calculator.
$A = \frac{1}{2}Pa$	Area of a regular polygon
$\approx \frac{1}{2}(30)(4.3)$	Replace P with 30 and a with 4.3.
≈ 64.5	Multiply.

So, the area of the base B is approximately 64.5 square centimeters.

Step 3 Find the surface area of the pyramid.

$S = \frac{1}{2}P\ell + 1$	Surface area of a regular pyramid
$= \frac{1}{2}(30)(8) + 64.5$	$P = 30$, $\ell = 8$, and $B \approx 64.5$
≈ 184.5	Simplify.

The surface area of the pyramid is about 184.5 square centimeters.

> **Review Vocabulary**
> Trigonometric Ratios
> $\sin A = \frac{\text{opp}}{\text{hyp}}$
> $\cos A = \frac{\text{adj}}{\text{hyp}}$
> $\tan A = \frac{\text{opp}}{\text{adj}}$

Guided Practice

3A. 8 ft, 6 ft — 87.6 ft^2

3B.

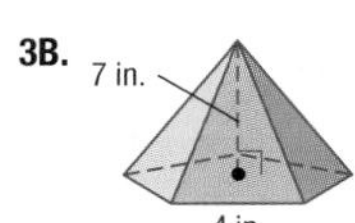

102.7 in^2

2 Lateral Area and Surface Area of Cones

Recall that a cone has a circular base and a vertex. The axis of a cone is the segment with endpoints at the vertex and the center of the base. If the axis is also the altitude, then the cone is a **right cone**. If the axis is not the altitude, then the cone is an **oblique cone**.

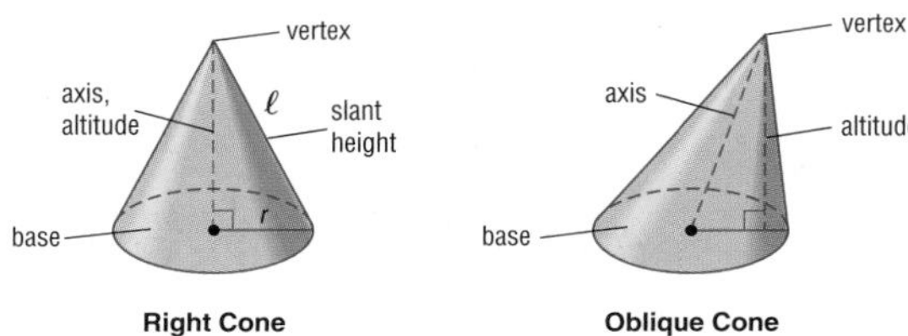

Right Cone   Oblique Cone

Watch Out!

Common Misconceptions A common error is to assume that the formulas in this lesson apply to any pyramid. Point out that these formulas apply only to *regular* pyramids. The lateral area of a non-regular pyramid would require finding the areas of triangles that are not congruent.

Teach with Tech

Video Recording Separate students into groups. Have them create videos teaching how to find the surface area of a pyramid or a cone. Share the videos with the entire class.

856 | Lesson 12-3 | Surface Areas of Pyramids and Cones

The net for a cone is shown at the right. The circle with radius r is the base of the cone. It has a circumference of $2\pi r$ and an area of πr^2. The sector with radius ℓ is the lateral surface of the cone. Its arc measure is $2\pi r$. You can use a proportion to find its area.

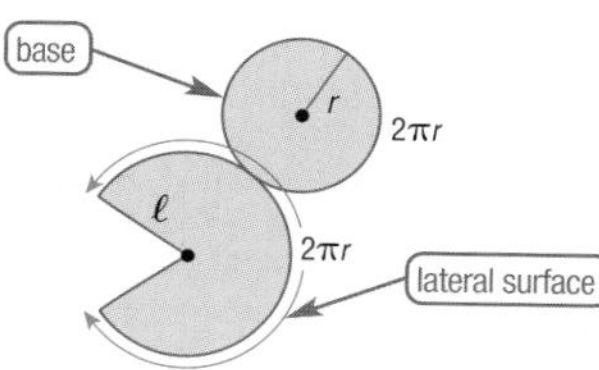

$$\frac{\text{area of sector}}{\text{area of circle}} = \frac{\text{measure of arc}}{\text{circumference of circle}}$$

$$\frac{\text{area of sector}}{\pi\ell^2} = \frac{2\pi r}{2\pi\ell}$$

$$\text{area of sector} = \pi\ell^2 \cdot \frac{2\pi r}{2\pi\ell} \text{ or } \pi r\ell$$

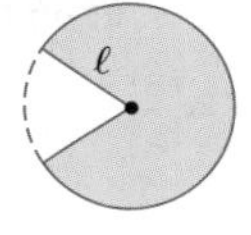

sector

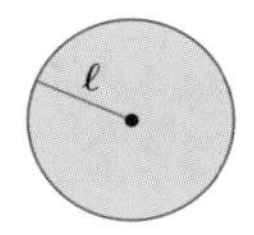

circle that contains the sector

StudyTip

CCSS Sense-Making Like a pyramid, the lateral area of a right circular cone L equals $\frac{1}{2}P\ell$. Since the base is a circle, the perimeter is the circumference of the base C. So, the lateral area is $\frac{1}{2}C\ell$.

$L = \frac{1}{2}C\ell$

$= \frac{1}{2}(2\pi r)$

$= \pi r\ell$

KeyConcept Lateral and Surface Area of a Cone

Words The lateral area L of a right circular cone is $L = \pi r\ell$, where r is the radius of the base and ℓ is the slant height.

The surface area S of a right circular cone is $S = \pi r\ell + \pi r^2$, where r is the radius of the base and ℓ is the slant height.

Model

Symbols $L = \pi r\ell \qquad S = \pi r\ell + \pi r^2$

Real-World Example 4 Lateral Area of a Cone

ARCHITECTURE The conical slate roof at the right has a height of 16 feet and a radius of 12 feet. Find the lateral area.

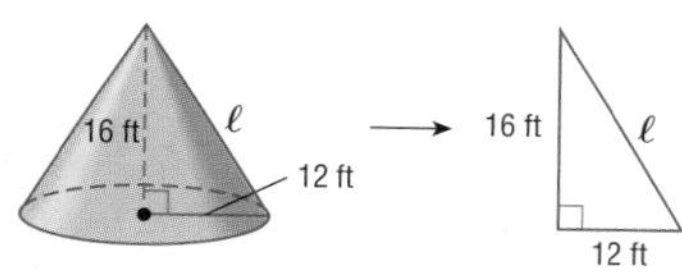

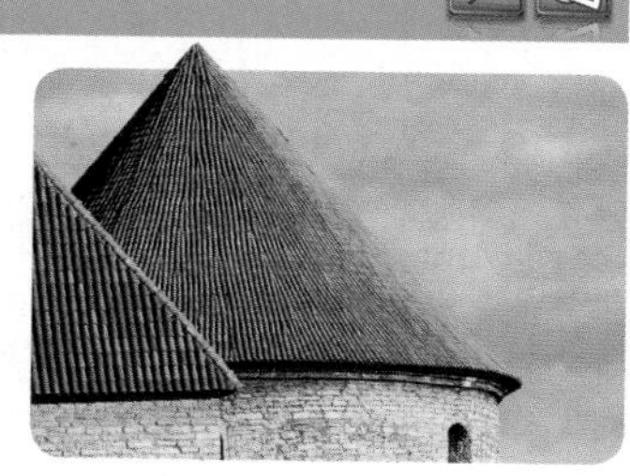

StudyTip

Draw a Diagram When solving word problems involving solids, it is helpful to draw a figure and label the known parts. Use a variable to label the measure or measures that you need to find.

Step 1 Find the slant height ℓ.

$\ell^2 = 16^2 + 12^2$	Pythagorean Theorem
$\ell^2 = 400$	Simplify.
$\ell = 20$	Take the positive square root of each side.

Step 2 Find the lateral area L.

Estimate $L \approx 3 \cdot 12 \cdot 20$ or 720 ft^2

$L = \pi r\ell$	Lateral area of a cone
$= \pi(12)(20)$	$r = 12$ and $\ell = 20$
≈ 754	Use a calculator.

The lateral area of the conical roof is about 754 square feet. The answer is reasonable compared to the estimate.

GuidedPractice

4. ICE CREAM A waffle cone is $5\frac{1}{2}$ inches tall and the diameter of the base is $2\frac{1}{2}$ inches. Find the lateral area of the cone. Round to the nearest tenth. **22.1 in^2**

2 Lateral Area and Surface Area of Pyramids

Example 4 shows how to find the lateral area of a cone. **Example 5** shows how to find the surface area of a cone.

Additional Example

4 ICE CREAM A sugar cone has an altitude of 8 inches and a diameter of $2\frac{1}{2}$ inches. Find the lateral area of the sugar cone. ≈ 31.8 in^2

CCSS Teaching the Mathematical Practices

Sense-Making Mathematically proficient students consider analogous problems and try simpler forms of the original problem in order to gain insight into its solution. Encourage students to make connections between lateral and surface areas of different solids.

Additional Example

5 Find the surface area of the cone. Round to the nearest tenth. 20.2 cm^2

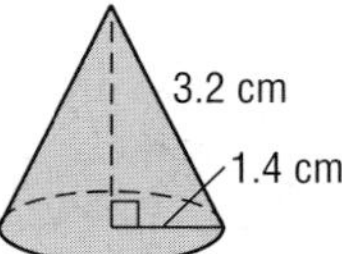

Example 5 Surface Area of a Cone

Find the surface area of a cone with a diameter of 14.8 centimeters and a slant height of 15 centimeters.

14.8 cm
15 cm

Estimate: $S \approx 3 \cdot 7 \cdot 20 + 3 \cdot 50$ or 570 cm^2

$S = \pi r\ell + \pi r^2$ Surface area of a cone

$= \pi(7.4)(15) + \pi(7.4)^2$ $r = 7.4$ and $\ell = 15$

≈ 520.8 Use a calculator.

The surface area of the cone is about 520.8 square centimeters. This is close to the estimate, so the answer is reasonable.

GuidedPractice

Find the surface area of each cone. Round to the nearest tenth.

5A. 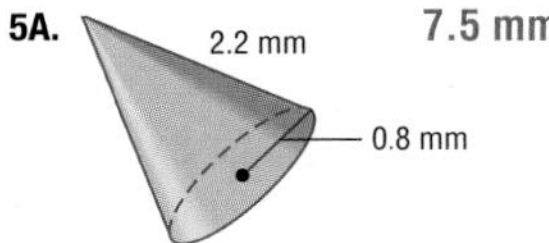

7.5 mm^2

5B. 6 in. 7 in. 286.9 in^2

The formulas for lateral and surface area are summarized below.

WatchOut!
Bases The bases of right prisms and right pyramids are not always regular polygons.

ConceptSummary Lateral and Surface Areas of Solids

Solid	Model	Lateral Area	Surface Area
prism	h, B, P	$L = Ph$	$S = L + 2B$ or $S = Ph + 2B$
cylinder	r, h	$L = 2\pi rh$	$S = L + 2B$ or $S = 2\pi rh + 2\pi r^2$
pyramid	ℓ, B, P	$L = \frac{1}{2}P\ell$	$S = \frac{1}{2}P\ell + B$
cone	ℓ, r	$L = \pi r\ell$	$S = \pi r\ell + \pi r^2$

858 | Lesson 12-3 | Surface Areas of Pyramids and Cones

Check Your Understanding

 = Step-by-Step Solutions begin on page R14. 

Examples 1–3 **Find the lateral area and surface area of each regular pyramid. Round to the nearest tenth if necessary.**

1. 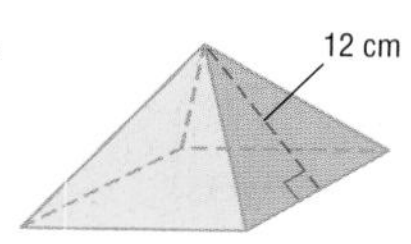

$L = 384\text{ cm}^2$; $S = 640\text{ cm}^2$

2. 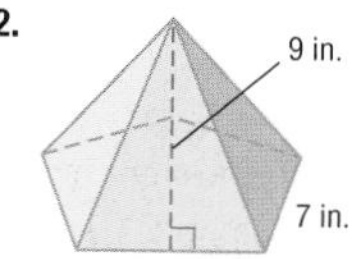

$L = 157.5\text{ in}^2$; $S \approx 241.8\text{ in}^2$

3. 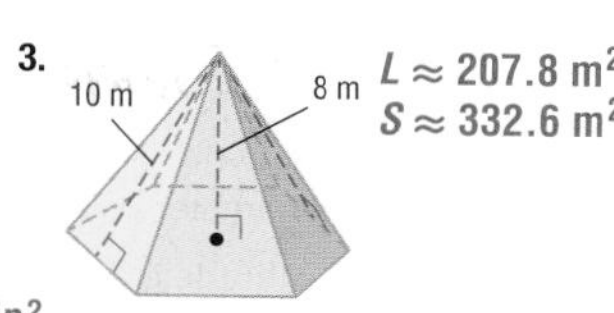

$L \approx 207.8\text{ m}^2$; $S \approx 332.6\text{ m}^2$

Examples 4–5 4. **TENTS** A conical tent is shown at the right. Round answers to the nearest tenth.

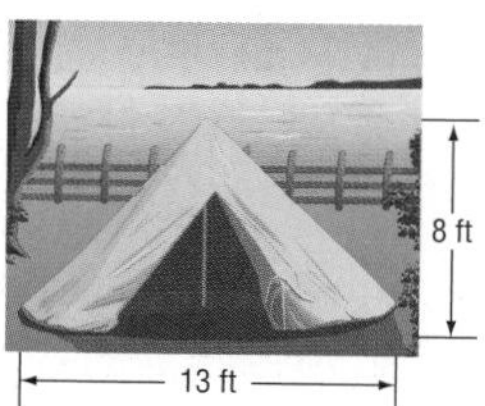

a. Find the lateral area of the tent and describe what it represents. 210.5 ft^2; the area of the curved surface

b. Find the surface area of the tent and describe what it represents. 343.2 ft^2; the area of the curved surface plus the area of the tent floor

CCSS SENSE-MAKING **Find the lateral area and surface area of each cone. Round to the nearest tenth.**

5. 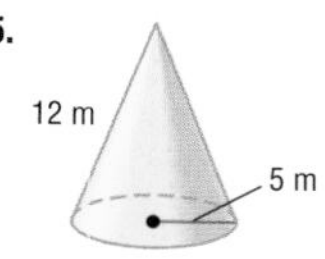

$L \approx 188.5\text{ m}^2$; $S \approx 267.0\text{ m}^2$

6. 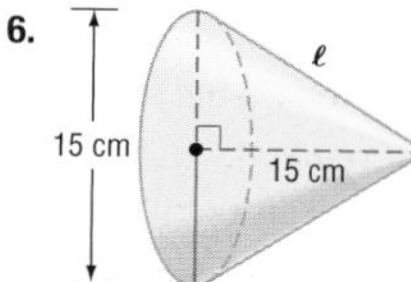

$L \approx 395.1\text{ cm}^2$; $S \approx 571.9\text{ cm}^2$

Practice and Problem Solving

Extra Practice is on page R12.

Examples 1–3 **Find the lateral area and surface area of each regular pyramid. Round to the nearest tenth if necessary.**

7. 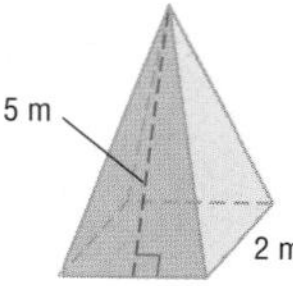

$L = 20\text{ m}^2$; $S = 24\text{ m}^2$

8. 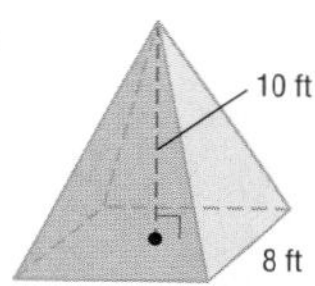

$L \approx 172.3\text{ ft}^2$; $S \approx 236.3\text{ ft}^2$

9. 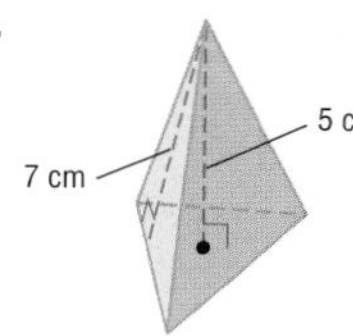

$L \approx 178.2\text{ cm}^2$; $S \approx 302.9\text{ cm}^2$

10. 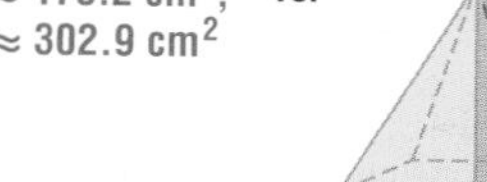

$L = 150\text{ ft}^2$; $S \approx 211.9\text{ ft}^2$

11. square pyramid with an altitude of 12 inches and a slant height of 18 inches $L \approx 966.0\text{ in}^2$; $S \approx 1686.0\text{ in}^2$

12. hexagonal pyramid with a base edge of 6 millimeters and a slant height of 9 millimeters $L = 162\text{ mm}^2$; $S \approx 255.5\text{ mm}^2$

13. **ARCHITECTURE** Find the lateral area of a pyramid-shaped building that has a slant height of 210 feet and a square base 332 feet by 332 feet. $139{,}440\text{ ft}^2$

3 Practice

Formative Assessment

Use Exercises 1–6 to check for understanding.

Use the chart at the bottom of this page to customize assignments for your students

Tips for New Teachers

Sense-Making Some students may have trouble finding lateral and surface areas of real-world objects. Point out that many objects that seem like a cylinder or cube may only have one base.

Teaching the Mathematical Practices

Sense-Making Mathematically proficient students start by explaining the meaning of a problem to themselves and looking for entry points to its solution. They plan a solution pathway rather than simply jumping into a solution attempt. In Exercises 5–6, encourage students to make a plan to solve each problem first.

Differentiated Homework Options

Level	Assignment	Two-Day Option	
AL Basic	7–19, 36–39, 41–57	7–19 odd, 42–45	8–18 even, 36–39, 41, 46–57
OL Core	7–21 odd, 22, 23–31 odd, 32–39, 41–57	7–19, 42–45	20–39, 41, 46–57
BL Advanced	20–54, (optional: 55–57)		

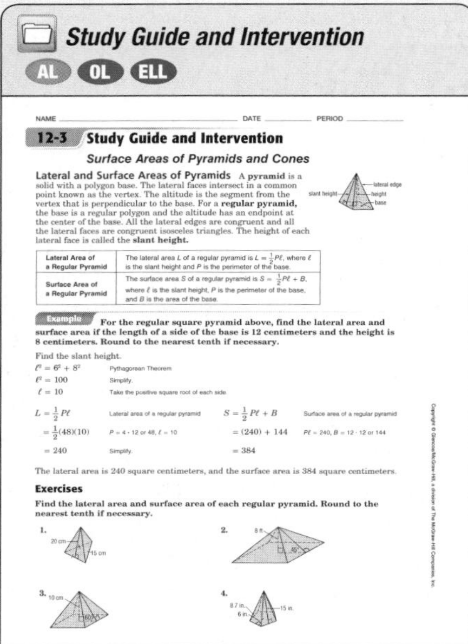

Study Guide and Intervention

AL OL ELL

NAME ______ DATE ______ PERIOD ______

12-3 Study Guide and Intervention

Surface Areas of Pyramids and Cones

Lateral and Surface Areas of Pyramids A pyramid is a solid with a polygon base. The lateral faces intersect in a common point known as the vertex. The altitude is the segment from the vertex that is perpendicular to the base. For a **regular pyramid**, the base is a regular polygon and the altitude has an endpoint at the center of the base. All the lateral edges are congruent and all the lateral faces are congruent isosceles triangles. The height of each lateral face is called the **slant height**.

Lateral Area of a Regular Pyramid	The lateral area L of a regular pyramid is $L = \frac{1}{2}P\ell$, where ℓ is the slant height and P is the perimeter of the base.
Surface Area of a Regular Pyramid	The surface area S of a regular pyramid is $S = \frac{1}{2}P\ell + B$, where ℓ is the slant height, P is the perimeter of the base, and B is the area of the base.

Example For the regular square pyramid above, find the lateral area and surface area if the length of a side of the base is 12 centimeters and the height is 8 centimeters. Round to the nearest tenth if necessary.

Find the slant height.

$\ell^2 = 6^2 + 8^2$ Pythagorean Theorem

$\ell^2 = 100$ Simplify.

$\ell = 10$ Take the positive square root of each side.

$L = \frac{1}{2}P\ell$ Lateral area of a regular pyramid; $S = \frac{1}{2}P\ell + B$ Surface area of a regular pyramid

$= \frac{1}{2}(48)(10)$ $P = 4 \cdot 12$ or 48, $\ell = 10$; $= (240) + 144$ $P\ell = 240$, $B = 12 \cdot 12$ or 144

$= 240$ Simplify; $= 384$

The lateral area is 240 square centimeters, and the surface area is 384 square centimeters.

Exercises

Find the lateral area and surface area of each regular pyramid. Round to the nearest tenth if necessary.

1. 2. 3. 4.

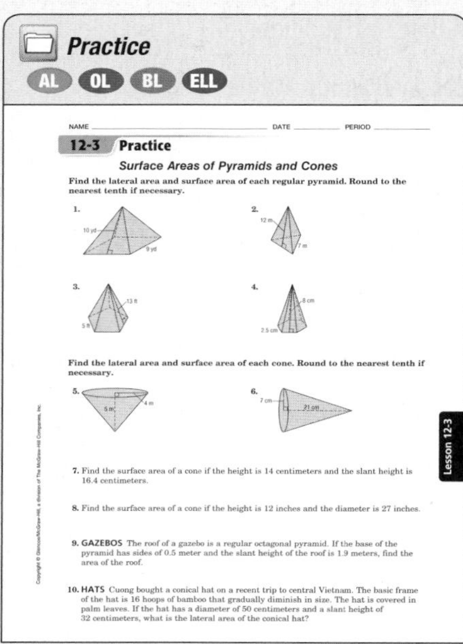

Practice

AL OL BL ELL

NAME ______ DATE ______ PERIOD ______

12-3 Practice

Surface Areas of Pyramids and Cones

Find the lateral area and surface area of each regular pyramid. Round to the nearest tenth if necessary.

1. 2. 3. 4.

Find the lateral area and surface area of each cone. Round to the nearest tenth if necessary.

5. 6.

7. Find the surface area of a cone if the height is 14 centimeters and the slant height is 16.4 centimeters.

8. Find the surface area of a cone if the height is 12 inches and the diameter is 27 inches.

9. GAZEBOS The roof of a gazebo is a regular octagonal pyramid. If the base of the pyramid has sides of 0.5 meter and the slant height of the roof is 1.9 meters, find the area of the roof.

10. HATS Cuong bought a conical hat on a recent trip to central Vietnam. The basic frame of the hat is 16 hoops of bamboo that gradually diminish in size. The hat is covered in palm leaves. If the hat has a diameter of 50 centimeters and a slant height of 32 centimeters, what is the lateral area of the conical hat?

Lesson 12-3

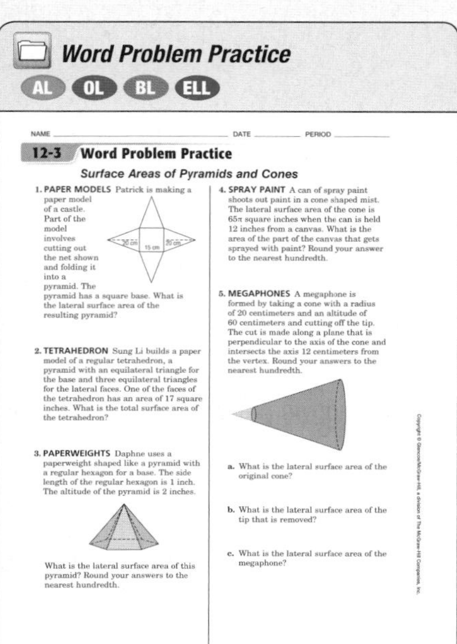

Word Problem Practice

AL OL BL ELL

NAME ______ DATE ______ PERIOD ______

12-3 Word Problem Practice

Surface Areas of Pyramids and Cones

1. PAPER MODELS Patrick is making a paper model of a castle. Part of the model involves cutting out the net shown and folding it into a pyramid. The pyramid has a square base. What is the lateral surface area of the resulting pyramid?

2. TETRAHEDRON Sung Li builds a paper model of a regular tetrahedron, a pyramid with an equilateral triangle for the base and three equilateral triangles for the lateral faces. One of the faces of the tetrahedron has an area of 17 square inches. What is the total surface area of the tetrahedron?

3. PAPERWEIGHTS Daphne uses a paperweight shaped like a pyramid with a regular hexagon for a base. The side length of the regular hexagon is 1 inch. The altitude of the pyramid is 2 inches. What is the lateral surface area of this pyramid? Round your answers to the nearest hundredth.

4. SPRAY PAINT A can of spray paint shoots out paint in a cone shaped mist. The lateral surface area of the cone is 65π square inches when the can is held 12 inches from a canvas. What is the area of the part of the canvas that gets sprayed with paint? Round your answer to the nearest hundredth.

5. MEGAPHONES A megaphone is formed by taking a cone with a radius of 20 centimeters and an altitude of 60 centimeters and cutting off the tip. The cut is made along a plane that is perpendicular to the axis of the cone and intersects the axis 12 centimeters from the vertex. Round your answers to the nearest hundredth.

a. What is the lateral surface area of the original cone?

b. What is the lateral surface area of the tip that is removed?

c. What is the lateral surface area of the megaphone?

Examples 4–5 Find the lateral area and surface area of each cone. Round to the nearest tenth.

14. 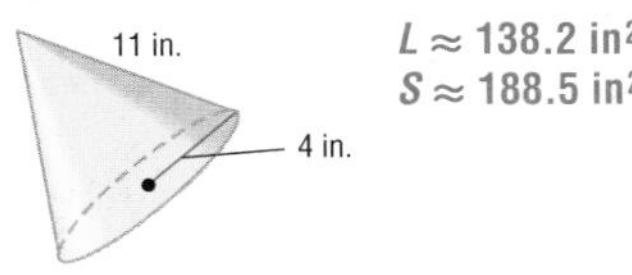

$L \approx 138.2$ in^2; $S \approx 188.5$ in^2

15. 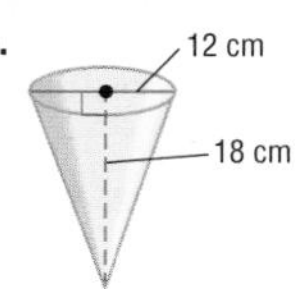

$L \approx 357.6$ cm^2; $S \approx 470.7$ cm^2

16. The diameter is 3.4 centimeters, and the slant height is 6.5 centimeters. $L \approx 34.7$ cm^2; $S \approx 43.8$ cm^2

17. The altitude is 5 feet, and the slant height is $9\frac{1}{2}$ feet. $L \approx 241.1$ ft^2; $S \approx 446.1$ ft^2

18. MOUNTAINS A conical mountain has a radius of 1.6 kilometers and a height of 0.5 kilometer. What is the lateral area of the mountain? 8.4 km^2

19 HISTORY Archaeologists recently discovered a 1500-year-old pyramid in Mexico City. The square pyramid measures 165 yards on each side and once stood 20 yards tall. What was the original lateral area of the pyramid? 28,013.6 yd^2

20. Describe two polyhedrons that have 7 faces. hexagonal pyramid, pentagonal prism

21. What is the sum of the number of faces, vertices, and edges of an octagonal pyramid? 34

22. TEPEES The dimensions of two canvas tepees are shown in the table at the right. Not including the floors, approximately how much more canvas is used to make Tepee B than Tepee A? about 219.9 ft^2

Tepee	Diameter (ft)	Height (ft)
A	14	6
B	20	9

23. The surface area of a square pyramid is 24 square millimeters and the base area is 4 square millimeters. What is the slant height of the pyramid? 5 mm

24. The surface area of a cone is 18π square inches and the radius of the base is 3 inches. What is the slant height of the cone? 3 in.

25. The surface area of a triangular pyramid is 532 square centimeters, and the base is 24 centimeters wide with a hypotenuse of 25 centimeters. What is the slant height of the pyramid? 16 cm

26. Find the lateral area of the tent to the nearest tenth. 311.2 ft^2

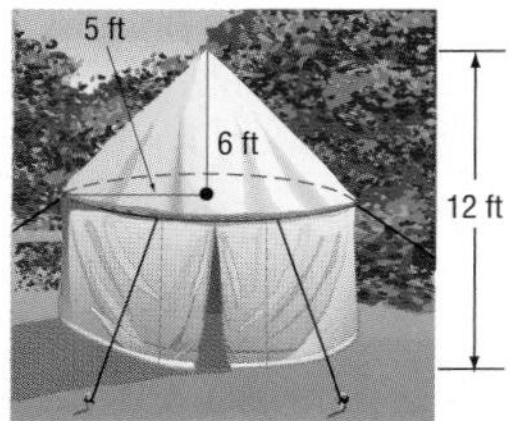

27. Find the surface area of the tank. Write in terms of π. 266π ft^2

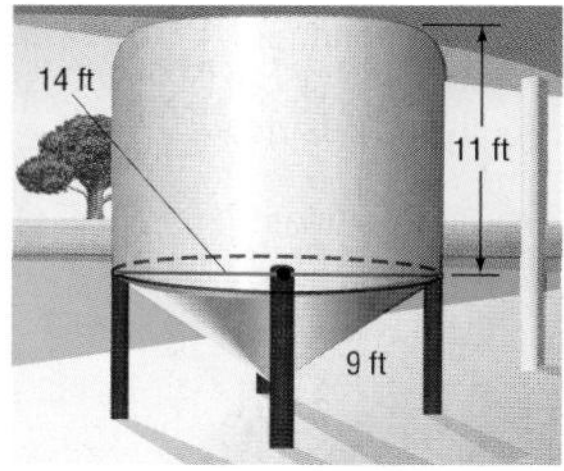

28. CHANGING DIMENSIONS A cone has a radius of 6 centimeters and a slant height of 12 centimeters. Describe how each change affects the surface area of the cone.

a. The radius and the slant height are doubled. The surface area is multiplied by 4.

b. The radius and the slant height are divided by 3. The surface area is divided by 9.

29. CCSS TOOLS A solid has the net shown at the right.

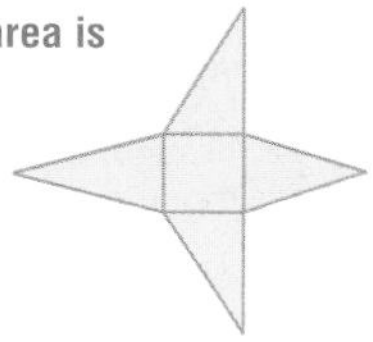

a. Describe the solid. nonregular pyramid with a square base

b. Make a sketch of the solid. See Ch. 12 Answer Appendix.

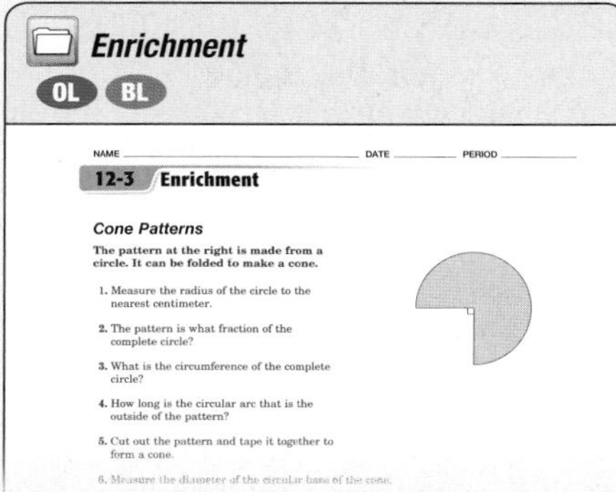

Enrichment

OL BL

NAME ______ DATE ______ PERIOD ______

12-3 Enrichment

Cone Patterns

The pattern at the right is made from a circle. It can be folded to make a cone.

1. Measure the radius of the circle to the nearest centimeter.
2. The pattern is what fraction of the complete circle?
3. What is the circumference of the complete circle?
4. How long is the circular arc that is the outside of the pattern?
5. Cut out the pattern and tape it together to form a cone.
6. Measure the diameter of the circular base of the cone.

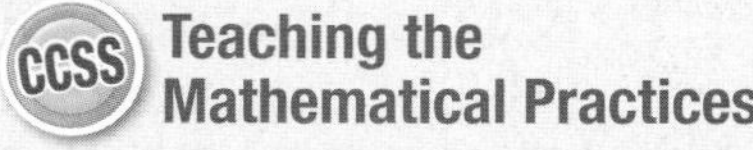

Teaching the Mathematical Practices

Tools Mathematically proficient students consider the available tools when solving a mathematical problem. In Exercise 29, encourage students to make a paper model of the net to verify their results.

Sketch each solid and a net that represents the solid.

30. hexagonal pyramid See margin.

31. rectangular pyramid See margin.

32. **PETS** A *frustum* is the part of a solid that remains after the top portion has been cut by a plane parallel to the base. The ferret tent shown at the right is a frustum of a regular pyramid.

a. Describe the faces of the solid. 4 trapezoids, 2 squares

b. Find the lateral area and surface area of the frustum formed by the tent. 690 in^2; 1015 in^2

c. Another pet tent is made by cutting the top half off of a pyramid with a height of 12 centimeters, slant height of 20 centimeters and square base with side lengths of 32 centimeters. Find the surface area of the frustum. 2240 cm^2

Find the lateral area and surface area of each solid. Round to the nearest tenth.

33.

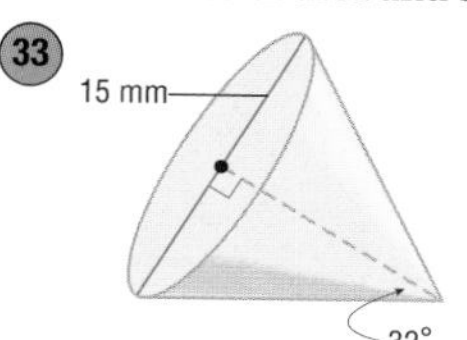

≈333.5 mm^2; ≈510.2 mm^2

34.

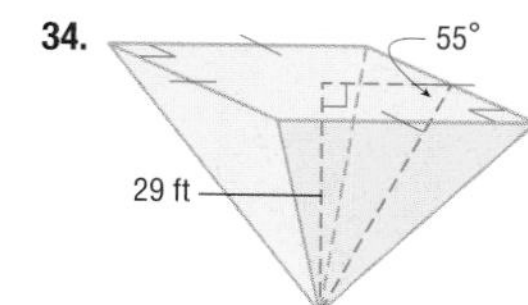

≈2875.5 ft^2; ≈4524.8 ft^2

35. **MULTIPLE REPRESENTATIONS** In this problem, you will investigate the lateral and surface area of a square pyramid with a base edge of 3 units.

a. **Geometric** Sketch the pyramid on isometric dot paper. See margin.

b. **Tabular** Make a table showing the lateral areas of the pyramid for slant heights of 1, 3, and 9 units. See margin.

c. **Verbal** Describe what happens to the lateral area of the pyramid if the slant height is tripled. The lateral area is tripled.

d. **Analytical** Make a conjecture about how the lateral area of a square pyramid is affected if both the slant height and the base edge are tripled. Then test your conjecture.

35d. The lateral area is multiplied by 3^2 or 9.

36. Sample answer: The distance from the vertex to the base is not the same for each point on the circumference of the base.

H.O.T. Problems Use Higher-Order Thinking Skills

36. **WRITING IN MATH** Why does an oblique solid not have a slant height?

37. **REASONING** Classify the following statement as *sometimes*, *always*, or *never* true. Justify your reasoning. Always; if the heights and radii are the same, the surface area of the cylinder will be greater since it has two circular bases and additional lateral area.

The surface area of a cone of radius r and height h is less than the surface area of a cylinder of radius r and height h.

38. **REASONING** A cone and a square pyramid have the same surface area. If the areas of their bases are also equal, do they have the same slant height as well? Explain. See margin.

39. **OPEN ENDED** Describe a pyramid that has a total surface area of 100 square units. See margin.

40. **CCSS ARGUMENTS** Determine whether the following statement is *true* or *false*. Explain your reasoning.

A regular polygonal pyramid and a cone both have height h units and base perimeter P units. Therefore, they have the same total surface area.

40. False; the lateral area and the base of the cone are greater than the lateral area and base of the pyramid.

41. **WRITING IN MATH** Describe how to find the surface area of a regular polygonal pyramid with an n-gon base, height h units, and an apothem of a units. See Ch. 12 Answer Appendix.

Exercise Alert

Isometric Dot Paper Exercise 35 requires the use of isometric dot paper.

Multiple Representations

In Exercise 35, students use a table and verbal description to investigate the lateral area of a square pyramid.

CCSS Teaching the Mathematical Practices

Arguments Mathematically proficient students understand and use stated assumptions and definitions in constructing arguments. They make conjectures and build a logical progression of statements to explore the truth of their conjectures. For Exercise 40, have students divide into pairs and have each student explain their reasoning to their partner.

Additional Answers

30. Sample answer:

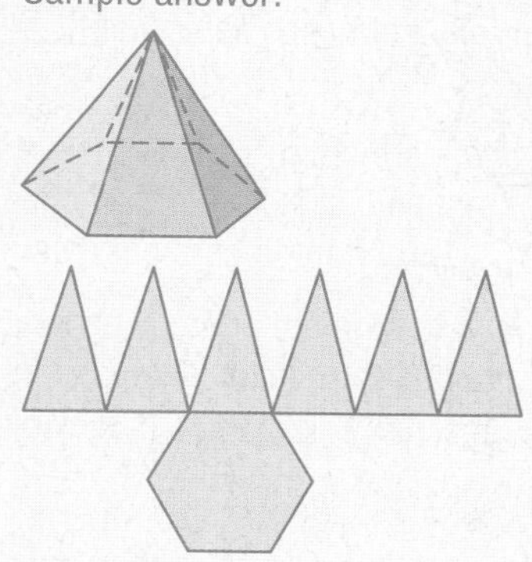

31. Sample answer:

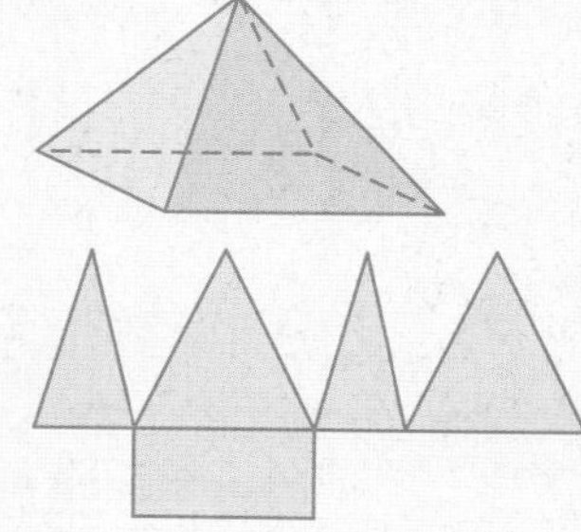

35b.

Slant Height (units)	Lateral Area (units^2)
1	6
3	18
9	54

38. They are not equal. The slant height of the cone is $\frac{2\sqrt{\pi}}{\pi}$ or about 1.13 times greater than the slant height of the square pyramid.

39. Sample answer: a square pyramid with a base edge of 5 units and a slant height of 7.5 units

35a. Sample answer:

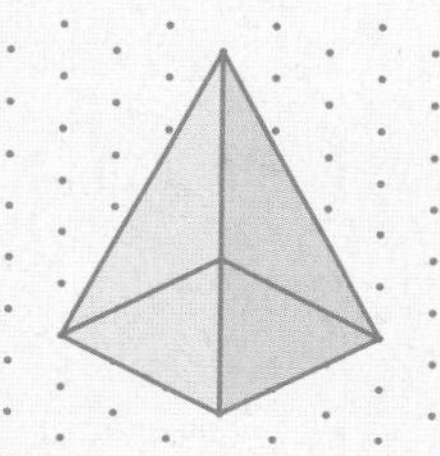

4 Assess

Crystal Ball Have students write how what they learned about surface areas of pyramids and cylinders will help them predict the volume of pyramids and cylinders.

Additional Answers

47.

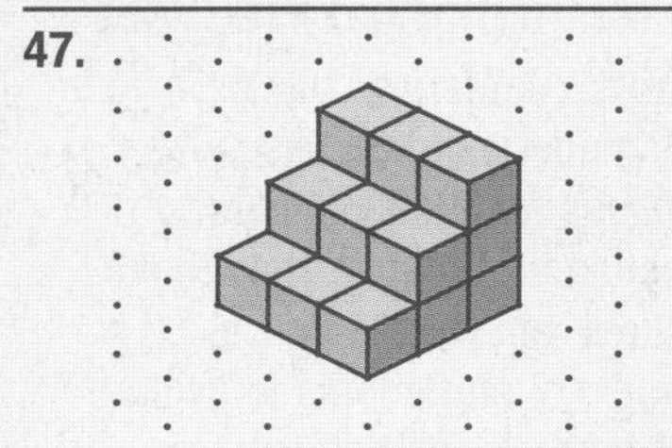

48.

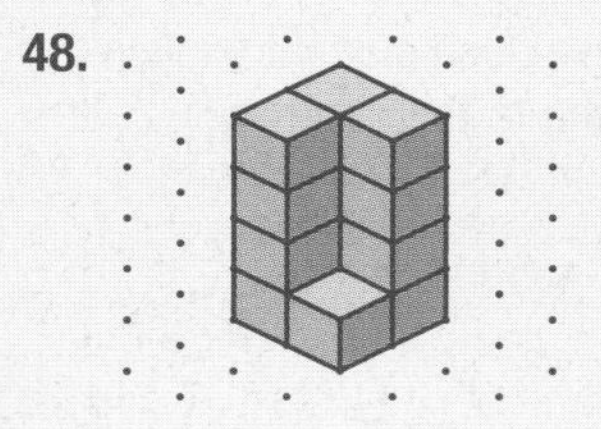

Standardized Test Practice

42. The top of a gazebo in a park is in the shape of a regular pentagonal pyramid. Each side of the pentagon is 10 feet long. If the slant height of the roof is about 6.9 feet, what is the lateral roof area? **C**

A 34.5 ft^2
B 50 ft^2
C 172.5 ft^2
D 250 ft^2

43. SHORT RESPONSE To the nearest square millimeter, what is the surface area of a cone with the dimensions shown? **3299 mm^2**

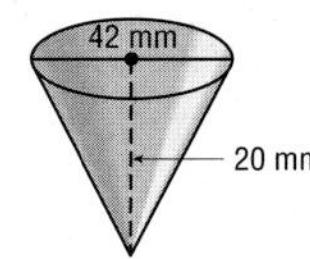

44. ALGEBRA Yu-Jun's craft store sells 3 handmade barrettes for \$9.99. Which expression can be used to find the total cost C of x barrettes? **H**

F $C = \frac{9.99}{x}$
G $C = 9.99x$
H $C = 3.33x$
J $C = \frac{x}{3.33}$

45. SAT/ACT What is the slope of a line perpendicular to the line with equation $2x + 3y = 9$? **D**

A $-\frac{3}{2}$
B $-\frac{2}{3}$
C $\frac{2}{3}$
D $\frac{3}{2}$
E $\frac{9}{2}$

Spiral Review

46. Find the surface area of a cylinder with a diameter of 18 cm and a height of 12 cm. (Lesson 12-2) **1187.5 cm^2**

Use isometric dot paper and each orthographic drawing to sketch a solid. (Lesson 12-1)

47.

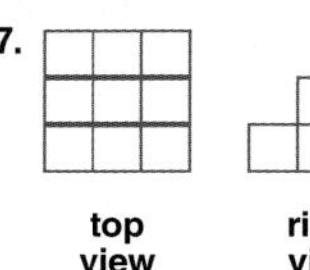

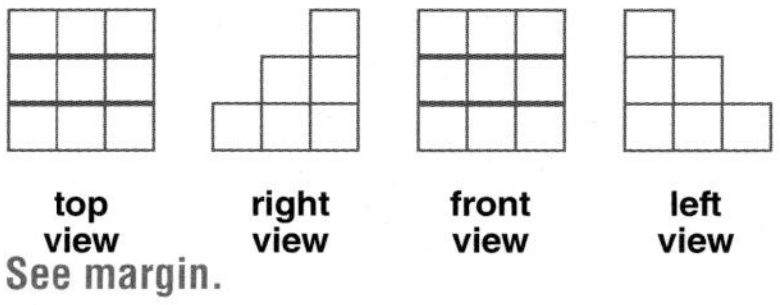

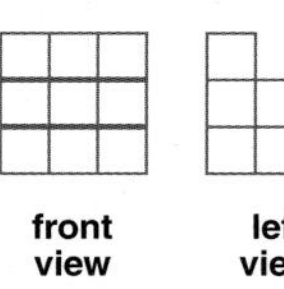

See margin.

48.

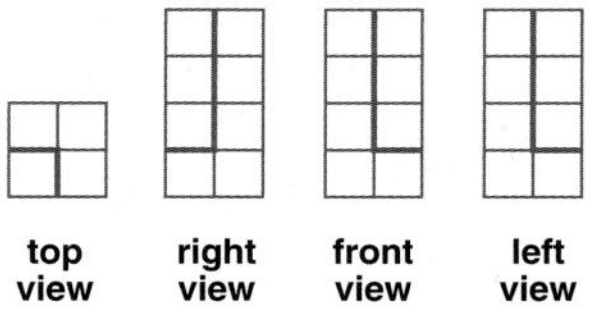

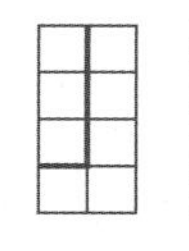

See margin.

Graph each figure and its image in the given line. (Lesson 9-1) **49–54. See Ch. 12 Answer Appendix.**

$J(2, 4), K(4, 0), L(7, 3)$

49. $\triangle JKL; x = 2$

50. $\triangle JKL; y = 1$

$Q(4, 8), R(1, 6), S(2, 1), T(5, 5)$

51. $QRST; y = -1$

52. $QRST; x = 4$

$A(-2, 6), B(-2, 1), C(3, 1), D(3, 4)$

53. $ABCD; x = 1$

54. $ABCD; y = -2$

Skills Review

Find the perimeter and area of each parallelogram, triangle, or composite figure. Round to the nearest tenth.

55. **57 m, 120 m^2**

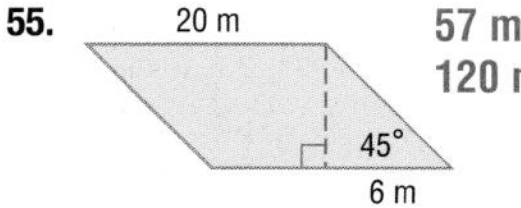

56. **73 mm, 180.5 mm^2**

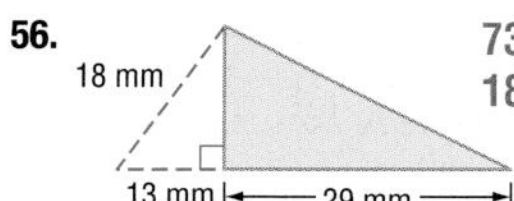

57. **183.1 in., 1887 in^2**

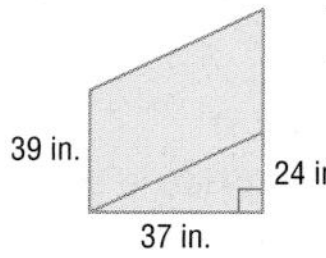

39 in.
24 in.
37 in.

Differentiated Instruction OL BL

Extension Ask students if the lateral faces of a regular pyramid are congruent. Then have them justify their conjectures. Sample answer: yes, by SSS

LESSON 12-4 Volumes of Prisms and Cylinders

Then

You found surface areas of prisms and cylinders.

Now

1 Find volumes of prisms.

2 Find volumes of cylinders.

Why?

Planters come in a variety of shapes and sizes. You can approximate the amount of soil needed to fill a planter by finding the volume of the three-dimensional figure that it most resembles.

Common Core State Standards

Content Standards

G.GMD.1 Give an informal argument for the formulas for the circumference of a circle, area of a circle, volume of a cylinder, pyramid, and cone.

G.GMD.3 Use volume formulas for cylinders, pyramids, cones, and spheres to solve problems. ★

Mathematical Practices

1 Make sense of problems and persevere in solving them.

7 Look for and make use of structure.

1 Volume of Prisms

Recall that the volume of a solid is the measure of the amount of space the solid encloses. Volume is measured in cubic units.

The rectangular prism at the right has 6 • 4 or 24 cubic units in the bottom layer. Since there are two layers, the total volume is 24 • 2 or 48 cubic units.

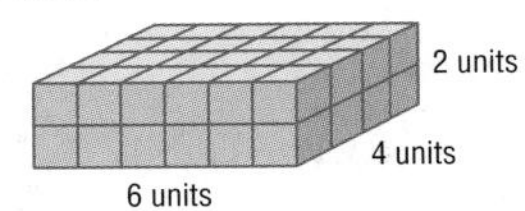

KeyConcept Volume of a Prism

Words The volume V of a prism is $V = Bh$, where B is the area of a base and h is the height of the prism.

Symbols $V = Bh$

Model

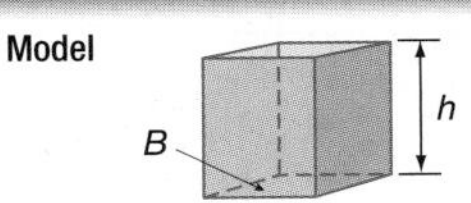

Example 1 Volume of a Prism

Find the volume of the prism.

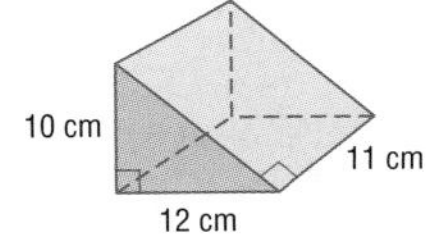

Step 1 Find the area of the base B.

$B = \frac{1}{2}bh$ Area of a triangle

$= \frac{1}{2}(12)(10)$ or 60 $b = 12$ and $h = 10$

Step 2 Find the volume of the prism.

$V = Bh$ Volume of a prism

$= 60(11)$ or 660 $B = 60$ and $h = 11$

The volume of the prism is 660 cubic centimeters.

GuidedPractice

1A. 340 mm^3

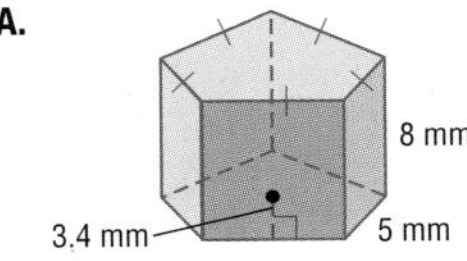

1B. 540 ft^3

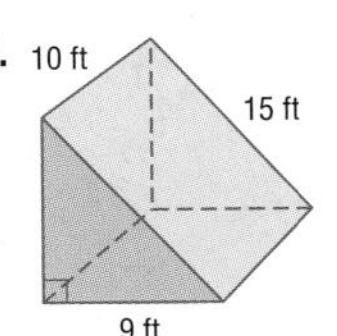

1 Focus

VerticalAlignment

Before Lesson 12-4 Find surface areas of prisms and cylinders.

Lesson 12-4 Find the volumes of prisms and cylinders.

After Lesson 12-4 Find the surface areas and volumes of spheres.

2 Teach

Scaffolding Questions

Have students read the **Why?** section of the lesson.

Ask:

- Why is the volume of the planter related to the amount of soil needed to fill it? Volume is the amount of space that a solid encloses. The space in the planter is filled with soil.
- What are some other real-world applications of volume? Sample answer: the volume of a cereal box affects the amount of cereal it contains; the volume of a building affects the size of heating or cooling system needed.

Lesson 12-4 Resources

Resource	Approaching Level AL	On Level OL	Beyond Level BL	English Learners ELL
Teacher Edition	▪ Differentiated Instruction, p. 865	▪ Differentiated Instruction, pp. 865, 868, 870	▪ Differentiated Instruction, pp. 868, 870	
Chapter Resource Masters	▪ Study Guide and Intervention, pp. 25–26 ▪ Skills Practice, p. 27 ▪ Practice, p. 28 ▪ Word Problem Practice, p. 29	▪ Study Guide and Intervention, pp. 25–26 ▪ Skills Practice, p. 27 ▪ Practice, p. 28 ▪ Word Problem Practice, p. 29 ▪ Enrichment, p. 30	▪ Practice, p. 28 ▪ Word Problem Practice, p. 29 ▪ Enrichment, p. 30	▪ Study Guide and Intervention, pp. 25–26 ▪ Skills Practice, p. 27 ▪ Practice, p. 28 ▪ Word Problem Practice, p. 29
Other	▪ 5-Minute Check 12-4 ▪ Study Notebook	▪ 5-Minute Check 12-4 ▪ Study Notebook	▪ 5-Minute Check 12-4 ▪ Study Notebook	▪ 5-Minute Check 12-4 ▪ Study Notebook

1 Volume of Prisms

Example 1 shows how to find the volume of prisms by using known area formulas.

Teach with Tech

Interactive Whiteboard Save your notes as you work through each example of finding the volume of prisms and cylinders. Send this file to your students so they can use it as a reference outside of class.

Formative Assessment

Use the Guided Practice exercises after each example to determine students' understanding of concepts.

Additional Example

1 Find the volume of the prism. 1500 cm^3

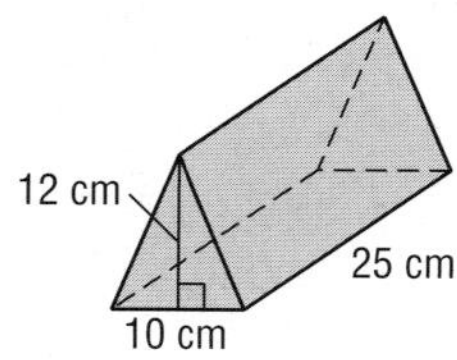

Additional Examples also in Interactive Classroom PowerPoint® Presentations

2 Volume of Cylinders

Examples 2 and 3 show how to use the area formula of circles to find the volume of a cylinder. **Example 4** shows how to compare volumes of prisms to find a missing measure.

Additional Example

2 Find the volume of the cylinder. Round to the nearest tenth. 18.3 cm^3

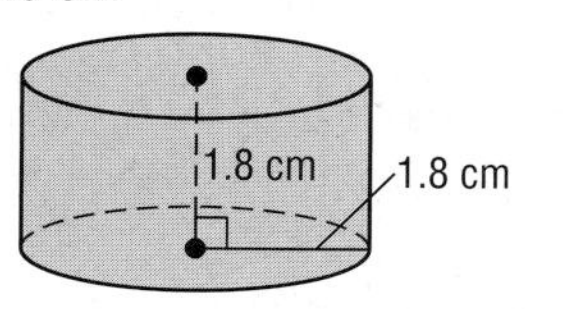

Real-WorldCareer

Architectural Engineer An architectural engineer applies the technical skills of engineering to the design, construction, operation, maintenance, and renovation of buildings.

Architectural engineers are required to have a bachelor's degree in engineering along with specialized coursework. Refer to Exercise 35.

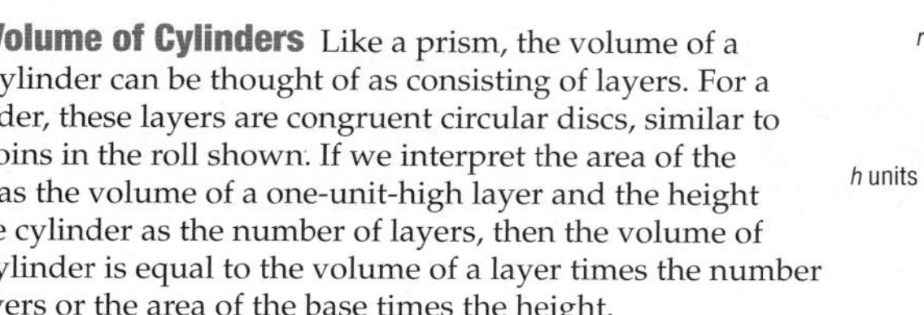

2 Volume of Cylinders

Like a prism, the volume of a cylinder can be thought of as consisting of layers. For a cylinder, these layers are congruent circular discs, similar to the coins in the roll shown. If we interpret the area of the base as the volume of a one-unit-high layer and the height of the cylinder as the number of layers, then the volume of the cylinder is equal to the volume of a layer times the number of layers or the area of the base times the height.

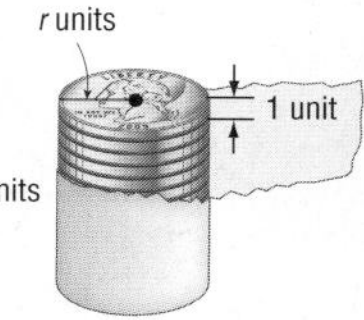

KeyConcept Volume of a Cylinder

Words	The volume V of a cylinder is $V = Bh$ or $V = \pi r^2 h$, where B is the area of the base, h is the height of the cylinder, and r is the radius of the base.	**Model**
Symbols	$V = Bh$ or $V = \pi r^2 h$	

Example 2 Volume of a Cylinder

Find the volume of the cylinder at the right.

9 in.

5 in.

Estimate: $V \approx 3 \cdot 5^2 \cdot 5$ or 375 in^3

$V = \pi r^2 h$ — Volume of a cylinder

$= \pi(4.5)^2(5)$ — $r = 4.5$ and $h = 5$

≈ 318.1 — Use a calculator.

The volume of the cylinder is about 318.1 cubic inches. This is fairly close to the estimate, so the answer is reasonable.

GuidedPractice

2. Find the volume of a cylinder with a radius of 3 centimeters and a height of 8 centimeters. Round to the nearest tenth. 226.2 cm^3

The first group of books at the right represents a right prism. The second group represents an oblique prism. Both groups have the same number of books. If all the books are the same size, then the volume of both groups is the same.

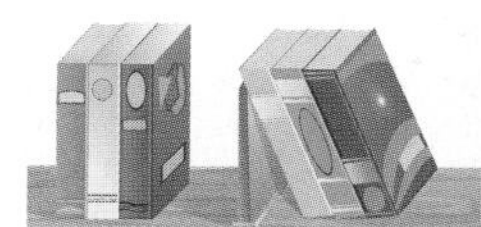

This demonstrates the following principle, which applies to all solids.

WatchOut!

Cross-Sectional Area For solids with the same height to have the same volume, their cross-sections must have the same area. The cross sections of the different solids do not have to be congruent polygons.

KeyConcept Cavalieri's Principle

Words If two solids have the same height h and the same cross-sectional area B at every level, then they have the same volume.

Models

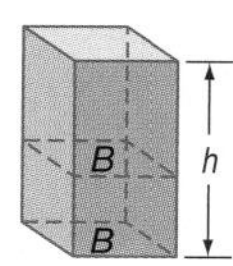

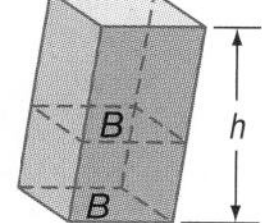

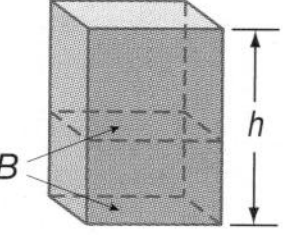

These prisms all have a volume of Bh.

Tips for New Teachers

Determining Height To help students see the difference between the height of the base of a triangular prism and the height of the prism, have them color the bases of the figures on their papers.

Area of Regular Polygons To review areas of regular polygons, see Lesson 11-4.

WatchOut!

Area and Volume Area is two-dimensional, so it is measured in square units. Volume is three-dimensional, so it is measured in cubic units.

Problem-Solving Tip

Make a Model When solving problems involving volume of solids, one way to help you visualize the problem is to make a model of the solid.

Example 3 Volume of an Oblique Solid

Find the volume of an oblique hexagonal prism if the height is 6.4 centimeters and the base area is 17.3 square centimeters.

$V = Bh$ Volume of a prism

$= 17.3(6.4)$ $B = 17.3$ and $h = 6.4$

$= 110.72$ Simplify.

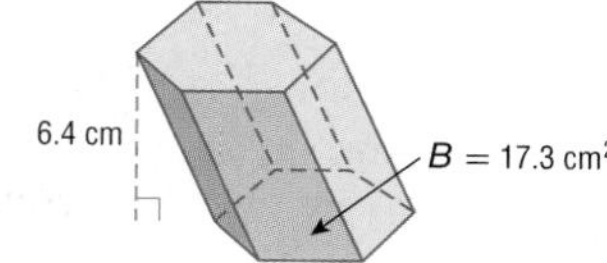

The volume is 110.72 cubic centimeters.

Guided Practice

3. Find the volume of an oblique cylinder that has a radius of 5 feet and a height of 3 feet. Round to the nearest tenth. 235.6 ft^3

Standardized Test Example 4 Comparing Volumes of Solids

Prisms A and B have the same length and width, but different heights. If the volume of Prism B is 150 cubic inches greater than the volume of Prism A, what is the length of each prism?

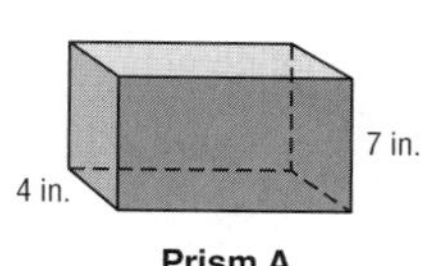

Prism A

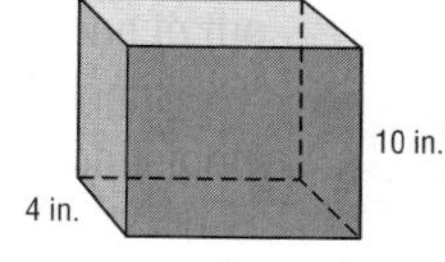

Prism B

A 10 in. **B** $11\frac{1}{2}$ in. **C** 12 in. **D** $12\frac{1}{2}$ in.

Read the Test Item

You know two dimensions of each solid and that the difference between their volumes is 150 cubic inches.

Solve the Test Item

Volume of Prism B − Volume of Prism A = 150 Write an equation.

$4\ell \cdot 10 - 4\ell \cdot 7 = 150$ Use $V = Bh$.

$12\ell = 150$ Simplify.

$\ell = 12\frac{1}{2}$ Divide each side by 12.

The length of each prism is $12\frac{1}{2}$ inches. The correct answer is D.

Test-Taking Tip

Writing Equations By choosing a variable to represent the unknown and setting up an equation, you make it easier to check for mistakes as you work out a problem.

Guided Practice

4. The containers at the right are filled with popcorn. About how many times as much popcorn does the larger container hold? G

F 1.6 times as much

G 2.5 times as much

H 3.3 times as much

J 5.0 times as much

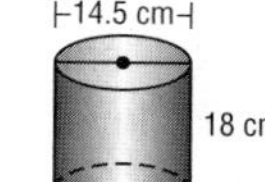

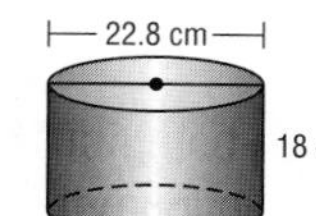

Differentiated Instruction AL OL

Logical Learners Students should reason that an oblique cylinder can also be likened to a stack of circles that has been shifted so that they make an oblique angle with the base. If a line segment is drawn connecting the center of each base (called the axis), then the axis is also an altitude for a right cylinder, but the axis is not an altitude for an oblique cylinder.

Additional Examples

3 Find the volume of an oblique cylinder. Round to the nearest tenth. $17{,}671.5 \text{ ft}^3$

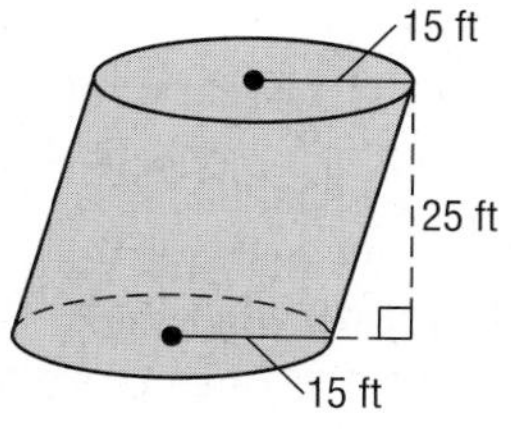

4 **STANDARDIZED TEST PRACTICE** Prisms A and B have the same width and height, but different lengths. If the volume of Prism B is 128 cubic inches greater than the volume of Prism A, what is the length of each prism? B

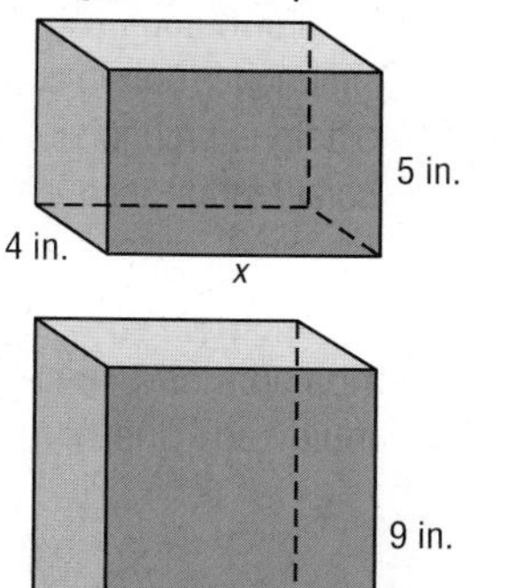

A 12 **C** 4

B 8 **D** 3.5

Focus on Mathematical Content

Modeling Give students hands-on experience finding the volumes of cylinders by having them measure the actual volume of juice cans or soup cans. Ask them to discuss how their measured volume compares with the volume printed on the can.

3 Practice

Formative Assessment

Use Exercises 1–9 to check for understanding.

Use the chart at the bottom of this page to customize assignments for your students.

Teaching the Mathematical Practices

Sense-Making Mathematically proficient students consider analogous problems and try simpler forms of the original problem in order to gain insight into its solution. In Exercises 10–13 and 16–19, encourage students to find the area of the base of each solid first.

Check Your Understanding

◯ = Step-by-Step Solutions begin on page R14.

Examples 1 and 3 **Find the volume of each prism.**

1. 108 cm^3

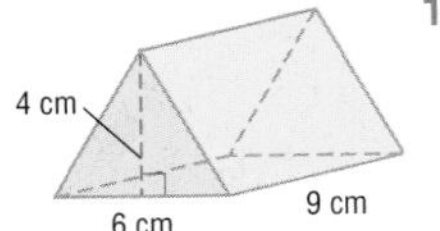

2. 396 in^3

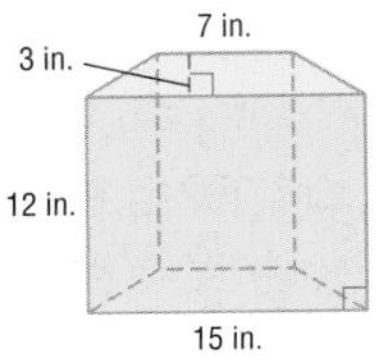

7 in.
3 in.
12 in.
15 in.

3. the oblique rectangular prism shown at the right 26.95 m^3

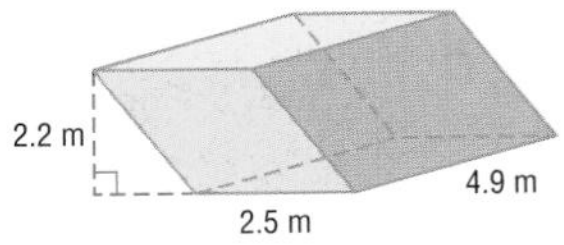

4. an oblique pentagonal prism with a base area of 42 square centimeters and a height of 5.2 centimeters 218.4 cm^3

2.2 m
2.5 m
4.9 m

Examples 2–3 **Find the volume of each cylinder. Round to the nearest tenth.**

5. 206.4 ft^3

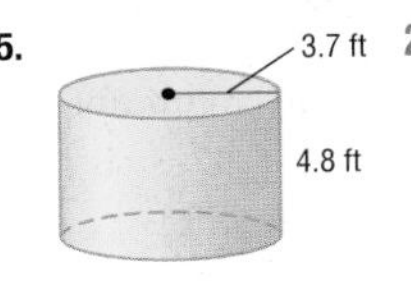

6. 1357.2 m^3

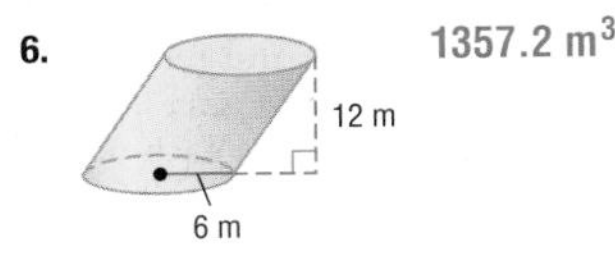

7. a cylinder with a diameter of 16 centimeters and a height of 5.1 centimeters 1025.4 cm^3

8. a cylinder with a radius of 4.2 inches and a height of 7.4 inches 410.1 in^3

Example 4 **9. MULTIPLE CHOICE** A rectangular lap pool measures 80 feet long by 20 feet wide. If it needs to be filled to four feet deep and each cubic foot holds 7.5 gallons, how many gallons will it take to fill the lap pool? D

A 4000 **B** 6400 **C** 30,000 **D** 48,000

Practice and Problem Solving

Extra Practice is on page R12.

Examples 1 and 3 CCSS **SENSE-MAKING** **Find the volume of each prism.**

10. 30 in^3

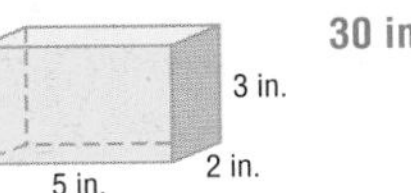

11. 539 m^3

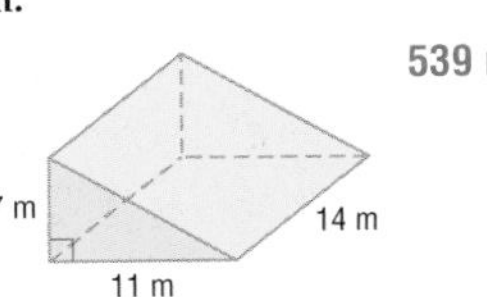

12. 324 cm^3

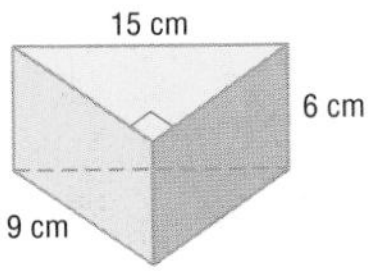

15 cm
6 cm
9 cm

13. 58.14 ft^3

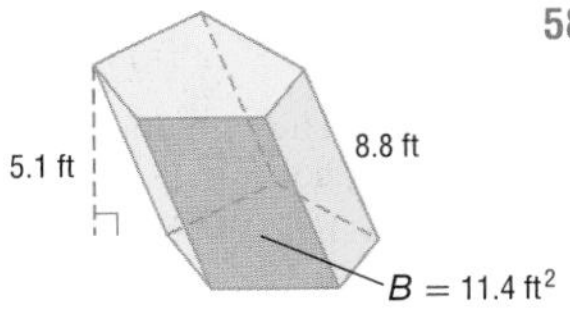

5.1 ft
8.8 ft
$B = 11.4\ ft^2$

14. an oblique hexagonal prism with a height of 15 centimeters and with a base area of 136 square centimeters 2040 cm^3

15. a square prism with a base edge of 9.5 inches and a height of 17 inches 1534.25 in^3

Differentiated Homework Options

Level	Assignment	Two-Day Option	
AL Basic	10–21, 42, 44–62	11–21 odd, 48–51	10–20 even, 42, 44–47, 52–62
OL Core	11–35 odd, 36–42, 44–62	10–21, 48–51	22–42, 44–47, 52–62
BL Advanced	22–59, (optional: 60–62)		

866 | Lesson 12-4 | Volumes of Prisms and Cylinders

Examples 2–3 CCSS SENSE-MAKING Find the volume of each cylinder. Round to the nearest tenth.

16. 1413.7 yd^3

17. 407.2 cm^3

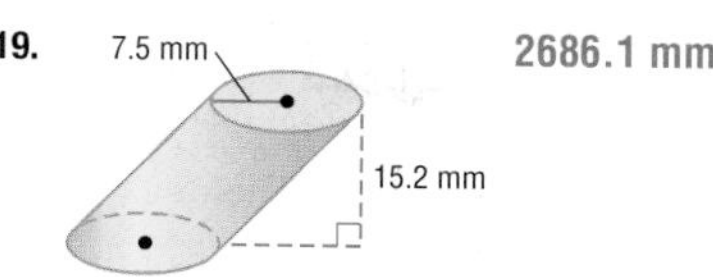

18. 823.0 in^3

19. 2686.1 mm^3

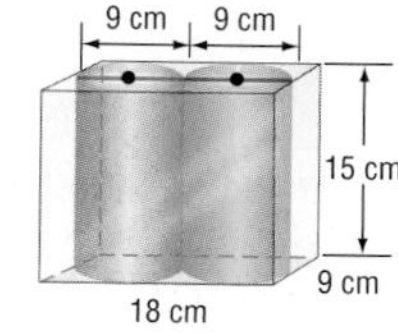

Example 4

20. **PLANTER** A planter is in the shape of a rectangular prism 18 inches long, $14\frac{1}{2}$ inches deep, and 12 inches high. What is the volume of potting soil in the planter if the planter is filled to $1\frac{1}{2}$ inches below the top? 2740.5 in^3

21. **SHIPPING** A box 18 centimeters by 9 centimeters by 15 centimeters is being used to ship two cylindrical candles. Each candle has a diameter of 9 centimeters and a height of 15 centimeters, as shown at the right. What is the volume of the empty space in the box? 521.5 cm^3

22. **SANDCASTLES** In a sandcastle competition, contestants are allowed to use only water, shovels, and 10 cubic feet of sand. To transport the correct amount of sand, they want to create cylinders that are 2 feet tall to hold enough sand for one contestant. What should the diameter of the cylinders be? 2.52 ft

Find the volume of the solid formed by each net.

23.

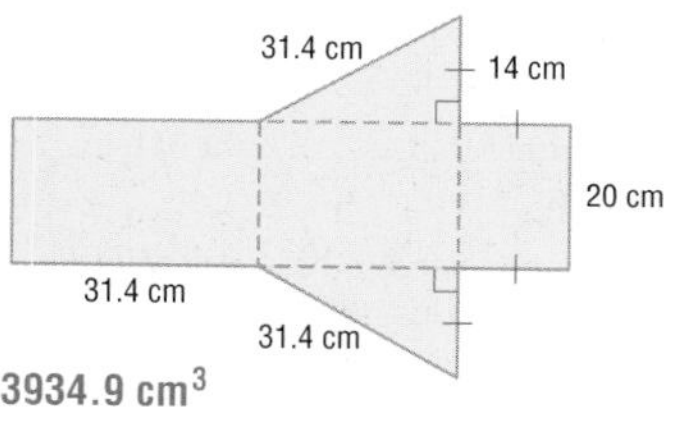

3934.9 cm^3

24. 48.9 m^3

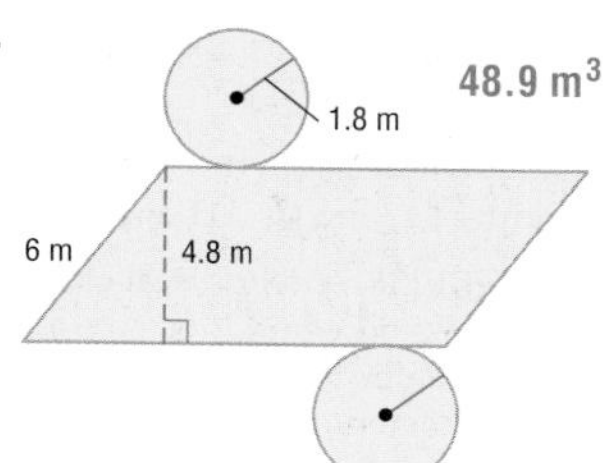

25. **FOOD** A cylindrical can of baked potato chips has a height of 27 centimeters and a radius of 4 centimeters. A new can is advertised as being 30% larger than the regular can. If both cans have the same radius, what is the height of the larger can? 35.1 cm

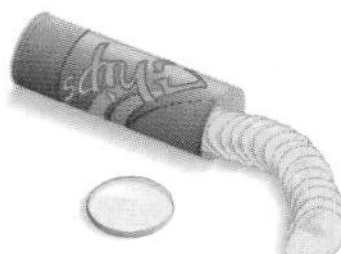

26. **CHANGING DIMENSIONS** A cylinder has a radius of 5 centimeters and a height of 8 centimeters. Describe how each change affects the volume of the cylinder.

a. The height is tripled. The volume is multiplied by 3.

b. The radius is tripled. The volume is multiplied by 3^2 or 9.

c. Both the radius and the height are tripled. The volume is multiplied by 3^3 or 27.

d. The dimensions are exchanged. The volume is multiplied by $\frac{8}{5}$.

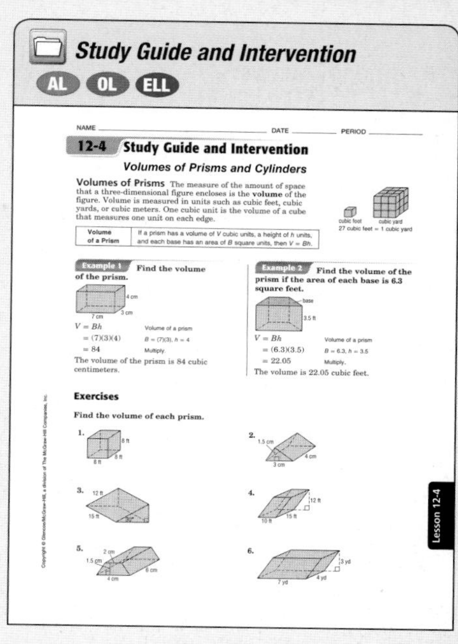

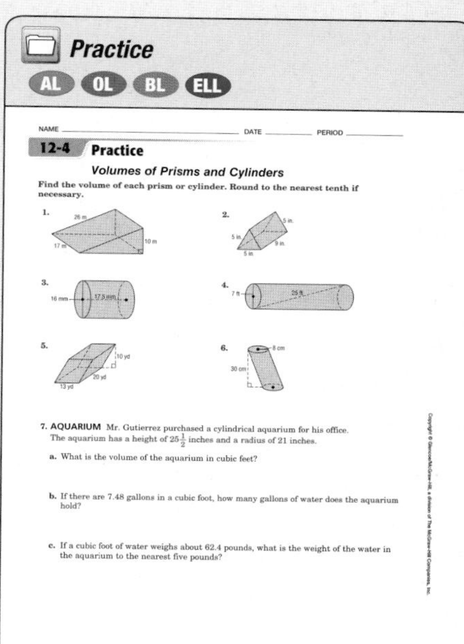

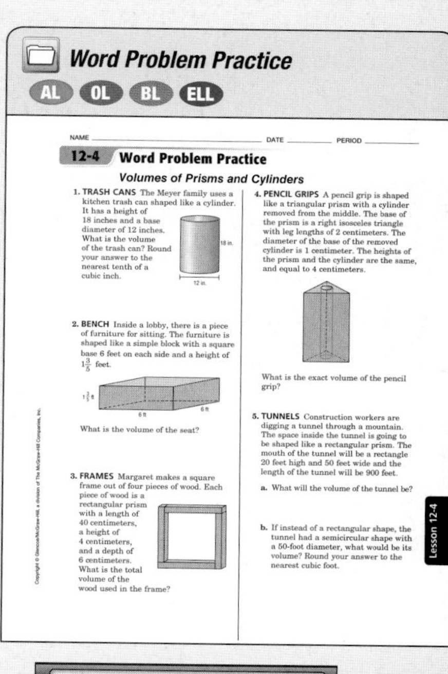

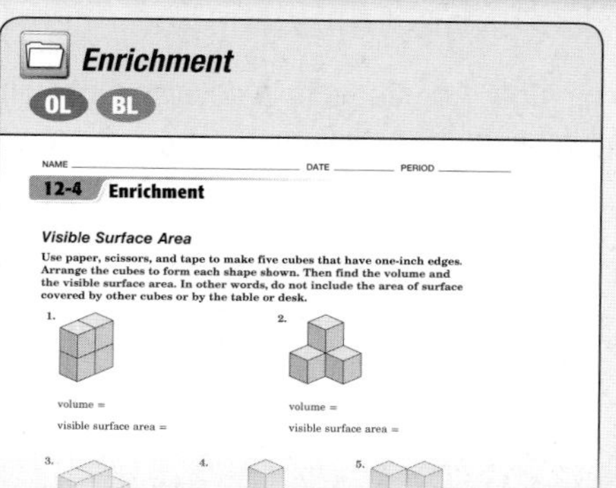

Additional Answer

38. Sample answers:

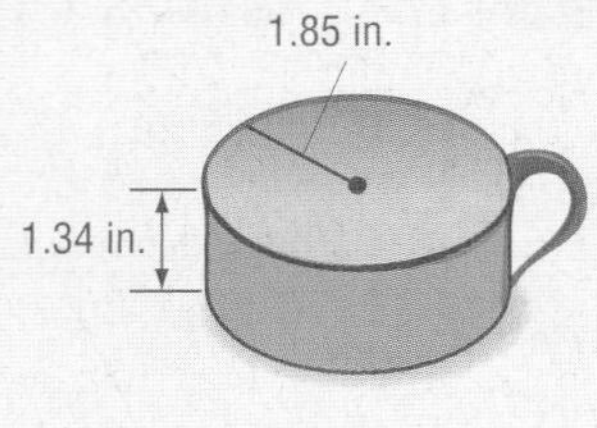

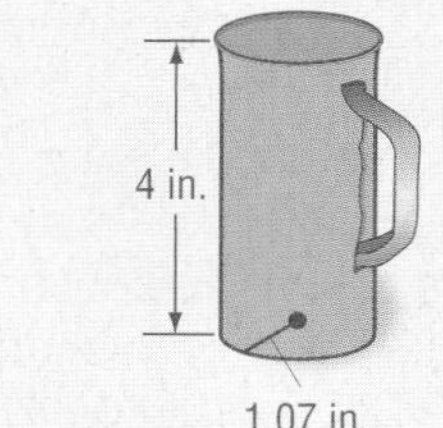

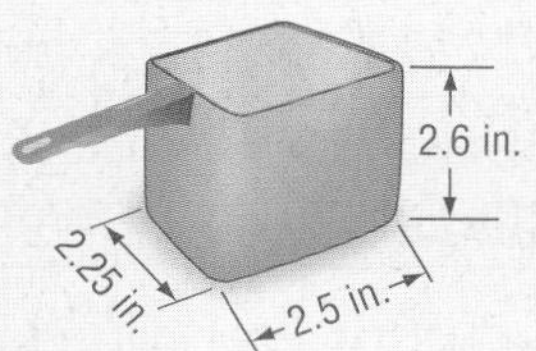

Follow-up

Students have explored surface area and volume.

Ask:

- How can the relationships between two-dimensional and three-dimensional figures help you solve problems? Sample answer: You can use the formulas and properties for two-dimensional figures that you know to solve problems involving three-dimensional figures. For example, the area of the base of a three-dimensional figure is used to calculate its volume.

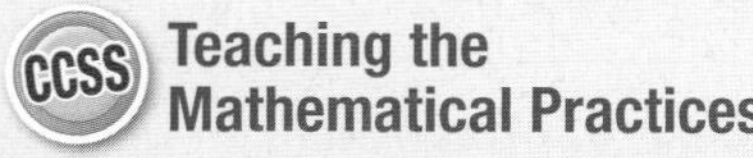

Teaching the Mathematical Practices

Modeling Mathematically proficient students can apply the mathematics they know to solve problems arising in everyday life. In Exercise 36, encourage students to divide the pool into rectangular and triangular pyramids.

27b. The plant should grow well in this soil since the bulk density of 0.019 lb/in^3 is close to the desired bulk density of 0.0018 lb/in^3.

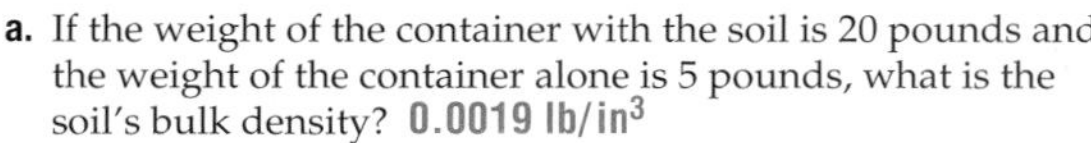

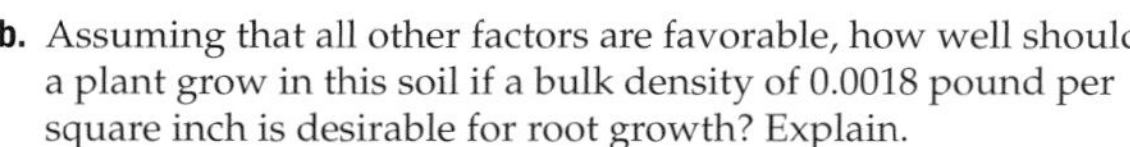

27. SOIL A soil scientist wants to determine the bulk density of a potting soil to assess how well a specific plant will grow in it. The density of the soil sample is the ratio of its weight to its volume.

a. If the weight of the container with the soil is 20 pounds and the weight of the container alone is 5 pounds, what is the soil's bulk density? **0.0019 lb/in^3**

b. Assuming that all other factors are favorable, how well should a plant grow in this soil if a bulk density of 0.0018 pound per square inch is desirable for root growth? Explain.

c. If a bag of this soil holds 2.5 cubic feet, what is its weight in pounds? **8.3 lb**

Find the volume of each composite solid. Round to the nearest tenth if necessary.

28. **225 cm^3**

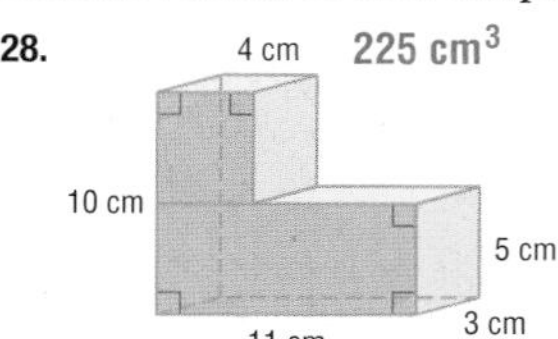

29. **120 m^3**

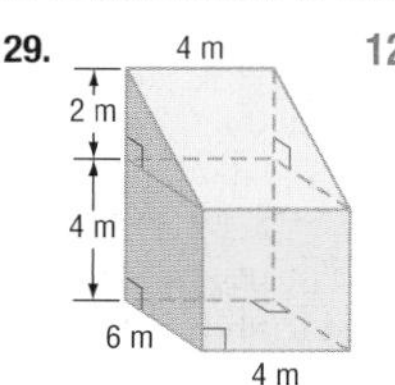

30. **260.5 in^3**

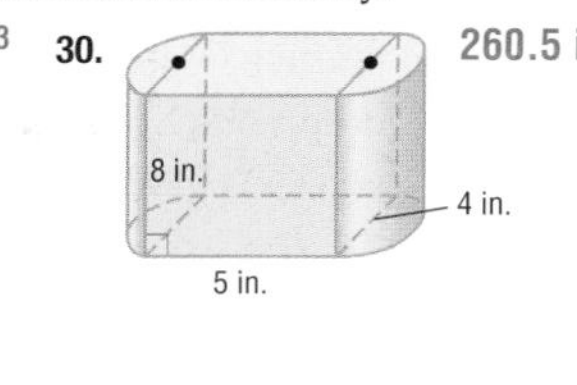

31. MANUFACTURING A can 12 centimeters tall fits into a rubberized cylindrical holder that is 11.5 centimeters tall, including 1 centimeter for the thickness of the base of the holder. The thickness of the rim of the holder is 1 centimeter. What is the volume of the rubberized material that makes up the holder? **304.1 cm^3**

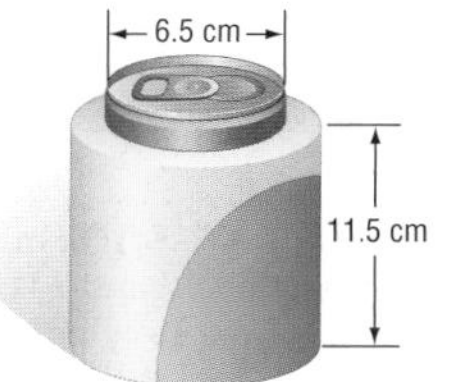

Find each measure to the nearest tenth.

32. A cylindrical can has a volume of 363 cubic centimeters. The diameter of the can is 9 centimeters. What is the height? **5.7 cm**

33. A cylinder has a surface area of 144π square inches and a height of 6 inches. What is the volume? **678.6 in^3**

34. A rectangular prism has a surface area of 432 square inches, a height of 6 inches, and a width of 12 inches. What is the volume? **576 in^3**

35. ARCHITECTURE A cylindrical stainless steel column is used to hide a ventilation system in a new building. According to the specifications, the diameter of the column can be between 30 centimeters and 95 centimeters. The height is to be 500 centimeters. What is the difference in volume between the largest and smallest possible column? Round to the nearest tenth cubic centimeter. **3,190,680.0 cm^3**

36. CCSS MODELING The base of a rectangular swimming pool is sloped so one end of the pool is 6 feet deep and the other end is 3 feet deep, as shown in the figure. If the width is 15 feet, find the volume of water it takes to fill the pool. **1575 ft^3**

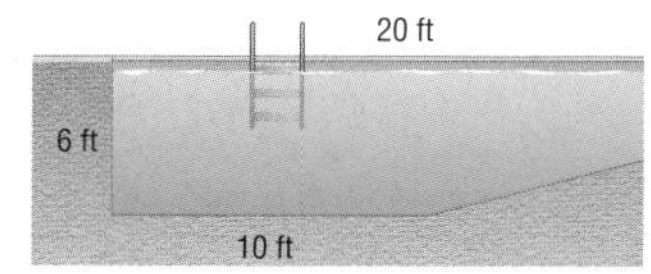

37. CHANGING DIMENSIONS A soy milk company is planning a promotion in which the volume of soy milk in each container will be increased by 25%. The company wants the base of the container to stay the same. What will be the height of the new containers? **$11\frac{1}{4}$ in.**

38. DESIGN Sketch and label (in inches) three different designs for a dry ingredient measuring cup that holds 1 cup. Be sure to include the dimensions in each drawing. (1 cup ≈ 14.4375 in^3) **See margin.**

Differentiated Instruction OL BL

Extension Ask students to develop a demonstration that shows how two different-shaped cylinders can have the same volume.

39. Find the volume of the regular pentagonal prism at the right by dividing it into five equal triangular prisms. Describe the base area and height of each triangular prism. **1100 cm^3; Each triangular prism has a base area of $\frac{1}{2}(8)(5.5)$ or 22 cm^2 and a height of 10 cm.**

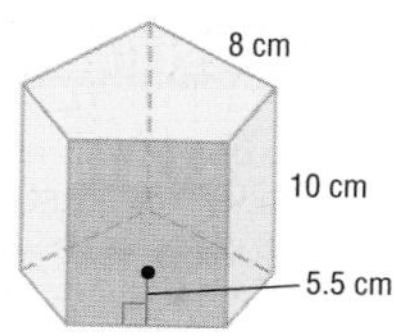

40. Because 2.96 yd^3 of concrete are needed, the second contractor is less expensive at $2181.50.

40. PATIOS Mr. Thomas is planning to remove an old patio and install a new rectangular concrete patio 20 feet long, 12 feet wide, and 4 inches thick. One contractor bid $2225 for the project. A second contractor bid $500 per cubic yard for the new patio and $700 for removal of the old patio. Which is the less expensive option? Explain.

41. MULTIPLE REPRESENTATIONS In this problem, you will investigate cylinders. **a–c. See margin.**

a. **Geometric** Draw a right cylinder and an oblique cylinder with a height of 10 meters and a diameter of 6 meters.

b. **Verbal** A square prism has a height of 10 meters and a base edge of 6 meters. Is its volume greater than, less than, or equal to the volume of the cylinder? Explain.

c. **Analytical** Describe which change affects the volume of the cylinder more: multiplying the height by x or multiplying the radius by x. Explain.

42. Francisco; Valerie incorrectly used $4\sqrt{3}$ as the length of one side of the triangular base. Francisco used a different approach, but his solution is correct.

H.O.T. Problems Use Higher-Order Thinking Skills

42. CCSS CRITIQUE Francisco and Valerie each calculated the volume of an equilateral triangular prism with an apothem of 4 units and height of 5 units. Is either of them correct? Explain your reasoning.

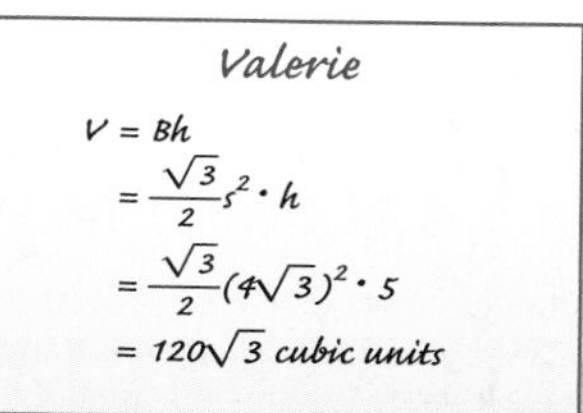

Francisco
$V = Bh$
$= \frac{1}{2}aP \cdot h$
$= \frac{1}{2}(4)(24\sqrt{3}) \cdot 5$
$= 240\sqrt{3}$ cubic units
Valerie
$V = Bh$
$= \frac{\sqrt{3}}{2}s^2 \cdot h$
$= \frac{\sqrt{3}}{2}(4\sqrt{3})^2 \cdot 5$
$= 120\sqrt{3}$ cubic units

43. CHALLENGE The cylindrical can below is used to fill a container with liquid. It takes three full cans to fill the container. Describe possible dimensions of the container if it is each of the following shapes.

a. rectangular prism **base 3 in. by 5 in., height 4π in.**

b. square prism **base 5 in. per side, height $\frac{12}{5}\pi$ in.**

c. triangular prism with a right triangle as the base

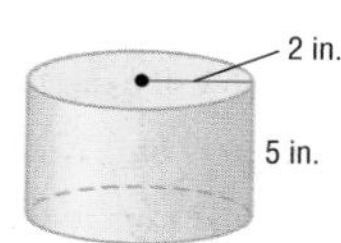

43c. base with legs measuring 3 in. and 4 in., height 10π in.

44. WRITING IN MATH Write a helpful response to the following question posted on an Internet gardening forum.

I am new to gardening. The nursery will deliver a truckload of soil, which they say is 4 yards. I know that a yard is 3 feet, but what is a yard of soil? How do I know what to order? **See margin.**

45. OPEN ENDED Draw and label a prism that has a volume of 50 cubic centimeters. **See margin.**

46. REASONING Determine whether the following statement is true or false. Explain.

Two cylinders with the same height and the same lateral area must have the same volume.

46. True; if two cylinders have the same height and the same lateral area, the circular bases must have the same area. Therefore, $\pi r^2 h$ is the same for each cylinder.

47. WRITING IN MATH How are the volume formulas for prisms and cylinders similar? How are they different? **See margin.**

Multiple Representations

In Exercise 41, students use drawings and verbal descriptions to investigate volumes of cylinders.

Teaching the Mathematical Practices

Critique Mathematically proficient students can distinguish correct logic from flawed reasoning. In Exercise 42, Valerie incorrectly used $4\sqrt{3}$ as one side of the triangle base.

Additional Answers

41a.

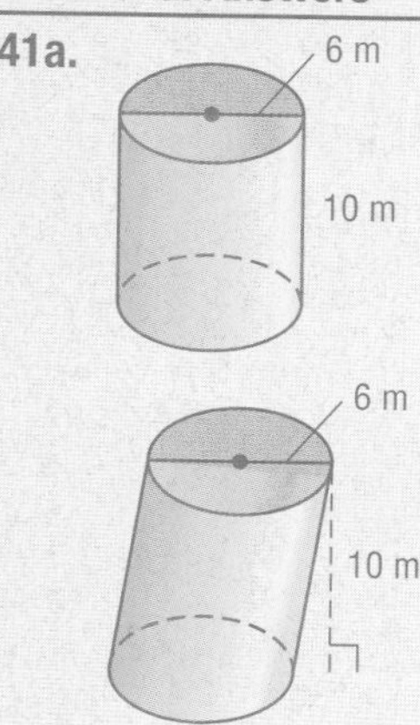

41b. Greater than; a square with a side length of 6 m has an area of 36 m^2. A circle with a diameter of 6 m has an area of 9π or 28.3 m^2. Since the heights are the same, the volume of the square prism is greater.

41c. Multiplying the radius by x; since the volume is represented by $\pi r^2 h$, multiplying the height by x makes the volume x times greater. Multiplying the radius by x makes the volume x^2 times greater, assuming $x > 1$.

44. Sample answer: The nursery means a cubic yard, which is 3^3 or 27 cubic feet. Find the volume of your garden in cubic feet and divide by 27 to determine the number of cubic yards of soil needed.

45. Sample answer:

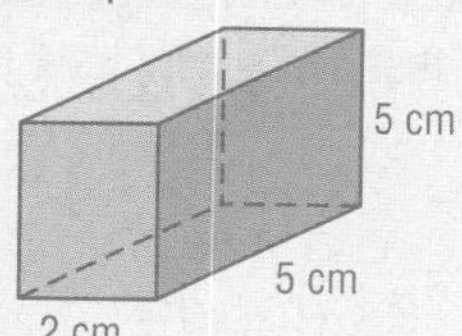

47. Sample answer: Both formulas involve multiplying the area of the base by the height. The base of a prism is a polygon, so the expression representing the area varies, depending on the type of polygon it is. The base of a cylinder is a circle, so its area is πr^2.

4 Assess

Name the Math Have students describe the similarities and differences between the volume of a cylinder and the volume of a prism.

Formative Assessment

Check for student understanding of Lessons 12-3 and 12-4.

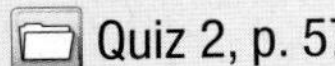 Quiz 2, p. 57

Standardized Test Practice

48. The volume of a triangular prism is 1380 cubic centimeters. Its base is a right triangle with legs measuring 8 centimeters and 15 centimeters. What is the height of the prism? B

A 34.5 cm **C** 17 cm
B 23 cm **D** 11.5 cm

49. A cylindrical tank used for oil storage has a height that is half the length of its radius. If the volume of the tank is 1,122,360 ft^3, what is the tank's radius? F

F 89.4 ft **H** 280.9 ft
G 178.8 ft **J** 561.8 ft

50. SHORT RESPONSE What is the ratio of the area of the circle to the area of the square? $\frac{\pi}{4}$

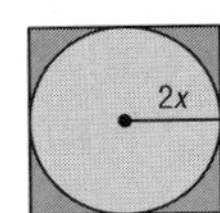

51. SAT/ACT A county proposes to enact a new 0.5% property tax. What would be the additional tax amount for a landowner whose property has a taxable value of $85,000? C

A $4.25 **D** $4250
B $170 **E** $42,500
C $425

Spiral Review

Find the lateral area and surface area of each regular pyramid. Round to the nearest tenth if necessary. (Lesson 12-3)

52. 212.1 ft^2; 255.4 ft^2
15 ft, 10 ft, 10 ft

53. 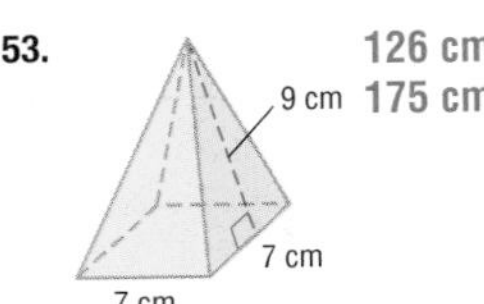

126 cm^2; 175 cm^2

54. 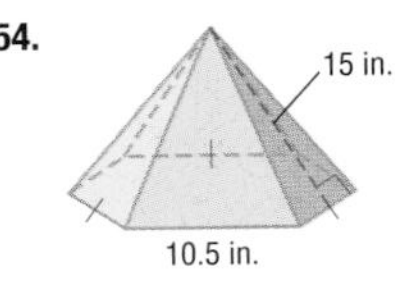

472.5 in^2; 758.9 in^2

55. BAKING Many baking pans are given a special nonstick coating. A rectangular cake pan is 9 inches by 13 inches by 2 inches deep. What is the area of the inside of the pan that needs to be coated? (Lesson 12-2) 205 in^2

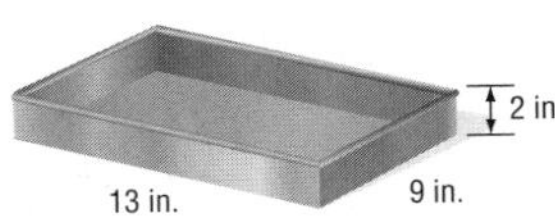

Find the indicated measure. Round to the nearest tenth. (Lesson 11-3)

56. The area of a circle is 54 square meters. Find the diameter. 8.3 m

57. Find the diameter of a circle with an area of 102 square centimeters. 11.4 cm

58. The area of a circle is 191 square feet. Find the radius. 7.8 ft

59. Find the radius of a circle with an area of 271 square inches. 9.3 in.

Skills Review

Find the area of each trapezoid, rhombus, or kite.

60. 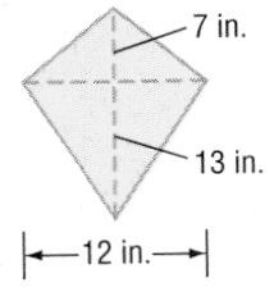

120 in^2

61. 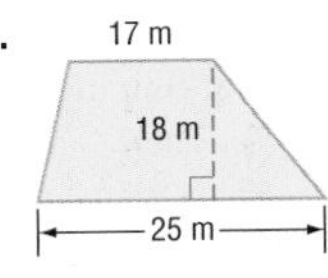

378 m^2

62. 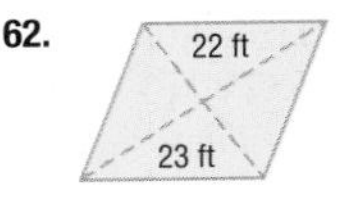

1012 ft^2

Differentiated Instruction OL BL

Extension Find the volume of a regular pentagonal prism with a height of 5 feet and a perimeter of 20 feet. $V \approx 137.6$ ft^3

12-4 Graphing Technology Lab
Changing Dimensions

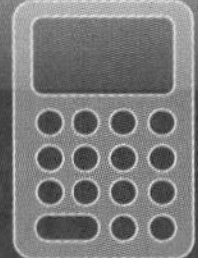

You can use TI-Nspire Technology to investigate how changes in dimension affect the surface area and volume of a rectangular prism.

Activity

Step 1 Open a new **Lists & Spreadsheet** page.

Step 2 Move the cursor to the space beside the letter in each column and label the columns ℓ for length, w for width, h for height, *sa* for surface area, and v for volume.

Step 3 Insert the values for length, width, and height shown into the table.

	A l	B w	C h	D sa	E v	F	G
1	1	2	3				
2	1	2	6				
3	1	4	6				
4	2	4	6				
5	3	6	9				

Step 4 Enter the formula for the surface area in terms of cells A1, B1, and C1 in cell D1.

Step 5 Enter the formula for the volume in terms of cells A1, B1, and C1 in cell E1.

Step 6 Highlight cell D1 and select **Fill Down** from the **Data** menu. Scroll down to fill in the surface areas for the other prisms. Repeat the process for volume.

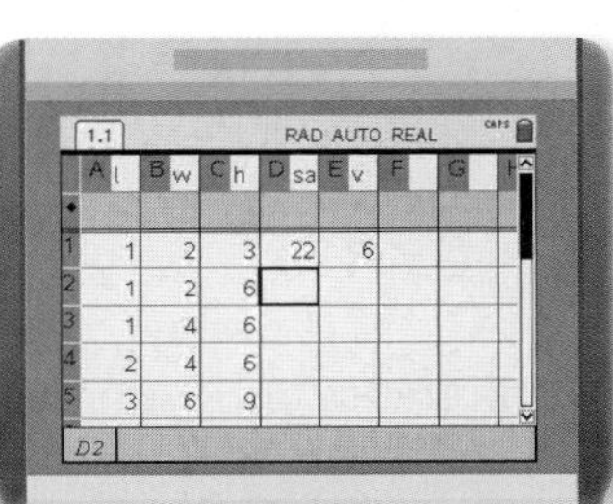

Step 7 Add additional values and observe the effect on surface area and volume as one or more of the dimensions changes.

Analyze the Results 1–4. See margin.

1. How does the surface area change when one of the dimensions is doubled? two of the dimensions? all three of the dimensions?
2. How does the volume change when one of the dimensions is doubled? two of the dimensions? all three of the dimensions?
3. How does the surface area change when all three of the dimensions are tripled?
4. How does the volume change when all three of the dimensions are tripled?
5. **MAKE A CONJECTURE** If the dimensions of a prism are all multiplied by a factor of 5, what do you think the ratio of the new surface area to the original surface area will be? the ratio of the new volume to the original volume? Explain.
6. **CHALLENGE** Write an expression for the ratio of the surface areas and the ratio of the volumes if all three of the dimensions of a prism are increased by a scale factor of k. Explain.

5–6. See Ch. 12 Answer Appendix.

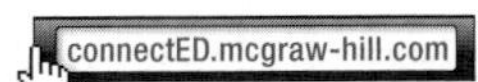
connectED.mcgraw-hill.com

Additional Answers

1. Sample answer: The surface area gets larger when one or two of the dimensions are doubled, but not by a constant factor. The surface area increases by a factor of 4 when all three of the dimensions are doubled.
2. Sample answer: The volume increases by a factor of 2 when one of the dimensions is doubled, 4 when two of the dimensions are doubled, and 8 when all three of the dimensions are doubled.
3. The surface area increases by a factor of 9 when all three of the dimensions are tripled.
4. The volume increases by a factor of 27 when all three of the dimensions are tripled.

1 Focus

Objective Explore how volume of a prism is affected by changing dimensions using the spreadsheet of the TI-Nspire Technology.

Materials

- TI-Nspire technology

Teaching Tip

Students may use the "fill-down" feature of a spreadsheet to enter the data in rows of the first three columns. Students should realize that they can find the surface area or volume of any prism by using spreadsheet features to copy formulas into columns.

2 Teach

Working in Cooperative Groups

Arrange students in groups of 2, mixing abilities. Groups should complete the activity and Exercises 1–4.

Practice Have students complete Exercises 1–4.

3 Assess

Formative Assessment

Use Exercises 5 and 6 to assess whether students comprehend how changing a dimension affects the volume or surface area of that prism.

From Concrete to Abstract

Give students a bag of beans and different sizes of prisms. Have them compare and contrast the volume of each prism by the amount of beans that fills each prism.

Formative Assessment

Use the Mid-Chapter Quiz to assess students' progress in the first half of the chapter.

Have students review the lesson indicated for the problems that they answered incorrectly.

Summative Assessment

Mid-Chapter Test, p. 59

eAssessment Customize and create multiple versions of your Mid-Chapter Quiz and their answer keys.

FOLDABLES® StudyOrganizer

Dinah Zike's Foldables®

Before students complete the Mid-Chapter Quiz, encourage them to review the information they have recorded for Lessons 12-1 through 12-4 in their Foldables.

CHAPTER 12 Mid-Chapter Quiz

Lessons 12-1 through 12-4

1. Describe how to use isometric dot paper to sketch the following figure. (Lesson 12-1) **See Ch. 12 Answer Appendix.**

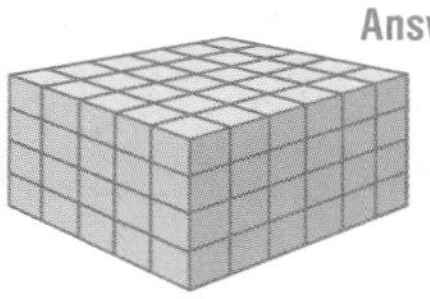

2. Use isometric dot paper to sketch a rectangular prism 2 units high, 3 units long, and 6 units wide. (Lesson 12-1) **See Ch. 12 Answer Appendix.**

3. Use isometric dot paper to sketch a triangular prism 5 units high, with two sides of the base that are 4 units long and 3 units long. (Lesson 12-1) **See Ch. 12 Answer Appendix.**

Find the lateral area of each prism. Round to the nearest tenth if necessary. (Lesson 12-2)

4. 3 m, 12 m **216 m²**

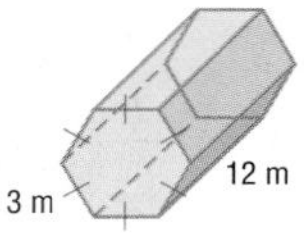

5.

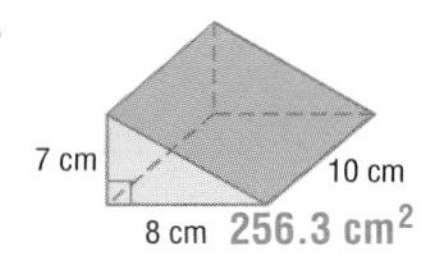

256.3 cm²

6. **MULTIPLE CHOICE** Coaxial cable is used to transmit long-distance telephone calls, cable television programming, and other communications. A typical coaxial cable contains 22 copper tubes and has a diameter of 3 inches. What is the approximate lateral area of a coaxial cable that is 500 feet long? (Lesson 12-2) **D**

A	16.4 ft²	**C**	294.5 ft²
B	196.3 ft²	**D**	392.7 ft²

Find the lateral area and surface area of each cylinder. Round to the nearest tenth if necessary. (Lesson 12-2)

7. 8 ft, 6 ft **301.6 ft²; 703.7 ft²**

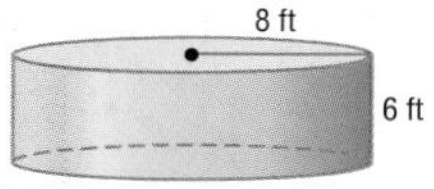

8.

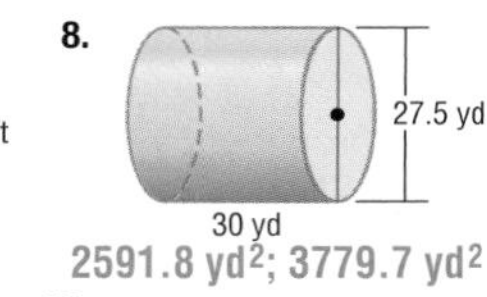

2591.8 yd²; 3779.7 yd²

9.

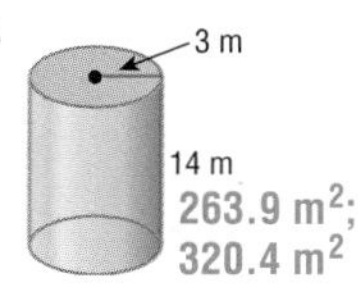

263.9 m²; 320.4 m²

10.

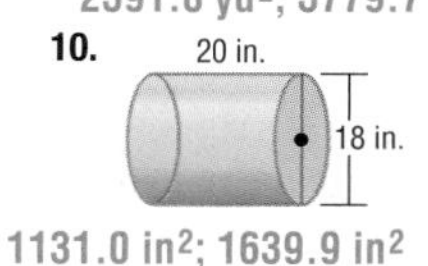

1131.0 in²; 1639.9 in²

11. **COLLECTIONS** Soledad collects unique salt and pepper shakers. She inherited a pair of tetrahedral shakers from her mother. (Lesson 12-3)
    a. Each edge of a shaker measures 3 centimeters. Make a sketch of one shaker. **See Ch. 12 Answer Appendix.**
    b. Find the total surface area of one shaker. **about 15.6 cm**

Find the surface area of each regular pyramid or cone. Round to the nearest tenth if necessary. (Lesson 12-3)

12. 5 ft, 12 ft **282.7 ft²**

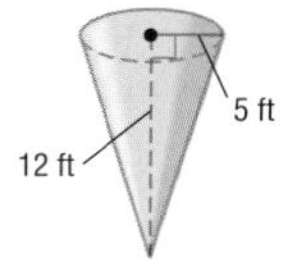

13.

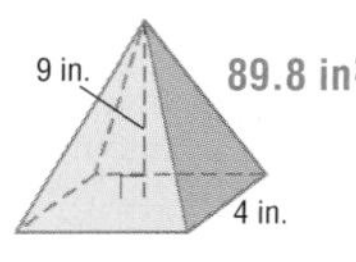

89.8 in²

Find the volume of each prism or cylinder. Round to the nearest tenth if necessary. (Lesson 12-4)

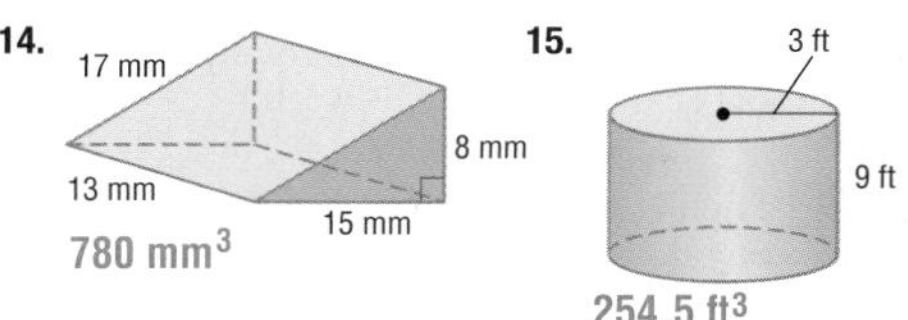

14. **780 mm³**

15. **254.5 ft³**

16. 12 cm, 6 cm, 2 cm **144 cm³**

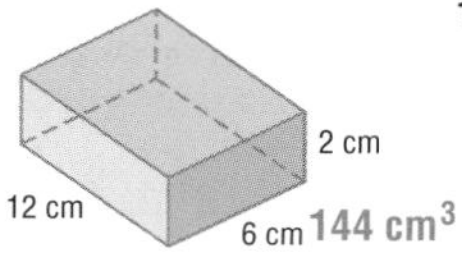

17.

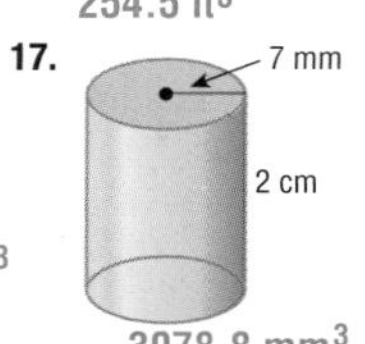

3078.8 mm³

18. 4 mm, 12 mm, 3 mm **72 mm³**

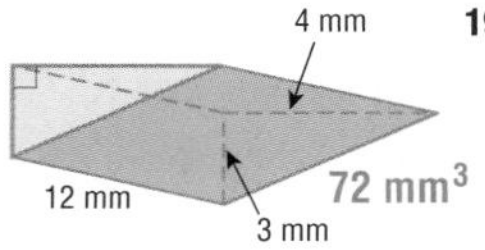

19.

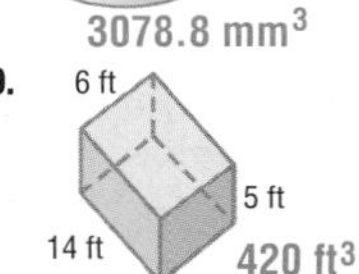

420 ft³

20. **METEOROLOGY** The TIROS weather satellites were a series of weather satellites that carried television and infrared cameras and were covered by solar cells. If the cylinder-shaped body of a TIROS had a diameter of 42 inches and a height of 19 inches, what was the volume available for carrying instruments and cameras? Round to the nearest tenth. (Lesson 12-4) **26,323.4 in²**

InterventionPlanner

TIER 1 On Level OL	TIER 2 Strategic Intervention AL approaching grade level	TIER 3 Intensive Intervention 2 or more grades below level
If students miss about 25% of the exercises or less,	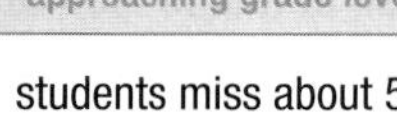 **If** students miss about 50% of the exercises,	**If** students miss about 75% of the exercises,
Then choose a resource: SE Lessons 12-1, 12-2, 12-3, and 12-4; Skills Practice, pp. 7, 14, 20, and 27; connectED.mcgraw-hill.com Self-Check Quiz	**Then** choose a resource:   Study Guide and Intervention, pp. 5, 12, 18, and 25; 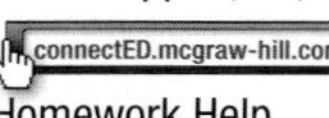 connectED.mcgraw-hill.com Extra Examples, Personal Tutor, Homework Help	**Then** use *Math Triumphs, Geometry*, Ch. 5; connectED.mcgraw-hill.com Extra Examples, Personal Tutor, Homework Help, Review Vocabulary

LESSON 12-5 Volumes of Pyramids and Cones

Then	Now	Why?
You found surface areas of pyramids and cones.	**1** Find volumes of pyramids. **2** Find volumes of cones.	Marta is studying crystals that grow on rock formations. For a project, she is making a clay model of a crystal with a shape that is a composite of two congruent rectangular pyramids. The base of each pyramid will be 1 by 1.5 inches, and the total height will be 4 inches. Why is determining the volume of the model helpful in this situation?

CCSS Common Core State Standards

Content Standards

G.GMD.1 Give an informal argument for the formulas for the circumference of a circle, area of a circle, volume of a cylinder, pyramid, and cone.

G.GMD.3 Use volume formulas for cylinders, pyramids, cones, and spheres to solve problems. ★

Mathematical Practices

1 Make sense of problems and persevere in solving them.

7 Look for and make use of structure.

1 Volume of Pyramids

A triangular prism can be separated into three triangular pyramids as shown. Since all faces of a triangular pyramid are triangles, any face can be considered a base of the pyramid.

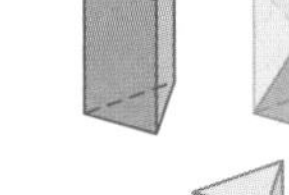

The yellow and orange pyramids have base area B_1 and height h_1. Therefore, by Cavalieri's Principle, they have the same volume. Likewise, the yellow and green pyramids have base area B_2 and height h_2, so they have the same volume.

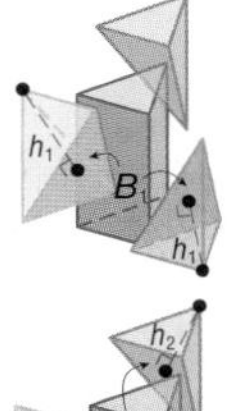

Since the orange and green pyramids have the same volume as the yellow pyramid, it follows that the volumes of all three pyramids are the same. Therefore, each pyramid has one third the volume of the prism with the same base area and height. This is true for a pyramid with any shape base.

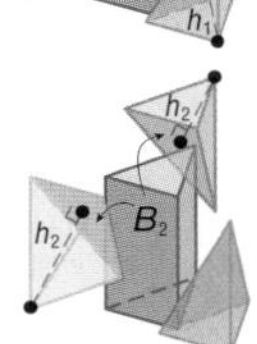

KeyConcept Volume of a Pyramid

Words The volume of a pyramid is $V = \frac{1}{3}Bh$, where B is the area of the base and h is the height of the pyramid.

Symbols $V = \frac{1}{3}Bh$

Models

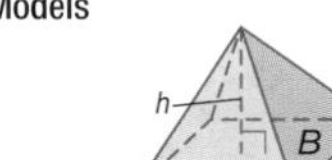

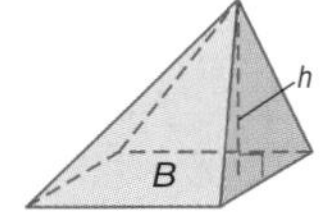

Example 1 Volume of a Pyramid

Find the volume of the pyramid.

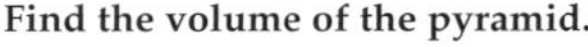

$V = \frac{1}{3}Bh$ Volume of a pyramid

$= \frac{1}{3}(9.5 \cdot 8)(9)$ $B = 9.5 \cdot 8$ and $h = 9$

$= 228$ Simplify.

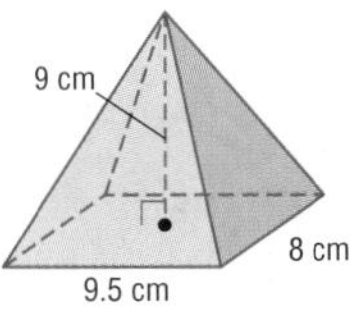

The volume of the pyramid is 228 cubic centimeters.

1 Focus

Vertical Alignment

Before Lesson 12-5 Find the surface areas of pyramids and cones.

Lesson 12-5 Find the volumes of pyramids and cones.

After Lesson 12-5 Find the surface areas and volumes of spheres.

2 Teach

Scaffolding Questions

Have students read the **Why?** section of the lesson.

Ask:

- What is the shape of a horizontal cross section of a pyramid? a rectangle
- When have you used the fact that the area of a figure is equal to the sum of the area of its pieces? Sample answer: when finding the area of a parallelogram

Lesson 12-5 Resources

Resource	Approaching Level AL	On Level OL	Beyond Level BL	English Learners ELL
Teacher Edition	▪ Differentiated Instruction, p. 875	▪ Differentiated Instruction, pp. 875, 879	▪ Differentiated Instruction, pp. 875, 879	
Chapter Resource Masters	▪ Study Guide and Intervention, pp. 31–32 ▪ Skills Practice, p. 33 ▪ Practice, p. 34 ▪ Word Problem Practice, p. 35	▪ Study Guide and Intervention, pp. 31–32 ▪ Skills Practice, p. 33 ▪ Practice, p. 34 ▪ Word Problem Practice, p. 35 ▪ Enrichment, p. 36	▪ Practice, p. 34 ▪ Word Problem Practice, p. 35 ▪ Enrichment, p. 36	▪ Study Guide and Intervention, pp. 31–32 ▪ Skills Practice, p. 33 ▪ Practice, p. 34 ▪ Word Problem Practice, p. 35
Other	▪ 5-Minute Check 12-5 ▪ Study Notebook	▪ 5-Minute Check 12-5 ▪ Study Notebook	▪ 5-Minute Check 12-5 ▪ Study Notebook	▪ 5-Minute Check 12-5 ▪ Study Notebook

1 Volume of Pyramids

Example 1 shows how to use the formula to find the volume of a pyramid.

Formative Assessment

Use the Guided Practice exercises after each Example to determine students' understanding of concepts.

Additional Example

1 Find the volume of the pyramid. 21 in^3

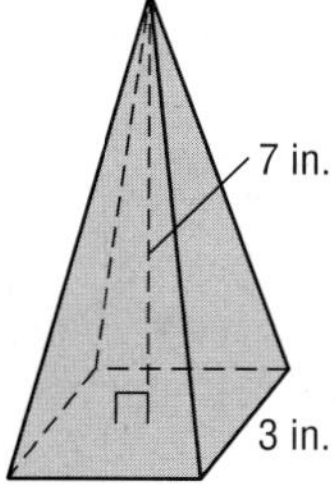

Additional Examples also in Interactive Classroom PowerPoint® Presentations

Interactive White Board READY

2 Volume of Cones

Example 2 shows how to find the volume of a cone. **Example 3** shows how to find the volume of a pyramidion in a real-world context.

Additional Example

2 Find the volume of each cone. Round to the nearest tenth.

a. 2167.6 ft^3

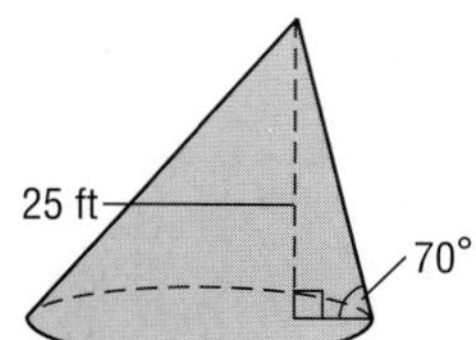

b. 314.2 in^3

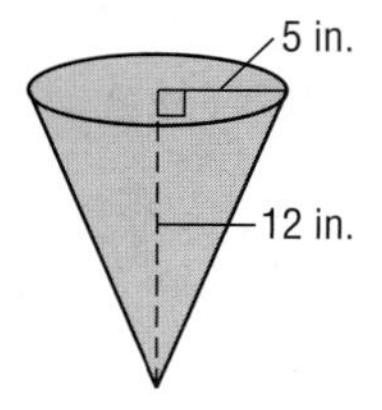

GuidedPractice

1A. **36.7 cm^3**

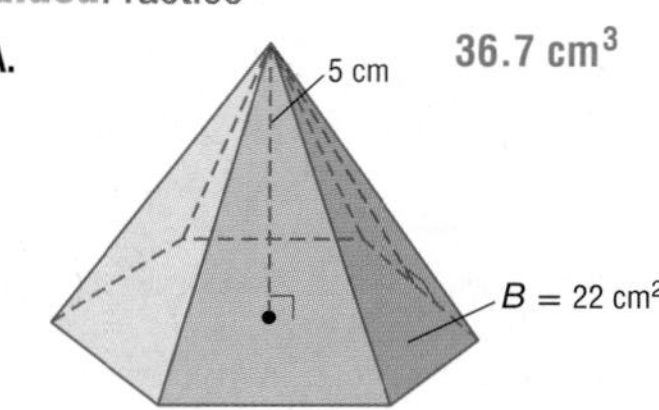

1B. **210 ft^3**

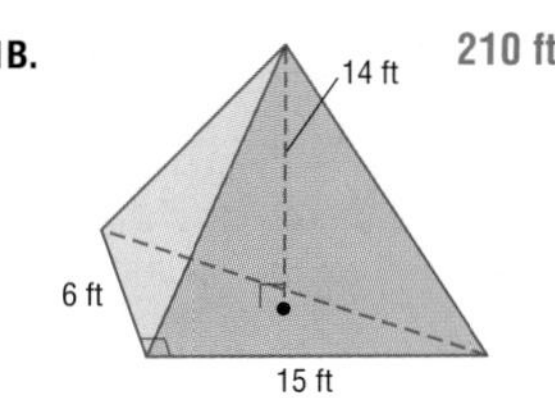

2 Volume of Cones The pyramid and prism shown have the same base area B and height h as the cylinder and cone. Since the volume of the pyramid is one third the volume of the prism, then by Cavalieri's Principle, the volume of the cone must be one third the volume of the cylinder.

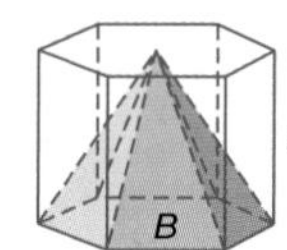

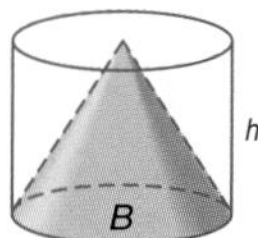

WatchOut!

Volumes of Cones The formula for the surface area of a cone only applies to right cones. However, the formula for volume applies to oblique cones as well as right cones.

KeyConcept Volume of a Cone

Words The volume of a circular cone is $V = \frac{1}{3}Bh$, or $V = \frac{1}{3}\pi r^2 h$, where B is the area of the base, h is the height of the cone, and r is the radius of the base.

Models

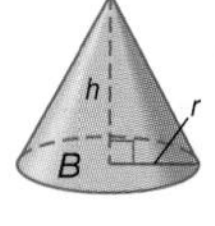

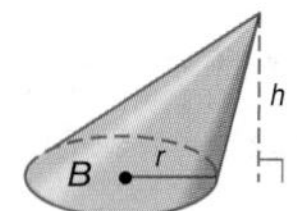

Symbols $V = \frac{1}{3}Bh$ or $V = \frac{1}{3}\pi r^2 h$

Example 2 Volume of a Cone

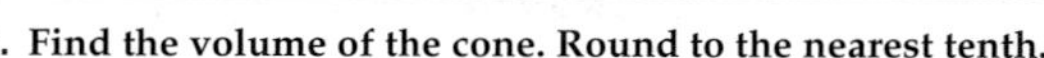

a. Find the volume of the cone. Round to the nearest tenth.

$V = \frac{1}{3}\pi r^2 h$	Volume of a cone
$\approx \frac{1}{3}\pi(3.2)^2(5.8)$	$r = 3.2$ and $h = 5.8$
≈ 62.2	Use a calculator.

The volume of the cone is approximately 62.2 cubic meters.

b. Find the volume of the cone. Round to the nearest tenth.

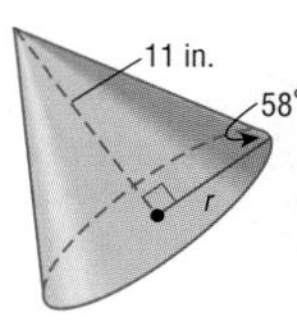

Step 1 Use trigonometry to find the radius.

$\tan 58° = \frac{11}{r}$	$\tan \theta = \frac{\text{opp}}{\text{adj}}$
$r = \frac{11}{\tan 58°}$	Solve for r.
$r \approx 6.9$	Use a calculator.

Focus on Mathematical Content

Formulas In Chapter 11, students found the areas of polygons and circles. Stress that in this chapter, the volume formulas include the area formulas of the polygons or circles as bases of the solids.

Step 2 Find the volume.

$V = \frac{1}{3}\pi r^2 h$ — Volume of a cone

$\approx \frac{1}{3}\pi(6.9)^2(11)$ — $r \approx 6.9$ and $h = 11$

≈ 548.4 — Use a calculator.

The volume of the cone is approximately 548.4 cubic inches.

Guided Practice

2A. $66.0\ \text{ft}^3$
2B. $1005.3\ \text{cm}^3$
2C. $392.7\ \text{cm}^3$

2A.

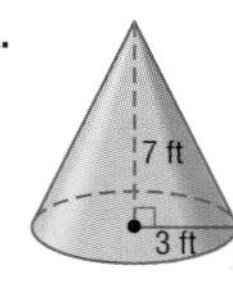

2B.

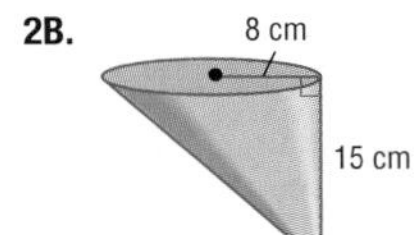

2C.

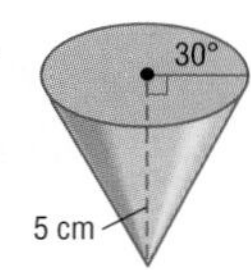

Real-World Example 3 Find Real-World Volumes

ARCHITECTURE At the top of the Washington Monument is a small square pyramid, called a *pyramidion*. This pyramid has a height of 55.5 feet with base edges of approximately 34.5 feet. What is the volume of the pyramidion? Round to the nearest tenth.

Sketch and label the pyramid.

55.5 ft
34.5 ft
34.5 ft

$V = \frac{1}{3}Bh$ — Volume of a pyramid

$= \frac{1}{3}(34.5 \cdot 34.5)(55.5)$ — $B = 34.5 \cdot 34.5$, $h = 55.5$

$\approx 22{,}019.6$ — Simplify.

The volume of the pyramidion atop the Washington Monument is about 22,019.6 cubic feet.

Real-World Link

The Washington Monument is the largest masonry structure in the world. By law, no other building in D.C. is allowed to be taller than the 555-foot-tall structure.

Source: Enchanted Learning

Guided Practice

3. ARCHAEOLOGY A pyramidion that was discovered in Saqqara, Egypt, in 1992 has a rectangular base 53 centimeters by 37 centimeters. It is 46 centimeters high. What is the volume of this pyramidion? Round to the nearest tenth. $30{,}068.7\ \text{cm}^3$

The formulas for the volumes of solids are summarized below.

Concept Summary Volumes of Solids

Solid	prism	cylinder	pyramid	cone
Model	h, B	r, h, B	h, B	h, r, B
Volume	$V = Bh$	$V = Bh$ or $V = \pi r^2 h$	$V = \frac{1}{3}Bh$	$V = \frac{1}{3}Bh$ or $V = \frac{1}{3}\pi r^2 h$

Additional Example

3 SCULPTURE At the top of a stone tower is a pyramidion in the shape of a square pyramid. This pyramid has a height of 52.5 centimeters and the base edges are 36 centimeters. What is the volume of the pyramidion? Round to the nearest tenth. $22{,}680\ \text{cm}^3$

Teach with Tech

Portable Media Player Create image files of pyramids and cones and the formulas for their volumes. Post the files on your class Web page for students to load onto their portable media players. Have them use these as "flashcards" to help them remember the formulas.

Follow-up

Students have explored the volumes of prisms, cylinders, pyramids, and cones.

Ask:

- Why is it helpful to have different formulas when finding volume? Sample answer: It may be easier to remember the formulas by using those involving base and height. However, depending upon which measures are known, it may be easier to use one formula instead of another.

Differentiated Instruction AL OL BL

Visual/Spatial Learners When you discuss cones and pyramids, show students that 3 cones fit into a cylinder with the same corresponding base and height by filling a cone with water, rice, or beans and pouring it into the corresponding cylinder or pyramid. This same relationship is true for three pyramids fitting in a prism with a corresponding base and height.

3 Practice

Formative Assessment

Use Exercises 1–9 to check for understanding.

Use the chart at the bottom of this page to customize assignments for your students.

Teaching the Mathematical Practices

Sense-Making Mathematically proficient students consider analogous problems and try simpler forms of the original problem in order to gain insight into its solution. In Exercises 10–13, encourage students to find the area of the base of each pyramid first.

Check Your Understanding

= Step-by-Step Solutions begin on page R14.

Example 1 **Find the volume of each pyramid.**

1. 75 in³

10 in. 5 in. 9 in.

2. 132 cm³

12 cm 4.4 cm 3 cm

3. a rectangular pyramid with a height of 5.2 meters and a base 8 meters by 4.5 meters **62.4 m³**

4. a square pyramid with a height of 14 meters and a base with 8-meter side lengths **298.7 m³**

Example 2 **Find the volume of each cone. Round to the nearest tenth.**

5. 51.3 in³

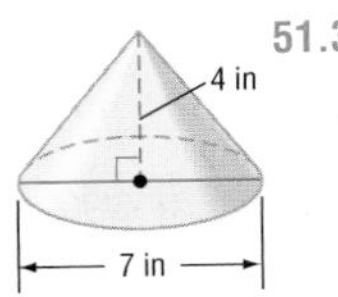

6. 168.1 cm³

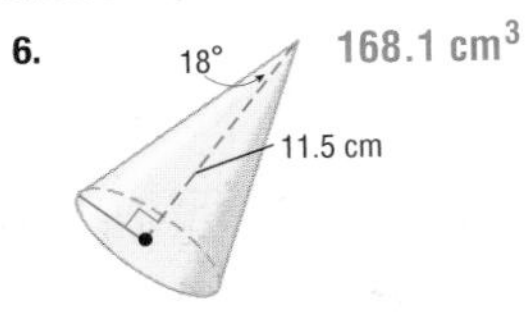

7. an oblique cone with a height of 10.5 millimeters and a radius of 1.6 millimeters **28.1 mm³**

8. a cone with a slant height of 25 meters and a radius of 15 meters **4712.4 m³**

Example 3 **9.** **MUSEUMS** The sky dome of the National Corvette Museum in Bowling Green, Kentucky, is a conical building. If the height is 100 feet and the area of the base is about 15,400 square feet, find the volume of air that the heating and cooling systems would have to accommodate. Round to the nearest tenth. **513,333.3 ft³**

Practice and Problem Solving

Extra Practice is on page R12.

Example 1 CCSS **SENSE-MAKING** **Find the volume of each pyramid. Round to the nearest tenth if necessary.**

10. 605 in³

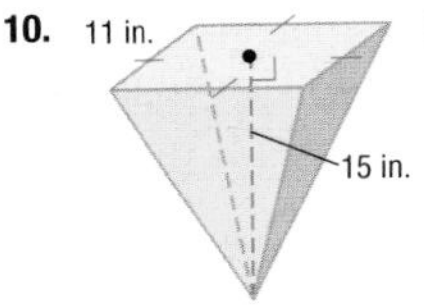

11. 105.8 mm³

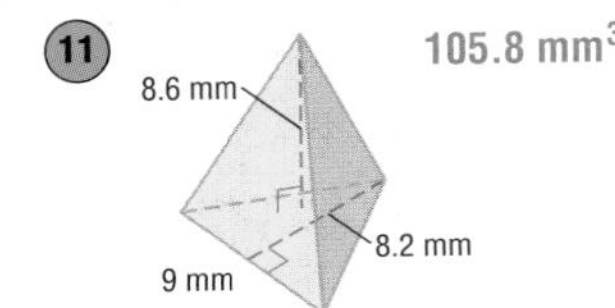

12. 482.1 m³

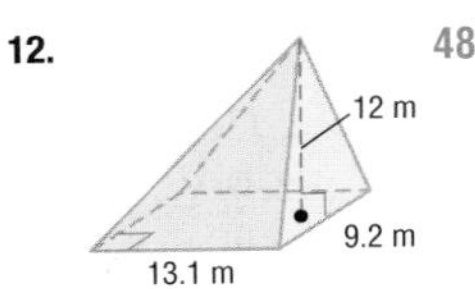

13. 233.8 cm³

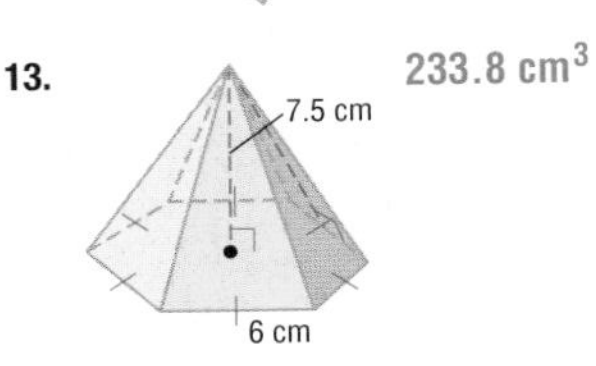

14. a pentagonal pyramid with a base area of 590 square feet and an altitude of 7 feet **1376.7 ft³**

15. a triangular pyramid with a height of 4.8 centimeters and a right triangle base with a leg 5 centimeters and hypotenuse 10.2 centimeters **35.6 cm³**

16. A triangular pyramid with a right triangle base with a leg 8 centimeters and hypotenuse 10 centimeters has a volume of 144 cubic centimeters. Find the height. **18 cm**

Differentiated Homework Options

Level	Assignment	Two-Day Option	
AL Basic	10–24, 37–52	11–23 odd, 41–44	10–24 even, 37–40, 45–52
OL Core	11–29 odd, 30, 31–35 odd, 37–52	10–24, 41–44	25–35, 37–40, 45–52
BL Advanced	25–48, (optional: 49–52)		

Example 2 **Find the volume of each cone. Round to the nearest tenth.**

17. 235.6 in³

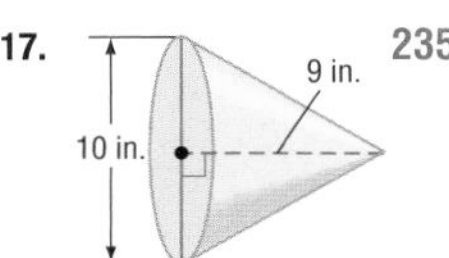

18. 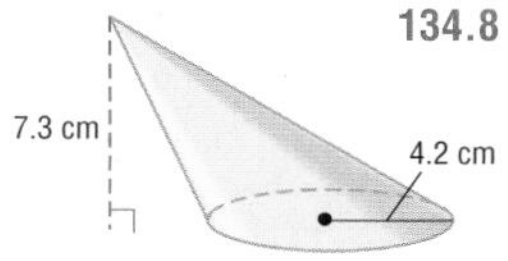 134.8 cm³

7.3 cm, 4.2 cm

19. 1473.1 cm³

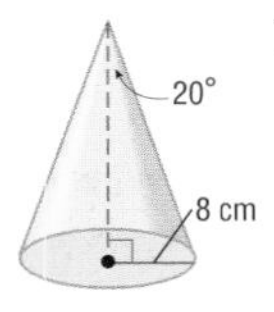

20. 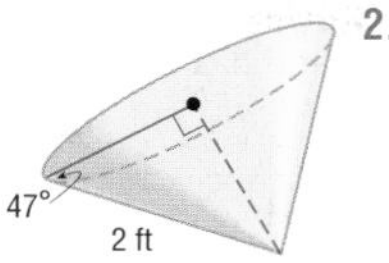 2.8 ft³

47°, 2 ft

21. an oblique cone with a diameter of 16 inches and an altitude of 16 inches 1072.3 in³

22. a right cone with a slant height of 5.6 centimeters and a radius of 1 centimeter 5.8 cm³

Example 3 **23.** **SNACKS** Approximately how many cubic centimeters of roasted peanuts will completely fill a paper cone that is 14 centimeters high and has a base diameter of 8 centimeters? Round to the nearest tenth. 234.6 cm³

24. **CCSS MODELING** The Pyramid Arena in Memphis, Tennessee, is the third largest pyramid in the world. It is approximately 350 feet tall, and its square base is 600 feet wide. Find the volume of this pyramid. 42,000,000 ft³

25. **GARDENING** The greenhouse at the right is a regular octagonal pyramid with a height of 5 feet. The base has side lengths of 2 feet. What is the volume of the greenhouse? 32.2 ft³

B

Find the volume of each solid. Round to the nearest tenth.

26.

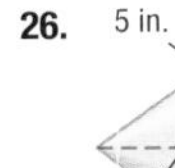

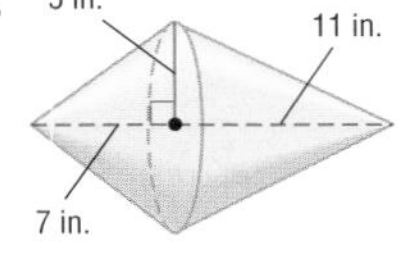

471.2 in³

27. 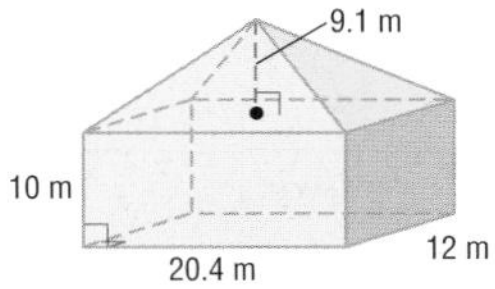 9.1 m, 10 m, 20.4 m, 12 m

3190.6 m³

28.

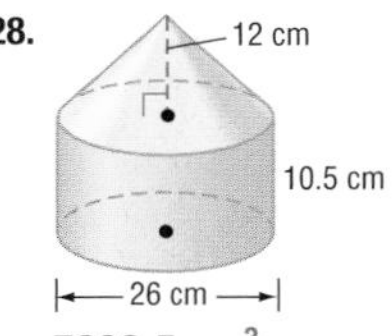

7698.5 cm³

29. **HEATING** Sam is building an art studio in her backyard. To buy a heating unit for the space, she needs to determine the BTUs (British Thermal Units) required to heat the building. For new construction with good insulation, there should be 2 BTUs per cubic foot. What size unit does Sam need to purchase? about 13,333 BTUs

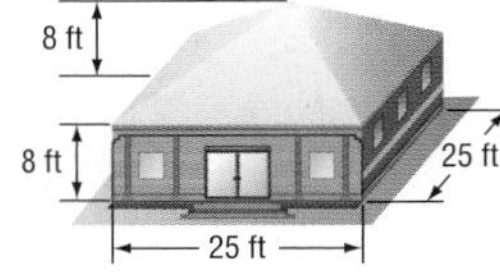

30. **SCIENCE** Refer to page 873. Determine the volume of the model. Explain why knowing the volume is helpful in this situation.

30. 2 in³; It tells Marta how much clay is needed to make the model.

CCSS Teaching the Mathematical Practices

Modeling Mathematically proficient students can apply the mathematics they know to solve problems arising in everyday life. In Exercise 24, encourage students to draw a diagram.

Enrichment

OL BL

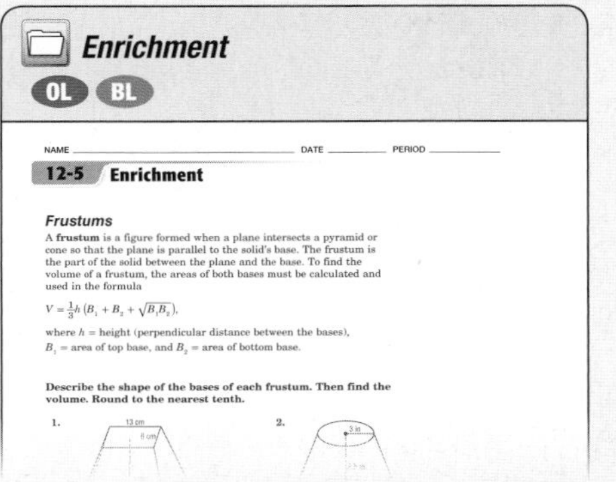

NAME ______ DATE ______ PERIOD ______

12-5 Enrichment

Frustums

A **frustum** is a figure formed when a plane intersects a pyramid or cone so that the plane is parallel to the solid's base. The frustum is the part of the solid between the plane and the base. To find the volume of a frustum, the areas of both bases must be calculated and used in the formula

$V = \frac{1}{3}h(B_1 + B_2 + \sqrt{B_1B_2})$,

where h = height (perpendicular distance between the bases), B_1 = area of top base, and B_2 = area of bottom base.

Describe the shape of the bases of each frustum. Then find the volume. Round to the nearest tenth.

1. 2.

Study Guide and Intervention

AL OL ELL

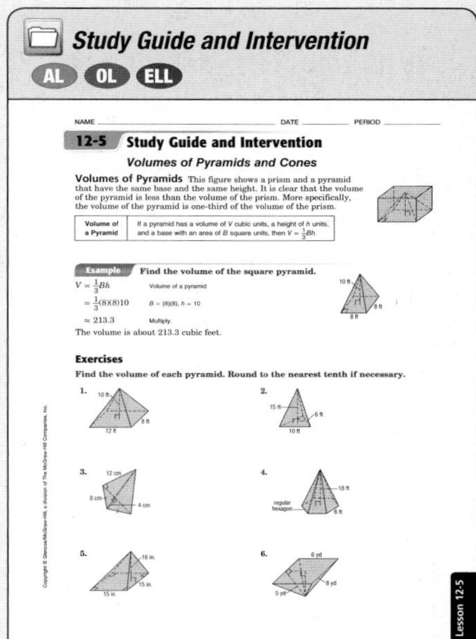

NAME ______ DATE ______ PERIOD ______

12-5 Study Guide and Intervention

Volumes of Pyramids and Cones

Volumes of Pyramids This figure shows a prism and a pyramid that have the same base and the same height. It is clear that the volume of the pyramid is less than the volume of the prism. More specifically, the volume of the pyramid is one-third of the volume of the prism.

Volume of a Pyramid	If a pyramid has a volume of V cubic units, a height of h units, and a base with an area of B square units, then $V = \frac{1}{3}Bh$.

Example Find the volume of the square pyramid.

$V = \frac{1}{3}Bh$ Volume of a pyramid

$= \frac{1}{3}(8)(8)10$ $B = (8)(8), h = 10$

≈ 213.3 Multiply.

The volume is about 213.3 cubic feet.

Exercises

Find the volume of each pyramid. Round to the nearest tenth if necessary.

1. 2. 3. 4. 5. 6.

Lesson 12-5

Practice

AL OL BL ELL

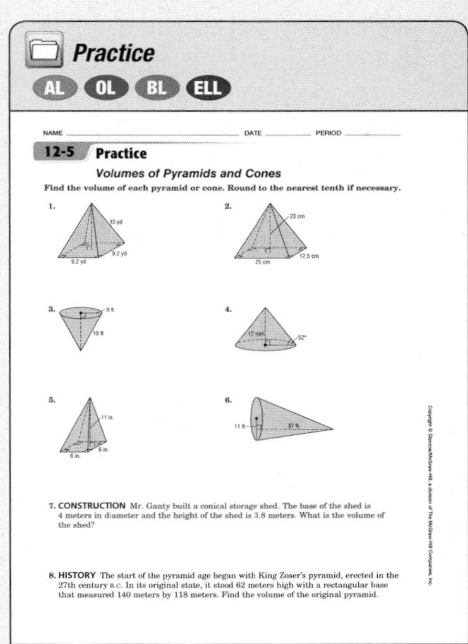

NAME ______ DATE ______ PERIOD ______

12-5 Practice

Volumes of Pyramids and Cones

Find the volume of each pyramid or cone. Round to the nearest tenth if necessary.

1. 2. 3. 4. 5. 6.

7. **CONSTRUCTION** Mr. Ganty built a conical storage shed. The base of the shed is 4 meters in diameter and the height of the shed is 3.8 meters. What is the volume of the shed?

8. **HISTORY** The start of the pyramid age began with King Zoser's pyramid, erected in the 27th century B.C. In its original state, it stood 62 meters high with a rectangular base that measured 140 meters by 118 meters. Find the volume of the original pyramid.

Word Problem Practice

AL OL BL ELL

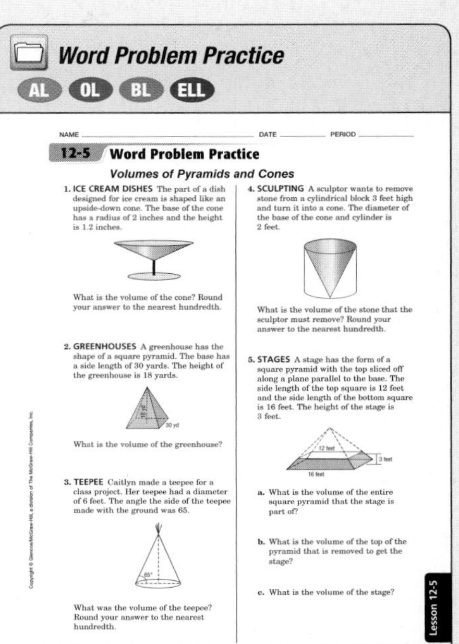

NAME ______ DATE ______ PERIOD ______

12-5 Word Problem Practice

Volumes of Pyramids and Cones

1. **ICE CREAM DISHES** The part of a dish designed for ice cream is shaped like an upside-down cone. The base of the cone has a radius of 2 inches and the height is 1.2 inches.

What is the volume of the cone? Round your answer to the nearest hundredth.

2. **GREENHOUSES** A greenhouse has the shape of a square pyramid. The base has a side length of 30 yards. The height of the greenhouse is 18 yards.

What is the volume of the greenhouse?

3. **TEEPEE** Caitlyn made a teepee for a class project. Her teepee had a diameter of 6 feet. The angle the side of the teepee made with the ground was 65.

What was the volume of the teepee? Round your answer to the nearest hundredth.

4. **SCULPTING** A sculptor wants to remove stone from a cylindrical block 3 feet high and turn it into a cone. The diameter of the base of the cone and cylinder is 2 feet.

What is the volume of the stone that the sculptor must remove? Round your answer to the nearest hundredth.

5. **STAGES** A stage has the form of a square pyramid with the top sliced off along a plane parallel to the base. The side length of the top square is 12 feet and the side length of the bottom square is 16 feet. The height of the stage is 3 feet.

a. What is the volume of the entire square pyramid that the stage is part of?

b. What is the volume of the top of the pyramid that is removed to get the stage?

c. What is the volume of the stage?

Lesson 12-5

Multiple Representations

In Exercise 35, students use drawings and verbal descriptions to investigate the volume of a rectangular pyramid.

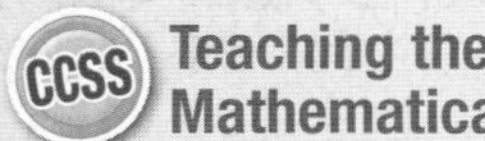

Teaching the Mathematical Practices

Arguments Mathematically proficient students understand and use stated assumptions and definitions in constructing arguments. In Exercise 36, encourage students to calculate and compare the volumes of a cone and prism with the same radius and height.

WatchOut!

Error Analysis In Exercise 37, students should recognize the difference between the height of the cone and the slant height. Alexandra used the slant height instead of the height in the formula.

Additional Answers

35a. Sample answer:

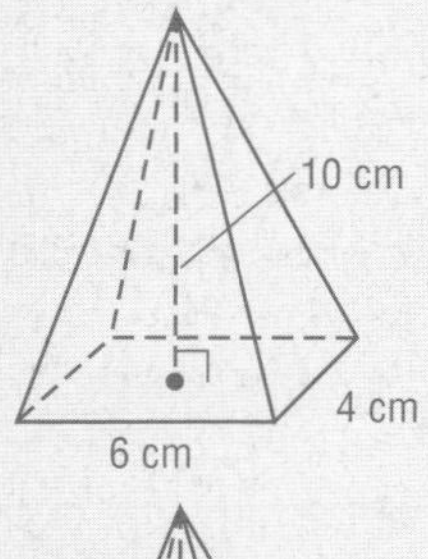

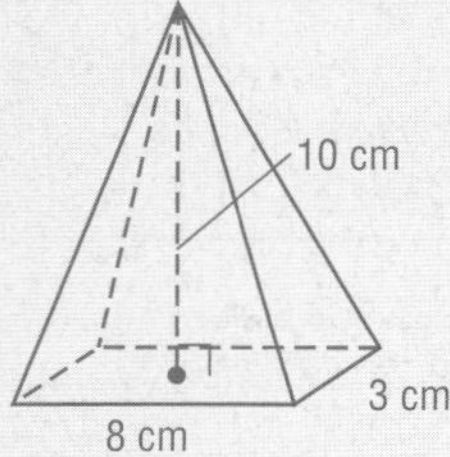

35b. The volumes are the same. The volume of a pyramid equals one third times the base area times the height. So, if the base areas of two pyramids are equal and their heights are equal, then their volumes are equal.

31. **CHANGING DIMENSIONS** A cone has a radius of 4 centimeters and a height of 9 centimeters. Describe how each change affects the volume of the cone.

a. The height is doubled. **The volume is doubled.**

b. The radius is doubled. **The volume is multiplied by 2^2 or 4.**

c. Both the radius and the height are doubled. **The volume is multiplied by 2^3 or 8.**

Find each measure. Round to the nearest tenth if necessary.

32. A square pyramid has a volume of 862.5 cubic centimeters and a height of 11.5 centimeters. Find the side length of the base. **15 cm**

33 The volume of a cone is 196π cubic inches and the height is 12 inches. What is the diameter? **14 in.**

34. The lateral area of a cone is 71.6 square millimeters and the slant height is 6 millimeters. What is the volume of the cone? **70.2 mm^3**

35. **MULTIPLE REPRESENTATIONS** In this problem, you will investigate rectangular pyramids. **a–c. See margin.**

a. **Geometric** Draw two pyramids with different bases that have a height of 10 centimeters and a base area of 24 square centimeters.

b. **Verbal** What is true about the volumes of the two pyramids that you drew? Explain.

c. **Analytical** Explain how multiplying the base area and/or the height of the pyramid by 5 affects the volume of the pyramid.

H.O.T. Problems Use Higher-Order Thinking Skills

36. **CCSS ARGUMENTS** Determine whether the following statement is *always*, *sometimes*, or *never* true. Justify your reasoning. **See margin.**

The volume of a cone with radius r and height h equals the volume of a prism with height h.

37. **ERROR ANALYSIS** Alexandra and Cornelio are calculating the volume of the cone at the right. Is either of them correct? Explain your answer. **See margin.**

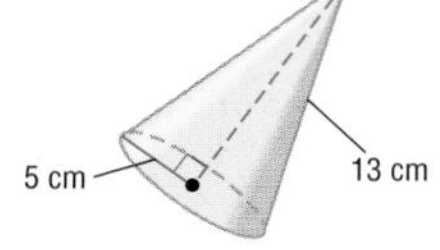

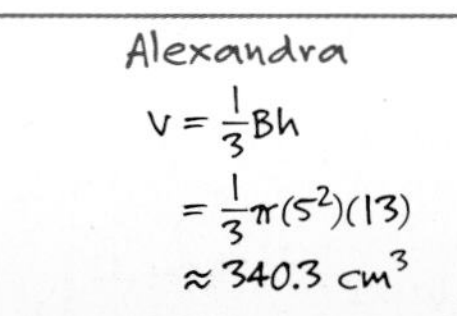

Cornelio

$5^2 + 12^2 = 13^2$

$V = \frac{1}{3}Bh$

$= \frac{1}{3}\pi(5^2)(12)$

$\approx 314.2 \text{ cm}^3$

40. To find the volume of each solid, you must know the area of the base and the height. The volume of a pyramid is one third the volume of a prism that has the same height and base area. The volume of a cone is one third the volume of a cylinder that has the same height and base area.

38. **REASONING** A cone has a volume of 568 cubic centimeters. What is the volume of a cylinder that has the same radius and height as the cone? Explain your reasoning. **See margin.**

39. **OPEN ENDED** Give an example of a pyramid and a prism that have the same base and the same volume. Explain your reasoning. **See margin.**

40. **WRITING IN MATH** Compare and contrast finding volumes of pyramids and cones with finding volumes of prisms and cylinders.

35c. If the base area is multiplied by 5, the volume is multiplied by 5. If the height is multiplied by 5, the volume is multiplied by 5. If both the base area and the height are multiplied by 5, the volume is multiplied by 5 • 5 or 25.

36. Sometimes; the statement is true if the base area of the cone is 3 times as great as the base area of the prism. For example, if the base of the prism has an area of 10 square units, then its volume is $10h$ cubic units. So, the cone must have a base area of 30 square units so that its volume is $\frac{1}{3}(30)h$ or $10h$ cubic units.

37. Cornelio; Alexandra incorrectly used the slant height.

Standardized Test Practice

41. A conical sand toy has the dimensions as shown below. How many cubic centimeters of sand will it hold when it is filled to the top? **A**

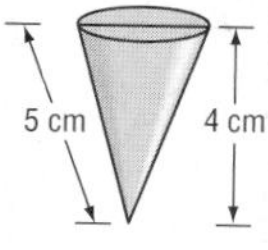

A 12π C $\frac{80}{3}\pi$

B 15π D $\frac{100}{3}\pi$

42. **SHORT RESPONSE** Brooke is buying a tent that is in the shape of a rectangular pyramid. The base is 6 feet by 8 feet. If the tent holds 88 cubic feet of air, how tall is the tent's center pole? **5.5 ft**

43. **PROBABILITY** A spinner has sections colored red, blue, orange, and green. The table below shows the results of several spins. What is the experimental probability of the spinner landing on orange? **F**

Color	Frequency
red	6
blue	4
orange	5
green	10

F $\frac{1}{5}$ H $\frac{9}{25}$

G $\frac{1}{4}$ J $\frac{1}{2}$

44. **SAT/ACT** For all $x \neq -2$ or 0, $\frac{x^2 - 2x - 8}{x^2 + 2x} = ?$ **E**

A -8 D $\frac{-8}{x+2}$

B $x - 4$ E $\frac{x-4}{x}$

C $\frac{-x-4}{x}$

Spiral Review

Find the volume of each prism. (Lesson 12-4)

45. 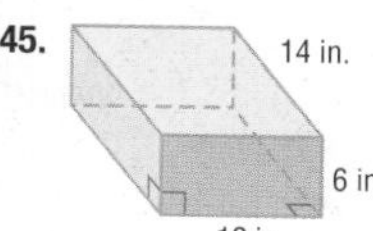

1008.0 in^3

46. 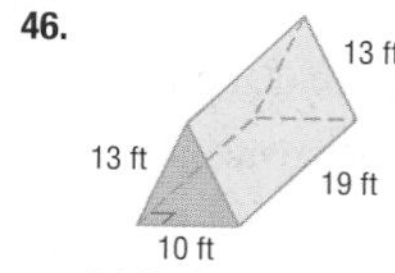

1140.0 ft^3

47. 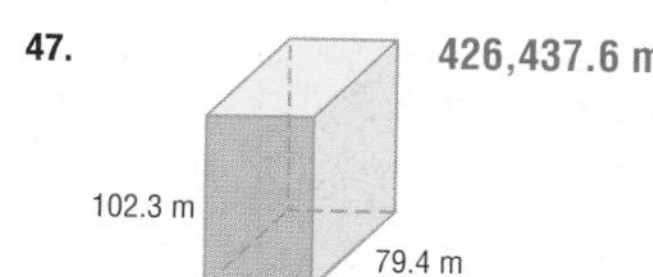

426,437.6 m^3

48. **FARMING** The picture shows a combination hopper cone and bin used by farmers to store grain after harvest. The cone at the bottom of the bin allows the grain to be emptied more easily. Use the dimensions in the diagram to find the entire surface area of the bin with a conical top and bottom. Write the exact answer and the answer rounded to the nearest square foot. (Lesson 12-3)
$\pi(216 + 9\sqrt{106} + 81\sqrt{2}) \approx 1330$ ft^2

Skills Review

Find the area of each shaded region. The polygons in Exercises 50-52 are regular.

49. 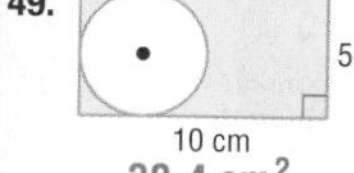

30.4 cm^2

50. 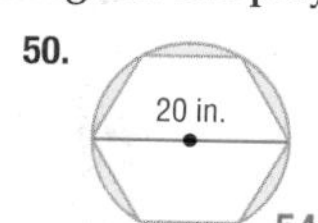

54.4 in^2

51. 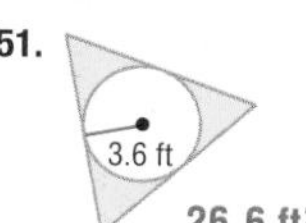

26.6 ft^2

52. 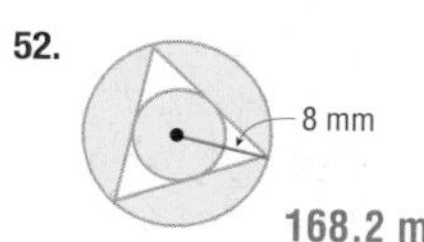

168.2 mm^2

Differentiated Instruction OL BL

Extension Have students find dimensions for a square pyramid and a cone that have the same height and approximately the same volume. Sample answer: cone with radius 6 cm and height 8 cm and square pyramid with base edge length 10.63 cm and height 8 cm.

4 Assess

Ticket Out the Door Ask students to list all the volume formulas they have learned thus far, along with an example of how to find each. Have students turn in their statements before they leave the classroom.

Additional Answers

38. 1704 cm^3; The volume of a cylinder is three times as much as the volume of a cone with the same radius and height.

39. Sample answer: A square pyramid with a base area of 16 and a height of 12, a prism with a square base area of 16 and a height of 4; if a pyramid and prism have the same base, then in order to have the same volume, the height of the pyramid must be 3 times as great as the height of the prism.

1 Focus

VerticalAlignment

Before Lesson 12-6 Find the surface areas of prisms and cylinders.

Lesson 12-6 Find the surface areas and volumes of spheres.

After Lesson 12-6 Investigate spherical geometry and compare and contrast with Euclidean geometry.

2 Teach

Scaffolding Questions

Have students read the **Why?** section of the lesson.

Ask:

- What is a cross section in any direction of a sphere? a circle
- What measurement do you think would be needed to find the volume of a sphere? Sample answer: the radius

LESSON 12-6 Surface Areas and Volumes of Spheres

Then

- You found surface areas of prisms and cylinders.

Now

1. Find surface areas of spheres.
2. Find volumes of spheres.

Why?

- When you blow bubbles, soapy liquid surrounds a volume of air. Because of surface tension, the liquid maintains a shape that minimizes the surface area surrounding the air. The shape that minimizes surface area per unit of volume is a sphere.

NewVocabulary
great circle
pole
hemisphere

Common Core State Standards

Content Standards

G.GMD.1 Give an informal argument for the formulas for the circumference of a circle, area of a circle, volume of a cylinder, pyramid, and cone.

G.GMD.3 Use volume formulas for cylinders, pyramids, cones, and spheres to solve problems. ★

Mathematical Practices

1 Make sense of problems and persevere in solving them.

6 Attend to precision.

1 Surface Area of Spheres

Recall that a *sphere* is the locus of all points in space that are a given distance from a given point called the *center* of the sphere.

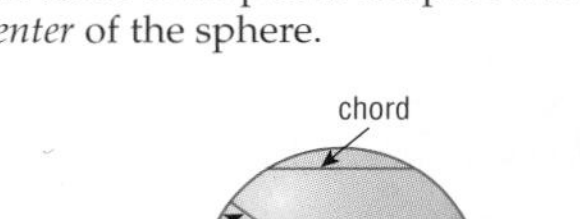

chord
radius
diameter
tangent

- A *radius* of a sphere is a segment from the center to a point on the sphere.
- A *chord* of a sphere is a segment that connects any two points on the sphere.
- A *diameter* of a sphere is a chord that contains the center.
- A *tangent* to a sphere is a line that intersects the sphere in exactly one point.

To develop a formula for the surface area of a sphere, consider a tennis ball. The covering of this sphere is comprised of two congruent dumbell-shaped pieces, each of which can be approximated by two congruent circles with radii equal to that of the sphere. So, the entire covering consists of approximately four congruent circles. The sum of these areas approximates the surface area of the sphere.

$S \approx 4A$ Sum of circles with area A

$\approx 4(\pi r^2)$ or $4\pi r^2$ $A = \pi r^2$

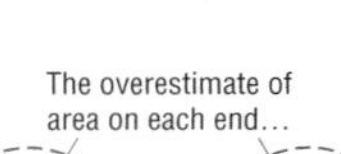

The overestimate of area on each end…
… approximates the underestimate in the middle.

While its derivation is beyond the scope of this course, the exact formula is in fact $S = 4\pi r^2$.

KeyConcept Surface Area of a Sphere

Words The surface area S of a sphere is $S = 4\pi r^2$, where r is the radius.

Symbols $S = 4\pi r^2$

Model

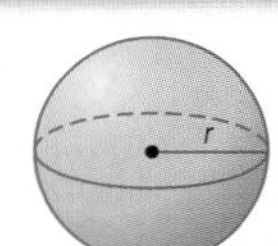

880 | Lesson 12-6

Lesson 12-6 Resources

Resource	Approaching Level AL	On Level OL	Beyond Level BL	English Learners ELL
Teacher Edition		▪ Differentiated Instruction, p. 883	▪ Differentiated Instruction, pp. 883, 886	
Chapter Resource Masters	▪ Study Guide and Intervention, pp. 37–38 ▪ Skills Practice, p. 39 ▪ Practice, p. 40 ▪ Word Problem Practice, p. 41	▪ Study Guide and Intervention, pp. 37–38 ▪ Skills Practice, p. 39 ▪ Practice, p. 40 ▪ Word Problem Practice, p. 41 ▪ Enrichment, p. 42	▪ Practice, p. 40 ▪ Word Problem Practice, p. 41 ▪ Enrichment, p. 42	▪ Study Guide and Intervention, pp. 37–38 ▪ Skills Practice, p. 39 ▪ Practice, p. 40 ▪ Word Problem Practice, p. 41
Other	▪ 5-Minute Check 12-6 ▪ Study Notebook	▪ 5-Minute Check 12-6 ▪ Study Notebook	▪ 5-Minute Check 12-6 ▪ Study Notebook	▪ 5-Minute Check 12-6 ▪ Study Notebook

Example 1 Surface Area of a Sphere

Find the surface area of the sphere. Round to the nearest tenth.

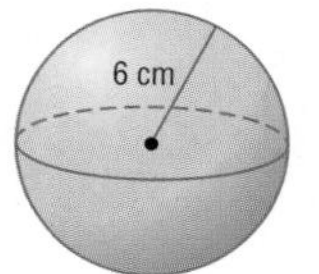

$S = 4\pi r^2$ Surface area of a sphere

$= 4\pi(6)^2$ Replace r with 6.

≈ 452.4 Use a calculator.

The surface area is about 452.4 square centimeters.

Guided Practice

1A. 633.5 mm^2

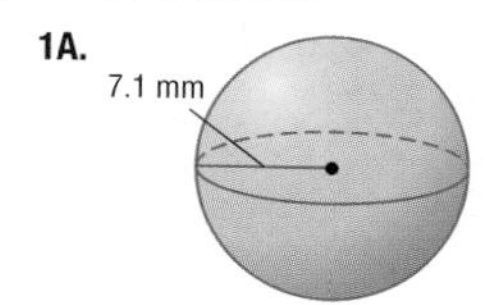

1B. 1520.5 ft^2

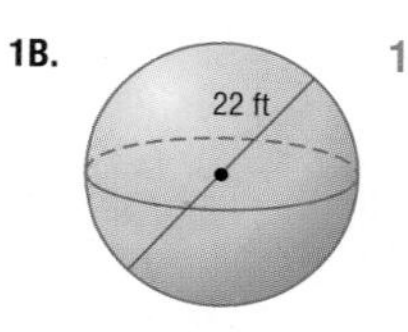

StudyTip

Great Circles A sphere has an infinite number of great circles.

A plane can intersect a sphere in a point or in a circle. If the circle contains the center of the sphere, the intersection is called a **great circle**. The endpoints of a diameter of a great circle are called **poles**.

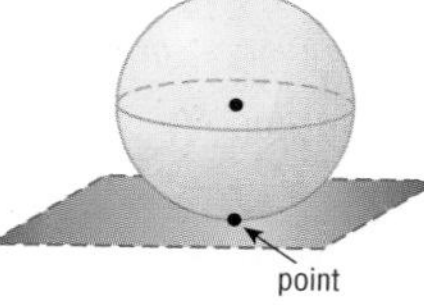

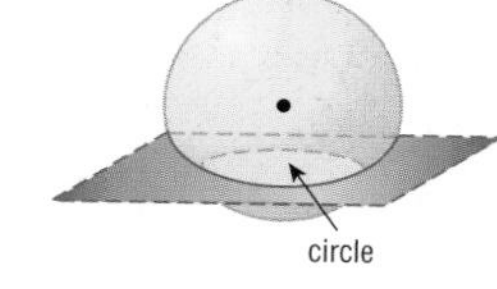

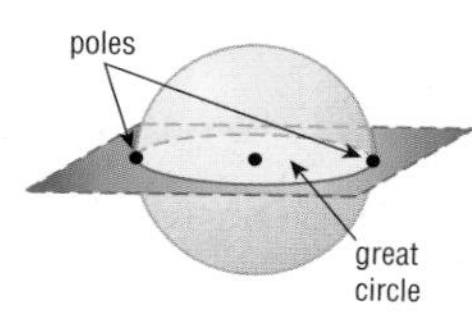

Since a great circle has the same center as the sphere and its radii are also radii of the sphere, it is the largest circle that can be drawn on a sphere. A great circle separates a sphere into two congruent halves, called **hemispheres**.

Example 2 Use Great Circles to Find Surface Area

WatchOut!

Area of Hemisphere When finding the surface area of a hemisphere, do not forget to include the area of the great circle.

a. Find the surface area of the hemisphere.

Find half the area of a sphere with a radius of 2.8 centimeters. Then add the area of the great circle.

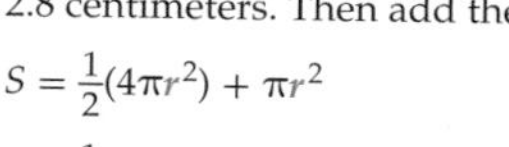

$S = \frac{1}{2}(4\pi r^2) + \pi r^2$ Surface area of a hemisphere

$= \frac{1}{2}[4\pi(2.8)^2] + \pi(2.8)^2$ Replace r with 2.8.

$\approx 73.9\text{ cm}^2$ Use a calculator.

b. Find the surface area of a sphere if the circumference of the great circle is 5π meters.

First, find the radius. The circumference of a great circle is $2\pi r$. So, $2\pi r = 5\pi$ or $r = 2.5$.

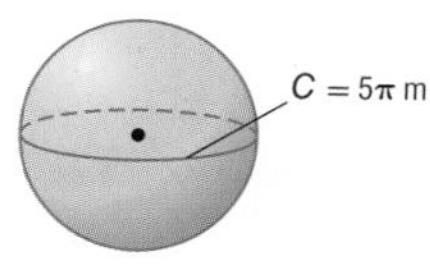

$S = 4\pi r^2$ Surface area of a sphere

$= 4\pi(2.5)^2$ Replace r with 2.5.

$\approx 78.5\text{ m}^2$ Use a calculator.

Teach with Tech

Document Camera Bring several different types of balls (tennis, baseball, golf ball, etc.) and have students find the surface area and volume of each. Choose a student to measure the circumference of a ball and explain to the class how that measurement is used to find the surface area and volume of the ball.

1 Surface Area of Spheres

Examples 1 and 2 show how to find the surface areas of spheres and hemispheres.

Formative Assessment

Use the Guided Practice exercises after each Example to determine students' understanding of concepts.

Additional Examples

1 Find the surface area of the sphere. Round to the nearest tenth.

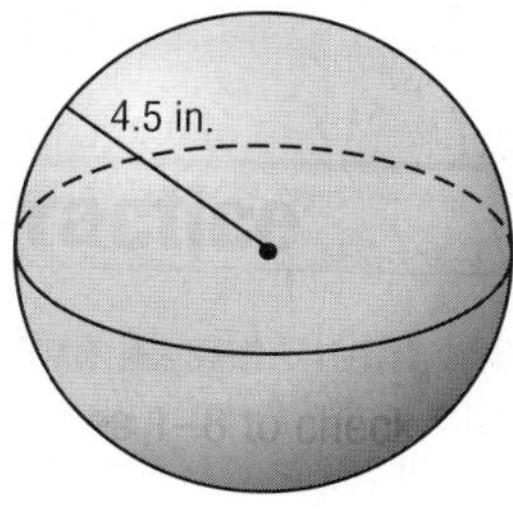

254.5 in^2

2 a. Find the surface area of the hemisphere. 129 mm^2

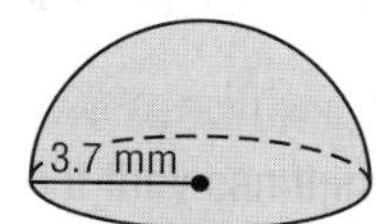

b. Find the surface area of a sphere if the circumference of the great circle is 10π feet. 314.2 ft^2

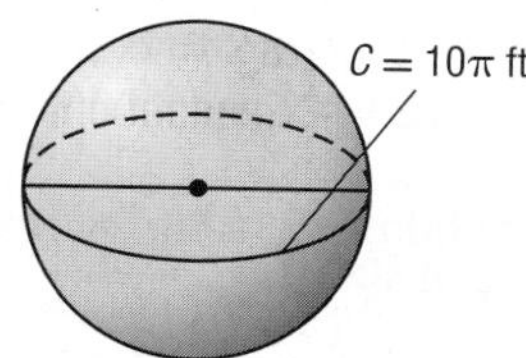

c. Find the surface area of a sphere if the area of the great circle is approximately 220 square meters. 886.7 m^2

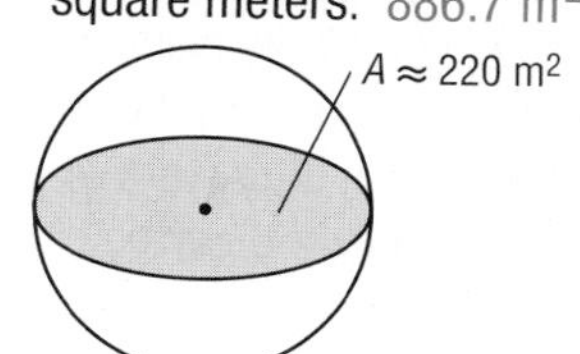

WatchOut!

Rounding In Example 2c, you could have also replaced πr^2 in the formula with 130. The answer may have been slightly different because of rounding.

2 Volume of Spheres

Example 3 shows how to find the volume of spheres and hemispheres. **Example 4** shows to use volume of a sphere in a real-world example.

Additional Example

3 Find the volume of each sphere or hemisphere. Round to the nearest tenth.

a. a sphere with a great circle circumference of 30π centimeters $14{,}137.2 \text{ cm}^3$

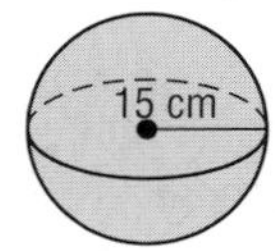

b. a hemisphere with a diameter of 6 feet 56.5 ft^3

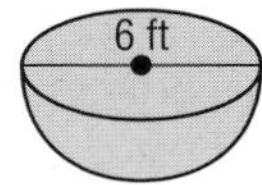

Additional Examples also in Interactive Classroom PowerPoint® Presentations

IWB Interactive White Board READY

Teaching the Mathematical Practices

Precision Mathematically proficient students are careful about specifying units of measure. They calculate accurately and efficiently. Encourage students to check their work to make sure that the units are correct.

c. Find the surface area of a sphere if the area of the great circle is approximately 130 square inches.

$A \approx 130 \text{ in}^2$

First, find the radius. The area of a great circle is πr^2. So, $\pi r^2 = 130$ or $r \approx 6.4$.

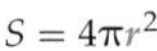

$S = 4\pi r^2$ Surface area of a sphere

$\approx 4\pi(6.4)^2$ or about 514.7 in^2 Replace r with 6.4. Use a calculator.

GuidedPractice

Find the surface area of each figure. Round to the nearest tenth if necessary.

2A. sphere: circumference of great circle $= 16.2\pi$ ft 824.5 ft^2

2B. hemisphere: area of great circle $\approx 94 \text{ mm}^2$ 282 mm^2

2C. hemisphere: circumference of great circle $= 36\pi$ cm 3053.6 cm^2

2 Volume of Spheres Suppose a sphere with radius r contains infinitely many pyramids with vertices at the center of the sphere. Each pyramid has height r and base area B. The sum of the volumes of all the pyramids equals the volume of the sphere.

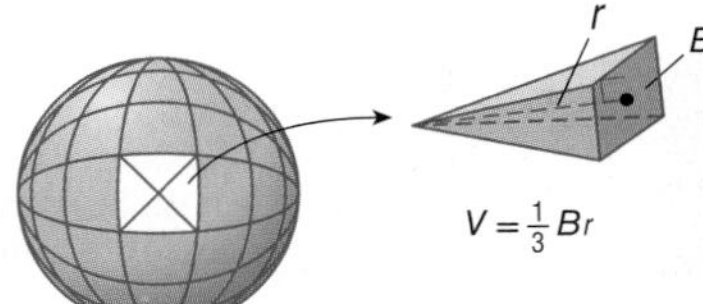

$V = \frac{1}{3}B_1r_1 + \frac{1}{3}B_2r_2 + \ldots + \frac{1}{3}B_nr_n$ Sum of volumes of pyramids

$= \frac{1}{3}r(B_1 + B_2 + \ldots + B_n)$ Distributive Property

$= \frac{1}{3}r(4\pi r^2)$ The sum of the pyramid base areas equals the surface area of the sphere.

$= \frac{4}{3}\pi r^3$ Simplify.

StudyTip

Draw a Diagram When solving problems involving volumes of solids, it is helpful to draw and label a diagram when no diagram is provided.

KeyConcept Volume of a Sphere

Words	The volume V of a sphere is $V = \frac{4}{3}\pi r^3$, where r is the radius of the sphere.	**Model**
Symbols	$V = \frac{4}{3}\pi r^3$	

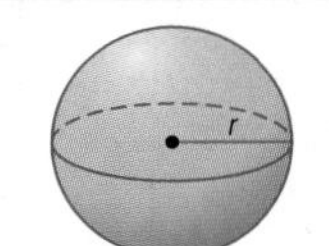

Example 3 Volumes of Spheres and Hemispheres

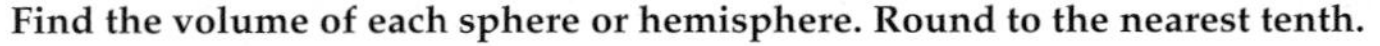

Find the volume of each sphere or hemisphere. Round to the nearest tenth.

a. a hemisphere with a radius of 6 meters

Estimate: $V \approx \frac{1}{2} \cdot \frac{4}{3} \cdot 3 \cdot 6^3$ or 432 m^3

$V = \frac{1}{2}\left(\frac{4}{3}\pi r^3\right)$ Volume of a hemisphere

$= \frac{2}{3}\pi(6)^3$ or about 452.4 m^3 Replace r with 6. Use a calculator.

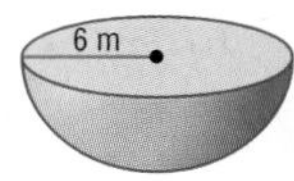

The volume of the hemisphere is about 452.4 cubic meters. This is close to the estimate, so the answer is reasonable.

StudyTip

CCSS Precision Remember to use the correct units when giving your answers. As with other solids, the surface area of a sphere is measured in square units, and volume is measured in cubic units.

Focus on Mathematical Content

Radius Point out that the intersection of any plane with a sphere in its interior is a circle with a radius less than or equal to the radius of the sphere.

b. **a sphere with a great circle circumference of 18π centimeters**

Step 1 Find the radius of the sphere.

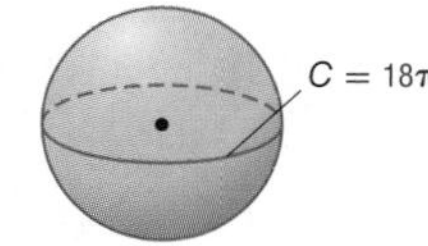

$C = 2\pi r$ Circumference of a circle

$18\pi = 2\pi r$ Replace C with 18π.

$r = 9$ Solve for r.

Step 2 Find the volume.

$V = \frac{4}{3}\pi r^3$ Volume of a sphere

$= \frac{4}{3}\pi(9)^3$ or about 3053.6 cm^3 Replace r with 9. Use a calculator.

GuidedPractice

3A. sphere: diameter = 7.4 in. **212.2 in^3**

3B. hemisphere: area of great circle $\approx 249 \text{ mm}^2$ **1477.9 mm^3**

Real-WorldLink

The University of North Carolina has won the greatest number of national championships in women's soccer since the first tournament in 1982. As of 2009, they have won 18 times.

Source: Fact Monster

Real-World Example 4 Solve Problems Involving Solids

SOCCER **The soccer ball globe at the right was constructed for the 2006 World Cup soccer tournament. It takes up $47{,}916\pi$ cubic feet of space. Assume that the globe is a sphere. What is the circumference of the globe?**

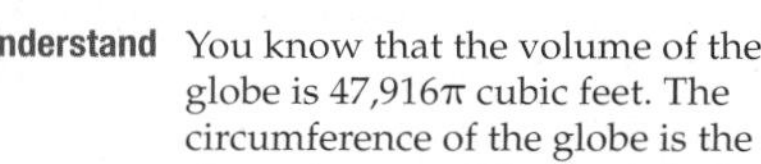

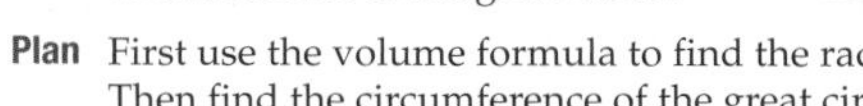

Understand You know that the volume of the globe is $47{,}916\pi$ cubic feet. The circumference of the globe is the circumference of the great circle.

Plan First use the volume formula to find the radius. Then find the circumference of the great circle.

Solve

$V = \frac{4}{3}\pi r^3$ Volume of a sphere

$47{,}916\pi = \frac{4}{3}\pi r^3$ Replace V with $47{,}916\pi$.

$35{,}937 = r^3$ Divide each side by $\frac{4}{3}\pi$.

Use a calculator to find $\sqrt[3]{35{,}937}$.

35937  [^] 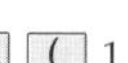 [(] 1  [÷] 3 [)]  [ENTER] 33

The radius of the globe is 33 feet. So, the circumference is $2\pi r = 2\pi(33)$ or approximately 207.3 feet.

Check You can work backward to check the solution.

If $C \approx 207.3$, then $r \approx 33$. If $r \approx 33$, then $V \approx \frac{4}{3}\pi \cdot 33^3$ or about $47{,}917\pi$ cubic feet. The solution is correct. ✓

GuidedPractice

4. **BALLOONS** Ren inflates a spherical balloon to a circumference of about 14 inches. He then adds more air to the balloon until the circumference is about 18 inches. What volume of air was added to the balloon? **about 52.1 in^3**

Additional Example

4 **ARCHEOLOGY** The stone spheres of Costa Rica were made by forming granodiorite boulders into spheres. One of the stone spheres has a volume of about $36{,}000\pi$ cubic inches. What is the diameter of the stone sphere? 60 in.

DifferentiatedInstruction OL BL

Naturalist Learners One way to compare moons is by their approximate diameters. Ask students to describe how to find the surface area of a moon. To find the surface area, determine the radius from the diameter. Then substitute the radius into the formula 4π times the square of the radius.

3 Practice

Formative Assessment

Use Exercises 1–9 to check for understanding.

Use the chart at the bottom of this page to customize assignments for your students.

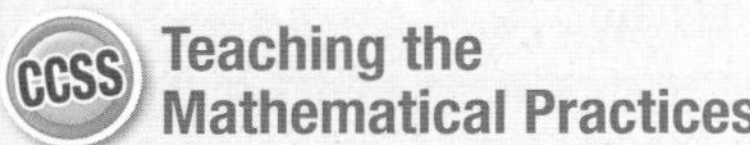

Teaching the Mathematical Practices

Precision Mathematically proficient students are careful about specifying units of measure. In Exercises 18–25, encourage students to check the units carefully.

Check Your Understanding

= Step-by-Step Solutions begin on page R14.

Examples 1–2 **Find the surface area of each sphere or hemisphere. Round to the nearest tenth.**

1. 9 m — 1017.9 m^2

2. 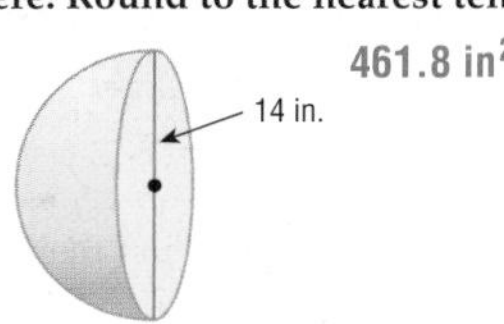

461.8 in^2

3. sphere: area of great circle = 36π yd^2 452.4 yd^2

4. hemisphere: circumference of great circle ≈ 26 cm 161.4 cm^2

Example 3 **Find the volume of each sphere or hemisphere. Round to the nearest tenth.**

5. sphere: radius = 10 ft 4188.8 ft^3

6. hemisphere: diameter = 16 cm 1072.3 cm^3

7. hemisphere: circumference of great circle = 24π m 3619.1 m^3

8. sphere: area of great circle = 55π in^2 1708.6 in^3

Example 4

9. **BASKETBALL** Basketballs used in professional games must have a circumference of $29\frac{1}{2}$ inches. What is the surface area of a basketball used in a professional game? 277.0 in^2

Practice and Problem Solving

Extra Practice is on page R12.

Examples 1–2 **Find the surface area of each sphere or hemisphere. Round to the nearest tenth.**

10. 50.3 ft^2
11. 113.1 cm^2
12. 109.0 mm^2
13. 680.9 in^2

10. 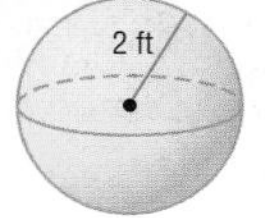

11. 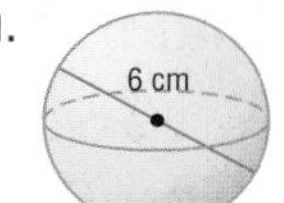

12. 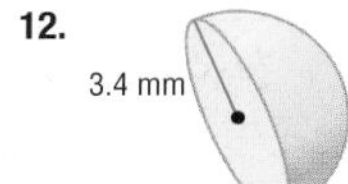

13. 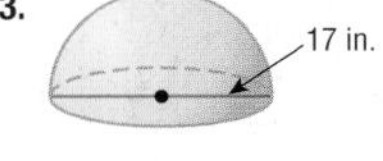

14. sphere: circumference of great circle = 2π cm 12.6 cm^2

15. sphere: area of great circle ≈ 32 ft^2 128 ft^2

16. hemisphere: area of great circle ≈ 40 in^2 120 in^2

17. hemisphere: circumference of great circle = 15π mm 530.1 mm^2

Example 3 CCSS **PRECISION** **Find the volume of each sphere or hemisphere. Round to the nearest tenth.**

18. 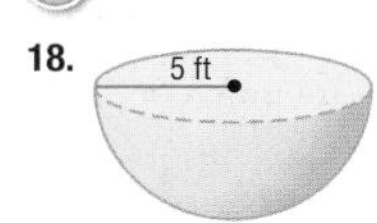

261.8 ft^3

19. 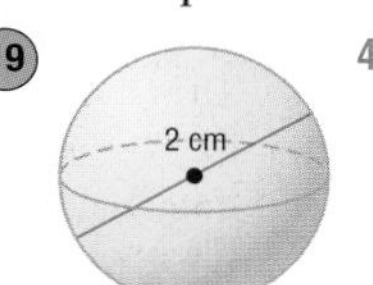

4.2 cm^3

20. sphere: radius = 1.4 yd 11.5 yd^3

21. hemisphere: diameter = 21.8 cm 2712.3 cm^3

22. sphere: area of great circle = 49π m^2 1436.8 m^3

23. sphere: circumference of great circle ≈ 22 in. 179.8 in^3

24. hemisphere: circumference of great circle ≈ 18 ft 49.2 ft^3

25. hemisphere: area of great circle ≈ 35 m^2 77.9 m^3

Differentiated Homework Options

Level	Assignment	Two-Day Option	
AL Basic	10–27, 46–65	11–27 odd, 49–52	10–26 even, 46–48, 53–65
OL Core	11–27 odd, 28, 29, 31, 32, 33–37 odd, 38, 39, 41, 43, 44, 46–65	10–27, 49–52	28–44, 46–48, 53–65
BL Advanced	28–61, (optional: 62–65)		

Example 4 **26. FISH** A *puffer fish* is able to "puff up" when threatened by gulping water and inflating its body. The puffer fish at the right is approximately a sphere with a diameter of 5 inches. Its surface area when inflated is about 1.5 times its normal surface area. What is the surface area of the fish when it is *not* puffed up? **about 52.4 in^2**

27. ARCHITECTURE The Reunion Tower in Dallas, Texas, is topped by a spherical dome that has a surface area of approximately 13,924π square feet. What is the volume of the dome? Round to the nearest tenth. **860,289.5 ft^3**

28. TREE HOUSE The spherical tree house, or *tree sphere*, shown at the right has a diameter of 10.5 feet. Its volume is 1.8 times the volume of the first tree sphere that was built. What was the diameter of the first tree sphere? Round to the nearest foot. **9 ft**

CCSS SENSE-MAKING **Find the surface area and the volume of each solid. Round to the nearest tenth.**

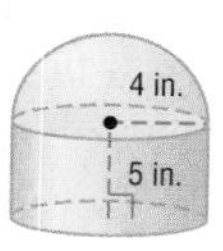

29. **276.5 in^2; 385.4 in^3**

30.

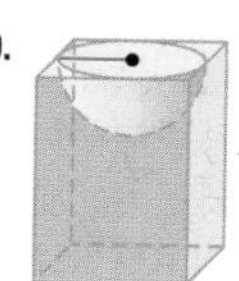

798.5 cm^2; 1038.2 cm^3

31. TOYS The spinning top at the right is a composite of a cone and a hemisphere.

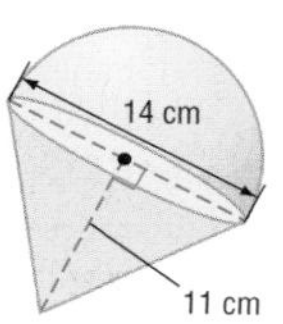

a. Find the surface area and the volume of the top. Round to the nearest tenth. **594.6 cm^2; 1282.8 cm^3**

b. If the manufacturer of the top makes another model with dimensions that are one-half of the dimensions of this top, what are its surface area and volume? **148.7 cm^2; 160.4 cm^3**

32. BALLOONS A spherical helium-filled balloon with a diameter of 30 centimeters can lift a 14-gram object. Find the size of a balloon that could lift a person who weighs 65 kilograms. Round to the nearest tenth. **The balloon would have to have a diameter of approximately 139,286 cm.**

Use sphere *S* to name each of the following.

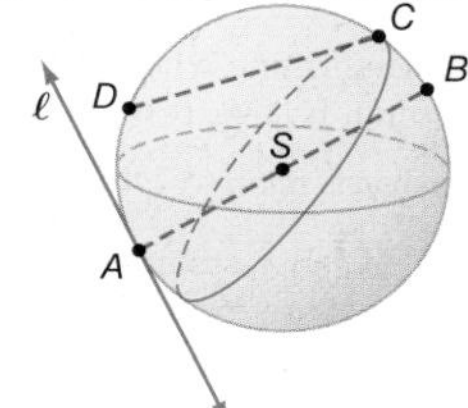

33. a chord **$\overline{DC}$**

34. a radius **Sample answer: $\overline{SA}$**

35. a diameter **$\overline{AB}$**

36. a tangent **line ℓ**

37. a great circle **⊙*S***

38. DIMENSIONAL ANALYSIS Which has greater volume: a sphere with a radius of 2.3 yards or a cylinder with a radius of 4 feet and height of 8 feet? **the sphere**

CCSS Teaching the Mathematical Practices

Sense-Making Mathematically proficient students start by explaining the meaning of a problem to themselves and looking for entry points to its solution. They plan a solution pathway rather than simply jumping into a solution attempt. In Exercises 29–30, encourage students to make a plan to solve each problem first.

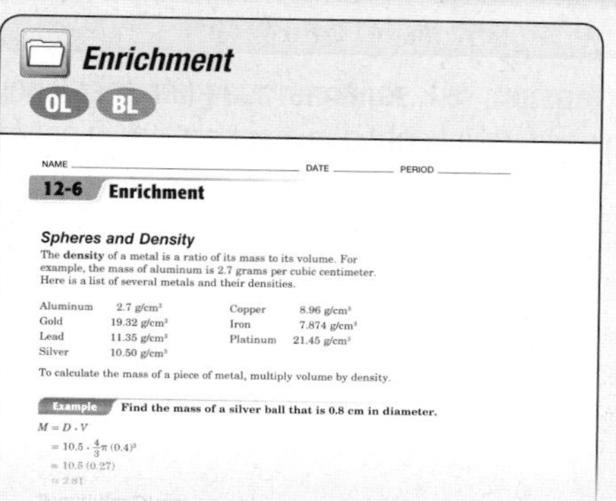

Enrichment
OL BL

NAME ______ DATE ______ PERIOD ______

12-6 Enrichment

Spheres and Density

The **density** of a metal is a ratio of its mass to its volume. For example, the mass of aluminum is 2.7 grams per cubic centimeter. Here is a list of several metals and their densities.

Aluminum	2.7 g/cm³	Copper	8.96 g/cm³
Gold	19.32 g/cm³	Iron	7.874 g/cm³
Lead	11.35 g/cm³	Platinum	21.45 g/cm³
Silver	10.50 g/cm³		

To calculate the mass of a piece of metal, multiply volume by density.

Example Find the mass of a silver ball that is 0.8 cm in diameter.

$M = D \cdot V$
$= 10.5 \cdot \frac{4}{3}\pi(0.4)^3$
$= 10.5(0.27)$
≈ 2.81

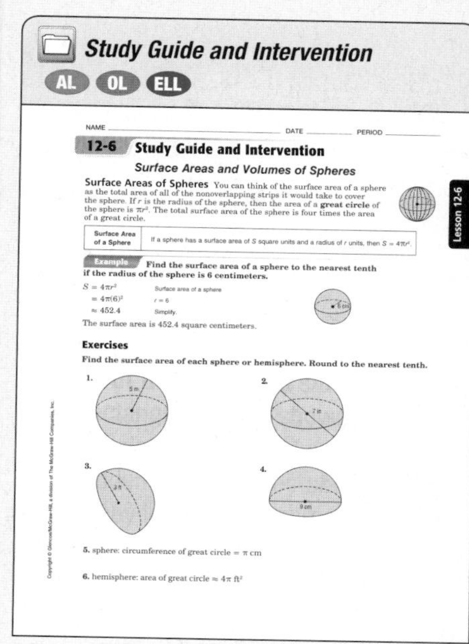

Study Guide and Intervention
AL OL ELL

NAME ______ DATE ______ PERIOD ______

12-6 Study Guide and Intervention

Surface Areas and Volumes of Spheres

Surface Areas of Spheres You can think of the surface area of a sphere as the total area of all of the nonoverlapping strips it would take to cover the sphere. If *r* is the radius of the sphere, then the area of a **great circle** of the sphere is πr^2. The total surface area of the sphere is four times the area of a great circle.

Surface Area of a Sphere	If a sphere has a surface area of *S* square units and a radius of *r* units, then $S = 4\pi r^2$.

Example Find the surface area of a sphere to the nearest tenth if the radius of the sphere is 6 centimeters.

$S = 4\pi r^2$ Surface area of a sphere
$= 4\pi(6)^2$ $r = 6$
≈ 452.4 Simplify.

The surface area is 452.4 square centimeters.

Exercises

Find the surface area of each sphere or hemisphere. Round to the nearest tenth.

1. 2. 3. 4.

5. sphere: circumference of great circle = π cm

6. hemisphere: area of great circle ≈ 4π ft²

Lesson 12-6

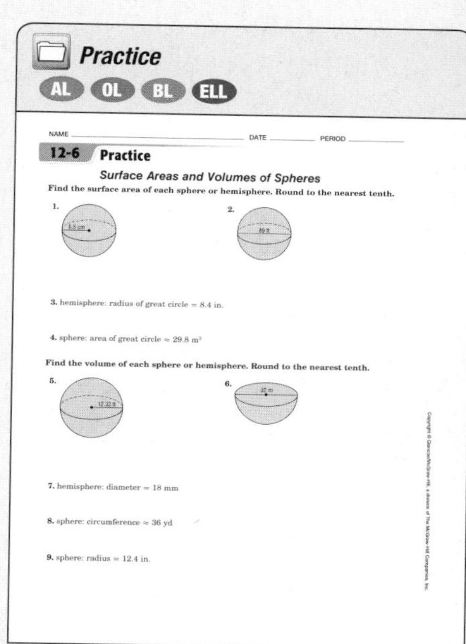

Practice
AL OL BL ELL

NAME ______ DATE ______ PERIOD ______

12-6 Practice

Surface Areas and Volumes of Spheres

Find the surface area of each sphere or hemisphere. Round to the nearest tenth.

1. 2.

3. hemisphere: radius of great circle = 8.4 in.

4. sphere: area of great circle = 29.8 m²

Find the volume of each sphere or hemisphere. Round to the nearest tenth.

5. 6.

7. hemisphere: diameter = 18 mm

8. sphere: circumference = 36 yd

9. sphere: radius = 12.4 in.

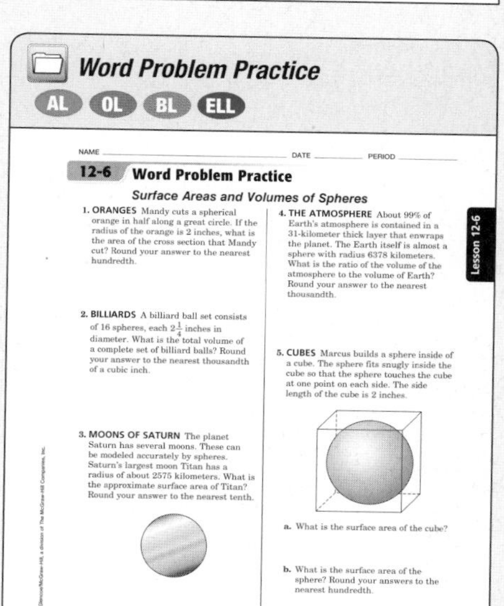

Word Problem Practice
AL OL BL ELL

NAME ______ DATE ______ PERIOD ______

12-6 Word Problem Practice

Surface Areas and Volumes of Spheres

1. **ORANGES** Mandy cuts a spherical orange in half along a great circle. If the radius of the orange is 2 inches, what is the area of the cross section that Mandy cut? Round your answer to the nearest hundredth.

2. **BILLIARDS** A billiard ball set consists of 16 spheres, each $2\frac{1}{4}$ inches in diameter. What is the total volume of a complete set of billiard balls? Round your answer to the nearest thousandth of a cubic inch.

3. **MOONS OF SATURN** The planet Saturn has several moons. These can be modeled accurately by spheres. Saturn's largest moon Titan has a radius of about 2575 kilometers. What is the approximate surface area of Titan? Round your answer to the nearest tenth.

4. **THE ATMOSPHERE** About 99% of Earth's atmosphere is contained in a 31-kilometer thick layer that enwraps the planet. The Earth itself is almost a sphere with radius 6378 kilometers. What is the ratio of the volume of the atmosphere to the volume of Earth? Round your answer to the nearest thousandth.

5. **CUBES** Marcus builds a sphere inside of a cube. The sphere fits snugly inside the cube so that the sphere touches the cube at one point on each side. The side length of the cube is 2 inches.

a. What is the surface area of the cube?

b. What is the surface area of the sphere? Round your answers to the nearest hundredth.

c. What is the ratio of the surface area of the cube to the surface area of the sphere? Round your answer to the nearest hundredth.

Lesson 12-6

connectED.mcgraw-hill.com

Additional Answers

39a. $\sqrt{r^2 - x^2}$

39c. The volume of the disc from the cylinder is $\pi r^2 y$ or $\pi y r^2$. The volume of the disc from the two cones is $\pi x^2 y$ or $\pi y x^2$. Subtract the volumes of the discs from the cylinder and cone to get $\pi y r^2 - \pi y x^2$, which is the expression for the volume of the disc from the sphere at height x.

39d. Cavalieri's Principle

39e. The volume of the cylinder is $\pi r^2(2r)$ or $2\pi r^3$. The volume of one cone is $\frac{1}{3}\pi r^2(r)$ or $\frac{1}{3}\pi r^3$, so the volume of the double napped cone is $2 \cdot \frac{1}{3}\pi r^3$ or $\frac{2}{3}\pi r^3$. Therefore, the volume of the hollowed out cylinder, and thus the sphere, is $2\pi r^3 - \frac{2}{3}\pi r^3$ or $\frac{4}{3}\pi r^3$.

40. There are infinitely many planes that produce reflection symmetry as long as they pass through the origin. Any angle of rotation will produce rotational symmetry.

41. There are infinitely many planes that produce reflection symmetry as long as they are vertical planes. Only rotation about the vertical axis will produce rotation symmetry through infinitely many angles.

42. The surface area is multiplied by 4^2 or 16. The volume is multiplied by 4^3 or 64.

43. The surface area is divided by 3^2 or 9. The volume is divided by 3^3 or 27.

44a. Sample answers:

JUICE
6.185 cm
6.185 cm
6.185 cm
Container C

39. INFORMAL PROOF A sphere with radius r can be thought of as being made up of a large number of discs or thin cylinders. Consider the disc shown that is x units above or below the center of the sphere. Also consider a cylinder with radius r and height $2r$ that is hollowed out by two cones of height and radius r.

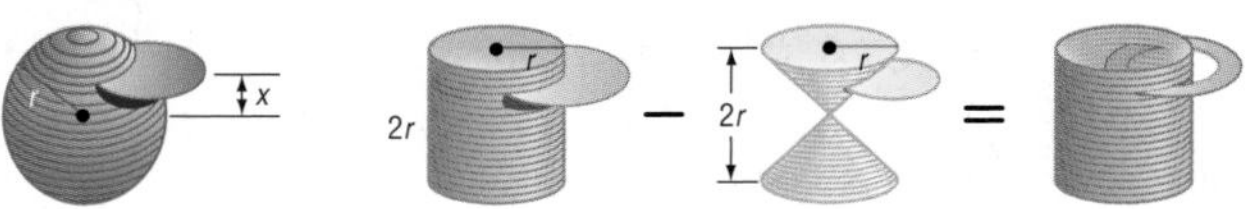

a. Find the radius of the disc from the sphere in terms of its distance x above the sphere's center. (*Hint:* Use the Pythagorean Theorem.) **a, c–e. See margin.**

b. If the disc from the sphere has a thickness of y units, find its volume in terms of x and y. $\pi\left(\sqrt{r^2 - x^2}\right)^2 \cdot y$ **or** $\pi y r^2 - \pi y x^2$

c. Show that this volume is the same as that of the hollowed-out disc with thickness of y units that is x units above the center of the cylinder and cone.

d. Since the expressions for the discs at the same height are the same, what guarantees that the hollowed-out cylinder and sphere have the same volume?

e. Use the formulas for the volumes of a cylinder and a cone to derive the formula for the volume of the hollowed-out cylinder and thus, the sphere.

CCSS TOOLS Describe the number and types of planes that produce reflection symmetry in each solid. Then describe the angles of rotation that produce rotation symmetry in each solid.

40. sphere **See margin.**

41. hemisphere **See margin.**

CHANGING DIMENSIONS A sphere has a radius of 12 centimeters. Describe how each change affects the surface area and the volume of the sphere. 42–43. See margin.

42. The radius is multiplied by 4.

43. The radius is divided by 3.

44. DESIGN A standard juice box holds 8 fluid ounces.

a. Sketch designs for three different juice containers that will each hold 8 fluid ounces. Label dimensions in centimeters. At least one container should be cylindrical. (*Hint:* 1 fl oz ≈ 29.57353 cm^3) **a–b. See margin.**

b. For each container in part **a**, calculate the surface area to volume (cm^2 per fl oz) ratio. Use these ratios to decide which of your containers can be made for the lowest materials cost. What shape container would minimize this ratio, and would this container be the cheapest to produce? Explain your reasoning.

H.O.T. Problems Use Higher-Order Thinking Skills

45. CHALLENGE A cube has a volume of 216 cubic inches. Find the volume of a sphere that is circumscribed about the cube. Round to the nearest tenth. **587.7 in^3**

46. REASONING Determine whether the following statement is *true* or *false*. If true, explain your reasoning. If false, provide a counterexample.

If a sphere has radius r, there exists a cone with radius r having the same volume.

46. True; a cone of radius r and height $4r$ has the same volume, $\frac{4}{3}\pi r^3$, as a sphere with radius r.

47. OPEN ENDED Sketch a sphere showing two examples of great circles. Sketch another sphere showing two examples of circles formed by planes intersecting the sphere that are *not* great circles. **See margin.**

48. WRITING IN MATH Write a ratio comparing the volume of a sphere with radius r to the volume of a cylinder with radius r and height $2r$. Then describe what the ratio means. **See margin.**

Differentiated Instruction BL

Extension Ask students, based on their knowledge of plane geometry, to develop definitions for a polyhedron inscribed in a sphere and a polyhedron circumscribed about a sphere. A polyhedron inscribed in a sphere touches the sphere with all of its vertices. A polyhedron circumscribed about a sphere has faces that are all tangent (intersect at one point) to the sphere.

Standardized Test Practice

49. **GRIDDED RESPONSE** What is the volume of the hemisphere shown below in cubic meters? **68.6**

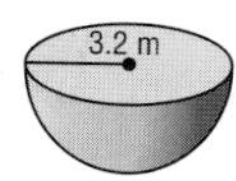

50. **ALGEBRA** What is the solution set of $3z + 4 < 6 + 7z$? **A**

A $\{z|z > -0.5\}$
B $\{z|z > -2\}$
C $\{z|z < -0.5\}$
D $\{z|z < -2\}$

51. If the area of the great circle of a sphere is 33 ft^2, what is the surface area of the sphere? **H**

F 42 ft^2
G 117 ft^2
H 132 ft^2
J 264 ft^2

52. **SAT/ACT** If a line ℓ is a perpendicular bisector of segment AB at E, how many points on line ℓ are the same distance from point A as from point B? **E**

A none
B one
C two
D three
E all points

Spiral Review

Find the volume of each pyramid. Round to the nearest tenth if necessary. (Lesson 12-5)

53. **58.9 ft^3**

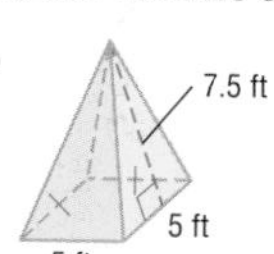

54. **240 in^3**

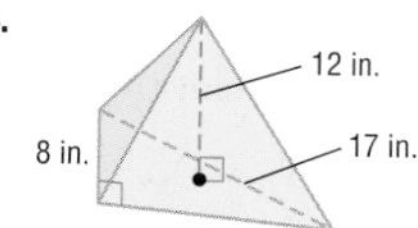

55. **232.4 m^3**

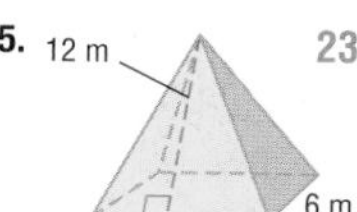

56. **ENGINEERING** The base of an oil drilling platform is made up of 24 concrete cylindrical cells. Twenty of the cells are used for oil storage. The pillars that support the platform deck rest on the four other cells. Find the total volume of the storage cells. (Lesson 12-4) **18,555,031.6 ft^3**

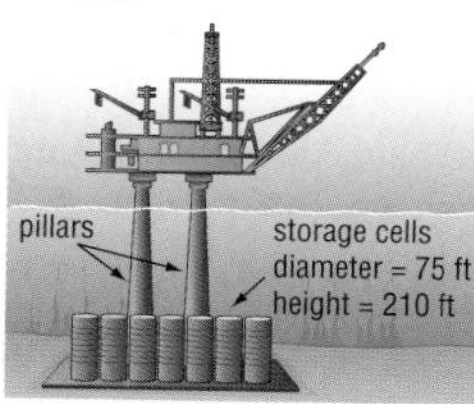

Find the area of each shaded region. Round to the nearest tenth. (Lesson 11-4)

57. **154.2 $units^2$**

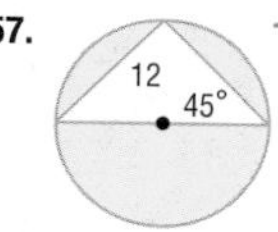

58. **42.1 $units^2$**

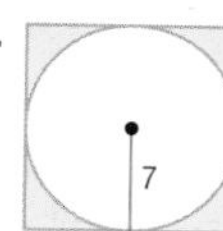

59. **80.2 $units^2$**

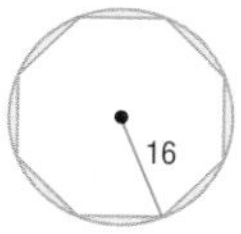

COORDINATE GEOMETRY **Find the area of each figure.** (Lesson 11-1)

60. $\square WXYZ$ with $W(0, 0)$, $X(4, 0)$, $Y(5, 5)$, and $Z(1, 5)$ **20 $units^2$**

61. $\triangle ABC$ with $A(2, -3)$, $B(-5, -3)$, and $C(-1, 3)$ **21 $units^2$**

Skills Review

Refer to the figure. **64–65. See margin.**

62. How many planes appear in this figure? **4**

63. Name three points that are collinear. ***D*, *B*, and *G***

64. Are points G, A, B, and E coplanar? Explain.

65. At what point do $\overleftrightarrow{EF}$ and $\overleftrightarrow{AB}$ intersect?

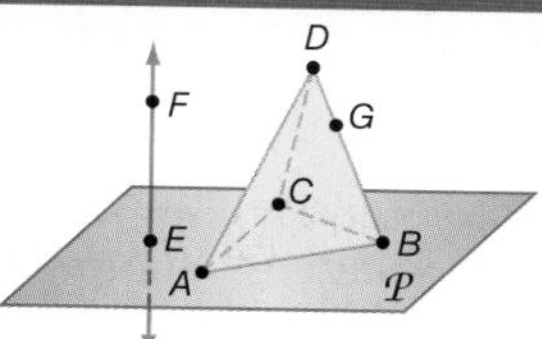

CCSS Teaching the Mathematical Practices

Tools Mathematically proficient students consider the available tools when solving a mathematical problem. Encourage students to use models of each solid.

4 Assess

Name the Math Ask students to describe how to find the surface area of a basketball that is sized by its circumference (usually 30 inches).

Formative Assessment

Check for understanding of Lessons 12-5 and 12-6.

 Quiz 3, p. 58

Additional Answers

44b. Sample answers: Container A, $\approx 27.02\ cm^2$ per fl oz; Container B, $\approx 26.48\ cm^2$ per fl oz; Container C, $\approx 28.69\ cm^2$ per fl oz; Of these three, Container B can be made for the lowest materials cost. The lower the surface area to volume ratio, the less packaging used for each fluid ounce of juice it holds. A spherical container with $r = 3.837$ cm would minimize this cost since it would have the least surface area to volume ratio of any shape, ≈ 23.13 cm per fl oz. However, a spherical container would likely be more costly to manufacture than a rectangular container since specially made machinery would be necessary.

47. Sample answer:

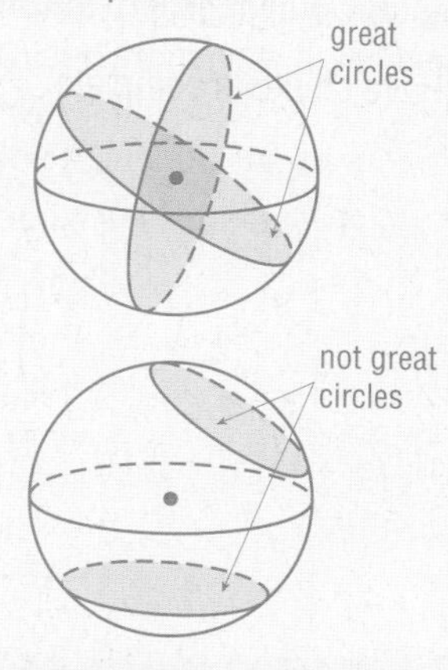

48. $\frac{2}{3}$; The volume of the sphere is two thirds the volume of the cylinder.

64. Points A, B, and E lie in plane $\mathcal{P}$, but point G does not lie in plane $\mathcal{P}$. Thus, they are not coplanar. Points A, G, and B lie in a plane, but point E does not lie in plane AGB.

65. $\overleftrightarrow{EF}$ and $\overleftrightarrow{AB}$ do not intersect. $\overleftrightarrow{AB}$ lies in plane $\mathcal{P}$, but only E lies in $\mathcal{P}$.

1 Focus

Objective Find the locus of points a given distance from the endpoints of a segment.

Materials

- ruler
- compass

Teaching Tip

Make sure students are clear that the points a given distance from the endpoint of a segment are points in space, and that they form the surface of a sphere.

2 Teach

Working in Cooperative Groups

Arrange students in groups of 2, mixing abilities. Have students do the experiments and discussion questions.

Activity 1

Ask:

- How could you demonstrate the points that are equidistant from the endpoint of a segment using a pencil or straw? Check students' work.

Practice Have students complete Exercises 1–4.

Activity 2

Ask:

- What is the difference between a circle and a sphere, as they relate to a locus of points? A circle is a locus of points on a plane, and a sphere is a locus of points in space.

Practice Have students complete Exercises 5–8.

EXTEND 12-6 Geometry Lab Locus and Spheres

Spheres are defined in terms of a locus of points in space. The definition of a sphere is the set of all points that are a given distance from a given point.

Activity 1 Locus of Points a Given Distance from Endpoints

Find the locus of all points that are equidistant from a segment.

Collect the Data

- Draw a given line segment with endpoints J and K
- Create a set of points that are equidistant from the segment.

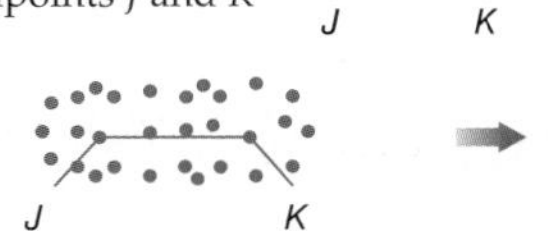

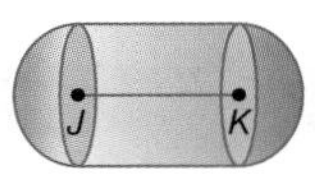

Analyze

1. Draw a figure and describe the locus of points in space that are 8 units from a segment that is 30 units long. See Ch. 12 Answer Appendix.
2. What three-dimensional shapes form the figure? two hemispheres and a cylinder
3. What are the radii and diameters of each hemisphere? 8 units; 16 units.
4. What are the diameter and the height of the cylinder? 16 units; 30 units.

Activity 2 Spheres That Intersect

Find the locus of all points that are equidistant from the centers of two intersecting spheres with the same radius.

Collect the Data

- Draw a line segment.
- Draw congruent overlapping spheres, with the centers at the endpoints of the given line segment.

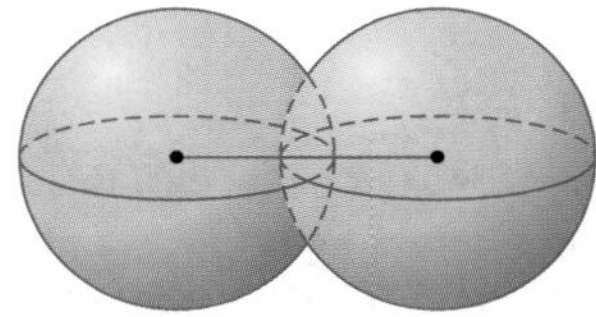

Analyze

5. What is the shape of the intersection of the upper hemispheres? semicircle
6. Can this be described as a locus of points in space or on a plane? Explain. See Ch. 12 Answer Appendix.
7. Describe this intersection as a locus. See Ch. 12 Answer Appendix.
8. FIREWORKS What is the locus of points that describes how particles from a fireworks explosion will disperse in an explosion at 400 feet above ground level if the expected distance a particle could travel is 200 feet? a sphere with radius 200 ft

3 Assess

Formative Assessment

Use Exercises 1–8 to assess whether students understand how to find the locus of points a given distance from the endpoints of a segment.

From Concrete to Abstract

Ask students what the locus of three or more coplanar points could be.

888 | Extend 12-6 | Geometry Lab: Locus and Spheres

LESSON 12-7 Spherical Geometry

Then	Now	Why?
You identified basic properties of spheres.	1 Describe sets of points on a sphere. 2 Compare and contrast Euclidean and spherical geometries.	Since Earth has a curved instead of a flat surface, the shortest path between two points on Earth is described by an arc of a great circle instead of a straight line.

NewVocabulary
Euclidean geometry
spherical geometry
non-Euclidean geometry

1 Geometry on a Sphere In this text, we have studied **Euclidean geometry**, either in the plane or in space. In plane Euclidean geometry, a *plane* is a flat surface made up of points that extend infinitely in all directions. In **spherical geometry**, or geometry on a sphere, a plane is the surface of a sphere.

Lines are also defined differently in spherical geometry.

KeyConcept Lines in Plane and Spherical Geometry

Plane Euclidean Geometry	Spherical Geometry
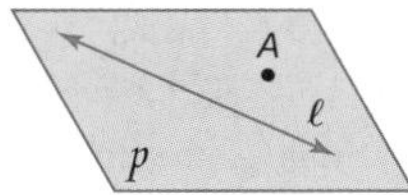	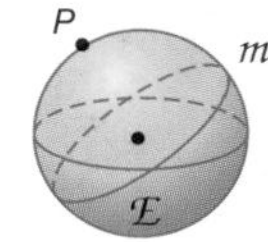
Plane $\mathcal{P}$ contains line ℓ and point A not on line ℓ.	Sphere $\mathcal{E}$ contains great circle m and point P not on m. Great circle m is a line on sphere $\mathcal{E}$.

Example 1 Describe Sets of Points on a Sphere

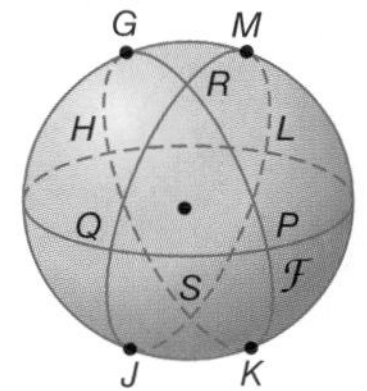

Name each of the following on sphere $\mathcal{F}$.

a. two lines containing point R

$\overleftrightarrow{GP}$ and $\overleftrightarrow{MQ}$ are lines on sphere $\mathcal{F}$ that contain point R.

b. a segment containing point K

$\overline{PS}$ is a segment on sphere $\mathcal{F}$ that contains point K.

c. a triangle

$\triangle RQP$ is a triangle on sphere $\mathcal{F}$.

GuidedPractice

Name each of the following on sphere $\mathcal{F}$ above.

1A. two lines containing point P $\overleftrightarrow{RK}$, $\overleftrightarrow{QP}$

1B. a segment containing point Q $\overline{PH}$

1C. a triangle $\triangle SQP$

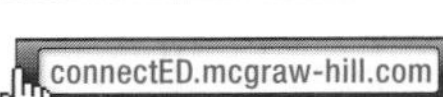

1 Focus

VerticalAlignment

Before Lesson 12-7 Identify basic properties of spheres.

Lesson 12-7 Describe sets of points on a sphere. Compare and contrast Euclidean and spherical geometries.

After Lesson 12-7 Investigate navigational coordinates.

2 Teach

Scaffolding Questions

Have students read the **Why?** section of the lesson.

Ask:

- What is the shortest path between two points on a sphere? an arc
- What is the line around the center of the earth that divides it into two equal parts? the equator
- When might it be important to know that the shortest distance between two points on the earth is not a straight line? Sample answer: when planning a flight path for a plane

Lesson 12-7 Resources

Resource	Approaching Level AL	On Level OL	Beyond Level BL	English Learners ELL
Teacher Edition	▪ Differentiated Instruction, p. 890	▪ Differentiated Instruction, pp. 890, 894	▪ Differentiated Instruction, pp. 890, 894	
Chapter Resource Masters	▪ Study Guide and Intervention, pp. 43–44 ▪ Skills Practice, p. 45 ▪ Practice, p. 46 ▪ Word Problem Practice, p. 47	▪ Study Guide and Intervention, pp. 43–44 ▪ Skills Practice, p. 45 ▪ Practice, p. 46 ▪ Word Problem Practice, p. 47 ▪ Enrichment, p. 48	▪ Practice, p. 46 ▪ Word Problem Practice, p. 47 ▪ Enrichment, p. 48	▪ Study Guide and Intervention, pp. 43–44 ▪ Skills Practice, p. 45 ▪ Practice, p. 46 ▪ Word Problem Practice, p. 47
Other	▪ 5-Minute Check 12-7 ▪ Study Notebook ▪ Teaching Geometry with Manipulatives	▪ 5-Minute Check 12-7 ▪ Study Notebook ▪ Teaching Geometry with Manipulatives	▪ 5-Minute Check 12-7 ▪ Study Notebook	▪ 5-Minute Check 12-7 ▪ Study Notebook ▪ Teaching Geometry with Manipulatives

1 Geometry on a Sphere

Examples 1 and 2 show how to describe sets of points on a sphere.

Formative Assessment

Use the Guided Practice exercises after each Example to determine students' understanding of concepts.

Additional Examples

1 Name each of the following on sphere $\mathcal{S}$.

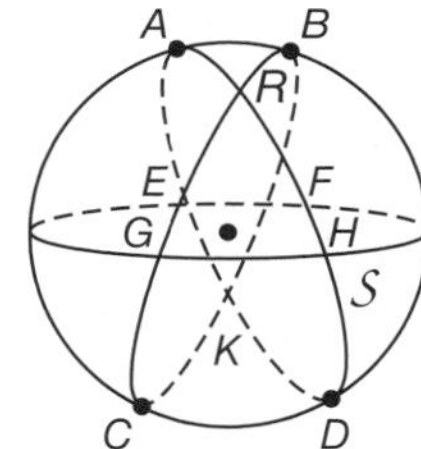

a. two lines containing point R $\overleftrightarrow{AD}$ and $\overleftrightarrow{BC}$

b. a segment containing point C $\overline{GK}$

c. a triangle $\triangle KGH$

2 **SPORTS** Determine whether the line h on the basketball shown is a line in spherical geometry. Explain.

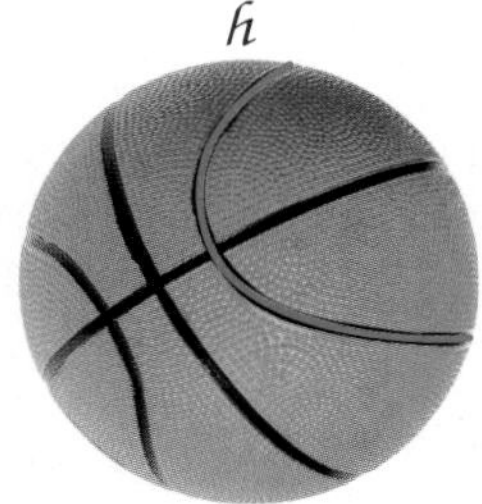

No; it is not a great circle.

Additional Examples also in Interactive Classroom PowerPoint® Presentations

Interactive White Board READY

2 Comparing Euclidean and Spherical Geometries

Example 3 shows how to compare postulates and properties of Euclidean geometry with those of spherical geometry.

2. Yes; figure p is a line because it goes through opposite poles of the sphere.

Real-World Example 2 Identify Lines in Spherical Geometry

ENTERTAINMENT Determine whether figure m on the mirror ball shown is a line in spherical geometry.

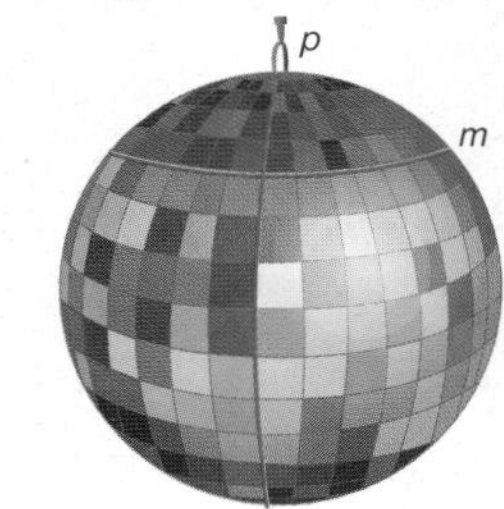

Notice that figure m does not go through the poles of the sphere. Therefore figure m is not a great circle and so not a line in spherical geometry.

Guided Practice

2. Determine whether figure p on the mirror ball shown is a line in spherical geometry.

Study Tip

Elliptical Geometry *Spherical geometry* is a subcategory of *elliptical geometry.*

2 Comparing Euclidean and Spherical Geometries

While some postulates and properties of Euclidean geometry are true in spherical geometry, others are not, or are true only under certain circumstances.

Example 3 Compare Plane Euclidean and Spherical Geometries

Tell whether the following postulate or property of plane Euclidean geometry has a corresponding statement in spherical geometry. If so, write the corresponding statement. If not, explain your reasoning.

a. Through any two points, there is exactly one line.

In the figure, notice that there is more than one great circle (line) through polar points A and B. However, there is only one great circle through nonpolar points C and D.

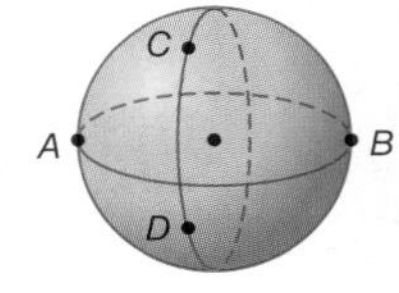

Therefore, a corresponding statement is that through any two nonpolar points, there is exactly one great circle (line).

b. If given a line and a point not on the line, then there exists exactly one line through the point that is parallel to the given line.

In the figure, notice that every great circle (line) containing point A will intersect line ℓ. Thus there exists no great circle through point A that is parallel to line ℓ.

ℓ

A

Guided Practice

3A. A line segment is the shortest path between two points.

3B. Through any two points, there is exactly one segment.

3A. An arc of a great circle is the shortest path between two points.
3B. Through any two arcs on a great circle, there are two segments—the major and minor arcs of the great circle determined by those points.

Study Tip

Finite Geometries *Planar networks* are another type of non-Euclidean geometry. You will learn about planar networks in Extend Lesson 13-6.

A **non-Euclidean geometry** is a geometry in which at least one of the postulates from Euclidean geometry fails. Notice in Example 3b that the Parallel Postulate does not hold true on a sphere. Lines, or great circles, cannot be parallel in spherical geometry. Therefore, spherical geometry is non-Euclidean.

Differentiated Instruction AL OL BL

Visual/Spatial Learners Have students create a map on a sheet of paper with lines indicating the shortest distance between two points. Wrap the map around a ball or globe, and use a piece of string to compare the original lines with the arcs connecting the points.

Check Your Understanding

  = Step-by-Step Solutions begin on page R14. 

Example 1 **Name each of the following on sphere $\mathcal{B}$.**

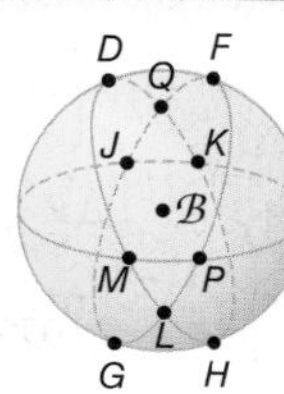

1. two lines containing point Q $\overleftrightarrow{DH}$, $\overleftrightarrow{FJ}$
2. a segment containing point L $\overline{HM}$
3. a triangle $\triangle JKQ$, $\triangle LMP$
4. two segments on the same great circle $\overline{LG}$ and $\overline{FJ}$

Example 2 **SPORTS Determine whether figure X on each of the spheres shown is a line in spherical geometry.**

5. 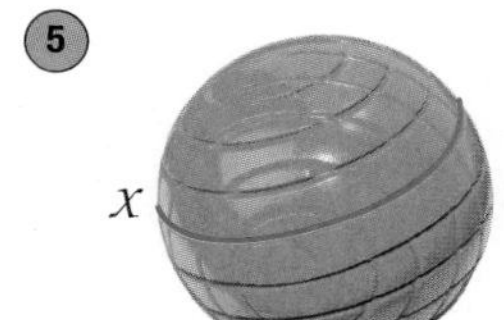

no

6. 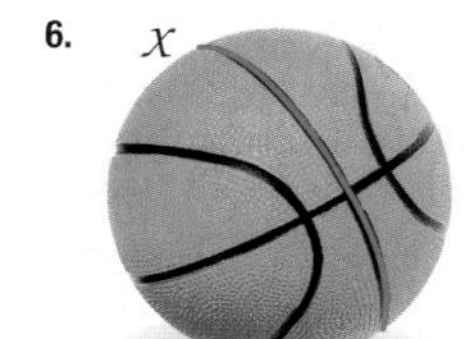

yes

Example 3 **CCSS REASONING Tell whether the following postulate or property of plane Euclidean geometry has a corresponding statement in spherical geometry. If so, write the corresponding statement. If not, explain your reasoning.**

7. The points on any line or line segment can be put into one-to-one correspondence with real numbers.
8. Perpendicular lines intersect at one point. Perpendicular great circles intersect at two points.

7. The points on any great circle or arc of a great circle can be put into one-to-one correspondence with real numbers.

Practice and Problem Solving

Extra Practice is on page R12.

Example 1 **Name two lines containing point M, a segment containing point S, and a triangle in each of the following spheres.**

9. 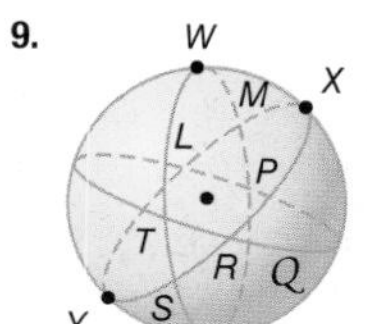

Sample answers: $\overleftrightarrow{WZ}$ and $\overleftrightarrow{XY}$, $\overline{RY}$ or $\overline{TZ}$, $\triangle RST$ or $\triangle MPL$

10. 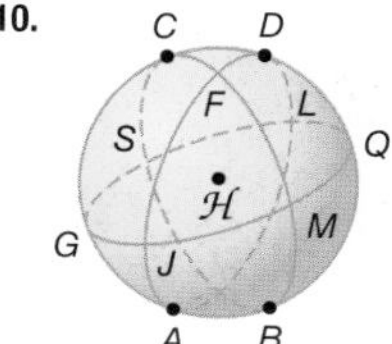

Sample answers: $\overleftrightarrow{FB}$ and $\overleftrightarrow{QJ}$, $\overline{CB}$ and $\overline{GL}$, $\triangle FJM$

11. **SOCCER** Name each of the following on the soccer ball shown.
    a. two lines containing point B $\overleftrightarrow{AD}$ and $\overleftrightarrow{FC}$
    b. a segment containing point F Sample answers: $\overline{BG}$ and $\overline{AH}$
    c. a triangle Sample answers: $\triangle BCD$ and $\triangle ABF$
    d. a segment containing point C $\overline{QD}$ and $\overline{BL}$
    e. a line $\overleftrightarrow{MJ}$
    f. two lines containing point A $\overleftrightarrow{MB}$ and $\overleftrightarrow{KF}$

Differentiated Homework Options

Level	Assignment	Two-Day Option	
AL Basic	9–18, 24, 26–45	9–17 odd, 31–34	10–18 even, 24, 26–30, 35–45
OL Core	9–19 odd, 21–24, 26–45	9–18, 31–34	19–24, 26–30, 35–45
BL Advanced	20–42, (optional: 43–45)		

Additional Example

3 Tell whether the following postulate or property of plane Euclidean geometry has a corresponding statement in spherical geometry. If so, write the corresponding statement. If not, explain your reasoning.

a. If two lines are parallel, they never intersect. True: Given a line, the only line on a sphere that is always the same distance from the line is the line itself.

b. Any two distinct lines are parallel or intersect once. False: Two distinct lines on a sphere intersect twice.

Teach with Tech

Web Search Use a Web search to find a circle mapping tool to find the distance between two points on the Earth. Have students name different locations, and enter them in the tool. On the resulting map, explain that the path shown is a curved line and is calculated using spherical geometry, based on the curvature of the Earth.

3 Practice

Formative Assessment

Use Exercises 1–8 to check for understanding.

Use the chart at the bottom of this page to customize assignments for your students.

Teaching the Mathematical Practices

Reasoning Mathematically proficient students make sense of quantities and their relationships in problem situations. In Exercises 7–8, students compare Euclidean geometry to spherical geometry.

Example 2 **ARCHITECTURE Determine whether figure w on each of the spheres shown is a line in spherical geometry.**

12.  yes

13. no

14. **CCSS MODELING** Lines of latitude and longitude are used to describe positions on the Earth's surface. By convention, lines of longitude divide Earth vertically, while lines of latitude divide it horizontally.

Lines of longitude
Equator
Lines of latitude

a. Are lines of longitude great circles? Explain.

b. Are lines of latitude great circles? Explain.

14a. Yes; sample answer: Since lines of longitude pass through poles of the sphere, they form great circles.

14b. No; sample answer: Of the lines of latitude, only the Equator is a great circle. It passes through opposite poles of the sphere. Other latitude lines do not pass through opposite poles of the sphere, so they cannot be great circles.

Example 3 **Tell whether the following postulate or property of plane Euclidean geometry has a corresponding statement in spherical geometry. If so, write the corresponding statement. If not, explain your reasoning.** 15–18. See Ch. 12 Answer Appendix.

15 A line goes on infinitely in two directions.

16. Perpendicular lines form four 90° angles.

17. If three points are collinear, exactly one is between the other two.

18. If M is the midpoint of $\overline{AB}$, then $\overline{AM} \cong \overline{MB}$.

B **On a sphere, there are two distances that can be measured between two points. Use each figure and the information given to determine the distance between points J and K on each sphere. Round to the nearest tenth. Justify your answer.**

19. See margin.

8 in.
H
K
J

$m\widehat{JK} = 100$

20. See margin.

H
J
5 cm
K

$m\widehat{JK} = 60$

21. **GEOGRAPHY** The location of Phoenix, Arizona, is 112° W longitude, 33.4° N latitude, and the location of Helena, Montana, is 112° W longitude, 46.6° N latitude. West indicates the location in terms of the prime meridian, and north indicates the location in terms of the equator. The mean radius of Earth is about 3960 miles. 21a–d. See Ch. 12 Answer Appendix.

a. Estimate the distance between Phoenix and Helena. Explain your reasoning.

b. Is there another way to express the distance between these two cities? Explain.

c. Can the distance between Washington, D.C., and London, England, which lie on approximately the same lines of latitude, be calculated in the same way? Explain your reasoning.

d. How many other locations are there that are the same distance from Phoenix, Arizona as Helena, Montana is? Explain.

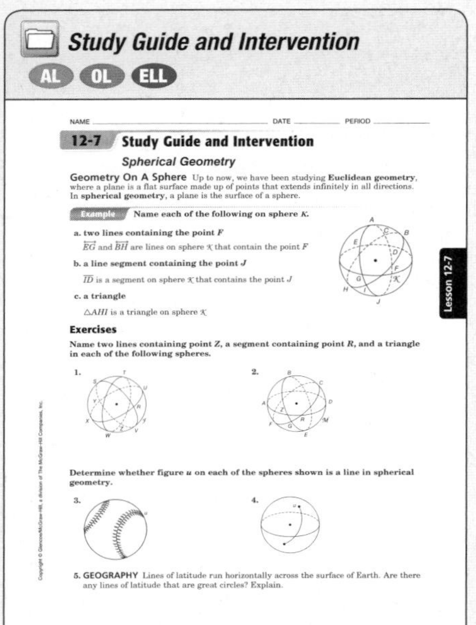

Study Guide and Intervention AL OL ELL

12-7 Study Guide and Intervention
Spherical Geometry

Geometry On A Sphere Up to now, we have been studying Euclidean geometry, where a plane is a flat surface made up of points that extends infinitely in all directions. In spherical geometry, a plane is the surface of a sphere.

Example Name each of the following on sphere K.

a. two lines containing the point F
b. a line segment containing the point J
c. a triangle

Exercises
Name two lines containing point Z, a segment containing point R, and a triangle in each of the following spheres.

Determine whether figure u on each of the spheres shown is a line in spherical geometry.

5. GEOGRAPHY Lines of latitude run horizontally across the surface of Earth. Are there any lines of latitude that are great circles? Explain.

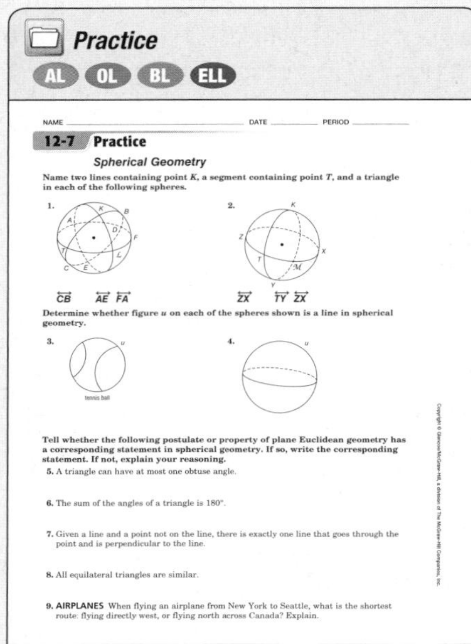

Practice AL OL BL ELL

12-7 Practice
Spherical Geometry

Name two lines containing point K, a segment containing point T, and a triangle in each of the following spheres.

Determine whether figure u on each of the spheres shown is a line in spherical geometry.

Tell whether the following postulate or property of plane Euclidean geometry has a corresponding statement in spherical geometry. If so, write the corresponding statement. If not, explain your reasoning.

5. A triangle can have at most one obtuse angle.
6. The sum of the angles of a triangle is 180°.
7. Given a line and a point not on the line, there is exactly one line that goes through the point and is perpendicular to the line.
8. All equilateral triangles are similar.
9. AIRPLANES When flying an airplane from New York to Seattle, what is the shortest route: flying directly west, or flying north across Canada? Explain.

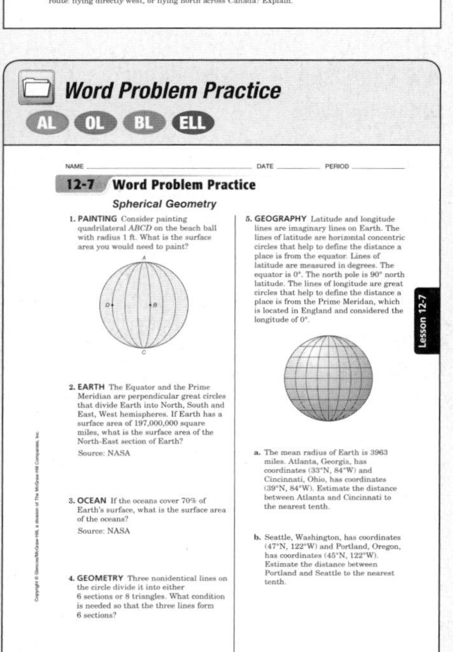

Word Problem Practice AL OL BL ELL

12-7 Word Problem Practice
Spherical Geometry

1. PAINTING Consider painting quadrilateral ABCD on the beach ball with radius 1 ft. What is the surface area you would need to paint?
2. EARTH The Equator and the Prime Meridian are perpendicular great circles that divide Earth into North, South and East, West hemispheres. If Earth has a surface area of 197,000,000 square miles, what is the surface area of the North-East section of Earth? Source: NASA
3. OCEAN If the oceans cover 70% of Earth's surface, what is the surface area of the oceans? Source: NASA
4. GEOMETRY Three nonidentical lines on the circle divide it into either 6 sections or 8 triangles. What condition is needed so that the three lines form 6 sections?
5. GEOGRAPHY Latitude and longitude lines are imaginary lines on Earth.

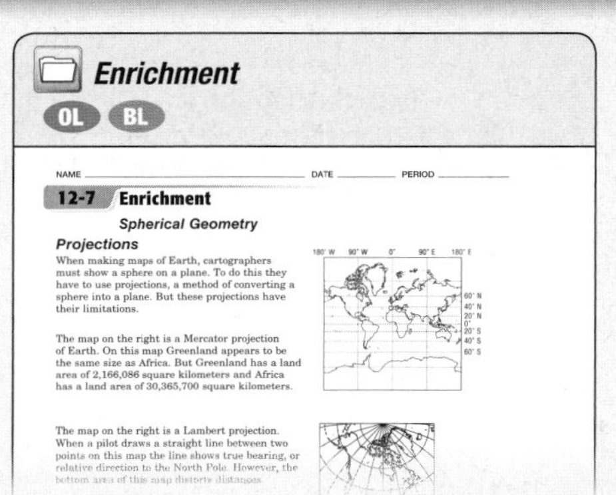

Enrichment OL BL

12-7 Enrichment
Spherical Geometry
Projections

When making maps of Earth, cartographers must show a sphere on a plane. To do this they have to use projections, a method of converting a sphere into a plane. But these projections have their limitations.

The map on the right is a Mercator projection of Earth. On this map Greenland appears to be the same size as Africa. But Greenland has a land area of 2,166,086 square kilometers and Africa has a land area of 30,365,700 square kilometers.

The map on the right is a Lambert projection.

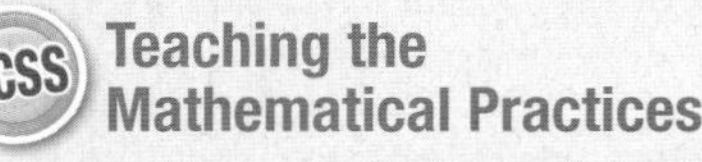

Teaching the Mathematical Practices

Modeling Mathematically proficient students can apply the mathematics they know to solve problems arising in everyday life. In Exercise 14, encourage students to review the definition of *great circle.*

22. **MULTIPLE REPRESENTATIONS** In this problem, you will investigate triangles in spherical geometry. **22b–c. See margin.**

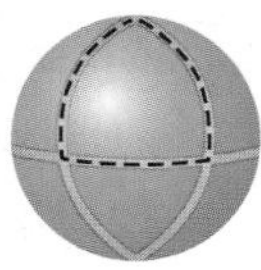

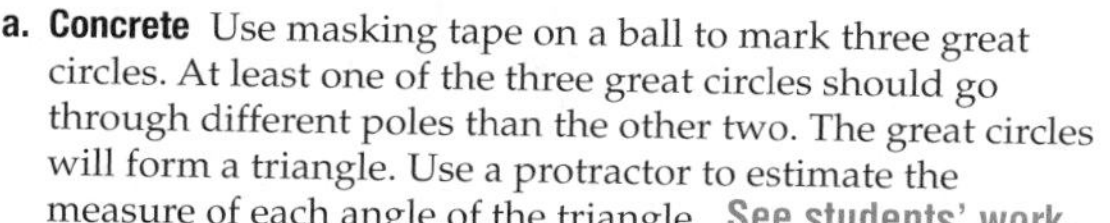

a. **Concrete** Use masking tape on a ball to mark three great circles. At least one of the three great circles should go through different poles than the other two. The great circles will form a triangle. Use a protractor to estimate the measure of each angle of the triangle. **See students' work.**

b. **Tabular** Tabulate the measure of each angle of the triangle formed. Remove the tape and repeat the process two times so that you have tabulated the measure of three different triangles. Record the sum of the measures of each triangle.

c. **Verbal** Make a conjecture about the sum of the measures of a triangle in spherical geometry.

23. **QUADRILATERALS** Consider quadrilateral *ABCD* on sphere $\mathcal{P}$. Note that it has four sides with $\overline{DC} \perp \overline{CB}$, $\overline{AB} \perp \overline{CB}$, and $\overline{DC} \cong \overline{AB}$.

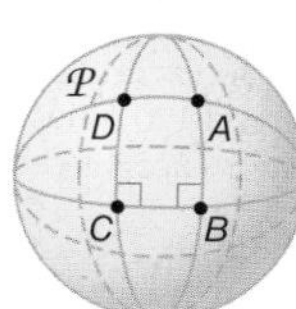

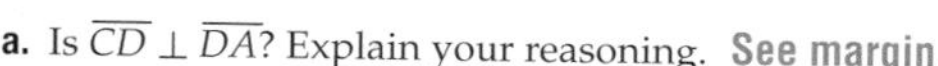

a. Is $\overline{CD} \perp \overline{DA}$? Explain your reasoning. **See margin.**

b. How does *DA* compare to *CB*? **$DA < CB$**

c. Can a rectangle, as defined in Euclidean geometry, exist in non-Euclidean geometry? Explain your reasoning. **No; the sides are not parallel.**

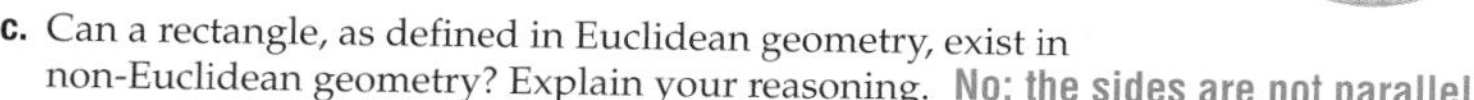

H.O.T. Problems Use Higher-Order Thinking Skills

24. **WRITING IN MATH** Compare and contrast Euclidean and spherical geometries. Be sure to include a discussion of planes and lines in both geometries. **See margin.**

25. **CHALLENGE** Geometries can be defined on curved surfaces other than spheres. Another type of non-Euclidean geometry is *hyperbolic geometry*. This geometry is defined on a curved saddle-like surface. Compare the sum of the angle measures of a triangle in hyperbolic, spherical, and Euclidean geometries. **See margin.**

Triangle in plane geometry

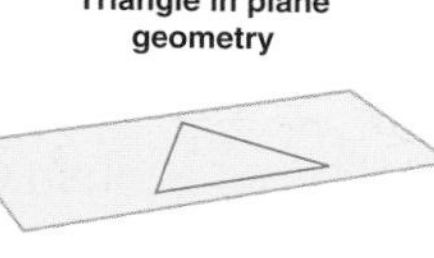

Triangle in spherical geometry

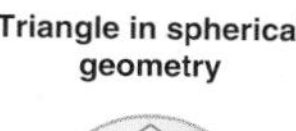

Triangle in hyperbolic geometry

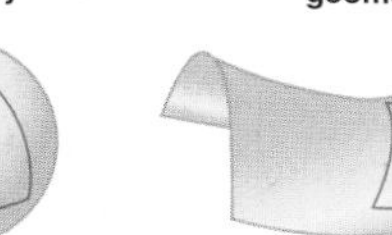

26. **OPEN ENDED** Sketch a sphere with three points so that two of the points lie on a great circle and two of the points do not lie on a great circle. **See Ch. 12 Answer Appendix.**

27. **CCSS ARGUMENTS** A *small circle* of a sphere intersects at least two points, but does not go through opposite poles. Points *A* and *B* lie on a small circle of sphere *Q*. Will two small circles *sometimes*, *always*, or *never* be parallel? Draw a sketch and explain your reasoning. **See Ch. 12 Answer Appendix.**

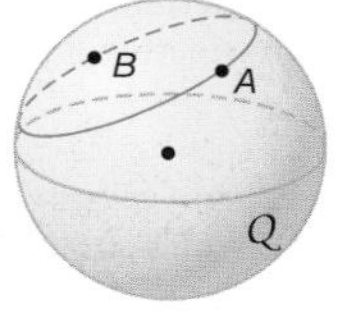

28. **WRITING IN MATH** Do similar or congruent triangles exist in spherical geometry? Explain your reasoning. **See Ch. 12 Answer Appendix.**

29. **REASONING** Is the statement *Spherical geometry is a subset of Euclidean geometry* true or false? Explain your reasoning. **See Ch. 12 Answer Appendix.**

30. **REASONING** Two planes are equidistant from the center of a sphere and intersect the sphere. What is true of the circles? Are they lines in spherical geometry? Explain.

30. The circles are congruent. They are not lines in spherical geometry because they are not great circles since they do not have their centers at the center of the sphere.

19. 14.0 in.; since 100 degrees is $\frac{5}{18}$ of 360 degrees, $\frac{5}{18}$ × circumference of great circle ≈ 14.0

20. 5.2 cm.; since 60 degrees is $\frac{1}{6}$ of 360 degrees, $\frac{1}{6}$ × circumference of great circle ≈ 5.2

25. Sample answer: In plane geometry, the sum of the measures of the angles of a triangle is 180. In spherical geometry, the sum of the measures of the angles of a triangle is greater than 180. In hyperbolic geometry, the sum of the measures of the angles of a triangle is less than 180.

Exercise Alert

Tape, Ball, and Protractor Exercise 22 requires the use of masking tape, a ball, and a protractor.

Multiple Representations

In Exercise 22, students use a physical model, a table, and verbal description to investigate triangles in spherical geometry.

Teaching the Mathematical Practices

Arguments Mathematically proficient students understand and use stated assumptions and definitions in constructing arguments. They make conjectures and build a logical progression of statements to explore the truth of their conjectures. In Exercise 27, point out to students that small circles on a sphere do not go through opposite poles.

Additional Answers

22b.

Triangle	$m\angle 1$	$m\angle 2$	$m\angle 3$	Sum
1	90	90	90	270
2	100	106	114	320
3	75	80	30	185

22c. Sample answer: The sum of the measures of the angles of a triangle in spherical geometry is greater than 180°.

23a. No; if $\overline{CD}$ was perpendicular to $\overline{DA}$, then $\overline{DA}$ would be parallel to $\overline{CB}$. This is not possible, because there are no parallel lines in spherical geometry.

24. Sample answer: Points, lines, and planes exist in both Euclidean and spherical geometries. In Euclidean geometry, lines continue indefinitely, and in spherical geometry, lines occur as great circles. In Euclidean geometry, planes extend indefinitely in two dimensions, and in spherical geometry, the plane is the surface of the sphere. Spherical geometry is non-Euclidean because the parallel postulate is invalid.

4 Assess

Ticket Out the Door Have students write a short summary of how spherical geometry is different from Euclidean geometry.

Additional Answer

42. $(3, -4)$; $(x - 3)^2 + (y + 4)^2 = 100$

Standardized Test Practice

31. Which of the following postulates or properties of spherical geometry is false? **C**

A The shortest path between two points on a circle is an arc.

B If three points are collinear, any of the three points lies between the other two.

C A great circle is infinite and never returns to its original starting point.

D Perpendicular great circles intersect at two points.

32. SAT/ACT A car travels 50 miles due north in 1 hour and 120 miles due west in 2 hours. What is the average speed of the car? **J**

F 50 mph　　H 60 mph

G 55 mph　　J none of the above

33. SHORT RESPONSE Name a line in sphere $\mathcal{P}$ that contains point D. **Sample answer: $\overleftrightarrow{BC}$**

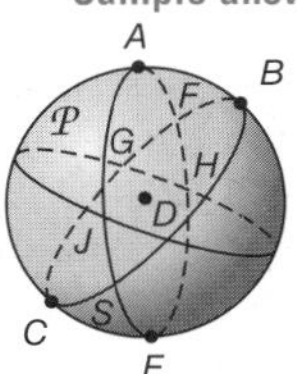

34. ALGEBRA The ratio of males to females in a classroom is 3:5. How many females are in the room if the total number of students is 32? **B**

A 12　　D 51

B 20　　E 53

C 29

Spiral Review

Find the volume of each sphere or hemisphere. Round to the nearest tenth. (Lesson 12-6)

35. sphere: area of great circle = 98.5 m² **735.4 m³**

36. sphere: circumference of great circle ≈ 23.1 in. **208.2 in³**

37. hemisphere: circumference of great circle ≈ 50.3 cm **1074.5 cm³**

38. hemisphere: area of great circle ≈ 3416 ft² **75,094.9 ft³**

Find the volume of each cone. Round to the nearest tenth. (Lesson 12-5)

39. **78.5 m³**

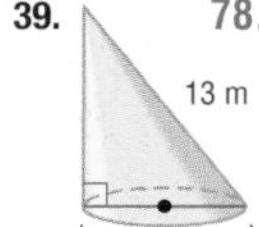

40.

4188.8 mm³

41. **0.1 m³**

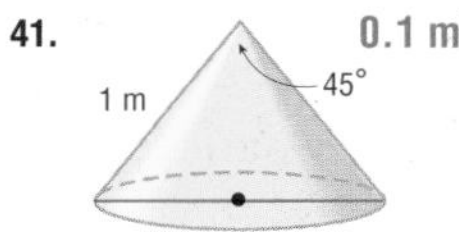

42. RADIOS Three radio towers are modeled by the points $A(-3, 4)$, $B(9, 4)$, and $C(-3, -12)$. Determine the location of another tower equidistant from all three towers, and write an equation for the circle which all three points lie on. (Lesson 10-8) **See margin.**

Skills Review

For each pair of similar figures, find the area of the green figure.

43. 6 cm　2 cm　A = 24 cm²　**2.7 cm²**

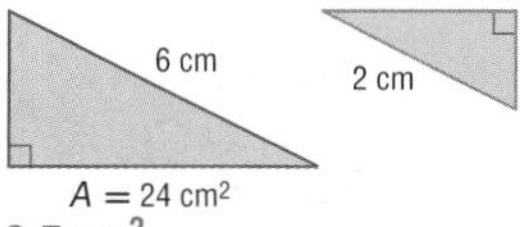

44. 11 ft　7 ft

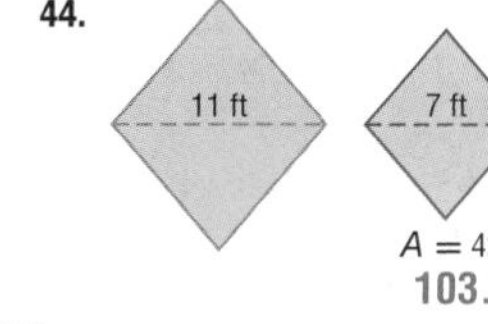

A = 42 ft²　**103.7 ft²**

45. 28 m　19 m

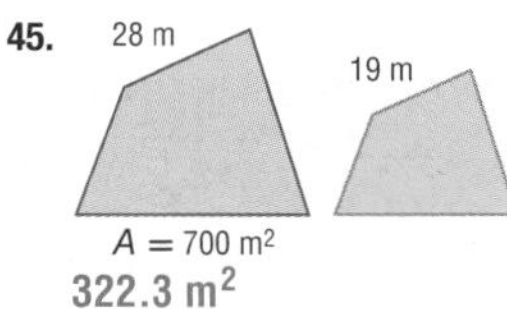

A = 700 m²　**322.3 m²**

Differentiated Instruction OL BL

Extension Using a graphing program with three-dimensional capabilities, have students investigate similar triangles drawn on a sphere. Is it possible for two spherical triangles to be similar without being congruent?

EXTEND 12-7 Geometry Lab
Navigational Coordinates

OBJECTIVE Use a latitude and longitude measure to identify the hemispheres on which the location lies and estimate the location of a city using a globe or map.

A grid system of imaginary lines on Earth is used for locating places and navigation. Imaginary vertical lines drawn around the Earth through the North and South Poles are called **meridians** and determine the measure of **longitude**. Imaginary horizontal lines parallel to the equator are called **parallels** and determine the measure of **latitude**.

The basic units for measurements are degrees, minutes, and seconds. 1 degree (°) = 60 minutes (‘), and 60 minutes = 60 seconds (″).

	Location of 0°	Direction	Maximum Degrees
Latitude (parallels)	equator	In northern hemisphere, all are degrees north. In southern hemisphere, all are degrees south.	180° at international dateline
Longitude (meridians)	Prime Meridian through Greenwich, England	In eastern hemisphere, all are degrees east. In western hemisphere, all are degrees west.	90° at each pole

1. City A: northern; City B: southern; City C: northern
2. City A: Lexington, Kentucky; City B: Adelaide, Australia; City C: Reykjavik, Iceland

Activity Investigate Latitude and Longitude

The table shows the latitude and longitude of three cities.

City	Latitude	Longitude
A	37°59′N	84°28′W
B	34°55′S	138°36′E
C	64°4′N	21°58′W

1. In which hemisphere is each city located?
2. Use a globe or map to name each city.
3. Earth is approximately a sphere with a radius of 3960 miles. The equator and all meridians are great circles. The circumference of a great circle is equal to the length of the equator or any meridian. Find the length of a great circle on Earth in miles. about 24,881.4 mi
4. Notice that the distance between each line of latitude is about the same. The distance from the equator to the North Pole is $\frac{1}{4}$ of the circumference of Earth, and each degree of latitude is $\frac{1}{90}$ of that distance. Estimate the distance between one pair of latitude lines in miles. about 69.1 mi

5. City F: southern; City G: northern; City H: southern
6. City F: Belem, Brazil; City G: Bangkok, Thailand; City H: Wellington, New Zealand
7. about 64 miles between meridians

Analyze

The table shows the latitude and longitude of three cities.

City	Latitude	Longitude
F	1°28′S	48°29′W
G	13°45′N	100°30′E
H	41°17′S	174°47′E

5. Name the hemisphere in which each city is located.
6. Use a globe or map to name each city.
7. Find the approximate distance between meridians at latitude of about 22° N. The direct distance between the two cities at the right is about 1646 miles.

Calcutta, India	22°34′N	88°24′E
Hong Kong, China	22°20′N	114°11′E

1 Focus

Objective
- Understand navigational coordinates.
- Find distances by using measurements of navigational coordinates.

Materials for Each Group
- world globe or map

Tips for New Teachers
Explain that the total number of degrees for latitude is 360° and that the northern and southern hemisphere each consist of 180°. The total number of degrees of longitude is 180° and the eastern and western hemisphere each consist of 90°.

2 Teach

Working in Cooperative Groups
Organize students in pairs, mixing abilities. Have pairs help each other to complete the Activity, Exercises 1–4.

Practice Have students complete Exercises 5–7.

3 Assess

Formative Assessment
Use Exercises 5–7 to assess whether students understand navigational coordinates.

From Concrete to Abstract
Ask students to describe the similarities and differences between meridians and parallels.

1 Focus

VerticalAlignment

Before Lesson 12-8 Compare surface areas and volumes of spheres.

Lesson 12-8 Identify congruent and similar solids, and use properties of similar solids.

After Lesson 12-8 Compute geometric probabilities.

2 Teach

Scaffolding Questions

Have students read the **Why?** section of the lesson.

Ask:

- What number relates the side lengths of two-dimensional similar figures? the scale factor
- Does the color of the gemstones determine whether they are similar? Sample answer: No; it matters only whether they are exactly the same shape.
- If the sides of one cube are twice the length of the sides of a second cube, how do you think the volume will change? Sample answer: The volume will be 8 times as much because the factor of 2 is multiplied three times for the volume.

LESSON 12-8 Congruent and Similar Solids

Then
- You compared surface areas and volumes of spheres.

Now
1. Identify congruent or similar solids.
2. Use properties of similar solids.

Why?
- The gemstones at the right are cut in exactly the same shape, but their sizes are different. Their shapes are *similar*.

NewVocabulary
similar solids
congruent solids

1 Identify Congruent or Similar Solids

Similar solids have exactly the same shape but not necessarily the same size. All spheres are similar and all cubes are similar.

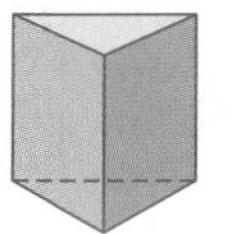
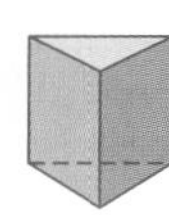
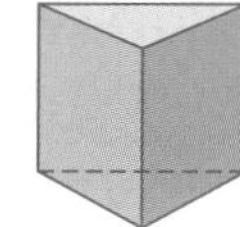
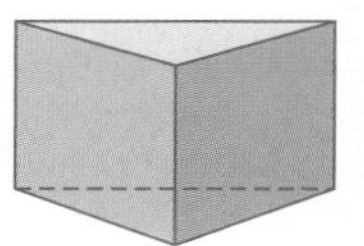

In similar solids, the corresponding linear measures, such as height and radius, have equal ratios. The common ratio is called the *scale factor.* If two similar solids are polyhedrons, their corresponding faces are similar.

KeyConcept Similar Solids

Words Two solids are similar if they have the same shape and the ratios of their corresponding linear measures are equal.

Models

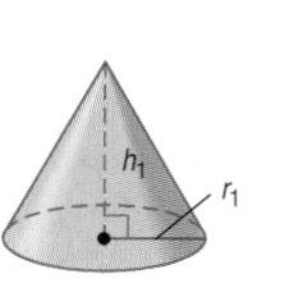

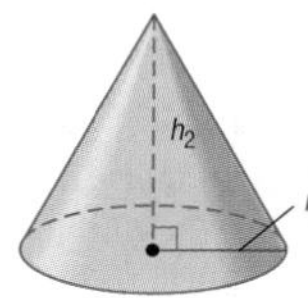

$$\frac{h_1}{h_2} = \frac{r_1}{r_2}$$

Congruent solids have exactly the same shape and the same size. Congruent solids are similar solids that have a scale factor of 1:1.

KeyConcept Congruent Solids

Words Two solids are congruent if they have the following characteristics.
- Corresponding angles are congruent.
- Corresponding edges are congruent.
- Corresponding faces are congruent.
- Volumes are equal.

Models

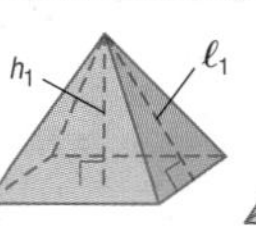

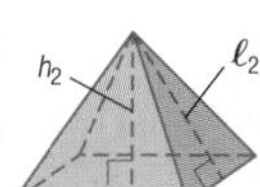

$$\frac{h_1}{h_2} = \frac{\ell_1}{\ell_2} = 1$$

896 | Lesson 12-8

Lesson 12-8 Resources

Resource	Approaching Level AL	On Level OL	Beyond Level BL	English Learners ELL
Teacher Edition	▪ Differentiated Instruction, p. 898	▪ Differentiated Instruction, pp. 898, 902	▪ Differentiated Instruction, pp. 898, 902	
Chapter Resource Masters	▪ Study Guide and Intervention, pp. 49–50 ▪ Skills Practice, p. 51 ▪ Practice, p. 52 ▪ Word Problem Practice, p. 53	▪ Study Guide and Intervention, pp. 49–50 ▪ Skills Practice, p. 51 ▪ Practice, p. 52 ▪ Word Problem Practice, p. 53 ▪ Enrichment, p. 54	▪ Practice, p. 52 ▪ Word Problem Practice, p. 53 ▪ Enrichment, p. 54	▪ Study Guide and Intervention, pp. 49–50 ▪ Skills Practice, p. 51 ▪ Practice, p. 52 ▪ Word Problem Practice, p. 53
Other	▪ 5-Minute Check 12-8 ▪ Study Notebook	▪ 5-Minute Check 12-8 ▪ Study Notebook	▪ 5-Minute Check 12-8 ▪ Study Notebook	▪ 5-Minute Check 12-8 ▪ Study Notebook

StudyTip

Similar and Congruent Solids If two solids are similar, then their corresponding linear measures are proportional. If two solids are congruent, then their corresponding linear measures are equal.

Example 1 Identify Similar and Congruent Solids

Determine whether each pair of solids is *similar*, *congruent*, or *neither*. If the solids are similar, state the scale factor.

a. the square pyramids

ratio of heights: $\frac{4}{6} = \frac{2}{3}$

ratio of base edges: $\frac{8}{12} = \frac{2}{3}$

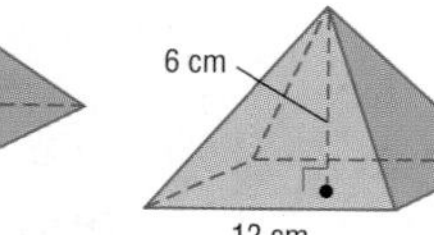

The ratios of the corresponding measures are equal, so the pyramids are similar. The scale factor is 2:3. Since the scale factor is not 1:1, the solids are not congruent.

b. the rectangular prisms

ratio of widths: $\frac{3}{1.7} \approx 1.76$

ratio of lengths: $\frac{6.2}{3.4} \approx 1.82$

ratio of heights: $\frac{2.5}{1.5} \approx 1.67$

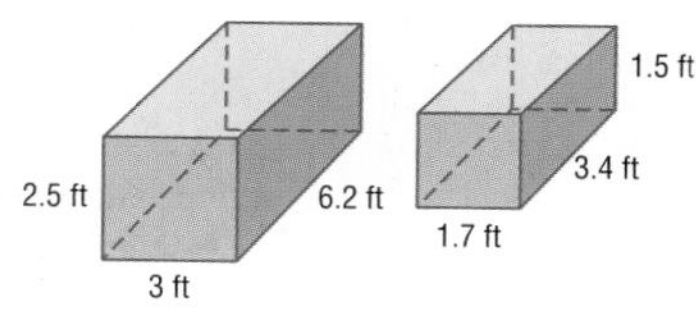

Since the ratios of corresponding measures are not equal, the prisms are neither congruent nor similar.

GuidedPractice

1A.

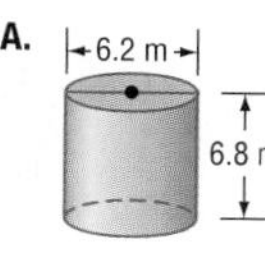

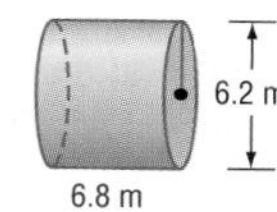

1B.

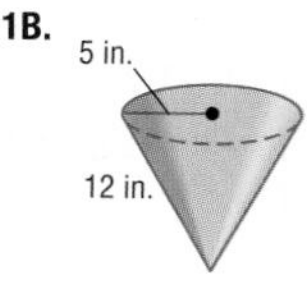

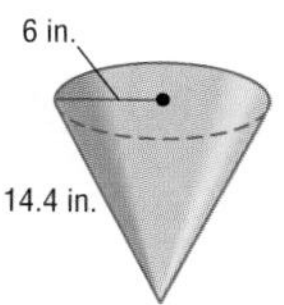

1A. congruent and similar; 1:1
1B. similar; 5:6

StudyTip

Check Solutions After finding missing measures of similar solids, work backward to check your solutions.

2 Properties of Congruent and Similar Solids

The cubes at the right are similar solids with a scale factor of 3:2.

ratio of surface areas: 54:24 or 9:4

ratio of volumes: 27:8

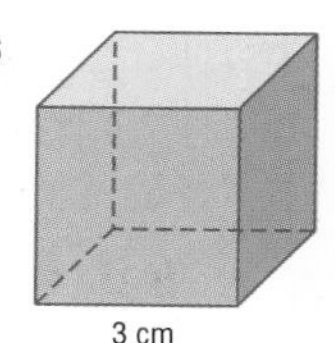

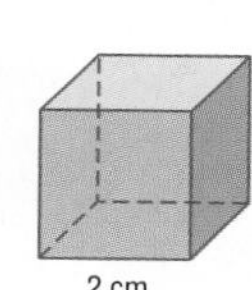

Notice that the ratio of surface areas, 9:4, can be written as $3^2:2^2$. The ratio of volumes, 27:8, can be written as $3^3:2^3$. This suggests the following theorem.

Theorem 12.1

		Models
Words	If two similar solids have a scale factor of $a:b$, then the surface areas have a ratio of $a^2:b^2$, and the volumes have a ratio of $a^3:b^3$.	  2 3
Examples	scale factor 2:3 ratio of surface area 4:9 ratio of volumes 8:27	

Figures must be similar in order for Theorem 12.1 to apply.

1 Identify Congruent or Similar Solids

Example 1 shows how to prove solids are congruent or similar.

Formative Assessment

Use the Guided Practice exercises after each Example to determine students' understanding of concepts.

Additional Example

1 Determine whether each pair of solids is *similar*, *congruent*, or *neither*. If the solids are similar, state the scale factor.

a.

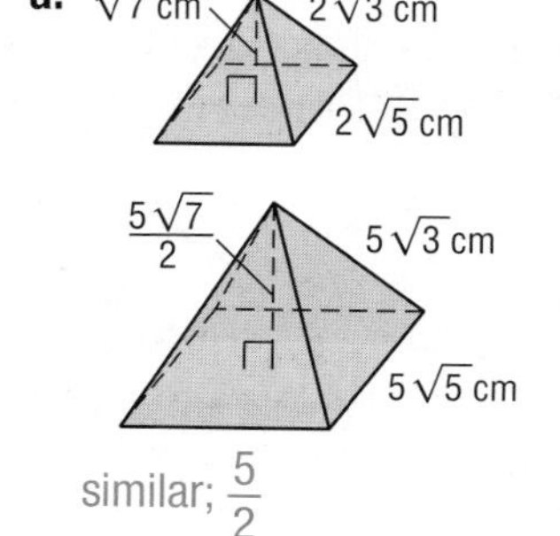

similar; $\frac{5}{2}$

b.

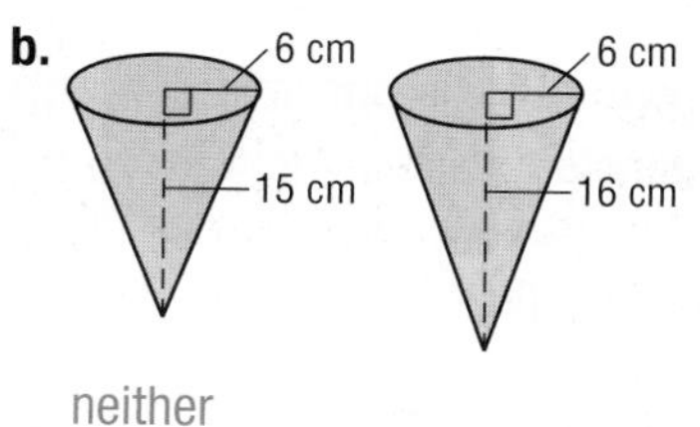

neither

Additional Examples also in Interactive Classroom PowerPoint® Presentations

IWB Interactive White Board READY

Tips for New Teachers

Corresponding Scales Point out that all corresponding dimensions of the two pyramids need to have the same scale factor for the pyramids to be similar.

2 Properties of Congruent and Similar Solids

Example 2 shows how to compare the volumes of two similar cones.
Example 3 shows how to use similar volumes to find an unknown measure.

Additional Examples

2 Two similar cones have radii of 9 inches and 12 inches. What is the ratio of the volume of the smaller cone to the volume of the larger cone? 27:64

3 **SOFTBALLS** The softballs below are similar spheres. If the radius of the larger softball is 1.9 inches, find the radius of the smaller softball.

$V = 9.15\pi \text{ in}^3$ $V = 4.06\pi \text{ in}^3$

$\approx$1.45 in.

Focus on Mathematical Content

Extension Point out that Theorem 12.1 can be used with any similar solids, including prisms.

Teach with Tech

Digital Camera Have students find and take pictures of objects at home that appear to be similar solids. Have them measure and find the volume of each solid to determine whether or not they are similar.

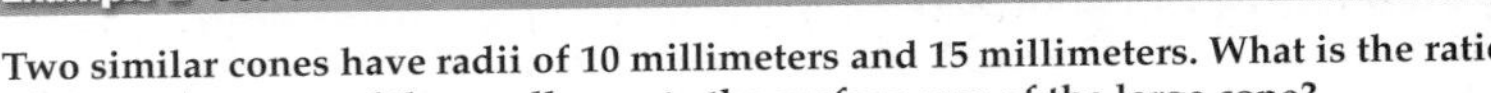

Example 2 Use Similar Solids to Write Ratios

Two similar cones have radii of 10 millimeters and 15 millimeters. What is the ratio of the surface area of the small cone to the surface area of the large cone?

First, find the scale factor.

$\frac{\text{radius of small cone}}{\text{radius of large cone}} = \frac{10}{15} \text{ or } \frac{2}{3}$ Write a ratio comparing the radii.

The scale factor is $\frac{2}{3}$.

$\frac{a^2}{b^2} = \frac{2^2}{3^2} \text{ or } \frac{4}{9}$ If the scale factor is $\frac{a}{b}$, then the ratio of surface areas is $\frac{a^2}{b^2}$.

So, the ratio of the surface areas is 4:9.

StudyTip
Similar Solids and Area If two solids are similar, then the ratio of any corresponding areas is $a^2 : b^2$. In Example 2, the ratio of the lateral areas of the cones is 4:25, and the ratio of the base areas of the cones is 4:25.

GuidedPractice

2. Two similar prisms have surface areas of 98 square centimeters and 18 square centimeters. What is the ratio of the height of the large prism to the height of the small prism? 7:3

Many real-world objects can be modeled by similar solids.

Real-World Example 3 Use Similar Solids to Find Unknown Values

CONTAINERS The containers at the right are similar cylinders. Find the height h of the smaller container.

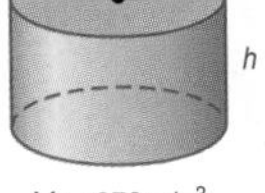

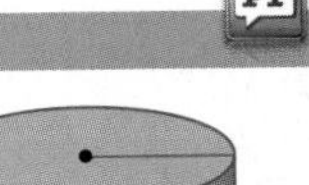

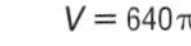

Understand You know the height of the larger container and the volumes of both containers.

Plan Use Theorem 12.1 to write a ratio comparing the volumes. Then find the scale factor and use it to find h.

Solve $\frac{\text{volume of small container}}{\text{volume of large container}} = \frac{270\pi}{640\pi}$ Write a ratio comparing volumes.

$= \frac{27}{64}$ Simplify.

$= \frac{3^3}{4^3}$ Write as $\frac{a^3}{b^3}$.

The scale factor is 3:4.

Ratio of heights $\rightarrow$ $\frac{h}{10} = \frac{3}{4}$ $\leftarrow$ Scale factor

$h \cdot 4 = 10 \cdot 3$ Find the cross products.

$h = 7.5$ Solve for h.

So, the height of the smaller container is 7.5 inches.

Check Since $\frac{7.5}{10} = 0.75 = \frac{3}{4}$, the solution is correct. ✓

Math HistoryLink
Georg F.B. Riemann (1826–1866) Spherical geometry is sometimes called *Riemann geometry*, after Georg Reimann, a German mathematician responsible for the Riemannian Postulate, which states that through a point not on a line, there are no lines parallel to the given line.

GuidedPractice

3. **VOLLEYBALL** A regulation volleyball has a circumference of about 66 centimeters. The ratio of the surface area of that ball to the surface area of a children's ball is approximately 1.6:1. What is the circumference of the children's ball? Round to the nearest centimeter. 52 cm

DifferentiatedInstruction AL OL BL

Verbal/Linguistic Learners Tell students that for the two-dimensional measurement of surface area, the ratio involves the power of two. For the three-dimensional measurement of volume, the ratio involves the power of three.

Check Your Understanding

= Step-by-Step Solutions begin on page R14.

Example 1 **Determine whether each pair of solids is *similar*, *congruent*, or *neither*. If the solids are similar, state the scale factor.**

1. similar; 4:3
2. neither

1.

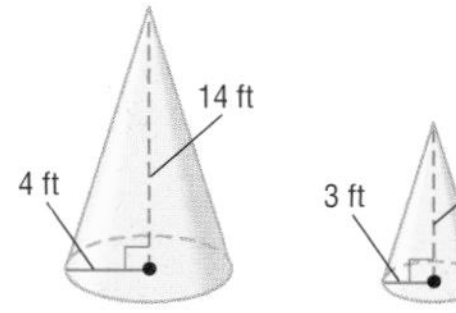

2.

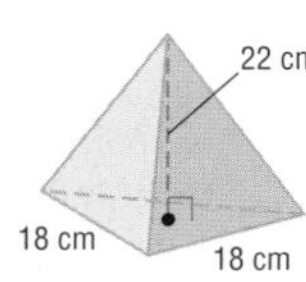

Example 2

3. Two similar cylinders have radii of 15 inches and 6 inches. What is the ratio of the surface area of the small cylinder to the surface area of the large cylinder? **4:25**

4. Two spheres have volumes of 36π cubic centimeters and 288π cubic centimeters. What is the ratio of the radius of the small sphere to the radius of the large sphere? **1:2**

Example 3

5. **EXERCISE BALLS** A company sells two different sizes of exercise balls. The ratio of the diameters is 15:11. If the diameter of the smaller ball is 55 centimeters, what is the volume of the larger ball? Round to the nearest tenth. **220,893.2 cm^3**

Practice and Problem Solving

Extra Practice is on page R12.

Example 1 CCSS **REGULARITY** **Determine whether each pair of solids is *similar*, *congruent*, or *neither*. If the solids are similar, state the scale factor.**

6. similar; 9:8
7. neither
8. similar and congruent; 1:1
9. similar; 6:5

6.

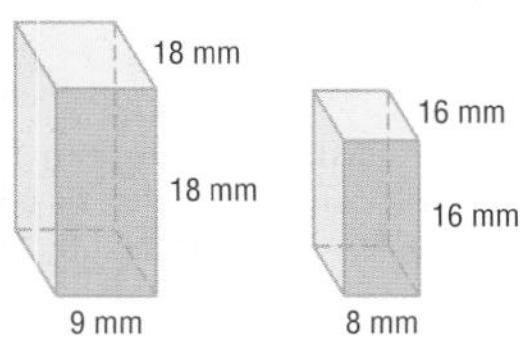

7.

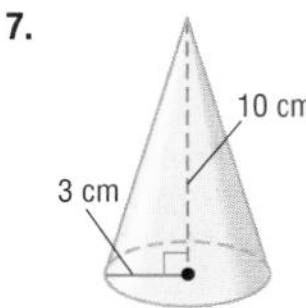

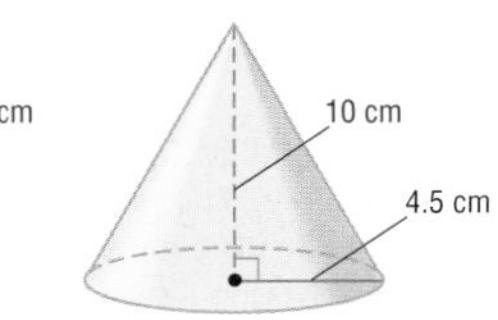

8.

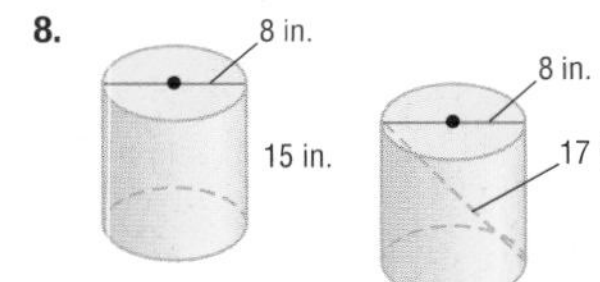

9.

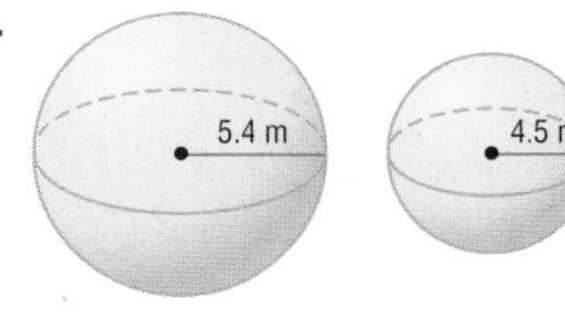

Example 2

10. Two similar pyramids have slant heights of 6 inches and 12 inches. What is the ratio of the surface area of the small pyramid to the surface area of the large pyramid? **1:4**

11. Two similar cylinders have heights of 35 meters and 25 meters. What is the ratio of the volume of the large cylinder to the volume of the small cylinder? **343:125**

12. Two spheres have surface areas of 100π square centimeters and 16π square centimeters. What is the ratio of the volume of the large sphere to the volume of the small sphere? **125:8**

13. Two similar hexagonal prisms have volumes of 250 cubic feet and 2 cubic feet. What is the ratio of the height of the large cylinder to the height of the small cylinder? **5:1**

14. **DIMENSIONAL ANALYSIS** Two rectangular prisms are similar. The height of the first prism is 6 yards and the height of the other prism is 9 feet. If the volume of the first prism is 810 cubic yards, what is the volume of the other prism? **101.25 yd^3**

Differentiated Homework Options

Level	Assignment	Two-Day Option	
AL Basic	6–16, 27, 29–47	7–15 odd, 33–36	6–16 even, 29–32, 37–47
OL Core	7–21 odd, 22–27, 29–47	6–16, 33–36	17–27, 29–32, 37–47
BL Advanced	17–43, (optional: 44–47)		

3 Practice

Formative Assessment

Use Exercises 1–5 to check for understanding.

Use the chart at the bottom of this page to customize assignments for your students.

Teaching the Mathematical Practices

Regularity Mathematically proficient students maintain oversight of the process, while attending to the details. They continually evaluate the reasonableness of their intermediate results. In Exercises 6–9, encourage students to check the reasonableness of their results.

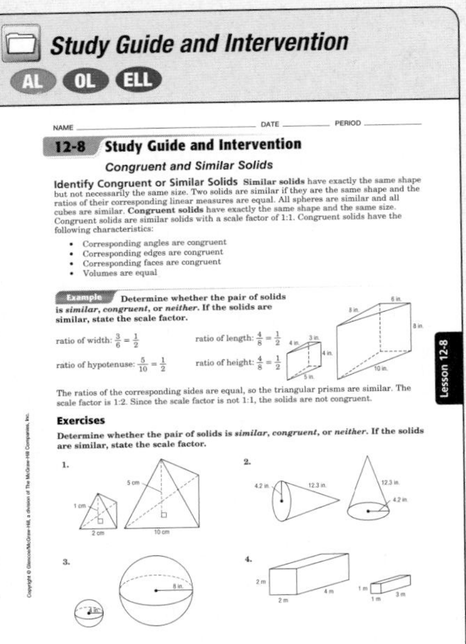

Study Guide and Intervention

AL OL ELL

NAME ________ DATE ________ PERIOD ________

12-8 Study Guide and Intervention

Congruent and Similar Solids

Identify Congruent or Similar Solids **Similar solids** have exactly the same shape but not necessarily the same size. Two solids are similar if they are the same shape and the ratios of their corresponding linear measures are equal. All spheres are similar and all cubes are similar. **Congruent solids** have exactly the same shape and the same size. Congruent solids are similar solids with a scale factor of 1:1. Congruent solids have the following characteristics:

- Corresponding angles are congruent
- Corresponding edges are congruent
- Corresponding faces are congruent
- Volumes are equal

Example **Determine whether the pair of solids is *similar*, *congruent*, or *neither*. If the solids are similar, state the scale factor.**

ratio of width: $\frac{3}{6} = \frac{1}{2}$ ratio of length: $\frac{4}{8} = \frac{1}{2}$

ratio of hypotenuse: $\frac{5}{10} = \frac{1}{2}$ ratio of height: $\frac{4}{8} = \frac{1}{2}$

The ratios of the corresponding sides are equal, so the triangular prisms are similar. The scale factor is 1:2. Since the scale factor is not 1:1, the solids are not congruent.

Exercises

Determine whether the pair of solids is *similar*, *congruent*, or *neither*. If the solids are similar, state the scale factor.

1. 2. 3. 4.

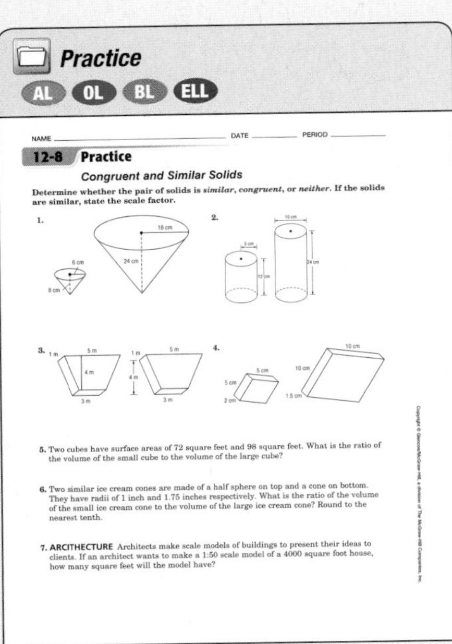

Practice

AL OL BL ELL

NAME ________ DATE ________ PERIOD ________

12-8 Practice

Congruent and Similar Solids

Determine whether the pair of solids is *similar*, *congruent*, or *neither*. If the solids are similar, state the scale factor.

1. 2. 3. 4.

5. Two cubes have surface areas of 72 square feet and 98 square feet. What is the ratio of the volume of the small cube to the volume of the large cube?

6. Two similar ice cream cones are made of a half sphere on top and a cone on bottom. They have radii of 1 inch and 1.75 inches respectively. What is the ratio of the volume of the small ice cream cone to the volume of the large ice cream cone? Round to the nearest tenth.

7. **ARCITHECTURE** Architects make scale models of buildings to present their ideas to clients. If an architect wants to make a 1:50 scale model of a 4000 square foot house, how many square feet will the model have?

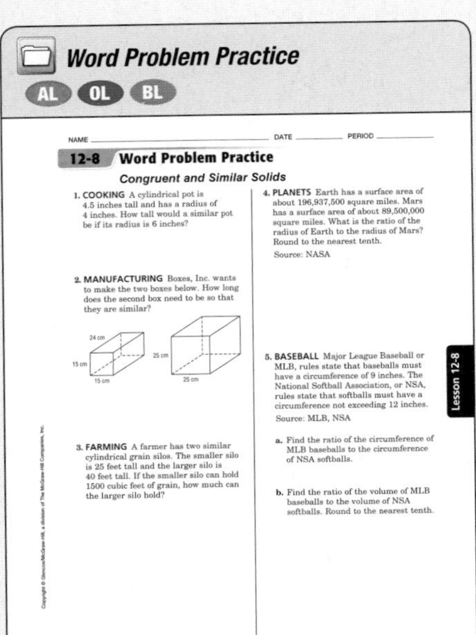

Word Problem Practice

AL OL BL

NAME ________ DATE ________ PERIOD ________

12-8 Word Problem Practice

Congruent and Similar Solids

1. **COOKING** A cylindrical pot is 4.5 inches tall and has a radius of 4 inches. How tall would a similar pot be if its radius is 6 inches?

2. **MANUFACTURING** Boxes, Inc. wants to make the two boxes below. How long does the second box need to be so that they are similar?

3. **FARMING** A farmer has two similar cylindrical grain silos. The smaller silo is 25 feet tall and the larger silo is 40 feet tall. If the smaller silo can hold 1500 cubic feet of grain, how much can the larger silo hold?

4. **PLANETS** Earth has a surface area of about 196,937,500 square miles. Mars has a surface area of about 89,500,000 square miles. What is the ratio of the radius of Earth to the radius of Mars? Round to the nearest tenth.
Source: NASA

5. **BASEBALL** Major League Baseball or MLB, rules state that baseballs must have a circumference of 9 inches. The National Softball Association, or NSA, rules state that softballs must have a circumference not exceeding 12 inches.
Source: MLB, NSA

a. Find the ratio of the circumference of MLB baseballs to the circumference of NSA softballs.

b. Find the ratio of the volume of MLB baseballs to the volume of NSA softballs. Round to the nearest tenth.

Example 3

15. **FOOD** A small cylindrical can of tuna has a radius of 4 centimeters and a height of 3.8 centimeters. A larger and similar can of tuna has a radius of 5.2 centimeters.

a. What is the scale factor of the cylinders? **10:13**

b. What is the volume of the larger can? Round to the nearest tenth. **419.6 cm³**

16. **SUITCASES** Two suitcases are similar rectangular prisms. The smaller suitcase is 68 centimeters long, 47 centimeters wide, and 27 centimeters deep. The larger suitcase is 85 centimeters long.

a. What is the scale factor of the prisms? **4:5**

b. What is the volume of the larger suitcase? Round to the nearest tenth. **168,539.1 cm³**

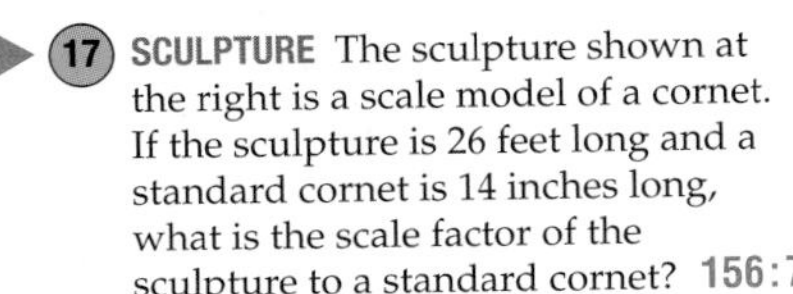

B 17. **SCULPTURE** The sculpture shown at the right is a scale model of a cornet. If the sculpture is 26 feet long and a standard cornet is 14 inches long, what is the scale factor of the sculpture to a standard cornet? **156:7**

18. The pyramids shown are congruent.

a. What is the perimeter of the base of Pyramid A? **24 cm**

b. What is the area of the base of Pyramid B? **24 cm²**

c. What is the volume of Pyramid B? **104 cm³**

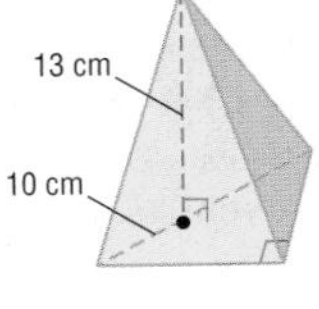

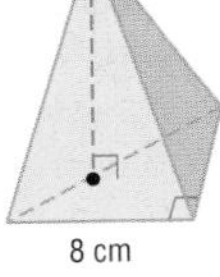

19. **TECHNOLOGY** Jalissa and Mateo each have the same type of MP3 player, but in different colors. The players are congruent rectangular prisms. The volume of Jalissa's player is 4.92 cubic inches, the width is 2.4 inches, and the depth is 0.5 inch. What is the height of Mateo's player? **4.1 in.**

CCSS SENSE-MAKING **Each pair of solids below is similar.**

20. What is the surface area of the smaller solid shown below? **946.3 cm²**

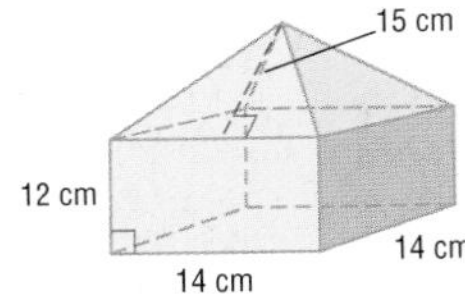

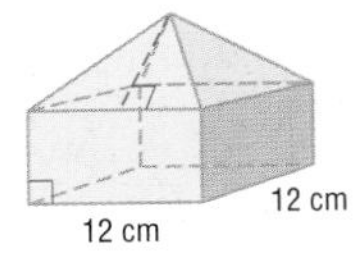

21. What is the volume of the larger solid shown below? **2439.6 cm³**

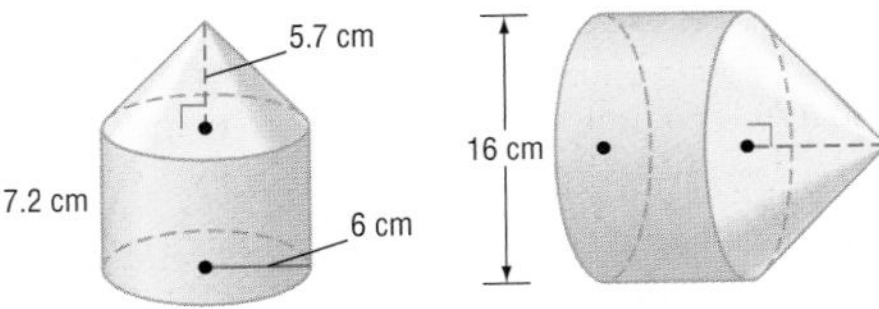

22. **DIMENSIONAL ANALYSIS** Two cylinders are similar. The height of the first cylinder is 23 cm and the height of the other cylinder is 8 in. If the volume of the first cylinder is 552π cm³, what is the volume of the other prism? Use 2.54 cm = 1 in. **380.65π cm³**

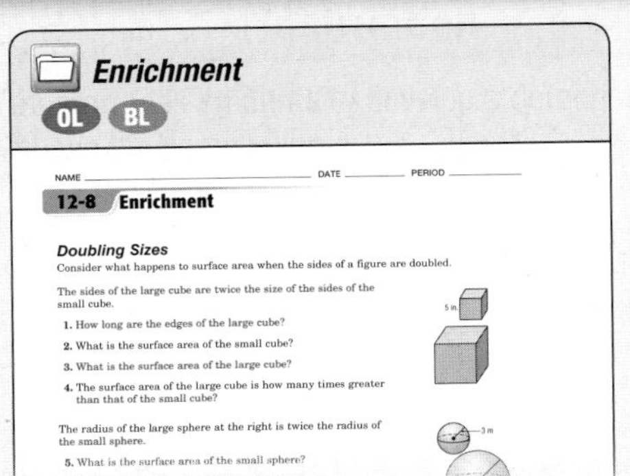

Enrichment

OL BL

NAME ________ DATE ________ PERIOD ________

12-8 Enrichment

Doubling Sizes

Consider what happens to surface area when the sides of a figure are doubled.

The sides of the large cube are twice the size of the sides of the small cube.

1. How long are the edges of the large cube?
2. What is the surface area of the small cube?
3. What is the surface area of the large cube?
4. The surface area of the large cube is how many times greater than that of the small cube?

The radius of the large sphere at the right is twice the radius of the small sphere.

5. What is the surface area of the small sphere?
6. What is the surface area of the large sphere?

CCSS Teaching the Mathematical Practices

Sense-Making Mathematically proficient students start by explaining the meaning of a problem to themselves and looking for entry points to its solution. They plan a solution pathway rather than simply jumping into a solution attempt. In Exercises 20–21, encourage students to make a plan to solve each problem first.

23. DIMENSIONAL ANALYSIS Two spheres are similar. The radius of the first sphere is 10 feet. The volume of the other sphere is 0.9 cubic meters. Use 2.54 cm = 1 in. to determine the scale factor from the first sphere to the second. **about 5.08 to 1**

24. ALGEBRA Two similar cones have volumes of 343π cubic centimeters and 512π cubic centimeters. The height of each cone is equal to 3 times its radius. Find the radius and height of both cones. **smaller cone: $r = 7$ cm, $h = 21$ cm; larger cone: $r = 8$ cm, $h = 24$ cm**

25. TENTS Two tents are in the shape of hemispheres, with circular floors. The ratio of their floor areas is 9 : 12.25. If the diameter of the smaller tent is 6 feet, what is the volume of the larger tent? Round to the nearest tenth. **89.8 ft^3**

26. MULTIPLE REPRESENTATIONS In this problem, you will investigate similarity. The heights of two similar cylinders are in the ratio 2 to 3. The lateral area of the larger cylinder is 162π square centimeters, and the diameter of the smaller cylinder is 8 centimeters.

a. **Verbal** What is the height of the larger cylinder? Explain your method.

b. **Geometric** Sketch and label the two cylinders. **See margin.**

c. **Analytical** How many times as great is the volume of the larger cylinder as the volume of the smaller cylinder? **3.375 times as great**

26a. 13.5 cm; The heights are in the ratio 2 to 3, so the scale factor is 2 : 3. Since $\frac{8}{12} = \frac{2}{3}$, the diameter of the larger cylinder is 12 cm. The lateral area of the larger cylinder is 162π cm^2, so the height is $162\pi \div 12\pi$ or 13.5 cm.

H.O.T. Problems Use Higher-Order Thinking Skills

27. ERROR ANALYSIS Cylinder X has a diameter of 20 centimeters and a height of 11 centimeters. Cylinder Y has a radius of 30 centimeters and is similar to Cylinder X. Did Laura or Paloma correctly find the height of Cylinder Y? Explain your reasoning.

27. Laura; because she compared corresponding parts of the similar figures. Paloma incorrectly compared the diameter of X to the radius of Y.

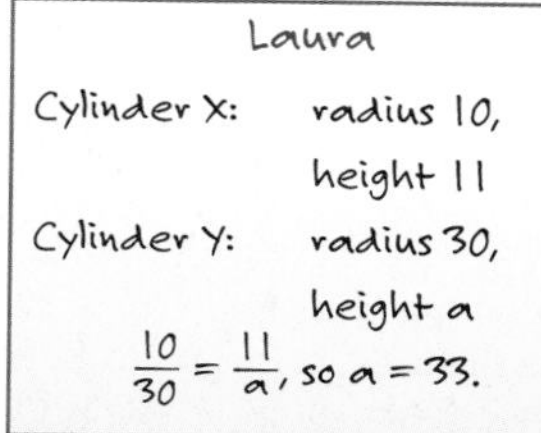

Laura
Cylinder X: radius 10, height 11
Cylinder Y: radius 30, height a
$\frac{10}{30} = \frac{11}{a}$, so a = 33.

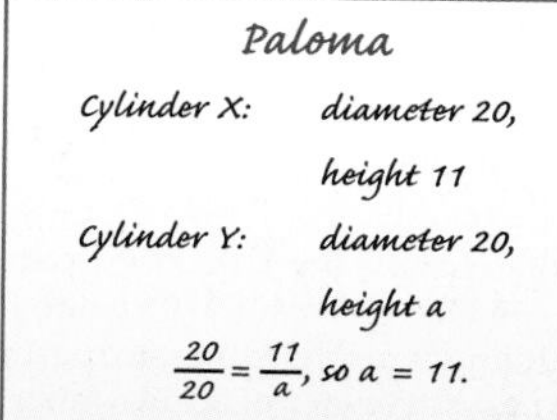

Paloma
Cylinder X: diameter 20, height 11
Cylinder Y: diameter 20, height a
$\frac{20}{20} = \frac{11}{a}$, so a = 11.

28. 8 : 135; The volume of Cylinder C is 8 times the volume of Cylinder A, and the volume of Cylinder D is 27 times the volume of Cylinder B. If the original ratio of volumes was $1x : 5x$, the new ratio is $8x : 135x$. So, the ratio of volumes is 8 : 135.

28. CHALLENGE The ratio of the volume of Cylinder A to the volume of Cylinder B is 1 : 5. Cylinder A is similar to Cylinder C with a scale factor of 1 : 2 and Cylinder B is similar to Cylinder D with a scale factor of 1 : 3. What is the ratio of the volume of Cylinder C to the volume of Cylinder D? Explain your reasoning.

29. WRITING IN MATH Explain how the surface areas and volumes of the similar prisms shown at the right are related. **See margin.**

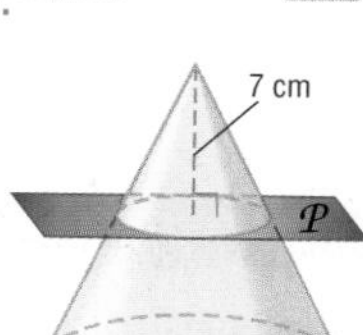

30. OPEN ENDED Describe two nonsimilar triangular pyramids with similar bases. **See margin.**

31. CCSS SENSE-MAKING Plane $\mathcal{P}$ is parallel to the base of cone C, and the volume of the cone above the plane is $\frac{1}{8}$ of the volume of cone C. Find the height of cone C. **14 cm**

7 cm
$\mathcal{P}$
• C

32. WRITING IN MATH Explain why all spheres are similar.

32. Sample answer: All spheres are the same shape. The only parameter that can vary is the radius, so all spheres are similar.

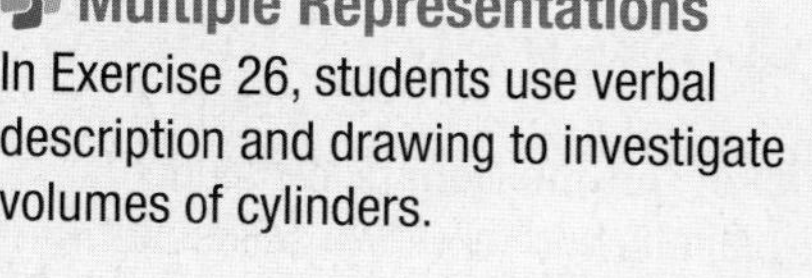

Multiple Representations

In Exercise 26, students use verbal description and drawing to investigate volumes of cylinders.

WatchOut!

Error Analysis For Exercise 27, students should write a proportion to find the height of Cylinder Y. Paloma incorrectly wrote that the diameter of Cylinder Y was 20.

Teaching the Mathematical Practices

Sense-Making Mathematically proficient students consider analogous problems and try simpler forms of the original problem in order to gain insight into its solution. In Exercise 31, encourage students to write a proportion comparing the two cones.

Additional Answers

26b. Sample answer:

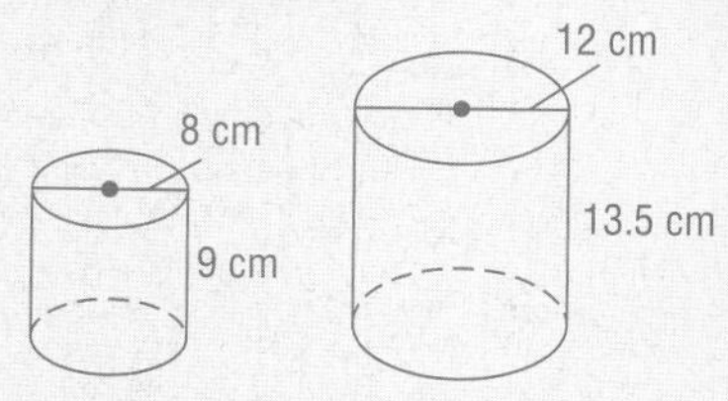

29. Since the scale factor is 15:9 or 5:3, the ratio of the surface areas is 25:9 and the ratio of the volumes is 125:27. So, the surface area of the larger prism is $\frac{25}{9}$ or about 2.8 times the surface area of the smaller prism. The volume of the larger prism is $\frac{125}{27}$ or about 4.6 times the volume of the smaller prism.

30. Sample answer: a pyramid with a right triangle base of 3, 4, and 5 units and a height of 6 units; a pyramid with a right triangle base of 6, 8, and 10 units and a height of 6 units.

4 Assess

Ticket Out the Door Have students explain how to tell if two solids are congruent. Have students turn in their statements before they leave the classroom.

Formative Assessment

Check for student understanding of Lessons 12-7 and 12-8.

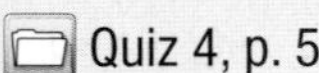 Quiz 4, p. 58

Standardized Test Practice

33. Two similar spheres have radii of 20π meters and 6π meters. What is the ratio of the surface area of the large sphere to the surface area of the small sphere? B

A $\frac{100}{3}$ B $\frac{100}{9}$ C $\frac{10}{3}$ D $\frac{10}{9}$

34. What is the scale factor of the similar figures? G

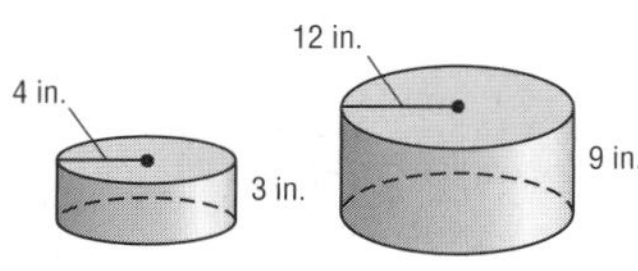

F 0.25
G 0.33
H 0.5
J 0.75

35. SHORT RESPONSE Point A and point B represent the locations of Timothy's and Quincy's houses. If each unit on the map represents one kilometer, how far apart are the two houses? $\sqrt{85} \approx 9.2$ km

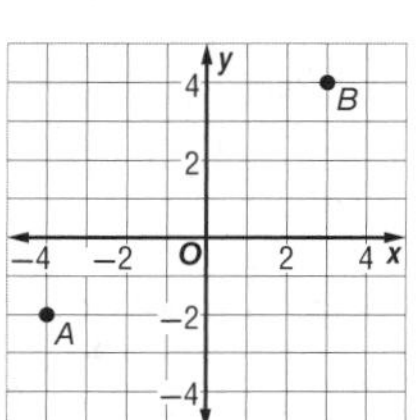

36. SAT/ACT If $\frac{x+2}{3} = \frac{(x+2)^2}{15}$, what is one possible value of x? D

A 0 B 1 C 2 D 3 E 4

Spiral Review

Determine whether figure χ **on each of the spheres shown is a line in spherical geometry.** (Lesson 12-7)

37. yes

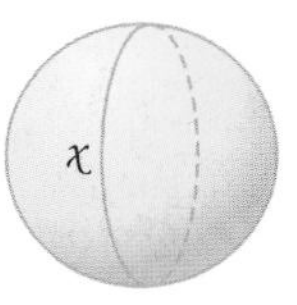

38. no

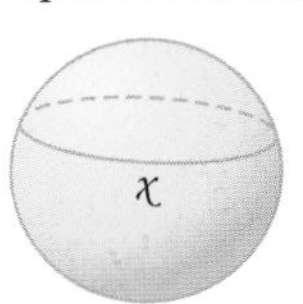

39. yes

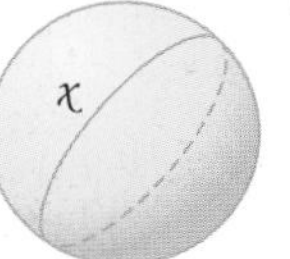

40. ENTERTAINMENT Some people think that the Spaceship Earth geosphere at Epcot in Disney World in Orlando, Florida, resembles a golf ball. The building is a sphere measuring 165 feet in diameter. A typical golf ball has a diameter of approximately 1.5 inches. (Lesson 12-6)

a. Find the volume of Spaceship Earth to the nearest cubic foot. 2,352,071 ft^3

b. Find the volume of a golf ball to the nearest tenth. 1.8 in^3

c. What is the scale factor that compares Spaceship Earth to a golf ball? 1320 to 1

d. What is the ratio of the volumes of Spaceship Earth to a golf ball? 1320^3 to 1 or 2,299,968,000 to 1

Find x. Assume that segments that appear to be tangent are tangent. (Lesson 10-7)

41. 5

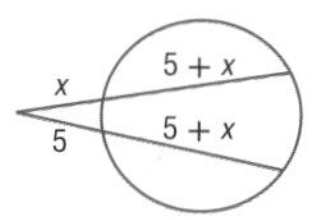

42. 4

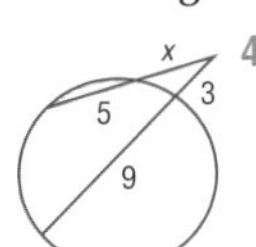

43. 6

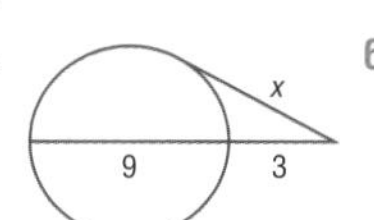

Skills Review

Express each fraction as a decimal to the nearest hundredth.

44. $\frac{8}{13}$ 0.62 **45.** $\frac{17}{54}$ 0.31 **46.** $\frac{11}{78}$ 0.14 **47.** $\frac{43}{46}$ 0.93

Differentiated Instruction OL BL

Extension Ask students to explain why food-processing companies might be concerned with maximizing volume for a given surface area of product packaging. Sample answer: The largest possible ratio of volume to ratio of surface area possible minimizes cost for packaging materials.

CHAPTER 12 Study Guide and Review

Study Guide

KeyConcepts

Representations of Three-Dimensional Figures (Lesson 12-1)

- Solids can be classified by bases, faces, edges, and vertices.

Surface Areas of Prisms and Cylinders (Lesson 12-2)

- Lateral surface area of a right prism: $L = Ph$
- Lateral surface area of a right cylinder: $L = 2\pi rh$

Surface Areas of Pyramids and Cones (Lesson 12-3)

- Lateral surface area of a pyramid: $L = \frac{1}{2}P\ell$
- Lateral surface area of a right cone: $L = \pi r\ell$

Volumes of Prisms and Cylinders (Lesson 12-4)

- Volume of prism or cylinder: $V = Bh$

Volumes of Pyramids and Cones (Lesson 12-5)

- Volume of a pyramid: $V = \frac{1}{3}Bh$
- Volume of a cone: $V = \frac{1}{3}\pi r^2h$

Surface Areas and Volumes of Spheres (Lesson 12-6)

- Surface area of a sphere: $S = 4\pi r^2$
- Volume of a sphere: $V = \frac{4}{3}\pi r^3$

Congruent and Similar Solids (Lesson 12-8)

- Similar solids have the same shape, but not necessarily the same size.
- Congruent solids are similar solids with a scale factor of 1.

FOLDABLES StudyOrganizer

Be sure the Key Concepts are noted in your Foldable.

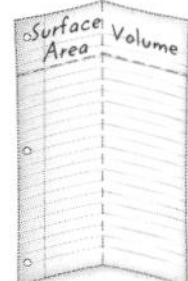

KeyVocabulary

altitude (p. 846)	lateral face (p. 846)
axis (p. 848)	non-Euclidean geometry (p. 890)
base edges (p. 846)	oblique cone (p. 856)
composite solid (p. 852)	oblique solid (p. 838)
congruent solid (p. 896)	regular pyramid (p. 854)
cross section (p. 840)	right cone (p. 856)
Euclidean geometry (p. 889)	right solid (p. 837)
great circle (p. 881)	similar solids (p. 896)
isometric view (p. 839)	slant height (p. 854)
lateral area (p. 846)	spherical geometry (p. 889)
lateral edge (p. 846)	topographic map (p. 845)

VocabularyCheck

State whether each sentence is *true* or *false*. If *false*, replace the underlined term to make a true sentence.

1. Euclidean geometry deals with a system of points, great circles (lines), and spheres (planes). **false, Spherical geometry**
2. Similar solids have exactly the same shape, but not necessarily the same size. **true**
3. A right solid has an axis that is also an altitude. **false, right cone**
4. The isometric view is when an object is viewed from a corner. **true**
5. The perpendicular distance from the base of a geometric figure to the opposite vertex, parallel side, or parallel surface is the altitude. **true**
6. Rotation symmetry is also called mirror symmetry. **false, reflection**
7. The intersection of two adjacent lateral faces is the lateral edge. **true**
8. Euclidean geometry refers to geometrical systems that are not in accordance with the Parallel Postulate. **false, Non-Euclidean geometry**
9. A composite solid is a three-dimensional figure that is composed of simpler figures. **true**
10. The slant height is the height of each lateral face of a pyramid or cone. **true**

Formative Assessment

KeyVocabulary The page references after each word denote where that term was first introduced. If students have difficulty answering questions 1–10, remind them that they can use these page references to refresh their memories about the vocabulary terms.

Summative Assessment

Vocabulary Test, p. 60

Vocabulary Review

Vocabulary Review provides students the opportunity to check their understanding of important concepts and terminology in an online game format.

FOLDABLES StudyOrganizer

Dinah Zike's Foldables®

Have students look through the chapter to make sure they have included examples in their Foldables for each lesson of the chapter. Suggest that students keep their Foldables handy while completing the Study Guide and Review pages. Point out that their Foldables can serve as a quick review when studying for the chapter test.

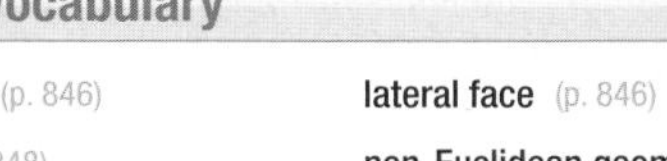

Lesson-by-Lesson Review

Intervention If the given examples are not sufficient to review the topics covered by the questions, remind students that the lesson references tell them where to review that topic in their textbook.

Two-Day Option Have students complete the Lesson-by-Lesson Review. Then you can use eAssessment to customize another review worksheet that practices all the objectives of this chapter or only the objectives on which your students need more help.

CHAPTER 12 Study Guide and Review *Continued*

Lesson-by-Lesson Review

12-1 Representations of Three-Dimensional Figures

Describe each cross section.

11.

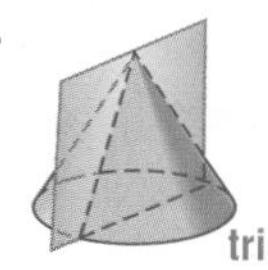

triangle

12. circle

13. CAKE The cake shown is cut in half vertically. Describe the cross section of the cake. rectangle

Example 1

Describe the vertical and horizontal cross sections of the figure shown below.

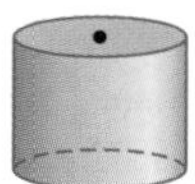

The vertical cross section is a rectangle.
The horizontal cross section is a circle.

12-2 Surface Areas of Prisms and Cylinders

Find the lateral area and surface area of each prism. Round to the nearest tenth if necessary.

14. 3 cm, 11 cm, 2 cm

Sample answer: 78 cm^2; 122 cm^2

15. 8 ft, 3 ft, 7 ft

Sample answer: 160 ft^2; 202 ft^2

Find the lateral area and surface area of each cylinder. Round to the nearest tenth.

16. 4 in., 5 in.

125.7 in^2; 226.2 in^2

17.

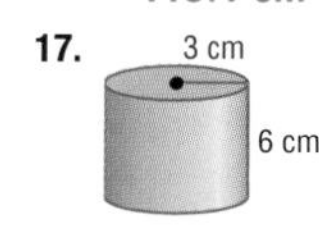

113.1 cm^2; 169.6 cm^2

Example 2

Find the surface area of the rectangular prism.

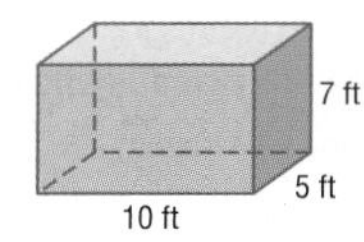

Use the 10-foot by 5-foot rectangle as the base.

$S = Ph + 2B$ Surface area of a prism

$= (2 \cdot 10 + 2 \cdot 5)(7) + 2(10 \cdot 5)$ Substitution

$= 310$ Simplify.

The surface area is 310 square feet.

12-3 Surface Areas of Pyramids and Cones

Find the lateral area and the surface area of each regular pyramid. Round to the nearest tenth.

18.

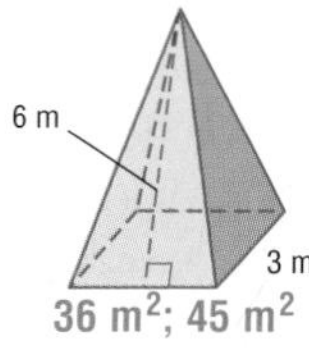

36 m^2; 45 m^2

19.

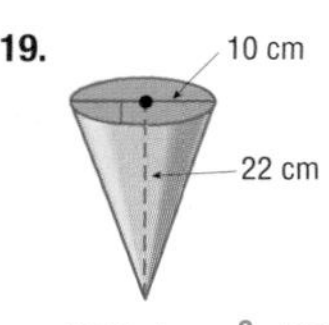

354.4 cm^2; 432.9 cm^2

Example 3

Find the surface area of the square pyramid. Round to the nearest tenth.

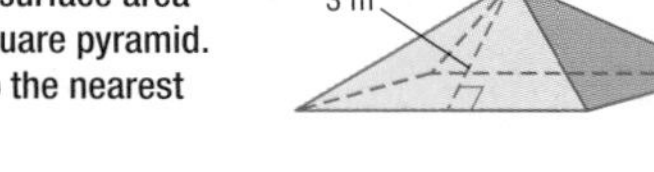

$S = \frac{1}{2}P\ell + B$ Surface area of a regular pyramid

$= \frac{1}{2}(4 \cdot 5)3 + 5 \cdot 5$ $P = 4 \cdot 5$ or 20, $\ell = 3$, $B = 4 \cdot 5$

$= 55$ Simplify.

The surface area is 55 square feet.

12-4 Volumes of Prisms and Cylinders

20. The volume of a cylinder is 770 cm^3. It has a height of 5 cm. Find its radius. **7 cm**

21. Find the volume of the triangular prism. **972 cm^3**

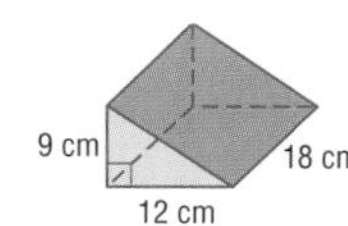

22. TRAILERS A semi-truck trailer is basically a rectangular prism. A typical height for the inside of these trailers is 108 inches. If the trailer is 8 feet wide and 20 feet long, what is the volume of the trailer? **1440 ft^3**

Example 4

Find the volume of the cylinder.

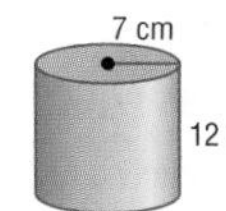

$V = \pi r^2 h$ Volume of a cylinder

$= \pi(7)^2(12)$ $r = 7$ and $h = 12$

≈ 1847.5 Use a calculator.

The volume is approximately 1847.5 cubic centimeters.

12-5 Volumes of Pyramids and Cones

23. Find the volume of a cone that has a radius of 1 cm and a height of 3.4 cm. **3.6 cm^3**

24. Find the volume of the regular pyramid. **18 cm^3**

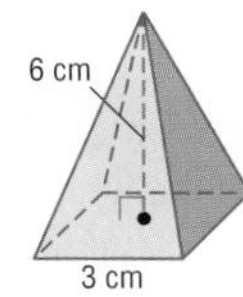

25. ARCHITECTURE The Great Pyramid measures 756 feet on each side of the base and the height is 481 feet. Find the volume of the pyramid. **91,636,272 ft^3**

Example 5

Find the volume of the pyramid.

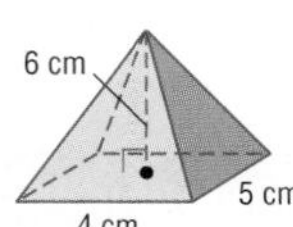

$V = \frac{1}{3}Bh$ Volume of a pyramid

$= \frac{1}{3}(4 \cdot 5)(6)$ $B = 4 \cdot 8$ and $h = 6$

$= 40$ Simplify.

The volume is 40 cubic centimeters.

12-6 Surface Areas and Volumes of Spheres

Find the surface area of each figure.

26.

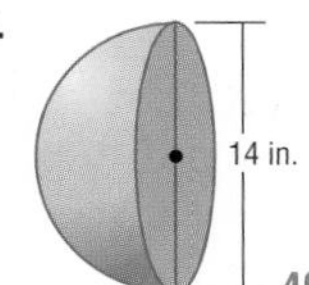

461.8 in^2

27.

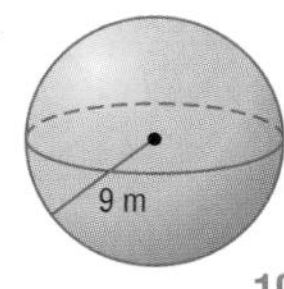

1017.9 m^2

Find the volume of each sphere or hemisphere. Round to the nearest tenth.

28. hemisphere: circumference of great circle $= 24\pi$ m **3619.1 m^3**

29. sphere: area of great circle $= 55\pi$ in^2 **1708.6 in^3**

30. CONSTRUCTION Cement is poured into a hemisphere that is 6 cm across. What is the volume of cement used? **56.5 cm^3**

Example 6

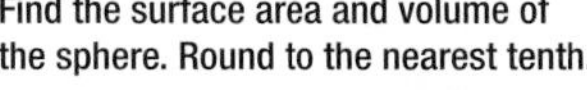

Find the surface area and volume of the sphere. Round to the nearest tenth.

14 cm

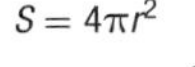

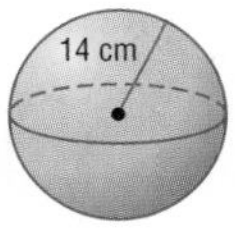

$S = 4\pi r^2$ Surface area of a sphere

$= 4\pi(14)^2$ Substitute.

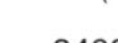

≈ 2463 Use a calculator.

The surface area is about 2463 square centimeters.

$V = \frac{4}{3}\pi r^3$ Volume of a sphere

$= \frac{4}{3}\pi(14)^3$ Replace r with 9.

$\approx 11{,}494$ cm^3 Use a calculator.

The volume is about 11,494 cubic centimeters.

connectED.mcgraw-hill.com 905

Anticipation Guide

Have students complete the Chapter 12 Anticipation Guide and discuss how their responses have changed now that they have completed Chapter 12.

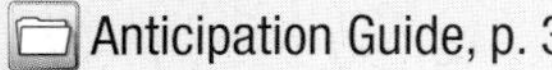

Additional Answers

31. $\overleftrightarrow{FG}$, $\overleftrightarrow{DJ}$
32. $\overline{DL}$
33. $\triangle CBD$
34. $\overleftrightarrow{HE}$, $\overleftrightarrow{GF}$
35. $\overline{KC}$
36. $\triangle JKL$

CHAPTER 12 Study Guide and Review *Continued*

12-7 Spherical Geometry

Name each of the following on sphere *A*. **31–36. See margin.**

31. two lines containing point *C*
32. a segment containing point *H*
33. a triangle containing point *B*
34. two lines containing point *L*
35. a segment containing point *J*
36. a triangle containing point *K*

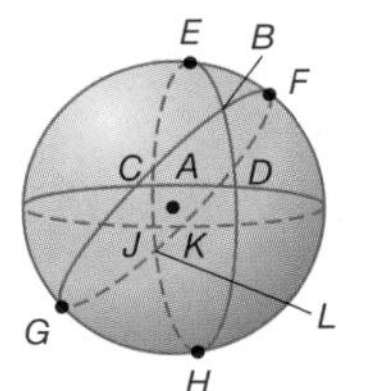

37. **MARBLES** Determine whether figure *y* on the sphere shown is a line in spherical geometry. **no**

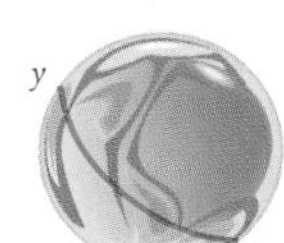

Example 7

Name each of the following on sphere *A*.

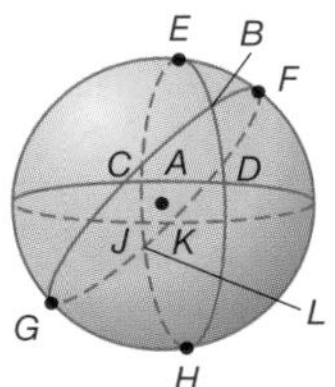

a. two lines containing point *D*
$\overleftrightarrow{EH}$, $\overleftrightarrow{CK}$

b. a segment containing point *E*
$\overline{DJ}$

12-8 Congruent and Similar Solids

Determine whether each pair of solids is *similar*, *congruent*, or *neither*. If the solids are similar, state the scale factor.

38. 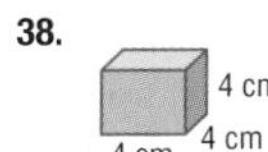

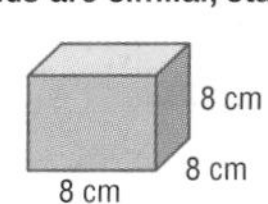

39. 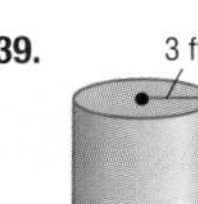

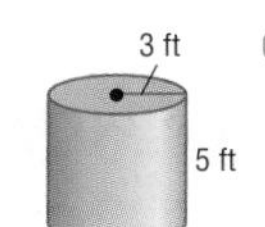

congruent

40. 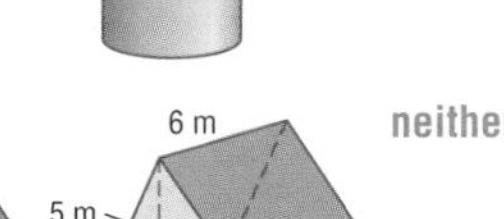

neither

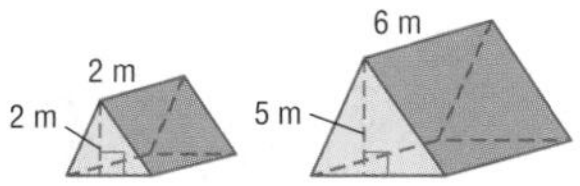

41. 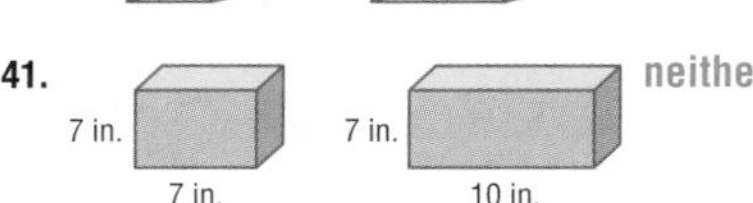

neither

42. **MODELS** A collector's model car is scaled so that 1 inch on the model equals $5\frac{3}{4}$ feet on the actual car. If the model is $\frac{4}{5}$ inches high, how high is the actual car? **$4\frac{3}{5}$ ft**

Example 8

Determine whether each pair of solids is similar, congruent, or neither. If the solids are similar, state the scale factor.

a.

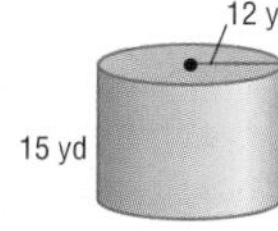

The ratios of the corresponding measures are equal and the scale factor is 1 : 1, so the solids are congruent.

b.

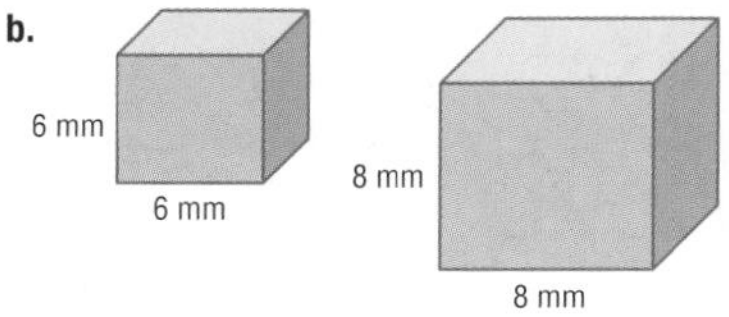

6 mm, 6 mm; 8 mm, 8 mm

ratio of widths: $\frac{6}{8} = 0.75$

ratio of heights: $\frac{6}{8} = 0.75$

The ratios of the corresponding measures are equal, so the cubes are similar. The scale factor is 3 : 4. Since the scale factor is not 1 : 1, the solids are not congruent.

Additional Answer (Practice Test)

1.

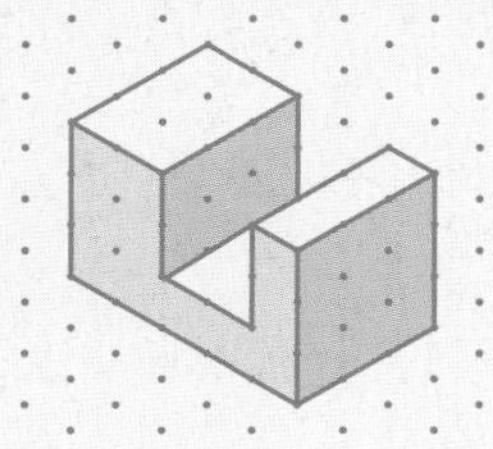

CHAPTER 12 Practice Test

1. Use isometric dot paper and the orthographic drawings to sketch the solid. **See margin.**

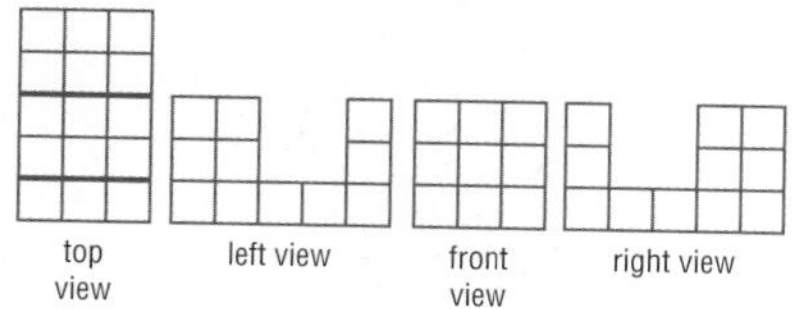

2. Describe the cross section. **ellipse**

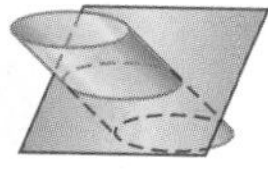

3. **SHORT RESPONSE** Find the surface area of the tent model. Round to the nearest tenth if necessary. **746.7 ft²**

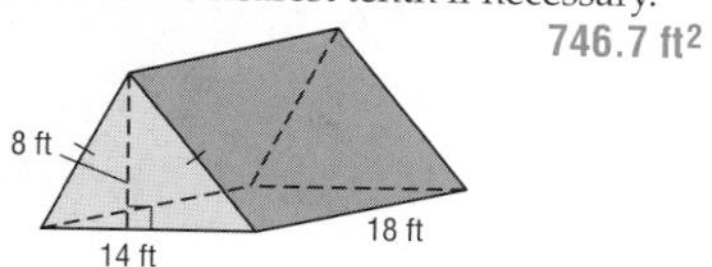

4. **CANDLES** A circular pillar candle is 2.8 inches wide and 6 inches tall. What are the lateral area and surface area of the candle? Round to the nearest tenth if necessary. **52.8 in², 65.1 in²**

5. **TEA** A tea bag is shaped like a regular square pyramid. Each edge of the base is 4 centimeters, and the slant height is 5 centimeters. What is the surface area of the tea bag in square centimeters? Round to the nearest tenth if necessary. **56**

6. **BEEHIVE** Estimate the lateral area and surface area of the Turkish beehive room. Round to the nearest tenth if necessary. **620.1 ft², 874.6 ft²**

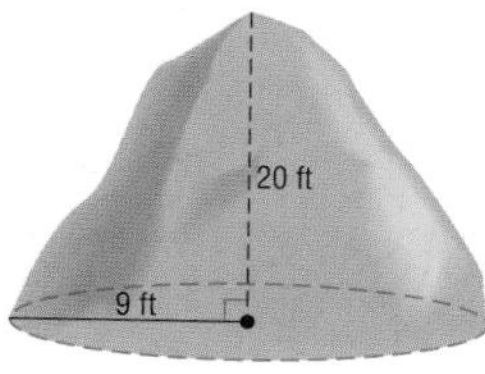

7. Find the volume of the candle in Exercise 4. Round to the nearest tenth if necessary. **36.9 in³**

8. Find the volume of the tea bag in Exercise 5. Round to the nearest tenth if necessary. **24.5 cm³**

9. **EARTH** Earth's radius is approximately 6400 kilometers. What are the surface area and volume of the Earth? Round to the nearest tenth if necessary. **514,718,540.4 km²; 1,098,066,219,443.5 km³**

10. **SOFTBALL** A regulation softball has a circumference of 12 inches. What is the volume of the softball? **29.2 in³**

Name each of the following on sphere $\mathcal{A}$.

11. two lines containing point S **$\overleftrightarrow{JL}$, $\overleftrightarrow{KN}$**
12. a segment containing point L **$\overline{CS}$**
13. a triangle **$\triangle DQP$**
14. two lines containing point D **$\overleftrightarrow{QC}$, $\overleftrightarrow{BP}$**
15. a segment containing point P **$\overline{DK}$**

16. Are these two cubes *similar*, *congruent*, or *neither*? Explain your reasoning. **See margin.**

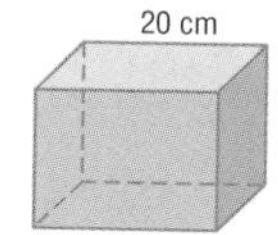

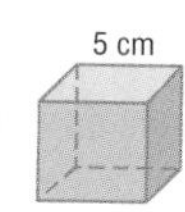

17. Two similar cylinders have heights of 75 centimeters and 25 centimeters. What is the ratio of the volume of the large cylinder to the volume of the small cylinder? **27:1**

18. **BAKING** Two spherical pieces of cookie dough have radii of 3 centimeters and 5 centimeters, respectively. The pieces are combined to form one large spherical piece of dough. What is the approximate radius of the new sphere of dough? Round to the nearest tenth. **5.3 cm**

19. **ALGEBRA** A rectangular prism has a base with side lengths x and $x + 3$ and height $2x$. Find the surface area and volume of the prism. **$10x^2 + 18x$; $2x^3 + 6x^2$**

20. **TRANSPORTATION** The traffic cone is 19 inches tall and has a radius of 5 inches.

a. Find the lateral area. **308.6 in²**

b. Find the surface area. **387.2 in²**

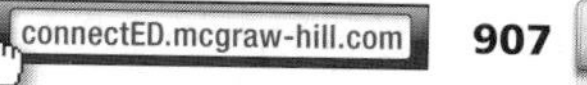

Summative Assessment

Use these alternate leveled chapter tests to differentiate assessment for your students.

Leveled Chapter 12 Tests

Form	Type	Level	Page(s)
1	MC	AL	61–62
2A	MC	OL	63–64
2B	MC	OL	65–66
2C	FR	OL	67–68
2D	FR	OL	69–70
3	FR	BL	71–72
Vocabulary Test			60
Extended-Response Test			73

MC = multiple-choice questions
FR = free-response questions

eAssessment Customize and create multiple versions of your chapter tests and their answer keys. All of the questions from the leveled chapter tests in the *Chapter 12 Resource Masters* are also available on eAssessment.

Additional Answer

16. Similar; all of the sides are not equal so the cubes are not congruent. The ratio of the larger cube's side to the smaller cube's side is always 4, so they are similar.

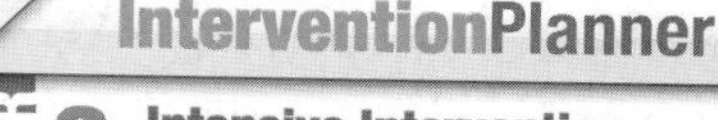

InterventionPlanner

TIER 1 On Level OL

If students miss about 25% of the exercises or less,

Then choose a resource:

SE Lessons 12-1, 12-2, 12-3, 12-4, 12-5, 12-6, 12-7, and 12-8

Skills Practice, pp. 7, 14, 20, 27, 33, 39, 45, and 51

connectED.mcgraw-hill.com Self-Check Quiz

TIER 2 Strategic Intervention AL
approaching grade level

If students miss about 50% of the exercises,

Then choose a resource:

Study Guide and Intervention, pp. 5, 12, 18, 25, 31, 37, 43, and 49

connectED.mcgraw-hill.com Extra Examples, Personal Tutor

TIER 3 Intensive Intervention
2 or more grades below level

If students miss about 75% of the exercises,

Then use *Math Triumphs, Geometry*, Ch. 5

connectED.mcgraw-hill.com Extra Examples, Personal Tutor, Homework Help, Review Vocabulary

1 Focus

Objective Learn the strategy of creating drawings to visualize how to solve a problem.

2 Teach

Scaffolding Questions

Ask:

- How can making a drawing help you understand the question being asked? Sample answer: Making a drawing can help you visualize how to solve a problem.
- How does labeling a drawing help you visualize how to solve a problem? Sample answer: Labeling the drawing can help you determine the units the answer should have (if any) and what information is missing from the drawing.
- Which steps to make a drawing can help you solve a problem? Sample answer: Sketching and labeling a drawing, as well as determining what information is missing from the drawing can help you determine what you are being asked to solve and what properties can be used to do so.

CHAPTER 12 Preparing for Standardized Tests

Make a Drawing

Making a drawing can be a very helpful way for you to visualize how to solve a problem. Sketch your drawings on scrap paper or in your test booklet (if allowed). Do not make any marks on your answer sheet other than your answers.

Strategies for Making a Drawing

Step 1

Read the problem statement carefully.

Ask yourself:

- What am I being asked to solve? What information is given?
- Would making a drawing help me visualize how to solve the problem?

Step 2

Sketch and label your drawing.

- Make your drawing as clear and accurate as possible.
- Label the drawing carefully. Be sure to include all of the information given in the problem statement.
- Fill in your drawing with information that can be gained from intermediate calculations.

Standardized Test Example

Solve the problem below. Responses will be graded using the short-response scoring rubric shown.

A regular pyramid has a square base with 10-centimeter sides and a height of 12 centimeters. What is the total surface area of the pyramid? Round to the nearest tenth if necessary.

Scoring Rubric	
Criteria	**Score**
Full Credit: The answer is correct and a full explanation is provided that shows each step.	2
Partial Credit: • The answer is correct, but the explanation is incomplete. • The answer is incorrect, but the explanation is correct.	1

Read the problem statement carefully. You are given the dimensions of a square pyramid and asked to find the surface area. Sketching a drawing may help you visualize the problem and how to solve it.

Example of a 2-point response:

Use the Pythagorean Theorem to find the slant height, ℓ.

$\ell^2 = 5^2 + 12^2$

$\ell^2 = 169$

$\ell = 13$

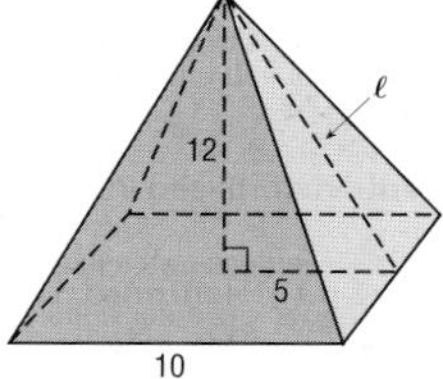

Find the lateral area.

$L = \frac{1}{2}P\ell$

$= \frac{1}{2}(40)(13)$

$= 260$

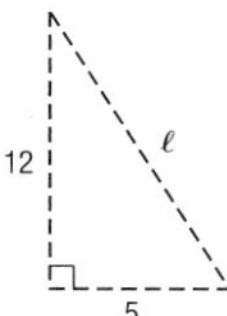

Add the area of the square base.

$S = 260 + 100$ or 360

The total surface area is 360 square centimeters.

The steps, calculations, and reasoning are clearly stated. The student also arrives at the correct answer. So, this response is worth the full 2 points.

Exercises

Solve each problem. Show your work. Responses will be graded using the short-response scoring rubric given at the beginning of the lesson.

1. A right circular cone has a slant height that is twice its radius. The lateral area of the cone is about 569 square millimeters. What is the radius of the cone? Round to the nearest whole millimeter. 9 mm

2. From a single point in her yard, Marti measures and marks distances of 18 feet and 30 feet with stakes for two sides of her garden. How far apart should the two stakes be if the garden is to be rectangular shaped? about 35 ft

3. A passing boat is 310 feet from the base of a lighthouse. The angle of depression from the top of the lighthouse is 24°. What is the height of the lighthouse to the nearest tenth of a foot? 138.0 ft

4. A regular hexagon is inscribed in a circle with a diameter of 12 centimeters. What is the exact area of the hexagon? $54\sqrt{3}$ cm^2

5. Luther is building a model rocket for a science fair project. He attaches a nosecone to a cylindrical body to form the rocket's fuselage. The rocket has a diameter of 4 inches and a total height (including the nosecone) of 2 feet 5 inches. The nosecone is 7 inches tall. What is the volume of the rocket? Give your answer rounded to the nearest tenth cubic inch. 305.8 in^3

6. Terry wants to measure the height of the top of the backboard of his basketball hoop. At 4:00, the shadow of a 4-foot fence post is 20 inches long, and the shadow of the backboard is 65 inches long. What is the height of the top of the backboard? 156 in. or 13 ft

Additional Example

Find the volume of the prism.

264 in^3

3 Assess

Use Exercises 1–6 to assess students' understanding.

Diagnose Student Errors

Survey student responses for each item. Class trends may indicate common errors and misconceptions.

1. A used incorrect formula
B correct
C used incorrect formula
D used incorrect formula

2. F correct
G forgot relationship of tangent and radius to point of tangency
H forgot relationship of tangent and radius to point of tangency
J forgot relationship of tangent and radius to point of tangency

3. A incorrect formula used
B correct
C incorrect formula used
D incorrect formula used

4. F correct
G arithmetic error
H arithmetic error
J arithmetic error

5. A found length of incorrect side
B correct
C used incorrect formula
D found length of incorrect side

6. F reversed inequality in Theorem 5.9
G correct
H reversed inequality in Theorem 5.9
J reversed inequality in Theorem 5.9

CHAPTER 12

Standardized Test Practice

Cumulative, Chapters 1 through 12

Multiple Choice

Read each question. Then fill in the correct answer on the answer document provided by your teacher or on a sheet of paper.

1. The Great Pyramid of Giza in Egypt originally had a height of about 148 meters. The base of the pyramid was a square with 230-meter sides. What was the original volume of the pyramid? Round to the nearest whole number. B

A $1{,}786{,}503\text{ m}^3$
B $2{,}609{,}733\text{ m}^3$
C $104{,}128{,}752\text{ m}^3$
D $122{,}716{,}907\text{ m}^3$

2. If $\overline{HK}$ is tangent to circle O, what is the radius of the circle? F

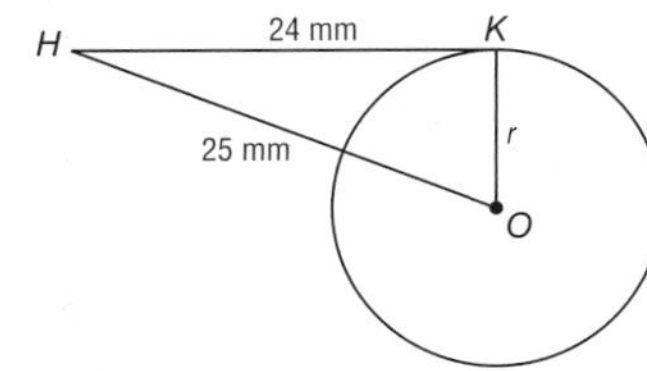

F 7 mm
G 8 mm
H 9 mm
J 10 mm

3. What is the sum of the interior angles of the figure? B

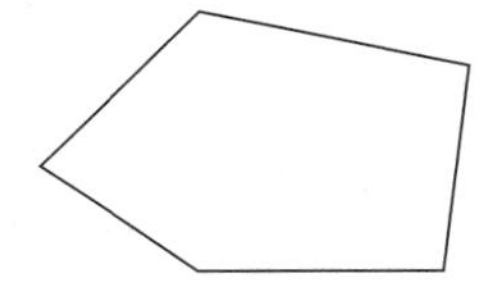

A 450°
B 540°
C 630°
D 720°

> **Test-Taking Tip**
> Question 1 You can eliminate some unreasonable answers by estimating first. Choices C and D are too large.

4. Eddie conducted a random survey of 50 students and found that 14 of them spend more than 2 hours each night doing homework. If there are 421 students at Eddie's school, predict how many of them spend more than 2 hours each night doing homework. F

F 118
G 124
H 125
J 131

5. $\overline{RS}$ represents the height of Mount Mitchell, the highest point in the state of North Carolina. If $TU = 5013$ feet, $UV = 6684$ feet, and $TV = 8355$ feet, use the ASA Theorem to find the height of Mount Mitchell. B

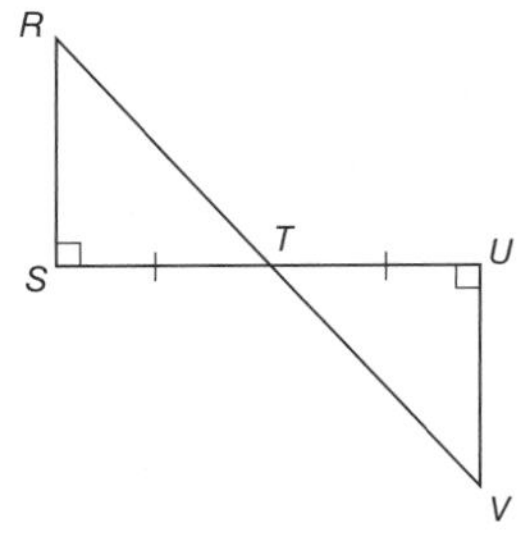

A 5013 ft
B 6684 ft
C 7154 ft
D 8355 ft

6. Triangle DEF is shown below.

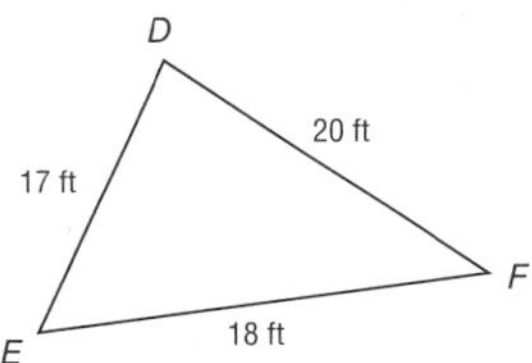

Which statement about this triangle is true? G

F $m\angle F > m\angle D$
G $m\angle E > m\angle F$
H $m\angle D < m\angle F$
J $m\angle E < m\angle D$

Short Response/Gridded Response

Record your answers on the answer sheet provided by your teacher or on a sheet of paper.

7. Suppose the length of one diagonal of a kite is three times the length of the other diagonal. If the area of the kite is 96 square inches, what are the lengths of the diagonals? Show your work. **8 in. and 24 in.**

8. Copy the figure and point Y. Then use a protractor and ruler to draw the rotation of the figure 75° clockwise about point Y. **See margin.**

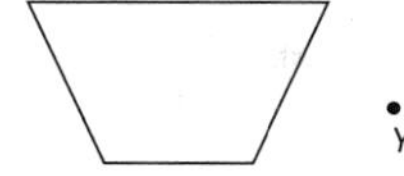

9. **GRIDDED RESPONSE** What is the perimeter of the isosceles triangle to the nearest tenth of a centimeter? **92.6**

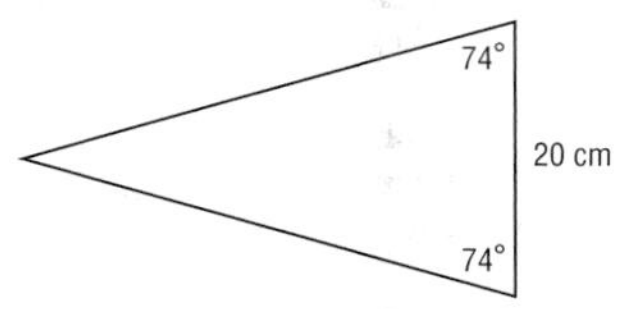

10. Determine whether the following statement is *sometimes*, *always*, or *never* true. Explain. **See margin.**

The orthocenter of a right triangle is located at the vertex of the right angle.

11. **GRIDDED RESPONSE** Given: $c \parallel d$

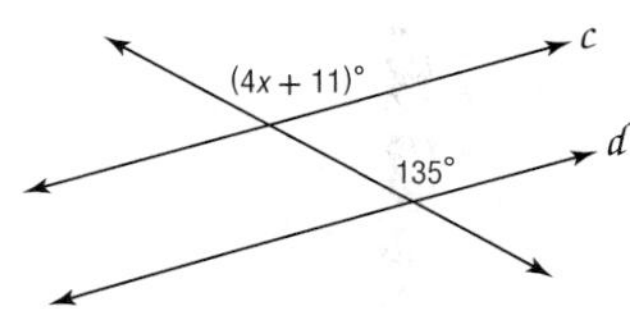

What is the value of x in the figure? **31**

12. What is the lateral area of the square pyramid below? Round to the nearest tenth if necessary. Show your work. **544 ft²**

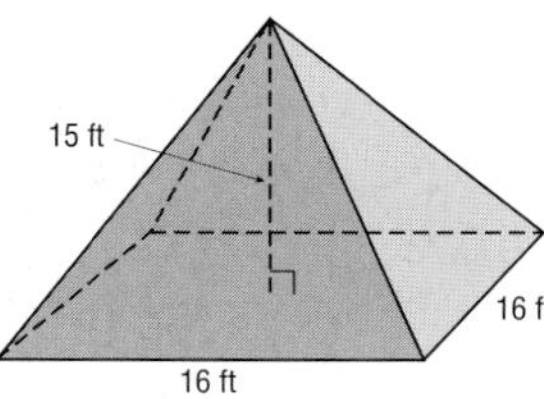

Extended Response

Record your answers on a sheet of paper. Show your work.

13. The two prisms below are similar figures.

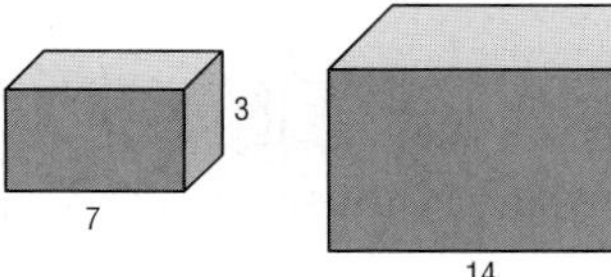

a. What is the scale factor from the smaller prism to the larger one? **2**

b. What are the volumes of the prisms? **42 cubic units, 336 cubic units**

c. How many times as great is the volume of the larger prism as the smaller prism? **8**

d. Suppose a solid figure has a volume of 40 cubic units. If its dimensions are scaled by a factor of 1.5, what will the volume of the new figure be? **135 cubic units**

Need ExtraHelp?

If you missed Question...	1	2	3	4	5	6	7	8	9	10	11	12	13
Go to Lesson...	12-5	10-5	6-1	7-1	4-5	5-3	11-2	9-3	8-4	5-2	3-2	12-3	12-8

Formative Assessment

You can use these pages to benchmark student progress.

Standardized Test Practice, pp. 74–76

Answer Sheet Practice

Have students simulate taking a standardized test by recording their answers on a practice recording sheet.

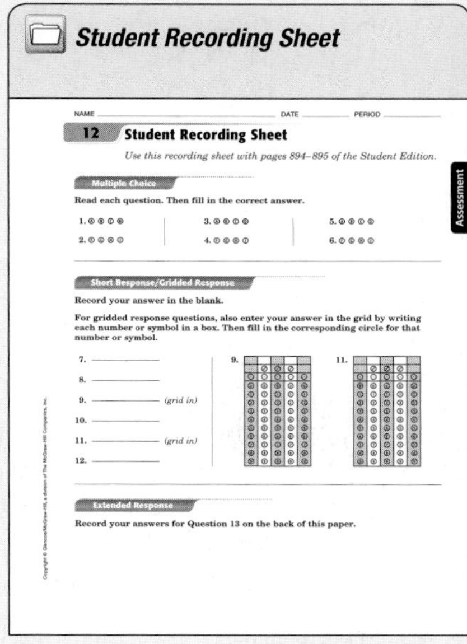
Student Recording Sheet

12 Student Recording Sheet

Use this recording sheet with pages 894–895 of the Student Edition.

Multiple Choice

Read each question. Then fill in the correct answer.

Short Response/Gridded Response

Record your answer in the blank.

For gridded response questions, also enter your answer in the grid by writing each number or symbol in a box. Then fill in the corresponding circle for that number or symbol.

Extended Response

Record your answers for Question 13 on the back of this paper.

eAssessment Create practice tests that align to your state standards, the Common Core State Standards, and other national standards such as TIMSS and NAEP.

Homework Option

Get Ready for Chapter 13 Assign students the exercises on page 913 as homework to assess whether they possess the prerequisite skills needed for the next chapter.

Additional Answers

8.

Y

10. Always; sample answer: In a right triangle, two of the altitudes are the legs of the triangle. The third altitude passes through the right angle. So, their point of intersection will always be the vertex of the right angle.

Lesson 12-1

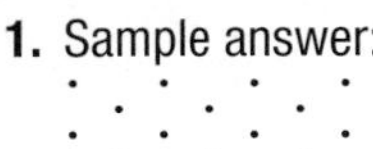

1. Sample answer:

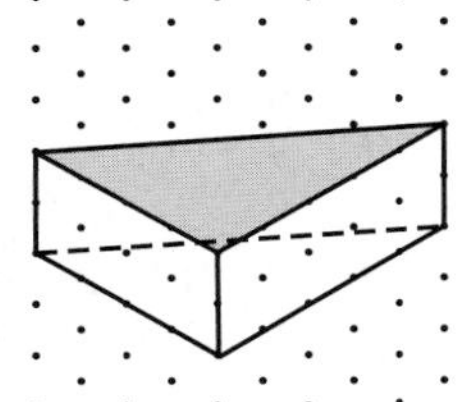

2. Sample answer:

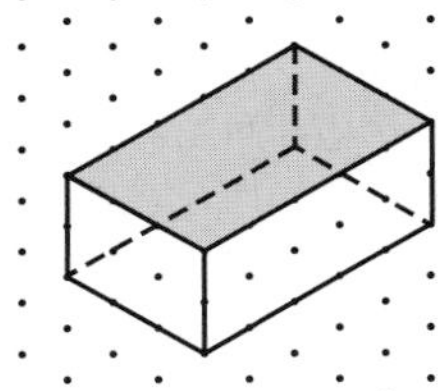

3.

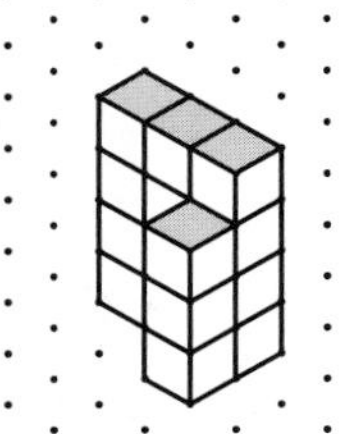

4.

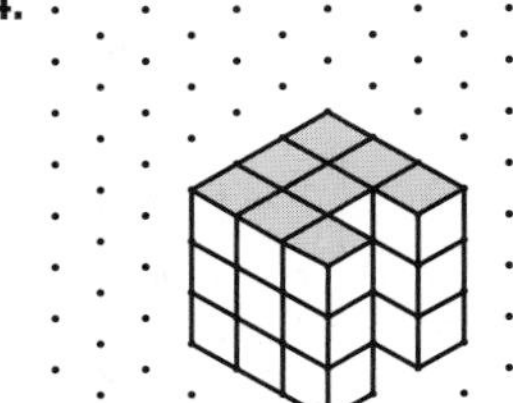

8.

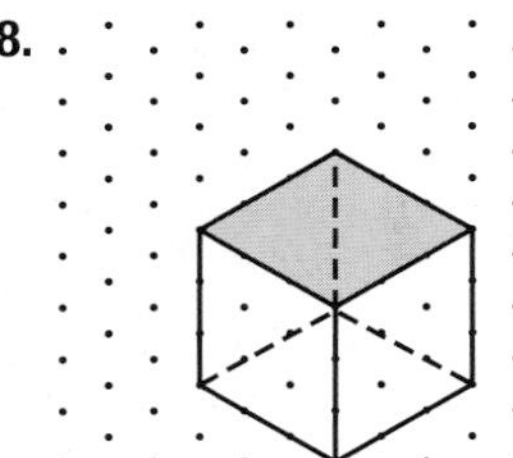

9. Sample answer:

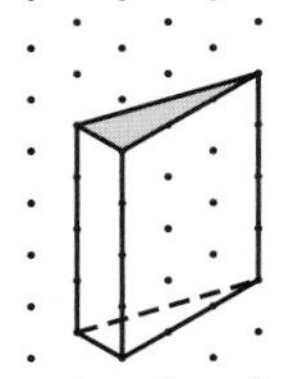

10. Sample answer:

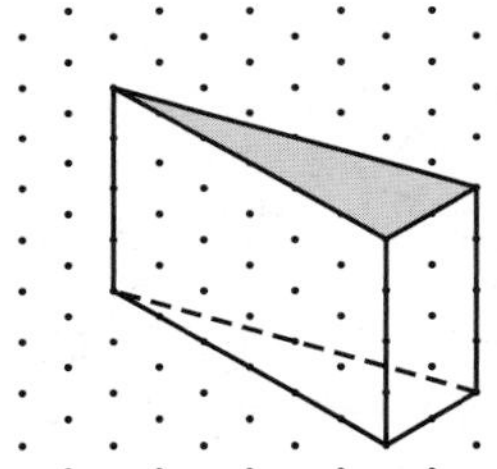

11.

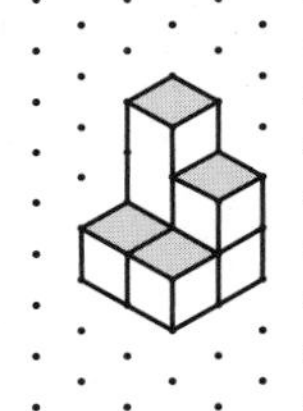

12.

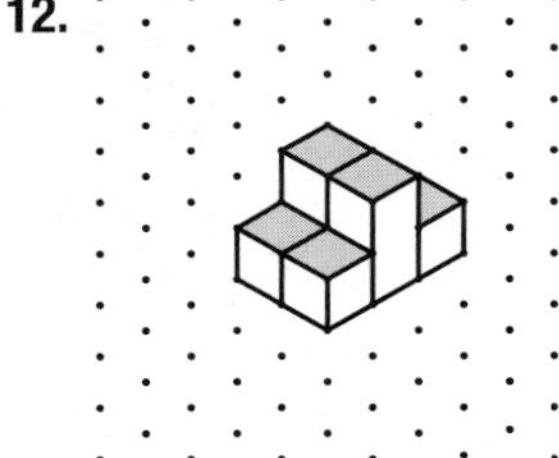

13.

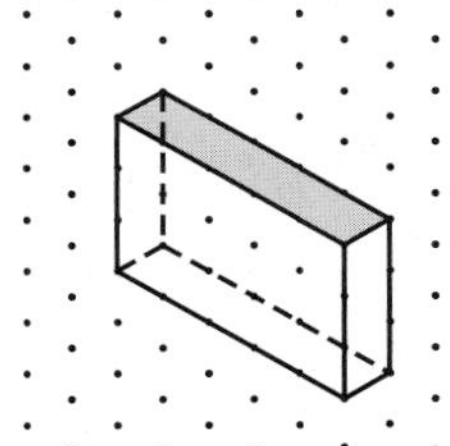

14.

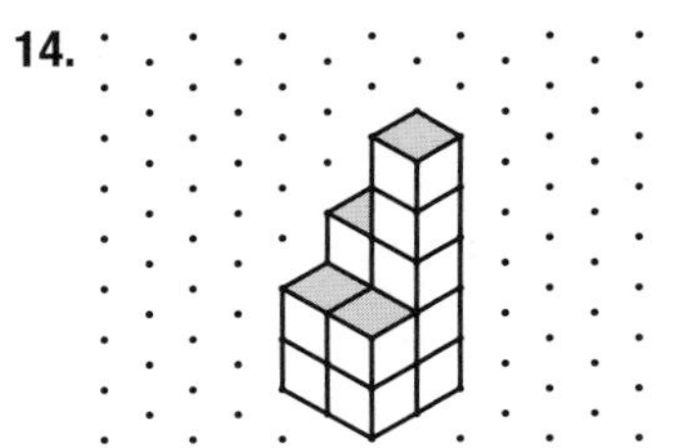

29a–b. Sample answer:

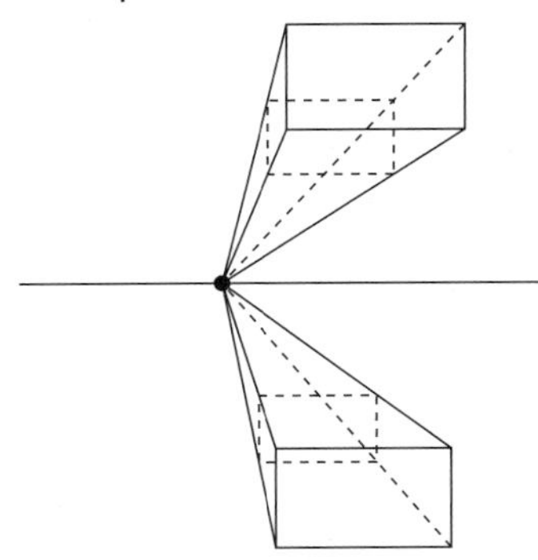

29c. Sample answer: The first drawing shows a view of the object from the bottom. The second drawing shows a view of the object from the top.

30.

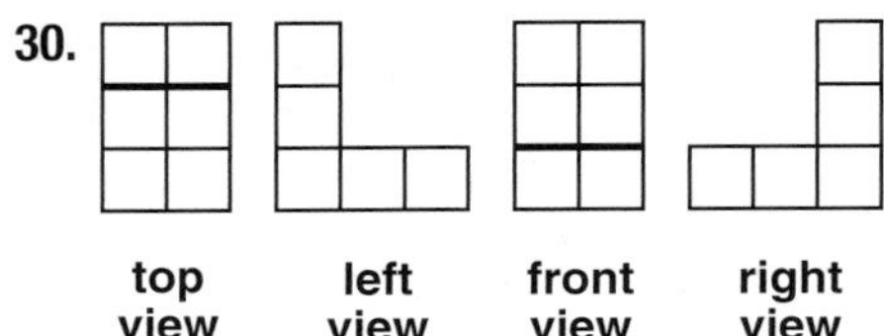

31.

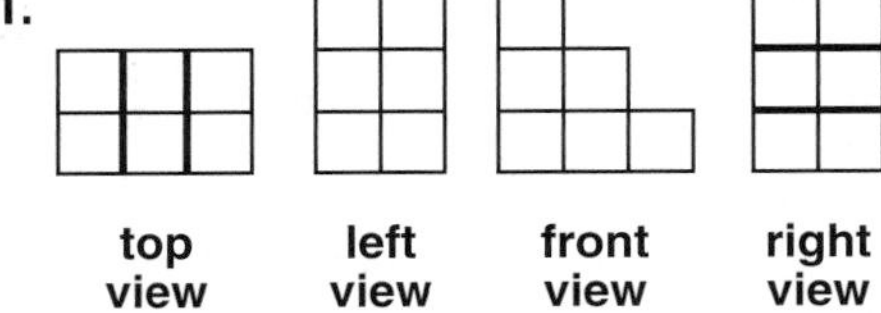

32.

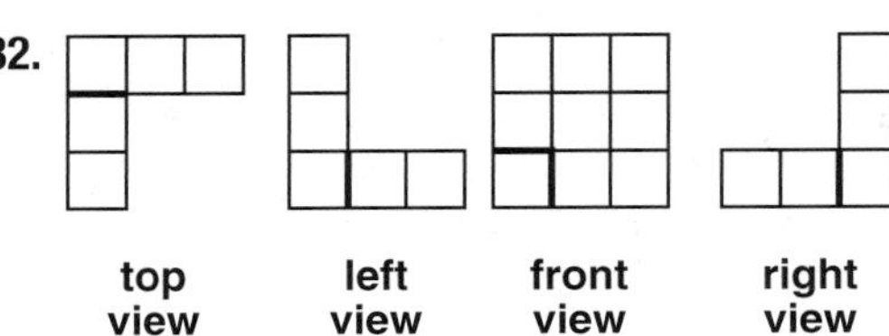

33a. Sample answer:

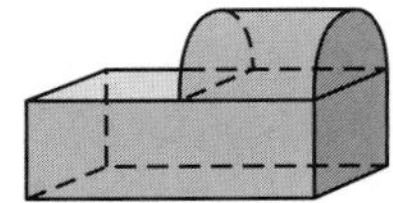

33b. Make a horizontal cut through the bottom part of the figure or make a vertical cut through the left side of the figure.

33c. The front view of the solid is the cross section when a vertical cut is made lengthwise. The right view of the solid is the cross section when a vertical cut is made through the right side of the figure.

34a. Sample answer:

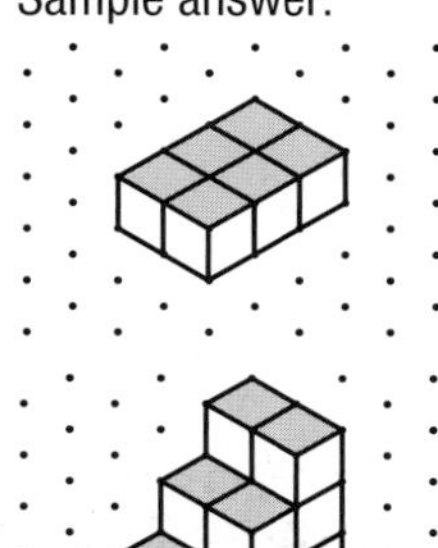

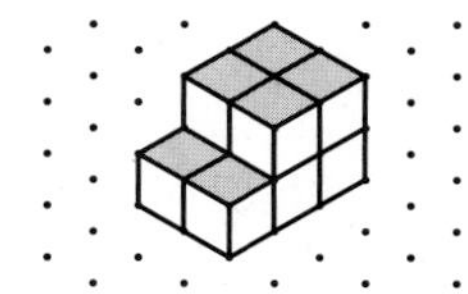

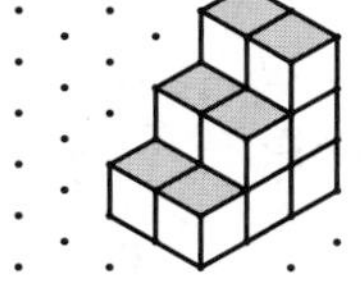

34b.

Number of Cubes	Number of Squares
6	11
10	15
12	18

34c. Sample answer: No; the number of squares in the isometric drawing will depend on the arrangement of the cubes that creates the figure.

37. Sample answer:

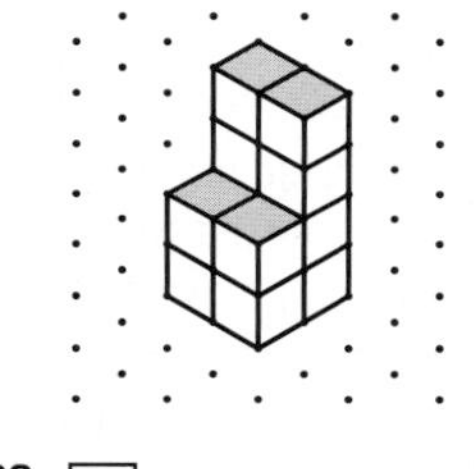

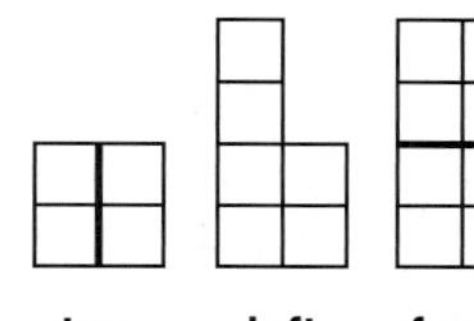

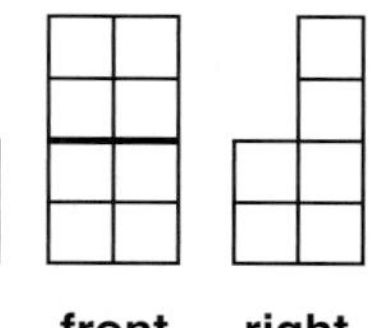

38.

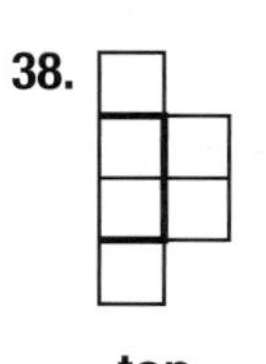

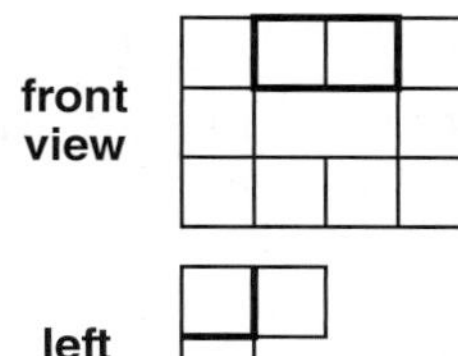

39. The cross section is a triangle. There are six different ways to slice the pyramid so that two equal parts are formed because the figure has six planes of symmetry. In each case, the cross section is an isosceles triangle. Only the side lengths of the triangles change.

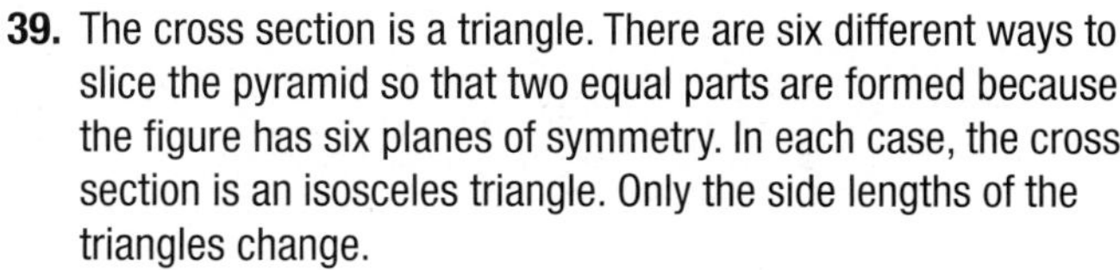

Lesson 12-3

29b. Sample answer:

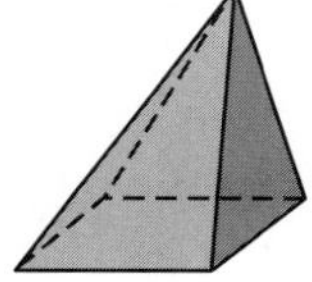

41. Use the apothem, the height, and the Pythagorean Theorem to find the slant height ℓ of the pyramid. Then use the central angle of the n-gon and the apothem to find the length of one side of the n-gon. Then find the perimeter. Finally, use $S = \frac{1}{2}P\ell + B$ to find the surface area. The area of the base B is $\frac{1}{2}Pa$.

49.

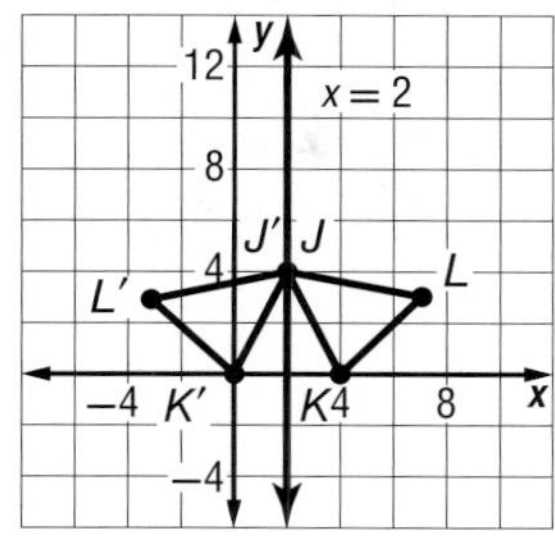

50.

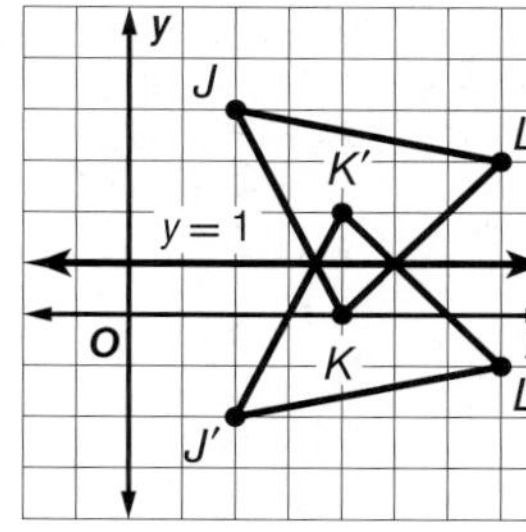

51.

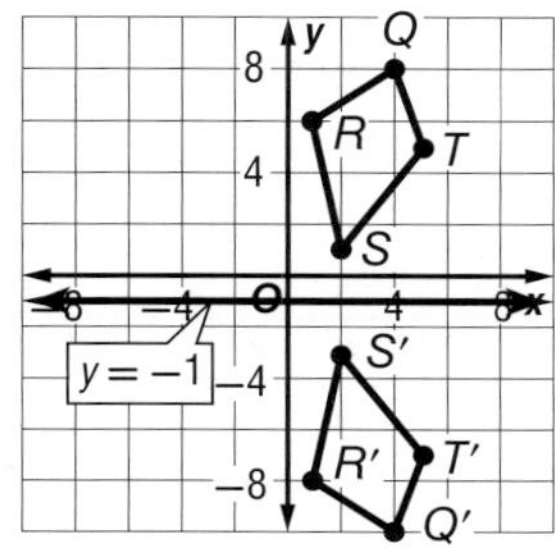

52.

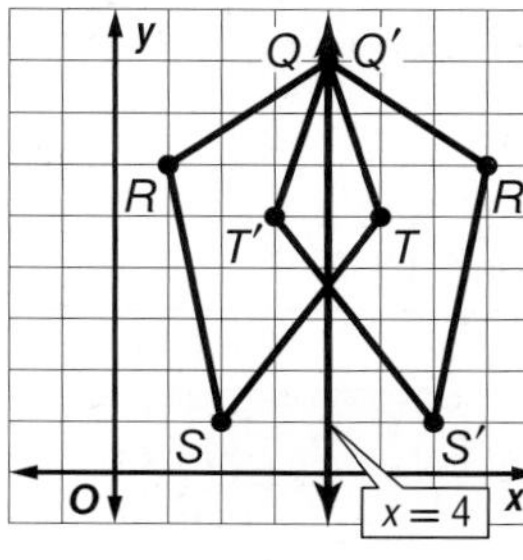

53.

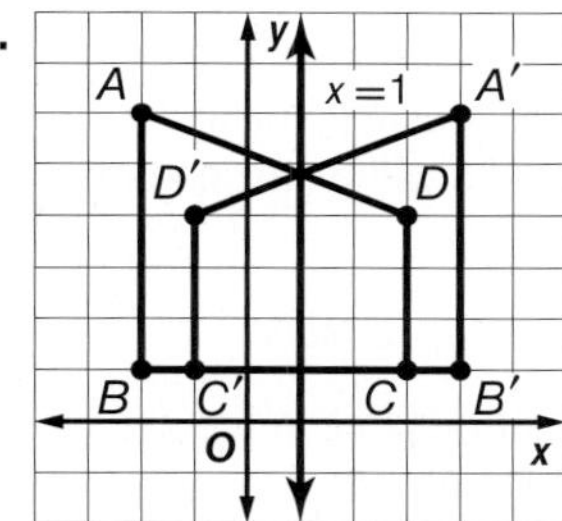

54.

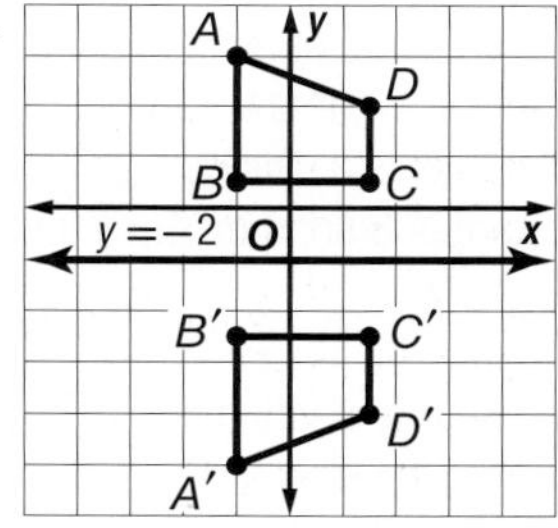

Extend 12-4

5. Sample answer: I think the surface area will be 25 times as great. When all of the dimensions were doubled it was 2^2 or 4 times as great and when all of the dimensions were tripled it was 3^2 or 9 times as great, so when the dimensions are multiplied by 5, it will be 5^2 times as great. I think the volume will be 125 times as great. When all of the dimensions were doubled it was 2^3 or 8 times as great and when all of the dimensions were tripled it was 3^3 or 27 times as great, so when the dimensions are multiplied by 5, it will be 5^3 times as great.

6. Surface area: k^2:1; sample answer: The ratio of the surface areas is the square of the factor that the sides are increased by if all three of the dimensions are increased by the same factor. Volume: k^3:1; sample answer: The ratio of the volumes is the cube of the factor that the sides are increased by if all three of the dimensions are increased by the same factor.

Mid-Chapter Quiz

1. Use isometric dot paper to sketch a rectangular prism 4 units high, 6 units long, and 5 units wide.

2.

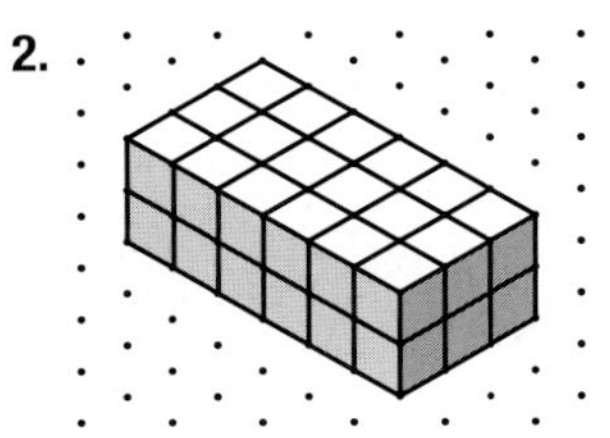

3.

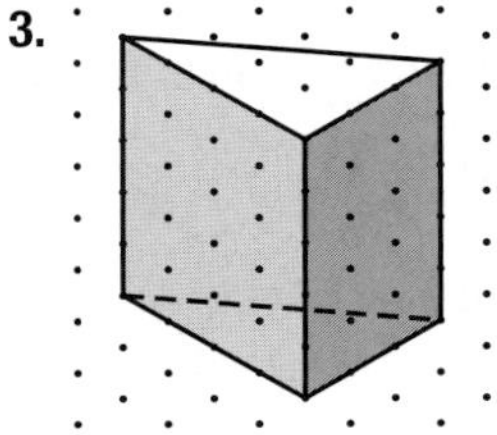

11a.

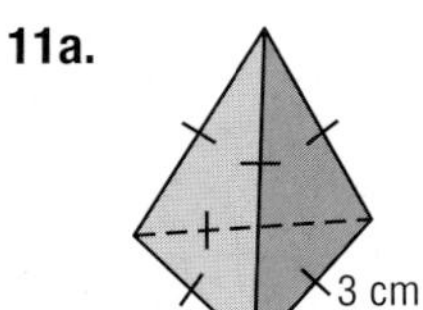

Extend 12-6

1.

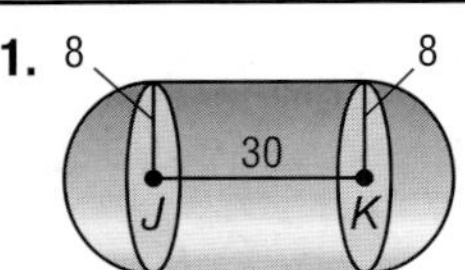

The locus of all points in space at a specific distance from a given point is a sphere. Thus, for this problem, the locus of points is a cylinder with height 30 units with hemispheres of radius 8 units on each end.

6. A semicircle is half of a locus of points on a plane.

7. The intersection is the set of all points located in the upper hemispheres and equidistant from the midpoint of the given line segment in the plane containing the perpendicular bisector of the given line segment.

Lesson 12-7

15. No; a great circle is finite and returns to its original starting point.

16. Yes; perpendicular great circles form eight 90° angles.

17. Yes; if three points are collinear, any one of the three points is between the other two.

18. Yes; if M is the midpoint of $\overline{AB}$ on a great circle, then $\overline{AM} \cong \overline{MB}$.

21a. about 912 mi; the cities are 13.2° apart on the same great circle, so $\frac{13.2}{360} \times 2\pi \times 3960$ gives the distance between them.

21b. Yes; sample answer: Since the cities lie on a great circle, the distance between the cities can be expressed as the major arc or the minor arc. The sum of the two values is the circumference of Earth.

21c. No; sample answer: Since lines of latitude do not go through opposite poles of the sphere, they are not great circles. Therefore, the distance cannot be calculated in the same way.

21d. Sample answer: Infinite locations. If Phoenix were a point on the sphere, then there are infinite points that are equidistant from that point.

26.

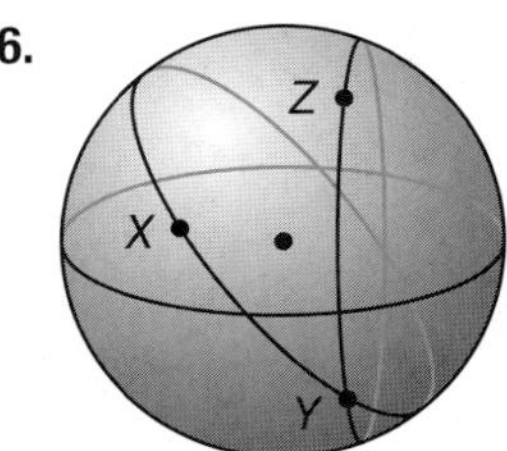

27. Sometimes; sample answer: Since small circles cannot go through opposite poles, it is possible for them to be parallel, such as lines of latitude. It is also possible for them to intersect when two small circles can be drawn through three points, where they have one point in common and two points that occur on one small circle and not the other.

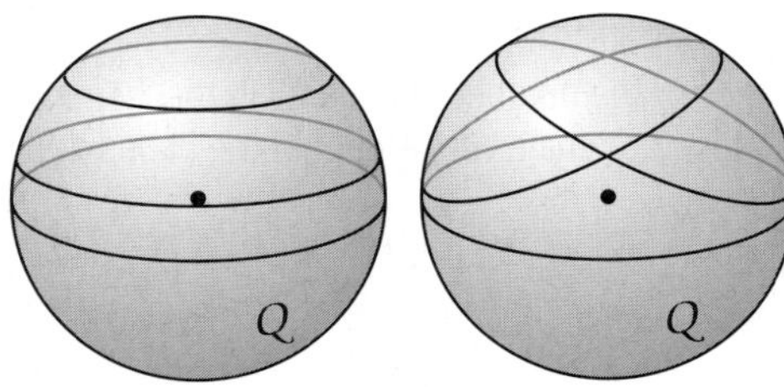

28. Sample answer: Congruent triangles exist, because three great circles that form a triangle will form identical triangles on opposite sides of the sphere. Similar triangles do not exist because the sum of the measures of the angles of a triangle is not constant. If two triangles in spherical geometry have the same angle measures, they are congruent.

29. False; sample answer: Spherical geometry is non-Euclidean, so it cannot be a subset of Euclidean geometry.

NOTES

Chapter Planner

Diagnostic Assessment
Quick Check

	LESSON 13-1 (45 min: 1 day; 90 min: 0.5 day)	LESSON 13-2 (45 min: 1 day; 90 min: 0.75 day)	LESSON 13-3 (45 min: 1 day; 90 min: 0.5 day)	LESSON 13-4 (45 min: 1 day; 90 min: 0.5 day)
Title	**Representing Sample Spaces**	**Probability with Permutations and Combinations**	**Geometric Probability**	**Simulations**
Objectives	▪ Represent sample spaces. ▪ Use the Fundamental Counting Principle to count outcomes.	▪ Use permutations with probability. ▪ Use combinations with probability.	▪ Find probabilities by using length. ▪ Find probabilities by using area.	▪ Design simulations to estimate probabilities. ▪ Summarize data from simulations.
Key Vocabulary	sample space tree diagram two-stage experiment multi-stage experiment Fundamental Counting Principle	permutation factorial circular permutation combination	geometric probability	probability model simulation random variable expected value Law of Large Numbers
CCSS		S.CP.9	S.MD.7	G.MG.3, S.MD.6
Multiple Representations	✓	✓		✓
Lesson Resources	connectED.mcgraw-hill.com Leveled Worksheets Vocabulary Personal Tutor Self-Check Quiz ▪ *5-Minute Check* ▪ *Study Notebook*	connectED.mcgraw-hill.com Leveled Worksheets Quiz 1 Vocabulary Personal Tutor Self-Check Quiz ▪ *5-Minute Check* ▪ *Study Notebook*	connectED.mcgraw-hill.com Leveled Worksheets Quiz 2 Vocabulary Personal Tutor Self-Check Quiz ▪ *5-Minute Check* ▪ *Study Notebook*	connectED.mcgraw-hill.com Leveled Worksheets Vocabulary Personal Tutor Virtual Manipulatives Self-Check Quiz ▪ *5-Minute Check* ▪ *Study Notebook* ▪ *Teaching Geometry with Manipulatives*
Resources for Every Lesson	IWB eStudent Edition IWB Interactive Classroom	▪ eTeacher Edition ▪ eSolutions Manual ▪ eAssessment		
Differentiated Instruction	pp. 916, 920	pp. 925, 929	pp. 932, 936	pp. 942, 945

Formative Assessment
Mid-Chapter Quiz

IWB All digital assets are Interactive Whiteboard ready.

Suggested Pacing			
Time Periods	Instruction	Review & Assess	Total
45-minute	7 days	2 days	9 days
90-minute	4 days	1 day	5 days

LESSON 13-5 (45 min: 1 day; 90 min: 0.75 day)	EXTEND 13-5 (45 min: 0.5 day; 90 min: 0.25 day)	LESSON 13-6 (45 min: 1 day; 90 min: 0.5 day)	EXTEND 13-6 (45 min: 0.5 day; 90 min: 0.25 day)
Probabilities of Independent and Dependent Events	**Spreadsheet Lab: Two-Way Frequency Tables**	**Probabilities of Mutually Exclusive Events**	**Geometry Lab: Graph Theory**
■ Find probabilities of independent and dependent events. ■ Find probabilities of events given the occurrence of other events.	■ Use two-way frequency tables to find marginal, joint, and relative frequencies.	■ Find probabilities of events that are mutually exclusive and events that are not mutually exclusive. ■ Find probabilities of complements.	■ Apply physical models, graphs, and networks to develop solutions in applied contexts.
compound event independent events dependent events conditional probability probability tree	two-way frequency table marginal frequencies joint frequencies relative frequency	mutually exclusive events complement	network node edge traceable network
S.CP.2, S.CP.3	S.CP.4, S.CP.6	S.CP.1, S.CP.7	
connectED.mcgraw-hill.com Leveled Worksheets Quiz 3 Vocabulary Personal Tutor Self-Check Quiz ■ *5-Minute Check* ■ *Study Notebook* ■ *Teaching Geometry with Manipulatives*	Vocabulary Personal Tutor **Materials** ■ computer ■ spreadsheet program	connectED.mcgraw-hill.com Leveled Worksheets Quiz 4 Vocabulary Personal Tutor Virtual Manipulatives Self-Check Quiz ■ *5-Minute Check* ■ *Study Notebook* ■ *Teaching Geometry with Manipulatives*	connectED.mcgraw-hill.com Vocabulary Animations ■ *Teaching Geometry with Manipulatives*
IWB eStudent Edition IWB Interactive Classroom	■ eTeacher Edition ■ eSolutions Manual ■ eAssessment		
pp. 948, 950, 953		pp. 960, 963	

Summative Assessment
Study Guide and Review
Practice Test

Assessment and Intervention

SE = Student Edition, **TE** = Teacher Edition, **CRM** = Chapter Resource Masters

	Diagnosis	Prescription
DIAGNOSTIC ASSESSMENT	**Beginning Chapter 13**	
	Get Ready for Chapter 13 **SE**	Response to Intervention **TE**
	Beginning Every Lesson	
	Then, Now, Why? **SE** 5-Minute Checks	Chapter 0 **SE**
FORMATIVE ASSESSMENT	**During/After Every Lesson**	
	Guided Practice **SE,** every example Check Your Understanding **SE** H.O.T. Problems **SE** Spiral Review **SE** Additional Examples **SE** Watch Out! **TE** Step 14, Assess **TE** Chapter 13 Quizzes **CRM,** pp. 45–46 Self-Check Quizzes connectED.mcgraw-hill.com	**TIER 1 Intervention** Skills Practice **CRM,** Ch. 1–13 connectED.mcgraw-hill.com **TIER 2 Intervention** Differentiated Instruction **TE** Differentiated Homework Options **TE** Study Guide and Intervention **CRM,** Ch. 1–13 **TIER 3 Intervention** *Math Triumphs, Geometry,* Ch. 6
	Mid-Chapter	
	Mid-Chapter Quiz **SE** Mid-Chapter Test **CRM**, p. 47 eAssessment	**TIER 1 Intervention** Skills Practice **CRM,** Ch. 1–13 connectED.mcgraw-hill.com **TIER 2 Intervention** Study Guide and Intervention **CRM**, Ch. 1–2 **TIER 3 Intervention** *Math Triumphs, Geometry,* Ch. 6
	Before Chapter Test	
	Chapter Study Guide and Review **SE** Practice Test **SE** Standardized Test Practice **SE** Chapter Test connectED.mcgraw-hill.com Standardized Test Practice connectED.mcgraw-hill.com Vocabulary Review connectED.mcgraw-hill.com eAssessment	**TIER 1 Intervention** Skills Practice **CRM,** Ch. 1–13 connectED.mcgraw-hill.com **TIER 2 Intervention** Study Guide and Intervention **CRM,** Ch. 1–13 **TIER 3 Intervention** *Math Triumphs, Geometry,* Ch. 6
SUMMATIVE ASSESSMENT	**After Chapter 13**	
	Multiple-Choice Tests, Forms 1, 2A, 2B **CRM,** pp. 49–54 Free-Response Tests, Forms 2C, 2D, 3 **CRM,** pp. 55–60 Vocabulary Test **CRM,** p. 48 Extended Response Test **CRM,** p. 61 Standardized Test Practice **CRM,** pp. 62–64 eAssessment	Study Guide and Intervention **CRM,** Ch. 1–13 connectED.mcgraw-hill.com

Differentiated Instruction

Option 1 Reaching All Learners

Logical Write the following menu choices on the board: 1. What size sundae would you like: small, medium, or large? 2. Would you like chocolate or vanilla ice cream? 3. Would you like caramel sauce, chocolate sauce, and/or strawberry sauce? 4. Would you like whipped cream? Ask students to create a tree diagram to show all of the possible sundae combinations.

Interpersonal Sketch a dart board on the board. Have students work together to measure the diameter of the bull's eye and how far each ring is spaced apart. Have them use this information to determine the probability of getting a bull's eye if they play.

Option 2 Approaching Level AL

Write the following question on the board: *Four blue blocks, two red blocks, a yellow block and a green block are placed in a bag. Suppose a red block is drawn and put back into the bag. Another block is drawn and put back, and this continues. What is the probability that a red block will be drawn each time if this continues for ten draws?* Ask students to solve the problem and show their work, explaining how they got their answer.

Option 3 English Learners ELL

Ask students to determine the probability of rolling a die five times and getting a two each time. Have them use paper, pencils and manipulatives to solve this problem with a partner. Ask them to explain their reasoning.

Option 4 Beyond Level BL

Have students work with a partner to design and conduct a simulation using dice, coins, or spinners. They should decide the question they want answered, the procedures they will follow, and record their data. Have them present their data to the class.

Focus on Mathematical Content

VerticalAlignment

Before Chapter 13

Related Topics from Grade 8

- Describe the resulting effect on volume when dimensions of a solid are changed proportionally.

Related Topics from Algebra 1

- Represent relationships using tables and graphs.
- Solve linear equations.

Chapter 13

Related Topics from Geometry

- Understand sample spaces and design simulations
- Compute probabilities for independent, dependent, mutually exclusive, not mutually exclusive, and conditional events.
- Calculate geometric probabilities.

After Chapter 13

Preparation for Precalculus

- Represent patterns using arithmetic and geometric sequences and series.
- Use properties of functions to analyze and solve problems and make predictions.

Lesson-by-LessonPreview

13-1 Representing Sample Spaces

The *sample space* of an experiment is the set of all possible outcomes. A sample space can be organized as a list, a table, or a tree diagram. Experiments for a sample space record the outcomes of repeated stages or events. When there is more than one stage, the experiment is a multistage event. The Fundamental Counting Principal states that the number of possible outcomes in a sample space can be found by multiplying together the number of possible outcomes at each stage of the event.

13-2 Probability With Permutations and Combinations

The factorial of a positive integer n, written $n!$, is the product of the integers less than or equal to n. Factorials are used to count arrangements of objects. A permutation is an arrangement of objects where order is important. The number of permutations of n distinct objects taken r at a time is given by ${}_nP_r = \frac{n!}{(n-r)!}$. If there are repetitions in the objects of the arrangement, with one object repeated r_1 times, a second object repeated r_2 times, and so on, the number of distinguishable permutations of n objects with repetitions is given by $\frac{n!}{r_1! \cdot r_2! \cdot \cdots \cdot r_k!}$. The number of distinguishable permutations of n objects arranged in a circle with no fixed reference point is $\frac{n!}{n} = (n-1)$. A *combination* is an arrangement of objects in which order is not important. A combination of n objects taken r at a time, or ${}_nC_r$, is calculated by dividing the number of permutations, ${}_nP_r$, by the number of arrangements containing the same elements, $r!$; ${}_nC_r = \frac{n!}{(n-r)!r!}$.

13-3 Geometric Probability

Probability that involves a geometric measure such as length or area is called a *geometric probability*. You can find the probability that a point lies in part of a figure by comparing the length or area of the part of the length or area of the whole figure. If a point in region A is chosen at random, then the probability $P(B)$ that the point is in region B, which is in the interior of region A is $P(B) = \frac{\text{area of region } B}{\text{area of region } A}$.

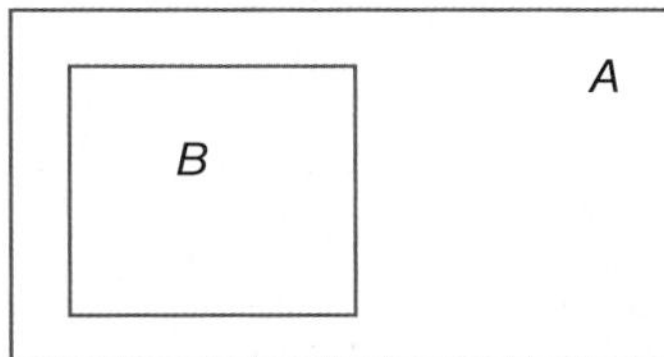

When determining the geometric probability with targets, assume that the object lands within the target area. You should also assume that it is equally likely that the object will land anywhere in the region.

13-4 Simulations

A probability model is a mathematical model used to match a random phenomenon. A simulation is the use of a probability model to recreate a situation again and again so that the likelihood of various outcomes can be estimated. Simulations can be constructed for geometric probabilities, and also with dice, coin tosses, random number tables, and random number generators.

A *random variable* is a variable that can assume a set of values, each with fixed probabilities. The *expected value* is the average value of a random variable that you would expect after repeating an experiment or simulation many times. Since the expected value is an average, an expected value does not have to be equal to a possible value of the random variable.

13-5 Probabilities of Independent and Dependent Events

A *compound* event consists of two or more simple events. Events A and B are independent if the probability that A occurs does not affect the probability that B occurs. The probability that two independent events both occur is the product of the probabilities of each individual event.

$$P(A + B) = P(A) \cdot P(B)$$

Events A and B are *dependent* if the probability that A occurs in some way changes the probability that B occurs. The probability that two dependent events both occur is the product of the probability that the first event occurs and the probability that the second event occurs after the first event already occurred.

$$P(A + B) = P(A) \cdot P(B|A)$$

In the formula for dependent probability, the notion of *conditional probability* is introduced. Conditional probability can be used when additional information is known about an event. The conditional probability of B occurring after A has occurred is $P(B|A) = \frac{P(A \text{ and } B)}{P(A)}$.

13-6 Probabilities of Mutually Exclusive Events

In Lesson 13-5 the intersection of events were examined. In this lesson the union of two events are studied. To find the probability that one event occurs or another event occurs, it must be known how the two events are related. If the two events cannot occur at the same time, they are mutually exclusive. That is, the events have no outcomes in common. If A and B are *mutually exclusive* events, then the probability that A occurs or B occurs is the sum of the probabilities of each individual event.

$$P(A \text{ or } B) = P(A) + P(B)$$

If two events are not mutually exclusive, then the sum of the probabilities of the individual events occurring would overestimate the probability by counting twice the probability that both events occur. If A and B are not mutually exclusive then the probability that A or B occurs is the sum of the individual probabilities minus the probability that both A and B occur.

$$P(A \text{ or } B) = P(A) + P(B) - P(A \text{ and } B)$$

Mc Graw Hill Professional Development

Targeted professional development has been articulated throughout Geometry. More quality, customized professional development is available from McGraw-Hill Professional Development. Visit connectED.mcgraw-hill.com for details on each product.

- Online Lessons emphasize the strategies and techniques used to teach Geometry. Includes streaming video, interactive pages, and online tools.
- Video Workshops allow mentors, coaches, or leadership personnel to facilitate on-site workshops on educational strategies in mathematics and mathematical concepts.
- MHPD Online (www.mhpdonline.com) offers online professional development with video clips of instructional strategies, links, student activities, and news and issues in education.
- Teaching Today (teachingtoday.glencoe.com) gives secondary teachers practical strategies and materials that inspire excellence and innovation in teaching.

Chapter Project

Fair Games

Students use what they have learned about probability and expected values to complete a project.

This chapter project addresses environmental literacy, as well as several specific skills identified as being essential to student success by the Framework for 21st Century Learning.

Visit connectED.mcgraw-hill.com for student and teacher handouts.

KeyVocabulary Introduce the key vocabulary in the chapter using the method below.

Define: The complement of an event A consists of all of the outcomes of a sample space that are not included as outcomes of event A.

Example: If A consists of rolling a 1 or a 5 on a die, then the complement of A is rolling a 2, 3, 4, or 6.

Ask: What is the probability that A or its complement occurs? 1

CHAPTER 13
Probability and Measurement
DARTS
Then
You learned about experiments, outcomes, and events. You also found probabilities of simple events.
Now
In this chapter, you will:
Represent sample spaces.
Use permutations and combinations with probability.
Find probabilities by using length and area.
Find probabilities of compound events.
Why?
GAMES Probability can be used to predict the likelihood of different outcomes of the games that we play.
Probability and Measurement
The of each colored region.
connectED.mcgraw-hill.com
Your Digital Math Portal
Animation
Vocabulary
eGlossary
Personal Tutor
Virtual Manipulatives
Graphing Calculator
Audio
Foldables
Self-Check Practice
Worksheets

Additional Answers (p. 913)

1. $\frac{7}{8}$
2. $1\frac{1}{9}$
3. $1\frac{11}{40}$
4. $\frac{1}{9}$
5. $\frac{3}{8}$
6. $\frac{1}{15}$
8. $\frac{5}{6}$ or 83%
10. $\frac{1}{6}$ or 17%

Get Ready for the Chapter

Diagnose Readiness | You have two options for checking prerequisite skills.

1 Textbook Option Take the Quick Check below. Refer to the Quick Review for help.

QuickCheck

Simplify. **1–6. See margin.**

1. $\frac{1}{2} + \frac{3}{8}$
2. $\frac{7}{9} + \frac{2}{6}$
3. $\frac{2}{5} + \frac{7}{8}$
4. $\frac{2}{9} \cdot \frac{4}{8}$
5. $\frac{3}{7} \cdot \frac{21}{24}$
6. $\frac{3}{10} \cdot \frac{2}{9}$
7. **SOCCER** A soccer team brings a 4.5-gallon cooler of water to their games. How many 4-ounce cups can the team drink per game? **144**

A die is rolled. Find the probability of each outcome.
8, 10. See margin.

8. P(greater than 1)
9. P(odd) $\frac{1}{2}$ **or 50%**
10. P(less than 2)
11. P(1 or 6) $\frac{1}{3}$ **or 33%**
12. **GAMES** Two friends are playing a game with a 20-sided die that has all of the letters of the alphabet except for Q, U, V, X, Y, and Z. What is the probability that the die will land on a vowel? $\frac{1}{5}$ **or 20%**

The table shows the results of an experiment in which a spinner numbered 1–4 was spun.

Outcome	Tally	Frequency
1	|||	3
2	𝍸 ||	7
3	𝍸 |	6
4	||||	4

13. What is the experimental probability that the spinner will land on a 4? $\frac{1}{5}$ **or 20%**
14. What is the experimental probability that the spinner will land on an odd number? $\frac{9}{20}$ **or 45%**
15. What is the experimental probability that the spinner will land on an even number? $\frac{11}{20}$ **or 55%**

QuickReview

Example 1 (Used in Lessons 13-5 and 13-6)

Simplify $\frac{6}{9} \cdot \frac{1}{2}$.

$\frac{6}{9} \cdot \frac{1}{2} = \frac{6 \cdot 1}{9 \cdot 2}$ Multiply the numerators and denominators.

$= \frac{6}{18}$ or $\frac{1}{3}$ Simplify.

Example 2 (Used in Lessons 13-1 and 13-3)

Suppose a die is rolled. What is the probability of rolling less than a five?

$P(\text{less than } 5) = \frac{\text{number of favorable outcomes}}{\text{number of possible outcomes}}$

$= \frac{4}{6}$ or $\frac{2}{3}$

The probability of rolling less than a five is $\frac{2}{3}$ or 67%.

Example 3 (Used in Lesson 13-1)

A spinner numbered 1–6 was spun. Find the experimental probability of landing on a 5.

Outcome	Tally	Frequency
1	||||	4
2	𝍸 ||	7
3	𝍸 |||	8
4	||||	4
5	||	2
6	𝍸	5

$P(5) = \frac{\text{number of times a 5 is spun}}{\text{total number of outcomes}}$ or $\frac{2}{30}$

The experimental probability of landing on a 5 is $\frac{2}{30}$ or 7%.

2 Online Option Take an online self-check Chapter Readiness Quiz at connectED.mcgraw-hill.com.

913

Essential Questions

- How can we predict the outcomes of events? Sample answers: You can conduct an experiment to determine the chance that the event will occur; you can use information from previous events; you can use new information that you've gathered.
- How can we quantify predictions? Sample answer: We can calculate or estimate the probability of the outcome occurring.

Get Ready for the Chapter

Response to Intervention (RtI)

Use the *Quick Check* results and the Intervention Planner chart to help you determine your Response to Intervention. The If-Then statements in the chart help you decide the appropriate tier of RtI and suggest intervention resources for each tier.

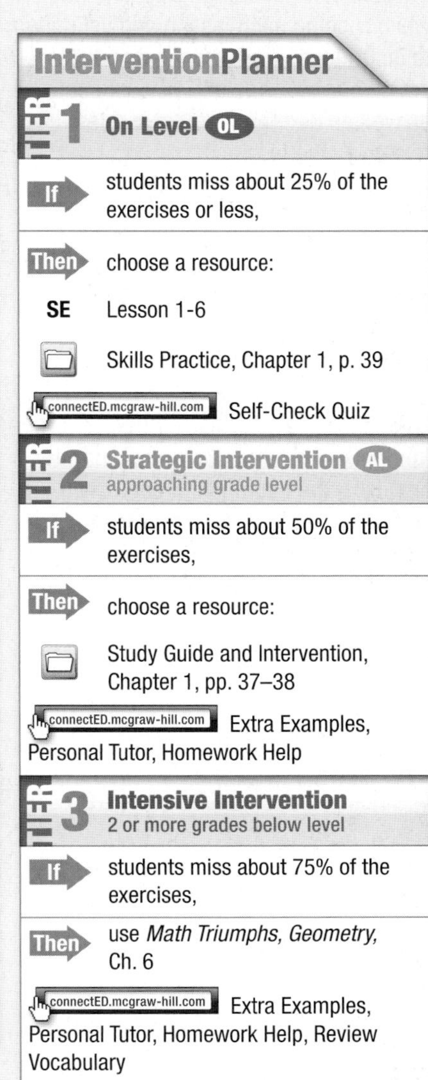

InterventionPlanner

TIER 1 On Level OL

If students miss about 25% of the exercises or less,

Then choose a resource:

SE Lesson 1-6

Skills Practice, Chapter 1, p. 39

connectED.mcgraw-hill.com Self-Check Quiz

TIER 2 Strategic Intervention AL approaching grade level

If students miss about 50% of the exercises,

Then choose a resource:

Study Guide and Intervention, Chapter 1, pp. 37–38

connectED.mcgraw-hill.com Extra Examples, Personal Tutor, Homework Help

TIER 3 Intensive Intervention 2 or more grades below level

If students miss about 75% of the exercises,

Then use *Math Triumphs, Geometry,* Ch. 6

connectED.mcgraw-hill.com Extra Examples, Personal Tutor, Homework Help, Review Vocabulary

FOLDABLES StudyOrganizer

Dinah Zike's Foldables®

Focus Students write the names of methods of counting and types of probabilities.

Teach After students make their Foldables, have them label the tabs to correspond to the six lessons in this chapter. Instruct students to take notes while reading each lesson and listening to instruction. They should include definitions of terms and key concepts, as well as diagrams and examples related to the lesson.

When to Use It Use the appropriate tabs as students cover each lesson in this chapter. Students can add to the vocabulary tab during each lesson.

Differentiated Instruction

Student Built Glossary p. 1

Students should complete the chart by providing the definition of each term and an example as they progress through Chapter 13. This study tool can also be used to review for the chapter test.

Get Started on the Chapter

You will learn several new concepts, skills, and vocabulary terms as you study Chapter 13. To get ready, identify important terms and organize your resources. You may wish to refer to Chapter 0 to review prerequisite skills.

FOLDABLES StudyOrganizer

Probability and Measurement Make this Foldable to help you organize your Chapter 13 notes about probability. Begin with one sheet of paper.

1 **Fold** a sheet of paper lengthwise.

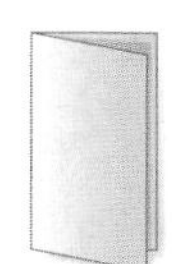

2 **Fold** in half two more times.

3 **Cut** along each fold on the left column.

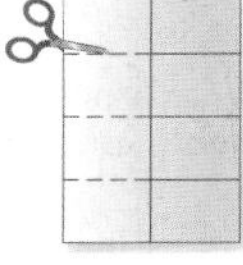

4 **Label** as shown.

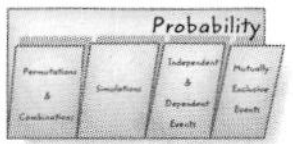

NewVocabulary

English		Español
sample space	p. 915	espacio muestral
tree diagram	p. 915	diagrama de árbol
permutation	p. 922	permutación
factorial	p. 922	factorial
circular permutation	p. 925	permutación circular
combination	p. 926	combinacion
geometric probability	p. 931	probabilidad geométrica
probability model	p. 939	modelo de la probabilidad
simulation	p. 939	simulacro
random variable	p. 941	variable aleatoria
expected value	p. 941	valor espenado
compound events	p. 947	eventos compuestos
independent events	p. 947	eventos independientes
dependent events	p. 947	eventos dependientes
conditional probability	p. 949	probabilidad condicional
probability tree	p. 949	árbol de la probabilidad
mutually exclusive	p. 956	mutuamente exclusivos
complement	p. 959	complemento

ReviewVocabulary

event evento one or more outcomes of an experiment

experiment experimento a situation involving chance such as flipping a coin or rolling a die

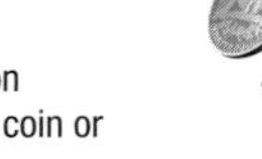

914 | Chapter 13 | Probability and Measurement

LESSON 13-1 Representing Sample Spaces

:: Then	:: Now	:: Why?
You calculated experimental probability.	1 Use lists, tables, and tree diagrams to represent sample spaces. 2 Use the Fundamental Counting Principle to count outcomes.	In a football game, a referee tosses a fair coin to determine which team will take possession of the football first. The coin can land on heads or tails.

NewVocabulary
sample space
tree diagram
two-stage experiment
multi-stage experiment
Fundamental Counting Principle

Common Core State Standards

Content Standards
Preparation for S.CP.9 (+) Use permutations and combinations to compute probabilities of compound events and solve problems.

Mathematical Practices
1 Make sense of problems and persevere in solving them.
2 Reason abstractly and quantitatively.

1 Represent a Sample Space

You have learned the following about experiments, outcomes, and events.

Definition	Example
An *experiment* is a situation involving chance that leads to results called *outcomes*.	In the situation above, the experiment is tossing the coin.
An *outcome* is the result of a single performance or *trial* of an experiment.	The possible outcomes are landing on heads or tails.
An *event* is one or more outcomes of an experiment.	One event of this experiment is the coin landing on tails.

The **sample space** of an experiment is the set of all possible outcomes. You can represent a sample space by using an organized list, a table, or a **tree diagram**.

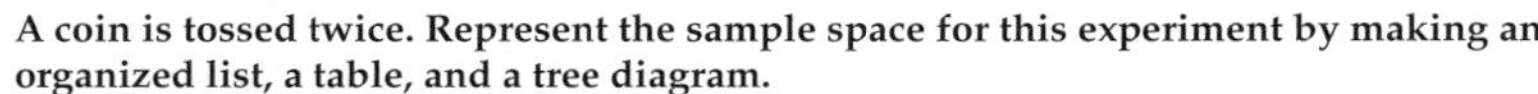

Example 1 Represent a Sample Space

A coin is tossed twice. Represent the sample space for this experiment by making an organized list, a table, and a tree diagram.

For each coin toss, there are two possible outcomes, heads H or tails T.

Organized List

Pair each possible outcome from the first toss with the possible outcomes from the second toss.

H, H　　T, T
H, T　　T, H

Table

List the outcomes of the first toss in the left column and those of the second toss in the top row.

Outcomes	Heads	Tails
Heads	H, H	H, T
Tails	T, H	T, T

Tree Diagram

Outcomes
First Toss: H, T
Second Toss: H, T (from H); H, T (from T)
Sample Space: H, H　H, T　T, H　T, T

GuidedPractice　**1. See Ch. 13 Answer Appendix.**

1. A coin is tossed and then a number cube is rolled. Represent the sample space for this experiment by making an organized list, a table, and a tree diagram.

1 Focus

VerticalAlignment

Before Lesson 13-1 Evaluate experiments, outcomes, and events.

Lesson 13-1 Represent sample spaces. Use the Fundamental Counting Principle to count outcomes.

After Lesson 13-1 Use permutations and combinations with probability.

2 Teach

Scaffolding Questions

Have students read the **Why?** section of the lesson.

Ask:

- What makes a coin fair? There is an equal chance that either side will land face up.
- What other ways are fair ways of determining who goes first in a game? Sample answers: roll of the die, blind card pick, paper-scissors-rock
- What factor determines a fair outcome? an equal chance for all possible outcomes

Lesson 13-1 Resources

Resource	Approaching Level AL	On Level OL	Beyond Level BL	English Learners ELL
Teacher Edition	▪ Differentiated Instruction, p. 916	▪ Differentiated Instruction, pp. 916, 920	▪ Differentiated Instruction, pp. 916, 920	
Chapter Resource Masters	▪ Study Guide and Intervention, pp. 5–6 ▪ Skills Practice, p. 7 ▪ Practice, p. 8 ▪ Word Problem Practice, p. 9	▪ Study Guide and Intervention, pp. 5–6 ▪ Skills Practice, p. 7 ▪ Practice, p. 8 ▪ Word Problem Practice, p. 9 ▪ Enrichment, p. 10	▪ Practice, p. 8 ▪ Word Problem Practice, p. 9 ▪ Enrichment, p. 10	▪ Study Guide and Intervention, pp. 5–6 ▪ Skills Practice, p. 7 ▪ Practice, p. 8 ▪ Word Problem Practice, p. 9
Other	▪ 5-Minute Check 13-1 ▪ Study Notebook	▪ 5-Minute Check 13-1 ▪ Study Notebook	▪ 5-Minute Check 13-1 ▪ Study Notebook	▪ 5-Minute Check 13-1 ▪ Study Notebook

1 Represent a Sample Space

Examples 1 and 2 show how to find the set of all possible outcomes by using an organized list, a table, and a tree diagram.

Formative Assessment

Use the Guided Practice exercises after each example to determine students' understanding of concepts.

Additional Examples

1 One red token and one black token are placed in a bag. A token is drawn and the color is recorded. It is then returned to the bag and a second draw is made. Represent the sample space for this experiment by making an organized list, a table, and a tree diagram. Organized List: R,R; B,B; R,B; B,R

Outcomes	Red	Black
Red	R,R	R,B
Black	B,R	B,B

Outcomes

First Draw	R		B	
Second Draw	R	B	R	B
Sample Space	R, R	R, B	B, R	B, B

2 **CHEF'S SALAD** A chef's salad at a local restaurant comes with a choice of French, ranch, or blue cheese dressings and optional toppings of cheese, turkey, and eggs. Draw a tree diagram to represent the sample space for salad orders. See students' work.

Additional Examples also in Interactive Classroom PowerPoint® Presentations

IWB Interactive White Board READY

The experiment in Example 1 is an example of a **two-stage experiment**, which is an experiment with two stages or events. Experiments with more than two stages are called **multi-stage experiments**.

WatchOut!

CCSS Sense-Making The words *and/or* in the third question for Example 2 suggest an additional stage in the ordering process. By making separate stages for choosing with or without tomato and with or without pickles, you allow for the possibility of choosing *both* tomato and pickles.

Real-World Example 2 Multi-Stage Tree Diagrams

HAMBURGERS To take a hamburger order, Keandra asks each customer the questions from the script shown. Draw a tree diagram to represent the sample space for hamburger orders.

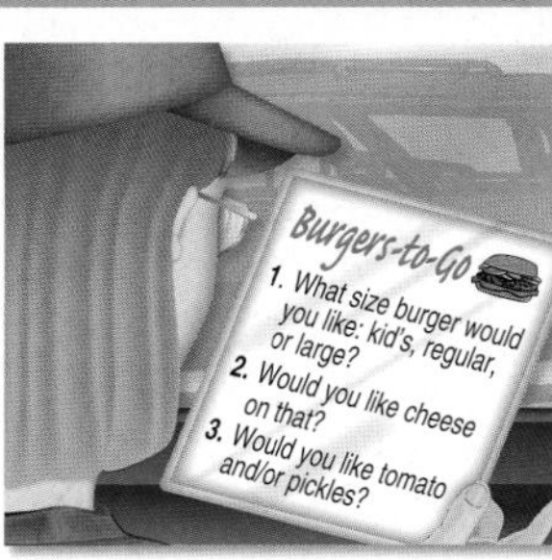

The sample space is the result of four stages.

- Burger size (K, R, or L)
- Cheese (C or NC)
- Tomato (T or NT)
- Pickles (P or NP)

Draw a tree diagram with four stages.

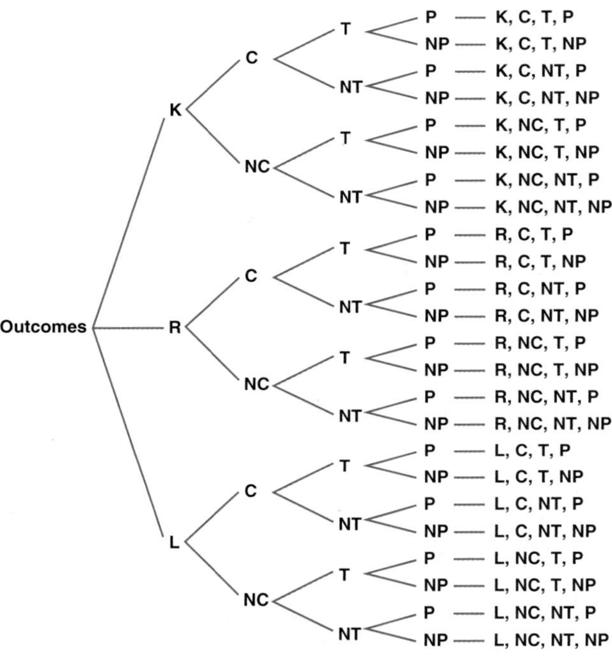

ReadingMath

Tree Diagram Notation Choose notation for outcomes in your tree diagrams that will eliminate confusion. In Example 2, *C* stands for *cheese*, while *NC* stands for *no cheese.* Likewise, *NT* and *NP* stand for *no tomato* and *no pickles*, respectively.

GuidedPractice 2. See Ch. 13 Answer Appendix.

2. **MUSIC** Yoki can choose a small MP3 player with a 4- or 8-gigabyte hard drive in black, teal, sage, or red. She can also get a clip and/or a dock to go with it. Make a tree diagram to represent the sample space for this situation.

DifferentiatedInstruction AL OL BL

Logical Learners Organize students in groups of three or four. Provide each group with a handful of four to six different manipulatives. Challenge each group to make as many unique groups of items as possible. Have students draw and record the total number of unique groups they can make by using one item, two items, three items, and so on. Challenge some groups to find the total number of unique groups if order is important (ABC and BCA are considered two separate groups) and if order is not important (ABC and BCA are considered the same group). Have groups share with the class their drawings and the total number of groups made.

2 Fundamental Counting Principle

For some two-stage or multi-stage experiments, listing the entire sample space may not be practical or necessary. To find the *number* of possible outcomes, you can use the **Fundamental Counting Principle**.

StudyTip

Multiplication Rule The Fundamental Counting Principle is sometimes called the *Multiplication Rule for Counting* or the *Counting Principle.*

KeyConcept Fundamental Counting Principle

Words The number of possible outcomes in a sample space can be found by multiplying the number of possible outcomes from each stage or event.

Symbols In a k-stage experiment, let

n_1 = the number of possible outcomes for the first stage.

n_2 = the number of possible outcomes for the second stage after the first stage has occurred.

⋮

n_k = the number of possible outcomes for the kth stage after the first $k - 1$ stages have occurred.

Then the total possible outcomes of this k-stage experiment is

$$n_1 \cdot n_2 \cdot n_3 \cdot \ldots \cdot n_k.$$

Real-WorldLink

More than 95 percent of high school students order a traditional ring style, which includes the name of the school, a stone, and the graduation year.

Source: *Fort Worth Star-Telegram*

Real-World Example 3 Use the Fundamental Counting System

PT

CLASS RINGS **Haley has selected a size and overall style for her class ring. Now she must choose from the ring options shown. How many different rings could Haley create in her chosen style and size?**

Ring Options	Number of Choices
metals	10
finishes	2
stone colors	12
stone cuts	5
side 1 activity logos	20
side 2 activity logos	20
band styles	2

Use the Fundamental Counting Principle.

metals		finishes		stone colors		stone cuts		side 1 logos		side 2 logos		band styles		possible outcomes
10	×	2	×	12	×	5	×	20	×	20	×	2	=	960,000

So, Haley could create 960,000 different rings.

GuidedPractice

3. Find the number of possible outcomes for each situation.

A. The answer sheet shown is completed. **65,536**

B. A die is rolled four times. **1296**

C. **SHOES** A pair of women's shoes comes in whole sizes 5 through 11 in red, navy, brown, or black. They can be leather or suede and are available in three different widths. **168**

Answer Sheet

1. Ⓐ Ⓑ Ⓒ Ⓓ
2. Ⓐ Ⓑ Ⓒ Ⓓ
3. Ⓐ Ⓑ Ⓒ Ⓓ
4. Ⓐ Ⓑ Ⓒ Ⓓ
5. Ⓐ Ⓑ Ⓒ Ⓓ
6. Ⓐ Ⓑ Ⓒ Ⓓ
7. Ⓣ Ⓕ
8. Ⓣ Ⓕ
9. Ⓣ Ⓕ
10. Ⓣ Ⓕ

WatchOut!

Choices For Example 2, remind students that just as choosing an option creates a unique outcome, not choosing also creates a unique outcome that must be included in the sample space.

2 Fundamental Counting Principle

Example 3 shows how to find the number of possible outcomes without respect to specific combinations.

Additional Example

3 **CARS** New cars are available with a wide selection of options for the consumer. One option is chosen from each category shown. How many different cars could a consumer create in the chosen make and model?

Car Options	Number of Choices
Exterior color	11
Interior color	7
Seat material	5
Engine	3
Computer navigation system	6
Wheels	4
Doors	3

83,160

Focus on Mathematical Content

Permutations Permutations are an extension of the Fundamental Counting Principle in which each unique order of outcomes is considered a unique event.

Tips for New Teachers

Fundamental Counting Principle The Fundamental Counting Principle can be used to check whether all possible outcomes have been considered in the sample space of a given event.

Teach with Tech

Digital Camera Have students name different combinations of photo settings available on the camera (photo size, photo quality, flash on/off, etc.). Use these settings to find how many different combinations of photo settings are possible on the camera. Have students summarize their results using a table or other display.

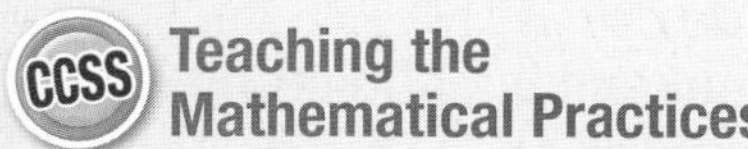

3 Practice

Formative Assessment

Use Exercises 1–5 to check for understanding.

Then use the chart at the bottom of this page to customize assignments for your students.

Teaching the Mathematical Practices

Reasoning Mathematically proficient students make sense of quantities and their relationships in problem situations. In Exercises 6–10, encourage students to list the possible outcomes first.

Additional Answer

21. Sample answer: 6 different ways:
$4(x + 6) + 2(3) + 2(x + 4)$;
$2(x + 11) + 2(x + 8) + 2(x)$;
$2(x + 4) + 2(x + 9) + 2(x + 6)$;
$2(x) + 2(3) + 4(x + 8)$;
$2(x) + 2(x + 8) + 2(3) + 2(x + 8)$;
$2(x) + 2(3) + 2(4) + 2(x + 6) + 2(x + 6)$

Check Your Understanding

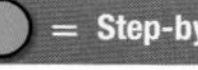 = Step-by-Step Solutions begin on page R14.

Example 1 **Represent the sample space for each experiment by making an organized list, a table, and a tree diagram.**

1. For each at bat, a player can either get on base or make an out. Suppose a player bats twice. **See Ch. 13 Answer Appendix.**

2. Quinton sold the most tickets in his school for the annual Autumn Festival. As a reward, he gets to choose twice from a grab bag with tickets that say "free juice" or "free notebook." **See Ch. 13 Answer Appendix.**

Example 2

3. **TUXEDOS** Patrick is renting a prom tuxedo from the catalog shown. Draw a tree diagram to represent the sample space for this situation. **See Ch. 13 Answer Appendix.**

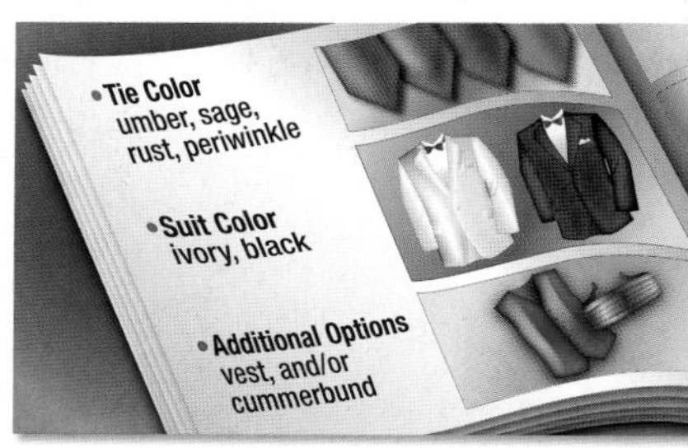

Example 3 **Find the number of possible outcomes for each situation.**

4. Marcos is buying a cell phone and must choose a plan. Assume one of each is chosen. **1800**

Cell Phone Options	Number of Choices
phone style	15
minutes package	5
Internet access	3
text messaging	4
insurance	2

5. Desirée is creating a new menu for her restaurant. Assume one of each item is ordered. **20,736**

Menu Titles	Number of Choices
appetizer	8
soup	4
salad	6
entree	12
dessert	9

Practice and Problem Solving

Extra Practice is on page R13.

Example 1 **CCSS REASONING** **Represent the sample space for each experiment by making an organized list, a table, and a tree diagram.** **6–10. See Ch. 13 Answer Appendix.**

6. Gina is a junior and has a choice for the next two years of either playing volleyball or basketball during the winter quarter.

7. Two different history classes in New York City are taking a trip to either the Smithsonian or the Museum of Natural History.

8. Simeon has an opportunity to travel abroad as a foreign exchange student during each of his last two years of college. He can choose between Ecuador or Italy.

9. A new club is formed, and a meeting time must be chosen. The possible meeting times are Monday or Thursday at 5:00 or 6:00 P.M.

10. An exam with multiple versions has exercises with triangles. In the first exercise, there is an obtuse triangle or an acute triangle. In the second exercise, there is an isosceles triangle or a scalene triangle.

Differentiated Homework Options

Level	Assignment	Two-Day Option	
AL Basic	6–16, 26–49	5–15 odd, 31–34	6–16 even, 26–30, 35–49
OL Core	5–19 odd, 20–24, 26–49	6–16, 31–34	17–24, 26–30, 35–49
BL Advanced	17–44, (optional: 45–49)		

11. **PAINTING** In an art class, students are working on two projects where they can use one of two different types of paints for each project. Represent the sample space for this experiment by making an organized list, a table, and a tree diagram. **See Ch. 13 Answer Appendix.**

oil paints

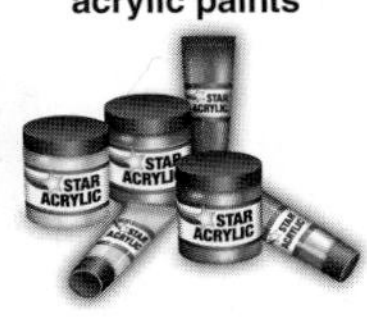
acrylic paints

Example 2 **Draw a tree diagram to represent the sample space for each situation.**

12. **BURRITOS** At a burrito stand, customers have the choice of beans, pork, or chicken with rice or no rice, and cheese and/or salsa. **See Ch. 13 Answer Appendix.**

13. **TRANSPORTATION** Blake is buying a vehicle and has a choice of sedan, truck, or van with leather or fabric interior, and a CD player and/or sunroof. **See Ch. 13 Answer Appendix.**

14. **TREATS** Ping and her friends go to a frozen yogurt parlor which has a sign like the one at the right. Draw a tree diagram for all possible combinations of cones with peanuts and/or sprinkles. **See Ch. 13 Answer Appendix.**

FROZEN YOGURT

Cones	Flavors
Cake Sugar Waffle	Strawberry Lime

Toppings: Peanuts and Sprinkles

Example 3 **CCSS PERSEVERANCE In Exercises 15–18, find the number of possible outcomes for each situation.**

15. In the Junior Student Council elections, there are 3 people running for secretary, 4 people running for treasurer, 5 people running for vice president, and 2 people running for class president. **120**

16. When signing up for classes during his first semester of college, Frederico has 4 class spots to fill with a choice of 4 literature classes, 2 math classes, 6 history classes, and 3 film classes. **144**

17. Niecy is choosing one each of 6 colleges, 5 majors, 2 minors, and 4 clubs. **240**

18. Evita works at a restaurant where she has to wear a white blouse, black pants or skirt, and black shoes. She has 5 blouses, 4 pants, 3 skirts, and 6 pairs of black shoes. **210**

19. **ART** For an art class assignment, Mr. Green gives students their choice of two quadrilaterals to use as a base. One must have sides of equal length, and the other must have at least one set of parallel sides. Represent the sample space by making an organized list, a table, and a tree diagram. **See Ch. 13 Answer Appendix.**

20. **BREAKFAST** A hotel restaurant serves omelets with a choice of vegetables, ham, or sausage that come with a side of hash browns, grits, or toast.

    a. How many different outcomes of omelet and one side are there if a vegetable omelet comes with just one vegetable? **18**

    b. Find the number of possible outcomes for a vegetable omelet if you can get any or all vegetables on any omelet. **45**

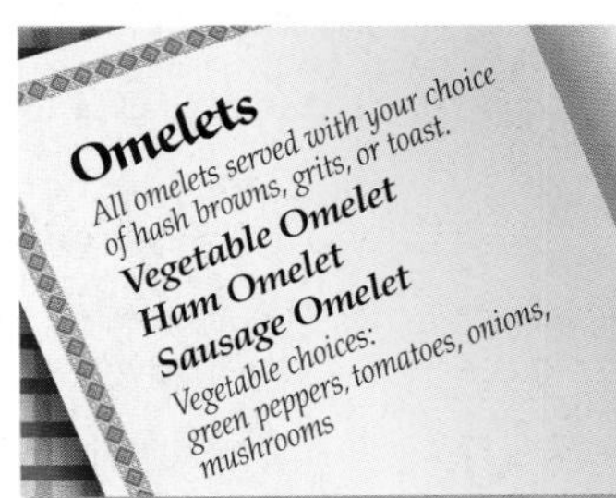

Omelets
All omelets served with your choice of hash browns, grits, or toast.
Vegetable Omelet
Ham Omelet
Sausage Omelet
Vegetable choices:
green peppers, tomatoes, onions, mushrooms

21. **COMPOSITE FIGURES** Carlito is calculating the area of the composite figure at the right. List six different ways he can do this. **See margin.**

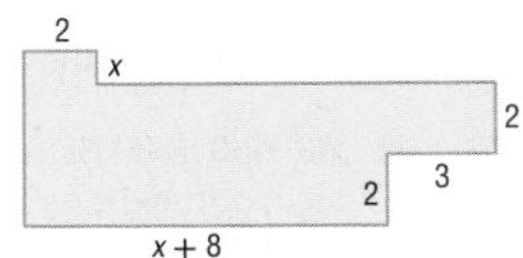

CCSS Teaching the Mathematical Practices

Perseverance Mathematically proficient students check their answers to problems using a different method, and they continually ask themselves, "does this make sense?" In Exercises 15–18, encourage students to check their answers for reasonableness.

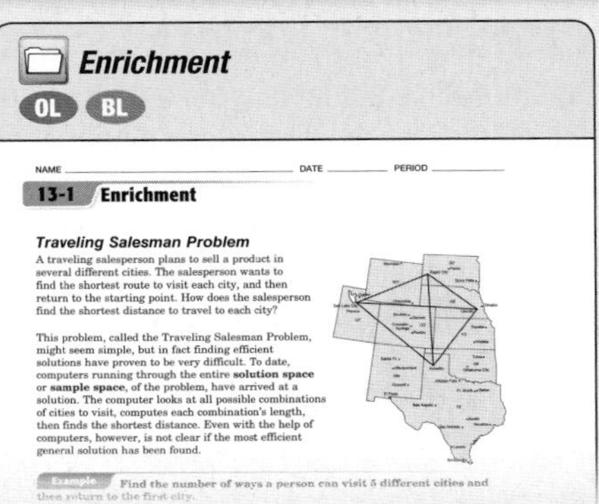

Enrichment
OL BL

NAME ______ DATE ______ PERIOD ______

13-1 Enrichment

Traveling Salesman Problem

A traveling salesperson plans to sell a product in several different cities. The salesperson wants to find the shortest route to visit each city, and then return to the starting point. How does the salesperson find the shortest distance to travel to each city?

This problem, called the Traveling Salesman Problem, might seem simple, but in fact finding efficient solutions have proven to be very difficult. To date, computers running through the entire **solution space** or **sample space**, of the problem, have arrived at a solution. The computer looks at all possible combinations of cities to visit, computes each combination's length, then finds the shortest distance. Even with the help of computers, however, is not clear if the most efficient general solution has been found.

Example Find the number of ways a person can visit 5 different cities and then return to the first city.

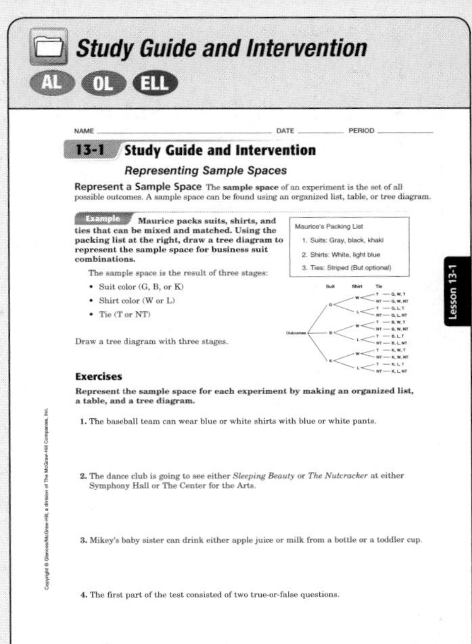

Study Guide and Intervention
AL OL ELL

NAME ______ DATE ______ PERIOD ______

13-1 Study Guide and Intervention

Representing Sample Spaces

Represent a Sample Space The **sample space** of an experiment is the set of all possible outcomes. A sample space can be found using an organized list, table, or tree diagram.

Example **Maurice packs suits, shirts, and ties that can be mixed and matched. Using the packing list at the right, draw a tree diagram to represent the sample space for business suit combinations.**

Maurice's Packing List
1. Suits: Gray, black, khaki
2. Shirts: White, light blue
3. Ties: Striped (But optional)

The sample space is the result of three stages:
- Suit color (G, B, or K)
- Shirt color (W or L)
- Tie (T or NT)

Draw a tree diagram with three stages.

Exercises

Represent the sample space for each experiment by making an organized list, a table, and a tree diagram.

1. The baseball team can wear blue or white shirts with blue or white pants.
2. The dance club is going to see either *Sleeping Beauty* or *The Nutcracker* at either Symphony Hall or The Center for the Arts.
3. Mikey's baby sister can drink either apple juice or milk from a bottle or a toddler cup.
4. The first part of the test consisted of two true-or-false questions.

Lesson 13-1

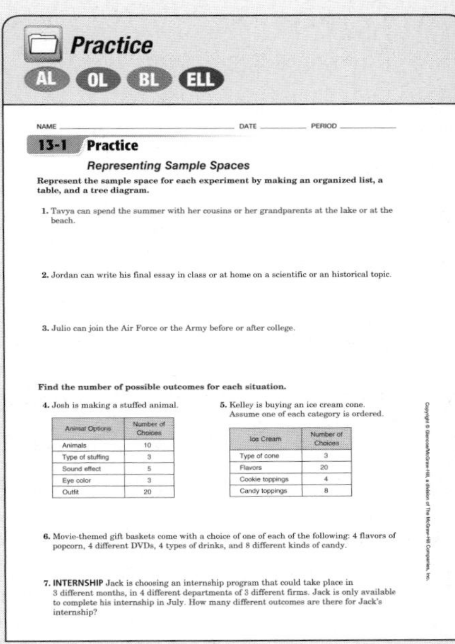

Practice
AL OL BL ELL

NAME ______ DATE ______ PERIOD ______

13-1 Practice

Representing Sample Spaces

Represent the sample space for each experiment by making an organized list, a table, and a tree diagram.

1. Tavya can spend the summer with her cousins or her grandparents at the lake or at the beach.
2. Jordan can write his final essay in class or at home on a scientific or an historical topic.
3. Julio can join the Air Force or the Army before or after college.

Find the number of possible outcomes for each situation.

4. Josh is making a stuffed animal.

Animal Options	Number of Choices
Animals	10
Type of stuffing	3
Sound effect	5
Eye color	3
Outfit	20

5. Kelley is buying an ice cream cone. Assume one of each category is ordered.

Ice Cream	Number of Choices
Type of cone	3
Flavors	20
Cookie toppings	4
Candy toppings	8

6. Movie-themed gift baskets come with a choice of one of each of the following: 4 flavors of popcorn, 4 different DVDs, 4 types of drinks, and 8 different kinds of candy.
7. **INTERNSHIP** Jack is choosing an internship program that could take place in 3 different months, in 4 different departments of 3 different firms. Jack is only available to complete his internship in July. How many different outcomes are there for Jack's internship?

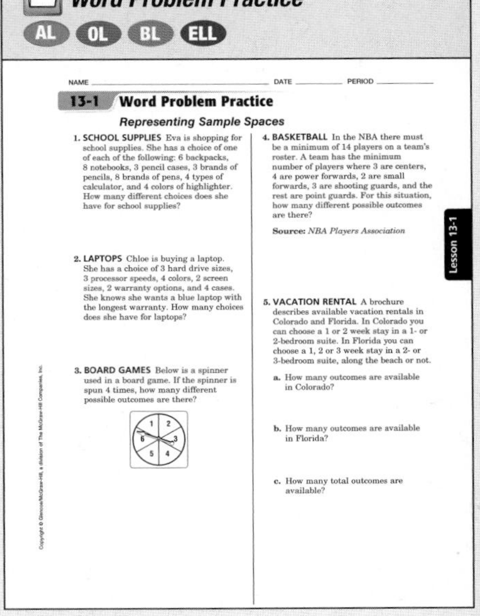

Word Problem Practice
AL OL BL ELL

NAME ______ DATE ______ PERIOD ______

13-1 Word Problem Practice

Representing Sample Spaces

1. **SCHOOL SUPPLIES** Eva is shopping for school supplies. She has a choice of one of each of the following: 6 backpacks, 8 notebooks, 3 pencil cases, 3 brands of pencils, 8 brands of pens, 4 types of calculator, and 4 colors of highlighter. How many different choices does she have for school supplies?
2. **LAPTOPS** Chloe is buying a laptop. She has a choice of 3 hard drive sizes, 3 processor speeds, 4 colors, 2 screen sizes, 2 warranty options, and 4 cases. She knows she wants a blue laptop with the longest warranty. How many choices does she have for laptops?
3. **BOARD GAMES** Below is a spinner used in a board game. If the spinner is spun 4 times, how many different possible outcomes are there?
4. **BASKETBALL** In the NBA there must be a minimum of 14 players on a team's roster. A team has the minimum number of players where 3 are centers, 4 are power forwards, 2 are small forwards, 3 are shooting guards, and the rest are point guards. For this situation, how many different possible outcomes are there?

   Source: *NBA Players Association*

5. **VACATION RENTAL** A brochure describes available vacation rentals in Colorado and Florida. In Colorado you can choose a 1 or 2 week stay in a 1- or 2-bedroom suite. In Florida you can choose a 1, 2 or 3 week stay in a 2- or 3-bedroom suite, along the beach or not.

   a. How many outcomes are available in Colorado?

   b. How many outcomes are available in Florida?

   c. How many total outcomes are available?

Lesson 13-1

Multiple Representations

In Exercise 24, students use a tree diagram and a Venn diagram to represent the sample space of an experiment.

Teaching the Mathematical Practices

Arguments Mathematically proficient students understand and use stated assumptions and definitions in constructing arguments. They make conjectures and build a logical progression of statements to explore the truth of their conjectures. In Exercise 28, encourage students to work together.

Additional Answers

22b. 5040; Sample answer: There are 10 possibilities for the first number in the combination. Since Miranda can use each number only once, there are only 9 possibilities for the second number in the combination, 8 possibilities for the third number in the combination, and 7 possibilities for the fourth number in the combination. The number of possible combinations is $10 \times 9 \times 8 \times 7$ or 5040.

25. $n^3 - 3n^2 + 2n$; Sample answer: There are n objects in the box when you remove the first object, so after you remove one object, there are $n - 1$ possible outcomes. After you remove the second object, there are $n - 2$ possible outcomes. The number of possible outcomes is the product of the number of outcomes of each experiment or $n(n - 1)(n - 2)$.

26. Sample answer: In an experiment, you choose between a blue box and a red box. You then remove a ball from the box that you chose without looking into the box. The blue box contains a red ball, a purple ball, and a green ball. The red box contains a yellow ball and an orange ball.

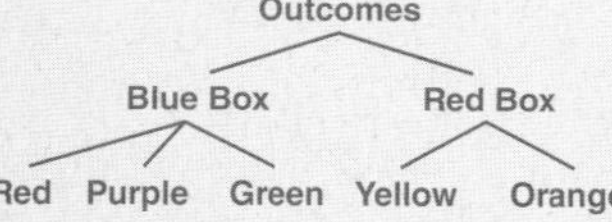

22. TRANSPORTATION Miranda got a new bicycle lock that has a four-number combination. Each number in the combination is from 0 to 9.

a. How many combinations are possible if there are no restrictions on the number of times Miranda can use each number? **10,000**

b. How many combinations are possible if Miranda can use each number only once? Explain. **See margin.**

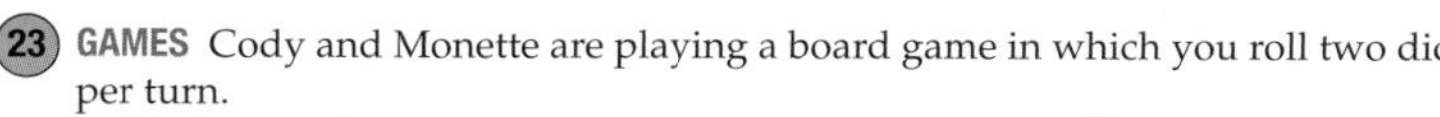

23. GAMES Cody and Monette are playing a board game in which you roll two dice per turn.

a. In one turn, how many outcomes result in a sum of 8? **5**

b. How many outcomes in one turn result in an odd sum? **18**

24. MULTIPLE REPRESENTATIONS In this problem, you will investigate a sequence of events. In the first stage of a two-stage experiment, you spin Spinner 1 below. If the result is red, you flip a coin. If the result is yellow, you roll a die. If the result is green, you roll a number cube. If the result is blue, you spin Spinner 2.

Spinner 1

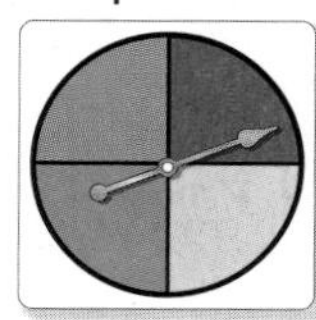

Spinner 2

a. **Geometric** Draw a tree diagram to represent the sample space for the experiment. **See Ch. 13 Answer Appendix.**

b. **Logical** Draw a Venn diagram to represent the possible outcomes of the experiment. **See Ch. 13 Answer Appendix.**

c. **Analytical** How many possible outcomes are there? **20**

d. **Verbal** Could you use the Fundamental Counting Principle to determine the number of outcomes? Explain. **Sample answer: No; since the second stage of the experiment depends on what happens in the first stage of the experiment, you cannot multiply the number of outcomes for each stage. You have to find the number of possible outcomes for each stage and add them.**

H.O.T. Problems Use Higher-Order Thinking Skills

25. CHALLENGE A box contains n different objects. If you remove three objects from the box, one at a time, without putting the previous object back, how many possible outcomes exist? Explain your reasoning. **See margin.**

26. OPEN ENDED Sometimes a tree diagram for an experiment is not symmetrical. Describe a two-stage experiment where the tree diagram is asymmetrical. Include a sketch of the tree diagram. Explain. **See margin.**

27. WRITING IN MATH Explain why it is not possible to represent the sample space for a multi-stage experiment by using a table. **See margin.**

Example 3

28. CCSS ARGUMENTS Determine if the following statement is *sometimes*, *always*, or *never* true. Explain your reasoning. **See margin.**

When an outcome falls outside the sample space, it is a failure.

29. REASONING A multistage experiment has n possible outcomes at each stage. If the experiment is performed with k stages, write an equation for the total number of possible outcomes P. Explain. **See margin.**

30. WRITING IN MATH Explain when it is necessary to show all of the possible outcomes of an experiment by using a tree diagram and when using the Fundamental Counting Principle is sufficient. **See margin.**

DifferentiatedInstruction OL BL

Extension Have students write a multi-stage experiment involving marketing, such as mix-and-match outfits, special-of-the-day dinner choices at a restaurant, or pizzas with a selection of toppings. Have students create a table listing all the choice options and then use the Fundamental Counting Principle to determine the number of possible outcomes. Then have students create a tree diagram to identify the sample space. Finally, have students create a marketing flyer highlighting the number of choices available for their product.

920 | Lesson 13-1 | Representing Sample Spaces

Standardized Test Practice

31. **PROBABILITY** Alejandra can invite two friends to go out to dinner with her for her birthday. If she is choosing among four of her friends, how many possible outcomes are there? **B**

A 4 C 8

B 6 D 9

32. **SHORT RESPONSE** What is the volume of the triangular prism shown below? **32 in^3**

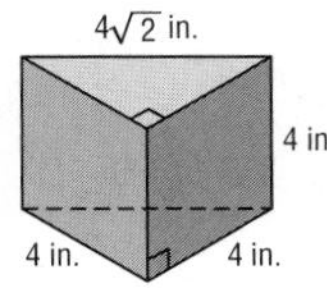

33. Brad's password must be five digits long, use the numbers 0–9, and the digits must not repeat. What is the maximum number of different passwords that Brad can have? **G**

F 15,120 H 59,049

G 30,240 J 100,000

34. **SAT/ACT** A pizza shop offers 3 types of crust, 5 vegetable toppings, and 4 meat toppings. How many different pizzas could be ordered by choosing 1 crust, 1 vegetable topping, and 1 meat topping? **D**

A 12 D 60

B 23 E infinite

C 35

Spiral Review

35. **ARCHITECTURE** To encourage recycling, the people of Rome, Italy, built a model of Basilica di San Pietro from empty beverage cans. The model was built to a 1:5 scale and was a rectangular prism that measured 26 meters high, 49 meters wide, and 93 meters long. Find the dimensions of the actual Basilica di San Pietro. (Lesson 12-8) **130 m high, 245 m wide, and 465 m long**

Using spherical geometry, name each of the following on sphere $\mathcal{W}$. (Lesson 12-7)

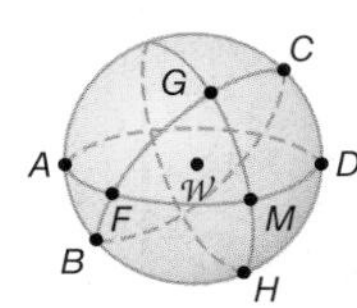

36. two lines containing point F **$\overleftrightarrow{BG}$, $\overleftrightarrow{AM}$**

37. a segment containing point G **$\overline{FC}$**

38. a triangle **$\triangle FGM$**

Find the lateral area and surface area of each cylinder. Round to the nearest tenth. (Lesson 12-2)

39.

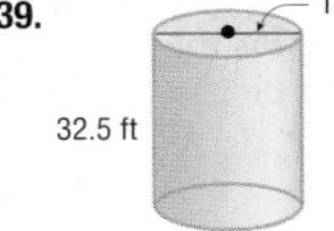

1429.4 ft^2
1737.3 ft^2

40.

37.7 in^2
51.8 in^2

41. 16.5 m, 16.5 m **1710.6 m^2** **3421.2 m^2**

42. **TELECOMMUNICATIONS** The signal from a tower follows a ray that has its endpoint on the tower and is tangent to Earth. Suppose a tower is located at sea level as shown. Determine the measure of the arc intercepted by the two tangents. (Lesson 10-6) **93.5**

86.5°

Note: Art not drawn to scale

COORDINATE GEOMETRY Determine whether the figure with the given vertices has *line* symmetry and/or *rotational* symmetry. (Lesson 9-5)

43. $Q(2, 2), R(7, 2), S(6, 6), T(3, 6)$ **line**

44. $J(-2, 2), K(-5, -1), L(-2, -4), M(1, -1)$ **line and rotational**

Skills Review

Find each quotient.

45. $\frac{5^2}{2}$ **12.5**

46. $\frac{3^3}{3 \cdot 2}$ **4.5**

47. $\frac{2^4 \cdot 6}{8}$ **12**

48. $\frac{2^3 \cdot 12}{6}$ **16**

49. $\frac{4^4 \cdot 3}{24}$ **32**

4 Assess

Crystal Ball Have students write about how learning to represent the sample space and to use the Fundamental Counting Principle will connect with permutations and combinations.

Additional Answers

27. Sample answer: You can list the possible outcomes for one stage of an experiment in the columns and the possible outcomes for the other stage of the experiment in the rows. Since a table is two dimensional, it would be impossible to list the possible outcomes for three or more stages of an experiment. Therefore, tables can only be used to represent the sample space for a two-stage experiment.

28. Sample answer: Never; the sample space is the set of all possible outcomes. An outcome cannot fall outside the sample space. A failure occurs when the outcome is in the sample space, but is not a favorable outcome.

29. $P = n^k$; Sample answer: The total number of possible outcomes is the product of the number of outcomes for each of the stages 1 through k. Since there are k stages, you are multiplying n by itself k times which is n^k.

30. Sample answer: Drawing a tree diagram is necessary if you want to show the sample space for an experiment or if you want to know the number of times a certain outcome occurs. Using the Fundamental Counting Principle only tells you how many possible outcomes there are, so it is only useful when you want to know how many outcomes there are.

1 Focus

Vertical Alignment

Before Lesson 13-2 Use the Fundamental Counting Principle.

Lesson 13-2 Use permutations with probability. Use combinations with probability.

After Lesson 13-2 Find probabilities by using length and area.

2 Teach

Scaffolding Questions

Have students read the **Why?** section of the lesson.

Ask:

- Why might order be important in the photograph? Sample answers: height of the people, color of the outfits, who is associated with whom
- In what other situations might the order of objects be important? Sample answer: mixing ingredients in baking
- In what situation might the order of objects not be important? Sample answer: when putting condiments on a hamburger

LESSON 13-2 Probability with Permutations and Combinations

Then

- You used the Fundamental Counting Principle.

Now

1. Use permutations with probability.
2. Use combinations with probability.

Why?

- Lina, Troy, Davian, and Mary are being positioned for a photograph. There are 4 choices for who can stand on the far left, leaving 3 choices for who can stand in the second position. For the third position, just 2 choices remain, and for the last position just 1 is possible.

New Vocabulary
permutation
factorial
circular permutation
combination

Common Core State Standards

Content Standards
S.CP.9 (+) Use permutations and combinations to compute probabilities of compound events and solve problems.

Mathematical Practices
1 Make sense of problems and persevere in solving them.
4 Model with mathematics.

1 Probability Using Permutations A **permutation** is an arrangement of objects in which order is important. One permutation of the four friends above is Troy, Davian, Mary, and then Lina. Using the Fundamental Counting Principle, there are $4 \cdot 3 \cdot 2 \cdot 1$ or 24 possible ordered arrangements of the friends.

The expression $4 \cdot 3 \cdot 2 \cdot 1$ used to calculate the number of permutations of these four friends can be written as 4!, which is read *4 factorial.*

KeyConcept Factorial

Words	The **factorial** of a positive integer n, written $n!$, is the product of the positive integers less than or equal to n.
Symbols	$n! = n \cdot (n-1) \cdot (n-2) \cdot \ldots \cdot 2 \cdot 1$, where $0! = 1$

Example 1 Probability and Permutations of *n* Objects

SPORTS **Chanise and Renee are members of the lacrosse team. If the 20 girls on the team are each assigned a jersey number from 1 to 20 at random, what is the probability that Chanise's jersey number will be 1 and Renee's will be 2?**

Step 1 Find the number of possible outcomes in the sample space. This is the number of permutations of the 20 girls' names, or 20!.

Step 2 Find the number of favorable outcomes. This is the number of permutations of the other girls' names given that Chanise's jersey number is 1 and Renee's is 2: (20 − 2)! or 18!.

Step 3 Calculate the probability.

$$P(\text{Chanise 1, Renee 2}) = \frac{18!}{20!}$$ ← number of favorable outcomes / ← number of possible outcomes

$$= \frac{\overset{1}{\cancel{18!}}}{20 \cdot 19 \cdot \underset{1}{\cancel{18!}}}$$ Expand 20! and divide out common factors.

$$= \frac{1}{380}$$ Simplify.

Guided Practice

1. PHOTOGRAPHY In the opening paragraph, what is the probability that Troy is chosen to stand on the far left and Davian on the far right for the photograph? $\frac{1}{12}$

922 | Lesson 13-2

Lesson 13-2 Resources

Resource	Approaching Level AL	On Level OL	Beyond Level BL	English Learners ELL
Teacher Edition		▪ Differentiated Instruction, pp. 925, 929	▪ Differentiated Instruction, pp. 925, 929	
Chapter Resource Masters	▪ Study Guide and Intervention, pp. 11–12 ▪ Skills Practice, p. 13 ▪ Practice, p. 14 ▪ Word Problem Practice, p. 15	▪ Study Guide and Intervention, pp. 11–12 ▪ Skills Practice, p. 13 ▪ Practice, p. 14 ▪ Word Problem Practice, p. 15 ▪ Enrichment, p. 16	▪ Practice, p. 14 ▪ Word Problem Practice, p. 15 ▪ Enrichment, p. 16	▪ Study Guide and Intervention, pp. 11–12 ▪ Skills Practice, p. 13 ▪ Practice, p. 14 ▪ Word Problem Practice, p. 15
Other	▪ 5-Minute Check 13-2 ▪ Study Notebook	▪ 5-Minute Check 13-2 ▪ Study Notebook	▪ 5-Minute Check 13-2 ▪ Study Notebook	▪ 5-Minute Check 13-2 ▪ Study Notebook

In the opening paragraph, suppose 6 friends were available, but the photographer wanted only 4 people in the picture. Using the Fundamental Counting Principle, the number of permutations of 4 friends taken from a group of 6 friends is $6 \cdot 5 \cdot 4 \cdot 3$ or 360.

Another way of describing this situation is the number of permutations of 6 friends taken 4 at a time, denoted $_6P_4$. This number can also be computed using factorials.

$$_6P_4 = 6 \cdot 5 \cdot 4 \cdot 3 = \frac{6 \cdot 5 \cdot 4 \cdot 3 \cdot 2 \cdot 1}{2 \cdot 1} = \frac{6!}{2!} = \frac{6!}{(6-4)!}$$

This suggests the following formula.

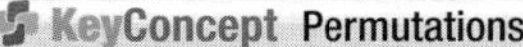

ReadingMath

CCSS Precision The phrase *distinct objects* means that the objects are distinguishable as being different in some way.

KeyConcept Permutations

Symbols The number of permutations of n distinct objects taken r at a time is denoted by $_nP_r$ and given by $_nP_r = \frac{n!}{n-r!}$.

Example The number of permutations of 5 objects taken 2 at a time is $_5P_2 = \frac{5!}{(5-2)!} = \frac{5 \cdot 4 \cdot 3!}{3!}$ or 20.

StudyTip

Randomness When outcomes are decided at random, they are equally likely to occur and their probabilities can be calculated using permutations and combinations.

PT

Example 2 Probability and $_nP_r$

A class is divided into teams each made up of 15 students. Each team is directed to select team members to be officers. If Sam, Valencia, and Deshane are on a team, and the positions are decided at random, what is the probability that they are selected as president, vice president, and secretary, respectively?

Step 1 Since choosing officers is a way of ranking team members, order in this situation is important. The number of possible outcomes in the sample space is the number of permutations of 15 people taken 3 at a time, $_{15}P_3$.

$$_{15}P_3 = \frac{15!}{(15-3)!} = \frac{15 \cdot 14 \cdot 13 \cdot 12!}{12!} \text{ or } 2730$$

Step 2 The number of favorable outcomes is the number of permutations of the 3 students in their specific positions. This is 1!, or 1.

Step 3 So the probability of Sam, Valencia, and Deshane being selected as the three officers is $\frac{1}{2730}$.

GuidedPractice

2. A student identification card consists of 4 digits selected from 10 possible digits from 0 to 9. Digits cannot be repeated.

A. How many possible identification numbers are there? **5040**

B. Find the probability that a randomly generated card has the exact number 4213. $\frac{1}{5040}$

1 Probability Using Permutations

Examples 1–4 show how to use permutations to find the number of possible ways to order objects.

Formative Assessment

Use the Guided Practice exercises after each example to determine students' understanding of concepts.

Additional Examples

1 **TALENT SHOW** Eli and Mia, along with 30 other people, sign up to audition for a talent show. Contestants are called at random to perform for the judges. What is the probability that Eli will be called to perform first and Mia will be called second? $\frac{1}{870}$

2 There are 12 puppies for sale at the local pet shop. Four are brown, four are black, three are spotted, and one is white. What is the probability that all the brown puppies will be sold first? $\frac{1}{495}$

Additional Examples also in Interactive Classroom PowerPoint® Presentations

Teach with Tech

Portable Media Player Have students find the total number of songs on their portable media player and the number of songs for each genre of music. Ask students to find the probability that a randomly chosen song will be from a chosen genre.

Focus on Mathematical Content

Permutations When writing permutations as $_nP_r$, r indicates the number of factors in the permutation, and n represents the first factor. The notation $_6P_4$ indicates taking 4 factors beginning with 6, or $6 \cdot 5 \cdot 4 \cdot 3$. This is the same as using the formula and canceling. This notation is also sometimes written as $P(n, r)$.

CCSS Teaching the Mathematical Practices

Precision Mathematically proficient students use clear definitions in discussion with others and in their own reasoning. To help students understand permutations, have the class act out the situation in Example 2.

Additional Example

3 TILES A box of floor tiles contains 5 blue (bl) tiles, 2 gold (gd) tiles, and 2 green (gr) tiles in random order. The desired pattern is bl, gd, bl, gr, bl, gd, bl, gr, bl. If you selected a permutation of these tiles at random, what is the probability that they would be chosen in the correct sequence? $\frac{1}{756}$

Tips for New Teachers

Sense-Making Remind students to re-read the question they are asked to answer, and to check the reasonableness of their answer. For instance, in Example 3 students may calculate the number of permutations and write an answer of 34,650. If they re-read the problem, they will see that the question is asking for the probability of a specific permutation, or $\frac{1}{34,650}$.

In a game, you must try to create a word using randomly selected letter tiles. Suppose you select the tiles shown. If you consider the letters O and O to be distinct, then there are 5! or 120 permutations of these letters.

Four of these possible arrangements are listed below.

POOLS POOLS SPOOL SPOOL

Notice that unless the Os are colored, several of these arrangements would look the same. Since there are 2 Os that can be arranged in 2! or 2 ways, the number of permutations of the letters O, P, O, L, and S can be written as $\frac{5!}{2!}$.

KeyConcept Permutations with Repetition

The number of distinguishable permutations of n objects in which one object is repeated r_1 times, another is repeated r_2 times, and so on, is

$$\frac{n!}{r_1! \cdot r_2! \cdot \ldots \cdot r_k!}.$$

Real-WorldLink

Created in 1956, *The Price is Right* is the longest-running game show in the United States.

Source: IMDB

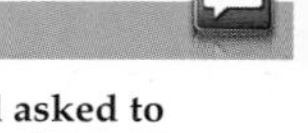

Example 3 Probability and Permutations with Repetition

GAME SHOW **On a game show, you are given the following letters and asked to unscramble them to name a U.S. river. If you selected a permutation of these letters at random, what is the probability that they would spell the correct answer of MISSISSIPPI?**

Step 1 There is a total of 11 letters. Of these letters, I occurs 4 times, S occurs 4 times, and P occurs 2 times. So, the number of distinguishable permutations of these letters is

$$\frac{11!}{4! \cdot 4! \cdot 2!} = \frac{39,916,800}{1152} \text{ or } 34,650.$$ Use a calculator.

Step 2 There is only 1 favorable arrangement—MISSISSIPPI.

Step 3 The probability that a permutation of these letters selected at random spells Mississippi is $\frac{1}{34,650}$.

GuidedPractice

3. **TELEPHONE NUMBERS** What is the probability that a 7-digit telephone number with the digits 5, 1, 6, 5, 2, 1, and 5 is the number 550-5211? $\frac{1}{420}$

So far, you have been studying objects that are arranged in *linear* order. Notice that when the spices below are arranged in a line, shifting each spice one position to the right produces a different permutation—curry is now first instead of salt. There are 5! distinct permutations of these spices.

924 | Lesson 13-2 | Probability with Permutations and Combinations

StudyTip

Turning the Circle Over If the circular object looks the same when it is turned over, such as a plain key ring, then the number of permutations must be divided by 2.

In a **circular permutation**, objects are arranged in a circle or loop. Consider the arrangements of these spices when placed on a turntable. Notice that rotating the turntable clockwise one position does *not* produce a different permutation—the order of the spices relative to each other remains unchanged.

Since 5 rotations of the turntable will produce the same permutation, the number of distinct permutations on the turntable is $\frac{1}{5}$ of the total number of arrangements when the spices are placed in a line.

$$\frac{1}{5} \cdot 5! = \frac{5 \cdot 4!}{5} \text{ or } 4!, \text{ which is } (5-1)!$$

KeyConcept Circular Permutations

The number of distinguishable permutations of n objects arranged in a circle with no fixed reference point is

$$\frac{n!}{n} \text{ or } (n-1)!.$$

If the n objects are arranged relative to a fixed reference point, then the arrangements are treated as linear, making the number of permutations $n!$.

Real-WorldCareer

Statisticians Statisticians collect statistical data for various subject areas, including sports and games. They use computer software to analyze, interpret, and summarize the data. Most statisticians have a master's degree.

PT

Example 4 Probability and Circular Permutations

Find the indicated probability. Explain your reasoning.

a. JEWELRY If the 6 charms on the bracelet shown are arranged at random, what is the probability that the arrangement shown is produced?

Since there is no fixed reference point, this is a circular permutation. So, there are $(6-1)!$ or $5!$ distinguishable permutations of the charms. Thus, the probability that the exact arrangement shown is produced is $\frac{1}{5!}$ or $\frac{1}{120}$.

b. DINING You are seating a party of 4 people at a round table. One of the chairs around this table is next to a window. If the diners are seated at random, what is the probability that the person paying the bill is seated next to the window?

Since the people are seated around a table with a fixed reference point, this is a linear permutation. So there are 4! or 24 ways in which the people can be seated around the table. The number of favorable outcomes is the number of permutations of the other 3 diners given that the person paying the bill sits next to the window, 3! or 6.

So, the probability that the person paying the bill is seated next to the window is $\frac{6}{24}$ or $\frac{1}{4}$.

Additional Example

4 Find the indicated probability. Explain your reasoning.

a. SEATING If 8 students sit at random in the circle of chairs shown, what is the probability that the students sit in the arrangement shown?

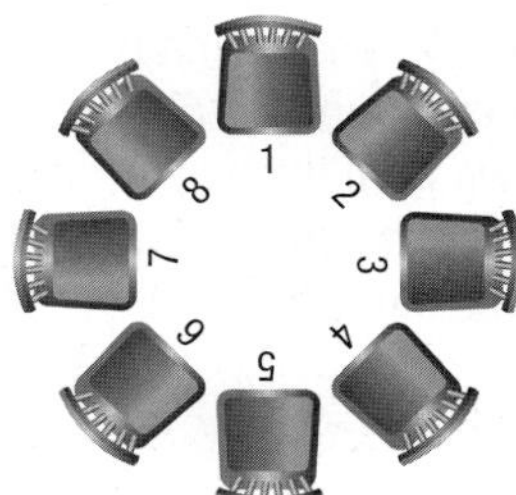

$\frac{1}{5040}$; Because there is no fixed reference point, this is a circular permutation.

b. You purchase a box of 8 crayons. If the crayons are packaged in random order, what is the probability that the crayon on the far left is red?

$\frac{1}{8}$; Because the crayons are in a row, this is a linear permutation.

DifferentiatedInstruction  

Visual/Spatial Learners Organize students in groups of three or four. Provide each group with a handful each of four different objects such as a variety of dry beans, color counters, or plastic beads. Have one group make as many unique combinations of two objects as possible. Have another group complete the same activity for permutations. Other groups can find combinations and permutations for groups of three or four objects. Have each group label a piece of paper and record all the different ways they arranged the objects. Allow groups to share their results with the class. Direct students to pay particular attention to the difference between the number of combinations and permutations made with the same number of objects.

2 Probability using Combinations

Example 5 shows how to find the number of ways a group of objects can be arranged when order is not important.

Additional Example

5 A set of alphabet magnets are placed in a bag. If 5 magnets are drawn from the bag at random, what is the probability that they will be the letters *a*, *e*, *i*, *o*, and *u*? $\frac{1}{65{,}780}$

Additional Answer (Guided Practice)

4A. $\frac{1}{10}$; Since there is no fixed reference point, this is a circular permutation. There are (11 − 1)! or 10! distinguishable permutations of the players. The number of favorable outcomes is the permutation of the other 9 players' positions in the huddle, or 9!. So, the probability that the fullback stands to the right of the quarterback is $\frac{9!}{10!}$ or $\frac{1}{10}$.

GuidedPractice

4. FOOTBALL A team's 11 football players huddle together before a play.

A. What is the probability that the fullback stands to the right of the quarterback if the team huddles together at random? Explain your reasoning. **See margin.**

B. If a referee stands directly behind the huddle, what is the probability that the referee stands directly behind the halfback? Explain your reasoning.

StudyTip

Permutations and Combinations Use permutations when the order of an arrangement of objects is important and combinations when order is not important.

4B. Since the players are huddled next to a fixed reference point, this is a linear permutation. There are 11! ways in which the players can be arranged in the huddle. The number of favorable outcomes is the number of permutations of the other 10 players given that the referee is standing behind the halfback, 10!. So, the probability that the referee stands behind the halfback is $\frac{10!}{11!}$ or $\frac{1}{11}$.

2 Probability Using Combinations

A **combination** is an arrangement of objects in which order is *not* important. Suppose you need to pack 3 of your 8 different pairs of socks for a trip. The order in which the socks are chosen does not matter, so the 3! or 6 groups of socks shown below would *not* be considered different. So, you would use combinations to determine the number of possible different sock choices.

A combination of n objects taken r at a time, or ${}_nC_r$, is calculated by dividing the number of permutations ${}_nP_r$ by the number of arrangements containing the same elements, $r!$.

KeyConcept Combinations

Symbols The number of combinations of n distinct objects taken r at a time is denoted by ${}_nC_r$ and is given by ${}_nC_r = \frac{n!}{(n-r)!\,r!}$.

Example The number of combinations of 8 objects taken 3 at a time is

$${}_8C_3 = \frac{8!}{(8-3)!\,3!} = \frac{8!}{5!3!} = \frac{8 \cdot 7 \cdot \cancel{6} \cdot \cancel{5!}}{\cancel{5!} \cdot \cancel{6}} \text{ or } 56.$$

Example 5 Probability and ${}_nC_r$

INVITATIONS For her birthday, Monica can invite 6 of her 20 friends to join her at a theme park. If she chooses to invite friends at random, what is the probability that friends Tessa, Guido, Brendan, Faith, Charlotte, and Rhianna are chosen?

Step 1 Since the order in which the friends are chosen does not matter, the number of possible outcomes in the sample space is the number of combinations of 20 people taken 6 at a time, ${}_{20}C_6$.

$${}_{20}C_6 = \frac{20!}{(20-6)!\,6!} = \frac{\cancel{20} \cdot 19 \cdot \cancel{18} \cdot 17 \cdot \overset{8}{\cancel{16}} \cdot 15 \cdot \cancel{14!}}{\cancel{14!} \cdot \cancel{6} \cdot \cancel{5} \cdot \cancel{4} \cdot \cancel{3} \cdot \cancel{2}} \text{ or } 38{,}760$$

Step 2 There is only 1 favorable outcome—that the six students listed above are chosen. The order in which they are chosen is not important.

Step 3 So the probability of these six friends being chosen is $\frac{1}{38{,}760}$.

GuidedPractice

5. GEOMETRY If three points are randomly chosen from those named on the rectangle shown, what is the probability that they all lie on the same line segment? $\frac{1}{14}$

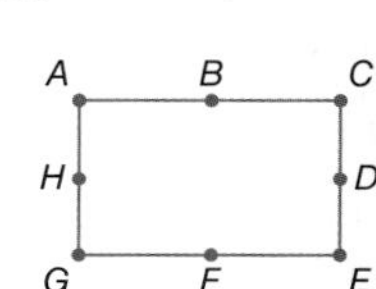

Check Your Understanding

= Step-by-Step Solutions begin on page R14.

Example 1

1. **GEOMETRY** Five students are asked to randomly select and name a polygon from the group shown below. What is the probability that the first two students choose the triangle and quadrilateral, in that order? $\frac{1}{20}$

   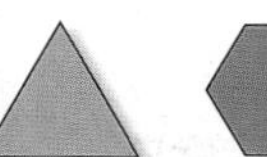

Example 2

2. **PLAYS** A high school performs a production of *A Raisin in the Sun* with each freshman English class of 18 students. If the three members of the crew are decided at random, what is the probability that Chase is selected for lighting, Jaden is selected for props, and Emelina for spotlighting? $\frac{1}{4896}$

Example 3

3. **DRIVING** What is the probability that a license plate using the letters C, F, and F and numbers 3, 3, 3, and 1 will be CFF3133? $\frac{1}{420}$

Example 4

4. **CHEMISTRY** In chemistry lab, you need to test six samples that are randomly arranged on a circular tray.

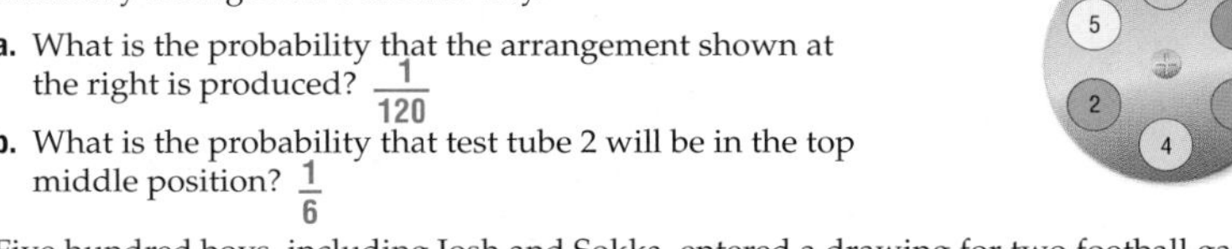

a. What is the probability that the arrangement shown at the right is produced? $\frac{1}{120}$

b. What is the probability that test tube 2 will be in the top middle position? $\frac{1}{6}$

Example 5

5. Five hundred boys, including Josh and Sokka, entered a drawing for two football game tickets. What is the probability that the tickets were won by Josh and Sokka? $\frac{1}{124,750}$

Practice and Problem Solving

Extra Practice is on page R13.

Example 1

6. **CONCERTS** Nia and Chad are going to a concert with their high school's key club. If they choose a seat on the row below at random, what is the probability that Chad will be in seat C11 and Nia will be in C12? $\frac{1}{132}$

7. **FAIRS** Alfonso and Colin each bought one raffle ticket at the state fair. If 50 tickets were randomly sold, what is the probability that Alfonso got ticket 14 and Colin got ticket 23? $\frac{1}{2450}$

Example 2

8. **CCSS MODELING** The table shows the finalists for a floor exercises competition. The order in which they will perform will be chosen randomly.

Floor Exercises Finalists
Eliza Hernandez
Kimi Kanazawa
Cecilia Long
Annie Montgomery
Shenice Malone
Caroline Smith
Jessica Watson

a. What is the probability that Cecilia, Annie, and Kimi are the first 3 gymnasts to perform, in any order? $\frac{1}{35}$

b. What is the probability that Cecilia is first, Annie is second, and Kimi is third? $\frac{1}{210}$

9. **JOBS** A store randomly assigns their employees work identification numbers to track productivity. Each number consists of 5 digits ranging from 1–9. If the digits cannot repeat, find the probability that a randomly generated number is 25938. $\frac{1}{15,120}$

10. **GROUPS** Two people are chosen randomly from a group of ten. What is the probability that Jimmy was selected first and George second? $\frac{1}{90}$

Differentiated Homework Options

Level	Assignment	Two-Day Option	
AL Basic	6–16, 23, 25–44	5–15 odd, 29–32	6–16 even, 23, 25–28, 33–44
OL Core	5–19 odd, 20–23, 25–44	6–16, 29–23	17–23, 25–28, 33–44
BL Advanced	17–38, (optional: 39–44)		

3 Practice

Formative Assessment

Use Exercises 1–5 to check for understanding.

Then use the chart at the bottom of this page to customize assignments for your students.

Teaching the Mathematical Practices

Modeling Mathematically proficient students can apply the mathematics they know to solve problems arising in everyday life. In Exercise 8, students will need to determine the number of favorable outcomes.

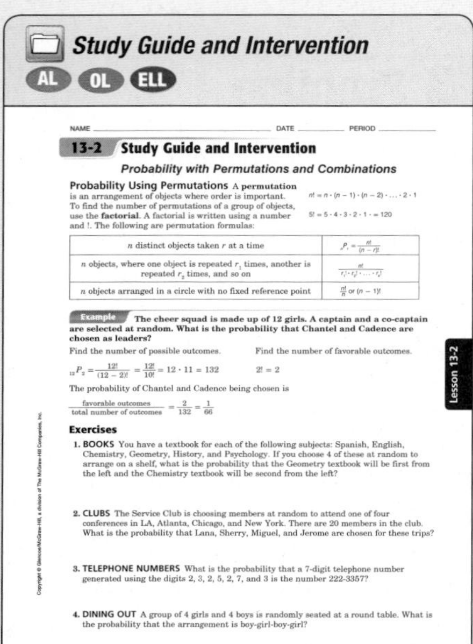

Study Guide and Intervention

AL OL ELL

NAME ______________ DATE ________ PERIOD ________

13-2 Study Guide and Intervention

Probability with Permutations and Combinations

Probability Using Permutations A **permutation** is an arrangement of objects where order is important. To find the number of permutations of a group of objects, use the **factorial**. A factorial is written using a number and !. The following are permutation formulas:

$n! = n \cdot (n-1) \cdot (n-2) \cdot \ldots \cdot 2 \cdot 1$

$5! = 5 \cdot 4 \cdot 3 \cdot 2 \cdot 1 \cdot = 120$

n distinct objects taken r at a time	${}_nP_r = \frac{n!}{(n-r)!}$
n objects, where one object is repeated r_1 times, another is repeated r_2 times, and so on	$\frac{n!}{r_1! \cdot r_2! \cdot \ldots \cdot r_k!}$
n objects arranged in a circle with no fixed reference point	$\frac{n!}{n}$ or $(n-1)!$

Example **The cheer squad is made up of 12 girls. A captain and a co-captain are selected at random. What is the probability that Chantel and Cadence are chosen as leaders?**

Find the number of possible outcomes. Find the number of favorable outcomes.

${}_{12}P_2 = \frac{12!}{(12-2)!} = \frac{12!}{10!} = 12 \cdot 11 = 132$ $\quad 2! = 2$

The probability of Chantel and Cadence being chosen is

$\frac{\text{favorable outcomes}}{\text{total number of outcomes}} = \frac{2}{132} = \frac{1}{66}$

Exercises

1. **BOOKS** You have a textbook for each of the following subjects: Spanish, English, Chemistry, Geometry, History, and Psychology. If you choose 4 of these at random to arrange on a shelf, what is the probability that the Geometry textbook will be first from the left and the Chemistry textbook will be second from the left?

2. **CLUBS** The Service Club is choosing members at random to attend one of four conferences in LA, Atlanta, Chicago, and New York. There are 20 members in the club. What is the probability that Lana, Sherry, Miguel, and Jerome are chosen for these trips?

3. **TELEPHONE NUMBERS** What is the probability that a 7-digit telephone number generated using the digits 2, 3, 2, 5, 2, 7, and 3 is the number 222-3357?

4. **DINING OUT** A group of 4 girls and 4 boys is randomly seated at a round table. What is the probability that the arrangement is boy-girl-boy-girl?

Lesson 13-2

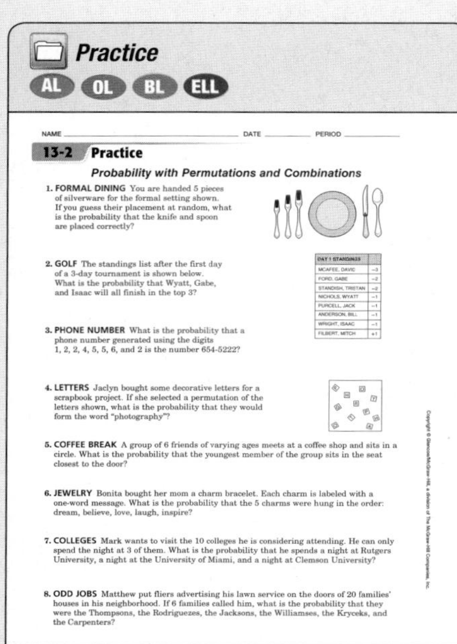

Practice

AL OL BL ELL

NAME ______________ DATE ________ PERIOD ________

13-2 Practice

Probability with Permutations and Combinations

1. **FORMAL DINING** You are handed 5 pieces of silverware for the formal setting shown. If you guess their placement at random, what is the probability that the knife and spoon are placed correctly?

2. **GOLF** The standings list after the first day of a 3-day tournament is shown below. What is the probability that Wyatt, Gabe, and Isaac will all finish in the top 3?

DAY 1 STANDINGS	
MCAFEE, DAVID	−3
FORD, GABE	−2
STANDISH, TRISTAN	−2
NICHOLS, WYATT	−1
PURCELL, JACK	−1
ANDERSON, BILL	−1
WRIGHT, ISAAC	−1
FILBERT, MITCH	+1

3. **PHONE NUMBER** What is the probability that a phone number generated using the digits 1, 2, 2, 4, 5, 5, 6, and 2 is the number 654-5222?

4. **LETTERS** Jaclyn bought some decorative letters for a scrapbook project. If she selected a permutation of the letters shown, what is the probability that they would form the word "photography"?

5. **COFFEE BREAK** A group of 6 friends of varying ages meets at a coffee shop and sits in a circle. What is the probability that the youngest member of the group sits in the seat closest to the door?

6. **JEWELRY** Bonita bought her mom a charm bracelet. Each charm is labeled with a one-word message. What is the probability that the 5 charms were hung in the order: dream, believe, love, laugh, inspire?

7. **COLLEGES** Mark wants to visit the 10 colleges he is considering attending. He can only spend the night at 3 of them. What is the probability that he spends a night at Rutgers University, a night at the University of Miami, and a night at Clemson University?

8. **ODD JOBS** Matthew put fliers advertising his lawn service on the doors of 20 families' houses in his neighborhood. If 6 families called him, what is the probability that they were the Thompsons, the Rodriguezes, the Jacksons, the Williamses, the Kryceks, and the Carpenters?

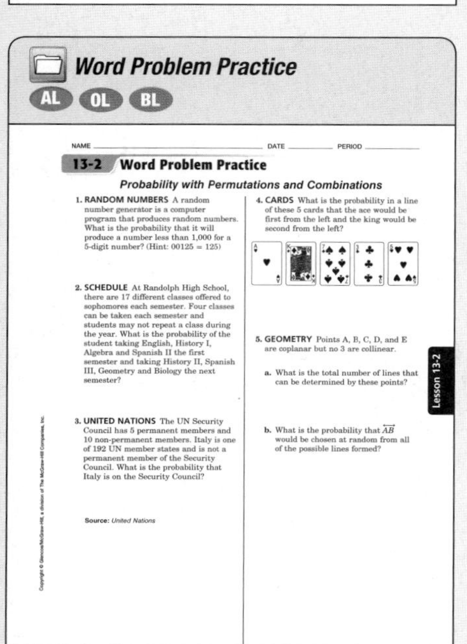

Word Problem Practice

AL OL BL

NAME ______________ DATE ________ PERIOD ________

13-2 Word Problem Practice

Probability with Permutations and Combinations

1. **RANDOM NUMBERS** A random number generator is a computer program that produces random numbers. What is the probability that it will produce a number less than 1,000 for a 5-digit number? (Hint: 00125 = 125)

2. **SCHEDULE** At Randolph High School, there are 17 different classes offered to sophomores each semester. Four classes can be taken each semester and students may not repeat a class during the year. What is the probability of the student taking English, History I, Algebra and Spanish II the first semester and taking History II, Spanish III, Geometry and Biology the next semester?

3. **UNITED NATIONS** The UN Security Council has 5 permanent members and 10 non-permanent members. Italy is one of 192 UN member states and is not a permanent member of the Security Council. What is the probability that Italy is on the Security Council?

Source: *United Nations*

4. **CARDS** What is the probability in a line of these 5 cards that the ace would be first from the left and the king would be second from the left?

5. **GEOMETRY** Points A, B, C, D, and E are coplanar but no 3 are collinear.

   a. What is the total number of lines that can be determined by these points?

   b. What is the probability that $\overleftrightarrow{AB}$ would be chosen at random from all of the possible lines formed?

Lesson 13-2

Example 3

11. **MAGNETS** Santiago bought some letter magnets that he can arrange to form words on his fridge. If he randomly selected a permutation of the letters shown below, what is the probability that they would form the word BASKETBALL? $\frac{1}{453{,}600}$

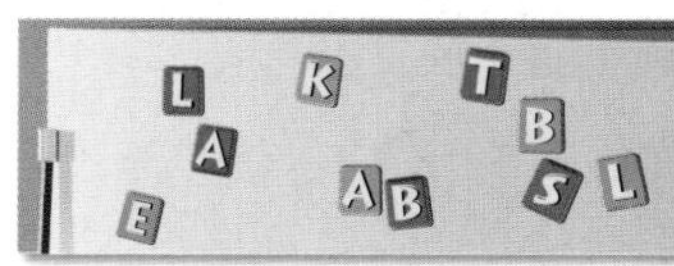

12. **ZIP CODES** What is the probability that a zip code randomly generated from among the digits 3, 7, 3, 9, 5, 7, 2, and 3 is the number 39372? $\frac{1}{3360}$

Example 4

13. **GROUPS** Keith is randomly arranging desks into circles for group activities. If there are 7 desks in his circle, what is the probability that Keith will be in the desk closest to the door? $\frac{1}{7}$

14. **AMUSEMENT PARKS** Sylvie is at an amusement park with her friends. They go on a ride that has bucket seats in a circle. If there are 8 seats, what is the probability that Sylvie will be in the seat farthest from the entrance to the ride? $\frac{1}{8}$

Example 5

15. **PHOTOGRAPHY** If you are randomly placing 24 photos in a photo album and you can place four photos on the first page, what is the probability that you choose the photos at the right? $\frac{1}{10{,}626}$

16. **ROAD TRIPS** Rita is going on a road trip across the U.S. She needs to choose from 15 cities where she will stay for one night. If she randomly pulls 3 city brochures from a pile of 15, what is the probability that she chooses Austin, Cheyenne, and Savannah? $\frac{1}{455}$

B 17. **CCSS SENSE-MAKING** Use the figure below. Assume that the balls are aligned at random.

a. What is the probability that in a row of 8 pool balls, the solid 2 and striped 11 would be first and second from the left? $\frac{1}{56}$

b. What is the probability that if the 8 pool balls were mixed up at random, they would end up in the order shown? $\frac{1}{40{,}320}$

c. What is the probability that in a row of seven balls, with three 8 balls, three 9 balls, and one 6 ball, the three 8 balls would be to the left of the 6 ball and the three 9 balls would be on the right? $\frac{1}{140}$

d. If the balls were randomly rearranged and formed a circle, what is the probability that the 6 ball is next to the 7 ball? $\frac{2}{7}$

18. How many lines are determined by 10 randomly selected points, no 3 of which are collinear? Explain your calculation. **45; Sample answer: The number of lines is the combination of 10 objects taken 2 at a time, which is $\frac{10!}{8!2!}$ or 45.**

19. Suppose 7 points on a circle are chosen at random, as shown at the right.

a. Using the letters A through E, how many ways can the points on the circle be named? **720**

b. If one point on the circle is fixed, how many arrangements are possible? **5040**

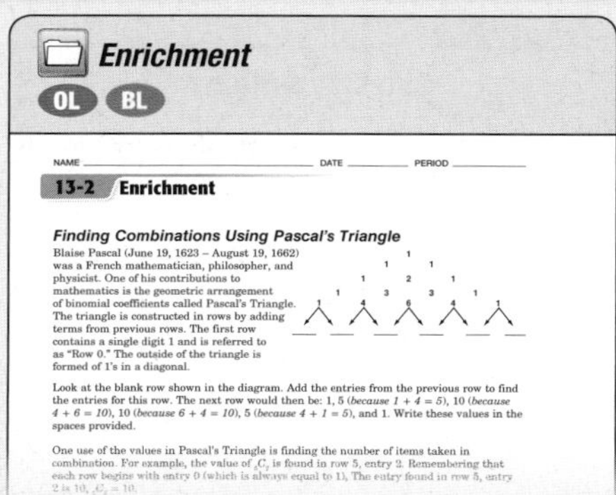

Enrichment

OL BL

NAME ______________ DATE ________ PERIOD ________

13-2 Enrichment

Finding Combinations Using Pascal's Triangle

Blaise Pascal (June 19, 1623 – August 19, 1662) was a French mathematician, philosopher, and physicist. One of his contributions to mathematics is the geometric arrangement of binomial coefficients called Pascal's Triangle. The triangle is constructed in rows by adding terms from previous rows. The first row contains a single digit 1 and is referred to as "Row 0." The outside of the triangle is formed of 1's in a diagonal.

1
1 1
1 2 1
1 3 3 1
1 4 6 4 1
__ __ __ __ __ __

Look at the blank row shown in the diagram. Add the entries from the previous row to find the entries for this row. The next row would then be: 1, 5 (*because 1 + 4 = 5*), 10 (*because 4 + 6 = 10*), 10 (*because 6 + 4 = 10*), 5 (*because 4 + 1 = 5*), and 1. Write these values in the spaces provided.

One use of the values in Pascal's Triangle is finding the number of items taken in combination. For example, the value of ${}_5C_2$ is found in row 5, entry 2. Remembering that each row begins with entry 0 (which is always equal to 1), The entry found in row 5, entry 2 is 10, ${}_5C_2 = 10$.

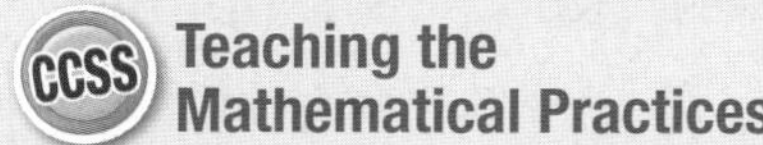

Teaching the Mathematical Practices

Sense-Making Mathematically proficient students start by explaining the meaning of a problem to themselves and looking for entry points to its solution. In Exercise 17, encourage students to determine whether order is important or not.

928 | Lesson 13-2 | Probability with Permutations and Combinations

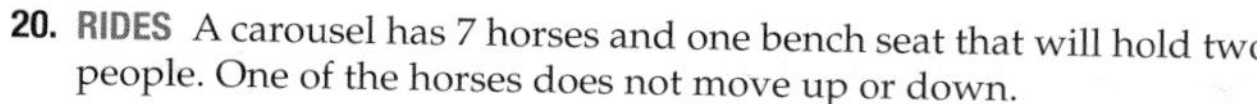

20. RIDES A carousel has 7 horses and one bench seat that will hold two people. One of the horses does not move up or down.

a. How many ways can the seats on the carousel be randomly filled by 9 people? **362,880**

b. If the carousel is filled randomly, what is the probability that you and your friend will end up in the bench seat? $\frac{1}{36}$

c. If 6 of the 9 people randomly filling the carousel are under the age of 8, what is the probability that a person under the age of 8 will end up on the horse that does not move up or down? $\frac{2}{3}$

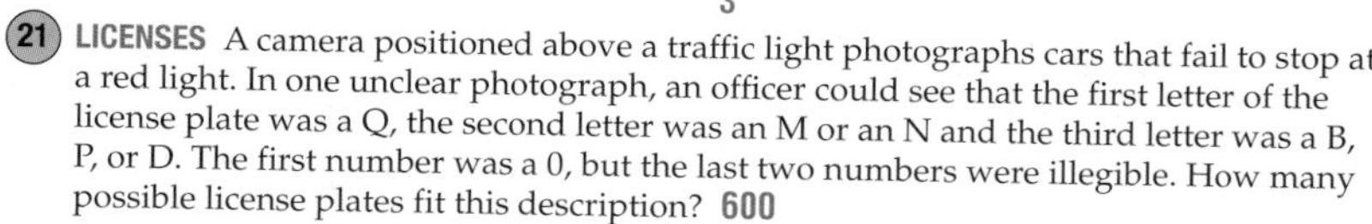

21. LICENSES A camera positioned above a traffic light photographs cars that fail to stop at a red light. In one unclear photograph, an officer could see that the first letter of the license plate was a Q, the second letter was an M or an N and the third letter was a B, P, or D. The first number was a 0, but the last two numbers were illegible. How many possible license plates fit this description? **600**

22. MULTIPLE REPRESENTATIONS In this problem, you will investigate permutations.

22a. Sample answer: 1, 4, 7; permutations 147, 174, 417, 471, 714, 741.
22c. Sample answer: The average of the permutations of three digits between 0 and 9 is the sum of the digits multiplied by 37.

a. **Numerical** Randomly select three digits from 0 to 9. Find the possible permutations of the three integers.

b. **Tabular** Repeat part **a** for four additional sets of three integers. You will use some digits more than once. Copy and complete the table below. **Sample answer:**

Integers	Permutations	Average of Permutations	Average of Permutations / 37
1, 4, 7	147, 174, 417, 471, 714, 741	444	12
2, 3, 5	235, 253, 325, 352, 523, 532	370	10
6, 8, 9	689, 698, 869, 896, 968, 986	851	23
1, 3, 5	135, 153, 315, 351, 513, 531	333	9
0, 4, 6	046, 064, 406, 460, 604, 640	370	10

c. **Verbal** Make a conjecture about the value of the average of the permutations of three digits between 0 and 9.

d. **Symbolic** If the three digits are x, y, and z, is it possible to write an equation for the average A of the permutations of the digits? If so, write the equation. If not, explain why not. **yes; $A = 37(x + y + z)$**

H.O.T. Problems Use Higher-Order Thinking Skills

23. CHALLENGE Fifteen boys and fifteen girls entered a drawing for four free movie tickets. What is the probability that all four tickets were won by girls? $\frac{13}{261}$

24. CHALLENGE A student claimed that permutations and combinations were related by $r! \cdot {}_nC_r = {}_nP_r$. Use algebra to show that this is true. Then explain why ${}_nC_r$ and ${}_nP_r$ differ by the factor $r!$. **See margin.**

25. OPEN ENDED Describe a situation in which the probability is given by $\frac{1}{{}_7C_3}$. **See margin.**

26. ARGUMENTS Is the following statement *sometimes*, *always*, or *never* true? Explain.

$${}_nP_r = {}_nC_r$$

Sometimes; sample answer: The statement is true when r is 1.

27. PROOF Prove that ${}_nC_{n-r} = {}_nC_r$. **See margin.**

28. WRITING IN MATH Compare and contrast permutations and combinations. **See margin.**

Differentiated Instruction OL BL

Extension Have students write about how understanding and applying the principles of probability might influence their decision making in some situations. Encourage students to use specific and detailed examples of situations that support their thought processes.

Multiple Representations

In Exercise 22, students use computations, a table, verbal descriptions, and symbolic representations to investigate permutations.

Teaching the Mathematical Practices

Arguments Mathematically proficient students understand and use stated assumptions and definitions in constructing arguments. They make conjectures and build a logical progression of statements to explore the truth of their conjectures. In Exercise 26, encourage students to analyze the equation for various values of r.

Additional Answers

24. Sample answer:

$$r! \cdot {}_nC_r = r! \cdot \frac{n!}{(n-r)!r!} = \frac{n!r!}{(n-r)!r!} = \frac{n!}{(n-r)!} = {}_nP_r$$

${}_nC_r$ and ${}_nP_r$ differ by the factor $r!$ because there are always $r!$ ways to order the groups that are selected. Therefore, there are $r!$ permutations of each combination.

25. Sample answer: A bag contains seven marbles that are red, orange, yellow, green, blue, purple, and black. The probability that the orange, blue, and black marbles will be chosen if three marbles are drawn at random can be calculated using a combination.

27.

$$C(n, n-r) \stackrel{?}{=} C(n, r)$$
$$\frac{n!}{[n-(n-r)]!(n-r)!} \stackrel{?}{=} \frac{n!}{(n-r)!r!}$$
$$\frac{n!}{r!(n-r)!} \stackrel{?}{=} \frac{n!}{(n-r)!r!}$$
$$\frac{n!}{(n-r)!r!} = \frac{n!}{(n-r)!r!} \checkmark$$

28. Sample answer: Both permutations and combinations are used to find the number of possible arrangements of a group of objects. The order of the objects is important in permutations, but not in combinations.

4 Assess

Name the Math Give students a probability scenario. Have them write the formula they would use to find the probability and state why the formula they chose is the most appropriate for the scenario given. Have students turn in their papers before they leave the classroom.

Formative Assessment

Check for student understanding of Lessons 13-1 and 13-2.

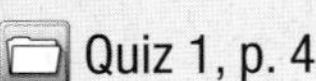 Quiz 1, p. 45

Standardized Test Practice

29. PROBABILITY Four members of the pep band, two girls and two boys, always stand in a row when they play. What is the probability that a girl will be at each end of the row if they line up in random order? **C**

A $\frac{1}{24}$ C $\frac{1}{6}$

B $\frac{1}{12}$ D $\frac{1}{2}$

30. SHORT RESPONSE If you randomly select a permutation of the letters shown below, what is the probability that they would spell GEOMETRY? $\frac{1}{20,160}$

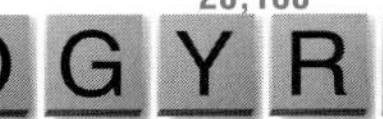

31. ALGEBRA Student Council sells soft drinks at basketball games and makes $1.50 from each. If they pay $75 to rent the concession stand, how many soft drinks would they have to sell to make $250 profit? **J**

F 116 H 167

G 117 J 217

32. SAT/ACT The ratio of 12:9 is equal to the ratio of $\frac{1}{3}$ to **A**

A $\frac{1}{4}$ D 2

B 1 E 4

C $\frac{5}{4}$

Spiral Review

33. SHOPPING A women's coat comes in sizes 4, 6, 8, or 10 in black, brown, ivory, and cinnamon. How many different coats could be selected? (Lesson 13-1) **16**

34. Two similar prisms have surface areas of 256 square inches and 324 square inches. What is the ratio of the height of the small prism to the height of the large prism? (Lesson 12-8) **8:9**

Find x. Round to the nearest tenth, if necessary. (Lesson 10-7)

35. **2**

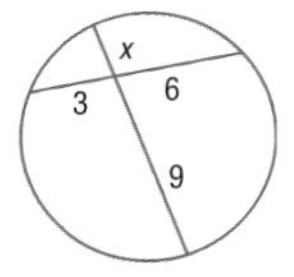

36. **3.2**

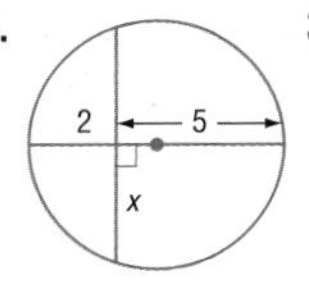

37. **4.5**

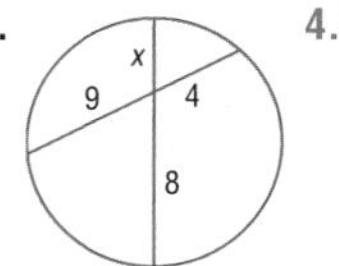

38. CHESS The bishop shown in square f8 can only move diagonally along dark squares. If the bishop is in c1 after two moves, describe the translation. (Lesson 9-2) **left 3 squares and down 7 squares**

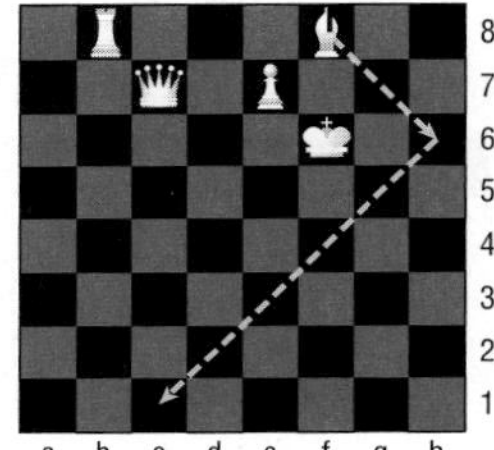

Skills Review

Use the number line to find each measure.

39. DF **3**

40. AE **10**

41. EF **1**

42. BD **6**

43. AC **5**

44. CF **6**

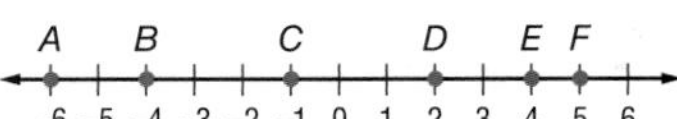

LESSON 13-3 Geometric Probability

Then	Now	Why?
You found probabilities of simple events.	1 Find probabilities by using length. 2 Find probabilities by using area.	The object of the popular carnival game shown is to collect points by rolling a ball up an incline and into one of several circular target areas. The point value of each area is assigned based on the probability of a person landing a ball in that area.

NewVocabulary
geometric probability

Common Core State Standards

Content Standards
S.MD.7 (+) Analyze decisions and strategies using probability concepts (e.g., product testing, medical testing, pulling a hockey goalie at the end of a game).

Mathematical Practices
1 Make sense of problems and persevere in solving them.
2 Reason abstractly and quantitatively.

1 Probability with Length The probability of winning the carnival game depends on the area of the target. Probability that involves a geometric measure such as length or area is called **geometric probability**.

KeyConcept Length Probability Ratio

Words If a line segment (1) contains another segment (2) and a point on segment (1) is chosen at random, then the probability that the point is on segment (2) is

$$\frac{\text{length of segment (2)}}{\text{length of segment (1)}}.$$

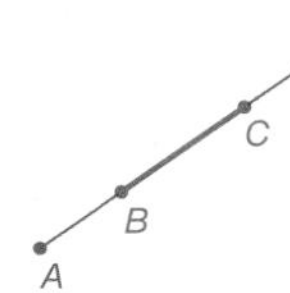

Example If a point E on $\overline{AD}$ is chosen at random, then $P(E \text{ is on } \overline{BC}) = \frac{BC}{AD}$.

Example 1 Use Lengths to Find Geometric Probability

Point X is chosen at random on $\overline{JM}$. Find the probability that X is on $\overline{KL}$.

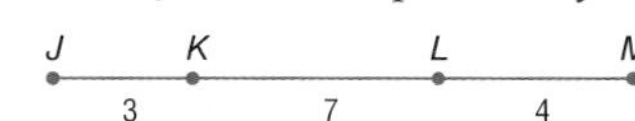

$P(X \text{ is on } \overline{KL}) = \frac{KL}{JM}$ — Length probability ratio

$= \frac{7}{14}$ — $KL = 7$ and $JM = 3 + 7 + 4$ or 14

$= \frac{1}{2}$, 0.5, or 50% — Simplify.

GuidedPractice **1A.** $\frac{2}{7}$, about 0.29, or about 29% **1B.** $\frac{11}{14}$, about 0.79, or about 79%

Point X is chosen at random on $\overline{JM}$. Find the probability of each event.

1A. $P(X \text{ is on } \overline{LM})$ **1B.** $P(X \text{ is on } \overline{KM})$

Geometric probability can be used in many real-world situations that involve an infinite number of outcomes.

1 Focus

VerticalAlignment

Before Lesson 13-3 Find probabilities of simple events.

Lesson 13-3 Find probabilities by using length.Find probabilities by using area.

After Lesson 13-3 Design simulations to estimate probabilities and summarize the data.

2 Teach

Scaffolding Questions

Have students read the **Why?** section of the lesson.

Ask:

- Which circular target area would it be easiest for the ball to land in? the outermost circle
- Which area would it be hardest for the ball to land in? one of the center circles
- What other factors affect the outcome of the game? Sample answer: the weight, speed, and composition of the ball

Lesson 13-3 Resources

Resource	Approaching Level AL	On Level OL	Beyond Level BL	English Learners ELL
Teacher Edition	■ Differentiated Instruction, p. 932	■ Differentiated Instruction, pp. 932, 936	■ Differentiated Instruction, pp. 932, 936	
Chapter Resource Masters	■ Study Guide and Intervention, pp. 17–18 ■ Skills Practice, p. 19 ■ Practice, p. 20 ■ Word Problem Practice, p. 21	■ Study Guide and Intervention, pp. 17–18 ■ Skills Practice, p. 19 ■ Practice, p. 20 ■ Word Problem Practice, p. 21 ■ Enrichment, p. 22 ■ Spreadsheet Activity, p. 23	■ Practice, p. 20 ■ Word Problem Practice, p. 21 ■ Enrichment, p. 22	■ Study Guide and Intervention, pp. 17–18 ■ Skills Practice, p. 19 ■ Practice, p. 20 ■ Word Problem Practice, p. 21
Other	■ 5-Minute Check 13-3 ■ Study Notebook	■ 5-Minute Check 13-3 ■ Study Notebook	■ 5-Minute Check 13-3 ■ Study Notebook	■ 5-Minute Check 13-3 ■ Study Notebook

1 Probability with Length

Examples 1 and 2 show how to find the probability of events involving length.

Formative Assessment

Use the Guided Practice exercises after each example to determine students' understanding of concepts.

Additional Examples

1 Point Z is chosen at random on $\overline{AD}$. Find the probability that Z is on $\overline{AB}$.

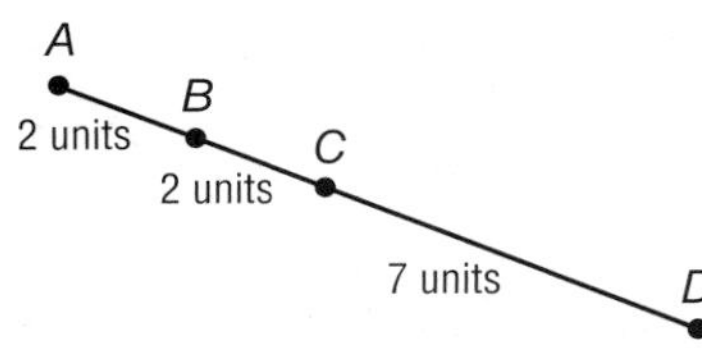

$\frac{2}{11}$, approximately 0.18, or approximately 18%

2 **ORBITS** Halley's Comet orbits the earth every 76 years. What is the probability that Halley's Comet will complete an orbit within the next decade?

$\frac{5}{38}$, approximately 0.13, or approximately 13%

Additional Examples also in Interactive Classroom PowerPoint® Presentations

WatchOut!

Intervals Remind students that the interval of the probability being considered is not necessarily equal to the entire interval of the event. Caution students to use only the units equal to the interval being considered.

Real-WorldLink

A Chicago Transit Authority train arrives or departs a station like Addison on the Red Line every 15 minutes.

Source: Chicago Transit Authority

Real-World Example 2 Model Real-World Probabilities

TRANSPORTATION **Use the information at the left. Assuming that you arrive at Addison on the Red Line at a random time, what is the probability that you will have to wait 5 or more minutes for a train?**

We can use a number line to model this situation. Since the trains arrive every 15 minutes, the next train will arrive in 15 minutes or less. On the number line below, the event of waiting 5 or more minutes is modeled by $\overline{BD}$.

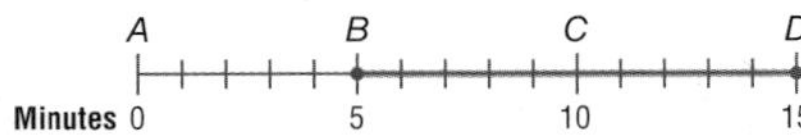

Find the probability of this event.

$P(\text{waiting 5 or more minutes}) = \frac{BD}{AD}$ Length probability ratio

$= \frac{10}{15}$ or $\frac{2}{3}$ $BD = 10$ and $AD = 15$

So, the probability of waiting 5 or more minutes for the next train is $\frac{2}{3}$ or about 67%.

GuidedPractice

2. **TEA** Iced tea at a cafeteria-style restaurant is made in 8-gallon containers. Once the level gets below 2 gallons, the flavor of the tea becomes weak.

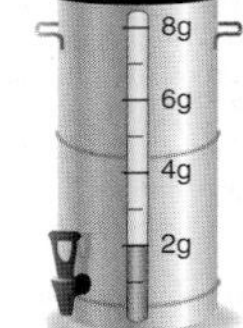

A. What is the probability that when someone tries to pour a glass of tea from the container, it is below 2 gallons? $\frac{1}{4}$ **or 25%**

B. What is the probability that the amount of tea in the container at any time is between 2 and 3 gallons? $\frac{1}{8}$ **or 12.5%**

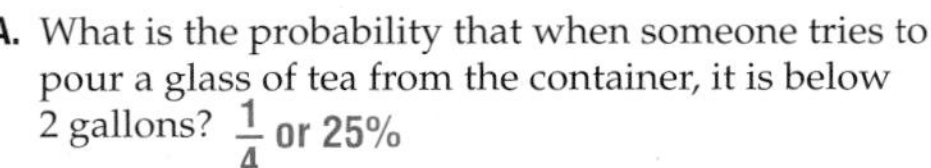

2 Probability with Area

Geometric probability can also involve area. The ratio for calculating geometric probability involving area is shown below.

KeyConcept Area Probability Ratio

Words If a region A contains a region B and a point E in region A is chosen at random, then the probability that point E is in region B is $\frac{\text{area of region } B}{\text{area of region } A}$.

Example If a point E is chosen at random in rectangle A, then $P(\text{point } E \text{ is in circle } B) = \frac{\text{area of region } B}{\text{area of region } A}$.

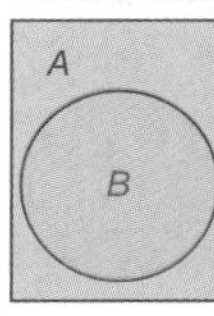

When determining geometric probabilities with targets, we assume

- that the object lands within the target area, and
- it is equally likely that the object will land anywhere in the region.

DifferentiatedInstruction AL OL BL

Logical Learners Have students model simple sample spaces by using geometric probabilities. Each event can be represented by a line segment whose length is proportional to the probability of the event. For example, flipping a coin can be represented by two lines of equal length, and the probability that a point is on either segment is 50%.

Real-WorldLink

Champion accuracy skydivers routinely land less than two inches away from the center of a target.

Source: *SkyDiving News*

Real-World Example 3 Use Area to Find Geometric Probability

SKYDIVING Suppose a skydiver must land on a target of three concentric circles. If the diameter of the center circle is 2 yards and the circles are spaced 1 yard apart, what is the probability that the skydiver will land in the red circle?

You need to find the ratio of the area of the red circle to the area of the entire target. The radius of the red circle is 1 yard, while the radius of the entire target is 1 + 1 + 1 or 3 yards.

$P(\text{skydiver lands in red circle}) = \dfrac{\text{area of red circle}}{\text{area of target}}$ — Area probability ratio

$= \dfrac{\pi(1)^2}{\pi(3)^2}$ — $A = \pi r^2$

$= \dfrac{\pi}{9\pi}$ or $\dfrac{1}{9}$ — Simplify.

The probability that the skydiver will land in the red circle is $\frac{1}{9}$ or about 11%.

GuidedPractice

3. **SKYDIVING** Find each probability using the example above.

A. P(skydiver lands in the blue region) $\frac{5}{9}$ **or about 56%**

B. P(skydiver lands in white region) $\frac{1}{3}$ **or about 33%**

You can also use an angle measure to find geometric probability. The ratio of the area of a sector of a circle to the area of the entire circle is the same as the ratio of the sector's central angle to 360. You will prove this in Exercise 27.

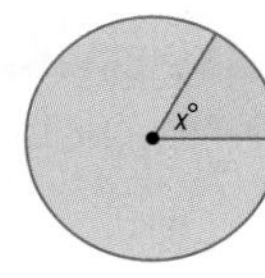

StudyTip

Use Estimation In Example 4b, the area of the purple sector is a little less than $\frac{1}{3}$ or 33% of the spinner. Therefore, an answer of 29% is reasonable.

Example 4 Use Angle Measures to Find Geometric Probability

Use the spinner to find each probability.

105°
45°
70°
50°
90°

a. P(pointer landing on yellow)

The angle measure of the yellow region is 45.

$P(\text{pointer landing on yellow}) = \dfrac{45}{360}$ or 12.5%

b. P(pointer landing on purple)

The angle measure of the purple region is 105.

$P(\text{pointer landing on purple}) = \dfrac{105}{360}$ or about 29%

c. P(pointer landing on neither red nor blue)

The combined angle measures of the red and blue region are 50 + 70 or 120.

$P(\text{pointer landing on neither red nor blue}) = \dfrac{360 - 120}{360}$ or about 67%

GuidedPractice

4A. P(pointer landing on blue) **4B.** P(pointer not landing on green)

4A. $\frac{7}{36}$ or about 19%

4B. $\frac{3}{4}$ or 75%

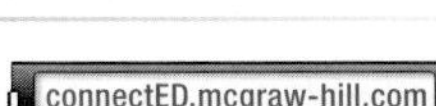

2 Probability with Area

Examples 3 and 4 show how to find the probability of events involving area.

Teach with Tech

Document Camera Use different colored objects to represent the areas of various regions within a figure. Have students model several problems involving area and geometric probability.

Additional Examples

3 **DARTS** The targets of a dartboard are formed by 3 concentric circles. If the diameter of the center circle is 4 inches and the circles are spread 3 inches apart, what is the probability that a player will throw a dart into the center circle? $\frac{1}{16}$ or approximately 6%

4 Use the spinner to find each probability.

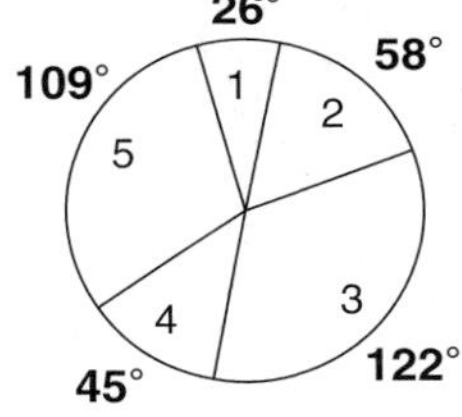

a. P(Pointer landing on section 3) $\frac{122}{360}$ or approximately 34%

b. P(Pointer landing on section 1) $\frac{26}{360}$ or approximately 7%

Focus on Mathematical Content

Area Remember that when comparing the area of similar figures, the ratio of the areas is the square of the ratio of the sides, as in Lesson 11-5.

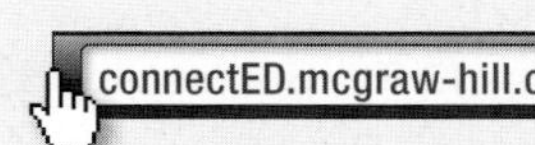

3 Practice

Formative Assessment

Use Exercises 1–5 to check for understanding.

Then use the chart at the bottom of this page to customize assignments for your students.

Teaching the Mathematical Practices

Reasoning Mathematically proficient students make sense of quantities and their relationships in problem situations. In Exercises 6–9 encourage students to draw a diagram for each exercise.

Additional Answer

27. Sample answer: The probability that a randomly chosen point will lie in the shaded region is the ratio of the area of the sector to the area of the circle.

$P(\text{point lies in sector})$

$= \dfrac{\text{area of sector}}{\text{area of circle}}$

$\dfrac{x}{360} \stackrel{?}{=} \dfrac{\frac{x}{360} \cdot \pi r^2}{\pi r^2}$

$\dfrac{x}{360} = \dfrac{x}{360}$ ✓

Check Your Understanding

= Step-by-Step Solutions begin on page R14.

Example 1 **Point X is chosen at random on $\overline{AD}$. Find the probability of each event.**

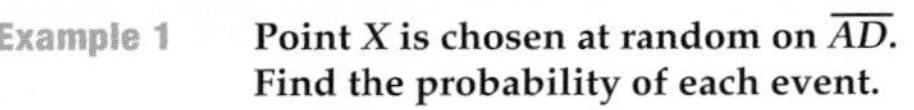

1. $P(X \text{ is on } \overline{BD})$ $\frac{1}{2}$, 0.5, or 50%

2. $P(X \text{ is on } \overline{BC})$ $\frac{3}{10}$, 0.3, or 30%

Example 2

3. **CARDS** In a game of cards, 43 cards are used, including one joker. Four players are each dealt 10 cards and the rest are put in a pile. If Greg doesn't have the joker, what is the probability that either his partner or the pile have the joker? $\frac{13}{33}$, 0.39, or about 39%

Examples 3–4

4. **ARCHERY** An archer aims at a target that is 122 centimeters in diameter with 10 concentric circles whose diameters decrease by 12.2 centimeters as they get closer to the center. Find the probability that the archer will hit the center. $\frac{1}{100}$, 0.01, or 1%

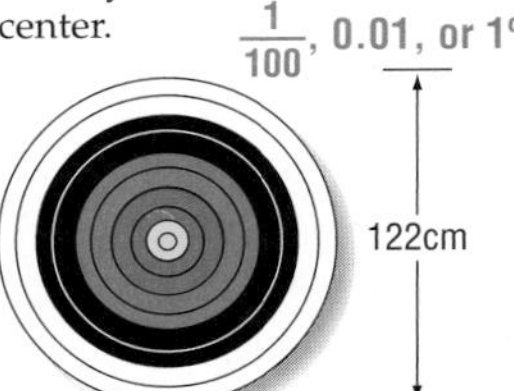

5. **NAVIGATION** A camper lost in the woods points his compass in a random direction. Find the probability that the camper is heading in the N to NE direction. $\frac{1}{8}$, 0.125, or 12.5%

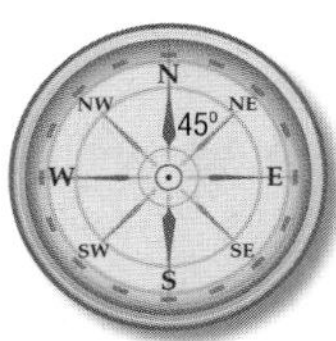

Practice and Problem Solving

Extra Practice is on page R13.

Example 1 CCSS **REASONING** **Point X is chosen at random on $\overline{FK}$. Find the probability of each event.**

F G H J K — 4, 12, 14, 6

6. $P(X \text{ is on } \overline{FH})$

7. $P(X \text{ is on } \overline{GJ})$

8. $P(X \text{ is on } \overline{HK})$

9. $P(X \text{ is on } \overline{FG})$

6. $\frac{4}{9}$, 0.44, or 44%
7. $\frac{13}{18}$, 0.72, or 72%
8. $\frac{5}{9}$, 0.56, or 56%
9. $\frac{1}{9}$, 0.11, or 11%

10. **BIRDS** Four birds are sitting on a telephone wire. What is the probability that a fifth bird landing at a randomly selected point between birds 1 and 4 will sit at some point between birds 3 and 4? $\frac{1}{3}$, 0.33, or 33%

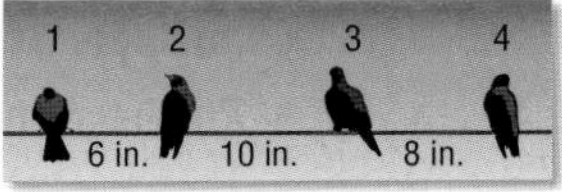

Example 2

11. **TELEVISION** Julio is watching television and sees an ad for a CD that he knows his friend wants for her birthday. If the ad replays at a random time in each 3-hour interval, what is the probability that he will see the ad again during his favorite 30-minute sitcom the next day? $\frac{1}{6}$, 0.17, or about 17%

Example 3 **Find the probability that a point chosen at random lies in the shaded region. Assume that figures that seem to be regular and congruent are regular and congruent.**

12. 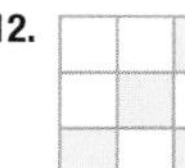 $\frac{3}{8}$, 0.375, or 37.5%

13. 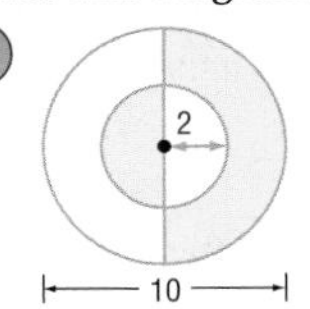

$\frac{1}{2}$, 0.5, or 50%

14. 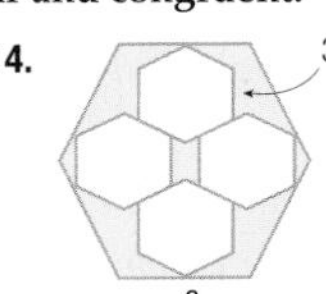

$\frac{7}{16}$, 0.4375, or 43.75%

Differentiated Homework Options

Level	Assignment	Two-Day Option	
AL Basic	6–22, 34, 36–53	7–21 odd, 40–43	6–22 even, 34, 36–39, 44–53
OL Core	7–25 odd, 26, 27–33 odd, 34, 36–53	6–22, 40–43	23–34, 36–39, 44–53
BL Advanced	23–50, (optional: 51–53)		

Example 4 **Use the spinner to find each probability. If the spinner lands on a line it is spun again.**

15. P(pointer landing on yellow) 12.2%
16. P(pointer landing on blue) 23.3%
17. P(pointer not landing on green) 69.4%
18. P(pointer landing on red) 25.6%
19. P(pointer landing on neither red nor yellow) 62.2%

Describe an event with a 33% probability for each model.

20. 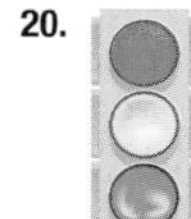
Sample answer: getting a red light

21. 10 20 30 40
Sample answer: a point between 10 and 20

22. 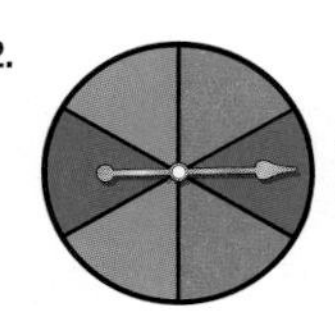
Sample answer: landing on green

Find the probability that a point chosen at random lies in the shaded region.

23. 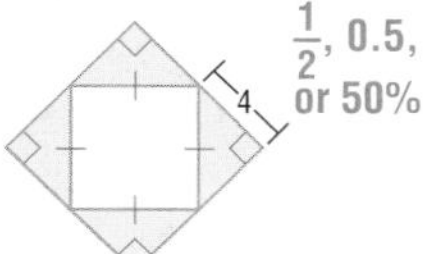

$\frac{1}{2}$, 0.5, or 50%

24. 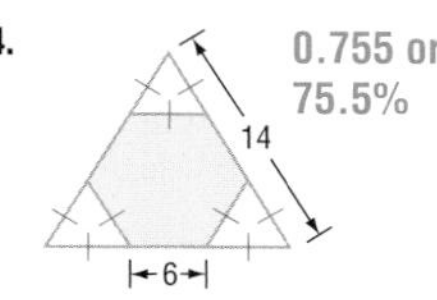

0.755 or 75.5%

25. 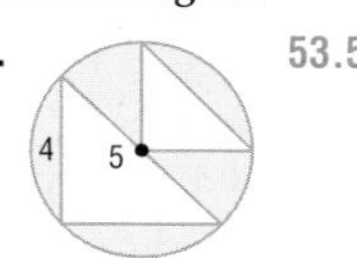

53.5%

26. **FARMING** The layout for a farm is shown with each square representing a plot. Estimate the area of each field to answer each question.

a. What is the approximate combined area of the spinach and corn fields? 67 square units

b. Find the probability that a randomly chosen plot is used to grow soybeans. 0.16 or 16%

27. **ALGEBRA** Prove that the probability that a randomly chosen point in the circle will lie in the shaded region is equal to $\frac{x}{360}$. See margin.

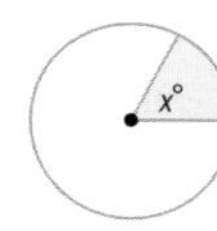

28. **COORDINATE GEOMETRY** If a point is chosen at random in the coordinate grid shown at the right, find each probability. Round to the nearest hundredth.

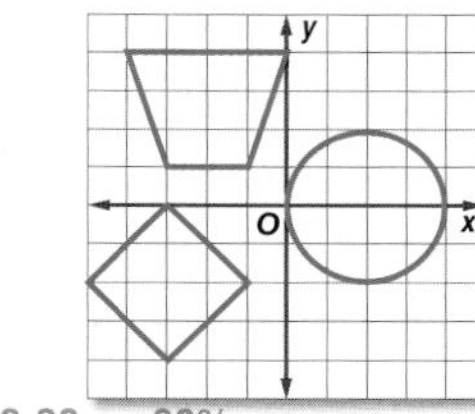

a. P(point inside the circle) $\frac{\pi}{25}$, 0.13, or 13%

b. P(point inside the trapezoid) $\frac{9}{100}$, 0.09, or 9%

c. P(point inside the trapezoid, square, or circle) $\frac{3}{10}$, 0.30, or 30%

CCSS SENSE-MAKING Find the probability that a point chosen at random lies in a shaded region.

29. 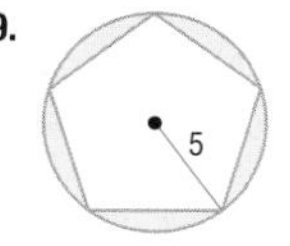

0.24 or 24%

30. 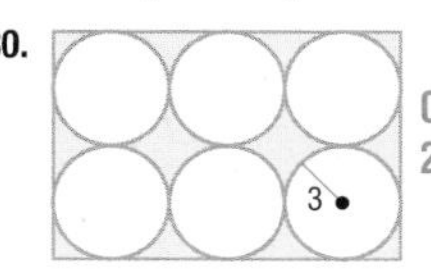

0.21 or 21%

31. 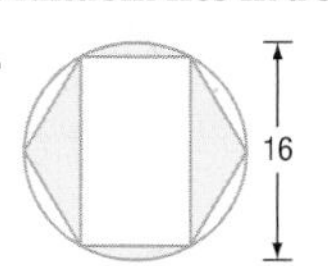

0.33 or 33%

CCSS Teaching the Mathematical Practices

Sense-Making Mathematically proficient students start by explaining the meaning of a problem to themselves and looking for entry points to its solution. They plan a solution pathway rather than simply jumping into a solution attempt. In Exercises 29–31, encourage students to make a plan to solve each problem first.

Enrichment
OL BL

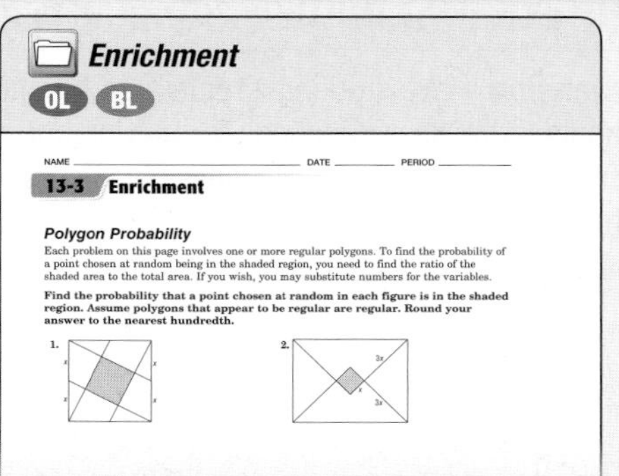
NAME DATE PERIOD

13-3 Enrichment

Polygon Probability

Each problem on this page involves one or more regular polygons. To find the probability of a point chosen at random being in the shaded region, you need to find the ratio of the shaded area to the total area. If you wish, you may substitute numbers for the variables.

Find the probability that a point chosen at random in each figure is in the shaded region. Assume polygons that appear to be regular are regular. Round your answer to the nearest hundredth.

1.

2.

Study Guide and Intervention
AL OL ELL

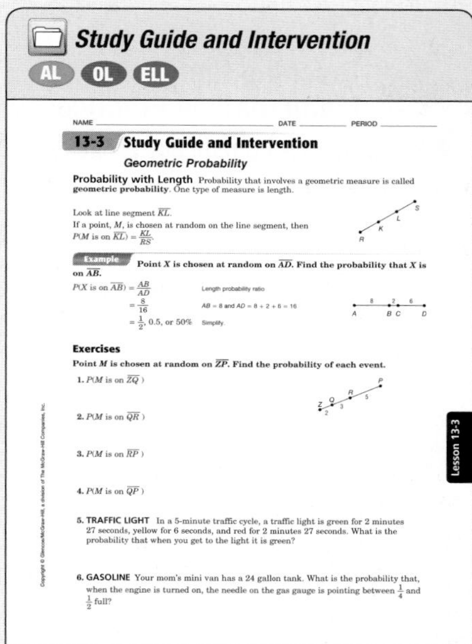
NAME DATE PERIOD

13-3 Study Guide and Intervention

Geometric Probability

Probability with Length Probability that involves a geometric measure is called **geometric probability**. One type of measure is length.

Look at line segment $\overline{KL}$.
If a point, M, is chosen at random on the line segment, then $P(M \text{ is on } \overline{KL}) = \frac{KL}{RS}$.

Example Point X is chosen at random on $\overline{AD}$. Find the probability that X is on $\overline{AB}$.

$P(X \text{ is on } \overline{AB}) = \frac{AB}{AD}$ Length probability ratio
$= \frac{8}{16}$ $AB = 8$ and $AD = 8 + 2 + 6 = 16$
$= \frac{1}{2}$, 0.5, or 50% Simplify.

Exercises

Point M is chosen at random on $\overline{ZP}$. Find the probability of each event.

1. $P(M \text{ is on } \overline{ZQ})$
2. $P(M \text{ is on } \overline{QR})$
3. $P(M \text{ is on } \overline{RP})$
4. $P(M \text{ is on } \overline{QP})$
5. **TRAFFIC LIGHT** In a 5-minute traffic cycle, a traffic light is green for 2 minutes 27 seconds, yellow for 6 seconds, and red for 2 minutes 27 seconds. What is the probability that when you get to the light it is green?
6. **GASOLINE** Your mom's mini van has a 24 gallon tank. What is the probability that, when the engine is turned on, the needle on the gas gauge is pointing between $\frac{1}{4}$ and $\frac{1}{2}$ full?

Lesson 13-3

Practice
AL OL BL ELL

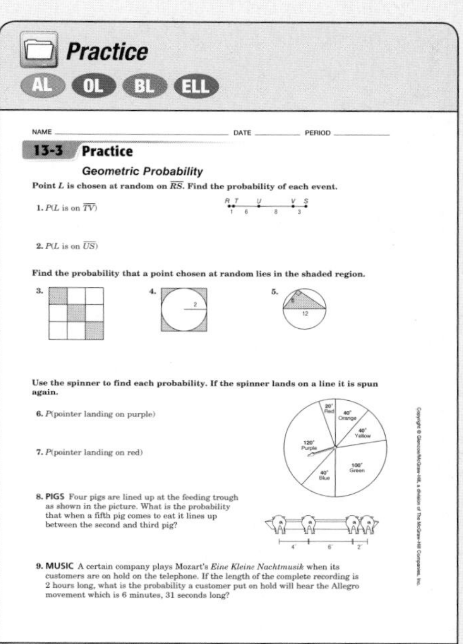
NAME DATE PERIOD

13-3 Practice

Geometric Probability

Point L is chosen at random on $\overline{RS}$. Find the probability of each event.

1. $P(L \text{ is on } \overline{TV})$
2. $P(L \text{ is on } \overline{US})$

Find the probability that a point chosen at random lies in the shaded region.

3.
4.
5.

Use the spinner to find each probability. If the spinner lands on a line it is spun again.

6. P(pointer landing on purple)
7. P(pointer landing on red)
8. **PIGS** Four pigs are lined up at the feeding trough as shown in the picture. What is the probability that when a fifth pig comes to eat it lines up between the second and third pig?
9. **MUSIC** A certain company plays Mozart's *Eine Kleine Nachtmusik* when its customers are on hold on the telephone. If the length of the complete recording is 2 hours long, what is the probability a customer put on hold will hear the Allegro movement which is 6 minutes, 31 seconds long?

Word Problem Practice
AL OL BL ELL

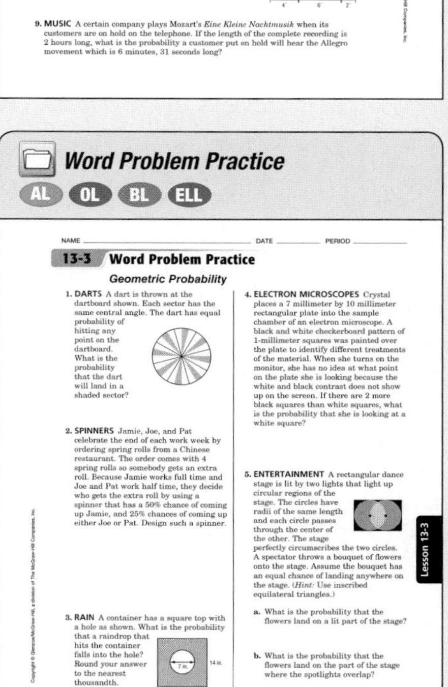
NAME DATE PERIOD

13-3 Word Problem Practice

Geometric Probability

1. **DARTS** A dart is thrown at the dartboard shown. Each sector has the same central angle. The dart has equal probability of hitting any point on the dartboard. What is the probability that the dart will land in a shaded sector?
2. **SPINNERS** Jamie, Joe, and Pat celebrate the end of each work week by ordering spring rolls from a Chinese restaurant. The order comes with 4 spring rolls so somebody gets an extra roll. Because Jamie works full time and Joe and Pat work half time, they decide who gets the extra roll by using a spinner that has a 50% chance of coming up Jamie, and 25% chances of coming up either Joe or Pat. Design such a spinner.
3. **RAIN** A container has a square top with a hole as shown. What is the probability that a raindrop that hits the container falls into the hole? Round your answer to the nearest thousandth.
4. **ELECTRON MICROSCOPES** Crystal places a 7 millimeter by 10 millimeter rectangular plate into the sample chamber of an electron microscope. A black and white checkerboard pattern of 1-millimeter squares was painted over the plate to identify different treatments of the material. When she turns on the monitor, she has no idea at what point on the plate she is looking because the white and black contrast does not show up on the screen. If there are 2 more black squares than white squares, what is the probability that she is looking at a white square?
5. **ENTERTAINMENT** A rectangular dance stage is lit by two lights that light up circular regions of the stage. The circles have radii of the same length and each circle passes through the center of the other. The stage perfectly circumscribes the two circles. A spectator throws a bouquet of flowers onto the stage. Assume the bouquet has an equal chance of landing anywhere on the stage. (*Hint:* Use inscribed equilateral triangles.)
a. What is the probability that the flowers land on a lit part of the stage?
b. What is the probability that the flowers land on the part of the stage where the spotlights overlap?

Lesson 13-3

Teaching the Mathematical Practices

Reasoning Mathematically proficient students make sense of quantities and their relationships in problem situations. In Exercise 36, encourage students to draw and label a diagram.

Additional Answers

37. No; Sample answer: Athletic events should not be considered random because there are other factors involved, such as pressure and ability that have an impact on the success of the event.

38. Sample answer: The probability that a randomly chosen point on $\overline{AC}$ lies between A and B is 20%.

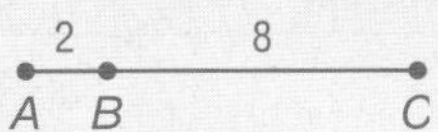

The probability that a randomly chosen point in the circle will lie in the shaded area is 20%.

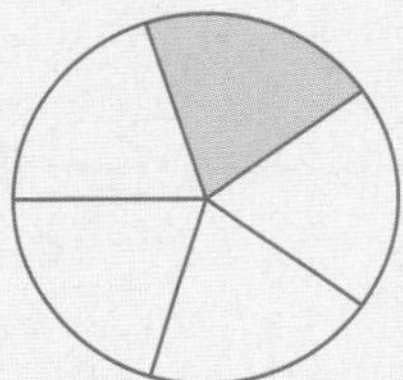

The probability that a randomly chosen point in the square will lie in the unshaded area is 20%.

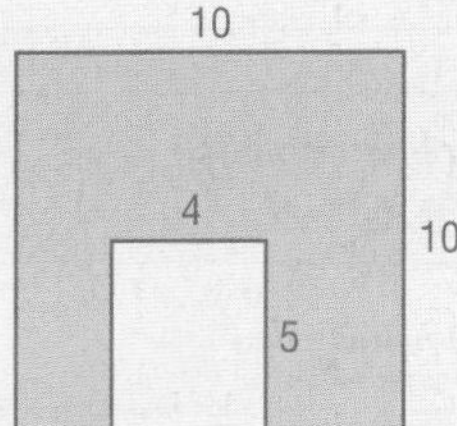

32. **COORDINATE GEOMETRY** Consider a system of inequalities, $1 \leq x \leq 6$, $y \leq x$, and $y \geq 1$. If a point (x, y) in the system is chosen at random, what is the probability that $(x - 1)^2 + (y - 1)^2 \geq 16$? **0.50 or 50%**

33. **VOLUME** The polar bear exhibit at a local zoo has a pool with the side profile shown. If the pool is 20 feet wide, what is the probability that a bear that is equally likely to swim anywhere in the pool will be in the incline region? **0.31 or 31%**

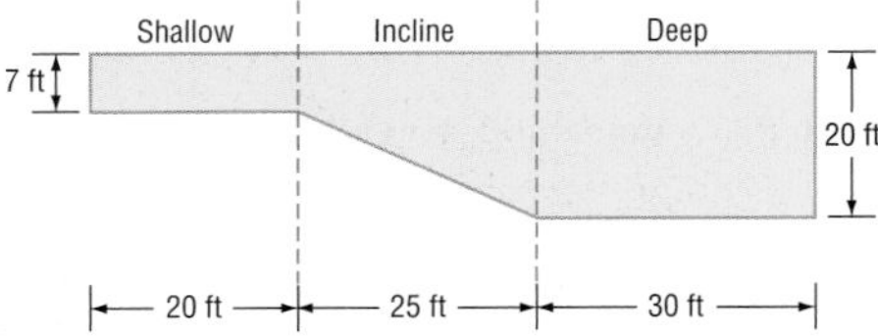

34. **DECISION MAKING** Meleah's flight was delayed and she is running late to make it to a national science competition. She is planning on renting a car at the airport and prefers car rental company A over car rental company B. The courtesy van for car rental company A arrives every 7 minutes, while the courtesy van for car rental company B arrives every 12 minutes.
    a. What is the probability that Meleah will have to wait 5 minutes or less to see each van? Explain your reasoning. (*Hint:* Use an area model.)
    b. What is the probability that Meleah will have to wait 5 minutes or less to see one of the vans? Explain your reasoning.
    c. Meleah can wait no more than 5 minutes without risking being late for the competition. If the van from company B should arrive first, should she wait for the van from company A or take the van from company B? Explain your reasoning.
    34a–c. See Ch. 13 Answer Appendix.

36. $\frac{1}{7}$; **sample answer: Using the Triangle Inequality Theorem, there are 7 isosceles triangles with integer side lengths and a perimeter of 32 centimeters. Of those triangles, only the one with side lengths 10, 10, and 12 has an area of exactly 48 square centimeters. Therefore, the probability is 1 in 7.**

H.O.T. Problems Use Higher-Order Thinking Skills

35. **CHALLENGE** Find the probability that a point chosen at random would lie in the shaded area of the figure. Round to the nearest tenth of a percent. **14.3%**

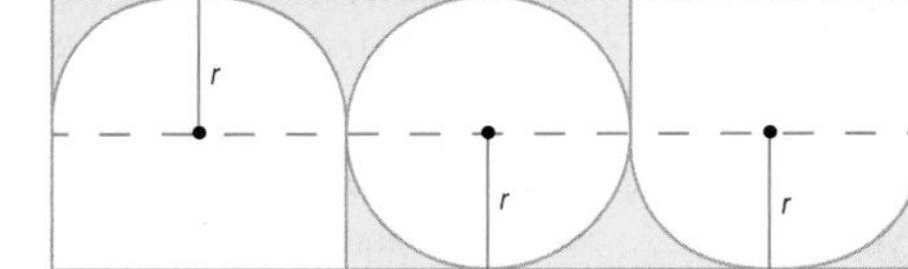

36. **REASONING** An isosceles triangle has a perimeter of 32 centimeters. If the lengths of the sides of the triangle are integers, what is the probability that the area of the triangle is exactly 48 square centimeters? Explain.

37.  **WRITING IN MATH** Can athletic events be considered random events? Explain. **See margin.**

38. **OPEN ENDED** Represent a probability of 20% using three different geometric figures. **See margin.**

39. **WRITING IN MATH** Explain why the probability of a randomly chosen point falling in the shaded region of either of the squares shown is the same. **See margin.**

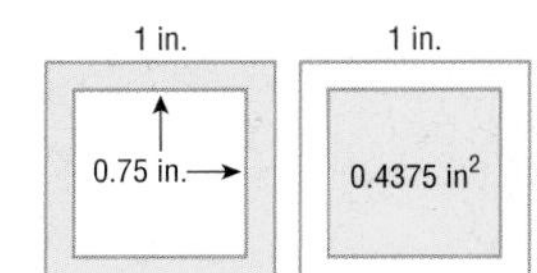

936 | Lesson 13-3 | Geometric Probability

Differentiated Instruction OL BL

Extension Have students create a game that applies the concepts of probability using area. Students should write clear directions for playing and winning the game. Directions should also include the probability of scoring for all possible events of the game. Allow students to play one another's games, checking to see whether the mathematical probabilities correspond to the experimental probabilities. Have students design games that are fair, very hard to win, or very easy to win.

Standardized Test Practice

40. PROBABILITY A circle with radius 3 is contained in a square with side length 9. What is the probability that a randomly chosen point in the interior of the square will also lie in the interior of the circle? C

A $\frac{1}{9}$ C $\frac{\pi}{9}$

B $\frac{1}{3}$ D $\frac{9}{\pi}$

41. ALGEBRA The area of Miki's room is $x^2 + 8x + 12$ square feet. A gallon of paint will cover an area of $x^2 + 6x + 8$ square feet. Which expression gives the number of gallons of paint that Miki will need to buy to paint her room? F

F $\frac{x+6}{x+4}$ H $\frac{x+4}{x+6}$

G $\frac{x-4}{x-6}$ J $\frac{x-4}{x+6}$

42. EXTENDED RESPONSE The spinner is divided into 8 equal sections.

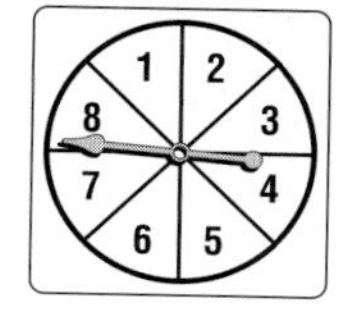

a. If the arrow lands on a number, what is the probability that it will land on 3? $\frac{1}{8}$

b. If the arrow lands on a number, what is the probability that it will land on an odd number? $\frac{1}{2}$

43. SAT/ACT A box contains 7 blue marbles, 6 red marbles, 2 white marbles, and 3 black marbles. If one marble is chosen at random, what is the probability that it will be red? C

A 0.11 D 0.39

B 0.17 E 0.67

C 0.33

Spiral Review

44. PROM Four friends are sitting at a table together at the prom. What is the probability that a particular one of them will sit in the chair closest to the dance floor? (Lesson 13-2) $\frac{1}{4}$

Represent the sample space for each experiment by making an organized list, a table, and a tree diagram. (Lesson 13-1)

45. Tito has a choice of taking music lessons for the next two years and playing drums or guitar. See Ch. 13 Answer Appendix.

46. Denise can buy a pair of shoes in either flats or heels in black or navy blue. See Ch. 13 Answer Appendix.

STAINED GLASS **In the stained glass window design, all of the small arcs around the circle are congruent. Suppose the center of the circle is point *O*.** (Lesson 10-4)

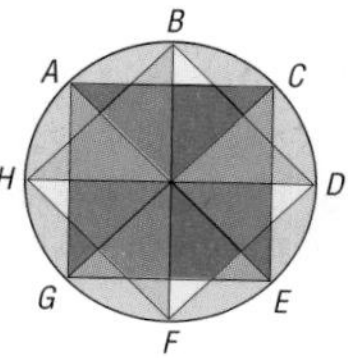

47. What is the measure of each of the small arcs? 45

48. What kind of figure is $\triangle AOC$? Explain. See margin.

49. What kind of figure is quadrilateral *BDFH*? Explain. See margin.

50. What kind of figure is quadrilateral *ACEG*? Explain. See margin.

Skills Review

Find the area of the shaded region. Round to the nearest tenth.

51. 57.1 m^2

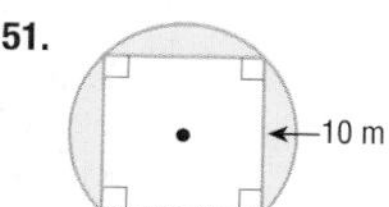

52. 42.1 in^2

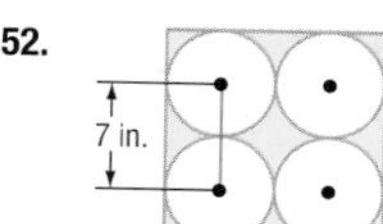

53. 66.3 cm^2

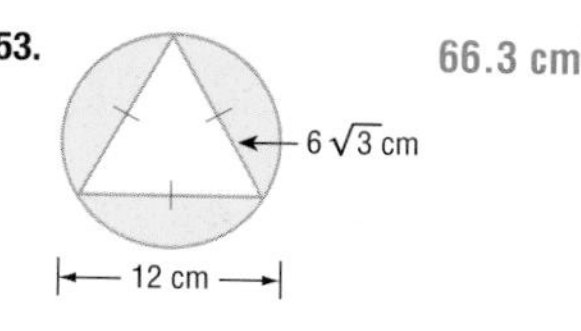

Follow-up

Students have explored geometric probability.

Ask:

- How can geometry be used to make predictions? Sample answer: You can find the probability of an event occurring by replacing the variables used for success and failure with measures of length or area. For example, you could find the probability of an event occurring in a specific sector of a circle by finding the ratio of the area of that sector to the area of the entire circle.

4 Assess

Crystal Ball Have students write a paragraph that explains how the lessons in probability might help them in evaluating simulations.

Formative Assessment

Check for student understanding of Lesson 13-3.

Quiz 2, p. 45

Additional Answers

39. Sample answer: The probability of a randomly chosen point lying in the shaded region of the square on the left is found by subtracting the area of the unshaded square from the area of the larger square and finding the ratio of the difference of the areas to the area of the larger square. The probability is $\frac{1^2 - 0.75^2}{1^2}$ or 43.75%. The probability of a randomly chosen point lying in the shaded region of the square on the right is the ratio of the area of the shaded square to the area of the larger square, which is $\frac{0.4375}{1}$ or 43.75%. Therefore, the probability of a randomly chosen point lying in the shaded area of either square is the same.

48. Isosceles right triangle; the sides are congruent radii, making it isosceles, and $\angle AOC$ is a central angle for an arc of 90°, making it a right angle.

49. Square; each angle intercepts a semicircle, making them 90° angles. Each side is a chord of congruent arcs, so the chords are congruent.

50. Square; each angle intercepts a semicircle, making them 90° angles. Each side is a chord of congruent arcs, so the chords are congruent.

Formative Assessment

Use the Mid-Chapter Quiz to assess students' progress in the first half of the chapter.

Have students review the lesson indicated for the problems that they answered incorrectly.

Summative Assessment

Mid-Chapter Test, p. 47

eAssessment Customize and create multiple versions of your Mid-Chapter Quiz and their answer keys.

FOLDABLES StudyOrganizer

Dinah Zike's Foldables®

Before students complete the Mid-Chapter Quiz, encourage them to review the information they have recorded for Lessons 13-1 through Lesson 13-3 in their Foldables.

CHAPTER 13 Mid-Chapter Quiz

Lessons 13-1 through 13-3

1. **LUNCH** A deli has a lunch special, which consists of a sandwich, soup, dessert, and a drink for $4.99. The choices are in the table below. (Lesson 13-1)

Sandwich	Soup	Dessert	Drink
chicken salad	tomato	cookie	tea
ham	chicken noodle	pie	coffee
tuna	vegetable		cola
roast beef			diet cola
			milk

   a. How many different lunches can be created from the items shown in the table? **120**

   b. If a soup and two desserts were added, how many different lunches could be created? **320**

2. **FLAGS** How many different signals can be made with 5 flags from 8 flags of different colors? (Lesson 13-1) **6720**

3. **CLOTHING** Marcy has six colors of shirts: red, blue, yellow, green, pink, and orange. She has each color in short-sleeved and long-sleeved styles. Represent the sample space for Marcy's shirt choices by making an organized list, a table, and a tree diagram. (Lesson 13-1) **See Ch. 13 Answer Appendix.**

4. **SPELLING** A bag contains one tile for each letter of the word TRAINS. If you selected a permutation of these letters at random, what is the probability that they would spell TRAINS? (Lesson 13-2) $\frac{1}{720}$

5. **CHANGE** Augusto has 3 pockets and 4 different coins. In how many ways can he put one coin in each pocket? (Lesson 13-2) **24**

6. **COINS** Ten coins are tossed simultaneously. In how many of the outcomes will the third coin turn up a head? (Lesson 13-2) 2^9

7. Find the probability that a point chosen at random lies in the shaded region. (Lesson 13-3) **about 51%**

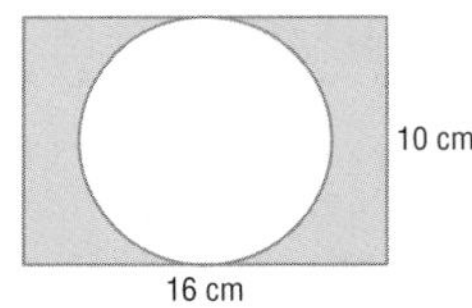

8. **EXTENDED RESPONSE** A 320 meter long tightrope is suspended between two poles. Assume that the line has an equal chance of breaking anywhere along its length. (Lesson 13-3)

   a. Determine the probability that a break will occur in the first 50 meters of the tightrope. **about 16%**

   b. Determine the probability that the break will occur within 20 meters of a pole. **about 13%**

Point A is chosen at random on $\overline{BE}$. Find the probability of each event. (Lesson 13-3)

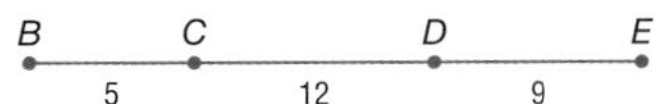

9. $P(A \text{ is on } \overline{CD})$ $\frac{6}{13}$

10. $P(A \text{ is on } \overline{BD})$ $\frac{17}{26}$

11. $P(A \text{ is on } \overline{CE})$ $\frac{21}{26}$

12. $P(A \text{ is on } \overline{DE})$ $\frac{9}{26}$

Use the spinner to find each probability. If the spinner lands on a line, it is spun again. (Lesson 13-3)

13. P(pointer landing on yellow) **about 64%**

14. P(pointer landing on blue) **about 7%**

15. P(pointer landing on red) **about 29%**

16. **GAMES** At a carnival, the object of a game is to throw a dart at the board and hit region III. (Lesson 13-3)

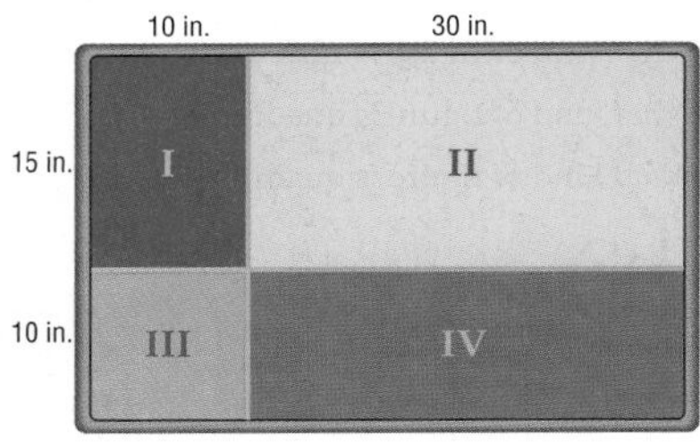

   a. What is the probability that it hits region I? **15%**

   b. What is the probability that it hits region II? **45%**

   c. What is the probability that it hits region III? **10%**

   d. What is the probability that it hits region IV? **30%**

InterventionPlanner

TIER 1 On Level OL

If students miss about 25% of the exercises or less,

Then choose a resource:

SE Lessons 13-1, 13-2, and 13-3

Skills Practice, pp. 7, 13, and 19

connectED.mcgraw-hill.com Self-Check Quiz

TIER 2 Strategic Intervention AL approaching grade level

If students miss about 50% of the exercises,

Then choose a resource:

Study Guide and Intervention, pp. 5, 11, 17

connectED.mcgraw-hill.com Extra Examples, Personal Tutor, Homework Help

TIER 3 Intensive Intervention 2 or more grades below level

If students miss about 75% of the exercises,

Then use *Math Triumphs, Geo.*, Ch. 6

connectED.mcgraw-hill.com Extra Examples, Personal Tutor, Homework Help, Review Vocabulary

938 | Chapter 13 | Mid-Chapter Quiz

LESSON 13-4 Simulations

:: Then

- You found probabilities by using geometric measures.

:: Now

1. Design simulations to estimate probabilities.
2. Summarize data from simulations.

:: Why?

- Based on practice, Allen knows that he makes 70% of his free throws. He wants to use this information to predict the number of free throws he is likely to make in games.

NewVocabulary

probability model
simulation
random variable
expected value
Law of Large Numbers

Common Core State Standards

Content Standards

G.MG.3 Apply geometric methods to solve problems (e.g., designing an object or structure to satisfy physical constraints or minimize cost; working with typographic grid systems based on ratios). ★

S.MD.6 (+) Use probabilities to make fair decisions (e.g., drawing by lots, using a random number generator).

Mathematical Practices

1 Make sense of problems and persevere in solving them.
4 Model with mathematics.

1 Design a Simulation A **probability model** is a mathematical model used to match a random phenomenon. A **simulation** is the use of a probability model to recreate a situation again and again so that the likelihood of various outcomes can be estimated. To design a simulation, use the following steps.

KeyConcept Designing a Simulation

Step 1 Determine each possible outcome and its theoretical probability.

Step 2 State any assumptions.

Step 3 Describe an appropriate probability model for the situation.

Step 4 Define what a trial is for the situation and state the number of trials to be conducted.

An appropriate probability model has the same probabilities as the situation you are trying to predict. Geometric models are common probability models.

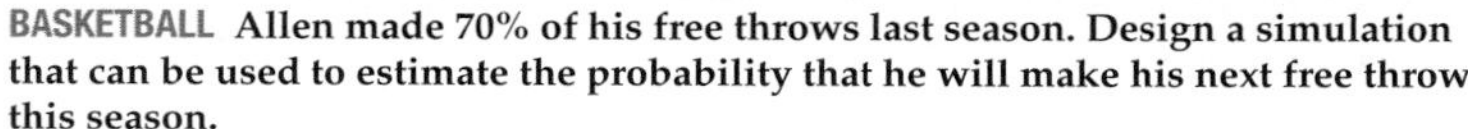

Example 1 Design a Simulation by Using a Geometric Model

BASKETBALL **Allen made 70% of his free throws last season. Design a simulation that can be used to estimate the probability that he will make his next free throw this season.**

Step 1

Possible Outcomes	Theoretical Probability
• Allen makes a free throw. →	70%
• Allen misses a free throw. →	(100 − 70)% or 30%

Step 2 Our simulation will consist of 40 trials.

Step 3 One device that could be used is a spinner divided into two sectors, one containing 70% of the spinner's area and the other 30%. To create such a spinner, find the measure of the central angle of each sector.

Make Free Throw	Miss Free Throw
70% of 360° = 252°	30% of 360° = 108°

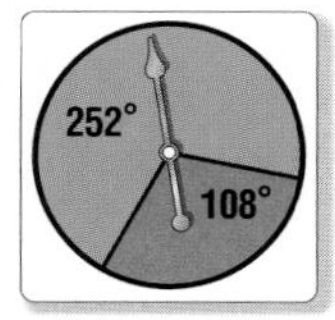

Make Free Throw
Miss Free Throw

Step 4 A trial, one spin of the spinner, will represent shooting one free throw. A successful trial will be a made free throw and a failed trial will be a missed free throw. The simulation will consist of 40 trials.

1 Focus

VerticalAlignment

Before Lesson 13-4 Use geometric measures to find probabilities.

Lesson 13-4 Design simulations to estimate probabilities. Summarize data from simulations.

After Lesson 13-4 Find probabilities of independent and dependent events.

2 Teach

Scaffolding Questions

Have students read the **Why?** section of the lesson.

Ask:

- If Allen took 50 free throws last season, how many did he make? 35
- If Allen can expect to take 60 free throws this season, how many can he predict he will make? 42
- What kind of reasoning does Allen use to predict the number of free throws he will make this season? inductive reasoning

Lesson 13-4 Resources

Resource	Approaching Level AL	On Level OL	Beyond Level BL	English Learners ELL
Teacher Edition	▪ Differentiated Instruction, p. 942	▪ Differentiated Instruction, pp. 942, 945	▪ Differentiated Instruction, p. 945	
Chapter Resource Masters	▪ Study Guide and Intervention, pp. 24–25 ▪ Skills Practice, p.26 ▪ Practice, p. 27 ▪ Word Problem Practice, p. 28	▪ Study Guide and Intervention, pp. 24–25 ▪ Skills Practice, p. 26 ▪ Practice, p. 27 ▪ Word Problem Practice, p. 28 ▪ Enrichment, p. 29 ▪ Graphing Calculator Activity, p. 30	▪ Practice, p. 27 ▪ Word Problem Practice, p. 28 ▪ Enrichment, p. 29	▪ Study Guide and Intervention, pp. 24–25 ▪ Skills Practice, p. 26 ▪ Practice, p. 27 ▪ Word Problem Practice, p. 28
Other	▪ 5-Minute Check 13-4 ▪ Study Notebook	▪ 5-Minute Check 13-4 ▪ Study Notebook	▪ 5-Minute Check 13-4 ▪ Study Notebook	▪ 5-Minute Check 13-4 ▪ Study Notebook

1 Design a Simulation

Examples 1 and 2 show how to create and use a probability model to predict the results of a concrete situation.

Formative Assessment

Use the Guided Practice exercises after each example to determine students' understanding of concepts.

Additional Examples

1 **BASEBALL** Maria got a hit 40% of the time she was at bat last season. Design a simulation that can be used to estimate the probability that she will get a hit at her next at bat this season. Sample answer: Use a spinner divided into two sectors, one containing 40% of the spinner's area or 144° and the other 60% of the spinner's area or 216°. A trial, one spin, will represent one at bat. The simulation will consist of 50 trials.

2 **PIZZA** A survey of Longmeadow High School students found that 30% preferred cheese pizza, 30% preferred pepperoni, 20% preferred peppers and onions, and 20% preferred sausage. Design a simulation that can be used to estimate the probability that a Longmeadow High School student prefers each of these choices. Sample answer: Use a random number generator to generate integers 0 through 10 where 0–2 represents cheese, 3–5 represents pepperoni, 6 and 7 represent peppers and onions, and 8 and 9 represent sausage. A trial will represent selecting a student at random and recording his or her pizza preference. The simulation will consist of 20 trials.

Additional Examples also in Interactive Classroom PowerPoint® Presentations

IWB Interactive White Board READY

GuidedPractice

1. **RESTAURANTS** A restaurant attaches game pieces to its large drink cups, awarding a prize to anyone who collects all 6 game pieces. Design a simulation using a geometric model that can be used to estimate how many large drinks a person needs to buy to collect all 6 game pieces. See Ch. 13 Answer Appendix.

Problem-SolvingTip

Use a Simulation Simulations often provide a safe and efficient problem-solving strategy in situations that otherwise may be costly, dangerous, or impossible to solve using theoretical techniques. Simulations should involve data that are easier to obtain than the actual data you are modeling.

In addition to geometric models, simulations can also be conducted using dice, coin tosses, random number tables, and random number generators, such as those available on graphing calculators.

Example 2 Design a Simulation by Using Random Numbers

EYE COLOR **A survey of East High School students found that 40% had brown eyes, 30% had hazel eyes, 20% had blue eyes, and 10% had green eyes. Design a simulation that can be used to estimate the probability that a randomly chosen East High student will have one of these eye colors.**

Step 1

Possible Outcomes		Theoretical Probability
Brown eyes	→	40%
Hazel eyes	→	30%
Blue eyes	→	20%
Green eyes	→	10%

Step 2 We assume that a student's eye color will fall into one of these four categories.

Step 3 Use the random number generator on your calculator. Assign the ten integers 0–9 to accurately represent the probability data. The actual numbers chosen to represent the outcomes do not matter.

Outcome	Represented by
Brown eyes	0, 1, 2, 3
Hazel eyes	4, 5, 6
Blue eyes	7, 8
Green eyes	9

Step 4 A trial will represent selecting a student at random and recording his or her eye color. The simulation will consist of 20 trials.

StudyTip

Random Number Generator To generate a set of random integers on a graphing calculator, press  MATH and select randInt(under the PRB menu. Then enter the beginning and ending integer values for your range and the number of integers you want in each trial.

GuidedPractice

2. **SOCCER** Last season, Yao made 18% of his free kicks. Design a simulation using a random number generator that can be used to estimate the probability that he will make his next free kick. See margin.

2 Summarize Data from a Simulation

After designing a simulation, you will need to conduct the simulation and report the results. Include both numerical and graphical summaries of the simulation data, as well as an estimate of the probability of the desired outcome.

Additional Answer (Guided Practice)

2. Sample answer: The theoretical probability that he will make his next free kick is 18%. I will use a random number generator to generate integers 1 through 50. The integers 1–9 will represent a made free kick and the integers 19–50 will represent a missed free kick. The simulation will consist of 50 trials.

Teach with Tech

Computer Projector Find a Web site with an applet that has a probability simulator (using coins, spinners, etc.). Find the theoretical probability of an event, and then use the simulator to obtain real experimental data.

Real-WorldLink

Mark Price holds the record for the highest career free-throw percentage in the NBA at 90.4%.

Source: National Basketball Association

Example 3 Conduct and Summarize Data from a Simulation

BASKETBALL Refer to the simulation in Example 1. Conduct the simulation and report the results using appropriate numerical and graphical summaries.

Make a frequency table and record the results after spinning the spinner 40 times.

Outcome	Tally	Frequency
Make Free Throw	𝍸 𝍸 𝍸 𝍸 𝍸 |	26
Miss Free Throw	𝍸 𝍸 ||||	14
Total		40

Based on the simulation data, calculate the probability that Allen will make his next free throw.

$\frac{\text{number of made free throws}}{\text{number of free throws attempted}} = \frac{26}{40}$ or 0.65   *This is an experimental probability.*

The probability that Allen makes his next free throw is 0.65 or 65%. Notice that this is close to the theoretical probability, 70%. So, the experimental probability of his missing the next free throw is $1 - 0.65$ or 35%.

Make a bar graph of these results.

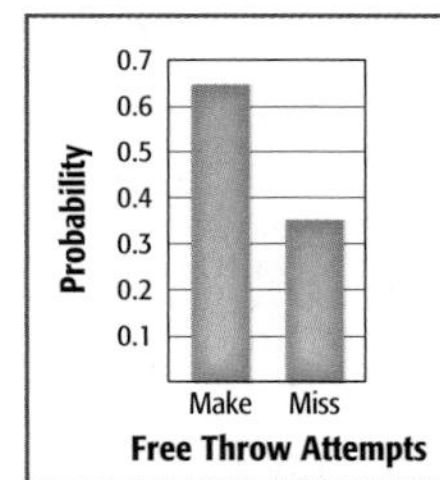

GuidedPractice

3. **EYE COLOR** Use a graphing calculator to conduct the simulation in Example 2. Then report the results using appropriate numerical and graphical summaries. **See margin.**

A **random variable** is a variable that can assume a set of values, each with fixed probabilities. For example, in the experiment of rolling two dice, the random variable X can represent the sums of the potential outcomes on the dice. The table shows some of the X-values assigned to outcomes from this experiment.

Sum of Outcomes of Rolling Two Dice	
Outcome	***X*-Value**
(1, 1)	2
(1, 2)	3
(2, 1)	3
(4, 5)	9
(6, 6)	12

Expected value, also known as mathematical expectation, is the average value of a random variable that one *expects* after repeating an experiment or simulation a theoretically infinite number of times. To find the expected value $E(X)$ of a random variable X, follow these steps.

KeyConcept Calculating Expected Value

Step 1 Multiply the value of X by its probability of occurring.

Step 2 Repeat Step 1 for all possible values of X.

Step 3 Find the sum of the results.

Since it is an average, an expected value does not have to be equal to a possible value of the random variable.

2 Summarize Data from a Simulation

Example 3 shows how to report the results of a simulation numerically and graphically. **Example 4** shows how to compute expected value and compare it with the results of a simulation.

Additional Example

3 **BASEBALL** Refer to the simulation in Additional Example 1. Conduct the simulation and report the results, using appropriate numerical and graphical summaries. Answers will vary, but should include a frequency table from the simulation and the corresponding bar graph.

Focus on Mathematical Content

Expected Value The expected value is the theoretical average value of the random variable expected after repeated trials. The actual value in a simulation may not be different.

Additional Answer (Guided Practice)

3. Sample answer: $P(\text{brown}) = 45\%$, $P(\text{hazel}) = 25\%$, $P(\text{blue}) = 20\%$, $P(\text{green}) = 10\%$

Outcome	Frequency
brown	9
hazel	5
blue	4
green	2

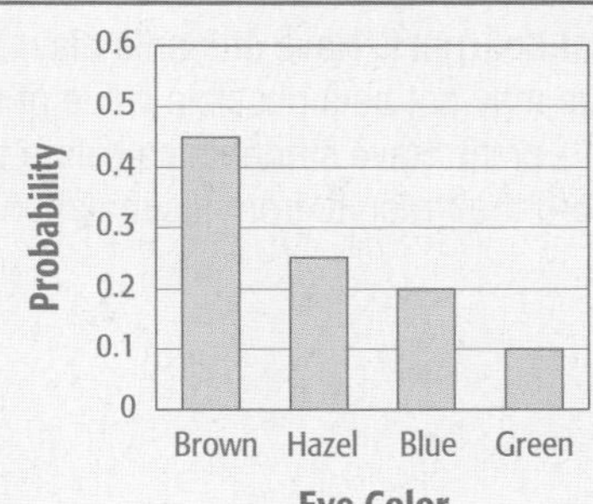

connectED.mcgraw-hill.com 941

Additional Example

4 ARCHERY Suppose that an arrow is shot at a target. The radius of the center circle is 3 inches, and each successive circle has a radius 5 inches greater than that of the previous circle. The point value for each region is shown.

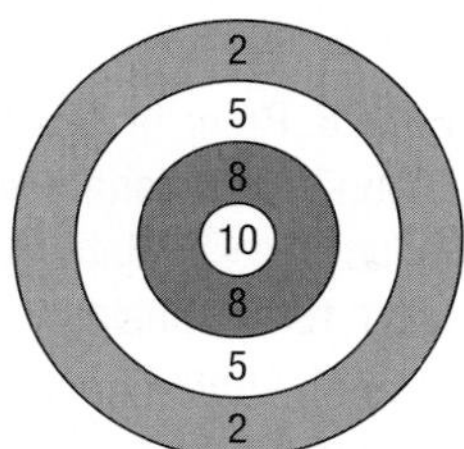

a. Let the random variable Y represent the point value assigned to a region on the target. Calculate the expected value $E(Y)$ for each shot of the arrow. $\frac{455}{108}$ or about 4.21

b. Design a simulation to estimate the average value, or the average of the results of your simulation, of shooting this game. How does this value compare with the expected value you found in part **a**? Answers will vary.

WatchOut!

Expected Value Remind students that they must multiply the value of the random variable by the probability of it occurring before summing the values to find the expected value.

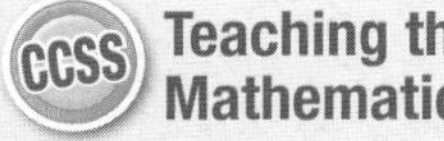

Teaching the Mathematical Practices

Modeling Mathematically proficient students can apply the mathematics they know to solve problems arising in everyday life. In Exercises 8–10, encourage students to list the possible outcomes first.

StudyTip

Geometric Probability Remember that when determining geometric probabilities with targets, we assume that the object lands within the target area, and that it is equally likely that the object will land anywhere in the region.

Math HistoryLink

Jakob Bernoulli (1654–1705) Bernoulli was a Swiss mathematician. It seemed obvious to him that the more observations made of a given situation, the better one would be able to predict future outcomes. He provided scientific proof of his Law of Large Numbers in his work *Ars Conjectandi* (Art of Conjecturing), published in 1713.

PT

Example 4 Calculate Expected Value

DARTS Suppose a dart is thrown at the dartboard. The radius of the center circle is 1 centimeter and each successive circle has a radius 4 centimeters greater than the previous circle. The point value for each region is shown.

a. Let the random variable Y represent the point value assigned to a region on the dartboard. Calculate the expected value $E(Y)$ from each throw.

First calculate the geometric probability of landing in each region.

$$\text{Region 5} = \frac{\pi(1)^2}{\pi(1+4+4+4+4)^2} = \frac{1}{289} \qquad \text{Region 4} = \frac{\pi(4+1)^2 - \pi(1)^2}{\pi(17)^2} = \frac{24}{289}$$

$$\text{Region 3} = \frac{\pi(4+5)^2 - \pi(5)^2}{\pi(17)^2} = \frac{56}{289} \qquad \text{Region 2} = \frac{\pi(4+9)^2 - \pi(9)^2}{\pi(17)^2} = \frac{88}{289}$$

$$\text{Region 1} = \frac{\pi(4+13)^2 - \pi(13)^2}{\pi(17)^2} = \frac{120}{289}$$

$$E(Y) = 1 \cdot \frac{120}{289} + 2 \cdot \frac{88}{289} + 3 \cdot \frac{56}{289} + 4 \cdot \frac{24}{289} + 5 \cdot \frac{1}{289} \text{ or about } 1.96$$

The expected value of each throw is about 1.96.

b. Design a simulation to estimate the average value, or the average of the results of your simulation, of this game. How does this value compare with the expected value you found in part a?

Assign the integers 0–289 to accurately represent the probability data.

Region 1 = integers 1–120   Region 2 = integers 121–208

Region 3 = integers 209–264   Region 4 = integers 265–288

Region 5 = integer 289

Use a graphing calculator to generate 50 trials of random integers from 1 to 289. Record the results in a frequency table. Then calculate the average value of the outcomes.

Outcome	Frequency
Region 1	16
Region 2	13
Region 3	13
Region 4	8
Region 5	0

$$\text{average value} = 1 \cdot \frac{16}{50} + 2 \cdot \frac{13}{50} + 3 \cdot \frac{13}{50} + 4 \cdot \frac{8}{50} + 5 \cdot \frac{0}{50} = 2.26$$

The average value 2.26 is greater than the expected value 1.96.

GuidedPractice

4. DICE If two dice are rolled, let the random variable X represent the sum of the potential outcomes.

A. Find the expected value $E(X)$. 7

B. Design and run a simulation to estimate the average value of this experiment. How does this value compare with the expected value you found in part A? See Ch. 13 Answer Appendix.

The difference in the average value from the simulation and the expected value in Example 4 illustrates the **Law of Large Numbers**: as the number of trials of a random process increases, the average value will approach the expected value.

DifferentiatedInstruction AL OL

Visual/Spatial Learners Have students play a simple game by flipping a coin to show them that the expected value may not be a possible value of the random variable. Have heads count as 0 points and tails count as 1 point. Have students calculate the expected value for several different odd numbers of trials and record their results from a simulation of each one.

Check Your Understanding

 = Step-by-Step Solutions begin on page R14. 

Examples 1, 3 **1. GRADES** Clara got an A on 80% of her first semester Biology quizzes. Design and conduct a simulation using a geometric model to estimate the probability that she will get an A on a second semester Biology quiz. Report the results using appropriate numerical and graphical summaries. See Ch. 13 Answer Appendix.

Examples 2–3 **2. FITNESS** The table shows the percent of members participating in four classes offered at a gym. Design and conduct a simulation to estimate the probability that a new gym member will take each class. Report the results using appropriate numerical and graphical summaries. See Ch. 13 Answer Appendix.

Class	Sign-Up %
tae kwon do	45%
yoga	30%
swimming	15%
kick-boxing	10%

Example 4 **3. CARNIVAL GAMES** The object of the game shown is to accumulate points by using a dart to pop the balloons. Assume that each dart will hit a balloon.

a. Calculate the expected value from each throw. 36

b. Design a simulation and estimate the average value of this game. See margin.

c. How do the expected value and average value compare? Sample answer: The expected value and average value are very close.

Practice and Problem Solving

Extra Practice is on page R13.

Examples 1, 3 **Design and conduct a simulation using a geometric probability model. Then report the results using appropriate numerical and graphical summaries.**

4. BOWLING Bridget is a member of the bowling club at her school. Last season she bowled a strike 60% of the time. See margin.

5. VIDEO GAMES Ian works at a video game store. Last year he sold 95% of the new-release video games. See Ch. 13 Answer Appendix.

6. MUSIC Kadisha is listening to a CD with her CD player set on the random mode. There are 10 songs on the CD. See Ch. 13 Answer Appendix.

7. BOARD GAMES Pilar is playing a board game with eight different categories, each with questions that must be answered correctly in order to win. See Ch. 13 Answer Appendix.

Examples 2–3 CCSS **MODELING** **Design and conduct a simulation using a random number generator. Then report the results using appropriate numerical and graphical summaries.**

8. MOVIES A movie theater reviewed sales from the previous year to determine which genre of movie sold the most tickets. The results are shown at the right. See Ch. 13 Answer Appendix.

Genre	Ticket %
drama	40%
mystery	30%
comedy	25%
action	5%

9. BASEBALL According to a baseball player's on-base percentages, he gets a single 60% of the time, a double 25% of the time, a triple 10% of the time, and a home run 5% of the time. See Ch. 13 Answer Appendix.

10. VACATION According to a survey done by a travel agency, 45% of their clients went on vacation to Europe, 25% went to Asia, 15% went to South America, 10% went to Africa, and 5% went to Australia. See Ch. 13 Answer Appendix.

11. TRANSPORTATION A car dealership's analysis indicated that 35% of the customers purchased a blue car, 30% purchased a red car, 15% purchased a white car, 15% purchased a black car, and 5% purchased any other color. See Ch. 13 Answer Appendix.

Differentiated Homework Options

Level	Assignment	Two-Day Option	
AL Basic	4–16, 20, 21, 23–36	5–15 odd, 26–29	4–16 even, 20, 21, 23–25, 30–36
OL Core	5–15 odd, 17–21, 23–36	4–16, 26–29	17–21, 23–25, 30–36
BL Advanced	17–35, (optional: 36)		

3 Practice

Formative Assessment

Use Exercises 1–3 to check for understanding.

Then use the chart at the bottom of this page to customize assignments for your students.

Additional Answers

3b. Sample answer: Use a random number generator to generate integers 1 through 25 where 1–16 represents 25 points, 17–24 represents 50 points, and 25 represents 100 points. Do 50 trials and record the results in a frequency table.

Outcome	Frequency
25	29
50	21
100	0

The average value is 35.5.

4. Sample answer: Use a spinner that is divided into two sectors, one containing 60% or 216° and the other containing 40% or 144°. Do 20 trials and record the results in a frequency table.

Outcome	Frequency
Strike	13
Not a strike	7
Total	20

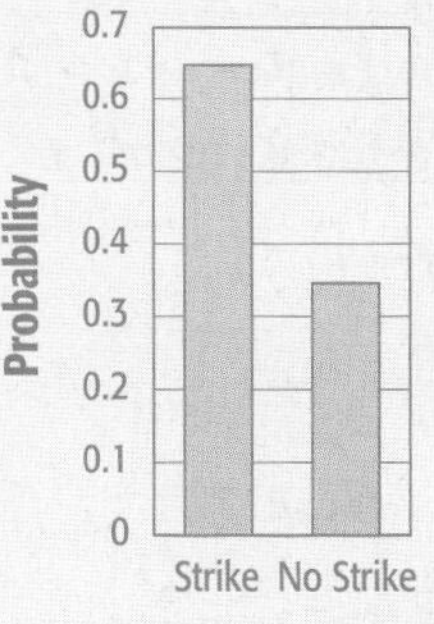

The probability of Bridget bowling a strike on her next turn is 0.65. The probability of bowling anything else is 1 – 0.65 or 0.35.

Study Guide and Intervention

AL OL ELL

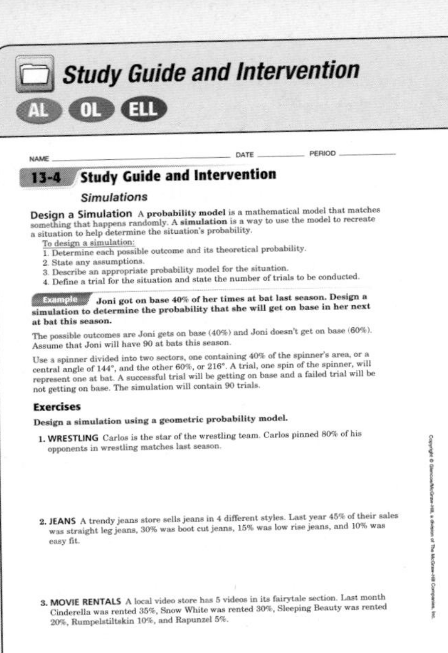

NAME ______ DATE ______ PERIOD ______

13-4 Study Guide and Intervention

Simulations

Design a Simulation A **probability model** is a mathematical model that matches something that happens randomly. A **simulation** is a way to use the model to recreate a situation to help determine the situation's probability.

To design a simulation:
1. Determine each possible outcome and its theoretical probability.
2. State any assumptions.
3. Describe an appropriate probability model for the situation.
4. Define a trial for the situation and state the number of trials to be conducted.

Example Joni got on base 40% of her times at bat last season. Design a simulation to determine the probability that she will get on base in her next at bat this season.

The possible outcomes are Joni gets on base (40%) and Joni doesn't get on base (60%). Assume that Joni will have 90 at bats this season.

Use a spinner divided into two sectors, one containing 40% of the spinner's area, or a central angle of 144°, and the other 60%, or 216°. A trial, one spin of the spinner, will represent one at bat. A successful trial will be getting on base and a failed trial will be not getting on base. The simulation will contain 90 trials.

Exercises

Design a simulation using a geometric probability model.

1. **WRESTLING** Carlos is the star of the wrestling team. Carlos pinned 80% of his opponents in wrestling matches last season.

2. **JEANS** A trendy jeans store sells jeans in 4 different styles. Last year 45% of their sales was straight leg jeans, 30% was boot cut jeans, 15% was low rise jeans, and 10% was easy fit.

3. **MOVIE RENTALS** A local video store has 5 videos in its fairytale section. Last month Cinderella was rented 35%, Snow White was rented 30%, Sleeping Beauty was rented 20%, Rumpelstiltskin 10%, and Rapunzel 5%.

Practice

AL OL BL ELL

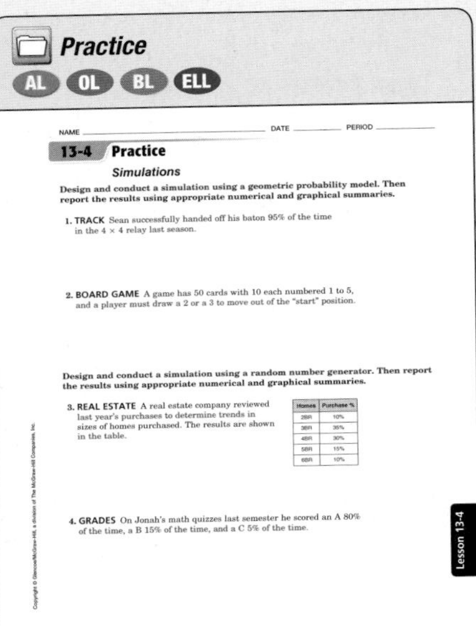

NAME ______ DATE ______ PERIOD ______

13-4 Practice

Simulations

Design and conduct a simulation using a geometric probability model. Then report the results using appropriate numerical and graphical summaries.

1. **TRACK** Sean successfully handed off his baton 95% of the time in the 4 × 4 relay last season.

2. **BOARD GAME** A game has 50 cards with 10 each numbered 1 to 5, and a player must draw a 2 or a 3 to move out of the "start" position.

Design and conduct a simulation using a random number generator. Then report the results using appropriate numerical and graphical summaries.

3. **REAL ESTATE** A real estate company reviewed last year's purchases to determine trends in sizes of homes purchased. The results are shown in the table.

4. **GRADES** On Jonah's math quizzes last semester he scored an A 80% of the time, a B 15% of the time, and a C 5% of the time.

Lesson 13-4

Word Problem Practice

AL OL BL ELL

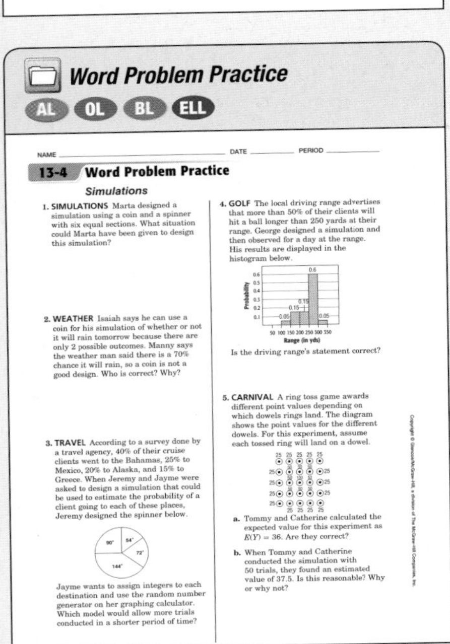

NAME ______ DATE ______ PERIOD ______

13-4 Word Problem Practice

Simulations

1. **SIMULATIONS** Marta designed a simulation using a coin and a spinner with six equal sections. What situation could Marta have been given to design this simulation?

2. **WEATHER** Isaiah says he can use a coin for his simulation of whether or not it will rain tomorrow because there are only 2 possible outcomes. Manny says the weather man said there is a 70% chance it will rain, so a coin is not a good design. Who is correct? Why?

3. **TRAVEL** According to a survey done by a travel agency, 40% of their cruise clients went to the Bahamas, 25% to Mexico, 20% to Alaska, and 15% to Greece. When Jeremy and Jayme were asked to design a simulation that could be used to estimate the probability of a client going to each of these places, Jeremy designed the spinner below.

Jayme wants to assign integers to each destination and use the random number generator on her graphing calculator. Which model would allow more trials conducted in a shorter period of time?

4. **GOLF** The local driving range advertises that more than 50% of their clients will hit a ball longer than 250 yards at their range. George designed a simulation and then observed for a day at the range. His results are displayed in the histogram below.

Is the driving range's statement correct?

5. **CARNIVAL** A ring toss game awards different point values depending on which dowels rings land. The diagram shows the point values for the different dowels. For this experiment, assume each tossed ring will land on a dowel.

a. Tommy and Catherine calculated the expected value for this experiment as $E(Y) = 36$. Are they correct?

b. When Tommy and Catherine conducted the simulation with 50 trials, they found an estimated value of 37.5. Is this reasonable? Why or why not?

Example 4 **DARTBOARDS** **The dimensions of each dartboard below are given in inches. There is only one shot per game. Calculate the expected value of each dart game. Then design a simulation to estimate each game's average value. Compare the average and expected values. In each figure, ■ = 25, □ = 50, and ■ = 100 points.** 12–14. See margin.

12.

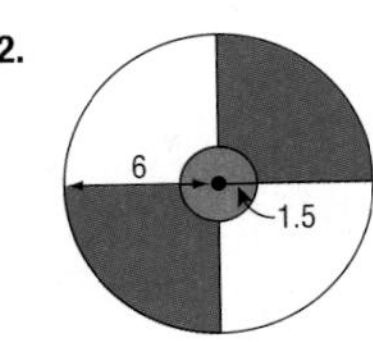

13

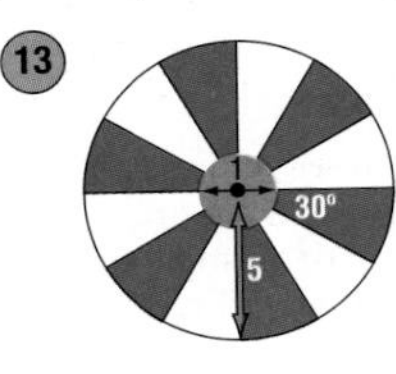

14.

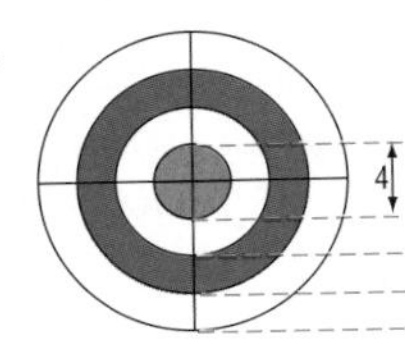

15. **CARDS** You are playing a team card game where a team can get 0 points, 1 point, or 3 points for a hand. The probability of your team getting 1 point for a hand is 60% and of getting 3 points for a hand is 5%.
    a. Calculate your team's expected value for a hand. 0.75
    b. Design a simulation and estimate your team's average value per hand. See margin.
    c. Compare the values for parts **a** and **b**. Sample answer: The two values are almost equal.

16. **DECISION MAKING** The object of the game shown is to win money by rolling a ball up an incline into regions with different payoff values. The probability that Susana will get $0 in a roll is 55%, $1 is 20%, $2 is 20%, and $3 is 5%. a–c. See margin.

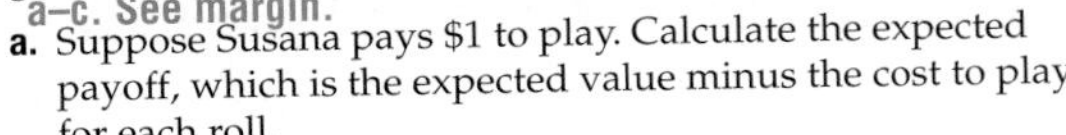

    a. Suppose Susana pays $1 to play. Calculate the expected payoff, which is the expected value minus the cost to play, for each roll.
    b. Design a simulation to estimate Susana's average payoff for this game after she plays 10 times.
    c. Should Susana play this game? Explain your reasoning.

B 17. **BASEBALL** Of his pitches thrown for strikes, a baseball pitcher wants to track which areas of the strike zone have a higher probability. He divides the strike zone into six congruent boxes as shown.

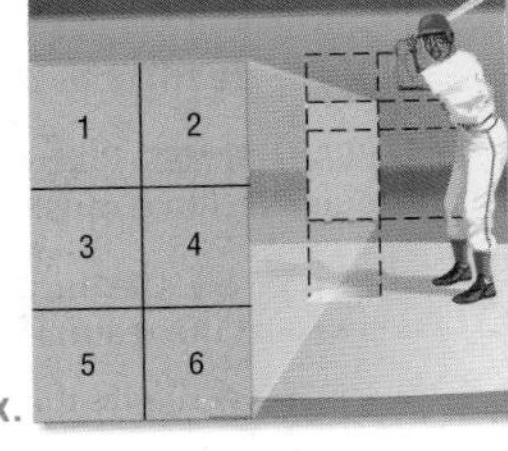

    a. If a strike is equally likely to hit each box, what is the probability that he will throw a strike in each box?
    b. Design a simulation to estimate the probability of a strike being thrown in each box. See Ch. 13 Answer Appendix.
    c. Compare the values for parts **a** and **b**.

17a. There is a $\frac{1}{6}$ or 16.7% probability of throwing a strike in each box.

17c. Sample answer: Some of the values are higher or lower, but most are very close to 16.7%.

18. **CCSS MODELING** Cynthia used her statistics from last season to design a simulation using a random number generator to predict what she would score each time she got possession of the ball.

Integer Values	Points Scored	Frequency
1–14	0	31
15	1	0
16–28	2	17
29–30	3	2

    a. Based on the frequency table, what did she assume was the theoretical probability that she would score two points in a possession? $\frac{13}{30}$ or 43.3%
    b. What is Cynthia's average value for a possession? her expected value? 0.8; 1.1
    c. Would you expect the simulated data to be different? If so, explain how. If not, explain why. See Ch. 13 Answer Appendix.

Enrichment

OL BL

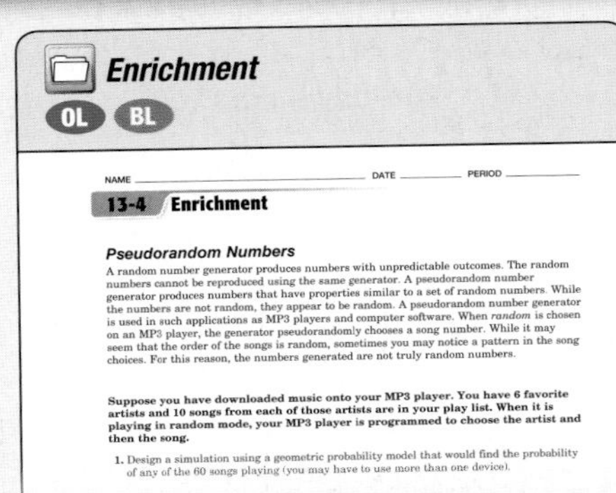

NAME ______ DATE ______ PERIOD ______

13-4 Enrichment

Pseudorandom Numbers

A random number generator produces numbers with unpredictable outcomes. The random numbers cannot be reproduced using the same generator. A pseudorandom number generator produces numbers that have properties similar to a set of random numbers. While the numbers are not random, they appear to be random. A pseudorandom number generator is used in such applications as MP3 players and computer software. When *random* is chosen on an MP3 player, the generator pseudorandomly chooses a song number. While it may seem that the order of the songs is random, sometimes you may notice a pattern in the song choices. For this reason, the numbers generated are not truly random numbers.

Suppose you have downloaded music onto your MP3 player. You have 6 favorite artists and 10 songs from each of those artists are in your play list. When it is playing in random mode, your MP3 player is programmed to choose the artist and then the song.

1. Design a simulation using a geometric probability model that would find the probability of any of the 60 songs playing (you may have to use more than one device).

Additional Answer

12. $E(Y) = 41.4$
Sample answer:

Outcome	Frequency
red	7
blue	20
white	23
total	50

Average value = 47; the average value is greater than the expected value.

 **19.** **MULTIPLE REPRESENTATIONS** In this problem, you will investigate expected value. **a–f. See Ch. 13 Answer Appendix.**

a. Concrete Roll two dice 20 times and record the sum of each roll.

b. Numerical Use the random number generator on a calculator to generate 20 pairs of integers between 1 and 6. Record the sum of each pair.

c. Tabular Copy and complete the table below using your results from parts **a** and **b**.

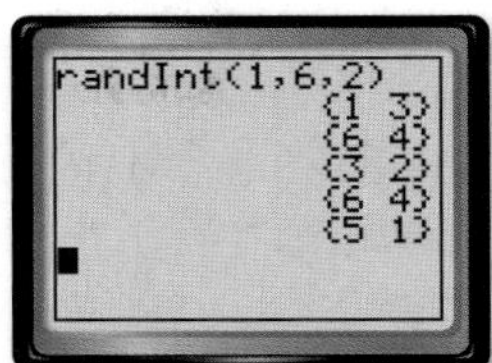

Trial	Sum of Die Roll	Sum of Output from Random Number Generator
1		
2		
...		
20		

d. Graphical Use a bar graph to graph the number of times each possible sum occurred in the first 5 rolls. Repeat the process for the first 10 rolls and then all 20 outcomes.

e. Verbal How does the shape of the bar graph change with each additional trial?

f. Graphical Graph the number of times each possible sum occurred with the random number generator as a bar graph.

g. Verbal How do the graphs of the die trial and the random number trial compare?

19g. Sample answer: They both have the most data points at the middle sums.

h. Analytical Based on the graphs, what do you think the expected value of each experiment would be? Explain your reasoning. **Sample answer: The expected value in both experiments is 7 because it is the sum that occurs most frequently.**

H.O.T. Problems Use Higher-Order Thinking Skills

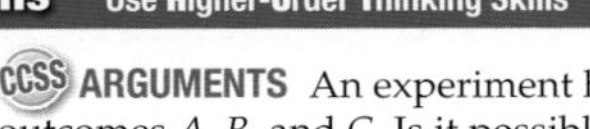

20. **CCSS ARGUMENTS** An experiment has three equally likely outcomes *A*, *B*, and *C*. Is it possible to use the spinner shown in a simulation to predict the probability of outcome C? Explain your reasoning. **See Ch. 13 Answer Appendix.**

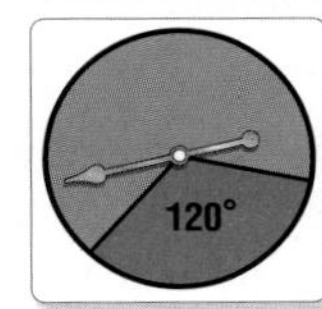

21. **REASONING** Can tossing a coin *sometimes*, *always*, or *never* be used to simulate an experiment with two possible outcomes? Explain. **See Ch. 13 Answer Appendix.**

22. **DECISION MAKING** A lottery consists of choosing 5 winning numbers from 31 possible numbers (0–30). The person who matches all 5 numbers, in any sequence, wins \$1 million. **a–b. See Ch. 13 Answer Appendix.**

a. If a lottery ticket costs \$1, should you play? Explain your reasoning by computing the expected payoff value, which is the expected value minus the ticket cost.

b. Would your decision to play change if the winnings increased to \$5 million? if the winnings were only \$0.5 million, but you chose from 21 numbers instead of 31 numbers? Explain.

23. **REASONING** When designing a simulation where darts are thrown at targets, what assumptions need to be made and why are they needed? **See Ch. 13 Answer Appendix.**

24. **OPEN ENDED** Describe an experiment in which the expected value is not a possible outcome. Explain. **See Ch. 13 Answer Appendix.**

25. **WRITING IN MATH** How is expected value different from probability? **See Ch. 13 Answer Appendix.**

Differentiated Instruction OL BL

Extension Have students write why they should expect the average value of the trials to get closer to the expected value as the number of trials of a simulation increase.

Additional Answers

13. $E(Y) = 38.1$

Sample answer:

Outcome	Frequency
red	0
blue	29
white	21
total	50

Average value = 35.5; the expected value is greater than the average value.

14. $E(Y) = 45.3$

Sample answer:

Outcome	Frequency
red	5
blue	16
white	29
total	50

Average value = 47; the average value is greater than the expected value.

15b. Sample answer: Use a random number generator to generate integers 1 through 20, where 1–7 represents 0 points, 8–19 represents 1 point, and 20 represents 3 points. Do 50 trials and record the results in a frequency table.

Outcome	Frequency
0	16
1	32
3	2

average value = 0.76

16a. –\$0.25

16b. Sample answer: Use a random number generator to generate integers 1 through 20, where 1–11 represents \$0, 12–15 represents \$1, 16–19 represents \$2, and 20 represents \$3. The average payoff after 10 trials is \$0.90 – \$1 or –\$0.10.

16c. Sample answer: No, both the theoretical and simulated expected payoff are less than what it costs to play the game.

4 Assess

Yesterday's News Have students write how what they learned about geometric probability helped them design simulations and compute expected value.

Follow-up

Students have explored simulations.

Ask:

- What should you consider when using the results of a simulation to make a prediction? Sample answers: the design of the simulation, how many trials were used, whether or not the theoretical and experimental probabilities are reasonably close

Standardized Test Practice

26. PROBABILITY Kaya tosses three coins at the same time and repeats the process 9 more times. Her results are shown below where H represents heads and T represents tails. Based on Kaya's data, what is the probability that at least one of the group of 3 coins will land with heads up? D

H H H	T T T
H H T	H T T
T T H	T T H
T H T	H T H
H H H	H H T

A 0.1 B 0.2 C 0.3 D 0.9

27. ALGEBRA Paul collects comic books. He has 20 books in his collection, and he adds 3 per month. In how many months will he have a total of 44 books in his collection? H

F 5 G 6 H 8 J 15

28. SHORT RESPONSE Alberto designed a simulation to determine how many times a player would roll a number higher than 4 on a die in a board game with 5 rolls. The table below shows his results for 50 trials. What is the probability that a player will roll a number higher than 4 two or more times in 5 rolls? $\frac{27}{50}$

Number of Rolls Greater Than 4	Frequency
0	8
1	15
2	18
3	9
4	0
5	0

29. SAT/ACT If a jar contains 150 peanuts and 60 cashews, what is the approximate probability that a nut selected from the jar at random will be a cashew? B

A 0.25 C 0.33 E 0.71
B 0.29 D 0.4

Spiral Review

Point X is chosen at random on $\overline{QT}$. Find the probability of each event. (Lesson 13-3)

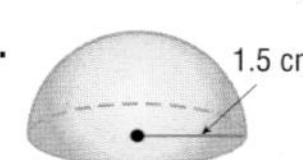

30. $P(X \text{ is on } \overline{QS})$ $\frac{9}{14}$, 0.64, or 64%

31. $P(X \text{ is on } \overline{RT})$ $\frac{4}{7}$, 0.57, or 57%

32. BOOKS Paige is choosing between 10 books at the library. What is the probability that she chooses 3 particular books to check out from the 10 initial books? (Lesson 13-2) $\frac{1}{120}$

Find the surface area of each figure. Round to the nearest tenth. (Lesson 12-6)

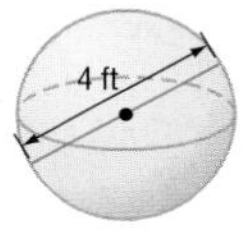

33. 50.3 ft^2

34. 1.5 cm 21.2 cm^2

35. 9 in. 1017.9 in^2

Skills Review

36. RECREATION A group of 150 students was asked what they like to do during their free time.

a. How many students like going to the movies or shopping? 117

b. Which activity was mentioned by 37 students? sports or shopping

c. How many students did *not* say they like movies? 56

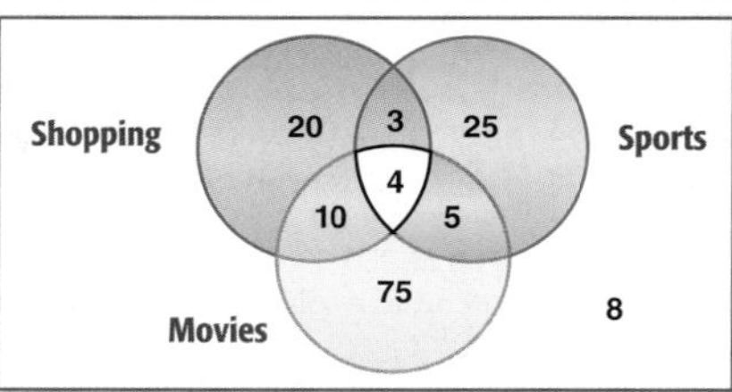

Additional Answers (Lesson 13-5, Guided Practice)

1A. Independent; since the first card is replaced, its selection in no way affects the outcome of the second card's selection.

1B. Dependent; since the first shirt is not put back, the sample space is reduced by one shirt choice.

LESSON 13-5 Probabilities of Independent and Dependent Events

Then

- You found simple probabilities

Now

1. Find probabilities of independent and dependent events.
2. Find probabilities of events given the occurrence of other events.

Why?

- The 18 students in Mrs. Turner's chemistry class are drawing names to determine who will give his or her presentation first. James is hoping to be chosen first and his friend Arturo wants to be second.

NewVocabulary
compound event
independent events
dependent events
conditional probability
probability tree

Common Core State Standards

Content Standards

S.CP.2 Understand that two events A and B are independent if the probability of A and B occurring together is the product of their probabilities, and use this characterization to determine if they are independent.

S.CP.3 Understand the conditional probability of A given B as $\frac{P(A \text{ and } B)}{P(B)}$, and interpret independence of A and B as saying that the conditional probability of A given B is the same as the probability of A, and the conditional probability of B given A is the same as the probability of B.

Mathematical Practices

2 Reason abstractly and quantitatively.
4 Model with mathematics.

1 Independent and Dependent Events

A **compound event** or *composite event* consists of two or more simple events. In the example above, James and Arturo being chosen to give their presentations first is a compound event. It consists of the event that James is chosen and the event that Arturo is chosen.

Compound events can be independent or dependent.

- Events A and B are **independent events** if the probability that A occurs does not affect the probability that B occurs.
- Events A and B are **dependent events** if the probability that A occurs in some way changes the probability that B occurs.

Consider choosing objects from a group of objects. If you replace the object each time, choosing additional objects are independent events. If you do not replace the object each time, choosing additional objects are dependent events.

PT

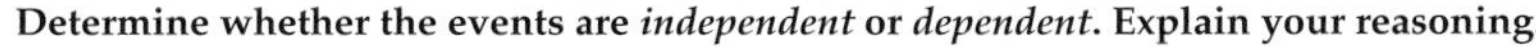

Example 1 Identify Independent and Dependent Events

Determine whether the events are *independent* or *dependent*. Explain your reasoning.

a. One coin is tossed, and then a second coin is tossed.

The outcome of the first coin toss in no way changes the probability of the outcome of the second coin toss. Therefore, these two events are *independent.*

b. In the class presentation example above, one student's name is chosen and not replaced, and then a second name is chosen.

After the first person is chosen, his or her name is removed and cannot be selected again. This affects the probability of the second person being chosen, since the sample space is reduced by one name. Therefore, these two events are *dependent.*

c. Wednesday's lottery numbers and Saturday's lottery numbers.

The numbers for one drawing have no bearing on the next drawing. Therefore, these two events are *independent*.

GuidedPractice 1A, 1B. See margin.

1A. A card is selected from a deck of cards and put back. Then a second card is selected.

1B. Andrea selects a shirt from her closet to wear on Monday and then a different shirt to wear on Tuesday.

1 Focus

VerticalAlignment

Before Lesson 13-5 Find simple probabilities.

Lesson 13-5 Find probabilities of independent and dependent events. Find the probabilities of events given the occurrence of other events.

After Lesson 13-5 Find probabilities of mutually exclusive events.

2 Teach

Scaffolding Questions

Have students read the **Why?** section of the lesson.

Ask:

- What factors affect the probability that James will be chosen first and Arturo will be chosen second? Sample answer: the number of students in the class
- If James is chosen first, what is the probability Arturo will be chosen second? $\frac{1}{17}$
- How does the choice of student that goes first affect if Arturo is chosen second? Arturo could be chosen first.

Lesson 13-5 Resources

Resource	Approaching Level AL	On Level OL	Beyond Level BL	English Learners ELL
Teacher Edition	▪ Differentiated Instruction, p. 950	▪ Differentiated Instruction, pp. 948, 950	▪ Differentiated Instruction, pp. 948, 953	▪ Differentiated Instruction, p. 950
Chapter Resource Masters	▪ Study Guide and Intervention, pp. 31–32 ▪ Skills Practice, p. 33 ▪ Practice, p. 34 ▪ Word Problem Practice, p. 35	▪ Study Guide and Intervention, pp. 31–32 ▪ Skills Practice, p. 33 ▪ Practice, p. 34 ▪ Word Problem Practice, p. 35 ▪ Enrichment, p. 36	▪ Practice, p. 34 ▪ Word Problem Practice, p. 35 ▪ Enrichment, p. 36	▪ Study Guide and Intervention, pp. 31–32 ▪ Skills Practice, p. 33 ▪ Practice, p. 34 ▪ Word Problem Practice, p. 35
Other	▪ 5-Minute Check 13-5 ▪ Study Notebook	▪ 5-Minute Check 13-5 ▪ Study Notebook	▪ 5-Minute Check 13-5 ▪ Study Notebook	▪ 5-Minute Check 13-5 ▪ Study Notebook

1 Independent and Dependent Events

Example 1 shows how to determine whether an event is independent or dependent. **Example 2** shows how to compute the probability of two independent events. **Example 3** shows how to compute the probability of two dependent events.

Formative Assessment

Use the Guided Practice exercises after each example to determine students' understanding of concepts.

Additional Examples

1 Determine whether the events are *independent* or *dependent*. Explain your reasoning.

a. A die is rolled, and then a second die is rolled. The two events are independent because the first roll in no way changes the probability of the second roll.

b. A card is selected from a deck of cards and not put back. Then a second card is selected. The two events are dependent because the first card is removed and cannot be selected again. This affects the probability of the second draw because the sample space is reduced by one.

2 **EATING OUT** Michelle and Christina are going out to lunch. They put 5 green slips of paper and 6 red slips of paper into a bag. If a person draws a green slip, they will order a hamburger. If they draw a red slip, they will order pizza.

Suppose that Michelle draws a slip. Not liking the outcome, she puts it back and draws a second time. What is the probability that on each draw her slip is green? $\frac{25}{121}$

Suppose a coin is tossed and the spinner shown is spun. The sample space for this experiment is

{(H, B), (H, R), (H, G), (T, B), (T, R), (T, G)}.

G
B
R

Using the sample space, the probability of the compound event of the coin landing on heads and the spinner on green is $P(\text{H and G}) = \frac{1}{6}$.

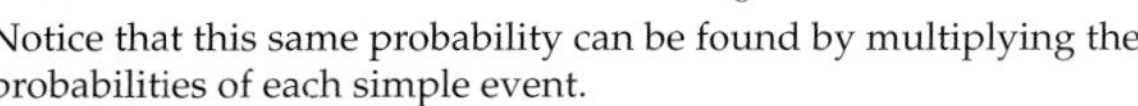

Notice that this same probability can be found by multiplying the probabilities of each simple event.

$$P(\text{H}) = \frac{1}{2} \qquad P(\text{G}) = \frac{1}{3} \qquad P(\text{H and G}) = \frac{1}{2} \cdot \frac{1}{3} \text{ or } \frac{1}{6}$$

This example illustrates the first of two Multiplication Rules for Probability.

ReadingMath

and The word *and* is a key word indicating to multiply probabilities.

KeyConcept Probability of Two Independent Events

Words	The probability that two independent events both occur is the product of the probabilities of each individual event.
Symbols	If two events A and B are independent, then $P(A \text{ and } B) = P(A) \cdot P(B)$.

This rule can be extended to any number of events.

StudyTip

Use an Area Model You can also use the area model shown below to calculate the probability that both slips are blue. The blue region represents the probability of drawing two successive blue slips. The area of this region is $\frac{9}{64}$ of the entire model.

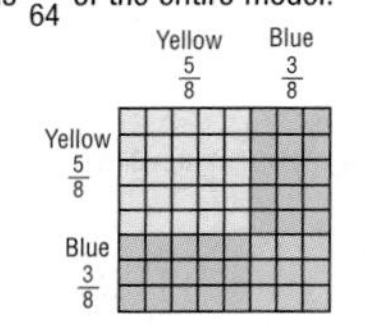

Real-World Example 2 Probability of Independent Events

TRANSPORTATION Marisol and her friends are going to a concert. They put the slips of paper shown into a bag. If a person draws a yellow slip, he or she will ride in the van to the concert. A blue slip means he or she rides in the car.

Suppose Marisol draws a slip. Not liking the outcome, she puts it back and draws a second time. What is the probability that on each draw her slip is blue?

These events are independent since Marisol replaced the slip that she removed. Let B represent a blue slip and Y a yellow slip.

	Draw 1		Draw 2	
$P(B \text{ and } B) =$	$P(B)$	$\cdot$	$P(B)$	Probability of independent events
$=$	$\frac{3}{8}$	$\cdot$	$\frac{3}{8}$ or $\frac{9}{64}$	$P(B) = \frac{3}{8}$

So, the probability of Marisol drawing two blue slips is $\frac{9}{64}$ or about 14%.

GuidedPractice

Find each probability. **2A.** $\frac{1}{12}$ or about 8% **2B.** $\frac{1}{16}$ or 6.25%

2A. A coin is tossed and a die is rolled. What is the probability that the coin lands heads up and the number rolled is a 6?

2B. Suppose you toss a coin four times. What is the probability of getting four tails?

DifferentiatedInstruction OL BL

Extension Have students calculate the probability of simple independent events, such as tossing a coin, using the formula for dependent probabilities. Students should see that the formula produces the same probabilities for independent events as the formula for calculating independent events.

The second of the Multiplication Rules of Probability addresses the probability of two dependent events.

KeyConcept Probability of Two Dependent Events

Words	The probability that two dependent events both occur is the product of the probability that the first event occurs and the probability that the second event occurs *after* the first event has already occurred.
Symbols	If two events A and B are dependent, then $P(A \text{ and } B) = P(A) \cdot P(B\mid A)$.

This rule can be extended to any number of events.

WatchOut!

Conditional Notation The "|" symbol in the notation $P(B\mid A)$ should not be interpreted as a division symbol.

The notation $P(B\mid A)$ is read *the probability that event B occurs given that event A has already occurred.* This is called **conditional probability**.

Example 3 Probability of Dependent Events

TRANSPORTATION Refer to Example 2. Suppose Marisol draws a slip and does not put it back. Then her friend Christian draws a slip. What is the probability that both friends draw a yellow slip?

These events are dependent since Marisol does not replace the slip that she removed.

$P(Y \text{ and } Y) = P(Y) \cdot P(Y\mid Y)$ — Probability of dependent events

$= \frac{5}{8} \cdot \frac{4}{7}$ or $\frac{5}{14}$ — After the first yellow slip is chosen, 7 total slips remain, and 4 of those are yellow.

So, the probability that both friends draw yellow slips is $\frac{5}{14}$ or about 36%.

CHECK You can use a tree diagram with probabilities, called a **probability tree**, to verify this result. Calculate the probability of each simple event at the first stage and each conditional probability at the second stage. Then multiply along each branch to find the probability of each outcome.

- $\frac{5}{8}$ Y
  - $\frac{4}{7}$ Y — $P(Y \text{ and } Y) = \frac{5}{8} \cdot \frac{4}{7}$ or $\frac{20}{56}$
  - $\frac{3}{7}$ B — $P(Y \text{ and } B) = \frac{5}{8} \cdot \frac{3}{7}$ or $\frac{15}{56}$
- $\frac{3}{8}$ B
  - $\frac{5}{7}$ Y — $P(B \text{ and } Y) = \frac{3}{8} \cdot \frac{5}{7}$ or $\frac{15}{56}$
  - $\frac{2}{7}$ B — $P(B \text{ and } B) = \frac{3}{8} \cdot \frac{2}{7}$ or $\frac{6}{56}$

The sum of the probabilities should be 1.

$\frac{20}{56} + \frac{15}{56} + \frac{15}{56} + \frac{6}{56} = \frac{56}{56}$ or 1 ✓

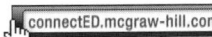

Real-WorldLink

A recent study found that with three or more teenage passengers, 85% of fatal crashes of passenger vehicles driven by teens involved driver error, almost 50% involved speeding, and almost 70% involved a single vehicle.

Source: National Safety Council

GuidedPractice $\frac{11}{850}$ **or about 1%**

3. Three cards are selected from a standard deck of 52 cards. What is the probability that all three cards are diamonds if neither the first nor the second card is replaced?

Additional Example

3 EATING OUT Refer to Additional Example 2. Suppose that Michelle draws a slip and does not put it back. Then her friend Christina draws a slip. What is the probability that both friends draw a green slip? $\frac{2}{11}$

Additional Examples also in Interactive Classroom PowerPoint® Presentations

Focus on Mathematical Content

Dependent Events The order of events occurring in a dependent event is important. For example, the probability of drawing a 3 from a deck of cards if a club has already been drawn is not the same as the probability of drawing a club if a 3 has already been drawn. In symbols, this is stated as $P(A\mid B) \neq P(B\mid A)$.

Teach with Tech

Interactive Whiteboard

Choose two students to work through an example in front of the class. Have one student explain how to find the probability of dependent events, and have the other student explain how to find the probability of independent events.

2 Conditional Probabilities

Example 4 shows how to compute a conditional probability.

Additional Example

4 STANDARDIZED TEST PRACTICE Mr. Monroe is organizing the gym class into two teams for a game. The 20 students randomly draw cards numbered with consecutive integers from 1 to 20.

- Students who draw odd numbers will be on the Red team.
- Students who draw even numbers will be on the Blue team.

If Monica is on the Blue team, what is the probability that she drew the number 10? B

A $\frac{1}{20}$ **C** $\frac{9}{20}$

B $\frac{1}{10}$ **D** $\frac{1}{2}$

2 Conditional Probabilities In addition to its use in finding the probability of two or more dependent events, conditional probability can be used when additional information is known about an event.

ReadingMath

Conditional Probability *P*(5|odd) is read *the probability that the number rolled is a 5 given that the number rolled is odd.*

Suppose a die is rolled and it is known that the number rolled is odd. What is the probability that the number rolled is a 5?

There are only three odd numbers that can be rolled, so our sample space is reduced from {1, 2, 3, 4, 5, 6} to {1, 3, 5}. So, the probability that the number rolled is a 5 is $P(5|\text{odd}) = \frac{1}{3}$.

Standardized Test Example 4 Conditional Probability

Ms. Fuentes' class is holding a debate. The 8 students participating randomly draw cards numbered with consecutive integers from 1 to 8.

- **Students who draw odd numbers will be on the Proposition Team.**
- **Students who draw even numbers will be on the Opposition Team.**

If Jonathan is on the Opposition Team, what is the probability that he drew the number 2?

A $\frac{1}{8}$ B $\frac{1}{4}$ C $\frac{3}{8}$ D $\frac{1}{2}$

Read the Test Item

Since Jonathan is on the Opposition Team, he must have drawn an even number. So you need to find the probability that the number drawn was 2 given that the number drawn was even. This is a conditional probability problem.

Solve the Test Item

Test-TakingTip

Use a Venn Diagram Use a Venn diagram to help you visualize the relationship between the outcomes of two events.

Let *A* be the event that an even number is drawn.
Let *B* be the event that the number 2 is drawn.

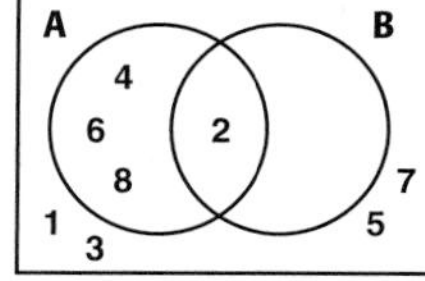

Draw a Venn diagram to represent this situation. There are only four even numbers in the sample space, and only one out of these numbers is a 2. Therefore, the $P(B|A) = \frac{1}{4}$. The answer is B.

GuidedPractice

4. When two dice are rolled, what is the probability that one die is a 4, given that the sum of the two die is 9? J

F $\frac{1}{6}$ G $\frac{1}{4}$ H $\frac{1}{3}$ J $\frac{1}{2}$

Since conditional probability reduces the sample space, the Venn diagram in Example 4 can be simplified as shown, with the intersection of the two events representing those outcomes in *A* and *B*. This suggests the following formula.

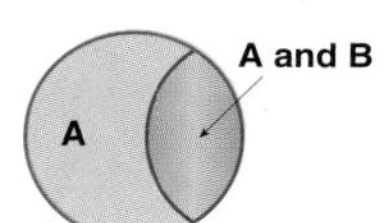

$$P(B|A) = \frac{P(A \text{ and } B)}{P(A)}$$

KeyConcept Conditional Probability

The conditional probability of *B* given *A* is $P(B|A) = \frac{P(A \text{ and } B)}{P(A)}$, where $P(A) \neq 0$.

DifferentiatedInstruction AL OL ELL

Verbal/Linguistic Learners Have students discuss the differences between finding probabilities for independent and dependent events and for conditional probabilities. This should include that the formulas for independent and dependent events calculate the probability of two or more events occurring, whereas conditional probability calculates the probability of one event given that another has occurred.

Check Your Understanding

Example 1 **Determine whether the events are *independent* or *dependent*. Explain.**

1. Jeremy took the SAT on Saturday and scored 1350. The following week he took the ACT and scored 23. **See margin.**

2. Alita's basketball team is in the final four. If they win, they will play in the championship game. **See margin.**

Example 2

3. **CARDS** A card is randomly chosen from a deck of 52 cards, replaced, and a second card is chosen. What is the probability of choosing both of the cards shown at the right? $\frac{1}{2704}$ **or** 3.7×10^{-4}

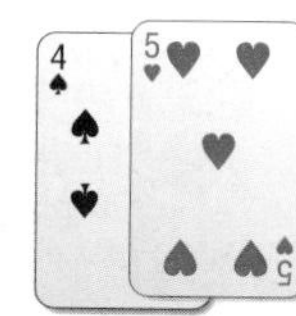

Example 3

4. **TRANSPORTATION** Isaiah is getting on the bus after work. It costs $0.50 to ride the bus to his house. If he has 3 quarters, 5 dimes, and 2 nickels in his pocket, find the probability that he will randomly pull out two quarters in a row. Assume that the events are equally likely to occur. $\frac{1}{15}$ **or 0.07**

Example 4

5. **GRIDDED RESPONSE** Every Saturday, 10 friends play dodgeball at a local park. To pick teams, they randomly draw cards with consecutive integers from 1 to 10. Odd numbers are on Team A, and even numbers are Team B. What is the probability that a player on Team B has drawn the number 10? $\frac{1}{5}$ **or 0.20**

Practice and Problem Solving

Extra Practice is on page R13.

Examples 1–3 **CCSS REASONING Determine whether the events are *independent* or *dependent*. Then find the probability.**

6. In a game, you roll an even number on a die and then spin a spinner numbered 1 through 5 and get an odd number. **independent;** $\frac{3}{10}$ **or 30%**

7. An ace is drawn, without replacement, from a deck of 52 cards. Then, a second ace is drawn. **dependent;** $\frac{1}{221}$ **or 0.5%**

8. In a bag of 3 green and 4 blue marbles, a blue marble is drawn and not replaced. Then, a second blue marble is drawn. **dependent;** $\frac{2}{7}$ **or about 29%**

9. You roll two dice and get a 5 each time. **independent;** $\frac{1}{36}$ **or about 3%**

10. **GAMES** In a game, the spinner at the right is spun and a coin is tossed. What is the probability of getting an even number on the spinner and the coin landing on tails? $\frac{1}{4}$ **or 25%**

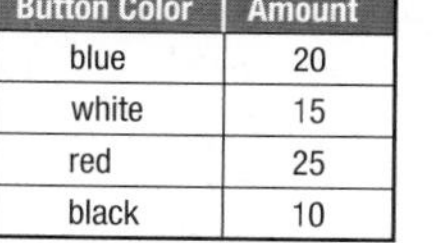

11. **GIFTS** Tisha's class is having a gift exchange. Tisha will draw first and her friend Brandi second. If there are 18 students participating, what is the probability that Brandi and Tisha draw each other's names? $\frac{1}{306}$ **or about 0.3%**

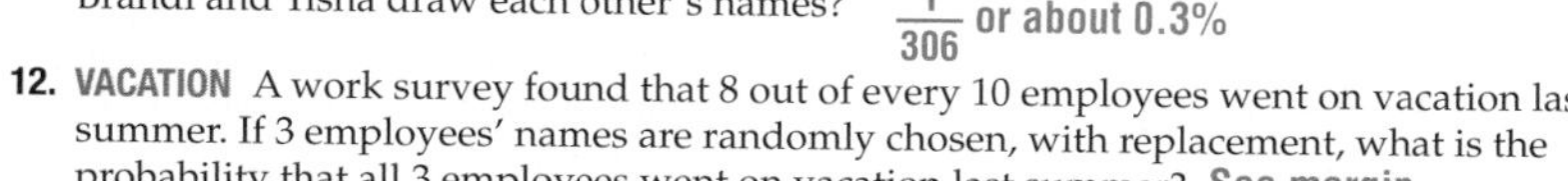

12. **VACATION** A work survey found that 8 out of every 10 employees went on vacation last summer. If 3 employees' names are randomly chosen, with replacement, what is the probability that all 3 employees went on vacation last summer? **See margin.**

13. **CAMPAIGNS** The table shows the number of each color of Student Council campaign buttons Clemente has to give away. If given away at random, what is the probability that the first and second buttons given away are both red? $\frac{20}{161}$ **or about 12%**

Button Color	Amount
blue	20
white	15
red	25
black	10

Differentiated Homework Options

Level	Assignment	Two-Day Option	
AL Basic	6–17, 23, 25–43	7–17 odd, 28–31	6–16 even, 23, 25–27, 32–43
OL Core	7–17 odd, 18–23, 25–43	6–17, 28–31	18–23, 25–27, 32–43
BL Advanced	18–39, (optional: 40–43)		

3 Practice

Formative Assessment

Use Exercises 1–5 to check for understanding.

Then use the chart at the bottom of this page to customize assignments for your students.

Additional Answers

1. The outcome of Jeremy taking the SAT in no way changes the probability of the outcome of his ACT test. Therefore, these two events are *independent*.
2. Alita's team will only go to the championship game if they win their game in the final four. Therefore, these two events are *dependent*.

12. $\frac{512}{1000}$ or about 51%

CCSS Teaching the Mathematical Practices

Reasoning Mathematically proficient students make sense of quantities and their relationships in problem situations. They use the ability to decontextualize—to abstract a given situation and represent it symbolically. In Exercises 6–9, encourage students to determine whether the events are independent or dependent and then apply multiplication rules for probability.

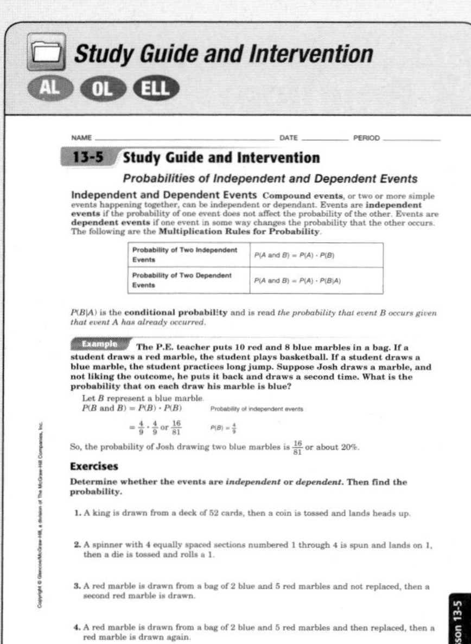

Study Guide and Intervention
AL OL ELL

NAME ______ DATE ______ PERIOD ______

13-5 Study Guide and Intervention

Probabilities of Independent and Dependent Events

Independent and Dependent Events Compound events, or two or more simple events happening together, can be independent or dependant. Events are **independent events** if the probability of one event does not affect the probability of the other. Events are **dependent events** if one event in some way changes the probability that the other occurs. The following are the **Multiplication Rules for Probability**.

Probability of Two Independent Events	$P(A \text{ and } B) = P(A) \cdot P(B)$
Probability of Two Dependent Events	$P(A \text{ and } B) = P(A) \cdot P(B\|A)$

$P(B|A)$ is the **conditional probability** and is read *the probability that event B occurs given that event A has already occurred.*

Example The P.E. teacher puts 10 red and 8 blue marbles in a bag. If a student draws a red marble, the student plays basketball. If a student draws a blue marble, the student practices long jump. Suppose Josh draws a marble, and not liking the outcome, he puts it back and draws a second time. What is the probability that on each draw his marble is blue?

Let *B* represent a blue marble.

$P(B \text{ and } B) = P(B) \cdot P(B)$ Probability of independent events

$= \frac{4}{9} \cdot \frac{4}{9}$ or $\frac{16}{81}$ $P(B) = \frac{4}{9}$

So, the probability of Josh drawing two blue marbles is $\frac{16}{81}$ or about 20%.

Exercises

Determine whether the events are *independent* or *dependent*. Then find the probability.

1. A king is drawn from a deck of 52 cards, then a coin is tossed and lands heads up.

2. A spinner with 4 equally spaced sections numbered 1 through 4 is spun and lands on 1, then a die is tossed and rolls a 1.

3. A red marble is drawn from a bag of 2 blue and 5 red marbles and not replaced, then a second red marble is drawn.

4. A red marble is drawn from a bag of 2 blue and 5 red marbles and then replaced, then a red marble is drawn again.

Lesson 13-5

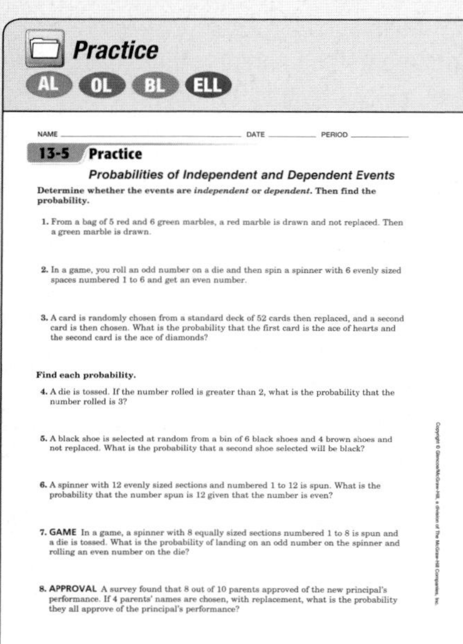

Practice
AL OL BL ELL

NAME ______ DATE ______ PERIOD ______

13-5 Practice

Probabilities of Independent and Dependent Events

Determine whether the events are *independent* or *dependent*. Then find the probability.

1. From a bag of 5 red and 6 green marbles, a red marble is drawn and not replaced. Then a green marble is drawn.

2. In a game, you roll an odd number on a die and then spin a spinner with 6 evenly sized spaces numbered 1 to 6 and get an even number.

3. A card is randomly chosen from a standard deck of 52 cards then replaced, and a second card is then chosen. What is the probability that the first card is the ace of hearts and the second card is the ace of diamonds?

Find each probability.

4. A die is tossed. If the number rolled is greater than 2, what is the probability that the number rolled is 3?

5. A black shoe is selected at random from a bin of 6 black shoes and 4 brown shoes and not replaced. What is the probability that a second shoe selected will be black?

6. A spinner with 12 evenly sized sections and numbered 1 to 12 is spun. What is the probability that the number spun is 12 given that the number is even?

7. **GAME** In a game, a spinner with 8 equally sized sections numbered 1 to 8 is spun and a die is tossed. What is the probability of landing on an odd number on the spinner and rolling an even number on the die?

8. **APPROVAL** A survey found that 8 out of 10 parents approved of the new principal's performance. If 4 parents' names are chosen, with replacement, what is the probability they all approve of the principal's performance?

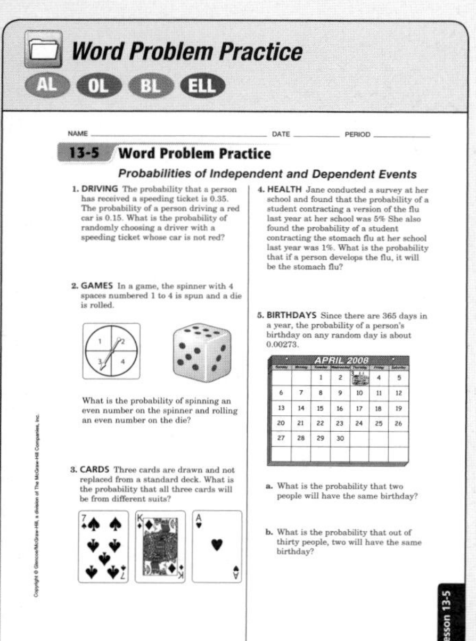

Word Problem Practice
AL OL BL ELL

NAME ______ DATE ______ PERIOD ______

13-5 Word Problem Practice

Probabilities of Independent and Dependent Events

1. **DRIVING** The probability that a person has received a speeding ticket is 0.35. The probability of a person driving a red car is 0.15. What is the probability of randomly choosing a driver with a speeding ticket whose car is not red?

2. **GAMES** In a game, the spinner with 4 spaces numbered 1 to 4 is spun and a die is rolled.

What is the probability of spinning an even number on the spinner and rolling an even number on the die?

3. **CARDS** Three cards are drawn and not replaced from a standard deck. What is the probability that all three cards will be from different suits?

4. **HEALTH** Jane conducted a survey at her school and found that the probability of a student contracting a version of the flu last year at her school was 5%. She also found the probability of a student contracting the stomach flu at her school last year was 1%. What is the probability that if a person develops the flu, it will be the stomach flu?

5. **BIRTHDAYS** Since there are 365 days in a year, the probability of a person's birthday on any random day is about 0.00273.

a. What is the probability that two people will have the same birthday?

b. What is the probability that out of thirty people, two will have the same birthday?

Lesson 13-5

Example 4

14. A red marble is selected at random from a bag of 2 blue and 9 red marbles and not replaced. What is the probability that a second marble selected will be red? $\frac{4}{5}$ or 80%

15. A die is rolled. If the number rolled is greater than 2, find the probability that it is a 6. $\frac{1}{4}$ or 25%

16. A quadrilateral has a perimeter of 12 and all of the side lengths are odd integers. What is the probability that the quadrilateral is a rhombus? $\frac{1}{5}$ or 20%

17. A spinner numbered 1 through 12 is spun. Find the probability that the number spun is an 11 given that the number spun was an odd number. $\frac{1}{6}$ or 17%

B

18. **CLASSES** The probability that a student takes geometry and French at Satomi's school is 0.064. The probability that a student takes French is 0.45. What is the probability that a student takes geometry if the student takes French? **0.14**

19. **TECHNOLOGY** At Bell High School, 43% of the students own a CD player and 28% own a CD player and an MP3 player. What is the probability that a student owns an MP3 player if he or she also owns a CD player? **0.65**

20. **PROOF** Use the formula for the probability of two dependent events $P(A \text{ and } B)$ to derive the conditional probability formula for $P(B|A)$. **See Ch. 13 Answer Appendix.**

C

21. **TENNIS** A double fault in tennis is when the serving player fails to land their serve "in" without stepping on or over the service line in two chances. Kelly's first serve percentage is 40%, while her second serve percentage is 70%.

    a. Draw a probability tree that shows each outcome. **See Ch. 13 Answer Appendix.**

    b. What is the probability that Kelly will double fault? **0.18 or 18%**

    c. Design a simulation using a random number generator that can be used to estimate the probability that Kelly double faults on her next serve.

21c. Sample answer: I would use a random number generator to generate integers 1 through 50. The integers 1–9 will represent a double fault, and the integers 10–50 will represent the other possible outcomes. The simulation will consist of 50 trials.

22. **VACATION** A random survey was conducted to determine where families vacationed. The results indicated that $P(B) = 0.6$, $P(B \cap M) = 0.2$, and the probability that a family did not vacation at either destination is 0.1.

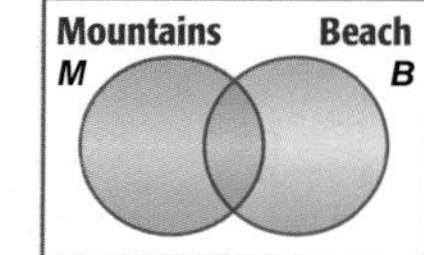

    a. What is the probability that a family vacations in the mountains? **0.3**

    b. What is the probability that a family visiting the beach will also visit the mountains? **0.33**

23. **DECISION MAKING** You are trying to decide whether you should expand a business. If you do not expand and the economy remains good, you expect \$2 million in revenue. If the economy is bad, you expect \$0.5 million. The cost to expand is \$1 million, but the expected revenue after the expansion is \$4 million in a good economy and \$1 million in a bad economy. You assume that the chances of a good and a bad economy are 30% and 70%, respectively. Use a probability tree to explain what you should do. **See Ch. 13 Answer Appendix.**

H.O.T. Problems Use Higher-Order Thinking Skills

24. **CCSS ARGUMENTS** There are n different objects in a bag. The probability of drawing object A and then object B without replacement is about 2.4%. What is the value of n? Explain. **See Ch. 13 Answer Appendix.**

25. **REASONING** If $P(A \mid B)$ is the same as $P(A)$, and $P(B \mid A)$ is the same as $P(B)$, what can be said about the relationship between events A and B? ***A* and *B* are independent events.**

26. **OPEN ENDED** Describe a pair of independent events and a pair of dependent events. Explain your reasoning. **See Ch. 13 Answer Appendix.**

27. **WRITING IN MATH** A medical journal reports the chance that a person smokes given that his or her parent smokes. Explain how you could determine the likelihood that a person's smoking and their parent's smoking are independent events. **See margin.**

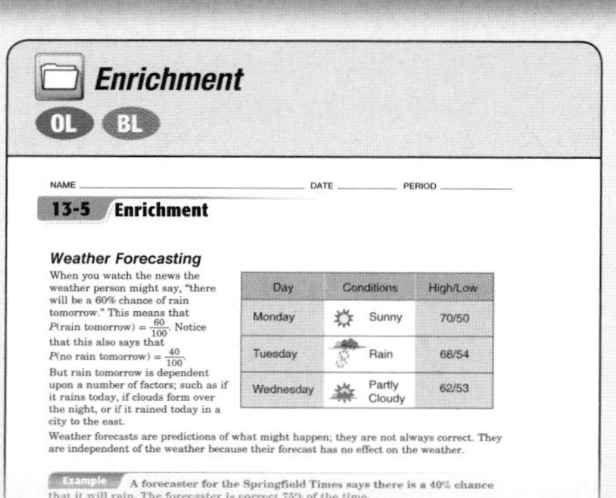

Enrichment
OL BL

NAME ______ DATE ______ PERIOD ______

13-5 Enrichment

Weather Forecasting

When you watch the news the weather person might say, "there will be a 60% chance of rain tomorrow." This means that $P(\text{rain tomorrow}) = \frac{60}{100}$. Notice that this also says that $P(\text{no rain tomorrow}) = \frac{40}{100}$. But rain tomorrow is dependent upon a number of factors; such as if it rains today, if clouds form over the night, or if it rained today in a city to the east.

Day	Conditions	High/Low
Monday	Sunny	70/50
Tuesday	Rain	68/54
Wednesday	Partly Cloudy	62/53

Weather forecasts are predictions of what might happen; they are not always correct. They are independent of the weather because their forecast has no effect on the weather.

Example A forecaster for the Springfield Times says there is a 40% chance that it will rain. The forecaster is correct 75% of the time.

Additional Answer

27. In order for the events to be independent, two things must be true: 1) the chance that a person smokes is the same as the chance that a person smokes given that the person's parent smokes, and 2) the chance that a person's parent smokes is the same as the chance that a person's parent smokes given that the person smokes.

Standardized Test Practice

28. PROBABILITY Shannon will be assigned at random to 1 of 6 P.E. classes throughout the day and 1 of 3 lunch times. What is the probability that she will be in the second P.E. class and the first lunch? **A**

A $\frac{1}{18}$ B $\frac{1}{9}$ C $\frac{1}{6}$ D $\frac{1}{2}$

29. ALGEBRA Tameron downloaded 2 videos and 7 songs to his digital media player for $10.91. Jake downloaded 3 videos and 4 songs for $9.93. What is the cost of each video? **J**

F $0.99 H $1.42

G $1.21 J $1.99

30. GRIDDED RESPONSE A bag of jelly beans contains 7 red, 11 yellow, and 13 green. Victoro picks two jelly beans from the bag without looking. What is the probability as a percent rounded to the nearest tenth that Victoro picks a green one and then a red one? **9.8**

31. SAT/ACT If the probability that it will snow on Tuesday is $\frac{4}{13}$, then what is the probability that it will *not* snow? **B**

A $\frac{4}{9}$ C $\frac{13}{9}$ E $\frac{13}{4}$

B $\frac{9}{13}$ D $\frac{13}{5}$

Spiral Review

32. SOFTBALL Zoe struck out during 10% of her at bats last season. Design and conduct a simulation to estimate the probability that she will strike out at her next at bat this season. (Lesson 13-4) **See margin.**

Use the spinner to find each probability. The spinner is spun again if it stops on a line. (Lesson 13-3)

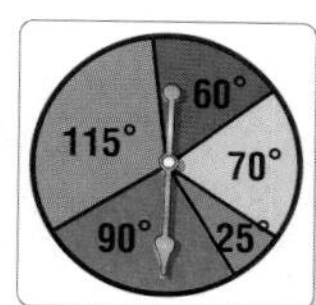

33. *P*(pointer landing on red) **0.25**

34. *P*(pointer landing on blue) **0.32**

35. *P*(pointer landing on green) **0.07**

36. *P*(pointer landing on yellow) **0.19**

Determine whether each pair of solids is *similar, congruent,* or *neither.* If the solids are similar, state the scale factor. (Lesson 12-8)

37. 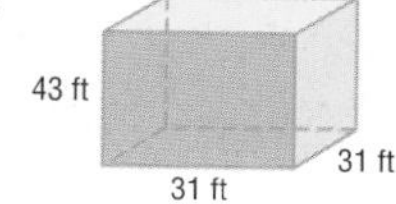

16 ft, 16 ft, 18 ft **neither**

38. 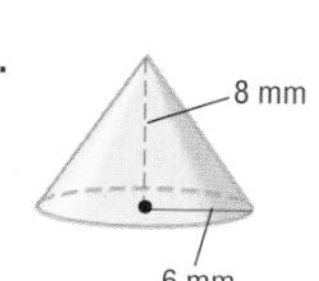

6 mm, 10 mm **congruent**

39. FIREWORKS Fireworks are shot from a barge on a river. There is an explosion circle inside which all of the fireworks will explode. Spectators sit outside a safety circle 800 feet from the center of the fireworks display. (Lesson 10-1)

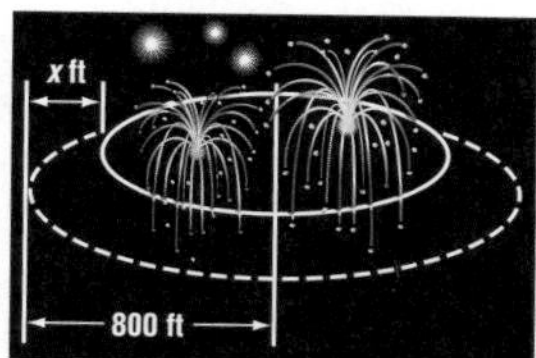

a. Find the approximate circumference of the safety circle. **5026.5 ft**

b. If the safety circle is 200 to 300 feet farther from the center than the explosion circle, find the range of values for the radius of the explosion circle. **500–600 ft**

c. Find the least and maximum circumferences of the explosion circle to the nearest foot. **3142 ft; 3770 ft**

Skills Review

Find the number of possible outcomes for each situation.

40. Blanca chooses from 5 different flavors of ice cream and 3 different toppings. **15**

41. Perry chooses from 6 colors and 2 seat designs for his new mountain bike. **12**

42. A rectangle has a perimeter of 12 and integer side lengths. **3**

43. Three number cubes are rolled simultaneously. **216**

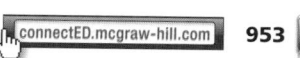

Differentiated Instruction BL

Extension The game show *Let's Make a Deal* has created controversy in the study of probability with the question: Switch or stay? Contestants on the show were asked to choose one door out of three. They were then shown one of the remaining doors that did not contain the one grand prize. The question was then asked, "Do you want to stay with your original choice, or switch to the remaining door?" Students can create a simulation or use an online applet to explore this question. Students should be able to explain why repeating an experiment many times forces the experimental and theoretical probabilities closer together.

CCSS Teaching the Mathematical Practices

Arguments Mathematically proficient students understand and use stated assumptions and definitions in constructing arguments. They are able to analyze situations by breaking them into cases, and can recognize and use counterexamples. In Exercise 24, encourage students to model this exercise using marbles in a bag.

4 Assess

Ticket Out the Door Have students write on a piece of paper the difference between independent and dependent events.

Formative Assessment

Check for student understanding of Lessons 13-4 and 13-5.

 Quiz 3, p. 46

Additional Answer

32. Sample answer: Use a spinner that is divided into two sectors, one containing 10% or 36° and the other containing 90% or 324°. Do 20 trials and record the results in a frequency table.

Outcome	Frequency
strike out	1
other	19
total	20

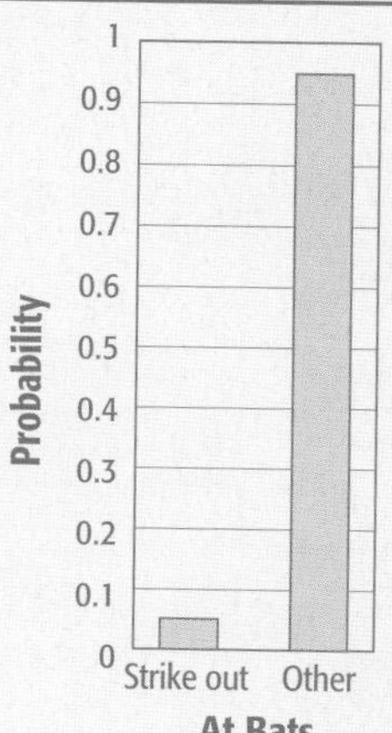

The probability that Zoe strikes out during her next at bat is 0.05. The probability of that she will not strike out is 0.95.

1 Focus

Objective Use two-way frequency tables to find marginal, joint, and relative frequencies.

Teaching Tip

Either of the tables in Activities 1 or 2 can be used to compute conditional probabilities like the one asked for in Activity 3. To find the conditional probability that a student attends the prom given that he or she is a senior using the table in Activity 1, divide the number of seniors attending the prom, 44, by the total number of seniors, 76. However, converting the two-way frequency table to a two-way relative frequency table will give you more information and allow you to answer questions more quickly.

2 Teach

Working in Cooperative Groups

Have student work in mixed ability pairs. Have students alternate the steps of the activities.

EXTEND 13-5 Geometry Lab Two-Way Frequency Tables

A **two-way frequency table** or *contingency table* is used to show the frequencies of data from a survey or experiment classified according to two variables, with the rows indicating one variable and the columns indicating the other.

CCSS Common Core State Standards
Content Standards
S.CP.4 Construct and interpret two-way frequency tables of data when two categories are associated with each object being classified. Use the two-way table as a sample space to decide if events are independent and to approximate conditional probabilities.
S.CP.6 Find the conditional probability of *A* given *B* as the fraction of *B*'s outcomes that also belong to *A*, and interpret the answer in terms of the model.
Mathematical Practices 5

Activity 1 Two-Way Frequency Table

PROM **Michael asks a random sample of 160 upperclassmen at his high school whether or not they plan to attend the prom. He finds that 44 seniors and 32 juniors plan to attend the prom, while 25 seniors and 59 juniors do not plan to attend. Organize the responses into a two-way frequency table.**

Step 1 Identify the variables. The students surveyed can be classified according *class* and *attendance.* Since the survey included only upperclassmen, the variable *class* has two categories: senior or junior. The variable *attendance* also has two categories: attending or not attending the prom.

Step 2 Create a two-way frequency table. Let the rows of the table represent *class* and the columns represent *attendance.* Then fill in the cells of the table with the information given.

Step 3 Add a *Totals* row and a *Totals* column to your table and fill in these cells with the correct sums.

Class	Attending the Prom	Not Attending the Prom	Totals
Senior	44	32	76
Junior	25	59	84
Totals	69	91	160

The frequencies reported in the *Totals* row and *Totals* column are called **marginal frequencies**, with the bottom rightmost cell reporting the total number of observations. The frequencies reported in the interior of the table are called **joint frequencies**. These show the frequencies of all possible combinations of the categories for the first variable with the categories for the second variable.

Analyze the Results

1. How many seniors were surveyed? **76**
2. How many of the students that were surveyed plan to attend the prom? **69**

A **relative frequency** is the ratio of the number of observations in a category to the total number of observations.

Activity 2 Two-Way Relative Frequency Table

PROM **Convert the table from Activity 1 to a table of relative frequencies.**

Step 1 Divide the frequency reported in each cell by the total number of respondents, 160.

Class	Attending the Prom	Not Attending the Prom	Totals
Senior	$\frac{44}{160}$	$\frac{32}{160}$	$\frac{76}{160}$
Junior	$\frac{25}{160}$	$\frac{59}{160}$	$\frac{84}{160}$
Totals	$\frac{69}{160}$	$\frac{91}{160}$	$\frac{160}{160}$

Step 2 Write each fraction as a percent rounded to the nearest tenth.

Class	Attending the Prom	Not Attending the Prom	Totals
Senior	27.5%	20%	47.5%
Junior	15.6%	36.9%	52.5%
Totals	43.1%	56.9%	100%

954 | Extend 13-5 | Geometry Lab: Two-Way Frequency Tables

Practice Have students complete Activities 1–4 and Exercises 1–6.

3 Assess

Formative Assessment

Use Exercises 7 and 8 to assess each student's ability to use two-way frequency tables to determine if events are independent.

From Concrete to Abstract

Ask students to summarize what they learned about two-way frequency tables.

You can use joint and marginal relative frequencies to approximate conditional probabilities.

Activity 3 Conditional Probabilities

PROM **Using the table from Activity 2, find the probability that a surveyed upperclassman plans to attend the prom given that he or she is a junior.**

The probability that a surveyed upperclassman plans to attend the prom given that he or she is a junior is the conditional probability *P*(attending the prom | junior).

$$P(\text{attending the prom} \mid \text{junior}) = \frac{P(\text{attending the prom and junior})}{P(\text{junior})}$$ Conditional Probability

$$\approx \frac{0.156}{0.525} \text{ or } 29.7\%$$ *P*(attending the prom and junior) = 15.6% or 0.156, *P*(junior) = 52.5% or 0.525

Analyze and Apply

Refer to Activities 2 and 3.

3. If there are 285 upperclassmen, about how many would you predict plan to attend the prom? **123 upperclassmen**
4. Find the probability that a surveyed student is a junior and does not plan to attend the prom. **≈36.9%**
5. Find the probability that a surveyed student is a senior given that he or she plans to attend the prom. **≈63.8%**
6. What is a possible trend you notice in the data? **Sample answer: It appears that more seniors plan to attend prom than juniors.**

When survey results are classified according to variables, you may want to decide whether these variables are independent of each other. Variable *A* is considered independent of variable *B* if $P(A \text{ and } B) = P(A) \cdot P(B)$. In a two-way frequency table, you can test for the independence of two variables by comparing the joint relative frequencies with the products of the corresponding marginal relative frequencies.

Activity 4 Independence of Events

PROM **Use the relative frequency table from Activity 2 to determine whether prom attendance is independent of class.**

Calculate the expected joint relative frequencies if the two variables were independent. Then compare them to the actual relative frequencies.

For example, if 47.5% of respondents were seniors and 43.1% of respondents plan to attend the prom, then one would expect 47.5% • 43.1% or about 20.5% of respondents are seniors who plan to attend the prom.

Since the expected and actual joint relative frequencies are not the same, prom attendance for these respondents is not independent of class.

Class	Attending the Prom	Not Attending the Prom	Totals
Senior	27.5% (20.5%)	20% (27%)	47.5%
Junior	15.6% (22.6%)	36.9% (29.9%)	52.5%
Totals	43.1%	56.9%	100%

Note: The numbers in parentheses are the expected relative frequencies.

COLLECT DATA **Design and conduct a survey of students at your school. Create a two-way relative frequency table for the data. Use your table to decide whether the data you collected indicate an independent relationship between the two variables. Explain your reasoning.**

7. student gender and whether a student's car insurance is paid by the student or the student's parent(s) **See students' work.**
8. student gender and whether a student buys or brings his or her lunch **See students' work.**

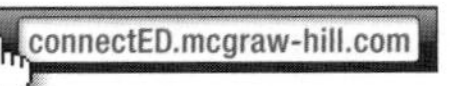

connectED.mcgraw-hill.com 955

1 Focus

VerticalAlignment

Before Lesson 13-6 Find probabilities of independent and dependent events.

Lesson 13-6 Find the probabilities of events that are mutually exclusive and events that are not mutually exclusive.

After Lesson 13-6 Investigate graph theory.

2 Teach

Scaffolding Questions

Have students read the **Why?** section of the lesson.

Ask:

- Why would Trayvon be thrilled if Katrina wins the election? She is a sophomore and female.
- Can a person win the election that both Dominic and Trayvon want? Yes; if the person is a junior or senior and female.
- Would either Dominic or Trayvon be happy if freshman Michael Monroe won the election? No; he is a freshman and male.

LESSON 13-6 Probabilities of Mutually Exclusive Events

Then

- You found probabilities of independent and dependent events.

Now

1. Find probabilities of events that are mutually exclusive and events that are not mutually exclusive.
2. Find probabilities of complements.

Why?

- At Wayside High School, freshmen, sophomores, juniors, and seniors can all run for Student Council president. Dominic wants either a junior or a senior candidate to win the election. Trayvon wants either a sophomore or a female to win, but says, "If the winner is sophomore Katina Smith, I'll be thrilled!"

NewVocabulary
mutually exclusive events
complement

Common Core State Standards

Content Standards

S.CP.1 Describe events as subsets of a sample space (the set of outcomes) using characteristics (or categories) of the outcomes, or as unions, intersections, or complements of other events ("or," "and," "not").

S.CP.7 Apply the Addition Rule, $P(A \text{ or } B) = P(A) + P(B) - P(A \text{ and } B)$, and interpret the answer in terms of the model.

Mathematical Practices

1 Make sense of problems and persevere in solving them.
4 Model with mathematics.

1 Mutually Exclusive Events

In Lesson 13-4, you examined probabilities involving the intersection of two or more events. In this lesson, you will examine probabilities involving the union of two or more events.

$P(A \text{ and } B)$ — Indicates an intersection of two sample spaces.

$P(A \text{ or } B)$ — Indicates a union of two sample spaces.

To find the probability that one event occurs *or* another event occurs, you must know how the two events are related. If the two events cannot happen at the same time, they are said to be **mutually exclusive**. That is, the two events have no outcomes in common.

Real-World Example 1 Identify Mutually Exclusive Events

ELECTIONS **Refer to the application above. Determine whether the events are *mutually exclusive* or *not mutually exclusive*. Explain your reasoning.**

a. a junior winning the election or a senior winning the election

These events are mutually exclusive. There are no common outcomes—a student cannot be both a junior and a senior.

b. a sophomore winning the election or a female winning the election

These events are not mutually exclusive. A female student who is a sophomore is an outcome that both events have in common.

c. drawing an ace or a club from a standard deck of cards.

Since the ace of clubs represents both events, they are not mutually exclusive.

GuidedPractice

Determine whether the events are *mutually exclusive* or *not mutually exclusive*. Explain your reasoning. 1B. not mutually exclusive

1A. selecting a number at random from the integers from 1 to 100 and getting a number divisible by 5 or a number divisible by 10 not mutually exclusive

1B. drawing a card from a standard deck and getting a 5 or a heart

1C. getting a sum of 6 or 7 when two dice are rolled mutually exclusive

Lesson 13-6 Resources

Resource	Approaching Level AL	On Level OL	Beyond Level BL	English Learners ELL
Teacher Edition	▪ Differentiated Instruction, p. 960	▪ Differentiated Instruction, pp. 960, 963	▪ Differentiated Instruction, pp. 960, 963	
Chapter Resource Masters	▪ Study Guide and Intervention, pp. 37–38 ▪ Skills Practice, p. 39 ▪ Practice, p. 40 ▪ Word Problem Practice, p. 41	▪ Study Guide and Intervention, pp. 37–38 ▪ Skills Practice, p. 39 ▪ Practice, p. 40 ▪ Word Problem Practice, p. 41 ▪ Enrichment, p. 42	▪ Practice, p. 40 ▪ Word Problem Practice, p. 41 ▪ Enrichment, p. 42	▪ Study Guide and Intervention, pp. 37–38 ▪ Skills Practice, p. 39 ▪ Practice, p. 40 ▪ Word Problem Practice, p. 41
Other	▪ 5-Minute Check 13-6 ▪ Study Notebook	▪ 5-Minute Check 13-6 ▪ Study Notebook	▪ 5-Minute Check 13-6 ▪ Study Notebook	▪ 5-Minute Check 13-6 ▪ Study Notebook

One way of finding the probability of two mutually exclusive events occurring is to examine their sample space.

When a die is rolled, what is the probability of getting a 3 or a 4? From the Venn diagram, you can see that there are two outcomes that satisfy this condition, 3 and 4. So,

$$P(3 \text{ and } 4) = \frac{2}{6} \text{ or } \frac{1}{3}.$$

Notice that this same probability can be found by adding the probabilities of each simple event.

$P(3) = \frac{1}{6}$ $\quad P(4) = \frac{1}{6}$ $\quad P(3 \text{ and } 4) = \frac{1}{6} + \frac{1}{6} = \frac{2}{6} \text{ or } \frac{1}{3}$

This example illustrates the first of two Addition Rules for Probability.

ReadingMath

or The word *or* is a key word indicating that at least one of the events occurs. *P*(*A* or *B*) is read as *the probability that A occurs or that B occurs.*

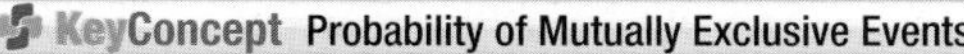

KeyConcept Probability of Mutually Exclusive Events

Words If two events *A* and *B* are mutually exclusive, then the probability that *A* or *B* occurs is the sum of the probabilities of each individual event.

Example If two events *A* or *B* are mutually exclusive, then $P(A \text{ or } B) = P(A) + P(B)$.

This rule can be extended to any number of events.

Math HistoryLink

Leonhard Euler **(1707–1783)** Euler introduced graph theory in 1736 in a paper titled *Seven Bridges of Konigsburg,* a famous solved mathematics problem inspired by an actual place and situation. Also, Euler's formula relating the number of edges, vertices, and faces of a convex polyhedron is the origin of graph theory. Refer to Extend 13-6.

Real-World Example 2 Mutually Exclusive Events

MUSIC Ramiro makes a playlist that consists of songs from three different albums by his favorite artist. If he lets his MP3 player select the songs from this list at random, what is the probability that the first song played is from Album 1 or Album 2?

Ramiro's Playlist

Album	Number of Songs
1	10
2	12
3	13

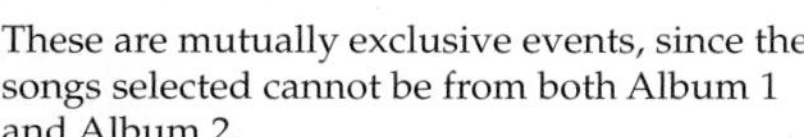

These are mutually exclusive events, since the songs selected cannot be from both Album 1 and Album 2.

Let event *A*1 represent selecting a song from Album 1.
Let event *A*2 represent selecting a song from Album 2.
There are a total of 10 + 12 + 13 or 35 songs.

$P(A1 \text{ or } A2) = P(A1) + P(A2)$ Probability of mutually exclusive events

$= \frac{10}{35} + \frac{12}{35}$ $\quad P(A1) = \frac{10}{35}$ and $P(A2) = \frac{12}{35}$

$= \frac{22}{35}$ Add.

So, the probability that the first song played is from Album 1 or Album 2 is $\frac{22}{35}$ or about 63%.

GuidedPractice

2A. Two dice are rolled. What is the probability that doubles are rolled or that the sum is 9? $\frac{5}{18}$ **or about 28%**

2B. CARNIVAL GAMES If you win the ring toss game at a certain carnival, you receive a stuffed animal. If the stuffed animal is selected at random from among 15 puppies, 16 kittens, 14 frogs, 25 snakes, and 10 unicorns, what is the probability that a winner receives a puppy, a kitten, or a unicorn?

2B. $\frac{41}{80}$ **or about 51%**

1 Mutually Exclusive Events

Example 1 shows how to determine whether an event is mutually exclusive or not mutually exclusive. **Example 2** shows how to compute the probability of two mutually exclusive events. **Example 3** shows how to compute the probability of two events that are not mutually exclusive.

Formative Assessment

Use the Guided Practice exercises after each example to determine students' understanding of concepts.

Additional Examples

1 CARDS Han draws one card from a standard deck. Determine whether the events are mutually exclusive or not mutually exclusive. Explain your reasoning.

a. an ace or a 9 Mutually exclusive; there are no common outcomes. A card cannot be both an ace and a 9.

b. a king or a club Not mutually exclusive; a king that is a club is an outcome that both events have in common.

2 COINS Trevor reaches into a can that contains 30 quarters, 25 dimes, 40 nickels and 15 pennies. What is the probability that the first coin he picks is a quarter or a penny? $\frac{9}{21}$ or about 43%

Additional Examples also in Interactive Classroom PowerPoint® Presentations

Interactive White Board READY

Tips for New Teachers

Reasoning Point out to students that the Venn diagram of two mutually exclusive events does not have overlapping circles. Also show them that the Venn diagrams of two events which are not mutually exclusive will have overlapping circles.

Teach with Tech

Interactive Whiteboard Draw a tree diagram on the board to show students how to find the probabilities of exclusive events. Save your work and send the diagram to students for reference.

Additional Example

3 ART Use the table from Example 3. What is the probability that Namiko selects a watercolor or a landscape? $\frac{1}{3}$ or about 33%

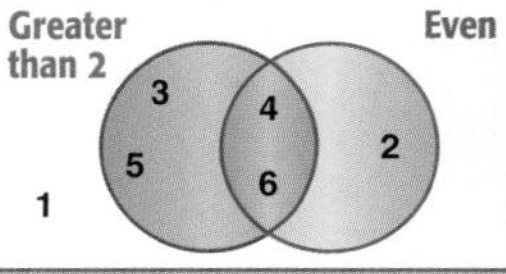

When a die is rolled, what is the probability of getting a number greater than 2 or an even number? From the Venn diagram, you can see that there are 5 numbers that are either greater than 2 or are an even number: 2, 3, 4, 5, and 6. So,

$$P(\text{greater than 2 or even}) = \frac{5}{6}.$$

Since it is possible to roll a number that is greater than 2 *and* an even number, these events are not mutually exclusive. Consider the probabilities of each individual event.

$$P(\text{greater than 2}) = \frac{4}{6} \qquad P(\text{even}) = \frac{3}{6}$$

If these probabilities were added, the probability of two outcomes, 4 and 6, would be counted twice—once for being numbers greater than 2 and once for being even numbers. You must subtract the probability of these common outcomes.

$$P(\text{greater than 2 or even}) = P(\text{greater than 2}) + P(\text{even}) - P(\text{greater than 2 and even})$$

$$= \frac{4}{6} + \frac{3}{6} - \frac{2}{6} \text{ or } \frac{5}{6}$$

This leads to the second of the Addition Rules for Probability.

KeyConcept Probability of Events That Are Not Mutually Exclusive

Words If two events *A* and *B* are not mutually exclusive, then the probability that *A* or *B* occurs is the sum of their individual probabilities minus the probability that both *A* and *B* occur.

Symbols If two events *A* and *B* are not mutually exclusive, then
$P(A \text{ or } B) = P(A) + P(B) - P(A \text{ and } B)$.

Real-World Example 3 Events That Are Not Mutually Exclusive

ART The table shows the number and type of paintings Namiko has created. If she randomly selects a painting to submit to an art contest, what is the probability that she selects a portrait or an oil painting?

Namiko's Paintings			
Media	Still Life	Portrait	Landscape
watercolor	4	5	3
oil	1	3	2
acrylic	3	2	1
pastel	1	0	5

Since some of Namiko's paintings are both portraits and oil paintings, these events are not mutually exclusive. Use the rule for two events that are not mutually exclusive. The total number of paintings from which to choose is 30.

$$P(\text{oil or portrait}) = P(\text{oil}) + P(\text{portrait}) - P(\text{oil and portrait})$$

$$= \frac{1+3+2}{30} + \frac{5+3+2+0}{30} - \frac{3}{30} \quad \text{Substitution}$$

$$= \frac{6}{30} + \frac{10}{30} - \frac{3}{30} \text{ or } \frac{13}{30} \quad \text{Simplify.}$$

The probability that Namiko selects a portrait or an oil painting is $\frac{13}{30}$ or about 43%.

Real-WorldLink

Juried art shows are shows in which artists are called to submit pieces and a panel of judges decides which art will be shown. They originated in the early 1800s to exhibit the work of current artists and educate the public.

Source: Humanities Web

GuidedPractice

3. What is the probability of drawing a king or a diamond from a standard deck of 52 cards? $\frac{4}{13}$ or about 31%

2 Probabilities of Complements

The **complement** of an event A consists of all the outcomes in the sample space that are not included as outcomes of event A.

When a die is rolled, the probability of getting a 4 is $\frac{1}{6}$. What is the probability of *not* getting a 4? There are 5 possible outcomes for this event: 1, 2, 3, 5, or 6. So, $P(\text{not } 4) = \frac{5}{6}$. Notice that this probability is also $1 - \frac{1}{6}$ or $1 - P(4)$.

KeyConcept Probability of the Complement of an Event

Words	The probability that an event will not occur is equal to 1 minus the probability that the event will occur.
Symbols	For an event A, $P(\text{not } A) = 1 - P(A)$.

Example 4 Complementary Events

RAFFLE Francisca bought 20 raffle tickets, hoping to win the $100 gift card to her favorite clothing store. If a total of 300 raffle tickets were sold, what is the probability that Francisca will not win the gift card?

Let event A represent selecting one of Francisca's tickets. Then find the probability of the complement of A.

$P(\text{not } A) = 1 - P(A)$ — Probability of a complement

$= 1 - \frac{20}{300}$ — Substitution

$= \frac{280}{300}$ or $\frac{14}{15}$ — Subtract and simplify.

The probability that one of Francisca's tickets *will not* be selected is $\frac{14}{15}$ or about 93%.

ReadingMath
Complement The complement of event A can also be noted as A^C.

GuidedPractice

4. If the chance of rain is 70%, what is the probability that it will not rain? **30%**

ConceptSummary Probability Rules

Types of Events	Words	Probability Rule
Independent Events	The outcome of a first event *does not affect* the outcome of the second event.	If two events A and B are independent, then $P(A \text{ and } B) = P(A) \cdot P(B)$.
Dependent Events	The outcome of a first event *does affect* the outcome of the other event.	If two events A and B are dependent, then $P(A \text{ and } B) = P(A) \cdot P(B\|A)$.
Conditional	Additional information is known about the probability of an event.	The conditional probability of A given B is $P(A\|B) = \frac{P(A \text{ and } B)}{P(B)}$.
Mutually Exclusive Events	Events *do not share* common outcomes.	If two events A or B are mutually exclusive, then $P(A \text{ or } B) = P(A) + P(B)$.
Not Mutually Exclusive Events	Events *do share* common outcomes.	If two events A and B are not mutually exclusive, then $P(A \text{ or } B) = P(A) + P(B) - P(A \text{ and } B)$.
Complementary Events	The outcomes of one event consist of all the outcomes in the sample space that are not outcomes of the other event.	For an event A, $P(\text{not } A) = 1 - P(A)$.

2 Probabilities of Complements

Example 4 shows how to compute the probability of complementary events. **Example 5** shows how to identify and use the appropriate probability rules to solve a problem.

Additional Example

4 GAMES Miguel bought 15 chances to pick the one red marble from a container to win a gift certificate to the bookstore. If there is a total of 200 marbles in the container, what is the probability that Miguel will not win the gift certificate? $\frac{37}{40}$ or about 93%

Focus on Mathematical Content

Complements For any event A, it is always true that either A will occur or not A will occur. The sum of the probabilities of a random variable is always 1. This can be seen in the formula for the probability of the complement of an event by rewriting it as $P(A) + P(\text{not } A) = 1$.

Additional Example

5 PETS A survey of Kingston High School students found that 63% of the students had a cat or a dog for a pet. If two students are chosen at random from a group of 100 students, what is the probability that at least one of them does not have a cat or a dog for a pet?
$\frac{333}{550}$ or about 61%

Real-WorldLink

About 81% of American motorists and their right-front passengers use a seat belt.

Source: National Highway Traffic Safety Administration

PT

Real-World Example 5 Identify and Use Probability Rules

SEAT BELTS **Refer to the information at the left. Suppose two people are chosen at random from a group of 100 American motorists and passengers. If this group mirrors the population, what is the probability that at least one of them does not wear a seat belt?**

Understand You know that 81% of Americans *do use* a seat belt. The phrase *at least one* means *one or more*. So, you need to find the probability that either

- the first person chosen does not use a seat belt *or*
- the second person chosen does not use a seat belt *or*
- both people chosen do not use a seat belt.

Plan The complement of the event described above is the event that both people chosen *do use* a seat belt. Find the probability of this event, and then find the probability of its complement.

Let event A represent choosing a person who does use a seat belt.

Let event B represent choosing a person who does use a seat belt after the first person has already been chosen.

These are two dependent events, since the outcome of the first event affects the probability of the outcome of the second event.

Solve

$P(A \text{ and } B) = P(A) \cdot P(B|A)$ Probability of dependent events

$= \frac{81}{100} \cdot \frac{80}{99}$ $P(A) = \frac{0.81(100)}{100}$ or $\frac{81}{100}$

$= \frac{6480}{9900}$ or $\frac{36}{55}$ Multiply.

$P[\text{not } (A \text{ and } B)] = 1 - P(A \text{ and } B)$ Probability of a complement

$= 1 - \frac{36}{55}$ Substitution

$= \frac{19}{55}$ Subtract.

So, the probability that at least one of the passengers does not use a seat belt is $\frac{19}{55}$ or about 35%.

Check Use logical reasoning to check the reasonableness of your answer.

The probability that one person chosen out of 100 *does not* wear his or her seat belt is (100 − 81)% or 19%. The probability that two people chosen out of 100 wear their seat belt should be greater than 19%. Since 35% > 19%, the answer is reasonable.

StudyTip

Key Probability Words When determining what type of probability you are dealing with in a situation, look for key words and correctly interpret their meaning.

and → independent or dependent events

or → mutually exclusive or not mutually exclusive

not → complementary events

and then → conditional

at least n → *n* or more

at most n → *n* or less

GuidedPractice

5. CELL PHONES According to an online poll, 35% of American motorists routinely use their cell phones while driving. Three people are chosen at random from a group of 100 motorists. What is the probability that

A. at least two of them use their cell phone while driving? **about 28%**

B. no more than one use their cell phone while driving? **about 72%**

DifferentiatedInstruction AL OL BL

Intrapersonal Learners Have students look at the Concept Summary on p. 941. Next, have students write in their own words when each probability rule is used and write an example of each.

Check Your Understanding

= Step-by-Step Solutions begin on page R14.

Example 1 **Determine whether the events are *mutually exclusive* or *not mutually exclusive*. Explain your reasoning.**

1. drawing a card from a standard deck and getting a jack or a club **not mutually exclusive; A jack of clubs is both a jack and a club.**
2. adopting a cat or a dog **mutually exclusive; A cat cannot be a dog and a dog cannot be a cat.**

Example 2

3. **JOBS** Adelaide is the employee of the month at her job. Her reward is to select at random from 4 gift cards, 6 coffee mugs, 7 DVDs, 10 CDs, and 3 gift baskets. What is the probability that an employee receives a gift card, coffee mug, or CD? **See margin.**

Example 3

4. **CLUBS** According to the table, what is the probability that a student in a club is a junior or on the debate team? **$\frac{11}{25}$ or about 44%**

Club	Soph.	Junior	Senior
Key	12	14	8
Debate	2	6	3
Math	7	4	5
French	11	15	13

Example 4 **Determine the probability of each event.**

5. If you have a 2 in 10 chance of bowling a spare, what is the probability of missing the spare? **The probability of missing the spare is $\frac{8}{10}$ or 80%.**
6. If the chance of living in a particular dorm is 75%, what is the probability of living in another dorm? **The probability of living in another dorm is $\frac{1}{4}$ or 25%.**

Example 5

7. **PROM** In Armando's senior class of 100 students, 91% went to the senior prom. If two people are chosen at random from the entire class, what is the probability that at least one of them did not go to prom? **17.3%**

Practice and Problem Solving

Extra Practice is on page R13.

Examples 1–3 **Determine whether the events are *mutually exclusive* or *not mutually exclusive*. Then find the probability. Round to the nearest tenth of a percent, if necessary.**

8. drawing a card from a standard deck and getting a jack or a six **mutually exclusive; $\frac{2}{13}$ or 15.4%**
9. rolling a pair of dice and getting doubles or a sum of 8 **not mutually exclusive; $\frac{10}{36}$ or 27.8%**
10. selecting a number at random from integers 1 to 20 and getting an even number or a number divisible by 3 **not mutually exclusive; $\frac{13}{20}$ or 65%**
11. tossing a coin and getting heads or tails **mutually exclusive; 100%**
12. drawing an ace or a heart from a standard deck of 52 cards **not mutually exclusive; $\frac{4}{13}$ or 30.8%**
13. rolling a pair of dice and getting a sum of either 6 or 10 **mutually exclusive; $\frac{2}{9}$ or about 22.2%**
14. **SPORTS** The table includes all of the programs offered at a sports complex and the number of participants aged 14–16. What is the probability that a player is 14 or plays basketball? **56%**

Graceland Sports Complex			
Age	Soccer	Baseball	Basketball
14	28	36	42
15	30	26	33
16	35	41	29

15. CCSS **MODELING** An exchange student is moving back to Italy, and her homeroom class wants to get her a going away present. The teacher takes a survey of the class of 32 students and finds that 10 people chose a card, 12 chose a T-shirt, 6 chose a video, and 4 chose a bracelet. If the teacher randomly selects the present, what is the probability that the exchange student will get a card or a bracelet? **$\frac{7}{16}$ or about 43.8%**

3 Practice

Formative Assessment

Use Exercises 1–7 to check for understanding.

Then use the chart at the bottom of this page to customize assignments for your students.

Additional Answer

3. $\frac{2}{3}$ or about 67%

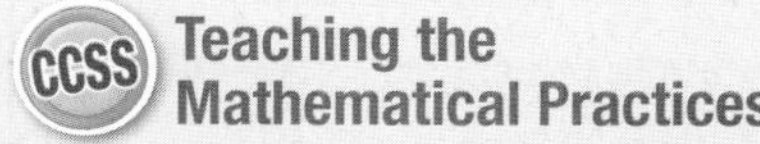

Teaching the Mathematical Practices

Modeling Mathematically proficient students can apply the mathematics they know to solve problems arising in everyday life. In Exercise 14, students should first determine whether the events are mutually exclusive or not.

Differentiated Homework Options

Level	Assignment	Two-Day Option	
AL Basic	8–22, 28, 30–44	9–21 odd, 35–38	8–22 even, 28, 30–34, 39–44
OL Core	9–21 odd, 22, 23–27 odd, 28, 30–44	8–22, 35–38	22–28, 30–34, 39–44
BL Advanced	23–41, (optional: 42–49)		

Example 4 **Determine the probability of each event.**

16. rolling a pair of dice and not getting a 3 $\frac{25}{36}$ **or about 69.4%**

17. drawing a card from a standard deck and not getting a diamond $\frac{3}{4}$ **or about 75%**

18. flipping a coin and not landing on heads $\frac{1}{2}$ **or about 50%**

19. spinning a spinner numbered 1–8 and not landing on 5 $\frac{7}{8}$ **or 87.5%**

20. **RAFFLE** Namid bought 20 raffle tickets. If a total of 500 raffle tickets were sold, what is the probability that Namid will not win the raffle? $\frac{24}{25}$ **or about 96%**

21. **JOBS** Of young workers aged 18 to 25, 71% are paid by the hour. If two people are randomly chosen out of a group of 100 young workers, what is the probability that exactly one is paid by the hour? **42%**

Example 5

22. **RECYCLING** Suppose 31% of Americans recycle. If two Americans are chosen randomly from a group of 50, what is the probability that at most one of them recycles? **about 90.4%**

B **CARDS Suppose you pull a card from a standard 52-card deck. Find the probability of each event.**

23. The card is a 4. $\frac{1}{13}$ **or 7.7%**

24. The card is red. $\frac{1}{2}$ **or 50%**

25. The card is a face card. $\frac{3}{13}$ **or 23.1%**

26. The card is not a face card. $\frac{10}{13}$ **or 76.9%**

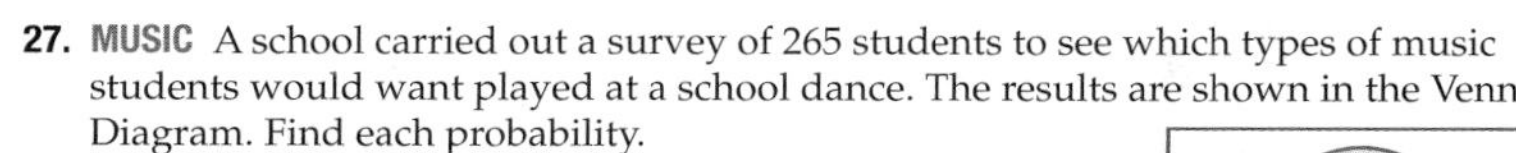

C 27. **MUSIC** A school carried out a survey of 265 students to see which types of music students would want played at a school dance. The results are shown in the Venn Diagram. Find each probability.

a. P(country or R&B) **71.3%**

b. P(rock and country or R&B and rock) **11.3%**

c. P(R&B but not rock) **36.2%**

d. P(all three) **3.8%**

Country 63
Rock 76
R&B 89
8
7
10
12

H.O.T. Problems Use Higher-Order Thinking Skills

28. **CCSS CRITIQUE** Tetsuya and Mason want to determine the probability that a red marble will be chosen out of a bag of 4 red, 7 blue, 5 green, and 2 purple marbles. Is either of them correct? Explain your reasoning.

Tetsuya	Mason
$P(R) = \frac{4}{17}$	$P(R) = 1 - \frac{4}{18}$

Neither; sample answer: The probability that a red marble will be chosen is $\frac{4}{18}$ or $1 - \frac{14}{18}$.

29. **CHALLENGE** You roll 3 dice. What is the probability that the outcome of at least two of the dice will be less than or equal to 4? Explain your reasoning. **See Ch. 13 Answer Appendix.**

REASONING Determine whether the following are mutually exclusive. Explain. **30–34. See margin.**

30. choosing a quadrilateral that is a square and a quadrilateral that is a rectangle

31. choosing a triangle that is equilateral and a triangle that is equiangular

32. choosing a complex number and choosing a natural number

33. **OPEN ENDED** Describe a pair of events that are mutually exclusive and a pair of events that are not mutually exclusive.

34. **WRITING IN MATH** Explain why the sum of the probabilities of two mutually exclusive events is not always 1.

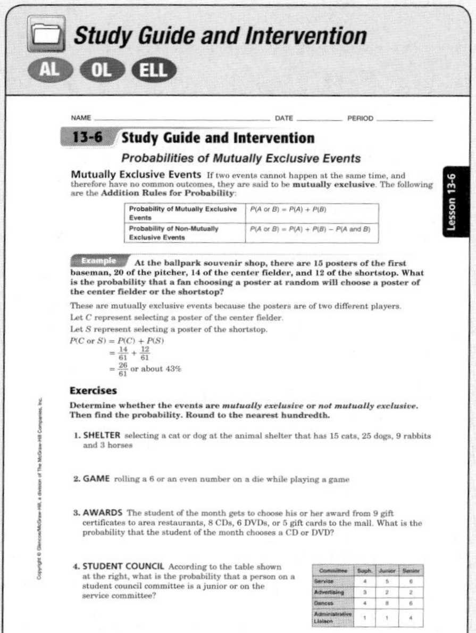

Study Guide and Intervention

AL OL ELL

NAME ________ DATE ________ PERIOD ________

13-6 Study Guide and Intervention

Probabilities of Mutually Exclusive Events

Mutually Exclusive Events If two events cannot happen at the same time, and therefore have no common outcomes, they are said to be **mutually exclusive**. The following are the **Addition Rules for Probability**:

Probability of Mutually Exclusive Events	$P(A \text{ or } B) = P(A) + P(B)$
Probability of Non-Mutually Exclusive Events	$P(A \text{ or } B) = P(A) + P(B) - P(A \text{ and } B)$

Example **At the ballpark souvenir shop, there are 15 posters of the first baseman, 20 of the pitcher, 14 of the center fielder, and 12 of the shortstop. What is the probability that a fan choosing a poster at random will choose a poster of the center fielder or the shortstop?**

These are mutually exclusive events because the posters are of two different players.

Let C represent selecting a poster of the center fielder.

Let S represent selecting a poster of the shortstop.

$P(C \text{ or } S) = P(C) + P(S)$

$= \frac{14}{61} + \frac{12}{61}$

$= \frac{26}{61}$ or about 43%

Exercises

Determine whether the events are *mutually exclusive* or *not mutually exclusive*. Then find the probability. Round to the nearest hundredth.

1. **SHELTER** selecting a cat or dog at the animal shelter that has 15 cats, 25 dogs, 9 rabbits and 3 horses

2. **GAME** rolling a 6 or an even number on a die while playing a game

3. **AWARDS** The student of the month gets to choose his or her award from 9 gift certificates to area restaurants, 8 CDs, 6 DVDs, or 5 gift cards to the mall. What is the probability that the student of the month chooses a CD or DVD?

4. **STUDENT COUNCIL** According to the table shown at the right, what is the probability that a person on a student council committee is a junior or on the service committee?

Committee	Soph.	Junior	Senior
Service	4	5	6
Advertising	3	2	2
Dances	4	8	6
Administrative Liaison	1	1	4

Lesson 13-6

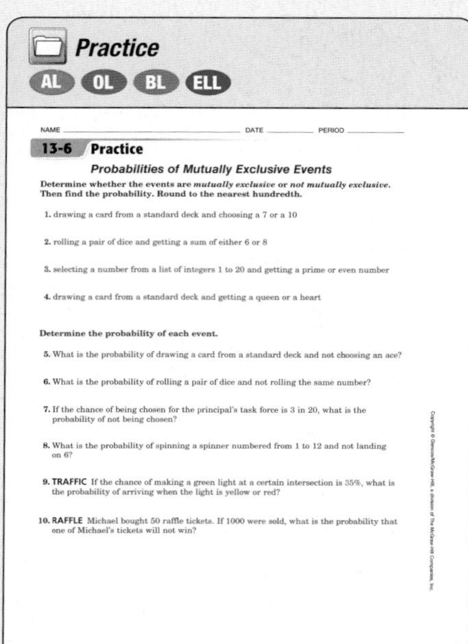

Practice

AL OL BL ELL

NAME ________ DATE ________ PERIOD ________

13-6 Practice

Probabilities of Mutually Exclusive Events

Determine whether the events are *mutually exclusive* or *not mutually exclusive*. Then find the probability. Round to the nearest hundredth.

1. drawing a card from a standard deck and choosing a 7 or a 10

2. rolling a pair of dice and getting a sum of either 6 or 8

3. selecting a number from a list of integers 1 to 20 and getting a prime or even number

4. drawing a card from a standard deck and getting a queen or a heart

Determine the probability of each event.

5. What is the probability of drawing a card from a standard deck and not choosing an ace?

6. What is the probability of rolling a pair of dice and not rolling the same number?

7. If the chance of being chosen for the principal's task force is 3 in 20, what is the probability of not being chosen?

8. What is the probability of spinning a spinner numbered from 1 to 12 and not landing on 6?

9. **TRAFFIC** If the chance of making a green light at a certain intersection is 35%, what is the probability of arriving when the light is yellow or red?

10. **RAFFLE** Michael bought 50 raffle tickets. If 1000 were sold, what is the probability that one of Michael's tickets will not win?

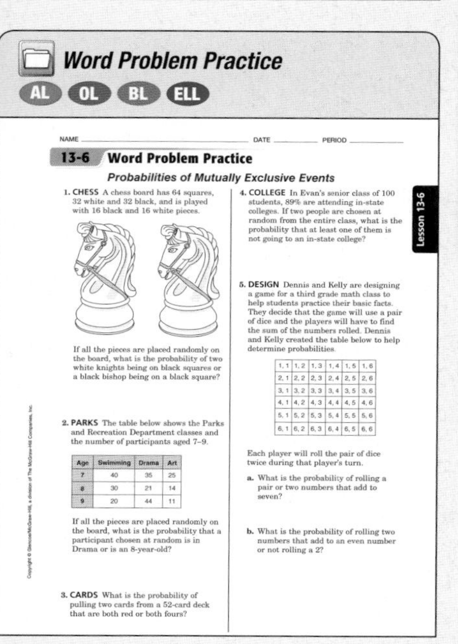

Word Problem Practice

AL OL BL ELL

NAME ________ DATE ________ PERIOD ________

13-6 Word Problem Practice

Probabilities of Mutually Exclusive Events

1. **CHESS** A chess board has 64 squares, 32 white and 32 black, and is played with 16 black and 16 white pieces.

If all the pieces are placed randomly on the board, what is the probability of two white knights being on black squares or a black bishop being on a black square?

2. **PARKS** The table below shows the Parks and Recreation Department classes and the number of participants aged 7–9.

Age	Swimming	Drama	Art
7	40	35	25
8	30	21	14
9	20	44	11

If all the pieces are placed randomly on the board, what is the probability that a participant chosen at random is in Drama or is an 8-year-old?

3. **CARDS** What is the probability of pulling two cards from a 52-card deck that are both red or both fours?

4. **COLLEGE** In Evan's senior class of 100 students, 89% are attending in-state colleges. If two people are chosen at random from the entire class, what is the probability that at least one of them is not going to an in-state college?

5. **DESIGN** Dennis and Kelly are designing a game for a third grade math class to help students practice their basic facts. They decide that the game will use a pair of dice and the players will have to find the sum of the numbers rolled. Dennis and Kelly created the table below to help determine probabilities.

1, 1	1, 2	1, 3	1, 4	1, 5	1, 6
2, 1	2, 2	2, 3	2, 4	2, 5	2, 6
3, 1	3, 2	3, 3	3, 4	3, 5	3, 6
4, 1	4, 2	4, 3	4, 4	4, 5	4, 6
5, 1	5, 2	5, 3	5, 4	5, 5	5, 6
6, 1	6, 2	6, 3	6, 4	6, 5	6, 6

Each player will roll the pair of dice twice during that player's turn.

a. What is the probability of rolling a pair or two numbers that add to seven?

b. What is the probability of rolling two numbers that add to an even number or not rolling a 2?

Lesson 13-6

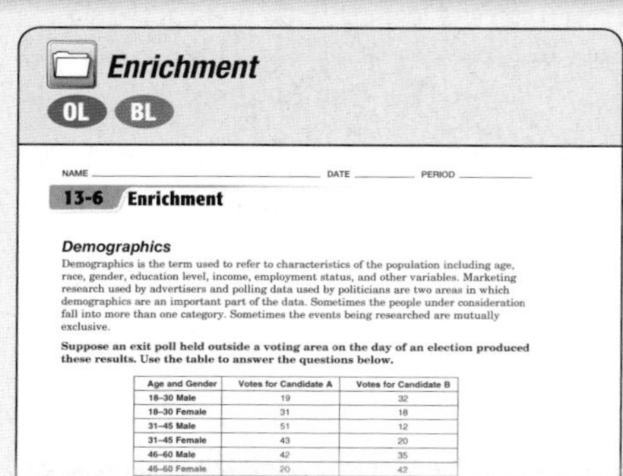

Enrichment

OL BL

NAME ________ DATE ________ PERIOD ________

13-6 Enrichment

Demographics

Demographics is the term used to refer to characteristics of the population including age, race, gender, education level, income, employment status, and other variables. Marketing research used by advertisers and polling data used by politicians are two areas in which demographics are an important part of the data. Sometimes the people under consideration fall into more than one category. Sometimes the events being researched are mutually exclusive.

Suppose an exit poll held outside a voting area on the day of an election produced these results. Use the table to answer the questions below.

Age and Gender	Votes for Candidate A	Votes for Candidate B
18–30 Male	19	32
18–30 Female	31	18
31–45 Male	51	12
31–45 Female	43	20
46–60 Male	42	35
46–60 Female	20	42
60+ Male	45	21
60+ Female	27	[illegible]

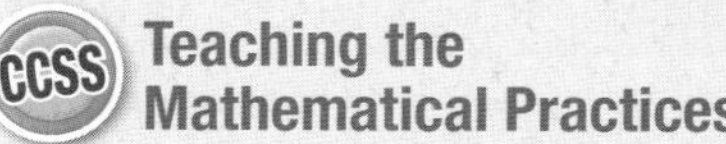

Teaching the Mathematical Practices

Critique Mathematically proficient students can distinguish correct logic from flawed reasoning. In Exercise 28, neither is correct. Tetsuya added the number of marbles incorrectly. Mason found the probability that any color but red would be chosen.

Standardized Test Practice

35. PROBABILITY Customers at a new salon can win prizes during opening day. The table shows the type and number of prizes. What is the probability that the first customer wins a manicure or a massage? **D**

Prize	Number
manicure	10
pedicure	6
massage	3
facial	1

A 0.075　　C 0.5

B 0.35　　D 0.65

36. SHORT RESPONSE A cube numbered 1 through 6 is shown.

If the cube is rolled once, what is the probability that a number less than 3 or an odd number shows on the top face of the cube? **$\frac{2}{3}$**

37. ALGEBRA What will happen to the slope of line p if it is shifted so that the y-intercept stays the same and the x-intercept approaches the origin? **J**

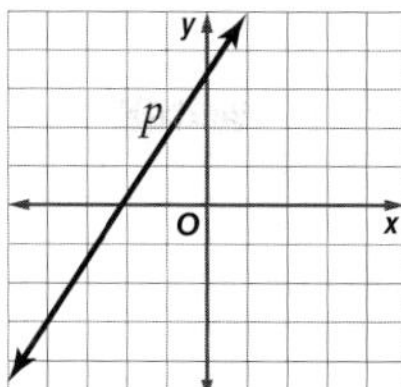

F The slope will become negative.

G The slope will become zero.

H The slope will decrease.

J The slope will increase.

38. SAT/ACT The probability of choosing a peppermint from a certain bag of candy is 0.25, and the probability of choosing a chocolate is 0.3. The bag contains 60 pieces of candy, and the only types of candy in the bag are peppermint, chocolate, and butterscotch. How many butterscotch candies are in the bag? **B**

A 25　　D 33

B 27　　E 45

C 30

Spiral Review

Determine whether the events are *independent* or *dependent*. Then find the probability. (Lesson 13-5)

39. A king is drawn, without replacement, from a standard deck of 52 cards. Then, a second king is drawn. **dependent; $\frac{1}{221}$ or 0.5%**

40. You roll a die and get a 2. You roll another die and get a 3. **independent; $\frac{1}{36}$ or about 3%**

41. SPORTS A survey at a high school found that 15% of the athletes at the school play only volleyball, 20% play only soccer, 30% play only basketball, and 35% play only football. Design a simulation that can be used to estimate the probability that an athlete will play each of these sports. (Lesson 13-4) **See Ch. 13 Answer Appendix.**

Copy the figure and point *P*. Then use a ruler to draw the image of the figure under a dilation with center *P* and the scale factor *r* indicated. (Lesson 9-6) **42–44. See Ch. 13 Answer Appendix.**

42. $r = \frac{1}{2}$

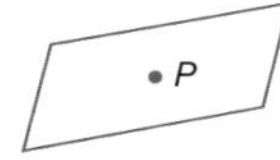

43. $r = 3$

44. $r = \frac{1}{5}$

Differentiated Instruction OL BL

Extension Have students create Venn diagrams to model each of the types of probabilities that they learned about in this chapter. Students should think of a situation to model with that type of probability and create a Venn diagram that models the events.

4 Assess

Name the Math Have students write on a sheet of paper the difference between mutually exclusive and not mutually exclusive events and the probability formula for each.

Formative Assessment

Check for student understanding of Lessons 13-5 and 13-6.

 Quiz 4, p. 46

Additional Answers

30. Not mutually exclusive; sample answer: Since squares are rectangles, but rectangles are not necessarily squares, a quadrilateral can be both a square and a rectangle, and a quadrilateral can be a rectangle but not a square.

31. Not mutually exclusive; sample answer: If a triangle is equilateral, it is also equiangular. The two can never be mutually exclusive.

32. Not mutually exclusive; sample answer: A natural number is also a complex number.

33. Sample answer: If you pull a card from a deck, it can be either a 3 or a 5. The two events are mutually exclusive. If you pull a card from a deck, it can be a 3 and it can be red. The two events are not mutually exclusive.

34. Sample answer: When two events are mutually exclusive, it means that they can't both happen, but it does not mean that one or the other of the events must happen. The sum of all possible outcomes in a sample space must be 1. For example, if Event *A* and Event *B* are mutually exclusive, the sample space includes the probability of Event *A*, the probability of Event *B*, and the probability of neither Event *A* or Event *B*, which must all sum to 1. The sum of the probabilities of Event *A* and Event *B* may be 1, but not necessarily.

1 Focus

Objective To apply physical models, graphs, and networks to develop solutions in applied contexts.

Teaching Tips

Relate the concept of a graph to a map of a city or country. Edges are like all of the two-way roads, and you could give weights to the roads by their type: two-lane, dirt road, highway, etc.

2 Teach

Working in Cooperative Groups

Organize students in pairs, mixing abilities. Have pairs help each other to complete Activities 1 and 2.

Practice Have students complete Analyze 1–5 and Model and Analyze 8–11.

Additional Answer

6a.

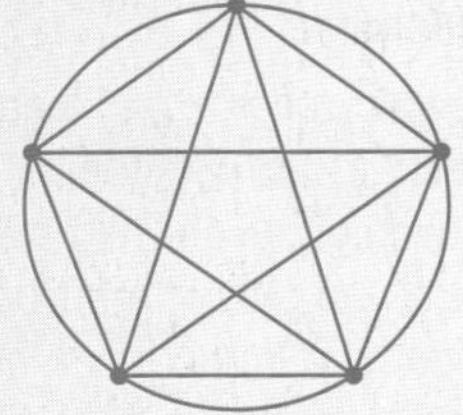

EXTEND 13-6 Geometry Lab Graph Theory

Mathematical structures can be used to model relationships in a set. The study of these graphs is called *graph theory*. These **vertex-edge graphs** are not like graphs that can be seen on a coordinate plane. Each graph, also called a **network**, is a collection of vertices, called **nodes**, and segments, called **edges**, that connect the nodes.

The bus route in the figure is an example of a network. The school, each stop, and the garage are nodes in the network. The connecting streets, such as Long Street, are edges.

This is an example of a **traceable network** because all of the nodes are connected, and each edge is used once in the network.

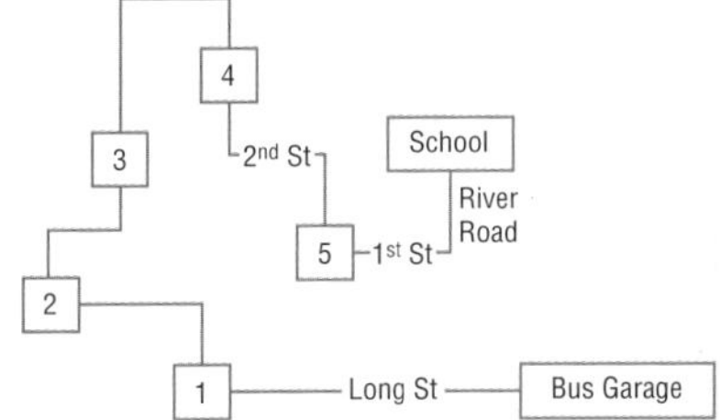

Activity 1

The graph represents the streets on Ava's newspaper route. To complete her route as quickly as possible, how can Ava ride her bike down each street only once?

Step 1 Copy the graph onto your paper.

Step 2 Beginning at Ava's home, trace over her route without lifting your pencil. Remember to trace each edge only once.

Step 3 Describe Ava's route.

Sample answer: Front St., Main St., Second Ave., State St., Elm St., First Ave., Town St.

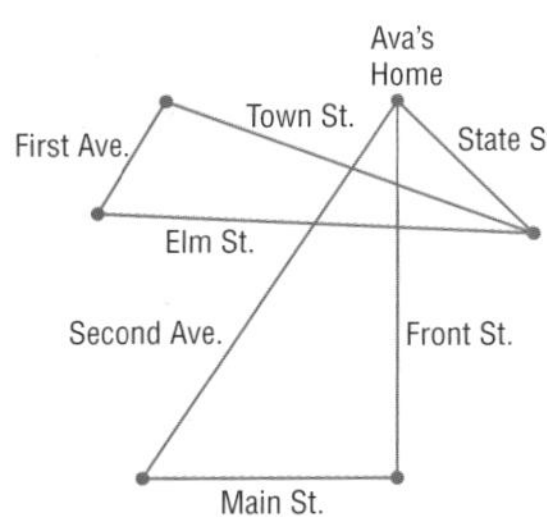

3. Yes; all nodes can be connected without retracing an edge.
4. No; not all of the edges can be used without retracing.
5. Yes; all nodes can be connected without retracing an edge.

Analyze

1. Is there more than one traceable route that begins at Ava's house? If so, how many? yes; 4
2. If it does not matter where Ava starts, how many traceable routes are possible? 8

Is each graph traceable? Write *yes* or *no*. Explain your reasoning.

3.

4. 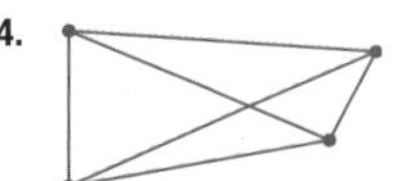

5. 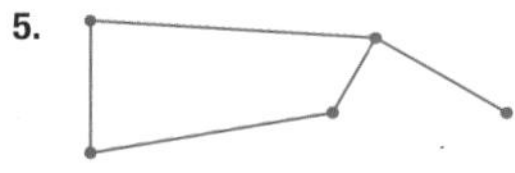

6. The campus for Centerburgh High School has five buildings built around the edge of a circular courtyard. There is a sidewalk between each pair of buildings.
   a. Draw a graph of the campus. Is the graph traceable? See margin.
   b. Suppose there are no sidewalks between pairs of adjacent buildings. Is it possible to reach all five buildings without walking down any sidewalk more than once? yes
7. **REASONING** Write a rule for determining whether a graph is traceable.

7. Sample answer: If you follow the edges of a graph, you should cover each edge only once.

In a network, routes from one vertex to another are also called *paths*. **Weighted vertex-edge graphs** are graphs in which a value, or **weight**, is assigned to each edge. The **weight of a path** is the sum of the weights of the edges along the path. The **efficient route** is the path with the minimum weight.

Activity 2

The edges of the network have different weights. Find the efficient route from A to B.

Step 1 Find all of the possible paths from A to B. Label each path with the letters of the nodes along the path.

Step 2 Trace each path and add the weights of each edge. The path with the least weight is the efficient route: A-U-X-Y-Z-B. The weight is 54.

Pay attention to the weights when determining the efficient route. It may not be the path with the fewest edges.

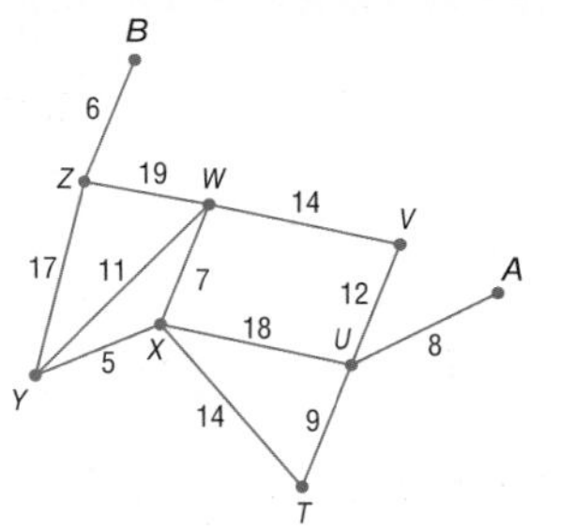

Model and Analyze

8. What is the longest path from A to B that does not cover any edges more than once? See margin.

Determine the efficient route from A to B for each network.

9. 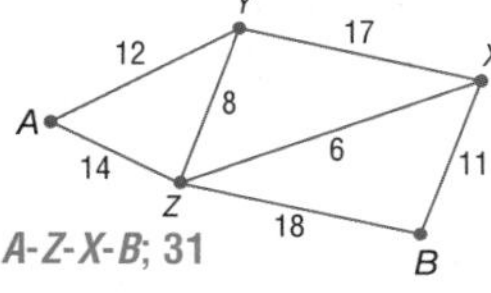
A-Z-X-B; 31

10. 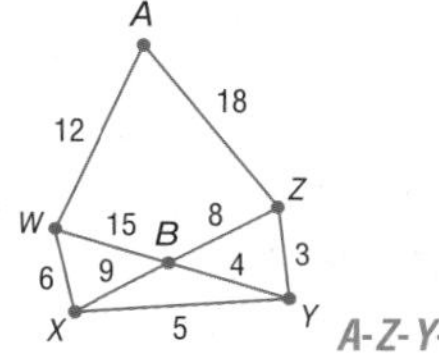
A-Z-Y-B; 25

11. 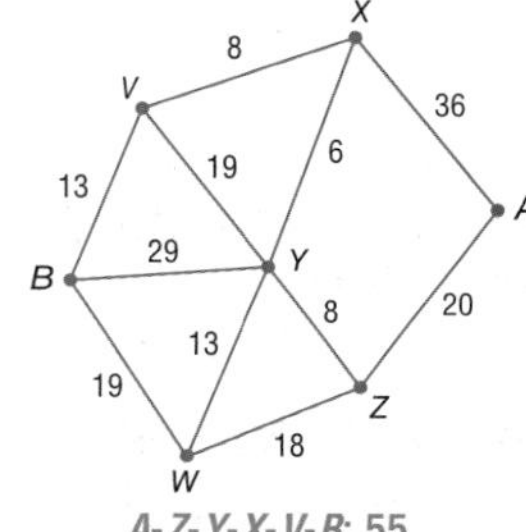
A-Z-Y-X-V-B; 55

12. **OPEN ENDED** Create a network with 8 nodes and an efficient route with a value of 25. See margin.

13. **WRITING IN MATH** Explain your method for determining the efficient route of a network. See margin.

14. **TRAVEL** Use the graph at the right to find each efficient route.
   a. from Phoenix to New York a–b. See margin.
   b. from Seattle to Atlanta

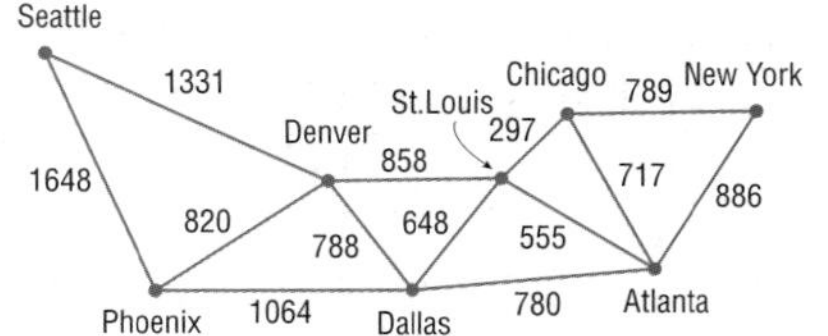

15. *Six Degrees of Separation* is a well-known example of graph theory. In this case, each person is a node and people are linked by an edge when they know each other.
   a. Make a graph of the situation. Directly connect yourself to three other people that you know personally. This represents the first degree of separation. See students' work.
   b. Expand the graph to show the first three degrees of separation. Name a person who is within 3 degrees of you, and list the path. See students' work.

3 Assess

Formative Assessment

Use Analyze 6 and 7 and Model and Analyze 12–15 to assess whether students understand vertex-edge maps.

From Concrete to Abstract

Ask students to consider graphs where you are only allowed to travel in one direction along an edge. Would this effect whether a graph is traceable?

Additional Answers

8. Sample answer: Any path that uses every edge except for the one weighted 17. An example is A-U-T-X-U-V-W-X-Y-W-Z-B.

12. Sample answer:

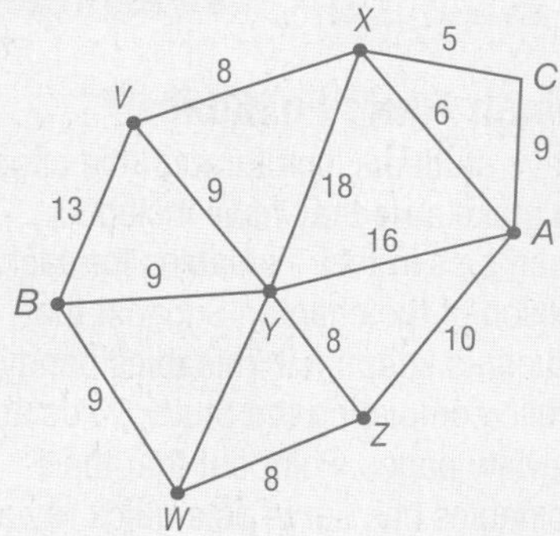

B-Y-A

13. Sample answer: Find all possible paths for the network and determine which is the shortest. Don't just look for the path with the fewest edges.

14a. Phoenix to Dallas to Atlanta to New York; 2730

14b. Seattle to Denver to St. Louis to Atlanta; 2744

Formative Assessment

KeyVocabulary The page references after each word denote where that term was first introduced. If students have difficulty completing Exercises 1–10, remind them that they can use these page references to refresh their memories about the vocabulary terms.

Summative Assessment

Vocabulary Test, p. 48

Vocabulary Review

Vocabulary Review provides students the opportunity to check their understanding of important concepts and terminology in an online game format.

FOLDABLES StudyOrganizer

Dinah Zike's Foldables®

Have students look through the chapter to make sure they have included examples in their Foldables for each lesson of the chapter. Suggest that students keep their Foldables handy while completing the Study Guide and Review pages. Point out that their Foldables can serve as a quick review when studying for the chapter test.

CHAPTER 13 Study Guide and Review

Study Guide

KeyConcepts

Representing Sample Spaces (Lesson 13-1)

- The sample space of an experiment is the set of all possible outcomes. It can be determined by using an organized list, a table, or a tree diagram.

Permutations and Combinations (Lesson 13-2)

- A permutation of n objects taken r at a time is given by $_nP_r = \frac{n!}{(n-r)!}$.
- A combination of n objects taken r at a time is given by $_nC_r = \frac{n!}{(n-r)!r!}$.
- Permutations should be used when order is important, and combinations should be used when order is not important.

Geometric Probability (Lesson 13-3)

- If a region A contains a region B and a point E in region A is chosen at random, then the probability that point E is in region B is $\frac{\text{area of region } B}{\text{area of region } A}$.

Simulations (Lesson 13-4)

- A simulation uses a probability model to recreate a situation again and again so that the likelihood of various outcomes can be estimated.

Probabilities of Compound Events (Lessons 13-5 and 13-6)

- If event A does not affect the outcome of event B, then the events are independent and $P(A \text{ and } B) = P(A) \cdot P(B)$.
- If two events A and B are dependent, then $P(A \text{ and } B) = P(A) \cdot P(B|A)$.
- If two events A and B cannot happen at the same time, they are mutually exclusive and $P(A \text{ or } B) = P(A) + P(B)$.
- If two events A and B are not mutually exclusive, then $P(A \text{ or } B) = P(A) + P(B) - P(A \text{ and } B)$.

FOLDABLES StudyOrganizer

Be sure the Key Concepts are noted in your Foldable.

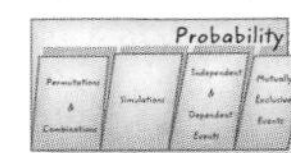

KeyVocabulary

circular permutation (p. 925)
combination (p. 926)
complement (p. 959)
compound events (p. 947)
conditional probability (p. 949)
dependent events (p. 947)
expected value (p. 941)
factorial (p. 922)
Fundamental Counting Principle (p. 917)
geometric probability (p. 931)
independent events (p. 947)
mutually exclusive events (p. 956)
permutation (p. 922)
probability model (p. 939)
probability tree (p. 949)
random variable (p. 941)
sample space (p. 915)
simulation (p. 939)
tree diagram (p. 915)

VocabularyCheck

State whether each sentence is *true* or *false*. If *false*, replace the underlined term to make a true sentence.

1. A tree diagram uses line segments to display possible outcomes. **true**
2. A permutation is an arrangement of objects in which order is NOT important. **false, combination**
3. Determining the arrangement of people around a circular table would require circular permutation. **true**
4. Tossing a coin and then tossing another coin is an example of dependent events. **false, independent**
5. Geometric probability involves a geometric measure such as length or area. **true**
6. $6! = 6 \cdot 5 \cdot 4 \cdot 3 \cdot 2 \cdot 1$, is an example of a factorial. **true**
7. The set of all possible outcomes is the sample space. **true**
8. Combining a coin toss and a roll of a die makes a simple event. **false, compound**
9. Grant flipped a coin 200 times to create a probability tree of the experiment. **false, simulation**
10. Drawing two socks out of a drawer without replacing them are examples of mutually exclusive events. **false, dependent e**

Lesson-by-Lesson Review

13-1 Representing Sample Spaces

11. POPCORN A movie theater sells small (S), medium (M), and large (L) size popcorn with the choice of no butter (NB), butter (B), and extra butter (EB). Represent the sample space for popcorn orders by making an organized list, a table, and a tree diagram. See margin.

12. SHOES A pair of men's shoes comes in whole sizes 5 through 13 in navy, brown, or black. How many different pairs could be selected? 27

Example 1

Three coins are tossed. Represent the sample space for this experiment by making an organized list.

Pair each possible outcome from the first toss with the possible outcomes from the second toss and third toss.

HHH, HHT, HTH, HTT, THH, THT, TTH, TTT

13-2 Probability with Permutations and Combinations

13. DINING Three boys and three girls go out to eat together. The restaurant only has round tables. Fred does not want any girl next to him and Gena does not want any boy next to her. How many arrangements are possible? 4

14. DANCE The dance committee consisted of 10 students. The committee will select three officers at random. What is the probability that Alice, David, and Carlene are selected? $\frac{1}{120}$

15. COMPETITION From 32 students, 4 are to be randomly chosen for an academic challenge team. In how many ways can this be done? 35,960

Example 2

For a party, Lucita needs to seat four people at a round table. How many combinations are possible?

Since there is no fixed reference point, this is a circular permutation.

$P_n = (n - 1)!$ Formula for circular permutation

$P_4 = (4 - 1)!$ $n = 4$

$= 3!$ or 6 Simplify.

So, there are 6 ways for Casey to seat four people at a round table.

13-3 Geometric Probability

16. GAMES Measurements for a beanbag game are shown. What is the probability of each event?

a. P(hole) 2.45%

b. P(no hole) 97.5%

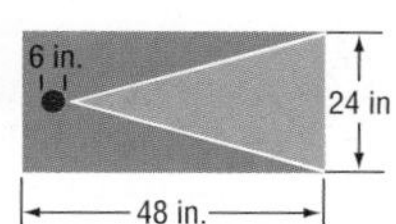

17. POOL Morgan, Phil, Callie, and Tyreese are sitting on the side of a pool in that order. Morgan is 2 feet from Phil. Phil is 4 feet from Callie. Callie is 3 feet from Tyreese. Oscar joins them.

a. Find the probability that Oscar sits between Morgan and Phil. $\frac{2}{9}$

b. Find the probability that Oscar sits between Phil and Tyreese. $\frac{7}{9}$

Example 3

A carnival game is shown.

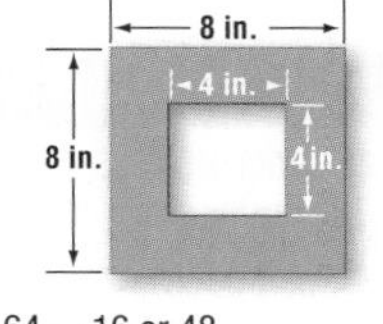

a. If Khianna threw 10 beanbags at the board, what is the probability that the beanbag went in the hole?

Area of hole $= 4 \cdot 4 = 16$

Area of board $= (8 \cdot 8) - 16 = 64 - 16$ or 48

$P(\text{hole}) = \frac{16}{64}$ or about 25%

b. What is the probability that the beanbag did not go in the hole?

$P(\text{no hole}) = \frac{48}{64}$ or about 75%

Lesson-by-Lesson Review

Intervention If the given examples are not sufficient to review the topics covered by the questions, remind students that the lesson references tell them where to review that topic in their textbook.

Two-Day Option Have students complete the Lesson-by-Lesson Review. Then you can use eAssessment to customize another review worksheet that practices all the objectives of this chapter or only the objectives on which your students need more help.

Additional Answer

11. S, NB; S, B; S, EB; M, NB; M, B; M, EB; L, NB; L, LB; L, EB

Outcomes	No Butter	Butter	Extra Butter
Small	S, NB	S, B	S, EB
Medium	M, NB	M, B	M, EB
Large	L, NB	L, B	L, EB

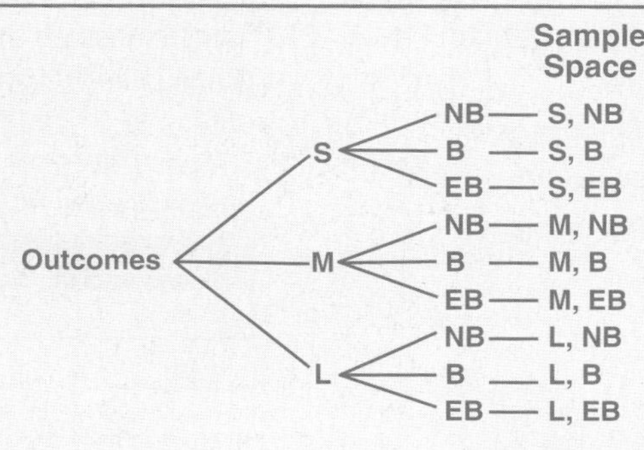

Anticipation Guide

Have students complete the Chapter 13 Anticipation Guide and discuss how their responses have changed now that they have completed Chapter 13.

Additional Answers

18. Sample answer: Use a spinner that is divided into two sectors, one containing 35% or 126° and the other containing 65% or 234°. Perform 50 trials and record the results in a frequency table. Use the results to determine the probability of Max scoring in the next match.
19. Sample answer: Use a spinner that is divided into 4 sectors, 108°, 79.2°, 82.8°, and 90°. Perform 50 trials and record the results in a frequency table. The results can be used to determine the probability of when a particular book will be purchased.
20. Sample answer: Use a spinner that is divided into 4 sectors, 226.8°, 87.48°, 28.08°, and 17.64°. Perform 50 trials and record the results in a frequency table. The results can be used to determine the probability for what a certain amount of oil would be used.

CHAPTER 13 Study Guide and Review *Continued*

13-4 Simulations

For each of the following, describe how you would use a geometric probability model to design a simulation. 18–20. See margin.

18. **POLO** Max scores 35% of the goals his team earns in each water polo match.
19. **BOOKS** According to a survey, people buy 30% of their books in October, November, and December, 22% during January, February, and March, 23% during April, May, and June, and 25% during July, August, and September.
20. **OIL** The United States consumes 17.3 million barrels of oil a day. 63% is used for transportation, 4.9% is used to generate electricity, 7.8% is used for heating and cooking, and 24.3% is used for industrial processes.

Example 4

Darius made 75% of his field goal kicks last season. Design a simulation that can be used to estimate the probability that he will make his next field goal kick this season.

Use a spinner that is divided into 2 sectors. Make one sector red containing 75% of the spinner's area and the other blue containing 25% of the spinner's area.

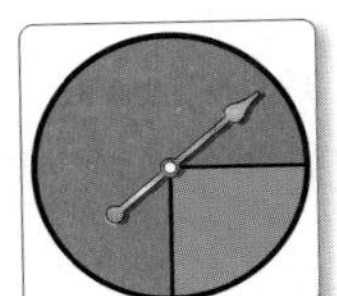

Spin the spinner 50 times. Each spin represents kicking a field goal. A successful trial will be a made field goal, and a failed trial will be a missed field goal.

13-5 Probabilities of Independent and Dependent Events

21. **MARBLES** A box contains 3 white marbles and 4 black marbles. What is the probability of drawing 2 black marbles and 1 white marble in a row without replacing any marbles? $\frac{6}{35}$
22. **CARDS** Two cards are randomly chosen from a standard deck of cards with replacement. What is the probability of successfully drawing, in order, a three and then a queen? $\frac{1}{169}$
23. **PIZZA** A nationwide survey found that 72% of people in the United States like pizza. If 3 people are randomly selected, what is the probability that all three like pizza? 37%

Example 5

A bag contains 3 red, 2 white, and 6 blue marbles. What is the probability of drawing, in order, 2 red and 1 blue marble without replacement?

Since the marbles are not being replaced, the events are dependent events.

$$P(\text{red, red, blue}) = P(\text{red}) \cdot P(\text{red}) \cdot P(\text{blue})$$
$$= \frac{3}{11} \cdot \frac{2}{10} \cdot \frac{6}{9}$$
$$= \frac{2}{55} \text{ or about } 3.6\%$$

13-6 Probabilities of Mutually Exclusive Events

24. **ROLLING DICE** Two dice are rolled. What is the probability that the sum of the numbers is 7 or 11? $\frac{2}{9}$
25. **CARDS** A card is drawn from a deck of cards. Find the probability of drawing a 10 or a diamond. $\frac{4}{13}$
26. **RAFFLE** A bag contains 40 raffle tickets numbered 1 through 40.
    a. What is the probability that a ticket chosen is an even number or less than 5? $\frac{11}{20}$
    b. What is the probability that a ticket chosen is greater than 30 or less than 10? $\frac{19}{40}$

Example 6

Two dice are rolled. What is the probability that the sum is 5 or doubles are rolled?

These are mutually exclusive events because the sum of doubles can never equal 5.

$$P(\text{sum is 5 or doubles}) = P(\text{sum is 5}) + P(\text{doubles})$$
$$= \frac{4}{36} + \frac{6}{36}$$
$$= \frac{5}{18} \text{ or about } 27.8\%$$

Additional Answers (Practice Test)

18. Not mutually exclusive; a person may own both a car and a truck.
19. Not mutually exclusive; you may roll 6 on one die and 1 on the other.
20. Mutually exclusive; a card cannot be both a spade and a club.
21. Sample answer: Use a spinner that is divided into two sectors, one containing 45% or 162° and the other containing 55% or 198°. Perform 50 trials and record the results in a frequency table.

Outcome	Frequency
A	23
Not an A	27
Total	50

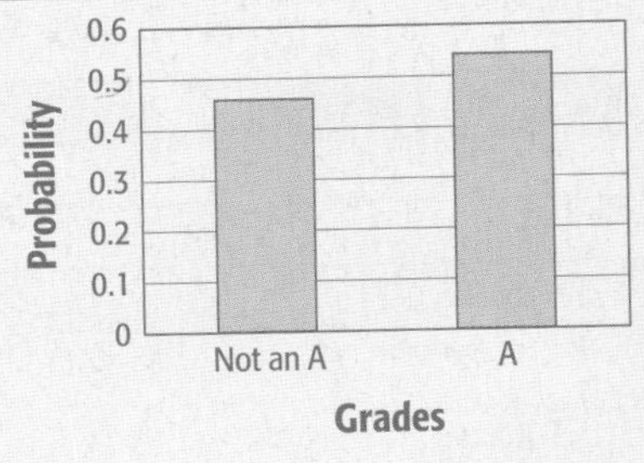

CHAPTER 13 Practice Test

Point X is chosen at random on $\overline{AE}$. Find the probability of each event. 1–2. See margin.

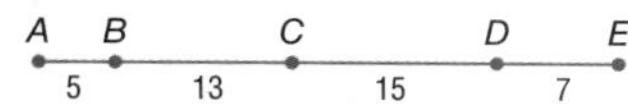

1. $P(X \text{ is on } \overline{AC})$
2. $P(X \text{ is on } \overline{CD})$

3. **BASEBALL** A baseball team fields 9 players. How many possible batting orders are there for the 9 players? 362,880

4. **TRAVEL** A traveling salesperson needs to visit four cities in her territory. How many distinct itineraries are there for visiting each city once? 24

Represent the sample space for each experiment by making an organized list, a table, and a tree diagram.

5. A box has 1 red ball, 1 green ball, and 1 blue ball. Two balls are drawn from the box one after the other, without replacement. See Ch. 13 Answer Appendix.
6. Shinsuke wants to adopt a pet and goes to his local humane society to find a dog or cat. While he is there, he decides to adopt two pets. See Ch. 13 Answer Appendix.
7. **ENGINEERING** An engineer is analyzing three factors that affect the quality of semiconductors: temperature, humidity, and material selection. There are 6 possible temperature settings, 4 possible humidity settings, and 6 choices of materials. How many combinations of settings are there? 144

8. **SPELLING** How many distinguishable ways are there to arrange the letters in the word "bubble"? 120

9. **PAINTBALL** Cordell is shooting a paintball gun at the target. What is the probability that he will shoot the shaded region? 0.16 or $\frac{4}{25}$

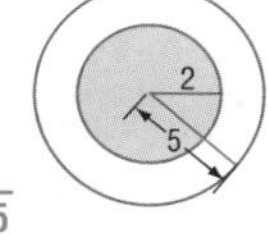

10. **SHORT RESPONSE** What is the probability that a phone number using the numbers 7, 7, 7, 2, 2, 2, and 6 will be 622-2777? $\frac{1}{140}$

11. **TICKETS** Fifteen people entered the drawing at the right. What is the probability that Jodi, Dan, and Pilar all won the tickets? $\frac{1}{455}$

Movie Ticket Giveaway!
Enter for a chance to win 3 tickets!

Determine whether the events are *independent* or *dependent*. Then find the probability.

12. A deck of cards has 5 yellow, 5 pink, and 5 orange cards. Two cards are chosen from the deck with replacement. Find P(the first card is pink and the second card is pink). independent, $\frac{1}{9}$
13. There are 6 green, 2 red, 2 brown, 4 navy, and 2 purple marbles in a hat. Sadie picks 2 marbles from the hat without replacement. What is the probability that the first marble is brown and the second marble is not purple? dependent, $\frac{13}{120}$

Use the spinner to find each probability. If the spinner lands on a line, it is spun again.

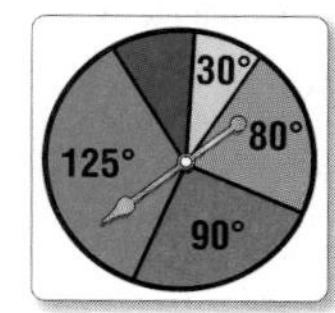

14. P(pointer landing on purple) 9.7%
15. P(pointer landing on red) 25%
16. P(pointer not landing on yellow) 91.7%

17. **FOOTBALL** According to a football team's offensive success rate, the team punts 40% of the time, kicks a field goal 30% of the time, loses possession 5% of the time, and scores a touchdown 25% of the time. Design a simulation using a random number generator. Report the results using appropriate numerical and graphical summaries. See Ch. 13 Answer Appendix.

18–20. See margin.

Determine whether the events are *mutually exclusive* or *not mutually exclusive*. Explain your reasoning.

18. a person owning a car and a truck
19. rolling a pair of dice and getting a sum of 7 and 6 on the face of one die
20. a playing card being both a spade and a club

21. **GRADES** This quarter, Todd earned As in his classes 45% of the time. Design and conduct a simulation using a geometric probability model. Then report the results using appropriate numerical and graphical summaries. See margin.

Summative Assessment

Use these alternate leveled chapter tests to differentiate assessment for your students.

Leveled Chapter 1 Tests

Form	Type	Level	Page(s)
1	MC	AL	49–50
2A	MC	OL	51–52
2B	MC	OL	53–54
2C	FR	OL	55–56
2D	FR	OL	57–58
3	FR	BL	59–60
Vocabulary Test			48
Extended-Response Test			61

MC = multiple-choice questions
FR = free-response questions

eAssessment Customize and create multiple versions of your chapter test and their answer keys. All of the questions from the leveled chapter tests in the Chapter 13 Resource Masters are also on eAssessment.

Additional Answers (Practice Test)

1. $\frac{9}{20}$, 0.45, or 45%
2. $\frac{3}{8}$, 0.375, or 37.5%

InterventionPlanner

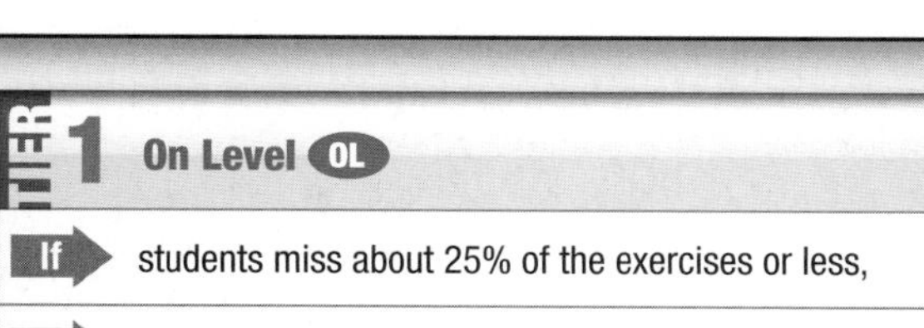

Tier 1 On Level OL

If students miss about 25% of the exercises or less,

Then choose a resource:

SE Lessons 13-1, 13-2, 13-3, 13-4, 13-5, and 13-6

Skills Practice, pp. 7, 13, 19, 26, 33, and 39

connectED.mcgraw-hill.com Self-Check Quiz

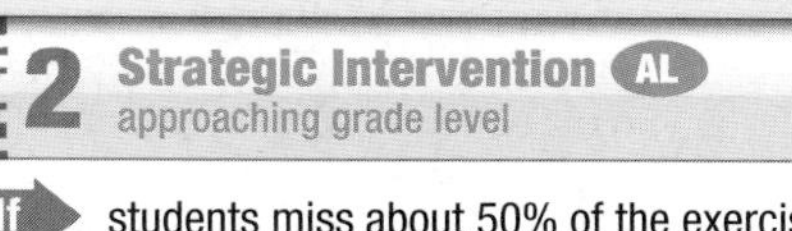

Tier 2 Strategic Intervention AL approaching grade level

If students miss about 50% of the exercises,

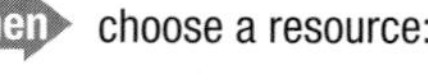

Then choose a resource:

Study Guide and Intervention, pp. 5, 11, 17, 24, 31, 37

connectED.mcgraw-hill.com Extra Examples, Personal Tutor

Tier 3 Intensive Intervention 2 or more grades below level

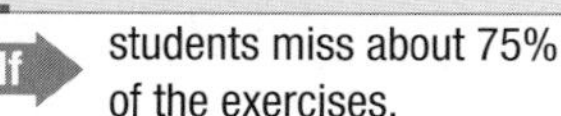

If students miss about 75% of the exercises,

Then use *Math Triumphs, Geo.*, Ch. 6

connectED.mcgraw-hill.com Extra Examples, Personal Tutor, Homework Help, Review Vocabulary

1 Focus

Objective Organize data in help analyze it and solve problems.

2 Teach

Scaffolding Questions

Ask:

- What are some ways that data could be given to you where it would need to be organized? Sample answer: Data can be given as part of a diagram or in the text of the problem.
- Can you think of any other different ways to organize data? Sample answer: Data can also be organized in a chart.
- What ways do you think organizing data can help you to solve a problem? Sample answer: It may be easier to find missing values and determine what techniques you need to use to solve a problem when the information given is clearly organized.

CHAPTER 13

Preparing for Standardized Tests

Organize Data

Sometimes you may be given a set of data that you need to analyze in order to solve items on a standardized test. Use this section to practice organizing data and to help you solve problems.

Strategies for Organizing Data

Step 1

When you are given a problem statement containing data, consider:

- **making a list** of the data.
- **using a table** to organize the data.
- **using a data display** (such as a *bar graph, Venn diagram, circle graph, line graph, box-and-whisker plot,* etc.) to organize the data.

Step 2

Organize the data.

- Create your table, list, or data display.
- If possible, fill in any missing values that can be found by intermediate computations.

Step 3

Analyze the data to solve the problem.

- Reread the problem statement to determine what you are being asked to solve.
- Use the properties of geometry and algebra to work with the organized data and solve the problem.
- If time permits, go back and check your answer.

Standardized Test Example

Read the problem. Identify what you need to know. Then use the information in the problem to solve.

Of the students who speak a foreign language at Marie's school, 18 speak Spanish, 14 speak French, and 16 speak German. There are 8 students who only speak Spanish, 7 who speak only German, 3 who speak Spanish and French, 2 who speak French and German, and 4 who speak all three languages. If a student is selected at random, what is the probability that he or she speaks Spanish or German, but not French?

A $\frac{7}{12}$ B $\frac{9}{16}$ C $\frac{2}{5}$ D $\frac{5}{18}$

970 | Chapter 13 | Preparing for Standardized Tests

Read the problem carefully. The data is difficult to analyze as it is presented. Use a Venn diagram to organize the data and solve the problem.

Step 1 Draw three circles, each representing a language.

Step 2 Fill in the data given in the problem statement.

Step 3 Fill in the missing values. For example, you know that 18 students speak Spanish and 14 students speak French.

$18 - 8 - 3 - 4 = 3$ (Spanish and German)
$14 - 3 - 4 - 2 = 5$ (only French)

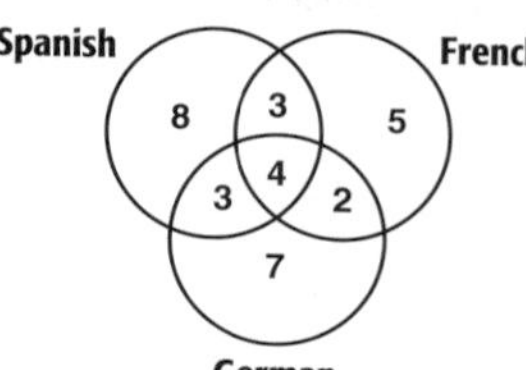

Step 4 Solve the problem. You are asked to find the probability that a randomly selected student speaks Spanish or German, but not French. From the Venn diagram, you can see that there are 32 total students. Of these, $8 + 3 + 7$, or 18 students speak Spanish or German, but not French. So, the probability is $\frac{18}{32}$ or $\frac{9}{16}$. So, the correct answer is B.

Exercises

Read the problem. Identify what you need to know. Then organize the data to solve the problem.

1. Alana has the letter tiles A, H, M, and T in a bag. If she selects a permutation of the tiles at random, what is the probability she will spell the word MATH? D

A $\frac{1}{4}$

B $\frac{1}{12}$

C $\frac{3}{50}$

D $\frac{1}{24}$

2. The table below shows the number of freshmen, sophomores, juniors, and seniors involved in basketball, soccer, and volleyball. What is the probability that a randomly selected student is a junior or plays volleyball? J

Sport	Fr	So	Jr	Sr
Basketball	7	6	5	6
Soccer	6	4	8	7
Volleyball	9	2	4	6

F $\frac{4}{21}$

G $\frac{5}{21}$

H $\frac{5}{17}$

J $\frac{17}{35}$

3. Find the probability that a point chosen at random lies in the shaded region. C

A 0.22

B 0.25

C 0.28

D 0.32

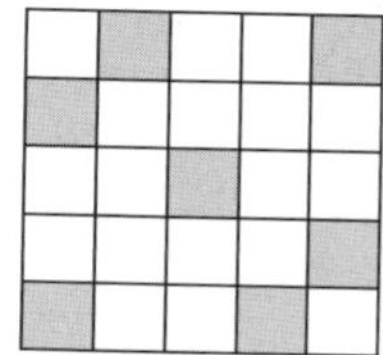

4. There are 10 sophomore, 8 junior, and 9 senior members in student council. Each member is assigned to help plan one school activity during the year. There are 4 sophomores working on the field day and 6 working on the pep rally. Of the juniors, 2 are working on the field day and 5 are working on the school dance. There are 2 seniors working on the pep rally. If each activity has a total of 9 students helping to plan it, what is the probability that a randomly selected student council member is a junior or is working on the field day? H

F $\frac{1}{5}$

G $\frac{4}{18}$

H $\frac{5}{9}$

J $\frac{2}{3}$

Additional Example

1 Of the students in Robert's class who have pets, 13 have dogs, 9 have cats, and 7 have fish. There are 6 students who have both a dog and a cat, 5 students who have both a dog and fish, 3 students who have both a cat and fish, and 2 students who have all three pets. If a student is chosen at random, what is the probability that he or she has a cat or a fish, but not a dog? B

A $\frac{1}{17}$

B $\frac{4}{17}$

C $\frac{6}{17}$

D $\frac{11}{17}$

3 Assess

Use Exercises 1–4 to assess students' understanding.

connectED.mcgraw-hill.com 971

Diagnose Student Errors

Survey student responses for each item. Class trends may indicate common errors and misconceptions.

1. A found difference of circumferences instead of difference of areas
B correct
C added areas instead of subtracting
D used diameters instead of radii in area formula

2. F correct
G used the height instead of the slant height in formula
H incorrectly applied the Pythagorean Theorem
J found volume instead of surface area

3. A correct
B there is no Reflection Property of Equality
C incorrect operation
D incorrectly applied property

4. F number of ways doubles can be rolled
G guess
H guess
J correct

5. A misread Venn diagram
B misread Venn diagram or misunderstood *or* in statement
C correct
D misread Venn Diagram

6. F listed measures in reverse order
G incorrectly ordered $m\angle S$ and $m\angle R$
H incorrectly ordered $m\angle T$ as the greatest measure
J correct

CHAPTER 13

Standardized Test Practice

Cumulative, Chapters 1 through 13

Multiple Choice

Read each question. Then fill in the correct answer on the answer document provided by your teacher or on a sheet of paper.

1. A machine is making steel washers by cutting out 10-millimeter circular disks from 34-millimeter circular disks as shown below. What is the area of each washer to the nearest tenth? B

A 75.4 mm^2
B 829.4 mm^2
C 986.5 mm^2
D 3317.5 mm^2

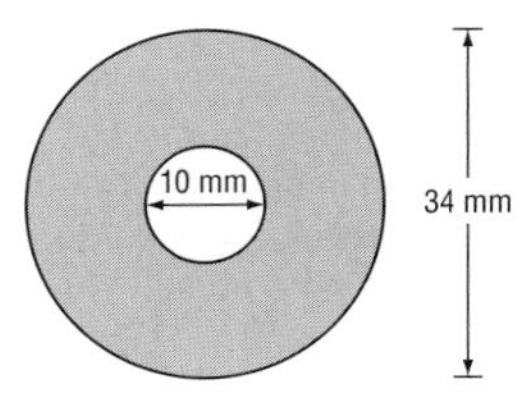

2. How much paper is needed to make the drinking cup below? Round to the nearest tenth. F

F 73.4 cm^2
G 70.7 cm^2
H 67.9 cm^2
J 58.8 cm^2

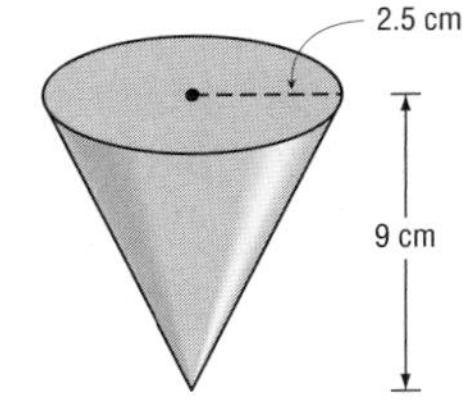

3. Which of the following properties of real numbers justifies the statement below? A

If $3x - 2 = 7x + 12$, then $3x - 2 + 2 = 7x + 12 + 2$.

A Addition Property of Equality
B Reflection Property of Equality
C Subtraction Property of Equality
D Symmetric Property of Equality

Test-Taking Tip

Question 4 What is the probability of rolling doubles with two number cubes? Multiply this by the number of trials.

4. What is the expected number of times Clarence will roll doubles with two number cubes in 90 trials? (Doubles occur when both number cubes show the same number in a trial.) J

F 6 G 9 H 10 J 15

5. The Venn diagram shows the states in the U.S. in which the population is greater than 10,000,000 and the population density is greater than 200 people per square mile. Which statement is false? C

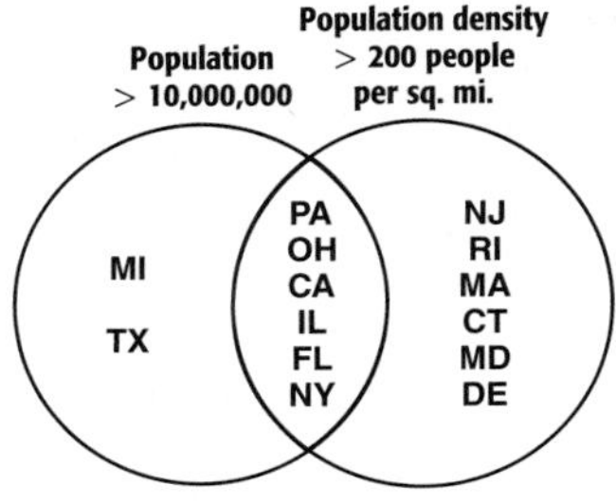

A In California (CA), the population is greater than 10,000,000, and the density is greater than 200.
B In Maryland (MD), the density is greater than 200.
C 14 states have a density greater than 200.
D 8 states have a population greater than 10,000,000.

6. Which of the following correctly shows the relationship between the angle measures of triangle *RST*? J

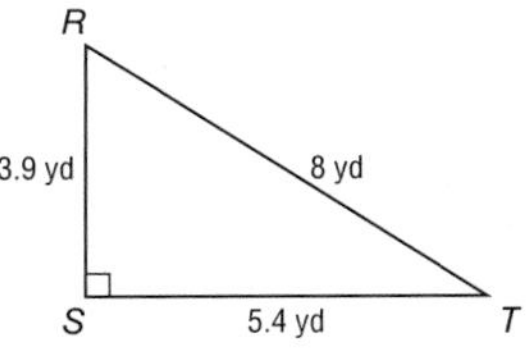

F $m\angle S < m\angle R < m\angle T$
G $m\angle T < m\angle S < m\angle R$
H $m\angle R < m\angle S < m\angle T$
J $m\angle T < m\angle R < m\angle S$

Short Response/Gridded Response

Record your answers on the answer sheet provided by your teacher or on a sheet of paper.

7. **GRIDDED RESPONSE** What is $m\angle S$ in the figure below? Express your answer in degrees. 77

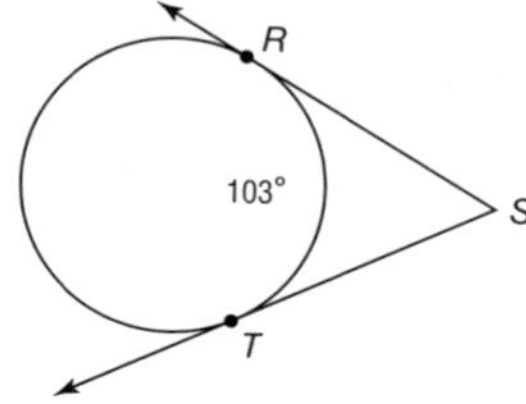

8. Does the figure have rotational symmetry? If so, give the order of symmetry. yes; order 2

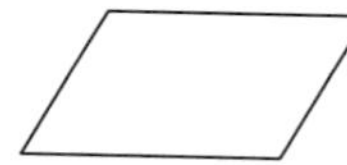

9. **GRIDDED RESPONSE** Segment AD bisects $\angle CAB$ in the triangle below. What is the value of x? 3

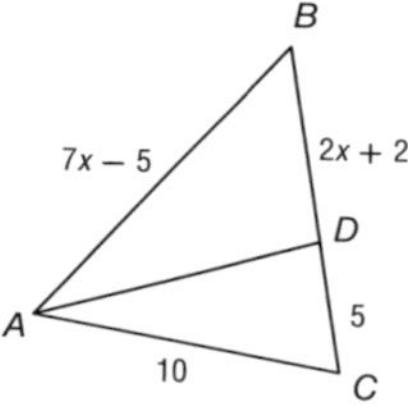

10. **GRIDDED RESPONSE** Armando leans an 18-foot ladder against the side of his house to clean out the gutters. The base of the ladder is 5 feet from the wall. How high up the side of the house does the ladder reach? Express your answer in feet, rounded to the nearest tenth. 17.3

11. Solve for x in the triangle below. 14

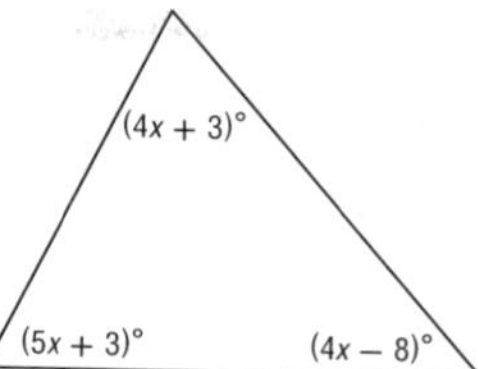

12. What effect does doubling the dimensions of the rectangle below have on its area and perimeter? See margin.

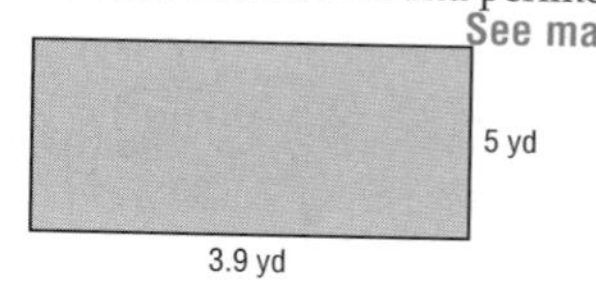

Extended Response

Record your answers on a sheet of paper. Show your work.

13. A bag contains 3 red chips, 5 green chips, 2 yellow chips, 4 brown chips, and 6 purple chips. One chip is chosen at random, the color noted, and the chip returned to the bag.
    a. Suppose two trials of this experiment are conducted. Are the events independent or dependent? Explain. See margin.
    b. What is the probability that both chips are purple? 0.09
    c. What is the probability that the first chip is green and the second is brown? 0.05

Need ExtraHelp?

If you missed Question...	1	2	3	4	5	6	7	8	9	10	11	12	13
Go to Lesson...	11-3	12-3	2-6	13-4	2-2	5-5	10-6	9-5	5-1	8-2	4-2	1-6	13-5

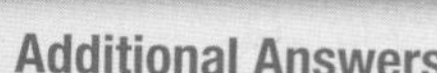

Additional Answers

12. The perimeter is doubled and the area is increased by a factor of 4.

13a. Independent; the outcome of choosing the first chip has no effect on the outcome of choosing the second chip because the chips are replaced after each trial.

Formative Assessment

You can use these pages to benchmark student progress.

Standardized Test Practice, pp. 62–64

Answer Sheet Practice

Have students simulate taking a standardized test by recording their answers on a practice recording sheet.

Student Recording Sheet

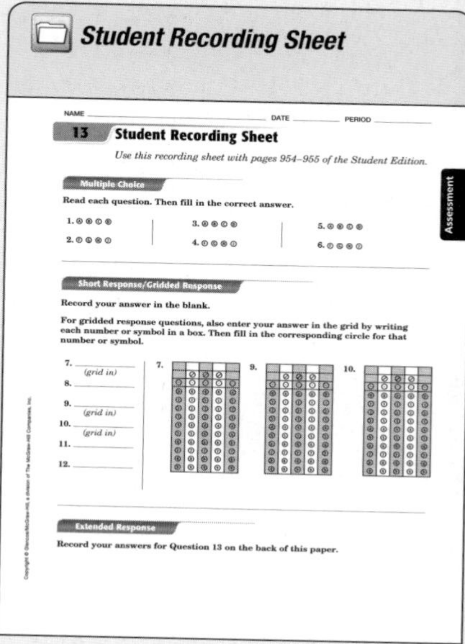

NAME DATE PERIOD

13 **Student Recording Sheet**

Use this recording sheet with pages 954–955 of the Student Edition.

Multiple Choice

Read each question. Then fill in the correct answer.

1. 2. 3. 4. 5. 6.

Short Response/Gridded Response

Record your answer in the blank.

For gridded response questions, also enter your answer in the grid by writing each number or symbol in a box. Then fill in the corresponding circle for that number or symbol.

7. (grid in)
8.
9. (grid in)
10. (grid in)
11.
12.

Extended Response

Record your answers for Question 13 on the back of this paper.

Assessment

eAssessment Create practice tests that align to your state standards, the Common Core State Standards, and other national standards such as TIMSS and NAEP.

Lesson 13-1 (Guided Practice)

1. H, 1; T, 1; H, 2; T, 2; H, 3; T, 3; H, 4; T, 4; H, 5; T, 5; H, 6; T, 6

Outcomes	1	2	3	4	5	6
Heads	H, 1	H, 2	H, 3	H, 4	H, 5	H, 6
Tails	T, 1	T, 2	T, 3	T, 4	T, 5	T, 6

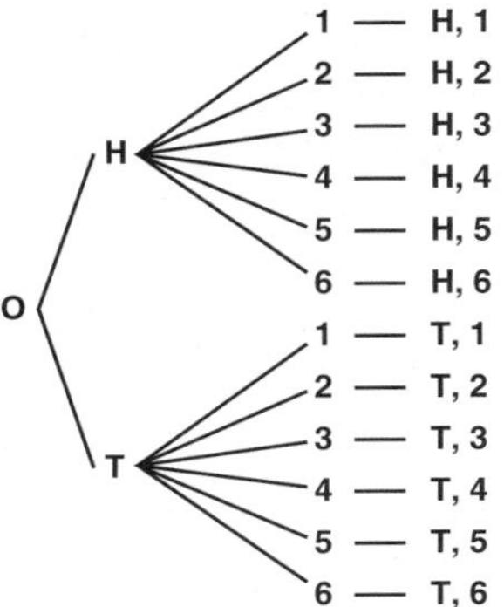

2.

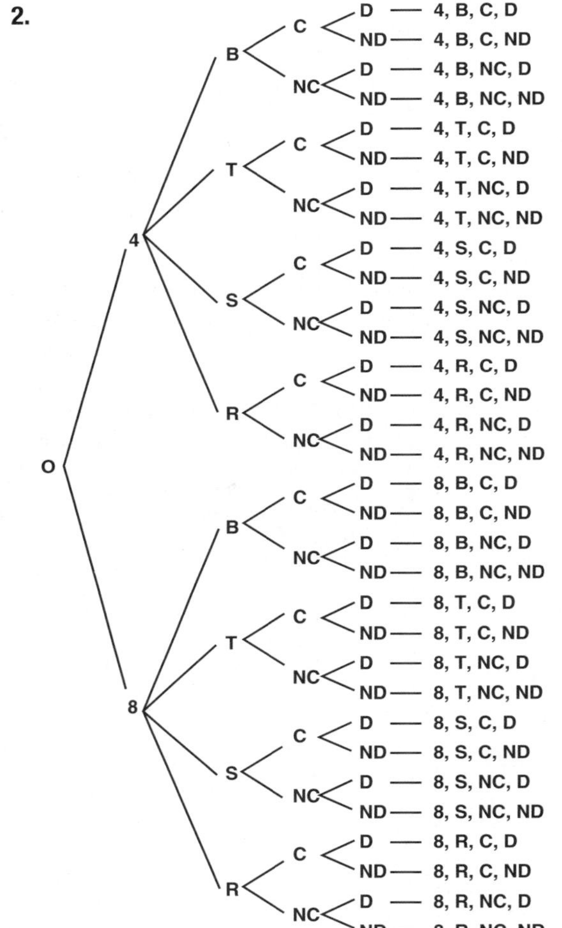

Lesson 13-1

1. S, S 0, 0
S, 0 0, S

Outcomes	Safe	Out
Safe	S, S	S, 0
Out	0, S	0, 0

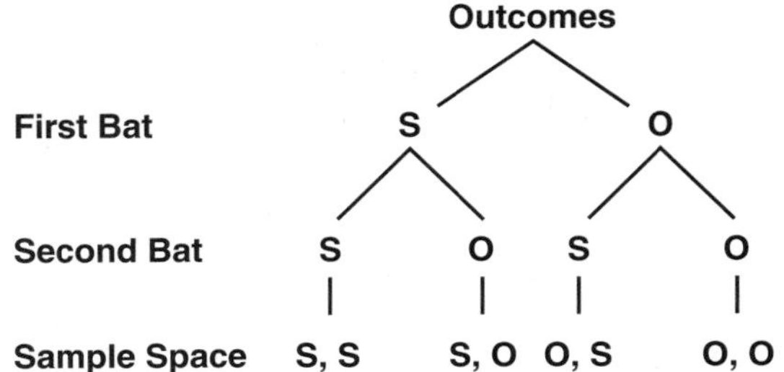

2. J, J N, N
J, N N, J

Outcomes	Juice	Notebook
Juice	J, J	J, N
Notebook	N, J	N, N

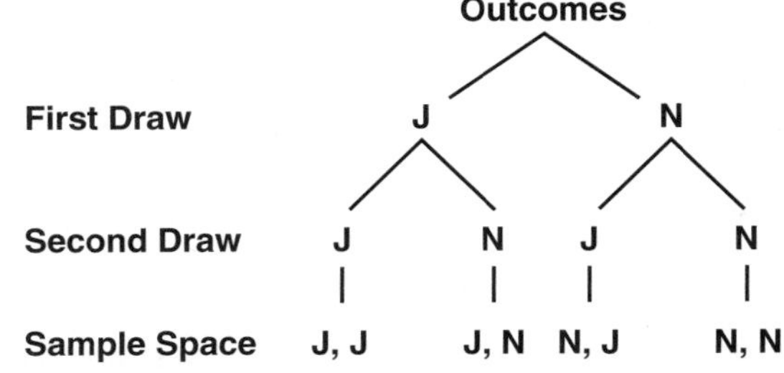

3.

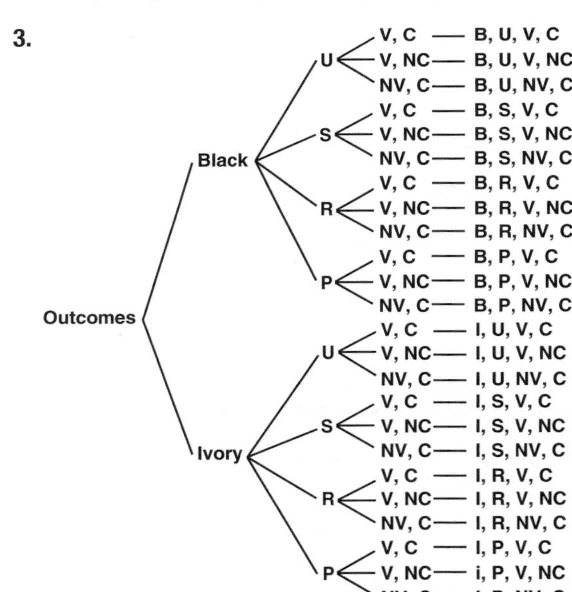

6. V, V B, B
V, B B, V

Outcomes	Volleyball	Basketball
Volleyball	V, V	V, B
Basketball	B, V	B, B

Outcomes

First Year V B

Second Year V B V B

Sample Space V, V V, B B, V B, B

7. S, S N, N
S, N N, S

Outcomes	Smithsonian	Natural
Smithsonian	S, S	S, N
Natural	N, S	N, N

Outcomes

First Class S N

Second Class S N S N

Sample Space S, S S, N N, S N, N

8. E, E I, I
E, I I, E

Outcomes	Italy	Ecuador
Italy	I, I	I, E
Ecuador	E, I	E, E

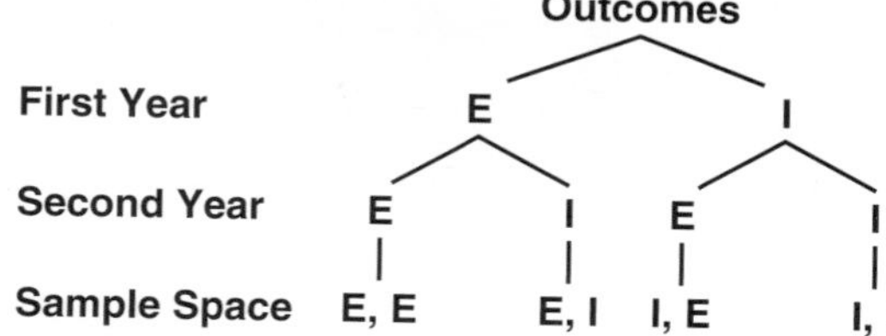

9. M, 5 T, 5
M, 6 T, 6

Outcomes	5	6
Monday	M, 5	M, 6
Thursday	T, 5	T, 6

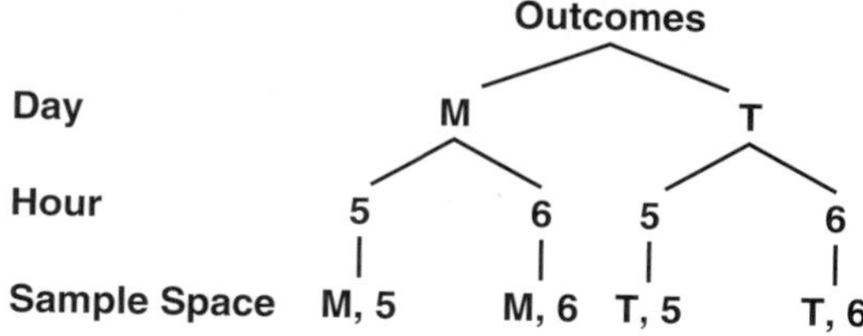

10. A, I A, S
O, I O, S

Outcomes	Isosceles	Scalene
Acute	A, I	A, S
Obtuse	O, I	O, S

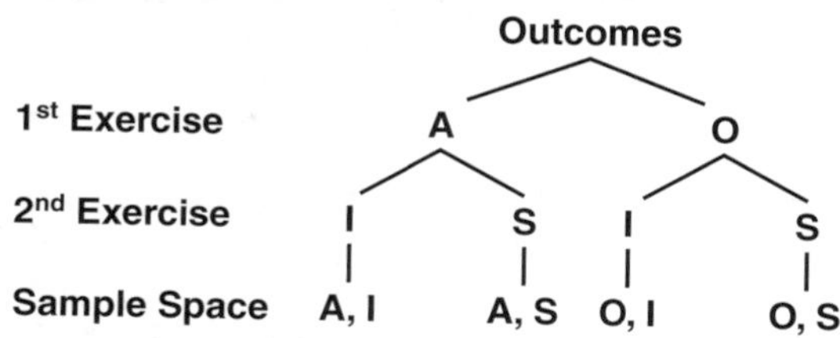

11. O, O A, A
O, A A, O

Outcomes	Oil	Acrylic
Oil	O, O	O, A
Acrylic	A, O	A, A

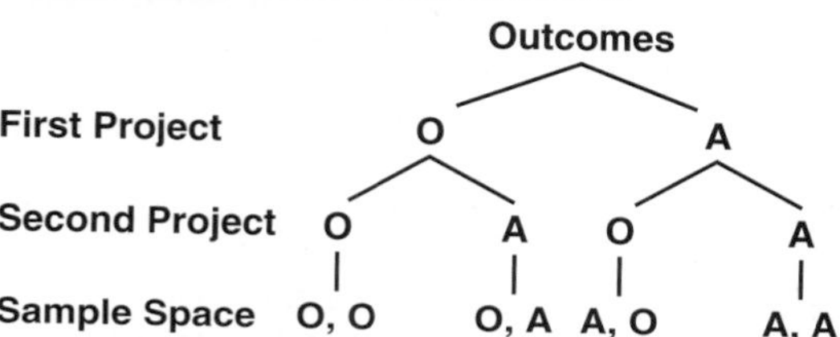

12. B = beans, P = pork, K = chicken, R = rice, NR = no rice, C = cheese, NC = no cheese, S = salsa, and NS = no salsa.

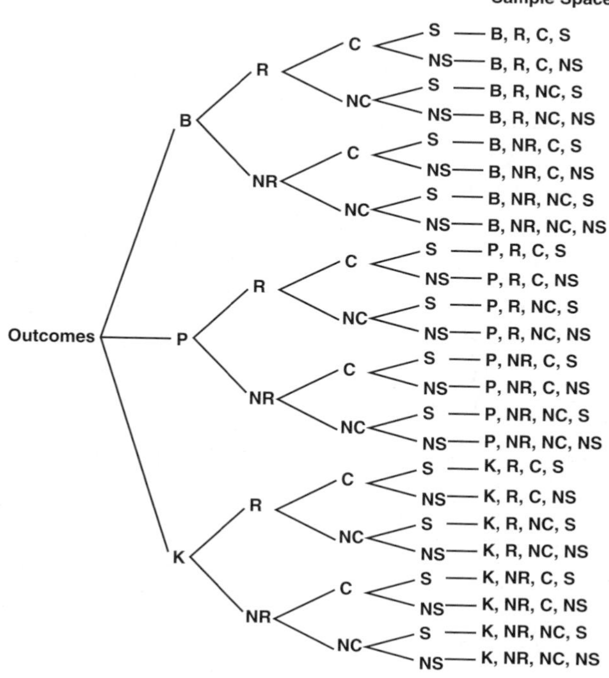

13. S = sedan, T = truck, V = van, L = leather, F = fabric, P = CD player, NP = no CD player, R = sunroof, NR = no sunroof

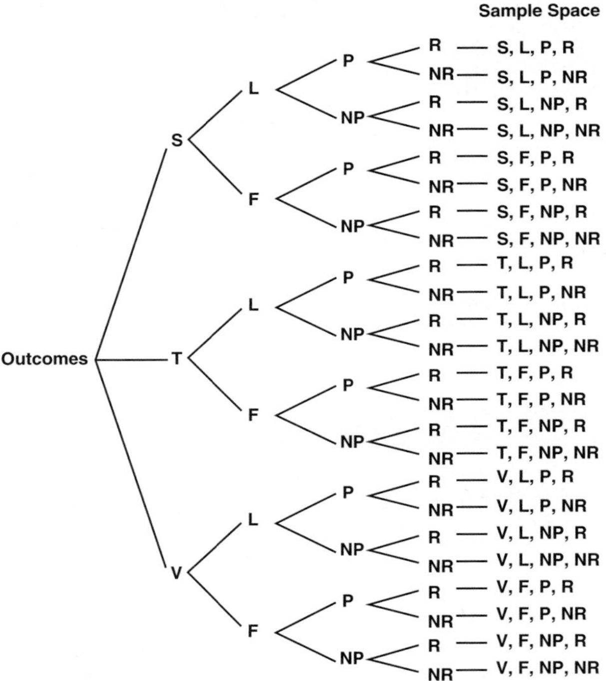

14. C = cake cone, G = sugar cone, W = waffle cone, S = strawberry, L = lime, P = peanuts, NP = no peanuts, K = sprinkles, NK = no sprinkles

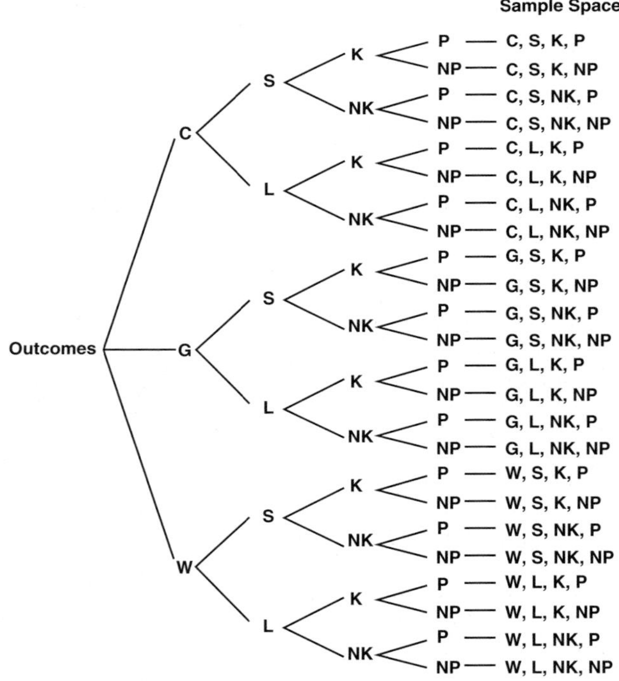

19. H = rhombus, P = parallelogram, R = rectangle, S = square, T = trapezoid; H, P; H, R; H, S; H, T; H, H; S, P; S, R; S, S; S, T; S, H

Outcomes	Rhombus	Square
parallelogram	H, P	S, P
rectangle	H, R	S, R
square	H, S	S, S
trapezoid	H, T	S, T
rhombus	H, H	S, H

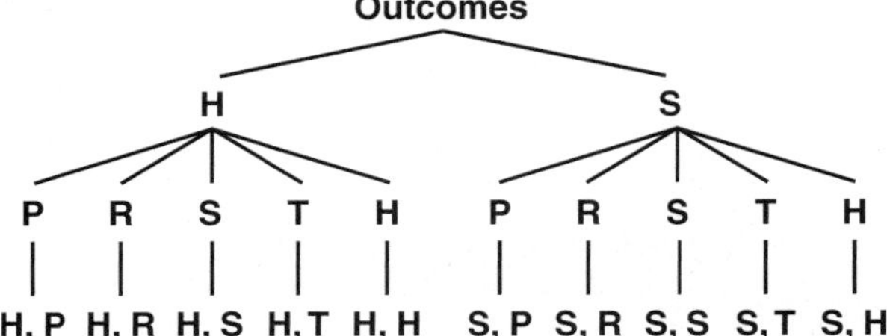

24a.

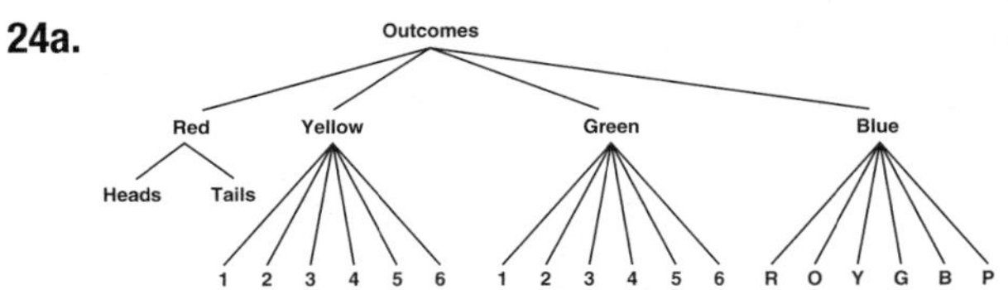

24b.

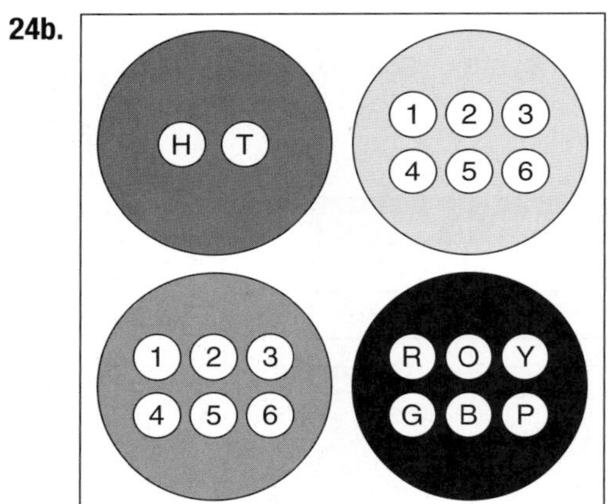

Lesson 13-3

34a. On a coordinate plane, graph $x = 7$ and shade between this line and the y-axis to represent the possible waiting times for the company A van. Graph $y = 12$ and shade between this line and the x-axis to represent the possible waiting times for the company B van. The area of the rectangle formed by the intersection is 84 units^2. Then graph $x = 5$ and $y = 5$ and shade the region bounded by these lines and the axes to represent the possible waiting times of 5 minutes or less for both vans. The area of the square is 25 square units. So the geometric probability is $\frac{25}{84}$ or about 30%.

34b. On a coordinate plane, graph the lines $x = 7$ and $y = 12$ and shade as before. The area of this rectangle is 84 units². Then graph $x = 7$ and $y = 5$. Shade the region bounded by the lines $y = 5$, $x = 7$, and the axes to represent the possible waiting times of 5 minutes or less for the company A van. The area of this rectangle is 35 units². Shade the region bounded by the lines $x = 5$, $y = 12$, and the axes to represent the possible waiting times of 5 minutes or less for the company B van. The area of this rectangle is 60 units². In each of these rectangles, the waiting time of 5 minutes or less for both vans has been counted twice. So the geometric probability is $\frac{60}{84} + \frac{35}{84} - \frac{25}{84} = \frac{70}{84}$, or about 83%.

34c. Sample answer: Since the chance of Meleah waiting 5 minutes or less to see the vans from both company A and B is only 30%, Meleah should take the van from company B.

45. D, D   G, G
D, G   G, D

Outcomes	Drums	Guitar
Drums	D, D	D, G
Guitar	G, D	G, G

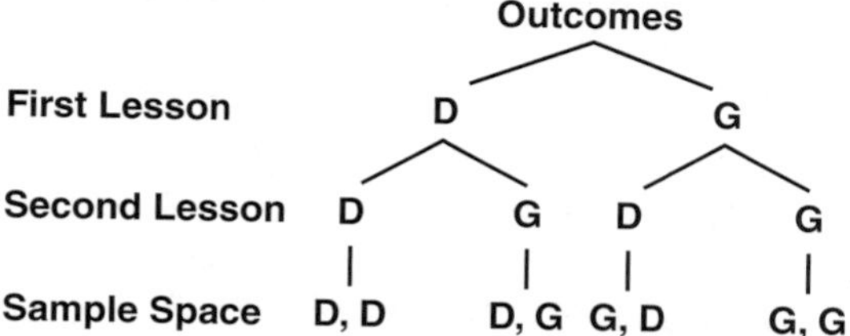

46. B, F   N, F
B, H   N, H

Outcomes	Flats	Heels
Black	B, F	B, H
Navy	N, F	N, H

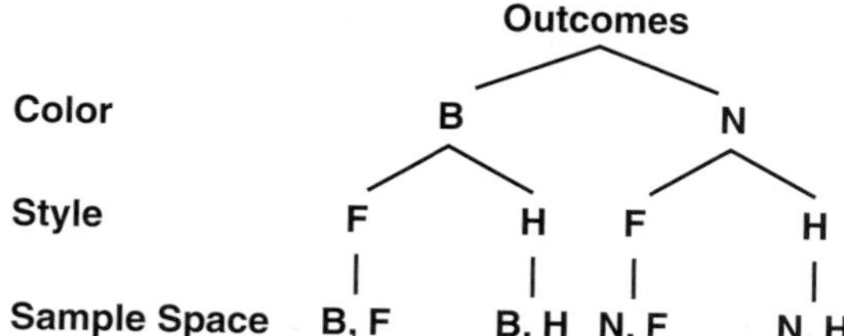

Mid-Chapter Quiz

3. R, S; R, L; B, S; B, L; Y, S; Y, L; G, S; G, L; P, S; P, L; O, S; O, L

Outcomes	Red	Blue	Yellow	Green	Pink	Orange
Short-sleeved	R, S	B, S	Y, S	G, S	P, S	O, S
Long-sleeved	R, L	B, L	Y, L	G, L	P, L	O, L

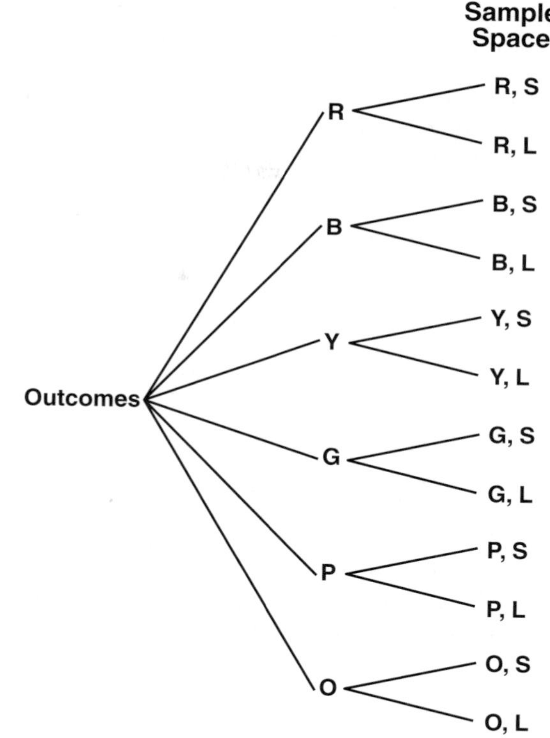

Lesson 13-4 (Guided Practice)

1. Sample answer:

Step 1

Possible outcomes		Theoretical Probability
• Game piece #1	→	$\frac{1}{6}$
• Game piece #2	→	$\frac{1}{6}$
• Game piece #3	→	$\frac{1}{6}$
• Game piece #4	→	$\frac{1}{6}$
• Game piece #5	→	$\frac{1}{6}$
• Game piece #6	→	$\frac{1}{6}$

Step 2 We assume that each game piece has an equal chance of being placed on a large drink cup, and that each drink cup has only 1 game piece on it.

Step 3 Create a spinner with 6 equal-sized sections numbered 1, 2, 3, 4, 5, and 6. Each sector of the spinner will have a central angle measuring 60°.

Step 4 A trial will consist of spinning the spinner until all every number has been spun and will represent someone buying large drinks until all 6 game pieces are collected.

4B. Sample answer: I will use a random number generator to generate pairs of integers 1–6. Each integer will represent the value of one of the die, so I will take the sum of the two integers. The simulation will consist of 20 trials.

Outcome	Frequency
2	1
3	0
4	1
5	4
6	1
7	7
8	2
9	2
10	1
11	1
12	0

The average value is 6.8. They are very close, but the average value is slightly less than the expected value.

Lesson 13-4

1. Sample answer: Use a spinner that is divided into two sectors, one containing 80% or 288° and the other containing 20% or 72°. Do 20 trials and record the results in a frequency table.

Outcome	Frequency
A	17
Below an A	3
Total	20

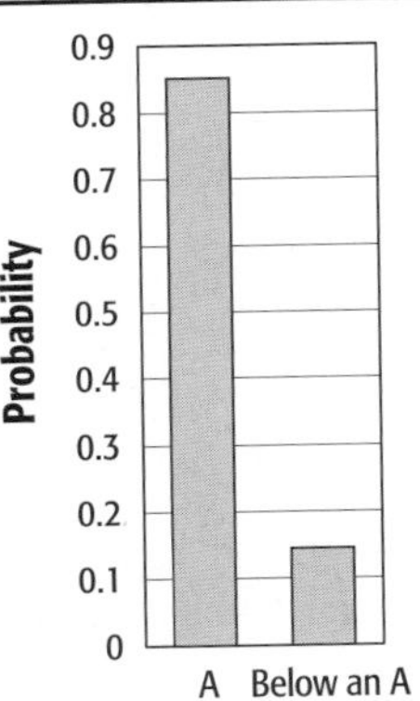

The probability of Clara getting an A on her next quiz is .85. The probability of earning any other grade is 1 − 0.85 or 0.15.

2. Sample answer: Use a random number generator to generate integers 1 through 20 where 1–9 represents tae kwon do, 10–15 represents yoga, 16–18 represents swimming, and 19–20 represents kick-boxing. Do 20 trials and record the results in a frequency table.

Outcome	Frequency
tae kwon do	9
yoga	7
swimming	1
kick-boxing	3
Total	20

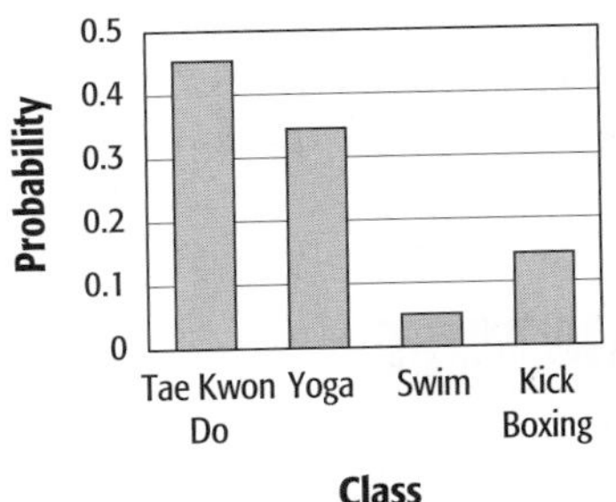

The probability of a customer taking the tae kwon do class is 0.45, taking yoga is 0.35, swimming is 0.05, and taking kick-boxing is 0.15.

5. Sample answer: Use a spinner that is divided into two sectors, one containing 95% or 342° and the other containing 5% or 18°. Do 50 trials and record the results in a frequency table.

Outcome	Frequency
Sale	46
No Sale	4
Total	50

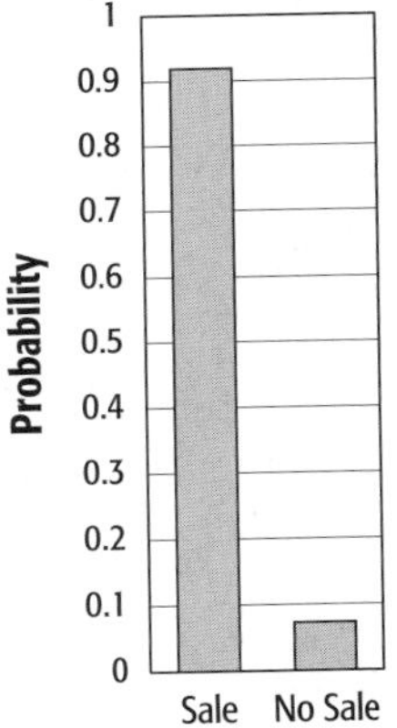

The probability of Ian selling a game is 0.92. The probability of not selling a game is 1 − 0.92 or 0.08.

6. Sample answer: Use a spinner that is divided into 10 equal sectors, each 36°. Do 10 trials and record the results in a frequency table.

Outcome	Frequency
Song 1	1
Song 2	0
Song 3	0
Song 4	0
Song 5	1
Song 6	1
Song 7	1
Song 8	2
Song 9	2
Song 10	2
Total	10

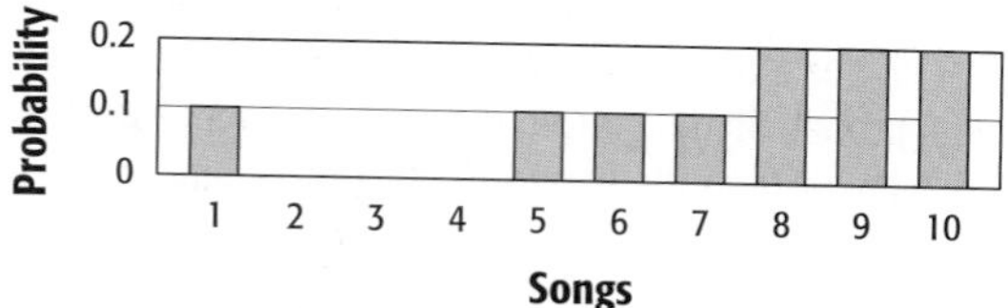

The probability of hearing song 1 is 0.1, songs 2–4 is 0, songs 5–7 is 0.1, and songs 8–10 is 0.2.

7. Sample answer: Use a spinner that is divided into 8 equal sectors, each 45°. Do 50 trials and record the results in a frequency table.

Outcome	Frequency
Category 1	3
Category 2	3
Category 3	6
Category 4	13
Category 5	4
Category 6	9
Category 7	7
Category 8	5
Total	50

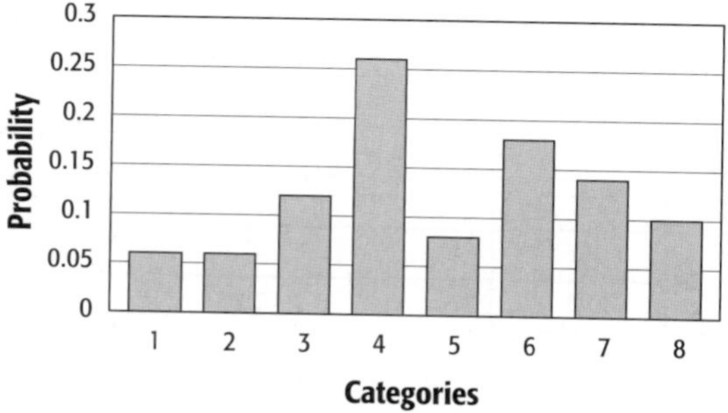

The probability of landing on Categories 1 and 2 is 0.06, Category 3 is 0.12, Category 4 is 0.26, Category 5 is 0.08, Category 6 is 0.18, Category 7 is 0.14, and Category 8 is 0.1.

8. Sample answer: Use a random number generator to generate integers 1 through 20, where 1–8 represents drama, 9–14 represents mystery, 15–19 represents comedy, and 20 represents action. Do 20 trials and record the results in a frequency table.

Outcome	Frequency
drama	11
mystery	3
comedy	6
action	0
Total	20

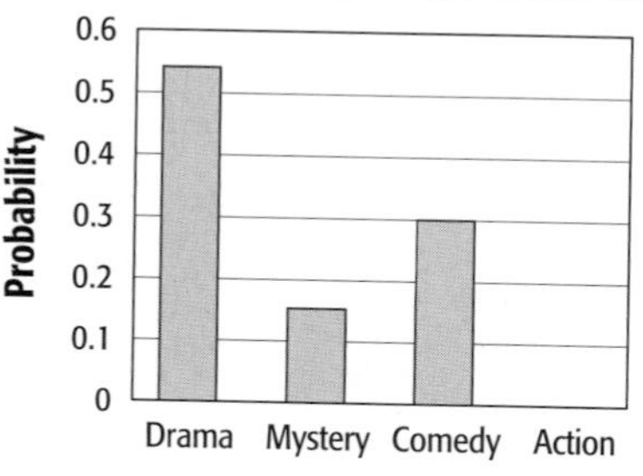

The probability of a customer choosing a drama is 0.55, choosing a mystery is 0.15, choosing a comedy is 0.3, and choosing an action film is 0.

9. Sample answer: Use a random number generator to generate integers 1 through 20, where 1–12 represents a single, 13–17 represents a double, 18–19 represents a triple, and 20 represents a home run. Do 20 trials and record the results in a frequency table.

Outcome	Frequency
single	13
double	4
triple	2
home run	1
Total	20

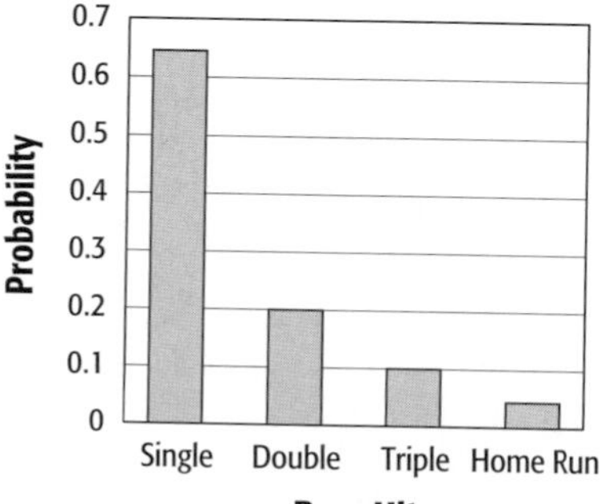

The probability of the baseball player hitting a single is 0.65, a double is 0.2, a triple is 0.1, and a home run is 0.05.

10. Sample answer: Use a random number generator to generate integers 1 through 20 where 1–9 represents Europe, 10–14 represents Asia, 15–17 represents South America, and 18–19 represents Africa, and 20 represents Australia. Do 20 trials and record the results in a frequency table.

Outcome	Frequency
Europe	7
Asia	6
South America	5
Africa	2
Australia	0
Total	20

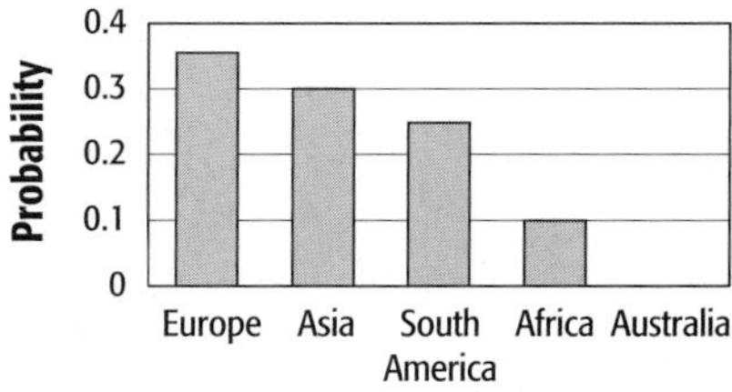

Travel Destinations

The probability of a customer traveling to Europe is 0.35, to Asia is 0.3, to South America is 0.25, to Africa is 0.1, and to Australia is 0.

11. Sample answer: Use a random number generator to generate integers 1 through 20, where 1–7 represents blue, 8–13 represents red, 14–16 represents white, 17–19 represents black, and 20 represents all other colors. Do 50 trials and record the results in a frequency table.

Outcome	Frequency
blue	17
red	14
black	7
white	10
other	2
Total	50

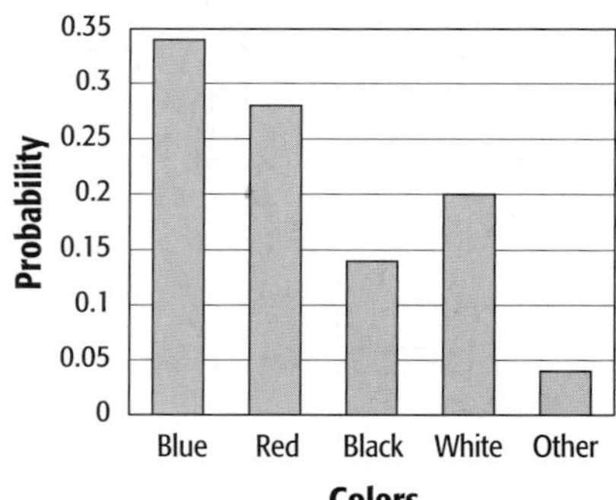

Colors

The probability of a customer buying a blue car is 0.34, buying a red car is 0.28, buying a black car is 0.14, buying a white car is 0.2, and any other color is 0.04.

17b. Sample answer: Since there are six equal outcomes, a die with the numbers 1 through 6 can be rolled to simulate each strike that is thrown. Roll the die 100 times and record the number on the die to indicate in which of the six boxes the strike was thrown. Record the percent of times a strike is thrown in each area.

Strike Area	Accuracy (%)
1	15
2	17
3	19
4	22
5	19
6	8
Total	100

18c. Sample answer: Yes; I would have expected fewer values between 1 and 14 and more values between 16 and 28. The theoretical probability of scoring 2 points in a possession is about 9% higher than the experimental probability and the theoretical probability of scoring 0 points in a possession is about 15% lower than the experimental probability.

19a. Sample answer: 9, 10, 6, 6, 7, 9, 5, 9, 5, 7, 6, 5, 7, 3, 9, 7, 6, 7, 8, 7

19b. Sample answer: 4, 10, 5, 10, 6, 7, 12, 3, 7, 4, 7, 9, 3, 6, 4, 11, 5, 7, 5, 3

19c. Sample answer:

Trial	Sum of Die Roll	Sum of Output from Random Number Generator
1	9	4
2	10	10
3	6	5
4	6	10
5	7	6
6	9	7
7	5	12
8	9	3
9	5	7
10	7	4
11	6	7
12	5	9
13	7	3
14	3	6
15	9	4
16	7	11
17	6	5
18	7	7
19	8	5
20	7	3

19d. Sample answer:

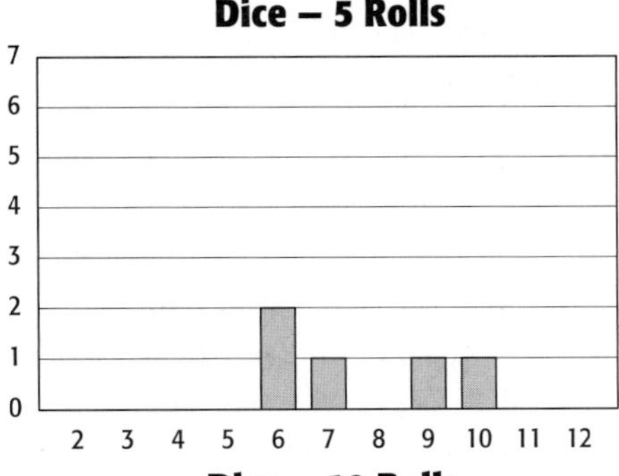

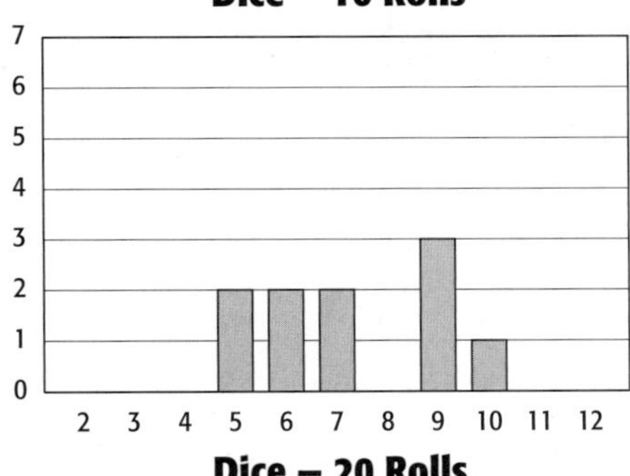

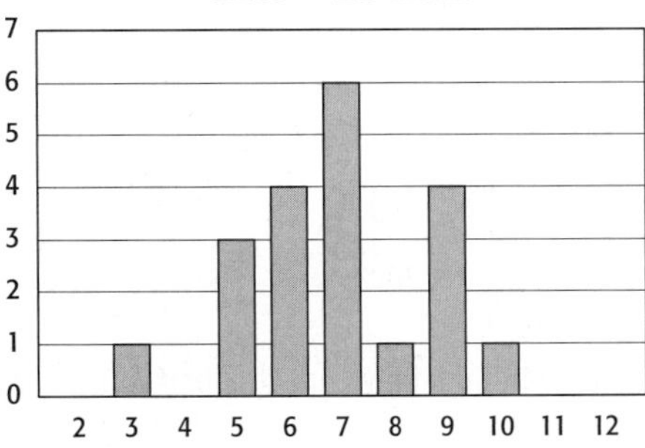

19e. Sample answer: The bar graph has more data points at the middle sums as more trials are added.

19f. Sample answer:

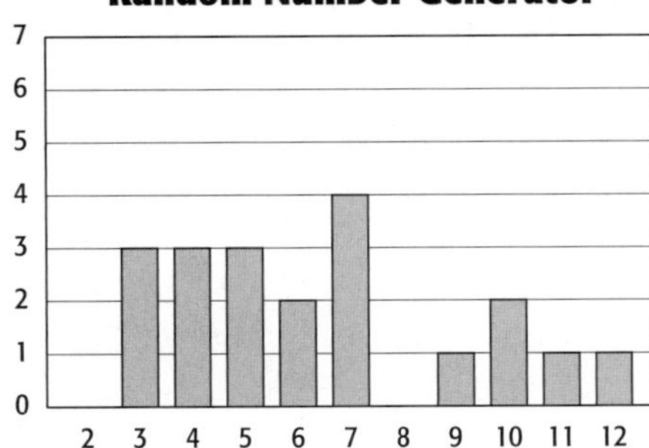

20. Yes; sample answer: If the spinner were going to be divided equally into three outcomes, each sector would measure 120. Since you only want to know the probability of outcome C, you can record spins that end in the red area as a success, or the occurrence of outcome C, and spins that end in the blue area as a failure, or an outcome of A or B.

21. Sometimes; sample answer: Flipping a coin can be used to simulate and experiment with two possible outcomes when both of the outcomes are equally likely. If the probabilities of the occurrence of the two outcomes are different, flipping a coin is not an appropriate simulation.

22a. Sample answer: The expected value is $\$1{,}000{,}000\left(\frac{1}{{}_{31}C_5}\right) \approx$ \$5.89. The expected payoff is \$5.89 − \$1 or \$4.89, which means that on average, a person can expect to gain \$4.89 for every \$1 he or she spends to buy a ticket. This is a low payoff value, so I may not play.

22b. Sample answer: The expected value is $\$5{,}000{,}000\left(\frac{1}{{}_{31}C_5}\right) \approx$ \$29.43. The expected payoff is \$29.43 − \$1 or \$28.43. This is a higher payoff, so I would play. The expected value from playing for \$0.5 million but only having to choose from 21 numbers is $500{,}000\left(\frac{1}{{}_{21}C_5}\right) \approx \$24.57$. The expected payoff is \$24.57 − \$1 or \$23.57. This is still a higher payoff value, so I would play.

23. Sample answer: We assume that the object lands within the target area, and that it is equally likely that the object will land anywhere in the region. These are needed because in the real world it will not be equally likely to land anywhere in the region.

24. Sample answer: Rolling a die has an expected value that is not a possible outcome. Each of the six faces of the die is equally likely to occur, so the probability of each is $\frac{1}{6}$. The expected value is $\frac{1}{6} \cdot 1 + \frac{1}{6} \cdot 2 + \frac{1}{6} \cdot 3 + \frac{1}{6} \cdot 4 + \frac{1}{6} \cdot 5 + \frac{1}{6} \cdot 6$ or 3.5. Since 3.5 is not a possible outcome, the expected value is not a possible outcome.

25. Sample answer: Expectation, or expected value, deals with all possible events, while probability typically deals with only one event. Probability is the likelihood that an event will happen, is between 0 and 1 inclusive, and is typically expressed as a decimal, fraction, or percent. Expectation is the weighted average of all possible events and can take on any value, even a value that is not a possible outcome. For example, the likelihood of rolling a "1" with a six-sided die is 1 out of every 6 rolls. So, the probability is $\frac{1}{6}$ or about 17%. When the same die is rolled, the expectation is 3.5, which is not a possible outcome.

Lesson 13-5

20.

$P(A \text{ and } B) = P(A) \cdot P(B \mid A)$	Formula for $P(A \text{ and } B)$
$\frac{P(A \text{ and } B)}{P(A)} = P(B \mid A)$	Divide each side by $P(A)$.

21a.

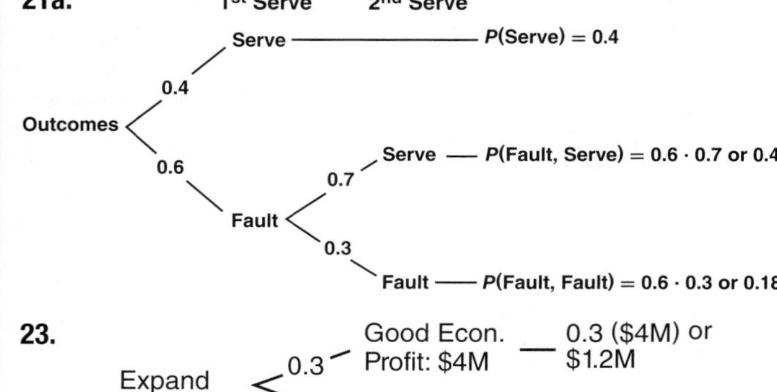

23.

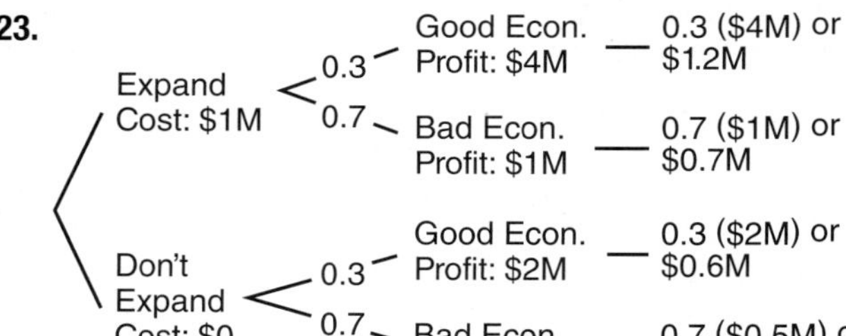

Sample answer: The expected value of choosing to expand is \$1.2M + \$0.7M or \$1.9M, and the expected value of choosing not to expand is \$0.95M. When we subtract the costs of expanding and of not expanding, we find the net expected value of expanding is \$1.9M − \$1M or \$0.9M and the net expected value of not expanding is \$0.95M − \$0 or \$0.95M. Since \$0.9M < \$0.95M, you should not expand the business.

24. 7; Sample answer: The probability of drawing object A is $\frac{1}{n}$, and the probability of drawing object B when object A is not replaced is $\frac{1}{n-1}$. Since we know that the probability is 2.4%, $\frac{1}{n} \cdot \frac{1}{n-1} = \frac{2.4}{100}$ or 0.024.Solve this equation to determine that n is 7.

26. Sample answer: Flipping a coin two times represents an independent event. Regardless of the outcome of the first flip, the probability of getting heads and tails on the second flip does not change. Drawing two colored marbles out of a bag without replacing the first marble represents a dependent event. Based on the color of the first marble, the probability that the second marble will be a specific color will change.

Lesson 13-6

29. 0.74; Sample answer: Consider an outcome to be an event in which at least two of the dice show a 4 or less. There are three outcomes in which the values of two or more of the dice are less than or equal to 4 and one outcome where the values of all three of the dice are less than or equal to 4. You have to find the probability of each of the four scenarios and add them together.

41. Sample answer: Use a random number generator to generate integers 1 through 20 in which 1–7 represent football, 8–13 represent basketball, 14–17 represent soccer, and 18–20 represent volleyball. Do 20 trials, and record the results in a frequency table.

Outcome	Frequency
football	7
basketball	6
soccer	5
volleyball	2
Total	20

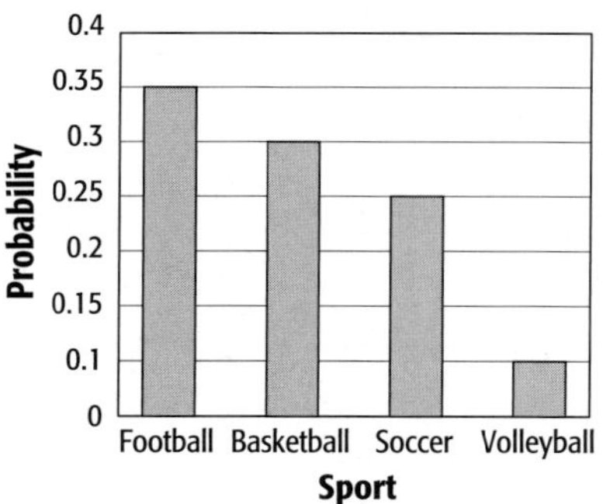

The probability that an athlete plays only football is 0.35, only basketball is 0.30, only soccer is 0.25, and only volleyball is 0.1.

42.

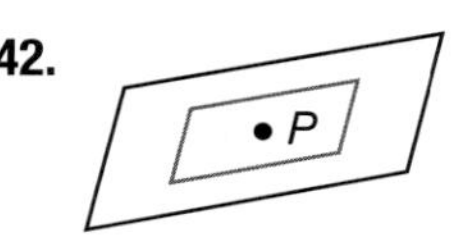

43.

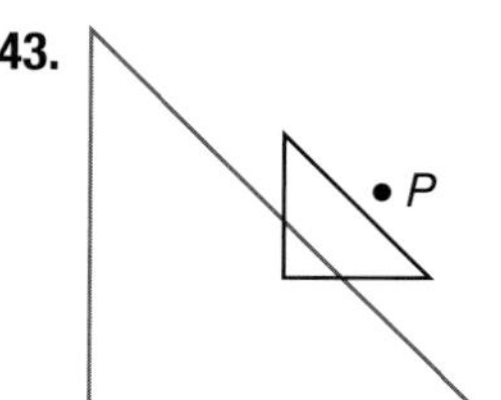

44.

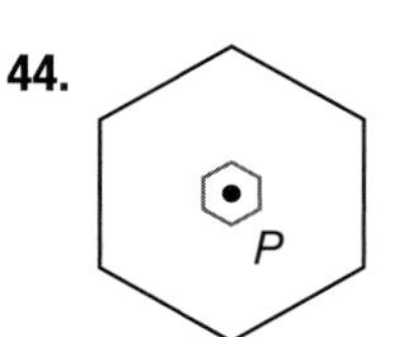

Practice Test

5. R, G; R, B; G, R; G, B; B, R; B, G;

Outcomes	Red	Green	Blue
Red		R, G	R, B
Green	G, R		G, B
Blue	B, R	B, G	

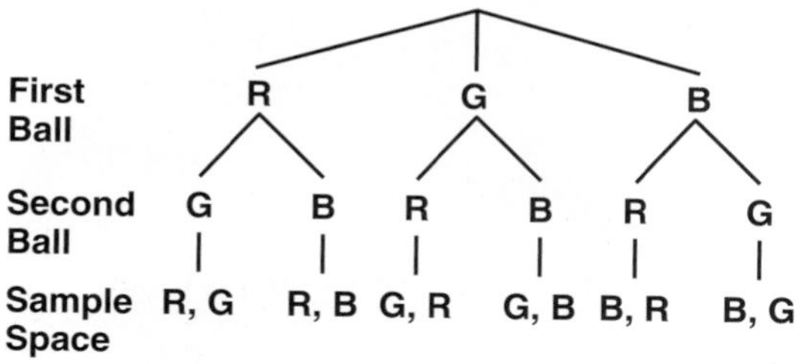

6. D, D; D, C; C, D; C, C;

Outcome	Dog	Cat
Dog	D, D	D, C
Cat	C, D	C, C

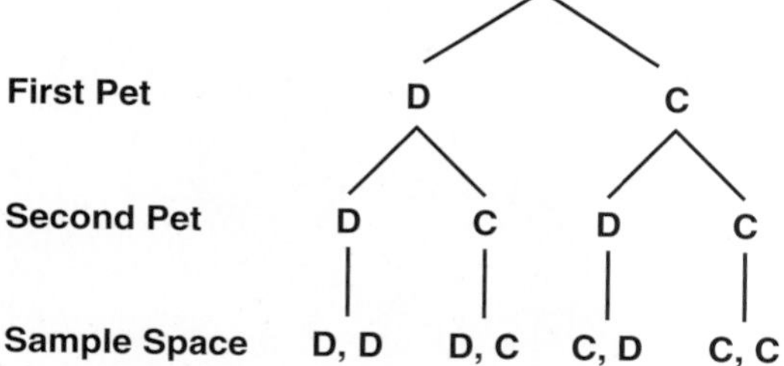

17. Sample answer: Use a random number generator to generate integers 1 through 20, where 1–8 represent a punt, 9–14 represent a field goal, 15 represents a turnover, and 16–20 represent touchdown. Do 20 trials and record the results in a frequency table. Use the results to find the probability of each hit.

Outcome	Frequency
Punt	8
Field Goal	6
Loss of Possession	1
Touchdown	5
Total	20

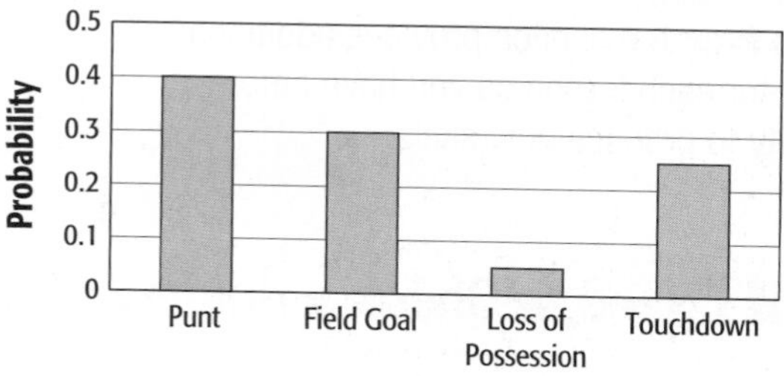

The probability of the team punting is 40%, kicking a field goal is 30%, losing possession is 5%, and scoring a touchdown is 25%.

Student Handbook

This **Student Handbook** can help you answer these questions.

What if I Need More Practice?

Extra Practice R1

The **Extra Practice** section provides additional problems for each lesson so you have ample opportunity to practice new skills.

What if I Need to Check a Homework Answer?

Selected Answers and Solutions R14

The answers to odd-numbered problems are included in **Selected Answers and Solutions**.

What if I Forget a Vocabulary Word?

Glossary/Glosario R115

The **English-Spanish Glossary** provides definitions and page numbers of important or difficult words used throughout the textbook.

What if I Need to Find Something Quickly?

Index R144

The **Index** alphabetically lists the subjects covered throughout the entire textbook and the pages on which each subject can be found.

What if I Forget a Formula?

Formulas and Measures, Symbols and Properties Inside Back Cover

Inside the back cover of your math book is a list of **Formulas and Symbols** that are used in the book.

Rubberball/Getty Images

Extra Practice

CHAPTER 1 Tools of Geometry

Refer to the figure. (Lesson 1-1)

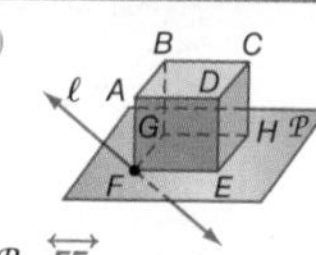

1. How many planes are shown in this figure? **6**
2. Name the intersection of plane ADE with plane $\mathcal{P}$. $\overleftrightarrow{FE}$
3. Name two noncoplanar lines that do not intersect. **Sample answer: lines ℓ and $\overleftrightarrow{CD}$**

Find the measurement of each segment. Assume that each figure is not drawn to scale. (Lesson 1-2)

4. $\overline{NQ}$ **6.7 cm**

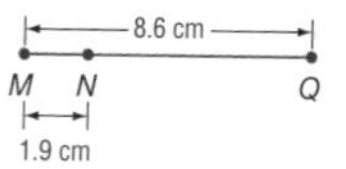

   M N Q; 8.6 cm; 1.9 cm

5. $\overline{BD}$ **7.8 mm**

   A B C D; 3.9 mm

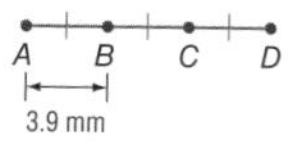

6. Find x and AB if B is between A and C, $AB = 3x$, $BC = 14$, and $AC = 41$. (Lesson 1-2) **9; 27**
7. **PLAYGROUND** The pivot or midpoint of a seesaw on a playground is 13.5 feet from the swing set. If the swing set is 8 feet from the edge of the seesaw when the seesaw is level, how long is the seesaw. (Lesson 1-3) **11 ft**
8. Find the coordinates of M if $N(1.5, 2.5)$ is the midpoint of $\overline{MP}$ and P has coordinates $(6, 9)$ (Lesson 1-3) **$(-3, -4)$**

Copy the diagram shown, and extend each ray. Classify each angle as *right*, *acute*, or *obtuse*. Then use a protractor to measure the angle to the nearest degree. (Lesson 1-4)

9. $\angle AFC$ **obtuse; 100**
10. $\angle DFB$ **right; 90**
11. $\angle CFD$ **acute; 25** 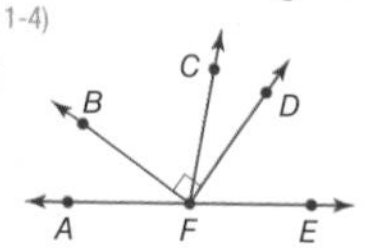
12. **SPORTS** When a ball is bounced on a smooth surface, the angles formed by the path of the ball are congruent. If the path of a ball forms a 53° angle with the floor, find $m\angle ABC$. (Lesson 1-5) **74**

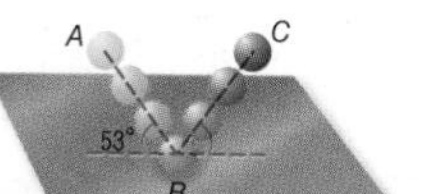

Determine whether each statement can be assumed from the figure. Explain. (Lesson 1-5)

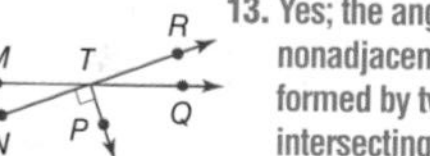

13. $\angle RTQ$ and $\angle MTN$ are vertical angles. **13. Yes; the angles are nonadjacent angles formed by two intersecting lines.**
14. $\overrightarrow{PT}$ is perpendicular to $\overrightarrow{TM}$ **No; $\angle PTM$ is not a right angle.**

Find the perimeter or circumference and area of each figure. Round to the nearest tenth, if necessary. (Lesson 1-6)

15.

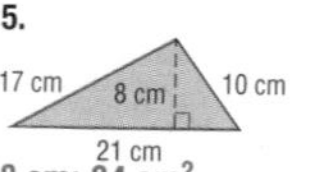

48 cm; 84 cm^2

16.

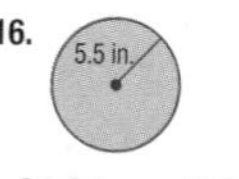

$\approx$34.6 in.; $\approx$95 in^2

17. **PLANNING** Tim is responsible for renting tables for an awards banquet. He needs 20 tables, and he can choose between circular tables with a diameter of 5.5 feet and square tables with a side length of 5 feet. Which option should Tim choose so that the tables cover the *smallest* area? (Lesson 1-6) **circular tables**

Find the surface area and volume of each solid to the nearest tenth. (Lesson 1-7)

18.

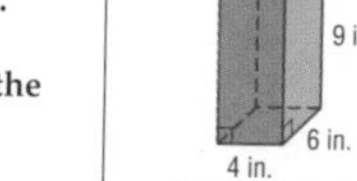

228 in^2; 216 in^3

19.

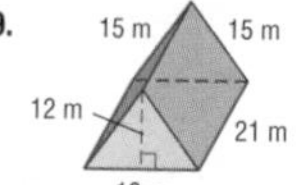

1224 m^2; 2268 m^3

20. **FISH** Sarah has a fish tank with the dimensions shown. (Lesson 1-7)
    a. What is the surface area of the fish tank? **1800 in^2**
    b. If Sarah fills the tank to a depth of 17 inches, what will be the volume of the water in the tank? **4896 in^3**

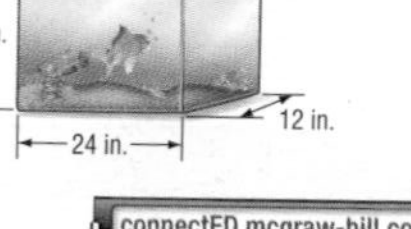

CHAPTER 2 Reasoning and Proof

1. Determine whether the statement below is *true* or *false*. If false, provide a counterexample. (Lesson 2-1)

   If $\overleftrightarrow{AB}$ is perpendicular to $\overleftrightarrow{CD}$, then exactly two right angles are formed.
   See Extra Practice Answer Appendix.

Use the following statements to write a compound statement for each conjunction or disjunction. Then find its truth value. Explain your reasoning. (Lesson 2-2)
p: A prism has two bases.
q: A pyramid has two bases.
r: A sphere has no bases.

2. $p \wedge r$
3. $q \vee \sim r$

2–3. See Extra Practice Answer Appendix.

COMMUNITY SERVICE **Refer to the Venn diagram that represents the organizations served by the students in a service club.** (Lesson 2-2)

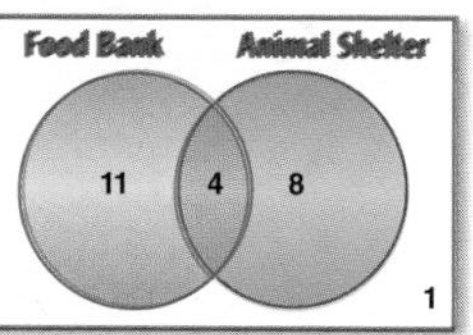

4. How many students volunteer in both organizations? **4**
5. How many students volunteer for only one organization? **19**
6. How many students are in the club? **24**

Determine the truth value of each conditional statement. If *true*, explain your reasoning. If *false*, give a counterexample. (Lesson 2-3)

7. If a number is divisible by 6, then it is divisible by 3. **7–8. See Extra Practice Answer Appendix.**
8. If $x^4 = 16$, then $x = 2$.
9. **GRADES** Draw a valid conclusion from the statement below, if possible. Then state whether your conclusion was drawn using the Law of Detachment or the Law of Syllogism. If no valid conclusion can be drawn, write *no valid conclusion* and explain your reasoning. (Lesson 2-4)

   If Amy scores above a 90 on her chemistry test, she will make an A. If she makes an A, her parents will take her to the theater. Amy scored a 93 on her chemistry test. **See Extra Practice Answer Appendix.**

Determine whether each conclusion is based on *inductive* or *deductive* reasoning. (Lesson 2-4)

10. Andrew's mom makes spaghetti for dinner on Mondays. Today is Monday. He concludes that his mom will make spaghetti for dinner. **deductive**
11. If Beth turns in her report early, she receives extra credit. Beth turned in her report early. She concludes that she will receive extra credit. **inductive**

Determine whether each statement is *always*, *sometimes*, or *never* true. Explain you reasoning. (Lesson 2-5) **12–15. See Extra Practice Answer Appendix.**

12. If planes $\mathcal{A}$ and $\mathcal{B}$ intersect, then their intersection is a line.
13. If point A lies in plane $\mathcal{P}$, then $\overleftrightarrow{AB}$ lies in plane $\mathcal{P}$.
14. Lines p and q intersect in points M and N.
15. **PHYSICS** The formula for pressure under water is $P = \rho gh$, where ρ is the density of water, g is gravity, and h is the height of the water. Given the water pressure, prove that you can calculate the height of the water using $h = \frac{P}{\rho g}$. (Lesson 2-6)
16. **PROOF** Write a two-column proof to verify that if $\overline{MN} \cong \overline{QP}$, then $x = 7$. (Lesson 2-6) **See Extra Practice Answer Appendix.**
17. **PROOF** Prove the following. (Lesson 2-7)
    Given: $\overline{AC} \cong \overline{BD}$, $\overline{EC} \cong \overline{ED}$
    Prove: $\overline{AE} \cong \overline{BE}$
    See Extra Practice Answer Appendix.

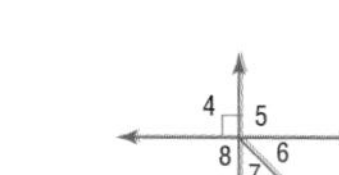

Find the measure of each numbered angle, and name the theorems that justify your work. (Lesson 2-8)

18. $\angle 2$ and $\angle 3$ are supplementary; $m\angle 2 = 149$
19. $\angle 6 \cong \angle 7$

18–19. See Extra Practice Answer Appendix.

20. **PROOF** Given that $\angle BEC$ is a right angle, prove that $\angle AEB$ and $\angle CED$ are complementary. (Lesson 2-8) **See Extra Practice Answer Appendix.**

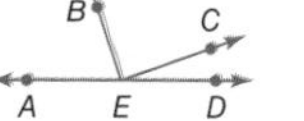

CHAPTER 3 Parallel and Perpendicular Lines

Classify the relationship between each pair of angles as *alternate interior*, *alternate exterior*, *corresponding*, or *consecutive interior* angles. (Lesson 3-1)

1. $\angle 5$ and $\angle 7$ **corresponding**
2. $\angle 2$ and $\angle 6$ **alternate interior**
3. $\angle 6$ and $\angle 7$ **consecutive interior**
4. $\angle 4$ and $\angle 8$ **alternate exterior**

5. **FENCES** Find the measures of $\angle 2$, $\angle 3$, and $\angle 4$ of the fence shown. (Lesson 3-2)

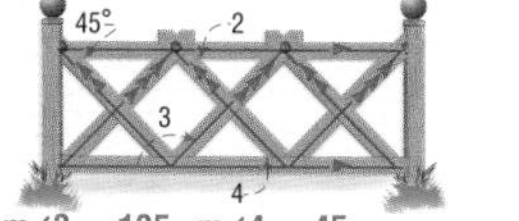

$m\angle 2 = 45$, $m\angle 3 = 135$, $m\angle 4 = 45$

Find the value of the variables in each figure. Explain your reasoning. (Lesson 3-2)

6. 7.

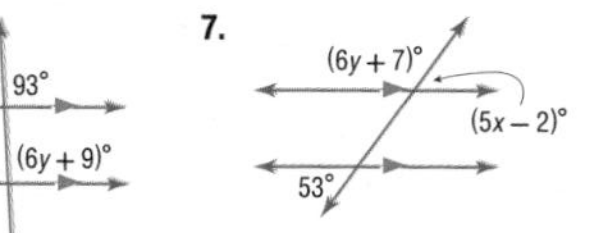

6–7. See Extra Practice Answer Appendix.

8. **JOBS** Katie mows lawns in the summer to earn extra money. She started with 3 lawns, and she now mows 12 lawns in her fourth summer. (Lesson 3-3) **8a–b. See Extra Practice Answer Appendix.**
   a. Graph the line that models the growth of Katie's business over time.
   b. What is the slope of the graph? What does it represent?
   c. Assuming that the business continues to grow at the same rate, how many lawns should Katie plan to mow during her sixth summer? **18**

Determine whether $\overleftrightarrow{AB}$ and $\overleftrightarrow{CD}$ are *parallel*, *perpendicular*, or *neither*. Graph each line to verify your answer. (Lesson 3-3)

9. $A(-4, -2)$, $B(0, 4)$, $C(-2, -4)$, $D(4, 5)$ **parallel**
10. $A(0, -3)$, $B(3, 9)$, $C(-4, 0)$, $D(8, 3)$ **neither**

9–10. See Extra Practice Answer Appendix for graphs.

Graph the line that satisfies each condition. (Lesson 3-3)

11. slope $= -\frac{1}{2}$, passes through $W(4, 5)$
12. passes through $M(-3, -5)$, perpendicular to $\overleftrightarrow{NP}$ with $N(-3, 2)$ and $P(9, 4)$ **11–12. See Extra Practice Answer Appendix.**

Write an equation in point-slope form of the line having the given slope that contains the given point. Then graph the line. (Lesson 3-4)

13. $m = -\frac{4}{5}$, $(10, -14)$
14. $m = 5$, $(-1, -3)$

13–14. See Extra Practice Answer Appendix.

Write an equation of the line through each pair of points in slope-intercept form. (Lesson 3-4)

15. $(4, 0)$ and $(-3, -7)$ $y = x - 4$
16. $(-1, 8)$ and $(5, -4)$ $y = -2x + 6$
17. **MOVIES** Wade watches movies online through an online movie rental company. His current plan costs \$7.99 per month with an additional charge of \$2.39 per movie. He is considering switching to a plan that costs \$14.99 per month with an additional charge of \$1.49 per movie. (Lesson 3-4)
    a. Write an equation to represent the total monthly cost for each plan.
    b. Graph the equations.
    c. If Wade watches an average of 10 movies per month, should he keep his current plan or change to the other plan? Explain.
    17a–c. See Extra Practice Answer Appendix.

Given the following information, determine which lines, if any, are parallel. State the postulate or theorem that justifies your answer. (Lesson 3-5)

18. $m\angle 4 + m\angle 7 = 180$
19. $\angle 1 \cong \angle 4$
20. $m\angle 6 = 90$

18–20. See Extra Practice Answer Appendix.

21. **PROOF** Write a two-column proof. (Lesson 3-5)
    Given: $\angle 1$ and $\angle 8$ are supplementary.
    Prove: $\ell \parallel m$
    See Extra Practice Answer Appendix.

Find the distance from P to ℓ. (Lesson 3-6)

22. Line ℓ contains points $(0, 3)$ and $(-4, -9)$. Point P has coordinates $(-6, -5)$. $\sqrt{10}$
23. Line ℓ contains points $(-5, 6)$ and $(1, -6)$. Point P has coordinates $(6, 4)$. $4\sqrt{5}$

Find the distance between each pair of parallel lines with the given equations. (Lesson 3-6)

24. $y = -4x - 6$, $y = -4x + 11$ $\sqrt{17}$
25. $y = \frac{1}{2}x + \frac{7}{2}$, $y = \frac{1}{2}x + 1$ $\sqrt{5}$

CHAPTER 4 Congruent Triangles

Classify each triangle as *acute*, *equiangular*, *obtuse*, or *right*, and as *equilateral*, *isosceles*, or *scalene*. (Lesson 4-1)

1. △ABC **obtuse; scalene**
2. △BCD **right; isosceles**
3. △BDF **equiangular; equilateral**

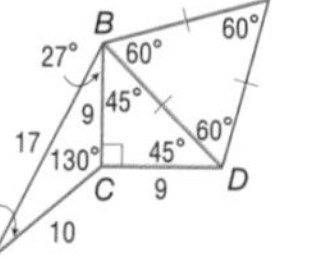

4. **BICYCLING** In the bicycle shown, $m\angle C = 60$ and $m\angle D = 105$. Find $m\angle B$. (Lesson 4-2) **45**

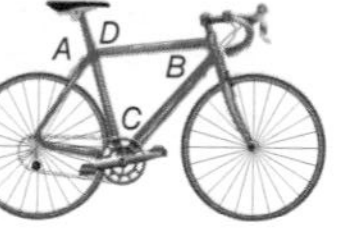

Find each measure. (Lesson 4-2)

5. $m\angle 1$ **57**
6. $m\angle 2$ **75**
7. $m\angle 3$ **44**

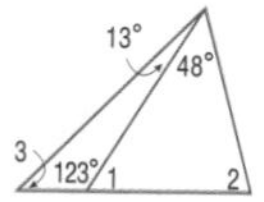

In the figure, △$ABC \cong$ △DEF. Find each value. (Lesson 4-3)

8. x **5**
9. y **8**
10. z **11**

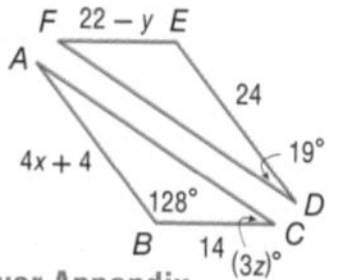

11–12. See Extra Practice Answer Appendix.

Determine whether △$PQR \cong$ △XYZ. Explain. (Lesson 4-4)

11. $P(-4, 2), Q(2, 2), R(2, 8)$; $X(-1, -3), Y(5, -3), Z(5, 4)$
12. $P(-2, 4), Q(-7, 3), R(0, 9)$; $X(3, 6), Y(2, 1), Z(8, 8)$

13. **PROOF** Write a two-column proof. (Lesson 4-4)
 Given: $\overline{AB} \cong \overline{DE}$, $\overline{AC} \cong \overline{DF}$, $\overline{AB} \parallel \overline{DE}$
 Prove: △$ABC \cong$ △DEF
 See Extra Practice Answer Appendix.

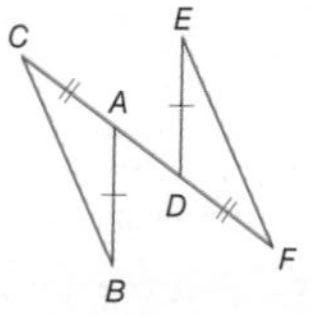

14. **PROOF** Write a paragraph proof. (Lesson 4-5)
 Given: $m\angle PRQ = 90$
 $m\angle RPT = 90$
 $\angle Q \cong \angle T$
 Prove: △$QRP \cong$ △TPR
 See Extra Practice Answer Appendix.

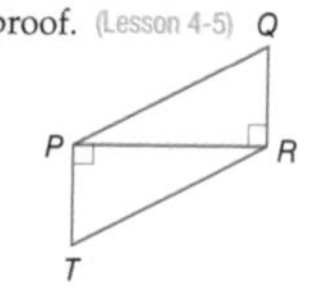

15. **NATURE** What is the approximate width of the creek shown below? Explain your reasoning. (Lesson 4-5)
 See Extra Practice Answer Appendix.

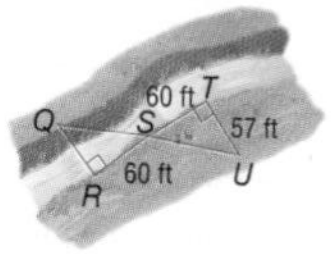

Find each measure. (Lesson 4-6)

16. $m\angle BDA$ **60**
17. BD **9**
18. $m\angle BCD$ **40**

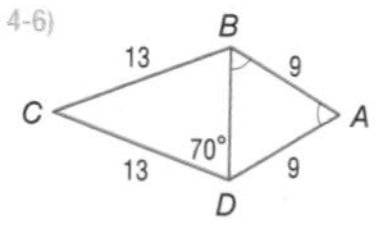

19. Identify the type of congruence transformation shown as a *reflection*, *translation*, or *rotation*. (Lesson 4-7) **rotation**

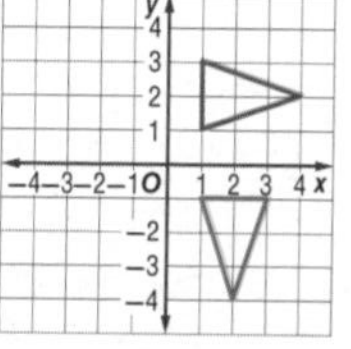

Graph each pair of triangles with the given vertices. Then, identify the transformation, and verify that it is a congruence transformation. (Lesson 4-7) **20–21. See Extra Practice Answer Appendix.**

20. $A(2, 2), B(4, -1), C(1, -2)$; $M(-4, -1), N(-1, -2), P(-2, 2)$
21. $A(-1, -1), B(-1, -4), C(2, -4)$; $M(-1, 1), N(-4, 1), P(-4, 4)$

22. **CAMPUS** The gym at Alex's school is located 70 feet south and 90 feet west of the main building. The vocational building is located 120 feet south and 200 feet east of the main building. Show that the triangle formed by these three buildings is scalene. Explain your reasoning. (Lesson 4-8) **See Extra Practice Answer Appendix.**

CHAPTER 5 Relationships in Triangles

1. **OFFICE DESIGN** The copy machine C, filing cabinet F, and supply shelves S are positioned in an office as shown. Copy the diagram, and find the location for the center of a work table so that it is the same distance from all three points. (Lesson 5-1)
 See Extra Practice Answer Appendix.

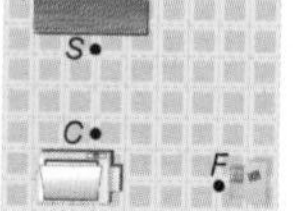

Point T is the incenter of △MNP. Find each measure below. Round to the nearest tenth, if necessary. (Lesson 5-1)

2. QT **4**
3. MT **10.2**
4. $m\angle PNT$ **51**

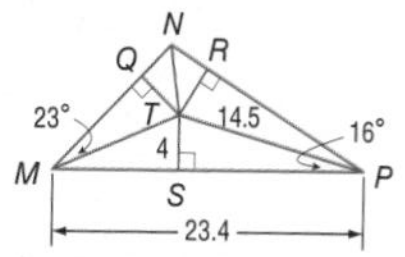

In △ABC, $CH = 70\frac{2}{3}$, $AG = 85$, and $DH = 20\frac{1}{3}$. Find each length. (Lesson 5-2)

5. FH **$35\frac{1}{3}$**
6. BD **61**
7. AH **$56\frac{2}{3}$**

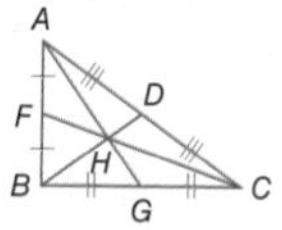

Find the indicated point of concurrency for each triangle with the given vertices. (Lesson 5-2)

8. centroid; $A(-4, -5), B(-1, 2), C(2, -4)$ **$\left(-1, -2\frac{1}{3}\right)$**
9. orthocenter; $M(-9, -2), N(1, 8), P(9, -8)$ **$(-1, 2)$**

List the angles and sides of each triangle in order from smallest to largest. (Lesson 5-3)

10. **$\angle R, \angle T, \angle S$; ST, RS, RT**
11. **$\angle Y, \angle X, \angle Z$; XZ, YZ, XY**

12. **MAPS** Three cities lie in a triangle as shown. Which two cities are the farthest apart? (Lesson 5-3)
 City A and City B

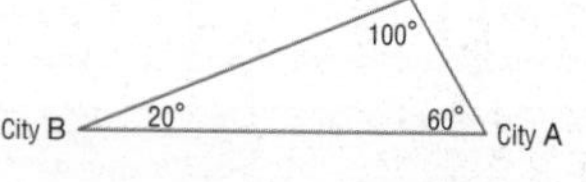

Write an indirect proof of each statement. (Lesson 5-4) **13–14. See Extra Practice Answer Appendix.**

13. If $-7 + 6x < 11$, then $x < 3$.
14. If $5 - 2x < -13$, then $x > 9$.

15. **JOBS** Nate worked for 6 hours today with two breaks. Use indirect reasoning to show that he worked for longer than two hours without a break at some point during his shift. (Lesson 5-4)
 See Extra Practice Answer Appendix.

16. Write an indirect proof of the statement below. (Lesson 5-4)
 A triangle can have at most one obtuse angle.
 See Extra Practice Answer Appendix.

17. Is it possible to form a triangle with side lengths 3 centimeters, 8 centimeters, and 11 centimeters? If not, explain why not. (Lesson 5-5)
 See Extra Practice Answer Appendix.

Find the range for the measure of the third side of a triangle given the measures of two sides. (Lesson 5-5)

18. 9 ft, 16 ft **$7 < x < 25$**
19. 1.7 m, 2.9 m **$1.2 < x < 4.6$**

20. Determine the possible values of x. (Lesson 5-5) **$x > \frac{7}{5}$ or 1.4**

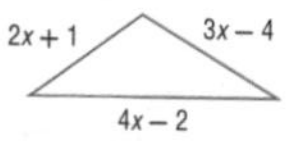

21. **SNOWSHOEING** Two groups of friends leave the same cabin to go snowshoeing. Group A goes 2.5 miles due north and then turns 79° east of north and travels an additional 2.5 miles. Group B goes 2.5 miles due south and then turns 86° east of south and travels an additional 2.5 miles. Who is now closer to the cabin? Use a diagram to explain your reasoning. (Lesson 5-6)
 See Extra Practice Answer Appendix.

Find the range of values containing x. (Lesson 5-6)

22. 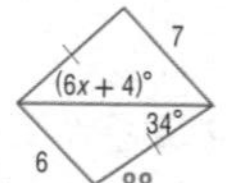 **$5 < x < \frac{88}{3}$**
23. 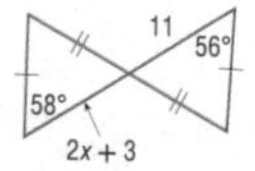 **$-1.5 < x < 4$**

24. **PROOF** Write a two-column proof. (Lesson 5-6)
 Given: $\overline{AB} \cong \overline{CD}$,
 $m\angle CDB > m\angle BAC$
 $m\angle BDA > m\angle CAD$
 Prove: $AC > DB$
 See Extra Practice Answer Appendix.

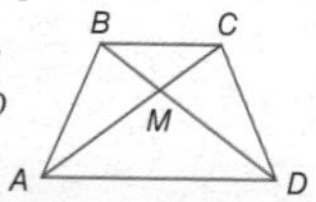

CHAPTER 6 Quadrilaterals

Find the value of x in each diagram. (Lesson 6-1)

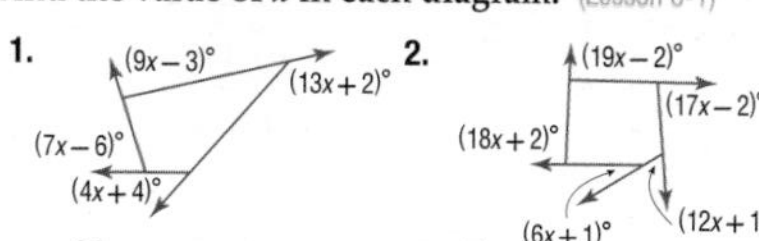

1. 11 **2.** 5

Use parallelogram $ABCD$ to find each measure. (Lesson 6-2)

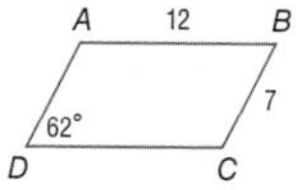

3. $m\angle A$ **118**

4. AD **7**

A 12 B, 7, 62°, D C

5. AUTO REPAIR A scissor jack is used to lift part of a car to make repairs. $ABCD$ is a parallelogram. As the jack is raised, $m\angle A$ and $m\angle C$ increase. Explain what must happen to $m\angle B$ and $m\angle D$. (Lesson 6-2) **See Extra Practice Answer Appendix.**

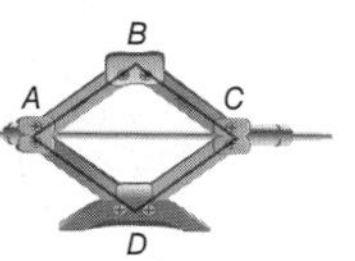

Find the value of each variable in each parallelogram. (Lesson 6-2)

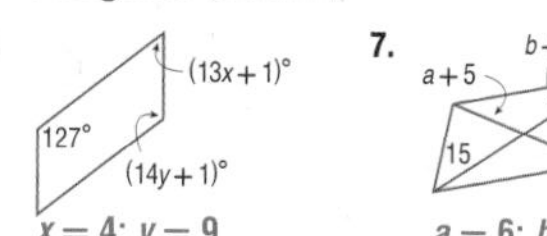

6. $x = 4$; $y = 9$ **7.** 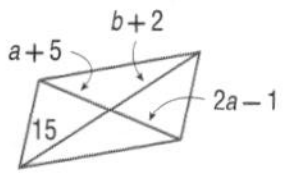 $a = 6$; $b = 13$

Determine whether each quadrilateral is a parallelogram. Justify your answer. (Lesson 6-3)

8. 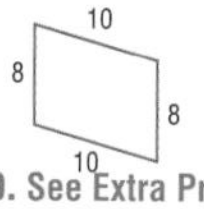 **9.**

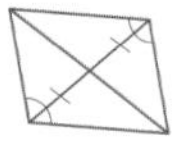

8–9. See Extra Practice Answer Appendix.

10. DESIGN Valerie is using the design shown for the front of a sweater. If all of the blocks of color are congruent parallelograms, write a two-column proof to show that $ACEG$ is a parallelogram. (Lesson 6-3) **See Extra Practice Answer Appendix.**

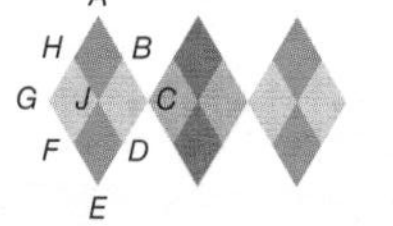

11. Graph the quadrilateral with vertices $A(0, 3)$, $B(10, 4)$, $C(6, -1)$, and $D(-4, -2)$. Determine whether $ABCD$ is a parallelogram. Justify your answer. (Lesson 6-3) **See Extra Practice Answer Appendix.**

12. SNOW Four boys are throwing snowballs, such that their positions are the vertices of a rectangle as shown. If Carl is 100 feet from Ben, and Abe and Ben throw snowballs along the diagonals at the same time and the snowballs collide in mid air, how far had the snowballs traveled at the time of collision? (Lesson 6-4) **50 ft**

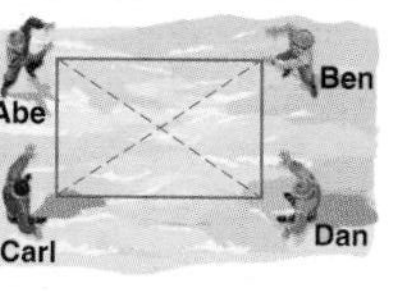

Quadrilateral $MNPQ$ is a rectangle. (Lesson 6-4)

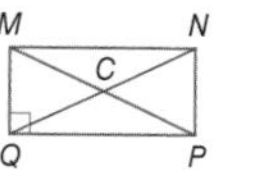

13. If $m\angle MNQ = 3x + 3$ and $m\angle QNP = 10x - 4$, find $m\angle MQN$. **66**

14. If $MC = 4.5x - 2.5$ and $NC = 4x + 1.5$, find QN. **67**

15. PROOF Write a proof to show that the four smaller triangles formed by the diagonals of a rectangle are isosceles. (Lesson 6-4) **See Extra Practice Answer Appendix.**

Quadrilateral $ABCD$ is a rhombus. Find each value or measure. (Lesson 6-5)

16. $m\angle DBC$ **53**

17. DC **15**

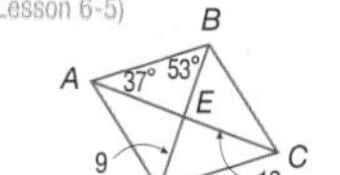

18. Determine whether ▱ $WXYZ$ with verticies $W(-2, 0)$, $X(1, 1)$, $Y(2, -2)$, $Z(-1, -3)$ is a *rhombus*, a *rectangle*, or a *square*. List all that apply. Explain. (Lesson 6-5) **See Extra Practice Answer Appendix.**

Find each measure. (Lesson 6-6)

19. $m\angle A$ **123**

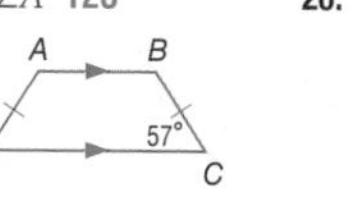

20. MR **12**

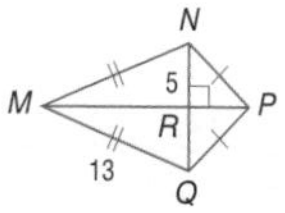

M N 5 R P 13 Q

CHAPTER 7 Proportions and Similarity

Find the measures of the angles or sides in each triangle. (Lesson 7-1)

1. The ratios of the measures of the three angles is 4 : 5 : 11. **36, 45, 99**

2. The ratio of the three sides is 5 : 3 : 6 and the perimeter is 98 centimeters. **35 cm, 21 cm, 42 cm**

3. FAMILY Shawn surveyed his homeroom class to find out how many of his classmates have at least 1 sibling. Of the 32 people in his homeroom, 25 have at least one sibling. (Lesson 7-1)

a. If there are 470 students in Shawn's school, write a proportion that could be used to predict the number of students in the school who have at least one sibling. $\frac{25}{32} = \frac{x}{470}$

b. What is the number of students in Shawn's school with at least one sibling? **≈367**

Determine whether each pair of figures is similar. If so, write the similarity statement and scale factor. If not, explain your reasoning. (Lesson 7-2)

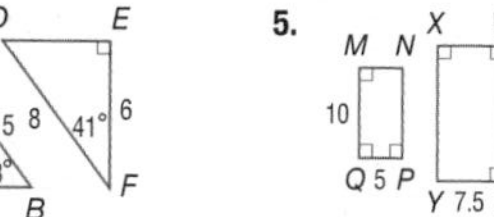

4. 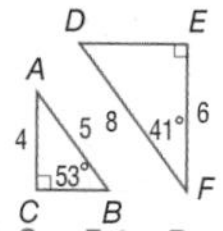 **5.**

4–5. See Extra Practice Answer Appendix.

Each pair of polygons is similar. Find the value of x. (Lesson 7-2) **6.** 5 **7.** 8.8

6. 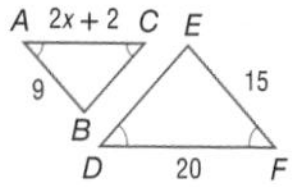 A 2x + 2 C E, 9, B, 15, D 20 F

7. 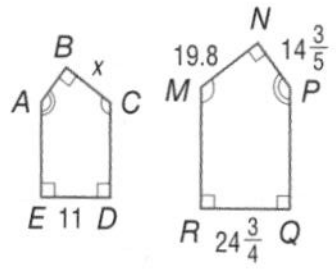 B x, A C, E 11 D, N, 19.8, $14\frac{3}{5}$, M P, R $24\frac{3}{4}$ Q

Determine whether the triangles are similar. If so, write a similarity statement. Explain your reasoning. (Lesson 7-3)

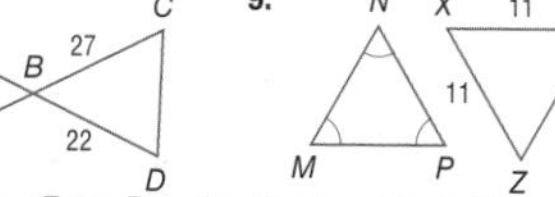

8. 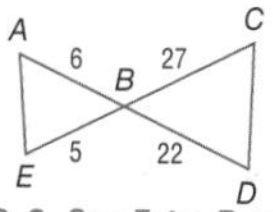 **9.**

8–9. See Extra Practice Answer Appendix.

10. HEIGHT When Rachel stands next to her cousin, Rachel's shadow is 2 feet long and her cousin's shadow is 1 foot long. If Rachel is 5 feet 6 inches tall, how tall is her cousin? (Lesson 7-3) **2 ft 9 in.**

Refer to the figure shown. (Lesson 7-4)

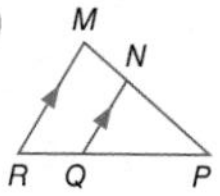

11. If $PN = 4$, $NM = 1$, and $PQ = 5$, find PR. **6.25**

12. If $PR = 13$, $PQ = 9$, and $NM = 3$, find PN. **6.75**

$\overline{DE}$, $\overline{EF}$, and $\overline{FD}$ **are midsegments of $\triangle ABC$. Find the value of x.** (Lesson 7-4)

13. 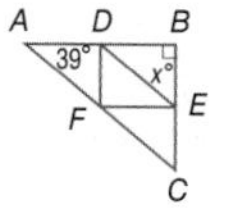 A D B, 39°, x°, F, E, C **51**

14. 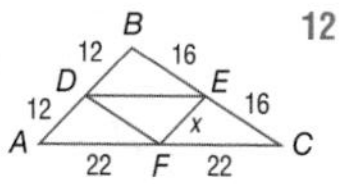 B, 12, 16, D, E, 12, x, 16, A, 22 F 22, C **12**

Find x. (Lesson 7-5)

15. 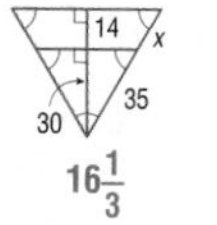 14, x, 30, 35 $16\frac{1}{3}$

16. 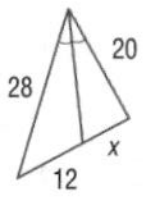 20, 28, x, 12 $8\frac{4}{7}$

17. FOOSBALL Jason wants to determine if his foosball table is a dilation of his school's soccer field. The dimension of the table are 30 inches by $55\frac{1}{2}$ inches, and the dimensions of the field are 60 yards by 110 yards. Is the table a dilation? Explain. (Lesson 7-6) **See Extra Practice Answer Appendix.**

Graph the original figure and its dilated image. Then verify that the dilation is a similarity transformation. (Lesson 7-6) **18–19. See Extra Practice Answer Appendix.**

18. $A(0, -2)$, $B(-1, 3)$, $C(3, -2)$; $X(0, -6)$, $Y(-3, 9)$, $Z(9, -6)$

19. $D(-6, 6)$, $E(6, 2)$, $F(-2, -4)$; $M(-3, 3)$, $N(3, 1)$, $P(-1, -2)$

20. ARCHITECTURE The blueprint below is a scale drawing of a proposed structure. (Lesson 7-7)

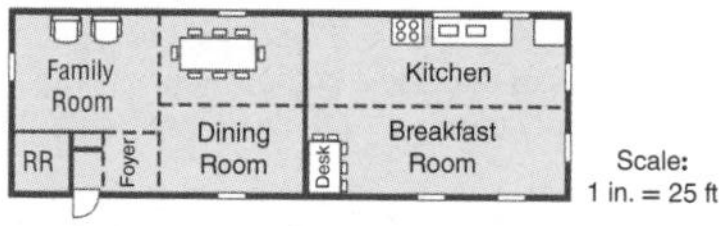

Family Room, Kitchen, Dining Room, Breakfast Room, RR, Foyer, Desk — Scale: 1 in. = 25 ft

a. What are the approximate dimensions of the family room? Round to the nearest 0.5 foot, if necessary. **15.5 ft by 12.5 ft**

b. What are the approximate dimensions of the dining room? Round to the nearest 0.5 foot, if necessary. **15.5 ft by 9.5 ft**

connectED.mcgraw-hill.com

CHAPTER 8 Right Triangles and Trigonometry

Find the geometric mean between each pair of numbers. (Lesson 8-1)

1. 7 and 12 $2\sqrt{21}$ **2.** 8 and 36 $12\sqrt{2}$

3. $x = 9\sqrt{5} \approx 20.1$, $y = 18\sqrt{5} \approx 40.2$, $z = 18$

Find x, y, and z. (Lesson 8-1)

3.

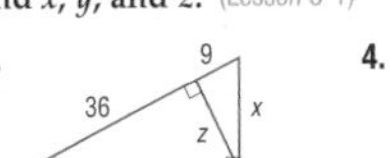

4.

4. $x = 5\sqrt{5} \approx 11.2$, $y = 10\sqrt{5} \approx 22.4$, $z = 20$

Find x. (Lesson 8-2)

5.

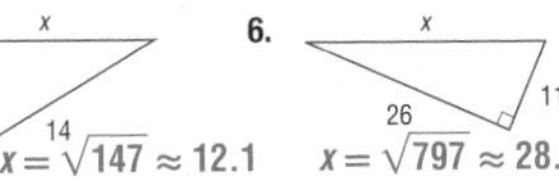

$x = \sqrt{147} \approx 12.1$

6. $x = \sqrt{797} \approx 28.2$

Determine whether each set of numbers can be the measures of the sides of a triangle. If so, classify the triangle as *acute*, *obtuse*, or *right*. Justify your answer. (Lesson 8-2)

7. 24, 32, 41 **8.** 17.5, 60, 62.5

7–8. See Extra Practice Answer Appendix.

Find x. (Lesson 8-3)

9. 22

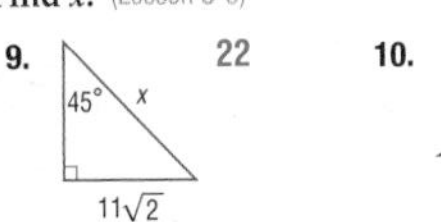

10. $7\sqrt{3}$

11. $9\sqrt{3}$ **12.** $14\sqrt{2}$

Find x. Round to the nearest tenth, if necessary. (Lesson 8-4)

13. 22.6

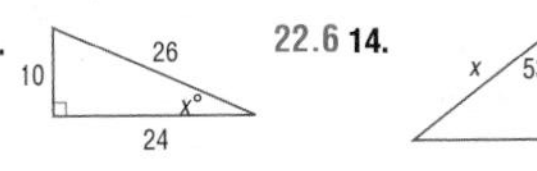

14. 13.3

15. SKATEBOARDING Lindsey is building a skateboard ramp. She wants the ramp to be 1 foot tall at the end and she wants it to make a 15° angle with the ground. What length of board should she buy for the ramp itself? Round to the nearest foot. (Lesson 8-4) **4 ft**

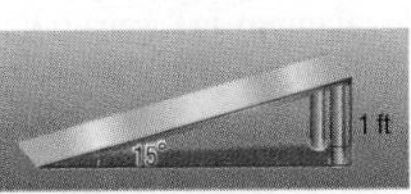

16. BUILDINGS Kara is standing about 50 feet from the base of her apartment building, looking up at it with an angle of elevation of 75°. What is the approximate height of Kara's building? (Lesson 8-5) **about 187 ft**

17. ROLLER COASTERS Evan is looking down the hill of a roller coaster from a height of 75 feet with an angle of depression of about 70°. What is the approximate horizontal distance from the top of the hill to the bottom of the hill? (Lesson 8-5) **about 27.3 ft**

18. MOVIES Kim is sitting in the row behind her friend Somi at the movies. Kim is looking at the screen with an angle of elevation of about 27° and Somi's angle of elevation is about 29°. If there are 3 feet between each row of seats, about how tall is the movie screen? (Lesson 8-5) **about 19 ft**

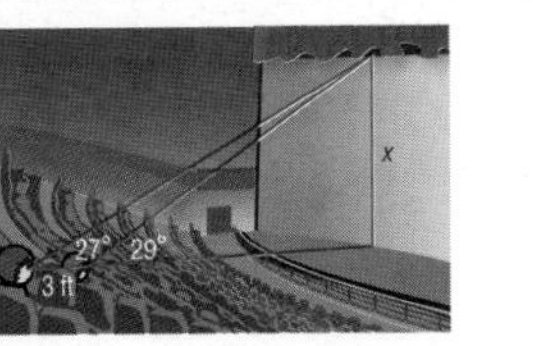

Solve each triangle. Round angle measures to the nearest degree and side measures to the nearest tenth. (Lesson 8-6)

19.

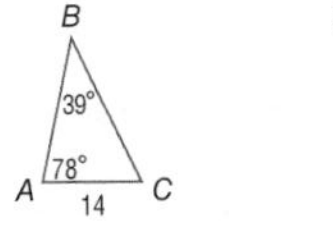

20.

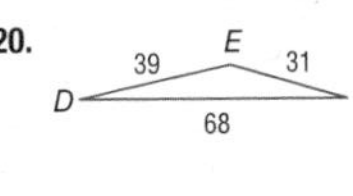

21.

22.

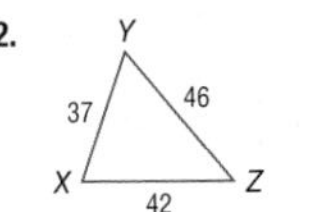

19–22. See Extra Practice Answer Appendix.

Copy the vectors to find each sum or difference. (Lesson 8-7)

23. $\vec{a} - \vec{b}$

24. $\vec{a} + \vec{c}$

23–24. See Extra Practice Answer Appendix.

25. SWIMMING Kendall is swimming due south at 4.5 feet per second. The current of the river is moving with a velocity of 2 feet per second due east. Find Kendall's resultant speed and direction. (Lesson 8-7) **about 4.9 ft/s, at an angle of about 24° east of south**

CHAPTER 9 Transformations and Symmetry

Graph each figure and its image under the given reflection. (Lesson 9-1) **1–3. See Extra Practice Answer Appendix.**

1. $\triangle ABC$ with vertices $A(-1, -4)$, $B(-5, 3)$, and $C(0, 5)$ in the line $y = x$

2. quadrilateral $WXYZ$ with vertices $W(-3, -2)$, $X(-4, 1)$, $Y(1, 4)$, and $Z(2, -2)$ in the y-axis

3. CAMPING Jin and Tom plan to hike to the rock bridge one day, return to camp, and then hike to the falls on the next day. Where along the trail should they place their camp in order to minimize the distance they must hike? (Lesson 9-1)

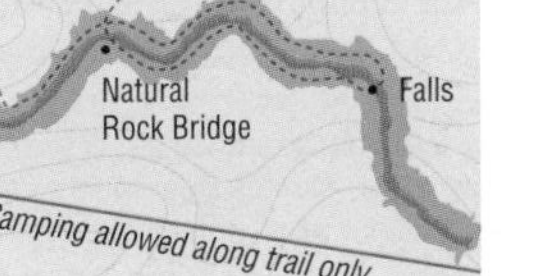

Graph each figure and its image along the given vector. (Lesson 9-2)

4. $\triangle XYZ$ with vertices $X(-2, -1)$, $Y(1, 3)$, and $Z(4, -2)$; $\langle -4, 2\rangle$

5. trapezoid $MNPQ$ with vertices $M(-4, -3)$, $N(-2, 2)$, $P(1, 2)$, and $Q(3, -3)$; $\langle 3, -1\rangle$

4–5. See Extra Practice Answer Appendix.

6. MAPS Caleb's house and several places he visits are shown on the grid. (Lesson 9-2)

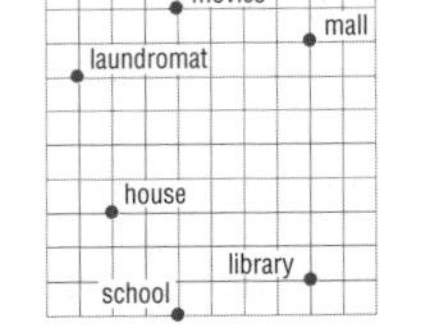

a. If Caleb leaves his house and goes one block west and four blocks north, what is his new location? **laundromat**

b. Write a translation vector that will take Caleb from the library to the movies. $\langle -4, 8\rangle$

7–8. See Extra Practice Answer Appendix.

Graph each figure and its image after the specified rotation about the origin. (Lesson 9-3)

7. $\triangle PQR$ with vertices $P(-1, -2)$, $Q(-5, -4)$, and $R(-3, -6)$; 90°

8. parallelogram $WXYZ$ with vertices $W(-3, 3)$, $X(-2, 7)$, $Y(4, 5)$ and $Z(3, 1)$; 180°

9. CLOCKS Anna looks at a clock at 11:05. When she looks at the clock for a second time during the same hour, the minute hand has rotated 270°. At what time does Anna look at the clock for the second time? (Lesson 9-3) **11:50**

Graph each figure with the given vertices and its image after the indicated glide reflection. (Lesson 9-4)

10. $\triangle DEF$: $D(-5, 1)$, $E(-3, 5)$, $F(0, 3)$
Translation: along $\langle -4, 3\rangle$; Reflection: in x-axis

11. $\triangle MNP$: $M(2, 5)$, $N(6, 2)$, $P(8, 6)$
Translation: along $\langle 2, 4\rangle$; Reflection: in $y = x$

10–11. See Extra Practice Answer Appendix.

Graph each figure with the given vertices and its image after the indicated composition of transformations. (Lesson 9-4)

12. $\overline{XY}$: $X(7, 9)$ and $Y(2, 1)$
Rotation: 90°; Translation: $\langle -5, -2\rangle$

13. $\overline{AB}$: $A(-4, -6)$ and $B(-2, 5)$
Reflection: in x-axis; Rotation: 270°

12–13. See Extra Practice Answer Appendix.

ALPHABET **Determine whether each letter below has *line* symmetry, *rotational* symmetry, *both*, or *neither*. Draw all lines of symmetry and state their number. Then determine the center of rotational symmetry and state the order and magnitude of rotational symmetry.** (Lesson 9-5)

14. B **15.** X

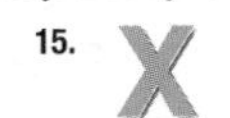

14–15. See Extra Practice Answer Appendix.

State whether the figure has *plane* symmetry, *axis* symmetry, *both*, or *neither*. (Lesson 9-5)

16. **both** **17.** **plane**

18. NATURE The diameter of a snowflake is 2 millimeters. If the diameter appears to be 3 centimeters when viewed under a microscope, what magnification setting (scale factor) was used? (Lesson 9-6) **15**

19–20. See Extra Practice Answer Appendix.

Find the image of each polygon with the given vertices after a dilation centered at the origin with the given scale factor. (Lesson 9-6)

19. $A(-5, -4)$, $B(-2, -3)$, $C(-1, -6)$, $D(-4, -8)$; $k = \frac{1}{2}$

20. $X(2, 4)$, $Y(4, 0)$, $Z(5, 5)$; $k = 1.5$

CHAPTER 10 Circles

The diameter of the smaller circle centered at A is 3 inches, and the diameter of the larger circle centered at A is 9 inches. The diameter of $\odot D$ is 11 inches. Find each measure. (Lesson 10-1)

1. BC **3 in.**
2. CD **2.5 in.**

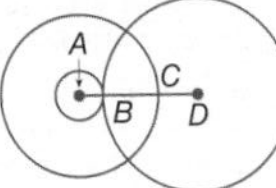

3. **DECORATIONS** To decorate for homecoming, Brittany estimates that she will need to purchase enough streamers to go around the school's circular fountain twice. If the diameter of the fountain is 88 inches, about how many feet of streamers should she buy? (Lesson 10-1) **about 46 ft**

Use $\odot C$ to find the length of each arc. Round to the nearest hundredth. (Lesson 10-2)

4. $\widehat{XY}$ if the radius is 5 feet **7.85 ft**
5. $\widehat{YZ}$ if the diameter is 8 meters **3.84 m**

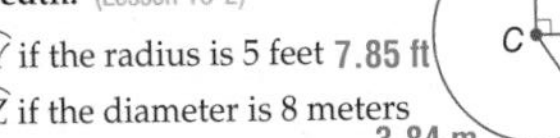

6. **TRANSPORTATION** The graph shows the results of a survey in which students at a high school were asked how they get to school. (Lesson 10-2)

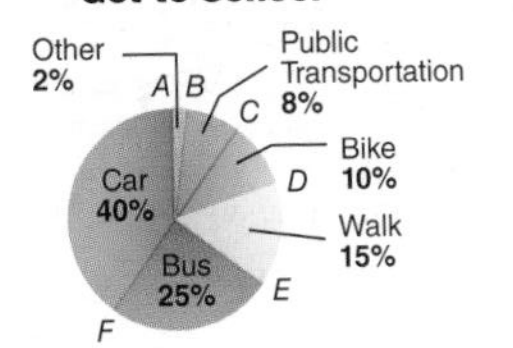

a. Find $m\widehat{CD}$. **36**
b. Find $m\widehat{BC}$. **28.8**

Find the value of x. (Lesson 10-3)

7. **15**
8. **25**

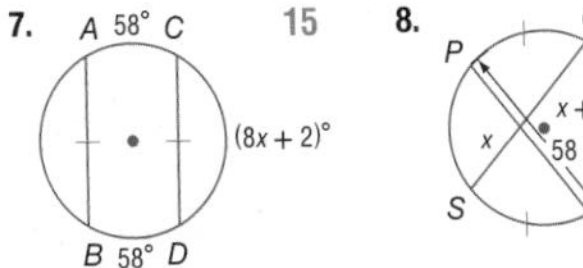

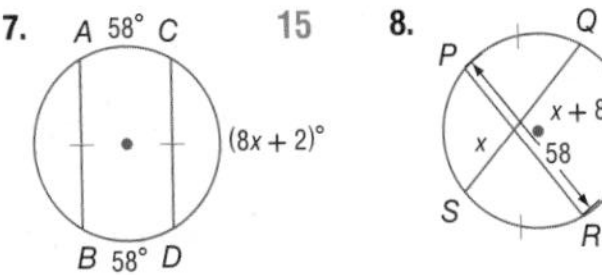

In $\odot M$, $MZ = 12$ and $WY = 20$. Find each measure. Round to the nearest hundredth. (Lesson 10-3)

9. CM **6.63**
10. XC **5.37**

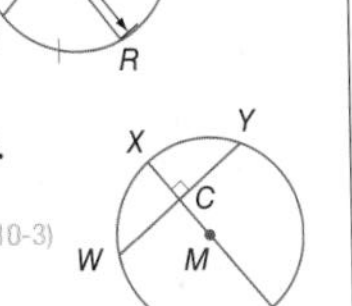

Find each measure. (Lesson 10-4)

11. $m\angle N$ **59**
12. $m\angle B$ **34**

13. Find x. Assume that segments that appear to be tangent are tangent. (Lesson 10-5) **15**

14. Quadrilateral $ABCD$ is circumscribed about $\odot H$. Find m. (Lesson 10-5) **33 mm**

Find each measure. Assume that segments that appear to be tangent are tangent. (Lesson 10-6)

15. $m\widehat{XYZ}$ **140**
16. $\widehat{MP}$ **40**

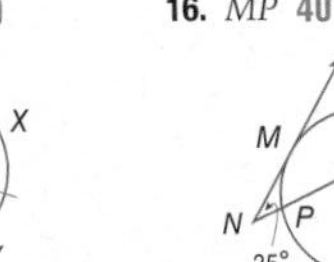

Find x to the nearest tenth. Assume that segments that appear to be tangent are tangent. (Lesson 10-7)

17. **3**
18. **2**

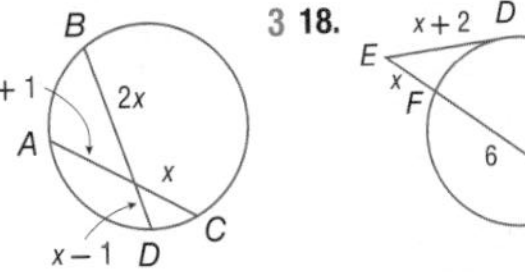

19. **CELL PHONES** A cell phone tower covers a circular area with a radius of 15 miles. (Lesson 10-8)
    a. If the tower is located at the origin, write an equation for this circular area of coverage. **19a. $x^2 + y^2 = 225$**
    b. Will a person 11 miles west and 12 miles south of the tower have coverage? Explain. **See Extra Practice Answer Appendix.**

20. Write an equation of a circle that contains points $A(-1, 5)$, $B(-5, 9)$, and $C(-9, 5)$. Then graph the equation. (Lesson 10-8) **See Extra Practice Answer Appendix.**

CHAPTER 11 Areas of Polygons and Circles

Find the perimeter and area of each figure. Round to the nearest tenth if necessary. (Lesson 11-1)

1. **43.8 cm, 84 cm²**
2. **45.8 in., 72 in²**

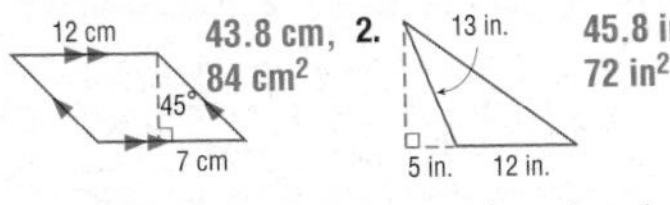

3. The height of a parallelogram is three times its base. If the area of the parallelogram is 108 square meters, find its base and height. (Lesson 11-1) **6 m; 18 m**

4. The height of a triangle is three feet less than its base. If the area of the triangle is 275 square feet, find its base and height. (Lesson 11-1) **25 ft; 22 ft**

Find the area of each trapezoid, rhombus, or kite. (Lesson 11-2)

5. **44 mm²**
6. **195 in²**
7. **190 cm²**

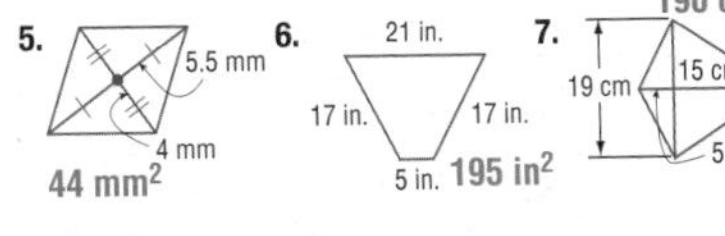

8. **MODELS** Joni is designing a mural for the side of a building. The wall is 15 feet high and 50 feet long. If she covers the wall with a kite as shown, what is the area of the kite? (Lesson 11-2) **375 ft²**

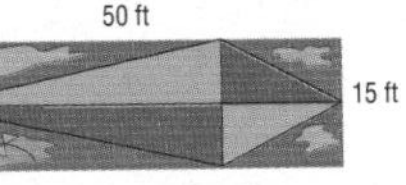

9. A trapezoid has a height of 12 inches, a base length of 9 inches, and an area of 150 square inches. What is the length of the other base? (Lesson 11-2) **16 in.**

Find the indicated measure. Round to the nearest tenth. (Lesson 11-3)

10. The area of a circle is 201 square meters. Find the radius. **8 m**

11. Find the diameter of a circle with an area of 79 square feet. **10 ft**

Find the area of each shaded sector. Round to the nearest tenth if necessary. (Lesson 11-3)

12. **18.8 cm²**
13. **288.3 in²**

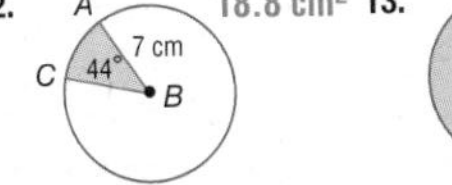

14. **GRAPHS** Len created a circle graph using the survey results shown in the table. (Lesson 11-3)

Preferred Type of Exercise	
Treadmill	62%
Stationary Bike	8%
Swimming	7%
Aerobics	12%
Other	11%

a. What is the angle measure of the sector representing swimming? **25.2**
b. If the graph has a 3-inch diameter, what is the area of the sector representing treadmill? **about 4.4 in²**

Find the area of each regular polygon. Round to the nearest tenth if necessary. (Lesson 11-4)

15. **509.2 mm²**
16. **110.9 ft²**
17. **85.6 m²**

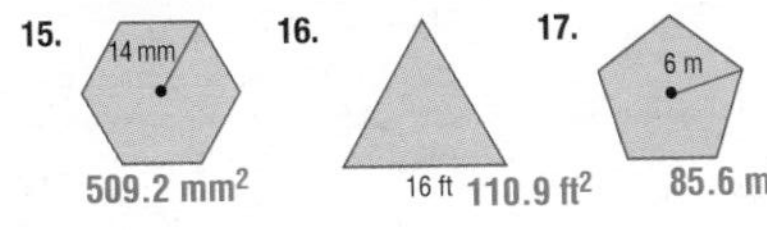

Find the area of each figure. Round to the nearest tenth if necessary. (Lesson 11-4)

18. **252.6 cm²**
19. **238.1 in²**

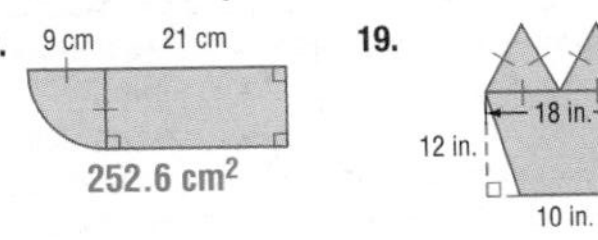

For each pair of similar figures, find the area of the green figure. (Lesson 11-5)

20. **$34\frac{2}{3}$ ft²**
21. **1087.5 mm²**

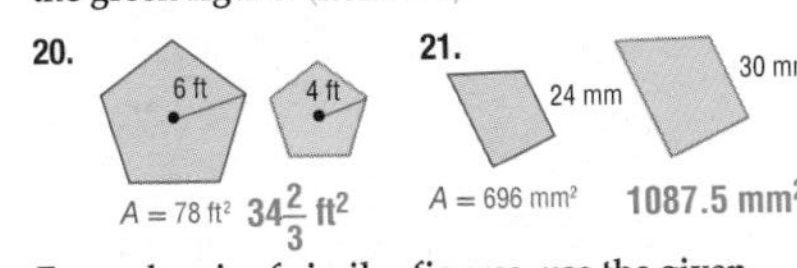

For each pair of similar figures, use the given areas to find the scale factor from the blue to the green figure. Then find x. (Lesson 11-5)

22. **$\frac{1}{2}$; 14**
23. **$\frac{6}{5}$; 10**

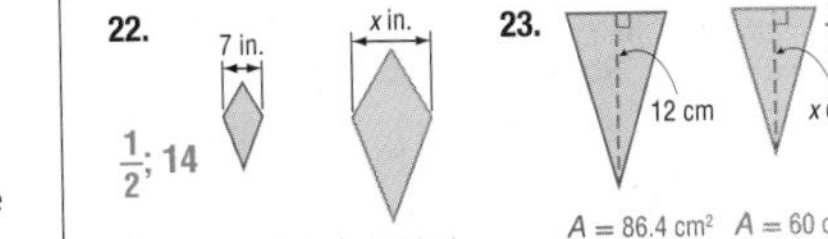

24. **MODELS** Anna is making a model of her house. The area of the model's living space is 70 square inches. If the area of the actual living space is 1750 square feet, how many feet are represented by each inch of the model? (Lesson 11-5) **5 ft**

CHAPTER 12 Extending Surface Area and Volume

Use isometric dot paper to sketch each prism. (Lesson 12-1) **1–3. See Extra Practice Answer Appendix.**

1. triangular prism 4 units high, with two sides of the base that are 3 units long and 4 units long
2. rectangular prism 1 unit high, 5 units wide, and 3 units long
3. Use isometric dot paper and the orthographic drawing to sketch the solid. (Lesson 12-1)

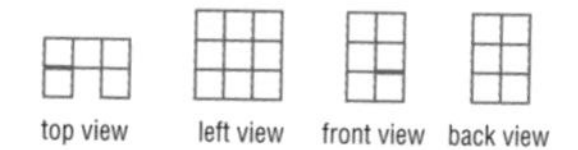

Find the lateral and surface area of each solid. Round to the nearest tenth. (Lesson 12-2)

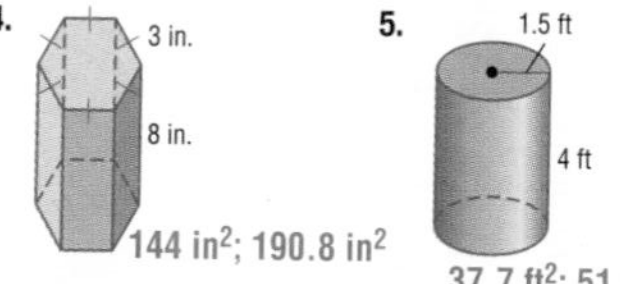

4. **144 in²; 190.8 in²**
5. **37.7 ft²; 51.8 ft²**

6. **MANUFACTURING** An office has recycling barrels that are cylindrical with cardboard sides and plastic lids and bases. Each barrel is 3 feet tall with a diameter of 30 inches. How many square feet of cardboard are used to make each barrel? (Lesson 12-2) **23.6 ft²**

Find the lateral and surface area of each regular pyramid or cone. Round to the nearest tenth if necessary. (Lesson 12-3)

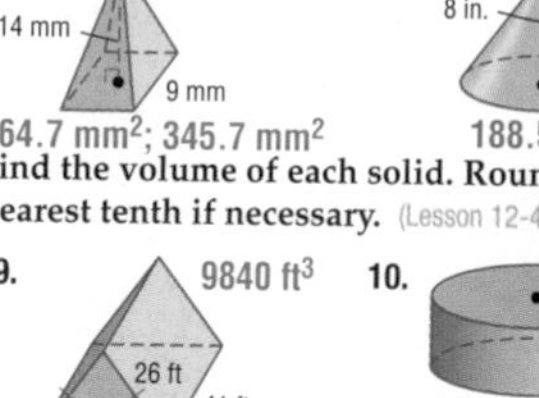

7. **264.7 mm²; 345.7 mm²**
8. **188.5 in²; 301.6 in²**

Find the volume of each solid. Round to the nearest tenth if necessary. (Lesson 12-4)

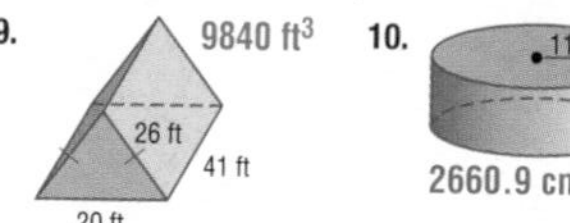

9. **9840 ft³**

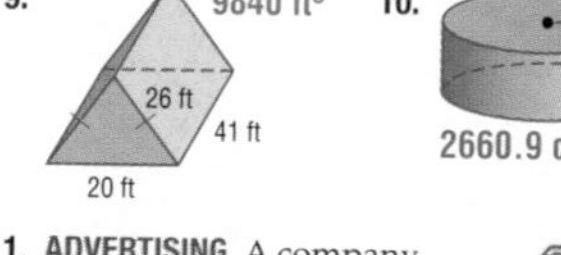

10. **2660.9 cm³**

11. **ADVERTISING** A company advertises that their juice boxes contain 20% more juice than their competitor's. If the base dimensions of the boxes are the same, how much taller are the larger boxes? (Lesson 12-4) **0.8 in.**

Find the volume of each solid. Round to the nearest tenth if necessary. (Lesson 12-5)

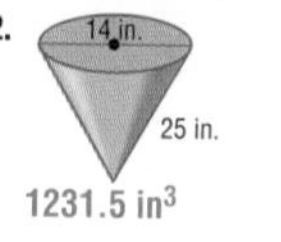

12. **1231.5 in³**

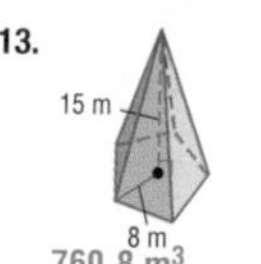

13. **760.8 m³**

Find the surface area and volume of each sphere or hemisphere. Round to the nearest tenth. (Lesson 12-6)

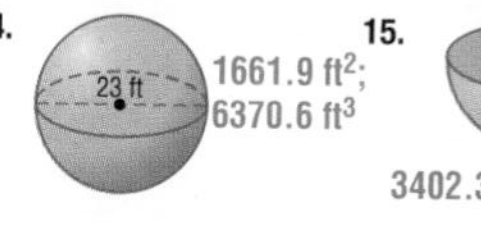

14. **1661.9 ft²; 6370.6 ft³**

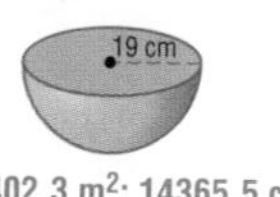

15. **3402.3 m²; 14365.5 cm³**

16. **SPORTS** The diameter of a tennis ball is 2.7 inches, and the diameter of a baseball is 2.9 inches. How many times as great is the volume of the baseball as the volume of the tennis ball? (Lesson 12-6) **1.24**

Name each of the following on sphere $\mathcal{A}$. (Lesson 12-7)

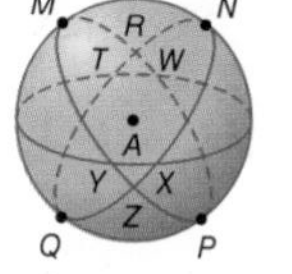

17. a triangle **Sample answer: $\triangle YXZ$**
18. two segments on the same great circle **Sample answer: $\overline{MZ}$ and $\overline{ZP}$**

Determine whether each pair of solids is *similar*, *congruent*, or *neither*. If the solids are similar, state the scale factor. (Lesson 12-8)

19. **similar; $\frac{2}{3}$**

9 cm, 8 cm; 27 cm, 12 cm

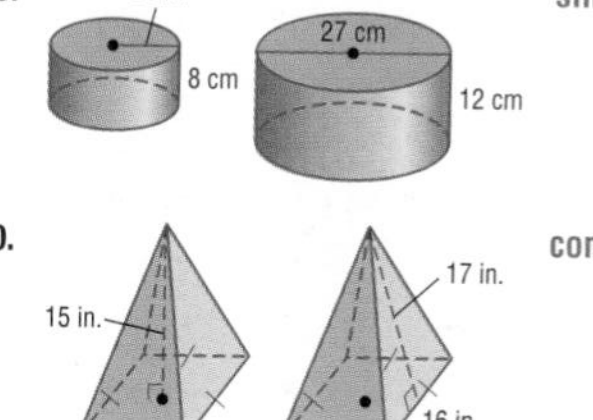

20. **congruent**

CHAPTER 13 Probability and Measurement

1. **FITNESS** Laura wants to go to a fitness class tomorrow. She can choose a 5:00 or a 7:30 class and spin or water aerobics. Represent the sample space for the situation by making an organized list, a table, and a tree diagram. (Lesson 13-1) **See Extra Practice Answer Appendix.**
2. **SCHOOL UNIFORMS** Susan has a school uniform that consists of a polo shirt, an oxford shirt, a skirt, and a pair of pants. She also has a sweater than she can wear if she chooses. Draw a tree diagram to represent the sample space for Susan's uniform. (Lesson 13-1) **See Extra Practice Answer Appendix.**
3. **CONSTRUCTION** Bert's family is building a house in a new neighborhood, and they must choose one option listed below for each feature. What is the number of possible outcomes for the situation? (Lesson 13-1) **108**

Feature	Options
floor plan	Elevation 1, Elevation 2
counters	formica, granite
cabinets	French antique glazed, oak, cherry
basement	unfinished, partially finished, finished
garage	none, one car, two car

4. **DIVING** At a swim meet, the order of the divers is randomly selected. If there are 12 divers, what is the probability that Danielle, Nora, and Li will dive first, second, and third, respectively? (Lesson 13-2) $\frac{1}{1320}$
5. **NUMBERS** Charlie's phone number is 555–3703. If he places each of the digits in a bowl and randomly selects one number at a time without replacement, what is the probability that he will choose his phone number? (Lesson 13-2) $\frac{1}{420}$
6. **RAFFLES** Participants in a raffle received tickets 1101 through 1125. If four winners are chosen, what is the probability that the winning tickets are 1103, 1111, 1118, and 1122? (Lesson 13-2) $\frac{1}{12,650}$
7. Point X is chosen at random on $\overline{AE}$. Find the probability that X is on $\overline{CE}$. (Lesson 13-3) **about 0.54 or 54%**

A 4 B 7 C 5 D 8 E

10. **$\frac{5}{12}$ or about 41.7%**

Find the probability that a point chosen at random lies in the shaded region. (Lesson 13-3)

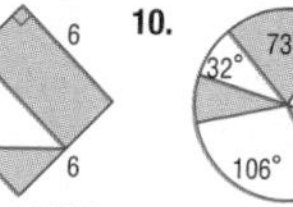

8. **≈0.553 or 55.3%**
9. **0.75 or 75%**

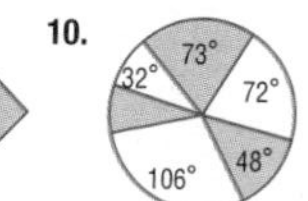

10.

11. **FOOTBALL** Wes made 92% of his point after touchdown attempts last season. Design and conduct a simulation using a random number generator that can be used to estimate the probability that he will make his next point after touchdown attempt. (Lesson 13-4) **See Extra Practice Answer Appendix.**

BASKETBALL For each field goal attempt in basketball, a player can earn 0, 2, or 3 points. The probability that a certain player will score 0 points on an attempt is 45%, 2 points is 40%, and 3 points is 15%. (Lesson 13-4)

12. Calculate the expected value for one attempt. **1.25**
13. Design a simulation using a geometric probability model and estimate the player's average value per field goal attempt. **See Extra Practice Answer Appendix.**
14. Compare the values for Exercises 12 and 13. **Sample answer: The values are about the same.**
15. A die is rolled twice. What is the probability that the first number rolled is a 3 and the second number rolled is a 5? (Lesson 13-5) $\frac{1}{36}$
16. Three cards are randomly chosen from a deck of 52 cards without replacement. What is the probability that they will all be red? (Lesson 13-5) **about 0.118 or 11.8%**
17. A spinner numbered 1 through 6 is spun. Find the probability that the number spun is a 3 given that it was less than 4. (Lesson 13-5) $\frac{1}{3}$

BOOKS The table shows the number and type of books that Sarah owns. Find each probability. (Lesson 13-6)

Medium	Classic	Mystery	Biography
print	29	8	32
audio	3	6	10
electronic	8	3	43

18. A randomly chosen title is a print or audio book. **about 0.62 or 62%**
19. A randomly chosen title is not a biography. **about 0.401 or 40.1%**
20. **DOGS** The table shows the ages and genders of the dogs at an animal shelter. What is the probability that a randomly chosen dog is a female or over 5 years old? (Lesson 13-6) **about 0.68 of 68%**

Age	Male	Female
under 1 year	6	5
1–5 years	8	7
6–10 years	4	6
over 10 years	3	5

Chapter 2

1. False; sample answer: If neither A nor B lie on $\overleftrightarrow{CD}$, then four right angles are not formed.

2. A prism has two bases, and a sphere has no bases; true, because p is true and r is true.

3. A pyramid has two bases, or a sphere has bases; false because q is false and $\sim r$ is false.

7. True; sample answer: If a number is divisible by 6, then it can be written as $6n$ for some integer n. $6n = 3 \cdot 2 \cdot n$ or $3(2n)$, so the number is also divisible by 3.

8. False; $(-2)^4$ is also 32.

9. Her parents will take her to the theater; Law of Syllogism.

12. Always; Postulate 2.7 states that the intersection of two planes is a line.

13. Sometimes; If point B also lies in plane P, then $\overleftrightarrow{AB}$ lies in plane P. If point B does not lie in plane P, then $\overleftrightarrow{AB}$ does not lie in plane P.

14. Never; Postulate 2.6 states that the intersection of two lines is exactly one point.

15. **Given:** $P = \rho gh$

Prove: $h = \frac{P}{\rho g}$

Proof:

Statements (Reasons)

1. $P = \rho gh$ (Given)
2. $\frac{P}{\rho g} = \frac{\rho gh}{\rho g}$ (Div. Prop.)
3. $\frac{P}{\rho g} = h$ (Simplify.)
4. $h = \frac{P}{\rho g}$ (Symm. Prop.)

16. **Given:** $\overline{MN} \cong \overline{QP}$

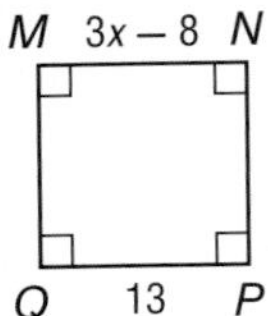

Prove: $x = 7$

Proof:

Statements (Reasons)

1. $\overline{MN} \cong \overline{QP}$ (Given)
2. $MN = QP$ (Def. of congruent segments)
3. $3x - 8 = 13$ (Subs. Prop.)
4. $3x - 8 + 8 = 13 + 8$ (Add. Prop.)
5. $3x = 21$ (Simplify.)
6. $\frac{3x}{3} = \frac{21}{3}$ (Div. Prop.)
7. $x = 7$ (Simplify.)

17. **Given:** $\overline{AC} \cong \overline{BD}$; $\overline{EC} \cong \overline{ED}$

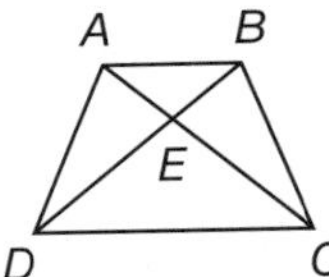

Prove: $\overline{AE} \cong \overline{BE}$

Proof:

Statements (Reasons)

1. $\overline{AC} \cong \overline{BD}$; $\overline{EC} \cong \overline{ED}$ (Given)
2. $AC = BD$; $EC = ED$ (Def. of $\cong$ segments)
3. $AE + EC = AC$; $BE + ED = BD$ (Seg. Add. Post.)
4. $AE + EC = BE + ED$ (Subs. Prop.)
5. $AE + EC = BE + EC$ (Subs. Prop.)
6. $AE + EC - EC = BE + EC - EC$ (Subt. Prop.)
7. $AE = BE$ (Simplify.)
8. $\overline{AE} \cong \overline{BE}$ (Def. of $\cong$ segments)

18. $m\angle 1 = 31$, $m\angle 2 = 149$, $m\angle 3 = 31$; Supplement Theorem

19. $m\angle 4 = 90$, $m\angle 5 = 90$, $m\angle 6 = 45$, $m\angle 7 = 45$, $m\angle 8 = 90$; Perpendicular lines intersect to form four right angles and Complement Theorem

20. **Given:** $\angle BEC$ is a right angle

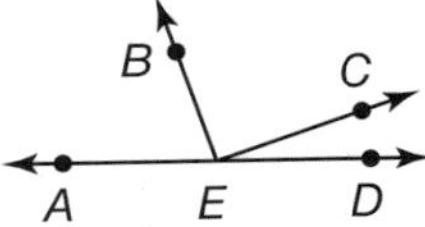

Prove: $\angle AEB$ and $\angle CED$ are complementary.

Proof:

Since $\angle AEB$, $\angle BEC$, and $\angle CED$ form a straight angle, we know that they are supplementary. That means that $m\angle AEB + m\angle BEC + m\angle CED = 180$. We are given that $\angle BEC$ is a right angle and by the definition of a right angle, we know that $m\angle BEC = 90$. Therefore, by the Substitution Property, $m\angle AEB + 90 + m\angle CED = 180$. Using the Subtraction Property of Equality, $m\angle AEB + m\angle CED = 90$. By definition, $\angle AEB$ and $\angle CED$ are complementary.

Chapter 3

6. $x = 29$, $y = 14$; Since $3x$ and 93 form a straight angle, they are supplementary. Therefore $3x + 93 = 180$ and so $x = 29$. Since $6y + 9$ and 93 are corresponding angles, they are congruent. Therefore $6y + 9 = 93$ and so $y = 14$.

7. $x = 11$, $y = 20$; Since $5x - 2$ and 53 are alternate exterior angles, they are congruent. Therefore $5x - 2 = 53$ and so $x = 11$. Since $6y + 7$ and $5x - 2$ form a straight angle, $6y + 7$ and 53 are supplementary. Therefore $6y + 7 + 53 = 180$ and so $y = 20$.

8a. **Katie's Lawn Mowing**

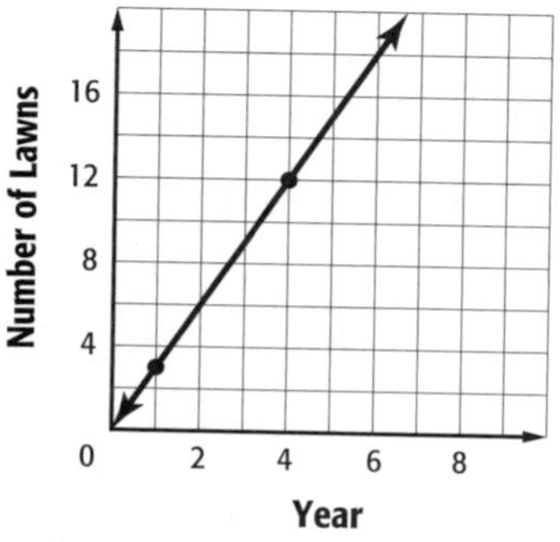

Number of Lawns

16

12

8

4

0 2 4 6 8

Year

8b. 3; Sample answer: The number of new lawns that Katie adds to her business each year.

9.

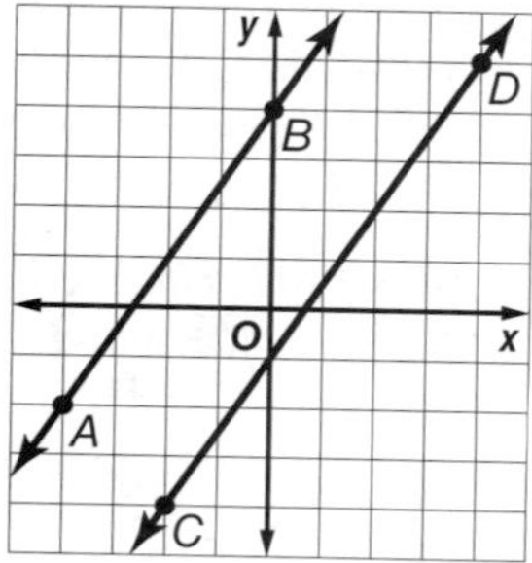

10.

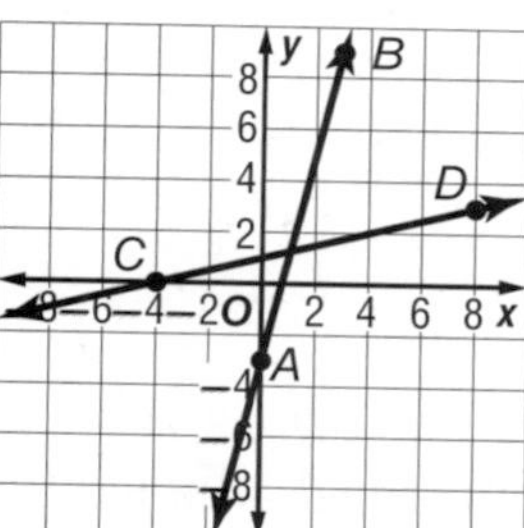

11.

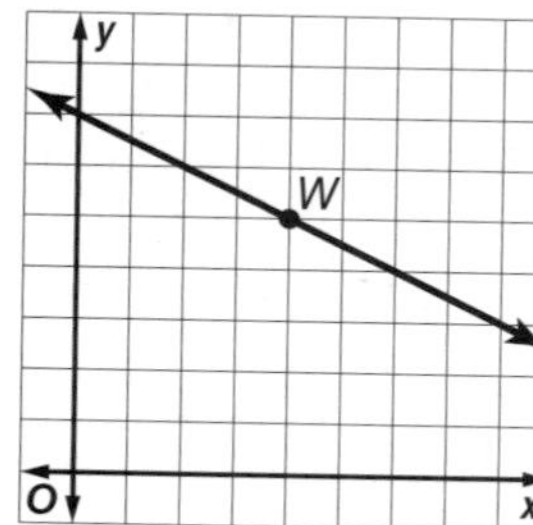

12.

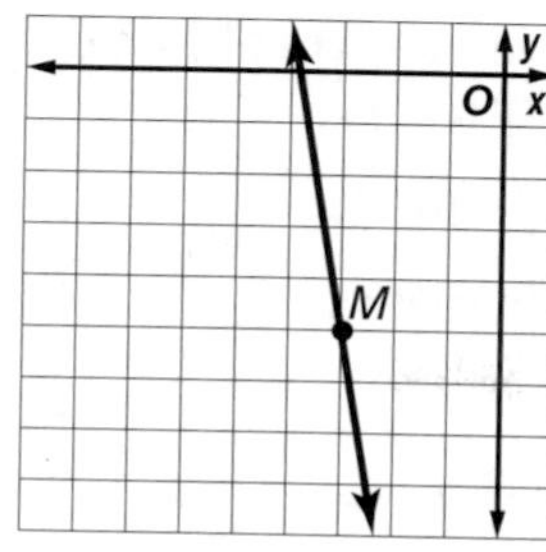

13. $y + 14 = -\frac{4}{5}(x - 10)$

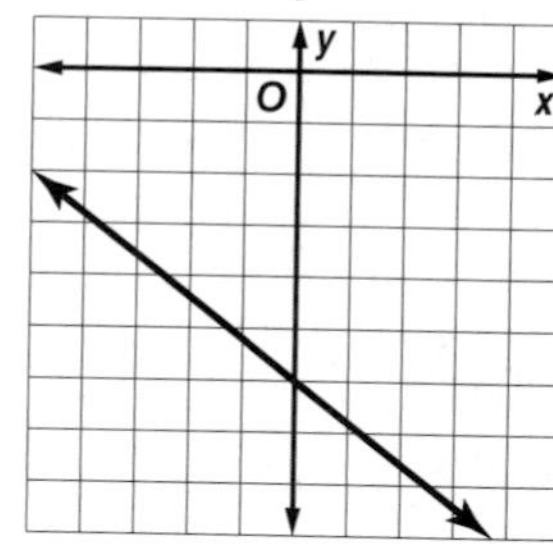

14. $y + 3 = 5(x + 1)$

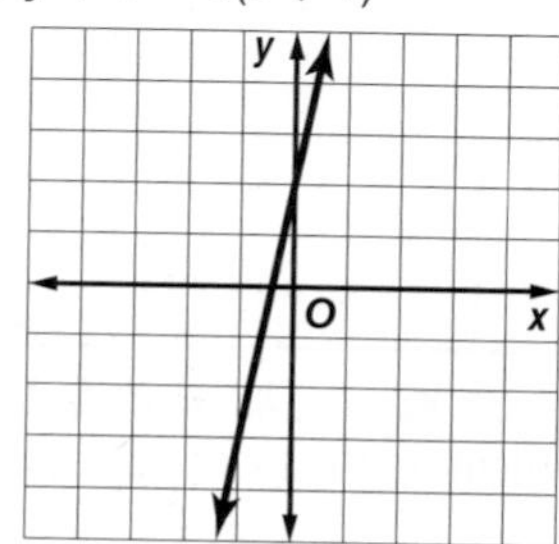

17a. Current plan: $y = 2.39x + 7.99$; Optional plan: $y = 1.49x + 14.99$

17b.

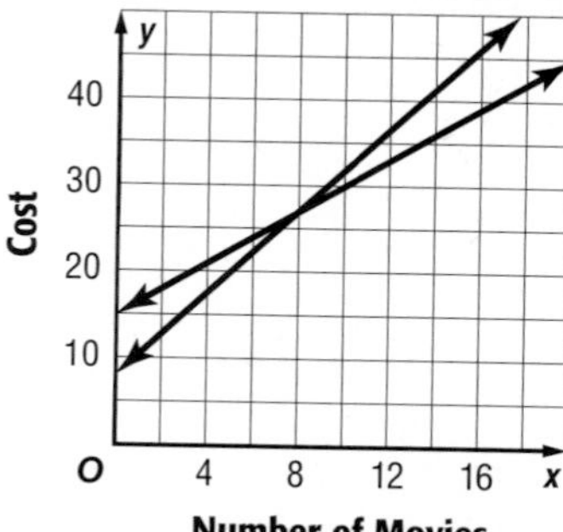

Extra Practice Answer Appendix

17c. Change; sample answer: His original plan costs \$31.89, and the optional plan would cost \$29.89.

18. $n \parallel p$; Consecutive Interior Angles Converse

19. $\ell \parallel m$; Alternate Exterior Angles Converse

20. $n \parallel p$; Perpendicular Transversal Converse

21. Given: $\angle 1$ and $\angle 8$ are supplementary.

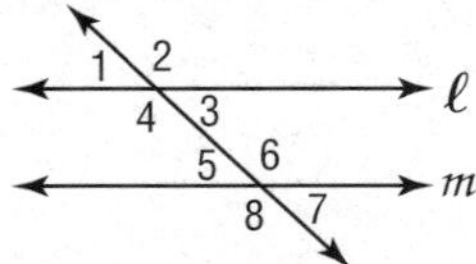

Prove: $\ell \parallel m$

Proof:

Statements (Reasons)

1. $\angle 1$ and $\angle 8$ are supplementary. (Given)
2. $m\angle 1 + m\angle 8 = 180$ (Def. of suppl. $\angle$s)
3. $m\angle 5 + m\angle 8 = 180$ (Suppl. Thm.)
4. $m\angle 1 + m\angle 8 = m\angle 5 + m\angle 8$ (Subs.)
5. $m\angle 1 = m\angle 5$ (Subt. Prop.)
6. $\angle 1 \cong \angle 5$ (Def. of $\cong$)
7. $\ell \parallel m$ (Conv. of Corr. $\angle$s Post.)

Chapter 4

11. $PQ = 6$, $QR = 6$, $PR = 6\sqrt{2}$, $XY = 6$, $YZ = 7$, $XZ = \sqrt{85}$. The corresponding sides are not congruent, so the triangles are not congruent.

12. $PQ = \sqrt{26}$, $QR = \sqrt{85}$, $PQ = \sqrt{29}$, $XY = \sqrt{26}$, $YZ = \sqrt{85}$, $XZ = \sqrt{29}$. Each pair of corresponding sides has the same measure, so the triangles are congruent. $\triangle PQR \cong \triangle XYZ$ by SSS.

13. Given: $\overline{AB} \cong \overline{DE}$, $\overline{AC} \cong \overline{DF}$, $\overline{AB} \parallel \overline{DE}$

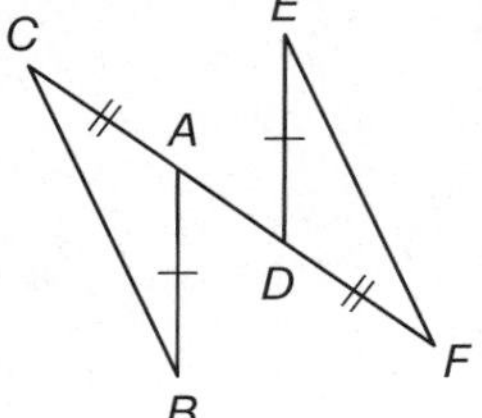

Prove: $\triangle ABC \cong \triangle DEF$

Proof:

Statements (Reasons)

1. $\overline{AB} \cong \overline{DE}$, $\overline{AC} \cong \overline{DF}$, $\overline{AB} \parallel \overline{DE}$ (Given)
2. $\angle BAC \cong \angle EDF$ (Alt. Ext. $\angle$s Thm.)
3. $\triangle ABC \cong \triangle DEF$ (SAS)

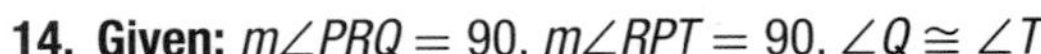

14. Given: $m\angle PRQ = 90$, $m\angle RPT = 90$, $\angle Q \cong \angle T$

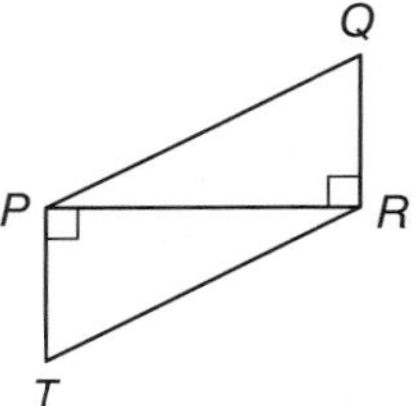

Prove: $\triangle QRP \cong \triangle TPR$

Proof:

We are given that $\angle Q \cong \angle T$, $m\angle PRQ = 90$, and $m\angle RPT = 90$. Using the Substitution Property and the definition of congruence, we can determine that $\angle PRQ \cong \angle RPT$. $\overline{RP} \cong \overline{PR}$ by the Reflexive Property. Therefore, $\triangle QRP \cong \triangle TPR$ by AAS.

15. 57 ft; Since $\angle T$ and $\angle R$ are both right angles, $\angle T \cong \angle R$. Because they are vertical angles, $\angle TSU \cong \angle RSQ$. $TS = RS = 60$, so $\overline{TS} \cong \overline{RS}$. Therefore, $\triangle UTS \cong \triangle QRS$ by ASA. That means that $QR = TU = 57$ ft.

20. reflection; $AB = \sqrt{13}$, $BC = \sqrt{10}$, $AC = \sqrt{17}$, $PM = \sqrt{13}$, $MN = \sqrt{10}$, $PN = \sqrt{17}$. So $\overline{AB} \cong \overline{PM}$, $\overline{BC} \cong \overline{MN}$, and $\overline{AC} \cong \overline{PN}$. By SSS, $\triangle ABC \cong \triangle PMN$.

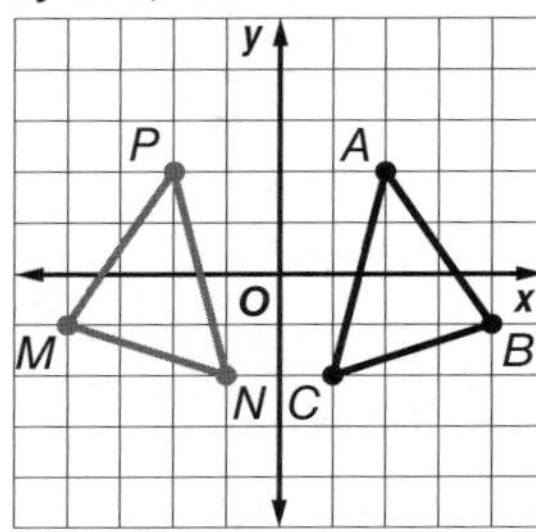

21. translation; $AB = 3$, $BC = 3$, $AC = \sqrt{18}$, $PN = 3$, $NM = 3$, and $PM = \sqrt{18}$. So $\overline{AB} \cong \overline{PN}$, $\overline{BC} \cong \overline{NM}$, and $\overline{AC} \cong \overline{PM}$. By SSS, $\triangle ABC \cong \triangle PNM$.

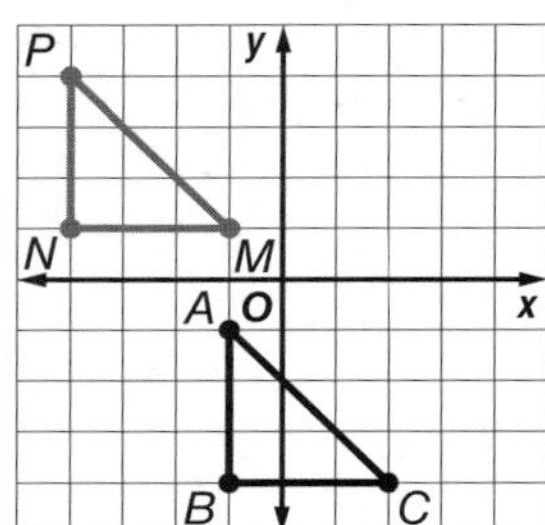

22. Sample answer: Let the coordinates (0, 0) represent the location of the main building, (−90, −70) represent the location of the gym, and (200, −120) represent the location of the vocational building. The distance from the main building to the gym is $\sqrt{(-90-0)^2+(-70-0)^2}$ or about 114 feet. The distance from the main building to the vocation building is $\sqrt{(200-0)^2+(-120-0)^2}$ or about 233 feet. The distance from the gym to the vocational building is $\sqrt{[200-(-90)]^2+[-120-(-70)]^2}$ or about 294 feet. Since none of these distances are the same, the triangle formed by these three buildings is scalene.

Chapter 5

1.

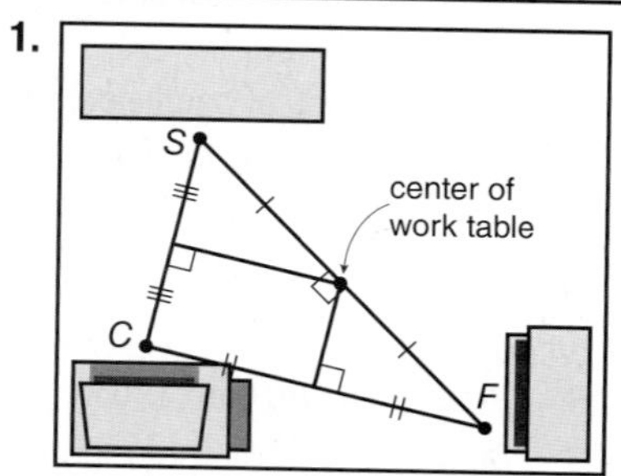

13. Given: $-7+6x<11$

Prove: $x<3$

Indirect Proof:

Step 1 Assume that $x>3$ or $x=3$ is true.

Step 2

x	3	4	5	6	7
$-7+6x$	11	17	23	29	35

When $x>3$, $-7+6x>11$ and when $x=3$, $-7+6x=11$.

Step 3 In both cases, the assumption leads to the contradiction of the given information that $-7+6x<11$. Therefore, the assumption that $x\geq 3$ must be false, so the original conclusion that $x<3$ must be true.

14. Given: $5-2x<-13$

Prove: $x>9$

Indirect Proof:

Step 1 Assume that $x<9$ or $x=9$ is true.

Step 2

x	9	8	7	6	5
$5-2x$	−13	−11	−9	−7	−5

When $x<9$, $5-2x>-13$ and when $x=9$, $5-2x=-13$.

Step 3 In both cases, the assumption leads to the contradiction of the given information that $-7+6x<11$. Therefore, the assumption that $x\geq 3$ must be false, so the original conclusion that $x<3$ must be true.

15. Let $x=$ the number of hours worked before the first break, $y=$ the number of hours worked between the first break and the second break, and $z=$ the number of hours worked after the second break.

Given: $x+y+z>6$

Prove: $x>2$, $y>2$, or $z>2$

Indirect Proof:

Step 1 Assume that no work session was more than 2 hours. That is, $x\leq 2$, $y\leq 2$, and $z\leq 2$.

Step 2 If $x\leq 2$, $y\leq 2$, and $z\leq 2$, then $x+y+z\leq 2+2+2$, or $x+y+z\leq 6$.

Step 3 This is a contradiction of the given statement. Therefore, the assumption is false and $x>2$, $y>2$, or $z>2$. That is, he worked for more than two hours without a break during his shift.

16. Given: $\triangle ABC$

Prove: $\triangle ABC$ can have at most one obtuse angle.

Indirect Proof:

Step 1 Assume that $\triangle ABC$ has two obtuse angles.

Step 2 By definition, an obtuse angle has a measure greater than 90. That means that the sum of the measures of two obtuse angles is greater than 90 + 90 or 180.

Step 3 This contradicts the fact that the sum of the measures of the three angles of a triangle is 180. Therefore, the assumption that $\triangle ABC$ has two obtuse angles must be false and the statement that a triangle can have at most one obtuse angle is true.

17. No; sample answer: Because $3+8\not>11$, the lengths cannot form a triangle.

21.

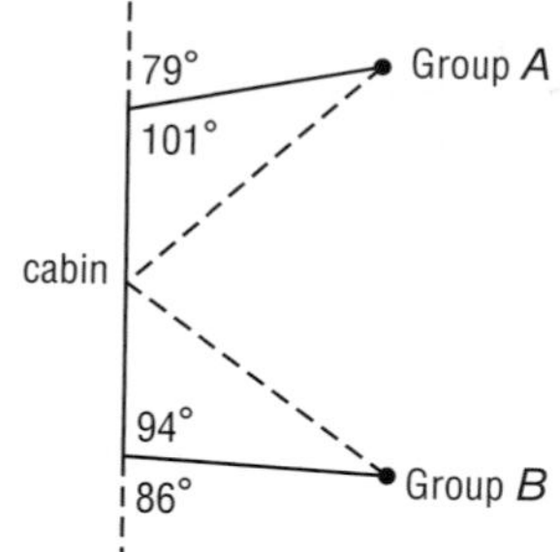

Group B is closer to the cabin. The included angle of the two legs of the path is smaller for Group B, and therefore the leg opposite the angle is shorter.

Extra Practice Answer Appendix

24. Given: $\overline{AB} \cong \overline{CD}$, $m\angle CDB > m\angle BAC$, $m\angle BDA > m\angle CAD$

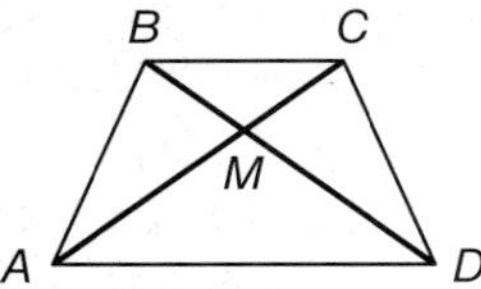

Prove: $AC > DB$

Proof:

Statements (Reasons)

1. $\overline{AB} \cong \overline{CD}$, $m\angle CDB > m\angle BAC$, $m\angle BDA > m\angle CAD$ (Given)
2. $\overline{AD} \cong \overline{DA}$ (Reflex. Prop.)
3. $m\angle CDB + m\angle BDA > m\angle BAC + m\angle BDA$ (Add. Prop. of Inequality)
4. $m\angle BAC + m\angle BDA > m\angle BAC + m\angle CAD$ (Add. Prop. of Inequality)
5. $m\angle CDB + m\angle BDA > m\angle BAC + m\angle CAD$ (Trans. Prop. of Ineq.)
6. $m\angle CDA = m\angle CDB + m\angle BDA$, $m\angle BAD = m\angle BAC + m\angle CAD$ ($\angle$ Add. Post.)
7. $m\angle CDA > m\angle BAD$ (Subs. Prop.)
8. $AC > DB$ (Hinge Theorem)

Chapter 6

5. Sample answer: Since $\angle B$ and $\angle D$ are supplementary to $\angle A$ and $\angle C$, as $m\angle A$ and $m\angle C$ increase, $m\angle B$ and $m\angle D$ must decrease so that their sum is still 180.

8. Yes; sample answer: Since both pairs of opposite sides of the quadrilateral are congruent, we can conclude that it is a parallelogram.

9. No; sample answer: Since we don't know if both pairs of opposite angles are congruent or the diagonals bisect each other, we do not have enough information to prove whether or not the quadrilateral is a parallelogram.

10. Given: *HABJ*, *JBCD*, *FJDE*, and *GHJF* are parallelograms; $\square HABJ \cong \square JBCD \cong \square FJDE \cong \square GHJF$.

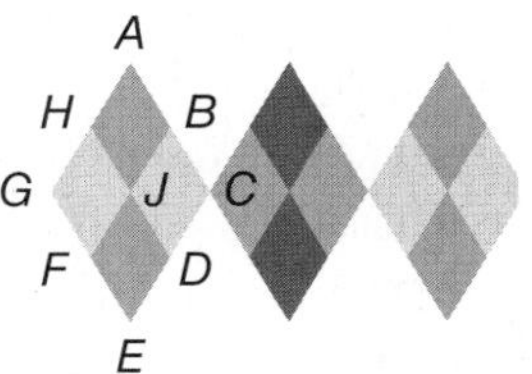

Prove: *ACEG* is a parallelogram.

Proof:

Statements (Reasons)

1. *HABJ*, *JBCD*, *FJDE*, and *GHJF* are parallelograms; $\square HABJ \cong \square JBCD \cong \square FJDE \cong \square GHJF$ (Given)
2. $\overline{GH} \cong \overline{FJ}$, $\overline{HA} \cong \overline{JB}$, $\overline{AB} \cong \overline{HJ}$, $\overline{BC} \cong \overline{JD}$ (Corr. parts of $\cong$ polygons are $\cong$.)
3. $\overline{FJ} \cong \overline{ED}$, $\overline{JB} \cong \overline{DC}$, $\overline{HJ} \cong \overline{GF}$, $\overline{JD} \cong \overline{FE}$ (Def. of parallelogram)
4. $\overline{GH} \cong \overline{ED}$, $\overline{HA} \cong \overline{DC}$, $\overline{AB} \cong \overline{GF}$, $\overline{BC} \cong \overline{FE}$ (Trans. Prop. of $\cong$)
5. $GH = ED$, $HA = DC$, $AB = GF$, $BC = FE$ (Def. of $\cong$)
6. $\overline{GH} \cong \overline{GH}$, $\overline{AB} \cong \overline{AB}$ (Refl. Prop.)
7. $GH = GH$, $AB = AB$ (Def. of $\cong$)
8. $GH + HA = GH + HA$, $AB + BC = AB + BC$ (Add. Prop.)
9. $GH + HA = ED + DC$, $AB + BC = GF + FE$ (Subs. Prop.)
10. $GA = EC$, $AC = GE$ (Seg. Add. Post.)
11. $\overline{GA} \cong \overline{EC}$, $\overline{AC} \cong \overline{GE}$ (Def. of $\cong$)
12. *ACEG* is a parallelogram. (If both pairs of opp. sides are $\cong$, then quad. is a parallelogram.)

11.

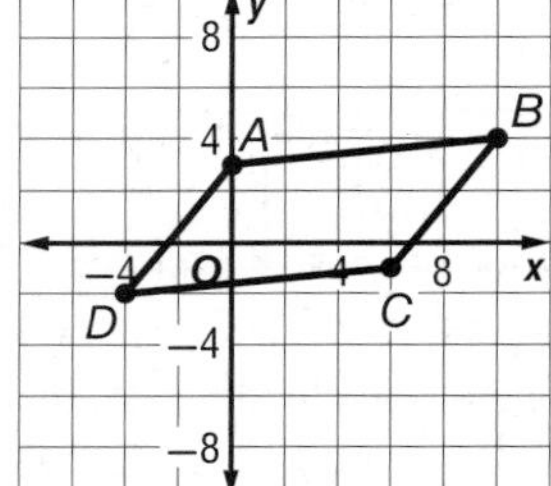

ABCD is a parallelogram. Sample answer: Since the slope of $\overline{AB}$ = slope of $\overline{DC} = \frac{1}{10}$, $\overline{AB} \parallel \overline{DC}$. The slope of $\overline{AD}$ = slope of $\overline{BC} = \frac{5}{4}$, so $\overline{AD} \parallel \overline{BC}$. Since both pairs of opposite sides of *ABCD* are parallel, *ABCD* is a parallelogram.

15. Given: *ABCD* is a rectangle.

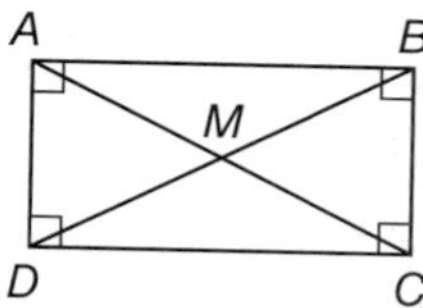

Prove: $\triangle AMB$, $\triangle BMC$, $\triangle CMD$, and $\triangle DMA$ are isosceles.

Proof:

Since *ABCD* is a rectangle and the diagonals of a rectangle are congruent, $\overline{AC} \cong \overline{BD}$ and $AC = BD$ by the definition of congruence. The diagonals of a rectangle bisect each other, so $AM = MC$ and $BM = MD$. Using the Segment Addition Postulate, $AM + MC = AC$ and $BM + MD = BD$. Using Substitution, $AM + MC = BM + MD$. Substituting again, $AM + AM = BM + BM$ and $MC + MC = MD + MD$ or $2AM = 2BM$ and $2MC = 2MD$. Using the Division Property, $AM = BM$ and $MC = MD$. We can conclude that $AM = BM = MC = MD$, and that $\overline{AM} \cong \overline{BM} \cong \overline{MC} \cong \overline{MD}$ by the definition of congruence. Therefore, $\triangle AMB$, $\triangle BMC$, $\triangle CMD$, and $\triangle DMA$ are isosceles by definition.

18. rhombus, rectangle, and square; Sample answer: The slope of $\overline{WX}$ = slope of $\overline{YZ} = \frac{1}{3}$. The slope of $\overline{WZ}$ = slope of $\overline{XY} = -3$. Since $\frac{1}{3} \cdot (-3) = -1$, $\overline{WX} \perp \overline{XY}$, $\overline{XY} \perp \overline{YZ}$, $\overline{YZ} \perp \overline{WZ}$, and $\overline{WZ} \perp \overline{WX}$. By the definition of perpendicular, $\angle WXY$, $\angle XYZ$, $\angle YZW$, and $\angle XWZ$ are right angles. Since $WX = XY = YZ = ZX = \sqrt{10}$, $\overline{WX} \cong \overline{XY} \cong \overline{YZ} \cong \overline{ZX}$ by the definition of congruence. Since ▱*WXYZ* has four right angles and four congruent sides, it is a square. If a parallelogram is a square, it is also a rhombus and a rectangle.

Chapter 7

4. No; sample answer: The measures of the angles of $\triangle ABC$ are 37, 53, and 90. The measures of the angles of $\triangle DEF$ are 41, 49, and 90. Since the corresponding angles of the figures are not congruent, the figures are not similar.

5. Yes; sample answer: $MNPQ \sim XWZY$ with a scale factor of $\frac{2}{3}$.

8. Not similar; sample answer: We know that the vertical angles are congruent, so we would need to show that the sides that include the angle are proportional. Since $\frac{6}{22} \neq \frac{5}{27}$, the triangles are not similar.

9. Similar; sample answer: $\triangle MNP \sim \triangle XYZ$; $\triangle XYZ$ is equilateral. Equilateral triangles are also equiangular. So $\triangle XYZ$ is equiangular. $\triangle MNP$ is also equiangular. All three angles in equiangular triangles measure 60. Therefore, $m\angle N = m\angle P = m\angle Y = m\angle Z = 60$, which means $\angle N \cong \angle Y$ and $\angle P \cong \angle Z$. So $\triangle MNP \sim \triangle XYZ$ by AA Similarity.

17. No; sample answer: Since $\frac{30}{60} \neq \frac{55.5}{110}$, the table is not a dilation of the field.

18.

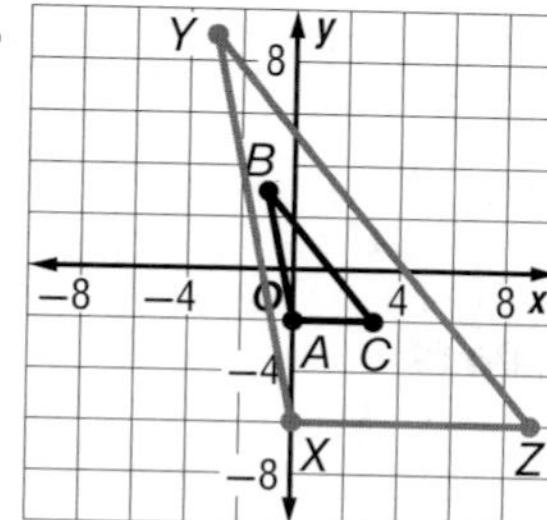

Since $\frac{AB}{XY} = \frac{\sqrt{26}}{3\sqrt{26}} = \frac{1}{3}$, $\frac{BC}{YZ} = \frac{\sqrt{41}}{3\sqrt{41}} = \frac{1}{3}$, and $\frac{AC}{XZ} = \frac{3}{9} = \frac{1}{3}$, the dilation is a similarity transformation.

19.

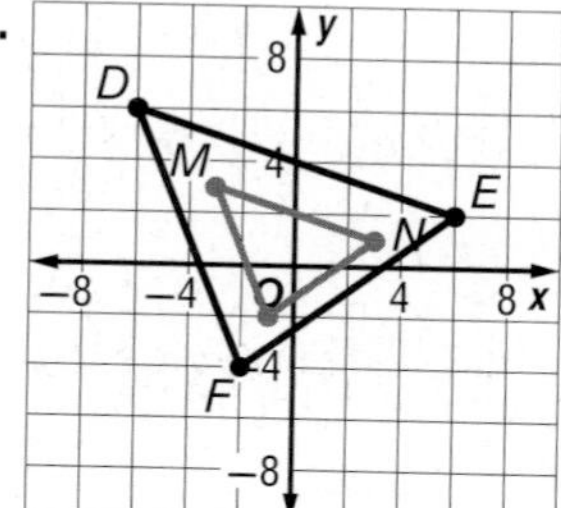

Since $\frac{DE}{MN} = \frac{4\sqrt{10}}{2\sqrt{10}} = 2$, $\frac{EF}{NP} = \frac{10}{5} = 2$, and $\frac{DF}{MP} = \frac{2\sqrt{29}}{\sqrt{29}} = 2$, the dilation is a similarity transformation.

Chapter 8

7. yes; obtuse

$41^2 \stackrel{?}{=} 24^2 + 32^2$

$1681 \stackrel{?}{=} 576 + 1024$

$1681 > 1600$

8. yes; right

$62.5^2 \stackrel{?}{=} 17.52^2 + 60^2$

$3906.25 \stackrel{?}{=} 306.25 + 3600$

$3906.25 = 3906.25$

19. $m\angle A = 78$, $m\angle B = 39$, $m\angle C = 63$, $AB = 19.8$, $BC = 21.8$, $AC = 14$

20. $m\angle D = 12$, $m\angle E = 153$, $m\angle F = 15$, $DE = 39$, $EF = 31$, $DF = 68$

21. $m\angle M = 28$, $m\angle N = 157$, $m\angle P = 25$, $MN = 15.2$, $NP = 16.5$, $MP = 28.4$

22. $m\angle X = 71$, $m\angle Y = 49$, $m\angle Z = 60$, $XY = 37$, $YZ = 46$, $XZ = 42$

23.

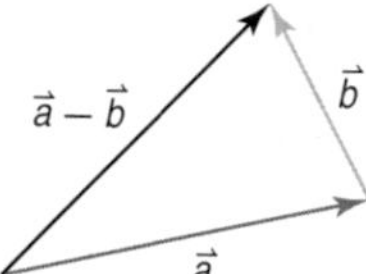

24.

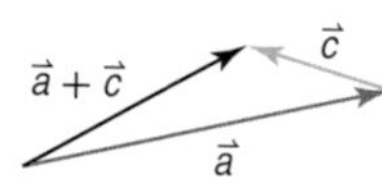

Chapter 9

1.

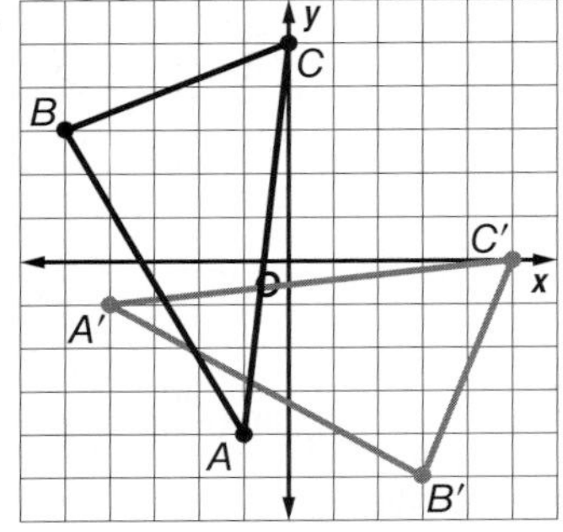

2.

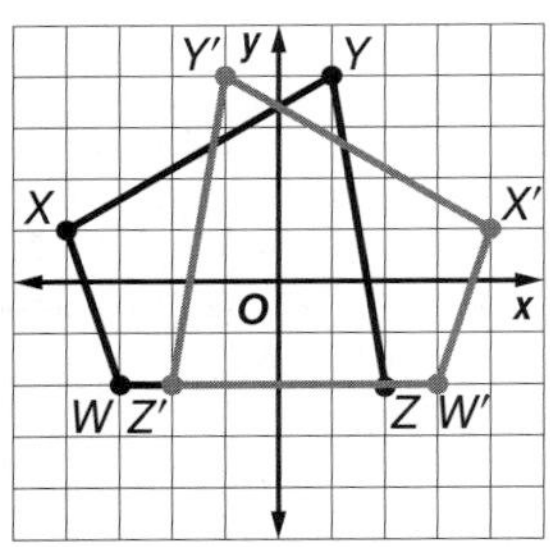

3.

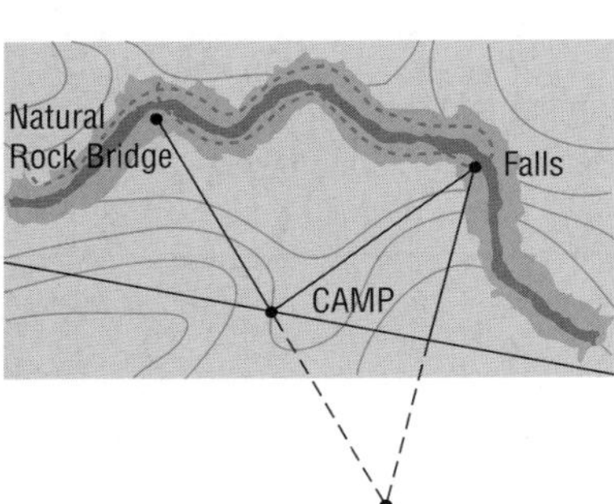

4.

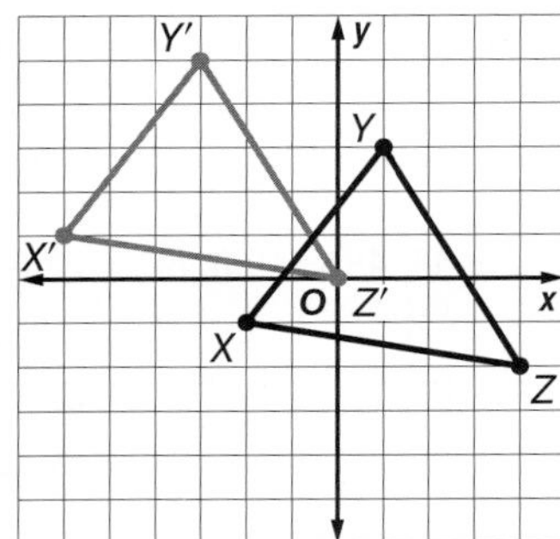

5.

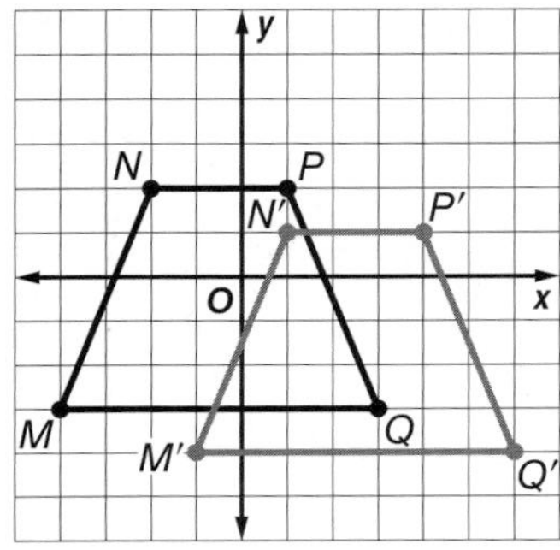

7.

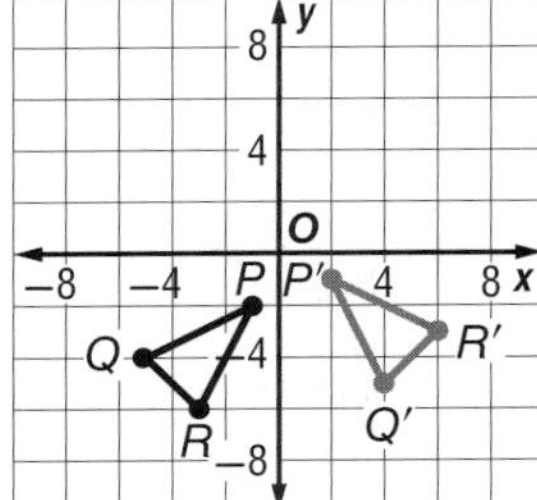

8.

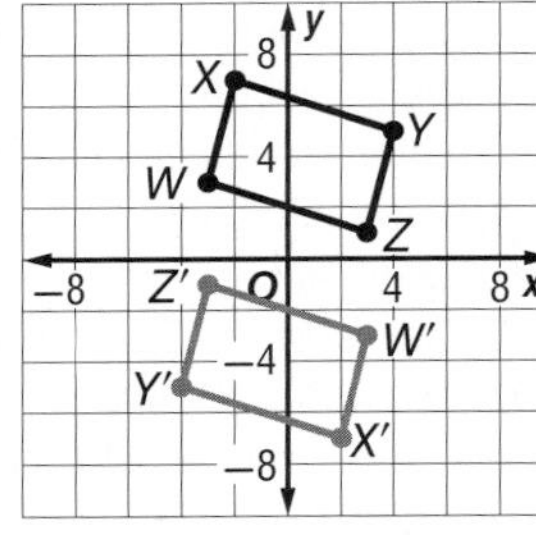

10.

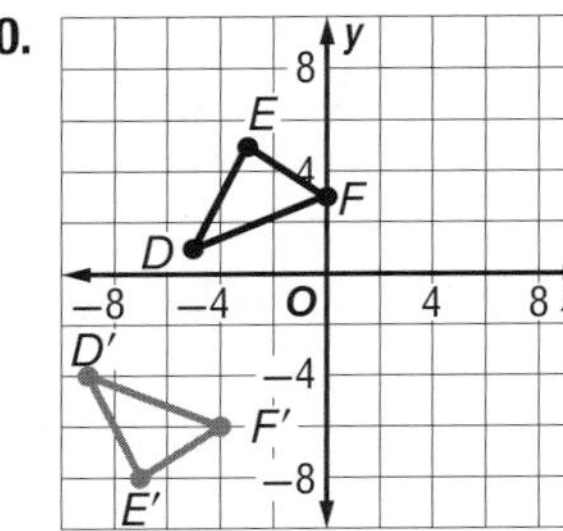

11.

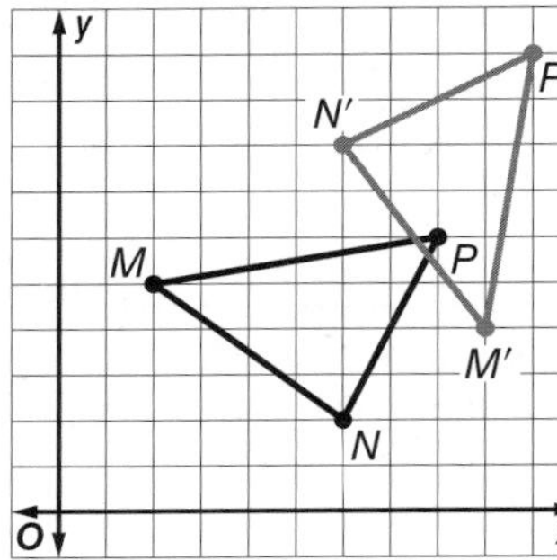

12.

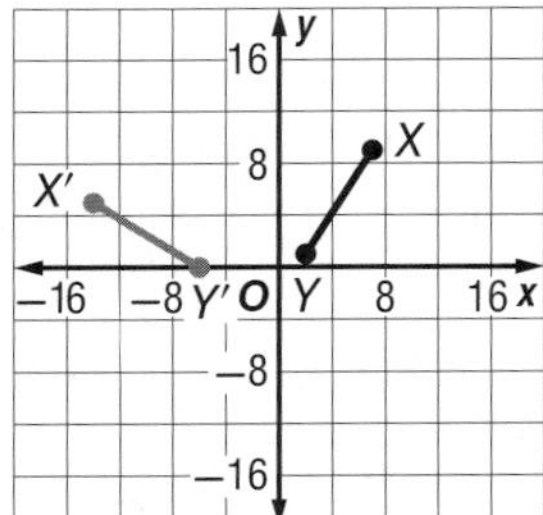

13.

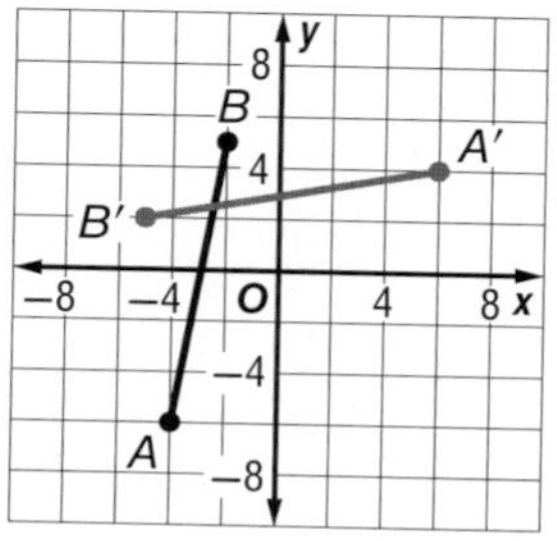

14. line; 1

15. both; 3 lines of symmetry; order of symmetry: 2; 180°

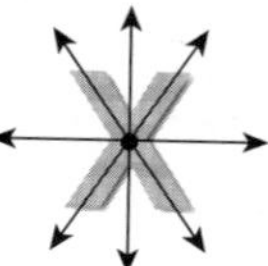

19.

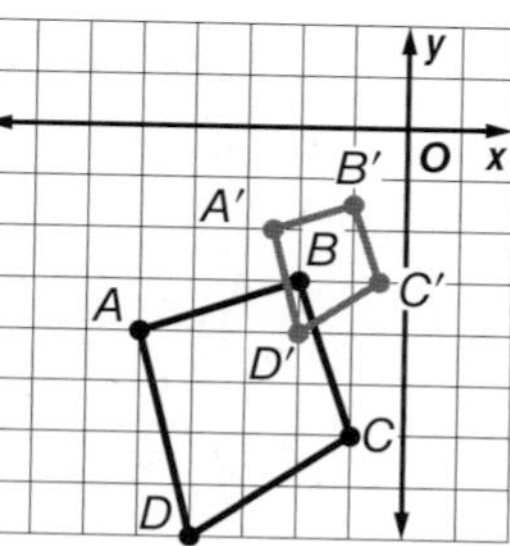

20.

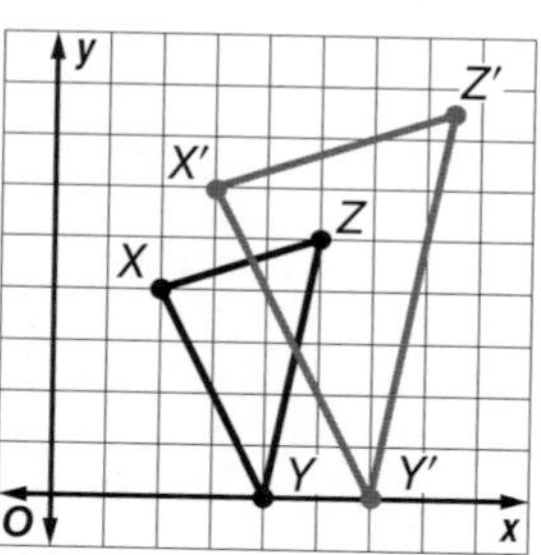

Chapter 10

19b. No; this location is $\sqrt{11^2 + 12^2}$ or about 16.3 mi from the tower, which is greater than the 15-mi radius of coverage.

20. $(x + 5)^2 + (y - 5)^2 = 16$

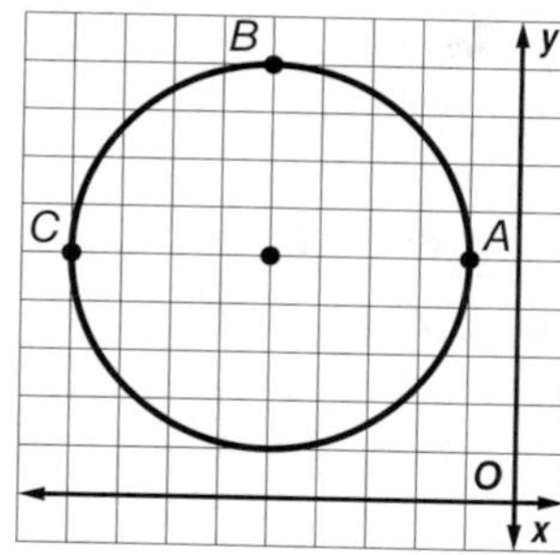

Chapter 12

1.

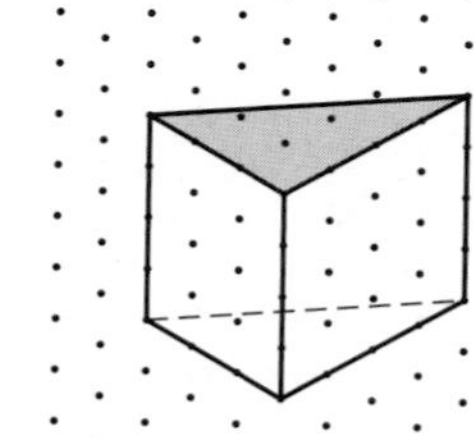

2.

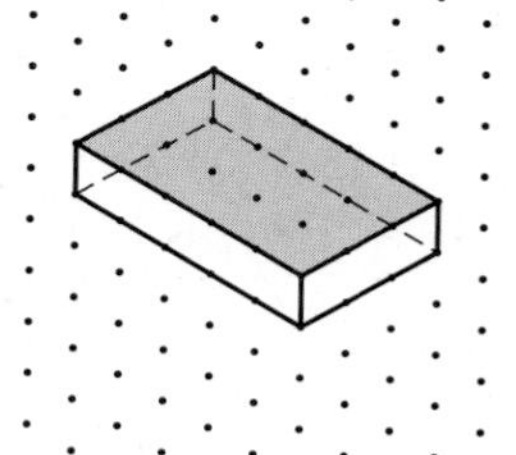

3.

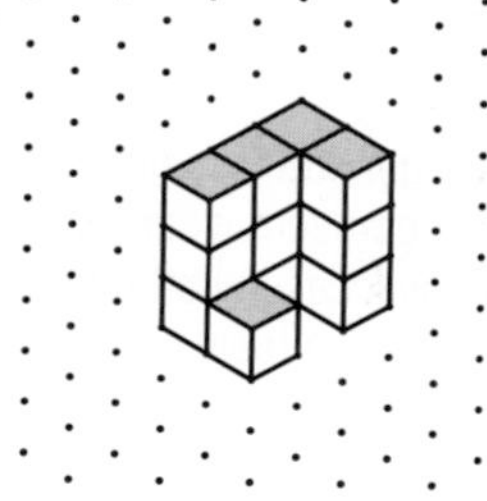

Extra Practice Answer Appendix

Chapter 13

1. 5:00, spin class
5:00, water aerobics
7:30, spin class
7:30, water aerobics

Outcomes	spin class	water aerobics
5:00	5:00, spin class	5:00, water aerobics
7:30	7:30, spin class	7:30, water aerobics

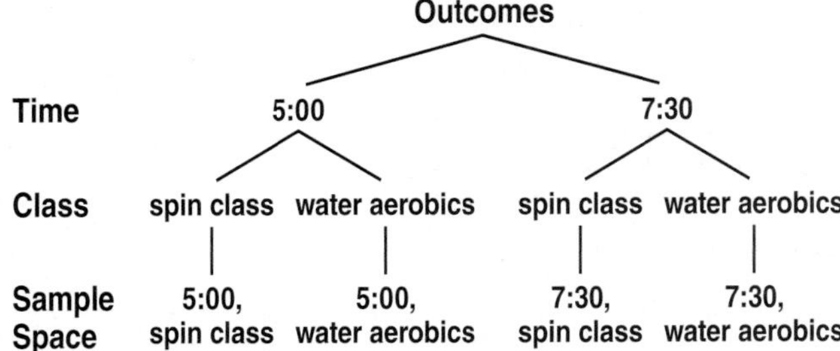

2.

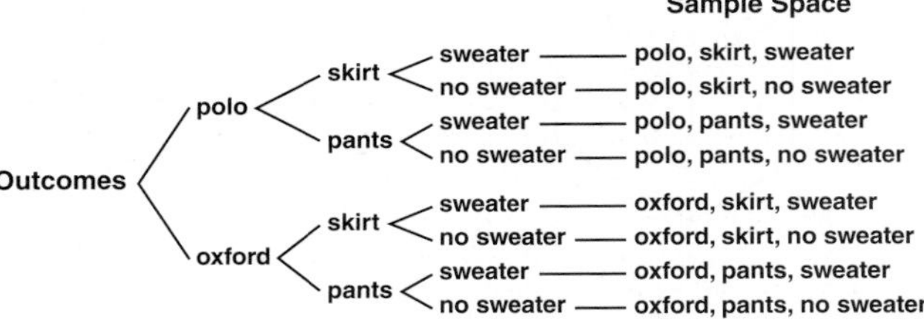

11. Sample answer: Use a random number generator to generate integers 1 through 100, where 1 – 92 represent a successful attempt, and 93 – 100 represent an unsuccessful attempt. Do 50 trials and record the results in a frequency table.

Outcome	Frequency
successful	46
unsuccessful	4

The probability that Wes' next point after touchdown attempt is successful is 0.92 or 92%, which is the same as the theoretical probability.

13. Sample answer: Use a spinner divided into sectors with angle measures of 162° to represent 0 points, 144° to represent 2 points, and 54° to represent 3 points. Do 20 trials and record the results in a frequency table.

Outcome	Frequency
0 points	8
2 points	11
3 points	1

The average value is 1.15 points per attempt.

NOTES

Selected Answers and Solutions

Go to Hotmath.com for step-by-step solutions of most odd-numbered exercises free of charge.

CHAPTER 0
Preparing for Geometry

Lesson 0-1

1. cm **3.** kg **5.** mL **7.** 10 **9.** 10,000 **11.** 0.18 **13.** 2.5 **15.** 24 **17.** 0.370 **19.** 4 **21.** 5 **23.** 16 **25.** 208 **27.** 9050

Lesson 0-2

1. 20 **3.** 12.1 **5.** 16 **7.** 12 **9.** 5.4 **11.** 22.47 **13.** 1.125 **15.** 5.4 **17.** 15 **19.** 367.9 g **21.** 735.8 g

Lesson 0-3

1. $\frac{1}{3}$ or 33% **3.** $\frac{2}{3}$ or 67% **5.** $\frac{1}{3}$ or 33% **7.** $\frac{13}{28}$ or about 46% **9.** $\frac{11}{14}$ or about 79% **11.** $\frac{9}{70}$ or about 13% **13.** $\frac{9}{28}$ or about 32% **15.** $\frac{1}{28}$ or about 3.6% **17.** $\frac{13}{28}$ or about 46% **19.** $\frac{13}{14}$ or about 93% **21.** $\frac{1}{10}$ or 10%; $\frac{1}{8}$ or 12.5% **23.** Sample answer: Assign each friend a different colored marble: red, blue, or green. Place all the marbles in a bag and without looking, select a marble from the bag. Whoever's marble is chosen gets to go first.

Lesson 0-4

1. 3 **3.** −2 **5.** −1 **7.** −26 **9.** 26 **11.** 15

Lesson 0-5

1. −8 **3.** 15 **5.** −72 **7.** $-\frac{15}{2}$ **9.** $\frac{7}{2}$ **11.** −15 **13.** −7 **15.** −7 **17.** −1 **19.** 60 **21.** −4 **23.** 4 **25.** 15 **27.** 21 **29.** −2 **31.** $-\frac{29}{2}$ **33.** −6 **35.** 1

Lesson 0-6

1. $\{x \mid x < 13\}$ **3.** $\{y \mid y < 5\}$ **5.** $\{t \mid t > -42\}$ **7.** $\{d \mid d \leq 4\}$ **9.** $\{k \mid k \geq -3\}$ **11.** $\{z \mid z < -2\}$ **13.** $\{m \mid m < 29\}$ **15.** $\{b \mid b \geq -16\}$ **17.** $\{z \mid z > -2\}$ **19.** $\{b \mid b \leq 10\}$ **21.** $\{q \mid q \geq 2\}$ **23.** $\left\{w \mid w \geq -\frac{7}{3}\right\}$

Lesson 0-7

1. (−2, 3) **3.** (2, 2) **5.** (−3, 1) **7.** (4, 1) **9.** (−1, −1) **11.** (3, 0) **13.** (2, −4) **15.** (−4, 2) **17.** none **19.** IV **21.** I **23.** III

25.

27.

29.

Lesson 0-8

1. (2, 0) **3.** no solution **5.** (2, −5) **7.** $\left(-\frac{4}{3}, 3\right)$ **9.** (4, 1) **11.** elimination, no solution **13.** elimination or substitution, (3, 0) **15.** elimination or substitution, (−6, 4)

Lesson 0-9

1. $4\sqrt{2}$ **3.** $10\sqrt{5}$ **5.** 6 **7.** $7x|y^3|\sqrt{2x}$ **9.** $\frac{9}{7}$ **11.** $\frac{3\sqrt{14}}{4}$ **13.** $\frac{p\sqrt{30p}}{9}$ **15.** $\frac{20+8\sqrt{3}}{13}$ **17.** $\frac{\sqrt{3}}{4}$ **19.** $\frac{6\sqrt{5}+3\sqrt{10}}{2}$

CHAPTER 1
Tools of Geometry

Chapter 1 Get Ready

1. **3.**

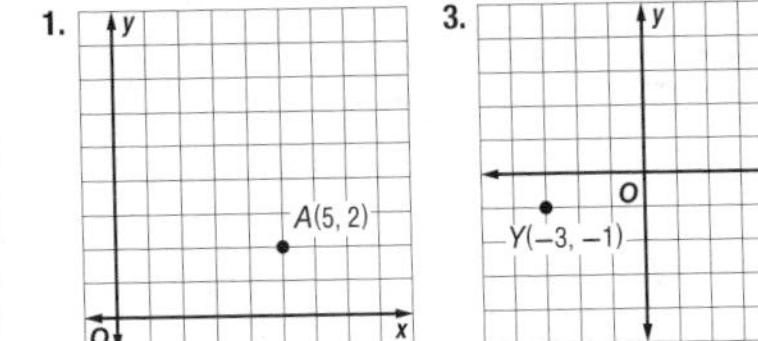

5. e5 **7.** $6\frac{29}{36}$ **9.** $5\frac{2}{15}$ **11.** 81 **13.** 153 **15.** 6

Lesson 1-1

1. Sample answer: m **3.** $\mathcal{B}$ **5.** plane **7.** Sample answer:

9. Sample answer: A, H, and B **11.** Yes; points B, D, and F lie in plane BDF.

13. Sample answer: n and q **15.** $\mathcal{R}$ **17** Sample answer: Points A, B, and C are contained in plane $\mathcal{R}$. Since point P is not contained in plane $\mathcal{R}$, it is not coplanar with points A, B, and C. **19.** points A and P **21.** Yes; line n intersects line q when the lines are extended. **23.** intersecting lines

25. two planes intersecting in a line **27.** point **29.** line **31.** intersecting planes **33.** Sample answer: **35.** Sample answer:

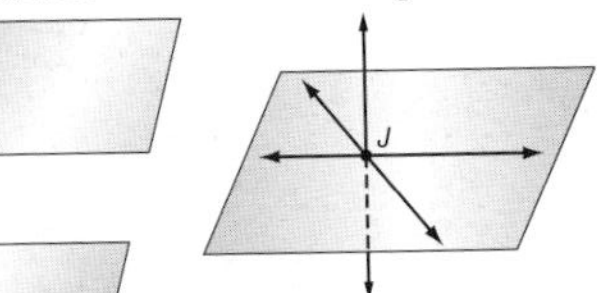

37. Sample answer: **39.** Sample answer:

41. edges **43.** Sample answer: M and N **45** The planes appear to be parallel. Since they do not have any lines in common, they do not intersect. **47.** No; V does not lie in the same plane. **49** **a.** The intersection between the signs and the pole is represented by a point. **b.** The two planes intersect in a line.

51a. Sample answer:

51b.

51c. Sample answer: They get closer together. **53.** Sample answer: The airplanes are in different horizontal planes.

55 **a.** There are four ways to choose three points: FGH, FGK, GHK, and FHK. Only one way, FGH, has three points collinear. So, the probability is $\frac{1}{4}$.

b. There is exactly one plane through any three noncollinear points and infinitely many planes through three collinear points. Therefore, the probability that the three points chosen are coplanar is 1.

57. Sample answer: **59.** 4 **61.** Sample answer: A table is a finite plane. It is not possible to have a real-life object that is an infinite plane because all real-life objects have boundaries.

63. H **65.** B **67.** $6\sqrt{7}$ **69.** $\frac{\sqrt{2}}{2}$ **71.** $\frac{|a^3|\sqrt{6}}{9}$ **73.** $4\sqrt{15} - 8\sqrt{3}$

75.

77. Sample answer: 424.5 g **79.** Sample answer: 1.1 kg **81.** > **83.** < **85.** >

Lesson 1-2

1. 5.7 cm or 57 mm **3.** $1\frac{7}{8}$ in. **5.** 3.8 in. **7**

$BD = 4x$ Given
$12 = 4x$ Substitution
$\frac{12}{4} = \frac{4x}{4}$ Divide each side by 4.
$3 = x$ Simplify.
$BC = 2x$ Given
$= 2(3)$ $x = 3$
$= 6$ Simplify.

9. $\overline{AG} \cong \overline{FG}$, $\overline{BG} \cong \overline{EG}$, $\overline{CG} \cong \overline{DG}$ **11.** 38 mm **13.** $\frac{15}{16}$ in. **15.** 1.1 cm **17.** 1.5 in. **19.** 4.2 cm **21.** $c = 18$; $YZ = 72$ **23.** $a = 4$; $YZ = 20$ **25.** $n = 4\frac{1}{3}$; $YZ = 1\frac{2}{3}$ **27** Yes; $KJ = 4$ in. and $HL = 4$ in. Since the segments have the same measure, they are congruent. **29.** no **31.** yes **33** Sample answer: All the segments that have one slash are congruent: $\overline{AB} \cong \overline{BC} \cong \overline{CD} \cong \overline{DE} \cong \overline{DG} \cong \overline{BG} \cong \overline{CG}$, $\overline{AC} \cong \overline{EC}$. All segments with two slashes are congruent: $\overline{AH} \cong \overline{HG} \cong \overline{GF} \cong \overline{FE}$, $\overline{AG} \cong \overline{HF} \cong \overline{GE}$. All segments with three slashes are congruent: $\overline{BH} \cong \overline{DF}$. **35.** Sample answer: $\overline{BD} \cong \overline{CE}$; $\overline{BD} \cong \overline{PQ}$; $\overline{YZ} \cong \overline{JK}$; $\overline{PQ} \cong \overline{RS}$; $\overline{GK} \cong \overline{KL}$ **37.** If point B is between points A and C, and you know AB and BC, add AB and BC to find AC. If you know AB and AC, subtract AB from

AC to find BC. **39.** $JK = 12, KL = 16$ **41.** Sample answer: Having a standard of measure is important so that there is a reference point against which other measures can be compared and evaluated. **43.** D **45.** D **47.** Sample answer: plane CDF **49.** points C, B, and F **51a.** about 2.1 s **51b.** about 9.7 in. **53.** $\{p|p > 9\}$ **55.** $\{x|x \leq -13\}$ **57.** 12 **59.** 5.5 **61.** $\sqrt{185}$

Lesson 1-3

1. 8

3 $AB = \sqrt{(x_2 - x_1)^2 + (y_2 - y_1)^2}$ Distance Formula

$= \sqrt{(2-4)^2 + (-3-9)^2}$ $(x_1, y_1) = (4, 9)$ and $(x_2, y_2) = (2, -3)$

$= \sqrt{(-2)^2 + (-12)^2}$ Subtract.

$= \sqrt{4 + 144}$ or $\sqrt{148}$ Simplify.

The distance between the time capsules is $\sqrt{148}$ or about 12.2 units.

5. $\sqrt{58}$ or about 7.6 units **7.** -3 **9.** $(4, -5.5)$

11 Let G be (x_1, y_1) and J be (x_2, y_2) in the Midpoint Formula.

$F\left(\frac{x_1 + 6}{2}, \frac{y_1 + (-2)}{2}\right) = F(1, 3.5)$ $(x_2, y_2) = (6, -2)$

Write two equations to find the coordinates of G.

$\frac{x_1 + 6}{2} = 1$ Midpoint Formula $\frac{y_1 + (-2)}{2} = 3.5$

$x_1 + 6 = 2$ Multiply each side by 2. $y_1 + (-2) = 7$

$x_1 = -4$ Simplify. $y_1 = 9$

The coordinates of G are $(-4, 9)$.

13. 5 **15.** 9 **17.** 12 **19.** $\sqrt{89}$ or about 9.4 units **21.** $\sqrt{58}$ or about 7.6 units **23.** $\sqrt{208}$ or about 14.4 units **25.** $\sqrt{65}$ or about 8.1 units **27.** $\sqrt{53}$ or about 7.3 units **29.** $\sqrt{18}$ or about 4.2 units **31.** 4.5 mi **33.** 6 **35.** -4.5 **37.** 3

39 $M\left(\frac{x_1 + x_2}{2}, \frac{y_1 + y_2}{2}\right)$ Midpoint Formula

$= M\left(\frac{22 + 15}{2}, \frac{4 + 7}{2}\right)$ $(x_1, y_1) = (22, 4)$ and $(x_2, y_2) = (15, 7)$

$= M\left(\frac{37}{2}, \frac{11}{2}\right)$ Simplify.

$= M(18.5, 5.5)$ Simplify.

The coordinates of the midpoint are $(18.5, 5.5)$.

41. $(-6.5, -3)$ **43.** $(-4.2, -10.4)$ **45.** $\left(-\frac{1}{2}, \frac{1}{2}\right)$ **47.** $A(1, 6)$ **49.** $C(16, -4)$ **51.** $C(-12, 13.25)$ **53.** 58 **55.** 4.5

57 **a.** If the center of the court is the origin, the player in the first is half of the length of the court or 47 feet to the right and half of the width of the court or 25 feet down. Since you go to the right, the x-coordinate is positive, and since you go down, the y-coordinate is negative. The ordered pair is $(47, -25)$. **b.** The distance that the ball travels is the distance between $(0, 0)$ and $(47, -25)$.

$d = \sqrt{(x_2 - x_1)^2 + (y_2 - y_1)^2}$ Distance Formula

$d = \sqrt{(47-0)^2 + (-25-0)^2}$ $(x_1, y_1) = (0, 0)$, $(x_2, y_2) = (47, -25)$

$d = \sqrt{2834}$ Simplify.

$d \approx 53.2$ Use a calculator.

The distance between the two players is about 53.2 feet.

59. =AVERAGE(B2, D2) **61.** $(-5, 0), (7, 0)$ **63.** $\left(-1\frac{1}{2}, -1\right)$ **65.** ± 5

67 **a.** Sample answer:

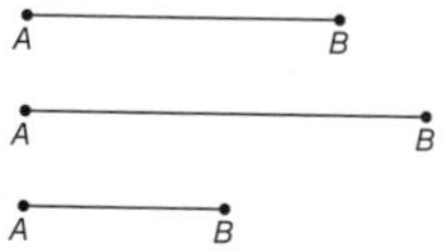

b. Sample answer:

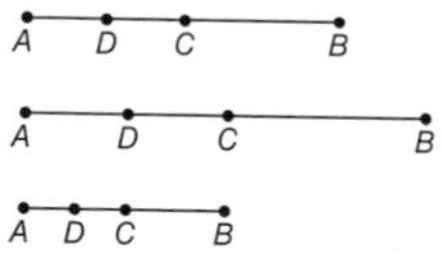

c. Sample answer:

line	AB (cm)	AC (cm)	AD (cm)
1	4	2	1
2	6	3	1.5
3	3	1.5	0.75

d. $AC = \frac{1}{2}AB$ Definition of midpoint

$AC = \frac{1}{2}x$ $AB = x$

$AD = \frac{1}{2}AC$ Definition of midpoint

$AD = \frac{1}{2}\left(\frac{1}{2}x\right)$ Substitution

$AD = \frac{1}{4}x$ Simplify.

e. Look for a pattern.

Number of Midpoints	Length of Smallest Segment
1	$\frac{1}{2}x$
2	$\frac{1}{2} \cdot \frac{1}{2}x = \frac{1}{2(2)}x$
3	$\frac{1}{2} \cdot \frac{1}{2(2)}x = \frac{1}{2^3}x$
4	$\frac{1}{2} \cdot \frac{1}{2(3)}x = \frac{1}{2^4}x$
n	$\frac{1}{2^n}x$

Sample answer: If n midpoints are found, then the smallest segment will have a measure of $\frac{1}{2^n}x$.

69. Sample answer: Sometimes; when the point (x_1, y_1) has coordinates $(0, 0)$.

71. Sample answer:

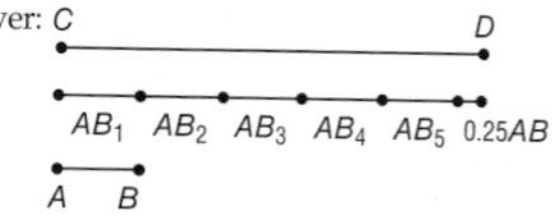

Draw $\overline{AB}$. Next, draw a construction line and place point C on it. From point C, strike 6 arcs in succession of length AB. On the sixth $\overline{AB}$ length, perform a segment bisector two times to create a $\frac{1}{4}AB$ length. Label the endpoint D. **73.** C **75.** C **77.** $2\frac{1}{8}$ in.

79.

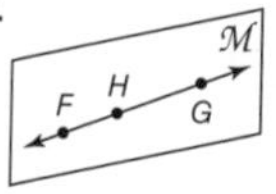

81. $4x + 38 \leq 75$; 9.25 lb or less **83.** 15.5 **85.** $2\frac{1}{3}$ **87.** 4

Lesson 1-4

1. U **3.** $\angle XYU$, $\angle UYX$ **5.** acute; 40 **7.** right; 90 **9.** 156 **11a.** 45; When joined together, the angles form a right angle, which measures 90. If the two angles that form this right angle are congruent, then the measure of each angle is $90 \div 2$ or 45. The angle of the cut is an acute angle. **11b.** The joint is the angle bisector of the frame angle. **13.** P **15.** M **17.** $\overrightarrow{NV}$, $\overrightarrow{NM}$ **19.** $\overrightarrow{RP}$, $\overrightarrow{RQ}$ **21.** $\angle TPQ$ **23.** $\angle TPN$, $\angle NPT$, $\angle TPM$, $\angle MPT$ **25.** $\angle 4$ **27.** S, Q

29 Sample answer: $\angle MPR$ and $\angle PRQ$ share points P and R.

31. 90, right **33.** 45, acute **35.** 135, obtuse

37 $m\angle ABE = m\angle EBF$ Definition of $\cong$ ∠s

$2n + 7 = 4n - 13$ Substitution

$7 = 2n - 13$ Subtract $2n$ from each side.

$20 = 2n$ Add 13 to each side.

$10 = n$ Divide each side by 2.

$m\angle ABE = 2n + 7$ Given

$= 2(10) + 7$ $n = 10$

$= 20 + 7$ or 27 Simplify.

39. 16 **41.** 47 **43a.** about 50 **43b.** about 140 **43c.** about 20 **43d.** 0 **45.** acute

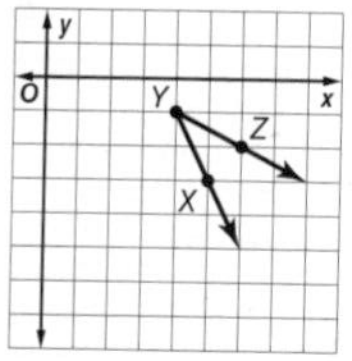

47 **a.** $m\angle 1 \approx 110$; since $110 > 90$, the angle is obtuse. **b.** $m\angle 2 \approx 85$; since $85 < 90$, the angle is acute. **c.** about 15; If the original path of the light is extended, the measure of the angle the original path makes with the refracted path represents the number of degrees the path of the light changed. The sum of the measure of this angle and the measure of $\angle 3$ is 180. The measure of $\angle 3$ is $360 - (110 + 85)$ or 165, so the measure of the angle the original path makes with the refracted path is $180 - 165$ or 15.

49. The two angles formed are acute angles. Sample answer: With my compass at point A, I drew an arc in the interior of the angle. With the same compass setting, I drew an arc from point C that intersected the arc from point A. From the vertex, I drew $\overrightarrow{BD}$. I used the same compass setting to draw the intersecting arcs, so $\overrightarrow{BD}$ divides $\angle ABC$ so that the measurement of $\angle ABD$ and $\angle DBC$ are equal. Therefore, $\overrightarrow{BD}$ bisects $\angle ABC$. **51.** Sometimes; sample answer: For example, if you add an angle measure of 4 and an angle measure of 6, you will have an angle measure of 10, which is still acute. But if you add angles with measure of 50 and 60, you will have an obtuse angle with a measure of 110. **53.** Sample answer: To measure an acute angle, you can fold the corner of the paper so that the edges meet. This would bisect the angle, allowing you to determine whether the angle was between 0° and 45° or between 45° and 90°. If the paper is folded two more times in the same manner and cut off this corner of the paper, the fold lines would form the increments of a homemade protractor that starts at 0° on one side and progresses in $90 \div 8$ or 11.25° increments, ending at the adjacent side, which would indicate 90°. You can estimate halfway between each fold line, which would give you an accuracy of $11.25° \div 2$ or about 6°. The actual measure of the angle shown is 52°. An estimate between 46° and 58° would be acceptable. **55.** Sample answer: Leticia's survey does not represent the entire student body because she did not take a random sample; she only took a sample of students from one major. **57.** E **59.** 8.25 **61.** 15.81 **63.** 10.07 **65.** $x = 11$; $ST = 22$ **67.** 4.5 **69.** 56 **71.** 14.75 **73.** 24.8 **75.** $17\frac{1}{3}$

Lesson 1-5

1. $\angle ZVY$, $\angle WVU$ **3a.** vertical **3b.** 15

5 If $x \perp y$, then $m\angle 2 = 90$ and $m\angle 3 = 90$.

$m\angle 2 = 3a - 27$ Given

$90 = 3a - 27$ Substitution

$117 = 3a$ Add 27 to each side.

$39 = a$ Divide each side by 3.

$m\angle 3 = 2b + 14$ Given

$90 = 2b + 14$ Substitution

$76 = 2b$ Subtract 14 from each side.

$38 = b$ Divide each side by 3.

7. Yes: they share a common side and vertex, so they are adjacent. Since $m\angle EDB + m\angle BDA + m\angle ADC = 90$, $\angle EDB$ and $\angle BDA$ cannot be complementary or supplementary. **9.** Sample answer: $\angle BFC$, $\angle DFE$ **11.** $\angle FDG$, $\angle GDE$ **13.** Sample answer: $\angle CBF$, $\angle ABF$ **15.** $\angle GDE$ **17.** $\angle CAE$ **19.** 65

21 $2x + 25 = 3x - 10$ Vertical ∠s are $\cong$ and have equal measures.

$25 = x - 10$ Subtract $2x$ from each side.

$35 = x$ Add 10 to each side.

$3x - 10 + y = 180$ Def. of supplementary ∠s

$3(35) - 10 + y = 180$ Substitution

$105 - 10 + y = 180$ Multiply.

$95 + y = 180$ Simplify.

$y = 85$ Subtract 95 from each side.

23. $x = 48$; $y = 21$ **25.** $m\angle F = 63$; $m\angle E = 117$ **27.** 40

29 If $\angle KNM$ is a right angle, then $m\angle KNM = 90$.

$m\angle KNL + m\angle LNM = m\angle KNM$ Sum of parts = whole

$6x - 4 + 4x + 24 = 90$ Substitution

$10x + 20 = 90$ Combine like terms.

$10x = 70$ Subtract 20 from each side.

$x = 7$ Divide each side by 10.

31. 92 **33.** 53; 37 **35.** $a = 8$; $b = 54$ **37.** Yes; the angles form a linear pair. **39.** No; the measures of each angle are unknown. **41.** No; the angles are not adjacent. **43.** Sample answer: $\angle 1$ and $\angle 3$

45 $\angle 1$ and $\angle 3$ are vertical angles, so they are congruent; $m\angle 3 = m\angle 1 = 110$. $\angle 1$ and $\angle 4$ are a linear pair, so they are supplementary.

$m\angle 4 + m\angle 1 = 180$	Def. of supplementary $\angle$s
$m\angle 4 + 110 = 180$	Substitution
$m\angle 4 = 70$	Subtract 110 from each side.

47. Sample answer: Yes; if the wing is not rotated at all, then all of the angles are right angles, which are neither acute nor obtuse. **49.** Yes; angles that are right or obtuse do not have complements because their measures are greater than or equal to 90. **51a.** Line a is perpendicular to plane $\mathcal{P}$. **51b.** Line m is in plane $\mathcal{P}$. **51c.** Any plane containing line a is perpendicular to plane $\mathcal{P}$. **53.** C **55.** J **57.** 125, obtuse **59.** 90, right **61.** $\left(-3\frac{1}{2}, 1\right)$ **63.** 81.5 cm **65.** $\overline{FG} \cong \overline{HJ} \cong \overline{JK} \cong \overline{FL}$, $\overline{GH} \cong \overline{LK}$; $\angle F \cong \angle J$, $\angle G \cong \angle H \cong \angle K \cong \angle L$ **67.** $\overline{WX} \cong \overline{XY} \cong \overline{YZ} \cong \overline{ZW}$; $\angle W \cong \angle Y$, $\angle X \cong \angle Z$

Lesson 1-6

1. pentagon; concave; irregular **3.** octagon; regular **5.** hexagon; irregular **7.** ≈ 40.2 cm; ≈ 128.7 cm² **9.** C **11.** triangle; convex; regular

13 The polygon has 8 sides, so it is an octagon. All of the lines containing the sides of the polygon will pass through the interior of the octagon, so it is concave. Since the polygon is not convex, it is irregular.

15. hendecagon; concave; irregular **17.** 7.8 m; ≈ 3.1 m² **19.** 26 in.; 42.3 in²

21

$c^2 = a^2 + b^2$	Pythagorean Theorem
$c^2 = 6.5^2 + 4.5^2$	$a = 6.5, b = 4.5$
$c^2 = 62.5$ or ≈ 7.9	Simplify.

$P = a + b + c$
$\approx 6.5 + 4.5 + 7.9$
≈ 18.9 cm

$A = \frac{1}{2}bh$
$= \frac{1}{2}(4.5)(6.5)$
≈ 14.6 cm²

23. ≈ 2.55 in.
25. triangle; $P = 5 + \sqrt{32} + \sqrt{17} \approx 14.78$ units; $A = 10$ units²

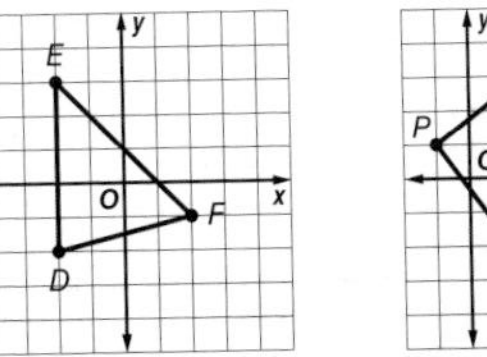

27. quadrilateral or square; $P = 20$ units; $A = 25$ units²

29a. 14 ft **29b.** 12 ft² **29c.** The perimeter doubles; the area quadruples. The perimeter of a rectangle with dimensions 6 ft and 8 ft is 28 ft, which is twice the perimeter of the original figure since 2 • 14 ft = 28 ft. The area of a rectangle with dimensions 6 ft and 8 ft is 48 ft², which is four times the area of the original figure, since 4 • 12 ft² = 48 ft². **29d.** The perimeter is halved; the area is divided by 4. The perimeter of a rectangle with dimensions 1.5 ft and 2 ft is 7 ft, which is half the perimeter of the original figure, since $\frac{1}{2}$ • 14 ft = 7 ft. The area of a rectangle with dimensions 1.5 ft and 2 ft is 3 ft², which is $\frac{1}{4}$ the area of the original figure, since $\frac{1}{4}$ • 12 ft² = 3 ft². **31.** 60 yd, 6 yd

33

$C = \pi d$	Circumference	$C = \pi d$	
$= \pi(8)$		$= \pi(10)$	
≈ 25.1	Simplify.	≈ 31.4	

minimum circumference: 25.1 in.; maximum circumference: 31.4 in.

$A = \pi r^2$	Area of a circle
$= \pi(4)^2$	$r = 4$
≈ 50.3	Simplify.

$A = \pi r^2$	Circumference
$= \pi(5)^2$	$r = 5$
≈ 78.5	Simplify.

minimum area: 50.3 in²; maximum area: 78.5 in²

35. 21.2 m **37.** $2\pi\sqrt{32}$ or about 35.5 units **39.** $12\sqrt{6}$ or about 29.4 in. **41.** 108 in.; 729 in²

43a–b. Sample answer:

Object	d (cm)	C (cm)	$\frac{C}{d}$
1	3	9.4	3.13
2	9	28.3	3.14
3	4.2	13.2	3.14
4	12	37.7	3.14
5	4.5	14.1	3.13
6	2	6.3	3.15
7	8	25.1	3.14
8	0.7	2.2	3.14
9	1.5	4.7	3.13
10	2.8	8.8	3.14

43c. Sample answer:

43d. Sample answer: $C = 3.14d$; the equation represents a formula for approximating the circumference of a circle. The slope represents an approximation for pi. **45.** 290.93 units² **47.** Sample answer: The pentagon is convex, since no points of the lines drawn on the edges are in the interior. The pentagon is regular since all of the angles and sides were constructed with the same measurement, making them congruent to each other. **49.** Sample answer: If a convex polygon is equiangular but not also equilateral, then it is not a regular polygon. Likewise, if a polygon is equiangular and equilateral, but not convex, then it is not a regular polygon. **51.** F **53.** C **55.** No; we do not know anything about these measures. **57.** Yes; they form a linear pair. **59.** elimination; $x = -3, y = -1$ **61.** substitution; $x = -4, y = -2.5$ **63.** 24 **65.** 169.6

Lesson 1-7

1. not a polyhedron; cylinder

3

$T = PH + 2B$	Surface area of a prism
$= (14)(3) + 2(12)$	$P = 14$ cm, $h = 3$ cm, $B = 12$ cm²
$= 66$ cm²	Simplify.
$V = BH$	Volume of a prism
$= (12)(3)$	$B = 12$ cm², $h = 3$ cm
$= 36$ cm³	Simplify.

5a. ≈ 27.2 in³ **5b.** 13.6π or about 42.7 in² **7.** pyramid; a polyhedron **9.** rectangular prism; a polyhedron **11.** cylinder; not a polyhedron **13.** not a polyhedron; cone **15.** not a polyhedron; sphere **17.** a polyhedron; pentagonal pyramid; base: $JHGFD$; faces: $JHGFD$, $\triangle JEH$, $\triangle HEG$, $\triangle GEF$, $\triangle FED$, $\triangle EDJ$; edges: $\overline{HG}$, $\overline{GF}$, $\overline{FD}$, $\overline{DJ}$, $\overline{JH}$, $\overline{EJ}$, $\overline{EH}$, $\overline{EG}$, $\overline{EF}$, $\overline{ED}$; vertices: J, H, G, F, D, E **19.** 121.5 m²; 91.1 m³

21

$T = PH + 2B$	$V = BH$
$= (24)(5) + 2(24)$	$= (24)(5)$
$= 168$ cm²	$= 120$ cm³

23. 150π or about 471.2 mm²; 250π or about 785.4 mm³

25 **a.**

$V = \pi r^2 h$	Volume of a cylinder
$= \pi\left(7\frac{3}{4}\right)^2\left(11\frac{3}{4}\right)$	$r = 7\frac{3}{4}$ in., $h = 11\frac{3}{4}$ in.
≈ 2217.1 in³	Simplify.

b.

$T = 2\pi rh + 2\pi r^2$	Surface area of a cylinder
$= 2\pi\left(7\frac{3}{4}\right)\left(11\frac{3}{4}\right) + 2\pi\left(7\frac{3}{4}\right)^2$	$r = 7\frac{3}{4}$ in., $h = 11\frac{3}{4}$ in.
≈ 949.5 in²	Simplify.

27. 3 in. **29.** 1212 in²; 1776 in³ **31a.** 96 in² **31b.** 113.1 in² **31c.** prism: 2 cans; cylinder: 3 cans **31d.** 2.18 in.; if the height is 10 in., then the surface area of the rectangular cake is 152 in². To find the radius of a cylindrical cake with the same height, solve the equation $152 = \pi r^2 + 20\pi r$. The solutions are $r = -22.18$ or $r = 2.18$. Using a radius of 2.18 in. gives surface area of about 152 in².

33 1 ft³ = (12 in.)³ = 1728 in³
$4320 \text{ in}^3 \cdot \frac{1 \text{ ft}^3}{1728 \text{ in}^3} = 2.5 \text{ ft}^3$

35. The volume of the original prism is 4752 cm³. The volume of the new prism is 38,016 cm³. The volume increased by a factor of 8 when each dimension was doubled. **37.** Neither; sample answer: the surface area is twice the sum of the areas of the top, front, and left side of the prism or 2(5 • 3 + 5 • 4 + 3 • 4), which is 94 in². **39a.** cone **39b.** cylinder **41.** 27 mm³ **43.** 55.2 **45.** F **47.** quadrilateral; convex; regular **49.** dodecagon; concave; irregular **51.** 10 **53.** The intersection of a plane and a line not in the plane is a point. **55.** Two lines intersect in one point.

57.

59.

Chapter 1 Study Guide and Review

1. plane **3.** perpendicular **5.** point P **7.** point W **9.** line **11.** $x = 6$, $XP = 27$ **13.** yes **15.** 1.5 mi **17.** 10 **19.** (16, −6.5) **21.** (−27, 16) **23.** G **25.** $\overrightarrow{CA}$ and $\overrightarrow{CH}$ **27.** Sample answer: $\angle A$ and $\angle B$ are right, $\angle E$ and $\angle C$ are obtuse, and $\angle D$ is acute. **29.** Sample answer: $\angle QWP$ and $\angle XWV$ **31.** 66 **33.** dodecagon, concave, irregular **35.** Option 1 = 12,000 ft², Option 2 = 12,100 ft², Option 3 ≈ 15,393.8 ft². Option 3 provides the greatest area. **37.** hexagonal prism. Bases: $ABCDEF$ and $GHJKLM$; Faces: ▱$ABHG$, ▱$BCJH$, ▱$CDKJ$, ▱$DELK$, ▱$EFML$, ▱$FAGM$; Edges: $\overline{AB}$, $\overline{BC}$, $\overline{CD}$, $\overline{DE}$, $\overline{EF}$, $\overline{FA}$, $\overline{GH}$, $\overline{HJ}$, $\overline{JK}$, $\overline{KL}$, $\overline{LM}$, $\overline{MG}$, $\overline{AG}$, $\overline{BH}$, $\overline{CJ}$, $\overline{DK}$, $\overline{EL}$, $\overline{FM}$; Vertices: $A, B, C, D, E, F, G, H, J, K, L, M$ **39.** 384 in²; 384 in³ **41.** 72 m², 36 m³ **43.** ≈ 23.6 in², ≈ 7.1 in³

CHAPTER 2
Reasoning and Proof

Chapter 2 Get Ready

1. 31 **3.** 14 **5.** 12 **7.** $x^2 + 3$ **9.** −7 **11.** 10.8 **13.** $4x = 52$; $13 **15.** $\angle CXD$, $\angle DXE$ **17.** 38

Lesson 2-1

1. Each cost is $2.25 more than the previous cost; $11.25. **3.** In each figure, the shading moves to the next point clockwise.

5 3, 3, 6, 9, 15
+3 +3 +6

Beginning with the third element, each element in the pattern is the sum of the previous two elements. So, the next element will be 15 + 9 or 24. **7.** The product of two even numbers is an even number. **9.** The set of points in a plane equidistant from point A is a circle.

11a. **Wireless Subscribership by Year**

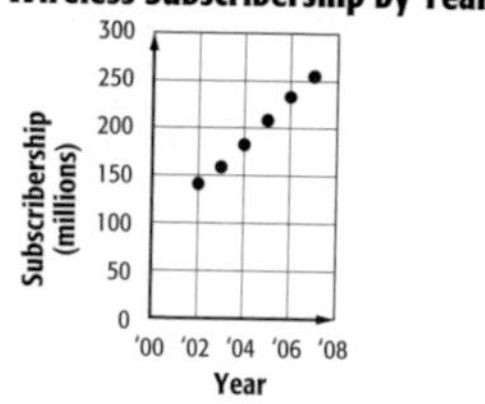

11b. Sample answer: About 372,000,000 Americans will have wireless subscriptions in 2012.

13 If a ray intersects a segment at its midpoint and forms adjacent angles that are not right angles, then the ray is not perpendicular to the segment. **15.** Each element in the pattern is three more than the previous element; 18.

17. Each element has an additional two as part of the number; 22222. **19.** Each element is one half the previous element; $\frac{1}{16}$. **21.** Each percentage is 7% less than the previous percentage; 79%. **23.** Each meeting is two months after the previous meeting; July.

25. In each figure, the shading moves to the next area of the figure counter clockwise.

27. The shading of the lower triangle in the upper right quadrant of the first figure moves clockwise through each set of triangles from one figure to the next.

29. Sample answer: It is drier in the west and hotter in the south than other parts of the country, so less water would be readily available.

31 First, list examples: $1 \cdot 3 = 3$, $3 \cdot 5 = 15$, $7 \cdot 9 = 63$, $11 \cdot 11 = 121$. All the products are odd numbers. So, a conjecture about the product of two odd numbers is that the product is an odd number.

33. They are equal. **35.** The points equidistant from A and B form the perpendicular bisector of $\overline{AB}$. **37.** The area of the rectangle is two times the area of the square.

39a. **Hockey Participation by Year**

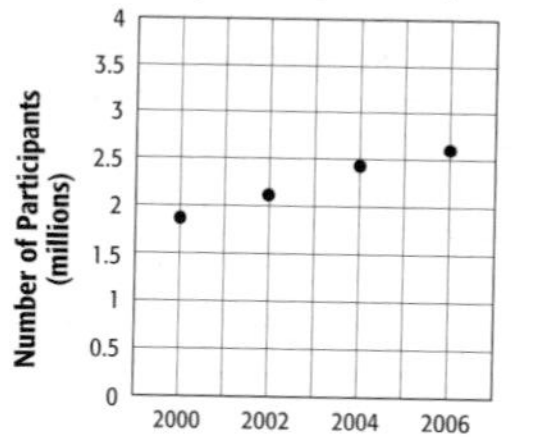

39b. Sample answer: More people over the age of 7 will play hockey in the future. The number of people playing hockey increases each year, so the graph suggests that even more people will play hockey in subsequent years. **41.** False; sample answer: Suppose $x = 2$, then $-x = -2$.

43. False; sample answer: A B C

45. False; sample answer: The length could be 4 m and the width could be 5 m. **47a.** 1, 4, 9, 16

47b. Sample answer: Start by adding 3 to 1 to get the second number, 4. Continue adding the next odd number to the previous number to get the next number in the sequence. **47c.** Sample answer: Each figure is the previous figure with an additional row and column of points added, which is 2 (position number) − 1. One is subtracted since 2 (position number) counts the corner point twice. 2 (position number) − 1 is always an odd number.

47d. 25, 36

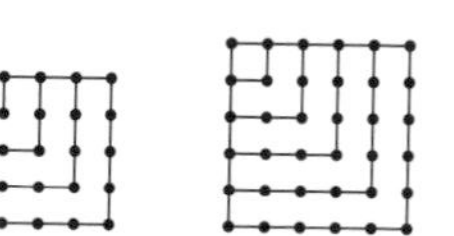

49a. 1, 5, 12, 22 **49b.** Sample answer: Start by adding 4 to 1 to get the second number, 5. Increase the amount added to the previous number by 3 each time to get the next number in sequence. So, add 4 + 3 or 7 to 5 to get 12, and add 4 + 3 + 3 or 10 to 12 to get 22. **49c.** Sample answer: The second figure is the previous figure with 4 points added to make a pentagon. The third figure is the previous figure with 7 more points added, which is 3 more than the last number of points added. The fourth figure is the previous figure with 10 points added, which is 3 more than the last number of points added.

49d. 35, 51

51 **a.** For each even number from 10 to 20, write the number as the sum of two primes. Sample answer: $10 = 5 + 5$, $12 = 5 + 7$, $14 = 7 + 7$, $16 = 5 + 11$, $18 = 7 + 11$, $20 = 7 + 13$ **b.** The number 3 can be written as $0 + 3$ and as $1 + 2$. Since neither 0 nor 1 is a prime number, 3 cannot be written as the sum of two primes. So, the conjecture is false.

53. In the sequence of perimeters, each measure is twice the previous measure. Therefore, doubling the side length of a regular hexagon appears to also double its perimeter. In the sequence of areas, each measure is four times the previous measure. Therefore, doubling the side length of a regular hexagon appears to quadruple its area.

55. Jack; 2 is an even prime number.

57. Sample answer: False; if the two points create a straight angle that includes the third point, then the conjecture is true. If the two points do not create a straight angle with the third point, then the conjecture is false. **59.** B **61.** G **63.** 132 m^2; 60 m^3 **65.** 54 cm^2; 27 cm^3 **67.** 26.69 **69.** plane **71.** 18 **73.** 8

Lesson 2-2

1. A week has seven days, and there are 60 minutes in an hour. p and r is true, because p is true and r is true.

3 $q \vee r$: There are 20 hours in a day, or there are 60 minutes in an hour. A disjunction is true if at least one of the statements is true. So, $q \vee r$ is true because r is true. It does not matter that q is false.

5. A week has seven days, or there are 60 minutes in an hour. $p \vee r$ is true, because p is true and r is true.

7.

p	q	$\sim q$	$p \vee \sim q$
T	T	F	T
T	F	T	T
F	T	F	F
F	F	T	T

9.

p	q	$\sim p$	$\sim q$	$\sim p \vee \sim q$
T	T	F	F	F
T	F	F	T	T
F	T	T	F	T
F	F	T	T	T

11. $\overrightarrow{DB}$ is the angle bisector of $\angle ADC$, and $\overline{AD} \cong \overline{DC}$. p and r is true because p is true and r is true.
13. $\overline{AD} \cong \overline{DC}$ or $\overrightarrow{DB}$ is not the angle bisector of $\angle ADC$. r or $\sim p$ is true because r is true and $\sim p$ is false.
15. $\overrightarrow{DB}$ is not the angle bisector of $\angle ADC$, or $\overline{AD} \not\cong \overline{DC}$. $\sim p$ or $\sim r$ is false because $\sim p$ is false and $\sim r$ is false. **17.** Springfield is the capital of Illinois, and Illinois shares a border with Kentucky. $p \wedge r$ is true because p is true and r is true. **19.** Illinois does not share a border with Kentucky, or Illinois is to the west of Missouri. $\sim r \vee s$ is false because $\sim r$ is false and s is false. **21.** Springfield is not the capital of Illinois, and Illinois does not share a border with Kentucky. $\sim p \wedge \sim r$ is false because $\sim p$ is false and $\sim r$ is false.

23.

p	q	$\sim p$	$\sim p \wedge q$
T	T	F	F
T	F	F	F
F	T	T	T
F	F	T	F

25.

p	r	$p \wedge r$
T	T	T
T	F	F
F	T	F
F	F	F

27.

p	r	$p \vee r$
T	T	T
T	F	T
F	T	T
F	F	F

29.

p	r	$\sim p$	$\sim p \wedge r$
T	T	F	F
T	F	F	F
F	T	T	T
F	F	T	F

31 **a.** The students who dive are represented by the intersection of the two sets and the nonintersecting portion of the Dive region. So, there are 3 + 4 or 7 students who dive. **b.** The students who participate in swimming or diving or both are represented by the union of the sets. There are 19 + 3 + 4 or 26 students who swim, dive, or do both. **c.** The students who swim and dive are represented by the intersection of the two sets. There are 3 students who both swim and dive.

33a. 50 **33b.** 40 **33c.** 110 **33d.** 20 **33e.** These teens do not use any of the listed electronics.

35 Make columns with the headings p, q, $\sim q$, r, $\sim q \vee r$, and $p \wedge (\sim q \vee r)$. List the possible combinations of truth values for p, q, and r. Use the truth values of q to find the truth values of $\sim q$. Use the truth values for each part of $\sim q \vee r$ to find the truth value of the compound statement. Then use the truth values for each part of $p \wedge (\sim q \vee r)$ to find the truth value of the compound statement.

p	q	$\sim q$	r	$\sim q \vee r$	$p \wedge (\sim q \vee r)$
T	T	F	T	T	T
T	F	T	T	T	T
T	T	F	F	F	F
T	F	T	F	T	T
F	T	F	T	T	F
F	F	T	T	T	F
F	T	F	F	F	F
F	F	T	F	T	F

If p and r are true, and q is true or false, then $p \wedge (\sim q \vee r)$ is true.

37.

p	q	$\sim q$	r	$\sim r$	$\sim q \wedge \sim r$	$p \vee (\sim q \wedge \sim r)$
T	T	F	T	F	F	T
T	F	T	T	F	F	T
T	T	F	F	T	F	T
T	F	T	F	T	T	T
F	T	F	T	F	F	F
F	F	T	T	F	F	F
F	T	F	F	T	F	F
F	F	T	F	T	T	T

true

Selected Answers and Solutions

39.

p	$\sim p$	q	r	$\sim r$	$(\sim p \vee q)$	$(\sim p \vee q) \vee \sim r$
T	F	T	T	F	T	T
T	F	F	T	F	F	F
T	F	T	F	T	T	T
T	F	F	F	T	F	T
F	T	T	T	F	T	T
F	T	F	T	F	T	T
F	T	T	F	T	T	T
F	T	F	F	T	T	T

If r is true or false, then $(\sim p \vee q) \vee \sim r$ is true.

41. Never; integers are rational numbers, not irrational. **43.** There exists at least one square that is not a rectangle. **45.** No students have classes in C-wing. **47.** Every segment has a midpoint. **49.** Sample answer: A triangle has three sides, and a square has four sides. Both are true, so the compound statement is true. **51.** 22 in^2; The area of a triangle is $\frac{1}{2}bh$. The base of the triangle is 11 inches and the height of the triangle is 4 inches, so the area of the triangle is $\frac{1}{2}(11)(4)$ or 22 in^2. **53.** A **55.** triangular prism; bases: $\triangle MNO$, $\triangle PQR$; faces: $\triangle MNO$, $\triangle PQR$, $OMPR$, $ONQR$, $PQNM$; edges: $\overline{MN}$, $\overline{NO}$, $\overline{OM}$, $\overline{PQ}$, $\overline{QR}$, $\overline{PR}$, $\overline{NQ}$, $\overline{MP}$, $\overline{OR}$; vertices: M, N, O, P, Q, and R **57.** triangular pyramid; base: $\triangle HJK$; faces: $\triangle HJK$, $\triangle HLK$, $\triangle KLJ$, $\triangle HLJ$; edges: $\overline{HK}$, $\overline{KJ}$, $\overline{HJ}$, $\overline{HL}$, $\overline{KL}$, $\overline{JL}$; vertices: H, K, J, and L **59.** −1 **61.** −7 **63.** 25 **65.** 14 **67.** 10

Lesson 2-3

1. H: today is Friday; C: tomorrow is Saturday. **3.** H: two angles are supplementary; C: the sum of the measures of the angles is 180.

5 **hypothesis:** You are sixteen years old.
conclusion: You are eligible to drive.
statement in if-then form: If you are sixteen years old, then you are eligible to drive.

7. If the angle is acute, then its measure is between 0 and 90. **9a.** If moisture in the air condenses and falls, then it rains. **9b.** If a cumulonimbus cloud has supercooled moisture, then hail forms. **9c.** If the temperature is freezing in all or most of the atmosphere, then precipitation falls as snow. **11.** False; Charlotte, Michigan; The hypothesis of the conditional is true, but the conclusion is false. The counterexample shows that the conditional statement is false. **13.** False; the animal could be a leopard. The hypothesis of the conditional is true, but the conclusion is false. This counterexample shows that the conditional statement is false. **15.** True; the hypothesis is false, since pigs cannot fly. A conditional with a false hypothesis is always true, so this conditional statement is true. **17.** If a number is a whole number, then it is an integer. Converse: If a number is an integer, then it is a whole number. False; sample answer: −3. Inverse: If a number is not a whole number, then it is not an integer. False: sample answer: −3. Contrapositive: If a number is not an integer, then it is not a whole number; true. **19.** H: you lead; C: I will follow. **21.** H: two angles are vertical; C: they are congruent. **23.** H: there is no struggle; C: there is no progress. **25.** H: a convex polygon has five sides; C: it is a pentagon. **27.** If you were at the party, then you received a gift. **29.** If a figure is a circle, then the area is πr^2. **31.** If an angle is right, then the angle measures 90 degrees. **33.** If the museum is the Andy Warhol Museum, then most of the collection is Andy Warhol's artwork.

35 To show that a conditional is false, you need only to find one counterexample. 9 is an odd number, but not divisible by 5. The hypothesis of the conditional is true, but the conclusion is false. So, this counterexample shows that the conditional statement is false.

37. False; the angle drawn is an acute angle whose measure is not 45. The hypothesis of the conditional is true, but the conclusion is false. This counterexample shows that the conditional statement is false. **39.** True; when this hypothesis is true, the conclusion is also true, since an angle and its complement's sum is 90. So, the conditional statement is true. **41.** True; the hypothesis is false, since red and blue paint make purple paint. A conditional with a false hypothesis is always true, so this conditional statement is true. **43.** False; the animal could be a falcon. The hypothesis of the conditional is true, but the conclusion is false. This counterexample shows that the conditional statement is false. **45.** False; these lines intersect, but do not form right angles. The hypothesis of the conditional is true, but the conclusion is false. This counterexample shows that the conditional statement is false.

47. Converse: If you live in Illinois, then you live in Chicago. False: You can live in Springfield. Inverse: If you do not live in Chicago, then you do not live in Illinois. False: You can live in Springfield. Contrapositive: If you do not live in Illinois, then you do not live in Chicago; true. **49.** Converse: If two angles are congruent, then they have the same measure; true. Inverse: If two angles do not have the same measure, then the angles are not congruent; true. Contrapositive: If two angles are not congruent, then they do not have the same measure; true. **51.** If segments are congruent, then they have the same length. Converse: If segments have the same length, then they are congruent; true. Inverse: If segments are not congruent, then they do not have the same length; true. Contrapositive: If segments do not have the same length, then they are not congruent; true. **53.** If an animal has stripes, then it is a zebra; false: a tiger has stripes.

55 The inverse is formed by negating both the hypothesis and the conclusion of the conditional. Inverse: If an animal does not have stripes, then it is not a zebra. This is a true statement.

57a. Sample answer: If a compound is an acid, it contains hydrogen. If a compound is a base, it contains hydroxide. If a compound is a hydrocarbon, it contains only hydrogen and carbon. **57b.** Sample answer: If a compound contains hydrogen, it is an acid. False; a hydrocarbon contains hydrogen. If a compound contains hydroxide, it is a base; true. If a compound contains only hydrogen and carbon, it is a hydrocarbon; true.

59 The blue area of the Venn diagram includes nonlinear functions but not quadratic functions. So, if a function is nonlinear, it may or may not be a quadratic function. Therefore, the conditional is false.

61. True; the deciduous area and the evergreen area have no common areas, so a deciduous tree cannot be evergreen. **63.** Sample answer: Kiri; when the hypothesis of a conditional is false, the conditional is always true. **65.** True; since the conclusion is false, the converse of the statement must be true. The converse and inverse are logically equivalent, so the inverse is also true. **67.** The hypothesis q of the inverse statement is *I received a detention*. The conclusion p of the inverse statement is *I did not arrive at school on time*. So the conditional A is $p \to q$: If I did not arrive at school on time, then I recieved a detention. So the converse of statement A is $\sim p \to \sim q$: If I did arrive at school on time, then I did not receive a detention. The contrapositve of Statement A is $\sim q \to \sim p$: If I did not receive a detention, then I arrived at school on time. **69.** A **71.** 0.00462

73.

p	q	p and q
T	T	T
T	F	F
F	T	F
F	F	F

75.

p	q	$\sim p$	$\sim p \wedge q$
T	T	F	F
T	F	F	F
F	T	T	T
F	F	T	F

77. H, J, and K are noncollinear.

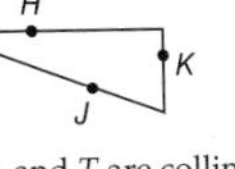

79. R, S, and T are collinear. **81.** $\overline{BC} \cong \overline{CD}$, $\overline{BE} \cong \overline{ED}$, $\overline{BA} \cong \overline{DA}$ **83.** about 9000 kg **85.** Divide each side by 8. **87.** Multiply each side by 3.

Lesson 2-4

1 Olivia is basing her conclusion on facts provided to her by her high school, not on a pattern of observations, so she is using deductive reasoning.

3. valid; Law of Detachment **5.** Invalid: Bayview could be inside or outside the public beach's circle.

Beaches

Public, Lifeguards

7. C **9.** No valid conclusion; $\angle 1$ and $\angle 2$ do not have to be vertical in order to be congruent. **11.** inductive reasoning **13.** deductive reasoning **15.** inductive reasoning

17 The given statement *Figure ABCD has four right angles* satisfies the conclusion of the true conditional. However, having a true conditional and a true conclusion does not make the hypothesis true. The figure could be a rectangle. So, the conclusion is invalid.

19. Invalid; your battery could be dead because it was old. **21.** valid; Law of Detachment **23.** Valid; Monday is outside of the days when the temperature drops below 32°F, so it cannot be inside the days when it snows circle either, so the conclusion is valid.

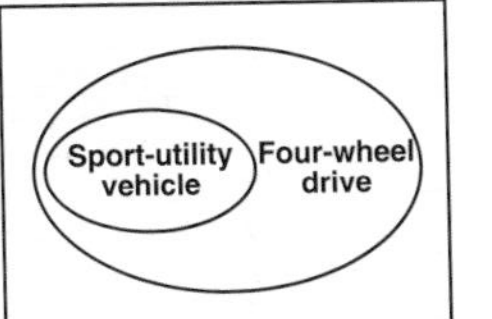

25. Invalid; Sabrina could be inside just the nurses' circle or inside the intersection of the circles, so the conclusion is invalid.

People who wear blue uniforms, Nurses, Sabrina?

27 The given statement *Ms. Rodriguez has just purchased a vehicle that has four-wheel drive* satisfies the conclusion of the true conditional. However, having a true conditional and a true conclusion does not make the hypothesis true. Ms. Rodriguez's car might be in the Four-wheel-drive section of the diagram that is not a sport-utility vehicle. So, the conclusion is invalid.

Sport-utility vehicle, Four-wheel drive

29. no valid conclusion **31.** no valid conclusion **33.** If two lines are not parallel, then they intersect in a point. **35.** Figure *ABCD* has all sides congruent; Law of Detachment.

37 You can reword the first given statement: If you are a ballet dancer, then you like classical music. Statement (1): If you are a ballet dancer, then you like classical music. Statement (2): If you like classical music, then you enjoy the opera. Since the conclusion of Statement (1) is the hypothesis of Statement (2), you can apply the Law of Syllogism. A valid conclusion: If you are a ballet dancer, then you enjoy the opera.

39. No valid conclusion; knowing a conclusion is true, does not imply the hypothesis will be true.

41a.

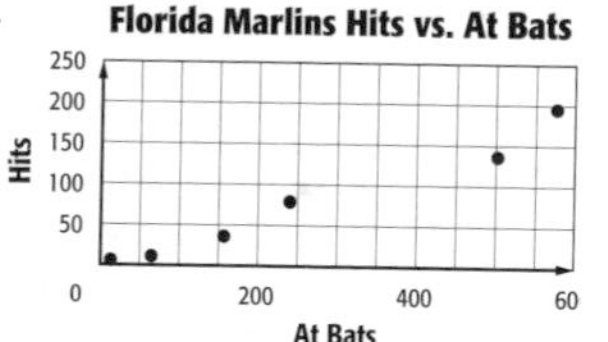

41b. Sample answer: About 91; inductive; a pattern was used to reach the conclusion. **41c.** Sample answer: The player with 240 at bats got more hits; deductive; the facts provided in the table were used to reach the conclusion. **43.** Law of Detachment: $[(p \rightarrow q) \wedge p] \rightarrow q$; Law of Syllogism: $[(p \rightarrow q) \wedge (q \rightarrow r)] \rightarrow (p \rightarrow r)$
45. Jonah's statement can be restated as, "Jonah is in group B and Janeka is in group B." In order for this compound statement to be true, both parts of the statement must be true. If Jonah was in group A, he would not be able to say that he is in group B, since students in group A must always tell the truth. Therefore the statement that Jonah is in group B is true. For the compound statement to be false, the statement that Janeka is in group B must be false. Therefore, Jonah is in group B and Janeka is in group A. **47.** D **49.** $\frac{26}{11}$
51a. If you live in Hawaii or Arizona then you do not observe Daylight Savings Time.
51b. If you do not observe Daylight Savings Time, then you live in Hawaii or Arizona; true.

53.

p	~p	q	~q	~p or ~q
T	F	T	F	F
T	F	F	T	T
F	T	T	F	T
F	T	F	T	T

55.

y	~y	z	~y or z
T	F	T	T
T	F	F	F
F	T	T	T
F	T	F	T

57. 18 **59.** Yes; the symbol denotes that $\angle DAB$ is a right angle. **61.** Yes; the sum of their measures is $m\angle ADC$, which is 90. **63.** No; we do not know $m\angle ABC$.

Lesson 2-5

1. The left side and front side have a common edge line *r*. Planes $\mathcal{P}$ and *Q* only intersect along line *r*. Postulate 2.7, which states if two planes intersect, then their intersection is a line. **3.** The front bottom edge of the figure is line *n* which contains points *D*, *C*, and *E*. Postulate 2.3, which states a line contains at least two points. **5.** Points *D* and *E*, which are on line *n*, lie in plane *Q*. Postulate 2.5, which states that if two points lie in a plane, then the entire line containing those points lies in that plane.

7 Postulate 2.7 states that if two planes intersect, then their intersection is a line. However, if three planes intersect, then their intersection may be a line or a point. So, the statement is sometimes true.

9. Always; Postulate 2.1 states through any two points, there is exactly one line. **11.** Postulate 2.3; a line contains at least two points. **13.** Postulate 2.4; a plane contains at least three noncollinear points. **15.** Since *C* is the midpoint of $\overline{AE}$ and $\overline{DB}$, $CA = CE = \frac{1}{2}AE$ and $CD = CB = \frac{1}{2}DB$ by the definition of midpoint. We are given $\overline{AE} \cong \overline{DB}$, so $AE = DB$ by the definition of congruent segments. By the multiplication property, $\frac{1}{2}DB = \frac{1}{2}AE$. So, by substitution, $AC = CB$. **17.** The edges of the sides of the bottom layer of the cake intersect. Plane $\mathcal{P}$ and *Q* of this cake intersect only once in line *m*. Postulate 2.7; if two planes intersect, then their intersection is a line. **19.** The top edge of the bottom layer of the cake is a straight line *n*. Points *C*, *D*, and *K* lie along this edge, so they lie along line *n*. Postulate 2.3; a line contains at least two points.

21 The bottom right part of the cake is a side. The side contains points *K*, *E*, *F*, and *G* and forms a plane. Postulate 2.2, which states that through any three noncollinear points, there is exactly one plane, shows that this is true.

23. The top edges of the bottom layer form intersecting lines. Lines *h* and *g* of this cake intersect only once at point *J*. Postulate 2.6; if two lines intersect, then their intersection is exactly one point. **25.** Never; Postulate 2.1 states through any two points, there is exactly one line. **27.** Always; Postulate 2.5 states if two points lie in a plane, then the entire line containing those points lies in that plane. **29.** Sometimes; the points must be noncollinear.

31. Given: *L* is the midpoint of $\overline{JK}$. $\overline{JK}$ intersects $\overline{MK}$ at *K*. $\overline{MK} \cong \overline{JL}$
Prove: $\overline{LK} \cong \overline{MK}$
Proof: We are given that *L* is the midpoint of $\overline{JK}$ and $\overline{MK} \cong \overline{JL}$. By the Midpoint Theorem, $\overline{JL} \cong \overline{LK}$. By the Transitive Property of Equality, $\overline{LK} \cong \overline{MK}$.

33a. Southside Blvd.; sample answer: Since there is a line between any two points, and Southside Blvd. is the line between point *A* and point *B*, it is the shortest route between the two. **33b.** I-295

35 Points *E*, *F*, and *G* lie along the same line. Postulate 2.3 states that a line contains at least two points.

37. Postulate 2.1; through any two points, there is exactly one line. **39.** Postulate 2.4; a plane contains at least three noncollinear points. **41.** Postulate 2.7; if two planes intersect, then their intersection is a line.

43a. A, B; A, B, C; A, B, C, D; A, B, C, D, E, F

43b.

Number of Computers	Number of Connections
2	1
3	3
4	6
5	10
6	15

43c. $n - 1$ **43d.** $\frac{n(n-1)}{2}$

45. Lisa is correct. Sample answer: The proof should begin with the given, which is that $\overline{AB}$ is congruent to $\overline{BD}$ and *A*, *B*, and *D* are collinear. Therefore, Lisa began the proof correctly. **47a.** Plane *Q* is perpendicular to plane $\mathcal{P}$. **47b.** Line *a* is perpendicular to plane $\mathcal{P}$. **49.** Sometimes; three coplanar lines may have 0, 1, 2, or 3 points of intersection, as shown in the figures below.

0 points 1 point 2 points 3 points

Postulates 2.1–2.5 were used. Through points *A* and *B* there is exactly one line, *n*, satisfying Postulate 2.1. For the noncollinear points *A*, *B*, and *C* there is exactly one plane, $\mathcal{P}$, satisfying Postulate 2.2. Line *n* contains points *A* and *B*, satisfying Postulate 2.3. Plane $\mathcal{P}$ contains the noncollinear points *A*, *B*, and *C*, satisfying Postulate 2.4. Line *n*, containing points *A* and *B*, lies entirely in plane $\mathcal{P}$, satisfying Postulate 2.5. **51.** A **53.** H
55. no conclusion **57.** If people are happy, then they rarely correct their faults. **59.** True; *M* is on $\overline{AB}$ and $AM + MB = AB$, so $p \wedge q$ is true. **61.** 19 m; 20 m of edging **63.** 5.5 **65.** 2, −2

Lesson 2-6

1. Trans. Prop. **3.** Sym. Prop.
5. Given: $\frac{y+2}{3} = 3$
Prove: $y = 7$
Proof:
Statements (Reasons)
a. $\frac{y+2}{3} = 3$ (Given)
b. $3\left(\frac{y+2}{3}\right) = 3(3)$ (Mult. Prop.)
c. $y + 2 = 9$ (Subst.)
d. $y = 7$ (Subt. Prop.)

7. Given: $\overline{AB} \cong \overline{CD}$
Prove: $x = 7$
Proof:
Statements (Reasons)
1. $\overline{AB} \cong \overline{CD}$ (Given)
2. $AB = CD$ (Def. of congruent segments)
3. $4x - 6 = 22$ (Subst. Prop.)
4. $4x = 28$ (Add. Prop.)
5. $x = 7$ (Div. Prop.)

9. Subt. Prop.

11
$4x - 5 = x + 12$ Original equation
$4x - 5 + 5 = x + 12 + 5$ Addition Property of Equality
$4x = x + 17$ Simplify.
If $4x - 5 = x + 12$, then $4x = x + 17$ by the Addition Property of Equality.

13. Dist. Prop. **15.** Trans. Prop.

17. Given: $\frac{8 - 3x}{4} = 32$
Prove: $x = -40$
Proof:
Statements (Reasons)
a. $\frac{8 - 3x}{4} = 32$ (Given)
b. $4\left(\frac{8 - 3x}{4}\right) = 4(32)$ (Mult. Prop.)
c. $8 - 3x = 128$ (Subst.)
d. $-3x = 120$ (Subt. Prop.)
e. $x = -40$ (Div. Prop.)

19. Given: $-\frac{1}{3}n = 12$
Prove: $n = -36$
Proof:
Statements (Reasons)
1. $-\frac{1}{3}n = 12$ (Given)
2. $-3\left(-\frac{1}{3}n\right) = -3(12)$ (Mult. Prop.)
3. $n = -36$ (Subst.)

21 **a.** Use properties of equality to justify each step in solving the equation for *a*.
Given: $d = vt + \frac{1}{2}at^2$
Prove: $a = \frac{2d - 2vt}{t^2}$
Proof:
Statements (Reasons)
1. $d = vt + \frac{1}{2}at^2$ (Given)
2. $d - vt = vt - vt + \frac{1}{2}at^2$ (Subtraction Property)
3. $d - vt = \frac{1}{2}at^2$ (Substitution)
4. $2(d - vt) = 2\left(\frac{1}{2}at^2\right)$ (Multiplication Property)

5. $2(d - vt) = at^2$ (Substitution)
6. $2d - 2vt = at^2$ (Distributive Property)
7. $\frac{2d - 2vt}{t^2} = \frac{at^2}{t^2}$ (Division Property)
8. $\frac{2d - 2vt}{t^2} = a$ (Substitution)
9. $a = \frac{2d - 2vt}{t^2}$ (Symmetric Property)

b. $a = \frac{2d - 2vt}{t^2}$ Given

$= \frac{2(2850) - 2(50)(30)}{30^2}$ $d = 2850, t = 30, v = 50$

$= 3$ Simplify.

The acceleration of the object is 3 ft/s^2. The Substitution Property of Equality justifies this calculation.

23. Given: $\overline{DF} \cong \overline{EG}$
Prove: $x = 10$
Proof:
Statements (Reasons)
1. $\overline{DF} \cong \overline{EG}$ (Given)
2. $DF = EG$ (Def. of ≅ segs)
3. $11 = 2x - 9$ (Subst.)
4. $20 = 2x$ (Add. Prop.)
5. $10 = x$ (Div. Prop.)
6. $x = 10$ (Symm. Prop.)

25 Use properties of equality and the definition of congruent angles to justify each step in proving $x = 100$.
Given: $\angle Y \cong \angle Z$
Prove: $x = 100$
Proof:
Statements (Reasons)
1. $\angle Y \cong \angle Z$ (Given)
2. $m\angle Y = m\angle Z$ (Definition of ≅ ∠s)
3. $x + 10 = 2x - 90$ (Substitution)
4. $10 = x - 90$ (Subtraction Property)
5. $100 = x$ (Addition Property)
6. $x = 100$ (Symmetric Property)

27a. Given: $V = \frac{P}{I}$
Prove: $\frac{V}{2} = \frac{P}{2I}$
Proof:
Statements (Reasons)
1. $V = \frac{P}{I}$ (Given)
2. $\frac{1}{2} \cdot V = \frac{1}{2} \cdot \frac{P}{I}$ (Mult. Prop.)
3. $\frac{V}{2} = \frac{P}{2I}$ (Mult. Prop.)

27b. Given: $V = \frac{P}{I}$
Prove: $2V = \frac{2P}{I}$
Proof:
Statements (Reasons)
1. $V = \frac{P}{I}$ (Given)
2. $2 \cdot V = 2 \cdot \frac{P}{I}$ (Mult. Prop)
3. $2V = \frac{2P}{I}$ (Mult. Prop.)

29. Given: $c^2 = a^2 + b^2$
Prove: $a = \sqrt{c^2 - b^2}$
Proof:
Statements (Reasons)
1. $a^2 + b^2 = c^2$ (Given)
2. $a^2 + b^2 - b^2 = c^2 - b^2$ (Subt. Prop.)
3. $a^2 = c^2 - b^2$ (Subs.)
4. $a = \pm\sqrt{c^2 - b^2}$ (Sq. Root Prop.)
5. $a = \sqrt{c^2 - b^2}$ (Length cannot be negative.)

31 The relation "is taller than" is not an equivalence relation because it fails the Reflexive and Symmetric properties. You cannot be taller than yourself (reflexive); if you are taller than your friend, then it does not imply that your friend is taller than you (symmetric).

33. The relation "≠" is not an equivalence relation because it fails the Reflexive Property, since $a \neq a$ is not true. **35.** The relation "≈" is not an equivalence relation because it fails the Reflexive Property, since $a \approx a$ is not true.

37. Given: $AP = 2x + 3$, $PB = \frac{3x + 1}{2}$, $AB = 10.5$
Prove: $\frac{AP}{AB} = \frac{2}{3}$

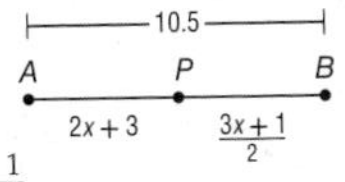

Proof:
Statements (Reasons)
1. $AP = 2x + 3$, $PB = \frac{3x + 1}{2}$, $AB = 10.5$ (Given)
2. $AP + PB = AB$ (Def. of a segment)
3. $2x + 3 + \frac{3x + 1}{2} = 10.5$ (Subt.)
4. $2 \cdot \left(2x + 3 + \frac{3x + 1}{2}\right) = 2 \cdot 10.5$ (Mult. Prop.)
5. $2 \cdot \left(2x + 3 + \frac{3x + 1}{2}\right) = 21$ (Subst.)
6. $2 \cdot 2x + 2 \cdot 3 + 2 \cdot \frac{3x + 1}{2} = 21$ (Dist. Prop.)
7. $4x + 6 + 3x + 1 = 21$ (Mult. Prop.)
8. $7x + 7 = 21$ (Add. Prop.)
9. $7x + 7 - 7 = 21 - 7$ (Subt. Prop.)
10. $7x = 14$ (Subs.)
11. $x = 2$ (Div. Prop.)
12. $AP = 2(2) + 3$ (Subst.)
13. $AP = 4 + 3$ (Mult. Prop.)
14. $AP = 7$ (Add. Prop.)
15. $\frac{AP}{AB} = \frac{7}{10.5}$ (Subst.)
16. $\frac{AP}{AB} = 0.\overline{6}$ (Div. Prop.)
17. $\frac{2}{3} = 0.\overline{6}$ (Div. Prop.)
18. $\frac{AP}{AB} = \frac{2}{3}$ (Trans. Prop.)

39. Sometimes; sample answer: If $a^2 = 1$ and $a = 1$, then $b = \sqrt{1}$ or 1. The statement is also true if $a = -1$, then $b = 1$. If $b = 1$, then $\sqrt{b} = 1$ since the square root of a number is nonnegative. Therefore, the statement is sometimes true. **41.** Sample answer: Depending on the purpose of the proof, one format may be preferable to another. For example, when writing an informal proof, you could use a paragraph proof to quickly convey your reasoning. When writing a more formal proof, a two-column proof may be preferable so that the justifications for each step are organized and easy to follow. **43.** 83° **45.** E **47.** Never; the sum of the measure of two supplementary angles is 180, so two obtuse angles can never be supplementary. **49.** Yes, by the Law of Detachment. **51.** (4, −3) **53.** (1, 2) **55.** (−1, −1) **57.** 2.4 cm

Lesson 2-7

1. Given: $\overline{LK} \cong \overline{NM}$, $\overline{KJ} \cong \overline{MJ}$
Prove: $\overline{LJ} \cong \overline{NJ}$
Proof:
Statements (Reasons)
a. $\overline{LK} \cong \overline{NM}$, $\overline{KJ} \cong \overline{MJ}$ (Given)
b. $LK = NM$, $KJ = MJ$ (Def. of ≅ segs.)
c. $LK + KJ = NM + MJ$ (Add. Prop.)
d. $LJ = LK + KJ$; $NJ = NM + MJ$ (Seg. Add. Post.)
e. $LJ = NJ$ (Subst.)
f. $\overline{LJ} \cong \overline{NJ}$ (Def. of ≅ segs.)

3 Use the definition of congruent segments and the Substitution Property of Equality.
Given: $\overline{AR} \cong \overline{CR}$; $\overline{DR} \cong \overline{BR}$
Prove: $AR + DR \cong CR + BR$
Proof:
Statements (Reasons)
1. $\overline{AR} \cong \overline{CR}$, $\overline{DR} \cong \overline{BR}$ (Given)
2. $AR = CR$, $DR = BR$ (Definition of ≅ segments)
3. $AR + DR = AR + BR$ (Addition Property)
4. $AR + DR = CR + BR$ (Substitution Property)

5. Given: $\overline{AB} \cong \overline{CD}$, $AB + CD = EF$
Prove: $2AB = EF$
Proof:
Statements (Reasons)
1. $\overline{AB} \cong \overline{CD}$, $AB + CD = EF$ (Given)
2. $AB = CD$ (Def. of ≅ segs.)
3. $AB + AB = EF$ (Subst.)
4. $2AB = EF$ (Subst.)

7 Use the Reflexive Property of Equality and the definition of congruent segments.
Given: $\overline{AB}$
Prove: $\overline{AB} \cong \overline{AB}$
Proof:
Statements (Reasons)
1. $\overline{AB}$ (Given)
2. $AB = AB$ (Reflexive Property)
3. $\overline{AB} \cong \overline{AB}$ (Definition of ≅ segments)

9. Given: $\overline{SC} \cong \overline{HR}$ and $\overline{HR} \cong \overline{AB}$
Prove: $\overline{SC} \cong \overline{AB}$
Proof:
Statements (Reasons)
1. $\overline{SC} \cong \overline{HR}$ and $\overline{HR} \cong \overline{AB}$ (Given)
2. $SC = HR$ and $HR = AB$ (Def. of ≅ segs.)
3. $SC = AB$ (Trans. Prop.)
4. $\overline{SC} \cong \overline{AB}$ (Def. of ≅ segs.)

11. Given: E is the midpoint of $\overline{DF}$ and $\overline{CD} \cong \overline{FG}$.
Prove: $\overline{CE} \cong \overline{EG}$
Proof:
Statements (Reasons)
1. E is the midpoint of $\overline{DF}$ and $\overline{CD} \cong \overline{FG}$. (Given)
2. $DE = EF$ (Def. of midpoint)
3. $CD = FG$ (Def. of ≅ segs.)
4. $CD + DE = EF + FG$ (Add. Prop.)
5. $CE = CD + DE$ and $EG = EF + FG$ (Seg. Add. Post.)
6. $CE = EG$ (Subst.)
7. $\overline{CE} \cong \overline{EG}$ (Def. of ≅ segs.)

13a. Given: $\overline{AC} \cong \overline{GI}$, $\overline{FE} \cong \overline{LK}$, $AC + CF + FE = GI + IL + LK$
Prove: $\overline{CF} \cong \overline{IL}$
Proof:
Statements (Reasons)
1. $\overline{AC} \cong \overline{GI}$, $\overline{FE} \cong \overline{LK}$, $AC + CF + FE = GI + IL + LK$ (Given)
2. $AC + CF + FE = AC + IL + LK$ (Subst.)
3. $AC - AC + CF + FE = AC - AC + IL + LK$ (Subt. Prop.)
4. $CF + FE = IL + LK$ (Subst.)
5. $CF + FE = IL + FE$ (Subs.)
6. $CF + FE - FE = IL + FE - FE$ (Subt. Prop.)
7. $CF = IL$ (Subst.)
8. $\overline{CF} \cong \overline{IL}$ (Def. of ≅ segs.)

13b. Sample answer: I measured $\overline{CF}$ and $\overline{IL}$, and both were 1.5 inches long, so the two segments are congruent.

15 **a.** Use the definition of midpoint and the segment addition postulate to prove.
Given: $\overline{SH} \cong \overline{TF}$; P is the midpoint of $\overline{SH}$ and $\overline{TF}$.
Prove: $\overline{SP} \cong \overline{TP}$
Proof:
Statements (Reasons)
1. $\overline{SH} \cong \overline{TF}$, P is the midpoint of $\overline{SH}$, P is the midpoint of $\overline{TF}$. (Given)
2. $SH = TF$ (Definition of ≅ segments)
3. $SP = PH$, $TP = PF$ (Definition of midpoint)
4. $SH = SP + PH$, $TF = TP + PF$ (Segment Addition Postulate)
5. $SP + PH = TP + PF$ (Substitution)
6. $SP + SP = TP + TP$ (Substitution)
7. $2SP = 2TP$ (Substitution)
8. $SP = TP$ (Division Property)
9. $\overline{SP} \cong \overline{TP}$ (Definition of ≅ segments)

b. $SP = \frac{1}{2}SH$ Definition of midpoint

$= \frac{1}{2}(127.3)$ or 63.54 Substitution

Since $\overline{TF} \cong \overline{SH}$, then $FP = SP = 63.54$.

Since $\triangle SPF$ is a right triangle, use the Pythagorean Theorem to find SF, the distance from first base to second base.

$c^2 = a^2 + b^2$ Pythagorean Theorem
$SF^2 = SP^2 + FP^2$ Substitution
$SF^2 = 63.54^2 + 63.54^2$ Substitution

$SF^2 \approx 8074.6632$	Simplify.
$SF \approx 90$	Take the positive square root of each side.

The distance from first base to second base is about 90 feet.

17. Neither; since $\overline{AB} \cong \overline{CD}$ and $\overline{CD} \cong \overline{BF}$, then $\overline{AB} \cong \overline{BF}$ by the Transitive Property of Congruence. **19.** No; congruence refers to segments. Segments cannot be added, only the measures of segments. **21.** A B C D (2 in.) **23.** D **25.** 18

27. Given: $AC = DF$, $AB = DE$
Prove: $BC = EF$
Proof:
<u>**Statements (Reasons)**</u>
1. $AC = DF$, $AB = DE$ (Given)
2. $AC = AB + BC$; $DF = DE + EF$ (Seg. Add. Post.)
3. $AB + BC = DE + EF$ (Subst.)
4. $BC = EF$ (Subt. Prop.)

29. 60, 30, 90, 60, 120, 60 **31.** $9\sqrt{2}$ **33.** $3y^4\sqrt{5x}$ **35.** 8

Lesson 2-8

1 $m\angle 1 = 90$ because $\angle 1$ is a right angle.

$m\angle 2 + m\angle 3 = 90$	Complement Theorem
$26 + m\angle 3 = 90$	$m\angle 2 = 26$
$26 + m\angle 3 - 26 = 90 - 26$	Subtraction Property
$m\angle 3 = 64$	Substitution

3. $m\angle 4 = 114$, $m\angle 5 = 66$; Suppl. Thm.

5. Given: $\angle 2 \cong \angle 6$
Prove: $\angle 4 \cong \angle 8$
Proof:
<u>**Statements (Reasons)**</u>
1. $\angle 2 \cong \angle 6$ (Given)
2. $m\angle 2 + m\angle 4 = 180$, $m\angle 6 + m\angle 8 = 180$ (Suppl. Thm.)
3. $m\angle 2 + m\angle 8 = 180$ (Subst.)
4. $m\angle 2 - m\angle 2 + m\angle 4 = 180 - m\angle 2$, $m\angle 2 - m\angle 2 + m\angle 8 = 180 - m\angle 2$ (Subt. Prop.)
5. $m\angle 4 = 180 - m\angle 2$, $m\angle 8 = 180 - m\angle 2$ (Subt. Prop.)
6. $m\angle 4 = m\angle 8$ (Subst.)
7. $\angle 4 \cong \angle 8$ (Def. $\cong$ ∡)

7. Given: $\angle 4 \cong \angle 7$
Prove: $\angle 5 \cong \angle 6$
Proof:
<u>**Statements (Reasons)**</u>
1. $\angle 4 \cong \angle 7$ (Given)
2. $\angle 4 \cong \angle 5$ and $\angle 6 \cong \angle 7$ (Vert. ∡ Thm.)
3. $\angle 7 \cong \angle 5$ (Subst.)
4. $\angle 5 \cong \angle 6$ (Subst.)

9. $m\angle 3 = 62$, $m\angle 1 = m\angle 4 = 45$ ($\cong$ Comp. and Suppl. Thm.) **11.** $m\angle 9 = 156$, $m\angle 10 = 24$ ($\cong$ Suppl. Thm.)

13

$m\angle 6 + m\angle 7 = 180$	Supplement Thm.
$2x - 21 + 3x - 34 = 180$	Substitution
$5x - 55 = 180$	Substitution
$5x - 55 + 55 = 180 + 55$	Addition Property
$5x = 235$	Substitution
$\frac{5x}{5} = \frac{235}{5}$	Division Property
$x = 47$	Substitution
$m\angle 6 = 2x - 21$	Given
$m\angle 6 = 2(47) - 21$ or 73	Substitution
$m\angle 7 = 3x - 34$	Given
$m\angle 7 = 3(47) - 34$ or 107	Substitution
$\angle 8 \cong \angle 6$	Vertical Angles Theorem
$m\angle 8 = m\angle 6$	Definition of $\cong$ ∡
$= 73$	Substitution

15. Given: $\angle 5 \cong \angle 6$
Prove: $\angle 4$ and $\angle 6$ are supplementary.
Proof:
<u>**Statements (Reasons)**</u>
1. $\angle 5 \cong \angle 6$ (Given)
2. $m\angle 5 = m\angle 6$ (Def. of $\cong$ ∡)
3. $\angle 4$ and $\angle 5$ are supplementary. (Def. of linear pairs)
4. $m\angle 4 + m\angle 5 = 180$ (Def. of ∡)
5. $m\angle 4 + m\angle 6 = 180$ (Subst.)
6. $\angle 4$ and $\angle 6$ are supplementary. (Def. of ∡)

17. Given: $\angle ABC$ is a right angle.
Prove: $\angle 1$ and $\angle 2$ are complementary angles.
Proof:
<u>**Statements (Reasons)**</u>
1. $\angle ABC$ is a right angle. (Given)
2. $m\angle ABC = 90$ (Def. of rt. ∡)
3. $m\angle ABC = m\angle 1 + m\angle 2$ ($\angle$ Add. Post.)
4. $90 = m\angle 1 + m\angle 2$ (Subst.)
5. $\angle 1$ and $\angle 2$ are complementary angles. (Def. of comp. ∡)

19. Given: $\angle 1 \cong \angle 2$, $\angle 2 \cong \angle 3$
Prove: $\angle 1 \cong \angle 3$
Proof:
<u>**Statements (Reasons)**</u>
1. $\angle 1 \cong \angle 2$, $\angle 2 \cong \angle 3$ (Given)
2. $m\angle 1 = m\angle 2$, $m\angle 2 = m\angle 3$ (Def. of $\cong$ ∡)
3. $m\angle 1 = m\angle 3$ (Trans. Prop.)
4. $\angle 1 \cong \angle 3$ (Def. of $\cong$ ∡)

21. Given: $\angle 1 \cong \angle 4$
Prove: $\angle 2 \cong \angle 3$
Proof:
<u>**Statements (Reasons)**</u>
1. $\angle 1 \cong \angle 4$ (Given)
2. $\angle 1 \cong \angle 2$, $\angle 3 \cong \angle 4$ (Vert. ∡ are $\cong$.)
3. $\angle 1 \cong \angle 3$ (Trans. Prop.)
4. $\angle 2 \cong \angle 3$ (Subst.)

23. Given: $\angle 1$ and $\angle 2$ are rt. ∡.
Prove: $\angle 1 \cong \angle 2$
Proof:
<u>**Statements (Reasons)**</u>
1. $\angle 1$ and $\angle 2$ are rt. ∡. (Given)
2. $m\angle 1 = 90$, $m\angle 2 = 90$ (Def. of rt. ∡)
3. $m\angle 1 = m\angle 2$ (Subst.)
4. $\angle 1 \cong \angle 2$ (Def. of $\cong$ ∡)

25. Given: $\angle 1 \cong \angle 2$, $\angle 1$ and $\angle 2$ are supplementary.
Prove: $\angle 1$ and $\angle 2$ are rt. ∡.
Proof:
<u>**Statements (Reasons)**</u>
1. $\angle 1 \cong \angle 2$, $\angle 1$ and $\angle 2$ are supplementary. (Given)
2. $m\angle 1 + m\angle 2 = 180$ (Def. of supp. ∡)
3. $m\angle 1 = m\angle 2$ (Def. of $\cong$ ∡)
4. $m\angle 1 + m\angle 1 = 180$ (Subst.)
5. $2(m\angle 1) = 180$ (Subst.)
6. $m\angle 1 = 90$ (Div. Prop.)
7. $m\angle 2 = 90$ (Subst. (steps 3, 6))
8. $\angle 1$ and $\angle 2$ are rt. ∡. (Def. of rt. ∡)

27. Since the path of the pendulum forms a right angle, $\angle ABC$ is a right angle, or measures 90. $\overrightarrow{BR}$ divides $\angle ABC$ into $\angle ABR$ and $\angle CBR$. By the Angle Addition Postulate, $m\angle ABR + m\angle CBR = m\angle ABC$, and, using substitution, $m\angle ABR + m\angle CBR = 90$. Substituting again, $m\angle 1 + m\angle 2 = 90$. We are given that $m\angle 1$ is 45°, so, substituting, $45 + m\angle 2 = 90$. Using the Subtraction Property, $45 - 45 + m\angle 2 = 90 - 45$, or $m\angle 2 = 45$. Since $m\angle 1$ and $m\angle 2$ are equal, $\overrightarrow{BR}$ is the bisector of $\angle ABC$ by the definition of angle bisector.

29 To prove lines ℓ and m are perpendicular, show that $\angle 1$, $\angle 3$, and $\angle 4$ are right ∡.
Given: $\angle 2$ is a right angle.
Prove: $\ell \perp m$
Proof:
<u>**Statements (Reasons)**</u>
1. $\angle 2$ is a right angle. (Given)
2. $m\angle 2 = 90$ (Definition of a rt. $\angle$)
3. $\angle 2 \cong \angle 3$ (Vert. ∡ are $\cong$.)
4. $m\angle 3 = 90$ (Substitution)
5. $m\angle 1 + m\angle 2 = 180$ (Supplement Theorem)
6. $m\angle 1 + 90 = 180$ (Substitution)
7. $m\angle 1 + 90 - 90 = 180 - 90$ (Subtraction Property)
8. $m\angle 1 = 90$ (Substitution)
9. $\angle 1 \cong \angle 4$ (Vertical ∡ are $\cong$.)
10. $\angle 4 \cong \angle 1$ (Symmetric Property)
11. $m\angle 4 = m\angle 1$ (Definition of $\cong$ ∡)
12. $m\angle 4 = 90$ (Substitution)
13. $\ell \perp m$ ($\perp$ lines intersect to form four rt. ∡.)

31. Given: $\overrightarrow{XZ}$ bisects $\angle WXY$, and $m\angle WXZ = 45$.
Prove: $\angle WXY$ is a right angle.
Proof:
<u>**Statements (Reasons)**</u>
1. $\overrightarrow{XZ}$ bisects $\angle WXY$ and $m\angle WXZ = 45$. (Given)
2. $\angle WXZ \cong \angle ZXY$ (Def. of $\angle$ bisector)
3. $m\angle WXZ = m\angle ZXY$ (Def. of $\cong$ ∡)
4. $m\angle ZXY = 45$ (Subst.)
5. $m\angle WXY = m\angle WXZ + m\angle ZXY$ ($\angle$ Add. Post.)
6. $m\angle WXY = 45 + 45$ (Subst.)
7. $m\angle WXY = 90$ (Subst.)
8. $\angle WXY$ is a right angle. (Def. of rt. ∡)

33. Each of these theorems uses the words "or to congruent angles" indicating that this case of the theorem must also be proven true. The other proofs only addressed the "to the same angle" case of the theorem.

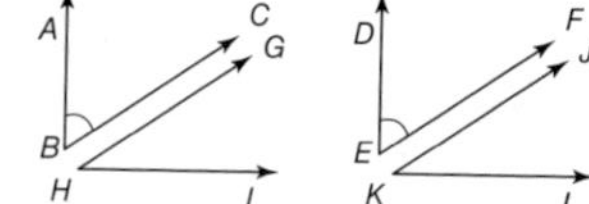

Given: $\angle ABC \cong \angle DEF$, $\angle GHI$ is complementary to $\angle ABC$, $\angle JKL$ is complementary to $\angle DEF$.
Prove: $\angle GHI \cong \angle JKL$
Proof:
<u>**Statements (Reasons)**</u>
1. $\angle ABC \cong \angle DEF$, $\angle GHI$ is complementary to $\angle ABC$, $\angle JKL$ is complementary to $\angle DEF$. (Given)
2. $m\angle ABC + m\angle GHI = 90$, $\angle DEF + \angle JKL = 90$ (Def. of compl. ∡)
3. $m\angle ABC + m\angle JKL = 90$ (Subst.)
4. $90 = m\angle ABC + m\angle JKL$ (Symm. Prop.)
5. $m\angle ABC + m\angle GHI = m\angle ABC + m\angle JKL$ (Trans. Prop.)
6. $m\angle ABC - m\angle ABC + m\angle GHI = m\angle ABC - m\angle ABC + m\angle JKL$ (Subt.)
7. $m\angle GHI = m\angle JKL$ (Subst.)
8. $\angle GHI \cong \angle JKL$ (Def. of $\cong$ ∡)

Given: $\angle ABC \cong \angle DEF$, $\angle GHI$ is supplementary to $\angle ABC$, $\angle JKL$ is supplementary to $\angle DEF$.
Prove: $\angle GHI \cong \angle JKL$
Proof:
<u>**Statements (Reasons)**</u>
1. $\angle ABC \cong \angle DEF$, $\angle GHI$ is supplementary to $\angle ABC$, $\angle JKL$ is supplementary to $\angle DEF$. (Given)
2. $m\angle ABC + m\angle GHI = 180$, $m\angle DEF + m\angle JKL = 180$ (Def. of suppl. ∡)
3. $m\angle ABC + m\angle JKL = 180$ (Subst.)
4. $180 = m\angle ABC + m\angle JKL$ (Symm. Property)
5. $m\angle ABC + m\angle GHI = m\angle ABC + m\angle JKL$ (Trans. Prop.)
6. $m\angle ABC - m\angle ABC + m\angle GHI = m\angle ABC - m\angle ABC + m\angle JKL$ (Subt.)
7. $m\angle GHI = m\angle JKL$ (Subst.)
8. $\angle GHI \cong \angle JKL$ (Def. of $\cong$ ∡)

35. Sample answer: Since protractors have the scale for both acute and obtuse angles along the top, the supplement is the measure of the given angle on the other scale. **37.** A **39.** B **41.** Subtratcion Prop. **43.** Substitution **45.** true **47.** true **49.** line n **51.** point W **53.** Yes; it intersects both m and n when all three lines are extended.

Chapter 2 Study Guide and Review

1. false; theorem **3.** true **5.** true **7.** true **9.** false; negation **11.** false; two nonadjacent supplementary angles **13.** Sample answer: Dogs or other pets may threaten or chase wildlife that might not be present in his local park. **15.** A plane contains at least three

noncollinear points and the sum of the measures of two complementary angles is not 180; true.
17a. 18 **17b.** 14 **17c.** 22 **19.** true **21.** *PQRS* is a parallelogram; Law of Detachment. **23.** valid; Law of Detachment **25.** Sometimes; if the three points are collinear, they will be contained in multiple planes, but if they are noncollinear, they will be contained in only one plane. **27.** Sometimes; if the angles are adjacent, they will form a right angle, but if they are not adjacent, they will not. **29.** Symmetric
31. Distributive Property **33.** Transitive Property
35. **Statements (Reasons)**
1. $PQ = RS$, $PQ = 5x + 9$, $RS = x - 31$ (Given)
2. $5x + 9 = x - 31$ (Subst.)
3. $4x = 9 = -31$ (Subt.)
4. $4x = -40$ (Subt. Prop.)
5. $x = -10$ (Div. Prop.)

37. **Statements (Reasons)**
1. X is the midpoint of $\overline{WX}$ and $\overline{VZ}$. (Given)
2. $\overline{WX} \cong \overline{YX}$, $\overline{VX} \cong \overline{ZX}$ (Def. of midpoint)
3. $WX = YX$, $VX = ZX$ (Def. of $\cong$)
4. $VX = VW = WX$, $ZX = ZY + YX$ (Seg. Add. Post.)
5. $VW + WX = ZY + YX$ (Subs.)
6. $VW = ZY$ (Subt. Prop.)

39. Segment Addition Postulate **41.** 127
43. **Statements (Reasons)**
1. $\angle 1 \cong \angle 4$, $\angle 2 \cong \angle 3$ (Given)
2. $m\angle 1 = m\angle 4$, $m\angle 2 = m\angle 3$ (Def. of $\cong$)
3. $m\angle 1 + m\angle 2 = m\angle 3 + m\angle 4$ (Add. Prop.)
4. $m\angle 1 + m\angle 2 = m\angle AFC$, $m\angle 3 + m\angle 4 = m\angle EFC$ ($\angle$ Add. Post.)
5. $m\angle AFC = m\angle EFC$ (Subst.)
6. $\angle AFC = \angle EFC$ (Def. of $\cong$)

CHAPTER 3
Parallel and Perpendicular Lines

Chapter 3 Get Ready

1. 4 **3.** Yes, points C and D lie in plane *CBD*.
5. 142 **7.** 90 **9.** −1 **11.** $\frac{1}{3}$

Lesson 3-1

1. *TUV* **3.** $\overline{YX}, \overline{TU}, \overline{ZW}$
5 Angle $\angle 1$ and $\angle 8$ are nonadjacent exterior angles that lie on opposite sides of the transversal. So, they are alternate exterior angles.
7. alternate interior **9.** line *n*; corresponding
11. line *m*; consecutive interior **13.** $\overline{CL}, \overline{EN}, \overline{BK}, \overline{AJ}$
15 The segments that do not intersect $\overline{BC}$ and are not in the same plane as $\overline{BC}$ are skew to $\overline{BC}$. Any of the following are skew to $\overline{BC}$: $\overline{EN}, \overline{AJ}, \overline{DM}, \overline{NM}, \overline{NJ}, \overline{JK}$, or $\overline{ML}$.
17. $\overline{KL}, \overline{CL}, \overline{BK}, \overline{ML}, \overline{DM}, \overline{NM}, \overline{KJ}$ **19.** $\overline{JK}$ **21.** line *s*; corresponding **23.** line *t*; alternate interior **25.** line *t*; alternate exterior **27.** line *t*; consecutive interior
29. line *s*; alternate exterior **31.** line *a*; vertical
33. line *c*; alternate interior **35.** line *f*; corresponding
37a. Sample answer: Since the lines are coplanar and they cannot touch, they are parallel. **37b.** Line *q* is a transversal of lines *p* and *m*. **39.** skew **41.** parallel
43. intersecting
45 **a.** The treads, or the upper horizontal parts of the stairs, are parallel. **b.** The treads of the two steps at the top of the incline lie in the same plane. So, they are coplanar. **c.** The treads of the steps on the incline of the escalator do not intersect and are not parallel to the treads of the steps on the bottom of the conveyor. So, they are skew.
47a.

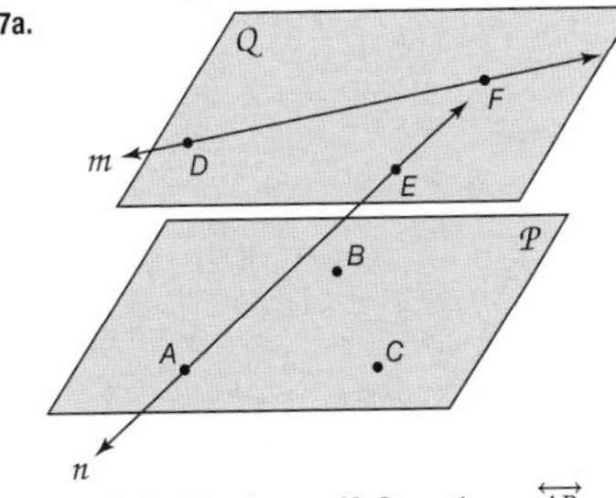

47b. parallel **47c.** skew **49.** Sometimes; $\overleftrightarrow{AB}$ intersects $\overleftrightarrow{EF}$ depending on where the planes intersect. **51.** B **53.** (0, 4), (−6, 0) **55.** $m\angle 9 = 86$, $m\angle 10 = 94$ **57.** $m\angle 19 = 140$, $m\angle 20 = 40$
59. 3.75 **61.** 90 **63.** 45

Lesson 3-2

1. 94; Corresponding Angle Postulate **3.** 86; Corresponding Angle Postulate and Supplement Angle Theorem **5.** 79; Vertical Angle Theorem, Consecutive Interior Angles Theorem **7.** $m\angle 2 = 93$, $m\angle 3 = 87$, $m\angle 4 = 87$ **9.** $x = 114$ by the Alternate Exterior Angles Theorem **11.** 62; Corresponding Angles Postulate **13.** 118; Def. of Supplementary Angles **15.** 38; Corresponding Angles Postulate **17.** 142; Supplement Angles Theorem **19.** 38; Alternate Exterior Angles Postulate
21 If the radiation rays form parallel lines, then $\angle 1$ and $\angle 3$ are corresponding angles. So, according to the Corresponding Angles Postulate, $\angle 1$ and $\angle 3$ are congruent.
23. Supplementary; since $\angle 3$ and $\angle 5$ are a linear pair, they are supplementary. $\angle 4$ and $\angle 5$ are congruent because they are alternate exterior angles, so $\angle 3$ is supplementary to $\angle 4$.
25 $3x - 15 = 105$ Corresponding Angles Postulate
$3x = 120$ Add 15 to each side.
$x = 40$ Divide each side by 3.
$(3x - 15) + (y + 25) = 180$ Supplement Theorem
$105 + y + 25 = 180$ Substitution
$y + 130 = 180$ Simplify.
$y = 50$ Subtract 130 from each side.
So, $x = 40$ by the Corresponding Angles Postulate; $y = 50$ by the Supplement Theorem.
27. $x = 42$ by the Consecutive Interior Angles Theorem; $y = 14$ by the Consecutive Interior Angles Theorem
29. $x = 60$ by the Consecutive Interior Angles Theorem; $y = 10$ by the Supplement Theorem **31.** Congruent; Alternate Interior Angles **33.** Congruent; vertical angles are congruent.
35. **Given:** $\ell \parallel m$
Prove: $\angle 1 \cong \angle 8$
$\angle 2 \cong \angle 7$
Proof:
Statements (Reasons)
1. $\ell \parallel m$ (Given)
2. $\angle 1 \cong \angle 5$, $\angle 2 \cong \angle 6$ (Corr. ∠s Post.)
3. $\angle 5 \cong \angle 8$, $\angle 6 \cong \angle 7$ (Vertical ∠s Thm.)
4. $\angle 1 \cong \angle 8$, $\angle 2 \cong \angle 7$ (Trans. Prop.)

37. **Given:** $m \parallel n$, $t \perp m$
Prove: $t \perp n$
Proof:
Statements (Reasons)
1. $m \parallel n$, $t \perp m$ (Given)
2. $\angle 1$ is a right angle. (Def. of $\perp$)
3. $m\angle 1 = 90$ (Def. of rt. ∠s)
4. $\angle 1 \cong \angle 2$ (Corr. ∠s Post.)
5. $m\angle 1 = m\angle 2$ (Def. of ≅ ∠s)
6. $m\angle 2 = 90$ (Subst.)
7. $\angle 2$ is a right angle. (Def. of rt. ∠s)
8. $t \perp n$ (Def. of $\perp$ lines)

39 Draw a line parallel to the two given lines and label angles 1, 2, 3, and 4. So, $x = m\angle 2 + m\angle 3$.

$m\angle 1 = 105$ because vertical angles are congruent and their measures are equal. $\angle 1$ and $\angle 2$ are supplementary by the Consecutive Interior Angles Theorem.
$m\angle 1 + m\angle 2 = 180$ Definition of supplementary angles
$105 + m\angle 2 = 180$ Substitution
$m\angle 2 = 75$ Subtract 105 from each side.
$m\angle 4 = 125$ because vertical angles are congruent and their measures are equal. $\angle 3$ and $\angle 4$ are supplementary by the Consecutive Interior Angles Theorem.
$m\angle 3 + m\angle 4 = 180$ Definition of supplementary angles
$m\angle 3 + 125 = 180$ Substitution
$m\angle 3 = 55$ Subtract 125 from each side.
$m\angle 2 + m\angle 3 = x$ Angle Addition Postulate
$75 + 55 = x$ Substitution
$130 = x$ Simplify.
41a. Sample answer for *m* and *n*:

41b. Sample answer:

$m\angle 1$	$m\angle 2$	$m\angle 3$	$m\angle 4$
60	120	60	120
45	135	45	135
70	110	70	110
90	90	90	90
25	155	25	155

41c. Sample answer: Angles on the exterior of a pair of parallel lines located on the same side of the transversal are supplementary. **41d.** Inductive; a pattern was used to make a conjecture.
41e. **Given:** parallel lines *m* and *n* cut by transversal *t*
Prove: $\angle 1$ and $\angle 4$ are supplementary.
Proof:
Statements (Reasons)
1. Lines *m* and *n* are parallel and cut by transversal *t*. (Given)
2. $m\angle 1 + m\angle 2 = 180$ (Suppl. Thm.)
3. $\angle 2 \cong \angle 4$ (Corr. ∠s are ≅.)
4. $m\angle 2 = m\angle 4$ (Def. of congruence)
5. $m\angle 1 + m\angle 4 = 180$ (Subst.)
6. $\angle 1$ and $\angle 4$ are supplementary. (Definition of supplementary angles)

43. In both theorems, a pair of angles is formed when two parallel lines are cut by a transversal. However, in the Alternate Interior Angles Theorem, each pair of alternate interior angles that is formed are congruent, whereas in the Consecutive Interior Angles Theorem, each pair of angles formed is supplementary.
45. $x = 171$ or $x = 155$; $y = 3$ or $y = 5$ **47.** C **49.** I and II **51.** Skew lines; the planes are flying in different directions and at different altitudes.
53. $m\angle 6 = 43$, $m\angle 7 = 90$ **55.** 15 **57.** $\frac{7}{3}$ **59.** 1
61. $-\frac{3}{5}$

Lesson 3-3

1. −1 **3.** $\frac{6}{5}$

(5) slope of $\overleftrightarrow{WX} = \frac{y_2 - y_1}{x_2 - x_1}$ Slope formula

$= \frac{5-4}{4-2}$ $(x_1, y_1) = (2, 4), (x_2, y_2) = (4, 5)$

$= \frac{1}{2}$ Simplify.

slope of $\overleftrightarrow{YZ} = \frac{y_2 - y_1}{x_2 - x_1}$ Slope formula

$= \frac{-7-1}{8-4}$ $(x_1, y_1) = (4, 1)$, $(x_2, y_2) = (8, -7)$

$= \frac{-8}{4}$ or −2 Simplify.

$\frac{1}{2}(-2) = -1$ Product of slopes

Since the product of the slopes is −1, $\overleftrightarrow{WX}$ is perpendicular to $\overleftrightarrow{YZ}$.

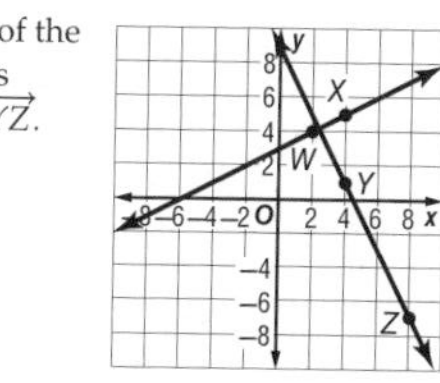
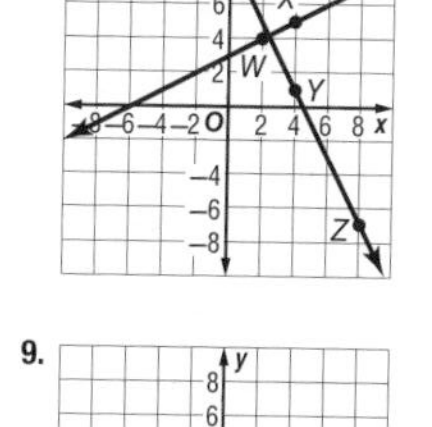

7. parallel

9.

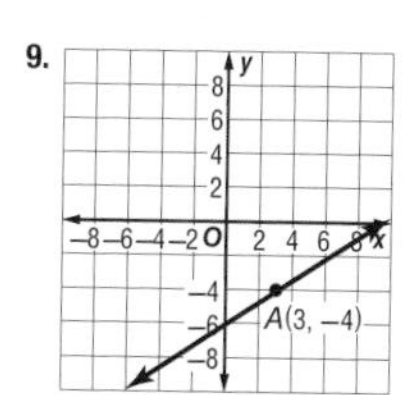
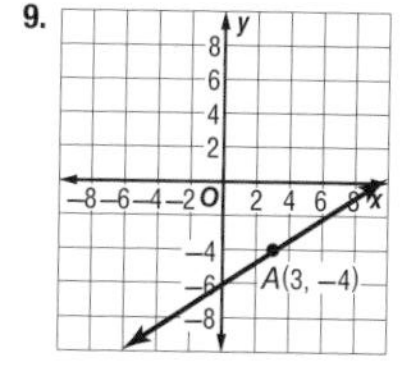

11.

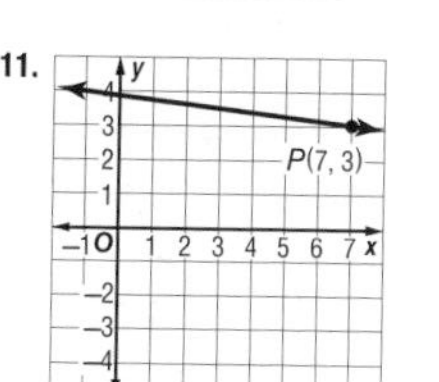

(13) Substitute (−3, 1) for (x_1, y_1) and (4, −2) for (x_2, y_2).

$m = \frac{y_2 - y_1}{x_2 - x_1}$ Slope formula

$= \frac{-2-1}{4-(-3)}$ Substitution

$= -\frac{3}{7}$ Simplify.

15. 8 **17.** undefined **19.** 1 **21.** 0 **23.** undefined

25. $-\frac{1}{6}$

27a.

27b. \$41.50
27c. \$84

29. parallel **31.** perpendicular

33. neither **35.**

37. **39.**

41. Line 2

(43) slope of Line 1 $= \frac{y_2 - y_1}{x_2 - x_1}$ Slope formula

$= \frac{0-(-4)}{7-(-9)}$ $(x_1, y_1) = (-9, -4)$, $(x_2, y_2) = (7, 0)$

$= \frac{4}{16}$ Subtract.

$= \frac{1}{4}$ Simplify.

slope of Line 2 $= \frac{y_2 - y_1}{x_2 - x_1}$ Slope formula

$= \frac{4-1}{7-0}$ $(x_1, y_1) = (0, 1)$, $(x_2, y_2) = (7, 4)$

$= \frac{3}{7}$ Subtract.

Since $\frac{1}{4} < \frac{3}{7}$, the slope of Line 2 is steeper than the slope of Line 1.

45a. the bald eagle

45b.

45c. 1189 bald eagles; 494 gray wolves

47. $y = -8$ **49.** $y = 0$

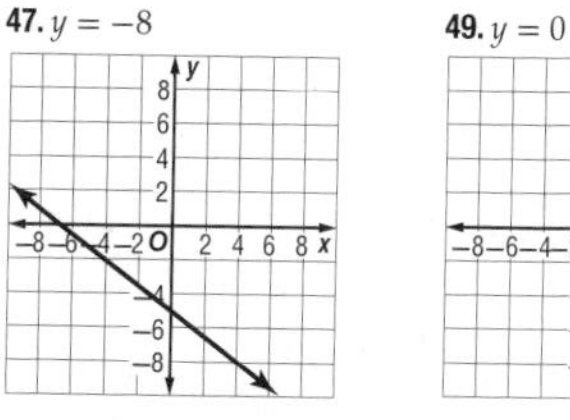

(51) a.

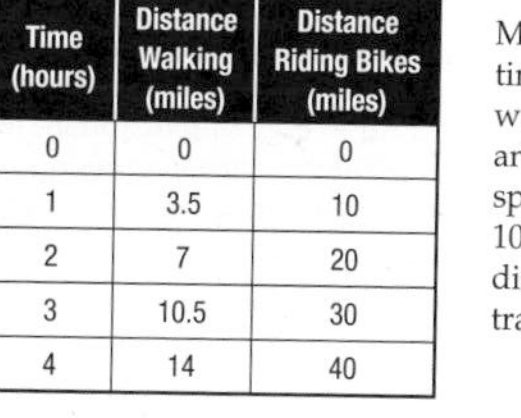

Time (hours)	Distance Walking (miles)	Distance Riding Bikes (miles)
0	0	0
1	3.5	10
2	7	20
3	10.5	30
4	14	40

Multiply the time spent walking by 3.5 and the time spent riding by 10 to find the distances travelled.

b. Use the table from part **a** to create a graph with time on the horizontal axis and distance on the vertical axis.

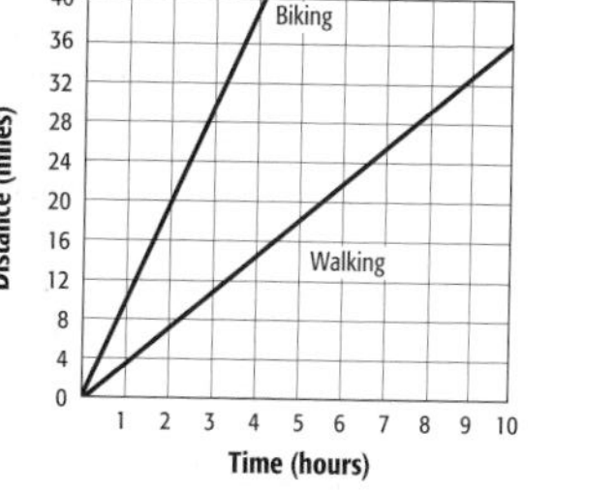
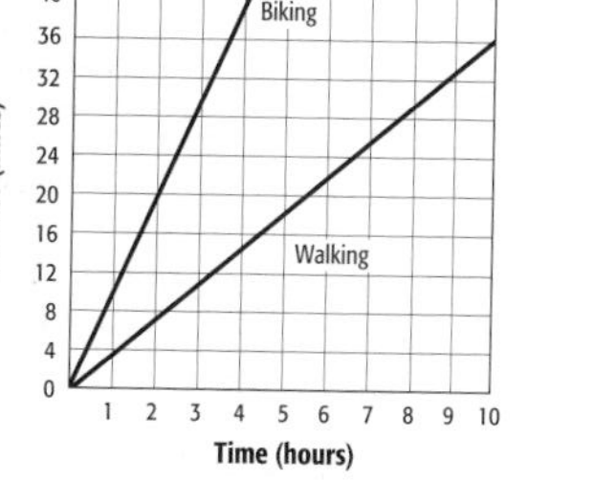

c. their speed **d.** Sample answer: Yes, they can make it if they ride their bikes. If they walk, it takes over two hours to go eight miles, so they wouldn't be home in time and they wouldn't get to spend any time in the store. If they ride their bikes, they can travel there in 24 minutes. If they spend 30 minutes in the store and spend 24 minutes riding home, the total amount of time they will use is 24 + 30 + 24 = 78 minutes, which is 1 hour and 18 minutes.

53. Terrell; Hale subtracted the x-coordinates in the wrong order. **55.** The Sears Tower has a vertical or undefined and the Leaning Tower of Pisa has a positive slope. **57.** Sample answer: (4, −3) and (5, −5) lie along the same line as point X and Y. The slope between all of the points is −2. To find additional points, you can take any point on the line and subtract 2 from the y-coordinate and add 1 to the x-coordinate. **59.** 2:5 **61.** C **63.** 123 **65.** 57 **67.** *ABC, ABQ, PQR, CDS, APU, DET* **69.** valid **71.** 6 **73.** $y = -2x + 3$

Lesson 3-4

1. $y = 4x - 3$ **3.** $y = -\frac{2}{3}x + 5$

5. $y + 3 = \frac{1}{4}(x + 2)$ **7.** $y = \frac{5}{4}x - 1$ **9.** $y = \frac{9}{7}x - \frac{19}{7}$ **11.** $y = 4x + 9$

13. $y = -5x - 2$ **15.** $y = 9x + 2$

17. $y = -\frac{3}{4}x + 4$

19 $y - y_1 = m(x - x_1)$ Point-slope form
$y - 11 = 2(x - 3)$ $m = 2, (x_1, y_1) = (3, 11)$
$y = 2x + 5$ Simplify.

Graph the given point (3, 11). Use the slope 2 or $\frac{2}{1}$ to find another point 2 units up and 1 unit to the right.

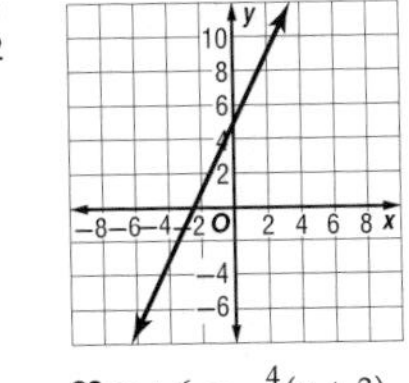

21. $y - 9 = -7(x - 1)$ **23.** $y + 6 = -\frac{4}{5}(x + 3)$

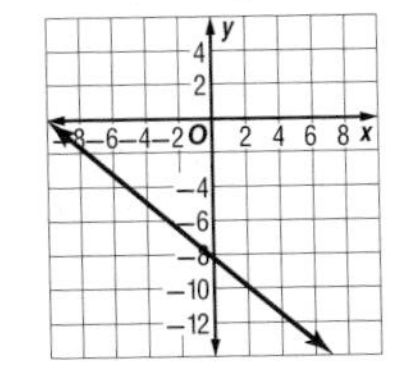

25. $y = -4$ **27.** $x = -3$ **29.** $y = -\frac{3}{4}x + 3$
31. $y = -\frac{10}{3}x + \frac{38}{3}$ **33.** $y = \frac{3}{2}x - \frac{1}{2}$ **35.** $y = \frac{2}{3}x - 2$
37. $y = -2x - 18$ **39.** $y = -\frac{2}{3}x + 6$

41 **a.** For each person, the cost increases \$5.50. So, the rate of change, or slope, is 5.5. The y-intercept represents the cost when there are 0 people, or \$400. Let y represent the total cost and x represent the number of people who attend the party.
$y = mx + b$ Slope-intercept form
$y = 5.5x + 400$ $m = 5.5, b = 400$
b. Let the x-axis represent the number of people and the y-axis represent the total cost.

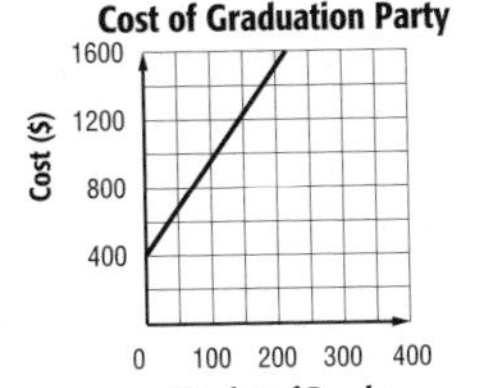

c. If $\frac{2}{3}$ of the class attends, then $\frac{2}{3} \cdot 285$ or 190 people attend.
$y = 5.5x + 400$ Write the equation.
$= 5.5(190) + 400$ $x = 190$
$= 1045 + 400$ Multiply.
$= 1445$ Simplify.
The party will cost \$1445.
d. $y = 5.5x + 400$ Write the equation.
$2000 = 5.5x + 400$ $y = 2000$
$1600 = 5.5x$ Subtract.
$y = 290.9$ Simplify.
If they raise \$2000, 290 people can attend the party.

43. p **45.** $n, p,$ or r **47.** perpendicular **49.** neither

51 First, find the slope of the line through (3, 2) and (−7, 2)
$m = \frac{y_2 - y_1}{x_2 - x_1}$ Slope formula
$= \frac{2-2}{-7-3}$ $(x_1, y_1) = (3, 2), (x_2, y_2) = (-7, 2)$
$= \frac{0}{-10}$ Subtract.
$= 0$ Simplify.
Since the slope of the line is 0, it is a horizontal line. A line is perpendicular to a horizontal line if it is vertical, so find the vertical line through the point (−8, 12). The line through the point (−8, 12) perpendicular to the line through (3, 2) and (−7, 2) is $x = -8$.

53. $C = 15(x - 1) + 40$ or $C = 15x + 25$ **55.** 14
57. Sample answer: $y = 2x - 1$, $y = -\frac{1}{2}x - \frac{17}{2}$ **59.** Sample answer: When given the slope and y-intercept, the slope-intercept form is easier to use. When given two points, the point-slope form is easier to use. When given the slope and a point, the point-slope form is easier to use.
61. H **63.** E **65.** 2 **67.** $x = 3, y \approx 26.33$
69. Gas-O-Rama is also a quarter mile from Lacy's home; the two gas stations are half a mile apart.
71. consecutive interior **73.** alternate exterior

Lesson 3-5

1. $j \parallel k$; Converse of Corresponding Angles Postulate

3 Angle 3 and ∠10 are alternate exterior angles of lines ℓ and m. Since ∠3 ≅ ∠10, ℓ ∥ m by the Alternate Exterior Angles Converse Theorem.

5. 20 **7.** Yes; Sample answer: Since the alternate exterior angles are congruent, the backrest and footrest are parallel. **9.** $u \parallel v$; Alternate Exterior ∡ Converse
11. $r \parallel s$; Consecutive Interior ∡ Converse
13. $u \parallel v$; Alternate Interior ∡ Converse **15.** $r \parallel s$; Corresponding ∡ Converse **17.** 22; Conv. Corr. ∡ Post.

19 The angles are consecutive interior angles. For lines m and n to be parallel, consecutive interior angles must be supplementary, according to the Consecutive Interior Angles Converse Theorem.
$(7x - 2) + (10 - 3x) = 180$ Definition of supp. ∡
$4x + 8 = 180$ Simplify.
$4x = 172$ Subtract 8 from each side.
$x = 43$ Divide each side by 4.

21. 36; Alt. Ext. ∡ Conv.
23a. ∠1 and ∠2 are supplementary. **23b.** Def. of linear pair **23c.** ∠2 and ∠3 are supplementary; Suppl. Thm.
23d. ≅ Suppl. Thm. **23e.** Converse of Corr. ∡ Post.

25. Given: ∠1 ≅ ∠3, $\overline{AC} \parallel \overline{BD}$
Prove: $\overline{AB} \parallel \overline{CD}$
Proof:
Statements (Reasons)
1. ∠1 ≅ ∠3, $\overline{AC} \parallel \overline{BD}$ (Given)
2. ∠2 ≅ ∠3 (Corr. ∡ Post.)
3. ∠1 ≅ ∠2 (Trans. Prop.)
4. $\overline{AB} \parallel \overline{CD}$ (If alternate ∡ are ≅, then lines are ∥.)

27. Given: ∠ABC ≅ ∠ADC, $m\angle A + m\angle ABC = 180$
Prove: $\overline{AB} \parallel \overline{CD}$
Proof:
Statements (Reasons)
1. ∠ABC ≅ ∠ADC, $m\angle A + m\angle ABC = 180$ (Given)
2. $m\angle ABC = m\angle ADC$ (Def. of ≅ ∡)
3. $m\angle A + m\angle ADC = 180$ (Substitution)
4. ∠A and ∠ADC are supplementary. (Def. of supplementary ∡)
5. $\overline{AB} \parallel \overline{CD}$ (If consec. int. ∡ are supplementary, then lines are ∥.)

29 The Converse of the Perpendicular Transversal Theorem states that two lines perpendicular to the same line are parallel. Since the slots, or the bottom of each rectangular opening, are perpendicular to each of the sides, the slots are parallel. Since any pair of slots is perpendicular to the sides, they are also parallel.

31. Given: ∠1 ≅ ∠2
Prove: ℓ ∥ m
Proof:
Statements (Reasons)
1. ∠1 ≅ ∠2 (Given)
2. ∠2 ≅ ∠3 (Vertical ∡ are ≅)
3. ∠1 ≅ ∠3 (Transitive Prop.)
4. ℓ ∥ m (If corr ∡ are ≅, then lines are ∥.)

33. $r \parallel s$; Sample answer: The corresponding angles are congruent. Since the angles are equal, the lines are parallel. **35.** $r \parallel s$; Sample answer: The alternate exterior angles are congruent. Since the angles are equal, the lines are parallel. **37.** Daniela; ∠1 and ∠2 are alternate interior angles for $\overline{WX}$ and $\overline{YZ}$, so if alternate interior angles are congruent, then the lines are parallel.

39. Sample answer:
Given: $a \parallel b$ and $b \parallel c$
Prove: $a \parallel c$
Statements (Reasons)
1. $a \parallel b$ and $b \parallel c$ (Given)
2. ∠1 ≅ ∠3 (Alt. Int. ∡ Thm.)
3. ∠3 ≅ ∠2 (Vert. ∡ are ≅)
4. ∠2 ≅ ∠4 (Alt. Int. ∡ Thm.)
5. ∠1 ≅ ∠4 (Trans. Prop.)
6. $a \parallel b$ (Alt. Int. ∡ Conv. Thm.)

41a. We know that $m\angle 1 + m\angle 2 = 180$. Since ∠2 and ∠3 are linear pairs, $m\angle 2 + m\angle 3 = 180$. By substitution, $m\angle 1 + m\angle 2 = m\angle 2 + m\angle 3$. By subtracting $m\angle 2$ from both sides we get $m\angle 1 = m\angle 3$. ∠1 ≅ ∠3, by the definition of congruent angles. Therefore, $a \parallel c$ since the corresponding angles are congruent. **41b.** We know that $a \parallel c$ and $m\angle 1 + m\angle 3 = 180$. Since ∠1 and ∠3 are corresponding angles, they are congruent and their measures are equal. By substitution, $m\angle 3 + m\angle 3 = 180$ or $2m\angle 3 = 180$. By dividing both sides by 2, we get $m\angle 3 = 90$. Therefore, $t \perp c$ since they form a right angle. **43.** Yes; sample answer: A pair of angles can be both supplementary and congruent if the measure of both angles is 90, since the sum of the angle measures would be 180.
45. G
47. J
49. $y = \frac{4}{5}x - 9$
51. 6 hours
53. W X Y Z (number line)
55. 8.6 m; 3.5 m^2 **57.** 10, 8.3

Lesson 3-6

1. **3.** The formation should be that of two parallel lines that are also parallel to the 50-yard line; the band members have formed two lines that are equidistant from the 50-yard line, so by Theorem 3.9, the two lines formed are parallel. **5.** $\sqrt{10}$ units

7 Let ℓ represent $y = -2x + 4$ and let m represent $y = -2x + 14$. The slope of the lines is −2. Write an equation for line p. The slope of p is the opposite reciprocal of −2, or $\frac{1}{2}$. Use the y-intercept of line ℓ, (0, 4), as one of the endpoints of the perpendicular segment.
$(y - y_1) = m(x - x_1)$ Point-slope form
$(y - 4) = \frac{1}{2}(x - 0)$ $(x_1, y_1) = (0, 4), m = \frac{1}{2}$
$y - 4 = \frac{1}{2}x$ Simplify.
$y = \frac{1}{2}x + 4$ Add 4 to each side.
Use a system of equations to find the point of intersection of lines m and p.
Equation for m: $y = -2x + 14$
Equation for p: $y = \frac{1}{2}x + 4$
$y = -2x + 14$ Equation for m
$\frac{1}{2}x + 4 = -2x + 14$ Use Equation p to substitute $\frac{1}{2}x + 4$ for y.
$\frac{5}{2}x + 4 = 14$ Add $2x$ to each side.

$\frac{5}{2}x = 10$ Subtract 4 from each side.
$x = 4$ Multiply each side by $\frac{2}{5}$.
$y = \frac{1}{2}x + 4$ Equation for p
$y = \frac{1}{2}(4) + 4$ Substitute 4 for x.
$y = 6$ Simplify.

The point of intersection is (4, 6). Use the Distance Formula to find the distance between (0, 4) and (4, 6).

$d = \sqrt{(x_2 - x_1)^2 + (y_2 - y_1)^2}$ Distance Formula
$= \sqrt{(4 - 0)^2 + (6 - 4)^2}$ $x_1 = 0, y_1 = 4, x_2 = 4, y_2 = 6$
$= \sqrt{20}$ or $2\sqrt{5}$ Simplify.

The distance between the lines is $2\sqrt{5}$ units.

9.

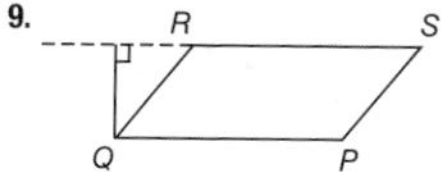

11.

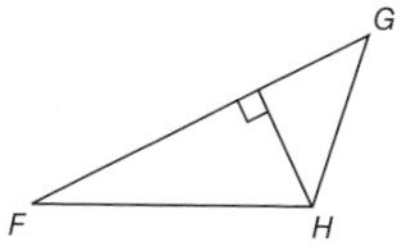

13. No; a driveway perpendicular to the road would be the shortest. The angle the driveway makes with the road is less than 90°, so it is not the shortest possible driveway.

(15) Find the slope and y-intercept of line ℓ and write the equation for the line.

$m = \frac{y_2 - y_1}{x_2 - x_1} = \frac{4 - (-3)}{7 - 0}$ or 1

Since ℓ contains (0, −3), the y-intercept is −3. So, the equation for line ℓ is $y = 1x + (-3)$ or $y = x - 3$. The slope of a line perpendicular to ℓ, line w, is −1. Write the equation of line w through (4, 3) with slope −1.

$y = mx + b$ Slope-intercept form
$3 = -1(4) + b$ $m = -1, (x, y) = (4, 3)$
$3 = -4 + b$ Simplify.
$7 = b$ Add 4 to each side.

So, the equation for line w is $y = -x + 7$. Solve the system of equations to determine the point of intersection.

line ℓ: $y = x - 3$
line w: $(+)\ y = -x + 7$
$2y = 4$ Add the two equations.
$y = 2$ Divide each side by 2.

Solve for x.

$y = x - 3$ Equation for line ℓ
$2 = x - 3$ $y = 2$
$5 = x$ Add 3 to each side.

The point of intersection is (5, 2). Let this be point Q. Use the Distance Formula to determine the distance between $P(4, 3)$ and $Q(5, 2)$.

$d = \sqrt{(x_2 - x_1)^2 + (y_2 - y_1)^2}$ Distance Formula
$= \sqrt{(5 - 4)^2 + (2 - 3)^2}$ $x_1 = 4, y_1 = 3, x_2 = 5, y_2 = 2$
$= \sqrt{2}$ Simplify.

The distance between the lines is $\sqrt{2}$ units.

17. 6 units **19.** $\sqrt{10}$ units **21.** 6 units **23.** $\sqrt{26}$ units **25.** 21 units **27.** $4\sqrt{17}$ units **29.** $\sqrt{14.76}$ units **31.** 5 units **33.** 6 units

(35) He can conclude that the right and left sides of the bulletin board are not parallel, since the perpendicular distance between one line and any point on the other line must be equal anywhere on the lines for the two lines to be parallel. In this case, the length of the top of the bulletin board is not equal to the length of the bottom of the bulletin board.

39b. Place point C any place on line m. The area of the triangle is $\frac{1}{2}$ the height of the triangle times the length of the base of the triangle. The numbers stay constant regardless of the location of C on line m. **39c.** 16.5 in^2

(41) To find out if the lines will intersect, determine if they are parallel. If they are parallel the perpendicular distance between the two lines at any point will be equal. Use a ruler to measure the distance between points A and C and points B and D. $AC = 1.2$ centimeters and $BD =$ 1.35 centimeters. The lines are not parallel, so they will intersect. Shenequa is correct.

43. $a = \pm 1$; $y = \frac{1}{2}x + 6$ and $y = \frac{1}{2}x + \frac{7}{2}$ or $y = -\frac{1}{2}x + 6$ and $y = -\frac{1}{2}x + \frac{7}{2}$

45a. Sample answer:

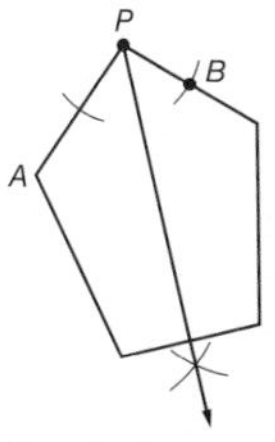

45b. Sample answer: Using a protractor, the measurement of the constructed angle is equal to 90. So, the line constructed from vertex P is perpendicular to the nonadjacent side chosen. **45c.** Sample answer: The same compass setting was used to construct points A and B. Then the same compass setting was used to construct the perpendicular line to the side chosen. Since the compass setting was equidistant in both steps, a perpendicular line was constructed.

47. Sample answer: First, a point on one of the parallel lines is found. Then the line perpendicular to the pair of parallel lines is found. Then the point of intersection is found between the perpendicular line and the other line not used in the first step. Last, the Distance Formula is used to determine the distance between the pair of intersection points. This value is the distance between the pair of parallel lines. **49.** C **51.** B **53.** $y + 1 = \frac{1}{4}(x - 3)$

55. $y - 3 = -(x + 2)$

57. Given: $AB = BC$
Prove: $AC = 2BC$
Proof:
Statements (Reasons)
1. $AB = BC$ (Given)
2. $AC = AB + BC$ (Seg. Add. Post.)
3. $AC = BC + BC$ (Substitution)
4. $AC = 2BC$ (Substitution)

59. Sample answer: Robin ⊥ Cardinal; Bluebird divides two of the angles formed by Robin and Cardinal into pairs of complementary angles. **61.** 5 **63.** 13 **65.** 5

Chapter 3 Study Guide and Review

1. false; parallel **3.** true **5.** true **7.** false; congruent **9.** corresponding **11.** alternate exterior **13.** skew lines **15.** 57; ∠5 ≅ ∠13 by Corr. ∠s Post. and 13 and 14 form a linear pair **17.** 123; ∠11 ≅ ∠5 by Alt. Int. ∠s Thm. and ∠5 ≅ ∠1 by Alt. Ext. ∠s Thm. **19.** 57; ∠1 ≅ ∠3 by Corr. ∠s Post. and ∠3 and ∠6 form a linear pair. **21.** perpendicular **23.** parallel

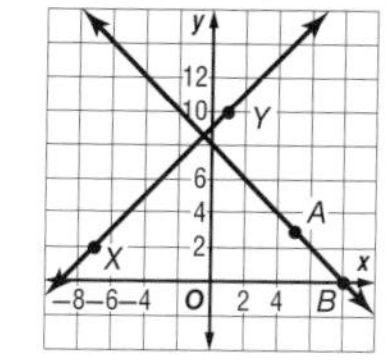

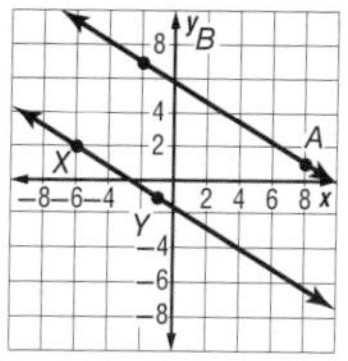

25.

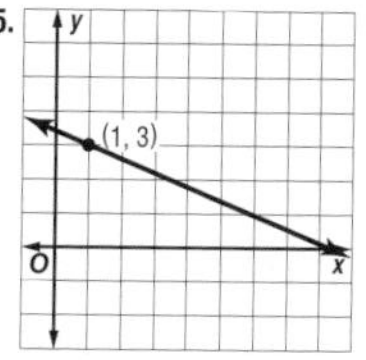

27. $y + 9 = 2(x - 4)$ **29.** $y = 5x - 3$ **31.** $y = -\frac{2}{3}x + 10$ **33.** $C = 20h + 50$ **35.** none **37.** $v \parallel z$; Alternate Exterior Angles Converse Thm.

39. 135 **41.**

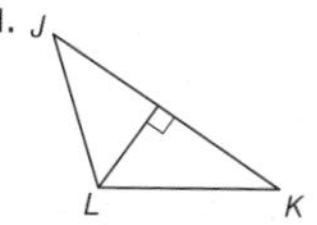

CHAPTER 4 Congruent Triangles

Get Ready

1. right **3.** obtuse **5.** 84°; Alternate Exterior Angles **7.** ≈10.8 **9.** ≈18.0 **11.** 144.2 mi

Lesson 4-1

1. right **3.** equiangular **5.** obtuse; ∠BDC > 90° **7.** isosceles

(9) By the definition of midpoint, $FK = KH$.

$FK + KH = FH$ Segment Addition Postulate
$KH + KH = FH$ Substitution
$2KH = FH$ Simplify.
$2(2.5) = FH$ Substitution
$5 = FH$ Simplify.

Since $\overline{GH} \cong \overline{FG}$, $GH = FG$ or 5. Since $GH = FG = FH = 5$, the triangle has three sides with the same measure. Therefore, the triangle has three congruent sides, so it is equilateral.

11. scalene **13.** $x = 5$, $QR = RS = QS = 25$ **15.** obtuse **17.** right **19.** acute **21.** obtuse **23.** acute **25.** right **27.** equilateral **29.** scalene **31.** scalene **33.** scalene **35.** equilateral

(37) Since △FGH is equilateral, $FG = GH$.

$FG = GH$ Given
$3x + 10 = 9x - 8$ Substitution
$10 = 6x - 8$ Subtract $3x$ from each side.
$18 = 6x$ Add 8 to each side.
$3 = x$ Divide each side by 3.

$FG = 3x + 10$ Given
$= 3(3) + 10$ or 19 $x = 3$

$FG = GH = HF = 19$

(39) Because the base of the prism formed is an equilateral triangle, the mirror tile must be cut into three strips of equal width. Since the original tile is a 12-inch square, each strip will be 12 inches long by 12 ÷ 3 or 4 inches wide.

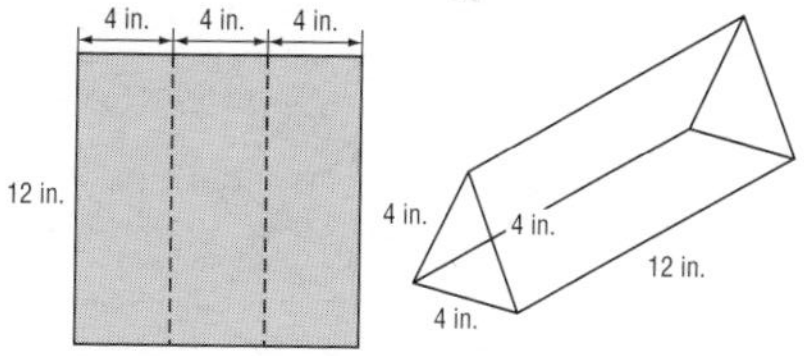

41. isosceles obtuse **43.** scalene; $XZ = 3\sqrt{5}$, $XY = \sqrt{113}$, $YZ = 2\sqrt{26}$ **45.** isosceles; $XZ = 2$, $XY = 2\sqrt{2}$, $YZ = 2$

47. Given: $m\angle ADC = 120$
Prove: △DBC is acute.
Proof: ∠ADC and ∠BDC form a linear pair. ∠ADC and ∠BDC are supplementary because if two angles form a linear pair, then they are supplementary. So, $m\angle ADC + m\angle BDC = 180$. We know $m\angle ADC = 120$, so by substitution, $120 + m\angle BDC = 180$. Subtract to find that $m\angle BDC = 60$. We already know that ∠B is acute because △ABC is acute. ∠BCD must also be acute because ∠C is acute and $m\angle C = m\angle ACD + m\angle BCD$. △DBC is acute by definition.

49. $x = 15$; $FG = 35$, $GH = 35$, $HF = 35$ **51.** $x = 3$; $MN = 13$, $NP = 13$, $PM = 11$

53.

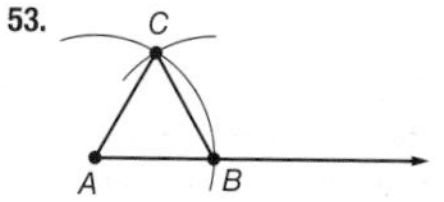

Sample answer: In △ABC, $AB = BC = AC = 1.3$ cm. Since all sides have the same length, they are

Selected Answers and Solutions
Selected Answers and Solutions

all congruent. Therefore the triangle is equilateral. $\triangle ABC$ was constructed using AB as the length of each side. Since the arc for each segment is the same, the triangle is equilateral.

55 **a.** Sample answer:
acute isosceles

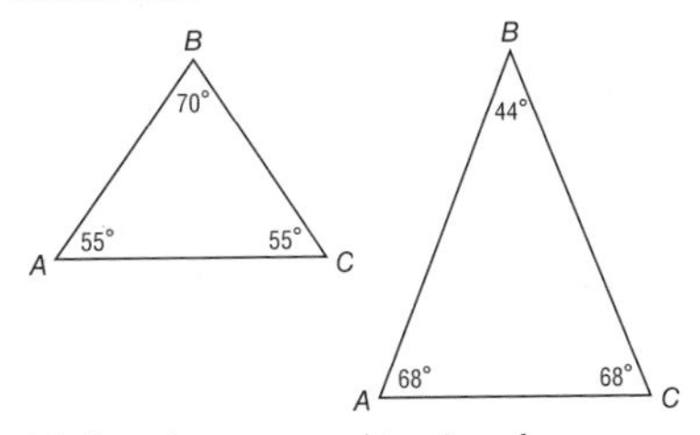

right isosceles   obtuse isosceles

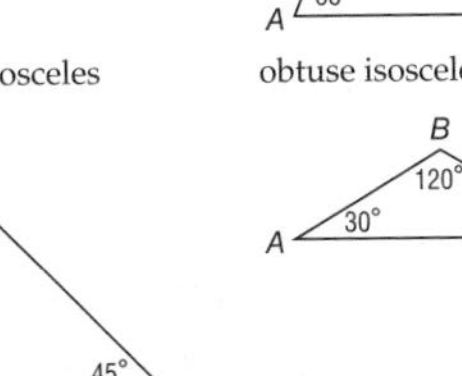

b.

$m\angle A$	$m\angle C$	$m\angle B$	Sum of Angle Measures
55	55	70	180
68	68	44	180
45	45	90	180
30	30	120	180

c. Sample answer: In an isosceles triangle, the angles opposite the congruent sides have the same measure. The sum of the angle measures of an isosceles triangle is 180. **d.** If the measures of the angles opposite the congruent sides of an isosceles triangle have the same measure, then if one angle measures x, then the other angle also measures x. If the sum of the measures of the angles of an isosceles triangle is 180, the measure of the third angle is $180 - (x + x)$ or $180 - 2x$. So, the other two angles measure x and $180 - 2x$.

57. Never; all equiangular triangles have three 60° angles, so they do not have a 90° angle. Therefore they cannot be right triangles. **59.** Never; all equilateral triangles are also equiangular, which means all of the angles are 60°. A right triangle has one 90° angle.

61. Sample answer: (triangle with sides 0.75 in., 0.9 in., 0.5 in.; angles 34°, 56°) **63.** Not possible; all equilateral triangles have three acute angles. **65.** A **67.** 13.5 **69.** 7 **71.** $2\sqrt{5}$ **73.** Two lines in a plane that are perpendicular to the same line are parallel. **75.** H: you are a teenager; C: you are at least 13 years old.

77. H: you have a driver's license; C: you are at least 16 years old **79.** Plane AEB intersects with plane $\mathcal{N}$ in $\overleftrightarrow{AB}$. **81.** Points D, C, and B lie in plane $\mathcal{N}$, but point E does not lie in plane $\mathcal{N}$. Thus, they are not coplanar. **83.** cons. int. **85.** alt. ext.

Lesson 4-2

1. 58 **3.** 80 **5.** 49 **7.** 78 **9.** 61 **11.** 151 **13.** 30

15
$m\angle L + m\angle M + m\angle 2 = 180$ Triangle Angle-Sum Theorem
$31 + 90 + m\angle 2 = 180$ Substitution
$121 + m\angle 2 = 180$ Simplify.
$m\angle 2 = 59$ Subtract 121 from each side.

$\angle 1$ and $\angle 2$ are congruent vertical angles. So, $m\angle 1 = 59$.

$m\angle 1 + m\angle 3 + m\angle P = 180$ Triangle Angle-Sum Theorem
$59 + m\angle 3 + 22 = 180$ Substitution
$81 + m\angle 3 = 180$ Simplify.
$m\angle 3 = 99$ Subtract 118 from each side.

$m\angle 1 = 59, m\angle 2 = 59, m\angle 3 = 99$

17. 79 **19.** 21

21
$m\angle A + m\angle B = 148$ Exterior Angle Theorem
$(2x - 15) + (x - 5) = 148$ Substitution
$3x - 20 = 148$ Simplify.
$3x = 168$ Add 20 to each side.
$x = 56$ Divide each side by 2.

So, $m\angle ABC = 56 - 5$ or 51.

23. 78 **25.** 39 **27.** 55 **29.** 35 **31.** $x = 30$; 30, 60

33 In $\triangle ABC$, $\angle B$ and $\angle C$ are congruent, so $m\angle B = m\angle C$.

$m\angle A = 3(m\angle B)$ $m\angle A$ is to be 3 times $m\angle B$.
$m\angle A + m\angle B + m\angle C = 180$ Triangle Angle-Sum Theorem
$3(m\angle B) + m\angle B + m\angle B = 180$ Substitution
$5(m\angle B) = 180$ Simplify.
$m\angle B = 36$ Divide each side by 5.

$m\angle C = m\angle B = 36$ $m\angle A = 3m\angle B = 3(36)$ or 108

35. Given: $\triangle MNO$; $\angle M$ is a right angle.
Prove: There can be at most one right angle in a triangle.
Proof: In $\triangle MNO$, M is a right angle. $m\angle M + m\angle N + m\angle O = 180$. $m\angle M = 90$, so $m\angle N + m\angle O = 90$. If N were a right angle, then $m\angle O = 0$. But that is impossible, so there cannot be two right angles in a triangle.
Given: $\triangle PQR$; $\angle P$ is obtuse.
Prove: There can be at most one obtuse angle in a triangle.
Proof: In $\triangle PQR$, $\angle P$ is obtuse. So $m\angle P > 90$. $m\angle P + m\angle Q + m\angle R = 180$. It must be that $m\angle Q + m\angle R < 90$. So, $\angle Q$ and $\angle R$ must be acute.

37. $m\angle 1 = 65, m\angle 2 = 20, m\angle 3 = 95, m\angle 4 = 40, m\angle 5 = 110, m\angle 6 = 45, m\angle 7 = 70, m\angle 8 = 65$ **39.** 67°, 23° **41.** $z < 23$; Sample answer: Since the sum of the measures of the angles of a triangle is 180 and $m\angle X = 157$, $157 + m\angle Y + m\angle Z = 180$, so $m\angle Y + m\angle Z = 23$. If $m\angle Y$ was 0, then $m\angle Z$ would equal 23. But since an angle must have a measure greater than 0, $m\angle Z$ must be less than 23, so $z < 23$.

43 Use the Triangle Angle-Sum Theorem and the Addition Property to prove the statement is true.
Given: $RSTUV$ is a pentagon.
Prove: $m\angle S + m\angle STU + m\angle TUV + m\angle V + m\angle VRS = 540$

Proof:
Statements (Reasons)
1. $RSTUV$ is a pentagon. (Given)
2. $m\angle S + m\angle 1 + m\angle 2 = 180$; $m\angle 3 + m\angle 4 + m\angle 7 = 180$; $m\angle 6 + m\angle V + m\angle 5 = 180$ (△ Sum. Thm.)
3. $m\angle S + m\angle 1 + m\angle 2 + m\angle 3 + m\angle 4 + m\angle 7 + m\angle 6 + m\angle V + m\angle 5 = 540$ (Addition Property)
4. $m\angle VRS = m\angle 1 + m\angle 4 + m\angle 5$; $m\angle TUV = m\angle 7 + m\angle 6$; $m\angle STU = m\angle 2 + m\angle 3$ (∠ Addition)
5. $m\angle S + m\angle STU + m\angle TUV + m\angle V + m\angle VRS = 540$ (Substitution)

45a. Sample answer:

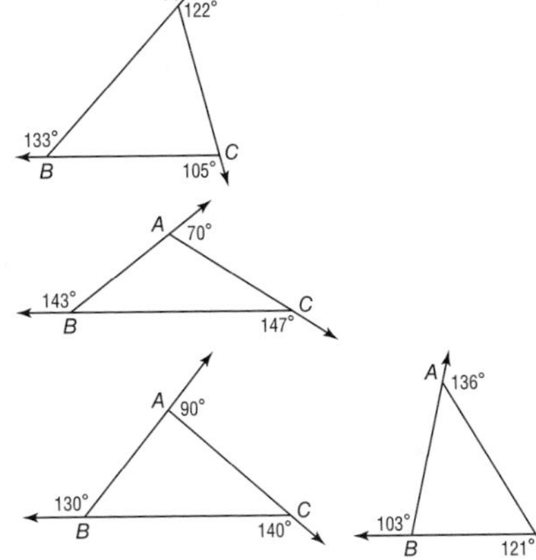

45b. Sample answer:

$m\angle 1$	$m\angle 2$	$m\angle 3$	Sum of Angle Measures
122	105	133	360
70	147	143	360
90	140	130	360
136	121	103	360
49	154	157	360

45c. Sample answer: The sum of the measures of the exterior angles of a triangle is 360.

45d. $m\angle 1 + m\angle 2 + m\angle 3 = 360$

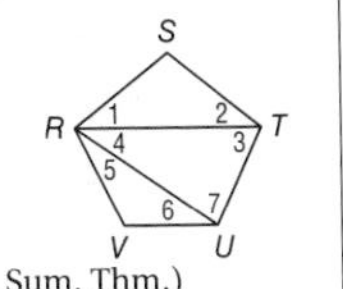

45e. The Exterior Angle Theorem tells us that $m\angle 3 = m\angle BAC + m\angle BCA$, $m\angle 2 = m\angle BAC + m\angle CBA$, $m\angle 1 = m\angle CBA + m\angle BCA$. Through substitution, $m\angle 1 + m\angle 2 + m\angle 3 = m\angle CBA + m\angle BCA + m\angle BAC + m\angle CBA + m\angle BAC + m\angle BCA$. This can be simplified to $m\angle 1 + m\angle 2 + m\angle 3 = 2m\angle CBA + 2m\angle BCA + 2m\angle BAC$. The Distributive Property can be applied and gives $m\angle 1 + m\angle 2 + m\angle 3 = 2(m\angle CBA + m\angle BCA + m\angle BAC)$. The Triangle Angle-Sum Theorem tells us that $m\angle CBA + m\angle BCA + m\angle BAC = 180$. Through substitution we have $m\angle 1 + m\angle 2 + m\angle 3 = 2(180) = 360$.

47. The measure of $\angle a$ is the supplement of the exterior angle with measure 110, so $m\angle a = 180 - 110$ or 70. Because the angles with measures b and c are congruent, $b = c$. Using the Exterior Angle Theorem, $b + c = 110$. By substitution, $b + b = 110$, so $2b = 110$ and $b = 55$. Because $b = c$, $c = 55$. **49.** $y = 13, z = 14$ **51.** Sample answer: Since an exterior angle is acute, the adjacent angle must be obtuse. Since another exterior angle is right, the adjacent angle must be right. A triangle cannot contain both a right and an obtuse angle because it would be more than 180 degrees. Therefore, a triangle cannot have an obtuse, acute, and a right exterior angle. **53.** 100°, 115°, 145° **55.** E **57.** obtuse **59.** $\sqrt{26}$ units

61. Each set of figures has one more triangle than the previous set and the direction of the triangles alternate between pointing up and and pointing to the right.

▲ △ ▲ △ ▲

63. Multiplication Property **65.** Addition Property **67.** Substitution Property

Lesson 4-3

1. $\angle Y \cong \angle S$, $\angle X \cong \angle R$, $\angle XZY \cong \angle RZS$, $\overline{YX} \cong \overline{SR}$, $\overline{YZ} \cong \overline{SZ}$, $\overline{XZ} \cong \overline{RZ}$; $\triangle YXZ \cong \triangle SRZ$ **3.** $\frac{1}{2}$ in.; Sample answer: The nut is congruent to the opening for the $\frac{1}{2}$-in. socket.

5
$\angle M \cong \angle R$ CPCTC
$m\angle M = m\angle R$ Definition of congruence
$y + 10 = 2y - 40$ Substitution
$10 = y - 40$ Subtract y from each side.
$50 = y$ Add 40 to each side.

7. 16; $\angle N$ corresponds to $\angle X$. By the Third Angles

Theorem, $m\angle N = 64$, so $4x = 64$. **9.** $\angle X \cong \angle A$, $\angle Y \cong \angle B$, $\angle Z \cong \angle C$, $\overline{XY} \cong \overline{AB}$, $\overline{XZ} \cong \overline{AC}$, $\overline{YZ} \cong \overline{BC}$; $\triangle XYZ \cong \triangle ABC$ **11.** $\angle R \cong \angle J$, $\angle T \cong \angle K$, $\angle S \cong \angle L$, $\overline{RT} \cong \overline{JK}$, $\overline{TS} \cong \overline{KL}$, $\overline{RS} \cong \overline{JL}$; $\triangle RTS \cong \triangle JKL$ **13.** 20

15

$\overline{ED} \cong \overline{UT}$	CPCTC
$ED = UT$	Definition of congruence
$3z + 10 = z + 16$	Substitution
$2z + 10 = 16$	Subtract z from each side.
$2z = 6$	Subtract 10 from each side.
$z = 3$	Divide each side by 3.

17a. $\triangle ABC \cong \triangle MNO$; $\triangle DEF \cong \triangle PQR$
17b. $\overline{AB} \cong \overline{MN}$, $\overline{BC} \cong \overline{NO}$, $\overline{AC} \cong \overline{MO}$, $\overline{DE} \cong \overline{PQ}$, $\overline{EF} \cong \overline{QR}$, $\overline{DF} \cong \overline{PR}$ **17c.** $\angle A \cong \angle M$, $\angle B \cong \angle N$, $\angle C \cong \angle O$, $\angle D \cong \angle P$, $\angle E \cong \angle Q$, $\angle F \cong \angle R$

19

$148 + 18 + a = 180$	Triangle Angle-Sum Theorem
$166 + a = 180$	Simplify.
$a = 14$	Subtract 166 from each side.

If two angles of one triangle are congruent to two angles of another triangle, then the third angles of the triangles are congruent. So, $3x + y = 14$ and $5x - y = 18$. Solve the system of equations.

$3x + y = 14$	
$(+)\ 5x - y = 18$	
$8x = 32$	Add the equations.
$x = 4$	Divide each side by 8.
$3x + y = 14$	Original equation
$3(4) + y = 14$	$x = 4$
$12 + y = 14$	Simplify.
$y = 2$	Subtract 12 from each side.

21. Given: $\angle A \cong \angle D$
$\angle B \cong \angle E$
Prove: $\angle C \cong \angle F$

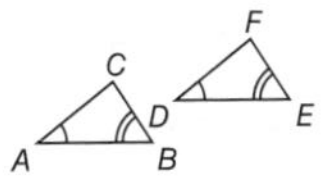

Proof:
Statements (Reasons)
1. $\angle A \cong \angle D$, $\angle B \cong \angle E$ (Given)
2. $m\angle A = m\angle D$, $m\angle B = m\angle E$ (Def. of $\cong$ ∡)
3. $m\angle A + m\angle B + m\angle C = 180$, $m\angle D + m\angle E + m\angle F = 180$ ($\angle$ Sum Theorem)
4. $m\angle A + m\angle B + m\angle C = m\angle D + m\angle E + m\angle F$ (Trans. Prop.)
5. $m\angle D + m\angle E + m\angle C = m\angle D + m\angle E + m\angle F$ (Subst.)
6. $m\angle C = m\angle F$ (Subt. Prop.)
7. $\angle C \cong \angle F$ (Def. of $\cong$ ∡)

23. Given: $\overline{BD}$ bisects $\angle B$.
$\overline{BD} \perp \overline{AC}$
Prove: $\angle A \cong \angle C$
Proof:
Statements (Reasons)
1. $\overline{BD}$ bisects $\angle B$, $\overline{BD} \perp \overline{AC}$. (Given)
2. $\angle ABD \cong \angle DBC$ (Def. of angle bisector)
3. $\angle ADB$ and $\angle BDC$ are right angles. ($\perp$ lines form rt. ∡.)
4. $\angle ADB \cong \angle BDC$ (All rt. ∡ are $\cong$.)
5. $\angle A \cong \angle C$ (Third $\angle$ Thm.)

25. Sample answer: Both of the punched flowers are congruent to the flower on the stamp, because it was used to create the images. According to the Transitive Property of Polygon Congruence, the two stamped images are congruent to each other because they are both congruent to the flowers on the punch.

27. Given: $\triangle DEF$
Prove: $\triangle DEF \cong \triangle DEF$

Proof:

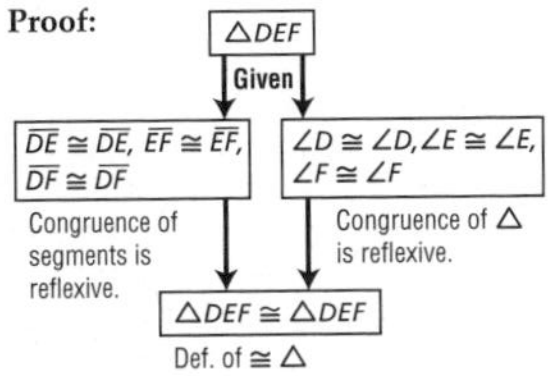

29.

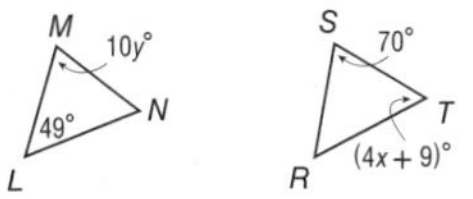

$x = 13$; $y = 7$

31 **a.** All the longer sides of the triangles are congruent and all the shorter sides are congruent. Sample answer: $\overline{AB} \cong \overline{CB}$, $\overline{AB} \cong \overline{DE}$, $\overline{AB} \cong \overline{FE}$, $\overline{CB} \cong \overline{DE}$, $\overline{CB} \cong \overline{FE}$, $\overline{DE} \cong \overline{FE}$, $\overline{AC} \cong \overline{DF}$ **b.** If the area is a square, then each of the four sides measures $\sqrt{100}$ or 10 feet. So, the perimeter of the square is 4(10) or 40 ft. The pennant string will need to be 40 ft long. **c.** Each pennant and the distance to the next pennant is 6 in. or 0.5 ft. So, the number of pennants is $40 \div 0.5$ or 80.

33a. If two triangles are congruent, then their areas are equal. **33b.** If the areas of a pair of triangles are equal, then the triangles are congruent; false; If one triangle has a base of 2 and a height of 6 and a second triangle has a base of 3 and a height of 4, then their areas are equal, but they are not congruent. **33c.** No; sample answer: Any pair of equilateral triangles that have the same base also have the same height, so it is not possible to draw a pair of equilateral triangles with the same area that are not congruent.
33d. yes;
sample answer:

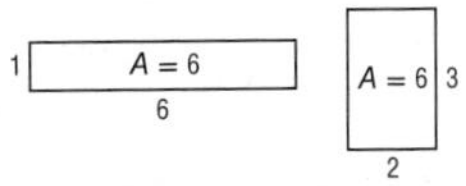

33e. No; any pair of squares that have the same area have the same side length, which is the square root of the area. If their areas are equal, they are congruent.
33f. Regular n-gons; If two regular n-gons are congruent, then they have the same area. All regular n-gons have the same shape, but may have different sizes. If two regular n-gons have the same area, then they not only have the same shape but also the same size. Therefore, they are congruent. **35.** diameter, radius, or circumerence; Sample answer: Two circles are the same size if they have the same diameter, radius, or circumference, so she can determine if the hoops are congruent if she measures any of them.
37. Both; Sample answer: $\angle A$ corresponds with $\angle Y$, $\angle B$ corresponds with $\angle X$, and $\angle C$ corresponds with $\angle Z$. $\triangle CAB$ is the same triangle as $\triangle ABC$ and $\triangle ZXY$ is the same triangle as $\triangle XYZ$. **39.** $x = 16$, $y = 8$
41. False; $\angle A \cong \angle X$, $\angle B \cong \angle Y$, $\angle C \cong \angle Z$, but corresponding sides are not congruent.

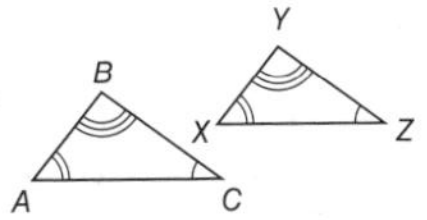

43. Sometimes; Equilateral triangles will be congruent if one pair of corresponding sides are congruent.
45. 5 **47.** C **49.** 59 **51.** $JK = 2\sqrt{146}$, $KL = \sqrt{290}$, $JL = \sqrt{146}$; scalene **53.** $JK = 5$, $KL = 5\sqrt{2}$, $JL = 5$; isosceles **55.** always **57.** complementary angles

Lesson 4-4

1a. two
1b. Given: $ABCD$ is a square
Prove: $\triangle ABC \cong \triangle CDA$
Proof:
Statements (Reasons)
1. $ABCD$ is a square (Given)
2. $\overline{AB} \cong \overline{CD}$, $\overline{BC} \cong \overline{DA}$ (Def. of $\cong$ a square)
3. $\overline{AC} \cong \overline{CA}$ (Reflex. Prop. $\cong$)
4. $\triangle ABC \cong \triangle CDA$ (SSS)

1c. Sample answer: $\overleftrightarrow{AB} \parallel \overleftrightarrow{CD}$; $\overleftrightarrow{AC}$ is a transversal to $\overleftrightarrow{AB}$ and $\overleftrightarrow{CD}$, so $\angle CAB$ and $\angle ACD$ are alternate interior angles. Since $\triangle ABC \cong \triangle CDA$, $\angle CAB$ and $\angle ACD$ are congruent corresponding angles. Therefore, the lines are parallel.

3 Sample answer: We are given that $\overline{LP} \cong \overline{NO}$ and $\angle LPM \cong \angle NOM$. Since $\triangle MOP$ is equilateral, $\overline{MO} \cong \overline{MP}$ by the definition of an equilateral triangle. So, two sides and the included angle of $\triangle LMP$ are congruent to two sides and the included angle of $\triangle NMO$. Therefore, $\triangle LMP$ is congruent to $\triangle NMO$ by the Side-Angle-Side Congruence Postulate.

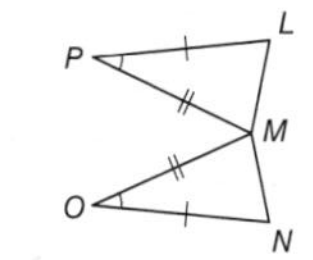

5. Given: $\overline{QR} \cong \overline{SR}$ and $\overline{ST} \cong \overline{QT}$
Prove: $\triangle QRT \cong \triangle SRT$
Proof: We know that $\overline{QR} \cong \overline{SR}$ and $\overline{ST} \cong \overline{QT}$. $\overline{RT} \cong \overline{RT}$ by the Reflexive Property. Since $\overline{QR} \cong \overline{SR}$, $\overline{ST} \cong \overline{QT}$, and $\overline{RT} \cong \overline{RT}$, $\triangle QRT \cong \triangle SRT$ by SSS.

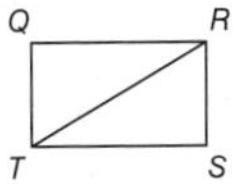

7. Given: $\overline{AB} \cong \overline{ED}$, $\angle ABC$ and $\angle EDC$ are right angles, and C is the midpoint of $\overline{BD}$.
Prove: $\triangle ABC \cong \triangle EDC$
Proof:
Statements (Reasons)
1. $\overline{AB} \cong \overline{ED}$, $\angle ABC$ and $\angle EDC$ are right angles, and C is the midpoint of $\overline{BD}$. (Given)
2. $\angle ABC \cong \angle EDC$ (All rt. ∡ $\cong$)
3. $\overline{BC} \cong \overline{DC}$ (Midpoint Thm.)
4. $\triangle ABC \cong \triangle EDC$ (SAS)

9 Use $d = \sqrt{(x_2 - x_1)^2 + (y_2 - y_1)^2}$ to find the lengths of the sides of $\triangle MNO$.

$MN = \sqrt{(-1-0)^2 + [-4-(-1)]^2}$	$(x_1, y_1) = (0, -1)$, $(x_2, y_2) = (-1, -4)$
$= \sqrt{1+9}$ or $\sqrt{10}$	Simplify.
$NO = \sqrt{[-4-(-1)]^2 + [-3-(-4)]^2}$	$(x_1, y_1) = (-1, -4)$, $(x_2, y_2) = (-4, -3)$
$= \sqrt{9+1}$ or $\sqrt{10}$	Simplify.
$MO = \sqrt{(-4-0)^2 + [-3-(-1)]^2}$	$(x_1, y_1) = (0, -1)$, $(x_2, y_2) = (-4, -3)$
$= \sqrt{16+4}$ or $\sqrt{20}$	Simplify.

Find the lengths of the sides of $\triangle QRS$.

$QR = \sqrt{(4-3)^2 + [-4-(-3)]^2}$	$(x_1, y_1) = (3, -3)$, $(x_2, y_2) = (4, -4)$
$= \sqrt{1+1}$ or $\sqrt{2}$	Simplify.
$RS = \sqrt{(3-4)^2 + [3-(-4)]^2}$	$(x_1, y_1) = (4, -4)$, $(x_2, y_2) = (3, 3)$
$= \sqrt{1+49}$ or $\sqrt{50}$	Simplify.
$QS = \sqrt{(3-3)^2 + [3-(-3)]^2}$	$(x_1, y_1) = (3, -3)$, $(x_2, y_2) = (3, 3)$
$= \sqrt{0+36}$ or 6	Simplify.

$MN = \sqrt{10}$, $NO = \sqrt{10}$, $MO = \sqrt{20}$, $QR = \sqrt{2}$, $RS = \sqrt{50}$, and $QS = 6$. The corresponding sides are not congruent, so the triangles are not congruent.

11. $MN = \sqrt{10}$, $NO = \sqrt{10}$, $MO = \sqrt{20}$, $QR = \sqrt{10}$, $RS = \sqrt{10}$, and $QS = \sqrt{20}$. Each pair of corresponding sides has the same measure, so they are congruent. $\triangle MNO \cong \triangle QRS$ by SSS.

13. Given: R is the midpoint of $\overline{QS}$ and $\overline{PT}$.
Prove: $\triangle PRQ \cong \triangle TRS$
Proof: Since R is the midpoint of $\overline{QS}$ and $\overline{PT}$, $\overline{PR} \cong \overline{RT}$ and $\overline{RQ} \cong \overline{RS}$ by definition of a midpoint. $\angle PRQ \cong \angle TRS$ by the Vertical Angles Theorem. So, $\triangle PRQ \cong \triangle TRS$ by SAS.

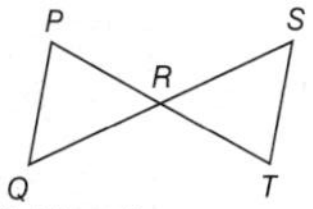

15. Given: $\triangle XYZ$ is equilateral.
$\overline{WY}$ bisects $\angle Y$.
Prove: $\overline{XW} \cong \overline{ZW}$
Proof: We know that $\overline{WY}$ bisects $\angle Y$, so $\angle XYW \cong \angle ZYW$. Also, $\overline{YW} \cong \overline{YW}$ by the Reflexive

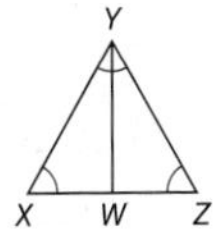

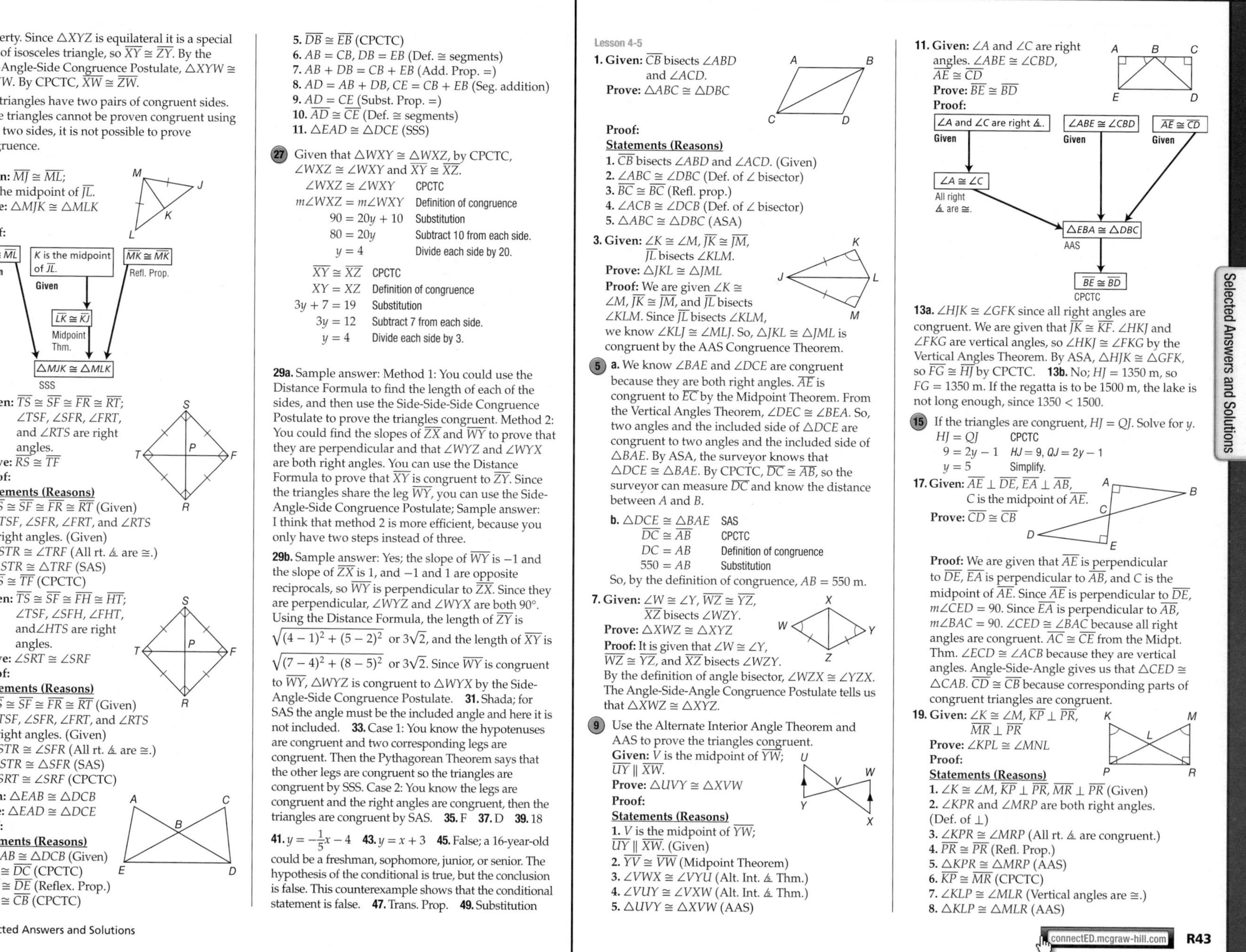

Property. Since $\triangle XYZ$ is equilateral it is a special type of isosceles triangle, so $\overline{XY} \cong \overline{ZY}$. By the Side-Angle-Side Congruence Postulate, $\triangle XYW \cong \triangle ZYW$. By CPCTC, $\overline{XW} \cong \overline{ZW}$.

17 The triangles have two pairs of congruent sides. Since triangles cannot be proven congruent using only two sides, it is not possible to prove congruence.

19. SAS

21. Given: $\overline{MJ} \cong \overline{ML}$; K is the midpoint of $\overline{JL}$.
Prove: $\triangle MJK \cong \triangle MLK$

Proof:

$\overline{MJ} \cong \overline{ML}$ (Given); K is the midpoint of $\overline{JL}$ (Given) → $\overline{LK} \cong \overline{KJ}$ (Midpoint Thm.); $\overline{MK} \cong \overline{MK}$ (Refl. Prop.) → $\triangle MJK \cong \triangle MLK$ (SSS)

23a. Given: $\overline{TS} \cong \overline{SF} \cong \overline{FR} \cong \overline{RT}$; $\angle TSF$, $\angle SFR$, $\angle FRT$, and $\angle RTS$ are right angles.
Prove: $\overline{RS} \cong \overline{TF}$
Proof:
Statements (Reasons)
1. $\overline{TS} \cong \overline{SF} \cong \overline{FR} \cong \overline{RT}$ (Given)
2. $\angle TSF$, $\angle SFR$, $\angle FRT$, and $\angle RTS$ are right angles. (Given)
3. $\angle STR \cong \angle TRF$ (All rt. ∡ are ≅.)
4. $\triangle STR \cong \triangle TRF$ (SAS)
5. $\overline{RS} \cong \overline{TF}$ (CPCTC)

23b. Given: $\overline{TS} \cong \overline{SF} \cong \overline{FH} \cong \overline{HT}$; $\angle TSF$, $\angle SFH$, $\angle FHT$, and $\angle HTS$ are right angles.
Prove: $\angle SRT \cong \angle SRF$
Proof:
Statements (Reasons)
1. $\overline{TS} \cong \overline{SF} \cong \overline{FR} \cong \overline{RT}$ (Given)
2. $\angle TSF$, $\angle SFR$, $\angle FRT$, and $\angle RTS$ are right angles. (Given)
3. $\angle STR \cong \angle SFR$ (All rt. ∡ are ≅.)
4. $\triangle STR \cong \triangle SFR$ (SAS)
5. $\angle SRT \cong \angle SRF$ (CPCTC)

25. Given: $\triangle EAB \cong \triangle DCB$
Prove: $\triangle EAD \cong \triangle DCE$
Proof:
Statements (Reasons)
1. $\triangle EAB \cong \triangle DCB$ (Given)
2. $\overline{EA} \cong \overline{DC}$ (CPCTC)
3. $\overline{ED} \cong \overline{DE}$ (Reflex. Prop.)
4. $\overline{AB} \cong \overline{CB}$ (CPCTC)
5. $\overline{DB} \cong \overline{EB}$ (CPCTC)
6. $AB = CB$, $DB = EB$ (Def. ≅ segments)
7. $AB + DB = CB + EB$ (Add. Prop. =)
8. $AD = AB + DB$, $CE = CB + EB$ (Seg. addition)
9. $AD = CE$ (Subst. Prop. =)
10. $\overline{AD} \cong \overline{CE}$ (Def. ≅ segments)
11. $\triangle EAD \cong \triangle DCE$ (SSS)

27 Given that $\triangle WXY \cong \triangle WXZ$, by CPCTC, $\angle WXZ \cong \angle WXY$ and $\overline{XY} \cong \overline{XZ}$.

$\angle WXZ \cong \angle WXY$	CPCTC
$m\angle WXZ = m\angle WXY$	Definition of congruence
$90 = 20y + 10$	Substitution
$80 = 20y$	Subtract 10 from each side.
$y = 4$	Divide each side by 20.

$\overline{XY} \cong \overline{XZ}$	CPCTC
$XY = XZ$	Definition of congruence
$3y + 7 = 19$	Substitution
$3y = 12$	Subtract 7 from each side.
$y = 4$	Divide each side by 3.

29a. Sample answer: Method 1: You could use the Distance Formula to find the length of each of the sides, and then use the Side-Side-Side Congruence Postulate to prove the triangles congruent. Method 2: You could find the slopes of $\overline{ZX}$ and $\overline{WY}$ to prove that they are perpendicular and that $\angle WYZ$ and $\angle WYX$ are both right angles. You can use the Distance Formula to prove that $\overline{XY}$ is congruent to $\overline{ZY}$. Since the triangles share the leg $\overline{WY}$, you can use the Side-Angle-Side Congruence Postulate; Sample answer: I think that method 2 is more efficient, because you only have two steps instead of three.

29b. Sample answer: Yes; the slope of $\overline{WY}$ is -1 and the slope of $\overline{ZX}$ is 1, and -1 and 1 are opposite reciprocals, so $\overline{WY}$ is perpendicular to $\overline{ZX}$. Since they are perpendicular, $\angle WYZ$ and $\angle WYX$ are both 90°. Using the Distance Formula, the length of $\overline{ZY}$ is $\sqrt{(4-1)^2 + (5-2)^2}$ or $3\sqrt{2}$, and the length of $\overline{XY}$ is $\sqrt{(7-4)^2 + (8-5)^2}$ or $3\sqrt{2}$. Since $\overline{WY}$ is congruent to $\overline{WY}$, $\triangle WYZ$ is congruent to $\triangle WYX$ by the Side-Angle-Side Congruence Postulate. **31.** Shada; for SAS the angle must be the included angle and here it is not included. **33.** Case 1: You know the hypotenuses are congruent and two corresponding legs are congruent. Then the Pythagorean Theorem says that the other legs are congruent so the triangles are congruent by SSS. Case 2: You know the legs are congruent and the right angles are congruent, then the triangles are congruent by SAS. **35.** F **37.** D **39.** 18

41. $y = -\frac{1}{5}x - 4$ **43.** $y = x + 3$ **45.** False; a 16-year-old could be a freshman, sophomore, junior, or senior. The hypothesis of the conditional is true, but the conclusion is false. This counterexample shows that the conditional statement is false. **47.** Trans. Prop. **49.** Substitution

Lesson 4-5

1. Given: $\overline{CB}$ bisects $\angle ABD$ and $\angle ACD$.
Prove: $\triangle ABC \cong \triangle DBC$

Proof:
Statements (Reasons)
1. $\overline{CB}$ bisects $\angle ABD$ and $\angle ACD$. (Given)
2. $\angle ABC \cong \angle DBC$ (Def. of ∠ bisector)
3. $\overline{BC} \cong \overline{BC}$ (Refl. prop.)
4. $\angle ACB \cong \angle DCB$ (Def. of ∠ bisector)
5. $\triangle ABC \cong \triangle DBC$ (ASA)

3. Given: $\angle K \cong \angle M$, $\overline{JK} \cong \overline{JM}$, $\overline{JL}$ bisects $\angle KLM$.
Prove: $\triangle JKL \cong \triangle JML$
Proof: We are given $\angle K \cong \angle M$, $\overline{JK} \cong \overline{JM}$, and $\overline{JL}$ bisects $\angle KLM$. Since $\overline{JL}$ bisects $\angle KLM$, we know $\angle KLJ \cong \angle MLJ$. So, $\triangle JKL \cong \triangle JML$ is congruent by the AAS Congruence Theorem.

5 **a.** We know $\angle BAE$ and $\angle DCE$ are congruent because they are both right angles. $\overline{AE}$ is congruent to $\overline{EC}$ by the Midpoint Theorem. From the Vertical Angles Theorem, $\angle DEC \cong \angle BEA$. So, two angles and the included side of $\triangle DCE$ are congruent to two angles and the included side of $\triangle BAE$. By ASA, the surveyor knows that $\triangle DCE \cong \triangle BAE$. By CPCTC, $\overline{DC} \cong \overline{AB}$, so the surveyor can measure $\overline{DC}$ and know the distance between A and B.

b.

$\triangle DCE \cong \triangle BAE$	SAS
$\overline{DC} \cong \overline{AB}$	CPCTC
$DC = AB$	Definition of congruence
$550 = AB$	Substitution

So, by the definition of congruence, $AB = 550$ m.

7. Given: $\angle W \cong \angle Y$, $\overline{WZ} \cong \overline{YZ}$, $\overline{XZ}$ bisects $\angle WZY$.
Prove: $\triangle XWZ \cong \triangle XYZ$
Proof: It is given that $\angle W \cong \angle Y$, $\overline{WZ} \cong \overline{YZ}$, and $\overline{XZ}$ bisects $\angle WZY$. By the definition of angle bisector, $\angle WZX \cong \angle YZX$. The Angle-Side-Angle Congruence Postulate tells us that $\triangle XWZ \cong \triangle XYZ$.

9 Use the Alternate Interior Angle Theorem and AAS to prove the triangles congruent.
Given: V is the midpoint of $\overline{YW}$; $\overline{UY} \parallel \overline{XW}$.
Prove: $\triangle UVY \cong \triangle XVW$
Proof:
Statements (Reasons)
1. V is the midpoint of $\overline{YW}$; $\overline{UY} \parallel \overline{XW}$. (Given)
2. $\overline{YV} \cong \overline{VW}$ (Midpoint Theorem)
3. $\angle VWX \cong \angle VYU$ (Alt. Int. ∡ Thm.)
4. $\angle VUY \cong \angle VXW$ (Alt. Int. ∡ Thm.)
5. $\triangle UVY \cong \triangle XVW$ (AAS)

11. Given: $\angle A$ and $\angle C$ are right angles. $\angle ABE \cong \angle CBD$, $\overline{AE} \cong \overline{CD}$
Prove: $\overline{BE} \cong \overline{BD}$
Proof:

$\angle A$ and $\angle C$ are right ∡. (Given) → $\angle A \cong \angle C$ (All right ∡ are ≅.); $\angle ABE \cong \angle CBD$ (Given); $\overline{AE} \cong \overline{CD}$ (Given) → $\triangle EBA \cong \triangle DBC$ (AAS) → $\overline{BE} \cong \overline{BD}$ (CPCTC)

13a. $\angle HJK \cong \angle GFK$ since all right angles are congruent. We are given that $\overline{JK} \cong \overline{KF}$. $\angle HKJ$ and $\angle FKG$ are vertical angles, so $\angle HKJ \cong \angle FKG$ by the Vertical Angles Theorem. By ASA, $\triangle HJK \cong \triangle GFK$, so $\overline{FG} \cong \overline{HJ}$ by CPCTC. **13b.** No; $HJ = 1350$ m, so $FG = 1350$ m. If the regatta is to be 1500 m, the lake is not long enough, since $1350 < 1500$.

15 If the triangles are congruent, $HJ = QJ$. Solve for y.

$HJ = QJ$	CPCTC
$9 = 2y - 1$	$HJ = 9$, $QJ = 2y - 1$
$y = 5$	Simplify.

17. Given: $\overline{AE} \perp \overline{DE}$, $\overline{EA} \perp \overline{AB}$, C is the midpoint of $\overline{AE}$.
Prove: $\overline{CD} \cong \overline{CB}$

Proof: We are given that $\overline{AE}$ is perpendicular to $\overline{DE}$, $\overline{EA}$ is perpendicular to $\overline{AB}$, and C is the midpoint of $\overline{AE}$. Since $\overline{AE}$ is perpendicular to $\overline{DE}$, $m\angle CED = 90$. Since $\overline{EA}$ is perpendicular to $\overline{AB}$, $m\angle BAC = 90$. $\angle CED \cong \angle BAC$ because all right angles are congruent. $\overline{AC} \cong \overline{CE}$ from the Midpt. Thm. $\angle ECD \cong \angle ACB$ because they are vertical angles. Angle-Side-Angle gives us that $\triangle CED \cong \triangle CAB$. $\overline{CD} \cong \overline{CB}$ because corresponding parts of congruent triangles are congruent.

19. Given: $\angle K \cong \angle M$, $\overline{KP} \perp \overline{PR}$, $\overline{MR} \perp \overline{PR}$
Prove: $\angle KPL \cong \angle MNL$
Proof:
Statements (Reasons)
1. $\angle K \cong \angle M$, $\overline{KP} \perp \overline{PR}$, $\overline{MR} \perp \overline{PR}$ (Given)
2. $\angle KPR$ and $\angle MRP$ are both right angles. (Def. of ⊥)
3. $\angle KPR \cong \angle MRP$ (All rt. ∡ are congruent.)
4. $\overline{PR} \cong \overline{PR}$ (Refl. Prop.)
5. $\triangle KPR \cong \triangle MRP$ (AAS)
6. $\overline{KP} \cong \overline{MR}$ (CPCTC)
7. $\angle KLP \cong \angle MLR$ (Vertical angles are ≅.)
8. $\triangle KLP \cong \triangle MLR$ (AAS)

9. $\angle KPL \cong \angle MRL$ (CPCTC)

21 Since $m\angle ACB = m\angle ADB = 44$, and $m\angle CBA = m\angle DBA = 68$, then $\angle ACB \cong \angle ADB$ and $\angle CBA \cong \angle DBA$ by the definition of congruence. $\overline{AB} \cong \overline{AB}$ by the Reflexive Property, so $\triangle ACB \cong \triangle ADB$ by AAS. Then $\overline{AC} \cong \overline{AD}$ by CPCTC. Since $AC = AD$ by the definition of congruence, the two seat stays are the same length.

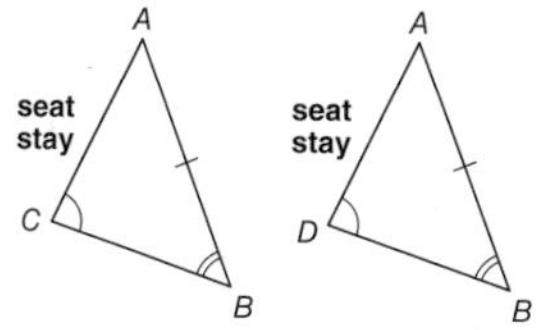

23. Tyrone; Lorenzo showed that all three corresponding angles were congruent, but AAA is not a proof of triangle congruence.

25.

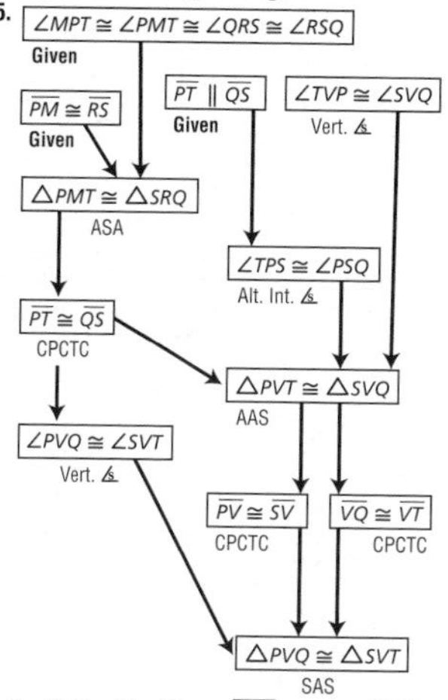

27. B 29. J 31. $AB = \sqrt{125}$, $BC = \sqrt{221}$, $AC = \sqrt{226}$, $XY = \sqrt{125}$, $YZ = \sqrt{221}$, $XZ = \sqrt{226}$. The corresponding sides have the same measure and are congruent. $\triangle ABC \cong \triangle XYZ$ by SSS.

33. $x = 19$; $y = 3$

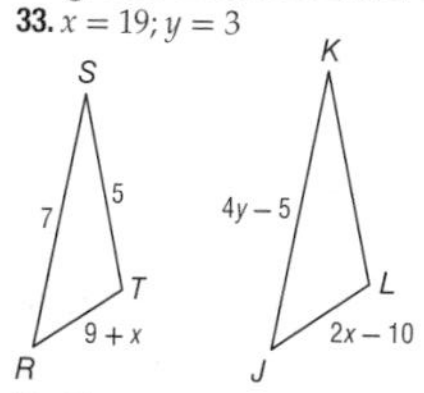

35.

p	q	$\sim p$	$\sim p \vee q$
F	T	T	T
T	T	F	T
F	F	T	T
T	F	F	F

37. **Given:** $\angle 2 \cong \angle 1$
$\angle 1 \cong \angle 3$
Prove: $\overline{AB} \parallel \overline{DE}$

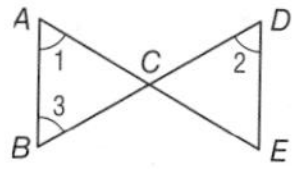

Statements (Reasons)
1. $\angle 2 \cong \angle 1$, $\angle 1 \cong \angle 3$ (Given)
2. $\angle 2 \cong \angle 3$ (Trans. Prop.)
3. $\overline{AB} \parallel \overline{DE}$ (If alt. int. ∠s are ≅, lines are ∥.)

Lesson 4-6

1. $\angle BAC$ and $\angle BCA$ 3. 12 5. 12

7. **Given:** $\triangle ABC$ is isosceles; $\overline{EB}$ bisects $\angle ABC$.
Prove: $\triangle ABE \cong \triangle CBE$
Proof:
Statements (Reasons)
1. $\triangle ABC$ is isosceles; $\overline{EB}$ bisects $\angle ABC$. (Given)
2. $\overline{AB} \cong \overline{BC}$ (Def. of isosceles)
3. $\angle ABE \cong \angle CBE$ (Def. of ∠ bisector)
4. $\overline{BE} \cong \overline{BE}$ (Refl. Prop.)
5. $\triangle ABE \cong \triangle CBE$ (SAS)

9 $\angle ABE$ is opposite $\overline{AE}$ and $\angle AEB$ is opposite $\overline{AB}$. Since $\overline{AE} \cong \overline{AB}$, $\angle ABE \cong \angle AEB$.

11. $\angle ACD$ and $\angle ADC$ 13. $\overline{BF}$ and $\overline{BC}$ 15. 60 17. 4

19 The triangle is equiangular, so it is also equilateral. All the sides are congruent.

$2x + 11 = 6x - 9$	Definition of congruence
$11 = 4x - 9$	Subtract $2x$ from each side.
$20 = 4x$	Add 9 to each side.
$5 = x$	Divide each side by 4.

21. $x = 11$, $y = 11$

23. **Given:** $\triangle HJM$ is an isosceles triangle and $\triangle HKL$ is an equilateral triangle. $\angle JKH$, $\angle HKL$ and $\angle HLK$, $\angle MLH$ are supplementary.
Prove: $\angle JHK \cong \angle MHL$

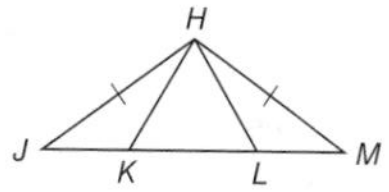

Proof: We are given that $\triangle HJM$ is an isosceles triangle and $\triangle HKL$ is an equilateral triangle, $\angle JKH$ and $\angle HKL$ are supplementary and $\angle HLK$ and $\angle MLH$ are supplementary. From the Isosceles Triangle Theorem, we know that $\angle HJK \cong \angle HML$. Since $\triangle HKL$ is an equilateral triangle, we know $\angle HLK \cong \angle LKH \cong \angle KHL$ and $\overline{HL} \cong \overline{KL} \cong \overline{HK}$. $\angle JKH$, $\angle HKL$ and $\angle HLK$, $\angle MLH$ are supplementary, and $\angle HKL \cong \angle HLK$, we know $\angle JKH \cong \angle MLH$ by the Congruent Supplements Theorem. By AAS, $\triangle JHK \cong \triangle MLH$. By CPCTC, $\angle JHK \cong \angle MHL$.

25a. 65°; Since $\triangle ABC$ is isosceles, $\angle ABC \cong \angle ACB$, so $180 - 50 = 130$ and $\frac{130}{2}$ or 65.

25b. **Given:** $\overline{BE} \cong \overline{CD}$
Prove: $\triangle AED$ is isosceles.
Proof:
Statements (Reasons)
1. $\overline{AB} \cong \overline{AC}$, $\overline{BE} \cong \overline{CD}$ (Given)
2. $AB = AC$, $BE = CD$ (Def. of congruence)
3. $AB + BE = AE$, $AC + CD = AD$ (Seg. Add. Post.)
4. $AB + BE = AC + CD$ (Add. Prop. of Eq.)
5. $AE = AD$ (Subst.)
6. $\overline{AE} \cong \overline{AD}$ (Def. of congruence)
7. $\triangle AED$ is isosceles. (Def. of isosceles)

25c. **Given:** $\overline{BC} \parallel \overline{ED}$ and $\overline{ED} \cong \overline{AD}$
Prove: $\triangle ADE$ is equilateral.
Proof:
Statements (Reasons)
1. $\overline{AB} \cong \overline{AC}$, $\overline{BC} \parallel \overline{ED}$ and $\overline{ED} \cong \overline{AD}$ (Given)
2. $\angle ABC \cong \angle ACB$ (Isos. △ Thm.)
3. $m\angle ABC = m\angle ACB$ (Def. of ≅)
4. $\angle ABC \cong \angle AED$, $\angle ACB \cong \angle ADE$ (Corr. ∠s Thm.)
5. $m\angle ABC = m\angle AED$, $m\angle ACB = m\angle ADE$ (Def. of ≅)
6. $m\angle AED = m\angle ACB$ (Subst.)
7. $m\angle AED = m\angle ADE$ (Subst.)
8. $\angle AED \cong \angle ADE$ (Def. of ≅)
9. $\overline{AD} \cong \overline{AE}$ (Conv. of Isos. △ Thm.)
10. $\triangle ADE$ is equilateral. (Def. of equilateral △)

25d. One pair of congruent corresponding sides and one pair of congruent corresponding angles; since you know that the triangle is isosceles, if one leg is congruent to a leg of $\triangle ABC$, then you know that both pairs of legs are congruent. Because the base angles of an isosceles triangle are congruent, if you know that $\angle K \cong \angle B$ you know that $\angle K \cong \angle L$, $\angle B \cong \angle C$, and $\angle C \cong \angle L$. Therefore, with one pair of congruent corresponding sides and one pair of congruent corresponding angles, the triangles can be proved congruent using either ASA or SAS.

27.

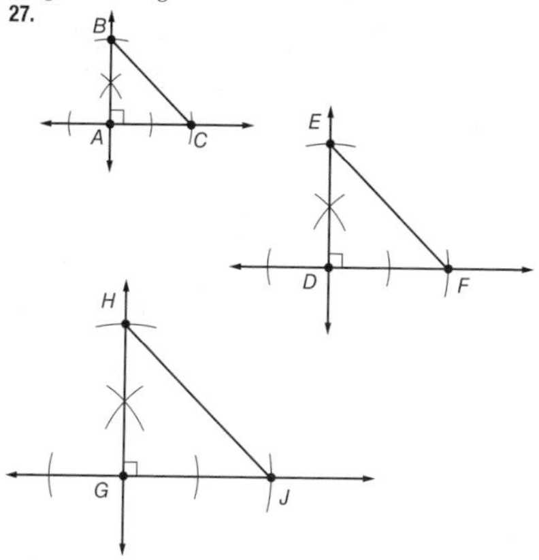

Sample answer: I constructed a pair of perpendicular segments and then used the same compass setting to mark points equidistant from their intersection. I measured both legs for each triangle. Since $AB = AC = 1.3$ cm, $DE = DF = 1.9$ cm, and $GH = GJ = 2.3$ cm, the triangles are isosceles. I used a protractor to confirm that $\angle A$, $\angle D$, and $\angle G$ are all right angles.

29 Since $\overline{AD} \cong \overline{CD}$, base angles CAD and ACD are congruent by the Isosceles Triangle Theorem. So, $m\angle CAD = m\angle ACD$.

$m\angle CAD + m\angle ACD + m\angle D = 180$	Triangle Angle-Sum Theorem
$m\angle CAD + m\angle CAD + 92 = 180$	Substitution
$2m\angle CAD + 92 = 180$	Simplify.
$2m\angle CAD = 88$	Subtract 92 from each side.
$m\angle CAD = 44$	Simplify.

31. 136

33. **Given:** Each triangle is isosceles, $\overline{BG} \cong \overline{HC}$, $\overline{HD} \cong \overline{JF}$, $\angle G \cong \angle H$, and $\angle H \cong \angle J$.
Prove: The distance from B to F is three times the distance from D to F.
Proof:
Statements (Reasons)
1. Each triangle is isosceles, $\overline{BG} \cong \overline{HC}$, $\overline{HD} \cong \overline{JF}$, $\angle G \cong \angle H$, and $\angle H \cong \angle J$. (Given)
2. $\angle G \cong \angle J$ (Trans. Prop.)
3. $\overline{BG} \cong \overline{CG}$, $\overline{HC} \cong \overline{HD}$, $\overline{JD} \cong \overline{JF}$ (Def. of Isosceles)
4. $\overline{BG} \cong \overline{JD}$ (Trans. Prop.)
5. $\overline{HC} \cong \overline{JD}$ (Trans. Prop.)
6. $\overline{CG} \cong \overline{JF}$ (Trans. Prop.)
7. $\triangle BCG \cong \triangle CDH \cong \triangle DFJ$ (SAS)
8. $\overline{BC} \cong \overline{CD} \cong \overline{DF}$ (CPCTC)
9. $BC = CD = DF$ (Def. of congruence)
10. $BC + CD + DF = BF$ (Seg. Add. Post.)
11. $DF + DF + DF = BF$ (Subst.)
12. $3DF = BF$ (Addition)

35. Case I
Given: $\triangle ABC$ is an equilateral triangle.
Prove: $\triangle ABC$ is an equiangular triangle.

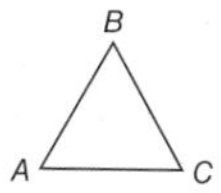

Proof:
Statements (Reasons)
1. $\triangle ABC$ is an equilateral triangle. (Given)
2. $\overline{AB} \cong \overline{AC} \cong \overline{BC}$ (Def. of equilateral △)
3. $\angle A \cong \angle B \cong \angle C$ (Isosceles △ Th.)
4. $\triangle ABC$ is an equiangular triangle. (Def. of equiangular)

Case II
Given: $\triangle ABC$ is an equiangular triangle.
Prove: $\triangle ABC$ is an equilateral triangle.

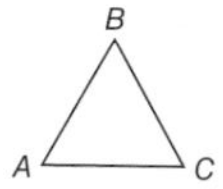

Proof:
Statements (Reasons)
1. $\triangle ABC$ is an equiangular triangle. (Given)
2. $\angle A \cong \angle B \cong \angle C$ (Def. of equiangular △)
3. $\overline{AB} \cong \overline{AC} \cong \overline{BC}$ (If 2 ∠s of a △ are ≅ then the sides opp. those ∠s are ≅.)
4. $\triangle ABC$ is an equilateral triangle. (Def. of equilateral)

37. **Given:** $\triangle ABC$, $\angle A \cong \angle C$
Prove: $\overline{AB} \cong \overline{CB}$

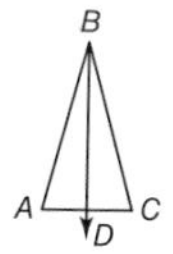

Proof:
Statements (Reasons)
1. Let $\overrightarrow{BD}$ bisect $\angle ABC$. (Protractor Post.)
2. $\angle ABD \cong \angle CBD$ (Def. of ∠ bisector)
3. $\angle A \cong \angle C$ (Given)

4. $\overline{BD} \cong \overline{BD}$ (Refl. Prop.)
5. $\triangle ABD \cong \triangle CBD$ (AAS)
6. $\overline{AB} \cong \overline{CB}$ (CPCTC)

39. 14

41

$m\angle LPM + m\angle LPQ = 180$	Supplement Theorem
$(3x - 55) + (2x + 10) = 180$	Substitution
$5x - 45 = 180$	Simplify.
$5x = 225$	Add 45 to each side.
$x = 45$	Divide each side by 45.

$m\angle LPM = 3x - 55$	Given
$= 3(45) - 55$	Substitution
$= 135 - 55$ or 80	Simplify.

Because $\overline{LM} \cong \overline{LP}$, base angles LMP and LPM are congruent by the Isosceles Triangle Theorem. So, $m\angle LMP = m\angle LPM = 80$.

43. 80

45. Given: $\triangle WJZ$ is equilateral, and $\angle ZWP \cong \angle WJM \cong \angle JZL$.

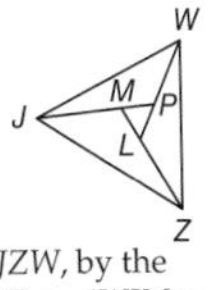

Prove: $\overline{WP} \cong \overline{ZL} \cong \overline{JM}$

Proof: We know that $\triangle WJZ$ is equilateral, since an equilateral $\triangle$ is equiangular, $\angle ZWJ \cong \angle WJZ \cong \angle JZW$. So, $m\angle ZWJ = m\angle WJZ = m\angle JZW$, by the definition of congruence. Since $\angle ZWP \cong \angle WJM \cong \angle JZL$, $m\angle ZWP = m\angle WJM = m\angle JZL$, by the definition of congruence. By the Angle Addition Postulate, $m\angle ZWJ = m\angle ZWP + m\angle PWJ$, $m\angle WJZ = m\angle WJM + m\angle MJZ$, $m\angle JZW = m\angle JZL + m\angle LZW$. By substitution, $m\angle ZWP + m\angle PWJ = m\angle WJM + m\angle MJZ = m\angle JZL + m\angle LZW$. Again by substitution, $m\angle ZWP + m\angle PWJ = m\angle ZWP + m\angle PJZ = m\angle ZWP + m\angle LZW$. By the Subtraction Property, $m\angle PWJ = m\angle PJZ = m\angle LZW$. By the definition of congruence, $\angle PWJ \cong \angle PJZ \cong \angle LZW$. So, by ASA, $\triangle WZL \cong \triangle ZJM \cong \triangle JWP$. By CPCTC, $\overline{WP} \cong \overline{ZL} \cong \overline{JM}$.

47. Never; the measure of the vertex angle will be 180 − 2(measure of the base angle) so if the base angles are integers, then 2(measure of the base angle) will be even and 180 − 2(measure of the base angle) will be even. **49.** It is not possible because a triangle cannot have more than one obtuse angle.

51. Sample answer: If a triangle is already classified, you can use the previously proven properties of that type of triangle in the proof. Doing this can save you steps when writing the proof. **53.** 185 **55.** E

57. $SU = \sqrt{17}$, $TU = \sqrt{2}$, $ST = 5$, $XZ = \sqrt{29}$, $YZ = 2$, $XY = 5$; the corresponding sides are not congruent; the triangles are not congruent.

59. Given: $AC = BD$
Prove: $AB = CD$

1. $AC = BD$ (Given)
2. $AC = AB + BC$, $BD = BC + CD$ (Seg. Add. Post.)
3. $AB + BC = BC + CD$ (Subst.)
4. $\overline{BC} \cong \overline{BC}$ (Reflexive)
5. $BC = BC$ (Def. of $\cong$ Segs.)
6. $AB = CD$ (Subt. Prop.)

61. Add. Prop. **63.** Trans. Prop. **65.** *A, K, B* or *B, J, C*

67. Given: $\angle ACB \cong \angle ABC$
Prove: $\angle XCA \cong \angle YBA$

Statements (Reasons)
1. $\angle ACB \cong \angle ABC$ (Given)
2. $\angle XCA$ and $\angle ACB$ are a linear pair. $\angle ABC$ and $\angle ABY$ are a linear pair. (Def. of linear pair)
3. $\angle XCA$, $\angle ACB$ and $\angle ABC$, $\angle ABY$ are supplementary. (Suppl. Thm.)
4. $\angle XCA \cong \angle YBA$ ($\angle$s suppl. to $\cong$ $\angle$s are $\cong$.)

Lesson 4-7

1. translation **3.** reflection **5.** $\triangle LKJ$ is a reflection of $\triangle XYZ$. $XY = 7$, $YZ = 8$, $XZ = \sqrt{113}$, $KJ = 8$, $LJ = \sqrt{113}$, $LK = 7$. $\triangle XYZ \cong \triangle LKJ$ by SSS. **7.** reflection

9 The image in green can be found by translating the blue figure to the right and up, by reflecting the figure in the line $y = -x$, or by rotating the figure 180° in either direction.

11. rotation **13.** translation **15.** rotation

17

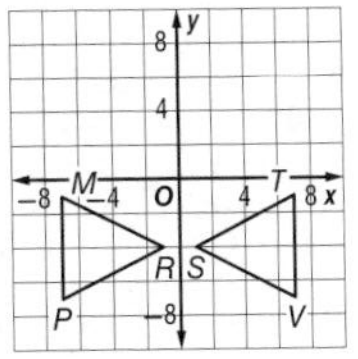

Use $d = \sqrt{(x_2 - x_1)^2 + (y_2 - y_1)^2}$ to find the lengths of the sides of $\triangle MPR$.

$MP = \sqrt{[-7 - (-7)]^2 + [-7 - (-1)]^2}$	$(x_1, y_1) = (-7, -1)$, $(x_2, y_2) = (-7, -7)$
$= \sqrt{0 + 36}$ or 6	Simplify.
$PR = \sqrt{[-1 - (-7)]^2 + [-4 - (-7)]^2}$	$(x_1, y_1) = (-7, -7)$, $(x_2, y_2) = (-1, -4)$
$= \sqrt{36 + 9}$ or $\sqrt{45}$	Simplify.
$MR = \sqrt{[-1 - (-7)]^2 + [-4 - (-1)]^2}$	$(x_1, y_1) = (-7, -1)$, $(x_2, y_2) = (-1, -4)$
$= \sqrt{36 + 9}$ or $\sqrt{45}$	Simplify.

Find the lengths of the sides of $\triangle TVS$.

$ST = \sqrt{(7 - 1)^2 + [-1 - (-4)]^2}$	$(x_1, y_1) = (1, -4)$, $(x_2, y_2) = (7, -1)$
$= \sqrt{36 + 9}$ or $\sqrt{45}$	Simplify.
$TV = \sqrt{(7 - 7)^2 + [-7 - (-1)]^2}$	$(x_1, y_1) = (7, -1)$, $(x_2, y_2) = (7, -7)$
$= \sqrt{0 + 36}$ or 6	Simplify.
$SV = \sqrt{(7 - 1)^2 + [-7 - (-4)]^2}$	$(x_1, y_1) = (1, -4)$, $(x_2, y_2) = (7, -7)$
$= \sqrt{36 + 9}$ or $\sqrt{45}$	Simplify.

In $\triangle MPR$, $MP = 6$, $PR = \sqrt{45}$, and $MR = \sqrt{45}$. In $\triangle TVS$, $ST = \sqrt{45}$, $TV = 6$, $SV = \sqrt{45}$. $\triangle MPR \cong \triangle TVS$ by SSS. $\triangle TVS$ is a reflection of $\triangle MPR$.

19.

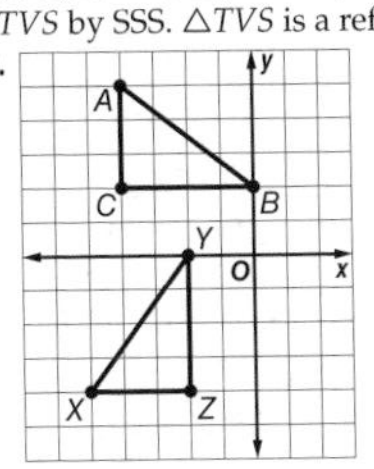

$\triangle XYZ$ is a rotation of $\triangle ABC$. $AB = 5$, $BC = 4$, $AC = 3$, $XY = 5$, $YZ = 4$, $XZ = 3$. Since $AB = XY$, $BC = YZ$, and $AC = XZ$, $\overline{AB} \cong \overline{XY}$, $\overline{BC} \cong \overline{YZ}$, and $\overline{AC} \cong \overline{XZ}$, $\triangle ABC \cong \triangle XYZ$ by SSS.

21. rotation
23. reflection
25. rotation

27. Rotation; the knob is the center of rotation.

29 **a.** Tionne used the stencil on one side, then flipped it and used the other side, then flipped it again to create the third flower in the design. She could have also used the stencil, then turned it to create the second flower, and turned it again to create the third flower. So, she could have used reflections or rotations. **b.** Tionne used the stamp, then turned it to create the second flower, and turned it again to create the third flower. So, she used rotations.

31a. translation, reflection **31b.** Sample answer: The triangles must be either isosceles or equilateral. When triangles are isosceles or equilateral, they have a line of symmetry, so reflections result in the same figure. **33.** Sample answer: A person looking in a mirror sees a reflection of himself or herself.

35. Sample answer: A faucet handle rotates when you turn the water on. **37.** no; 75% **39.** J **41.** 4
43. 10 **45.** yes; Law of Detachment **47.** (8, 9.5)
49. (−7.5, 3.5) **51.** (1, 9.5)

Lesson 4-8

1.

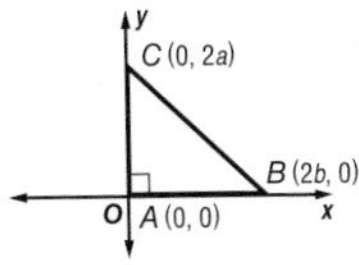

3. $T(2a, 0)$

5. $DC = \sqrt{[-a - (-a)]^2 + (b - 0)^2}$ or b

$GH = \sqrt{(a - a)^2 + (b - 0)^2}$ or b

Since $DC = GH$, $\overline{DC} \cong \overline{GH}$.

$DF = \sqrt{(0 - a)^2 + \left(\frac{b}{2} - b\right)^2}$ or $\sqrt{a^2 + \frac{b^2}{4}}$

$GF = \sqrt{(a - 0)^2 + \left(b - \frac{b}{2}\right)^2}$ or $\sqrt{a^2 + \frac{b^2}{4}}$

$CF = \sqrt{(0 - a)^2 + \left(\frac{b}{2} - 0\right)^2}$ or $\sqrt{a^2 + \frac{b^2}{4}}$

$HF = \sqrt{(a - 0)^2 + \left(0 - \frac{b}{2}\right)^2}$ or $\sqrt{a^2 + \frac{b^2}{4}}$

Since $DF = GF = CF = HF$, $\overline{DF} \cong \overline{GF} \cong \overline{CF} \cong \overline{HF}$. $\triangle FGH \cong \triangle FDC$ by SSS.

7.

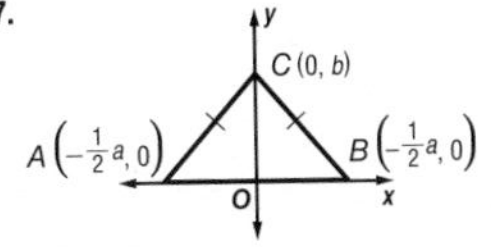

9 Since this is a right triangle, each of the legs can be located on an axis. Placing the right angle of the triangle, $\angle T$, at the origin will allow the two legs to be along the x- and y-axes. Position the triangle in the first quadrant. Since R is on the y-axis, its x-coordinate is 0. Its y-coordinate is $3a$ because the leg is $3a$ units long. Since S is on the x-axis, its y-coordinate is 0. Its x-coordinate is $3a$ because the leg is $3a$ units long.

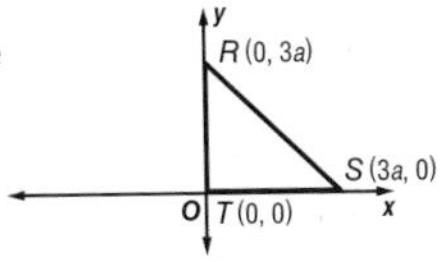

11.

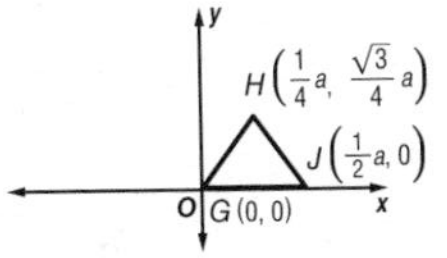

13. $C(a, a)$, $Y(a, 0)$

15 Vertex N is positioned at the origin. So, its coordinates are (0, 0). Vertex L is on the x-axis, so its y-coordinate is 0. The coordinates of vertex L are $(3a, 0)$. $\triangle NJL$ is isosceles, so the x-coordinate of J is located halfway between 0 and $3a$, or $1.5a$. The coordinates of vertex J are $(1.5a, b)$. So, the vertices are $N(0, 0)$, $J(1.5a, b)$, $L(3a, 0)$.

17. $H(2b, 2b\sqrt{3})$, $N(0, 0)$, $D(4b, 0)$

19. Given: Isosceles $\triangle ABC$ with $\overline{AC} \cong \overline{BC}$; R and S are midpoints of legs $\overline{AC}$ and $\overline{BC}$.
Prove: $\overline{AS} \cong \overline{BR}$

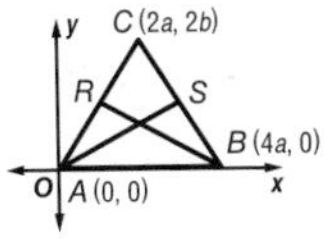

Proof:
The coordinates of S are $\left(\frac{2a + 4a}{2}, \frac{2b + 0}{2}\right)$ or $(3a, b)$.

The coordinates of R are $\left(\frac{2a + 0}{2}, \frac{2b + 0}{2}\right)$ or (a, b).

$AS = \sqrt{(3a - 0)^2 + (b - 0)^2}$ or $\sqrt{9a^2 + b^2}$

$BR = \sqrt{(4a - a)^2 + (0 - b)^2}$ or $\sqrt{9a^2 + b^2}$

Since $AS = BR$, $\overline{AS} \cong \overline{BR}$.

21. Given: Right $\triangle ABC$ with right $\angle BAC$; P is the midpoint of $\overline{BC}$.
Prove: $AP = \frac{1}{2}BC$

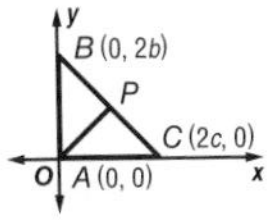

Proof:
Midpoint P is $\left(\frac{0 + 2c}{2}, \frac{2b + 0}{2}\right)$ or (c, b).

$AP = \sqrt{(c - 0)^2 + (b - 0)^2}$ or $\sqrt{c^2 + b^2}$

$BC = \sqrt{(2c - 0)^2 + (0 - 2b)^2} = \sqrt{4c^2 + 4b^2}$ or $2\sqrt{c^2 + b^2}$

$\frac{1}{2}BC = \sqrt{c^2 + b^2}$

So, $AP = \frac{1}{2}BC$.

23. The distance between Raleigh and Durham is about 0.32 units, between Raleigh and Chapel Hill is about 0.41 units, and between Durham and Chapel Hill is about 0.15 units. Since none of these distances are the same, the Research Triangle is scalene.

25. slope of $\overline{XY} = 1$, slope of $\overline{YZ} = -1$, slope of $\overline{ZX} = 0$; since $1(-1) = -1$, $\overline{XY} \perp \overline{YZ}$. Therefore, $\triangle XYZ$ is a right triangle.

27. The slope between the tents is $-\frac{4}{3}$. The slope between the ranger's station and the tent located at (12, 9) is $\frac{3}{4}$. Since $-\frac{4}{3} \cdot \frac{3}{4} = -1$, the triangle formed by the tents and ranger's station is a right triangle.

29 a.

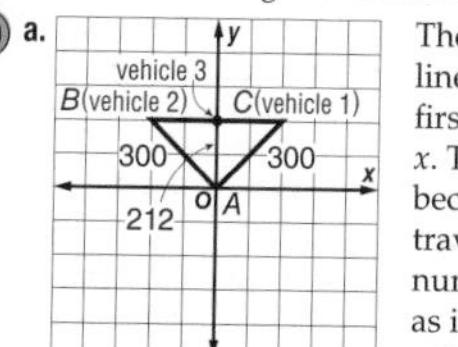

The equation of the line along which the first vehicle lies is $y = x$. The slope is 1 because the vehicle travels the same number of units north as it does east of the origin and the y-intercept is 0. The equation of the line along which the second vehicle lies is $y = -x$. The slope is -1 because the vehicle travels the same number of units north as it does west of the origin and the y-intercept is 0.

b. The paths taken by both the first and second vehicles are 300 yards long. Therefore, the paths are congruent. If two sides of a triangle are congruent, then the triangle is isosceles. You can also write a coordinate proof to prove the triangle formed is isosceles.

Given: $\triangle ABC$

Prove: $\triangle ABC$ is an isosceles right triangle.

Proof: By the Distance Formula,

$AB = \sqrt{(-a - 0)^2 + (a - 0)^2}$ or $\sqrt{2a^2}$ and

$AC = \sqrt{(a - 0)^2 + (a - 0)^2}$ or $\sqrt{2a^2}$. So, $AB = AC$

and $\overline{AB} \cong \overline{AC}$. The triangle is isosceles. By the Slope Formula, the slope of $\overline{AB}$ is $\frac{a}{-a}$ or -1 and the slope of $\overline{AC}$ is $\frac{a}{a}$ or 1. Since the slopes are negative reciprocals, the sides of the triangle are perpendicular and therefore form a right angle. So, $\triangle ABC$ is an isosceles right triangle.

c. The paths taken by the first two vehicles form the hypotenuse of isosceles right triangles.

$a^2 + b^2 = c^2$	Pythagorean Theorem
$a^2 + a^2 = 300^2$	$b = a$
$2a^2 = 90{,}000$	Simplify.
$a^2 = 45{,}000$	Divide each side by 2.
$a = 150\sqrt{2}$	Take the positive square root of each side.

First vehicle: $(a, a) = (150\sqrt{2}, 150\sqrt{2})$; second vehicle: $(-a, a) = (-150\sqrt{2}, 150\sqrt{2})$. The third vehicle travels due north and therefore, remains on the y-axis; third vehicle: (0, 212)

d. The y-coordinates of the first two vehicles are $150\sqrt{2} \approx 212.13$, while the y-coordinate of the third vehicle is 212. Since all three vehicles have approximately the same y-coordinate, they are approximately collinear. The midpoint between the first and second vehicles is

$\left(\frac{150\sqrt{2} + (-150\sqrt{2})}{2}, \frac{150\sqrt{2} + 150\sqrt{2}}{2}\right)$

or approximately (0, 212.13). This is the approximate location of the third vehicle.

31. Sample answer: $(a, 0)$ **33.** Sample answer: $(4a, 0)$

35. Given: $\triangle ABC$ with coordinates $A(0, 0)$, $B(a, b)$, and $C(c, d)$ and $\triangle DEF$ with coordinates $D(0 + n, 0 + m)$, $E(a + n, b + m)$, and $F(c + n, d + m)$

Prove: $\triangle DEF \cong \triangle ABC$

Proof:

$AB = \sqrt{(a - 0)^2 + (b - 0)^2}$ or $\sqrt{a^2 + b^2}$

$DE = \sqrt{[a + n - (0 + n)]^2 + [b + m - (0 + m)]^2}$ or $\sqrt{a^2 + b^2}$

Since $AB = DE$, $\overline{AB} \cong \overline{DE}$.

$BC = \sqrt{(c - a)^2 + (d - b)^2}$ or $\sqrt{c^2 - 2ac + a^2 + d^2 - 2bd + b^2}$

$EF = \sqrt{[c + n - (a + n)]^2 + [d + m - (b + m)]^2}$ or $\sqrt{c^2 - 2ac + a^2 + d^2 - 2bd + b^2}$

Since $BC = EF$, $\overline{BC} \cong \overline{EF}$.

$CA = \sqrt{(c - 0)^2 + (d - 0)^2}$ or $\sqrt{c^2 + d^2}$

$FD = \sqrt{[0 + n - (c + n)]^2 + [0 + m - (d + m)]^2}$ or $\sqrt{c^2 + d^2}$

Since $CA = FD$, $\overline{CA} \cong \overline{FD}$.

Therefore, $\triangle DEF \cong \triangle ABC$ by the SSS Postulate.

37a. Using the origin as a vertex of the triangle makes calculations easier because the coordinates are (0, 0). **37b.** Placing at least one side of the triangle on the x- or y-axis makes it easier to calculate the length of the side since one of the coordinates will be 0. **37c.** Keeping a triangle within the first quadrant makes all of the coordinates positive, and makes the calculations easier. **39.** D **41.** C **43.** reflection, translation, or rotation **45.** Sample answer: $\angle TSR \cong \angle TRS$ **47.** Sample answer: $\triangle RQV \cong \triangle SQV$ **49.** 4.2 **51.** 3.6

Chapter 4 Study Guide & Review

1. true **3.** true **5.** false; base **7.** true **9.** false; coordinate proof **11.** obtuse **13.** right **15.** $x = 6$, $JK = KL = JL = 24$ **17.** 70 **19.** 82 **21.** $\angle D \cong \angle J$, $\angle A \cong \angle F$, $\angle C \cong \angle H$, $\angle B \cong \angle G$, $\overline{AB} \cong \overline{FG}$, $\overline{BC} \cong \overline{HG}$, $\overline{DC} \cong \overline{JH}$, $\overline{DA} \cong \overline{JF}$; polygon $ABCD \cong$ polygon $FGHJ$ **23.** $\triangle BFG \cong \triangle CGH \cong \triangle DHE \cong \triangle AEF$, $\triangle EFG \cong \triangle FGH \cong \triangle GHE \cong \triangle HEF$ **25.** No, the corresp. sides of the 2 $\triangle$s are not $\cong$. **27.** not possible

29. Given: $\overline{AB} \parallel \overline{DC}$, $\overline{AB} \cong \overline{DC}$

Prove: $\triangle ABE \cong \triangle CDE$

Proof:

Statements (Reasons)

1. $\overline{AB} \parallel \overline{DC}$ (Given)
2. $\angle A \cong \angle DCE$ (Alt. Int. $\angle$s Thm.)
3. $\overline{AB} \parallel \overline{DC}$ (Given)
4. $\angle ABE \cong \angle D$ (Alt. Int. $\angle$s Thm.)
5. $\triangle ABE \cong \triangle CDE$ (ASA)

31. 3 **33.** 77.5 **35.** reflection **37.** rotation **39.**

41. Given: $\triangle DSH$ with vertices $D(8, 28)$, $S(0, 0)$, and $H(19, 7)$

Prove: $\triangle DSH$ is scalene.

Proof:

Statements (Reasons)

1. $D(8, 28)$, $S(0, 0)$, and $H(19, 7)$ (Given)
2. $\overline{DS} = \sqrt{(8 - 0)^2 + (28 - 0)^2}$ or $\sqrt{848}$ (Distance Formula)
3. $\overline{SH} = \sqrt{(19 - 0)^2 + (7 - 0)^2}$ or $\sqrt{410}$ (Distance Formula)
4. $\overline{DH} = \sqrt{(8 - 19)^2 + (28 - 7)^2}$ or $\sqrt{562}$ (Distance Formula)
5. $\overline{DS} \ncong \overline{SH} \ncong \overline{DH}$
6. $\triangle DSH$ is a scalene triangle. (Definition of scalene)

CHAPTER 5 Relationships in Triangles

Chapter 5 Get Ready

1. 9 **3.** 10 ft **5.** $JK = KL = LM = MJ$ **7.** Sometimes; the conjecture is true when E is between D and F, otherwise it is false. **9.** $-6 > x$ **11.** $x < 41$

Lesson 5-1

1. 12 **3.** 15 **5.** 8 **7.** 12

9 $\overrightarrow{MP}$ is the perpendicular bisector of $\overline{LN}$.

$LP = NP$	Perpendicular Bisector Theorem
$2x - 4 = x + 5$	Substitution
$x - 4 = 5$	Subtract x from each side.
$x = 9$	Add 4 to each side.

$NP = 9 + 5$ or 14

11. 6 **13.** 4 **15.** M **17.** $\overline{CD}$, $\overline{BD}$ **19.** $\overline{BH}$ **21.** 11

23 Since $\overline{QM} \perp \overrightarrow{NM}$, $\overline{QP} \perp \overrightarrow{NP}$, and $QM = QP$, Q is equidistant from the sides of $\angle PNM$. By the Converse of the Angle Bisector Theorem, $\overrightarrow{NQ}$ bisects $\angle PNM$.

$\angle PNQ \cong \angle QNM$	Definition of angle bisector
$m\angle PNQ = m\angle QNM$	Definition of congruent angles
$4x - 8 = 3x + 5$	Substitution
$x - 8 = 5$	Subtract $3x$ from each side.
$x = 13$	Add 8 to each side.

$m\angle PNM = m\angle PNQ + m\angle QNM$	Angle Addition Postulate
$= (4x - 8) + (3x + 5)$	Substitution
$= 7x - 3$	Simplify.
$= 7(13) - 3$ or 88	$x = 13$

25. 42 **27.** 7.1 **29.** 33

31 Sketch the table and draw the three angle bisectors of the triangle.

Find the point of concurrency of the angle bisectors of the triangle, the incenter. This point is equidistant from each side of the triangle. So, the centerpiece should be placed at the incenter.

33. No; we need to know whether the perpendicular segments are congruent to each other. **35.** No; we need to know whether the hypotenuses of the triangles are congruent.

37. Given: $\overline{CA} \cong \overline{CB}$, $\overline{AD} \cong \overline{BD}$

Prove: C and D are on the perpendicular bisector of $\overline{AB}$.

Proof:

Statements (Reasons)

1. $\overline{CA} \cong \overline{CB}$, $\overline{AD} \cong \overline{BD}$ (Given)
2. $\overline{CD} \cong \overline{CD}$ (Congruence of segments is reflexive.)
3. $\triangle ACD \cong \triangle BCD$ (SSS)
4. $\angle ACD \cong \angle BCD$ (CPCTC)
5. $\overline{CE} \cong \overline{CE}$ (Congruence of segments is reflexive.)
6. $\triangle CEA \cong \triangle CEB$ (SAS)
7. $\overline{AE} \cong \overline{BE}$ (CPCTC)
8. E is the midpoint of $\overline{AB}$. (Def. of midpoint)
9. $\angle CEA \cong \angle CEB$ (CPCTC)
10. $\angle CEA$ and $\angle CEB$ form a linear pair. (Def. of linear pair)
11. $\angle CEA$ and $\angle CEB$ are supplementary.

(Supplement Theorem)
12. $m\angle CEA + m\angle CEB = 180$ (Def. of supplementary)
13. $m\angle CEA + m\angle CEA = 180$ (Substitution Prop.)
14. $2m\angle CEA = 180$ (Substitution Prop.)
15. $m\angle CEA = 90$ (Division Prop.)
16. $\angle CEA$ and $\angle CEB$ are rt. $\angle$. (Def. of rt. $\angle$)
17. $\overline{CD} \perp \overline{AB}$ (Def. of $\perp$)
18. $\overline{CD}$ is the perpendicular bisector of $\overline{AB}$. (Def. of $\perp$ bisector)
19. C and D are on the perpendicular bisector of $\overline{AB}$. (Def. of point on a line)

39. Given: $\overline{CD}$ is the $\perp$ bisector of $\overline{AB}$. E is a point on $\overline{CD}$.
Prove: $EA = EB$
Proof: $\overline{CD}$ is the $\perp$ bisector of $\overline{AB}$. By definition of $\perp$ bisector, D is the midpoint of $\overline{AB}$. Thus, $\overline{AD} \cong \overline{BD}$ by the Midpoint Theorem. $\angle CDA$ and $\angle CDB$ are right angles by the definition of perpendicular. Since all right angles are congruent, $\angle CDA \cong \angle CDB$. Since E is a point on $\overline{CD}$, $\angle EDA$ and $\angle EDB$ are right angles and are congruent. By the Reflexive Property, $\overline{ED} \cong \overline{ED}$. Thus, $\triangle EDA \cong \triangle EDB$ by SAS. $\overline{EA} \cong \overline{EB}$ because CPCTC, and by definition of congruence, $EA = EB$.

41. $y = -\frac{7}{2}x + \frac{15}{4}$; The perpendicular bisector bisects the segment at the midpoint of the segment. The midpoint is $\left(\frac{1}{2}, 2\right)$. The slope of the given segment is $\frac{2}{7}$, so the slope of the perpendicular bisector is $-\frac{7}{2}$.

43. Given: $\overline{PX}$ bisects $\angle QPR$. $\overline{XY} \perp \overline{PQ}$ and $\overline{XZ} \perp \overline{PR}$
Prove: $\overline{XY} \cong \overline{XZ}$
Proof:
Statements (Reasons)
1. $\overline{PX}$ bisects $\angle QPR$, $\overline{XY} \perp \overline{PQ}$, and $\overline{XZ} \perp \overline{PR}$. (Given)
2. $\angle YPX \cong \angle ZPX$ (Definition of angle bisector)
3. $\angle PYX$ and $\angle PZX$ are right angles. (Definition of perpendicular)
4. $\angle PYX \cong \angle PZX$ (Right angles are congruent.)
5. $\overline{PX} \cong \overline{PX}$ (Reflexive Property)
6. $\triangle PYX \cong \triangle PZX$ (AAS)
7. $\overline{XY} \cong \overline{XZ}$ (CPCTC)

45 The circumcenter is the point where the perpendicular bisectors of a triangle intersect. You can find the circumcenter by locating the point of intersection of two of the perpendicular bisectors.

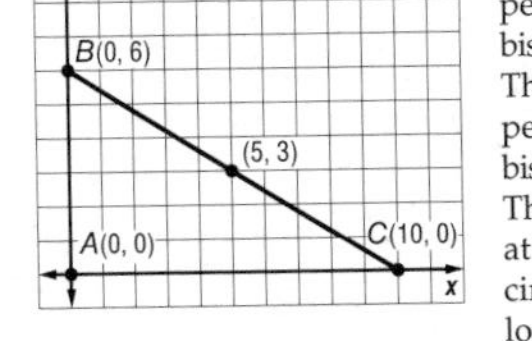

The equation of the perpendicular bisector of $\overline{AB}$ is $y = 3$. The equation of the perpendicular bisector of $\overline{AC}$ is $x = 5$. These lines intersect at (5, 3). The circumcenter is located at (5, 3).

47. a plane perpendicular to the plane in which $\overline{CD}$ lies and bisecting $\overline{CD}$

49. Sample answer:

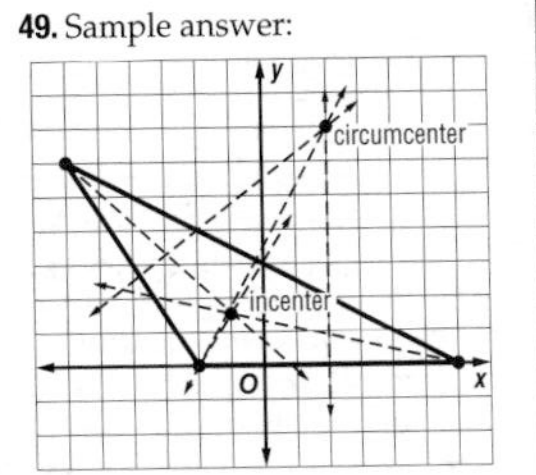

51. always
Given: $\triangle ABC$ is isosceles with legs $\overline{AB}$ and $\overline{BC}$; $\overline{BD}$ is the $\perp$ bisector of $\overline{AC}$.
Prove: $\overline{BD}$ is the angle bisector of $\angle ABC$.
Proof:
Statements (Reasons)
1. $\triangle ABC$ is isosceles with legs $\overline{AB}$ and $\overline{BC}$. (Given)
2. $\overline{AB} \cong \overline{BC}$ (Def. of isosceles $\triangle$)
3. $\overline{BD}$ is the $\perp$ bisector of $\overline{AC}$. (Given)
4. D is the midpoint of $\overline{AC}$. (Def. of segment bisector)
5. $\overline{AD} \cong \overline{DC}$ (Def. of midpoint)
6. $\overline{BD} \cong \overline{BD}$ (Reflexive Property)
7. $\triangle ABD \cong \triangle CBD$ (SSS)
8. $\angle ABD \cong \angle CBD$ (CPCTC)
9. $\overline{BD}$ is the angle bisector of $\angle ABC$. (Def. of $\angle$ bisector)

53. Given: Plane $\mathcal{Z}$ is an angle bisector of $\angle KJH$. $\overline{KJ} \cong \overline{HJ}$
Prove: $\overline{MH} \cong \overline{MK}$
Proof:
Statements (Reasons)
1. Plane $\mathcal{Z}$ is an angle bisector of $\angle KJH$; $\overline{KJ} \cong \overline{HJ}$ (Given)
2. $\angle KJM \cong \angle HJM$ (Definition of angle bisector)
3. $\overline{JM} \cong \overline{JM}$ (Reflexive Property)
4. $\triangle KJM \cong \triangle HJM$ (SAS)
5. $\overline{MH} \cong \overline{MK}$ (CPCTC)

55. A **57.** D **59.** $L(a, b)$ **61.** $S(-2b, 0)$ and $R(0, c)$
63. $\triangle JKL$ is a translation of $\triangle XYZ$; $JK = 2$, $KL = 4$, $JL = \sqrt{20}$, $XY = 2$, $YZ = 4$, $XZ = \sqrt{20}$. $\triangle JKL \cong \triangle XYZ$ by SSS.
65. $\sqrt{5}$
67. $m = 42t + 450$; \$1164

69. Given: $\triangle MLP$ is isosceles. N is the midpoint of $\overline{MP}$.
Prove: $\overline{LN} \perp \overline{MP}$
Proof:
Statements (Reasons)
1. $\triangle MLP$ is isosceles. (Given)
2. $\overline{ML} \cong \overline{PL}$ (Definition of isosceles $\triangle$)
3. $\angle M \cong \angle P$ (Isosceles $\triangle$ Th.)
4. N is the midpoint of $\overline{MP}$. (Given)
5. $\overline{MN} \cong \overline{PN}$ (Def. of midpoint)
6. $\triangle MNL \cong \triangle PNL$ (SAS)
7. $\angle LNM \cong \angle LNP$ (CPCTC)
8. $m\angle LNM = m\angle LNP$ (Def. of $\cong \angle$s)
9. $\angle LNM$ and $\angle LNP$ are a linear pair. (Def. of a linear pair)
10. $m\angle LNM + m\angle LNP = 180$ (Sum of measure of linear pair of $\angle$s $= 180$)
11. $2m\angle LNM = 180$ (Substitution)
12. $m\angle LNM = 90$ (Division)
13. $\angle LNM$ is a right angle. (Def. of rt. $\angle$)
14. $\overline{LN} \perp \overline{MP}$ (Def. of $\perp$)

Lesson 5-2

1
$PC = \frac{2}{3}FC$	Centroid Theorem
$PC = \frac{2}{3}(PF + PC)$	Segment Addition and Substitution
$PC = \frac{2}{3}(6 + PC)$	$PF = 6$
$PC = 4 + \frac{2}{3}PC$	Distributive Property
$\frac{1}{3}PC = 4$	Subtract $\frac{2}{3}PC$ from each side.
$PC = 12$	Multiply each side by 3.

3. (5, 6) **5.** 4.5 **7.** 13.5 **9.** 6 **11.** (3, 6)

13 The centroid is the point of balance for a triangle. Use the Midpoint Theorem to find the midpoint M of the side with endpoints at (0, 8) and (6, 4). The centroid is two-thirds the distance from the opposite vertex to that midpoint.
$M\left(\frac{0+6}{2}, \frac{8+4}{2}\right) = M(3, 6)$
The distance from $M(3, 6)$ to the point at (3, 0) is $6 - 0$ or 6 units. If P is the centroid of the triangle, then $P = \frac{2}{3}(6)$ or 4 units up from the point at (3, 0). The coordinates of P are $(3, 0 + 4)$ or (3, 4).

15. (−4, −4) **17.** median **19.** median **21.** 3 **23.** $\frac{1}{2}$

25
$\overline{AC} \cong \overline{DC}$	Definition of median
$AC = DC$	Definition of congruence
$4x - 3 = 2x + 9$	Substitution
$2x - 3 = 9$	Subtract $2x$ from each side.
$2x = 12$	Add 3 to each side.
$x = 6$	Divide each side by 2.

$m\angle ECA = 15x + 2$	Given
$= 15(6) + 2$	$x = 6$
$= 90 + 2$ or 92	Simplify.

$\overline{EC}$ is not an altitude of $\triangle AED$ because $m\angle ECA = 92$. If $\overline{EC}$ were an altitude, then $m\angle ECA$ must be 90.

27. altitude **29.** median
31. Given: $\triangle XYZ$ is isosceles. $\overline{WY}$ bisects $\angle Y$.
Prove: $\overline{WY}$ is a median.
Proof: Since $\triangle XYZ$ is isosceles, $\overline{XY} \cong \overline{ZY}$. By the definition of angle bisector, $\angle XYW \cong \angle ZYW$. $\overline{YW} \cong \overline{YW}$ by the Reflexive Property. So, by SAS, $\triangle XYW \cong \triangle ZYW$. By CPCTC, $\overline{XW} \cong \overline{ZW}$. By the definition of a midpoint, W is the midpoint of $\overline{XZ}$. By the definition of a median, $\overline{WY}$ is a median.

33a.

33b. Sample answer: The four points of concurrency of an equilateral triangle are all the same point.

33c.

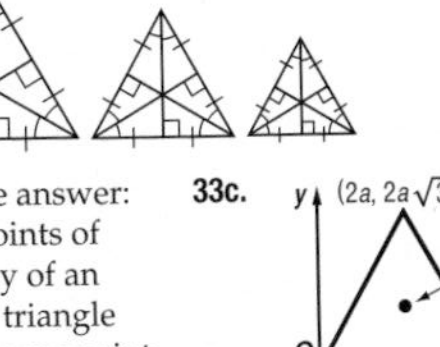

35. 7

37 Sample answer: Kareem is correct. According to the Centroid Theorem, $AP = \frac{2}{3}AD$. The segment lengths are transposed.

39. $\left(1, \frac{5}{3}\right)$; Sample answer: I found the midpoint of $\overline{AC}$ and used it to find the equation for the line that contains point B and the midpoint of $\overline{AC}$, $y = \frac{10}{3}x - \frac{5}{3}$. I also found the midpoint of $\overline{BC}$ and the equation for the line between point A and the midpoint of $\overline{BC}$, $y = -\frac{1}{3}x + 2$. I solved the system of two equations for x and y to get the coordinates of the centroid, $\left(1, \frac{5}{3}\right)$.

41. $2\sqrt{13}$ **43.** Sample answer: Each median divides the triangle into two smaller triangles of equal area, so the triangle can be balanced along any one of those lines. To balance the triangle on one point, you need to find the point where these three balance lines intersect. The balancing point for a rectangle is the intersection of the segments connecting the midpoints of the opposite sides, since each segment connecting these midpoints of a pair of opposite sides divides the rectangle into two parts with equal area. **45.** 3 **47.** B **49.** 5

51. **53.** neither

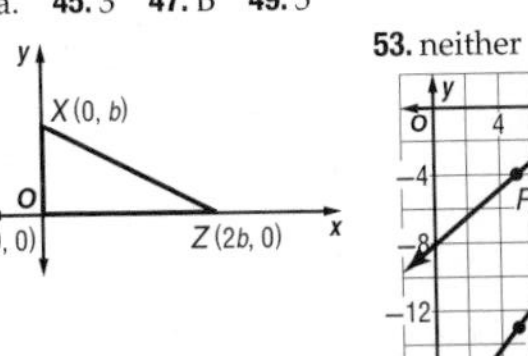

55. Because the lines are perpendicular, the angles formed are right angles. All right angles are congruent. Therefore, $\angle 1$ is congruent to $\angle 2$.

Lesson 5-3

1. $\angle 1$, $\angle 2$ **3.** $\angle 4$ **5.** $\angle A$, $\angle C$, $\angle B$; $\overline{BC}$, $\overline{AB}$, $\overline{AC}$ **7.** $\overline{BC}$; Sample answer: Since the angle across from segment $\overline{BC}$ is larger than the angle across from $\overline{AC}$, $\overline{BC}$ is longer. **9.** $\angle 1$, $\angle 2$ **11.** $\angle 1$, $\angle 3$, $\angle 6$, $\angle 7$ **13.** $\angle 5$, $\angle 9$

15. The sides from shortest to longest are $\overline{RT}, \overline{RS}, \overline{ST}$. The angles opposite these sides are $\angle S, \angle T$, and $\angle R$, respectively. So the angles from smallest to largest are $\angle S, \angle T$, and $\angle R$.

17. $\angle L, \angle P, \angle M$; $\overline{PM}, \overline{ML}, \overline{PL}$ **19.** $\angle C, \angle D, \angle E$; $\overline{DE}, \overline{CE}, \overline{CD}$

21. To use Theorem 5.9, first show that the measure of the angle opposite $\overline{YZ}$ is greater than the measure of the angle opposite $\overline{XZ}$. If $m\angle X = 90$, then $m\angle Y + m\angle Z = 90$, so $m\angle Y < 90$ by the definition of inequality. So $m\angle X > m\angle Y$. According to Theorem 5.9, if $m\angle X > m\angle Y$, then the length of the side opposite $\angle X$ must be greater than the length of the side opposite $\angle Y$. Since $\overline{YZ}$ is opposite $\angle X$, and $\overline{XZ}$ is opposite $\angle Y$, then $YZ > XZ$. So YZ, the length of the top surface of the ramp, must be greater than the length of the ramp.

23. $\angle P, \angle Q, \angle M$; $\overline{MQ}, \overline{PM}, \overline{PQ}$ **25.** $\angle 2$ **27.** $\angle 3$ **29.** $\angle 8$ **31.** $m\angle BCF > m\angle CFB$ **33.** $m\angle DBF < m\angle BFD$ **35.** $RP > MP$ **37.** $RM > RQ$

39. Use the Distance Formula

$d = \sqrt{(x_2 - x_1)^2 + (y_2 - y_1)^2}$ to find the lengths of the sides.

$AB = \sqrt{[-2-(-4)]^2 + (1-6)^2}$ $x_1 = -4, x_2 = -2, y_1 = 6, y_2 = 1$

$= \sqrt{29}$ Simplify.

≈ 5.4 Use a calculator.

$BC = \sqrt{[5-(-2)]^2 + (6-1)^2}$ $x_1 = -2, x_2 = 5, y_1 = 1, y_2 = 6$

$= \sqrt{74}$ Simplify.

≈ 8.6 Use a calculator.

$AC = \sqrt{[5-(-4)]^2 + (6-6)^2}$ $x_1 = -4, x_2 = 5, y_1 = 6, y_2 = 6$

$= \sqrt{81}$ or 9   Simplify.

Since $AB < BC < AC$, $\angle C < \angle A < \angle B$. The angles in order from smallest to largest are $\angle C, \angle A, \angle B$.

41. AB, BC, AC, CD, BD; In $\triangle ABC$, $AB < BC < AC$ and in $\triangle BCD$, $BC < CD < BD$. By the figure $AC < CD$, so $BC < AC < CD$. **43.** Sample answer: $\angle R$ is an exterior angle to $\triangle PQR$, so by the Exterior Angle Inequality, $m\angle R$ must be greater than $m\angle Q$. The markings indicate that $\angle R \cong \angle Q$, indicating that $m\angle R = m\angle Q$. This is a contradiction of the Exterior Angle Inequality Theorem, so the markings are incorrect. **45.** Sample answer: 10; $m\angle C > m\angle B$, so if $AB > AC$, Theorem 5.10 is satisfied. Since $10 > 6$, $AB > AC$. **47.** $m\angle 1, m\angle 2 = m\angle 5, m\angle 4, m\angle 6, m\angle 3$; Sample answer: The side opposite $\angle 5$ is the smallest side in that triangle and $m\angle 2 = m\angle 5$, so we know that $m\angle 4$ and $m\angle 6$ are both greater than $m\angle 2$ and $m\angle 5$. The side opposite $\angle 6$ is greater than the side opposite $\angle 4$, Since the side opposite $\angle 2$ is greater than the side opposite $\angle 1$, we know that $m\angle 1 < m\angle 2$ and $m\angle 5$. Since $m\angle 2 = m\angle 5$, $m\angle 1 + m\angle 3 = m\angle 4 + m\angle 6$. Since $m\angle 1 < m\angle 4$, then $m\angle 3 > m\angle 6$. **49.** D

51a. $t = 2.5h + 198$

51b. 6 **51c.** \$180 **53.** 9 **55.** $y = -5x + 7$; The perpendicular bisector bisects the segment at the midpoint of the segment. The midpoint is $\left(\frac{1}{2}, \frac{9}{2}\right)$. The slope of the given segment is $\frac{1}{5}$, so the slope of the perpendicular bisector is -5.

57. Given: T is the midpoint of $\overline{SQ}$.
$\overline{SR} \cong \overline{QR}$

Prove: $\triangle SRT \cong \triangle QRT$

Proof:

Statements (Reasons)

1. T is the midpoint of $\overline{SQ}$. (Given)
2. $\overline{ST} \cong \overline{TQ}$ (Def. of midpoint)
3. $\overline{SR} \cong \overline{QR}$ (Given)
4. $\overline{RT} \cong \overline{RT}$ (Reflexive Prop.)
5. $\triangle SRT \cong \triangle QRT$ (SSS)

59. false **61.** true

Lesson 5-4

1. $\overline{AB} \not\cong \overline{CD}$

3. The conclusion of the conditional statement is $x < 6$. If $x < 6$ is false, then x must be greater than or equal to 6. The negation of the conclusion is $x \geq 6$.

5. Given: $2x + 3 < 7$

Prove: $x < 2$

Indirect Proof: Step 1

Assume that $x > 2$ or $x = 2$ is true.

Step 2

x	2	3	4	5	6
$2x + 3$	7	9	11	13	15

When $x > 2$, $2x + 3 > 7$ and when $x = 2$, $2x + 3 = 7$.

Step 3 In both cases, the assumption leads to the contradiction of the given information that $2x + 3 < 7$. Therefore, the assumption that $x \geq 2$ must be false, so the original conclusion that $x < 2$ must be true.

7. Use a = average or $\frac{\text{number of points scored}}{\text{number of games played}}$.

Proof:

Indirect Proof: Step 1 Assume that Christina's average points per game was greater than or equal to 3, $a \geq 3$.

Step 2

CASE 1	CASE 2
$a = 3$	$a > 3$
$3 \stackrel{?}{=} \frac{13}{6}$	$\frac{13}{6} \stackrel{?}{>} 3$
$3 \neq 2.2$	$2.2 \not> 3$

Step 3 The conclusions are false, so the assumption must be false. Therefore, Christina's average points per game was less than 3.

9. Given: $\triangle ABC$ is a right triangle; $\angle C$ is a right angle.

Prove: $AB > BC$ and $AB > AC$

Indirect Proof: Step 1 Assume that the hypotenuse of a right triangle is not the longest side. That is, $AB < BC$ and $AB < AC$.

Step 2 If $AB < BC$, then $m\angle C < m\angle A$. Since $m\angle C = 90$, $m\angle A > 90$. So, $m\angle C + m\angle A > 180$.

By the same reasoning, $m\angle C + m\angle B > 180$.

Step 3 Both relationships contradict the fact that the sum of the measures of the angles of a triangle equals 180. Therefore, the hypotenuse must be the longest side of a right triangle.

11. $x \leq 8$ **13.** The lines are not parallel. **15.** The triangle is equiangular.

17. To write an indirect proof, first identify the conclusion. Find the negation of the conclusion and assume that it is true. Make a table of values to show that the negation of the conclusion is false. Since the assumption leads to a contradiction, you can conclude that the original conclusion must be true.

Given: $2x - 7 > -11$

Prove: $x > -2$

Indirect Proof: Step 1 The negation of $x > -2$ is $x \leq -2$. So, assume that $x \leq -2$ is true.

Step 2 Make a table with several possibilities for x assuming $x < -2$ or $x = -2$.

x	−6	−5	−4	−3	−2
$2x - 7$	−19	−17	−15	−13	−11

When $x < -2$, $2x - 7 < -11$ and when $x = -2$, $2x - 7 = -11$.

Step 3 In both cases, the assumption leads to the contradiction of the given information that $2x - 7 > -11$. Therefore, the assumption that $x \leq -2$ must be false, so the original conclusion that $x > -2$ must be true.

19. Given: $-3x + 4 < 7$

Prove: $x > -1$

Indirect Proof: Step 1 Assume that $x \leq -1$ is true.

Step 2 When $x < -1$, $-3x + 4 > 7$ and when $x = -1$, $-3x + 4 = 7$.

x	−5	−4	−3	−2	−1
$-3x + 4$	19	16	13	10	7

Step 3 In both cases, the assumption leads to the contradiction of the given information that $-3x + 4 < 7$. Therefore, the assumption that $x \leq -1$ must be false, so the original conclusion that $x > -1$ must be true.

21. Let the cost of one game be x and the other be y.

Given: $x + y > 80$

Prove: $x > 40$ or $y > 40$

Indirect Proof: Step 1 Assume that $x \leq 40$ and $y \leq 40$.

Step 2 If $x \leq 40$ and $y \leq 40$, then $x + y \leq 40 + 40$ or $x + y \leq 80$. This is a contradiction because we know that $x + y > 80$.

Step 3 Since the assumption that $x \leq 40$ and $y \leq 40$ leads to a contradiction of a known fact, the assumption must be false. Therefore, the conclusion that $x > 40$ or $y > 40$ must be true. Thus, at least one of the games had to cost more than \$40.

23. Given: xy is an odd integer.

Prove: x and y are odd integers.

Indirect Proof: Step 1 Assume that x and y are not both odd integers. That is, assume that either x or y is an even integer.

Step 2 You only need to show that the assumption that x is an even integer leads to a contradiction, since the argument for y is an even integer follows the same reasoning. So, assume that x is an even integer and y is an odd integer. This means that $x = 2k$ for some integer k and $y = 2m + 1$ for some integer m.

$xy = (2k)(2m + 1)$ Subst. of assumption

$= 4km + 2k$ Dist. Prop.

$= 2(km + k)$ Dist. Prop.

Since k and m are integers, $km + k$ is also an integer. Let p represent the integer $km + k$. So xy can be represented by $2p$, where p is an integer. This means that xy is an even integer, but this contradicts the given that xy is an odd integer.

Step 3 Since the assumption that x is an even integer and y is an odd integer leads to a contradiction of the given, the original conclusion that x and y are both odd integers must be true.

25. Given: x is an odd number.

Prove: x is not divisible by 4.

Indirect Proof: Step 1 Assume x is divisible by 4. In other words, 4 is a factor of x.

Step 2 Let $x = 4n$, for some integer n.
$x = 2(2n)$

So, 2 is a factor of x which means x is an even number, but this contradicts the given information.

Step 3 Since the assumption that x is divisible by 4 leads to a contradiction of the given, the original conclusion x is not divisible by 4 must be true.

27. Given: $XZ > YZ$

Prove: $\angle X \not\cong \angle Y$

Indirect Proof: Step 1

Assume that $\angle X \cong \angle Y$.

Step 2 $\overline{XZ} \cong \overline{YZ}$ by the converse of the isosceles $\triangle$ theorem.

Step 3 This contradicts the given information that $XZ > YZ$. Therefore, the assumption $\angle X \cong \angle Y$ must be false, so the original conclusion $\angle X \not\cong \angle Y$ must be true.

29. Given: $\triangle ABC$ is isosceles.

Prove: Neither of the base angles is a right angle.

Indirect Proof: Step 1

Assume that $\angle B$ is a right angle.

Step 2 By the Isosceles $\triangle$ Theorem, $\angle C$ is also a right angle.

Step 3 This contradicts the fact that a triangle can have no more than one right angle. Therefore, the assumption that $\angle B$ is a right angle must be false, so the original conclusion neither of the base angles is a right angle must be true.

31. Given: $m\angle A > m\angle ABC$
Prove: $BC > AC$

Proof:
Assume $BC \not> AC$. By the Comparison Property, $BC = AC$ or $BC < AC$.
Case 1: If $BC = AC$, then $\angle ABC \cong \angle A$ by the Isosceles Triangle Theorem. (If two sides of a triangle are congruent, then the angles opposite those sides are congruent.) But, $\angle ABC \cong \angle A$ contradicts the given statement that $m\angle A > m\angle ABC$. So, $BC \neq AC$.
Case 2: If $BC < AC$, then there must be a point D between A and C so that $\overline{DC} \cong \overline{BC}$. Draw the auxiliary segment $\overline{BD}$. Since $DC = BC$, by the Isosceles Triangle Theorem $\angle BDC \cong \angle DBC$. Now $\angle BDC$ is an exterior angle of $\triangle BAD$ and by the Exterior Angles Inequality Theorem (the measure of an exterior angle of a triangle is greater than the measure of either corresponding remote interior angle) $m\angle BDC > m\angle A$. By the Angle Addition Postulate, $m\angle ABC = m\angle ABD + m\angle DBC$. Then by the definition of inequality, $m\angle ABC > m\angle DBC$. By Substitution and the Transitive Property of Inequality, $m\angle ABC > m\angle A$. But this contradicts the given statement that $m\angle A > m\angle ABC$. In both cases, a contradiction was found, and hence our assumption must have been false. Therefore, $BC > AC$.

33. We know that the other team scored 3 points, and Katsu thinks that they made a three point shot. We also know that a player can score 3 points by making a basket and a foul shot.
Step 1 Assume that a player for the other team made a two-point basket and a foul shot.
Step 2 The other team's score before Katsu left was 26, so their score after a two-point basket and a foul shot would be 26 + 3 or 29.
Step 3 The score is correct when we assume that the other team made a two-point basket and a foul shot, so Katsu's assumption may not be correct. The other team could have made a three-point basket or a two-point basket and a foul shot.

35 a. To write an indirect proof, first identify the conclusion. Find the negation of the conclusion and assume that it is true. Then use the data to prove that the assumption is false.
Step 1 50% is half, and the statement says more than half of the teens polled said that they recycle, so assume that less than 50% recycle.
Step 2 The data shows that 51% of teens said that they recycle, and 51% > 50%, so the number of teens that recycle is not less than half.
Step 3 This contradicts the data given. Therefore, the assumption is false, and the conclusion more than half of the teens polled said they recycle must be true.
b. According to the data, 23% of 400 teenagers polled said that they participate in Earth Day. Verify that 23% of 400 is 92.

$400 \cdot 23\% \stackrel{?}{=} 92$
$400 \cdot 0.23 \stackrel{?}{=} 92$
$92 = 92$

37 Given: $\overline{AB} \perp$ line p
Prove: $\overline{AB}$ is the shortest segment from A to line p.
Indirect Proof: Step 1
Assume $\overline{AB}$ is not the shortest segment from A to p.
Step 2 Since $\overline{AB}$ is not the shortest segment from A to p, there is a point C such that $\overline{AC}$ is the shortest distance. $\triangle ABC$ is a right triangle with hypotenuse $\overline{AC}$, the longest side of $\triangle ABC$ since it is across from the largest angle in $\triangle ABC$ by the Angle-Side Relationships in Triangles Theorem.
Step 3 This contradicts the fact that $\overline{AC}$ is the shortest side. Therefore, the assumption is false, and the conclusion, $\overline{AB}$ is the shortest side, must be true.

39a. $n^3 + 3$ **39b.** Sample answer:

n	$n^3 + 3$
2	11
3	30
10	1003
11	1334
24	13,827
25	15,628
100	1,000,003
101	1,030,304
526	145,531,579
527	146,363,186

39c. Sample answer: When $n^3 + 3$ is even, n is odd.
39d. Indirect Proof: Step 1
Assume that n is even. Let $n = 2k$, where k is some integer.

Step 2
$n^3 + 3 = (2k)^3 + 3$ Substitute assumption
$= 8k^3 + 3$ Simplify.
$= (8k^3 + 2) + 1$ Replace 3 with 2 + 1 and group the first two terms.
$= 2(4k^3 + 1) + 1$ Distributive Property

Since k is an integer, $4k^3 + 1$ is also an integer. Therefore, $n^3 + 3$ is odd.
Step 3 This contradicts the given information that $n^3 + 3$ is even. Therefore, the assumption is false, so the conclusion that n is odd must be true.

41. Sample answer: $\triangle ABC$ is scalene.
Given: $\triangle ABC$; $AB \neq BC$; $BC \neq AC$; $AB \neq AC$
Prove: $\triangle ABC$ is scalene.
Indirect Proof:
Step 1 Assume that $\triangle ABC$ is not scalene.
Case 1: $\triangle ABC$ is isosceles.
Step 2 If $\triangle ABC$ is isosceles, then $AB = BC$, $BC = AC$, or $AB = AC$.
Step 3 This contradicts the given information, so $\triangle ABC$ is not isosceles.

Case 2: $\triangle ABC$ is equilateral.
In order for a triangle to be equilateral, it must also be isosceles, and Case 1 proved that $\triangle ABC$ is not isosceles. Thus, $\triangle ABC$ is not equilateral. Therefore, $\triangle ABC$ is scalene. **43.** Neither; sample answer: Since the hypothesis is true when the conclusion is false, the statement is false. **45.** $y = 2x - 7$ **47.** J

49. Given: $\overline{RQ}$ bisects $\angle SRT$.
Prove: $m\angle SQR > m\angle SRQ$
Proof:
<u>Statements (Reasons)</u>
1. $\overline{RQ}$ bisects $\angle SRT$. (Given)
2. $\angle SRQ \cong \angle QRT$ (Def. of bisector)
3. $m\angle QRS = m\angle QRT$ (Def. of $\cong$ ∠s)
4. $m\angle SQR = m\angle T + m\angle QRT$ (Exterior Angles Theorem)
5. $m\angle SQR > m\angle QRT$ (Def. of Inequality)
6. $m\angle SQR > m\angle SRQ$ (Substitution)

51. $\left(1\frac{2}{5}, 2\frac{3}{5}\right)$ **53.** 64 **55.** $\sqrt{5} \approx 2.2$ **57.** true **59.** false

Lesson 5-5

1 Yes; check each inequality.
$5 + 7 \stackrel{?}{>} 10$ $\quad 5 + 10 \stackrel{?}{>} 7$ $\quad 7 + 10 \stackrel{?}{>} 5$
$12 > 10$ ✓ $\quad 15 > 7$ ✓ $\quad 17 > 5$ ✓
Since the sum of each pair of side lengths is greater than the third side length, sides with lengths 5 cm, 7 cm, and 10 cm will form a triangle.
3. yes; $6 + 14 > 10$, $6 + 10 > 14$, and $10 + 14 > 6$
5. Given: $\overline{XW} \cong \overline{YW}$
Prove: $YZ + ZW > XW$
Proof:
<u>Statements (Reasons)</u>
1. $\overline{XW} \cong \overline{YW}$ (Given)
2. $XW = YW$ (Def. of $\cong$ segs.)
3. $YZ + ZW > YW$ (△ Inequal. Thm.)
4. $YZ + ZW > XW$ (Subst.)

7. yes **9.** no; $2.1 + 4.2 \not> 7.9$ **11.** yes **13.** 6 m < n < 16 m **15.** 5.4 in. < n < 13 in. **17.** $5\frac{1}{3}$ yd < n < 10 yd
19. Given: $\overline{JL} \cong \overline{LM}$
Prove: $KJ + KL > LM$
Proof:
<u>Statements (Reasons)</u>
1. $\overline{JL} \cong \overline{LM}$ (Given)
2. $JL = LM$ (Def. of $\cong$ segments)
3. $KJ + KL > JL$ (△ Inequal. Thm.)
4. $KJ + KL > LM$ (Subst.)

21
$XY + YZ > XZ$
$(4x - 1) + (2x + 7) > x + 13$
$6x + 6 > x + 13$
$5x > 7$
$x > \frac{7}{5}$

$XY + XZ > YZ$
$(4x - 1) + (x + 13) > 2x + 7$
$5x + 12 > 2x + 7$
$3x > -5$
$x > -\frac{5}{3}$

$YZ + XZ > XY$
$(2x + 7) + (x + 13) > 4x - 1$
$3x + 20 > 4x - 1$
$21 > x$

Since x must be greater than $\frac{7}{5}$, greater than $-\frac{5}{3}$, and less than 21, possible values of x are $\frac{7}{5} < x < 21$.

23. Given: $\triangle ABC$
Prove: $AC + BC > AB$
Proof:
<u>Statements (Reasons)</u>
1. Construct $\overline{CD}$ so that C is between B and D and $\overline{CD} \cong \overline{AC}$. (Ruler Post.)
2. $CD = AC$ (Def. of $\cong$ segments)
3. $\angle CAD \cong \angle ADC$ (Isos. △ Thm.)
4. $m\angle CAD = m\angle ADC$ (Def. of $\cong$ ∠s)
5. $m\angle BAC + m\angle CAD = m\angle BAD$ (∠ Add. Post.)
6. $m\angle BAC + m\angle ADC = m\angle BAD$ (Subst.)
7. $m\angle ADC < m\angle BAD$ (Def. of inequality)
8. $AB < BD$ (Thoerem 5.10)
9. $BD = BC + CD$ (Seg. Add. Post.)
10. $AB < BC + CD$ (Subst.)
11. $AB < BC + AC$ (Subst. (Steps 2, 10))

25. $2 < x < 10$ **27.** $1 < x < 11$ **29.** $x > 0$ **31.** Yes; sample answer: The measurements on the drawing do not form a triangle. According to the Triangle Inequality Theorem, the sum of the lengths of any two sides of a triangle is greater than the length of the third side. The lengths in the drawing are 1 ft, $3\frac{7}{8}$ ft, and $6\frac{3}{4}$ ft. Since $1 + 3\frac{7}{8} \not> 6\frac{3}{4}$, the triangle is impossible. They should recalculate their measurements before they cut the wood.

33 A triangle 3 feet by 4 feet by x feet is formed. The length of the third side x must be less than the sum of the lengths of the other two sides. So, $x < 3 + 4$ or $x < 7$. Since the awning drapes 6 inches or 0.5 feet over the front, the total length should be less than 7 + 0.5 or 7.5 feet. She should buy no more than 7.5 feet.

35. Yes; $\sqrt{99} \approx 9.9$ since $\sqrt{100} = 10$, $\sqrt{48} \approx 6.9$ since $\sqrt{49} = 7$, and $\sqrt{65} \approx 8.1$ since $\sqrt{64} = 8$. $6.9 + 8.1 > 9.9$, so it is possible.
37. no; $\sqrt{122} \approx 11.1$ since $\sqrt{121} = 11$, $\sqrt{5} \approx 2.1$ since $\sqrt{4} = 2$, and $\sqrt{26} \approx 5.1$ since $\sqrt{25} = 5$. So, $2.1 + 5.1 \not> 11.1$.

39 Use the Distance Formula
$d = \sqrt{(x_2 - x_1)^2 + (y_2 - y_1)^2}$ to find the lengths of the sides.

$FG = \sqrt{[3 - (-4)]^2 + (-3 - 3)^2}$ $\quad x_1 = -4, x_2 = 3, y_1 = 3, y_2 = -3$
$= \sqrt{85}$ $\quad$ Simplify.
≈ 9.2 $\quad$ Use a calculator.
$GH = \sqrt{(4 - 3)^2 + [6 - (-3)]^2}$ $\quad x_1 = 3, x_2 = 4, y_1 = -3, y_2 = 6$

$= \sqrt{82}$ Simplify.
≈ 9.1 Use a calculator.

$FH = \sqrt{[4-(-4)]^2 + (6-3)^2}$ $x_1 = -4, x_2 = 4, y_1 = 3, y_2 = 6$
$= \sqrt{73}$ Simplify.
≈ 8.5 Use a calculator.

$FG + GH \overset{?}{>} FH$	$FG + FH \overset{?}{>} GH$	$GH + FH \overset{?}{>} FG$
$9.2 + 9.1 \overset{?}{>} 8.5$	$9.2 + 8.5 \overset{?}{>} 9.1$	$9.1 + 8.5 \overset{?}{>} 9.2$
$18.3 > 8.5$	$17.7 > 9.1$	$17.6 > 9.2$

Since $FG + GH > FH$, $FG + FH > GH$, and $GH + FH > FG$, the coordinates are the vertices of a triangle.

41. yes; $QR + QS > RS$, $QR + RS > QS$, and $QS + RS > QR$ **43.** The perimeter is greater than 36 and less than 64. Sample answer: From the diagram we know that $\overline{AC} \cong \overline{EC}$ and $\overline{DC} \cong \overline{BC}$, and $\angle ACB \cong \angle ECD$ because vertical angles are congruent, so $\triangle ACB \cong \triangle ECD$. Using the Triangle Inequality Theorem, the minimum value of AB and ED is 2 and the maximum value is 16. Therefore, the minimum value of the perimeter is greater than 2(2 + 7 + 9) or 36, and the maximum value of the perimeter is less than 2(16 + 7 + 9) or 64.
45. Sample answers: whether or not the side lengths actually form a triangle, what the smallest and largest angles are, whether the triangle is equilateral, isosceles, or scalene
47.

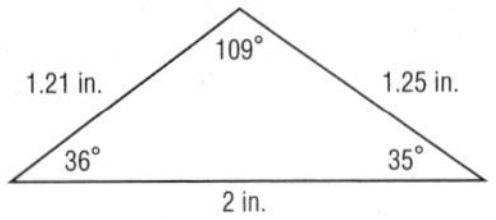

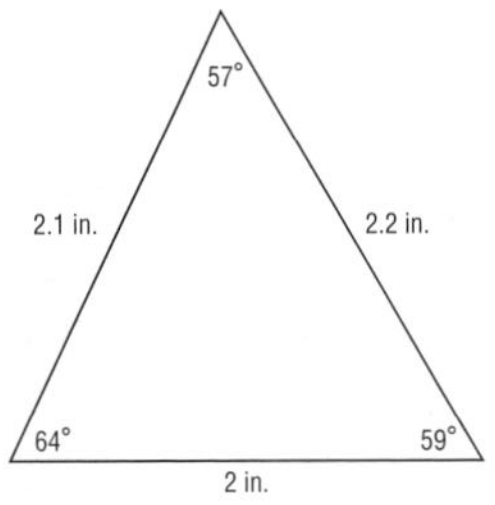

49. B **51.** H **53.** $y > 6$ or $y < 6$ **55.** 132 mi < d < 618 mi **57.** 15; Alt. Ext. ∡ Thm. **59.** $x = \frac{4}{3} \approx 1.3$; $JK = 4$ **61.** $x = 2$; $JK = KL = JL = 14$ **63.** $x = 7$; $SR = RT = 24$, $ST = 19$

Lesson 5-6

1. $m\angle ACB > m\angle GDE$

3 $\overline{QR} \cong \overline{SR}$, $\overline{TR} \cong \overline{TR}$, and $m\angle QRT < m\angle SRT$. By the Hinge Theorem, $QT < ST$.

5a. $\overline{AB} \cong \overline{DE}$, $\overline{AC} \cong \overline{DF}$ **5b.** $\angle D$; Sample answer: Since $EF > BC$, according to the converse of the Hinge Theorem, $m\angle D > m\angle A$ **7.** $\frac{5}{3} < x < B$

9. Given: $\overline{AD} \cong \overline{CB}$, $DC < AB$
Prove: $m\angle CBD < m\angle ADB$

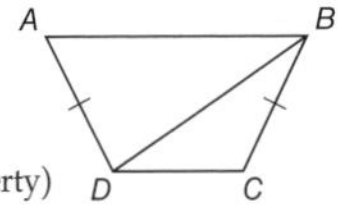

Statements (Reasons)
1. $\overline{AD} \cong \overline{CB}$ (Given)
2. $\overline{DB} \cong \overline{DB}$ (Reflexive Property)
3. $DC < AB$ (Given)
4. $m\angle CBD < m\angle ADB$ (SSS Inequality)

11. $m\angle MLP < m\angle TSR$

13 $\overline{TU} \cong \overline{VU}$, $\overline{WU} \cong \overline{WU}$, and $WT < WV$. By the Converse of the Hinge Theorem, $m\angle TUW > m\angle VUW$.

15. $JK > HJ$ **17.** $2 < x < 6$

19 Two sides of one triangle are congruent to two sides of the other triangle and the third side of the first triangle is less than the third side of the second triangle. So, by the Converse of the Hinge Theorem, the included angle of the first triangle is less than the included angle of the second triangle.
$0 < x + 20 < 41$ Converse of Hinge Theorem
$-20 < x < 21$ Subtract 20 from each.
The range of values containing x is $-20 < x < 21$.

21. $\overline{RS}$; sample answer: The height of the crane is the same and the length of the crane arm is fixed, so according to the Hinge Theorem, the side opposite the smaller angle is shorter. Since 29° < 52°, $RS < MN$.

23. Given: $\overline{LK} \cong \overline{JK}$, $\overline{RL} \cong \overline{RJ}$, K is the midpoint of $\overline{QS}$, $m\angle SKL > m\angle QKJ$
Prove: $RS > QR$

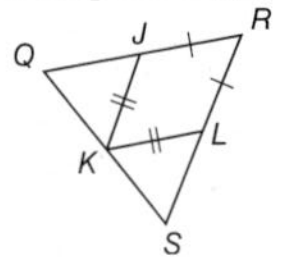

Statements (Reasons)
1. $\overline{LK} \cong \overline{JK}$, $\overline{RL} \cong \overline{RJ}$, K is the midpoint of $\overline{QS}$, $m\angle SKL > m\angle QKJ$ (Given)
2. $SK = QK$ (Def. of midpoint)
3. $SL > QJ$ (Hinge Thm.)
4. $RL = RJ$ (Def. of ≅ segs.)
5. $SL + RL > RL + RJ$ (Add. Prop.)
6. $SL + RL > QJ + RJ$ (Subst.)
7. $RS = SL + RL$, $QR = QJ + RJ$ (Seg. Add. Post.)
8. $RS > QR$ (Subst.)

25. Given: $\overline{XU} \cong \overline{VW}$, $VW > XW$, $\overline{XU} \parallel \overline{VW}$
Prove: $m\angle XZU > m\angle UZV$

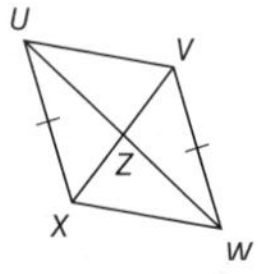

Statements (Reasons)
1. $\overline{XU} \cong \overline{VW}$, $\overline{XU} \parallel \overline{VW}$ (Given)
2. $\angle UXV \cong \angle XVW$, $\angle XUW \cong \angle UWV$ (Alt. Int. ∡ Thm.)
3. $\triangle XZU \cong \triangle VZW$ (ASA)
4. $\overline{XZ} \cong \overline{VZ}$ (CPCTC)
5. $\overline{WZ} \cong \overline{WZ}$ (Refl. Prop.)
6. $VW > XW$ (Given)
7. $m\angle VZW > m\angle XZW$ (Converse of Hinge Thm.)
8. $\angle VZW \cong \angle XZU$, $\angle XZW \cong \angle VZU$ (Vert. ∡ are ≅.)
9. $m\angle VZW = m\angle XZU$, $m\angle XZW = m\angle VZU$ (Def. of ≅ ∡)
10. $m\angle XZU > m\angle UZV$ (Subst.)

27 **a.** Sample answer: Use a ruler to measure the distance from her shoulder to her fist for each position. The distance is 1.6 cm for Position 1 and 2 cm for Position 2. Therefore, the distance from her shoulder to her fist is greater in Position 2.
b. Sample answer: In each position, a triangle formed. The distance from her shoulder to her elbow and from her elbow to her wrist is the same in both triangles. Using the measurements in part **a** and the Converse of the Hinge Theorem, you know that the measure of the angle opposite the larger side is larger, so the angle formed by Anica's elbow is greater in Position 2.

29. Given: $\overline{PR} \cong \overline{PQ}$, $SQ > SR$
Prove: $m\angle 1 < m\angle 2$

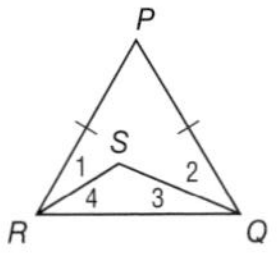

Statements (Reasons)
1. $\overline{PR} \cong \overline{PQ}$ (Given)
2. $\angle PRQ \cong \angle PQR$ (Isos. △ Thm.)
3. $m\angle PRQ = m\angle 1 + m\angle 4$, $m\angle PQR = m\angle 2 + m\angle 3$ (Angle Add. Post.)
4. $m\angle PRQ = m\angle PQR$ (Def. of ≅ ∡)
5. $m\angle 1 + m\angle 4 = m\angle 2 + m\angle 3$ (Subst.)
6. $SQ > SR$ (Given)
7. $m\angle 4 > m\angle 3$ (Angle Side Relationship Thm.)
8. $m\angle 4 = m\angle 3 + x$ (Def. of inequality)
9. $m\angle 1 + m\angle 4 - m\angle 4 = m\angle 2 + m\angle 3 - (m\angle 3 + x)$ (Subt. Prop.)
10. $m\angle 1 = m\angle 2 - x$ (Subst.)
11. $m\angle 1 + x = m\angle 2$ (Add. Prop.)
12. $m\angle 1 < m\angle 2$ (Def. of inequality)

31. $CB < AB$ **33.** $m\angle BGC < m\angle FBA$

35 $\overline{WZ} \cong \overline{YZ}$, $\overline{ZU} \cong \overline{ZU}$, and $m\angle WZU > m\angle YZU$. By the Hinge Theorem, $WU > YU$.

37a.

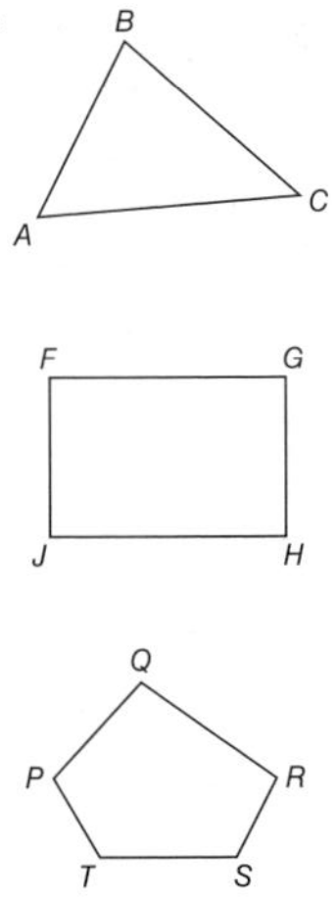

37b. ∠ measures: 59, 76, 45; 90, 90, 90, 90; 105, 100, 96, 116, 123; Sum of ∡: 180, 360, 540
37c. Sample answer: The sum of the angles of the polygon is equal to 180 times two less than the number of sides of the polygon.
37d. Inductive; sample answer: Since I used a pattern to determine the relationship, the reasoning I used was inductive.
37e. $(n - 2)180$

39.

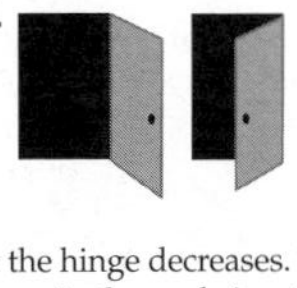

A door; as the door opens, the door opening increases as the angle made by the hinge increases. As the door closes, the door opening decreases as the angle made by the hinge decreases. This is similar to the side opposite the angle in a triangle, because as the side opposite an angle increases the measure of the angle also increases. As the side decreases, the angle also decreases. **41.** Never; from the Converse of the Hinge Theorem, $\angle ADB < \angle BDC$. $\angle ADB < \angle BDC$ form a linear pair. So, $m\angle ADB + m\angle BDC = 180$. Since, $m\angle BDC > m\angle ADB$, $m\angle BDC$ must be greater than 90 and $m\angle ADB$ must be smaller than 90. So, by the definition of obtuse and acute angles, $m\angle BDC$ is always obtuse and $m\angle ADB$ is always acute. **43.** $2.8 < x < 12$ **45.** F **47.** 1.2 cm < n < 7.6 cm **49.** 6 m < n < 12 m **51.** $x = 8$ **53.** A **55.** ∠3, ∠ACB **57.** $x = 66$ by the Consecutive Interior Angles Theorem; $y = 35$ by the Consecutive Interior Angles Theorem

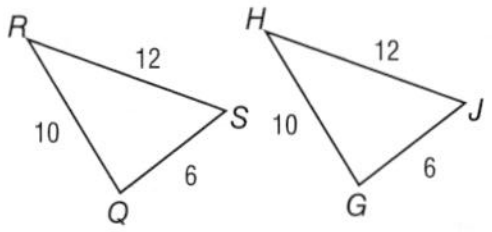

Chapter 5 Study Guide and Review

1. false; orthocenter **3.** true **5.** false; median **7.** false; false **9.** false; the vertex opposite that side **11.** 5 **13.** 34 **15.** (2, 3) **17.** ∠S, ∠R, ∠T; $\overline{RT}$, $\overline{TS}$, $\overline{SR}$ **19.** The shorter path is for Sarah to get Irene and then go to Anna's house. **21.** △FGH is not congruent to △MNO. **23.** $y \geq 4$
25. Let the cost of one DVD be x, and the cost of the other DVD be y.
Given: $x + y > 50$
Prove: $x > 25$ or $y > 25$
Indirect proof: Step 1 Assume that $x \leq 25$ and $y \leq 25$.
Step 2 If $x \leq 25$ and $y \leq 25$, then $x + y \leq 25 + 25$, or $x + y \leq 50$. This is a contradiction because we know that $x + y > 50$.
Step 3 Since the assumption that $x \leq 25$ and $y \leq 25$ leads to a contradiction of a known fact, the assumption must be false. Therefore, the conclusion that $x > 25$ or $y > 25$ must be true. Thus, at least one DVD had to be over $25.
27. no; 3 + 4 < 8 **29.** Let x be the length of the third side. 6.5 cm < x < 14.5 cm **31.** $m\angle ABC > m\angle DEF$ **33.** Rose

CHAPTER 6 Quadrilaterals

Chapter 6 Get Ready

1. 150 **3.** 54 **5.** 137 **7.** $x = 1$, $WX = XY = YW = 9$ **9.** Des Moines to Phoenix = 1153 mi, Des Moines to Atlanta = 738 mi, Phoenix to Atlanta = 1591 mi

Lesson 6-1

1. 1440 **3.** $m\angle X = 36, m\angle Y = 72, m\angle Z = 144, m\angle W = 108$

5 $(n - 2) \cdot 180 = (16 - 2) \cdot 180 \quad n = 6$
$= 14 \cdot 180$ or 2520 Simplify.
The sum of the interior angle measures is 2520. So, the measure of one interior angle is $2520 \div 16$ or 157.5.

7. 36 **9.** 68 **11.** 45 **13.** 3240 **15.** 5400

17 $(n - 2) \cdot 180 = (4 - 2) \cdot 180 \quad n = 4$
$= 2 \cdot 180$ or 360 Simplify.
The sum of the interior angle measures is 360.
$360 = m\angle J + m\angle K + m\angle L + m\angle M$ Sum of interior angle measures
$360 = (3x - 6) + (x + 10) + x + (2x - 8)$ Substitution
$360 = 7x - 4$ Combine like terms.
$364 = 7x$ Add 4 to each side.
$52 = x$ Simplify.

$m\angle J = 3x - 6 = 3(52) - 6$ or 150 $\quad m\angle K = x + 10 = 52 + 10$ or 62
$m\angle L = x = 52 \quad m\angle M = 2x - 8 = 2(52) - 8$ or 96

19. $m\angle U = 60, m\angle V = 193, m\angle W = 76, m\angle Y = 68, m\angle Z = 143$ **21.** 150 **23.** 144 **25a.** 720 **25b.** Yes, 120; sample answer: Since the measures of the sides of the hexagon are equal, it is regular and the measures of the angles are equal. That means each angle is $720 \div 6$ or 120. **27.** 4 **29.** 15

31 $21 + 42 + 29 + (x + 14) + x + (x - 10) + (x - 20) = 360$
$4x + 76 = 360$
$4x = 284$
$x = 71$

33. 37 **35.** 72 **37.** 24 **39.** 51.4, 128.6 **41.** 25.7, 154.3
43. Consider the sum of the measures of the exterior angles N for an n-gon.
N = sum of measures of linear pairs − sum of measures of interior angles
$= 180n - 180(n - 2)$
$= 180n - 180n + 360$
$= 360$
So, the sum of the exterior angle measures is 360 for any convex polygon. **45.** 105, 110, 120, 130, 135, 140, 160, 170, 180, 190

47 **a.** 60 ft $\div$ 8 = 7.5 ft Perimeter $\div$ number of sides
b. $(n - 2) \cdot 180 = (8 - 2) \cdot 180 \quad n = 8$
$= 6 \cdot 180$ or 1080 Simplify.
Sample answer: The sum of the interior angle measures is 1080. So, the measure of each angle of a regular octagon is $1080 \div 8$ or 135. So if each side of the board makes up half of the angle, each one measures $135 \div 2$ or 67.5.

49. Liam; by the Exterior Angle Sum Theorem, the sum of the measures of any convex polygon is 360.

51. Always; by the Exterior Angle Sum Theorem, $m\angle QPR = 60$ and $m\angle QRP = 60$. Since the sum of the interior angle measures of a triangle is 180, the measure of $\angle PQR = 180 - m\angle QPR - m\angle QRP = 180 - 60 - 60 = 60$. So, $\triangle PQR$ is an equilateral triangle. **53.** The Interior Angles Sum Theorem is derived from the pattern between the number of sides in a polygon and the number of triangles. The formula is the product of the sum of the measures of the angles in a triangle, 180, and the number of triangles in the polygon. **55.** 72 **57** C
59. $ML < JM$ **61.** 3 **63.** $\angle E \cong \angle G$; $\angle EFH \cong \angle GHF$; $\angle EHF \cong \angle GFH$; $\overline{EF} \cong \overline{GH}$; $\overline{EH} \cong \overline{GF}$; $\overline{FH} \cong \overline{HF}$; $\triangle EFH \cong \triangle GHF$ **65.** $\angle 1$ and $\angle 5$, $\angle 4$ and $\angle 6$, $\angle 2$ and $\angle 8$, $\angle 3$ and $\angle 7$

Lesson 6-2

1a. 148 **1b.** 125 **1c.** 4 **3.** 15 **5.** $w = 5, b = 4$
7. Given: $\square ABCD$, $\angle A$ is a right angle.
Prove: $\angle B$, $\angle C$, and $\angle D$ are right angles. (Theorem 6.6)
Proof: By definition of a parallelogram, $\overline{AB} \parallel \overline{CD}$. Since $\angle A$ is a right angle, $\overline{AC} \perp \overline{AB}$. By the Perpendicular Transversal Theorem, $\overline{AC} \perp \overline{CD}$. $\angle C$ is a right angle, because perpendicular lines form a right angle. $\angle B \cong \angle C$ and $\angle A \cong \angle D$ because opposite angles in a parallelogram are congruent. $\angle C$ and $\angle D$ are right angles, since all right angles are congruent.

9 $m\angle R + m\angle Q = 180$ Consecutive angles are supplementary.
$m\angle R + 128 = 180$ Substitution
$m\angle R = 52$ Subtract 128 from each side.

11. 5

13 **a.** $\overline{JH} \cong \overline{FG}$ Opposite sides are congruent.
$JH = FG$ Definition of congruence
$= 1$ in. Substitution
b. $\overline{GH} \cong \overline{FJ}$ Opposite sides are congruent.
$GH = FJ$ Definition of congruence
$= \frac{3}{4}$ in. Substitution
c. $\angle JFG \cong \angle JHG$ Opposite angles are congruent.
$m\angle JFG = m\angle JHG$ Definition of congruence
$= 62$ Substitution
d. $m\angle FJH + m\angle JHG = 180$ Consecutive angles are supplementary.
$m\angle FJH + 62 = 180$ Substitution
$m\angle FJH = 118$ Subtract 62 from each side.

15. $a = 7, b = 11$ **17.** $x = 5, y = 17$ **19.** $x = 58, y = 63.5$ **21.** (2.5, 2.5)
23. Given: $WXTV$ and $ZYVT$ are parallelograms.
Prove: $\overline{WX} \cong \overline{ZY}$
Proof:
Statements (Reasons)
1. $WXTV$ and $ZYVT$ are parallelograms. (Given)
2. $\overline{WX} \cong \overline{VT}$, $\overline{VT} \cong \overline{YZ}$ (Opp. sides of a ▱ are ≅.)
3. $\overline{WX} \cong \overline{ZY}$ (Trans. Prop.)

25. Given: $\triangle ACD \cong \triangle CAB$
Prove: $\overline{DP} \cong \overline{PB}$
Proof:
Statements (Reasons)
1. $\triangle ACD \cong \triangle CAB$ (Given)
2. $\angle ACD \cong \angle CAB$ (CPCTC)
3. $\angle DPC \cong \angle BPA$ (Vert. ∡ are ≅.)
4. $\overline{AB} \cong \overline{CD}$ (CPCTC)
5. $\triangle ABP \cong \triangle CDP$ (AAS)
6. $\overline{DP} \cong \overline{PB}$ (CPCTC)

27. Given: $\square WXYZ$
Prove: $\triangle WXZ \cong \triangle YZX$ (Theorem 6.8)
Proof:
Statements (Reasons)
1. $\square WXYZ$ (Given)
2. $\overline{WX} \cong \overline{ZY}$, $\overline{WZ} \cong \overline{XY}$ (Opp. sides of a ▱ are ≅.)
3. $\angle ZWX \cong \angle XYZ$ (Opp. ∡ of a ▱ are ≅.)
4. $\triangle WXZ \cong \triangle YZX$ (SAS)

29. Given: $ACDE$ is a parallelogram.
Prove: $\overline{EC}$ bisects $\overline{AD}$. (Theorem 6.7)
Proof: It is given that $ACDE$ is a parallelogram. Since opposite sides of a parallelogram are congruent, $\overline{EA} \cong \overline{DC}$. By definition of a parallelogram, $\overline{EA} \parallel \overline{DC}$. $\angle AEB \cong \angle DCB$ and $\angle EAB \cong \angle CDB$ because alternate interior angles are congruent. $\triangle EBA \cong \triangle CBD$ by ASA. $\overline{EB} \cong \overline{BC}$ and $\overline{AB} \cong \overline{BD}$ by CPCTC. By the definition of segment bisector, $\overline{EC}$ bisects $\overline{AD}$ and $\overline{AD}$ bisects $\overline{EC}$.

31. 3

33 $\angle AFB$ and $\angle BFC$ form a linear pair.
$\angle AFB + \angle BFC = 180$ Supplement Theorem
$\angle AFB + 49 = 180$ Substitution
$\angle AFB = 131$ Subtract 49 from each side.

35. 29 **37.** $(-1, -1)$; Sample answer: Opposite sides of a parallelogram are parallel. Since the slope of $\overline{BC} = \frac{-6}{2}$, the slope of $\overline{AD}$ must also be $\frac{-6}{2}$. To locate vertex D, start from vertex A and move down 6 and right 2.

39 First, use properties involving opposite angles and opposite sides of a parallelogram to help prove that $\triangle YUZ$ and $\triangle VXW$ are right angles. Then use the Hypotenuse-Angle Congruence Theorem to prove the triangles are congruent.
Given: $\square YWVZ$, $\overline{VX} \perp \overline{WY}$, $\overline{YU} \perp \overline{VZ}$
Prove: $\triangle YUZ \cong \triangle VXW$
Proof:
Statements (Reasons)
1. $\square YWVZ$, $\overline{VX} \perp \overline{WY}$, $\overline{YU} \perp \overline{VZ}$ (Given)
2. $\angle Z \cong \angle W$ (Opp. ∡ of a ▱ are ≅.)
3. $\overline{WV} \cong \overline{ZY}$ (Opp. sides of a ▱ are ≅.)
4. $\angle VXW$ and $\angle YUZ$ are rt. ∡. (⊥ lines form four rt. ∡.)
5. $\triangle VXW$ and $\triangle YUZ$ are rt. △s. (Def. of rt. △s)
6. $\triangle YUZ \cong \triangle VXW$ (HA)

41. 7
43.

45. Sample answer: In a parallelogram, the opposite sides and angles are congruent. Two consecutive angles in a parallelogram are supplementary. If one angle of a parallelogram is right, then all the angles are right. The diagonals of a parallelogram bisect each other. **47.** 13 **49.** B **51.** 9 **53.** 18 **55.** 100
57. not a polyhedron; cylinder
59. not a polyhedron; cone
61. diagonal; $-\frac{4}{5}$

Lesson 6-3

1. Yes; each pair of opposite angles are congruent.
3. $AP = CP, BP = DP$; sample answer: If the diagonals of a quadrilateral bisect each other, then the quadrilateral is a parallelogram, so if $AP = CP$ and $BP = DP$, then the string forms a parallelogram.

5 If both pairs of opposite sides are congruent, then the quadrilateral is a parallelogram.
$2x + 3 = x + 7$ Congruent sides have equal measures.
$x + 3 = 7$ Subtract x from each side.
$x = 4$ Subtract 3 from each side.

$3y - 5 = y + 11$ Congruent sides have equal measures.
$2y - 5 = 11$ Subtract y from each side.
$2y = 16$ Add 5 to each side.
$y = 8$ Divide each side by 2.

7 If the diagonals bisect each other, then it is a parallelogram.

midpoint of $\overline{WY}$: $\left(\frac{-5+1}{2}, \frac{4+(-3)}{2}\right) = \left(-2, \frac{1}{2}\right)$

midpoint of $\overline{XZ}$: $\left(\frac{3+(-7)}{2}, \frac{4+(-3)}{2}\right) = \left(-2, \frac{1}{2}\right)$

The midpoint of $\overline{WY}$ and $\overline{XZ}$ is $\left(-2, \frac{1}{2}\right)$. Since the diagonals bisect each other, $WXYZ$ is a parallelogram.

9. Yes; both pairs of opposite sides are congruent.
11. No; none of the tests for parallelograms are fulfilled. **13.** Yes; the diagonals bisect each other.

15. $\square ACDH$ (Given) → $\overline{AC} \parallel \overline{HD}$ (Def. of ▱)
B is the midpoint of $\overline{AC}$. (Given) → $\overline{AB} \cong \overline{BC}$ (Def. of midpoint)
F is the midpoint of $\overline{HD}$. (Given) → $\overline{HF} \cong \overline{FD}$ (Def. of midpoint)
→ $\overline{AB} \cong \overline{BC} \cong \overline{HF} \cong \overline{FD}$ (Def. of ▱)
→ $\overline{AB} \parallel \overline{HF}$ and $\overline{BC} \parallel \overline{FD}$ (Def. of ▱)
→ $ABFH$ is a ▱. (Opp. sides are $\parallel$ and $\cong$.)

17. Given: $ABEF$ is a parallelogram; $BCDE$ is a parallelogram.
Prove: $ACDF$ is a parallelogram.

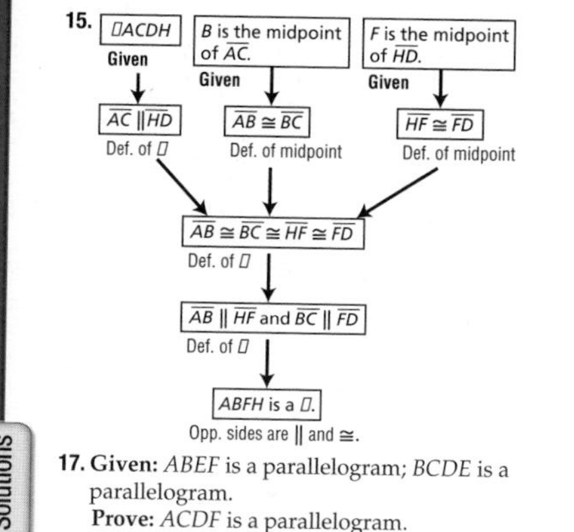

Proof:
Statements (Reasons)
1. $ABEF$ is a parallelogram; $BCDE$ is a parallelogram. (Given)
2. $\overline{AF} \cong \overline{BE}$, $\overline{BE} \cong \overline{CD}$, $\overline{AF} \parallel \overline{BE}$, $\overline{BE} \parallel \overline{CD}$ (Def. of ▱)
3. $\overline{AF} \cong \overline{CD}$, $\overline{AF} \parallel \overline{CD}$ (Trans. Prop.)
4. $ACDF$ is a parallelogram. (If one pair of opp. sides is $\cong$ and $\parallel$, then the quad. is a ▱.)

19. $x = 8, y = 9$ **21.** $x = 11, y = 7$ **23.** $x = 4, y = 3$

25. No; both pairs of opposite sides must be congruent. The distance between K and L is $\sqrt{53}$. The distance between L and M is $\sqrt{37}$. The distance between M and J is $\sqrt{50}$. The distance between J and K is $\sqrt{26}$. Since, both pairs of opposite sides are not congruent, $JKLM$ is not a parallelogram.

27. Yes; a pair of opposite sides must be parallel and congruent. Slope of $\overline{QR} = \frac{7}{2} =$ slope of $\overline{ST}$, so $\overline{QR} \parallel \overline{ST}$. The distance between Q and $R = \sqrt{53} =$ distance between S and T, so $\overline{QR} \cong \overline{ST}$. So, $QRST$ is a parallelogram.

29. Given: $ABCD$ is a parallelogram. $\angle A$ is a right angle.
Prove: $\angle B$, $\angle C$, and $\angle D$ are right angles.
Proof:
slope of $\overline{BC} = \left(\frac{b-b}{a-0}\right)$ or 0
The slope of $\overline{CD}$ is undefined.
slope of $\overline{AD} = \left(\frac{0-0}{a-0}\right)$ or 0
The slope of $\overline{AB}$ is undefined.
Therefore, $\overline{BC} \perp \overline{CD}$, $\overline{CD} \perp \overline{AD}$, and $\overline{AB} \perp \overline{BC}$. So, $\angle B$, $\angle C$, and $\angle D$ are right angles.

31 **a.** Use the Segment Addition Postulate to rewrite AC and CF each as the sum of two measures. Then use substitution, the Subtraction Property, and the Transitive Property to show that $\overline{BC} \cong \overline{DE}$. By proving that $BCDE$ is a parallelogram, you can prove that $\overline{BE} \parallel \overline{CD}$.
Given: $\overline{AC} \cong \overline{CF}$, $\overline{AB} \cong \overline{CD} \cong \overline{BE}$, and $\overline{DF} \cong \overline{DE}$
Prove: $\overline{BE} \parallel \overline{CD}$
Proof: We are given that $\overline{AC} \cong \overline{CF}$, $\overline{AB} \cong \overline{CD} \cong \overline{BE}$, and $\overline{DF} \cong \overline{DE}$. $AC = CF$ by the definition of congruence. $AC = AB + BC$ and $CF = CD + DF$ by the Segment Addition Postulate and $AB + BC = CD + DF$ by substitution. Using substitution again, $AB + BC = AB + DF$, and $BC = DF$ by the Subtraction Property. $\overline{BC} \cong \overline{DF}$ by the definition of congruence, and $\overline{BC} \cong \overline{DE}$ by the Transitive Property. If both pairs of opposite sides of a quadrilateral are congruent, then the quadrilateral is a parallelogram, so $BCDE$ is a parallelogram. By the definition of a parallelogram, $\overline{BE} \parallel \overline{CD}$.
b. Let x = width of the copy. If $AB = 12$, then $CD = BE = 12$. So, $CF = 12 + 8$ or 20.
$\frac{CF}{BE} = \frac{\text{width of copy}}{\text{width of original}}$
$\frac{20}{12} = \frac{x}{5.5}$ Substitution
$20(5.5) = 12x$ Cross multiply.
$110 = 12x$ Simplify.
$9.2 \approx x$ Divide each side by 12.
The width of the original object is about 9.2 in.

33. Given: $\overline{AB} \cong \overline{DC}$, $\overline{AB} \parallel \overline{DC}$
Prove: $ABCD$ is a parallelogram.
Proof:
Statements (Reasons)
1. $\overline{AB} \cong \overline{DC}$, $\overline{AB} \parallel \overline{DC}$ (Given)
2. Draw $\overline{AC}$. (Two points determine a line.)
3. $\angle 1 \cong \angle 2$ (If two lines are $\parallel$, then alt. int. ∠s are $\cong$.)
4. $\overline{AC} \cong \overline{AC}$ (Refl. Prop.)
5. $\triangle ABC \cong \triangle CDA$ (SAS)
6. $\overline{AD} \cong \overline{BC}$ (CPCTC)
7. $ABCD$ is a parallelogram. (If both pairs of opp. sides are $\cong$, then the quad. is ▱.)

35 Opposite sides of a parallelogram are parallel and congruent. Since the slope of $\overline{AB}$ is 0, the slope of $\overline{DC}$ must be 0. The y-coordinate of vertex D must be c. The length of $\overline{AB}$ is $(a + b) - 0$ or $a + b$. So the length of $\overline{DC}$ must be $a + b$. If the x-coordinate of D is $-b$ and the x-coordinate of C is a, then the length of $\overline{DC}$ is $a - (-b)$ or $a + b$. So, the coordinates are $C(a, c)$ and $D(-b, c)$.

37 Sample answer: Since the two vertical rails are both perpendicular to the ground, he knows that they are parallel to each other. If he measures the distance between the two rails at the top of the steps and at the bottom of the steps, and they are equal, then one pair of sides of the quadrilateral formed by the handrails is both parallel and congruent, so the quadrilateral is a parallelogram. Since the quadrilateral is a parallelogram, the two hand rails are parallel by definition.

39a. Sample answer:

39b. Sample answer:

Rectangle	Side	Length
ABCD	$\overline{AC}$	3.3 cm
	$\overline{BD}$	3.3 cm
MNOP	$\overline{MO}$	2.8 cm
	$\overline{NP}$	2.8 cm
WXYZ	$\overline{WY}$	2.0 cm
	$\overline{XZ}$	2.0 cm

39c. Sample answer: The diagonals of a rectangle are congruent.

41. Sample answer: The theorems are converses of each other. The hypothesis of Theorem 6-3 is "a figure is a parallelogram," and the hypothesis of 6-9 is "both pairs of opposite sides of a quadrilateral are congruent." The conclusion of Theorem 6-3 is "opposite sides are congruent," and the conclusion of 6-9 is "the quadrilateral is a parallelogram."

43. $D(b-a, c)$, $C(b, c)$, $A(-a, 0)$, $B(0, 0)$

45. Sample answer: You can show that: both pairs of opposite sides are congruent or parallel, both pairs of opposite angles are congruent, diagonals bisect each other, or one pair of opposite sides is both congruent and parallel. **47.** 4 **49.** E **51.** (4.5, 1.5) **53.** 35

55. Given: $P + W > 2$ (P is time spent in the pool; W is time spent lifting weights.)
Prove: $P > 1$ or $W > 1$
Proof:
Step 1: Assume $P \leq 1$ and $W \leq 1$.
Step 2: $P + W \leq 2$
Step 3: This contradicts the given statement. Therefore he did at least one of these activities for more than an hour.

57.
$\overline{MN} \cong \overline{PQ}$ (Given) → $MN = PQ$ (Def. of $\cong$ seg.) → $MN + NP = NP + PQ$ (Addition Prop.) ← $NP = NP$ (Reflective Prop.)
→ $MP = NQ$ (Substitution) ← $MN + NP = MP$, $NP + PQ = NQ$ (Seg. Addition Post.)
→ $\overline{MP} \cong \overline{NQ}$ (Def. of $\cong$ seg.)
→ $\triangle MLP \cong \triangle QLN$ (ASA) ← $\angle M \cong \angle Q$, $\angle 2 \cong \angle 3$ (Given)

59. not perpendicular

Lesson 6-4

1. 7 ft **3.** 33.5 **5.** 11

7. Given: $ABDE$ is a rectangle; $\overline{BC} \cong \overline{DC}$.
Prove: $\overline{AC} \cong \overline{EC}$
Proof:
Statements (Reasons)
1. $ABDE$ is a rectangle; $\overline{BC} \cong \overline{DC}$. (Given)
2. $ABDE$ is a parallelogram. (Def. of rectangle)
3. $\overline{AB} \cong \overline{DE}$ (Opp. sides of a ▱ are $\cong$.)
4. $\angle B$ and $\angle D$ are right angles. (Def. of rectangle)
5. $\angle B \cong \angle D$ (All rt. ∠s are $\cong$.)
6. $\triangle ABC \cong \triangle EDC$ (SAS)
7. $\overline{AC} \cong \overline{EC}$ (CPCTC)

9. Yes; $AB = 5 = CD$ and $BC = 8 = AD$. So, $ABCD$ is a parallelogram. $BD = \sqrt{89} = AC$, so the diagonals are congruent. Thus, $ABCD$ is a rectangle.

11 Since all angles in a rectangle are right angles, $\angle ABD$ is a right triangle.
$AD^2 + AB^2 = BD^2$ Pythagorean Theorem
$2^2 + 6^2 = BD^2$ Substitution
$40 = BD^2$ Simplify.
$6.3 \approx BD$ Take the positive square root of each side.
$BD \approx 6.3$ ft

13. 25 **15.** 43 **17.** 38 **19.** 46

21. Given: $QTVW$ is a rectangle; $\overline{QR} \cong \overline{ST}$.
Prove: $\triangle SWQ \cong \triangle RVT$
Proof:
Statements (Reasons)
1. $QTVW$ is a rectangle; $\overline{QR} \cong \overline{ST}$. (Given)
2. $QTVW$ is a parallelogram. (Def. of rectangle)
3. $\overline{WQ} \cong \overline{VT}$ (Opp sides of a ▱ are $\cong$.)
4. $\angle Q$ and $\angle T$ are right angles. (Def. of rectangle)
5. $\angle Q \cong \angle T$ (All rt. ∠s are $\cong$.)

6. $QR = ST$ (Def. of ≅ segs.)
7. $\overline{RS} \cong \overline{RS}$ (Refl. Prop.)
8. $RS = RS$ (Def. of ≅ segs.)
9. $QR + RS = RS + ST$ (Add. prop.)
10. $QS = QR + RS$, $RT = RS + ST$ (Seg. Add. Post.)
11. $QS = RT$ (Subst.)
12. $\overline{QS} \cong \overline{RT}$ (Def. of ≅ segs.)
13. $\triangle SWQ \cong \triangle RVT$ (SAS)

23. No; $JK = \sqrt{65} = LM$, $KL = \sqrt{37} = MJ$, so $JKLM$ is a parallelogram. $KM = \sqrt{106}$; $JL = \sqrt{98}$. $KM \neq JL$, so the diagonals are not congruent. Thus, $JKLM$ is not a rectangle.

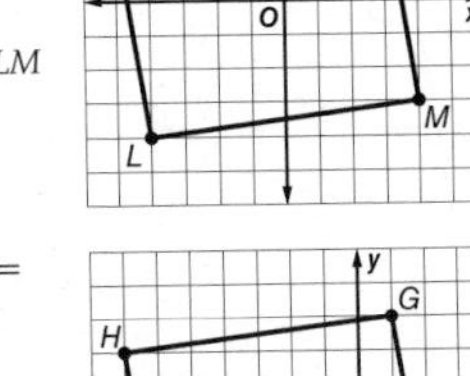

25. No; slope of $\overline{GH} = \frac{1}{8}$ = slope of $\overline{JK}$ and slope of $\overline{HJ} = -6$ = slope of $\overline{KG}$. So, $GHJK$ is a parallelogram. The product of the slopes of consecutive sides $\neq -1$, so the consecutive sides are not perpendicular. Thus, $GHJK$ is not a rectangle. **27.** 40

29 A rectangle has four right angles, so $m\angle CDB = 90$. Since a rectangle is a parallelogram, opposite sides are parallel. Alternate interior angles of parallel lines are congruent. So, $\angle 3 \cong \angle 2$ and $m\angle 3 = m\angle 2 = 40$. $m\angle 4 = 90 - 40$ or 50. Since diagonals of a rectangle are congruent and bisect each other, the triangle with angles 4, 5, and 6 is isosceles with $m\angle 6 = m\angle 4$.

$m\angle 4 + m\angle 5 + m\angle 6 = 180$	Triangle Angle-Sum Theorem
$m\angle 4 + m\angle 5 + m\angle 4 = 180$	$m\angle 6 = m\angle 4$
$50 + m\angle 5 + 50 = 180$	Substitution
$100 + m\angle 5 = 180$	Simplify.
$m\angle 5 = 80$	Subtract 100 from each side.

31. 100

33. Given: $WXYZ$ is a rectangle with diagonals $\overline{WY}$ and $\overline{XZ}$.
Prove: $\overline{WY} \cong \overline{XZ}$
Proof:
Statements (Reasons)
1. $WXYZ$ is a rectangle with diagonals $\overline{WY}$ and $\overline{XZ}$. (Given)
2. $\overline{WX} \cong \overline{ZY}$ (Opp. sides of a ▱ are ≅.)
3. $\overline{WZ} \cong \overline{WZ}$ (Refl. Prop.)
4. $\angle XWZ$ and $\angle YZW$ are right angles. (Def. of ▭)
5. $\angle XWZ \cong \angle YZW$ (All right ∠s are ≅.)
6. $\triangle XWZ \cong \triangle YZW$ (SAS)
7. $\overline{WY} \cong \overline{XZ}$ (CPCTC)

35. $ABCD$ is a parallelogram, and $\angle B$ is a right angle. Since $ABCD$ is a parallelogram and has one right angle, then it has four right angles. So by the definition of a rectangle, $ABCD$ is a rectangle.

37. Sample answer: Since $\overline{RP} \perp \overline{PQ}$ and $\overline{SQ} \perp \overline{PQ}$, $m\angle P = m\angle Q = 90$. Lines that are perpendicular to the same line are parallel, so $\overline{RP} \parallel \overline{SQ}$. The same compass setting was used to locate points R and S, so $\overline{RP} \cong \overline{SQ}$. If one pair of opposite sides of a quadrilateral is both parallel and congruent, then the quadrilateral is a parallelogram. A parallelogram with right angles is a rectangle. Thus, $PRSQ$ is a rectangle. **39.** 5 **41.** No; sample answer: Both pairs of opposite sides are congruent, so the sign is a parallelogram, but no measure is given that can be used to prove that it is a rectangle.

43 Draw ▱ $ABCD$ on the coordinate plane.
Find the slopes of $\overline{AD}$ and $\overline{AB}$ and show that the lines are perpendicular.
Given: ▱$ABCD$ and $\overline{AC} \cong \overline{BD}$
Prove: ▱$ABCD$ is a rectangle.
Proof:

$AC = \sqrt{(a + b - 0)^2 + (c - 0)^2}$

$BD = \sqrt{(b - a)^2 + (c - 0)^2}$

But $AC = BD$ and

$$\sqrt{(a + b - 0)^2 + (c - 0)^2} = \sqrt{(b - a)^2 + (c - 0)^2}.$$
$$(a + b - 0)^2 + (c - 0)^2 = (b - a)^2 + (c - 0)^2$$
$$(a + b)^2 + c^2 = (b - a)^2 + c^2$$
$$a^2 + 2ab + b^2 + c^2 = b^2 - 2ab + a^2 + c^2$$
$$2ab = -2ab$$
$$4ab = 0$$
$$a = 0 \text{ or } b = 0$$

Because A and B are different points, $a \neq 0$. Then $b = 0$. The slope of $\overline{AD}$ is undefined and the slope of $\overline{AB} = 0$. Thus, $\overline{AD} \perp \overline{AB}$. $\angle DAB$ is a right angle and $ABCD$ is a rectangle.

45. $x = 6$, $y = -10$ **47.** 6 **49.** Sample answer: All rectangles are parallelograms because, by definition, both pairs of opposite sides are parallel. Parallelograms with right angles are rectangles, so some parallelograms are rectangles, but others with non-right angles are not. **51.** J **53.** E **55.** $x = 8$, $y = 22$ **57.** (2.5, 0.5) **59.** $\overline{AH}$ and $\overline{AJ}$ **61.** $\angle AJK$ and $\angle AKJ$ **63.** $\sqrt{101}$

Lesson 6-5

1. 32

3. Given: $ABCD$ is a rhombus with diagonal $\overline{DB}$.
Prove: $\overline{AP} \cong \overline{CP}$
Proof:
Statements (Reasons)
1. $ABCD$ is a rhombus with diagonal $\overline{DB}$. (Given)
2. $\angle ABP \cong \angle CBP$ (Diag. of rhombus bisects ∠)
3. $\overline{PB} \cong \overline{PB}$ (Refl. Prop.)
4. $\overline{AB} \cong \overline{CB}$ (Def. of rhombus)
5. $\triangle APB \cong \triangle CPB$ (SAS)
6. $\overline{AP} \cong \overline{CP}$ (CPCTC)

5. Rectangle, rhombus, square; consecutive sides are perpendicular, all sides are congruent. **7.** 14 **9.** 28

11

$m\angle ABC + m\angle BCD = 180$	Consecutive ∠s are supp.
$(2x - 7) + (2x + 3) = 180$	Substitution
$4x - 4 = 180$	Simplify.
$4x = 184$	Add 4 to each side.
$x = 46$	Divide each side by 4.
$m\angle BCD = 2x + 3$	Given
$= 2(46) + 3$ or 95	Substitution
$\angle DAB \cong \angle BCD$	Opposite angles are congruent.
$m\angle DAB = m\angle BCD$	Definition of congruence
$= 95$	Substitution

13. Given: $\overline{WZ} \parallel \overline{XY}$, $\overline{WX} \parallel \overline{ZY}$, $\overline{WZ} \cong \overline{ZY}$
Prove: $WXYZ$ is a rhombus.
Proof:
Statements (Reasons)
1. $\overline{WZ} \parallel \overline{XY}$, $\overline{WX} \parallel \overline{ZY}$, $\overline{WZ} \cong \overline{ZY}$ (Given)
2. $WXYZ$ is a ▱. (Both pairs of opp. sides are ∥.)
3. $WXYZ$ is a rhombus. (If one pair of consecutive sides of a ▱ are ≅, the ▱ is a rhombus.)

15. Given: $JKQP$ is a square. $\overline{ML}$ bisects $\overline{JP}$ and $\overline{KQ}$.
Prove: $JKLM$ is a parallelogram.
Proof:
Statements (Reasons)
1. $JKQP$ is a square. $\overline{ML}$ bisects $\overline{JP}$ and $\overline{KQ}$. (Given)
2. $JKQP$ is a parallelogram. (All squares are parallelograms.)
3. $\overline{JM} \parallel \overline{KL}$ (Def. of ▱)
4. $\overline{JP} \cong \overline{KQ}$ (Opp. Sides of ▱ are ≅)
5. $JP = KQ$ (Def of ≅ segs.)
6. $JM = MP$, $KL = LQ$ (Def. of bisects)
7. $JP = JM + MP$, $KQ = KL + LQ$ (Seg. Add Post.)
8. $JP = 2JM$, $KQ = 2KL$ (Subst.)
9. $2JM = 2KL$ (Subst.)
10. $JM = KL$ (Division Prop.)
11. $\overline{KL} \cong \overline{JM}$ (Def. of ≅ segs.)
12. $JKLM$ is a parallelogram. (If one pair of opp. sides is ≅ and ∥, then the quad. is a ▱.)

17. Rhombus; Sample answer: The measure of angle formed between the two streets is 29, and vertical angles are congruent, so the measure of one angle of the quadrilateral is 29. Since the crosswalks are the same length, the sides of the quadrilateral are congruent. Therefore, they form a rhombus. **19.** Rhombus; the diagonals are perpendicular. **21.** None; the diagonals are not congruent or perpendicular.

23 The diagonals of a rhombus are perpendicular, so $\triangle ABP$ is a right triangle.

$AP^2 + PB^2 = AB^2$	Pythagorean Theorem
$AP^2 + 12^2 = 15^2$	Substitution
$AP^2 + 144 = 225$	Simplify.
$AP^2 = 81$	Subtract 144 from each side.
$AP = 9$	Take the square root of each side.

25. 24 **27.** 6 **29.** 90 **31.** square **33.** rectangle

35. Given: $ABCD$ is a parallelogram; $\overline{AC} \perp \overline{BD}$.
Prove: $ABCD$ is a rhombus.
Proof: We are given that $ABCD$ is a parallelogram. The diagonals of a parallelogram bisect each other, so $\overline{AE} \cong \overline{EC}$. $\overline{BE} \cong \overline{BE}$ because congruence of segments is reflexive. We are also given that $\overline{AC} \perp \overline{BD}$. Thus, $\angle AEB$ and $\angle BEC$ are right angles by the definition of perpendicular lines. Then $\angle AEB \cong \angle BEC$ because all right angles are congruent. Therefore, $\triangle AEB \cong \triangle CEB$ by SAS. $\overline{AB} \cong \overline{CB}$ by CPCTC. Opposite sides of parallelograms are congruent, so $\overline{AB} \cong \overline{CD}$ and $\overline{BC} \cong \overline{AD}$. Then since congruence of segments is transitive, $\overline{AB} \cong \overline{CD} \cong \overline{BC} \cong \overline{AD}$. All four sides of $ABCD$ are congruent, so $ABCD$ is a rhombus by definition.

37. Given: $ABCD$ is a parallelogram; $\overline{AB} \cong \overline{BC}$.
Prove: $ABCD$ is a rhombus.
Proof: Opposite sides of a parallelogram are congruent, so $\overline{BC} \cong \overline{AD}$ and $\overline{AB} \cong \overline{CD}$. We are given that $\overline{AB} \cong \overline{BC}$. So, by the Transitive Property, $\overline{BC} \cong \overline{CD}$. So, $\overline{BC} \cong \overline{CD} \cong \overline{AB} \cong \overline{AD}$. Thus, $ABCD$ is a rhombus by definition.

39. Sample answer: The diagonals bisect each other, so the quadrilateral is a parallelogram. Since the diagonals of the parallelogram are perpendicular to each other, the parallelogram is a rhombus.

41. Given: $ABCD$ is a square.
Prove: $\overline{AC} \perp \overline{DB}$
Proof:
slope of $\overline{DB} = \frac{0 - a}{a - 0}$ or -1
slope of $\overline{AC} = \frac{0 - a}{0 - a}$ or 1
The slope of $\overline{AC}$ is the negative reciprocal of the slope of $\overline{DB}$, so they are perpendicular.

43 Use the properties of exterior angles to classify the quadrilaterals. Sample answer: Since the octagons are regular, each side is congruent, and the quadrilaterals share common sides with the octagons, so the quadrilaterals are either rhombuses or squares. The vertices of the quadrilaterals are formed by the exterior angles of the sides of the octagons adjacent to the vertices. The sum of the measures of the exterior angles of a polygon is always 360 and since a regular octagon has 8 congruent exterior angles, each one measures 360 ÷ 8 or 45. As shown in the diagram, each angle of the quadrilaterals in the pattern measures 45 + 45 or 90. Therefore, the quadrilateral is a square.

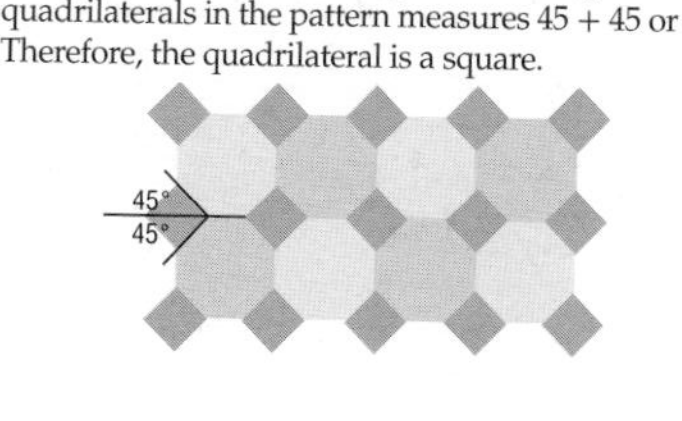

45a.

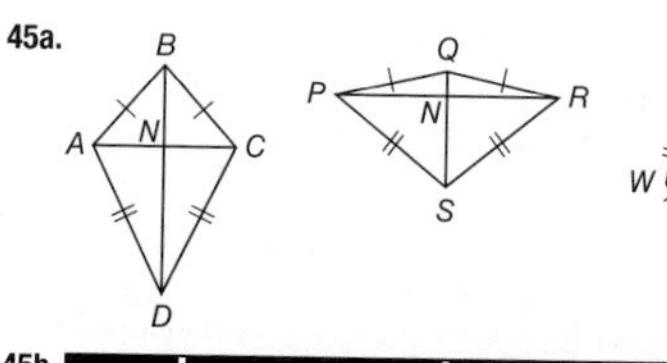

45b.

Figure	Distance from N to each vertex along shorter diagonal		Distance from N to each vertex along longer diagonal	
ABCD	0.8 cm	0.8 cm	0.9 cm	1.5 cm
PQRS	1.2 cm	1.2 cm	0.3 cm	0.9 cm
WXYZ	0.2 cm	0.2 cm	1.1 cm	0.4 cm

45c. Sample answer: The shorter diagonal of a kite is bisected by the longer diagonal. **47.** True; sample answer: A rectangle is a quadrilateral with four right angles and a square is both a rectangle and a rhombus, so a square is always a rectangle.
Converse: If a quadrilateral is a rectangle then it is a square. False; sample answer: A rectangle is a quadrilateral with four right angles. It is not necessarily a rhombus, so it is not necessarily a square.
Inverse: If a quadrilateral is not a square, then it is not a rectangle. False; sample answer: A quadrilateral that has four right angles and two pairs of congruent sides is not a square, but it is a rectangle.
Contrapositive: If a quadrilateral is not a rectangle, then it is not a square. True; sample answer: If a quadrilateral is not a rectangle, it is also not a square by definition. **49.** Sample answer: (0, 0), (6, 0), (0, 6), (6, 6) ; the diagonals are perpendicular, and any four points on the lines equidistant from the intersection of the lines will be the vertices of a square. **51.** B **53.** H **55.** 52 **57.** 38 **59.** Yes; both pairs of opposite sides are congruent. **61.** No; the Triangle Inequality Theorem states that the sum of the lengths of any two sides of a triangle must be greater than the length of the third side. Since 22 + 23 = 45, the sides of Monifa's backyard cannot be 22 ft, 23 ft and 45 ft. **63.** 2 **65.** $\frac{5}{4}$

Lesson 6-6

1. 101 **3.** $\overline{BC} \parallel \overline{AD}$, $\overline{AB} \nparallel \overline{CD}$; $ABCD$ is a trapezoid. **5.** 1.2 **7.** 70 **9.** 70

11

$\overline{XZ} \cong \overline{YW}$	Diagonals are congruent.
$XZ = YW$	Definition of congruence.
$18 = YW$	Substitution
$18 = YP + PW$	Segment Addition Postulate
$18 = 3 + PW$	Substitution
$15 = PW$	Subtract 3 from each side.

13. $\overline{JK} \parallel \overline{LM}$, $\overline{KL} \nparallel \overline{JM}$; $JKLM$ is a trapezoid, but not isosceles since $KL = \sqrt{26}$ and $JM = 5$. **15.** $\overline{XY} \parallel \overline{WZ}$, $\overline{WX} \nparallel \overline{YZ}$; $WXYZ$ is a trapezoid, but not isosceles since $XZ = \sqrt{74}$ and $WY = \sqrt{68}$. **17.** 10 **19.** 8 **21.** 17

23 The G key represents the midsegment of the trapezoid. Use the Trapezoid Midsegment Theorem to find the length of the key.

length of G key $= \frac{1}{2}$(length of C key + length of D key)

$= \frac{1}{2}(6 + 1.8)$ Substitution

$= \frac{1}{2}(7.8)$ or 3.9 Simplify.

The length of the G key is 3.9 in.

25. $\sqrt{20}$ **27.** 75

29. Given: $ABCD$ is a trapezoid; $\angle D \cong \angle C$.
Prove: Trapezoid $ABCD$ is isosceles.
Proof: By the Parallel Postulate, we can draw the auxillary line $\overline{EB} \parallel \overline{AD}$. $\angle D \cong \angle BEC$, by the Corr. ∠s Thm. We are given that $\angle D \cong \angle C$, so by the Trans. Prop, $\angle BEC \cong \angle C$. So, $\triangle EBC$ is isosceles and $\overline{EB} \cong \overline{BC}$. From the definition of a trapezoid, $\overline{AB} \parallel \overline{DE}$. Since both pairs of opposite sides are parallel, $ABED$ is a parallelogram. So, $\overline{AD} \cong \overline{EB}$. By the Transitive Property, $\overline{BC} \cong \overline{AD}$. Thus, $ABCD$ is an isosceles trapezoid.

31. Given: $ABCD$ is a kite with $\overline{AB} \cong \overline{BC}$ and $\overline{AD} \cong \overline{DC}$.
Prove: $\overline{BD} \perp \overline{AC}$
Proof: We know that $\overline{AB} \cong \overline{BC}$ and $\overline{AD} \cong \overline{DC}$. So, B and D are both equidistant from A and C. If a point is equidistant from the endpoints of a segment, then it is on the perpendicular bisector of the segment. The line that contains B and D is the perpendicular bisector of $\overline{AC}$, since only one line exists through two points. Thus, $\overline{BD} \perp \overline{AC}$.

33. Given: $ABCD$ is a trapezoid with median $\overline{EF}$.
Prove: $\overline{EF} \parallel \overline{AB}$ and $\overline{EF} \parallel \overline{DC}$ and $EF = \frac{1}{2}(AB + DC)$

Proof:
By the definition of the median of a trapezoid, E is the midpoint of $\overline{AD}$ and F is the midpoint of $\overline{BC}$.

Midpoint E is $\left(\frac{a+0}{2}, \frac{d+0}{2}\right)$ or $\left(\frac{a}{2}, \frac{d}{2}\right)$.

Midpoint F is $\left(\frac{a+b+a+b+c}{2}, \frac{d+0}{2}\right)$ or $\left(\frac{2a+2b+c}{2}, \frac{d}{2}\right)$.

The slope of $\overline{AB} = 0$, the slope of $\overline{EF} = 0$, and the slope of $\overline{DC} = 0$. Thus, $\overline{EF} \parallel \overline{AB}$ and $\overline{EF} \parallel \overline{DC}$.

$AB = \sqrt{[(a+b)-a]^2 + (d-d)^2} = \sqrt{b^2}$ or b

$DC = \sqrt{[(a+b+c)-0]^2 + (0-0)^2}$
$= \sqrt{(a+b+c)^2}$ or $a+b+c$

$EF = \sqrt{\left(\frac{2a+2b+c-a}{2}\right)^2 + \left(\frac{d}{2}-\frac{d}{2}\right)^2}$
$= \sqrt{\left(\frac{a+2b+c}{2}\right)^2}$ or $\frac{a+2b+c}{2}$

$\frac{1}{2}(AB + DC) = \frac{1}{2}[b + (a+b+c)]$
$= \frac{1}{2}(a+2b+c)$
$= \frac{a+2b+c}{2}$
$= EF$

Thus, $\frac{1}{2}(AB + DC) = EF$.

35. 15 **37.** 28 ft **39.** 70 **41.** 2 **43.** 20 **45.** 10 in. **47.** 105

49 $\angle ZWX \cong \angle ZYX$ because one pair of opposite sides of a kite is congruent and $\angle ZWX \cong \angle ZYX$. So, $m\angle ZYX = m\angle ZWX = 10x$.

$m\angle ZWX + m\angle WXY + m\angle ZYX + m\angle WZY = 360$	Polygon Interior Angles Sum Theorem
$10x + 120 + 10x + 4x = 360$	Substitution
$24x + 120 = 360$	Simplify.
$24x = 240$	Subtract 120 from each side.
$x = 10$	Divide each side by 24.

So, $m\angle ZYX = 10x$ or 100.

51. Given: $ABCD$ is an isosceles trapezoid.
Prove: $\angle DAC \cong \angle CBD$
Proof:
Statements (Reasons)
1. $ABCD$ is an isosceles trapezoid. (Given)
2. $\overline{AD} \cong \overline{BC}$ (Def. of isos. trap.)
3. $\overline{DC} \cong \overline{DC}$ (Refl. Prop.)
4. $\overline{AC} \cong \overline{BD}$ (Diags. of isos. trap. are ≅.)
5. $\triangle ADC \cong \triangle BCD$ (SSS)
6. $\angle DAC \cong \angle CBD$ (CPCTC)

53. Sometimes; opp ∠s are supplementary in an isosceles trapezoid. **55.** Always; by def. a square is a quadrilateral with 4 rt. ∠s and 4 ≅ sides. Since by def., a rhombus is a quadrilateral with 4 ≅ sides, a square is always a rhombus. **57.** Sometimes; only if the parallelogram has 4 rt. ∠s and/or congruent diagonals, is it a rectangle.

59.

Parallelograms (Opp. sides are ∥.)
Rectangles (4 rt ∠s)
Squares
Rhombi (4 ≅ sides)
Trapezoids (exactly 1 pair of ∥ sides)
Isosceles Trapezoids (Legs are ≅.)
Kites (exactly 2 pair of ≅ sides)

61 slope of $\overline{WX} = \frac{4-4}{3-(-3)} = 0$

slope of $\overline{XY} = \frac{3-4}{5-3} = -\frac{1}{2}$

slope of $\overline{YZ} = \frac{1-3}{-5-5} = \frac{1}{5}$

slope of $\overline{WZ} = \frac{1-4}{-5-(-3)} = \frac{3}{2}$

Since the figure has no parallel sides, it is just a quadrilateral.

63. Given: isosceles trapezoid $ABCD$ with $\overline{AD} \cong \overline{BC}$
Prove: $\overline{BD} \cong \overline{AC}$
Proof:
$DB = \sqrt{(a-b)^2 + (0-c)^2}$ or $\sqrt{(a-b)^2 + c^2}$
$AC = \sqrt{[(a-b)-0]^2 + (c-0)^2}$ or $\sqrt{(a-b)^2 + c^2}$
$BD = AC$ and $\overline{BD} \cong \overline{AC}$

65. Belinda; $m\angle D = m\angle B$. So $m\angle A + m\angle B + m\angle C + m\angle D = 360$ or $m\angle A + 100 + 45 + 100 = 360$. So, $m\angle A = 115$. **67.** Never; a square has all 4 sides ≅, while a kite does not have any opposite sides congruent. **69.** A quadrilateral must have exactly one pair of sides parallel to be a trapezoid. If the legs are congruent, then the trapezoid is an isosceles trapezoid. If a quadrilateral has exactly two pairs of consecutive congruent sides with the opposite sides not congruent, the quadrilateral is a kite. A trapezoid and a kite both have four sides. In a trapezoid and isosceles trapezoid, both have exactly one pair of parallel sides. **71.** 76 **73.** B **75.** 18 **77.** 9

79. No; slope of $\overline{JK} = \frac{1}{8}$ = slope of $\overline{LM}$ and slope of $\overline{KL} = -6$ = slope of $\overline{MJ}$. So, $JKLM$ is a parallelogram. The product of the slopes of consecutive sides $\neq -1$, so the consecutive sides are not perpendicular. Thus, $JKLM$ is not a rectangle.

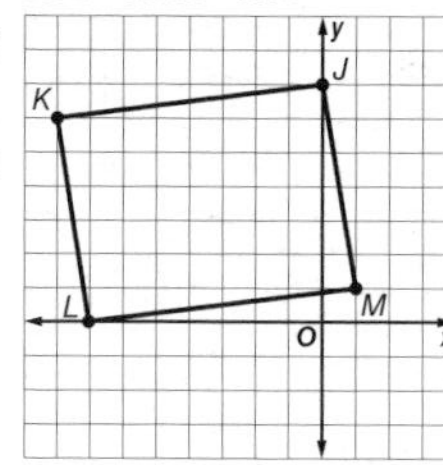

81. Given: $\angle CMF \cong \angle EMF$, $\angle CFM \cong \angle EFM$
Prove: $\triangle DMC \cong \triangle DME$
Proof:
Statements (Reasons)
1. $\angle CMF \cong \angle EMF$, $\angle CFM \cong \angle EFM$ (Given)
2. $\overline{MF} \cong \overline{MF}$, $\overline{DM} \cong \overline{MF}$ (Reflexive Property)
3. $\triangle CMF \cong \triangle EMF$ (ASA)
4. $\overline{CM} \cong \overline{EM}$ (CPCTC)
5. $\angle DMC$ and $\angle CMF$ are supplementary and $\angle DME$ and $\angle EMF$ are supplementary. (Supplement Th.)
6. $\angle DMC \cong \angle DME$ (∡ suppl. to ≅ ∡ are ≅.)
7. $\triangle DMC \cong \triangle DME$ (SAS)

83. 1

Chapter 6 Study Guide and Review

1. false, both pairs of base angles **3.** false, diagonal **5.** true **7.** false, is always **9.** true **11.** 1440 **13.** 720 **15.** 26 **17.** 18 **19.** 115 **21.** $x = 37, y = 6$ **23.** yes, Theorem 6.11

25. Given: ▱$ABCD$, $\overline{AE} \cong \overline{CF}$
Prove: Quadrilateral $EBFD$ is a parallelogram

Statements (Reasons)
1. $ABCD$, $\overline{AE} \cong \overline{CF}$ (Given)
2. $AE = CF$ (Def. of ≅ segs)
3. $\overline{BC} \cong \overline{AD}$ (Opp. sides of a ▱ are ≅)
4. $BC = AD$ (Def. of ≅ segs)
5. $BC = BF + CF$, $AD = AE + ED$ (Seg. Add. Post.)
6. $BF + CF = AE + ED$ (Subst.)
7. $BF + AE = AE + ED$ (Subst.)
8. $BF = ED$ (Subt. Prop.)
9. $\overline{BF} \cong \overline{ED}$ (Def. of ≅ segs)
10. $\overline{BF} \parallel \overline{ED}$ (Def. of ▱)
11. Quadrilateral $EBFD$ is a parallelogram. (If one pair of opposite sides is parallel and congruent then it is a parallelogram.)

27. $x = 5, y = 12$ **29.** 33 **31.** 64 **33.** 6 **35.** 55 **37.** 35 **39.** Rectangle, rhombus, square; all sides are ≅, consecutive sides are ⊥. **41.** 19.2 **43a.** Sample answer: The legs of the trapezoids are part of the diagonals of the square. The diagonals of a square bisect opposite angles, so each base angle of a trapezoid measures 45°. One pair of sides is parallel and the base angles are congruent. **43b.** $16 + 8\sqrt{2} \approx 27.3$ in.

CHAPTER 7
Proportions and Similarity

Chapter 7 Get Ready

1. 4 or –4 **3.** –37 **5.** 64 **7.** 64.5

Lesson 7-1

1. 23:50 **3.** 30, 75, 60 **5.** 16 **7.** 8 **9.** 18 **11.** Movie A; 1:2

13 The ratio of the sides can be written as $9x:7x:5x$.

$9x + 7x + 5x = 191.1$	Perimeter of a triangle
$21x = 191.1$	Combine like terms.
$x = 9.1$	Divide each side by 21.

The measures of the sides are 9(9.1) or 81.9 inches, 7(9.1) or 63.7 inches, and 5(9.1) or 45.5 inches.

15. 2.2 ft **17.** 54, 108, 18 **19.** 75, 60, 45 **21.** $\frac{15}{8}$ **23.** 3 **25.** 8 **27.** 3

29

$\frac{7}{500} = \frac{x}{350}$	← 13- to 17-year-old vegetarians ← 13- to 17-year olds
$7 \cdot 350 = 500 \cdot x$	Cross Products Property
$2450 = 500x$	Simplify.
$4.9 = x$	Divide each side by 500.

About 5 13- to 17-year-olds would be vegetarian.

31. 3, –3.5 **33.** 12.9, –0.2 **35.** 2541 in^2 **37.** 48, 96, 144, 72 **39a.** No; the HDTV aspect ratio is 1.77778 and the standard aspect ratio is 1.33333. Neither television set is a golden rectangle since the ratios of the lengths to the widths are not the golden ratio. **39b.** 593 pixels and 367 pixels

41. Given: $\frac{a}{b} = \frac{c}{d}$, $b \neq 0$, $d \neq 0$
Prove: $ad = bc$
Proof:
Statements (Reasons)
1. $\frac{a}{b} = \frac{c}{d}$ $b \neq 0$, $d \neq 0$ (Given)
2. $(bd)\frac{a}{b} = (bd)\frac{c}{d}$ (Mult. Prop.)
3. $da = bc$ (Subst. Prop.)
4. $ad = bc$ (Comm. Prop.)

43 **a.**

b.

Triangle	ABC	MNO	PQR
Leg length	1 in.	2 in.	0.5 in.
Perimeter	2.5 in.	5 in.	1.25 in.

c. Sample answer: When the vertex angle of an isosceles triangle is held constant and the leg length is increased or decreased by a factor, the perimeter of the triangle increases or decreases by the same factor.

45. 5:2 **47.** $\frac{2}{3} = \frac{5}{7.5}$; You need to multiply $\frac{2}{3}$ by a factor of 2.5 to get $\frac{5}{7.5}$. The factor of the other three proportions is 2.8. **49.** Both are written with fractions. A ratio compares two quantities with division, while a proportion equates two ratios. First, ratios are used to write proportions. Then the cross products are used to solve the proportion. **51.** F **53.** D **55.** 2.5 **57.** Since a square is a parallelogram, the diagonals bisect each other. Since a square is a rhombus, the diagonals are congruent. Therefore, the distance from first base to third base is equal to the distance between home plate and second base. Thus, the distance from home plate to the center of the infield is 127 ft $3\frac{3}{8}$ in. divided by 2 or 63 ft $7\frac{11}{16}$ in. This distance is longer than the distance from home plate to the pitcher's mound so the pitcher's mound is not located in the center of the field. It is about 3 feet closer to home. **59.** $-\frac{4}{7} < x < \frac{136}{7}$ **61.** ∠1, ∠4, ∠11 **63.** ∠2, ∠6, ∠9, ∠4

65. Given: $\triangle ABC \cong \triangle DEF$, $\triangle DEF \cong \triangle GHI$
Prove: $\triangle ABC \cong \triangle GHI$

Proof:
You are given that $\triangle ABC \cong \triangle DEF$. Because corresponding parts of congruent triangles are congruent, $\angle A \cong \angle D$, $\angle B \cong \angle E$, $\angle C \cong \angle F$, $\overline{AB} \cong \overline{DE}$, $\overline{BC} \cong \overline{EF}$, and $\overline{AC} \cong \overline{DF}$. You are also given that $\triangle DEF \cong \triangle GHI$. So $\angle D \cong \angle G$, $\angle E \cong \angle H$, $\angle F \cong \angle I$, $\overline{DE} \cong \overline{GH}$, $\overline{EF} \cong \overline{HI}$, and $\overline{DF} \cong \overline{GI}$ by CPCTC. Therefore, $\angle A \cong \angle G$, $\angle B \cong \angle H$, $\angle C \cong \angle I$, $\overline{AB} \cong \overline{GH}$, $\overline{BC} \cong \overline{HI}$, and $\overline{AC} \cong \overline{GI}$ because congruence of angles and segments is transitive. Thus, $\triangle ABC \cong \triangle GHI$ by the definition of congruent triangles.

Lesson 7-2

1 Using the similarity statement, ∠A and ∠Z are corresponding angles, ∠B and ∠Y are corresponding angles, and ∠C and ∠X are corresponding angles. So, $\angle A \cong \angle Z$, $\angle B \cong \angle Y$, and $\angle C \cong \angle X$. $\overline{AC}$ and $\overline{ZX}$ are corresponding sides, $\overline{BC}$ and $\overline{YX}$ are corresponding sides, and $\overline{AB}$ and $\overline{ZY}$ are corresponding sides. So, $\frac{AC}{ZX} = \frac{BC}{YX} = \frac{AB}{ZY}$.

3. no; $\frac{NQ}{WZ} \neq \frac{QR}{WX}$ **5.** 6 **7.** 22 ft **9.** $\angle J \cong \angle P$, $\angle F \cong \angle S$, $\angle M \cong \angle T$; $\angle H \cong \angle Q$, $\frac{PQ}{JH} = \frac{TS}{MF} = \frac{SQ}{FH} = \frac{TP}{MJ}$

11. $\angle D \cong \angle K$, $\angle F \cong \angle M$, $\angle G \cong \angle J$; $\frac{DF}{KM} = \frac{FG}{MJ} = \frac{GD}{JK}$

13 Two sides and the included angle of $\triangle LTK$ are congruent to two sides and the included angle of $\triangle MTK$, so $\triangle LTK \cong \triangle MTK$. By CPCTC, the triangles have all corresponding angles congruent and all corresponding sides congruent. So, $\triangle LTK \sim \triangle MTK$, with a scale factor of 1.

15. no; $\frac{AD}{WM} \neq \frac{DK}{ML}$ **17.** Yes; sample answer:
The ratio of the longer dimensions of the screens is approximately 1.1 and the ratio of the shorter dimensions of the screens is approximately 1.1.

19

$\frac{SB}{JH} = \frac{BP}{HT}$	Similarity proportion
$\frac{2}{3} = \frac{x+3}{2x+2}$	$SB = 2, JH = 3, BP = x + 3, HT = 2x + 2$
$2(2x + 2) = 3(x + 3)$	Cross Products Property
$4x + 4 = 3x + 9$	Distributive Property
$x + 4 = 9$	Subtract $3x$ from each side.
$x = 5$	Subtract 4 from each side.

21. 3 **23.** 10.8 **25.** 18.9 **27.** 40 m **29.** $\angle A \cong \angle V$, $\angle B \cong \angle X$, $\angle D \cong \angle Z$, $\angle F \cong \angle T$; $\frac{AB}{VX} = \frac{BD}{XZ} = \frac{DF}{ZT} = \frac{FA}{TV} = 2$ **31.** $\overline{AC}, \overline{AD}$ **33.** ∠ABH, ∠ADF

35

$\angle D \cong \angle P$	Corresponding angles of similar polygons are congruent.
$m\angle D = m\angle P$	Definition of congruence
$x + 34 = 97$	Substitution
$x = 63$	Subtract 34 from each side.
$\angle C \cong \angle R$	Corresponding angles of similar polygons are congruent.
$m\angle C = m\angle R$	Definition of congruence
$83 = 3y - 13$	Substitution
$96 = 3y$	Add 13 to each side.
$32 = y$	Divide each side by 3.

37. 52 in. by 37 in. **39.** no; $\frac{BC}{XY} \neq \frac{AB}{WX}$ **41.** Never; sample answer: Parallelograms have both pairs of opposite sides parallel. Trapezoids have exactly one pair of parallel legs. Therefore, the two figures cannot be similar because they can never be the same type of figure. **43.** Sometimes; sample answer: If corresponding angles are congruent and corresponding sides are proportional, two isosceles triangles are similar. **45.** Always; sample answer: Equilateral triangles always have three 60° angles, so the angles of one equilateral triangle are always congruent to the angles of a second equilateral triangle. The three sides of an equilateral triangle are always congruent, so the ratio of each pair of legs of one triangle to a second triangle will always be the same. Therefore, a pair of equilateral triangles is always similar.

47 Let ℓ = new length and w = new width.

$\frac{2\frac{1}{3}}{\ell} = \frac{2}{3}$	Use the lengths and scale factor to write a proportion.
$2\frac{1}{3} \cdot 3 = \ell \cdot 2$	Cross Products Property
$\frac{7}{3} \cdot 3 = 2\ell$	Write $2\frac{1}{3}$ as $\frac{7}{3}$.
$7 = 2\ell$	Multiply.
$\frac{7}{2} = \ell$	Divide each side by 7.

The new length is $\frac{7}{2}$ inches or $3\frac{1}{2}$ inches.

$\frac{1\frac{2}{3}}{w} = \frac{2}{3}$	Use the widths and scale factor to write a proportion.
$1\frac{2}{3} \cdot 3 = w \cdot 2$	Cross Products Property
$\frac{5}{3} \cdot 3 = 2w$	Write $1\frac{2}{3}$ as $\frac{5}{3}$.
$5 = 2w$	Multiply.
$\frac{5}{2} = w$	Divide each side by 2.

The new width is $\frac{5}{2}$ inches or $2\frac{1}{2}$ inches.

49a. $\frac{a}{3a} = \frac{b}{3b} = \frac{c}{3c} = \frac{a+b+c}{3(a+b+c)} = \frac{1}{3}$

49b. No; the sides are no longer proportional. **51.** 4 **53.** Sample answer:

55. Sample answer: The figures could be described as congruent if they are the same size and shape, similar if their corresponding angles are congruent and their corresponding sides are proportional, and equal if they are the same exact figure. **57.** G **59.** E

61. Given: E and C are midpoints of $\overline{AD}$ and $\overline{DB}$. $\overline{AD} \cong \overline{DB}$; $\angle A \cong \angle 1$

Prove: $ABCE$ is an isosceles trapezoid.

Proof:

- E and C are midpoints of $\overline{AD}$ and $\overline{DB}$. (Given)
- $\overline{AD} \cong \overline{DB}$ (Given)
- $\frac{1}{2}AD = \frac{1}{2}DB$ (Def. of Midpt.)
- $AE = BC$ (Substitution)
- $\overline{AE} \cong \overline{BC}$ (Def. of ≅)
- $\angle A \cong \angle 1$ (Given)
- $\overline{EC} \parallel \overline{AB}$ (If corr. ∡ are ≅, lines are ∥.)
- $ABCE$ is an isos. trapezoid. (Def. of isos. trapezoid)

63. $x \leq 4$ **65.** The angle bisector of the vertex angle of an isosceles triangle is not an altitude of the triangle. **67.** 128 **69.** 68 **71.** $x = 2$, $RT = 8$, $RS = 8$

Lesson 7-3

1. Yes; $\triangle YXZ \sim \triangle VWZ$ by AA Similarity. **3.** No; corresponding sides are not proportional. **5.** C **7.** $\triangle QVS \sim \triangle RTS$; 20 **9.** Yes; $\triangle XUZ \sim \triangle WUY$ by SSS Similarity.

11 $\frac{CB}{DB} = \frac{10}{6}$ or $\frac{5}{3}$ and $\frac{BA}{BF} = \frac{9+6}{9} = \frac{15}{9}$ or $\frac{5}{3}$. $m\angle CBA = m\angle DBF = 38$, so $\angle CBA \cong \angle DBF$. Since the length of the sides that include the congruent angles are proportional, $\triangle CBA \sim \triangle DBF$ by SAS Similarity.

13. No; not enough information to determine. If $JH = 3$ or $WY = 24$, then $\triangle JHK \sim \triangle XWY$ by SSS Similarity. **15.** Yes; sample answer: Since $\overline{AB} \cong \overline{EB}$ and $\overline{CB} \cong \overline{DB}$, $\frac{AB}{CB} = \frac{EB}{DB}$. $\angle ABE \cong \angle CBD$ because vertical angles are congruent. Therefore, $\triangle ABE \sim \triangle CBD$ by SAS Similarity.

17 Since $\overline{RS} \parallel \overline{PT}$, $\angle QRS \cong \angle QPT$ and $\angle QSR \cong \angle QTP$ because they are corresponding angles. By AA Similarity, $\triangle QRS \sim \triangle QPT$.

$\frac{RS}{PT} = \frac{QS}{QT}$	Definition of similar polygons
$\frac{12}{16} = \frac{x}{20}$	$RS = 12$, $PT = 16$, $QS = x$, $QT = 20$
$12 \cdot 20 = 16 \cdot x$	Cross Products Property
$240 = 16x$	Simplify.
$15 = x$	Divide each side by 16.

Since $QS + ST = 20$ and $QS = 15$, then $ST = 5$.

19. $\triangle HJK \sim \triangle NQP$; 15, 10 **21.** $\triangle GHJ \sim \triangle GDH$; 14, 20 **23.** about 12.8 ft

25. Given: $\angle B \cong \angle E$, $\overline{QP} \parallel \overline{BC}$; $\overline{QP} \cong \overline{EF}$, $\frac{AB}{DE} = \frac{BC}{EF}$

Prove: $\triangle ABC \sim \triangle DEF$

Proof:

Statements (Reasons)

1. $\angle B \cong \angle E$, $\overline{QP} \parallel \overline{BC}$; $\overline{QP} \cong \overline{EF}$, $\frac{AB}{DE} = \frac{BC}{EF}$ (Given)
2. $\angle APQ \cong \angle C$, $\angle AQP \cong \angle B$ (Corr. ∡ Post.)
3. $\angle AQP \cong \angle E$ (Trans. Prop.)
4. $\triangle ABC \sim \triangle AQP$ (AA Similarity)
5. $\frac{AB}{AQ} = \frac{BC}{QP}$ (Def. of ~ △s)
6. $AB \cdot QP = AQ \cdot BC$; $AB \cdot EF = DE \cdot BC$ (Cross products)
7. $QP = EF$ (Def. of ≅ segs.)
8. $AB \cdot EF = AQ \cdot BC$ (Subst.)
9. $AQ \cdot BC = DE \cdot BC$ (Subst.)
10. $AQ = DE$ (Div. Prop.)
11. $\overline{AQ} \cong \overline{DE}$ (Def. of ≅ segs.)
12. $\triangle AQP \cong \triangle DEF$ (SAS)
13. $\angle APQ \cong \angle F$ (CPCTC)
14. $\angle C \cong \angle F$ (Trans. Prop.)
15. $\triangle ABC \sim \triangle DEF$ (AA Similarity)

27. Given: $\triangle XYZ$ and $\triangle ABC$ are right triangles; $\frac{XY}{AB} = \frac{YZ}{BC}$.

Prove: $\triangle YXZ \sim \triangle BAC$

Proof:

Statements (Reasons)

1. $\triangle XYZ$ and $\triangle ABC$ are right triangles. (Given)
2. $\angle XYZ$ and $\angle ABC$ are right angles. (Def. of rt. △)
3. $\angle XYZ \cong \angle ABC$ (All rt. ∡ are ≅.)
4. $\frac{XY}{AB} = \frac{YZ}{BC}$ (Given)
5. $\triangle YXZ \sim \triangle BAC$ (SAS Similarity)

29. 20 in.

31 Use $d = \sqrt{(x_2 - x_1)^2 + (y_2 - y_1)^2}$ to find the side lengths of $\triangle XYZ$ and $\triangle WYV$.

$XY = \sqrt{[5-(-1)]^2 + [3-(-9)]^2} = 6\sqrt{5}$
$(x_1, y_1) = (-1, -9)$, $(x_2, y_2) = (5, 3)$

$YZ = \sqrt{(-1-5)^2 + (6-3)^2} = 3\sqrt{5}$
$(x_1, y_1) = (5, 3)$, $(x_2, y_2) = (-1, 6)$

$XZ = \sqrt{[-1-(-1)]^2 + [6-(-9)]^2} = 15$
$(x_1, y_1) = (-1, -9)$, $(x_2, y_2) = (-1, 6)$

$WY = \sqrt{(5-1)^2 + [3-(-5)]^2} = 2\sqrt{5}$
$(x_1, y_1) = (1, -5)$, $(x_2, y_2) = (5, 3)$

$YV = \sqrt{(1-5)^2 + (5-3)^2} = 2\sqrt{5}$
$(x_1, y_1) = (5, 3)$, $(x_2, y_2) = (1, 5)$

$WV = \sqrt{(1-1)^2 + [5-(-5)]^2} = 10$
$(x_1, y_1) = (1, -5)$, $(x_2, y_2) = (1, 5)$

Since the perimeter of $\triangle XYZ = 6\sqrt{5} + 3\sqrt{5} + 15$ or $9\sqrt{5} + 15$ and the perimeter of $\triangle WYV = 4\sqrt{5} + 2\sqrt{5} + 10$ or $6\sqrt{5} + 10$, the ratio of the perimeters is $\frac{9\sqrt{5}+15}{6\sqrt{5}+10} = \frac{3(3\sqrt{5}+5)}{2(3\sqrt{5}+5)}$ or $\frac{3}{2}$.

33. $\angle C \cong \angle C'$, since all right angles are congruent. Line ℓ is a transversal of parallel segments $\overline{BC}$ and $\overline{B'C'}$, so $\angle ABC \cong \angle A'B'C'$ since corresponding angles of parallel lines are congruent. Therefore, by AA Similarity, $\triangle ABC \sim \triangle A'B'C'$. So $\frac{BC}{AC}$, the slope of line ℓ through points A and B, is equal to $\frac{B'C'}{A'C'}$, the slope of line ℓ through points A' and B'.

35 Since $\angle CAB \cong \angle CAB$ by the Reflexive Property and $\angle ABC \sim \angle ADE$ by the definition of right angles, $\triangle ABC \sim \triangle ADE$ by the AA Similarity Postulate.

$\frac{AB}{BC} = \frac{AD}{DE}$	Definition of similar polygons
$\frac{100}{15} = \frac{100+5}{DE}$	Substitution
$100 \cdot DE = 105 \cdot 15$	Cross Products Property
$100DE = 1575$	Simplify.
$DE = 15.75$	Divide each side by 100.

Since the △s formed by the laser sources are ≅, $\overline{DE} \cong \overline{GE}$. So, $DG = 15.75 + 15.75$ or 31.5. Since $\overline{AD}$ and $\overline{FG}$ are ∥, $AF = DG$. So, $AF = 31.5$. The laser sources should be placed 31.5 cm apart.

37. Sample answer: The AA Similarity Postulate, SSS Similarity Theorem, and SAS Similarity Theorem are all tests that can be used to determine whether two triangles are similar. The AA Similarity Postulate is used when two pairs of congruent angles on two triangles are given. The SSS Similarity Theorem is used when the corresponding side lengths of two triangles are given. The SAS Similarity Theorem is used when two proportional side lengths and the included angle on two triangles are given. **39.** 6

41. Sample answer: You could consider the amount of space that the actual object occupies and compare it to the amount of space that is available for the scale model or drawing. Then, you could determine the amount of detail that you want the scale model or drawing to have, and you could use these factors to choose an appropriate scale. **43a.** $\frac{6}{x-2} = \frac{4}{5}$

43b. 9.5; 7.5 **45.** B **47.** $\angle X \cong \angle R$, $\angle W \cong \angle Q$, $\angle Y \cong \angle S$; $\angle Z \cong \angle T$, $\frac{WX}{QR} = \frac{ZY}{TS} = \frac{WZ}{QT} = \frac{XY}{RS}$

49. 12 **51.** 52.3 **53.** Sample answer: If one pair of opposite sides are congruent and parallel, the quadrilateral is a parallelogram. **55.** not possible

57. Given: $r \parallel t$; $\angle 5 \cong \angle 6$
Prove: $\ell \parallel m$

Proof:
Statements (Reasons)
1. $r \parallel t$; $\angle 5 \cong \angle 6$ (Given)
2. $\angle 4$ and $\angle 5$ are supplementary. (Consecutive Interior Angles Theorem)
3. $m\angle 4 + m\angle 5 = 180$ (Def. of Suppl. ∡)
4. $m\angle 5 = m\angle 6$ (Def. of ≅ ∡)
5. $m\angle 4 + m\angle 6 = 180$ (Substitution)
6. $\angle 4$ and $\angle 6$ are supplementary. (Def. of Suppl. ∡)
7. $\ell \parallel m$ (If cons. int. ∡ are suppl., then lines are ∥.)

Lesson 7-4

1. 10 **3.** Yes; $\frac{AD}{DC} = \frac{BE}{EC} = \frac{2}{3}$, so $\overline{DE} \parallel \overline{AB}$. **5.** 11
7. 2360.3 ft **9.** $x = 20$; $y = 2$

11 If $AB = 12$ and $AC = 16$, then $BC = 4$.

$\frac{AB}{BC} = \frac{AE}{ED}$ Triangle Proportionality Theorem
$\frac{12}{4} = \frac{AE}{5}$ Substitute.
$12 \cdot 5 = 4 \cdot AE$ Cross Products Property
$60 = 4AE$ Multiply.
$15 = AE$ Divide each side by 4.

13. 10 **15.** yes; $\frac{ZV}{VX} = \frac{WY}{YX} = \frac{11}{5}$ **17.** no; $\frac{ZV}{VX} \neq \frac{WY}{YX}$

19 $m\angle PHM + m\angle PHJ + m\angle JHL = 180$ Definition of a straight angle
$44 + m\angle PHJ + 76 = 180$ Substitution
$120 + m\angle PHJ = 180$ Simplify.
$m\angle PHJ = 60$ Subtract 120 from each side.

By the Triangle Midsegment Theorem, $\overline{PH} \parallel \overline{KL}$.
$\angle PHJ \cong \angle JHL$ Alternate Interior Angles Theorem
$m\angle PHJ = m\angle JHL$ Definition of congruence
$60 = x$ Substitution

21. 1.35 **23.** 1.2 in. **25.** $x = 18$; $y = 3$ **27.** $x = 48$; $y = 72$

29. Given: $\overleftrightarrow{AD} \parallel \overleftrightarrow{BE} \parallel \overleftrightarrow{CF}$, $\overline{AB} \cong \overline{BC}$
Prove: $\overline{DE} \cong \overline{EF}$

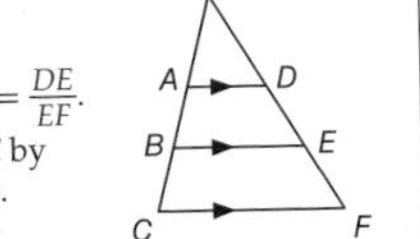

Proof:
From Corollary 7.1, $\frac{AB}{BC} = \frac{DE}{EF}$.
Since $\overline{AB} \cong \overline{BC}$, $AB = BC$ by definition of congruence.
Therefore, $\frac{AB}{BC} = 1$.
By substitution, $1 = \frac{DE}{EF}$. Thus, $DE = EF$. By definition of congruence, $\overline{DE} \cong \overline{EF}$.

31. Given: $\frac{DB}{AD} = \frac{EC}{AE}$
Prove: $\overline{DE} \parallel \overline{BC}$

Proof:
Statements (Reasons)
1. $\frac{DB}{AD} = \frac{EC}{AE}$ (Given)
2. $\frac{AD}{AD} + \frac{DB}{AD} = \frac{AE}{AE} + \frac{EC}{AE}$ (Add. Prop.)
3. $\frac{AD + DB}{AD} = \frac{AE + EC}{AE}$ (Subst.)
4. $AB = AD + DB$, $AC = AE + EC$ (Seg. Add. Post.)
5. $\frac{AB}{AD} = \frac{AC}{AE}$ (Subst.)
6. $\angle A \cong \angle A$ (Refl. Prop.)
7. $\triangle ADE \sim \triangle ABC$ (SAS Similarity)
8. $\angle ADE \cong \angle ABC$ (Def. of ~ polygons)
9. $\overline{DE} \parallel \overline{BC}$ (If corr. ∡ are ≅, then the lines are ∥.)

33. 9

35 If $CA = 10$ and $CD = 2$, then $DA = 8$.

$\frac{CE}{EB} = \frac{CD}{DA}$ Triangle Proportionality Theorem
$\frac{t-2}{t+1} = \frac{2}{8}$ Substitute.
$(t-2)(8) = (t+1)(2)$ Cross Products Property
$8t - 16 = 2t + 2$ Distributive Property
$6t - 16 = 2$ Subtract $2t$ from each side.
$6t = 18$ Add 16 to each side.
$t = 3$ Divide each side by 6.

If $t = 3$, then $CE = 3 - 2$ or 1.

37. 8, 7.5
39. $\triangle ABC \sim \triangle ADE$ SAS Similarity **41.** 6
$\frac{AD}{AB} = \frac{DE}{BC}$ Def. ~ △s
$\frac{40}{100} = \frac{DE}{BC}$ Substitution
$\frac{2}{5} = \frac{DE}{BC}$ Simplify.
$\frac{2}{5}BC = DE$ Multiply.

43 All the triangles are isosceles. Segment EH is the midsegment of triangle ABC. Therefore, segment EH is half of the length of AC, which is $35 \div 2$ or 17.5 feet. Similarly, FG is the midsegment of triangle BEH, so $FG = 17.5 \div 2$ or 8.75 feet. To find DJ, use the vertical altitude which is 12 feet. Let the altitude from B to the segment AC meet the segment DJ at K. Find BC using the Pythagorean Theorem.

$BC^2 = BK^2 + KC^2$
$BC^2 = 12^2 + 17.5^2$
$BC = \sqrt{12^2 + 17.5^2}$
$BC \approx 21.22$ in.

Since the width of each piece of siding is the same, $BJ = \frac{3}{4}BC$, which is about $\frac{3}{4}(21.22)$ or 15.92 in.
Now, use the Triangle Proportionality Theorem.

$\frac{AC}{BC} = \frac{DJ}{BJ}$
$\frac{35}{21.22} = \frac{DJ}{15.92}$
$21.22(DJ) = (15.92)(35)$
$21.22(DJ) = 557.2$
$DJ \approx 26.25$ in.

45. Sample answer:

47a. Sample answer:

47b.

Triangle	Length		Ratio	
ABC	AD	1.1 cm	$\frac{AD}{CD}$	1.0
	CD	1.1 cm		
	AB	2.0 cm	$\frac{AB}{CB}$	1.0
	CB	2.0 cm		
MNP	MQ	1.4 cm	$\frac{MQ}{PQ}$	0.8
	PQ	1.7 cm		
	MN	1.6 cm	$\frac{MN}{PN}$	0.8
	PN	2.0 cm		
WXY	WZ	0.8 cm	$\frac{WZ}{YZ}$	0.7
	YZ	1.2 cm		
	WX	2.0 cm	$\frac{WX}{YX}$	0.7
	YX	2.9 cm		

47c. Sample answer: The proportion of the segments created by the angle bisector of a triangle is equal to the proportion of their respective consecutive sides.
49. Always; sample answer: $\overline{FH}$ is a midsegment. Let $BC = x$, then $FH = \frac{1}{2}x$. $FHCB$ is a trapezoid, so $DE = \frac{1}{2}(BC + FH) = \frac{1}{2}\left(x + \frac{1}{2}x\right) = \frac{1}{2}x + \frac{1}{4}x = \frac{3}{4}x$.
Therefore, $DE = \frac{3}{4}BC$.

51.

By Corollary 7.1, $\frac{a}{b} = \frac{c}{d}$.

53. 8 **55.** G **57.** $\triangle ABE \sim \triangle CDE$ by AA Similarity; 6.25

59. $\triangle WZT \sim \triangle WXY$ by AA Similarity; 7.5
61. $\overline{QR} \parallel \overline{TS}$, $\overline{QT} \nparallel \overline{RS}$; $QRST$ is an isosceles trapezoid since $RS = \sqrt{26} = QT$. **63.** 6 **65.** 56 **67.** $\frac{2}{3}$
69. 2.1 **71.** 8.7

Lesson 7-5

1 The triangles are similar by AA Similarity.
$\frac{x}{10} = \frac{12}{15}$ ~△s have corr. medians proportional to the corr. sides.
$x \cdot 15 = 10 \cdot 12$ Cross Products Property
$15x = 120$ Simplify.
$x = 8$ Divide each side by 15.

3. 35.7 ft **5.** 20 **7.** 8.5 **9.** 18

11 $\frac{15}{27} = \frac{28 - b}{b}$ Triangle Angle Bisector Theorem
$15 \cdot b = 27(28 - b)$ Cross Products Property
$15b = 756 - 27b$ Multiply.
$42b = 756$ Add $27b$ to each side.
$b = 18$ Divide each side by 42.

13. 15

15 $\frac{AB}{JK} = \frac{AD}{JM}$ ~△s have corr. altitudes proportional to the corr. sides.
$\frac{9}{21} = \frac{4x - 8}{5x + 3}$ Substitute.
$9(5x + 3) = 21(4x - 8)$ Cross Products Property
$45x + 27 = 84x - 168$ Distributive Property
$27 = 39x - 168$ Subtract $45x$ from each side.
$195 = 39x$ Add 168 to each side.
$5 = x$ Divide each side by 39.

17. 4
19. Given: $\triangle ABC \sim \triangle RST$
$\overline{AD}$ is a median of $\triangle ABC$.
$\overline{RU}$ is a median of $\triangle RST$.
Prove: $\frac{AD}{RU} = \frac{AB}{RS}$
Proof:
Statements (Reasons)
1. $\triangle ABC \sim \triangle RST$; $\overline{AD}$ is a median of $\triangle ABC$; $\overline{RU}$ is a median of $\triangle RST$. (Given)
2. $CD = DB$; $TU = US$ (Def. of median)
3. $\frac{AB}{RS} = \frac{CB}{TS}$ (Def. of ~ △s)
4. $CB = CD + DB$; $TS = TU + US$ (Seg. Add. Post.)
5. $\frac{AB}{RS} = \frac{CD + DB}{TU + US}$ (Subst.)
6. $\frac{AB}{RS} = \frac{DB + DB}{US + US}$ or $\frac{2(DB)}{2(US)}$ (Subst.)
7. $\frac{AB}{RS} = \frac{DB}{US}$ (Subst.)
8. $\angle B \cong \angle S$ (Def. of ~ △s)
9. $\triangle ABD \sim \triangle RSU$ (SAS Similarity)
10. $\frac{AD}{RU} = \frac{AB}{RS}$ (Def. of ~ △s)

21. 3 **23.** 70
25. Given: $\overline{CD}$ bisects $\angle ACB$.
By construction, $\overline{AE} \parallel \overline{CD}$.
Prove: $\frac{AD}{DB} = \frac{AC}{BC}$

Proof:

Statements (Reasons)

1. $\overline{CD}$ bisects $\angle ACB$; By construction, $\overline{AE} \parallel \overline{CD}$. (Given)
2. $\frac{AD}{DB} = \frac{EC}{BC}$ ($\triangle$ Prop. Thm.)
3. $\angle 1 \cong \angle 2$ (Def. of $\angle$ Bisector)
4. $\angle 3 \cong \angle 1$ (Alt. Int. $\angle$s Thm.)
5. $\angle 2 \cong \angle E$ (Corr. $\angle$s Post.)
6. $\angle 3 \cong \angle E$ (Trans. Prop.)
7. $\overline{EC} \cong \overline{AC}$ (Converse of Isos. $\triangle$ Thm.)
8. $EC = AC$ (Def. of $\cong$ segs.)
9. $\frac{AD}{DB} = \frac{AC}{BC}$ (Subst.)

27. Given: $\triangle QTS \sim \triangle XWZ$, $\overline{TR}$, $\overline{WY}$ are $\angle$ bisectors.

Prove: $\frac{TR}{WY} = \frac{QT}{XW}$

Proof:

Statements (Reasons)

1. $\triangle STQ \sim \triangle ZWX$, $\overline{TR}$ and $\overline{WY}$ are angle bisectors. (Given)
2. $\angle STQ \cong \angle ZWX$, $\angle Q \cong \angle X$ (Def of $\sim \triangle$s)
3. $\angle STR \cong \angle QTR$, $\angle ZWY \cong \angle XWY$ (Def. $\angle$ bisector)
4. $m\angle STQ = m\angle STR + m\angle QTR$, $m\angle ZWX = m\angle ZWY + m\angle XWY$ ($\angle$ Add. Post.)
5. $m\angle STQ = 2m\angle QTR$, $m\angle ZWX = 2m\angle XWY$ (Subst.)
6. $2m\angle QTR = 2m\angle XWY$ (Subst.)
7. $m\angle QTR = m\angle XWY$ (Div. Prop.)
8. $\angle QTR \cong \angle XWY$ (Def. of $\cong$ Angles)
9. $\triangle QTR \sim \triangle XWY$ (AA Similarity)
10. $\frac{TR}{WY} = \frac{QT}{XW}$ (Def. of $\sim \triangle$s)

29 Since the segment from Trevor to Ricardo is an angle bisector, the segments from Ricardo to Craig and from Ricardo to Eli are proportional to the segments from Trevor to Craig and from Trevor to Eli. Since Craig is closer to Trevor than Eli is, Craig is also closer to Ricardo than Eli is. So, Craig will reach Ricardo first.

31. Chun; by the Angle Bisector Theorem, the correct proportion is $\frac{5}{8} = \frac{15}{x}$. **33.** $PS = 18.4$, $RS = 24$

35. Both theorems have a segment that bisects an angle and have proportionate ratios. The Triangle Angle Bisector Theorem pertains to one triangle, while Theorem 7.9 pertains to similar triangles. Unlike the Triangle Angle Bisector Theorem, which separates the opposite side into segments that have the same ratio as the other two sides, Theorem 7.9 relates the angle bisector to the measures of the sides. **37.** 2.2 **39.** C

41. $x = 2$; $y = 3$ **43.** $KP = 5$, $KM = 15$, $MR = 13\frac{1}{3}$, $ML = 20$, $MN = 12$, $PR = 16\frac{2}{3}$

45. Given: $\overline{EF} \cong \overline{HF}$

G is the midpoint of $\overline{EH}$.

Prove: $\triangle EFG \cong \triangle HFG$

Proof:

Statements (Reasons)

1. $\overline{EF} \cong \overline{HF}$; G is the midpoint of $\overline{EH}$. (Given)
2. $\overline{EG} \cong \overline{GH}$ (Def. of midpoint)
3. $\overline{FG} \cong \overline{FG}$ (Reflexive Prop.)
4. $\triangle EFG \cong \triangle HFG$ (SSS)

47. 5 **49.** $\sqrt{137} \approx 11.7$ **51.** $\sqrt{340} \approx 18.4$

Lesson 7-6

1. enlargement; 2

3 The ratio comparing the widths is $\frac{152.5}{27} \approx 5.6$.

The ratio comparing the lengths is $\frac{274}{78} \approx 3.5$.

Sample answer: Since $\frac{152.5}{27} \neq \frac{274}{78}$, a table tennis table is not a dilation of a tennis court.

5. $\frac{RJ}{KJ} = \frac{SJ}{LJ} = \frac{RS}{KL} = \frac{1}{2}$, so $\triangle RSJ \sim \triangle KLJ$ by SSS Similarity. **7.** reduction; $\frac{1}{2}$ **9.** enlargement; 2

11. reduction **13.** No; sample answer: Since $\frac{1.2}{2.5} \neq \frac{1.25}{3}$, the design and the actual tattoo are not proportional. Therefore, the tattoo is not a dilation of the design.

15.

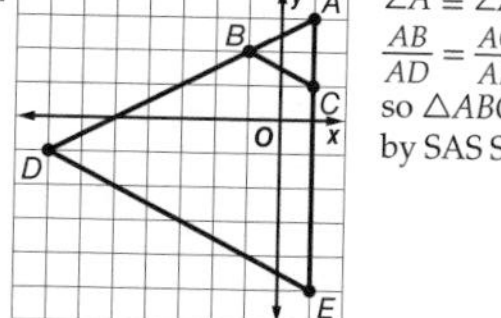

$\angle A \cong \angle A$ and $\frac{AB}{AD} = \frac{AC}{AE} = \frac{1}{4}$, so $\triangle ABC \sim \triangle ADE$ by SAS Similarity.

17. $\frac{JK}{DG} = \frac{KL}{GH} = \frac{JL}{DH} = \frac{1}{2}$, so $\triangle JKL \sim \triangle DGH$ by SSS Similarity.

19

$\frac{AC}{AB} = \frac{AZ}{AY}$	Definition of similar polygons
$\frac{4}{AB} = \frac{12}{6}$	$AC = 4$, $AZ = 12$, $AY = 6$
$4 \cdot 6 = AB \cdot 12$	Cross Products Property
$24 = 12AB$	Simplify.
$2 = AB$	Divide each side by 12.

Since $AB = 2$, the coordinates of B are $(0, -2)$.

21 **a.** Sample answer: $\triangle ABC$: $A(0, 0)$, $B(1, 3)$, $C(4, 2)$. Draw points D and E so that $AD = 2AB$ and $AE = 2AC$. Connect the points to form $\triangle ADE$: $A(0, 0)$, $D(2, 6)$, $E(8, 4)$.

b. Sample answer: $\triangle MNP$: $M(0, 0)$, $N(1, 2)$, $P(3, 1)$ Draw points Q and R so that $MQ = 3MN$ and $MR = 3MP$. Connect the points to form $\triangle MQR$: $M(0, 0)$, $Q(3, 6)$, $R(9, 3)$.

$\triangle TWX$: $T(0, 0)$, $W(0, 7)$, $X(4, 0)$

Draw points Y and Z so that $TY = 0.5TW$ and $TZ = 0.5TX$. Connect the points to form $\triangle TYZ$: $T(0, 0)$, $Y(0, 3.5)$, $Z(2, 0)$.

c.

Coordinates											
$\triangle ABC$		$\triangle ADE$		$\triangle MNP$		$\triangle MQR$		$\triangle TWX$		$\triangle TYZ$	
A	(0, 0)	A	(0, 0)	M	(0, 0)	M	(0, 0)	T	(0, 0)	T	(0, 0)
B	(1, 3)	D	(2, 6)	N	(1, 2)	Q	(3, 6)	W	(0, 7)	Y	(0, 3.5)
C	(4, 2)	E	(8, 4)	P	(3, 1)	R	(9, 3)	X	(4, 0)	Z	(2, 0)

d. Sample answer: Multiply the coordinates of the given triangle by the scale factor to get the coordinates of the dilated triangle.

$\triangle ADE$: $A(0 \cdot 2, 0 \cdot 2)$ or $A(0, 0)$, $D(1 \cdot 2, 3 \cdot 2)$ or $D(2, 6)$, $E(4 \cdot 2, 2 \cdot 2)$ or $E(8, 4)$

$\triangle MQR$: $M(0 \cdot 3, 0 \cdot 3)$ or $M(0, 0)$, $Q(1 \cdot 3, 2 \cdot 3)$ or $Q(3, 6)$, $R(3 \cdot 3, 1 \cdot 3)$ or $R(9, 3)$

$\triangle TYZ$: $T(0 \cdot 0.5, 0 \cdot 0.5)$ or $T(0, 0)$, $Y(0 \cdot 0.5, 7 \cdot 0.5)$ or $Y(0, 3.5)$, $Z(4 \cdot 0.5, 0 \cdot 0.5)$ or $Z(2, 0)$

23. No; sample answer: Since the x-coordinates are multiplied by 3 and the y-coordinates are multiplied by 2, $\triangle XYZ$ is 3 times as wide and only 2 times as tall as $\triangle PQR$. Therefore, the transformation is not a dilation. **25.** Sample answer: Architectural plans are reductions. **27.** Sample answer: If a transformation is an enlargement, the lengths of the transformed object will be greater than the original object, so the scale factor will be greater than 1. If a transformation is a reduction, the lengths of the transformed object will be less than the original object, so the scale factor will be less than 1, but greater than 0. If the transformation is a congruence transformation, the scale factor is 1, because the lengths of the transformed object are equal to the lengths of the original object. **29.** $\frac{1}{2}$ **31.** E

33. yes; $\frac{AC}{BD} = \frac{DE}{CE} = \frac{4}{3}$ **35.** no; $\frac{AB}{CD} \neq \frac{AE}{CE}$ **37.** 117

39. Given: $\triangle ABC$

S is the midpoint of $\overline{AC}$.

T is the midpoint of $\overline{BC}$.

Prove: $\overline{ST} \parallel \overline{AB}$

Proof:

Midpoint S is $\left(\frac{b+0}{2}, \frac{c+0}{2}\right)$ or $\left(\frac{b}{2}, \frac{c}{2}\right)$.

Midpoint T is $\left(\frac{a+b}{2}, \frac{0+c}{2}\right)$ or $\left(\frac{a+b}{2}, \frac{c}{2}\right)$.

Slope of $\overline{ST} = \frac{\frac{c}{2} - \frac{c}{2}}{\frac{a+b}{2} - \frac{b}{2}} = \frac{0}{\frac{a}{2}}$ or 0.

Slope of $\overline{AB} = \frac{0-0}{a-0} = \frac{0}{a}$ or 0.

$\overline{ST}$ and $\overline{AB}$ have the same slope so, $\overline{ST} \parallel \overline{AB}$.

41. 8 **43.** 0.003 **45.** 0.17

Lesson 7-7

1. about 117 mi **3a.** 6 in.:50 ft **3b.** $\frac{1}{100}$ **5.** 380 km **7.** 173 km

9 **a.** $\frac{\text{replica height}}{\text{statue height}} = \frac{10 \text{ in.}}{10 \text{ ft}} = \frac{1 \text{ in.}}{1 \text{ ft}}$

The scale of the replica is 1 inch:1 foot.

b. $\frac{10 \text{ in.}}{10 \text{ ft}} = \frac{10 \text{ in.}}{10 \text{ ft}} \cdot \frac{1 \text{ ft}}{12 \text{ in.}} = \frac{1}{12}$

The scale factor is 1:12. So, the replica is $\frac{1}{12}$ times as tall as the actual sculpture.

11. Sample answer: 1 in. = 12 ft

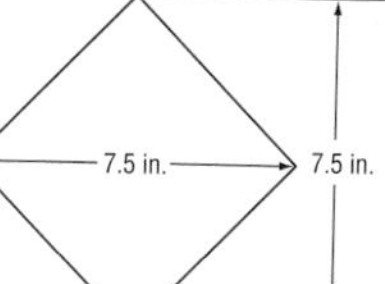

13. about 2.7 h or 2 h and 42 min **15.** 1.61 km

17 **a.** Scale = Model to Rocket

$\frac{1 \text{ in.}}{12 \text{ ft}} = \frac{7 \text{ in.}}{x \text{ ft}}$	Write a proportion.
$1 \cdot x = 12 \cdot 7$	Cross Product Property
$x = 84$	Simplify.

The height of the rocket is 84 feet.

b. Since 12 ft = 144 in., $\frac{1 \text{ in.}}{12 \text{ ft}} = \frac{1 \text{ in.}}{144 \text{ in.}}$.

Scale = Model to Rocket

$\frac{1 \text{ in.}}{144 \text{ in.}} = \frac{x \text{ in.}}{70 \text{ in.}}$	Write a proportion.
$1 \cdot 70 = 144 \cdot x$	Cross Product Property
$70 = 144x$	Simplify.
$0.5 \approx x$	Divide each side by 144.

The diameter of the model is about 0.5 inch.

19 Scale = Actual Tower to Replica

$\frac{3}{1} = \frac{986 \text{ ft}}{x \text{ ft}}$	Write a proportion.
$3 \cdot x = 1 \cdot 986$	Cross Product Property
$3x = 986$	Simplify.
$x \approx 329$	Divide each side by 3.

The height of the ride is about 329 feet.

21. Felix; sample answer: The ratio of the actual high school to the replica is $\frac{75}{1.5}$ or 50:1. **23.** The first drawing will be larger. The second drawing will be $\frac{1}{6}$ the size of the first drawing, so the scale factor is 1:6. **25.** Both can be written as ratios comparing lengths. A scale factor must have the same unit of measure for both measurements. **27.** D **29.** C **31.** 12 **33.** 17.5 **35.** 29.3 **37.** 3.5 **39.** 10.5 **41.** 8 **43.** $JK = \sqrt{10}$, $KL = \sqrt{10}$, $JL = \sqrt{20}$, $XY = \sqrt{10}$, $YZ = \sqrt{10}$, and $XZ = \sqrt{20}$. Each pair of corresponding sides has the same measure so they are congruent. $\triangle JKL \cong \triangle XYZ$ by SSS. **45.** 8 **47.** 48 **49.** $3\sqrt{77}$

Chapter 7 Study Guide and Review

1. j; ratio **3.** g; AA Similarity Postulate **5.** d; extremes **7.** b; proportion **9.** 49 **11.** 10 or −10 **13.** 120 in. **15.** No, the polygons are not similar because the corresponding sides are not proportional. **17.** 16.5 **19.** Yes, $\triangle ABE \sim \triangle ADC$ by the SAS ~ Thm. **21.** No, the triangles are not similar because not all corresponding angles are congruent. **23.** 34.2 feet **25.** 22.5 **27.** 6 **29.** 633 mi **31.** enlargement; 2 **33.** 10.5 inches **35.** 95.8 mi

CHAPTER 8 Right Angles and Trigonometry

Chapter 8 Get Ready

1. $4\sqrt{7}$ **3.** $10\sqrt{3}$ **5.** $\frac{3}{4}$ **7.** 10 **9.** $x = 17.2$ in., 68.8 in. of trim

11.

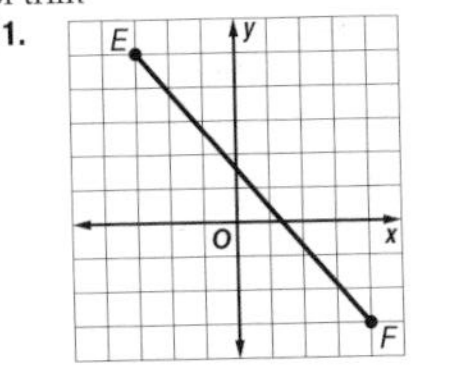
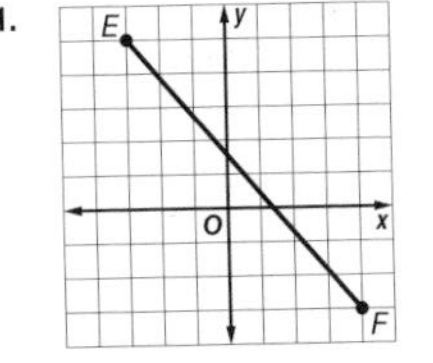

Lesson 8-1

1. 10 **3.** $10\sqrt{6}$ or 24.5 **5.** $x = 6$; $y = 3\sqrt{5} \approx 6.7$; $z = 6\sqrt{5} \approx 13.4$ **7.** 18 ft 11 in.

9 $x = \sqrt{ab}$ — Definition of geometric mean
$= \sqrt{16 \cdot 25}$ — $a = 16$ and $b = 25$
$= \sqrt{(4 \cdot 4) \cdot (5 \cdot 5)}$ — Factor.
$= 4 \cdot 5$ or 20 — Simplify.

11. $12\sqrt{6} \approx 29.4$ **13.** $3\sqrt{3} \approx 5.2$ **15.** $\triangle WXY \sim \triangle XZY \sim \triangle WZX$ **17.** $\triangle HGF \sim \triangle HIG \sim \triangle GIF$

19 $17 = \sqrt{6 \cdot (y - 6)}$ — Geometric Mean (Altitude) Theorem
$289 = 6 \cdot (y - 6)$ — Square each side.
$\frac{289}{6} = y - 6$ — Divide each side by 6.
$54\frac{1}{6} = y$ — Add 6 to each side.
$54.2 \approx y$ — Write as a decimal.

$x = \sqrt{6 \cdot y}$ — Geometric Mean (Leg) Theorem
$= \sqrt{6 \cdot 54\frac{1}{6}}$ — $y = 54\frac{1}{6}$
$= \sqrt{325}$ — Multiply.
$= 5\sqrt{13}$ — Simplify.
≈ 18.0 — Use a calculator.

$z = \sqrt{(y - 6) \cdot y}$ — Geometric Mean (Leg) Theorem
$= \sqrt{\left(54\frac{1}{6} - 6\right) \cdot 54\frac{1}{6}}$ — $y = 54\frac{1}{6}$
$= \sqrt{48\frac{1}{6} \cdot 54\frac{1}{6}}$ — Subtract.
≈ 51.1 — Use a calculator.

21. $x \approx 4.7$; $y \approx 1.8$; $z \approx 13.1$ **23.** $x = 24\sqrt{2} \approx 33.9$; $y = 8\sqrt{2} \approx 11.3$; $z = 32$ **25.** 161.8 ft **27.** $\frac{\sqrt{30}}{7}$ or 0.8 **29.** $x = \frac{3\sqrt{3}}{2} \approx 2.6$; $y = \frac{3}{2}$; $z = 3$ **31.** 11 **33.** 3.5 ft **35.** 5 **37.** 4

39. Given: $\angle PQR$ is a right angle. $\overline{QS}$ is an altitude of $\triangle PQR$.
Prove: $\triangle PSQ \sim \triangle PQR$
$\triangle PQR \sim \triangle QSR$
$\triangle PSQ \sim \triangle QSR$

Proof:
Statements (Reasons)
1. $\angle PQR$ is a right angle. $\overline{QS}$ is an altitude of $\triangle PQR$. (Given)
2. $\overline{QS} \perp \overline{RP}$ (Definition of altitude)
3. $\angle 1$ and $\angle 2$ are right angles. (Definition of perpendicular lines)
4. $\angle 1 \cong \angle PQR$, $\angle 2 \cong \angle PQR$ (All right ∠s are ≅.)
5. $\angle P \cong \angle P$, $\angle R \cong \angle R$ (Congruence of angles is reflexive.)
6. $\triangle PSQ \sim \triangle PQR$, $\triangle PQR \sim \triangle QSR$ (AA Similarity Statements 4 and 5)
7. $\triangle PSQ \sim \triangle QSR$ (Similarity of triangles is transitive.)

41. Given: $\angle ADC$ is a right angle. $\overline{DB}$ is an altitude of $\triangle ADC$.
Prove: $\frac{AB}{AD} = \frac{AD}{AC}$
$\frac{BC}{DC} = \frac{DC}{AC}$

Proof:
Statements (Reasons)
1. $\angle ADC$ is a right angle. $\overline{DB}$ is an altitude of $\triangle ADC$. (Given)
2. $\triangle ADC$ is a right triangle. (Definition of right triangle)
3. $\triangle ABD \sim \triangle ADC$, $\triangle DBC \sim \triangle ADC$ (If the altitude is drawn from the vertex of a rt. ∠ to the hypotenuse of a rt. △, then the 2 △s formed are similar to the given △ and to each other.)
4. $\frac{AB}{AD} = \frac{AD}{AC}$, $\frac{BC}{DC} = \frac{DC}{AC}$ (Def. of similar triangles)

43 $x = \sqrt{ab}$ — Definition of geometric mean
$= \sqrt{7 \cdot 12}$ — $a = 7$ and $b = 12$
$= \sqrt{84}$ — Multiply.
≈ 9 — Simplify.

The average rate of return is about 9%.

45 Sample answer: The geometric mean of two consecutive integers is $\sqrt{x(x+1)}$ and the average of two consecutive integers is $\frac{x + (x+1)}{2}$.

$\sqrt{x(x+1)} \stackrel{?}{=} \frac{x + (x+1)}{2}$
$\sqrt{x^2 + x} \stackrel{?}{=} \frac{2x+1}{2}$
$\sqrt{x^2 + x} \stackrel{?}{=} x + \frac{1}{2}$
$x^2 + x \stackrel{?}{=} \left(x + \frac{1}{2}\right)^2$
$x^2 + x \stackrel{?}{=} x^2 + x + \frac{1}{4}$
$0 \neq \frac{1}{4}$

If you set the two expressions equal to each other, the equation has no solution. So, the statement is never true.

47. Sometimes; sample answer: When the product of the two integers is a perfect square, the geometric mean will be a positive integer. **49.** Neither; sample answer: On the similar triangles created by the altitude, the leg that is x units long on the smaller triangle corresponds with the leg that is 8 units long on the larger triangle, so the correct proportion is $\frac{4}{x} = \frac{x}{8}$ and x is about 5.7. **51.** Sample answer: 9 and 4, 8 and 8; In order for two whole numbers to result in a whole-number geometric mean, their product must be a perfect square. **53.** Sample answer: Both the arithmetic and the geometric mean calculate a value between two given numbers. The arithmetic mean of two numbers a and b is $\frac{a+b}{2}$, and the geometric mean of two numbers a and b is $\sqrt{ab}$. The two means will be equal when $a = b$.

Justification:
$\frac{a+b}{2} = \sqrt{ab}$
$\left(\frac{a+b}{2}\right)^2 = ab$
$\frac{(a+b)^2}{4} = ab$
$(a+b)^2 = 4ab$
$a^2 + 2ab + b^2 = 4ab$
$a^2 - 2ab + b^2 = 0$
$(a-b)^2 = 0$
$a - b = 0$
$a = b$

55. 10 **57.** C

59. $\frac{AB}{DE} = \frac{BC}{EF} = \frac{AC}{DF} = 3$, so $\triangle ABC \sim \triangle DEF$ by SSS Similarity.

61. $\angle M \cong \angle Q$ and $\frac{PM}{SQ} = \frac{MN}{QR} = \frac{1}{2}$, so $\triangle MNP \sim \triangle QRS$ by SAS Similarity.

63. octagon **65.** $x = 34$, $y = \pm 5$ **67.** hexagonal pyramid; base: $ABCDEF$, faces: $ABCDEF$, AGF, FGE, EGD, DGC, CGB, BGA; edges: $\overline{AF}$, $\overline{FE}$, $\overline{ED}$, $\overline{DC}$, $\overline{CB}$, $\overline{BA}$, $\overline{AG}$, $\overline{FG}$, $\overline{EG}$, $\overline{DG}$, $\overline{CG}$, and $\overline{BG}$; vertices: A, B, C, D, E, F, and G **69.** cone; base: circle Q; vertex: P **71.** $\frac{16\sqrt{3}}{3}$ **73.** $\frac{3\sqrt{55}}{11}$

Lesson 8-2

1. 12

3 The side opposite the right angle is the hypotenuse, so $c = 16$.
$a^2 + b^2 = c^2$ — Pythagorean Theorem
$4^2 + x^2 = 16^2$ — $a = 4$ and $b = x$
$16 + x^2 = 256$ — Simplify.
$x^2 = 240$ — Subtract 16 from each side.
$x = \sqrt{240}$ — Take the positive square root of each side.
$x = 4\sqrt{15}$ — Simplify.
$x \approx 15.5$ — Use a calculator.

5. D **7.** yes; obtuse
$26^2 \stackrel{?}{=} 16^2 + 18^2$
$676 > 256 + 324$
9. 20 **11.** $\sqrt{21} \approx 4.6$ **13.** $\frac{\sqrt{10}}{5} \approx 0.6$

15 16 and 30 are both multiples of 2: $16 = 2 \cdot 8$ and $30 = 2 \cdot 15$. Since 8, 15, 17 is a Pythagorean triple, the missing hypotenuse is $2 \cdot 17$ or 34.

17. 70 **19.** about 3 ft
21. yes; obtuse
$21^2 \stackrel{?}{=} 7^2 + 15^2$
$441 > 49 + 225$
23. yes; right
$20.5^2 \stackrel{?}{=} 4.5^2 + 20^2$
$420.25 = 20.25 + 400$
25. yes; acute
$7.6^2 \stackrel{?}{=} 4.2^2 + 6.4^2$
$57.76 < 17.64 + 40.96$
27. 15 **29.** $4\sqrt{6} \approx 9.8$

31. acute; $XY = \sqrt{29}$, $YZ = \sqrt{20}$, $XZ = \sqrt{13}$; $(\sqrt{29})^2 < (\sqrt{20})^2 + (\sqrt{13})^2$ **33.** right; $XY = 6$, $YZ = 10$, $XZ = 8$; $6^2 + 8^2 = 10^2$

35. Given: $\triangle ABC$ with sides of measure a, b, and c, where $c^2 = a^2 + b^2$
Prove: $\triangle ABC$ is a right triangle.
Proof:
Draw $\overline{DE}$ on line ℓ with measure equal to a. At D, draw line $m \perp \overline{DE}$. Locate point F on m so that $DF = b$. Draw $\overline{FE}$ and call its measure x. Because $\triangle FED$ is a right triangle, $a^2 + b^2 = x^2$. But $a^2 +$

$b^2 = c^2$, so $x^2 = c^2$ or $x = c$. Thus, $\triangle ABC \cong \triangle FED$ by SSS. This means $\angle C \cong \angle D$. Therefore, $\angle C$ must be a right angle, making $\triangle ABC$ a right triangle.

37. Given: In $\triangle ABC$, $c^2 > a^2 + b^2$ where c is the length of the longest side.
Prove: $\triangle ABC$ is an obtuse triangle.
Proof:

Statements (Reasons)
1. In $\triangle ABC$, $c^2 > a^2 + b^2$ where c is the length of the longest side. In $\triangle PQR$, $\angle R$ is a right angle. (Given)
2. $a^2 + b^2 = x^2$ (Pythagorean Theorem)
3. $c^2 > x^2$ (Substitution Property)
4. $c > x$ (A property of square roots)
5. $m\angle R = 90$ (Definition of a right angle)
6. $m\angle C > m\angle R$ (Converse of the Hinge Theorem)
7. $m\angle C > 90$ (Substitution Property of Equality)
8. $\angle C$ is an obtuse angle. (Definition of an obtuse angle)
9. $\triangle ABC$ is an obtuse triangle. (Definition of an obtuse triangle)

39. $P = 36$ units; $A = 60$ square units^2 **41.** 15

43 **Scale** **Width to Length**

$\frac{16}{9} = \frac{41 \text{ in.}}{x \text{ in.}}$ Write a proportion.
$16 \cdot x = 9 \cdot 41$ Cross Product Property
$16x = 369$ Simplify.
$x = \frac{369}{16}$ Divide each side by 16.

The length of the television is about 23 inches.

$a^2 + b^2 = c^2$ Pythagorean Theorem
$\left(\frac{369}{16}\right)^2 + 41^2 = c^2$ $a = \frac{369}{16}$ and $b = 41$
$\sqrt{\left(\frac{369}{16}\right)^2 + 41^2} = c$ Take the positive square root of each side.
$47.0 \approx c$ Use a calculator.

The screen size is about 47 inches.

45 The side opposite the right angle is the hypotenuse, so $c = x$.

$a^2 + b^2 = c^2$ Pythagorean Theorem
$8^2 + (x - 4)^2 = x^2$ $a = 8$ and $b = x - 4$
$64 + x^2 - 8x + 16 = x^2$ Find 8^2 and $(x - 4)^2$.
$-8x + 80 = 0$ Simplify.
$80 = 8x$ Add $8x$ to each side.
$10 = x$ Divide each side by 8.

47. $\frac{1}{2}$ **49.** 5.4 **51.** Right; sample answer: If you double or halve the side lengths, all three sides of the new triangles are proportional to the sides of the original triangle. Using the Side-Side-Side Similarity Theorem, you know that both of the new triangles are similar to the original triangle, so they are both right.

53. D **55.** 250 units **57.** 6 **59.** $6\sqrt{5} \approx 13.4$

61. 1 in. = 2 ft; 6 in. × 4 in. **63.** yes; AA

65. Given: $\overline{FG} \perp \ell$; $\overline{FH}$ is any nonperpendicular segment from F to ℓ.
Prove: $FH > FG$
Proof:

Statements (Reasons)
1. $\overline{FG} \perp \ell$ (Given)
2. $\angle 1$ and $\angle 2$ are right angles. ($\perp$ lines form right angles.)
3. $\angle 1 \cong \angle 2$ (All right angles are congruent.)
4. $m\angle 1 = m\angle 2$ (Definition of congruent angles)
5. $m\angle 1 > m\angle 3$ (Exterior Angle Inequality Thm.)
6. $m\angle 2 > m\angle 3$ (Substitution Property.)
7. $FH > FG$ (If an $\angle$ of a $\triangle$ is > a second $\angle$, then the side opposite the greater $\angle$ is longer than the side opposite the lesser $\angle$.)

67. 50 **69.** 40 **71.** $\frac{7\sqrt{5}}{5}$ **73.** $2\sqrt{3}$ **75.** 2

Lesson 8-3

1. $5\sqrt{2}$ **3.** 22 **5.** $x = 14$; $y = 7\sqrt{3}$ **7.** Yes; sample answer: The height of the triangle is about $3\frac{1}{2}$ in., so since the height of the plaque is less than the diameter of the opening, it will fit. **9.** $\frac{15\sqrt{2}}{2}$ or $7.5\sqrt{2}$

11 In a 45°-45°-90° triangle, the length of the hypotenuse is $\sqrt{2}$ times the length of a leg.

$h = x\sqrt{2}$ Theorem 8.8
$= 18\sqrt{3} \cdot \sqrt{2}$ Substitution
$= 18\sqrt{6}$ $\sqrt{3} \cdot \sqrt{2} = \sqrt{6}$

13. $20\sqrt{2}$ **15.** $\frac{11\sqrt{2}}{2}$ **17.** $8\sqrt{2}$ or 11.3 cm **19.** $x = 10$; $y = 20$ **21.** $x = \frac{17\sqrt{3}}{2}$; $y = \frac{17}{2}$ **23.** $x = \frac{14\sqrt{3}}{3}$; $y = \frac{28\sqrt{3}}{3}$ **25.** $16\sqrt{3}$ or 27.7 ft **27.** 22.6 ft

29 In a 45°-45°-90° triangle, the length of the hypotenuse is 2 times the length of a leg.

$h = x\sqrt{2}$ Theorem 8.8
$6 = x\sqrt{2}$ Substitution
$\frac{6}{\sqrt{2}} = x$ Divide each side by $\sqrt{2}$.
$\frac{6}{\sqrt{2}} \cdot \frac{\sqrt{2}}{\sqrt{2}} = x$ Rationalize the denominator.
$\frac{6 \cdot \sqrt{2}}{\sqrt{2} \cdot \sqrt{2}} = x$ Multiply.
$\frac{6\sqrt{2}}{2} = x$ $\sqrt{2} \cdot \sqrt{2} = 2$
$3\sqrt{2} = x$ Simplify.
$h = x\sqrt{2}$ Theorem 8.8
$y = 6\sqrt{2}$ Substitution

31. $x = 5$; $y = 10$ **33.** $x = 45$; $y = 12\sqrt{2}$

35 In a 30°-60°-90° triangle, the length of the hypotenuse is 2 times the length of the shorter leg.

$h = 2s$ Theorem 8.9
$= 2(25)$ or 50 Substitution

The zip line's length is 50 feet.

37. $x = 9\sqrt{2}$; $y = 6\sqrt{3}$; $z = 12\sqrt{3}$
39. 7.5 ft; 10.6 ft; 13.0 ft **41.** (6, 9) **43.** (4, −2)

45 **a.**

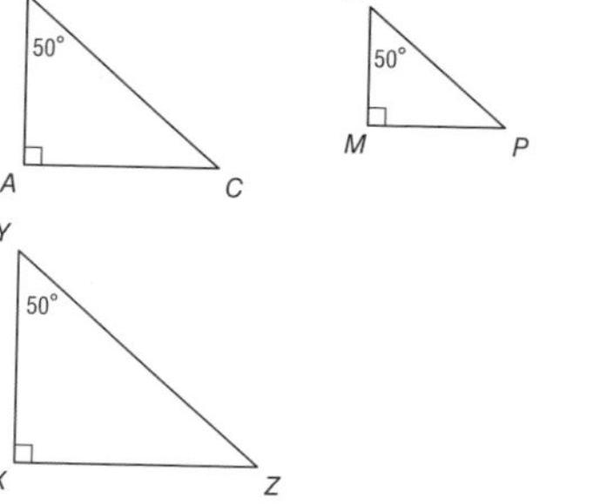

b. Measure the sides of the triangles to the nearest tenth of a centimeter. Find the ratios to the nearest tenth of a centimeter. Sample answer:

Triangle	Length				Ratio	
ABC	AC	2.4 cm	BC	3.2 cm	$\frac{BC}{AC}$	1.3
MNP	MP	1.7 cm	NP	2.2 cm	$\frac{NP}{MP}$	1.3
XYZ	XZ	3.0 cm	YZ	3.9 cm	$\frac{YZ}{XZ}$	1.3

c. Sample answer: In a right triangle with a 50° angle, the ratio of the leg opposite the 50° angle to the hypotenuse will always be the same, 1.3.

47. Sample answer: Let ℓ represent the length. $\ell^2 + w^2 = (2w)^2$; $\ell^2 = 3w^2$; $\ell = w\sqrt{3}$.

49. 37.9 **51.** B **53.** (−13, −3) **55.** 15 ft **57.** $x \approx 16.9$, $y \approx 22.6$, $z \approx 25.0$ **59.** 36, 90, 54 **61.** 45, 63, 72 **63.** $\angle 1$, $\angle 4$, $\angle 11$ **65.** $\angle 2$, $\angle 6$, $\angle 9$, $\angle 8$, $\angle 7$ **67.** 12.0

Lesson 8-4

1. $\frac{16}{20} = 0.80$ **3.** $\frac{12}{20} = 0.60$ **5.** $\frac{16}{20} = 0.80$ **7.** $\frac{\sqrt{3}}{2} \approx 0.87$
9. 27.44 **11.** about 1.2 ft **13.** 44.4 **15.** $RS \approx 6.7$; $m\angle R \approx 42$; $m\angle T \approx 48$

17 $\sin J = \frac{\text{opp}}{\text{hyp}} = \frac{56}{65} \approx 0.86$ $\cos J = \frac{\text{adj}}{\text{hyp}} = \frac{33}{65} \approx 0.51$

$\tan J = \frac{\text{opp}}{\text{adj}} = \frac{56}{33} \approx 1.70$ $\sin L = \frac{\text{opp}}{\text{hyp}} = \frac{33}{65} \approx 0.51$

$\cos L = \frac{\text{adj}}{\text{hyp}} = \frac{56}{65} \approx 0.86$ $\tan L = \frac{\text{opp}}{\text{adj}} = \frac{33}{56} \approx 0.59$

19. $\frac{84}{85} = 0.99$; $\frac{13}{85} = 0.15$; $\frac{84}{13} = 6.46$; $\frac{13}{85} = 0.15$; $\frac{84}{85} = 0.99$; $\frac{13}{84} = 0.15$ **21.** $\frac{\sqrt{3}}{2} = 0.87$; $\frac{2\sqrt{2}}{4\sqrt{2}} = 0.50$; $\frac{2\sqrt{6}}{2\sqrt{2}} = \sqrt{3} = 1.73$; $\frac{2\sqrt{2}}{4\sqrt{2}} = 0.50$; $\frac{\sqrt{3}}{2} = 0.87$; $\frac{\sqrt{3}}{3} = 0.58$
23. $\frac{\sqrt{3}}{2} \approx 0.87$ **25.** $\frac{1}{2}$ or 0.5 **27.** $\frac{1}{2}$ or 0.5 **29.** 28.7
31. 57.2 **33.** 17.4

35 Let $m\angle A = 55$ and let x be the height of the roller coaster.

$\sin A = \frac{\text{opp}}{\text{hyp}}$ Definition of sine ratio
$\sin 55 = \frac{x}{98}$ Substitution
$98 \cdot \sin 55 = x$ Multiply each side by 98.
$80 \approx x$ Use a calculator.

The height of the roller coaster is about 80 feet.

37. 61.4 **39.** 28.5 **41.** 21.8 **43.** $WX = 15.1$; $XZ = 9.8$; $m\angle W = 33$ **45.** $ST = 30.6$; $m\angle R = 58$; $m\angle T = 32$

47 $JL = \sqrt{[-2 - (-2)]^2 + [4 - (-3)]^2} = 7$
$KJ = \sqrt{[-2 - (-7)]^2 + [-3 - (-3)]^2} = 5$
$\tan K = \frac{\text{opp}}{\text{adj}}$ Definition of tangent ratio
$= \frac{7}{5}$ Substitution
$m\angle K = \tan^{-1}\left(\frac{7}{5}\right) \approx 54.5$ Use a calculator.

49. 51.3 **51.** 13.83 in.; 7.50 in^2 **53.** 8.74 ft; 3.41 ft^2
55. 0.92

57 The triangle is isosceles, so two sides measure 32 and the two smaller triangles each have a side that measures x. Let $m\angle A = 54$.

$\cos A = \frac{\text{adj}}{\text{hyp}}$ Definition of cosine ratio
$\cos 54 = \frac{x}{32}$ Substitution
$32 \cdot \cos 54 = x$ Multiply each side by 32.
$18.8 \approx x$ Simplify.
$\sin A = \frac{\text{opp}}{\text{hyp}}$ Definition of sine ratio
$\sin 54 = \frac{y}{32}$ Substitution
$32 \cdot \sin 54 = y$ Multiply each side by 32.
$25.9 \approx y$ Simplify.

59. $x = 9.2$; $y = 11.7$
61a.

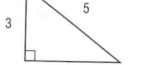

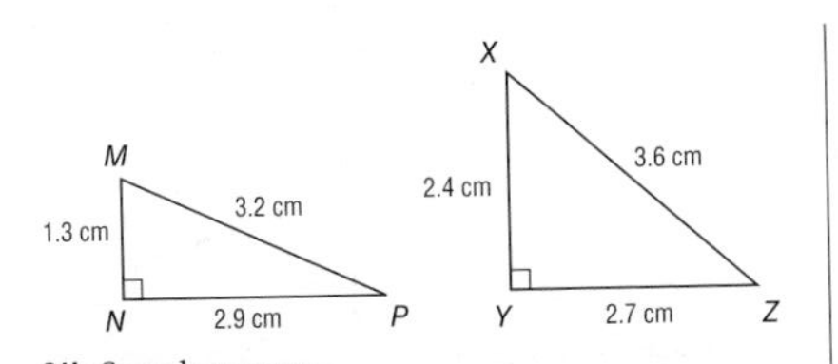

61b. Sample answer:

Triangle	Trigonometric Ratios				Sum of Ratios Squared	
ABC	cos A	0.677	sin A	0.742	$(\cos A)^2 + (\sin A)^2$	1
	cos C	0.742	sin C	0.677	$(\cos C)^2 + (\sin C)^2$	1
MNP	cos M	0.406	sin M	0.906	$(\cos M)^2 + (\sin M)^2$	1
	cos P	0.906	sin P	0.406	$(\cos P)^2 + (\sin P)^2$	1
XYZ	cos X	0.667	sin X	0.75	$(\cos X)^2 + (\sin X)^2$	1
	cos Z	0.75	sin Z	0.667	$(\cos Z)^2 + (\sin Z)^2$	1

61c. Sample answer: The sum of the cosine squared and the sine squared of an acute angle of a right triangle is 1. **61d.** $(\sin X)^2 + (\cos X)^2 = 1$
61e. Sample answer:

$(\sin A)^2 + (\cos A)^2 \stackrel{?}{=} 1$ Conjecture

$\left(\frac{y}{r}\right)^2 + \left(\frac{x}{r}\right)^2 \stackrel{?}{=} 1$ $\sin A = \frac{y}{r}, \cos A = \frac{x}{r}$

$\frac{y^2}{r^2} + \frac{x^2}{r^2} \stackrel{?}{=} 1$ Simplify.

$\frac{y^2 + x^2}{r^2} \stackrel{?}{=} 1$ Combine fractions with like denominators.

$\frac{r^2}{r^2} \stackrel{?}{=} 1$ Pythagorean Theorem

$1 = 1$ Simplify.

63. Sample answer: Yes; since the values of sine and cosine are both calculated by dividing one of the legs of a right triangle by the hypotenuse, and the hypotenuse is always the longest side of a right triangle, the values will always be less than 1. You will always be dividing the smaller number by the larger number. **65.** Sample answer: To find the measure of an acute angle of a right triangle, you can find the ratio of the leg opposite the angle to the hypotenuse and use a calculator to find the inverse sine of the ratio, you can find the ratio of the leg adjacent to the angle to the hypotenuse and use a calculator to find the inverse cosine of the ratio, or you can find the ratio of the leg opposite the angle to the leg adjacent to the angle and use a calculator to find the inverse tangent of the ratio. **67.** H **69.** E **71.** $x = 7\sqrt{2}$; $y = 14$
73. yes; right
$17^2 \stackrel{?}{=} 8^2 + 15^2$
$289 = 64 + 225$
75. yes; obtuse
$35^2 \stackrel{?}{=} 30^2 + 13^2$
$1225 > 900 + 169$

77. no; $8.6 > 3.2 + 5.3$ **79.** $5\frac{7}{15}$ h or 5 h 28 min
81. $x = 1, y = \frac{3}{2}$ **83.** 260 **85.** 18.9 **87.** 157.1

Lesson 8-5

1. 27.5 ft **3.** 14.2 ft
5 Make a sketch.

$\tan A = \frac{BC}{AC}$ $\tan = \frac{\text{opposite}}{\text{adjacent}}$

$\tan x° = \frac{348.5}{155}$ $m\angle A = x$, $BC = 350 - 1.5$ or 348.5, $AC = 155$

$x = \tan^{-1}\left(\frac{348.5}{155}\right)$ Solve for x.

$x \approx 66.0$ Use a calculator.

The angle of elevation is about 66°.
7. 14.8°
9 Make a sketch.

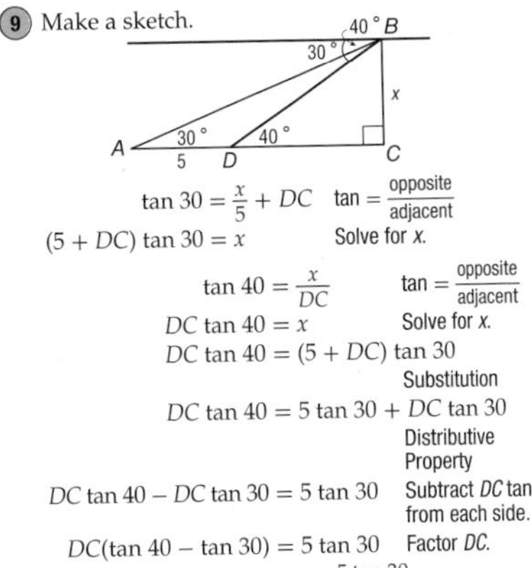

$\tan 30 = \frac{x}{5} + DC$ $\tan = \frac{\text{opposite}}{\text{adjacent}}$

$(5 + DC) \tan 30 = x$ Solve for x.

$\tan 40 = \frac{x}{DC}$ $\tan = \frac{\text{opposite}}{\text{adjacent}}$

$DC \tan 40 = x$ Solve for x.

$DC \tan 40 = (5 + DC) \tan 30$ Substitution

$DC \tan 40 = 5 \tan 30 + DC \tan 30$ Distributive Property

$DC \tan 40 - DC \tan 30 = 5 \tan 30$ Subtract $DC \tan 30$ from each side.

$DC(\tan 40 - \tan 30) = 5 \tan 30$ Factor DC.

$DC = \frac{5 \tan 30}{\tan 40 - \tan 30}$ Divide each side by $\tan 40 - \tan 30$.

$DC \approx 11.0$ Use a calculator.

$\tan A = \frac{BC}{AC}$ $\tan = \frac{\text{opposite}}{\text{adjacent}}$

$\tan 30 = \frac{x}{16.0}$ $A = 30$, $BC = x$, $AC = 5 + 11.0$ or 16.0

$16.0 \tan 30 = x$ Multiply each side by 16.0.

$9.3 \approx x$ Use a calculator.

The platform is about 9.3 feet high.
11. about 1309 ft **13.** 16.6° **15.** 240.2 ft
17 Make a sketch.

$\tan A = \frac{BC}{AC}$ $\tan = \frac{\text{opposite}}{\text{adjacent}}$

$\tan 38° = \frac{121}{x}$ $m\angle A = 38$, $BC = 124 - 3$ or 121, $AC = x$

$x = \frac{121}{\tan 38°}$ Solve for x.

$x \approx 154.9$ Use a calculator.

You should place the tripod about 154.9 feet from the monument.
19a. 74.8° **19b.** 110.1 m
21 Make two sketches.

$\tan x° = \frac{0.3}{8.5}$ $\tan = \frac{\text{opp}}{\text{adj}}$

$x = \tan^{-1}\left(\frac{0.3}{8.5}\right)$ Solve for x.

$x \approx 2.02$ Use a calculator.

José throws at an angle of depression of 2.02°.

$\tan x° = \frac{0.7}{8.5}$ $\tan = \frac{\text{opp}}{\text{adj}}$

$x = \tan^{-1}\left(\frac{0.7}{8.5}\right)$ Solve for x.

$x \approx 4.71$ Use a calculator.

Kelsey throws at an angle of elevation of 4.71°.
23. Rodrigo; sample answer: Since your horizontal line of sight is parallel to the other person's horizontal line of sight, the angles of elevation and depression are congruent according to the Alternate Interior Angles Theorem. **25.** True; sample answer: As a person moves closer to an object, the horizontal distance decreases, but the height of the object is constant. The tangent ratio will increase, and therefore the measure of the angle also increases. **27.** Sample answer: If you sight something with a 45° angle of elevation, you don't have to use trigonometry to determine the height of the object. Since the legs of a 45°-45°-90° are congruent, the height of the object will be the same as your horizontal distance from the object. **29.** 6500 ft **31.** B
33. $\frac{20}{15} = 1.33$ **35.** $\frac{15}{20} = 0.75$ **37.** $\frac{20}{25} = 0.80$
39. Given: $\overline{CD}$ bisects $\angle ACB$. By construction, $\overline{AE} \parallel \overline{CD}$.
Prove: $\frac{AD}{DB} = \frac{AC}{BC}$
Proof:
Statements (Reasons)
1. $\overline{CD}$ bisects $\angle ACB$. By construction, $\overline{AE} \parallel \overline{CD}$. (Given)
2. $\frac{AD}{DB} = \frac{EC}{BC}$ (Triangle Proportionality Theorem)
3. $\angle 1 \cong \angle 2$ (Definition of Angle Bisector)
4. $\angle 3 \cong \angle 1$ (Alternate Interior Angle Theorem)
5. $\angle 2 \cong \angle E$ (Corresponding Angle Postulate)
6. $\angle 3 \cong \angle E$ (Transitive Prop.)
7. $\overline{EC} \cong \overline{AC}$ (Isosceles △ Thm.)
8. $EC = AC$ (Def. of congruent segments)
9. $\frac{AD}{DB} = \frac{AC}{BC}$ (Substitution)

41. (7, 4) **43.** (−5, 6) **45.** 2 **47.** 2.1

Lesson 8-6

1. 6.1
3 By the Triangle Angle Sum Theorem, the remaining angle measures $180 - (60 + 55)$ or 65.

$\frac{\sin A}{a} = \frac{\sin B}{b}$ Law of Sines

$\frac{\sin 65°}{73} = \frac{\sin 60°}{x}$ $m\angle A = 65, a = 73, m\angle B = 60, b = x$

$x \sin 65° = 73 \sin 60°$ Cross Products Property

$x = \frac{73 \sin 60°}{\sin 65°}$ Divide each side by sin 65°.

$x \approx 69.8$ Use a calculator.

5. 8.3 **7.** 47.1 ft **9.** $m\angle N = 42$, $MP \approx 35.8$, $NP \approx 24.3$
11. $m\angle D \approx 73$, $m\angle E \approx 62$, $m\angle F \approx 45$ **13.** 4.1 **15.** 22.8
17. 15.1 **19.** 2.0 **21.** 2.8 in.
23 $a^2 = b^2 + c^2 - 2bc \cos A$ Law of Cosines

$x^2 = 1.2^2 + 3.0^2 - 2(1.2)(3.0) \cos 123°$ Substitution

$x^2 = 10.44 - 7.2 \cos 123°$ Simplify.

$x = \sqrt{10.44 - 7.2 \cos 123°}$ Take the square root of each side.

$x \approx 3.8$ Use a calculator.

25. 98 **27.** 112 **29.** 126.2 ft **31.** $m\angle B = 34$, $AB \approx 9.5$, $CA \approx 6.7$
33 $j^2 = k^2 + \ell^2 - 2k\ell \cos J$ Law of Cosines

$29.7^2 = 30.0^2 + 24.6^2 - 2(30.0)(24.6) \cos J$ $j = 29.7, k = 30.0, \ell = 24.6$

$882.09 = 1505.16 - 1476 \cos J$ Simplify.

$-623.07 = -1476 \cos J$ Subtract 1505.16 from each side.

$\frac{-623.07}{-1476} = \cos J$ Divide each side by −1476.

$m\angle J = \cos^{-1}\left(\frac{623.07}{1476}\right)$ Use the inverse cosine ratio.

$m\angle J \approx 65$ Use a calculator.

$\frac{\sin J}{j} = \frac{\sin K}{k}$ Law of Sines

$\frac{\sin 65°}{29.7} = \frac{\sin K}{30.0}$ $m\angle J \approx 65, j = 29.7$, and $k = 30.0$

$30.0 \sin 65° = 29.7 \sin K$ Cross Products Property

$\frac{30.0 \sin 65°}{29.7} = \sin K$ Divide each side by 29.7.

$m\angle K = \sin^{-1}\left(\frac{30.0 \sin 65°}{29.7}\right)$ Use the inverse sine ratio.

$m\angle K \approx 66$ Use a calculator.

By the Triangle Angle-Sum Theorem, $m\angle L \approx 180 - (65 + 66)$ or 49.

35. $m\angle G = 75$, $GH \approx 19.9$, $GJ \approx 11.8$ **37.** $m\angle P \approx 35$, $m\angle R \approx 75$, $RP \approx 14.6$ **39.** $m\angle C \approx 23$, $m\angle D \approx 67$,

$m\angle E \approx 90$ **41.** $m\angle A = 35$, $AB \approx 7.5$, $BC \approx 9.8$
43. ≈ 96.2 ft **45a.** Def. of sine **45b.** Mult. Prop.
45c. Subst. **45d.** Div. Prop. **47.** 24.3

49

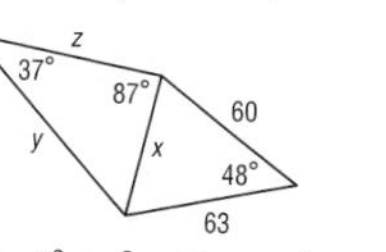

$a^2 = b^2 + c^2 - 2bc \cos A$	Law of Cosines
$x^2 = 60^2 + 63^2 - 2(60)(63) \cos 48°$	Substitution
$x^2 = 7569 - 7560 \cos 48°$	Simplify.
$x = \sqrt{7569 - 7560 \cos 48°}$	Take the square root of each side.
$x \approx 50.1$	Use a calculator.
$\frac{\sin A}{a} = \frac{\sin B}{b}$	Law of Sines
$\frac{\sin 37°}{50.1} = \frac{\sin 87°}{y}$	$m\angle A = 37°, a = x = 50.1,$ $m\angle B = 87°, b = y$
$y \sin 37° = 50.1 \sin 87°$	Cross Products Property
$y = \frac{50.1 \sin 87°}{\sin 37°}$	Divide each side by sin 37°.
$y \approx 83.1$	Use a calculator.

By the Triangle Angle-Sum Theorem, the angle opposite side z measures $180 - (37 + 87)$ or 56.

$\frac{\sin A}{a} = \frac{\sin B}{b}$	Law of Sines
$\frac{\sin 37°}{50.1} = \frac{\sin 56°}{z}$	$m\angle A = 37°, a = x = 50.1,$ $m\angle B = 87°, b = z$
$z \sin 37° = 50.1 \sin 56°$	Cross Products Property
$z = \frac{50.1 \sin 56°}{\sin 37°}$	Divide each side by sin 37°.
$z \approx 69.0$	Use a calculator.

perimeter $= 60 + 63 + y + z$
$\approx 60 + 63 + 83.1 + 69.0$ or 275.1

51

$a^2 = b^2 + c^2 - 2bc \cos A$	Law of Cosines
$x^2 = 8^2 + 6^2 - 2(8)(6) \cos 71.8°$	Substitution
$x^2 = 100 - 96 \cos 71.8°$	Simplify.
$x = \sqrt{100 - 96 \cos 71.8°}$	Take the square root of each side.
$x \approx 8.4$ in.	Use a calculator.

53a.

53b. $h = AB \sin B$ **53c.** $A = \frac{1}{2}(BC)(AB \sin B)$

53d. 57.2 units² **53e.** $A = \frac{1}{2}(BC)(CA \sin C)$ **55.** 5.6

57a. Sample answer: **57b.** Sample answer:

59. A **61.** 325.6 **63.** 269.6 ft **65.** 45 **67.** Never; sample answer: Since an equilateral triangle has three congruent sides and a scalene triangle has three noncongruent sides, the ratios of the three pairs of sides can never be equal. Therefore, an equilateral triangle and a scalene triangle can never be similar.
69. $Q(a, a)$, $P(a, 0)$ **71.** $\sqrt{80} \approx 8.9$ **73.** 8.5

Lesson 8-7

1. 1 in. : 60 mi/h

3.

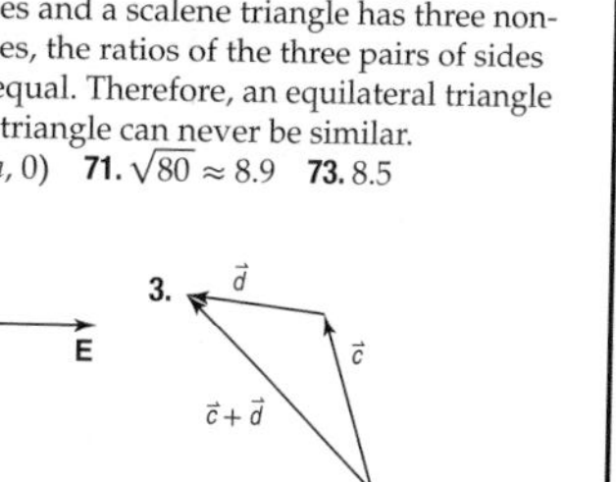

5

$\overrightarrow{YZ} = \langle x_2 - x_1, y_2 - y_1 \rangle$	Component form of a vector
$= \langle 5 - 0, 5 - 0 \rangle$	$(x_1, y_1) = (0, 0)$ and $(x_2, y_2) = (5, 5)$
$= \langle 5, 5 \rangle$	Simplify.

7. $\sqrt{20}$; $\approx 296.6°$
9. $\langle -1, 6 \rangle$

11. ≈ 354.3 mi/h at angle of 8.9° east of north
13. 1 in. : 5 m

15. 1 in. : 50 km/h

17.

19.

21.

23. $\langle 5, 0 \rangle$ **25.** $\langle -6, -3 \rangle$ **27.** $\langle -3, -6 \rangle$
29. $\sqrt{34}$; $\approx 31.0°$ **31.** $\sqrt{50}$; $\approx 171.9°$

33 Use the distance formula to find the magnitude.

$\lvert \vec{r} \rvert = \sqrt{(x_2 - x_1)^2 + (y_2 - y_1)^2}$	Distance Formula
$= \sqrt{(-3 - 0)^2 + (-6 - 0)^2}$	$(x_1, y_1) = (0, 0)$ and $(x_2, y_2) = (-3, -6)$
$= \sqrt{45}$ or about 6.7	Simplify.

Use the inverse tangent function to find θ.

$\tan \theta = \frac{6}{3}$	$\tan \theta = \frac{\text{opp}}{\text{adj}}$
$\theta = \tan^{-1} \frac{6}{3} \approx 63.4°$	Def. of inverse tangent

The direction of $\vec{r}$ is about $180° + 63.4°$ or $243.4°$.

35. $\langle 5, 3 \rangle$ **37.** $\langle -1, 5 \rangle$

39. $\langle 9, 3 \rangle$ **41a.** 2 mi, 3 mi

41b. In component form, the vectors representing Amy's hikes due east and due south are $\langle 2, 0 \rangle$ and $\langle 0, -3 \rangle$, respectively. So, the resultant vector is $\langle 2, 0 \rangle + \langle 0, -3 \rangle$ or $\langle 2, -3 \rangle$. The resultant distance is about 3.6 mi. The direction of $\vec{r}$ is about $90° - 56.3°$ or $33.7°$ east of south.
43. $\langle 4, -4 \rangle$ **45.** $\langle 26, 5 \rangle$ **47.** 2.3 ft/s **49.** Sometimes; sample answer: Parallel vectors can either have the same or opposite direction.

51.
$$\begin{aligned} k(\vec{a} + \vec{b}) &= k(\langle x_1, y_1 \rangle + \langle x_2, y_2 \rangle) \\ &= k\langle x_1 + x_2, y_1 + y_2 \rangle \\ &= \langle k(x_1 + x_2), k(y_1 + y_2) \rangle \\ &= \langle kx_1 + kx_2, ky_1 + ky_2 \rangle \\ &= \langle kx_1, ky_1 \rangle + \langle kx_2, ky_2 \rangle \\ &= k\langle x_1, y_1 \rangle + k\langle x_2, y_2 \rangle \\ &= k\vec{a} + k\vec{b} \end{aligned}$$

53. The initial point of the resultant starts at the initial point of the first vector in both methods. However, in the parallelogram method, both vectors start at the same initial point, whereas, in the triangle method, the resultant connects the initial point of the first vector and the terminal point of the second. The resultant is the diagonal of the parallelogram formed using the parallelogram method. **55.** B **57.** D **59.** 72.0 **61.** 376.4 ft **63.** 30 **65.** 30 **67.** 60 **69.** Δs 1–4, Δs 5–12, Δs 13–20

Chapter 8 Study Guide and Review

1. false, geometric **3.** false, sum **5.** true **7.** true
9. false, Law of Cosines **11.** 6 **13.** $\frac{8}{3}$ **15.** 50 ft
17. $9\sqrt{3} \approx 15.6$
19. yes; acute
$16^2 \stackrel{?}{=} 13^2 + 15^2$
$256 < 169 + 225$
21. 18.4 m **23.** $x = 4\sqrt{2}$, $y = 45°$ **25.** $\frac{5}{13}$, 0.38
27. $\frac{12}{13}$, 0.92 **29.** $\frac{5}{12}$, 0.42 **31.** 32.2 **33.** 63.4° and 26.6°
35. 86.6 feet **37.** 15.2 **39.** $\langle -6, -5 \rangle$ **41.** $\langle -8, 1 \rangle$

CHAPTER 9 Transformations and Symmetry

Chapter 9 Get Ready

1. rotation **3.** translation **5.** $\langle -16, -28 \rangle$
7. reduction; $\frac{1}{2}$

Lesson 9-1

1.

3.

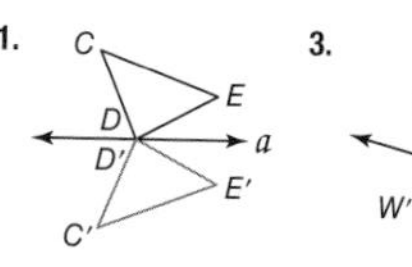

5.

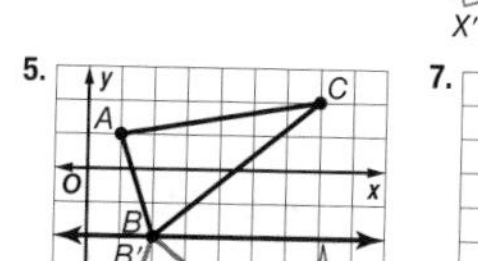

7.

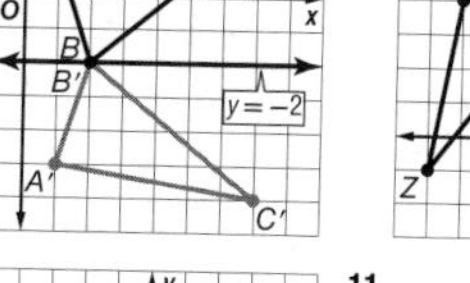

9.

11.

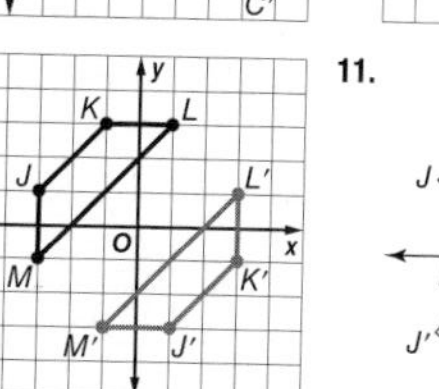

13 Draw a line through each vertex that is perpendicular to line t. Measure the distance from point A to line t. Then locate A' the same distance from line t on the opposite side. Repeat to locate points B', C', and D'. Then connect vertices A', B', C' and D' to form the reflected image.

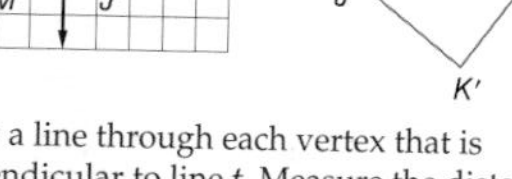

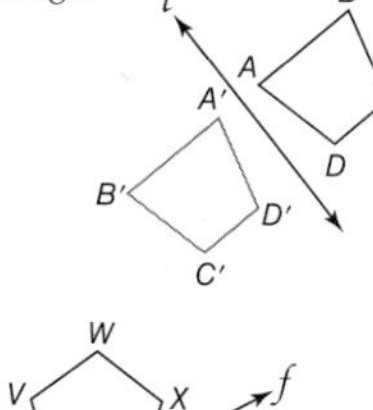

15.

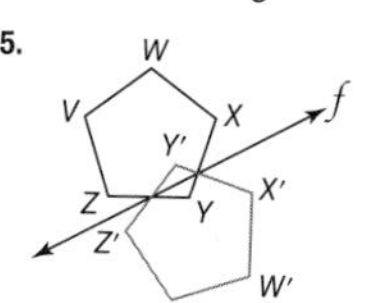

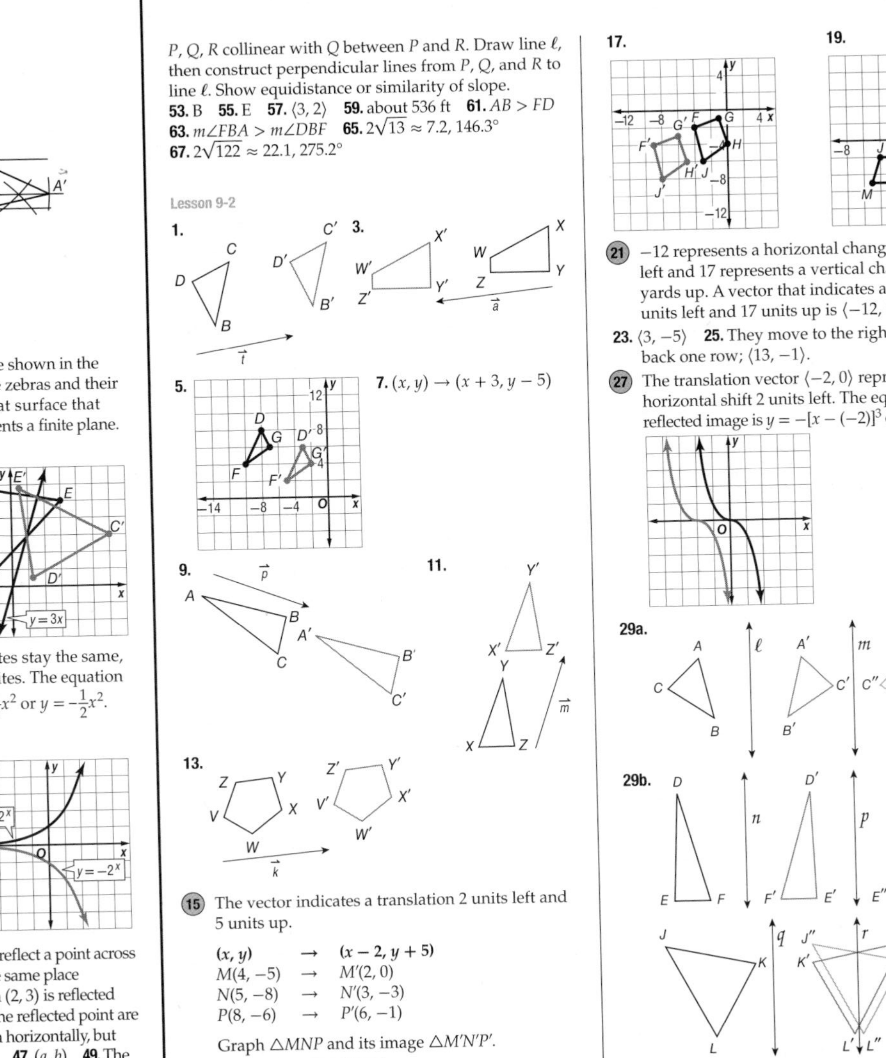

17. **19.** 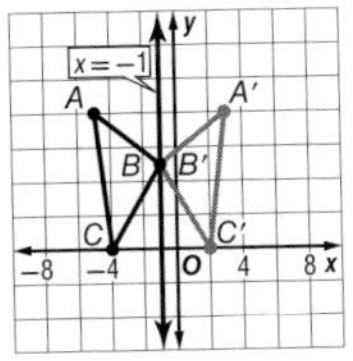 **21.** 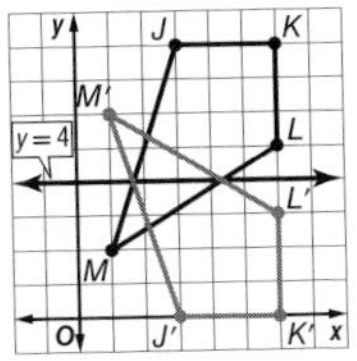 **23.**

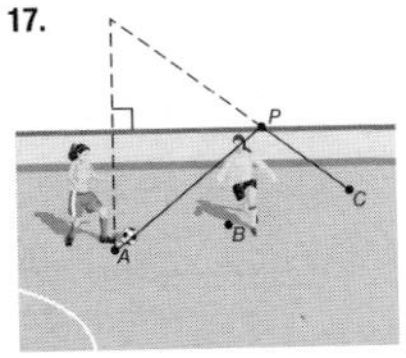

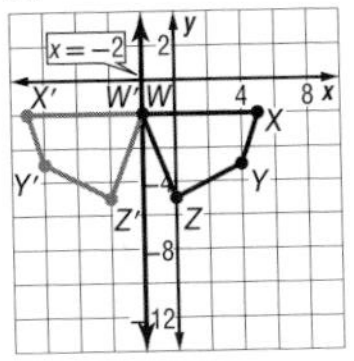

25 Multiply the x-coordinate of each vertex by -1.

(x, y)	→	$(-x, y)$
$J(-4, 6)$	→	$J'(4, 6)$
$K(0, 6)$	→	$K'(0, 6)$
$L(0, 2)$	→	$L'(0, 2)$
$M(-4, 2)$	→	$M'(4, 2)$

Graph $JKLM$ and its image $J'K'L'M'$

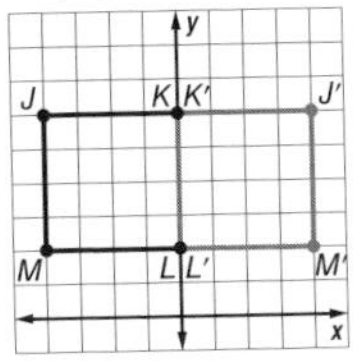

27. 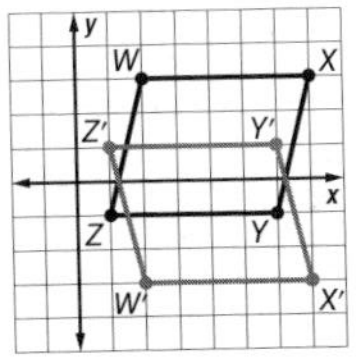 **29.** 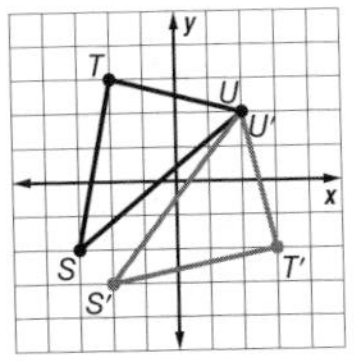 **31.**

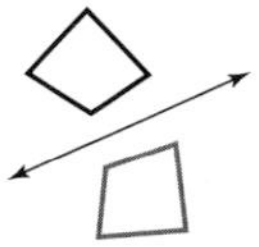

33.

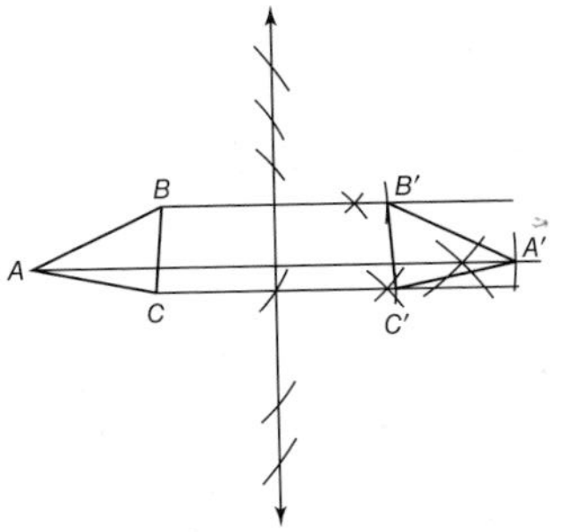

35 **a.** The reflections of the zebras are shown in the water. So, the water separates the zebras and their reflections. **b.** The water is a flat surface that extends in all directions. It represents a finite plane.

37. **39.**

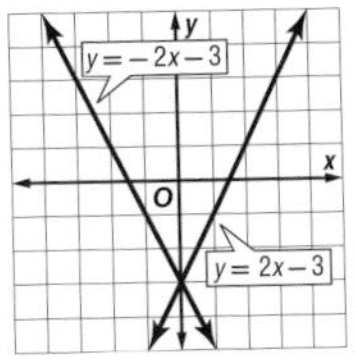

41 In the reflection, the x-coordinates stay the same, but the y-coordinates are opposites. The equation of the reflected image is $-y = \frac{1}{2}x^2$ or $y = -\frac{1}{2}x^2$.

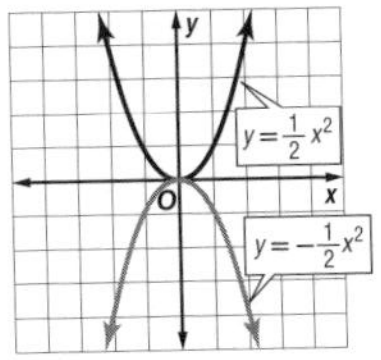

43.

45. Jamil; sample answer: When you reflect a point across the x-axis, the reflected point is in the same place horizontally, but not vertically. When (2, 3) is reflected across the x-axis, the coordinates of the reflected point are (2, −3) since it is in the same location horizontally, but the other side of the x-axis vertically. **47.** (a, b) **49.** The slope of the line connecting the two points is $\frac{3}{5}$. The Midpoint Formula can be used to find the midpoint between the two points, which is $\left(\frac{3}{2}, \frac{3}{2}\right)$. Using the point-slope form, the equation of the line is $y = -\frac{5}{3}x + 4$. (The slope of the bisector is $-\frac{5}{3}$ because it is the negative reciprocal of the slope $\frac{3}{5}$.) **51.** Construct P, Q, R collinear with Q between P and R. Draw line ℓ, then construct perpendicular lines from P, Q, and R to line ℓ. Show equidistance or similarity of slope.
53. B **55.** E **57.** $\langle 3, 2\rangle$ **59.** about 536 ft **61.** $AB > FD$
63. $m\angle FBA > m\angle DBF$ **65.** $2\sqrt{13} \approx 7.2$, 146.3°
67. $2\sqrt{122} \approx 22.1$, 275.2°

Lesson 9-2

1. **3.** **5.**

7. $(x, y) \rightarrow (x + 3, y - 5)$

9. **11.** **13.**

15 The vector indicates a translation 2 units left and 5 units up.

(x, y)	→	$(x - 2, y + 5)$
$M(4, -5)$	→	$M'(2, 0)$
$N(5, -8)$	→	$N'(3, -3)$
$P(8, -6)$	→	$P'(6, -1)$

Graph $\triangle MNP$ and its image $\triangle M'N'P'$.

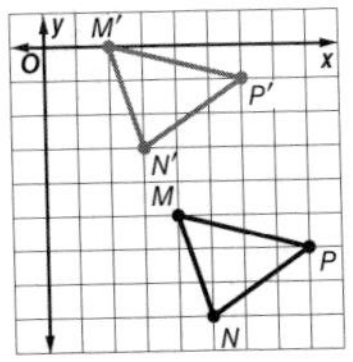

17. **19.**

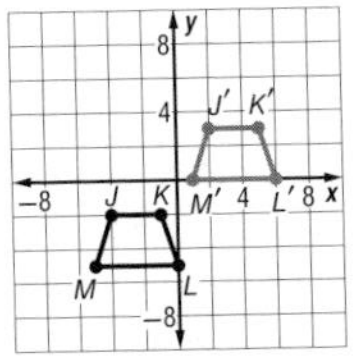

21 −12 represents a horizontal change of 12 yards left and 17 represents a vertical change of 17 yards up. A vector that indicates a translation 12 units left and 17 units up is $\langle -12, 17\rangle$.

23. $\langle 3, -5\rangle$ **25.** They move to the right 13 seats and back one row; $\langle 13, -1\rangle$.

27 The translation vector $\langle -2, 0\rangle$ represents a horizontal shift 2 units left. The equation of the reflected image is $y = -[x - (-2)]^3$ or $y = -(x + 2)^3$.

29a. **29b.**

29c.

Distance Between Corresponding Points (cm)		Distance Between Parallel Lines (cm)	
A and A'', B and B'', C and C''	4.4	ℓ and m	2.2
D and D'', E and E'', F and F''	5.6	n and p	2.8
J and J'', K and K'', L and L''	2.8	q and r	1.4

29d. Sample answer: The composition of two reflections in vertical lines can be described by a horizontal translation that is twice the distance between the two vertical lines. **31.** $y = m(x - a) + 2b$; $2b - ma$ **33.** Sample answer: Both vector notation and function notation describe the distance a figure is translated in the horizontal and vertical directions. Vector notation does not give a rule in terms of initial location, but function notation does. For example, the translation a units to the right and b units up from the point (x, y) would be written $\langle a, b\rangle$ in vector notation and $(x, y) \longrightarrow (x + a, y + b)$ in function notation. **35.** D **37.** F

39.

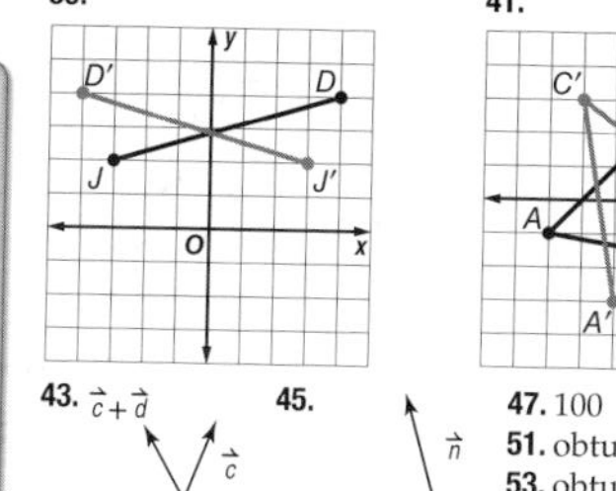

41.

43. $\vec{c} + \vec{d}$ **45.**

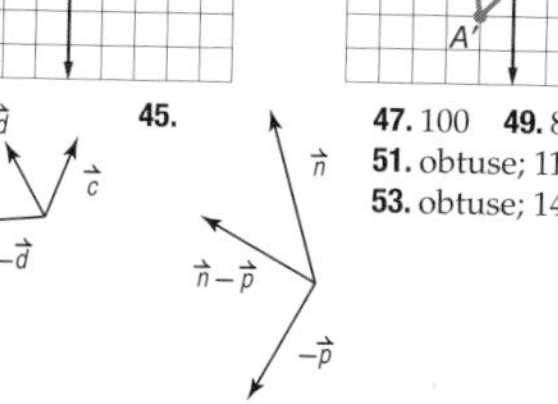

47. 100 **49.** 80
51. obtuse; 110
53. obtuse; 140

Lesson 9-3

1.

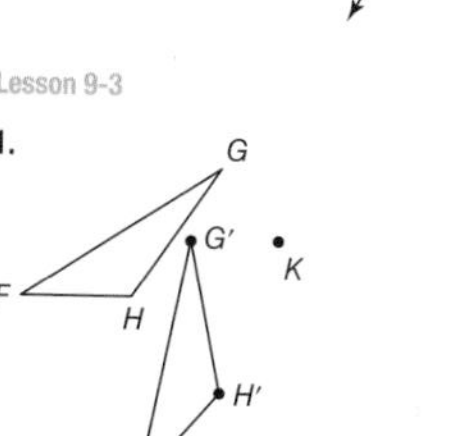

3 Multiply the x- and y-coordinates by -1.

(x, y)	$\rightarrow$	$(-x, -y)$
$D(-2, 6)$	$\rightarrow$	$D'(2, -6)$
$F(2, 8)$	$\rightarrow$	$F'(-2, -8)$
$G(2, 3)$	$\rightarrow$	$G'(-2, -3)$

Graph $\triangle DFG$ and its image $\triangle D'F'G'$.

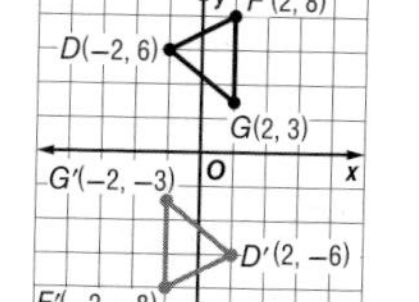

5. **7.** **9.**

11. 120°; 360° ÷ 6 petals = 60° per petal. Two petal turns is 2 • 60° or 120°.
13. 154.2°; 360° ÷ 7 petals = 51.4° per petal. Three petal turns is 3 • 51.4° or 154.2°.

15.

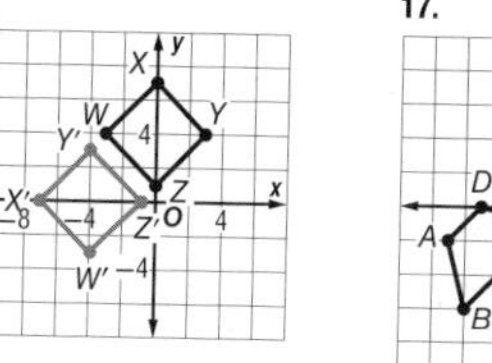

17.

19.

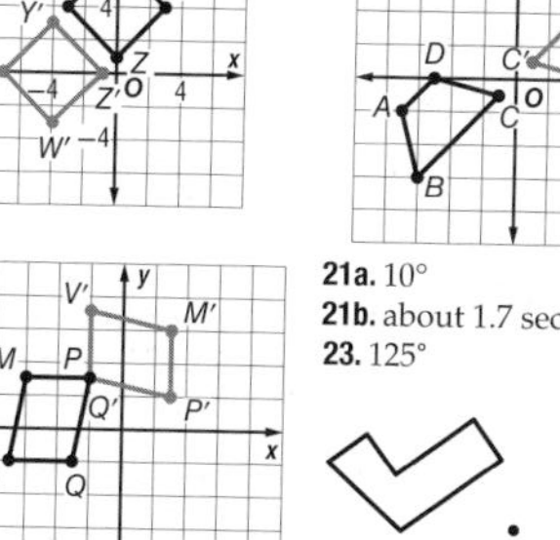

21a. 10°
21b. about 1.7 seconds
23. 125°

25. $y = -x + 2$; parallel **27.** $y = -x - 2$; collinear
29. x-intercept: $y = 2x + 4$; y-intercept: $y = 2x + 4$

31 After 31 seconds, the ride will have rotated 31 • 0.25 or 7.75 times. So, she will be in the bottom position of the ride, with the car having the center at (0, −4). After 31 seconds, the car will have rotated 31 • 0.5 or 15.5 times. So, she will be in the position directly across from her starting position. Her position after 31 seconds would be (2, −4).

33 **a.**

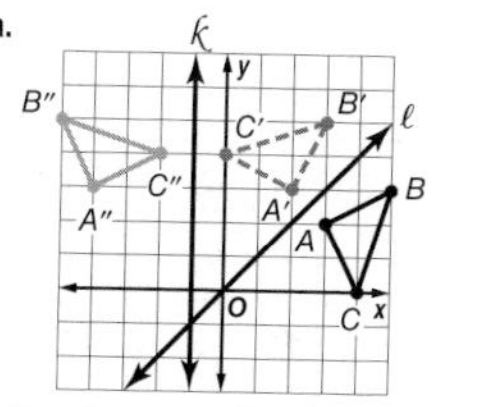

b. Sample answer: Let the x-axis be line n and the y-axis be line p. Draw $\triangle DEF$ with vertices $D(-4, 1)$, $E(-2, 3)$, and $F(0, 1)$. Reflect $\triangle DEF$ in the line n to get $\triangle D'E'F'$ with vertices $D'(-4, -1)$, $E'(-2, -3)$, and $F'(0, -1)$. Reflect $\triangle D'E'F'$ in the line p to get $\triangle D''E''F''$ with vertices $D''(4, -1)$, $E''(2, -3)$, and $F''(0, -1)$.

Sample answer: Let the line $y = -x$ be line q and the line $y = 0.5$ be line r. Draw $\triangle MNP$ with vertices $M(0, -4)$, $N(1, 2)$, and $P(3, -5)$. Reflect $\triangle MNP$ in the line q to get $\triangle M'N'P'$ with vertices $M'(4, 0)$, $N'(2, -1)$, and $P'(5, -3)$. Reflect $\triangle M'N'P'$ in the line r to get $\triangle M''N''P''$ with vertices $M''(4, 1)$, $N''(2, 2)$, and $P''(5, 4)$.

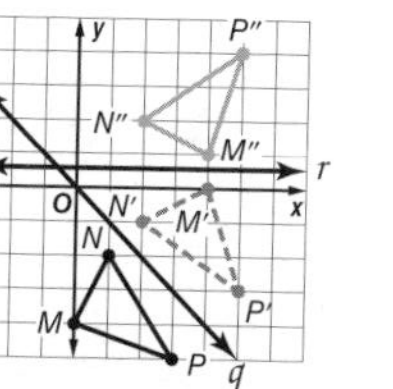

c.

Angle of Rotation Between Figures		Angle Between Intersecting Lines	
$\triangle ABC$ and $\triangle A''B''C''$	90°	ℓ and m	45°
$\triangle DEF$ and $\triangle D''E''F''$	180°	n and p	90°
$\triangle MNP$ and $\triangle M''N''P''$	90°	q and r	45°

d. Sample answer: The measure of the angle of rotation about the point where the lines intersect is twice the measure of the angle between the two intersecting lines.

35. Sample answer: (−1, 2); Since $\triangle CC'P$ is isosceles and the vertex angle of the triangle is formed by the angle of rotation, both $m\angle PCC'$ and $m\angle PC'C$ are 40° because the base angles of isosceles triangles are congruent. When you construct a 40° angle with a vertex at C and a 40° angle with a vertex at C′, the intersection of the rays forming the two angles intersect at the point of rotation, or (−1, 2).

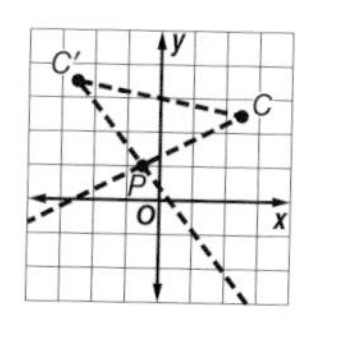

37. No; sample answer: When a figure is reflected about the x-axis, the x-coordinates of the transformed figure remain the same, and the y-coordinates are negated. When a figure is rotated 180° about the origin, both the x- and y-coordinates are negated. Therefore, the transformations are not equivalent. **39.** D **41.** J
43. 50 mi **45.**

47. reflection **49.** rotation or reflection

Lesson 9-4

1. **3.**

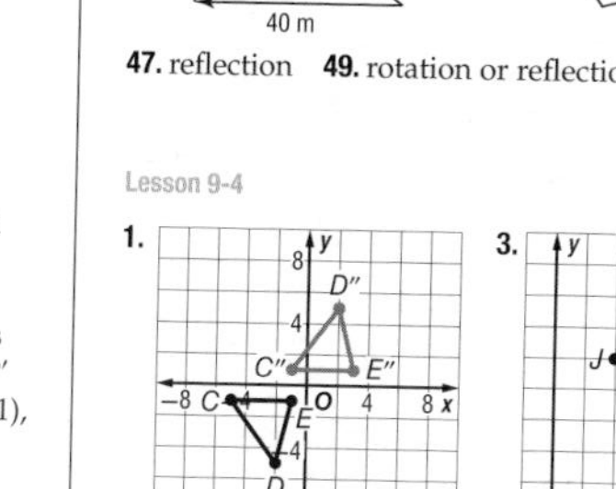

5.

rotation clockwise 100° about the point where lines m and p intersect.

7 translation along $\langle 2, 0\rangle$ reflection in x-axis

(x, y)	$\rightarrow$	$(x + 2, y)$	(x, y)	$\rightarrow$	$(x, -y)$
$R(1, -4)$	$\rightarrow$	$R'(3, -4)$	$R'(3, -4)$	$\rightarrow$	$R''(3, 4)$
$S(6, -4)$	$\rightarrow$	$S'(8, -4)$	$S'(8, -4)$	$\rightarrow$	$S''(8, 4)$
$T(5, -1)$	$\rightarrow$	$T'(7, -1)$	$T'(7, -1)$	$\rightarrow$	$T''(7, 1)$

Graph $\triangle RST$ and its image $\triangle R''S''T''$.

9. **11.**

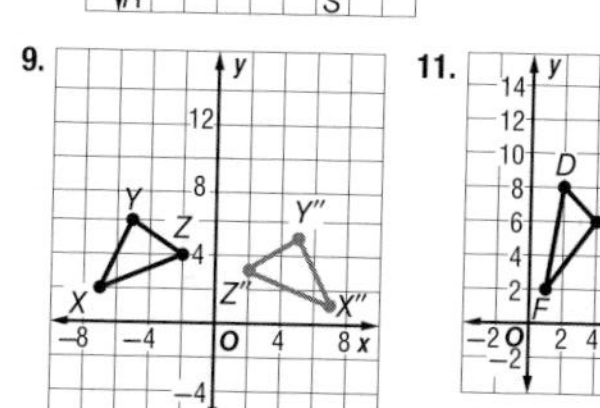

13.

15.

17. horizontal translation 4 cm to the right.

19. 70° rotation about the point where lines m and p intersect

21. translation **23.** reflection

25 rotation 90° about origin

(x, y)	→	$(-y, x)$
$(-2, -5)$	→	$(5, -2)$
$(0, 1)$	→	$(-1, 0)$

reflection in x-axis

(x, y)	→	$(x, -y)$
$(5, -2)$	→	$(5, 2)$
$(-1, 0)$	→	$(-1, 0)$

Graph line y' through points at (5, −2) and (−1, 0). Graph line y'' through points at (5, 2) and (−1, 0).

27. $A''(3, 1)$, $B''(2, 3)$, $C''(1, 0)$

29 A translation occurs from Step 1 to Step 2. A rotation 90° counterclockwise occurs from Step 2 to Step 3. So, the transformations are a translation and a 90° rotation.

31. $(x + 5.5, y)$ reflected in the line that separates the left prints from the right prints **33.** double reflection **35.** rotation 180° about the origin and reflection in the x-axis

37. Given: Lines ℓ and m intersect at point P. A is any point not on ℓ or m.

Prove: a. If you reflect point A in line m, and then reflect its image A' in line ℓ, A'' is the image of A after a rotation about point P.

b. $m\angle APA'' = 2(m\angle SPR)$

Proof: We are given that line ℓ and line m intersect at point P and that A is not on line ℓ or line m. Reflect A over line m to A' and reflect A' over line ℓ to A''. By the definition of reflection, line m is the perpendicular bisector of $\overline{AA'}$ at R, and line ℓ is the perpendicular bisector of $\overline{A'A''}$ at S. $\overline{AR} \cong \overline{A'R}$ and $\overline{A'S} \cong \overline{A''S}$ by the definition of a perpendicular bisector. Through any two points there is exactly one line, so we can draw auxiliary segments $\overline{AP}$, $\overline{A'P}$, and $\overline{A''P}$. $\angle ARP$, $\angle A'RP$, $\angle A'SP$ and $\angle A''SP$ are right angles by the definition of perpendicular bisectors. $\overline{RP} \cong \overline{RP}$ and $\overline{SP} \cong \overline{SP}$ by the Reflexive Property. $\triangle ARP \cong \triangle A'RP$ and $\triangle A'SP \cong \triangle A''SP$ by the SAS Congruence Postulate. Using CPCTC, $\overline{AP} \cong \overline{A'P}$ and $\overline{A'P} \cong \overline{A''P}$, and $\overline{AP} \cong \overline{A''P}$ by the Transitive Property. By the definition of a rotation, A'' is the image of A after a rotation about point P. Also using CPCTC, $\angle APR \cong \angle A'PR$ and $\angle A'PS \cong \angle A''PS$. By the definition of congruence, $m\angle APR = m\angle A'PR$ and $m\angle A'PS = m\angle A''PS$. $m\angle APR + m\angle A'PR + m\angle A'PS + m\angle A''PS = m\angle APA''$ and $m\angle A'PS + m\angle A'PR = m\angle SPR$ by the Angle Addition Postulate. $m\angle A'PR + m\angle A'PR + m\angle A'PS + m\angle A'PS = m\angle APA''$ by Substitution, which simplifies to $2(m\angle A'PR + m\angle A'PS) = m\angle APA''$. By Substitution, $2(m\angle SPR) = m\angle APA''$.

39. Sample answer: No; there are not invariant points in a glide reflection because all of the points are translated along a vector. Perhaps for compositions of transformations, there may be invariant points when a figure is rotated and reflected, rotated twice, or reflected twice. **41.** Yes; sample answer: If a segment with endpoints (a, b) and (c, d) is to be reflected about the x-axis, the coordinates of the endpoints of the reflected image are $(a, -b)$ and $(c, -d)$. If the segment is then reflected about the line $y = x$, the coordinates of the endpoints of the final image are $(-b, a)$ and $(-d, c)$. If the original image is first reflected about $y = x$, the coordinates of the endpoints of the reflected image are (b, a) and (d, c). If the segment is then reflected about the x-axis, the coordinates of the endpoints of the final image are $(b, -a)$ and $(d, -c)$.

43 Sample answer: When two rotations are performed on a single image, the order of the rotations does not affect the final image when the two rotations are centered at the same point. For example, if $\triangle ABC$ is rotated 45° clockwise about the origin and then rotated 60° clockwise about the origin, $\triangle A''B''C''$ is the same as if the figure were first rotated 60° clockwise about the origin and then rotated 45° clockwise about the origin. If $\triangle ABC$ is rotated 45° clockwise about the origin and then rotated 60° clockwise about $P(2, 3)$, $\triangle A''B''C''$ is different than if the figure were first rotated 60° clockwise about $P(2, 3)$ and then rotated 45° clockwise about the origin. So, the order of the rotations sometimes affects the location of the final image.

45. A **47.** H

49.

51.

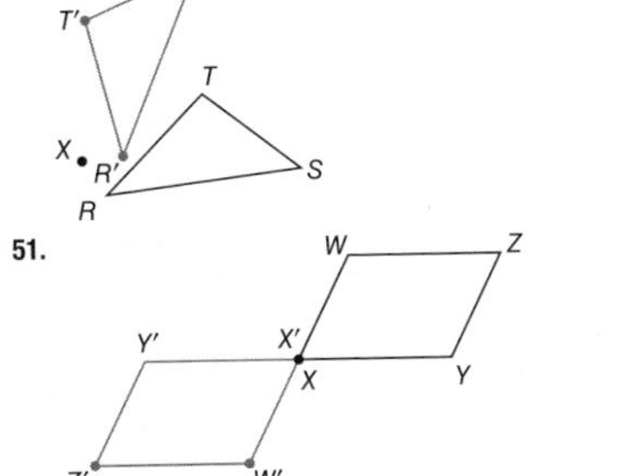

53. **55.** **57.**

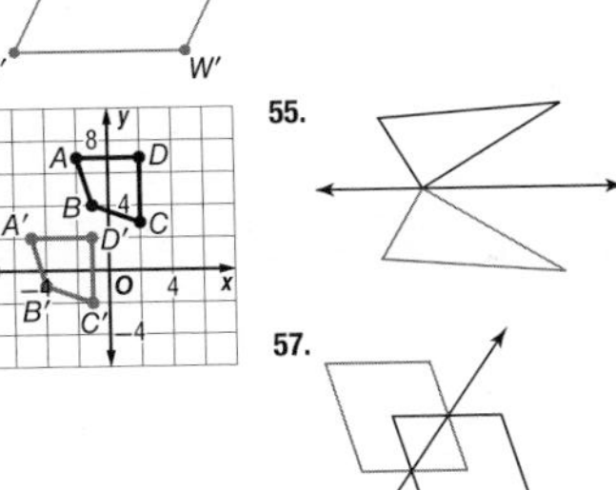

Lesson 9-5

1. yes; 4 **3.** yes; 1 **5.** yes; 2; 180

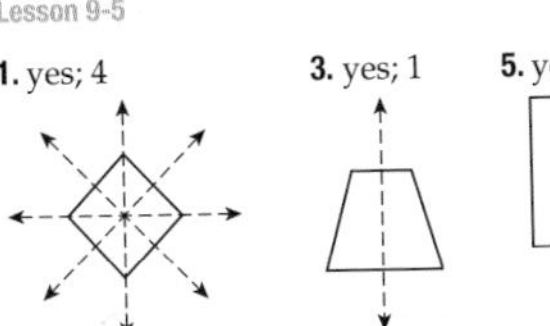

7 **a.** There is no plane in which the dome can be reflected onto itself horizontally. So, there are no horizontal planes of symmetry. The dome has 18 • 2 or 36 vertical planes of symmetry. **b.** The dome has order 36 symmetry and magnitude 360° ÷ 36 or 10°.

9. no **11.** yes; 6 **13.** yes; 1

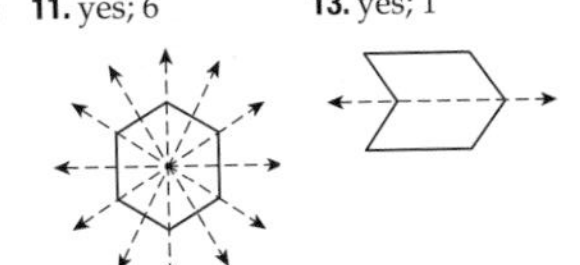

15. no **17.** yes; 1

19. yes; 3; 120°

21 No; there is no rotation between 0° and 360° that maps the shape onto itself. So, the figure does not have rotational symmetry.

23. yes; 8; 45°

25. yes; 8; 45° **27.** both **29.** both

31. no horizontal, infinitely many vertical

33. 1 horizontal, infinitely many vertical

35 Figure $ABCD$ is a square. It has 4 lines of symmetry and has order 4 symmetry and magnitude 360° ÷ 4 or 90°. So, it has line symmetry and rotational symmetry.

37. line and rotational

39. rotational; 2; 180°; line symmetry; $y = -x$ **41.** rotational; 2; 180°

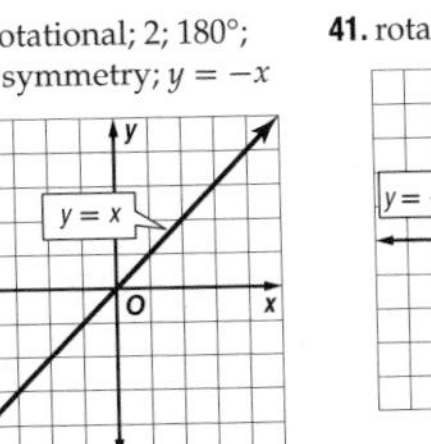

43. plane and axis; 180

45a. 3 **45b.** 3

45c.

Polygon	Lines of Symmetry	Order of Symmetry
equilateral triangle	3	3
square	4	4
regular pentagon	5	5
regular hexagon	6	6

45d. Sample answer: A regular polygon with n sides has n lines of symmetry and order of symmetry n.

47. Sample answer: $(-1, 0)$, $(2, 3)$, $(4, 1)$, and $(1, -2)$

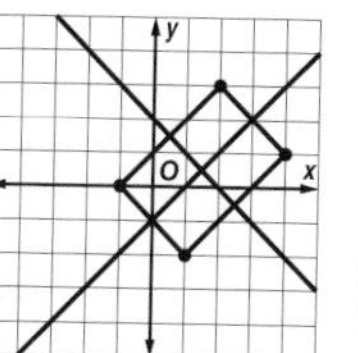

49.  Sample answer: An isosceles triangle has line symmetry from the vertex angle to the base of the triangle, but it does not have rotational symmetry because it cannot be rotated from 0° to 360° and map onto itself. **51.** B **53.** H

55.

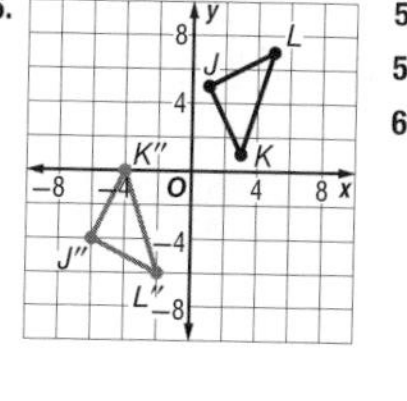

57. $(7, -7)$
59. reduction; $\frac{1}{2}$
61. enlargement; 3

Lesson 9-6

1.

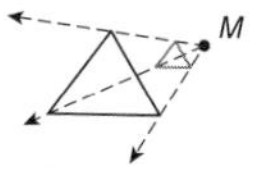

3 The figure increases in size from B to B', so it is an enlargement.

$$\frac{\text{image length}}{\text{preimage length}} = \frac{QB'}{QB} = \frac{8}{6} \text{ or } \frac{4}{3}$$

$$QB + BB' = QB'$$
$$6 + x = 8$$
$$x = 2$$

5.

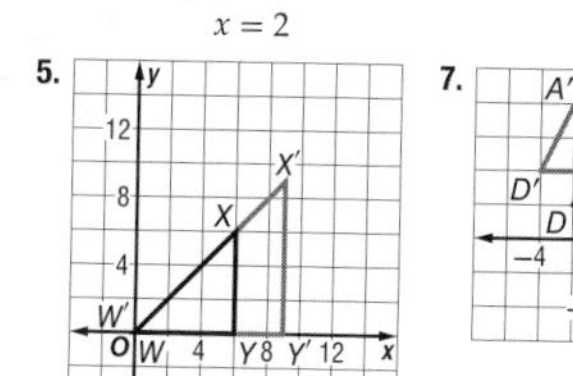

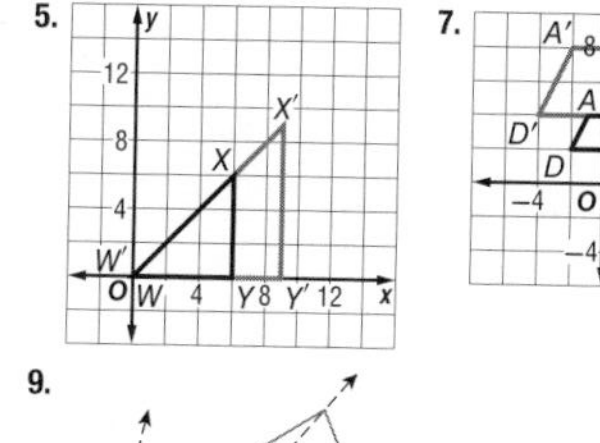

7.

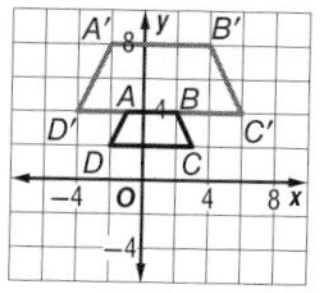

9.

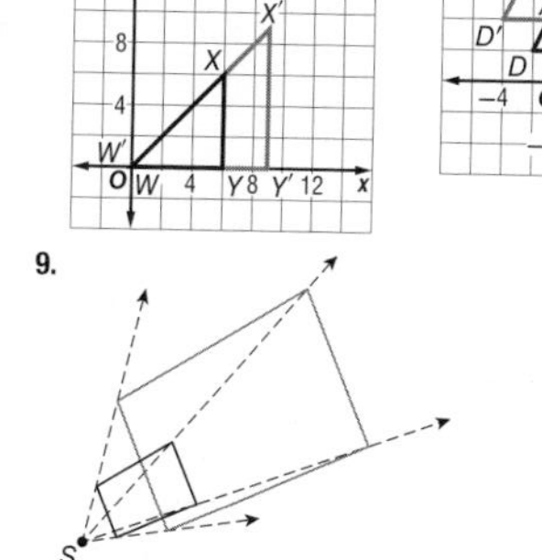

11. 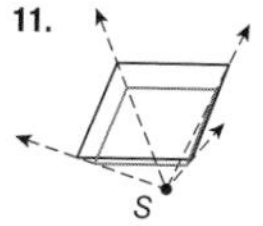 **13.**

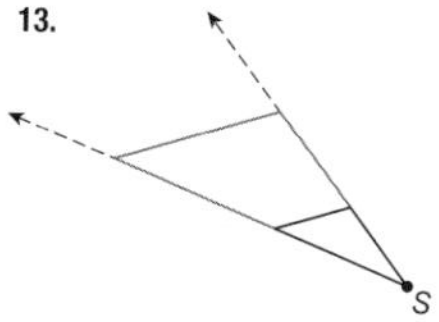

15. enlargement; 2; 4.5 **17.** reduction; $\frac{3}{4}$; 3.5

19. 15×; The insect's image length in millimeters is 3.75 • 10 or 37.5 mm. The scale factor of the dilation is $\frac{37.5}{2.5}$ or 15.

21 Multiply the x- and y-coordinates of each vertex by the scale factor, 0.5.

$(x, y) \rightarrow (0.5x, 0.5y)$
$J(-8, 0) \rightarrow J'(-4, 0)$
$K(-4, 4) \rightarrow K'(-2, 2)$
$L(-2, 0) \rightarrow L'(-1, 0)$

Graph JKL and its image $J'K'L'$.

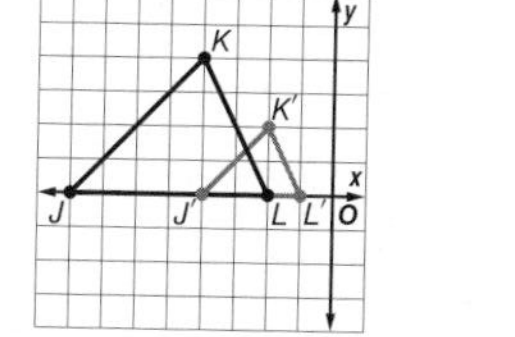

23. 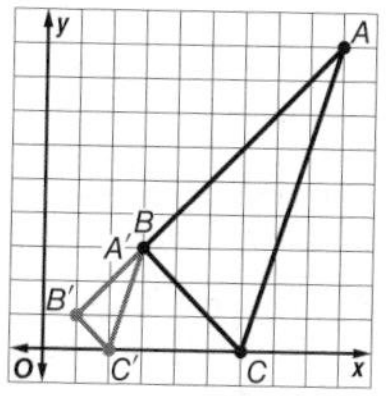 **25.**

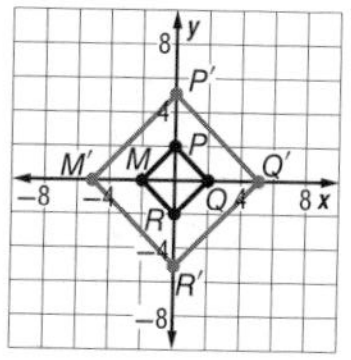

27a. 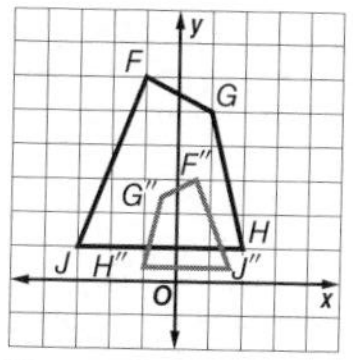 **27b.**

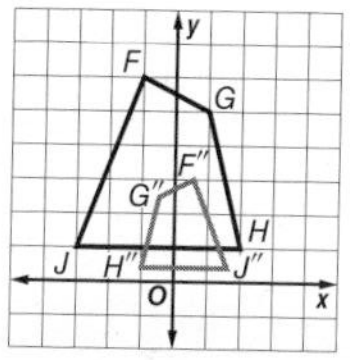

27c. no **27d.** Sometimes; sample answer: For the order of a composition of a dilation centered at the origin and a reflection to be unimportant, the line of reflection must contain the origin, or must be of the form $y = mx$.
29. No; sample answer: The measures of the sides of the rectangles are not proportional, so they are not similar and cannot be a dilation.

31 **a.**
$T = Ph + 2B$ — Surface area of a prism
$= (16)(4) + 2(12)$ — $P = 16$ cm, $h = 4$ cm, $B = 12$ cm²
$= 88$ cm² — Simplify.

$V = Bh$ — Volume of a prism
$= (12)(4)$ — $B = 12$ cm², $h = 4$ cm
$= 48$ cm³ — Simplify.

b. Multiply the dimensions by the scale factor 2: length = 6 • 2 or 12 cm, width = 2 • 2 or 4 cm, height = 4 • 2 or 8 cm.

$T = Ph + 2B$ — Surface area of a prism
$= (32)(8) + 2(48)$ — $P = 32$ cm, $h = 8$ cm, $B = 48$ cm²
$= 352$ cm² — Simplify.

$V = Bh$ — Volume of a prism
$= (48)(8)$ — $B = 48$ cm², $h = 8$ cm
$= 384$ cm³ — Simplify.

c. Multiply the dimensions by the scale factor $\frac{1}{2}$: length = $6 \cdot \frac{1}{2}$ or 3 cm, width = $2 \cdot \frac{1}{2}$ or 1 cm, height = $4 \cdot \frac{1}{2}$ or 2 cm.

$T = Ph + 2B$ — Surface area of a prism
$= (8)(2) + 2(3)$ — $P = 8$ cm, $h = 2$ cm, $B = 3$ cm²
$= 22$ cm² — Simplify.

$V = Bh$ — Volume of a prism
$= (3)(2)$ — $B = 3$ cm², $h = 2$ cm
$= 6$ cm³ — Simplify.

d. surface area of preimage: 88 cm²
surface area of image with scale factor 2: 352 cm² or (88 • 4) cm²
surface area of image with scale factor $\frac{1}{2}$: 22 cm² or $\left(88 \cdot \frac{1}{4}\right)$ cm²
The surface area is 4 times greater after dilation with scale factor 2, $\frac{1}{4}$ as great after dilation with scale factor $\frac{1}{2}$.

volume of preimage: 48 cm³
volume of image with scale factor 2: 384 cm³ or (48 • 8) cm³
volume of image with scale factor $\frac{1}{2}$: 6 cm³ or $\left(48 \cdot \frac{1}{8}\right)$ cm²
The volume is 8 times greater after dilation with scale factor 2; $\frac{1}{8}$ as great after dilation with scale factor $\frac{1}{2}$.

e. The surface area of the preimage would be multiplied by r^2. The volume of the preimage would be multiplied by r^3.

33 **a.**
$$k = \frac{\text{diameter of image}}{\text{diameter of preimage}} = \frac{2 \text{ mm}}{1.5 \text{ mm}} = \frac{2}{1\frac{1}{2}} = 2 \cdot \frac{2}{3} = \frac{4}{3} \text{ or } 1\frac{1}{3}$$

b.
$A = \pi r^2$ — Area of a circle
$= \pi(0.75)^2$ — $r = 1.5 \div 2$ or 0.75
≈ 1.77 mm² — Use a calculator.

$A = \pi r^2$ — Area of a circle
$= \pi(1)^2$ — $r = 2 \div 2$ or 1
≈ 3.14 mm² — Use a calculator.

35. $\frac{11}{5}$ **37.** $y = 4x - 3$

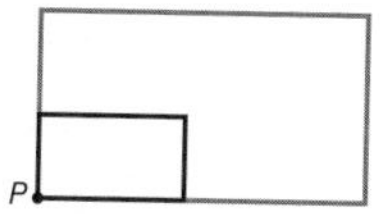

39a. Always; sample answer: Since a dilation of 1 maps an image onto itself, all four vertices will remain invariant under the dilation. **39b.** Always; sample answer: Since the rotation is centered at B, point B will always remain invariant under the rotation.
39c. Sometimes: sample answer: If one of the vertices is on the x-axis, then that point will remain invariant under reflection. If two vertices are on the x-axis, then the two vertices located on the x-axis will remain invariant under reflection. **39d.** Never; when a figure is translated, all points move an equal distance. Therefore, no points can remain invariant under translation. **39e.** Sometimes; sample answer: If one of the vertices of the triangle is located at the origin, then that vertex would remain invariant under the dilation. If none of the points on $\triangle XYZ$ are located at the origin, then no points will remain invariant under the dilation.
41. Sample answer: Translations, reflections, and rotations produce congruent figures because the sides and angles of the preimage are congruent to the corresponding sides and angles of the image. Dilations produce similar figures, because the angles of the preimage and the image are congruent and the sides of the preimage are proportional to the corresponding sides of the image. A dilation with a scale factor of 1 produces an equal figure because the image is mapped onto its corresponding parts in the preimage.
43. A **45.** D
47. yes; 1 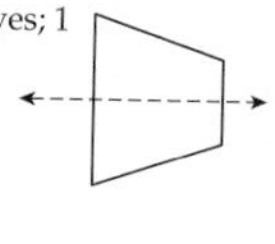
49. translation along $\langle -1, 8 \rangle$ and reflection in the y-axis
51. $2\sqrt{51}$ ft ≈ 14.3 ft
53. 34.6 **55.** 107.1

Chapter 9 Study Guide and Review

1. composition of transformations **3.** dilation
5. line of reflection **7.** translation **9.** reflection
11. **13.**

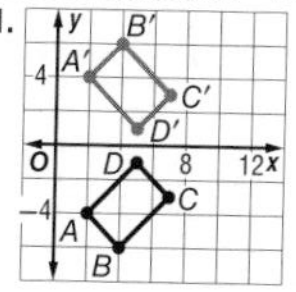

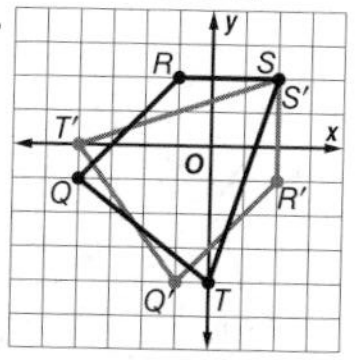

15. 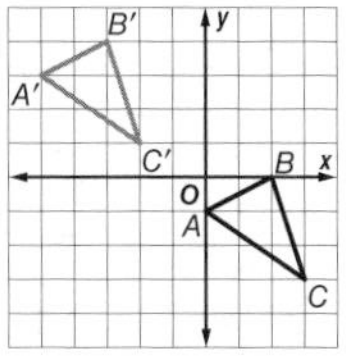

17. 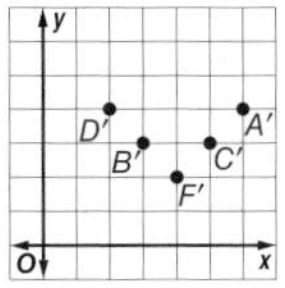

19. 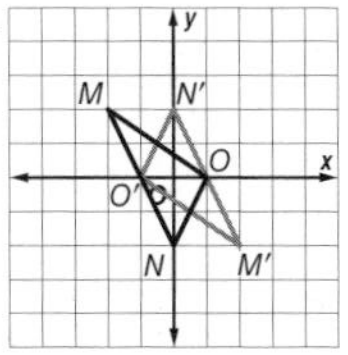

21. 90° 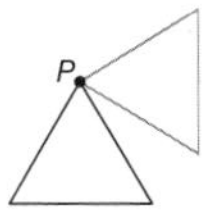

23. 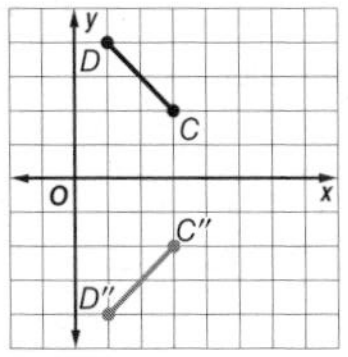

25. Sample answer: translation right and down, translation of result right and up.

27. yes; 2 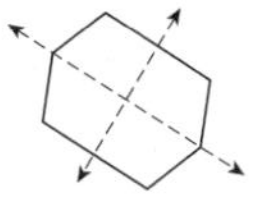

29. yes; 4; 90° 

31. 4 **33.** reduction; 8.25; 0.45

CHAPTER 10
Circles

Chapter 10 Get Ready

1. 130 **3.** 15.58 **5.** 82.8 **7.** $5.85 **9.** 8.5 ft **11.** −3, 4

Lesson 10-1

1. $\odot N$ **3.** 8 cm **5.** 14 in. **7.** 22 ft; 138.23 ft **9.** $4\pi\sqrt{13}$ cm **11.** $\overline{SU}$ **13.** 8.1 cm

(15) $d = 2r$ Diameter formula
$= 2(14)$ or 28 in. Substitute and simplify.

17. 3.7 cm **19.** 14.6 **21.** 30.6 **23.** 13 in.; 81.68 in. **25.** 39.47 ft; 19.74 ft **27.** 830.23 m; 415.12 m

(29) $a^2 + b^2 = c^2$ Pythagorean Theorem
$(6\sqrt{2})^2 + (6\sqrt{2})^2 = c^2$ Substitution
$144 = c^2$ Simplify.
$12 = c$ Take the positive square root of each side.

The diameter is 12π feet.
$C = \pi d$ Circumference formula
$= \pi(12)$ Substitution
$= 12\pi$ ft Simplify.

31. 10π in. **33.** 14π yd **35a.** 31.42 ft **35b.** 4 ft **37.** 22.80 ft; 71.63 ft **39.** $0.25x$; $0.79x$ **41.** neither

(43) The radius is 3 units, or 3 • 25 = 75 feet.
$C = 2\pi r$ Circumference formula
$= 2\pi(75)$ Substitution
$= 150\pi$ Simplify.
≈ 471.2 ft Use a calculator.

45a. Sample answer: 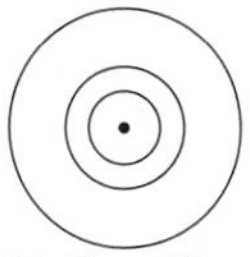

45b.

Circle Radius (cm)	Circumference (cm)
0.5	3.14
1	6.28
2	12.57

45c. They all have the same shape—circular. **45d.** The ratio of their circumferences is also 2.

45e. $(C_B) = \frac{b}{a}(C_A)$ **45f.** 4 in.

(47) **a.** $C = 2\pi r$ Circumference formula
$= 2\pi(30)$ Substitution
$= 60\pi$ Simplify.

$C = 2\pi r$ Circumference formula
$= 2\pi(5)$ Substitution
$= 10\pi$ Simplify.

$60\pi - 10\pi = 50\pi \approx 157.1$ mi

b. If $r = 5$, $C = 10\pi$; if $r = 10$, $C = 20\pi$; if $r = 15$, $C = 30\pi$, and so on. So, as r increases by 5, C increases by 10π or by about 31.4 miles.

49a. $8r$ and $6r$; Twice the radius of the circle, $2r$ is the side length of the square, so the perimeter of the square is $4(2r)$ or $8r$. The regular hexagon is made up of six equilateral triangles with side length r, so the perimeter of the hexagon is $6(r)$ or $6r$. **49b.** less; greater; $6r < C < 8r$ **49c.** $3d < C < 4d$; The circumference of the circle is between 3 and 4 times its diameter. **49d.** These limits will approach a value of πd, implying that $C = \pi d$. **51.** Always; a radius is a segment drawn between the center of the circle and a point on the circle. A segment drawn from the center to a point inside the circle will always have a length less than the radius of the circle.

53. $\frac{8\pi}{\sqrt{3}}$ or $\frac{8\pi\sqrt{3}}{3}$ **55.** 40.8 **57.** J **59.** 

61. 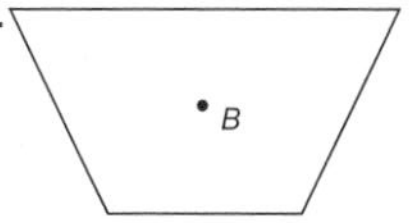

63. no **65.** no

67. True; sample answer: Since the hypothesis is true and the conclusion is true, then the statement is true for the conditions. **69.** 90 **71.** 20

Lesson 10-2

1. 170 **3.** major arc; 270 **5.** semicircle; 180 **7.** 147 **9.** 123 **11.** 13.74 cm

(13) $65 + 70 + x = 360$ Sum of central angles
$135 + x = 360$ Simplify.
$x = 225$ Subtract 135 from each side.

15. 40 **17.** minor arc; 125 **19.** major arc; 305 **21.** semicircle; 180 **23.** major arc; 270 **25a.** 280.8; 36 **25b.** major arc; minor arc **25c.** No; no categories share the same percentage of the circle. **27.** 60 **29.** 300 **31.** 180 **33.** 220 **35.** 120

(37) $\ell = \frac{x}{360} \cdot 2\pi r$ Arc length equation
$= \frac{112}{360} \cdot 2\pi(4.5)$ Substitution.
≈ 8.80 cm Use a calculator.

39. 17.02 in. **41.** 12.04 m **43.** The length of the arc would double. **45.** 40.84 in. **47.** 9.50 ft **49.** 142

(51) **a.** $m\widehat{AB} = m\angle ACB$ $\widehat{AB}$ is a minor arc.
$= 180 - (22 + 22)$ Angle Addition Postulate
$= 180 - 44$ or 136 Simplify.

b. $\ell = \frac{x}{360} \cdot 2\pi r$ Arc length equation
$= \frac{136}{360} \cdot 2\pi(62)$ Substitution.
≈ 147.17 ft Use a calculator.

(53) **a.** 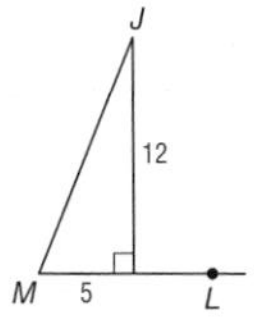

$\tan \angle JML = \frac{12}{5}$
$m\angle JML = \tan^{-1}\left(\frac{12}{5}\right)$
$\approx 67.4°$
$m\widehat{JL} = m\angle JML \approx 67.4°$

b. 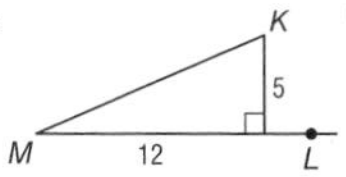

$\tan \angle KML = \frac{5}{12}$
$m\angle KML = \tan^{-1}\left(\frac{5}{12}\right)$
$\approx 22.6°$

$m\widehat{KL} = m\angle KML \approx 22.6°$

c. $m\angle JMK = m\angle JML - m\angle KML$
$\approx 67.4 - 22.6$
$\approx 44.8°$
$m\widehat{JK} = m\angle JMK \approx 44.8°$

d. $r = \sqrt{(x_2 - x_1)^2 + (y_2 - y_1)^2}$ Distance Formula
$= \sqrt{(5 - 0)^2 + (12 - 0)^2}$ $(x_1, y_1) = (0, 0)$ and $(x_2, y_2) = (5, 12)$
$= 13$ Simplify.

$\ell = \frac{x}{360} \cdot 2\pi r$ Arc length equation
$= \frac{67.4}{360} \cdot 2\pi(13)$ Substitution
≈ 15.29 units Use a calculator.

e. $\ell = \frac{x}{360} \cdot 2\pi r$ Arc length equation
$= \frac{44.8}{360} \cdot 2\pi(13)$ Substitution
≈ 10.16 units Use a calculator.

55. Selena; the circles are not congruent because they do not have congruent radii. So, the arcs are not congruent. **57.** Never; obtuse angles intersect arcs between 90° and 180° **59.** $m\widehat{LM} = 150$, $m\widehat{MN} = 90$, $m\widehat{NL} = 120$ **61.** 175 **63.** B **65.** H **67.** J **69.** 6.2

71. 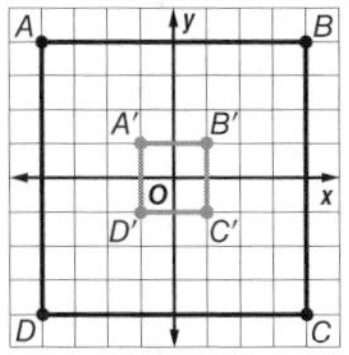

73. $x = \frac{50}{3}$; $y = 10$; $z = \frac{40}{3}$ **75.** 10, −10 **77.** 46.1, −46.1

Lesson 10-3

(1) $\widehat{ST}$ is a minor arc, so $m\widehat{ST} = 93$. $\overline{RS}$ and $\overline{ST}$ are congruent chords, so the corresponding arcs $\widehat{RS}$ and $\widehat{ST}$ are congruent.
$\widehat{RS} \cong \widehat{ST}$ Corresponding arcs are congruent.
$m\widehat{RS} = m\widehat{ST}$ Definition of congruent arcs
$x = 93$ Substitution

3. 3 **5.** 3.32 **7.** 21 **9.** 127 **11.** 7

(13) $\overline{KL}$ and $\overline{AJ}$ are congruent chords in congruent circles, so the corresponding arcs $\widehat{KL}$ and $\widehat{AJ}$ are congruent.
$\widehat{KL} \cong \widehat{AJ}$ Corresponding arcs are congruent.
$m\widehat{KL} = m\widehat{AJ}$ Definition of congruent arcs
$5x = 3x + 54$ Substitution
$2x = 54$ Subtract $3x$ from each side.
$x = 27$ Divide each side by 2.

15. 122.5° **17.** 5.34 **19.** 6.71

(21) $DE + EC = DC$ Segment Addition Postulate
$15 + EC = 88$ Substitution
$EC = 73$ Subtract 15 from each side.
$EC^2 + EB^2 = CB^2$ Pythagorean Theorem
$73^2 + EB^2 = 88^2$ Substitution
$EB^2 = 2415$ Subtract 73^2 from each side.
$EB \approx 49.14$ the positive square root of each side.
$EB = \frac{1}{2}AB$ $\overline{DC} \perp \overline{AB}$, so $\overline{DC}$ bisects $\overline{AB}$.
$2EB = AB$ Multiply each side by 2.
$2(49.14) \approx AB$ Substitution
$98.3 \approx AB$ Simplify.

23. 4

25. Proof:
Because all radii are congruent, $\overline{QP} \cong \overline{PR} \cong \overline{SP} \cong \overline{PT}$. You are given that $\overline{QR} \cong \overline{ST}$, so $\triangle PQR \cong \triangle PST$ by SSS. Thus, $\angle QPR \cong \angle SPT$ by CPCTC. Since the central angles have the same measure, their intercepted arcs have the same measure and are therefore congruent.
Thus, $\widehat{QR} \cong \widehat{ST}$.

27. Each arc is 90°, and each chord is 2.12 ft.

29. Given: $\odot L$, $\overline{LX} \perp \overline{FG}$, $\overline{LY} \perp \overline{JH}$, $\overline{LX} \cong \overline{LY}$
Prove: $\overline{FG} \cong \overline{JH}$

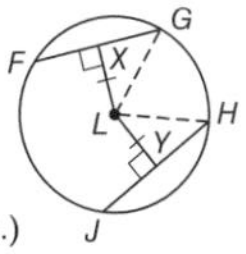

Proof:
Statements (Reasons)
1. $\overline{LG} \cong \overline{LH}$ (All radii of a ⊙ are ≅.)
2. $\overline{LX} \perp \overline{FG}$, $\overline{LY} \perp \overline{JH}$, $\overline{LX} \cong \overline{LY}$ (Given)
3. $\angle LXG$ and $\angle LYH$ are right ∡. (Def. of ⊥ lines)
4. $\triangle XGL \cong \triangle YHL$ (HL)
5. $\overline{XG} \cong \overline{YH}$ (CPCTC)

6. $XG = YH$ (Def. of ≅ segments)
7. $2(XG) = 2(YH)$ (Multiplication Property)
8. $\overline{LX}$ bisects $\overline{FG}$; $\overline{LY}$ bisects $\overline{JH}$. (A radius ⊥ to a chord bisects the chord.)
9. $FG = 2(XG)$, $JH = 2(YH)$ (Def. of seg. bisector)
10. $FG = JH$ (Substitution)
11. $\overline{FG} \cong \overline{JH}$ (Def. of ≅ segments)

31 Since $\overline{AB} \perp \overline{CE}$ and $\overline{DF} \perp \overline{CE}$, $\overline{CE}$ bisects $\overline{AB}$ and $\overline{DF}$.
Since $\overline{AB} \cong \overline{DF}$, $AB = DF$.

$CB = \frac{1}{2}AB$ Definition of bisector
$CB = \frac{1}{2}DF$ Substitution
$CB = DE$ Definition of bisector
$9x = 2x + 14$ Substitution
$7x = 14$ Subtract $2x$ from each side.
$x = 2$ Divide each side by 7.

33. 5 **35.** About 17.3; P and Q are equidistant from the endpoints of $\overline{AB}$ so they both lie on the perpendicular bisector of $\overline{AB}$, so $\overline{PQ}$ is the perpendicular bisector of $\overline{AB}$. Hence, both segments of $\overline{AB}$ are 5. Since $\overline{PS}$ is perpendicular to chord $\overline{AB}$, $\angle PSA$ is a right angle. So, $\triangle PSA$ is a right triangle.
By the Pythagorean Theorem, $PS = \sqrt{(PA)^2 - (AS)^2}$.
By substitution, $PS = \sqrt{11^2 - 5^2}$ or $\sqrt{96}$.
Similarly, $\triangle ASQ$ is a right triangle with
$SQ = \sqrt{(AQ)^2 - (AS)^2} = \sqrt{9^2 - 5^2}$ or $\sqrt{56}$.
Since $PQ = PS + SQ$, $PQ = \sqrt{96} + \sqrt{56}$ or about 17.3.

37a. Given: $\overline{CD}$ is the perpendicular bisector of chord $\overline{AB}$ in ⊙X.
Prove: $\overline{CD}$ contains point X.
Proof:
Suppose X is not on $\overline{CD}$. Draw $\overline{XE}$ and radii $\overline{XA}$ and $\overline{XB}$. Since $\overline{CD}$ is the perpendicular bisector of $\overline{AB}$, E is the midpoint of $\overline{AB}$ and $\overline{AE} \cong \overline{EB}$. Also, $\overline{XA} \cong \overline{XB}$, since all radii of a ⊙ are ≅. $\overline{XE} \cong \overline{XE}$ by the Reflexive Property. So, $\triangle AXE \cong \triangle BXE$. By CPCTC, $\angle XEA \cong \angle XEB$. Since $\angle XEA$ and $\angle XEB$ are congruent adjacent angles that make up $\angle AEB$, $\overline{XE} \perp \overline{AB}$. Then $\overline{XE}$ is the perpendicular bisector of $\overline{AB}$. But $\overline{CD}$ is also the perpendicular bisector of $\overline{AB}$. This contradicts the uniqueness of a perpendicular bisector of a segment. Thus, the assumption is false, and center X must be on $\overline{CD}$.

37b. Given: In ⊙X, X is on $\overline{CD}$ and $\overline{FG}$ bisects $\overline{CD}$ at O.
Prove: Point O is point X.
Proof:
Since point X is on $\overline{CD}$ and C and D are on ⊙X, $\overline{CD}$ is a diameter of ⊙X. Since $\overline{FG}$ bisects $\overline{CD}$ at O, O is the midpoint of $\overline{CD}$. Since the midpoint of a diameter is the center of a circle, O, is the center of the circle.

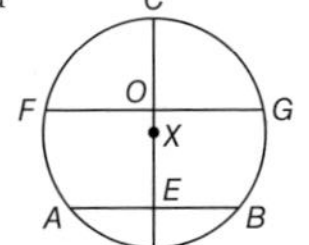

Therefore, point O is point X.

39. No; sample answer: In a circle with a radius of 12, a 60° arc would include a chord of 12. If the arc is tripled to 180°, the included chord is 24, which is not a triple of 12.
41. F **43.** E **45.** 170 **47.** 275 in.
49. yes; obtuse **51.** ±11
$31^2 \stackrel{?}{=} 20^2 + 21^2$
$961 > 400 + 441$

Lesson 10-4

1. 30 **3.** 66 **5.** 54
7. Given: $\overline{RT}$ bisects $\overline{SU}$.
Prove: $\triangle RVS \cong \triangle UVT$
Proof:
Statements (Reasons)
1. $\overline{RT}$ bisects $\overline{SU}$. (Given)
2. $\overline{SV} \cong \overline{VU}$ (Def. of segment bisector)
3. $\angle SRT$ intercepts $\widehat{ST}$. $\angle SUT$ intercepts $\widehat{ST}$. (Def. of intercepted arc)
4. $\angle SRT \cong \angle SUT$ (Inscribed ∡ of same arc are ≅.)
5. $\angle RVS \cong \angle UVT$ (Vertical ∡ are ≅.)
6. $\triangle RVS \cong \triangle UVT$ (AAS)

9. 25 **11.** 162

13 $m\widehat{NP} + m\widehat{PQ} + m\widehat{QN} = 360$ Addition Theorem
$120 + 100 + m\widehat{QN} = 360$ Substitution
$220 + m\widehat{QN} = 360$ Simplify.
$m\angle QN = 140$ Subtract 220 from each side.
$m\angle P = \frac{1}{2}m\widehat{QN}$ $\angle P$ intercepts $\widehat{QN}$.
$= \frac{1}{2}(140)$ or 70 Substitution

15. 140 **17.** 32 **19.** 20
21. Given: $m\angle T = \frac{1}{2}m\angle S$
Prove: $m\widehat{TUR} = 2m\widehat{URS}$
Proof:
$m\angle T = \frac{1}{2}m\angle S$ means that $m\angle S = 2m\angle T$. Since $m\angle S = \frac{1}{2}m\widehat{TUR}$ and $m\angle T = \frac{1}{2}m\widehat{URS}$, the equation becomes $\frac{1}{2}m\widehat{TUR} = 2\left(\frac{1}{2}m\widehat{URS}\right)$. Multiplying each side of the equation by 2 results in $m\widehat{TUR} = 2m\widehat{URS}$.

23. 30 **25.** 12.75 **27.** 135 **29.** 106
31. Given: Quadrilateral $ABCD$ is inscribed in ⊙O.
Prove: $\angle A$ and $\angle C$ are supplementary. $\angle B$ and $\angle D$ are supplementary.
Proof: By arc addition and the definitions of arc measure and the sum of central angles, $m\widehat{DCB} + m\widehat{DAB} = 360$. Since $m\angle C = \frac{1}{2}m\widehat{DAB}$ and $m\angle A = \frac{1}{2}m\widehat{DCB}$, $m\angle C + m\angle A = \frac{1}{2}\left(m\widehat{DCB} + m\widehat{DAB}\right)$, but $m\widehat{DCB} + m\widehat{DAB} = 360$, so $m\angle C + m\angle A = \frac{1}{2}(360)$ or 180. This makes $\angle C$ and $\angle A$ supplementary. Because the sum of the measures of the interior angles of a quadrilateral is 360, $m\angle A + m\angle C + m\angle B + m\angle D = 360$. But $m\angle A + m\angle C = 180$, so $m\angle B + m\angle D = 180$, making them supplementary also.

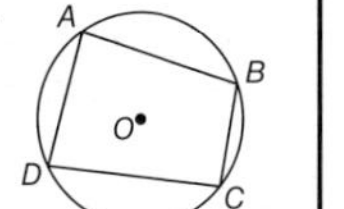

33 Since all the sides of the sign are congruent, all the corresponding arcs are congruent.
$8m\widehat{QR} = 360$, so $m\widehat{QR} = \frac{360}{8}$ or 45.
$m\angle RLQ = \frac{1}{2}m\widehat{QR}$
$= \frac{1}{2}(45)$ or 22.5

35. 135
37. Proof:
Statements (Reasons)
1. $m\angle ABC = m\angle ABD + m\angle DBC$ (∠ Addition Th.)
2. $m\widehat{ADC} = m\widehat{AD} + m\widehat{DC}$ (Arc Addition Theorem)
3. $\frac{1}{2}m\widehat{ADC} = \frac{1}{2}m\widehat{AD} + \frac{1}{2}m\widehat{DC}$ (Multiplication Property)
4. $m\angle ABD = \frac{1}{2}m\widehat{AD}$, $m\angle DBC = \frac{1}{2}m\widehat{DC}$ (The measure of an inscribed ∠ whose side is a diameter is half the measure of the intercepted arc (Case 1).)
5. $\frac{1}{2}m\widehat{ADC} = m\angle ABD + m\angle DBC$ (Substitution (Steps 3, 4))
6. $\frac{1}{2}m\widehat{ADC} = m\angle ABC$ (Substitution (Steps 5, 1))

39 Use the Inscribed Angle Theorem to find the measures of $\angle FAE$ and $\angle CBD$. Then use the definition of congruent arcs and the Multiplication Property of Equality to help prove that the angles are congruent.
Given: $\angle FAE$ and $\angle CBD$ are inscribed; $\widehat{EF} \cong \widehat{DC}$
Prove: $\angle FAE = \angle CBD$
Proof:
Statements (Reasons)
1. $\angle FAE$ and $\angle CBD$ are inscribed; $\widehat{EF} \cong \widehat{DC}$ (Given)
2. $m\angle FAE = \frac{1}{2}m\widehat{EF}$; $m\angle CBD = \frac{1}{2}m\widehat{DC}$ (Measure of an inscribed ∠ = half measure of intercepted arc.)
3. $m\widehat{EF} = m\widehat{DC}$ (Def. of ≅ arcs)
4. $\frac{1}{2}m\widehat{EF} = \frac{1}{2}m\widehat{DC}$ (Mult. Prop.)
5. $m\angle FAE = m\angle CBD$ (Substitution)
6. $\angle FAE \cong \angle CBD$ (Def. of ≅ ∡)

41a.
41b. Sample answer: $m\angle A = 30$, $m\angle D = 30$; $m\widehat{AC} = 60$, $m\widehat{BD} = 60$; The arcs are congruent because they have equal measures.
41c. Sample answer: In a circle, two parallel chords cut congruent arcs.
41d. 70; 70 **43.** Always; rectangles have right angles at each vertex, therefore opposite angles will be inscribed in a semicircle. **45.** Sometimes; a rhombus can be inscribed in a circle as long as it is a square. Since the opposite angles of rhombi that are not squares are not supplementary, they can not be inscribed in a circle. **47.** $\frac{\pi}{2}$ **51.** A **53.** $d = 17$ in., $r = 8.5$ in., $C = 17\pi$ or about 53.4 in. **55.** 48 **57.** 24
59. 107 **61.** 144 **63.** 54 **65.** $\frac{1}{2}$

Lesson 10-5

1. no common tangent

3 $FG^2 + GE^2 \stackrel{?}{=} FE^2$
$36^2 + 15^2 \stackrel{?}{=} (24 + 15)^2$
$1521 = 1521$
$\triangle EFG$ is a right triangle with right angle EGF. So $\overline{FG}$ is perpendicular to radius $\overline{EG}$ at point G. Therefore, by Theorem 10.10, $\overline{FG}$ is tangent to ⊙E.

5. 16 **7.** $x = 250$; $y = 275$; 1550 ft
9.
11.
13. yes; $625 = 625$

15 $XY^2 + YZ^2 \stackrel{?}{=} XZ^2$
$8^2 + 5^2 \stackrel{?}{=} (3 + 5)^2$
$89 \neq 64$
Since $\triangle XYZ$ is not a right triangle, $\overline{XY}$ is not perpendicular to radius $\overline{YZ}$. So, $\overline{XY}$ is not tangent to ⊙Z.

17 $\overrightarrow{QP}$ is tangent to ⊙N at P. So, $\overrightarrow{QP} \perp \overline{PN}$ and $\triangle PQN$ is a right triangle.
$QP^2 + PN^2 = QN^2$ Pythagorean Theorem
$24^2 + 10^2 = x^2$ $QP = 24$, $PN = 10$, and $QN = x$
$576 + 100 = x^2$ Multiply.
$676 = x^2$ Simplify.
$26 = x$ Take the positive square root of each side.

19. 9 **21.** 4 **23a.** 37.95 in. **23b.** 37.95 in. **25.** 8; 52 cm
27. 8.06
29. Given: Quadrilateral $ABCD$ is circumscribed about ⊙P.
Prove: $AB + CD = AD + BC$
Statements (Reasons)
1. Quadrilateral $ABCD$ is circumscribed about ⊙P. (Given)
2. Sides $\overline{AB}$, $\overline{BC}$, $\overline{CD}$, and $\overline{DA}$ are tangent to ⊙P at points H, G, F, and E, respectively. (Def. of circumscribed)
3. $\overline{EA} \cong \overline{AH}$; $\overline{HB} \cong \overline{BG}$; $\overline{GC} \cong \overline{CF}$; $\overline{FD} \cong \overline{DE}$ (Two segments tangent to a circle from the same exterior point are ≅.)

4. $AB = AH + HB$, $BC = BG + GC$, $CD = CF + FD$, $DA = DE + EA$ (Segment Addition)
5. $AB + CD = AH + HB + CF + FD$; $DA + BC = DE + EA + BG + GC$ (Substitution)
6. $AB + CD = AH + BG + GC + FD$; $DA + BC = FD + AH + BG + GC$ (Substitution)
7. $AB + CD = FD + AH + BG + GC$ (Commutative Prop. of Add.)
8. $AB + CD = DA + BC$ (Substitution)

31

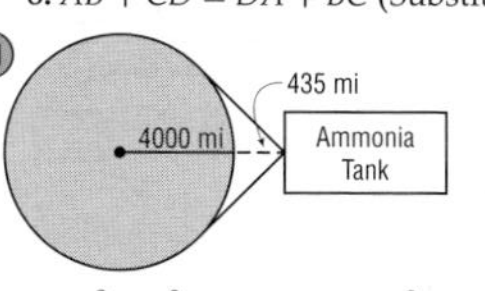

$4000^2 + x^2 = (4000 + 435)^2$	Pythagorean Theorem
$x^2 = 3{,}669{,}225$	Subtract 4000^2 from each side.
$x \approx 1916$ mi	Take the positive square root of each side.

33. Proof: Assume that ℓ is not tangent to $\odot S$. Since ℓ intersects $\odot S$ at T, it must intersect the circle in another place. Call this point Q. Then $ST = SQ$. $\triangle STQ$ is isosceles, so $\angle T \cong \angle Q$. Since $\overline{ST} \perp \ell$, $\angle T$ and $\angle Q$ are right angles. This contradicts that a triangle can only have one right angle.

35. Sample answer: Using the Pythagorean Theorem, $2^2 + x^2 = 10^2$, so $x \approx 9.8$. Since $PQST$ is a rectangle, $PQ = x = 9.8$.

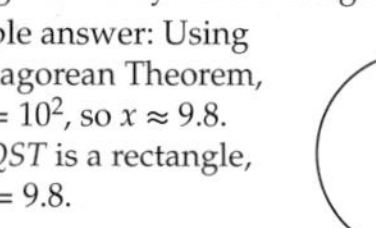

37. Sample answer:

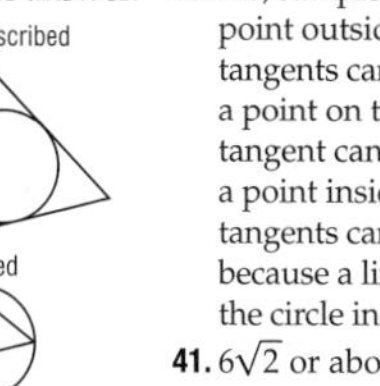

39. No; sample answer: From a point outside the circle, two tangents can be drawn. From a point on the circle, one tangent can be drawn. From a point inside the circle, no tangents can be drawn because a line would intersect the circle in two points.

41. $6\sqrt{2}$ or about 8.5 in.

43. D **45.** 61 **47.** 71 **49.** 109 **51.** Yes; $\triangle AEC \sim \triangle BDC$ by AA Similarity. **53.** 110 **55.** 58

Lesson 10-6

1. 110 **3.** 73 **5.** 248

7 Draw and label a diagram.

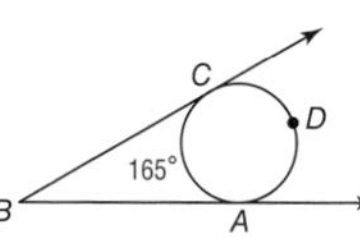

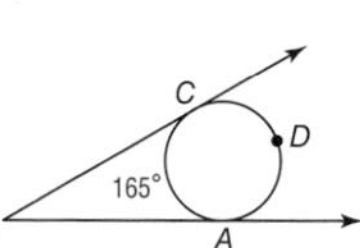

$m\angle B = \frac{1}{2}(m\widehat{CDA} - m\widehat{CA})$	Theorem 10.14
$= \frac{1}{2}[(360 - 165) - 165]$	Substitution
$= \frac{1}{2}(195 - 165)$ or 15	Simplify.

9. 71.5

11

$51 = \frac{1}{2}(m\widehat{RQ} + m\widehat{NP})$	Theorem 10.12
$51 = \frac{1}{2}(m\widehat{RQ} + 74)$	Substitution
$102 = m\widehat{RQ} + 74$	Multiply each side by 2.
$28 = m\widehat{RQ}$	Subtract 74 from each side.

13. 144 **15.** 125 **17a.** 100 **17b.** 20 **19.** 74 **21.** 185 **23.** 22 **25.** 168

27

$3 = \frac{1}{2}[(5x - 6) - (4x + 8)]$	Theorem 10.14
$6 = (5x - 6) - (4x + 8)$	Multiply each side by 2.
$6 = x - 14$	Simplify.
$20 = x$	Add 14 to each side.

29a. 145 **29b.** 30

31. <u>Statements (Reasons)</u>
1. $\overrightarrow{FM}$ is a tangent to the circle and $\overrightarrow{FL}$ is a secant to the circle. (Given)
2. $m\angle FLH = \frac{1}{2}m\widehat{HG}$, $m\angle LHM = \frac{1}{2}m\widehat{LH}$ (The meas. of an inscribed $\angle = \frac{1}{2}$ the measure of its intercepted arc.)
3. $m\angle LHM = m\angle FLH + m\angle F$ (Exterior ∡ Th.)
4. $\frac{1}{2}m\widehat{LH} = \frac{1}{2}m\widehat{HG} + m\angle F$ (Substitution)
5. $\frac{1}{2}m\widehat{LH} - \frac{1}{2}m\widehat{HG} = m\angle F$ (Subtraction Prop.)
6. $\frac{1}{2}(m\widehat{LH} - m\widehat{HG}) = m\angle F$ (Distributive Prop.)

33a. Proof: By Theorem 10.10, $\overline{OA} \perp \overline{AB}$. So, $\angle FAE$ is a right $\angle$ with measure 90, and $\widehat{FCA}$ is a semicircle with measure of 180. Since $\angle CAE$ is acute, C is in the interior of $\angle FAE$. By the Angle and Arc Addition Postulates, $m\angle FAE = m\angle FAC + m\angle CAE$ and $m\widehat{FCA} = m\widehat{FC} + m\widehat{CA}$. By substitution, $90 = m\angle FAC + m\angle CAE$ and $180 = m\widehat{FC} + m\widehat{CA}$. So, $90 = \frac{1}{2}m\widehat{FC} + \frac{1}{2}m\widehat{CA}$ by Division Prop., and $m\angle FAC + m\angle CAE = \frac{1}{2}m\widehat{FC} + \frac{1}{2}m\widehat{CA}$ by substitution. $m\angle FAC = \frac{1}{2}m\widehat{FC}$ since $\angle FAC$ is inscribed, so substitution yields $\frac{1}{2}m\widehat{FC} + m\angle CAE = \frac{1}{2}m\widehat{FC} + \frac{1}{2}m\widehat{CA}$. By Subt. Prop., $m\angle CAE = \frac{1}{2}m\widehat{CA}$. **33b.** Use same reasoning to prove $m\angle CAB = \frac{1}{2}m\widehat{CDA}$

35 **a.** Sample answer:

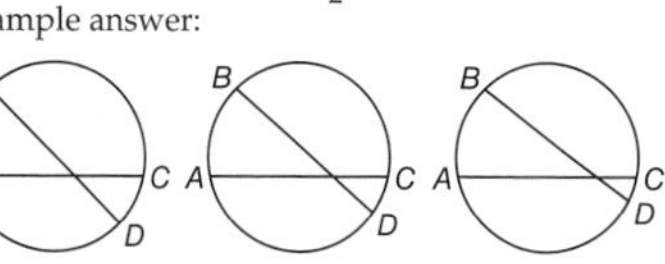

b. Sample answer:

	Circle 1	Circle 2	Circle 3
$\widehat{CD}$	25	15	5
$\widehat{AB}$	50	50	50
x	37.5	32.5	27.5

c. As the measure of $\widehat{CD}$ gets closer to 0, the measure of x approaches half of $m\widehat{AB}$; $\angle AEB$ becomes an inscribed angle.

d. Theorem 10.12 states that if two chords intersect in the interior of a circle, then the measure of an angle formed is one half the sum of the measure of the arcs intercepted by the angle and its vertical angle. Use this theorem to write an equation relating x, $m\widehat{AB}$, and $m\widehat{CD}$. Then let $m\widehat{CD} = 0$ and simplify. The result is Theorem 10.6, the Inscribed Angle Theorem.

$x = \frac{1}{2}(m\widehat{AB} + m\widehat{CD})$
$x = \frac{1}{2}(m\widehat{AB} + 0)$
$x = \frac{1}{2}m\widehat{AB}$

37. 15

39a. $m\angle G \le 90$; $m\angle G < 90$ for all values except when $\overleftrightarrow{JG} \perp \overleftrightarrow{GH}$ at G, then $m\angle G = 90$. **39b.** $m\widehat{KH} = 56$; $m\widehat{HJ} = 124$; Because a diameter is involved the intercepted arcs measure $(180 - x)$ and x degrees. Hence, solving $\frac{180 - x - x}{2} = 34$ leads to the answer.

41. Sample answer: Using Theorem 10.14, $60° = \frac{1}{2}[(360° - x) - x]$ or 120°; repeat for 50° to get 130°. The third arc can be found by adding 50° and 60° and subtracting from 360° to get 110°. **43.** J **45.** B **47.** 8

49. Given: $\widehat{MHT}$ is a semicircle. $\overline{RH} \perp \overline{TM}$.
Prove: $\frac{TR}{RH} = \frac{TH}{HM}$

Proof:
<u>Statements (Reasons)</u>
1. $\widehat{MHT}$ is a semicircle; $\overline{RH} \perp \overline{TM}$. (Given)
2. $\angle THM$ is a right angle. (If an inscribed $\angle$ intercepts a semicircle, the $\angle$ is a rt. $\angle$.)
3. $\angle TRH$ is a right angle. (Def. of $\perp$ lines)
4. $\angle THM \cong \angle TRH$ (All rt. angles are $\cong$.)
5. $\angle T \cong \angle T$ (Reflexive Prop.)
6. $\triangle TRH \sim \triangle THM$ (AA Sim.)
7. $\frac{TR}{RH} = \frac{TH}{HM}$ (Def. of $\sim \triangle$s)

51. 54.5° **53.** −4, −9 **55.** 0, −5 **57.** −6

Lesson 10-7

1. 2 **3.** 5

5 Let T be the endpoint of $\overline{QT}$, the diameter that passes through point S.

$PS \cdot SR = QS \cdot ST$	Theorem 10.15
$10 \cdot 10 = 6 \cdot ST$	Substitution
$100 = 6ST$	Simplify.
$\frac{50}{3} = ST$	Divide each side by 6.

So, the diameter of the circle is $6 + \frac{50}{3}$ or $\frac{68}{3}$ centimeters.

$C = \pi d$	Circumference formula
$= \pi\left(\frac{68}{3}\right)$	Substitution
≈ 71.21 cm	Use a calculator.

7. 5 **9.** 14 **11.** 3.1

13

$CD^2 = CB \cdot CA$	Theorem 10.17
$12^2 = x \cdot (x + 12)$	Substitution
$144 = x^2 + 12x$	Simplify.
$0 = x^2 + 12x - 144$	144 from each side.
$x = \frac{-b \pm \sqrt{b^2 - 4ac}}{2a}$	Quadratic Formula
$= \frac{-12 \pm \sqrt{12^2 - 4(1)(-144)}}{2(1)}$	$a = 1, b = 12, c = -144$
$= \frac{-12 \pm \sqrt{720}}{2}$	Disregard the negative solution.
≈ 7.4	Use a calculator.

15. 13 in. **17.** 7.1 **19.** $a = 15$; $b \approx 11.3$ **21.** $c \approx 22.8$; $d \approx 16.9$

23 Inscribed angles that intercept the same arc are congruent. Use this theorem to find two pairs of congruent angles. Then use AA Similarity to show that two triangles in the figure are similar. Finally, use the definition of similar triangles to write a proportion. Find the cross products.
Proof:
<u>Statements (Reasons)</u>
1. $\overline{AC}$ and $\overline{DE}$ intersect at B. (Given)
2. $\angle A \cong \angle D$, $\angle E \cong \angle C$ (Inscribed ∡ that intercept the same arc are $\cong$.)
3. $\triangle ABE \sim \triangle DBC$ (AA Similarity)
4. $\frac{AB}{BD} = \frac{EB}{BC}$ (Def. of $\sim \triangle$s)
5. $AB \cdot BC = EB \cdot BD$ (Cross products)

25. Proof:
<u>Statements (Reasons)</u>
1. tangent $\overline{JK}$ and secant $\overline{JM}$ (Given)
2. $m\angle KML = \frac{1}{2}m\widehat{KL}$ (The measure of an inscribed $\angle$ equals half the measure of its intercept arc.)
3. $m\angle JKL = \frac{1}{2}m\widehat{KL}$ (The measure of an $\angle$ formed by a secant and a tangent = half the measure of its intercepted arc.)
4. $m\angle KML = m\angle JKL$ (Substitution)
5. $\angle KML \cong m\angle JKL$ (Definition of $\cong$ ∡)
6. $\angle J \cong \angle J$ (Reflexive Property)
7. $\triangle JMK \sim \triangle JKL$ (AA Similarity)
8. $\frac{JK}{JL} = \frac{JM}{JK}$ (Definition of $\sim \triangle$s)
9. $JK^2 = JL \cdot JM$ (Cross products)

27. Sample answer: When two secants intersect in the exterior of a circle, the product equation equates the product of the exterior segment measure and the whole segment measure for each secant. When a secant and a tangent intersect, the product involving the tangent segment becomes (measure of tangent segments)^2 because the exterior segments and the whole segments are the same segment.
29. Sometimes; they are equal when the chords are perpendicular. **31.** Sample answer: The product of the parts on one intersecting chord equals the product of the parts of the other chord. **33.** G **35.** E

37.

39.

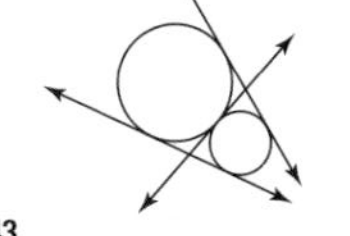

41.

43.

45. $y = 2x + 8$ **47.** $y = \frac{2}{9}x + \frac{1}{3}$ **49.** $y = -\frac{1}{12}x + 1$

Lesson 10-8

1. $(x - 9)^2 + y^2 = 25$

3 $r = \sqrt{(x_2 - x_1)^2 + (y_2 - y_1)^2}$ Distance Formula

$= \sqrt{(2 - 0)^2 + (2 - 0)^2}$ $(x_1, y_1) = (0, 0)$ and $(x_2, y_2) = (2, 2)$

$= \sqrt{8}$ Simplify.

$(x - h)^2 + (y - k)^2 = r^2$ Equation of a circle

$(x - 0)^2 + (y - 0)^2 = (\sqrt{8})^2$ $h = 0, k = 0$, and $r = \sqrt{8}$

$x^2 + y^2 = 8$ Simplify.

5. $(x - 2)^2 + (y - 1)^2 = 4$

7. $(3, -2)$; 4 **9.** $(2, -1)$; $(x - 2)^2 + (y + 1)^2 = 40$ **11.** $(1, 2), (-1, 0)$ **13.** $x^2 + y^2 = 16$ **15.** $(x + 2)^2 + y^2 = 64$ **17.** $(x + 3)^2 + (y - 6)^2 = 9$ **19.** $(x + 5)^2 + (y + 1)^2 = 9$

21 The third ring has a radius of 15 + 15 + 15 or 45 miles.

$(x - h)^2 + (y - k)^2 = r^2$ Equation of a circle

$(x - 0)^2 + (y - 0)^2 = 45^2$ $h = 0, k = 0$, and $r = 45$

$x^2 + y^2 = 2025$ Simplify

23. $(0, 0)$; 6

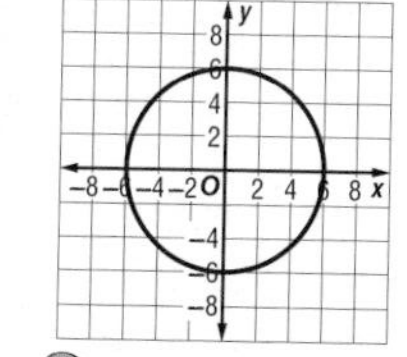

25 Write equation in standard form.

$x^2 + y^2 + 8x - 4y = -4$ Original equation

$x^2 + 8x + y^2 - 4y = -4$ Isolate and group like terms.

$x^2 + 8x + 16 + y^2 - 4y + 4 = -4 + 20$ Complete the squares.

$(x + 4)^2 + (y - 2)^2 = 16$ Factor and simplify.

$[x - (-4)]^2 + (y - 2)^2 = 4^2$ Write + 4 as − (−4) and 16 as 4^2.

So $h = -4, k = 2$, and $r = 4$. The center is at $(-4, 2)$ and the radius is 4.

27. $(x - 3)^2 + (y - 3)^2 = 13$ **29.** $(-2, -1), (2, 1)$ **31.** $(-2, -4), (2, 0)$ **33.** $\left(\frac{\sqrt{2}}{2}, \frac{3\sqrt{2}}{2}\right)$, $\left(-\frac{\sqrt{2}}{2}, -\frac{3\sqrt{2}}{2}\right)$ **35.** $(x - 3)^2 + y^2 = 25$

37a. $x^2 + y^2 = 810{,}000$ **37b.** 3000 ft

39a. $(x + 4)^2 + (y - 5)^2 = 36$ **39b.** The circle represents the boundary of the delivery region. All homes within the circle get free delivery. Consuela's home at (0, 0) is located outside the circle, so she cannot get free delivery.

41 The radius of a circle centered at the origin and containing the point (0, −3) is 3 units. Therefore, the equation of the circle is $(x - 0)^2 + (y - 0)^2 = 3^2$ or $x^2 + y^2 = 9$. The point $(1, 2\sqrt{2})$ lies on the circle, since evaluating $x^2 + y^2 = 9$ for $x = 1$ and $y = 2\sqrt{2}$ results in a true equation.

$1^2 + (2\sqrt{2})^2 = 9$

$1 + 8 = 9$

$9 = 9$ ✓

43. $(x + 5)^2 + (y - 2)^2 = 36$ **45.** $(x - 8)^2 + (y - 2)^2 = 16$; the first circle has its center at (5, −7). If the circle is shifted 3 units right and 9 units up, the new center is at (8, 2), so the new equation becomes $(x - 8)^2 + (y - 2)^2 = 16$. **47a.** 4 **47b–c.** Method 1: Draw a circle of radius 200 centered on each station. Method 2: Use the Pythagorean Theorem to identify pairs of stations that are more than 200 miles apart. Using Method 2, plot the points representing the stations on a graph. Stations that are more than 4 units apart on the graph will be more than 200 miles apart and will thus be able to use the same frequency. Assign station A to the first frequency. Station B is within 4 units of station A, so it must be assigned the second frequency. Station C is within 4 units of both stations A and B, so it must be assigned a third frequency. Station D is also within 4 units of stations A, B, and C, so it must be assigned a fourth frequency. Station E is $\sqrt{29}$ or about 5.4 units away from station A, so it can share the first frequency. Station F is $\sqrt{29}$ or about 5.4 units away from station B, so it can share the second frequency. Station G is $\sqrt{32}$ or about 5.7 units away from station C, so it can share the third frequency. Therefore, the least number of frequencies that can be assigned is 4. **49.** (−6.4, 4.8) **51.** A **53.** Step 1 **55.** 3 **57.** 5.6 **59.** 53 **61.** 28.3 ft **63.** 32 cm; 64 cm²

Chapter 10 Study Guide and Review

1. false, chord **3.** true **5.** true **7.** false, two **9.** false, congruent **11.** $\overline{DM}$ or $\overline{DP}$ **13.** 13.69 cm; 6.84 cm **15.** 34.54 ft; 17.27 ft **17.** 163 **19a.** 100.8 **19b.** 18 **19c.** minor arc **21.** 131 **23.** 50.4 **25.** 56

27.

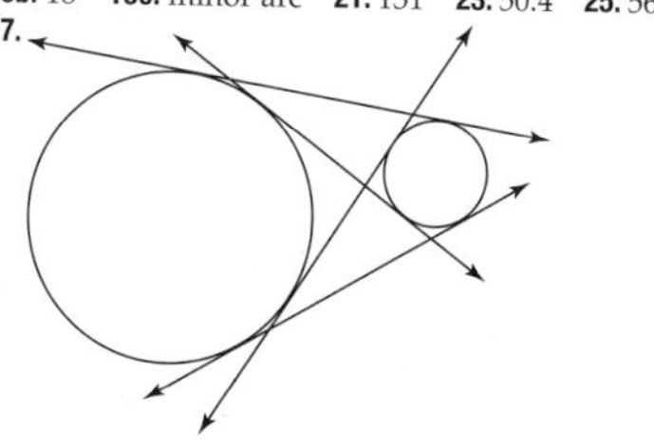

29. 97 **31.** 214 **33.** 4 **35.** $(x + 2)^2 + (y - 4)^2 = 25$ **37.** The radius of the circle is 19 + 15 or 34 inches, and (h, k) is (0, 0). Therefore the equation is $(x - 0)^2 + (y - 0)^2 = 34^2$ or $x^2 + y^2 = 34^2$.

CHAPTER 11

Areas of Polygons and Circles

Chapter 11 Get Ready

1. 5 **3.** 20 **5.** 11 ft **7.** 123 **9.** 78 **11.** 11 **13.** $3\sqrt{2}$ cm

Lesson 11-1

1. 56 in., 180 in² **3.** 64 cm, 207.8 cm² **5.** 43.5 in., 20 in² **7.** 28.5 in., 33.8 in² **9.** 11 cm

11 Perimeter = 21 + 17 + 21 + 17 or 76 ft

Use the Pythagorean Theorem to find the height.

$8^2 + h^2 = 17^2$ Pythagorean Theorem

$64 + h^2 = 289$ Simplify.

$h^2 = 225$ Subtract 64 from each side.

$h = 15$ Take the positive square root of each side.

$A = bh$ Area of a parallelogram

$= 21(15)$ or 315 ft² $b = 21$ and $h = 15$

13. 69.9 m, 129.9 m² **15.** 174.4 m, 1520 m² **17.** 727.5 ft² **19.** 338.4 cm² **21.** 480 m²

23

$\cos 26° = \frac{h}{158}$ $\cos = \frac{\text{adjacent}}{\text{hypotenuse}}$

$158 \cos 26° = h$ Multiply each side by 158.

$142 \approx h$ Use a calculator.

$A = bh$ Area of a parallelogram

$\approx 394(142)$ or 55,948 mi² $b = 394$ and $h = 142$

25. $b = 12$ cm; $h = 3$ cm **27.** $b = 11$ m; $h = 8$ m **29.** 1 pint yellow, 3 pints of blue **31.** 9.19 in.; 4.79 in²

33 Graph the parallelogram then measure the length of the base and the height and calculate the area.

$A = bh$ Area of a parallelogram

$\approx 6(6)$ or 36 units² $b = 6$ and $h = 6$

35a. 10.9 units²

35b. $\sqrt{s(s - a)(s - b)(s - c)} \stackrel{?}{=} \frac{1}{2}bh$

$\sqrt{15(15 - 5)(15 - 12)(15 - 13)} \stackrel{?}{=} \frac{1}{2}(5)(12)$

$\sqrt{15(10)(3)(2)} \stackrel{?}{=} 30$

$\sqrt{900} \stackrel{?}{=} 30$

$30 = 30$

37. 15 units²; Sample answer: I inscribed the triangle in a 6-by-6 square. I found the area of the square and subtracted the areas of the three right triangles inside the square that were positioned around the given triangle. The area of the given triangle is the difference, or 15 units². **39.** Sample answer: The area will not change as K moves along line p. Since lines m and p are parallel, the perpendicular distance between them is constant. That means that no matter where K is on line p, the perpendicular distance to line p, or the height of the triangle, is always the same. Since point J and L are not moving, the distance between them, or the length of the base, is constant. Since the height of the triangle and the base of the triangle are both constant, the area will always be the same. **41.** Sample answer: To find the area of the parallelogram, you can measure the height $\overline{PT}$ and then measure one of the bases $\overline{PQ}$ or $\overline{SR}$ and multiply the height by the base to get the area. You can also measure the height $\overline{SW}$ and measure one of the bases $\overline{QR}$ or $\overline{PS}$ and then multiply the height by the base to get the area. It doesn't matter which side you choose to use as the base, as long as you use the height that is perpendicular to that base to calculate the area. **43.** 6 **45.** B **47.** $x^2 + y^2 = 36$ **49.** $(x - 1)^2 + (y + 4)^2 = 17$ **51.** 5.6 **53.** Sample answer: if each pair of opposite sides are parallel, the quadrilateral is a parallelogram. **55.** 9 **57.** 12

Lesson 11-2

1. 132 ft^2 **3.** 178.5 m^2 **5.** 8 cm **7.** 6.3 ft **9.** 678.5 ft^2 **11.** 136 in^2 **13.** 137.5 ft^2

15 $A = \frac{1}{2}d_1d_2$ Area of a kite

$= \frac{1}{2}(4.8)(10.2)$ $d_1 = 4.8$ and $d_2 = 10.2$

$= 24.48$ Simplify.

The area is about 24.5 square microns.

17. 784 ft^2

19 Let x represent the length of one diagonal. Then the length of the other diagonal is $3x$.

$A = \frac{1}{2}d_1d_2$ Area of a rhombus

$168 = \frac{1}{2}(x)(3x)$ $A = 168$, $d_1 = x$, and $d_2 = 3x$

$168 = \frac{3}{2}x^2$ Simplify.

$112 = x^2$ Multiply each side by $\frac{2}{3}$.

$\sqrt{112} = x$ Take the positive square root of each side.

So the lengths of the diagonals are $\sqrt{112}$ or about 10.6 centimeters and $3(\sqrt{112})$ or about 31.7 centimeters.

21. 4 m **23.** The area of $\triangle HJF = \frac{1}{2}d_1\left(\frac{1}{2}d_2\right)$ and the area of $\triangle HGF = \frac{1}{2}d_1\left(\frac{1}{2}d_2\right)$. Therefore, the area of $\triangle HJF = \frac{1}{4}d_1d_2$, and the area of $\triangle HGF = \frac{1}{4}d_1d_2$. The area of kite $FGHJ$ is equal to the area of $\triangle HJF$ + the area of $\triangle HGF$ or $\frac{1}{4}d_1d_2 + \frac{1}{4}d_1d_2$. After simplification, the area of kite $FGHJ$ is equal to $\frac{1}{2}d_1d_2$. **25a.** 24 in^2 each of yellow, red, orange, green, and blue; 20 in^2 of purple **25b.** Yes; her kite has an area of 140 in^2, which is less than 200 in^2. **27.** 18 sq. units **29.** The area of a trapezoid is $\frac{1}{2}h(b_1 + b_2)$. So, $A = \frac{1}{2}(x + y)(x + y)$ or $\frac{1}{2}(x^2 + xy + y^2)$. The area of $\triangle 1 = \frac{1}{2}(y)(x)$, $\triangle 2 = \frac{1}{2}(z)(z)$, and $\triangle 3 = \frac{1}{2}(x)(y)$. The area of $\triangle 1 + \triangle 2 + \triangle 3 = \frac{1}{2}xy + \frac{1}{2}z^2 + \frac{1}{2}xy$. Set the area of the trapezoid equal to the combined areas of the triangles to get $\frac{1}{2}(x^2 + 2xy + y^2) = \frac{1}{2}xy + \frac{1}{2}z^2 + \frac{1}{2}xy$. Multiply by 2 on each side: $x^2 + 2xy + y^2 = 2xy + z^2$. When simplified, $x^2 + y^2 = z^2$.

31 The length of the base of the triangle is $\frac{12 - 8}{2}$ or 2. Use trigonometry to find the height of the triangle (and trapezoid).

$\tan 30 = \frac{\text{opposite}}{\text{adjacent}}$

$\frac{\sqrt{3}}{3} = \frac{2}{h}$

$\sqrt{3}h = 6$

$h = \frac{6}{\sqrt{3}}$

$h = 2\sqrt{3}$

Use the Pythagorean Theorem to find the hypotenuse of the triangle.

$a^2 + b^2 = c^2$

$2^2 + (2\sqrt{3})^2 = c^2$

$4 + 12 = c^2$

$16 = c^2$

$4 = c$

Find the perimeter and area of the trapezoid.

perimeter $= 12 + 8 + 4 + 4$

$= 28$ in.

$= \frac{28}{12}$ ft

≈ 2.3 ft

area $= \frac{1}{2}(b_1 + b_2)h$

$= \frac{1}{2}(8 + 12)(2\sqrt{3})$

$= 20\sqrt{3}\text{in}^2$

$= 20\sqrt{3}\text{in}^2 \cdot \frac{1 \text{ ft}}{12 \text{ in.}} \cdot \frac{1 \text{ ft}}{12 \text{ in.}}$

$= \frac{20\sqrt{3}}{144}$ ft^2

≈ 0.2 ft^2

33a. 2 cm; 4 cm; 12 cm

33b. 4 cm; 4 cm; 12 cm; 8 cm; 4 cm; 12 cm; 6 cm; 4 cm; 12 cm; 10 cm; 4 cm; 12 cm

33c.

x	P
2 cm	26.1 cm
4 cm	25.4 cm
6 cm	25.3 cm
8 cm	25.4 cm
10 cm	26.1 cm

33d. P; 26.8; 26.4; 26; 25.6; 25.2; 2 4 6 8 10 12; Length of x (cm)

33e. Sample answer: Based on the graph, the perimeter will be minimized when $x = 6$. This value is significant because when $x = 6$, the figure is a rhombus. **35.** 7.2 **37.** Sometimes; sample answer: If the areas are equal, it means that the products of the diagonals are equal. The only time that the perimeters will be equal is when the diagonals are also equal, or when the two rhombi are congruent. **39.** A **41.** J **43.** 17.5 units^2 **45.** $x^2 + y^2 = 1600$ **47.** $x = 9$; $y = 9\sqrt{3}$ **49.** always **51.** never **53.** 18.8 in.; 28.3 in^2 **55.** 36.4 ft; 105.7 ft^2

Lesson 11-3

1. 1385.4 yd^2

3 $A = \pi r^2$ Area of a circle

$74 = \pi r^2$ $A = 74$

$23.55 \approx r^2$ Divide each side by π.

$4.85 \approx r$ Take the positive square root of each side.

So, the diameter is $2 \cdot 4.85$ or about 9.7 millimeters.

5. 4.5 in^2 **7a.** 10.6 in^2 **7b.** \$48 **9.** 78.5 yd^2 **11.** 14.2 in^2 **13.** 78.5 ft^2 **15.** 10.9 mm **17.** 8.1 ft

19 $A = \frac{x}{360} \cdot \pi r^2$ Area of a sector

$= \frac{72}{360} \cdot \pi(8)^2$ $x = 72$ and $r = 8$

≈ 40.2 cm^2 Use a calculator.

21. 322 m^2 **23.** 284 in^2 **25a.** 1.7 cm^2 each **25b.** about 319.4 mg **27.** 13 **29.** 9.8

31 **a.** $C = \pi d$ Circumference of a circle

$2.5 = \pi d$ $C = 2.5$

$0.8 \text{ ft} \approx d$ Divide each side by π.

b. age = diameter · growth factor

$= 0.8 \cdot 4.5$ or 3.6 yr

33. 53.5 m^2 **35.** 10.7 cm^2 **37.** 7.9 in^2 **39.** 30 mm^2

41 The area equals the area of the large semicircle with a radius of 6 in. plus the area of a small semicircle minus 2 times the area of a small semicircle. The radius of each small semicircles is 2 in.

$A = \frac{1}{2}\pi(6)^2 + \frac{1}{2}\pi(2)^2 - 2\left[\frac{1}{2}\pi(2)^2\right]$

$= 18\pi + 2\pi - 4\pi$

$= 16\pi$

≈ 50.3 in^2

43a. $A = \frac{x\pi r^2}{360} - r^2\left[\sin\left(\frac{x}{2}\right)\cos\left(\frac{x}{2}\right)\right]$

43b.

x	A
10	0.1
20	0.5
30	1.7
40	4.0
45	5.6
50	7.7
60	13.0
70	20.3
80	29.6
90	41.1

43c. Area and Central Angles; Area of Segment; 0 5 10 15 20 25 30 35 40 45 50; 10 20 30 40 50 60 70 80 90; Central Angle Measure

43d. Sample answer: From the graph, it looks like the area would be about 15.5 when x is 63°. Using the formula, the area is 15.0 when x is 63°. The values are very close because I used the formula to create the graph. **45.** 449.0 cm^2 **47.** Sample answer: You can find the shaded area of the circle by subtracting x from 360° and using the resulting measure in the formula for the area of a sector. You could also find the shaded area by finding the area of the entire circle, finding the area of the unshaded sector using the formula for the area of a sector, and subtracting the area of the unshaded sector from the area of the entire circle. The method in which you find the ratio of the area of a sector to the area of the whole circle is more efficient. It requires less steps, is faster, and there is a lower probability for error. **49.** Sample answer: If the radius of the circle doubles, the area will not double. If the radius of the circle doubles, the area will be four times as great. Since the radius is squared, if you multiply the radius by 2, you multiply the area by 2^2, or 4. If the arc length of a sector is doubled, the area of the sector is doubled. Since the arc length is not raised to a power, if the arc length is doubled, the area would also be twice as large. **51.** $x = 56$; $m\angle MTQ = 117$; $m\angle PTM = 63$ **53.** E **55.** 13.2 cm, 26.4 cm **57.** 178.2 ft^2 **59.** 7 **61.** 31

Lesson 11-4

1. center: point F, radius: $\overline{FD}$, apothem: $\overline{FG}$, central angle: $\angle CFD$, 90° **3.** 162 in^2 **5.** 239 ft^2

7 **a.** The blue area equals the area of the center circle with a radius of 3 ft plus 2 times the quantity of the area a rectangle 19 ft by 12 ft minus the area of a semicircle with a radius of 6 ft.

Area

= Area of circle + 2 · (Area of rectangle − Area of semicircle)

$= \pi r^2 + 2 \cdot \left(\ell w - \frac{1}{2}\pi r^2\right)$

$= \pi(3)^2 + 2\left[(19(12) - \frac{1}{2}\pi(6)^2\right]$

$= 9\pi + 2(228 - 18\pi)$

$= 9\pi + 456 - 36\pi$

$= 456 - 27\pi$

≈ 371 ft^2

b. The red area equals the area of the center circle with a radius of 6 ft minus the center circle with a radius of 3 ft plus 2 times the area of a circle with a radius of 6 ft.

Area

= Area of large circle − Area of small circle + 2 · Area of circle

$= \pi r^2 - \pi r^2 + 2 \cdot \pi r^2$

$= \pi(6)^2 - \pi(3)^2 + 2\pi(6)^2$

$= 36\pi - 9\pi + 72\pi$

$= 99\pi$

≈ 311 ft^2

9. center: point R, radius: $\overline{RL}$, apothem: $\overline{RS}$, central angle: $\angle KRL$, 60° **11.** 59.4 cm^2 **13.** 584.2 in^2

15 The figure can be separated into a rectangle with a length of 12 cm and a width of 10 cm and a triangle with a base of 12 cm and a height of 16 cm − 10 cm or 6 cm.

Area of figure = Area of rectangle + Area of triangle

$= \ell w + \frac{1}{2}bh$

$= 12(10) + \frac{1}{2}(12)(6)$

$= 120 + 36$ or 156 cm^2

17. 55.6 in^2 **19.** 42.1 yd^2 **21a.** 29.7 in., 52.3 in^2 **21b.** 16 **23.** 1.9 in^2 **25a.** 50.9 ft^2 **25b.** 4 boxes **27.** 58.1 mm; 232.4 mm^2

29 To find the area of the shaded region, find the area of the rectangle 8 units by 4 units minus the area of the semicircle with a radius of 2 units minus the area of the trapezoid with bases 4 units and 2 units and height 2 units.

Area of figure

= Area of rectangle − Area of semicircle − Area of trapezoid

$= \ell w - \frac{1}{2}\pi r^2 - \frac{1}{2}h(b_1 + b_2)$

$= 8(4) - \frac{1}{2}\pi(2)^2 - \frac{1}{2}(2)(4 + 2)$

$= 32 - 2\pi - 6$

$= 26 - 2\pi$

≈ 19.7 units^2

31. 24 units^2 **33.** 0.43 in^2; 0.56 in^2; 0.62 in^2; 0.65 in^2; Sample answer: When the perimeter of a regular polygon is constant, as the number of sides increases, the area of the polygon increases.

35. Chloe; sample answer: The measure of each angle of a regular hexagon is 120°, so the segments from the center to each vertex form 60° angles. The triangles formed by the segments from the center to each vertex are equilateral, so each side of the hexagon is 11 in. The perimeter of the hexagon is 66 in. Using trigonometry, the length of the apothem is about 9.5 in. Putting the values into the formula for the area of a regular polygon and simplifying, the area is about 313.5 in^2.

37. Sample answer:

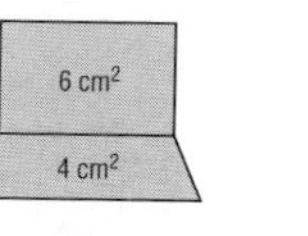

39. Sample answer: You can decompose the figure into shapes of which you know the area formulas. Then, you can sum all of the areas to find the total area of the figure. **41.** F **43.** D **45.** 254.5 cm^2 **47.** 490.9 mm^2 **49.** 272 in^2 **51.** semicircle; 180 **53.** major arc; 270 **55.** 30

Lesson 11-5

1. 9 yd^2 **3.** $\frac{5}{3}$; 35 **5.** 5.28 in^2

7 The scale factor between the parallelograms is $\frac{7.5}{15}$ or $\frac{1}{2}$, so the ratio of their areas is $\left(\frac{1}{2}\right)^2$ or $\frac{1}{4}$.

$\frac{\text{area of small figure}}{\text{area of large figure}} = \frac{1}{4}$ Write a proportion.

$\frac{60}{\text{area of large figure}} = \frac{1}{4}$ Substitution

$60 \cdot 4 = \text{area of large figure} \cdot 1$ Cross multiply.

$240 = \text{area of large figure}$ Simplify.

So the area of the large parallelogram is 240 ft^2.

9. 672 cm^2 **11.** $\frac{4}{5}$; 17.5 **13.** $\frac{3}{2}$; 36 **15a.** 4 in.

15b. Larger; sample answer: The area of a circular pie pan with an 8 in. diameter is about 50 in^2. The area of the larger pan is 52.6 in^2, and the area of the smaller pan is 41.6 in^2. The area of the larger pan is closer to the area of the circle, so Kaitlyn should choose the larger pan to make the recipe. **17a.** If the area is doubled, the radius changes from 24 in. to 33.9 in. **17b.** If the area is tripled, the radius changes from 24 in. to 41.6 in. **17c.** If the area changes by a factor of x, then the radius changes from 24 in. to $24\sqrt{x}$ in.

19 Area of $\triangle JKL = \frac{1}{2}bh$

$= \frac{1}{2}(5)(6)$ or 15 square units

The scale factor between the triangles is $\frac{5}{3}$, so the ratio of their areas is $\left(\frac{5}{3}\right)^2$ or $\frac{25}{9}$.

$\frac{\text{area of } \triangle JKL}{\text{area of } \triangle J'K'L'} = \frac{25}{9}$ Write a proportion.

$\frac{15}{\triangle J'K'L'} = \frac{25}{9}$ Area of $\triangle JKL = 15$

$15 \cdot 9 = \text{area of } \triangle J'K'L' \cdot 25$ Cross multiply.

$5.4 = \text{area of } \triangle J'K'L'$ Divide each side by 25.

So the area of $\triangle J'K'L'$ is 5.4 units^2.

21. area of $ABCD = 18$; area of $A'B'C'D' \approx 56.2$

23 **a.** Sample answer: The graph is misleading because the tennis balls used to illustrate the number of participants are similar circles. When the diameter of the tennis ball increases, the area of the tennis ball also increases. For example, the diameter of the tennis ball representing 1995 is about 2.6 and the diameter of the tennis ball representing 2000 is about 3. So, the rate of increase in the diameters is $\frac{3 - 2.6}{2000 - 1995}$ or about 8%. The area of the circle representing 1995 is $\pi(1.3)^2$ and the area of the circle representing 2000 is $\pi(1.5)^2$. So, the rate of increase in the areas is $\frac{2.25\pi - 1.69\pi}{2000 - 1995}$ or about 35%. The area of the tennis ball increases at a greater rate than the diameter of the tennis ball, so it looks like the number of participants in high school tennis is increasing more than it actually is.

b. Sample answer: If you use a figure with a constant width to represent the participation in each year and only change the height, the graph would not be misleading. For example, use rectangles of equal width and height that varies.

25. Neither; sample answer: In order to find the area of the enlarged circle, you can multiply the radius by the scale factor and substitute it into the area formula, or you can multiply the area formula by the scale factor squared. The formula for the area of the enlargment is $A = \pi(kr)^2$ or $A = k^2\pi r^2$.

27. $P_{\text{enlarged}} = Q\sqrt{R}$ **29.** Sample answer: If you know the area of the original polygon and the scale factor of the enlargement, you can find the area of the enlarged polygon by multiplying the original area by the scale factor squared. **31.** J **33.** E **35.** 66.3 cm^2 **37.** 37.4 in^2 **39.** 142.5 **41.** both **43.** $\overline{LP}$ **45.** $\overline{BM}$, $\overline{AL}$, $\overline{EP}$, $\overline{OP}$, $\overline{PL}$, $\overline{LM}$, $\overline{MN}$

Chapter 11 Study Guide and Review

1. false; height **3.** false; radius **5.** true **7.** false; height of a parallelogram **9.** false; base **11.** $P = 50$ cm; A = 60 cm^2 **13.** $P = 13.2$ mm; $A = 6$ mm^2 **15.** 132 ft^2 **17.** 96 cm^2 **19.** 336 cm^2 **21.** 1.5 m^2 **23.** 59 in^2 **25.** 166.3 ft^2 **27.** 65.0 m^2 **29.** ≈ 695 in^2 **31.** $\frac{1}{2}$; 8 **33.** area of $\triangle RST = 18$ square units; area of $\triangle R'S'T' =$ 4.5 square units **35.** 16.4 miles

CHAPTER 12 Extending Surface Area and Volume

Chapter 12 Get Ready

1. true **3.** true **5.** true **7.** 168 in^2 **9.** 176 in^2 **11.** ±15

Lesson 12-1

1. Sample answer: **3.**

5a. slice vertically **5b.** slice horizontally **5c.** slice at an angle **7.** triangle

9 Sample answer: First mark the corner of the solid. Then draw 4 units down, 1 unit to the left, and 3 units to the right. Draw a triangle for the top of the solid. Draw segments 4 units down from each vertex for the vertical edges. Connect the appropriate vertices. Use a dashed line for the hidden edge.

11. **13.**

15 **a.** The cross section is a four-sided figure with opposite sides parallel and congruent and with all angles right angles. So, the cross section is a rectangle.
b. To make the cross section of a triangle, cut off the corner of the clay through one of the vertices to the opposite face of the figure.

17. hexagon **19.** trapezoid **21.** Make a vertical cut. **23.** Make an angled cut. **25.** Sample answer: **27.** Sample answer:

29a–b. Sample answer: **29c.** Sample answer: The first drawing shows a view of the object from the bottom. The second drawing shows a view of the object from the top.

31 Top view: There are two rows and 3 columns when viewed from above. Use dark segments to indicate that there are different heights. Left view: The figure is 3 units high and two units wide. Front view: The first column is 3 units high, the second is 2 units high, and the third is 1 unit high. Right view: The figure is 3 units high and 2 units wide. Use dark segments to indicate that there are two breaks in this surface.

top view left view front view right view

33a. Sample answer: **33b.** Make a horizontal cut through the bottom part of the figure or make a vertical cut through the left side of the figure.

33c. The front view of the solid is the cross section when a vertical cut is made lengthwise. The right view of the solid is the cross section when a vertical cut is made through the right side of the figure. **35.** Sample answer: A cone is sliced at an angle through its lateral side and base.
37. Sample answer:

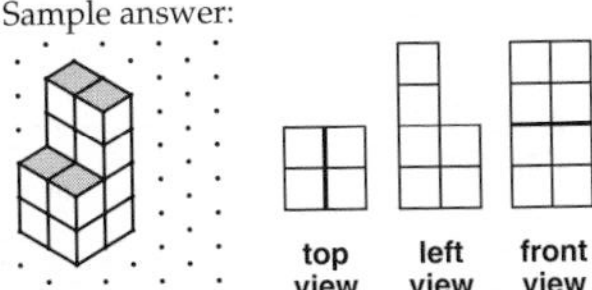

top view | left view | front view | right view

39. The cross section is a triangle. There are six different ways to slice the pyramid so that two equal parts are formed because the figure has six planes of symmetry. In each case, the cross section is an isosceles triangle. Only the side lengths of the triangles change. **41a.** inner side of deck = circumference of pool = 81.64 ÷ π ≈ 26 ft; outer side of deck = 26 + 3 + 3 = 32 ft; outer perimeter of deck = 4 × 32 = 128 ft **41b.** area of deck = (2 × 3 × 32) + (2 × 3 × 26) = 348 square feet **43.** E **45.** $\frac{3}{2}$; 9 **47.** about 3.6 yd² **49.** 28.9 in.; 66.5 in²

Lesson 12-2

1. 112.5 in² **3.** $L = 288$ ft²; $S = 336$ ft² **5.** $L \approx 653.5$ yd²; $S \approx 1715.3$ yd²

7
$S = 2\pi rh + 2\pi r^2$ Surface area of a cylinder
$286.3 = 2\pi(3.4)h + 2\pi(3.4)^2$ Replace S with 286.3 and r with 3.4.
$286.3 \approx 21.4h + 72.6$ Use a calculator to simplify.
$213.7 \approx 21.4h$ Subtract 72.6 from each side.
$10.0 \approx h$ Divide each side by 21.4.
The height of the can is about 10.0 cm.

9 Find the missing side length of the base.
$c^2 = 4^2 + 3^2$ Pythagorean Theorem
$c^2 = 25$ Simplify.
$c = 5$ Take the square root of each side.

$L = Ph$ Lateral area of a prism
$= (4 + 3 + 5)2$ Substitution
$= 24$ Simplify.
The lateral area is 24 ft².

$S = Ph + 2B$ Surface area of a prism
$= (4 + 3 + 5)(2) + 2\left(\frac{1}{2} \cdot 4 \cdot 3\right)$ Substitution
$= 24 + 12$ or 36 Simplify.
The surface area is 36 ft².

11. Sample answer: $L = 64$ in²; $S = 88$ in² **13.** $L = 11.2$ m²; $S = 13.6$ m² **15.** $L = 1032$ cm²; $S = 1932$ cm² (18 × 25 base); $L = 1332$ cm²; $S = 1932$ cm² (25 × 12 base); $L = 1500$ cm²; $S = 1932$ cm² (18 × 12 base) **17.** $L = 1484.8$ cm²; $S = 1745.2$ cm² **19.** $L \approx 282.7$ mm²; $S \approx 339.3$ mm² **21.** $L \approx 155.8$ in²; $S \approx 256.4$ in² **23.** 42.5 m² **25.** $r = 9.2$ cm

27
$S = 2\pi rh + 2\pi r^2$ Surface area of a cylinder
$256\pi = 2\pi r(8) + 2\pi r^2$ Replace S with 256π and h with 8.
$128 = 8r + r^2$ Divide each side by 2π.
$0 = r^2 + 8r - 128$ Subtract 128 from each side.
$0 = (r + 16)(r - 8)$ Factor.
$r + 16 = 0$ or $r - 8 = 0$ Zero Product Property
$r = -16$ $r = 8$
Since the radius cannot be negative, $r = 8$. So, the diameter is 8 • 2 or 16 millimeters.

29a. First, find the area of the sector and double it. Then find 73% of the the lateral area of the cylinder. Next, find the areas of the two rectangles formed by the radius and height when a portion is cut. Last, find the sum of all the areas. **29b.** 283.7 in² **31.** $L = 1392.0$ cm²; $S = 2032$ cm² **33.** about 299.1 cm²

35 The composite figure has trapezoid bases. The trapezoids have bases 20 cm and 13 cm and a height of 21 cm. To find the length of the fourth side of the trapezoid x, use the Pythagorean Theorem.

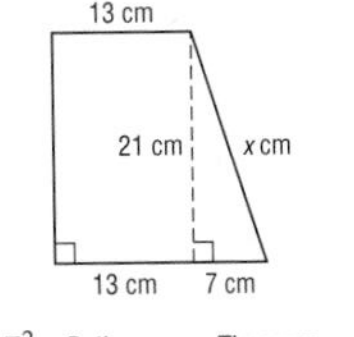

$x^2 = 21^2 + 7^2$ Pythagorean Theorem
$x^2 = 490$ Simplify.
$x \approx 22.136$ Take the square root of each side.

$S = Ph + 2B$ Surface area of a prism
$\approx (21 + 13 + 22.136 + 20)(28) + 2\left[\frac{1}{2}(21)(20 + 13)\right]$ Substitution
$\approx 2131.8 + 693$ or 2824.8 cm² Simplify.

37. 1059.3 cm² **39.** Derek; sample answer: $S = 2\pi r^2 + 2\pi rh$, so the surface area of the cylinder is $2\pi(6)^2 + 2\pi(6)(5)$ or 132π cm² **41.** To find the surface area of any solid figure, find the area of the base (or bases) and add to the area of the lateral faces of the figure. The lateral faces and bases of a rectangular prism are rectangles. Since the bases of a cylinder are circles, the lateral faces of a cylinder is a rectangle. **43.** $\frac{\sqrt{3}}{2}\ell^2 + 3\ell h$; the area of an equilateral triangle of side ℓ is $\frac{\sqrt{3}}{4}\ell^2$ and the perimeter of the triangle is 3ℓ. So, the total surface area is $\frac{\sqrt{3}}{2}\ell^2 + 3\ell h$. **45.** A **47.** H

49.

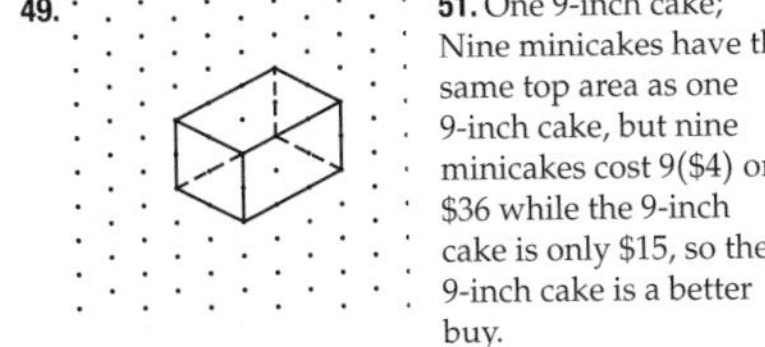

51. One 9-inch cake; Nine minicakes have the same top area as one 9-inch cake, but nine minicakes cost 9($4) or $36 while the 9-inch cake is only $15, so the 9-inch cake is a better buy.
53. 2.5 in. **55.** 20.5

Lesson 12-3

1. $L = 384$ cm²; $S = 640$ cm² **3.** $L \approx 207.8$ m²; $S \approx 332.6$ m² **5.** $L \approx 188.5$ m²; $S \approx 267.0$ m²

7
$L = \frac{1}{2}P\ell$ Lateral area of a regular pyramid
$= \frac{1}{2}(8)(5)$ $P = 2 \cdot 4$ or 8, $\ell = 5$
$= 20$ m² Simplify.

$S = \frac{1}{2}P\ell + B$ Surface area of a regular pyramid
$= 20 + 4$ $\frac{1}{2}P\ell = 20$, $B = 4$
$= 24$ m² Simplify.

9. $L \approx 178.2$ cm²; $S \approx 302.9$ cm² **11.** $L \approx 966.0$ in²; $S \approx 1686.0$ in² **13.** 139,440 ft² **15.** $L \approx 357.6$ cm²; $S \approx 470.7$ cm² **17.** $L \approx 241.1$ ft²; $S \approx 446.1$ ft²

19 Use the Pythagorean Theorem to find the slant height ℓ.

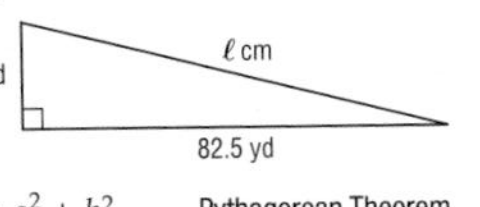

$c^2 = a^2 + b^2$ Pythagorean Theorem
$\ell^2 = 20^2 + 82.5^2$ $a = 20$, $b = 82.5$, $c = \ell$
$\ell^2 = 7206.25$ Simplify.
$\ell = \sqrt{7206.25}$ Take the square root of each side.

$L = \frac{1}{2}P\ell$ Lateral area of a regular pyramid
$= \frac{1}{2}(660)(\sqrt{7206.25})$ $P = 154 \cdot 4$ or 660, $\ell = 6$
$\approx 28{,}013.6$ yd² Use a calculator.

21. 34 **23.** 5 mm **25.** 16 cm **27.** 266π ft²
29a. nonregular pyramid with a square base
29b. Sample answer: **31.** Sample answer:

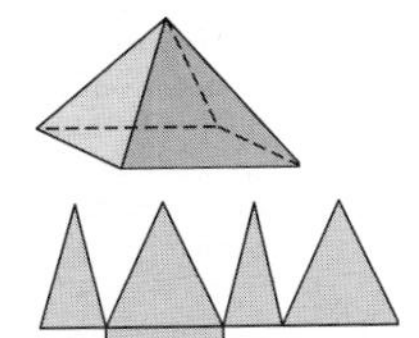

33 The lateral area of a cone is $L = \pi r\ell$. The radius is half the diameter, or 7.5 mm. Find the slant height ℓ.

7.5 mm, 32°, ℓ

$\sin 32° = \frac{\text{opposite}}{\text{hypotenuse}}$
$\sin 32° = \frac{7.5}{\ell}$
$\ell = \frac{7.5}{\sin 32°}$ or about 14.15 mm
$L = \pi(7.5)(14.15)$ or about 333.5 mm².
The surface area of a cone is $S = L + \pi r^2$.
$S = 333.5 + \pi(7.5)^2$ or about 510.2 mm².

35a. Sample answer:

35b.

Slant Height (units)	Lateral Area (units)²
1	6
3	18
9	54

35c. The lateral area is tripled. **35d.** The lateral area is multiplied by 3² or 9. **37.** Always; if the heights and radii are the same, the surface area of the cylinder will be greater since it has two circular bases and additional lateral area. **39.** Sample answer: a square pyramid with a base edge of 5 units and a slant height of 7.5 units **41.** Use the apothem, the height, and the Pythagorean Theorem to find the slant height ℓ of the pyramid. Then use the central angle of the n-gon and the apothem to find the length of one side of the n-gon. Then find the perimeter. Finally, use $S = \frac{1}{2}P\ell + B$ to find the surface area. The area of the base B is $\frac{1}{2}Pa$. **43.** 3299 mm² **45.** D

47.

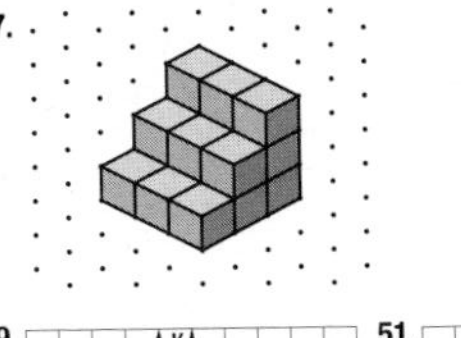

49. **51.**

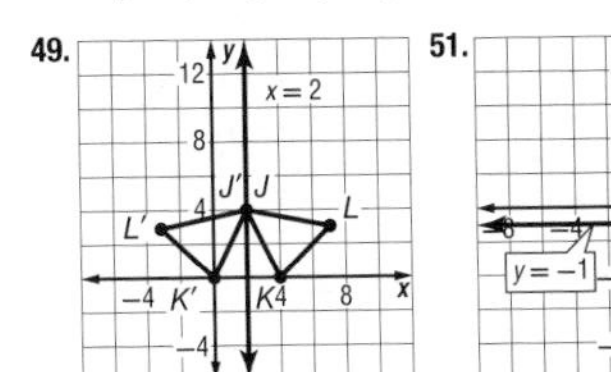

53.

55. 57 m, 120 m^2
57. 183.1 in., 1887 in^2

Lesson 12-4

1. 108 cm^3 **3.** 26.95 m^3 **5.** 206.4 ft^3 **7.** 1025.4 cm^3 **9.** D

(11) $V = Bh$ — Volume of a prism
$= 38.5(14)$ — $B = \frac{1}{2}(11)(7)$ or 38.5, $h = 14$
$= 539$ m^3 — Simplify.

13. 58.14 ft^3 **15.** 1534.25 in^3

(17) $V = \pi r^2 h$ — Volume of a cylinder
$= \pi(6)^2(3.6)$ — Replace r with $12 \div 2$ or 6 and h with 3.6.
≈ 407.2 cm^3 — Use a calculator.

19. 2686.1 mm^3 **21.** 521.5 cm^3 **23.** 3934.9 cm^3 **25.** 35.1 cm **27a.** 0.0019 lb/in^3 **27b.** The plant should grow well in this soil since the bulk density of 0.0019 lb/in^3 is close to the desired bulk density of 0.0018 lb/in^3. **27c.** 8.3 lb **29.** 120 m^3

(31) Find the volume of the cylinder with a height of 11.5 cm and a radius of $8.5 \div 2$ or 4.25 cm. Subtract from that the volume of the cylinder with a height of 11.5 cm and a radius of $6.5 \div 2$ or 3.25 cm. Add the volume of the bottom cylinder that has a height of 1 cm and a radius of $6.5 \div 2$ or 3.25 cm.

Volume = Volume of large cylinder − Volume of small cylinder + Volume of bottom
$= \pi r_1^2 h_1 - \pi r_2^2 h_1 + \pi r_2^2 h_2$
$= \pi(4.25)^2(11.5) - \pi(3.25)^2(11.5) + \pi(3.25)^2(1)$ — $r_1 = 4.25, r_2 = 3.25, h_1 = 10.5, h_2 = 1$
≈ 304.1 cm^3 — Use a calculator.

33. 678.6 in^3 **35.** 3,190,680.0 cm^3 **37.** $11\frac{1}{4}$ in.

(39) Each triangular prism has a base area of $\frac{1}{2}(8)(5.5)$ or 22 cm^2 and a height of 10 cm. The volume of each triangular prism is $22 \cdot 10$ or 220 cm^3. So, the volume of five triangular prisms is $220 \cdot 5$ or 1100 cm^3.

41a.

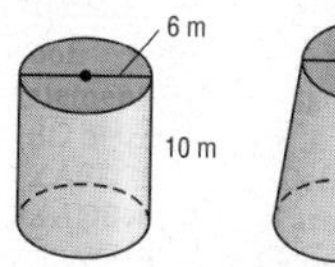

41b. Greater than; a square with a side length of 6 m has an area of 36 m^2. A circle with a diameter of 6 m has an area of 9π or 28.3 m^2. Since the heights are the same, the volume of the square prism is greater assuming $x > 1$. **41c.** Multiplying the radius by x; since the volume is represented by $\pi r^2 h$, multiplying the height by x makes the volume x times greater. Multiplying the radius by x makes the volume x^2 times greater. **43.** Sample answer: The can holds $\pi(2)^2(5)$ or 20π in^3 of liquid. Therefore, the container holds 60π in^3. **43a.** base 3 in. by 5 in., height 4π in. **43b.** base 5 in. per side, height $\frac{12}{5}\pi$ in. **43c.** base with legs measuring 3 in. and 4 in., height 10π in.

45. Sample answer:

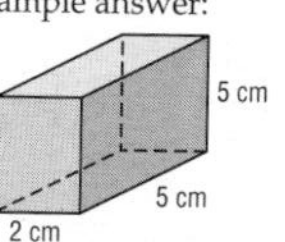

47. Sample answer: Both formulas involve multiplying the area of the base by the height. The base of a prism is a polygon, so the expression representing the area varies, depending on the type of polygon it is. The base of a cylinder is a circle, so its area is πr^2. **49.** F **51.** C **53.** 126 cm^2; 175 cm^2 **55.** 205 in^2 **57.** 11.4 cm **59.** 9.3 in. **61.** 378 m^2

Lesson 12-5

1. 75 in^3 **3.** 62.4 m^3 **5.** 51.3 in^3 **7.** 28.1 mm^3 **9.** 513,333.3 ft^3

(11) $V = \frac{1}{3}Bh$ — Volume of a pyramid
$= \frac{1}{3}(36.9)(8.6)$ — $B = \frac{1}{2} \cdot 9 \cdot 8.2$ or 36.9, $h = 8.6$
≈ 105.8 mm^3 — Simplify.

13. 233.8 cm^3 **15.** 35.6 cm^3 **17.** 235.6 in^3 **19.** 1473.1 cm^3 **21.** 1072.3 in^3

(23) $V = \frac{1}{3}\pi r^2 h$ — Volume of a cone
$= \frac{1}{3}\pi(4)^2(14)$ — Replace r with $\frac{8}{2}$ or 4 and h with 14.
≈ 234.6 cm^3 — Use a calculator.

25. 32.2 ft^3 **27.** 3190.6 m^3 **29.** about 13,333 BTUs **31a.** The volume is doubled. **31b.** The volume is multiplied by 2^2 or 4. **31c.** The volume is multiplied by 2^3 or 8.

(33) $V = \frac{1}{3}\pi r^2 h$ — Volume of a cone
$196\pi = \frac{1}{3}\pi r^2(12)$ — Replace V with 196π and h with 12.
$196\pi = 4\pi r^2$ — Simplify.
$49 = r^2$ — Divide each side by 4π.
$7 = r$ — Take the square root of each side.

The radius of the cone is 7 inches, so the diameter is $7 \cdot 2$ or 14 inches.

35a. Sample answer:

35b. The volumes are the same. The volume of a pyramid equals one third times the base area times the height. So, if the base areas of two pyramids are equal and their heights are equal, then their volumes are equal. **35c.** If the base area is multiplied by 5, the volume is multiplied by 5. If the height is multiplied by 5, the volume is multiplied by 5. If both the base area and the height are multiplied by 5, the volume is multiplied by $5 \cdot 5$ or 25. **37.** Cornelio; Alexandra incorrectly used the slant height. **39.** Sample answer: A square pyramid with a base area of 16 and a height of 12, a prism with a square base of area 16 and height of 4; if a pyramid and prism have the same base, then in order to have the same volume, the height of the pyramid must be 3 times as great as the height of the prism. **41.** A **43.** F **45.** 1008.0 in^3 **47.** 426,437.6 m^3 **49.** 30.4 cm^2 **51.** 26.6 ft^2

Lesson 12-6

1. 1017.9 m^2 **3.** 452.4 yd^2 **5.** 4188.8 ft^3 **7.** 3619.1 m^3 **9.** 277.0 in^2 **11.** 113.1 cm^2 **13.** 680.9 in^2 **15.** 128 ft^2 **17.** 530.1 mm^2

(19) $V = \frac{4}{3}\pi r^3$ — Volume of a sphere
$= \frac{4}{3}\pi(1)^3$ — $r = \frac{2}{2}$ or 1
≈ 4.2 cm^3 — Use a calculator.

21. 2712.3 cm^3 **23.** 179.8 in^3 **25.** 77.9 m^3 **27.** 860,289.5 ft^3

(29) Surface area $= \frac{1}{2} \cdot$ Area of sphere + Lateral area of cylinder + Area of circle
$= \frac{1}{2}(4\pi r^2) + 2\pi rh + \pi r^2$
$= \frac{1}{2}(4\pi)(4)^2 + 2\pi(4)(5) + \pi(4)^2$
≈ 276.5 in^2

Volume = Volume of hemisphere + Volume of cylinder
$= \frac{1}{2}\left(\frac{4}{3}\pi r^3\right) + \pi r^2 h$
$= \frac{1}{2}\left(\frac{4}{3}\pi \cdot 4^3\right) + \pi(4)^2(5)$
≈ 385.4 in^3

31a. 594.6 cm^2; 1282.8 cm^3 **31b.** 148.7 cm^2; 160.4 cm^3 **33.** $\overline{DC}$ **35.** $\overline{AB}$ **37.** $\odot S$ **39a.** $\sqrt{r^2 - x^2}$ **39b.** $\pi\left(\sqrt{r^2 - x^2}\right)^2 \cdot y$ or $\pi y r^2 - \pi y x^2$ **39c.** The volume of the disc from the cylinder is $\pi r^2 y$ or $\pi y r^2$. The volume of the disc from the two cones is $\pi x^2 y$ or $\pi y x^2$. Subtract the volumes of the discs from the cylinder and cone to get $\pi y r^2 - \pi y x^2$, which is the expression for the volume of the disc from the sphere at height x. **39d.** Cavalieri's Principle **39e.** The volume of the cylinder is $\pi r^2(2r)$ or $2\pi r^3$. The volume of one cone is $\frac{1}{3}\pi r^2(r)$ or $\frac{1}{3}\pi r^3$, so the volume of the double napped cone is $2 \cdot \frac{1}{3}\pi r^3$ or $\frac{2}{3}\pi r^3$. Therefore, the volume of the hollowed out cylinder, and thus the sphere, is $2\pi r^3 - \frac{2}{3}\pi r^3$ or $\frac{4}{3}\pi r^3$.

(41) Vertical: There is an infinite number of vertical planes that produce reflection symmetry. When any vertical plane intersects the hemisphere through a diameter, both sides of the hemisphere are mirror images. Horizontal: There are no horizontal planes that produce reflection symmetry. When any horizontal plane intersects the hemisphere, the part on top will always be slightly smaller than the bottom. Rotation: There is an infinite number of angles of rotation. When the axis of rotation passes through the center of the sphere perpendicular to its base, the hemisphere can be mapped onto itself by a rotation of any angle between 0° and 360° in the axis.

(43) The surface area is divided by 3^2 or 9. The volume is divided by 3^3 or 27. **45.** 587.7 in^3

47.

49. 68.6 **51.** H **53.** 58.9 ft^3 **55.** 232.4 m^3 **57.** 154.2 units^2 **59.** 80.2 units^2 **61.** 21 units^2 **63.** D, B, and G **65.** $\overleftrightarrow{EF}$ and $\overleftrightarrow{AB}$ do not intersect. $\overleftrightarrow{AB}$ lies in plane $\mathcal{P}$, but only E lies in plane $\mathcal{P}$.

Lesson 12-7

1. $\overleftrightarrow{DH}$, $\overleftrightarrow{FJ}$ **3.** $\triangle JKQ$, $\triangle LMP$

(5) Figure x does not go through the poles of the sphere. So, figure x is not a great circle and so not a line in spherical geometry.

7. The points on any great circle or arc of a great circle can be put into one-to-one correspondence with real numbers. **9.** Sample answers: $\overleftrightarrow{WZ}$ and $\overleftrightarrow{XY}$, $\overleftrightarrow{RY}$ or $\overline{TZ}$, $\triangle RST$ or $\triangle MPL$ **11a.** $\overleftrightarrow{AD}$ and $\overleftrightarrow{FC}$ **11b.** Sample answers: $\overline{BG}$ and $\overline{AH}$ **11c.** Sample answers: $\triangle BCD$ and $\triangle ABF$ **11d.** $\overline{QD}$ and $\overline{BL}$ **11e.** $\overleftrightarrow{MJ}$ **11f.** $\overleftrightarrow{MB}$ and $\overleftrightarrow{KF}$ **13.** no

(15) Every great circle (line) is finite and returns to its original starting point. Thus, there exists no great circle that goes on infinitely in two directions.

17. Yes; If three points are collinear, any one of the three points is between the other two. **19.** 14.0 in.; since 100 degrees is $\frac{5}{18}$ of 360 degrees, $\frac{5}{18}$ × circumference of the great circle ≈ 14.0. **21a.** about 913 mi; the cities are 13.2° apart on the same great circle, so $\frac{13.2}{360} \times 2\pi \times 3963$ give the distance between them. **21b.** Yes; sample answer: Since the cities lie on a great circle, the distance between the cities can be expressed as the major arc or the minor arc. The sum of the two values is the circumference of Earth. **21c.** No; sample answer:

Since lines of latitude do not go through opposite poles of the sphere, they are not great circles. Therefore, the distance cannot be calculated in the same way. **21d.** Sample answer: Infinite locations. If Phoenix were a point on the sphere, then there are infinite points that are equidistant from that point.

23 **a.** No; if $\overline{CD}$ were perpendicular to $\overline{DA}$, then $\overline{DA}$ would be parallel to $\overline{CB}$. This is not possible, since there are no parallel lines in spherical geometry. **b.** $DA < CB$ because $\overline{CB}$ appears to lie on a great circle. **c.** No; since there are no parallel lines in spherical geometry, the sides of a figure cannot be parallel. So, a rectangle, as defined in Euclidean geometry, cannot exist in non-Euclidean geometry.

25. Sample answer: In plane geometry, the sum of the measures of the angles of a triangle is 180. In spherical geometry, the sum of the measures of the angles of a triangle is greater than 180. In hyperbolic geometry, the sum of the measures of the angles of a triangle is less than 180. **27.** Sometimes; sample answer: Since small circles cannot go through opposite poles, it is possible for them to be parallel, such as lines of latitude. It is also possible for them to intersect when two small circles can be drawn through three points, where they have one point in common and two points that occur on one small circle and not the other.

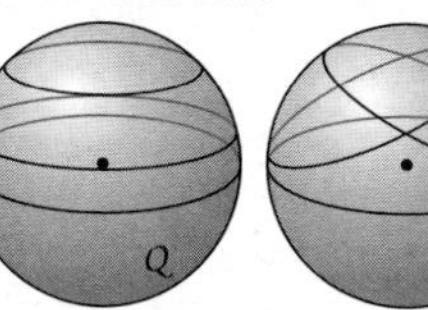

29. False; sample answer; Spherical geometry is non-Euclidean, so it cannot be a subset of Euclidean geometry. **31.** C **33.** Sample answer: $\overline{BC}$ **35.** 735.4 m^3 **37.** 1074.5 cm^3 **39.** 78.5 m^3 **41.** 0.1 m^3 **43.** 2.7 cm^2 **45.** 322.3 m^2

Lesson 12-8

1. similar; 4:3 **3.** 4:25 **5.** 220,893.2 cm^3 **7.** neither **9.** similar; 6:5

11 $\frac{\text{height of large cylinder}}{\text{height of small cylinder}} = \frac{35}{25}$ or $\frac{7}{5}$

The scale factor is $\frac{7}{5}$. If the scale factor is $\frac{a}{b}$, then the ratio of volumes is $\frac{a^3}{b^3} = \frac{7^3}{5^3}$ or $\frac{343}{125}$. So, the ratio of the volumes is 343:125.

13. 5:1 **15a.** 10:13 **15b.** 419.6 cm^3

17 scale factor $= \frac{26 \text{ ft}}{14 \text{ in.}}$ — Write a ratio comparing the lengths.

$= \frac{312 \text{ in.}}{14 \text{ in.}}$ — 26 ft = 26 • 12 or 312 in.

$= \frac{156}{7}$ — Simplify.

The scale factor is 156:7.

19. 4.1 in. **21.** 2439.6 cm^3 **23.** about 5.08 to 1

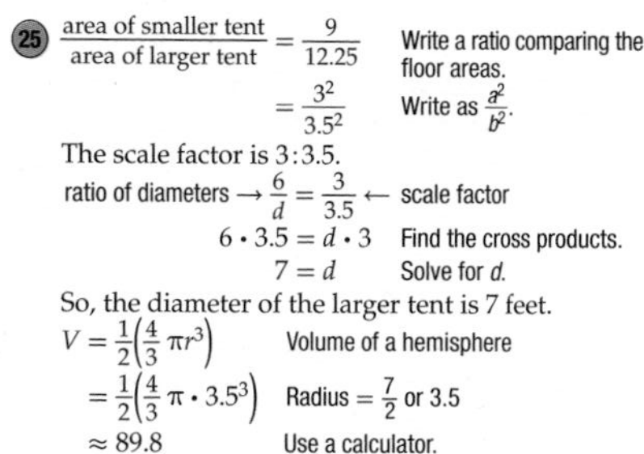

25 $\frac{\text{area of smaller tent}}{\text{area of larger tent}} = \frac{9}{12.25}$ — Write a ratio comparing the floor areas.

$= \frac{3^2}{3.5^2}$ — Write as $\frac{a^2}{b^2}$.

The scale factor is 3:3.5.

ratio of diameters $\rightarrow \frac{6}{d} = \frac{3}{3.5} \leftarrow$ scale factor

$6 \cdot 3.5 = d \cdot 3$ — Find the cross products.

$7 = d$ — Solve for d.

So, the diameter of the larger tent is 7 feet.

$V = \frac{1}{2}\left(\frac{4}{3}\pi r^3\right)$ — Volume of a hemisphere

$= \frac{1}{2}\left(\frac{4}{3}\pi \cdot 3.5^3\right)$ — Radius $= \frac{7}{2}$ or 3.5

≈ 89.8 — Use a calculator.

The volume of the larger tent is about 89.8 ft^3.

27. Laura; because she compared corresponding parts of the similar figures. Paloma incorrectly compared the diameter of X to the radius of Y. **29.** Since the scale factor is 15:9 or 5:3, the ratio of the surface areas is 25:9 and the ratio of the volumes is 125:27. So, the surface area of the larger prism is $\frac{25}{9}$ or about 2.8 times the surface area of the smaller prism. The volume of the larger prism is $\frac{125}{27}$ or about 4.6 times the volume the smaller prism. **31.** 14 cm **33.** B **35.** $\sqrt{85} \approx 9.2$ km **37.** yes **39.** yes **41.** 5 **43.** 6 **45.** 0.31 **47.** 0.93

Chapter 12 Study Guide and Review

1. false, Spherical geometry **3.** false, right cone **5.** true **7.** true **9.** true **11.** triangle **13.** rectangle **15.** Sample answer: 160 ft^2; 202 ft^2 **17.** 113.1 cm^2; 169.6 cm^2 **19.** 354.4 cm^2; 432.9 cm^2 **21.** 972 cm^3 **23.** 3.6 cm^3 **25.** 91,636,272 ft^3 **27.** 1017.9 m^2 **29.** 1708.6 in^3 **31.** $\overleftrightarrow{FG}$, $\overleftrightarrow{DJ}$ **33.** $\triangle CBD$ **35.** $\overline{KC}$ **37.** no **39.** congruent **41.** neither

CHAPTER 13 Probability and Measurement

Chapter 13 Get Ready

1. $\frac{7}{8}$ **3.** $1\frac{11}{40}$ **5.** $\frac{3}{8}$ **7.** 144 **9.** $\frac{1}{2}$ or 50% **11.** $\frac{1}{3}$ or 33% **13.** $\frac{1}{5}$ or 20% **15.** $\frac{11}{20}$ or 55%

Lesson 13-1

1. S, S O, O
S, O O, S

Outcomes	Safe	Out
Safe	S, S	S, O
Out	O, S	O, O

Outcomes
First Bat: S, O
Second Bat: S → S, O; O → S, O
Sample Space: S, S | S, O | O, S | O, O

3.
Outcomes
- Black
  - U: V, C — B, U, V, C; V, NC — B, U, V, NC; NV, C — B, U, NV, C
  - S: V, C — B, S, V, C; V, NC — B, S, V, NC; NV, C — B, S, NV, C
  - R: V, C — B, R, V, C; V, NC — B, R, V, NC; NV, C — B, R, NV, C
  - P: V, C — B, P, V, C; V, NC — B, P, V, NC; NV, C — B, P, NV, C
- Ivory
  - U: V, C — I, U, V, C; V, NC — I, U, V, NC; NV, C — I, U, NV, C
  - S: V, C — I, S, V, C; V, NC — I, S, V, NC; NV, C — I, S, NV, C
  - R: V, C — I, R, V, C; V, NC — I, R, V, NC; NV, C — I, R, NV, C
  - P: V, C — I, P, V, C; V, NC — i, P, V, NC; NV, C — I, P, NV, C

5 Possible Outcomes
= Appetizers × Soups × Salads × Entrees × Desserts
= 8 × 4 × 6 × 12 × 9 or 20,736

7. S, S N, N
S, N N, S

Outcomes	Smithsonian	Natural
Smithsonian	S, S	S, N
Natural	N, S	N, N

Outcomes
First Class: S, N
Second Class: S → S, N; N → S, N
Sample Space: S, S | S, N | N, S | N, N

9. M, 5 T, 5
M, 6 T, 6

Outcomes	5	6
Monday	M, 5	M, 6
Thursday	T, 5	T, 6

Outcomes
Day: M, T
Hour: M → 5, 6; T → 5, 6
Sample Space: M, 5 | M, 6 | T, 5 | T, 6

11. O, O A, A
O, A A, O

Outcomes	Oil	Acrylic
Oil	O, O	O, A
Acrylic	A, O	A, A

Outcomes
First Project: O, A
Second Project: O → O, A; A → O, A
Sample Space: O, O | O, A | A, O | A, A

13. S = sedan, T = truck, V = van, L = leather, F = fabric, P = CD player, NP = no CD player, R = sunroof, NR = no sunroof

Outcomes — Sample Space
- S
  - L: P — R: S, L, P, R; NR: S, L, P, NR; NP — R: S, L, NP, R; NR: S, L, NP, NR
  - F: P — R: S, F, P, R; NR: S, F, P, NR; NP — R: S, F, NP, R; NR: S, F, NP, NR
- T
  - L: P — R: T, L, P, R; NR: T, L, P, NR; NP — R: T, L, NP, R; NR: T, L, NP, NR
  - F: P — R: T, F, P, R; NR: T, F, P, NR; NP — R: T, F, NP, R; NR: T, F, NP, NR
- V
  - L: P — R: V, L, P, R; NR: V, L, P, NR; NP — R: V, L, NP, R; NR: V, L, NP, NR
  - F: P — R: V, F, P, R; NR: V, F, P, NR; NP — R: V, F, NP, R; NR: V, F, NP, NR

15 Possible Outcomes = Secretary × Treasurer × Vice President × President
= 3 × 4 × 5 × 2 or 120

17. 240 **19.** H = rhombus, P = parallelogram, R = rectangle, S = square, T = trapezoid; H, P; H, R; H, S; H, T; H, H; S, P; S, R; S, S; S, T; S, H

Outcomes	Rhombus	Square
Parallelogram	H, P	S, P
Rectangle	H, R	S, R
Square	H, S	S, S
Trapezoid	H, T	S, T
Rhombus	H, H	S, H

Outcomes
H → P, R, S, T, H; S → P, R, S, T, H
H, P | H, R | H, S | H, T | H, H | S, P | S, R | S, S | S, T | S, H

21. Sample answer: 6 different ways:
$4(x + 6) + 2(3) + 2(x + 4)$;

$2(x + 11) + 2(x + 8) + 2(x)$;
$2(x + 4) + 2(x + 9) + 2(x + 6)$;
$2(x) + 2(3) + 4(x + 8)$;
$2(x) + 2(x + 8) + 2(3) + 2(x + 8)$;
$2(x) + 2(3) + 2(4) + 2(x + 6) + 2(x + 6)$

23 **a.** The rolls that result in a sum of 8 are 2 and 6, 3 and 5, 4 and 4, 5 and 3, 6 and 2. So, there are 5 outcomes.
b. The rolls that result in an odd sum are shown.

1, 2   1, 4   1, 6
2, 1   2, 3   2, 5
3, 2   3, 4   3, 6
4, 1   4, 3   4, 5
5, 2   5, 4   5, 6
6, 1   6, 3   6, 5

So, there are 18 outcomes.

25. $n^3 - 3n^2 + 2n$; Sample answer: There are n objects in the box when you remove the first object, so after you remove one object, there are $n - 1$ possible outcomes. After you remove the second object, there are $n - 2$ possible outcomes. The number of possible outcomes is the product of the number of outcomes of each experiment or $n(n - 1)(n - 2)$.
27. Sample answer: You can list the possible outcomes for one stage of an experiment in the columns and the possible outcomes for the other stage of the experiment in the rows. Since a table is two dimensional, it would be impossible to list the possible outcomes for three or more stages of an experiment. Therefore, tables can only be used to represent the sample space for a two-stage experiment.
29. $P = n^k$; Sample answer: The total number of possible outcomes is the product of the number of outcomes for each of the stages 1 through k. Since there are k stages, you are multiplying n by itself k times which is n^k. **31.** B **33.** G **35.** 130 m high, 245 m wide, and 465 m long **37.** Sample answer: $\overline{FC}$
39. 1429.4 ft^2, 1737.3 ft^2 **41.** 1710.6 m^2, 3421.2 m^2
43. line **45.** 12.5 **47.** 12 **49.** 32

Lesson 13-2

1. $\frac{1}{20}$ **3.** $\frac{1}{420}$ **5.** $\frac{1}{124,750}$

7 The number of possible outcomes is 50!. The number of favorable outcomes is $(50 - 2)!$ or 48!.
P(Alfonso 14, Colin 23)

$= \frac{48!}{50!}$ $\frac{\text{Number of favorable outcomes}}{\text{Number of possible outcomes}}$

$= \frac{\cancel{48!}^{1}}{50 \cdot 49 \cdot \cancel{48!}_{1}}$ Expand 48! and divide out common factors.

$= \frac{1}{2450}$ Simplify.

9. $\frac{1}{15,120}$

11 There is a total of 10 letters. Of these letters, B occurs 2 times, A occurs 2 times, and L occurs 2 times. So, the number of distinguishable permutations of these letters is

$\frac{10!}{2! \cdot 2! \cdot 2!} = \frac{3,628,800}{8}$ or 453,600   Use a calculator.

There is only 1 favorable arrangement—BASKETBALL. So, the probability that a permutation of these letters selected at random spells basketball is $\frac{1}{453,600}$.

13. $\frac{1}{7}$ **15.** $\frac{1}{10,626}$ **17a.** $\frac{1}{56}$ **17b.** $\frac{1}{40,320}$ **17c.** $\frac{1}{140}$
17d. $\frac{2}{7}$ **19a.** 720 **19b.** 5040

21 Find the number of ways to choose the second letter times the number of ways to choose the third letter times the number of ways to choose the last two numbers.

possible license plates $= {}_2C_1 \cdot {}_3C_1 \cdot {}_{10}C_1 \cdot {}_{10}C_1$
$= 2 \cdot 3 \cdot 10 \cdot 10$ or 600

23. $\frac{13}{261}$ **25.** Sample answer: A bag contains seven marbles that are red, orange, yellow, green, blue, purple, and black. The probability that the orange, blue, and black marbles will be chosen if three marbles are drawn at random can be calculated using a combination.

27. $C(n, n - r) \stackrel{?}{=} C(n, r)$

$\frac{n!}{[n - (n - r)]!(n - r)!} \stackrel{?}{=} \frac{n!}{(n - r)!r!}$

$\frac{n!}{r!(n - r)!} \stackrel{?}{=} \frac{n!}{(n - r)!r!}$

$\frac{n!}{(n - r)!r!} = \frac{n!}{(n - r)!r!}$ ✓

29. C **31.** J **33.** 16 **35.** 2 **37.** 4.5 **39.** 3 **41.** 1 **43.** 5

Lesson 13-3

1. $\frac{1}{2}$, 0.5, or 50% **3.** $\frac{13}{33}$, 0.39, or about 39% **5.** $\frac{1}{8}$, 0.125, or 12.5% **7.** $\frac{13}{18}$, 0.72, or 72% **9.** $\frac{1}{9}$, 0.11, or 11%
11. $\frac{1}{6}$, 0.17, or about 17%

13 You need to find the ratio of the area of the shaded region to the area of the entire region. The area of shaded region equals the area of the large semicircle minus the area of the small semicircle plus the area of the small semicircle. So, the area of the shaded region equals the area of the large semicircle. Since the area of the large semicircle equals half the total area, P(landing in shaded region) $= \frac{1}{2}$, 0.5, or 50%.

15 P(pointer landing on yellow) $= \frac{44}{360}$ or about 12.2%

17. 69.4% **19.** 62.2% **21.** Sample answer: a point between 10 and 20 **23.** $\frac{1}{2}$, 0.5, or 50%
25. 53.5% **27.** Sample answer: The probability that a randomly chosen point will lie in the shaded region is ratio of the area of the sector to the area of the circle.

$P(\text{point lies in sector}) = \frac{\text{area of sector}}{\text{area of circle}}$

$\frac{x}{360} \stackrel{?}{=} \frac{\frac{x}{360} \cdot \pi r^2}{\pi r^2}$

$\frac{x}{360} = \frac{x}{360}$ ✓

29. 0.24 or 24% **31.** 0.33 or 33%

33 volume of shallow region $= Bh = (7 \cdot 20) \cdot 20$ or 2800 ft^3

volume of incline region $= Bh = \frac{1}{2}(25)(7 + 20) \cdot 20$ or 6750 ft^3

volume of deep region $= Bh = (20 \cdot 30) \cdot 20$ or 12,000 ft^3

P(bear swims in the incline region)

$= \frac{\text{volume of incline region}}{\text{volume of pool}}$

$= \frac{6750}{2800 + 6750 + 12,000}$

≈ 0.31 or 31%

35. 14.3% **37.** No; sample answer: Athletic events should not be considered random because there are other factors involved, such as pressure and ability, that have an impact on the success of the event.
39. Sample answer: The probability of a randomly chosen point lying in the shaded region of the square on the left is found by subtracting the area of the unshaded square from the area of the larger square and finding the ratio of the difference of the areas to the area of the larger square. The probability is $\frac{1^2 - 0.75^2}{1^2}$ or 43.75%. The probability of a randomly chosen point lying in the shaded region of the square on the right is the ratio of the area of the shaded square to the area of the larger square, which is $\frac{0.4375}{1}$ or 43.75%. Therefore, the probability of a randomly chosen point lying in the shaded area of either square is the same. **41.** F **43.** C

45. D, D   G, G
D, G   G, D

Outcomes	Drums	Guitar
Drums	D, D	D, G
Guitar	G, D	G, G

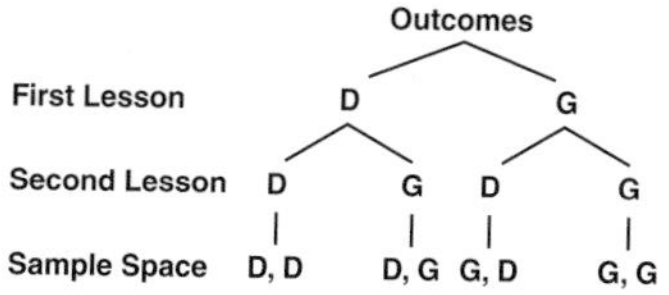

Outcomes

First Lesson: D, G
Second Lesson: D, G (from D); D, G (from G)
Sample Space: D, D   D, G   G, D   G, G

47. 45 **49.** Square; each angle intercepts a semicircle, making them 90° angles. Each side is a chord of congruent arcs, so the chords are congruent.
51. 57.1 m^2 **53.** 66.3 cm^2

Lesson 13-4

1. Sample answer: Use a spinner that is divided into two sectors, one containing 80% or 288° and the other containing 20% or 72°. Do 20 trials and record the results in a frequency table.

Outcome	Frequency
A	17
below an A	3
Total	20

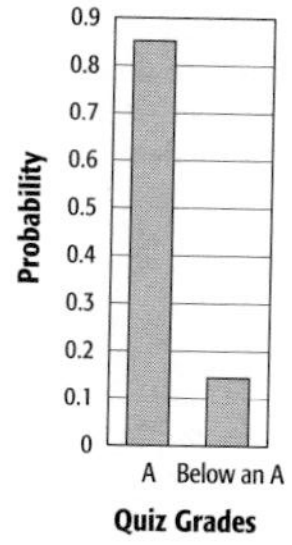

Probability
0.9
0.8
0.7
0.6
0.5
0.4
0.3
0.2
0.1
0
A   Below an A
Quiz Grades

The probability of Clara getting an A on her next quiz is 0.85. The probability of earning any other grade is $1 - 0.85$ or 0.15. **3a.** 36 **3b.** Sample answer: Use a random number generator to generate integers 1 through 25 where 1–16 represents 25 points, 17–24 represents 50 points, and 25 represents 100 points. Do 50 trials and record the results in a frequency table.

Outcome	Frequency
25	29
50	21
100	0

The average value is 35.5. **3c.** Sample answer: The expected value and average value are very close.

5 Sample answer: Use a spinner that is divided into two sectors, one containing 95% or 342° and the other containing 5% or 18°.
Sale: 95% of 360 = 342°
No Sale: 5% of 360 = 18°
Do 50 trials and record the results in a frequency table.

Outcome	Frequency
sale	46
no sale	4
Total	50

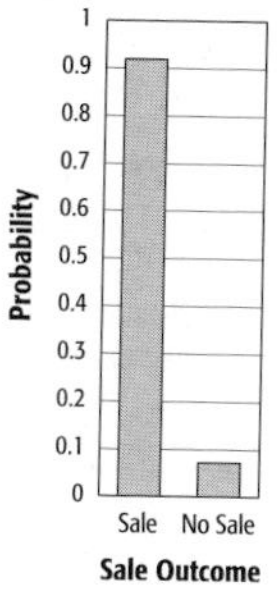

Probability
1
0.9
0.8
0.7
0.6
0.5
0.4
0.3
0.2
0.1
0
Sale   No Sale
Sale Outcome

Based on the simulation, the experimental probability of Ian selling a game is 0.92. The experimental probability of not selling a game is $1 - 0.92$ or 0.08.

7. Sample answer: Use a spinner that is divided into 8 equal sectors, each 45°. Do 50 trials and record the results in a frequency table.

Outcome	Frequency
Category 1	3
Category 2	3
Category 3	6
Category 4	13
Category 5	4
Category 6	9
Category 7	7
Category 8	5
Total	50

Selected Answers and Solutions

The probability of landing on Categories 1 and 2 is 0.06, Category 3 is 0.12, Category 4 is 0.26, Category 5 is 0.08, Category 6 is 0.18, Category 7 is 0.14, and Category 8 is 0.1.

9. Sample answer: Use a random number generator to generate integers 1 through 20, where 1–12 represents a single, 13–17 represents a double, 18–19 represents a triple, and 20 represents a home run. Do 20 trials and record the results in a frequency table.

Outcome	Frequency
single	13
double	4
triple	2
home run	1
Total	20

The probability of the baseball player hitting a single is 0.65, a double is 0.2, a triple is 0.1, and a home run is 0.05.

11. Sample answer: Use a random number generator to generate integers 1 through 20, where 1–7 represents blue, 8–13 represents red, 14–16 represents white, 17–19 represents black, and 20 represents all other colors. Do 50 trials and record the results in a frequency table.

Outcome	Frequency
blue	17
red	14
black	7
white	10
other	2
Total	50

The probability of a customer buying a blue car is 0.34, buying a red car is 0.28, buying a black car is 0.14, buying a white car is 0.2, and any other color is 0.04.

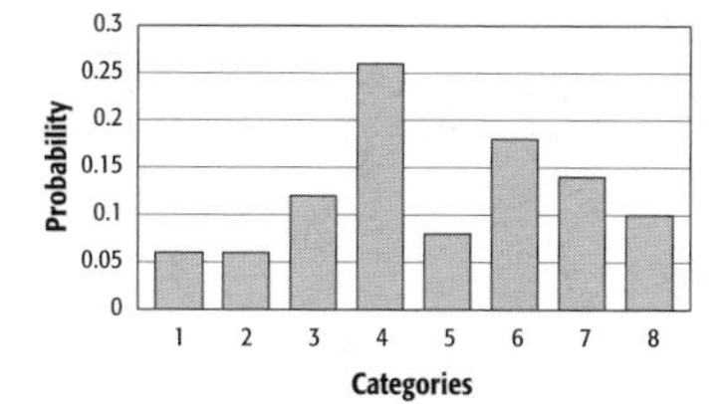

13 Calculate the geometric probability of landing on each color.

$P(\text{red}) = \frac{\text{area of red}}{\text{area of circle}}$

$= \frac{\pi(0.5)^2}{\pi(5)^2}$

$= 0.01$

The blue and white areas are equal. Their total area is the area of the large circle minus the area of the red circle or $\pi(5)^2 - \pi(0.5)^2$ or about 77.8 square units. So, the blue area and the white area are each about 38.9 square units.

$P(\text{blue}) = \frac{\text{area of blue}}{\text{area of circle}}$

$= \frac{38.9}{\pi(5)^2}$

≈ 0.495

$P(\text{white}) = P(\text{blue}) \approx 0.495$

$E(Y) = 25 \cdot 0.495 + 50 \cdot 0.495 + 0.01 \cdot 100$

$E(Y) = 38.125$

Sample answer: Assign the integers 1–1000 to accurately represent the probability data. Blue = integers 1–495, White = integers 496–990, Red = integers 991–1000. Use the calculator to generate 500 trials of random integers from 1 to 1000. Record the results in a frequency table.

Outcome	Frequency
red	0
blue	29
white	21
total	50

Then calculate the average value of the outcomes.

$\frac{0}{50} \cdot 100 + \frac{29}{50} \cdot 25 + \frac{21}{50} \cdot 50 = 35.5$

Average value = 35.5; the expected value is greater than the average value.

15a. 0.75 **15b.** Sample answer: Use a random number generator to generate integers 1 through 20, where 1–7 represents 0 points, 8–19 represents 1 point, and 20 represents 3 points. Do 50 trials and record the results in a frequency table; average value = 0.76.

Outcome	Frequency
0	16
1	32
3	2

15c. Sample answer: the two values are almost equal.

17a. There is a $\frac{1}{6}$ or 16.7% probability of throwing a strike in each box. **17b.** Sample answer:

Strike Area	Accuracy (%)
1	15
2	17
3	19
4	22
5	19
6	8
Total	100

17c. Sample answer: Some of the values are higher or lower, but most are very close to 16.7%.

19a. Sample answer:

Sum of Die Roll
9
10
6
6
7
9
5
9
5
7
6
5
7
3
9
7
6
7
8
7

19b. Sample answer:

Sum of Output from Random Number Generator
4
10
5
10
6
7
12
3
7
4
7
9
3
6
4
11
5
7
5
3

19c. Sample answer:

Trial	Sum of Die Roll	Sum of Output from Random Number Generator
1	9	4
2	10	10
3	6	5
4	6	10
5	7	6
6	9	7
7	5	12
8	9	3
9	5	7
10	7	4
11	6	7
12	5	9
13	7	3
14	3	6
15	9	4
16	7	11
17	6	5
18	7	7
19	8	5
20	7	3

19d. Sample answer:

Dice–5 Rolls

Dice–10 Rolls

Dice – 20 Rolls

19e. Sample answer: The bar graph has more data points at the middle sums as more trials are added.
19f. Sample answer:

Random Number Generator

19g. Sample answer: They both have the most data points at the middle sums. **19h.** Sample answer: The expected value in both experiments is 7 because it is the sum that occurs most frequently.

21 Sometimes; sample answer: Flipping a coin can be used to simulate and experiment with two possible outcomes when both of the outcomes are equally likely. For example, if there is an equal number of boys and girls in a class, then flipping a coin can be used to simulate choosing one person from the class. If the probabilities of the occurrence of the two outcomes are different, flipping a coin is not an appropriate simulation. For example, if 55% of the class is girls and 45% is boys, then flipping a coin cannot be used to simulate choosing one person from the class.

23. Sample answer: We assume that the object lands within the target area, and that it is equally likely that the object will land anywhere in the region. These are needed because in the real world it will not be

equally likely to land anywhere in the region.
25. Sample answer: Expectation, or expected value, deals with all possible events, while probability typically deals with only one event. Probability is the likelihood that an event will happen, is between 0 and 1 inclusive, and is typically expressed as a decimal, fraction, or percent. Expectation is the weighted average of all possible events and can take on any value, even a value that is not a possible outcome. For example, the likelihood of rolling a "1" with a six-sided die is 1 out of every 6 rolls. So, the probability is $\frac{1}{6}$ or about 17%. When the same die is rolled, the expectation is 3.5, which isn't even a possible outcome. **27.** H **29.** B **31.** $\frac{4}{7}$, 0.57, or 57% **33.** 50.3 ft^2 **35.** 1017.9 in^2

Lesson 13-5

1. The outcome of Jeremy taking the SAT in no way changes the probability of the outcome of his ACT test. Therefore, these two events are *independent*.
3. $\frac{1}{2704}$ or 3.7×10^{-4} **5.** $\frac{1}{5}$ or 0.20

7 These events are dependent since the card is not replaced.

$P(A \text{ and } A) = P(A) \cdot P(A|A)$ — Probability of dependent events

$= \frac{4}{52} \cdot \frac{3}{51}$ — After first ace is drawn, 51 cards remain, and 3 of those are aces.

$= \frac{12}{2652}$ or $\frac{1}{221}$ — Multiply.

The probability is $\frac{1}{221}$ or about 0.5%.

9. independent; $\frac{1}{36}$ or about 3% **11.** $\frac{1}{306}$ or about 0.3% **13.** $\frac{20}{161}$ or about 12% **15.** $\frac{1}{4}$ or 25% **17.** $\frac{1}{6}$ or 17%

19 $P(\text{own MP3 player} \mid \text{own CD player})$

$= \frac{P(\text{own MP3 player and CD player})}{P(\text{own CD player})}$

$= \frac{0.28}{0.43}$

≈ 0.65

21a.

1st Serve — 2nd Serve
Outcomes → 0.4 Serve — P(Serve) = 0.4
Outcomes → 0.6 Fault → 0.7 Serve — P(Fault, Serve) = 0.6 · 0.7 or 0.42
Outcomes → 0.6 Fault → 0.3 Fault — P(Fault, Fault) = 0.6 · 0.3 or 0.18

21b. 0.18 or 18% **21c.** Sample answer: I would use a random number generator to generate integers 1 through 50. The integers 1–9 will represent a double fault, and the integers 10–50 will represent the other possible outcomes. The simulation will consist of 50 trials.

23.

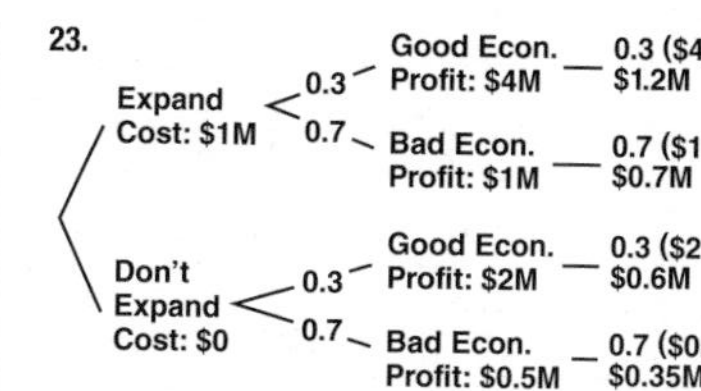

Sample answer: The expected value of choosing to expand is \$1.2M + \$0.7M or \$1.9M, and the expected value of choosing not to expand is \$0.95M. When we subtract the costs of expanding and of not expanding, we find the net expected value of expanding is \$1.9M − \$1M or \$0.9M and the net expected value of not expanding is \$0.95M − \$0 or \$0.95M. Since \$0.9M < \$0.95M, you should not expand the business.
25. *A* and *B* are independent events.
27. In order for the events to be independent, two things must be true: 1) the chance that a person smokes is the same as the chance that a person smokes given that the person's parent smokes, and 2) the chance that a person's parent smokes is the same as the chance that a person's parent smokes given that the person smokes. **29.** J **31.** B **33.** 0.25 **35.** 0.07 **37.** neither **39a.** 5026.5 ft **39b.** 500–600 ft **39c.** 3142 ft; 3770 ft **41.** 12 **43.** 216

Lesson 13-6

1. not mutually exclusive **3.** $\frac{2}{3}$ or about 67%

5. The probability of missing the spare is $\frac{8}{10}$ or 80%.

7. 17.3%

9 Since rolling two fours is both getting doubles and getting a sum of 8, the events are not mutually exclusive.

$P(\text{doubles or a sum of 8})$

$= P(\text{doubles}) + P(\text{a sum of 8}) - P(\text{doubles and a sum of 8})$

$= \frac{6}{36} + \frac{5}{36} - \frac{1}{36}$

$= \frac{10}{36}$ or about 27.8%

11. mutually exclusive; 100% **13.** mutually exclusive; $\frac{2}{9}$ or about 22.2% **15.** $\frac{7}{16}$ or about 43.8% **17.** $\frac{3}{4}$ or about 75% **19.** $\frac{7}{8}$ or about 87.5%

21 Find the probability that the first worker is paid by the hour plus the probability that that the second worker is paid by the hour. The probability that a worker is not paid by the hour is 1 − 0.71 or 0.29.

$P(\text{first paid}) + P(\text{second paid})$

$= P(\text{first paid}) \cdot P(\text{second not paid}) + P(\text{second paid}) \cdot P(\text{first not paid})$

$= 0.71(0.29) + 0.71(0.29)$

$\approx 0.21 + 0.21$ or 0.42

The probability is about 0.42 or 42%.

23. $\frac{1}{13}$ or 7.7% **25.** $\frac{3}{13}$ or 23.1%

27a. 71.3% **27b.** 11.3% **27c.** 36.2% **27d.** 3.8%
29. 0.74; sample answer: There are three outcomes in which the values of two or more of the dice are less than or equal to 4 and one outcome where the values of all three of the dice are less than or equal to 4. You have to find the probability of each of the four scenarios and add them together. **31.** Not mutually exclusive; sample answer: If a triangle is equilateral, it is also equiangular. The two can never be mutually exclusive. **33.** Sample answer: If you pull a card from a deck, it can be either a 3 or a 5. The two events are mutually exclusive. If you pull a card from a deck, it can be a 3 and it can be red. The two events are not mutually exclusive. **35.** D **37.** J **39.** dependent; $\frac{1}{221}$ or 0.5%

41. Sample answer: Use a random number generator to generate integers 1 through 20 in which 1–7 represent football, 8–13 represent basketball, 14–17 represent soccer, and 18–20 represent volleyball. Do 20 trials, and record the results in a frequency table.

Outcome	Frequency
football	7
basketball	6
soccer	5
volleyball	2
Total	20

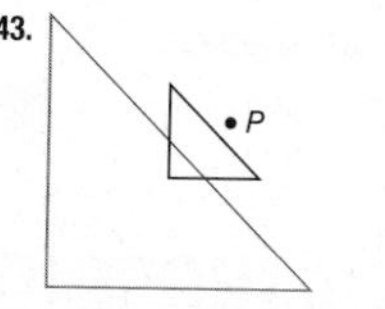

The probability that an athlete plays only football is 0.35, only basketball is 0.30, only soccer is 0.25, and only volleyball is 0.1.

43. [diagram: triangle with point P]

Chapter 13 Study Guide and Review

1. true **3.** true **5.** true **7.** true **9.** false, simulation **11.** S, NB; S, B; S, EB; M, NB; M, B; M, EB; L, NB; L, LB; L, EB

Outcomes	No Butter	Butter	Extra Butter
Small	S, NB	S, B	S, EB
Medium	N, NB	M, B	M, EB
Large	L, NB	L, B	L, EB

Outcomes — Sample Space
S: NB — S, NB; B — S, B; EB — S, EB
M: NB — M, NB; B — M, B; EB — M, EB
L: NB — L, NB; B — L, B; EB — L, EB

13. 4 **15.** 35,960 **17a.** $\frac{2}{9}$ **17b.** $\frac{7}{9}$ **19.** Sample answer: Use a spinner that is divided into 4 sectors, 108°, 79.2°, 82.8°, and 90°. Perform 50 trials and record the results in a frequency table. The results can be used to determine the probability of when a particular book will be purchased. **21.** $\frac{6}{35}$ **23.** 37% **25.** $\frac{4}{13}$

Glossary/Glosario

MultilingualeGlossary

Go to connectED.mcgraw-hill.com for a glossary of terms in these additional languages:

Arabic	Chinese	Hmong	Spanish	Vietnamese
Bengali	English	Korean	Tagalog	
Brazilian Portuguese	Haitian Creole	Russian	Urdu	

English

A

acute angle (p. 38) An angle with a degree measure less than 90.

$0 < m\angle A < 90$

acute triangle (p. 237) A triangle in which all of the angles are acute angles.

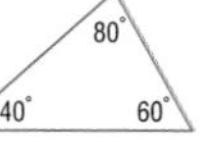

three acute angles

adjacent angles (p. 46) Two angles that lie in the same plane, have a common vertex and a common side, but no common interior points.

adjacent arcs (p. 708) Arcs in a circle that have exactly one point in common.

algebraic proof (p. 136) A proof that is made up of a series of algebraic statements. The properties of equality provide justification for many statements in algebraic proofs.

alternate exterior angles (p. 174) In the figure, transversal t intersects lines ℓ and m. $\angle 5$ and $\angle 3$, and $\angle 6$ and $\angle 4$ are alternate exterior angles.

Español

ángulo agudo Ángulo cuya medida en grados es menos de 90.

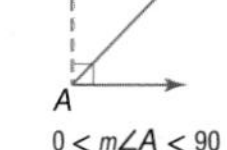

$0 < m\angle A < 90$

triángulo acutángulo Triángulo cuyos ángulos son todos agudos.

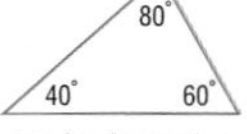

tres ángulos agudos

ángulos adyacentes Dos ángulos que yacen sobre el mismo plano, tienen el mismo vértice y un lado en común, pero ningún punto interior en común.

arcos adyacentes Arcos en un círculo que tienen un solo punto en común.

demostración algebraica Demostración que se realiza con una serie de enunciados algebraicos. Las propiedades de la igualdad proveen justificación para muchas enunciados en demostraciones algebraicas.

ángulos alternos externos En la figura, la transversal t interseca las rectas ℓ y m. $\angle 5$ y $\angle 3$, y $\angle 6$ y $\angle 4$ son ángulos alternos externos.

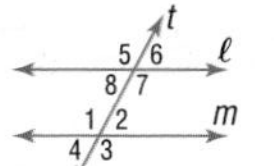

alternate interior angles (p. 174) In the figure at the bottom of page R115, transversal t intersects lines ℓ and m. $\angle 1$ and $\angle 7$, and $\angle 2$ and $\angle 8$ are alternate interior angles.

altitude **1.** (p. 337) In a triangle, a segment from a vertex of the triangle to the line containing the opposite side and perpendicular to that side. **2.** (p. 846) In a prism or cylinder, a segment perpendicular to the bases with an endpoint in each plane. **3.** (p. 854) In a pyramid or cone, the segment that has the vertex as one endpoint and is perpendicular to the base.

ambiguous case of the Law of Sines (p. 598) Given the measures of two sides and a nonincluded angle, there exist two possible triangles.

angle (p. 36) The intersection of two noncollinear rays at a common endpoint. The rays are called *sides* and the common endpoint is called the *vertex*.

angle bisector (p. 39) A ray that divides an angle into two congruent angles.

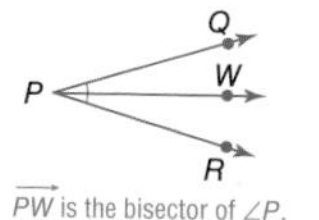

$\overrightarrow{PW}$ is the bisector of $\angle P$.

angle of depression (p. 580) The angle between the line of sight and the horizontal when an observer looks downward.

angle of elevation (p. 580) The angle between the line of sight and the horizontal when an observer looks upward.

angle of rotation (p. 640) The angle through which a preimage is rotated to form the image.

apothem (p. 807) A segment that is drawn from the center of a regular polygon perpendicular to a side of the polygon.

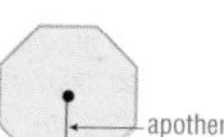

arc (p. 706) A part of a circle that is defined by two endpoints.

area (p. 58) The number of square units needed to cover a surface.

auxiliary line (p. 246) An extra line or segment drawn in a figure to help complete a proof.

axiom (p. 127) A statement that is accepted as true.

ángulos alternos internos En la figura anterior, la transversal t interseca las rectas ℓ y m. $\angle 1$ y $\angle 7$, y $\angle 2$ y $\angle 8$ son ángulos alternos internos.

altura **1.** En un triángulo, segmento trazado desde uno de los vértices del triángulo hasta el lado opuesto y que es perpendicular a dicho lado. **2.** En un prisma o un cilindro, segmento perpendicular a las bases con un extremo en cada plano. **3.** En una pirámide o un cono, segmento que tiene un extremo en el vértice y que es perpendicular a la base.

caso ambiguo de la ley de los senos Dadas las medidas de dos lados y de un ángulo no incluido, existen dos triángulos posibles.

ángulo La intersección de dos rayos no colineales en un extremo común. Las rayos se llaman *lados* y el punto común se llama *vértice*.

bisectriz de un ángulo Rayo que divide un ángulo en dos ángulos congruentes.

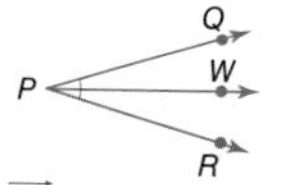

$\overrightarrow{PW}$ es la bisectriz del $\angle P$.

ángulo de depresión Ángulo formado por la horizontal y la línea de visión de un observador que mira hacia abajo.

ángulo de elevación Ángulo formado por la horizontal y la línea de visión de un observador que mira hacia arriba.

ángulo de rotación Ángulo a través del cual se rota una preimagen para formar la imagen.

apotema Segmento trazado desde el centro de un polígono regular hasta uno de sus lados y que es perpendicular a dicho lado.

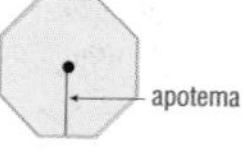

arco Parte d e un círculo definida por dos extremos.

área Número de unidades cuadradas para cubrir una superficie.

línea auxiliar Recta o segmento de recta adicional que es traza en una figura para ayudar a completar una demostración.

axioma Enunciado que se acepta como verdadero.

axis **1.** (p. 848) In a cylinder, the segment with endpoints that are the centers of the bases. **2.** (p. 856) In a cone, the segment with endpoints that are the vertex and the center of the base.

axis symmetry (p. 665) Symmetry in a three-dimensional figure that occurs if the figure can be mapped onto itself by a rotation between 0° and 360° in a line.

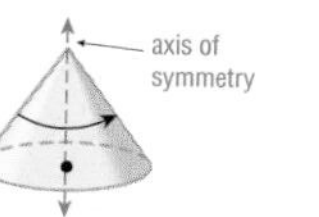

B

base angle of an isosceles triangle (p. 285) See *isosceles triangle* and isosceles trapezoid.

base edges (p. 846) The intersection of the lateral faces and bases in a solid figure.

base of parallelogram (p. 779) Any side of a parallelogram.

base of a polyhedron (p. 67) The two parallel congruent faces of a polyhedron.

between (p. 15) For any two points A and B on a line, there is another point C between A and B if and only if A, B, and C are collinear and $AC + CB = AB$.

betweenness of points (p. 15) See *between*.

biconditional (p. 116) The conjunction of a conditional statement and its converse.

C

center of circle (p. 697) The central point where radii form a locus of points called a circle.

center of dilation (p. 511) The center point from which dilations are performed.

center of rotation (p. 640) A fixed point around which shapes move in a circular motion to a new position.

center of symmetry (p. 664) See *point of symmetry*.

central angle (p. 706) An angle that intersects a circle in two points and has its vertex at the center of the circle.

eje **1.** En un cilindro, el segmento cuyos extremos son el centro de las bases. **2.** En un cono, el segmento cuyos extremos son el vértice y el centro de la base.

eje simetría Simetriá que ocurre en una figura tridimensional si la figura se puede aplicar sobre sí misma, mientras se gira entre 0° y 360° sobre una recta.

ángulo de la base de un triángulo isósceles Ver *triángulo isósceles* y trapecio isósceles.

aristas de las bases Intersección de las base con las caras laterales en una figura sólida.

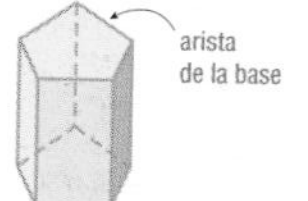

base de un paralelogramo Cualquier lado de un paralelogramo.

base de poliedro Las dos caras paralelas y congruentes de un poliedro.

entre Para cualquier par de puntos A y B de una recta, existe un punto C ubicado entre A y B si y sólo si A, B y C son colineales y $AC + CB = AB$.

intermediación de puntos Ver *entre*.

bicondicional Conjunción entre un enunciado condicional y su recíproco.

centro de un círculo Punto central desde el cual los radios forman un lugar geométrico de puntos llamado círculo.

centro de la homotecia Punto fijo en torno al cual se realizan las homotecias.

centro de rotación Punto fijo alrededor del cual gira una figura hasta alcanzar una posición dada.

centro de la simetría Vea *el punto de simetría*.

ángulo central Ángulo que interseca un círculo en dos puntos y cuyo vértice está en el centro del círculo.

central angle of a regular polygon (p. 807) An angle that has its vertex at the center of a polygon and with sides that pass through consecutive vertices of the polygon.

centroid (p. 335) The point of concurrency of the medians of a triangle.

chord **1.** (p. 697) For a given circle, a segment with endpoints that are on the circle. **2.** (p. 880) For a given sphere, a segment with endpoints that are on the sphere.

chord segments (p. 750) Segments that form when two chords intersect inside a circle.

circle (p. 697) The locus of all points in a plane equidistant from a given point called the *center* of the circle.

P is the center of the circle.

circular permutation (p. 925) A permutation of objects that are arranged in a circle or loop.

circumcenter (p. 325) The point of concurrency of the perpendicular bisectors of a triangle.

circumference (pp. 58, 699) The distance around a circle.

circumscribed (p. 700) A circle is circumscribed about a polygon if the circle contains all the vertices of the polygon.

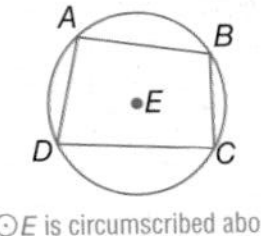

$\odot E$ is circumscribed about quadrilateral $ABCD$.

collinear (p. 5) Points that lie on the same line.

P, Q, and R are collinear.

combination (p. 926) An arrangement or listing in which order is not important.

common tangent (p. 732) A line or segment that is tangent to two circles in the same plane.

complement (p. 959) The complement of an event A consists of all the outcomes in the sample space that are not included as outcomes of event A.

complementary angles (p. 47) Two angles with measures that have a sum of 90.

ángulo central de un polígono regular Ángulo cuyo vértice esta en el centro del polígono y cuyos lados pasan por vértices consecutivas del polígono.

baricentro Punto de intersección de las medianas de un triángulo.

cuerda **1.** Para cualquier círculo, segmento cuyos extremos están en el círculo. **2.** Para cualquier esfera, segmento cuyos extremos están en la esfera.

segmentos de cuerda Segmentos que se forman cuando dos cuerdas se intersecan dentro de un círculo.

círculo Lugar geométrico formado por todos los puntos en un plano, equidistantes de un punto dado llamado *centro* del círculo.

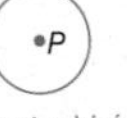

P es el centro del círculo.

permutación circular Permutación de objetos que se arreglan en un círculo o un bucle.

circuncentro Punto de intersección de las mediatrices de un triángulo.

circunferencia Distancia alrededor de un círculo.

circunscrito Un polígono está circunscrito a un círculo si todos sus vértices están contenidos en el círculo.

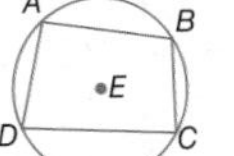

$\odot E$ está circunscrito al cuadrilátero $ABCD$.

colineal Puntos que yacen sobre la misma recta.

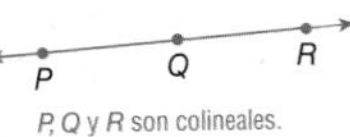

P, Q y R son colineales.

combinación Arreglo o lista en que el orden no es importante.

tangente común Recta o segmento de recta tangente a dos círculos en el mismo plano.

complemento El complemento de un evento A consiste en todos los resultados en el espacio muestral que no se incluyen como resultados del evento A.

ángulos complementarios Dos ángulos cuyas medidas suman 90.

component form (p. 602) A vector expressed as an ordered pair, ⟨change in x, change in y⟩.

composite figure (p. 809) A figure that can be separated into regions that are basic figures.

composite solid (p. 852) A three-dimensional figure that is composed of simpler figures.

composition of reflections (p. 652) Successive reflections in parallel lines.

composition of transformations (p. 651) The resulting transformation when a transformation is applied to a figure and then another transformation is applied to its image.

compound event (p. 947) An event that consists of two or more simple events.

compound statement (p. 99) A statement formed by joining two or more statements.

concave polygon (p. 56) A polygon for which there is a line containing a side of the polygon that also contains a point in the interior of the polygon.

concentric circles (p. 698) Coplanar circles with the same center.

conclusion (p. 107) In a conditional statement, the statement that immediately follows the word *then*.

concurrent lines (p. 325) Three or more lines that intersect at a common point.

conditional probability (p. 949) The probability of an event under the condition that some preceding event has occurred.

conditional statement (p. 107) A statement that can be written in *if-then* form.

cone (p. 67) A solid with a circular base, a vertex not contained in the same plane as the base, and a lateral surface area composed of all points in the segments connecting the vertex to the edge of the base.

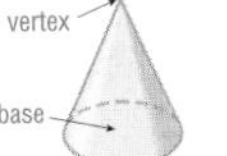

congruence transformations (p. 296) A mapping for which a geometric figure and its image are congruent.

congruent (pp. 16, 255) Having the same measure.

congruent arcs (p. 707) Arcs in the same circle or in congruent circles that have the same measure.

componente Vector expresado en forma de par ordenado, ⟨cambio en x, cambio en y⟩.

figura compuesta Figura que se puede separar en regiones formas de figuras básicas.

solido compuesto Figura tridimensional formada por figuras más simples.

composición de reflexiones Reflexiones sucesivas en rectas paralelas.

composición de transformaciones Transformación que resulta cuando se aplica una transformación a una figura y luego se le aplica otra transformación a su imagen.

evento compuesto Evento que consiste de dos o más eventos simples.

enunciado compuesto Enunciado formado por la unión de dos o más enunciados.

polígono cóncavo Polígono para el cual existe una recta que contiene un lado del polígono y un punto en el interior del polígono.

círculos concéntricos Círculos coplanarios con el mismo centro.

conclusión Parte de un enunciado condicional que está escrito justo después de la palabra *entonces*.

rectas concurrentes Tres o más rectas que se intersecan en un punto común.

probabilidad condicional La probabilidad de un acontecimiento bajo condición que ha ocurrido un cierto acontecimiento precedente.

enunciado condicional Enunciado escrito en la forma *si-entonces*.

cono Sólido de base circular cuyo vértice no yace en el mismo plano que la base y cuya área de superficie lateral está formada por todos los puntos en los segmentos que conectan el vértice con el bonde de la base.

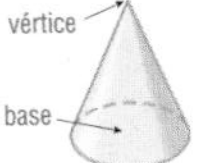

transformaciones de congruencia Aplicación en la cual una figura geométrica y su imagen son congruentes.

congruente Que tienen la misma medida.

arcos congruentes Arcos que tienen la misma medida y que pertenecen al mismo círculo o a círculos congruentes.

congruent polygons (p. 255) Polygons in which all matching parts are congruent.

congruent solids (p. 896) Two solids with the same shape, size and scale factor of 1:1.

conic section (p. 764) Any figure that can be obtained by slicing a cone.

conjecture (p. 91) An educated guess based on known information.

conjunction (p. 99) A compound statement formed by joining two or more statements with the word *and.*

consecutive interior angles (p. 174) In the figure, transversal t intersects lines ℓ and m. There are two pairs of consecutive interior angles: $\angle 8$ and $\angle 1$, and $\angle 7$ and $\angle 2$.

construction (p. 17) A method of creating geometric figures without the benefit of measuring tools. Generally, only a pencil, straightedge, and compass are used.

contrapositive (p. 109) The statement formed by negating both the hypothesis and conclusion of the converse of a conditional statement.

converse (p. 109) The statement formed by exchanging the hypothesis and conclusion of a conditional statement.

convex polygon (p. 56) A polygon for which there is no line that contains both a side of the polygon and a point in the interior of the polygon.

coordinate proofs (p. 303) Proofs that use figures in the coordinate plane and algebra to prove geometric concepts.

coplanar (p. 5) Points that lie in the same plane.

corner view (p. 839) The view from a corner of a three-dimensional figure, also called the *isometric view.*

corollary (p. 249) A statement that can be easily proved using a theorem is called a corollary of that theorem.

polígonos congruentes Polígonos cuyas partes correspondientes son todas congruentes.

sólidos congruentes Dos sólidos con la misma forma, tamaño y factor de escala de 1:1.

sección cónica Cualquier figura obtenida mediante el corte de un cono doble.

conjetura Juicio basado en información conocida.

conjunción Enunciado compuesto que se obtiene al unir dos o más enunciados con la palabra *y.*

ángulos internos consecutivos En la figura, la transversal t interseca las rectas ℓ y m. La figura presenta dos pares de ángulos internos consecutivos; $\angle 8$ y $\angle 1$; y $\angle 7$ y $\angle 2$.

construcción Método para dibujar figuras geométricas sin el uso de instrumentos de medición. En general, sólo requiere de un lápiz, una regla y un compás.

antítesis Enunciado formado por la negación tanto de la hipótesis como de la conclusión del recíproco de un enunciado condicional.

recíproco Enunciado que se obtiene al intercambiar la hipótesis y la conclusión de un enunciado condicional dado.

polígono convexo Polígono para el cual no existe recta alguna que contenga un lado del polígono y un punto en el interior del polígono.

demostraciones en coordinadas Demostraciones que usan figuras en el plano de coordinados y álgebra para demostrar conceptos geométricos.

coplanar Puntos que yacen en el mismo plano.

vista de esquina Vista desde una de las esquinas de una figura tridimensional. También se conoce como *vista en perspectiva.*

corolario Un enunciado que se puede demostrar fácilmente usando un teorema se conoce como corolario de dicho teorema.

corresponding angles (p. 174) In the figure, transversal t intersects lines ℓ and m. There are four pairs of corresponding angles: $\angle 5$ and $\angle 1$, $\angle 8$ and $\angle 4$, $\angle 6$ and $\angle 2$, and $\angle 7$ and $\angle 3$.

corresponding parts (p. 255) Matching parts of congruent polygons.

cosecant (p. 578) The reciprocal of the sine of an angle in a right triangle.

cosine (p. 568) For an acute angle of a right triangle, the ratio of the measure of the leg adjacent to the acute angle to the measure of the hypotenuse.

cotangent (p. 578) The ratio of the adjacent to the opposite side of a right triangle.

counterexample (p. 94) An example used to show that a given statement is not always true.

cross products (p. 462) In the proportion $\frac{a}{b} = \frac{c}{d}$, where $b \neq 0$ and $d \neq 0$, the cross products are ad and bc. The proportion is true if and only if the cross products are equal.

cross section (p. 840) The intersection of a solid and a plane.

cylinder (p. 67) A figure with bases that are formed by congruent circles in parallel planes.

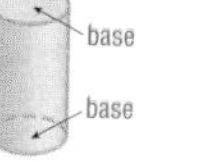

ángulos correspondientes En la figura, la transversal t interseca las rectas ℓ y m. La figura muestra cuatro pares de ángulos correspondientes: $\angle 5$ y $\angle 1$, $\angle 8$ y $\angle 4$, $\angle 6$ y $\angle 2$; y $\angle 7$ y $\angle 3$.

partes correspondientes Partes que coinciden de polígonos congruentes.

cosecante Recíproco del seno de un ángulo en un triángulo rectangulo.

coseno Para cualquier ángulo agudo de un triángulo rectángulo, razón de la medida del cateto adyacente al ángulo agudo a la medida de la hipotenusa.

cotangente Razón de la medida del cateto adyacente a la medida de cateto opuesto de un triángulo rectángulo.

contraejemplo Ejemplo que se usa para demostrar que un enunciado dado no siempre es verdadero.

productos cruzados En la proporción $\frac{a}{b} = \frac{c}{d}$, donde $b \neq 0$ y $d \neq 0$, los productos cruzados son ad y bc. La proporción es verdadera si y sólo si los productos cruzados son iguales.

sección transversal Intersección de un sólido con un plano.

cilindro Figura cuyas bases son círculos congruentes ubicados en planos paralelos.

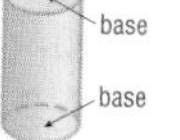

D

deductive argument (p. 129) A proof formed by a group of algebraic steps used to solve a problem.

deductive reasoning (p. 117) A system of reasoning that uses facts, rules, definitions, or properties to reach logical conclusions.

degree (p. 37) A unit of measure used in measuring angles and arcs. An arc of a circle with a measure of 1° is $\frac{1}{360}$ of the entire circle.

dependent events (p. 947) Two or more events in which the outcome of one event affects the outcome of the other events.

argumento deductivo Demostración que consta de un conjunto de pasos algebraicos que se usan para resolver un problema.

razonamiento deductivo Sistema de razonamiento que emplea hechos, reglas, definiciones o propiedades para obtener conclusiones lógicas.

grado Unidad de medida que se usa para medir ángulos y arcos. El arco de un círculo que mide 1° equivale a $\frac{1}{360}$ del círculo completo.

eventos dependientes Dos o más eventos en que el resultado de un evento afecta el resultado de los otros eventos.

diagonal (p. 393) In a polygon, a segment that connects nonconsecutive vertices of the polygon.

$\overline{SQ}$ is a diagonal.

diameter 1. (p. 697) In a circle, a chord that passes through the center of the circle. 2. (p. 880) In a sphere, a segment that contains the center of the sphere, and has endpoints that are on the sphere.

dilation (pp. 511, 674) A transformation that enlarges or reduces the original figure proportionally. A dilation with center C and positive scale factor k, $k \neq 1$, is a function that maps a point P in a figure to its image such that

- if point P and C coincide, then the image and preimage are the same point, or
- if point P is not the center of dilation, then P' lies on $\overrightarrow{CP}$ and $CP' = k(CP)$.

If $k < 0$, P' is the point on the ray opposite $\overrightarrow{CP}$ such that $CP' = |k|(CP)$.

direct isometry (p. 298) An isometry in which the image of a figure is found by moving the figure intact within the plane.

direction (p. 600) The measure of the angle that a vector forms with the positive x-axis or any other horizontal line.

directrix (p. 765) The fixed line in a parabola that is equidistant from the locus of all points in a plane.

disjunction (p. 100) A compound statement formed by joining two or more statements with the word *or*.

distance between two points (p. 25) The length of the segment between two points.

diagonal Recta que conecta vértices no consecutivos de un polígono.

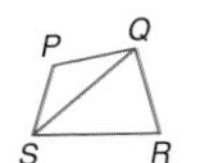

$\overline{SQ}$ es una diagonal.

diámetro 1. En un círculo cuerda que pasa por el centro. 2. En una estera segmento que incluye el centro de la esfera y cuyos extremos están ubicados en la esfera.

homotecia Transformación que amplía o disminuye proporcionalmente el tamaño de una figura. Una homotecia con centro C y factor de escala positivo k, $k \neq 1$, es una función que aplica un punto P a su imagen, de modo que si el punto P coincide con el punto C, entonces la imagen y la preimagen son el mismo punto, o si el punto P no es el centro de la homotecia, entonces P' yace sobre $\overrightarrow{CP}$ y $CP' = k(CP)$. Si $k < 0$, P' es el punto sobre el rayo opuesto a $\overrightarrow{CP}$, tal que $CP' = |k|(CP)$.

isometría directa Isometría en la cual se obtiene la imagen de una figura, al mover la figura intacta dentro del plano.

dirección Medida del ángulo que forma un vector con el eje x positivo o con cualquier otra recta horizontal.

directriz Línea fija en una parábola que está equidistante del lugar geométrico de todos los puntos en un plano.

disyunción Enunciado compuesto que se forma al unir dos o más enunciados con la palabra *o*.

distancia entre dos puntos Longitud del segmento entre dos puntos.

E

edge (p. 964) A line that connects two nodes in a network.

edge of a polyhedron (p. 67) A line segment where the faces of a polyhedron intersect.

efficient route (p. 965) The path in a network with the least weight.

enlargement (p. 511) An image that is larger that the original figure.

equiangular polygon (p. 57) A polygon with all congruent angles.

arista Recta que conecta dos nodos en una red.

arista de un poliedro Segmento de recta donde se intersecan las caras de un poliedro.

ruta eficiente Ruta en una red con el menor peso.

ampliación Imagen que es más grande que la figura original.

polígono equiangular Polígono cuyos ángulos son todos congruentes.

equiangular triangle (p. 237) A triangle with all angles congruent.

equidistant (p. 218) The distance between two lines measured along a perpendicular line is always the same.

equilateral polygon (p. 57) A polygon with all congruent sides.

equilateral triangle (p. 238) A triangle with all sides congruent.

equivalent vectors (p. 601) Vectors that have the same magnitude and direction.

Euclidean geometry (p. 889) A geometrical system in which a plane is a flat surface made up of points that extend infinitely in all directions.

expected value (p. 941) Also *mathematical expectation*, is the average value of a random variable that one expects after repeating an experiment or simulation an infinite number of times.

extended ratios (p. 461) Ratios that are used to compare three or more quantities.

exterior (p. 36) A point is in the exterior of an angle if it is neither on the angle nor in the interior of the angle.

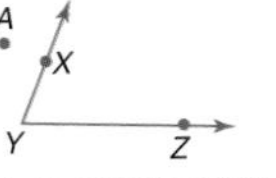

A is in the exterior of $\angle XYZ$.

exterior angle (p. 248) An angle formed by one side of a triangle and the extension of another side.

$\angle 1$ is an exterior angle.

exterior angles (p. 174) An angle that lies in the region that is not between two transversals that intersect the same line.

external secant segment (p. 752) A secant segment that lies in the exterior of the circle.

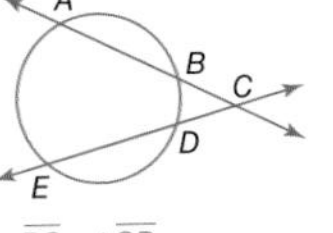

$\overline{BC}$ and $\overline{CD}$ are external secant segments.

extremes (p. 462) In $\frac{a}{b} = \frac{c}{d}$, the numbers a and d.

triángulo equiangular Triángulo cuyos ángulos son todos congruentes.

equidistante La distancia entre dos rectas que siempre permanece constante cuando se mide a lo largo de una perpendicular.

polígono equilátero Polígono cuyos lados son todos congruentes.

triángulo equilátero Triángulo cuyos lados son todos congruentes.

vectores iguales Vectores con la misma magnitud y dirección.

geometría euclidiana Sistema en el cual un plano es una superficie plana formada por puntos que se extienden infinitamente en todas las direcciones.

valor esperado También *expectativa matemática*, el valor promedio de una variable aleatoria que uno *espera* después de repetir un experimento o un simulacro un número infinito de veces.

razones extendmientes Razones que se utilizan para comparar tres o más cantidades.

exterior Un punto yace en el exterior de un ángulo si no se ubica ni en el ángulo ni en el interior del ángulo.

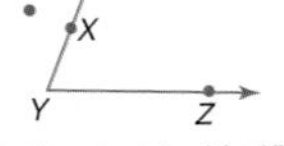

A está en el exterior del $\angle XYZ$.

ángulo externo Ángulo formado por un lado de un triángulo y la prolongación de otro de sus lados.

$\angle 1$ es un ángulo externo.

ángulos externos Un ángulo que está en la región que no está entre dos transversals que cruzan la misma línea.

segmento secante externo Segmento secante que yace en el exterior del círculo.

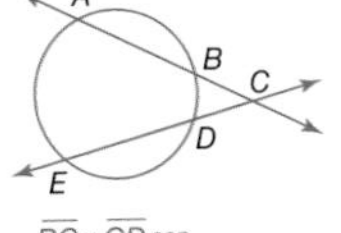

$\overline{BC}$ y $\overline{CD}$ son segmentos secantes externos.

extremos Los números a y d en $\frac{a}{b} = \frac{c}{d}$.

F

face of a polyhedron (p. 67) A flat surface of a polyhedron.

factorial (p. 922) The product of the integers less than or equal to a positive integer n, written as $n!$

finite plane (p. 10) A plane that has boundaries or does not extend indefinitely.

flow proof (p. 248) A proof that organizes statements in logical order, starting with the given statements. Each statement is written in a box with the reason verifying the statement written below the box. Arrows are used to indicate the order of the statements.

focus (p. 765) The fixed point in a parabola that is equidistant from the locus of all points in a plane.

formal proof (p. 137) A two-column proof containing statements and reasons.

fractal (p. 509) A figure generated by repeating a special sequence of steps infinitely often. Fractals often exhibit self-similarity.

frustum (p. 861) The part of a solid that remains after the top portion has been cut by a plane parallel to the base.

Fundamental Counting Principle (p. 917) A method used to determine the number of possible outcomes in a sample space by multiplying the number of possible outcomes from each stage or event.

cara de un poliedro Superficie plana de un poliedro.

factorial Producto de los enteros menores o iguales a un número positivo n, escrito como $n!$

plano finito Plano que tiene límites o que no se extiende indefinidamente.

demostración de flujo Demostración que organiza los enunciados en orden lógico, comenzando con los enunciados dados. Cada enunciado se escribe en una casilla y debajo de cada casilla se escribe el argumento que verifica dicho enunciado. El orden de los enunciados se indica con flechas.

foco Punto fijo en una parábola que está equidistante del lugar geométrico de todos los puntos en un plano.

demostración formal Demostración en dos columnas que contiene enunciados y razonamientos.

fractal Figura que se obtiene mediante la repetición infinita de una sucesión particular de pasos. Los fractales a menudo exhiben autosemejanza.

tronco Parte de un sólido que queda después de que la parte superior ha sido cortada por un plano paralelo a la base.

principio fundamental de contar Método para determinar el número de resultados posibles en un espacio muestral multiplicando el número de resultados posibles de cada etapa o evento.

G

geometric mean (p. 537) For any positive numbers a and b, the positive number x such that $\frac{a}{x} = \frac{x}{b}$.

geometric probability (p. 931) Using the principles of length and area to find the probability of an event.

glide reflection (p. 651) The composition of a translation followed by a reflection in a line parallel to the translation vector.

great circle (p. 881) A circle formed when a plane intersects a sphere with its center at the center of the sphere.

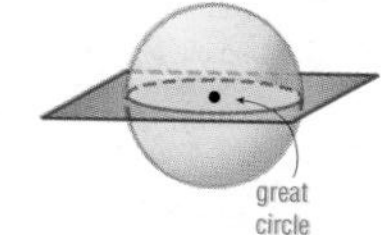

media geométrica Para todo número positivo a y b, existe un número positivo x tal que $\frac{a}{x} = \frac{x}{b}$.

probabilidad geométrica Uso de los principios de longitud y área para calcular la probabilidad de un evento.

reflexión del deslizamiento Composición de una traslación seguida por una reflexión en una recta paralela al vector de la traslación.

círculo mayor Círculo que se forma cuando un plano interseca una esfera y cuyo centro es el mismo que el centro de la esfera.

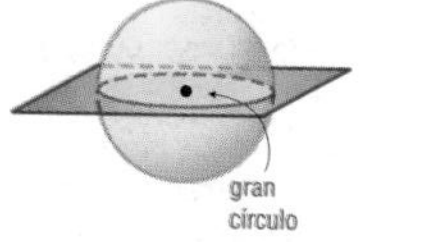

H

height of a parallelogram (p. 779) The length of an altitude of a parallelogram.

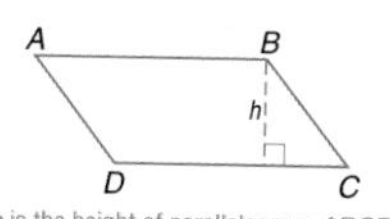

h is the height of parallelogram $ABCD$.

height of a trapezoid (p. 789) The perpendicular distance between the bases of a trapezoid.

h is the height of trapezoid $ABCD$.

height of a triangle (p. 781) The length of an altitude drawn to a given base of a triangle.

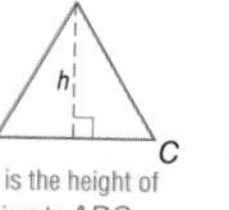

h is the height of triangle ABC.

hemisphere (p. 881) One of the two congruent parts into which a great circle separates a sphere.

hypothesis (p. 107) In a conditional statement, the statement that immediately follows the word *if*.

altura de un paralelogramo Longitud del segmento perpendicular que va desde la base hasta el vértice opuesto a ella.

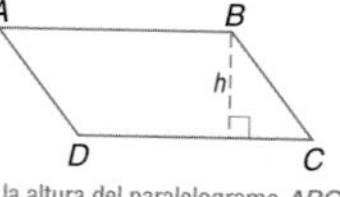

h es la altura del paralelogramo $ABCD$.

altura de un trapecio Distancia perpendicular entre las bases de un trapecio.

h es la altura del trapecio $ABCD$.

altura de un triángulo Longitud de una altura trazada a una base dada de un triángulo.

h es la altura de triángulo ABC.

hemisferio Una de las dos partes congruentes en las cuales un círculo mayor divide una esfera.

hipótesis Enunciado escrito inmediatamente después de la palabra *si* en un enunciado condicional.

I

if-then statement (p. 107) A compound statement of the form "if p, then q," where p and q are statements.

image (p. 296) A figure that results from the transformation of a geometric figure.

incenter (p. 328) The point of concurrency of the angle bisectors of a triangle.

included angle (p. 266) In a triangle, the angle formed by two sides is the included angle for those two sides.

included side (p. 275) The side of a polygon that is a side of each of two angles.

enunciado si-entonces Enunciado compuesto de la forma "si p, entonces q," donde p y q son enunciados.

imagen Figura que resulta de la transformación de una figura geométrica.

incentro Punto de intersección de las bisectrices interiores de un triángulo.

ángulo incluido En un triángulo, el ángulo formado por dos lados es el ángulo incluido de esos dos lados.

lado incluido Lado de un polígono común a dos de sus ángulos.

independent events (p. 947) Two or more events in which the outcome of one event does not affect the outcome of the other events.

indirect isometry (p. 298) An isometry that cannot be performed by maintaining the orientation of the points, as in a direct isometry.

indirect proof (p. 355) In an indirect proof, one assumes that the statement to be proved is false. One then uses logical reasoning to deduce that a statement contradicts a postulate, theorem, or one of the assumptions. Once a contradiction is obtained, one concludes that the statement assumed false must in fact be true.

indirect reasoning (p. 355) Reasoning that assumes that the conclusion is false and then shows that this assumption leads to a contradiction of the hypothesis like a postulate, theorem, or corollary. Then, since the assumption has been proved false, the conclusion must be true.

inductive reasoning (p. 91) Reasoning that uses a number of specific examples to arrive at a plausible generalization or prediction. Conclusions arrived at by inductive reasoning lack the logical certainty of those arrived at by deductive reasoning.

informal proof (p. 129) A paragraph proof.

inscribed (p. 700) A polygon is inscribed in a circle if each of its vertices lie on the circle.

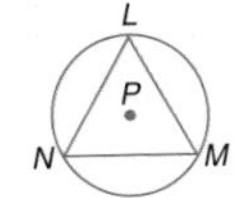

$\triangle LMN$ is inscribed in $\odot P$.

inscribed angle (p. 723) An angle that has a vertex on a circle and sides that contain chords of the circle.

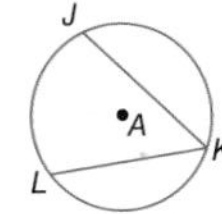

In $\odot A$, $\angle JKL$ is an inscribed angle.

intercepted arc (p. 723) An angle intercepts an arc if and only if each of the following conditions are met.
1. The endpoints of the arc lie on the angle.
2. All points of the arc except the endpoints are in the interior of the circle.
3. Each side of the angle has an endpoint of the arc.

eventos independientes El resultado de un evento no afecta el resultado del otro evento.

isometría indirecta Tipo de isometría que no se puede obtener manteniendo la orientación de los puntos, como ocurre con la isometría directa.

demostración indirecta En una demostración indirecta, se supone que el enunciado a demostrar es falso. Después, se deduce lógicamente que existe un enunciado que contradice un postulado, un teorema o una de las conjeturas. Una vez hallada una contradicción, se concluye que el enunciado que se suponía falso debe ser, en realidad, verdadero.

razonamiento indirecto Razonamiento en que primero se supone que la conclusión es falsa y luego se demuestra que esta conjetura lleva a una contradicción de la hipótesis como un postulado, un teorema o un corolario. Finalmente, como se ha demostrado que la conjetura es falsa, la conclusión debe ser verdadera.

razonamiento inductivo Razonamiento que usa varios ejemplos específicos para lograr una generalización o una predicción pausible. Las conclusiones obtenidas por razonamiento inductivo carecen de la certeza lógica de aquellas obtenidas por razonamiento deductivo.

demostración informal Demostración en forma de párrafo.

inscrito Un polígono está inscrito en un círculo si todos sus vértices yacen en el círculo.

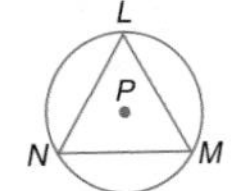

$\triangle LMN$ está inscrito en $\odot P$.

ángulo inscrito Ángulo cuyo vértice esté en un círculo y cuyos lados contienen cuerdas del círculo.

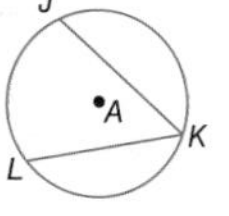

En $\odot A$, $\angle JKL$ es un ángulo inscrito.

arco intersecado Un ángulo interseca un arco si y sólo si se cumple cada una de las siguientes condiciones.
1. Los extremos del arco yacen en el ángulo.
2. Todos los puntos del arco, excepto los extremos, yacen en el interior del círculo.
3. Cada lado del ángulo tiene un extremo del arco.

interior (p. 36) A point is in the interior of an angle if it does not lie on the angle itself and it lies on a segment with endpoints that are on the sides of the angle.

M is in the interior of $\angle JKL$.

interior angles (p. 174) Angles that lie between two transversals that intersect the same line.

intersection (p. 6) A set of points common to two or more geometric figures.

inverse (p. 109) The statement formed by negating both the hypothesis and conclusion of a conditional statement.

inverse cosine (p. 571) The inverse function of cosine, or $\cos^{-1}$. If the cosine of an acute $\angle A$ is equal to x, then $\cos^{-1} x$ is equal to the measure of $\angle A$.

inverse sine (p. 571) The inverse function of sine, or $\sin^{-1}$. If the sine of an acute $\angle A$ is equal to x, then $\sin^{-1} x$ is equal to the measure of $\angle A$.

inverse tangent (p. 571) The inverse function of tangent, or $\tan^{-1}$. If the tangent of an acute $\angle A$ is equal to x, then $\tan^{-1} x$ is equal to the measure of $\angle A$.

irrational number (p. 26) A number that cannot be expressed as a terminating or repeating decimal.

irregular figure (p. 57) A polygon with sides and angles that are not all congruent.

isometric view (p. 839) Corner views of three-dimensional objects on two-dimensional paper.

isometry (p. 296) A mapping for which the original figure and its image are congruent.

isosceles trapezoid (p. 439) A trapezoid in which the legs are congruent, both pairs of base angles are congruent, and the diagonals are congruent.

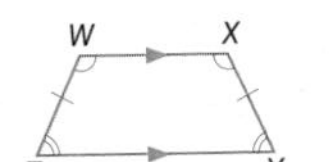

interior Un punto se encuentra en el interior de un ángulo si no yace en el ángulo como tal y si está en un segmento cuyos extremos están en los lados del ángulo.

M está en el interior del $\angle JKL$.

ángulos interiores Ángulos que yacen entre dos transversales que intersecan la misma recta.

intersección Conjunto de puntos comunes a dos o más figuras geométricas.

inverso Enunciado que se obtiene al negar tanto la hipótesis como la conclusión de un enunciado condicional.

inverso del coseno Función inversa del coseno, o $\cos^{-1}$. Si el coseno de un $\angle A$ agudo es igual a x, entonces $\cos^{-1} x$ es igual a la medida del $\angle A$.

inverso del seno Función inversa del seno, o $\sin^{-1}$. Si el seno de un $\angle A$ agudo es igual a x, entonces $\sin^{-1} x$ es igual a la medida del A.

inverse del tangente Función inversa de la tangente, o $\tan^{-1}$. Si la tangente de un $\angle A$ agudo es igual a x, entonces $\tan^{-1} x$ es igual a la medida del $\angle A$.

número irracional Número que no se puede expresar como un decimal terminal o periódico.

figura irregular Polígono cuyos lados y ángulos no son todo congruentes.

vista isométrica Vistas de las esquinas de sólidos geométricos tridimensionales sobre un papel bidimensional.

isometría Aplicación en la cual la figura original y su imagen son congruentes.

trapecio isósceles Trapecio cuyos catetos son congruentes, ambos pares de ángulos de las bases son congruentes y las diagonales son congruentes.

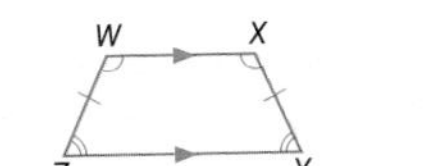

isosceles triangle (p. 238, 285) A triangle with at least two sides congruent. The congruent sides are called *legs*. The angles opposite the legs are *base angles*. The angle formed by the two legs is the *vertex angle*. The side opposite the vertex angle is the *base*.

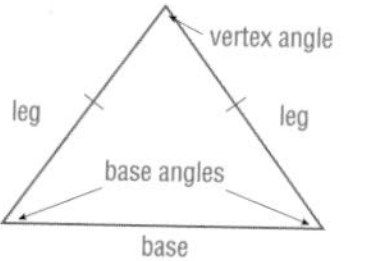

iteration (p. 509) A process of repeating the same procedure over and over again.

J

joint frequencies (p. 954) In a two-way frequency table, the frequencies reported in the cells in the interior of the table.

K

kite (p. 442) A quadrilateral with exactly two distinct pairs of adjacent congruent sides.

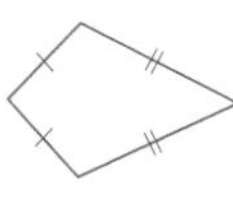

L

lateral area (p. 846) For prisms, pyramids, cylinders, and cones, the area of the faces of the figure not including the bases.

lateral edges **1.** (p. 846) In a prism, the intersection of two adjacent lateral faces. **2.** (p. 854) In a pyramid, lateral edges are the edges of the lateral faces that join the vertex to vertices of the base.

lateral faces **1.** (p. 846) In a prism, the faces that are not bases. **2.** (p. 854) In a pyramid, faces that intersect at the vertex.

latitude (p. 895) A measure of distance north or south of the equator.

Law of Cosines (p. 589) Let $\triangle ABC$ be any triangle with a, b, and c representing the measures of sides opposite the angles with measures A, B, and C respectively. Then the following equations are true.

$a^2 = b^2 + c^2 - 2bc \cos A$

$b^2 = a^2 + c^2 - 2ac \cos B$

$c^2 = a^2 + b^2 - 2ab \cos C$

triángulo isósceles Triángulo que tiene por lo menos dos lados congruentes. Los lados congruentes se llaman *catetos*. Los ángulos opuestos a los catetos son los *ángulos de la base*. El ángulo formado por los dos catetos es el *ángulo del vértice*. El lado opuesto al ángulo del vértice es la *base*.

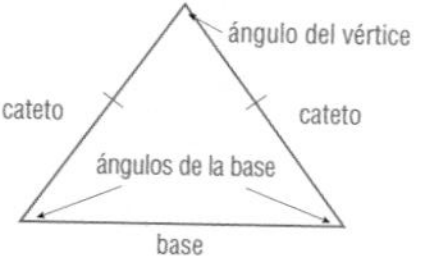

iteración Proceso de repetir el mismo procedimiento una y otra vez.

frecuencias conjuntas En una tabla de double entrada o de frecuencias, las frecuencias reportadas en las celdas en el interior de la tabla.

cometa Cuadrilátero que tiene exactamente dos pares differentes de lados congruentes y adyacentes.

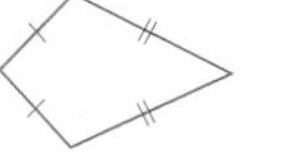

área lateral En prismas, pirámides, cilindros y conos, es el área de la caras de la figura sin incluir el área de las bases.

aristas laterales **1.** En un prisma, la intersección de dos caras laterales adyacentes. **2.** En una pirámide, las aristas de las caras laterales que unen el vértice de la pirámide con los vértices de la base.

caras laterales **1.** En un prisma, las caras que no forman las bases. **2.** En una pirámide, las caras que se intersecan en el vértice.

latitud Medida de la distancia al norte o al sur del ecuador.

ley de los cosenos Sea $\triangle ABC$ cualquier triángulo donde a, b y c son las medidas de los lados opuestos a los ángulos que miden A, B y C respectivamente. Entonces las siguientes ecuaciones son verdaderas.

$a^2 = b^2 + c^2 - 2bc \cos A$

$b^2 = a^2 + c^2 - 2ac \cos B$

$c^2 = a^2 + b^2 - 2ab \cos C$

Law of Detachment (p. 117) If $p \rightarrow q$ is a true conditional and p is true, then q is also true.

Law of Large Numbers (p. 942) Law that states that as the number of trials of a random process increases, the average value will approach the expected value.

Law of Sines (p. 588) Let $\triangle ABC$ be any triangle with a, b, and c representing the measures of sides opposite the angles with measures A, B, and C respectively.

Then, $\frac{\sin A}{a} = \frac{\sin B}{b} = \frac{\sin C}{c}$.

Law of Syllogism (p. 119) If $p \rightarrow q$ and $q \rightarrow r$ are true conditionals, then $p \rightarrow r$ is also true.

legs of a right triangle (p. 26) The shorter sides of a right triangle.

legs of a trapezoid (p. 439) The nonparallel sides of a trapezoid.

legs of an isosceles triangle (p. 285) The two congruent sides of an isosceles triangle.

line (p. 5) A basic undefined term of geometry. A line is made up of points and has no thickness or width. In a figure, a line is shown with an arrowhead at each end. Lines are usually named by lowercase script letters or by writing capital letters for two points on the line, with a double arrow over the pair of letters.

line of reflection (p. 623) A line in which each point on the preimage and its corresponding point on the image are the same distance from this line.

line of symmetry (p. 663) A line that can be drawn through a plane figure so that the figure on one side is the reflection image of the figure on the opposite side.

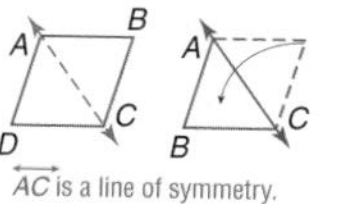

$\overleftrightarrow{AC}$ is a line of symmetry.

line segment (p. 14) A measurable part of a line that consists of two points, called endpoints, and all of the points between them.

linear pair (p. 46) A pair of adjacent angles whose non-common sides are opposite rays.

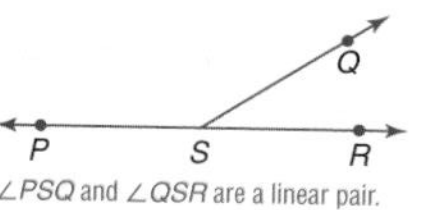

$\angle PSQ$ and $\angle QSR$ are a linear pair.

ley de indiferencia Si $p \rightarrow q$ es un enunciado condicional verdadero y p es verdadero, entonces q también es verdadero.

ley de los grandes números Ley que establece que a medida que aumenta el número de ensayos de un proceso aleatorio, el valor promedio se aproximará al valor esperado.

ley de los senos Sea $\triangle ABC$ cualquier triángulo donde a, b y c representan las medidas de los lados opuestos a los ángulos que miden A, B y C respectivamente.

Entonces, $\frac{\text{scn } A}{a} = \frac{\text{scn } B}{b} = \frac{\text{scn } C}{c}$.

ley del silogismo Si $p \rightarrow q$ y $q \rightarrow r$ son enunciados condicionales verdaderos, entonces $p \rightarrow r$ también es verdadero.

catetos de un triángulo rectángulo Lados más cortos de un triángulo rectángulo.

catetos de un trapecio Los lados no paralelos de un trapecio.

catetos de un triángulo isósceles Las dos lados congruentes de un triángulo isósceles.

recta Término geometrico basico no definido. Una recta está formada por puntos y carece de grosor o ancho. En una figura, una recta se representa con una flecha en cada extremo. Generalmente se designan con letras minúsculas o con las dos letras mayúsculas de dos puntos sobre la recta y una flecha doble sobre el par de letras.

línea de reflexión Una línea en la cual cada punto en el preimage y el su corresponder senalañ en la imagen es la misma distancia de esta línea.

eje de simetría Recta que se traza a través de una figura plana, de modo que un lado de la figura es la imagen reflejada del lado opuesto.

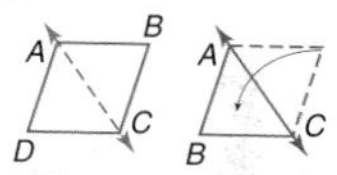

$\overleftrightarrow{AC}$ es un eje de simetría.

segmento de recta Sección medible de una recta que consta de dos puntos, llamados extremos, y todos los puntos entre ellos.

par lineal Par de ángulos adyacentes cuyos lados no comunes forman rayos opuestos.

P S R Q

$\angle PSQ$ y $\angle QSR$ forman un par lineal.

locus (p. 11) The set of points that satisfy a given condition.

logically equivalent (p. 110) Statements that have the same truth values.

longitude (p. 895) A measure of distance east or west of the Prime Meridian.

M

magnitude (p. 600) The length of a vector.

magnitude of symmetry (p. 664) The smallest angle through which a figure can be rotated so that it maps onto itself.

major arc (p. 707) An arc with a measure greater than 180. $\widehat{ACB}$ is a major arc.

marginal frequencies (p. 954) In a two-way frequency table, the accumulated frequencies reported in the Totals row and Totals column.

matrix logic (p. 353) A rectangular array in which learned clues are recorded in order to solve a logic or reasoning problem.

means (p. 462) In $\frac{a}{b} = \frac{c}{d}$, the numbers b and c.

median (p. 335) In a triangle, a line segment with endpoints that are a vertex of a triangle and the midpoint of the side opposite the vertex.

meridians (p. 895) Imaginary vertical lines drawn around the Earth through the North and South Poles.

midpoint (p. 27) The point on a segment exactly halfway between the endpoints of the segment.

midsegment of trapezoid (p. 441) A segment that connects the midpoints of the legs of a trapezoid.

midsegment of triangle (p. 491) A segment with endpoints that are the midpoints of two sides of a triangle.

minor arc (p. 707) An arc with a measure less than 180. $\widehat{AB}$ is a minor arc.

lugar geométrico Conjunto de puntos que satisfacen una condición dada.

lógicamente equivalentes Enunciados que poseen los mismos valores verdaderos.

longitud Medida de la distancia del este o al oeste del Primer Meridiano.

magnitud Longitud de un vector.

magnitud de la simetria El angulo mas pequeno con el cual una figura puede serrotada de modo que traz sobre si mismo.

arco mayor Arco que mide más de 180. $\widehat{ACB}$ es un arco mayor.

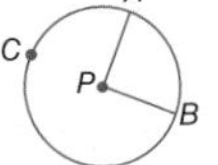

frecuencias marginales En una tabla de double entrada o de frecuencias, las frecuencias acumuladas que se reportan en la hilera de los totales y en la columna de los totales.

lógica matricial Arreglo rectangular en que las claves aprendidas se escriben en orden para resolver un problema de lógica o razonamiento.

medias Los números b y c en la proporción $\frac{a}{b} = \frac{c}{d}$.

mediana En un triángulo, Segmento de recta de cuyos extremos son un vértice del triángulo y el punto medio del lado opuesto a dicho vértice.

meridianos Líneas verticales imaginarias dibujadas alrededor de la Tierra que von del polo norte al polo sur.

punto medio Punto en un segmento que yace exactamente en la mitad, entre los extremos del segmento.

segmento medio de un trapecio Segmento que conecta los puntos medios de los catetos de un trapecio.

segmento medio de un triángulo Segmento cuyas extremos son los puntos medianos de dos lados de un triángulo.

arco menor Arco que mide menos de 180. $\widehat{AB}$ es un arco menor.

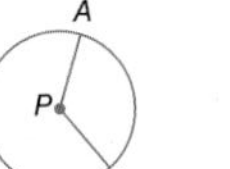

multi-stage experiments (p. 916) Experiments with more than two stages.

mutually exclusive (p. 956) Two events that have no outcomes in common.

N

negation (p. 99) If a statement is represented by p, then *not p* is the negation of the statement.

net (p. 76) A two-dimensional figure that when folded forms the surfaces of a three-dimensional object.

network (p. 964) A graph of interconnected vertices.

n-gon (p. 57) A polygon with n sides.

node (p. 964) A collection of vertices.

non-Euclidean geometry (p. 890) The study of geometrical systems that are not in accordance with the Parallel Postulate of Euclidean geometry.

O

oblique cone (p. 856) A cone that is not a right cone.

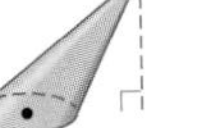

oblique cylinder (p. 848) A cylinder that is not a right cylinder.

oblique prism (p. 846) A prism in which the lateral edges are not perpendicular to the bases.

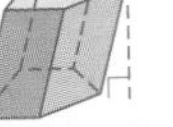

oblique solid (p. 838) A solid with base(s) that are not perpendicular to the edges connecting the two bases or vertex.

obtuse angle (p. 38) An angle with degree measure greater than 90 and less than 180.

experimentos multietápicos Experimentos con más de dos etapas.

mutuamente exclusivos Eventos que no tienen resultados en común.

negación Si p representa un enunciado, entonces *no p* es la negación del enunciado.

red Figura bidimensional que al ser plegada forma las superficies de un objeto tridimensional.

red Gráfico de vértices interconectados.

*en*ágono Polígono con n lados.

nodo Colección de vértices.

geometría no euclidiana El estudio de sistemas geométricos que no satisfacen el postulado de las paralelas de la geometría euclidiana.

cono oblicuo Cono que no es un cono recto.

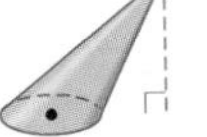

cilindro oblicuo Cilindro que no es un cilindro recto.

prisma oblicuo Prisma cuyas aristas laterales no son perpendiculares a las bases.

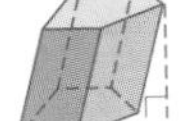

sólido oblicuo Sólido con base o bases que no son perpendiculares a las aristas, las cuales conectan las dos bases o vértice.

ángulo obtuso Ángulo que mide más de 90 y menos de 180.

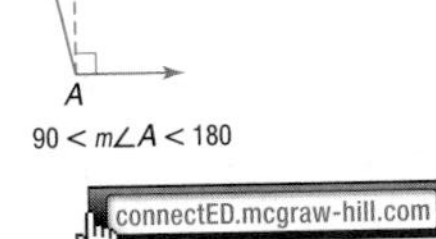

obtuse triangle (p. 237) A triangle with an obtuse angle.

one obtuse angle

opposite rays (p. 36) Two rays $\overrightarrow{BA}$ and $\overrightarrow{BC}$ such that *B* is between *A* and *C*.

opposite vectors (p. 601) Vectors that have the same magnitude but opposite direction.

order of symmetry (p. 664) The number of times a figure can map onto itself as it rotates from 0° to 360°.

ordered triple (p. 556) Three numbers given in a specific order used to locate points in space.

orthocenter (p. 337) The point of concurrency of the altitudes of a triangle.

orthographic drawing (p. 75) The two-dimensional top view, left view, front view, and right view of a three-dimensional object.

triángulo obtusángulo Triángulo con un ángulo obtuso.

un ángulo obtuso

rayos opuestos Dos rayos $\overrightarrow{BA}$ y $\overrightarrow{BC}$ donde *B* esta entre *A* y *C*.

vectores opuestos Vectores que tienen la misma magnitud pero enfrente de la dirección.

orden de la simetría Número de veces que una figura se puede aplicar sobre sí misma mientras gira de 0° a 360°.

triple ordenado Tres números dados en un orden específico que sirven para ubicar puntos en el espacio.

ortocentro Punto de intersección de las alturas de un triángulo.

proyección ortogonal Vista bidimensional superior, del lado izquierda, frontal y del lado derecho de un objeto tridimensional.

P

parabola (p. 764) The graph of a quadratic function. The set of all points in a plane that are the same distance from a given point, called the focus, and a given line, called the directrix.

paragraph proof (p. 129) An informal proof written in the form of a paragraph that explains why a conjecture for a given situation is true.

parallel lines (p. 173) Coplanar lines that do not intersect.

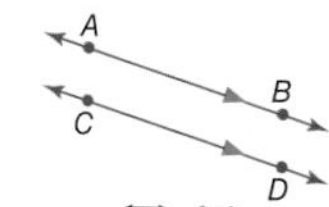

$\overleftrightarrow{AB} \parallel \overleftrightarrow{CD}$

parallel planes (p. 173) Planes that do not intersect.

parallel vectors (p. 601) Vectors that have the same or opposite direction.

parallelogram (p. 403) A quadrilateral with parallel opposite sides. Any side of a parallelogram may be called a *base*.

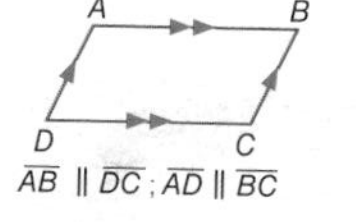

$\overline{AB} \parallel \overline{DC}$; $\overline{AD} \parallel \overline{BC}$

parábola La grafica de una funcion cuadratica. Conjunto de todos los puntos de un plano que estan a la misma distancia de un punto dado, llamado foco, y de una recta dada, llamada directriz.

demostración de párrafo Demostración informal escrita en párrafo que explica por qué una conjetura para una situación dada es verdadera.

rectas paralelas Rectas coplanares que no se intersecan.

$\overleftrightarrow{AB} \parallel \overleftrightarrow{CD}$

planos paralelos Planos que no se intersecan.

vectores paralelos Vectores con la misma dirección o dirección opuesta.

paralelogramo Cuadrilátero cuyos lados opuestos son paralelos y cuya *base* puede ser cualquier de sus lados.

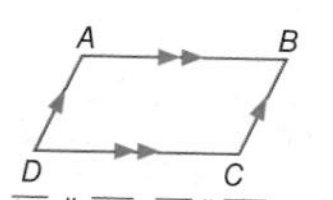

$\overline{AB} \parallel \overline{DC}$; $\overline{AD} \parallel \overline{BC}$

parallelogram method (p. 601) A method used to find the resultant of two vectors in which you place the vectors at the same initial point, complete a parallelogram, and draw the diagonal.

parallels (p. 895) Imaginary horizontal lines parallel to the equator.

perimeter (p. 58) The sum of the lengths of the sides of a polygon.

permutation (p. 922) An arrangement of objects in which order is important.

perpendicular bisector (p. 324) In a triangle, a line, segment, or ray that passes through the midpoint of a side and is perpendicular to that side.

D is the midpoint of $\overline{BC}$.

perpendicular lines (p. 48) Lines that form right angles.

line $m \perp$ line n

pi (π) (p. 699) An irrational number represented by the ratio of the circumference of a circle to the diameter of the circle.

plane (p. 5) A basic undefined term of geometry. A plane is a flat surface made up of points that has no depth and extends indefinitely in all directions. In a figure, a plane is often represented by a shaded, slanted four-sided figure. Planes are usually named by a capital script letter or by three noncollinear points on the plane.

plane Euclidean geometry (p. 889) Geometry based on Euclid's axioms dealing with a system of points, lines, and planes.

plane symmetry (p. 665) Symmetry in a three- dimensional figure that occurs if the figure can be mapped onto itself by a reflection in a plane.

Platonic solids (p. 68) The five regular polyhedra: tetrahedron, hexahedron, octahedron, dodecahedron, or icosahedron.

point (p. 5) A basic undefined term of geometry. A point is a location. In a figure, points are represented by a dot. Points are named by capital letters.

point of concurrency (p. 325) The point of intersection of concurrent lines.

método del paralelogramo Método que se usa para hallar la resultante de dos vectores en que se dibujan los vectores con el mismo punto de origen, se completa un paralelogramo y se traza la diagonal.

paralelos Rectas horizontales imaginarias paralelas al ecuador.

perímetro Suma de la longitud de los lados de un polígono.

permutación Disposicion de objetos en la cual el orden es importante.

mediatriz Recta, segmento de recta o rayo perpendicular que corta un lado del triángulo en su punto medio.

D es el punto medio de $\overline{BC}$.

rectas perpendiculares Rectas que forman ángulos rectos.

recta $m \perp$ recta n

pi (π) Número irracional representado por la razón de la circunferencia de un círculo al diámetro del mismo.

plano Término geométrico básico no definido. Superficie plana sin espesor formada por puntos y que se extiende hasta el infinito en todas direcciones. En una figura, los planos a menudo se representan con una figura inclinada y sombreada y se designan con una letra mayúscula o con tres puntos no colineales del plano.

geometría del plano euclidiano Geometría basada en los axiomas de Euclides, los cuales abarcan un sistema de puntos, rectas y planos.

simetría plana Simetría en una figura tridimensional que ocurre si la figura se puede aplicar sobre sí misma mediante una reflexión en el plano.

sólidos platónicos Los cinco poliedros regulares siguientes: tetraedro, hexaedro, octaedro, dodecaedro e icosaedro.

punto Término geométrico básico no definido. Un punto representa un lugar o ubicación. En una figura, se representa con una marca puntual y se designan con letras mayúsculas.

punto de concurrencia Punto de intersección de rectas concurrentes.

point of symmetry (p. 664) A figure that can be mapped onto itself by a rotation of 180°.

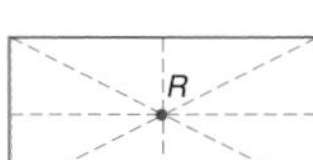

R is a point of symmetry.

point of tangency (p. 732) For a line that intersects a circle in only one point, the point at which they intersect.

point-slope form (p. 198) An equation of the form $y - y_1 = m(x - x_1)$, where (x_1, y_1) are the coordinates of any point on the line and m is the slope of the line.

poles (p. 881) The endpoints of the diameter of a great circle.

polygon (p. 56) A closed figure formed by a finite number of coplanar segments called *sides* such that the following conditions are met:

1. The sides that have a common endpoint are noncollinear.
2. Each side intersects exactly two other sides, but only at their endpoints, called the *vertices*.

polyhedrons (p. 67) Closed three-dimensional figures made up of flat polygonal regions. The flat regions formed by the polygons and their interiors are called *faces*. Pairs of faces intersect in segments called *edges*. Points where three or more edges intersect are called *vertices*.

population density (p. 797) A measurement of population per unit of area.

postulate (p. 127) A statement that describes a fundamental relationship between the basic terms of geometry. Postulates are accepted as true without proof.

preimage (p. 296) The graph of an object before a transformation.

principle of superposition (p. 682) Two figures are congruent if and only if there is a rigid motion or a series of rigid motions that maps one figure exactly onto the other.

prism (p. 67) A solid with the following characteristics:

1. Two faces, called *bases*, are formed by congruent polygons that lie in parallel planes.
2. The faces that are not bases, called *lateral faces*, are formed by parallelograms.

punto de simetría Una figura que se puede traz sobre sí mismo por una rotación de 180°.

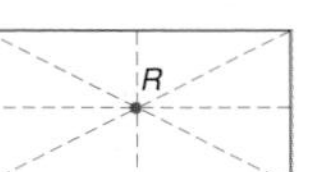

R es un punto de simetría.

punto de tangencia Punto de intersección de una recta en un círculo en un solo punto.

forma punto-pendiente Ecuación de la forma $y - y_1 = m(x - x_1)$, donde (x_1, y_1) representan las coordenadas de un punto cualquiera sobre la recta y m representa la pendiente de la recta.

postes Las extremos del diámetro de un círculo mayor.

polígono Figura cerrada formada por un número finito de segmentos coplanares llamados *lados*, tal que satisface las siguientes condiciones:

1. Los lados que tienen un extremo común son no colineales.
2. Cada lado interseca exactamente dos lados mas, pero sólo en sus extremos, llamados *vértices*.

poliedros Figuras tridimensionales cerrada formadas por regiones poligonales planas. Las regiones planas definidas por un polígono y sus interiores se llaman *caras*. Cada intersección entre dos caras se llama *arista*. Los puntos donde se intersecan tres o más aristas se llaman *vértices*.

densidad demográfica Medida de la población por unidad de área.

postulado Enunciado que describe una relación fundamental entre los términos geométricos básicos. Los postulados se aceptan como verdaderos sin necesidad de demostración.

preimagen Gráfica de una figura antes de una transformación.

principio de superposición Dos figuras son congruentes si y sólo si existe un movimiento rígido o una serie de movimientos rígidos que aplican una de las figuras exactamente sobre la otra.

prisma Sólido con las siguientes características:

1. Dos caras llamadas *bases*, formadas por polígonos congruentes que yacen en planos paralelos.
2. Las caras que no son las bases, llamadas *caras laterales*, son paralelogramos.

3. The intersections of two adjacent lateral faces are called *lateral edges* and are parallel segments.

base
lateral edge
lateral face

triangular prism

probability model (p. 939) A mathematical model used to match a random phenomenon.

probability tree (p. 949) An organized table of line segments (branches) that shows the probability of each outcome.

proof (p. 128) A logical argument in which each statement you make is supported by a statement that is accepted as true.

proof by contradiction (p. 355) An indirect proof in which one assumes that the statement to be proved is false. One then uses logical reasoning to deduce a statement that contradicts a postulate, theorem, or one of the assumptions. Once a contradiction is obtained, one concludes that the statement assumed false must in fact be true.

proportion (p. 462) An equation of the form $\frac{a}{b} = \frac{c}{d}$ that states that two ratios are equal.

pyramid (p. 67) A solid with the following characteristics:

1. All of the faces, except one face, intersect at a point called the *vertex*.
2. The face that does not contain the vertex is called the *base* and is a polygonal region.
3. The faces meeting at the vertex are called *lateral faces* and are triangular regions.

vertex
lateral face
base

rectangular pyramid

Pythagorean triple (p. 548) A group of three whole numbers that satisfies the equation $a^2 + b^2 = c^2$, where c is the greatest number.

3. Las intersecciones de dos caras laterales adyacentes se llaman *aristas laterales* y son segmentos paralelos.

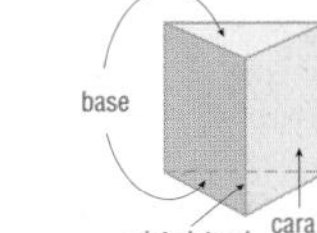

prisma triangular

modelo de probabilidad Modelo matemático que se usa para relacionar un fenómeno aleatorio.

árbol de la probabilidad Tabla organizada de segmentos de recta (ramas) que muestra la probabilidad de cada resultado.

demostración Argumento lógico en el cual cada enunciado que se hace está respaldado por un enunciado que se acepta como verdadero.

demostración por contradicción Demostración indirecta en la cual se supone que el enunciado a demostrarse es falso. Luego, se usa el razonamiento lógico para inferir un enunciado que contradiga el postulado, teorema o una de las conjeturas. Una vez que se obtiene una contradicción, se concluye que el enunciado que se supuso falso es, en realidad, verdadero.

proporción Ecuación de la forma $\frac{a}{b} = \frac{c}{d}$ que establece que dos razones son iguales.

pirámide Sólido con las siguientes características:

1. Todas las caras, excepto una, se intersecan en un punto llamado *vértice*.
2. La cara sin el vértice se llama *base* y es una región poligonal.
3. Las caras que se encuentran en los vértices se llaman *caras laterales* y son regiones triangulares.

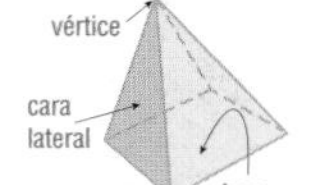

pirámide rectangular

triplete pitágorico Grupo de tres números enteros que satisfacen la ecuación $a^2 + b^2 = c^2$, donde c es el número mayor.

Glossary/Glosario

R

radius 1. (p. 697) In a circle, any segment with endpoints that are the center of the circle and a point on the circle. **2.** (p. 880) In a sphere, any segment with endpoints that are the center and a point on the sphere.

radius of a regular polygon (p. 807) The radius of a circle circumscribed about a polygon.

random variable (p. 941) A variable that can assume a set of values, each with fixed probabilities.

rate of change (p. 189) Describes how a quantity is changing over time.

ratio (p. 461) A comparison of two quantities using division.

ray (p. 36) $\overrightarrow{PQ}$ is a ray if it is the set of points consisting of $\overline{PQ}$ and all points S for which Q is between P and S.

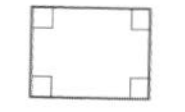

rectangle (p. 423) A quadrilateral with four right angles.

reduction (p. 511) An image that is smaller than the original figure.

reflection (pp. 296, 623) A transformation representing the flip of a figure over a point, line or plane. A reflection in a line is a function that maps a point to its image such that

- if the point is on the line, then the image and preimage are the same point, or
- if the point is not on the line, the line is the perpendicular bisector of the segment joining the two points.

regular polygon (p. 57) A convex polygon in which all of the sides are congruent and all of the angles are congruent.

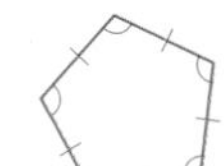

regular polyhedron (p. 68) A polyhedron in which all of the faces are regular congruent polygons.

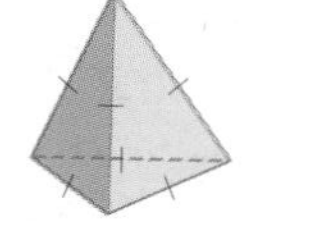

radio **1.** En un círculo, cualquier segmento cuyos extremos son en el centro y un punto del círculo. **2.** En una esfera, cualquier segmento cuyos extremos son el centro y un punto de la esfera.

radio de un polígono regular Radio de un círculo circunscrito alrededor de un polígono.

variable aleatoria Variable que puede tomar un conjunto de valores, cada uno con probabilidades fijas.

tasa de cambio Describe cómo cambia una cantidad a través del tiempo.

razón Comparación de dos cantidades mediante división.

rayo $\overrightarrow{PQ}$ es un rayo si se el conjunto de puntos formado por $\overline{PQ}$ y todos los puntos S para los cuales Q se ubica entre P y S.

rectángulo Cuadrilátero con cuatro ángulos rectos.

reducción Imagen más pequeña que la figura original.

reflexión Transformación en la cual una figura se "voltea" a través de un punto, una recta o un plano. Una reflexión en una recta es una función que aplica un punto a su imagen, de modo que si el punto yace sobre la recta, entonces la imagen y la preimagen son el mismo punto, o si el punto no yace sobre la recta, la recta es la mediatriz del segmento que une los dos puntos.

polígono regular Polígono convexo cuyos los lados y ángulos son congruentes.

poliedro regular Poliedro cuyas caras son polígonos regulares congruentes.

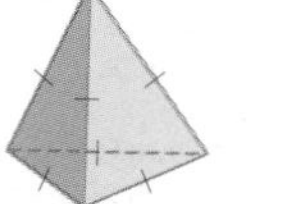

regular prism (p. 67) A right prism with bases that are regular polygons.

regular pyramid (p. 854) A pyramid with a base that is a regular polygon.

regular tessellation (p. 660) A tessellation formed by only one type of regular polygon.

related conditionals (p. 109) Statements that are based on a given conditional statement.

relative frequency (p. 954) In a frequency table, the ratio of the number of observations in a category to the total number of observations.

remote interior angles (p. 248) The angles of a triangle that are not adjacent to a given exterior angle.

resultant (p. 601) The sum of two vectors.

rhombus (p. 430) A quadrilateral with all four sides congruent.

right angle (p. 38) An angle with a degree measure of 90.

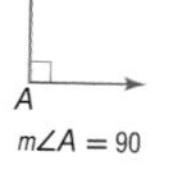

right cone (p. 856) A cone with an axis that is also an altitude.

right cylinder (p. 848) A cylinder with an axis that is also an altitude.

right prism (p. 846) A prism with lateral edges that are also altitudes.

right solid (p. 837) A solid with base(s) that are perpendicular to the edges connecting them or connecting the base and the vertex of the solid.

right triangle (p. 237) A triangle with a right angle. The side opposite the right angle is called the *hypotenuse*. The other two sides are called *legs*.

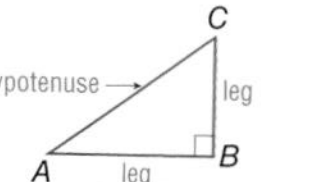

prisma regular Prisma recto cuyas bases son polígonos regulares.

pirámide regular Pirámide cuya base es un polígono regular.

teselado regular Teselado formado por un solo tipo de polígono regular.

condicionales relacionados Enunciados que se basan en un enunciado condicional dado.

frecuencia relativa En una tabla de frecuencias, la razón del número de observaciones en una categoría al número total de observaciones.

ángulos internos no adyacentes Ángulos de un triángulo que no son adyacentes a un ángulo exterior dado.

resultante Suma de dos vectores.

rombo Cuadrilátero con cuatro lados congruentes.

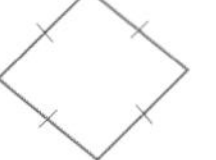

ángulo recto Ángulo que mide 90.

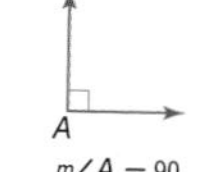

cono recto Cono cuyo eje es también su altura.

cilindro recto Cilindro cuyo eje es también su altura.

prisma recto Prisma cuyas aristas laterales también son su altura.

sólido recto Sólido con base o bases perpendiculares a las aristas, conectándolas entre sí o conectando la base y el vértice del sólido.

triángulo rectángulo Triángulo con un ángulo recto. El lado opuesto al ángulo recto se conoce como *hipotenusa*. Los otros dos lados se llaman *catetos*.

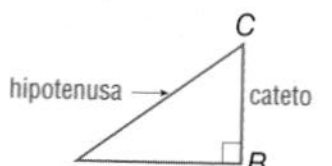

rotation (pp. 296, 640) A transformation that turns every point of a preimage through a specified angle and direction about a fixed point, called the *center of rotation*. A rotation about a fixed point through an angle of $x°$ is a function that maps a point to its image such that

- if the point is the center of rotation, then the image and preimage are the same point, or
- if the point is not the center of rotation, then the image and preimage are the same distance from the center of rotation and the measure of the angle of rotation formed by the preimage, center of rotation, and image points is x.

rotational symmetry (p. 664) If a figure can be rotated less than 360° about a point so that the image and the preimage are indistinguishable, the figure has rotational symmetry.

S

sample space (p. 915) The set of all possible outcomes of an experiment.

scalar (p. 606) A constant multiplied by a vector.

scalar multiplication (p. 606) Multiplication of a vector by a scalar.

scale factor (p. 470) The ratio of the lengths of two corresponding sides of two similar polygons or two similar solids.

scale factor of dilation (p. 511) The ratio of a length on an image to a corresponding length on the preimage.

scalene triangle (p. 238) A triangle with no two sides congruent.

secant (p. 741) Any line that intersects a circle in exactly two points.

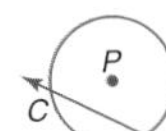

$\overleftrightarrow{CD}$ is a secant of $\odot P$.

secant segment (p. 752) A segment of a secant line that has exactly one endpoint on the circle.

sector of a circle (p. 799) A region of a circle bounded by a central angle and its intercepted arc.

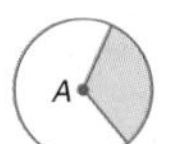

The shaded region is a sector of $\odot A$.

rotación Transformación en la cual se hace girar cada punto de la preimagen a través de un ángulo y una dirección determinadas alrededor de un punto llamado *centro de rotación*. La rotación de $x°$ es una función que aplica un punto a su imagen, de modo que si el punto es el centro de rotación, entonces la imagen y la preimagen están a la misma distancia del centro de rotación y la medida del ángulo formado por los puntos de la preimagen, centro de rotación e imagen es x.

simetría rotacional Si una imagen se puede girar menos de 360° alrededor de un punto, de modo que la imagen y la preimagen sean idénticas, entonces la figura tiene simetría rotacional.

espacio muestral El conjunto de todos los resultados posibles de un experimento.

escalar Constante multiplicada por un vector.

multiplicación escalar Multiplicación de un vector por un escalar.

factor de escala Razón entre las longitudes de dos lados correspondientes de dos polígonos o sólidos semejantes.

factor de escala de homotecia Razon de una longitud en la imagen a una longitud correspondiente en la preimagen.

triángulo escaleno Triángulo que no tiene dos lados congruentes.

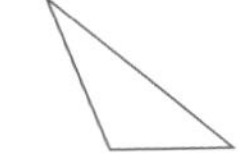

secante Cualquier recta que interseca un círculo exactamente en dos puntos.

$\overleftrightarrow{CD}$ es una secante de $\odot P$.

segmento secante Segmento de una recta secante que tiene exactamente un extremo en el círculo.

sector circular Región de un círculo limitada por un ángulo central y su arco de intersección.

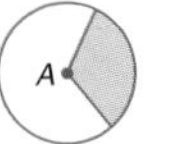

La región sombreada es un sector de $\odot A$.

segment (p. 14) See *line segment.*

segment bisector (p. 29) A segment, line, or plane that intersects a segment at its midpoint.

segment of a circle (p. 803) The region of a circle bounded by an arc and a chord.

The shaded region is a segment of $\odot A$.

self-similar (p. 509) If any parts of a fractal image are replicas of the entire image, the image is self-similar.

semicircle (p. 707) An arc that measures 180.

semi-regular tessellation (p. 660) A uniform tessellation formed using two or more regular polygons.

sides of an angle (p. 36) The rays of an angle.

Sierpinski Triangle (p. 509) A self-similar fractal described by Waclaw Sierpinski. The figure was named for him.

similar solids (p. 896) Solids that have exactly the same shape, but not necessarily the same size.

similarity ratio (p. 470) The scale factor between two similar polygons

similarity transformation (p. 511) When a figure and its transformation image are similar.

simulation (p. 939) A probability model used to recreate a situation again and again so the likelihood of various outcomes can be estimated.

sine (p. 568) For an acute angle of a right triangle, the ratio of the measure of the leg opposite the acute angle to the measure of the hypotenuse.

skew lines (p. 173) Lines that do not intersect and are not coplanar.

slant height (p. 854) The height of the lateral side of a pyramid or cone.

segmento Ver *segmento de recta.*

bisector del segmento Segmento, recta o plano que interseca un segmento en su punto medio.

segmento de un círculo Región de un círculo limitada por un arco y una cuerda.

La región sombreada es un segmento de $\odot A$.

autosemejante Si cualquier parte de una imagen fractal es una réplica de la imagen completa, entonces la imagen es autosemejante.

semicírculo Arco que mide 180.

teselado semiregular Teselado uniforme compuesto por dos o más polígonos regulares.

lados de un ángulo Los rayos de un ángulo.

triángulo de Sierpinski Fractal autosemejante descrito por el matemático Waclaw Sierpinski. La figura se nombró en su honor.

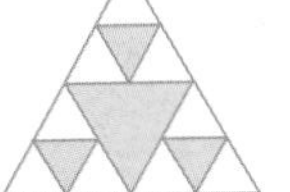

sólidos semejantes Sólidos que tienen exactamente la misma forma, pero no necesariamente el mismo tamaño.

razón de semejanza Factor de escala entre dos polígonos semejantes.

transformación de semejanza cuando una figura y su imagen transformada son semejantes.

simulacro Modelo de la probabilidad que se usa para reconstruir una situación repetidas veces y así poder estimar la probabilidad de varios resultados.

seno Para un ángulo agudo de un triángulo rectángulo, razón entre la medida del cateto opuesto al ángulo agudo a la medida de la hipotenusa.

rectas alabeadas Rectas que no se intersecan y que no son coplanares.

altura oblicua Altura de la cara lateral de una pirámide o un cono.

Glossary/Glosario

Glossary/Glosario

slope (p. 188) For a (nonvertical) line containing two points (x_1, y_1) and (x_2, y_2), the number m given by the formula $m = \frac{y_2 - y_1}{x_2 - x_1}$ where $x_2 \neq x_1$.

slope-intercept form (p. 198) A linear equation of the form $y = mx + b$. The graph of such an equation has slope m and y-intercept b.

solid of revolution (p. 647) A three-dimensional figure obtained by rotating a plane figure about a line.

solving a triangle (p. 591) Finding the measures of all of the angles and sides of a triangle.

space (p. 7) A boundless three-dimensional set of all points.

sphere (p. 67) In space, the set of all points that are a given distance from a given point, called the *center*.

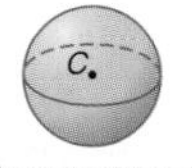

C is the center of the sphere.

spherical geometry (p. 889) The branch of geometry that deals with a system of points, great circles (lines), and spheres (planes).

square (p. 431) A quadrilateral with four right angles and four congruent sides.

standard position (p. 602) When the initial point of a vector is at the origin.

statement (p. 99) Any sentence that is either true or false, but not both.

supplementary angles (p. 47) Two angles with measures that have a sum of 180.

surface area (p. 69) The sum of the areas of all faces and side surfaces of a three-dimensional figure.

symmetry (p. 663) A figure has symmetry if there exists a rigid motion—reflection, translation, rotation, or glide reflection—that maps the figure onto itself.

pendiente Para una recta (no vertical) que contiene dos puntos (x_1, y_1) y (x_2, y_2), tel número m viene dado por la fórmula $m = \frac{y_2 - y_1}{x_2 - x_1}$ donde $x_2 \neq x_1$.

forma pendiente-intersección Ecuación lineal de la forma $y = mx + b$ donde, la pendiente es m y la intersección y es b.

sólido de revolución Figura tridimensional que se obtiene al rotar una figura plana alrededor de una recta.

resolver un triángulo Calcular las medidas de todos los ángulos y todos los lados de un triángulo.

espacio Conjunto tridimensional no acotado de todos los puntos.

esfera En el espacio, conjunto de todos los puntos a cierta distancia de un punto dado llamado *centro*.

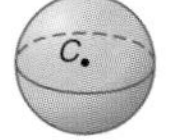

C es el centro de la esfera.

geometría esférica Rama de la geometría que estudia los sistemas de puntos, los círculos mayores (rectas) y las esferas (planos).

cuadrado Cuadrilátero con cuatro ángulos rectos y cuatro lados congruentes.

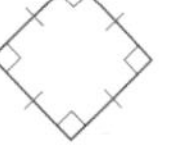

posición estándar Cuando el punto inicial de un vector es el origen.

enunciado Cualquier suposición que puede ser falsa o verdadera, pero no ambas.

ángulos suplementarios Dos ángulos cuya suma es igual a 180.

área de superficie Suma de las áreas de todas las caras y superficies laterales de una figura tridimensional.

simetría Una figura tiene simetría si existe un movimiento rígido (reflexión, translación, rotación, o reflexión con deslizamiento) que aplica la figura sobre sí misma.

T

tangent 1. (p. 568) For an acute angle of a right triangle, the ratio of the measure of the leg opposite the acute angle to the measure of the leg adjacent to the acute angle. 2. (p. 732) A line in the plane of a circle that intersects the circle in exactly one point. The point of intersection is called the *point of tangency*. 3. (p. 880) A line that intersects a sphere in exactly one point.

tangent segment (p. 752) A segment of a tangent with one endpoint on a circle that is both the exterior and whole segment.

tessellation (p. 660) A pattern that covers a plane by transforming the same figure or set of figures so that there are no overlapping or empty spaces.

theorem (p. 129) A statement or conjecture that can be proven true by undefined terms, definitions, and postulates.

topographic map (p. 845) A representation of a three-dimensional surface on a flat piece of paper.

traceable network (p. 964) A network in which all of the nodes are connected and each edge is used once when the network is used.

transformation (p. 511) In a plane, a mapping for which each point has exactly one image point and each image point has exactly one preimage point.

translation (pp. 296, 632) A transformation that moves a figure the same distance in the same direction. A translation is a function that maps each point to its image along a vector such that each segment joining a point and its image has the same length as the vector, and this segment is also parallel to the vector.

translation vector (p. 632) The vector in which a translation maps each point to its image.

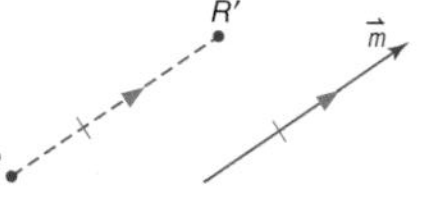

Point *R′*, is a translation of point *R* along translation vector *m*.

tangente 1. Para un ángulo agudo de un triángulo rectángulo, razón de la medida del cateto opuesto al ángulo agudo a la medida del cateto adyacente al ángulo agudo. 2. Recta en el plano de un círculo que interseca el círculo en exactamente un punto. El punto de intersección se conoce como *punto de tangencia*. 3. Recta que interseca una esfera en exatamente un punto.

segmento tangente Segmento de la tangente con un extremo en un círculo que es tanto el segmento externo como el segmento completo.

teselado Patrón con que se cubre un plano aplicando la misma figura o conjunto de figuras, sin que haya traslapes ni espacios vacíos.

teorema Enunciado o conjetura que se puede demostrar como verdadera mediante términos geométricos básicos, definiciones y postulados.

mapa topográfico Representación de una superficie tridimensional sobre una hoja del papel.

red detectable Red en la cual todos los nodos estén conectados y cada arista se utiliza una vez al usarse la red.

transformación En un plano, aplicación para la cual cada punto del plano tiene un único punto de la imagen y cada punto de la imagen tiene un único punto de la preimagen.

traslación Transformación que mueve una figura la misma distancia en la misma dirección. Una traslación es una función que aplica cada punto a su imagen a lo largo de un vector, de modo que cada segmento que une un punto a su imagen tiene la misma longitud que el vector y este segmento es también paralelo al vector.

vector de traslación Vector en el cual una traslación aplica cada punto a su imagen.

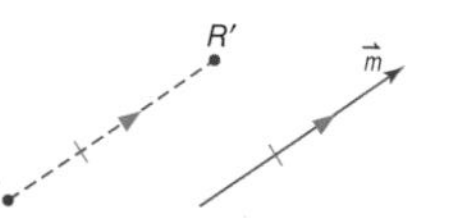

El punta *R′*, es la traslación del punto *R* a lo largo del vector *m* de traslación.

transversal (p. 174) A line that intersects two or more lines in a plane at different points.

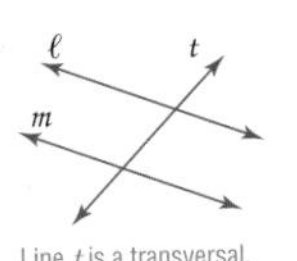

Line *t* is a transversal.

trapezoid (p. 439) A quadrilateral with exactly one pair of parallel sides. The parallel sides of a trapezoid are called *bases*. The nonparallel sides are called *legs*. The pairs of angles with their vertices at the endpoints of the same base are called *base angles*.

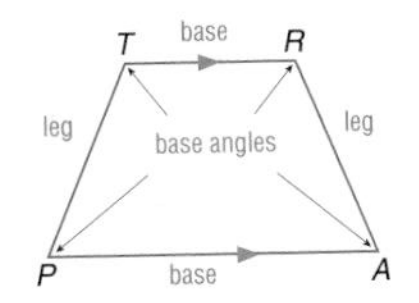

tree diagram (p. 915) An organized table of line segments (branches) which shows possible experiment outcomes.

triangle method (p. 602) A method used to find the resultant of two vectors in which the second vector is connected to the terminal point of the first and the resultant is drawn from the initial point of the first vector to the terminal point of the second vector.

trigonometric ratio (p. 568) A ratio of the lengths of sides of a right triangle.

trigonometry (p. 568) The study of the properties of triangles and trigonometric functions and their applications.

truth table (p. 101) A table used as a convenient method for organizing the truth values of statements.

truth value (p. 99) The truth or falsity of a statement.

two-column proof (p. 137) A formal proof that contains statements and reasons organized in two columns. Each step is called a *statement*, and the properties that justify each step are called *reasons*.

two-stage experiment (p. 916) An experiment with two stages or events.

two-way frequency table (p. 954) A table used to show the frequencies or relative frequencies of data from a survey or experiment classified according to two variables, with the rows indicating one variable and the columns indicating the other.

transversal Recta que interseca dos o más rectas en el diferentes puntos del mismo plano.

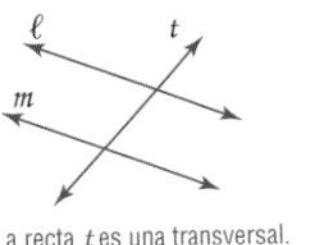

La recta *t* es una transversal.

trapecio Cuadrilátero con sólo un par de lados paralelos. Los lados paralelos del trapecio se llaman *bases*. Los lados no paralelos se llaman *catetos*. Los pares de ángulos cuyos vértices coinciden en los extremos de la misma base son los *ángulos de la base*.

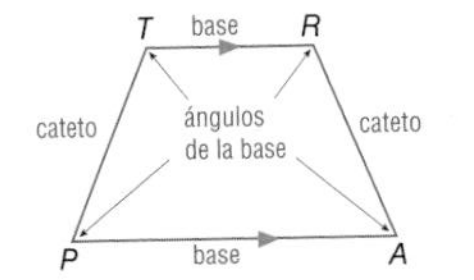

diagrama del árbol Tabla organizada de segmentos de recta (ramas) que muestra los resultados posibles de un experimento.

método del triangulo Método para calcular la resultante de dos vectores en cual el segundo vector está conectado al extremo del primer y la resultante se traza desde el punto inicial del primer vector al extremo del segundo vector.

razón trigonométrica Razón de las longitudes de los lados de un triángulo rectángulo.

trigonometría Estudio de las propiedades de los triángulos, de las funciones trigonométricas y sus aplicaciones.

tabla de validez Tabla que se utiliza para organizar de una manera conveniente los valores de verdaderos de los enunciados.

valor de verdad Condición de un enunciado de ser verdadero o falso.

demostración de dos columnas Demostración formal que contiene enunciados y razones organizadas en dos columnas. Cada paso se llama *enunciado* y las propiedades que lo justifican son las *razones*.

experimento de dos pasos Experimento que consta de dos pasos o eventos.

tabla de doble entrada o de frecuencias Tabla que se usa para mostrar las frecuencias o frecuencias relativas de los datos de una encuesta o experimento clasificado de acuerdo con dos variables, en la cual las hileras indican una variable y las columnas indican la otra variable.

U

undefined term (p. 5) Words, usually readily understood, that are not formally explained by means of more basic words and concepts. The basic undefined terms of geometry are point, line, and plane.

uniform tessellations (p. 660) Tessellations containing the same arrangement of shapes and angles at each vertex.

término geométrico básico no definido Palabras que por lo general se entienden fácilmente y que no se explican formalmente mediante palabras o conceptos más básicos. Los términos geométricos básicos no definidos son el punto, la recta y el plano.

teselado uniforme Teselados con el mismo patrón de formas y ángulos en cada vértice.

V

vector (p. 600) A directed segment representing a quantity that has both magnitude, or length, and direction.

vertex angle of an isosceles triangle (p. 285) See *isosceles triangle*.

vertex-edge graphs (p. 964) A collection of nodes connected by edges.

vertex of an angle (pp. 36, 67) The common endpoint of an angle.

vertex of a polygon (p. 56) The vertex of each angle of a polygon.

vertex of a polyhedron (p. 67) The intersection of three edges of a polyhedron.

vertical angles (p. 46) Two nonadjacent angles formed by two intersecting lines.

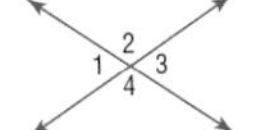

∠1 and ∠3 are vertical angles.
∠2 and ∠4 are vertical angles.

volume (p. 69) A measure of the amount of space enclosed by a three-dimensional figure.

vector Segmento dirigido que representa una cantidad, la cual posee tanto magnitud o longitud como dirección.

ángulo del vértice un triángulo isosceles Ver *triángulo isósceles*.

gráficas de vértice-arista Colección de nodos conectados por aristas.

vértice de un ángulo Extremo común de un ángulo.

vertice de un polígono Vértice de cada ángulo de un polígono.

vértice de un poliedro Intersección de las aristas de un poliedro.

ángulos opuestos por el vértice Dos ángulos no adyacentes formados por dos rectas que se intersecan.

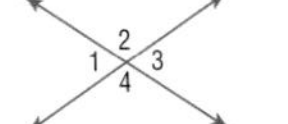

∠1 y ∠3 son ángulos opuestos por el vértice.
∠2 y ∠4 son ángulos opuestos por el vértice.

volumen La medida de la cantidad de espacio contiene una figura tridimensional.

W

weight (p. 946) The value assigned to an edge in a vertex-edge graph.

weight of a path (p. 946) The sum of the weights of the edges along a path.

weighted vertex-edge graphs (p. 946) A collection of nodes connected by edges in which each edge has an assigned value.

peso Valor asignado a una arista en una gráfica de vértice-arista.

peso de una ruta Suma de los pesos de las aristas a lo largo de una ruta.

gráficas ponderadas de vértice-arista Colección de nodos conectados por aristas en que cada arista tiene un valor asignado.

Index

B

C

Index

Index

D

E

Index

G

L

Index

M

Index

Index

Index

Q

R

Index

Index

S

Index

Index

Formulas

Coordinate Geometry

Slope	$m = \frac{y_2 - y_1}{x_2 - x_1}$
Distance on a number line:	$d = \lvert a - b \rvert$
Distance on a coordinate plane:	$d = \sqrt{(x_2 - x_1)^2 + (y_2 - y_1)^2}$
Distance in space:	$d = \sqrt{(x_2 - x_1)^2 + (y_2 - y_1)^2 + (z_2 - z_1)^2}$
Distance arc length:	$\ell = \frac{x}{360} \cdot 2\pi r$
Midpoint on a number line:	$M = \frac{a + b}{2}$
Midpoint on a coordinate plane:	$M = \left(\frac{x_1 + x_2}{2}, \frac{y_1 + y_2}{2}\right)$
Midpoint in space:	$M = \left(\frac{x_1 + x_2}{2}, \frac{y_1 + y_2}{2}, \frac{z_1 + z_2}{2}\right)$

Perimeter and Circumference

square	$P = 4s$	**rectangle**	$P = 2\ell + 2w$	**circle**	$C = 2\pi r$ or $C = \pi d$

Area

square	$A = s^2$	**triangle**	$A = \frac{1}{2}bh$
rectangle	$A = \ell w$ or $A = bh$	**regular polygon**	$A = \frac{1}{2}Pa$
parallelogram	$A = bh$	**circle**	$A = \pi r^2$
trapezoid	$A = \frac{1}{2}h(b_1 + b_2)$	**sector of a circle**	$A = \frac{x}{360} \cdot \pi r^2$
rhombus	$A = \frac{1}{2}d_1 d_2$ or $A = bh$		

Lateral Surface Area

prism	$L = Ph$	**pyramid**	$L = \frac{1}{2}P\ell$
cylinder	$L = 2\pi rh$	**cone**	$L = \pi r\ell$

Total Surface Area

prism	$S = Ph + 2B$	**cone**	$S = \pi r\ell + \pi r^2$
cylinder	$S = 2\pi rh + 2\pi r^2$	**sphere**	$S = 4\pi r^2$
pyramid	$S = \frac{1}{2}P\ell + B$		

Volume

cube	$V = s^3$	**pyramid**	$V = \frac{1}{3}Bh$
rectangular prism	$V = \ell wh$	**cone**	$V = \frac{1}{3}\pi r^2 h$
prism	$V = Bh$	**sphere**	$V = \frac{4}{3}\pi r^3$
cylinder	$V = \pi r^2 h$		

Equations for Figures on a Coordinate Plane

slope-intercept form of a line	$y = mx + b$	**circle**	$(x - h)^2 + (y - k)^2 = r^2$
point-slope form of a line	$y - y_1 = m(x - x_1)$		

Trigonometry

Law of Sines	$\frac{\sin A}{a} = \frac{\sin B}{b} = \frac{\sin C}{c}$	**Law of Cosines**	$a^2 = b^2 + c^2 - 2bc \cos A$ $b^2 = a^2 + c^2 - 2ac \cos B$ $c^2 = a^2 + b^2 - 2ab \cos C$
Pythagorean Theorem	$a^2 + b^2 = c^2$		

Symbols

$\neq$	is not equal to
$\approx$	is approximately equal to
$\cong$	is congruent to
$\sim$	is similar to
$\angle$, $\measuredangle$	angle, angles
$m\angle A$	degree measure of $\angle A$
$^\circ$	degree
$\overleftrightarrow{AB}$	line containing points *A* and *B*
$\overline{AB}$	segment with endpoints *A* and *B*
$\overrightarrow{AB}$	ray with endpoint *A* containing *B*
AB	measure of $\overline{AB}$, distance between points *A* and *B*
$\sim p$	negation of *p*, not *p*
$p \wedge q$	conjunction of *p* and *q*
$p \vee q$	disjunction of *p* and *q*
$p \longrightarrow q$	conditional statement, if *p* then *q*
$p \longleftrightarrow q$	biconditional statement, *p* if and only if *q*
$\parallel$	is parallel to
$\nparallel$	is not parallel to
$\perp$	is perpendicular to
$\triangle$	triangle
$>, \geq$	is greater than, is greater than or equal to
$<, \leq$	is less than, is less than or equal to
$\square$	parallelogram
n-gon	polygon with *n* sides
$a:b$	ratio of *a* to *b*
(x, y)	ordered pair
(x, y, z)	ordered triple
$\sin x$	sine of *x*
$\cos x$	cosine of *x*
$\tan x$	tangent of *x*
$\vec{a}$	vector *a*
$\overrightarrow{AB}$	vector from *A* to *B*
$\lvert\overrightarrow{AB}\rvert$	magnitude of the vector from *A* to *B*
A'	the image of preimage *A*
$\rightarrow$	is mapped onto
$\odot A$	circle with center *A*
π	pi
$\widehat{AB}$	minor arc with endpoints *A* and *B*
$\widehat{ABC}$	major arc with endpoints *A* and *C*
$m\widehat{AB}$	degree measure of arc *AB*
$f(x)$	*f* of *x*, the value of *f* at *x*
!	factorial
${}_nP_r$	permutation of *n* objects taken *r* at a time
${}_nC_r$	combination of *n* objects taken *r* at a time
$P(A)$	probability of *A*
$P(A\|B)$	the probability of *A* given that *B* has already occurred

Measures

Metric	Customary
Length	
1 kilometer (km) = 1000 meters (m) 1 meter = 100 centimeters (cm) 1 centimeter = 10 millimeters (mm)	1 mile (mi) = 1760 yards (yd) 1 mile = 5280 feet (ft) 1 yard = 3 feet 1 yard = 36 inches (in.) 1 foot = 12 inches
Volume and Capacity	
1 liter (L) = 1000 milliliters (mL) 1 kiloliter (kL) = 1000 liters	1 gallon (gal) = 4 quarts (qt) 1 gallon = 128 fluid ounces (fl oz) 1 quart = 2 pints (pt) 1 pint = 2 cups (c) 1 cup = 8 fluid ounces
Weight and Mass	
1 kilogram (kg) = 1000 grams (g) 1 gram = 1000 milligrams (mg) 1 metric ton (t) = 1000 kilograms	1 ton (T) = 2000 pounds (lb) 1 pound = 16 ounces (oz)